Stay o

Join our Executi
We'll keep you
products

MW00635889

Name*

Address

City State Zip

Phone

Fax

Email

*Kennedy Information does not release customer information to outside parties

Please give us your comments or suggestions for next year's directory. Or share your career success stories.

KENNEDY INFORMATION 1-800-531-0007

28TH

EDITION

THE DIRECTORY OF EXECUTIVE RECRUITERS 1999

KENNEDY INFORMATION

Compiled and published by Kennedy Information, LLC
publishers of **Executive Recruiter News, The Directory of Executive Recruiters, SearchSelect®, The Directory of Outplacement & Career Management Firms, Consultants News** and **The Directory of Management Consultants.**

One Kennedy Place, Route 12 South, Fitzwilliam, NH 03447
Phone:603-585-6544 • Fax:603-585-9555
E-mail: bookstore@kennedyinfo.com
Internet: http://www.kennedyinfo.com

Library of Congress Catalog Card Number 73-642226
ISBN # 1-885922-30-2

Price $44.95

ISSN 0090-6484
ISBN 1-885922-30-2

Foreword

We are proud to present the 28th annual edition of *The Directory of Executive Recruiters,* the most complete listing of executive recruiters prepared today. The Directory, published since 1971, is continually researched, added to and updated by our full-time staff. It is the most in-depth and comprehensive reference for executive recruiters available.

Whether you're buying this guide in order to manage your career over the long-term or to make an immediate change, you will find listed 4,363 search firms, comprehensively cross-indexed by management function, geography and industry. We also identify 11,179 key recruiters, together with their areas of specialty in many cases. *To the best of our knowledge, none of the firms listed here charge the individual job-seeker. Please notify us of any listees who appear to be operating in violation of this restriction.*

Before you dig in to this wealth of information, read the Introduction, which will give you important advice on your search and how best to use this book.

It is our objective to make *The Directory of Executive Recruiters* as complete and as easy to use as possible. Accordingly, we always welcome your comments and suggestions on how we can improve the book.

Wayne E. Cooper
Publisher

Kathleen Kennedy Burke
Directory Editor

Constance C. Kennedy
Database Department Manager

Note:
Every effort has been made to verify the information included in this book. However, we assume no responsibility for any errors or omissions and reserve the right to include or eliminate company listings and otherwise edit the list.

Table of Contents

INTRODUCTION

What You Need to Know about Executive Recruiters vii
Four Facts You Should Know vii
Question & Answer Session: 14 Valuable Tips ix
How to Use This Directory xi
How to Read a Listing xii

LISTINGS

Retainer Recruiting Firms, A to Z 1
Contingency Recruiting Firms, A to Z 231

INDEXES

Job Functions 635
Industries 845
Recruiter Specialties 1015
Key Principals 1171
Geographical 1281
Firms 1335

APPENDIX

Other Useful Recruiter Resources 1363
Directory Data Services and SearchSelect® Order Form 1365
Labels, Reports, PC Disks and Mailing Service 1366
Kennedy's Pocket Guide to Working with Executive Recruiters..... 1367
SearchSelect® for Windows 1368

What You Need to Know about Executive Recruiters

There are entire books on how to use executive recruiting services to your best advantage. In the next few pages we give you a brief overview of the subject. This is followed by a question and answer session with tips on why, when and how to interact with recruiters.

We also highly recommend our companion publication, *Kennedy's Pocket Guide to Working with Executive Recruiters.* It contains 30 short chapters of frank advice, including how and when to contact recruiters and how to respond when a headhunter calls. See page 1367 for more details.

Four Facts You Should Know

1) Individuals do not pay fees to search firms.

Executive search firms are paid by the companies who hire them to fill a position, typically a fee of one-third of the job's first year compensation. Search firms are not working for you, but for their paying clients. Therefore, do not expect firms to be overly responsive when you contact them.

If your resume is impressive, they may add you to their database of executives. They may contact you if they have a position that fits your profile or to ask you to recommend other people who might be interested in the job. In either case, you will be starting the process of building a relationship with the recruiter. Every phone call or meeting will probably be noted in the firm's database.

Some companies advertise career counseling and resume mailing services to executives. These services, which can be expensive, are not offered by any of the executive search firms listed in this directory.

2) The difference between retainer and contingency search firms is important.

There are two types of recruiters. 36% of the firms listed in this directory are retainer, while the remaining 64% are contingency. Both charge the client employer a fee and neither should ever charge the prospective employee.

The distinctions between retainer and contingency firms are:

Retainer Firms:

- Retainer recruiters are hired by a client company for an assignment, typically for 90-120 days, and are paid regardless of the results of the search. They may also be kept on retainer by their clients, to fill whatever assignments they have.
- One retainer firm is hired by a client company for a given job opening.
- They are more often used to fill higher level positions with salaries of $70,000 and above.
- For these assignments they will assemble a short "slate" of candidates. Therefore, if a retainer firm seriously considers you for a position, you will probably be part of a small group of candidates.
- While your file is being used by a retained recruiter for an assignment, no other recruiter at that firm can contact you, even if you would be the perfect candidate. As a result, you are unlikely to be contacted by a firm for more than one or two positions a year, at most.
- If you work for a company that has hired the search firm during the last year or two, you will be "off-limits" for any other position it may have, no matter how well qualified you are. For this reason alone, it is important to be known to multiple search firms.

Contingency Firms:

- Contingency recruiters are more often used for junior and mid-level executives, typically for positions with salaries below $70,000.
- Contingency recruiters receive payment only when their candidate is hired.
- Contingency recruiters do not usually work on an exclusive basis with their clients. Since they are competing with other recruiters to provide candidates for each assignment, they tend to work fast and to submit to the client company as many candidates as they can. This means you may be one of many candidates for a given job.
- Contingency recruiters provide you with a great deal of exposure, since they send many resumes to their clients. This can be useful to you early in your career or if you are unemployed. However, bear in mind that you may not always want your resume widely distributed if you are happy in your current job.

When a headhunter calls you, it can be hard to tell whether they are from a contingency or retainer search firm. This directory helps clarify that information. Even so, contingency firms occasionally work on a retainer basis and some retainer firms do contingency work from time to time. Our advice is to ask explicitly the nature of the assignment before giving your permission to any recruiter to distribute your resume.

3) Some search firms specialize, while others don't. Consider both kinds.

Recruiting firms are often generalists, covering many different management functions (e.g. sales) and industries (e.g. textiles). Quite a few firms and many individual recruiters, however, do specialize. To make your search as effective as possible, consider recruiters who cover your function and specialize in your industry. Generalist firms should not be ignored, especially at the higher executive ranks. The largest multiple-office search firms tend to cover all functions and industries, but will often have practice areas for particular areas of expertise.

4) Most recruiters work nationally, so don't limit your search by geography.

At the lower salary levels, companies may be reluctant to consider out-of-town executives because of the expense of interviewing and relocating them. In these instances, search firms may focus on local candidates. However, for many executive appointments, search firms will look nationally or even internationally. It is in your interest to be known to search firms who fill positions in your industry, function and salary range, no matter where they are. A New York recruiter is as likely to have an assignment in Los Angeles as in Boston.

Question & Answer Session: 14 Valuable Tips

Q: What's the best way to contact an executive recruiter: phone, fax, e-mail or mail?
A: Always mail a resume with cover letter, and don't follow up by phone, e-mail or mail. Executive recruiters are interested only in the job-seekers who fit their current openings. Don't risk alienating a recruiter who may find an opening for you later by taking up his or her valuable time now. Some firms in the directory list web sites. Most of these give detailed advice on whom to contact.

Q: Should I send my resume to retainer firms, contingency firms, or both?
A: It depends. Early in your career and for mid-level positions, contingency firms are more likely to help you. Contingency firms also tend to be strong in industries with high turnover such as retailing, advertising, EDP, publishing and healthcare. Senior positions are more likely to be handled by retainer firms. If you are unemployed, it is fine to contact many firms of both kinds. If you are happy in your current job but want to actively manage your career, be careful not to contact any retainer firms your employer uses.

Q: How many resumes should I send out?
A: Resumes are cheap to send, while perfect job openings are scarce. Since different search firms know about different job opportunities, you should send your resume and cover letter widely. It makes sense to cover all of the firms in your industry and function. It's also smart to include leading generalist firms and firms in your area or places you're interested in moving to. Your initial objective is to get into multiple firms' databases so that when they have an assignment that matches your background, your name will come up.

Q: Should I include a cover letter?
A: Absolutely. But keep it brief, direct, and adopt a confident tone.

Q: How can I make sure that my resume gets to the right specialist at a recruiting firm?
A: Use the information in this directory wherever possible. Make sure that your resume clearly communicates your employment history and accomplishments. Many recruiters scan resumes into databases. This means you should use standard typefaces and formats, generally following the reverse-chronology model.

Q: How long should I wait before I can expect a response?
A: You won't get a response unless you fit an opening.

Q: Can I count on a headhunter to get me a job?
A: Working with a recruiter should be part of a multi-faceted job search. Recruiters work most effectively for everyone involved when you have made contact before you want to make a job change. They can also be helpful in keeping you abreast of developments within your industry, in newly important skills and specialties you have already or may want to acquire. You can make a good impression with recruiters if you are knowledgeable and helpful to them, possibly recommending other people for positions. Other important steps to take in your job search:

- Network with family, friends, acquaintances, and business contacts.
- Contact target firms directly.
- Reply to position listings in newspapers, association and university publications, online services, etc.
- Subscribe to services that mail you information about job openings.

Q: When is the best time to contact a recruiter?
A: Immediately, and on a continuing basis. We do recommend that executives actively manage their careers whether or not they are looking to

change jobs. This includes keeping selected recruiters up-to-date with your career progress and accomplishments. Whenever you do want to make a change, recruiters will already know you and understand what your objectives are.

Q: How do I keep my boss from finding out I'm looking for a job?
A: Tell your boss that you often get calls from headhunters because you have given helpful advice in the past. Be careful not to let any recruiter send your resume to companies unless you give specific approval.

Q: Can I cover a single national or international firm with one resume?
A: Spring for the extra postage. Even large firms vary in the way they handle resumes, so it's best to be on the safe side and send a resume to each office: some firms centralize, others don't.

Q: Should I concentrate on headhunters that specialize in my job function, or go by industry?
A: Normally both. Review both the list of management functions (on page 635) and the list of industries (on page 845) carefully. Some people may be primarily a specialist in a function (such as a Chief Financial Officer) while others may have general skills but expertise in a particular industry. For many people, both dimensions are relevant. (See recruiter specialty index, page 1015.)

Q: How long can I use *The Directory of Executive Recruiters* before getting a new issue?
A: One year. Turnover in this business is high; new firms are constantly being formed, partnerships dissolved, addresses changed. Three-quarters of the listings change in some way. Using a current directory pays for itself in time and postage savings alone. For the most up-to-date listings, consider *SearchSelect® for Windows*, our electronic version of the directory, which is updated monthly.

Q: I've heard a few horror stories — is there any way to tell whether a headhunting firm is trustworthy?
A: There is only one professional association for search firms: the Association of Executive Search Consultants (AESC). It has 119 members. Membership in AESC is indicated in the listings and is indicative of a commitment to professionalism in executive recruiting.

International Association of Corporate and Professional Recruitment (IACPR) is an organization of senior-level HR executives and retained executive search consultants. Membership in IACPR is also indicated in the listings.

Q: What other services does Kennedy Information recommend?
A: 1)This directory may also be purchased in electronic form, enabling you to perform speedy and sophisticated searches on the most up-to-date listings. ***SearchSelect® for Windows*** can also execute mail merges for cover letters and maintain records of your contacts with firms. A sample of this full-featured and easy-to-use program is provided on the "Strategies for Working with Recruiters" disk included with this book. Find details on the inside back cover.

2) **Labels, Reports, and PC Disks:** If you wish to send letters to a large number of recruiting firms, we have a mailing label service to speed things up. See page 1366 for details.

3) Our companion book, ***Kennedy's Pocket Guide to Working with Executive Recruiters,*** described on page 1367, contains invaluable advice and guidance for your job search. The "Strategies" disk also provides a sampling of these advice articles.

4) An expanded hardbound **Corporate Edition** of this directory is available to assist client organizations seeking executive search assistance. It includes key data on revenues, number of professionals, fee structures, and international contacts.

How to Use This Directory

The Directory of Executive Recruiters has been designed to be useful in a number of ways:

1. Start by referring to the index of 65 management functions (page 635) and 65 industries (page 845). These indexes enable you to find recruiting firms that specialize in your area(s). They also show whether the firm operates on a retainer or contingency basis. Review generalist firms too, a category that includes many of the largest search firms.
2. In addition, you may search for individual recruiters according to their areas of specialization. An index of 453 recruiter specialties begins on page 1,015 and lists 7,877 individual recruiters.
3. You may want to narrow your search to concentrate on recruiting firms in certain locations. To do this, consult our geographic index, which begins on page 1,281. Remember that many firms fill executive positions nationally, so it doesn't pay to limit yourself.
4. If you know of a particular headhunter, or receive a call from someone, find them by using our key principals index (page 1,171) which includes 11,179 recruiters at offices throughout North America.

You will build your own list of target executive recruiters by using the various indexes. The directory listings contain a wealth of information about each firm, including contact information, brief descriptions and key individual recruiters.

How to Read A Listing

	ABC Recruiting, Inc. 10 Any Street Anytown, State, Zip	Recruiting firm's name and main office mailing address
Phone, fax, e-mail and web addresses	(555) 123-4567 *Fax:* (555) 644-2477 *E-Mail:* recruit@aol.com *Web:* http://www.abc.com	
	Key Contact - Specialty: Mr. Joe Green - *Senior executives* Ms. Mary Brown - *Financial services, consulting*	Whom to contact and individual recruiter specialties
General description of the firm	*Description:* Executive recruiters to U.S. and European companies for senior managers. Special emphasis on banking, insurance and management consulting.	
Specific functional and industry areas covered by the firm	*Salary minimum:* $100,000 *Functions:* Generalist, Directors, CFOs *Industries:* Generalist, Banking, Mgmt. Consulting, Insurance	Lowest salary for positions handled by this firm
	Professional Associations: AESC, IACPR	Membership in AESC or IACPR
Branch office contact information and specialties	*Branches:* 200 New Street Newtown, State, Zip (666) 987-6543 *Key Contact - Specialty:* Mr. John Gray- *CEOs, COOs, CFOs*	
	International Branches: Frankfurt, London	Location of overseas offices
Affiliated firms	*Affiliates:* DEF Financial Recruiting, Inc.	
	Networks: XYZ Recruiting Associates	Membership in networks of independent recruiting firms

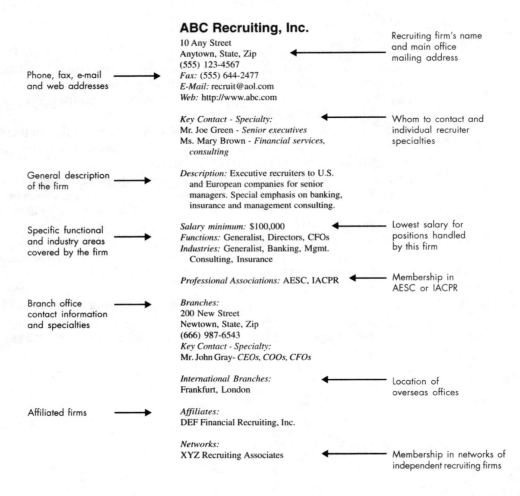

Retainer Recruiting Firms, A to Z

Firms in this section are retained by the hiring entity and paid at least a portion of their fee immediately to initiate the search. In this edition, we acknowledge that some executive search firms in this category occasionally accept assignments on a contingency basis. These firms are denoted with the symbol (†).

Full street addresses are listed for all U.S., Canada and Mexico locations, when known.

City only for overseas locations.

See page 231 for a parallel A to Z listing of firms charging on a contingency basis all or part of the time.

A la Carte Int'l., Inc. †
3330 Pacific Ave., Ste. 500
Virginia Beach, Virginia 23451-2983
(757) 425-6111
(800) 446-3037
Fax: (757) 425-8507
Email: alacarte@pilot.infi.net
Web: www.alacarte.com

Key Contact - Specialty:
Mr. Michael J. Romaniw - *Sales, marketing, general management, food manufacturers*

Description: Executive and retainer search firm that functions as a source for marketing, sales, operations and technical management personnel for food manufacturers. Compensation and competitive evaluation studies. Comprehensive personality profiles.

Salary Minimum: $65,000
Functions: Directors, Senior mgmt., Middle mgmt., Product dev., Mkt. research, Sales mgmt., Risk mgmt.
Industries: Food/bev/tobacco, Computer equip., Hospitality, Entertainment, Advertising/PR

Affiliates:
Career Assessment Center
Hollander Horizon Int'l.
OSAGUI S.A. de C.V.

A-L Assoc., Inc. †
546 Fifth Ave.
New York, New York 10036
(212) 878-9000
Fax: (212) 878-9096
Email: smanning@alassoc.com
Web: www.alassoc.com

Key Contact - Specialty:
Mr. Curt Miller - *Financial services, technical*
Mr. Edward Orchant - *Financial services, capital markets*

Description: Expedient, value added global executive search. Function specializations include most within financial services as well as a broad spectrum of legal and technical disciplines.

Salary Minimum: $150,000
Functions: General mgmt., Finance, IT, Mgmt. consultants, Attorneys
Industries: Finance, Legal, Computer svcs., Accounting, Mgmt. consulting, High tech, Software

International Branches:
Tokyo

A.K.S. Assoc., Ltd.
175 Derby St., Ste. 27
Hingham, Massachusetts 02043-4054
(781) 740-1704
Fax: (781) 740-4383
Email: salmeladux@aol.com

Key Contact - Specialty:
Mr. Alexander K. Salmela - *Finance, MIS, general management*

Description: Senior level search focused on general management, financial, MIS and operations functions in the financial services and manufacturing sectors. Personalized approach using quality standards at competitive fee arrangements.

Salary Minimum: $90,000
Functions: Senior mgmt., Middle mgmt., Admin. svcs., Health admin., CFO's, MIS mgmt., Mgmt. consultants
Industries: Energy/utilities, Finance, Higher ed., Legal, Mgmt. consulting, Insurance, Healthcare

Abbott Associates
225 B St.
Davis, California 95616
(530) 757-2770

Key Contact - Specialty:
Ms. Brenda L. Abbott - *Generalist*

Description: Executive search and research concentrating on senior level search, generalists.

Salary Minimum: $60,000
Functions: Generalist, Senior mgmt., Mfg., Sales & mktg., HR mgmt., Finance, IT
Industries: Generalist, Finance, Hospitality, Communications, High tech, Software

The Abbott Group, Inc.
530 College Pkwy.
Annapolis, Maryland 21401
(410) 757-4100
Web: www.abbottgroup.com

Key Contact - Specialty:
Mr. Peter D. Abbott - *Senior management*
Mr. D. Clarke Havener - *Senior management*
Ms. Barrie Atwood
Ms. Carolyn Jacobsen
Mr. Todd Houchins
Ms. Mary Ann Herbst

Description: Senior level executive search firm with strong practices in high technology and manufacturing.

Salary Minimum: $150,000
Functions: Senior mgmt., Product dev., Materials Plng., Mktg. mgmt., Benefits, CFO's, MIS mgmt.
Industries: Generalist, Printing, Machinery/Appliances, Defense, Aerospace, High tech, Software
Professional Associations: AESC

Branches:
8201 Greensboro Dr., Ste. 1000
McLean, Virginia 22102
(703) 714-6938

Key Contact - Specialty:
Ms. Mary Ann Herbst

Abécassis Conseil
507 Place d'Armes, Bureau 240
Montreal, Quebec H2Y 2W8
Canada
(514) 842-8213
Fax: (514) 842-8128
Email: abecasis@aei.ca

Key Contact - Specialty:
Ms. Pauline P. Abécassis - *Generalist*

Description: Our firm with each achievement throughout the years, have developed a global vision of a company. Our team is dedicated to the search for competent personnel who best reflect your business image.
Functions: Generalist, Mfg., Materials, Sales & mktg., HR mgmt., Finance, Engineering
Industries: Wholesale, Brokers, Non-profits, Mgmt. consulting, Telecoms, Insurance, High tech

Abeln, Magy & Assoc., Inc.
800 E. Wayzata Blvd., Ste. 200
Wayzata, Minnesota 55391
(612) 476-4938
Fax: (612) 404-7470
Email: info@abelnmagy.com

Key Contact - Specialty:
Mr. David S. Magy
Ms. Mary Abeln
Mr. Kenneth E. Abeln

Description: Professional retainer search consultants with 65 years of combined experience in a variety of functions.
Functions: General mgmt., Mfg., Materials, Healthcare, Sales & mktg., HR mgmt., Finance
Industries: Generalist

Adams & Assoc. Int'l.
22456 N. Brookside Way
Barrington, Illinois 60010
(847) 400-0798
Email: search@adamsassoc.com

Key Contact - Specialty:
Ms. Sheila Cunningham - *General management*
Ms. Joan Bennett - *General management*
Mr. Bill Lewis - *General management*

Description: General management recruiting in manufacturing, technology and professional services sectors.
Functions: General mgmt., Mfg., Sales & mktg., IT, Engineering, Int'l.
Industries: Mfg., Svcs., High tech, Software

† occasional contingency assignment

G. Adams Partners

39 S. Lasalle St., Ste. 714
Chicago, Illinois 60603
(312) 577-5648
Fax: (312) 577-5651
Email: gadamsptrs@aol.com

Key Contact - Specialty:
Mr. Gerald Adams - *Construction, architecture, engineering, real estate*

Description: Responsive, client-oriented boutique firm offering tailored services to the nations leading building and design firms.

Salary Minimum: $70,000
Functions: Directors, Senior mgmt., Middle mgmt., Engineering, Architects, Int'l.
Industries: Construction, Real estate

Affiliates:
Briant Assoc., Inc.
Glines Assoc., Inc.

Adler Management, Inc. †

66 Witherspoon St., Ste. 315
Princeton, New Jersey 08542
(609) 443-3300
Fax: (609) 443-4439
Email: jadler@webspan.net

Key Contact - Specialty:
Mr. Jack E. Adler
Mr. John Sherman

Description: Specialize in high technology markets, recruiting management teams for venture backed start-ups as well as Fortune 500 companies.

Salary Minimum: $100,000
Functions: Senior mgmt., Middle mgmt., Mktg. mgmt., Sales mgmt., IT
Industries: Venture cap., Publishing, New media, Telecoms, High tech, Software

Advanced Executive Resources

1740 44th St., Ste. 140
Grand Rapids, Michigan 49509-6421
(616) 942-4030
Fax: (616) 942-9950
Email: advexres@aol.com

Key Contact - Specialty:
Mr. Michael D. Harvey
Ms. Arlene Toy
Mr. Ray Saxe
Mr. Jim Loser
Ms. Annette Anderson

Description: We provide Michigan organizations their only local source for executive search. Majority of assignments are mid and high level technical and/or managerial searches across a variety of industries including die cast, automotive, food, plastics, environmental, oil and retail.

Salary Minimum: $50,000
Functions: Generalist, General mgmt., Mfg., Materials, Sales & mktg., Finance, Engineering
Industries: Mfg., Food/bev/tobacco, Lumber/furniture, Plastics/rubber, Aerospace, High tech, Software

Advantage Partners, Inc.

27600 Chagrin Blvd., Ste. 210
Cleveland, Ohio 44122
(216) 514-1212
Fax: (216) 514-1213
Email: advprtnrs@aol.com

Key Contact - Specialty:
Ms. Nikki C. Bondi - *General management*
Mr. James B. McPolin - *General management*

Description: Retained search firm specializing in recruiting of senior managers and executive talent for both public and private corporations.

Salary Minimum: $80,000
Functions: General mgmt., Directors, Senior mgmt., Mktg. mgmt., HR mgmt., CFO's, MIS mgmt.
Industries: Generalist, Mfg., Finance, Insurance

The Advisory Group, Inc.

266 Los Gatos-Saratoga Rd.
Los Gatos, California 95030
(408) 395-5960
Fax: (408) 446-5060
Email: tagsearch@aol.com

Key Contact - Specialty:
Mr. George Vaccaro - *High technology*

Description: A 26-year-old retained search firm providing technical, executive and management professionals for San Francisco Bay Area high-technology firms, with a special emphasis on start-ups.

Salary Minimum: $75,000
Functions: General mgmt., Mfg., Materials, Sales & mktg., Finance, R&D, Engineering
Industries: Computer equip., Test/measurement equip., Venture cap., New media, Telecoms, High tech, Software

Ahrensdorf & Assoc.

1489 Baltimore Pike
Springfield, Pennsylvania 19064
(610) 543-7888
Fax: (610) 543-4965
Email: leeahrensdorf@worldnet.att.net

Key Contact - Specialty:
Mr. Lee Ahrensdorf - *Financial services, healthcare, transportation*

Description: Generalist, retainer search firm that stresses service, quality and recruits with the goal of building partnerships with its client base.

Salary Minimum: $75,000
Functions: Generalist, Senior mgmt., Plant mgmt., Mktg. mgmt., Sales mgmt., HR mgmt., CFO's
Industries: Drugs mfg., Plastics/rubber, Transportation, Finance, Svcs., Biotech, Healthcare

J. R. Akin & Co.

14 Griffin Rd., Ste. 1
South Hamilton, Massachusetts 01982
(978) 468-9024

Key Contact - Specialty:
Mr. J. R. Akin - *General management, human resources, electrical*

Description: A very disciplined, professional and responsive firm with mature, corporate-trained search professionals. Superior research in most disciplines and industries, with particular focus on high technology, aerospace, packaged goods, financial services, healthcare, transportation and the electrical industry.

Salary Minimum: $100,000
Functions: Senior mgmt., Plant mgmt., Health admin., Sales mgmt., HR mgmt., CFO's, MIS mgmt.
Industries: Energy/utilities, Computer equip., Human resource svcs., Telecoms, Packaging, Healthcare

Alexander Associates

993 Lenox Drive, Ste. 200
Lawrenceville, New Jersey 08648
(609) 844-7580
Fax: (609) 844-7582
Email: search@alexassociates.com
Web: www.alexassociates.com

Key Contact - Specialty:
Mr. Richard J. Alexander - *Finance & accounting, information technology, management consultants, sales & marketing*

Description: We are the premier retainer-based executive search firm for the Philadelphia to New York business corridor. Because we are a central New Jersey-based firm, we are attuned to the executive needs and personalities of this important business community.

Salary Minimum: $70,000
Functions: Sales & mktg., Finance, IT, MIS mgmt., Mgmt. consultants
Industries: Mfg., Drugs mfg., Finance, Misc. financial, Computer svcs., Mgmt. consulting, Telecoms

The Alexander Group
(Firm declined to update.)
P.O. Box 316
West Berlin, New Jersey 08091-0316
(609) 768-0692
Email: tag_hldgs@msn.com

Key Contact - Specialty:
Mr. Preston Beckley

Description: As a minority-owned, retained generalist firm, we are committed to sourcing highly qualified individuals from under-represented groups for inclusion in every candidate slate we present for client approval.

Salary Minimum: $75,000
Functions: Generalist, General mgmt., Mfg., Sales & mktg., IT, Mgmt. consultants, Minorities
Industries: Mfg., Finance, Svcs., Telecoms, Aerospace, High tech, Healthcare

The Alexander Group
1330 Post Oak Blvd., Ste. 2800
Houston, Texas 77056
(713) 993-7900
Fax: (713) 993-7979
Email: jhowze@thealexandergroup.com
Web: thealexandergroup.com

Key Contact - Specialty:
Ms. Jane S. Howze
Mr. John C. Lamar

Description: We believe that fees should relate to the effort expected.Therefore, we establish a budget for each search and bill for the time on an hourly billing rate. Our fees are not dependent on the compensation of the position. We are an obvious choice for recruiting practice groups, partners or for multiple positions.

Salary Minimum: $80,000
Functions: General mgmt., HR mgmt., Budgeting, IT, MIS mgmt., Minorities, Int'l.
Industries: Energy/utilities, Banking, Legal, Computer svcs., Human resource svcs., High tech, Biotech

Branches:
4370 LaJolla Village Drive 400
San Diego, California 92122
(619) 755-0226
Fax: (619) 755-8233
Email: judyhudson@compuserve.com
Key Contact - Specialty:
Ms. Judith S. Hudson

250 Sutter St., 470
San Francisco, California 94108
(415) 677-8668
Fax: (415) 677-8674
Email:
rbrizendine@thealexandergroup.com
Key Contact - Specialty:
Mr. Raymond E. Brizendine

Ten Post Office Sq., Ste. 600 S.
Boston, Massachusetts 02109
(617) 988-0577
Email: rmitchell@thealexandergroup.com
Key Contact - Specialty:
Mr. Robert A. Mitchell

Alexander Ross & Co.
21 East 40th St. at Madison Ave.
New York, New York 10016
(212) 889-9333
Fax: (212) 481-3565
Email: benrl@ix.netcom.com

Key Contact - Specialty:
Mr. Ben Lichtenstein

Description: Executive search firm dedicated solely to human resource functions. Known for extensive human resources candidate database and in-depth assessment of human resource management and change management executives.

Salary Minimum: $80,000
Functions: HR mgmt., Benefits, Personnel, Training, Mgmt. consultants
Industries: Generalist

The Alfus Group
353 Lexington Ave., 8th Floor
New York, New York 10016
(212) 599-1000
Fax: (212) 599-1253
Email: mail@thealfusgroup.com

Key Contact - Specialty:
Mr. Phillip Alfus - *Hospitality, hotels, restaurant, leisure*
Mr. David Casey - *Gaming, hotels, resorts, casinos, amusements parks*
Ms. Susan Wilner - *Hotels, resorts, conference centers*
Mr. Joshua Reich - *Country clubs, culinary, food service, restaurants*
Ms. Sherrie Moore - *Hospitals, healthcare*
Mr. Pat Thompson - *Real estate*
Ms. Danielle Padwa - *Sports*
Ms. Michelle Hill - *Food, security, service industry, convention centers*
Ms. Lisa Vendetti - *Advertising, marketing*

Description: International executive search specializing in leisure time/hospitality/ real estate/entertainment/sports event management and related healthcare industries including hotel, restaurant, cruise line, airline, club, hospitals and managed care facilities.

Salary Minimum: $70,000
Functions: Senior mgmt., Healthcare, Sales & mktg., HR mgmt., Finance, MIS mgmt., Engineering
Industries: Hospitality, Entertainment, Mgmt. consulting, Human resource svcs., Advertising/PR, Real estate, Healthcare

International Branches:
Rome

David Allen Assoc. †
P. O. Box 56
Haddonfield, New Jersey 08033-0048
(609) 795-6470
Fax: (609) 795-0175
Email: david.allen.search@worldnet.att.net
Web: www.quikpage.com/A/allendavid

Key Contact - Specialty:
Mr. David Ritchings - *Finance, marketing, financial services, multimedia*

Description: Small, highly focused firm providing value added services to industry leaders as they build for the future. We have consistently found the right people for clients for over 17 years.

Salary Minimum: $50,000
Functions: General mgmt., Product dev., Productivity, Advertising, Finance, MIS mgmt., R&D
Industries: Energy/utilities, Food/bev/ tobacco, Finance, Entertainment, Communications, Software, Healthcare

Allen Austin Lowe & Powers
4543 Post Oak Place, Ste. 217
Houston, Texas 77027
(713) 355-1900
Fax: (713) 355-1901
Email: aalpsearch@aol.com

Key Contact - Specialty:
Mr. Robert L. Andrews - *Retail, manufacturing, sales & marketing, advertising, food industry*
Mr. Tom Arledge - *Supermarket, other retail, food manufacturing, food industry*
Mr. Michael Howard - *Construction*
Mr. Jake A. Baker - *Food manufacturing, hi-tech*
Mr. Edward T. Conlin - *Hi-tech, advertising, strategic marketing communications*
Mr. James Wilkson - *Telecommunications, food service, real estate, hospitality*
Mr. Joseph Dell'Aquilla - *Advertising, marketing communications, media*
Mr. William A. Scarpino - *Real Estate*
Mr. Sidney McClendon, III - *Law*
Mr. Abel Garcia - *Supermarkets, food service, programming, hi-tech, advertising*
Ms. Suzy Hannes
Ms. B. K. Whetstone-Smith - *Finance & accounting*
Mr. Philip Harrell
Ms. Linda Dailey - *Finance & accounting*
Ms. Kelly Rehmeyer - *Finance & accounting, programming*
Mr. Robert Milstead
Mr. Rudy Elizando
Ms. Robin Frishman
Ms. Kathy Insinger

Description: Retained search firm specializing in the recruitment of senior and middle level officers across a broad range of industries. We are proven performers and offer an unprecedented performance

† occasional contingency assignment

guarantee.

Salary Minimum: $60,000
Functions: General mgmt., Mfg., Sales & mktg., HR mgmt., Finance, IT, Attorneys
Industries: Generalist, Energy/utilities, Mfg., Wholesale, Svcs., Communications, High tech

Branches:
952 Hickory Way, Ste. 100
Fremont, California 94536
(510) 745-8287
Fax: (510) 745-9895
Key Contact - Specialty:
Mr. Jake Baker

4230 S. MacDill Ave., Ste. 222
Tampa, Florida 33611
(813) 902-0092
Fax: (813) 902-0050
Key Contact - Specialty:
Mr. James C. Wilkson

701 Brazos, Ste. 1000
Austin, Texas 78701
(512) 372-6594
Fax: (512) 372-9895
Key Contact - Specialty:
Mr. Ed Conlin

Allen Evans Assoc.
157 E. 57th St., 17th Floor
New York, New York 10022
(212) 486-7111
Fax: (212) 755-6952
Email: bklein@allenevans.com

Key Contact - Specialty:
Mr. Robert Klein

Description: Generalist executive search firm - technology (software/hardware), information/publishing, multimedia, consumer packaged goods, retail.

Salary Minimum: $75,000
Functions: Generalist, Senior mgmt., Mktg. mgmt., MIS mgmt., Systems anal., Systems dev., Systems implem.
Industries: Generalist, Retail, Misc. financial, Entertainment, High tech, Software

Allen/Associates
650 Westlake Ctr.
4555 Lake Forest Drive
Cincinnati, Ohio 45242
(513) 563-3040

Key Contact - Specialty:
Mr. Michael Allen - *Senior level (building products, consumer products)*

Description: Executive search consultants exclusively focused on critical assignments for senior decision makers and board members. Fifty percent of practice is at the executive vice president - CEO level.

Salary Minimum: $150,000
Functions: Generalist, General mgmt., Directors, Senior mgmt., Mfg., Mktg. mgmt., CFO's
Industries: Generalist, Textiles/apparel, Misc. mfg., Wholesale, Retail

Allerton Heneghan & O'Neill
70 W. Madison St., Ste. 2015
Three First National Plaza
Chicago, Illinois 60602
(312) 263-1075
Fax: (312) 263-1450
Email: aho@interaccess.com

Key Contact - Specialty:
Mr. Donald Allerton - *High technology, general management, human resources, diversity*
Mr. Donald A. Heneghan - *Finance & accounting, information technology*
Mr. Donald Wilson - *Senior management, diversity, automotive, retail*

Description: Retainer-based search firm with long-standing client relationships with large, multi-national companies and smaller, entrepreneurial organizations. Principal and professional support person work in tandem on each assignment.

Salary Minimum: $100,000
Functions: Senior mgmt., Plant mgmt., Mktg. mgmt., Training, CFO's, MIS mgmt., Minorities
Industries: Drugs mfg., Motor vehicles, Finance, Mgmt. consulting, Telecoms, High tech, Software
Professional Associations: IACPR

Affiliates:
KPMG Peat Marwick

Alliance Executive Search, Inc.
53 Webster Street
North Falmouth, Massachusetts 02556
(508) 548-7464
Fax: (508) 548-6356
Email: allianceex@capecod.net
Web: allianceexecsearch.com

Key Contact - Specialty:
Mr. Edward Starecheski
Ms. Lisa Nash
Ms. Betty Shaughnessy
Mr. Matthew Sutherland

Description: Full service retained search firm with the expertise, relationships and resources to successfully execute the most challenging search assignments while providing the highest level of personalized service.

Salary Minimum: $100,000
Functions: Senior mgmt., Mfg., Sales & mktg., HR mgmt., Finance, IT
Industries: Generalist, Misc. mfg., Finance, Hospitality, Entertainment, Communications, Environmental svcs.

Alliance Search Management Inc.
25307 I-45 North, Ste. 102
The Woodlands, Texas 77380
(281) 367-8630
Email: kflorip@flex,net

Key Contact - Specialty:
Ms. Kathy Powell-Florip - *Healthcare management*

Functions: Nurses, Allied health, Health admin.
Industries: Hospitality, Higher ed., Human resource svcs., Insurance, Healthcare

ALW Research Int'l.
60 Canterbury Rd.
Chatham, New Jersey 07928
(973) 701-9700
Fax: (973) 701-9619
Email: alwri@mail.idt.net
Web: www.alwri.com

Key Contact - Specialty:
Ms. Abbe L. Rosenthal - *Medical devices, pharmaceuticals, consumer products, electronics, industrial products*

Description: An executive search consultancy specializing in senior and middle management, female and minority recruitment and market-based compensation studies for public and private corporations.

Salary Minimum: $60,000
Functions: Mfg., Materials, HR mgmt., Finance, R&D, Engineering, Mgmt. consultants
Industries: Energy/utilities, Mfg., Transportation, Finance, Pharmaceutical svcs., Mgmt. consulting, Human resource svcs.
Professional Associations: IACPR

Affiliates:
Smith, Roth & Squires

AM & G Certified Public Accountants & Consultants
30 S. Wacker Drive, Ste. 2600
Chicago, Illinois 60606
(312) 207-2800
Fax: (312) 207-0368
Email: nvanheve@amgnet.com
Web: amgnet.com

Key Contact - Specialty:
Mr. Nicholaas Van Hevelingen - *Senior financial leadership (privately held companies), senior financial & operations leadership (professional partnerships)*

Description: Our search practice is a department of AM&G CPA's and Consultants, the 7th largest accounting and consulting firm in Chicago. It specializes in senior level management positions across all industries and disciplines, with a special emphasis in recruiting chief financial officers.

Salary Minimum: $75,000
Functions: Generalist, Senior mgmt., CFO's
Industries: Generalist, Construction, Mfg., Wholesale, Retail, Legal, Accounting

Peter W. Ambler Co.

14651 Dallas Pkwy., Ste. 402
Dallas, Texas 75240-7477
(972) 404-8712
Fax: (972) 404-8761
Email: amblera@dmans.com

Key Contact - Specialty:
Mr. Peter W. Ambler - *Generalist*

Description: Director level to senior executive level positions in a wide range of industries including high technology chemical, manufacturing, retail, services, energy and transportation.

Salary Minimum: $60,000
Functions: Generalist, Senior mgmt., Plant mgmt., Purchasing, Sales mgmt., CFO's, MIS mgmt.
Industries: Generalist, Printing, Plastics/rubber, Machinery/Appliances, Consumer electronics, Retail, High tech

American Executive Management, Inc.

30 Federal St.
Salem, Massachusetts 01970
(978) 744-5923
Email: amexec@tiac.com

Key Contact - Specialty:
Mr. E. J. Cloutier - *General management (USA, Europe, Middle East, Asia)*
Mr. H. Cygan - *International*
Ms. S. Smith
Ms. L. Shelton - *Telecommunications*
Mr. J. Gagola - *Oil, gas, chemical (Europe)*
Mr. P. Pitman - *Hospitality, entertainment*

Description: Leading international search firm. Extensive experience with major international corporations including such firms as: ABB, Fluor, Exxon, G.E. and Raytheon. Excellent performance and references.

Salary Minimum: $100,000
Functions: Senior mgmt., Middle mgmt., Sales & mktg., HR mgmt., Finance, IT, Engineering
Industries: Energy/utilities, Construction, Entertainment, Equip. svcs., Communications, Telecoms, Defense

American Group Practice, Inc.

420 Madison Ave., 5th Floor
New York, New York 10017
(212) 371-3091

Key Contact - Specialty:
Mr. Ralph Herz, Jr.

Description: Retainer search for practicing physicians, physician executives and senior-level healthcare executives; medical staff planning and medical group practice development, PHO's, MSO's, GPWW's and other physician/hospital relations activities.

Salary Minimum: $80,000
Functions: Healthcare, Physicians, Nurses, Allied health, Health admin.
Industries: Healthcare

Ames & Ames

P.O. Box 7404
Menlo Park, California 94026
(650) 322-4000

Key Contact - Specialty:
Mr. A. P. Ames - *Medical devices, medical electronics*

Description: Executive search, nationwide, since 1981. Medical device and medical electronics focus only.

Salary Minimum: $100,000
Functions: Generalist, Mfg., Sales & mktg.
Industries: Drugs mfg., Medical devices

Amrop International

Jaime Balmes No. 11, Torre "A" - P.H.
Colonia Los Morales Polanco
Mexico City, Mexico DF 11510
Mexico
52 5 557 5642
52 5 557 9403
Fax: 52 5 395 6677
Email: 100765.1453@compuserve.com

Key Contact - Specialty:
Mr. Carlos A. Rojas
Ms. Ma. Elena Juarez
Mr. Rodolfo Tames
Mr. Pedro Peniche

Description: Amrop International committed to helping private and public sector client organizations achieve greater profitability, performance and efficiency through the engagement of outstanding chief executives and senior managers.

Salary Minimum: $80,000
Functions: Generalist
Industries: Generalist

Branches:
Av. Lazaro Cardenas 2400 Pte.
Edificio Los Soles, C-13
Garza Garcia, Nuevo Leon 66270
Mexico
52 8 363 2969
Fax: 52 8 363 2301
Key Contact - Specialty:
Mr. Jose G. Carrillo
Mr. Ricardo Pacheco

Networks:
Amrop International

AMS Int'l.

9836 Fairfax Sq., Ste. 254
Fairfax, Virginia 22031
(703) 383-9740
Fax: (703) 383-9745
Email: ams@huskynet.com

Key Contact - Specialty:
Mr. Adam M. Smith
Mr. Mark Roth

Description: Client-centered retained executive search for the institutional client. Original, comprehensive research and thorough candidate assessment. Specializing in senior level critical needs.

Salary Minimum: $85,000
Functions: Senior mgmt., Mfg., HR mgmt., CFO's, MIS mgmt., R&D, Int'l.
Industries: Generalist, Mfg., Finance, Svcs., High tech, Software, Biotech

Anderson & Associates

112 S. Tryon St., Ste. 800
Charlotte, North Carolina 28284
(704) 347-0090
Fax: (704) 347-0064

Key Contact - Specialty:
Mr. Douglas K. Anderson

Description: Search and related consulting services for a nationwide clientele. Emphasis in software technology, environmental services, financial institutions, graphic arts, healthcare and manufacturing. Functional experience: searches for CEO/CFO, directors and senior executives.

Salary Minimum: $70,000
Functions: Generalist, Physicians, Allied health, Health admin.
Industries: Generalist, Food/bev/tobacco, Finance, Hospitality, Packaging, Real estate, Healthcare
Professional Associations: AESC

Anderson & Schwab, Inc.

444 Madison Ave., Ste. 807
New York, New York 10022-6903
(212) 758-6800
Fax: (212) 755-9576

† occasional contingency assignment

Key Contact - Specialty:
Mr. Frank Schwab, Jr. - *Top management*
Mr. Klaus G. Scheye - *Top management*
Mr. Harleigh V. S. Tingley - *Senior economics*
Ms. Ivy S. Wilensky - *Senior financial*
Mr. Thomas Parker - *Generalist*
Mr. Simon Handelsman - *Senior operating, technical*
Mr. Colin Smith - *Senior operating, technical*
Mr. Ian D. Buckingham - *Geology, exploration*

Description: Specializes in providing a broad variety of consulting services to include business, operations management and personnel work, to the international extractive and processing industries.

Salary Minimum: $75,000
Functions: Generalist, Directors, Senior mgmt., CFO's, Engineering, Environmentalists, Int'l.
Industries: Agri/forestry/mining, Energy/utilities, Chemicals, Metal products, Machinery/Appliances, Finance, Environmental svcs.

Branches:
707 Seventeenth St., 23rd Floor
Denver, Colorado 80202
(303) 295-5563
Fax: (303) 382-7455
Key Contact - Specialty:
Mr. Thomas Parker

International Branches:
Melbourne

Affiliates:
KPMG Australia

Anderson Bradshaw Assoc., Inc. †

P.O. Box 924045
Houston, Texas 77292-4045
(713) 869-6789

Key Contact - Specialty:
Mr. Robert W. Anderson - *International engineering, construction, oil & gas, on/off shore, process plant operations & maintenance (refineries, chemical, petrochemical plants)*

Description: Domestic and international. Assignments in engineering and construction, oil and gas, environmental and manufacturing for energy and power industry.

Salary Minimum: $60,000
Functions: Senior mgmt., Middle mgmt., Plant mgmt., HR mgmt., Engineering, Environmentalists, Int'l.
Industries: Energy/utilities, Construction, Chemicals, Human resource svcs., Defense, Haz. waste, Aerospace

Andre David & Assoc., Inc.

P.O. Box 700967
Dallas, Texas 75370
(972) 250-1986
Fax: (972) 250-2243

Key Contact - Specialty:
Mr. Terry Patch - *Human resources*

Description: A management consulting firm engaging in executive search. We perform searches with a high degree of professionalism, a sense of urgency and a commitment to excellence. We bring client and external expertise to search engagements.

Salary Minimum: $75,000
Functions: Plant mgmt., Mktg. mgmt., Benefits, Personnel, Budgeting, Mgmt. consultants, Minorities
Industries: Food/bev/tobacco, Entertainment, Mgmt. consulting

The Andre Group, Inc.

(Firm declined to update.)
500 N. Gulph Rd., Ste. 210
King of Prussia, Pennsylvania 19406
(610) 337-0600

Key Contact - Specialty:
Mr. Larry Cozzillio - *Human resources*

Description: Recognized leader in recruitment and search of HR professionals, representing over 85% of Fortune 500 clients on nationwide basis. Largest in USA.

Salary Minimum: $75,000
Functions: HR mgmt., Benefits, Personnel
Industries: Mfg., Finance, Svcs., High tech, Biotech, Healthcare
Professional Associations: IACPR

APA Search, Inc.

721 W. Boston Post Rd.
Mamaroneck, New York 10543
(914) 698-2800
Fax: (914) 698-8787
Email: apasearch@aol.com

Key Contact - Specialty:
Mr. Howard Kesten

Description: Highly professional and specialized automotive executive search firm. Extensive network of automotive manufacturing and distribution executives. Senior management, sales, marketing, operations, manufacturing and financial positions.
Functions: Senior mgmt., Middle mgmt., Mfg., Sales & mktg., Finance, Engineering, Int'l.
Industries: Paints/petroleum products, Metal products, Motor vehicles, Wholesale, Retail, Communications, Packaging

Argonaut Partners, LLC

3 Embarcadero Ctr., Ste. 2260
San Francisco, California 94111
(415) 765-6540
Fax: (415) 288-6905
Email: peter@argonautpart.com

Key Contact - Specialty:
Mr. Peter V. Hall - *Real estate, mortgage finance, financial services, chief financial officers*
Mr. Matthew B. Slepin - *Real estate, information technology, financial services*

Description: We believe the strength of the company lies in both its industry experience (financial service and real estate) as well as its hands-on approach to executing search. Senior members of the firm are intimately involved in the search strategy and everyday sourcing of candidates.

Salary Minimum: $100,000
Functions: Directors, Mktg. mgmt., Training, CFO's, Cash mgmt., MIS mgmt., Minorities
Industries: Banking, Invest. banking, Brokers, Venture cap., Misc. financial, Real estate

Argus National, Inc.

98 Mill Plain Rd., Ste. 301
Danbury, Connecticut 06811-5148
(203) 790-8420

Key Contact - Specialty:
Ms. Constance Gruen
Mr. Ronald J. Guido
Mr. William E. Bruder

Description: Management search and recruitment designed for one company...yours.

Salary Minimum: $50,000
Functions: Generalist, Senior mgmt., Product dev., Plant mgmt., Mktg. mgmt., CFO's, Engineering
Industries: Generalist, Paints/petroleum products, Metal products, Machinery/Appliances, Motor vehicles, Computer equip., Test/measurement equip.

ARI Int'l.

1501A Ocean Ave.
Seal Beach, California 90740
(562) 795-5111
Fax: (562) 421-6407

Key Contact - Specialty:
Mr. Ronald L. Curci

Description: Provides (retained) domestic and international executive and technical search.

Salary Minimum: $100,000

Functions: Generalist, Int'l.
Industries: Generalist

Ariail & Assoc.
210 Friendly Ave., Ste. 200
Greensboro, North Carolina 27401
(910) 275-2906
Email: ariailassoc@msn.com
Web: www.ariailassoc.com

Key Contact - Specialty:
Mr. Randolph C. Ariail - *Senior executives, furniture & related industries*

Description: A retained search firm specializing in the procurement of senior level executives in the household furniture and institutional furnishing industry. A twenty-six year history of successful procurement of CEO's and VP's of sales/marketing, manufacturing, general management and CFO's.

Salary Minimum: $100,000
Functions: Senior mgmt., Plant mgmt., Sales mgmt., CFO's
Industries: Lumber/furniture

Ariel Recruitment Assoc.
410 W. 53rd St., Ste. 126
New York, New York 10019
(212) 765-8300
Fax: (212) 765-3450
Email: arielxl@ibm.net

Key Contact - Specialty:
Mr. Eugene Fixler - *Publishing, media, marketing*
Ms. Lynn Ruttanai-Fanelli - *Publishing*
Ms. Rona Wexler - *Publishing*

Description: Specializing in publishing professionals for consumer and trade magazines, journals, newsletters, electronic publishing and database publishing nationwide. Place publishing and media professionals in marketing and sales management positions outside publishing.

Salary Minimum: $85,000
Functions: Senior mgmt., Product dev., Sales mgmt., Direct mktg., Training, CFO's, Minorities
Industries: Entertainment, Publishing, New media, Broadcast & Film, Software

---

Armitage Associates Ltd.
151 Yonge St., Ste. 1210
Toronto, Ontario M5C 2W7
Canada
(416) 863-0576
Fax: (416) 863-0092
Email: armitage@interlog.com

Key Contact - Specialty:
Mr. John D. Armitage - *Financial services, high technology*
Ms. Karen Wood - *Financial services, high technology*

Description: Boutique specializing in mid to senior level assignments.

Salary Minimum: $80,000
Functions: Directors, Senior mgmt., CFO's, M&A, MIS mgmt.
Industries: Finance, Hospitality, Insurance, Real estate, High tech, Software

---

J. S. Armstrong & Assoc., Inc.
Three Embarcadero Ctr., Ste. 2260
San Francisco, California 94111
(415) 288-6900
Fax: (415) 288-6905
Email: jarmstrong@jsaa.com

Key Contact - Specialty:
Ms. Jennifer Sheehan-Armstrong - *High technology*

Description: Our firm's success is based on industry exceeding standards for performance, execution and highly personalized service. We achieve results by targeting, aggressively recruiting and thoroughly evaluating the leaders who fit clients' needs.

Salary Minimum: $200,000
Functions: Senior mgmt., Mktg. mgmt., Sales mgmt., CFO's, MIS mgmt., R&D, Engineering
Industries: High tech

William B. Arnold Assoc., Inc.
600 S. Cherry St., Ste. 1105
Denver, Colorado 80246-1716
(303) 393-6662

Key Contact - Specialty:
Mr. William B. Arnold - *Generalist*
Ms. Sheridan J. Arnold - *Generalist*

Description: Generalist search practice -- most industries and functions, senior and middle management. We are the oldest retained executive search firm in the Rocky Mountain Region.

Salary Minimum: $75,000
Functions: Generalist
Industries: Generalist

Affiliates:
Darmody & Associates, Inc.

Patrick Arnone & Assoc. Inc.
11921 Freedom Drive, Ste. 550
Reston, Virginia 20190
(703) 925-5950
Fax: (703) 925-5952
Email: patrick@arnone-assoc.com
Web: www.arnone-assoc.com

Key Contact - Specialty:
Mr. Patrick J. Arnone - *High technology, information technology, software, communications, internet*

Description: Patrick Arnone is committed to using the experience and knowledge he gained during his 32-year tenure in the IT industry, from start-up to large established companies. He knows what it takes for a company to grow profitably and with excellence. His commitment is to recruit professionals who will make that possible for his clients.

Salary Minimum: $100,000
Functions: Generalist, General mgmt., Directors, Senior mgmt., Sales & mktg., Finance, IT
Industries: Generalist, Computer equip., Computer svcs., Mgmt. consulting, Communications, High tech, Software

---

Artgo, Inc.
545 Hanna Bldg.
Cleveland, Ohio 44115-1901
(216) 241-1548
Fax: (216) 696-3944

Key Contact - Specialty:
Mr. Arthur D. Baldwin, II - *Generalist*

Description: Executive search for corporate needs including special capabilities in middle management assignments.
Functions: Senior mgmt., Production, Purchasing, CFO's, MIS mgmt., Systems anal., Engineering
Industries: Generalist, Metal products, Motor vehicles, Hospitality, Aerospace

---

The Ascher Group
7 Becker Farm Rd.
Roseland, New Jersey 07068
(973) 597-1900
Fax: (973) 597-1911
Email: sa@Aschergroup.com

Key Contact - Specialty:
Ms. Susan Ascher - *Generalist*

Description: We are a generalist interim executive/retained search firm which recruits middle and senior-level managers and executives for diverse industries. The firm's practice is national in scope with a geographical concentration in the Northeast.

Salary Minimum: $50,000
Functions: Purchasing, Distribution, Benefits, Training, CFO's, Budgeting
Industries: Generalist, Accounting, Mgmt. consulting, Human resource svcs., High tech

---

Ashford Management Group, Inc.
2295 Parklake Drive NE, Ste. 425
Atlanta, Georgia 30345
(770) 938-6260
Fax: (770) 621-9529

Email: ashfordgroup@mindspring.com

Key Contact - Specialty:
Ms. Janis E. Martinez - *Retail*
Ms. Lynn Nelson - *Retail*
Ms. Karen Cooper - *Retail*

Description: We also provide other services, including management consulting and interview training for the interviewer and the interviewee. Our clients include some of the nation's largest retailers.
Functions: Directors, Senior mgmt., Product dev., Direct mktg., HR mgmt., Benefits, MIS mgmt.
Industries: Retail

Branches:
3550 Watt Ave., Ste. 425
Sacramento, California 95821
(916) 978-9246
Fax: (916) 978-0371
Key Contact - Specialty:
Ms. Annette Griffey - *Retail*

Ashlar-Stone Management Consultants Inc.
50 Burnhamthorpe Rd. W., Ste. 401
Mississauga, Ontario L5B 3C2
Canada
(905) 615-0900
Fax: (905) 615-0917

Key Contact - Specialty:
Mr. Stuart K.J. Moore
Mr. Robert D. Chisholm

Description: Small, responsive firm providing high quality executive search services with superior results in all industries.

Salary Minimum: $75,000
Functions: General mgmt., Mfg., Materials, Sales & mktg., HR mgmt., Finance, MIS mgmt.
Industries: Mfg., Retail, Communications, Packaging

Affiliates:
The Peter Riches Partnership

Ashworth Consultants, Inc.
53 Fulton St.
Boston, Massachusetts 02109-1401
(617) 720-0350
Fax: (617) 720-0360

Key Contact - Specialty:
Mr. Robert I. Ash - *Consulting firms*

Description: Provides board level consulting in compensation, management planning & personnel selection for start-ups, threshold companies and established organizations.

Salary Minimum: $75,000
Functions: Senior mgmt., Middle mgmt., Benefits, CFO's, MIS mgmt., Mgmt. consultants
Industries: Energy/utilities, Textiles/apparel, Paper, Drugs mfg., Computer equip., Pharmaceutical svcs., Mgmt. consulting

---

Association Executive Resources Group
P.O. Box 3880
Gaithersburg, Maryland 20885-3880
(301) 417-7045
Fax: (301) 417-7049

Key Contact - Specialty:
Mr. Gerard F. Hurley - *National associations, golf, city social clubs, philanthropic groups, fraternal groups*
Mr. Charles D. Rumbarger - *National associations*

Description: Dedicated exclusively to searches for CEO and professional staff positions for national trade and professional associations and golf/city clubs and other not-for-profit organizations. Principals and senior associates total more than 60 years association management experience.

Salary Minimum: $55,000
Functions: Senior mgmt., Middle mgmt.
Industries: Hospitality, Non-profits

AST/BRYANT
One Atlantic St.
Stamford, Connecticut 06901
(203) 975-7188
Fax: (203) 977-7353
Email: astbry@ix.netcom.com

Key Contact - Specialty:
Mr. Steven T. Ast - *Non-profit institutions, CEOs, chief development executives*

Description: Providing professional services in the recruitment of presidents and CEO's and chief development executives for colleges and universities, hospitals and medical centers and other not-for-profit institutions and organizations nationally.

Salary Minimum: $75,000
Functions: Senior mgmt., Specialized services, Non-profits, Environmentalists
Industries: Svcs., Non-profits, Higher ed.
Professional Associations: AESC

Branches:
2716 Ocean Park Blvd., Ste. 3001
Santa Monica, California 90405
(310) 314-2424
Fax: (310) 399-5774
Key Contact - Specialty:
Mr. Christopher P. Bryant - *Non-profit institutions, CEOs, chief development executives*

Aster Search Group
555 Madison Ave., Ste. 2300
New York, New York 10022
(212) 888-6182

Key Contact - Specialty:
Ms. Eve Cohen - *Healthcare*

Description: We conduct assignments for hospitals, integrated delivery networks, physician practice management companies, managed care companies, long term care facilities and home care companies, healthcare agencies. Please send only healthcare resumes.

Salary Minimum: $70,000
Functions: Health admin.
Industries: Healthcare

Affiliates:
Stanton Healthcare Group

Atlanta Executive Partners, Inc.
P.O. Box W
Teaticket, Massachusetts 02536
(508) 495-4300
Fax: (508) 495-4301
Web: aep@mindspring.com

Key Contact - Specialty:
Mr. Robert J. Sweet - *Technology, telecommunications, manufacturing, communications, aerospace*

Description: A systems approach, providing leaders who enhance company performance and competitive standing. Benchmarking to establish clear criteria for acquiring or aligning with executives and companies. Real world solutions from line-management experienced consultants.

Salary Minimum: $100,000
Functions: Generalist, General mgmt., Mfg., Sales & mktg., Finance, IT, R&D
Industries: Computer equip., Test/measurement equip., Mgmt. consulting, Government, Aerospace, High tech, Software

---

Aubin Int'l. Inc.
30 Rowes Wharf, 4th Floor
Boston, Massachusetts 02110
(617) 443-9922
Fax: (617) 443-9955
Email: info@aubin.com
Web: www.aubin.com

Key Contact - Specialty:
Mr. Richard E. Aubin - *High technology*
Mr. J. David Lyons - *High technology*

Description: An international retainer practice offering a partnering philosophy; swift, successful results; leading-edge information systems and fifteen years experience. Specialists in borderless

search, an innovative team-based approach that attracts world-class candidates for every assignment.
Functions: Directors, Senior mgmt., Mktg. mgmt., Sales mgmt., CFO's, MIS mgmt., Int'l.
Industries: Computer svcs., New media, Telecoms, High tech, Software
Professional Associations: AESC, IACPR

Auerbach Associates, Inc.
65 Franklin St., Ste. 400
Boston, Massachusetts 02110
(617) 451-0095
Fax: (617) 451-5199

Key Contact - Specialty:
Ms. Judith A. Auerbach - *Higher education, healthcare, non-profit institutions*
Ms. Paula B. Hurley - *Higher education, non-profit, healthcare*

Description: Specializes in executive search for colleges and universities, healthcare, not-for-profit institutions, the public sector. Special emphasis on recruitment of women and under-represented groups.

Salary Minimum: $60,000
Functions: Senior mgmt., Middle mgmt., Health admin., CFO's, MIS mgmt., Minorities, Non-profits
Industries: Non-profits, Higher ed., Government, Healthcare

A. M. Auster Associates
283 N. Northlake Blvd., Ste. 111
Altamonte Springs, Florida 32701
(407) 831-2400

Key Contact - Specialty:
Mr. A. Marc Auster - *Insurance, technology consulting, healthcare*

Description: Retained search firm in most industries and within most functional areas. Limitation of clients in smaller industries.

Salary Minimum: $80,000
Functions: Generalist, Senior mgmt., Legal, Mfg., Benefits, Risk mgmt., Mgmt. consultants
Industries: Mfg., Transportation, Hospitality, Mgmt. consulting, Aerospace, Insurance, Healthcare

Austin Group Int'l./Marlar Int'l.
117 Laura Lane, Ste. 200
Austin, Texas 78746
(512) 329-8077
Fax: (512) 327-3997
Email: ausgrpintl@aol.com

Key Contact - Specialty:
Mr. Ray Holley - *Marketing & sales, general management*
Ms. Jane O'Neal - *Sales, sales management, marketing & channel management, technical & customer support, human factors*
Mr. Phillip Kuhlenbeck - *Sales, sales management, marketing, product development*
Mr. Brian Riley - *Sales, sales management, marketing, product management*
Ms. Suzanne Bushong
Ms. Pamela Speciale - *Sales, marketing, technical support, call center operations*

Description: Computer industry specialists recruiting marketing, sales, technical, customer service and management candidates. Retained and hourly search rates. Extensive in-house research capability. Domestic and international high-tech search. Over 30 offices in 17 countries.

Salary Minimum: $75,000
Functions: Senior mgmt., Middle mgmt., Mkt. research, Mktg. mgmt., Sales mgmt., Direct mktg., Int'l.
Industries: Computer equip., Consumer electronics, Computer svcs., Software

Affiliates:
Marlar International

Austin-McGregor Int'l.
12005 Ford Rd., Ste. 720
Dallas, Texas 75234
(972) 488-0500
Fax: (972) 488-0535
Email: amidallas@aol.com
Web: amidallas.com

Key Contact - Specialty:
Mr. Charles McCreary - *High technology, consumer, entertainment, industrial*
Mr. Marc England - *High technology*

Description: For 20 years, we've identified and recruited the best talent from around the world, from hard-to-find contributors to chief executives to board members; the kind of people that make a far-reaching impact on an organization, its strategic direction and its bottom line.

Salary Minimum: $70,000
Functions: Mfg., Materials, Healthcare, Sales & mktg., Finance, IT, R&D
Industries: Mfg., Transportation, Wholesale, Retail, Svcs., Communications, High tech

Affiliates:
DPSC Int'l (Benelux) NV
Reyes Consulting Group

Avalon Health Group, Inc.
245 E. 54th St., Ste. 3-T
New York, New York 10022
(212) 758-3786
Fax: (212) 758-5304
Email: jpufahl@avalonhealth.com

Key Contact - Specialty:
Dr. John P. Pufahl - *Managed care*
Ms. Linda Tierney - *Operations*

Description: Specializing in executive search and professional development for physician managers and senior managed care executives.

Salary Minimum: $100,000
Functions: General mgmt., Senior mgmt., Sales & mktg., Finance, CFO's, IT, MIS mgmt.
Industries: Healthcare

Avery Assoc.
3 1/2 N. Santa Cruz Ave., Ste. B
Los Gatos, California 95030
(408) 399-4424
Fax: (408) 399-4423

Key Contact - Specialty:
Ms. Sue Whitfield - *Public sector*
Mr. Paul Kimura - *Private sector*

Description: Public sector practice is focused on city and county government and agencies throughout western U.S. Private sector search is focused on administrative positions in technology, communications and financial/general services.

Salary Minimum: $75,000
Functions: General mgmt., Materials, Sales & mktg., Benefits, Personnel, Training, Finance
Industries: Communications, Government, High tech, Software, Biotech

Avondale Search Int'l., Inc. †
4651 Salisbury Rd., Ste. 295
Jacksonville, Florida 32256
(904) 296-4449
Fax: (904) 296-6478
Email: esc@mediaone.net
Web: www.asii.com

Key Contact - Specialty:
Ms. Margot E. Finley - *High tech sales*
Mr. Tom Philipp-Edmonds
Ms. Trish Jewell

Description: Our firm offers a variety of recruitment solutions that we tailor to each client. Put your most important search assignment in our hands.
Functions: General mgmt., Distribution, Sales & mktg., IT, MIS mgmt., Systems anal., Systems dev.
Industries: Transportation, Computer svcs., High tech, Software

The Ayers Group, Inc.
370 Lexington Ave., 25th Floor
New York, New York 10017
(212) 599-5656
(212) 889-7788
Fax: (212) 889-6689

† occasional contingency assignment

Email: bob.deissig@ayers.com

Key Contact - Specialty:
Mr. William L. Ayers, Jr. - *Technology, capital markets*
Mr. Robert Deissig

Description: Specialists in information systems placement for retained search. Career counseling and outplacement specifically for information systems. Management and executive search specialists in internal audit.

Salary Minimum: $150,000
Functions: Personnel, Training, Cash mgmt., M&A, Risk mgmt., MIS mgmt., Systems implem.
Industries: Banking, Invest. banking, Brokers, Computer svcs., Accounting, Insurance, Healthcare
Professional Associations: IACPR

The Badger Group
4125 Blackhawk Plaza Circle, Suite 270
Danville, California 94506
(925) 736-5553
Fax: (925) 736-5554
Email: info@badgergroup.com
Web: www.badgergroup.com

Key Contact - Specialty:
Mr. Fred H. Badger - *Information technology*
Mr. Dick Bruce - *Information technology*
Mr. Jim Watkinson - *Information technology*

Description: We are committed to bringing an elite level of service, professionalism and ethics to retained executive recruiting.

Salary Minimum: $120,000
Functions: Generalist, Directors, Senior mgmt., Mktg. mgmt., Sales mgmt., CFO's, MIS mgmt.
Industries: Generalist, Medical devices, Computer equip., Computer svcs., New media, Aerospace, Software
Professional Associations: AESC

Baeder Kalinski Int'l. Group, Inc.
40 S. River Rd.
Bedford Place, U-64
Bedford, New Hampshire 03110
(603) 669-1570
Fax: (603) 625-1417
Email: felixk@bkig.com
Web: www.bkig.com

Key Contact - Specialty:
Mr. Felix Kalinski, Jr. - *Management consulting, engineering, construction*

Description: We apply a unique methodology called Search Alliance (SM) to bring value added recruiting ideas to global clients. We have Search Alliance (SM) relationships served continuously for over fourteen years.

Salary Minimum: $75,000
Functions: Generalist, Directors, Senior mgmt., CFO's, Systems implem., Engineering, Mgmt. consultants
Industries: Generalist, Mfg., Mgmt. consulting, Haz. waste, Insurance, Healthcare

---

The Baer Group
3161 Coleridge Rd., Ste. 300
Cleveland, Ohio 44118
(216) 371-9982
Fax: (216) 371-6284
Email: GHerbruck@aol.com

Key Contact - Specialty:
Ms. Gretchen S. Herbruck - *Healthcare*

Description: Provides retained search for mid to senior level executives in most functions and industries with a specialization in healthcare. Other services include search, industry and market research.

Salary Minimum: $60,000
Functions: Generalist, General mgmt., Mfg., Healthcare, HR mgmt., Specialized services, Mgmt. consultants
Industries: Generalist, Mfg., Svcs., Healthcare

Baldwin Associates, LLC
39 Locust Ave.
New Canaan, Connecticut 06840
(203) 966-5355
Fax: (203) 966-1924
Web: BaldwinAssociates@worldnet.att.net

Key Contact - Specialty:
Mr. Robert J. Kammerer
Mr. Peter Robohm
Ms. Marsha L. Shannon

Description: Professionally staffed firm, specializing in general management and senior executive recruiting for prestigious clients, companies which offer high technology products and services, or where information is a competitive differentiator.

Salary Minimum: $125,000
Functions: Generalist, Senior mgmt., Sales & mktg., CFO's, IT, Mgmt. consultants
Industries: Computer equip., Computer svcs., Mgmt. consulting, Communications, High tech, Software

---

The Baldwin Group
550 W. Campus Drive
Arlington Heights, Illinois 60004
(847) 394-4303
Fax: (847) 394-0576
Web: www.thebaldgrp.com

Key Contact - Specialty:
Mr. Keith R. Baldwin

Description: Our clients receive dependability, thoroughness and professionalism which culminates in attracting outstanding persons which we guarantee for one full year after hire.

Salary Minimum: $75,000
Functions: Generalist
Industries: Food/bev/tobacco, Paints/petroleum products, Machinery/Appliances, Motor vehicles, Computer svcs., Mgmt. consulting, Defense

---

Allen Ballach Assoc. Inc.
11 Parkview Blvd., Ste. 100
Whitby, Ontario L1N 3M8
Canada
(905) 725-0314
Fax: (905) 725-3418
Email: allen@aballach.com
Web: www.aballach.com

Key Contact - Specialty:
Mr. Allen Ballach - *Manufacturing, engineering, advanced technologies*

Description: 20 years experience providing senior management and executive level search and selection solutions to the advanced technology market sectors throughout North America.

Salary Minimum: $80,000
Functions: Senior mgmt., Production, Sales mgmt., CFO's, MIS mgmt., R&D, Engineering
Industries: Energy/utilities, Motor vehicles, Consumer electronics, Computer svcs., Broadcast & Film, Aerospace, Software

---

Ballantyne & Assoc.
P.O. Box 810
Moss Beach, California 94038
(650) 634-9464
Email: der@headhunter-usa.com

Key Contact - Specialty:
Mr. Tom Ballantyne - *Marketing & advertising (consumer products)*

Description: Specializing in the search for consumer product, business, entertainment and educational software marketing and advertising management professionals for Fortune 1000, startups and non-profits.

Salary Minimum: $100,000
Functions: Middle mgmt., Advertising, Mkt. research, Mktg. mgmt., Minorities, Non-profits, Environmentalists
Industries: Food/bev/tobacco, Soap/perfume/cosmetics, Consumer electronics, Entertainment, Advertising/PR, Publishing, New media

---

Ballos & Co., Inc.
45 Fieldstone Drive
Morristown, New Jersey 07960-2634
(973) 538-4609

Key Contact - Specialty:
Mr. Constantine J. Ballos - *Generalist*
Mr. H. P. Ballos - *Generalist*

Description: Effective, ethical, professional search firm with high percentage repeat business: process, chemical, pharmaceutical, biotechnology, manufacturing and technology driven industries.

Salary Minimum: $80,000
Functions: Generalist, General mgmt., Mfg., Materials, Sales & mktg., R&D, Engineering
Industries: Generalist, Paper, Chemicals, Drugs mfg., Plastics/rubber, Paints/ petroleum products, Environmental svcs.

James Bangert & Assoc., Inc.
15500 Wayzata Blvd., Ste. 1022
Wayzata, Minnesota 55391
(612) 475-3454
Fax: (612) 473-4306
Email: jab@bangertassoc.com

Key Contact - Specialty:
Mr. James Bangert

Description: We serve both large corporate clients as well as small start-ups. Successful search assignments range from department/division manager to officer level positions.

Salary Minimum: $60,000
Functions: General mgmt., Mfg., Materials, Sales & mktg., HR mgmt., R&D, Engineering
Industries: Medical devices, Computer equip., Test/measurement equip., Finance, Computer svcs., Telecoms, High tech

---

The Barack Group, Inc. †
The Chrysler Bldg.
405 Lexington Ave., 50th Floor
New York, New York 10174
(212) 867-9700
Fax: (212) 681-9555
Email: execsearch@aol.com
Web: execsearch@earthlink.net

Key Contact - Specialty:
Ms. Brianne Barack

Description: A specialized recruiting firm for consumer goods and service companies.

Salary Minimum: $75,000
Functions: Directors, Senior mgmt., Middle mgmt., Advertising, Mktg. mgmt.
Industries: Food/bev/tobacco, Entertainment, Communications, Advertising/PR, New media, Broadcast & Film

---

Barger & Sargeant, Inc.
131 Windermere Rd., Ste. 400
P.O. Box 1420
Center Harbor, New Hampshire 03226-1420
(603) 253-4700

Key Contact - Specialty:
Mr. H. Carter Barger - *Senior executives, boards of directors*

Description: Founded in 1973. Twice selected in top 50 U.S. search firms by ERN. Noted for thoroughness in consulting, interviewing and board recruiting. A fixed fee is established at commencement of search.

Salary Minimum: $100,000
Functions: Generalist, Directors, Senior mgmt., Plant mgmt., Mktg. mgmt., Direct mktg., CFO's
Industries: Generalist, Retail, Banking, Insurance, High tech, Healthcare
Professional Associations: AESC, IACPR

J. W. Barleycorn, Renard & Assoc., Inc.
1614 Lancaster Ave.
Reynoldsburg, Ohio 43068-2639
(614) 861-4400
Fax: (614) 861-5558

Key Contact - Specialty:
Mr. James W. Barleycorn
Ms. Susan Erwin
Mr. James A. Renard

Description: Expertise in small and medium size companies in the midwest with concentration in engineering, human resources, legal, sales/marketing, finance and senior level executives.

Salary Minimum: $60,000
Functions: Generalist, Senior mgmt., Plant mgmt., Health admin., Sales mgmt., CFO's, Engineering
Industries: Generalist, Metal products, Machinery/Appliances, Finance, Computer svcs., Human resource svcs., Healthcare

---

Barnes Development Group, LLC
1017 W. Glen Oaks Lane, Ste. 108
Mequon, Wisconsin 53092
(414) 241-8468
Fax: (414) 241-8438
Email: BarnesDG@aol.com

Key Contact - Specialty:
Mr. Richard E. Barnes - *Manufacturing, service*
Ms. Roanne L. Barnes - *Long term care, non-profit, service industries*

Description: Practice dedicated to retained executive search consulting; midwest client base.

Salary Minimum: $50,000
Functions: Generalist, General mgmt., Mfg., Health admin., Sales & mktg., HR mgmt., MIS mgmt.
Industries: Generalist, Chemicals, Plastics/ rubber, Metal products, Machinery/ Appliances, Non-profits, Healthcare
Professional Associations: AESC

Fred A. Barnette & Assoc.
1213 Culbreth Drive
Wilmington, North Carolina 28405
(910) 256-0883
Fax: (910) 256-1183

Key Contact - Specialty:
Mr. Fred A. Barnette - *Generalist, healthcare*

Description: Consultants in executive search. Exclusively healthcare (biotechnology, pharmaceuticals, diagnostics, services, health services, consumer health, CRO's, managed care, life sciences). All functions, middle to top management.
Functions: General mgmt., Mfg., Materials, Healthcare, Sales & mktg., M&A, R&D
Industries: Mfg., Drugs mfg., Medical devices, Svcs., Pharmaceutical svcs., Biotech, Healthcare

Branches:
P.O. Box 190
27 Beach Rd.
Monmouth Beach, New Jersey 07750
(732) 870-3232
Fax: (732) 870-8432
Key Contact - Specialty:
Mr. Fred A. Barnette - *Generalist, healthcare*

Barone-O'Hara Assoc., Inc.
29 Emmons Drive
Princeton, New Jersey 08540
(609) 452-1980
Fax: (609) 452-0053

Key Contact - Specialty:
Ms. Marialice Barone - *Medical devices*
Mr. James J. O'Hara - *Medical devices*

Description: Executive search exclusively to manufacturers of healthcare devices. Especially successful with small companies: startups, restarts, fast growth. Consulting provided as adjunct to executive search.

Salary Minimum: $60,000
Functions: Senior mgmt., Product dev., Plant mgmt., Mkt. research, Mktg. mgmt., Sales mgmt., Int'l.
Industries: Medical devices

Affiliates:
Richmond Healthcare Consultants

† occasional contingency assignment

Barrett Hospitality Search
23591 El Toro Rd., Ste. 213
Lake Forest, California 92630
(714) 458-6789

Key Contact - Specialty:
Mr. Peter Barrett - *Hospitality*
Ms. Pat McCormick - *Hospitality*
Mr. Steve Pitzer - *Hospitality*
Mr. Sal Sarabosing
Ms. Tracy Thomas

Description: Specialize in selection and recruitment of senior/middle level hospitality executives, e.g. CEO, CFO, COO, sales, marketing, financial, human resources and regional, district and general managers.

Salary Minimum: $60,000
Functions: Senior mgmt., Middle mgmt., Mktg. mgmt., Sales mgmt., HR mgmt., CFO's, MIS mgmt.
Industries: Hospitality

Barrington Hart, Inc.
20 N. Wacker Drive
Chicago, Illinois 60606
(312) 332-3344
Fax: (312) 332-3617
Email: bhart20@aol.com

Key Contact - Specialty:
Ms. Gloria J. Rosemarin - *Finance & unique individual contributor*

Description: Multi-specialty firm emphasizing responsiveness, resourcefulness, creativity, flexibility. Offering full service executive search and innovative variations. Will unbundle assignments to meet needs for research/sourcing, interviewing assistance and reference checking.

Salary Minimum: $60,000
Functions: Generalist, Middle mgmt., Production, Sales & mktg., Finance, Graphic artists
Industries: Generalist, Agri/forestry/mining, Plastics/rubber, Computer equip., Finance, Equip. svcs., Communications

Nathan Barry Assoc., Inc.
301 Union Wharf
Boston, Massachusetts 02109
(617) 227-6067
Fax: (617) 227-9105

Key Contact - Specialty:
Mr. Nathan Barry - *CEO's for venture funded medical device companies*

Description: Nathan Barry Associates has a unique search capability. Our prime focus is to participate with the management/investors in helping to build and grow the client company.

Salary Minimum: $100,000
Functions: Directors, Senior mgmt., Mfg., Sales & mktg., CFO's, R&D, Engineering
Industries: Drugs mfg., Medical devices, Venture cap., Biotech, Healthcare

Barth Smith Company
1000 Skokie Blvd.
Wilmette, Illinois 60091
(847) 853-8860

Key Contact - Specialty:
Mr. David K. Barth - *Senior management*
Mr. Paul C. Smith

Description: Small generalist firm with considerable industrial experience. Searches conducted expeditiously by senior principals with few conflicts of interest and a strong link to successful strategy implementation.

Salary Minimum: $100,000
Functions: General mgmt., Directors, Senior mgmt., Materials, Sales & mktg., Finance, CFO's
Industries: Generalist, Metal products, Machinery/Appliances, Wholesale, Retail, Venture cap., Non-classifiable industries

Bartholdi & Co., Inc.
1515 Arapahoe St., Ste. 450
Denver, Colorado 80202
(303) 606-4783
Fax: (303) 606-4787
Email: tmalouf@bartholdi-marlar.com
Web: www.bartholdi-marlar.com

Key Contact - Specialty:
Mr. Terry Malouf - *High technology, contract electronics manufacturing*

Description: Retained senior level executive search and management consulting firm with strength and specialization in venture funded start-up firms as well as electronics, software, computer, telecommunications, investment banking and venture capital funds.

Salary Minimum: $70,000
Functions: Senior mgmt., Mktg. mgmt., Sales mgmt., CFO's, IT, Systems dev., Engineering
Industries: Computer equip., Consumer electronics, Test/measurement equip., Invest. banking, Venture cap.

Branches:
10040 E. Happy Valley Rd., Ste. 244
Scottsdale, Arizona 85255
(602) 502-2178
Fax: (602) 502-5992
Email: tgbartholdi@bartholdi-marlar.com
Key Contact - Specialty:
Mr. Theodore G. Bartholdi, Sr. - *High technology, venture capital partners & associates*

24387 Saddlebag Court, Ste. 200
Murrieta, California 92562-6103
(909) 698-5757
Fax: (909) 698-4010
Email: tcourbat@bartholdi-marlar.com
Key Contact - Specialty:
Mr. Thomas Courbat - *High technology*

637 S. Broadway, Ste B-217
Boulder, Colorado 80303-5932
(303) 664-5088
Fax: (303) 664-5089
Email: ifred@bartholdi-marlar.com
Key Contact - Specialty:
Mr. J. Fred Henderson - *High technology*

P.O. Box 947
Leadville, Colorado 80461
(719) 486-2918
Fax: (719) 486-0522
Key Contact - Specialty:
Ms. Terry Stevenson - *High technology, contract electronics manufacturing*

14 Douglass Way
Exeter, New Hampshire 03833
(603) 772-4228
Fax: (603) 778-4746
Email: tedbartholdijr@batholdi-marlar.com
Key Contact - Specialty:
Mr. Theodore G. Bartholdi, Jr. - *High technology*

12020 Sunrise Valley Drive, Ste. 160
Reston, Virginia 20191-3429
(703) 476-5519
Fax: (703) 391-0029
Email: cholt@bartholdi-marlar.com
Key Contact - Specialty:
Ms. Carol Holt - *High technology, investment banking*

Networks:
Marlar International

Barton Assoc., Inc.
(Firm declined to update.)
One Riverway, Ste. 2500
Houston, Texas 77056
(713) 961-9111
Fax: (713) 993-9399

Key Contact - Specialty:
Mr. Gary Barton - *Generalist, consumer marketing, general management, human resources*
Ms. Kathleen Johnson - *Human resources, learning, finance, consulting, energy*
Ms. Pat Kelso - *Generalist, human resources, systems integration*
Ms. Rachelle Vento - *Research*
Ms. Mara Van Nostrand - *Consumer marketing*
Ms. Juliet Giries - *Consumer marketing, organization development*
Ms. Barbara Keller - *Consumer marketing, human resources*
Ms. Allison Parsons - *Consumer marketing, general management*
Ms. Kim Turner - *Consulting*
Ms. Maria Harris - *Consulting*

Mr. Steve Williams - *Energy, refining, consulting*

Description: A global retainer practice built on strong client relationships and timely execution of projects. Expertise encompasses most industries and functional areas.

Salary Minimum: $75,000
Functions: Generalist, General mgmt., Mktg. mgmt., HR mgmt., Finance, IT, Mgmt. consultants
Industries: Generalist, Energy/utilities, Food/bev/tobacco, Chemicals, Computer equip., Finance, Banking, Computer svcs., Accounting, Mgmt. consulting, Human resource svcs., Communications, Advertising/PR, Telecoms, Aerospace, High tech, Software

Bason Associates

11311 Cornell Park Drive, Ste. 200
Cincinnati, Ohio 45242
(513) 469-9881
Fax: (513) 469-9691
Email: bason@one.net
Web: www.bason.com

Key Contact - Specialty:
Mr. Maurice L. Bason - *General management, packaging, capital equipment, plastics*
Ms. L. Christine Visnich - *Healthcare services, pharmaceutical devices, medical devices, venture capital, general management*
Mr. Barry Joffe - *Manufacturing operations, human resources, financial, public services*
Ms. Elizabeth Hall - *Telecommunications, high technology, global search*
Mr. Ted W. Plattenburg - *Consumer packaged goods*

Description: Experienced consultants emphasize a team approach to bring outstanding, timely results in the domestic and international market. The principles of integrity, commitment and professionalism form the foundation of the firm.

Salary Minimum: $75,000
Functions: General mgmt., Mfg., Sales & mktg., HR mgmt., Finance, IT, Engineering
Industries: Generalist, Mfg., Transportation, Finance, Communications, High tech, Healthcare

Battalia Winston Int'l./The Euram Consultants Group

300 Park Ave., 23rd Floor
New York, New York 10022
(212) 308-8080
Email: information@battaliawinston.com
Web: www.battaliawinston.com

Key Contact - Specialty:
Ms. Dale Winston
Mr. Terence M. Gallagher

Description: A long-established and highly-respected domestic and international executive search firm with expertise in most industries and all functions at the senior level with emphasis on a professional, responsive and quality service to our clients.

Salary Minimum: $100,000
Functions: General mgmt., Directors, Senior mgmt., Admin. svcs., Legal, Mfg., Product dev., Production, Automation, Plant mgmt., Quality, Materials, Purchasing, Materials Plng., Distribution, Health admin., Sales & mktg., Mktg. mgmt., Sales mgmt., PR, HR mgmt., Benefits, Personnel, Finance, CFO's, Budgeting, Cash mgmt., Taxes, M&A, Risk mgmt., IT, MIS mgmt., Systems anal., Systems dev., Systems implem., Network admin., DB admin., Specialized services, Mgmt. consultants, Non-profits, Attorneys, Int'l.
Industries: Energy/utilities, Mfg., Food/bev/tobacco, Paper, Chemicals, Soap/perfume/cosmetics, Drugs mfg., Medical devices, Plastics/rubber, Metal products, Machinery/Appliances, Motor vehicles, Computer equip., Consumer electronics, Test/measurement equip., Misc. mfg., Finance, Banking, Invest. banking, Venture cap., Svcs., Entertainment, Non-profits, Pharmaceutical svcs., Legal, Computer svcs., Mgmt. consulting, Human resource svcs., Communications, Publishing, Defense, Aerospace, Insurance, High tech, Software, Healthcare
Professional Associations: AESC, IACPR

Branches:
1888 Century Park E.
Los Angeles, California 90067
(310) 284-8080
Key Contact - Specialty:
Mr. Michael McClain
Mr. William E. Mason

One Sansome St.
San Francisco, California 94104
(415) 984-3180
Key Contact - Specialty:
Mr. Dave Thompson

150 S. Wacker Drive, Ste. 1220
Chicago, Illinois 60606
(312) 704-0050
Email: chicagoBWI@aol.com
Key Contact - Specialty:
Mr. James F. McSherry
Mr. Richard W. Folts
Mr. James P. O'Neill

20 William St.
Wellesley Hills, Massachusetts 02181
(781) 239-1400
Key Contact - Specialty:
Mr. Steven M. Garfinkle

33 Wood Ave. S.
Iselin, New Jersey 08830
(732) 603-5265
Key Contact - Specialty:
Mr. Terence M. Gallagher

Networks:
Euram Consultants Group

R. Gaines Baty Assoc., Inc.

12750 Merit Drive, Ste. 990
Dallas, Texas 75251
(972) 386-7900
Fax: (972) 387-2224
Email: gbaty@RGBA.com
Web: www.rgba.com

Key Contact - Specialty:
Mr. R. Gaines Baty - *Information technology management, consulting management, general management (technology companies)*

Description: Full scale national executive search for specialized mid-to-upper level management in technology, systems and consulting fields and general and sales management for technology companies. Personal attention, results orientation and long term approach.

Salary Minimum: $80,000
Functions: General mgmt., Distribution, Sales mgmt., IT, MIS mgmt., Systems implem., Mgmt. consultants
Industries: Mfg., Wholesale, Retail, Computer svcs., Mgmt. consulting, High tech, Software

Branches:
2870 Peachtree Rd., Ste. 256
Atlanta, Georgia 30305
(770) 859-9980
Fax: (770) 992-2631
Key Contact - Specialty:
Ms. Marcia Dickens - *Financial management (US and international), bilingual candidates*

Martin H. Bauman Assoc., Inc.

375 Park Ave., Ste. 2002
New York, New York 10152
(212) 752-6580

Key Contact - Specialty:
Mr. Martin H. Bauman - *Finance, P&L, venture capital, transportation*
Ms. Nina Proct - *Generalist*
Mr. Steven A. Heller - *Generalist*

Description: Our firm offers a highly personalized service in executive recruitment and assessment, at the core of which is our peerless assessment capability, recognized worldwide.

Salary Minimum: $165,000
Functions: Generalist, Senior mgmt., Mfg., Distribution, Sales & mktg., HR mgmt., CFO's
Industries: Generalist, Food/bev/tobacco, Soap/perfume/cosmetics, Transportation, Wholesale, Finance, Insurance

Professional Associations: AESC

Branches:
625 N. Michigan Ave., Ste. 500
Chicago, Illinois 60611-3108
(312) 751-5407
Key Contact - Specialty:
Ms. Audrey Hellinger - *Financial services, generalist*

Networks:
Transearch Int'l.

The Bauman Group
220 Main St., Ste. 200
Los Altos, California 94024
(650) 941-0800
Fax: (650) 941-1729
Email: BaumanGrp@aol.com

Key Contact - Specialty:
Ms. Ina Bauman - *Medical, biotechnology, pharmaceuticals*
Ms. Stephanie Greenblatt - *Medical devices, biotechnology*

Description: Retained search firm which provides senior level clinical and regulatory, research & business development expertise to biotechnology, pharmaceutical, medical device and medical instrumentation companies.

Salary Minimum: $90,000
Functions: Middle mgmt., Physicians, Mkt. research, Mktg. mgmt., Sales mgmt.
Industries: Drugs mfg., Medical devices, Pharmaceutical svcs., Biotech, Healthcare

Affiliates:
Kazan Int'l.

BayResearch Group, Inc.
425 N. Martingale Rd., Ste. 1560
Schaumburg, Illinois 60173
(847) 413-4000
Fax: (847) 413-4025
Email: BayRecruit@aol.com
Web: BayResearch.com

Key Contact - Specialty:
Mr. Michael T. Peterson - *Financial services, marketing, sales, strategic planning*
Mr. Vaughn Emory - *Healthcare, biotechnology, information systems, engineering*

Description: We typically guarantee a presentation of five (5) qualified and interested candidates, strategically sourced from targeted organizations, within a 2-4 week time frame.

Salary Minimum: $60,000
Functions: Directors, Product dev., HR mgmt., Taxes, Risk mgmt., Mgmt. consultants, Environmentalists
Industries: Computer equip., Consumer electronics, Mgmt. consulting, High tech, Software, Biotech, Healthcare

BCG Search, Inc.
(Firm declined to update.)
9172 Wickham Way
Orlando, Florida 32836
(407) 876-0390

Key Contact - Specialty:
Mr. R. Michael Hornbuckle - *Senior management*

Description: Our searches are often directed at finding a specific problem and require us to be very insightful about organization dynamics and issues.

Salary Minimum: $75,000
Functions: Directors, Senior mgmt., Health admin., CFO's, Budgeting, Cash mgmt., MIS mgmt.
Industries: Construction, Hospitality, Nonprofits, Real estate, Healthcare

Branches:
9690 Deerco Rd., Ste. 250
Timonium, Maryland 21093
(410) 583-1722
Key Contact - Specialty:
Mr. Chris Stevens

Beach Executive Search Inc.
10100 W. Sample Rd., Ste. 325
Cumber Executive Plaza
Coral Springs, Florida 33065-3975
(954) 340-7337

Key Contact - Specialty:
Mr. William L. Beach - *Generalist*

Description: Generalist retained search firm providing a highly personalized service to a wide range of clients located throughout central and south Florida requiring national searches.

Salary Minimum: $75,000
Functions: Mfg., Sales & mktg., HR mgmt., Finance, IT, R&D, Engineering
Industries: Generalist, Svcs., Aerospace, Real estate, High tech, Software

The Beam Group
11 Penn Ctr. Plaza, Ste. 502
Philadelphia, Pennsylvania 19103
(215) 988-2100
Fax: (215) 988-1558
Email: beamgrouprag@msn.com

Key Contact - Specialty:
Mr. Russell A. Glicksman - *Senior executives (marketing, human resources, MIS, direct marketing, finance)*
Mr. Scott McKenna - *Human resources, marketing, financial services*
Ms. Suzanne Martin - *Consumer products, operations research, technology, sales & marketing*

Description: Generalist search firm with a diverse group of both large and small insurance, financial services, consumer products and high-tech companies. Particular expertise in candidate assessment.

Salary Minimum: $70,000
Functions: Senior mgmt., Mfg., Mktg. mgmt., Direct mktg., CFO's, Cash mgmt., MIS mgmt.
Industries: Mfg., Food/bev/tobacco, Retail, Finance, Communications, Insurance, Healthcare

Branches:
111 North Ave.
Barrington, Illinois 60010-3257
(847) 382-6040
Fax: (847) 382-6510
Key Contact - Specialty:
Mr. Michael Puestow - *Actuarial, managed care*

600 Third Ave.
New York, New York 10016
(212) 476-4100
Fax: (212) 986-7798
Key Contact - Specialty:
Mr. Al Swann - *Consumer products, technology*
Mr. Jay Santamaria - *Consumer products, operations research, technology, sales & marketing, pharmaceuticals*
Ms. Susan Merjos - *Administration, human resources, finance*

Becker, Norton & Co.
4088 Alpha Drive, Alpha Bldg.
Allison Park, Pennsylvania 15101
(412) 486-5553
Fax: (412) 487-8576

Key Contact - Specialty:
Mr. Robert C. Becker

Description: A strong regional firm with capability of conducting national searches. The company has extensive expertise in conducting searches and experience in marketing, finance, data processing systems and management disciplines.

Salary Minimum: $60,000
Functions: Senior mgmt., Production, Sales mgmt., Benefits, CFO's, Taxes, Engineering
Industries: Construction, Metal products, Retail, Banking, Real estate

The Bedford Consulting Group Inc.
The Bedford House, 60 Bedford Rd.
Toronto, Ontario M5R 2K2
Canada
(416) 963-9000
Fax: (416) 963-9998

Email: search@bedfordgroup.com

Key Contact - Specialty:
Mr. Steven G. Pezim - *General management, sales & marketing, technology, retail, consumer products*
Mr. Howard J. Pezim - *Generalist, healthcare, consumer products, industrial, senior management*
Mr. G. Russell Buckland - *Mining, pulp & paper, engineering, construction*

Description: Well established, research based generalist firm; senior and middle management searches across most functions and industries.

Salary Minimum: $75,000
Functions: Senior mgmt., Middle mgmt., Mktg. mgmt., Sales mgmt., Personnel, CFO's, MIS mgmt.
Industries: Agri/forestry/mining, Food/bev/tobacco, Paper, Drugs mfg., Hospitality, Software, Healthcare
Professional Associations: AESC, IACPR

Networks:
Transearch Int'l.

The Bedford Group †

154 Quicksand Pond Rd.
Little Compton, Rhode Island 02837
(401) 635-4646
Fax: (401) 635-8466
Email: bedgroup@meganet.net

Key Contact - Specialty:
Mr. John W. Edwards - *Electronics*
Ms. Lillian E. Edwards - *Electronics*

Description: Extensive senior executive experience in electronics, medical devices, telecommunications industries. Outstanding completion record. Off limit recruiting strictly observed.

Salary Minimum: $70,000
Functions: Middle mgmt., Product dev., Production, Quality, Mkt. research, Mktg. mgmt., R&D
Industries: Medical devices, Computer equip., Computer svcs., Telecoms, Aerospace, High tech, Software

Behavioral Science Assoc., Inc. †

2135 E. University Drive, Ste. 121
Mesa, Arizona 85213
(602) 833-2629
Fax: (602) 833-1029
Email: bsa@bsassoc.com
Web: www.bsassoc.com

Key Contact - Specialty:
Mr. Robert E. King - *Insurance*
Mr. Vincent L. Cauallo - *Insurance*

Description: Retained executive search firm that blends the best of traditional executive search with modern psychological assessment and evaluation. This powerful combination provides well qualified people that will work effectively within the hiring company's own corporate environment.
Functions: Senior mgmt., Middle mgmt., Mktg. mgmt., Benefits, M&A, Systems dev., Mgmt. consultants
Industries: Brokers, Misc. financial, Mgmt. consulting, Human resource svcs., Insurance, High tech, Software

Affiliates:
Tesauro Management Counselors

Neail Behringer Consultants Inc.

24 E. 38th St., Ste. 4B
New York, New York 10016
(212) 689-7555
Fax: (212) 689-6868

Key Contact - Specialty:
Mr. Neail Behringer - *Generalist*
Mr. Charles Seitz - *Generalist*
Ms. Marie Antoniazzi - *Generalist*
Ms. Mary Lou Martin - *Healthcare*
Mr. Dan Danford - *Generalist*

Description: We specialize in recruiting middle and top level management for the fashion and healthcare markets.

Salary Minimum: $50,000
Functions: Generalist, General mgmt., Senior mgmt., Healthcare, Health admin., Sales & mktg., Finance
Industries: Generalist, Textiles/apparel, Printing, Retail, Mgmt. consulting, Healthcare

Branches:
11 Wagstaff Lane
West Islip, New York 11795
(516) 669-6542
Fax: (516) 669-6542
Key Contact - Specialty:
Mr. Neail Behringer

Bell Wishingrad Partners Inc.

230 Park Ave., Ste. 1000
New York, New York 10169
(212) 949-6666

Key Contact - Specialty:
Mr. Nelson C. Bell - *Financial services*
Ms. Vivian Wishingrad - *Financial services*

Description: A practice focused upon senior management positions in financial services and affiliated industries. Search activities performed only by partners with limited client base avoiding off-limit conflicts. All resumes should be directed to the Stamford office.

Salary Minimum: $150,000
Functions: Senior mgmt., Mktg. mgmt., Sales mgmt., Cash mgmt., M&A
Industries: Finance, Banking, Invest. banking, Brokers, Venture cap., Misc. financial

Branches:
2701 Summer St.,
Stamford, Connecticut 06905
(203) 921-2600
Key Contact - Specialty:
Ms. Vivian Wishingrad - *Financial services*

Joy Reed Belt Search Consultants, Inc.

P.O. Box 18446
Oklahoma City, Oklahoma 73154
(405) 842-6336
Fax: (405) 842-6357
Email: drbelt@aol.com

Key Contact - Specialty:
Ms. Joy Reed Belt - *CEOs, senior management, generalist*
Mr. Dalon W. Schuckman - *Mid level management (generalist)*
Ms. Carolyn Stuart - *Research*
Ms. Lynn Watson - *Banking, healthcare*

Description: Human resources consulting firm specializing in executive search. Our highly qualified professionals are trained in business and the behavioral sciences and are able to present only those candidates who will fit with your company's philosophy and corporate culture.

Salary Minimum: $60,000
Functions: Middle mgmt., Health admin., Advertising, Benefits, M&A, MIS mgmt., Attorneys, Paralegals
Industries: Generalist, Energy/utilities, Food/bev/tobacco, Human resource svcs., Advertising/PR, Real estate, Healthcare

Branches:
6002 S. Atlanta Court
Tulsa, Oklahoma 74170-0688
(918) 748-8844
Fax: (918) 742-6172
Email: jrbtulsa@aol.com
Key Contact - Specialty:
Mr. Nick Ratanasin

Bench Int'l. Search, Inc.

116 N. Robertson Blvd., Ste. 503
Los Angeles, California 90048
(310) 854-9900
Fax: (310) 652-2081
Email: careerlink@benchinternational.com
Web: www.benchinternational.com

Key Contact - Specialty:
Ms. Denise DeMan - *Pharmaceutical, biotechnology*

Description: We provide both recruiting and staffing development consulting services to our client base. We are limited to recruiting professionals with advanced degrees for the pharmaceutical, biotechnology and high technology industries. We serve both the technical and administrative tracks up through executive management.

Salary Minimum: $100,000

† occasional contingency assignment

Functions: Directors, Senior mgmt., Middle mgmt., Mkt. research, R&D, Minorities
Industries: Chemicals, Drugs mfg., Medical devices, Pharmaceutical svcs., Biotech, Healthcare

---

Bender Executive Search Management Consulting

45 N. Station Plaza, Ste. 315
Great Neck, New York 11021
(516) 773-4300
Fax: (516) 482-5355
Email: Benderexec@aol.com

Key Contact - Specialty:
Mr. Alan Bender - *Marketing, sales promotion, market research, sales. communications for manufacturers*

Description: Tailor-made consultative approach by a former marketing executive with 15 years specializing in marketing search nationwide. Multi-resource firm with sophisticated research capability. Known for quality, thoroughness, fast results, pro-active personalized service and close collaborative relationships.

Salary Minimum: $75,000
Functions: Senior mgmt., Middle mgmt., Advertising, Mkt. research, Mktg. mgmt., Sales mgmt., Direct mktg.
Industries: Mfg., Retail, Finance, Svcs., Communications, Insurance, High tech
Professional Associations: IACPR

The Bennett Group, Inc.

5640 Professional Circle
Indianapolis, Indiana 46241
(317) 247-1240
Fax: (317) 247-6533
Email: recruserv@aol.com

Key Contact - Specialty:
Mr. Charles T. Gelatka - *Automotive, electronics (mostly engineering & manufacturing)*
Mr. M.D. Bennett - *Automotive, electronics (mostly engineering & manufacturing)*

Description: The founder of the firm was trained, during the mid-seventies, by Elmer R. Davis, one of the true pioneers of the search industry. Founded in 1981, the firm consists of professionals whose backgrounds have kept pace with technology in all facets of the electronics and automotive industries.

Salary Minimum: $60,000
Functions: Senior mgmt., Middle mgmt., Production, Productivity, Systems dev., R&D, Engineering
Industries: Machinery/Appliances, Motor vehicles, Computer equip., Consumer electronics, High tech, Software

---

Bennett Search & Consulting Co.

7065 Dennis Circle, #103
Naples, Florida 34104
(941) 352-2820
Fax: (941) 353-7719

Key Contact - Specialty:
Mr. Robert C. Bennett, Jr. - *Banks, country clubs, generalist*
Dr. James D. Carter - *Generalist*
Dr. Jane Carter - *Generalist*
Ms. Colleen Shue - *Computer hardware, software*
Mr. Beirne Brown - *Restaurants, hotels*

Description: Generalist USA - hardware/software, banking, electronics, security, real estate development, golf club staffing, restaurant/hotel management. Senior management, general management, sales, manufacturing, engineering and human resources. 25 years quality diversity recruitment and training.

Salary Minimum: $60,000
Functions: Directors, Senior mgmt., Sales & mktg., Finance, IT, Minorities, Attorneys, Paralegals
Industries: Generalist, Finance, Banking, Hospitality, Law enfcmt., Real estate

---

C. Berger And Company †

327 E. Gundersen Drive
Carol Stream, Illinois 60188
(630) 653-1115
(800) 382-4CBC
Fax: (630) 653-1691
Email: cberger@dupagels.lib.il.us
Web: www.cberger.com

Key Contact - Specialty:
Ms. Carol A. Berger - *Library & records personnel*
Ms. Catherine Bartholomew - *Library & records personnel*
Ms. Christine Bodine - *Library & records personnel*

Description: CBC conducts searches for managerial, marketing and subject specialists in libraries, information centers and related businesses; supplies temporaries to libraries and offers library/records management consulting and project support services.

Salary Minimum: $50,000
Functions: Admin. svcs., Purchasing, Personnel, IT, Specialized services
Industries: Finance, Non-profits, Communications, Government, Insurance, High tech, Non-classifiable industries

---

Berkhemer/Clayton, Inc.

Union Station
800 N. Alameda St., Ste. 200
Los Angeles, California 90012
(213) 621-2300
Fax: (213) 621-2303
Email: bcsearch@aol.com

Key Contact - Specialty:
Ms. Betsy Berkhemer-Credaire
Mr. Fred J. Clayton
Ms. Melba Sanders
Mr. Cris Credaire

Description: Multi-ethnic-owned; partners are African-American, Asian and Anglo. We handle communications, marketing, financial and management searches at senior levels.

Salary Minimum: $70,000
Functions: Directors, Senior mgmt., Mktg. mgmt., PR, Minorities
Industries: Food/bev/tobacco, Banking, Hospitality, Advertising/PR, New media, High tech, Healthcare

---

Best, Coleman & Co., Inc.

1085 Commonwealth Ave., Ste. 325
Boston, Massachusetts 02115

Key Contact - Specialty:
Mr. Robert Best
Ms. Claudia A. Coleman

Description: Senior management and sales and marketing positions within the retail and wholesale industries. Retainer only.

Salary Minimum: $90,000
Functions: Senior mgmt., Mkt. research, Mktg. mgmt., Sales mgmt.
Industries: Wholesale, Retail

BEST/World Assoc. Inc.

505 W. Abram St., 3rd Floor
Arlington, Texas 76010
(817) 861-0000
Fax: (817) 459-BEST
Email: email@bestworld.com
Web: www.bestworld.com

Key Contact - Specialty:
Mr. G. Tim Best - *Senior management*
Ms. April Grady - *Generalist*

Description: Modular and full service, executive search and research support services to corporate recruiters. Services offered on an hourly basis for all phases of the search process from target list development through face-to-face interviews. Competitor organization analysis and pre-employment screening services are also available.

Salary Minimum: $70,000

Functions: Generalist, General mgmt., CFO's, MIS mgmt., Systems implem., Mgmt. consultants, Minorities
Industries: Generalist, Food/bev/tobacco, Soap/perfume/cosmetics, Finance, Mgmt. consulting, High tech, Software

---

Bialecki Inc.

780 Third Ave., Ste. 4203
New York, New York 10017
(212) 755-1090
Web: www.bialecki.com

Key Contact - Specialty:
Ms. Linda Bialecki - *Mission critical or difficult searches*

Description: Highly specialized investment banking, capital markets, sales, trading, research and product development, corporate finance and money management searches primarily for investment banks. Expertise in investment banking industry heads, structured products and derivatives. U.S. based clients, worldwide searches. Substantial repeat business.

Salary Minimum: $450,000
Functions: M&A
Industries: Invest. banking
Professional Associations: AESC

Bialla & Assoc. Inc.

4000 Bridgeway, Ste. 201
Sausalito, California 94965
(415) 332-7111
Fax: (415) 332-3964
Web: www.bialla.com

Key Contact - Specialty:
Mr. Vito Bialla
Mr. H. Scott Thomson
Mr. W. Jeff Hastings

Description: Specialists in all aspects of marketing, advertising and senior management. Domestic and international client base with Western states emphasis. Partners experienced in wide variety of industries, particularly consumer goods and services.

Salary Minimum: $100,000
Functions: Directors, Senior mgmt., Middle mgmt., Mktg. mgmt., Direct mktg., CFO's, Int'l.
Industries: Food/bev/tobacco, Computer equip., Consumer electronics, Entertainment, Communications, High tech, Software

---

Paul J. Biestek Assoc., Inc.

10600 W. Higgins Rd., Ste. 300
Rosemont, Illinois 60018
(847) 825-5131

Key Contact - Specialty:
Mr. Paul J. Biestek - *Generalist*

Description: We draw on 30 years of executive search consulting and corporate human resources management experience.

Salary Minimum: $70,000
Functions: Mfg., Materials, Sales mgmt., IT, R&D, Engineering, Architects
Industries: Energy/utilities, Mfg., Food/bev/tobacco, Medical devices, Machinery/Appliances, Defense, Aerospace
Professional Associations: IACPR

Billington & Assoc. †

3250 Wilshire Blvd., Ste. 900
Los Angeles, California 90010
(213) 386-7511
Fax: (213) 386-7025

Key Contact - Specialty:
Mr. Brian J. Billington - *Finance, general management, administration*

Description: Primary emphasis on middle management recruitment for financial/administrative professionals. Consulting includes finance/organizational areas plus specialty in full range of fundraising activities for non profit organizations.

Salary Minimum: $60,000
Functions: Senior mgmt., Middle mgmt., Purchasing, Health admin., CFO's, Credit, Non-profits
Industries: Generalist

Affiliates:
Thomure Associates

Biomedical Search Consultants †

52 Federal Rd.
P.O. Box 1070
Danbury, Connecticut 06813-1070
(203) 744-4027
Fax: (203) 748-2122
Email: ta4nabio@prodigy.com

Key Contact - Specialty:
Mr. Thomas A. Fornabaio

Description: Pharmaceutical, medical devices, diagnostics and cosmetic industry specialists.
Functions: Production, Plant mgmt., Productivity, Purchasing, Packaging, R&D, Engineering
Industries: Chemicals, Soap/perfume/cosmetics, Drugs mfg., Medical devices, Biotech

Affiliates:
Carta Group Inc.

BioQuest Inc.

100 Spear St., Ste. 1125
San Francisco, California 94105
(415) 777-2422
Fax: (415) 777-4363
Email: anderson@bioquestinc.com
Web: www.bioquestinc.com

Key Contact - Specialty:
Mr. Roger J. Anderson
Dr. H. Jurgen Weber

Description: Areas of specialization include: executive management, corporate development; marketing/sales management, operations, research and development, engineering, manufacturing and regulatory.

Salary Minimum: $100,000
Functions: Directors, Senior mgmt., Middle mgmt., Mktg. mgmt., Sales mgmt., CFO's, R&D
Industries: Drugs mfg., Medical devices, Pharmaceutical svcs., Biotech

---

Deborah Bishop & Assoc.

1070 Marina Village Pkwy., Ste. 203
Alameda, California 94501
(510) 523-2305

Key Contact - Specialty:
Ms. Deborah Bishop

Description: We specialize in high-tech industry. We do retained search only. Integrated circuits, LAN, peripherals, computers.

Salary Minimum: $85,000
Functions: Directors, Senior mgmt., Mfg., Sales & mktg., Engineering
Industries: Computer equip., Telecoms, High tech, Software

Bishop Partners

708 Third Ave., Ste. 2200
New York, New York 10017
(212) 986-3419
Fax: (212) 986-3350
Email: info@bishopnet.com
Web: www.BishopPartners.com

Key Contact - Specialty:
Ms. Susan Bishop - *Media, entertainment, publishing, telecommunications*
Mr. Vincent Morgan - *Information technology, media*
Ms. Mary Jane Range - *Information technology, commercial banking, insurance*
Ms. Laura Timoney - *Cable, broadcasting, new media, telecommunications*
Ms. Christina Burz - *Cable, broadcasting, publishing*
Ms. Sheila Yossem - *Information technology, media*
Ms. Kristin Scorce

Description: Industry expertise in media, communications and entertainment; all functional areas covered with a specialty in information technology.

Salary Minimum: $120,000
Functions: General mgmt., Senior mgmt., Sales & mktg., HR mgmt., IT, MIS mgmt., Mgmt. consultants

† occasional contingency assignment

Industries: Entertainment, Computer svcs., Communications, Publishing, New media, Broadcast & Film, Telecoms
Professional Associations: AESC

Blackshaw, Olmstead, Lynch & Koenig

3414 Peachtree Rd. NE
1010 Monarch Plaza
Atlanta, Georgia 30326
(404) 261-7770
Fax: (404) 261-4469
Web: bolandk@mindspring.com

Key Contact - Specialty:
Ms. Lisa Shalet - *Generalist*
Mr. Brian Blackshaw - *Generalist*
Mr. George T. Olmstead - *Generalist*
Mr. Joel S. Koenig - *Generalist*
Ms. Barbara Anderson

Description: BOL&K is a retainer only, generalist firm, specializing in senior management. Our client base is international.

Salary Minimum: $100,000
Functions: Generalist
Industries: Generalist
Professional Associations: IACPR

Branches:
60 Arch St.
Greenwich, Connecticut 06830
(203) 869-7727
Fax: (203) 661-7261
Key Contact - Specialty:
Mr. John P. Lynch, III

Networks:
Transearch Int'l.

Blake/Hansen Ltd.

1920 Bayshore Drive
Englewood, Florida 34223
(941) 475-1300

Key Contact - Specialty:
Mr. Ty E. Hansen - *Aviation, aerospace, defense, high technology*

Description: Board member, officer, senior and middle echelon executive search. Consulting since 1974. Specializing in aviation/aerospace and high-technology industries contracting with DOD and the intelligence community.

Salary Minimum: $80,000
Functions: Generalist
Industries: Motor vehicles, Transportation, Defense, Aerospace, High tech

Branches:
102 W. 75th St., Ste. 40
New York, New York 10023
(212) 874-4933
Key Contact - Specialty:
Ms. Jeri E. Schmidt - *Packaging industry (all functions)*

J: Blakslee Int'l., Ltd.

49 Hillside Ave.
Mill Valley, California 94941
(415) 389-7300
Fax: (415) 389-7302
Email: jblakslee@msn.com

Key Contact - Specialty:
Mr. Jan H. Blakslee - *Medical device, pharmaceutical, biotechnology*
Ms. Joyce Mustin - *Medical device, pharmaceutical, biotechnology*

Description: Senior level retained executive search to the pharmaceutical, biotechnology and medical device/instrument industry and international capability, especially Europe.

Salary Minimum: $125,000
Functions: Directors, Senior mgmt., Product dev., Mktg. mgmt., CFO's, R&D, Engineering
Industries: Drugs mfg., Medical devices, Test/measurement equip., Venture cap., Biotech, Healthcare
Professional Associations: IACPR

Blaney Executive Search

Damon Mill Sq.
Concord, Massachusetts 01742
(978) 371-2192
Fax: (978) 369-9066
Email: blaexesrch@aol.com
Web: www.blaexesrch.com

Key Contact - Specialty:
Mr. John A. Blaney - *Marketing & sales vice presidents, engineering vice presidents, CEOs, COOs*

Description: Small firm providing quality search services to large and small organizations in the high technology fields. Extensive experience in working with start-up and emerging organizations.

Salary Minimum: $100,000
Functions: Senior mgmt., Product dev., Mkt. research, CFO's, MIS mgmt., R&D, Engineering
Industries: Medical devices, Computer equip., Test/measurement equip., Venture cap., New media, Telecoms, Software

Blau Mancino Schroeder

12 Roszel Rd., Ste. C-101
Princeton, New Jersey 08540
(609) 520-8400
Fax: (609) 520-8993

Key Contact - Specialty:
Mr. Gene Mancino

Description: We provide retained executive search services for the healthcare industry, including pharmaceuticals, biotechnology, medical device, diagnostics and healthcare services. Clients include major and developing corporations in North America.

Salary Minimum: $100,000
Functions: Directors, Senior mgmt., Middle mgmt., Product dev., Mktg. mgmt., MIS mgmt., R&D
Industries: Drugs mfg., Venture cap., Pharmaceutical svcs., Mgmt. consulting, Biotech, Healthcare

Branches:
800 FirsTier Bank Bldg.
Lincoln, Nebraska 68508
(402) 434-1494
Key Contact - Specialty:
Mr. Lee Schroeder

4800 Juan Tabo, Ste. D
Albuquerque, New Mexico 87111
(505) 271-0702
Fax: (505) 298-3939
Key Contact - Specialty:
Mr. Steven J. Schroeder

Block & Assoc.

20 Sunnyside Ave., Ste. A 332
Mill Valley, California 94941
(415) 389-9710
Fax: (415) 389-0314
Email: randsrch@aol.com

Key Contact - Specialty:
Mr. Randall T. Block

Description: We offer a thorough search process for director level and above in the high tech industry. Clients range from start-ups to established companies. Search consulting also available.

Salary Minimum: $90,000
Functions: Directors, Senior mgmt., Middle mgmt., Mktg. mgmt., Sales mgmt., IT, Engineering
Industries: Computer equip., Human resource svcs., New media, Broadcast & Film, Telecoms, High tech, Software

D. R. Blood & Assoc.

5900 E. Thomas Rd., Ste. H206
Scottsdale, Arizona 85251
(602) 675-2794
Email: den4ray@aol.com

Key Contact - Specialty:
Mr. Dennis R. Blood - *Entertainment, manufacturing*
Mr. Burwood O. Blood - *Supply chain management*
Mr. James L. Blood - *Sports administration, professional, sales management*
Ms. Candy Fox - *Audit, EDP*

Description: Clients: we isolate, select, evaluate and refer only candidates you will hire. Candidates: we only refer professionals with a solid vertical career history.

Salary Minimum: $75,000

Functions: Senior mgmt., Production, Materials Plng., Distribution, Packaging, CFO's, MIS mgmt.
Industries: Drugs mfg., Motor vehicles, Misc. mfg., Entertainment, Broadcast & Film, Software

---

Blum & Co.

1412 N. Lapham St.
Oconomowoc, Wisconsin 53066
(414) 569-8853

Key Contact - Specialty:
Mr. D. L. Buzz Blum

Description: A dedicated firm offering flexible, personalized service. Our reputation is built on experience, confidentiality, integrity and professionalism. Our unique fee schedule limits your exposure and assures results.

Salary Minimum: $40,000
Functions: Generalist, Senior mgmt., Middle mgmt., Engineering, Environmentalists
Industries: Generalist

Boardroom Consultants/Kenny Kindler Tholke

530 Fifth Ave., Ste. 2100
New York, New York 10036
(212) 328-0440

Key Contact - Specialty:
Mr. Roger M. Kenny - *Consumer, high technology, healthcare, heavy manufacturing, board director*
Mr. Peter A. Kindler - *Finance, information technology, board governance*
Mr. William E. Tholke - *High technology, insurance, healthcare, general management, board directors*
Mr. John A. Coleman - *Generalist, financial services*

Description: We are a generalist firm which recruits senior-level management for all industries. In addition, the firm specializes in the recruitment of corporate board directors and advisory board members through Boardroom Consultants. The firm's practice is national in scope and currently includes four executive recruiters based in New York.

Salary Minimum: $90,000
Functions: Generalist, Directors, Senior mgmt., CFO's, MIS mgmt., Engineering, Mgmt. consultants
Industries: Generalist, Motor vehicles, Finance, Banking, Computer svcs., Mgmt. consulting, Healthcare
Professional Associations: AESC, IACPR

Networks:
The Hever Group

Boettcher Assoc.

120 Bishops Way, Ste. 126
Brookfield, Wisconsin 53005
(414) 782-2205

Key Contact - Specialty:
Mr. Jack W. Boettcher - *Generalist*

Description: National generalist executive search firm in all functions in all industries and management consulting in human resource areas including outplacement.

Salary Minimum: $50,000
Functions: Generalist, General mgmt., Mfg., Materials, Sales & mktg., HR mgmt., Finance
Industries: Generalist, Metal products, Machinery/Appliances, Transportation, Computer svcs., Human resource svcs., Software

---

Bonell Ryan Inc.

630 5th Ave., Ste. 2607
Rockefeller Center
New York, New York 10111
(212) 332-3340
Fax: (212) 332-3335
Email: debgryan@aol.com
Web: www.bonnellryan.com

Key Contact - Specialty:
Ms. Debra Ryan - *Marketing, operations, risk management*

Salary Minimum: $100,000
Functions: Advertising, Mktg. mgmt., Direct mktg., Customer svc., Credit, Risk mgmt., Non-profits
Industries: Finance, Misc. financial, Mgmt. consulting, New media, High tech

---

Bonnell Assoc. Ltd.

2960 Post Rd. S., Ste. 200
Southport, Connecticut 06490
(203) 319-7214
Fax: (203) 319-7219
Email: info@bonnellassociates.com
Web: bonnellassociates.com

Key Contact - Specialty:
Mr. William R. Bonnell - *Financial services, managed care, healthcare, finance, marketing*
Ms. Linda Buggy - *Customer service, diversity, healthcare, managed care*
Ms. Cynthia Pallman-David - *Technology, healthcare, managed care, insurance, sales*

Description: Retained executive search firm offering focus on organizations which are rebuilding or in a turnaround. Industry experience includes concentration in healthcare, insurance, telecommunications, airline, banking, hotel and non-profit. Significant international experience.

Salary Minimum: $100,000
Functions: Sales & mktg., HR mgmt., Finance, Mgmt. consultants, Minorities, Int'l.
Industries: Generalist, Finance, Hospitality, Human resource svcs., Publishing, Insurance, Healthcare
Professional Associations: IACPR

John C. Boone & Co.

1807 Henley St.
Glenview, Illinois 60025
(847) 998-1905

Key Contact - Specialty:
Mr. John C. Boone - *Generalist*

Description: An individual practitioner with over 20 years executive search experience in multi-disciplines and diverse industries.

Salary Minimum: $60,000
Functions: Generalist
Industries: Generalist, Food/bev/tobacco, Paper, Drugs mfg., Medical devices, Machinery/Appliances, Motor vehicles

---

The Borton Wallace Co.

P.O. Box 8816
Asheville, North Carolina 28814
(828) 258-1831
Fax: (828) 251-0989
Email: mbp@gte.net

Key Contact - Specialty:
Mr. Murray B. Parker - *Pulp & paper*

Description: Most functions within pulp & paper, polymeric, nonwoven and vertically integrated industries. Executive search, organizational development and staffing consulting services to most manufacturing industries.

Salary Minimum: $60,000
Functions: Middle mgmt., Mfg., Materials, Sales & mktg., IT, R&D, Engineering
Industries: Paper, Chemicals, Packaging

Branches:
6504 Lake Shadows
Chattanooga, Tennessee 37343
(423) 842-7867
Fax: (423) 842-9336
Key Contact - Specialty:
Mr. Charles Andrews - *Marketing, sales, paper, chemicals, packaging*

Affiliates:
Brandywine Consulting Group

Bosch & Assoc., LLC

P.O. Box 1030
Greens Farms, Connecticut 06436
(203) 255-8700
Fax: (203) 259-4959

Email: ebosch@sprintmail.com

Key Contact - Specialty:
Mr. Eric E. Bosch - *Sales, marketing, finance, general management*
Mr. Brian Gardner - *Sales, marketing, public relations*
Mr. Don Doyle - *Sales, marketing, general management*
Ms. Diane Bosch - *Human resources, sales, marketing, general management*
Ms. Heather Madden - *Sales, marketing*

Description: We subscribe to a strict and proven executive search methodology. We consistently deliver to our clients executives of superior performance. We are extremely well networked in our chosen industries and functional areas.

Salary Minimum: $80,000
Functions: Mkt. research, Mktg. mgmt., Sales mgmt., Direct mktg., PR, HR mgmt., Finance
Industries: Food/bev/tobacco, Drugs mfg., Finance, Communications, Telecoms, High tech, Software

---

Bosland Gray Assoc.
Waterview Plaza
2001 Route 46, Ste. 310
Parsippany, New Jersey 07054
(201) 402-4964

Key Contact - Specialty:
Mr. Andrew Gray
Mr. Richard Bosland

Description: Fee fixed at beginning of search; proven expertise within technical and specialized areas; each assignment commands the direct and personal attention of one of the firm's principals.

Salary Minimum: $70,000
Functions: Generalist, Distribution, Mktg. mgmt., Sales mgmt., MIS mgmt., R&D, Mgmt. consultants
Industries: Generalist, Chemicals, Drugs mfg., Consumer electronics, Misc. mfg., Retail, Mgmt. consulting

---

Boulware & Assoc. Inc.
175 W. Jackson St., Ste. 1841
Chicago, Illinois 60604
(312) 322-0088
Fax: (312) 322-0092
Email: boulware1@aol.com

Key Contact - Specialty:
Ms. Christine Boulware - *Public, non-profit, private sectors*
Mr. David Erickson-Pearson - *Transportation, economic development, non-profit, real estate*
Ms. Jaye Stovall
Mr. Haskel Levi
Ms. Rhyan Zweifler - *Non-profit, community development, economic development, family services*
Ms. Etta Ish Henderson - *Healthcare, social services, managed care*
Mr. William Geller - *Public sector*
Ms. Kavita Visayan
Ms. Marian Alexander deBerry - *Human resources, financial services*

Description: A national retained executive search firm doing work in the private, not-for-profit and public sectors. Our work ranges from recruiting senior executives in major corporations to serving executive directors, governors and mayors.

Salary Minimum: $60,000
Functions: General mgmt., Health admin., Sales & mktg., HR mgmt., Finance, Minorities, Non-profits
Industries: Generalist, Mfg., Finance, Non-profits, Human resource svcs., Government, Real estate

---

Bowden & Co., Inc.
P.O. Box 39427
Cleveland, Ohio 44139
(440) 248-2313
Fax: (440) 248-6528
Email: bowdenandco@bowdenandco.com
Web: www.bowdenandco.com

Key Contact - Specialty:
Mr. Chester W. Dickey - *Generalist, manufacturing, information technology*
Mr. Harrison R. Magee - *Generalist, manufacturing*
Ms. Dorothy A. Teresko

Description: Develops focused candidate and position specifications honed to client requirements. Quality execution, assured integrity, successful results evidenced by over two decades of successful consulting practice.

Salary Minimum: $100,000
Functions: Senior mgmt., Middle mgmt., Mfg., Sales & mktg., HR mgmt., MIS mgmt., Int'l.
Industries: Generalist, Energy/utilities, Mfg., Finance, Svcs., Aerospace, Insurance

Affiliates:
Robert W. Dingman Co., Inc.
L. W. Foote Co.
Gunlock Associates, Inc.
Lasher Assoc.
Ott & Hansen, Inc.
Questar Partners, Inc.
Van Dyke Assoc.

BowdenGlobal, Ltd.
6450 Rockside Woods Blvd. S., Ste. 100
Corporate Plaza I
Cleveland, Ohio 44131
(216) 328-2088

Key Contact - Specialty:
Mr. Otis H. Bowden, II - *General management*

Description: Quality, satisfied client performance consistent with founders three times national recognition within The Career Makers.

Salary Minimum: $100,000
Functions: Generalist, Senior mgmt., Middle mgmt., Product dev., Mktg. mgmt., CFO's, Attorneys
Industries: Generalist, Chemicals, Plastics/rubber, Motor vehicles, Finance, Aerospace, Insurance

---

Boyden
100 Park Ave., 34th Floor
New York, New York 10017
(212) 843-0200
Email: boydenhaw@aol.com
Web: www.boyden.com

Key Contact - Specialty:
Mr. Richard Foy

Description: Pioneers in the world of search; globally leading the way.

Salary Minimum: $90,000
Functions: Generalist, Directors, Senior mgmt., Plant mgmt., Quality, Distribution, Packaging, Health admin., Mktg. mgmt., Sales mgmt., Direct mktg., PR, HR mgmt., CFO's, Cash mgmt., M&A, Risk mgmt., MIS mgmt., Minorities, Non-profits, Environmentalists, Int'l.
Industries: Generalist, Energy/utilities, Food/bev/tobacco, Textiles/apparel, Lumber/furniture, Paper, Printing, Chemicals, Drugs mfg., Medical devices, Paints/petroleum products, Machinery/Appliances, Motor vehicles, Computer equip., Misc. mfg., Transportation, Wholesale, Retail, Finance, Non-profits, Pharmaceutical svcs., Accounting, Human resource svcs., Communications, New media, Telecoms, Environmental svcs., High tech, Software, Healthcare
Professional Associations: AESC, IACPR

Branches:
275 Battery St., Ste. 420
Embarcadero Center West Tower
San Francisco, California 94111
(415) 981-7900
Email: boydensf@aol.com
Key Contact - Specialty:
Ms. Lynne Koll Martin
Ms. Julia C. Hirsch
Mr. Frederick J. Greene
Mr. James K. Stack
Mr. Putney Westerfield
Mr. Ronald Goerss
Mr. John O'Shaughnessy

2445 M St. NW, Ste. 250
Washington, District of Columbia
20037-1435
(202) 342-7200

Email: boydendc@aol.com
Key Contact - Specialty:
Mr. William H. Marumoto
Ms. S. Hope Johnson
Mr. Stanley Krejci
Mr. Jeffrey Bergman
Mr. Ed Bitar

Broward Financial Ctr., Ste. 1050
500 E. Broward Blvd.
Ft. Lauderdale, Florida 33394
(954) 522-8885
Email: boydenfla@mindspring.com
Key Contact - Specialty:
Mr. Jean Bellin

1360 Peachtree St. NE
2 Midtown Plaza, Ste. 1740
Atlanta, Georgia 30309-3214
(404) 876-9986
Email: boyden@mindspring.com
Key Contact - Specialty:
Mr. Thomas C. Zay
Mr. Geary D. Martin
Mr. William H. Leslie

2 Prudential Plaza
180 N. Stetson Ave., Ste. 2500
Chicago, Illinois 60601
(312) 565-1300
Email: ram@boydenchi.com
Key Contact - Specialty:
Mr. Richard A. McCallister
Ms. Janet L. Fischer
Ms. Trina D. Gordon
Mr. John S. Gude
Mr. John McNicholas
Mr. Robert Knopik

300 E. Long Lake, Ste. 375
Bloomfield Hills, Michigan 48304
(810) 647-4201
Key Contact - Specialty:
Mr. John Slosar
Mr. Peter Viall

12444 Powerscourt Drive, Ste. 301
St. Louis, Missouri 63131
(314) 984-2590
Email: boydenstl@earthlink.net
Key Contact - Specialty:
Mr. George Zamborsky

55 Madison Ave., Ste. 300
Morristown, New Jersey 07960-7354
(973) 267-0980
Email: boydennj@aol.com
Key Contact - Specialty:
Mr. Peter R. Schmidt
Mr. Mark Velten
Mr. Joseph DiPiazza
Ms. Terry Myers

100 Park Ave., 34th floor
New York, New York 10017
(212) 843-0200
Email: boyden-ny@mindspring.com
Key Contact - Specialty:
Mr. Rolfe I. Kopelan - *Financial services*
Mr. Daniel G. Jarvis - *Information technology*
Mr. Keith Roberts - *Corporate finance*
Ms. Allison Bush
Mr. George Lumsby

625 Stanwix St., Ste. 2405
Allegheny Twr.
Pittsburgh, Pennsylvania 15222-1423
(412) 391-3020
Email: boydenpgh@aol.com
Key Contact - Specialty:
Mr. E. Wade Close, Jr.
Mr. Malcolm MacGregor

333 Clay St., Ste. 3810
Houston, Texas 77002-4102
(713) 655-0123
Email: boydenhou@mindspring.com
Key Contact - Specialty:
Mr. Thomas C. Zay, Jr.
Mr. James N. J. Hertlein

2200, 520 - 5th Ave. SW
Calgary, Alberta T2P 3R7
Canada
(403) 237-6603
Email: sam@advantagetech.com
Key Contact - Specialty:
Mr. Sam Travis
Mr. Robert Travis

2610 Limestone Place
Coquitlam, British Columbia V3E 2V1
Canada
(604) 944-8081
Email: hummingb@axionet.com
Key Contact - Specialty:
Mr. Roger Gurr

130 Adelaide St. W., Ste. 2000
Toronto, Ontario M5H 3P5
Canada
(416) 863-0153
Email: boyden@ilap.com
Key Contact - Specialty:
Mr. John D. Crawford
Ms. Lynne de Munnik
Mr. Peter Spellisex

1250, Blvd. René-Lévesque O.
Bureau 4110
Montreal, Quebec H3B 4W8
Canada
(514) 935-4560
Email: pbourbeau@ibm.net
Key Contact - Specialty:
Mr. Paul J. Bourbeau
Ms. Martine Deschamps

Paseo de la Reforma 509, 11o Piso
Mexico City, Mexico DF 06500
Mexico
52 5 553 7777
Email: boydenmex@iserve.net.mx
Key Contact - Specialty:
Mr. Alberto F. Rivas
Mr. Bernardo Gitlin

International Branches:
Amsterdam, Athens, Auckland, Bad Homburg, Bangalore, Bangkok, Berlin, Bogota, Bombay, Boulogne, Brussels, Buenos Aires, Caracas, Central Hong Kong, Copenhagen, Geneva, Helsinki, Jakarta, Johannesburg, Kuala Lumpur, Lima, Lisbon, London, Madrid, Makati City, Melbourne, Milan, Minato-ku, New Delhi, Oslo, Paris, Prague, Pune, Rio de Janeiro, Rome, Santiago, Sao Paulo, Seoul, Shanghai, Singapore, St. Petersburg, Stockholm, Sydney, Taipei, Valencia, Warsaw, Zollikon

Boyle/Ogata Executive Search

18301 Von Karman Ave., Ste. 810
Irvine, California 92612
(949) 474-0115
Fax: (949) 474-2204
Email: info@boyleogata.com
Web: www.boyleogata.com

Key Contact - Specialty:
Mr. Mike Boyle - *Senior management*
Mr. Keith Ogata - *Senior management*
Mr. Mark Bregman - *Senior management*
Ms. Sharon Baker

Description: We are generalists with focus areas in: high-tech, aerospace, medical products, telecommunications and manufacturing. We ensure that only A players are hired for key leadership positions.

Salary Minimum: $80,000
Functions: Senior mgmt., Mfg., Healthcare, Sales & mktg., HR mgmt., Finance, Engineering
Industries: Generalist, Mfg., Medical devices, Aerospace, High tech, Software, Biotech

The Bradbury Management Group, Inc.

1999 S. Bascom Ave., Ste. 910
Campbell, California 95008
(408) 377-5400
Fax: (408) 377-1112
Email: pwbradbury@aol.com

Key Contact - Specialty:
Mr. Paul W. Bradbury, Jr. - *High technology (upper management)*
Ms. Elizabeth Campbell - *High technology (upper management)*

Description: Responsive, thorough, high quality executive search for the high technology (microcomputer, peripheral, software, semiconductor, biomedical, telecommunications) and environmental industries.

Salary Minimum: $100,000
Functions: General mgmt., Mfg., Sales & mktg., HR mgmt., Finance, IT, Engineering
Industries: Medical devices, Computer equip., Test/measurement equip., Environmental svcs., High tech, Software, Biotech
Professional Associations: IACPR

The Brand Co., Inc.
8402 Red Bay Court
Vero Beach, Florida 32963
(561) 231-1807
Email: home1.gte.net/brand

Key Contact - Specialty:
Mr. J. Brand Spangenberg - *Senior management*

Description: Responsive and personalized client focus on senior level searches for board directors, general management executives, functional heads and critical technology specialists. Generalist practice with particular experience in manufacturing, distribution and service businesses.

Salary Minimum: $75,000
Functions: Generalist, Senior mgmt., Plant mgmt., Mktg. mgmt., Sales mgmt., HR mgmt., CFO's
Industries: Generalist, Energy/utilities, Metal products, Machinery/Appliances, Misc. mfg., Packaging, High tech

Brandywine Consulting Group
5 Great Valley Pkwy., Ste. 356
Malvern, Pennsylvania 19355
(610) 407-4600
Fax: (610) 407-4605

Key Contact - Specialty:
Mr. Richard H. Beatty

Description: Broad-based practice with some specialization in chemical process, pulp & paper, packaging, pharmaceuticals and consumer products. Senior level retained assignments, include behavioral; based interview design and psychological assessment. Minimum compensation cutoff of $70,000.

Salary Minimum: $70,000
Functions: Directors, Senior mgmt., Middle mgmt., Production, Plant mgmt., Mktg. mgmt., Sales mgmt.
Industries: Paper, Drugs mfg., Medical devices, Pharmaceutical svcs., Healthcare

Brandywine Management Group
8 Drawbridge Rd.
Berlin, Maryland 21811
(410) 208-9791
Fax: (410) 208-9792

Key Contact - Specialty:
Mr. Jeffrey A. Morse - *Pulp & paper, healthcare, technical, senior level executives*
Mr. Stewart Schwartz - *Technical research*
Mrs. Sally Harrison - *Healthcare, semiconductors*
Mr. F. William Gaw - *Pulp & paper, technical*
Mrs. Markey Burke - *Healthcare, physicians*

Description: Retained search, consulting and outplacement firm engaged in technical, general, senior level management practices.

Salary Minimum: $45,000
Functions: Senior mgmt., Production, Plant mgmt., Packaging, Healthcare, Sales & mktg., HR mgmt.
Industries: Generalist, Lumber/furniture, Chemicals, Drugs mfg., Metal products, Misc. mfg., Healthcare

Branches:
82 Lake Drive
Mountain Lakes, New Jersey 07046
(800) 860-8812
Key Contact - Specialty:
Mrs. Sally Harrison - *Outplacement, senior level*

Affiliates:
Brandywine Consulting Group

Brandywine Retained Ventures, Inc.
75 Glen Rd., Ste. 301
Sandy Hook, Connecticut 06482
(203) 270-6355
Fax: (203) 270-6369
Email: brv75es@aol.com
Web: www.brv-inc.com

Key Contact - Specialty:
Mr. Clemente Alvear - *Generalist*
Ms. Joanne Bellontine - *Generalist*
Mr. Joel Johns - *Generalist*
Mr. Jeff Muthersbaugh - *Generalist*
Mr. Tom Sullivan - *Generalist*
Mr. John Vialosky - *Generalist*

Description: Successful senior management retained practice with a diverse group of client industries and functional areas. Assignments have included clients through North America, Latin America and Western Europe. Language capabilities in Spanish and Portuguese.

Salary Minimum: $80,000
Functions: Directors, Senior mgmt., Middle mgmt., Production, Sales mgmt., HR mgmt., IT
Industries: Generalist, Mfg., Svcs., Law enfcmt., Telecoms, High tech, Biotech

Branches:
5051 Arroyo Chamisa NE
Albuquerque, New Mexico 87111
(505) 271-8871
Fax: (505) 293-8978
Key Contact - Specialty:
Ms. Cherri Hoffman

Brault & Assoc., Ltd.
9117 Maria Ave.
Great Falls, Virginia 22066
(703) 759-2728
Fax: (703) 759-9404

Key Contact - Specialty:
Mr. J. P. Brault - *High technology*

Description: Executive search firm specializing in the high technology industry, biotechnology, energy and environment, DOD and intelligence systems, systems engineering and integration, information engineering, life sciences, healthcare and agribusiness.

Salary Minimum: $75,000
Functions: Directors, Senior mgmt., Sales & mktg., CFO's, MIS mgmt., Mgmt. consultants
Industries: Generalist, Finance, Computer svcs., Mgmt. consulting, High tech, Software

Bredeson Executive Recruitment, LLC †
P.O. Box 160203
Austin, Texas 78716-0203
(512) 306-9466
Fax: (512) 306-9488
Email: bredeson@worldnet.att.net
Web: www.bredeson.com

Key Contact - Specialty:
Ms. Sheri Bredeson - *Finance & accounting, management consulting*
D. A. Bredeson - *Legal*

Description: Retained search firm providing talented and productive professionals to clients nationwide. Expertise includes the placement of mid to senior level executives excelling in accounting, audit, tax, information technology, legal and management consulting disciplines.

Salary Minimum: $75,000
Functions: General mgmt., Legal, Materials, Finance, IT, Mgmt. consultants, Attorneys
Industries: Energy/utilities, Mfg., Finance, Svcs., New media, High tech, Software

The Brentwood Group, Inc.
170 Kinnelon Rd., Ste. 29B
Kinnelon, New Jersey 07405
(973) 283-1000
Fax: (973) 283-1220
Email: brentwood@nac.net

Key Contact - Specialty:
Ms. Doris Banach-Osenni - *Management consulting, direct marketing, financial services, publishing, senior management*
Ms. Barbara Benkwitt - *Chemical insurance, pharmaceuticals, consulting, information technology*
Ms. Kathy Sabbio - *Management (mid to senior), pharmaceuticals, communications, advertising, investment banking*
Ms. Pat Pagana - *Engineering, consulting, pharmaceuticals, publishing, travel*

Description: Our firm provides experience, consistency, quality and results. We are a cohesive team who have been together a long while and understand, execute and are the ones who actually fill your search.

Salary Minimum: $50,000
Functions: Mktg. mgmt., Direct mktg., HR mgmt., CFO's, MIS mgmt., Mgmt. consultants, Minorities
Industries: Chemicals, Drugs mfg., Medical devices, Paints/petroleum products, Invest. banking, Entertainment, Insurance

The Brentwood Group Ltd.

9 Monroe Pkwy., Ste. 230
Lake Oswego, Oregon 97035
(503) 697-8136
Fax: (503) 697-8161
Email: brentwood@transport.com

Key Contact - Specialty:
Mr. Frank Moscow - *High technology (senior management)*
Mr. Lenny White - *High technology (middle management)*
Mr. James O'Leary - *High technology (middle management)*

Description: We are a results driven search firm exclusively dedicated to serving high technology clients.

Salary Minimum: $65,000
Functions: Directors, Senior mgmt., Middle mgmt., Product dev., Plant mgmt., Mktg. mgmt., CFO's
Industries: Computer equip., Consumer electronics, Computer svcs., Telecoms, High tech, Software, Biotech

Brentwood Int'l.

9841 Airport Blvd., Ste. 420
Los Angeles, California 90045
(310) 216-0033
Fax: (310) 338-5484
Email: brentwd001@aol.com

Key Contact - Specialty:
Mr. James Keenan - *Generalist*
Ms. Marilyn Bennett - *Marketing & sales*
Ms. Linda Barr - *High technology*
Ms. Susan Cole-Hill - *High technology, consumer products*
Ms. Cynthia Whittaker - *High technology, aerospace*
Ms. Liz Denis - *High technology, aerospace*
Ms. Michelle Curtin - *Financial services*
Mr. Ed Rardin - *Manufacturing, marketing*
Ms. Bittian Kaplan - *Technology marketing*
Ms. Jennifer Neiman - *Human resources, technology*

Description: Exclusively executive search specializing in high technology, aerospace, financial services, manufacturing, systems, engineering, public sector, management, marketing and consumer products.

Salary Minimum: $75,000
Functions: Generalist, General mgmt., Sales & mktg., HR mgmt., Systems dev., R&D, Engineering
Industries: Computer equip., Consumer electronics, Hospitality, Entertainment, Aerospace, High tech, Software

Briant Assoc., Inc.

39 S. LaSalle St., Ste. 714
Chicago, Illinois 60603
(312) 577-5640
Fax: (312) 577-5651
Email: rbingham1@earthlink.net

Key Contact - Specialty:
Mr. Rick Bingham - *Food*
Ms. Larissa R. Klavins - *Consumer products*

Description: Professional industry expertise in evaluating and understanding our clients unique staffing needs, coupled with the work ethic to execute an effective and timely search.

Salary Minimum: $55,000
Functions: General mgmt., Mfg., Materials, Sales & mktg., Finance, R&D, Engineering
Industries: Mfg., Food/bev/tobacco, Textiles/apparel, Metal products, Machinery/Appliances, Consumer electronics, Mgmt. consulting

Affiliates:
BGA Partners

Brigade, Inc.

P.O. Box 1974
Cupertino, California 95015-1974
(408) 871-2200
Fax: (408) 871-2206
Email: brigadeinc@aol.com
Web: www.brigadeinc.com

Key Contact - Specialty:
Mr. Gary B. Barnes - *Marketing, sales, finance, corporate communications, public relations*
Ms. Aida Regina - *Finance, engineering*
Ms. Erica Kremer - *Information systems*

Description: A proven retained executive search firm specializing in high technology, telecommunications, financial services and board member searches.

Salary Minimum: $125,000
Functions: General mgmt., Mfg., Sales & mktg., HR mgmt., Finance, IT, Engineering
Industries: Computer equip., Finance, Mgmt. consulting, Communications, Advertising/PR, High tech, Software

Brindisi Search

10751 Falls Rd., Ste. 250
Greenspring Station
Lutherville, Maryland 21093
(410) 339-7673
Fax: (410) 823-0146
Email: tbrindisi@aol.com
Web: www.brindisisearch.com

Key Contact - Specialty:
Mr. Thomas J. Brindisi - *Human resources, change management, strategic planning, business development*

Description: We provide aggressive search capabilities for business-linked human resource functions. We work with leading-edge Fortune 500 firms to enhance their competitiveness by identifying world class human resource talent.

Salary Minimum: $60,000
Functions: Senior mgmt., HR mgmt., Benefits, Personnel, Training, Mgmt. consultants
Industries: Generalist, Finance, Hospitality, Communications

Affiliates:
Chesapeake Consulting Group

Brissenden, McFarland, Fuccella & Reynolds, Inc.

1130 Rte. 202, Ste. E-7
Raritan, New Jersey 08869
(908) 704-9100
Email: inquiry@bmfr.com
Web: www.bmfr.com

Key Contact - Specialty:
Mr. Hoke Brissenden - *Pharmaceuticals, medical devices, diagnostics*
Mr. Carl J. Fuccella - *Utilities*
Dr. John H. Reynolds - *Pharmaceuticals, nuclear utilities, engineering*
Mr. Bernard J. Ryan - *Finance*

Description: The practice focuses on senior management positions, both line and staff, in major industries: utilities, healthcare, electronics, telecommunications, chemical and allied manufacturing and services. Professional staff averages 20 years executive search experience.

Salary Minimum: $90,000
Functions: General mgmt., Mfg., Sales & mktg., HR mgmt., Finance, R&D, Engineering
Industries: Energy/utilities, Chemicals, Drugs mfg., Medical devices, Metal products, High tech, Biotech

Branches:
11270 W. Park Place, Ste. 270
One Park Plaza
Milwaukee, Wisconsin 53224-3623
(414) 359-5625
Key Contact - Specialty:
Mr. Robert Cutler - *Nuclear utilities*

The Broadmoor Group, L.L.C. (a division of Tuttle Venture Group Inc.)

5151 Beltline Rd., Ste. 955
Dallas, Texas 75240
(972) 980-1960
Fax: (972) 980-1689

Email: rneal@tvg.com

Key Contact - Specialty:
Mr. Randall Neal
Mr. James Leverette

Description: A firm specializing in the recruitment of individual contributors, middle management to executive level professionals

Salary Minimum: $80,000
Functions: Generalist
Industries: Energy/utilities, Medical devices, Venture cap., Computer svcs., Communications, High tech, Software

---

Brooke Chase Assoc., Inc.
505 N. Lake Shore Drive, Ste. 5507
Chicago, Illinois 60611
(312) 744-0033
Fax: (312) 822-0475
Email: HDHNTRJOE@aol.com

Key Contact - Specialty:
Mr. Joseph J. McElmeel - *Sales, marketing, general management*

Description: Specialists in the recruitment of sales/marketing and general management for manufacturers within the hardware/plumbing/building materials/ consumer electronics/housewares/lawn and garden industries.

Salary Minimum: $50,000
Functions: Senior mgmt., Middle mgmt., Plant mgmt., Quality, Mkt. research, Mktg. mgmt., Sales mgmt.
Industries: Lumber/furniture, Paper, Plastics/rubber, Paints/petroleum products, Metal products, Consumer electronics, Packaging

---

Bernard E. Brooks & Assoc., Inc.
187 N. Church St., Ste. 555
Spartanburg, South Carolina 29307
(864) 948-1005
Fax: (864) 948-1007
Email: bbrooks2@compuserve.com

Key Contact - Specialty:
Mr. Bernard E. Brooks - *Generalist*

Description: Retained executive search firm with strong record of success recruiting for higher education, healthcare and not for profit organizations. Excellent record in diversity recruiting.

Salary Minimum: $75,000
Functions: Senior mgmt., Plant mgmt., Health admin., CFO's, MIS mgmt., R&D, Minorities
Industries: Computer equip., Transportation, Higher ed., Mgmt. consulting, Telecoms, Healthcare

---

Brown Venture Assoc.
3000 Sand Hill Rd., Ste. 110, Bldg. 3
Menlo Park, California 94025
(650) 233-0205
Fax: (650) 233-1902
Email: info@bva.com

Key Contact - Specialty:
Mr. Jerry Brown
Ms. Kerstin Barley

Description: Retained search firm specializing in CEO and vice president searches for venture backed start-ups and high growth companies. Principals have engineering backgrounds with significant operation experience.

Salary Minimum: $85,000
Functions: Senior mgmt., Mktg. mgmt., Sales mgmt., CFO's
Industries: Computer equip., Venture cap., New media, Telecoms, High tech, Software

---

Brush Creek Partners
One Ward Pkwy., Ste. 345
Kansas City, Missouri 64112
(816) 960-0999
Fax: (816) 554-8390
Email: Brushcrk@sprynet.com

Key Contact - Specialty:
Mr. Jerry D. Lunn - *Generalist*

Description: We devote the resources, expertise and perseverance to conduct broad-based searches with the highest level of quality in the most efficient time frame. We are supported by comprehensive state of the art research and retrieval capabilities, databases and an extensive network of industry sources.

Salary Minimum: $75,000
Functions: Generalist, Senior mgmt., Sales & mktg., HR mgmt., CFO's, MIS mgmt., R&D
Industries: Generalist, Chemicals, Computer equip., Misc. mfg., Finance, Telecoms, Biotech

Branches:
521 SE 2nd St., Ste. C
Lees Summit, Missouri 64063
(816) 554-2500
Fax: (816) 554-8390
Email: brushcrk@sprynet.com
Key Contact - Specialty:
Ms. Tracy L. Howard - *Generalist*

Brystol Cove Assoc. †
4660 La Jolla Village Drive, Ste. 500
San Diego, California 92122
(619) 535-4860
(619) 401-2050
Fax: (619) 593-8815
Email: hrpros@brystol.com

Key Contact - Specialty:
Ms. Cecelia Gonzalez - *Human resources*
Mr. Joe Gonzalez - *Human resources*
Ms. Patricia Paredes - *Latin America, human resources*

Description: We are committed to continued education, comprehensive research and exceptional listening skills that will empower us to remain informed about the industries we serve. We bring human resource corporate experience to the search by having individuals out of industry with our firm.

Salary Minimum: $55,000
Functions: HR mgmt., Benefits, Training
Industries: Generalist

BT&A, LLC
6527 Main St.
Trumbull, Connecticut 06611
(203) 452-3660
Fax: (203) 452-9153
Email: Ray@btallc.com
Web: www.btallc.com

Key Contact - Specialty:
Mr. Colin Bunges - *Information technology*
Mr. Raymond Tomasco - *Information technology*
Ms. Karen Vacheron Alexander - *Information technology*

Description: We are a national full-service search firm specializing exclusively in recruitment for the information technology industries.

Salary Minimum: $100,000
Functions: General mgmt., Sales & mktg., IT, MIS mgmt., R&D, Engineering
Industries: Computer svcs., New media, High tech, Software

Branches:
700 Canal St.
Stamford, Connecticut 06902
(203) 328-3099
Key Contact - Specialty:
Mr. Raymond Tomasco - *Information technology*

Charles Buck & Assoc., Inc.
400 E. 59th St.
New York, New York 10022
(212) 759-2356

Key Contact - Specialty:
Mr. Charles A. Buck, Jr. - *Senior management, marketing, design*

Description: Small quality searches with a distinct emphasis on partnering with clients.

Salary Minimum: $85,000
Functions: Generalist, Senior mgmt., Mkt. research, Mktg. mgmt., Sales mgmt., Mgmt. consultants, Graphic artists

Industries: Generalist, Entertainment, Non-profits, Legal, Mgmt. consulting, Advertising/PR, Publishing

---

Bullis & Co., Inc.

120 Quintara St.
San Francisco, California 94116
(415) 753-6140
Fax: (415) 753-6653

Key Contact - Specialty:
Mr. Richard J. Bullis

Description: Small retainer firm working with most industries and all functions, with specific interest in high technology, engineering, manufacturing, finance and general management.

Salary Minimum: $90,000
Functions: Generalist, Senior mgmt., Plant mgmt., CFO's, MIS mgmt., Mgmt. consultants, Int'l.
Industries: Generalist, Agri/forestry/mining, Motor vehicles, Computer equip., Computer svcs., Mgmt. consulting, High tech

---

The Burgess Group-Corporate Recruiters Int'l., Inc. †

160 E. 26th St., Ste. 6-G
New York, New York 10010-1826
(212) 686-5598
(203) 746-6629
Fax: (212) 679-1868
Email: BurgessGrp@worldnet.att.net
Web: www.home.att.net/~burgessgrp

Key Contact - Specialty:
Mr. William H. Burgess, III - *Sales, marketing, finance, information technology, non-profit management*

Salary Minimum: $50,000
Functions: Production, Mktg. mgmt., Sales mgmt., Budgeting, Systems anal., Minorities, Non-profits
Industries: Generalist, Energy/utilities, Mfg., Finance, Svcs., Communications, Insurance

Branches:
Candlewood Knolls, 5 Almargo Rd.
New Fairfield, Connecticut 06812-3416
(203) 746-6629
Fax: (203) 746-6629
Key Contact - Specialty:
Mr. William H. Burgess, III

Burke, O'Brien & Bishop Assoc., Inc.

1000 Herrontown Rd.
Princeton, New Jersey 08540
(609) 921-3510
Fax: (609) 683-1578

Key Contact - Specialty:
Mr. James F. Bishop

Description: Executive search consulting assignments range from president, CEO, positions with compensation exceeding $1 million to middle management level from a minimum of $100,000. Most functions, with emphasis on general management, finance, marketing and human resources.

Salary Minimum: $100,000
Functions: Generalist
Industries: Generalist

J. Burkey Assoc.

900 Laurel Ave.
River Edge, New Jersey 07661
(201) 262-7990
Fax: (201) 262-7955
Email: jburkey@erols.com

Key Contact - Specialty:
Ms. Julie V. Burkey - *Pharmaceutical, medical device industries*

Description: Executive search services at an hourly-based fee. This cost-effective and highly productive approach allows for a full search or just a part of the process.

Salary Minimum: $75,000
Functions: Directors, Middle mgmt., Product dev., Mkt. research, Mktg. mgmt., R&D
Industries: Drugs mfg., Medical devices

Joseph R. Burns & Assoc., Inc.

2 Shunpike Rd.
Madison, New Jersey 07940
(973) 377-1350

Key Contact - Specialty:
Mr. Joseph R. Burns - *Generalist*

Description: Executive search firm with excellent recruitment skills and a demonstrated record of success in servicing our clients with the highest degree of professionalism.

Salary Minimum: $75,000
Functions: Generalist, Senior mgmt., Plant mgmt., Health admin., Mktg. mgmt., CFO's, MIS mgmt.
Industries: Generalist, Computer equip., Finance, Communications, New media, Software, Healthcare
Professional Associations: IACPR

Busch International

One First St., Ste. One
Los Altos, California 94022-2754
(650) 949-1115
Email: jack@buschint.com
Web: www.buschint.com

Key Contact - Specialty:
Mr. Jack Busch
Mrs. Olga Ocon

Description: Our firm consists of senior consultants specializing in high-technology electronics exclusively. Assignments are with growth companies requiring CEO's, VP's, COO's in marketing, sales, engineering, operations and finance worldwide.

Salary Minimum: $125,000
Functions: Senior mgmt., CFO's
Industries: Computer equip., High tech, Software

Networks:
Transearch Int'l.

Butterfass, Pepe & MacCallan Inc.

P.O. Box 721
Mahwah, New Jersey 07430
(201) 512-3330
Fax: (201) 512-0272
Email: bpm@carroll.com
Web: www.bpmi.com

Key Contact - Specialty:
Mr. Stanley W. Butterfass
Ms. Leonida R. Pepe
Ms. Deirdre MacCallan

Description: Boutique search firm. Teams are assigned with strengths in areas of assignment, assuring client of consistent, personal attention. Specialties include: fixed income, equities, private placement, M&A, corporate finance, real estate and money management.

Salary Minimum: $50,000
Functions: HR mgmt., CFO's, Cash mgmt., M&A, Risk mgmt., Minorities
Industries: Banking, Invest. banking, Brokers, Venture cap., Human resource svcs., Insurance
Professional Associations: IACPR

Buzhardt Assoc.

1385 Narrow Gauge Rd.
Bolton, Mississippi 39041
(601) 852-8042
Email: joebuz@netprocon.com

Key Contact - Specialty:
Mr. J. F. Buzhardt

Description: Specializing in evaluating and recruiting management skills for the functional areas of operations, marketing/sales, finance and human resources.

Salary Minimum: $60,000
Functions: General mgmt., Mfg., Sales & mktg., HR mgmt., Finance, IT
Industries: Mfg., Wholesale, Retail

Byron Leonard Int'l., Inc.

2659 Townsgate Rd., Ste. 100
Westlake Village, California 91361
(805) 373-7500
Fax: (805) 373-5531

† occasional contingency assignment

Email: bli@bli-inc.com
Web: www.bli-inc.com

Key Contact - Specialty:
Mr. Leonard M. Linton - *Generalist, high technology*
Mr. Stephen M. Wolf - *Generalist, high technology*

Description: Over 10 years search experience in growth industries, emphasizing: custom fit of candidates to the enterprise, disciplined recruitment methodology, exceptional research. Principals have domestic and international experience. Satisfied clients: start-ups to multinationals.

Salary Minimum: $60,000
Functions: Generalist, Senior mgmt., Product dev., Mkt. research, Mktg. mgmt., CFO's, MIS mgmt.
Industries: Generalist, Machinery/ Appliances, Computer equip., Computer svcs., New media, High tech, Software

---

C. G. & Assoc. †
Box 11160
Pittsburgh, Pennsylvania 15237
(724) 935-1288
Fax: (724) 935-1430

Key Contact - Specialty:
Mr. Charles C. Groom

Description: We specialize in real estate and construction, development, property management, syndication, financial and controllers.

Salary Minimum: $40,000
Functions: Finance, Specialized services, Architects
Industries: Energy/utilities, Construction, Real estate

C. M. Management Services, Inc.
(a Hamilton-Ryker company)
698 Perimeter Drive, Ste. 200
Lexington, Kentucky 40517
(606) 266-5000
Fax: (606) 269-8711

Key Contact - Specialty:
Mr. Richard E. Blanchard, Sr. - *General management*
Ms. Marsha Brook - *Generalist, human resources, marketing, financial, manufacturing*
Mr. Bill Thornton - *General management*

Description: Firm specializes in search activities for engineers and manufacturing, data processing, banking and finance, personnel, all disciplines. Also outplacement, management consulting and temporary staffing.

Salary Minimum: $40,000
Functions: Senior mgmt., Mfg., Purchasing, Mktg. mgmt., HR mgmt., Finance, IT
Industries: Generalist, Motor vehicles, Finance, Accounting, Human resource svcs., Communications, Insurance

---

C. P. Consulting
Box 469, The Hideout
Lake Ariel, Pennsylvania 18436
(717) 698-8321
Fax: (717) 698-8321

Key Contact - Specialty:
Ms. Catherine Phillips - *Financial services*

Description: Resumes cannot be responded to.

Salary Minimum: $75,000
Functions: Directors, Mktg. mgmt., Benefits, Personnel, Training, CFO's, R&D
Industries: Generalist, Banking, Misc. financial, Pharmaceutical svcs., Legal, Insurance

---

Robert Caldwell & Assoc.
12021 Wilshire Blvd., Ste. 650
Los Angeles, California 90025
(310) 454-1946

Key Contact - Specialty:
Mr. Robert Caldwell

Description: National firm specializing in difficult to fill executive positions. Each search is conducted by the president of the firm - never delegated. Successful completion of each search guaranteed in writing.

Salary Minimum: $100,000
Functions: Generalist
Industries: Generalist

The Caldwell Partners Amrop International
64 Prince Arthur Ave.
Toronto, Ontario M5R 1B4
Canada
(416) 920-7702
Fax: (416) 922-8646
Email: leaders@caldwellpartners.com
Web: www.caldwellpartners.com

Key Contact - Specialty:
Ms. Kelly A. Blair
Mr. Francis W. H. Brunelle
Mr. C. Douglas Caldwell
Mr. Ronald D. Charles
Mr. Ralph A. Chauvin
Ms. Heather Connelly
Ms. Anne M. Fawcett
Ms. Betsy Gibbons
Mr. Timothy J. Hamilton
Mr. Clarke H. Jackson
Mr. R. David Kinley
Mr. Christopher J. Laubitz
Mr. Kevin McBurney
Mr. Robert McGill
Ms. Sharon Neelin
Mr. Donald Prior
Mr. L. Grant Spitz
Mr. Robert J. Sutton
Mr. Daniel Lacoste
Mr. Guy Hebert
Mr. Richard Joly
Ms. Lori Moffat

Description: Leading Canadian executive search firm.
Functions: Generalist
Industries: Generalist
Professional Associations: AESC, IACPR

Branches:
400-3rd. Ave. SW, Ste. 3450
Calgary, Alberta T2P 4H2
Canada
(403) 265-8780
Fax: (403) 263-6508
Key Contact - Specialty:
Mr. Robert J. Sutton

999 W. Hastings St., Ste. 750
Vancouver, British Columbia V6C 2W2
Canada
(604) 669-3550
Fax: (604) 669-5095
Key Contact - Specialty:
Mr. Kevin McBurney

1840 Sherbrooke St. W.
Montreal, Quebec H3H 1E4
Canada
(514) 935-6969
Fax: (514) 935-7402
Key Contact - Specialty:
Mr. Buy Hebert

Networks:
Amrop International

Lee Calhoon & Co., Inc.
P.O. Box 201
1621 Birchrun Rd.
Birchrunville, Pennsylvania 19421
(610) 469-9000
Fax: (610) 469-0398
Email: leecalhoon@aol.com

Key Contact - Specialty:
Mr. Lee Calhoon - *Managed care*

Description: A retained executive search firm founded in 1970 that has specialized exclusively in the managed care industry for the past twelve years.

Salary Minimum: $75,000
Functions: Generalist
Industries: Healthcare

Branches:
123 Black Rock
P.O. Box 504
Redding Ridge, Connecticut 06876-0504
(203) 938-7495
Key Contact - Specialty:
Ms. Courtney F. Lake

Caliber Associates

125 Strafford Ave., Ste. 112
Wayne, Pennsylvania 19087
(610) 971-1880
Fax: (610) 971-1887
Email: steve@caliberassoc.com

Key Contact - Specialty:
Mr. Steven P. Hochberg - *Life sciences*
Ms. Leslie Finkel

Description: We support the life sciences industries, both emerging organizations and major pharmaceutical companies, in identifying and selecting key scientific, technical and general management. Our focus areas include: discovery research, development, regulatory/medical affairs, operations/manufacturing, sales, marketing and business development.

Salary Minimum: $80,000
Functions: Senior mgmt., Middle mgmt., Product dev., Plant mgmt., Physicians, Mktg. mgmt., R&D
Industries: Chemicals, Soap/perfume/cosmetics, Drugs mfg., Medical devices, Pharmaceutical svcs., Biotech, Healthcare

Callan Assoc., Ltd.

2021 Spring Rd., Ste. 175
Oak Brook, Illinois 60523
(630) 574-9300
Email: callan@enteract.com

Key Contact - Specialty:
Mr. Robert M. Callan - *General management, board of director*
Ms. Elizabeth C. Beaudin - *Marketing, sales, engineering, R&D, purchasing*
Ms. Marianne C. Ray - *Finance, software, banking*
Mr. James W. Jacobs - *Information services, purchasing, board of director, manufacturing, general management*
Mr. James R. Stranberg - *Manufacturing*
Mr. Ronald T. Brzezinski - *Information technology*

Description: A firm of experienced professionals dedicated to recruiting exceptional management. Client base includes companies throughout North America, Europe, Asia and Latin America. Especially strong capability in the Midwest.

Salary Minimum: $100,000
Functions: General mgmt., Materials, Sales & mktg., HR mgmt., Finance, IT, Engineering
Industries: Generalist, Chemicals, Metal products, Computer svcs., Accounting, Packaging, Software
Professional Associations: IACPR

Cambridge Management Planning

2323 Yonge St., Ste. 203
Toronto, Ontario M4P 2C9
Canada
(416) 484-8408
Fax: (416) 484-0151
Email: admin@cambridgemgmt.com
Web: www.cambridgemgmt.com

Key Contact - Specialty:
Mr. Graham Carver
Mr. Robert Graham
Mr. Barrie Sprawson

Description: Executive search-middle to senior management searches for a wide range of corporations in Canada and internationally. Emphasis placed on highly targeted, in-house market research capabilities.

Salary Minimum: $85,000
Functions: Generalist, Senior mgmt., Plant mgmt., Sales mgmt., CFO's, MIS mgmt., Engineering
Industries: Generalist, Motor vehicles, Banking, Pharmaceutical svcs., Aerospace, High tech, Healthcare

Networks:
I-I-C Partners Executive Search Worldwide

Cameron Consulting Group

1112 Austin Ave.
Pacific Grove, California 93950
(408) 646-8415
Fax: (408) 646-8626

Key Contact - Specialty:
Mr. James W. Cameron

Description: A broad and general executive recruiting and human resource consulting practice serving all industries.

Salary Minimum: $60,000
Functions: Generalist
Industries: Generalist

Affiliates:
Dwyer Consulting Group, Inc.

Campa & Assoc.

1 Yonge St., Ste. 2203
Toronto, Ontario M5E 1E5
Canada
(416) 407-7777
Fax: (416) 214-5764

Key Contact - Specialty:
Mr. Carl Campa

Description: We recruit high performance management talent for world class engineered products manufacturers with a global focus.

Salary Minimum: $65,000
Functions: General mgmt., Mfg., Plant mgmt., Materials, Sales & mktg., Engineering, Mgmt. consultants
Industries: Plastics/rubber, Metal products, Machinery/Appliances, Motor vehicles, Misc. mfg., Aerospace, High tech

T. M. Campbell Co. †

1111 Third Ave., Ste. 2500
Seattle, Washington 98101
(206) 583-8355
Fax: (206) 780-1705
Email: tmcampbell@msn.com

Key Contact - Specialty:
Ms. Terri Campbell

Description: Nationwide executive searches in many industries, including government, telecommunications, software, consumer products and professional services. Special expertise in placing information technology professionals. Flexible pricing and services.

Salary Minimum: $60,000
Functions: Sales & mktg., HR mgmt., Finance, IT, MIS mgmt., Systems implem., Mgmt. consultants
Industries: Mfg., Computer svcs., Accounting, Mgmt. consulting, Telecoms, Government, Software

Canadian Career Partners

Ste. 500, 707-7th Ave. SW
Calgary, Alberta T2P 0Z2
Canada
(403) 290-0466
Fax: (403) 294-0513
Email: debra.johnstone@career-partners.com
Web: career-partners.com

Key Contact - Specialty:
Ms. Debra J. Johnstone
Mr. Clive L. MacRaild
Mr. Gary R. Agnew
Mr. Bruce Green

Description: Successfully conduct searches in a broad range of industries and government. Treat every engagement as a partnership with our client, determining the best way to streamline the process without compromising thoroughness.

Salary Minimum: $50,000
Functions: Generalist, General mgmt., Senior mgmt., Mfg., Sales mgmt., Finance, IT
Industries: Generalist, Energy/utilities, Mfg., Transportation, Finance, Government, Environmental svcs.

Canny, Bowen Inc.

200 Park Ave.
New York, New York 10166
(212) 949-6611
Fax: (212) 949-5191

Email: jneuberth@aol.com

Key Contact - Specialty:
Mr. Carl W. Menk
Mr. David R. Peasback - *Generalist, senior management, human resources, attorneys, finance*
Ms. Mary Rose Schiavone - *General management, manufacturing, marketing, CFOs, information technology*
Mr. William K. Sur - *General management, senior management, CFOs, international, directors*
Ms. Debra Erder - *Generalist, senior management, marketing, personnel, CFOs*
Mr. Greg Gabel - *Generalist, general management, directors, finance, manufacturing*

Description: Specialize in senior executive search. We will accept only those assignments which we feel are feasible. Forty-three years in retainer-based executive search assisting our clients to select and recruit their top management.

Salary Minimum: $125,000
Functions: Generalist, General mgmt., Directors, Senior mgmt., Middle mgmt., Mfg., Production, Quality, Sales & mktg., Mktg. mgmt., Direct mktg., PR, HR mgmt., Benefits, Personnel, Finance, CFO's, Cash mgmt., M&A, IT, MIS mgmt., R&D, Mgmt. consultants, Non-profits, Attorneys, Int'l.
Industries: Generalist, Energy/utilities, Construction, Food/bev/tobacco, Textiles/apparel, Paper, Chemicals, Soap/perfume/cosmetics, Drugs mfg., Medical devices, Metal products, Motor vehicles, Computer equip., Consumer electronics, Transportation, Wholesale, Retail, Finance, Banking, Invest. banking, Venture cap., Hospitality, Pharmaceutical svcs., Legal, Accounting, Human resource svcs., New media, Broadcast & Film, Telecoms, Environmental svcs., Packaging, Insurance, Real estate, High tech, Software, Biotech, Healthcare
Professional Associations: AESC

Affiliates:
Christopher Beale Associates Ltd.

The Cantor Concern, Inc. †
330 W. 58th St., Ste. 216
New York, New York 10019
(212) 333-3000
Fax: (212) 245-1012
Email: cantorcrn@compuserve.com
Web: www.cantorconcern.com

Key Contact - Specialty:
Ms. Marie T. Raperto - *Public, government, investor relations*

Description: A national search firm with professional staff experienced in business, government, not-for-profit, management consulting search. Company serves all industries and specializes in public affairs, public relations, corporate communications, IR.

Salary Minimum: $35,000
Functions: PR, Minorities
Industries: Generalist, Food/bev/tobacco, Finance, Hospitality, Communications, Software, Healthcare

Affiliates:
The Cantor Concern Staffing Options, Inc.

Capital Consulting & Research, Inc.
(Firm declined to update.)
51 Locust Ave.
New Canaan, Connecticut 06840
(203) 966-3200
Email: staffing@capconres.com
Web: www.capconres.com

Key Contact - Specialty:
Mr. John R. Bingle
Ms. Maryellen James

Description: Assists the world's largest professional service firms/Fortune 500 companies grow by developing business strategies to improve their success in critical markets while also establishing well managed, cost effective staffing programs.
Functions: Senior mgmt., Sales mgmt., Systems implem., Mgmt. consultants
Industries: Invest. banking, Venture cap., Computer svcs., Accounting, Mgmt. consulting

Capital Consulting Group, Inc.
8323 Cherry Lane, Ste. A-13
Laurel, Maryland 20707
(301) 470-2411
Fax: (301) 470-1347
Email: mail@capitalconsulting.com

Key Contact - Specialty:
Mr. Dale Legal - *Telecommunications, IT, finance, sales & marketing, satellite*
Mr. Karl King - *Telecommunications, IT, sales & marketing, satellite, consulting*
Mr. Vern Barnes - *Sales & marketing, sales support, software/hardware*
Mr. Dan Brest - *Sales & marketing, legal, general, consulting*
Ms. Sandy Landwerb - *Software, hardware, data communications*

Description: Our clients represent a broad spectrum of national, international and multinational organizations. Sizes range from start-up to Fortune 50 companies. Over 65% of our annual business is repeat clients.
Functions: Generalist, Directors, Advertising, Benefits, CFO's, MIS mgmt., Engineering
Industries: Generalist, Drugs mfg., Invest. banking, Mgmt. consulting, Publishing, Defense, High tech

Caplan Assoc., Inc.
201 Rte. 17 N., Ste. 302
Rutherford, New Jersey 07070
(201) 438-2002
Fax: (201) 438-7670
Email: info@caplanassoc.com
Web: www.caplanassoc.com

Key Contact - Specialty:
Ms. Shellie Caplan - *Pharmaceutical, biotechnology, general management, business development, marketing*

Description: Management, executive level search firm servicing all facets of healthcare industry including pharmaceuticals, biotechnology, general management, business development, marketing, sales, healthcare, clinical regulatory, healthcare publishing, managed care, medical education, advertising.

Salary Minimum: $70,000
Functions: Directors, Senior mgmt., Middle mgmt., Sales & mktg., M&A, R&D
Industries: Drugs mfg., Pharmaceutical svcs., Advertising/PR, Publishing, New media, Biotech, Healthcare

The Caplan-Taylor Group
101 First St., Ste. 610
Los Altos, California 94022
(650) 941-3030
Fax: (650) 941-7259
Email: jacaplan@att.net

Key Contact - Specialty:
Mr. John Caplan - *Senior executives, drugs, pharmaceuticals, healthcare, biotechnology*
Mr. Len Perry - *Functional heads, drugs, pharmaceuticals, healthcare, biotechnology*

Description: We specialize in recruiting executives for various healthcare industries. The worldwide emphasis is in the pharmaceutical, biotechnology, medical instrumental/device, diagnostic and related healthcare areas.

Salary Minimum: $100,000
Functions: General mgmt., Mfg., Sales & mktg., HR mgmt., Finance, R&D, Engineering
Industries: Drugs mfg., Medical devices, Biotech, Healthcare

Branches:
2045 Big Horn Mountain Drive
Tucson, Arizona 85737
(520) 825-8505
Fax: (520) 825-2861
Email: tayaz@aol.com
Key Contact - Specialty:
Mr. John Taylor - *Senior executives, drugs, pharmaceuticals, biotechnology, healthcare*

Affiliates:
Archer Group

Caprio & Assoc. Inc.

721 E. Madison Ave., Ste. 100
Villa Park, Illinois 60181
(630) 832-8825
Fax: (630) 832-8925

Key Contact - Specialty:
Mr. Jerry Caprio - *Printing, publishing, packaging, converting*

Description: Specialist in recruiting senior level management for the printing, publishing, converting and packaging industries.

Salary Minimum: $75,000
Functions: Senior mgmt., Plant mgmt., Packaging, Advertising, Sales mgmt., Direct mktg.
Industries: Paper, Printing, Chemicals, Paints/petroleum products, Advertising/PR, Publishing, Packaging

Capstone Consulting, Inc.

703 S. Dearborn St.
Printers Row
Chicago, Illinois 60605
(312) 922-9556
Fax: (312) 922-9558
Email: capstoneconsulting@msn.com
Web: www.capstoneconsulting.com

Key Contact - Specialty:
Mr. Mark R. Ormond - *Senior executives, plant management, sales & marketing, human resources, engineering*
Ms. Lori K. Pedelty - *Manufacturing, senior executives*

Description: A highly focused search-driven consultancy offering a wide range of stategic business planning services. Committed to the highest level of client partnership; detailed, methodical and personalized attention are our hallmarks.

Salary Minimum: $75,000
Functions: Generalist, Senior mgmt., Middle mgmt., Mfg., Sales mgmt., HR mgmt., Engineering
Industries: Generalist, Mfg., Metal products, Consumer electronics, Misc. mfg.

Capstone Inc.

One Global View
Rensselaer Technology Park
Troy, New York 12180
(518) 285-7328
Fax: (518) 285-7467
Email: amy.johnson@mapinfo.com

Key Contact - Specialty:
Ms. Amy M. Johnson

Description: We offer a turnkey approach to retained search including organizational analysis, position definition, compensation surveys, interview training and final candidate selection as requested.

Salary Minimum: $60,000
Functions: Senior mgmt., Mfg., Automation, Sales & mktg., CFO's, Systems dev., Engineering
Industries: Generalist, Paper, Chemicals, Plastics/rubber, Computer svcs., High tech, Software

Cardwell Enterprises Inc.

P.O. Box 59418
Chicago, Illinois 60659
(773) 273-5774
Fax: (847) 475-6792

Key Contact - Specialty:
Ms. Jean Cardwell - *Corporate communications (including media relations, public relations), employee communications, integrated marketing communications, corporate advertising, editorial services (speech writing)*

Description: We recruit quality candidates for positions in corporate communications, investor relations, public relations, government and public affairs on behalf of Fortune 500.

Salary Minimum: $80,000
Functions: Advertising, PR, Minorities
Industries: Generalist, Energy/utilities, Finance, Pharmaceutical svcs., Communications, Telecoms, High tech

Career Consultants

(Firm declined to update.)
107 N. Pennsylvania, Ste. 400
Indianapolis, Indiana 46204
(317) 639-5601

Key Contact - Specialty:
Mr. Richard R. Butz

Description: We have successfully provided quality search services to corporations across the United States for over 30 years. We have successfully helped our clients fill over 60,000 openings.

Salary Minimum: $40,000
Functions: Senior mgmt., Middle mgmt., Automation, Sales mgmt., CFO's, MIS mgmt., Engineering
Industries: Generalist, Plastics/rubber, Paints/petroleum products, Metal products, Banking, Invest. banking, Human resource svcs.

Career Specialists, Inc. †

155-108th Ave. NE, Ste. 200
Bellevue, Washington 98004
(425) 455-0582
Fax: (425) 646-9738
Email: prolfe@msn.com

Key Contact - Specialty:
Ms. Pamela Rolfe - *CEOs, senior management, generalist*

Description: Founded in 1969 we specialize in senior management and highly technical positions.

Salary Minimum: $60,000
Functions: Generalist, Directors, Senior mgmt., Mfg., CFO's, IT
Industries: Textiles/apparel, Lumber/furniture, Metal products, Misc. mfg., Finance, High tech, Software

Affiliates:
Rolfe & Associates

Careers Plus

24955 Pacific Coast Hwy., Ste. B201
Malibu, California 90265
(310) 317-6113
Fax: (310) 317-6119
Email: careers@careers.com
Web: www.careersplus.com

Key Contact - Specialty:
Mr. Thomas Myers - *Senior management electronics*

Description: Search for technical sales managers and marketing, general management, executives in electronics.

Salary Minimum: $70,000
Functions: Senior mgmt., Mkt. research, Mktg. mgmt., Sales mgmt., Engineering
Industries: Computer equip., Test/measurement equip., Telecoms, High tech

Carlsen Resources, Inc.

800 Belford Ave., Ste. 200
Grand Junction, Colorado 81501
(970) 242-9462
Fax: (970) 242-9074
Email: carlsenres@aol.com

Key Contact - Specialty:
Ms. Ann R. Carlsen
Mr. Justin Rallis
Ms. Kate Hampford
Ms. Kristine Smith
Ms. Terri Thompson
Mr. Mike Schaack
Ms. Anne La Iond

Description: Executive level management positions in cable TV, telephone, cellular, DBS, wireless, entertainment, multimedia and information technology.

Salary Minimum: $70,000
Functions: Generalist, Mktg. mgmt., Personnel, CFO's, MIS mgmt., Minorities, Int'l.
Industries: Advertising/PR, New media, Broadcast & Film, Telecoms

† occasional contingency assignment

Carlson & Czeswik

Northland Plaza, Ste. 995
3800 W. 80th St.
Minneapolis, Minnesota 55431
(612) 896-8343

Key Contact - Specialty:
Mr. Frederick R. Czeswik - *Generalist*

Description: Executives and senior managers for banking, manufacturing, consumer packaged goods, insurance, healthcare and financial services. Exceptional quality.

Salary Minimum: $75,000
Functions: Generalist, Senior mgmt., Middle mgmt., Plant mgmt., Mktg. mgmt., CFO's, MIS mgmt.
Industries: Generalist, Food/bev/tobacco, Chemicals, Retail, Finance, Insurance, Healthcare

Branches:
1601 48th St., Ste. 250
Des Moines, Iowa 50266
(515) 225-2525
Key Contact - Specialty:
Mr. Gregory P. Carlson - *Generalist*

The Carlyle Group, Ltd.

625 N. Michigan Ave., Ste. 2100
Chicago, Illinois 60611
(312) 587-3030
Fax: (312) 587-0491

Key Contact - Specialty:
Mr. Max DeZara - *Management consulting*
Mr. Mitchell Berman - *Management consulting*
Mr. Larry S. Loubet - *Real estate*
Mr. Ward P. Feste - *Real estate*
Mr. Jon Schultz - *Real estate*

Description: We have distinguished ourselves as a premier retained executive search and human resource consulting firm. As a nationwide firm, we provide staffing and human resource consulting services at every organizational level - from middle through top level executive professionals.

Salary Minimum: $75,000
Functions: Middle mgmt., Personnel, Training, Mgmt. consultants
Industries: Mgmt. consulting, Human resource svcs., Real estate, Healthcare
Professional Associations: IACPR

Carnegie Partners, Inc.

1286 Amaranth Drive
Naperville, Illinois 60564-9331
(630) 236-6336
Fax: (630) 236-6283
Email: r-hollis@uchicago.edu

Key Contact - Specialty:
Mr. Robert W. Hollis - *Generalist*
Ms. Christa A. Capello - *Generalist*
Mr. Clarke Caldwell - *Generalist*
Mr. Michael Morrical - *Staffing*
Mr. Brian D. Wasiele - *Metals*
Mr. Charles F. Schlabach - *Electronics*
Mr. Fred Hickman - *Sales*

Description: Professional consulting and execution in the areas of executive search, selection, appraisal and management development. Specialists in behavioral interviewing and competency-based selection. Interview training included with each search.

Salary Minimum: $50,000
Functions: General mgmt., Mfg., Materials, Sales & mktg., HR mgmt., Finance, Engineering
Industries: Generalist, Mfg., Metal products, Finance, Svcs., Communications, Non-classifiable industries

Branches:
10195 Overhill Drive
Santa Ana, California 92705
(714) 730-2066
Fax: (714) 730-9380
Key Contact - Specialty:
Mr. Gary Colacci

219 E. Main St.
Mechanicsburg, Pennsylvania 17055-6555
(717) 737-3911
Fax: (717) 737-5300
Key Contact - Specialty:
Ms. Christa A. Capello

Affiliates:
Herbert William Consulting, Inc.

Carpenter Assoc., Inc.

20 S. Clark St., Ste. 2210
Chicago, Illinois 60603
(312) 263-4004
Fax: (312) 263-5083
Email: JudiCarpenter@msn.com

Key Contact - Specialty:
Ms. Judi Carpenter - *Direct marketing*

Description: After 16 years experience with direct marketing industry I understand clients' needs and consistently make successful matches. This high success rate is a result of a rare blend of experience, personality and intuitive people skills. I develop long term relationships with clients based on trust and genuine friendships.
Functions: Senior mgmt., Advertising, Mkt. research, Mktg. mgmt., Direct mktg., Int'l.
Industries: Advertising/PR, Publishing, New media, Broadcast & Film, Telecoms

Carpenter, Shackleton & Company

58 Foxwood Lane, Ste. 100
Barrington, Illinois 60010-1615
(847) 381-2555

Key Contact - Specialty:
Mr. George M. Shackleton - *Generalist*
Mr. Eric G. Carpenter - *Generalist*
Dr. Robert Denker - *Generalist*
Ms. Dora Lee Shackleton - *Sales & marketing*
Ms. Louise Rodriguez - *Minorities*

Description: Specialize in recruiting for publicly and privately owned Chicago area clients for all functions. Primary industries represented are manufacturing, financial services, higher education, transportation, communications and museums.
Functions: General mgmt., Mfg., Sales & mktg., HR mgmt., Finance, IT, Int'l.
Industries: Generalist, Mfg., Transportation, Finance, Non-profits, Higher ed., Communications

Branches:
253 E. Delaware Place, Ste. 9F
Chicago, Illinois 60611
(312) 944-5484
Key Contact - Specialty:
Mr. Michael Shackleton - *Generalist*

Carrington & Carrington, Ltd.

39 S. LaSalle St., Ste. 700
Chicago, Illinois 60603
(312) 606-0015
Fax: (312) 606-0501
Email: cclltd@worldnet.att.net

Key Contact - Specialty:
Mr. Willie E. Carrington
Ms. Marian H. Carrington

Description: We work across all functional and industry lines with a specific focus on identification of culturally diverse professionals. We are considered specialists in diversity and we have earned our reputation by successfully placing senior executives in specialized areas.

Salary Minimum: $100,000
Functions: Materials, Healthcare, Sales & mktg., HR mgmt., Finance, IT, Minorities
Industries: Generalist, Food/bev/tobacco, Drugs mfg., Finance, Telecoms
Professional Associations: AESC

Carris, Jackowitz Assoc.

201 E. 79th St.
New York, New York 10021
(212) 879-5482

Key Contact - Specialty:
Mr. S. Joseph Carris - *Generalist*
Mr. Ronald N. Jackowitz

Salary Minimum: $75,000
Functions: Generalist
Industries: Generalist

Branches:
Box 54
Andover, New Jersey 07821
(973) 786-5884

Key Contact - Specialty:
Mr. Ronald N. Jackowitz - *Generalist*

Caruso & Assoc., Inc.
1489 N. Military Trail, Ste. 216
West Palm Beach, Florida 33409
(561) 683-2336
Fax: (561) 683-3676
Email: caruso22@sprintmail.com

Key Contact - Specialty:
Mr. Dennis Caruso - *Real estate*

Description: Searches are performed by partners of firm and not handed off to other recruiters, a personal hands-on approach to develop a close working relationship with our clients.
Functions: Senior mgmt., Mktg. mgmt., Sales mgmt., CFO's, MIS mgmt., Architects
Industries: Construction, Finance, Hospitality, Environmental svcs., Real estate, High tech, Healthcare

Caruthers & Co., L.L.C.
50 Riverside Avenue
Westport, Connecticut 06880
(203) 222-3758
Fax: (203) 454-2310

Key Contact - Specialty:
Mr. Robert D. Caruthers - *Marketing, public relations, marketing services*

Description: National practice focused on senior level corporate communications, public affairs, marketing services, advertising and marketing assignments. Special expertise in financial services/ insurance, consumer and industrial categories.

Salary Minimum: $75,000
Functions: Advertising, Mkt. research, Mktg. mgmt., Direct mktg., Customer svc., PR
Industries: Generalist

Cary & Assoc.
P.O. Box 2043
Winter Park, Florida 32790-2043
(407) 647-1145

Key Contact - Specialty:
Mr. Con Cary - *Generalist, retail, wholesale, manufacturing*

Description: Principal was a Senior Vice President for a $600 million (annual volume) retail chain in addition to having 3 years of experience with a recognized search firm.

Salary Minimum: $35,000
Functions: Generalist, Senior mgmt., Middle mgmt., Distribution, Sales mgmt., CFO's, MIS mgmt.
Industries: Generalist, Food/bev/tobacco, Transportation, Wholesale, Retail, Hospitality, Entertainment

Rosemary Cass Ltd.
215 Main St.
Westport, Connecticut 06880
(203) 454-2920
Fax: (203) 454-4643

Key Contact - Specialty:
Ms. Rosemary Cass

Description: Specializes in pharmaceutical, biotechnology, medical devices and related healthcare industries. Searches in all disciplines within these industries.
Functions: General mgmt., Mfg., Sales & mktg., HR mgmt., Finance, IT, R&D
Industries: Drugs mfg., Medical devices, Invest. banking, Venture cap., Biotech

The Cassie Group
26 Main St.
Toms River, New Jersey 08753
(732) 473-1779
Web: cassigrp@cassie.com

Key Contact - Specialty:
Mr. Ronald L. Cassie - *Medical industry*

Description: Executive recruiting for the healthcare industry by experienced healthcare executives. Associate locations: U.S., Europe, Australia. Across all functions including but not limited to: general management, marketing, sales, R&D, operations, HR, QA/QC, regulatory, Info systems.

Salary Minimum: $50,000
Functions: General mgmt., Mfg., Sales & mktg., HR mgmt., Finance, R&D, Engineering
Industries: Medical devices, Pharmaceutical svcs., Biotech, Healthcare

Branches:
12 Running Brook Rd.
Bridgewater, New Jersey 08807
(908) 429-1335
Fax: (908) 218-0213
Key Contact - Specialty:
Fred P. Hauck - *Biotechnology manufacturers, senior level*

328 S. Front St, Ste. 5
P.O. Box 1674
New Bern, North Carolina 28563
(252) 634-9355
Fax: (252) 634-3090
Key Contact - Specialty:
Mr. John T. Shipherd - *Medical device manufacturers, senior level*

3655 Rt 202, Ste. 116
Doylestown, Pennsylvania 18901
(215) 348-1222
Fax: (215) 348-9186
Key Contact - Specialty:
Mr. Carl E. Berke - *Pharmaceutical manufacturers (senior level positions)*
Mr. Paul Edgerton - *Diagnostic manufacturers (senior level positions)*

Affiliates:
Ruston Poole International
George Walck & Associates

Catalyx Group
One Harkness Plaza, Ste. 300
61 W. 62nd St.
New York, New York 10023
(212) 956-3525
Fax: (212) 956-3763
Email: catalyx@erols.com
Web: www.catalyx.com

Key Contact - Specialty:
Mr. Lawrence D. Poster - *Life sciences, e-commerce, scientists, board of directors, CEOs*

Description: Recruits exceptional senior executives, turn-around specialists and scientists. Focus on emerging growth companies (all industries), biotechnology/high technology/e-commercial and information technology companies, and CEO/board of director searches.

Salary Minimum: $90,000
Functions: Generalist, Directors, Senior mgmt., CFO's, MIS mgmt., R&D, Int'l.
Industries: Drugs mfg., Medical devices, Venture cap., New media, High tech, Software, Biotech

Branches:
20 Stonepark Lane, Ste. 100
Nepean, Ontario K2H 9H4
Canada
(613) 726-7379
Key Contact - Specialty:
Mr. Peter Winter - *Life sciences, executives, scientists, engineers*

Michael J. Cavanagh & Assoc. Inc.
60 St. Clair Ave. E., Ste. 905
Toronto, Ontario M4T 1N5
Canada
(416) 324-9661
Email: cavsearch@sympatico.ca

Key Contact - Specialty:
Mr. Michael Cavanagh
Ms. Helena Beran

Description: One of Canada's most experienced recruiters in aerospace, automotive, electrical and packaged goods industries. A generalist operative at a senior level in Canada.

Salary Minimum: $100,000
Functions: Senior mgmt., Plant mgmt., Purchasing, Mktg. mgmt., Sales mgmt., CFO's, MIS mgmt.

† occasional contingency assignment

Industries: Generalist, Drugs mfg., Motor vehicles, Hospitality, Aerospace, High tech, Healthcare

---

Caywood Partners, Ltd.
1022 Main St., Ste. C
St. Helena, California 94574
(707) 967-0800
Fax: (707) 967-0700
Email: doug@caywood.com
Web: www.caywood.com

Key Contact - Specialty:
Mr. Doug Griffith - *LAN, MAN, WAN, telecommunications, data communications*

Description: We are one of the few retained search firms in the high tech sector focused exclusively on the computer networking industry - specializing in technical marketing, product management and research/development.

Salary Minimum: $80,000
Functions: Directors, Middle mgmt., Mkt. research, Mktg. mgmt., PR, R&D, Engineering
Industries: Computer equip., Venture cap., New media, Telecoms, High tech, Software

---

CEC Associates †
(Firm declined to update.)
52 Accord Park Drive
Norwell, Massachusetts 02061
(781) 982-0205

Key Contact - Specialty:
Ms. Claire E. Connolly - *Healthcare, biotechnology, securities*

Description: Retained recruitment of senior management executives in the healthcare field with a particular emphasis on senior housing, longterm care and home care. Other areas of focus include biotechnology and information technology in the securities industry.

Salary Minimum: $60,000
Functions: Senior mgmt., Middle mgmt., Nurses, Health admin., Sales mgmt., CFO's, MIS mgmt.
Industries: Invest. banking, Brokers, Biotech, Healthcare

Cejka Healthcare Executive Search Services (CHESS)
222 S. Central, Ste. 400
St. Louis, Missouri 63105
(314) 726-1603
Email: gstaub@cejka.com
Web: www.cejka.com

Key Contact - Specialty:
Ms. Susan Cejka - *Healthcare*
Mr. James Schmidt - *Healthcare*
Mr. Michael Taylor - *Healthcare*
Ms. Carrie Hackett - *Healthcare*

Description: We are a national healthcare search and consulting firm specializing in integration, physician group development and managed care.

Salary Minimum: $60,000
Functions: Directors, Senior mgmt., Middle mgmt., Physicians, Health admin., CFO's, Mgmt. consultants
Industries: Healthcare

Affiliates:
Cejka Healthcare Consulting
Trow Corps.

Cendea Connection Int'l. †
13740 Research Blvd., Bldg. 0-1
Austin, Texas 78750
(512) 219-6000
Email: info@cendea.com
Web: www.cendea.com

Key Contact - Specialty:
Mr. Wade H. Allen
Mr. Steven G. Ledbetter
Mr. William L. Pryor

Description: Specializing in all levels of sales, marketing and management positions throughout the high tech industries. Ethics, integrity and confidentiality are core components of our business.

Salary Minimum: $75,000
Functions: General mgmt., Mfg., Materials, Sales & mktg., IT, R&D, Int'l.
Industries: Computer equip., Computer svcs., Equip. svcs., Telecoms, High tech, Software

---

cFour Partners
100 Wilshire Blvd., Ste. 1840
Santa Monica, California 90401
(310) 394-2639
Fax: (310) 394-2669
Email: bbellano@cfour.com
Web: www.cfour.com

Key Contact - Specialty:
Mr. Robert W. Bellano - *Technology, digital media, venture capital*
Ms. Jennifer Happillon - *Digital media, entertainment*
Mr. David Shay - *Technology, professional services, customer support*
Mr. Shaun Corrales - *Technology, software, telecommunications*
Ms. Christina Romstein - *Digital media, entertainment, software*

Description: Specialized search firm serving vendors, service providers and end users involved in high technology, digital media, entertainment, telecommunications, software, internet commerce, applications, venture capital across all functional roles.

Salary Minimum: $100,000
Functions: General mgmt., Mfg., Sales & mktg., HR mgmt., Finance, IT, Engineering
Industries: Mfg., Finance, Svcs., Communications, Aerospace, High tech, Software

Branches:
1980 Post Oak Blvd., Ste. 2280
Houston, Texas 77056
(713) 840-7101
Fax: (713) 840-7260
Email: pkors@cfour.com
Key Contact - Specialty:
Mr. Paul Kors - *Technology, telecommunications*

Networks:
International Technology Partners

Chaloner Assoc. †
Box 1097, Back Bay Station
Boston, Massachusetts 02117-1097
(617) 451-5170
Fax: (617) 451-8160
Email: chaloner@chaloner.com
Web: www.chaloner.com

Key Contact - Specialty:
Mr. Edward H. Chaloner - *Public relations, corporate communications*
Ms. Sally Burke - *Advertising, marketing*
Mr. Chris McLean - *Marketing, investor relations*
Mr. Kirk Hazlett - *Public relations*
Ms. Michelle Shea - *Public relations*
Mr. Rich Young - *Corporate communications*

Description: We work in the fields of corporate communications, public relations, advertising, investor relations, marketing communications & sales promotion.

Salary Minimum: $50,000
Functions: Advertising, Mkt. research, Mktg. mgmt., Direct mktg., PR, Non-profits, Graphic artists
Industries: Generalist

David Chambers & Assoc., Inc.
2 Greenwich Plaza, Ste. 100
Greenwich, Connecticut 06830
(203) 622-1333

Key Contact - Specialty:
Mr. David E. Chambers - *General management, board searches*

Description: 25 year old generalist search firm with over 90% repeat business each year. Clients are large and small corporations and partnerships including investment bankers and venture capitalists; manufacturing dispersed in U.S. and Canada.

Salary Minimum: $150,000

Functions: Directors, Senior mgmt., Mfg., HR mgmt., CFO's, Int'l.
Industries: Generalist, Energy/utilities, Construction, Mfg., Entertainment, Aerospace, Healthcare

Affiliates:
Anthony Whitmee & Assoc.

Joseph Chandler & Assoc., Inc.
121 Stonegate
La Grange Park, Illinois 60526
(708) 482-7463
Fax: (708) 482-7469

Key Contact - Specialty:
Mr. Joseph J. Chandler - *Generalist, manufacturing*

Description: Well established generalist working nationwide.

Salary Minimum: $60,000
Functions: Generalist
Industries: Generalist, Plastics/rubber, Metal products, Machinery/Appliances, Misc. mfg.

Chanko-Ward, Ltd.
2 W. 45th St.
New York, New York 10036
(212) 869-4040

Key Contact - Specialty:
Mr. Jim Chanko
Mr. Dick Ward

Description: Functional specialists for 30 years in the identification and selection of finance, accounting, MIS and planning executives.

Salary Minimum: $100,000
Functions: Senior mgmt., Finance, MIS mgmt.
Industries: Generalist

Chase Partners
BCE Place, 181 Bay St., Ste. 3740
P.O. Box 798
Toronto, Ontario M5J 2T3
Canada
(416) 364-6404
Fax: (416) 364-2875

Key Contact - Specialty:
Mr. John S. Harrison - *Senior executive*

Description: Exclusively executive search for all business sectors. Strengths in recruiting marketing, finance and administration. Broad base of clients in manufacturing, service industries (including financial services) and consumer packaged goods.

Salary Minimum: $80,000
Functions: Senior mgmt.
Industries: Mfg., Finance

ChaseAmerica, Inc.
11211 Prosperity Farms Road, #210C
Palm Beach Gardens, Florida 33410
(561) 622-1120
Fax: (561) 626-4646
Email: chase22@ix.netcom.com
Web: chase22@ix.netcom.com

Key Contact - Specialty:
Mr. David E. Stefan - *Sports, golf, apparel, sports products companies*

Description: Our clients are sports apparel companies, sport marketing firms, professional sports teams, golf equipment, major golf resorts, golf course developments.

Salary Minimum: $100,000
Industries: Entertainment

A. D. Check Assoc., Inc.
204 S. Franklin St.
Wilkes-Barre, Pennsylvania 18701
(717) 829-5066
Fax: (717) 820-8293
Email: check204@aol.com

Key Contact - Specialty:
Mr. Andrew D. Check - *Manufacturing*

Description: Near 100% completion rate; deep long-term client commitments; 75% of volume is repeat business; performance-based contracts; competitively favorable fee and expense structures; clients state our outperformance of major retainer firms previously used.

Salary Minimum: $60,000
Functions: Generalist, Senior mgmt., Middle mgmt., Plant mgmt., Mktg. mgmt., Sales mgmt., Int'l.
Industries: Generalist, Medical devices, Metal products, Machinery/Appliances, Motor vehicles, Test/measurement equip., Misc. mfg.

The Cherbonnier Group, Inc.
(a division of TCG International, Inc.)
3050 Post Oak Blvd., Ste. 1600
Houston, Texas 77056
(713) 688-4701
Fax: (713) 960-1168
Email: consult@chergroup.com

Key Contact - Specialty:
Mr. L. Michael Cherbonnier

Description: Extensive domestic and international experience. Searches have crossed most industry lines and most senior positions both line and staff. Twenty five years executive search experience on worldwide scale. Provide in-depth candidate evaluations.

Salary Minimum: $80,000

Functions: Generalist, Product dev., CFO's, MIS mgmt., Engineering, Environmentalists, Int'l.
Industries: Generalist, Energy/utilities, Construction, Computer equip., Computer svcs., Human resource svcs., High tech

Branches:
1520 140th Ave. NE, Ste. 100
Bellevue, Washington 98005
(425) 664-9435
Fax: (425) 664-2092
Key Contact - Specialty:
Mr. W. Gene Burden

Chicago Research Group, Inc.
P.O. Box 3757
Chapel Hill, North Carolina 27515
(919) 968-0120
Email: chgoresgrp@mindspring.com

Key Contact - Specialty:
Ms. Deborah Marshall
Mr. Robert Ross

Description: We were founded with one single goal in mind: provide the highest quality business research in the industry... business research that is accurate, thorough and timely.

Salary Minimum: $75,000
Functions: Generalist
Industries: Generalist

Branches:
P.O. Box 230
Lake Forest, Illinois 60045
(847) 234-9220
Key Contact - Specialty:
Ms. Pat Ensing

China Human Resources Group
29 Airpark Rd.
Princeton, New Jersey 08540
(609) 683-4521
Fax: (609) 683-9670

Key Contact - Specialty:
Ms. Christine Casati - *General management (China-related)*

Description: The China Human Resources Group meets the growing demand for experienced management talent in the People's Republic of China by offering consulting and search services for all China-related business.

Salary Minimum: $50,000

International Branches:
Shanghai

Chrisman & Co. Inc.
350 S. Figueroa St., Ste. 550
Los Angeles, California 90071
(213) 620-1192
Fax: (213) 620-1693

† occasional contingency assignment

Email: lachrisman@worldnet.att.net

Key Contact - Specialty:
Mr. Timothy Chrisman - *Generalist*

Description: Board member, middle and upper echelon executive searches, nationally.

Salary Minimum: $75,000
Functions: Generalist
Industries: Generalist

Christenson Hutchison McDowell, LLC

466 Southern Blvd.
Chatham, New Jersey 07928-1462
(973) 966-1600
Fax: (973) 966-6933

Key Contact - Specialty:
Mr. H. Alan Christenson
Mr. William K. Hutchison
Mr. Robert N. McDowell

Description: Established in 1976. Partner management of all assignments. Nationwide practice, serving large public corporations, small privately held companies in banking, insurance, financial services, healthcare, manufaturing, not-for-profit and government agencies.

Salary Minimum: $120,000
Functions: Senior mgmt., Mfg., Sales & mktg., HR mgmt., Finance, IT, Non-profits
Industries: Generalist, Mfg., Finance, Computer svcs., Human resource svcs., Government, Insurance
Professional Associations: AESC, IACPR

Christian & Timbers, Inc.

One Corporate Exchange
25825 Science Park Drive, Suite 400
Cleveland, Ohio 44122
(216) 464-8710
Fax: (216) 464-6160
Email: comments@ctnet.com
Web: www.ctnet.com

Key Contact - Specialty:
Mr. Jeffrey E. Christian - *CEOs, board of directors, senior executive level management, Internet, software*
Mr. Adam Kohn - *Professional consulting services, systems integration, telephony services, environmental services, architectural engineering*
Mr. Steve Mader - *Telecommunications, computing, software, data communications, electronic media*
Mr. David Mather - *Telecommunications, multimedia, interactive media, Internet-related, consumer electronics*
Mr. Gregory Selker - *Software, interactive media, on-line services, networking, data communications*
Mr. Mark Esposito - *Banking, insurance, asset management, venture capital, financial information providers*
Mr. Marc Lewis - *Computing (hardware & software), internet, interactive media, telecommunications, data communications*
Mr. John Daily - *Information technology (senior level executives), CIO's (large companies), generalist*
Mr. Buster Houchins - *Information technology, medical devices, electronics*
Ms. Margaret King - *CEO, senior level management, internet, software, multimedia*
Mr. Chuck Pappalardo - *Information technology, consulting information services, professional services, interactive media, software development*
Ms. Vici Wayne - *Senior executive management, internet, emerging technologies, consumer products, media businesses*
Ms. Penny Mooney - *Consumer package & durable goods, consumer technology & services, consumer & retail start-ups, industrial, automotive*
Mr. Morgan McKeown - *Consumer services & products, professional services, internet/new media, information technology, healthcare*
Mr. David Nocifora
Mr. Leo Shulman

Description: Provide executive search and management consulting to upper management and boards in information technology, financial services, healthcare, environmental services, professional services, consumer products, manufacturing and general industry.

Salary Minimum: $150,000
Functions: Generalist, Directors, Senior mgmt., Health admin., Mktg. mgmt., Sales mgmt., CFO's, MIS mgmt., Minorities, Int'l.
Industries: Generalist, Energy/utilities, Chemicals, Medical devices, Computer equip., Consumer electronics, Finance, Banking, Venture cap., Pharmaceutical svcs., Publishing, New media, Broadcast & Film, Telecoms, Environmental svcs., Haz. waste, Insurance, High tech, Software, Biotech, Healthcare

Branches:
20833 Stevens Creek Blvd., Ste. 200
Cupertino, California 95014
(408) 446-5440
Fax: (408) 446-5445
Key Contact - Specialty:
Mr. David R. Mather - *Telecommunications, multimedia, interactive media, internet-related, consumer electronics*

191 Post Rd. W.
Westport, Connecticut 06880
(203) 221-2660
Fax: (203) 221-2726
Key Contact - Specialty:
Ms. Penny Mooney - *Consumer package goods, durable goods, consumer technology, consumer services, consumer & retail start-ups*

8840 Stanford Blvd., Ste. 2900
Columbia, Maryland 21045
(410) 872-0200
Fax: (410) 872-0208
Key Contact - Specialty:
Mr. William C. Buster Houchins - *Information technology, electronics, manufacturing, medical devices, technology*

24 New England Executive Park
Burlington, Massachusetts 01803
(781) 229-9515
Fax: (781) 229-8608
Key Contact - Specialty:
Mr. Stephen P. Mader - *Telecommunications, computing, software, data communications, electronic media*

570 Lexington Ave., 19th Floor
New York, New York 10022
(212) 588-3500
Fax: (212) 688-5754
Key Contact - Specialty:
Mr. Morgan McKeown - *Internet, new media, consumer services & products, professional consulting services, healthcare*

3000 Towers Cresent Drive
Vienna, Virginia 22182
(703) 448-1700
Fax: (703) 447-1740
Key Contact - Specialty:
Ms. Jane-Scott Cantus - *Financial services, aerospace/defense, telecommunications, emerging technologies, new media industries*

William J. Christopher Assoc., Inc.

307 N. Walnut St.
West Chester, Pennsylvania 19380
(610) 696-4397
Fax: (610) 692-5177
Email: wjc@wjca.com
Web: www.wjca.com

Key Contact - Specialty:
Mr. John Jeffrey Bole

Description: We specialize in professional staffing for the following industries: paper mills, paper coaters and converters, printers, packaging converters and laminators, graphic art equipment and supply manufacturers.

Salary Minimum: $50,000
Functions: Senior mgmt., Middle mgmt., Plant mgmt., Quality, Sales mgmt., Direct mktg., Personnel
Industries: Paper, Printing, Packaging

Christopher-Westmont & Assoc., Inc.

14077 Cedar Rd., Ste. 201
Cleveland, Ohio 44118
(216) 321-1429
Fax: (216) 321-1734

Key Contact - Specialty:
Mr. John R. Donnelly - *Automotive manufacturing, original equipment manufacturing, suppliers to OEM (Tier 1, Tier 2)*
Mr. Patrick Donnelly - *Financial services-academia*
Mr. Christopher Donnelly - *Manufacturing*
Mr. Larry Gregg - *High tech, electronics, human resources*

Description: Firm is focused on high technology including manufacturing, engineering and operations in automotive and general industry.

Salary Minimum: $50,000
Functions: Middle mgmt., Quality, Materials Plng., Sales mgmt., MIS mgmt., Minorities, Int'l.
Industries: Generalist, Drugs mfg., Motor vehicles, Human resource svcs., Packaging, High tech

---

Churchill & Affiliates, Inc.
1200 Bustleton Pike, Ste. 3
Feasterville, Pennsylvania 19053
(215) 364-8070
Fax: (215) 322-4391
Email: hwasserman@churchillsearch.com
Web: churchillsearch.com

Key Contact - Specialty:
Mr. Harvey Wasserman - *Telecommunications*

Description: Executive search and recruitment for the telecommunications industry. Specializing in sales, marketing, engineering and support from senior management to field sales and support, domestically and internationally.

Salary Minimum: $50,000
Functions: Senior mgmt., Sales & mktg., Advertising, Mkt. research, PR, CFO's, Mgmt. consultants
Industries: Test/measurement equip., Communications, Advertising/PR, Telecoms, High tech, Software

---

M. A. Churchill & Assoc., Inc.
Morelyn Plaza, 1111 Street Rd., #307
Southampton, Pennsylvania 18966
(215) 953-0300
Fax: (215) 953-1419
Email: searchmac@aol.com
Web: www.machurchill.com

Key Contact - Specialty:
Mr. Lawrence Sher
Mr. Stuart S. Borden
Mr. John H. Spicher
Mr. Brian M. Hochberg
Ms. Pamela A. Wylie
Ms. Dolores Garzone
Mr. Gary Konefsky

Description: A highly focused search firm for the information technology, banking/Wall Street/financial systems vendors-worldwide. Recruiting disciplines are sales, marketing, management, support, pre/post sales support, product/marketing-management, project management, and senior systems development.

Salary Minimum: $50,000
Functions: General mgmt., Sales & mktg., Finance, IT, Int'l.
Industries: Computer equip., Finance, Computer svcs., Accounting, Communications, High tech, Software

---

Cizek Assoc., Inc.
2390 E. Camelback Rd., Ste. 300
Biltmore Financial Ctr.
Phoenix, Arizona 85016
(602) 553-1066
Email: cizekassoc@aol.com

Key Contact - Specialty:
Ms. Marti J. Cizek - *Generalist*

Description: Generalist firm with strength in manufacturing, consumer products, technology, healthcare, non-profit and banking/financial services. With offices in Phoenix and Chicago, we serve clients coast to coast.

Salary Minimum: $75,000
Functions: Generalist, General mgmt., Mfg., Sales & mktg., HR mgmt., Finance, Minorities
Industries: Generalist, Mfg., Finance, Svcs., Aerospace, High tech, Healthcare

Branches:
2021 Midwest Rd., Ste. 200
Oak Brook, Illinois 60523
(630) 953-8570
Key Contact - Specialty:
Mr. John T. Cizek - *Generalist*

CJA-The Adler Group, Inc.
17852 17th St., Ste. 209
Tustin, California 92780
(714) 573-1820
Fax: (714) 731-3952
Email: coach@cja-careers.com
Web: www.cja-careers.com

Key Contact - Specialty:
Mr. Louis S. Adler - *High technology, manufacturing, sales, marketing*
Mr. Brad M. Remillard - *Distribution, finance, accounting*

Description: We offer performance-based job descriptions; pre-planned, structured interviews and in-house hiring training for our clients. This training includes on-line POWER Staffing Software System. A unique Windows-based interactive hiring system including applicant tracking and evaluation.

Salary Minimum: $75,000
Functions: Senior mgmt., Plant mgmt., Purchasing, Materials Plng., Mkt. research, Sales mgmt., CFO's
Industries: Plastics/rubber, Computer equip., Entertainment, Telecoms, High tech, Software

Branches:
5757 Century Blvd., #700
Los Angeles, California 90045
(310) 378-4571
Fax: (310) 791-4434
Key Contact - Specialty:
Mr. Barry A. Deutsch

921 Harwood Terrace
Bedford, Texas 76021
(817) 281-3444
Fax: (817) 428-8414
Key Contact - Specialty:
Mr. Carl Bradford

Arlene Clapp, Ltd. †
3800 W. 80th St.
1000 Northland Plaza
Minneapolis, Minnesota 55431
(612) 831-1888
Fax: (612) 831-1212
Email: clapp006@tc.umn.edu

Key Contact - Specialty:
Ms. Arlene Clapp - *Real estate (commercial), construction*

Description: We specialize in placements in commercial real estate (office, retail, industrial) and construction industries.
Functions: Directors, Senior mgmt., Middle mgmt., Sales & mktg., Sales mgmt., Specialized services, Non-profits
Industries: Generalist, Construction, Finance, Misc. financial, Real estate

---

Clarey & Andrews, Inc.
1200 Shermer Rd., Ste. 108
Northbrook, Illinois 60062
(847) 498-2870

Key Contact - Specialty:
Mr. J. Douglas Andrews
Mr. Jack R. Clarey

Description: We are a small generalist firm whose assignments are conducted only by experienced principals.

Salary Minimum: $120,000
Functions: Generalist, General mgmt., Mfg., Sales & mktg., HR mgmt., Finance
Industries: Generalist, Mfg.
Professional Associations: AESC

Networks:
Penrhyn International

Clarey/Napier Int'l., L.C.
600 Travis St., Ste. 6500
Houston, Texas 77002
(713) 238-6705
Fax: (713) 236-4778
Email: cnintl@icct.net

Key Contact - Specialty:
Mr. William A. Clarey, II

† occasional contingency assignment

Ms. Ginger L. Napier

Description: Worldwide executive search specializing in all phases of the energy industry including oil and gas, chemicals, power, refining, petrochemicals, engineering and construction, environmental and management consulting services.

Salary Minimum: $100,000
Functions: Senior mgmt., HR mgmt., Finance, IT, Engineering, Mgmt. consultants, Int'l.
Industries: Generalist, Energy/utilities, Chemicals, Computer svcs., Accounting, Mgmt. consulting, Human resource svcs.

Ken Clark Int'l.

Five Independence Way, Ste. 210
Princeton, New Jersey 08540
(609) 514-2600
Fax: (609) 514-2700
Email: info@kenclark.com
Web: www.kenclark.com

Key Contact - Specialty:
Mr. Kenneth Clark - *Presidents, CEOs, board level*
Mr. Robert Hennessy - *Healthcare, consumer products, scientific products, industrial products*
Mr. Robert Majczan - *Pharmaceutical & diagnostic products & services*
Mr. William O'Callaghan - *Medical products & services*
Ms. Rosemarie Ciak - *Marketing, sales*
Mr. Alan George - *Manufacturing, supply chain*
Mr. Keith Jones - *R&D*
Ms. Carolyn Maye - *Regulatory affairs, quality assurance*
Ms. Andrea Schutz - *Human resources*

Description: We specialize in the healthcare, scientific, consumer and industrial products and services industries. We were founded by former partners of global executive search firms and former executives of global corporations. We guarantee quality work and service excellence.

Salary Minimum: $100,000
Functions: General mgmt., Mfg., Materials, Sales & mktg., IT, R&D, Engineering
Industries: Mfg., Medical devices, Test/measurement equip., Pharmaceutical svcs., Human resource svcs., Biotech, Healthcare

Branches:
255 Alhambra Circle, Ste. 710
Coral Gables, Florida 33134
(305) 774-1183
Fax: (305) 774-5677
Key Contact - Specialty:
Mr. Sundeep Shankwalkar

International Branches:
Singapore, Windsor

Affiliates:
Ken Clark Int'l.

Richard Clarke Assoc., Inc.

9 West 95th St., Ste. C-1
New York, New York 10025
(212) 222-5600

Key Contact - Specialty:
Mr. Richard Clarke

Description: Minority recruiting, all skill areas, i.e. accounting, finance, sales, marketing, engineering, systems, law and human resources.

Salary Minimum: $60,000
Functions: Generalist
Industries: Generalist

Clayman & Co.

20 Park Plaza, Ste. 483
Boston, Massachusetts 02116
(617) 578-9999
Fax: (617) 578-9929
Email: clayco@ma.ultranet.com

Key Contact - Specialty:
Mr. Steven G. Clayman - *High technology, sales & marketing*
Mr. John H. Crawford - *High technology, sales & marketing*
Mr. Vincent Brennan - *High technology, sales & marketing*

Description: Proud of over twenty-five years of recruiting of sales and marketing executives for high technology clients. We rely on our original research plus our database of 30,000+ previously interviewed sales/marketing executives.

Salary Minimum: $150,000
Functions: Directors, Senior mgmt., Mkt. research, Mktg. mgmt., Sales mgmt., PR, Mgmt. consultants
Industries: Computer svcs., Advertising/PR, New media, Telecoms, High tech, Software

---

Coastal Int'l., Inc.

28 Green St.
Newbury, Massachusetts 01951
(978) 462-2436
Fax: (978) 462-9198
Web: www.coastal-intl.com

Key Contact - Specialty:
Mr. Lew Boyd
Ms. Cary Stratton

Description: Experienced in senior-level search for IT and energy/environmental firms throughout North America, including multiple searches and staffing new organizations. Completed numerous searches for subsidiaries of international or Fortune 500 companies.

Salary Minimum: $50,000
Functions: Directors, Senior mgmt., Middle mgmt., Mkt. research, Mktg. mgmt., Sales mgmt., CFO's
Industries: Energy/utilities, Mgmt. consulting, Environmental svcs., High tech, Software

---

COBA Executive Search

14947 E. Wagon Trail Place
Aurora, Colorado 80015
(303) 693-8382
Fax: (303) 693-3960
Email: mkiken@isp.incc.net

Key Contact - Specialty:
Mr. Mark E. Kiken - *Sales & marketing, finance & accounting, international food & beverage, communications, software*
Ms. Lesia Korytko - *Manufacturing, biotech, healthcare*

Description: We specialize in searches for: U.S., Eastern Europe, Pacific Rim and the Americas. Candidates are selected for on-site market experience, linguistic/historical understanding and ability to grow business.

Salary Minimum: $75,000
Functions: General mgmt., Mfg., Sales & mktg., Finance, Int'l.
Industries: Mfg., Food/bev/tobacco, Communications, Telecoms, High tech, Biotech, Healthcare

---

Cochran, Cochran & Yale, Inc.

955 E. Henrietta Rd.
Rochester, New York 14623
(716) 424-6060
Fax: (716) 424-6069
Email: ccyale@frontiernet.net
Web: www.ccy.com

Key Contact - Specialty:
Mr. Gary M. Baker - *Finance, human resources, marketing executives, manufacturing, supply chain*
Mr. Walter Y. Critchley - *CIO, marketing, general management, operations, manufacturing*

Description: Retained search with specialized divisions: finance, software, electronics, process manufacturing and consumer products marketing. Industries include pharmaceuticals, plastics, high tech electronics, aerospace, consumer products, banking and consulting.

Salary Minimum: $45,000
Functions: Directors, Senior mgmt., Production, Materials Plng., CFO's, MIS mgmt., Engineering
Industries: Energy/utilities, Food/bev/tobacco, Chemicals, Soap/perfume/cosmetics, Plastics/rubber, Machinery/Appliances, Banking

Branches:
1333 W. 120th Ave., Ste. 311
Westminster, Colorado 80234
(303) 252-4600
Fax: (303) 252-7810
Key Contact - Specialty:
Mr. Chet Marino - *Engineering, accounting, finance, MIS, human resources*

5166 Main St.
Williamsville, New York 14221
(716) 631-1300
Fax: (716) 631-1319
Email: yale@ccy.com
Key Contact - Specialty:
Mr. Walter Critchley - *Manufacturing, operations, systems, human resources, finance*

Coe & Co. Int'l. Inc./EMA Partners Int'l.

1400, 400-3rd Ave. SW
Canterra Tower
Calgary, Alberta T2P 4H2
Canada
(403) 232-8833
Fax: (403) 232-0165
Email: coe@coeandcompany.com
Web: www.coeandcompany.com

Key Contact - Specialty:
Dr. Karen Coe - *High technology, telecommunications, oil & gas, consumer services, research & development*
Ms. Lynda Costello - *Oil & gas, education, communications*
Mr. Robert Caple - *Oil & gas, manufacturing*
Ms. Kalyna Bilinski - *consumer packaged goods, pharmaceuticals, sales & marketing, food*

Description: A generalist firm which recruits middle to senior level executives for agriculture/forestry, communication, consumer products, education, energy/utilities, financial services, healthcare/hospitals, high tech, telecommunications, information technology, legal, manufacturing, oil and gas, petroleum, public administration, publishing/media, and transportation/distribution industries, among others. The firm's practice is national and international in scope.

Salary Minimum: $60,000
Functions: Senior mgmt., Plant mgmt., Customer svc., Benefits, CFO's, MIS mgmt., R&D
Industries: Energy/utilities, Mfg., Transportation, Communications, Packaging, High tech, Biotech
Professional Associations: AESC

Networks:
EMA Partners Int'l.

Dean M. Coe Assoc.

1 Financial Center
Boston, Massachusetts 02110
(617) 210-6850
Email: dcoe@dmcassociates.com

Key Contact - Specialty:
Ms. Jane E. Carlson

Description: Generalist firm serving most industries. Partners have extensive background in real estate, finance, insurance,, non-profit administration, creative services, corporate communications, HR.

Salary Minimum: $100,000
Functions: Generalist, Senior mgmt.
Industries: Generalist, Insurance, Real estate, Healthcare
Professional Associations: AESC

The Coelyn Group

1 Park Plaza, Ste. 600
Irvine, California 92614
(949) 553-8855
Fax: (949) 363-0837

Key Contact - Specialty:
Mr. Ronald H. Coelyn - *Life sciences*
Ms. Carol L. Moson - *Life sciences*
Ms. Lynn S. Nishimoto - *Life sciences*

Description: Retainer-based executive search firm specializing in senior level executive positions strictly in life sciences.
Functions: Directors, Senior mgmt., Middle mgmt., CFO's, R&D
Industries: Drugs mfg., Medical devices, Biotech, Healthcare

Cole, Warren & Long, Inc.

2 Penn Center Plaza, Ste. 312
Philadelphia, Pennsylvania 19102
(215) 563-0701
Fax: (215) 563-2907
Email: cwlserch@itw.com
Web: www.cwl-inc.com

Key Contact - Specialty:
Mr. Ronald Cole - *General management*
Mr. Richard Warren - *General management*
Mr. Richard Lewis - *Technical, manufacturing*

Description: An executive search and general management consulting firm, servicing clients domestic and int'l. Broad range of clients including: financial services, insurance, mfg., retail, electronics, utilities, healthcare, retail and government. Unique hourly rate offers many options to clients.

Salary Minimum: $90,000
Functions: Generalist, Senior mgmt., Mfg., Sales & mktg., HR mgmt., Finance, IT
Industries: Generalist, Mfg., Finance, Svcs., Computer svcs., Insurance, Healthcare
Professional Associations: IACPR

Affiliates:
Baladi & Company
Leaders Trust International
MSL Belgium SA
Shirley Associates

J. Kevin Coleman & Assoc., Inc.

416 Hermosa Place
South Pasadena, California 91030
(818) 403-0704

Key Contact - Specialty:
Mr. J. Kevin Coleman - *Generalist*

Description: Specializes from mid-management to general management assignments in manufacturing, engineering, finance, marketing and human resources. Industries served include: communications, entertainment, engineering services, industrial products and high technology.

Salary Minimum: $75,000
Functions: General mgmt., Mfg., HR mgmt., Finance, MIS mgmt., Engineering
Industries: Generalist, Mfg., Aerospace, High tech

Coleman Lew & Assoc., Inc.

326 W. Tenth St.
Charlotte, North Carolina 28202
(704) 377-0362
Fax: (704) 377-0424
Email: clakdc@aol.com

Key Contact - Specialty:
Mr. Charles E. Lew
Mr. Kenneth D. Carrick, Jr.
Ms. Ann N. Whitlock
Mr. Thomas M. Brinkley

Description: Established in 1979, firm is a regional generalist search firm with national clients. Expertise in the food industry with an extensive database supported by a strong research staff.
Functions: Generalist, Senior mgmt., Production, Distribution, Mktg. mgmt., CFO's, Mgmt. consultants
Industries: Generalist, Misc. mfg., Transportation, Wholesale, Retail, Legal, Accounting
Professional Associations: AESC

Colton Bernard Inc.

870 Market St., Ste. 822
San Francisco, California 94102
(415) 399-8700
Fax: (415) 399-0750
Email: rcolton@coltonbernard.com
Web: www.fashionmall.com/coltonbernard

Key Contact - Specialty:
Mr. Harry Bernard - *Senior management*
Mr. Roy C. Colton - *Senior management*

Description: A full range of marketing, information, organizational and management recruiting services for the apparel industry exclusively. Also, licensing, sales training programs, image development, seminars and workshops; interactive consumer testing.

Salary Minimum: $75,000
Functions: Directors, Senior mgmt., Mktg. mgmt., CFO's, MIS mgmt., Mgmt. consultants, Int'l.
Industries: Textiles/apparel, Retail

The Colton Partnership, Inc.

63 Wall St.
New York, New York 10005
(212) 509-1800
Fax: (212) 509-1633
Email: citi2901@aol.com

Key Contact - Specialty:
Mr. W. Hoyt Colton - *Financial services*
Mr. Scott C. Colton - *Information technology*
Mr. Charles Guevara - *Technology consultants*

Description: We are generalists with an expertise in financial services and information technology. We adhere to a dedicated personal service that demands the highest standards of professionalism, honesty and integrity. Our corporate creed is excellence and our quality of work is never compromised in the commitment to our clients requirements.

Salary Minimum: $75,000
Functions: HR mgmt., CFO's, Cash mgmt., M&A, Risk mgmt., IT
Industries: Finance, New media, High tech, Software

Affiliates:
Colton Information Technology, Inc.

Colucci, Blendow & Johnson

P.O. Box 10
Half Moon Bay, California 94019
(650) 712-0103
Fax: (650) 712-0105
Email: EXSEARCH@IT.NETCOM.COM

Key Contact - Specialty:
Mr. Bart A. Colucci

Description: Twenty nine years of retained search experience in medical technology including pharmaceuticals, diagnostics, biotechnology, medical devices and instrumentation.

Salary Minimum: $80,000
Functions: Generalist
Industries: Drugs mfg., Medical devices, Pharmaceutical svcs., Biotech

Columbia Consulting Group

20 S. Charles St., 9th Floor
Sun Life Bldg.
Baltimore, Maryland 21201
(410) 385-2525
Fax: (410) 385-0044
Email: ccgbal@erols.com
Web: www.columbiaconsultinggroup.com

Key Contact - Specialty:
Mr. Lawrence J. Holmes
Mr. Robert C. Gauthier
Mr. Thomas J. McMahon
Ms. Julie Mercer
Mr. Cory T. Holmes
Ms. Laurie Hoffman
Ms. Cynthia Belt
Mr. Phil Grantham

Description: Client retained executive search consultants serving most industries and functions.

Salary Minimum: $95,000
Functions: Generalist, Mfg., Healthcare, Sales & mktg., HR mgmt., Finance, IT
Industries: Generalist, Finance, Svcs., Communications, High tech, Biotech
Professional Associations: AESC, IACPR

Branches:
582 Forest Highlands
Flagstaff, Arizona 86001
(520) 525-1946
Fax: (520) 525-1709
Key Contact - Specialty:
Mr. Joseph P. Johnson

353 Sacramento St., Ste. 600
San Francisco, California 94111
(415) 392-2525
Fax: (415) 433-5994

185 Helios Drive
Jupiter, Florida 33477
(561) 748-0232
Fax: (561) 748-0234
Key Contact - Specialty:
Mr. Larry D. Mingle

230 Park Ave., Ste. 456
The Helmsley Bldg.
New York, New York 10169
(212) 983-2525
Fax: (212) 983-2541
Key Contact - Specialty:
Ms. Ann Fulgham-MacCarthy
Ms. Trish Gill
Mr. David Bullock
Mr. Joseph P. Johnson
Ms. Carol Lawson
Mr. William Johnson

Networks:
Global Search Partners

Combined Resources Inc.

25300 Lorain Rd., Ste. 2C
North Olmsted, Ohio 44070
(800) 738-2451
(440) 716-2244
Fax: (800) 838-5627
Email: info@cri-search.com
Web: www.cri-search.com

Key Contact - Specialty:
Mr. Gilbert Sherman - *Information technology professionals*
Mr. David Danner - *Information technology professionals*

Description: We provide comprehensive information technology staffing services to law firms, accounting firms, consulting firms and financial institutions. Founded in 1987, we have distinguished our firm by providing excellent, cost-effective service to our clients and confidential, respectful service to our candidates. We guarantee the success of our executive search assignments for one full year.
Functions: MIS mgmt., Systems anal., Systems dev., Systems implem., Systems support, Network admin., DB admin.
Industries: Finance, Legal, Computer svcs., Accounting, Mgmt. consulting, High tech, Software

Compass Group Ltd.

401 S. Old Woodward, Ste. 460
Birmingham, Michigan 48009
(248) 540-9110
Email:
executivesearch@compassgroup.com
Web: www.compassgroup.com

Key Contact - Specialty:
Mr. Paul Czamanske - *CEOs, COOs, board searches*
Ms. Christina L. Balian - *Generalist, strategy, finance, general management*
Mr. Jerold L. Lipe - *Generalist, general management, purchasing, human resources*
Ms. Katherine T. Slaughter - *Generalist, non-profit, higher education*
Mr. James W. Sturtz - *Generalist, automotive*
Mr. Peter M. Czamanske - *Generalist, information technologies*
Ms. Renee L. Naud

Description: A leading Midwest based firm, working internationally, accepting only retained engagements. Emphasis in automotive, manufacturing, high-tech and service industries. Most disciplines.

Salary Minimum: $100,000
Functions: Senior mgmt., Mfg., Materials, Sales & mktg., CFO's, Non-profits, Int'l.
Industries: Generalist, Construction, Mfg., Finance, Svcs., Communications, High tech
Professional Associations: AESC

Branches:
Two Mid America Plaza, Ste. 800
Oakbrook Terrace, Illinois 60181
(630) 954-2255
Key Contact - Specialty:
Mr. Jerold L. Lipe - *Generalist*

Networks:
The Hever Group

Computer Professionals

3601 Algonquin Rd., Ste. 129
Rolling Meadows, Illinois 60008
(847) 577-6266
Email: compro@interaccess.com

Key Contact - Specialty:
Mr. Kevin B. Hogan

Description: Single practitioner specialized in retained executive searches involved in all aspects of information technology.

Salary Minimum: $225,000
Functions: Directors, Senior mgmt., Middle mgmt.
Industries: High tech, Software

Computer Search Group, Ltd.

20 N. Wacker Drive, Ste. 2200
Chicago, Illinois 60606
(312) 269-9950
Fax: (312) 269-9952
Email: CSGforIT@aol.com

Key Contact - Specialty:
Mr. James E. Johnston - *Information systems*

Description: Professional and executive recruiting of information systems, banking and finance professionals. Especially expert in the mid-range and client server computer markets.

Salary Minimum: $45,000
Functions: MIS mgmt., Systems anal., Systems dev., Systems implem., Systems support
Industries: Generalist

Conard Associates, Inc.

74 Northeastern Blvd., Unit #22A
Nashua, New Hampshire 03062
(603) 886-0600
Fax: (603) 886-8886
Email: rodconard@earthlink.net

Key Contact - Specialty:
Dr. Rodney J. Conard

Description: Our executive search capabilities complement our consulting services. We help companies develop competitive excellence programs which integrate TQM, process re-engineering and performance management. Capable leadership is essential to competitive excellence.

Salary Minimum: $100,000
Functions: Generalist, Senior mgmt., Plant mgmt., Sales mgmt., CFO's, MIS mgmt., Mgmt. consultants
Industries: Generalist, Paper, Finance, Higher ed., Packaging, High tech, Healthcare

Conasa de Mexico, S.C.

San Francisco No 1838, Suite 303
Col. de Valle
Mexico City, Mexico DF 03100
Mexico
52 5 534 3265
Fax: 52 5 534 4629

Key Contact - Specialty:
Mr. Fernando Zambrana - *Top management industry, services, commerce*
Ms. Victoria Villareal - *Middle management industry, services, commerce*

Description: The most professional and effective middle size executive search firm in Mexico, characterized for diversifying its clients in different lines of business, acting without any interference in order to provide the best available candidates, under a strict profile previously agreed upon.

Salary Minimum: $75,000
Functions: General mgmt., Mfg., Materials, Sales & mktg., HR mgmt., Finance, IT
Industries: Mfg., Wholesale, Retail, Finance, Svcs., High tech, Software

Affiliates:
Columbia Consulting Group

Networks:
Global Search Partners

Conex Inc./InterSearch

150 E. 52nd St., 2nd Floor
New York, New York 10022
(212) 371-3737
Fax: (212) 371-3897
Email: conexny@aol.com
Web: www.intersearch.org

Key Contact - Specialty:
Mr. Fred Siegel - *Generalist*
Mr. Nicholas A. Leone - *Generalist*
Ms. Christina Lopez - *Generalist*
Ms. Ann Marie Pizzariello - *Generalist*

Description: Generalist firm with broad domestic and international client base; most industries and functions.

Salary Minimum: $70,000
Functions: Senior mgmt., Middle mgmt., Mktg. mgmt., Sales mgmt., Finance, IT, Int'l.
Industries: Generalist

Networks:
InterSearch

Robert Connelly & Assoc., Inc.

P.O. Box 24028
Minneapolis, Minnesota 55424
(612) 925-3039
Fax: (612) 922-5762
Email: Robtconn@aol.com

Key Contact - Specialty:
Mr. Robert F. Olsen - *Real estate, construction, architecture, agribusiness*

Description: A generalist firm with national client base. Expertise in medium and large corporations at the middle and upper management ranks. Specializing in consumer packaged goods, agribusiness, architectural/engineering, real estate, construction and environmental engineering.

Salary Minimum: $40,000
Functions: Senior mgmt., Mkt. research, Mktg. mgmt., CFO's, Engineering, Environmentalists, Architects
Industries: Agri/forestry/mining, Construction, Food/bev/tobacco, Environmental svcs., Real estate

Conroy Partners Ltd.

250 - 6 Ave. SW, 2140 Bow Valley Sq. 4
Calgary, Alberta T2P 3H7
Canada
(403) 261-8080
Fax: (403) 261-8085
Email: mail@conroypartners.com
Web: www.conroypartners.com

Key Contact - Specialty:
Mr. M. J. Conroy - *Oil & gas, financial, oil field services, general management*
Mr. Peter G. Edwards - *Oil & gas, oil field services*
Mr. S. Scott Doupe - *Finance, public sector, human resources, general management*
Ms. Cathy G. Simpson - *High technology, information technology, utilities, environmental*

Description: Retainer based senior, professional, managerial and executive search firm whose business is largely focused in western Canada. Consulting services are provided to our clients utilizing our extensive knowledge of domestic and international recruitment.
Functions: Senior mgmt., Sales & mktg., Mktg. mgmt., CFO's, MIS mgmt., Specialized services, Non-profits
Industries: Energy/utilities, Mfg., Finance, Human resource svcs., Government, High tech, Software

Consulpro †
(a division of Mel Spotswood Int'l. Inc.)

470 Somerset St. W.
Ottawa, Ontario K1R 5J8
Canada
(613) 236-3417
Fax: (613) 236-7964
Email: consulpro@istar.ca

Key Contact - Specialty:
Mr. Mel Spotswood - *IT*
Ms. Zora Arnautovic - *Legal, patent agent*

Description: Retained search in a variety of industries - majority high tech. Owner has 30 years business experience.

Salary Minimum: $50,000
Functions: Generalist, General mgmt., Sales mgmt., PR, CFO's, MIS mgmt.
Industries: Generalist, Legal, Advertising/PR, Telecoms, High tech, Software

† occasional contingency assignment

The Consulting Group Ltd.

501 Madison Ave., 26th Floor
New York, New York 10022
(212) 751-8484
Fax: (212) 980-5935

Key Contact - Specialty:
Mr. J. Michael Mitchell - *Securities, real estate*
Ms. Jessica S. Flagg - *Securities, real estate*
Ms. Terri Nava - *Securities, real estate*

Description: Specialist in the global securities markets with a subspecialty in real estate. Clients include international and domestic banks, investment banks, insurance companies, pension managers and other institutional money sources.

Salary Minimum: $100,000
Industries: Finance, Invest. banking, Brokers, Venture cap., Misc. financial, Insurance, Real estate

International Branches:
Central Hong Kong, London, Singapore

ContactBridge, Inc.

1051 Perimeter Drive, Ste. 501
Schaumburg, Illinois 60173
(847) 517-7256
Fax: (847) 517-7600
Email: blingle@psctou.com
Web: cbsearch.com

Key Contact - Specialty:
Mr. Bruce Lingle - *MIS, midrange, client server, network*

Description: Recruiting and source research services, of MIS professionals, offered as an hourly, value added consultive service.

Salary Minimum: $30,000
Functions: Systems anal., Systems dev., Systems implem., Systems support, Network admin., DB admin., Mgmt. consultants
Industries: Generalist, Construction, Mfg., Wholesale, Retail, Svcs., Packaging

Conway & Assoc.

1007 Church St., Ste. 408
Evanston, Illinois 60201
(847) 866-6832
Fax: (847) 866-6265
Web: conwayassc@aol.com

Key Contact - Specialty:
Ms. Maureen Conway

Description: Provide industry research, candidate identification, screening and recommendations to corporate clients. Services range from research to full search services with in-depth personal interviews and reference checks.
Functions: Middle mgmt., Sales mgmt., Direct mktg., Benefits, Personnel, Systems implem., R&D
Industries: Chemicals, Drugs mfg., Human resource svcs., Advertising/PR, Telecoms, Haz. waste

Philip Conway Management

320 Hampton Place
Hinsdale, Illinois 60521
(630) 655-4566

Key Contact - Specialty:
Mr. Philip A. Conway

Description: Specialists in the recruitment of senior and middle managers. Each assignment handled by one designated professional from research through final negotiations and follow up.

Salary Minimum: $60,000
Functions: Senior mgmt., Middle mgmt., Plant mgmt., Quality, Sales mgmt., Personnel, CFO's
Industries: Generalist

P. G. Cook Assoc. †

5103 Jackson Lane
Brentwood, Tennessee 37027
(615) 373-8263
(615) 373-4009
Fax: (615) 371-8215

Key Contact - Specialty:
Mr. P. Gene Cook - *Administrative, technical, operations & senior managers in healthcare & manufacturing*

Description: Recruiting for manufacturing and healthcare industries throughout the U.S.

Salary Minimum: $45,000
Functions: Automation, Materials Plng., Health admin., Benefits, Budgeting, MIS mgmt., Engineering
Industries: Mfg., Medical devices, Plastics/rubber, Motor vehicles, Consumer electronics, Pharmaceutical svcs., Healthcare

Cook Assoc.,® Inc.

212 W. Kinzie St.
Chicago, Illinois 60610
(312) 329-0900
Fax: (312) 329-1528
Email: info@cookassociates.com
Web: www.cookassociates.com

Key Contact - Specialty:
Mr. Jeffrey Posselt - *Banking, professional services, financial services*
Ms. Mary Kier - *Consumer, housewares, hardware*
Mr. John Olson - *Equipment, instrumentation, valves*
Ms. Kate Dussling - *Office products, furniture*
Mr. Arnie Kins - *High technology, medical*
Mr. James Evan-Cook - *Insurance*
Mr. John Kins - *International*
Mr. Frank Whiting - *Sporting goods, apparel, footwear*
Ms. Betty Moy - *Retail, wholesale*
Mr. John Wynn - *Film converting, packaging, paper, plastics, thermoforming*
Ms. Miranda Knapp - *Film converting, graphics, paper, printing, packaging*
Ms. Janet McNeil - *Home furnishings, textiles*
Mr. Walter Rach - *Food & beverage*
Ms. Carolyn Peart - *Architects, interior design*
Ms. Kristyn Chapas - *Catalog, direct marketing*
Mr. Christian Schiller - *Mergers & acquisitions*
Ms. Jane McDowell - *Adhesives, chemicals, coatings, polymers, resins*
Mr. Bob Cavoto - *Construction, engineering*
Ms. Adrienne Boyer - *Giftware, tabletops, toys, crafts, hobby*
Ms. Christine Noone - *Consumer packaged goods, health & beauty care*
Mr. Art Pawelczyk - *Residential furniture, institutional furniture*
Ms. Elizabeth Hassel - *Housewares, hardware*
Ms. Sarah Wolohan - *Building supplies, automotive aftermarket*

Description: We provide executive search to over 50 specialized industries nationwide and internationally. Lasting client relationships are built on integrity, performance and follow-through.

Salary Minimum: $75,000
Functions: Generalist, Senior mgmt., Plant mgmt., Mktg. mgmt., CFO's, Engineering, Int'l.
Industries: Generalist, Construction, Misc. mfg., Retail, Finance, Packaging, Insurance

The Cooke Group

1001 W. Glen Oaks Lane, Ste. 102
Mequon, Wisconsin 53092
(414) 241-9842
Fax: (414) 241-1004
Email: cookegroupinc@execpc.com

Key Contact - Specialty:
Mr. Jeffrey R. Cooke - *Senior management, middle management, privately-held manufacturing companies, family-owned manufacturing companies*

Description: Boutique firm offering executive search. Business planning and restructuring and organizational development services to privately-held or family-owned businesses ($5MM to 50MM+).

Salary Minimum: $75,000
Functions: Generalist, Senior mgmt., Middle mgmt., Mfg., Mktg. mgmt., Sales mgmt., CFO's
Industries: Generalist, Mfg., Metal products, Machinery/Appliances, Misc. mfg., Wholesale, Packaging

Affiliates:
Robert H. Marshall & Associates

The Cooper Executive Search Group Inc.

P.O. Box 375
Wales, Wisconsin 53183-0375
(414) 968-9049
Fax: (414) 968-9059

Key Contact - Specialty:
Mr. Robert M. Cooper - *Generalist*

Description: Full service firm with particular strengths in transitional and middle market companies. Significant client-side experience provides for unusual sensitivity to client needs.

Salary Minimum: $75,000
Functions: Generalist
Industries: Generalist

Cornell Group Int'l. Consulting, Inc.

68 N. Plank Rd., Ste. 202
Newburgh, New York 12550
(914) 565-8905
Fax: (914) 565-5688
Email: cornellgroup@juno.com
Web: www.worldemployment.com

Key Contact - Specialty:
Mr. Alan Guarino - *Financial services, CEOs, generalist*
Ms. Kathleen Guarino - *CEOs, COOs*
Mr. Al Aruza - *Financial services, CFOs, generalist*
Mr. Robert Wysocki - *Financial services, telecommunications*
Mr. Joe Chin - *Corporate finance, re-engineering, risk management*

Description: Dynamic group of professionals with 100% success rate on retained search. We offer 15 years experience in varied disciplines of executive search.

Salary Minimum: $50,000
Functions: Directors, Senior mgmt., Quality, Cash mgmt., M&A, Risk mgmt., Mgmt. consultants
Industries: Banking, Invest. banking, Venture cap., Misc. financial, Mgmt. consulting, Telecoms, Insurance

Branches:
16 Cherokee Drive
Brookfield, Connecticut 06804-3116
(203) 775-3131
Key Contact - Specialty:
Mr. Robert A. Wysocki

Affiliates:
Cornell Group
CyberSource
World Wide Employment Center

The Corporate Advisory Group

256 Columbia Tnpk., Ste. 101
Florham Park, New Jersey 07932
(973) 377-2466
Fax: (973) 377-7741

Key Contact - Specialty:
Mr. Richard T. Barkauskas - *Senior management (general & functional)*

Description: Senior level executive search across all major business functions within the telecommunications industry.

Salary Minimum: $100,000
Functions: Senior mgmt., Mfg., Materials, Mktg. mgmt., HR mgmt., CFO's, MIS mgmt.
Industries: Generalist, Food/bev/tobacco, Textiles/apparel, Drugs mfg., Wholesale, Retail, Telecoms

Branches:
16763 E. Point Drive
Sugarloaf Key, Florida 33042
(305) 745-1652
Fax: (305) 745-2140
Key Contact - Specialty:
Mr. Roy M. Nunn - *Telecommunications senior management (general & functional)*

Corporate Environment Ltd.

P.O. Box 798
Crystal Lake, Illinois 60039-0798
(815) 455-6070
Fax: (815) 455-0124

Key Contact - Specialty:
Mr. Tom McDermott - *Technical intensive industrial process equipment, environmental, industrial process, materials handling & finishing, biotechnical*

Description: General industrial - specializing in environmental equipment/service industry/industrial process equipment/services, key technical specialist, middle and senior management assignments/environmental attorneys; $60-250K compensation. All functions/disciplines. Domestic/international clientele.

Salary Minimum: $60,000
Functions: Senior mgmt., Mfg., Purchasing, Sales mgmt., R&D, Engineering, Environmentalists
Industries: Energy/utilities, Construction, Mfg., Svcs., Haz. waste, High tech, Biotech

Corporate Leadership Strategies, Inc.

15 Constitution Drive, Ste. 121
Bedford, New Hampshire 03110
(603) 471-7184
Fax: (603) 471-7101
Email: fjgreaney@aol.com

Key Contact - Specialty:
Mr. Francis J. Greaney - *Managed care*

Description: Nationwide practice in managed care search. Each search viewed as a strategic initiative. Ethical and professional representation of client organizations. Mr. Greaney was CEO of a general hospital, a senior officer in two Blue Cross Blue Shield Plans and CEO of a managed care company.

Salary Minimum: $100,000
Functions: Generalist, General mgmt., Senior mgmt., Healthcare, Personnel
Industries: Generalist, Insurance, Biotech, Healthcare

The Corporate Source Group, Inc.

1 Cranberry Hill
Lexington, Massachusetts 02173
(781) 862-1900
Fax: (781) 862-6367
Web: www.csg-search.com

Key Contact - Specialty:
Mr. Dana Willis

Description: Broad based, professional firm specializing in targeted search for difficult assignments. Performance guaranteed, uncompromising standards.

Salary Minimum: $100,000
Functions: Generalist, Senior mgmt., Finance, IT, Engineering, Int'l.
Industries: Finance, Communications, High tech, Software

Branches:
11601 Wilshire Blvd., Ste. 500
Los Angeles, California 90025
(310) 575-4863
Fax: (310) 575-1890
Key Contact - Specialty:
Ms. Karen Hudson

4830 W. Kennedy Blvd., Ste. 495
Tampa, Florida 33609
(813) 286-4422
Fax: (813) 286-4431
Key Contact - Specialty:
Mr. Mark Hausherr

625 N. Michigan Ave., 5th Floor
Chicago, Illinois 60611
(312) 751-4250
Fax: (312) 751-2731
Key Contact - Specialty:
Ms. Barbara McLean

14725 Pommel Drive
Rockville, Maryland 20850
(301) 217-5868
Fax: (301) 217-0599
Key Contact - Specialty:
Ms. Tara Stotz

90 Park Ave., Ste. 1600
New York, New York 10016
(212) 984-0738
Fax: (212) 687-8119
Key Contact - Specialty:
Ms. Carolyn Culbreth

301 Grant St., Ste. 1500
One Oxford Centre
Pittsburgh, Pennsylvania 15219-1417
(412) 577-2962
Fax: (412) 942-1395
Key Contact - Specialty:
Mr. J. Ronald Hagy

The Corrigan Group
1333 Ocean Ave.
Santa Monica, California 90401
(310) 260-9488

Key Contact - Specialty:
Mr. Gerald F. Corrigan - *Generalist*

Description: Retained search firm providing highly professional services to clients in most industries and the not-for-profit sector. Principal has 20 years experience in search profession.

Salary Minimum: $90,000
Functions: Generalist
Industries: Generalist
Professional Associations: IACPR

Corso, Mizgala + French
Scotia Plaza, Ste. 3003, P.O. Box 1005
40 King St. W.
Toronto, Ontario M5H 3Y2
Canada
(416) 369-9222
Web: www.intersearch-canada.com

Key Contact - Specialty:
Mr. John J. Corso
Mr. Anthony B. Mizgala
Mr. Guy P. French

Description: Serve private, public sector clients and non-profit organizations. Broad experience - 50+ combined years of successful middle to senior recruiting assignments in Canada, Europe and the United States.

Salary Minimum: $90,000
Functions: Generalist
Industries: Food/bev/tobacco, Drugs mfg., Motor vehicles, Banking, Hospitality, Telecoms, Healthcare

Affiliates:
AG Lennox & Assoc.
Pacific Executive Search Inc.
Societe Jean Pierre Brisebois
Wilson Associates Inc.

Networks:
InterSearch

Courtright & Assoc., Inc.
P.O. Box 503
Clarks Summit, Pennsylvania 18411-0503
(717) 586-0735
Fax: (717) 586-0764
Email: rjcxx@ptd.net
Web: www.courtrightassoc.com

Key Contact - Specialty:
Mr. Robert J. Courtright - *Biotechnology, NE PA general management, construction panel industry*

Description: Specialize in recruiting for biotechnology and pharmaceutical firms and the construction panel industry.

Salary Minimum: $70,000
Functions: Generalist
Industries: Construction, Drugs mfg., Biotech

Cowell & Associates, Ltd.
100 Forest Place, Ste. P22
Oak Park, Illinois 60301
(708) 383-6618
Fax: (708) 383-9012
Email: RoyCowell@aol.com

Key Contact - Specialty:
Mr. Roy A. Cowell - *General management*

Description: Provide specialized highly focused services in organization development and evaluation/recruitment of executive talent. Consultative approach coupled with limited number of concurrent assignments yields timely quality results and meaningful relationships.

Salary Minimum: $75,000
Functions: Senior mgmt., Mktg. mgmt., CFO's, MIS mgmt., Mgmt. consultants
Industries: Computer equip., Retail, Mgmt. consulting, Telecoms, Insurance, High tech, Software

---

Cowin Assoc. †
1 Old Country Rd.
Carle Place, New York 11514
(516) 741-3020
Fax: (516) 741-4953
Email: cowinone@aol.com

Key Contact - Specialty:
Mr. David M. Cowin - *Aerospace management*

Description: Serving large and small companies in the aerospace and related high technology industries since 1959.

Salary Minimum: $60,000
Functions: Middle mgmt., Product dev., Production, Mktg. mgmt., Systems anal., R&D, Engineering
Industries: Metal products, Computer equip., Aerospace, High tech

---

Creative Management Strategies, Ltd.
305 Madison Ave., Ste. 2033
New York, New York 10165
(212) 697-7207
Fax: (212) 697-3509
Email: jprufeta@creativegroupny.com
Web: creativegroupny.com

Key Contact - Specialty:
Mr. John R. Prufeta
Mr. Ira N. Gottlieb
Mr. Scott Stern
Ms. Sharon Adair
Ms. Tara J. Nicholas
Mr. Patrick Blair
Mr. John P. Cole
Mr. Robert J. Paufeta
Mr. John Schoonmaker

Description: Innovative, national healthcare search practice organized around provider delivery systems, health insurance and health technology disciplines.

Salary Minimum: $75,000
Functions: Senior mgmt., Physicians, Health admin., Sales mgmt., CFO's, MIS mgmt., Mgmt. consultants
Industries: Insurance, Healthcare

Affiliates:
The Creative Group Development
Creative Health Concepts
Creative Staffing Strategies, Inc.

Creative-Leadership, Inc.
11777 Bernardo Plaza Court, Ste. 101
San Diego, California 92128
(619) 592-0506
Fax: (619) 592-0413
Email: bob_spence@clci.com
Web: www.clci.com

Key Contact - Specialty:
Mr. Bob Spence - *Senior management*
Ms. Elizabeth Cooper - *Finance*
Ms. Susan Collins - *Manufacturing*
Mr. Jim Horton - *High technology*
Mr. Terry Norris - *Human resources*

Description: We offer a new paradigm in executive search; the Choosing Winners ™ System, behavioral assessments and interviewer training.

Salary Minimum: $50,000
Functions: Middle mgmt., Plant mgmt., Quality, Sales mgmt., Personnel, CFO's, Engineering
Industries: Construction, Motor vehicles, Computer equip., Retail, Hospitality, Human resource svcs., Government

---

The Cris Group, Inc.
501 Madison Ave.
New York, New York 10022
(212) 752-2838
Fax: (212) 888-3870

Key Contact - Specialty:
Ms. Jan Cris

Description: Known for key management assignments, long client relationships and high quality of research and service.

Salary Minimum: $125,000
Functions: Generalist, General mgmt., Sales & mktg., Benefits, Finance, IT
Industries: Generalist, Food/bev/tobacco, Finance, Accounting, Mgmt. consulting, High tech, Healthcare

Crispi, Wagner & Co., Inc.

420 Lexington Ave.
New York, New York 10170
(212) 687-2340
Fax: (212) 949-5936
Email: crispico@aol.com
Web: members.aol.com/crispco/cw.html

Key Contact - Specialty:
Mr. Nicholas Crispi - *Investment professionals*
Mr. Martin Katz - *Sales, portfolio management*

Description: We are an executive recruitment and search firm which specializes in the placement of investment professionals. Almost all disciplines are covered due to clients changing needs. International activity has been a portion of our business. Strategic consulting to the investment industry.

Salary Minimum: $100,000
Functions: Directors, Cash mgmt., M&A, Risk mgmt., Mgmt. consultants
Industries: Invest. banking, Brokers, Venture cap., Misc. financial, Mgmt. consulting

Crist Partners, Ltd.

303 W. Madison St., Ste. 2650
Chicago, Illinois 60606
(312) 920-0609
Fax: (312) 920-0608
Email: cristpartners.com

Key Contact - Specialty:
Mr. Peter D. Crist - *CEOs, CFOs, COOs, board member*
Mr. Kevin Hanrahan - *Finance*
Mr. Rob Tillman - *Finance*

Description: Senior recruiters handling select searches at the CEO, COO, CFO or board level, minimum fee of $150,000. Focus on succession situations.

Salary Minimum: $400,000
Functions: Directors, Senior mgmt., Mktg. mgmt., CFO's
Industries: Food/bev/tobacco, Chemicals, Machinery/Appliances, Consumer electronics, Banking, Invest. banking, Brokers

Cromwell Partners, Inc.

441 Lexington Ave.
New York, New York 10017
(212) 953-3220
Fax: (212) 953-4688
Email: webmaster@cromwell-partners.com
Web: www.cromwell-partners.com

Key Contact - Specialty:
Mr. Joseph Ziccardi - *Financial services*
Mr. Paul M. Heller - *Financial services*

Description: Our areas of expertise have included capital markets, corporate finance, global derivatives, treasury, risk management, structured finance, emerging markets, project finance, real estate finance and information technology.

Salary Minimum: $100,000
Functions: CFO's, Cash mgmt., M&A, Risk mgmt., Systems anal., Systems dev., Int'l.
Industries: Banking, Invest. banking, Misc. financial

Affiliates:
CP Interactive
CP Selection
Emerging Markets Search & Select

Crowder & Company

2050 N. Woodward Ave., Ste. 335
Bloomfield Hills, Michigan 48304
(248) 645-0909
Fax: (248) 645-2366
Email: Crowder@teleweb.net

Key Contact - Specialty:
Mr. Edward W. Crowder - *Generalist*
Mr. Mark D. Hokanson - *Generalist*
Ms. Kristin C. Nestor

Description: Results-oriented consulting firm providing multi-disciplinary executive search at the senior management level.

Salary Minimum: $80,000
Functions: Generalist, General mgmt., Mfg., Sales & mktg., HR mgmt., Finance, Engineering
Industries: Generalist, Plastics/rubber, Metal products, Machinery/Appliances, Motor vehicles, Misc. mfg., Packaging

Timothy D. Crowe, Jr.

26 Higate Rd., Ste. 101
Chelmsford, Massachusetts 01824-4440
(508) 256-2008
Email: tcrowecons@aol.com

Key Contact - Specialty:
Mr. Timothy D. Crowe, Jr.

Description: Our firm is a small consulting organization dedicated to providing service to only a few companies in the greater Boston area.

Salary Minimum: $50,000
Functions: Plant mgmt., Purchasing, Mktg. mgmt., Sales mgmt., CFO's, Systems dev., Engineering
Industries: Medical devices, Machinery/Appliances, Computer equip., Test/measurement equip., Misc. mfg., High tech

Crown Advisors, Inc.

239 Ft. Pitt Blvd.
Pittsburgh, Pennsylvania 15222
(412) 566-1100
Fax: (412) 566-1256
Email: info@crownsearch.com

Key Contact - Specialty:
Mr. Tom Callahan - *Construction*
Mr. John Cigna - *Real estate finance, real estate management, real estate development*
Mr. Philip Canzian - *Real estate finance, real estate management, real estate development*
Mr. Bert McDermott - *Real estate finance, real estate management, real estate development*
Mr. Kevin Jones - *Construction*

Description: More than six decades of national experience enables us to recruit the precise talent necessary to aid clients in achieving their goals.

Salary Minimum: $60,000
Functions: Senior mgmt., Middle mgmt.
Industries: Construction, Banking, Invest. banking, Real estate, High tech

CTR

4699 Old Ironsides Drive, Ste. 390
Santa Clara, California 95054
(408) 980-8082
Fax: (408) 727-0651
Email: ctrhr@ix.netcom.com

Key Contact - Specialty:
Mr. Timothy J. Outman - *High technology*

Description: Mid level to executive level recruitment services to corporate clients in high-technology environments.
Functions: General mgmt., Senior mgmt., Middle mgmt., Product dev., CFO's, MIS mgmt., Engineering
Industries: High tech

M. J. Curran & Assoc., Inc.

1 Beacon St., Ste. 1600
Boston, Massachusetts 02108
(617) 723-7002
Fax: (617) 742-4022

Key Contact - Specialty:
Mr. Martin Curran - *Generalist*

Description: Firm makes use of extensive international & national contacts to provide clients with high degree of services and professionalism in seeking senior management talent.

† occasional contingency assignment

Salary Minimum: $75,000

Curran Partners, Inc.
One Landmark Sq., 18th Floor
Stamford, Connecticut 06901
(203) 363-5350
Fax: (203) 363-5353
Email: wsawyer@curranpartners.com

Key Contact - Specialty:
Mr. Michael N. Curran
Ms. Whitney A. Sawyer
Mr. Joel I. Barad

Description: Executive search firm working exclusively on retained assignments.

Salary Minimum: $100,000
Functions: Generalist, Senior mgmt., Mktg. mgmt., Sales mgmt., CFO's, MIS mgmt., Int'l.
Industries: Generalist, Food/bev/tobacco, Textiles/apparel, Soap/perfume/ cosmetics, Drugs mfg., Pharmaceutical svcs., Biotech

Curry, Telleri Group, Inc.
22 North Drive
East Brunswick, New Jersey 08816
(732) 828-3883
Fax: (732) 846-2085

Key Contact - Specialty:
Dr. Michael J. Curry - *Biotechnology, pharmaceuticals & allied industries*
Mr. Frank C. Telleri - *Chemicals, coatings, plastics & allied industries*

Description: Focus on retainer search engagements for middle and upper level management and technical positions for all functional areas within the chemical, plastics, coatings and allied industries including pharmaceutical and biotechnology.

Salary Minimum: $40,000
Functions: Mfg., Materials, Sales & mktg., HR mgmt., IT, R&D, Engineering
Industries: Chemicals, Drugs mfg., Plastics/ rubber, Paints/petroleum products, Computer equip., Software, Biotech

Branches:
Harmon Cove, Twr. 3
Ste. 4-A, A/L Level
Secaucus, New Jersey 07094
(201) 223-1700
Fax: (201) 223-1818
Key Contact - Specialty:
Mr. George Sedak - *Engineering, information technology*

The Curtiss Group International
301 Yamato Rd., Ste. 2112
Northern Trust Plaza
Boca Raton, Florida 33431
(561) 997-0011
Fax: (561) 997-0087
Email: curtissgroup@compuserv.com

Key Contact - Specialty:
Mr. William E. Frank, Jr. - *Senior executives, board of directors*
Mr. Robert L. Beatty, Jr. - *General management, high technology*
Mr. David B. Miner - *Senior executives, general management*
Mr. Lynn H. Bentley - *High technology, human resources*
Mr. Joseph M. Bujold - *General management*
Mr. John A. Farrell - *Corporate finance, financial services*
Mr. John M. Rose - *General management, manufacturing*
Mr. Allyn Lean - *Real estate*

Description: We are the largest retainer-based search firm headquartered in Florida. Our clientele includes a select and limited base of corporations and government agencies requiring national and international expertise.

Salary Minimum: $100,000
Functions: Generalist, Directors, Senior mgmt., Middle mgmt., CFO's, MIS mgmt., Int'l.
Industries: Generalist

Branches:
550 North Reo Street, Suite 300
Tampa, Florida 33609
(813) 287-5049
Key Contact - Specialty:
Mr. John A. Farrell - *Financial services*

International Branches:
Brussels

Networks:
I-I-C Partners Executive Search Worldwide

Cusack Consulting
P.O. Box 689
Croton-on-Hudson, New York 10520
(914) 271-1399

Key Contact - Specialty:
Mr. Peter Cusack - *Generalist*
Ms. Glenna Q. McNally - *Generalist*

Description: Generalist firm with primary focus on corporate management disciplines.

Salary Minimum: $100,000
Functions: Generalist, General mgmt., Mfg., Materials, HR mgmt., R&D, Engineering
Industries: Generalist, Mfg., Communications

Judith Cushman & Assoc.
1125 12th Ave. NW, Ste. B-1A
Issaquah, Washington 98027
(425) 392-8660
Fax: (425) 391-9190
Email: jcushman@jc-a.com
Web: www.jc-a.com

Key Contact - Specialty:
Ms. Judith Cushman

Description: Offering full spectrum recruiting solutions in our niche--public relations, corporate communications and investor relations with a strength in high tech. A state of the art business model coupled with in-depth service and strategy.

Salary Minimum: $40,000
Functions: PR, Minorities
Industries: Generalist, Communications, Advertising/PR, New media, High tech, Software, Healthcare
Professional Associations: IACPR

Branches:
PO Box 1749
Seattle, Washington 98111
(630) 466-0860
Fax: (630) 466-0861
Key Contact - Specialty:
Ms. Isabel Soderlind

The Custer Group, Inc.
P.O. Box 3372
5115 Maryland Way
Brentwood, Tennessee 37024-3372
(615) 377-0787
Fax: (615) 309-0577
Email: jdcuster@ix.netcom.com

Key Contact - Specialty:
Mr. J. Dwight Custer
Mr. B.W. Custer

Description: Consultants to management for executive selection at the senior management level in all industries and in all functional areas.

Salary Minimum: $75,000
Functions: Generalist, General mgmt., Mfg., Healthcare, Sales & mktg., Finance, IT
Industries: Generalist, Agri/forestry/mining, Mfg., Finance, Svcs., High tech, Healthcare

Cyntal Int'l. Ltd.
310 Madison Ave., Ste. 1212
New York, New York 10017
(212) 661-1271
Fax: (212) 661-1589
Email: cyntal@aol.com

Key Contact - Specialty:
Ms. Cynthia D. Vroom

Salary Minimum: $75,000
Functions: Senior mgmt., Middle mgmt., Mfg., Sales & mktg., HR mgmt., Finance
Industries: Generalist, Mfg., Entertainment, Communications, High tech, Non-classifiable industries

Cypress Int'l., Inc.
6305 Songbird Way
Tampa, Florida 33625-1620
(813) 962-3300

Key Contact - Specialty:
Mr. Robert Murphy - *Generalist*
Mr. Thomas Cook - *Generalist*
Ms. Rita Dreyfus - *Generalist*
Mr. Paul Hill - *Generalist*
Mr. John Murray - *Generalist*
Mr. Bruce Wheeler - *Generalist*
Mr. Steve Williams - *Generalist*
Mr. Pat Antonochi - *Generalist*
Mr. Jack Cunningham - *Generalist*
Ms. Lynda Michaels - *Generalist*

Description: Quality executive search firm specializing in senior/middle management in most industries. Particular emphasis on hard to fill positions. Principals work with you from start to finish.

Salary Minimum: $75,000
Functions: Generalist, Directors, Senior mgmt., Automation, Physicians, Allied health, Health admin., Sales & mktg., HR mgmt., Benefits, Personnel, Training, CFO's, M&A, Risk mgmt., MIS mgmt., Systems anal., Systems dev., Systems implem., Systems support, Mgmt. consultants, Int'l.
Industries: Generalist, Food/bev/tobacco, Chemicals, Drugs mfg., Medical devices, Computer equip., Finance, Banking, Invest. banking, Brokers, Venture cap., Misc. financial, Entertainment, Pharmaceutical svcs., Computer svcs., Equip. svcs., Mgmt. consulting, Human resource svcs., Communications, Advertising/PR, Publishing, New media, Broadcast & Film, Telecoms, Insurance, High tech, Software, Biotech, Healthcare

D.A.I Human Resources Consultants †
1010 Sherbrooke St. W., Ste. 1800
Montreal, Quebec H3A 2R7
Canada
(514) 282-9855
Fax: (514) 286-6078
Email: daican@ican.net

Key Contact - Specialty:
Mr. Daniel Ascher - *General management, sales & marketing management*
Mr. Michael Vice - *Senior clinical research, regulatory affairs, pharmaco-economics*

Description: Owner operated, detail oriented sharpshooters. Well connected throughout North America and Europe in pharmaceutical, medical, biotech, CRO's and chemical related.

Salary Minimum: $70,000
Functions: Senior mgmt., Middle mgmt., Advertising, Mkt. research, Mktg. mgmt., Sales mgmt., CFO's
Industries: Mfg., Drugs mfg., Medical devices, Svcs., Pharmaceutical svcs., Communications, Advertising/PR

D.A.L. Associates, Inc.
2777 Summer St.
Stamford, Connecticut 06905
(203) 961-8777
Fax: (203) 324-2812

Key Contact - Specialty:
Mr. Donald A. Lotufo
Mr. Michael E. Rush
Mr. Joseph E. Farrell, III
Ms. Linda Reiner

Description: A generalist executive-management retainer search firm. Experienced in multi-industries and multi-functions.

Salary Minimum: $70,000
Functions: General mgmt., Mfg., Sales & mktg., HR mgmt., Finance, IT, R&D
Industries: Medical devices, Computer equip., Test/measurement equip., Finance, Communications, Biotech, Healthcare

Affiliates:
Bennett Associates Limited
Civitas International
Dieter Schulz & Partners GmbH
Executive Access Ltd.
Smith Search, S.C.
Societe Europeenne de Participations Industrielles
Studio Bossi

D.R. Assoc.
718 N. Monterey St., Ste. 301
Alhambra, California 91801
(626) 284-7480
Fax: (626) 284-7480

Key Contact - Specialty:
Mr. Dan Royfe - *Metalworking, machine tool industries, fabricators*

Description: Executive search and management consulting; specialty in all disciplines of metalworking, fabrication & machine tool industries; sales, service, technical, managerial engineering and executive level positions.

Salary Minimum: $75,000
Functions: Mfg., Engineering
Industries: Mfg.

Daggett & Kvistad
3015 Hopyard Rd., Ste. N
Pleasanton, California 94566
(510) 484-9050
Fax: (510) 484-9054
Email: jdaggett@daggettkvistad.com

Key Contact - Specialty:
Mr. James W. Daggett
Mr. Niles K. Kvistad

Description: High technology general management, sales, marketing, engineering, manufacturing and operations specialists. Semiconductor, semiconductor capital equipment industries.

Salary Minimum: $70,000
Functions: Senior mgmt., Purchasing, Materials Plng., Mktg. mgmt., Customer svc., Engineering, Int'l.
Industries: Chemicals, Test/measurement equip., Accounting, High tech

Dahl-Morrow Int'l.
12020 Sunrise Valley Drive, Ste. 100
Reston, Virginia 20191
(703) 860-6868
Fax: (703) 860-2962
Email: dmiintl@aol.com
Web: www.dahl-morrowintl.com

Key Contact - Specialty:
Ms. Barbara Steinem
Ms. Andy Steinem
Mr. Charles B. Clark

Description: Extensive executive and entrepreneurial experience, plus expertise in executive search. Founded in January, 1991 to provide seasoned executives for interim and permanent management assignments worldwide.

Salary Minimum: $80,000
Functions: Senior mgmt., Mktg. mgmt., Sales mgmt., CFO's, MIS mgmt., Engineering, Int'l.
Industries: Computer equip., Venture cap., New media, Telecoms, Environmental svcs., High tech, Biotech

The Dalley Hewitt Co.
1401 Peachtree St. NE, Ste. 500
Atlanta, Georgia 30309
(404) 885-6642
Fax: (404) 885-6665
Email: rives@interserv.com
Web: dalleyhewitt.com

Key Contact - Specialty:
Ms. Rives D. Hewitt - *Generalist*

Description: We are a management recruiting and consulting firm that provides domestic and international clients with a flexible package of executive search services.

† occasional contingency assignment

Salary Minimum: $50,000
Functions: Senior mgmt., Mfg., Mktg. mgmt., Sales mgmt., HR mgmt., Personnel, MIS mgmt.
Industries: Mfg., Printing, Finance, Higher ed., New media, High tech, Biotech
Professional Associations: IACPR

Alfred Daniels & Assoc., Inc.
5795 Waverly Ave.
La Jolla, California 92037
(619) 459-4009

Key Contact - Specialty:
Mr. Alfred Daniels - *Investment banking*
Ms. Lynn Scullion Reisfeld - *Investment banking*

Description: Worldwide investment banking; debt/equity: derivatives, institutional sales, trading, research; capital markets; corporate finance; mergers/acquisitions; money management; information and biotechnology. Clients: commercial and investment banks, money managers, hedge funds, biotech companies.

Salary Minimum: $50,000
Functions: Senior mgmt., Middle mgmt., Mktg. mgmt., Sales mgmt., Cash mgmt., Risk mgmt., Systems dev.
Industries: Finance, Banking, Invest. banking, Brokers, Venture cap., Accounting, Biotech

---

Alan Darling Consulting
374 Dover Road, Ste. 18
South Newfane, Vermont 05351
(802) 348-6365

Key Contact - Specialty:
Mr. Alan Darling - *Generalist*

Description: Search services for most industries. Features detailed presearch survey with written report and stresses original research as the major source for candidates. Clients served are typically in New England and upstate New York.

Salary Minimum: $60,000
Functions: Generalist, General mgmt., Mfg., Health admin., Sales & mktg., MIS mgmt., Non-profits
Industries: Generalist, Mfg., Retail, Banking, High tech, Healthcare

---

The Dartmouth Group
1200 Broadway, 7D-8D
New York, New York 10001
(212) 689-2713
Fax: (212) 532-6519
Email: storf@aol.com

Key Contact - Specialty:
Mr. Herbert F. Storfer - *Cosmetics, health & beauty aids, packaging, materials management, purchasing*
Mr. Paul D. Storfer - *Pharmaceuticals*

Description: A highly professional, specialized executive search firm offering focused, personalized service and competency-based selection for major companies in the cosmetics, pharmaceutical, healthcare, food, new electronic media and packaging industries. Established in 1976.

Salary Minimum: $70,000
Functions: Senior mgmt., Mfg., Materials, Sales & mktg., HR mgmt.
Industries: Generalist, Food/bev/tobacco, Soap/perfume/cosmetics, Drugs mfg., Plastics/rubber, Pharmaceutical svcs., Packaging

---

Data Bank Executive Search
635 W. 7th St., Ste. 100
Cincinnati, Ohio 45203
(513) 241-9955
Fax: (513) 333-6364
Email: jobs@databankcorp.com
Web: www.databankcorp.com

Key Contact - Specialty:
Mr. Wayne Ivey - *Executive information systems*
Mr. Harry Molloy - *Executive information systems*
Mr. Walt Reep - *Executive information systems*

Description: Our mission is to fullfill the career needs of our client, candidates and employees by matching well qualified, pre-screened information systems executives with rewarding, high-quality career opportunities.

Salary Minimum: $125,000
Functions: IT, MIS mgmt.
Industries: Generalist, Retail, Finance, Computer svcs., Insurance, High tech, Software

Branches:
851 Orchard Lane, Ste. B
Beavercreek, Ohio 45434
(937) 431-9955
Fax: (937) 461-9956
Email: jobs@databankcorp.com
Web: www.databankcorp.com
Key Contact - Specialty:
Mr. Bryan Whitaker - *Information systems*

Daubenspeck & Associates, Ltd.
411 W. Ontario St., Ste. 724B
Chicago, Illinois 60610
(312) 255-0952
Fax: (312) 255-0411
Email: daubenspec@aol.com

Key Contact - Specialty:
Mr. Kenneth Daubenspeck - *Information technology, consulting fields*
Mrs. Rima Daubenspeck - *Information technology, general management, professional services*

Description: The firm specializes in providing executive search and executive team building, for example placing entire management teams. Additionally, the firm trains its clients in building staffing mechanisms.

Salary Minimum: $110,000
Functions: Senior mgmt., Distribution, Personnel, CFO's, IT, Mgmt. consultants, Minorities
Industries: Finance, Hospitality, Communications, Insurance, High tech, Software

---

Daudlin, De Beaupre & Co., Inc.
18530 Mack Ave., Ste. 315
Grosse Pointe Farms, Michigan 48236
(810) 771-0029
Fax: (810) 771-2941

Key Contact - Specialty:
Mr. Paul T. Daudlin - *Healthcare*
Ms. Mary Anne De Beaupre - *Healthcare*
Ms. Jill Hodgins Verros - *Healthcare*
Mr. James Delmotte - *Healthcare*

Description: Search consultants specializing in the recruitment of executives and professionals in the healthcare field throughout the United States.

Salary Minimum: $50,000
Functions: Physicians, Nurses, Allied health, Health admin.
Industries: Healthcare

Davies, Park
10235-101 St., Ste. 904
Oxford Twr.
Edmonton, Alberta T5J 3G1
Canada
(403) 420-9900
Fax: (403) 426-2936
Email: gdavies@daviespark.ab.ca
Web: www.daviespark.ab.ca

Key Contact - Specialty:
Mr. A. Gerry Davies - *Healthcare private industry (general)*
Mr. K. Darwin Park - *Municipal government, education, private industry*

Description: Proven track in national/international search for western Canadian employers. Principals have 30+ years in business.

Salary Minimum: $60,000
Functions: Generalist, Senior mgmt., Physicians, Health admin., HR mgmt., CFO's, Engineering
Industries: Generalist, Agri/forestry/mining, Energy/utilities, Retail, Hospitality, Government, Healthcare

Branches:
530 Alberta Stock Exchange Twr.
300-5th Ave. SW
Calgary, Alberta T2P 3C4
Canada
(403) 263-0600
Fax: (403) 269-1080
Email: anelson@daviespark.ab.ca
Key Contact - Specialty:
Mr. Allan C. Nelson - *Finance & accounting, generalist, oil & gas*

Affiliates:
Renaud Foster Management Consultants
The Robert Thompson Partnership
Michael Stern Assoc., Inc./Euram

Alan Davis & Assoc. Inc.
538 Main Rd.
Hudson Heights, Quebec J0P 1J0
Canada
(514) 458-3535
Fax: (514) 458-3530
Email: adavis@alandavis.com
Web: www.alandavis.com

Key Contact - Specialty:
Mr. Alan Davis
Ms. Diane Bates
Ms. Robin Flax
Ms. Angie Jackson

Description: A bilingual HR consulting practice specializing in recruitment. Services include search (management and specialists), recruitment advertising, international recruitment, strategic recruitment planning, recruitment operations audits and consulting.
Functions: Mfg., Sales & mktg., HR mgmt., IT, R&D, Engineering, Int'l.
Industries: Agri/forestry/mining, Mfg., Communications, Government, Aerospace, High tech, Software

Branches:
1255 University St., #906
Montreal, Quebec H3B 3W4
Canada
(514) 393-7203
Fax: (514) 393-9647
Key Contact - Specialty:
Ms. Robin Flax

John J. Davis & Assoc., Inc.
521 Fifth Ave., Ste. 1740
New York, New York 10175
(212) 286-9489
Fax: (973) 467-3706
Email: jdavis1013@aol.com

Key Contact - Specialty:
Mr. John J. Davis - *Information systems management*
Mr. Thomas D. Bell - *Information systems management*
Mr. Jack P. Long - *Information systems management*
Mr. Jack Davis - *Information systems management*
Mr. John D. Simon - *Information systems management*

Description: A highly specialized firm focused exclusively in the senior and middle management areas of information systems and telecommunications. The practice is nationwide.

Salary Minimum: $135,000
Functions: MIS mgmt.
Industries: Generalist

Davis & Company
3419 Via Lido, Ste. 615
Newport Beach, California 92663
(800) 600-4417
(714) 376-6995
Fax: (714) 376-6995

Key Contact - Specialty:
Mr. G. Gordon Davis - *Generalist*
Mr. Troy M. Davis - *Generalist*
Ms. Valerie D. Treaster - *Research*

Description: Generalist firm serving a limited clientele for maximum effectiveness.

Salary Minimum: $50,000
Functions: Generalist
Industries: Generalist, Metal products, Motor vehicles, Test/measurement equip., Transportation, Aerospace, High tech

Joseph A. Davis Consultants, Inc.
104 E. 40th St., Ste. 203
New York, New York 10016
(212) 682-4006
Email: 71327.1715@compuserve.com

Key Contact - Specialty:
Mr. Joseph A. Davis
Ms. Winifred R. Davis

Description: Black-owned firm specializing in recruiting minority and women professionals.

Salary Minimum: $75,000
Functions: Generalist, General mgmt., Sales & mktg., HR mgmt., Finance, IT, Specialized services
Industries: Generalist, Energy/utilities, Finance, Computer svcs., Human resource svcs., Communications, High tech

Bert Davis Executive Search, Inc.
425 Madison Ave., Ste. 14A
New York, New York 10017
(212) 838-4000
Fax: (212) 888-3823
Email: bdavis2289@aol.com

Key Contact - Specialty:
Mr. Paul F. Gravelle
Ms. Lauren Aaron
Ms. Tracey Wilmot
Ms. Katharine Berlowe

Description: Premier executive search firm specializing in the publishing, communications, multimedia and direct marketing industries. Practice extends nationwide and internationally.

Salary Minimum: $100,000
Functions: Generalist, Middle mgmt., Product dev., PR, CFO's, Systems implem., DB admin.
Industries: Communications, Advertising/PR, Publishing, New media

Branches:
One Sansome St.
San Francisco, California 94104
(415) 951-4788
Fax: (415) 951-4775
Key Contact - Specialty:
Ms. Harriet Reitman

De Funiak & Edwards
1602 Hidden Hills Trail
Long Beach, Indiana 46360
(219) 878-9790

Key Contact - Specialty:
Mr. William S. de Funiak - *Insurance, information technology*

Description: High concentration of searches in life and property casualty insurance companies, insurance consulting firms with insurance administration and information systems specialists. Positions from project manager to president.

Salary Minimum: $50,000
Functions: MIS mgmt., Mgmt. consultants
Industries: Computer svcs., Mgmt. consulting, Insurance

Branches:
P.O. Box 459
Leonardtown, Maryland 20650
(301) 475-2801
Key Contact - Specialty:
Mr. Randolph J. Edwards - *Insurance, information technology*

Dean-MacDonald
3201 Enterprise Pkwy., Ste. 250
Beachwood, Ohio 44122
(216) 514-2611

Key Contact - Specialty:
Mr. Roderick P. Deighen - *General executive*

Description: Particularly experienced in assessing executive potential, the match with client organization and its culture. Have over twenty years of close, one-on-one analysis of executives plus thorough understanding of corporate operations.

Salary Minimum: $100,000

† occasional contingency assignment

Functions: Generalist, General mgmt., Mfg., Materials, Sales & mktg., HR mgmt., Finance
Industries: Generalist, Mfg., Finance, Communications, Defense, Aerospace, Packaging

---

Defrain Mayer

6900 College Blvd., Ste. 300
Overland Park, Kansas 66211
(913) 345-0500
Fax: (913) 345-0172
Email: ses@defrain.com

Key Contact - Specialty:
Mr. Stephen E. Snodgrass

Description: Specialize in human resources management consulting, executive search, employee relations, outplacement counseling, compensation, total quality management and productivity.

Salary Minimum: $60,000
Functions: Senior mgmt., Plant mgmt., Mktg. mgmt., HR mgmt., CFO's, Cash mgmt., Engineering
Industries: Generalist, Energy/utilities, Finance, Invest. banking, Non-profits, Communications, Telecoms

Affiliates:
DeFrain Mayer LLC

Thorndike Deland Assoc. LLC

275 Madison Ave., Ste. 1300
New York, New York 10016
(212) 661-6200
Fax: (212) 661-8438
Email: cbinen@aol.com

Key Contact - Specialty:
Mr. Howard Bratches - *Consumer goods, direct marketing, financial services*
Mr. Joseph J. Carideo - *Retailing, fashion, apparel*
Ms. Dene Doino
Mr. Louis A. Hoyda - *Direct marketing, publishing, healthcare, technology*
Ms. Carol Binen - *Research (all fields)*
Mr. Jeffrey G. Swiff - *Financial services, insurance, consumer*
Mr. William Venable - *Financial services, investment banking, technology*
Ms. Ellen Reiser - *Retail, consumer services, technology, consulting*
Mr. Richard G. Moyse - *Insurance, financial services, consulting*
Ms. Joan Higbee - *International consumer, industrial & service industries*

Description: Seventy years of excellence in executive search. Specialize in retailing, consumer goods and services and industrial search. Includes financial services, direct marketing, publishing, apparel manufacturers and insurance.

Salary Minimum: $100,000
Functions: Senior mgmt., Mkt. research, Mktg. mgmt., Sales mgmt., Direct mktg., CFO's, IT
Industries: Food/bev/tobacco, Textiles/apparel, Wholesale, Retail, Finance, Communications, Insurance

Networks:
Greenwich International Group

S. W. Delano & Co. †

750 Main St., 6th Floor
Hartford, Connecticut 06103
(860) 278-5186

Key Contact - Specialty:
Mr. Steven W. Delano

Description: 15 years experience serving financial services/investment companies. Extensive database, thoughtful screening.

Salary Minimum: $70,000
Functions: CFO's, Cash mgmt., Risk mgmt.
Industries: Invest. banking, Brokers, Venture cap., Misc. financial, Insurance

---

Delphi Systems, Ltd.

6740 Pennsylvania Ave.
Kansas City, Missouri 64113
(816) 333-6944
Fax: (816) 333-6944
Email: delphi@aviary.share.net
Web: aviary.share.net/delphi/search.html

Key Contact - Specialty:
Mr. P. W. Reagan

Description: Founded in 1971, Delphi is a retianed executive search firm conduction a world-wide general practice. Our competitive distinction lies in the use of the WingSpread skills-based decision support system for position definition, candidate sourcing, selection, acquisition and post search development.

Salary Minimum: $200,000
Functions: Generalist
Industries: Generalist

Delta Services

225 Matlage Way
P.O. Box 1294
Sugar Land, Texas 77487
(281) 494-9300
Fax: (281) 494-9394
Email: delta3@msn.com

Key Contact - Specialty:
Mr. John F. Jansen

Description: Executive recruitment to oil and gas, refining, chemical and banking industries. We specialize in key operations, engineering, research and financial disciplines ranging from staff level to executive management.

Salary Minimum: $70,000
Functions: General mgmt., Sales & mktg., Finance, R&D, Engineering, Minorities, Int'l.
Industries: Energy/utilities, Chemicals, Plastics/rubber, Paints/petroleum products, Banking, Mgmt. consulting, Environmental svcs.

Derhak Ireland & Partners Ltd.

65 International Blvd., Ste. 100
Toronto, Ontario M9W 6L9
Canada
(416) 675-7600
Fax: (416) 675-7833
Email: alderhak@aol.com

Key Contact - Specialty:
Mr. Allen R. Derhak
Mr. Murray W. Clarke
Mr. William M. Derhak
Mr. Howard Kleiman
Mr. Vincent J. McKnight
Mr. David E. Van Schaik

Description: We are a firm of senior executive recruitment profesionals, all of whom have extensive management experience in pharmaceuticals, high-tech, automotive, telecommunications and consumer goods.

Salary Minimum: $75,000
Functions: Generalist, General mgmt., Mfg., Healthcare, Sales & mktg., Finance, Engineering
Industries: Generalist, Mfg., Finance, Aerospace, Packaging, High tech, Healthcare

---

Development Resource Group

104 E. 40th St., Ste. 304
New York, New York 10016
(212) 983-1600
Fax: (212) 983-1687
Web: drgdell@aol.com

Key Contact - Specialty:
Ms. Linda Low

Description: Specialist in search for all not-for-profit executive directors, senior managers and development specialists.
Functions: Directors, Senior mgmt., Health admin., Non-profits
Industries: Non-profits, Higher ed., Advertising/PR, Healthcare

Branches:
1629 K St. NW., Ste. 802
Washington, District of Columbia 20006
(202) 223-6528
Fax: (202) 775-7465
Key Contact - Specialty:
Mr. David Edell

Development Search Specialists
W3072 First National Bank Bldg.
St. Paul, Minnesota 55101-1308
(612) 224-3750

Key Contact - Specialty:
Mr. Fred J. Lauerman

Description: Highly personalized searches for and recruitment of executive directors and senior-level, fund-raising executives for non-profit institutions and organizations.

Salary Minimum: $50,000
Functions: Senior mgmt., Non-profits
Industries: Non-profits, Higher ed., Healthcare

Rob Dey Executive Search †
2869 S. Bumby Ave.
Orlando, Florida 32806-8704
(407) 896-6500
(407) 240-7447
Fax: (407) 896-0145
Email: robdey@robdey.com
Web: www.robdey.com

Key Contact - Specialty:
Mr. Robert L. Dey - *CEOs, CFOs, independent sector, not-for-profits executives*
Dr. Janice Hopkins Howell - *Physicians, physician executives*
James A. Mullenhoff - *Law, management information systems*
Ms. Irene Dey - *Hospitality (executive committee), law*
Mr. Benjamin Bauer - *Human resources, hospitality*
Mr. Peter J. Kenny - *Actuaries, finance & accounting*

Description: Specialize in CEOs and key executives reporting to CEOs in the independent, private and public sectors. We are now a multi-discipline firm focusing on difficult to fill executive positions in a broad range of sectors, both domestic and international.

Salary Minimum: $50,000
Functions: Senior mgmt., Physicians, HR mgmt., Finance, IT, Non-profits, Attorneys
Industries: Finance, Hospitality, Non-profits, Higher ed., Communications, High tech, Healthcare

Branches:
113 Fireside Circle
Baltimore, Maryland 21212
(410) 532-6878
Fax: (410) 532-9478
Email: carlton@jhunix.hef.jhu.edu
Web: saracarlton@robdey.com
Key Contact - Specialty:
Ms. Sara B. Carlton - *Physicians*

Affiliates:
Charitable Alliance

DHR Int'l., Inc.
10 S. Riverside Plaza, Ste. 2220
Chicago, Illinois 60606
(312) 782-1581
Fax: (312) 782-2096
Web: www.dhrintl.com

Key Contact - Specialty:
Mr. David H. Hoffmann
Mr. Craig E. Randall
Mr. Warren K. Hendriks, Jr.
Mr. Robert E. Reilly, Jr.
Mr. T. Michael Brock
Mr. David J. O'Gorman - *Financial services*
Mr. Joseph E. Gale
Mr. Stephen P. Campbell
Mr. John S. Pope
Mr. Kim Murlas
Mr. Robert J. Aylsworth
Ms. Maureen Martin
Ms. Lynn Small
Ms. Tonay Tucker
Ms. Kimberly Walley
Mr. Bob Wittebort
Mr. Dudley Morton
Mr. Steve Ethington
Mr. John Lafferty
Mr. Joseph W. Shenton, Jr.
Mr. David Chyla
Ms. Carolyn Oakley-Lowe
Mr. Frank McCloskey - *Technology*
Mr. Richard McIntire
Ms. Andrea Moran
Ms. Heidi Muecke
Mr. Jim Nalepa
Mr. Clarence Nails
Mr. Tal Newhart

Description: Generalist firm with specialty practices and national and international coverage. Geographical coverage and lack of client blockage major plus. Two years placement guarantee.

Salary Minimum: $60,000
Functions: Generalist
Industries: Generalist

Branches:
11811 N. Tatum, Ste. 3031
Phoenix, Arizona 85028
(602) 953-7810
Fax: (602) 953-7811
Key Contact - Specialty:
Mr. David A. Bruno - *Retail operations*
Mr. Kent Schmidtke
Ms. Jessica Jewell
Ms. Karin Sparber
Ms. Susan Schepman
Mr. Mark Tudi - *Sports, entertainment*

19200 Von Karman Ave., Ste. 500
Irvine, California 92612-1540
(714) 622-5520
Fax: (714) 622-5521
Key Contact - Specialty:
Mr. Ronald E. LaGrow
Mr. Larry Cabaldon
Ms. Michelle Amici
Mr. Mark Hoinacki
Mr. Oscar Obledo

1888 Century Park E., Ste. 1917
Los Angeles, California 90067
(310) 284-3131
Fax: (310) 284-3139
Key Contact - Specialty:
Mr. John Wasley
Mr. Jamieson Allen
Mr. Andrew Abramowicz
Mr. David Dean

2465 E. Bayshore Rd., Ste. 310
Palo Alto, California 94303
(650) 354-0296
Fax: (650) 424-8463
Key Contact - Specialty:
Ms. Mary Lasko

11455 El Camino Real, Ste. 210
San Diego, California 92130-2045
(619) 792-7654
Fax: (619) 792-7447
Key Contact - Specialty:
Mr. Joel T. Grushkin
Ms. Bente K. Hansen - *Biotechnology*
Mr. Bradley Janik
Mr. John Pacheco
Mr. Lee Sharp - *Information technology*
Ms. Joyce Lang
Ms. Teresa Mahfood
Ms. Bree O'Shea

50 California St., Ste. 1500
San Francisco, California 94111
(415) 439-5213
Fax: (415) 439-5217
Key Contact - Specialty:
Ms. Joyce Lang
Mr. Gerald Parsons

1200 17th St.
One Tabor Ctr., Ste. 1000
Denver, Colorado 80202
(303) 629-0730
Fax: (303) 629-0724
Key Contact - Specialty:
Mr. Martin M. Pocs
Mr. Thomas C. Maitland
Mr. Thomas Laxgang
Ms. Jill Spinner
Ms. Joanna Hubble
Mr. Dave Sandusky

7900 E. Union Ave., Ste. 1100
Denver Tech Ctr.
Denver, Colorado 80237
(303) 694-5360
Fax: (303) 694-5361
Key Contact - Specialty:
Mr. Lawrence J. Winslow

10 Main St. S., Ste. 2B
Southbury, Connecticut 06488
(203) 262-8740
Fax: (203) 262-8742
Key Contact - Specialty:
Mr. Anthony T. DelNegro
Mr. Ralph B. DeCristoforo - *Healthcare practice*

† occasional contingency assignment

1717 Pennsylvania Ave. NW, Ste. 650
Washington, District of Columbia 20006
(202) 822-9555
Fax: (202) 822-9525
Key Contact - Specialty:
Mr. Stephen A. Hayes
Mr. James Martin
Mr. Bruce Babashan
Mr. Steve Leo
Mr. William Gelbard
Ms. Delia Morris
Mr. William Gaggiano
Ms. Marci Greenfield
Ms. Gale Molovinsky

One E. Broward, Ste. 700
Ft. Lauderdale, Florida 33301
(954) 713-2886
Fax: (954) 713-2887
Key Contact - Specialty:
Mr. Russell H. Miller

2810 E. Oakland Park Blvd., Ste. 104
Ft. Lauderdale, Florida 33306
(954) 564-6110
Fax: (954) 564-6119
Key Contact - Specialty:
Mr. Victor P. Viglino

Two Sawgrass Village, Ste. 4
Ponte Vedra Beach, Florida 32082
(904) 273-4656
Fax: (904) 273-4617
Key Contact - Specialty:
Mr. William Elston

Four Sawgrass Village
Ponte Vedra Beach, Florida 32082
(904) 285-6655
Fax: (904) 285-2846
Key Contact - Specialty:
Mr. Don Reek
Mr. Ron Preston
Mr. Sean Collins
Mr. Robert Fitzmorris
Mr. Samuel Shake

8875 Hidden River Pkwy., Ste. 300
Lakeview Bldg.
Tampa, Florida 33637
(813) 975-7261
Fax: (813) 975-7261
Key Contact - Specialty:
Mr. James Adams

3201 W. Parkland Blvd.
Tampa, Florida 33609
(813) 348-0931
Fax: (813) 348-9525
Key Contact - Specialty:
Mr. John T. Watters

400 Perimeter Ctr. Terrace, Ste. 900
Atlanta, Georgia 30346
(770) 392-4275
Fax: (770) 392-4273
Key Contact - Specialty:
Mr. Jerry Franzel
Mr. Matthew Klein
Mr. Charles H. Teller, Jr.
Mr. Jeremy C. King
Mr. Richard Dean
Ms. Heather Harris
Mr. Joseph Lupton
Mr. Bill Turner

1901 N. Roselle Rd., Ste. 800
Schaumburg, Illinois 60195
(847) 490-6450
Fax: (847) 490-5892
Key Contact - Specialty:
Mr. Michael Setze

101 W. Ohio St., 20th Floor
Indianapolis, Indiana 46201-4215
(317) 684-6948
Fax: (317) 684-6945
Key Contact - Specialty:
Mr. James Doan

9393 W. 110th St., Ste. 500
Overland Park, Kansas 66210
(913) 451-6950
Fax: (913) 451-6951
Key Contact - Specialty:
Ms. Stephanie Klaus

67 Willow Grove Rd.
Brunswick, Maine 04011
(207) 720-1308
Fax: (207) 721-9765
Key Contact - Specialty:
Mr. Lee Lindeman

1419 Forest Drive, Ste. 205
Annapolis, Maryland 21403
(410) 295-0938
Fax: (410) 295-0938
Key Contact - Specialty:
Mr. Jack F. Hildner

1304 St. Paul's Way
Crownsville, Maryland 21031
(410) 849-5115
Fax: (410) 849-2844
Key Contact - Specialty:
Mr. Jack Hildner

84 State St., 6th Floor
Boston, Massachusetts 02109
(617) 742-5899
Fax: (617) 720-1390
Key Contact - Specialty:
Mr. Christopher Dona
Mr. Michael Loiacano
Mr. Jesse Cooper
Mr. Robert T. Zuzack
Ms. Jennifer L. Hatcher
Mr. Christopher R. Seitz
Ms. Jill Cooper
Ms. Lisa Parato
Mr. Brendan Reen

30 Monument Sq., Ste. 155
Concord, Massachusetts 01742
(508) 369-1350
Fax: (508) 369-9442
Key Contact - Specialty:
Mr. John L. Alexanderson

1461 Cambridge Rd.
Lansing, Michigan 48911
(517) 487-9586
Fax: (517) 487-9387
Key Contact - Specialty:
Mr. Gordon White

6429 James Ave. S.
Richfield, Minnesota 55423
(612) 866-0781
Fax: (612) 866-6188
Key Contact - Specialty:
Mr. John Soll

8182 Maryland Ave., Ste. 200
Clayton, Missouri 63105
(314) 725-1191
Fax: (314) 725-9286
Key Contact - Specialty:
Mr. Steven N. Wood
Ms. Stacy Godat
Ms. Jami Pritchett
Mr. Ronald W. Hind
Mr. Herb Aten
Mr. Kevin Burford
Mr. Darren Eden
Ms. Chris Gagliano
Ms. Stephanie Gregorius
Ms. Elaine Mattison
Mr. Larry Munson
Mr. C. Scott Salmon

5000 Central Park Drive, Ste. 204
Lincoln, Nebraska 68504
(402) 464-0566
Fax: (402) 464-0871
Key Contact - Specialty:
Mr. Ted Balistreri
Mrs. Bonnie Balistreri

1 Springfield Ave.
Summit, New Jersey 07901
(908) 598-4757
Fax: (908) 598-4758
Key Contact - Specialty:
Mr. James McIntosh

560 Valley Rd.
Upper Montclair, New Jersey 07043
(201) 746-2100
Fax: (201) 746-8716
Key Contact - Specialty:
Mr. David M. Richardson

280 Park Ave., 29th Floor
New York, New York 10017
(212) 883-6800
Fax: (212) 883-9507
Key Contact - Specialty:
Mr. Booker Rice, Jr.
Mr. Frank T. Spencer - *Retail*
Mr. Robert J. Isacco
Ms. Elizabeth Alvarez
Ms. Lizzette Claudio
Ms. Wendy Converse
Ms. Deborah DeMaria
Ms. Wendy Friedman
Mr. Andrew Hussar
Ms. Michele Lieblich
Mr. Greer Meisels
Mr. Joel Raven
Mr. Chris Ruggeri
Mr. Declan Maguire

65 E. State St., Ste. 1000
Columbus, Ohio 43215
(614) 460-3516
Fax: (614) 221-9834
Key Contact - Specialty:
Mr. Hayes Reilly

155 B Ave., Ste. 240
Lake Oswego, Oregon 97034
(503) 699-7994
Fax: (503) 699-8162
Key Contact - Specialty:
Mr. James Scheetz

301 Grant St., Ste. 150
One Oxford Centre
Pittsburgh, Pennsylvania 15219-1417
(412) 255-3740
Fax: (412) 255-3701
Key Contact - Specialty:
Mr. Jack Nicholas

2843 S. County Trail, Ste. C11
East Greenwich, Rhode Island 02818
(401) 884-1695
Fax: (401) 884-2394
Key Contact - Specialty:
Mr. Stephen P. Bartlett
Mr. Scott Newton

3200 W. End Ave., Ste. 500
Nashville, Tennessee 37203
(615) 783-1690
Fax: (615) 783-1689
Key Contact - Specialty:
Mr. David Higgins
Ms. Leslie Edwards
Mr. Mark Spinale

5215 N. O'Connor Blvd., Ste. 200
Irving, Texas 75240
(972) 868-9075
Fax: (972) 868-9076
Key Contact - Specialty:
Mr. Victor Arias, Jr.
Mr. Rick Burgess

4001 S. 700 E, Ste. 586
Salt Lake City, Utah 84107
(801) 263-7033
Fax: (801) 263-7038
Key Contact - Specialty:
Ms. Cynthia C. Hammond
Ms. Allyson Ralphs
Ms. Kristen DeShano

22525 SE 64th Place, Ste. 201
Issaquah, Washington 98027
(425) 557-3681
Fax: (425) 557-3684
Key Contact - Specialty:
Mr. James L. Black
Mr. Clint Merriman
Ms. Allison Bizzano

300 N. Corporate Drive, Ste. 120
P.O. Box 589
Brookfield, Wisconsin 53045
(414) 879-0850
Fax: (414) 879-0855
Key Contact - Specialty:
Mr. Robert W. Stanislaw

Ms. Denise Moore
Mr. Dennis Hood
Ms. Susan Foley
Ms. Terri Courtney-Couch

Networks:
InterSearch

Dieckmann & Assoc., Ltd.

180 N. Stetson Ave., Ste. 5555
Two Prudential Plaza
Chicago, Illinois 60601
(312) 819-5900
Email: dieckxsearch@ameritech.net

Key Contact - Specialty:
Mr. Ralph E. Dieckmann - *General management, insurance, CFOs*
Mr. Edward J. Sheedy, III - *Pharmaceutical, consulting, high technology*
Mr. Steven A. Jablo - *Real estate, banking, mortgage banking, insurance*
Mr. Richard B. Jeffers - *General management, consulting*

Description: Professionalism and quality are our hallmarks; long-term client value generated by our placements' effectiveness is our focus; manufacturing, insurance, financial services, consumer goods and consulting searches are our strengths.

Salary Minimum: $100,000
Functions: Senior mgmt., Middle mgmt., CFO's, M&A, Risk mgmt., MIS mgmt., Mgmt. consultants
Industries: Drugs mfg., Metal products, Banking, Mgmt. consulting, Insurance, Real estate, High tech
Professional Associations: AESC, IACPR

Networks:
International Search Associates (ISA)

DieckMueller Group

1500 N. Casaloma Drive, Ste. 409
Appleton, Wisconsin 54915
(920) 733-8500
Fax: (920) 733-8818
Email: execsearch@dieckmueller.com

Key Contact - Specialty:
Mr. Daniel W. Dieck - *Manufacturing corporations (all disciplines)*
Mr. Michael S. Mueller - *Manufacturing corporations (all disciplines)*
Mr. Charles R. Magee - *Manufacturing corporations (all disciplines)*

Description: Retained search firm that operates exclusively with manufacturing corporations. Operate throughout North America recruiting sales, marketing, finance, research, engineering, human resource, technical, operations and senior management personnel.

Salary Minimum: $80,000
Functions: Senior mgmt., Plant mgmt., HR mgmt., CFO's, MIS mgmt., Engineering, Int'l.
Industries: Food/bev/tobacco, Paper, Printing, Chemicals, Plastics/rubber, Machinery/Appliances, Packaging
Professional Associations: IACPR

The Diestel Group

19 E. 200th South, Ste. 1000
Salt Lake City, Utah 84111
(801) 532-1000
Fax: (801) 532-7676
Email: brent@jespersen.org

Key Contact - Specialty:
Mr. Brent Jespersen
Ms. Jill Perelson

Description: Skilled consultants utilizing a collaborative, partnering approach to executive search and organizational consulting.

Salary Minimum: $80,000
Functions: Senior mgmt., Middle mgmt., Mfg., Mktg. mgmt., HR mgmt., CFO's, MIS mgmt.
Industries: Generalist, Mfg., Finance, Svcs., New media, Aerospace, High tech

DiMarchi Partners

7107 LaVista Place, Ste. 200
Niwot, Colorado 80503
(303) 415-9300

Key Contact - Specialty:
Mr. Paul DiMarchi
Ms. Patricia McKeown
Mr. C. Scott Walters

Description: A generalist practice, specializing in key contributors; our consultants/partners possess over 70 years of combined experience in successfully evaluating human potential and ability.

Salary Minimum: $100,000
Functions: Generalist, Senior mgmt., Mktg. mgmt., Sales mgmt., CFO's, MIS mgmt., Engineering
Industries: Generalist, Misc. mfg., Venture cap., Communications, Telecoms, High tech, Software

J. Dinerstein & Co., Inc.

45 Rockefeller Plaza, Ste. 2000
New York, New York 10111
(212) 332-3200
Fax: (212) 332-3202
Email: jdinerstein@compuserve.com

Key Contact - Specialty:
Ms. Jan Dinerstein

Description: Results oriented executive and management consulting firm with focus on fashion and retail, consumer products, technology, financial services and media. Diversified client base includes venture capital and private equity companies.

† occasional contingency assignment

Salary Minimum: $150,000
Functions: Generalist, Senior mgmt., Advertising, Mktg. mgmt., PR, HR mgmt., CFO's
Industries: Generalist, Food/bev/tobacco, Textiles/apparel, Retail, Venture cap., Advertising/PR, New media

---

Robert W. Dingman Co., Inc.

650 Hampshire Rd., Ste. 116
Westlake Village, California 91361
(805) 778-1777
Fax: (805) 778-9288
Email: info@dingman.com
Web: www.dingman.com

Key Contact - Specialty:
Mr. Robert W. Dingman
Mr. Bruce Dingman
Mr. Bret Dalton

Description: Senior management level assignments where need emphasizes a compatible management style, values, personality and goals between the candidates and the client. Ranked as a "Top Fifty" search firm.

Salary Minimum: $100,000
Functions: Generalist, Senior mgmt., Middle mgmt., Mktg. mgmt., Sales mgmt., CFO's, Non-profits
Industries: Generalist, Mfg., Consumer electronics, Hospitality, Entertainment, High tech, Software
Professional Associations: AESC

Dinte Resources, Inc.

8300 Greensboro Drive, Ste. 880
McLean, Virginia 22102
(703) 448-3300
Fax: (703) 448-0215
Web: www.dinte.com

Key Contact - Specialty:
Mr. Paul Dinte
Ms. Leah Rogers

Description: High quality retained firm providing executive search and interim executive solutions to corporations and associations thereby assisting them in meeting business objectives.

Salary Minimum: $100,000
Functions: Generalist, Senior mgmt., Sales & mktg., HR mgmt., CFO's, MIS mgmt., Mgmt. consultants
Industries: Generalist, Energy/utilities, Transportation, Finance, Mgmt. consulting, Human resource svcs., High tech

---

Dise & Co.

20600 Chagrin Blvd., Ste. 610
Shaker Heights, Ohio 44122
(216) 752-1700
Fax: (216) 752-6640
Email: diseco@aol.com
Web: www.diseco.com

Key Contact - Specialty:
Mr. Ralph A. Dise, Jr. - *Senior executives, board members*
Mr. Brad J. Attewell - *Manufacturing, marketing, human resources*
Mr. P. William Marshall - *Banking, finance, accounting, investment banking*
Ms. Carolyn Risher - *Client services and support*

Description: Our strength is the rapid identification of the most appropriate candidates given the client's strategic objectives and corporate cultures.

Salary Minimum: $75,000
Functions: Middle mgmt., Plant mgmt., Mktg. mgmt., Training, Cash mgmt., M&A, Minorities
Industries: Food/bev/tobacco, Plastics/rubber, Computer equip., Banking, Venture cap., Aerospace

---

R. J. Dishaw & Assoc.

P.O. Box 671262
Dallas, Texas 75367
(972) 924-5000
Fax: (972) 924-5003
Email: exsearch@msn.com

Key Contact - Specialty:
Mr. Raymond J. Dishaw - *Managerial, scientific, engineering, manufacturing*

Description: A generalist firm specializing in quality service. M.S., Ph.D. level in technical, managerial, financial and manufacturing fields.

Salary Minimum: $60,000
Functions: General mgmt., Mfg., Materials, Sales & mktg., IT, R&D, Engineering
Industries: Generalist

Diversified Health Search
(an affiliate of Diversified Search, Inc.)

One Commerce Sq.
2005 Market St., Ste. 3300
Philadelphia, Pennsylvania 19103
(215) 732-6666
Fax: (215) 568-8399
Email: Diversified@Divsearch.com
Web: www.divsearch.com

Key Contact - Specialty:
Ms. Judith M. von Seldeneck
Mr. Stephen S. Morreale

Description: Executive search firm serving the management and physician needs of healthcare providers, managed care organizations and integrated healthcare delivery systems nationwide.

Salary Minimum: $120,000
Functions: Senior mgmt., Admin. svcs., Materials, Physicians, HR mgmt., Finance, IT
Industries: Healthcare
Professional Associations: AESC

Networks:
International Network Associated Consultants

Diversified Search, Inc.
(an affiliate of The Diversified Search Companies)

One Commerce Sq.
2005 Market St., Ste. 3300
Philadelphia, Pennsylvania 19103
(215) 732-6666
Fax: (215) 568-8399
Email: Diversified@Divsearch.com

Key Contact - Specialty:
Ms. Judith M. von Seldeneck
Mr. Stephen S. Morreale

Description: Generalist executive search firm, founded 1971, serving clients nationwide. Areas of specialty include financial services, manufacturing, healthcare, consumer products, education, not-for-profit and boards of directors.

Salary Minimum: $100,000
Functions: Generalist, Directors, Senior mgmt., Middle mgmt., Admin. svcs., Purchasing, Materials Plng., Physicians, Nurses, Health admin., Advertising, Mkt. research, Mktg. mgmt., Sales mgmt., Direct mktg., Customer svc., PR, Benefits, Personnel, Training, CFO's, Budgeting, Cash mgmt., Credit, Taxes, M&A, Risk mgmt., MIS mgmt., Systems anal., Systems implem., Systems support, R&D, Engineering, Mgmt. consultants, Minorities, Non-profits, Environmentalists, Attorneys, Int'l.
Industries: Generalist, Energy/utilities, Food/bev/tobacco, Textiles/apparel, Printing, Chemicals, Drugs mfg., Medical devices, Plastics/rubber, Motor vehicles, Computer equip., Consumer electronics, Test/measurement equip., Misc. mfg., Transportation, Retail, Finance, Banking, Invest. banking, Brokers, Venture cap., Hospitality, Entertainment, Non-profits, Higher ed., Pharmaceutical svcs., Legal, Computer svcs., Accounting, Equip. svcs., Mgmt. consulting, Human resource svcs., Law enfcmt., Communications, Advertising/PR, Publishing, Telecoms, Government, Environmental svcs., Aerospace, Insurance, Real estate, High tech, Biotech, Healthcare
Professional Associations: AESC

Networks:
International Network Associated Consultants

DLB Assoc.

271 Madison Ave., Ste. 1406
New York, New York 10016
(212) 953-6460

Key Contact - Specialty:
Mr. Lawrence E. Brolin - *Marketing, advertising, direct response, corporate communications*
Ms. Dorothy Goodman-Brolin - *Marketing, advertising, direct response, corporate communications*

Description: Boutique firm with a national practice specializing in the recruitment of general management, marketing, advertising, direct response, interactive and corporate communications professionals for consumer and service industries.

Salary Minimum: $75,000
Functions: General mgmt., Advertising, Mktg. mgmt., Direct mktg., PR, Mgmt. consultants, Minorities
Industries: Mfg., Finance, Entertainment, Mgmt. consulting, Communications, High tech, Software

DLG Assoc., Inc.

1515 Mockingbird Lane, Ste. 560
Charlotte, North Carolina 28209
(704) 522-9993
Fax: (704) 522-7730

Key Contact - Specialty:
Mr. David J. Guilford - *Financial services management, mortgage banking, real estate, corporate lending, capital markets*
Mr. W. Kenneth Goodson, Jr. - *Mortgage banking, real estate lending, corporate banking, capital markets*

Description: Specialize in financial services, real estate and MIS/DP custom search; senior officers of the company and affiliate firm each have 50(+) years executive management experience in banking and/or MIS.

Salary Minimum: $65,000
Functions: Senior mgmt., Middle mgmt., Mkt. research, CFO's, Cash mgmt., MIS mgmt.
Industries: Banking, Invest. banking, Venture cap., Misc. financial, Computer svcs., Accounting, Human resource svcs.

L. J. Doherty & Assoc.

65 Ford Rd.
Sudbury, Massachusetts 01776
(508) 443-9603
Email: ljdassoc@aol.com

Key Contact - Specialty:
Mr. Leonard J. Doherty - *Computer, communications*

Description: Computer industry focus: systems, software, networking/communications and information technology services.

Salary Minimum: $90,000
Functions: General mgmt., Sales & mktg., IT, Engineering, Int'l.
Industries: Computer equip., Mgmt. consulting, New media, Telecoms, High tech, Software

Doherty Int'l., Inc.

300 W. Washington St., Ste. 704
Chicago, Illinois 60606
(312) 845-3040
Fax: (312) 845-3969
Email: dohertyint@aol.com

Key Contact - Specialty:
Mr. John J. Doherty - *Logistics, human resources*

Description: Our success is dramatically reflected in our energized, comprehensive approach to the total transition process. With over 20 years of experience in the transition field, the leadership of the organization feels professionally comfortable and competent in delivering effective programs to a growing list of clients.

Salary Minimum: $100,000
Functions: Middle mgmt., Plant mgmt., Materials, Mkt. research, Mktg. mgmt., HR mgmt., IT
Industries: Generalist, Mfg., Transportation, Non-profits, Higher ed., Packaging, Biotech

Affiliates:
Options Unlimited, Inc.

Doleman Enterprises †

1474 N. Point Village Ctr., Ste. 236
Reston, Virginia 20194-1190
(703) 742-5454
Fax: (703) 708-6992
Email: doleman@patriot.net
Web: www.patriot.net/users/doleman

Key Contact - Specialty:
Ms. Linda J. Howard - *Pharmaceutical, information technology*
Mr. Robert J. Doleman - *Engineering, research economists, research analysts*
Mr. Howard Miller - *Generalist*

Description: Executive search and professional recruitment, engineering and computer science, pharmaceutical, logistics, information systems and hospitality management.

Salary Minimum: $40,000
Functions: Generalist, Sales & mktg., HR mgmt., IT, R&D, Engineering, Minorities
Industries: Generalist, Drugs mfg., Hospitality, Pharmaceutical svcs., Defense, High tech, Software

The Domann Organization

P.O. Box 1717
Glen Ellen, California 95442
(800) 923-6626
Fax: (707) 527-0780
Email: domorg@aol.com

Key Contact - Specialty:
Mr. William A. Domann, Jr. - *Research & development, medical, clinical, operations, manufacturing*

Description: We are particularly versed in identifying qualified candidates and providing information services to companies and individuals in the biotechnology, medical device, diagnostics and pharmaceutical marketplaces.

Salary Minimum: $75,000
Functions: General mgmt., Mfg., Healthcare, R&D
Industries: Drugs mfg., Medical devices, Pharmaceutical svcs., Biotech

Dominguez-Metz & Assoc.

12 Geary St., Ste. 604
San Francisco, California 94108
(415) 765-1505
Fax: (415) 765-1534
Email: dominguez-metz@prodigy.net

Key Contact - Specialty:
Ms. Nancy Metz - *Retailing, manufacturing*
Ms. Connie Dominguez - *Retailing, manufacturing*

Description: Both my partner and myself come from retailing so we have a strong understanding of the retail world.

Salary Minimum: $50,000
Functions: General mgmt., Product dev., Distribution, Sales & mktg., HR mgmt., Finance, MIS mgmt.
Industries: Textiles/apparel, Retail, Human resource svcs.

Domres Professional Search †

P.O. Box 103
Coleman, Wisconsin 54112
(920) 897-4890
Fax: (920) 897-4891
Email: noszwet@ez-net.com

Key Contact - Specialty:
Mr. Terry A. Domres - *Pulp & paper*

Description: We recruit for all disciplines in the pulp, paper and related industries. Nationwide.
Functions: Middle mgmt., Production, Purchasing, Mkt. research, Budgeting, MIS mgmt., Systems anal.
Industries: Paper, Printing, Machinery/Appliances

† occasional contingency assignment

Donahue/Bales Assoc.

303 W. Madison, Ste. 1150
Chicago, Illinois 60606
(312) 732-0999
Fax: (312) 732-0990

Key Contact - Specialty:
Mr. E. M. Mick Donahue
Mr. L. Patrick Bales

Description: General practice encompasses most functions and industries.

Salary Minimum: $80,000
Functions: General mgmt., Mfg., Sales & mktg., HR mgmt., Finance, R&D, Mgmt. consultants
Industries: Generalist

Affiliates:
Associates In Executive Search, Ltd.
East-West Consulting, K.K.

Donini Assoc.

6231 Kellogg Drive
McLean, Virginia 22101
(703) 893-8109
Fax: (703) 893-7980
Email: doniniassociates@erols.com

Key Contact - Specialty:
Mr. Jerry P. Donini
Ms. Patricia Donini

Description: Principals have direct hands-on management experience in the industries served. Personalized service and accountability - all assignments are handled directly by the principals of the firm and are not delegated to someone else.

Salary Minimum: $50,000
Functions: General mgmt., Healthcare, Sales & mktg., HR mgmt., Finance, IT, Mgmt. consultants
Industries: Retail, Svcs., Hospitality, Mgmt. consulting, Human resource svcs., High tech, Healthcare

Dotson & Assoc.

412 E. 55th St., Ste. 8A
New York, New York 10022
(212) 593-3651

Key Contact - Specialty:
Ms. M. Ileen Dotson - *Marketing & sales*

Description: Specializing in placement of middle and senior level marketing, communications, sales and service quality professionals. Expertise in financial services, technology and general communications including direct mail and telemarketing.

Salary Minimum: $75,000
Functions: Health admin., Advertising, Mkt. research, Mktg. mgmt., Sales mgmt., Direct mktg., Minorities
Industries: Banking, Entertainment, New media, Broadcast & Film, Telecoms, High tech, Healthcare

Cal Douglas Executive Search, Inc.

604 Cottingham Court
Allison Park, Pennsylvania 15101
(412) 364-8106
(800) 886-8106
Fax: (412) 364-6367
Email: caldoug@usaor.net

Key Contact - Specialty:
Mr. Calvin H. Douglas - *Non-profit senior management*

Description: A national recruiting service specializing in the placement of CEOs, chief development officers and planned giving executives for the non-profit sector.

Salary Minimum: $50,000
Functions: Non-profits
Industries: Non-profits, Higher ed., Healthcare

Douglas-Allen, Inc.

1500 Main St., 24th Floor
Springfield, Massachusetts 01115
(413) 739-0900
Fax: (413) 734-9109
Email: rosdai@javanet.com

Key Contact - Specialty:
Mr. Robert D. Stevens - *Investment management*
Ms. Kimberly A. Leask

Description: Serving the nation's top financial institutions in the recruitment of portfolio managers, sales and marketing professionals and analysts.

Salary Minimum: $100,000
Functions: Mkt. research, Sales mgmt., Cash mgmt.
Industries: Invest. banking, Misc. financial, Insurance

CS Dowling Executive Services

1700 Rte. 23 N., Ste. 100
Wayne, New Jersey 07470
(973) 696-4022
Fax: (973) 696-1964
Email: dow@csdowling.com
Web: csdowling.com

Key Contact - Specialty:
Mr. Dan Bruder - *HVAC, building automation, energy services*

Description: We provide executive level search and selection throughout North America. Positions focus on Director, Vice President, General Manager, CEO, COO levels.

Salary Minimum: $150,000
Functions: General mgmt., Directors, Senior mgmt., Mktg. mgmt., Sales mgmt., Engineering

Affiliates:
Dow-Tech Assoc

Drew Assoc. Int'l.

25 Pompton Ave., Ste. 305
Verona, New Jersey 07044
(973) 571-9735
Fax: (973) 571-9747

Key Contact - Specialty:
Mr. Robert R. Detore - *Healthcare executive*
Ms. Roberta Cowan - *Physician*
Richard F. Grady - *Medical director*

Description: Healthcare industry consultants for physician and executive recruitment and physician practice valuation and acquisition consulting services.

Salary Minimum: $80,000
Functions: Physicians, Health admin., Mkt. research, Sales mgmt., CFO's, Mgmt. consultants, Int'l.
Industries: Mgmt. consulting, Healthcare

Affiliates:
Associated Health Consultants
Trans-Phil Manpower Resources, Inc.

Robert Drexler Assoc., Inc. †

210 River St.
Hackensack, New Jersey 07601
(201) 342-0200
Fax: (201) 342-9062
Email: 74672.122@compuserve.com

Key Contact - Specialty:
Mr. Robert C. Drexler

Description: Engineering, technical and executive search consultants. Our clients include pharmaceutical, chemical, petrochemical, petroleum, industrial, commercial, environmental, bridge and highway: engineering and construction.

Salary Minimum: $50,000
Functions: Product dev., Automation, Plant mgmt., MIS mgmt., Engineering, Environmentalists, Architects
Industries: Energy/utilities, Construction, Chemicals, Plastics/rubber, Pharmaceutical svcs., Environmental svcs., Biotech

Drinkwater & Assoc.

One Beach St., #1
Beverly Farms, Massachusetts 01915
(978) 922-3676
Email: wdrinkwater@msn.com

Key Contact - Specialty:
Ms. Wendy A. Drinkwater - *Generalist, technology, consulting, financial services, professional services, retail*

Ms. Ashley B. Ullstein - *Generalist, technology*
Ms. Patti D. Edington - *Generalist, consulting, tax/audit, research*
Mr. Brian McElroy - *Generalist, technology, financial services, consulting, tax/audit*
Ms. Diane P. Esecson - *Generalist, retail, technology*
Ms. Julie Davidson - *Generalist, financial services, tax, audit, technology*

Description: Seasoned search consultant with experience from Korn/Ferry Int'l. and as an independent for 7 years. Provide research, interview prospective candidates by telephone and rapidly deliver qualified resumes to clients. High quality, cost effective.
Functions: Generalist, Senior mgmt., Middle mgmt., Sales & mktg., Finance, Systems anal., Mgmt. consultants
Industries: Generalist, Retail, Invest. banking, Mgmt. consulting, Telecoms, High tech, Software

Dromeshauser Assoc.

70 Walnut St.
Wellesley, Massachusetts 02181
(781) 239-0222

Key Contact - Specialty:
Mr. Peter Dromeshauser - *Computers, telecommunications*

Description: Primary area of concentration in hi tech and senior management including computers, software, communications information services and consulting services.

Salary Minimum: $150,000
Functions: Directors, Senior mgmt., Middle mgmt., Mktg. mgmt., Sales mgmt., MIS mgmt.
Industries: Computer equip., Communications, Telecoms, High tech, Software

J. H. Dugan & Assoc., Inc.

225 Crossroads Blvd., Ste. 416
Carmel, California 93923
(408) 625-5880
Fax: (408) 625-2504
Email: plastic-recruiter@jhdugan.com
Web: www.jhdugan.com

Key Contact - Specialty:
Mr. John H. Dugan - *Plastics*

Description: Plastics industry specialists, all functions and markets including commercial development, mergers, acquisitions, market research and compensation analysis. Industry experienced staff with focused approach toward growth oriented market segments and technologies.

Salary Minimum: $50,000
Functions: General mgmt., Mfg., Packaging, Sales & mktg., M&A, R&D, Engineering
Industries: Chemicals, Plastics/rubber, Paints/petroleum products, Misc. mfg., Packaging, High tech, Non-classifiable industries

Affiliates:
Casting Industrie
M. W. McDonald & Assoc.
Plastics Career Registry
Plastics Search Alliance, Inc.
SearchNet*Asia

Dunlap & Sullivan Assoc.

100 W. Long Lake Rd., Ste. 112
Bloomfield Hills, Michigan 48304-2773
(248) 540-0315
Fax: (248) 642-4732
Email: DunSul@aol.com

Key Contact - Specialty:
Mr. Stanley R. Dunlap
Mr. Richard A. Dunlap

Description: Offer executive search-concentrating on senior executive appointments, across a wide spectrum of industries. Building a personal relationship with clients, creating a high percentage of repeat business.

Salary Minimum: $50,000
Functions: General mgmt., Mfg., Sales & mktg., HR mgmt., CFO's, IT, Engineering
Industries: Energy/utilities, Lumber/furniture, Printing, Machinery/Appliances, Motor vehicles, Misc. mfg.

Branches:
29 Pearl St. NW, Ste. 227
Grand Rapids, Michigan 49503
(616) 458-4142
Fax: (616) 458-4203
Key Contact - Specialty:
Mr. John P. Sullivan

Dunn Associates †

229 Limberline Drive
Greensburg, Pennsylvania 15601
(724) 832-9822
Fax: (724) 832-9836
Email: maddunn@aol.com
Web: maddunn@aol.com

Key Contact - Specialty:
Ms. Margaret A. Dunn - *Generalist*
Ms. Jean Pistentis - *Generalist*

Description: Quality recruiting for substantially less. Honesty. Integrity. Timeliness. Attention to details. Telephone screening. Full search except face to face interviews.

Salary Minimum: $60,000
Functions: Generalist, Mfg., Materials, Sales & mktg., Finance, IT, Engineering
Industries: Generalist, Lumber/furniture, Chemicals, Plastics/rubber, Metal products, Machinery/Appliances, Motor vehicles

C. A. Durakis Assoc., Inc.

5550 Sterrett Place, Ste. 302
Columbia, Maryland 21044
(410) 740-5590
Fax: (410) 740-5422
Email: cad@durakis.com
Web: www.durakis.com

Key Contact - Specialty:
Mr. Charles A. Durakis, Jr. - *Generalist*
Mr. Fredric L. Fields - *Non-profit*

Description: General practice searches. Senior executive and middle management - all industries.

Salary Minimum: $100,000
Functions: Senior mgmt., Advertising, Mktg. mgmt., Sales mgmt., CFO's, MIS mgmt., Non-profits
Industries: Drugs mfg., Computer equip., Consumer electronics, Pharmaceutical svcs., Insurance, High tech, Healthcare

Branches:
66 Bayberry Lane
Westport, Connecticut 06880
(203) 227-3840
Key Contact - Specialty:
Ms. Lynn Medoff

3003 Gulf Shore Blvd.
Naples, Florida 33940
(941) 261-9277
Key Contact - Specialty:
Mr. Charles A. Durakis, Sr. - *Generalist*

620 Massachusetts Ave.
Cambridge, Massachusetts 02138
(617) 497-7769
Fax: (617) 868-5101
Key Contact - Specialty:
Mr. Richard Tufenkjian - *Generalist*

Donald F. Dvorak & Co.

1000 Skokie Blvd., Ste. 200
Wilmette, Illinois 60091-1136
(847) 853-8110
Fax: (847) 853-8202
Email: kpmgdfd@msn.com

Key Contact - Specialty:
Mr. Donald F. Dvorak

Description: Quality performance in search for most management functions. Engagements performed only by firm principals.

Salary Minimum: $90,000
Functions: Directors, Senior mgmt., Production, CFO's, Taxes, MIS mgmt., Non-profits
Industries: Generalist

Affiliates:
A.K.S. Assoc., Ltd.
Lynn Dwigans & Co.
Krueger Assoc.
Telford, Adams & Alexander

† occasional contingency assignment

Dwyer Consulting Group, Inc.

2 Cecil Place
Wheeling, West Virginia 26003
(304) 243-1600
Fax: (304) 243-1692
Email: dwyer@1st.net

Key Contact - Specialty:
Mr. Gilbert E. Dwyer

Description: A broad and general executive recruiting and consulting practice with particular interest in senior line and staff executives in technology-based companies.

Salary Minimum: $100,000
Functions: Directors, Senior mgmt., CFO's
Industries: Generalist, Energy/utilities, Pharmaceutical svcs., High tech, Biotech

Affiliates:
Cameron Consulting Group

Dynamic Synergy Corp. †

2730 Wilshire Blvd., Ste. 550
Santa Monica, California 90403-4747
(310) 586-1000
Fax: (310) 586-1010
Web: www.dynamicsynergy.com

Key Contact - Specialty:
Mr. Mark Landay - *Software industry*

Description: Our corporation's special talent is to find the best candidate to fulfill the requirements. We provide an extremely high level of service, quickly generating a short list of qualified candidates. Our short turn around time results in cost effectiveness. Partners with our clients, we offer unique options to exchange equity for our professional search services.

Salary Minimum: $80,000
Functions: Directors, Senior mgmt., Mktg. mgmt., Systems dev., R&D, Engineering
Industries: Computer equip., Consumer electronics, Computer svcs., Aerospace, High tech, Software

Earley Kielty & Assoc., Inc.

2 Pennsylvania Plaza
New York, New York 10121
(212) 736-5626
Fax: (212) 643-0409
Email: ekainfo@earleykielty.com

Key Contact - Specialty:
Mr. John L. Kielty, III
Mr. Eugene Herman
Mr. Jay Sterling
Ms. Eileen McCauley
Mr. Nick Leone

Description: Professional executive search firm conducting retained searches for senior and mid level executives in all size corporations in a variety of industries including consumer products, distribution, manufacturing and service.

Salary Minimum: $100,000
Functions: General mgmt., Sales & mktg., HR mgmt., Finance, CFO's, IT, Mgmt. consultants
Industries: Misc. mfg., Finance, Entertainment, Mgmt. consulting, Communications, High tech, Software
Professional Associations: IACPR

Branches:
35 Mason St.
Greenwich, Connecticut 06830
(203) 661-7420
Key Contact - Specialty:
Mr. Chuck Stroble

Early Cochran & Olson

401 N. Michigan Ave., Ste. 515
Chicago, Illinois 60611-4205
(312) 595-4200
Fax: (312) 595-4209
Email: ECO94@aol.com

Key Contact - Specialty:
Mr. Bert H. Early - *Senior lawyers*
Mr. B. Tucker Olson - *Senior lawyers*
Ms. Corinne Cochran - *Senior lawyers*
Mr. Bruce R. LeMar - *Senior lawyers*

Description: National practice limited to retainer searches for lawyers to fill senior corporate and law firm positions. Experienced consultants serve Fortune 500 corporations and major law firms. References furnished.

Salary Minimum: $100,000
Functions: Legal, Attorneys
Industries: Generalist

Eastbourne Assoc. Inc.

330 Motor Pkwy.
Hauppauge, New York 11788
(516) 231-2555
Fax: (516) 231-2570
Email: ea330@aol.com

Key Contact - Specialty:
Ms. Rosemary Kissel
Mr. Herbert Sokol

Description: Accept only 3 clients in any one industry. Founding principals personally work on each assignment, providing complete status report and candidate slate in 6-8 weeks. 2 year candidate replacement policy.
Functions: Senior mgmt., Mkt. research, Direct mktg., Customer svc., MIS mgmt., Systems implem., R&D
Industries: Mfg., Drugs mfg., Svcs., Telecoms, High tech, Software, Biotech

Eastman & Beaudine, Inc.

1370 One Galleria Twr.
13355 Noel Rd., LB-31
Dallas, Texas 75240
(972) 661-5520
Fax: (972) 980-8540

Key Contact - Specialty:
Mr. Robert E. Beaudine - *Sports, insurance brokerage, real estate, retail, venture capital (emerging companies)*
Mr. Frank R. Beaudine - *Sports, general management, retail, entertainment*

Description: Consultants to management in executive selection.

Salary Minimum: $70,000
Functions: Generalist, Directors, Senior mgmt., Mktg. mgmt., Sales mgmt., CFO's, MIS mgmt.
Industries: Generalist, Food/bev/tobacco, Venture cap., Entertainment, Human resource svcs., Insurance, Real estate

Branches:
1 Ravinia Drive, Ste. 1110
Atlanta, Georgia 30346
(770) 390-2720
Fax: (770) 390-2729
Key Contact - Specialty:
Mr. Frank R. Beaudine, Jr. - *Human resources, communications, manufacturing, marketing*

EBA Group

17 Leighton Lane
Lakehurst, New Jersey 08733
(732) 657-9300
Fax: (732) 657-9393

Key Contact - Specialty:
Mr. Thomas E. Barker - *Telecommunications, computers, software*

Description: Contract retained executive search specialists in mid to upper management levels concentrating on telecommunications, telephone/cable and computer industries.

Salary Minimum: $60,000
Functions: Generalist, Senior mgmt., Production, Purchasing, Systems dev., Engineering, Mgmt. consultants
Industries: Generalist, Computer equip., Mgmt. consulting, Broadcast & Film, Telecoms, High tech, Software

Bruce Edwards & Associates, Inc.

1000 Park Forty Plaza, Ste. 290
Durham, North Carolina 27713
(919) 544-9911

Key Contact - Specialty:
Mr. S. Bruce Edwards - *Vice presidents, executive vice presidents, COOs, presidents, CEOs*

Mr. George D. Smith - *Vice presidents, executive vice presidents, COOs, presidents, CEOs*
Mr. Donald Fish

Description: Retainer type search firm, located in the Research Triangle area of North Carolina. Clients primarily headquarted in U.S. Senior level searches for corporations, organizations and institutions.

Salary Minimum: $85,000
Functions: Generalist, Middle mgmt., Mfg., Sales mgmt., CFO's, IT, Non-profits
Industries: Generalist, Computer equip., Retail, Venture cap., High tech, Software, Biotech

---

Effective Search, Inc.

11718 N. Main
Roscoe, Illinois 61073-9566
(815) 623-7400
Web: www.esintl.net

Key Contact - Specialty:
Mr. John A. Cain
Mr. Bob H. Mullins
Mr. Christian A. Anderson

Description: Specializing in managers for sales, marketing, accounting, engineering manufacturing and general management, especially those requiring technical degrees (including senior engineer). All searches evaluate candidates working style and interpersonal skills.

Salary Minimum: $40,000
Functions: General mgmt., Mfg., Materials, Sales & mktg., HR mgmt., Finance, Engineering
Industries: Drugs mfg., Plastics/rubber, Metal products, Machinery/Appliances, Computer equip., Consumer electronics, High tech

Branches:
Suite 402
Berea, Ohio 44017
(440) 234-2205
Key Contact - Specialty:
Mr. Craig B. Toedtman

925 Harvest Drive, Ste. 190
Blue Bell, Pennsylvania 19422
(215) 628-4177
Key Contact - Specialty:
Mr. Chris Bilotta

Affiliates:
Resource Development Co., Inc.

EFL Assoc.

7101 College Blvd., Ste. 550
Overland Park, Kansas 66210-1891
(913) 451-8866
Fax: (913) 451-3219
Email: eflinfo@eflkc.com
Web: www.transearch.com

Key Contact - Specialty:
Mr. Peter K. Lemke
Ms. Evelyn C. Davis
Mr. David A. Wolfram
Mr. Jason M. Meschke

Description: National/international executive search practice specializing in senior/upper management levels for a broad base of client companies.

Salary Minimum: $75,000
Functions: Generalist
Industries: Generalist

Affiliates:
EFL Assoc.

Networks:
Transearch Int'l.

EFL Int'l.

8777 E. Via De Ventura, Ste. 300
Scottsdale, Arizona 85258-9734
(602) 483-0496
Fax: (602) 483-2832
Email: info@eflinternational.com
Web: www.eflinternational.com

Key Contact - Specialty:
Mr. William R. Franquemont - *Generalist*
Mr. Jeffrey D. Franquemont - *Generalist, high technology*

Description: Provide search consulting services to senior management.

Salary Minimum: $60,000
Functions: Generalist
Industries: Generalist, Food/bev/tobacco, Computer equip., Misc. mfg., Hospitality, High tech, Software

Affiliates:
EFL Assoc.

Egan & Assoc.

White House Ctr., 128 S. Sixth Ave.
West Bend, Wisconsin 53095
(414) 335-0707
Fax: (414) 335-0625

Key Contact - Specialty:
Mr. Daniel K. Egan - *Generalist*
Ms. Joy V. Massar - *Generalist*

Description: Perform executive searches on a retainer basis only. No contingency work performed. The vast majority of clients are manufacturers with searches being performed for all major disciplines within manufacturing.

Salary Minimum: $60,000
Functions: Generalist
Industries: Mfg.

Egan Search Group

Two Penn Plaza, Ste. 1500
New York, New York 10121
(212) 292-5070
Fax: (212) 292-5071

Key Contact - Specialty:
Mr. John Egan - *Financial services, generalist*

Description: Twenty five years of specialty search experience within financial services plus a deliberate effort to work with a limited number of clients in order to provide a more personalized and focused service.

Salary Minimum: $100,000
Functions: Generalist
Industries: Banking, Invest. banking

EGM Consulting, Inc. †

8333 W. McNab Rd., Ste. 231
Tamarac, Florida 33321
(954) 720-9645
Fax: (954) 720-5813
Web: stanley@satelnet.org

Key Contact - Specialty:
Mr. Eric G. Mankuta - *Pharmaceutical, biotechnology*

Description: Healthcare-biotechnology, pharmaceuticals, diagnostics, devices, hospitals, services-senior and middle level executives, medical, scientific, other technical. Principal has 15 years recruiting experience in healthcare industry.

Salary Minimum: $50,000
Functions: Senior mgmt., Quality, Physicians, Mkt. research, Mktg. mgmt., R&D, Engineering
Industries: Drugs mfg., Medical devices, Pharmaceutical svcs., Biotech

---

Richard A. Eisner & Co., LLP

575 Madison Ave.
New York, New York 10022
(212) 355-1700
Fax: (212) 355-2414
Email: ileff@eisner.rae.com
Web: www.rae.com

Key Contact - Specialty:
Ms. Ilene J. Leff - *CFOs, COOs, general managers*
Mr. Richard Fisher - *Financial services, CFOs*

Description: Senior executive searches, compensation and management consulting services for a wide range of companies including mid-sized companies, portfolio companies of venture capital and buyout firms, new USA ventures of non-USA based companies.

Salary Minimum: $80,000
Functions: Generalist, General mgmt., Mktg. mgmt., HR mgmt., Finance, IT, Mgmt. consultants
Industries: Generalist, Mfg., Finance, Svcs., Communications, Software, Healthcare

† occasional contingency assignment

Branches:
100 Campus Drive
Florham Park, New Jersey 07932
(973) 593-7000
Key Contact - Specialty:
Mr. Eli Hoffman

Affiliates:
Summit Int'l. Assoc., Inc.

William J. Elam & Assoc.
434 Greentree Court Bldg.
Lincoln, Nebraska 68505-2438
(402) 467-5638

Key Contact - Specialty:
Mr. William J. Elam, Jr. - *Generalist*

Description: Group of professionals out of industry, with extensive management background. Focus on middle to top level assignments on a nationwide basis. Concentration in automotive parts, biotech and pharmaceutical.

Salary Minimum: $75,000
Functions: Senior mgmt., Plant mgmt., Nurses, Health admin., Mktg. mgmt., CFO's, R&D
Industries: Drugs mfg., Motor vehicles, Wholesale, Banking, Biotech, Healthcare

Elite Resources Group
71 Baker Blvd., Ste. 204
Fairlawn, Ohio 44333
(330) 867-9412
Fax: (330) 867-0468
Email: elite-rg@neo.lrun.com

Key Contact - Specialty:
Mr. Gary T. Suhay - *Transportation, engineering, research & development, quality, technical service & sales*

Description: A full-service human resource consulting and staffing based business. We focus on conducting executive/management/professional searches in the context of your mission, culture and direction.

Salary Minimum: $30,000
Functions: Generalist, Production, Purchasing, Materials Plng., Distribution, R&D, Engineering
Industries: Generalist, Chemicals, Plastics/rubber, Machinery/Appliances, Misc. mfg., Transportation, Packaging

Yves Elkas Inc. †
485 McGill St., Ste. 601
Montreal, Quebec H2Y 2H4
Canada
(514) 845-0088
Fax: (514) 845-2518
Email: elkas@total.net
Web: www.elkas.com

Key Contact - Specialty:
Mr. Yves Elkas - *Generalist, senior management, human resources*
Mr. Jacques E. Ouellet - *Finance, human resources*
Mr. Simon Parisien - *Sales, marketing*

Description: We provide expertise in executive search and evaluation of prospective candidates. Over the years, we have devised original and sound methodologies in recruitment.

Salary Minimum: $50,000
Functions: General mgmt., Mfg., Materials, Sales & mktg., HR mgmt., Finance, Engineering
Industries: Food/bev/tobacco, Misc. mfg., Transportation, Retail, Venture cap., Communications, Packaging

Elliot Assoc. Inc. †
104 S. Broadway
Tarrytown, New York 10591
(914) 631-4904
Fax: (914) 631-6481
Web: www.elliotassociates.com

Key Contact - Specialty:
Ms. Alice Elliot - *Hospitality, service*

Description: Nationwide executive search in the hospitality and service industries handling retainer and contingency searches.

Salary Minimum: $80,000
Functions: Directors, Senior mgmt., Middle mgmt., Sales & mktg., HR mgmt., Finance, Int'l.
Industries: Svcs., Hospitality, Entertainment

Branches:
5227 W. Acapulco Lane
Glendale, Arizona 85306
(602) 978-0218
Fax: (602) 547-9830
Key Contact - Specialty:
Ms. Libby Gordon

186 N Crescent Dr.
Beverly Hills, California 90210
(310) 285-0377
Fax: (310) 285-0378
Key Contact - Specialty:
Mr. Don Fitzgerald

131 Roswell St., Ste. B2-2
Alpharetta Executive Ctr.
Alpharetta, Georgia 30201-1964
(770) 664-5354
Fax: (770) 664-0233
Key Contact - Specialty:
Ms. Joan Ray

42 Pleasant St.
Newburyport, Massachusetts 01950-2715
(978) 462-5657
Fax: (978) 462-7872
Key Contact - Specialty:
Mr. Richard Giannino

10901 Reed Hartman Hwy., Ste. 321
Cincinnati, Ohio 45242-2835
(513) 792-0113
Fax: (513) 792-0117
Key Contact - Specialty:
Mr. Rick Badgley

16 Muirfield Court
Bridgeville, Pennsylvania 15017
(412) 221-6428
Fax: (412) 221-6458
Key Contact - Specialty:
Mr. Greg Palmer

505 Powell St.
Austin, Texas 78703
(512) 472-4484
Fax: (512) 472-5165
Key Contact - Specialty:
Mr. Troy Erb

Affiliates:
Elliot Solutions, LLC

H. J. Elliot, Inc.
5136 Eau Claire Court
Gurnee, Illinois 60031
(847) 249-1091
Email: hjelliot@earthlink.net
Web: home.earthlink.net/~hjelliot/index.html

Key Contact - Specialty:
Mr. Elliot Hoffenberg - *Human resources information systems, finance, financial information systems, sales*

Description: Searches in HRIS, IS, financials, HR. Sales searches performed either on retainer or on an hourly consulting basis.

Salary Minimum: $60,000
Functions: Middle mgmt., Sales mgmt., Benefits, CFO's, MIS mgmt., Systems anal., Systems implem.
Industries: Generalist, Finance, Computer svcs., Mgmt. consulting, Human resource svcs., Software

The Elliott Company
5 Burlington Woods Drive, Ste. 203
Burlington, Massachusetts 01803-4542
(781) 270-5380
Fax: (617) 270-5375
Email:
roger.elliott@theelliottcompany.com
Web: www.theelliottcompany.com

Key Contact - Specialty:
Mr. Roger S. Elliott

Description: Executive resource dedicated to serving companies and supporting clients' profitable growth through retained leadership acquisition, as well as our performance management and business development activities. Practice no conflict of interest.

Salary Minimum: $80,000

Functions: General mgmt., Mfg., Sales & mktg., HR mgmt., Finance, Specialized services, Int'l.
Industries: Generalist, Mfg., Finance, Svcs., Communications, Software, Biotech

Affiliates:
Slayton Int'l., Inc.

David M. Ellner Assoc.
2 Penn Plaza, Ste. 1500
New York, New York 10121
(212) 279-0665
Web: www.elldoda@aol.com

Key Contact - Specialty:
Mr. David M. Ellner - *Generalist*

Description: Executive search services tailored to the small and medium sized organization.

Salary Minimum: $60,000
Functions: Senior mgmt., Mktg. mgmt., MIS mgmt., Systems anal., Systems dev., Systems support, Engineering
Industries: Computer equip., Misc. financial, Entertainment, Legal, Mgmt. consulting, Publishing, Software

---

Elwell & Assoc., Inc.
3100 W. Liberty St., Ste. E
Ann Arbor, Michigan 48103
(734) 662-8775
Fax: (734) 662-2045
Email: elwellas@elwellassociates.com

Key Contact - Specialty:
Mr. Richard F. Elwell
Mr. David A. Gilmore
Mr. Stephen R. Elwell

Description: Specializing in searches for senior executives, across functions and industries, throughout North America.

Salary Minimum: $90,000
Functions: Senior mgmt., Mfg., Materials, Sales & mktg., HR mgmt., Finance, Engineering
Industries: Generalist

Affiliates:
M/J/A Partners
RWS Partners
Michael Stern Assoc., Inc./Euram

EMN/Witt/Kieffer
(a division of Witt/Kieffer, Ford, Hadelman & Lloyd)
98 Old South Rd.
Nantucket, Massachusetts 02554-6000
(508) 228-6700
Fax: (508) 228-6484
Email: info@emnemn.com
Web: www.emnemn.com

Key Contact - Specialty:
Ms. Nancy A. Martin - *Presidents, vice presidents, deans, directors*

Description: The nation's largest executive search firm dedicated to serving education, healthcare, the arts and the not-for-profit community.

Salary Minimum: $75,000
Functions: Senior mgmt., Health admin., CFO's, MIS mgmt., Non-profits
Industries: Non-profits, Higher ed., Healthcare

Branches:
1920 Main St., Ste. 310
Irvine, California 92614
(949) 851-5070
Fax: (949) 851-2412
Key Contact - Specialty:
Ms. Paula Corabelli - *Higher education*

5143 N. Stanford Drive
Nashville, Tennessee 37215
(615) 665-3388
Fax: (615) 665-3389
Key Contact - Specialty:
Mr. Gary J. Posner - *Presidents, vice presidents, deans, directors*

Empire International
1147 Lancaster Ave.
Berwyn, Pennsylvania 19312
(610) 647-7976
Fax: (610) 647-8488
Email: emhunter@erols.com
Web: empire-internal.com

Key Contact - Specialty:
Mr. Charles V. Combe, II
Mr. M. J. Stanford
Mr. Thomas MacCarthy
Mr. Samuel Shay Gillin
Mr. John Flowers
Mr. Bryan Shea
Mr. Robert Banks

Description: We are a generalist retainer search firm addressing senior-level management engagements throughout the English-speaking world including the United States, Canada, the United Kingdom and the Pacific Rim.

Salary Minimum: $100,000
Functions: Generalist, Senior mgmt., Sales mgmt., CFO's, MIS mgmt., R&D, Engineering
Industries: Generalist, Chemicals, Metal products, Computer equip., Invest. banking, New media, High tech

---

The Energists
10260 Westheimer, Ste. 300
Houston, Texas 77042
(713) 781-6881
Fax: (713) 781-2998
Email: search@energists.com
Web: www.energists.com

Key Contact - Specialty:
Mr. Alex Preston - *Exploration, production*
Mr. Bradford Macurda - *Exploration, production*

Description: Specialists (each consultant has a minimum of sixteen years technical/business energy industry and search experience) in executive search to the upstream and midstream energy industry.

Salary Minimum: $80,000
Functions: Senior mgmt., Middle mgmt., R&D, Engineering, Int'l.
Industries: Energy/utilities

Networks:
Transearch Int'l.

ENI
P.O. Box 073
Wilton, Connecticut 06897
(203) 834-0587

Key Contact - Specialty:
Mr. Edgar F. Newman - *Generalist*

Description: 20 years of professional search experience servicing a broad range of multinational clients in all functional areas. Strong background in healthcare, consumer products, high technology and service industries.

Salary Minimum: $75,000
Functions: Middle mgmt., Health admin., Mktg. mgmt., Sales mgmt., IT, Mgmt. consultants, Int'l.
Industries: Generalist, Energy/utilities, Mfg., Computer equip., Mgmt. consulting, Real estate, Healthcare

Affiliates:
Sheila Greco Assoc.
Princeton HR Consulting

The Enns Partners Inc.
70 University Ave., Ste. 410
P.O. Box 14
Toronto, Ontario M5J 2M4
Canada
(416) 598-0012
Fax: (416) 598-4328

Key Contact - Specialty:
Mr. George Enns
Mr. Roy Miller
Mr. Alan Burns
Ms. Rita Eskudt
Mr. Jim Lundy

Description: Experienced consulting firm serving senior executive search requirements.

Salary Minimum: $100,000
Functions: Generalist
Industries: Generalist
Professional Associations: AESC

Networks:
The Hever Group

Entelechy Group Ltd.
133 E. Main St., 2C
Westminster, Maryland 21157
(904) 620-8303
Fax: (904) 620-8305

Email: entelechia@aol.com

Key Contact - Specialty:
Mr. William Cebak - *Medical communications*
Ms. Cindy Chambers - *Medical communications*

Description: We are dedicated to the development and growth of our chosen customers by providing them with professional executive search consulting services to aid them in the fulfillment of critical personnel needs.
Functions: Healthcare
Industries: Communications, Healthcare

The Enterprise Group
1075 Washington St.
West Newton, Massachusetts 02165
(617) 964-1855
Fax: (617) 964-8377
Email: hwigder@world.std.com

Key Contact - Specialty:
Mr. T. Harvey Wigder - *Privately held businesses*

Description: Broad focus on these issues: Does company have right organization structure?; Do key executives have needed skills?; Does environment motivate success behavior? Searches result from improvement opportunities.

Salary Minimum: $75,000
Functions: Generalist, General mgmt., Directors, Senior mgmt., Middle mgmt.
Industries: Generalist

Epsen, Fuller & Assoc., LLC
3 S. Mountain Terrace
Montclair, New Jersey 07042
(973) 783-1880
Fax: (973) 783-1881
Email: tjfuller@viconet.com

Key Contact - Specialty:
Mr. Thomas Fuller - *Retail, apparel, consumer products*

Description: Strategic executive search services with in-depth industry and functional knowledge in each area of practice.

Salary Minimum: $50,000
Functions: Senior mgmt., Middle mgmt., Product dev., Distribution, Sales & mktg., Finance, IT
Industries: Computer equip., Consumer electronics, Wholesale, Retail, New media, High tech, Software

Affiliates:
Kulper & Co.

Mary R. Erickson & Assoc.
(Firm declined to update.)
8300 Norman Center Drive, Ste. 545
Minneapolis, Minnesota 55437
(612) 914-9694

Key Contact - Specialty:
Ms. Mary R. Erickson - *Senior executives, strategic organizational consulting*

Description: Twenty-seven years of experience as a nationally retained generalist practice, serving senior management in multiple industries. Focused on executive acquisition and organizational consulting offering services unparalleled in the industry.

Salary Minimum: $100,000
Functions: Generalist
Industries: Generalist

Erikson Consulting Assoc., Inc.
230 Park Ave., Ste. 1000
New York, New York 10169
(212) 808-3052
Fax: (212) 661-2238
Email: econsult@compuserve.com

Key Contact - Specialty:
Mr. Theodore J. Erikson - *Investment banking, technology*

Description: Senior level executive search and consulting services to the investment banking, asset management, emerging technologies industries and information technology disciplines.

Salary Minimum: $100,000
Functions: CFO's, MIS mgmt.
Industries: Finance, Invest. banking, Venture cap., High tech, Biotech

---

Erlanger Assoc.
2 Soundview Drive
Greenwich, Connecticut 06830
(203) 629-5410
Fax: (203) 629-5444

Key Contact - Specialty:
Mr. Richard A. Erlanger - *CEOs, COOs, general managers*
Ms. Carolyn M. Desley - *CEOs, COOs, general managers*

Description: Focus on searches for operating general partners and line executives in buyouts and turnaround portfolio companies and their parent firms.

Salary Minimum: $170,000
Functions: Generalist, Senior mgmt., Plant mgmt., Mktg. mgmt., CFO's, MIS mgmt., Engineering
Industries: Generalist, Mfg., Wholesale, Finance, Svcs., Packaging, Healthcare

Branches:
777 S. Flagler Drive
8th Floor, W. Twr.
West Palm Beach, Florida 33401
(561) 820-9461
Fax: (561) 835-1774
Key Contact - Specialty:
Ms. Lynn Hayden - *CFOs, operations, marketing*

Erwin Assoc.
2021 Midwest Rd., Ste. 200
Oak Brook, Illinois 60521
(708) 953-8519

Key Contact - Specialty:
Mr. Ronald R. Erwin

Description: Generalist firm serving clients in manufacturing and services businesses. Extensive experience in recruiting for entrepreneurial companies and for rigorously competitive environments. Serve overseas firms investing in U.S.

Salary Minimum: $75,000
Functions: Middle mgmt., Product dev., Automation, Materials Plng., Sales mgmt., CFO's, Engineering
Industries: Mfg., Lumber/furniture, Plastics/rubber, Metal products, Machinery/Appliances, Motor vehicles, Test/measurement equip.

ESA
141 Durham Rd., Ste. 16
Madison, Connecticut 06443
(203) 245-1983
Fax: (203) 245-8428
Email: esa.search@snet.net
Web: www.esa-search.com

Key Contact - Specialty:
Mr. Barry L. Dicker - *High technology*
Mr. Geoffrey M. Kerrigan - *High technology*
Mr. Vincent Bongiovanni - *High technology*
Mr. Mark Freeman - *High technology*

Description: Concentration in high tech industries. Specializing in the full range of functional areas found in most high technology manufacturing companies.

Salary Minimum: $40,000
Functions: Directors, Senior mgmt., Mktg. mgmt., MIS mgmt., Systems anal., Systems dev., Engineering
Industries: Mfg., Aerospace, High tech, Software

Branches:
McPherson Business Complex, Office #3
P.O. Box 1028
Littleton, North Carolina 27850
(919) 586-3931
Fax: (919) 586-4133
Email: www.ndpigott@msn.com
Key Contact - Specialty:
Mr. A. Daniel Pigott - *High technology*

ESS (Executive Search Services)

2925 Fourth St., Ste. 11
Santa Monica, California 90405
(310) 392-3244
Email: mms@sprintmail.com
Web: home.sprintmail.com/~mms

Key Contact - Specialty:
Mr. Matthew M. Susleck - *Engineering, marketing, management, key technical positions*

Description: Our methodology is based on up-to-the-minute sector research and implemented with an exclusive custom software suite developed specifically for retained search production. Searches are quick, current and comprehensive.

Salary Minimum: $75,000
Functions: Senior mgmt., Middle mgmt., Plant mgmt., Sales mgmt., MIS mgmt., Engineering, Int'l.
Industries: Energy/utilities, Construction, Mfg., Transportation, Telecoms, Environmental svcs., High tech

Ethos Consulting, Inc.

100 Drakes Landing Rd., Ste. 100
Greenbrae, California 94904
(415) 397-2211
(800) 297-5087
Fax: (415) 397-0856
Email: resumes@ethosconsulting.com
Web: www.ethosconsulting.com

Key Contact - Specialty:
Mr. Conrad E. Prusak - *General management*
Ms. Julie J. Prusak - *Consulting, marketing, consumer goods*
Mr. David Whelan - *High technology, communications, media*
Mr. Michael Truesdell - *High technology, hospitality, entertainment*
Ms. Andrea Danforth - *Human resources, healthcare, finance*

Description: Highly personalized, senior level executive search practice that concentrates on delivering the results a client needs in a timely and professional manner.

Salary Minimum: $120,000
Functions: General mgmt., Sales & mktg., HR mgmt., CFO's, Engineering, Mgmt. consultants
Industries: Generalist, Mfg., Finance, Svcs., Communications, High tech, Healthcare
Professional Associations: IACPR

ETI Search Int'l.

990 Hammond Drive, Ste. 825
Bldg. 1
Atlanta, Georgia 30328
(770) 399-8492
Fax: (770) 399-8487

Key Contact - Specialty:
Mr. William Chambers, III
Mr. David F. Brown
Ms. Donna Grayson

Description: Retained executive search specializing in telecommunications, high tech and healthcare, with significant capabilities in other industries.

Salary Minimum: $85,000
Functions: Senior mgmt., Middle mgmt., Mktg. mgmt., Sales mgmt., HR mgmt., CFO's, MIS mgmt.
Industries: Svcs., Mgmt. consulting, Communications, Telecoms, High tech, Healthcare

The Evans Search Group

One Darling Drive
Avon, Connecticut 06001
(860) 677-6770
Email: rreinc@connix.com

Key Contact - Specialty:
Mr. Ronald R. Evans

Description: Specialize in serving family owned or closely held businesses across diverse industries.

Salary Minimum: $90,000
Functions: Senior mgmt., Mktg. mgmt., PR, CFO's, M&A, MIS mgmt.
Industries: Invest. banking, Accounting, Advertising/PR, High tech, Software

Branches:
12900 Preston Rd., #925
Dallas, Texas 75230
(972) 960-8640
Key Contact - Specialty:
Dr. Nancy Polk

Excalibur Human Resources, Inc.

5 Independence Way
Princeton Corporate Center
Princeton, New Jersey 08540
(609) 452-0952
Fax: (609) 452-8818
Email: pgraver@aol.com

Key Contact - Specialty:
Ms. Patricia Graver - *Healthcare*
Ms. Beth Conyngham - *Healthcare*

Description: Progressive executive search firm specializing in the healthcare/hi-tech industries providing superior service with particular strengths on complex assignments in executive and scientific areas.

Salary Minimum: $80,000
Functions: General mgmt., Mfg., Sales & mktg., HR mgmt., Finance, IT, R&D
Industries: Drugs mfg., Pharmaceutical svcs., Biotech, Healthcare

ExeConnex, LLC

1030 Huntwick Court
Roswell, Georgia 30075
(770) 650-3821
Email: colette@execonnex.com

Key Contact - Specialty:
Ms. Colette Davis - *Project management*

Description: We are a search firm specializing in project management in the technology sector.

Salary Minimum: $75,000
Functions: Directors, Middle mgmt., Product dev., Production, Systems anal., Systems implem., Mgmt. consultants
Industries: Energy/utilities, Mfg., Finance, Svcs., Communications, High tech, Software

ExecuGroup, Inc. †

Box 5040
Grenada, Mississippi 38901
(601) 226-9025
Fax: (601) 226-9090
Email: ExecuGroup@aol.com
Web: members.aol.com/ExecuGroup

Key Contact - Specialty:
Mr. Robert T. Ray - *Mid to senior level management positions in most industries*

Description: Executive search specializing in mid to senior level management positions for both operational and staffing needs.

Salary Minimum: $75,000
Functions: General mgmt., Mktg. mgmt., Sales mgmt., HR mgmt., Finance, MIS mgmt.
Industries: Generalist, Finance, Human resource svcs.

Branches:
26 Bethlehem Plaza
Bethlehem, Pennsylvania 18018
(610) 954-9977
Fax: (610) 954-9511
Email: ExecuGroup@aol.com
Web: http://members.aol.com/ExecuGroup
Key Contact - Specialty:
Mr. James O. Norwine - *Mid to senior level management positions in most industries*

ExecuQuest, Inc.

2050 Breton SE, Ste. 103
Grand Rapids, Michigan 49546-5547
(616) 949-1800
Fax: (616) 949-0561
Email: execuquest@aol.com

Key Contact - Specialty:
Mr. William L. Waanders - *Generalist*
Ms. Patricia J. Waanders

Description: Midwest executive search firm focused on mid-level and senior management positions in manufacturing, banking

† occasional contingency assignment

and financial services industries. Also handle CFO, controller and treasurer searches in all industries.

Salary Minimum: $75,000
Functions: Generalist, General mgmt., Mfg., Sales & mktg., HR mgmt., Finance, MIS mgmt.
Industries: Generalist, Lumber/furniture, Metal products, Misc. mfg., Wholesale, Finance, Svcs.

Executech

500 S. Depeyster St.
Kent, Ohio 44240
(330) 677-0010

Key Contact - Specialty:
Mr. J. Mark Seaholts

Description: Customized search in chemical industry with emphasis in adhesives, electromechanical industry with emphasis in motors and appliances, healthcare industry with emphasis in physicians, administrators and medical equipment industry. General.
Functions: Generalist, Senior mgmt., Mfg., Sales mgmt., Benefits, Engineering, Int'l.
Industries: Generalist, Mfg., Printing, Chemicals, Plastics/rubber, Machinery/ Appliances, Misc. mfg.

Affiliates:
National Search, Inc.
SilverCrest Search

Executive Access Inc. †

590 Madison Ave., 26th Floor
New York, New York 10022
(212) 308-6888
Fax: (212) 308-3288
Email: mgonzales@eany.com

Key Contact - Specialty:
Mr. Michael T. Brookes - *Investment banking, emerging markets, capital markets, investment banking*

Description: The newly established American subsidiary of Asia's largest and most successful executive search firm focusing on the investment banking industry.
Functions: Senior mgmt., Middle mgmt., Personnel, CFO's, Cash mgmt., Systems anal., Int'l.
Industries: Finance, Invest. banking, Venture cap.

International Branches:
Central Hong Kong, London, Mumbai, New Delhi, Singapore

Executive Alliance

(Firm declined to update.)
2 Mount Royal Ave., Ste. 300
Marlborough, Massachusetts 01752
(508) 481-7777
Email: info@executivealliance.com

Key Contact - Specialty:
Mr. Don Bateman
Ms. Cary Morrill
Mr. James Campbell

Description: Generalist executive search practice with experience in most industries and in all functional disciplines. Practice is one of five in full-service HR consulting firm.

Salary Minimum: $100,000
Functions: Generalist, General mgmt., Senior mgmt., Sales & mktg., Engineering, Int'l.
Industries: Generalist, High tech, Software

Affiliates:
DPSC International

Executive Careers †

1801 Ave. of the Stars, Ste. 640
Los Angeles, California 90067
(310) 552-3455
(310) 306-0360
Fax: (310) 578-7524

Key Contact - Specialty:
Ms. Annette R. Segil - *Generalist*

Description: Search generalist with strong specialization in logistics and distribution, retail, catalogue, direct marketing, community based social services and museums, family and emerging and middle market businesses.

Salary Minimum: $50,000
Functions: Senior mgmt., Health admin., Sales & mktg., Direct mktg., HR mgmt., Finance, Non-profits
Industries: Generalist, Retail, Finance, Hospitality, Entertainment, Non-profits, Communications

Executive Dimensions

P.O. Box 801
Amherst, New York 14231-0801
(716) 632-9034
Fax: (716) 631-5253
Email:
execsearch@executivedimensions.com
Web: www.executivedimensions.com

Key Contact - Specialty:
Ms. Gwen O. Arcara - *Senior level*

Description: Experienced consultants providing exceptional executive search and interim executive services. Dedicated to delivering value-oriented services to our clients. Specialize in the recruitment of senior executives and contract (interim) professionals.

Salary Minimum: $90,000
Functions: Directors, Senior mgmt., Health admin., HR mgmt., Finance, MIS mgmt., Mgmt. consultants
Industries: Food/bev/tobacco, Drugs mfg., Finance, Pharmaceutical svcs., Mgmt. consulting, Human resource svcs., Healthcare

Branches:
One Perimeter Park S., Ste. 100N
Birmingham, Alabama 35243-2359
(205) 970-6024
Fax: (205) 678-7533
Email: execsearch@executivedimensions.com
Web: www.executivedimensions.com
Key Contact - Specialty:
Mr. Arlen Reynolds - *Interim executives*

Executive Directions

4919 Spruce Hill Drive NW
Canton, Ohio 44718
(330) 499-1001
Fax: (330) 499-2579
Email: execudir@staffing.net
Web: executive-directions.com

Key Contact - Specialty:
Mr. Paul E. Richards - *Automotive, plastic molding industries*
Mr. R. Glenn Richards - *Flexible packaging, resins, compounds, converting*

Description: Provide small, medium and large corporations with executive search, team building and corporate consulting services while requiring only a minimal initial investment/retainer. Industry specialization includes: automotive, plastics, converting and packaging.

Salary Minimum: $50,000
Functions: Generalist, Senior mgmt., Product dev., Production, Plant mgmt., Quality, Sales mgmt.
Industries: Paper, Printing, Plastics/rubber, Metal products, Computer equip., Packaging

Affiliates:
Pinnacle Int'l.

The Executive Group, Inc.

9191 Towne Centre Drive, Ste. 105
San Diego, California 92122
(619) 457-8100
Fax: (619) 457-1277
Email: exegroup@aol.com
Web: home.aol.com/exegroup

Key Contact - Specialty:
Mr. Paul X. Bouzan - *Generalist, executives, technical, managerial*
Mr. Larry Rossi - *Generalist, executives*
Mr. Robert Kaplan - *Generalist, attorneys*

Description: General industrial search practice; hi-tech, engineering, legal, finance, banking and biotechnology.

Salary Minimum: $60,000
Functions: Middle mgmt., Physicians, Mkt. research, Benefits, M&A, Systems anal., Non-profits
Industries: Generalist

Executive Manning Corp.

3000 NE 30th Place, Ste. 405
Ft. Lauderdale, Florida 33306
(954) 561-5100
Fax: (954) 564-7483
Email: emccg@aol.com
Web: www.exmanning.com

Key Contact - Specialty:
Mr. Richard L. Hertan - *Generalist*

Description: We are one of the country's premier executive search and management consulting firms, providing a full spectrum of services relating to human resources.

Salary Minimum: $75,000
Functions: Generalist, Senior mgmt., Production, Materials Plng., Health admin., MIS mgmt., R&D
Industries: Generalist, Paper, Computer equip., Finance, Pharmaceutical svcs., Computer svcs., Healthcare

Affiliates:
EMC Consulting Group
Missing Link Consultants

Executive Recruitment Specialists, Inc.

6407 Idlewild Rd., Ste. 103
Charlotte, North Carolina 28212
(704) 536-8830
Fax: (704) 536-8893
Email: esklut@aol.com
Web: free.websight.com/recruitmentspecialistsinc/

Key Contact - Specialty:
Mr. Eric Sklut - *Executive, general management*

Description: Unparalleled level of service, direct efforts by experienced search professionals and company principals, 100% completion rate, flexible, adaptable, able to meet any demands, highly ethical practices.

Salary Minimum: $50,000
Functions: Senior mgmt., Nurses, Allied health, CFO's, IT, Engineering, Mgmt. consultants
Industries: Mfg., Retail, Mgmt. consulting, Government, High tech, Software, Healthcare

Executive Resource Group, Inc.

29 Oakhurst Rd.
Cape Elizabeth, Maine 04107
(207) 871-5527
Email: sibyl@mindspring.com

Key Contact - Specialty:
Ms. Sibyl Masquelier - *Publishing*

Description: We are our client's representative in the marketplace. Qualified women are always included in the final presentation of each search. We represent the character of the client and handle all actions professionally.

Salary Minimum: $65,000
Functions: Plant mgmt., Advertising, Mkt. research, HR mgmt., Benefits, Network admin., DB admin.
Industries: Printing, Human resource svcs., Publishing, New media, Broadcast & Film, Telecoms
Professional Associations: IACPR

Executive Search Consultants

(Firm declined to update.)
28211 McCall Blvd.
Sun City, California 92585
(909) 679-4792

Key Contact - Specialty:
Dr. James J. Sheridan - *School administrators*
Ms. Helen Archer - *School administrators*
Mr. Frank Clayton - *School administrators*

Description: All our consultants are retired educators who have served in top level executive positions as superintendents, assistant superintendents of business, instruction and personnel. All have served also as middle managers (principals and assistant principals).
Functions: Generalist, Directors, Senior mgmt., Middle mgmt., Admin. svcs.

Executive Search Consultants International, Inc.

350 Fifth Ave., Ste. 5501
New York, New York 10118
(212) 330-1900
Fax: (212) 330-1906
Email: carlcarro@aol.com

Key Contact - Specialty:
Mr. Carl R. Carro
Mr. James W. Doyle
Mr. Mark S. Thrapp

Description: Our firm provides executive search and management consulting services on a retainer basis to domestic and international corporations in retailing, wholesale, direct marketing, media, technology, manufacturing, finance and consumer packaged goods.

Salary Minimum: $100,000
Functions: General mgmt., Materials, Sales & mktg., Finance, IT, Mgmt. consultants, Int'l.
Industries: Generalist, Retail, Finance, Svcs., Communications, High tech

Executive Search Inc.

5401 Gamble Drive, Ste. 275
Parkdale One
Minneapolis, Minnesota 55416
(612) 541-9153
Fax: (612) 541-9979

Key Contact - Specialty:
Mr. James G. Gresham

Description: We are devoted to identifying and tracking high performers in many areas of business. Dedication to results gives us the unique ability to effectively conclude the most demanding assignments.

Salary Minimum: $50,000
Functions: Generalist
Industries: Generalist

Executive Search Int'l./Transearch

60 Walnut St.
Wellesley, Massachusetts 02181
(781) 239-0303
Fax: (781) 235-5975
Email: esits@tiac.net

Key Contact - Specialty:
Mr. Les Gore - *Consumer products, direct marketing*
Ms. Gayle Gorfinkle - *Logistics, supply chain management, professional services*

Description: Industry specialists who add value by being true consultative partners with our clients. We have access to top executive talent, globally through Transearch, an elite international alliance of locally-owned search firms, with over 60 offices operating in 42 countries.

Salary Minimum: $70,000
Functions: Generalist, General mgmt., Mfg., Materials, Sales & mktg., Specialized services, Int'l.
Industries: Generalist, Mfg., Retail, Svcs., Communications, High tech

Networks:
Transearch Int'l.

Executive Search Partners

444 Park Ave. S., Ste. 1202
New York, New York 10016
(212) 686-2929
Fax: (212) 686-2172
Email: exsearch@interport.net

Key Contact - Specialty:
Mr. Kenneth B. Collins - *Generalist, publishing, new media*

Description: Executive search consultants specializing in magazines, books, newspapers and broadcasting and the electronic information industry.

Salary Minimum: $75,000

Functions: Senior mgmt., Middle mgmt., Mktg. mgmt., Sales mgmt., Benefits, CFO's, MIS mgmt.
Industries: Printing, Invest. banking, Human resource svcs., Communications, Advertising/PR, Publishing, New media

Executive Solutions
(a division of Larson, Allen, Weishair & Co.)
220 S. Sixth St., Ste. 1000
Minneapolis, Minnesota 55402-4505
(773) 376-4583
Fax: (773) 376-4820
Email: cindy.s.hedberg@lawcollp.com
Web: www.lawcollp.com

Key Contact - Specialty:
Mr. Jerry Clark - *Healthcare administration*
Dr. Patrick A. Auman - *Healthcare administration*
Ms. Cindy Hedberg - *Healthcare administration*
Mr. Peter D. Kozachok - *Generalist*
Ms. Barbara Kolh - *Generalist*

Description: 3 divisions: one recruits senior-level management for a variety of healthcare entities. The second recruits executives for interim assignments. The third recruits for executive positions/ director level other than healthcare.

Salary Minimum: $60,000
Functions: Senior mgmt., Middle mgmt., Health admin., HR mgmt., CFO's, MIS mgmt., Mgmt. consultants
Industries: Mfg., Finance, Computer svcs., Accounting, Advertising/PR, Packaging, Healthcare

Branches:
640 CEPI Drive, Ste. #A
St. Louis, Missouri 63005-1200
(314) 532-3250
Fax: (314) 532-5275
Email: elizabeth.s.wesolich@lawcollp.com
Key Contact - Specialty:
Ms. Debbie Staggemeier - *Healthcare administration*
Mr. John J. Bogdajewicz - *Healthcare administration*
Ms. Elizabeth S. Wesolich - *Healthcare administration*

The Executive Source Inc.
55 Fifth Ave., 19th Floor
New York, New York 10003-4301
(212) 691-5505
Fax: (212) 691-9839
Email: tes5505@aol.com

Key Contact - Specialty:
Ms. Sarah J. Marks
Mr. Richard C. Plazza

Description: We focus on providing permanent and interim senior human resources professionals specializing in financial services and insurance.

Salary Minimum: $75,000
Functions: Benefits, Personnel, Training
Industries: Banking, Invest. banking, Mgmt. consulting, Human resource svcs.
Professional Associations: IACPR

The Executive Tree
3751 Dunes Rd.
Palm Beach, Florida 33410
(561) 776-0016
Fax: (561) 776-9517
Email: exectree@gate.net
Web: www.gate.net/~exectree

Key Contact - Specialty:
Mr. Lewis James Jordan - *Technologies*
Ms. Kathryn Purcell - *Financial*
Ms. Carol Purcell - *Human resources*
Mr. Randolph Denton - *Sales & marketing*
Dr. Johnathon Victor - *Education, medical*

Description: A national firm specializing in industry recruitment, an hourly, researched based process that identifies and develops candidates at a price that is almost always less than contingent, retained or ad search.

Salary Minimum: $50,000
Functions: Senior mgmt., Mfg., Sales & mktg., HR mgmt., Finance, IT, Engineering
Industries: Generalist, Mfg., Transportation, Finance, Svcs., Communications, Non-classifiable industries

Branches:
2636 Maseth Ave.
Baltimore, Maryland 21219
(888) 745-8743
Email: exectree@gate.net
Web: www.gate.net/~exectree
Key Contact - Specialty:
Ms. Peggy Antoniak - *Government*

Raymond L. Extract & Assoc.
7337 Hyannis Drive
West Hills, California 91307
(818) 999-2837
Fax: (818) 704-7275
Web: rle50967@csun.edu

Key Contact - Specialty:
Mr. Raymond L. Extract - *General management, human resources management*

Description: Broad range of executive search, corporate outplacement and human resources management consulting services. Serve all industries, emphasizing high tech in early growth stages, from entrepreneurial to managerial, other manufacturing, medical.

Salary Minimum: $80,000
Functions: Generalist, Senior mgmt., Sales & mktg., HR mgmt., CFO's, MIS mgmt.
Industries: Generalist, Computer equip., Test/measurement equip., Misc. mfg., High tech, Biotech, Healthcare

Eyler Assoc., Inc.
400 Locust St., Ste. 170
Des Moines, Iowa 50309
(515) 245-4244
Fax: (515) 244-3216

Key Contact - Specialty:
Mr. Richard N. Eyler - *Senior level*

Description: Twenty-four years search experience completing in excess of 350 senior level assignments and five years managing a 450 million profit center for Deere & Co. Broad exposure to manufacturing, banking, financial services, insurance and healthcare.

Salary Minimum: $75,000
Functions: Senior mgmt., Product dev., Plant mgmt., Health admin., CFO's, MIS mgmt., Engineering
Industries: Energy/utilities, Lumber/ furniture, Metal products, Machinery/ Appliances, Banking, Insurance, Healthcare

Fagan & Company
Robb Rd., P.O. Box 611
Ligonier, Pennsylvania 15658
(724) 238-9571

Key Contact - Specialty:
Ms. Stephanie L. Bronder - *Non-profit, institutional advancement, fund-raising, human resources*
Mr. Charles A. Fagan, III - *Senior management, financial services, healthcare, administration*
Mr. Alfred N. Pilz - *Heavy industry*

Description: Full range domestic and international executive search in industrial, healthcare and financial services. Search and appraisal related consulting; e.g. organizational development and competitive analysis.

Salary Minimum: $100,000
Functions: Generalist, Directors, Senior mgmt., Plant mgmt., Health admin., CFO's, Non-profits
Industries: Metal products, Machinery/ Appliances, Finance, Invest. banking, Misc. financial, Non-profits, Telecoms

Affiliates:
Kessler & Associates
Richard W. Montague/Executive Search
Osprey-Clarke Executive Search

Fairfaxx Corp.
17 High St.
Norwalk, Connecticut 06851
(203) 838-8300
Fax: (203) 851-5844

Key Contact - Specialty:
Mr. Jeffrey Thomas - *Apparel, retail, consumer products*
Mr. Joseph Tucci - *High technology, banking*

Description: Services include executive search worldwide. 2 affiliates internationally, 4 domestic affiliates. Heavy emphasis in the apparel industry.

Salary Minimum: $75,000
Functions: Senior mgmt., Production, Distribution, Sales mgmt., CFO's, MIS mgmt., Engineering
Industries: Textiles/apparel, Test/measurement equip., Retail, Entertainment

---

Fairfield Int'l. Resources

725 Fifth Ave., Trump Twr.
New York, New York 10022-2519
(212) 838-0220
Fax: (212) 838-3456
Email: buchholt@fairfieldinternational.com
Web: fairfieldinternational.com

Key Contact - Specialty:
Dr. Bruce Barton Buchholtz - *Retail, wholesale, apparel manufacturing*
Mr. Richard P. Hirshorn - *Retail, wholesale*
Mr. Harvey Levine - *Retail, wholesale*

Description: International is our middle name. For nearly 2 decades we've been in the vanguard of the retail and wholesale industries. As these businesses have become more global we have been fortunate to share our unique perspective with our clients. Hard copy resumes will not be responded to. E-mail resumes will be acknowledged within 24 hours.

Salary Minimum: $75,000
Functions: Senior mgmt., Product dev., Purchasing, Materials Plng., Mkt. research, Sales mgmt., Int'l.
Industries: Textiles/apparel, Soap/perfume/cosmetics, Wholesale, Retail, Entertainment, Advertising/PR, Broadcast & Film

Branches:
9701 Wilshire Blvd.
Beverly Hills, California 90212-2011
(310) 858-5250
Fax: (310) 858-5247
Key Contact - Specialty:
Mr. Bruce Barton Buchholtz

International Branches:
Causeway Bay, London, Milan, Paris

Paul Falcone Assoc.

14 Ridgedale Ave., Ste. 207
Cedar Knolls, New Jersey 07927
(201) 984-1010
Fax: (201) 984-6844

Key Contact - Specialty:
Mr. Paul S. Falcone, Jr.

Description: Specializing in consumer packaged goods, telecommunications, hospitality and media.

Salary Minimum: $65,000
Functions: Directors, Distribution, Mktg. mgmt., Sales mgmt., HR mgmt.
Industries: Food/bev/tobacco, Soap/perfume/cosmetics, Hospitality, Communications

---

Family-Business Roundtable, Inc.

727 E. Bethany Home Rd., Ste. 125
Phoenix, Arizona 85014
(602) 285-1207
Fax: (602) 285-0663
Email: gcrosby@fbrinc.com
Web: www.fbrinc.com

Key Contact - Specialty:
Dr. Georgann Crosby - *Family businesses*

Description: We specialize in recruiting for senior management positions for family businesses.

Salary Minimum: $75,000
Functions: Senior mgmt.
Industries: Generalist

Leon A. Farley Assoc.

468 Jackson St.
San Francisco, California 94111
(415) 989-0989
Fax: (415) 989-5908

Key Contact - Specialty:
Mr. Leon A. Farley - *Senior level executives (generalist)*
Ms. Patricia L. Wilson - *Senior level executives (generalist)*
Mr. Charles R. Zellerbach

Description: Senior searches (over $150,000 compensation) in all industries and functions. Emphasis on general management. Extensive experience in financial services, technology, communications and professional service (partner level lawyers and consultants). International.

Salary Minimum: $150,000
Functions: Generalist, Directors, Senior mgmt., Mktg. mgmt., CFO's, Mgmt. consultants, Int'l.
Industries: Generalist, Construction, Food/bev/tobacco, Finance, Legal, Aerospace, High tech
Professional Associations: AESC

Networks:
Penrhyn International

James Farris Assoc.

4101 N. Classen, Ste. E
Oklahoma City, Oklahoma 73118
(405) 525-5061

Key Contact - Specialty:
Mr. James W. Farris - *Generalist*

Description: Retained searches for mid to top level in finance; management; healthcare; insurance; manufacturing; human resources; information systems and technical professions; sales and marketing; along with outplacement and consulting services.

Salary Minimum: $40,000
Functions: Generalist
Industries: Generalist

The Fawcett Group

416 Puritan Rd.
Swampscott, Massachusetts 01907
(781) 592-9555
Email: mfawcett@fawcett-group.com

Key Contact - Specialty:
Ms. Marcia A. Fawcett - *Senior management, executive staff*

Description: Our specialty is in high technology, small to medium firms. Our strength is in general management, sales and marketing, IS/IT, R&D/engineering and human resources.

Salary Minimum: $80,000
Functions: Senior mgmt., Sales & mktg., HR mgmt., MIS mgmt.
Industries: Hospitality, Entertainment, Human resource svcs., New media, Telecoms, High tech, Software

---

FCI, Inc.

621 Shrewsbury Ave.
Shrewsbury, New Jersey 07702
(732) 576-8522
Fax: (732) 576-8098
Email: fci.jobs@ix.netcom.com

Key Contact - Specialty:
Mr. Douglas L. Sheeran
Ms. Pamela Siedlecki
Ms. Denise Gonzalez

Description: A generalist search practice for professional, technical and managerial positions providing customized response to client needs with a focus on time and cost effective performance.

Salary Minimum: $65,000
Functions: Generalist
Industries: Generalist

Fell & Nicholson Technology Resources

1731 Embarcadero Rd., Ste. 210
Palo Alto, California 94303
(650) 856-9200
Fax: (650) 856-1328
Email: fellnich@aol.com

Key Contact - Specialty:
Mr. Robert M. Fell - *Senior executives, entertainment, information technology*
Mr. Jack F. Nicholson - *Senior executives, information technology*

Mr. Joe Shakes - *Senior executives, mid level, information technology*
Ms. Kerry O'Connor - *Information technology research*

Description: Specialists in structuring executive teams for start up, early stage and high growth established organizations. Major focus on data communications and telecommunications, software, internet, information services and leading edge technologies.

Salary Minimum: $100,000
Functions: General mgmt., Directors, Senior mgmt., Mktg. mgmt., Sales mgmt., CFO's, Engineering
Industries: Computer svcs., High tech, Software

Branches:
1921 Palomar Oaks Way #105
Carlsbad, California 92008
(760) 929-9200
Fax: (760) 929-9243
Email: fellnich@aol.com
Key Contact - Specialty:
Ms. Virgina Bradley - *Information technology research*

Fenwick Partners
57 Bedford St., Ste. 101
Lexington, Massachusetts 02173
(781) 862-3370
Fax: (781) 861-7546
Web: www.fenwickpartners.com

Key Contact - Specialty:
Ms. Patricia C. Kelleher - *Information technology*
Mr. Charles A. Polachi, Jr. - *Information technology*
Mr. William S. Starner - *Information technology*
Mr. Peter V. Polachi - *Information technology*
Ms. Debra Germaine - *Information technology*
Mr. Paul Moran - *Information technology*
Ms. Brigid Oliveri Siegel - *Information technology*
Mr. Cortland Stiles, Jr. - *Information technology*

Description: We are the leading retained executive search firm focused exclusively in the high technology markets. We specialize in senior level executive leadership positions across all functional disciplines. We serve the executive staffing needs of a wide spectrum of clients from Fortune 500 companies to emerging, high growth, venture capital backed organizations.

Salary Minimum: $150,000
Functions: Generalist, Directors, Senior mgmt., Mfg., Product dev., Production, Automation, Productivity, Sales & mktg., Mkt. research, Mktg. mgmt., Sales mgmt., Direct mktg., Customer svc., PR, Benefits, Personnel, Training, CFO's, M&A, IT, MIS mgmt., R&D, Engineering, Mgmt. consultants, Int'l.
Industries: Computer equip., Consumer electronics, Test/measurement equip., Venture cap., Computer svcs., Mgmt. consulting, New media, Telecoms, High tech, Software

Networks:
International Technology Partners

Ferneborg & Assoc., Inc.
1450 Fashion Island Blvd., Ste. 650
San Mateo, California 94404
(650) 577-0100
Fax: (650) 577-0122
Email: mailbox@execsearch.com
Web: www.execsearch.com

Key Contact - Specialty:
Mr. John R. Ferneborg
Mr. Jay W. Ferneborg
Mr. John C. Tincu

Description: Multi-specialty practice serving clients nationwide at the senior management/board level. All searches are conducted by principals highly experienced in a wide range of industries and functions.

Salary Minimum: $80,000
Functions: Generalist, General mgmt., Mfg., Sales & mktg., HR mgmt., Finance, IT
Industries: Generalist, Food/bev/tobacco, Retail, Entertainment, Communications, High tech, Software
Professional Associations: AESC

Networks:
The Hever Group

Fidelity Search Group, Inc. †
P.O. Box 466
Wayne, Pennsylvania 19087-0466
(610) 581-0590
Fax: (610) 581-0594
Email: fisearch@ix.netcom.com
Web: www.fidelitysearch.com

Key Contact - Specialty:
Ms. Beth C. Hare - *Financial, human resources*

Description: We are dedicated to high quality executive search.

Salary Minimum: $70,000
Functions: Senior mgmt., Middle mgmt., HR mgmt., CFO's, Cash mgmt., M&A
Industries: Mfg., Drugs mfg., Finance, Banking, Packaging, High tech, Healthcare

Financial Plus Management Solutions Inc. †
49 Wellington St. E., 4th Floor
The Gooderham Flatiron Bldg.
Toronto, Ontario M5E 1C9
Canada
(416) 594-9232
Fax: (416) 594-9233

Key Contact - Specialty:
Mr. Roman M. Skrypuch - *Financial services, sales*

Description: We are a firm which has built a reputation of providing high calibre individuals who bring added value to our clients.

Salary Minimum: $40,000
Functions: General mgmt., Sales & mktg., HR mgmt., Finance, IT
Industries: Finance, Accounting, Equip. svcs., Human resource svcs., High tech, Software

Financial Search Group, Inc. †
800 Turnpike St., Ste. 300
North Andover, Massachusetts 01845
(978) 682-4123
Fax: (978) 685-1048

Key Contact - Specialty:
Mr. Paul T. Luther - *Equipment leasing, financial services*

Description: Performs mid and senior level executive retained searches for corporate finance organizations, including money/investment management positions, equipment lessors and investment banks.

Salary Minimum: $50,000
Functions: Cash mgmt.
Industries: Invest. banking, Misc. financial, Equip. svcs.

Neil Fink Assoc.
900 N. Point St., Ste. 410
Ghirardelli Sq.
San Francisco, California 94109
(415) 441-3777
Fax: (415) 775-4925
Email: njf@well.com

Key Contact - Specialty:
Mr. Neil Fink

Description: We are a specialized executive search firm servicing the entertainment and communications technology industries. Our searches have covered almost every discipline, including general management, marketing, sales, creative, production, editorial, publishing and technical search assignments.
Functions: General mgmt., Product dev., Mktg. mgmt., Sales mgmt., Engineering, Graphic artists, Int'l.

Industries: Computer equip., Consumer electronics, Communications, Publishing, New media, Broadcast & Film, Software

Branches:
2002-A Guadalupe St., Ste. 177
Austin, Texas 78705
(512) 858-1942
Fax: (512) 858-5032
Key Contact - Specialty:
Ms. Abigail Tourish

Affiliates:
F.I.R.S.T. (First Interactive Recruiting Specialists)
Lipson & Co.

Finnegan & Assoc.
P.O. Box 1183
Palos Verdes Estates, California 90274-1938
(310) 375-8555
Email: finney8311@aol.com

Key Contact - Specialty:
Mr. Richard Finnegan
Mr. Gerald F. Finnegan

Description: A national and international management consulting/executive search firm specializing in recruiting CEO's, sales/marketing, financial, operations, development executives and managers. A venture capital fund allows investment in high growth companies.

Salary Minimum: $100,000
Functions: General mgmt., Mfg., Sales & mktg., CFO's, IT, Mgmt. consultants
Industries: Computer equip., Consumer electronics, Banking, Mgmt. consulting, Telecoms, High tech, Software

First Advisory Services Int'l., Inc.
(a division of The Systech Organization Inc.)
9735 Magledt Rd.
Baltimore, Maryland 21234
(410) 665-6033
(410) 223-2800
Fax: (410) 665-8843
Email: aasoma@aol.com

Key Contact - Specialty:
Mr. Walter J. Sistek - *Generalist*
Mr. George Hankins - *Financial services*
Mr. William M. Fleishman - *High technology, biotechnology*
Mr. Donald Shandler - *Human resource development*
Mr. Dana C. Goodrich, III - *Manufacturing*
Ms. Catherine E. Meehling - *University*
Mr. Jack M. Hawkins, Jr. - *Global financial, public sector*
Mr. Stephen McSpadden - *Legal, healthcare*
Mr. Joseph J. Diblasi - *High technology, biotechnology*

Description: Full service consulting corporation, offering global executive search services to new and existing clients.

Salary Minimum: $75,000
Functions: Generalist, Senior mgmt., Physicians, MIS mgmt., R&D, Engineering, Int'l.
Industries: Generalist, Finance, Hospitality, Mgmt. consulting, High tech, Biotech, Healthcare

Affiliates:
AIB Int'l. Consultants
Resolution Technology Ltd.

First Choice Search
P.O. Box 16574
Seattle, Washington 98116
(206) 938-1944

Key Contact - Specialty:
Ms. Michele J. Hale

Description: Partner with select group of clients to act as an extension of their human resource function for the term of a project. Assists in analyzing, researching and recommending organizational changes and needs in relation to the search assignment.

Salary Minimum: $50,000
Functions: Middle mgmt., Product dev., Plant mgmt., Quality, Training, R&D, Engineering
Industries: Agri/forestry/mining, Paper, Chemicals, Soap/perfume/cosmetics, Paints/petroleum products, Leather/stone/glass/clay

First Union Executive Search
301 S. College St., Ste. 2525
Charlotte, North Carolina 28288-0102
(704) 383-9969
Fax: (704) 383-9897
Email: gail.breen@firstunion.com

Key Contact - Specialty:
Mr. Harry W. Wilson - *Financial services*
Mr. Tom Miller

Description: Multi-disciplined recruiting at mid/senior levels for super-regional financial institutions.

Salary Minimum: $80,000
Functions: Generalist, Middle mgmt., Mktg. mgmt., Direct mktg., Finance, MIS mgmt., Minorities
Industries: Banking, Invest. banking, Brokers, Misc. financial, Mgmt. consulting

Howard Fischer Assoc. Int'l., Inc.
1800 JFK Blvd., 7th Floor
Philadelphia, Pennsylvania 19103
(215) 568-8363
Fax: (215) 568-4815
Email: howard.fischer@hfischer.com

Key Contact - Specialty:
Mr. Howard Fischer - *Directors, CEOs, telecommunications*
Mr. Evan Scott - *Information technology, consultants*

Description: To help our clients improve their lives and their businesses through leadership recruitment and selection.

Salary Minimum: $150,000
Functions: Directors, Senior mgmt., Mktg. mgmt., Sales mgmt., HR mgmt., CFO's, MIS mgmt., Mgmt. consultants, Minorities, Int'l.
Industries: Generalist, Chemicals, Drugs mfg., Misc. mfg., Mgmt. consulting, Broadcast & Film, Telecoms, Insurance, High tech, Biotech, Healthcare

Branches:
13750 San Pedro Ave., Ste. 810
San Antonio, Texas 78232
(210) 491-0844
Fax: (210) 494-4461
Key Contact - Specialty:
Mr. Howard Fischer - *Directors, CEOs, telecommunications*
Ms. Jani Stevenson - *Biotechnology, pharmaceutical, manufacturing*

Affiliates:
Delta Management Consultants GmbH
TASA International

Fisher & Assoc.
1063 Lenor Way
San Jose, California 95128
(408) 554-0156

Key Contact - Specialty:
Mr. Gary E. Fisher - *CEO's, marketing, sales executives*

Description: We are a retained executive search firm specializing in the placement of high tech marketing, sales and engineering executives.

Salary Minimum: $100,000
Functions: Directors, Senior mgmt., Middle mgmt., Mkt. research, Mktg. mgmt., Sales mgmt., Engineering
Industries: Computer equip., High tech, Software

The Fisher Group
250-6th Ave., SW
1500 Bow Valley Sq. IV
Calgary, Alberta T2P 3H7
Canada
(403) 251-3040
Email: fisher_group@msn.com

Key Contact - Specialty:
Mr. Mel V. Fisher - *Mid/senior management, sales & marketing, finance, information technology, information systems*

Description: Administrative and executive

search services for major multi-national, national, western companies in the information related industries. Technology, telecommunication, information systems and oil & gas.

Salary Minimum: $30,000
Functions: Generalist, Senior mgmt., Plant mgmt., Sales mgmt., CFO's, MIS mgmt., Network admin.
Industries: Generalist, Energy/utilities, Mfg., Printing, Communications, Telecoms, High tech

---

Fisher Personnel Management Services

1219 Morningside Drive
Manhattan Beach, California 90266
(310) 546-7507
Fax: (310) 546-7574
Email: fisherpm@gte.net

Key Contact - Specialty:
Mr. Neal Fisher - *Generalist, aircraft, aerospace, defense, consumer electronics, automotive*
Ms. Marilyn Hamilton - *Generalist, aircraft, aerospace, defense, consumer electronics, automotive*

Description: Services to aircraft, automotive, aerospace, consumer electronics, industrial and truck equipment, industrial materials, computer equipment and software manufacturing companies with functional management searches in engineering, manufacturing, sales, marketing, finance and human resources.

Salary Minimum: $75,000
Functions: General mgmt., Mfg., Materials, Sales & mktg., IT, R&D, Engineering
Industries: Metal products, Machinery/Appliances, Motor vehicles, Computer equip., Publishing, Aerospace, High tech
Professional Associations: IACPR

A. G. Fishkin & Assoc., Inc. †

P.O. Box 34413
Bethesda, Maryland 20827
(301) 983-0303
Fax: (301) 983-0415
Email: afishkin@us.net

Key Contact - Specialty:
Ms. Anita Fishkin - *Information technology, software engineering, telecommunications*
Mr. Paul F. Kallfelz - *Marketing, sales management*

Description: Recruit medium to senior level management for voice/data/wireless communications, software engineering, systems integration, information technology. Functions - sales/marketing management, product management, software development, information engineering, management consulting and program management.

Salary Minimum: $50,000
Functions: General mgmt., Mktg. mgmt., Sales mgmt., IT, Systems implem., Network admin., Mgmt. consultants
Industries: Computer svcs., Mgmt. consulting, New media, Telecoms, High tech, Software

---

Fitzgerald Associates

21 Muzzey St.
Lexington, Massachusetts 02173
(781) 863-1945
Fax: (781) 863-8872
Email: fitzsearch@aol.com

Key Contact - Specialty:
Mr. Geoffrey Fitzgerald - *Managed care, information management, demand management, disease management*
Ms. Diane Fitzgerald - *Managed care, clinical professionals, medical directors, medical management experts*

Description: Extensive, exclusive experience in recruiting managed care, healthcare information, demand/disease management and services professionals for HMO's, PHO's, hospitals, managed care firms, consulting firms and vendors to those organizations.

Salary Minimum: $60,000
Functions: Healthcare, IT
Industries: Pharmaceutical svcs., Insurance, Software, Healthcare

---

FitzGibbon & Assoc.

P.O. Box 1108
Media, Pennsylvania 19063
(610) 565-7566
Email: mfitzgi388@aol.com

Key Contact - Specialty:
Mr. Michael T. FitzGibbon - *Retail, direct mail*

Description: Specialist in sensitive searches requiring highest standards of professional representation of the corporations' image in retail and direct response industries.

Salary Minimum: $80,000
Functions: Senior mgmt., Middle mgmt., Distribution, Direct mktg., Customer svc., MIS mgmt.
Industries: Retail, Non-profits

The Flagship Group

C-8 Shipway Place, 13th St.
Boston, Massachusetts 02129
(617) 241-9000
Fax: (617) 242-1549

Key Contact - Specialty:
Ms. Anna Coppola - *Investment management, financial services*

Description: We are committed to providing our clients with outstanding, customized, quality service that delivers exceptional candidates.

Salary Minimum: $150,000
Functions: General mgmt., Sales & mktg., HR mgmt., Finance, Cash mgmt., Risk mgmt., IT
Industries: Finance

Robert M. Flanagan & Assoc., Ltd.

Fields Lane, JMKB Bldg.
North Salem, New York 10560
(914) 277-7210
Fax: (914) 244-8867
Email: RFlana8827@aol.com

Key Contact - Specialty:
Mr. Robert M. Flanagan - *General management, marketing & sales, investment management*
Ms. Amy Normann - *Marketing, sales*

Description: National practice built on reputation for doing quality search work at the senior levels of management. Ninety percent of business is with established client base.

Salary Minimum: $100,000
Functions: General mgmt., Mfg., Materials, Sales & mktg., HR mgmt., Finance, IT
Industries: Generalist, Mfg., Wholesale, Finance, Svcs., Communications, Packaging

---

Flesher & Assoc., Inc.

445 S. San Antonio Rd., Ste. 102
Los Altos, California 94022
(650) 917-9900
Fax: (650) 917-9903
Web: www.flesher.com

Key Contact - Specialty:
Ms. Susan Flesher - *High technology, public relations, corporate communications, marketing communications*

Description: We are an executive search firm specialzing in building strategic communications teams for high technology corporations and agencies. Includes middle and senior level management searches.
Functions: PR

Florapersonnel, Inc.

1740 Lake Markham Rd.
Sanford, Florida 32771-8964
(407) 320-8177
Fax: (407) 320-8083
Email: hortsearch@aol.com
Web: www.florapersonnel.com

Key Contact - Specialty:
Mr. Robert F. Zahra - *Horticulture*
Mr. Joseph Dalton - *Horticulture*

Description: International search firm for the greater horticulture industry. Retained only.
Industries: Agri/forestry/mining, Chemicals, Publishing, Environmental svcs., Biotech

J. G. Flynn & Assoc. Inc.
650 W. Georgia St., Ste. 1750
Vancouver, British Columbia V6B 4N7
Canada
(604) 689-7205
Fax: (604) 689-2584
Email: recruit@jgflynn.com
Web: www.jgflynn.com

Key Contact - Specialty:
Mr. Jerry Flynn - *Senior management, general management*

Description: We have established our firm as one of the pre-eminent search firms in North America - particularly in the mining and related consulting engineering industries. We don't rely on advertising, our research-based approach is thorough, efficient and discreet.

Salary Minimum: $70,000
Functions: Generalist, General mgmt., Mfg., HR mgmt., R&D, Engineering, Int'l.
Industries: Generalist, Agri/forestry/mining, Energy/utilities, Construction, Mfg., Advertising/PR, Aerospace

Flynn, Hannock, Inc.
1001 Farmington Ave.
West Hartford, Connecticut 06107-2121
(860) 521-5005
Fax: (860) 561-5294
Email: fhi@ntplx.net

Key Contact - Specialty:
Mr. Elwin W. Hannock, III - *General management, human resources, marketing, banking*
Mr. Ronald L. Gibbons - *Marketing, insurance, managed care, interim management*

Description: Executive search in banking, insurance, manufacturing, healthcare and utilities. The firm has a general practice coupled with a concentration in human resources. We also provide interim management services.

Salary Minimum: $90,000
Functions: Generalist, Senior mgmt., Middle mgmt., Mktg. mgmt., HR mgmt., Benefits, Training
Industries: Generalist, Energy/utilities, Mfg., Misc. mfg., Banking, Insurance, Healthcare

Branches:
P.O. Box 8027
Stamford, Connecticut 06905
(203) 357-0009
Fax: (203) 961-8141

Key Contact - Specialty:
Mr. Richard Sandor - *Human resources, generalist*

Affiliates:
GMS Consultancy Ltd.

Fogec Consultants, Inc.
P.O. Box 28806
Milwaukee, Wisconsin 53228
(414) 427-0690
Fax: (414) 427-0691
Email: tfogec@execpc.com
Web: www.recruitersonline.com/414-427-0690.html

Key Contact - Specialty:
Mr. Thomas G. Fogec - *Banking, finance & accounting, human resources*

Description: Specialize in executive, managerial and professional positions across industry lines. Extensive client-side experience provides for highly personalized service and strong sensitivity to client needs.

Salary Minimum: $50,000
Functions: Quality, Benefits, Personnel, Budgeting, Cash mgmt., Credit, Systems dev.
Industries: Finance, Banking, Invest. banking, Brokers, Computer svcs., Accounting, Human resource svcs.

Foley Proctor Yoskowitz
One Cattano Ave.
Morristown, New Jersey 07960-6820
(973) 605-1000
Fax: (973) 605-1020
Email: fpassoc@aol.com

Key Contact - Specialty:
Mr. Richard W. Proctor - *Healthcare executives, middle management, physicians (PCP's)*
Mrs. Reggie Yoskowitz - *Healthcare executives, senior physician executives (department chairs)*

Description: The three partners are trained hospital executives with a 90% repeat business in recruiting CEOs, senior administrators, physician chairmen/executives, product line/department managers, managed care/practice administrators and staff physicians.

Salary Minimum: $50,000
Functions: Physicians, Nurses, Allied health, Health admin., CFO's, MIS mgmt., Minorities
Industries: Accounting, Human resource svcs., Advertising/PR, Insurance, Healthcare
Professional Associations: IACPR

Branches:
24 E. 39th St.
New York, New York 10016
(212) 928-1110

Key Contact - Specialty:
Mr. Thomas J. Foley - *Senior healthcare executives, senior physicians (department chairs)*

L. W. Foote Co.
110-110th Ave. NE, Ste. 603
Bellevue, Washington 98004-5840
(425) 451-1660
Fax: (425) 451-1535
Email: email@lwfoote.com
Web: www.lwfoote.com

Key Contact - Specialty:
Mr. Leland W. Foote
Mr. James E. Bloomer

Description: We have recruited exceptional individuals for clients in a broad range of industries with emphasis in technology (both hardware and software), consumer products and telecommunications.

Salary Minimum: $80,000
Functions: Generalist
Industries: Food/bev/tobacco, Textiles/apparel, Computer equip., Computer svcs., Telecoms, High tech, Software
Professional Associations: AESC

The Forbes Group
3475 Lenox Rd. NE, Ste. 400
Atlanta, Georgia 30326
(404) 264-0600
Fax: (404) 264-9022
Email: search@theforbesgroup.com
Web: www.theforbesgroup.com

Key Contact - Specialty:
Ms. Kathy Forbes - *Senior management, technology companies*

Description: We are a retained executive search firm which exclusively recruits senior management for emerging technology companies.

Salary Minimum: $130,000
Functions: Senior mgmt.
Industries: High tech, Software

The Ford Group, Inc.
485 Devon Park Drive, Ste. 110
Wayne, Pennsylvania 19087
(610) 975-9007
Fax: (610) 975-9008
Web: www.thefordgroup.com

Key Contact - Specialty:
Ms. Sandra D. Ford - *Management consulting, finance, human resources, information systems*

Description: We are a boutique firm specializing in retained executive search for international management consulting firms and selected general management positions for industry leaders.

Salary Minimum: $100,000

Functions: Senior mgmt., HR mgmt., Finance, CFO's, MIS mgmt., Systems implem., Mgmt. consultants
Industries: Drugs mfg., Finance, Mgmt. consulting, Human resource svcs., Telecoms, High tech, Healthcare

Forray Assoc., Inc.

950 Third Ave., 16th Floor
New York, New York 10022
(212) 279-0404
Fax: (212) 279-4223

Key Contact - Specialty:
Ms. Karen Forray
Ms. Marni Layton

Description: Specialize in finance, marketing and sales - all industries - mid to senior level management - long standing reputation with Fortune 500 companies and smaller, entrepreneurial environments.

Salary Minimum: $80,000
Functions: Directors, Senior mgmt., Middle mgmt., Mkt. research, Mktg. mgmt., CFO's, Budgeting
Industries: Generalist

F-O-R-T-U-N-E Personnel Consultants of Boise

960 Broadway Ave., Ste. 540
Boise, Idaho 83706
(208) 343-5190
Fax: (208) 343-6067
Email: fortune@dmi.net

Key Contact - Specialty:
Mr. Garn Christensen - *Pulp & paper, general management*
Ms. Vicki Norrie - *Pulp & paper*
Mr. V. Thomas Rose - *Pulp & paper*
Ms. Sandra K. Bishop - *Banking, financial*

Description: Consultants in executive search for middle and top management and boards of directors positions. Firm is composed of former senior executives from Fortune 500 companies.

Salary Minimum: $80,000
Functions: Directors, Senior mgmt., Automation, Plant mgmt., HR mgmt., MIS mgmt., Engineering
Industries: Food/bev/tobacco, Paper, Motor vehicles, Banking, Invest. banking, Human resource svcs., High tech

Fortune Group Int'l., Inc. †

1410 W. Street Rd.
Warminster, Pennsylvania 18974
(215) 675-3100
Fax: (215) 675-3080
Email: search@fortunegroup.com
Web: fortunegroup.com

Key Contact - Specialty:
Mr. Michael G. Strand - *Pharmaceutical, medical device, biotechnology*
Ms. Roseann Pfannenstiel - *Healthcare, pharmaceutical*
Mr. Chris Adams - *Engineering, operations, business development*
Ms. Lauren Adams - *Pharmaceutical, CRO, medical device*
Ms. Patricia Wells - *Biostatistics, data management, information systems*
Dr. Beverlee Ciccone - *Regulatory affairs, quality assurance*

Description: We are dedicated to finding individuals who will be the leaders of your firm in the future. Primary focus is the pharmaceutical, CRO, chemical, medical devices and communications markets.

Salary Minimum: $75,000
Functions: Senior mgmt., Middle mgmt., Production, Sales & mktg., IT, Engineering, Int'l.
Industries: Chemicals, Drugs mfg., Medical devices, Pharmaceutical svcs., Telecoms, High tech, Biotech

Foster Partners
(an alliance firm of KPMG Peat Marwick LLP)

570 Lexington Ave., 14th Floor
New York, New York 10022
(212) 893-2300
Fax: (212) 893-2309
Email: fosterp@kpmg.com

Key Contact - Specialty:
Mr. Dwight E. Foster - *International*
Ms. Karen Weiss - *International*
Ms. Gail Amsterdam - *Retail*
Mr. Gregory Frumess - *Banking, investment services*
Ms. Barbara Kolburne - *Information, communications and entertainment*
Mr. Robert T. Hart - *Fortune 100 & 500 corporations*

Description: We were formed in January 1990 through a management buyout of KPMG Peat Marwick's executive search practice, which was established in 1962. We conduct senior level search assignments domestically and internationally and across all industry disciplines, including general management, finance, banking and capital markets and retail.

Salary Minimum: $90,000
Functions: Generalist, General mgmt., Directors, Senior mgmt., Middle mgmt., Admin. svcs., Mfg., Product dev., Production, Automation, Plant mgmt., Quality, Productivity, Materials, Purchasing, Materials Plng., Distribution, Packaging, Healthcare, Physicians, Nurses, Allied health, Health admin., Advertising, Mkt. research, Mktg. mgmt., Sales mgmt., Direct mktg., Customer svc., PR, HR mgmt., Benefits, Personnel, Training, Finance, CFO's, Budgeting, Cash mgmt., Credit, Taxes, M&A, Risk mgmt., IT, MIS mgmt., Systems anal., Systems dev., Systems implem., Systems support, R&D, Engineering, Specialized services, Mgmt. consultants, Minorities, Non-profits, Environmentalists, Architects, Technicians, Attorneys, Graphic artists, Int'l.
Industries: Generalist, Agri/forestry/mining, Energy/utilities, Construction, Food/bev/tobacco, Textiles/apparel, Lumber/furniture, Paper, Printing, Chemicals, Soap/perfume/cosmetics, Drugs mfg., Medical devices, Plastics/rubber, Paints/petroleum products, Leather/stone/glass/clay, Metal products, Machinery/Appliances, Motor vehicles, Computer equip., Consumer electronics, Test/measurement equip., Misc. mfg., Transportation, Wholesale, Retail, Finance, Banking, Invest. banking, Brokers, Venture cap., Misc. financial, Hospitality, Entertainment, Non-profits, Higher ed., Pharmaceutical svcs., Legal, Computer svcs., Accounting, Equip. svcs., Mgmt. consulting, Human resource svcs., Law enfcmt., Communications, Advertising/PR, Publishing, New media, Broadcast & Film, Telecoms, Government, Defense, Environmental svcs., Haz. waste, Aerospace, Packaging, Insurance, Real estate, High tech, Software, Biotech, Healthcare, Non-classifiable industries

Branches:
2001 M St. NW
Washington, District of Columbia 20036
(202) 467-3597
Fax: (202) 785-0683
Key Contact - Specialty:
Mr. Dann P. Stringer - *High technology*
Mr. Pete Metzger - *Trade associations, corporate communications, defense*

One Biscayne Twr.
2 S. Biscayne Blvd., Ste. 2900
Miami, Florida 33131
(305) 577-3684
Fax: (305) 577-3682
Key Contact - Specialty:
Mr. Mark E. Young - *Agribusiness*

303 Peachtree St. NE, Ste. 2000
Atlanta, Georgia 30308
(404) 222-3440
Fax: (404) 221-2396
Key Contact - Specialty:
Mr. Gerald J. Bump - *Generalist*

Peat Marwick Plaza
303 E. Wacker Drive, 26th Floor
Chicago, Illinois 60601-5255
(312) 938-1201
Fax: (312) 938-0449
Key Contact - Specialty:
Mr. Terry Burns - *Financial services*

2800 Two First Union Ctr.
Charlotte, North Carolina 28282
(704) 335-5511
Fax: (704) 335-5357
Key Contact - Specialty:
Mr. Jeffrey M. Siegrist - *Pulp & paper*

200 Crescent Court, Ste. 300
Dallas, Texas 75201-1885
(214) 754-2241
Fax: (214) 754-2104
Key Contact - Specialty:
Mr. William Rowe - *High technology, financial services*
Mr. Rod McNahan - *Technology*

International Branches:
Birmingham

Affiliates:
3P Executive Search
Ibarra, Molina, Foster Partners, S.A. de C.V.
Knight Consulting Group Limited
KPMG
PEAT Executive Search AG
Peat Marwick Management Consultants pte ltd.
PMM Management Consultants GmbH
Daniel Porte Consultants
Eliane Volpert Executive Search

Foy, Schneid & Daniel, Inc.

555 Madison Ave., 12th Floor
New York, New York 10022
(212) 980-2525

Key Contact - Specialty:
Mr. James C. Foy
Ms. Beverly R. Daniel - *Management, manufacturing, chemicals, logistics, market information & research*

Description: Professional executive search practice with targeted experience in most industries. The ability and experience of our consultants ensures that clients achieve efficient and quality results.

Salary Minimum: $75,000
Functions: Generalist, Senior mgmt., Plant mgmt., Distribution, Mkt. research, HR mgmt., MIS mgmt.
Industries: Food/bev/tobacco, Chemicals, Misc. mfg., Retail, Non-profits, Mgmt. consulting, New media

Franchise Recruiters Ltd.

3500 Innsbruck
Lincolnshire Country Club
Crete, Illinois 60417
(708) 757-5595
Fax: (708) 758-8222
Email: franchise@worldnet.att.net

Key Contact - Specialty:
Mr. Jerry C. Wilkerson - *Franchise executives*

Description: For franchisors with franchise experienced candidates only. Candidates guaranteed one year unconditionally. Excellent corporate client references. Specialties: candidates for sales and marketing, operations, training, real estate, financial, legal, executive, international development.

Salary Minimum: $40,000
Functions: Directors, Senior mgmt., Middle mgmt., Sales mgmt., IT, Int'l.

Branches:
20 Holly St., Ste. 203
Toronto, Ontario M4S 3B1
Canada
(416) 322-5730
Fax: (416) 363-8474
Key Contact - Specialty:
Mr. George Kinzie - *Franchising management*

Francis & Assoc.

6923 Vista Drive
West Des Moines, Iowa 50266
(515) 221-9800
Fax: (515) 221-9806
Email: FranSearch@aol.com

Key Contact - Specialty:
Mr. Dwaine Francis
Ms. N. Kay Francis
Ms. Karen Novak

Description: Very professional firm, known for high quality and timely work. Work done on national and international basis.

Salary Minimum: $100,000
Functions: Generalist
Industries: Generalist
Professional Associations: AESC

Neil Frank & Co.

P.O. Box 3570
Redondo Beach, California 90277-1570
(310) 937-8950
Fax: (310) 937-9477
Email: neilnick@aol.com
Web: neilfrank.com

Key Contact - Specialty:
Mr. Neil Frank - *Public relations, corporate communications, marketing communications*

Description: Functional specialist in public relations, corporate communications, and marketing communications. Retained solo practice.

Salary Minimum: $50,000
Functions: PR
Industries: Advertising/PR

Franklin Allen Consultants, Ltd.

401 Franklin Ave., Ste. 102
Garden City, New York 11530-5943
(516) 248-4511
Fax: (516) 294-6646
Web: frnklnalln@aol.com

Key Contact - Specialty:
Mr. Howard F. Roher - *Senior management, board directors*
Mr. Allen B. Kupchik - *Healthcare*

Description: We are a generalist firm in business for over 16 years. We recruit for middle management and senior management positions.
Functions: Senior mgmt., Middle mgmt., Health admin., Mktg. mgmt., CFO's, M&A, R&D
Industries: Soap/perfume/cosmetics, Drugs mfg., Invest. banking, Hospitality, Pharmaceutical svcs., Biotech, Healthcare

The Franklin Search Group, Inc./Medzilla

(Firm declined to update.)
14522 54th Place W.
Edmonds, Washington 98026-3811
(425) 742-4292
Email: info@medzilla.com
Web: www.medzilla.com

Key Contact - Specialty:
Dr. Franklin A. Heasley - *Management positions requiring technical expertise*

Description: Specialized in the recruitment of executives for the biotechnical, pharmaceutical and medical device industries.

Salary Minimum: $50,000
Functions: Directors, Senior mgmt., Middle mgmt., Physicians, Nurses, Mktg. mgmt., R&D
Industries: Drugs mfg., Medical devices, Venture cap., Non-profits, Biotech, Healthcare

KS Frary & Assoc.

One Salem Green, Ste. 403
Salem, Massachusetts 01970
(978) 741-5201
Fax: (978) 741-5203
Email: ksfrary@tiac.net
Web: www.ksfrary.com

Key Contact - Specialty:
Mr. Kevin S. Frary - *Manufacturing industries, high technology*
Mr. Ted L. Hubbard - *Manufacturing industries, financial services*

Description: Aggressive, ethical full service firm with proven assessment skills, strong customer focus and in-depth research capabilities with a record of recruiting leaders who produce results.

Salary Minimum: $75,000
Functions: Senior mgmt., Plant mgmt., Mktg. mgmt., Sales mgmt., CFO's, MIS mgmt., Engineering
Industries: Food/bev/tobacco, Medical devices, Computer equip., Test/measurement equip., Misc. mfg., High tech, Software

Affiliates:
Travis & Co., Inc.

P. N. French Assoc., Inc.
126 Noell Farm Rd.
Carlisle, Massachusetts 01741
(978) 369-4569

Key Contact - Specialty:
Mr. Peter N. French - *Non-profit*

Description: Executive search for colleges and universities and related not-for-profit organizations. Conduct searches in a variety of functional areas, but specialize in searches for senior administrators. Excellent reputation for confidentiality.

Salary Minimum: $60,000
Functions: Generalist, Senior mgmt., Purchasing, CFO's, MIS mgmt., Engineering, Non-profits
Industries: Energy/utilities, Entertainment, Non-profits, Higher ed., Computer svcs., Broadcast & Film

---

Friedman Eisenstein Raemer & Schwartz, LLP †
401 N. Michigan Ave., Ste. 2600
Chicago, Illinois 60611
(312) 245-1729
Fax: (312) 644-9866
Email: srodriquez@fers.com
Web: www.fers.com

Key Contact - Specialty:
Ms. Susan Raemer-Rodriguez - *Financial*

Description: We represent mostly small to medium sized, privately or closely held businesses, in a wide variety of industry and service areas. We specialized in financial and accounting, human resources, manufacturing operations and technology related positions. Salary ranges are from 40k -125k.

Salary Minimum: $40,000
Functions: Plant mgmt., Sales mgmt., HR mgmt., CFO's, Budgeting, MIS mgmt., Network admin.
Industries: Construction, Plastics/rubber, Metal products, Misc. financial, Accounting, Human resource svcs., Telecoms

---

Gerald Frisch Assoc., Inc.
181 E. 73rd St.
New York, New York 10021
(212) 737-4810

Key Contact - Specialty:
Mr. Gerald Frisch - *General management, MIS*

Description: Offering the exclusive GFA planned executive search system.

Salary Minimum: $70,000
Functions: Senior mgmt., Mktg. mgmt., Customer svc., PR, MIS mgmt., Mgmt. consultants
Industries: Food/bev/tobacco, Drugs mfg., Banking, Invest. banking, Pharmaceutical svcs., Mgmt. consulting, Publishing

---

Furlong Search, Inc.
550 Tyndall St., #11
Los Altos, California 94022
(650) 856-8484
Fax: (650) 941-7059
Email: jwfsearch@aol.com

Key Contact - Specialty:
Mr. James W. Furlong

Description: Oldest retained search firm serving the electronic industry exclusively, filling middle managers to CEO positions in all disciplines.

Salary Minimum: $120,000
Functions: Generalist
Industries: Computer equip., Consumer electronics, Test/measurement equip., High tech, Software

Branches:
19312 Romar St.
Northridge, California 91324
(818) 885-7044
Fax: (818) 885-7588
Key Contact - Specialty:
Mr. James W. Furlong

634 E. Main St.
Hillsboro, Oregon 97123
(503) 640-3221
Fax: (503) 640-3897
Key Contact - Specialty:
Mr. James W. Furlong

C. F. Furr & Co.
6135 Park S. Drive, Ste. 104
Charlotte, North Carolina 28210
(704) 552-6868
Fax: (704) 554-1830
Email: cffurrco@mindspring.com

Key Contact - Specialty:
Mr. C. Franklin Furr - *Financial services, healthcare, generalist*

Description: History of achieving excellent results for clients, commitment to successful search completion, principal involvement in every search, exceptional research capabilities, thorough sourcing and screening, comprehensive candidate reports, disciplined communications and follow through, replacement search guarantee.

Salary Minimum: $50,000
Functions: Generalist, Middle mgmt., Sales mgmt., Benefits, Cash mgmt., MIS mgmt.
Industries: Generalist, Finance, Banking, Brokers, Misc. financial, Pharmaceutical svcs., Healthcare

---

The Furst Group, Inc.
1639 N. Alpine Rd.
Rockford, Illinois 61107
(815) 229-7800
Fax: (815) 394-0239
Email: tom@furstsearch.com
Web: www.furstsearch.com

Key Contact - Specialty:
Mr. Thomas C. Furst
Dr. Martin E. Pschirrer
Ms. Lynn M. Momberger
Mr. Steven J. Bois
Ms. Lori M. Burke

Description: Retained recruiting and human resource consulting within manufacturing, financial and service marketplaces.

Salary Minimum: $50,000
Functions: Senior mgmt., Mfg., Materials, Sales mgmt., HR mgmt., CFO's, Engineering
Industries: Energy/utilities, Food/bev/tobacco, Plastics/rubber, Metal products, Machinery/Appliances, Computer equip., Banking

---

Furst Group/MPI
555 S. Perryville Rd.
Rockford, Illinois 61108-2509
(815) 229-9111
Fax: (815) 229-8926
Web: www.furstgroup.com

Key Contact - Specialty:
Mr. J. Robert Clarke - *Healthcare*
Mr. Tyler P. Pratt - *Healthcare*
Ms. Sherrie L. Barch - *Healthcare*
Mr. Dennis L. Pankratz - *Healthcare*
Mr. Brad L. Newpoff - *Healthcare*

Description: Specialists in medical management, cost containment and health insurance markets including HMO's, PPO's, medical group practices, indemnity, hospital, pharmacy, home health and ancillary markets.

Salary Minimum: $100,000
Functions: Senior mgmt., Physicians, Health admin., Sales & mktg., HR mgmt., CFO's, MIS mgmt.
Industries: Pharmaceutical svcs., Mgmt. consulting, Insurance, Healthcare

Branches:
8009 34th Ave., Ste. 1450
Riverview Office Twr.
Minneapolis, Minnesota 55425-1608
(612) 851-9213
Fax: (612) 851-9232
Web: www.furstgroup.com
Key Contact - Specialty:
Mr. Brad J. Chandler - *Healthcare*
Mr. Timothy Frischman - *Healthcare*

Futures Int'l. †

120 Post Rd W., Ste. 202
Westport, Connecticut 06880
(203) 221-6488
Fax: (203) 221-6499
Email: futuresintl.com

Key Contact - Specialty:
Mr. Richard Stein

Description: Based in NY, CT and London, we have a totally integrated approach to recruitment. Used extensively for strategic advisory, communication analysis, organizational development. Work with only a handful of elite clients to board level.
Functions: Risk mgmt.
Industries: Invest. banking, Brokers, Misc. financial

International Branches:
London

GAAP Inc.

1524 Summerhill
Montreal, Quebec H3H 1B9
Canada
(514) 935-3253
Fax: (514) 935-0852
Email: ehughes@gaapsearch.com

Key Contact - Specialty:
Mr. Emerson Hughes - *Senior executives*
Mr. Steve Johnstone - *Senior executives*
Ms. Shawn Davidson - *Senior executives*
Mr. John Hussey - *Senior executives*
Ms. Jacqueline Gilbert - *Middle management*

Description: A boutique senior level retainer executive search firm serving a select list of Fortune 100 companies coast to coast in North America.

Salary Minimum: $75,000
Functions: Directors, Senior mgmt., Plant mgmt., Distribution, Mktg. mgmt., CFO's, MIS mgmt.
Industries: Generalist, Agri/forestry/mining, Energy/utilities, Computer equip., Telecoms, High tech, Non-classifiable industries

Branches:
114 Lakeshore Rd. E.
Oakville, Ontario L6J 6N2
Canada
(905) 337-0155
Fax: (905) 337-0157
Email: lleduc@gaapsearch.com
Key Contact - Specialty:
Ms. Lauren Leduc - *Senior executives*

Gable Healthcare Group, Inc. †

(Firm declined to update.)
4701 N. Federal Hwy., Ste. 445, Box C-14
Lighthouse Point, Florida 33064
(954) 942-7878

Key Contact - Specialty:
Ms. Jacqueline S. Gable - *Healthcare*

Description: A comprehensive physician and healthcare executive recruiting firm committed to providing quality candidates which meet client's specific needs. Our goal is to assist you in finding the best candidate possible.

Salary Minimum: $50,000
Functions: Physicians, Nurses, Allied health, Health admin.
Industries: Healthcare

Gaffney Management Consultants

35 N. Brandon Drive
Glendale Heights, Illinois 60139-2087
(630) 307-3380
Fax: (630) 307-3381
Email: gaffneymgt@aol.com

Key Contact - Specialty:
Mr. Keith Gaffney - *Middle management, directors, vice presidents, generalist (functional)*
Mr. William Gaffney - *Executive level, presidents, CEOs, vice presidents*

Description: Retained executive search firm servicing the needs of major manufacturing and engineering related organizations both public and private. Effective recruitment in the areas of general management, manufacturing operations, quality, purchasing/materials, finance/accounting, information technology/MIS, engineering, human resources, sales and marketing.

Salary Minimum: $50,000
Functions: General mgmt., Mfg., Materials, Sales & mktg., HR mgmt., Finance, Engineering
Industries: Generalist, Construction, Chemicals, Metal products, Machinery/ Appliances, Motor vehicles, Consumer electronics

Gahan Assoc. †

11 Ambrose Ave.
Malverne, New York 11565
(516) 593-3621
Fax: (516) 593-3625

Key Contact - Specialty:
Mrs. Ann M. Gahan - *Management consultants, financial executives*
Mr. Thomas M. Gahan - *Senior management, middle management, marketing, financial executives*
Ms. Carolyn M. Gahan - *Human resource management, non-profit executives, middle management*
Mr. Anthony Cioffoletti - *Information technology*

Description: Over twenty years successful recruiting experience to corporate and management consulting clients.

Salary Minimum: $80,000
Functions: Generalist, Middle mgmt., Direct mktg., HR mgmt., Risk mgmt., MIS mgmt., Non-profits
Industries: Finance, Svcs., Pharmaceutical svcs., Mgmt. consulting, Insurance, High tech, Healthcare

Affiliates:
BTAG

Gaines & Assoc. Int'l., Inc.

650 N. Dearborn St., Ste. 450
Chicago, Illinois 60610
(312) 654-2900
Fax: (312) 654-2903
Email: general@gainesintl.com
Web: www.gainesintl.com

Key Contact - Specialty:
Ms. Donna Gaines - *Architecture, interior design, construction, real estate, engineering*

Description: We are a professional search firm specializing in the design and building industries. We conduct in-depth searches with a level of expertise founded on years of experience. We dedicate ourselves to providing timely effective solutions by assessing needs, finding the right individuals and facilitating communications that benefit both employer and candidate.

Salary Minimum: $50,000
Functions: Directors, Senior mgmt., Production, Mktg. mgmt., Engineering, Architects, Graphic artists
Industries: Generalist, Construction, Retail, Real estate, Non-classifiable industries

Branches:
2221 Peachtree Rd., Ste. P-33
Atlanta, Georgia 30309
(404) 355-7008
Fax: (404) 355-9142
Key Contact - Specialty:
Mr. Grant Heath
Ms. Peggy Johnson

4108 Rancho Alegre NW
Albuquerque, New Mexico 87120
(505) 890-2900
Fax: (505) 890-5110
Key Contact - Specialty:
Ms. Cathie Kempf

300 Park Ave., 17th Floor
New York, New York 10022
(212) 721-7689
Fax: (212) 721-7217
Key Contact - Specialty:
Ms. Tracy McNair

Jay Gaines & Company, Inc.

450 Park Ave.
New York, New York 10022
(212) 308-9222
Fax: (212) 308-5146

Email: jgandco@jaygaines.com

Key Contact - Specialty:
Mr. Jay Gaines - *General management, information technology*
Mr. Tarin Anwar - *Investment banking, capital markets, risk management, investment management*
Ms. Valerie Germain - *Information technology, operations*
Ms. Marie Rice - *Generalist*
Ms. Susan Schaller - *Generalist*
Mr. Dick Kurth

Description: We are a generalist executive search firm that recruits senior-level management primarily in the areas of financial services, high technology, information technology, management consulting and publishing, among others.

Salary Minimum: $200,000
Functions: Generalist, Senior mgmt., Sales & mktg., HR mgmt., Finance, IT, Mgmt. consultants
Industries: Generalist, Mfg., Finance, Communications, Insurance, High tech, Software
Professional Associations: AESC

Gaming Consultants, Inc.
P.O. Box 641247
Kenner, Louisiana 70064
(504) 469-9894

Key Contact - Specialty:
Mr. Frank H. Rutherford - *Gaming*

Description: 20 years in executive search, highly confidential, top management positions, within the gaming industry exclusively; hotels, clubs and casinos. National and international clients preferred, but not limited to candidates with gaming credentials.

Salary Minimum: $100,000
Functions: Senior mgmt., Purchasing, Advertising, Mktg. mgmt., Benefits, CFO's, MIS mgmt.
Industries: Hospitality, Entertainment

Gans, Gans & Assoc., Inc.
4129 E. Fowler Ave.
Tampa, Florida 33617
(813) 971-6501
Fax: (813) 971-6966
Email: mkelly@gansgans.com
Web: www.gansgans.com

Key Contact - Specialty:
Ms. Simone Gans Barefield - *Management consultants, medical healthcare, information technology, specialized services*

Description: We specialize in diversity search, recruiting individuals of diverse backgrounds, including women and people of various ethnic and racial backgrounds, for executive, management, professional, technical and sales positions.

Salary Minimum: $75,000
Functions: Senior mgmt., CFO's, MIS mgmt., Specialized services, Mgmt. consultants
Industries: Mgmt. consulting, Communications, Insurance, Healthcare

Branches:
175 N. Franklin, Ste. 401
Chicago, Illinois 60606
(312) 357-9600
Fax: (312) 357-9613
Email: mkelly@gansgans.com
Key Contact - Specialty:
Mr. George Wright Anderson - *Information technology, finance, government*

107 N. 22nd St.
Philadelphia, Pennsylvania 19103
(215) 751-1724
Fax: (215) 751-1730
Email: mkelly@gansgans.com
Key Contact - Specialty:
Mr. Ernest Barefield - *Accounting & finance, specialized services, general management, information technology*

Affiliates:
GGA Contract Staffing Services

W. N. Garbarini & Assoc.
961 Cherokee Court
Westfield, New Jersey 07090
(908) 232-2737
Fax: (908) 232-2326

Key Contact - Specialty:
Mr. William N. Garbarini
Ms. Linda Lauchiere

Description: Boutique general search firm with unique personalized service approach.

Salary Minimum: $75,000
Functions: Generalist, Senior mgmt., Mktg. mgmt., Sales mgmt., CFO's, MIS mgmt., R&D
Industries: Generalist, Food/bev/tobacco, Medical devices, Pharmaceutical svcs., Healthcare

---

Gardiner, Townsend & Assoc.
101 E. 52nd St.
New York, New York 10022
(212) 230-1889
Fax: (212) 838-0424

Key Contact - Specialty:
Mr. E. Nicholas P. Gardiner - *Financial services, energy, communications, media*
Mr. John W. Townsend - *Financial services*

Description: We provide our clients with the best available candidates for top level recruitment regardless of geographic location with a single consultant in charge from start to finish across int'l. barriers using advanced information technology, global industry expertise, cross-cultural judgement.

Salary Minimum: $180,000
Functions: Senior mgmt., Mkt. research, CFO's, M&A, MIS mgmt., Mgmt. consultants, Int'l.
Industries: Energy/utilities, Banking, Invest. banking, Mgmt. consulting, Publishing, Broadcast & Film, Telecoms
Professional Associations: AESC

Gardner-Ross Assoc., Inc.
300 Madison Ave.
New York, New York 10017
(212) 687-6615

Key Contact - Specialty:
Mr. Marvin Gardner
Ms. Elsa Ross - *Publishing, service, new media*
Mr. Al Griffin - *High technology, packaging, printing*

Description: We are a generalist firm with several sub-specialties such as packaging, magazine publishing, printing, healthcare and high technology. Our assignments range from CEO, COO, marketing/sales management and most upper management positions.

Salary Minimum: $75,000
Functions: Middle mgmt., Plant mgmt., Health admin., Direct mktg., IT, MIS mgmt., Mgmt. consultants
Industries: Drugs mfg., Misc. mfg., Finance, Publishing, Packaging, High tech, Software

---

Dick Garland Consultants
31 E. 32nd St.
New York, New York 10016
(212) 481-8484
Fax: (212) 481-9582

Key Contact - Specialty:
Mr. Dick Garland - *Credit card*

Description: We never fail. 100% completion rate. Clients deal solely with the owner.
Functions: Sales mgmt., Budgeting
Industries: Misc. financial, Non-classifiable industries

Branches:
5 Crest Drive
White Plains, New York 10607
(914) 347-5525
Fax: (914) 347-5280
Key Contact - Specialty:
Mr. Dick Garland - *Credit card*

The Garms Group
12 Ferndale Rd.
Barrington, Illinois 60010
(847) 382-7200
Fax: (847) 382-7222

Email: dangarms@garms.com
Web: www.garms.com

Key Contact - Specialty:
Mr. Daniel S. Garms
Mr. Val Babic

Description: Recruitment specialists for start-up and emerging high technology companies focused in computer graphics, internet, CAD, database, client server, product data management (PDM) and imaging related technologies.

Salary Minimum: $75,000
Functions: General mgmt., Mfg., Sales & mktg., IT, R&D, Engineering, Mgmt. consultants
Industries: Computer equip., Consumer electronics, Computer svcs., New media, Telecoms, High tech, Software

The Garret Group †

342 Parsippany Rd.
Parsippany, New Jersey 07054
(973) 884-0711
Fax: (973) 884-1307
Email: jwharton@staffing.net

Key Contact - Specialty:
Mr. John P. Wharton - *Engineering, operations*
Mr. Bernd Stecker - *Engineering, operations*

Description: Specialists in recruiting engineering, operations, quality assurance and regulatory affairs professionals for the pharmaceutical, medical device and consumer packaged goods industries.

Salary Minimum: $50,000
Functions: Product dev., Production, Plant mgmt., Quality, R&D, Engineering
Industries: Food/bev/tobacco, Soap/perfume/cosmetics, Drugs mfg., Medical devices, Consumer electronics, Packaging, Biotech

Branches:
6610 Gasparilla Pines Blvd., Unit 235
Englewood, Florida 34224
(941) 698-0118
Fax: (941) 698-1158
Key Contact - Specialty:
Mr. James N. Finn - *Engineering*

International Branches:
Lyngby

Garrett Assoc. Inc.

P.O. Box 53359
Atlanta, Georgia 30355
(404) 364-0001
Fax: (404) 364-0726
Email: lgarr95868@aol.com

Key Contact - Specialty:
Ms. Linda M. Garrett - *Healthcare*
Mr. Donald L. Garrett - *Healthcare*
Ms. Janis Morrison - *Healthcare*

Description: Coast to coast healthcare/executive search. Outside healthcare candidates generally come from banking, hotels, consulting, marketing administration and MIS.

Salary Minimum: $50,000
Functions: Senior mgmt., Nurses, Health admin., CFO's, MIS mgmt., Mgmt. consultants, Minorities
Industries: Healthcare

The Garrison Organization

1501 42nd St.
One Corporate Place, Ste. 468
Des Moines, Iowa 50266
(515) 223-8755
Fax: (515) 223-0996

Key Contact - Specialty:
Mr. Ed Garrison - *Life insurance sales, management, marketing*
Mr. Dwight Liggett

Description: Executive recruiting in and for the life insurance industry, primarily specialist in marketing agency and marketing officers, agency managers. Advanced underwriting attorneys, training specialist.

Salary Minimum: $60,000
Functions: Middle mgmt., Sales mgmt.
Industries: Insurance

Branches:
400 South Colorado Blvd., Ste. 600
Denver, Colorado 80222
(303) 394-9877
Key Contact - Specialty:
Mr. Randall Garrison

Garrison-Randall, Inc. †

480 Second St., Ste. 304
San Francisco, California 94107
(415) 995-8400
Fax: (415) 995-8422

Key Contact - Specialty:
Ms. Rita M. Fornino - *Healthcare*

Description: Specializing in placement of management within the healthcare industry. Our position expertise encompasses administration, finance, ancillary, performance improvement and patient care services.

Salary Minimum: $60,000
Functions: Senior mgmt., Middle mgmt., Healthcare, Nurses, Health admin., HR mgmt., Finance
Industries: Healthcare

Branches:
One Sansome St.
San Francisco, California 94104
(415) 433-2330
Key Contact - Specialty:
Ms. Rita M. Fornino - *Healthcare*

Peter Gasperini & Assoc., Inc.

42 Crane Rd.
Scarsdale, New York 10583
(914) 723-0004

Key Contact - Specialty:
Mr. Peter Gasperini - *Financial services*

Description: Concentration in financial services industry on a retained basis. Fifteen years of search experience on a global basis. Special concentration on investment management.

Salary Minimum: $100,000
Industries: Banking, Invest. banking, Brokers, Misc. financial

Gaudry, Shink, Levasseur

1155 University Ave., Ste. 505
Montreal, Quebec H3B 3A7
Canada
(514) 878-1199

Key Contact - Specialty:
Mr. Jean Gaudry
Mr. Marc Levasseur
Mr. Gilles Shink

Description: The three associates combine close to 30 years in executive search. We merged our three separate practices in early 1997 to become the fastest growing executive search firm in the province of Quebec.

Salary Minimum: $60,000
Functions: Generalist, Mfg., Materials, Sales & mktg., HR mgmt., Finance, Engineering
Industries: Generalist, Agri/forestry/mining, Mfg., Finance, Communications, Aerospace, Packaging

Gavin Forbes & Price

2207 Garnet Ave., Ste. F
San Diego, California 92109
(619) 483-6696
Fax: (619) 581-2025

Key Contact - Specialty:
Mr. Daniel Price - *Banking*

Description: Major international banks, state, regionals, local institutuions in California exclusively, accept search assignments on selective basis, principal conducts search only.

Salary Minimum: $60,000
Functions: CFO's, Budgeting, Cash mgmt., Credit, Taxes, M&A, Risk mgmt.
Industries: Banking

Affiliates:
Du Parc, Lyons & Assoc. Inc.

† occasional contingency assignment

Geddes & Rubin Management Inc. †

10 Bay St., Ste. 1501
Toronto, Ontario M5J 2R8
Canada
(416) 365-7770
Fax: (416) 365-7669
Email: gr@grsearch.com
Web: www.grsearch.com

Key Contact - Specialty:
Mr. Murray Geddes - *Generalist*
Mr. Ron Rubin - *Generalist, sales & marketing*

Description: Providing expedient and creative executive search services using competency based human resources management.

Salary Minimum: $50,000
Functions: Generalist, General mgmt., Mfg., Sales & mktg., HR mgmt., Finance, IT
Industries: Mfg., Finance, Svcs., Communications, High tech, Software, Biotech

Genesis Consulting Partners

306 S. Philip St.
Philadelphia, Pennsylvania 19106
(215) 627-3350
Fax: (215) 625-3920

Key Contact - Specialty:
Mr. Kendall A. Elsom, Jr. - *Biotechnology*
Ms. Catrayl Dalyan

Description: Ten years specialization in pharmaceutical, medical products and biotechnology. Unusually strong ability to counsel boards of directors, chairmen of high technology ventures on organization, planning development, staffing and other HR matters. Selective senior level outplacement services.

Salary Minimum: $100,000
Functions: Generalist, Senior mgmt., Sales & mktg., Finance, IT, R&D, Mgmt. consultants
Industries: Drugs mfg., Medical devices, Venture cap., Healthcare, Non-classifiable industries

Geneva Group Int'l.

4 Embarcadero Ctr., Ste. 1400
San Francisco, California 94111
(415) 433-4646
Fax: (415) 433-6635
Email: isill@aol.com
Web: www.genevagroup.com

Key Contact - Specialty:
Mr. Igor M. Sill - *Software*

Description: Specializes in presidential, board member and officer level searches for high technology companies. Special emphasis on key officers for venture capital backed, privately held emerging technologies with a focus on software, Internet and multimedia companies.

Salary Minimum: $100,000
Functions: Directors, Senior mgmt.
Industries: Venture cap., New media, High tech, Software

International Branches:
Kent

GES Services, Inc.

630 Fifth Ave., 20th Floor
Rockefeller Ctr.
New York, New York 10111
(212) 332-3260
Fax: (212) 332-3261
Email: gessvc@aol.com

Key Contact - Specialty:
Mr. Christy Guzzetta - *Wealth management*
Ms. Abby J. Norris

Description: Recruit senior and middle management professionals for personal trust, private banking, financial planning, investment management and related wealth management disciplines.
Functions: Sales mgmt., Cash mgmt., Credit, Taxes, Risk mgmt., Systems anal., Non-profits
Industries: Finance, Banking, Invest. banking, Brokers, Misc. financial

Gibson & Co., Inc.

250 N. Sunnyslope Rd., Ste. 300
Brookfield, Wisconsin 53005
(414) 785-8100
(414) 367-5100

Key Contact - Specialty:
Mr. Bruce Gibson - *CEOs, COO's, CFOs, CIO's, officer level positions*

Description: Principal has 29 years of experience in officer level executive search, specializing in CEO, COO, CFO, CIO and functional vice presidency assignments in marketing, sales, manufacturing, engineering, human resources and finance; board directors.

Salary Minimum: $180,000
Functions: Generalist
Industries: Generalist

Gielow Assoc., Inc.

306 N. Milwaukee St.
Milwaukee, Wisconsin 53202
(800) 969-7715
Fax: (414) 226-4131
Email: gielow@execpc.com
Web: www.execpc.com/~gielow

Key Contact - Specialty:
Mr. Curtis C. Gielow - *Healthcare, sports, non-profit organizations*

Description: The firm serves service sector industries including non-profit organizations. Special search expertise and experience in healthcare, sports and public assembly and transfusion medicine and blood banking.

Salary Minimum: $50,000
Functions: Senior mgmt., Middle mgmt., Physicians, Allied health, Health admin., Personnel, CFO's
Industries: Banking, Non-profits, Pharmaceutical svcs., Mgmt. consulting, Human resource svcs., Insurance, Healthcare

Gilbert & Van Campen Int'l.
(J. B. Gilbert Assoc., Inc.)

420 Lexington Ave.
New York, New York 10170
(212) 661-2122
Fax: (212) 599-0839
Email: vcassoc@aol.com

Key Contact - Specialty:
Mr. Jerry Gilbert - *Executive level (150K salary minimum)*
Mr. Stephen B. Van Campen - *Executive level (150K salary minimum)*
Mr. Jerry Van Campen - *MIS, on line Internet research, E-mail, web*

Description: Worldwide executive search consultants to U.S. and international management. Confidential assignments completed in more than thirty-five countries in a wide spectrum of industry and executive functions.

Salary Minimum: $150,000
Functions: Senior mgmt., Materials, Sales & mktg., Benefits, R&D, Specialized services, Int'l.
Industries: Generalist, Mfg., Transportation, Finance, Svcs., Communications, Healthcare

Branches:
Operations Resarch Ctr.
99 Lake Side Drive
Belvidere, New Jersey 07823
(908) 475-2222
Fax: (908) 475-2241
Email: vcassoc@aol.com
Key Contact - Specialty:
Ms. Gloria Takacs

Gilbert Tweed Assoc. Inc.

415 Madison Ave.
New York, New York 10017
(212) 758-3000
Fax: (212) 832-1040
Email: gtany@aol.com
Web: www.gilberttweed.com

Key Contact - Specialty:
Ms. Janet Tweed
Ms. Stephanie Pinson
Ms. Joan Gagan
Ms. Karen DelPrete

Mr. Jack Lusk

Description: Generalist search practice providing broad range of support services to assure successful completion of every search - strong track record recruiting female and minority candidates. Also provides organizational profiling service, seminars-Picking Winners and Keeping Winners.

Salary Minimum: $150,000
Functions: Generalist, Directors, Senior mgmt., Plant mgmt., Quality, Productivity, Packaging, Physicians, Mktg. mgmt., Sales mgmt., Direct mktg., CFO's, MIS mgmt., R&D, Mgmt. consultants, Minorities, Int'l.
Industries: Generalist, Energy/utilities, Food/bev/tobacco, Paper, Printing, Chemicals, Soap/perfume/cosmetics, Drugs mfg., Medical devices, Plastics/rubber, Paints/petroleum products, Machinery/Appliances, Motor vehicles, Computer equip., Consumer electronics, Test/measurement equip., Transportation, Invest. banking, Venture cap., Misc. financial, Pharmaceutical svcs., Computer svcs., Mgmt. consulting, Human resource svcs., Broadcast & Film, Telecoms, Environmental svcs., Haz. waste, Packaging, High tech, Software, Biotech, Healthcare
Professional Associations: IACPR

Branches:
155 Prospect Ave.
West Orange, New Jersey 07052
(201) 731-3033
Key Contact - Specialty:
Ms. Jane Greenwald
Mr. John Ebeling
Ms. Linda Paul

Howard Gilmore & Assoc.

15 Chelsea Court
Beachwood, Ohio 44122
(216) 831-6249

Key Contact - Specialty:
Mr. Howard A. Gilmore - *Industrial sales & marketing*

Description: Search and outplacement services in the sales, marketing, management areas, concentration more in the industrial, technical areas domestically.

Salary Minimum: $30,000
Functions: Middle mgmt., Mktg. mgmt., Sales mgmt., Training, Mgmt. consultants
Industries: Metal products, Misc. mfg.

Gilreath Weatherby Inc.

P.O. Box 1483
Manchester by the Sea, Massachusetts 01944
(508) 526-8771
Email: jmpg@tiac.net
Web: www.gilreathweatherby.com

Key Contact - Specialty:
Mr. James M. Gilreath - *Consumer products (all functions), venture capital acquisitions*
Ms. Diane C. Gilreath

Description: Mr. Gilreath will handle your search assignment from assisting with position specs formulation through the job offer and candidate acceptance. He has 30 years of experience to offer.

Salary Minimum: $80,000
Functions: Generalist, Senior mgmt., Middle mgmt., Plant mgmt., Mktg. mgmt., Sales mgmt., CFO's
Industries: Generalist, Construction, Plastics/rubber, Metal products, Venture cap., Aerospace, Packaging

The Glazin Group

555 Burrard St., Ste. 1795
Vancouver, British Columbia V7X 1M9
Canada
(604) 687-3828
Fax: (604) 687-3875
Email: search@glazin.com

Key Contact - Specialty:
Ms. Lynne Glazin - *Real estate, construction, hospitality, entertainment*
Ms. Lindy Arnold - *Retail, construction, healthcare, public sector*

Description: We not only employ a research-based approach to search, we define ourselves by that approach. Our dedication to research means that we are able to reach the top individuals in any field, discreetly determining their appropriateness and level of interest in an assignment.
Functions: General mgmt., Mfg., Sales & mktg., HR mgmt., Finance, IT, Specialized services
Industries: Generalist, Construction, Retail, Svcs., Real estate, High tech, Healthcare
Professional Associations: AESC

Affiliates:
Michael Stern Assoc., Inc./Euram

J. P. Gleason Assoc., Inc.

P.O. Box 33
Cary, Illinois 60013-0033
(847) 516-8900
Fax: (847) 516-8928
Email: jpgsearch@aol.com

Key Contact - Specialty:
Mr. James P. Gleason - *Human resources, marketing, sales, finance, manufacturing*

Description: Higher level search in marketing, sales, finance, HR and operations for clients in transportation, manufacturing, retail and other industries. Personal, consultative approach with limited number of clients.

Salary Minimum: $100,000
Functions: General mgmt., Mfg., Sales & mktg., HR mgmt., Finance
Industries: Food/bev/tobacco, Lumber/furniture, Metal products, Computer equip., Banking, Entertainment, High tech

Glines Assoc., Inc.

39 S. LaSalle St., Ste. 714
Chicago, Illinois 60603
(312) 577-5645
Fax: (312) 577-5651
Email: laglines@earthlink.net

Key Contact - Specialty:
Mr. Larry Glines - *Medical industry*

Description: Medical industry executive search dedicated to quality service and results. Our industry network and comprehensive methodology provides precise recruitment and selection. We customize our services and function as a knowledgeable partner.
Functions: General mgmt., Mfg., Materials, Sales & mktg., M&A, R&D, Engineering
Industries: Drugs mfg., Medical devices, Biotech

Global Data Services, Inc. †

694 Ft. Salonga Rd.
Northport, New York 11768
(516) 754-0771
Fax: (516) 754-0590
Email: info@globaldatasearch.com
Web: www.globaldatasearch.com

Key Contact - Specialty:
Mr. Garry Silivanch

Description: We specialize in outsourcing large recruiting efforts on a fixed fee basis under a program called Pace. Also, individual searches at standard fee depending on project size.

Salary Minimum: $100,000
Functions: General mgmt., Sales & mktg., IT, R&D, Mgmt. consultants
Industries: Energy/utilities, Mfg., Finance, Svcs., Mgmt. consulting, High tech, Software

Global Employer's Network, Inc. †

12222 Merit Drive, Ste. 450
Dallas, Texas 75251-2229
(972) 934-2100
Fax: (972) 788-1893
Email: geni@geni-jobnet.com
Web: www.geni-jobnet.com

Key Contact - Specialty:
Mr. Bob Lowrance

Description: Staffing consulting firm providing large-scale recruitment outsourcing, executive search, research, internet services and other staffing related

† occasional contingency assignment

products and services. Functional emphasis in technologically driven organizations.

Salary Minimum: $50,000
Functions: Generalist, General mgmt., Mfg., Finance, IT, Engineering, Int'l.
Industries: Generalist, Mfg., Finance, New media, Telecoms, High tech, Software

Global HealthCare Partners
(a division of Global Net Partners)

7431 E. State St., Ste. 221
Rockford, Illinois 61108
(815) 398-1052
Fax: (815) 398-1057
Email: ceofinder@aol.com

Key Contact - Specialty:
Mr. Brad L. Newpoff - *Healthcare executives*

Description: We are a retained executive search and consulting firm that is in the business of providing solutions to the obstacles that stand in the way of our client's goals.

Salary Minimum: $50,000
Functions: General mgmt., Healthcare, Sales & mktg., HR mgmt., Finance, IT, Specialized services
Industries: Venture cap., Pharmaceutical svcs., Insurance, High tech, Software, Healthcare

Branches:
P.O. Box 685
Unionville, Pennsylvania 19375
(610) 793-4645
Fax: (610) 793-2157
Key Contact - Specialty:
Dr. Allen Silberman - *Healthcare executives*

Global Research Partnership Inc.

130 Garth Rd., Ste. 114
Scarsdale, New York 10583
(914) 723-4229
Fax: (914) 623-8763
Email: imrbwt@aol.com

Key Contact - Specialty:
Ms. Betty Wong Tomita - *International (Asia Pacific, Europe)*
Ms. Gai Galitzine - *International (Latin America, Europe)*

Description: We provide US based search management of overseas recruitment utilizing a worldwide network of experienced professionals familiar with local markets and the needs of US multinationals. We advise/consult regarding local cultures and customs.
Functions: Generalist, General mgmt., Mfg., Sales & mktg., R&D, Minorities, Int'l.
Industries: Generalist, Mfg., Drugs mfg., Retail, Svcs., Communications, High tech

Global Resources Group

7676 Hazard Center Drive, Ste. 1320
San Diego, California 92108
(619) 291-2300
Fax: (619) 291-7300
Email: info@grgi.com
Web: www.grgi.com

Key Contact - Specialty:
Mr. Donn E. Bleau - *Healthcare, managed care, employee benefits, human resources*

Description: A search firm committed to excellence with the uncanny ability to attract and secure the most sought after professionals who then make a positive impact on our clients' bottom-line.

Salary Minimum: $75,000
Functions: Directors, Senior mgmt., Physicians, Health admin., Mktg. mgmt., Sales mgmt., Mgmt. consultants
Industries: Pharmaceutical svcs., Mgmt. consulting, Human resource svcs., Insurance, Healthcare

F. Gloss Int'l.

1595 Spring Hill Rd., Ste. 350
Vienna, Virginia 22182
(703) 847-0010
Fax: (703) 847-3044
Email: fred_gloss@fgloss.com

Key Contact - Specialty:
Mr. Fred C. Gloss

Description: Clientele includes international information technology, transportation, telecommunications, aerospace and national defense/security companies. Also assist clients in mergers and acquisition, organizational development and attracting capital and key personnel for promising start-ups.

Salary Minimum: $70,000
Functions: Senior mgmt., Mktg. mgmt., Sales mgmt., IT, R&D, Mgmt. consultants, Int'l.
Industries: Transportation, Misc. financial, Computer svcs., Defense, Aerospace, High tech, Software

Glou Int'l., Inc.

687 Highland Ave.
Needham, Massachusetts 02194-2232
(781) 449-3310
Fax: (781) 449-3358
Email: glou@glou.com

Key Contact - Specialty:
Mr. Alan Glou - *Management, executives, board members (US & international)*

Description: Retained executive management searches since 1960. Serving both domestic and international firms specializing in the chemistry of the management team. Also consulting providing people audits, cross-cultural and organizational training and networking services.

Salary Minimum: $80,000
Functions: Directors, Senior mgmt., Mktg. mgmt., PR, CFO's, MIS mgmt., Int'l.
Industries: Medical devices, Computer equip., Computer svcs., New media, Telecoms, High tech, Software

The Tracy Glover Co.

P.O. Box 1982
Frisco, Texas 75034
(972) 346-3838
(972) 346-2121
Fax: (972) 346-3303
Email: glover@cmpu.net

Key Contact - Specialty:
Ms. Tracy Glover

Description: The firm, with offices in New York and Dallas, provides comprehensive retained search services to the financial services industry with unique expertise to deliver diverse slates of candidates.
Functions: Directors, Senior mgmt., CFO's, Cash mgmt., M&A, Risk mgmt., Minorities
Industries: Finance, Banking, Invest. banking, Brokers, Insurance, Real estate, High tech

Affiliates:
Warren Int'l.

The Gobbell Co.

1601 Dove St., Ste. 145
Newport Beach, California 92660
(714) 476-2258
Email: jgobbell@pacbell.net

Key Contact - Specialty:
Mr. John J. Gobbell - *Senior management*

Description: Small, high quality retainer firm specializing in California based clients. Emphasize senior management in: entertainment, publishing, telecommunications, engineering, construction, healthcare, food, aerospace, investment, financial services and real estate.

Salary Minimum: $80,000
Functions: Generalist, Senior mgmt., Admin. svcs., HR mgmt., CFO's, R&D, Engineering
Industries: Computer equip., Consumer electronics, Transportation, Finance, Entertainment, Aerospace, High tech

Affiliates:
Hergenrather & Co.

Robert G. Godfrey Assoc. Ltd. †

P.O. Box 3392
Oak Park, Illinois 60303-3392
(708) 771-2374
Fax: (708) 771-2615

Email: godfreyrg@aol.com

Key Contact - Specialty:
Mr. Robert G. Godfrey - *Market research, healthcare, information technology*

Description: Highly personalized national executive search practice with an emphasis on efficient, high quality and professional service. Firm has reputation for long-term placements. Also offers recruitment consulting services to include contract recruitment.
Functions: Generalist, Senior mgmt., Middle mgmt., Production, Health admin., HR mgmt., IT
Industries: Generalist, Mfg., Higher ed.

The Gogates Group, Inc.
630 Fifth Ave., 20th Floor
New York, New York 10111
(212) 355-4117
Email: agogates@cybernex.net
Web: www2.cybernex.net/~agogates

Key Contact - Specialty:
Mr. Andrew Gogates - *Financial services, quantitative analysts, risk management*

Description: Executive search specialist for the financial services industry for over 20 years. Emphasis on quantitatively oriented research analysts, traders and money managers for investment banks hedge funds and private investment firms.

Salary Minimum: $75,000
Functions: Cash mgmt., Risk mgmt., R&D
Industries: Finance, Banking, Invest. banking, Brokers, Misc. financial

---

The Goldman Group Inc. †
381 Park Ave. S., Ste. 1520
New York, New York 10016
(212) 685-9311
Fax: (212) 532-2740

Key Contact - Specialty:
Ms. Elaine Goldman
Ms. Anna Mintzer
Ms. Maria Pell

Description: The Goldman Group, Inc. is one of the largest and fastest growing specialized search and management consulting firms in the country, specializing in public relations, corporate and marketing communications, public affairs, investor relations and related fields.

Salary Minimum: $55,000
Functions: PR
Industries: Misc. financial, Pharmaceutical svcs., Accounting, Mgmt. consulting, Communications, Advertising/PR, New media

Affiliates:
Goldman+Bell, LLC

Fred J. Goldsmith Assoc.
14056 Margate St.
Sherman Oaks, California 91401
(818) 783-3931
Fax: (818) 907-9724

Key Contact - Specialty:
Mr. Fred J. Goldsmith - *Technology, distribution, food, consumer packaged goods, natural resources*

Description: Executive search - transportation, technology, consumer products, distribution, oil and exploration industries, food services and human resource services.

Salary Minimum: $65,000
Functions: Senior mgmt., Quality, Distribution, Sales mgmt., Benefits, CFO's, Mgmt. consultants
Industries: Chemicals, Computer equip., Transportation, Mgmt. consulting, Human resource svcs., High tech, Software

---

David Gomez & Assoc., Inc. †
20 N. Clark St., 35th Floor
Chicago, Illinois 60602
(312) 346-5525
Fax: (312) 346-1438
Email: dgomez@dgai.com
Web: www.dgai.com

Key Contact - Specialty:
Mr. David P. Gomez - *Information Technology and senior management*
Mr. Robert H. Mittenthal - *Accounting/Finance, Marketing/Advertising, real estate and senior management*
Mr. Patrick Dudasik

Description: Our uniqueness is that we offer a one-stop shop for our clients. We place no limitations on our abilities nor sacrifice our exceptional level of service. We guarantee success.

Salary Minimum: $70,000
Functions: Generalist, Directors, Senior mgmt., Sales & mktg., Finance, IT, Minorities
Industries: Generalist, Accounting, Mgmt. consulting, Advertising/PR, Real estate, High tech, Software

---

The Goodman Group
P.O. Box J
San Rafael, California 94913-3908
(415) 472-6500
Email: mail@goodmangroup.com
Web: www.goodmangroup.com

Key Contact - Specialty:
Mr. Lion Goodman - *Healthcare information systems, management consulting, information systems*
Ms. Lynda Sheridan - *Healthcare information systems & services, medical products*
Mr. Brad Buehler - *Healthcare information systems, software, consulting*

Description: Specialists in the application of information systems and technologies to healthcare, insurance, and other vertical markets. Extensive experience locating senior staff for management consulting firms and start-up companies, especially software and technology ventures. Recruitment of chief executives, partners, and senior managers of sales, marketing, information systems, operations, and software development.

Salary Minimum: $75,000
Functions: Senior mgmt., Middle mgmt., Mktg. mgmt., Sales mgmt., MIS mgmt., Systems implem., Mgmt. consultants
Industries: Medical devices, Computer svcs., Mgmt. consulting, High tech, Software, Healthcare

---

Goodrich & Sherwood Assoc., Inc.
521 Fifth Ave.
New York, New York 10175
(212) 697-4131
Fax: (212) 983-7499

Key Contact - Specialty:
Mr. Andrew Sherwood - *General management*

Description: The nation's largest full service human resource management consulting firm specializing in strategic human resource systems, executive search, outplacement counseling, pre-retirement counseling, organization assessment and management development.

Salary Minimum: $80,000
Functions: Generalist, Directors, Senior mgmt., Product dev., Plant mgmt., Packaging, Mkt. research, Mktg. mgmt., Sales mgmt., Benefits, Personnel, CFO's, M&A, MIS mgmt., Mgmt. consultants
Industries: Food/bev/tobacco, Textiles/apparel, Lumber/furniture, Paper, Soap/perfume/cosmetics, Drugs mfg., Medical devices, Paints/petroleum products, Computer equip., Consumer electronics, Misc. mfg., Invest. banking, Hospitality, Entertainment, Pharmaceutical svcs., Computer svcs., Mgmt. consulting, Advertising/PR, Environmental svcs., Packaging, High tech, Software, Healthcare
Professional Associations: IACPR

Branches:
401 Merritt Seven
Norwalk, Connecticut 06851
(203) 847-2525
Fax: (203) 846-2880

† occasional contingency assignment

Key Contact - Specialty:
Mr. Richard E. Spann - *Consumer products, general management*

4 Armstrong Rd.
Shelton, Connecticut 06484
(203) 944-2828
Fax: (203) 944-2838
Key Contact - Specialty:
Mr. John P. Schegg - *Generalist*

6 Century Drive
Parsippany, New Jersey 07054
(201) 455-7100
Fax: (201) 898-0730
Key Contact - Specialty:
Mr. Frank R. Palma - *Manufacturing, general management*

1 Independence Way
Princeton, New Jersey 08540
(609) 452-0202
Fax: (609) 452-0555
Key Contact - Specialty:
Mr. Don Doele - *Human resources, compensation*

250 Mill St.
Rochester, New York 14614
(716) 777-4060
Fax: (716) 777-4105
Key Contact - Specialty:
Mr. Cornelius J. Murphy - *Research & development, manufacturing*

Torre Caballito Piso 19
Reforma 10 Centro
Mexico City, Mexico DF 06400
Mexico
52 5 628 1282
Key Contact - Specialty:
Mr. Peter R. Laskowski - *Generalist*

International Branches:
Santpoort-Zuid

Goodwin & Co.
1150 Connecticut Ave. NW, Ste. 200
Washington, District of Columbia 20036
(202) 785-9292
Fax: (202) 785-9297
Email: goodco@aol.com

Key Contact - Specialty:
Mr. Tom Goodwin
Mr. Dan Sherman
Ms. Shari Curtis

Description: A national executive search firm serving corporate and not-for-profit clients in finance, environmental, advocacy, education and philanthropy.

Salary Minimum: $60,000
Functions: Generalist, Senior mgmt., PR, CFO's, Minorities, Non-profits, Environmentalists
Industries: Generalist

Gordon/Tyler
2220 Brandywine St.
Philadelphia, Pennsylvania 19130
(215) 569-2344

Key Contact - Specialty:
Dr. Fern Polaski

Description: Specialists in research and development, technical services and engineering for consumer products and services companies.

Salary Minimum: $80,000
Functions: Product dev., R&D, Engineering, Minorities
Industries: Food/bev/tobacco, Soap/perfume/cosmetics, Drugs mfg.

Gossage Regan Assoc.
25 W. 43rd St., Ste. 812
New York, New York 10036
(212) 869-3348
Fax: (212) 997-1127

Key Contact - Specialty:
Mr. Wayne Gossage - *Library executives (directors, deans of libraries)*
Ms. Joan Neumann - *Library executives (directors, deans of libraries)*

Description: Executive search and screening for directors, deans of libraries, CIOs and information managers for libraries (public, academic, law), information centers (business and nonprofits), other information operations, both external and internal information.

Salary Minimum: $70,000
Functions: Directors, Senior mgmt., Middle mgmt.
Industries: Generalist, Non-profits

Gould, McCoy & Chadick, Inc.
300 Park Ave.
New York, New York 10022
(212) 688-8671
Fax: (212) 308-4510
Email:
slchadick@gouldmccoychadick.com
Web: www.gouldmccoychadick.com

Key Contact - Specialty:
Mr. William E. Gould - *Generalist (senior level), international*
Ms. Millington F. McCoy - *Generalist (senior level), financial services*
Ms. Susan L. Chadick - *Generalist (senior level), human resources, financial services (all functions)*

Description: Executive search firm providing comprehensive services to corporations in the identification, assessment and selection of their management personnel. Known for our thoroughness, our assessment ability and quality of our service.

Salary Minimum: $125,000
Functions: Generalist, Directors, Senior mgmt., Mktg. mgmt., Benefits, Personnel, Training, CFO's, MIS mgmt., R&D
Industries: Generalist, Food/bev/tobacco, Paper, Chemicals, Soap/perfume/cosmetics, Drugs mfg., Medical devices, Finance, Banking, Brokers, Venture cap., Misc. financial, Hospitality, Entertainment, Pharmaceutical svcs., Mgmt. consulting, Human resource svcs., Publishing, Telecoms, Packaging, Insurance, Real estate, High tech, Biotech, Healthcare
Professional Associations: AESC, IACPR

The Governance Group, Inc.
P.O. Box H
Short Hills, New Jersey 07078
(908) 277-1800
Fax: (908) 277-4445
Email: tgg4u@aol.com

Key Contact - Specialty:
Mr. Steven N. Schrenzel - *Insurance, mutual funds, sales, marketing, technology (senior executives & professionals)*

Description: Generalist firm, committed to diversity. Emphasizes executive resources consulting approach supporting relocation, merger, acquisition, divestiture or restructuring. Exceptional expertise in consulting, recruitment for retirement and benefit plan service providers.

Salary Minimum: $75,000
Functions: Senior mgmt., Production, Mktg. mgmt., Benefits, Finance, MIS mgmt., Minorities
Industries: Energy/utilities, Computer equip., Finance, Mgmt. consulting, Advertising/PR, Insurance, High tech

Affiliates:
The Alexander Group
Management Alliance Group, Inc.

Graham & Co. †
34 Sycamore Ave., Bldg. 2 South
Little Silver, New Jersey 07739
(908) 747-8000
Fax: (908) 576-1676

Key Contact - Specialty:
Mr. Harold Scott - *Manufacturing, automotive OE parts (all levels, all positions), specialty chemicals.*

Description: Executive search firm with a diversified portfolio of clients in traditional and technology-driven organizations handling executive management assignments in most functional areas.

Salary Minimum: $60,000
Functions: Middle mgmt., Production, Plant mgmt., Quality, Purchasing, Materials Plng.

Industries: Plastics/rubber, Metal products, Motor vehicles

Affiliates:
Brain Transearch
Groupe Ranger Inc.
Proper Transearch
Raggatt International
Thomas Cole Kinder
Transearch France

Robert Graham Assoc.
3 Regency Plaza, Ste. 114
Providence, Rhode Island 02903
(401) 455-7777

Key Contact - Specialty:
Mr. Robert W. Graham - *CFOs, COO's, consultants, marketing, human resources*

Description: Experienced generalist firm, most industries and functions. Represent Fortune 10 firm in area of business development. Top consulting firm experience required. Also marketing and human resources.

Salary Minimum: $100,000
Functions: Generalist, Senior mgmt., Health admin., Mktg. mgmt., CFO's, Mgmt. consultants
Industries: Generalist, Misc. mfg., Finance, Banking, Mgmt. consulting, Human resource svcs., Healthcare

Granger, Counts & Assoc.
728 Trade Sq. W.
Troy, Ohio 45373
(937) 339-1119

Key Contact - Specialty:
Mr. Robert L. Counts

Description: Highly responsive search firm for management, professional and technical personnel.

Salary Minimum: $30,000
Functions: Senior mgmt., Plant mgmt., Materials Plng., Mktg. mgmt., Personnel, CFO's, Engineering
Industries: Generalist, Food/bev/tobacco, Machinery/Appliances, Motor vehicles, Misc. mfg., Misc. financial, Accounting

A. Davis Grant & Co.
295 Pierson Avenue
Edison, New Jersey 08837
(732) 494-2266
Fax: (732) 494-3626
Email: mail@adg.net
Web: www.adg.net

Key Contact - Specialty:
Mr. Allan D. Grossman - *CIO's, information technology (executives)*
Ms. Lynn Lewis - *Senior information technology management*

Description: Executive recruiting firm dedicated exclusively to information systems and technology professionals from project management through chief information officers.

Salary Minimum: $75,000
Functions: MIS mgmt.
Industries: Generalist
Professional Associations: IACPR

Grant Cooper & Assoc., Inc.
795 Office Pkwy., Ste. 117
St. Louis, Missouri 63141-7166
(314) 567-4690
Fax: (314) 567-4697
Email: mail@grantcooper.com
Web: www.grantcooper.com

Key Contact - Specialty:
Ms. Cynthia J. Kohlbry - *Financial services*
Mr. Stephen H. Loeb - *Generalist*
Mr. J. Dale Meier - *Generalist*
Mr. William Tunney, Jr. - *Generalist*
Mr. Richard L. Anderson - *Generalist*
Mr. A. Ray Einsel - *Financial Services*
Ms. Susan T. Goldenberg - *Financial services*

Description: Executive search consultants specializing in upper and middle management searches for over 40 years. Broad experience in most industries including manufacturing, healthcare, retail, not-for-profit and financial services, including most investment banking and capital markets disciplines.

Salary Minimum: $100,000
Functions: Generalist, Senior mgmt., Mfg., Sales & mktg., HR mgmt., Finance, MIS mgmt.
Industries: Generalist, Mfg., Wholesale, Finance, Invest. banking, Svcs., Healthcare
Professional Associations: IACPR

Affiliates:
The Bird Moore Partnership

Grantham & Co., Inc.
136 Erwin Rd.
Chapel Hill, North Carolina 27514-2293
(919) 932-5650
Fax: (919) 932-5568
Web: granthamco@aol.com

Key Contact - Specialty:
Mr. John D. Grantham - *COOs, CFOs, general managers, senior vice presidents, vp's of marketing*

Description: Small, intensive generalist firm which is highly responsive to client needs, with over 19 years search experience serving North America; strong long-term relationships with clients.

Salary Minimum: $90,000
Functions: Senior mgmt., Purchasing, Mkt. research, Benefits, Personnel, CFO's, R&D
Industries: Generalist, Energy/utilities, Mfg., Retail, Finance, Aerospace, Packaging

Annie Gray Assoc., Inc.
12400 Olive Blvd., Ste. 555
St. Louis, Missouri 63141
(314) 275-4405
Fax: (314) 523-4523
Email: anniegray9@aol.com

Key Contact - Specialty:
Ms. Annie Gray

Description: Firm excels in bringing corporations and tomorrows leaders together. We help create multi-million dollar success stories. From Fortune 50's to start-ups. Our goal is to out-do our previous effort for each client.

Salary Minimum: $100,000
Functions: Directors, Senior mgmt., Mfg., CFO's, Non-profits
Industries: Generalist

Affiliates:
Executaries by Gray

Greenhaven & Assoc., Inc.
90 Park Ave., Ste. 1700
New York, New York 10016
(212) 984-0747

Key Contact - Specialty:
Ms. L. Catherine Ehrenreich - *Sales & marketing, computers, telecommunications*
Mr. Chester P. Evans - *Management consulting*
Mr. Bennett A. Ellis - *Publishing*

Description: Retained search firm nationally placing high technology, publishing professionals and management consultants. $75,000 and up.

Salary Minimum: $75,000
Functions: Generalist, Sales mgmt., Direct mktg., Mgmt. consultants
Industries: Computer svcs., Mgmt. consulting, Communications, Publishing, Telecoms, High tech

Greger/Peterson Assoc., Inc.
321 12th St., Ste. 210
Manhattan Beach, California 90266
(310) 546-8555
Email: jspsearch@aol.com

Key Contact - Specialty:
Mr. John S. Peterson - *Senior executives*

Description: Retained only. Culture-sensitive, organizational approach dedicated to quality results and client service. General practice - hospitality/leisure and entertainment/new media specialty.

Salary Minimum: $125,000
Functions: Senior mgmt., Mktg. mgmt., Sales mgmt., CFO's

† occasional contingency assignment

Industries: Hospitality, Entertainment, New media

Branches:
5335 SW Meadows Rd., Ste. 401
Lake Oswego, Oregon 97035
(503) 620-6800
Email: hotelGPA@aol.com
Key Contact - Specialty:
Mr. Kenneth R. Greger - *Hospitality, entertainment, new media*

Gregory Michaels & Assoc., Inc.

8410 W. Bryn Mawr Ave., Ste. 400
Chicago, Illinois 60631
(773) 380-1333
Fax: (773) 380-1223

Key Contact - Specialty:
Mr. Gregory P. Crecos
Mr. Joseph J. Scodius
Ms. Kambrea R. Wendler
Ms. Mary K. Simon
Ms. Lorrie A. Hopp
Ms. Kelly L. McNulty

Description: Boutique executive search firm recruiting upper level management.

Salary Minimum: $250,000
Functions: Generalist
Industries: Generalist

David M. Griffith & Assoc., Ltd.

4320 Auburn Blvd., Ste. 2000
Sacramento, California 95841
(916) 485-8102
Fax: (916) 485-0111

Key Contact - Specialty:
Mr. Robert W. Murray - *Public sector*
Ms. Bobbi Peckham - *Public sector*
Mr. Chuck Neumayer - *Public sector*

Description: The nation's leading public sector consulting firm with over 30 offices nationwide. Public sector search specialists with West and East coast offices.
Industries: Government

Branches:
1621 Metropolitan Blvd., Ste. 201
Tallahassee, Florida 32308
(904) 386-1101
Fax: (904) 386-3599
Key Contact - Specialty:
Mr. Renée Narlock - *Public sector*

650 Dundee Rd., Ste. 275
Northbrook, Illinois 60062
(708) 564-9270
Fax: (708) 564-9136
Key Contact - Specialty:
Mr. Mike Casey - *Public sector*
Mr. Matt O'Biern - *Public sector*

Griffith & Werner, Inc.

10691 N. Kendall Drive, Ste. 212
Miami, Florida 33176
(305) 598-5600
Fax: (305) 598-8020

Key Contact - Specialty:
Mr. Warland Griffith, III - *Latin America, Puerto Rico*

Description: Senior executive and upper management search consulting services for regional level and locally based positions in Latin/Central America, as well as senior level domestic assignments in the continental United States.

Salary Minimum: $75,000
Functions: Senior mgmt., Plant mgmt., Materials Plng., Mktg. mgmt., HR mgmt., CFO's, Int'l.
Industries: Food/bev/tobacco, Drugs mfg., Medical devices, Transportation, Finance, Communications, Broadcast & Film

Affiliates:
Clive & Stokes International

Grossberg & Assoc.

1100 Jorie Blvd., Ste. 301
Oak Brook, Illinois 60521
(630) 574-0066
Fax: (630) 573-0552
Email: bobgsearch@aol.com

Key Contact - Specialty:
Mr. Robert M. Grossberg - *Generalist*
Mr. Bob Williamson - *Marketing, sales*

Description: Human resource professionals whose sole function is to assist clients in developing a talented management staff.

Salary Minimum: $60,000
Functions: Generalist, Mfg., Materials, Sales & mktg., HR mgmt., Finance, Engineering
Industries: Generalist, Mfg., Plastics/rubber, Machinery/Appliances, Misc. mfg., Accounting, High tech

Groton Planning Group

5 Bradford Rd.
Wiscasset, Maine 04578
(207) 882-6001
Fax: (207) 882-6832
Email: sjk@midcoast.com

Key Contact - Specialty:
Mr. Stephan J. Kornacki

Description: Sole practitioner.
Functions: Product dev., Materials Plng., Distribution, Mkt. research, Mktg. mgmt., Sales mgmt., MIS mgmt.
Industries: Drugs mfg., Computer equip., Pharmaceutical svcs., High tech, Software, Biotech, Healthcare

Groussman & Assoc., Inc.

One Bent Tree Twr.
16475 N. Dallas Pkwy, Ste. 280
Dallas, Texas 75248
(972) 381-1721
Fax: (972) 381-1727

Key Contact - Specialty:
Ms. Maria Groussman - *Retail, international, finance, merchandise, marketing*

Description: We specialize in retail international and domestic searches. As generalists, we serve clients with a broad expertise in all functions.

Salary Minimum: $55,000
Functions: Senior mgmt., Middle mgmt., Sales mgmt., CFO's, Minorities, Int'l.
Industries: Generalist, Wholesale, Retail, Finance

Grover & Assoc.

4414 Zachary Court
Dublin, Ohio 43017-5049
(614) 718-9418

Key Contact - Specialty:
Mr. James R. Grover

Description: Small nationwide firm with clientele in chemicals, pharmaceuticals, minerals and metals. Excellent knowledge of technologies in industries served. Since 1973, providing confidential executive search and consulting services.

Salary Minimum: $90,000
Functions: Generalist, Directors, Senior mgmt., Plant mgmt., Sales & mktg., R&D, Engineering
Industries: Chemicals, Drugs mfg., Plastics/rubber, Leather/stone/glass/clay, Metal products, Human resource svcs., Environmental svcs.

Growth Consultants of America

629 Perry Creek Dr.
Grand Blanc, Michigan 48439
(615) 383-0550
Email: johnhgd2@aol.com

Key Contact - Specialty:
Mr. John H. Haggard, Jr. - *Healthcare, broadcast media, radio, cable*

Description: Place senior level executives in sales and marketing, CEO, COO, CFO, director positions.

Salary Minimum: $60,000
Functions: Senior mgmt., Physicians, Nurses, Health admin., Advertising, Sales mgmt.
Industries: Wholesale, Retail, Broadcast & Film, Healthcare

Growth Strategies, Inc.

19801 E. Country Club Drive, Ste. 4501
Aventura, Florida 33180
(305) 937-2055
Email: steve-nathasingh@bigfoot.com

Key Contact - Specialty:
Mr. Steve Nathasingh - *High technology, general management*

Description: We have international experience in working with many segments of the high technology industry to provide senior and middle management leadership with functional expertise in sales, marketing, corporate development and management consulting.

Salary Minimum: $75,000
Functions: Senior mgmt., Mktg. mgmt., Sales mgmt., M&A, MIS mgmt., Mgmt. consultants, Int'l.
Industries: Computer equip., Consumer electronics, Mgmt. consulting, New media, Telecoms, High tech, Biotech

David E. Grumney Co. Inc. †

P.O. Box 1690
Eastsound, Washington 98245
(360) 376-2066
Fax: (360) 376-3097
Email: grumney@pacificrim.net

Key Contact - Specialty:
Mr. David E. Grumney - *Graphic arts, printing*

Description: Executive recruitment for North America printing and related industries including business forms manufacturers, commercial printers (heat-set web and sheet-fed), direct mail, direct response, graphic arts equipment manufacturers, pressure sensitive label converters, publication printers, etc.

Salary Minimum: $50,000
Functions: Senior mgmt., Middle mgmt., Plant mgmt., Mktg. mgmt., Sales mgmt., Direct mktg., CFO's
Industries: Printing, Advertising/PR, Publishing, Packaging

GSW Consulting Group, Inc.

401 B St., Ste. 340
San Diego, California 92101
(619) 696-7900
Fax: (619) 696-1666

Key Contact - Specialty:
Mr. Joel M. Winitz - *Executive, senior management, corporate directors*

Description: Provide executive search, executive compensation and organization planning consulting services to senior management, primarily in the U.S., U.K., Europe and Latin America.

Salary Minimum: $100,000
Functions: Directors, Senior mgmt., Mktg. mgmt., Sales mgmt., CFO's, MIS mgmt., Engineering
Industries: Computer equip., Venture cap., New media, Telecoms, High tech, Software, Biotech

Wolf Gugler & Assoc. Ltd.

1370 Don Mills Rd., Ste. 300
Toronto, Ontario M3B 3N7
Canada
(416) 386-1719
Email: gugler@pathcom.com
Web: www.nrex.com/ipage/headhunter.html

Key Contact - Specialty:
Mr. Wolf Gugler - *Sales & marketing, retailer/supplier*

Description: Company principal possesses 15 years expertise in recruitment of top performers. In-depth knowledge of hardlines retail and also the sales and marketing discipline.

Salary Minimum: $55,000
Functions: Middle mgmt., Mfg., Purchasing, Materials Plng., Distribution, Sales & mktg., HR mgmt.
Industries: Mfg., Lumber/furniture, Paints/petroleum products, Metal products, Retail, Entertainment, New media

Guidarelli Assoc., Inc.

2933 W. John Beers Rd.
Stevensville, Michigan 49127
(616) 429-7001
Fax: (616) 429-7003
Email: guidarelli@qtm.net

Key Contact - Specialty:
Ms. Shelley Guidarelli - *Consumer products marketing*

Description: Consumer products marketing recruitment and placement specialists for mid and upper management.

Salary Minimum: $60,000
Functions: Mktg. mgmt.
Industries: Food/bev/tobacco, Soap/perfume/cosmetics, Drugs mfg.

Guidry & East Healthcare Search Consultants †

2607 Heatherbend Drive
Pearland, Texas 77584
(281) 997-2200
Fax: (281) 997-5550
Email: jguidry@prohealth.com
Web: www.prohealth.com

Key Contact - Specialty:
Mr. Jim Guidry - *Administrative, department directors, healthcare*

Description: Client-retained medical, healthcare and biomedical searches and related consulting services in recruiting executives, middle-management, physicians and physician extenders. Healthcare and biomedical marketing, strategic planning and management consultants.

Salary Minimum: $50,000
Functions: Physicians, Nurses, Allied health, Health admin., Mkt. research, HR mgmt., MIS mgmt.
Industries: Healthcare

Affiliates:
The ProHealth Group

Gundersen Partners, L.L.C.

230 W. 17th St.
New York, New York 10011
(212) 675-2300
Fax: (212) 675-6965
Web: MarketingAlumni.com

Key Contact - Specialty:
Mr. Steven G. Gundersen - *Advertising, general management*
Mr. Jeff Cahn - *Promotion, merchandising*
Ms. Tina Moore - *Creative services*
Mr. Dennis Troyanos - *Direct marketing*
Mr. Jeff Gundersen - *International & financial services*

Description: Specializes in all facets of consumer marketing. Blue chip client base includes multi-national corporations and advertising, direct marketing, marketing services agencies.

Salary Minimum: $100,000
Functions: Senior mgmt., Advertising, Mktg. mgmt., Sales mgmt., Direct mktg., Graphic artists, Int'l.
Industries: Mfg., Retail, Finance, Svcs., Communications, Insurance, High tech

Branches:
74 W. Long Lake Rd., Ste. 102
Bloomfield Hills, Michigan 48304
(248) 258-3800
Fax: (248) 644-4122
Email: jhbissell@compuserve.com
Key Contact - Specialty:
Mr. John Bissell - *Corporate marketing*
Mr. Ed Tazzia - *Corporate marketing, technology*

Affiliates:
Bucher/Rugman & Partners
Maesina International Search

Gustin Partners, Ltd.

The Ware Mill
Newton Lower Falls, Massachusetts 02162-1452
(617) 332-0800
Fax: (617) 332-0882
Email: info@gustinpartners.com
Web: www.gustinpartners.com

Key Contact - Specialty:
Ms. Vivian C. Brocard
Mr. Charles A. Gustin

† occasional contingency assignment

Mr. Andrew Rafey

Description: Highly specialized, senior-level expertise in executive and entire management team selection within the information technology industry. All engagements executed by senior partners. Clients range from early-stage to Fortune 500 worldwide.

Salary Minimum: $200,000
Functions: Senior mgmt., Mktg. mgmt., Sales mgmt., CFO's, MIS mgmt., Systems implem., Int'l.
Industries: Computer equip., Venture cap., New media, Broadcast & Film, Telecoms, High tech, Software

---

William Guy & Assoc., Inc.
P.O. Box 57407
Sherman Oaks, California 91413
(818) 763-2514

Key Contact - Specialty:
Mr. C. William Guy

Description: Cornerstone World Headquarters; largest executive search consortium; offices in major cities throughout the world; searches entail board of directors, chairman and other upper echelon management/professional levels.

Salary Minimum: $50,000
Functions: Generalist, Directors, Senior mgmt., CFO's, MIS mgmt., Minorities, Int'l.
Industries: Generalist, Mfg., Retail, Finance, Svcs., High tech, Healthcare

---

GWS Partners
Two N. Riverside Plaza, #1745
Chicago, Illinois 60606
(312) 454-5501
Fax: (312) 454-5512
Email: gsilver123@aol.com

Key Contact - Specialty:
Mr. Gary Silverman - *Senior management, board of directors*

Description: Practice focuses on conducting senior-level management and board director search engagements for Fortune 500 corporations.

Salary Minimum: $225,000
Functions: Directors, Senior mgmt., Materials, Benefits, CFO's, Budgeting, MIS mgmt.
Industries: Food/bev/tobacco, Paper, Drugs mfg., Motor vehicles, Wholesale, Publishing, Packaging

Branches:
28 Colonial Drive
Rancho Mirage, California 92270
(760) 324-4293

Key Contact - Specialty:
Mr. Gary Silverman - *Senior management, board of directors*

Habelmann & Assoc.
P.O. Box 1186
Birmingham, Michigan 48012-1186
(734) 207-1815
Fax: (734) 207-1815

Key Contact - Specialty:
Mr. Gerald B. Habelmann - *Generalist, accounting, finance, tax, information technology, state & local government*

Description: Consultants to management in executive search and selection in most functions and industries throughout North America.

Salary Minimum: $55,000
Functions: Generalist, General mgmt., Mfg., Healthcare, HR mgmt., Finance, IT
Industries: Generalist, Energy/utilities, Mfg., Retail, Finance, Government, Real estate

---

Haddad Assoc.
P.O. Box 462
Tarpon Springs, Florida 34688-0462
(813) 939-8078508-747-9777
Fax: (813) 934-4322
Email: rjhaddad@gte.net

Key Contact - Specialty:
Mr. Ronald J. Haddad

Description: Small executive search firm providing retained search services for mid and senior management positions. Emphasis in consulting industry.

Salary Minimum: $70,000
Functions: Generalist, Senior mgmt., Mktg. mgmt., Direct mktg., IT, Engineering, Mgmt. consultants
Industries: Generalist, Computer equip., Mgmt. consulting, Communications, Environmental svcs., High tech, Biotech

---

Hadley Lockwood, Inc.
17 State St.
New York, New York 10004
(212) 785-4405
Fax: (212) 785-4415

Key Contact - Specialty:
Mr. Irwin Brandon - *Securities (all functions)*
Mr. David Hart - *Securities (all functions)*

Description: Executive search and recruitment for financial and investment companies, with concentration in investment banking, capital markets, securities research. Consulting services regarding entire reorganizations, additional departments and new businesses for the same client.

Salary Minimum: $100,000
Industries: Finance, Invest. banking, Brokers, Venture cap., Misc. financial

---

M. A. Haggith Consultants Ltd.
5160 Yonge St., Ste. 810
North York, Ontario M2N 6L9
Canada
(416) 229-2527
Fax: (416) 229-4710
Email: haggith@istar.ca
Web: www.haggith.com

Key Contact - Specialty:
Mr. Marvin Haggith - *Generalist*

Description: We provide executive search services to a wide variety of clients in varied market sectors. Emphasis is on fit using various technologies to provide objective measurements.
Functions: Generalist, Directors, Senior mgmt., Middle mgmt.
Industries: Generalist

Halbrecht Lieberman Assoc., Inc.
1200 Summer St.
Stamford, Connecticut 06905
(203) 327-5630
Fax: (203) 327-0187
Email: admin@hlassoc.com
Web: www.hlassoc.com

Key Contact - Specialty:
Ms. Beverly Lieberman - *Senior level information technology (executives)*

Description: Specialists-information management, telecom, advanced technologies, business process re-engineering, strategic and management consulting. General management executive search for high tech firms.

Salary Minimum: $150,000
Functions: Senior mgmt., MIS mgmt., Systems anal., Systems implem., Systems support, Mgmt. consultants
Industries: Energy/utilities, Drugs mfg., Retail, Finance, Svcs., Communications, Healthcare
Professional Associations: AESC

Hale Assoc.
1816 N. Sedgwick St.
Chicago, Illinois 60614
(312) 337-3288
Fax: (312) 337-3451

Key Contact - Specialty:
Ms. Maureen D. Hale - *General management, senior executives*

Description: We service the executive search industry and specialize in research and sourcing services. The firm customizes these services to meet client needs.

Salary Minimum: $50,000

Functions: Generalist, Senior mgmt., Mktg. mgmt., Sales mgmt., CFO's, Cash mgmt., Mgmt. consultants
Industries: Generalist, Metal products, Banking, Invest. banking, Brokers, Accounting, Mgmt. consulting

---

K. C. Hale, Inc.
20 Avon Meadow Lane
P.O. Box 1215
Avon, Connecticut 06001
(860) 677-7511
Fax: (860) 677-0354

Key Contact - Specialty:
Ms. Kathryn Hale Dumanis
Ms. Kathleen M. McCormack

Description: Extensive search capability and experience in investment, pension, marketing, financial and operational sectors.

Salary Minimum: $100,000
Functions: Directors, Senior mgmt., Mkt. research, Sales mgmt., Cash mgmt., Risk mgmt.
Industries: Invest. banking, Brokers, Misc. financial, Accounting, Human resource svcs., Insurance, Healthcare

---

Haley Associates
526 Ramona St.
Palo Alto, California 94301
(650) 323-0456
Fax: (650) 323-2904

Key Contact - Specialty:
Ms. Carol F. Dressler - *High technology (CEOs, vice presidents)*

Description: A fully retained executive search firm specializing in CEO, vice president and board member level positions for technology based, venture funded companies.

Salary Minimum: $130,000
Functions: Senior mgmt., Mktg. mgmt., Sales mgmt., Engineering
Industries: Computer equip., Venture cap., New media, Telecoms, High tech, Software

---

Michael J. Hall & Co. †
19880 NE 7th Ave., Ste. D
Poulsbo, Washington 98370
(360) 598-3700
Fax: (360) 598-3703
Email: hallco@job.com
Web: www.job.com

Key Contact - Specialty:
Ms. Sheila Brown-Alcala - *Architectural, engineering managers & specialists*
Mr. Michael J. Hall - *Architectural, engineering executives*
Ms. Tina Glymph - *Architects, planners, inspectors*
Mr. Robert Graham - *Civil engineers, electrical engineers, mechanical engineers*
Ms. Christine Simkanin - *Information systems, environmental engineers, technicians*

Description: We are a management consulting firm to the A/E industry. Our recruiting group was added in 1994 and has become a vital service to many of our clients.

Salary Minimum: $24,000
Functions: Mktg. mgmt., M&A, Risk mgmt., Engineering, Environmentalists, Architects, Technicians
Industries: Construction, Transportation, Government, Environmental svcs., High tech, Non-classifiable industries

---

The Halyburton Co., Inc.
6201 Fairview Rd., Ste. 200
Charlotte, North Carolina 28210
(704) 556-9892
Fax: (803) 547-0175
Email: halyburton@aol.com

Key Contact - Specialty:
Mr. Robert R. Halyburton - *Senior level management*

Description: We offer search experience in most industries and disciplines. We strive for excellence in representing our clients and in evaluating prospective candidates.

Salary Minimum: $60,000
Functions: Generalist, Senior mgmt.
Industries: Generalist

The Hamilton Group
6701 Democracy Blvd., Ste. 300
Bethesda, Maryland 20817
(301) 530-9407
Fax: (301) 530-9409
Email: boguski@erols.com
Web: www.hamiltongroup.com

Key Contact - Specialty:
Mr. Ronald T. Boguski - *Senior level executives (professional services, telecommunications, network computing, software)*

Description: Clients consist of Fortune 500, venture capital funded/emerging companies in the high technology industry. Partners, former executives from industry, serve as advisors to board of directors, presidents, CEO's and senior management.

Salary Minimum: $100,000
Functions: Directors, Senior mgmt., Mfg., Sales & mktg., CFO's, MIS mgmt., Mgmt. consultants
Industries: Computer equip., Computer svcs., New media, Telecoms, Aerospace, High tech, Software

Branches:
9403 Lagovista Ct.
Great Falls, Virginia 22066
(703) 759-9201
Fax: (703) 759-9203
Email: jim@hamiltongroup.com
Web: www.hamiltongroup.com
Key Contact - Specialty:
Mr. James B. Lawrence - *Network computing, software, telecommunications (senior level executives)*

Hamilton-Chase & Assoc., Inc.
Seaport Professional Bldg.
P.O. Box 237
Gloucester, Massachusetts 01930
(978) 281-1759
Fax: (978) 281-8023

Key Contact - Specialty:
Mr. Joseph E. Russo - *Generalist*

Description: Executive and technical search firm specializing in high-technology. Client organizations range in size from start-ups to Fortune 500. It employs quantitative interviewing/reference checking methodology, significantly improving candidate selection.

Salary Minimum: $80,000
Functions: Generalist
Industries: Generalist

Branches:
Custance Place
76 Bedford St., Ste. 18
Lexington, Massachusetts 02173
(617) 863-2811
Fax: (508) 281-8023
Key Contact - Specialty:
Mr. Joseph E. Russo - *Generalist*

R. C. Handel Assoc. Inc.
117 New London Turnpike
Glastonbury Common
Glastonbury, Connecticut 06033
(860) 633-3900

Key Contact - Specialty:
Mr. Richard C. Handel, Jr.

Description: A firm focused upon client service. In addition to providing professional search and staffing related consulting, we will tailor our service to the specific needs of the client.

Salary Minimum: $50,000
Functions: Generalist, Senior mgmt., Middle mgmt., Mfg., Sales & mktg., HR mgmt., Finance
Industries: Generalist, Mfg., Finance, Insurance, Healthcare

W. L. Handler & Assoc.
2255 Cumberland Parkway NW
Bldg. 1500
Atlanta, Georgia 30339
(770) 805-5000
Fax: (770) 805-5011

† occasional contingency assignment

Email: info@wlhandler.com
Web: www.wlhandler.com

Key Contact - Specialty:
Mr. William L. Handler - *Generalist*

Description: Middle and senior management and technical positions. Noted for rapid response and percent of completion. All assignments are performance guaranteed. Unconditional employment guarantee. More than 18 years of service to our clients.

Salary Minimum: $75,000
Functions: General mgmt., Mfg., Materials, Sales & mktg., HR mgmt., Finance, IT
Industries: Generalist, Mfg., Finance, Svcs., Communications, High tech

Networks:
World Search Group

Hands-on Broadcast †
124 W. 24th St., Ste. 6B
New York, New York 10011
(212) 924-5036
Fax: (212) 604-9036
Email: bgspeed@aol.com
Web: jobopts.com

Key Contact - Specialty:
Ms. Lorraine Bege - *Broadcast, cable, television, animation, entertainment*

Description: We place designers in cable, television and post-production--animators in feature film and multimedia in the US and internationally. Animation has become a strong focus.
Functions: Directors, Middle mgmt., Mktg. mgmt., Graphic artists, Int'l.
Industries: Finance, Entertainment, Communications, Advertising/PR, Publishing, New media, Broadcast & Film

Handy HRM
(a division of Compagnie General des Eaux)
250 Park Ave.
New York, New York 10177
(212) 557-0400
Fax: (212) 557-3531

Key Contact - Specialty:
Mr. J. Gerald Simmons - *Board of directors*
Mr. Richard K. Phillips - *Investment banking, corporate banking*
Mr. James R. Clovis, Jr. - *General management, corporate staff*
Mr. Chester A. Hopkins - *General management, marketing, corporate communications*
Mr. Franklin Key Brown - *Asset management*
Mr. Marc D. Lewis - *General management, finance, technology*
Mr. Patrick Brennan - *Banking, finance*
Mr. David G. Olsen - *Information technology, CIO's*
Mr. John C. Daily - *Information technology, CIO's*
Mr. R. Kevin Hughes - *Banking, corporate staff*
Mr. David W. Patenge - *Investment & commercial banking, finance*
Ms. Carolyn Dorsi

Description: Consultants in executive recruiting and executive compensation.

Salary Minimum: $100,000
Functions: Directors, Senior mgmt., Mktg. mgmt., PR, HR mgmt., CFO's, Cash mgmt., Taxes, M&A, MIS mgmt.
Industries: Generalist, Food/bev/tobacco, Computer equip., Consumer electronics, Finance, Banking, Invest. banking, Brokers, Venture cap., Misc. financial, Communications, Advertising/PR, Publishing, High tech, Software

International Branches:
Paris

Hanley & Assoc.
5150 N.Tamiami Trail, Ste. 501
Naples, Florida 34103
(941) 643-7474
Fax: (941) 643-1778
Web: www.hanleyassociates.com

Key Contact - Specialty:
Ms. Dorothy Hanley
Mr. Jim Lowrie

Description: Special strengths in placing middle and upper management, information technology managers in medical/healthcare, financial services and high technology industries.

Salary Minimum: $75,000
Functions: General mgmt., Healthcare, Health admin., Sales & mktg., Finance, IT
Industries: Computer equip., Banking, Computer svcs., Insurance, High tech, Software, Healthcare

Hanzel & Co., Inc.
60 E. 42nd St., Ste. 1146
New York, New York 10165
(212) 972-1832

Key Contact - Specialty:
Mr. Bruce S. Hanzel
Mr. Robert T. Anderson

Description: Principal area of practice is in senior management for revenue producing functions of investment banking.

Salary Minimum: $80,000
Functions: Cash mgmt., M&A
Industries: Invest. banking, Brokers, Venture cap.

Harcor Quest & Assoc. †
27389 Detroit Rd., Ste. J-23
Cleveland, Ohio 44145
(216) 871-5177
Fax: (216) 871-5185

Key Contact - Specialty:
Ms. Rachel Taylor - *Senior management*

Description: As generalists, we are a full service executive search and recruitment firm meeting the wide range of management needs of client companies from both the service and industrial sectors.

Salary Minimum: $70,000
Functions: Generalist, General mgmt., Mfg., Materials, IT, R&D, Engineering
Industries: Generalist, Mfg., Svcs., Computer svcs., High tech, Software, Biotech

Harcourt Group Ltd.
2178 Harcourt Drive
Cleveland Heights, Ohio 44106
(216) 791-6000
Email: jph@harcourtgroup.com

Key Contact - Specialty:
Mr. James P. Herget - *Industrial, financial services*
Mrs. Jane K. Herget - *Industrial, financial services*

Description: Together the principals combine the highest level of achievement in research and search methodology. A boutique format has allowed them to deliver the quality and attention which clients deserve.

Salary Minimum: $75,000
Functions: General mgmt., Mfg., Materials, Sales & mktg., HR mgmt., Finance, IT
Industries: Generalist, Mfg., Finance, Svcs., Aerospace, High tech, Software

Hardison & Company
4975 Preston Park Blvd., Ste. 150
Plano, Texas 75093
(972) 985-6990
Fax: (972) 985-6991

Key Contact - Specialty:
Mr. Richard L. Hardison - *Senior management, board members*

Description: Founded to provide the highest quality executive search services to a select group of clients committed to excellence in the recruitment of senior level executive talent.

Salary Minimum: $150,000
Functions: Directors, Senior mgmt., Mktg. mgmt., CFO's, M&A, MIS mgmt., Minorities

Industries: Energy/utilities, Chemicals, Computer equip., Venture cap., Entertainment, Telecoms, High tech

The Harris Consulting Corp.

444 St. Mary Ave., Ste. 1400
Winnipeg, Manitoba R3C 3T1
Canada
(204) 942-8735
Fax: (204) 944-8941
Email: harris@solutions.mb.ca

Key Contact - Specialty:
Mr. Russell H. May
Mr. Kenneth Poole
Mr. Alan Thorlakson

Description: Offering proactive and research driven search for management, professional and executive positions with particular depth of experience (17 years in business) in manufacturing, financial services, agribusiness and not-for-profit sectors.

Salary Minimum: $50,000
Functions: Senior mgmt., Middle mgmt., Plant mgmt., Materials Plng., Sales mgmt., Personnel, CFO's
Industries: Generalist, Agri/forestry/mining, Mfg., Finance, Aerospace, Insurance, High tech

Affiliates:
Verity Filion Inc.

Harris Heery & Assoc., Inc.

One Norwalk W., 40 Richards Ave.
Norwalk, Connecticut 06854
(203) 857-0808
Fax: (203) 857-0822
Web: bheery@harrisheery.com

Key Contact - Specialty:
Mr. William J. Heery - *Consumer marketing*
Mr. Andrew S. Harris - *Consumer marketing*
Ms. Linda Leonard - *Consumer marketing*
Ms. Suzanne Douglass - *Consumer marketing*

Description: A specialized firm for consumer goods and services companies recruiting on a domestic and international basis.

Salary Minimum: $80,000
Functions: Senior mgmt., Middle mgmt., Mkt. research, Mktg. mgmt., Direct mktg., Int'l.
Industries: Food/bev/tobacco, Soap/perfume/cosmetics, Computer equip., Entertainment, Telecoms, Insurance, High tech

Hartman & Barnette

P.O. Box 7966
Charlottesville, Virginia 22906
(804) 979-0993

Key Contact - Specialty:
Mr. Robert J. Hartman - *Healthcare*

Description: Specializing in personal, confidential search for middle and senior management in all functional areas. Extensive experience with highly specialized technology based products and companies. Activity divided between start-ups, medium and multinationals.

Salary Minimum: $70,000
Functions: General mgmt., Directors, Senior mgmt., Mfg., Sales & mktg., R&D, Int'l.
Industries: Drugs mfg., Medical devices, Venture cap., Pharmaceutical svcs., Biotech, Healthcare

Branches:
1213 Culbreth Dr., Bldg. 100
Wilmington, North Carolina 28405
(910) 256-0883
Key Contact - Specialty:
Mr. Fred A. Barnette - *Healthcare*

Hartsfield Group, Inc.

P.O. Box 421217
Atlanta, Georgia 30342
(770) 901-9000
(770) 901-6392
Fax: (770) 901-9100

Key Contact - Specialty:
Mr. Vincent W. Dee - *General management, those reporting directly to the CEOs*

Description: Fifteen year record of improving clients' competitiveness through leadership selection at the CEO and key functional levels. Clients range from Fortune 1000, mid-size emerging companies to high technology start-ups.

Salary Minimum: $100,000
Functions: Generalist, Senior mgmt., Sales & mktg., Finance, IT, MIS mgmt., Mgmt. consultants
Industries: New media, Telecoms, Aerospace, High tech

Harvard Aimes Group

6 Holcomb St., P.O. Box 16006
West Haven, Connecticut 06516
(203) 933-1976
Fax: (203) 933-0281
Email: JDG@RiskMgtSearch.com
Web: www.RiskMgtSearch.com

Key Contact - Specialty:
Mr. James J. Gunther - *Corporate risk management*

Description: Retained search for risk management (including safety and claims), benefits and insurance professionals in corporate environment only. All consultants have extensive experience working in the field in which they now recruit.

Salary Minimum: $50,000
Functions: Risk mgmt.
Industries: Generalist

Harvard Group Int'l.

5505 Roswell Rd., 3rd Floor
Atlanta, Georgia 30342
(404) 459-9045
Fax: (404) 459-9044
Email: karaf@mindspring.com

Key Contact - Specialty:
Mr. Thomas Gordy - *Communications, aerospace, high technology*

Description: Proven track record of prompt professional services from very experienced personnel who assist senior management in improving organizational and market performance in the communications, aerospace and high technology industries.
Functions: General mgmt., Mfg., Materials, Sales & mktg., HR mgmt., Finance, IT
Industries: Communications, Telecoms, Aerospace, High tech

Branches:
2743 Flintridge Drive
Colorado Springs, Colorado 80918
(719) 266-1980
Fax: (719) 266-1980
Email: goody@concentric.net
Key Contact - Specialty:
Mr. Goody Goodman - *Communications, aerospace, high technology*

Harvey Hohauser & Assoc., LLC

5600 New King St., Ste. 355
Troy, Michigan 48098
(248) 641-1400
Fax: (248) 641-1929
Email: hohauser@mailexcite.com

Key Contact - Specialty:
Mr. Harvey Hohauser
Ms. Debra Schlutow
Ms. Mary Mastripolito

Description: Management consultants specializing in executive recruitment, management appraisals and organization analysis.

Salary Minimum: $70,000
Functions: General mgmt., Mfg., Sales & mktg., HR mgmt., Finance, IT, Engineering
Industries: Generalist, Chemicals, Plastics/rubber, Metal products, Motor vehicles, Finance, Non-profits

Branches:
P.O. Box 717
Okemos, Michigan 48805
(517) 349-7007
Fax: (517) 349-7027
Key Contact - Specialty:
Mr. Kenneth S. Glickman

Affiliates:
Ramsey Hall Ltd.

Bruce W. Haupt Assoc. †
P.O. Box 21599, Kalorama Station NW
Washington, District of Columbia 20009
(202) 364-0793

Key Contact - Specialty:
Bruce W. Haupt - *Legal, medical, R&D scientist)*

Description: Primarily a legal and legal-medical search firm. We have previously completed two (2) searches at the level of Associate Justice of the U.S. Supreme Court.

Salary Minimum: $60,000
Functions: Directors, Legal, Physicians, R&D, Attorneys
Industries: Generalist, Legal, Healthcare

The Hawkins Co.
5455 Wilshire Blvd., Ste. 1406
Los Angeles, California 90036
(213) 933-3337
Fax: (213) 933-9765
Email: hawkins95@aol.com

Key Contact - Specialty:
Mr. William D. Hawkins

Description: Retained executive search firm specializing in public and private sector recruitment with strong emphasis on diversity recruitment.

Salary Minimum: $100,000
Functions: Product dev., Production, Mkt. research, Sales mgmt., CFO's, Engineering, Minorities
Industries: Energy/utilities, Food/bev/tobacco, Motor vehicles, Hospitality, Communications, Government

William E. Hay & Co.
Two First National Plaza
20 S. Clark St., Ste. 2305
Chicago, Illinois 60603
(312) 782-6510

Key Contact - Specialty:
Mr. William E. Hay - *Senior level executives (all functional areas)*

Description: A generalist firm representing equal time in the private manufacturing, service and not-for-profit sectors across all functional categories.

Salary Minimum: $50,000
Functions: Generalist, Senior mgmt., Middle mgmt., Plant mgmt., Mktg. mgmt., CFO's, MIS mgmt.
Industries: Generalist, Construction, Transportation, Hospitality, Non-profits, Mgmt. consulting, Government

Hayden Group, Inc.
One Post Office Sq., Ste. 3830
Boston, Massachusetts 02109
(617) 482-2445
Fax: (617) 482-2444

Key Contact - Specialty:
Mr. Robert E. Hawley - *Financial services, senior level*
Mr. Harry B. McCormick - *Financial services, senior level*

Description: Broad range of senior management, middle management and board search assignments conducted on an exclusive basis for regional, national and international clients with particular emphasis in financial services companies.

Salary Minimum: $100,000
Functions: Directors, Senior mgmt., Sales mgmt., CFO's, MIS mgmt.
Industries: Finance, Banking, Misc. financial

Hayman & Co.
4311 Oak Lawn Ave. #450
Dallas, Texas 75219
(214) 953-1900
Fax: (214) 559-2838
Email: hayman@airmail.net

Key Contact - Specialty:
Mr. Thomas C. Hayman

Salary Minimum: $80,000
Functions: Generalist
Industries: Generalist

The Haystack Group, Inc.
7 Mountain St.
P.O. Box 823
Vinalhaven, Maine 04863-0823
(207) 863-2793
Fax: (207) 863-9916
Email: islandman@haystack-group.com
Web: www.haystack-group.com

Key Contact - Specialty:
Mr. John Gasbarre - *Medical devices, biotechnology, pharmaceuticals, healthcare information technology*

Description: Our areas of expertise are needle in haystack searches within medical devices, biotechnology pharmaceuticals, healthcare information technology. We rely heavily on search research and competitive intelligence to insure our work is exhaustive.

Salary Minimum: $80,000
Functions: Directors, Product dev., Mkt. research, Mktg. mgmt., Sales mgmt., R&D, Engineering
Industries: Drugs mfg., Medical devices, Pharmaceutical svcs., Biotech, Healthcare

Hazlett Associates
2340 Orrington Ave.
Evanston, Illinois 60201
(847) 866-8382
Fax: (847) 866-8390
Email: tomhazlett@aol.com

Key Contact - Specialty:
Mr. Thomas M. Hazlett

Description: National searches with emphasis on direct/database marketing, marketing communications, consumer products/services. Only accept limited number of engagements at one time to ensure personal service and timely results.

Salary Minimum: $75,000
Functions: General mgmt., Sales & mktg., Mkt. research, Mktg. mgmt., Sales mgmt., Direct mktg., DB admin.
Industries: Food/bev/tobacco, Printing, Computer svcs., Communications, Advertising/PR, New media

Headden Assoc.
777 108th Ave. NE, Ste. 600
Bellevue, Washington 98004
(425) 451-2427
Fax: (425) 646-3015

Key Contact - Specialty:
Mr. William P. Headden, Jr. - *Telecommunications, generalist*
Mr. Alex Mott - *Telecommunications, sales & marketing*
Ms. Carol Reid

Description: We conduct mid to senior level retained search over a broad range of disciplines. We are generalists but have developed a special expertise in wireless communications including cellular, two way, paging and SMR.

Salary Minimum: $90,000
Functions: Generalist, Senior mgmt., Middle mgmt., Mktg. mgmt., CFO's
Industries: Generalist, New media, Telecoms, High tech

Healey Executive Search, Inc.
(Firm declined to update.)
2925 Dean Pkwy., Ste. 300
Minneapolis, Minnesota 55416
(612) 928-7633

Key Contact - Specialty:
Mr. David Healey - *General management*

Description: Generalist firm conducting search in the upper Midwest for directors, presidents, marketing, manufacturing, human resources, non-profit.

Salary Minimum: $60,000

Functions: Directors, Senior mgmt., Plant mgmt., Mktg. mgmt., Benefits, CFO's, Non-profits
Industries: Generalist, Mfg., Metal products, Computer equip., Finance, Non-profits, Telecoms

Health Industry Consultants, Inc.

9250 E. Costilla Ave., Ste. 600
Englewood, Colorado 80112
(303) 790-2009
Fax: (303) 790-2021

Key Contact - Specialty:
Mr. Jon K. Fitzgerald - *Medical devices, officer level, board of directors*

Description: Middle and upper management retained search in general management, engineering, operations, QA/RA, marketing and sales for medical companies. 90% of searches for CEO's or board directorships.

Salary Minimum: $100,000
Functions: General mgmt., Directors, Senior mgmt., Mfg., Sales & mktg., R&D, Engineering
Industries: Medical devices

Healthcare Management Resources, Inc.

P.O. Box 450149
Atlanta, Georgia 31145
(404) 329-9314
Fax: (404) 320-3114
Email: admin@hmratlanta.com

Key Contact - Specialty:
Ms. Mary Bowman - *Venture funded start-up companies, medical devices, diagnostics, biotechnology*
Ms. Diane Westmore - *Venture funded start-up companies, medical devices, diagnostics, biotechnology*
Ms. Louise Sawhill - *Venture funded start-up companies, medical devices, diagnostics, biotechnology*

Description: Specialize in venture-funded start-up companies in medical devices, diagnostics and biotechnology.

Salary Minimum: $75,000
Functions: Senior mgmt., Product dev., Sales mgmt., CFO's, MIS mgmt., R&D, Int'l.
Industries: Drugs mfg., Medical devices, Venture cap., Biotech, Healthcare

F. P. Healy & Co., Inc.

230 Park Ave., Ste. 232
New York, New York 10169
(212) 661-0366
Fax: (212) 661-0383

Key Contact - Specialty:
Mr. Frank P. Healy
Mr. Richard P. Healy

Description: We are an executive search firm that serves all industries.

Salary Minimum: $50,000
Functions: Senior mgmt., Plant mgmt., Mktg. mgmt., Direct mktg., CFO's, MIS mgmt., Engineering
Industries: Drugs mfg., Motor vehicles, Computer equip., Finance, High tech, Software, Healthcare

Heath/Norton Assoc., Inc.

545 Eighth Ave.
New York, New York 10018
(212) 695-3600

Key Contact - Specialty:
Mr. Richard S. Stoller - *Senior level sales & marketing, general management*
Mr. Richard Rosenow - *Senior level engineering, manufacturing, general management*

Description: With experience dating back to 1966, Heath/Norton is considered to be one of the more prestigious search firms in the country. The retainer firm specializes in sales, marketing, engineering, manufacturing and general management.

Salary Minimum: $75,000
Functions: General mgmt., Senior mgmt., Middle mgmt., Mfg., Plant mgmt., Quality, Materials, Purchasing, Sales & mktg., Mkt. research, Mktg. mgmt., Sales mgmt., Engineering
Industries: Food/bev/tobacco, Printing, Medical devices, Machinery/Appliances, Consumer electronics, Misc. mfg., Aerospace, High tech, Healthcare

R. W. Hebel Assoc.

4833 Spicewood Springs Rd., Ste. 202
Austin, Texas 78759
(512) 338-9691
Fax: (512) 338-1308

Key Contact - Specialty:
Mr. Robert W. Hebel - *Healthcare, pharmaceutical, device, diagnostic, biotechnology*

Description: Retainer search firm specializing in senior healthcare executive recruitment specific to the biotechnology, pharmaceutical; diagnostic and device healthcare sectors.

Salary Minimum: $100,000
Functions: Senior mgmt., Product dev., Mkt. research, CFO's, R&D
Industries: Drugs mfg., Medical devices, Venture cap., Pharmaceutical svcs., Biotech

Hechkoff/Work Executive Search Inc.

444 Madison Ave., Ste. 710
New York, New York 10022
(212) 935-2100
Fax: (212) 935-2199
Email: results@hwsearch.com

Key Contact - Specialty:
Mr. Robert B. Hechkoff - *Information technology, management consulting, telecommunications*
Mr. Alan J. Work - *Information technology, management consulting, financial services*

Description: Our extensive network of contacts gives our recruiters a considerable advantage in identifying potential candidates and referrals. Our focused, client centered approach has resulted in hundreds of successful placements.

Salary Minimum: $100,000
Functions: Directors, Senior mgmt., Middle mgmt., Mktg. mgmt., MIS mgmt., Systems implem., Mgmt. consultants
Industries: Computer equip., Computer svcs., Mgmt. consulting, New media, Telecoms, High tech, Software

Hedman & Assoc. †

3312 Woodford, Ste. 200
Arlington, Texas 76013-1139
(817) 277-0888
Email: hedman@onramp.net

Key Contact - Specialty:
Mr. Kent R. Hedman - *General management*

Description: 25 years recruiting experience; strictly confidential; emphasis on identification and assessment of high impact performers and matching client needs; special competence identifying profit center management talent.

Salary Minimum: $40,000
Functions: Generalist, Int'l.
Industries: Generalist

Heffelfinger Assoc., Inc. †

470 Washington St.
Chestnut Green
Norwood, Massachusetts 02062
(781) 769-6650
Fax: (781) 769-6652
Email: heffone@wn.net

Key Contact - Specialty:
Mr. Thomas V. Heffelfinger - *CIO's, CEOs, senior vice presidents, technology oriented companies & CTO's*

Description: Founded in 1965, specialize in computer/communication industry, both vendor and corporate IS management positions. National and international coverage through NASA-North American Search Alliance partners.

† occasional contingency assignment

Salary Minimum: $100,000
Functions: General mgmt., Mfg., Sales & mktg., Finance, IT, R&D, Int'l.
Industries: Computer equip., Computer svcs., Telecoms, High tech, Software

Affiliates:
Dennis & Gemmill International Limited

Heidrick & Struggles, Inc.

233 S. Wacker Drive, Ste. 4200
Sears Tower
Chicago, Illinois 60606-6303
(312) 496-1000
(312) 496-1200
Fax: (312) 496-1290
Web: www.h-s.com

Key Contact - Specialty:
Mr. Gerard R. Roche
Mr. John T. Thompson
Mr. Patrick S. Pittard
Mr. Richard D. Nelson
Mr. Donald M. Kilinski

Description: Consultants in executive search assisting client organizations in identifying, attracting and retaining executive talent for specific opportunities within middle and top management and for boards of directors.

Salary Minimum: $150,000
Functions: Generalist
Industries: Generalist
Professional Associations: AESC, IACPR

Branches:
19200 Von Karman Ave., Ste. 600
Irvine, California 92612
(714) 477-8011
Fax: (714) 477-8012
Key Contact - Specialty:
Mr. Michael T. Kristy

300 S. Grand Ave., Ste. 2400
Los Angeles, California 90071
(213) 625-8811
Fax: (213) 617-7216
Key Contact - Specialty:
Mr. Thomas M. Mitchell

2740 Sand Hill Rd.
Menlo Park, California 94025-7096
(650) 234-1500
Fax: (650) 854-4191
Key Contact - Specialty:
Mr. Wesley D. Richards

Four Embarcadero Ctr., Ste. 3570
San Francisco, California 94111
(415) 981-2854
Fax: (415) 981-0482
Key Contact - Specialty:
Mr. Jeff Hodge

Greenwich Office Park, #3
51 Weaver St.
Greenwich, Connecticut 06831-5150
(203) 629-3200
Fax: (203) 629-1331
Key Contact - Specialty:
Mr. Marvin B. Berenblum

1301 K St. NW, Ste. 500 E.
Washington, District of Columbia 20005-3317
(202) 289-4450
Fax: (202) 289-4451
Key Contact - Specialty:
Mr. Roger W. Stoy, Jr.

76 S. Laura St., Ste. 2110
Jacksonville, Florida 32202-5448
(904) 355-6674
Fax: (904) 355-6841
Key Contact - Specialty:
Mr. Charles R. Hoskins

5301 Blue Lagoon Drive, Ste. 590
Miami, Florida 33125
(305) 262-2606
Fax: (305) 262-6697
Key Contact - Specialty:
Ms. Jean-Dominique Virchaux

303 Peachtree St. NE, Ste. 3100
Sun Trust Plaza
Atlanta, Georgia 30308-3201
(404) 577-2410
Fax: (404) 577-4048
Key Contact - Specialty:
Mr. A. Wayne Luke
Mr. Patrick S. Pittard

223 S. Wacker Drive, Ste. 7000
Chicago, Illinois 60606-6402
(312) 496-1000
Fax: (312) 496-1046
Key Contact - Specialty:
Ms. Linda Heagy

One Post Office Sq., Ste. 3570
Boston, Massachusetts 02109-0199
(617) 423-1140
Fax: (617) 423-0895
Key Contact - Specialty:
Mr. George A. Rossi

245 Park Ave., Ste. 4300
New York, New York 10167-0152
(212) 867-9876
Fax: (212) 370-9035
Key Contact - Specialty:
Ms. Joie A. Gregor

227 W. Trade St., Ste. 1600
Charlotte, North Carolina 28202
(704) 333-1953
Fax: (704) 335-7274
Key Contact - Specialty:
Mr. Eugene M. Rackley

600 Superior Ave. E., Ste. 2500
Cleveland, Ohio 44114-2650
(216) 241-7410
Fax: (216) 241-2217
Key Contact - Specialty:
Mr. Charles E. Wallace, Jr.

One Logan Sq., Ste. 3075
18th & Cherry Streets
Philadelphia, Pennsylvania 19103
(215) 988-1000
Fax: (215) 988-9496
Key Contact - Specialty:
Mr. Kenneth L. Kring

2200 Ross Ave., Ste. 4700E
Texas Commerce Bank Bldg.
Dallas, Texas 75201-2787
(214) 220-2130
Fax: (214) 220-1029
Key Contact - Specialty:
Mr. David C. Anderson

1221 McKinney St., Ste. 3050
One Houston Center
Houston, Texas 77010
(713) 237-9000
Fax: (713) 751-3018
Key Contact - Specialty:
Mr. David A. Morris

8000 Towers Crescent Drive, Ste. 555
Vienna, Virginia 22182-2700
(703) 761-4830
Fax: (703) 761-4831
Key Contact - Specialty:
Mr. Kevin A. McNerney

BCE Place, 161 Bay St., Ste. 2310
P.O. Box 601
Toronto, Ontario M5J 2S1
Canada
(416) 361-4700
Fax: (416) 361-4770
Key Contact - Specialty:
Mr. David R. Pasahow

Torre Chapultepec
Ruben Dario No. 281 Ofna. 1403
Col. Bosque de Chapultepec
Mexico City, Mexico DF 11580
Mexico
52 5 280 5200
Fax: 52 5 280 5230
Key Contact - Specialty:
Mr. Adolfo Medina-Haro

International Branches:
Amsterdam, Barcelona, Berlin, Brussels, Buenos Aires, Caracas, Chiyoda-ku, Copenhagen, Dresden, Dusseldorf, Dusseldorf, Frankfurt, Hamburg, Helsinki, Hong Kong, Lima, Lisbon, London, Madrid, Milan, Moscow, Munich, Munich, Oslo, Paris, Prague, Santiago, Sao Paulo, Singapore, Stockholm, Sydney, Warsaw, Zurich

The Heidrick Partners, Inc.

20 N. Wacker Drive, Ste. 2850
Chicago, Illinois 60606-3171
(312) 845-9700

Key Contact - Specialty:
Mr. Robert L. Heidrick
Mr. Gardner W. Heidrick
Mr. Theodore W. Seweloh
Ms. Melanie F. Davis
Ms. Susan M. Coffin

Description: In general executive recruiting with a specialization of counseling and searching for outside corporate directors.

Salary Minimum: $120,000

Functions: Generalist, Directors, Senior mgmt., Purchasing, Mktg. mgmt., Sales mgmt., CFO's, MIS mgmt.
Industries: Generalist, Energy/utilities, Food/bev/tobacco, Printing, Metal products, Machinery/Appliances, Misc. mfg., Real estate
Professional Associations: AESC

Heinze & Assoc. Inc.

6125 Blue Circle Drive, Suite 218
Minnetonka, Minnesota 55343
(612) 938-2828

Key Contact - Specialty:
Mr. David Heinze - *General management*

Description: Custom designed search strategy conducted by experienced professionals. Guaranteed performance.

Salary Minimum: $75,000
Functions: Generalist, Senior mgmt., Plant mgmt., Mktg. mgmt., Sales mgmt., CFO's, MIS mgmt.
Industries: Generalist, Medical devices, Machinery/Appliances, Consumer electronics, Misc. mfg., Insurance, High tech

---

Helbling & Assoc., Inc.

117 VIP Drive, Ste. 320
Northridge Office Plaza
Wexford, Pennsylvania 15090
(724) 935-7500
Fax: (724) 935-7531
Email: helb@nauticom.com

Key Contact - Specialty:
Mr. Thomas J. Helbling - *Construction, real estate*

Description: Staff offers more than 30 years of national construction recruiting experience and is recognized for its ability to successfully recruit professionals in all levels of management with 90% of business coming from repeat clients.
Functions: Senior mgmt., Middle mgmt., Mktg. mgmt., Personnel, CFO's, Mgmt. consultants
Industries: Construction, Real estate

Helfer Executive Consultants

P.O. Box 50239
Nashville, Tennessee 37205-0239
(615) 356-2777

Key Contact - Specialty:
Mr. Frederick W. Helfer - *Manufacturing, engineering, technical*

Description: Southeastern retainer firm specializing in high performance candidates for managerial, professional and technical positions. Especially strong in mfg, eng and MIS. Also recruit sales and marketing, HR and financial positions.

Salary Minimum: $75,000
Functions: General mgmt., Mfg., Materials, Sales & mktg., HR mgmt., Finance, IT
Industries: Generalist, Printing, Plastics/rubber, Metal products, Misc. mfg., Finance, Packaging

---

Heller Assoc., Ltd.

One Northfield Plaza, Ste. 300
Northfield, Illinois 60093
(847) 441-2626
Fax: (847) 441-2645
Email: info@hellerassociates.com
Web: www.hellerassociates.com

Key Contact - Specialty:
Mr. Gary A. Heller - *Generalist*

Description: Executive search specializing in mid to senior sales, marketing and general management functions within commercial and consumer industries. We have affiliate arrangements with other search firms in New York, Atlanta, Los Angeles, San Francisco, Europe and Asia.

Salary Minimum: $75,000
Functions: Generalist, Directors, Senior mgmt., Middle mgmt., Product dev., Sales mgmt., CFO's
Industries: Generalist, Food/bev/tobacco, Machinery/Appliances, Computer equip., Consumer electronics, Communications, Software

---

The Helms Int'l. Group †

8000 Towers Crescent Drive, Ste. 1350
Vienna, Virginia 22182
(703) 760-7881
Fax: (703) 556-4271
Email: helmsintl@aol.com

Key Contact - Specialty:
Ms. Mary P. Helms - *Human Resources*

Description: Executive search which supports the intended strategy of clients experiencing organizational change. Aligned with executive development process. Emphasis on human resource positions.

Salary Minimum: $60,000
Functions: Mktg. mgmt., HR mgmt., Training, IT, Mgmt. consultants, Non-profits
Industries: Generalist, Non-profits, Human resource svcs., Communications, High tech, Software

---

G. W. Henn & Co.

42 E. Gay St., Ste. 1312
Columbus, Ohio 43215-3119
(614) 469-9666
Fax: (614) 469-8304

Key Contact - Specialty:
Mr. George W. Henn, Jr. - *General management*

Description: General recruiting practice focusing on senior management positions, all industries. Significant experience in insurance, banking, manufacturing, information systems and automotive.

Salary Minimum: $100,000
Functions: Senior mgmt., Mktg. mgmt., Sales mgmt., CFO's, MIS mgmt.
Industries: Energy/utilities, Paper, Medical devices, Machinery/Appliances, Banking, Pharmaceutical svcs., Packaging

---

Bruce Henry Assoc. Inc.

465 California St. #450
San Francisco, California 94104
(415) 398-6540
Fax: (415) 438-2112
Email: bh@brucehenry.com
Web: www.brucehenry.com

Key Contact - Specialty:
Mr. Bruce Henry - *Healthcare, dentistry*

Description: We provide executive search for the dental industry. Shifting our focus in 1997, we specialize in both general practice and specialist dentists. We also offer search services for dental practice administrators.

Salary Minimum: $50,000
Functions: Senior mgmt., Middle mgmt., Physicians, Nurses, Mktg. mgmt., CFO's, MIS mgmt.
Industries: Healthcare

Branches:
234 W. Bandera, Ste. 109
Boerne, Texas 78006
(830) 510-4598
Fax: (830) 510-4598
Email: bd@brucehenry.com
Web: www.brucehenry.com
Key Contact - Specialty:
Mr. Bill Dye - *Healthcare, dentistry*

The Hensge Co.

2100 Manchester Rd., Ste. 507
Wheaton, Illinois 60187-4586
(630) 871-1818
Email: sgeteam@aol.com

Key Contact - Specialty:
Mr. Bill Hensge - *Senior management*

Description: Our practice is aimed at helping clients execute their business strategy by better alignment of their organization with their strategic objectives.

Salary Minimum: $100,000
Functions: Senior mgmt., Mfg., Materials, Sales & mktg., HR mgmt., Finance, Mgmt. consultants

† occasional contingency assignment

Industries: Agri/forestry/mining, Mfg., Transportation, Wholesale, Mgmt. consulting, Communications, Packaging

---

Herbeck Kline & Assoc.

Three Hawthorne Pkwy., Ste. 235
Vernon Hills, Illinois 60061
(847) 247-1400
Fax: (847) 247-1576
Email: jbherbeck@Ameritech.net

Key Contact - Specialty:
Mr. J. Brad Herbeck
Mr. Dennis Kline

Description: Demonstrated ability to work successfully for middle market companies (closely/privately held) to Fortune 500 clients. Experience both domestic and international in all functional areas.

Salary Minimum: $100,000
Functions: General mgmt., Mfg., Sales & mktg., HR mgmt., Finance, IT, R&D
Industries: Mfg., Transportation, Retail, Communications, Aerospace, High tech, Biotech

---

Hergenrather & Co.

401 W. Charlton Ave.
Spokane, Washington 99208
(509) 466-6700
Fax: (509) 466-7500
Email: rhergenrather@whitworth.edu

Key Contact - Specialty:
Dr. Richard A. Hergenrather - *Generalist*
Mr. Edmund R. Hergenrather - *Generalist*

Description: The first professional executive search organization in the West established at Los Angeles in 1954. Engaged in senior level searches in every functional area and in most industries.

Salary Minimum: $75,000
Functions: Generalist, General mgmt., Mfg., Sales & mktg., HR mgmt., Finance, Engineering
Industries: Generalist, Mfg., Transportation, Finance, Svcs., Aerospace, High tech

---

Hermann & Westmore

9800 D Topanga Canyon Blvd., Ste. 345
Chatsworth, California 91311
(818) 717-9000
Fax: (818) 717-9099
Email: HermWest@aol.com

Key Contact - Specialty:
Mr. Robert J. Westmore - *Audit, tax, MAS*

Description: We are a niche firm focused on providing partner level individuals in all disciplines to the CPA and management consulting communities.

Salary Minimum: $120,000
Functions: Directors, Senior mgmt., Finance, CFO's, IT, MIS mgmt., Mgmt. consultants
Industries: Accounting, Mgmt. consulting

Branches:
14 N. Chatsworth Ave., Ste. 4D
Larchmont, New York 10538
(914) 833-7723
Fax: (914) 833-7719
Email: GeoHermann@aol.com
Key Contact - Specialty:
Mr. George A. Hermann - *Audit, tax, MAS*

A. Herndon & Assoc., Inc.

5100 Westheimer, Ste. 200
Houston, Texas 77056
(713) 968-6577

Key Contact - Specialty:
Mr. Martin Buss
Ms. Angela Herndon

Description: Provide significantly lower recruiting costs without sacrificing service quality through effective utilization of proprietary database, in-house ability to access numerous commercial databases and hourly billing structure.

Salary Minimum: $75,000
Functions: Directors, Senior mgmt., Middle mgmt., Sales & mktg., Finance, IT, Attorneys
Industries: Generalist

Herrerias & Assoc. †

330 Sir Francis Drake Blvd., Ste. E
San Anselmo, California 94960
(415) 721-7001
Fax: (415) 721-7003
Email: paul@herrerias.com
Web: www.herrerias.com

Key Contact - Specialty:
Mr. Paul Herrerias - *Finance, marketing, human resources*

Description: We are the premier retained executive search firm for technology companies in the North Bay.

Salary Minimum: $75,000
Functions: Directors, Sales & mktg., HR mgmt., Finance, Mgmt. consultants
Industries: Accounting, New media, Software, Biotech

The Herrmann Group Ltd.

60 Bloor St. W., Ste. 1100
Toronto, Ontario M4W 3B8
Canada
(416) 922-4242
Fax: (416) 922-4366
Email: gherrmanngroup.com
Web: www.herrmanngroup.com

Key Contact - Specialty:
Ms. Gerlinde Herrmann - *Generalist, mid to senior level*

Description: We specialize in building and retaining strong business alliances with our clients. We become an integral part of their organizations and are thereby able to offer valuable support and services. We go beyond supplying people.

Salary Minimum: $60,000
Functions: Generalist, Senior mgmt., Mkt. research, Personnel, Cash mgmt., Systems anal., Mgmt. consultants

---

Hersher Assoc., Ltd.

3000 Dundee Rd., Ste. 314
Northbrook, Illinois 60062
(847) 272-4050
Fax: (847) 272-1998
Email: hersher@hersher.com

Key Contact - Specialty:
Ms. Betsy S. Hersher - *Healthcare*
Ms. Linda B. Hodges - *Healthcare*

Description: Exclusively healthcare. National CIO and information systems experts. Experience in integrated delivery networks, academic medical centers, managed care organizations and physician organizations. Established track record in executive nursing, information systems, finance, administration and clinical department heads. Nationally recognized as recruitment and retention consulting experts.

Salary Minimum: $50,000
Functions: Health admin., Mktg. mgmt., Sales mgmt., CFO's, MIS mgmt., Mgmt. consultants
Industries: Healthcare

Stanley Herz & Co.

Mill Pond Office Complex, Ste. 103
Somers, New York 10589
(914) 277-7500
Fax: (914) 277-7749
Web: www.stanleyherz.com

Key Contact - Specialty:
Mr. Stanley Herz - *Senior management*

Description: Executive search and search consulting. Finance, technology, MIS, marketing, general management. Clients are national. Emphasis on mid-size and emerging companies. Firm profiled in Business Week and Inc. magazine.

Salary Minimum: $90,000
Functions: Senior mgmt., Plant mgmt., Mktg. mgmt., CFO's, MIS mgmt.
Industries: Generalist

The Hetzel Group, Inc.

Williamsburg Village
1601 Colonial Pkwy.
Inverness, Illinois 60067
(847) 776-7000

Key Contact - Specialty:
Mr. William G. Hetzel - *Generalist*
Ms. Karen M. Ross - *Generalist*

Description: Most proud of the long term client relationships and success of candidates placed. Each search performed by an officer.

Salary Minimum: $100,000
Functions: Generalist, Senior mgmt., Sales mgmt., CFO's, MIS mgmt., R&D, Engineering
Industries: Generalist, Drugs mfg., Plastics/rubber, Machinery/Appliances, Computer equip., Aerospace, High tech
Professional Associations: IACPR

Affiliates:
Nagler, Robins & Poe, Inc.

Heyman Assoc., Inc.
341 Madison Ave., 12th Floor
New York, New York 10017
(212) 681-7818
Email: hai@heymanassociates.com
Web: www.heymanassociates.com

Key Contact - Specialty:
Mr. William C. Heyman
Ms. Elisabeth A. Ryan
Ms. Maryanne B. Rainone
Mr. Robert L. Ferrante
Ms. Elizabeth Krumenacker
Mr. James Masuga
Ms. Susanne deLemos

Description: As specialists in public relations, corporate communications, investor relations and public affairs,we are in contact with the industry's leaders and maintain a database with the names and backgrounds of thousands of communications and public affairs professionals.

Salary Minimum: $75,000
Functions: PR
Industries: Generalist, Advertising/PR

HG & Assoc.
1110 Lake Cook Rd., Ste. 268
Buffalo Grove, Illinois 60089
(847) 459-9516
(847) 433-5494
Fax: (847) 459-0340
Email: hgassoc@aol.com

Key Contact - Specialty:
Mr. Herb Greenberg - *Privately held companies (small to mid-size)*

Description: Demonstrated ability to work successfully for middle market companies (closely/privately held) to Fortune 500 clients. Experience both domestic and international in all functional areas.

Salary Minimum: $60,000
Functions: Generalist
Industries: Generalist

Higdon Prince Inc.
230 Park Ave., Ste. 1455
New York, New York 10169
(212) 986-4662
Fax: (212) 986-5002
Web: higprin@aol.com

Key Contact - Specialty:
Mr. Henry G. Higdon - *Financial services, investment management, investment banking*
Ms. Marylin L. Prince - *Financial services, investment management, investment banking*
Ms. Maryann C. Bovich - *Financial services, investment management, investment banking*
Ms. Sloan Satenstein - *Financial services, investment management, investment banking*
Mr. Joseph B. Goldsmith - *Financial services, investment management, investment banking*

Description: A medium size high-powered firm with searches conducted by owners/professionals with no less than 10 years of experience and recognized as leaders in the business.

Salary Minimum: $150,000
Functions: General mgmt., Senior mgmt., Mktg. mgmt., Sales mgmt., HR mgmt., CFO's, Int'l.
Industries: Generalist, Finance, Banking, Invest. banking, Brokers, Venture cap., Misc. financial
Professional Associations: AESC

Higgins Assoc., Inc.
P.O. Box 916
Northbrook, Illinois 60065-0916
(847) 940-4800

Key Contact - Specialty:
Mr. John B. Higgins

Description: Retainer fee, generalist search firm.

Salary Minimum: $200,000
Functions: Generalist, General mgmt., Directors, Sales & mktg., Finance, IT, MIS mgmt.
Industries: Generalist

Highland Search Group, L.L.C.
565 Fifth Ave., 22nd Floor
New York, New York 10017
(212) 328-1100
Email: highland@searchers.com
Web: www.searchers.com

Key Contact - Specialty:
Mr. Steven B. Potter - *Investment banking, merchant banking, CEOs*
Mr. Georges L. Holzberger - *Investment banking, global banking*
Mr. James L. Phillips, Jr. - *Investment management, real estate*
Mr. Michael Liebowitz - *Investment banking*
Mr. Michael P. Castine - *Investment management, CFOs*

Description: We specialize in providing executive recruiting services to the financial services industry to include insurance, real estate, investment banking, commercial banking, investment management and direct investments. We also specialize in recruiting CFOs, CEOs and directors accross a wide spectrum of corporate America.

Salary Minimum: $150,000
Functions: Directors, Senior mgmt., Purchasing, HR mgmt., CFO's, Mgmt. consultants
Industries: Banking, Invest. banking, Brokers, Venture cap., Misc. financial, Real estate

Higley, Hall & Co., Inc.
112 Turnpike Rd., Westboro Executive Park
Westborough, Massachusetts 01581
(508) 836-4292
Fax: (508) 836-4294
Email: donhall1@aol.com

Key Contact - Specialty:
Mr. Donald L. Hall - *Financial, banking*

Description: Executive banking background on part of principal - quality firm.

Salary Minimum: $50,000
Functions: Directors, Senior mgmt., Middle mgmt., CFO's, MIS mgmt.
Industries: Finance, Banking, Misc. financial

Frank P. Hill
Rio Guadalquivir 38-701
Col. Cuauhtemoc
Mexico City, Mexico DF 06500
Mexico
52 5 208 4902
Email: fphill@acnet.net
Web: www.iicpartners-esw.com

Key Contact - Specialty:
Mr. Frank P. Hill - *Generalist*
Ms. Andrea Garcia Sauer - *Generalist*
Mr. Roberto E. Tattersfield - *Generalist*

Description: Specializing in upper-level executives search. Particularly strong in sales, marketing, finance, manufacturing and human resources.

Salary Minimum: $50,000
Functions: General mgmt., Plant mgmt., Materials, Sales & mktg., HR mgmt., Finance, CFO's
Industries: Chemicals, Soap/perfume/cosmetics, Drugs mfg., Retail

Networks:
I-I-C Partners Executive Search Worldwide

The Hindman Co.
2000 Warrington Way
Browenton Place, Ste. 110
Louisville, Kentucky 40222
(502) 426-4040

Key Contact - Specialty:
Mr. Neil C. Hindman - *Manufacturing, industrial, banking, finance (all management functions)*
Mr. Harold B. Berry - *Manufacturing, industrial, banking, finance (all management functions)*
Mr. James H. Palmer - *Manufacturing, industrial, banking, finance (all management functions)*
Ms. Deborah F. Bruno - *Manufacturing, industrial, banking, finance (all management functions)*

Description: North America and Europe: executive/management search, regional, national, international. U.S. and multinational corporate clientele. Emphasize all management functions: manufacturing/industrial and banking/financial sectors.

Salary Minimum: $50,000
Functions: Generalist, Senior mgmt., Plant mgmt., Mktg. mgmt., Sales mgmt., CFO's, Engineering
Industries: Generalist, Chemicals, Plastics/rubber, Metal products, Motor vehicles, Consumer electronics, Finance

Branches:
270 Jefferson Place
Canfield, Ohio 44406
(330) 533-5450
Key Contact - Specialty:
Mr. James E. Rimmel

The Tower at Williams Square, Ste. 200
5215 North O'Connor Road
Irving, Texas 75039
(972) 868-9122
Key Contact - Specialty:
Mr. Thomas A. Fowler

325 Springlake Rd.
Bristol, Virginia 24201
(540) 669-5006
Key Contact - Specialty:
Mr. Ted K. Ellis

Affiliates:
David Dillistone & Company, Ltd.

Hite Executive Search
P.O. Box 43217
Cleveland, Ohio 44143-0217
(440) 461-1600
Fax: (440) 461-9177
Email: wahite@hite-mgmt.com
Web: www.hite-mgmt.com

Key Contact - Specialty:
Mr. William A. Hite, III - *General management*
Mr. Lauren R. Pacini - *Information technology*
Ms. Bonnie L. Page

Description: Executive, senior and middle management specialists. Convenient North-Central US headquarters. Computerized research and database, plus extensive worldwide resource network. Quality documentary procedures. Percentage or fixed fee arrangements. Retainer only.

Salary Minimum: $100,000
Functions: Generalist, General mgmt., Mfg., Sales & mktg., MIS mgmt., Engineering, Specialized services
Industries: Generalist, Plastics/rubber, Metal products, Computer equip., Finance, High tech

Hockett Associates, Inc.
One First St., Ste. 1
P.O. Box 1765
Los Altos, California 94023
(650) 941-8815
Fax: (650) 941-8817
Email: whockett@aol.com

Key Contact - Specialty:
Mr. Bill Hockett - *Life sciences, technology, education, environment*

Description: Senior management search for life science, environment and other companies, characterized by comprehensive targeting and networking, personal contact, a limited practice size, high quality and an unusual success rate.

Salary Minimum: $125,000
Functions: Generalist, Senior mgmt., Product dev., Mktg. mgmt., Sales mgmt., CFO's, R&D
Industries: Drugs mfg., Medical devices, Venture cap., Entertainment, Pharmaceutical svcs., Biotech, Healthcare

Hodge-Cronin & Assoc., Inc.
9575 W. Higgins Rd., Ste. 904
Rosemont, Illinois 60018
(847) 692-2041
Fax: (847) 692-2197

Key Contact - Specialty:
Ms. Kathleen A. Cronin
Mr. Richard J. Cronin - *Generalist*

Description: Worked in most industries and disciplines, international.

Salary Minimum: $90,000
Functions: Generalist, Senior mgmt., Automation, Plant mgmt., Mktg. mgmt., Sales mgmt., Benefits
Industries: Generalist, Textiles/apparel, Lumber/furniture, Printing, Plastics/rubber, Consumer electronics, Test/measurement equip., Publishing
Professional Associations: AESC

Hoglund & Assoc., Inc.
303 W. Madison St., Ste. 1150
Chicago, Illinois 60606
(312) 357-1037
Fax: (312) 732-0990

Key Contact - Specialty:
Mr. Gerald C. Hoglund - *Generalist, marketing, sales, engineering, human resources*

Description: 18 year search firm; results-oriented, takes great pride in providing superior client service and committed to unwavering professional ethics and standards.

Salary Minimum: $70,000
Functions: Senior mgmt., Product dev., Mktg. mgmt., Sales mgmt., Personnel, CFO's, Engineering
Industries: Generalist

Richard D. Holbrook Assoc.
51 Atlantic Ave., Ste. 10
P.O. Box 43
Marblehead, Massachusetts 01945-0043
(781) 639-6200
Email: rdhassoc@aol.com
Web: www.binghamton.com/holbrook/hb.htm

Key Contact - Specialty:
Mr. Richard D. Holbrook

Description: Responsive firm with a quality, solutions-oriented approach to executive search. Our procedure: define the need; understand client's organization, mission, culture; determine the appropriate functional solution; find the right fit.

Salary Minimum: $75,000
Functions: Generalist

Holland & Assoc., Inc.
P.O. Box 488
Chelsea, Michigan 48118-0488
(734) 475-3701
Fax: (734) 475-7032
Email: holland1@wwnet.com
Web: www.wwnet.com/~holland1

Key Contact - Specialty:
Mr. Thomas A. Parr - *Sales & marketing, manufacturing, operations*
Mr. Paul D. Alman - *General management, software*

Description: We provide professional and personalized service to clients involved in the design, development, manufacture, marketing and sales of technologically-advanced products for consumer and commercial markets.

Salary Minimum: $50,000

Functions: Senior mgmt., Purchasing, Healthcare, Mktg. mgmt., Sales mgmt., MIS mgmt., Engineering
Industries: Computer equip., Consumer electronics, Broadcast & Film, Telecoms, High tech, Software, Healthcare

Branches:
2700 Porter Rd.
Plover, Wisconsin 54467
(715) 344-6646
Fax: (715) 344-1674
Key Contact - Specialty:
Mr. Daniel O. Holland - *Electrical engineers*

Holland Rusk & Assoc.

211 E. Ontario St., Ste. 1110
Chicago, Illinois 60611
(312) 266-9595
Fax: (312) 266-8650
Web: Kylerusk@msn.com

Key Contact - Specialty:
Ms. Susan R. Holland - *Diversity management roles*
Mr. Kyle R. Holland

Description: A highly personalized, customized approach to accurately and professionally serve national and international clients. Have developed diverse networks within senior management to offer an array of talented finalists. 100% woman-owned.

Salary Minimum: $75,000
Functions: Generalist, Directors, Senior mgmt., Mfg., Sales & mktg., Finance, Specialized services
Industries: Generalist, Energy/utilities, Construction, Mfg., Transportation, Environmental svcs.

Hollander Horizon Int'l.

1617 Pacific Coast Hwy., Ste. C
Redondo Beach, California 90277
(310) 540-3231
Fax: (310) 540-4230
Email: arnoldzimm@aol.com
Web: hhisearch.com

Key Contact - Specialty:
Mr. Arnold Zimmerman - *Food, consumer products (technical)*

Description: Executive search to the food and consumer products industries. Our practice is limited to and highly accomplished in the areas of research and development, manufacturing, engineering and quality control.

Salary Minimum: $60,000
Functions: Plant mgmt., Quality, R&D, Engineering
Industries: Food/bev/tobacco, Soap/perfume/cosmetics, Drugs mfg.

Branches:
2668 McNair Drive
Robbinsdale, Minnesota 55422
(612) 521-9568
Fax: (612) 521-9645
Key Contact - Specialty:
Mr. Joseph Ayers - *Food, consumer products (technical)*

16 Wall St.
Princeton, New Jersey 08540
(609) 924-7577
Fax: (609) 924-8626
Key Contact - Specialty:
Mr. Michael Hollander - *Food, consumer products (technical)*

The Hollins Group, Inc.

225 W. Wacker Drive, Ste. 2125
Chicago, Illinois 60606-1229
(312) 606-8000
Fax: (312) 606-0213

Key Contact - Specialty:
Mr. Lawrence I. Hollins - *Generalist*
Ms. Pamela Talbott Creed - *Healthcare, generalist*
Ms. Dena Dodd Perry - *Financial services*
Mr. Derrick R. Buckingham - *Generalist*
Ms. Lynn Oda - *Generalist*
Ms. Angela Winters - *Generalist*
Ms. April M. Williams - *Generalist*
Ms. Courtney A. Jones - *Generalist*

Description: Provides senior and board of director level search services to major corporations and privately held firms across a wide range of industries and functional disciplines.

Salary Minimum: $90,000
Functions: Generalist, General mgmt., Healthcare, Sales & mktg., HR mgmt., Finance, Minorities
Industries: Generalist, Food/bev/tobacco, Banking, Non-profits, Higher ed., Telecoms

Branches:
1401 Peachtree St. NE, Ste. 500
Atlanta, Georgia 30309
(404) 870-8070
Fax: (404) 870-8084
Key Contact - Specialty:
Ms. Nancy M. Hall - *Information technology, academia, financial services*

Two Penn Plaza, Ste. 1500
New York, New York 10121
(212) 292-4929
Fax: (212) 292-4930
Key Contact - Specialty:
Mr. Lawrence I. Hollins

Networks:
Cross Border Search & Consulting Partners

Holohan Group, Ltd.

755 S. New Ballas Rd., Ste. 260
St. Louis, Missouri 63141-8714
(314) 997-3393
Fax: (314) 997-9103
Email: holohangroup@compuserve.com

Key Contact - Specialty:
Mr. Barth A. Holohan, Jr. - *Medical and regulatory affairs, quality assurance*
Ms. Marie Falbo Holohan
Ms. Margaret O. Pautler - *Business research*
Dr. K. Wayne Ratts - *Science, technology*
Dr. Arnold Hershman - *Science, technology*
Dr. Ellen B. Lawrence - *Science, technology, research & development, engineering, information systems*
Dr. Fyllis L. Otsuka - *Science, technology, research & development, engineering, business development*
Dr. Melvin L. Rueppel - *Science, technology, manufacturing, engineering*

Description: Quality executive, management and technical recruitment management consulting firm, primarily serving a core group of technology driven clients in most functional areas, featuring a strong professional staff of Ph.D. recruiters, a persistent focus on each assignment and development of long-term client/consultant relationships.

Salary Minimum: $85,000
Functions: Generalist, General mgmt., Mfg., Sales & mktg., IT, R&D, Engineering
Industries: Generalist, Agri/forestry/mining, Chemicals, Drugs mfg., Entertainment, High tech, Biotech

J. B. Homer Assoc. Inc.

420 Lexington Ave., Ste. 2328
Graybar Bldg.
New York, New York 10170
(212) 697-3300
Fax: (212) 986-5086
Email: jhomer@jbhomer.com
Web: www.jbhomer.com

Key Contact - Specialty:
Ms. Judy B. Homer - *Information technology*

Description: As specialists in executive recruitment, we are dedicated to the principle that a corporation's executives hold the key to the success of any enterprise.

Salary Minimum: $150,000
Functions: MIS mgmt., Systems implem., Systems support
Industries: Generalist
Professional Associations: AESC

Affiliates:
Nicholson International

Hornberger Management Company

One Commerce Ctr., 7th Floor
Wilmington, Delaware 19801-5401
(302) 573-2541
Fax: (302) 573-2507
Email: recruitment@hmc.com
Web: www.hmc.com

Key Contact - Specialty:
Mr. Frederick C. Hornberger, Jr. - *Construction*

Description: Board and executive search exclusively for the construction industry (general & specialty contractors, design-build, construction management, real estate developer/owner/builders). Specializing in CEO, COO & officer-level positions with compensation levels exceeding $100,000. In addition we find outside directors and excutives for interum and contract positions.

Salary Minimum: $100,000
Functions: Directors, Senior mgmt., Middle mgmt., Sales mgmt., CFO's, Int'l.
Industries: Construction

Affiliates:
Consultec
Executive Talent/Transearch
SMCL

Horton Int'l. Inc.

420 Lexington Ave., Ste. 810
New York, New York 10170
(212) 973-3780
Fax: (212) 973-3798
Email: newyork@horton-intl.com
Web: www.horton-intl.com

Key Contact - Specialty:
Mr. Robert H. Horton - *General management, international*
Ms. Helga Long - *Pharmaceutical, consumer products*
Mr. John C. Fischer - *Information technology*
Mr. Franklin Key Brown - *Financial services*

Description: Senior line executives with strong general management and corporate development credentials conducting searches in all operating disciplines and most staff positions for most industries. Specialties in telecommunications, healthcare, packaged consumer products and capital markets.

Salary Minimum: $100,000
Functions: Generalist, Senior mgmt., Mfg., Sales & mktg., HR mgmt., Finance, IT, Engineering, Int'l.
Industries: Generalist, Food/bev/tobacco, Chemicals, Drugs mfg., Medical devices, Metal products, Machinery/Appliances, Motor vehicles, Computer equip., Consumer electronics, Test/measurement equip., Finance, Communications, Aerospace, Insurance, Software, Biotech
Professional Associations: AESC

Branches:
24405 Chestnut St., Ste. 107
Santa Clarita, California 91321
(805) 222-2272
Fax: (805) 222-2374
Key Contact - Specialty:
Mr. William H. Parry - *Manufacturing, general management*

10 Tower Lane
Avon, Connecticut 06001
(860) 674-8701
Fax: (860) 676-9753
Key Contact - Specialty:
Ms. Katherine H. Cooke - *Financial services, industrial, engineering*
Ms. Susan A. Pace - *Insurance, pharmaceuticals*
Mr. Robert J. Gilchrist - *Insurance, marketing and sales, engineering*
Mr. Larry Brown - *Human resources management, healthcare*
Mr. C. Edward Snyder - *Human resources management, healthcare*
Mr. Robert F. Savard, Jr. - *Financial services*

33 Sloan St.
Roswell, Georgia 30075
(770) 640-1533
Fax: (770) 640-6242
Key Contact - Specialty:
Mr. David C. Reddick - *Consumer products*

463 W. Russell St., Ste. D
Barrington, Illinois 60010
(847) 304-5300
Fax: (847) 381-2215
Email: chicago@horton-intl.com
Key Contact - Specialty:
Mr. Adam Zak - *Manufacturing, international, high technology*

Redwood Tower
217 E. Redwood St.
Baltimore, Maryland 21202-3316
(410) 625-3800
Fax: (410) 625-3801
Key Contact - Specialty:
Mr. Timothy C. McNamara - *Transportation, public admin., government*

International Branches:
Birmingham, Dubendorf, Frankfurt, Hong Kong, London, Shanghai, South Melbourne, Sydney

Networks:
Horton International

Hospitality Executive Search, Inc.

729 Boylston St
Boston, Massachusetts 02116-2639
(617) 266-7700
Fax: (617) 267-2033

Key Contact - Specialty:
Mr. Jonathan M. Spatt - *Hospitality, senior level, board level*

Description: Years of experience and commitment show in our reputation. We succeed... and will continue to. We undertake retained hospitality search projects for senior level and board level. Individual projects commence at $75K. Retained national executive selection and national executive placement since 1976.

Salary Minimum: $75,000
Functions: Directors, Senior mgmt., Product dev., HR mgmt., Training, CFO's, MIS mgmt.
Industries: Food/bev/tobacco, Hospitality, Entertainment

Houtz•Strawn & Arnold, Inc.

11402 Bee Caves Rd. W.
Austin, Texas 78733
(512) 263-1131
Fax: (512) 263-4149
Email: hsainc@ix.netcom.com

Key Contact - Specialty:
Mr. William M. Strawn - *Pharmaceutical, biotechnology*
Mr. Jerome M. Arnold - *Pharmaceutical, biotechnology*
Mr. David M. Leech - *Pharmaceutical, biotechnology medical device*

Description: Senior level assignments with pharmaceutical and biotechnology companies. Major corporations and venture capital start-ups.

Salary Minimum: $150,000
Functions: Senior mgmt., Product dev., Mktg. mgmt., Sales mgmt., CFO's, R&D, Mgmt. consultants
Industries: Drugs mfg., Medical devices, Pharmaceutical svcs., Biotech

William C. Houze & Co.

48249 Vista De Nopal
La Quinta, California 92253
(760) 564-6400
Fax: (760) 564-8429

Key Contact - Specialty:
Mr. William C. Houze - *Generalist*
Mr. Geoffry Clayton Houze - *Generalist*

Description: All searches performed with care, in compliance with AESC standards, personally conducted and managed by Bill Houze. Bill has 12 years recruiting experience with GE and Rockwell and 22 years as a search consultant to worldwide clientele.

Salary Minimum: $90,000
Functions: General mgmt., Mfg., Materials, Sales & mktg., HR mgmt., Finance, Engineering
Industries: Machinery/Appliances, Motor vehicles, Consumer electronics, Defense, Haz. waste, Aerospace, High tech
Professional Associations: AESC

Affiliates:
Dennis & Gemmill International Limited

Randall Howard & Assoc., Inc.

P.O. Box 382397
Memphis, Tennessee 38183-2397
(901) 754-3333
Fax: (901) 758-5578

Email: RHAssociat@aol.com

Key Contact - Specialty:
Mr. Randall C. Howard

Description: Executive search and corporate outplacement (individuals/groups) in the Southern region...and throughout the USA.

Salary Minimum: $50,000
Functions: General mgmt., Mfg., HR mgmt., Finance, Engineering
Industries: Generalist

The Howard-Sloan-Koller Group †

353 Lexington Ave., 11th Floor
New York, New York 10016
(212) 661-5250
Fax: (212) 557-9178
Email: hsk@hsksearch.com
Web: www.hsksearch.com

Key Contact - Specialty:
Mr. Edward R. Koller, Jr. - *General management, sales*
Ms. Karen Danziger - *Editorial, creative*

Description: Executive search and consulting in the magazine, newspaper, newsletter and book publishing fields. Executive search in direct marketing, public relations, information technology, new media and cable. Executive search in advertising agency account management and creative.

Salary Minimum: $50,000
Functions: Senior mgmt., Middle mgmt., Advertising, Sales mgmt., PR, CFO's
Industries: Advertising/PR, Publishing, New media, Broadcast & Film, Telecoms

Affiliates:
Jerry Fields Assoc.
Howard-Sloan Assoc.

Howe & Assoc.

5 Radnor Corp. Ctr., Ste. 448
Radnor, Pennsylvania 19087
(610) 975-9124
Fax: (610) 975-0574
Email: execsearch@howe-assoc.com

Key Contact - Specialty:
Mr. Edward R. Howe, Jr. - *Generalist*
Mr. John R. Fell, III - *Financial services, telecommunications*
Mr. George T. Corrigan, Jr. - *Packaging*

Description: Serves corporations headquartered in the mid-Atlantic region and nationwide. Clients represent a variety of industries, including manufacturing, consumer products, financial services, packaging and telecommunications.

Salary Minimum: $100,000
Functions: Generalist, Senior mgmt., Product dev., Packaging, Mktg. mgmt., CFO's, MIS mgmt.
Industries: Generalist, Food/bev/tobacco, Misc. mfg., Banking, Invest. banking, Telecoms, Packaging

---

Robert Howe & Assoc. †

35 Glenlake Pkwy., Ste. 164
Atlanta, Georgia 30328
(770) 390-0030

Key Contact - Specialty:
Mr. Robert W. Hamill - *Manufacturing, hospitality (mid-upper management)*

Description: Representing small to large manufacturing and service companies, nationally and internationally in recruiting at mid-upper level management positions.

Salary Minimum: $60,000
Functions: General mgmt., Mfg., Materials, Sales & mktg., HR mgmt., IT, Engineering
Industries: Food/bev/tobacco, Textiles/apparel, Chemicals, Medical devices, Metal products, Hospitality, High tech

Affiliates:
J. W. Bauder Assoc.

HRCS

5245 Pacific Concourse Drive
Los Angeles, California 90045
(310) 643-0743
(800) 660-HRCS
Fax: (310) 643-0740
Web: www.hrcs.com

Key Contact - Specialty:
Mr. Michael Martin
Mr. Vince Anderson
Ms. Suzanne Manns

Description: We are the nation's premiere consulting firm specializing in contract recruiting, executive search and recruitment research.

Salary Minimum: $60,000
Functions: General mgmt., Mfg., Healthcare, Sales & mktg., HR mgmt., Finance, IT
Industries: Energy/utilities, Drugs mfg., Medical devices, Entertainment, Non-profits, New media, Broadcast & Film

Branches:
90 Park Ave., 17th Floor
New York, New York 10016
(800) 660-4727
Key Contact - Specialty:
Mr. Michael Martin

HRD Consultants, Inc.

60 Walnut Ave.
Clark, New Jersey 07066
(732) 815-7825
Fax: (732) 815-7810
Email: hrd@aol.com

Key Contact - Specialty:
Ms. Marcia Glatman - *Human resources*

Description: We offer our clients a long history in human resource recruitment, an extensive network, information regarding trends in human resources and a commitment to excellence.

Salary Minimum: $120,000
Functions: Benefits, Personnel, Training, Mgmt. consultants, Minorities
Industries: Generalist
Professional Associations: IACPR

HRS, Inc.

P.O. Box 4499
Pittsburgh, Pennsylvania 15205
(412) 331-4700
Fax: (412) 331-2540

Key Contact - Specialty:
Mr. David P. Smith - *Telecommunications, information technology, manufacturing*
Mr. Jeffrey D. Latterell - *Metals*

Description: Performance, personal service, integrity. Serving national corporations, start-up and nonprofit organizations. Experienced staff. Employ state-of-the-art market research, background investigation and validated evaluation techniques.

Salary Minimum: $50,000
Functions: Generalist, General mgmt., Mfg., Sales & mktg., Finance, IT, Int'l.
Industries: Generalist, Metal products, Finance, Telecoms, High tech, Software

---

Arnold Huberman Assoc., Inc. †

51 E. 25th St., Ste. 501
New York, New York 10010
(212) 545-9033
Fax: (212) 779-9641
Email: arnie@huberman.com
Web: www.huberman.com

Key Contact - Specialty:
Mr. Arnold Huberman - *Public relations executives*
Ms. Rachel Schwartz - *Public relations executives*

Description: Specialists in management recruiting in the areas of corporate communications and public relations across all industries. Specific expertise in finding public relations agencies for corporations.
Functions: PR
Industries: Advertising/PR

Affiliates:
Bird & Company

† occasional contingency assignment

Huff Assoc.

95 Reef Drive
Ocean City, New Jersey 08226
(609) 399-2867

Key Contact - Specialty:
Mr. William Z. Huff - *Manufacturing, healthcare, sales & marketing, hospitality, software*
Ms. Margaret L. Huff - *Manufacturing, healthcare, sales & marketing, hospitality, software*

Description: Specialize in being results oriented, budget conscious, confidential, giving individual personalized & flexible services throughout industries & organizations related to physicians, healthcare, hospitality/casino, paper & allied products, biotech/genetic engineering & all manufacturing.

Salary Minimum: $50,000
Functions: Mfg., Healthcare, Physicians, Sales & mktg., IT, R&D, Engineering
Industries: Generalist, Drugs mfg., Hospitality, Entertainment, Software, Biotech, Healthcare

E. A. Hughes & Co., Inc.

146 E. 37th St.
New York, New York 10016
(212) 689-4600
Fax: (212) 689-4975
Email: general@eahughes.com

Key Contact - Specialty:
Ms. Elaine A. Hughes - *Apparel, textile, home fashions, catalog & retail, direct marketing*
Ms. Mary Anne Glynn - *Apparel, textile, home fashions, catalog & retail, direct marketing*
Mr. Marvin Lord - *Apparel, textile, home fashions, catalog & retail, direct marketing*

Description: A full service, generalist search firm with a hands on approach.

Salary Minimum: $100,000
Functions: Directors, Senior mgmt., Product dev., Mkt. research, Mktg. mgmt., Sales mgmt., Direct mktg.
Industries: Textiles/apparel, Retail
Professional Associations: AESC

Hughes & Company

1626 Belle View Blvd.
P.O. Box 7365
Alexandria, Virginia 22307-0365
(703) 765-8853
Email: DJHughes@CareerResources.com
Web: www.CareerResources.com

Key Contact - Specialty:
Mr. Donald J. Hughes - *COOs, food, grocery, sales, management, consumer goods*
Mr. Martin Smith - *Brand management, consumer marketing, consumer promotions, pet food*
Mr. J. Reid Johnston - *CEOs, CFOs, information systems, management, pharmaceutical*

Description: We are an executive search firm with a mission to help client companies worldwide identify, recruit and hire the best and brightest sales, marketing and management talent available in the consumer products and services industry. We work quickly, discreetly and efficiently with a focus on mid and senior level positions.

Salary Minimum: $70,000
Functions: Directors, Senior mgmt., Middle mgmt., Mktg. mgmt., Sales mgmt., MIS mgmt., Int'l.
Industries: Food/bev/tobacco, Paper, Soap/perfume/cosmetics, Drugs mfg., Hospitality, Pharmaceutical svcs., New media

The Human Resource Consulting Group, Inc.

165 S. Union Blvd., Ste. 456
Lakewood, Colorado 80228-2211
(303) 987-8888

Key Contact - Specialty:
Mr. Joseph L. Zaccaro - *Middle to top management*
Mr. John F. Kane - *Middle to top management*
Ms. Susan M. Behm - *Middle to top management*

Description: A national executive search practice with highly experienced business executives and consultants with backgrounds in consumer goods, high technology, telecommunications, healthcare and diversified multinational corporations.

Salary Minimum: $75,000
Functions: Generalist
Industries: Generalist

Branches:
800 Turnpike St., Ste. 300
North Andover, Massachusetts 01845
(978) 686-5338
Key Contact - Specialty:
Mr. Al Zink - *Middle to top management*
Mr. Daniel D. Cantor - *Middle to top management*

8330 Corporate Dr., #3
Racine, Wisconsin 53406
(414) 884-8674
Key Contact - Specialty:
Ms. Terri Ladzinski - *Middle to top management*

The Human Resource Department Ltd.

23240 Chagrin Blvd., Ste. 845
4 Commerce Park Sq.
Cleveland, Ohio 44122-5403
(216) 292-6996
Fax: (216) 292-6336
Email: thrd2@en.com

Key Contact - Specialty:
Mr. Charles K. Niles - *Human resources*

Description: We are a human resources project management firm that provides various human resources functional expertise to clients. Because of our human resources focus, we are able to source the most qualified and talented HR professionals for our clients.
Functions: General mgmt., Mfg., HR mgmt., Benefits, Personnel, Training, Mgmt. consultants
Industries: Energy/utilities, Mfg., Transportation, Finance, Svcs., Packaging, Healthcare

The Human Resource Group, Inc.

8221 Brecksville Rd.
Bldg. #1, Ste. 103
Cleveland, Ohio 44141
(216) 838-5818
Fax: (216) 838-5940
Email: hrgroup@ix.netcom.com
Web: www.hrgroupinc.com

Key Contact - Specialty:
Mr. Michael J. Coman
Mr. John H. Markt
Mr. Michael R. English
Mr. Ted J. Moore

Description: The only middle and senior management retained search consultants that offer a complete refund of your retainer if we can't find candidates that meet your specifications!

Salary Minimum: $75,000
Functions: General mgmt., Mfg., Materials, Sales & mktg., HR mgmt., IT, Engineering
Industries: Mfg., Computer svcs., Human resource svcs., Defense, Aerospace, High tech, Software

Human Resource Solutions

1333 Corporate Drive, Ste. 117
Irving, Texas 76040
(972) 550-9116
Fax: (972) 580-7929
Email: slamotta@people-solutions.com
Web: www.people-solutions.com

Key Contact - Specialty:
Mr. Steve LaMotta - *Executives, human resources*
Mr. Ed Rankin - *Executives, human resources*

Description: Proven and specialized experience in mid to executive level human resource professionals nationally. Highly specialized service and strategic solutions combining research, sourcing and technology with an expansive network - focused on results.

Salary Minimum: $60,000
Functions: Directors, Senior mgmt., Middle mgmt., HR mgmt., Benefits, Personnel, Training
Industries: Generalist, Mfg., Retail, Finance, Svcs., High tech, Healthcare

Branches:
11782 Jollyville Rd., Ste. 111
Austin, Texas 78759
(512) 219-4065
Fax: (512) 219-4064
Email: lkhaines@aol.com
Web: www.people-solutions.com
Key Contact - Specialty:
Ms. Linda Haines - *Human resources*

1550 Eastchase Pkwy., Ste. 600
Ft. Worth, Texas 76120
(817) 461-1558
Fax: (817) 461-1559
Email: larryc@humressol.com
Web: www.people-solutions.com
Key Contact - Specialty:
Mr. Larry Cox - *Human resources*

Human Resource Technologies, Inc.
(a division of Raymond Karsan Associates)
2200 E. Devon Ave., Ste. 183
Des Plaines, Illinois 60018
(847) 297-8000
Email: RSondhi@raymondkarsan.com
Web: www.raymondkarsan.com

Key Contact - Specialty:
Mr. Rick Sondhi - *Executive and professional level search*

Description: Creative, solution oriented, client driven group provides cost effective, fixed fee retained professional search and employment services nationwide. Educated, experienced salaried staff provide customized, documented employment related programs.

Salary Minimum: $40,000
Functions: General mgmt., Mfg., Sales & mktg., HR mgmt., Finance, IT, Minorities
Industries: Generalist, Mfg., Transportation, Finance, High tech, Software, Healthcare

---

Human Resources Personnel Agency †
916 Garland St.
Little Rock, Arkansas 72201
(501) 376-4622
Email: jobs@employment4u.com
Web: www.employment4u.com

Key Contact - Specialty:
Mr. M. Ben Traylor - *Manufacturing (all areas)*
Ms. Cherie Harrington - *Accounting, data processing, information systems*
Ms. Rita A. Price - *Plastics, quality control, materials*
Mr. Wayne Martin - *Paper, pulp, wood products*

Description: Firm only works with manufacturing related positions. Plant start ups a specialty. Staff offers over 75 years of hands on manufacturing experience.
Functions: Generalist, Automation, Productivity, Packaging, Benefits, Systems dev., Engineering
Industries: Generalist, Textiles/apparel, Printing, Plastics/rubber, Metal products, Machinery/Appliances, Consumer electronics

Affiliates:
Human Resources Outplacement Services

H.I. Hunt & Co., Ltd.
99 Summer St., #940
Boston, Massachusetts 02110
(617) 261-1611
Fax: (617) 443-9444
Email: hihunt@tiac.net

Key Contact - Specialty:
Mr. Herbert I. Hunt, III - *Financial services*
Mr. Peter Schibli - *Financial services*
Mr. Roy Walters - *Staffing industry*
Ms. Janeen Rivers - *Staffing industry*
Mr. Alex G. Power - *Financial services*

Description: Worldwide executive search firm specializing in the areas of investment banking, structured finance and fund management businesses. Industry leader in the placement of senior management within the staffing profession.

Salary Minimum: $50,000
Functions: Finance
Industries: Finance, Human resource svcs.

Affiliates:
T. Seaden & Co., Ltd.

Hunt & Howe Inc.
1 Dag Hammarskjold Plaza, 34th Floor
New York, New York 10017
(212) 758-2800
Fax: (212) 758-7710

Key Contact - Specialty:
Mr. James E. Hunt - *MIS, legal, financial, investment management, general management*
Mr. William S. Howe - *Management consulting, strategy, general management, human resources*

Description: Skilled veterans whose focus is on finding and attracting senior level executives for major corporations and institutions throughout the U.S. and abroad.

Salary Minimum: $100,000
Functions: Generalist, Senior mgmt., CFO's, MIS mgmt., Engineering, Mgmt. consultants, Attorneys
Industries: Generalist, Motor vehicles, Banking, Invest. banking, Legal, Computer svcs., Mgmt. consulting
Professional Associations: AESC

Networks:
The Hever Group

The Hunt Co.
274 Madison Ave.
New York, New York 10016
(212) 889-2020

Key Contact - Specialty:
Mr. Bridgford H. Hunt

Description: Generalist firm. Maintain confidential relationships with clients before, during and after assignments. We will not accept assignments that involve conflicts of interest.

Salary Minimum: $100,000
Functions: Generalist, Directors, Senior mgmt., CFO's, MIS mgmt.
Industries: Generalist

The Hunt Group, Inc.
20344 Havenview Drive
Cornelius, North Carolina 28031
(704) 895-2660
Fax: (704) 895-2665
Email: joehunt@jbhunt.net
Web: www.jbhunt.net

Key Contact - Specialty:
Mr. Joseph B. Hunt - *Senior management*

Description: As partners we take the time and invest the energy to understand our clients' corporate culture and personality. Our industry specialized search practice can track and identify the executives who excel.

Salary Minimum: $75,000
Functions: General mgmt., Mfg., Production, Plant mgmt., Materials, R&D, Engineering
Industries: Mfg., Food/bev/tobacco, Chemicals, Soap/perfume/cosmetics, Drugs mfg., Transportation, Wholesale

---

Hunter Douglas Group, Inc.
1143 West North Shore Ave.
Chicago, Illinois 60626
(773) 338-7865
(773) 262-0345
Fax: (773) 338-7869
Email: hunter@enteract.com
Web: www.hunterdouglasgroup.com

Key Contact - Specialty:
Mr. Bob Douglas - *Management consultants, healthcare*
Mr. Jim Schneider - *Research/Systems*

† occasional contingency assignment

Description: The group specializes in completing searches for middle management within eight weeks. Superior recruitment with personalized service and positive results.

Salary Minimum: $50,000
Functions: Middle mgmt., Healthcare, Physicians, Nurses, Allied health, Health admin., Mgmt. consultants
Industries: Drugs mfg., Svcs., Mgmt. consulting, Human resource svcs., Insurance, Healthcare

Hunter Int'l., Inc.
262 S. Britain Rd.
Southbury, Connecticut 06488
(203) 264-1000

Key Contact - Specialty:
Mr. Ron Kelly - *Generalist*

Description: Results oriented general practice that achieves long term client relationships. Mostly repeat business in finding MID and senior management in healthcare, insurance, financial services, consumer and industrial arenas. Research intensive!

Salary Minimum: $75,000
Functions: Generalist, Senior mgmt., Middle mgmt., Sales & mktg., HR mgmt., Finance
Industries: Generalist, Food/bev/tobacco, Medical devices, Finance, Hospitality, Insurance, Healthcare

Affiliates:
Cappon Associates

Huntington Group
6527 Main St.
Trumbull, Connecticut 06611
(203) 261-1166
Fax: (203) 452-9153
Email: hg@hgllc.com
Web: www.hgllc.com

Key Contact - Specialty:
Mr. Raymond Tomasco - *Information technology*

Description: We develop one year contracts with some of our clients giving us exclusive responsibility to fulfill a forecasted number and type of assignments. In these cases we become an outsourced recruiting effort, offering the client efficient, cost effective service.

Salary Minimum: $100,000
Functions: MIS mgmt., Systems anal., Systems dev., Systems implem., Systems support
Industries: Computer svcs., Mgmt. consulting, High tech, Software

Branches:
700 Canal St., 3rd Floor
Stamford, Connecticut 06902
(203) 328-3790
Fax: (203) 328-3791
Key Contact - Specialty:
Ms. Karen Vacheron Alexander - *Information technology*

Huntress Real Estate Executive Search †
P.O. Box 8667
Kansas City, Missouri 64114
(913) 383-8180
Fax: (913) 383-8184
Email: info@huntress.net
Web: www.huntress.net

Key Contact - Specialty:
Mr. Stan Stanton - *Mid to senior level executives (all functions)*
Mr. Glenn Hoffman - *Asset management, property management*
Ms. Marilyn Jacob - *Retail*

Description: Real estate related consulting advisory services; management consultants to the real estate, finance and construction industry including organizational planning, compensation studies and specializing in executive staffing.

Salary Minimum: $40,000
Functions: Senior mgmt., Middle mgmt., Sales & mktg., CFO's, M&A, Mgmt. consultants, Int'l.
Industries: Construction, Retail, Finance, Mgmt. consulting, Real estate

W. Hutt Management Resources Ltd.
2349 Fairview St., Ste. 110
Burlington, Ontario L7R 2E3
Canada
(905) 637-3800
Fax: (905) 637-3221
Email: whuttmgt@skyline.net

Key Contact - Specialty:
Mr. Wayne Hutt - *Generalist*
Ms. Gayle Hutt - *Administration*

Description: We are an executive search firm that provides expert, low profile search activity, in the industrial/commercial segments of business; with candidates ranging from design engineers to presidents.

Salary Minimum: $40,000
Functions: General mgmt., Mfg., Materials, Sales & mktg., HR mgmt., Finance, Engineering
Industries: Generalist, Agri/forestry/mining, Mfg., Transportation, Finance, Aerospace, Packaging

Hutton Merrill & Assoc.
2465 E. Bayshore Rd., Ste. 301
Palo Alto, California 94303
(650) 494-0666

Key Contact - Specialty:
Mr. Thomas J. Hutton
Ms. Barbara Merrill
Ms. Vera Wong

Description: We are a high technology executive search firm with a primary focus on semiconductors, semiconductor equipment, software and networking. We conduct extensive, original research for every assignment.

Salary Minimum: $150,000
Functions: General mgmt., Mfg., Sales & mktg., Engineering
Industries: Computer equip., Test/measurement equip., High tech, Software

HVS Executive Search
372 Willis Ave.
Mineola, New York 11501
(516) 248-8828
Fax: (516) 742-1905
Email: kxk@hvs.intl.com
Web: www.hvs-intl.com

Key Contact - Specialty:
Mr. Keith Kefgen
Ms. Dena Blum-Rothman
Mr. Stephen Rushmore

Description: We are a retainer search firm specializing in the recruitment of senior level executives in the hospitality industry.

Salary Minimum: $75,000
Functions: Directors, Senior mgmt., Middle mgmt., Mktg. mgmt., CFO's, M&A, MIS mgmt.
Industries: Hospitality
Professional Associations: AESC, IACPR

Affiliates:
HVS Eco Services
HVS Technology Services

Hyde Danforth & Co.
5950 Berkshire Lane, Ste. 1040
Dallas, Texas 75225
(214) 691-5966
Fax: (214) 369-7317
Web: www.hdco.net

Key Contact - Specialty:
Mr. W. Michael Danforth - *Generalist*
Mr. W. Jerry Hyde - *Generalist*

Description: Over 85% of engagements performed for existing or referred clients. A quality boutique practice serving industry, attorneys, professionals and academia. Also provide H/R career and transition consulting.

Salary Minimum: $60,000

Functions: Generalist, Mfg., Sales & mktg., HR mgmt., Finance, Attorneys
Industries: Generalist, Banking, Hospitality, Legal, Accounting, Insurance, Real estate

The Hyde Group, Inc.
209 Palmer Point, River Rd.
Cos Cob, Connecticut 06807
(203) 661-0413
Fax: (203) 622-6314
Email: ahydethg@aol.com

Key Contact - Specialty:
Ms. Anne P. Hyde - *Management consultants, women, minorities, non-profit, marketing*

Description: Nationwide knowledge and network in all facets of management consulting recruiting and business process re-engineering/change management. Maintain a very strong capability regarding women and minorities in all disciplines.

Salary Minimum: $100,000
Functions: Senior mgmt., Admin. svcs., Mktg. mgmt., PR, HR mgmt., Training, Non-profits
Industries: Non-profits, Mgmt. consulting, Human resource svcs., Advertising/PR, Telecoms

IM Independent Management Recruiters
4507 Montview Drive
Chattanooga, Tennessee 37411
(423) 622-8217

Key Contact - Specialty:
Ms. Charlotte Pierce
Ms. Ann Lacy

Description: We are the best when it comes to finding candidates for our clients, large or small. We are so sure of our placements that we will replace our candidate if, she/he does not meet our client's expectations, six months after a candidate is placed.

Salary Minimum: $100,000
Functions: Directors, Physicians, Health admin., CFO's, MIS mgmt., Attorneys, Int'l.
Industries: Finance, Banking, Higher ed., Telecoms, Government, Aerospace, Real estate

IMA Search, Inc.
106 Peninsula Drive, Ste. A
Babylon, New York 11702
(516) 422-3900
(212) 683-7200
Fax: (516) 587-3556
Email: imasearch@aol.com

Key Contact - Specialty:
Mr. Paul D. Steinberg - *Generalist, high technology, packaging, retail, travel*
Ms. Suzanne Welling - *Generalist, real estate*

Description: IMA's experienced business professionals provide a broad range of confidential services to management including: executive search, general consulting, unique talent reserve bank, executive appraisal, background checks, outplacement. Brochure available.

Salary Minimum: $60,000
Functions: Generalist, Health admin., Mktg. mgmt., Finance, Budgeting, Systems anal., Non-profits
Industries: Generalist, Medical devices, Computer equip., Finance, Communications, Aerospace, Healthcare

John Imber Assoc., Ltd.
3601 Algonquin Rd., Ste. 129
Rolling Meadows, Illinois 60008
(847) 506-1700
Fax: (847) 577-1651
Email: rebmi@aol.com

Key Contact - Specialty:
Mr. John Imber

Description: Utilizing a search process designed to attract, select and retain individuals fittingly prepared and motivated to thrive within your unique corporate environment.

Salary Minimum: $50,000
Functions: Generalist
Industries: Generalist

The IMC Group of Companies
14 E. 60th St., Ste. 1200
New York, New York 10022
(212) 838-9535
Fax: (212) 486-2964
Email: imcgroup@interport.net
Web: www.imcgroupofcos.com

Key Contact - Specialty:
Mr. Herbert Regehly
Ms. Laurie Raiber

Description: 30 years hospitality/leisure, media/entertainment industry related retained search firm for senior level positions.

Salary Minimum: $95,000
Functions: Directors, Senior mgmt., Mktg. mgmt., Sales mgmt., CFO's, MIS mgmt., Mgmt. consultants
Industries: Hospitality, Entertainment, Mgmt. consulting, Human resource svcs.

Branches:
2600 Douglas Rd.
Coral Gables, Florida 33134
(305) 444-2211
Fax: (305) 445-5097
Key Contact - Specialty:
Ms. Karine Gill

Affiliates:
HLR Associates Limited

Ingram & Aydelotte, Inc.
430 Park Ave., 7th Floor
New York, New York 10022
(212) 319-7777
Fax: (212) 319-1632
Email:
ingram_aydelotte@compuserve.com

Key Contact - Specialty:
Mr. D. John Ingram - *Generalist*
Mr. G. Thomas Aydelotte - *Generalist*
Mr. Christopher J. Shea - *Information technology*
Mr. Edward C. P. Edwards - *Generalist*

Description: Experienced consultants working in most industries and functions on senior management and board of director searches. Dedicated partner attention to each search. Extensive research. Retainer only.

Salary Minimum: $150,000
Functions: Health admin., Sales & mktg., HR mgmt., Finance, IT, Non-profits
Industries: Soap/perfume/cosmetics, Transportation, Finance, Legal, Mgmt. consulting, Communications, Healthcare

Networks:
I-I-C Partners Executive Search Worldwide

Innovative Partnerships
11828 Rancho Bernardo Rd., Ste. 123-408
San Diego, California 92128-1999
(619) 676-1999
Fax: (619) 676-1999
Email: inpartners@aol.com

Key Contact - Specialty:
Ms. Catherine Burton - *Public relations, fund development, public affairs, community relations*

Description: We specialize in executive search in public relations, fund development (fund raising) and public affairs/community relations. We work nationwide and fill retained, senior level positions.

Salary Minimum: $75,000
Functions: Senior mgmt., Middle mgmt., Health admin., Mktg. mgmt., PR, Minorities, Non-profits
Industries: Finance, Non-profits, Higher ed., Advertising/PR, Broadcast & Film, Government, Software

† occasional contingency assignment

Innovative Search Group, Inc.

8097 Roswell Rd., Ste. C101
Atlanta, Georgia 30350-3936
(800) 589-3587
(770) 399-9093
Fax: (770) 399-9094
Email: innovative@innovativesearch.com
Web: www.innovativesearch.com

Key Contact - Specialty:
Ms. Sarah J. H. Bajc
Ms. Euris Bell
Mr. Daniel A. Peat

Description: Consulting firm specializing in direct search and recruitment for clients in all industries nationwide. All services are billed on an hourly basis.
Functions: Generalist
Industries: Generalist

Intech Summit Group, Inc.

5075 Shoreham Place, Ste. 280
San Diego, California 92122
(619) 452-2100
Fax: (619) 452-8500
Email: isg@isgsearch.com
Web: www.isgsearch.com

Key Contact - Specialty:
Mr. Robert C. Cohen - *High technology, healthcare, data processing, network communications*
Mr. Michael R. Cohen - *Healthcare administration, consulting, information technology, human resources, engineering*

Description: Principals have over 40 years of combined professional search experience at all levels of executive recruitment in healthcare, hi-tech, government, human resources, network communications, finance, educational services, information technology and consulting services industry.

Salary Minimum: $80,000
Functions: Senior mgmt., Health admin., HR mgmt., CFO's, MIS mgmt., Systems implem., Mgmt. consultants
Industries: Finance, Mgmt. consulting, Human resource svcs., Telecoms, Government, High tech, Healthcare

Branches:
3150 Pio Pico Drive
Suite 100A
Carlsbad, California 92008
(760) 720-2120
Fax: (760) 720-2121
Key Contact - Specialty:
Ms Kathy Kinley

Integrated Search Solutions Group, LLC (ISSG)

33 Main St.
Port Washington, New York 11050
(516) 767-3030
Email: mainst.33@aol.com

Key Contact - Specialty:
Mr. Laurence Janis - *Information technology*
Mr. Vincent J. Sessa - *Information technology*

Description: Our focus is information technology, with involvement in outsourcing, business and systems re-engineering and client server technologies. Our practice bridges business and technology with the provider and user communities.

Salary Minimum: $100,000
Functions: Directors, Senior mgmt., Mktg. mgmt., Sales mgmt., Personnel, MIS mgmt., Mgmt. consultants
Industries: Computer equip., Computer svcs., Mgmt. consulting, High tech, Software

Integrity Search, Inc.

1489 Baltimore Pike, Ste. 232
Victoria Business Ctr.
Springfield, Pennsylvania 19064
(610) 543-8590
Fax: (610) 543-3668
Email: isearch221@aol.com

Key Contact - Specialty:
Ms. Janet R. Long - *Communications, marketing, management consulting*

Description: Offering a consultive, strategic approach to executive search and management coaching on interviewing and hiring process, plus an unrivaled reputation for treating both candidates and clients with respect and integrity.

Salary Minimum: $75,000
Functions: Mkt. research, Mktg. mgmt., PR, Benefits, MIS mgmt., Mgmt. consultants
Industries: Finance, Mgmt. consulting, Human resource svcs., Communications, New media, Telecoms, Healthcare

InteliSearch, Inc. †

350 Bedford St., Ste. 304
Stamford, Connecticut 06901
(203) 325-1389
Fax: (203) 325-1678
Email: intlsrch@erols.com

Key Contact - Specialty:
Mr. George L. Rodriguez - *Finance, human resources, sales & marketing, general management, senior attorneys*

Description: Building corporate strength through client-centered processes which leverage executive human resources and business-side experience. Unique results-tracking enable assessment of capabilities. National minority development council-certified; with strong bi-cultural executive relationships.

Salary Minimum: $70,000
Functions: Senior mgmt., Advertising, Mkt. research, Benefits, Personnel, CFO's, Budgeting
Industries: Banking, Brokers, Misc. financial, Publishing, Broadcast & Film, Telecoms, Insurance

Interactive Search Network †

3330 Pierce St., Ste. 306
San Francisco, California 94123
(415) 921-0663
Fax: (415) 776-9361
Email: dougexecs@aol.com

Key Contact - Specialty:
Mr. Douglas Perlstadt - *Retail, direct mail, interactive commerce*

Description: Recruit mid-senior level executives primarily in the area of commerce (retail, catalog, internet) in a wide range of diciplines including merchandising, marketing, operations, finance and human resources.
Functions: Middle mgmt., Product dev., Sales & mktg., Advertising, HR mgmt., CFO's, MIS mgmt.
Industries: Textiles/apparel, Retail, Non-profits, New media

International Management Services Inc. †

6300 N. River Rd., Ste. 205
Rosemont, Illinois 60018
(847) 698-2800
Fax: (847) 698-4606

Key Contact - Specialty:
Mr. Carl A. Johnson - *Electronics, general management*
Mr. Byron T. Garoufalis - *Engineering*
Mr. James M. Barz - *Factory automation, process control*
Ms. Betsy Brace - *Healthcare*
Mr. Peter B. Steinau - *Healthcare*

Description: Executive retainer search and management consulting firm to most industries since 1970. Principals are former corporate senior operating managers from technically oriented and retail corporations. Will not recruit from clients.

Salary Minimum: $50,000
Functions: General mgmt., Mfg., Healthcare, Sales & mktg., Finance, IT, Engineering
Industries: Generalist, Mfg., Svcs., Telecoms, High tech, Software, Healthcare

Branches:
6642 Trident Way
Naples, Florida 34108
(941) 596-3300
Fax: (941) 591-4879
Key Contact - Specialty:
Mr. Carl Johnson

Affiliates:
Bertrand, Ross & Assoc., Inc.

International Management Advisors, Inc.
P.O. Box 174, FDR Station
New York, New York 10150-0174
(212) 758-7770

Key Contact - Specialty:
Ms. Constance W. Klages - *Information systems, human resources, generalist*
Mr. Paul J. Harbaugh, Jr. - *Chemical, retail, marketing*
Mr. Henri J. P. Manassero - *Hospitality*
Mr. George N. Lumsby

Description: Quality, medium size generalist firm serving multinational and national organizations. We conduct searches in most functional areas. Results through teamwork.

Salary Minimum: $75,000
Functions: Generalist, Senior mgmt., Mktg. mgmt., HR mgmt., IT, Engineering, Minorities
Industries: Generalist, Energy/utilities, Non-profits, Mgmt. consulting, Human resource svcs., High tech, Biotech

Affiliates:
Clives & Stokes International

Networks:
International Search Associates (ISA)

International Research Group
(a subsidiary of Wilkins & Wilkins Int'l., Inc.)
345 Manzanita Ave., Ste. 103
Palo Alto, California 94306-1023
(650) 833-1040
(650) 833-1050
Fax: (650) 833-1047
Email: swilkins@best.com
Web: www.internationalresearchgrp.com

Key Contact - Specialty:
Ms. Sherrie Wilkins - *Medical technology, biotechnology*
Mr. Sid Wilkins - *Medical technology*
Ms. A. M. Wilkins - *Medical, biotechnology*
Ms. Mary Lou Fasola

Description: All principals have held key positions in science and technology organizations and have recruited for technical, managerial and executive positions in medical technology and biotechnology industries.

Salary Minimum: $60,000
Functions: Mfg., Mktg. mgmt., R&D, Engineering, Int'l.
Industries: Drugs mfg., Medical devices, Test/measurement equip., Biotech

Branches:
44817 E. Foxtail Rd.
P.O. Box 1495
Coarsegold, California 93614
(209) 683-8798
Fax: (209) 683-8798
Key Contact - Specialty:
Dr. Mark Wilder - *Medical technology*

Interquest, Inc.
599 Lexington Ave., Ste. 2300
New York, New York 10022
(212) 319-0790
Fax: (212) 753-0596

Key Contact - Specialty:
Mr. Meyer Haberman - *General counsel, lateral partner*

Description: Recruitment of senior lawyers for corporations and law firms both domestically and internationally. Cover all industries and all legal disciplines. Specialization in general counsel and partner searches.

Salary Minimum: $100,000
Functions: Directors, Senior mgmt., Legal, Mgmt. consultants, Attorneys
Industries: Generalist, Medical devices, Finance, Entertainment, Legal, Communications, Healthcare

Branches:
98 Cutter Mill Rd., Ste. 337 S
Great Neck, New York 11021
(516) 482-2330
Fax: (516) 482-2114
Key Contact - Specialty:
Ms. Sylvia Miller

Affiliates:
TempLaw Ltd.

Intersource, Ltd. †
87 Vickery St.
Roswell, Georgia 30075
(770) 645-0015
Fax: (770) 645-0035
Email: resumes@intersourceltd.com
Web: www.intersourceltd.com

Key Contact - Specialty:
Ms. Vikki Loving
Mr. Ginger Wallis - *Contract division, human resources*
Ms. Robin Hangartner - *Human resources, technology, executive search*
Ms. Linda Trocina - *Contract division, human resources*
Ms. Allis Fox - *Human resources, technology, executive search*

Description: Executive search firm specializing in human resource, accounting, finance and technology placement across all industries. Particular emphasis on high technology/entrepreneurial start up companies and specialized recruitment searches for diversity candidates.

Salary Minimum: $60,000
Functions: Benefits, Personnel, Training, CFO's, Credit, MIS mgmt., Minorities
Industries: Generalist, Mfg., Svcs., Communications, High tech, Software

Branches:
1509A W. 6th St.
Austin, Texas 78703
(512) 457-0883
Fax: (512) 457-0889
Email: phalladay@aol.com
Web: www.intersourceltd.com
Key Contact - Specialty:
Ms. Patti Halladay - *Accounting, finance, human resources, high technology*

1523 Pecan Trace Court
Houston, Texas 77479
(281) 343-7851
Fax: (281) 545-8794
Email: isource@compassnet.com
Key Contact - Specialty:
Mr. Thom Besso - *Human resources, accounting & finance, high technology, sales & marketing, consumer products*
Ms. Sandy Besso - *Human resources, accounting & finance, high technology, sales & marketing, consumer products*

IPR, Inc. †
11417 Sunset Hills Rd., Ste. 215
Reston, Virginia 20190
(703) 318-9600
Fax: (703) 318-9121
Email: gthomas@iprinc.com
Web: www.iprinc.com

Key Contact - Specialty:
Mr. G. Alan Thomas - *Information technology*
Mr. Gordon K. Thomas

Description: Full service HR and management consulting firm. Established in Washington D.C. area for 15 plus years. Specialists in retained executive search. Active in all areas of human resource consulting.
Functions: HR mgmt., Mgmt. consultants
Industries: Mgmt. consulting, Human resource svcs.

IR Search
7777 Greenback Lane, Ste. 201
Citrus Heights, California 95610
(916) 721-5511
Fax: (916) 721-5007
Email: richshoe@irgroupco.com
Web: www.irgroupco.com

Key Contact - Specialty:
Mr. Richard Shoemaker - *Board members, CEOs, COOs, CFOs*
Ms. Sandra Simmons - *Life, HMOs, PPOs, TPAs, annuities*
Mr. Jeff Batozech - *Reinsurance, alternative risk, public entity*
Mr. Michael Priseler - *Retail brokerage, standard carriers, agri-business*

† occasional contingency assignment

Description: A strategic consulting, M&A and executive search firm specializing in services to the insurance industry.

Salary Minimum: $65,000
Functions: Directors, Senior mgmt., Middle mgmt., Mktg. mgmt., Sales mgmt., CFO's, M&A
Industries: Hospitality, Insurance

Branches:
P.O. Box 470248
San Francisco, California 94147
(415) 346-0910
Fax: (415) 346-0919
Key Contact - Specialty:
Mr. Gene Boscacci - *E&S, surety, retail brokerage, workers' compensation*

Jeffrey Irving Assoc., Inc.

(Firm declined to update.)
216 S. Payne St.
Alexandria, Virginia 22314-2904
(703) 836-7770

Key Contact - Specialty:
Mr. Jeffrey J. Irving - *Generalist*

Description: A small, generalist firm particularly skilled in search for clients working through significant organization change where application of behavioral science expertise can be helpful beyond the search process itself.

Salary Minimum: $90,000
Functions: Generalist, General mgmt., Sales & mktg., HR mgmt., Finance, IT
Industries: Generalist, Finance, Communications, Publishing, High tech, Software

Isaacson, Miller

334 Boylston St., Ste. 500
Boston, Massachusetts 02116-3805
(617) 262-6500
Fax: (617) 262-6509
Email: jisaacson@imsearch.com
Web: www.execsearches.com

Key Contact - Specialty:
Mr. John Isaacson - *Healthcare, universities, non-profit*
Mr. Arnie Miller

Description: A national retained search firm, completing 125 senior executive searches per year. Civic and high-tech practice. Clients include transportation, universities, foundations, environmental defense, healthcare institutions, non-profit organizations, community economic development, governments, high-tech firms and publishing.

Salary Minimum: $50,000
Functions: Generalist, Directors, Senior mgmt., Middle mgmt., Admin. svcs., Physicians, Nurses, Allied health, Health admin., Mkt. research, Mktg. mgmt., Sales mgmt., PR, Benefits, Personnel, Training, CFO's, MIS mgmt., Systems anal., Systems dev., Systems implem., R&D, Engineering, Mgmt. consultants, Minorities, Non-profits, Environmentalists, Attorneys
Industries: Computer equip., Transportation, Banking, Invest. banking, Venture cap., Non-profits, Higher ed., Legal, Computer svcs., Mgmt. consulting, Publishing, New media, Broadcast & Film, Government, Environmental svcs., High tech, Software, Healthcare

J. Nicholas Arthur

One Financial Ctr.
Boston, Massachusetts 02111
(617) 204-9000
Fax: (617) 423-2776
Email: ncb@tlp-llc.com

Key Contact - Specialty:
Mr. Nicholas C. Bogard - *Senior level financial services*
Mr. Arthur P. Beecher - *Senior level financial services*

Description: Specializes in senior management positions within financial services.

Salary Minimum: $100,000
Functions: Senior mgmt., Mktg. mgmt., Sales mgmt., Direct mktg., CFO's, Cash mgmt., M&A
Industries: Banking, Invest. banking, Brokers, Venture cap., Misc. financial

J. Robert Scott
(a Fidelity Investments company)

27 State St.
Boston, Massachusetts 02109
(617) 563-2770
Fax: (617) 723-1282
Email: info@j-robert-scott.com
Web: j-robert-scott.com

Key Contact - Specialty:
Mr. William A. Holodnak - *Financial services, biotechnology, healthcare services, venture capital*
Mr. Todd Jackowitz - *Financial services, biotechnology, specialty retailing, cataloging*
Mr. Aaron Lapat - *Software*
Ms. Katie E. Vande Water - *Information technology, financial services*
Mr. Richard J. McCarthy

Description: Process based approach, proven commitment and dedication to clients. Exceptionally strong research capability and performance based billing. Quality of work is guaranteed. A Fidelity Investments company.

Salary Minimum: $80,000
Functions: Generalist
Industries: Generalist, Mfg., Svcs., Communications, Software, Biotech, Healthcare

J.B.A. Assoc.

3020 Issaquah Pine Lake Rd., Ste. 547
Issaquah, Washington 98029
(206) 557-8804
Fax: (206) 727-8512

Key Contact - Specialty:
Mr. James L. Black - *Retail*

Description: A full service retained firm for retail and food services industries.

Salary Minimum: $50,000
Functions: Generalist, Personnel
Industries: Retail, Hospitality

J.D.G. y Asociados, S.A. de C.V.

Boulevard Rodriguez No. 78
Hermosillo, Sonora 83000
Mexico
52 62 14 82 76
52 62 14 28 75
Fax: 52 62 14 82 76

Key Contact - Specialty:
Mr. Jose D. Gurrola - *Multinational companies operating in Mexico and the U.S.A. Southwest*

Description: Highly regarded generalist firm in Northern Mexico, with profound knowledge of the U.S.-Mexico Maquiladoras (in-bond industry) executive market and the general Mexico business sphere.

Salary Minimum: $25,000
Functions: General mgmt., Mfg., Materials, Sales & mktg., HR mgmt., Finance, Int'l.
Industries: Mfg., Wholesale, Retail, Finance, Svcs., Communications, Healthcare

J.J. & H., Ltd.

120 S. LaSalle St., Ste. 1410
Chicago, Illinois 60603
(312) 726-1578
Fax: (312) 726-2295
Email: chicago@jacobson-associates.com
Web: www.jacobson-associates.com

Key Contact - Specialty:
Mr. David N. Jacobson - *Insurance*
Ms. Margaret Resce Milkint - *Insurance*

Description: Providing quality, ethical nationwide services since 1971 in the field of insurance, risk management and healthcare.

Salary Minimum: $50,000
Functions: Risk mgmt.
Industries: Insurance, Healthcare

Branches:
1775 The Exchange, Ste. 240
Atlanta, Georgia 30339
(770) 952-3877
Fax: (770) 952-0061
Key Contact - Specialty:
Mr. Gregory P. Jacobson - *Insurance*
Mr. John Baumann - *Healthcare*

Five Neshaminy Interplex, Ste. 113
Trevose, Pennsylvania 19053
(215) 639-5860
Fax: (215) 639-8096
Key Contact - Specialty:
Mr. Nate Bass - *Insurance*

Affiliates:
Jacobson Assoc.

Jackson Resources †
101 W. 6th St., Ste. 505
Austin, Texas 78701
(512) 236-1227
Fax: (512) 435-6667
Email: jjj@jacksonresources.com

Key Contact - Specialty:
Ms. Jennifer Jackson - *Sales & marketing, computers*
Mr. Tim Scoggins - *Sales, marketing*

Description: Our searches are fast, efficient and economical. By canvassing the competition, our clients get a market analysis of their hiring prospects, not just a stack of resumes.
Functions: Sales & mktg.
Industries: Computer equip., Computer svcs., High tech, Software

Jacobs & Co.
Pocket Knife Sq.
P.O. Box 1686
Lakeville, Connecticut 06039-0353
(860) 435-1012
Email: dmj@snet.net

Key Contact - Specialty:
Mr. David M. Jacobs - *Generalist, key management, top sales talent, SEC, NASD, compliance*

Description: Search and consulting within the securities industry with an emphasis on compliance professionals who have an expertise in investment adviser and broker dealer regulations, also key senior management within this industry.

Salary Minimum: $75,000
Functions: Generalist, Sales & mktg.
Industries: Generalist, Brokers, Non-classifiable industries

JAG Group
311 Lindbergh Blvd., Ste. 109
Ross Communications Bldg.
St. Louis, Missouri 63141
(314) 432-6565

Key Contact - Specialty:
Mr. John A. Green - *Healthcare administration, general management, manufacturing, marketing management*
Mr. Don Goldstein - *Healthcare administration*
Ms. Jean Pompelli - *Quality management, purchasing, environmental & healthcare administration*
Ms. Heide Green - *Healthcare administration*

Description: The firm prides itself in being confidential, thorough and rapid response without sacrificing quality. Specialize in managed care and hospital administration. Rather unique fee arrangements.

Salary Minimum: $50,000
Functions: Senior mgmt., Production, Healthcare, Mktg. mgmt., R&D, Engineering, Environmentalists
Industries: Mfg., Lumber/furniture, Legal, Advertising/PR, Aerospace, Healthcare

Affiliates:
R. F. Mulvaney & Assoc., Inc.

Jakobs & Assoc. Int'l.
(Firm declined to update.)
79 Burda Ave.
New City, New York 10956-1518
(914) 638-9432

Key Contact - Specialty:
Mr. Frederick H. Jakobs - *General executive, senior management, board of directors*

Description: 35 years experience as senior human resource executive and business consultant in high-growth, highly competitive industries represents added value to clients addressing today's multiple challenges of diversity, productivity, quality and organizational effectiveness.

Salary Minimum: $75,000
Functions: Generalist, Directors, Mfg., Sales & mktg., Benefits, Finance, Mgmt. consultants
Industries: Generalist, Energy/utilities, Lumber/furniture, Computer equip., Hospitality, Entertainment, Environmental svcs.

Pendleton James Assoc., Inc.
200 Park Ave., Ste. 4520
New York, New York 10166
(212) 557-1599
Email: pjassoc@aol.com

Key Contact - Specialty:
Mr. E. Pendleton James - *Senior general management & corporate boards*

Description: Senior management level searches.

Salary Minimum: $150,000
Functions: Directors, Senior mgmt., Sales mgmt., CFO's, Cash mgmt., MIS mgmt.
Industries: Retail, Finance, Invest. banking, Brokers, Venture cap.
Professional Associations: AESC

Branches:
One International Place, Ste. 2350
Boston, Massachusetts 02110
(617) 261-9696
Key Contact - Specialty:
Mr. Durant A. Hunter - *Senior management*

Affiliates:
GKR Associates Ltd.

January Management Group
432 E. Rich St., Ste. 2F
Columbus, Ohio 43215
(614) 463-1820

Key Contact - Specialty:
Mr. Bruce M. Bastoky - *Generalist*

Description: Generalist firm staffed by former human resources executives conducting search with high sense of urgency and discretion, making this firm particularly effective during crisis or unexpected executive changes. No unsolicited resumes please.

Salary Minimum: $90,000
Functions: Generalist, Mfg., Materials
Industries: Generalist, Mfg., Retail

JDavid Assoc., Inc.
P.O. Box 1056
Madison, Connecticut 06443
(203) 245-7303

Key Contact - Specialty:
Mr. Joe D. Tuschman

Description: Provide executive search expertise, on a retainer basis, working within most functional areas and in many industries. Consumer product clients represent 75% of practice.

Salary Minimum: $100,000
Functions: Generalist
Industries: Generalist

Jender & Company
800 W. 5th Ave., Ste. 205B
Naperville, Illinois 60563
(630) 355-7797
Fax: (630) 355-7806
Email: jpj1935@aol.com
Web: jpj1935@aol.com

Key Contact - Specialty:
Mr. Jesse Jender

Description: Generalist firm, representing companies that manufacture a product, all functional areas. Emphasis on general management, engineering management, marketing/sales management, financial and H.R.

Salary Minimum: $50,000

† occasional contingency assignment

Functions: Generalist, Mfg., Materials, Sales & mktg., IT, Engineering
Industries: Generalist, Mfg., Computer svcs., Broadcast & Film, Telecoms, High tech, Software

JG Consultants, Inc.
8350 N. Central Expwy., Ste. M2000
Dallas, Texas 75206
(214) 696-9196
Fax: (214) 696-9205
Web: www.jandg@flash.net

Key Contact - Specialty:
Ms. Jay Stephenson - *High technology*

Description: Recognized for completing difficult searches when others have not produced results. Have performed many multi-location, multi-hire searches as well as recruiting impossible to find candidates. All candidates are pre-interviewed and referenced.

Salary Minimum: $80,000
Functions: Senior mgmt., Product dev., Sales & mktg., Sales mgmt., Systems support, Int'l.
Industries: Venture cap., Computer svcs., Telecoms, High tech, Software

JLI-Boston
230 Commercial St.
Boston, Massachusetts 02109-1305
(617) 227-4030
Fax: (617) 227-6008
Email: contact@jli-boston.com
Web: www.jli-boston.com

Key Contact - Specialty:
Mr. N. G. Fountas - *Plastics*
Ms. M. Lincoln

Description: Exclusively in the plastics, packaging and medical device industries. Conducts critical searches for Best-in-Class executives, managers and technical specialists who can significantly impact its clients' capabilities, profits and market positions.

Salary Minimum: $60,000
Functions: General mgmt., Mfg., Packaging, Sales & mktg., R&D, Engineering, Mgmt. consultants
Industries: Chemicals, Medical devices, Plastics/rubber, Paints/petroleum products, Mgmt. consulting, Packaging

JM & Company
P.O. Box 285
Wayne, Pennsylvania 19087
(610) 964-0200
Fax: (610) 964-8596

Key Contact - Specialty:
Mr. John C. Marshall - *Packaging*
Mr. John D. Hildebrand - *Plastics*
Mr. Robert A. Sargent - *Packaging*
Ms. Kristen Cossa - *Printing*
Mr. Craig Baker - *Corrugated*

Description: Our firm works on a search basis with companies that require very detailed recruiting, confidentiality and a thorough knowledge of the industries that we specialize in.

Salary Minimum: $100,000
Functions: Senior mgmt., Middle mgmt., Plant mgmt., Packaging, Mktg. mgmt., Sales mgmt., Graphic artists
Industries: Paper, Printing, Chemicals, Plastics/rubber, Packaging

John & Powers, Inc.
12935 N. Forty Drive, Ste. 214
St. Louis, Missouri 63141
(314) 453-0080

Key Contact - Specialty:
Mr. Harold A. John - *Generalist*

Description: Consulting firm which exclusively specializes in executive search to all industries. Clients represented include Fortune 500 companies, medium size organizations and turnaround situations.

Salary Minimum: $100,000
Functions: Generalist
Industries: Generalist

John Michael Assoc. †
Washington Dulles Int'l. Airport
P.O. Box 17130
Washington, District of Columbia 20041
(703) 471-6300
Fax: (703) 471-4064
Email: gf@searchjma.com
Web: www.searchjma.com

Key Contact - Specialty:
Mr. Gary J. Fossett - *Corporate securities, intellectual property, healthcare, international transactions, telecommunications*

Description: An executive retained search company for law firms and corporations seeking legal talent. Experience includes work with over 100 law firms and corporations in Los Angeles, New York, Washington D.C.

Salary Minimum: $80,000
Functions: Attorneys
Industries: Legal

Johnson & Assoc., Inc.
101 First St., Ste. 282
Los Altos, California 94022
(650) 941-4244
Fax: (650) 941-9093
Email: cherijai@aol.com
Web: www.best.com/~cherijai

Key Contact - Specialty:
Ms. Cheri Johnson - *High technology technical positions & management*

Description: Personnel search specialists primarily in hi-tech, bio-medical, medical instrumentation, hi-volume disposables, computer telephony, telecommunications, computers and peripherals industry. Other assignments have included Big Eight, golf course professionals & related club management.

Salary Minimum: $50,000
Functions: Senior mgmt., Middle mgmt., Mkt. research, Sales mgmt., Systems dev., R&D, Engineering
Industries: Agri/forestry/mining, Medical devices, Computer equip., Computer svcs., New media, Telecoms, Software

John H. Johnson & Assoc., Inc.
310 S. Michigan Ave., Ste. 2300
Chicago, Illinois 60604
(312) 663-4257
Fax: (312) 663-9761

Key Contact - Specialty:
Mr. John H. Johnson

Description: Professional retainer-based executive search firm for all industries/ functional areas.

Salary Minimum: $75,000
Functions: Generalist, General mgmt., Mfg., Sales & mktg., HR mgmt., Finance, Engineering
Industries: Generalist, Paper, Printing, Metal products, Machinery/Appliances, Aerospace, Packaging

L. J. Johnson & Co. †
815 Newport Rd.
Ann Arbor, Michigan 48103
(734) 663-6446
Fax: (734) 663-8114
Email: jobs@jobsbyjohnson.com

Key Contact - Specialty:
Mr. L. J. Johnson - *Manufacturing (all)*

Description: Retained searches for management, logistics, technical and administrative personnel. Financial and management consultants. Strong emphasis on manufacturing, engineering, automotive TIER 1 and logistics/food/ consumer personnel.

Salary Minimum: $40,000
Functions: Mfg., Materials, Distribution, HR mgmt., Finance, Engineering, Mgmt. consultants
Industries: Generalist, Food/bev/tobacco, Plastics/rubber, Motor vehicles, Transportation, Mgmt. consulting, Human resource svcs.

Johnson & Company

11 Grumman Hill Rd.
Wilton, Connecticut 06897
(203) 761-1212
Fax: (203) 762-7269

Key Contact - Specialty:
Mr. Stanley C. Johnson - *Functional heads, general managers*

Description: Quality reputation for recruiting functional heads and general managers.

Salary Minimum: $90,000
Functions: Generalist, Senior mgmt., Mktg. mgmt., Sales mgmt., Direct mktg., CFO's, Mgmt. consultants
Industries: Generalist, Food/bev/tobacco, Textiles/apparel, Metal products, Retail, Mgmt. consulting, Publishing
Professional Associations: IACPR

Ronald S. Johnson Assoc., Inc.

11661 San Vicente Blvd., Ste. 400
Los Angeles, California 90049
(310) 820-5855
Fax: (310) 207-1815
Email: searchrsj@aol.com

Key Contact - Specialty:
Mr. Ronald S. Johnson
Ms. Pat Kriste

Description: Retainer search firm specializing in senior management for medium to high technology, venture backed companies in hardware, software, network/telecommunications and transportation.

Salary Minimum: $90,000
Functions: Senior mgmt., Product dev., Mktg. mgmt., Sales mgmt., CFO's, MIS mgmt., Engineering
Industries: Generalist, Computer equip., Computer svcs., New media, Telecoms, High tech, Software

Johnson Smith & Knisely

100 Park Ave., 15th Floor
New York, New York 10017
(212) 885-9100
Fax: (212) 661-3778
Email: mokeefe@jsk.com

Key Contact - Specialty:
Mr. Gary Knisely
Ms. Mary E. O'Keefe - *Corporate*
Mr. William J. Maher - *Fashion, retail*
Mr. David S. Kanal - *Fashion, retail*
Mr. Robert Barron - *Fashion, retail*
Ms. Barbara Pickens - *Consumer markets*
Mr. David Barnes - *Consumer markets*
Mr. Joel C. Millonzi - *Financial services*
Mr. Scott Coff - *Financial services*
Ms. C.C. Leslie - *Financial services*
Mr. Ashton S. McFadden - *Financial services, portfolio management*
Mr. Edward J. Pierson - *Financial services*
Mr. David S. Stevens, III - *Financial services*
Mr. Anthony Whiting - *Financial services*
Ms. Patricia May - *Financial services*
Ms. Sandra Rupp - *Financial services*
Ms. Janice Abert - *Financial services*
Ms. Stephanie Cohen - *Financial services*
Ms. Lisa Gurliacci - *Financial services*
Mr. Dan Johnson - *Financial services*
Ms. Elizabeth Klebanoff - *Financial services*
Ms. Kate Zadek - *Financial services*
Ms. Jennifer Brown - *Financial services*
Ms. Juliet Blair - *Financial services*
Ms. Rachel Hamlin - *Financial services*
Ms. Pat Mastandrea - *Media, entertainment, communications*
Ms. Susan Denison - *Media, entertainment, communications*
Mr. Peter Eldredge - *Media, entertainment, communications*
Ms. Cara Erickson - *Media, entertainment*
Mr. John W. Malcom - *Media, entertainment, communications, publishing*
Ms. Marci Pepper - *Media, entertainment*
Ms. Jennifer Emerzian - *Media, entertainment, communications*
Ms. Susan Sachs - *Media, entertainment*
Ms. Carole Schwartz - *Professional services*
Ms. Rochelle Block - *Professional services*
Ms. Annie Austn - *Professional services*
Ms. Kari Sheehan - *Professional services*
Mr. Jeffrey Neuberth - *Professional services*

Description: We are an international firm of specialists that recruits senior level management within particular sectors. Currently there are 10 sectors represented which include financial services, media & entertainment, consumer products, fashion & retail, technology, telecom, business services, professional services, healthcare & industrial.

Salary Minimum: $150,000
Functions: General mgmt., Mfg., Sales & mktg., HR mgmt., Finance, IT, Specialized services
Industries: Mfg., Retail, Finance, Svcs., Communications, High tech, Healthcare

Branches:
39350 Civic Center Drive, Ste. 440
Fremont, California 94538
(510) 713-0840
Fax: (510) 713-1209
Key Contact - Specialty:
Mr. Larry Dillon - *Technology*
Mr. Howard Nitchke - *Technology*

1888 Century Park E., Ste. 1900
Los Angeles, California 90067
(310) 284-3238
Fax: (310) 284-3239
Key Contact - Specialty:
Ms. Franca Virgili - *Media, entertainment, communications*
Mr. Roger Comstock - *Business services*

44 Montgomery St., Ste. 3060
San Francisco, California 94104
(415) 397-0846
Fax: (415) 397-0848
Key Contact - Specialty:
Ms. Sara Kampmann - *Financial services*
Mr. William von Stein - *Financial services*
Ms. Kathleen Ursin - *Financial services*

1 Prestige Drive, Ste. 203
Meriden, Connecticut 06450
(203) 237-3000
Fax: (203) 634-6860
Key Contact - Specialty:
Mr. Robert Simon - *Technology*
Mr. Spencer Ingram - *Technology*
Ms. Melissa Moreno - *Technology*

600 Peachtree St., Ste. 3860
Atlanta, Georgia 30308
(404) 874-2100
Fax: (404) 874-0150
Key Contact - Specialty:
Mr. Donald R. Duckworth
Mr. Colin Brady - *Industrial*
Mr. Dan Bailey - *Industrial*
Ms. Helene Eversbush - *Professional services*
Ms. Rebecca Bass - *Technology*
Mr. Russell Gray - *Telecommunications*
Ms. F. Colleen Stewart - *Telecommunications*

181 West Madison St., Ste. 4850
Chicago, Illinois 60602
(312) 920-9400
Fax: (312) 920-9410
Key Contact - Specialty:
Ms. Linda Mack - *Financial services*
Ms. Jill Hendrickson - *Financial services*
Mr. Terry McSherry - *Industrial*
Mr. Tim O'Donnell - *Industrial*
Ms. Christine Wojeik - *Industrial*
Ms. Anna McCormick-Kelch - *Media, entertainment, communications*
Anne Bishop - *Media, entertainment*
Ms. Sara Nehring - *Technology*
Mr. Vince Schwartz - *Technology*

137 Elmer St.
Westfield, New Jersey 07090
(908) 301-0440
Fax: (908) 301-0445
Key Contact - Specialty:
Mr. Walt Trosin - *Healthcare, pharmaceuticals*
Ms. E. Leigh Marshall - *Telecommunications*

Jonas, Walters & Assoc., Inc.

1110 N. Old World Third St., Ste. 510
Milwaukee, Wisconsin 53203-1102
(414) 291-2828
Fax: (414) 291-2822
Email: tpappas@aol.com

Key Contact - Specialty:
Mr. William F. Walters - *Consumer products, electronics, metal working, engineered products, telecommunications*

Mr. Peter Flannery - *Medical devices, medical instruments, industrial equipment, electrical equipment*
Mr. Donald Hucko - *Sales & marketing, finance, manufacturing, engineering*
Mr. Scott Roberts - *Consumer products, industrial gases, financial services, engineered products*
Ms. Donna Daniels - *Healthcare, medical devices, medical instruments, biotechnology, telecommunications*

Description: Wisconsin's oldest and largest retained search firm with strong Midwest presence. Focus is on recruitment of mid/senior executives for major manufacturers. Excellent client retention record. Managed care division.

Salary Minimum: $75,000
Functions: General mgmt., Mfg., Materials, Healthcare, Sales & mktg., HR mgmt., Finance
Industries: Generalist, Medical devices, Plastics/rubber, Leather/stone/glass/clay, Metal products, Machinery/Appliances, Misc. mfg.

Affiliates:
Riverfront Search Partners, Inc.

The Jonathan Stevens Group, Inc. †

116 Village Blvd., Ste. 200
Princeton Forrestal Village
Princeton, New Jersey 08540
(609) 734-7444
Fax: (732) 431-3815

Key Contact - Specialty:
Mr. Steven G. Goldstein - *Finance, investment banking, consumer products, information technology, consulting*
Ms. Ruth F. Reifersen - *Specialty retail, sales & marketing, industrial, cosmetics*

Description: Boutique search firm that has long lasting relationships with companies and that recruits in many different disciplines. The principal has total contact with the client at all times. We will generate 5 to 8 candidates over a 3 week period of time from the inception of the assignment that meet the must factors. Search to completion ratio is extremely high.

Salary Minimum: $50,000
Functions: Senior mgmt., Product dev., Direct mktg., Cash mgmt., MIS mgmt., Engineering, Mgmt. consultants
Industries: Food/bev/tobacco, Textiles/apparel, Finance, Banking, Invest. banking, Mgmt. consulting, High tech

Jones and Jones

10250 SW Greenburg Rd.
Lincoln Center, Ste. 219
Portland, Oregon 97223
(503) 452-6116
Fax: (503) 452-6115
Email: jonesjones@aol.com
Web: www.jones-jones.com

Key Contact - Specialty:
Ms. Pamela K. Jones - *High technology companies*

Description: We are a 14 year old firm serving high technology companies exclusively. The firm provides a full range of retained services associated with executive and technical searches.
Functions: Senior mgmt., Mktg. mgmt., Sales mgmt., Training, CFO's, MIS mgmt., Engineering
Industries: High tech

Jones Management Co.

1 Dock St., Ste. 112
Stamford, Connecticut 06902
(203) 353-1140
Email: fjones@jones-mgt.com
Web: www.jones-mgt.com

Key Contact - Specialty:
Mr. Francis E. Jones - *Generalist*
Ms. Denise Guest - *Finance*

Description: We are a consulting firm dedicated to providing quality executive search and professional consulting services in areas including finance, accounting, audit, taxation, treasury, branding, marketing and sales, human resources, brokerage, insurance, operations, information technology and general management.

Salary Minimum: $75,000
Functions: Finance, Budgeting, Credit, M&A, IT, Engineering, Mgmt. consultants
Industries: Finance, Communications, Environmental svcs., Packaging, Real estate, Software, Healthcare
Professional Associations: IACPR

Branches:
555 Fifth Ave.
New York, New York 10017
(212) 697-8647
Email: fjones@jones-mgt.com
Key Contact - Specialty:
Ms. Bonnie Jones - *Administrative*

Jones-Parker/Starr

207 S. Elliott Rd., Ste. 155
Chapel Hill, North Carolina 27514
(919) 542-5977
(919) 542-1527
Fax: (919) 542-1622
Email: jonespark1@aol.com

Key Contact - Specialty:
Ms. Janet Jones-Parker - *Professional services, executive search firms, management consulting*

Description: Firm specializes in recruiting experienced consultants or industry executives seeking to enter the consulting profession.
Functions: Mgmt. consultants
Industries: Mgmt. consulting

Branches:
103 Pinegate Rd.
Peachtree City, Georgia 30269
(770) 486-6494
Fax: (770) 486-6491
Email: jonstarr@aol.com
Key Contact - Specialty:
Mr. Jonathan Starr - *Professional services, management consulting, executive search firms*

Jordan-Sitter Assoc.

23995 Bat Cave Rd., Ste. 200
San Antonio, Texas 78266
(210) 651-5561
Fax: (210) 651-5562
Email: info@jordan-sitter.com
Web: www.jordan-sitter.com

Key Contact - Specialty:
Mr. William P. Sitter - *Construction, mining, industrial & agricultural equipment manufacturers & distributors (not contractors)*

Description: Construction, mining, industrial and agricultural equipment manufacturers, dealers and related businesses on an exclusive and retained basis, only.

Salary Minimum: $70,000
Functions: General mgmt., Senior mgmt., Middle mgmt., Mfg., Sales & mktg., Engineering, Int'l.
Industries: Agri/forestry/mining, Construction, Metal products, Machinery/Appliances

Jordon & Jordon, Inc.

101 Greenwood Ave., Ste. LC-10
Jenkintown, Pennsylvania 19046
(215) 885-1644
Fax: (215) 885-1680
Email: info@jordonandjordon.com
Web: www.jordonandjordon.com

Key Contact - Specialty:
Mr. Bud Jordon - *All field of endeavor*
Ms. Carole Bowman - *All fields of endeavor*

Description: Specialize in retail on a national level and all other fields of endeavor.

Salary Minimum: $24,000

Functions: Generalist, General mgmt., Healthcare, Sales & mktg., HR mgmt., IT, Minorities
Industries: Generalist, Retail, Svcs., Communications, High tech, Software, Healthcare

J. M. Joseph Assoc.

P.O. Box 104
High Bridge, New Jersey 08829-0104
(908) 638-6877
Fax: (908) 638-8220
Email: research@jmjoseph.com
Web: www.jmjoseph.com

Key Contact - Specialty:
Mr. C. Russell Ditzel

Description: Targeted professional and executive recruiting in most functional areas. Principals and associates have solid corporate and operating company experience. Provide database development and competitor analysis research.

Salary Minimum: $40,000
Functions: Senior mgmt., Mfg., Mktg. mgmt., Sales mgmt., Personnel, MIS mgmt., Minorities
Industries: Generalist, Food/bev/tobacco, Medical devices, Computer svcs., Packaging, Software, Healthcare

JSG Group Management Consultants

4 Library Lane
Unionville, Ontario L3R 5T6
Canada
(905) 477-3625
Fax: (905) 477-8211
Email: rbirarda@istar.ca
Web: www.jsggroup.com

Key Contact - Specialty:
Mr. Richard W. Birarda - *Technology, automotive*

Description: Retainer-based executive search firm specializing in the automotive and technology sectors.

Salary Minimum: $70,000
Functions: Middle mgmt., Productivity, Customer svc., CFO's, Systems implem., Engineering, Mgmt. consultants
Industries: Computer equip., Misc. financial, Mgmt. consulting, Telecoms, Insurance, High tech, Software

Judd Associates

85 Greenwood Rd., Morganville Farms
Morganville, New Jersey 07751
(732) 970-0234
Email: Heidi@Judd.net

Key Contact - Specialty:
Ms. Heidi Judd

Description: We never take on more than 2 to 3 assignments at a time - allowing every client to be our #1 priority. The president of our company personally conducts every assignment.

Salary Minimum: $80,000
Functions: Generalist, Senior mgmt., Health admin., Mktg. mgmt., CFO's, MIS mgmt., Systems anal.
Industries: Generalist, Food/bev/tobacco, Soap/perfume/cosmetics, Computer equip., High tech, Software, Healthcare

Kacevich, Lewis & Brown, Inc.

300 W. Main St., Bldg. B
Northborough, Massachusetts 01532
(508) 393-6002
Email: joek@klbinc.com

Key Contact - Specialty:
Mr. Joseph B. Kacevich, Jr. - *Network, internet*

Description: Specialize in the search and replacement of sales support, hardware and software engineering and product and marketing management professionals in the networking, internetworking and communications industries.

Salary Minimum: $80,000
Functions: Mktg. mgmt., Sales mgmt., Engineering
Industries: Computer equip., Telecoms, High tech

Kanzer Assoc., Inc.

500 N. Michigan Ave., Ste. 620
Chicago, Illinois 60611
(312) 464-0831
Fax: (312) 464-3719
Email: kanzer@kanzer.com
Web: www.kanzer.com

Key Contact - Specialty:
Mr. William F. Kanzer - *Finance, human resources, manufacturing, sales & marketing, public relations*

Description: Provides clients with quality focus, aggressive timing, technical competence and commitment to communication, follow-through and delivery of a quality product.

Salary Minimum: $90,000
Functions: Generalist, Quality, Advertising, Benefits, Credit, MIS mgmt., Graphic artists
Industries: Generalist, Energy/utilities, Medical devices, Test/measurement equip., Computer svcs., Communications, Insurance
Professional Associations: IACPR

Gary Kaplan & Assoc.

201 S. Lake Ave., Ste. 600
Pasadena, California 91101
(626) 796-8100
Fax: (626) 796-1003
Email: resumes@gkasearch.com

Key Contact - Specialty:
Mr. Gary Kaplan - *Generalist*
Mr. Walter B. McNichols - *Generalist*

Description: International executive search firm committed to quality of effort, service and timely completion of assignments. Diversified clients include financial services, entertainment, high technology, consumer products, higher education, hospitality, natural resources.

Salary Minimum: $75,000
Functions: Generalist, Senior mgmt., Sales & mktg., HR mgmt., CFO's, MIS mgmt., Non-profits
Industries: Generalist, Agri/forestry/mining, Energy/utilities, Mfg., Finance, Higher ed., Communications

Kaplan & Assoc., Inc.

1220 Wyngate Rd.
Wynnewood, Pennsylvania 19096
(610) 642-5644

Key Contact - Specialty:
Mr. Alan J. Kaplan - *Technology, telecommunications firms, financial services organizations, start-up & venture-backed companies*
Ms. Stacy N. Deuel

Description: Our mission is to help organizations achieve their long term business objectives by ensuring they can identify and attract the finest executive talent. We are a generalist firm with particular expertise in financial services, information technology, telecommunications and startup companies.

Salary Minimum: $100,000
Functions: Senior mgmt., Mktg. mgmt., Sales mgmt., HR mgmt., CFO's, Cash mgmt., MIS mgmt.
Industries: Finance, Banking, Venture cap., Computer svcs., New media, Telecoms, High tech

Karel & Co. †

13522 Delano St.
Van Nuys, California 91401
(818) 785-6700
Fax: (818) 785-5656
Email: karel-co@primenet.com

Key Contact - Specialty:
Mr. Stephen A. Karel - *Environmental engineering, engineering, architectural & engineering, construction, real estate*

Description: Over 17 years of proven

† occasional contingency assignment

performance globally. The retention rate of our candidates for our clients is outstanding.

Salary Minimum: $50,000
Functions: PR, Benefits, M&A, Engineering, Architects, Attorneys, Int'l.
Industries: Energy/utilities, Construction, Retail, Human resource svcs., Environmental svcs., Haz. waste, Real estate

Howard Karr & Assoc., Inc.
1777 Borel Place, Ste. 408
San Mateo, California 94402
(650) 574-5277
Fax: (650) 574-0310
Email: search@karr.com
Web: www.karr.com

Key Contact - Specialty:
Ms. Cynthia Karr - *CFOs, controllers*
Mr. Howard L. Karr - *CFOs*
Ms. Liz Karr - *CFOs, controllers*

Description: Specialized retained executive search firm recruiting chief financial officers, controllers and other senior financial positions. We work in all industries. Most of our client companies are located in the western states.

Salary Minimum: $100,000
Functions: Finance, CFO's, Budgeting, Cash mgmt., M&A
Industries: Generalist, Medical devices, Venture cap., Communications, High tech, Software, Biotech
Professional Associations: AESC

Allan Karson Assoc., Inc.
8200 Blvd. E.
North Bergen, New Jersey 07047
(201) 868-4344
Email: karson@intac.com
Web: www.karson.com

Key Contact - Specialty:
Mr. Allan Karson - *High technology corporations, software, data & telecommunication system (both U.S. and European-based corporations)*

Description: Executive search specializing in leadership positions for corporations that develop information and communication systems, computers and software. The positions are for top management, senior marketing and sales, technology and product development and product management. Approximately thirty percent of assignments are from European-based corporations.

Salary Minimum: $200,000
Functions: Senior mgmt., Mkt. research, Mktg. mgmt., Systems dev., Systems implem., R&D, Int'l.
Industries: Computer equip., Consumer electronics, Computer svcs., New media, Telecoms, High tech, Software

Martin Kartin & Co., Inc.
211 E. 70th St.
New York, New York 10021
(212) 628-7676
Fax: (212) 628-8838

Key Contact - Specialty:
Mr. Martin C. Kartin

Description: Individualized service, 20 years of retained search expertise emphasizing consumer products. Affordable fees based on proven results.

Salary Minimum: $50,000
Functions: Generalist, Senior mgmt., Mfg., Materials, Sales & mktg., Finance, R&D
Industries: Generalist, Food/bev/tobacco, Textiles/apparel, Soap/perfume/cosmetics, Drugs mfg., Retail, Communications

Chris Kauffman & Company
P.O. Box 53218
Atlanta, Georgia 30305
(404) 233-3530
Fax: (404) 262-7960
Email: chris@kauffco.com
Web: www.kauffco.com

Key Contact - Specialty:
Mr. Christopher C. Kauffman - *Restaurant*

Description: National executive search in the restaurant industry working with national chains, regional companies, franchisees and independent operators.

Salary Minimum: $50,000
Functions: Senior mgmt.
Industries: Hospitality

Kaufman Assoc.
2471 E. Bayshore Rd., Ste. 520
Palo Alto, California 94303
(650) 424-0151

Key Contact - Specialty:
Ms. Susan Kaufman - *Technology management, sales, financial, investment banking*

Salary Minimum: $80,000
Functions: Senior mgmt., Middle mgmt., Mkt. research, Sales mgmt., CFO's, Systems dev., R&D
Industries: Finance, High tech, Software

Kaye/Bassman Int'l. Corp.
18333 Preston Rd., Ste. 500
Dallas, Texas 75252-5477
(972) 931-5242
Fax: (972) 931-9683
Email: kbic@kbic.com
Web: www.kbic.com

Key Contact - Specialty:
Mr. Bob Bassman
Mr. Jeff Kaye
Ms. Sandy Bassman
Ms. Suzanne Clark
Mr. Bill Baker
Ms. Jamie Smith

Description: Helping companies in specialized fields identify, recruit and hire those professionals who clearly stand out as exceptional in their profession.

Salary Minimum: $75,000
Functions: Healthcare, Sales & mktg., Finance, IT, R&D, Engineering
Industries: Construction, Chemicals, Computer svcs., Insurance, Real estate, Biotech, Healthcare

Kazan International, Inc.
5 Cold Hill Rd. S., Ste. 26
Mendham, New Jersey 07945
(973) 543-0300
Fax: (973) 543-4235

Key Contact - Specialty:
Mr. J. Neil Kazan - *Healthcare, pharmaceutical, biotechnology, medical devices, diagnostics*

Description: Retainer executive search firm dedicated to the healthcare industry. Specialization includes senior management positions in medical devices, diagnostics, biotechnology and pharmaceuticals.

Salary Minimum: $100,000
Functions: General mgmt., Mfg., Sales & mktg., Finance, R&D, Int'l.
Industries: Drugs mfg., Medical devices, Venture cap., Pharmaceutical svcs., Biotech

Affiliates:
Euromedica

Keane Assoc.
676 Commonwealth Ave.
Newton, Massachusetts 02159
(617) 965-1600

Key Contact - Specialty:
Mr. Kevin Keane

Description: We specialize in technology based companies and maintain an extensive national database. All searches are conducted by principals. Also provide human resource consulting in compensation, benefits and policies.

Salary Minimum: $75,000
Functions: Senior mgmt., Sales mgmt., CFO's, MIS mgmt., Systems dev., Systems implem., Mgmt. consultants
Industries: Computer equip., Mgmt. consulting, New media, Telecoms, High tech, Software, Biotech

A.T. Kearney Executive Search

222 W. Adams St.
Chicago, Illinois 60606
(312) 648-0111
Fax: (312) 223-6369
Email: executive_search@atkearney.com
Web: www.executive_search.atkearney.com

Key Contact - Specialty:
Mr. Charles W. Sweet - *Generalist*

Description: Broad line firm serving most industries and all functions. A division of a global management consulting firm and a wholly owned subsidiary of an international information services company. Emphasis is on quality, tangible results and value-added service.

Salary Minimum: $90,000
Functions: Generalist, Directors, Senior mgmt., Middle mgmt., Admin. svcs., Legal, Mfg., Product dev., Production, Automation, Plant mgmt., Quality, Productivity, Materials, Purchasing, Materials Plng., Distribution, Packaging, Healthcare, Physicians, Nurses, Allied health, Health admin., Sales & mktg., Advertising, Mkt. research, Mktg. mgmt., Sales mgmt., Direct mktg., Customer svc., PR, HR mgmt., Benefits, Personnel, Training, Finance, CFO's, Budgeting, Cash mgmt., Credit, Taxes, M&A, Risk mgmt., IT, MIS mgmt., Systems anal., Systems dev., Systems implem., Systems support, Network admin., DB admin., R&D, Engineering, Specialized services, Mgmt. consultants, Minorities, Non-profits, Environmentalists, Architects, Technicians, Attorneys, Graphic artists, Paralegals, Int'l.
Industries: Generalist, Agri/forestry/mining, Energy/utilities, Construction, Mfg., Food/bev/tobacco, Textiles/apparel, Lumber/furniture, Paper, Printing, Chemicals, Soap/perfume/cosmetics, Drugs mfg., Medical devices, Plastics/rubber, Paints/petroleum products, Leather/stone/glass/clay, Metal products, Machinery/Appliances, Motor vehicles, Computer equip., Consumer electronics, Test/measurement equip., Misc. mfg., Transportation, Wholesale, Retail, Finance, Banking, Invest. banking, Brokers, Venture cap., Misc. financial, Svcs., Hospitality, Entertainment, Non-profits, Higher ed., Pharmaceutical svcs., Legal, Computer svcs., Accounting, Equip. svcs., Mgmt. consulting, Human resource svcs., Law enfcmt., Communications, Advertising/PR, Publishing, New media, Broadcast & Film, Telecoms, Government, Defense, Environmental svcs., Haz. waste, Aerospace, Packaging, Insurance, Real estate, High tech, Software, Biotech, Healthcare, Non-classifiable industries

Professional Associations: AESC, IACPR

Branches:
Park One
2141 E. Highland, Ste. 135
Phoenix, Arizona 85016
(602) 994-3032
Fax: (602) 947-6362
Key Contact - Specialty:
Ms. Jill S. Faber - *Generalist*

Biltmore Twr.
500 S. Grand Ave., Ste. 1780
Los Angeles, California 90071
(213) 689-6800
Fax: (213) 689-6857
Key Contact - Specialty:
Mr. Jack L. Groban - *Information technology, generalist*
Mr. Otis Booth, III - *Generalist*

Three Lagoon Drive, Ste. 160
Redwood Shores, California 94065
(650) 637-6600
Fax: (650) 637-6699
Key Contact - Specialty:
Mr. Carl M. Olsen - *Generalist*

4909 Murphy Canyon Rd., Ste. 120
San Diego, California 92123
(619) 278-8835
Fax: (619) 278-6725
Key Contact - Specialty:
Ms. Sue Major

One Tabor Ctr.
1200 17th St., Ste. 950
Denver, Colorado 80202
(303) 626-7300
Fax: (303) 626-7302
Key Contact - Specialty:
Ms. Marcia P. Pryde - *Generalist*

One Landmark Sq., Ste. 426
Stamford, Connecticut 06901
(203) 969-2222
Fax: (203) 326-8600
Key Contact - Specialty:
Mr. Mark J. McMahon - *Generalist*

200 S. Biscayne Blvd.
First Union Financial Ctr., Ste. 3500
Miami, Florida 33131
(305) 577-0046
Fax: (305) 577-3837
Key Contact - Specialty:
Mr. John T. Mestepey - *Generalist*

1100 Abernathy Rd., Ste. 900
Atlanta, Georgia 30328-5603
(770) 393-9900
Fax: (770) 395-9312
Key Contact - Specialty:
Mr. Richard A. Citarella - *Generalist*

One Liberty Square, 5th Floor
Boston, Massachusetts 02109
(617) 832-0500
Fax: (617) 832-0515
Key Contact - Specialty:
Mr. Andy R. Zaleta - *Generalist*

8500 Normandale Lake Blvd., Ste. 1630
Bloomington, Minnesota 55437
(612) 921-8436
Fax: (612) 921-8465
Key Contact - Specialty:
Mr. Don Hykes - *Generalist*

153 E. 53rd St.
New York, New York 10022
(212) 751-7040
Fax: (212) 350-3150
Key Contact - Specialty:
Mr. James Abruzzo - *Generalist*

1200 Bank One Ctr.
600 Superior Ave. E.
Cleveland, Ohio 44114-2650
(216) 241-6880
Fax: (216) 241-2763
Key Contact - Specialty:
Mr. David R. Lauderback - *Generalist*

One World Trade Ctr.
121 SW Salmon, Ste. 1100
Portland, Oregon 97204
(503) 471-1320
Fax: (503) 827-3668
Key Contact - Specialty:
Ms. Cathy Griffin - *Generalist*

Lincoln Plaza
500 N. Akard St., Ste. 4170
Dallas, Texas 75201
(214) 969-0010
Fax: (214) 720-5902
Key Contact - Specialty:
Mr. Robert Johnson - *Generalist*

Pennzoil Place
711 Louisiana, Ste. 2250
Houston, Texas 77002
(713) 222-1276
Fax: (713) 222-1856
Key Contact - Specialty:
Mr. Les Csorba - *Generalist*

225 Reinekers Lane
Alexandria, Virginia 22314
(703) 739-4624
Fax: (703) 519-0391
Key Contact - Specialty:
Mr. Roger I. Sekera - *Generalist*

130 Adelaide St. W., Ste. 2710
Toronto, Ontario M5H 3P5
Canada
(416) 947-1990
Fax: (416) 947-0255
Key Contact - Specialty:
Mr. Gerry Baker - *Generalist*

Ruben Dario 281, Piso 15
Col. Bosques de Chapultepec
Mexico City, Mexico CP 11580
Mexico
52 5 282 0050
Fax: 52 5 282 0631
Key Contact - Specialty:
Mr. Javier Valle - *Generalist*

International Branches:
Amsterdam, Brussels, Dusseldorf, Hong

Kong, London, Madrid, Minato-ku, Neuilly-sur-Seine, Oslo, Sao Paulo, Singapore, Sydney, Zurich

Affiliates:
Cambridge Consulting Services, Ltd.
M. J. Freitas Assoc.

The Keith-Murray Partnership
17 Sword St.
Toronto, Ontario M5A 3N3
Canada
(416) 926-0491
Fax: (416) 924-0688
Email: murray@astral.magic.ca

Key Contact - Specialty:
Ms. M. Keith-Murray

Description: As a research-driven generalist search firm dedicated to personalized, value-added service, we work with non-competitive clients to ensure unhindered search capabilities and the highest standards of confidentiality and integrity.
Functions: Advertising, Mktg. mgmt., Direct mktg., PR, HR mgmt., IT, Non-profits
Industries: Generalist

Thomas A. Kelley & Assoc.
3000 Sand Hill Rd., Ste. 120, Bldg. 2
Menlo Park, California 94025
(650) 854-3247
Fax: (650) 854-3509
Email: tom@tak.com

Key Contact - Specialty:
Mr. Tom A. Kelley
Ms. Susan Zelezny

Description: Specialize in top management for high technology start-up firms. Perform searches at vice president and CEO levels for Silicon Valley based companies in telecommunications, computer, software, internet and multi-media industries.

Salary Minimum: $100,000
Functions: Senior mgmt.
Industries: High tech, Software

S. D. Kelly & Assoc., Inc. †
990 Washington St., Ste. 314 S
Dedham, Massachusetts 02026-6719
(781) 326-8038
Fax: (781) 326-6123
Email: search@sdkelly.com
Web: www.sdkelly.com

Key Contact - Specialty:
Ms. Susan D. Kelly - *Electronic components/subassemblies, contract manufacturing, T/M instrumentation, assembly/test equipment, factory automation/controls*

Description: Specialize in retained and exclusive search and market-related research projects in the areas of sales, marketing, engineering, manufacturing, operations and general management within the electronics industry.

Salary Minimum: $60,000
Functions: Senior mgmt., Mfg., Automation, Materials, Sales & mktg., Engineering, Int'l.
Industries: Mfg., Computer equip., Test/measurement equip., High tech, Software

Kelly Assoc.
4021 B Monona Drive
Madison, Wisconsin 53716
(608) 222-5330
(760) 324-2466
Fax: (608) 222-5330

Key Contact - Specialty:
Mr. Ronald Kelly - *Private clubs managers, golf professionals, golf course superintendents*
Ms. Mary K. Kelly - *Private clubs managers, golf professionals, golf course superintendents*

Description: The company targets existing private golf clubs as well as new golf courses and associated golf clubs that are searching for a club manager, head golf professional or a golf course superintendent.

Salary Minimum: $75,000
Functions: Personnel, Mgmt. consultants
Industries: Hospitality, Entertainment, Mgmt. consulting

Kelly Associates †
5626 Colony Drive
Bethlehem, Pennsylvania 18017
(610) 868-6831
Fax: (610) 868-8657

Key Contact - Specialty:
Mr. Michael V. Palos - *Human resources, plant management, general management, environmental, health & safety*
Mr. Timothy J. Donahue - *Industrial gases, welding products, distribution*
Ms. Debbie Ruthrauff - *Food (all functions), retail management, consumer goods, accounting*
Ms. Bonnie Raub
Ms. Anjanette Curzi
Mr. John Keefe - *Materials management, manufacturing, sales & marketing*

Description: For HR people, we are well connected. For our industry specializations, we work very hard and try to work very smart. Our practice is generalist in nature and nationwide in scope. We have been successful with companies from Greenfield to Fortune 25.

Salary Minimum: $40,000
Functions: Generalist, Mfg., Materials, HR mgmt., Engineering, Mgmt. consultants, Minorities
Industries: Energy/utilities, Food/bev/tobacco, Chemicals, Plastics/rubber, Misc. mfg., Transportation, Telecoms

David Warwick Kennedy & Assoc.
1075 W. Georgia St., Ste. 1390
Vancouver, British Columbia V6E 3C9
Canada
(604) 685-9494
Fax: (604) 669-5156
Email: dwksearch@lightspeed.bc.ca

Key Contact - Specialty:
Mr. David Kennedy - *Generalist*

Description: We are a management consulting firm based in Vancouver, BC. The firm has one main specialty area: executive search. We strive to provide major firm quality at 2/3 the price and less than half the arrogance.

Salary Minimum: $40,000
Functions: Purchasing, Distribution, CFO's, Taxes, MIS mgmt., Mgmt. consultants
Industries: Generalist, Agri/forestry/mining, Food/bev/tobacco, Wholesale, Accounting, Mgmt. consulting

Kennedy & Co.
20 N. Wacker Drive, Ste. 1745
Chicago, Illinois 60606
(312) 372-0099
Fax: (312) 372-0629

Key Contact - Specialty:
Mr. Thomas J. Moran
Ms. Diane Dombeck
Mr. William M. O'Connor
Mr. Robert Mayer
Ms. Lenore Meyer

Description: Executive search practice serving clients nationwide in most functions and industries with expertise in finance.

Salary Minimum: $75,000
Functions: Directors, Senior mgmt., CFO's, Cash mgmt., M&A, MIS mgmt., Non-profits
Industries: Finance, Banking, Invest. banking, Brokers, Misc. financial

The Kennett Group, Inc. †
15 W. Third St.
Media, Pennsylvania 19063
(610) 565-8080
Fax: (610) 565-8085
Email: kennett_group@msn.com
Web: www.kennettgroup.com/tkg

Key Contact - Specialty:
Mr. Patrick B. Sweeney
Mr. David Gillespie
Ms. Linda Resch
Mr. Stephen Cammarota

Description: Search services for senior management within the financial services and information systems arena. Vertical specialties in trust operations and internet companies.

Salary Minimum: $60,000
Functions: Directors, Senior mgmt., CFO's, MIS mgmt., Systems implem., Network admin., DB admin.
Industries: Misc. financial, Computer svcs., Mgmt. consulting, High tech, Software, Non-classifiable industries

---

Kensington Int'l., Inc.
1415 W. 22nd St., Ste. 750
Oak Brook, Illinois 60521
(630) 571-0123
Fax: (630) 571-3139

Key Contact - Specialty:
Mr. Brian G. Clarke - *Senior level marketing, sales, corporate finance, Fortune 250*
Mr. Richard George - *Senior level manufacturing management, heavy manufacturing, Fortune 1000 & equivalent*
Mr. Scott Robinson - *Senior level manufacturing, sales, marketing management, mid cap companies $50-500 million sales*
Mr. Kevin Duffy - *Retail, consumer mass & grocery*

Description: Highly flexible and strategy-oriented firm that seeks strategic partnerships with a relatively small group of clients worldwide. Strong practice in the sourcing and placement of senior-level women and individuals of color.

Salary Minimum: $80,000
Functions: Senior mgmt., Middle mgmt., Plant mgmt., Mktg. mgmt., Sales mgmt., CFO's, Cash mgmt.
Industries: Food/bev/tobacco, Chemicals, Plastics/rubber, Metal products, Banking, Insurance, Healthcare

---

Kensington International
2130 Fillmore St., #231
San Francisco, California 94115-2224
(415) 776-1509
Email: kii@best.com

Key Contact - Specialty:
Ms. Holland Kensington - *Food & beverage, consumer packaged goods, transportation, financial services, high technology*

Description: Retained search. Client base includes: consumer package goods, food and beverage, transportation and financial services, high technology, healthcare. Professionals: operations, marketing/sales, accounting/finance and technical.

Salary Minimum: $75,000
Functions: IT, Systems anal., Systems dev., Systems implem., Systems support, Engineering
Industries: Communications, Telecoms, High tech, Software, Biotech, Healthcare

---

Kent & Assoc.
6477 Quarry Lane, Ste. 100
Dublin, Ohio 43017
(614) 798-9501
Fax: (614) 798-9502

Key Contact - Specialty:
Mr. Melvin Kent - *Generalist*

Description: Boutique firm best known for matching of chemistry between client and candidate offering high degree of personal service.

Salary Minimum: $80,000
Functions: Generalist, Senior mgmt., Healthcare, Sales & mktg., Direct mktg., CFO's, Int'l.
Industries: Generalist, Misc. mfg., High tech, Software, Healthcare

---

Kenzer Corp.
777 Third Ave.
New York, New York 10017
(212) 308-4300
Fax: (212) 308-1842
Email: ny@kenzer.com

Key Contact - Specialty:
Mr. Robert D. Kenzer - *Retail, financial services, manufacturing, high tech, hospitality & gaming*
Mr. Eric B. Segal - *Retail, financial services, manufacturing, high tech, hospitality & gaming*
Ms. Elaine Erickson - *Retail, financial services, manufacturing, high tech, hospitality & gaming*
Ms. Robin Russell - *Retail, financial services, manufacturing, high tech, hospitality & gaming*
Ms. Deborah Spiegel - *Retail, financial services, manufacturing, high tech, hospitality & gaming*

Description: A full service executive search firm with nationwide computer integrated offices. Over a twenty year history of operating with a high air of urgency and the highest standard of professionalism.
Functions: Directors, Senior mgmt., Product dev., Materials, Purchasing, Distribution, Advertising, Mkt. research, Mktg. mgmt., Sales mgmt., Direct mktg., Customer svc., PR, Personnel, CFO's, Budgeting, Cash mgmt., M&A, Risk mgmt., IT, MIS mgmt., Network admin., DB admin.
Industries: Mfg., Textiles/apparel, Transportation, Wholesale, Retail, Finance, Hospitality, Entertainment, Non-profits, Pharmaceutical svcs., Human resource svcs., Advertising/PR, Real estate, High tech

Branches:
6033 W. Century Blvd., Ste. 700
Los Angeles, California 90045
(310) 417-8577
Fax: (310) 417-3083
Email: la@kenzer.com
Key Contact - Specialty:
Mr. Daniel Guerrero - *Retail, financial services, manufacturing, high tech, hospitality & gaming*

1600 Parkwood Circle NW, Ste. 310
Atlanta, Georgia 30339
(770) 955-7210
Fax: (770) 955-6504
Email: atlanta@kenzer.com
Key Contact - Specialty:
Ms. Marie Powell - *Retail, financial services, manufacturing, high tech, hospitality & gaming*

625 N. Michigan Ave., Ste. 1244
Chicago, Illinois 60611
(312) 266-0976
Fax: (312) 266-0994
Email: chicago@kenzer.com
Key Contact - Specialty:
Ms. Mary Allgire - *Retail, financial services, manufacturing, high tech, hospitality & gaming*

150 S. Fifth St., Ste. 1400
Fifth Street Twrs.
Minneapolis, Minnesota 55402
(612) 332-7770
Fax: (612) 332-7707
Email: minn@kenzer.com
Key Contact - Specialty:
Ms. Elizabeth Bothereau - *Financial services, retail, manufacturing, high tech, hospitality & gaming*

3030 LBJ Frwy., Ste. 1430
Triwest Plaza
Dallas, Texas 75234
(972) 620-7776
Fax: (972) 243-7570
Email: dallas@kenzer.com
Key Contact - Specialty:
Mr. Donald Jones - *Retail, financial services, manufacturing, high tech, hospitality & gaming*

Affiliates:
R.R. Beyma, Ltd.
Howgate Sable & Partners

Kershner & Co.
514 Tenth St. NW, 8th Floor
Washington, District of Columbia 20004
(202) 347-2129
Fax: (202) 347-2134
Email: bkershner@kershnerandco.com
Web: www.kershnerandco.com

Key Contact - Specialty:
Mr. Bruce Kershner - *Financial services, REIT's*

Description: We are a boutique search and consulting firm. We perform mid and senior level searches in most industries, with emphasis in the financial service arena.

Salary Minimum: $50,000
Functions: Directors, Senior mgmt., Middle mgmt., Finance, CFO's, Cash mgmt., M&A
Industries: Banking, Invest. banking, Brokers, Venture cap., Misc. financial, Insurance, Real estate

Daniel J. Kerstein, Consultant to Management

9332 E. Jewell Circle
Denver, Colorado 80231
(303) 695-1114
Email: dk@dank.com

Key Contact - Specialty:
Mr. Daniel J. Kerstein - *Medical instrumentation, machinery*

Description: We use a consultive method to do executive search. We have found that openings are the effect of problems, we address the cause.

Salary Minimum: $40,000
Functions: Generalist, Sales & mktg., Finance, R&D, Engineering
Industries: Medical devices, Metal products, Machinery/Appliances, Misc. mfg., Accounting

Michael L. Ketner & Assoc., Inc.

221 Penn Ave., Ste. 3700
Pittsburgh, Pennsylvania 15221
(412) 731-8100
Fax: (412) 731-9224
Email: ketner@ketner.com
Web: www.ketner.com

Key Contact - Specialty:
Mr. Michael L. Ketner - *Construction*
Mr. Keith A. Maxin - *Construction*

Description: With twenty-seven years experience and more than 2000 successful search assignments under our belt we are uniquely qualified to fill any construction executive need paying over $80,000 per year.

Salary Minimum: $80,000
Functions: General mgmt., Directors, Senior mgmt., Middle mgmt., Admin. svcs., Sales mgmt., CFO's
Industries: Construction

Kiley, Owen & McGovern, Inc.

P.O. Box 68
Blackwood, New Jersey 08012
(609) 227-5332
Fax: (609) 227-5530
Email: kilowen@voicenet.com
Web: wwwvoicenet.com/kilowen

Key Contact - Specialty:
Ms. Sheila M. McGovern - *Data communications, sales & marketing*
Mr. Tom Vandegrift - *Data communications, telecommunications engineering, software*
Mr. Ralph Owen - *Data communications, sales & marketing*
Mr. Ed Bryant - *Data communications, sales support, applications engineering*

Description: International retainer search firm specializing in sales and marketing management, software, engineering in the computer, telecommunications and data communications industries.

Salary Minimum: $50,000
Functions: Mkt. research, Mktg. mgmt., Sales mgmt., Customer svc., Systems support, Engineering, Int'l.
Industries: Computer equip., Computer svcs., Telecoms, Software, Non-classifiable industries
Professional Associations: IACPR

The Kilman Advisory Group

406 Farmington Ave.
Farmington, Connecticut 06032-1964
(860) 676-7817
Fax: (860) 676-7839
Email: contact@kilman.com
Web: www.kilman.com

Key Contact - Specialty:
Mr. Paul H. Kilman - *Legal*

Description: Provide search, outplacement and human resource consulting services primarily for the law departments of multinational companies. Successful in recruiting native attorneys in Europe, Canada, South America and the Pacific Rim for U.S. operations abroad.
Functions: Attorneys, Int'l.
Industries: Generalist

Kincannon & Reed

2106-C Gallows Rd.
Vienna, Virginia 22182
(703) 761-4046
Fax: (703) 790-1533
Email: krsearch@aol.com
Web: krsearch.com

Key Contact - Specialty:
Mr. Kelly Kincannon
Ms. Donna N. Lee

Description: The firm provides senior executive and board level recruitment services in agribusiness, food and biotechnology both in the US and overseas.

Salary Minimum: $100,000
Functions: Generalist
Industries: Agri/forestry/mining, Food/bev/tobacco, Chemicals, Drugs mfg., Pharmaceutical svcs., Biotech, Healthcare
Professional Associations: AESC

Kingsbury • Wax • Bova †

60 Hamilton St.
Cambridge, Massachusetts 02139
(617) 868-6166
Fax: (617) 868-0817
Email: mail@kwb.com

Key Contact - Specialty:
Mr. Robert M. Wax - *Corporate finance, leasing*
Mr. Scott C. Kingsbury - *Printing management*

Description: We provide middle and senior management search and corporate advisory services to assist our clients to meet financial and operational goals while expanding internationally.

Salary Minimum: $60,000
Functions: Senior mgmt., Middle mgmt., Plant mgmt., Sales mgmt., Direct mktg., Finance
Industries: Paper, Printing, Finance
Professional Associations: IACPR

Branches:
230 Park Ave., Ste. 1000
New York, New York 10169
(212) 808-3006
Fax: (212) 297-0331
Key Contact - Specialty:
Mr. Barry A. Bova - *Financial management*

Affiliates:
Robert Walters Associates

Kingsley Allen Partners Inc.

2 Bloor St. W., Ste. 1730, Box 28
Toronto, Ontario M4W 3E2
Canada
(416) 969-7218
Fax: (416) 920-3165
Email: info@kingsleyallen.com
Web: www.executiverecruitments.com

Key Contact - Specialty:
Mr. Richard Belanger - *Marketing, direct marketing, sales, communications*
Mr. Sean Magennis - *Generalist, psychometric testing, aptitude testing*

Description: A dynamic downtown boutique with a focus on service excellence and a dedicated relationship to a leading suite of assessment tools.

Salary Minimum: $70,000
Functions: Generalist

The Kingsley Group

44 Montgomery St., Ste. 3850
San Francisco, California 94104
(415) 291-9395
Fax: (415) 291-9373
Email: laurak@kingsley-group.com
Web: www.kingsley-group.com

Key Contact - Specialty:
Ms. Laura Kirkendorfer - *Transportation, supply chain, marketing*

Description: We are a general management consulting and executive search firm, with over a decade of experience in the transportation, supply chain and marketing industries. Our international expertise extends to Mexico, Latin America, Southeast Asia and Europe.

Salary Minimum: $60,000
Functions: General mgmt., Distribution, Sales & mktg., HR mgmt., Mgmt. consultants, Int'l.
Industries: Generalist, Transportation

Kingsley Quinn/USA
500 Morris Ave.
Springfield, New Jersey 07081
(973) 376-0044
Fax: (973) 376-6969
Email: kqusa@kingsleyquinn.com
Web: www.KingsleyQuinn.com

Key Contact - Specialty:
Mr. Kenneth A. Mortensen - *High technology*
Mr. Hugh Bever - *Pharmaceutical*
Mr. Frank M. Dework - *Food*
Mr. William Koppelman - *Information systems, MIS*

Description: Medium sized retainer based specializing in pharmaceutical and high tech industries. Principals all have senior management experience in industries served.

Salary Minimum: $75,000
Functions: General mgmt., Mfg., Healthcare, Sales & mktg., IT, R&D, Engineering
Industries: Food/bev/tobacco, Drugs mfg., Medical devices, Computer equip., Pharmaceutical svcs., High tech, Biotech

Branches:
7032 County Rd. 37
Springwater, New York 14560
(716) 669-2120
Key Contact - Specialty:
Mr. William J. Doyle - *High technology*

Affiliates:
Euromedica, Limited

The Kinlin Co., Inc.
749 Main St.
Osterville, Massachusetts 02655
(508) 420-1165
Fax: (508) 428-8525
Email: 104571,2471@compuserv.com

Key Contact - Specialty:
Ms. Ellen C. Kinlin - *Investment executives (senior)*
Ms. Molly Lee - *Researcher*
Mr. Dickson Smith - *Senior investment analysts (both buy side & sell side)*
Mr. Michael Hatch - *Investment management*

Description: Specializing in financial services industry on senior management $200,000+. Additional office space in Boston.

Salary Minimum: $200,000
Functions: Mktg. mgmt., Sales mgmt., Cash mgmt., M&A
Industries: Finance, Invest. banking, Brokers, Misc. financial

Branches:
60 State St.
Boston, Massachusetts 02109
(617) 742-7877
Key Contact - Specialty:
Ms. Karen Costa - *Financial services*

Richard Kinser & Assoc.
919 Third Ave., 10th Floor
New York, New York 10022
(212) 735-2740
Fax: (212) 735-2741

Key Contact - Specialty:
Mr. Richard Kinser - *Generalist*
Ms. Astrid von Baillou - *Communications, marketing*

Description: Assignments done by experienced search professionals. Successful search experience with top corporations and new ventures. Extensive candidate source contacts. Management and board of directors searches.

Salary Minimum: $100,000
Functions: Generalist, Directors, Senior mgmt., Plant mgmt., Mktg. mgmt., PR, CFO's
Industries: Generalist, Mfg., Computer equip., Finance, Mgmt. consulting, Communications, High tech
Professional Associations: AESC

Kip Williams, Inc.
355 Lexington Ave., 11th Floor
New York, New York 10017-6603
(212) 661-1225
Fax: (212) 867-2784
Email: kipwill@ix.netcom.com

Key Contact - Specialty:
Ms. Luanne S. Kip - *Strategic planning, corporate development, marketing, venture capital*

Description: Client driven, solutions-oriented approach combined with personal attention for exceptionally high completion rate. Proven source of difficult-to-recruit strategic management consultants. Focus on consumer industries, venture capital firms.

Salary Minimum: $90,000
Functions: General mgmt., Sales & mktg., HR mgmt., M&A, Mgmt. consultants, Minorities, Int'l.
Industries: Generalist, Misc. mfg., Venture cap., Mgmt. consulting, Human resource svcs., Communications, Healthcare

---

Kiradjieff & Goode, Inc.
70 Walnut St.
Wellesley, Massachusetts 02181-2199
(781) 239-8244
Fax: (781) 239-8241
Email: cgoode@kg-inc.com
Web: www.kg-inc.com

Key Contact - Specialty:
Mr. Richard W. Goode, Jr.
Ms. Laura K. Goode

Description: Board member, upper and middle echelon executive searches. Broad experience with a passionate commitment to personal service, consistent results and developing long-term client relationships.

Salary Minimum: $90,000
Functions: Generalist, General mgmt., Mfg., Sales & mktg., HR mgmt., Finance, IT
Industries: Generalist, Mfg., Finance, Svcs., Real estate, Biotech, Healthcare

---

Kirby Assoc.
P.O. Box 753-B
Collegeville, Pennsylvania 19426
(610) 489-8460
Fax: (610) 489-8467

Key Contact - Specialty:
Mr. William P. Kirby - *Generalist, human resources*

Description: Thirty years experience in recruiting and selecting general management and key functional management candidates (human resources, sales, production, etc.) in manufacturing and wholesale distribution industries.
Functions: Generalist, Senior mgmt., Plant mgmt., Distribution, Benefits, Personnel
Industries: Generalist, Paper, Wholesale

Kittleman & Assoc.,LLC
300 S. Wacker Drive, Ste. 1710
Chicago, Illinois 60606
(312) 986-1166
Fax: (312) 986-0895
Email: kittleman@aol.com

Key Contact - Specialty:
Mr. Richard M. King
Ms. Jeanne M. Halvorsen
Mr. Scott W. Bates
Ms. Mary Beth Malone

Description: Executive search, management consulting and leadership development exclusively for non-profit organizations including professional associations and private foundations nationwide.

† occasional contingency assignment

Salary Minimum: $50,000
Functions: Senior mgmt., Health admin., Mktg. mgmt., PR, CFO's, Non-profits
Industries: Non-profits, Higher ed., Advertising/PR

The Kleinstein Group, Inc.

33 Wood Ave. S.
Iselin, New Jersey 08830
(732) 494-7500
Fax: (732) 494-7579

Key Contact - Specialty:
Mr. Jonah A. Kleinstein

Description: The firm's unique research approach enables us to present candidates within 3 to 4 weeks from the initiation of assignment. The firm works on a retainer basis with a wide range of clients, from emerging growth-oriented organizations, to specialty industries, to Fortune 100 companies.

Salary Minimum: $100,000
Functions: Generalist, Senior mgmt., Finance, R&D, Attorneys, Int'l.
Industries: Generalist, Mfg., Chemicals, Drugs mfg., Finance, Packaging, Healthcare

Raymond J. Klemmer & Assoc.

(Firm declined to update.)
316 S. Bedford Rd.
Chappaqua, New York 10514
(914) 238-8598

Key Contact - Specialty:
Mr. Raymond J. Klemmer - *General management*

Description: High level recruiting for general managers, deep experience. Much faster yet higher quality. Much more research and better matching of experience and expertise to each search. Total client focus including consulting as needed.

Salary Minimum: $150,000
Functions: General mgmt., Mfg., Sales & mktg., HR mgmt., IT, Mgmt. consultants, Int'l.
Industries: Food/bev/tobacco, Plastics/rubber, Computer equip., Test/measurement equip., Non-profits, Human resource svcs., High tech

The Kleven Group, Inc. - Executive Search Division

(a division of StaffMark, Inc.)
1 Cranberry Hill, P.O. Box 636
Lexington, Massachusetts 02173
(781) 861-1020
Fax: (781) 861-1047
Email: kleven@kleven.com
Web: www.kleven.com

Key Contact - Specialty:
Mr. Robert Kleven - *High technology executives*
Ms. Michele White - *General executive*

Description: Retained search for scarce specialties and senior management executives at reduced cost for true search process. In-house research staff, national capability. Research packages available for corporate clients only. Video conferencing available in-house.

Salary Minimum: $80,000
Functions: Senior mgmt., Middle mgmt., MIS mgmt., Systems dev., Systems support, DB admin., Engineering
Industries: Computer equip., Consumer electronics, Test/measurement equip., Aerospace, High tech, Software, Biotech

Knapp Consultants

184 Old Ridgefield Rd.
Wilton, Connecticut 06897
(203) 762-0790
Fax: (203) 762-0747
Email: raknapp@aol.com

Key Contact - Specialty:
Mr. Ronald A. Knapp - *High technology, manufacturing*

Description: Nationwide executive search/management consulting firm specializing in aerospace, high technology, electronics, general manufacturing and gas turbine industries.

Salary Minimum: $90,000
Functions: General mgmt., Mfg., Materials, Sales & mktg., Finance, IT, Engineering
Industries: Medical devices, Metal products, Machinery/Appliances, Computer equip., Defense, Aerospace, High tech
Professional Associations: IACPR

Koehler & Co.

700 N. Pilgrim Pkwy., Ste. 104
Elm Grove, Wisconsin 53122
(414) 796-8010
Fax: (414) 796-8788
Email: koehlerj@execpc.com

Key Contact - Specialty:
Mr. Jack Koehler

Description: Conduct searches in all disciplines for manufacturing and technology oriented clients. Inquiries invited; references gladly offered.

Salary Minimum: $100,000
Functions: General mgmt., Senior mgmt., Mfg., Materials, Sales & mktg., HR mgmt.
Industries: Mfg.

Lee Koehn Assoc., Inc.

4380 SW Macadam Ave., Ste. 185
Portland, Oregon 97201
(503) 224-9067
Fax: (503) 224-8122
Email: koehn@lkassociates.com

Key Contact - Specialty:
Mr. Lee Koehn
Ms. Michael James

Description: A boutique retained search firm known for quality, timeliness and results serving its West Coast clients. Major emphasis in financial services, hi-tech, telecommunications, manufacturing and healthcare.

Salary Minimum: $80,000
Functions: Senior mgmt., Mfg., Health admin., Sales mgmt., Finance, MIS mgmt., Engineering
Industries: Energy/utilities, Metal products, Banking, Telecoms, Packaging, High tech, Healthcare

T. J. Koellhoffer & Assoc.

250 Rte. 28, Ste. 206
Bridgewater, New Jersey 08807
(908) 526-6880
Fax: (908) 725-2653
Email: tkoell@aol.com

Key Contact - Specialty:
Mr. Thomas J. Koellhoffer - *Engineering, applied research, telecommunications, biomedical*

Description: Specializing in technical and executive recruiting of senior management, manufacturing, R&D, business development and engineering talent for the broadcasting, information processing, telecommunications, scientific instrumentation and biotechnology industries.

Salary Minimum: $70,000
Functions: Senior mgmt., Mfg., Mktg. mgmt., MIS mgmt., R&D, Engineering, Mgmt. consultants
Industries: New media, Broadcast & Film, Telecoms, Aerospace, High tech, Software, Biotech

Fred Koffler Assoc.

942 Greenfield Rd.
Woodmere, New York 11598
(516) 569-6582

Key Contact - Specialty:
Mr. Fred Koffler

Description: Executive search firm specializing in senior management positions. Retained by client companies to recruit key executives in the area of sales, marketing, finance, engineering R&D, manufacturing and general management.

Salary Minimum: $80,000
Functions: General mgmt., Senior mgmt., Mfg., Materials, Sales & mktg., Finance, Engineering
Industries: Generalist

Koltnow & Company

1120 Ave. of the Americas, 4th Floor
New York, New York 10036
(212) 626-6606
Fax: (212) 626-6607

Key Contact - Specialty:
Ms. Emily Koltnow - *Apparel related industries*
Ms. Sharon Naulty - *Apparel related industries*

Description: Specializing in apparel related services including design, sales, production and senior management. Additional expertise in accessories, catalog and specialty retailers. Work closely with clients to identify needs and find candidates who match specific profiles.

Salary Minimum: $75,000
Functions: Senior mgmt., Middle mgmt., Product dev., Mkt. research, Sales mgmt.
Industries: Textiles/apparel, Wholesale, Retail

Koontz, Jeffries & Assoc., Inc. †

3623 Countryplace Blvd.
Sarasota, Florida 34233
(941) 922-3832

Key Contact - Specialty:
Mr. Donald N. Koontz - *Generalist*
Mr. David C. Foreman - *Generalist*
Mr. A. R. Kurkowski - *Generalist*
Mr. Gary Nichols - *Generalist*

Description: National generalist firm; written performance guarantee; written off-limits policy.

Salary Minimum: $80,000
Functions: General mgmt., Mfg., Healthcare, Sales & mktg., HR mgmt., Finance, Engineering
Industries: Generalist, Chemicals, Drugs mfg., Medical devices, Metal products, Insurance, Healthcare

Kopplin Search, Inc.

50-855 Washington St., Ste. C233
La Quinta, California 92253
(760) 564-0231
Fax: (760) 564-7331
Email: kopplin@kopplinsearch.com
Web: www.kopplinsearch.com

Key Contact - Specialty:
Mr. Richard M. Kopplin - *Club, golf (senior executives)*

Description: Specializing in executive management placement for private and resort golf clubs and golf related industries. We place general managers, head golf pros, course superintendents and sales and marketing executives.

Salary Minimum: $75,000
Functions: Senior mgmt., Middle mgmt., Mktg. mgmt., CFO's, Mgmt. consultants
Industries: Hospitality, Entertainment, Mgmt. consulting

Korban Associates

312 W. State St.
Kennett Square, Pennsylvania 19348
(610) 444-8611
Fax: (610) 444-8612
Email: korbanro@korban.com

Key Contact - Specialty:
Mr. Richard O. Korban - *Medical, healthcare, technology based manufacturing*
Mr. John R. Wolfe

Description: A strategically small firm conducting personalized searches in businesses/functions where the principals have direct line management experience. Speed, quality, professionalism, flexibility.

Salary Minimum: $60,000
Functions: General mgmt., Mfg., Healthcare, Sales & mktg., IT, R&D, Engineering
Industries: Mfg., Communications, High tech, Software, Biotech, Healthcare

Koren, Rogers Assoc. Inc. †

701 Westchester Ave., Ste. 212W
White Plains, New York 10604
(914) 686-5800
Fax: (914) 686-4116
Email: mkoren@korenrogers.com
Web: www.korenrogers.com

Key Contact - Specialty:
Mr. Michael Koren - *Finance, general management*

Description: Provide finance and accounting executive recruiting services with emphasis in consumer/pharmaceutical, entertainment, media and communication industries.

Salary Minimum: $75,000
Functions: Senior mgmt., CFO's, Cash mgmt., Taxes, M&A, MIS mgmt., Minorities
Industries: Food/bev/tobacco, Drugs mfg., Computer equip., Entertainment, Pharmaceutical svcs., Telecoms, Software

Korn/Ferry Int'l.

200 Park Ave., 37th Floor
New York, New York 10166
(212) 687-1834
Fax: (212) 986-5684

Key Contact - Specialty:
Mr. Richard Ferry
Mr. Michael Boxberger
Mr. Windle B. Priem - *Financial services*
Mr. Peter Dunn
Mr. Ed Kelley
Mr. Horacio McCoy
Mr. Michael Wellman

Description: Handling full range of industries. Specialty practices include financial services, consumer products, technology, retail, energy, healthcare, education and board services.

Salary Minimum: $100,000
Functions: Directors, Senior mgmt., Mfg., Materials, Physicians, Health admin., Sales & mktg., HR mgmt., Finance, IT, R&D, Engineering, Mgmt. consultants, Non-profits, Int'l.
Industries: Generalist, Agri/forestry/mining, Energy/utilities, Construction, Food/bev/tobacco, Textiles/apparel, Lumber/furniture, Paper, Printing, Chemicals, Soap/perfume/cosmetics, Drugs mfg., Medical devices, Plastics/rubber, Paints/petroleum products, Leather/stone/glass/clay, Metal products, Machinery/Appliances, Motor vehicles, Computer equip., Consumer electronics, Test/measurement equip., Misc. mfg., Transportation, Wholesale, Retail, Finance, Hospitality, Communications, Government, Environmental svcs., Aerospace, Packaging, Insurance, Real estate, High tech, Software, Biotech, Healthcare, Non-classifiable industries
Professional Associations: AESC, IACPR

Branches:
17100 Gillette Ave.
Irvine, California 92614
(949) 851-1834
Fax: (949) 833-7608
Key Contact - Specialty:
Mr. Elliot Gordon

1800 Century Park E., Ste. 900
Los Angeles, California 90067
(310) 552-1834
Fax: (310) 553-6452
Key Contact - Specialty:
Ms. Caroline Nahas

3 Lagoon Dr., Ste. 280
Redwood City, California 94065
(650) 632-1834
Fax: (650) 632-1835
Key Contact - Specialty:
Mr. Geoffrey Champion - *Advanced technology*

600 Montgomery St., 31st Floor
The Transamerica Pyramid
San Francisco, California 94111
(415) 956-1834
Fax: (415) 956-1988
Key Contact - Specialty:
Mr. David Nosal

† occasional contingency assignment

One Landmark Sq.
Stamford, Connecticut 06901
(203) 359-3350
Fax: (203) 327-2044
Key Contact - Specialty:
Mr. Terence P. McGovern

900 19th St. NW, #800
Presidential Plaza
Washington, District of Columbia 20006
(202) 822-9444
Fax: (202) 822-8127
Key Contact - Specialty:
Mr. Michael Kirkman
Mr. Craig Fuller - *Global board services*

200 S. Biscayne Blvd., Ste. 2790
Miami, Florida 33131
(305) 377-4121
Fax: (305) 377-4428
Key Contact - Specialty:
Ms. Marjorie Kean

303 Peachtree St. NE, Ste. 1600
Atlanta, Georgia 30308
(404) 577-7542
Fax: (404) 584-9781
Key Contact - Specialty:
Mr. James E. Boone

233 S. Wacker Drive, Ste. 3300
Sears Twr.
Chicago, Illinois 60606
(312) 466-1834
Fax: (312) 466-0451
Key Contact - Specialty:
Mr. Scott Kingdom

One International Place, 11th Floor
Boston, Massachusetts 02110
(617) 345-0200
Fax: (617) 345-0544
Key Contact - Specialty:
Mr. Mark L. Smith - *Professional services*

4816 IDS Center
Minneapolis, Minnesota 55402
(612) 333-1834
Fax: (612) 333-8971
Key Contact - Specialty:
Mr. Allan H. Raymond

1 Palmer Sq., Ste. 330
Princeton, New Jersey 08542
(609) 921-8811
Fax: (609) 921-0230
Key Contact - Specialty:
Mr. Richard Arons - *Healthcare devices, biotechnology*

2 Logan Square, Suite 2530
Philadelphia, Pennsylvania 19103
(215) 496-6666
Fax: (215) 568-9911
Key Contact - Specialty:
Mr. David Shabot - *Healthcare provider*

111 Congress Ave., Ste. 2230
Austin, Texas 78701
(512) 236-1834
Fax: (512) 236-1835
Key Contact - Specialty:
Mr. Rob Golding

500 N. Akard St., 3232 Lincoln Plaza
Dallas, Texas 75201
(214) 954-1834
Fax: (214) 954-1849
Key Contact - Specialty:
Mr. Bill Funk - *Education*

1100 Louisiana, Ste. 2850
Houston, Texas 77002
(713) 651-1834
Fax: (713) 651-0848
Key Contact - Specialty:
Mr. John Brock - *Energy*

8045 Leesburg Pike, Ste. 540
Vienna, Virginia 22182
(703) 761-7020
Fax: (703) 761-7023
Key Contact - Specialty:
Mr. James M. Searing - *Telecommunications, information systems, technology, utilities*

One Union Square, 600 University St., #3428
Seattle, Washington 98101-1114
(206) 447-1834
Fax: (206) 447-9261
Key Contact - Specialty:
Mr. Herschel Jones

Simcoe Place
200 Front St. W., Ste. 2200
Toronto, Ontario M5V 3J1
Canada
(416) 593-5776
Fax: (416) 593-9350
Key Contact - Specialty:
Mr. P. J. Fennell

Montes Urales 641
Lomas de Chapultepec
Del Miguel Hidalgo
Mexico City, Mexico DF 11000
Mexico
52 5 202 0046
Fax: 52 5 202 4469
Key Contact - Specialty:
Mr. Horacio McCoy
Mr. Manuel Papayanopulos - *Advanced technology*
Mr. Thurston R. Hamer
Ms. Maria Elena Valdes - *Consumer, retailing*
Mr. Fernando Tello - *Professional, consulting services*

Daniel Zambrano 52S
Col. Chepe Vera
Monterrey, Nuevo Leon 64030
Mexico
52 8 348 4355
Fax: 52 8 333 7362
Key Contact - Specialty:
Mr. Juan Llaguno
Mr. Romulo Gonzalez

International Branches:
Amsterdam, Athens, Bangkok, Barcelona, Beijing, Birmingham, Bombay, Bratislava, Brussels, Bucharest, Budapest, Buenos Aires, Caracas, Chiyoda-ku, Copenhagen, Dusseldorf, Frankfurt, Geneva, Goteborg, Helsinki, Hong Kong, Istanbul, Jakarta, Kuala Lumpur, Lima, London, Luxembourg, Madrid, Melbourne, Milan, Moscow, New Delhi, Oslo, Paris, Prague, Rio de Janeiro, Rome, Santafe de Bogota, Santiago, Sao Paulo, Seoul, Shanghai, Singapore, Stockholm, Sydney, Vienna, Warsaw, Wellington, Zurich

Korn/Ferry, Int'l., S.A. de C.V.

Montes Urales 641
Lomas de Chapultepec
Del Miguel Hidalgo
Mexico City, Mexico DF 11000
Mexico
52 5 202 0046
Fax: 52 5 202 4469

Key Contact - Specialty:
Mr. Horacio McCoy
Mr. Manuel Papayanopulos - *Advanced technology*
Mr. Thurston R. Hamer
Ms. Maria Elena Valdes - *Consumer, retailing*
Mr. Fernando Tello - *Professional, consulting services*

Description: By far Mexico's leading and largest executive search firm.

Salary Minimum: $75,000

Branches:
Daniel Zambrano 525
Col. Chepe Vera
Monterrey, Nuevo Leon 64030
Mexico
52 8 348 4355
Fax: 52 8 333 7362
Key Contact - Specialty:
Mr. Juan F. Llaguno - *General practice*
Mr. Romulo Gonzalez - *General practice*
Mr. Eduardo Trafer

Kors Montgomery Int'l.

1980 Post Oak Blvd., Ste. 2280
Houston, Texas 77056
(713) 840-7101
Fax: (713) 840-7260
Email: info@korsmontgomery.com
Web: www.korsmontgomery.com

Key Contact - Specialty:
Mr. R. Paul Kors - *Technology & energy executives*

Description: Majority of assignments have an international content. Concentrating on technology, energy, chemicals, engineering and construction. Strategic alliance with leading independent firms in Europe, North America and Japan.

Salary Minimum: $120,000
Functions: Senior mgmt., Mktg. mgmt., Sales mgmt., CFO's, MIS mgmt., Systems dev., Int'l.

Industries: Energy/utilities, Chemicals, Computer svcs., Broadcast & Film, Telecoms, High tech, Software

Networks:
International Technology Partners

Kossuth & Assoc., Inc.

800 Bellevue Way NE, Ste. 400
Bellevue, Washington 98004
(425) 450-9050
Fax: (425) 450-0513
Email: kossuth@halcyon.com
Web: www.halcyon.com/kossuth

Key Contact - Specialty:
Ms. Jane Kossuth - *Wireless, software, internet*
Mr. David Kossuth - *Wireless, software, internet*

Description: Retained search in all functional areas above $50,000 including industry specialization in wireless communications, software, electronics and multimedia.

Salary Minimum: $50,000
Functions: General mgmt., Mfg., Materials, Sales & mktg., HR mgmt., Finance, Engineering
Industries: Computer equip., Test/measurement equip., Venture cap., Broadcast & Film, Telecoms, High tech, Software

Kostmayer Assoc., Inc.

111 Hamlet Hill Rd., Ste. 1410
Baltimore, Maryland 21210
(410) 435-2288
Fax: (410) 435-2293
Email: rogerkos@earthlink.net

Key Contact - Specialty:
Mr. Roger C. Kostmayer - *Financial services*

Description: We are a three-generation executive search consulting firm, founded by John H. Kostmayer over 25 years ago in Princeton, N.J. The firm specializes in senior financial services positions and has been recognized for its high quality, fast results, effective communications and unusual methodology.

Salary Minimum: $100,000
Functions: Senior mgmt., Middle mgmt., Advertising, Mktg. mgmt., Sales mgmt., CFO's, MIS mgmt.

Branches:
1120 Ave. of the Americas, 4th Floor
New York, New York 10036
(212) 626-6664
Fax: (212) 626-6665
Email: sikost@erols.com
Key Contact - Specialty:
Mr. John B. Kostmayer - *Financial services*

The J. Kovach Group

201 Penn Ctr. Blvd., Ste. 460
Pittsburgh, Pennsylvania 15235
(412) 825-5168

Key Contact - Specialty:
Mr. Jerry Kovach - *Real estate, construction, healthcare industries*

Description: Twenty-five years experience in executive search for the real estate and construction industry. Recently added healthcare specialty ('95) doing administrative and physician recruiting plus will be adding locum tenens in '98.

Salary Minimum: $50,000
Functions: Directors, Senior mgmt., Middle mgmt., Physicians, Health admin., CFO's
Industries: Construction, Hospitality, Real estate, Healthcare

KPMG Executive Search
(a division of KPMG Canada)

Commerce Court W., Ste. 3300
Box 31, Stn Commerce Court
Toronto, Ontario M5L 1B2
Canada
(416) 777-8500
Fax: (416) 777-8070
Email: executivesearch@kpmg.ca
Web: www.kpmg.ca/es/main.htm

Key Contact - Specialty:
Mr. James A. Parr - *Executive search*
Mr. Douglas Colling - *Municipal government, utilities, information technology, communications*
Mr. William Berlet - *Manufacturing, distribution, transportation, mining*
Mr. Paul Perras - *Generalist, senior level*
Mr. Wilfred C. Stewart - *Manufacturing, distribution, financial services, consumer products*
Ms. Jordene Lyttle - *Public, non-profit, healthcare, education*

Description: Leading, full-service management consulting firm established in 1936, now a division of KPMG Canada. Executive search practice headquartered in Toronto with professionals in 11 other offices across Canada. Affiliated with KPMG International, with search practices in 50 cities worldwide.

Salary Minimum: $70,000
Functions: Generalist
Industries: Generalist

Branches:
205 Fifth Ave. SW, Ste. 1200
Calgary, Alberta T2P 4B9
Canada
(403) 691-8300
Fax: (403) 691-8304
Key Contact - Specialty:
Mr. Merv Manthey - *Oil & gas industry*
Mr. Arnold Rand

Canada Trust Tower, Ste. 2800
10104-103 Ave.
Edmonton, Alberta T5J 3V8
Canada
(403) 429-7300
Fax: (403) 424-2465
Key Contact - Specialty:
Mr. Jeff Uhlich - *Government, oil & gas, transportation*

P.O. Box 10426 Pacific Centre
900-777 Dunsmuir St.
Vancouver, British Columbia V7Y 1K3
Canada
(604) 691-3000
Fax: (604) 691-3425
Key Contact - Specialty:
Ms. Anne Moore - *Generalist*
Ms. Barbara Segovia - *Generalist*

800-200 Graham Ave.
Winnipeg, Manitoba R3C 4M1
Canada
(204) 957-1770
Fax: (204) 943-4913
Key Contact - Specialty:
Mr. Paul Croteau - *Generalist*

100 New Gower St., Ste. 800
Cabot Place
St. John's, Newfoundland A1C 6K3
Canada
(709) 722-5804
Fax: (709) 722-1758
Key Contact - Specialty:
Mr. Lloyd Powell - *Generalist*

Purdy's Wharf Twr. One
#1505, 1959 Upper Water St.
Halifax, Nova Scotia B3J 3N2
Canada
(902) 492-6000
Fax: (902) 429-9248
Key Contact - Specialty:
Ms. Susan Letson - *Education, crown corporations, manufacturing, distribution*

World Exchange Plaza
45 O'Connor St., Ste. 1000
Ottawa, Ontario K1P 1A4
Canada
(613) 560-0011
Fax: (613) 238-3698
Key Contact - Specialty:
Mr. Gary Reid - *Government, high technology*
Mr. Chris Klus

Marsland Centre
20 Erb St. W., 3rd Floor
Waterloo, Ontario N2L 1T2
Canada
(519) 747-8800
Fax: (519) 747-8830
Key Contact - Specialty:
Mr. Robert Curry - *Generalist*

2000 McGill College, Ste. 2000
Montreal, Quebec H3A 3H8
Canada
(514) 840-2500
Fax: (514) 840-2339

Key Contact - Specialty:
Mr. Robert Nadeau - *Generalist*

#2000-1881 Scarth St.
Regina, Saskatchewan S4P 4K9
Canada
(306) 791-1200
Fax: (306) 525-0616
Key Contact - Specialty:
Ms. Mary Anne Davidson - *Government, agriculture*

Affiliates:
Allerton Heneghan & O'Neill

Katherine R. Kraemer
160 Main St.
Los Altos, California 94022
(650) 941-1552
Fax: (650) 941-1968
Email: kkexesrch@aol.com

Key Contact - Specialty:
Ms. Katherine R. Kraemer - *Senior level management, high technology, systems, software, components*

Description: 50% of the business practice is realized in companies ranging from $600M to Fortune 500 high technology corporations. The remaining 50% of the practice is comprised of assignments in start-up environments. Other client consulting services include assistance in aligning strategic alliances, co-development partnerships and raising capital funding.

Salary Minimum: $100,000
Functions: Directors, Senior mgmt., Sales & mktg., CFO's, Engineering, Mgmt. consultants
Industries: Computer equip., Consumer electronics, Venture cap., New media, Broadcast & Film, Telecoms, High tech

C. R. Krafski & Assoc., Inc.
P.O. Box 584
Barrington, Illinois 60011
(847) 382-7870
Fax: (847) 382-0035

Key Contact - Specialty:
Ms. Charlene Krafski - *Insurance*
Mr. John T. Weaver - *Insurance*
Mr. W. Lawrence Howe - *Insurance*

Description: Executive search and management consulting services provided for the insurance and financial services industries.

Salary Minimum: $60,000
Functions: Senior mgmt., Middle mgmt.
Industries: Insurance

Krakower Group, Inc.
3224 Vista Arroyo
Santa Barbara, California 93109
(805) 898-0447
Fax: (805) 898-0151

Key Contact - Specialty:
Mr. Bernard H. Krakower - *High technology*

Description: Over twenty five years serving the computer and telecommunications industries in executive search, management audits, organizational planning and consulting.

Salary Minimum: $100,000
Functions: General mgmt., Sales & mktg., CFO's, IT, Engineering
Industries: Computer equip., Computer svcs., New media, Telecoms, Software

J. Krauss Assoc.
28091 Winthrop Circle SW
Bonita Springs, Florida 34134
(941) 947-8320

Key Contact - Specialty:
Mr. Jack Krauss - *General managers, presidents*

Description: Domestic/international executive search, assessment, organization planning of mid-upper and top management including chairmanship.

Salary Minimum: $50,000
Functions: Directors, Senior mgmt., Middle mgmt., Production, Plant mgmt., Mktg. mgmt., Sales mgmt.
Industries: High tech, Software, Non-classifiable industries

Krauthamer & Assoc.
5530 Wisconsin Ave., Ste. 1202
Chevy Chase, Maryland 20815
(301) 654-7533
Fax: (301) 654-0136
Email: krauthamer@AOL.com

Key Contact - Specialty:
Mr. Gary L. Krauthamer
Ms. Ellen S. Dorfman
Mr. Todd Dorfman

Description: National/international executive search consultants.

Salary Minimum: $75,000
Functions: Generalist
Industries: Generalist

Krecklo Executive Search Inc.
Scotia Plaza, Ste. 4900
40 King St. W.
Toronto, Ontario M5H 4A2
Canada
(416) 777-6799
Email: bdk@krecklo.com

Key Contact - Specialty:
Mr. Brian D. Krecklo - *Information technology*
Mr. Wayne Hussey - *Information technology*

Description: We are an information systems and technology senior executive search firm which has accumulated 23 years of experience.

Salary Minimum: $100,000
Functions: MIS mgmt.
Industries: Generalist
Professional Associations: AESC

Branches:
1115 Sherbrooke St. W., Ste. 2401
Montreal, Quebec H3A 1H3
Canada
(514) 281-9999
Key Contact - Specialty:
Mr. Brian D. Krecklo

Kremple & Meade, Inc.
P.O. Box 426
Pacific Palisades, California 90272
(310) 459-4221
Fax: (310) 459-9642
Email: tomnet@gte.net

Key Contact - Specialty:
Mr. Thomas M. Meade
Ms. Jeannette Clemens

Description: National search firm engaged for senior executive searches in various industries. Experience spans venture-backed start-ups to medium-size companies. CEO's, COO's, management teams.

Salary Minimum: $125,000
Functions: Directors, Senior mgmt., Plant mgmt., Mktg. mgmt., CFO's
Industries: Generalist, Food/bev/tobacco, Machinery/Appliances, Computer equip., Finance, Equip. svcs., High tech

Kremple Consulting Group
222 Reward St.
Nevada City, California 95959
(530) 478-9050
(530) 265-5688
Fax: (530) 478-9051
Email: jkremple@gv.net

Key Contact - Specialty:
Mr. Robert J. Kremple
Mr. Jeffrey J. Kremple

Description: A national firm serving our clients with the highest degree of integrity and the optimum amount of personal attention by a partner of the firm.

Salary Minimum: $70,000
Functions: Senior mgmt., Middle mgmt., Mktg. mgmt., HR mgmt., CFO's, MIS mgmt., R&D

Industries: Generalist, Computer equip., Consumer electronics, Entertainment, Telecoms, High tech, Software

D. A. Kreuter Assoc., Inc.
1100 E. Hector St., Ste. 388, R
Conshohocken, Pennsylvania 19428
(610) 834-1100
Fax: (610) 834-7722

Key Contact - Specialty:
Mr. Daniel A. Kreuter
Mr. Joel Harrison
Mr. Steven M. Clark
Ms. Corinne Weston
Ms. Jeanne Zimbehl

Description: National executive search and selection consultants for the diversified, financial services sector, IBID. Handle all functions; specialize in investment management, marketing, sales and senior management.

Salary Minimum: $100,000
Functions: Senior mgmt., Sales & mktg.
Industries: Finance

Kreutz Consulting Group, Inc.
585 N. Bank Lane, Ste. 2000
Lake Forest, Illinois 60045
(847) 234-9115
Fax: (847) 234-9175

Key Contact - Specialty:
Mr. Gary L. Kreutz - *Heavy manufacturing, high technology, software, telecommunications, consumer products*

Description: Fully computerized, hands-on personalized service, extremely wide and thorough market coverage, domestic and international practice with affilates worldwide, senior/upper middle management and board of director levels.

Salary Minimum: $75,000
Functions: Generalist, General mgmt., Mfg., Sales & mktg., IT, Engineering, Int'l.
Industries: Generalist, Mfg., Transportation, Svcs., Communications, High tech, Software
Professional Associations: AESC, IACPR

Affiliates:
The Mattson Jack Group

Networks:
Transearch Int'l.

Krueger Assoc.
1000 Skokie Blvd.
Wilmette, Illinois 60091
(847) 853-0550
Fax: (847) 853-8202

Key Contact - Specialty:
Mr. Kurt Krueger

Description: We are a general practice search firm specializing in manufacturing and service organizations.

Salary Minimum: $100,000
Functions: Generalist, Mfg., Sales & mktg., HR mgmt., Finance, IT, Engineering
Industries: Generalist, Construction, Mfg., Packaging

John Kuhn & Assoc., Inc.
641 Monroe, Ste. 109
P.O. Box 3, Brickner Sq.
Sheboygan Falls, Wisconsin 53085
(920) 467-1320

Key Contact - Specialty:
Mr. John J. Kuhn - *Manufacturing operations (all middle to upper management), manufacturing search (all functional disciplines)*

Description: Retained exclusively by clients at the middle to upper management level. Our clients are involved in all manufacturing and service disciplines. Salary requirements $50,000 minimum.

Salary Minimum: $50,000
Functions: Middle mgmt., Productivity, Materials Plng., Sales mgmt., Training, MIS mgmt., Engineering
Industries: Generalist, Lumber/furniture, Plastics/rubber, Metal products, Machinery/Appliances, Consumer electronics, Accounting

Kukoy Associates
1009 Soda Creek Drive
Evergreen, Colorado 80439
(303) 670-9545
Fax: (303) 670-9545
Email: kukoyassoc@aol.com

Key Contact - Specialty:
Mr. Stephen J. Kukoy - *CIOs, CTOs, VP-1.5, directors & their direct reports*

Description: A well known and respected search firm specializing in information systems executive search, CIOs and their direct reports.

Salary Minimum: $60,000
Functions: IT, MIS mgmt., Systems anal., Systems dev., Systems implem., Network admin.
Industries: Generalist, Computer svcs., Telecoms, High tech, Software

Paul Kull & Co.
18 Meadow Brook Rd.
Randolph, New Jersey 07869
(201) 361-7440

Key Contact - Specialty:
Mr. Paul Kull - *High technology, industrial, service companies*

Description: Since 1966-searches in management, engineering, manufacturing, sales/ marketing, software/ programming for industries & service companies in electronics, medical electronics, instruments, controls, components, devices, optics, lasers, computers, global position satellite systems, cellular/RF.

Salary Minimum: $50,000
Functions: Senior mgmt., Product dev., Mktg. mgmt., Sales mgmt., R&D, Engineering, Int'l.
Industries: Medical devices, Machinery/ Appliances, Computer equip., Consumer electronics, Test/measurement equip., Packaging, Software

Kulper & Co., L.L.C.
P.O. Box 1445
Morristown, New Jersey 07962-1445
(973) 285-3850
Fax: (973) 285-3851
Email: kulper-company-1@worldnet.att.net

Key Contact - Specialty:
Mr. Keith D. Kulper - *Telecommunications, financial services, high technology, not-for-profit, senior level*

Description: We are a retained executive search firm specializing in fulfilling senior level search assignments in the telecommunications, high tech, financial services and not-for-profit arenas.

Salary Minimum: $100,000
Functions: Senior mgmt., Quality, Training, Taxes, Network admin., Non-profits, Attorneys
Industries: Computer equip., Finance, Pharmaceutical svcs., Human resource svcs., Telecoms, Insurance, Software

Affiliates:
Epsen, Fuller & Assoc., Inc.

Kunzer Assoc., Ltd.
1415 W. 22nd St.
Oak Brook, Illinois 60523
(630) 574-0010
Fax: (630) 574-2774

Key Contact - Specialty:
Mr. William J. Kunzer - *Generalist*
Mrs. Diane S. Kunzer - *Generalist*

Description: Serve clients in most industries and in all functional areas of senior and middle management, domestic and international.

Salary Minimum: $50,000
Functions: General mgmt., Mfg., Sales & mktg., HR mgmt., Finance, IT, Engineering
Industries: Generalist

John Kurosky & Assoc.

3 Corporate Park Drive, Ste. 210
Irvine, California 92606-5111
(949) 851-6370
Fax: (949) 851-8465
Email: jka@ix.netcom.com

Key Contact - Specialty:
Mr. John Kurosky - *High technology, generalist, middle management, senior management*
Mr. Scott McCutcheon - *Franchising*
Mr. John McClosky - *Manufacturing*
Mr. David Renwick - *Networking, software*
Ms. Donna Brauerman - *Retail*
Ms. Susan Page - *Hospitality*
Ms. Christine Jensen - *Data, telecommunications*
Mr. Ted Bauly - *Legal*
Mr. Kenneth Schwartz - *Financial services*

Description: Placement of executives and technical specialists for traditional and high tech driven organizations. All disciplinary functions. Manufacturing, computer/communications products, software, biomed/biotech, legal, hospitality. Clients also include investment banking firms, venture capital firms, and law firms. This is s worldwide practice.

Salary Minimum: $80,000
Functions: Generalist, General mgmt., Mfg., Sales & mktg., IT, Engineering, Attorneys
Industries: Mfg., Invest. banking, Venture cap., Hospitality, Legal, Communications, High tech, Biotech

L O R †
(a division of Nat'l. Institute of HR Research, Inc.)

418 Wall St.
Princeton, New Jersey 08540
(609) 921-6580
Fax: (609) 921-0483

Key Contact - Specialty:
Ms. Joan Aller - *Finance*
Mr. M. Don Lyons - *Management, manufacturing, information technology, engineers*
Mr. Dennis Marshall - *Telecommunications, data communications*

Description: Established in 1973; recruit professional and management level for most manufacturing industries; all disciplines. Clients in $10-$450 million sales range, salaries 35-125K. Cover USA, Eastern Block and Pacific Rim. Recruit, test, check references of candidates.

Salary Minimum: $35,000
Functions: Mfg., Sales mgmt., HR mgmt., Finance, IT, Engineering, Int'l.
Industries: Agri/forestry/mining, Drugs mfg., Medical devices, Metal products, Finance, Pharmaceutical svcs., Software

L. Patrick Group

300 Executive Drive, Ste. 250
West Orange, New Jersey 07052
(973) 364-1001

Key Contact - Specialty:
Mr. Louis P. Giordano - *Generalist*

Description: Full and modified retained search services. Generalist firm serving most industries and functions.

Salary Minimum: $75,000
Functions: Generalist, Senior mgmt., Middle mgmt., Mfg., Materials, MIS mgmt., Engineering
Industries: Generalist

Marvin Laba & Assoc.

6255 Sunset Blvd., Ste. 617
Los Angeles, California 90028
(213) 464-1355
Fax: (213) 465-0330

Key Contact - Specialty:
Mr. Marvin Laba - *Retail & the vendors that supply them*
Ms. Bonnie Milstein - *Retail & the vendors that supply them*

Description: The company specializes in department, specialty store and mass retailers and their vendors and suppliers. Wholesale and retail senior management positions of all descriptions are worked on.

Salary Minimum: $50,000
Functions: Senior mgmt., Product dev., Purchasing, Sales mgmt., Personnel, CFO's, MIS mgmt.
Industries: Textiles/apparel, Soap/perfume/cosmetics, Retail, Misc. financial, Entertainment, Human resource svcs., Advertising/PR

Branches:
250 Ridgedale Ave., Ste. A1
Florham Park, New Jersey 07932
(973) 966-2888
Fax: (973) 966-6626
Key Contact - Specialty:
Mr. Stuart Laba - *Retail & the vendors that supply them*

Rene LaFlamme & Associes

(Firm declined to update.)
59 St. Charles W.
Longueuil, Quebec J4H 1C5
Canada
(514) 677-3399
Email: laflamm@odyssee.net

Key Contact - Specialty:
Mr. Rene LaFlamme

Description: In order to ensure we find the very best candidates, we apply a rigorous search methodology. And one of our associates is personally involved in the recruitment process and selection.

Salary Minimum: $60,000
Functions: Generalist, General mgmt., Mfg., Healthcare, Sales & mktg., HR mgmt., Finance
Industries: Mfg., Finance, Svcs., Communications, Packaging, High tech, Biotech

Laguzza Assoc., Ltd.

McGuire Lane
Croton-on-Hudson, New York 10520
(914) 271-4002
Fax: (212) 399-7082

Key Contact - Specialty:
Mr. John Laguzza - *Vice president of finance, controller, treasurer, MIS, tax (financial functions only)*

Description: Specializing in financial functions. Recruiting finance, control executives, vice president of finance, controllers and treasurers.

Salary Minimum: $75,000
Functions: CFO's, MIS mgmt.
Industries: Drugs mfg., Machinery/Appliances, Pharmaceutical svcs., Defense, Insurance, Biotech, Healthcare

Branches:
810 Seventh Ave.
New York, New York 10019
(212) 247-8190
Fax: (212) 399-7082
Key Contact - Specialty:
Mr. John Laguzza - *Financial (function only)*

Networks:
ACES (Associated Consultants in Executive Search)

LAI Ward Howell

200 Park Ave., Ste. 3100
New York, New York 10166-0136
(212) 953-7900
Email: gowxxrod@lai.usa.com

Key Contact - Specialty:
Ms. Jean E. Allen - *Corporate & marketing communications*
Mr. Theodore H. Borman - *Healthcare*
Mr. Michael Brenner - *Information services, financial services, professional services*
Mr. Anthony B. Cashen - *Financial services*
Mr. William M. Cicchino - *Financial services*
Mr. Dale M. Flanagan - *Financial services*
Mr. Roderick C. Gow - *Financial services*
Mr. Harold E. Johnson - *Human resources*
Ms. Susan J. Landon - *Communications, entertainment, technology, financial services*
Ms. Dina K. S. Lewisohn - *Financial services*
Mr. Jeffrey R. L'Hote - *Financial services*
Mr. Erik W. Matson - *Technology*
Ms. Eileen M. Merrigan - *Financial services*
Mr. Martin D. Nass - *Real estate*
Mr. Bruce J. Robertson - *Consumer products*

Dr. Mark G. Scher
Mr. Michael J. Sullivan - *Professional services*

Description: Senior-level generalist practice which serves a broad base of corporate and institutional clients. The firm has focused practice capabilities in the areas of boards of directors, consumer and industrial products, financial services, healthcare and technology.

Salary Minimum: $125,000
Functions: Generalist
Industries: Generalist
Professional Associations: AESC, IACPR

Branches:
2525 E. Arizona Biltmore Circle
Phoenix, Arizona 85016-2129
(602) 955-3800
Key Contact - Specialty:
Mr. Vance A. Howe - *Consumer, higher education, energy*
Mr. Richard E. Nosky - *Energy, communications, entertainment, technology*

16255 Ventura Blvd., Ste. 400
Encino, California 91436-2394
(818) 905-6010
Key Contact - Specialty:
Mr. Jerry L. Kay - *Healthcare*
Mr. Neal L. Maslan - *Healthcare, pharmaceuticals*
Mr. Marty Ross - *Healthcare*

1801 Century Park E., Ste. 2300
Los Angeles, California 90067-2325
(310) 277-0550
Key Contact - Specialty:
Mr. Dana B. Ardi - *Communications, entertainment, technology*

Embarcadero Ctr. W., Ste. 2180
275 Battery St.
San Francisco, California 94111-3305
(415) 296-0600
Key Contact - Specialty:
Mr. Glen S. Corso - *Financial services*
Mr. Howard C. Crane - *Financial services, technology, telecommunications*
Mr. David de Wilde - *Financial services*
Mr. Rick M. Flam - *Financial services, legal*

Metro Ctr., One Station Place
Stamford, Connecticut 06902-6800
(203) 324-4445
Key Contact - Specialty:
Mr. Austin Broadhurst, Jr. - *Healthcare*
Ms. Jodie A. Emery - *Healthcare*
Ms. Lee Ann Howard - *Healthcare*
Mr. F. Clawson Smith - *Financial services*
Mr. Robert Ryder Stone - *Financial services*

Barnett Plaza, Ste. 3000
101 E. Kennedy Blvd.
Tampa, Florida 33602-6150
(813) 221-7727
Key Contact - Specialty:
Mr. Walter U. Baker - *International, consumer, industrial*
Mr. John B. Henard - *Information technology, electronics, consumer products, retail*
Ms. M. Ellen Pollin - *Retail*

Northdale Plaza, Ste. 200E
3903 Northdale Blvd.
Tampa, Florida 33624-1864
(813) 961-7494
Key Contact - Specialty:
Mr. Jack P. Wissman

191 Peachtree St. NE, Ste. 800
Atlanta, Georgia 30303-1747
(404) 688-0800
Key Contact - Specialty:
Ms. Judy D. Benjamin - *Healthcare*
Mr. Joseph W. Colavito, II - *Professional services*
Mr. David W. Gallagher - *Consumer products, hospitality, retail, entertainment*
Mr. Joe D. Goodwin - *Consumer products, energy, manufacturing, board of directors*
Mr. Dale E. Jones - *Communications technology, consumer products*
Mr. James B. Norton, III - *Financial Services*
Mr. Rafael A. Sierra - *Healthcare, academic medicine*
Mr. Charles E. Taylor - *Information technology, general management, education, government, non-profit*
Mr. Noah W. Waldman - *Healthcare services, managed care, long term care, integrated delivery systems, physician practice management*
Mr. Jeffrey P. Watkins - *Technology*
Mr. Robert C. Chandler - *Healthcare*
Mr. Charles R. Edwards - *Communications, entertainment, technology*
Mr. William R. Robertson - *Energy, natural resources (chemicals & plastics-subspecialty)*
Mr. Ernest A. Taylor - *Finance, consumer*

1300 Grove Ave., Ste. 100
Barrington, Illinois 60010-5246
(847) 382-2206
Key Contact - Specialty:
Mr. Michael J. Berke - *Consumer products, industrial*
Mr. Douglas M. Smith - *Automotive, industrial, manufacturing*

225 W. Wacker Drive, Ste. 2100
Chicago, Illinois 60606-1229
(312) 782-3113
Key Contact - Specialty:
Ms. Pamela J. Andrews - *Professional services, technology*
Mr. James S. Aslaksen - *Chemicals, oil & gas, industrial*
Mr. Arthur J. Davidson - *Industrial, automotive*
Ms. Diane M. Barowsky - *Healthcare*
Mr. Barry R. Cesafsky - *Healthcare, technology, professional services*
Ms. Constance W. Kling - *Information technology, telecommunications*
Mr. Bradford B. Marion - *Industrial*
Mr. Paul McG. Miller - *Utilities, industrial*
Mr. Lawrence F. Nein - *Financial services, consumer products*
Mr. Larry D. Poore - *Industrial, manufacturing, energy, aerospace, defense*
Mr. Thomas G. Putrim - *Financial services*
Mr. John S. Rothschild - *Technology, professional services*
Mr. Paul W. Schmidt - *Consumer products, industrial*
Mr. David J. Shimp - *Technology, professional services*
Mr. Donald R. Utroska - *Industrial, commercial, consumer products*

99 High St., 27th Floor
Boston, Massachusetts 02110-2320
(617) 292-6242
Key Contact - Specialty:
Mr. Kevin E. Conley - *Financial services*
Ms. Kathy J. Epstein - *Global technology practice, energy, natural resources*
Mr. Walter E. Williams - *Financial services*

99 Park Ave., Ste. 2000
New York, New York 10016-1699
(212) 697-3730
Key Contact - Specialty:
Mr. A. Donald Ikle - *Insurance, financial services*
Mr. Anthony W. G. Lord - *Financial services*
Mr. Stephen M. McPherson - *Financial services*
Catherine R. Nathan - *Legal*
Ms. Carrie Looms Pryor - *Communications, entertainment, technology*
Mr. Henry J. Scherck, III - *Pharmaceuticals, healthcare*
Mr. Michael A. Tappan - *Financial services (Russia Practice)*

Key Twr., Ste. 4110
127 Public Sq.
Cleveland, Ohio 44114-1216
(216) 694-3000
Key Contact - Specialty:
Mr. Glenn G. Anderson, Jr. - *Industrial manufacturing, financial services*
Mr. Robert H. Crumbaker - *Industrial, high technology, banking*
Mr. Carson E. Dye - *Healthcare, human resources, physician executive*
Mr. Mark P. Elliott - *Industrial*
Mr. David W. Fell - *Information technology, industrial, human resources*
Mr. John F. Johnson - *Automotive, industrial, board of directors, human resources*
Mr. Dean D. Trilling - *Information technology, retail, consumer products (packaged goods)*

One Oxford Ctr., Ste. 1500
301 Grant St.
Pittsburgh, Pennsylvania 15219-1417
(412) 255-3730
Key Contact - Specialty:
Mr. John E. Hughes, Jr. - *Intercollegiate & professional sports, industrial, consumer, financial practices*

San Jacinto Ctr., Ste. 1400
98 San Jacinto Blvd.
Austin, Texas 78701-4039
(512) 236-0394
Key Contact - Specialty:
Ms. Tara L. Pettersson - *Information technology, consumer products*
Mr. Scott Uhrig - *Information technology, communications, entertainment, technology emerging companies*
Mr. Martin F. Wood - *Industrial/consumer durable manufacturing*

Thanksgiving Twr., Ste. 4150
1601 Elm St.
Dallas, Texas 75201-4768
(214) 754-0019
Key Contact - Specialty:
Mr. Timothy A. Brown - *Financial services, healthcare*
Mr. Frederick A. Halstead - *Healthcare*
Mr. M. Steven Kendrick - *Technology, information technology, airlines, electronic commerce, credit card*
Mr. Gregory C. Konstans - *Financial services, technology*
Mr. Arnold Kuypers - *Healthcare*
Ms. Patricia Davison McNicholas - *Professional services*
Mr. David W. Palmlund, III - *Consumer retail, food service, technology*
Mr. Robert L. Pearson - *Board of directors, information technology, telecommunications, consumer goods, manufacturing*
Ms. Barbara Z. Settles - *Technology*
Ms. Judy N. Stubbs - *Generalist*
Ms. Melinda M. Sumurdy - *Retail, consumer goods*
Mr. Thomas M. Watkins, III - *Financial services*

Three Riverway, Ste. 1800
Houston, Texas 77056
(713) 739-8602
Key Contact - Specialty:
Mr. Ray J. Daugbjerg - *Energy*
Mr. Kevin E. Hofner - *Energy, natural resources*
Mr. J. Ewing Walker, Jr. - *Energy*
Mr. Thomas H. Wilson - *Energy, natural resources, financial services*
Mr. David L. Witte - *Energy, natural resources, consumer*
Ms. Deborah T. Woods - *Energy*

401 E. Host Drive
Lake Geneva, Wisconsin 53147-2500
(414) 249-5200
Key Contact - Specialty:
Mr. Michael J. Corey - *Insurance, financial services, professional services*
Mr. Terry M. Clarke - *Insurance, financial services*
Mr. Patrick M. Corey - *Insurance, communications, entertainment, technology, professional services*
Mr. Gary P. DeMarlie - *Insurance, financial services*
Mr. Paul David Hanson - *Insurance, financial services*
Mr. Paul L. Hanson - *Insurance, financial services*
Mr. Douglas G. Mann - *Insurance*
Mr. Thomas F. Moran - *Insurance, financial services*
Mr. Scott B. Smith - *Insurance, financial services*

International Branches:
London

Lamay Assoc., Inc. †

P.O. Box 517
Riverside, Connecticut 06878
(914) 764-4020
Fax: (914) 764-4054
Email: dmsearch_lamay@msn.com

Key Contact - Specialty:
Mr. Lawrence S. Mayers - *Direct marketing, catalog management*
Ms. Barbara P. Bliss - *Direct marketing, database management*
Ms. Donna L. Viglione

Description: Comprehensive management selection and consultation for all disciplines of direct marketing; particularly adept at building staff and professional teams for new or expanding direct marketing activities.

Salary Minimum: $50,000
Functions: Senior mgmt., Middle mgmt., Sales & mktg., MIS mgmt., Systems implem.
Industries: Generalist, Mfg., Banking, Misc. financial, Svcs., Communications

Affiliates:
The Lloyd Group

Lamon + Stuart + Michaels Inc.

20 Bay St., Ste. 1200
Toronto, Ontario M5J 2N8
Canada
(416) 361-7033
Fax: (416) 361-0728
Email: office@lsmconsulting.com

Key Contact - Specialty:
Mr. Wayne Lamon - *Generalist*
Mr. Bob Stuart - *Generalist*
Ms. Faith Atkinson - *Generalist*
Mr. Dave Clarkson - *Generalist*
Ms. Jennifer Hill - *Generalist*

Description: We offer a broad range of services, products and approaches that provide competitive value to our clients. We offer four areas of expertise that form the building blocks for development and implementation of organizational excellence in the workplace.
Functions: Generalist, Mfg., Materials, Sales & mktg., Finance, IT, Mgmt. consultants
Industries: Generalist, Mfg., Finance, Human resource svcs., Insurance, High tech, Software

Branches:
353 St. Nicolas St., Ste. 310
Montreal, Quebec M2Y 2P1
Canada
(514) 842-7771
Fax: (514) 842-0200
Email: psagrh@login.net
Key Contact - Specialty:
Mr. Gilles Rouleau - *Generalist*

Affiliates:
Wayne Perry & Associates

Langley & Associates, Inc. (Executive Search Consultants)

P.O. Box 261606
Highlands Ranch, Colorado 80163-1606
(303) 694-2228
Fax: (303) 694-2216

Key Contact - Specialty:
Ms. Carol M. Langley - *Utility, (senior level management, CEOs, general managers, presidents)*

Description: Specialize in placing middle and senior level management positions within the utility industry (CEO, COO, president, GM, senior VP, etc.) work in all areas of the utility industry, i.e. electric, gas, nuclear power, telecommunications, oil, geothermal, with IOU's, REC's, G & T's and municipal utilities.
Functions: Directors, Senior mgmt., Engineering
Industries: Energy/utilities, Telecoms

Lawrence L. Lapham, Inc.

80 Park Ave., Ste. 3K
New York, New York 10016
(212) 599-0644

Key Contact - Specialty:
Mr. Lawrence L. Lapham - *Diversified financial services, direct marketing, managed health, HMOs, consumer products*

Description: Specialize in diversified financial services including life, P & C insurance and other financial services. Also general management for consumer products both consumer and durable, healthcare and high technology.

Salary Minimum: $100,000
Functions: Senior mgmt., Health admin., Mktg. mgmt., Direct mktg., CFO's, MIS mgmt., Int'l.
Industries: Generalist, Banking, Misc. financial, Human resource svcs., Insurance, High tech, Healthcare

---

Larkin & Co.

582 Market, Ste. 1115
San Francisco, California 94104
(415) 433-5338

Key Contact - Specialty:
Mr. Dick Larkin - *General management, business development, environmental, research, technology*

Description: Long term involvement with communications and information technologies, defense/space sectors. Also, engineer-construction, environmental restoration and waste management, research and technology.

Salary Minimum: $100,000
Functions: Senior mgmt., Mktg. mgmt., Sales mgmt., HR mgmt., R&D, Engineering, Environmentalists
Industries: Generalist, Energy/utilities, Construction, Telecoms, Defense, Haz. waste, High tech

---

R. H. Larsen & Assoc., Inc.

3900 NE 21 Ave.
Ft. Lauderdale, Florida 33308
(954) 763-9000
Web: rlarsen.com

Key Contact - Specialty:
Mr. Robert H. Larsen - *Executive level*
Ms. Elizabeth A. McDonald - *Generalist*

Description: Founded in 1972, the firm's search expertise is in finance/accounting, manufacturing, sales/marketing, EDP/MIS, general management and corporate development in both the North American and Latin American markets.

Salary Minimum: $100,000
Functions: General mgmt., Mfg., Materials, Sales & mktg., HR mgmt., Finance, IT
Industries: Generalist

Larsen & Lee, Inc. †

4915 St. Elmo Ave., Ste. 504
Bethesda, Maryland 20814
(301) 718-4280

Key Contact - Specialty:
Mr. Joseph J. Lee - *Tax, financial*

Description: Nationwide tax and financial executive search specialists. Knowledgeable, insightful and timely. Guaranteed!

Salary Minimum: $60,000
Functions: Cash mgmt., Taxes
Industries: Generalist, Finance, Banking, Accounting

Larsen Int'l., Inc.

660 Preston Forest Ctr., Ste. 114
Dallas, Texas 75230
(214) 987-0026
Fax: (214) 987-4301
Email: larsenintl@internetmci.com

Key Contact - Specialty:
Mr. Donald J. Larsen
Ms. Judith Keljo

Description: Domestic and international (Middle East) experience in executive search. Specialties in mid-to-upper management executives. Senior level assignments, nationwide, with strong expertise in the consulting engineering and security alarm industries.

Salary Minimum: $70,000
Functions: Senior mgmt., Engineering, Environmentalists, Architects
Industries: Construction, Test/measurement equip., Environmental svcs.

Affiliates:
Larsen & Lee, Inc.

Larsen, Whitney, Blecksmith & Zilliacus, Inc.

888 W. Sixth St., Ste. 500
Los Angeles, California 90017
(213) 243-0033
Fax: (213) 243-0030
Web: www.directnet.com/~sandy

Key Contact - Specialty:
Mr. Edward L. Blecksmith - *Generalist, leisure, hospitality, real estate*
Mr. William A. Whitney - *Generalist, leisure, hospitality, entertainment (themed), non-profit*
Ms. Sandra M. Hogan - *Generalist, publishing, financial*
Mr. Patrick W. Zilliacus - *CEOs, directors, technical, operations*
Mr. Richard F. Larsen - *Banking, financial executives*

Description: Generalist firm, international, retainer based.

Salary Minimum: $75,000
Functions: Generalist, Senior mgmt., Middle mgmt., HR mgmt., MIS mgmt., Attorneys, Int'l.
Industries: Generalist, Banking, Invest. banking, Hospitality, Entertainment, High tech, Healthcare

---

Larson Assoc. †

P.O. Box 9005
Brea, California 92621
(714) 529-4121
Fax: (714) 572-3606

Key Contact - Specialty:
Mr. Ray Larson - *Management, sales, industrial*

Description: Executive and professional search for chemical, electronics, high tech, environmental, industrial firms, management, marketing, sales and technical people. Also, management consulting for human resource and organizational development functions.

Salary Minimum: $50,000
Functions: Generalist, Senior mgmt., Middle mgmt., Mktg. mgmt., Sales mgmt., MIS mgmt., Mgmt. consultants
Industries: Generalist, Chemicals, Plastics/rubber, Metal products, Computer equip., Test/measurement equip., Misc. mfg.

LAS Management Consulting Group, Inc.

23 Kilmer Drive, Bldg. #1, Ste. G
Morganville, New Jersey 07751
(732) 972-8800
Fax: (732) 972-6770
Email: jobs@lasmanagement.com
Web: www.lasmanagement.com

Key Contact - Specialty:
Mr. Philip A. Salvatore - *Information systems audit, information systems security, electronic commerce, SAP, ORACLE*

Description: Specialist management recruiting firm in information systems audit, information systems security, electronic commerce, SAP, BAAN, ORACLE, Peoplesoft and controls consulting. Providing our search services to the premier firms in financial services, consumer products, manufacturing and public accounting consulting industries.

Salary Minimum: $55,000
Functions: Risk mgmt., Systems anal., Systems dev., Systems implem., Network admin., DB admin., Mgmt. consultants
Industries: Invest. banking, Pharmaceutical svcs., Computer svcs., Accounting, Mgmt. consulting, High tech, Software

---

Lasher Assoc.

1200 S. Pine Island Rd., Ste. 370
Ft. Lauderdale, Florida 33324
(954) 472-5658
Email: mick@lasherassociates.com
Web: www.lasherassociates.com

Key Contact - Specialty:
Mr. Charles M. Lasher - *Generalist*
Mr. Daniel B. Bronson - *Generalist*

Description: Boutique firm, serving the largest corporations to emerging companies in most industries. Committed to the highest level of performance, confidentiality and professionalism. Specialties in technology based companies and early stage companies.

Salary Minimum: $95,000
Functions: General mgmt., Mfg., Sales & mktg., Finance, IT, R&D, Engineering
Industries: Generalist, Drugs mfg., Medical devices, Computer equip., New media, High tech, Biotech

---

Michael Latas & Assoc., Inc. †

1311 Lindbergh Plaza Ctr.
St. Louis, Missouri 63132
(314) 993-6500
Fax: (314) 993-0632

† occasional contingency assignment

Email: latas@latas.com
Web: www.latas.com

Key Contact - Specialty:
Mr. Michael Latas - *Generalist*
Mr. Richard L. Latas - *Generalist*
Mr. Gary H. Jesberg - *General contractors, CM, design-build, treatment plant builders, owners reps*
Mr. Edward L. Nickels - *Electrical contracting, power transmission, distribution, telecommunications*
Mr. William E. Ragan - *Electrical contracting, power transmission, distribution, telecommunications*
Mr. Rodney L. Robinson - *Concrete & asphalt paving, bridge, utilities, dirt, materials*
Mr. Daniel J. Conroy - *General contractors, CM, design-build, owners reps, manufacturers*
Mr. Kent L. Lawrence - *Architects, consulting engineers, facility engineering, construction management*
Mr. William C. Leonard - *General contractors, CM, design-build, owners reps*
Mr. Michael J. Palumbo - *Concrete & asphalt paving, bridge, utilities, dirt, materials*
Mr. Robert A Haentzler - *Concrete & asphalt paving, bridge, utilities, dirt, materials*
Mr. John M. Dupilka - *Architects, consulting engineers, facility engineering, construction management*
Mr. Nicholas J. Gavura - *Architects, consulting engineers, facility engineering, construction management*
Ms. Nancy Creasy - *Mechanical contracting, fire protection, HVAC service, manufacturing*
Mr. Jody W. Waller - *Concrete & asphalt paving, bridge, utilities, dirt, materials*
Mr. Jeffrey D. Bono - *General contractors, CM, design-build, owners reps, municipal*
Mrs. Cindi M. Love - *Architects, consulting engineers, facilities engineering, construction management*
Mr. James P. Fox - *Real estate development, land acquisition, property management*
Ms. Kathie Foster - *General contractors, CM, design/build, owners reps*
Mr. John H. Patterson - *Residential, multi-family*
Mr. Allen Beller - *Real estate development, land acquisition, property management*

Description: Dedicated exclusively to serving the construction A/E/P and real estate industry nationwide since 1975. Your premier source for senior mgmt., middle mgmt. and difficult-to-fill professional level needs. Organized into division specialization backed up by exhaustive research library and support staff of research, sourcing and recruiting specialists. Strictly confidential.

Salary Minimum: $50,000
Functions: Generalist, Senior mgmt., Middle mgmt., CFO's, Engineering, Environmentalists, Architects
Industries: Generalist, Construction, Environmental svcs., Real estate

Branches:
P.O. Box 4503
Youngstown, Ohio 44515
(216) 799-9445
Key Contact - Specialty:
Mr. Samuel Rusnov - *Material handling, metal processing, packaging*

Latham International, Ltd.
300 Craig Rd., 2nd Floor
Manalapan, New Jersey 07726
(732) 761-1230
Fax: (732) 761-1616
Email: latham@lathamintl.com
Web: www.lathamintl.com

Key Contact - Specialty:
Ms. Audrey Lynn

Description: Established in 1979, we focus on recruiting top-tier MBAs with fast-track business experience. Our clients include leading strategy, Big-Six and boutique consulting firms nationwide.

Salary Minimum: $75,000
Functions: Generalist, Middle mgmt., Sales & mktg., Finance, Mgmt. consultants, Minorities, Int'l.
Industries: Generalist, Machinery/ Appliances, Finance, Mgmt. consulting, High tech

---

Lauer, Sbarbaro Assoc., EMA Partners Int'l.
30 N. LaSalle St., Ste. 4030
Chicago, Illinois 60602-2588
(312) 372-7050
Fax: (312) 704-4393
Email: sbarbs@aol.com

Key Contact - Specialty:
Mr. Richard D. Sbarbaro - *Generalist*
Mr. William J. Yacullo - *Generalist*
Ms. Joan H. Blumenthal - *Generalist*

Description: Medium size generalist firm operating worldwide with principal participation on every assignment. Known for its long term client relationships and professional approach to clients and candidates alike. Excellent placement success record.

Salary Minimum: $75,000
Functions: Generalist, General mgmt., Mfg., Healthcare, Sales & mktg., Finance, IT
Industries: Generalist, Mfg., Retail, Finance, Svcs., Communications, Healthcare
Professional Associations: AESC

Networks:
EMA Partners Int'l.

Lautz, Grotte, Engler & Swimley
One Bush St., Ste. 550
San Francisco, California 94104
(415) 834-3101
Fax: (415) 834-3113
Email: piket@searchexec.com
Web: searchexec.com

Key Contact - Specialty:
Mr. Lindsay A. Lautz - *Generalist*
Mr. Lawrence C. Grotte - *Generalist*
Mr. Peter G. Engler - *Generalist*
Mr. E. Scott Swimley - *Software*

Description: Provide senior level executive search and consulting services to emerging technology, telecommunications, consumer products, new media and medical technology clients. Specialists in early-stage and high-growth client companies.

Salary Minimum: $150,000
Functions: Generalist, Directors, Senior mgmt., Sales & mktg., CFO's, IT, Engineering
Industries: Generalist, Consumer electronics, Finance, Venture cap., Communications, High tech, Software

---

Lawrence-Leiter & Co.
4400 Shawnee Mission Pkwy., #204
Shawnee Mission, Kansas 66205
(913) 677-5500
Fax: (913) 677-1975
Email: lleiter@sky.net

Key Contact - Specialty:
Mr. William B. Beeson - *Upper management (all industries)*

Description: Human resources oriented general management consulting firm with long established executive search division.

Salary Minimum: $50,000
Functions: Generalist, General mgmt., Senior mgmt., Plant mgmt., Mktg. mgmt., CFO's, Engineering
Industries: Generalist

W. R. Lawry, Inc. †
6 Wilcox St., P.O. Box 832
Simsbury, Connecticut 06070
(860) 651-0281
Fax: (860) 651-8324
Email: wlawry@aol.com

Key Contact - Specialty:
Mr. William R. Lawry - *Engineering, telecommunications, quality, medical device, plastics*

Description: Technical recruiting firm specializing in locating specific, highly qualified individuals or managers.

Salary Minimum: $50,000
Functions: Generalist, Middle mgmt., Product dev., Plant mgmt., Quality, R&D, Engineering
Industries: Generalist, Energy/utilities, Chemicals, Drugs mfg., Medical devices, Telecoms, High tech

---

Layne-Mendez & Co.

222 W. Las Colinas Blvd., Ste. 1750
Irving, Texas 75039
(972) 462-9419
Fax: (972) 462-8577
Email: larry.mendez@mcione.com

Key Contact - Specialty:
Mr. Larry W. Mendez - *Finance, information technology, natural resources*

Description: We limit our consultants to 5 concurrent searches to ensure personalized service. We will not accept similar concurrent searches, providing access to the largest candidate pool available.

Salary Minimum: $90,000
Functions: General mgmt., Finance, IT, Mgmt. consultants, Non-profits
Industries: Energy/utilities, Invest. banking, Venture cap., Non-profits, Higher ed., Computer svcs., Mgmt. consulting

---

Leader Search Inc.

44 Barclay Walk SW
Calgary, Alberta T2P 4V9
Canada
(403) 262-8545
Fax: (403) 262-8549
Email: leadfind@cadvision.com

Key Contact - Specialty:
Mr. R. W. Johnson
Ms. Kendra Koss
Ms. Kathy Stankievech
Ms. Maureen Lemiuex
Ms. Pat Massitti

Description: Retainer firm specializing in fitting right character candidates to the right culture of our clients.
Functions: General mgmt., Mfg., Materials, Sales & mktg., Finance, Engineering, Specialized services
Industries: Generalist, Energy/utilities, Mfg., Finance, Hospitality, Entertainment, Non-classifiable industries

---

Leaders-Trust Int'l./Carce y Asociados, S.C.

Pico de Verapaz 449-A D. 101
Col. Jardines en la Montana
Mexico City DF, Mexico CP 14210
Mexico
52 5 630 01 32
52 5 630 02 65
Fax: 52 5 631 33 47
Email: carce@dp1.telmex.net

Key Contact - Specialty:
Ms. Elizabeth Falcon - *Automotive industrial, consumer & retail, finance*
Ms. Leticia Barranco - *Automotive, industrial, consumer & retail, finance*

Description: We are an executive search firm which provides excellent professional counsel to national and international firms in top executives search. We build a successful management organization that can fully understand top companies culture, needs and goals in order to link them to top performer individuals who will contribute to their goals.

Salary Minimum: $60,000
Functions: Directors, Plant mgmt., Mktg. mgmt., HR mgmt., Credit, MIS mgmt., Mgmt. consultants
Industries: Food/bev/tobacco, Printing, Plastics/rubber, Motor vehicles, Banking, Brokers, Packaging

Affiliates:
Leaders-Trust International
Odgers International Ltd.

The Lear Group, Inc.

Clock Tower Office, Ste. 1
660 Dover Center Rd.
Cleveland, Ohio 44140
(216) 892-9828
Fax: (216) 892-9757
Email: leargroup@aol.com

Key Contact - Specialty:
Mr. Larry Gregg - *Senior management*

Description: We offer executive search and recruitment services to a wide variety of industrial clients. Areas of concentration include sales, marketing, engineering and manufacturing.

Salary Minimum: $80,000
Functions: Senior mgmt., Mfg., Quality, Purchasing, Sales mgmt., Engineering, Int'l.
Industries: Generalist, Mfg., Medical devices, Plastics/rubber, Machinery/ Appliances, Misc. mfg., High tech

---

Ledbetter/Davidson Int'l., Inc.

101 Park Ave., 25th Floor
New York, New York 10178
(212) 687-6600
Fax: (212) 687-1113
Email:
cLedbetter@LedbetterDavidson.com
Web: www.biospace.com

Key Contact - Specialty:
Ms. Charlene Ledbetter - *Life sciences, technology*
Ms. Jennifer A. Stevens - *Pharmaceuticals, sales & marketing*
Ms. Jennifer P. Hamburg - *Biotechnology, healthcare*
Ms. Claudia Ribeiro - *Finance, technology*

Description: We provide management consulting services to the healthcare, (biotechnology, pharmaceutical, device and managed care), technology and financial services industries, specializing in retained engagements for the recruitment of executive, scientific and technical management.

Salary Minimum: $100,000
Functions: Directors, Senior mgmt., Middle mgmt., Sales mgmt., CFO's, MIS mgmt., R&D
Industries: Drugs mfg., Medical devices, Finance, Pharmaceutical svcs., High tech, Biotech, Healthcare

---

The Conrad Lee Co. Inc.

7280 W. Palmetto Park Rd., Ste. 208
Boca Raton, Florida 33433
(561) 447-0561
Fax: (561) 347-1244
Web: www.conradlee.com

Key Contact - Specialty:
Mr. Conrad P. Lee
Ms. Nancellen Stahl
Mr. Brad Jensen

Description: Full service search firm with solid experience, relationships and research. We cover the Americas for multinational clients. Search specialty areas include technology, consumer products, consulting, retail, manufacturing and Latin America.

Salary Minimum: $75,000
Functions: General mgmt., Materials, Sales & mktg., HR mgmt., Finance, IT, Int'l.
Industries: Computer equip., Consumer electronics, Transportation, Retail, Hospitality, Entertainment, Real estate

---

V. J. Lehman & Assoc., Inc.

4600 S. Ulster St., Ste. 240
Denver, Colorado 80237
(303) 846-3003
Fax: (303) 220-8705
Email: vlehman@ix.netcom.com

Key Contact - Specialty:
Mr. Victor J. Lehman - *Generalist*

Description: Generalist retained search firm with a diverse client base with experience in most industries and functions.

Salary Minimum: $75,000
Functions: General mgmt., Mfg., Materials, Sales & mktg., HR mgmt., Finance, Engineering
Industries: Generalist, Mfg., Transportation, Finance, Svcs., Communications, High tech

Lehman McLeskey
98 San Jacinto Blvd., Ste. 440
San Jacinto Office Center
Austin, Texas 78701
(512) 478-1131
Fax: (512) 478-1985
Email: lehman@io.com

Key Contact - Specialty:
Ms. Jan A. Lehman - *Executive level management*
Ms. Penny McLeskey - *Executive level management*

Description: Senior level executives in financial services, manufacturing, technology, consumer products.

Salary Minimum: $80,000
Functions: Plant mgmt., Mktg. mgmt., Sales mgmt., CFO's, MIS mgmt., Attorneys
Industries: Energy/utilities, Mfg., Telecoms, Software, Healthcare

Lekan & Assoc., Inc. †
815 Superior Ave., Ste. 1325
Cleveland, Ohio 44114
(216) 781-6400
Fax: (216) 781-6547
Email: search@lekan.com

Key Contact - Specialty:
Dr. Dennis Lekan - *Senior executives*
Dr. Richard Vardaris - *Assessment*
Mr. Joseph Morris - *Technical*
Ms. C J Nelson - *Technical*

Description: We are unique in our partnership approach to our clients, understanding the nature of their business, cultural fit and objectives. We believe in continuous communication to ensure on-going satisfaction.

Salary Minimum: $60,000
Functions: Generalist, General mgmt., Materials, Sales & mktg., HR mgmt., Finance, IT
Industries: Generalist, Mfg., Finance, Non-profits, Legal, Accounting, Packaging

Lemming/LeVan, Inc.
1040 Crown Pointe Pkwy., Ste. 1055
Atlanta, Georgia 30338
(770) 551-6979
Fax: (770) 551-6977
Email: lemminglevan@lemminglevan.com

Key Contact - Specialty:
Ms. Salli LeVan - *Retail, apparel (manufacturing)*
Mr. Jeff Lemming - *Retail, consumer goods*

Description: Full service retained executive search firm composed of former executives from retail and retail related industries; forms partnerships with organizations to provide recruitment executive search & consulting services.

Salary Minimum: $100,000
Functions: Directors, Product dev., Purchasing, Advertising, Benefits, CFO's, MIS mgmt.
Industries: Textiles/apparel, Retail
Professional Associations: AESC

Branches:
545 Fifth Ave., Ste. 609
New York, New York 10017
(212) 682-8828
Fax: (212) 682-8281
Key Contact - Specialty:
Ms. Gloria Cappellini - *Retail; Apparel Manufacturing*

AG Lennox & Assoc.
(Firm declined to update.)
2001, 500 - 4th Ave. SW
Calgary, Alberta T2P 2V6
Canada
(403) 265-4222
Email: admin@aglennox.cia.com
Web: www.intersearch-canada.com

Key Contact - Specialty:
Mr. Allan Lennox - *Executives*

Description: The firm prides itself on quality of work and attention to detail. The professional staff is implementation and results-oriented. All subscribe to stringent rules of professional conduct and ethics.
Functions: General mgmt., Healthcare, Sales & mktg., HR mgmt., Finance, IT, Engineering
Industries: Agri/forestry/mining, Energy/utilities, Transportation, Misc. financial, Non-profits, Human resource svcs., Healthcare

Affiliates:
Societe Jean Pierre Brisebois
Wilson Associates Inc.

Networks:
InterSearch

Jacques LePage Executive Search Inc.
800 Rene-Levesque Blvd., Ste. 2450
Montreal, Quebec H3B 4V7
Canada
(514) 874-1987
(514) 876-9876
Email: jlepage@executivesearch.qc.ca

Key Contact - Specialty:
Mr. Jacques LePage

Description: Top #1 in Quebec; bilingual firm (French & English) national and international search experience, research based generalist firm; senior and middle management searches across most functions and industries.

Salary Minimum: $60,000
Functions: General mgmt., Mfg., Materials, Sales & mktg., HR mgmt., Engineering, Int'l.
Industries: Agri/forestry/mining, Energy/utilities, Mfg., Communications, Aerospace, High tech, Software
Professional Associations: IACPR

J. E. Lessner Assoc., Inc.
2143 E. Newark Rd.
Lapeer, Michigan 48446
(810) 667-9335
Fax: (810) 667-3470
Email: lessner@tir.com

Key Contact - Specialty:
Mr. Jack Lessner - *Organizational development, executive search activities*
Ms. Mary Ann Lessner
Ms. Lori Thomas - *Medium management, functional*
Mr. Mark Lessner - *Manufacturing, sales, engineering*
Ms. Jan Roodvoets - *Sales, manufacturing, materials*

Description: Perform executive searches, organizational development and outplacement activities.

Salary Minimum: $65,000
Functions: General mgmt., Mfg., Materials, Sales & mktg., Finance, Engineering, Int'l.
Industries: Mfg., Plastics/rubber, Metal products, Motor vehicles, Transportation, Aerospace, High tech

Levin & Company, Inc.
#1 Kendall Sq., Bldg. 200, Ste. 2200
Cambridge, Massachusetts 02139
(617) 621-7122
Fax: (617) 621-7048
Email: levinco@aol.com

Key Contact - Specialty:
Ms. Becky Levin - *Biotechnology, pharmaceuticals, biomedical*

Description: We look beyond resumes to character and build complementary teams with special emphasis on workplace diversity. We focus on life sciences, pharmaceuticals and biomedical companies.

Salary Minimum: $75,000
Functions: Directors, Senior mgmt., CFO's, MIS mgmt.
Industries: Drugs mfg., Medical devices, Biotech

Branches:
1301 Page St.
San Francisco, California 94117
(415) 552-9522
Fax: (415) 552-9608
Key Contact - Specialty:
Ms. Mari Paul

Alan Levine Assoc. †
275 Turnpike St., Ste. 202
Canton, Massachusetts 02021-2357
(781) 821-1131
Fax: (781) 821-0601
Email: alevine@sprintmail.com

Key Contact - Specialty:
Mr. Alan C. Levine - *Retail, consumer packaged goods, catalog, Big 6 consulting*

Description: Specialized, personalized, quality search firm with over 17 years of service to the retail, wholesale, direct mail and consumer packaged goods industries.

Salary Minimum: $60,000
Functions: General mgmt., Sales & mktg., HR mgmt., Finance, IT, Specialized services, Mgmt. consultants
Industries: Mfg., Transportation, Wholesale, Retail, Hospitality, Non-profits, Real estate

Michael Levine Search Consultants
11 E. 44th St., 16th Floor
New York, New York 10017
(212) 328-1940
Email: mikwill@aol.com

Key Contact - Specialty:
Mr. Michael Levine
Ms. Diane Cohen - *International, marketing*

Description: A boutique firm who can guarantee personalized care in every search. Our contacts are wide and we can find people in places not normally covered by a large firm.

Salary Minimum: $75,000
Functions: Senior mgmt., Middle mgmt., Advertising, Mkt. research, PR, Int'l.
Industries: Mfg., Soap/perfume/cosmetics, Retail, Entertainment, Broadcast & Film, High tech, Software

Levison Search Assoc. †
P.O. Box 1009
Kenwood, California 95452-1009
(707) 538-3324
Fax: (707) 538-1602
Email: levison-associates@worldnet.att.net

Key Contact - Specialty:
Ms. Regina Levison - *Healthcare (all)*
Mr. Michael Levison - *Healthcare (all)*
Ms. C. Lynn Adamson - *Healthcare (all)*

Description: Firm specializes in recruiting for hospitals, HMOs, medical groups and clinics at the department supervisor/manager level and above.

Salary Minimum: $50,000
Functions: Physicians, Health admin.
Industries: Healthcare

The Levton Group Inc.
140 Symington Ave.
Toronto, Ontario M6P 3W4
Canada
(416) 532-0161
Fax: (416) 532-0161
Email: levton@pathcom.com
Web: www.pathcom.com/~levton

Key Contact - Specialty:
Mr. Nick Breaks - *Human resource bureau*

Description: The firm offers recruitment and other human resource services on an hourly rated basis. Strengths include senior clerical, accounting all levels, computer professionals and management.
Functions: Plant mgmt., Sales mgmt., HR mgmt., Credit, Systems support, Network admin., Technicians
Industries: Metal products, Computer equip., Consumer electronics, Wholesale, Retail, High tech, Healthcare

Lewis & Blank Int'l.
520 S. El Camino Real, Ste. 342
San Mateo, California 94402-1716
(650) 685-6855
Fax: (650) 685-0671
Email: lbint@lewis-blank.com
Web: www.lewis-blank.com

Key Contact - Specialty:
Ms. Daphne V. Lewis - *Biomedical, pharmaceutical, venture, device*
Ms. Paula Blank - *Biomedical, pharmaceutical, venture, device*

Description: We build teams for established and emerging biomedical companies recognized as leaders in their markets. Principals have supported the growth of the industry over the past 20 years.

Salary Minimum: $125,000
Functions: Directors, Senior mgmt., Product dev., Health admin., Mkt. research, CFO's, R&D
Industries: Drugs mfg., Medical devices, Invest. banking, Venture cap., Biotech, Healthcare
Professional Associations: AESC

Lewis Companies Inc.
162 Cumberland St., Suite 305
Renaissance Court
Toronto, Ontario M5R 3N2
Canada
(416) 929-1506
Fax: (416) 929-8470
Email: lewiscos@interlog.com

Key Contact - Specialty:
Ms. Lorraine Lewis - *Generalist*
Mr. Stephen Morrison - *Generalist*
Ms. Ann Curran - *Corporate development*

Description: This practice is client, results-driven and creative. It operates in most industry and functional sectors. All project activity is conducted in an ethical professional manner. Selection capability is exceptional.

Salary Minimum: $70,000
Functions: Generalist, General mgmt., Mfg., Materials, Sales & mktg., HR mgmt., Finance
Industries: Generalist, Agri/forestry/mining, Mfg., Transportation, Finance, Svcs., Communications

Lindsey & Co., Inc.
484 Boston Post Rd., P.O. Box 1273
Darien, Connecticut 06820
(203) 655-1590
Fax: (203) 655-3798

Key Contact - Specialty:
Mr. Lary L. Lindsey - *Generalist*
Mr. Thomas K. McInerney - *Generalist*
Ms. Marilyn B. Vojta - *Generalist*
Ms. Hillary A. Morgan - *Generalist*
Mr. Anthony T. Hwang - *Generalist*

Description: General search in all industries and functions.
Functions: Generalist
Industries: Generalist

Branches:
438 E. Wilson Bridge Rd., Ste. 200
Worthington, Ohio 43085
(614) 431-8262
Fax: (614) 431-8263
Key Contact - Specialty:
Mr. Philip Perry - *Generalist*

Lipsky Group, Inc. †
220 Nice Lane, Ste. 112
Newport Beach, California 92663
(949) 645-4300
Fax: (949) 645-4522
Email: lipsky@ix.netcom.com

Key Contact - Specialty:
Ms. Marla J. Lipsky - *High technology start-ups (computer related), upper management, sales & marketing*

Description: We are a boutique executive search and consulting firm. We specialize in start-ups and turnarounds. Specifically in the computer communication marketplace. We do everything from complete executive staff to full departments (ie sales & marketing).

Salary Minimum: $75,000
Functions: Senior mgmt., Middle mgmt., Mktg. mgmt., Sales mgmt., Customer svc., CFO's, Int'l.
Industries: Computer equip., Venture cap., Mgmt. consulting, Advertising/PR, High tech, Software

Lipson & Co.
1900 Ave. of the Stars, Ste. 2810
Los Angeles, California 90067
(310) 277-4646
Fax: (310) 277-8585
Email: hrlipson@aol.com

Key Contact - Specialty:
Mr. Howard R. Lipson - *Entertainment, multimedia, consumer goods*
Ms. Harriet L. Lipson - *Entertainment, multimedia, consumer goods*

Description: The company's principals have years of client side experience in the industries in which they specialize. This fact, coupled with personal, hands-on attention throughout a search by company's principals, results in satisfied clients and repeat business.

Salary Minimum: $75,000
Functions: Directors, Senior mgmt., Mkt. research, Mktg. mgmt., Int'l.
Industries: Publishing, New media, Broadcast & Film, Software

Affiliates:
F.I.R.S.T. (First Interactive Recruiting Specialists)
Neil Fink Assoc.

Lipton Assoc., Inc.
575 Lexington Ave., Ste. 410
New York, New York 10022
(212) 838-0900
Email: blipton@regentvc.com

Key Contact - Specialty:
Mr. Robert J. Lipton - *Legal*

Description: We are a professional services company dedicated to providing partner level, retained search services to law firms. We help law firms fulfill strategic planning objectives through the acquisition of law partners and practice groups.

Salary Minimum: $200,000
Functions: Legal, Attorneys
Industries: Legal

Litchfield & Willis, Inc.
3900 Essex Lane, Ste. 650
Houston, Texas 77027-5111
(713) 439-8200
Fax: (713) 439-8201
Email: landw@swbell.net
Web: litchwillis.com

Key Contact - Specialty:
Ms. Barbara H. Litchfield
Ms. Cristina Caram
Ms. Missy Wilborn

Description: A retained search firm, we provide interim professionals as well as consulting services. Special expertise for clients in: professional services industry, oil & gas, emerging companies, Japanese owned and NAFTA-related organizations, large national corporations.
Functions: Generalist
Industries: Generalist

Livingston, Robert & Co.
Two Greenwich Plaza
Greenwich, Connecticut 06830
(203) 622-4901
Email: prlsearch@aol.com

Key Contact - Specialty:
Mr. Peter R. Livingston - *Senior level general management, investment banking*
Ms. Dorothy C. Pickering - *Communications, fashion, marketing, sports*

Description: Small, research oriented, general management oriented, clients are both large corporations and start-ups. Only the principals work on assignments.

Salary Minimum: $100,000
Functions: Senior mgmt., Mfg., Purchasing, HR mgmt., CFO's, MIS mgmt., Int'l.
Industries: Generalist, Chemicals, Invest. banking, Entertainment, Publishing, High tech, Software

Lloyd Associates †
35 Glenlake Pkwy., Ste. 164
Atlanta, Georgia 30328
(770) 390-0001

Key Contact - Specialty:
Ms. Carolyn T. Lloyd - *Banking*

Description: Generalist practice with emphasis on commercial banks (CEO, CFO, senior lending and credit officers), including community, major regional, money center banks and consulting firms serving these banks.

Salary Minimum: $50,000
Functions: Generalist, Senior mgmt., Middle mgmt., CFO's, MIS mgmt., Mgmt. consultants, Minorities
Industries: Generalist, Lumber/furniture, Banking, Invest. banking, Non-profits, Computer svcs., Mgmt. consulting

Lloyd Prescott & Churchill, Inc.
4902 Eisenhower Blvd., Ste. 185
One President's Plaza
Tampa, Florida 33634
(813) 881-1110
Fax: (813) 889-8458
Email: headhunt7@earthlink.net
Web: www.lloydprescott.com

Key Contact - Specialty:
Mr. Sheldon M. Ginsberg - *Senior management*
Mr. Manuel F. Gordon - *Senior management*
Mr. Daniel D. Katzman

Description: Generalist firm providing international and national executive and professional search. Offering our clients the best and the brightest candidates in their field and unique retainer driven custom search programs to accomodate their problems and long and short term goals as it relates to executive management.

Salary Minimum: $100,000
Functions: Generalist, Senior mgmt., Mfg., Healthcare, Finance, IT, Attorneys
Industries: Generalist, Mfg., Svcs., Legal, Insurance, High tech, Healthcare

Branches:
8753 Yates Drive, Ste. 200
Westminster, Colorado 80030
(303) 301-2651
Key Contact - Specialty:
Mr. William D. Ray - *Senior management*

7000 Central Pkwy. Ste. 1700
Atlanta, Georgia 30328
(770) 821-5330
Key Contact - Specialty:
Mr. Gene R. Kash - *Senior Management*

500 N. Michigan Ave., Suite 300
Chicago, Illinois 60611
(312) 396-4154
(708) 532-5447
Key Contact - Specialty:
Mr. Thomas J. Dato - *Senior management*
Mr. Daniel P. Barus - *Senior management*

509 Olive St., Ste. 600
St. Louis, Missouri 63101
(314) 259-4152
Key Contact - Specialty:
Mr. Christopher P. Otto - *Senior management*

300 Vanderbilt Motor Pkwy., Ste. 200
Hauppauge, New York 11788
(516) 439-6836
Key Contact - Specialty:
Mr. Gino Comparetto - *Senior management*

4210 W. Ridge Rd.
Rochester, New York 14626
(716) 225-2350
Key Contact - Specialty:
Mr. Steven M. Eisele - *Senior Management*

1373 E. Morehead #27
Charlotte, North Carolina 28204-2979
(704) 372-3463
Key Contact - Specialty:
Mr. Ronald N. Jackson - *Senior Management*

94 Northwoods Blvd.
Columbus, Ohio 43235
(614) 847-8205
Key Contact - Specialty:
Mr. Alan L. Gabriel - *Senior management*

Two Gateway Ctr., Ste. 620
Pittsburgh, Pennsylvania 15222-1402
(412) 355-2373
Key Contact - Specialty:
Mr. Richard F. Getzug - *Senior management*

Affiliates:
Lloyd Prescott Assoc., Inc.

Locke & Assoc.

2410 NationsBank Plaza
Charlotte, North Carolina 28280
(704) 372-6600
Email: flocke@mindspring.com

Key Contact - Specialty:
Mr. M. Fred Locke, Jr. - *General management*

Description: Executive search engagements conducted exclusively on a retainer basis in a broad variety of professional disciplines. Extensive experience serving engineering and construction, manufacturing, financial and service industries.

Salary Minimum: $70,000
Functions: Senior mgmt., Plant mgmt., Sales mgmt., Benefits, CFO's, Engineering, Int'l.
Industries: Generalist, Energy/utilities, Construction, Textiles/apparel, Metal products, Banking, Accounting
Professional Associations: AESC

Branches:
4144 Carmichael Rd., Ste. 20
Montgomery, Alabama 36106
(334) 272-7400
Key Contact - Specialty:
Mr. Glen O. Pruitt - *Engineering, construction*

Loewenstein & Assoc., Inc.

5847 San Felipe, Ste. 1250
Houston, Texas 77057
(713) 952-1840
Fax: (713) 952-4534
Email: loewenst@att.net
Web: loewenstein.com

Key Contact - Specialty:
Mr. Ron Loewenstein - *IT, sales & marketing, engineering*

Description: Specialists in executive search for information technology and management consultants, technical sales, marketing, engineering and management professionals, principally in the process, manufacturing and high technology industries.

Salary Minimum: $50,000
Functions: Senior mgmt., Production, Automation, Sales mgmt., MIS mgmt., Systems implem., Mgmt. consultants
Industries: Energy/utilities, Chemicals, Computer equip., Computer svcs., Mgmt. consulting, High tech, Software

Affiliates:
Authent® Executive Placements

J. P. Logan & Co., Inc.

144 E. 44th St., 6th Floor
New York, New York 10017
(212) 832-1800
Fax: (212) 808-9808

Key Contact - Specialty:
Mr. James P. Logan, III

Description: Consultants to management in executive selection. Generalist firm specializing in strategically critical assignments.

Salary Minimum: $100,000
Functions: Generalist
Industries: Generalist

The Logan Group, Inc.

7710 Carondelet, Ste. 507
St. Louis, Missouri 63105
(314) 862-2828
Fax: (314) 862-3007
Email: lgi@inlink.com
Web: www.ador.com/~logan/

Key Contact - Specialty:
Mr. Brian Ryan - *Generalist*

Description: National/international search firm engaged in quality search and surveys. Activity tailored to clients' needs.

Salary Minimum: $50,000
Functions: Generalist, Senior mgmt., Mkt. research, Mktg. mgmt., CFO's, MIS mgmt., Non-profits
Industries: Generalist, Hospitality, Computer svcs., Telecoms, High tech, Healthcare

Logistics Management Resources, Inc.

(Firm declined to update.)
P.O. Box 2204
New York, New York 10956-0588
(914) 638-4224

Key Contact - Specialty:
Ms. Marjorie Slater - *Logistics, materials management, purchasing*

Description: Researching, sourcing and identifying candidates not responding to advertisements. This leads to improved quality of potential individuals. We prepare salary studies based on skill sets, in addition, candidate profiles compare functional background vs. client requirements.

Salary Minimum: $55,000
Functions: Materials, Purchasing, Distribution, Customer svc., Mgmt. consultants
Industries: Generalist, Mfg., Transportation, Svcs., Packaging, Software

Longshore + Simmons

625 Ridge Pike, Ste. 410
Plymouth Corporate Center
Conshohocken, Pennsylvania 19428
(610) 941-3400
Fax: (610) 941-2424

Key Contact - Specialty:
Mr. George F. Longshore
Mr. H. J. Simmons
Mr. Dennis J. Kain
Ms. Stephaine J. Underwood
Mr. Richard Lohkamp
Mr. William Morrison
Mr. Doris W. Posthes

Description: Healthcare executive search, including managed care; recruitment for physician leadership, hospital and community-based specialists, primary care; healthcare consulting specializing in compensation, hospital-based practice, market studies, hospital/physician strategies, practice valuation and sales.

Salary Minimum: $75,000
Functions: Directors, Senior mgmt., Physicians, Health admin., CFO's, MIS mgmt.
Industries: Drugs mfg., Human resource svcs., Insurance, Healthcare

J. S. Lord & Company, Inc.

266 Main St., Ste. 7B
Olde Medfield Sq.
Medfield, Massachusetts 02052
(508) 359-5100
Fax: (508) 359-5660
Email: jsl&co@aol.com

Key Contact - Specialty:
Mr. J. Scott Lord - *Consumer products, pharmaceuticals, biotechnology, high technology*

Description: Firm founded to provide clients with the focus, commitment and communications necessary to complete searches in a timely manner. Original research and candidate development will be undertaken on each assignment with the goal of presenting final candidates within three to five weeks. Founder has twenty years of recruitment experience.

Salary Minimum: $75,000
Functions: Generalist, Mfg., Sales & mktg., Finance, MIS mgmt., R&D, Non-profits
Industries: Generalist, Food/bev/tobacco, Textiles/apparel, Soap/perfume/cosmetics, Drugs mfg., High tech, Biotech

The John Lucht Consultancy Inc.

The Olympic Twr.
641 Fifth Ave.
New York, New York 10022
(212) 935-4660

Key Contact - Specialty:
Mr. John Lucht - *Senior management*

Description: Outstanding generalist firm. Will recruit CEO's, outside board members, senior management. Will evaluate current staff. All industries, all functions. Noted for thoroughness of searching, referencing and documentation.

Salary Minimum: $150,000
Functions: Generalist, Directors, Senior mgmt., Mktg. mgmt., HR mgmt., CFO's, MIS mgmt.
Industries: Generalist, Drugs mfg., Publishing, New media, Broadcast & Film, Insurance, High tech
Professional Associations: AESC, IACPR

The Luciani Group †

200 Gate Five Rd., Ste. 201
Sausalito, California 94965
(415) 289-0212
Email: tluc4fun@lanminds.com

Key Contact - Specialty:
Mr. Thomas G. Luciani - *Finance executives (treasury, high technology)*
Ms. Stacey McGurk - *Finance executives (high technology)*

Description: Search, consulting organization that does retained searches. Specializing in financial executive placement exclusively, primarily in treasury area. Firm's clients are in the high technology industry in the SF Bay area.
Functions: CFO's, Budgeting, Cash mgmt., Taxes, M&A, Risk mgmt., Mgmt. consultants
Industries: Computer equip., New media, Broadcast & Film, Telecoms, High tech, Software, Biotech

Fran Luisi Assoc.

168 Smoke Rise Rd.
Basking Ridge, New Jersey 07920
(908) 306-0395
Fax: (908) 306-0397
Email: fluisi@erols.com

Key Contact - Specialty:
Mr. Francis J. Luisi - *Human resources*

Description: Boutique firm that recruits the progressive human resource professional on a global basis.

Salary Minimum: $75,000
Functions: Benefits, Personnel, Training, Mgmt. consultants, Minorities, Int'l.
Industries: Generalist, Motor vehicles, Human resource svcs., Communications, New media, Broadcast & Film, Software

Charles Luntz & Assoc., Inc.

14323 S. Outer Forty, Ste. 400 S.
Chesterfield, Missouri 63017
(314) 275-7992
Fax: (314) 275-7063

Key Contact - Specialty:
Mr. Charles E. Luntz
Ms. Joy Brother
Ms. Mary Ahearn
Mr. Michael C. Luntz

Description: Generalist firm representing companies in urban and rural locations. Fill positions considered key to employer. Principal in executive search since 1968.

Salary Minimum: $40,000
Functions: Generalist, General mgmt., Mfg., Sales & mktg., HR mgmt., IT, Minorities
Industries: Generalist, Chemicals, Paints/petroleum products, Metal products, Banking, Advertising/PR, Aerospace

P. J. Lynch Assoc.

P.O. Box 967
Ridgefield, Connecticut 06877
(203) 438-8475
Fax: (203) 438-9315

Key Contact - Specialty:
Mr. Patrick J. Lynch - *Publishing, information products*
Dr. Arlene Heissan - *Consumer products, organizational development*
Mr. Phil Bartlett - *Manufacturing, information products*

Description: Quality orientation to matching highly skilled managers to performance driven organizations. Timely and effective utilization of search process. Resource in providing value added service to our clients.

Salary Minimum: $80,000
Functions: Senior mgmt., Mfg., Sales & mktg., Mktg. mgmt., Finance, IT
Industries: Food/bev/tobacco, Drugs mfg., Communications, Publishing, New media, High tech, Software

Lynch Miller Moore Partners, Inc.

10 S. Wacker Drive, Ste. 2935
Chicago, Illinois 60606
(312) 876-1505
Fax: (312) 876-0245
Web: www.lmminc.com

Key Contact - Specialty:
Mr. Michael C. Lynch
Mr. Michael R. Miller
Mr. David S. Moore
Mr. Richard G. Hypes, Jr.
Mr. Daniel M. O'Hara
Mr. Torrey N. Foster, Jr.
Ms. Patricia G. Gilbert
Ms. Ellen T. Reid

Description: We are committed to professionalism and client service. We emphasize senior level assignments in manufacturing, high technology, financial services, venture capital and healthcare.

Salary Minimum: $90,000
Functions: Generalist, Senior mgmt., Mfg., Sales & mktg., HR mgmt., Finance, IT
Industries: Generalist

Lyons Assoc. †

270 River St., Ste. 401
Troy, New York 12180
(518) 273-9113
Fax: (518) 273-6152
Email: lyonssj@aol.com

Key Contact - Specialty:
Mr. Sean J. Lyons - *Hospitality*

Description: A generalist retained search firm exclusively to the hospitality industry. Emphasizing the recruitment of middle and upper level management.

Salary Minimum: $40,000
Functions: Generalist
Industries: Hospitality

Lyons Pruitt Int'l.

2020 Downyflake, Ste. 102
Allentown, Pennsylvania 18103
(610) 791-0100
(800) 827-5776
Fax: (610) 791-0112
Email: search@lyonspruitt.com
Web: www.lyonspruitt.com

Key Contact - Specialty:
Mr. Jim Pruitt - *Credit card banks*
Mr. Scott Lyons - *Financial services*
Mr. Olin Lyons - *Plastics*

Description: We have been providing executive search services of the highest caliber for a combined 29 years. We specialize in identifying exceptional professionals with a verifiable track record of performance and accomplishment.

Salary Minimum: $75,000
Functions: Senior mgmt., Production, Sales mgmt., CFO's, Cash mgmt., Risk mgmt., MIS mgmt.
Industries: Chemicals, Plastics/rubber, Banking, Invest. banking, Venture cap., High tech, Software

M/J/A Partners
1100 Jorie Blvd., Ste. 301
Oak Brook, Illinois 60521
(630) 990-0033
Fax: (630) 573-0552

Key Contact - Specialty:
Mr. Manuel J. Alves - *General management, finance, human resources*

Description: Forging a partnership with every client, we understand their business strategy, corporate culture and management style. Over 60% of our clients are those previously served. Our target search activity is in the upper middle management to top management levels.

Salary Minimum: $75,000
Functions: Senior mgmt., Materials Plng., Direct mktg., HR mgmt., CFO's, MIS mgmt., Mgmt. consultants
Industries: Misc. mfg., Banking, Misc. financial, Higher ed., Accounting, Mgmt. consulting, High tech
Professional Associations: IACPR

Affiliates:
RWS Partners

The Macdonald Group, Inc.
301 Rte. 17, Ste. 800
Rutherford, New Jersey 07070
(201) 939-2312
Fax: (201) 939-7754
Email: macdgrp@aol.com

Key Contact - Specialty:
Mr. G. William Macdonald

Description: Generalist firm with national practice. Personal service, cost effective, quality results with urgency!

Salary Minimum: $75,000
Functions: Generalist
Industries: Generalist, Drugs mfg., Machinery/Appliances, Misc. mfg., Pharmaceutical svcs., High tech, Healthcare
Professional Associations: IACPR

The Mackenzie Group †
213 Canvasback Drive
Havre de Grace, Maryland 21078
(410) 642-0096
Fax: (410) 642-0094

Key Contact - Specialty:
Mr. Keith Barkley - *Healthcare, biotechnology, pharmaceutical, diagnostic, managed care, hospital administration*

Description: As national experts in our specialties - our clients ultimately hire the best person. As industry specialists, we recruit from a longer list of companies to achieve our client's goals.

Salary Minimum: $100,000
Functions: Directors, Senior mgmt., Middle mgmt., Mktg. mgmt., Sales mgmt., Mgmt. consultants
Industries: Drugs mfg., Medical devices, Pharmaceutical svcs., Biotech, Healthcare

MacNaughton Assoc.
3600 Lime St., Ste. 323
Riverside, California 92501
(909) 788-4951
Fax: (909) 788-4953
Email: sperrym.pacbell.net

Key Contact - Specialty:
Mr. Sperry MacNaughton - *Higher education, organization development, marketing, development*

Description: We handle non-profit, higher education, healthcare and organization development searches. We offer full search services and have extensive experience working with academic search committees and senior management.

Salary Minimum: $75,000
Functions: Senior mgmt., Plant mgmt., Sales mgmt., Training, CFO's, MIS mgmt., Non-profits
Industries: Generalist, Finance, Higher ed., Computer svcs., Accounting, Human resource svcs., Healthcare

Maczkov-Biosciences, Inc.
(Firm declined to update.)
405 Enfrente Rd., Ste. 120
Novato, California 94949
(415) 884-5680
Email: mzkbioex@aol.com

Key Contact - Specialty:
Mr. Nicholas Maczkov - *Healthcare*
Mr. Russell Crone - *Healthcare services*

Description: Offer percentage of first year's compensation and hourly billing rates. 15 years of recruiting senior level executives in life sciences and information technology sectors.

Salary Minimum: $90,000
Functions: Directors, Senior mgmt., Plant mgmt., Physicians, Mktg. mgmt., CFO's, R&D
Industries: Biotech, Healthcare

Affiliates:
McGrath & Assoc., Inc.

The Madeira Group
(a division of HR Unlimited, Inc.)
924 Old Logger Rd., P.O. Box 896
Moscow, Pennsylvania 18444-0896
(717) 842-8959
Fax: (717) 842-9838
Email: rvierra@aol.com

Key Contact - Specialty:
Mr. Ronald Vachon-Vierra - *Healthcare*

Description: We are committed to providing a quality executive search service to our clients in a cost effective manner. Our success is defined by one factor... client satisfaction.

Salary Minimum: $70,000
Functions: Generalist
Industries: Healthcare

The Madison Group
342 Madison Ave., Ste. 1060
New York, New York 10173-1060
(212) 599-0032

Key Contact - Specialty:
Mr. David Soloway
Ms. Lynn Fernandez
Ms. Ruth Gold
Mr. Philip Tesoriero

Description: Committed to quality service and unblocked access to candidates in each market served. We strive to provide very personal service to a select group of clients.

Salary Minimum: $75,000
Functions: General mgmt., Mfg., Sales & mktg., Finance, CFO's, R&D, Minorities
Industries: Chemicals, Misc. mfg., Finance, Venture cap., Hospitality, High tech, Biotech

Madison MacArthur Inc.
33 Madison Ave.
Toronto, Ontario M5R 2S2
Canada
(416) 920-0092
Fax: (416) 920-0099
Email: madmac@idirect.com
Web: www.macarthursearch.com

Key Contact - Specialty:
Mr. Ian MacArthur - *Retail sales & marketing (all sectors), financial services (all sectors)*
Ms. Sylvia MacArthur - *Communications, marketing, advertising (all sectors)*
Mr. Roger Oxenham - *Sales & marketing management (all sectors)*
Ms. Leanna MacDowell - *Retail & sales management (all sectors)*
Ms. Samantha Yarwood - *Marketing & communications (all sectors)*

Description: "Established a true partnership with real concern for my needs."-VP Marketing Merisel, Canada. "Really listened to our needs, produced such excellent candidates we hired two."-The Body Shop, Canada. "Probably the best experience I ever had with an executive search firm." VP Marketing Sprint, Canada.

Salary Minimum: $50,000
Functions: Advertising, Mkt. research, Mktg. mgmt., Sales mgmt., Direct mktg., Customer svc., PR

† occasional contingency assignment

Industries: Food/bev/tobacco, Drugs mfg., Banking, Advertising/PR, New media, Broadcast & Film, Telecoms

Maglio & Co., Inc.

450 N. Sunnyslope Rd.
Brookfield, Wisconsin 53005
(414) 784-6020
Fax: (414) 784-6046

Key Contact - Specialty:
Mr. Charles J. Maglio
Ms. Vicki Peterson

Description: Board and executive search consultants, with a diverse base of clients both domestically and internationally. Extensive experience establishing North American staff for off-shore corporations.

Salary Minimum: $75,000
Functions: General mgmt., Mfg., Materials, Sales & mktg., HR mgmt., Finance, Engineering
Industries: Generalist, Construction, Hospitality, Aerospace, Packaging, High tech

Maiorino & Weston Assoc., Inc.

90 Grove St., Ste. 205
The Executive Pavilion
Ridgefield, Connecticut 06877
(203) 431-0600
Fax: (203) 431-8646
Email: contact@mwasearch.com
Web: www.mwasearch.com

Key Contact - Specialty:
Mr. Robert V. Maiorino

Description: Generalist, servicing the consumer goods, entertainment, sports, communications and hospitality industries both domestic and international. Concentrations in marketing and sales management, finance, human resources and general management.

Salary Minimum: $75,000
Functions: Generalist, General mgmt., Mfg., HR mgmt., Finance, Minorities, Int'l.
Industries: Food/bev/tobacco, Soap/perfume/cosmetics, Consumer electronics, Hospitality, Entertainment, Human resource svcs., Communications

Management & Human Resources

20 Mohegan Rd.
Acton, Massachusetts 01720-2535
(978) 264-4270
Email: airedale@ma.ultranet.com
Web: www.ultranet.com/~airedale

Key Contact - Specialty:
Mr. John J. Donnelly - *Healthcare management, recycling management*

Description: Assuring our client organizations' satisfaction and on-going relationships by delivering quality services coupled with extensive experience, outstanding listening, communications and problem-solving skills together with scrupulous attention to detail and especially responsiveness and client service.

Salary Minimum: $85,000
Functions: General mgmt., Healthcare, Health admin., Sales & mktg., HR mgmt., Finance, Mgmt. consultants
Industries: Non-profits, Mgmt. consulting, Human resource svcs., Environmental svcs., High tech, Software, Healthcare

Management Alliance Group, Inc.

33 Union Place, 3rd Floor
Summit, New Jersey 07901
(908) 598-0400
Email: maginc@village.ios.com

Key Contact - Specialty:
Mr. Carlyle Newell - *Flavor & food ingredients, consumer products, pharmaceutical*
Mr. Wayne Newell - *Technical, environmental, health & safety, engineering, operation*
Mr. Darryl Miller - *Financial services, consumer products*
Dr. Thomas Bachhuber - *University relations, human resource consulting*
Mr. Arthur Perkins - *Sales & marketing, purchasing, logistics, distribution, materials management*

Description: We deliver solutions in executive search, diversity management and university resources, enabling clients to maintain a competitive edge by leveraging human capital to achieve corporate objectives.

Salary Minimum: $70,000
Functions: Senior mgmt., Materials, Sales & mktg., Cash mgmt., IT, Engineering, Minorities
Industries: Mfg., Food/bev/tobacco, Drugs mfg., Invest. banking, Misc. financial, Mgmt. consulting, Haz. waste

Branches:
295 Madison Ave.
New York, New York 10017
(212) 481-3606
Key Contact - Specialty:
Ms. Michele Parker - *Investment management, general senior level management*

Affiliates:
The Governance Group, Inc.

Management Catalysts

P.O. Box 70
Ship Bottom, New Jersey 08008
(609) 597-0079
Fax: (609) 597-2860
Email: MgmtCat@aol.com

Key Contact - Specialty:
Dr. J. R. Stockton - *Food, beverage, consumer product, drug & allied companies (technical positions)*
Ms. N. O. Boyd

Description: Specializing for 15-20 years in filling R&D and other key technical positions in the food, beverage, consumer product, drug and allied industries, where the right science and engineering professionals can truly make a difference.
Functions: Product dev., Quality, Packaging, R&D, Engineering
Industries: Food/bev/tobacco, Soap/perfume/cosmetics, Drugs mfg., Medical devices, Biotech

Management Dimensions Ltd.

7 Park Brook Place
Thornhill, Ontario L3T 2J9
Canada
(905) 771-8485

Key Contact - Specialty:
Mr. John G. Dunn - *Information technology (all levels of management)*

Description: Over 20 years specializing in the recruiting of all levels of management for information technology companies.

Salary Minimum: $100,000
Functions: Senior mgmt., Middle mgmt., Mktg. mgmt., Sales mgmt., CFO's, MIS mgmt., Mgmt. consultants
Industries: Computer equip., Computer svcs., High tech, Software

Management Recruiters of Nassau, Inc. †

2303 Grand Ave., 2nd Floor
Baldwin, New York 11510
(516) 771-1200
Fax: (516) 771-1205
Email: mriny@netcom.com

Key Contact - Specialty:
Mr. Thomas Wieder - *Banking, financial institutions*
Mr. James Humes - *Investment management, asset management*
Mr. Warren Harvey - *Mutual funds, investment management*
Mr. Chris Hebert - *Engineering, software development, telecommunications, satellite communications, information technology, networking*
Mr. Peter Caracciolo - *Sales & marketing, metals, building materials*

Description: We offer staffing consultation services and customized executive search solutions to fill the needs of leading financial and industrial organizations.
Functions: Senior mgmt., Middle mgmt., Sales mgmt., Cash mgmt., Systems dev., Engineering
Industries: Generalist, Energy/utilities, Metal products, Finance, Banking, Invest. banking, High tech

Management Resources Int'l.

160 E. 88th St., Ste. 12G
New York, New York 10028
(212) 722-4885

Key Contact - Specialty:
Mr. F. J. Rotundo

Description: Executive search assignments conducted for Fortune 500, banking, financial and institutions in most functional areas.

Salary Minimum: $25,000
Functions: Generalist
Industries: Generalist

Management Search of R.I. Inc. †

One State St., Ste. 501
Providence, Rhode Island 02908
(401) 273-5511
Fax: (401) 273-5573
Email: msi1@edgenet.net
Web: msi1.com

Key Contact - Specialty:
Mr. James L. Meyer
Mr. Stephen E. Judge

Description: One of New England's largest privately held professional search firms - team focused search; multi-disciplined, corporately mandated minimal industry blacklists. Specialists in mid-level ($50-$200K) search.

Salary Minimum: $50,000
Functions: Senior mgmt., Middle mgmt., Mfg., Sales mgmt., Finance, IT, Engineering
Industries: Generalist, Mfg., Plastics/rubber, Consumer electronics, Finance, High tech, Software

Mannard & Assoc., Inc.
(a member of The Lincoln Group)

1600 Golf Rd., Ste. 1200
Rolling Meadows, Illinois 60008
(847) 981-5170
Fax: (847) 981-5189

Key Contact - Specialty:
Mr. Thomas B. Mannard - *Manufacturing (Fortune 500 to entrepreneurially run)*
Mr. James E. Chavoen
Ms. Kathleen Weinrauch

Description: Boutique firm; President primary consultant on all engagements; only market to manufacturing companies strongly niche plastics, packaging, metals & metal fabrication. Firm characterized by quality, service, flexibility; strong repeat client base.

Salary Minimum: $70,000
Functions: Generalist, Senior mgmt., Plant mgmt., Sales & mktg., HR mgmt., Finance, Engineering
Industries: Generalist, Food/bev/tobacco, Paper, Plastics/rubber, Metal products, Machinery/Appliances, Packaging
Professional Associations: IACPR

F. L. Mannix & Co.

10 Village Rd.
Weston, Massachusetts 02193
(781) 894-9660
Fax: (781) 237-7779

Key Contact - Specialty:
Mr. Francis L. Mannix - *Information systems, broadcasting, high technology*

Description: 39 years experience in search for all middle and upper management functions and the hard to find technologist in the traditional manufacturing, hi-tech, institutional and TV/broadcast fields.

Salary Minimum: $30,000
Functions: Senior mgmt., Sales mgmt., Systems anal., Systems implem., Systems support, Engineering, Minorities
Industries: Plastics/rubber, Computer equip., Non-profits, Computer svcs., Broadcast & Film, High tech, Software

Manuso, Alexander & Associates, Inc.

44 Pondfield Rd., Ste. 1
Bronxville, New York 10708
(914) 337-5000
Fax: (914) 337-6028

Key Contact - Specialty:
Dr. James S. J. Manuso - *Senior management, manufacturing, physicians, marketing, CFOs*
Ms. Susan M. Alexander - *Senior management, manufacturing, physicians, marketing, CFOs*
Ms. Alden F. Prouty - *Senior management, manufacturing, physicians, marketing, CFOs*
Dr. Emile M. Hiesiger - *Senior management, manufacturing, physicians, marketing, CFOs*
Mr. David M. Fineman - *Senior management, manufacturing, physicians, marketing, CFOs*
Mr. M. Blanton Whitlow - *Senior management, manufacturing, physicians, marketing, CFOs*

Description: Why MA&A? Strategic focus on start up to mid-size companies; senior team with operating experience and extensive personal networks; computerized industry database and history of accomplishment and success.

Salary Minimum: $80,000
Functions: Directors, Senior mgmt., Plant mgmt., Physicians, Mkt. research, CFO's, R&D
Industries: Drugs mfg., Medical devices, Pharmaceutical svcs., Biotech, Healthcare

Mark Adam Assoc.

256 Canterbury Rd.
Westfield, New Jersey 07090-1905
(908) 654-8999
Fax: (908) 654-1536
Email: dp-markadam@msn.com

Key Contact - Specialty:
Mr. Donald Pizzi

Description: Boutique practice with a twenty-eight year track record, offering a highly personalized, tightly controlled service, focused on director-up level information systems/technology assignments.

Salary Minimum: $80,000
Functions: MIS mgmt., Systems anal., Systems dev., Systems implem., Systems support
Industries: Generalist, Food/bev/tobacco, Drugs mfg., Entertainment, Advertising/PR, Publishing, Broadcast & Film

Networks:
Marlar International

J. L. Mark Assoc., Inc.

2000 Arapahoe St., Ste. 505
Denver, Colorado 80205
(303) 292-0360
Fax: (303) 292-0361
Web: www.jlmark.com

Key Contact - Specialty:
Mr. John L. Mark - *Generalist*
Ms. Lynne B. Mark - *Generalist*
Ms. Catherine B. Hoover - *Financial*
Ms. Christine Burtt
Ms. Megan Sharp
Ms. Sandy Bushnell

Description: Generalists with over 15 years retained search experience at middle through general to senior management levels. Focus on chemistry: selecting candidates complementary to and compatible with client management style. 12 month guarantee.

Salary Minimum: $100,000
Functions: General mgmt., Healthcare, Sales & mktg., HR mgmt., Finance, IT, Minorities
Industries: Computer equip., Finance, Computer svcs., Communications, Insurance, High tech, Healthcare
Professional Associations: IACPR

† occasional contingency assignment

Mark Stanley & Co./EMA Partners International
P.O. Box 149071
Coral Gables, Florida 33114
(530) 751-5232
Fax: (202) 331-4212
Email: jhramsey@bridge.net
Web: www.coral.net/ema/

Key Contact - Specialty:
Mr. John H. Ramsey
Dr. Dabney G. Park

Description: Senior management, all industries. International a specialty.

Salary Minimum: $80,000
Functions: Generalist, Senior mgmt., Sales mgmt., CFO's, Minorities, Attorneys, Int'l.
Industries: Generalist, Agri/forestry/mining, Food/bev/tobacco, Government, Environmental svcs., Biotech, Healthcare
Professional Associations: AESC

Branches:
1629 K St. NW, Ste. 1100
Washington, District of Columbia 20006
(202) 785-6711
Fax: (202) 331-4212
Key Contact - Specialty:
Mr. John H. Ramsey
Mr. Paul S. Weller - *Agribusiness*

Networks:
EMA Partners Int'l.

Marks & Co., Inc.
304 Main Ave., Ste. 364
Norwalk, Connecticut 06851
(203) 849-0888

Key Contact - Specialty:
Ms. Sharon Marks
Ms. Whitney Reese

Description: National practices in EDP audit, data security, general audit and disaster recovery. Founder is a former Fortune 500 executive with above experience. Associates also have directly related industry experience.

Salary Minimum: $50,000
Functions: MIS mgmt., Systems dev., Systems support, Network admin.
Industries: Generalist

Paula Marks Inc.
280 Madison Ave., Ste. 1202
New York, New York 10016
(212) 252-0444
Fax: (212) 252-1113
Email: PaulaMarks@aol.com

Key Contact - Specialty:
Ms. Paula F. Marks

Description: Specialize in human resources, general management and diversified.

Salary Minimum: $85,000
Functions: Directors, Product dev., Distribution, Sales & mktg., HR mgmt., CFO's, MIS mgmt.
Industries: Generalist, Mfg., Retail, Svcs., Communications

Brad Marks Int'l.
1888 Century Park E., Ste. 1040
Los Angeles, California 90067
(310) 286-0600
Fax: (310) 286-0479
Email: bodysnatcher@bradmarks.com
Web: www.bradmarks.com

Key Contact - Specialty:
Mr. Brad Marks - *Entertainment*
Mr. Neil Pennella - *International TV, cable, legal*
Ms. Aurora Christidis - *Management consulting, international. TV, cable, legal*
Mr. Bob Miggins - *Broadcasting, sales & marketing*
Ms. Linda Nicolai - *New media*
Ms. Lyn Cason - *Financial, general management, information technology*
Mr. Morgan O'Bryant - *Research*

Description: A specialist firm which recruits senior-level management for the entertainment and media-related industries. The firm's practice is national and international in scope and currently includes 7 recruiters with over 40 years of combined search experience.

Salary Minimum: $100,000
Functions: General mgmt., Sales & mktg., HR mgmt., Finance, IT, Attorneys, Int'l.
Industries: Entertainment, Legal, Communications

The Marlow Group
5 Great Plain Ave.
P.O. Box 812707
Wellesley, Massachusetts 02482
(781) 237-7012
Fax: (781) 237-7012

Key Contact - Specialty:
Mr. Paul M. Jones

Description: Generalist firm serving emerging high-technology companies-sales, marketing, operations and technical.

Salary Minimum: $70,000
Functions: Senior mgmt., Mktg. mgmt., Sales mgmt., Direct mktg., CFO's, M&A, MIS mgmt.
Industries: Medical devices, Computer equip., Advertising/PR, New media, High tech, Software, Biotech

The Maroon Group
246 Chestnut Hill Rd.
Litchfield, Connecticut 06759
(860) 567-3644
Fax: (860) 567-3108
Email: MaroonG@aol.com

Key Contact - Specialty:
Mr. K. Michael Blount - *Information technology, insurance management*

Description: Provides full range services specializing in knowing your company, its personality and needs. Minimum three year replacement guarantee on hired executive.

Salary Minimum: $50,000
Functions: General mgmt., Mfg., Sales & mktg., HR mgmt., Finance, IT
Industries: Generalist, Misc. mfg., Computer svcs., Telecoms, Insurance, High tech, Software

Marra Peters & Partners
Millburn Esplanade
Millburn, New Jersey 07041
(973) 376-8999
Email: jmarra8405@aol.com
Web: www.marrapeters.com

Key Contact - Specialty:
Mr. John Marra, Jr. - *General management, finance, accounting, information technology, marketing*
Mr. Charles J. Pelisson - *Marketing, human resources, research & development, sales & distribution*

Description: Clients are assured of their importance as they receive a sophisticated service in a highly personalized and responsive manner. We provide a consultative approach to retain the executive who will impact your business in the most contributory way.

Salary Minimum: $70,000
Functions: General mgmt., Mfg., Sales & mktg., HR mgmt., Finance, IT, Specialized services
Industries: Generalist, Construction, Retail, Mgmt. consulting, Communications, Government, Real estate

Branches:
7040 Palmetto Park Rd., Ste. 145
Boca Raton, Florida 33433
(561) 347-7778
Key Contact - Specialty:
Mr. John Marra
Ms. Marie Gensch

10612-D Providence Rd., Ste. 305
Charlotte, North Carolina 28277
(704) 841-8000
Key Contact - Specialty:
Ms. Jenny K. Lyon - *General management, finance, accounting, operations*

Affiliates:
Cleas
Euromedica, Limited

Marshall Consultants, Inc. †

360 E. 65th St.
New York, New York 10021
(212) 628-8400
Fax: (212) 628-8449
Email: marshcons@msn.com
Web: www.marshallconsultants.com

Key Contact - Specialty:
Mr. Larry Marshall - *Corporate & marketing communications, public relations, investor relations, public affairs, advertising & marketing*
Mr. Hugh McCandless - *Corporate & marketing communications, public relations, investor relations, public affairs, advertising & marketing*
Ms. Gail Quinn - *Corporate & marketing communications, public relations, investor relations, public affairs, advertising & marketing*
Ms. Marjorie Silverman - *Investor relations, corporate & marketing communications, public relations, investor relations, public affairs, advertising & marketing*

Description: First search firm specializing in corporate and marketing communications, public relations, public affairs, investor relations, advertising and marketing. Only firm in function with eastern and western offices, jointly serving over half the Fortune 500 companies nationally.

Salary Minimum: $25,000
Functions: Advertising, Mktg. mgmt., PR
Industries: Generalist
Professional Associations: IACPR

Branches:
24172 Malibu Rd.
Malibu, California 90265
(310) 456-0666
Fax: (310) 456-8886
Web: www.marshallconsultants.co
Key Contact - Specialty:
Ms. Kathleen DesRosiers
Mr. Larry Marshall
Ms. Wendy Tanenbaum

The Marshall Group †

31 Cambridge Lane
Lincolnshire, Illinois 60069
(847) 940-0021
Fax: (847) 940-7031
Web: marshall_group@compuserve.com

Key Contact - Specialty:
Mr. Don Marshall - *Generalist*

Description: Personal retained search designed to locate and provide management and non-management personnel to high growth clients.
Functions: Generalist
Industries: Generalist

Donovan Martin & Assoc.

1000 Elwell Court, Ste. 217
Palo Alto, California 94303
(650) 969-8235

Key Contact - Specialty:
Mr. Donovan Martin - *Executives, CEOs, marketing & sales (vice presidents), CFOs*

Description: We provide executive and professional search services for a variety of companies, from large, long established firms to the newest start-ups.

Salary Minimum: $100,000
Functions: Senior mgmt., Mktg. mgmt., Sales mgmt., CFO's, MIS mgmt.
Industries: Computer equip., High tech, Software

J. Martin & Assoc.

10820 Holman Ave., Ste. 103
Los Angeles, California 90024
(310) 475-5380

Key Contact - Specialty:
Ms. Judy R. Martin - *Computer, high technology, healthcare services*

Description: Specialization computer/high technology-medical/healthcare venture capital backed start-up, emerging, high growth, Fortune 500, CEO to senior sales and marketing levels. Quick results, high quality.

Salary Minimum: $70,000
Functions: Directors, Senior mgmt., Middle mgmt., Mktg. mgmt., Sales mgmt., IT, Engineering
Industries: Mfg., Computer equip., Telecoms, High tech, Software, Healthcare

George R. Martin

P.O. Box 673
Doylestown, Pennsylvania 18901-0673
(215) 348-8146
Email: exsearch@comcat.com

Key Contact - Specialty:
Mr. George R. Martin

Description: Concentrate on marketing, sales, technical and operations functions. Twenty four year completion rate is high, with excellent stick and promotion ratios. Highly qualified research staff.

Salary Minimum: $60,000
Functions: Middle mgmt., Plant mgmt., Quality, Mkt. research, Mktg. mgmt., R&D, Engineering
Industries: Chemicals, Drugs mfg., Plastics/rubber, Metal products, Test/measurement equip., Misc. mfg., Biotech

The Martin Group

508 Bridle Court
Walnut Creek, California 94596
(925) 942-2550
Fax: (925) 942-2552

Key Contact - Specialty:
Ms. Lois G. Martin
Mr. Timothy P. Martin

Description: Multi-specialty practice serving clients ranging from entrepreneurial, venture capital financed start-ups to Fortune 500 companies. The principals of the firm personally conduct all search assignments.

Salary Minimum: $75,000
Functions: General mgmt., Mfg., Materials, HR mgmt., Finance, IT, Mgmt. consultants
Industries: Generalist, Food/bev/tobacco, Wholesale, Retail, Finance, Mgmt. consulting, Software

Martin Partners, L.L.C.

224 S. Michigan Ave., Ste. 620
Chicago, Illinois 60604
(312) 922-1800
Fax: (312) 922-1813
Email: webmaster@martinptrs.com
Web: www.martinptrs.com

Key Contact - Specialty:
Mr. Theodore B. Martin, Jr. - *Generalist*
Mr. Michael B. Wyman - *Generalist*
Mr. Thomas A. Jagielo - *Generalist*
Ms. Kathleen Lehman Hajek - *Generalist*
Ms. Sally Frantz - *Generalist*
Ms. Lynn K. Cherney - *Generalist*
Ms. Adrianne Kalyna - *Generalist*

Description: Our goal is to partner with every client, providing the highest quality of senior level search work possible with a total committment to client/candidate customer service. Integrity and teamwork are our most important assets. Quality and speed are our drivers.

Salary Minimum: $120,000
Functions: Senior mgmt., Mfg., Sales & mktg., CFO's, IT, Mgmt. consultants, Int'l.
Industries: Mfg., Food/bev/tobacco, Invest. banking, Venture cap., Communications, Software, Healthcare
Professional Associations: AESC, IACPR

Maschal/Connors Inc.

306 S. Bay Ave., P. O. Box 1301
Beach Haven, New Jersey 08008
(609) 492-3400

Key Contact - Specialty:
Mr. Chuck Maschal - *Generalist*
Ms. Jennifer Mancini

Description: A management consulting

† occasional contingency assignment

firm specializing in recruitment of senior level management (through CEO and board) for manufacturers in specified industries.

Salary Minimum: $100,000
Functions: Generalist
Industries: Generalist, Metal products, Machinery/Appliances, Motor vehicles, Computer equip., Misc. mfg., Law enfcmt.
Professional Associations: IACPR

Mason & Nicastri Ltd.
2118 Wilshire Blvd., Ste. 650
Santa Monica, California 90403
(310) 317-0747
Fax: (310) 317-0098
Email: mnltd@ni.net

Key Contact - Specialty:
Ms. Morgan Mason - *Food, beverage*

Description: We are a retained search firm specializing in the food industry. We provide superior middle and upper level management candidates to restaurant, hotel, retail and entertainment companies throughout the United States. We are exclusive to these industries, in business since 1986, we enjoy an excellent reputation.

Salary Minimum: $40,000
Industries: Food/bev/tobacco, Hospitality

Branches:
9121 Atlanta Ave., #336
Huntington Beach, California 92646
(714) 960-2120
Fax: (714) 960-6329
Email: mnltdoc@ni-net
Key Contact - Specialty:
Ms. Diane Nicastri - *Food, beverage*

Masserman & Assoc., Inc.
70 West Red Oak Lane
White Plains, New York 10604
(914) 697-4884
Fax: (914) 697-4885
Email: bruce@masserman.com

Key Contact - Specialty:
Mr. Bruce Masserman - *Information technology (financial services, publishing & database marketing industries)*

Description: Specialized search firm dedicated to the information technology marketplace. Emphasis on systems development and emerging technology professionals for the financial services industries.

Salary Minimum: $85,000
Functions: MIS mgmt., Systems anal., Systems dev., Systems implem., Systems support, Network admin., DB admin.
Industries: Banking, Invest. banking, Brokers, Misc. financial, Computer svcs., Mgmt. consulting, High tech

Massey-Horton Int'l.
330 Bay Street, Suite 1104
Toronto, Ontario M5H 2S8
Canada
(416) 861-0077
Fax: (416) 363-2976
Email: toronto@horton-intl.com
Web: massey@horton-intl.com

Key Contact - Specialty:
Mr. Bruce Massey - *Generalist*
Mr. Guy W. Redwood - *Generalist*
Mr. Ralph Hanson - *Food, packaged goods*

Description: Senior management recruiting firm servicing clients nationally and internationally through partners in 25 countries worldwide.

Salary Minimum: $90,000
Functions: Generalist, Senior mgmt., Plant mgmt., Sales mgmt., CFO's, MIS mgmt., Mgmt. consultants
Industries: Food/bev/tobacco, Drugs mfg., Finance, Mgmt. consulting, Communications, Aerospace, Insurance

Networks:
Horton International

Louis Thomas Masterson & Co.
1375 E. Ninth St., Ste. 1950
Cleveland, Ohio 44114-1724
(216) 621-2112
Fax: (216) 621-7320
Web: lmasterson@sprintmail.com

Key Contact - Specialty:
Mr. Louis T. Masterson - *General management*

Description: We provide high quality, responsive executive recruiting service. Searches cover many industries and multiple disciplines.

Salary Minimum: $70,000
Functions: Generalist, Senior mgmt., Mfg., Healthcare, Physicians, Health admin., HR mgmt.
Industries: Generalist, Mfg., Chemicals, Paints/petroleum products, Finance, Svcs., Healthcare

Matté & Company, Inc.
124 W. Putnam Ave.
Greenwich, Connecticut 06830
(203) 661-2224
Fax: (203) 661-5927

Key Contact - Specialty:
Mr. Norman E. Matté

Description: Consulting services in executive search, management assessment and benchmarking. Learn how your business compares in meeting 21st century organizational requirements. Branch office in London.

Salary Minimum: $125,000
Functions: General mgmt., Mfg., Distribution, HR mgmt., Finance, IT, Int'l.
Industries: Food/bev/tobacco, Drugs mfg., Computer equip., Finance, Computer svcs., Human resource svcs., High tech

Affiliates:
D. C. Tucker & Assoc.

Matte Consulting Group Inc.
1010 Sherbrooke W., Ste. 1200
Montreal, Quebec H3A 2R7
Canada
(514) 848-1008
Fax: (514) 848-9157

Key Contact - Specialty:
Mr. Richard Matte - *Manufacturing, information technology, general management*
Ms. Dominique Lanctot - *Finance & accounting, general management*

Description: An affiliate of IIC Partners, we are a highly dynamic Montreal based executive search firm specializing in senior recruitments on both a national and international scale.

Salary Minimum: $100,000
Functions: Generalist, General mgmt., Mfg., Healthcare, Sales & mktg., Finance, IT
Industries: Generalist, Energy/utilities, Mfg., Finance, Communications, Packaging, Healthcare

Affiliates:
Cambridge Management Planning

Networks:
I-I-C Partners Executive Search Worldwide

Maxecon Executive Search Consultants
9500 S. Dadeland Blvd., Ste. 601
Miami, Florida 33156
(305) 670-1933
Fax: (305) 670-8396
Email: maxecon@aol.com

Key Contact - Specialty:
Mr. Ronald Gerstl - *Senior management multinationals (Latin America)*

Description: Specializing in executives for Latin American divisions of multinational companies: U.S.-based regional headquarter personnel responsible for the area and executives for subsidiary operations in Latin America/Caribbean.

Salary Minimum: $90,000
Functions: Generalist, Senior mgmt., Middle mgmt., Mktg. mgmt., Sales mgmt., CFO's, Int'l.
Industries: Generalist, Food/bev/tobacco, Soap/perfume/cosmetics, Drugs mfg., Computer equip., Consumer electronics, Advertising/PR

K. Maxin & Assoc.

Allegheny Ctr., Bldg. 10, Ste. 421
Pittsburgh, Pennsylvania 15212
(412) 322-2595
(800) 867-8447
Fax: (412) 322-7027
Email: kmaxin@usa.net

Key Contact - Specialty:
Mr. Keith A. Maxin - *Construction, real estate*

Description: Executive search in the construction and real estate industries.

Salary Minimum: $60,000
Functions: Senior mgmt., Middle mgmt., Mktg. mgmt., CFO's, Engineering, Architects
Industries: Construction, Telecoms, Real estate

Mary L. Mayer, Ltd.

P.O. Box 250
Medina, Minnesota 55340
(612) 473-7700
Fax: (612) 449-0772
Email: mlmayer@worldnet.att.net
Web: mlmayer@worldnet.att.net

Key Contact - Specialty:
Ms. Mary L. Mayer - *Insurance, loss prevention, risk management, sales & marketing (insurance related)*

Description: Licensed insurance agent specializing in the areas of insurance, risk management, sales, marketing, mid to high level management, claims, loss prevention, company and brokerage. 25 years sales and marketing experience in the insurance industry.

Salary Minimum: $50,000
Functions: Senior mgmt., Benefits, Risk mgmt.
Industries: Insurance

The Mayes Group, Ltd. †

P.O. Box 399, Daisy Point
St. Peters, Pennsylvania 19470
(610) 469-6900
Fax: (610) 469-6088
Email: mayesgroup@aol.com

Key Contact - Specialty:
Ms. Abby Mayes - *Managed care*
Ms. Megan Murray - *Managed care*

Description: We are a retained executive search firm specializing in managed care. Clients include: HMOs, PPOs, health systems, disease management, pharmaceutical and information system companies.

Salary Minimum: $75,000
Functions: Senior mgmt., Healthcare, Physicians, Nurses, Health admin., Sales mgmt., MIS mgmt.
Industries: Healthcare

The Mazzitelli Group, Ltd.

603 E. Lake St., Ste. 200
Wayzata, Minnesota 55391
(612) 449-9490
Fax: (612) 475-4932
Email: mmazzitell@aol.com
Web: www.visi.com/~dbrekke/mazzitelli.html

Key Contact - Specialty:
Ms. Teresa Mazzitelli - *Generalist*

Description: Generalist retainer search firm.
Functions: Generalist, General mgmt., Mfg., Sales & mktg., HR mgmt., Finance, IT
Industries: Generalist, Mfg., Wholesale, Retail, Svcs., Communications, High tech

The McAulay Firm

100 N. Tryon St., Ste. 5220
NationsBank Corporate Ctr.
Charlotte, North Carolina 28202
(704) 342-1880
Fax: (704) 342-0825

Key Contact - Specialty:
Mr. Albert L. McAulay, Jr. - *Generalist*
Mr. Charles C. Lucas, III - *Generalist*
Mr. Steven B. Smith - *Generalist*

Description: All functions and industries.

Salary Minimum: $75,000
Functions: Generalist
Industries: Generalist, Energy/utilities, Mfg., Textiles/apparel, Finance, Insurance, Real estate
Professional Associations: AESC

McBride Assoc., Inc.

1511 K St. NW
Washington, District of Columbia 20005-1497
(202) 638-1150

Key Contact - Specialty:
Mr. Jonathan E. McBride - *Problem-solving*

Description: Discreet, comprehensive, thorough, small; specialize in select high-level assignments; make every effort to represent clients in the same thoughtful and professional manner as they would seek to represent themselves.

Salary Minimum: $150,000
Functions: General mgmt., Directors, Sales & mktg., PR, HR mgmt., Finance, IT
Industries: Drugs mfg., Finance, Svcs., Communications, High tech, Software, Biotech
Professional Associations: AESC

McCann, Choi & Associates, LLC

590 Madison Ave., 26th Floor
New York, New York 10022
(212) 755-7051
Fax: (212) 355-2610
Email: JMcCann@McCannChoi.com/

Key Contact - Specialty:
Mr. Joseph H. McCann, III - *Financial services*
Ms. Julie A. Choi - *Financial services*

Description: Completely client driven, very consultative boutique search firm with exclusive focus on financial institutions.

Salary Minimum: $200,000
Functions: Senior mgmt., CFO's, M&A, Risk mgmt.
Industries: Invest. banking, Misc. financial

McCartan Assoc.

P.O. Box 25
Medford, New Jersey 08055
(609) 797-1969
Fax: (609) 797-0282
Email: padraig@prodigy.net

Key Contact - Specialty:
Mr. Charles P. McCartan

Description: High quality, precise execution for a select group of client companies possessing the highest standards is our only interest.

Salary Minimum: $40,000
Functions: Generalist
Industries: Generalist

K. E. McCarthy & Assoc.

9800 S. Sepulveda Blvd., Ste. 720
Los Angeles, California 90045
(310) 568-4070
Fax: (310) 568-4077
Email: kemassoc@aol.com

Key Contact - Specialty:
Mr. Kevin E. McCarthy

Description: The firm has wide experience serving financial institutions general management emphasizing finance, treasury, capital markets and information technology executives. Expertise in search and consultation to growth companies in high technology and financial services.

Salary Minimum: $75,000
Functions: Generalist, Senior mgmt., Middle mgmt., CFO's, Cash mgmt., MIS mgmt., Mgmt. consultants
Industries: Finance, Banking, Higher ed., Computer svcs., Mgmt. consulting, High tech, Software

† occasional contingency assignment

McCooe & Assoc., Inc.
615 Franklin Tnpk.
Ridgewood, New Jersey 07450-1929
(201) 445-3161
Fax: (201) 445-8958
Email:
mccooe@mccooe@mccooeassoc.com
Web: www.mccooeassoc.com

Key Contact - Specialty:
Mr. John J. McCooe - *Senior management*
Mr. Sean J. McCooe - *Senior management*
Mr. Glenn C. Lambre - *Chemicals, healthcare, industrial manufacturing*

Description: Specializes in executive recruitment of strategic human resources. Exceptional discernment of best candidate fit in an organization. Offers management consulting in compensation planning, job evaluation, organization development, training and career development.

Salary Minimum: $80,000
Functions: Senior mgmt., Plant mgmt., Distribution, R&D, Engineering, Int'l.
Industries: Generalist, Construction, Chemicals, Medical devices, Plastics/rubber, Higher ed., Healthcare

McCormack & Assoc.
5042 Wilshire Blvd., Ste. 505
Los Angeles, California 90036
(213) 549-9200
Fax: (213) 549-9222
Email: JMSearch@aol.com

Key Contact - Specialty:
Mr. Joseph A. McCormack - *Gay & lesbian, minorities, not-for-profit, diversity recruiting*

Description: Specialty practice in diversity recruiting for corporations, service providers and not-for-profit organizations. Recruit people of color and alternative sexual orientation for boards of directors and senior management. Secondary focus on environmental consulting and outdoor recreation products.

Salary Minimum: $60,000
Functions: Directors, Senior mgmt., CFO's, Minorities, Non-profits, Environmentalists
Industries: Generalist, Non-profits, Pharmaceutical svcs., Environmental svcs., Haz. waste, Healthcare
Professional Associations: AESC

Branches:
353 Sacramento St., #600
San Francisco, California 94111
(415) 421-3300
Fax: (415) 421-3350
Key Contact - Specialty:
Mr. Adam Forest - *Environmental consulting, outdoor recreation products*
Ms. Adrienne Graf

McCormack & Farrow
695 Town Center Drive, Ste. 660
Costa Mesa, California 92626
(714) 549-7222

Key Contact - Specialty:
Mr. Jerry M. Farrow
Mr. Kenneth L. Thompson
Ms. Helen E. Friedman
Mr. Gene Phelps
Mr. Jim Wade
Mr. Dave Mildrew

Description: General practice retained search in most industries, nationwide. Special emphasis on high technology, start-up and emerging companies, manufacturing, healthcare, financial services, not-for-profit and privately owned businesses.

Salary Minimum: $75,000
Functions: Generalist, General mgmt., Mfg., Sales & mktg., Finance, IT, R&D
Industries: Generalist, Mfg., Medical devices, Retail, Aerospace, High tech, Healthcare

Branches:
19426 N. 87th Drive
Peoria, Arizona 85382
(602) 566-2142
Key Contact - Specialty:
Mr. Gene Phelps

McCray, Shriver, Eckdahl & Assoc., Inc.
10880 Wilshire Blvd., Ste. 2050
Los Angeles, California 90024
(310) 479-7667
Fax: (310) 479-8608
Email: principal@mccray-inc.com
Web: www.mccray-inc.com

Key Contact - Specialty:
Mr. Harold C. McCray - *Chairman, CEO, presidents*
Mr. Martin J. Hewett - *Chairman, CEO, presidents*
Mr. William J. Sheweloff - *Senior officer, general management, internet/intranet, communications*
Mr. Maurice Mason - *High technology, manufacturing, telecommunications*

Description: Board-level, presidential and general management solutions in high technology, industrial and consumer industries. 25 years of proven success.

Salary Minimum: $100,000
Functions: Senior mgmt., Product dev., Plant mgmt., Mktg. mgmt., Sales mgmt., CFO's, Int'l.
Industries: Computer equip., Consumer electronics, Computer svcs., Broadcast & Film, Telecoms, Aerospace, Software

McDonald Assoc. Int'l.
1290 N. Western Ave., Ste. 209
Lake Forest, Illinois 60045-1257
(847) 234-6889
Fax: (847) 234-6889
Email: sbmlf@aol.com

Key Contact - Specialty:
Mr. Stanleigh B. McDonald - *Generalist*

Description: Retainer executive search; assist clients with special staffing needs below normal salary level. Depends on the client and client need!

Salary Minimum: $70,000
Functions: Senior mgmt., Productivity, Mktg. mgmt., Benefits, CFO's, MIS mgmt., Specialized services
Industries: Mfg., Plastics/rubber, Finance, Svcs., Telecoms, High tech, Biotech

Affiliates:
Hogg Clarke International

McDonald, Long & Assoc., Inc.
670 White Plains Rd.
Scarsdale, New York 10583
(914) 723-5400
Fax: (914) 723-5699
Email: ehpx32a@prodigy.com

Key Contact - Specialty:
Mr. William G. Long - *Financial services (all functions)*

Description: Senior level general management search with specialties in the corporate financial (CFO, treasurer, controller and tax), banking (commercial, thrift, investment and international banking), insurance industries and human resource function.

Salary Minimum: $75,000
Functions: Generalist, Mfg., Sales & mktg., Finance, IT, Attorneys, Int'l.
Industries: Generalist, Finance, Non-profits, Legal, Publishing, Insurance, Real estate

G. E. McFarland & Co.
(Firm declined to update.)
535 Colonial Park Drive
Roswell, Georgia 30075
(770) 992-0900

Key Contact - Specialty:
Mr. Charles P. Beall
Mr. Dennis A. Desmond
Mr. Carleton A. Palmer
Mr. Wayne F. Carmichael
Ms. Nancy Drake

Description: Serve a broad cross-section of client organizations representing most industries, with particular emphasis on aerospace, information and communication systems, electronics, biomedical technology, construction/construction materials and financial services.

Salary Minimum: $100,000
Functions: Generalist, Int'l.
Industries: Generalist

Networks:
Nimrod International Search

Clarence E. McFeely, Inc.
20 N. Wacker Drive, Ste. 3110
Chicago, Illinois 60606
(312) 641-2977
(847) 381-0475
Fax: (312) 641-2367
Email: okaalphie@aol.com

Key Contact - Specialty:
Mr. Clarence E. McFeely - *CEO, president, COO, CFO, corporate CIO*

Description: National generalist practice concentrates on CEO, COO, corporate CFO, CIO and senior executive level positions. Clients include healthcare, financial services, biotechnology, conglomerates, electronic goods, LBO's, entertainment, broadcasting, medical products and new venture start-ups.

Salary Minimum: $300,000
Functions: Generalist, Directors, Senior mgmt., Finance, CFO's, IT, Specialized services
Industries: Generalist
Professional Associations: AESC

Robert E. McGrath & Assoc.
256 Post Rd. E.
Westport, Connecticut 06880
(203) 221-8335

Key Contact - Specialty:
Mr. Robert E. McGrath - *Chemicals, paper, pharmaceuticals*
Mr. T.M. Johnson

Description: Firm specializes in paper, pulp, nonwovens, pharmaceuticals, chemicals and publishing.

Salary Minimum: $80,000
Functions: Senior mgmt., Middle mgmt., Production, Plant mgmt., Packaging, Mktg. mgmt., Environmentalists
Industries: Paper, Chemicals, Drugs mfg., Medical devices, Plastics/rubber

McGrath & Assoc., Inc.
993 Lenox Drive, Ste. 200
Lawrenceville, New Jersey 08648
(609) 844-7594
Fax: (609) 844-7548
Email: contactus@mcgrathassociates.com
Web: mcgrathassociates.com

Key Contact - Specialty:
Mr. Steven L. McGrath - *Sales & marketing, finance, consultants*
Mr. Peter T. Lins - *Information technologies, business development*
Mr. Kenneth A. Hirshman - *Manufacturing, operations, information technology*
Mr. Robert Glass - *Security*

Description: We are a retainer-based search firm. A boutique with a functional specialization: information technology, financial planning and control, sales and marketing and consulting. Primary industries served: telecommunications, healthcare, financial consulting.

Salary Minimum: $75,000
Functions: General mgmt., Mfg., Sales & mktg., HR mgmt., Finance, IT, Mgmt. consultants
Industries: Mfg., Finance, Pharmaceutical svcs., Telecoms, High tech, Software, Healthcare

McHale & Assoc.
1001 Fourth Ave. Plaza, Ste. 3200
Seattle, Washington 98154
(206) 230-9062
Email: jmchale@concentric.net

Key Contact - Specialty:
Mr. John P. McHale - *Finance, high technology, healthcare, international, sales*
Ms. Laurie Jackson - *Public relations, media relations*

Description: Internationally oriented; North America, Pacific Rim and Europe. Retained executive search firm oriented toward Northwestern U.S., functionally dealing in international, high technology, medical, public and private sectors.

Salary Minimum: $40,000
Functions: Senior mgmt., Health admin., CFO's, Systems dev., Systems implem., Int'l.
Industries: Misc. financial, Computer svcs., Accounting, High tech, Software, Healthcare

McIntyre Assoc.
3 Forest Park Drive
Forest Park Office Green
Farmington, Connecticut 06032
(860) 284-1000
Fax: (860) 284-1111
Email: mcassoc@tiac.net

Key Contact - Specialty:
Mr. Jeffrey F. McIntyre - *Wireless, telecommunications executives, electronic commerce software, supply chain solutions software*

Description: Recruitment of key executives involved in breaking ground in and/or financing emerging technology niche markets, with emphasis on the growing telecom/software-centric convergence of wireless and wireline markets on a global basis.

Salary Minimum: $100,000
Functions: Directors, Senior mgmt., Mkt. research, Sales mgmt., CFO's, Int'l.
Industries: High tech, Software

McKeen & Company †
P.O. Box 850143
Richardson, Texas 75085-0143
(214) 231-9999

Key Contact - Specialty:
Ms. S. L. Nyvall
Mr. J. J. McKeen

Description: The established semiconductor industry specialists: IC assembly and packaging international, semiconductor equipment and materials international.

Salary Minimum: $100,000
Functions: General mgmt., Mfg., Engineering

McKinley•Arend Int'l.
The Phoenix Twr., 33rd Floor
3200 Southwest Frwy.
Houston, Texas 77027-7526
(713) 623-6400
Fax: (713) 975-0022
Email: mckinleyarend.com

Key Contact - Specialty:
Mr. James M. McKinley - *Generalist*
Mr. Lewis Arend - *Generalist*

Description: International firm conducting technical & non-technical searches; offices worldwide.
Functions: Senior mgmt., Plant mgmt., Mkt. research, CFO's, R&D, Engineering, Int'l.
Industries: Generalist, Energy/utilities, Paper, Chemicals, Drugs mfg., Metal products, Human resource svcs.

International Branches:
London

The McLeod Group, Inc.
253 Post Rd. W.
Westport, Connecticut 06880
(203) 454-1234
Email: mcleod@discovernet.net

Key Contact - Specialty:
Mr. Anthony N. Schenck
Mr. Reuel A. Dorman

Description: Represents only a few clients to avoid conflicts. Carries out assignments with imagination and urgency. Exploits the search process for information and ideas useful to the client. Always exceeds expectations.

Salary Minimum: $125,000
Functions: M&A
Industries: Invest. banking

† occasional contingency assignment

McManners Assoc., Inc.
2525 Ontario Drive
San Jose, California 95124
(408) 559-9232

Key Contact - Specialty:
Mr. Donald E. McManners - *Generalist*

Description: Senior level searches conducted for all functions. Strong candidate/industry research capability. Firm has successful, continuing, client relationships with Fortune 500 corporations for over 15 years. Professionalism and quality guarantee.

Salary Minimum: $150,000
Functions: General mgmt., Mfg., Healthcare, Sales & mktg., R&D, Engineering, Int'l.
Industries: Generalist, Medical devices, Computer equip., Misc. mfg., Publishing, Aerospace, High tech
Professional Associations: IACPR

McNichol Assoc.
620 Chestnut St., Ste. 1031
Philadelphia, Pennsylvania 19106
(215) 922-4142
Email: JMcNichol@McNicholAssoc.com

Key Contact - Specialty:
Mr. John McNichol, Jr. - *Senior management for professional design, construction engineering, construction, environmental firms*

Description: Specialists in recruiting management for architectural, engineering, construction and environmental industries as well as senior facilities (project, environmental, etc.) managers for institutions and industry.

Salary Minimum: $75,000
Functions: Generalist, Senior mgmt., Middle mgmt., Engineering, Environmentalists, Architects
Industries: Construction, Environmental svcs., Haz. waste
Professional Associations: IACPR

Jon McRae & Associates, Inc.
1930 N. Druid Hills Rd. NE, Ste. 200
Atlanta, Georgia 30319-4120
(404) 325-3252
Fax: (404) 325-9610
Email: jma@mindspring.com

Key Contact - Specialty:
Mr. O. Jon McRae - *Non-profit, presidents, education*
Dr. William W. Kelly - *Non-profit, presidents, education*
Dr. Charles E. Glassick - *Non-profit, presidents, education*
Mr. Kenneth B. Orr - *Non-profit, presidents, education*
Ms. Ellen Adair Wyche - *Non-profit, presidents, education*

Description: Executive search counsel for governing boards and presidents of not-for-profit institutions with a focus in higher education. Excellence-oriented professionalism accentuated with a personal and intuitive style.

Salary Minimum: $90,000
Functions: Senior mgmt., CFO's
Industries: Non-profits, Higher ed.

MCS Assoc.
18300 Von Karman, Ste. 1000
Irvine, California 92612
(949) 263-8700
Fax: (949) 553-0168
Email: mcs@earthlink.net

Key Contact - Specialty:
Mr. Norman Katz - *Banking management, finance, lending*
Mr. Thomas J. Haupert - *Banking management, finance, lending*

Description: Consulting firm that specializes in banking, real estate, financial services. Established in 1973, clients are nationwide, including large and small organizations.

Salary Minimum: $75,000
Functions: Senior mgmt., Middle mgmt., Admin. svcs., Benefits, CFO's, Cash mgmt., Credit
Industries: Banking, Misc. financial, Legal, Insurance, Real estate

Affiliates:
Stafford Consulting Group

James Mead & Co.
164 Kings Hwy. N.
Westport, Connecticut 06880
(203) 454-5544
Fax: (203) 454-5695
Email: jim@jmeadco.com

Key Contact - Specialty:
Mr. James D. Mead - *Consumer packaged/durable goods sales & marketing, and related industries*
Ms. Katherine W. Cizynski - *Consumer packaged goods, sales & marketing*

Description: Search firm offering highly personalized, targeted service operating in consumer packaged goods and related industries. A focus against marketing, sales and general management positions.

Salary Minimum: $100,000
Functions: Directors, Senior mgmt., Middle mgmt., Advertising, Mkt. research, Mktg. mgmt., Sales mgmt.
Industries: Food/bev/tobacco, Paper, Soap/perfume/cosmetics, Drugs mfg., Consumer electronics, Entertainment, Mgmt. consulting

Meads & Assoc.
6700 S. Florida Ave., Ste. 4
Lakeland, Florida 33813
(941) 644-0411
Fax: (941) 647-3866
Web: www.meads.net

Key Contact - Specialty:
Mr. Walter F. Meads - *Advertising agencies*
Ms. Joyce Goheen - *Advertising agencies*

Description: Executive recruitment for advertising agencies. We work in all disciplines: management, account, creative, media, research, public relations, sales promotion, TV promotion, et al.
Functions: Advertising, PR
Industries: Advertising/PR

Meder & Assoc., Inc.
102 Wilmot Rd., Ste. 500
Deerfield, Illinois 60015
(847) 914-0200
Fax: (847) 914-0209

Key Contact - Specialty:
Mr. Peter F. Meder
Ms. Kathleen A. McCarthy
Ms. Laura Henzlik
Mr. Jerome B. Herb
Mr. William Wright
Ms. Camille Rudy
Mr. Christopher Bertchy
Ms. Anne Driscoll

Description: The firm engages in senior and executive level search for a wide variety of companies and professional service firms. Positions are normally associated with compensation levels above $100,000. The practice is national in scope of clients and search.

Salary Minimum: $100,000
Functions: Generalist, Senior mgmt., Production, Health admin., Mktg. mgmt., CFO's, Mgmt. consultants
Industries: Generalist, Energy/utilities, Food/bev/tobacco, Motor vehicles, Finance, Mgmt. consulting, Packaging

Media Management Resources, Inc. †
6464 S. Quebec
Englewood, Colorado 80111
(303) 290-9800
Fax: (303) 290-9596
Email: mwein@mediamanagement.com

Key Contact - Specialty:
Mr. Michael S. Wein

Description: International executive search firm specializing in middle and upper management in entertainment, entertainment delivery, information services and telecommunications.

Salary Minimum: $50,000
Functions: Senior mgmt., Engineering, Mgmt. consultants, Technicians
Industries: Broadcast & Film, Telecoms

Branches:
31B Gulf Breeze Pkwy.
Gulf Breeze, Florida 32561
(850) 934-4880
Fax: (850) 934-4756
Email: bwein@mediamanagement.com
Key Contact - Specialty:
Mr. William Wein

Affiliates:
Intelligent Management Solutions, Inc. (IMS)

Martin H. Meisel Assoc., Inc.
55 E. 87th St.
New York, New York 10128
(212) 369-4300

Key Contact - Specialty:
Martin H. Meisel - *Healthcare*
Norman Metzger - *Healthcare*

Description: Retainer search assignments limited to select group of clients. Research built search firm - emphasis presently in medical and healthcare fields.

Salary Minimum: $100,000
Functions: Physicians, Nurses, Allied health, Benefits, Personnel
Industries: Healthcare

Melancon & Co.
P.O. Box 2383
McKinney, Texas 75070-2383
(972) 231-9963

Key Contact - Specialty:
Mr. Robert M. Melancon - *Generalist*

Description: We specialize in the identification, recruitment and retention of key executive talent for mid and upper level management positions on a regional, national and international basis. Originally established over 25 years ago, the company has earned the reputation as one of the oldest and most highly regarded regional search firms in the Southwest.

Salary Minimum: $60,000
Functions: Generalist, General mgmt., Mfg., Mktg. mgmt., HR mgmt., Finance, Engineering
Industries: Generalist, Energy/utilities, Mfg., Finance, Svcs., High tech

---

Meng, Finseth & Assoc., Inc.
Del Amo Executive Plaza
3858 Carson St., Ste. 202
Torrance, California 90503
(310) 316-0706

Key Contact - Specialty:
Ms. Cameron E. Meng
Mr. Carl L. Finseth
Mr. Charles M. Meng
Ms. Marlene M. Rafferty
Ms. Diane Natvig

Description: Retainer search firm established 1970, serving broad range clientele - public and private sector.

Salary Minimum: $100,000
Functions: Senior mgmt., Physicians, Mkt. research, HR mgmt., CFO's, MIS mgmt., Non-profits
Industries: Energy/utilities, Hospitality, Higher ed., Accounting, Communications, Aerospace, Healthcare
Professional Associations: IACPR

Mercedes & Co., Inc.
(Firm declined to update.)
6 Whittier Place, Ste. #16-B
Boston, Massachusetts 02114-1400
(617) 227-4277
Email: mercedesco@sprynet.com

Key Contact - Specialty:
Ms. Linda Mercedes Correia
Ms. Randy Cabell

Description: Executive search practice which focuses on the following industries: biotechnology, medical devices and instrumentation, pharmaceutical, software, high technology and healthcare services. Personal and responsive attention to a national client base.

Salary Minimum: $100,000
Functions: Middle mgmt., Production, Mkt. research, CFO's, Systems anal., Engineering, Minorities
Industries: Drugs mfg., Consumer electronics, Pharmaceutical svcs., High tech, Software, Biotech, Healthcare

---

The Mercer Group, Inc.
535 Cordova Rd., Ste. 234
Santa Fe, New Mexico 87501
(505) 466-9500
Fax: (505) 466-1274
Email: mercer@mindspring.com
Web: www.mindspring.com/~mercer

Key Contact - Specialty:
Mr. James L. Mercer - *Government (state & local)*

Description: Specialize in public sector. Full-fledged management consulting firm offering services in strategy, market research, organization studies, organization development, executive search, compensation, et al.

Salary Minimum: $50,000
Functions: Senior mgmt., Personnel, Mgmt. consultants
Industries: Higher ed., Mgmt. consulting, Human resource svcs., Government

Branches:
5579B Chambler Dunwoody Rd., Ste. 511
Atlanta, Georgia 30338
(770) 551-0403
Fax: (770) 399-9749
Key Contact - Specialty:
James L. Mercer
Stephen D. Egan, Jr.

3036 Lake Lansing Rd.. Ste. 117
East Lansing, Michigan 48823
(517) 333-1781
Fax: (517) 332-2547
Key Contact - Specialty:
Mr. Thomas Dority

5667 Stone Rd.
Centerville, Virginia 20120
(703) 631-2718
Fax: (703) 803-7517
Key Contact - Specialty:
Mr. Gene Swearingen

MESA, Inc.
6019 Belmont Way
Parker, Colorado 80134
(303) 841-4512
Email: mesacook@aol.com

Key Contact - Specialty:
Mr. Dennis F. Cook - *Manufacturing, general industry, high technology*

Description: Superior executive search record in industrial companies for general management and senior management of all functional disciplines. Industrial, government and commercial sectors. Firm's principals are seasoned former industrial executives.

Salary Minimum: $90,000
Functions: Senior mgmt., Mfg., Materials, Mktg. mgmt., HR mgmt., MIS mgmt., Int'l.
Industries: Mfg., Metal products, Machinery/Appliances, Motor vehicles, Transportation, Aerospace, High tech

---

Messett Assoc., Inc.
7700 N. Kendall Drive, Ste. 304
Miami, Florida 33156
(305) 275-1000
Fax: (305) 274-4462
Email: messett@messett.com
Web: www.messett.com

Key Contact - Specialty:
Mr. William J. Messett, III - *Generalist (top level US domestic & int'l.)*

Description: We undertake executive searches, acquisitions, mergers, plus joint venture partner identification on a worldwide basis from our Miami headquarters and affiliate offices in US, Europe, Latin America and Asia. A partner in International Executive Search, Inc. (IES).

Salary Minimum: $75,000
Functions: Generalist, Senior mgmt., Sales & mktg., HR mgmt., CFO's, MIS mgmt., Int'l.
Industries: Generalist, Energy/utilities, Food/bev/tobacco, Drugs mfg., Finance, Insurance, Software

Affiliates:
Int'l. Executive Search, Inc.

META/MAT, Ltd.
2 Park Way & Rte. 17 S.
Upper Saddle River, New Jersey 07458
(201) 818-0101
Fax: (201) 818-6885

Key Contact - Specialty:
Mr. Fred Kopff

Description: We offer unusual depth and breadth of knowledge in finance, high technology and consumer products businesses.

Salary Minimum: $100,000
Functions: Generalist, Directors, Senior mgmt., Purchasing, CFO's, MIS mgmt., Engineering
Industries: Soap/perfume/cosmetics, Medical devices, Paints/petroleum products, Invest. banking, Pharmaceutical svcs., Human resource svcs., Telecoms

Walter Meyer & Assoc.
P.O. Box 133
Orchard Park, New York 14127-0133
(716) 662-0427

Key Contact - Specialty:
Mr. Walter E. Meyer - *Operating management*

Description: Small company oriented.

Salary Minimum: $50,000
Functions: Senior mgmt., Middle mgmt., Quality, Productivity, Materials Plng., Sales mgmt.
Industries: Medical devices, Metal products, Misc. mfg., Banking

Meyer Assoc., Inc.
5079 Riverhill Road
Marietta, Georgia 30068
(770) 565-2020

Key Contact - Specialty:
Mr. Rick M. Meyer - *Management consulting services, manufacturing, information technology*

Description: Our goal is straightforward - give to clients real value - we recognize that use of recruiting services is an investment that must produce exceptional returns and tangible benefits.

Salary Minimum: $75,000
Functions: Senior mgmt., Middle mgmt., Mfg., Plant mgmt., Mktg. mgmt., Mgmt. consultants
Industries: Generalist, Mgmt. consulting, Telecoms, Healthcare

Michael Assoc.
613 Poplar Ave.
Elmhurst, Illinois 60126
(630) 832-2550

Key Contact - Specialty:
Mr. Michael S. Golding - *Manufacturing, management, engineering*

Description: Searches for general management, specializing in manufacturing management, technical and engineering supervision and personnel.

Salary Minimum: $40,000
Functions: Middle mgmt., Product dev., Production, Purchasing, Materials Plng., Engineering, Architects
Industries: Construction, Mfg., Lumber/furniture, Plastics/rubber, Metal products, Machinery/Appliances, Misc. mfg.

Michigan Consulting Group
3037 Benjamin
Royal Oak, Michigan 48073
(810) 795-5687
Fax: (810) 795-5687

Key Contact - Specialty:
Mr. David E. Southworth - *Officers (CEO, COO, CFO, president), senior & general management, engineers, manufacturing, sales*
Ms. Kathy Palazzolo - *Manufacturing management, engineers, operations, senior & middle management (females, minorities)*
Mr. Pedro Salinas Gasga - *Manufacturing management, engineers, administration, operations, senior and middle management (Mexico, South and Central America)*
Mr. Jack Lynch - *Senior, operations, manufacturing management, sales management, engineering (Vietnam, China)*
Mr. Rich Krezo - *Stamping, metal forming management, engineers, manufacturing, sales*

Description: Consultants in executive search assisting Fortune 500 companies including automotive OEMs and Tier I, II and III suppliers, stamping and metal forming, plastics and rubber industry and general manufacturing. Provide related consulting services in interim senior managers, organizational restructuring and Greenfield projects.

Salary Minimum: $75,000
Functions: General mgmt., Senior mgmt., Mfg., Sales & mktg., CFO's, Engineering, Minorities
Industries: Generalist, Plastics/rubber, Metal products, Machinery/Appliances, Motor vehicles, Aerospace, Software

Affiliates:
Charles E. Day & Assoc., Inc.
Fred Gallagher & Associates
Midwest Consulting

Millar Walker & Gay
379 Dundas St. E., 2nd Floor
Toronto, Ontario M5A 2A6
Canada
(416) 365-7818
Fax: (416) 368-6716
Email: mwgmt@idirect.com

Key Contact - Specialty:
Mr. James G. Millar - *Corporate finance*
Mr. Warren T. Walker - *Accounting*

Description: Specialists in accounting and corporate finance including banking, investment banking, merger acquisition, valuation, fixed income and taxation. We have successful searches as far away as Russia, UK, USA and Canada.

Salary Minimum: $50,000
Functions: CFO's, Budgeting, Cash mgmt., Credit, Taxes, M&A, Risk mgmt.
Industries: Generalist, Agri/forestry/mining, Banking, Invest. banking, Brokers, Venture cap., Real estate

Millennium Search Group, Inc.
4025 Camino del Rio S., Ste. 300
San Diego, California 92108
(619) 542-7777
Fax: (619) 542-7773
Web: www.msgiusa.com

Key Contact - Specialty:
Mr. David M. Ferrara - *Management consulting*
Mr. Bryan L. Gragg - *Management consulting*
Mr. Stephen J. Abkin - *Management consulting*

Description: Retained executive search firm specializing exclusively in placement of senior-level management consultants (partners, vice presidents, principals, senior managers).

Salary Minimum: $100,000
Functions: Directors, Senior mgmt., Personnel, Systems anal., Systems dev., Systems implem., Mgmt. consultants
Industries: Mfg., Retail, Finance, Mgmt. consulting, Communications, High tech, Healthcare

Million & Assoc., Inc.
Carew Tower, Ste. 1831
Cincinnati, Ohio 45202
(513) 579-8770

Key Contact - Specialty:
Mr. Ken Million
Ms. Kim Kramer

Description: Search and recruitment for executive, managerial, professional and technical talent for all types of industries, banking and financial organizations and hospital and healthcare industries, exclusively for clients.

Salary Minimum: $40,000
Functions: Generalist
Industries: Generalist

Milo Research

60 E. 42nd St., Ste. 1762
New York, New York 10165
(212) 972-2780
Fax: (212) 983-5854
Email: miloresearch@msn.com

Key Contact - Specialty:
Mr. Lance M. Goulbourne

Description: We are a full service research and executive recruiting firm specializing in the recruitment of middle and senior level management professionals.

Salary Minimum: $50,000
Functions: Generalist, Middle mgmt., Sales mgmt., Direct mktg., HR mgmt., MIS mgmt., Minorities
Industries: Generalist, Mfg., Finance, Svcs., Communications, Telecoms, High tech

---

Mims & Associates

4615 Post Oak Place, Ste. 140
Houston, Texas 77027
(713) 877-8402
Email: ssmims@msn.com

Key Contact - Specialty:
Mr. Stephen S. Mims - *Law*

Description: Former practicing attorney engaged in retained search for senior level attorneys since 1984.

Salary Minimum: $60,000
Functions: Attorneys
Industries: Legal

Herbert Mines Assoc., Inc.

375 Park Ave., Ste. 301
New York, New York 10152
(212) 355-0909

Key Contact - Specialty:
Mr. Herbert Mines
Mr. Harold Reiter
Ms. Jane Vergari
Ms. Elaine Gilbert
Ms. Linda Pettibone
Mr. Howard Gross
Mr. Robert Nahas
Mr. Brian Meany
Ms. Maxine Martens
Ms. Barbara North
Ms. Tracey Levine
Ms. Kristin Dennehy
Ms. Kate Benson
Ms. Emily Shannon
Ms. Anne Loftus

Description: Consulting services and retainer search for senior management for retail, direct marketing, textiles, specialty food, cosmetics, fashion manufacturing and consumer businesses. Clients range from small to multi-billion dollar conglomerates. Over 80% of assignments are from existing clients.

Salary Minimum: $100,000
Functions: Directors, Senior mgmt., Admin. svcs., Product dev., Production, Plant mgmt., Quality, Productivity, Advertising, Mkt. research, Mktg. mgmt., Sales mgmt., Direct mktg., PR, HR mgmt., CFO's, MIS mgmt., Mgmt. consultants, Graphic artists, Int'l.
Industries: Food/bev/tobacco, Textiles/apparel, Soap/perfume/cosmetics, Wholesale, Retail, Hospitality, Entertainment, Non-profits, Mgmt. consulting, Human resource svcs., Advertising/PR, Real estate
Professional Associations: AESC

Affiliates:
Floriane de Saint Pierre
International Management Consultants

Mirtz Morice, Inc.

One Dock St., 3rd Floor
Stamford, Connecticut 06902
(203) 964-9266
Fax: (203) 324-3925

Key Contact - Specialty:
Mr. P. John Mirtz - *Generalist*
Mr. James L. Morice - *Generalist*

Description: Beyond executive recruiting, certain consulting services are provided that relate to, support and enhance the search practice. Included are assignments related to management organization and succession planning and compensation.

Salary Minimum: $100,000
Functions: Generalist, Senior mgmt., Mktg. mgmt., Personnel, CFO's, MIS mgmt., Mgmt. consultants
Industries: Generalist, Food/bev/tobacco, Soap/perfume/cosmetics, Hospitality, Mgmt. consulting, Human resource svcs., Insurance

---

Laurie Mitchell & Co., Inc. †

25018 Hazelmere Rd.
Cleveland, Ohio 44122-3241
(216) 292-6001

Key Contact - Specialty:
Ms. Laurie Mitchell - *Advertising, public relations, consumer marketing*

Description: Serving corporate, agency and individual needs with discretion and integrity. Bundled or unbundled search services in public relations, marketing communications, financial communications, advertising and sales promotion.

Salary Minimum: $35,000
Functions: Advertising, Mkt. research, Mktg. mgmt., Direct mktg., PR
Industries: Generalist, Communications, Advertising/PR, Publishing, New media

---

Mitchell/Wolfson, Assoc.

600 Central Ave., Ste. 375
Highland Park, Illinois 60035
(708) 266-0600

Key Contact - Specialty:
Mr. Robert H. Wolfson - *Insurance, actuarial, risk management*

Description: Within the insurance industry, we work with primary carriers, reinsurers, brokerage firms, consultants and corporate risk management.

Salary Minimum: $100,000
Functions: Benefits, Risk mgmt.
Industries: Insurance

MIXTEC Group

31255 Cedar Valley Drive, Ste. 327-317
Westlake Village, California 91362
(818) 889-8819
Fax: (818) 889-9025
Email: mixtec@mixtec.net
Web: mixtec.net

Key Contact - Specialty:
Dr. Ward A. Fredericks - *Food, top management*
Mr. William Heintz - *Produce, packaged food*
Mr. Christopher Nelson - *Produce, packaged fresh cut produce*
Ms. Joyce Cripe - *Healthcare*
Ms. Julie Spiedel - *Research direction*
Mr. Peter May - *Sales & marketing*
Mr. Ted Thiras - *Food service distribution*
Mr. Jerry Knotts - *Technology*
Mr. John Donnelly - *Packaged food*
Mr. Jay Holford - *Citrus, produce*

Description: Specialists in senior search in the food, produce, food service, medical and technology driven industries. Our search efforts are based on in-depth knowledge of industry sectors based on top management experience.

Salary Minimum: $80,000
Functions: Generalist, Directors, Senior mgmt., Production, Mktg. mgmt., Sales mgmt., CFO's
Industries: Generalist, Food/bev/tobacco, Packaging, Biotech, Healthcare

Branches:
13626 Tierra Spur
Salinas, California 93906
(408) 484-9391
Key Contact - Specialty:
Mr. William Heintz - *Produce, packaged foods industry*

P.O. Box 662
Vero Beach, Florida 32961
(407) 569-3220
Key Contact - Specialty:
Mr. Jay Holford - *Food industry*

MK & Assoc.
775 E. Blithedale, #351
Mill Valley, California 94941
(415) 389-5994
Fax: (415) 389-5993
Email: mkennedy@mkandassociates.com
Web: mkandassociates.com

Key Contact - Specialty:
Mr. Mike Kennedy - *Software, networking*
Ms. Sharon Kennedy - *Software, networking*

Description: Consulting organization focused on executive and middle management search requirements for software and high technology companies with emphasis on growth planning and organizational development. Execute middle and upper level searches for software and high technology companies.

Salary Minimum: $100,000
Functions: Directors, Senior mgmt., Middle mgmt.
Industries: High tech, Software

Moffitt Int'l., Inc.
Park Terrace Ctr., Ste. 1316A
Asheville, North Carolina 28806
(704) 251-4550
Fax: (704) 251-4555
Email: moffitt@aol.com
Web: www.moffittsearch.com

Key Contact - Specialty:
Mr. Timothy D. Moffitt - *Generalist*
Mr. James Vockley - *Generalist*

Description: An internationally recognized, research-based generalist firm with strong market niches.

Salary Minimum: $75,000
Functions: Generalist, Senior mgmt., Physicians, HR mgmt., CFO's, IT, Engineering
Industries: Generalist, Construction, Drugs mfg., Finance, Real estate, Software, Healthcare

Branches:
6 Commerce Drive, Ste. 2000
Cranford, New Jersey 07016
(908) 709-1680
Fax: (908) 709-8946
Key Contact - Specialty:
Mr. Joe Mrozek - *Generalist*

Affiliates:
Condicio Arnfrid Wuttke & Co., GMBH
MBTT/MII

Molloy Partners
340 Broadway
Saratoga Springs, New York 12866
(518) 581-2532
Fax: (518) 581-2832
Email: tom@molloypartners.com

Key Contact - Specialty:
Mr. Thomas Molloy - *Senior level, higher education, senior level finance, marketing*

Description: We are engaged by both corporate clients and colleges/universities. On the corporate side we specialize in sales, marketing, finance and manufacturing. In higher education we are retained for senior level assignments in fundraising, public relations, finance and administration.

Salary Minimum: $75,000
Functions: Directors, Senior mgmt., Sales mgmt., HR mgmt., CFO's, MIS mgmt., Non-profits
Industries: Higher ed., Human resource svcs., High tech, Software, Healthcare

---

Oscar Montaño, Inc.
200 N. Glendora Ave., Ste. J
Glendora, California 91741
(626) 335-7342
Fax: (626) 335-8683
Email: oscwmon@aol.com

Key Contact - Specialty:
Mr. Oscar W. Montaño - *Consumer finance, automotive*

Description: Specializing in consumer and automotive finance, we provide the complete search process plus industry knowledge. We also do salary surveys, organizational consulting and specialized outplacement.

Salary Minimum: $80,000
Functions: Senior mgmt., Sales mgmt., CFO's, Budgeting, Credit, M&A, Risk mgmt.
Industries: Transportation, Banking, Misc. financial, Accounting, Mgmt. consulting

---

Montenido Assoc.
481 Cold Canyon Rd.
Calabasas, California 91302-2204
(818) 222-2744
(805) 373-7500
Fax: (805) 373-5531
Email: swolf@bli-inc.com

Key Contact - Specialty:
Mr. Stephen M. Wolf - *High technology, information technology*

Description: Perform middle and upper level searches for the computer hardware/software, financial services and professional services industries. Specialize in nationwide staffing for field marketing, including sales and technical support for high technology start-ups.

Salary Minimum: $75,000
Functions: Senior mgmt., Mktg. mgmt., Sales mgmt., MIS mgmt., Systems anal., Systems implem., Mgmt. consultants
Industries: Computer equip., Entertainment, Computer svcs., Mgmt. consulting, New media, High tech, Software

---

Montgomery West
99 Almaden Blvd., Ste. 600
San Jose, California 95113
(408) 292-9876
Fax: (408) 292-2127
Email: info@mwest.sanjose.com
Web: www.montgomerywest.com

Key Contact - Specialty:
Mr. Greg Goodere - *High technology, sales & marketing, finance, human resources, engineering*
Ms. Barbara Estrada - *High technology, public sector, healthcare, biotechnology, multimedia*
Ms. Cesca Cecilio - *Generalist, high technology, entertainment, advertising, diversity*
Ms. Lina Fafard - *Information technology, CIO, software, diversity*

Description: We use a creative approach to identifying and recruiting senior level executives in multiple industries and functions. Dedicated to client satisfaction, quality and results, with a commitment to diversity.

Salary Minimum: $100,000
Functions: General mgmt., Sales & mktg., HR mgmt., Finance, IT, R&D, Minorities
Industries: Generalist, Mfg., Finance, Communications, Government, High tech, Healthcare

Branches:
595 Market St., Ste. 1100
San Francisco, California 94105
(415) 905-1133
Fax: (415) 905-1132
Email: info@mwest.sanfrancisco.com
Key Contact - Specialty:
Mr. Robert Gragg - *Consumer, finance, human resources, marketing, procurement*

Thomas R. Moore Executive Search
2000 E. Lamar St., Ste. 600
Bank of America Bldg.
Arlington, Texas 76006
(817) 548-8766

Key Contact - Specialty:
Mr. Thomas R. Moore - *Non-profit institutions (development/advancement)*

Description: Executive recruiting service

specializing in development personnel. This service is offered to gift-supported institutions seeking executive staff personnel in development, public relations, planned giving, alumni affairs, annual support and foundation management.

Salary Minimum: $50,000
Functions: Direct mktg., Non-profits
Industries: Non-profits, Higher ed., Healthcare

Moore Research Assoc.

25 Karena Lane
Lawrenceville, New Jersey 08648
(609) 844-0020
Fax: (609) 844-0030
Email: sandeeMRA@aol.com

Key Contact - Specialty:
Ms. Sandee Moore - *Healthcare, pharmaceutical, manufacturing, engineering*

Description: Full-service search research firm. Name generation, candidate development and market research skills available

Salary Minimum: $50,000
Functions: General mgmt., Mfg., Materials, Healthcare, Sales & mktg., R&D, Engineering
Industries: Generalist, Energy/utilities, Mfg., Finance, Communications, Biotech, Healthcare

Morgan Int'l., Inc.

551 Crest Court
Lake Forest, Illinois 60045
(847) 615-8660
Fax: (847) 615-8629
Email: blayton2@ix.netcom.com

Key Contact - Specialty:
Mr. Bernard Layton - *Construction, engineering, pharmaceutical, biotechnology*

Salary Minimum: $100,000
Functions: Directors, Production, Purchasing, Physicians, Sales mgmt., CFO's
Industries: Construction, Food/bev/tobacco, Chemicals, Medical devices, Mgmt. consulting, Software, Biotech

Morgan Samuels Co.
(a division of Executive Decision Int'l., LLC)

9171 Wilshire Blvd., Ste. 428
Beverly Hills, California 90210
(310) 278-9660
Fax: (310) 278-2878
Email: bhensley@executive-decisions.com

Key Contact - Specialty:
Mr. Bert C. Hensley - *Generalist*
Mr. Lew Samuels - *Engineering, construction, oil & gas, energy utilities*
Mr. Richard Morgan - *Engineering, construction, oil & gas, petroleum, energy utilities*
Mr. Will Gates - *Healthcare, information technology, consumer products, entertainment*
Ms. Stephanie Davis - *Financial services, high technology, healthcare*
Ms. Nancy Schlect - *Construction, environmental, energy, utilities, petroleum*
Mr. Chip James - *Entertainment, high technology, information technology, real estate, telecommunications*
Mr. Daniel Johnson - *Entertainment, financial services, high technology, information technology, legal*
Ms. Christine Borkenhagen - *Consumer products, entertainment, financial services, hospitality, telecommunications*

Description: We are a boutique firm which applies a consultative approach to recruit senior level management for the following industries: engineering and construction, real estate, environmental, financial services, manufacturing, information technology, healthcare and entertainment.

Salary Minimum: $90,000
Functions: Senior mgmt., Allied health, Sales & mktg., HR mgmt., Finance, Engineering, Mgmt. consultants
Industries: Energy/utilities, Construction, Mfg., Transportation, Environmental svcs., Aerospace, Real estate

Morgan/Webber, Inc.

(Firm declined to update.)
5510 Merrick Rd.
Massapequa, New York 11758
(516) 799-2650
Email: lavsearch@juno.com

Key Contact - Specialty:
Mr. Steven M. Lavender - *Generalist*

Description: We tailor our searches to the style, needs and culture of our clients. We bring two decades of successful executive search and consulting to facilitate clients needs, large and small.

Salary Minimum: $75,000
Functions: General mgmt., Mfg., Sales & mktg., HR mgmt., IT, Specialized services, Int'l.
Industries: Generalist, Entertainment, Advertising/PR, Publishing, Broadcast & Film, High tech, Biotech

Moriarty/Fox, Inc.

20 N. Wacker Drive, Ste. 2410
Chicago, Illinois 60606
(312) 332-4600

Key Contact - Specialty:
Mr. Philip S. J. Moriarty
Mr. J. Thomas Kenny

Description: We have prided ourselves on establishing long and productive professional relationships with our many and varied client organizations. We are interested in helping our clients grow.

Salary Minimum: $75,000
Functions: Generalist
Industries: Generalist

Affiliates:
Robert Sellery Assoc., Ltd.

Morris & Berger

201 S. Lake Ave., Ste. 700
Pasadena, California 91101
(626) 795-0522
Fax: (626) 795-6330

Key Contact - Specialty:
Ms. Kristine A. Morris
Mr. Jay V. Berger

Description: Retained, generalist executive search firm with specialty practice in non-profit sector including academic, arts, social services, foundations. Other clients range from start-up, privately held to Fortune 500 corporations.

Salary Minimum: $50,000
Functions: Generalist, Directors, Senior mgmt., Middle mgmt., Mktg. mgmt., CFO's, Non-profits
Industries: Generalist, Misc. mfg., Misc. financial, Non-profits, Higher ed., Government

Morton, McCorkle & Assoc. Inc.

2190 S. Mason Rd., Ste. 309
St. Louis, Missouri 63131-1637
(314) 984-9494
Fax: (314) 984-9460
Email: mmacnslt@aol.com

Key Contact - Specialty:
Mr. Sam B. McCorkle
Mr. R. C. Morton
Mr. John F. Truex

Description: Upper level retained search encompassing most all functions and industries. International in scope with emphasis on general management, marketing and other key line positions. Twenty-six years of exceptional performance.

Salary Minimum: $70,000
Functions: Generalist, Senior mgmt., Plant mgmt., Materials, R&D, Engineering, Int'l.
Industries: Generalist, Agri/forestry/mining, Food/bev/tobacco, Chemicals, Machinery/Appliances, Packaging, Biotech

Moss & Co.
12145 Arrow Point Loop
Bainbridge Island, Washington 98110
(206) 842-4035

Key Contact - Specialty:
Ms. Barbara Moss - *Real estate development, construction, property management*

Description: We are unique in that we charge only by the hour. It typically takes an average of 65 hours to complete a search. Clients can start and stop the process at any time, maintaining their control and keeping costs to a mininum.

Salary Minimum: $40,000
Functions: Engineering, Architects
Industries: Construction, Real estate

Branches:
14747 Henderson Rd. NE
Bainbridge Island, Washington 98110
(206) 855-8300
Key Contact - Specialty:
Ms. Theresa Torseth

6358 NE 151st St.
Kenmore, Washington 98011-4388
(425) 402-7095
Key Contact - Specialty:
Mr. Jeff Harris

13816 NE 87th St.
Redmond, Washington 98052
(425) 869-6622
Key Contact - Specialty:
Ms. Wanda Ross

1116 NW 83rd St.
Seattle, Washington 98117
(206) 781-7062
Key Contact - Specialty:
Ms. Teri Thompson

19232 Ridge Rd. SW
Vashon, Washington 98070
(206) 463-1694
Key Contact - Specialty:
Ms. Kirsten Jennings

Moyer, Sherwood Assoc., Inc.
1285 Ave. of the Americas, 35th Floor
New York, New York 10019
(212) 554-4008

Key Contact - Specialty:
Mr. David S. Moyer - *Corporate communications, public relations*

Description: We offer highly personal service, rooted in the combination of three approaches: traditional, thorough, confidential executive search consulting; modern, computer-based methodology and a commitment to creativity in our search work.

Salary Minimum: $90,000
Functions: PR
Industries: Generalist, Advertising/PR, New media

Branches:
65 High Ridge Rd., Ste. 502
Stamford, Connecticut 06905
(203) 656-2220
Key Contact - Specialty:
Ms. Margaret L. O'Donnell

Affiliates:
Redden-Shaffer Group

MPA Executive Search Inc.
7900 Blvd. Taschereau Ouest
Bureau A-204
Brossard, Quebec J4X 1C2
Canada
(514) 875-3996
(450) 465-6998
Fax: (450) 465-9215
Email: courrier@mparechdecadres.qc.ca
Web: www.mparechdecadres.dc.ca

Key Contact - Specialty:
Mr. Marc Paquet - *Generalist*

Description: We specialize in the search of intermediate and executive level personnel. Strong experience in engineering and manufacturing.

Salary Minimum: $40,000
Functions: Generalist, Production, Distribution, Sales mgmt., Personnel, Taxes, Engineering
Industries: Generalist, Textiles/apparel, Transportation, Human resource svcs., Haz. waste, High tech, Healthcare

Mruk & E.M.A. Partners
230 Park Ave., Ste. 1000
New York, New York 10169
(212) 808-3076
Email: emruk@chcn.org

Key Contact - Specialty:
Mr. Edwin S. Mruk - *Board of directors, general management, healthcare*
Ms. Carol Buckner - *Law firm administration*

Salary Minimum: $100,000
Functions: Directors, Plant mgmt., Health admin., Mktg. mgmt., CFO's, Systems dev., Attorneys
Industries: Generalist
Professional Associations: AESC

Networks:
EMA Partners Int'l.

MSA Executive Search
(a division of MMI Companies)
MSA Bldg., Ste. 300
4801 Cliff Ave.
Independence, Missouri 64055
(816) 373-9988
Fax: (816) 478-1929
Email: jgroves@mgmtscience.com
Web: www.mgmtscience.com

Key Contact - Specialty:
Ms. Jane Groves - *Healthcare executives*

Description: Firm is largest employee relations/human resource consulting firm in healthcare industry. This division provides executive search for retained clients only. Provides in depth executive assessment and candidate profiles.
Functions: Health admin., Mgmt. consultants
Industries: Human resource svcs., Insurance, Healthcare

MTA Partners
2828 W. Parker Rd., #207
Plano, Texas 75075
(972) 758-8646
Web: mwtucker@airmail.net

Key Contact - Specialty:
Mr. Michael Tucker - *Healthcare*
Mr. Jim Henry - *Healthcare*
Ms. Marsha Murphy - *Healthcare*
Mr. Roger Toney - *Healthcare*
Ms. Sandy Bradley - *Healthcare*
Ms. Angie Kirkman - *Healthcare*

Description: Retained healthcare firm for all levels.

Salary Minimum: $75,000
Functions: Directors, Senior mgmt., Middle mgmt., Mktg. mgmt., Sales mgmt., Non-profits
Industries: Drugs mfg., Medical devices, Pharmaceutical svcs., Biotech, Healthcare

Much & Co.
237 Park Ave., Park Ave. Atrium
New York, New York 10017
(212) 551-3578
(212) 217-0600
Fax: (212) 217-0613
Email: muchandco@aol.com

Key Contact - Specialty:
Mr. Isaac Much - *Global investment management, investment strategy, investment research, investment banking*

Description: Financial services, worldwide: specializing in investment management, investment research and investment banking in all the major financial capitals and in the emerging markets.

Salary Minimum: $200,000
Functions: CFO's, Cash mgmt., M&A, Risk mgmt.
Industries: Invest. banking, Brokers, Venture cap., New media, Telecoms, Insurance, Biotech

Mullen Assoc., Inc.
65 Community Rd., P.O. Box 365
Pinehurst, North Carolina 28370
(910) 295-0077
Fax: (910) 295-4419

Key Contact - Specialty:
Mr. James J. Mullen - *Paint & coatings, specialty chemicals, ink, adhesives*
Mr. Lawrence C. Fisher - *Paint & coatings, specialty chemicals, ink, adhesives*

Description: Retained only - boutique type firm - highly personalized service never more than six on-going searches.

Salary Minimum: $85,000
Functions: Generalist, General mgmt., Mfg., Sales & mktg., R&D
Industries: Generalist, Printing, Chemicals, Plastics/rubber, Paints/petroleum products, Packaging

Pamela L. Mulligan, Inc.

56 Hopkins Green Rd.
Hopkinton, New Hampshire 03229
(603) 226-2262
Fax: (603) 226-2212

Key Contact - Specialty:
Ms. Pamela L. Mulligan - *Managed care, healthcare, insurance*

Description: Recruiting expertise in managed care and insurance (to include direct marketing, TPA, special risk and employee benefits). Functional titles and areas include: sales, marketing, underwriting, claims, systems, human resources, medical directors, CFO, psychiatrists, utilization and care management and operations.

Salary Minimum: $60,000
Functions: Senior mgmt., Nurses, Mktg. mgmt., Sales mgmt., CFO's, MIS mgmt., Systems implem.
Industries: Insurance, High tech, Healthcare

The Mulshine Co., Inc.

2517 Rte. 35, Ste. D-201
Manasquan, New Jersey 08736
(732) 528-8585
Fax: (732) 223-9803
Email: mulshine@monmouth.com

Key Contact - Specialty:
Mr. Michael A. Mulshine

Description: Dedicated to search for general and middle management and senior individual contributors in R&D, engineering, manufacturing, document management, accounting, finance, venture capital and emerging high tech companies.

Salary Minimum: $70,000
Functions: General mgmt., Mfg., Materials, Sales & mktg., IT, Engineering, Specialized services
Industries: Generalist, Chemicals, Computer equip., Finance, Aerospace, High tech, Software

Affiliates:
The Mulshine Company, Ltd.

The Mulshine Company, Ltd.

48 Helen Drive
Queensbury, New York 12804
(518) 743-9301
Email: mulshine@interpcs.net

Key Contact - Specialty:
Mr. Michael G. Mulshine

Description: Fifteen year's experience in specialized scientific and R&D, packaging, product and process development, engineering and manufacturing oriented searches to VP levels for the consumer brands, pharmaceutical, biotech and food industries.

Salary Minimum: $50,000
Functions: Senior mgmt., Middle mgmt., Product dev., Automation, Packaging, R&D, Engineering
Industries: Food/bev/tobacco, Chemicals, Soap/perfume/cosmetics, Drugs mfg., Plastics/rubber, Packaging, Biotech

Affiliates:
The Mulshine Co., Inc.

Multi Processing, Inc.

20 Crown Hill Rd.
Atkinson, New Hampshire 03811
(603) 362-6300
Fax: (603) 362-8844
Email: jvito@multiprocessing.com

Key Contact - Specialty:
Mr. Joseph Vito - *Senior engineering, sales & marketing (senior)*

Description: Recruiting professionals for computer development; hardware and software; sales marketing and end user applications development.

Salary Minimum: $60,000
Functions: Directors, Senior mgmt., Mktg. mgmt., Sales mgmt., MIS mgmt., Systems anal., Engineering
Industries: Computer svcs., Communications, New media, Broadcast & Film, Telecoms, High tech, Software

R. F. Mulvaney & Assoc., Inc.

10420 Old Olive, Ste. 112
St. Louis, Missouri 63141-5937
(314) 993-3222
Fax: (314) 993-3528
Email: mulvaney@ix.netcom.com

Key Contact - Specialty:
Mr. Ronald F. Mulvaney - *Manufacturing, managed healthcare*

Description: Established in 1974 serving national clients at search for mid and executive levels. Specialize in manufacturing, managed healthcare and managed mental healthcare.

Salary Minimum: $60,000
Functions: Senior mgmt., Middle mgmt., Plant mgmt., Health admin.
Industries: Chemicals, Plastics/rubber, Metal products, Machinery/Appliances, Misc. mfg., Healthcare

Jennifer Munro & Partners, Inc.

33 Normandy Rd.
Greenville, South Carolina 29615
(864) 268-6482
Fax: (864) 268-7137
Email: jlmunro10@aol.com

Key Contact - Specialty:
Ms. Jennifer Munro - *Capital management, finance, banking*

Description: Specialize in performance-driven companies; strong emphasis on behavioral as well as functional compatibility.

Salary Minimum: $100,000
Functions: Senior mgmt., Middle mgmt., Plant mgmt., Mktg. mgmt., Sales mgmt., Cash mgmt., MIS mgmt.
Industries: Generalist, Construction, Invest. banking, Brokers, Hospitality, Broadcast & Film, High tech

Munroe, Curry & Bond Assoc.
(a division of Associated Business Consultants, Inc.)

43 North Main St.
P.O. Box 1299
Medford, New Jersey 08055
(609) 953-8600

Key Contact - Specialty:
Ms. M. Louise Milnes
Ms. Delores Bond
Mr. David W. Deming
Mr. Mike Bastian
Mr. Michael P. Harkins
Mr. Gerald Curry
Mr. Michael Munroe

Description: Unique and creative approach, hourly billing, 3-year placement guarantee, 98% retention rate over 3-year period. Candidate assessment includes extensive face-to-face interactive testing to skim the top 2%. The process guarantees market share increase when combining sales search with sales force assessment.

Salary Minimum: $65,000
Functions: Directors, Senior mgmt., Middle mgmt., Product dev., Automation, R&D, Engineering
Industries: Drugs mfg., Medical devices, Biotech

P. J. Murphy & Assoc., Inc.

735 N. Water St.
Milwaukee, Wisconsin 53202
(414) 277-9777
Fax: (414) 277-7626
Web: www.pjmurphy.com

Key Contact - Specialty:
Dr. Patrick J. Murphy - *General management*
Mr. Craig S. Zaffrann
Mr. James F. Zahradka - *Physicians, healthcare executives*
Mr. Kurt J. Thomas

Description: Established firm; retainer only; considerable work with boards in selecting senior people; national in scope.

Salary Minimum: $60,000
Functions: Generalist, Directors, Senior mgmt., Physicians, Sales & mktg., HR mgmt., CFO's
Industries: Generalist

Murphy Partners Int'l.

956 Shoreline Rd.
Barrington, Illinois 60010
(847) 304-1599
Fax: (847) 304-1844
Email: murphy@mpivips.com

Key Contact - Specialty:
Mr. Bob Murphy - *Directors, senior management, CFOs, mergers & acquisitions, international*
Ms. V. Kolacia - *Hospitality, higher education, accounting, entertainment, insurance*
Ms. K. Froelich - *Food, paper, chemicals, drugs, computer equipment*

Description: High level, high quality search practice with focus on personal service. President was partner with Big 6 accounting firm. He has 24+ years search experience; been responsible for over 900 engagements; significant, 150+ international assignments.

Salary Minimum: $100,000
Functions: Generalist, Distribution, Mktg. mgmt., HR mgmt., Taxes, MIS mgmt., Mgmt. consultants
Industries: Generalist, Retail, Real estate, High tech, Software, Biotech, Healthcare

Mycoff & Assoc.

26689 Pleasant Park Rd., Ste. 260
Conifer, Colorado 80433
(303) 838-7445
Fax: (303) 838-7428
Email: mail@mycoffassociates.com
Web: www.MycoffAssociates.com

Key Contact - Specialty:
Mr. Carl A. Mycoff

Description: Specialists in executive search for electric, natural gas, telecommunications and water industries.

Salary Minimum: $70,000
Functions: Senior mgmt., Middle mgmt., Mktg. mgmt., CFO's, Cash mgmt., MIS mgmt., Engineering
Industries: Energy/utilities, Telecoms

DDJ Myers, Ltd.

2303 N. 44th St., #14-400
Phoenix, Arizona 85008
(602) 840-9595
(800) 574-8877
Fax: (602) 840-6486
Email: deedeem@ddjmyers-ltd.com
Web: www.ddjmyers-ltd.com

Key Contact - Specialty:
Ms. Deedee Myers - *Treasury management, finance, interest rate risk, asset & liability, securitization*

Description: We provide executive recruiting, career pathing and succession planning for financial executives. Financial organizations use our services for internal and external searches, development and execution of career management processes and comprehensive succession plans.
Functions: Senior mgmt., HR mgmt., CFO's, Cash mgmt., Risk mgmt., IT
Industries: Transportation, Banking, Invest. banking, Brokers, Equip. svcs., Mgmt. consulting, Human resource svcs.

Branches:
331 Shawmut Ave., 2nd Floor
Boston, Massachusetts 02118
(617) 267-2141
Fax: (617) 267-4829
Key Contact - Specialty:
Mr. John Myers - *Treasury management, finance, interest rate risk, asset & liability, securitization*

Nadzam, Lusk, Horgan & Assoc., Inc.

3211 Scott Blvd., Ste. 205
Santa Clara, California 95054-3091
(408) 727-6601
Fax: (408) 727-6605
Email: @nlh.com

Key Contact - Specialty:
Mr. Richard J. Nadzam
Mr. Thomas F. Horgan
Mr. J. Kevin Day

Description: Consultants to corporate management in executive search, primarily for technology companies, i.e., electronics, information technology, healthcare manufacturing and aerospace. Clients range from Fortune 50 to start-up new technology companies.

Salary Minimum: $120,000
Functions: General mgmt., Mfg., Sales & mktg., HR mgmt., IT, Engineering, Int'l.
Industries: Mfg., Communications, Aerospace, High tech, Software, Biotech, Healthcare
Professional Associations: AESC

Nagler, Robins & Poe, Inc.

65 William St.
Wellesley, Massachusetts 02481-3802
(781) 431-1330
Email: jpoe@nrpinc.com
Web: www.nrpinc.com

Key Contact - Specialty:
Mr. Leon G. Nagler - *Consulting, financial services, manufacturing*
Ms. Jeri N. Robins - *Consulting, consumer products, marketing, sales*
Mr. James B. Poe - *Technology*

Description: Servicing clients nationally from offices in Boston and Chicago. A 20+ year record of quickly meeting client needs coupled with one of the highest success rates in the search industry.

Salary Minimum: $100,000
Functions: Generalist
Industries: Generalist, Misc. mfg., Finance, Mgmt. consulting, New media, High tech, Software

Affiliates:
The Hetzel Group, Inc.

National Restaurant Search, Inc. †

135 Beech Tree Lane, Ste. 100
Roswell, Georgia 30075
(770) 650-1800
Email: headhunter@sisna.com

Key Contact - Specialty:
Mr. John W. Chitvanni - *Restaurant executives*

Description: Corporate - work exclusively in the restaurant/hospitality industry. Assignments include president, CEO, COO, finance, franchising, real estate and construction, marketing, human resources and operations at the executive level. All NRS executives have restaurant/hotel operations experience.

Salary Minimum: $50,000
Functions: Generalist
Industries: Hospitality, Entertainment

Branches:
617 N. Tyler Rd., Ste. 100
St. Charles, Illinois 60174
(630) 584-8448
Key Contact - Specialty:
Mr. Ronald F. Stockman

National Search, Inc.

(Firm declined to update.)
514 Daniels St., Ste. 350
Raleigh, North Carolina 27605
(919) 460-9000

Email: mailhost@nasearch.com

Key Contact - Specialty:
Mr. Marshall E. Molliver - *Pesticides, specialty chemicals, inorganic chemicals*

Description: Thorough investigative searches to find and recruit the most qualified people. Most of our business is repeat business with corporations in our specialization.

Salary Minimum: $80,000
Functions: General mgmt., Mfg., Sales & mktg., R&D, Engineering
Industries: Chemicals, Drugs mfg., Medical devices

Affiliates:
Executech
SilverCrest Search

NDI Services
43000 Nine Mile Rd.
Novi, Michigan 48375
(248) 348-8040
Fax: (248) 348-8276

Key Contact - Specialty:
Mr. David Kosteva - *Healthcare finance, purchasing (all industries)*

Description: Human resources consulting firm with specialization in HR planning, executive search and database management. Administrator - HFMA Exec-u-Trak, NAPM Employment Services.

Salary Minimum: $50,000
Functions: Purchasing, Health admin.
Industries: Generalist, Healthcare

The Neil Michael Group, Inc./ Global Partners
350 Fifth Ave., Ste. 2711
New York, New York 10118
(212) 631-0999
Fax: (212) 631-0011
Email: neils@idt.net

Key Contact - Specialty:
Dr. Neil M. Solomon
Mr. Alfred Middleton - *Board searches*
Mr. Andrew R. Newcorn

Description: Retainer search firm with special emphasis in healthcare and biotechnology. Extensive focus on emerging growth companies. Broad investment banking and venture capital relationships. International capabilities.

Salary Minimum: $100,000
Functions: Directors, Senior mgmt., Product dev., Mktg. mgmt., Sales mgmt., CFO's, R&D
Industries: Soap/perfume/cosmetics, Drugs mfg., Medical devices, Venture cap., Pharmaceutical svcs., Biotech, Healthcare

Affiliates:
Pact & Partners Int'l.
Ruston Poole International, Ltd.

Networks:
Global Partners

J. Fielding Nelson & Assoc., Inc.
(Firm declined to update.)
P.O. Box 307
Layton, Utah 84041-0307
(801) 546-4665

Key Contact - Specialty:
Mr. Randy H. Craig - *Executives, technology industries*

Description: Mostly Mountain states-management, technical, manufacturing, sales, marketing, healthcare and finance.

Salary Minimum: $50,000
Functions: Senior mgmt., Middle mgmt., Product dev., Sales mgmt., CFO's, Systems dev., Engineering
Industries: Chemicals, Metal products, Computer equip., Computer svcs., High tech, Software

New World Healthcare Solutions, Inc.
380 Lexington Ave., Ste. 1700
New York, New York 10168
(212) 551-7867
Fax: (914) 267-0894
Email: ies1221@aol.com
Web: www.newworldhealthcare.com

Key Contact - Specialty:
Mr. Ira E. Shapiro - *Healthcare (domestic & international)*
Ms. Irene Ross - *Healthcare (domestic & international)*

Description: An international firm that specializes in healthcare and provides a unique hiring process which will ensure the hiring of the right candidate. Our organization actively participates in the evaluation process and truly understands the healthcare industry.

Salary Minimum: $70,000
Functions: Senior mgmt., Healthcare, Health admin., Sales mgmt., CFO's, MIS mgmt., Int'l.
Industries: Healthcare

Affiliates:
New World Healthcare, International

Newell Assoc.
89 Devonshire Rd.
New Rochelle, New York 10804
(914) 636-3254
Fax: (914) 654-1709

Key Contact - Specialty:
Mr. Donald Pierce Newell - *Senior management (all functions), CEOs*

Description: Strongly relationship oriented. We handle all management functions and general managers. We're best recruiting exceptional talent. Our chief present focus is the leasing industry.

Salary Minimum: $50,000
Functions: Generalist, Senior mgmt., Health admin., CFO's, Minorities
Industries: Generalist, Lumber/furniture, Metal products, Computer svcs., Equip. svcs., Software

Nicholaou & Co.
56 West Piers Drive
Westmont, Illinois 60559-3227
(630) 960-2382

Key Contact - Specialty:
Ms. Jean Nicholaou

Description: Personalized search service, mid to upper management-nationwide.

Salary Minimum: $50,000
Functions: Generalist, General mgmt., Mfg., Sales & mktg., Engineering, Specialized services
Industries: Generalist, Mfg.

Nichols & Company
P.O. Box 3561
Boulder, Colorado 80307-3561
(303) 494-3383
Fax: (303) 494-3383

Key Contact - Specialty:
Mr. Charles H. Nichols

Description: Retained executive search firm working with international network of clients in industrial and technological specialties. Recruiting senior management and board members.

Salary Minimum: $75,000
Functions: Directors, Senior mgmt., Mfg., CFO's, M&A, MIS mgmt., Int'l.
Industries: Generalist, Food/bev/tobacco, Plastics/rubber, Metal products, Motor vehicles, Misc. mfg., Mgmt. consulting

Affiliates:
Crowder & Company
Jarl Hallin International, AB

Nichols Brown Int'l.
330 Madison Ave., 11th Floor
New York, New York 10017
(212) 561-0690
Email: ednny@aol.com

Key Contact - Specialty:
Ms. E. Diane Nichols - *Executive recruiters*

Description: Executive search practice specializing in the placement of senior level executive recruiters and on assignments to identify national and international merger-suitable and/or joint venture search firms.

Salary Minimum: $250,000
Functions: Generalist, HR mgmt., Finance, M&A, Int'l.
Industries: Invest. banking, Misc. financial, Human resource svcs.

The Niemond Corp.

P.O. Box 4106
San Marcos, California 92069
(619) 591-4127

Key Contact - Specialty:
Ms. Nancy A. Niemond
Mr. Wesley E. Niemond

Description: Founder has 20 years of nationwide retained executive search experience, with emphasis in the communications, electronics, data processing and defense systems industries.

Salary Minimum: $100,000
Functions: Middle mgmt., Plant mgmt., Materials, Mktg. mgmt., HR mgmt., Budgeting, MIS mgmt.
Industries: Medical devices, Computer equip., Test/measurement equip., Haz. waste, Aerospace

---

NMC & Kay Int'l.

P.O. Box 3209
Englewood, Colorado 80112
(303) 768-9282
Fax: (303) 768-8365
Email: NmcKay303@aol.com
Web: www.occ.com/nki/

Key Contact - Specialty:
Ms. Debra Clarke - *Telecommunications, high technology, engineering*
Mr. Peter Kay - *Automotive, aerospace*
Mr. David Binney - *Finance & accounting*
Mr. Ian Gilmour - *Materials management*

Description: Serious search firm with guaranteed results. All consultants have held positions at the senior management level. International in scope with many multinational clients.
Functions: General mgmt., Mfg., Materials, Finance, R&D, Engineering, Int'l.
Industries: Generalist, Mfg., Transportation, Retail, Communications, Aerospace, High tech

International Branches:
London

W. D. Nolte & Company

6 Middlesex Rd.
Darien, Connecticut 06820
(203) 323-5858
Fax: (203) 323-0164

Key Contact - Specialty:
Mr. William D. Nolte, Jr. - *Generalist*

Description: Over 20 years as a management consultant serving public and private businesses and institutions in the U.S. and abroad. National and international coverage through NASA- North American Search Alliance partners.

Salary Minimum: $80,000
Functions: General mgmt., Mfg., Materials, Sales & mktg., Finance, IT, Mgmt. consultants
Industries: Mfg., Finance, Computer svcs., Accounting, Mgmt. consulting, Insurance, Software

---

Nordeman Grimm, Inc.

717 Fifth Ave.
New York, New York 10022
(212) 935-1000
Fax: (212) 980-1443

Key Contact - Specialty:
Mr. Jacques C. Nordeman - *General management, investment companies, new media investment banking, finance*
Mr. Peter G. Grimm - *General management, finance, marketing, corporate communication, human resources*

Description: Nordeman Grimm specializes in recruiting exceptional senior executives. We are known for quality, teamwork and long-term relationships.

Salary Minimum: $150,000
Functions: Generalist, Directors, Senior mgmt., Admin. svcs., Advertising, Mktg. mgmt., Sales mgmt., Direct mktg., PR, HR mgmt., Finance, CFO's, MIS mgmt., Mgmt. consultants, Non-profits
Industries: Generalist, Mfg., Food/bev/tobacco, Computer equip., Consumer electronics, Misc. mfg., Retail, Finance, Invest. banking, Brokers, Venture cap., Misc. financial, Svcs., Hospitality, Entertainment, Non-profits, Legal, Computer svcs., Mgmt. consulting, Human resource svcs., Communications, Advertising/PR, Publishing, New media, Broadcast & Film, Telecoms, Insurance, Real estate, High tech, Software
Professional Associations: AESC, IACPR

Paul Winston Norman & Assoc.

5357 W. Montrose Ave., Ste. 2
Chicago, Illinois 60641
(773) 685-4389
Fax: (773) 685-4415
Email: pwnco@aol.com

Key Contact - Specialty:
Mr. Paul W. Norman - *Healthcare, information technology, telecommunications*

Description: Retained industry focused firm conducting quality recruitment, assessment and delivery of executive talent in healthcare, information technology and biotechnology worldwide.

Salary Minimum: $60,000
Functions: Senior mgmt., Middle mgmt., Healthcare, Health admin., Sales mgmt., MIS mgmt., Systems dev.
Industries: Medical devices, Computer equip., Computer svcs., Telecoms, High tech, Biotech, Healthcare

---

Norman Broadbent Int'l., Inc.

200 Park Ave.
New York, New York 10166
(212) 953-6990
Fax: (212) 599-3673
Email: info@nbisearch.com
Web: www.nbisearch.com

Key Contact - Specialty:
Mr. Michael Flood - *Financial industry*

Description: Executive search firm with the resources to work effectively across a number of functions/industries serving clients in financial services, professional services, consumer, industrial, information technology, new media and entertainment as well as healthcare/pharmaceuticals with senior level requirements.

Salary Minimum: $100,000
Functions: Generalist, Directors, Senior mgmt., Middle mgmt., Product dev., Production, Automation, Plant mgmt., Quality, Productivity, Purchasing, Physicians, Nurses, Allied health, Health admin., Advertising, Mkt. research, Mktg. mgmt., Sales mgmt., Direct mktg., PR, Benefits, Personnel, Training, CFO's, Budgeting, Cash mgmt., Credit, Taxes, M&A, Risk mgmt., MIS mgmt., Systems anal., Systems dev., Systems implem., Systems support, Mgmt. consultants, Int'l.
Industries: Generalist, Food/bev/tobacco, Textiles/apparel, Lumber/furniture, Paper, Printing, Chemicals, Soap/perfume/cosmetics, Drugs mfg., Medical devices, Motor vehicles, Computer equip., Consumer electronics, Retail, Finance, Banking, Invest. banking, Brokers, Venture cap., Misc. financial, Hospitality, Entertainment, Computer svcs., Accounting, Mgmt. consulting, Human resource svcs., Communications, Advertising/PR, Publishing, New media, Broadcast & Film, Telecoms, Insurance, Software, Healthcare
Professional Associations: AESC, IACPR

Branches:
Metro Corporate Ctr.
1840 Gateway Drive, 2nd Floor
San Mateo, California 94404
Key Contact - Specialty:
Mr. Kelvin Thompson - *Technology*

233 S. Wacker Drive, Ste. 9850
Sears Tower
Chicago, Illinois 60606
(312) 876-3300
Fax: (312) 876-3640

Key Contact - Specialty:
Mr. Roger A. Quick - *Healthcare*

International Branches:
Beijing, Central Hong Kong, London

Networks:
The International Search Partnership

North American Recruiters, Inc.

4725 Olson Memorial Hwy.,#100
Parkdale Plaza, Ste. 519
Golden Valley, Minnesota 55422
(612) 591-1951
Fax: (612) 591-5850

Key Contact - Specialty:
Mr. David A. Knutson - *Generalist*

Description: A generalist search firm whose search process provides clients with detailed candidate background information. We participate with clients during interviews. Searches are performed under strict timelines.

Salary Minimum: $75,000
Functions: Generalist, Senior mgmt., Middle mgmt., Plant mgmt., Materials, Sales mgmt.
Industries: Generalist

Northern Consultants Inc.

17 Western Ave.
P.O. Box 220
Hampden, Maine 04444-0220
(207) 862-2323
Fax: (207) 862-2325

Key Contact - Specialty:
Dr. Alta L. Chase
Mr. James D. Brown - *Plastics*

Description: Specialize in search and operational audits: custom injection molding, plastics packaging and machinery. Also career counseling and alternate career path identification.

Salary Minimum: $60,000
Functions: Senior mgmt., Plant mgmt., Mktg. mgmt., Sales mgmt., Engineering
Industries: Paper, Plastics/rubber, Machinery/Appliances, Mgmt. consulting, Human resource svcs., Packaging

NPF Assoc. Ltd. Inc.

1999 University Drive, Ste. 405
Coral Springs, Florida 33071-6032
(954) 753-8560
Fax: (954) 753-8611
Web: npfnick@worldnet.att.net

Key Contact - Specialty:
Mr. Nick P. Fischler - *Human resources*

Description: Executive search firm specializing in human resources, with a client base of Fortune 500 companies.

Salary Minimum: $70,000
Functions: HR mgmt., Benefits, Personnel, Training
Industries: Generalist, Food/bev/tobacco, Soap/perfume/cosmetics, Misc. mfg., Transportation, Retail, Hospitality

Nuessle, Kurdziel & Weiss, Inc.

1601 Market St., 5 Penn Ctr. Plaza
Philadelphia, Pennsylvania 19103
(215) 561-3700
Fax: (215) 561-3745

Key Contact - Specialty:
Mr. John F. Kurdziel
Mr. Warren G. Nuessle
Mr. Gerald E. Weiss

Description: Executive search assignments in most functional areas with emphasis on general management, finance, human resources and marketing in most industry classifications. Also perform compensation studies.

Salary Minimum: $80,000
Functions: Generalist, General mgmt., Mfg., Distribution, Sales & mktg., Finance, MIS mgmt.
Industries: Generalist, Metal products, Retail, Finance, Accounting, Human resource svcs., Communications

Nursing Technomics
(a division of National Technomics, Inc.)

(Firm declined to update.)
814 Sunset Hollow Rd.
West Chester, Pennsylvania 19380
(610) 436-4551
Web: jimccrea@bellatlantic.net

Key Contact - Specialty:
Ms. Joan I. McCrea - *Nurses (administrative & management)*

Description: Specializing in executive search for executive, management and specialty nurses.

Salary Minimum: $50,000
Functions: Nurses, Training, Mgmt. consultants

O'Brien & Bell

812 Huron Rd., Ste. 535
Cleveland, Ohio 44115
(216) 575-1212
Fax: (216) 575-7502
Email: obrienbell@aol.com

Key Contact - Specialty:
Mr. Timothy M. O'Brien - *General management, manufacturing, industrial, consumer products, professional services (senior-level functions directly below the GM)*
Mr. Peter Holmes
Mr. Henry C. Hecker
Mr. William Faber

Description: An executive recruiting firm focusing on the recruitment of all functions of senior managers and executives for manufacturing, professional service firms, consumer products and retail organizations.

Salary Minimum: $100,000
Functions: Senior mgmt., Plant mgmt., Distribution, Mktg. mgmt., Sales mgmt., R&D, Engineering
Industries: Plastics/rubber, Metal products, Machinery/Appliances, Motor vehicles, Misc. mfg., Banking, Mgmt. consulting

O'Brien Consulting Services

171 Swanton St., Unit #72
Winchester, Massachusetts 01890-1965
(781) 721-4404
Email: ocs@mediaone.net

Key Contact - Specialty:
Mr. James J. O'Brien, Jr. - *Senior level executives, all functions*

Description: Previous line management experience in both high technology and manufacturing/distribution industries combined with partner positions with 2 major search firms.

Salary Minimum: $75,000
Functions: Directors, Senior mgmt., Middle mgmt., Sales & mktg., HR mgmt., CFO's, MIS mgmt.
Industries: Generalist, Machinery/Appliances, Misc. mfg., Finance, High tech, Software, Biotech

O'Callaghan Honey/Ray & Berndtson Inc.

400 5th Ave. SW, Ste. 400
Calgary, Alberta T2P 0L6
Canada
(403) 269-3277
Fax: (403) 262-9347

Key Contact - Specialty:
Mr. Terry K. O'Callaghan
Mr. W. Michael M. Honey
Mr. W. John McKay

Description: Calgary's most experienced executive search consultants serving domestic/international clientele worldwide.

Salary Minimum: $90,000
Functions: Generalist, Senior mgmt., CFO's, MIS mgmt., Non-profits, Attorneys, Int'l.
Industries: Energy/utilities, Food/bev/tobacco, Transportation, Finance, Non-profits, Legal, High tech

† occasional contingency assignment

O'Connor, O'Connor, Lordi, Ltd.

707 Grant St., Ste. 2727, Gulf Tower
Pittsburgh, Pennsylvania 15219-1908
(412) 261-4020
Fax: (412) 261-4480
Email: oolltd@aol.com

Key Contact - Specialty:
Mr. Thomas F. O'Connor - *Fortune 500*
Mr. Richard E. Brown - *Fortune 500*

Description: Custom tailored executive recruitment program for middle to upper echelon management with emphasis on sales, marketing, R&D, manufacturing, MIS, finance and general management.

Salary Minimum: $100,000
Functions: Senior mgmt., Plant mgmt., Materials, Mktg. mgmt., Sales mgmt., CFO's, MIS mgmt.
Industries: Energy/utilities, Food/bev/tobacco, Chemicals, Paints/petroleum products, Metal products, Machinery/Appliances, High tech

O'Keefe & Assoc., Inc.

P.O. Box 1092
Southport, Connecticut 06490
(203) 254-2544
Fax: (203) 254-2126
Email: jvokeefe@aol.com
Web: www.1anet.com/okeefe

Key Contact - Specialty:
Ms. Kathy O'Keefe
Mr. John O'Keefe
Mr. Kevin Keating
Mr. Paul Sampson
Mr. Tom Wilczynski
Ms. Diane Sweeney
Ms. Susan Moore
Ms. Kelly O'Keefe
Mr. Athan Crist
Ms. Eileen Vita
Mr. Bill Tohill

Description: We specialize in the consumer packaged goods industry to include sales, marketing, promotion, research, advertising and general management. Washington office specializes in high tech management.

Salary Minimum: $90,000
Functions: General mgmt., Mfg., Materials, Sales & mktg., HR mgmt., Finance, IT
Industries: Food/bev/tobacco, Drugs mfg., Misc. mfg., Finance, Entertainment, Human resource svcs., Advertising/PR

Branches:
54-585 Southern Hills
La Quinta, California 92253
(619) 771-0142
Fax: (619) 771-3717
Key Contact - Specialty:
Mr. Robert Wallace

7900 SE 28th St., Ste. 400
Mercer Island, Washington 98040
(206) 236-6199
Fax: (206) 236-6160
Key Contact - Specialty:
Mr. Jack O'Keefe

O'Neill & Co.

One Norwalk W., 40 Richards Ave.
Norwalk, Connecticut 06854
(203) 857-0344
Fax: (203) 857-0822
Web: soneillco@aol.com

Key Contact - Specialty:
Mr. Stephen A. O'Neill - *Finance, marketing*

Description: Nationwide recruitment of upper level finance, marketing and consulting professionals.

Salary Minimum: $75,000
Functions: Advertising, Mkt. research, CFO's, Budgeting, Cash mgmt., Risk mgmt., Mgmt. consultants
Industries: Mfg., Finance, Entertainment, Mgmt. consulting, Communications, Software, Biotech

Affiliates:
Harris Heery & Assoc., Inc.

O'Rourke Companies, Inc.

4100 International Plaza
Twr. II, Ste. 530
Ft. Worth, Texas 76109
(817) 735-8697
Fax: (817) 731-9130
Email: o'rourke1@flash.net

Key Contact - Specialty:
Mr. Dennis M. O'Rourke
Ms. Patti Cox
Ms. Rachel O'Rourke
Mr. Marshall Utterson
Mr. Jim McAllister
Ms. Vikki L. Dose

Description: Executive search/management consulting firm led by senior human resource professionals serving a broad base of industrial clients. Perform full range of human resource services designed to meet needs of the client.

Salary Minimum: $80,000
Functions: Generalist, Senior mgmt., Middle mgmt., Plant mgmt., Training, CFO's, Engineering
Industries: Generalist, Energy/utilities, Paper, Misc. mfg., Non-profits

O'Shea, Divine & Co., Inc.

4 Civic Plaza, Ste. #350
Newport Beach, California 92660
(949) 720-9070
Fax: (949) 720-9628
Email: DvinSrch@gte.net

Key Contact - Specialty:
Mr. Robert S. Divine
Mr. Kenneth D. Jones
Ms. Susan Hase

Description: Generalist firm recruiting senior-level management, primarily manufacturing, distribution, healthcare, financial services, telecommunications, not-for-profit. National in scope, with concentration in southern California. Affiliates in the major industrial nations.

Salary Minimum: $75,000
Functions: Generalist, General mgmt., Mfg., Sales & mktg., Finance, IT, Engineering
Industries: Medical devices, Plastics/rubber, Test/measurement equip., Finance, Telecoms, High tech, Biotech

Networks:
EMA Partners Int'l.

Dennis P. O'Toole & Assoc. Inc.

1865 Palmer Ave., Ste. 210
Larchmont, New York 10538
(914) 833-3712
(914) 833-3713
Email: dpotoole@aol.com

Key Contact - Specialty:
Mr. Dennis P. O'Toole - *Hospitality, entertainment*

Description: A select executive search firm known for personalized service and in-depth recruitment of senior management and hard to find specialists for resort, hotel, club and entertainment industries.

Salary Minimum: $70,000
Functions: Senior mgmt., Middle mgmt., Purchasing, Mktg. mgmt., Sales mgmt., HR mgmt., CFO's
Industries: Generalist, Hospitality, Entertainment
Professional Associations: AESC

O'Toole & Company, Inc.

1047 Forest
Oak Park, Illinois 60302
(708) 848-6200

Key Contact - Specialty:
Mr. William R. O'Toole
Ms. Nancy L. O'Toole

Description: Professional and experienced search for senior and middle management.

Salary Minimum: $60,000
Functions: Generalist, Senior mgmt., Middle mgmt., Sales mgmt., Cash mgmt., IT, Mgmt. consultants
Industries: Generalist, Retail, Finance, Banking, Invest. banking, Svcs., Mgmt. consulting

Oak Assoc.
P.O. Box 624
San Anselmo, California 94960
(415) 456-2225
Fax: (415) 456-2299
Email: oak101@pacbell.net

Key Contact - Specialty:
Mr. Matthew G. Raggio - *Officer level, software*

Description: We are a retained executive search firm specializing in the recruitment of key management talent in the technology industry. Areas of focus include general management, sales and marketing in the software industry.

Salary Minimum: $150,000
Functions: Senior mgmt., Mktg. mgmt., Sales mgmt.
Industries: High tech, Software

Ober & Company
11777 San Vicente Blvd., Ste. 860
Los Angeles, California 90049
(310) 207-1127

Key Contact - Specialty:
Ms. Lynn W. Ober - *Generalist*

Description: Broad based executive search practice with expertise in high technology, financial services, information technology, logistics, manufacturing, healthcare and consulting.

Salary Minimum: $100,000
Functions: General mgmt., Mfg., Healthcare, Sales & mktg., HR mgmt., Finance, IT
Industries: Mfg., Finance, Svcs., High tech, Software, Biotech, Healthcare

Affiliates:
CPM Search International

Oberlander & Co., Inc.
223 E. State St., P.O. Box 789
Geneva, Illinois 60134
(630) 232-2600
Fax: (630) 232-9240

Key Contact - Specialty:
Mr. Howard I. Oberlander

Description: Specialize in providing professional, confidential guidance in management selection.

Salary Minimum: $75,000
Functions: Generalist, General mgmt., Mfg., Sales & mktg., HR mgmt., Finance, R&D
Industries: Generalist, Mfg., Transportation, Svcs., Packaging, High tech, Biotech

The Odessa Group
523 W. 6th St., Ste. 807
Los Angeles, California 90014
(213) 629-9181
Fax: (213) 629-1481

Key Contact - Specialty:
Mr. Odessa J. Felactu - *High technology, medical*

Description: A high impact consulting group whose single purpose is to add value, increase profits and/or solve difficult problems.

Salary Minimum: $75,000
Functions: Generalist, Directors, Senior mgmt., Production, Plant mgmt., CFO's, Engineering
Industries: Generalist, Computer equip., Misc. mfg., Finance, Aerospace, High tech, Healthcare

The Ogdon Partnership
(a division of The Ogdon Group, Inc.)
375 Park Ave., Ste. 2409
New York, New York 10152-0175
(212) 308-1600
Fax: (212) 755-3819
Email: ogdonptnrs@aol.com
Web: members.aol.com/ogdonptnrs

Key Contact - Specialty:
Mr. Thomas H. Ogdon - *Venture portfolios (CEO's & directors), communications, consumer products (general management executives)*
Ms. Cathy N. Hughes - *Communications, publishing (edit & business side)*
Mr. Edward C. Mattes, Jr. - *New media/ internet, legal, medical*
Ms. Nina Leighton - *Communications, legal, financial*

Description: General recruiting; emphasis on marketing including advertising and P.R.; publishing including editorial; legal including partner-to-partner; financial services; top management and board positions for ventures; consumer packaged goods. New media, including general management, marketing and sales management; club management.

Salary Minimum: $100,000
Functions: Generalist, Directors, Senior mgmt., Sales mgmt., Direct mktg., CFO's, Attorneys
Industries: Generalist, Venture cap., Hospitality, Legal, Advertising/PR, Publishing, New media
Professional Associations: IACPR

Affiliates:
Executive Search Consultants
Groupe Mercator
John McCarthy Associates

The Oldani Group
188 - 106th Ave. NE, Ste. 420
Bellevue, Washington 98004
(425) 451-3938
Fax: (425) 453-6786
Email: searches@theoldanigroup.com
Web: www.theoldanigroup.com

Key Contact - Specialty:
Mr. Jerrold Oldani

Description: Firm has nationally prominent public sector practice and well established regional practice in not-for-profit. Exceptional skills in targeted recruitments, candidate evaluations and background checks.

Salary Minimum: $75,000
Functions: Directors, Senior mgmt., Health admin., Mktg. mgmt., MIS mgmt., Minorities
Industries: Construction, Non-profits, Law enfcmt., Government

Branches:
3331 Beard Road
Fremont, California 94555
(510) 713-8292
Fax: (510) 795-1949
Key Contact - Specialty:
Ms. Jo Ann Wexler

5 Klakring Court
Annapolis, Maryland 21403
(410) 216-9664
Fax: (410) 216-9660
Key Contact - Specialty:
Mr. Ronald J. Weisinger

P.O. Box 752089
Houston, Texas 77275-2089
(281) 485-8623
Fax: (281) 485-3666
Key Contact - Specialty:
Mr. David K. Wasson

188-106th Ave., N.E., Ste 420
Bellevue, Washington 98004
(425) 451-3938
Fax: (425) 453-6786
Key Contact - Specialty:
Mr. Dennis Lencioni
Mr. Jerry Oldani

Oliver & Rozner Assoc., Inc.
823 Walton Ave.
Mamaroneck, New York 10543
(914) 381-6242

Key Contact - Specialty:
Mr. Burton L. Rozner

Description: In-depth recruitment expertise in general management, marketing, sales management, manufacturing, engineering, R&D, finance, information systems and other key staff functions. Reputation for thoroughness, penetrating assessment and careful attention to detail, planning and strategy.

Salary Minimum: $100,000
Functions: Senior mgmt., Plant mgmt., Materials Plng., Mktg. mgmt., HR mgmt., CFO's, R&D
Industries: Food/bev/tobacco, Drugs mfg., Medical devices, Metal products, Motor vehicles, High tech, Healthcare
Professional Associations: AESC

Ollinger Partners
P.O. Box 2815
Duxbury, Massachusetts 02331
(781) 934-7106
Fax: (781) 934-7108
Email: casho@idt.net

Key Contact - Specialty:
Mr. Chuck Ollinger - *Hospitality, retailing, financial services*
Ms. Deborah Schwartz - *Retail, hospitality, financial services*

Description: A boutique firm of experienced professionals in hospitality and specialty retailing/consumer goods and services which specializes in senior management, marketing and human resource assignments.

Salary Minimum: $80,000
Functions: Senior mgmt., Advertising, Benefits, Personnel, CFO's, MIS mgmt., Int'l.
Industries: Retail, Misc. financial, Hospitality, Human resource svcs., Insurance

---

Olsen/Clark
649 Al Dorsey Lane NW
P.O. Box 11697
Bainbridge Island, Washington 98110-5697
(206) 842-2522
Fax: (206) 842-2527
Email: olsenclark@msn.com

Key Contact - Specialty:
Ms. Elizabeth Clark Olsen - *Healthcare, automotive, high technology, restaurants*
Mr. Rex Olsen - *Medical devices, high technology, food & beverage*

Description: Our firm's principals have both corporate and consulting experience in our specialty areas, enabling us to quickly identify appropriate candidates. Executive assessment using the Birkman Method¬ is available.

Salary Minimum: $75,000
Functions: Directors, Senior mgmt., Plant mgmt., Mktg. mgmt., Sales mgmt., HR mgmt., CFO's
Industries: Food/bev/tobacco, Medical devices, Computer equip., Transportation, Hospitality, High tech, Healthcare

---

Onsite Staffing Solutions
(a division of Right Services, Inc.)
53 W. Jackson Blvd., Ste. 1315
Chicago, Illinois 60604
(312) 939-2208
Fax: (312) 427-3403

Key Contact - Specialty:
Mr. Robert W. Otto
Mr. Randall W. Schorle
Mr. John T. Boyd

Description: Consultants providing assessment and design of solutions to staffing related issues. We provide assistance during all phases of the recruitment process. Also provide human resource professionals on an interim or project basis.

Branches:
477 E. Butterfield Rd.
Lombard, Illinois 60148
(708) 969-7010
Key Contact - Specialty:
Ms. Susan Murphy

The Onstott Group
60 William St.
Wellesley, Massachusetts 02181
(781) 235-3050
Fax: (781) 235-8653
Email: hneal@onstott.com
Web: www.onstott.com

Key Contact - Specialty:
Mr. Ben Beaver
Ms. Patricia Campbell
Mr. Joe Onstott
Ms. Joan Lucarelli

Description: Retainer-based search firm specializing in recruiting executives for most functional disciplines and industries. Concentration in high technology, telecommunications, manufacturing, consumer goods, financial and other service businesses and growth industries. International capability.

Salary Minimum: $100,000
Functions: Senior mgmt., Mfg., Sales & mktg., HR mgmt., CFO's, MIS mgmt., Mgmt. consultants
Industries: Mfg., Finance, Mgmt. consulting, Communications, High tech, Software
Professional Associations: AESC

Networks:
World Search Group

Opalka Dixon Consultants to Management
1215 Confederate Ave.
Richmond, Virginia 23227
(804) 358-0119

Key Contact - Specialty:
Ms. Violet Dixon - *Direct marketing*

Description: Services the direct marketing industry exclusively. Searches include management, marketing, operations, MIS and finance. Consult to emerging DM companies in management and organizational development.

Salary Minimum: $80,000
Functions: Direct mktg.
Industries: Non-classifiable industries

Oppedisano & Co., Inc.
370 Lexington Ave., Ste. 1200
New York, New York 10017
(212) 696-0144
Fax: (212) 686-3006

Key Contact - Specialty:
Mr. Edward Oppedisano - *Investment management, sales & marketing of investment management products, investment research*

Description: Our firm provides executive search, merger/acquisition and other consultative services exclusively to the investment management industry.
Functions: Sales mgmt., Cash mgmt.
Industries: Misc. financial

Opportunity Resources, Inc.
25 W. 43rd St., Ste. 1017
New York, New York 10036
(212) 575-1688
Fax: (212) 575-0297
Email: orisrch@ix.netcom.com

Key Contact - Specialty:
Ms. Freda Mindlin - *Non-profit organizations (CEO & mid-management levels)*

Description: We have the distinction of being a very specialized and nationally recognized, retained executive search firm for not-for-profit organizations. We are results-oriented and tailor each search to meet our clients' needs.

Salary Minimum: $75,000
Functions: Senior mgmt., Non-profits
Industries: Non-profits, Higher ed.
Professional Associations: AESC

Opus Marketing
23151 Moulton Pkwy.
Laguna Hills, California 92653
(949) 581-0962
Fax: (949) 581-1497
Email: bob@opusmarketing.com
Web: www.opusmarketing.com

Key Contact - Specialty:
Mr. Robert S. Kreisberg - *High technology sales, sales management, pre sales, technical support, professional services*

Description: We offer fully integrated staffing services - including search plans, hiring models and thorough screening of candidates - our clients have cut turnover and improved new hire retention rates significantly.

Salary Minimum: $40,000
Functions: Sales mgmt., Systems anal., Systems dev., Systems implem., Systems support, Network admin., DB admin.
Industries: Computer equip., Computer svcs., Telecoms, High tech, Software, Biotech

Branches:
10180 Bluff Rd.
Eden Prairie, Minnesota 55347
(612) 828-9642
Fax: (612) 828-9553
Email: shughes@opusmarketing.com
Key Contact - Specialty:
Ms. Susan F. Hughes - *High technology sales, technical support*

Organization Consulting Ltd.
1 Eglinton Ave. E., Ste. 501
Toronto, Ontario M4P 3A1
Canada
(416) 480-1333
Fax: (416) 322-7753
Email:
organizationconsulting@compuserve.com

Key Contact - Specialty:
Mr. Robert Johnston
Mr. Terry MacGorman
Mr. Hugh Farrell

Description: Retainer based firm, over 15 years of Canadian and U.S. experience at executive, professional and board levels.

Salary Minimum: $100,000
Functions: Generalist, General mgmt., Mfg., Sales & mktg., HR mgmt., Finance, IT
Industries: Generalist, Mfg., Retail, Svcs., High tech, Software, Biotech

Affiliates:
SR Int'l.

Organization Resources Inc.
63 Atlantic Ave., Boston Harbor
Boston, Massachusetts 02110
(617) 742-8970
Fax: (617) 523-9093
Email: OrgResInc@aol.com

Key Contact - Specialty:
Mr. John R. Kris - *Top management*
Mr. Peter T. Austin - *High technology*
Mr. John C. Jay - *Emerging companies*
Mr. Robert C. Bray - *Financial services*

Description: We are dedicated to assisting clients achieve operating and strategic objectives by providing highly individualized organizational consulting and executive selection services. Particularly experienced with fast growth companies and non-profit organizations.

Salary Minimum: $125,000
Functions: General mgmt., Mfg., Materials, Healthcare, Sales & mktg., Finance, R&D
Industries: Generalist, Printing, Medical devices, Finance, Non-profits, High tech, Software

---

Orion Consulting, Inc.
115 Rte. 46, Bldg. B, Ste. 13/14
Mountain Lakes, New Jersey 07046
(973) 402-8866
Fax: (973) 402-9258
Email: oci@planet.net

Key Contact - Specialty:
Mr. James V. Dromsky

Description: Management consulting firm providing retained executive search, organizational development, general on and off-site human resource services.

Salary Minimum: $45,000
Functions: Generalist
Industries: Generalist

Ott & Hansen, Inc.
136 S. Oak Knoll, Ste. 300
Pasadena, California 91101
(626) 578-0551
Fax: (626) 578-0570

Key Contact - Specialty:
Mr. George W. Ott - *Top management, general, directors*
Mr. David G. Hansen - *Top management, general, hospitality*

Description: Boutique firm. Two principals have over 30 years each search generalist experience. Over 60% of clients are privately owned/closely controlled public companies with $30-300 million revenue.

Salary Minimum: $80,000
Functions: Generalist, General mgmt., Mfg., Sales & mktg., HR mgmt., Finance, IT
Industries: Generalist, Construction, Mfg., Hospitality, Entertainment, Aerospace, High tech

---

Robert Ottke Assoc.
P.O. Box 7553
Newport Beach, California 92660
(949) 737-2100
Email: rottke@pacbell.net

Key Contact - Specialty:
Mr. Robert C. Ottke - *Pharmaceutical, biomedical*

Description: General executive search-special emphasis: high technology, healthcare, medical, pharmaceutical, biomedical devices.

Salary Minimum: $50,000
Functions: Senior mgmt., Physicians, Nurses, Health admin., MIS mgmt., R&D, Int'l.
Industries: Drugs mfg., Medical devices, Pharmaceutical svcs., Computer svcs., Mgmt. consulting, Biotech

---

Ovca Assoc. Inc.
7 Overbrook Rd.
Louisville, Kentucky 40207
(502) 893-6114
Fax: (502) 893-5410

Key Contact - Specialty:
Mr. William J. Ovca, Jr.

Description: National generalist practice delivering high-valued added services to clients in a wide range of industries.

Salary Minimum: $75,000
Functions: Generalist
Industries: Generalist

Overton Consulting
10535 N. Port Washington Rd.
Mequon, Wisconsin 53092
(414) 241-0200
Fax: (414) 241-8291
Email: overtonconsulting.com
Web: overtonconsulting.com

Key Contact - Specialty:
Mr. Justin V. Strom - *Banking, credit card, legal*
Mr. Raymond N. Thurber - *Office products*
Mr. Michael S. Krier - *Consumer products, not-for-profit, construction*
Mr. Robert Hutchison - *Financial services, human resources*
Mr. Andrew J. Lane - *Plastics, chemicals, manufacturing, logistics*
Ms. Nancy R. Noeske - *Academic, not-for-profit*
Mr. William Thomas Brown - *Financial services*

Description: Largest retained executive search firm in Wisconsin offering tailored recruitment services at executive and director levels. Full in-house research capabilities.

Salary Minimum: $70,000
Functions: Senior mgmt., Materials, Mktg. mgmt., HR mgmt., Finance, Non-profits, Attorneys
Industries: Mfg., Finance, Higher ed.

LaMonte Owens, Inc. †
P.O. Box 27742
Philadelphia, Pennsylvania 19118
(215) 248-0500
Fax: (215) 233-3737
Email: lowens@voicenet.com
Web: www.voicenet.com/~lowens/index.html

† occasional contingency assignment

Key Contact - Specialty:
Mr. LaMonte Owens - *Generalist, diversity recruiting*

Description: 29 years in specialized recruiting of minority and female professional, managerial and executive placement. Diversity recruiters.

Salary Minimum: $40,000
Functions: Generalist, Admin. svcs., Production, Distribution, Sales mgmt., Systems dev., Minorities
Industries: Generalist, Energy/utilities, Drugs mfg., Finance, Human resource svcs., Software

---

P.A.R. Assoc., Inc.

Sixty State St., Ste. 1040
Boston, Massachusetts 02109
(617) 367-0320
Fax: (617) 367-0521
Email: peter@parassoc.com
Web: www.parassoc.com

Key Contact - Specialty:
Mr. Peter A. Rabinowitz - *Healthcare, insurance, real estate, general commerce*

Description: General business practice, healthcare, non-profit organizations (academia, arts), banking and financial services, manufacturing and professional services.

Salary Minimum: $120,000
Functions: Directors, Senior mgmt., Health admin., Mktg. mgmt., CFO's, Minorities
Industries: Generalist, Energy/utilities, Construction, Hospitality, Non-profits, Insurance, Healthcare

Networks:
International Search Associates (ISA)

P.R.H. Management, Inc.

2777 Summer St.
Stamford, Connecticut 06905
(203) 327-3900
Fax: (203) 327-6324
Email: peter@prhmanagement.com
Web: www.prhmanagement.com

Key Contact - Specialty:
Mr. Peter R. Hendelman - *Telecommunications, high technology*

Description: Since 1973, we have offered a personal service giving each professional the attention needed to attain their unique career objectives. 80% of our candidates are promoted in two years.

Salary Minimum: $50,000
Functions: Senior mgmt., Mktg. mgmt., Sales mgmt., CFO's, MIS mgmt., Engineering, Minorities
Industries: Misc. financial, Computer svcs., Equip. svcs., New media, Telecoms, High tech, Software

---

Page-Wheatcroft & Co., Ltd.

The Whitehouse on Central Expwy.
9850 N. Central Expwy., Ste. 226
Dallas, Texas 75231
(214) 696-4333
Email: ceo@www.electronicresume.com

Key Contact - Specialty:
Mr. Stephen J. L. Page - *Senior-level partners & senior executives (law firms, consulting firms, technology-driven businesses)*
Mr. Mark E. Rich - *Senior level partners & senior executives (consulting firms, technology-driven businesses)*
Mr. S. John Byington - *Legal*
Mr. Ralph P. Stow - *Technology, consulting*
Mr. Steven H. Boykin
Ms. Martha Goodwin

Description: National general management search practice with expertise in: financial services; law firms; strategy, management and information technology consulting firms and technology driven, Fortune 500 companies.

Salary Minimum: $300,000
Functions: Generalist, Senior mgmt., Legal, Mktg. mgmt., MIS mgmt., Mgmt. consultants, Attorneys
Industries: Generalist, Finance, Legal, Computer svcs., Mgmt. consulting, High tech, Software

Branches:
1555 King St., Ste. 300
Alexandria, Virginia 22314
(703) 836-9695
Key Contact - Specialty:
Mr. S. John Byington

The Pailin Group Professional Search Consultants

8500 N. Stemmons Frwy., Ste. 6070
LB-55
Dallas, Texas 75247-3832
(214) 630-1703
Fax: (214) 630-1704
Email: pailingrouppsc@compuserve.com

Key Contact - Specialty:
Mr. David L. Pailin, Sr. - *Accounting & finance, sales & marketing*
Ms. Cheryl Pailin - *Contract administration, manufacturing, engineering*
Ms. Debra Hosey - *Human resources, organizational development, organizational design*
Mr. Robert Martin, Sr. - *Healthcare, legal*
Ms. Roxxanne Miller - *Insurance, financial services, banking*
Ms. Joan Cox - *Accounting & finance*

Description: We offer targeted search consulting in accounting/finance, sales/marketing, legal, general management, MIS, engineering and healthcare. We are uniquely qualified with the capabilities to source candidates of diverse backgrounds.

Salary Minimum: $50,000
Functions: Plant mgmt., Purchasing, Advertising, Personnel, Cash mgmt., Systems anal., Attorneys
Industries: Energy/utilities, Mfg., Finance, Communications, High tech, Software, Healthcare

---

J. Palacios & Assoc., Inc. †

P.O. Box 362437
San Juan, Puerto Rico 00936-2437
(787) 723-6433
Fax: (787) 723-3040
Email: jpalacio@coqui.net

Key Contact - Specialty:
Ms. Jeannette C. De Palacios

Description: Professional executive search with strong emphasis on ethics and confidentiality. Search leader for the pharmaceuticals, chemicals and medical devices industries, serving most positions: consultant on the Myers Briggs type psychological indicators and its applications. Over 80% repeated business every year.

Salary Minimum: $50,000
Functions: Generalist
Industries: Generalist

Kirk Palmer & Assoc., Inc.

6 E. 43rd St., Ste. 2004
New York, New York 10017
(212) 983-6477
Fax: (212) 599-2597
Email: Kirk@KirkPalmer.com
Web: www.Kirkpalmer.com

Key Contact - Specialty:
Mr. Kirk Palmer

Description: Recognized authorities in the retail and apparel industries. Client base includes many of the top retail and apparel companies in America. Proven expertise in senior management searches within all functional areas.

Salary Minimum: $75,000
Functions: General mgmt., Product dev., Purchasing, Sales & mktg., HR mgmt., Graphic artists
Industries: Wholesale, Retail

Branches:
306 Moulton St.
Hamilton, Massachusetts 01982
(508) 468-2485
Fax: (508) 468-4663
Key Contact - Specialty:
Ms. Leslie Cook

Pamenter, Pamenter, Brezer & Deganis Ltd.

(Firm declined to update.)
4 Eva Rd., Ste. 400
Etobicoke, Ontario M9C 2A8
Canada
(416) 620-5980

Key Contact - Specialty:
Mr. Fred Pamenter - *University administration, senior executive*
Mr. Craig Pamenter - *Mid-level management*

Description: Our search work is usually performed in conjunction with reorganization projects. Recently we conducted a major human resources restructuring project for a leading business school using our employment model.

Salary Minimum: $50,000
Functions: General mgmt., Senior mgmt., Middle mgmt., Mktg. mgmt., PR, HR mgmt., CFO's
Industries: Food/bev/tobacco, Printing, Misc. mfg., Higher ed., Packaging

The PAR Group - Paul A. Reaume, Ltd.

100 N. Waukegan Rd., Ste. 200
Lake Bluff, Illinois 60044
(847) 234-0005
Fax: (847) 234-8309
Email: pargroup@interaccess.com

Key Contact - Specialty:
Mr. Paul A. Reaume - *Generalist*
Mr. Gerald R. Plock - *Generalist*

Description: Searches for top management and senior staff in local government and related organizations and not-for-profit associations (i.e. city manager, police chief, public works director; executive director and association managers).

Salary Minimum: $45,000
Functions: Senior mgmt., Middle mgmt., CFO's, Budgeting, Minorities, Non-profits, Environmentalists
Industries: Entertainment, Non-profits, Law enfcmt., Government, Non-classifiable industries

Parenica & Co. †

19250 Stableford Lane
Cornelius, North Carolina 28031
(704) 896-0060
Fax: (704) 896-0240
Email: parenica@sprintmail.com

Key Contact - Specialty:
Mr. Jim Parenica - *Technology, information technology, telecommunications, general management, human resources*

Description: I conduct 10-12 retained executive search assignments per year, resulting in a more thorough and timely effort on each search.

Salary Minimum: $100,000
Functions: General mgmt., Senior mgmt., HR mgmt., IT, MIS mgmt., Mgmt. consultants
Industries: Energy/utilities, Mfg., Textiles/apparel, Finance, Computer svcs., High tech

Jim Parham & Assoc., Inc. †

6700 S. Florida Ave., Ste. 33
Lakeland, Florida 33813-3312
(941) 644-7097

Key Contact - Specialty:
Mr. Jim Parham - *Transportation*

Description: Specialized executive search for the motor freight industry (LTL,T/L, hazardous haulers, flatbed, tank carriers, refrigerated, van, logistics).

Salary Minimum: $35,000
Functions: General mgmt., Directors, Senior mgmt., Middle mgmt., Distribution, CFO's, MIS mgmt.
Industries: Transportation

Frank Parillo & Assoc.

1801 E. Heim Ave., Ste. 200
Orange, California 92665
(714) 921-8008

Key Contact - Specialty:
Mr. Frank Parillo

Description: Serving large, middle and small companies in the biotechnology, medical diagnostic and device industries, as well as venture capital-based start-ups. Focused on middle and senior management. Conduct searches for all executives' functions.

Salary Minimum: $50,000
Functions: Senior mgmt., Middle mgmt., Product dev., Production, Mktg. mgmt., Sales mgmt., R&D
Industries: Chemicals, Drugs mfg., Medical devices, Biotech

D. P. Parker & Assoc., Inc.

372 Washington St.
Wellesley, Massachusetts 02181
(781) 237-1220
Fax: (781) 237-4702
Email: information@dpparker.com
Web: www.dpparker.com

Key Contact - Specialty:
Dr. David P. Parker

Description: Founded by David P. Parker (ScD.,MIT-Metallurgy). Specialize in R&D/marketing/operations and general management in specialty materials and chemicals, biotechnology, aerospace, electronics and other technically based industries.

Salary Minimum: $90,000
Functions: Senior mgmt., Product dev., Automation, Plant mgmt., Mktg. mgmt., R&D, Engineering
Industries: Chemicals, Drugs mfg., Plastics/rubber, Metal products, Aerospace, High tech, Biotech
Professional Associations: AESC

R. Parker & Assoc., Inc. †

551 5th Ave., Ste. 222
New York, New York 10176
(212) 661-8074

Key Contact - Specialty:
Ms. Roberta Parker - *Sales & marketing, consumer packaged goods*

Description: Conventional and outlet retail. Consumer marketing and sales - packaged goods and durables - areas of specialization include food, health and beauty aids, cosmetics, tabletop.

Salary Minimum: $50,000
Functions: Generalist, Product dev., Advertising, Mkt. research, Mktg. mgmt., Sales mgmt., Direct mktg.
Industries: Generalist, Food/bev/tobacco, Textiles/apparel, Soap/perfume/cosmetics, Drugs mfg.

Michael W. Parres & Assoc.

21 Kercheval, Ste. 200
Grosse Pointe Farms, Michigan 48236
(313) 886-8080

Key Contact - Specialty:
Mr. Mike Parres - *Manufacturing & sales of product to the OE automotive manufacturers (all disciplines)*

Description: We are dedicated to providing a service that clients find extraordinarily supportive in their pursuit of exceptional talent. This commitment is backed by many years of management resourcing experience.

Salary Minimum: $70,000
Functions: Senior mgmt., Middle mgmt., Plant mgmt., Distribution, Sales mgmt., CFO's, Engineering
Industries: Metal products, Motor vehicles, Misc. mfg., Transportation

Parsons Assoc. Inc.

601 Forest Ave.
Glen Ellyn, Illinois 60137
(630) 469-7660
Email: jwp@ix.netcom.com

Key Contact - Specialty:
Ms. Sue N. Parsons - *Generalist*

Description: Small firm that emphasizes a

† occasional contingency assignment

strong degree of communication and close relationships with a select group of client companies in need of highly talented middle and senior management executives.

Salary Minimum: $70,000
Functions: Generalist, Senior mgmt., Middle mgmt., Plant mgmt., Sales mgmt., CFO's, MIS mgmt.
Industries: Generalist

Partners Executive Search Consultants Inc.

163 Glenvale Blvd.
Toronto, Ontario M4G 2W4
Canada
(416) 467-6812
Fax: (416) 467-8892
Email: randyq@ultratech.net

Key Contact - Specialty:
Mr. Randy Quarin

Description: We will become your human resource partner in the marketplace to bring the best candidates to your front door.
Functions: Middle mgmt., Advertising, Mkt. research, Mktg. mgmt., Sales mgmt., Direct mktg., Graphic artists
Industries: Entertainment, Advertising/PR, Publishing, New media, Broadcast & Film, Telecoms, Software

Affiliates:
Mandrake Management Consultants

Partners In Human Resources Int'l., Inc.

9 E. 37th St., 9th Floor
New York, New York 10016-2822
(212) 685-0400
Email: partners@ingress.com

Key Contact - Specialty:
Mr. Max Neufeld - *Human resources, marketing, finance, information technology*

Description: Professional, personalized service; broad-based expertise in mid to upper management searches. Particular expertise in financial services, consumer products and pharmaceutical industries and information technology.

Salary Minimum: $75,000
Functions: General mgmt., Mfg., Sales & mktg., Finance, IT, Mgmt. consultants, Int'l.
Industries: Soap/perfume/cosmetics, Drugs mfg., Medical devices, Finance, Mgmt. consulting, Human resource svcs., Broadcast & Film

Networks:
IMSA

The Partnership Group

7 Becker Farm Rd.
Roseland, New Jersey 07068
(201) 535-8566
Fax: (201) 535-6408
Web: SearchNJ@Bellatlantic.net

Key Contact - Specialty:
Mr. Peter T. Maher - *Financial services, other service industries, senior management*
Mr. Raymond Schwartz - *Pharmaceutical, telecommunications, vice presidents, top management*
Mr. Silas E. G. Edman - *Banking, mortgage, director, top management*
Mr. Tim Christy - *Manufacturing, technical, operations, middle to high level management*
Mr. Michael T. Bucci - *Consumer packaged goods, advertising, middle to senior management*
Mr. Richard G. Schoon - *Non-profit senior management*

Description: Human resource consultancy specializing in retained executive search with emphasis on strategic client partnerships. We offer sustained size and critical mass to be effective but are committed to intense personal service.

Salary Minimum: $75,000
Functions: Middle mgmt., Plant mgmt., Health admin., Mktg. mgmt., Benefits, CFO's, Mgmt. consultants
Industries: Generalist, Leather/stone/glass/clay, Test/measurement equip., Finance, Human resource svcs., High tech, Healthcare

Branches:
3 Regency Plaza
Providence, Rhode Island 02903
(401) 621-1361
Key Contact - Specialty:
Mr. Richard G. Schoon

Affiliates:
Deven Anderson International

Partnervision Consulting Group Inc.

1 Frizzell Ave.
Toronto, Ontario M4K 1H8
Canada
(416) 406-6247
(416) 406-0739
Fax: (416) 406-0755
Web: www.partnercontracting.com

Key Contact - Specialty:
Ms. Lynn Lefebvre - *Generalist*
Mr. Peter Flynn - *Generalist*
Ms. Dianne Kenton - *Human resources*
Ms. Amanda Cook - *Generalist*
Mr. Dennis Mogg - *Diversity (aboriginal and people with disabilities)*

Description: We opened our doors in 1991 as an executive search firm. We've differentiated ourselves in three ways: we're a 'relationship management' based organization; we take a business perspective in our recruiting solutions; and we service our clients at all management levels. We are your 'One stop recruiting team'.
Functions: Middle mgmt., HR mgmt., Finance, CFO's, IT, Mgmt. consultants, Minorities
Industries: Energy/utilities, Food/bev/tobacco, Finance, Mgmt. consulting, Human resource svcs., Telecoms, High tech

Affiliates:
Partnercontracting Inc.

Partridge Assoc., Inc. †

1200 Providence Hwy.
Sharon, Massachusetts 02067
(781) 784-4144
Fax: (781) 784-4780

Key Contact - Specialty:
Mr. Robert J. Partridge

Description: Executive search organization specializing in recruitment for corporate and unit level positions in the hospitality industry. Twenty years of industry experience in hotels, restaurants and food service.

Salary Minimum: $50,000
Functions: Generalist, Senior mgmt., Middle mgmt., Mkt. research, Mktg. mgmt., CFO's, MIS mgmt.
Industries: Hospitality
Professional Associations: IACPR

Carolyn Smith Paschal Int'l. †

1155 Camino Del Mar, Ste. 506
Del Mar, California 92014
(619) 587-1366
Fax: (619) 792-9511

Key Contact - Specialty:
Ms. Carolyn Smith Paschal - *Fundraising, public relations, marketing communications, investor relations*

Description: We find executives in public relations and advertising agencies, hospitals, educational institutions, arts organizations and other non-profit organizations, in fundraising, PR, IR and marketing communications positions.

Salary Minimum: $35,000
Functions: Senior mgmt., PR, IT, Minorities, Non-profits
Industries: Generalist, Food/bev/tobacco, Non-profits, Higher ed., Communications, Advertising/PR, Healthcare

Paul-Tittle Assoc., Inc.
1485 Chain Bridge Rd., Ste. 304
McLean, Virginia 22101
(703) 442-0500
Fax: (703) 893-3871
Email: pta@paul-tittle.com
Web: www.careermosaic.com/cm/pta/pta1.html

Key Contact - Specialty:
Mr. David M. Tittle - *Information technology*
Mr. Ron Cimino - *Telecommunications marketing*

Description: Executive search and dedicated recruiting projects for information technology, telecommunications, Internet and interactive multi-media industries. Specializes in mid and senior level management and individual contributors in sales, marketing and technology components of above industries.

Salary Minimum: $60,000
Functions: Mktg. mgmt., Customer svc., CFO's, MIS mgmt., Systems anal., Systems implem., Mgmt. consultants
Industries: Computer svcs., Mgmt. consulting, New media, Telecoms, High tech, Software, Healthcare

Pawlik/Dorman Partners
2639 N. Southport, Ste. B
Chicago, Illinois 60614
(773) 296-0950
Fax: (773) 296-0629
Email: bpawlik@compuserve.com

Key Contact - Specialty:
Ms. Bernadette Pawlik - *Generalist*

Description: 15 years retained search experience. Each search conducted exclusively by the partner. Conducting traditional and unbundled search.

Salary Minimum: $70,000
Functions: Generalist, Senior mgmt., Middle mgmt., Sales & mktg., HR mgmt., Finance, Mgmt. consultants
Industries: Generalist, Mfg., Computer equip., Consumer electronics, Svcs., Telecoms, High tech

PCD Partners
101 W. Eagle Rd.
Havertown, Pennsylvania 19083
(610) 449-1000
Fax: (610) 449-2066

Key Contact - Specialty:
Mr. James Pappas - *Healthcare*

Description: Generalist firm operating nationally-marketing, manufacturing and finance-all areas; including healthcare administration, physician recruitment and practice acquisition network.

Salary Minimum: $60,000
Functions: General mgmt., Directors, Senior mgmt., Admin. svcs., Healthcare, Physicians, Health admin.
Industries: Healthcare

Peachtree Executive Search
10800 Alpharetta Hwy., Ste. 481
Roswell, Georgia 30076
(770) 998-2272

Key Contact - Specialty:
Mr. Mark F. Snoddy, Jr. - *General practice*

Description: A small firm focusing on quality service to clients, primarily in the southeast U.S. with a broad client base.

Salary Minimum: $70,000
Functions: Senior mgmt., Plant mgmt., Mktg. mgmt., Sales mgmt., MIS mgmt., R&D, Technicians
Industries: Chemicals, Drugs mfg., Advertising/PR, Packaging, Insurance, High tech, Software

Pearson, Caldwell & Farnsworth
One California St., Ste. 1950
San Francisco, California 94111
(415) 982-0300
Fax: (415) 982-0333

Key Contact - Specialty:
Mr. John R. Pearson
Mr. William R. Caldwell
Mr. John A. Farnsworth
Mr. Thomas R.B. Boesch

Description: Full range senior level executive search with emphasis on the financial services industry and recruitment of corporate financial officers.

Salary Minimum: $100,000
Functions: Directors, Senior mgmt., Mktg. mgmt., Sales mgmt., CFO's, Risk mgmt., Mgmt. consultants
Industries: Finance, Banking, Invest. banking, Misc. financial, Accounting, Mgmt. consulting

Branches:
250 Park Ave., 17th Floor
New York, New York 10177
(212) 983-5850
Fax: (212) 983-5855
Key Contact - Specialty:
Ms. Paula L. Whitton

Peck & Assoc., Ltd.
250 S. Main St.
Thiensville, Wisconsin 53092
(414) 238-8700
Fax: (414) 238-9525
Email: jdowning@execpc.com

Key Contact - Specialty:
Ms. Judi Downing

Description: Our goal is to exceed our client's expectations. We use a project driven methodology. Each project is custom designed to meet your needs. We help you make informed choices.
Functions: Directors, Senior mgmt., Mfg., Product dev., Benefits, MIS mgmt., Mgmt. consultants
Industries: Plastics/rubber, Finance, High tech

Affiliates:
Kilvington Saville

Peeney Assoc., Inc.
146 Second St.
Fanwood, New Jersey 07023
(908) 322-2324
Fax: (908) 322-2332

Key Contact - Specialty:
Mr. James D. Peeney - *Automotive industry, healthcare*
Mr. John J. Juelis

Description: Specialists in general management, manufacturing, human resources, marketing, finance, automotive, utilities, banking and machine tool industries.

Salary Minimum: $75,000
Functions: General mgmt., Mfg., Sales & mktg., HR mgmt., Finance
Industries: Generalist, Metal products, Machinery/Appliances, Motor vehicles, Human resource svcs.

Paul S. Pelland, P.C.
2431 Stono Watch Dr.
Johns Island, South Carolina 29455-3116
(843) 559-9798
Email: search@scsupernet.com

Key Contact - Specialty:
Mr. Paul S. Pelland - *Foundry, primary metals, metal working*
Ms. Jane A. Taylor - *Foundry, primary metals, metal working*

Description: Foundry and secondary machining/forming specialists. Emphasis on executive and senior management, marketing and technological professionals. Most metal working areas. Emphasis on foundry clients industry worldwide.

Salary Minimum: $60,000
Functions: Senior mgmt., Middle mgmt., Plant mgmt., Quality, Mktg. mgmt., Engineering
Industries: Metal products, Misc. mfg.

Penn Associates
Two Penn Center Plaza, Ste. 200
1500 JFK Blvd.
Philadelphia, Pennsylvania 19102
(215) 854-6336
Fax: (215) 592-9079

† occasional contingency assignment

Email: dickersn@concentric.net

Key Contact - Specialty:
Mr. Joseph A. Dickerson - *Human resources*

Description: Consulting firm specializing in the recruitment of middle and upper level human resource executives. We handle assignments worldwide and provide research services. We bring innovative solutions to staffing problems.

Salary Minimum: $75,000
Functions: HR mgmt., Benefits, Personnel, Training, Mgmt. consultants, Minorities
Industries: Generalist, Finance, Hospitality, Communications, Environmental svcs., High tech, Healthcare

The Penn Partners, Inc.
230 S. Broad St., 19th Floor
Philadelphia, Pennsylvania 19102
(215) 568-9285
Fax: (215) 568-1277

Key Contact - Specialty:
Ms. Kathleen M. Shea - *Generalist*
Mr. John F. Smith - *Generalist*
Ms. Karen M. Swartz - *Generalist*
Ms. Cheryl L. Littman - *Generalist*

Description: Generalist retainer based search practice. Specializing at the senior and middle management level.

Salary Minimum: $75,000
Functions: Generalist, General mgmt., Senior mgmt., Middle mgmt., Sales & mktg., HR mgmt., Finance
Industries: Mfg., Food/bev/tobacco, Machinery/Appliances, Consumer electronics, Finance, Mgmt. consulting
Professional Associations: IACPR

People Management Mid-South, LLC
3310 W. End Ave., Ste. 575
Nashville, Tennessee 37203
(615) 463-2800
Fax: (615) 463-2944
Email: twt@jobfitmatters.com
Web: www.jobfitmatters.com

Key Contact - Specialty:
Mr. Tommy Thomas - *Generalist*
Ms. Joyce Morgan - *Generalist*

Description: We specialize in retained executive search, selection and consultation on issues related to job fit.

Salary Minimum: $70,000
Functions: Generalist, General mgmt., Mfg., Health admin., CFO's, IT, Non-profits
Industries: Generalist, Mfg., Finance, Svcs., Government, High tech, Healthcare

Affiliates:
People Management Northeast, Inc.

People Management Northeast, Inc.
1 Darling Drive
Avon, Connecticut 06001
(860) 678-8900
Web: www.jobfit-pmi.com

Key Contact - Specialty:
Mr. Steven Darter - *Generalist, insurance, managed care, manufacturing, general management*
Mr. James Bond - *Generalist, information systems, life insurance, general management, managed care*
Ms. Karla Hammond - *Generalist, human resources, public relations, communications*

Description: Our focus is on achieving a sound job fit. This objective is enhanced by our SIMA® assessment process which provides an extra dimension of insight into individuals' natural operating style and motivated abilities to perform well in a given position.

Salary Minimum: $75,000
Functions: Generalist, General mgmt., Mfg., Sales & mktg., HR mgmt., Finance, IT
Industries: Generalist, Mfg., Finance, Computer svcs., Insurance, Software, Healthcare

Affiliates:
People Management Mid-South, LLC
People Management, Inc.

Perez-Arton Consultants, Inc.
23 Spring St., Room 304
Ossining-on-Hudson, New York 10562
(914) 762-2100
Email: perezart@bestweb.net

Key Contact - Specialty:
Ms. Maria M. Perez
Dr. Julius Elias
Ms. Mary Ellen Rudolph

Description: Higher education administration at the presidential, VP, deans and directors level. Presidential and board evaluations, board development and institutional assessments. All programmatic and operational areas in higher education and non-profit institutions.

Salary Minimum: $75,000
Functions: Minorities, Non-profits
Industries: Non-profits, Higher ed.

The Perkins Group †
7621 Little Ave., Ste. 216
Charlotte, North Carolina 28226
(704) 543-1111
Fax: (704) 543-0945
Email: perk@vnet.net
Web: www.perkinsgroup@aol.com

Key Contact - Specialty:
Mr. R. Patrick Perkins - *Generalist, manufacturing, distribution*
Mr. Richard Krumel - *Manufacturing, distribution*
Mr. William Bright - *Manufacturing, distribution*

Description: A 15 year national multi-service retained search firm focused primarily in manufacturing and distribution who provides our clients with staffing programs designed to reduce cycle time and lower costs per hire.

Salary Minimum: $65,000
Functions: Generalist, General mgmt., Mfg., Materials, Sales & mktg., Finance, Engineering
Industries: Generalist, Mfg., Transportation, Finance, Aerospace, Packaging, High tech

Branches:
318 South Fork Rd.
Mooresville, North Carolina 28115
(704) 660-1000
Fax: (704) 543-0945
Web: www.perkinsgroup.com
Key Contact - Specialty:
Mr. Richard G. Krumel - *Generalist*

R. H. Perry & Assoc., Inc.
2607 31st St., NW
Washington, District of Columbia 20008
(202) 965-6464
Fax: (202) 338-3953
Email: r.h.perry@worldnet.att.net
Web: ourworld.compuserve.com/homepages/rhperry

Key Contact - Specialty:
Mr. R. H. Perry - *College & university presidents*
Mr. Neil A. Stein - *Private sector senior level executives, senior level positions in not-for-profit organizations*
Ms. Sandra Ellis

Description: Search and personnel consulting firm based in Washington, DC.
Functions: Generalist
Industries: Generalist, Higher ed.

Branches:
1127 Rosebank Drive
Columbus, Ohio 43235
(614) 431-1551
Fax: (614) 431-1252
Email: akoenig@worldnet.att.net
Key Contact - Specialty:
Dr. Allen E. Koenig - *Higher education*

Affiliates:
The Registry for Interim College & University Presidents

Perry-D'Amico & Assoc.
P.O. Box 671
Half Moon Bay, California 94019
(650) 726-3132

Key Contact - Specialty:
Mr. Len Perry - *Medical products*
Ms. Virginia Perry - *Medical products*

Description: Small, highly-focused firm in medical products, targeting V.P. level in all management, staff, technical and related functions. Exceptional network in regulatory affairs, QA/QR in device, pharmaceutical and biotechnology.

Salary Minimum: $80,000
Functions: Generalist, Mfg., Sales & mktg., HR mgmt., Finance, R&D, Engineering
Industries: Drugs mfg., Medical devices, Human resource svcs., Biotech

Perry-Martel Int'l., Inc. †

430 Gilmour St.
Ottawa, Ontario K2P 0R8
Canada
(613) 236-6995
Fax: (613) 236-8240
Email: pmi@istar.ca
Web: www.technogate.com

Key Contact - Specialty:
Mr. David Perry - *Senior executives, information technology*
Ms. Anita Martel

Description: We combine the proprietary tools in our S.M.A.R.T. search process with industry knowledge to design and mount a tightly focused marketing and recruiting campaign.

Salary Minimum: $60,000
Functions: Senior mgmt., Sales mgmt., PR, CFO's, MIS mgmt., Systems anal., Systems dev.
Industries: Computer equip., Computer svcs., New media, Aerospace, High tech, Software

Barry Persky & Co., Inc.

256 Post Rd. E.
Westport, Connecticut 06880-3617
(203) 454-4500
Fax: (203) 454-3318
Email: bpco@mags.net

Key Contact - Specialty:
Mr. Barry Persky

Description: Since 1971 the firm has specialized in recruitment of senior executives and managers, serving domestic and international clients in capital equipment, high technology, basic manufacturing, public services, consumer products and communications industries.

Salary Minimum: $50,000
Functions: Generalist, Senior mgmt., Product dev., Mktg. mgmt., CFO's, Engineering, Int'l.
Industries: Generalist, Metal products, Machinery/Appliances, Transportation, Publishing, Government, High tech

Professional Associations: IACPR

The Personnel Group, Inc.

5821 Cedar Lake Rd.
Sunset Ridge Business Park
Minneapolis, Minnesota 55416
(612) 525-1557
Fax: (612) 525-1088

Key Contact - Specialty:
Mr. David G. Nelson - *Manufacturing, finance, sales & marketing*
Mr. Thomas H. Bodin - *General management, healthcare, communications, human resources*
Mr. Wayne A. Carter - *General management, engineering, human resources*

Description: Search practice is enhanced by executives from the Fortune 100. Practice has internal psychological/behavioral assessment capability. Provides customer with a variety of services including retained search, on-site recruiters and strategic recruiting/search consulting.

Salary Minimum: $60,000
Functions: General mgmt., Mfg., Healthcare, Sales & mktg., HR mgmt., Finance, Engineering
Industries: Mfg., Finance, Svcs., Communications, Aerospace, Healthcare

Alec Peters Assoc. Inc./DLR

Two Concourse Pkwy., Ste. 155
Atlanta, Georgia 30328
(770) 650-9707
Fax: (770) 650-9710
Email: AlecPETE@aol.com

Key Contact - Specialty:
Mr. Alec Peters - *Staffing industry*

Description: Specialty search practices: IS staffing and consulting, contract technical, outsourcing, staff leasing and permanent placement search industries.

Salary Minimum: $75,000
Functions: General mgmt., Sales & mktg., HR mgmt., Finance, IT
Industries: Non-classifiable industries

Richard Peterson & Assoc., Inc.

5064 Roswell Rd., Ste. C-201
Atlanta, Georgia 30342
(404) 256-1661
Fax: (404) 257-1280

Key Contact - Specialty:
Mr. Richard A. Peterson

Description: Executive search for the financial services industry.

Salary Minimum: $50,000
Functions: Senior mgmt., Middle mgmt., Mktg. mgmt., Benefits, Personnel, CFO's, MIS mgmt.
Industries: Finance, Banking

Petrie Partners, Inc.

P.O. Box 618663
Orlando, Florida 32861
(407) 521-7703
Fax: (407) 521-6080
Web: cpetrie@msn.com

Key Contact - Specialty:
Mr. Christopher J. Petrie
Ms. Colleen Gavigan

Description: Our firm combines an exceptionally successful track record with highly personalized service. Outstanding references from clients and candidates over the past decade.

Salary Minimum: $90,000
Functions: Generalist, Senior mgmt., Middle mgmt., Distribution, HR mgmt., Personnel, Training
Industries: Generalist, Drugs mfg., Medical devices, Entertainment, Human resource svcs.

Peyser Assoc., Inc.

1717 N. Bayshore Drive, Ste. 4051
Miami, Florida 33132
(305) 374-9010

Key Contact - Specialty:
Mr. Robert E. Peyser - *Financial services*

Description: President has over 20 years experience in executive search and handles all his searches personally assuring high level expertise and accountability.

Salary Minimum: $50,000
Functions: Senior mgmt., Automation, Mkt. research, Systems implem., Engineering, Int'l.
Industries: Generalist, Food/bev/tobacco, Finance, Insurance, High tech, Software

Pharmaceutical Recruiters, Inc.

271 Madison Ave., Ste. 1200
New York, New York 10016
(212) 557-5627
Fax: (212) 557-5866

Key Contact - Specialty:
Ms. Linda S. Weiss - *Pharmaceuticals*

Description: We recruit upper, middle and senior executives for the pharmaceutical industry.

Salary Minimum: $75,000
Functions: Directors, Senior mgmt., Middle mgmt., Product dev., Plant mgmt., Mkt. research, Mktg. mgmt.

† occasional contingency assignment

Industries: Drugs mfg., Pharmaceutical svcs.

Phase II Management

25 Stonybrook Rd.
Westport, Connecticut 06880
(203) 226-7252
Fax: (203) 226-3263

Key Contact - Specialty:
Mr. Richard P. Fincher - *Generalist*

Description: Specialists in packaging, related industries, manufacturing, equipment, electrical/electronics, industrial sales, marketing and distribution. Frequent work for U.S. subsidiaries of foreign companies.

Salary Minimum: $65,000
Functions: Senior mgmt., Middle mgmt., Mfg., Materials, Sales & mktg., CFO's, Engineering
Industries: Generalist, Mfg., Packaging

J. R. Phillip & Assoc., Inc.

555 Twin Dolphin Drive, Ste. 120
Redwood City, California 94065
(650) 631-6700
Fax: (650) 631-6710
Email: jr_phillip@msn.com

Key Contact - Specialty:
Mr. John R. Phillip - *Senior management, board level*
Mr. Glenn P. Ambra - *Senior management, board level*

Description: Over 25 years of search experience. Clients nationwide. Venture capital backed to Fortune 500 clients.

Salary Minimum: $110,000
Functions: Senior mgmt., Product dev., Mktg. mgmt., CFO's
Industries: Drugs mfg., Medical devices, Test/measurement equip., Pharmaceutical svcs., Software, Biotech, Healthcare

Phillips & Assoc. †

62 Derby St., Unit 1
Hingham, Massachusetts 02043-3718
(781) 740-9699
Fax: (781) 740-9064
Email: dphillips@phillipsearch.com
Web: www.phillipsearch.com

Key Contact - Specialty:
Mr. Daniel J. Phillips

Description: We are a healthcare specialized search and recruitment firm. The benefits to prospective clients include: healthcare professional performing the search, a shorter recruiting cycle, an extensive database and national network of healthcare professionals.

Salary Minimum: $50,000
Functions: Directors, Middle mgmt., Health admin., Sales mgmt., CFO's, Risk mgmt., MIS mgmt.
Industries: Higher ed., Mgmt. consulting, Software, Healthcare

Phoenix Search

Viaducto Miguel Aleman 259-102
Col. Roma Sur
Mexico City, Mexico DF 06760
Mexico
525 564-6583
Email: phoenix_search@ibm.net

Key Contact - Specialty:
Mr. L. Ignacio Garrote - *Information technology*

Description: Covering all Latin America from offices in Mexico, Brasil and Puerto Rico, we are the region's leading information technology firm. Our practice is well rounded with successful searches in many industries.

Salary Minimum: $50,000
Functions: Directors, Senior mgmt., Mktg. mgmt., Sales mgmt., CFO's, MIS mgmt., Int'l.
Industries: Generalist, Energy/utilities, Mfg., Transportation, Retail, High tech, Software

International Branches:
Sao Paulo

Affiliates:
Executive Search Associates

Physician Executive Management Center

4014 Gunn Hwy., Ste. 160
Tampa, Florida 33624-4787
(813) 963-1800
Email:
PhysicianExecutive@compuserve.com
Web: PhysicianExecutive.com

Key Contact - Specialty:
Mr. David R. Kirschman - *Physician executives*
Ms. Jennifer R. Grebenschikoff - *Physician executives*

Description: Only national firm specializing in physician executives. Our clients are hospital systems, group practices, managed care and insurance companies who ask us to find physician-only CEOs, vice presidents of medical affairs, medical directors and department chiefs.

Salary Minimum: $100,000
Functions: Senior mgmt., Physicians
Industries: Healthcare

Picard Int'l., Ltd.

125 E. 38th St.
New York, New York 10016
(212) 252-1620
Fax: (212) 252-0973
Email: office@picardintl.com
Web: www.picardintl.com

Key Contact - Specialty:
Mr. Daniel A. Picard - *Financial services, technology, healthcare, management consulting*

Description: Senior executive searches in a broad range of functions including general management, corporate strategy, technology, capital markets in financial services, management consulting, healthcare and high technology industries.

Salary Minimum: $150,000
Functions: Health admin., CFO's, Cash mgmt., Risk mgmt., MIS mgmt., Mgmt. consultants
Industries: Banking, Invest. banking, Mgmt. consulting, Human resource svcs., High tech, Software, Healthcare
Professional Associations: IACPR

International Branches:
Sao Paulo

Pierce & Crow

(Firm declined to update.)
100 Drakes Landing Rd., Ste. 300
Greenbrae, California 94904
(415) 925-1191
Email: pac@piercecrow.com
Web: www.piercecrow.com

Key Contact - Specialty:
Mr. Richard Pierce
Mr. Dennis Crow

Description: Recruitment of corporate officers in the high tech industry, specializing in sales, marketing, engineering and general management positions.

Salary Minimum: $125,000
Functions: Senior mgmt., Mktg. mgmt., Sales mgmt., Engineering, Int'l.
Industries: High tech, Software

Pinsker and Company, Inc.

P.O. Box 3269
Saratoga, California 95070
(408) 867-5161
Email: pinskerinc@earthlink.net

Key Contact - Specialty:
Mr. Richard J. Pinsker - *Board members, key executives*

Description: Executive selection consultants. Client results: locate best candidates through retained search engagements; select best candidates through hiring decision-making workshops. Pinsker is author of "Hiring Winners" (AMACOM

Books).

Salary Minimum: $100,000
Functions: Generalist, Directors, Senior mgmt., Middle mgmt.
Industries: Generalist, Computer equip., Test/measurement equip., Misc. mfg., High tech

Pinton Forrest & Madden/EMA Partners Int'l.

1055 W. Hastings St., Ste. 1220
Guinness Twr.
Vancouver, British Columbia V6E 2E9
Canada
(604) 689-9970
Fax: (604) 689-9943
Email: pfm_emapartners@bc.sympatico.ca

Key Contact - Specialty:
Mr. Garth Pinton
Mr. Casey Forrest
Mr. George Madden

Description: We build long-term client relationships through the partners' 40 combined years of recruitment and business management experience plus our direct involvement in each search assignment, backed by quality research.

Salary Minimum: $70,000
Functions: Purchasing, Materials Plng., Mktg. mgmt., Sales mgmt., Credit, M&A, MIS mgmt.
Industries: Energy/utilities, Mfg., Finance, Hospitality, Entertainment, Communications, Government
Professional Associations: AESC

Networks:
EMA Partners Int'l.

DNPitchon Assoc.

60 W. Ridgewood Ave.
Ridgewood, New Jersey 07450
(201) 612-8350

Key Contact - Specialty:
Mr. Daniel N. Pitchon - *Generalist*
Ms. Linda A. Belen - *Generalist*

Description: Consultancy based executive search practice.

Salary Minimum: $100,000
Functions: Generalist, Senior mgmt., Middle mgmt., Mktg. mgmt., HR mgmt., CFO's
Industries: Generalist, Food/bev/tobacco, Paper, Chemicals, Motor vehicles, Transportation, Hospitality

Plante & Moran, LLP

27400 Northwestern Hwy.
Southfield, Michigan 48034
(248) 352-2500
Fax: (248) 352-0018
Email: careers@plante-moran.com
Web: www.plante-moran.com

Key Contact - Specialty:
Dr. Dennis Blender

Description: Specialize in recruiting financial, accounting, administrative, human resources and information technology positions with emphasis in the manufacturing, healthcare, not-for-profit and financial industries. We utilize psychological assessment services to assist in matching candidates to a position.

Salary Minimum: $30,000
Functions: Allied health, Customer svc., Training, M&A, Risk mgmt., Systems support, Non-profits
Industries: Misc. mfg., Banking, Accounting, Human resource svcs., Telecoms, Real estate, Healthcare

Plemmons Assoc., Inc.

535-B Colonial Park Drive, Ste. 202
Roswell, Georgia 30075
(770) 993-6073
(770) 998-1074
Fax: (770) 993-8657

Key Contact - Specialty:
Mr. Patrick F. Plemmons

Description: Your search is done by a senior-level, experienced professional. We offer craftsmanship, personalized service, attention to detail and concern for the unique needs of your organization.

Salary Minimum: $75,000
Functions: Senior mgmt., Middle mgmt., Physicians, Health admin.
Industries: Healthcare

Rene Plessner Assoc., Inc.

375 Park Ave.
New York, New York 10152
(212) 421-3490
Fax: (212) 421-3999

Key Contact - Specialty:
Mr. Rene Plessner

Description: A boutique executive search firm specializing in cosmetics, accessories, apparel and fashion-related areas, also consumer packaged goods, retail, and high technology, with an emphasis on entrepreneurial companies.

Salary Minimum: $75,000
Functions: General mgmt., Mfg., Sales & mktg., Advertising, Mktg. mgmt., Sales mgmt., PR
Industries: Textiles/apparel, Soap/perfume/cosmetics, Computer equip., Advertising/PR, Aerospace, High tech
Professional Associations: IACPR

R. L. Plimpton Assoc., Inc.

(Firm declined to update.)
900 E. Logan Circle
Greenwood Village, Colorado 80121
(303) 771-1311

Key Contact - Specialty:
Mr. Ralph L. Plimpton - *Information technology*
Ms. Edie Shearer - *Information technology*
Ms. Adrienne Robinson - *Information technology*

Description: Exceptionally quick response. Performance-based selection techniques coupled with attention to fit with the corporate culture, management chemistry and strategic objectives. General management, financial, high technology, manufacturing and marketing.

Salary Minimum: $65,000
Functions: Middle mgmt., Automation, Distribution, Mktg. mgmt., Cash mgmt., Systems anal., Engineering
Industries: Energy/utilities, Mfg., Computer equip., Finance, Computer svcs., Insurance, Software

Yves Plouffe & Assoc.

209, 9th St.
Rouyn-Noranda, Quebec J9X 2C1
Canada
(819) 764-6432
Fax: (819) 764-6888
Email: yplouffe@cablevision.qc.ca

Key Contact - Specialty:
Mr. Yves J. Plouffe - *Management, sales & marketing, engineering, international*
Mr. Normand Gélinas - *Manufacturing, engineering, general management, human resources*
Ms. Christine Marenger - *Human resources, manufacturing, finance & accounting*
Mr. Georges H. Désilets - *International, finance & accounting, sales & marketing*

Description: Their solid record demonstrates their capabilities in personnel search and recruiting, remuneration surveys and personnel ouplacement. Active files on natural resources personnel, rapid achievement of results, confidentiality, thoroughness and their warranty.

Salary Minimum: $62,000
Functions: General mgmt., Mfg., Sales & mktg., HR mgmt., Finance, Engineering, Int'l.
Industries: Agri/forestry/mining, Energy/utilities, Mfg., Finance, Svcs., Communications, Environmental svcs.

Affiliates:
Sociogest

Plummer & Assoc., Inc.

65 Rowayton Avenue
Rowayton, Connecticut 06853
(203) 899-1233
Fax: (203) 838-0887
Email: resume@plummersearch.com
Web: www.plummersearch.com

Key Contact - Specialty:
Mr. John Plummer
Ms. Kathy Mackenna
Mr. Jeff Hunt
Ms. Heidi Plummer

Description: Specializes in CEO/COO/ senior officer level assignments for the retail industry: wholesale trade, retail services, quick serve/casual dining, catalogs/direct marketing, manufacturers for the retail industry (toys, cosmetics, apparel) and retail consulting firms.

Salary Minimum: $125,000
Functions: Directors, Senior mgmt., Middle mgmt., Advertising, CFO's, MIS mgmt., Mgmt. consultants
Industries: Textiles/apparel, Wholesale, Retail, Venture cap., Hospitality, Entertainment, Mgmt. consulting

Branches:
231 Washington Ave.
Marietta, Georgia 30060
(770) 429-9007
Fax: (770) 426-6374
Key Contact - Specialty:
Ms. Susan Gill

Poirier, Hoevel & Co.

12400 Wilshire Blvd., Ste. 915
Los Angeles, California 90025
(310) 207-3427
Fax: (310) 820-7431

Key Contact - Specialty:
Mr. Michael J. Hoevel - *Generalist*
Mr. Roland L. Poirier - *Generalist*

Description: California based professional firm - national and international Fortune 1000 base with emphasis on manufacturing, financial institutions, entertainment, public accounting, consumer products, aerospace, service and hi-tech.

Salary Minimum: $75,000
Functions: Generalist, Senior mgmt., Mktg. mgmt., CFO's, Taxes, MIS mgmt., Engineering
Industries: Generalist, Wholesale, Retail, Finance, Telecoms, Aerospace, High tech

Ray Polhill & Assoc.

P.O. Box 470653
Charlotte, North Carolina 28247
(704) 365-4522
Fax: (704) 365-6224
Email: rlpohill@aol.com

Key Contact - Specialty:
Mr. Ray L. Polhill

Description: Principals with strong industry credentials provide searches for CEO, sales, marketing, product support management. Focus: construction equipment, material handling, engine/power generation, forestry, and ag equipment - manufacturer and dealer clients. High standards, client satisfaction.

Salary Minimum: $60,000
Functions: Senior mgmt., Middle mgmt., Mfg., Mktg. mgmt., Sales mgmt., Customer svc., Int'l.
Industries: Generalist, Agri/forestry/mining, Construction, Mfg., Machinery/ Appliances

Polson & Co., Inc.

15 S. Fifth St., Ste. 750
Minneapolis, Minnesota 55402
(612) 332-6607
Fax: (612) 332-6296
Email: polson29@idt.net

Key Contact - Specialty:
Ms. Martha Spriggs
Mr. Christopher C. Polson - *Generalist*
Mr. Ed McLellan

Description: Full service, retainer fee, executive search firm; generalist.

Salary Minimum: $100,000
Functions: Generalist, General mgmt., Mfg., Sales & mktg., HR mgmt., Finance, IT
Industries: Generalist, Agri/forestry/mining, Mfg., Communications, High tech, Healthcare

David Powell, Inc.

2995 Woodside Rd., Ste. 150
Woodside, California 94062
(650) 851-6000
Fax: (650) 851-5514
Email: dpi@davidpowell.com
Web: www.davidpowell.com

Key Contact - Specialty:
Mr. David Powell
Ms. Jean Bagileo
Mr. Bill Wraith
Mr. David Powell, Jr.
Mr. Robb Kundtz
Mr. Steve Balogh
Ms. Parm Williams
Ms. Sheila Trombadore
Mr. Gary Rockow
Ms. Lindsay White

Description: Our primary focus is officer-level searches for emerging and established companies in high technology industries. We also have extensive background in healthcare, biotechnology, environmental, construction and natural resources.

Salary Minimum: $125,000
Functions: Senior mgmt., Mfg., Sales & mktg., HR mgmt., CFO's, MIS mgmt., Engineering
Industries: Mfg., Communications, Environmental svcs., High tech, Software, Biotech, Healthcare

Powers Consultants, Inc. †

2241A S. Brentwood Blvd., Ste. IV
St. Louis, Missouri 63144
(314) 961-8787
(314) 961-6437
Fax: (314) 968-0758
Email: np7969@aol.com

Key Contact - Specialty:
Mr. William D. Powers - *Architecture, engineering, construction (all disciplines), hospitality*

Description: Serves nationally many of the largest and smallest professional service firms within the design and construction industries, providing clients with a unique two-year performance guarantee on placements plus an extremely high (87%) retention stick ratio over past fifteen years.

Salary Minimum: $40,000
Functions: Senior mgmt., Sales mgmt., MIS mgmt., Systems implem., Engineering, Architects
Industries: Construction, Food/bev/tobacco, Drugs mfg., Hospitality, Environmental svcs., Real estate, Biotech

Branches:
22 Oak Bend Court
Ladue, Missouri 63124
(314) 961-8792
Key Contact - Specialty:
Ms. Janet Powers - *Banking, food processing, environmental, management systems*

Prairie Resource Group, Inc. †

137 N. Oak Park Ave., Ste. 307
Oak Park, Illinois 60301
(708) 763-9100
Fax: (708) 763-9200
Email: search@prgchicago.com
Web: www.prgchicago.com

Key Contact - Specialty:
Mr. M. Kent Taylor - *High technology, general operations management, consulting*
Mr. Richard Gertler - *Sales & marketing, software implementation & development*

Description: Specialized to recruit unique talent for high-tech traditional manufacturing industries. Most effective on technically demanding personnel specifications, where in-depth engineering/ scientific knowledge is required, along with solid business and people skills. Also extremely cost effective on multiple positions in all industries.

Salary Minimum: $50,000
Functions: Generalist, General mgmt., Mfg., Finance, IT, R&D, Engineering
Industries: Generalist, Mfg., Finance, Mgmt. consulting, Telecoms, High tech, Software

Elan Pratzer & Partners Inc.
40 King St. W., Ste. 4714
Box 404
Toronto, Ontario M5H 3Y2
Canada
(416) 365-1841
Fax: (416) 365-0851

Key Contact - Specialty:
Mr. Elan Pratzer
Mr. Dov Zevy
Mr. John Mealia
Mr. Tom Summers
Ms. Barbara Bruner

Description: Retainer firm which is dedicated to building resilient executive teams. Areas of expertise include financial services, real estate, merchant banking, high tech and manufacturing.

Salary Minimum: $100,000
Functions: Generalist, Senior mgmt., Product dev., Mktg. mgmt., CFO's, M&A, MIS mgmt.
Industries: Generalist, Banking, Venture cap., Computer svcs., Real estate, High tech, Software
Professional Associations: AESC

PRAXIS Partners
5004 Monument Ave., Ste. 102
Richmond, Virginia 23230
(804) 739-5809
(804) 359-0104
Fax: (804) 739-5547
Email: vapraxis@aol.com
Web: www.praxispartners.com

Key Contact - Specialty:
Mr. David H. DeBaugh - *General management, manufacturing, human resources*
Mr. Samuel Davis, III - *Retail, venture capital, information technology*
Mr. Donald J. Pliszka - *Generalist*
Mr. Larry D. Olszewski - *Manufacturing, automotive*
Mr. Allen Moore - *Information technology*

Description: Boutique firm offering partner involvement in all aspects of retained search for senior leadership positions. Complementary consulting services in executive compensation and business strategy. Client base ranges from family-owned businesses to Fortune 200.

Salary Minimum: $60,000
Functions: Directors, Senior mgmt., Plant mgmt., Sales mgmt., HR mgmt., CFO's, IT
Industries: Generalist, Mfg., Paper, Metal products, Retail, Venture cap., High tech

Predictor Systems Corp.
1796 Equestrian Drive
Pleasanton, California 94588
(510) 846-9396
Fax: (510) 849-9392
Email: ldillon984@aol.com
Web: dillon1@msn.com

Key Contact - Specialty:
Mr. Larry A. Dillon - *High technology*
Ms. Helen Schultz - *High technology*

Description: Searches are conducted using advanced interactive CD-ROM candidate comparisons developed around a custom designed four-dimensional interviewing approach which evaluates a candidate's fit in regards to position, organizational, behavioral and technical factors.

Salary Minimum: $100,000
Functions: Senior mgmt., Middle mgmt., Product dev., MIS mgmt.
Industries: Computer equip., High tech, Software

George Preger & Associates Inc.
41 MacPherson Ave.
Toronto, Ontario M5R 1W7
Canada
(416) 922-6336
Fax: (416) 922-4902
Email: consult@georgepreger.com
Web: www.georgepreger.com

Key Contact - Specialty:
Mr. G. A. Preger

Description: A leading independent executive search firm in Canada. All industries and functions. Senior management oriented. We are unique in Canada in the emphasis we place on research and direct servicing.

Salary Minimum: $70,000
Functions: Directors, Senior mgmt., Plant mgmt., Sales mgmt., CFO's, MIS mgmt., Engineering
Industries: Mfg., Textiles/apparel, Medical devices, Motor vehicles, Consumer electronics, Test/measurement equip., Aerospace

International Branches:
Haita

Preng & Assoc., Inc.
2925 Briarpark, Ste. 1111
Houston, Texas 77042
(713) 266-2600
Fax: (713) 266-3070
Web: www.preng.com

Key Contact - Specialty:
Mr. David E. Preng - *Energy, chemicals, natural resources*
Mr. William G. French - *Energy, manufacturing, management consulting, international (former Soviet Union & Europe)*
Mr. William J. Mathias - *Energy exploration, production, engineering, information systems*
Mr. Ralph Stevens - *Energy, management consulting, manufacturing*

Description: Worldwide executive search capabilities specializing in oil and gas, chemicals, power, refining, manufacturing, natural resources, petrochemicals, engineering and construction and environmental services. Special expertise in CIS.

Salary Minimum: $75,000
Functions: Directors, Senior mgmt., Middle mgmt., CFO's, MIS mgmt., Engineering, Mgmt. consultants
Industries: Energy/utilities, Construction, Chemicals, Mgmt. consulting, Environmental svcs.
Professional Associations: AESC

International Branches:
London, Moscow, Vienna

Preston & Co. †
461 Route 625
Pittstown, New Jersey 08867
(908) 730-7411
Email: joepre@ix.netcom.com

Key Contact - Specialty:
Mr. Joe Preston - *Financial services*

Description: We specialize in the investment and mutual fund industries and financial services in general. With 13 years of experience, we have an extensive network of contacts.
Functions: Senior mgmt., Middle mgmt., Mktg. mgmt., Sales mgmt., Budgeting, Cash mgmt., Mgmt. consultants
Industries: Banking, Invest. banking, Brokers, Misc. financial, Computer svcs., Accounting, Mgmt. consulting

Preston-Hunter, Inc.
105 N. 10th
Mattoon, Illinois 61938
(217) 235-1051
Fax: (217) 235-2053

Key Contact - Specialty:
Mr. Paul Bailey - *Manufacturing, consumer products, high technology, general management*

Description: A general search practice firm with a strong track record in consumer products, manufacturing and high technology. Concentrate in the midwest and southwest including midsize and large cities.

† occasional contingency assignment

Salary Minimum: $60,000
Functions: Generalist, General mgmt., Mfg., Sales & mktg., Finance, IT, Mgmt. consultants
Industries: Generalist, Mfg., Svcs., Communications, High tech, Software, Healthcare

Prestonwood Assoc.
266 Main St., Olde Medfield Sq.
Ste. 12A
Medfield, Massachusetts 02052
(508) 359-7100
Fax: (508) 359-4007
Email: prestnwd@ix.netcom.com

Key Contact - Specialty:
Ms. Diane Coletti

Description: Specialists in marketing and sales disciplines-heavy emphasis in high tech, software, communications, consulting services, medical devices and consumer products. Provide a high quality retained search resource to highly professional companies. Clients typically small to medium companies.

Salary Minimum: $80,000
Functions: Directors, Senior mgmt., Mkt. research, Sales mgmt., PR, MIS mgmt., Mgmt. consultants
Industries: Medical devices, Computer equip., Mgmt. consulting, Human resource svcs., Telecoms, High tech, Software

PricewaterhouseCoopers Executive Search
Rio de la Plata No. 48 - 9° Piso
Colonia Cuauhtémoc
Mexico City, Mexico DF 06500
Mexico
52 5 722 17 00
Fax: 52 5 553 92 11
Email:
francisco_noriega@mexico.notes.pw.com
Web: www.pw.com.mx

Key Contact - Specialty:
Mr. Francisco Noriega Muñoz - *Generalist*
Ms. Laura Chávez Flores - *Generalist*
Ms. Lorena Zuñiga Rios - *Generalist*

Description: We are an international business advisory firm rendering audit, tax, consulting, legal and foreign trade services.
Functions: General mgmt., Mfg., Materials, Sales & mktg., HR mgmt., Finance, IT
Industries: Generalist, Transportation, Svcs., Communications, Packaging, High tech, Software

PricewaterhouseCoopers Executive Search
Ste. 300, Box 82
Royal Trust Tower, Toronto Dominion Centre
Toronto, Ontario M5K 1G8
Canada
(416) 863-1133
Fax: (416) 365-8215
Email: pw.tor.exec.search@pwcglobal.com
Web: www.pwcglobal.com/ca

Key Contact - Specialty:
Mr. Paul F. Crath - *Generalist, financial services, mining, manufacturing, high technology*
Mr. B. Keith McLean - *Generalist, education, non-profit*
Mr. Tom Sinclair - *Generalist*
Ms. Margaret Campbell - *Generalist*
Ms. Deborah Caplan - *Generalist, distribution, sales & marketing*
Mr. Bob Eaton - *Generalist*
Mr. Charles Lennox - *Information technology, consulting, high technology*
Ms. Barbara Nixon - *Healthcare, non-profit*
Ms. Margaret Pelton - *Healthcare, non-profit*
Mr. Clarke Wallace - *Public sector, municipal, government*

Description: Senior level consultants work with public, private, government and not-for-profit clients on a broad range of middle management and senior executive searches. Fixed fee arrangement ensures complete objectivity throughout the process.

Salary Minimum: $70,000
Functions: Senior mgmt., Middle mgmt., Plant mgmt., Health admin., Sales & mktg., Finance, MIS mgmt.
Industries: Generalist, Energy/utilities, Mfg., Finance, Communications, High tech, Healthcare
Professional Associations: IACPR

Branches:
425 - 1st St. SW, Ste. 1200
Calgary, Alberta T2P 3V7
Canada
(403) 267-1200
Fax: (403) 266-1419
Key Contact - Specialty:
Ms. Irene Pfeiffer - *Generalist, oil & gas*

2401 Toronto Dominion Twr.
Edmonton Centre
Edmonton, Alberta T5J 2Z1
Canada
(403) 493-8200
Fax: (403) 428-8069
Key Contact - Specialty:
Ms. Rose Mary Holland - *Generalist*

601 W. Hastings St., Ste. 1400
Vancouver, British Columbia V6B 5A5
Canada
(604) 682-4711
(604) 661-5700
Fax: (604) 662-5300
Key Contact - Specialty:
Mr. Robert McMillin - *Generalist, manufacturing, associations*
Mr. Grant Smith - *Generalist, mining, club management*
Mr. Rob VanNus - *Generalist*

2200 One Lombard Place
Winnipeg, Manitoba R3B 0X7
Canada
(204) 943-7321
Fax: (204) 943-7774
Key Contact - Specialty:
Ms. Karen Swystun - *Generalist*

1250 Rene-Levesque Boulevard West
Montreal, Quebec H3B 2G4
Canada
(514) 938-5600
Fax: (514) 938-5709
Key Contact - Specialty:
Mr. Joe Beaupre - *Generalist*
Mr. Claude Daigneault - *Generalist*

Prichard Kymen Inc.
12204 - 106 Ave., Ste. 302
Edmonton, Alberta T5N 3Z1
Canada
(403) 448-0128
Fax: (403) 453-5246
Email: lawink4774@aol.com

Key Contact - Specialty:
Mr. Pat McKinney - *Executive, technical, middle management*
Ms. Linda Weiss - *Technical sales, human resource personnel administrative*

Description: We have recruited in the technical, engineering and mid-senior management areas. Our client base includes an increasing number of Canadian and North American organizations.
Functions: Senior mgmt., Production, Distribution, Allied health, Mktg. mgmt., HR mgmt., Engineering
Industries: Generalist, Agri/forestry/mining, Construction, Lumber/furniture, Drugs mfg., Machinery/Appliances, Transportation

The Primary Group, Inc. †
P.O. Box 916160
Longwood, Florida 32791-6160
(407) 869-4111
Fax: (407) 682-3321

Key Contact - Specialty:
Mr. Ken Friedman - *Mutual funds, insurance*
Mr. Jerry Goldsmith - *Bank securities & investments, insurance, banking*

Description: Executive search for investment and insurance products in financial institutions and broker dealers. Expertise in management and sales from senior to regional levels. Other areas: legal, healthcare and employee benefits.

Salary Minimum: $50,000
Functions: Senior mgmt., Mkt. research, Mktg. mgmt., Sales mgmt., Cash mgmt., Risk mgmt., Attorneys
Industries: Banking, Invest. banking, Brokers, Misc. financial, Legal, Insurance, Real estate

Primus Assoc., L.C.

13915 Burnet Rd., Ste. 440
Austin, Texas 78728
(512) 246-2266
Fax: (512) 246-1333
Email: info@primusnet.com
Web: www.primusnet.com

Key Contact - Specialty:
Mr. Sam Gassett - *High technology (executive level)*
Ms. Becky Gates - *High technology, senior level, executive level*
Mr. Charles Leadford - *High technology, senior level, executive level*

Description: Our high technology sector specialization enables us to identify and contact target candidates faster and more effectively than generalist firms.
Functions: Directors, Senior mgmt., Middle mgmt., Sales mgmt., CFO's, MIS mgmt., Engineering
Industries: High tech, Software

Princeton Search Partners, Inc.

475 Wall St.
Princeton, New Jersey 08540
(609) 430-9600
Fax: (609) 924-8270
Email: pspinc@ix.netcom.com

Key Contact - Specialty:
Mr. Anthony A. Latini - *Financial services, technology, healthcare*
Dr. M. Katherine Kraft - *Human resources*
Mr. William J. Brickner - *Healthcare*

Description: Generalist boutique executive search firm providing highly personalized and responsive service to prestigious clients.

Salary Minimum: $75,000
Functions: Generalist, Senior mgmt., Middle mgmt., Health admin., Direct mktg., Finance, IT
Industries: Generalist, Finance, Computer svcs., Accounting, Mgmt. consulting, Insurance, Healthcare

Prior/Martech Assoc., Inc.

16000 Christensen Rd., Ste. 310
Seattle, Washington 98188-2928
(206) 242-1141
Fax: (206) 242-1255
Email: priormar@ix.netcom.com
Web: www.expert-market.com/priormartech

Key Contact - Specialty:
Mr. Paul R. Meyer
Mr. Michael E. McGahan

Description: We assist owners, board members, or CEOs in meeting their staffing requirements both from inside the organization through management appraisal or from outside through executive recruiting. We help organizations in governance issues.

Salary Minimum: $75,000
Functions: Generalist, Senior mgmt., Health admin., CFO's, MIS mgmt.
Industries: Agri/forestry/mining, Construction, Mfg., Healthcare

Affiliates:
Martech Assoc., Inc.

Professional Research Services, Inc.

1101 Perimeter Drive, Ste. 610
Schaumburg, Illinois 60173
(847) 995-8800
Fax: (847) 995-8812
Email: prs1@netwave.net
Web: www.prs1.com

Key Contact - Specialty:
Mr. Tom DeBourcy
Mr. Mike Silber

Description: Nationwide firm providing search and unbundled employment research. The firm provides services in most industries and functions. We primarily deal with mid-level positions in the $30,000 - $100,000 salary range.
Functions: Generalist, Mfg., Materials, Healthcare, Sales & mktg., Finance, Minorities
Industries: Generalist, Mfg., Finance, Svcs., Software, Biotech, Healthcare

Professional Search †

521 Cambridge Drive
Muskegon, Michigan 49441
(616) 798-3537
Fax: (616) 798-8062
Email: info@professionalsearch.net
Web: www.professionalsearch.net

Key Contact - Specialty:
Mr. George McKenzie
Ms. Ingrid McKenzie

Description: Our staff size, team approach and extensive resources enable us to offer recruiting services in a comprehensive range of areas. Our approach enables us to complete the assignment significantly faster than the industry average time.

Salary Minimum: $50,000
Functions: Generalist, Mfg., Sales & mktg., HR mgmt., Finance, IT, Engineering
Industries: Generalist, Mfg., Finance, Svcs., Communications, High tech, Software

Professional Selection Services

4780 Ashford Dunwoody Rd., Ste. 426
Atlanta, Georgia 30338
(770) 393-0109
Fax: (770) 512-0211
Email: smcdowell@profselection.com
Web: www.profselection.com

Key Contact - Specialty:
Ms. Sally A. McDowell - *Middle management*

Description: Mid-management search and selection services. We combine internet research with effective sourcing and screening techniques to identify, screen and present qualified short-list candidates.

Salary Minimum: $70,000
Functions: Middle mgmt., Healthcare, Sales & mktg., HR mgmt., Finance, IT, Mgmt. consultants
Industries: Finance, Svcs., Mgmt. consulting, Communications, Telecoms, High tech, Healthcare

Professional Team Search, Inc.

P.O. Box 30185
Phoenix, Arizona 85046-0185
(602) 482-3600
Fax: (602) 788-0710
Email: pts@ww-web.com

Key Contact - Specialty:
Ms. Denise M. Chaffin - *Computer engineering, electrical engineering, wireless telecommunications*

Description: Our company focus is to work with individual company management teams on a one-to-one basis. Our search efforts are targeted toward mid-level management to executive level professionals.

Salary Minimum: $55,000
Functions: Senior mgmt., MIS mgmt., Systems anal., Systems dev., Systems implem., Systems support, Engineering
Industries: Computer equip., Consumer electronics, Telecoms, Aerospace, High tech, Software, Biotech

† occasional contingency assignment

ProLinks Inc.
1626 Belle View Blvd.
P.O. Box 7365
Alexandria, Virginia 22307-0365
(703) 765-6873
Email: Prolinks@aol.com
Web: www.CareerResources.com

Key Contact - Specialty:
Mr. Don Hughes - *Golf professionals, golf course superintendents, sports*
Ms. J. Reilly Hughes - *Private club managers*

Description: A highly regarded specialized recruiting firm that has both a national and international practice. We are small, cohesive and results oriented. This allows us to provide highly personalized service to a limited clientele.

Salary Minimum: $60,000
Functions: Mgmt. consultants, Int'l.
Industries: Hospitality, Entertainment, Mgmt. consulting, Non-classifiable industries

Pursuant Legal Consultants †
P.O. Box 2347
Seattle, Washington 98111
(206) 682-2599
Email: plclawrs@ix.netcom.com

Key Contact - Specialty:
Mr. Allen G. Norman - *Legal*

Description: Founded in 1984, exclusively executive & legal search firm. Working with Fortune 500 companies as well as law firms. Specialty areas include: in-house counsel, environmental law, partners in transition. Have recently expanded company to include high tech industries of the Pacific Northwest.

Salary Minimum: $60,000
Functions: Attorneys
Industries: Legal

Quantum Int'l., Ltd.
1915 E. Bay Drive, Ste. 2B
Largo, Florida 33771
(813) 587-0000
Fax: (813) 587-0015
Email: quantumnet@pipeline.com

Key Contact - Specialty:
Mr. Douglas L. Anderson - *Technical management*
Ms. Carol D. Small - *Technical management, marketing management*

Description: Retained search; may include specialties (such as sales, finance, training, etc.) designated by clients.

Salary Minimum: $60,000
Functions: Senior mgmt., Middle mgmt., Mktg. mgmt., R&D, Engineering, Mgmt. consultants
Industries: Construction, Mfg., Textiles/apparel, Chemicals, Plastics/rubber, Accounting, Mgmt. consulting

Quetico Corp.
The Towers at Williams Sq.
5215 N. O'Conner, 2nd Floor
Irving, Texas 75039
(972) 868-9150
Fax: (972) 868-9048
Email: quetico@esptx.com

Key Contact - Specialty:
Mr. C. Robert Morrison - *Human resources, retail, restaurant*
Ms. Susan S. Morrison - *Finance, healthcare*

Description: A retained search firm specializing in placement of human resources and finance professionals in all industries and retail restaurant professionals for all functions.

Salary Minimum: $60,000
Functions: General mgmt., Health admin., HR mgmt., Finance
Industries: Generalist, Retail, Finance, Hospitality, Human resource svcs., Real estate, Healthcare

Quigley Assoc.
145 Versailles Circle, Ste. B
Towson, Maryland 21204
(410) 821-1306

Key Contact - Specialty:
Mr. Jack Quigley

Description: Personalized, high quality firm serving all segments of the healthcare field. Emphasis on senior management and physician search. National practice backed by over twenty years experience.

Salary Minimum: $75,000
Functions: Healthcare, Physicians, Health admin., HR mgmt.
Industries: Human resource svcs., Insurance, Healthcare

L. J. Quinn & Assoc., Inc.
260 S. Los Robles Ave., Ste. 301
Pasadena, California 91101-2824
(626) 793-6044
Fax: (626) 793-7183
Email: ljq@pacbell.net

Key Contact - Specialty:
Mr. Leonard J. Quinn

Salary Minimum: $60,000
Functions: Directors, Health admin., Mktg. mgmt., Personnel, M&A, MIS mgmt., Attorneys
Industries: Computer equip., Misc. mfg., Venture cap., Misc. financial, Telecoms, Real estate, Software

Branches:
90 Park Ave., Ste. 1600
New York, New York 10016
(212) 687-7798
Key Contact - Specialty:
Mr. L. J. Quinn

QVS Int'l.
3005 River Drive, Ste. 501
Savannah, Georgia 31404
(912) 353-7773
Email: qvsconsult@aol.com

Key Contact - Specialty:
Mr. B. V. Cooper - *Generalist, middle management, senior management, foreign-based firms in U.S.*
Mr. Eric W. Robyn - *Generalist, middle management, senior management, foreign-based firms in U.S.*

Description: International generalist firm, retained. Serves U.S. and foreign firms. Also provides management consulting in marketing, HR, mergers/acquisitions, organizational development. Two U.S., four foreign affiliates. Also has retained support staffing division.

Salary Minimum: $50,000
Functions: Generalist, General mgmt., Mfg., Sales & mktg., Finance, IT, Engineering
Industries: Generalist, Mfg., Paper, Chemicals, Svcs., Environmental svcs., Packaging

R & L Assoc., Ltd.
235 W. 56th St., Ste. 15J
New York, New York 10019
(212) 247-5735
Fax: (212) 247-7249
Email: RnL711@aol.com

Key Contact - Specialty:
Ms. Rochelle Schumer
Mr. Leonard Rehner - *Financial services, investment banking, consulting*
Mr. Marvin Schumer - *Information technology, information systems*

Description: We are specialists in retained search recruiting. We are the go-getters of executive search. Our searches include: strategy partners, managing directors, consultants, recruiters, research directors, nationwide.
Functions: Senior mgmt., Middle mgmt., Sales mgmt., Training, CFO's, MIS mgmt., Mgmt. consultants
Industries: Generalist, Retail, Finance, Communications, Insurance, High tech, Healthcare

R M Associates
P.O. Box 155
Dublin, Ohio 43017
(614) 846-4432
Fax: (614) 764-3808

Key Contact - Specialty:
Mr. Richard A. Marling - *Generalist*

Description: Generalist, national scope-manager level and up. Heavy emphasis in manufacturing, engineering and finance. Principal has 15+ years in retained search - major clients.

Salary Minimum: $60,000
Functions: Generalist, Middle mgmt., Plant mgmt., Distribution, Sales mgmt., CFO's, Engineering
Industries: Generalist

R/K International Inc.
191 Post Rd. West
Westport, Connecticut 06880
(203) 221-2747
Fax: (203) 221-2754
Email: rk.walsh@worlnet.att.net

Key Contact - Specialty:
Mr. Kenneth A. Walsh
Mr. Richard M. Dubrow

Description: We bring over 45 years of experience to the search process in a collaborative effort with our clients. All assignments are managed from start to finish by the principals. Integrity and performance are the key to our success.

Salary Minimum: $75,000
Functions: General mgmt., Mfg., Materials, Sales & mktg., HR mgmt., Finance, Engineering
Industries: Plastics/rubber, Metal products, Computer equip., Test/measurement equip., Telecoms, High tech, Software

Radosevic Assoc.
4350 La Jolla Village Drive, Ste. 870
San Diego, California 92122-1247
(619) 642-0900

Key Contact - Specialty:
Mr. Frank Radosevic - *High technology generalist*
Ms. Tanya C. Radosevic - *High technology generalist*

Description: President has 28 years experience locating outstanding professionals for multi-disciplined clients, with an emphasis in medical electronics, bioscience, computers, engineering industrial and telecommunications products.

Salary Minimum: $75,000
Functions: Generalist
Industries: Medical devices, Computer equip., Consumer electronics, Test/measurement equip., Aerospace, High tech, Biotech

Raines Int'l. Inc.
1120 Ave. of the Americas, FL 21
New York, New York 10036
(212) 997-1100
Fax: (212) 997-6892
Web: www.rainesintl.com

Key Contact - Specialty:
Mr. Bruce R. Raines

Description: International generalist firm specializing in middle to upper management executives. Concentrations include general management, finance and accounting, marketing, information technology (MIS), strategic planning, operations/procurement, investment banking, real estate/finance, human resources and insurance.

Salary Minimum: $100,000
Functions: General mgmt., Mfg., Materials, Sales & mktg., Finance, IT, Mgmt. consultants
Industries: Generalist, Food/bev/tobacco, Drugs mfg., Transportation, Finance, Communications, High tech
Professional Associations: IACPR

Rand Assoc.
204 Lafayette Ctr.
Kennebunk, Maine 04043
(207) 985-7700

Key Contact - Specialty:
Mr. Rand W. Gesing - *Manufacturing, financial services*

Description: Generalist with a concentration within manufacturing and financial services firms.
Functions: Generalist, Senior mgmt., Middle mgmt., Plant mgmt., Materials Plng., Mktg. mgmt., CFO's
Industries: Generalist, Food/bev/tobacco, Paper, Plastics/rubber, Metal products, Machinery/Appliances, High tech

The Rankin Group, Ltd.
P.O. Box 1120
Lake Geneva, Wisconsin 53147
(414) 279-5005
Fax: (414) 279-6705
Email: mrankin716@aol.com

Key Contact - Specialty:
Mr. Jeffrey A. Rankin
Ms. M. J. Rankin

Description: National search firm specializing in the recruitment of wealth management professionals for institutional and personal trust, private banking, investment and family office positions.

Salary Minimum: $100,000
Functions: Senior mgmt., Middle mgmt., Mktg. mgmt., Sales mgmt., CFO's, Non-profits
Industries: Finance, Invest. banking, Misc. financial, Mgmt. consulting

The Ransford Group
10497 Town & Country Way, Ste. 800
Houston, Texas 77024
(713) 722-7281
Fax: (713) 722-0950
Web: Ransford.com

Key Contact - Specialty:
Mr. Dean E. McMann - *Management consulting, software, high technology*
Mr. Thomas W. Smith
Mr. David J. Kasbaum - *Management consulting, energy*
Mr. Mark Malinski - *COO*
Mr. William Hayes - *Management consulting*
Ms. Maria Anderson - *Research*
Mr. Richard Whittier - *Management consulting, change management*

Description: We are built upon 3 concepts: in-depth research, methodical search and industry specialty.

Salary Minimum: $100,000
Functions: General mgmt., Directors, Senior mgmt., Mktg. mgmt., CFO's, Mgmt. consultants
Industries: Mgmt. consulting, Telecoms, High tech, Software

Ray & Berndtson
301 Commerce St., Ste. 2300
Ft. Worth, Texas 76102
(817) 334-0500
Fax: (817) 334-0779
Web: www.rayberndtson.com

Key Contact - Specialty:
Mr. Paul R. Ray, Jr.
Mr. Paul R. Ray, Sr.
Mr. Reece Pettigrew

Description: Executive search and management consulting firm serving major worldwide companies in a variety of industries.

Salary Minimum: $120,000
Functions: Generalist
Industries: Generalist, Energy/utilities, Food/bev/tobacco, Chemicals, Soap/perfume/cosmetics, Drugs mfg., Medical devices, Metal products, Machinery/Appliances, Motor vehicles, Computer equip., Consumer electronics, Finance, Banking, Invest. banking, Brokers, Venture cap., Pharmaceutical svcs., Computer svcs., Accounting, Equip. svcs., Mgmt. consulting, Human resource svcs., New media, Telecoms, Insurance, High tech, Software, Healthcare
Professional Associations: AESC, IACPR

† occasional contingency assignment

Branches:
2029 Century Park E., Ste. 1000
Los Angeles, California 90067
(310) 557-2828
Fax: (310) 277-0674
Key Contact - Specialty:
Mr. Scott D. Somers - *Business, professional services*

2479 E. Bayshore Rd., Ste. 801
Palo Alto, California 94303
(650) 494-2500
Fax: (650) 494-3800
Email: hma@execsearchfirm.com
Web: www.execsearchfirm.com
Key Contact - Specialty:
Mr. James A. McFadzean
Mr. John A. Holland

191 Peachtree St. NE, Ste. 3800
Atlanta, Georgia 30303-1757
(404) 215-4600
Fax: (404) 215-4620
Key Contact - Specialty:
Mr. Charles B. Eldridge - *Business, professional services*

233 S. Wacker Drive, Ste. 4020
Sears Twr.
Chicago, Illinois 60606-6310
(312) 876-0730
Fax: (312) 876-6850
Key Contact - Specialty:
Mr. Donald B. Clark - *Financial services*

245 Park Ave., 33rd Floor
New York, New York 10167
(212) 370-1316
Fax: (212) 370-1462
Key Contact - Specialty:
Mr. Kenneth M. Rich - *Financial services*

Texas Commerce Tower
2200 Ross Ave., Ste. 4500W
Dallas, Texas 75201
(214) 969-7620
Fax: (214) 754-0646
Key Contact - Specialty:
Mr. Breck Ray - *Energy, utilities, industrial*

301 Commerce St., Ste. 2300
Ft. Worth, Texas 76102
(817) 334-0500
Fax: (817) 870-9838
Key Contact - Specialty:
Mr. Breck Ray - *Energy, utilities, industrial*

500 Dallas, Ste. 3010
One Allen Ctr.
Houston, Texas 77002
(713) 309-1400
Fax: (713) 309-1401
Key Contact - Specialty:
Mr. Steven Raben - *Energy, utilities, industrial*

400 5th Ave. SW, Ste. 400
Calgary, Alberta T2P 0L6
Canada
(403) 269-3277
Fax: (403) 262-9347
Key Contact - Specialty:
Mr. Terry K. O'Callaghan
Mr. W. Michael M. Honey
Mr. W. John McKay

710-1050 W. Pender St.
Vancouver, British Columbia V6E 3S7
Canada
(604) 685-0261
Fax: (604) 684-7988
Email: vancouver@raybern.ca
Web: www.prb.com
Key Contact - Specialty:
Mr. Kyle Mitchell - *Generalist*
Mr. John Tanton - *Generalist*
Ms. Catherine Van Alstine
Mr. Alec Wallace
Mr. Craig Hemer

155 S. Queen St., Ste. 900
Ottawa, Ontario K1P 6L1
Canada
(613) 786-3191
Fax: (613) 569-1661
Key Contact - Specialty:
Mr. Richard Morgan - *Generalist, senior executives*

200 Bay St., Ste. 3150, South Twr.
Royal Bank Tower
Toronto, Ontario M5J 2J3
Canada
(416) 366-1990
Fax: (416) 366-7353
Email: lmk@prbcan.com
Key Contact - Specialty:
Mr. W. Carl Lovas - *Generalist, senior executives*
Mr. Paul R. A. Stanley - *Generalist, senior executives*
Mr. Gordon Wilson - *Financial, senior executives*
Mr. David Murray - *Finance, senior executives*
Mr. Michael O'Keefe - *Senior executives, healthcare*

1250 W. Rene-Levesque Blvd., Ste. 3925
Montreal, Quebec H3B 4W8
Canada
(514) 937-1000
Fax: (514) 937-1264
Email: bernardlabrecque@ray-berndtson.ca
Web: www.ray-berndtson.ca
Key Contact - Specialty:
Mr. B. F. Labrecque - *Pharmaceuticals, telecommunications, information technology*
Mr. J. E. Laurendeau - *Financial services, manufacturing, professional services*
Mr. Roger Lachance - *Manufacturing, paper, forestry*
Mr. Jacques Woods - *Consumer packaged goods, communications, automotive*

Palo Santo No. 6
Colonia Lomas Altas
Mexico City, Mexico DF 11950
Mexico
52 5 570 74 62
Fax: 52 5 259 4000
Email: cdudley@Rayberndtson.com
Key Contact - Specialty:
Mr. Craig J. Dudley
Mr. Luis Lezama
Ms. Paulina Robles Cuellar
Mr. Pedro Cortina Del Valle

International Branches:
Amsterdam, Bangalore, Barcelona, Beijing, Budapest, Buenos Aires, Caracas, Central Hong Kong, Chiyoda-ku, Copenhagen, Frankfurt, Helsinki, Istanbul, Lisbon, London, Madrid, Melbourne, Milan, Mumbai, Oslo, Paris, Prague, Sao Paulo, Shanghai, Singapore, Stockholm, Sydney, Vienna, Warsaw, Zavantem

Ray & Berndtson/Laurendeau Labrecque

1250 W. Rene-Levesque Blvd., Ste. 3925
Montreal, Quebec H3B 4W8
Canada
(514) 937-1000
Fax: (514) 937-1264
Email: bernardlabrecque@ray-berndtson.ca
Web: www.ray-berndtson.ca

Key Contact - Specialty:
Mr. B. F. Labrecque - *Pharmaceuticals, telecommunications, information technology*
Mr. J. E. Laurendeau - *Financial services, manufacturing, professional services*
Mr. Roger Lachance - *Manufacturing, paper, forestry*
Mr. Jacques Woods - *Consumer packaged goods, communications, automotive*

Description: We recruit senior-level management and business leaders who integrate well into the unique culture of our client organizations and achieve their position's objectives as well as personal growth ambitions.

Salary Minimum: $75,000
Functions: General mgmt., Mfg., Sales & mktg., Finance, IT, R&D, Engineering
Industries: Agri/forestry/mining, Energy/utilities, Mfg., Finance, Insurance, High tech, Biotech
Professional Associations: AESC

Ray & Berndtson/Lovas Stanley †

200 Bay St., Ste. 3150, South Twr.
Royal Bank Tower
Toronto, Ontario M5J 2J3
Canada
(416) 366-1990
Fax: (416) 366-7353
Email: lmk@prbcan.com

Key Contact - Specialty:
Mr. W. Carl Lovas - *Generalist, senior executives*
Mr. Paul R. A. Stanley - *Generalist, senior executives*
Mr. Gordon Wilson - *Financial, senior executives*

Mr. David Murray - *Finance, senior executives*
Mr. Michael O'Keefe - *Senior executives, healthcare*

Description: Canada's leading executive search firm serving major organizations worldwide on matters of management, leadership and human resources.

Salary Minimum: $75,000
Functions: Generalist, Senior mgmt., Product dev., Sales mgmt., Benefits, CFO's, MIS mgmt.
Industries: Generalist, Food/bev/tobacco, Finance, Communications, Government, High tech, Healthcare
Professional Associations: AESC, IACPR

Branches:
155 S. Queen St., Ste. 900
Ottawa, Ontario K1P 6L1
Canada
(613) 786-3191
Fax: (613) 569-1661
Key Contact - Specialty:
Mr. Richard Morgan - *Generalist, senior executives*

Ray & Berndtson/Tanton Mitchell

710-1050 W. Pender St.
Vancouver, British Columbia V6E 3S7
Canada
(604) 685-0261
Fax: (604) 684-7988
Email: vancouver@raybern.ca
Web: www.prb.com

Key Contact - Specialty:
Mr. Kyle Mitchell - *Generalist*
Mr. John Tanton - *Generalist*
Ms. Catherine Van Alstine
Mr. Alec Wallace
Mr. Craig Hemer

Description: The largest executive and management search firm in Western Canada with eleven professional staff providing search services to major organizations in every industry group.

Salary Minimum: $70,000
Functions: Senior mgmt., Middle mgmt., Admin. svcs., Health admin., CFO's, MIS mgmt., Non-profits
Industries: Generalist
Professional Associations: AESC

RCE Assoc.

39 Tamarack Circle
Skillman, New Jersey 08558
(609) 688-1190
(609) 688-0797
Email: jwg@plasticsearch.com
Web: www.plasticsearch.com

Key Contact - Specialty:
Mr. John W. Guarniere - *Tooling, custom injection molding, precision metal stamping, electronic connector*

Description: We have completed 100+ technical and hard to find executive searches.

Salary Minimum: $85,000
Functions: General mgmt., Plant mgmt., Mktg. mgmt., Sales mgmt.

International Branches:
Horsham St. Faith

Redden & McGrath Assoc., Inc.

427 Bedford Rd.
Pleasantville, New York 10570
(914) 747-3900
Fax: (914) 747-3984

Key Contact - Specialty:
Ms. Mary Redden - *Marketing research, marketing*
Ms. Laura McGrath Faller - *General search including: direct response marketing, magazine publishing, television/home video marketing, production and distribution, finance and accounting, human resources*

Description: Nationwide practice specializing in marketing, marketing research, direct marketing and sales promotion for consumer and service industries. All searches directly managed by partner with emphasis on service and quality.

Salary Minimum: $60,000
Functions: Mkt. research, Mktg. mgmt., Direct mktg., Customer svc., HR mgmt., Finance
Industries: Food/bev/tobacco, Soap/perfume/cosmetics, Banking, Misc. financial, Hospitality, Publishing, Broadcast & Film

Redden-Shaffer Group

290 Maple Court, Ste. 108
Ventura, California 93003-3510
(805) 642-3670
Fax: (805) 642-3847
Email: rsg@vcnet.com

Key Contact - Specialty:
Mr. Bradford W. Shaffer
Mr. Daniel J. Redden

Description: Executive level searches across major functional units with emphasis in computers, biotechnology, financial services, telecommunications and higher education. Additional emphasis on serving U.S. companies with operations in Asia.

Salary Minimum: $100,000
Functions: General mgmt., Mfg., Sales & mktg., HR mgmt., Finance, IT, Engineering
Industries: Computer equip., Consumer electronics, Banking, Higher ed., Telecoms, High tech, Biotech

Affiliates:
Moyer, Sherwood Assoc., Inc.

Redwood Partners Ltd.

152 Madison Ave., 22nd Floor
New York, New York 10016
(212) 843-8585
Fax: (212) 843-9093
Email: redwood@redwoodpartners.com
Web: www.redwoodpartners.com/

Key Contact - Specialty:
Mr. Michael Flannery - *Sales, marketing, new media, Internet & interactive services, electronic commerce software*
Mr. Randy Schoenfeld - *Marketing Services, new media, internet and interactive services*

Description: Our searches will be in the areas of marketing, direct marketing (continuities, clubs, magazines, catalogs and interactive/www sites), sales promotion, brand/product development, advertising sales, production, special markets and new business development.

Salary Minimum: $50,000
Functions: Sales & mktg., Advertising, Mktg. mgmt., Sales mgmt., IT
Industries: Computer svcs., Communications, New media, High tech, Software

Reece & Mruk Partners/EMA Partners Int'l.

75 Second Ave., Ste. 305
Needham, Massachusetts 02194-2800
(781) 449-3603

Key Contact - Specialty:
Mr. Christopher S. Reece - *Generalist*

Description: We are a retainer-based executive search firm. We are part of a global alliance, EMA Partners Int'l. which includes 25 offices in 18 countries.
Functions: Generalist, General mgmt., Mfg., Healthcare, Sales & mktg., CFO's, MIS mgmt.
Industries: Generalist, Mfg., Finance, Svcs., Communications, Biotech, Healthcare
Professional Associations: AESC

Networks:
EMA Partners Int'l.

Reeder & Assoc., Ltd.

1095 Old Roswell Rd., Ste. F
Roswell, Georgia 30076-1665
(770) 649-7523
Fax: (770) 649-7543
Email: administrator@reederassoc.com
Web: www.reederassoc.com

Key Contact - Specialty:
Mr. Michael S. Reeder - *Managed care, healthcare*

Description: We are a national executive search/consulting firm specializing in managed care and healthcare. We believe our firm, compared to larger, generalist firms can provide greater insight, knowledge and value.

Salary Minimum: $200,000
Functions: Senior mgmt., Physicians, Health admin., Mktg. mgmt., HR mgmt., CFO's, MIS mgmt.
Industries: Healthcare
Professional Associations: AESC

Reese Assoc.

10475 Perry Hwy.
Wexford, Pennsylvania 15090
(724) 935-8644

Key Contact - Specialty:
Mr. Charles D. Reese, Jr. - *Metals, machinery, basic industrial products*
Mr. Robert L. Kirkpatrick - *Mining, metals, machinery, basic products*

Description: Retainer search firm plus some related consulting specializes in metals, metals fabricating, mining, capital equipment, building products, fluid power, miscellaneous manufacturing industries.

Salary Minimum: $75,000
Functions: Generalist
Industries: Leather/stone/glass/clay, Metal products, Machinery/Appliances, Test/measurement equip., Misc. mfg.

The Regis Group, Ltd. †

4292 Revere Circle
Marietta, Georgia 30062
(770) 998-2188
Fax: (770) 998-2188

Key Contact - Specialty:
Mr. Stephan W. Kirschner
Mr. Kenneth D. Lee

Description: Retained firm committed to servicing our clients' requirements in most disciplines through professionalism, confidentiality and integrity while maintaining an attractive fee structure.

Salary Minimum: $40,000
Functions: Generalist, General mgmt., Mfg., Materials, Sales & mktg., Engineering, Specialized services
Industries: Generalist, Mfg., Finance, Svcs., Packaging, High tech, Healthcare

---

Michael James Reid & Co.

595 Market St., Ste. 2500
San Francisco, California 94105
(415) 956-6010
Fax: (415) 495-1482
Email: mjrandco@best.com

Key Contact - Specialty:
Mr. Michael J. Reid - *Human resources, financial, information technology minorities*

Description: We believe that all high performing organizations must foster workplace diversity to enhance their competitive potential.

Salary Minimum: $60,000
Functions: Generalist, Senior mgmt., Benefits, Personnel, Training, Finance, IT
Industries: Generalist

Reifel & Assoc.

617 Riford Rd.
Glen Ellyn, Illinois 60137-3923
(630) 469-6651
Fax: (630) 469-6659

Key Contact - Specialty:
Ms. Laurie L. Reifel - *Generalist*

Description: Generalist search firm specializing in retained recruiting and industry researching.

Salary Minimum: $75,000
Functions: General mgmt., Plant mgmt., Mktg. mgmt., CFO's, R&D, Mgmt. consultants, Minorities
Industries: Generalist, Chemicals, Paints/petroleum products, Misc. financial, Mgmt. consulting, Human resource svcs.

Rein & Co., Inc.

150 Airport Rd., Ste. 700
Lakewood, New Jersey 08701
(732) 367-3300
Fax: (732) 367-8948

Key Contact - Specialty:
Mr. David Rein
Mr. Steve Rein

Description: Company caters primarily to venture capitalists and major I.T. corporations, geography covered: continental U.S., some European and Far Eastern activity. The firm often co-invests with the venture capitalists.

Salary Minimum: $75,000
Functions: Generalist, General mgmt., Directors, Senior mgmt.
Industries: Generalist

The Douglas Reiter Co., Inc.

610 SW Alder, Ste. 1221
Portland, Oregon 97205
(503) 228-6916
Email: dmreiter@aol.com
Web: reiterco.com

Key Contact - Specialty:
Mr. Douglas Reiter

Description: Senior and upper middle management; executive search, interim executives, project teams, consultants, senior executive reviews. For all industries, domestic and international, for interim assignments or permanent placements.
Functions: Directors, Senior mgmt., Middle mgmt., CFO's, MIS mgmt.
Industries: Agri/forestry/mining, Lumber/furniture, Plastics/rubber, High tech

Networks:
SearchNet Int'l.

The Remington Group

111 Lions Drive, Ste. 219
Barrington, Illinois 60010
(847) 577-2000
Fax: (847) 577-2066

Key Contact - Specialty:
Ms. Eleanor Anne Sweet - *Consumer marketing, consumer packaged goods, hardlines, sales executives, management*

Description: We specialize in the consumer products area concentrating in the houseware and hardware industries. Our expertise covers consumer packaged goods to hard good durables primarily in the marketing and sales executive area both domestically and internationally.

Salary Minimum: $50,000
Functions: Product dev., Advertising, Mkt. research, Mktg. mgmt., Sales mgmt., Minorities, Int'l.
Industries: Food/bev/tobacco, Textiles/apparel, Lumber/furniture, Soap/perfume/cosmetics, Plastics/rubber, Paints/petroleum products, Machinery/Appliances

---

Renaissance Resources, LLC

9100 Arboretum Pkwy., Ste. 270
Richmond, Virginia 23236
(804) 330-3088
Fax: (804) 330-7188
Email: Renaiss96@aol.com
Web: www.renaissanceresources.com

Key Contact - Specialty:
Mr. Robert L. Bryant - *Banking, finance, manufacturing, information systems*
Mr. David L. Ambruster - *Manufacturing, engineering, quality, power generation, pulp & paper*
Mr. Alfred Hinkle - *Banking, finance, information systems, telecommunications*
Ms. Lori Bryant

Description: We specialize in providing exceptional search consulting across a spectrum of industries and disciplines. We do this by combining the art and science of conducting search.

Salary Minimum: $60,000
Functions: General mgmt., Mfg., Materials, Sales & mktg., Finance, IT, Engineering

Industries: Generalist, Energy/utilities, Mfg., Finance, Svcs., High tech, Software

Affiliates:
Tierney Assoc., Inc.

The Repovich-Reynolds Group (TRRG, Inc.)
709 E. Colorado Blvd., Ste. 200
Pasadena, California 91101
(626) 585-9455
Email: trrg@pacbell.net
Web: trrg.com

Key Contact - Specialty:
Ms. Smooch S. Reynolds - *Communications, investor relations, marketing*
Ms. Kathleen N. Johnson - *Communications, investor relations, marketing*
Ms. Monet M. LeMon - *Communications, investor relations, marketing*
Ms. Jean T. Watkins - *Communications, investor relations, marketing*

Description: National firm with a staff comprised of former, senior level communications, marketing and investor relations executives. We're commited to identifying exceptional communications, marketing and investor relations professionals whose contributions will play a critical role in our clients' success.

Salary Minimum: $85,000
Functions: Advertising, Mkt. research, Mktg. mgmt., PR, Mgmt. consultants
Industries: Generalist

Reserve Technology Institute †
9039 Katy Frwy., Ste. 342
Houston, Texas 77024
(713) 468-3877
Fax: (713) 468-6507
Email: mneedham@iAmerica.net

Key Contact - Specialty:
Ms. Mary Needham - *Engineering, senior management*

Description: Process and power engineering specialists, senior management, business/project development, engineering management. Refining, chemical, petrochem, power and process control.

Salary Minimum: $70,000
Functions: Senior mgmt., Sales mgmt., Engineering, Int'l.
Industries: Energy/utilities, Construction, Environmental svcs.

Resolve Assoc. Int'l. †
440 SE 13th Ave.
Pompano Beach, Florida 33060
(954) 942-8344
Fax: (954) 943-6607
Email: resolve@gate.net
Web: www.resolveassociates.com

Key Contact - Specialty:
Mr. John Juanito Finch - *Latin America, domestic Hispanic*

Description: International firm specializing in senior level Hispanic/Latin American Executives. Generalist, with a client base ranging from Fortune 500 to emerging industry leaders. Specialties include regional and in-country Latin American assignments.

Salary Minimum: $75,000
Functions: Generalist, Int'l.
Industries: Generalist

The Resource Group
(a division of The Direct Marketing Resource Group LLC)
1575 Boston Post Rd.
Guilford, Connecticut 06437
(203) 453-7070
Fax: (203) 453-7580
Email: r.peragine@the-resource-group.com

Key Contact - Specialty:
Mr. Ralph P. Peragine - *Direct marketing, direct mail, telemarketing, database, internet marketing*

Description: Executive recruiting in the direct marketing, direct mail and telemarketing areas.

Salary Minimum: $75,000
Functions: Directors, Senior mgmt., Middle mgmt., Mkt. research, Mktg. mgmt., Direct mktg., Customer svc.
Industries: Non-classifiable industries

Branches:
26 Pearl Street
Norwalk, Connecticut 06850
(203) 846-3333
Fax: (203) 846-4134
Key Contact - Specialty:
Mr. Ralph Peragine - *Direct marketing, direct mail, telemarketing, database, internet marketing*

The Resource Group †
P.O. Box 331
Red Bank, New Jersey 07701
(732) 842-6555

Key Contact - Specialty:
Mr. Timothy L. Howe - *Business development, power generation, process equipment & services*

Description: We fill key sales and management positions with companies involved in the sales of equipment and services for cogeneration; power generation; resource recovery and the process industry. We have set up business development groups, domestically and internationally for utilities, oil/gas companies and equipment suppliers.

Salary Minimum: $75,000
Functions: Senior mgmt., Middle mgmt., Mktg. mgmt., Sales mgmt., Engineering, Int'l.
Industries: Energy/utilities, Machinery/Appliances

Resource Inc.
P.O. Box 620
Marshfield Hills, Massachusetts 02051
(617) 837-8113
Fax: (617) 837-8063

Key Contact - Specialty:
Mr. Thomas C. Healy - *Senior management*

Description: Specialize in search within the foods and consumer products industry. Work with mid to senior level managers within manufacturing, R&D, sales and marketing, engineering and logistics.

Salary Minimum: $50,000
Functions: Senior mgmt., Plant mgmt., Quality, Purchasing, Distribution, Sales mgmt., Engineering
Industries: Food/bev/tobacco, Paper, Soap/perfume/cosmetics, Medical devices, Transportation

Resource Perspectives, Inc.
535 Anton Blvd., Ste. 860
Costa Mesa, California 92626
(714) 662-4947
(714) 662-4967
Fax: (714) 662-4953
Email: cherneysd@aol.com
Email: rpidelany@aol.com

Key Contact - Specialty:
Dr. Steven D. Cherney - *Consumer oriented industries, technical, marketing*
Mr. Donald F. DeLany - *Consumer packaged goods, technical, operations, sales & marketing*

Description: Serving the consumer packaged goods and related industries. Specialists in research and development, safety, regulatory, engineering, manufacturing, operations, marketing and sales for foods, beverages, paper, household, toiletries and personal care product categories.

Salary Minimum: $50,000
Functions: Senior mgmt., Product dev., Plant mgmt., Mkt. research, Mktg. mgmt., R&D, Engineering
Industries: Food/bev/tobacco, Paper, Soap/perfume/cosmetics, Drugs mfg., Hospitality, Packaging

Resources for Management
221 7th St., Ste. 302
Pittsburgh, Pennsylvania 15238
(412) 820-7559

† occasional contingency assignment

Key Contact - Specialty:
Mr. Thomas T. Flannery - *Generalist, domestic, international*
Ms. Stacey M. Holland
Mr. Richard W. Reed, Jr.
Mr. James H. Knowles, Jr.
Mr. David W. Christopher

Description: With consulting fees based on an hourly rate, we can provide search flexibility and value. Can execute complete search, assist in individual elements of search process and agreement.

Salary Minimum: $50,000
Functions: Generalist, Senior mgmt., Plant mgmt., Mktg. mgmt., Sales mgmt., CFO's, Engineering
Industries: Mfg., Paper, Chemicals, Test/measurement equip., Misc. mfg., Pharmaceutical svcs.

Retained Search Assoc.

2915 Providence Rd., Ste. 300
Charlotte, North Carolina 28211
(704) 442-9840
Fax: (704) 442-9670
Email: gjm333@aol.com

Key Contact - Specialty:
Mr. Gregg J. McCormick - *Retail banking, consumer products, technology*
Mr. Michael Cognac - *HRIS, personnel, PeopleSoft*
Ms. Julie Gotheif

Description: A retained firm that has significant focus in technology, HRMS, retail banking and consumer products.

Salary Minimum: $85,000
Functions: Generalist, Mfg., HR mgmt., Finance, IT, MIS mgmt., Systems anal.
Industries: Generalist, Food/bev/tobacco, Finance, Computer svcs., Human resource svcs.

The Revere Assoc., Inc.

1947 Cleveland-Massillon Rd., P.O. Box 498
Bath, Ohio 44210-0498
(216) 666-6442
Fax: (216) 666-0586

Key Contact - Specialty:
Mr. Michael W. Fremon - *Process, plastics, chemical, pulp & paper (management & technical)*

Description: Search firm specializing in plastics, paper and other process industries. Work with small privately owned companies as well as Fortune 500's. Adept at high technology searches.

Salary Minimum: $60,000
Functions: Generalist, Product dev., Plant mgmt., Mkt. research, Mktg. mgmt., Sales mgmt., R&D
Industries: Generalist, Construction, Paper, Printing, Chemicals, Plastics/rubber, Test/measurement equip.

S. Reyman & Assoc., Ltd.

20 N. Michigan Ave., Ste. 520
Chicago, Illinois 60602
(312) 580-0808

Key Contact - Specialty:
Ms. Susan Reyman - *Generalist*

Description: Each consultant dedicates exclusive efforts to one client assignment at a time, producing extremely thorough and expeditious results. Our average turnaround time is three to four weeks. Our goal is to meet and exceed our clients' expectations. We believe individual client focus along with our search expertise is what makes that possible.

Salary Minimum: $70,000
Functions: Generalist, Senior mgmt., Distribution, Mktg. mgmt., Personnel, CFO's, MIS mgmt.
Industries: Generalist, Food/bev/tobacco, Medical devices, Plastics/rubber, Metal products, Equip. svcs., Healthcare
Professional Associations: IACPR

Russell Reynolds Assoc., Inc.

200 Park Ave.
New York, New York 10166-0002
(212) 351-2000
Fax: (212) 370-0896
Email: info@russreyn.com
Web: www.russreyn.com

Key Contact - Specialty:
Mr. Hobson Brown, Jr. - *Board of directors*

Description: Executive recruiting consultants. Clients in all major industries including financial services, consumer markets, healthcare, manufacturing, natural resources and technology are served through a global network of 33 wholly-owned offices.

Salary Minimum: $150,000
Functions: Generalist, Directors, Senior mgmt., Legal, Mfg., Materials, Healthcare, Health admin., Advertising, Mkt. research, Mktg. mgmt., Sales mgmt., Direct mktg., Customer svc., PR, HR mgmt., Benefits, CFO's, Budgeting, Cash mgmt., Credit, Taxes, M&A, Risk mgmt., MIS mgmt., Systems anal., Systems dev., Systems implem., Network admin., DB admin., R&D, Engineering, Minorities, Non-profits, Environmentalists, Technicians, Attorneys, Int'l.
Industries: Generalist, Agri/forestry/mining, Energy/utilities, Food/bev/tobacco, Textiles/apparel, Paper, Chemicals, Soap/perfume/cosmetics, Drugs mfg., Medical devices, Plastics/rubber, Paints/petroleum products, Leather/stone/glass/clay, Metal products, Machinery/Appliances, Motor vehicles, Computer equip., Consumer electronics, Test/measurement equip., Misc. mfg., Transportation, Retail, Finance, Banking, Invest. banking, Brokers, Venture cap., Misc. financial, Hospitality, Entertainment, Non-profits, Higher ed., Pharmaceutical svcs., Legal, Computer svcs., Accounting, Human resource svcs., Law enfcmt., Communications, Advertising/PR, Publishing, New media, Broadcast & Film, Telecoms, Government, Environmental svcs., Aerospace, Insurance, Real estate, High tech, Software, Biotech, Healthcare, Non-classifiable industries
Professional Associations: AESC, IACPR

Branches:
333 S. Grand Ave., Ste. 3500
Los Angeles, California 90071
(213) 253-4400
Fax: (213) 253-4444
Key Contact - Specialty:
Mr. Richard B. Krell - *Financial services, general industry*

2500 Sand Hill Rd., Ste. 105
Menlo Park, California 94025
(650) 233-2400
Fax: (650) 233-2499
Key Contact - Specialty:
Mr. Barry Obrand - *Technology*

101 California St., Ste. 3140
San Francisco, California 94111
(415) 352-3300
Fax: (415) 781-7690
Key Contact - Specialty:
Mr. P. Anthony Price - *Industrial*

1700 Pennsylvania Ave. NW, Ste. 850
Washington, District of Columbia 20006
(202) 628-2150
Fax: (202) 331-9348
Key Contact - Specialty:
Mr. Eric L. Vautour - *Government affairs, trade associations*

The Hurt Bldg., 50 Hurt Plaza, Ste. 600
Atlanta, Georgia 30303
(404) 577-3000
Fax: (404) 577-2832
Key Contact - Specialty:
Mr. Joseph T. Spence, Jr. - *Financial services*

200 S. Wacker Drive, Ste. 3600
Chicago, Illinois 60606
(312) 993-9696
Fax: (312) 876-1919
Key Contact - Specialty:
Ms. Andrea Redmond - *Insurance, financial services, boards of directors*
Mr. Charles A. Tribbett, III - *Diversity, legal, boards of directors*

Old City Hall, 45 School St.
Boston, Massachusetts 02108
(617) 523-1111
Fax: (617) 523-7305

Key Contact - Specialty:
Mr. J. Nicholas Hurd - *Commercial banking*

3050 Norwest Ctr., 90 S. Seventh St.
Minneapolis, Minnesota 55402
(612) 332-6966
Fax: (612) 332-2629
Key Contact - Specialty:
Mr. Robert W. Macdonald, Jr. - *Industrial, legal*

200 Park Ave.
New York, New York 10166
(212) 351-2000
Fax: (212) 370-0896
Key Contact - Specialty:
Mr. Clarke Murphy - *Global banking*
Mr. James M. Bagley - *Human resources, financial services*

1900 Trammell Crow Ctr., 2001 Ross Ave.
Dallas, Texas 75201
(214) 220-2033
Fax: (214) 220-3998
Key Contact - Specialty:
Mr. Joseph A. Bailey, III - *Consumer markets, sports, entertainment*

500 Dallas St., Ste. 2840
Houston, Texas 77002-4708
(713) 658-1776
Fax: (713) 658-9461
Key Contact - Specialty:
Mr. Joseph A. Bailey, III - *Consumer markets, sports, entertainment*

Scotia Plaza, Ste. 3500
40 King St. W.
Toronto, Ontario M5H 3Y2
Canada
(416) 364-3355
Fax: (416) 364-5174
Key Contact - Specialty:
Mr. Richard C. E. Moore - *Financial services*

Arquímedes 130-3
Colonia Polanco
Mexico City, Mexico 11560
Mexico
52 5 281 0440
Fax: 52 5 281 3121
Key Contact - Specialty:
Ms. Luz Lajous - *Latin America*

International Branches:
Amsterdam, Barcelona, Brussels, Buenos Aires, Central Hong Kong, Chiyoda-ku, Copenhagen, Edinburgh, Frankfurt, Hamburg, London, Madrid, Melbourne, Milan, Paris, Sao Paulo, Shanghai, Singapore, Sydney, Warsaw

Affiliates:
Reynolds Consulting Int'l.

Reynolds Consulting Int'l.
(a division of Russell Reynolds Assoc.)

181 University Ave., Ste. 1904
Toronto, Ontario M5H 3M7
Canada
(416) 304-1702
Fax: (416) 304-1723

Key Contact - Specialty:
Mr. Jock McGregor - *Manufacturing, financial, professional services*
Mr. Morris Tambor - *Manufacturing, retail, technology*
Ms. Birgit Westphal - *Automotive, manufacturing, financial*

Description: We offer the best of both worlds - the personalized focus of a boutique service and the extensive resources of a multi-disciplinary firm.

Salary Minimum: $75,000
Functions: Senior mgmt., Purchasing, Mktg. mgmt., CFO's, MIS mgmt., Mgmt. consultants, Non-profits
Industries: Motor vehicles, Transportation, Banking, Mgmt. consulting, Telecoms, Aerospace, High tech

Branches:
630 Bow Valley Square 1
202 6th Ave. SW
Calgary, Alberta T2P 2R9
Canada
(403) 781-1850
Fax: (403) 205-4888
Key Contact - Specialty:
Ms. Noranne Dickin - *Oil & gas, natural resources*

885 West Georgia St., Ste. 1500
Vancouver, British Columbia V6C 3E8
Canada
(604) 608-0844
Fax: (604) 608-0846
Key Contact - Specialty:
Ms. Noranne Dickin - *Oil & gas, natural resources*

1, Place Ville-Marie, Bureau 300
Montreal, Quebec H3B 4T9
Canada
(514) 393-5513
Fax: (514) 390-4126
Key Contact - Specialty:
Mr. Jean Pierre Hurtubise - *Manufacturing, distribution, telecommunications*

Reynolds Partners

380 Madison Ave., 7th Floor
New York, New York 10017-2513
(212) 856-4466

Key Contact - Specialty:
Ms. Sydney Reynolds

Description: Small personal service firm. Specialists: nonprofit leadership, chief executive, board diversity, genetic engineers, geneticists and other positions that are an outgrowth of the Genome Project which includes positions in agriculture and biotechnology.

Salary Minimum: $75,000
Functions: Healthcare, Mktg. mgmt., HR mgmt., R&D, Mgmt. consultants, Minorities, Non-profits
Industries: Pharmaceutical svcs., Mgmt. consulting, Human resource svcs., Communications, Aerospace, Biotech, Healthcare

Rhodes Associates

555 Fifth Ave., 5th Floor
New York, New York 10017
(212) 983-2000
Fax: (212) 983-8333
Web: rhodesassociates.com

Key Contact - Specialty:
Mr. Stephen Littman - *Real estate*
Mr. Dominic Castriota - *Financial services*
Ms. Wendy C. Weiler - *Financial services*
Ms. Jane Lyons - *Real estate*
Mr. Anthony J. LoPinto - *Real estate*

Description: A general search practice with specializations in real estate and financial services, including capital markets, emerging markets high yield and investment banking. Domestic and international in scope.

Salary Minimum: $100,000
Industries: Finance, Banking, Invest. banking, Venture cap., Real estate

RIC Corp.

900 E. Ocean Blvd., #232
Stuart, Florida 34994
(561) 287-5409
(561) 288-1811
Web: www.workhappy.com

Key Contact - Specialty:
Mr. R. Thomas Welch - *Generalist*
Ms. Kathleen A. O'Neill - *Generalist*

Description: Highly regarded small firm solving problems for clients in a fair, efficient and cost effective manner. Expertise in executive, management, technical and sales for domestic, international and emerging markets.

Salary Minimum: $75,000
Functions: Generalist, Senior mgmt., Middle mgmt., Distribution, Mktg. mgmt., Cash mgmt., MIS mgmt.
Industries: Generalist, Motor vehicles, Computer equip., Transportation, Retail, Telecoms, High tech

Marshall Rice Assoc.

40 Boulder Ave., P.O. Box 1485
Charlestown, Rhode Island 02813
(401) 322-1993
Fax: (401) 322-9886

Email: mtrice@compuserve.com

Key Contact - Specialty:
Mr. Marshall T. Rice

Description: We serve exclusively the senior management needs of non-profit institutions such as universities, colleges, schools, foundations, libraries, museums, churches, dioceses, medical centers, hospitals and other health related, social service and educational organizations.

Salary Minimum: $50,000
Functions: Generalist, Senior mgmt., Health admin., CFO's, Non-profits
Industries: Non-profits, Higher ed.

Rice Cohen Int'l.

301 Oxford Valley Rd., Ste. 1505-1506
Yardley, Pennsylvania 19067
(215) 321-4100
Fax: (215) 321-6370
Email: sconsultant@sprintmail.com
Web: www.mrinet.com/scphill

Key Contact - Specialty:
Mr. Gene Rice - *Consultants, designers, senior executives (consulting & training industry), management consulting, assessment*
Mr. Jeff Cohen - *Temporary, outsourcing*
Mr. Mark Green - *Human resources, I/O psychology, internal O.D.*
Mr. John Shalinsky - *Food, beverage*
Mr. Fred Schrandt - *Building products*
Ms. Kim Dorfman - *Consumer sales, HBA*
Ms. Sharin Phillips - *Managed healthcare, property & casualty insurance*
Ms. Eileen Capecci - *Multimedia training, distance training*
Ms. Liz DeForrest - *Electronics, electrical*
Mr. Martin Allen - *Software applications*
Mr. Leon Kasperski - *Credit risk, debt recovery, financial*

Description: Interactive videoconferencing for interviews/business meetings/ training. Relocation consulting - discounts on vanline services, mortgages, cost of living reports. Compensation consulting. Assessment and selection consulting. Delivery of top talent by utilizing our exclusive 25 step search and selection process.

Salary Minimum: $75,000
Functions: Directors, Senior mgmt., Mfg., Healthcare, Mkt. research, Mktg. mgmt., Sales mgmt., Direct mktg., Benefits, Training, IT, Mgmt. consultants
Industries: Energy/utilities, Construction, Mfg., Consumer electronics, Misc. financial, Mgmt. consulting, New media, Environmental svcs., High tech, Software, Healthcare, Non-classifiable industries

Richards Assoc., Inc. †

1562 First Ave., Ste. 218
New York, New York 10028
(212) 717-2670
Fax: (212) 717-2668
Email: richsearch@aol.com

Key Contact - Specialty:
Ms. Sharon Richards - *Entertainment marketing, promotions, licensing, interactive, public relations*

Description: Having worked in entertainment marketing for nearly ten years prior to becoming a recruiter, president offers a first hand understanding of her clients' business needs and her candidates' accomplishments.

Salary Minimum: $50,000
Functions: Senior mgmt., Middle mgmt., Advertising, Mkt. research, Mktg. mgmt., PR
Industries: Food/bev/tobacco, Entertainment, Communications, Advertising/PR, New media, Broadcast & Film

Riddle & McGrath LLC

1040 Crown Pointe Pkwy., Ste. 310
Atlanta, Georgia 30338
(770) 804-3190
Fax: (770) 804-3194
Email: ridmcgrath@aol.com

Key Contact - Specialty:
Mr. James E. Riddle - *General management, sales & marketing, manufacturing, engineering*
Mr. Patrick McGrath - *Transportation, logistics*

Description: We were established by two veterans of the executive search business to provide the highest level of professional service to a select list of clients.

Salary Minimum: $90,000
Functions: Senior mgmt., Mfg., Distribution, Sales & mktg., HR mgmt., Finance, MIS mgmt.
Industries: Generalist, Paper, Printing, Misc. mfg., Transportation, Packaging

Ridenour & Assoc.

1 E. Wacker Drive, Ste. 3500
Chicago, Illinois 60601
(312) 644-1888
Fax: (312) 644-1883
Email: ssridenour@aol.com
Web: www.RidenourAssociates.com

Key Contact - Specialty:
Ms. Suzanne S. Ridenour - *Direct marketing, new media, interactive executives (including all integrated marketing areas)*

Description: Domestic and international executive search specializing in the recruitment of direct marketing and integrated communications professionals.

Salary Minimum: $75,000
Functions: Senior mgmt., Advertising, Sales mgmt., Direct mktg., MIS mgmt., Systems implem., Int'l.
Industries: Misc. financial, Hospitality, Entertainment, Non-profits, Mgmt. consulting, Advertising/PR, New media

Rieser & Assoc., Inc.

P.O. Box 220138
St. Louis, Missouri 63122
(314) 984-9001
Fax: (314) 821-1395
Email: riesearch@aol.com

Key Contact - Specialty:
Mr. John D. Rieser - *Generalist*

Description: A highly professional generalist firm, concentrating on senior level management positions, providing individualized retainer search, stressing discretion and confidentiality. We are dedicated to personalized service, comprehensive research and ethical search.

Salary Minimum: $75,000
Functions: Generalist, Senior mgmt., Mktg. mgmt., CFO's, R&D, Engineering
Industries: Generalist, Agri/forestry/mining, Food/bev/tobacco, Finance, Human resource svcs.

Wilson Riles & Assoc., Inc.

400 Capitol Mall, Ste. 1540
Sacramento, California 95814-4408
(916) 448-0600
Fax: (916) 448-5457
Email: wriles@wredu.com
Web: www.wredu.com/

Key Contact - Specialty:
Dr. Wilson Riles - *School district superintendents, university administrators, other education administrative personnel*

Description: Specialty includes the recruitment of highly qualified administrators to fill positions in the field of education, including superintendents of schools, university administrators and legal counsels for school districts.
Industries: Higher ed., Government

Riotto-Jones Assoc.
(a division of A. R. Riotto & Co., Inc.)

600 Third Ave.
New York, New York 10016
(212) 697-4575
Fax: (212) 370-9395
Email: riottojones.com
Web: www.riottojones.com

Key Contact - Specialty:
Mr. Anthony R. Riotto - *Investment management*
Ms. Lynn M. Klein

Description: Specializing in investment management, trust, private banking and institutional services both national and international. Primary clients are money-center, regional and boutique banks, mutual fund and investment management firms.

Salary Minimum: $100,000
Functions: Senior mgmt., Middle mgmt., Mkt. research, Mktg. mgmt., Sales mgmt., Cash mgmt., Risk mgmt.
Industries: Banking, Invest. banking, Brokers, Venture cap., Misc. financial

Affiliates:
Thomas Hancock Associates Pty. Ltd.

RJN Consulting
355 Lexington Ave., 17th Floor
New York, New York 10017
(212) 972-5140
Fax: (212) 370-7174

Key Contact - Specialty:
Mr. Richard J. Newman - *Beverage industry*
Ms. E. Linda Alvarez - *Beverage industry*
Ms. Robin Mesger

Description: A generalist firm specializing in management consulting and recruiting senior level and middle management executives for consumer products, including beverages, food and tobacco.

Salary Minimum: $60,000
Functions: Senior mgmt., Middle mgmt., Plant mgmt., Mkt. research, Mktg. mgmt., Sales mgmt., PR
Industries: Food/bev/tobacco, Soap/perfume/cosmetics, Advertising/PR

RLM Assoc., Ltd.
420 Lexington Ave., Ste. 501
New York, New York 10170
(212) 661-3220
Fax: (212) 661-0240
Email: rlmassoc@ix.netcom.com

Key Contact - Specialty:
Ms. Rusty Myer
Mr. James Benedict
Mr. Rick Savior

Description: Retained executive search focused on senior management engagements across the functional spectrum for clients seeking to leverage emerging technology and optimize customer information.

Salary Minimum: $200,000
Functions: Senior mgmt., Middle mgmt., Personnel, CFO's, M&A, Systems anal., Systems implem.
Industries: Finance, High tech, Software

RMA Search
101 Continental Place, Ste. 105
Brentwood, Tennessee 37027
(615) 377-9603
Fax: (615) 370-5768

Key Contact - Specialty:
Ms. Mary Bowles - *Generalist*

Description: Consultants specializing in executive search, corporate outplacement, employee appraisal, attitude surveys and operational consulting projects.

Salary Minimum: $30,000
Functions: Generalist
Industries: Generalist

Branches:
301 Gallaher View Rd., Ste. 111
Knoxville, Tennessee 37919
(615) 691-4733
Fax: (615) 691-4787
Key Contact - Specialty:
Ms. Ellen E. Bowling

1355 Lynnfield Rd.
Memphis, Tennessee 38119
(901) 763-1818
Key Contact - Specialty:
Mr. David Dunn

Robert Lowell Int'l.
13154 Coit Rd., Ste. 224
Dallas, Texas 75240
(972) 233-2270
Fax: (972) 490-1510

Key Contact - Specialty:
Mr. Robert M. Bryza - *Heavy machinery*

Description: Highly regarded firm with middle management and senior-level professionals conducting executive search. Specialized management consulting services: management assessment, development and succession planning, labor relations, organization design and outplacement.

Salary Minimum: $60,000
Functions: Generalist
Industries: Generalist, Energy/utilities, Medical devices, Metal products, Computer equip., Transportation, Aerospace

Norman Roberts & Assoc., Inc.
1800 Century Park E., Ste. 430
Los Angeles, California 90067-1507
(310) 552-1112
Fax: (310) 552-1113
Email: NRAssoc@aol.com

Key Contact - Specialty:
Mr. Norman C. Roberts
Ms. Valerie S. Frank

Description: Specialize in nationwide recruitment for: public sector/not-for-profit, transportation, utilities, engineering, environmental services, manufacturing, healthcare, education and real estate. Recruit in all functional areas within these industries.

Salary Minimum: $70,000
Functions: Senior mgmt., Health admin., HR mgmt., Finance, IT, Engineering, Non-profits
Industries: Energy/utilities, Transportation, Non-profits, Higher ed., Telecoms, Government, Healthcare

Roberts Ryan & Bentley, Inc.
1107 Kenilworth Drive, Ste. 208
Baltimore, Maryland 21204
(410) 321-6600
Fax: (410) 321-1347
Email: rrbentley@aol.com

Key Contact - Specialty:
Mr. Richard R. Cappe
Mr. Richard A. Dannenberg

Description: Research based retained executive search for mid and upper management. Operates within most functional areas with emphasis on general management, finance, information services and marketing.

Salary Minimum: $100,000
Functions: Directors, Advertising, Personnel, Taxes, Systems dev., Mgmt. consultants, Minorities
Industries: Energy/utilities, Banking, Computer svcs., Mgmt. consulting, Insurance, Software, Healthcare

Branches:
3206 Sandy Ridge Drive
Clearwater, Florida 34621
(813) 786-1312
Fax: (813) 786-3349
Key Contact - Specialty:
Ms. Sue Ann Whitley

7315 Wisconsin Ave., Ste. 333E
Bethesda, Maryland 20814
(301) 469-3150
Fax: (301) 469-3108
Key Contact - Specialty:
Mr. Gregory Reynolds

Robertson-Surrette Ltd.
10th Floor, Barrington Twr., Scotia Sq.
P.O. Box 2166
Halifax, Nova Scotia B3J 3C4
Canada
(902) 421-1330
Fax: (902) 425-1108
Email: resume@robsur.com
Web: www.robsur.com

Key Contact - Specialty:
Mr. Mark J. Surrette - *Senior executives, vice president & above*
Mr. Steve Ashton
Mr. Jamie Baillie

Salary Minimum: $60,000
Functions: Generalist
Industries: Generalist

Branches:
100 Cameron St.
Moncton, New Brunswick E1C 5Y6
Canada
(506) 855-8169
Fax: (506) 854-8464
Key Contact - Specialty:
Mr. Pierre Battan

29 Beechwood Ave., Ste. 200
Ottawa, Ontario K1M 1M2
Canada
(613) 749-9909
Fax: (613) 749-9599
Key Contact - Specialty:
Mr. Ron Robertson

Bruce Robinson Assoc.
Harmon Cove Towers
Ste. 8, A/L Tower 1
Secaucus, New Jersey 07094
(201) 617-9595
Fax: (201) 617-1434
Email: bra1970@aol.com

Key Contact - Specialty:
Mr. Bruce Robinson - *Generalist*
Mr. Eric Robinson - *Generalist*
Mr. John Robinson - *Generalist*

Description: Organization formed in 1970 by Bruce Robinson who recognized the need to recruit top flight minority and female talent on an executive search basis. Company has grown and now works successfully with major Fortune 500 companies in all areas of search.

Salary Minimum: $75,000
Functions: General mgmt., Mfg., Healthcare, Sales & mktg., HR mgmt., Finance, IT
Industries: Generalist, Mfg., Svcs., Communications, Insurance, Healthcare, Non-classifiable industries
Professional Associations: AESC

Robinson, Fraser Group Ltd.
10 Bay St., Ste. 700
Toronto, Ontario M5J 2R8
Canada
(416) 864-9174
Fax: (416) 864-1133
Email: rfg@interlog.com

Key Contact - Specialty:
Mr. Stephen Robinson - *Building competent executive teams*

Description: As generalists, we provide value driven hiring solutions that drive shareholder value.

Salary Minimum: $80,000
Functions: Directors, Senior mgmt., Finance, CFO's, IT, MIS mgmt., Mgmt. consultants
Industries: Generalist

Robison & Associates
1350 First Citizens Plaza
128 S. Tryon St.
Charlotte, North Carolina 28202
(704) 376-0059
Fax: (704) 371-5178

Key Contact - Specialty:
Mr. John H. Robison - *Generalist*
Mr. H. Heath Massey, III - *Generalist*

Description: Serve all industries including governmental, institutional, professional-legal and medical.

Salary Minimum: $50,000
Functions: Generalist, Mfg., Sales & mktg., Finance, IT, Engineering, Int'l.
Industries: Generalist, Energy/utilities, Construction, Mfg., Finance, Svcs., Insurance

---

Robison Humphreys & Assoc., Inc.
295 The West Mall, 7th Floor
Etobicoke, Ontario M9C 4Z4
Canada
(416) 626-6346
Fax: (416) 622-9672

Key Contact - Specialty:
Mr. William M. Humphreys - *CEO, COO, marketing, advertising, sales, CFO, publishing*
Ms. Margaret H. Robison - *Advertising, printing, publishing*
Mr. Scott W. Humphreys - *Sales management, marketing, food & beverage, communications*

Description: Direct sourcing (no advertising) executive search; over 85% of annual fees from repeat clients or referral from clients/candidates. Client base: Canada, United States, United Kingdom.

Salary Minimum: $50,000
Functions: Senior mgmt., Middle mgmt., Advertising, Mktg. mgmt., Sales mgmt., CFO's
Industries: Construction, Food/bev/tobacco, Lumber/furniture, Printing, Metal products, Motor vehicles, Publishing

---

Robsham & Assoc., Inc.
4 S. Marketplace, Faneuil Hall
Boston, Massachusetts 02109
(617) 742-2944
Fax: (617) 523-0464
Email: robsham1@aol.com

Key Contact - Specialty:
Ms. Beverly H. Robsham - *Finance, marketing*

Description: Generous and complete involvement in each client's search; detailed screening and interviewing - extensive candidate reports. We work with a sense of urgency.

Salary Minimum: $75,000
Functions: General mgmt., Sales & mktg., Finance, Specialized services
Industries: Generalist, Finance, Communications, Software
Professional Associations: IACPR

Rodzik & Assoc., Inc.
8601 Six Forks Rd., Ste. 403
Raleigh, North Carolina 27615
(919) 846-8150
Fax: (919) 846-9130

Key Contact - Specialty:
Mr. Gerald F. Rodzik - *Generalist*
Ms. C. L. Rodzik - *Generalist*
Mr. T. A. Rodzik - *Legal*
Mr. A. D. Bray - *Generalist*

Description: Full service firm with optional services and customized pricing to meet client requirements.

Salary Minimum: $70,000
Functions: Generalist, Mfg., Sales & mktg., HR mgmt., Finance, R&D, Engineering
Industries: Energy/utilities, Mfg., Finance, Svcs., Communications, High tech, Software

---

Rogers - McManamon Executive Search
33781 Via Cascada
San Juan Capistrano, California 92675
(949) 496-1614
Fax: (949) 496-2305
Email: tim@mcmanamon.com

Key Contact - Specialty:
Mr. Tim McManamon - *Communications, (marketing & engineering), CIO*
Ms. Gay Rogers - *Communications, (marketing & engineering), CIO*

Description: We offer our national clients extensive enterprise networking arena contacts along with a strong perception for technical trends and the ever-changing direction of the communications industry.

Salary Minimum: $100,000
Functions: Directors, Middle mgmt., Mkt. research, Mktg. mgmt., MIS mgmt., Engineering
Industries: Computer equip., Telecoms, High tech

ROI Assoc. †
P.O. Box 136
Massapequa Park, New York 11762
(516) 746-4842

Email: 75273.1636@compuserve.com

Key Contact - Specialty:
Mr. Peter M. Portanova - *Manufacturing, materials management, purchasing*

Description: Executive search consultants specializing in manufacturing, quality, materials management, purchasing, systems and manufacturing consulting professionals. Principal is a nationally known speaker on career planning.

Salary Minimum: $50,000
Functions: Plant mgmt., Quality, Purchasing, Materials Plng., Mgmt. consultants
Industries: Food/bev/tobacco, Chemicals, Soap/perfume/cosmetics, Drugs mfg., Medical devices, Computer equip., Consumer electronics

---

ROI International, Inc. †
16040 Christensen Rd., Ste. 316
Seattle, Washington 98188
(206) 248-5000
Fax: (206) 248-5005
Email: roi@roi-intl.com
Web: www.roi-intl.com

Key Contact - Specialty:
Mr. Marc Goyette - *Telecommunications, information technology*
Ms. Margo Goyette - *Telecommunications*

Description: Executive retained search consulting specializing in the telecommunications industry.

Salary Minimum: $100,000
Functions: Directors, Senior mgmt., Mktg. mgmt., Sales mgmt., MIS mgmt., Systems anal., Engineering
Industries: Venture cap., Broadcast & Film, Telecoms, High tech, Software

---

Rojek Marketing Group, Inc. †
489 Walmar Drive
Bay Village, Ohio 44140
(330) 468-0072
Fax: (330) 468-3555
Email: RMGITW@aol.com

Key Contact - Specialty:
Ms. Tina Wascovich - *Senior marketing management, corporate communications, public relations, brand management, product management*
Ms. Lorraine Rojek - *Senior marketing, advertising executives*
Mr. Scott Montgomery - *Executive level marketing, advertising professionals*

Description: Specialized recruitment services offered for executive and management level marketing, advertising and communications professionals. Industry focus - consumer packaged goods companies, retail, finance, healthcare, insurance, manufacturing.

Salary Minimum: $50,000
Functions: Advertising, Mkt. research, Mktg. mgmt., PR
Industries: Mfg., Soap/perfume/cosmetics, Retail, Finance, Svcs., Communications, Healthcare

---

Rolland Ressources Humaines Inc.
560 boul. Henri-Bourassa O., Ste. 202
Montreal, Quebec H3L 1P4
Canada
(514) 333-6619
Fax: (514) 334-5985

Key Contact - Specialty:
Mr. Guy Rolland - *Financial services, manufacturing, telecommunications*

Salary Minimum: $50,000
Functions: General mgmt., Mfg., Materials, Sales & mktg., HR mgmt., Finance, Minorities
Industries: Mfg., Paper, Chemicals, Drugs mfg., Invest. banking, Venture cap., Telecoms

---

Rollo Assoc.
725 S. Figueroa St., Ste. 808
Los Angeles, California 90017
(213) 688-9444
Fax: (213) 688-8358
Email: info@rolloassoc.com
Web: www.rolloassoc.com

Key Contact - Specialty:
Mr. Robert S. Rollo - *Generalist (senior level)*
Mr. Peter W. Kelly - *Financial services*
Ms. Bethany W. George - *Generalist, consumer services*
Ms. Jane Hurd - *Healthcare*
Ms. Kristine M. Anderson - *Generalist*

Description: Specialists in senior level assignments for top tier corporations/institutions with multi-industry capability and an impressive worldwide placement record for significant client companies.

Salary Minimum: $150,000
Functions: Generalist, Directors, Senior mgmt., Healthcare, Sales & mktg., CFO's, Minorities
Industries: Generalist, Energy/utilities, Mfg., Finance, Hospitality, Insurance, Healthcare
Professional Associations: AESC

Romac Int'l. Inc.
175 Federal St., Ste. 900
Boston, Massachusetts 02110
(617) 350-0945
Fax: (617) 542-8570
Email: bcuddy@romac.com
Web: www.romacintl.com

Key Contact - Specialty:
Mr. Brian C. Cuddy - *CFO, controller*
Mr. William J. Griffiths - *CFO, controller*
Mr. William A. Grady - *Senior level information technology*

Description: We provide world class senior level financial, accounting and information technology professionals on a retained (permanent) or interim (contract) basis.

Salary Minimum: $100,000
Functions: CFO's, Budgeting, Cash mgmt., Taxes, M&A, MIS mgmt., Mgmt. consultants
Industries: Venture cap., Mgmt. consulting, Telecoms, Real estate, High tech, Software, Biotech

---

Rooney Assoc., Inc.
501 Pennsylvania Ave.
Glen Ellyn, Illinois 60137
(630) 469-7102
Fax: (630) 469-0749
Email: jrooney@exec-recruit.com
Web: www.exec-recruit.com

Key Contact - Specialty:
Mr. Joseph J. Rooney - *Vice president (sales & marketing), general management, high technology, telecommunications, consumer electronics*

Description: Boutique firm, highly personalized service. Practice adept in aiding cultural changes, or assignments requiring sensitivity, along with creativity.

Salary Minimum: $75,000
Functions: Senior mgmt., Middle mgmt., Mktg. mgmt., Sales mgmt.
Industries: Computer equip., Consumer electronics, New media, Telecoms, High tech, Software

---

Ropella & Assoc.
6988 Pine Blossom Rd.
Milton, Florida 32570
(850) 983-4777
Fax: (850) 983-6677
Email: ropella@spydee.net
Web: www.ropella.com

Key Contact - Specialty:
Mr. Patrick B. Ropella - *Chemical industry*

Description: The chemical industry is our focus everyday. We track business and employment trends and monitor current developments within commodity, specialty, organic and inorganic chemical manufacturers and distributors around the globe.

Salary Minimum: $50,000
Functions: Directors, Senior mgmt., Middle mgmt., Mkt. research, Mktg. mgmt., Sales mgmt., R&D

† occasional contingency assignment

Industries: Chemicals

Ropes Associates, Inc.

333 N. New River Drive E., 3rd Floor
Ft. Lauderdale, Florida 33301-2240
(954) 525-6600
Fax: (954) 779-7279
Email: jropes@ropesassociates.com
Web: www.ropesassociates.com

Key Contact - Specialty:
Mr. John Ropes - *Real estate*

Description: Executive search: real estate industry including developers, builders and operators of residential, resort, commercial and industrial properties.

Salary Minimum: $120,000
Functions: Senior mgmt., Middle mgmt., Mktg. mgmt., Sales mgmt., CFO's
Industries: Construction, Hospitality, Entertainment, Real estate
Professional Associations: AESC

W. R. Rosato & Assoc., Inc.

61 Broadway, 26th Floor
New York, New York 10006
(212) 509-5700
Fax: (212) 968-0855
Email: wrrinc@aol.com

Key Contact - Specialty:
Mr. William R. Rosato - *Senior financial technology management*
Mr. Frank M. Colasanto - *Senior financial technology management*
Mr. Jack Federman - *Quantitative research, sales & trading*

Description: Over twenty successful years of search experience dedicated to the support of the investment banking, broker dealer community. Expertise in capital markets, technology, quantitative research, analytics, sales and trading.

Salary Minimum: $125,000
Functions: Risk mgmt., MIS mgmt., Systems anal., Systems dev., Systems implem.
Industries: Invest. banking, Misc. financial

Ross & Company, Inc.

35 Old Post Rd.
Southport, Connecticut 06490
(203) 221-8200

Key Contact - Specialty:
Mr. H. Lawrence Ross

Description: General management recruiters, specializing in venture and risk capital backed companies. Particular expertise in biotech/lifesciences, healthcare services/managed care, medical informatics and partners for risk capital funds.

Salary Minimum: $150,000

Rovner & Assoc., Inc. †

20 N. Wacker Drive, Ste. 3121
Chicago, Illinois 60606
(312) 332-9960
Fax: (312) 332-9965
Email: melissao@rovner.com
Web: www.rovner.com

Key Contact - Specialty:
Ms. Bettyann Rovner - *Information technology*
Ms. Lesly Schlender - *Information technology*

Description: Specializing in information technology. We pride ourselves in building long-term client relationships, providing quality search services with uncompromising thoroughness, integrity, confidentiality and delivery.

Salary Minimum: $75,000
Functions: Middle mgmt., Mktg. mgmt., Sales mgmt., HR mgmt., IT, MIS mgmt., Systems implem.
Industries: Mfg., Finance, Svcs., Communications, High tech, Software

Rovner Gerner & Assoc.

21031 Ventura Blvd., Ste. 704
Woodland Hills, California 91364
(818) 348-0696
Fax: (818) 348-2775
Email: zcar93a@prodigy.com

Key Contact - Specialty:
Dr. Louis Rovner - *Generalist, psychological evaluation*
Ms. Jeri Gerner - *Generalist*

Description: Psychological evaluation for compatibility and appropriateness is included as a standard element of our assessment procedure. Our exclusive nine-step process insures the perfect blend of experience, skills and character.

Salary Minimum: $60,000
Functions: Generalist, General mgmt., Mfg., Sales & mktg., HR mgmt., Finance, IT
Industries: Generalist, Mfg., Retail, Finance, Svcs., Communications, Insurance

David Rowe & Assoc., Inc.

9047 Monroe Ave.
Brookfield, Illinois 60513
(708) 387-1000

Key Contact - Specialty:
Mr. David E. Rowe - *Healthcare providers*
Ms. Lydia Imler-Diskin - *Healthcare providers*
Ms. Carol E. Rozenboom - *Healthcare providers*

Description: Conducts searches for all management levels in hospitals, hospital systems, organized physician group practices, and managed care companies.

Salary Minimum: $80,000
Functions: Physicians, Nurses, Health admin.
Industries: Healthcare

RSMR, Inc.

300 S. Wacker Drive, Ste. 670
Chicago, Illinois 60606
(312) 957-0337
Fax: (312) 957-0335
Email: rsmr@sprynet.com

Key Contact - Specialty:
Mr. John Ryan - *Corporate & project finance*
Mr. Christopher Swan - *Engineering, energy, utilities*
Mr. Michael Morrow - *Manufacturing, industrial products*
Mr. Stephen Rotter - *Corporate finance, electronic commerce, chip card technology*

Description: Retained executive search firm. Our consultative approach and commitment to specialized industry practices enable us to build lasting, performance-driven client relationships.

Salary Minimum: $60,000
Functions: General mgmt., Mfg., Materials, Sales mgmt., Cash mgmt., Risk mgmt., Engineering
Industries: Energy/utilities, Construction, Machinery/Appliances, Finance, Environmental svcs., Real estate

Ruppert Comann Assoc., Inc.

8151 S. St. Paul Way
Littleton, Colorado 80122
(303) 488-0108

Key Contact - Specialty:
Mr. William J. Ruppert
Ms. Eleanora T. Ruppert

Description: Executive search devoted to mining, minerals and related industries. Owned by a metallurgical engineer with over 25 years experience. Searches include management, professional, sales/marketing, financial and administrative.

Salary Minimum: $70,000
Functions: Generalist, Senior mgmt., Middle mgmt., Engineering, Int'l.
Industries: Agri/forestry/mining, Construction

Rurak & Assoc., Inc

1350 Connecticut Ave. NW, Ste. 801
Washington, District of Columbia 20036
(202) 293-7603
Fax: (202) 296-2435

Email: z.rurak@rurak-assoc.com

Key Contact - Specialty:
Mr. Zbigniew T. Rurak
Mr. Richard H. Hutchison
Ms. Carol M. Balsamo
Ms. Krissa Johnson

Description: Generalist practice serving senior management in executive search, selection and development. Clients range from domestic venture-capitalized start-ups to foreign multinational corporations. Search and consulting engagements conducted worldwide.

Salary Minimum: $100,000
Functions: Generalist
Industries: Generalist
Professional Associations: AESC

Affiliates:
Kensington Consulting Group Ltd.

Rusher, Loscavio & LoPresto
180 Montgomery St., Ste. 1616
San Francisco, California 94104-4239
(415) 765-6600
Fax: (415) 397-2842

Key Contact - Specialty:
Mr. William H. Rusher, Jr. - *Insurance*
Mr. J. Michael Loscavio - *Insurance, finance*
Mr. Frank A. Juska - *High technology, finance*
Mr. Robert W. Kile - *Not-for-profits*

Description: Retained executive search in financial services, high technology, biotechnology, manufacturing, non-profit and service industries. Function specialties in general management, manufacturing, distribution, finance, marketing/sales, MIS, HR, engineering & technical management, executive directors and fund development.

Salary Minimum: $75,000
Functions: Directors, Senior mgmt., Benefits, CFO's, MIS mgmt., Non-profits
Industries: Metal products, Computer equip., Misc. financial, Insurance, High tech, Software, Non-classifiable industries
Professional Associations: AESC

Branches:
2479 E. Bayshore Rd., Ste. 700
Palo Alto, California 94303
(650) 494-0883
Fax: (650) 494-7231
Key Contact - Specialty:
Mr. Robert L. LoPresto - *High technology positions (executive level)*
Ms. G. Kay Sullivan - *High technology positions (executive level)*
Ms. Geraldine Whitaker - *High technology positions (executive level)*

Rushmore • Judge Inc.
65 Queen St. W., Ste. 1602
P.O. Box 94
Toronto, Ontario M5H 2M5
Canada
(416) 363-4238
Fax: (416) 363-4239
Email: goodmgmt@torfree.net

Key Contact - Specialty:
Mr. G. Michael Wolkensperg - *Senior management*
Mr. Derek Redwood - *Financial services management*
Ms. Lisa Butler
Mr. Bill Branston

Description: As search consultants, we are also students of organizational dynamics - deciphering the nuances of external market conditions and internal political realities. This knowledge becomes a factor in our assessments and our recommendations.

Salary Minimum: $75,000
Functions: Senior mgmt., Plant mgmt., Distribution, Health admin., CFO's, Non-profits
Industries: Generalist

Rust & Assoc., Inc.
1009 Ashley Lane
Libertyville, Illinois 60048-3813
(847) 816-7878
Fax: (847) 816-7905
Email: rust29@allways.net

Key Contact - Specialty:
Mr. John R. Rust - *Generalist*

Description: International generalist firm: guarantee search filled or money back; unconditional two year guarantee on candidate retention; off limits, lifetime candidates, two year clients; only expenses charged, travel outside metro Chicago.

Salary Minimum: $60,000
Functions: Senior mgmt., Middle mgmt., Mkt. research, Mktg. mgmt., Sales mgmt., CFO's, Mgmt. consultants
Industries: Mfg., Finance, Svcs., Communications, High tech, Biotech, Healthcare

W. A. Rutledge & Assoc.
51 Sherman Hill Rd., Ste. A103
Cornerstone Professional Park, Bldg. A
Woodbury, Connecticut 06798
(203) 266-0200
Fax: (203) 266-0213

Key Contact - Specialty:
Mr. William A. Rutledge
Ms. Laraine Petersen

Description: Senior/executive management search across most functional areas in technology based consumer and industrial product companies; heavy pharmaceutical, chemicals, electronics, communications.
Functions: Generalist, Senior mgmt., Middle mgmt.
Industries: Generalist, Chemicals, Drugs mfg., Consumer electronics, Misc. financial, Aerospace, Biotech

The S C Group LLC
315 Seventh Ave., Ste. 12A
New York, New York 10001-6006
(212) 634-6754
Fax: (212) 634-6765
Email: JimFarah@aol.com

Key Contact - Specialty:
Mr. James C. Farah - *Board members, executives (family and closely-held firms)*

Description: Our core business is recruiting for board of directors for closely-held firms, family business offices and family foundations. Our principals have special experience and knowledge in executive management of and advising to closely-held firms.
Functions: Generalist
Industries: Generalist

The Sager Co.
9540 Midwest Ave.
Cleveland, Ohio 44125
(216) 459-1300
Fax: (216) 459-2740

Key Contact - Specialty:
Mr. Robert Ianni
Ms. Joan Cianciolo

Description: Multi-discipline practice identifying regional and national talent for senior and executive opportunities in engineering, finance, general management, human resources, information systems, production/operations and sales/marketing throughout greater Midwest.

Salary Minimum: $75,000
Functions: Generalist
Industries: Generalist, Machinery/Appliances, Motor vehicles, Test/measurement equip., Misc. mfg.

Sales Builders, Inc. †
10680 Main St., Ste. 230
Fairfax, Virginia 22030
(703) 591-3232
Fax: (703) 591-2849
Email: jcebrowski@salesbuilders.com
Web: www.salesbuilders.com

Key Contact - Specialty:
Mr. John W. Cebrowski - *Sales & marketing (international)*

Dr. J. Brett Fenwick - *International generalist*

Description: Specialist practice that focuses on upper and senior level international sales and marketing search and global organization consulting. Firm performs cross-cultural and expatriate assessments. Searches executed worldwide.

Salary Minimum: $75,000
Functions: Senior mgmt., Mkt. research, Mktg. mgmt., Sales mgmt., Direct mktg., Customer svc., Int'l.
Industries: Energy/utilities, Mfg., Wholesale, Environmental svcs., Packaging, High tech, Healthcare
Professional Associations: IACPR

Salveson Stetson Group, Inc.

992 Old Eagle School Rd., Ste. 917
Wayne, Pennsylvania 19087
(610) 341-9020
Fax: (610) 341-9025
Email: salveson@salvstet.com

Key Contact - Specialty:
Mr. John Salveson
Ms. Sally Stetson

Description: We are highly consultative in our approach to search. We perform an in-depth organization assessment to begin a search and remain after the search to help the new executive assimilate.

Salary Minimum: $100,000
Functions: General mgmt., Mfg., Materials, Sales & mktg., HR mgmt., Finance, Mgmt. consultants
Industries: Generalist

Salzmann Gay Assoc., Inc.

275 Commerce Drive, Ste. 236
Ft. Washington, Pennsylvania 19034
(215) 654-0285

Key Contact - Specialty:
Ms. Martha Gay - *Senior management, finance, marketing*

Description: Retained executive search firm serving clients domestically and internationally.

Salary Minimum: $80,000
Functions: Generalist, Senior mgmt., Direct mktg., CFO's, Mgmt. consultants, Minorities
Industries: Generalist, Retail, Banking, Misc. financial, Mgmt. consulting, Insurance, Healthcare

---

Norm Sanders Assoc., Inc.

2 Village Court
Hazlet, New Jersey 07730
(908) 264-3700
Email: nsa@normsanders.com
Web: www.normsanders.com

Key Contact - Specialty:
Mr. Norman D. Sanders - *Senior level information systems*
Mr. Burton H. Helgeson - *Senior level information systems*
Mr. Walter J. McGuigan - *Senior level information systems*
Mr. John Boag - *Senior level information systems*
Ms. Mary M. Lindsey - *Senior level information systems*
Ms. Karen M. Sanders - *Senior level information systems*
Mr. Todd A. Sanders - *Senior level information systems*
Mr. Louis B. Hughes - *Senior level information systems and consulting partners*

Description: One of the leading firms recruiting chief information officers (CIO's), senior level information systems executives and technology leaders. The firm has in-depth capabilities to assess both business and technical acumen and utilizes database of senior level I.S. talent.

Salary Minimum: $175,000
Functions: MIS mgmt.
Industries: Generalist, Transportation, Retail, Finance, Hospitality, Publishing, High tech

---

Sanford Rose Assoc. - Lake Forest

655 Rockland Rd., Ste. 105
Lake Bluff, Illinois 60044
(847) 482-1210
Fax: (847) 482-1213
Email: bluduncan@aol.com

Key Contact - Specialty:
Mr. James W. Duncan - *Medical products, devices, services, biotechnology (all levels & functions)*

Description: Highly specialized, experienced resource for top management of early/mid-stage entrepreneurial medical ventures to find, attract and integrate top-notch talent throughout their organization.

Salary Minimum: $75,000
Functions: Generalist, General mgmt., Mfg., Sales & mktg., Finance, R&D, Engineering
Industries: Drugs mfg., Medical devices, Pharmaceutical svcs., Biotech, Healthcare

---

Allan Sarn Assoc., Inc.

230 Park Ave., Ste. 1522
New York, New York 10169
(212) 687-0600
Fax: (212) 687-6216

Key Contact - Specialty:
Mr. Allan G. Sarn - *Human resources*

Description: We are the only retainer-based executive search firm that specializes exclusively in human resources and we have been providing our diverse client base with senior HR executives who add strategic value to their organizations.

Salary Minimum: $100,000
Functions: HR mgmt.
Industries: Generalist
Professional Associations: IACPR

Sathe & Associates, Inc.

5821 Cedar Lake Rd.
Minneapolis, Minnesota 55416
(612) 546-2100
Fax: (612) 546-6930

Key Contact - Specialty:
Mr. Mark Sathe - *Generalist (mid, upper level management)*

Description: Industry specialties include financial services, manufacturing, banking, environment, medical products, healthcare, hospitality and high tech. Founded in 1974. Retainer only since 1989. 90% completion ratio, 95% successful hiring ratio.

Salary Minimum: $60,000
Functions: Generalist, General mgmt., Mfg., Sales & mktg., Finance, IT, Engineering
Industries: Generalist, Construction, Mfg., Finance, Svcs., Communications, Packaging

---

Satterfield & Assoc., Inc.

7875 Annesdale Drive
Cincinnati, Ohio 45243
(513) 561-3679
Email: dick@satterfield3.com
Web: www.satterfield3.com

Key Contact - Specialty:
Mr. Richard W. Satterfield, Jr. - *General management, sales management*

Description: Retained search firm that specializes in consumer packaged goods and technology/telecommunications industries. Focus against general management, sales and marketing naturally.

Salary Minimum: $100,000
Functions: Senior mgmt., Mktg. mgmt., Sales mgmt., Mgmt. consultants
Industries: Food/bev/tobacco, Soap/perfume/cosmetics, Computer equip., Mgmt. consulting, Telecoms, High tech, Software

---

Savoy Partners, Ltd.

1620 L St. NW, Ste. 801
Washington, District of Columbia 20036
(202) 887-0666
Fax: (202) 887-4991

Key Contact - Specialty:
Mr. Robert J. Brudno - *Generalist*
Ms. Elizabeth Clauhsen - *Generalist*

Description: An independent, highly-regarded, senior level executive search firm whose principals each have more than fifteen years of retainer executive search experience. Management consulting complements our partner-level-only search practice.

Salary Minimum: $100,000
Functions: General mgmt., Sales & mktg., HR mgmt., Finance, IT, Specialized services, Int'l.
Industries: Generalist, Finance, Svcs., Communications, Aerospace, High tech, Healthcare

---

David Saxner & Assoc., Inc. (DSA, Inc.)

3 First National Plaza, Ste. 1400
Chicago, Illinois 60602
(312) 214-3360
Fax: (312) 214-3787

Key Contact - Specialty:
Mr. David Saxner - *Commercial real estate*
Ms. Rikke Vognsen - *Commercial real estate*

Description: Established to recruit senior level and middle management executives in the real estate industry. We work closely with our clients to facilitate and bring continuity to the recruitment process.

Salary Minimum: $75,000
Functions: Senior mgmt., Middle mgmt., Mktg. mgmt., CFO's, Engineering, Architects
Industries: Real estate

Schall Executive Search Partners

601 Second Ave. S.
4390 First Bank Place
Minneapolis, Minnesota 55402
(612) 338-3119
Fax: (612) 336-4509
Email: schallpartners@att.net

Key Contact - Specialty:
Mr. David M. Lyman - *Financial services, consumer products*
Mr. David R. Schall - *Retail, financial services, human resources*

Description: We tailor our search strategy to meet the needs of your company. We limit the number of searches we handle at any one time which allows us to focus our efforts on your assignment and complete it faster.

Salary Minimum: $70,000
Functions: Senior mgmt., Distribution, Mktg. mgmt., Sales mgmt., Benefits, CFO's, Cash mgmt.
Industries: Generalist, Food/bev/tobacco, Medical devices, Misc. mfg., Retail, Finance, Insurance

Affiliates:
Network Careers

F. B. Schmidt Int'l.

30423 Canwood Place, Ste. 239
Agoura Hills, California 91301
(818) 706-0500
Fax: (818) 707-0784
Email: info@fbschmidt.com
Web: fbschmidt.com

Key Contact - Specialty:
Mr. Frank B. Schmidt - *Senior level executives (consumer products & services companies)*

Description: Exclusive recruitment specialists in senior level management functions for consumer oriented firms in the consumer packaged goods, financial, healthcare, telecommunications, electronics, leisure, health and beauty aids, retail, food, quick serve/restaurant industries.

Salary Minimum: $100,000
Functions: Senior mgmt., Advertising, Mkt. research, Mktg. mgmt., Sales mgmt., Direct mktg., Int'l.
Industries: Food/bev/tobacco, Soap/perfume/cosmetics, Drugs mfg., Consumer electronics, Finance, Hospitality, Communications

---

Schneider, Hill & Spangler, Inc.

Rose Tree Corp. Ctr., P.O. Box 70
Media, Pennsylvania 19063-0070
(610) 566-9550
Fax: (610) 566-9555

Key Contact - Specialty:
Mr. Steven A. Schneider - *Healthcare, technology (senior level & outside directors)*
Mr. J.W. White - *Food, consumer packaged goods (senior level & outside directors)*
Mr. Skip W. Schneider

Description: One of the nation's oldest executive search firms successfully representing over eighty industry groups from the new venture start-up to the multinationals at the senior, officer and outside director levels.

Salary Minimum: $100,000
Functions: General mgmt., Directors, Senior mgmt., Sales & mktg., HR mgmt., Finance, CFO's
Industries: Food/bev/tobacco, Drugs mfg., Medical devices, Pharmaceutical svcs., High tech, Biotech, Healthcare

---

Schuyler Assoc., Ltd.

400 Perimeter Ctr. Terrace, Ste. 900
Atlanta, Georgia 30346
(770) 352-9414
Fax: (770) 512-0211
Email: Bert@Schuyler-Associates.com

Key Contact - Specialty:
Mr. Lambert Schuyler - *Senior management*

Description: Specialists in attracting super stars for senior management positions.

Salary Minimum: $150,000
Functions: General mgmt., Healthcare, Sales & mktg., Finance, IT, R&D, Int'l.
Industries: Energy/utilities, Finance, Svcs., Insurance, High tech, Software, Healthcare

Networks:
The Hever Group

Schuyler, Baker & Parker, Inc.

Two Concourse Pkwy., Ste. 775
Atlanta, Georgia 30328-5347
(770) 804-1996
Fax: (770) 804-1917
Email: confidential@sbpsearch.com
Web: www.sbpsearch.com

Key Contact - Specialty:
Mr. Lambert Schuyler
Mr. Jerry H. Baker
Mr. Daniel F. Parker, Sr.
Mr. Gary L. Daugherty

Description: We specialize in value added senior management searches for most industries and institutions of higher education. Significant experience serving international companies.

Salary Minimum: $90,000
Functions: Generalist
Industries: Mfg., Finance, Svcs., Communications, High tech, Software, Healthcare

Networks:
The Hever Group

Schwab-Carrese Assoc., Inc. Executive Search

128 S. Tryon St., Ste. 1570
Charlotte, North Carolina 28202
(704) 331-4229
Fax: (704) 376-5988
Email: schcar@aol.com
Web: www.schwab-carrese.com

Key Contact - Specialty:
Mr. James K. Schwab
Ms. Shauna Daly
Mr. Mike Keenan
Ms. Anna Hancock
Mr. Frank Carrese
Mr. David Salls
Mr. Buddy LeTourneau
Ms. Annamarie Phillips

Description: Retained executive search firm serving all industries and professions.

Salary Minimum: $85,000
Functions: Generalist
Industries: Generalist

Schweichler Assoc., Inc.

200 Tamal Vista, Ste. 100, Bldg. 200
Corte Madera, California 94925
(415) 924-7200
Fax: (415) 924-9152
Email: search@schweichler.com
Web: www.schweichler.com

Key Contact - Specialty:
Mr. Lee Schweichler - *High technology*
Ms. Ann Peckenpaugh - *High technology*
Ms. Claudia Cole Bluhm - *High technology*
Ms. Linda Mikula - *High technology*

Description: Reputation for locating exceptional individuals for organizations undergoing rapid growth or change. Focus on recruiting President, CEO, COO, Vice President and director levels. Particularly effective in entrepreneurial (high-tech) environments.

Salary Minimum: $125,000
Functions: Senior mgmt., Mktg. mgmt., Sales mgmt., Direct mktg., Customer svc., R&D, Engineering
Industries: Computer equip., Consumer electronics, Communications, New media, Telecoms, High tech, Biotech

Networks:
International Technology Partners

Scott Executive Search, Inc.

61 Woodbury Place, Ste. 200
Rochester, New York 14618
(716) 264-0330
Email: eannscott@worldnet.att.net

Key Contact - Specialty:
Ms. E. Ann Scott - *Food, consumer packaged goods, telecommunications*

Description: Quality retainer based executive recruiting for management positions - focus on service and results.

Salary Minimum: $70,000
Functions: Senior mgmt., Product dev., Production, Plant mgmt., Purchasing, Mktg. mgmt., Personnel
Industries: Food/bev/tobacco, Soap/perfume/cosmetics, New media, Telecoms, Packaging
Professional Associations: IACPR

Search Advisors Int'l. Corp.

One Harbour Place, Ste. 925
777 S. Harbour Island Blvd.
Tampa, Florida 33602-5747
(813) 221-7555
Fax: (813) 221-7557
Email: admin@searchadvisorsintl.com

Key Contact - Specialty:
Mr. Mark N. Strom - *Executive management (all areas)*
Mr. Edward Wilson - *Executive management (all areas)*
Mr. Gordon Scott - *Executive management, domestic, international*
Mr. Ariel B. Matucan - *Executive management (all areas)*

Description: Retained executive search consultants who specialize in long term client relationships, rather than a functional or industry focus. We succeed while maintaining the highest professional and ethical standards.

Salary Minimum: $75,000
Functions: General mgmt., Mfg., Sales & mktg., HR mgmt., Finance, Engineering, Int'l.
Industries: Energy/utilities, Mfg., Retail, Finance, Svcs., Aerospace, High tech

---

The Search Alliance, Inc.
(T. A. Byrnes/Human Resources, Inc.)

311 Centre St., Ste. 206
Fernandina Beach, Florida 32034
(904) 277-2535
Email: tsainc@net-magic.net

Key Contact - Specialty:
Mr. Tom Byrnes
Mr. David J. Beed

Description: Worldwide industry specific executive search with an exemplary record of success and repeat business. Extensive experience in executive team evaluation for restructuring, mergers and acquisitions and succession planning.

Salary Minimum: $90,000
Functions: General mgmt., Sales & mktg., HR mgmt., Finance, IT, R&D, Engineering
Industries: Computer equip., Finance, Computer svcs., Insurance, High tech, Software, Healthcare

Branches:
998 Farmington Ave., Ste. 210
West Hartford, Connecticut 06107
(860) 232-2300
Key Contact - Specialty:
Mr. David J. Beed
Mr. Bill Thomas

203 S. Main St.
Providence, Rhode Island 02903
(401) 861-2550
Key Contact - Specialty:
Mr. John Sahagian

The Search Company
(a division of Strategic Search Solutions Inc.)

8 Oriole Gardens
Toronto, Ontario M4V IV7
Canada
(416) 315-8594
Fax: (416) 960-3590

Key Contact - Specialty:
Ms. Rosemary Kaczanowski

Description: A specialty agency made up of experienced communications professionals. Focus on the communications, public affairs and corporate research disciplines. All searches are handled by senior individuals. The firm works exclusively on a retained basis.

Salary Minimum: $60,000
Functions: Senior mgmt., Middle mgmt., Advertising, Mkt. research, PR, Risk mgmt., Non-profits
Industries: Energy/utilities, Finance, Banking, Invest. banking, Communications, Advertising/PR, New media

Affiliates:
Firm Research

Search Excellence

2060 Ave De Los Arboles, Ste. 306
Thousand Oaks, California 91362
(805) 241-8950

Key Contact - Specialty:
Mr. Andrew Smith

Description: Our search methodology represents an innovative and personalized approach to executive search. Extremely high ethical standards always maintained.

Salary Minimum: $50,000
Functions: Generalist
Industries: Generalist

Search Group Inc.

505 Third St. SW, Ste. 950
Calgary, Alberta T2P 3E6
Canada
(403) 292-0950
Fax: (403) 292-0959
Email: van_biesen@searchgroupinc.com
Web: www.searchgroupinc.com

Key Contact - Specialty:
Mr. Jacques A. H. van Biesen - *Senior executive management, senior technical staff*
Ms. Coby van Biesen - *Generalist*
Ms. Catherine Bell

Description: We specialize in providing worldwide executive search services to clients that seek exceptional staff for executive management and senior technical positions.

Salary Minimum: $80,000

Functions: Generalist, Senior mgmt., Mfg., CFO's, R&D, Engineering, Int'l.
Industries: Generalist, Misc. mfg., Finance, Svcs., Communications, Environmental svcs., High tech

Search Innovations, Inc.

405 Beaumont Circle
West Chester, Pennsylvania 19380
(610) 692-2000
(610) 692-6066
Email: vkessler@nni.com

Key Contact - Specialty:
Ms. Vivian Kessler - *Generalist*
Mr. Ehud Israel - *Generalist*

Description: A firm providing premium service for hourly rates, significantly lowering costs per hire. We cater to the mutual fund, mortgage banking, credit card, direct marketing and insurance industries.

Salary Minimum: $70,000
Functions: Middle mgmt., Mktg. mgmt., Direct mktg., Benefits, Personnel, Training, Cash mgmt.
Industries: Banking, Invest. banking, Misc. financial, Pharmaceutical svcs., Human resource svcs., Advertising/PR, Insurance

Search Int'l. †

P.O. Box 81
Newburyport, Massachusetts 01950
(978) 465-4000
Fax: (978) 465-4069
Email: searchfirm@aol.com
Web: www.searchinternationalinc.com

Key Contact - Specialty:
Mr. Brian Eagar - *Hospitality, investment banking, training, culinary, micro brew*
Mr. Michael Schweiger - *Senior level administration, hospitality*
Ms. Christine Hawthorne - *Household management, estate management, hospitality sales*
Mrs. Maria Johnson - *Information systems*
Mr. Andrew Lowery - *Hospitality, generalist*
Mr. John Stanley - *General hospitality, culinary*
Mr. Elliott Wade - *Management information services, consulting*
Mr. Stephan Thieringer - *Hotels, resorts*
Mr. Joseph Laite - *Services, sales*

Description: Boston Business Journal independently ranks us as the 4th largest overall firm in New England and the highest ranking in the hospitality industry for 5 consecutive years. Additional offices in California, Connecticut, Framingham, MA, New York, Philadelphia, Israel, Nassau, and the United Kingdom.

Salary Minimum: $70,000

Functions: Middle mgmt., Sales mgmt., CFO's, MIS mgmt., Systems dev., Systems support, Int'l.
Industries: Food/bev/tobacco, Computer equip., Invest. banking, Svcs., Hospitality, Entertainment

Search Masters Int'l.

500 Foothills S., Ste. 2
Sedona, Arizona 86336
(520) 282-3553
Fax: (520) 282-5881
Email: smi@sedona.net
Web: smi.bio.com/

Key Contact - Specialty:
Mr. David G. Jensen - *Biotechnology*

Description: Administrative, technical and marketing/operations, etc. for companies in the industrial life sciences, i.e. biotechnology, medical device, pharmaceutical industries.

Salary Minimum: $50,000
Functions: Directors, Senior mgmt., Plant mgmt., Mktg. mgmt., Sales mgmt., CFO's, R&D
Industries: Chemicals, Drugs mfg., Medical devices, Pharmaceutical svcs., Biotech, Healthcare

Affiliates:
Management Consulting Munchen

Search Research Assoc., Inc.

(Firm declined to update.)
100 Tower Office Park, Ste. K
Woburn, Massachusetts 01801
(781) 938-0990
Email: gordon@sra,tiac.net
Web: www.searchresearch.com/

Key Contact - Specialty:
Mr. Gordon S. Scott - *Financial management, marketing, non-profit, insurance*
Mr. John Doyle - *Insurance, non-profit, marketing*
Mr. George T. Kenney - *Insurance, MIS, manufacturing*
Mr. Peter Dexter - *Sales & marketing, utilities, petrochemical*

Description: 70% retained search salaries 60K to 120K range, 30% research. We work with approx. 5 search firms across the USA. We also have 3 dedicated researches on our staff just for research.

Salary Minimum: $60,000
Functions: Middle mgmt., Health admin., Mktg. mgmt., Personnel, CFO's, M&A, MIS mgmt.
Industries: Generalist, Energy/utilities, Misc. financial, Non-profits, Human resource svcs., Insurance, Healthcare

SearchCom, Inc.

12860 Hillcrest, Ste. 101
Dallas, Texas 75230-1519
(972) 490-0300
Email: susana1@airmail.net

Key Contact - Specialty:
Ms. Susan Abrahamson - *Marketing, advertising, public relations*

Description: Executive search for marketing, advertising and public relations talent for corporations and their agencies, across all industries.

Salary Minimum: $50,000
Functions: Advertising, Mkt. research, Mktg. mgmt., Direct mktg., PR, Graphic artists
Industries: Food/bev/tobacco, Computer equip., Consumer electronics, Advertising/PR, Publishing, High tech, Healthcare

Searchforce, Inc.

2907 W. Bay Drive
Belleair Bluffs, Florida 34640
(813) 588-4400
Fax: (813) 588-0116
Email: sfi@searchforce.com
Web: www.searchforce.com

Key Contact - Specialty:
Mr. Al DiPalo
Ms. Vicki Carr
Mr. James Kitt

Description: Entry level Ph.D.'s/MD's to division president. Small focused firm acting as an extension of your company. Represent small number of clients - no ethical problems.

Salary Minimum: $65,000
Functions: Senior mgmt., Middle mgmt., Product dev., R&D, Mgmt. consultants
Industries: Chemicals, Soap/perfume/cosmetics, Drugs mfg., Medical devices, Pharmaceutical svcs., Biotech, Healthcare

Secura/Burnett Partners

555 California St., Ste. 3950
San Francisco, California 94104
(415) 398-0700
Fax: (415) 398-2274

Key Contact - Specialty:
Mr. Louis C. Burnett
Ms. Kathleen Van Boven
Ms. Jenifer H. Hartwell
Ms. Sarah R. Ashby

Description: An international retained executive search firm dedicated to identifying and recruiting senior level managers for the financial services industry.

Salary Minimum: $200,000

† occasional contingency assignment

Functions: Directors, Senior mgmt., Personnel, CFO's, MIS mgmt., Int'l.
Industries: Finance, Banking, Invest. banking, Brokers, Venture cap., Insurance, Real estate

Branches:
590 Madison Ave., 32nd Floor
New York, New York 10022
(212) 754-0200
Fax: (212) 223-0054
Key Contact - Specialty:
Mr. Robert J. Friedland
Mr. Lawrence J. Fraser
Mr. John V. Jazylo

Sedlar & Miners
1120 Ave. of the Americas, 4th Floor
New York, New York 10036
(212) 628-1616

Key Contact - Specialty:
Mr. Richard A. Miners - *Information technology, consumer goods & services, general management, sales & marketing, management consultants*
Ms. Jeri L. Sedlar - *Information technology, general management, sales & marketing, management consultants*

Description: Senior management searches in technology and the consumer products and services categories. Both principals work on each individual assignment.

Salary Minimum: $125,000
Functions: General mgmt., Sales & mktg., Direct mktg., Finance, IT, Mgmt. consultants
Industries: Drugs mfg., Finance, Misc. financial, Mgmt. consulting, New media, High tech, Software
Professional Associations: IACPR

Affiliates:
Sheila Greco Assoc.

J. R. Seehusen Assoc., Inc.
805 S. Main St.
Fairfield, Iowa 52556
(515) 469-2600
Fax: (515) 472-8580
Email: jrsausa@lisco.com

Key Contact - Specialty:
Mr. Joseph R. Seehusen - *CIO, CFO*

Description: High quality custom senior search and consulting work. 260 assignments completed in Fortune 500 and major global financial clients.

Salary Minimum: $75,000
Functions: CFO's, MIS mgmt.
Industries: Food/bev/tobacco, Banking, Misc. financial, Healthcare

Seiden Krieger Assoc., Inc.
375 Park Ave.
New York, New York 10152
(212) 688-8383
Email: ska@interport.net

Key Contact - Specialty:
Mr. Steven A. Seiden - *CEOs; directors*
Mr. Dennis F. Krieger - *Operating management*

Description: Retainer firm specializing in CEO's and professionals who report to CEO's. Frequently such searches are for companies in transition. Particular expertise in recruiting executives with hands-on experience in world class manufacturing philosophies.

Salary Minimum: $90,000
Functions: Generalist, Directors, Senior mgmt., Middle mgmt., Mktg. mgmt., CFO's, Engineering
Industries: Generalist, Metal products, Machinery/Appliances, Computer equip., Misc. mfg., Telecoms, Aerospace
Professional Associations: IACPR

Affiliates:
Leaders-Trust International
Withey & Vedi

Seitchik Corwin & Seitchik Inc.
3443 Clay St.
San Francisco, California 94118-2008
(415) 928-5717

Key Contact - Specialty:
Mr. J. Blade Corwin - *Apparel, textiles, footwear & related areas, retail*
Mr. Jack Seitchik - *Apparel, textiles, footwear & related areas, retail*

Description: Specialize in apparel, textile, footwear, handbag, accessories and related needletrades industries.

Salary Minimum: $50,000
Functions: Generalist
Industries: Textiles/apparel, Retail

Branches:
330 E. 38th St., Ste. 5P
New York, New York 10016
(212) 370-3592
Key Contact - Specialty:
Mr. William Seitchik - *Apparel, textiles, footwear & related areas, retail*

Robert Sellery Assoc., Ltd.
1155 Connecticut Ave. NW, Ste. 500
Washington, District of Columbia 20036
(202) 331-0090
Fax: (202) 452-8654
Email: rselleryjr@aol.com
Web: www.sellery.com

Key Contact - Specialty:
Mr. Robert A. Sellery, Jr. - *Not-for-profit organizations*

Description: We find presidents, executive directors, chief development, communication, financial and academic officers and program officers, along with people reporting to these positions for non-profit organizations.
Functions: Minorities, Non-profits, Environmentalists, Int'l.
Industries: Non-profits, Higher ed., Human resource svcs., Government, Healthcare

Affiliates:
Moriarty/Fox, Inc.

Senior Careers
120 Wall St., 16th Floor
New York, New York 10005
(212) 475-8837
(800) 464-0456
Fax: (212) 228-3958

Key Contact - Specialty:
Mr. David R. Willcox - *Generalist*

Description: We are an executive search firm which places into non-profit and for-profit companies executives who have demonstrated outstanding management talent throughout their careers.
Functions: Generalist, Int'l.
Industries: Generalist

Sensible Solutions, Inc.
239 W. Coolidge Ave.
Barrington, Illinois 60010
(847) 382-0070
Email: pdelaney@sensibleinc.com
Web: sensibleinc.com

Key Contact - Specialty:
Mr. Patrick J. Delaney - *Senior level core team employees & portfolio workers*

Description: We are an executive search consultancy. We deliver client specific results within two practice concentrations: 1. searches for senior level executives and portfolio workers (external people resources) and 2. consulting for best practices in managing portfolio workers.

Salary Minimum: $8,000
Functions: Generalist, General mgmt., Senior mgmt., Mfg., Finance, IT, Mgmt. consultants
Industries: Generalist, Computer svcs., Accounting, Mgmt. consulting, Human resource svcs., Telecoms, Healthcare

Sevcor Int'l., Inc.
1 Pierce Place, Ste. 400E
Itasca, Illinois 60143
(630) 250-3088
Email: sevcor@sevcor-int.com
Web: www.sevcor-int.com

Key Contact - Specialty:
Mr. J. Randy Severinsen
Mr. William R. Lange

Description: We partner with clients who view recruitment as a strategic business objective, offering retingency search for partner projects, plus contracts. Consulting services. Specialty IT areas include SAP, Baan, PeopleSoft and Oracle.

Salary Minimum: $35,000
Functions: Middle mgmt., Systems anal., Systems dev., Systems implem., Systems support, Engineering, Mgmt. consultants
Industries: Misc. financial, Computer svcs., Mgmt. consulting, Human resource svcs., Insurance, High tech, Software

Shannahan & Co., Inc.

655 Redwood Hwy., Ste. 133
Mill Valley, California 94941
(415) 381-3613
Fax: (415) 381-3879
Web: peter@shannahan.com

Key Contact - Specialty:
Mr. Peter Shannahan - *Financial services*

Description: Specialize in senior sales, management, marketing and executive level placements for financial services, with emphasis in the institutional retirement plan arena.

Salary Minimum: $90,000
Functions: Senior mgmt., Middle mgmt., Mkt. research, Mktg. mgmt., Sales mgmt.
Industries: Banking, Invest. banking, Brokers, Venture cap., Misc. financial

M. B. Shattuck & Assoc., Inc.

100 Bush St., Ste. 1675
San Francisco, California 94104
(415) 421-6264
Fax: (415) 421-0434
Email: mbshattuck@aol.com

Key Contact - Specialty:
Mr. M. B. Shattuck - *Senior level executives, high technology, general manufacturing*

Description: Nationwide client base in most industries/functions, for senior/upper middle levels. Special competence in high technology (computer related), distribution, telecommunications (networking), general manufacturing and health/medical.

Salary Minimum: $80,000
Functions: General mgmt., Mfg., Materials, Sales & mktg., HR mgmt., IT, Engineering
Industries: Generalist, Medical devices, Metal products, Machinery/Appliances, Computer equip., High tech, Software
Professional Associations: AESC

Affiliates:
Hodge-Cronin & Assoc., Inc.

Peggy Shea & Assoc. †

2660 Townsgate Rd., Ste. 800
Westlake Village, California 91361
(818) 889-5350
Fax: (818) 379-5343
Email: Peggyshea@earthlink.net

Key Contact - Specialty:
Ms. Peggy Shea - *Healthcare*
Mr. James Peck - *Healthcare*
Ms. Shannon Warden - *Healthcare*

Description: A West coast healthcare executive search firm placing administrative, nursing and ancillary executives within the hospital setting. Our goal is building a lasting partnership with our client hospitals.

Salary Minimum: $60,000
Functions: Senior mgmt., Middle mgmt., Nurses, Allied health, Health admin.

Shelton, Wiseman & Leon †

16980 Via Tazon, Ste. 240
San Diego, California 92127
(619) 673-6000
Fax: (619) 673-6006
Email: swl@sheltonsearch.com
Web: www.sheltonsearch.com

Key Contact - Specialty:
Mr. Frederick L. Shelton - *Attorneys*
Ms. Diana Leon-Shelton - *Attorneys*
Ms. Lynn C. Curry

Description: We accept only 2-3 clients per city. Our clients receive exclusivity of candidates. We have filled searches other search firms were unsuccessful at completing. Specialties: intellectual property, corporate, litigation, health, labor, tax, ERISA, international.
Functions: Attorneys

Shepherd Bueschel & Provus, Inc.

401 N. Michigan Ave., Ste. 3020
Chicago, Illinois 60611
(312) 832-3020
Fax: (312) 832-0001
Email: sbp4019aol.com

Key Contact - Specialty:
Mr. David A. Bueschel
Ms. Barbara L. Provus
Mr. Daniel M. Shepherd

Description: Three principals and two associates with significant and diverse experience, responsible as a team both for conducting assignments and maintaining client relationships. All three principals are included in the new "Career Makers".

Salary Minimum: $125,000
Functions: Generalist, Directors, Senior mgmt., Sales mgmt., HR mgmt., MIS mgmt., Mgmt. consultants
Industries: Generalist, Mfg., Retail, Mgmt. consulting, Publishing, High tech, Software
Professional Associations: AESC, IACPR

Sheridan Search
(a division of Sheridan Consulting LLC)

401 N. Franklin St., 2nd Floor
Chicago, Illinois 60610
(312) 822-0232
Fax: (312) 822-9840
Email: info@sheridan-consulting.com
Web: www.sheridan-consulting.com

Key Contact - Specialty:
Mr. John A. Sheridan

Description: The firm specializes in human resources search assignments.

Salary Minimum: $100,000
Functions: HR mgmt., Benefits, Personnel, Training
Industries: Generalist

Sherwood Lehman Massucco, Inc.

3455 W. Shaw Ave., Ste. 110
Fresno, California 93711-3201
(209) 276-8572
Fax: (209) 276-2351
Email: slinc@slinc.com
Web: www.slinc.com

Key Contact - Specialty:
Mr. Robert F. Sherwood - *General management, technical management*
Mr. Neal G. Lehman - *Information systems, general management, financial*
Mr. Harry A. Massucco - *Banking, general management*

Description: Nationwide search for companies that are headquartered or have division offices in Central California.

Salary Minimum: $60,000
Functions: Generalist, Mfg., Materials, Sales & mktg., HR mgmt., Finance, IT
Industries: Generalist, Agri/forestry/mining, Construction, Mfg., Transportation, Finance, High tech

Shinn & Assoc.

631 O'Farrell St., Ste. 1904
San Francisco, California 94109
(415) 567-1380
Fax: (415) 567-1393
Email: mshinn@aol.com

Key Contact - Specialty:
Mr. Michael Shinn - *High tech: semiconductor, software, hardware, telecom*

Description: We are a small firm concentrating on middle to upper middle management levels in the Silicon Valley. We also place technical individual contributors. Specialize in software, telecommunications, and semiconductor.

Salary Minimum: $75,000

† occasional contingency assignment

Functions: General mgmt., Mfg., Materials, Sales & mktg., Finance, IT, Engineering
Industries: Computer equip., Consumer electronics, Test/measurement equip., Communications, Telecoms, High tech, Software

---

Michael Shirley Assoc. Inc.

7300 W. 110th St., Ste. 230
Overland Park, Kansas 66210
(913) 491-0240
Email: msassociates@earthlink.net

Key Contact - Specialty:
Mr. Michael R. Shirley - *Generalist*
Ms. Lyn Pilley
Ms. Theresa Leinwetter - *Generalist*
Ms. Pat Cassady - *Generalist*
Ms. Mary Reusser - *Generalist*
Mr. Kim Jerabek
Ms. Melissa Watkins - *Generalist*
Ms. Donna Overson - *Generalist*
Ms. Laura Dryer - *Generalist*

Description: Generalist executive search and senior level outplacement firm with strong experience in the services industries in the Central Midwest. Healthcare, banking/financial, utilities/energy services and restaurant have been significant industry specialties.

Salary Minimum: $60,000
Functions: Generalist, Senior mgmt., Health admin., Mktg. mgmt., Sales mgmt., CFO's, MIS mgmt.
Industries: Generalist, Energy/utilities, Food/bev/tobacco, Finance, Hospitality, Insurance, Healthcare

---

Shoemaker & Assoc.

1862 Independence Sq., Ste. A
Atlanta, Georgia 30338
(770) 395-7225
Email: shoemakerassoc@mindspring.com

Key Contact - Specialty:
Mr. Larry Shoemaker

Description: Highly professional generalist practice conducting a broad range of executive searches on a national scope at upper levels and middle management levels in management, marketing, sales, finance, research, quality, manufacturing and operations.

Salary Minimum: $60,000
Functions: Generalist, Senior mgmt., Plant mgmt., Mktg. mgmt., Sales mgmt., CFO's, Budgeting
Industries: Generalist, Food/bev/tobacco, Soap/perfume/cosmetics, Drugs mfg., Pharmaceutical svcs., Advertising/PR, Packaging

---

E. L. Shore & Assoc.

2 St. Clair Ave. E., Ste. 1201
Toronto, Ontario M4T 2T5
Canada
(416) 928-9399
Fax: (416) 928-6509
Email: elshore@netcom.ca

Key Contact - Specialty:
Mr. Earl Shore
Mr. Keith Hall
Mr. Marty Collis

Description: Search practice covers most industries with an emhasis on senior management. Typical searches include retail management, financial services, high tech, manufacturing and IT. In-depth knowledge of the Canadian market. Dedicated to providing personalized, professional service having a track record of superior results.

Salary Minimum: $75,000
Functions: Generalist, Senior mgmt., Middle mgmt., Distribution, HR mgmt., Finance, MIS mgmt.
Industries: Generalist, Mfg., Retail, Finance, Svcs., Aerospace, High tech

Networks:
The International Search Partnership

Shore Asociados Ejecutivos, S. A. de C.V. †

Av. Constituentes # 117-5o Piso
Col. San Miguel Chapultepec
Mexico City, Mexico DF 11850
Mexico
52 5 277 30 04
Fax: 52 5 515 39 79
Email: shorel@spin.com.mx

Key Contact - Specialty:
Mr. Fernando Fernandez De Cordova - *Generalist*
Ms. Linda Shore - *Generalist*
Ms. Virginia Franco - *Generalist*
Mr. Oscar Adams - *Generalist*
Ms. Susan Shore - *Generalist*

Description: Most complete personnel service in Mexico, a no nonsense operation, executive placement all levels, bicultural and bilingual associates. Turnkey operations in human resources, consulting in HR.

Salary Minimum: $25,000
Functions: Generalist, General mgmt., Materials, Sales & mktg., HR mgmt., Finance, IT
Industries: Generalist, Construction, Food/bev/tobacco, Transportation, Finance, Hospitality, Communications

Branches:
Av. Lazaro Cardenas #4145-5o Piso
Guadalajara, Jalisco 45040
Mexico
52 3 647 9012
Fax: 52 3 647 7916
Key Contact - Specialty:
Mr. Jorge Coello

Paseo Del Otono 100-304
Naucalpan, Mexico 53160
Mexico
52 5 360 1436
Fax: 52 5 360 0989
Key Contact - Specialty:
Ms. Susan Shore

Av. Lazaro Cardenas # 2400 Pte.
Monterrey, Nuevo Leon
Mexico
52 8 363 27 69
Fax: 52 8 363 27 68
Key Contact - Specialty:
Mr. Alfonso Calderon

Networks:
InterSearch

The Shorr Group

500 N. Michigan Ave., Ste. 820
Chicago, Illinois 60611
(312) 644-5100
Fax: (312) 644-7122
Email: shorrgrp@aol.com
Web: members.aol.com/shorrgrp/homepage/index

Key Contact - Specialty:
Ms. Carol Kurz-Shorr
Ms. Helene Fronteras
Ms. Joanne Roper
Ms. Gracemarie Soper
Ms. Karen Shorr

Description: On a retained basis, we identify candidates who will excel in your workplace in order to help you hire your organization's future and we guarantee satisfaction on each assignment.

Salary Minimum: $30,000
Functions: Generalist, General mgmt., Mfg., HR mgmt., Finance, Engineering, Specialized services
Industries: Generalist, Mfg., Finance, Human resource svcs., Communications, Insurance, Healthcare

---

The Shotland Group

6345 Balboa Blvd., Ste. 335
Encino, California 91316
(818) 995-1501
Fax: (818) 776-1430
Email: shotgrp@aol.com

Key Contact - Specialty:
Mr. David R. Shotland - *Manufacturing, marketing, engineering, generalist*

Description: A generalist practice emphasizing recruitment of middle and upper level management. Primary areas of specialization include disciplines within a manufacturing organization.

Salary Minimum: $50,000
Functions: Senior mgmt., Middle mgmt., Materials Plng., Distribution, Sales mgmt., CFO's, Engineering
Industries: Soap/perfume/cosmetics, Drugs mfg., Medical devices, Plastics/rubber, Metal products, Consumer electronics, Misc. mfg.

M. Shulman, Inc.

44 Montgomery St., Ste. 3085
San Francisco, California 94104-4804
(415) 398-3488
Fax: (415) 398-2208
Email: mel@mshulman.com

Key Contact - Specialty:
Mr. Mel Shulman - *Generalist with emphasis on high technology computer, medical, retail, high technology, entertainment*

Description: National generalist practice concentrates on CEO, COO and senior executive level positions. Clients include aerospace, financial services, biotechnology, conglomerates, electronic goods, LBO's, entertainment, broadcasting, medical products, new venture start-ups.

Salary Minimum: $300,000
Functions: Generalist, Directors, Senior mgmt., CFO's, MIS mgmt.
Industries: Generalist

John Sibbald Assoc., Inc.

7733 Forsyth Blvd., Ste. 2010
St. Louis, Missouri 63105-1817
(314) 727-0227
Email: Jsibbald@aol.com

Key Contact - Specialty:
Mr. John R. Sibbald - *Generalist*
Ms. Kathryn J. Costick - *Hospitality*
Mr. John B. Hunter, Jr. - *Hospitality*
Mr. Randall Martin - *Hospitality*

Description: Generalist recruiting firm with nationwide practice. Small, by design, to provide highly personalized service to limited clientele with emphasis on repeat business. Hospitality industry division serving clubs, resorts and hotels.

Salary Minimum: $80,000
Functions: Generalist, General mgmt., Mfg., Sales & mktg., HR mgmt., Finance, R&D
Industries: Generalist, Food/bev/tobacco, Soap/perfume/cosmetics, Drugs mfg., Machinery/Appliances, Retail, Hospitality

Larry Siegel & Assoc.

1111 Third Ave., Ste. 2880
Seattle, Washington 98101
(206) 622-4282
Fax: (206) 622-4058
Email: 102532.1505@compuserve.com

Key Contact - Specialty:
Mr. Larry Siegel

Description: A highly experienced generalist firm specializing in recruitment of senior level management in all functional disciplines with expertise in a wide range of manufacturing, distribution and service industries.

Salary Minimum: $70,000
Functions: Senior mgmt., Mfg., Materials, Sales & mktg., HR mgmt., Finance, Engineering
Industries: Mfg., Metal products, Machinery/Appliances, Consumer electronics, Misc. mfg., Communications, Aerospace

RitaSue Siegel Resources, Inc.

20 E. 46th St.
New York, New York 10017-2417
(212) 682-2100
Fax: (212) 682-2946
Email: RitaSueS@aol.com
Web: www.core77.com/RitaSueSiegel/index.html

Key Contact - Specialty:
Ms. RitaSue Siegel - *Design management, industrial design, interior design, architecture, consultant firms*
Ms. Jessica Ragaza - *Interactive media, industrial design, retail interiors, creative directors, collateral*
Ms. Marilyn Moran - *Package design, corporate interior design, gift and tabletop, graphic design management*

Description: Design management and staff; graphics: packaging, coporate, brand and retail identity, creative services, corporate communication; industrial design: product-automotive, toys, medical, computers, office products, telecommunications, tabletop/housewares; interior design and architecture. User-interface, usability.

Salary Minimum: $40,000
Functions: Product dev., Advertising, Mktg. mgmt., Engineering, Mgmt. consultants, Architects, Graphic artists
Industries: Food/bev/tobacco, Medical devices, Consumer electronics, Transportation, Entertainment, New media, High tech

L. A. Silver Assoc., Inc.

463 Worcester Rd., Ste. 205
Framingham, Massachusetts 01701
(508) 879-2603
Fax: (508) 879-8425
Email: lasilver@sprynet.com

Key Contact - Specialty:
Mr. Lee Silver - *Software, high technology*

Description: A multinational software telecommunications management recruitment firm with worldwide contacts and significant worldwide networks at senior management levels. All assignments managed hands on by principals only.

Salary Minimum: $88,000
Functions: General mgmt., Mfg., Sales & mktg., Finance, IT, R&D, Int'l.
Industries: Generalist, Computer equip., Communications, High tech, Software

Daniel A. Silverstein Assoc. Inc.

5355 Town Ctr. Rd., Ste. 1001
Boca Raton, Florida 33486
(561) 391-0600
Fax: (561) 391-0180

Key Contact - Specialty:
Mr. Daniel A. Silverstein - *Healthcare*

Description: Executive search for pharmaceuticals, biotechnology, diagnostics and managed care. Venture capital-presidents for early stage companies. Top management for HMO's, practice management companies and pharmacy benefit managers.

Salary Minimum: $100,000
Functions: Directors, Senior mgmt., IT, R&D, Mgmt. consultants
Industries: Drugs mfg., Medical devices, Venture cap., Pharmaceutical svcs., Mgmt. consulting, Biotech, Healthcare

D. J. Simpson Assoc. Inc.

1900 Minnesota Court, Ste. 118
Mississauga, Ontario L5N 3C9
Canada
(905) 821-2727
Fax: (905) 821-3800
Email: djsai@inforamp.net

Key Contact - Specialty:
Mr. David Simpson
Mr. Karl Hagglund

Description: We combine search with one of the most powerful assessment tools available today to ensure our clients outperform their most worthy opponents. And we have the track record to prove it.

Salary Minimum: $80,000

Functions: Directors, Senior mgmt., Plant mgmt., Mktg. mgmt., Sales mgmt., CFO's, MIS mgmt.
Industries: Generalist, Food/bev/tobacco, Misc. mfg., Retail, Venture cap., High tech, Healthcare

Sinclair & Co., Inc. †

831 Beacon St., Ste. 320
Newton Centre, Massachusetts 02159
(617) 969-4242
Fax: (617) 969-4248
Email: sinclair@ss4jobs.com
Web: www.sinclair.qpg.com

Key Contact - Specialty:
Mr. Douglas L. Sinclair - *Executive management*

Description: Executive serach for the computer industry with focus on software tools, advanced applications, manufacturing systems (MRP, MES, ERP), supply chain management, telecommunications, finance and insurance industries.

Salary Minimum: $65,000
Functions: Mfg., Mktg. mgmt., CFO's, IT, MIS mgmt., Systems anal., Mgmt. consultants
Industries: Computer equip., Computer svcs., Mgmt. consulting, High tech, Software

Branches:
4701 S. Atlantic Ave.
New Smyrna Beach, Florida 32169
(904) 428-9610
Fax: (904) 428-3055
Key Contact - Specialty:
Ms. Carolyn J. Buxton - *Marketing*

Affiliates:
SilverSands Int'l.

Sink, Walker, Boltrus Int'l.

60 Walnut St., 3rd Floor
Wellesley Hills, Massachusetts 02181
(781) 237-1199
Web: www.swbi.com

Key Contact - Specialty:
Mr. Douglas G. Walker - *High technology, financial services, manufacturing, CEO's & BOD*
Mr. Richard Boltrus - *High technology, operations, research, scientists, semiconductors*
Ms. Sushila A. Desai
Mr. Cornel Faucher - *Telecommunications, data communications, internet software, multimedia*
Mr. Douglas G. Shufelt - *Telecommunications, high technology, financial services, manufacturing, fashion & retail*
Mr. Lee L'Archevesque - *High technology, operations, research, scientists, semiconductors*

Description: Primary search assignments for individual contributors and management: high technology; communications - public and private networks; capital equipment - ATE and semiconductor industry; general manufacturers; consulting firms; financial services; VC/LBO firms represented.

Salary Minimum: $85,000
Functions: General mgmt., Mfg., Sales & mktg., Finance, IT, Specialized services, Int'l.
Industries: Computer equip., Test/measurement equip., Misc. mfg., Finance, Telecoms, High tech, Software

Branches:
2055 Gateway Place, Ste. 400
San Jose, California 95110
(408) 451-3977
Key Contact - Specialty:
Mr. Dick Boltrus

16479 Dallas Pkwy., Ste. 540
Dallas, Texas 75248
(972) 380-8686
Email: cwsink21@ix.netcom.com
Key Contact - Specialty:
Mr. Clifton W. Sink - *Telecommunications, high technology, capital equipment, semiconductors*

Ruth Sklar Assoc., Inc. (RSA Executive Search) †

475 Park Ave. S., 8th Floor
New York, New York 10016-6901
(212) 213-2929
Fax: (212) 779-9617
Email: ruthsklar@EarthLink.net

Key Contact - Specialty:
Ms. Ruth Sklar - *Consumer products, services, healthcare, finance, banking*
Mr. Daniel R. Mazziota - *High technology, biotechnology, senior financial*

Description: Multi-resource firm emphasizing principal involvement in all phases of search. Recruitment of key executives from finance, healthcare, consumer products, services, microwave electronics and aerospace industries. Specializing in entrepreneurial environments.

Salary Minimum: $80,000
Functions: Senior mgmt., Mktg. mgmt., Sales mgmt., CFO's, MIS mgmt., Engineering, Int'l.
Industries: Soap/perfume/cosmetics, Drugs mfg., Misc. financial, Entertainment, Telecoms, High tech, Healthcare

Skott/Edwards Consultants

500 Fifth Avenue
New York, New York 10110
(212) 382-1166
Fax: (212) 382-2926
Email: burkland@skottedwards.com
Web: www.skottedwards.com

Key Contact - Specialty:
Mr. Skott B. Burkland - *Senior level general management, life sciences*
Mr. James H. Cornehlsen - *Media, communications, marketing, database, information services*
Mrs. Elaine Burfield - *Information technology, emerging life sciences, senior level general management*

Description: Industry expertise emphasizing healthcare, pharmaceuticals, financial services, electronic publishing, high tech, consumer products and insurance. All functions including management, finance, human resource, manufacturing, sales and marketing, legal, procurement and board of directors.

Salary Minimum: $100,000
Functions: General mgmt., Mfg., Healthcare, Sales & mktg., Finance, IT, R&D
Industries: Generalist, Food/bev/tobacco, Drugs mfg., Medical devices, Retail, Finance, Biotech
Professional Associations: AESC

Branches:
1776 On the Green
Morristown, New Jersey 07960
(973) 644-0900
Fax: (973) 644-0991
Key Contact - Specialty:
Mr. Franklin J. Barbosa - *High technology, computer systems, communications, information systems, CAD/CAM*
Dr. Charles R. Grebenstein - *Emerging life sciences, information technology, senior level general management*

Affiliates:
M. B. Shattuck & Assoc., Inc.

Networks:
Penrhyn International

Slayton Int'l., Inc.

181 W. Madison, Ste. 4510
Chicago, Illinois 60602
(312) 456-0080
Fax: (312) 456-0089
Email: slayton@slaytonintl.com
Web: www.slaytonintl.com

Key Contact - Specialty:
Mr. Richard C. Slayton
Mr. Richard S. Slayton
Mr. Daniel Nigg
Ms. Arliss Kacedan
Mr. Thomas Jacob

Description: A growing influence in international executive search consulting. Ranked the seventeenth largest retained search practice in the world by Executive Recruiter News.

Salary Minimum: $120,000
Functions: General mgmt., Mfg., Sales & mktg., HR mgmt., Finance, MIS mgmt., Int'l.

Industries: Metal products, Machinery/ Appliances, Motor vehicles, Finance, Telecoms, Aerospace, High tech
Professional Associations: IACPR

Networks:
I-I-C Partners Executive Search Worldwide

Christopher Smallhorn Executive Recruiting, Inc.

One Boston Place
Boston, Massachusetts 02108
(617) 723-8180

Key Contact - Specialty:
Mr. Christopher Smallhorn

Description: Serve a range of industries in the recruiting of senior managers. Fees are fixed. The business is ethical, profitable and has loyal clients.

Salary Minimum: $125,000
Functions: Directors, Senior mgmt., Healthcare, Mktg. mgmt., CFO's
Industries: Generalist, Food/bev/tobacco, Soap/perfume/cosmetics, Drugs mfg., Medical devices, Venture cap., Healthcare

---

Smith & Laue Search

4370 NE Halsey St.
Portland, Oregon 97213
(503) 460-9181
Fax: (503) 460-9182
Email: smithlaue@aol.com

Key Contact - Specialty:
Mr. Charles D. Smith - *Senior search, food processing, agribusiness, food ingredients, pet food*
Ms. Elizabeth Laue - *Food processing*

Description: We specialize in mid and senior level professionals in the agribusiness, food processing, ingredients, flavor and the pet food industries both in the United States and internationally.

Salary Minimum: $100,000
Functions: Directors, Senior mgmt., Middle mgmt., Packaging, Mkt. research, CFO's
Industries: Agri/forestry/mining, Food/bev/ tobacco, Drugs mfg., Misc. financial, Packaging, Biotech

---

Smith & Sawyer, Inc.

230 Park Ave., 33rd Floor
New York, New York 10169
(212) 490-4390

Key Contact - Specialty:
Ms. Patricia L. Sawyer
Mr. Robert L. Smith

Description: Senior management positions in information industries, high technology, software, telecommunications, consulting, consumer products and services, retail and financial services. General managers (CEO, COO, division GM), directors and functional heads of marketing, finance, corporate development, information services and HR.

Salary Minimum: $200,000
Functions: Directors, Senior mgmt., Mktg. mgmt., CFO's, MIS mgmt., Mgmt. consultants, Minorities
Industries: Generalist, Retail, Mgmt. consulting, New media, Telecoms, High tech, Software
Professional Associations: AESC

Smith & Syberg, Inc.

825 Washington St., Ste. 2A
Columbus, Indiana 47201
(812) 372-7254
Fax: (812) 372-7275
Email: sands@hsonline.net

Key Contact - Specialty:
Mr. Joseph E. Smith - *Airline, accounting & finance*
Mr. Keith A. Syberg - *World class manufacturing companies*
Mr. Patrick Smith - *Food processing companies*

Description: Generalist recruiters serving primarily airlines, manufacturing, distribution and service companies. Our philosophy: form collaborative, long-term relationships with clients; represent clients professionally and positively; fill clients needs with the best qualified candidates.

Salary Minimum: $60,000
Functions: Senior mgmt., Middle mgmt., Product dev., Plant mgmt., Materials, HR mgmt., Finance
Industries: Food/bev/tobacco, Medical devices, Metal products, Motor vehicles, Consumer electronics, Transportation, Aerospace

---

Howard W. Smith Assoc.

Old State House Station
P.O. Box 230877
Hartford, Connecticut 06123-0877
(860) 549-2060
Email: hwsmith9@aol.com

Key Contact - Specialty:
Mr. Howard W. Smith

Description: Mostly repeat clients, financial service related including investment management, real estate, mortgage banking, marketing, finance and general management.

Salary Minimum: $70,000
Functions: Generalist, Health admin., CFO's, Minorities, Non-profits, Attorneys
Industries: Generalist, Finance, Legal, Insurance, Real estate, Healthcare

---

Abbott Smith Assoc., Inc.

P.O. Box 318, Franklin Ave.
Millbrook, New York 12545
(914) 677-5300
Fax: (914) 677-3315

Key Contact - Specialty:
Mr. David W. Brinkerhoff - *Human resources*
Ms. Sara P. McWilliams - *Human resources*

Description: As specialists in the area of human resources, the major emphasis for thirty years has been the recruitment of candidates worldwide.

Salary Minimum: $75,000
Functions: HR mgmt., Benefits, Personnel, Training, Int'l.
Industries: Generalist, Human resource svcs.
Professional Associations: IACPR

Branches:
2600 Lexington St.
Broadview, Illinois 60153
(708) 649-3318
Fax: (708) 344-1912
Key Contact - Specialty:
Mr. David D. Dalenberg - *Human resources*
Mr. Frank Calzaretta - *Human resources*

International Branches:
London

Herman Smith Executive Initiatives Inc.

161 Bay St., Ste. 3600, BCE Place
Canada Trust Twr., P.O. Box 629
Toronto, Ontario M5J 2S1
Canada
(416) 862-8830
Fax: (416) 869-1809
Email: hsei@globalserve.net

Key Contact - Specialty:
Mr. Herman M. Smith - *CEO, board of directors*
Ms. Janice N. Kussner - *Management (middle to senior level)*
Mr. Steven Wilson - *Management (middle to senior level)*
Mr. Sussannah Kelly - *Management (middle to senior level)*

Description: International specialists in recruitment, as well as recruitment program design.

Salary Minimum: $75,000
Functions: Senior mgmt., Middle mgmt., Mfg., Sales & mktg., HR mgmt., CFO's, MIS mgmt.
Industries: Generalist, Energy/utilities, Mfg., Transportation, Finance, Government, High tech

Networks:
EMA Partners Int'l.

† occasional contingency assignment

Smith James Group, Inc.
11660 Alpharetta Hwy., Ste. 515
Roswell, Georgia 30076
(770) 667-0212
Fax: (770) 667-0868
Email: resumes@smithjames.com
Web: www.smithjames.com

Key Contact - Specialty:
Mr. James Soutouras - *Generalist*
Mr. Michael Smith - *Generalist*
Ms. Stacy Smith - *Banking, finance, telecommunications*
Mr. Charles E. Milton - *High technology, utilities, internet, telecommunications*

Description: Expertise in telecommunications, high technology, banking, service, utilities industry. Concentration is on senior/middle management and key technical positions. Firm bills on an hourly basis, guaranteed not to exceed 30% fee.

Salary Minimum: $50,000
Functions: Generalist, Mfg., Materials, Sales & mktg., HR mgmt., Finance, IT
Industries: Generalist, Energy/utilities, Mfg., Svcs., Communications, High tech, Software

H. C. Smith Ltd.
20600 Chagrin Blvd., Ste. 200
Tower East
Shaker Heights, Ohio 44122
(216) 752-9966
Fax: (216) 752-9970
Email: hcsmith@stratos.net

Key Contact - Specialty:
Dr. Herbert C. Smith
Ms. Rebecca Ruben Smith

Description: Professionally managed generalist practice with broad range of global resources. Recognized ability to evaluate and recruit talented minorities and women for executive and board positions.

Salary Minimum: $75,000
Functions: Generalist
Industries: Generalist

Smith, Roth & Squires
237 Park Ave., 21st Floor
New York, New York 10017
(516) 767-9480
Web: srs-execsearch.com

Key Contact - Specialty:
Mr. Ronald P. Roth - *Generalist*
Mr. R. James Squires - *Generalist*

Description: Executive search generalists in telecommunications, medical technology, pharmaceuticals and consumer products. Accessible, principal-directed, multinational scope. Serving a select group of clients with individualized effort.

Salary Minimum: $85,000
Functions: Generalist, General mgmt., Mfg., Sales & mktg., IT, Engineering, Mgmt. consultants
Industries: Generalist, Food/bev/tobacco, Soap/perfume/cosmetics, Medical devices, Computer equip., Telecoms, High tech

Branches:
6987 N. Oracle Rd.
Tucson, Arizona 85704
(520) 544-3600
Email: rjbaf@aol.com
Key Contact - Specialty:
Mr. Robert J. Butler - *Generalist*

Affiliates:
ALW Research Int'l.
Peter Kirby Int'l.

Smith Search, S.C.
Barranca del Muerto, No. 472
Col. Alpes, Del. A. Obregon
Mexico City, Mexico DF 01010
Mexico
525 593 8766
Fax: 525 593 8969
Email: smith@mail.internet.com.mx

Key Contact - Specialty:
Mr. John E. Smith, Jr. - *Generalist*
Ms. Maria Elena Pardo
Ms. Ana Luz Smith

Description: Mexico's leading independent executive recruitment firm, specializing in the cross-cultural, bilingual executive for companies primarily in Mexico but also the US and most Latin American countries.

Salary Minimum: $75,000
Functions: Generalist, Directors, Plant mgmt., Mktg. mgmt., CFO's, MIS mgmt.
Industries: Food/bev/tobacco, Chemicals, Banking, Invest. banking, Computer svcs., Telecoms, High tech
Professional Associations: AESC

A. William Smyth, Inc.
P.O. Box 380
Ross, California 94957
(415) 457-8383

Key Contact - Specialty:
Mr. William Smyth

Description: Experience includes related categories; i.e., entertainment, transportation, high technology, software where sophisticated marketing is required. Management consulting, M&A, organization planning, salary surveys and channel planning.

Salary Minimum: $80,000
Functions: General mgmt., Sales & mktg., Finance, IT, Int'l.
Industries: Food/bev/tobacco, Soap/perfume/cosmetics, Computer equip., Finance, Entertainment, High tech, Software

Snyder & Co.
35 Old Avon Village, Rte. 44, Ste. 185
Avon, Connecticut 06001-3822
(860) 521-9760
Fax: (860) 521-2495
Email: JamesSnyder@compuserve.com

Key Contact - Specialty:
Mr. James F. Snyder, Jr. - *Healthcare, financial services, consumer products*

Description: The firm's professional work is characterized by its exhaustive sourcing methodology and in-depth candidate assessment skills.

Salary Minimum: $100,000
Functions: General mgmt., Mfg., Healthcare, Sales & mktg., HR mgmt., Finance, R&D
Industries: Food/bev/tobacco, Drugs mfg., Medical devices, Finance, Insurance, Biotech, Healthcare

Sockwell & Assoc.
227 W. Trade St., Ste. 1930
Charlotte, North Carolina 28202
(704) 372-1865
Fax: (704) 372-8960
Email: email@sockwell.com
Web: www.sockwell.com

Key Contact - Specialty:
Mr. J. Edgar Sockwell
Ms. Lyttleton Rich
Ms. Susan N. Jernigan
Mr. John A. Hendrix
Mr. B. Harrison Turnbull

Description: Senior level functional search for North American clients in for-profit and not-for-profit sectors; most assignments at CEO/COO/CFO or division executive level; client-focus and internal quality initiatives.

Salary Minimum: $125,000
Functions: Generalist, Senior mgmt., Health admin., Mktg. mgmt., CFO's, MIS mgmt., Non-profits
Industries: Generalist, Printing, Invest. banking, Higher ed., Real estate, Biotech, Healthcare
Professional Associations: AESC

Networks:
Transearch Int'l.

Soderlund Assoc. Inc.
105 W. Fourth St., Ste. 1005
Cincinnati, Ohio 45202
(513) 721-1005
Fax: (513) 721-1057
Email: eric@soderlund.com
Web: www.soderlund.com

Key Contact - Specialty:
Mr. Eric Soderlund - *High technology, directors, VP's, SVP's*
Ms. Terri Ross - *Staffing, human resources*
Ms. Paige Sutkamp - *Staffing, human resources*

Description: We recruit senior executives for the computer industry in product development, marketing & sales, service, staffing and human resources.

Salary Minimum: $150,000
Functions: Mfg., Materials, Sales & mktg., HR mgmt., R&D, Engineering, Int'l.
Industries: High tech

Solomon-Page Healthcare Group
1140 Ave. of the Americas, 8th Floor
New York, New York 10036
(212) 764-9200
Fax: (212) 824-1505
Email: mgouran@spges.com
Web: www.solomonpagegroup.com

Key Contact - Specialty:
Mr. Marc S. Gouran - *Healthcare*

Description: Highly focused, nationwide, retained executive search in most functional areas for managed healthcare, group insurance, HMO's, hospitals and related healthcare companies and institutions.

Salary Minimum: $50,000
Functions: Generalist, Senior mgmt., Middle mgmt., Physicians, Nurses, Mktg. mgmt., CFO's
Industries: Pharmaceutical svcs., Insurance, Healthcare

Branches:
514 Via de la Valle, Ste. 309
Solana Beach, California 92075
(619) 259-8770
Fax: (619) 259-8977
Email: mgamboa@spgeswest.com
Key Contact - Specialty:
Mr. Mark Gamboa - *Healthcare*

Soltis Management Services
876 Brower Rd.
Radnor, Pennsylvania 19087-2208
(610) 687-4200
Web: soltis@earthlink.net

Key Contact - Specialty:
Mr. Charles W. Soltis - *Generalist*

Description: Management consultants in executive search, executive assessment, organization issues and management development. Since 1971, an inimitable reputation for confidential, results oriented service to corporate clients. Search assignments 98% successful.

Salary Minimum: $100,000
Functions: Generalist, Senior mgmt., Plant mgmt., Sales mgmt., CFO's, MIS mgmt., Non-profits
Industries: Generalist

Solutions Group
P.O. Box 360805
Birmingham, Alabama 35236
(205) 663-1301
Fax: (205) 663-1306
Email: SGSearch@aol.com

Key Contact - Specialty:
Mr. Michael Wheless - *Generalist*
Mr. Hinky Verchot - *Generalist*

Description: Specialize in management search for healthcare and general industry.

Salary Minimum: $60,000
Functions: General mgmt., Mfg., Materials, Health admin., HR mgmt., MIS mgmt., Engineering
Industries: Generalist, Mfg., Finance, Higher ed., Telecoms, Insurance, Healthcare

Stephen M. Sonis Assoc. †
275 Turnpike St., Ste. 202
Canton, Massachusetts 02021
(781) 821-0303
Fax: (781) 821-0601
Email: smsonis@aol.com

Key Contact - Specialty:
Mr. Stephen M. Sonis

Description: We specialize in focused, personalized service for both start-ups and major companies. We are totally client-driven. We represent a creative, intelligent, cost and time effective search alternative.

Salary Minimum: $40,000
Functions: Generalist, Materials, Sales & mktg., Mktg. mgmt., Direct mktg., HR mgmt., Finance
Industries: Generalist, Wholesale, Retail, Hospitality, Entertainment, Human resource svcs., Communications

Souder & Assoc. †
P.O. Box 71
Bridgewater, Virginia 22812
(540) 828-2365
Fax: (540) 828-2851
Email: soudereg@cfw.com
Web: www.souderandassociates.com

Key Contact - Specialty:
Mr. E. G. Souder, Jr. - *Human resources, operations, technical, sales, accounting*
Ms. Deana A. Griffin - *Human resources, operations, technical, sales, accounting*

Description: A national executive search firm and recruitment services provider with over a decade of experience in executive search. The practice provides recruitment services for manufacturing, food and technology oriented industries.

Salary Minimum: $40,000
Functions: General mgmt., Mfg., Sales & mktg., HR mgmt., R&D, Engineering
Industries: Mfg., Transportation, Finance, Svcs., Communications, High tech, Healthcare

Southern Research Services †
3837 Northdale Blvd., Ste. 364
Tampa, Florida 33624
(813) 269-9595
Fax: (813) 264-6847
Email: srsbloch@aol.com

Key Contact - Specialty:
Mr. Thomas L. Bloch

Description: Specialize in locating and qualifying technical/engineering management professionals with solid business sense in the battery, medical products, electric utility industry and electronic components.

Salary Minimum: $50,000
Functions: Senior mgmt., Middle mgmt., Plant mgmt., Personnel, R&D, Engineering, Environmentalists
Industries: Energy/utilities, Medical devices, Plastics/rubber, Metal products, Misc. mfg., Environmental svcs., High tech

Special Markets Group, Inc.
4732 Old Countryside Circle S.
Stone Mountain, Georgia 30083
(404) 508-0834
Fax: (404) 296-7999

Key Contact - Specialty:
Mr. Kenneth D. Lee - *Generalist, minorities*

Description: Retained firm dedicated to providing executive search and human resource consulting to both small entrepreneurial organizations as well as large corporate entities. Expertise in diversity/minority positions and general business.

Salary Minimum: $50,000
Functions: Generalist, Senior mgmt., Mktg. mgmt., Sales mgmt., CFO's, MIS mgmt., Minorities
Industries: Generalist, Food/bev/tobacco, Computer equip., Finance, Hospitality, Communications, Insurance

Affiliates:
Universal Consulting Group, Inc.

Specialty Consultants Inc.
2710 Gateway Towers
Pittsburgh, Pennsylvania 15222-1189
(412) 355-8200
Fax: (412) 355-0498

† occasional contingency assignment

Web: www.info@specon.com

Key Contact - Specialty:
Mr. Charles J. Abbott
Mr. Joseph R. DiSanti

Description: Executive search - real estate and construction industries; pharmaceutical and biotech research industries.

Salary Minimum: $50,000
Functions: Generalist
Industries: Construction, Drugs mfg., Banking, Invest. banking, Pharmaceutical svcs., Real estate, Biotech

---

Spectrum Consultants

12625 High Bluff Drive, Ste. 215
San Diego, California 92130-2054
(619) 259-3232
Fax: (619) 792-7064
Email: spectcon@earthlink.net

Key Contact - Specialty:
Mr. G. W. Christiansen
Mr. Stanley Bass

Description: Telecommunications, hi-tech, aerospace, golf industry, engineering, scientists, advanced materials, general management, marketing.

Salary Minimum: $50,000
Functions: Senior mgmt., Product dev., Quality, Mktg. mgmt., Sales mgmt., R&D, Engineering
Industries: Medical devices, Computer equip., Broadcast & Film, Telecoms, Aerospace, High tech, Software

---

SpencerStuart

277 Park Ave., 29th Floor
New York, New York 10172
(212) 336-0200
Fax: (212) 336-0296
Email:
firstinitiallastname@spencerstuart.com
Web: www.spencerstuart.com

Key Contact - Specialty:
Mr. Robert A. Damon - *Consumer goods & services, restaurant, hospitality, general management, sports management*
Mr. Denis B. K. Lyons - *Financial services, investment & commercial banking*
Mr. E. Peter McLean - *Generalist, consumer manufacturing, industrial manufacturing, financial services, communications*
Mr. Thomas J. Neff - *General management, board services*
Mr. Thomas G. Hardy - *Consumer goods & services*
Ms. Andrea de Cholnoky - *Financial services, global securities, wholesale banking*
Mr. Joseph H. Boccuzi - *Healthcare, pharmaceuticals, biotechnology*
Ms. Julie H. Daum - *Consumer goods, board services*
Ms. Marnie McBryde - *Financial services*
Mr. David S. Daniel - *Consumer goods & services, apparel, retail*
Ms. Barbara Selbach - *Financial services, global securities, wholesale banking*
Ms. Judith Bacher - *Boards, finance, strategic planning, human resources, multimedia*
Mr. Norbert Gottenberg - *High technology*
Mr. Nicholas Young - *Financial services, natural resources, industrial manufacturing*
Ms. Robin Soren - *Financial services*
Mr. Brian Offutt - *Communications*
Mr. John Wood - *Consumer goods and services*
Ms. Betty Hudson - *Communications*

Description: CEO, senior level executive and board of director search consulting services.

Salary Minimum: $150,000
Functions: Generalist, General mgmt., Directors, Senior mgmt., Middle mgmt., Admin. svcs., Mfg., Product dev., Production, Automation, Plant mgmt., Quality, Productivity, Materials, Purchasing, Materials Plng., Distribution, Packaging, Healthcare, Physicians, Nurses, Allied health, Health admin., Sales & mktg., Advertising, Mkt. research, Mktg. mgmt., Sales mgmt., Direct mktg., Customer svc., PR, HR mgmt., Benefits, Personnel, Training, Finance, CFO's, Budgeting, Cash mgmt., Credit, Taxes, M&A, Risk mgmt., IT, MIS mgmt., Systems anal., Systems dev., Systems implem., Systems support, R&D, Engineering, Specialized services, Mgmt. consultants, Minorities, Non-profits, Environmentalists, Architects, Technicians, Attorneys, Graphic artists, Int'l.
Industries: Generalist, Agri/forestry/mining, Energy/utilities, Construction, Food/bev/tobacco, Textiles/apparel, Lumber/furniture, Paper, Printing, Chemicals, Soap/perfume/cosmetics, Drugs mfg., Medical devices, Plastics/rubber, Paints/petroleum products, Leather/stone/glass/clay, Metal products, Machinery/Appliances, Motor vehicles, Computer equip., Consumer electronics, Test/measurement equip., Misc. mfg., Transportation, Wholesale, Retail, Finance, Banking, Invest. banking, Brokers, Venture cap., Misc. financial, Hospitality, Entertainment, Non-profits, Higher ed., Pharmaceutical svcs., Legal, Computer svcs., Accounting, Equip. svcs., Mgmt. consulting, Human resource svcs., Law enfcmt., Communications, Advertising/PR, Publishing, New media, Broadcast & Film, Telecoms, Government, Defense, Environmental svcs., Haz. waste, Aerospace, Packaging, Insurance, Real estate, High tech, Software, Biotech, Healthcare, Non-classifiable industries
Professional Associations: AESC

Branches:
10900 Wilshire Blvd., Ste. 800
Los Angeles, California 90024-6524
(310) 209-0610
Key Contact - Specialty:
Mr. Anthony V. Pfannkuche - *Healthcare*
Mr. Michael C. Bruce - *Financial services*
Mr. Steven Rodriguez - *High technology, telecommunications*

3000 Sand Hill Rd.
Bldg. 2, Ste. 175
Menlo Park, California 94025
(650) 688-1285
Key Contact - Specialty:
Mr. Bradley A. Stirn - *High technology*
Mr. Stephen R. Strain - *High technology*
Mr. John Ware - *High technology*
Mr. Rick Gostyla - *High technology*
Ms. Nayla Rizk - *High technology*
Mr. Jane Carmena - *High technology, communications*
Mr. Phil Johnston - *High technology*

525 Market St., Ste. 3700
San Francisco, California 94105-2161
(415) 495-4141
Key Contact - Specialty:
Mr. Joseph E. Griesedieck, Jr. - *Consumer products, retail, telecommunications, boards*
Ms. Carol B. Emmott - *Healthcare*
Mr. E. C. Grayson - *Energy, industrial*
Ms. Kimberlee O'Maley - *Generalist, consumer goods, telecommunications, financial services*
Ms. Janis M. Zivic - *Generalist, healthcare, financial services, non-profit, communications*
Ms. MaryAnn Walter - *Healthcare*
Mr. Jonathan O. White - *High technology, life sciences*
Mr. T. Christopher Butler - *Financial services*

695 E. Main St.
Financial Centre
Stamford, Connecticut 06901
(203) 324-6333
Key Contact - Specialty:
Mr. H. James Krauser - *Real estate, mortgage banking*
Mr. J. Rick Richardson - *Financial services*
Mr. Thomas W. Wasson - *High technology*
Mr. Richard B. White - *Consumer products, financial services, publishing, advertising, public relations*
Mr. Dayton Ogden - *General management, financial services, board services*
Mr. Carlton W. Thompson - *Entertainment, communications*
Ms. Susan S. Hart - *Consumer goods & services, apparel, retail*
Ms. Claudia L. Kelly - *Financial services, consumer marketing*
Mr. Daniel P. Romanello - *High technology*
Mr. James M. Citrin - *Consumer goods & services, finance, multimedia, hospitality*
Mr. Bill Clemens - *Financial services, professional services*

Mr. Robert E. Kaufmann - *Non-profit, education*
Mr. Kevin Butler - *Life sciences, high technology*
Ms. Tammy Kien-Jersey - *Financial services*

220 Alhambra Circle, Ste. 700
Coral Gables, Florida 33134
(305) 443-9911
Key Contact - Specialty:
Mr. Kenneth V. Eckhart - *Generalist, multi-national, industrial*
Mr. Michael Bell - *Generalist, aviation, board services*

3424 Peachtree Rd., NE
Monarch Twr., Ste. 1100
Atlanta, Georgia 30326
(404) 504-4400
Fax: (404) 504-4401
Key Contact - Specialty:
Mr. William B. Reeves - *Generalist, financial services, insurance*
Mr. Samuel H. Pettway - *Consumer goods & services, non-profit*
Mr. J. Michael Allred - *High technology*
Mr. Robert D. Mattox - *Generalist*
Ms. Sharon Hall - *Consumer goods*
Mr. Carl Gilchrist - *High technology*

401 N. Michigan Ave., Ste. 3400
Chicago, Illinois 60611
(312) 822-0080
Key Contact - Specialty:
Mr. James J. Drury, III - *General management, industrial, consumer goods, manufacturing, transportation*
Mr. Richard J. Brennen - *High technology*
Mr. Kevin M. Connelly - *Financial services*
Mr. Paul W. Earle - *Healthcare, board services*
Mr. J. Curtis Fee - *Financial services, consumer financial services, retail banking, board services*
Mr. Joseph M. Kopsick - *Generalist, consumer goods & services, industrial*
Ms. Patricia Meagher-Clare - *Generalist, consumer goods & services*
Mr. Christopher C. Nadherny - *Consumer goods & services, direct marketing*
Ms. Toni S. Smith - *Non-profit*
Mr. Thomas J. Snyder - *Consumer goods & services, retail*
Mr. Gilbert R. Stenholm - *Consumer goods & services*
Ms. Gail H. Vergara - *Healthcare*
Mr. Robert G. Shields - *Utilities, energy*
Mr. Alvan Turner - *Global industrial*
Ms. Ginny Mowatt - *Financial services*

601 Second Ave. S., Ste. 4125
Minneapolis, Minnesota 55402
(612) 938-0583
Key Contact - Specialty:
Mr. Matt Christoff - *General, communications, consumer goods & services, professional services*
Ms. Susan Boren - *General, boards, consumer goods & services, financial services*

2005 Market St., Ste. 2350
Philadelphia, Pennsylvania 19103
(215) 814-1681
Key Contact - Specialty:
Ms. Connie B. McCann - *Financial services, consumer financial services, retail banking*
Mr. Dennis C. Carey - *Board services, general management, high technology, communications*
Mr. Franklin D. Marsteller - *Insurance*
Mr. Jeff Bell - *Financial services, global banking, asset management*

1717 Main St., Ste. 5600
Dallas, Texas 75201-4605
(214) 672-5200
Key Contact - Specialty:
Mr. O. D. Cruse - *High technology, general management*
Mr. Randall D. Kelley - *High technology, consumer goods, professional services*
Ms. Matrice Ellis-Kirk - *Financial services, consumer goods and services*
Mr. John W. Schroeder - *Consumer packaged goods, capital goods manufacturing, financial services, transportation*
Mr. Ronald J. Zera - *Education, non-profit, healthcare, industrial*

1111 Bagby, Ste. 1616
Houston, Texas 77002-2594
(713) 225-1621
Key Contact - Specialty:
Mr. Louis J. Rieger - *Generalist, energy, boards, financial services, manufacturing*
Mr. Joseph A. Collard - *Energy*
Mr. Jonathan A. Crystal - *Energy, financial services, real estate, healthcare*
Mr. Thomas M. Simmons - *Financial services, energy*
Mr. Richard J. Preng - *Generalist, energy*
Mr. George J. Donnelly - *Generalist, energy, board services*
Ms. Mary Bass - *High technology*

One University Ave., Ste. 801
Toronto, Ontario M5J 2P1
Canada
(416) 361-0311
Key Contact - Specialty:
Mr. Jerry Bliley - *Manufacturing, high technology, professional services, financial services*
Mr. Jeffrey M. Hauswirth - *High technology, real estate, consumer goods*
Mr. Andrew J. MacDougall - *Financial services, generalist, board services, insurance*
Mr. David MacEachern - *Entertainment, communications, manufacturing, consumer goods*
Ms. Michelle Morin - *Insurance, human resources, financial services*
Ms. Michelle Savoy - *Financial services*
Mr. Roger Clarkson - *Consumer goods, services*

1981 Ave. McGill College
Montreal, Quebec H3A 2Y1
Canada
(514) 288-3377
Key Contact - Specialty:
Ms. Manon Vennat - *Board services, communications*
Mr. Jérôme Piché - *Telecommunications, media, high technology*

Edificio Omega
Campos Eliseos 345, 6th Floor
Col. Polanco
Mexico City, Mexico DF 11560
Mexico
52 5 281 4050
Fax: 52 5 281 4184
Key Contact - Specialty:
Mr. Grant Lussier - *Consumer goods & services, energy, financial services*
Mr. Rafael Escandon - *Financial services, energy*

International Branches:
Amsterdam, Barcelona, Beijing, Brussels, Buenos Aires, Chiyoda-ku, Dusseldorf, Frankfurt, Geneva, Hong Kong, Johannesburg, Leeds, London, Madrid, Manchester, Melbourne, Milan, Munich, Paris, Rome, Sao Paulo, Shanghai, Singapore, Stuttgart, Sydney, Zurich

The Spiegel Group
P.O. Box 9121
Newton, Massachusetts 02164
(617) 558-5545
Fax: (617) 558-2807
Email: gspiegel@mediaone.net

Key Contact - Specialty:
Ms. Gayle Spiegel - *High technology, international*

Description: We offer proven performance in finding local nationals all over the world for both American and European based companies. We work with both start-up, venture funded firms and publicly held high technology companies in the U.S. and abroad.

Salary Minimum: $80,000
Functions: Mktg. mgmt., Sales mgmt., Customer svc., CFO's, MIS mgmt., R&D, Int'l.
Industries: Computer equip., Venture cap., Mgmt. consulting, Telecoms, High tech, Software, Biotech

Spilman & Assoc.
3102 Oak Lawn Ave., Ste. 700
The Centrum
Dallas, Texas 75219
(214) 528-8994
Fax: (214) 528-9011
Email: spilman@airmail.com

Key Contact - Specialty:
Ms. Mary P. Spilman - *Vertically integrated distribution industries*

Description: Focus is the distribution and retail arenas and consulting firms that specialize in those arenas.

Salary Minimum: $50,000
Functions: Generalist, General mgmt., HR mgmt., Finance, IT, Mgmt. consultants, Minorities
Industries: Food/bev/tobacco, Drugs mfg., Consumer electronics, Finance, Packaging, High tech, Software

---

Splaine & Assoc., Inc.

15951 Los Gatos Blvd.
Los Gatos, California 95032
(408) 354-3664
Fax: (408) 356-6329
Email: info@exec-search.com
Web: www.exec-search.com

Key Contact - Specialty:
Mr. Charles Splaine - *High technology*

Description: Senior level search assignments for high technology companies, i.e., computer systems, software services, data/voice communications and semiconductors. Recent searches have been for internet and software related companies and high tech start-ups.

Salary Minimum: $150,000
Functions: Generalist, General mgmt., Mfg., Finance, IT, Engineering, Environmentalists
Industries: Computer equip., Legal, Human resource svcs., New media, Environmental svcs., High tech, Software

---

Sports Group Int'l.

804 Salem Woods Drive, Ste. 103
Raleigh, North Carolina 27615
(919) 846-1860
Fax: (919) 848-0236
Email: sportsgrup@aol.com.

Key Contact - Specialty:
Mr. Joseph A. White - *Apparel, footwear, consumer, golf, sporting goods*

Description: Specialists in recruiting general management, marketing/sales and international for recreational products and services organizations.

Salary Minimum: $75,000
Functions: Senior mgmt., Middle mgmt., Product dev., Mkt. research, Mktg. mgmt., Sales mgmt., PR
Industries: Textiles/apparel, Entertainment

Spriggs & Co., Inc.

1701 Lake Ave., Ste. 265
Glenview, Illinois 60025
(847) 657-7181
Fax: (847) 657-7186
Email: robertspriggs@compuserve.com

Key Contact - Specialty:
Mr. Robert D. Spriggs
Mr. William H. Billington
Mr. Tom McGrath
Mr. John R. Goldrick

Description: Search and management consulting.
Functions: Senior mgmt., Product dev., Mkt. research, Sales mgmt., CFO's, M&A, MIS mgmt.
Industries: Food/bev/tobacco, Chemicals, Soap/perfume/cosmetics, Invest. banking, Computer svcs., Broadcast & Film, Telecoms

---

Spring Assoc., Inc. †

10 East 23rd St.
New York, New York 10010-4402
(212) 473-0013
Email: thehiringline@msn.com
Web: www.springassociates.com

Key Contact - Specialty:
Mr. Dennis Spring - *Public relations, marketing communications, corporate communications*

Description: A leader in our field for over 15 years. Our clients are both communications departments of major corporations and the public relations firms which serve them.

Salary Minimum: $75,000

M. H. Springer & Assoc.

(Firm declined to update.)
5855 Topanga Canyon Blvd., Ste. 230
Woodland Hills, California 91367
(818) 710-8955

Key Contact - Specialty:
Mr. Mark H. Springer - *Financial services*

Description: Small retained firm specializing in financial services, i.e. banks, savings & loans and mortgage banking.

Salary Minimum: $100,000
Functions: Senior mgmt., CFO's, Risk mgmt.
Industries: Finance, Invest. banking, Misc. financial

Springer Souder & Assoc. L.L.C.

180 N. Stetson Ave., Ste. 3050
Two Prudential Plaza
Chicago, Illinois 60601
(312) 803-2600
Fax: (312) 803-2606
Web: www.springersouder.com

Key Contact - Specialty:
Mr. Neil A. Springer - *Transportation, industrial equipment, automotive*
Ms. Elizabeth W. Souder - *Automotive, high technology, chemical, furniture*

Description: Retained generalist search firm focused on serving our clients in a strategic and consultative manner across a broad range of needs including Board of Director and senior level executive search.

Salary Minimum: $100,000
Functions: Generalist, Senior mgmt., Mktg. mgmt., CFO's, MIS mgmt., Minorities
Industries: Generalist, Lumber/furniture, Chemicals, Motor vehicles, Transportation, Telecoms, High tech

---

SSA Executive Search Int'l.

4350 E. Camelback Rd., Ste. B200
Phoenix, Arizona 85018
(602) 998-1744
Fax: (602) 998-1082
Email: ssaexec@aol.com

Key Contact - Specialty:
Ms. Susan F. Shultz - *Generalist, boards*

Description: Retained search firm completing management, professional, international, board, legal, non-profit and public sector and financial assignments for clients throughout the U.S. and internationally. SS&A has a division devoted to corporate board recruitment.

Salary Minimum: $70,000
Functions: Generalist, Directors, Int'l.
Industries: Generalist

Affiliates:
Bennett Associates Limited
Morgan & Partner
Morgan & Partners

Stafford Consulting Group

P.O. Box 16566
San Diego, California 92176-6566
(619) 285-8161
Fax: (619) 285-8162
Email: stafford@electriciti.com

Key Contact - Specialty:
Mr. Peter B. Stafford - *Financial services, land development, service industries*
Ms. Norma Stafford - *Title insurance, mortgage banking*
Mr. Chris Stafford - *Mortgage banking (subprime), regional managers, branch managers, loan officers*

Description: Primarily represent Southern California firms for their corporate and national/regional expansion needs; and represent nationally oriented firms in their need to hire western regional talent.
Functions: Senior mgmt., Middle mgmt., Admin. svcs., Sales mgmt., Direct mktg., CFO's, Attorneys
Industries: Finance, Banking, Venture cap., Misc. financial, Legal, Accounting, Insurance

---

Stanton Chase Int'l.

100 E. Pratt St., Ste. 2530
Baltimore, Maryland 21202
(410) 528-8400
Fax: (410) 528-8409

Email: scibw@aol.com
Web: www.stantonchase.com

Key Contact - Specialty:
Mr. H. Edward Muendel - *Generalist*
Mr. James W. Paxton - *Healthcare*
Mr. James M. Matthews - *Generalist*
Mr. Ralph H. Lightner Jr. - *Information technology, aerospace defense, electronics, financial services*
Mr. Robin Scott - *Generalist*

Description: With world headquarters in Amsterdam, we are a medium sized firm of 16 offices in 9 countries. We employ over 90 professionals worldwide. International strengths are banking/financial services, high technology, distribution, mining/natural resources, healthcare and general manufacturing.

Salary Minimum: $70,000
Functions: Directors, Senior mgmt., Middle mgmt., Product dev., Production, Automation, Plant mgmt., Quality, Productivity, Purchasing, Distribution, Physicians, Nurses, Health admin., Mktg. mgmt., Sales mgmt., CFO's, Cash mgmt., R&D, Engineering
Industries: Food/bev/tobacco, Lumber/furniture, Chemicals, Drugs mfg., Plastics/rubber, Paints/petroleum products, Metal products, Machinery/Appliances, Computer equip., Consumer electronics, Misc. mfg., Retail, Finance, Non-profits, Higher ed., Telecoms, Environmental svcs., High tech, Software, Healthcare
Professional Associations: IACPR

Branches:
10866 Wilshire Blvd., Ste. 870
Los Angeles, California 90024-4111
(310) 474-1029
Fax: (310) 474-6747
Email: schaseint@aol.com
Key Contact - Specialty:
Mr. Edward J. Savage - *Generalist*
Ms. Imbi Leetma
Mr. Christos Richards - *Healthcare, telecommunications, high technology*
Mr. Tim Smith
Ms. Pam McGranaham

4370 La Jolla Village Dr., 4th floor
San Diego, California 92122
(619) 546-4779
Fax: (619) 458-0853
Key Contact - Specialty:
Mr. Christos Richards - *Healthcare, telecommunications, high technology*

225 W. Washington St., Ste. 2200
Chicago, Illinois 60606
(312) 422-8162
Fax: (312) 422-8163
Email: JRPiperJr@aol.com
Key Contact - Specialty:
Mr. James R. Piper, Jr.
Mr. Jeff Levitt

5420 LBJ Frwy., Ste. 780
Dallas, Texas 75240
(972) 404-8411
Fax: (972) 404-8415
Email: dallas@stantonchase.com
Key Contact - Specialty:
Mr. Ed H. Moerbe
Mr. Douglas C. Potter
Ms. Carole Campbell
Mr. Fred Reed
Mr. Kevin Anderson
Mr. Jerry McFarland
Ms. Aimee Fogle

20 Adelaide St. P., #401
Toronto, Ontario M5C 2T6
Canada
(416) 868-0118
Fax: (416) 868-0121
Email: jbotrie@botrie.com
Key Contact - Specialty:
Mr. Jim Botrie
Mr. David Nirenberg
Ms. Ellen Barbieri
Mr. Peter Caven
Mr. Randy DePiero
Ms. Deborah Lee

International Branches:
Amsterdam, Berlin, Bratislava, Capetown, Central Hong Kong, Frankfurt, Kronberg, London, Lyon, Melville, Orleans, Paris, Rio de Janeiro, Sao Paulo, Singapore, Sydney, Wellington

Affiliates:
Alta Decision
Dott. Ing. Giorgio Rebua
Douglas Walker Int'l.
Emory & Marlow
Fernaud y Asociados
PMC Int'l.
Stratega Consultories

The Stark Wilton Group

P.O. Box 4924
East Lansing, Michigan 48826
(517) 332-4100
Fax: (517) 332-2733
Email: starkwiltongroup@worldnet.att.net

Key Contact - Specialty:
Ms. Mary Stark - *Healthcare, consumer products, services*
Mr. Wilton Smith - *Telecommunications, high technology, manufacturing*

Description: We are a highly personalized firm. All hiring companies have the opportunity to meet our professional staff, who have worked in industry, banking or management consulting before joining the firm.

Salary Minimum: $85,000
Functions: Senior mgmt., Mkt. research, Mktg. mgmt., Budgeting, Cash mgmt., Risk mgmt., Mgmt. consultants
Industries: Food/bev/tobacco, Drugs mfg., Medical devices, Plastics/rubber, Invest. banking, Mgmt. consulting, High tech

Branches:
P.O. Box 20067
Saginaw, Michigan 48602
(517) 791-7077
Fax: (517) 791-2523
Key Contact - Specialty:
Ms. Mary Stark

Staub, Warmbold & Assoc., Inc.

575 Madison Ave.
New York, New York 10022
(212) 605-0554
Fax: (212) 759-7304
Web: bluedevil33@msn.com

Key Contact - Specialty:
Mr. Robert A. Staub
Mr. Herman P. Warmbold

Description: Provides executive search services to corporations and the not-for-profit sector. Functional areas include general management, finance, marketing and manufacturing. Salary minimum of $100,000.

Salary Minimum: $100,000
Functions: Generalist
Industries: Generalist

Steeple Resources & Consulting

623 Eagle Rock Ave., Ste. 117
West Orange, New Jersey 07052
(201) 364-2500
Fax: (201) 364-1069

Key Contact - Specialty:
Ms. Dianne Eden - *Accounting, finance, sales & marketing administration, operations*

Description: Business background with Fortune, medium and small company exposure. Accounting, financial and sales and marketing recruitment specialists.

Salary Minimum: $70,000
Functions: Senior mgmt., Middle mgmt., Purchasing, Materials Plng., Sales mgmt., Finance, Mgmt. consultants
Industries: Generalist

Stentiford & Berardi Assoc. Ltd.
(a division of The Solomon-Page Group Ltd.)

1140 Ave. of the Americas
New York, New York 10036
(212) 382-1616
Fax: (212) 764-9690
Email: ismith@spges.com
Web: www.solomonpagegroup.com

Key Contact - Specialty:
Ms. Loretta A. Berardi - *Book & new media publishing management*
Mr. Charles M. Stentiford - *Magazine publishing management*

† occasional contingency assignment

Ms. Susan Gold - *Magazine publishing management*

Description: Individual executive search in the broadcast, magazine publishing, book publishing and alternative media industries by media professionals with a total of more than 75 years in the industry.
Functions: Senior mgmt., Middle mgmt., Advertising, Mktg. mgmt., Sales mgmt., Direct mktg., CFO's
Industries: Higher ed., Publishing, New media

Stephens Assoc. Ltd., Inc.

480 S. Third St.
P.O. Box 151-114
Columbus, Ohio 43215
(614) 469-9990
Fax: (614) 469-0177

Key Contact - Specialty:
Mr. Stephen A. Martinez - *Generalist, high technology*
Mr. William Coleman - *Manufacturing, generalist*
Ms. Judith Mitchell - *Generalist*
Ms. Denise Fooce - *Generalist*

Description: Industry focused, full service, all functions, retainer based firm, w/ strong concentration in computer, telecommunications, environmental services, manufacturing and research technology industries. Selected client work in financial services (banking, investment banking) and venture capital.

Salary Minimum: $75,000
Functions: Generalist
Industries: Energy/utilities, Mfg., Finance, Communications, Environmental svcs., High tech, Biotech

Sterling Int'l. †
(a Kodi Management company)

710 Rte. 46 E., Ste. 200
Fairfield, New Jersey 07004
(973) 227-0017
Fax: (973) 808-1644
Email: linda@employment-networking.com
Web: www.employment-networking.com

Key Contact - Specialty:
Ms. Linda Weiner
Ms. Margot Schwartz
Mr. Dan Trout

Description: Specialize in the areas of information technology, cost management, operational & supply chain improvement, merger and acquisition services, business & financial process reengineering. National placement of senior management in consulting and corporate.

Salary Minimum: $100,000
Functions: M&A, MIS mgmt., Systems implem., Mgmt. consultants
Industries: Mfg., Retail, Finance, Computer svcs., Mgmt. consulting, Communications, Healthcare

Affiliates:
Century Staffing

Michael Stern Assoc., Inc./ Euram

70 University Ave., Ste. 370
Toronto, Ontario M5J 2M4
Canada
(416) 593-0100
Fax: (416) 593-5716
Email: search@michaelstern.com

Key Contact - Specialty:
Mr. Michael Stern - *Generalist*
Mr. Bob Sturgess - *Generalist*
Mr. Bill Lampert - *Generalist*
Mr. Dave MacCarthy - *Generalist*

Description: Recruiting corporate leaders since 1982, we are committed to providing superior results with personnel service.

Salary Minimum: $70,000
Functions: Senior mgmt., Mfg., Healthcare, Sales & mktg., HR mgmt., CFO's, MIS mgmt.
Industries: Mfg., Retail, Svcs., Communications, Real estate, High tech, Healthcare
Professional Associations: IACPR

Networks:
Euram Consultants Group

The Stevens Group

4612 Willow Bend Drive
Arlington, Texas 76003-1079
(817) 483-7300
Fax: (817) 483-2718
Email: kgsgrp@aol.com
Web: www.thestevensgroup.com

Key Contact - Specialty:
Mr. Ken G. Stevens - *Generalist*

Description: We recruit superior executive and technical management talent for corporations and management worldwide, providing a tailored approach and access to top candidates unequaled by large search firms.

Salary Minimum: $60,000
Functions: Generalist
Industries: Generalist, Test/measurement equip., Banking, Legal, Accounting, Real estate, Biotech
Professional Associations: IACPR

The Stevenson Group, Inc. (N.J.)

560 Sylvan Avenue
Englewood Cliffs, New Jersey 07632
(201) 568-1900
Fax: (201) 568-5132
Email: stevesrch1@aol.com

Key Contact - Specialty:
Mr. Stephen M. Steinman - *Chemicals, information technology, consumer products*
Mr. Donald Harshman - *Apparel, textile*
Ms. Harriet Maphet - *Healthcare, chemicals*
Ms. Leslie Wright - *Organization studies, international*
Mr. Marc Roberts - *Information technology*
Ms. Elisabeth Ammann - *International*
Ms. Barbara Butcher - *Retail*
Ms. Jane Johnson

Description: Broadly based executive search services on a cross-industry basis. Emphasis on general management, sales and marketing management, administrative and research and development positions within pharmaceuticals, healthcare, information technology, consumer and personal care industries.

Salary Minimum: $90,000
Functions: Senior mgmt., Middle mgmt., Mktg. mgmt., CFO's, MIS mgmt., R&D, Int'l.
Industries: Textiles/apparel, Chemicals, Drugs mfg., Paints/petroleum products, Computer svcs., Software, Healthcare
Professional Associations: IACPR

Branches:
2255 Glades Rd.
Boca Raton, Florida 33431
(561) 989-5445
Key Contact - Specialty:
Mr. William Schall - *Biotechnology, pharmaceuticals*
Mr. Victor Kleinman - *Biotechnology, pharmaceuticals*

Stewart, Stein & Scott, Ltd.

1000 Shelard Pkwy., Ste. 606
Minneapolis, Minnesota 55426
(612) 545-8151
Fax: (612) 545-8464
Email: sssltd@mail.winternet.com

Key Contact - Specialty:
Mr. Terry W. Stein - *Generalist*
Mr. Jeffrey O. Stewart - *Generalist*

Description: Consultants to management in executive recruitment and selection. Generalist practice serving a broad base of clients. Partners have 50 years of diverse corporate management experience, both domestic and international.

Salary Minimum: $75,000
Functions: Generalist, Senior mgmt., Health admin., Mktg. mgmt., HR mgmt., CFO's, MIS mgmt.

Industries: Generalist, Mfg., Finance, Svcs., Communications, High tech, Healthcare
Professional Associations: IACPR

Networks:
Transearch Int'l.

Stewart/Laurence Assoc., Inc. †

P.O. Box 1156, Atrium Executive Park
Englishtown, New Jersey 07726
(732) 972-8000
Fax: (732) 972-8003
Email: mel@stewartlaurence.com
Web: www.stewartlaurence.com

Key Contact - Specialty:
Mr. Mel Stewart Klein - *High technology executives (international & domestic) level*

Description: Professional recruitment, executive search and outplacement for all areas of high technology; professions include executive, marketing, finance and legal (including venture capital IPO's).

Salary Minimum: $75,000
Functions: Senior mgmt., Middle mgmt., Mktg. mgmt., Sales mgmt., CFO's, Mgmt. consultants, Int'l.
Industries: Printing, Computer equip., Computer svcs., Mgmt. consulting, Telecoms, Software, Biotech

Affiliates:
Strategic Alternatives

Charles Stickler Assoc.

P.O. Box 5312C
Lancaster, Pennsylvania 17606
(717) 569-2881
Web: www.CharlesTickler.com

Key Contact - Specialty:
Mr. Charles W. Stickler, III - *Metals*
Mr. Charles W. Stickler, IV - *Metals*

Description: Recruiting specialists for the metals and metal distribution industries.

Salary Minimum: $50,000
Functions: General mgmt., Mfg., Materials, Sales & mktg., Engineering
Industries: Metal products

Linford E. Stiles & Assoc., L.L.C.

46 Newport Rd., Ste. 210
The Gallery
New London, New Hampshire 03257
(603) 526-6566
(800) 322-5185
Fax: (603) 526-6185
Email: lstiles@lesasearch.com
Web: www.lesasearch.com

Key Contact - Specialty:
Mr. Linford E. Stiles - *Senior executives*
Mr. Jake Stiles - *Manufacturing management, consulting*
Ms. Sabine Fischer - *Computer & electronics executives*

Description: Specializing in executives for all functions in a manufacturing company environment.

Salary Minimum: $60,000
Functions: Senior mgmt., Production, Plant mgmt., Purchasing, Systems implem., Systems support, Mgmt. consultants
Industries: Machinery/Appliances, Test/measurement equip., Misc. mfg., Computer svcs., Aerospace, High tech, Software

Networks:
World Search Group

Stillinger & Assoc.

1148 Patterson Lane
Pacific Grove, California 93950
(408) 655-2602
Fax: (408) 648-1544
Email: stillinger@aol.com

Key Contact - Specialty:
Mr. Scott R. Stillinger - *Management consulting, information technology, reinvention, process redesign, change management*
Mrs. Regina V. Stillinger - *Organization development, change management consulting*

Description: We create competitive advantage for our clients by understanding their business, culture and values. Finding executives for any organization who have not only the skills, but also the right temperament and passion for their work is the key to success.

Salary Minimum: $75,000
Functions: General mgmt., Sales & mktg., HR mgmt., IT, Specialized services, Mgmt. consultants
Industries: Generalist, Svcs., Computer svcs., Mgmt. consulting, Human resource svcs., Communications, High tech

Branches:
P.O. Box 274
7017 8th Ave.
Tahoma, California 96142
(916) 525-5545
Fax: (916) 525-5544
Email: skylarc@ibm.net
Key Contact - Specialty:
Mr. Skip Stillinger - *Information technology, management consulting*

STM Assoc.

230 S. 500 East, Ste. 500
Salt Lake City, Utah 84102
(801) 531-6500
Fax: (801) 531-6062
Email: stm@utw.com

Key Contact - Specialty:
Mr. Gerald W. Cooke - *Mining, natural resources, energy, utilities*
Mr. Robert L. Roylance - *Mining, natural resources, energy, utilities*

Description: Specialize in natural resources, including mining, metals, pulp & paper, chemicals, as well as energy, utilities, national, international. Twenty-five year repeat business record based on extensive database, original research and personal service.

Salary Minimum: $75,000
Functions: General mgmt., Mfg., Materials, HR mgmt., Finance, Engineering, Int'l.
Industries: Agri/forestry/mining, Energy/utilities, Paper, Chemicals

Allan Stolee Inc.

6278 N. Federal Hwy., Ste. 450
Ft. Lauderdale, Florida 33308
(954) 564-9111
Fax: (954) 564-9111
Email: stolee@rcrt.com
Web: www.rcrt.com

Key Contact - Specialty:
Mr. Allan J. Stolee - *Generalist*

Description: A professional firm, we provide executive search consulting and recruitment services locally, nationally and internationally. We are business generalists experienced in recruiting for most forms of commercial enterprise.

Salary Minimum: $100,000
Functions: General mgmt., Mfg., Materials, Sales & mktg., R&D, Engineering, Int'l.
Industries: Generalist, Construction, Chemicals, Drugs mfg., Medical devices, Plastics/rubber, Biotech

Stone, Murphy & Olson

5500 Wayzata Blvd., Ste. 1020
Minneapolis, Minnesota 55416
(612) 591-2300

Key Contact - Specialty:
Ms. Toni M. Barnum - *Financial services*
Mr. Gary J. Murphy - *Human resources*
Ms. Kathy A. Mathias - *Marketing, sales*
Mr. Al Giesen
Ms. Alicia Aeziman

Description: Executive retained search firm engaged in general practice committed to serving the best interests of clients.

Salary Minimum: $75,000
Functions: General mgmt., Mfg., Sales & mktg., HR mgmt., Finance, Engineering, Specialized services
Industries: Generalist, Energy/utilities, Mfg., Finance, Svcs., Insurance, High tech

† occasional contingency assignment

Stoopen Asociados, S.C./EMA Partners Int'l.

Minerva No. 92-702
Mexico City, Mexico DF 01030
Mexico
52 5 661 7243
52 5 661 8119
Fax: 52 5 661 5872
Email: intl@stoopen.com.mx
Web: jstoopen@stoopen.com.mx

Key Contact - Specialty:
Ms. Josefina Stoopen - *Generalist*
Ms. Lucia Trueba - *Generalist*
Ms. Lyn A. Juarez - *Generalist*
Ms. Ines Ruf - *Generalist*

Description: We are involved in executive search in all professional disciplines. Our company policy stresses quality above volume. We keep the organization at a size that allows the partners to get involved personally in every assignment.

Salary Minimum: $60,000
Functions: Senior mgmt., Plant mgmt., Materials Plng., Sales & mktg., HR mgmt., CFO's, IT
Industries: Construction, Mfg., Banking, Entertainment, Computer svcs., Mgmt. consulting, Telecoms

Networks:
EMA Partners Int'l.

Straight & Co.

3415 Merganser Lane
Alpharetta, Georgia 30022
(770) 663-0448
Fax: (770) 442-1001
Email: straightco@aol.com

Key Contact - Specialty:
Mr. Gary R. Straight - *Financial services, marketing management, information processing*

Description: Search specialists for financial services, investment management, insurance and banking - strengths in general management, finance, marketing and information processing.

Salary Minimum: $75,000
Functions: Senior mgmt., Middle mgmt., Mktg. mgmt., Sales mgmt., CFO's, Credit, Risk mgmt.
Industries: Finance, Misc. financial

Mark Stranberg & Assoc. Inc. †

4 Wadsworth Rd
Sudbury, Massachusetts 01776
(978) 440-8800
Fax: (978) 440-8354
Email: mstranberg@worldnet.att.net

Key Contact - Specialty:
Mr. Mark Stranberg - *Investment industry, banking, insurance, mutual fund*

Description: We specialize in the investment industry. We conduct searches for senior management whose income ranges from $100K - 500K in disciplines such as portfolio management, pensions, sales, marketing, operations and trading.

Salary Minimum: $100,000
Functions: Directors, Senior mgmt., Mktg. mgmt., Sales mgmt.
Industries: Banking, Invest. banking, Brokers, Misc. financial, Insurance, Software

Strategic Advancement Inc.

242 Old New Brunswick Rd., Ste. 100
Piscataway, New Jersey 08854
(908) 562-1222
Fax: (908) 562-9448

Key Contact - Specialty:
Mr. Andrew Borkin
Ms. Lisa Gold - *Banking and insurance*

Description: We have created a network of contacts that can assist you in finding the right candidate for the position you wish to fill -- in the shortest amount of time.

Salary Minimum: $50,000
Functions: Middle mgmt., Mfg., Materials, Mktg. mgmt., Sales mgmt., HR mgmt., Finance
Industries: Generalist, Mfg., Paper, Drugs mfg., Finance, Insurance

Strategic Alternatives †

3 Portola Rd.
Portola Valley, California 94028
(650) 851-2211
Fax: (650) 851-2288
Email: imarks@strategicalternatives.com
Web: www.strategicalternatives.com

Key Contact - Specialty:
Mr. Ira M. Marks - *High technology, internet, marketing, software executives*

Description: Specialize in the recruitment of senior executive, mid-level and key technical contributors for start-ups to mature high-technology companies, national and international. Expertise in electronic commerce, R&D, HW/SW product development, marketing, sales and operations.

Salary Minimum: $110,000
Functions: Senior mgmt., Sales & mktg., Mkt. research, IT, R&D, Engineering, Int'l.
Industries: Computer equip., Consumer electronics, Venture cap., New media, Telecoms, High tech, Software

Affiliates:
Stewart/Laurence Assoc., Inc.
Tactical Alternatives

Strategic Executives, Inc.

6 Landmark Square, 4th Floor
Stamford, Connecticut 06901
(203) 359-5757
Fax: (203) 978-1785
Email: gulian@strategicexecutives.com
Web: www.strategicexecutives.com

Key Contact - Specialty:
Mr. Randolph S. Gulian - *Financial services, information services*

Description: National search and selection programs designed to identify management consultants, marketing executives and corporate business planning and development professionals for client companies wishing to enhance their competitive position.

Salary Minimum: $80,000
Functions: Generalist, General mgmt., Senior mgmt., Sales & mktg., Mktg. mgmt., Finance, Mgmt. consultants
Industries: Generalist, Food/bev/tobacco, Computer equip., Finance, Mgmt. consulting, Communications, Healthcare

Branches:
980 N. Michigan Ave., Ste. 1400
Chicago, Illinois 60611
(312) 988-4821
Fax: (312) 642-6545
Key Contact - Specialty:
Mr. James A. Perry - *Telecommunications, information services*

One Dag Hammarskjold Plaza, 7th Floor
New York, New York 10017
(212) 207-9866
Fax: (212) 207-9864
Key Contact - Specialty:
Mr. Harlan R. Halper - *Management consulting*

Strategic Search Corp.

645 N. Michigan Ave., Ste. 800
Chicago, Illinois 60611
(312) 944-4000
Email: scottsargis@sprintmail.com

Key Contact - Specialty:
Mr. Scott R. Sargis - *Technical, manufacturing*

Description: Technical and manufacturing specialists from staff to vice president levels including R&D, quality assurance, manufacturing and product development.

Salary Minimum: $50,000
Functions: Product dev., Production, Automation, Plant mgmt., Quality, R&D, Engineering
Industries: Mfg., Chemicals, Drugs mfg., Medical devices, Computer equip., Packaging, High tech

StratfordGroup
6120 Parkland Blvd.
Cleveland, Ohio 44124
(440) 460-3232
(800) 536-4384
Fax: (440) 460-3230
Web: www.stratfordgroup.com

Key Contact - Specialty:
Mr. Larry S. Imely - *Generalist*
Mr. John M. Thornton - *Generalist*
Mr. Eric N. Peterson - *Generalist*
Mr. Paul C. Stefunek - *New media, information technology, telecommunications*
Ms. Julie A. Jochems - *Generalist*

Description: Technological resources, experienced professional staff, a commitment to serve our clients and our unconditional guarantee help make us a nationwide leader in executive search.

Salary Minimum: $95,000
Functions: Generalist, Senior mgmt., Plant mgmt., Sales mgmt., Benefits, CFO's, MIS mgmt.
Industries: Generalist, Construction, Food/bev/tobacco, Mgmt. consulting, Broadcast & Film, High tech, Healthcare

Branches:
475 Sansome St., Ste. 710
San Francisco, California 94111
(415) 291-1699
Fax: (415) 291-1688
Key Contact - Specialty:
Mr. Stephen Combs - *High technology, venture capital, general management, sales & marketing*
Ms. Irene Murphy - *High technology, general management, sales & marketing*
Ms. Kathy Lockton - *High technology, general management, sales & marketing*
Mr. Hani Elnaggar
Ms. Christina Gomez

475 Sansome St., Ste. 700
San Francisco, California 94111
(415) 788-7800
Fax: (415) 788-7710
Key Contact - Specialty:
Mr. Bob Concannon - *Consumer products*
Ms. Donna Clark - *High technology sales*
Ms. Meredith Moore - *Consumer products*
Mr. Fred Whelan - *Marketing*
Mr. Bob Jacobs - *Hardware, software*

2150 N. 1st St., Ste. 250
San Jose, California 95131
(408) 436-2900
Fax: (408) 436-0643
Key Contact - Specialty:
Mr. Ron Bates - *High technology*

7887 E. Bellview Ave., Ste. 700
Denver, Colorado 80111
(303) 689-2233
Fax: (303) 689-2244
Key Contact - Specialty:
Mr. Bruce Stover - *Cable, telecommunications*
Mr. Frederick M. Schaefer, Jr. - *Manufacturing, not-for-profit*
Ms. Catherine M. Forbes - *Cable, telecommunications*

6905 Rockledge Drive, Ste. 600
Bethesda, Maryland 20817
(301) 896-9333
Key Contact - Specialty:
Mr. Lawrence A. Dilworth

1760 Manley Rd.
Maumee, Ohio 43537
(419) 893-5919
Fax: (419) 893-2491
Key Contact - Specialty:
Mr. Joel P. Epstein - *Financial services, venture capital*
Ms. Deborah M. Galbraith - *Generalist*
Mr. Theodore A. Bruccoleri - *Financial services, real estate, high technology*
Ms. Carole A. Chandler - *Human resource services, high technology, healthcare*

445 Byers Rd.
Miamisburg, Ohio 45342
(937) 859-1717
Fax: (937) 859-1767
Key Contact - Specialty:
Mr. John D. O'Reilly - *Generalist*

610 W. Germantown Pike, Ste. 150
Plymouth Meeting, Pennsylvania 19462
(610) 828-0713
Fax: (610) 825-5890
Key Contact - Specialty:
Mr. Frank A. Garofolo - *Generalist*
Mr. Robert J. Altieri - *Medical, healthcare*

One Lincoln Ctr.
5400 LBJ Freeway, Ste. 1070
Dallas, Texas 75240
(972) 386-9053
Fax: (972) 386-9050
Key Contact - Specialty:
Mr. Frank J. Laux - *Consumer products, food & beverage*

700 Louisiana St., Ste. 2250
Houston, Texas 77002
(713) 223-7270
Fax: (713) 223-7279
Key Contact - Specialty:
Mr. Jack W. Bradshaw - *Generalist*
Mr. John Stanton - *Generalist*

The Concourse West
1595 Spring Hill Rd., Ste. 220
Vienna, Virginia 22182
(703) 442-5280
Fax: (703) 790-8349
Key Contact - Specialty:
Mr. Lawrence A. Dilworth - *Generalist*

W. R. Strathmann Assoc.
150 Fifth Ave.
New York, New York 10011
(212) 243-8660

Key Contact - Specialty:
Mr. Winfried R. Strathmann - *Generalist*

Description: Firm specializes in senior level recruiting for the European business community in the US, with emphasis on German organizations. Partners and staff members are multilingual.

Salary Minimum: $100,000
Functions: Generalist, Directors, Senior mgmt., Int'l.
Industries: Generalist, Construction, Finance, Banking, Invest. banking, Communications, Real estate
Professional Associations: AESC

Straube Associates
Willows Professional Park
855 Turnpike Rd.
North Andover, Massachusetts 01845-6105
(978) 687-1993
Fax: (978) 687-1886
Email: sstraube@straubeassociates
Web: www.straubeassociates.com

Key Contact - Specialty:
Mr. Stan Straube - *Generalist*
Ms. Kathy Kelley - *Marketing & sales*
Mr. Bill Marlow - *Engineering, high technology*
Ms. Leslie Allen - *Generalist*
Ms. Carla Pope - *Generalist*

Description: Generalists, servicing all industries, special emphasis in high-tech, financial services, hospitality and manufacturing. International capabilities. Specialists in the human resources and environmental, health and safety disciplines. Women and minorities, target recruiting.

Salary Minimum: $70,000
Functions: Generalist, Senior mgmt., Product dev., Mktg. mgmt., Personnel, CFO's, Environmentalists
Industries: Generalist, Medical devices, Computer equip., Misc. mfg., Hospitality, High tech, Software

Affiliates:
Leonard Assoc.
Edward O'Brien

Strelcheck & Assoc., Inc.
(Firm declined to update.)
1009 Glen Oaks Lane, Ste. 211
Mequon, Wisconsin 53092
(414) 241-9500

Key Contact - Specialty:
Mr. Robert R. Strzelczyk

Description: Physician search: occupational health and most other specialties. National scope.

J. Stroll Assoc., Inc. †
(Firm declined to update.)
980 Post Rd. E., Ste. 3
Westport, Connecticut 06880
(203) 227-3688

† occasional contingency assignment

Email: joe-stroll@mindspring.com

Key Contact - Specialty:
Mr. Joseph Stroll - *Vice presidents, corporate law*
Mr. Ray Peters - *Paralegals, general corporate, of counsel*

Description: Identifies suitable candidates for corporate law EEO, general, contracts, patents, civil, partnerships.

Salary Minimum: $80,000
Functions: Generalist
Industries: Mfg., Drugs mfg., Pharmaceutical svcs., Legal, Environmental svcs., Biotech, Healthcare

---

Stroman Int'l., Inc.

5299 DTC Pkwy., Ste. 815
Englewood, Colorado 80111
(303) 689-9552
Fax: (303) 689-9661
Email: stroman@executive-recruiting.com
Web: www.executive-recruiting.com

Key Contact - Specialty:
Mr. Alfred L. Stroman, III - *Generalist, senior executives, corporations-venture capital deals*
Ms. Laura K. Clement - *Generalist, senior executives, corporations-venture capital deals*

Description: We are a generalist firm, specializing in recruiting senior executives for corporations and venture capital deals with an emphasis in manufacturing industries, healthcare, higher education, high tech and construction.

Salary Minimum: $100,000
Functions: Generalist, Senior mgmt., Mktg. mgmt., HR mgmt., CFO's, MIS mgmt., Int'l.
Industries: Generalist, Construction, Mfg., Venture cap., Higher ed., High tech, Healthcare

---

Sullivan & Assoc.

344 N. Old Woodward, Ste. 304
Birmingham, Michigan 48009
(248) 258-0616
Fax: (248) 258-2823
Email: sullivan@kennon.com
Web: www.glolink.com/sullivan

Key Contact - Specialty:
Mr. Dennis B. Sullivan
Mr. Jeffrey A. Evans
Ms. Dodie C. David
Mr. Douglas Allen
Mr. Kevin Mahoney

Description: Widely recognized as most prestigious Michigan-based retainer firm serving growing client base. Diversified practice re: client size and industry, including healthcare, banking, manufacturing, not-for-profit, etc.

Salary Minimum: $75,000
Functions: Senior mgmt., Production, Health admin., Sales mgmt., Benefits, CFO's, MIS mgmt.
Industries: Plastics/rubber, Motor vehicles, Non-profits, Higher ed., Accounting, Software, Healthcare
Professional Associations: AESC

Joe Sullivan & Assoc., Inc.

#9 Feather Hill
P.O. Box 612
Southold, New York 11971
(516) 765-5050

Key Contact - Specialty:
Mr. Joseph J. Sullivan, Jr.

Description: Executive search and recruitment in broadcasting, cable, entertainment and satellite industries.

Salary Minimum: $100,000
Functions: Generalist, Senior mgmt., Sales & mktg., HR mgmt., CFO's, Engineering
Industries: Generalist, Entertainment, Communications, Broadcast & Film

---

Sullivan & Company

20 Exchange Place, 50th Floor
New York, New York 10005-3201
(212) 422-3000
Fax: (212) 422-9100
Email:
lastnamefirstnameinitial@sullivanco.com
Web: www.sullivanco.com/

Key Contact - Specialty:
Mr. Brian M. Sullivan - *Financial services*
Ms. Brendan G. Burnett - *Financial services*
Mr. Jory J. Marino - *Financial services, information technology*
Ms. Marguerite A. McMahon - *Financial services*
Mr. Leslie W. Stern - *Financial services*
Mr. Steven M. Davis - *Financial services*
Ms. Anne G. McCool
Mr. Barry I. Bregman - *Financial services*
Mr. Gene S. Manheim - *Financial services*
Mr. Keith S. Macomber - *Financial services*
Mr. Jack H. Cage - *Financial services*

Description: International executive search firm with expertise in investment banking, capital markets, portfolio management, technology, banking, legal, human resources and management consulting. Our clients include major investment banks, hedge funds, investment management firms, regional banks, law firms and management consulting firms.

Salary Minimum: $200,000
Functions: Senior mgmt., IT, MIS mgmt., Systems anal., Systems implem.
Industries: Finance, Banking, Invest. banking, Brokers, Venture cap., Misc. financial, Insurance
Professional Associations: AESC, IACPR

Summit Executive Search Consultants, Inc. †

420 Lincoln Rd., Ste. 265
Miami Beach, Florida 33139
(305) 672-5008
Fax: (305) 672-5007
Email: summitsearch@compuserve.com

Key Contact - Specialty:
Mr. Alfred J. Holzman

Description: Highly personalized retainer based search assignments in all functions and industries. Special attention given to occupational safety, industrial hygiene, engineering, manufacturing, automotive, diversity/affirmative action/minority searches.

Salary Minimum: $50,000
Functions: Production, Automation, Quality, Purchasing, Materials Plng., Engineering, Minorities
Industries: Plastics/rubber, Metal products, Machinery/Appliances, Motor vehicles, Misc. mfg., Human resource svcs.

Summit Group Int'l., Inc. †

2295 Henry Clower Blvd., Suite 201
Snellville, Georgia 30078
(770) 736-9701
Fax: (770) 736-0640
Email: sgi@summit_group.com
Web: summit_group.com

Key Contact - Specialty:
Mr. Dotson Benefield
Mr. Jan Eason

Description: Quality, service, integrity and professionalism combined with over 20 years of completion of successful recruiting assignments have been the key to our successful reputation and results.

Salary Minimum: $60,000
Functions: Generalist, Middle mgmt., Mfg., Distribution, Sales mgmt., HR mgmt., Engineering
Industries: Generalist, Construction, Leather/stone/glass/clay, Transportation, Equip. svcs., Insurance, Real estate

---

Swartz & Assoc., Inc.

P.O. Box 14167
Scottsdale, Arizona 85267
(602) 998-0363
Fax: (602) 596-1960
Email: bill@swartz.com
Web: www.swartz.com

Key Contact - Specialty:
Mr. William K. Swartz - *Technology industry*
Ms. Pamela L. Swartz

Description: Retained search in all functional categories, at the VP level and above, on behalf of middle-market, technology-based growth companies worldwide.

Salary Minimum: $100,000
Functions: Directors, Senior mgmt., CFO's, Int'l.
Industries: Computer equip., Computer svcs., New media, High tech, Software

Sweeney Harbert & Mummert, Inc.

777 S. Harbour Island Blvd., Ste. 130
Tampa, Florida 33602
(813) 229-5360
Fax: (813) 229-0018

Key Contact - Specialty:
Mr. David O. Harbert - *Generalist*
Mr. James W. Sweeney - *Generalist*
Mr. Dennis D. Mummert - *Generalist*
Mr. David A. Gallagher - *Generalist*

Description: Specialists in senior-level executive search. A generalist firm serving clients on a nationwide basis. Number of clients per industry limited to two, avoiding blocking conflicts.

Salary Minimum: $100,000
Functions: Generalist
Industries: Generalist

Synapse Human Resource Consulting Group

7557 Rambler Rd., Ste. 1425
Dallas, Texas 75231
(214) 891-5977

Key Contact - Specialty:
Mr. Michael Schwartz - *Senior management, management consultants, senior sales & marketing*

Description: Small, high quality retained search firm with experience in multiple industries. Limited size of practice to insure high quality work with no conflicts of interest. Seek to become strategic business partner with clients. Also offer human resource consulting services.

Salary Minimum: $50,000
Functions: Senior mgmt., Healthcare, Sales & mktg., HR mgmt., Finance, MIS mgmt., Mgmt. consultants
Industries: Mfg., Finance, Svcs., Mgmt. consulting, Communications, High tech, Healthcare

Affiliates:
M. S. Schwartz & Company, Inc.

Synergistics Assoc. Ltd.

400 N. State St., Ste. 400
Chicago, Illinois 60610
(312) 467-5450
Fax: (312) 822-0246
Email: AJBsynerg@aol.com

Key Contact - Specialty:
Mr. Alvin J. Borenstine - *Information technology, CIO's*

Description: Specialists in data processing executives from $100,000 to $250,000. Principals are former directors MIS from Fortune 100 firms. We have placed more MIS executives than any Chicago firm.

Salary Minimum: $100,000
Functions: Middle mgmt., IT, Mgmt. consultants
Industries: Generalist
Professional Associations: AESC

The Synergy Organization

3070 Bristol Pike, Bldg. II, Ste. 209
Bensalem, Pennsylvania 19020
(215) 638-9777

Key Contact - Specialty:
Dr. Kenneth R. Cohen - *Healthcare*

Description: Progressive and established executive search/management consulting firm incorporates personalized interviews and proven standardized testing with employers and prospective employees to guarantee compatibility, productivity and retention! Unconditional one year guarantee!

Salary Minimum: $60,000
Functions: Directors, Senior mgmt., Nurses, Allied health, Health admin., CFO's, MIS mgmt.
Industries: Human resource svcs., Healthcare

Tabb & Assoc. †

1460 W. Lane Ave., Ste. 250
Columbus, Ohio 43221
(614) 486-8888
Fax: (614) 486-3950

Key Contact - Specialty:
Mr. Roosevelt Tabb - *General management*

Description: We specialize in senior and middle level executives in a diverse group of industrial and consumer firms. Our work is quiet...confidential... and on-target.

Salary Minimum: $75,000
Functions: General mgmt., Mfg., Sales & mktg., HR mgmt., Finance, Engineering
Industries: Chemicals, Plastics/rubber, Metal products, Machinery/Appliances, Misc. mfg., Human resource svcs.

Tactical Alternatives

2819 Crow Canyon Rd., Ste. 210
San Ramon, California 94583
(925) 831-3800
Fax: (925) 831-3808
Email: alsal@pacbell.net

Key Contact - Specialty:
Mr. Al Salottolo - *Computer, high-tech*

Description: Conducts searches for senior level, hardware/software individuals for computer high tech companies. Expertise in: R&D, process development, marketing, sales and operations. Assignments are performed with the highest degree of professionalism, sense of urgency and integrity.

Salary Minimum: $65,000
Functions: Directors, Production, Mktg. mgmt., Sales mgmt., MIS mgmt., Systems dev., Engineering
Industries: Computer equip., Computer svcs., Human resource svcs., New media, Telecoms, High tech, Software

Affiliates:
Strategic Alternatives

The Talley Group †

P.O. Box 2918
Staunton, Virginia 24402
(540) 248-7009
Fax: (540) 248-7046
Email: talley@cfw.com
Web: www.talley-group.com

Key Contact - Specialty:
Mr. J. L. Burkhill - *Marketing, engineering, human resources*
Mr. T. C. Jorgensen - *Finance & accounting, engineering*
Ms. S. Estes - *Information systems*
Ms. C. Szabad - *Human resources, accounting*

Description: Conducts searches for growth oriented companies, strong emphasis on mid-senior level positions. For the past 11 years we have specialized in human resources and, more recently, information systems, finance, marketing and engineering recruiting.

Salary Minimum: $40,000
Functions: Sales & mktg., Benefits, Personnel, Training, Finance, IT, Engineering
Industries: Food/bev/tobacco, Paper, Printing, Motor vehicles, Banking, Accounting, Equip. svcs.

The Talon Group

16801 Addison Rd., Ste. 255
Dallas, Texas 75248
(972) 931-8223
Fax: (972) 931-8063
Email: talongrp@gte.net

Key Contact - Specialty:
Mr. Robert A. Piper - *Real estate, home building, multi-family, development*
Mr. Rodney Hall - *Real estate, home building, multi-family, development*

† occasional contingency assignment

Mr. Anthony Cleveland - *Real estate, home building, multi-family, development*
Ms. Jean Mason - *Real estate, home building, multi-family, development*

Description: We have been assisting home building and real estate clients through quality driven management consulting and executive search.

Salary Minimum: $60,000
Functions: Directors, Senior mgmt., Middle mgmt., Sales & mktg., HR mgmt., Finance, Specialized services
Industries: Construction, Mgmt. consulting, Human resource svcs., Publishing, Real estate

Affiliates:
Piper/Knight, Inc.

Martin Stevens Tamaren & Assoc., Inc. †

26842 Bridlewood Drive
Laguna Hills, California 92653
(949) 582-6900
(800) 527-2509
Fax: (949) 582-8125
Email: martystevens@earthlink.net

Key Contact - Specialty:
Mr. Martin Stevens - *Computer, communication, networking, software, telecommunication*
Mr. Thomas Bakehorn - *Computer, communication, networking, software, telecommunication*

Description: Retained director level and up in the computer, telecommunications, satellite and wireless industries.

Salary Minimum: $90,000
Functions: Senior mgmt., Mktg. mgmt., Sales mgmt., Cash mgmt., Systems anal., Systems dev., Engineering
Industries: Computer equip., Venture cap., New media, Broadcast & Film, Telecoms, High tech, Software

Affiliates:
Global Executive Search

Tanner & Assoc., Inc.

15851 Dallas Pkwy., Ste. 600
Dallas, Texas 75248
(972) 371-5740
Fax: (972) 371-5741
Email: mikeb@intnetc.net
Web: www.tanner-assoc.com

Key Contact - Specialty:
Mr. Mike Boate - *Telecommunications*

Description: Focused and personalized attention with sincere interest in your company's long term success. Combined with guaranteed results.

Salary Minimum: $80,000
Functions: Senior mgmt., Middle mgmt., Product dev., Mktg. mgmt., Sales mgmt., Engineering, Int'l.
Industries: Telecoms

Tannura & Assoc., Inc.

One Tower Lane, Ste. 1700
Oakbrook Terrace, Illinois 60181-4631
(630) 573-2929
Fax: (630) 954-0022
Email: tannura@aol.com

Key Contact - Specialty:
Mr. Robert P. Tannura - *Information systems & technology*

Description: Specializing in information systems and technology ranging from high level technical through executive management including leading edge technology, traditional systems, telecommunications, sales and customer support.

Salary Minimum: $75,000
Functions: IT
Industries: Generalist

Tarnow Int'l.

150 Morris Ave.
Springfield, New Jersey 07081
(201) 376-3900
Fax: (201) 376-0340
Email: tarnowint@aol.com

Key Contact - Specialty:
Mr. Emil Vogel - *Senior management*
Mr. William A. Myers
Ms. Karen Gordon Knapp - *Senior management*

Description: A generalist firm working at senior levels with established market niches in a broad range of industries and disciplines.

Salary Minimum: $100,000
Functions: Generalist, General mgmt., Mfg., Sales & mktg., HR mgmt., Finance, IT
Industries: Generalist
Professional Associations: IACPR

TASA International

750 Lexington Ave., 17th Floor
New York, New York 10022
(212) 486-1490
Fax: (212) 486-2518

Key Contact - Specialty:
Mr. John Mclaughlin
Mr. R. Fred Rijke
Mr. Michael Franzino
Mr. Robert B. Whaley
Mr. Jeffrey C. Wierichs
Mr. Klaus Jacobs
Ms. Abbe S. GoldFarb
Ms. Anne-Marie Finnell

Description: Consultants to management on executive search, worldwide.

Salary Minimum: $120,000
Functions: Generalist, Int'l.
Industries: Generalist
Professional Associations: AESC

Branches:
Embarcadero Corporate Center
2483 Bayshore Rd., Ste. 101
Palo Alto, California 94303
(650) 424-9233
Fax: (650) 424-9253
Key Contact - Specialty:
Mr. Herman De Kesel
Ms. Jo Carol Conover
Ms. Christine Venditti

7061 S. Tamiami Trail
Sarasota, Florida 34231
(941) 922-8856
Fax: (941) 924-9138
Key Contact - Specialty:
Mr. Richard L. Fleming

3340 Peachtree St. NE, Ste. 2440
Atlanta, Georgia 30326
(404) 812-8272
Fax: (404) 812-8280
Key Contact - Specialty:
Mr. W. H. Peter Keesom
Mr. Robert P. Milne
Mr. L. Lee Weber
Ms. Amanda Grimes

430 Bedford St. Ste. 350
Lexington, Massachusetts 02173
(781) 861-8099
Fax: (781) 861-8081
Email: TASA_Boston@compuserve.com
Key Contact - Specialty:
Ms. Claudia B. Liebesny
Mr. Mike Ahearn
Mr. Charlie Watt
Ms. Marie A. Laliberte

5420 LBJ Frwy., Ste. 1475
Dallas, Texas 75240
(972) 458-1212
Fax: (972) 702-0710
Key Contact - Specialty:
Mr. James P. Demchak
Mr. Duane R. Goar
Mr. Harvey D. Letcher
Mr. J. Herbert Wise
Mr. Jon A. Lewis
Mr. Roger B. Cortez
Mr. Keith D. Pearson
Mr. Michael McMillin

Paseo de las Palmas 731-1002
Mexico City, Mexico DF 11010
Mexico
52 5 540 5505
Fax: 52 5 540 4277
Key Contact - Specialty:
Mr. Francisco Albisua
Mr. Juan Manuel Farias
Mr. Antonio Larrea

International Branches:
Amsterdam, Barcelona, Bogota, Brisbane, Brussels, Buenos Aires, Caracas, Central Hong Kong, Frankfurt, Jakarta, Johannesburg, London, Madrid, Melbourne, Milan, Munich, Paris, Rome, Santiago, Sao Paulo, Singapore, Sydney, Vienna, Wellington, Zurich

Tate & Assoc., Inc.
1020 Springfield Ave., Ste. 201
Westfield, New Jersey 07090
(908) 232-2443
Fax: (908) 232-5959

Key Contact - Specialty:
Mr. Gene M. Tate - *Generalist*

Description: Highly successful retained search firm recognized for timeliness, customization and quality service. Dedicated to results, professional integrity and commitment to success reflected by 90% repeat business.

Salary Minimum: $50,000
Functions: Senior mgmt., Product dev., Mktg. mgmt., Finance, IT, R&D, Engineering
Industries: Generalist, Food/bev/tobacco, Drugs mfg., Medical devices, Finance, Communications, Packaging

Tate Consulting, Inc.
10647 Avenida Santa Ana
Boca Raton, Florida 33498
(561) 852-8283
Fax: (561) 852-2385
Email: info@tateinc.com
Web: www.tateinc.com

Key Contact - Specialty:
Mr. Andrew Tate - *Computer engineering*

Description: We are committed to providing high quality solutions to our clients in the hi-tech industry with our on-site consulting, outsourcing and full time placement services.
Functions: MIS mgmt., Systems anal., Systems dev., Systems implem., Systems support, R&D, Engineering
Industries: Computer equip., High tech, Software

TaxSearch Inc. †
6102 S. Memorial Drive
Tulsa, Oklahoma 74133-1937
(918) 252-3100
Fax: (918) 252-3063
Email: taxsearch@taxsearchinc.com
Web: www.taxsearchinc.com

Key Contact - Specialty:
Mr. Anthony Santiago - *Tax*
Ms. Sam Bynum - *Tax*

Description: Our mission is to develop a level of trust and respect with our clients that creates a long-term partnership for solving personnel and recruitment needs in the tax field.

Salary Minimum: $75,000
Functions: Taxes
Industries: Generalist, Energy/utilities, Mfg., Finance, Svcs., Communications, High tech

Carl J. Taylor & Co.
11551 Forest Central Dr. Ste. 329
Dallas, Texas 75243
(214) 340-1188
Fax: (214) 340-1175

Key Contact - Specialty:
Mr. Carl J. Taylor

Description: Executive search practice with a reputation for completing challenging mid and senior level position assignments in a timely and professional manner.

Salary Minimum: $75,000
Functions: General mgmt., Finance, IT, R&D, Mgmt. consultants
Industries: Energy/utilities, Drugs mfg., Mgmt. consulting, Communications, Healthcare

Taylor Winfield
12801 N. Central Expwy., Ste. 1260
Dallas, Texas 75243
(972) 392-1400
Fax: (972) 392-1455
Email: administrator@taylorwinfield.com
Web: www.taylorwinfield.com

Key Contact - Specialty:
Ms. Nancy L. Albertini - *Directors & officers*
Ms. Connie Adair
Ms. Jane Ann Nelson
Ms. Shelley Henry
Mr. Bob Bozman

Description: Clients include computer hardware and software companies, telecommunications with special focus on the public network and or related technology firms. Specific knowledge of private, start-up firms with venture capital funding.

Salary Minimum: $120,000
Functions: Directors, Senior mgmt., Mktg. mgmt., CFO's, MIS mgmt., Mgmt. consultants
Industries: Computer equip., Venture cap., Computer svcs., Mgmt. consulting, Telecoms, High tech, Software

Branches:
5875 Mallview Court
Columbus, Ohio 43231
(614) 895-6757
Fax: (614) 895-2208
Key Contact - Specialty:
Ms. Judy Redeker

The TBI Group
34 Militia Hill Drive
Chesterbrook, Pennsylvania 19087
(610) 251-2147
Fax: (610) 251-2148
Email: mjrandels@aol.com
Web: thetbigroup.hypermart.net

Key Contact - Specialty:
Mr. Michael J. Randels

Description: Boutique consulting firm primarily engaged in retained executive search. Provides high quality, individualized, executive and management recruitment services to a limited number of companies.
Functions: Generalist, Senior mgmt., Middle mgmt., Admin. svcs., Distribution, Sales mgmt., HR mgmt.
Industries: Generalist, Food/bev/tobacco, Lumber/furniture, Soap/perfume/cosmetics, Misc. mfg., Retail, High tech

Affiliates:
Belknap & Assoc.

TechFind, Inc.
P.O. Box 626
Natick, Massachusetts 01760
(508) 647-0111
Fax: (508) 647-0110
Email: tfind@worldnet.att.net

Key Contact - Specialty:
Ms. Amy B. Lurier - *Pharmaceuticals, biotechnology*

Description: Retained search firm specializing in the placement of highly trained scientists and medical professionals. Our recruiters are trained scientists in the life science area. We have all worked in a chemical, biotech or pharmaceutical company and have experience in placing scientists.

Salary Minimum: $80,000
Functions: Directors, Senior mgmt., Middle mgmt., Product dev., Nurses, R&D
Industries: Drugs mfg., Medical devices, Pharmaceutical svcs., Biotech

Technical Skills Consulting Inc. †
220 Yonge Street, Toronto Eaton Centre
Galleria Offices, Box 507, Ste. 214
Toronto, Ontario M5B 2H1
Canada
(416) 586-7971
Fax: (416) 586-0416
Email: tsc@tscinc.on.ca

Key Contact - Specialty:
Mr. Paul MacBean - *Engineering, technology, science*
Ms. Roxanne Mars - *Engineering, technology, science*
Mr. Don Phaneuf

† occasional contingency assignment

Description: Specializing in the recruitment of engineering, technology and science professionals for Canadian industry.

Salary Minimum: $50,000
Functions: Product dev., Purchasing, Mkt. research, MIS mgmt., Engineering, Environmentalists, Architects
Industries: Agri/forestry/mining, Mfg., Textiles/apparel, Paper, Environmental svcs., Aerospace, High tech

---

The Technology Group

585 Tollgate Rd., Ste. E&F
Elgin, Illinois 60123
(847) 695-7800
Fax: (847) 695-7211
Email: i-schwan@tec-group.com
Web: www.tec-group.com

Key Contact - Specialty:
Mr. John Schwan - *Information technology*
Ms. Susan Burns - *Sales & marketing*
Ms. Betty Baum - *Business re-engineering*

Description: Our firm specializes in management personnel and key individual contributors for information technology companies.

Salary Minimum: $75,000
Functions: Senior mgmt., Middle mgmt., Product dev., Mktg. mgmt., Sales mgmt., MIS mgmt.
Industries: Generalist, Computer equip., Computer svcs., Broadcast & Film, Telecoms, High tech, Software

Affiliates:
SearchNet Int'l.

Technology Management Partners

1000 Fremont Ave., Ste. 270
Los Altos, California 94024
(650) 948-2100
Fax: (650) 948-8282
Email: webstertmp@batnet.com

Key Contact - Specialty:
Mr. Larry Webster - *Executives, communications, new media*

Description: Specialize in executive and management placement for venture financed startup and emerging growth technology based companies.

Salary Minimum: $90,000
Functions: Senior mgmt., Middle mgmt., Mkt. research, Sales mgmt., Systems dev., R&D, Engineering
Industries: Computer equip., Consumer electronics, New media, Telecoms, High tech, Software

---

Telford, Adams & Alexander

650 Town Ctr. Drive, Ste. 850-A
Costa Mesa, California 92626
(714) 850-4309
Fax: (714) 850-4488

Key Contact - Specialty:
Mr. John H. Telford, Jr. - *General management, finance, human resources, marketing*
Ms. Debra M. Zaslav - *Information technology management, distribution*

Description: The firm will accept only those assignments where we are certain we can be successful. We rely heavily on repeat business from satisfied clients. All of our work is guaranteed.

Salary Minimum: $75,000
Functions: Senior mgmt., Middle mgmt., Materials Plng., Health admin., Mktg. mgmt., CFO's, MIS mgmt.
Industries: Soap/perfume/cosmetics, Computer equip., Transportation, Finance, Government, Biotech, Healthcare

Affiliates:
Foster Partners
Telford, Adams & Alexander

TEMCO-The Executive Management Consulting Organization

P.O. Box 303
Oconomowoc, Wisconsin 53066-0303
(414) 567-2069

Key Contact - Specialty:
Mr. Thomas E. Masson

Description: HR management consultants with broad range of services including: executive search, personnel management, organization analysis, management training/development, employee/supervisory counseling, team-building workshops and personnel function audits.

Salary Minimum: $50,000
Functions: Generalist
Industries: Generalist

Tennyson Advisors

237 Park Ave., Ste. 2100
New York, New York 10017
(212) 551-1450
Fax: (212) 551-1114

Key Contact - Specialty:
Mr. Michael Martinolich - *Investment management, domestic, international*

Description: We focus exclusively on the recruitment of domestic & international investment management professionals domiciled worldwide. Our firm was founded by Michael Martinolich who has been recruiting since 1985.

Salary Minimum: $100,000
Functions: Sales mgmt., CFO's, Cash mgmt., Risk mgmt.
Industries: Finance, Invest. banking, Brokers, Venture cap., Misc. financial

---

Tesar-Reynes, Inc.

500 N. Michigan Ave., Ste. 1400
Chicago, Illinois 60611
(312) 661-0700
Fax: (312) 661-1598
Email: tony@tesar-reynes.com
Web: www/tesar-reynes.com

Key Contact - Specialty:
Mr. Tony Reynes
Mr. Bob Tesar

Description: One of the largest specialists in advertising, media, sales promotion, direct marketing, public relations, research and integrated marketing management. Will fill most searches in 60-90 days.

Salary Minimum: $50,000
Functions: Advertising, Mktg. mgmt., Direct mktg., PR
Industries: Generalist

Thomas Mangum Co.

1655 Hastings Ranch Drive
Pasadena, California 91107
(818) 351-0866
Fax: (818) 351-0856
Email: mangum@earthlink.net

Key Contact - Specialty:
Mr. William T. Mangum - *General management, operations management*
Ms. Maria Mangum - *Administrative, board of directors*
Ms. Carolyn Carter - *Technical*

Description: Founded 1960 with long established reputation as a leader in hi-tech oriented search industry involving difficult assignments (electronics, aerospace, systems, R&D, information tech, etc.) and manufacturing, general management and senior management search.

Salary Minimum: $75,000
Functions: Generalist, Senior mgmt., Mfg., Materials, Sales & mktg., Finance, IT
Industries: Generalist, Mfg., Finance, Svcs., Aerospace, High tech, Healthcare
Professional Associations: IACPR

Branches:
2469 Cahuilla Hills Rd.
Palm Springs, California 92264
(619) 323-0174
Key Contact - Specialty:
Mr. William T. Mangum - *General management, operations management*

22607 N.E. 19th St.
Redmond, Washington 98053
(425) 836-3305

Key Contact - Specialty:
Ms. Stacy Mangum

Thomas Resource Group
(formerly Montague Enterprises)
1630 Tiburon Blvd.
Tiburon, California 94920
(415) 435-5123
Web: tthomas@infoasis.com

Key Contact - Specialty:
Mr. Terry Thomas
Dr. Norm Mitroff

Description: Executive search consultant since 1978 who commits an extraordinary amount of time to and personally conducts each assignment, limits self to three concurrent searches and has a cost effective fee structure and a highly responsive, personalized, client tailored approach.

Salary Minimum: $90,000
Functions: Directors, Senior mgmt., Mktg. mgmt., Sales mgmt., Direct mktg., HR mgmt., CFO's
Industries: Food/bev/tobacco, Drugs mfg., Medical devices, New media, Telecoms, Biotech, Healthcare

Richard Thompson Assoc., Inc.
701 4th Ave. S., Ste. 500
Minneapolis, Minnesota 55415
(612) 339-6060
Fax: (612) 337-9099

Key Contact - Specialty:
Mr. Richard P. Thompson

Description: Senior management and board of directors search consulting services for both non-profit and for- profit organizations.

Salary Minimum: $60,000
Functions: Generalist, Senior mgmt., Mfg., HR mgmt., CFO's, Mgmt. consultants, Non-profits
Industries: Generalist, Medical devices, Machinery/Appliances, Finance, Non-profits, High tech, Biotech

Thorne, Brieger Assoc., Inc.
11 E. 44th St.
New York, New York 10017
(212) 682-5424
Fax: (212) 557-4926
Email: sbrieger@earthlink.net

Key Contact - Specialty:
Mr. Steven M. Brieger
Mr. Mike Jacobs
Mr. Jeffrey M. Stark

Description: Skilled recruiters and assessors bringing a consultant's approach to solving organizational problems. Assignments carried out by principals only, each with more than 25 years of successful generalist experience.

Salary Minimum: $90,000
Functions: Generalist, General mgmt., Mfg., Materials, HR mgmt., Finance, Engineering
Industries: Generalist, Textiles/apparel, Chemicals, Medical devices, Machinery/ Appliances, Retail, Insurance

Tierney Assoc., Inc.
51 Downing St.
Wilkes-Barre, Pennsylvania 18702
(717) 825-9500
Fax: (717) 825-9568
Email: gtierney@microserve.net

Key Contact - Specialty:
Mr. George F. Tierney - *Electronic, electrical connectors, metal stamping, CIM*
Mr. Donald G. Symanski - *High precision metal fab, rubber, plastics*
Ms. Carol A. Newcomb - *Electronics, paper industry*
Mr. Paul J. Argenio - *Electronics, metal fab & consumer products*
Ms. Lisa Simon

Description: Client base largely electronic components & systems (connectors, sensors, switches, power elex, sm & assembly) for computer, automotive, consumer (DIY), industrial, lighting and telecom markets. Extensive marketing and sales/product, smt assembly management, engineering and technical/ marketing and sales oriented general managers.

Salary Minimum: $60,000
Functions: General mgmt., Mfg., Materials, Sales & mktg., Mktg. mgmt., Sales mgmt., Engineering
Industries: Mfg., Medical devices, Plastics/ rubber, Metal products, Computer equip., Consumer electronics, Test/measurement equip.

Tirocchi, Wright, Inc.
2055 Gateway Place, Ste. 400
San Jose, California 95110
(408) 292-6033
Fax: (408) 441-9152
Email: twisearch@aol.com

Key Contact - Specialty:
Mr. Fred Tirocchi - *High technology (all functions)*

Description: Consultants in executive search. Primary focus in high tech: systems, semiconductors and miscellaneous manufacturing with vertical integration.

Salary Minimum: $100,000
Functions: General mgmt., Mfg., Materials, Sales & mktg., HR mgmt., IT, Engineering
Industries: Computer equip., Consumer electronics, Test/measurement equip., Computer svcs., Packaging, High tech, Software

Branches:
3017 Douglas Blvd., Ste. 300
Roseville, California 95661
(916) 624-1700
Fax: (916) 624-3600
Key Contact - Specialty:
Ms. Paula G. Wright - *High technology (all functions)*

TNS Partners, Inc.
8140 Walnut Hill Lane, Ste. 301
Dallas, Texas 75231
(214) 369-3565
Fax: (214) 369-9865
Email: tnspartner@aol.com
Web: mailbox@tnspartners.com

Key Contact - Specialty:
Mr. John K. Semyan
Mr. Craig C. Neidhart
Mr. Alan R. St. Clair
Mr. James Peters

Description: Generalist firm with an emphasis on senior management positions in high technology, telecommunications, consumer and industrial manufacturing, services and information technology.

Salary Minimum: $100,000
Functions: Generalist, General mgmt., Mfg., Materials, HR mgmt., Finance, IT
Industries: Generalist, Energy/utilities, Mfg., Wholesale, Svcs., Aerospace, High tech

Skip Tolette Executive Search Consulting
577 W. Saddle River Rd.
Upper Saddle River, New Jersey 07458
(201) 327-8214
Email: skiptol@aol.com

Key Contact - Specialty:
Mr. Skip Tolette - *Information technology*

Description: Functional strength information technology - CIO, development, operations, strategy, telecommunications and consulting.

Salary Minimum: $100,000
Functions: MIS mgmt., Systems anal., Systems dev., Systems implem., Systems support, Network admin., DB admin.
Industries: Generalist

Tower Consultants, Ltd.
621B Swedesford Rd.
Swedesford Corporate Ctr.
Malvern, Pennsylvania 19355
(610) 722-9300
Fax: (610) 722-9310

Email: towercons@aol.com
Web: www.towerconsultants.com

Key Contact - Specialty:
Ms. Donna DeHart - *Human resources*
Ms. Kim deVry - *Human resources*

Description: Nationwide search: human resources, benefits and compensation, staffing, HR generalists, diversity, development/organizational effectiveness, international human resources. Represent major corporations, insurance carriers and consulting/brokerage firms and not-for-profit.

Salary Minimum: $75,000
Functions: HR mgmt., Benefits, Personnel, Training, Mgmt. consultants, Minorities, Int'l.
Industries: Textiles/apparel, Chemicals, Paints/petroleum products, Computer equip., Misc. mfg., Aerospace, High tech
Professional Associations: IACPR

Branches:
943 Central Pkwy.
Stuart, Florida 34994-3904
(561) 288-3590
Fax: (561) 288-3540
Key Contact - Specialty:
Ms. Donna L. Friedman - *Human resources*
Mr. Thomas J. Regan - *Human resources*

Trac One †
239 Route 22 E.
Green Brook, New Jersey 08812
(732) 968-1600
Fax: (732) 968-9437

Key Contact - Specialty:
Mr. Thomas C. Wood - *Data processing*

Description: We conduct executive searches for MIS professionals exclusively as a subsidiary of Team One, Inc. - a family of companies dedicated to data processing recruitment, search and consulting services.

Salary Minimum: $75,000
Functions: Generalist, MIS mgmt., Systems anal., Systems dev., Systems implem., Systems support, Engineering
Industries: Generalist, Computer svcs., Mgmt. consulting, Human resource svcs., Telecoms, High tech, Software

Travaille Executive Search †
1730 Rhode Island Ave. NW, Ste. 401
Washington, District of Columbia 20036
(202) 463-6342
Email: travaille@lazer.net

Key Contact - Specialty:
Mr. Benjamin H. Long - *Communications*

Description: We have an in-depth understanding of corporate communications and marketing communications, plus national and international public affairs. Excellent in finding financial communicators for start-up companies.

Salary Minimum: $45,000
Functions: PR, Graphic artists
Industries: Advertising/PR, Publishing, New media

Travis & Co., Inc.
325 Boston Post Rd.
Sudbury, Massachusetts 01776
(978) 443-4000
Fax: (978) 443-3251

Key Contact - Specialty:
Mr. John A. Travis - *Medical devices, biotechnology, pharmaceuticals*
Mrs. Mary K. Morse - *Biotechnology, medical services, telecommunications, financial services*
Mr. Michael J. Travis - *Computer software & hardware, multimedia*

Description: Top quality search for executive management. Clients in a wide range of industries; recognized for expertise in medical devices, pharmaceuticals, biotechnology, telecommunications, multimedia and computer hardware and software.

Salary Minimum: $100,000
Functions: Senior mgmt., Plant mgmt., Mktg. mgmt., Sales mgmt., CFO's, R&D, Engineering
Industries: Drugs mfg., Medical devices, Computer equip., New media, Software, Biotech, Healthcare

Van Treadaway Assoc., Inc. †
564 Greystone Trace NE
Marietta, Georgia 30068
(770) 578-0985
Fax: (770) 578-8626
Email: treads@mindspring.com
Web: www.vtassociates.com

Key Contact - Specialty:
Mr. Van Treadaway - *Information systems, software engineering, telecommunications*
Mr. Joe Payne - *Information systems, software engineering, sales & marketing*

Description: Twenty years experience in high technology recruiting, on both sides of the desk, allows for a tailored approach to meet the need of each client at all professional levels.

Salary Minimum: $50,000
Functions: Personnel, MIS mgmt., Systems anal., Systems dev., Systems implem., Systems support, Mgmt. consultants
Industries: Computer svcs., Mgmt. consulting, Human resource svcs., Telecoms, High tech, Software

Trebor Weldon Lawrence, Inc.
355 Lexington Ave.
New York, New York 10017
(212) 867-0066
Fax: (212) 867-2784

Key Contact - Specialty:
Mr. Lawrence Levine - *Promotion marketing*
Mr. Robert Ornstein - *Database management, research and analysis*
Ms. Gayle W. Parker - *Market research*

Description: Promotion marketing, marketing services/research, public relations, general communications, M&A. Wage and salary consulting, departmental structure and job description consulting; unbundled services include reference checking, interviewing only, resume review, etc.

Salary Minimum: $45,000
Functions: Advertising, Mktg. mgmt., Sales mgmt., Direct mktg., Mgmt. consultants
Industries: Generalist, Food/bev/tobacco, Soap/perfume/cosmetics, Drugs mfg., Mgmt. consulting, Advertising/PR

TRH Assoc., Inc.
310 Madison Ave., Ste. 1212
New York, New York 10017
(212) 661-1271

Key Contact - Specialty:
Ms. Tala R. Hoffman - *Finance, banking, consulting, strategic planning, operations*

Description: Search recruiting and competitive research conducted on an hourly retainer basis.

Salary Minimum: $100,000
Functions: Generalist, HR mgmt., Finance, Mgmt. consultants
Industries: Banking, Invest. banking, Accounting, Mgmt. consulting, Human resource svcs.

Triumph Consulting, Inc.
2550 Middle Rd., Ste. 600
Bettendorf, Iowa 52722
(319) 344-7300
Fax: (319) 355-3633
Email: Triumphcon@aol.com

Key Contact - Specialty:
Mr. Daniel G. DePuydt
Mr. Scott M. White

Description: We are a national practice concentrating in manufacturing, technology, transportation and healthcare. The principals have extensive prior senior management experience. Each assignment is specifically handled by a designated professional through all phases of the search process.

Salary Minimum: $75,000

Functions: Senior mgmt., Plant mgmt., Health admin., Mktg. mgmt., HR mgmt., CFO's, MIS mgmt.
Industries: Chemicals, Plastics/rubber, Machinery/Appliances, Consumer electronics, Banking, Publishing, Healthcare

Trout & Assoc. Inc.

15 Gatehouse Lane
Sandy, Utah 84092
(801) 576-1547
Fax: (801) 576-1541

Key Contact - Specialty:
Mr. Thomas L. Trout - *Generalist*

Description: Human resources consulting services with emphasis on executive search/staffing services and career counselling outplacement services.

Salary Minimum: $45,000
Functions: Senior mgmt., Finance, IT, Engineering, Environmentalists
Industries: Generalist, Finance, Defense, Environmental svcs., Aerospace, Software, Healthcare

Trowbridge & Co., Inc.

105 Chestnut St., Ste. 22
Needham, Massachusetts 02492
(781) 444-4200
Email: RLT80@aol.com

Key Contact - Specialty:
Mr. Robert L. Trowbridge - *Technology products & services*

Description: Consultants in executive search and selection assisting a select number of U.S. and international clients in identifying, attracting and retaining senior level executives for all disciplines, including general management.

Salary Minimum: $80,000
Functions: General mgmt., Mfg., Healthcare, Sales & mktg., Finance, IT, R&D, Engineering
Industries: Energy/utilities, Mfg., Finance, Communications, High tech, Software, Biotech, Healthcare

Tryon & Heideman, LLC

8301 State Line Rd., Ste. 204
Kansas City, Missouri 64114
(816) 822-1976
Fax: (816) 822-9333
Email: tryonheideman@sprintmail.com

Key Contact - Specialty:
Ms. Katey Tryon
Ms. Mary Marren Heideman

Description: Emphasize consensus building on criteria for executive positions before initiating search. Develop in-depth understanding of clients' organizational culture to ensure best match.

Salary Minimum: $65,000
Functions: Generalist, General mgmt., Senior mgmt., HR mgmt., Finance, Engineering, Int'l.
Industries: Generalist, Energy/utilities, Mfg., Finance, Svcs., Non-profits, Communications

Tschudin Inc.

215 River Vale Rd.
River Vale, New Jersey 07675
(201) 666-3456
Fax: (201) 666-8470
Email: accessusa@tschudin.com
Web: www.tschudin.com

Key Contact - Specialty:
Dr. Hugo Tschudin - *Generalist*
Ms. Ruth Tschudin - *Generalist*
Mr. Richard Danoff - *Generalist*

Description: Searches for executives who are crucial for company success. Especially strong in assignments requiring extraordinary care/depth. Examples: niche businesses, searches involving European and American companies.

Salary Minimum: $70,000
Functions: Generalist, Senior mgmt., Middle mgmt., Plant mgmt., Mktg. mgmt., Sales mgmt., CFO's
Industries: Generalist, Food/bev/tobacco, Drugs mfg., Medical devices, Metal products, Machinery/Appliances, Test/measurement equip.

Affiliates:
Portland International HR Consultants Ltd.

TSW Assoc., LLC †

1 Selleck St., Ste. 570
Norwalk, Connecticut 06855
(203) 866-7300
Fax: (203) 838-7390
Email: wilcom@discovernet.net

Key Contact - Specialty:
Mr. Frank M. Wilkinson - *Investment management, information systems, marketing investment services, investment research*
Mr. Robert E. Schultz
Mr. Spencer L. Timm

Description: Provide investment advisors, and financial service organizations, also recruit financial professionals for non-financial corporations.

Salary Minimum: $70,000
Functions: Directors, Senior mgmt., Mkt. research, CFO's, Cash mgmt., Risk mgmt., Systems anal.
Industries: Invest. banking, Brokers, Venture cap., Misc. financial, Computer svcs., Accounting

W. G. Tucker & Assoc.

2908 McKelvey Rd., Ste. 2
Pittsburgh, Pennsylvania 15221-4569
(412) 244-9309
Fax: (412) 244-9195
Email: wgtucker@ix.netcom.com

Key Contact - Specialty:
Ms. Weida G. Tucker - *Generalist, diversity*

Description: Generalist recruitment firm with heavy recruitment emphasis in human resources, manufacturing, finance and accounting, sales and marketing and materials management.

Salary Minimum: $60,000
Functions: General mgmt., Materials, Health admin., Sales & mktg., HR mgmt., Finance, IT
Industries: Energy/utilities, Chemicals, Drugs mfg., Non-profits, Computer svcs., Accounting, Human resource svcs.

Tucker Assoc.

1015 Mercer Rd.
Princeton, New Jersey 08540
(609) 921-0800
Fax: (609) 921-1293
Web: tuckerassociates@worldnet.att.net

Key Contact - Specialty:
Mr. John J. Tucker
Ms. Merlene K. Tucker

Description: Retained executive search for client companies in financial services: insurance, banking and securities, nationwide and international. Practice covers all upper and middle management positions.

Salary Minimum: $100,000
Functions: Generalist, Senior mgmt., Sales & mktg., IT, Mgmt. consultants, Minorities, Attorneys
Industries: Generalist, Finance, Communications, Insurance

The Thomas Tucker Co.

44 Montgomery St., Ste. 3085
San Francisco, California 94104
(415) 693-5900
Fax: (415) 398-2208
Email: tatco@a.crl.com

Key Contact - Specialty:
Mr. Thomas A. Tucker
Mr. Andrew Price
Ms. Maryanne Zadfar

Description: Provide a highly personalized service to operating executives and human resources professionals accountable for officer and board level staffing. Eighty percent of our work is repeat business and we conduct no more than three searches per consultant at any one time.

Salary Minimum: $150,000

† occasional contingency assignment

Functions: Senior mgmt., Production, Health admin., CFO's, MIS mgmt., R&D, Engineering
Industries: Generalist, Computer equip., Consumer electronics, Invest. banking, Computer svcs., High tech, Software

Branches:
2465 E. Bayshore Rd.
Palo Alto, California 94303
(415) 693-5900
Key Contact - Specialty:
Ms. Kirsten Smith
Mr. Mark Bentley

Tuft & Assoc., Inc.
1209 Astor St.
Chicago, Illinois 60610
(312) 642-8889
Fax: (312) 642-8883
Email: matuft@aol.com

Key Contact - Specialty:
Ms. Mary Ann Tuft - *Not-for-profit associations*
Dr. Peggy Sullivan - *Library, information centers*
Dr. LaVerne Gallman - *Nursing*
Ms. Betty J. Thomas - *Nursing*
Dr. Patricia Estok - *Nursing*
Dr. Billye Brown - *Nursing*
Ms. Carole Badger

Description: Specialized executive search firm. National in scope, the firm focuses on CEO and key management staff of not-for-profit associations, philanthropic, nursing, libraries and information centers.

Salary Minimum: $50,000
Functions: Senior mgmt., Middle mgmt., Nurses, Health admin., CFO's, R&D, Non-profits
Industries: Non-profits, Higher ed., Human resource svcs., Publishing, Healthcare

Tully/Woodmansee Int'l. Inc.
1088 US 27 N.
Lake Placid, Florida 33852
(941) 465-1024
Fax: (941) 465-0787
Email: twi@ct.net

Key Contact - Specialty:
Ms. Margo L. Tully - *Generalist*

Description: When you engage our firm, we will not establish a client relationship with another business like yours. This is to your advantage in that it permits us to exclusively service your needs and not be blocked from sourcing candidates from any targeted companies in your type of business.

Salary Minimum: $70,000
Functions: General mgmt., Directors, Senior mgmt., Sales & mktg., HR mgmt., Finance, IT
Industries: Generalist, Food/bev/tobacco, Retail, Banking, Legal, Accounting, Human resource svcs.

Branches:
1021 Shadowoak Dr.
Ballwin, Missouri 63021
(314) 227-9052
Key Contact - Specialty:
Mr. Dick Dale - *Generalist*

9 Woody Lane
Sparta, New Jersey 07871
(201) 726-8645
Fax: (201) 726-0167
Email: ldltw@aol.com
Key Contact - Specialty:
Ms. Lucy Lardner - *Generalist*

7220 Rivers Edge Dr., Ste. 101
Columbus, Ohio 43235
(614) 844-5480
Fax: (614) 844-5680
Key Contact - Specialty:
Mr. Bruce Woodmansee - *Generalist*

524 6th Ave. W., Ste. 210
Seattle, Washington 98119
(206) 285-9200
Fax: (206) 285-9299
Email: mbbdtnon@msn.com
Key Contact - Specialty:
Ms. Mary Beth Barbour - *Generalist*

International Branches:
London

Tuttle Venture Group, Inc.
5151 Beltline Rd., Ste. 955
Dallas, Texas 75240
(972) 980-1688
Fax: (972) 980-1689
Email: dtuttle@tvg.com
Web: www.tvg.com

Key Contact - Specialty:
Mr. Donald E. Tuttle
Mr. Dan Meyer

Description: A firm specializing in high technology industries, from emerging growth companies to the Fortune 1000, and possessing international experience and a large repeat client base.

Salary Minimum: $125,000
Functions: Generalist
Industries: Medical devices, Venture cap., Computer svcs., Communications, Aerospace, High tech, Software

Tyler & Company
1000 Abernathy Rd. NE, Ste. 1400
Atlanta, Georgia 30328-5655
(770) 396-3939
Fax: (770) 396-6693
Email: info@tylerandco.com
Web: www.tylerandco.com

Key Contact - Specialty:
Mr. J. Larry Tyler - *CEO's*
Ms. Robin Singleton
Ms. Mary Wynkoop
Mr. Chip Nagle
Mr. Stephen J. Kratz - *Managed care*
Mr. Bruce McClearen
Dr. George Linney - *Physician executives*
Ms. Katie Mazzuckelli - *Healthcare information technology*
Mr. Mark Reinecke - *Managed care*

Description: National searches for healthcare management and physician executives.

Salary Minimum: $60,000
Functions: Health admin., Minorities
Industries: Healthcare

Branches:
Chadds Ford Business Campus
Brandywine Two Bldg., Ste. 208
Chadds Ford, Pennsylvania 19317-9667
(610) 558-6100
Fax: (610) 558-6101
Email: phoffmeir@tylerandco.com
Key Contact - Specialty:
Ms. Patty Hoffmeir
Mr. Bill Wilson
Mr. Fred Hollander

2000 E. Lamar Blvd., Ste. 330
Arlington, Texas 76006-7347
(817) 460-4242
Fax: (817) 460-6991
Email: mhill@tylerandco.com
Key Contact - Specialty:
Mr. Mike Hill
Mr. Michael McAndrew

The Ultimate Source
2147 Avy
Menlo Park, California 94025
(650) 854-1849
Fax: (650) 854-4555

Key Contact - Specialty:
Ms. Jean M. Martin - *Management*

Description: Specializing in high technology industries: computers, software, hardware, wireless communication, networks and portable computing. General management for non technical companies.

Salary Minimum: $85,000
Functions: Senior mgmt., Mkt. research, Sales mgmt., Engineering, Int'l.
Industries: Mfg., Communications, High tech, Software, Biotech, Healthcare

Van Dyke Assoc.
1755 S. Naperville Rd., Ste. 100
Wheaton, Illinois 60187
(630) 221-0191

Key Contact - Specialty:
Mr. Roger Van Dyke - *Generalist*

Description: Small owned-operated firm providing high quality professional executive search consulting services to Christian organizations, manufacturing companies and service companies/ organizations.

Salary Minimum: $70,000
Functions: Generalist, Senior mgmt., Middle mgmt., Health admin., HR mgmt., CFO's, Non-profits
Industries: Generalist, Mfg., Food/bev/ tobacco, Healthcare

Peter Van Leer & Assoc.

15500 Wayzata Blvd., Ste. 1022
Wayzata, Minnesota 55391
(612) 473-3793
Fax: (612) 473-4306

Key Contact - Specialty:
Mr. Peter Van Leer - *Property & casualty insurance*

Description: Retainer search specialized in the insurance industry with emphasis on property and casualty.

Salary Minimum: $60,000
Functions: Senior mgmt., Direct mktg., Risk mgmt.
Industries: Insurance

Van Leeuwen Assoc.

11661 San Vicente Blvd., Ste. 708
Los Angeles, California 90049
(310) 207-6883

Key Contact - Specialty:
Mr. Lee Van Leeuwen - *Real estate, hospitality, retail grocery, service industries, public sector*

Description: Thirty years of recruiting experience in real estate, retail, hospitality, service industries and public sector. Highly adept at working with demanding, owner/founder dominated companies. Small and responsive firm.

Salary Minimum: $100,000
Functions: Generalist, Senior mgmt., CFO's, Non-profits
Industries: Generalist, Construction, Retail, Hospitality, Entertainment, Government, Real estate

---

VanMaldegiam Assoc., Inc.

500 Park Blvd., Ste. 800
Itasca, Illinois 60143
(630) 250-8338

Key Contact - Specialty:
Mr. Norman E. VanMaldegiam - *Generalist*

Description: A small exclusive 100% generalist retainer executive search consulting firm-30 years experience-maximum of three concurrent assignments-5 year no-raid agreement-fixed fee retainer, research driven-minimal client restrictions.

Salary Minimum: $90,000
Functions: Generalist, Senior mgmt., Mfg., Materials, Mktg. mgmt., HR mgmt., CFO's
Industries: Generalist, Mfg., Svcs.

VanReypen Enterprises, Ltd.

P.O. Box 407
Walworth, New York 14568-0407
(315) 986-3042

Key Contact - Specialty:
Mr. Robert D. VanReypen - *Direct selling industry (all functional management disciplines)*
Ms. Shirley VanReypen - *Direct selling industry (all functional management disciplines)*

Description: International executive recruiters with 46 years personal international management experience and 18 years executive recruiting covering all functional disciplines in all industries.

Salary Minimum: $40,000
Functions: Senior mgmt., Middle mgmt., Admin. svcs., Mktg. mgmt., Sales mgmt., Direct mktg., CFO's
Industries: Generalist

Venture Resources, Inc.

2659 Townsgate Rd., Ste. 119
Westlake Village, California 91361
(805) 371-3600
Fax: (805) 371-8720
Email: vri1@ix.netcom.com

Key Contact - Specialty:
Mr. William C. White - *High technology*

Description: Highly specialized executive search firm working with venture capital based and emerging publicly held, high technology companies at chief executive officer and first line functional vice president level.

Salary Minimum: $120,000
Functions: Directors, Senior mgmt., Mktg. mgmt., Sales mgmt., CFO's
Industries: Medical devices, Computer equip., Test/measurement equip., Human resource svcs., Broadcast & Film, High tech, Biotech

Networks:
Marlar International

Verkamp-Joyce Assoc., Inc.

Westwood of Lisle
2443 Warrenville Rd., Ste. 600
Lisle, Illinois 60532
(630) 955-3750

Key Contact - Specialty:
Ms. Sheila M. Joyce
Mr. J. Frank Verkamp

Description: Management consulting firm specializing in executive selection. Assist clients in identifying upper and middle executive management talent for every major industry throughout the United States.

Salary Minimum: $80,000
Functions: Generalist, General mgmt., Mfg., Materials, Sales & mktg., Finance, Engineering
Industries: Generalist, Food/bev/tobacco, Soap/perfume/cosmetics, Medical devices, Metal products, Misc. mfg., Finance

---

The Verriez Group Inc. †

205 John St.
London, Ontario N6A 1N9
Canada
(519) 673-3463
Fax: (519) 673-4748
Email: verriez@verriez.com
Web: www.verriez.com

Key Contact - Specialty:
Mr. Paul M. Verriez - *Accounting & finance, sales & marketing management*
Ms. Lynn Sveinbjornson - *Accounting & finance, human resources management*

Description: Experience, small and personal, combination of skills and expertise, any discipline, strong finance and accounting. When confidentiality is required, when advertising is unsuccessful. 75% of business is from repeat clients.

Salary Minimum: $60,000
Functions: General mgmt., Sales & mktg., HR mgmt., Finance, CFO's, Taxes, Int'l.
Industries: Generalist, Mfg., Finance, Svcs., Communications, Insurance, High tech

Affiliates:
Management Solutions Consulting Inc.
The Nichols Consultancy

Claude Vezina, Conseil en recherche de cadres inc.

417, rue Saint-Nicolas, Bureau 100
Montreal, Quebec H2Y 2P4
Canada
(514) 849-2333
Fax: (514) 849-5619
Email: cv@ergonet.com

Key Contact - Specialty:
Mr. Claude Vezina
Mrs. Veronique Kezerli
Mr. Richard Laniel

Description: A leader in Quebec in senior executive search and members of board of directors.

Salary Minimum: $70,000
Functions: Generalist, Int'l.
Industries: Generalist

† occasional contingency assignment

Networks:
EMA Partners Int'l.

Vick & Assoc.

(Firm declined to update.)
3325 Landershire Lane, Ste. 1001
Plano, Texas 75023
(972) 612-8425
Email: billvick@ipa.com
Web: www.ipa.com/bvick

Key Contact - Specialty:
Mr. Bill Vick - *Marketing executives, software*

Description: National search firm working with microcomputer companies staffing sales and marketing positions with focus on mid level to senior positions.

Salary Minimum: $70,000
Functions: Sales & mktg.
Industries: Software

Villareal & Assoc., Inc.

427 S. Boston, Ste. 215
Tulsa, Oklahoma 74103
(918) 584-0808
Fax: (918) 584-6281
Email: villarea@swbell.net

Key Contact - Specialty:
Mr. Morey J. Villareal - *General management*

Description: Human resources consulting firm specializing in compensation, organization analysis and executive search.

Salary Minimum: $40,000
Functions: Generalist
Industries: Generalist

The Viscusi Group, Inc.

P.O. Box 261
New York, New York 10023-0261
(212) 595-3811
Web: www.viscusigroup.com

Key Contact - Specialty:
Mr. Stephen P. Viscusi - *Office & home furniture*

Description: Specialize in sales and marketing personnel in contract and home furnishings and interior textiles industry. Contract, residential, floor/wall covering.

Salary Minimum: $75,000
Functions: Sales & mktg., Sales mgmt.
Industries: Textiles/apparel, Lumber/furniture, Misc. mfg.

International Branches:
London

Vlcek & Company, Inc.

620 Newport Center Drive, 11th Floor
Newport Beach, California 92660
(714) 752-0661
Fax: (714) 752-5205
Email: mail@vlcekco.com

Key Contact - Specialty:
Mr. Thomas J. Vlcek - *General management, human resources, operations*
Ms. Suzanne Galante - *Medical, financial services*
Mr. Jeffrey T. McDermott - *Medical, finance, human resources, sales & marketing*

Description: 24 years experience as general search consultants serving clients nationally with emphasis in the consumer sector, healthcare/life sciences, and financial services. Preferred provider for a number of major corporations on upper-mid to senior level searches.

Salary Minimum: $80,000
Functions: Generalist, Senior mgmt., Mfg., Sales & mktg., HR mgmt., CFO's, MIS mgmt.
Industries: Generalist, Mfg., Retail, Finance, Svcs., Human resource svcs., Biotech
Professional Associations: IACPR

Voigt Assoc.

601 Skokie Rd., Ste. 301
Northbrook, Illinois 60062
(847) 564-4152

Key Contact - Specialty:
Mr. Raymond R. Voigt

Description: Search consultant since 1978; serves biotechnology and pharmaceutical industries exclusively. Majority of search assignments are for senior level scientists and scientific managers.

Salary Minimum: $75,000
Functions: Middle mgmt., Product dev., Plant mgmt., Quality, Mktg. mgmt., R&D, Engineering
Industries: Drugs mfg., Pharmaceutical svcs., Biotech

Fred Wackerle, Inc.

20 N. Wacker Drive, Ste. 3110
Chicago, Illinois 60606
(312) 641-2977
Email: wackerle@aol.com

Key Contact - Specialty:
Mr. Frederick W. Wackerle - *CEOs, CEO successors only*

Description: National generalist practice concentrates on CEO, COO positions only. Clients include aerospace, financial services, biotechnology, conglomerates, electronic goods, LBO's, entertainment, broadcasting, med. products, new venture start-ups.

Salary Minimum: $800,000
Functions: Generalist, Directors, Senior mgmt.
Industries: Generalist
Professional Associations: AESC

Robert H. Wadsworth & Assoc., Inc.

4455 E. Camelback Rd., Ste. 261E
Phoenix, Arizona 85018
(602) 952-1100
Fax: (602) 952-8520
Email: rhw@rhwadsworth.com

Key Contact - Specialty:
Mr. Robert H. Wadsworth - *Mutual fund management*

Description: Focusing exclusively on the mutual fund industry, we conduct searches for senior legal, operations, marketing, financial and administrative executives. This specialization results in the most efficient and thorough service available.
Functions: Generalist
Industries: Finance, Misc. financial

Wakefield Talabisco Int'l.

342 Madison Ave., Ste. 808
New York, New York 10173
(212) 661-8600
Fax: (212) 661-8832
Email: Barbara@wtali.com
Web: www.wtali.com

Key Contact - Specialty:
Ms. Barbara Talabisco - *Consumer businesses, marketing, specialty retail, direct selling, direct marketing*

Description: Boutique international search focusing in consumer related businesses such as direct selling, direct marketing, specialty retail and not-for-profit.

Salary Minimum: $125,000
Functions: Senior mgmt., Middle mgmt., Mktg. mgmt., Direct mktg., Personnel, CFO's, Minorities
Industries: Soap/perfume/cosmetics, Drugs mfg., Hospitality, Entertainment, Non-profits, Human resource svcs.

Branches:
Mendon Meadows, Ste. 8, Rte. 4
Mendon, Vermont 05701
(802) 747-5901
Fax: (802) 749-5904
Key Contact - Specialty:
Mr. J. Alvin Wakefield - *Consumer businesses, non-profit, industrial, service businesses*

Walker Group, Inc.

5305 Ximines Lane
Minneapolis, Minnesota 55442
(612) 553-1356
Fax: (612) 553-1371

Key Contact - Specialty:
Mr. Walter G. Walker - *Managed healthcare, retail*

Description: The firm specializes in retailing, and healthcare industry searches on a national basis.

Salary Minimum: $75,000
Functions: General mgmt., Directors, Senior mgmt., Middle mgmt., Mktg. mgmt., Sales mgmt., CFO's
Industries: Retail, Healthcare

Wallace Management Co.

P.O. Box 92286
Nashville, Tennessee 37209
(615) 385-0338
Fax: (615) 279-0075

Key Contact - Specialty:
Mr. William J. Wallace - *General management, finance & accounting, sales & marketing, human resources, information technology*

Description: Company created to serve corporate clients in the Mid-South region. Primarily in service sector as opposed to manufacturing. Most business will be done with executives in the $75K to $225K range.
Functions: Generalist, General mgmt., Sales & mktg., HR mgmt., Finance, IT, Non-profits
Industries: Generalist, Transportation, Wholesale, Finance, Svcs., Communications, Healthcare

J. D. Walsh & Co.

456 Lost District Drive
New Canaan, Connecticut 06840
(203) 966-2893
Fax: (203) 966-1296

Key Contact - Specialty:
Mr. John Walsh - *Telecommunications*

Description: Specialization with telecommunication and information services industries.

Salary Minimum: $75,000
Functions: Sales mgmt., MIS mgmt., Mgmt. consultants
Industries: Computer svcs., Mgmt. consulting, Telecoms, Software

Deborah Snow Walsh, Inc.

1500 Skokie Boulevard, Suite 540
Northbrook, Illinois 60062
(847) 564-0089
Fax: (847) 564-0884
Email: deborahsnowwalshinc.att.net

Key Contact - Specialty:
Ms. Deborah Snow Walsh
Ms. Hilary Dexter
Ms. Alice J. Anson
Ms. Lynda Moore McKay
Ms. Ava D. Youngblood

Description: Retained, executive search firm focusing on senior level candidates covering all functions and industries, with the reputation for presenting a diverse slate of candidates.

Salary Minimum: $150,000
Functions: General mgmt., Sales & mktg., Finance, IT
Industries: Generalist

Lee H. Walton & Assoc.

379 Jeffrey Place
Valley Cottage, New York 10989
(914) 268-0292

Key Contact - Specialty:
Ms. Lee H. Walton - *Generalist*

Description: Executive recruiting services for domestic and international clients in a wide range of industries and functions. 24 years of experience with expertise in management consulting/strategic planning, financial services, consumer products, venture capital backed small companies.

Salary Minimum: $100,000
Functions: Middle mgmt., Sales & mktg., HR mgmt., Finance, MIS mgmt.
Industries: Mfg., Finance, Svcs., Insurance, Healthcare
Professional Associations: IACPR

The Ward Group

8 Cedar St., Ste. 68
Woburn, Massachusetts 01801
(617) 938-4000
Fax: (617) 938-4100
Email: thewardgrp@aol.com

Key Contact - Specialty:
Mr. James M. Ward - *Marketing, communications*
Mr. Jerry Grady - *Marketing, communications*
Mr. Lou Nagy - *Marketing, communications*

Description: Our consultative approach to executive search enables us to successfully recruit talented marketing and communications professionals in a timely manner. Our expertise in assessing the professional and personal variables of both clients and candidates has been the cornerstone of our success.
Functions: Senior mgmt., Advertising, Mkt. research, Mktg. mgmt., Direct mktg., PR
Industries: Food/bev/tobacco, Banking, Brokers, Communications, Advertising/PR, New media, High tech

Ward Liebelt Assoc. Inc.

50 Riverside Ave.
Westport, Connecticut 06880
(203) 454-0414
Fax: (203) 454-2310

Key Contact - Specialty:
Mr. Anthony C. Ward
Mr. Michael Iserson
Mr. Rolly Allen
Ms. Joan Gagan

Description: Highly specialized consumer packaged goods, general management, senior marketing management, sales management and recruitment of management consultants.

Salary Minimum: $75,000
Functions: Directors, Senior mgmt., Advertising, Mkt. research, Mktg. mgmt., Direct mktg., Mgmt. consultants
Industries: Food/bev/tobacco, Soap/perfume/cosmetics, Drugs mfg., Hospitality, Entertainment, Mgmt. consulting

Warren Int'l.

(Firm declined to update.)
303 E. 51st St.
New York, New York 10022
(212) 752-7025

Key Contact - Specialty:
Mr. Robert Warren - *Financial*

Description: We are a retained search firm serving the investment management area of financial services for positions in excess of $200,000.
Functions: CFO's, Cash mgmt.

Warring & Assoc.

5673 Stetson Court
Anaheim Hills, California 92807
(714) 998-8228

Key Contact - Specialty:
Mr. J. T. Warring - *Financial services*

Description: Practice limited to retained executive search/business strategy assistance to companies in life and casualty insurance, and related enterprise. Extensively engaged in int'l. insurance regulatory & business-operational advisory services.

Salary Minimum: $150,000

† occasional contingency assignment

Functions: Generalist, Directors, Senior mgmt., Physicians, Mgmt. consultants, Non-profits, Int'l.
Industries: Generalist, Insurance, Healthcare

Branches:
2727 Allen Pkwy.
Houston, Texas 77019
(713) 831-3308
Key Contact - Specialty:
Mr. Benjamin N. Woodson - *Insurance*

Affiliates:
Warring Int'l. Insurance Advisory Services, Ltd.

The Washington Firm, Ltd.
2 Nickerson, Courtyard Suite
Seattle, Washington 98109
(206) 284-4800
Fax: (206) 284-8844
Email: wafirm@wafirm.com

Key Contact - Specialty:
Mr. A. R. Battson - *Senior management*
Ms. Kristina Moris - *Senior management*

Description: In addition to retained executive search, we support our clients with highly experienced human resource and organizational consultants.

Salary Minimum: $60,000
Functions: General mgmt., Sales & mktg., HR mgmt., IT
Industries: Telecoms, High tech, Software

Affiliates:
The Pacific Firm

R. J. Watkins & Co., Ltd.
625 Broadway, Ste. 1210
San Diego, California 92101
(619) 239-3094
Fax: (619) 239-5125
Email: bwatkins@rjwatkins.com
Web: www.rjwatkins.com

Key Contact - Specialty:
Mr. Robert J. Watkins - *Senior executives (for technology companies), biomedical, information tech, software*

Description: We are a boutique search firm that specializes in creating value by attracting high-impact candidates for growth-oriented firms.

Salary Minimum: $100,000
Functions: Directors, Senior mgmt., Product dev., Mkt. research, CFO's, MIS mgmt., R&D
Industries: Generalist, Computer equip., Finance, Pharmaceutical svcs., Mgmt. consulting, Biotech

Branches:
1621 D Placerita Canyon Rd.
Santa Clarita, California 91321-3302
(805) 284-7500
Fax: (805) 284-7555

Key Contact - Specialty:
Mr. Gary Saenger

International Branches:
London

Scott Watson & Assoc., Inc. †
100 Second Ave. S., #200-S
St. Petersburg, Florida 33701
(800) 610-5770
Fax: (800) 927-4716
Email: scott@scottwatson.com
Web: www.scottwatson.com

Key Contact - Specialty:
Mr. Scott Watson - *Banking, finance, law*
Ms. Martha Watson

Description: Executive search consultants specializing in banking, finance and law.

Salary Minimum: $70,000
Functions: Generalist, Senior mgmt., Mktg. mgmt., CFO's, Cash mgmt., M&A, Attorneys
Industries: Generalist, Finance, Banking, Legal, Accounting

Watson Int'l., Inc.
25 W. 43rd St., Ste. 914
New York, New York 10036-7406
(212) 354-3344
Fax: (212) 354-3348
Email: hswatson@aol.com

Key Contact - Specialty:
Ms. Hanan S. Watson - *Energy/utilities, generalist*

Description: Known for high quality service and long and deep relationships with clients.

Salary Minimum: $120,000
Functions: General mgmt., Sales & mktg., Finance, IT, Mgmt. consultants
Industries: Generalist, Energy/utilities, Mgmt. consulting
Professional Associations: IACPR

Waveland Int'l.
1 E. Wacker Drive, Ste. 3630
Chicago, Illinois 60601
(312) 739-9600
Fax: (312) 739-0250

Key Contact - Specialty:
Mr. Phillip D. Greenspan
Mr. Steven Recsetar

Description: Our firm is a relationship driven and preferred provider focused organization dedicated to long term partnerships with our clients and providing a high level of customer service.

Salary Minimum: $100,000
Functions: General mgmt., Plant mgmt., Materials, Sales & mktg., HR mgmt., CFO's, MIS mgmt.
Industries: Food/bev/tobacco, Chemicals, Svcs., Communications, New media, Telecoms, High tech

Branches:
2601 E. Thomas Rd., Ste. 255
Phoenix, Arizona 85016
(602) 553-8400
Fax: (602) 553-8363
Key Contact - Specialty:
Mr. Thomas J. Bolger

2700 Westchester Ave.
Purchase, New York 10577
(914) 253-0800
Fax: (914) 253-0801
Key Contact - Specialty:
Mr. Michael J. Koeller
Mr. Thomas J. Bolger

17304 Preston Rd., Ste. 800
Dallas, Texas 75252
(972) 733-6555
Fax: (972) 733-6809
Key Contact - Specialty:
Mr. Louis A. Freda

Webb, Johnson Assoc., Inc.
280 Park Ave.
New York, New York 10017
(212) 661-3700
Fax: (212) 986-4765
Email: WJFinder@aol.com

Key Contact - Specialty:
Mr. George H. Webb, Jr.
Mr. John W. Johnson, Jr.
Ms. Margaret Chan
Mr. James K. Makrianes, Jr.
Mr. Russell E. Marks, Jr.
Mr. U. W. Runquist
Mr. Silas Spengler
Ms. Elvira F. Ryder

Salary Minimum: $125,000
Functions: Generalist, General mgmt., Mfg., Sales & mktg., Finance, IT, Specialized services
Industries: Generalist, Mfg., Finance, Svcs., Communications, High tech, Healthcare

Weber Executive Search
(a division of Weber Management Consultants, Inc.)
205 E. Main St., Ste. 2-3A
Huntington, New York 11743
(516) 673-4700
Fax: (516) 673-4885
Web: WeberExec@msn.com

Key Contact - Specialty:
Mr. Ronald R. Weber - *Consumer products*

Description: A general management consulting and executive search firm specializing in consumer products, including beverage, food and packaged goods industries.

Salary Minimum: $75,000

Functions: General mgmt., Mfg., Sales & mktg., HR mgmt., Finance, Engineering, Int'l.
Industries: Food/bev/tobacco, Soap/ perfume/cosmetics, Wholesale, Hospitality, Entertainment, Packaging

S. B. Webster & Associates
P.O. Box 1007
Duxbury, Massachusetts 02331
(617) 934-6603

Key Contact - Specialty:
Mr. William L. Webster - *General management, information systems, consulting*

Description: Our success is a direct result of our professional competence in search, our commitment to quality client service and our effective client relationships.

Salary Minimum: $80,000
Functions: Middle mgmt., Quality, Materials Plng., Sales mgmt., CFO's, Systems dev., Mgmt. consultants
Industries: Misc. mfg., Brokers, Computer svcs., Mgmt. consulting

Weinstein & Co.
One Apple Hill, Ste. 316
Natick, Massachusetts 01760
(508) 655-3838

Key Contact - Specialty:
Mr. Lewis R. Weinstein - *Consulting firms, high technology, media, entertainment, convergence*

Description: Founder (MIT, Harvard Business School, Bain & Co.) handles all work; few searches at a time, very high service level. National practice: consulting firms, hi tech, media/entertainment/convergence, consumer products, financial services.

Salary Minimum: $100,000
Functions: Generalist, General mgmt., Sales & mktg., HR mgmt., Finance, IT, Mgmt. consultants
Industries: Food/bev/tobacco, Finance, Entertainment, Mgmt. consulting, Communications, High tech, Software

S. E. Weinstein Co.
1830 Second Ave., Ste. 240
Rock Island, Illinois 61201
(309) 794-1992
Fax: (309) 794-1993
Email: hunter1830@aol.com

Key Contact - Specialty:
Mr. Stanley E. Weinstein - *Executive, domestic, international*

Description: Highly personalized, detailed approach with experience in the development of long term client-company working relationships, worldwide.

Salary Minimum: $60,000
Functions: Senior mgmt., Production, Mktg. mgmt., CFO's, MIS mgmt., Engineering, Int'l.
Industries: Generalist, Food/bev/tobacco, Banking, Accounting, Advertising/PR

Affiliates:
The Beatrice Weinstein Group

D. L. Weiss & Assoc.
18201 Von Karman Ave., Ste. 310
Irvine, California 92612-1005
(949) 833-5001
(800) 862-7743
Fax: (949) 833-5073
Email: dlweiss1@aol.com
Web: www.dlweiss.com

Key Contact - Specialty:
Mr. David L. Weiss
Mr. Roger J. Peterson

Description: Retained executive search firm conducting searches in a wide variety of industries, focusing on automotive, aerospace, electronics, manufacturing, consumer products, utilities/energy and communications. Special emphasis on matching candidate/client chemistry.

Salary Minimum: $100,000
Functions: Generalist
Industries: Mfg., Motor vehicles, Finance, Svcs., Communications, Aerospace, High tech

The Wellesley Group, Inc.
23576 N. Melody Lane
Lake Zurich, Illinois 60047
(847) 726-8100
Fax: (847) 726-8168
Email: wellesley@earthlink.net

Key Contact - Specialty:
Ms. Cathleen Faerber - *All industries*

Description: Retainer executive search firm recruiting for professional, technical and executive level positions in all industries on a nationwide basis.

Salary Minimum: $45,000
Functions: Directors, Senior mgmt., Middle mgmt., Mkt. research, Sales mgmt., R&D, Engineering
Industries: Drugs mfg., Finance, Human resource svcs., Telecoms, High tech, Biotech, Healthcare

Wellington Management Group
1601 Market St., Ste. 2902
Philadelphia, Pennsylvania 19103
(215) 569-8900
Fax: (215) 569-4902
Email: welmgmtgrp@aol.com

Key Contact - Specialty:
Mr. Walter R. Romanchek - *Pharmaceutical, biotechnology, healthcare, chemical*
Mr. Robert Scott Campbell - *Telecommunications, information services, computer, consumer products, new media*
Ms. Elizabeth Ann Kelly - *Telecommunications, information services, computer, new media*
Mr. Joseph J. Panchella - *Telecommunications, information services, computer, new media*
Ms. Theresa E. Hoffman - *Healthcare, information services, telecommunications, pharmaceutical*
Ms. Mary Ellen McCann - *Information services, telecommunications, pharmaceutical, healthcare*

Description: Senior and middle echelon executive search consulting with concentration in telecommunications/ information services, computer, chemical, pharmaceutical, biotechnology and healthcare industries. Consultative services to help clients link management selection with strategic goals.

Salary Minimum: $75,000
Functions: Senior mgmt., Purchasing, Health admin., Mktg. mgmt., CFO's, MIS mgmt., R&D
Industries: Drugs mfg., Venture cap., New media, Telecoms, Software, Biotech, Healthcare

The Wentworth Co., Inc.
479 W. 6th St., Ste. 108
The Arcade Bldg.
San Pedro, California 90731
(310) 519-0113
(800) 995-9678
Fax: (310) 519-8402
Email: info@wentco.com

Key Contact - Specialty:
Mr. John Wentworth
Mr. Ken Bertok

Description: Recruiting department management, on-site contract recruiting, mid-range single position searches. Training for recruiters. Consulting regarding employment department operations and hiring manager satisfaction.

Salary Minimum: $45,000
Functions: Generalist
Industries: Generalist

Branches:
8033 Bolt Dr. SE
Ada, Michigan 49301
(616) 682-9567
Fax: (616) 682-9573
Key Contact - Specialty:
Mr. Dennis R. Woolley

Jude M. Werra & Assoc.

205 Bishop's Way, Ste. 226
Brookfield, Wisconsin 53005
(414) 797-9166
Fax: (414) 797-9540
Email: jmwa@execpc.com

Key Contact - Specialty:
Mr. Jude M. Werra - *Generalist*
Ms. Patricia DeLaney - *Generalist*
Ms. Nora Finnigan Werra - *Generalist*
Mr. Timothy C. Pappas - *Generalist*

Description: Human resource consultants, working exclusively under retainer in executive search and selection, succession planning, performance management assessment.

Salary Minimum: $105,000
Functions: Generalist, Senior mgmt., Mfg., Sales & mktg., HR mgmt., CFO's, MIS mgmt.
Industries: Generalist, Chemicals, Metal products, Machinery/Appliances, Motor vehicles, Environmental svcs., Packaging

Affiliates:
Richard Glynn Consultants Pte. Ltd.
Imaconsult S.A.
Messett Assoc., Inc.

Wesley Brown & Bartle Co., Inc.

(Firm declined to update.)
152 Madison Ave., 21st Floor
New York, New York 10016
(212) 684-6900

Key Contact - Specialty:
Mr. Wesley Poriotis - *Telecommunications, generalist*
Ms. Barbara Mendez-Tucker
Mr. Tom Bartle - *Diversity staffing, corporate communications*
Mr. Jeff Greene - *Diversity staffing*
Mr. Edwin Berkowitz - *Manufacturing, information technology*
Ms. Tina Belvedere - *Administration, treasury*

Description: Nation's oldest diversity and minority search firm with longstanding diversity and military search and consulting practices. Unconditional two year guarantees.

Salary Minimum: $50,000
Functions: Directors, Middle mgmt., Plant mgmt., Mktg. mgmt., PR, MIS mgmt., Minorities
Industries: Paper, Drugs mfg., Consumer electronics, Advertising/PR, Telecoms

Affiliates:
The Center For Military and Private Sector Initiatives
The Center for Minority Professional Development

West & West

(Firm declined to update.)
5090 Shoreham Place, Ste. 206
San Diego, California 92122
(619) 550-3877
Email: westseek@aol.com

Key Contact - Specialty:
Mr. Paul A. West - *Executive, senior management, technical*
Ms. Rosemary G. Cobb-West - *Executive, senior management, technical*

Description: Multi-industry experience with a successful track record; 60 years of experience in filling nationwide jobs; searches are conducted by the principals.

Salary Minimum: $75,000
Functions: Generalist, Plant mgmt., Mkt. research, Personnel, R&D, Engineering, Int'l.
Industries: Generalist, Energy/utilities, Mfg., Communications, Aerospace, Software, Biotech

Western Management Assoc.

8351 Vicksburg Ave.
Los Angeles, California 90045-3924
(310) 645-1091
Fax: (310) 645-1092
Email: cfoforrent@aol.com

Key Contact - Specialty:
Mr. Gene Siciliano - *CFOs, controllers*

Description: With 30+ years experience as CFO and financial management consultant, I work only in the financial management area, selecting only the best candidates for companies seeking top notch CFOs.

Salary Minimum: $75,000
Functions: CFO's
Industries: Mfg., Wholesale, Svcs., Environmental svcs., Packaging, High tech, Software

Western Management Consultants

1188 W. Georgia St., Ste. 2000
Vancouver, British Columbia V6E 4A2
Canada
(604) 687-0391
Fax: (604) 687-2315
Email: search@westernmgmt.com

Key Contact - Specialty:
Mr. Brian M. Morrison
Mr. Roger Welch
Mr. Adrian Palmer

Description: Executive search/strategic planning/human resources/information technology/general management consulting firm. Local, regional, national and international clients.

Salary Minimum: $80,000
Functions: Directors, Senior mgmt., Middle mgmt., Sales & mktg., HR mgmt., CFO's, Engineering
Industries: Energy/utilities, Transportation, Finance, Pharmaceutical svcs., Aerospace, Real estate, High tech

Branches:
333-5th Ave. SW, Ste. 1100
Calgary, Alberta T2P 3B6
Canada
(403) 531-8200
Fax: (403) 531-8218
Key Contact - Specialty:
Mr. Mauro Meneghetti

10250-101 St., Ste. 1500
Edmonton, Alberta T5J 3P4
Canada
(403) 428-1501
Fax: (403) 429-0256
Key Contact - Specialty:
Mr. John E. Steffensen
Mr. John M. Schiel
Mr. Allen Snart
Mr. Rick Harvey

65 Queen St. W., Ste. 800
Toronto, Ontario M5H 2M5
Canada
(416) 362-6863
Fax: (416) 362-0761
Key Contact - Specialty:
Mr. George Toner
Mr. Mike Bell

1004 University Drive
Saskatoon, Saskatchewan S7N 0K3
Canada
(306) 242-6191
Fax: (306) 665-0025
Key Contact - Specialty:
Mr. Brian Pratt

The Westminster Group, Inc.

40 Westminster St., Ste. 300
Providence, Rhode Island 02903
(401) 273-9300
Fax: (401) 273-6951
Email: Westminster@westmin.com

Key Contact - Specialty:
Mr. James B. King - *Financial services*

Description: Experienced executive search consultants working in most industries and functions on senior management and board of directors search. Retained search only.

Salary Minimum: $100,000
Functions: Generalist
Industries: Generalist

International Branches:
Kensington

Networks:
Global Search Partners

Weston Consultants, Inc.
P.O. Box 216
Weston, Massachusetts 02193
(781) 890-3750
Fax: (781) 890-2007

Key Contact - Specialty:
Mr. Edmund J. Walsh

Description: Executive search in all functional disciplines, in high-technology and other industries. Human resource management consulting: organization and succession planning; compensation, incentives, benefits, performance evaluation and professional development.

Salary Minimum: $60,000
Functions: Generalist
Industries: Generalist

S. J. Wexler Assoc., Inc.
1120 Ave. of the Americas, 4th Floor
New York, New York 10036
(212) 626-6599
Fax: (212) 626-6598

Key Contact - Specialty:
Ms. Suzanne Wexler - *Human resources*

Description: Specializing in placing executives at the mid and senior management level in human resources, finance.

Salary Minimum: $65,000
Functions: HR mgmt., Finance
Industries: Generalist, Mfg., Finance, Svcs., Communications, Packaging, High tech
Professional Associations: IACPR

Wheeler Assoc.
19 Berkeley Rd. II
Westport, Connecticut 06880
(203) 454-3370
Fax: (203) 454-1632
Email: STracy@wheelerassociates.com
Web: www.wheelerassociates.com

Key Contact - Specialty:
Ms. Susan Tracy - *Information technology & consulting, outsouring, services, HR, financial shared services*

Description: Focused boutique specializing in leading edge technology executives, consultants and business leaders.

Salary Minimum: $110,000
Functions: Directors, Senior mgmt., Mktg. mgmt., HR mgmt., CFO's, MIS mgmt., Mgmt. consultants
Industries: Computer svcs., Mgmt. consulting, High tech, Software
Professional Associations: IACPR

Wheeler, Moore & Elam Co.
14800 Quorum Drive, Ste. 200
Dallas, Texas 75240
(972) 386-8806
Fax: (972) 867-8591
Email: drmark@msn.com

Key Contact - Specialty:
Dr. Mark H. Moore - *Generalist*
Mr. Robert W. Elam - *Generalist*

Description: A comprehensive, retained national search firm with in-depth research capabilities. A general search practice with broad-based expertise in middle and senior management assignments.

Salary Minimum: $60,000
Functions: Generalist
Industries: Generalist

Wheelless Group
49 E. Elm St.
Chicago, Illinois 60611
(312) 642-1377
Fax: (312) 642-9387
Email: wheelless@aol.com

Key Contact - Specialty:
Ms. Pat Wheelless
Ms. Neysa Bennett
Ms. Darlene Mroczek

Description: The Wheelless Group is a retained search firm serving all areas of the direct marketing community. We accept assignments from client companies who need to fill professional positions.
Functions: Direct mktg., PR
Industries: Advertising/PR, New media, Telecoms

Whitbeck & Assoc.
P.O. Box 873
Stillwater, Minnesota 55082
(612) 337-0887
(612) 430-0096

Key Contact - Specialty:
Ms. Elizabeth C. Whitbeck - *Legal, generalist*

Description: Retained general executive search. Retained legal search serving law firms and corporations, placing partners, associates and in-house counsel. Law firm mergers/acquisitions involve situation-specific fee agreements. Management consulting involves hourly fees.

Salary Minimum: $50,000
Functions: Generalist, Attorneys
Industries: Generalist, Legal

Arch S. Whitehead Assoc. Inc. (ASWA)
51 Terry Drive, P.O. Box 1424
Sag Harbor, New York 11963
(516) 725-4226
Fax: (516) 725-4718
Email: aswaco@aol.com

Key Contact - Specialty:
Mr. Arch S. Whitehead, III - *Information technology (search & recruiting research)*

Description: Our database of diverse sales, marketing and technical information technology and software professionals identified by ethnicity and gender and enlarged by 2,000 additional professionals monthly, supports our recruiting and recruiting research assignments.

Salary Minimum: $100,000
Functions: Automation, MIS mgmt., Systems anal., Systems dev., Systems implem., Systems support, Minorities
Industries: Computer equip., Consumer electronics, Computer svcs., High tech, Software

K. L. Whitney Company
(Firm declined to update.)
6 Aspen Drive
North Caldwell, New Jersey 07006
(973) 228-7124

Key Contact - Specialty:
Mr. Kenneth L. Whitney, Jr. - *Investment management (portfolio), sales & marketing*

Description: Retainer search for equity and fixed income portfolio management, securities research, Erisa and taxable sales and marketing; senior level administrative roles.

Salary Minimum: $75,000
Functions: Cash mgmt.
Industries: Misc. financial

The Whitney Group
(a subsidiary of Headway Corporate Resources)
850 Third Ave., 11th Floor
New York, New York 10022
(212) 508-3500
Fax: (212) 508-3589
Web: www.whitneygroup.com

Key Contact - Specialty:
Mr. Gary S. Goldstein
Ms. Alicia C. Lazaro
Mr. Eugene Y. Shen
Ms. Louise M. Cannavo
Ms. Julia Harris
Ms. Eileen Tierney

Description: Financial services specialist firm focused on capital markets related activities which include: investment banking, sales and trading, research,

† occasional contingency assignment

derivatives, emerging markets, merchant banking, leveraged transactions, money management and insurance.

Salary Minimum: $100,000
Functions: Cash mgmt., M&A, Risk mgmt., MIS mgmt., Int'l.
Industries: Finance, Banking, Invest. banking, Brokers, Venture cap., Misc. financial, Real estate

International Branches:
Central Hong Kong, London, Minato-ku, Singapore

Whittlesey & Assoc., Inc.

300 S. High St.
West Chester, Pennsylvania 19382
(610) 436-6500
Fax: (610) 344-0018
Email: jameshogg@internetmci.com

Key Contact - Specialty:
Mr. James G. Hogg, Jr.
Ms. Barbara L. Lyons
Mr. Robert J. McManus
Ms. Toni J. Ritchey

Description: Focus on assignments with organizations who place a very high value on total quality and who believe that human resource practices and systems are the key to competitive advantage.

Salary Minimum: $70,000
Functions: General mgmt., Mfg., Sales & mktg., HR mgmt., Finance, IT, Mgmt. consultants
Industries: Generalist, Mfg., Finance, Svcs., Communications, High tech, Healthcare

The Whyte Group, Inc. †

4701 Sangamore Rd., Ste. S-210
Bethesda, Maryland 20816
(301) 263-0724
Fax: (301) 263-0725
Email: whytegroup@gslink.com

Key Contact - Specialty:
Mr. Roger J. Whyte - *Hospitality*
Ms. Deborah McCarthy - *General management*
Ms. Catherine T. Gildea - *Healthcare*
Mr. Gene Elliott - *Finance*
Mr. Richard Gardella - *IT*
Ms. Elizabeth Lamond - *Hospitality*

Description: Well-established national firm whose principal goal is to assist clients in obtaining and sustaining the competitive edge. Our focus is in marketing, HRD and general management in the hospitality industry.

Salary Minimum: $45,000
Functions: Senior mgmt., Middle mgmt., Healthcare, Mktg. mgmt., Sales mgmt., HR mgmt., IT
Industries: Hospitality, Entertainment, Human resource svcs., Advertising/PR, Real estate, Software, Healthcare

Branches:
P.O. Box 1765
New Seabury, Massachusetts 02649
(508) 477-2248
Fax: (508) 477-2833
Key Contact - Specialty:
Ms. Catherine T. Gildea

Daniel Wier & Assoc.

333 S. Grand Ave., Ste. 1880
Los Angeles, California 90071
(213) 628-2580
Fax: (213) 628-2581
Email: danwier@aol.com

Key Contact - Specialty:
Mr. Daniel C. Wier - *Professional services*

Description: Significant experience in placement of director and senior management in profit and not-for-profit sector. Over twenty years successful search experience. Personal attention given every assignment. Documented exceptional placement results.

Salary Minimum: $90,000
Functions: Directors, Senior mgmt., Mfg., Sales & mktg., HR mgmt., Finance, Mgmt. consultants
Industries: Energy/utilities, Food/bev/tobacco, Misc. mfg., Banking, Invest. banking, Mgmt. consulting, Human resource svcs.

Wilcox Bertoux & Miller

100 Howe Ave., Ste. 155N
Sacramento, California 95825
(916) 977-3700
Fax: (916) 977-3733
Email: wbmcareer@wbmcareer.com
Web: www.wbmcareer@wbmcareer.com

Key Contact - Specialty:
Mr. Fred T. Wilcox - *Healthcare (financial), operational management (senior), financial management*
Mr. Michael P. Bertoux - *Banking*
Ms. Diane Miller - *Associate management, senior management*

Description: Executive search firm specializing in middle and upper executives, financial managers, financial healthcare professionals, bankers, MIS, human resources, associate management resources and outplacement consulting.

Salary Minimum: $60,000
Functions: Senior mgmt., Middle mgmt., Plant mgmt., Health admin., CFO's, Budgeting, Systems anal.
Industries: Banking, Misc. financial, Accounting, Mgmt. consulting, Software, Healthcare

Wilcoxen, Blackwell, Niven & Assoc.

1918 Harrison Street. Siote 104
Hollywood, Florida 33020
(954) 922-4569
Fax: (954) 922-4594

Key Contact - Specialty:
Mr. C. E. Wilcoxen
Mr. Richard N. Boynton
Mr. A. Ashley McGinnis

Description: Retainer-based firm specializing in senior-level and upper-middle level assignments in travel and hospitality services.

Salary Minimum: $60,000
Functions: Directors, Senior mgmt., Middle mgmt., Advertising, Customer svc., CFO's, Systems implem.
Industries: Transportation, Hospitality, Entertainment, Software

Wilder, Gammel Partners, Ltd.

1901 Avenue of the Stars, Ste. 1800
Los Angeles, California 90067
(310) 203-9470
Fax: (310) 203-9473
Email: wgpsearch@aol.com

Key Contact - Specialty:
Mr. Barry S. Wilder
Mr. Matthew C. Gammel

Description: Specialist firm focused in real estate, investment banking, financial services and capital markets.

Salary Minimum: $100,000
Functions: Generalist, HR mgmt., Finance, Architects
Industries: Construction, Finance, Insurance, Real estate

The Wilkie Group Int'l.

P.O. Box 407
One First Canadian Place
Toronto, Ontario M5X 1E3
Canada
(416) 214-1979
Fax: (416) 214-1980
Email: wilkieg@wilkgrpintl.com

Key Contact - Specialty:
Mr. Glenn A. Wilkie - *CEO, board, COO, CFO*

Description: We are a Canadian based mid-size firm who with United Kingdom based PA Consulting Group, provide executive search and selection services in North America and internationally.

Salary Minimum: $100,000
Functions: Senior mgmt., Mktg. mgmt., Sales mgmt., CFO's, Taxes, Mgmt. consultants, Int'l.

Industries: Transportation, Retail, Banking, Invest. banking, Publishing, Insurance, High tech

Affiliates:
PA Consulting Group

Walter K. Wilkins & Co.

330 Hartford Rd.
South Orange, New Jersey 07079
(973) 378-8877
Fax: (973) 378-8834
Email: waltwilkins@compuserve.com

Key Contact - Specialty:
Mr. Walter K. Wilkins - *Physicians, occupational medicine, environmental health, insurance medicine, managed care*
Ms. Barbara King - *Employee assistance professionals (EAP)*

Description: Medical search boutique. 25 years experience in healthcare (medicine and EAP professionals). Focus: physicians for insurance industry (life underwriting, health, claims) and general industry (environmental health and safety, occupational medicine, toxicology, epidemiology, HMOs and managed care).

Salary Minimum: $100,000
Functions: Physicians, Health admin., R&D, Environmentalists, Int'l.
Industries: Generalist, Misc. mfg., Pharmaceutical svcs., Environmental svcs., Insurance, Biotech, Healthcare

Wilkinson & Ives

100 Shoreline Drive, Ste. 275A
Mill Valley, California 94941
(415) 289-7500
Web: w-ives.com

Key Contact - Specialty:
Mr. Richard K. Ives - *High technology (senior executives, CEO's, board of directors)*
Ms. Suzanne Snyder - *High technology (generalist, senior level)*

Description: Senior level, retained-only firm specializing in engagements at board, CEO and first line of management levels.

Salary Minimum: $150,000
Functions: Generalist, Directors, Senior mgmt., Mfg., Sales & mktg., IT, Engineering
Industries: Generalist, Computer equip., Consumer electronics, Computer svcs., Telecoms, High tech, Software

Williams Executive Search, Inc.

4200 Norwest Ctr., 90 S. Seventh St.
Minneapolis, Minnesota 55402
(612) 339-2900
Fax: (612) 305-5040
Email: wdubbs@kpmg.com

Key Contact - Specialty:
Mr. Bill Dubbs

Description: Highly regarded, Minneapolis headquartered firm representing clients requiring national searches. Member of IACPR. Recent ('95-'96) searches include: president, COO, VP of marketing, CFO, VP of major accounts, executive director of project finance and director of financial controls.

Salary Minimum: $100,000
Functions: Generalist, Senior mgmt., CFO's
Industries: Generalist, Venture cap.
Professional Associations: IACPR

Williams, Roth & Krueger, Inc.

20 N. Wacker Drive, Ste. 3450
Chicago, Illinois 60606
(312) 977-0800
Fax: (312) 977-0159
Email: wrkexecsearch1@compuserve.com

Key Contact - Specialty:
Mr. Robert J. Roth - *Generalist*
Mr. Roger K. Williams - *Generalist*
Mr. Alan P. Hanley - *Generalist*

Description: Specialize in upper-middle and senior level searches-all industries and functions. Specific expertise in healthcare, banking/financial services, electronics, plastics, electromechanical, computer hardware/software/services, telecommunications, aerospace, consumer products.

Salary Minimum: $100,000
Functions: Generalist, Directors, Senior mgmt., Middle mgmt., CFO's, R&D, Engineering
Industries: Generalist

Willis & Assoc.

5122 Spencer Rd.
Lyndhurst, Ohio 44124
(440) 461-3709
Fax: (440) 446-9340

Key Contact - Specialty:
Ms. Francille Willis

Description: Our principal works closely with the client and can customize the search to suit specific needs. Strong experience in manufacturing, insurance, banking and information technology. Unsolicited resumes are retained for approximately six months.

Salary Minimum: $70,000
Functions: Mfg., Materials, Healthcare, HR mgmt., Finance, IT, Engineering
Industries: Mfg., Finance, Computer svcs., Communications, Packaging, Insurance, Software

William Willis Worldwide Inc.

P.O. Box 4444
Greenwich, Connecticut 06831-0408
(203) 532-9292
Fax: (203) 532-1919
Email: wwwinc@aol.com

Key Contact - Specialty:
Mr. William H. Willis, Jr. - *CEO's, food, financial services, international, research & developing*

Description: International practice, hands-on, personalized consultants to management on executive selection.

Salary Minimum: $85,000
Functions: Directors, Senior mgmt., Mktg. mgmt., HR mgmt., CFO's, R&D, Int'l.
Industries: Food/bev/tobacco, Chemicals, Soap/perfume/cosmetics, Drugs mfg., Invest. banking, Broadcast & Film, Biotech
Professional Associations: AESC, IACPR

Networks:
World Search Group

N. Willner & Co., Inc. †

P.O. Box 746
Matawan, New Jersey 07747
(732) 566-8882
Fax: (732) 566-2001
Email: info@nwillner.com
Web: www.nwillner.com

Key Contact - Specialty:
Mr. Nathaniel Willner - *Consumer marketing & sales*

Description: Specializing in all areas of consumer marketing from the manager level thru VP/GM. Strengths are in marketing management, sales promotion, marketing research and sales management.

Salary Minimum: $65,000
Functions: Advertising, Mkt. research, Mktg. mgmt., Sales mgmt.
Industries: Food/bev/tobacco, Textiles/apparel, Paper, Soap/perfume/cosmetics, Drugs mfg., Consumer electronics, Misc. mfg.

Wills Consulting Assoc. Inc.

2 Greenwich Plaza, Ste. 100
Greenwich, Connecticut 06830
(203) 622-4930
Fax: (203) 622-4931

† occasional contingency assignment

Email: jwwca@aol.com

Key Contact - Specialty:
Mr. James C. Wills - *Public affairs, corporate communications, investor relations, marketing communications*

Description: We entered the recruiting field fifteen years ago. Pre-search experience, which I bring to the search process, includes communications posts with a Fortune 500 corporation and world leading consulting firms.

Salary Minimum: $85,000
Functions: Advertising, Mkt. research, Mktg. mgmt., PR
Industries: Chemicals, Drugs mfg., Consumer electronics, Banking, Invest. banking, Mgmt. consulting, Advertising/PR

Wilson Assoc. Inc.

5945 Spring Garden Rd.
Halifax, Nova Scotia B3H 1Y4
Canada
(902) 423-1657
Fax: (902) 423-0277
Email: lbennett@wilson-associates.com
Web: www.wilson-associates.com

Key Contact - Specialty:
Mr. Jim Wilson - *Generalist*
Mr. Chris Schulz - *Generalist*
Mr. G.H. Wilson - *Generalist*

Description: Generalist private sector firm covering the Atlantic Region with national and international affiliates. Strong expertise in the oil and gas and information technology/telecommunications sectors. A memeber of InterSearch.

Salary Minimum: $80,000
Functions: Generalist
Industries: Generalist

Branches:
140 Water St., Ste. 603
St. John's, Newfoundland A1C 6H6
Canada
(709) 722-5000
Fax: (709) 726-9890
Email: lbennett@wilson-associates.com
Web: wilson-associates.com
Key Contact - Specialty:
Mr. Jim Wilson

Networks:
InterSearch

The Winchester Group

100 S. Ellsworth Ave., Ste. 400
San Mateo, California 94401
(650) 696-3266
Fax: (650) 696-3186

Key Contact - Specialty:
Mr. J. Barry Ryan

Description: Recruiting for all functions in all industries since 1979. The firm includes specialists in healthcare, legal, agribusiness, marketing, finance, human resources and operations.

Salary Minimum: $70,000
Functions: Senior mgmt., Production, Distribution, Physicians, Mktg. mgmt., Finance, Engineering
Industries: Generalist, Drugs mfg., Misc. mfg., Hospitality, Pharmaceutical svcs., Broadcast & Film, Telecoms

The Windham Group

114 Winchester Rd.
Fairlawn, Ohio 44333
(330) 867-1075
Email: rj-windham@msn.com

Key Contact - Specialty:
Mr. Rick Jacobson - *Information systems, manufacturing, asset management, insurance*

Description: Dynamic and resourceful firm dedicated to pursuing the best executive talent capable of improving the performance of North American clients.

Salary Minimum: $75,000
Functions: Generalist, Senior mgmt., Materials, Sales & mktg., HR mgmt., Finance, MIS mgmt.
Industries: Generalist, Plastics/rubber, Consumer electronics, Retail, Finance, Insurance, Software

Windsor International

3350 Cumberland Circle, Ste. 1900
Atlanta, Georgia 30339-3363
(770) 438-2300
Fax: (770) 984-5414
Email: windsori@mindspring.com
Web: www.mindspring.com/~windsori/windsor.html

Key Contact - Specialty:
Mr. Edmund A. M. Wooller - *Sales & marketing, finance, general management, international*

Description: Most of our clients have overseas parents or customers. We are glad to recommend other resources if we can not address a client need effectively.

Salary Minimum: $50,000
Functions: Generalist, General mgmt., Sales & mktg., Finance, Engineering, Int'l.
Industries: Generalist, Chemicals, Leather/stone/glass/clay, Computer equip., Finance, Svcs.

Winguth, Grant & Donahue

417 Montgomery St., Ste. 910
San Francisco, California 94104
(415) 283-1970
Fax: (415) 986-1630
Email: wgdsf@aol.com
Web: research@wgdsearch.com

Key Contact - Specialty:
Ms. Susan G. Grant - *High growth companies*
Mr. Patrick D. Donahue - *High growth companies*

Description: Generalist practice focusing on emerging growth and owner-managed companies. In practice our clients are private, public and not-for-profit ranging from start-up to a billion in revenues.

Salary Minimum: $75,000
Functions: General mgmt., Senior mgmt., Mfg., Sales & mktg., HR mgmt., CFO's, IT
Industries: Generalist, Construction, Mfg., Transportation, Wholesale, Retail, High tech

Winston Search, Inc.

16 Greenmeadow Drive, Ste. 305
Timonium, Maryland 21093
(410) 560-1111
Fax: (410) 560-0112
Email: winston@bellatlantic.net
Web: www.winstonsearch.com

Key Contact - Specialty:
Mr. Thomas Winston - *Technical & senior management*
Mr. Mark Hofmeister - *Technical & senior management*

Description: Technical and upper management placement, with corporations worldwide.

Salary Minimum: $50,000
Functions: Senior mgmt., Plant mgmt., Sales mgmt., M&A, MIS mgmt., Systems implem., Engineering
Industries: Energy/utilities, Mfg., Transportation, Communications, Aerospace, High tech, Software

Winthrop Partners, Inc.

2900 Westchester Ave., Ste. 104
Purchase, New York 10577
(914) 253-8282
Fax: (914) 253-6440
Email: winthrop@winthroppartners.com

Key Contact - Specialty:
Mr. Steven Goldshore - *Marketing, human resources, financial*
Mr. Vincent Battipaglia - *Information systems*
Ms. Dominique Molina - *Manufacturing*
Ms. Evelyn Sirena - *Information systems*

Description: A generalist firm with practice leaders in marketing, information systems, human resources, general management and financial functions.

Salary Minimum: $75,000
Functions: Middle mgmt., Plant mgmt., Health admin., Mktg. mgmt., Personnel, Taxes, Systems anal.

Industries: Generalist, Food/bev/tobacco, Medical devices, Misc. mfg., Pharmaceutical svcs., Publishing, Healthcare

---

Wisnewski & Assoc.

3089 Alexander Ave.
Santa Clara, California 95051
(408) 260-0621
(800) 640-0981
Fax: (408) 246-9563
Email: edwisnewski@ejwassociates.com
Web: ejwassociates.com

Key Contact - Specialty:
Mr. Edward J. Wisnewski - *Information technology, telecommunications, MIS, sales*

Description: A national executive search practice with highly experienced business executives with backgrounds in information technology, telecommunications, MIS and sales management.

Salary Minimum: $70,000
Functions: General mgmt., Sales & mktg., HR mgmt., Finance, IT, Engineering
Industries: Generalist, Finance, Communications, High tech, Software, Biotech

---

Witt/Kieffer, Ford, Hadelman & Lloyd

2015 Spring Rd., Ste. 510
Oak Brook, Illinois 60523
(630) 990-1370
Fax: (630) 990-1382
Web: www.wittkieffer.com

Key Contact - Specialty:
Mr. Jordan M. Hadelman - *Healthcare administration*
Mr. John S. Lloyd - *Healthcare administration*
Mr. J. Daniel Ford - *Healthcare administration*

Description: We are a specialist firm which recruits senior-level management for integrated healthcare systems, hospitals, managed care and health insurance companies, physician group practices, associations, professional societies, colleges and universities. The firm's practice is national in scope with increasing business from selected international clients.

Salary Minimum: $75,000
Functions: General mgmt., Senior mgmt., Healthcare, Physicians, Nurses, Mktg. mgmt., MIS mgmt.
Industries: Higher ed., Insurance, Healthcare
Professional Associations: AESC

Branches:
432 N. 44th St., Ste. 360
Phoenix, Arizona 85008
(602) 267-1370
Fax: (602) 244-2722
Key Contact - Specialty:
Mr. Michael F. Meyer - *Managed care, health insurance companies*

2100 Powell St., Ste. 890
Emeryville, California 94608
(510) 420-1370
Fax: (510) 420-0363
Key Contact - Specialty:
Ms. Elaina Spitaels Genser - *Healthcare administration*

1920 Main St., Ste. 310
Irvine, California 92714-7224
(949) 851-5070
Fax: (949) 851-2412
Key Contact - Specialty:
Mr. James Gauss - *Healthcare administration*
Mr. Richard A. Swan - *Healthcare administration*
Ms. Paula Carabelli - *Higher education*
Mr. Gary Hamm - *Healthcare administration*

2015 Spring Rd., Ste. 510
Oak Brook, Illinois 60523
(630) 990-1370
Fax: (630) 990-1382
Key Contact - Specialty:
Mr. Michael F. Doody - *Healthcare administration*
Ms. Kathleen Ballein - *Healthcare administration*
Ms. Anne Zenzer - *Healthcare administration*
Ms. Karen Otto - *Healthcare administration*
Mr. Michael J. Corey - *Healthcare administration*

4550 Montgomery Ave., Ste. 615N
Bethesda, Maryland 20814
(301) 654-5070
Fax: (301) 654-1318
Key Contact - Specialty:
Ms. Anna W. Phillips - *Healthcare administration*

25 Burlington Mall Rd., 6th Floor
Burlington, Massachusetts 01803
(781) 272-8899
Fax: (781) 272-6677
Key Contact - Specialty:
Mr. Michael J. Patlovich - *Healthcare administration*

8000 Maryland Ave., Ste. 1080
St. Louis, Missouri 63105
(314) 862-1370
Fax: (314) 727-5662
Key Contact - Specialty:
Mary Francis Lyons - *Physician executives*

Three Park Ave., 29th Floor
New York, New York 10016
(212) 686-2676
Fax: (212) 686-2527
Key Contact - Specialty:
Mr. Alexander H. Williams - *Healthcare administration, physicians executives*

5420 LBJ Freeway, Ste. 460
Two Lincoln Centre
Dallas, Texas 75240
(972) 490-1370
Fax: (972) 490-3472
Key Contact - Specialty:
Mr. Keith Southerland - *Healthcare administration*
Mr. Peter Goodspeed - *Healthcare Administration*

10375 Richmond Ave., Ste. 1625
Houston, Texas 77042
(713) 266-6779
Fax: (713) 266-8133
Key Contact - Specialty:
Ms. Marvene Eastham - *Healthcare administration*

Wojdula & Assoc., Ltd.

700 Rayovac Drive, Ste. 204
Madison, Wisconsin 53711
(608) 271-2000
Fax: (608) 271-7475
Email: wojdulaltd@wojdula.com
Web: www.wojdula.com

Key Contact - Specialty:
Mr. Andrew G. Wojdula
Ms. Donna M. Wojdula

Description: Executive and management recruiting and contract staffing services.

Salary Minimum: $75,000
Functions: Generalist, General mgmt., Mfg., Materials, Sales & mktg., HR mgmt., IT
Industries: Generalist, Construction, Mfg., Svcs.

Branches:
N7645 E. Lakeshore Drive
Whitewater, Wisconsin 53190
(414) 473-3023
Fax: (414) 473-3092
Key Contact - Specialty:
Ms. Donna Wojdula

D. S. Wolf Assoc., Inc.

(Firm declined to update.)
330 Madison Ave., 20th Floor
New York, New York 10017
(212) 692-9400

Key Contact - Specialty:
Mr. David A. Wolf

Description: Specialists in executive recruiting for international, domestic and investment banking clients, primarily within the areas of corporate finance, sales and trading, capital markets, accounting, operations, research and systems.
Functions: HR mgmt., Finance, Taxes, Attorneys

Industries: Finance, Banking, Invest. banking, Brokers, Misc. financial, Legal, Accounting

S. R. Wolman Assoc., Inc.

133 E. 35th St.
New York, New York 10016
(212) 685-2692
Fax: (212) 889-4379

Key Contact - Specialty:
Mr. Steve Wolman
Ms. Nannette Willner
Ms. Ann E. Fonfa
Ms. Stacey Mann

Description: Generalists with strong specialty in luxury products, traditional packaged goods, design consulting and international. Require monthly retainer, but substantial part of fee is earned when we successfully complete assignment.

Salary Minimum: $50,000
Functions: Generalist, Senior mgmt., Plant mgmt., Purchasing, Mktg. mgmt., Sales mgmt., Int'l.
Industries: Food/bev/tobacco, Textiles/apparel, Soap/perfume/cosmetics, Drugs mfg., Entertainment, Advertising/PR, Packaging

Woltz & Assoc., Inc.

P.O. Box 189
West Dundee, Illinois 60118
(847) 836-9380
Fax: (847) 836-9385
Email: woltz10050.com@aol
Web: woltz@msn.com

Key Contact - Specialty:
Mr. Kenneth A. Woltz - *Information technology*

Description: Over 18 years search experience in executive search and organization development, specializing in information technology.

Salary Minimum: $70,000
Functions: MIS mgmt., Systems anal., Systems dev., Systems implem., Systems support, DB admin., Mgmt. consultants
Industries: Mfg., Wholesale, Svcs., Communications, High tech, Software, Healthcare

M. Wood Company

10 N. Dearborn St., Ste. 700
Chicago, Illinois 60602
(312) 368-0633
Fax: (312) 368-5052
Email: poracky@mwoodco.com
Web: www.mwoodco.com

Key Contact - Specialty:
Mr. John W. Poracky - *Information systems, generalist*
Mr. Milton M. Wood - *Information systems, generalist*

Description: Firm's two retained search practices - (1) generalist, (2) information technology - search practices emphasize detailed research, consultative approach and quality in identifying, assessing and recruiting talented senior professionals and managers.

Salary Minimum: $70,000
Functions: Senior mgmt., Middle mgmt., Mktg. mgmt., CFO's, MIS mgmt., Systems implem., Mgmt. consultants
Industries: Generalist, Hospitality, Pharmaceutical svcs., Computer svcs., Accounting, Mgmt. consulting, Healthcare

Wood, Franchot Inc.

1550 Utica Ave. S., Ste. 425
Minneapolis, Minnesota 55416
(612) 546-6997
Fax: (612) 546-6743
Email: woodfranco@aol.com

Key Contact - Specialty:
Mr. Michael D. Wood - *General management, marketing, finance*
Mr. Douglas W. Franchot - *Promotional marketing, general management*

Description: Partners draw on broad range of experience, most notably extensive senior line management in both large and small companies. We recognize our most important responsibility is to represent the client company with discretion, insight and professionalism.

Salary Minimum: $80,000
Functions: Generalist, General mgmt., Mfg., Sales & mktg., Finance
Industries: Generalist, Finance, Communications, Healthcare

Branches:
379 Dawson St.
Philadelphia, Pennsylvania 19128
(215) 482-3143
Fax: (215) 483-6046
Key Contact - Specialty:
Ms. Linda Bayrd

Wood-Glavin, Inc.

8695 College Blvd., Ste. 260
Overland Park, Kansas 66210
(913) 451-2015
Fax: (913) 451-2017

Key Contact - Specialty:
Mr. William M. Wood - *Insurance*
Mr. James E. Glavin - *Information systems*

Description: A small firm conducting retained searches, developing a close relationship with a small number of corporate clients.

Salary Minimum: $75,000
Functions: Senior mgmt., Middle mgmt., Mkt. research, Mktg. mgmt., HR mgmt., CFO's, MIS mgmt.
Industries: Generalist

Bruce G. Woods Executive Search

25 Highland Park Village, Ste. 100171
Dallas, Texas 75205
(214) 522-9888
(214) 522-8833
Email: woods@cyberramp.net
Web: contractexecutives.com

Key Contact - Specialty:
Mr. Bruce Gilbert Woods - *High tech, telecommunications, healthcare, financial services, hospitality*

Description: Privately owned firm offering 22 years of personal attention to clientele. North American & international practice. Specialties high tech, software, wireless, telecom, Big 6 accounting, real estate, healthcare.

Salary Minimum: $100,000
Functions: Materials, Healthcare, Finance, MIS mgmt., Systems implem., Network admin., Mgmt. consultants
Industries: Energy/utilities, Computer svcs., Mgmt. consulting, Telecoms, High tech, Software, Healthcare

The Woodstone Consulting Company, Inc.

43500 Elk River Rd.
Steamboat Springs, Colorado 80487
(970) 879-1079
(970) 879-5435
Email: wcc@cmn.net

Key Contact - Specialty:
Mr. Edward A. Meagher, III - *Hospitality, retail, restaurants, service industries*
Ms. Linda J. Meagher - *Hospitality, retail, restaurants, service industries*

Description: Highly personalized programs and services with commitment to client success. Strategic staffing, executive coaching and performance effectiveness are only 3 of our specialties.

Salary Minimum: $75,000
Functions: Middle mgmt., Purchasing, Distribution, Mkt. research, Personnel, R&D, Mgmt. consultants
Industries: Retail, Svcs., Hospitality, Entertainment, Mgmt. consulting, Human resource svcs.

Woodworth Int'l. Group

620 SW Fifth Ave., Ste. 1225
Portland, Oregon 97204
(503) 225-5000
Fax: (503) 225-5005

Email: gwoodworth@woodworth.com

Key Contact - Specialty:
Ms. Gail L. Woodworth
Mr. Floyd Hunsaker
Ms. Kathleen Papasadero
Mr. Steffen Brown
Ms. Dalena Bradley
Ms. Peggy Phipps
Mr. John P. Dudley

Description: Team oriented consulting in executive search, human resources, mergers and acquistions.

Salary Minimum: $60,000
Functions: Generalist, General mgmt., Mfg., Sales & mktg., Finance, IT, Engineering
Industries: Generalist, Mfg., Finance, Communications, High tech, Software, Healthcare

Branches:
2591 White Owl Drive
Encinitas, California 92024
(760) 634-6893
Fax: (760) 634-6874
Key Contact - Specialty:
Ms. Alexa Saxon

Dick Wray & Consultants, Inc.
540 N. Santa Cruz, Ste. 269
Los Gatos, California 95030
(800) 525-WRAY
Fax: (408) 436-9696
Email: wray96@aol.com
Web: www.DickWray.com

Key Contact - Specialty:
Mr. Dick Wray - *Corporate restaurant staff*

Description: Retained searches - for corporate retail restaurant and retail business.

Salary Minimum: $50,000
Functions: Senior mgmt., Middle mgmt., Mktg. mgmt., CFO's, Minorities
Industries: Hospitality

Branches:
835 Amigos Way, #5
Newport Beach, California 92660
(800) 967-WRAY
Fax: (800) 915-WRAY
Key Contact - Specialty:
Mr. Jim Walker

1001 Mayport Rd., Ste. 330467
Atlantic Beach, Florida 32233-0467
(800) 710-WRAY
Fax: (800) 711-WRAY
Key Contact - Specialty:
Mr. Jim Osborn

133 Shinnecock Lane
East Islip, New York 11730
(800) 946-WRAY
Fax: (800) 947-WRAY
Key Contact - Specialty:
Mr. Terry O'Halloran

3810 Chippenham Rd
Mechanicsburg, Pennsylvania 17055
(800) 720-WRAY
Fax: (800) 721-WRAY
Key Contact - Specialty:
Mr. Richard Kostiuk

8323 Alamo Rd.
Brentwood, Tennessee 37027-7328
(800) 958-WRAY
Fax: (800) 318-WRAY
Key Contact - Specialty:
Mr. Benny Ball

14027 Memorial Drive, Ste. 152
Houston, Texas 77079
(800) 410-WRAY
Fax: (800) 994-WRAY
Key Contact - Specialty:
Mr. Peter Langlois

11261 E. Big Cotton Wood Hwy.
Brighton, Utah 84121
(800) 610-WRAY
Fax: (800) 610-5566
Key Contact - Specialty:
Mr. Dan Murphy

WTW Assoc., Inc.
675 Third Ave., Ste. 2808
New York, New York 10017
(212) 972-6990
Fax: (212) 297-0546
Email: wtwassoc@aol.com

Key Contact - Specialty:
Mr. Warren T. Wasp, Jr. - *Entertainment, multimedia, communications*
Ms. Nancy Lombardi - *Legal, communications, finance, human resources*
Mr. David W. Morris - *Financial services, marketing, insurance*
Mr. Thomas P. Schneider - *Multimedia, information technology, telecommunications*
Ms. Christiana Zidwick - *MIS, data processing, publishing, media*

Description: A generalist firm with an international orientation. Industry expertise includes media/entertainment, professional services, high technology and financial services. Functional emphasis is in general management, finance, information technology and marketing.

Salary Minimum: $75,000
Functions: Middle mgmt., Production, Mktg. mgmt., HR mgmt., M&A, MIS mgmt., Int'l.
Industries: Generalist, Computer equip., Finance, Entertainment, Legal, Telecoms, High tech
Professional Associations: IACPR

Networks:
I-I-C Partners Executive Search Worldwide

Wyatt & Jaffe
9900 Bren Rd. E., Ste. 550
Minnetonka, Minnesota 55343-9668
(612) 945-0099
Fax: (612) 945-9900
Email: jwyatt@wyattjaffe.com
Web: www.wyattjaffe.com

Key Contact - Specialty:
Mr. James R. Wyatt
Mr. Mark Jaffe

Description: Competitive markets demand exceptional leaders. We are the firm ambitious corporations select to attract high-level management talent typically perceived as unattainable.

Salary Minimum: $120,000
Functions: Generalist
Industries: High tech

R. S. Wyatt Assoc., Inc. †
501 St. James Court
P.O. Box 92786
Southlake, Texas 76092-9371
(817) 421-8726
Fax: (817) 421-1374
Email: rswassoc@aol.com

Key Contact - Specialty:
Robert S. Wyatt - *Retail, consumer products, Big 6 consulting firms*

Description: We provide executive search and consulting services to a limited list of retail, consumer products and consulting firms. Consequently the firm is not blocked from recruiting at many of the country's top companies. All searches are conducted by the principal.

Salary Minimum: $60,000
Functions: Senior mgmt., Middle mgmt., Distribution, Advertising, Direct mktg., Training, Mgmt. consultants
Industries: Wholesale, Retail, Venture cap., Entertainment, Mgmt. consulting

Wyndham Mills Int'l., Inc. †
Two Barrett Lakes Office Ctr.
1825 Barrett Lakes Blvd., 5th Floor
Kennesaw, Georgia 30144
(770) 792-1962
Fax: (770) 792-1963
Email: info@wyndmill.com
Web: www.wyndmill.com

Key Contact - Specialty:
Mr. Cabell M. Poindexter

Description: Global search consultants providing executive, managerial and professional level search services to client organizations around the world.
Functions: Generalist, General mgmt., Mfg., Sales & mktg., Finance, Engineering, Int'l.
Industries: Generalist, Energy/utilities, Construction, Retail, Brokers, Telecoms, Healthcare

† occasional contingency assignment

Branches:
1856 Pembrook Rd., Ste. 4
Greensboro, North Carolina 27408
(336) 275-2622
Fax: (336) 275-3811
Key Contact - Specialty:
Ms. Beth Holly

Xagas & Assoc.
1127 Fargo Blvd., Ste. 1
Geneva, Illinois 60134
(630) 232-7044

Key Contact - Specialty:
Mr. Steve Xagas - *Quality managers, automation specialists*

Description: The firm's market specialty is in the recruitment of individual contributors, middle managers and senior executives in World Class Quality Initiatives.

Salary Minimum: $50,000
Functions: Automation, Plant mgmt., Quality, Productivity, Materials Plng., Engineering, Minorities
Industries: Food/bev/tobacco, Medical devices, Plastics/rubber, Metal products, Motor vehicles, Misc. mfg., High tech

Xavier Associates, Inc. †
1350 Belmont St., Ste. 106
Williamsburg Sq.
Brockton, Massachusetts 02401-4430
(508) 584-9414
Fax: (508) 588-2578
Email: info@xavierassociates.com
Web: www.xavierassociates.com

Key Contact - Specialty:
Mr. Frank X. McCarthy - *Diversity*

Description: Focus in diversity recruiting on a retainer basis. Our research company provides research to client companies and recruiting firms.

Salary Minimum: $45,000
Functions: Generalist, CFO's, MIS mgmt., Minorities
Industries: Generalist, Retail, Finance, Communications, Insurance, High tech, Healthcare

Yelverton Executive Search
15951 Los Gatos Blvd., Ste. 11-A
Los Gatos, California 95032
(408) 358-3890
Fax: (408) 358-8150
Email: yelvrtn@mbay.net

Key Contact - Specialty:
Mr. Jack R. Yelverton

Description: Small, independent firm specializing in recruitment of senior management for emerging high-technology companies.

Salary Minimum: $75,000
Functions: Senior mgmt., Mktg. mgmt., Sales mgmt., CFO's, R&D, Engineering, Int'l.
Industries: Chemicals, Machinery/ Appliances, Computer equip., Test/ measurement equip., High tech, Software, Biotech

Affiliates:
Battles & Associates Pty. Ltd.

Steven Yungerberg Assoc., Inc.
P.O. Box 458
Minneapolis, Minnesota 55331-0458
(612) 470-2288
Fax: (612) 470-3940

Key Contact - Specialty:
Mr. Steven A. Yungerberg - *Investment management, financial services*

Description: Management consulting firm specializing in executive selection and recruitment.

Salary Minimum: $50,000
Functions: Senior mgmt., Mkt. research, Benefits, CFO's, Cash mgmt., M&A, Int'l.
Industries: Finance

Yungner & Bormann
(a division of Healthcare Recruiters Int'l. • Minnesota, Inc.)
6442 City W. Pkwy., Ste. 303
Eden Prairie, Minnesota 55344
(612) 942-5414
Fax: (612) 942-5452
Email: dbormann@juno.com

Key Contact - Specialty:
Mr. David C. Bormann - *Medical device, pharmaceuticals, biotechnology, healthcare*
Mr. Steven J. Yungner - *Medical device, pharmaceuticals, biotechnology, healthcare*

Description: Industry/specialization: medical device, pharmaceuticals, healthcare and biotechnology. We profile both the work environment as well as candidates. Association with a national recruiting firm. Clients only work with a principal.

Salary Minimum: $90,000
Functions: Senior mgmt., Product dev., Mkt. research, Sales mgmt., MIS mgmt., R&D, Engineering
Industries: Drugs mfg., Medical devices, Venture cap., Pharmaceutical svcs., Biotech, Healthcare

The Zammataro Company
P.O. Box 339
Hudson, Ohio 44236
(330) 656-1055
Fax: (330) 653-3337
Email: fzam@gwis.com

Key Contact - Specialty:
Mr. Frank Zammataro

Description: A generalist firm dedicated to high quality, timely, retainer based recruiting. Experience spans 25 years and includes assignments completed in twenty plus industries.

Salary Minimum: $70,000
Functions: General mgmt., Mfg., Distribution, Sales & mktg., HR mgmt., Finance, MIS mgmt.
Industries: Generalist, Chemicals, Medical devices, Plastics/rubber, Metal products, Computer equip., Misc. mfg.

ZanExec L.L.C. †
2063 Madrillon Rd.
Vienna, Virginia 22182
(703) 734-7070
Fax: (703) 734-9440
Email: zanni@msn.com

Key Contact - Specialty:
Ms. Zan Vourakis - *High technology (line management)*
Mr. Peter Johnson - *Professional services, management consulting in IT*

Description: We are a retained executive search firm with over 20+ years of experience specializing in the areas of high technology line management. Concentration in information systems, systems integration, software development and telecommunications.

Salary Minimum: $100,000
Functions: Senior mgmt., Middle mgmt., Mktg. mgmt., MIS mgmt., Systems anal., Systems dev., Mgmt. consultants
Industries: Computer svcs., New media, Telecoms, Defense, Aerospace, High tech, Software

The Zarkin Group, Inc.
550 Mamaroneck Ave., Ste. 310
Harrison, New York 10528-1636
(914) 777-0500
Fax: (914) 777-0536
Email: nzarkin@aol.com

Key Contact - Specialty:
Mr. Norman Zarkin - *Retail, distribution, real estate*
Mr. Douglas Skirbe - *Retail, logistics, manufacturing*
Ms. Antonella Russo - *Human resources, sales & marketing*

Description: National search firm. 26 years of experience. Principals involved in every search. Quick response.

Salary Minimum: $60,000
Functions: General mgmt., Mfg., Materials, Sales & mktg., HR mgmt., IT

Industries: Generalist, Construction, Mfg., Lumber/furniture, Wholesale, Retail, Real estate

---

Egon Zehnder Int'l. Inc.

350 Park Ave., 8th Floor
New York, New York 10022
(212) 519-6000
Fax: (212) 519-6060

Key Contact - Specialty:
Mr. A. Daniel Meiland
Mr. Fortunat F. Mueller-Maerki
Mr. Victor H. Loewenstein
Mr. Marc P. Schappell
Ms. Juliana A. Zinger
Mr. T. Lee Pomeroy, II
Mr. Peter K. Gonye
Mr. Justus J. O'Brien
Mr. Alan D. Hilliker
Mr. Russell E. Boyle
Ms. Gwen L. Feder
Ms. S. Marcella Butler
Mr. Anthony T. Brown
Mr. Carter L. Burgess, Jr.

Description: Professional management consulting in areas of search, management appraisals, board appointments.

Salary Minimum: $150,000
Functions: Generalist
Industries: Generalist

Branches:
350 S. Grand Ave., Ste. 3580
California Plaza II
Los Angeles, California 90071
(213) 621-8900
Fax: (213) 621-8901
Key Contact - Specialty:
Mr. George C. Fifield
Mr. S. Ross Brown
Ms. Cathy Anterasian
Mr. Bradley J. Little

435 Tasso St., Ste. 200
Palo Alto, California 94303
(650) 847-3000
Fax: (650) 847-3050
Key Contact - Specialty:
Mr. S. Ross Brown
Mr. Jon F. Carter
Ms. Susan Darwin
Ms. Susan L. Hailey
Mr. Reynold H. Lewke

100 Spear St., Ste. 920
San Francisco, California 94105
(415) 904-7800
Fax: (415) 904-7801
Key Contact - Specialty:
Mr. S. Ross Brown
Ms. Martha Josephson

3424 Peachtree Rd. NE
1275 Monarch Twr.
Atlanta, Georgia 30326
(404) 875-3000
Fax: (404) 876-4578
Key Contact - Specialty:
Mr. Joel M. Koblentz
Mr. Douglas W. Edwards
Mr. Jonathan Stroup
Mr. Kevin McGonigle
Dr. Ira Isaacson

One First National Plaza, Ste. 3004
Chicago, Illinois 60603
(312) 782-4500
Fax: (312) 782-2846
Key Contact - Specialty:
Mr. Kai Lindholst
Mr. Ronald O. Tracy
Mr. Kenneth W. Taylor
Mr. Louis Kacyn
Mr. Bradford McLane
Mr. John Puisis
Mr. Karl Aavik
Mr. George Davis

181 Bay St., Ste. 2900
Toronto, Ontario M5J 2T3
Canada
(416) 364-0222
Key Contact - Specialty:
Mr. Gregory T. Carrott
Ms. Jan J. Stewart
Mr. David P. Harris
Mr. Jon N. G. Martin
Mr. Thomas E. Long
Ms. Pamela A. Warren

1 Place Ville-Marie, Ste. 3310
Montreal, Quebec H3B 3N2
Canada
(514) 876-4249
Key Contact - Specialty:
Mr. Pierre Payette
Mr. J. Robert Swidler
Mr. Andre LeComte
Mr. Gilbert Forest

Edificio Torre Optima
Paseo de las Palmas, No. 405 Desp 703
Col. Lomas de Chapultepec
Mexico City, Mexico DF 11000
Mexico
52 5 540 7635
Key Contact - Specialty:
Mr. Dario Pastrana
Mr. Jose Sanchez Padilla

International Branches:
Amsterdam, Athens, Barcelona, Berlin, Brussels, Budapest, Buenos Aires, Copenhagen, Dusseldorf, Frankfurt, Geneva, Hamburg, Helsinki, Hong Kong, Istanbul, Kuala Lumpur, Lisbon, London, Luxembourg, Lyon, Madrid, Melbourne, Milan, Munich, New Delhi, Paris, Prague, Rome, Sao Paulo, Shanghai, Singapore, Sydney, Tokyo, Vienna, Warsaw, Zurich

---

Zingaro & Company
(a subsidiary of Preferred Professional Recruiters)

4200 Green Cliffs Rd.
Austin, Texas 78746
(512) 327-7277
Fax: (512) 327-1774
Email: search@zingaro.com
Web: www.zingaro.com

Key Contact - Specialty:
Dr. Ron Zingaro
Ms. Paulette Stepp

Description: An executive search firm specializing in the retained search and selection of senior management for the healthcare industry, including: pharmaceuticals, devices, diagnostics, venture/biotechnology, and pharmaceutical services.

Salary Minimum: $100,000
Functions: General mgmt., Mfg., Healthcare, Sales & mktg., Finance, IT, R&D
Industries: Drugs mfg., Medical devices, Venture cap., Pharmaceutical svcs., Biotech, Healthcare

---

Michael D. Zinn & Assoc., Inc.

601 Ewing St., Ste. C-11
Princeton, New Jersey 08540
(609) 921-8755
Web: www.zinnassociates.com

Key Contact - Specialty:
Mr. Michael D. Zinn - *General management, technology, banking, financial services*

Description: Retainer based search firm, distinguished by its strong commitment to client service, integrity and productivity.

Salary Minimum: $90,000
Functions: Senior mgmt., Middle mgmt., Sales & mktg., Sales mgmt., HR mgmt., IT, R&D
Industries: Mfg., Drugs mfg., Medical devices, Finance, High tech, Software, Biotech

Branches:
1120 Ave. of the Americas, 4th Floor
New York, New York 10036
(212) 391-0070
Key Contact - Specialty:
Mr. Michael D. Zinn

Zurick, Davis & Co., Inc.

85 Tower Office Park
Woburn, Massachusetts 01801-2120
(781) 938-1975
Fax: (781) 938-0599
Email: zurickdavis@earthlink.net

Key Contact - Specialty:
Mr. Peter E. Davis
Mr. Jeffrey M. Zegas - *Healthcare*

Description: Nationwide practice serving healthcare clients including integrated networks, teaching/community hospitals, medical groups, insurance companies, service companies, PHO's, MSO's, rehab/nursing homes, subacute, home health, assisted living, managed care companies, academic medical centers.

Salary Minimum: $70,000
Functions: Generalist, Directors, Senior mgmt., Middle mgmt., Physicians, Allied health, Health admin.
Industries: Pharmaceutical svcs., Biotech, Healthcare

Zweig White & Assoc., Inc.

600 Worcester St., Box 8325
Natick, Massachusetts 01760
(508) 651-1559
Fax: (508) 653-6522
Email: JKreiss@zwa.com
Web: www.zwa.com

Key Contact - Specialty:
Mr. John P. Kreiss - *Architecture, consulting, engineering, environmental consulting*
Ms. Kathryn Sprankle - *Architecture, consulting, engineering, environmental consulting*

Description: Full-service management consultants and publishers serving the A/E/P and environmental consulting industry, including retained executive searches and annual recruiting contracts.
Functions: Mktg. mgmt., M&A, Mgmt. consultants
Industries: Environmental svcs., Non-classifiable industries

Branches:
243 Vallejo St.
San Francisco, California 94111
81 3 5512 4711
Fax: (415) 296-8003
Key Contact - Specialty:
Ms. Chris Lea Catton - *Architecture, engineering, environmental consulting*

1025 Thomas Jefferson St., NW #305E
Washington, District of Columbia 20007
(202) 965-3341
Fax: (202) 965-3394
Key Contact - Specialty:
Ms. Kathryn Sprankle - *Architecture, engineering, environmental consulting*

Zwell Int'l.

300 S. Wacker Drive, Ste. 650
Chicago, Illinois 60606
(312) 663-3737
Fax: (312) 663-4455
Email: info@zwell.com
Web: www.zwell.com

Key Contact - Specialty:
Dr. Michael Zwell
Mr. Ed Westfall

Description: Professional and executive recruiting with a special emphasis on core competency assessment.

Salary Minimum: $80,000
Functions: Directors, Senior mgmt., Middle mgmt., Plant mgmt., CFO's, MIS mgmt., Int'l.
Industries: Mfg., Motor vehicles, Retail, Finance, Entertainment, Accounting, High tech

Branches:
2 Embarcadero Ctr., Ste. 200
San Francisco, California 94111
(415) 835-4337
Fax: (415) 835-1355
Key Contact - Specialty:
Mr. John Francis

Contingency Recruiting Firms, A to Z

Agencies and other firms in executive recruiting operating **all** or **part** of the time on a fee-paid basis payable on placement. Percentages of retainer and contingency work vary; check with individual firms.

The 500 Granary Inc.

105 Robinson St.
Oakville, Ontario L6J 1G1
Canada
(905) 845-0045
Fax: (905) 845-2100
Email: fretz@granary.com
Web: www.mega-granary.com/

Key Contact - Specialty:
Mr. William Fretz - *Generalist*

Description: Our executive search division offers Canada-wide mid to senior level sales, marketing and manufacturing search capabilities within the following industry sectors: automotive, communications, technology and medical/ pharmaceutical.

Salary Minimum: $70,000
Functions: Mfg., Materials, Sales & mktg., HR mgmt., Finance, IT, Engineering
Industries: Motor vehicles, Wholesale, Pharmaceutical svcs., Aerospace, High tech, Software

Branches:
Oxford St. E., Unit 6
London, Ontario N5V 4L8
Canada
(519) 457-0400
Fax: (519) 457-3419
Key Contact - Specialty:
Mr. Mike Johnson - *Automotive manufacturing*

48 Village Centre Place, 3rd Floor
Mississauga, Ontario L4Z 1V9
Canada
(905) 281-0500
Fax: (905) 273-4233
Key Contact - Specialty:
Ms. Joanne Robinson - *Generalist*

O'Connor St., Ste. 1318
Ottawa, Ontario K1P 6L2
Canada
(613) 237-2888
Fax: (613) 237-2070
Key Contact - Specialty:
Ms. Carol-Anne Scanlon - *Generalist*

615 ouest, boul. Rene-Levesque, bureau 600
Montreal, Quebec H3B 1P6
Canada
(514) 861-8373
Fax: (514) 866-6180
Key Contact - Specialty:
Mr. Gille Lavoie - *Generalist*

Affiliates:
Ian Martin Information Technology Inc.
Ian Martin Ltd.

A C Personnel Services, Inc.

2400 S. Mac Arthur, Ste. 217
P.O. Box 271052
Oklahoma City, Oklahoma 73137
(405) 728-3503
Fax: (405) 681-7070
Email: acemp777@aol.com

Key Contact - Specialty:
Ms. Delores Lantz - *Sales, management*

Description: Leaders in professional placements.
Functions: Direct mktg., MIS mgmt., Systems anal., Systems dev., Systems implem., Systems support
Industries: Food/bev/tobacco, Computer equip., Hospitality, Computer svcs., Communications, Telecoms, Environmental svcs.

A First Resource

P.O. Box 15451
Winston-Salem, North Carolina 27113
(336) 784-5898
Fax: (336) 784-6702
Email: siburt@a1stresource.com

Key Contact - Specialty:
Ms. Karen L. Siburt - *Manufacturing, engineering, textiles/apparel*
Ms. Yvonne Easterling - *MIS, information technology*
Mr. Jeremy Henry - *Manufacturing, engineering, automotive*
Ms. Holly Foster - *Manufacturing, engineering*

Description: Providing excellence in candidate selection to those companies who expect no less.

Salary Minimum: $30,000
Functions: Middle mgmt., Mfg., Plant mgmt., IT, MIS mgmt., Systems dev., Engineering
Industries: Generalist, Mfg., Textiles/ apparel, Lumber/furniture, Computer svcs., High tech, Non-classifiable industries

A Permanent Success Employment Services

12658 Washington Blvd., Ste. 104
Los Angeles, California 90066
(310) 305-7376
Fax: (310) 306-2929
Email: permjobs@flash.net
Web: www.flash.net/~permjobs

Key Contact - Specialty:
Mr. Darrell W. Gurney - *Sales & marketing, accounting & finance, human resources, MIS, computer professionals*

Description: Our firm recruits in our specialties locally and nationwide. We are affiliated with 400 executive search firms nationwide, which allows us to source and place candidates throughout the U.S.
Functions: Middle mgmt., Mfg., Sales & mktg., HR mgmt., Finance, IT
Industries: Mfg., Finance, Svcs., Real estate, High tech, Software

A-K-A (Anita Kaufmann Assoc.)

1301 Ave. of the Americas, 41st Floor
New York, New York 10019
(212) 581-8166
Fax: (212) 581-8173

Key Contact - Specialty:
Anita D. Kaufmann - *Lawyers, paralegals, compliance professionals*

Description: We specialize in the placement of attorneys in legal, quasilegal and nonlegal positions with corporations, both domestically and internationally. Industry expertise includes financial services (investment banks, commercial banks, hedge funds), management consulting, fashion, pharmaceutical and consumer products companies.
Functions: Legal, Attorneys
Industries: Legal

A-Linko & Assoc.

(Firm declined to update.)
13467 Wetmore Rd.
San Antonio, Texas 78247
(210) 499-1011

Key Contact - Specialty:
Mr. Jim Lay - *Food processing, engineering, plant/production management, quality control management*
Mr. Raymond Cruz - *Food processing, engineering, production management, quality control management*

Description: Specializing in bi-lingual (spanish speaking) candidates in all disciplines.

Salary Minimum: $20,000
Functions: Minorities
Industries: Food/bev/tobacco, Chemicals, Soap/perfume/cosmetics, Drugs mfg., Medical devices, Hospitality

A. D. & Assoc. Executive Search, Inc.

5589 Woodsong Drive, Ste. 100
Atlanta, Georgia 30338-2933
(770) 393-0021
Fax: (770) 393-9060
Email: hawks@mindspring.com
Web: www.executiverecruiters.com/ searchhtml

Key Contact - Specialty:
Mr. A. Dwight Hawksworth - *Telecommunications, high technology*

Description: Finding the best! Generalist firm that values human importance and is committed to excellence. Search practice covers a broad functional and industry base with typical assignments being in telecommunications, information technology, financial services and human resource management. Creative approach leads to getting the right people in the right jobs in a timely and economical manner... strong client representation.

Salary Minimum: $50,000
Functions: Generalist, General mgmt., Sales & mktg., HR mgmt., Finance, IT, Minorities
Industries: Generalist, Finance, Computer svcs., Accounting, Human resource svcs., Telecoms, High tech

Branches:
P.O. Box 88005
Dunwoody, Georgia 30356-8005
(770) 279-1746

A.J. & Assoc.
1333 Snell Isle Blvd., Ste. 120
St. Petersburg, Florida 33704
(813) 551-0013
Fax: (813) 551-2018
Email: ajnassoc@aol.com

Key Contact - Specialty:
Mr. Joe Walsh - *Retail sales, sales support*
Mr. Andrew Rodriguez - *Consumer marketing*

Description: Expertise in placing sales, trade marketing, category management, sales technology, consumer marketing and minority professionals in the consumer packaged goods industry. A significant percentage of all fees are donated to charity.

Salary Minimum: $50,000
Functions: Senior mgmt., Middle mgmt., Mkt. research, Mktg. mgmt., Sales mgmt., Minorities, Int'l.
Industries: Food/bev/tobacco, Paper, Soap/perfume/cosmetics, Hospitality, Mgmt. consulting

A.L.S. Group
104 Mt. Joy Road
Milford, New Jersey 08848
(908) 995-9500
Fax: (908) 995-7032

Key Contact - Specialty:
Mr. Scott Lysenko - *Banking, finance*
Ms. Lisa Lysenko - *Banking, finance*

Description: Specializing in corporate lending, commercial lending, investment banking and finance.

Salary Minimum: $35,000
Functions: General mgmt., Sales & mktg., Finance, Cash mgmt., Credit, M&A, Risk mgmt.
Industries: Finance, Banking, Invest. banking, Venture cap., Misc. financial, Accounting, Real estate

A.M.C.R., Inc.
83 N. Miller Rd., Ste. 102
Akron, Ohio 44333
(330) 869-0777
Fax: (330) 869-0978

Key Contact - Specialty:
Ms. Karen S. Jacobs
Mr. William R. Hinebough

Description: Executive recruiting, contingency search, placement, employee relations, outplacement, attitude surveys, training, some organizational development interventions.

Salary Minimum: $50,000
Functions: Production, Plant mgmt., Purchasing, IT, R&D, Engineering
Industries: Chemicals, Plastics/rubber, Metal products, Human resource svcs., Environmental svcs., High tech, Software

Branches:
6005 Heron Pond Dr.
Port Orange, Florida 32124
(904) 322-4982
Key Contact - Specialty:
Mr. Randy L. Farabee

Aaron Consulting, Inc.
P.O. Box 9436
St. Louis, Missouri 63117
(314) 367-2627
Fax: (314) 367-2919
Email: aaron@aaronlaw.com
Web: aaronlaw.com

Key Contact - Specialty:
Mr. Aaron Williams - *Attorneys*

Description: Exclusively represents attorney employers and candidates worldwide. Since 1980, 80-90% of placements have been with corporate law departments. Opportunities include: Fortune 100 - small companies, general counsel - staff attorney positions.

Salary Minimum: $55,000
Functions: Attorneys
Industries: Generalist, Legal

Abacus Group LLC
Two Penn Plaza, Ste. 1500
New York, New York 10121
(212) 292-4999
Fax: (212) 292-4998
Web: abacusllc@aol.com

Key Contact - Specialty:
Mr. Brian Bereck - *Accounting, finance*
Mr. Len Frankel - *Accounting, finance*
Mr. Bart O'Rourke - *Accounting, finance*

Description: Specialist in the recruitment of accounting, financial and tax professionals. Industries include (not limited to): financial services (banking/brokerage), communications, entertainment, real estate, manufacturing, insurance and public accounting.

Salary Minimum: $30,000
Functions: Finance, CFO's, Budgeting, Cash mgmt., Credit, Taxes, Risk mgmt.
Industries: Generalist, Finance, Banking, Invest. banking, Communications, Insurance, Real estate

Cathy Abelson Legal Search
1601 Market St., Ste. 300
Philadelphia, Pennsylvania 19103
(215) 561-3010
Fax: (215) 561-3001
Email: CAbelson@aol.com
Web: www.abelsonlegalsearch.com

Key Contact - Specialty:
Ms. Cathy B. Abelson - *Law*
Ms. Sandra G. Mannix - *Law*
Ms. Liz Shapiro - *Law*

Description: An established company whose skilled professional recruiters identify and place experienced attorneys with firms and corporations primarily in the Philadelphia area, Delaware and New Jersey, and also throughout the United States and several foreign countries.
Functions: Legal, Taxes, M&A, Attorneys
Industries: Legal

Abraham & London Ltd.
7 Old Sherman Tnpk., Ste. 209
Danbury, Connecticut 06810
(203) 730-4000
Fax: (203) 798-1784
Email: stu@abrahamlondon.com

Key Contact - Specialty:
Mr. Stuart R. Laub - *Telecommunications*

Description: Middle management through executive level appointments nationwide with emphasis in staffing sales and marketing support professionals. Specializing in telecommunications, data communications, computer and other related hi-tech industries.

Salary Minimum: $35,000
Functions: Sales & mktg., Mkt. research, Mktg. mgmt., Sales mgmt., Systems implem., Systems support, Engineering
Industries: Medical devices, Computer equip., New media, Telecoms, High tech, Software

Branches:
237 Danbury Rd.
Wilton, Connecticut 06897
(203) 834-2500
Fax: (203) 834-9981
Key Contact - Specialty:
Ms. Patty Walsh - *Telecommunications*

B. J. Abrams & Assoc. Inc.
550 Frontage Rd., #3600
Northfield, Illinois 60093
(847) 446-2966
Fax: (847) 446-2973
Email: BJRec@aol.com

Key Contact - Specialty:
Mr. Burton J. Abrams - *Generalist, HR, manufacturing*
Ms. Sharman McGurn - *Generalist, healthcare, marketing*

Description: Can handle searches in manufacturing, front door to back, healthcare searches also active. But a generalist firm, a contingency firm that functions like a retainer firm.

Salary Minimum: $50,000
Functions: Generalist, Mfg., Materials, Healthcare, Sales & mktg., HR mgmt., Finance
Industries: Generalist, Mfg., Communications, Healthcare

Abraxas Technologies, Inc.
100 Alexandria Blvd., Ste. 8
Oviedo, Florida 32765
(407) 359-0020
Fax: (407) 359-9922
Email: michelle@abraxas.com
Web: www.abraxas.com

Key Contact - Specialty:
Ms. Michelle McCosh

Description: Broad ranging consulting and placement company covering all areas of IT recruiting.
Functions: MIS mgmt., Systems anal., Systems dev., Systems implem., Systems support
Industries: Plastics/rubber, Computer svcs., Broadcast & Film, Telecoms, Insurance, High tech, Software

ACC Consultants, Inc.
P.O. Box 91240
Albuquerque, New Mexico 87199
(505) 856-6528
Fax: (505) 856-6472
Email: accdentem@aol.com
Web: www.accdentemps.com

Key Contact - Specialty:
Mr. Jerry Berger - *Dental, dental administration, dental management*
Ms. Virginia Seebinger - *Dental*
Mr. Larry Seebinger - *Dental*

Description: Contingent and retained searches in dental field throughout the U.S. Administration, management and clinical dental functions covered temporary and permanent placement of dentists, dental hygienists, dental assistants and front office management and staff.
Functions: Allied health, Health admin.
Industries: Healthcare

ACC Technical Services
475 Wolf Ledges Pkwy., P. O. Box 569
Akron, Ohio 44309
(330) 762-9188
Fax: (330) 762-1113
Email: acc@accautomation.com

Key Contact - Specialty:
Mr. Kevin Pierson - *Engineering, information technology*

Description: We offer in-house design services and staffing of engineering personnel. Engineering staffing is our forte. 70% of our clients are located in the Midwest.

Salary Minimum: $35,000
Functions: Middle mgmt., Product dev., Production, Automation, Plant mgmt., IT, Engineering
Industries: Plastics/rubber, Metal products, Machinery/Appliances, Motor vehicles, Consumer electronics, Misc. mfg., Packaging

Accelerated Data Decision, Inc.
P.O. Box 152
Augusta, New Jersey 07822
(973) 875-8375
Fax: (973) 875-0706

Key Contact - Specialty:
Mr. Walter M. Sullivan
Ms. Linda Price

Description: A specialized firm working with owners and high level managers. Searches done on a strictly confidential basis usually recruiting from the competitor.

Salary Minimum: $25,000
Functions: Generalist, Purchasing, Sales mgmt., Personnel, Cash mgmt., Engineering, Int'l.
Industries: Generalist, Food/bev/tobacco, Chemicals, Soap/perfume/cosmetics, Metal products, Environmental svcs., High tech

Affiliates:
Hog Sports

Accent On Achievement, Inc.
3190 Rochester Rd., Dept. K
Troy, Michigan 48083
(248) 528-1390
Fax: (248) 528-9335
Email: achieve@home.msen.com
Web: accent-on-achievement.com

Key Contact - Specialty:
Ms. Charlene N. Brown - *Accounting, finance, auditors, employee benefits professionals*
Ms. Betty Gray - *Accounting & finance*

Description: We focus on candidate's goals/objectives. Owner is a former Deloitte & Touche CPA. Offer packages range from $35,000 to $100,000+. Recruiting for staff to director levels in accounting, SEC reporting and audit.

Salary Minimum: $30,000
Functions: CFO's, Budgeting, Cash mgmt., Taxes, M&A, Minorities
Industries: Generalist, Energy/utilities, Invest. banking, Accounting, High tech, Software

Access Assoc. Inc.
1107 Kenilworth Drive, Ste. 307
Towson, Maryland 21204
(410) 821-7190
Fax: (410) 821-7823
Email: hedhntr@erols.com

Key Contact - Specialty:
Ms. Barbara Barrett - *Technology*
Ms. Greta Rose - *Human resources*

Description: We conduct thorough market research to find the best candidates with strong technical skills or leadership profiles and managerial experience. All assignments are managed by principals of the firm with assistance from our market research team.

Salary Minimum: $50,000
Functions: Generalist, Product dev., Automation, Benefits, Systems anal., Systems dev., Engineering
Industries: Generalist, Medical devices, Motor vehicles, Human resource svcs., Aerospace, High tech, Software

Access Data Personnel, Inc.
649 Second St.
Manchester, New Hampshire 03102
(603) 641-6300
Fax: (603) 641-8987
Email: accessdata@aol.com
Web: members.aol.com/accessdata/personnel.html

Key Contact - Specialty:
Mr. Glen A. Axne - *Information services*

Description: We work exclusively in the data processing field. Our areas of specialization include: systems and application programming, database, network and communications, operations and management. We work on a regional and national basis.

Salary Minimum: $20,000
Functions: MIS mgmt., Systems anal., Systems dev., Systems implem., Systems support, Network admin., DB admin.
Industries: Generalist, Computer svcs., Telecoms, High tech, Software

ACCESS Technology

4000 Barranca Pkwy., Ste. 250
Irvine, California 92604
(949) 850-1000
Fax: (949) 262-0386
Email: rnadel@earthlink.net

Key Contact - Specialty:
Mr. R. J. Nadel - *High technology*

Description: Over 15 years dedicated work with California high technology firms.

Salary Minimum: $50,000
Functions: Middle mgmt., Product dev., Automation, Mktg. mgmt., Sales mgmt., Systems implem., Engineering
Industries: Computer equip., Test/measurement equip., Human resource svcs., Telecoms, Aerospace, High tech, Software

Access/Resources, Inc.

P.O. Box 194
Osterville, Massachusetts 02655-0194
(508) 428-4637
Fax: (508) 428-8892

Key Contact - Specialty:
Mr. Peter V. Vangel - *Financial, general management*

Description: Middle and upper management recruiting for industrial clients throughout the Midwest with special capabilities in financial, operational and general management assignments.

Salary Minimum: $50,000
Functions: Purchasing, Mkt. research, Benefits, CFO's, Budgeting, Cash mgmt., M&A
Industries: Mfg., Medical devices, Plastics/rubber, Machinery/Appliances, Motor vehicles, Computer equip., Accounting

Branches:
37450 Schoolcraft Rd., Ste. 150
Livonia, Michigan 48150
(734) 462-3214
Key Contact - Specialty:
Ms. Joan Vangel

Affiliates:
Henry Group
Manufacturing Edge, Inc.

Acclaim Services, Inc.

5445 La Sierra, #317
Dallas, Texas 75231
(214) 750-1818
Fax: (214) 750-4403
Email: info@acclaimsvc.com

Key Contact - Specialty:
Mr. Wayne Rampey

Description: We specialize in the recruitment of object oriented, client server and internet related professionals. A separate division specializes in interactive voice response technologies.

Salary Minimum: $50,000
Functions: IT, MIS mgmt., Systems anal., Systems dev., Systems implem., Systems support
Industries: Computer svcs., Software

Account Ability Now

333 Bridge St. NW
1210 Bridgewater Place
Grand Rapids, Michigan 49504
(616) 235-1149
Fax: (616) 235-1148
Email: aan@accountability.com
Web: www.accountability.com

Key Contact - Specialty:
Ms. Julie Schalk - *Accounting, information systems*

Description: Specialized in superior accounting and information systems personnel for the West Michigan marketplace.

Salary Minimum: $20,000
Functions: Finance, MIS mgmt., Systems anal., Systems dev., Systems implem., Systems support, Network admin.
Industries: Finance

Accountancies
(a division of DM Stone, Inc.)

100 Bush St., Ste. 675
San Francisco, California 94104
(415) 433-6900
Fax: (415) 433-6901
Email: rael@dmstone.com
Web: www.dmstone.com

Key Contact - Specialty:
Ms. Rael Parker - *Accounting & finance temporaries*
Mr. Doug Wasmuth - *Accounting & finance direct hire*
Mr. Jeffrey Starr

Description: We are a CPA-owned and operated agency for temporary, temp-to-hire and direct hire placements. Serving clients in a diverse group of industries, the firm focuses exclusively on accounting and finance.
Functions: Finance, CFO's, Budgeting, Cash mgmt., Credit, Taxes, M&A
Industries: Generalist

Branches:
333 Cobalt Way, Ste. 107
Sunnyvale, California 94086
(408) 774-6774
Fax: (408) 774-6777
Email: Allison@dmstone.com
Web: www.dmstone.com
Key Contact - Specialty:
Ms. Allison Bui - *Accounting & finance (direct hire & temporaries)*
Mr. Tim Wenzel

Affiliates:
DM Stone Personnel Services

Accountants Executive Search

2777 Summer St.
Stamford, Connecticut 06905
(203) 327-5100
Fax: (203) 327-5567
Email: aocstamford@usa.net
Web: www.aocnet.com

Key Contact - Specialty:
Mr. Bernard Simon - *Accounting & finance*
Mr. Marvin Sternlicht - *Accounting & finance*

Description: Searches for accounting and financial personnel in all areas of private industry and public accounting, including financial services - from entry level and staff accounting professionals to CFOs and CPAs; permanent and temporary positions.

Salary Minimum: $35,000
Functions: Purchasing, CFO's, Budgeting, Cash mgmt., Credit, Int'l.
Industries: Generalist, Finance

Accountants Executive Search

2005 Market St., Ste. 520
Philadelphia, Pennsylvania 19103
(215) 568-5600
Fax: (215) 569-2211
Email: jobs@aocsearch.com
Web: www.aocnet.com

Key Contact - Specialty:
Mr. Mark S. Libes - *Accounting & finance*

Description: Through professional memberships, long-term relationships and constant recruiting, we maintain regular contact with professionals who have the experience, skills and bottom-line accomplishments employers are seeking.
Functions: Middle mgmt., CFO's, Budgeting, Cash mgmt., Credit, Taxes, Specialized services
Industries: Generalist

Affiliates:
Millennium Staffing

Accountants On Call
(a division of Adecco Employment Services Inc.)

Park 80 W., Plaza II, Garden State Pkwy.
Interstate 80, 9th Floor
Saddle Brook, New Jersey 07663
(201) 843-0006
Fax: (201) 712-1033
Web: www.aocnet.com

Key Contact - Specialty:
Mr. Stewart C. Libes
Ms. Doris J. Fitzsimmons
Ms. Dory Libes
Ms. Diane O'Meally
Ms. Debbie Buchsbaum
Ms. Linda Krutzsch
Mr. Larry Saltzman
Mr. Brad Violette
Mr. Alexander deGreve
Mr. Ed Blust

Description: International specialists in the placement of temporary and permanent accounting, bookkeeping, data entry and other financial personnel.
Functions: Finance, IT
Industries: Generalist

Branches:
1201 S. Alma School Rd., Ste. 6750
Mesa, Arizona 85210
(602) 644-0500
Fax: (602) 644-9550
Key Contact - Specialty:
Ms. Robin Bumgarner
Ms. Stacy Boase

2111 E. Highland, Ste. B-420
Park One
Phoenix, Arizona 85016
(602) 957-1200
Fax: (602) 957-1222
Key Contact - Specialty:
Mr. John Kuzmick

3500 W. Olive Ave., Ste. 550
Burbank, California 91505
(818) 845-6600
Fax: (818) 845-6330
Key Contact - Specialty:
Mr. William DeMario
Ms. Laurie Matthews
Ms. Victoria Kaleta

The Plaza 1
1921 Palomar Oaks Way, #314
Carlsbad, California 92008
(760) 431-7770
Fax: (760) 431-3709
Key Contact - Specialty:
Ms. Ellen Deason

17700 Castleton St., Ste. 305
Puente Hills Business Ctr. III
City of Industry, California 91748
(626) 912-0090
Fax: (626) 912-8292

1 Centerpointe Dr., Ste. 250
La Palma, California 90623
(949) 739-1300
Fax: (949) 521-6500

10960 Wilshire Blvd., Ste. 1115
Los Angeles, California 90024-3705
(310) 312-3330
Fax: (310) 444-0606
Key Contact - Specialty:
Mr. Steve Shapiro
Ms. Alissa Grand
Ms. Mia Bilbao

5000 Birch St., Ste. 550
Newport Beach, California 92660-2132
(949) 955-0100
Fax: (949) 955-1347
Key Contact - Specialty:
Ms. Traci Carter

The Ordway Bldg.
One Kaiser Plaza, #1030
Oakland, California 94612
(510) 986-1800
Fax: (510) 986-8760
Key Contact - Specialty:
Mr. David Walker
Ms. Sherri Bohlke

525 University Ave., Ste. 23
Palo Alto, California 94301
(650) 328-8400
Fax: (650) 328-8570
Key Contact - Specialty:
Ms. Michelle Pletkin

6140 Stoneridge Mall Rd., Ste. 360
Pleasanton, California 94588
(925) 734-8666
Fax: (925) 734-5550
Key Contact - Specialty:
Mr. David Walker

1650 Spruce St., Ste. 412
Riverside, California 92507
(909) 686-2100
Fax: (909) 686-2662
Key Contact - Specialty:
Mr. Vic Shneider

100 Howe Ave., Ste. 210N
Sacramento, California 95825
(916) 483-6666
Fax: (916) 483-6816
Key Contact - Specialty:
Mr. Ron Garner
Ms. Ann Garner

4180 La Jolla Village Drive, Ste. 200
San Diego, California 92037
(619) 453-0666
Fax: (619) 453-3373
Key Contact - Specialty:
Mr. David Walker

44 Montgomery St., Ste. 2310
San Francisco, California 94104
(415) 398-3366
Fax: (415) 398-2618
Key Contact - Specialty:
Ms. Sara Boyd
Ms. Lynda Galliano

970 W. 190th St., Ste. 870
Torrance, California 90502
(310) 527-2777
Fax: (310) 527-0109
Key Contact - Specialty:
Mr. Randy Wagaman

2175 N. California Blvd., Ste. 615
Walnut Creek, California 94596
(925) 937-1000
Fax: (925) 939-3716
Key Contact - Specialty:
Ms. Lynda Galliano

21800 Oxnard St., Ste. 750
Woodland Hills, California 91367
(818) 992-7676
Fax: (818) 992-1360
Key Contact - Specialty:
Ms. Erin Spitzer

1200 17th St., Ste. 2160
1 Tabor Ctr.
Denver, Colorado 80202
(303) 571-1110
Fax: (303) 571-1102
Key Contact - Specialty:
Mr. Monte Merz

1775 K St. NW, Ste. 290
Washington, District of Columbia 20006
(202) 829-0003
Fax: (202) 829-1694
Key Contact - Specialty:
Mr. Tony Zambrano

1 Alhambra Plaza, Ste. 1435
Coral Gables, Florida 33134
(305) 443-9333
Fax: (305) 443-6589
Key Contact - Specialty:
Mr. Daniel Perron

1801 Lee Rd., Ste. 375
Winter Park, Florida 32789
(407) 629-2999
Fax: (407) 629-2927
Key Contact - Specialty:
Mr. Don Phillips

3355 Lenox Rd. NE, Ste. 530
Atlanta, Georgia 30326
(404) 261-4800
Fax: (404) 233-1853
Web: www.aocnet.com
Key Contact - Specialty:
Ms. Amy Noland

200 N. LaSalle St., Ste. 1745
Chicago, Illinois 60601
(312) 782-7788
Fax: (312) 782-0171
Key Contact - Specialty:
Mr. George Lessmeister
Ms. Nicole Deibert

3400 Dundee Rd., Ste. 260
Northbrook, Illinois 60062-2334
(847) 205-0800
Fax: (847) 205-1230
Key Contact - Specialty:
Ms. Bridget O'Connell
Ms. Cheryl Scassellati

1 Lincoln Centre, Ste. 1108
Oakbrook Terrace, Illinois 60181
(630) 261-1300
Fax: (630) 261-1334
Key Contact - Specialty:
Ms. Alison Gentry

1750 E. Golf Rd., Ste. 200
Schaumburg, Illinois 60173
(847) 413-8800
Fax: (847) 413-9066
Key Contact - Specialty:
Mr. Carl Barnard

111 Monument Circle, Ste. 3510
Bank 1 Center/Tower
Indianapolis, Indiana 46204
(317) 686-0001
Fax: (317) 686-0007
Key Contact - Specialty:
Ms. Vicki Herrod
Ms. Diana Koester

The Springs Office Ctr.
950 Breckenridge Lane, #175
Louisville, Kentucky 40207
(502) 893-8333
Fax: (502) 893-5599
Key Contact - Specialty:
Ms. Janet Newcomb

201 N. Charles St., #1106
Baltimore, Maryland 21202
(410) 685-5700
Fax: (410) 685-5736
Key Contact - Specialty:
Mr. David Watson

15200 Shady Grove Rd., Ste. 350 #12
Rockville, Maryland 20850
(301) 519-2300
Fax: (301) 519-3637
Key Contact - Specialty:
Mr. John Ryder

99 Summer St., Ste. 1240
Boston, Massachusetts 02110
(617) 345-0440
Fax: (617) 345-0423
Key Contact - Specialty:
Ms. Lynn Cogavin

28411 Northwestern Hwy., Ste. 910
Southfield, Michigan 48034
(248) 356-0660
Fax: (248) 356-8740
Key Contact - Specialty:
Ms. Vicki Herrod
Ms. Rachelle Iaquinto

2301 W. Big Beaver Rd., Ste. 105
Troy, Michigan 48084
(248) 649-0700
Fax: (248) 649-5110
Key Contact - Specialty:
Ms. Vicki Herrod

45 S. 7th St., Ste. 3004
Plaza VII Bldg.
Minneapolis, Minnesota 55402
(612) 341-9900
Fax: (612) 341-3284
Key Contact - Specialty:
Ms. Darlene Kluck

911 Main St., Ste. 620
Commerce Twr.
Kansas City, Missouri 64105
(816) 421-7774
Fax: (816) 421-8224
Key Contact - Specialty:
Ms. Brenda Hunzeker

515 N. 6th St., Ste. 1340, 1 City Centre
St. Louis, Missouri 63101
(314) 436-0500
Fax: (314) 436-0833
Key Contact - Specialty:
Ms. Debra CoHen

10805 Sunset Office Drive, Ste. 208
Sunset Hills, Missouri 63127
(314) 966-4900
Fax: (314) 966-6663
Key Contact - Specialty:
Mr. Scott Scheibel

111 Westport Plaza, Ste. 512
Westport, Missouri 63146
(314) 576-0006
Fax: (314) 576-7345
Key Contact - Specialty:
Mr. Louis Hanses

6787 W. Tropicana Ave., Ste. 239
Las Vegas, Nevada 89103
(702) 284-7112
Fax: (702) 284-7191
Key Contact - Specialty:
Ms. Donna Kelly

379 Thornall St., 10th Floor
Edison, New Jersey 08837
(732) 321-1700
Fax: (732) 494-4386
Key Contact - Specialty:
Mr. Ted Fitzgerald

30 Montgomery St., Ste. 620
Jersey City, New Jersey 07302
(201) 333-4227
Fax: (201) 333-4248
Key Contact - Specialty:
Ms. Mary Berntsen

354 Eisenhower Pkwy.
Livingston, New Jersey 07039
(973) 533-0600
Fax: (973) 533-1504
Key Contact - Specialty:
Ms. Rita Silverstein

The Atrium, E. 80 Rte. 4, Ste. 230
Paramus, New Jersey 07652
(201) 843-8882
Fax: (201) 843-8572
Key Contact - Specialty:
Ms. Bess Epstein
Ms. Donna Mahan
Mr. Neil Lebovits

136 Main St.
Princeton, New Jersey 08540
(609) 452-7117
Fax: (609) 987-0681
Key Contact - Specialty:
Mr. Robert Meixner

450 Harmon Meadow Blvd., 1st Floor
Secaucus, New Jersey 07094
(201) 330-0080
Fax: (201) 330-8729
Key Contact - Specialty:
Mr. Eric Alpern
Mr. Louis Schuckman

500 N. Broadway, Ste. 237
The Jericho Atrium
Jericho, New York 11753
(516) 935-0050
Fax: (516) 935-1343
Key Contact - Specialty:
Ms. Sheila Frank
Ms. Melissa Bindrim

535 Fifth Ave. #1200
New York, New York 10017
(212) 953-7400
Fax: (212) 953-8921
Key Contact - Specialty:
Mr. Bernard M. Simon

227 W. Trade St., Ste. 1810
The Carillon Bldg.
Charlotte, North Carolina 28202
(704) 376-0006
Fax: (704) 376-4787
Key Contact - Specialty:
Ms. Patricia Comer

1801 Stanley Rd., Ste. 206
Greensboro, North Carolina 27407
(336) 292-3800
Fax: (336) 292-2245
Key Contact - Specialty:
Mr. Larry Basel

5540 Centerview Drive, Ste. 208
Raleigh, North Carolina 27606
(919) 859-5550
Fax: (919) 859-5575
Key Contact - Specialty:
Mr. Mark Gregory
Mr. Anthony Caggiano

250 E. Fifth St., Ste. 1630
Chiquita Ctr.
Cincinnati, Ohio 45202
(513) 381-4545
Fax: (513) 381-4672
Key Contact - Specialty:
Mr. Gary Merrifield
Mr. Joseph Vitale

10260 Alliance Rd. #130
Cincinnati, Ohio 45242
(513) 791-4300
Fax: (513) 791-9299
Key Contact - Specialty:
Ms. Heather Ray

700 Ackerman Rd., Ste. 390
Columbus, Ohio 43202
(614) 267-7200
Fax: (614) 267-7595
Key Contact - Specialty:
Mr. Russell Sheets

Rockside Square II
6133 Rockside Rd., #206
Independence, Ohio 44131
(216) 328-0888
Fax: (216) 328-1709
Key Contact - Specialty:
Mr. Michael Golenberke

222 SW Columbia St., Ste. 1115
Portland, Oregon 97201
(503) 228-0400
Fax: (503) 220-2529
Key Contact - Specialty:
Mr. David Adams
Mr. Martin Ryan

1150 First Ave., Ste. 482
Parkview Twr.
King of Prussia, Pennsylvania 19406
(610) 337-8500
Fax: (610) 337-7344
Key Contact - Specialty:
Mr. Mark S. Libes

The Frick Bldg.
437 Grant St., Ste. 1615A
Pittsburgh, Pennsylvania 15219
(412) 391-0900
Fax: (412) 391-8288
Key Contact - Specialty:
Mr. Robert Fleming

10 Weybosset St., Ste. 201
Providence, Rhode Island 02903
(401) 277-9944
Fax: (401) 277-0660
Key Contact - Specialty:
Ms. Linda Meschke
Mr. Michael Alcott

250 Commonwealth Drive, Ste. 104
Greenville, South Carolina 29607
(864) 987-0123
Fax: (864) 288-3044
Key Contact - Specialty:
Ms. Angela Tucker

8310 Capital of Texas Hwy. N., Ste. 150
Austin, Texas 78731
(512) 346-6000
Fax: (512) 346-6683
Key Contact - Specialty:
Mr. Lace Archibald

2828 Routh St., Ste. 690
Quadrangle Bldg.
Dallas, Texas 75201
(214) 979-9001
Fax: (214) 969-0046
Key Contact - Specialty:
Ms. Karen Vang
Ms. Kay Morgan

5550 LBJ Frwy., Ste. 310
Dallas, Texas 75240
(972) 980-4184
Fax: (972) 980-2359
Key Contact - Specialty:
Mr. Doug Hall

1200 Summit Ave., #306
Ft. Worth, Texas 76102-3182
(817) 870-1800
Fax: (817) 870-1890
Key Contact - Specialty:
Mr. Mark Wegesin

1990 Post Oak Blvd., Ste. 720
Houston, Texas 77056
(713) 961-5603
Fax: (713) 961-3256
Key Contact - Specialty:
Mr. Richard Thompson

170 S. Main St., Ste. 550
Salt Lake City, Utah 84101
(801) 328-3338
Fax: (801) 328-3324
Key Contact - Specialty:
Ms. Sara Boyd

701 E. Franklin St., Ste. 1408
Richmond, Virginia 23219
(804) 225-0200
Fax: (804) 225-0217
Key Contact - Specialty:
Ms. Jean Jordan

8000 Towers Crescent Drive, Ste. 825
Vienna, Virginia 22182
(703) 448-7500
Fax: (703) 448-7538
Key Contact - Specialty:
Mr. Michael Parbs
Ms. Susan Gallagher

600 108th Ave. NE, Ste. 650
Bellevue, Washington 98004
(425) 635-0700
Fax: (425) 635-0315
Key Contact - Specialty:
Mr. David Adams

601 Union St., Two Union Sq.
Seattle, Washington 98101
(206) 467-0700
Fax: (206) 467-9986
Key Contact - Specialty:
Ms. Jeaneen Reinhart
Ms. Shauna Menner

3333 N. Mayfair Rd., Ste. 213
Milwaukee, Wisconsin 53222
(414) 771-1900
Fax: (414) 771-2586
Key Contact - Specialty:
Ms. Dottie Mahnke

1730-505 Burrard St.
Vancouver, British Columbia V7X 1M4
Canada
(604) 669-9096
Fax: (604) 669-9196
Key Contact - Specialty:
Ms. Paula Hollander

Toronto Dominion Center Royal #2522
Royal Trust Tower- 77 King St. W.
Toronto, Ontario M5K 1K2
Canada
(416) 363-7747
Fax: (416) 363-8499
Key Contact - Specialty:
Ms. Anna Marie Hubbard

International Branches:
Leeds, London, Richmond

Affiliates:
Financial Operations Group
Millennium Staffing
MIS Search

Accountants Executive Search

2001 Gateway Place, Ste. 200
San Jose, California 95110
(408) 437-9779
Fax: (408) 437-0716
Web: www.aocnet.com

Key Contact - Specialty:
Mr. Nick Schichtle - *Accounting, finance*

Description: Nationwide firm specializing in recruitment and placement of accounting and finance professionals.
Functions: Finance, CFO's, Budgeting, Cash mgmt., Credit, Taxes, M&A
Industries: Generalist, Mfg., Svcs., Communications, High tech, Software, Biotech

Accountants On Call

1715 N. Westshore Blvd., Ste. 460
Westshore Ctr.
Tampa, Florida 33607
(813) 289-0051
Fax: (813) 289-6004

Key Contact - Specialty:
Mr. Jeffrey Waldon - *Accounting personnel*
Ms. Maita Waldon - *Bookkeeping personnel*

Description: Our knowledge of accounting and finance enables us to test, screen and qualify only the best candidates available. We offer the most professional service and follow through in our industry.
Functions: Generalist, CFO's, Budgeting, Cash mgmt., Credit, Taxes, M&A
Industries: Finance, Misc. financial, Accounting, Insurance, Real estate, High tech, Healthcare

Accountants On Call

1101 Kermit Drive, Ste. 600
Nashville, Tennessee 37217
(615) 399-0200
Fax: (615) 399-2285
Email: aocjobs@bellsouth.net

Key Contact - Specialty:
Mr. Milton H. Ellis - *Accounting*

Description: Full service accounting and finance placements.
Functions: CFO's, Budgeting, Cash mgmt., Credit, Taxes, M&A, Risk mgmt.
Industries: Generalist

Accounting & Bookkeeping Personnel, Inc.

1702 E. Highland Ave., Ste. 200
Phoenix, Arizona 85016
(602) 277-3700
Fax: (602) 277-8212
Email: ActgAndBkp@aol.com
Web: www.aafa.com

Key Contact - Specialty:
Mr. Michael Nolan - *Accounting & finance*
Ms. Marybeth Howard - *Accounting & finance*

Description: Firm is owned and operated by accountants. We specialize in placing accountants in permanent or temporary positions.

Salary Minimum: $40,000
Functions: CFO's, Budgeting, Cash mgmt., Credit, Taxes, M&A, Risk mgmt.
Industries: Generalist

Branches:
4400 E. Broadway, Ste. 600
Tucson, Arizona 85711
(602) 323-3600
Fax: (602) 795-4753
Email: ActgAndBkp@aol.com
Web: www.AAFA.com
Key Contact - Specialty:
Mr. Duane Etter - *Accounting & finance*

Accounting & Computer Personnel
200 Salina Meadows Pkwy., Ste. 180
Syracuse, New York 13212
(315) 457-8000
Fax: (315) 457-0029
Email: wew@a-c-p.com
Web: www.a-c-p.com

Key Contact - Specialty:
Mr. William E. Winnewisser - *Computer (IS), technical & management professionals, accounting & financial management professionals, bankers, business attorneys*

Description: Over twenty-five years experience in recruitment and placement of professionals in: accounting, financial management, computer systems, programming and operations, information systems management, computer hardware/software sales and banking.

Salary Minimum: $20,000
Functions: Finance, IT, Mgmt. consultants, Attorneys
Industries: Generalist

Accounting Additions
1000 Fourth St., Ste. 150
San Rafael, California 94901
(415) 459-2300
Fax: (415) 459-2471
Email: acctadd@dnai.com

Key Contact - Specialty:
Mr. Neil L. Kreuzberger

Description: We continue to be a leading Bay Area supplier of temporary, contract and permanent professionals in the accounting and finance arenas.

Salary Minimum: $30,000
Functions: CFO's, Budgeting, Cash mgmt., Credit, Taxes
Industries: Generalist, Food/bev/tobacco, Computer equip., Finance, Real estate, High tech, Software

Branches:
115 Sansome St., Ste. 1200
San Francisco, California 94104
(415) 398-3995
Key Contact - Specialty:
Mr. Chris Rand - *Accounting & finance (contract & full-time)*

Accounting Personnel & Engineering Personnel Consultants
210 Baronne St., Ste. 922
New Orleans, Louisiana 70112
(504) 581-7800
(504) 581-1400
Fax: (504) 568-1222
Email: apcepc@apcepc.com
Web: www.apcepc.com

Key Contact - Specialty:
Mr. Frank Loria - *Accounting, information systems, engineering*

Description: Twenty-seven years of specialization in full time and temporary placement of accounting and financial executives, information systems professionals, bookkeeping and clerical personnel.
Functions: General mgmt., HR mgmt., Finance, IT, Engineering
Industries: Generalist, Energy/utilities, Wholesale, Finance, Svcs., Communications

---

Ackerman Johnson Inc.
333 N. Sam Houston Pkwy. E., Ste. 1210
Houston, Texas 77060
(281) 999-8879
Fax: (281) 999-7570
Email: ajhoust@ackermanjohnson.com
Web: www.ackermanjohnson.com

Key Contact - Specialty:
Mr. Frederick W. Stang

Description: We specialize in sales, sales management, marketing and marketing management positions in medical, pharmaceutical, voice and data communications, consulting, computer hardware/software, business products/services, industrial, consumer products and energy.
Functions: Senior mgmt., Middle mgmt., Distribution, Mktg. mgmt., Sales mgmt., Mgmt. consultants, Int'l.
Industries: Medical devices, Computer equip., Hospitality, Pharmaceutical svcs., Mgmt. consulting, Telecoms, Software

---

ACSYS Resources, Inc.
1300 Market St., Ste. 501
Wilmington, Delaware 19801
(302) 658-6181
Email: dom@acsysresources.com
Web: www.@acsysresources.com

Key Contact - Specialty:
Mr. Domenic L. Vacca - *Accounting, finance, financial services, data processing, human resources*

Description: Permanent/temp/contract specialists in accounting, finance, banking and data processing - contingency and retainer.

Salary Minimum: $15,000
Functions: Mkt. research, Customer svc., HR mgmt., IT, Systems anal., Systems dev., Systems implem.
Industries: Drugs mfg., Invest. banking, Brokers, Broadcast & Film, Telecoms, Real estate, Software

Branches:
1300 Market St., Ste. 501
Wilmington, Delaware 19801
(302) 658-6181
Email: dom@acsysresources.com
Web: www.acsysresources.com
Key Contact - Specialty:
Mr. Domenic L. Vacca - *Accounting, finance, financial services, banking, information technology*

1820 Chapel Avenue W., Ste. 168
Cherry Hill, New Jersey 08002
(609) 910-1824
Email: info@acsysresources.com
Key Contact - Specialty:
Mr. Michael Shedroff - *Accounting, finance, financial services, banking, information technology*

379 Thornall St., Sixth Floor
Edison, New Jersey 08837
(732) 205-1900
Email: info@acsysresources.com
Key Contact - Specialty:
Mr. Ben V. Holsopple - *Financial systems, information technology, business consulting services, project management*

120 Wood Ave. S., Ste. 200
Iselin, New Jersey 08830
(908) 494-8686
Key Contact - Specialty:
Ms. Lisa Lucifero - *Accounting, finance, financial services, data processing*

5 Independence Way
Princeton, New Jersey 08540
(610) 452-6448
Email: info@acsysresources.com
Key Contact - Specialty:
Mr. Ben V. Holsopple - *Financial systems, information technology, business consulting services, project management*

1850 William Penn Way, Ste. 106
Lancaster, Pennsylvania 17601
(717) 390-0888
Email: info@acsysresources.com
Key Contact - Specialty:
Ms. Jill Smith - *Accounting, finance, financial services, banking, information technology*

1700 Market St., Ste. 3110
Philadelphia, Pennsylvania 19103
(215) 568-6810
Email: info@acsysresources.com
Key Contact - Specialty:
Mr. Harry Sauer - *Accounting, finance, financial services, banking, information technology*

500 E. Swedesford Rd., Ste. 100
Wayne, Pennsylvania 19087
(610) 687-6107
Email: info@acsysresources.com
Key Contact - Specialty:
Mr. David Laderman - *Accounting, finance, financial services, banking, information technology*

Action Executive Personnel Consulting Inc.
365 Bay St., Ste. 304
Toronto, Ontario M5H 2V1
Canada
(416) 363-1399
Fax: (416) 363-9271
Email: aepi@passport.ca
Web: www.actionex.com

Key Contact - Specialty:
Mr. Dennis Black - *Information systems*
Ms. Wallamena Folletta - *Information systems, clerical*
Mr. Marc Roberts - *Information systems*

Description: Recruitment of permanent and contract information systems professionals.

Salary Minimum: $40,000
Functions: Directors, Mktg. mgmt., Systems dev., Systems support, Network admin., DB admin., Mgmt. consultants

Action Management Corp.
915 S. Grand Traverse St.
Flint, Michigan 48502
(810) 234-2828
Fax: (810) 234-5159
Email: info@ActionManagement.com
Web: www.ActionManagement.com

Key Contact - Specialty:
Ms. Valerie L. June - *Women, minorities*

Description: Minority-owned firm specializing in recruitment of minorities and women. We'll provide you with a complete and precise analysis of each candidate's skills, expertise, interests, goals and salary requirements.

Salary Minimum: $30,000
Functions: Senior mgmt., Middle mgmt., Plant mgmt., Sales mgmt., Personnel, MIS mgmt., Engineering
Industries: Generalist, Machinery/Appliances, Motor vehicles, Human resource svcs., Communications, Telecoms, Software

Branches:
1655 N. Fort Myer Dr., Ste. 700
Arlington, Virginia 22209
(800) 771-8571
Fax: (810) 234-5159
Key Contact - Specialty:
Ms. Claude High - *Minorities, women*

Active Search & Placement Inc.
2041 Business Ctr. Drive, Ste. 102
Irvine, California 92612
(949) 833-9900
Fax: (949) 833-7988
Email: asap97@pacbell.net
Web: home.pacbell.net/asap97/index.html

Key Contact - Specialty:
Ms. Nada D. Williston - *Investment management, mutual funds, trust*

Description: We conduct targeted searches for portfolio managers, research analysts, business development officers, trust and operations administrators for clients who are investment management, mutual funds and trust companies.

Salary Minimum: $45,000
Functions: Finance, Cash mgmt.
Industries: Invest. banking, Brokers, Misc. financial

Acuity Medical Recruitment
500 Wright Rd.
Goodman, Mississippi 39079
(601) 472-2889
Fax: (601) 472-2889
Email: acuitymed@usa.net
Web: members.spree.com/acuitymed/

Key Contact - Specialty:
Ms. Linda Wright - *Physicians*

Description: Quality healthcare depends on qualified, dedicated and reliable physicians - providing the best physicians to fulfill your mandate in giving Americans integrity in healthcare, this is our mission.

Salary Minimum: $15,000
Functions: Healthcare, Physicians, Minorities

Affiliates:
American Medical Recruiting Co. Inc.
Recruiters Professional Network

Adam-Bryce Inc.
77 Maple Ave.
New City, New York 10956
(914) 634-1772
Fax: (914) 634-1912

Key Contact - Specialty:
Ms. Nadine Rubin - *Information technology, telecommunications*
Ms. Phyllis Reiss - *Information technology, telecommunications*
Ms. Naomi Laks - *Information technology, telecommunications*
Ms. Elaine Thibault - *Information technology, telecommunications*
Ms. Tina Buonavita - *Information technology, telecommunications*

Description: We have been involved in staffing and identifying high potential candidates who through the use of technology have moved their IT organizations into the forefront of their industries.
Functions: IT, MIS mgmt., Systems anal., Systems dev., Systems implem., Systems support, Int'l.
Industries: Computer svcs., Broadcast & Film, Telecoms, High tech

Arthur Adams & Assoc.
1046 Ravine Ridge Drive, Ste. 200
Worthington, Ohio 43085-2907
(614) 846-5075
Fax: (614) 846-5076
Email: art.adams@adamsrecruiting.com
Web: www.adamsrecruiting.com

Key Contact - Specialty:
Mr. Arthur Adams - *Computer networking sales*

Description: Contingency/retainer search in the computer networking sales field on a worldwide basis.

Salary Minimum: $100,000
Functions: Sales mgmt.
Industries: Computer equip., Computer svcs., Software

The Addison Consulting Group
12 Strafford Circle Rd.
Medford, New Jersey 08055
(609) 953-7650

Key Contact - Specialty:
Mr. Sandy Korkuch - *Medical devices (all management functions)*

Description: We are a specialty firm recruiting all management functions for medical device, biotech and related industries, offering extensive industry experience and a broad business perspective to discerning, growth-oriented companies.

Salary Minimum: $50,000
Functions: General mgmt., Mfg., Product dev., Quality, Sales & mktg., Engineering
Industries: Medical devices

ADECCO Employment Services

(Firm declined to update.)
7335 Timberlake Rd.
Lynchburg, Virginia 24502
(804) 239-0013

Key Contact - Specialty:
Ms. Ellen Dodson - *Engineering, information technology*

Description: A full service personnel staffing company providing assistance in: professional recruiting and temporary services. Temporary and full-time placement of clerical, light industrial, technical and professional employees. Also do on-site alliance and outsourcing.

Adel-Lawrence Assoc., Inc.

1208 Hwy. 34, Ste. 18
Aberdeen, New Jersey 07747
(732) 566-4914
Fax: (732) 566-9326

Key Contact - Specialty:
Mr. Larry Radzely - *Engineering, software, technical*

Description: Nationwide placement of engineering/technical personnel. Specializing in electrical/mechanical/software engineers; computers (networking, help desk, system analysts); telecommunications; biomedical/x-ray service and field service/repair.

Salary Minimum: $25,000
Functions: Systems anal., Systems dev., Systems implem., Systems support, Network admin., Engineering, Technicians
Industries: Medical devices, Computer equip., Consumer electronics, Test/ measurement equip., Computer svcs., High tech, Software

Adept Tech Recruiting, Inc.

219 Glendale Rd.
Scarsdale, New York 10583
(914) 725-8583

Key Contact - Specialty:
Mr. Fredrick R. Press - *Information technology, healthcare, equity analysts, stockbrokers, securities industry*

Description: Primarily, placement of personnel in all areas of information technology, personnel in all areas of healthcare and equity analysts and stockbrokers in the securities industry.

Salary Minimum: $25,000
Functions: Nurses, Allied health, Cash mgmt., Systems anal., Systems dev., Systems implem., Systems support
Industries: Finance, Computer svcs., New media, Telecoms, High tech, Software, Healthcare

Adirect Recruiting Corp.

468 Queen St. E., Ste. 206, Box 22
Toronto, Ontario M5A 1T7
Canada
(416) 365-9889
Fax: (416) 365-3123
Email: adirect@inforamp.net

Key Contact - Specialty:
Mr. Bob Copp
Ms. Susan Fox

Description: We provide cost and time effective mid to mid-senior level managerial/professional/technical search services to major Canadian companies. We offer three to five week turnaround times with fees ranging from $6,000 to $12,000. Over 96% of our assignments are completed successfully.

Salary Minimum: $50,000
Functions: Middle mgmt., Mfg., Materials, Sales & mktg., HR mgmt., Finance, R&D
Industries: Mfg., Retail, Svcs., Communications, Aerospace, Biotech, Healthcare

ADR Accounting Management Recruiters

15 Wakefield Crescent
Toronto, Ontario M1W 2C1
Canada
(416) 298-3781
Fax: (416) 298-4512

Key Contact - Specialty:
Mr. J. Alan Lomax - *Accounting, finance, insurance, marketing, property management*

Description: Selective and thorough approach to selecting and screening candidates for specific positions.
Functions: Middle mgmt., Admin. svcs., Health admin., Customer svc., Budgeting, Cash mgmt., Credit
Industries: Generalist, Drugs mfg., Misc. mfg., Pharmaceutical svcs., Accounting, Advertising/PR, Insurance

Advanced Corporate Search

3885-J Cochran St., #317
Simi Valley, California 93063
(805) 522-1997
Email: acsigtxecs@aol.com

Key Contact - Specialty:
Ms. Jan Gibson - *Satellite, GPS, VSAT, communication systems, software & hardware*

Description: Long term proven abilities to secure a proper match. We have the skills to analyze, evaluate and to motivate both company and candidate into a career marriage. Strong business tendencies enable us to ascertain technical abilities and inter-personal characteristics.

Salary Minimum: $60,000
Functions: Senior mgmt., Mkt. research, Mktg. mgmt., Sales mgmt., IT, R&D, Engineering
Industries: Computer equip., New media, Telecoms, Defense, High tech, Software

Advanced Recruiting, Inc.

7300 NW Expwy., Ste. 183
Oklahoma City, Oklahoma 73132
(405) 720-9445
Fax: (405) 720-9133
Email: advrec@icon.net
Web: www.icon.net/~advrec

Key Contact - Specialty:
Mr. Len Branch - *MIS, data processing*

Description: We take a professional and highly ethical apprach while conducting a candidate search for our clients. We listen to our clients, do our homework, and provide qualified candidates for your consideration.
Functions: MIS mgmt., Systems anal., Systems dev., Systems implem., Systems support, Network admin., DB admin.
Industries: New media, Telecoms, High tech, Software

Branches:
1947 Wadsworth Blvd., Ste. 394
Lakewood, Colorado 80227
(303) 936-5699
Fax: (303) 935-2204
Email: advrec@icon.net
Web: www.icon.net/~advrec
Key Contact - Specialty:
Ms. Lynn Owens - *MIS, data processing*

Advanced Recruitment, Inc.

6025 Stage Rd., Ste. 42-299
Bartlett, Tennessee 38134
(901) 373-1195
Fax: (901) 373-5682
Email: ar.tturkal@mindspring.com

Key Contact - Specialty:
Ms. Terry Turkal - *Manufacturing, engineering, human resources*
Ms. Nancy Cougle - *Manufacturing, engineering, human resources*

Description: We offer much experience in recruiting for manufacturing, engineering and human resources. A principal worked for 9 years at another recruitment agency.
Functions: Mfg., Product dev., Production, Automation, Plant mgmt., Quality, Engineering
Industries: Mfg., Paper, Plastics/rubber, Metal products, Machinery/Appliances, Computer equip., Misc. mfg.

Advanced Resources, Inc.

(Firm declined to update.)
7730 Carondelet Ave., Ste. 450
St. Louis, Missouri 63105
(314) 725-5777
Email: rhoehne@advr.com
Web: www.advr.com

Key Contact - Specialty:
Ms. Rebecca Hoehne - *Information systems*

Description: We offer over fifteen years of professional information systems recruiting service.
Functions: MIS mgmt., Systems anal., Systems dev., Systems implem., Systems support
Industries: High tech, Software

Advancement Recruiting Services

P.O. Box 209
Avon, Ohio 44011
(440) 930-5151
Fax: (440) 930-5153

Key Contact - Specialty:
Mr. Rudy Socha - *Manufacturing, data processing, engineering, physicians*

Description: We handle all disciplines and industries. Be sure to include your current or last salary, relocation preference and home ownership status.

Salary Minimum: $40,000
Functions: Senior mgmt., Product dev., Production, Automation, Quality, Physicians, Systems dev.
Industries: Generalist, Chemicals, Plastics/rubber, Metal products, High tech, Software, Healthcare

Advancement, Inc.

721 Fair Links Way
Gurnee, Illinois 60031-4706
(847) 247-2100
Fax: (847) 247-2105
Email: info@advancement.com
Web: www.advancement.com

Key Contact - Specialty:
Mr. Scott Hall - *Technical, data communications, telecommunications, computers, multimedia*

Description: Knowledge of our clients' markets, resourcing large internal and external databases and industry contacts can fill clients' needs in the telecom, datacom wireless, multimedia and IC markets.

Salary Minimum: $35,000
Functions: Directors, Product dev., Mkt. research, Mktg. mgmt., Sales mgmt., R&D, Engineering
Industries: Computer equip., Consumer electronics, New media, Broadcast & Film, Telecoms, High tech, Software

Advice Personnel Inc.

230 Park Ave., Ste. 903
New York, New York 10169
(212) 682-4400
Fax: (212) 697-0343

Key Contact - Specialty:
Ms. Shelley Lieff - *CPA firms, consulting firms, tax, financial, CFO's*
Mr. Alan Schwartz - *Financial service, real estate, commercial, closely-held businesses, all financial*

Description: We specialize in accounting, administrative and financial management placements across diverse industry lines. From CFO controller and chief administrative officers to entry level positions we provide confidential recruitment services tailored to each client.

Salary Minimum: $40,000
Functions: Generalist, Senior mgmt., Admin. svcs., CFO's, Budgeting, Taxes, M&A
Industries: Generalist, Wholesale, Finance, Accounting, Communications, Real estate, High tech

Advisors' Search Group, Inc.

370 Lexington Ave., Ste. 1506
New York, New York 10017
(212) 557-7533
Fax: (212) 573-9412

Key Contact - Specialty:
Mr. Michael A. Weinstock - *Portfolio management, investment advisory*

Description: We place support staff exclusively to 130+ of New York's most prominent investment advisory firms and portfolio managers. To include portfolio administration, marketing support performance measurement, operations and systems.

Salary Minimum: $30,000
Functions: Mktg. mgmt., Cash mgmt., Systems dev., Systems support, DB admin.
Industries: Finance, Invest. banking, Venture cap., Misc. financial

AES Search

1 Kalisa Way, Ste. 103
Paramus, New Jersey 07652
(201) 261-1600
(800) 545-4518
Fax: (201) 261-4343
Email: aesnj@aol.com
Web: www.AESrecruiting.com

Key Contact - Specialty:
Mr. Michael Goldstein
Mr. Stuart Zweighaft
Ms. Midge Mooney
Ms. Erica Haber
Mr. Nicholas J. Palermo
Mr. Paul Stevens
Ms. Lourdes Garcia
Ms. Jennifer Abdulla

Description: Reputation for professional, confidential search that gets results backed by guarantees on both retainer and contingency searches.
Functions: Mfg., Healthcare, Sales & mktg., Finance, IT, R&D, Engineering
Industries: Chemicals, Drugs mfg., Telecoms, Packaging, Insurance, Software, Healthcare

Affinity Executive Search

17860 NE 9th Place
North Miami Beach, Florida 33162-1117
(305) 770-1177
Fax: (305) 770-4010
Email: kohn@ix.netcom.com

Key Contact - Specialty:
Mr. Steven Kohn - *Sales & marketing, engineering, manufacturing, presidents, CEOs*
Ms. Renee Leavy - *Research & development, operations, software engineers, electronic engineers*

Salary Minimum: $50,000
Functions: Senior mgmt., Product dev., Mktg. mgmt., Sales mgmt., Direct mktg., Systems dev., Engineering
Industries: Consumer electronics, Test/measurement equip., Misc. mfg., High tech, Software

Affordable Executive Recruiters

5518 Lemona Ave.
Sherman Oaks, California 91411
(818) 782-8554
Fax: (818) 779-0395

Key Contact - Specialty:
Mr. Fred Gerson - *Financial*

Description: Specializing in CFO's, CEO's, CPA's, controllers, accountants, payroll personnel. Also human resources, credit managers.

Salary Minimum: $30,000
Functions: Sales mgmt., Direct mktg., Personnel, Credit, M&A, Attorneys, Paralegals
Industries: Mfg., Food/bev/tobacco, Misc. financial, Entertainment, Accounting, Communications, Insurance

Aggressive Corporation

4701 Auvergne Ave., Ste. 101
Lisle, Illinois 60532
(630) 852-3400
Fax: (630) 852-5072

Key Contact - Specialty:
Mr. Adam Gaspar
Mr. Raymond J. Kagee
Mr. Thomas J. Lane
Mr. Howard Vernon

Description: A middle to senior level search and assignment firm, founded in 1967, whose practice covers all of North America.

Salary Minimum: $70,000
Functions: General mgmt., Mfg., Materials, Sales & mktg., HR mgmt., Finance, Engineering
Industries: Food/bev/tobacco, Textiles/apparel, Lumber/furniture, Metal products, Machinery/Appliances, Motor vehicles, Misc. mfg.

Agra Placements, Ltd.

4949 Pleasant St., Ste. 1
West 50th Place III
West Des Moines, Iowa 50266-5494
(515) 225-6562
Fax: (515) 225-7733
Email: agraia@netins.net
Web: www.agraplacements.com

Key Contact - Specialty:
Ms. Lori Chenoweth

Description: The nation's leading firm specializing in the recruitment, screening and selection of management, marketing and technical professionals for international, national, regional and local agribusiness, horticultural and food firms.

Salary Minimum: $25,000
Functions: Mfg., Materials, Sales & mktg., Engineering
Industries: Agri/forestry/mining, Food/bev/tobacco

Branches:
2200 N. Kickapoo, Ste. 2
Lincoln, Illinois 62656
(217) 735-4373
Fax: (217) 732-2041
Key Contact - Specialty:
Mr. Perry M. Schneider

55 South Wabash Street, P.O. Box 4
Peru, Indiana 46970
(765) 472-1988
Fax: (765) 472-7568
Key Contact - Specialty:
Mr. Doug Rice

710 N. Broadway St.
New Ulm, Minnesota 56073-1202
(507) 354-4900
Fax: (507) 354-4909
Key Contact - Specialty:
Mr. Denny Sjogren

AGRI-associates

500 Nichols Rd.
Kansas City, Missouri 64112
(816) 531-7980
Fax: (816) 531-7982
Email: personpj@msn.com
Web: www.agriassociates.com

Key Contact - Specialty:
Mr. Glenn J. Person - *Agricultural personnel*

Description: Specialist in personnel search and recruiting for agribusiness, including suppliers of agricultural production inputs, agriculture commodity processors and agricultural production enterprises.

Salary Minimum: $30,000
Functions: General mgmt., Product dev., Quality, Purchasing, Packaging, Sales mgmt., CFO's
Industries: Agri/forestry/mining

Branches:
Woodstone Office Plaza
18915 Nordhoff St.
Northridge, California 91324
(818) 701-3094
Fax: (818) 701-5190
Key Contact - Specialty:
Mr. Les E. Reardanz
Ms. Eileen Reardanz

5200 NW 43rd St., Ste. 102-179
Gainesville, Florida 32606-4482
(352) 372-4200
Fax: (352) 371-6607
Key Contact - Specialty:
Mr. W. E. Gene Pope

895-B McFarland Rd.
Alpharetta, Georgia 30004
(770) 475-2201
Fax: (770) 475-1136
Key Contact - Specialty:
Mr. Michael T. Deal

300 NW Bank Twr.
2550 Middle Rd.
Bettendorf, Iowa 52722
(319) 344-6974
Fax: (319) 344-9199
Email: agridav@earthlink.net
Key Contact - Specialty:
Mr. Michael S. Vinzenz

7800 Metro Parkway, Ste. 300
Bloomington, Minnesota 55425
(612) 851-9196
Fax: (612) 851-9197
Key Contact - Specialty:
Mr. Dana Hansen

10330 Regency Parkway Drive
304 Regency Westpoint, P.O. Box 24046
Omaha, Nebraska 68124-0046
(402) 397-4410
Fax: (402) 397-4411
Key Contact - Specialty:
Mr. Richard W. Robertson

2632 Maplewood Drive
Columbus, Ohio 43231
(614) 891-3362
Fax: (614) 891-3382
Email: jillmcg@ix.netcom.com
Key Contact - Specialty:
Ms. Jill E. McGregor

1669 Glenn Rd.
Lancaster, Pennsylvania 17601
(717) 392-6692
Key Contact - Specialty:
Mr. Frank R. Rauba

7777 Walnut Grove Rd.
Memphis, Tennessee 38120
(901) 757-8787
Fax: (901) 751-1639
Email: agriline@aol.com
Key Contact - Specialty:
Mr. Richard E. Thompson

131 Degan, Ste. 203
Sundance Square
Lewisville, Texas 75057-3664
(972) 221-7568
Fax: (972) 221-1409
Email: agri.dallas@mail.usld.net
Key Contact - Specialty:
Mr. Lawrence W. Pete Keeley
Ms. Nancy Harris

International Branches:
Amstelveen, Cheltenham, Larrach, Ste. Vrain, Tel Aviv

Agri-Personnel
(a division of Bluechip Properties, Inc.)

5120 Old Bill Cook Rd.
Atlanta, Georgia 30349
(404) 768-5701
Fax: (404) 768-5705

Key Contact - Specialty:
Mr. David J. Wicker

Description: Search and placement for agribusiness and other industries nationwide and worldwide. All disciplines of executive, professional and technical levels.

Salary Minimum: $40,000
Functions: General mgmt., Sales & mktg., HR mgmt., Finance, Engineering, Int'l.
Industries: Agri/forestry/mining, Food/bev/tobacco

Agri-Tech Personnel, Inc.

3113 NE 69th St.
Kansas City, Missouri 64119
(816) 453-7200
Fax: (816) 453-6001
Email: DalePick@aol.com

Key Contact - Specialty:
Mr. Dale Pickering - *Agriculture, food*

Description: International agri-business recruiters for the grain storage and processing, food manufacturing, drug and chemical industries, finding candidates to fill positions in management, manufacturing, engineering, marketing, R&D, Q.C., administration, etc.

Salary Minimum: $30,000
Functions: Senior mgmt., Middle mgmt., Production, Plant mgmt., CFO's, R&D, Engineering
Industries: Agri/forestry/mining, Food/bev/tobacco, Chemicals, Drugs mfg., Transportation, Human resource svcs., Packaging

---

Agriesti & Assoc.
16291 Country Day Rd.
Poway, California 92064
(619) 451-7766
Fax: (619) 451-7843

Key Contact - Specialty:
Ms. Kay Agriesti - *Sales & marketing, consumer products, medical, pharmaceutical*
Ms. Lisa Tumbiolo - *Sales & marketing, consumer products*

Description: We are a nationwide search firm specializing in consumer products, sales and marketing professionals also medical and pharmaceuticals sales. We are affiliated with partners across the U.S. to facilitate our searches.
Functions: Middle mgmt., Mkt. research, Mktg. mgmt., Sales mgmt.
Industries: Healthcare

AJM Professional Services
(formerly Andersen, Jones & Muller Assoc.)
803 West Big Beaver Rd., Ste. 357
Troy, Michigan 48084-4734
(248) 244-2222
Fax: (248) 244-2233
Email: ajmps@aol.com
Web: www.ajmps.com

Key Contact - Specialty:
Mr. Charles A. Muller - *Information technology*
Mr. Jeffrey Jones - *Information technology*

Description: Specialists in contingency and retained search for information systems and software engineering professionals at managerial and staff levels. Access to a national candidate and client base through various networks and affiliations.

Salary Minimum: $30,000
Functions: IT, MIS mgmt., Systems anal., Systems dev., Systems implem., Systems support, Network admin.
Industries: Generalist

AKH Executive Search
8957 SW Terwilliger Blvd.
Portland, Oregon 97219
(503) 244-2411
Fax: (503) 244-8655
Email: arielelk@aol.com

Key Contact - Specialty:
Ms. Ariel Klein - *Advertising*
Ms. Alexis Halmy

Description: We specialize in the national recruitment of advertising and marketing professionals in the areas of account services, creative, media, interactive and account planning.

Salary Minimum: $25,000
Functions: Advertising, Direct mktg., PR
Industries: Advertising/PR

Alaska Executive Search, Inc.
821 N St., Ste. 204
Anchorage, Alaska 99501-6093
(907) 276-5707
Fax: (907) 279-3731
Email: aes@alaska.net

Key Contact - Specialty:
Mr. Robert E. Bulmer - *Engineering, management*

Description: Executive and medical search, consulting business and technical/medical temporaries specializing in the Alaskan marketplace.

Salary Minimum: $30,000
Functions: Generalist
Industries: Construction, Finance, Svcs., Communications, Environmental svcs., Insurance, Healthcare

---

Albrecht & Assoc., Executive Search Consultants
(a Management Recruiters Int'l. company)
10700 Richmond, Ste. 217
Houston, Texas 77042-4900
(713) 784-7444
Fax: (713) 784-5049
Email: albrecht@albrecht-assoc.com
Web: albrecht-assoc.com

Key Contact - Specialty:
Ms. Franke M. Albrecht

Description: Specialize in energy (to include oil, gas and electric power), pharmaceutical, biotechnology and managed healthcare. Our database includes virtually every company in these industries and we have an extensive network of clients and professionals in these organizations.

Salary Minimum: $60,000
Functions: Directors, Senior mgmt., Middle mgmt., Mfg., Health admin., R&D, Engineering
Industries: Energy/utilities, Drugs mfg., Pharmaceutical svcs., Mgmt. consulting, Insurance, Biotech, Healthcare

---

Alexander & Co.
33 Ora Way
San Francisco, California 94131
(415) 824-9803
Fax: (415) 206-1525
Email: palex@hooked.net

Key Contact - Specialty:
Ms. Penelope Alexander - *Marketing, communications, computers*

Description: Specialized recruitment of marketing and public relations professionals with technology experience (computer technology).

Salary Minimum: $50,000
Functions: Advertising, Mkt. research, Mktg. mgmt., Direct mktg., PR
Industries: Computer equip., Consumer electronics, Advertising/PR, Publishing, New media, High tech, Software

---

Alexander & Collins
1888 Century Park E., Ste. 1900
Los Angeles, California 90067
(310) 277-4656
Fax: (310) 277-7098
Email: lalawsrch@aol.com

Key Contact - Specialty:
Ms. Sara E. Collins - *Attorneys*

Description: Company provides both executive and attorney search services to aerospace, finance, high technology, legal and transportation related industries within the United States and Asia.

Salary Minimum: $80,000
Functions: Attorneys
Industries: Legal

Alexander Enterprises, Inc.
P.O. Box 148
Center Square, Pennsylvania 19422
(610) 279-0100
Fax: (610) 279-0124
Web: www.stephyoung@aol.com

Key Contact - Specialty:
Ms. Florence D. Young - *Pharmaceutical*
Ms. Stephanie Young - *Pharmaceutical*

Description: We conduct recruitment searches for all types of pharmaceutical professionals (M.D.'s, Ph.D.'s, quality, regulatory, data management and etc.)

Salary Minimum: $45,000

Functions: Directors, Senior mgmt., Middle mgmt., Product dev , Physicians, MIS mgmt., R&D
Industries: Drugs mfg., Medical devices, Pharmaceutical svcs., Human resource svcs., Biotech

The Alice Groves Co., Inc.
Harbour Sq., 700 Canal St.
Stamford, Connecticut 06902
(203) 324-3225

Key Contact - Specialty:
Mr. Raymond J. Leavee - *Retail*
Mr. Kenneth S. Leavee - *Retail*

Description: Our firm is dedicated to the thoughtful search and selection of retail and fashion executives who positively and dramatically influence our clients' profit pictures.

Salary Minimum: $40,000
Functions: Generalist
Industries: Retail

Allard Associates
44 Montgomery St., Ste. 500
San Francisco, California 94104
(800) 291-5279
Fax: (800) 526-7791
Email: recruit@allardassociates.com
Web: www.allardassociates.com

Key Contact - Specialty:
Ms. Kathryn Trott
Ms. Susan Allard

Description: Founded by former industry executives, we have a proven track record in disciplines critical to success in the consumer credit and retail banking industries, including: credit card, secured and unsecured consumer loans and lines, EFT, ATM, POS, deposit products and related emerging markets (smart card, on-line and internet banking).

Salary Minimum: $50,000
Functions: Senior mgmt., Mktg. mgmt., Direct mktg., Credit, Risk mgmt., DB admin., Mgmt. consultants
Industries: Misc. financial

Branches:
1059 Court St., Ste. 114
Woodland, California 95695
(800) 291-5279
Fax: (800) 526-7791
Key Contact - Specialty:
Ms. Nina Bates
Ms. Lucie Fox
Ms. Kay Hampshire
Ms. Linda Sprowls
Ms. Sue Daugherty

111 John St., Ste. 210
New York, New York 10038
(800) 291-5279
Key Contact - Specialty:
Mr. Louis Giacalone

Allen & Assoc.
1700 E. Desert Inn Rd., Ste. 118
Las Vegas, Nevada 89109
(702) 731-2066
Fax: (702) 731-5734
Email: ballen@wizard.com
Web: link4success.com/allen-ats/

Key Contact - Specialty:
Ms. Barbara A. Allen - *Finance, accounting*
Mr. Ken Thompson - *Information technology*
Ms. Marla Allen - *Sales & marketing*

Description: Executive search for hospitality, gaming, development, manufacturing and distribution.
Functions: Mktg. mgmt., Sales mgmt., CFO's, Cash mgmt., MIS mgmt., Systems anal., Systems dev.
Industries: Mfg., Food/bev/tobacco, Computer equip., Misc. financial, Hospitality, Computer svcs., Software

Frank E. Allen & Assoc.
15 James St.
Florham Park, New Jersey 07932
(201) 966-1606
Fax: (201) 966-9749
Email:
f.allenhumanresources@worldnet.att.net
Web: www.frankallen.com

Key Contact - Specialty:
Mr. Frank Allen - *Human resources*
Mr. Mark Allen - *Human resources*
Ms. Catherine Hind - *Human resources*
Mr. Rick A. Swaak - *International human resources*

Description: An executive search resource specializing in employee relations and human resources. Domestic and international.

Salary Minimum: $45,000
Functions: HR mgmt.
Industries: Energy/utilities, Mfg., Finance, Communications, Aerospace, Insurance, High tech

Jay Allen & Assoc.
300 S. Pine Island Rd., Ste. 265
Plantation, Florida 33324
(954) 423-3090
(800) 650-2139
Fax: (800) 793-8028
Email: JayAllen@worldnet.att.net

Key Contact - Specialty:
Mr. Jay Allen - *Physicians*
Mr. Cole Perry - *Executives, physicians*

Description: We are a leader in the industry of physician recruitment specializing in emergency medicine and primary care.

Salary Minimum: $150,000
Functions: Physicians, Health admin.
Industries: Healthcare

D. S. Allen Assoc.
1119 Raritan Rd., Ste. 2
Clark, New Jersey 07066
(732) 574-1600
Fax: (732) 574-2778
Email: dsahunt@aol.com

Key Contact - Specialty:
Mr. Don Allen
Ms. Mary Ann Ulrich

Description: Specializing in the information technology, hi-tech and communications industries for corporate and major consulting organizations. Areas of expertise: CEO, president, vice president, partner and manager levels plus leading sales/marketing executives.

Salary Minimum: $60,000
Functions: Directors, Senior mgmt., Mktg. mgmt., Sales mgmt., HR mgmt., IT, Int'l.
Industries: Mgmt. consulting, New media, Telecoms, High tech, Software

Branches:
28188 Moulton Pkwy., Ste. 820
Laguna Niguel, California 92677
(949) 360-4449
Fax: (949) 360-6543
Key Contact - Specialty:
Ms. Muriel Levitt

24200 Chagrin Blvd., Ste. 222
Beachwood, Ohio 44122
(216) 831-1701
Fax: (216) 831-2071
Key Contact - Specialty:
Mr. John Falk

Affiliates:
Gunther Conseils SA
I.T. APPS

Allen Consulting Group, Inc.
10805 Sunset Office Drive, Ste. 214
St. Louis, Missouri 63127
(314) 227-9994
Fax: (314) 227-9994
Email: toma@allencg.com
Web: www.allencg.com

Key Contact - Specialty:
Mr. Thomas R. Allen - *Information systems, data processing*

Description: Owner has 25 years experience in the information systems industry. He has been programmer, manager and director. He personally works with each client and candidate to determine and match their unique requirements.
Functions: MIS mgmt., Systems anal., Systems dev., Systems implem., Systems support, Network admin., DB admin.
Industries: Generalist

Allen, Wayne & Co. LLC
5321 N. Port Washington Rd.
Glendale, Wisconsin 53217
(414) 962-4426
(888) 403-3400
Fax: (414) 962-3610
Email: Allen_Wayne@hotmail.com

Key Contact - Specialty:
Mr. Charles N. Wallens - *Generalist*

Description: We provide executive placement services for top level professionals and organizations interested in hiring the very best. Our services are confidential, thorough, and produce results quickly. Nationwide service since 1960.

Salary Minimum: $40,000
Functions: Generalist, Senior mgmt., Middle mgmt., Production, Sales mgmt., Finance, Engineering
Industries: Generalist, Plastics/rubber, Motor vehicles, Finance, Human resource svcs., Insurance, High tech

Branches:
1436 W. Grey St., Ste. 512
Houston, Texas 77019
(877) 804-2104
Fax: (877) 804-2105
Key Contact - Specialty:
Mr. Daniel F. Norris

900 NE Loop 410 Ste. D-427
San Antonio, Texas 78209
(877) 804-2104
Fax: (877) 804-2105
Key Contact - Specialty:
Mr. Donald A. Quesnell

Allen-Jeffers Assoc.
23716 Marlin Cove
Laguna Niguel, California 92677
(949) 495-1096
Fax: (949) 495-5009
Email: BobJeffers@aol.com
Web: www.ipa.com/eoffice/949-495-1096.html

Key Contact - Specialty:
Mr. Robert Jeffers - *Medical device, pharmaceuticals (executive, senior technical)*

Description: We are an executive and technical search frim specializing in the medical and electronics industries. The measure of a search firm is in the quality and suitability of its candidates.
Functions: Automation, Plant mgmt., Mktg. mgmt., Sales mgmt., Systems dev., R&D, Engineering
Industries: Mfg., Medical devices, Plastics/rubber, Computer equip., Venture cap., Biotech, Healthcare

Allhands Placement Consultants
1209 Kossuth St.
Lafayette, Indiana 47905
(765) 742-1985
Fax: (765) 742-8061
Email: kallhands@aol.com

Key Contact - Specialty:
Ms. Kelly Allhands - *Surgery specialties, FP's, IM's, OB/Gyns, physicians only*

Description: Executive search and placement within healthcare settings across the U.S. Extensive use of database matching and candidate profiling, to send the right candidate to prospective clients. Competitive fees.
Functions: Physicians
Industries: Healthcare

Allied Search, Inc.
2030 Union St., Ste. 206
San Francisco, California 94123
(415) 921-1971
Fax: (415) 921-5309
Web: alliedsrch@aol.com

Key Contact - Specialty:
Mr. Donald C. May - *Information technology consulting, management consulting, systems, finance & accounting*

Description: Place professionals and executives nationwide and worldwide. Fields covered are consulting (IT and management), systems (CIOs, etc.), financal (CFOs, treasurers, controllers, etc.) and human resources (VP-human resources, etc.).

Salary Minimum: $40,000
Functions: General mgmt., HR mgmt., Finance, IT, Mgmt. consultants, Attorneys, Int'l.
Industries: Generalist

Branches:
8530 Wilshire Blvd., Ste. 404
Beverly Hills, California 90211
(213) 680-4040
Fax: (415) 921-5309
Key Contact - Specialty:
Mr. Donald C. May

Tom Allison Assoc.
625 Stagecoach Rd. SE
Albuquerque, New Mexico 87123
(505) 275-7771
Fax: (505) 275-7771

Key Contact - Specialty:
Mr. Tom Allison - *Food, consumer products, agriculture, produce*

Description: We are a successful nationwide experienced executive search company specializing in the food, consumer products and agriculture industries. We specialize in supervisory to executive level positions in all classifications.

Salary Minimum: $40,000
Functions: Generalist, Senior mgmt., Middle mgmt., Production, Purchasing, Sales mgmt., Benefits
Industries: Generalist, Agri/forestry/mining, Food/bev/tobacco, Machinery/Appliances, Wholesale, Retail, Hospitality

Allman & Co., Inc.
P.O. Box 4573
Wilmington, North Carolina 28406
(910) 395-5219
Fax: (910) 395-2703
Email: s.allman@worldnet.att.net

Key Contact - Specialty:
Mr. Steven L. Allman - *Trust banking, retirement plan services*

Description: 20 years helping trust companies with staffing requirements. Past agency of the year by NCAPS and Steven L. Allman, CPC, as consultant of the year by NCAPS.

Salary Minimum: $40,000
Functions: Cash mgmt., Attorneys
Industries: Banking, Invest. banking, Brokers, Accounting

Allstaff, Inc.
2015 S. Arlington Heights Rd., Ste. 102
Arlington Heights, Illinois 60005
(847) 640-9777
Fax: (847) 640-9779
Email: allstaff@mindspring.com
Web: www.net-temps.com/allstaff

Key Contact - Specialty:
Mr. Joseph R. Frankian - *Software, information technology*
Mr. Devlin Endres - *Hardware, software, telecommunications*
Mr. William McCabe - *Hardware, software, telecommunications*

Description: We are a contract and placement company who specializes in the placement of software and hardware engineers, developers to our high-tech and telephony clients (Fortune 100-500) here in the Chicago land area.
Functions: Mktg. mgmt., Systems anal., Systems dev., Systems implem., Systems support, Network admin., DB admin.
Industries: Computer equip., Consumer electronics, Telecoms, Software

Alpha Executive Search
P.O. Box 305
Pointe Clear, Alabama 36564
(334) 990-9909
Fax: (334) 990-7732

Email: jjl@mobile.gulf.net

Key Contact - Specialty:
Mr. John J. Little - *Manufacturing, engineering, plant management, sales, purchasing*

Description: I specialize in the valve, pump, actuator/electric motor industry. I cover all disciplines within these industries on a national basis.

Salary Minimum: $40,000
Functions: Product dev., Production, Plant mgmt., Quality, Purchasing, Sales mgmt., Engineering
Industries: Metal products, Machinery/ Appliances, Test/measurement equip., Misc. mfg., Real estate, Non-classifiable industries

---

Alpha Resource Group, Inc.
1916 Brabant Drive
Plano, Texas 75025
(972) 527-1616
Fax: (972) 527-4244

Key Contact - Specialty:
Mr. Sewell B. Pappas - *Hotel, resort*

Description: Through our worldwide recruitment network, we specialize in professional executive search and placement to many of the industry's finest hotels, resorts, clubs and casinos.

Salary Minimum: $25,000
Functions: Directors, Senior mgmt., Middle mgmt., Sales mgmt., Personnel, CFO's, MIS mgmt.
Industries: Hospitality, Entertainment, Human resource svcs.

Alpha Resources
One Tower Lane, Ste. 1700
Oakbrook Terrace, Illinois 60181
(630) 573-2913
Fax: (630) 954-0833
Email: alpharesou@aol.com

Key Contact - Specialty:
Mr. Daniel P. Cook - *Sales & marketing, electrical/electronics*

Description: Specializes in marketing & sales for semiconductor, integrated circuit and electrical industries. Principal has been in recruiting since July 1979. Work national and some international.

Salary Minimum: $40,000
Functions: Mktg. mgmt., Sales mgmt., Int'l.
Industries: Test/measurement equip., High tech

Alpha Search
(a subsidiary of CMI)
P.O. Box 1379
Deland, Florida 32721
(904) 734-0776
Fax: (904) 734-9853
Email: alphasch@n-jcenter.com

Key Contact - Specialty:
Mr. Bob Stillings - *Supermarkets, wholesale, logistics, human resources*
Ms. Eleanor Stillings - *Food service distribution, distribution*

Description: Offering over 20 years of professional recruiting experience oriented to the supermarket, wholesale grocery and food service distribution industries. Career advancement opportunities available nationally.

Salary Minimum: $40,000
Functions: Senior mgmt., Middle mgmt., Admin. svcs., Purchasing, Distribution, Sales mgmt., Risk mgmt.
Industries: Food/bev/tobacco, Drugs mfg., Misc. mfg., Wholesale, Retail, Finance, Hospitality

---

The Altco Group
100 Menlo Park
Edison, New Jersey 08837
(908) 549-6100
Fax: (908) 549-6105
Email: box100@altco.com
Web: www.altco.com

Key Contact - Specialty:
Mr. Ken Altreuter - *Consumer packaged goods (operation & technical)*
Mr. John Shea - *Consumer packaged goods (operation & technical)*

Description: We specialize in technical, scientific and operations positions for consumer packaged goods and pharmaceutical/medical device companies. Our experience, extensive database and industry contacts allow us to quickly identify the best candidates.

Salary Minimum: $40,000
Functions: Product dev., Plant mgmt., Quality, Packaging, R&D, Engineering, Minorities
Industries: Food/bev/tobacco, Chemicals, Soap/perfume/cosmetics, Drugs mfg., Medical devices, Plastics/rubber, Packaging

---

Altec/HRC
2820 W. Maple Rd., Ste. 236
Troy, Michigan 48084
(248) 643-8520
Fax: (248) 643-8521

Key Contact - Specialty:
Mr. Frank A. Cowall - *Technical, middle management, upper management (all levels)*

Description: Specialize in the placement of engineers and all types of various management positions found in manufacturing companies. The emphasis is on making good matches and a hard sell is not used on either side. We also recruit in industrial and technical sales.

Salary Minimum: $30,000
Functions: Generalist, Middle mgmt., Mfg., Materials, Sales mgmt., HR mgmt., Engineering
Industries: Generalist, Plastics/rubber, Metal products, Machinery/Appliances, Motor vehicles, Misc. mfg.

The Alternatives Group, Inc.
4004 Beltline Rd., Ste. 210
Dallas, Texas 75244-2328
(972) 788-9393
(800) 599-2133
Fax: (972) 788-1928
Email: altgroup@cyberramp.net

Key Contact - Specialty:
Ms. Michele Benum Sparks - *Data processing, sales, telecommunications*
Ms. Gina Lawrence

Description: Specialize in the nationwide placement of data processing, telecommunications, technical support and sales personnel.

Salary Minimum: $30,000
Functions: Sales mgmt., MIS mgmt., Systems anal., Systems dev., Systems implem., Systems support, Mgmt. consultants
Industries: Computer equip., Computer svcs., Telecoms, High tech, Software

---

Alynco, Inc.
10709 Platte Valley Drive
Little Rock, Arkansas 72212-3629
(501) 221-0066
Fax: (501) 221-0068
Email: fausett@swbell.net

Key Contact - Specialty:
Mr. A. Smith Fausett - *Logistics*

Description: Prior to starting my firm 10 years ago, my personal background was in distribution and transportation. As a result, I feel we are uniquely positioned to assist both clients and candidates in this area.

Salary Minimum: $30,000
Functions: Distribution

Amato & Assoc., Inc.
388 Market St., Ste. 500
San Francisco, California 94111
(415) 781-7664

Key Contact - Specialty:
Mr. Joseph D. Amato - *Insurance*

Description: Commercial insurance specialty, production oriented positions such as sales, underwriting, A/E's, etc. to upper level management, carriers, brokers, reinsurers.

Salary Minimum: $80,000
Functions: Senior mgmt., Middle mgmt., Mktg. mgmt., Sales mgmt., Risk mgmt., Systems implem., Systems support
Industries: Insurance

Amato & Associates Insurance Recruiters
1313 Medford Rd., Ste. 100
Wynnewood, Pennsylvania 19096-2418
(610) 642-9696
Fax: (610) 642-9797

Key Contact - Specialty:
Ms. Bobbi Amato - *Insurance*

Description: Commercial property/casualty/workers compensation, insurance underwriters, account executives, producers, claims, loss control for carriers, agents/brokers, reinsurers, risk management concentrating in mid-Atlantic and East Coast.

Salary Minimum: $25,000
Functions: Middle mgmt., Mkt. research, Sales mgmt., Direct mktg., Customer svc., CFO's, Risk mgmt.
Industries: Insurance

Ambridge Management Corp.
36 Toronto St., Ste. 850
Toronto, Ontario M5C 2C5
Canada
(416) 367-3810
Fax: (416) 367-9458
Email: ambridge@caspar.net

Key Contact - Specialty:
Mr. Gordon K. Sherwin - *Banking, financial services*
Ms. Catherine Regush - *Banking, leasing*

Description: We specialize in investment banking, project finance, treasury and trading positions and risk management positions attached to these roles.

Salary Minimum: $60,000
Functions: Finance, Cash mgmt., Credit, M&A, Risk mgmt.
Industries: Finance, Banking

Affiliates:
Synagent Inc.

AMD & Associates
3455 Peachtree Industrial Blvd.
Ste. 305-266
Duluth, Georgia 30096
(770) 395-1202
Email: amdassoc@bellsouth.net

Key Contact - Specialty:
Ms. Anna Marie Denman - *Generalist, sales & marketing*

Description: Excellent skills in building lasting client relationships. Experienced in both senior level and mid-level retained and contingency search in a broad range of industries. Broad exposure to generalist recruiting with heavy concentration in sales/sales management in medical/healthcare.
Functions: Health admin., Mkt. research, Mktg. mgmt., Sales mgmt., IT
Industries: Food/bev/tobacco, Drugs mfg., Medical devices, Misc. mfg., Pharmaceutical svcs., Computer svcs., Healthcare

---

American Executive Search
(a division of American Recruiters Consolidated Inc.)
800 Cypress Creek Rd. W., Ste. 310
Ft. Lauderdale, Florida 33309
(954) 771-6663
(954) 493-9200
Fax: (954) 351-9323
Email: www.americanrecruiters.com
Web: www.americanrecruiters.com

Key Contact - Specialty:
Mr. Carl R. Carieri - *Food service equipment, appliance, sales & marketing, engineering, manufacturing*

Description: Search and recruitment in sales, engineering, manufacturing and technical positions. Middle and upper level are our main focus. Serve food, data communications, food equipment and supplies and appliance industries.
Functions: Generalist, Mfg., Allied health, Sales & mktg., IT, R&D, Engineering
Industries: Food/bev/tobacco, Metal products, Machinery/Appliances, Computer equip., High tech, Software, Healthcare

---

American Heritage Group, Inc.
1301 W. Long Lake Rd., Ste. 330
Troy, Michigan 48098
(248) 267-6880
Fax: (248) 267-6886
Email: info@ahginc.com
Web: www.ahcinc.com

Key Contact - Specialty:
Mr. John Holliday - *Computer professionals*
Mr. Robert Drohan - *Computer professionals*

Description: We are a triple disciplined, duel faceted executive recruiting, consulting firm. Placing all levels of the computer, automotive engineering, clerical worlds.
Functions: Admin. svcs., Plant mgmt., Materials Plng., Direct mktg., Personnel, Systems implem., Mgmt. consultants
Industries: Paints/petroleum products, Machinery/Appliances, Computer equip., Consumer electronics, High tech, Software

Branches:
32670 Concord
Madison Heights, Michigan 48071
(248) 577-1170
Fax: (248) 577-1176
Email: info@ahginc.cncoffice.com
Web: www.ahglnc.com
Key Contact - Specialty:
Mr. John Holliday - *Automotive, computer, secretarial*

American Logistics Consultants, Inc.
(a division of American Services Group, Int'l.)
2215 York Rd.
Oak Brook, Illinois 60523
(630) 990-9499
Fax: (630) 990-1009
Email: alc@asgworld.com
Web: www.asgworld.com

Key Contact - Specialty:
Mr. Terrence McDorman - *Logistics, transportation, traffic, shipping*
Mr. Raymond Lilja

Description: Full service recruitment of middle management and executives in the transportation industry.

Salary Minimum: $50,000
Functions: Materials, Purchasing, Materials Plng., Distribution, Packaging
Industries: Mfg., Transportation, Wholesale, Retail, Svcs.

American Medical Consultants, Inc.
11625 SW 110th Rd.
Miami, Florida 33176
(305) 271-9225
Fax: (305) 271-8664
Email: AMC-Miami@prodigy.net
Web: www.ammedcon.com

Key Contact - Specialty:
Mr. Martin H. Osinski - *Physicians, physician executives*

Description: A nationwide physician and healthcare recruitment organization that assists hospitals, group practices, HMOs and solo practitioners in meeting their physician and personnel needs.

Salary Minimum: $75,000
Functions: Physicians, Nurses, Allied health, Health admin.
Industries: Healthcare

Branches:
471 Lexington Ave.
Ft. Lauderdale, Florida 33325
(954) 424-8777
Fax: (954) 370-1341
Email: amcfl@bellsouth.net
Key Contact - Specialty:
Mr. Michael Kirschner - *Physicians, physician executives*

American Medical Recruiters

325 Krameria St.
Denver, Colorado 80220
(719) 593-1629
Fax: (719) 593-1911
Email: gmberquist@aol.com
Web: www.medrecruit.com

Key Contact - Specialty:
Ms. Gailmarie Berquist - *Healthcare*
Ms. Patty Koff

Description: Recruit for hospital systems across the country, medical supply companies and for healthcare information system companies.
Functions: Healthcare, Nurses, Allied health, Health admin., MIS mgmt., Systems anal.
Industries: Healthcare

Branches:
173 Dolomite Dr.
Colorado Springs, Colorado 80919
(719) 593-1629
Key Contact - Specialty:
Ms. Patty Koff

American Medical Recruiting Co. Inc.

P.O. Box 12810
Jackson, Mississippi 39236
(601) 898-9963
(800) 813-3191
Fax: (601) 898-7577
Email: amrc@misnet.com

Key Contact - Specialty:
Mr. Paul Pinkerton - *Physicians*
Ms. Dara Bariola - *Physicians*

Description: Specializing in physician recruitment for many clients nationwide.
Functions: Physicians, Nurses, Health admin.
Industries: Healthcare

American Professional Search, Inc.

6805 Arno Allisona Rd.
College Grove, Tennessee 37046-9216
(615) 368-7979
Fax: (615) 368-7981
Email: amprosinc@sprynet.com

Key Contact - Specialty:
Mr. Ray O'Steen - *Manufacturing engineering*
Ms. Gloria O'Steen

Description: Twenty-four years as a manager and engineer plus eight as a recruiter allows a thorough understanding of client requirements, resulting in the ability to select individuals who will have an immediate positive impact on the hiring organization.
Functions: Quality, Productivity, Distribution, Packaging, Budgeting, Cash mgmt., Engineering
Industries: Agri/forestry/mining, Mfg., Plastics/rubber, Metal products, Machinery/Appliances, Motor vehicles, Misc. mfg.

American Resources Corp.

213 W. Institute Place, Ste. 412
Chicago, Illinois 60610
(312) 587-9000
(800) 587-9001
Fax: (312) 587-9160
Email: arc@ameritech.net
Web: www.american-resources.com

Key Contact - Specialty:
Mr. Osita Oruche - *Executive management, information technology*
Dr. Chuck Mojek - *Engineering, plant manufacturing, operations*
Mr. Gene Spencer - *Banking & financial communities*
Mr. Larry Stewart - *General management, sales, marketing*
Mr. Emmett Vaughn - *Human resources (general)*
Ms. Rachel Erbach

Description: Our dedicated consulting specialists know the most effective recruitment techniques, the overall professional market and how to attract the best candidates.

Salary Minimum: $35,000
Functions: Mfg., Production, Plant mgmt., Sales & mktg., HR mgmt., Finance, IT
Industries: Generalist

Branches:
27424 Winchester Terrace
Brownstown, Michigan 48183
(313) 692-1933
Key Contact - Specialty:
Mr. Raymond Herbert

4206 West North Avenue
Milwaukee, Wisconsin 53208
(414) 548-9000
Key Contact - Specialty:
Mr. Roy Evans

American Services Group

2215 York Rd., Ste. 204
Oak Brook, Illinois 60523
(630) 990-1001
Fax: (630) 990-1009
Email: asg@asgx.com
Web: www.asgx.com

Key Contact - Specialty:
Mr. Raymond Lilja - *Engineering, manufacturing, logistics, information technology*

Description: We recruit! By utilizing this direct-referral method plus other networking and cross-referencing techniques, we quickly and accurately construct a matrix of high-performing candidates according to the exact parameters defined by our client.
Functions: General mgmt., Mfg., Materials, Sales & mktg., IT, R&D, Engineering
Industries: Energy/utilities, Construction, Mfg., Transportation, Aerospace, High tech, Software

Affiliates:
American Contract Services, Inc.
American Information Solutions, Inc.
American Logistics Consultants, Inc.
American Technical Search, Inc.

AmeriPro Search, Inc.

20468 Chartwell Centre Drive, Ste. A
Cornelius, North Carolina 28031
(704) 896-8991
Fax: (704) 896-8855
Email: ameriprosearch.com
Web: www.ameriprosearch.com

Key Contact - Specialty:
Ms. Elaine Brauninger - *General manufacturing, building products*
Mr. John C. Brauninger - *Sales, marketing, MIS, SAP, accounting*

Description: Full service contingency search with emphasis on technical (engineering, design, manufacturing and quality control), sales (industrial), marketing (industrial & international) and electronic data processing (midrange & mainframe). Heavy emphasis in MIS, SAP and Oracle.

Salary Minimum: $30,000
Functions: General mgmt., Mfg., Materials, Sales & mktg., Finance, IT, Engineering
Industries: Generalist, Mfg., Medical devices, Plastics/rubber, Machinery/Appliances, Motor vehicles, Software

AmeriResource Group Inc.

2525 NW Expwy., Ste. 532
Oklahoma City, Oklahoma 73112
(405) 842-5900
Fax: (405) 843-9879
Email: staffing@flash.net
Web: www.flash.net/~staffing

Key Contact - Specialty:
Mr. Nick Martire - *MIS, engineering, finance, human resources, executive management*
Mr. Richard Nimmo - *MIS, engineering, finance and accounting, executive management, sales*

Description: We are a fully integrated human resource company. We provide employees (permanent, contract and temporary) to companies nationwide from entry level to executive management.

Salary Minimum: $35,000
Functions: General mgmt., Mfg., Healthcare, HR mgmt., Finance, IT, Engineering
Industries: Construction, Finance, Computer svcs., Accounting, Communications, Aerospace, Software

Branches:
5840 S. Memorial Drive, Ste. 212
Tulsa, Oklahoma 74145
(918) 627-4900
Fax: (918) 627-4984
Key Contact - Specialty:
Mrs. Diane Hewitt - *Engineering, medical, healthcare, finance and accounting*

Ames Assoc. Inc.
6935 Wisconsin Ave., Ste. 300
Chevy Chase, Maryland 20815
(301) 656-5222
Fax: (301) 652-0216

Key Contact - Specialty:
Ms. Mildred S. Ames - *Mortgage banking, property management*

Description: Recruiting for the real estate and banking industries, primarily mortgage banking, property management, construction, in the Mid-Atlantic area; Maryland; Virginia; Washington, D.C.
Functions: Senior mgmt., Middle mgmt., Admin. svcs.
Industries: Finance, Banking, Invest. banking, Misc. financial, Real estate

Affiliates:
Million & Associates

Ames-O'Neill Assoc., Inc.
330 Vanderbilt Motor Pkwy.
Hauppauge, New York 11788
(516) 582-4800
Fax: (516) 234-6094
Email: ames@frontiernet.net

Key Contact - Specialty:
Mr. George C. Ames - *Commercial, military electronics, avionics, software engineering, telecommunications*

Description: We specialize in the recruitment of high-technology specialists in electronics, avionics, aerospace, telecommunications, software engineering and related support functions for commercial and military clients.

Salary Minimum: $40,000
Functions: Mfg., Materials, Sales & mktg., Finance, IT, R&D, Engineering
Industries: Medical devices, Computer equip., Consumer electronics, Test/ measurement equip., Aerospace, High tech, Software

---

Amherst Human Resource Group, Ltd.
401 N. Michigan Ave., Ste. 360
Chicago, Illinois 60611
(312) 245-0050
Fax: (312) 245-9583
Email: amherst_hrg@msn.com

Key Contact - Specialty:
Ms. Sylvia E. Emerick - *Association management*
Ms. Stephanie Rubin - *Manufacturing*

Description: Generalists in middle/upper management arena with selected specialties such as healthcare, manufacturing, consumer products and services, association management; candidate generation through computerized database, networking resources and research staff.

Salary Minimum: $40,000
Functions: Generalist, Senior mgmt., Plant mgmt., Health admin., Sales & mktg., Finance, Minorities
Industries: Generalist, Food/bev/tobacco, Misc. mfg., Misc. financial, Svcs., Human resource svcs., Healthcare

---

Amherst Personnel Group Inc.
550 W. Old Country Rd.
Hicksville, New York 11801-4116
(516) 433-7610
Fax: (516) 433-7848

Key Contact - Specialty:
Mr. Charles J. Eibeler
Mr. Donald Porter

Description: 25th year specializing in sales and marketing and retailing management.

Salary Minimum: $20,000
Functions: Sales & mktg., Advertising, Mktg. mgmt., Sales mgmt.
Industries: Food/bev/tobacco, Soap/ perfume/cosmetics, Drugs mfg., Medical devices, Retail, Healthcare

---

Aminex Corp.
148 State St., Ste. 405
Boston, Massachusetts 02109
(617) 248-6883
Fax: (617) 248-8650
Email: aminex@thecia.net
Web: www.aminex.com

Key Contact - Specialty:
Mr. Lucius F. Sinks - *Insurance, technical, management, marketing*
Mr. Rick Tolstrup - *Insurance, technical, management, marketing*
Ms. Lisa Lepore Perry - *Insurance, technical, management, marketing, managed care, worker's compensation*

Description: We have devoted our full resources and capabilites to provide the insurance industry with talented executives. We believe that attracting leadership talent is of paramount importance to a company's success.

Salary Minimum: $30,000
Functions: Mkt. research, Mktg. mgmt., Sales mgmt., Customer svc., Benefits, Personnel, Risk mgmt.
Industries: Insurance

Analog Solutions
7 Heather Trail
Rochester, New York 14624
(716) 426-2647
Email: analog@analogsolutions.com
Web: www.analogsolutions.com

Key Contact - Specialty:
Mr. Gary Fowler - *Electrical engineering, hardware, software*

Description: We set ourself apart from other recruiting firms by offering a specialized service to a select group of growing companies. We offer our clients the opportunity to work with the industry's very best, low volume, high service organization.

Salary Minimum: $50,000
Functions: R&D, Engineering
Industries: Computer equip., Consumer electronics, Software

Analytic Recruiting, Inc.
12 E. 41st St., 9th Floor
New York, New York 10017
(212) 545-8511
Fax: (212) 545-8520
Email: analytic@pipeline.com
Web: www.analyticrecruiting.com

Key Contact - Specialty:
Mr. Daniel Raz
Ms. Rita Raz

Description: Specialize in the identification and recruitment of candidates with strong quantitative/analytical business problem solving skills from analyst through director levels across industry and functional lines.

Salary Minimum: $45,000
Functions: Production, Mkt. research, Direct mktg., Cash mgmt., M&A, Risk mgmt., IT
Industries: Food/bev/tobacco, Drugs mfg., Finance, Banking, Invest. banking, Mgmt. consulting, Advertising/PR

Anderson Industrial Assoc., Inc.
P.O. Box 2266
Cumming, Georgia 30028
(770) 844-9027
Fax: (770) 844-9656
Email: aia@atl.mindspring.com
Web: www.ipa.com/eoffice/770-844-9027.html

Key Contact - Specialty:
Mr. Gregory D. Anderson - *Surface mount technology, RF design, electric motor design & application, mechanical engineering, other engineering*

Description: Professional recruiting firm; degreed engineers placement in electrical, electronics, chemicals, plastics, HVAC, metals, telecommunications and instrumentation; all functions permanent/temporary.

Salary Minimum: $25,000
Functions: Product dev., Automation, Quality, Productivity, Purchasing, Packaging, Engineering
Industries: Paper, Chemicals, Medical devices, Plastics/rubber, Metal products, Machinery/Appliances, Consumer electronics

Anderson Network Group
P.O. Box 274-WBB
Dayton, Ohio 45409-0274
(937) 299-7601
Fax: (937) 299-7602
Email: abg@megisnet.net

Key Contact - Specialty:
Mr. Wayne F. Anderson - *Accounting, human resources, logistics & distribution*

Description: Executive placement for manufacturing, third-party logistics and distribution clients with needs in financial, manufacturing/distribution operations and human resources areas.

Salary Minimum: $35,000
Functions: Distribution, HR mgmt., Benefits, Finance, CFO's, Budgeting, MIS mgmt.
Industries: Mfg., Motor vehicles, Misc. mfg., Transportation, Human resource svcs., Non-classifiable industries

Andex Executive Search
101 River St.
Milford, Connecticut 06460
(203) 783-1616
Fax: (203) 783-3939
Email: jobs@andex.com
Web: www.andex.com

Key Contact - Specialty:
Mr. Harry Anderson - *Information technology*

Description: A technical recruiting firm specializing in the computer industry. Salaries typically range from 30,000 to 250,000+.
Functions: IT, MIS mgmt., Systems anal., Systems dev., Systems implem., Systems support, Network admin.
Industries: Energy/utilities, Mfg., Finance, Svcs., Aerospace, Insurance, High tech

Andrews & Assoc.
6100 Fairview Rd., Ste. 1420
Charlotte, North Carolina 28210
(704) 556-0088
Fax: (704) 556-0350

Key Contact - Specialty:
Mr. Dwight L. Andrews - *Accounting, financial*
Mr. Kevin M. Beste - *Accounting, financial*

Description: We have been assisting companies in locating CFOs and senior level financial managers in the Carolinas for over 20 years.
Functions: CFO's, Budgeting, Cash mgmt., Taxes, M&A
Industries: Mfg., Wholesale, Retail, Misc. financial, Accounting

Andrews & Wald Group
5344 Monterey Circle, Ste. 88
Delray Beach, Florida 33484-8377
(561) 496-2931
Fax: (561) 496-3245

Key Contact - Specialty:
Mr. E. Steven Wald - *Management*

Description: We do executive search for management in all disciplines, with years of expertise in sales and marketing, on a contingent fixed reasonable fee basis anywhere in North America.

Salary Minimum: $30,000
Functions: Senior mgmt., Middle mgmt., Plant mgmt., Mktg. mgmt., Sales mgmt., CFO's, MIS mgmt.
Industries: Medical devices, Metal products, Machinery/Appliances, Computer equip., Test/measurement equip., Entertainment, Non-profits

Angel Group Int'l.
4360 Brownsboro Rd., Ste. 240
Louisville, Kentucky 40207
(502) 897-0333
Fax: (502) 897-0496
Email: info@angel-group.com
Web: www.angel-group.com

Key Contact - Specialty:
Mr. Steve Angel - *Accounting, financial*
Mr. Bruce Thomas - *General manufacturing*
Mr. Matthew Grimes - *Sales management*
Ms. Barbara Beard - *MIS*
Ms. Paula Bryan - *Human resources*
Ms. Janine Stubblefield - *Accounting, financial*

Functions: Production, Distribution, Sales mgmt., Benefits, Cash mgmt., Systems dev., Int'l.
Industries: Mfg., Transportation, Retail, Banking, Accounting, Communications

Tryg R. Angell, Ltd.
354 Shelton Rd.
Nichols, Connecticut 06611
(203) 377-4541
Fax: (203) 377-4545

Key Contact - Specialty:
Mr. Tryg R. Angell - *Paper, sales, marketing, technical*

Description: Senior positions in the pulp and paper industries. National and regional sales and marketing positions as well as technical and production positions for paper, chemical and other industrial companies.

Salary Minimum: $30,000
Functions: Senior mgmt., Product dev., Plant mgmt., Mkt. research, Sales mgmt., Benefits, Engineering
Industries: Energy/utilities, Construction, Paper, Printing, Chemicals, Paints/petroleum products, Metal products

Angus Employment Ltd.
1100 Burloak Drive, 5th Floor
Royal Bank Bldg.
Burlington, Ontario L7L 6B2
Canada
(905) 319-0773
Fax: (905) 336-9445
Email: resumes@angusemployment.com
Web: www.angusemployment.com

Key Contact - Specialty:
Mr. Evan Stewart - *Generalist*

Description: As a general placement firm, we recruit on behalf of many high-profile firms in all industries for professional occupations at every level.
Functions: Generalist, Senior mgmt., Product dev., Mktg. mgmt., CFO's, MIS mgmt., Engineering
Industries: Motor vehicles, Test/measurement equip., Transportation, Equip. svcs., Human resource svcs., New media, Software

The Angus Group, Ltd.
2337 Victory Pkwy.
Cincinnati, Ohio 45206
(513) 961-5575
Fax: (513) 961-5616
Email: angus@skycorp.net
Web: www.angusgroup.com

Key Contact - Specialty:
Mr. Thomas R. Angus - *Human resources, general management*
Mr. Dave Hartig - *Manufacturing, engineering, operations, general management*
Mr. Pete Nadherny - *Banking, finance, accounting, general management*

Description: Recruiting services to businesses, most disciplines. Most professionals in office have 10 years + of experience.

Salary Minimum: $50,000
Functions: Plant mgmt., Mktg. mgmt., Sales mgmt., HR mgmt., Finance, IT, Engineering
Industries: Generalist, Mfg., Retail, Finance, Accounting, Human resource svcs., Advertising/PR

Ansara, Bickford & Fiske
95 Elm St., Ste. #5
P.O. Box 239
West Springfield, Massachusetts 01089
(413) 733-0791
Fax: (413) 731-1486
Email: pa@ansara.com
Web: www.ansara.com

Key Contact - Specialty:
Mr. Peter Ansara - *High technology manufacturing, semiconductors, electronics, automation, telecommunications*
Mr. Peter Kratimenos - *Packaging, HVAC, mechanical & environmental computers, web masters, network*

Description: Fully automated, state-of-the-art research capability. Deep and concise databases drawn from all sources. Attract hard to find engineers in specialty niches.

Salary Minimum: $30,000
Functions: Production, Automation, Plant mgmt., Materials Plng., Distribution, Packaging, Engineering
Industries: Machinery/Appliances, Computer equip., Test/measurement equip., Pharmaceutical svcs., Telecoms, Packaging, High tech

Fred Anthony Assoc.
P.O. Box 372
Lake Geneva, Wisconsin 53147
(414) 248-8133
Fax: (414) 248-8121
Email: faa13@genevaonline.com

Key Contact - Specialty:
Mr. Fred Anthony - *Chemical sales & marketing*

Description: Specialty - chemical coatings and the raw materials for that industry (resins, additives)

Salary Minimum: $50,000
Functions: Middle mgmt., Sales & mktg., Mkt. research, Mktg. mgmt., Sales mgmt., R&D, Int'l.
Industries: Mfg., Chemicals, Paints/petroleum products

Anthony Michael & Co.
800 Hingham St., Ste. 2000
Rockland, Massachusetts 02370
(781) 871-9600
Fax: (781) 982-9006
Email: amc@baycolony.com
Web: www.anthonymichael.baycolony.com

Key Contact - Specialty:
Mr. Michael Kulesza - *Investment industry*
Mr. Robert E. Burr, Jr.

Description: Our assignments span middle to senior management in the following areas: portfolio management and research, sales and marketing, defined contribution, global custody, compliance and legal.

Salary Minimum: $75,000
Functions: Directors, Senior mgmt., Mktg. mgmt., Sales mgmt., Attorneys, Int'l.
Industries: Invest. banking, Brokers, Misc. financial

APA Employment Agency Inc.
700 NE Multnomah, Ste. 274
Port of Portland Bldg.
Portland, Oregon 97232-4102
(503) 233-1200
(800) 715-4562
Fax: (503) 233-0071
Web: www.apaemployment.com

Key Contact - Specialty:
Mr. Les Swanson
Mr. Dave Knox - *Warehouse, production management, industrial, drivers*
Mr. Jeff Voigt - *Office/administrative, human resources, customer service, accounting, management*
Ms. Darbi Sadlier

Description: We have a large client base in the Portland Oregon area. We place many new candidates weekly. Our name would be a good lead for someone trying to relocate.

Salary Minimum: $20,000
Functions: Admin. svcs., Customer svc., Personnel, Training
Industries: Generalist, Mfg., Misc. mfg., Transportation, Retail, Svcs., Non-classifiable industries

Branches:
10260 SW Greenburg Rd., #400
Beaverton, Oregon 97223
(503) 293-7694
Fax: (503) 293-7695
Key Contact - Specialty:
Mr. Les Swanson
Ms. Darbi Sadlier

4804-G NE Thurston Way
Vancouver, Washington 98662
(360) 253-1200
(888) 715-4563
Fax: (360) 253-4674
Key Contact - Specialty:
Ms. Amy Leggett - *Administrative, industrial, professional, management, sales*
Ms. Michelle Salter

David Aplin & Assoc.
10235 - 101 St., 2306 Oxford Twr.
Edmonton, Alberta T5J 3G1
Canada
(403) 428-6663
Fax: (403) 421-4680
Email: david@aplin.ab.ca
Web: www.aplin.ab.ca

Key Contact - Specialty:
Mr. David Aplin - *Information technology*
Mr. Jeff Aplin - *Information technology*
Ms. Jennifer Ward - *Information technology*

Description: We are one of Canada's leading professional search organizations offering clients and candidates a full range of recruitment services in IT, accounting/finance, sales/marketing, engineering, HR and office personnel from intermediate to executive levels.

Salary Minimum: $40,000
Functions: General mgmt., Mfg., Sales & mktg., HR mgmt., Finance, IT, Engineering
Industries: Leather/stone/glass/clay, Metal products, Wholesale, Human resource svcs., New media, High tech, Healthcare

Affiliates:
David Aplin & Assoc.

R. W. Apple & Assoc.
200 Atlantic Ave., Box 200
Manasquan, New Jersey 08736
(732) 223-4305
Fax: (732) 223-4325
Web: applepics@usamailbox.com

Key Contact - Specialty:
Mr. Richard W. Apple - *Consulting (general), environmental consulting*

Description: Provide executive search services to environmental consulting firms. Concentrations include environmental engineering, process development, sales and marketing.

Salary Minimum: $30,000
Functions: Benefits, Personnel, Environmentalists
Industries: Environmental svcs., Haz. waste

Applied Resources
(Firm declined to update.)
42 High St., Ste. 2
P.O. Box 525
Medford, Massachusetts 02155
(781) 391-1202
Fax: (781) 391-8011
Email: alf@applres.com
Web: www.applres.com

Key Contact - Specialty:
Dr. Alton J. Frabetti - *Energy*

Description: Energy cost reduction professionals, nationwide. Including engineering, sales and management, performance contracting, energy service companies, utilities, project finance, power marketing, construction management and cogeneration.

Salary Minimum: $50,000
Functions: Senior mgmt., Sales mgmt., Engineering
Industries: Energy/utilities

Applied Resources, Inc.
7200 Hemlock Lane N., Ste. 324
Maple Grove Executive Centre
Maple Grove, Minnesota 55369
(612) 391-6000
Email: ari@winternet.com
Web: www.winternet.com/~ari/

Key Contact - Specialty:
Mr. Michael G. Weiss - *Engineering, manufacturing, management*

Description: Specialists in identifying engineering and manufacturing professionals. Dedicated to serving technology driven growth companies in Minnesota. Have developed extensive networks in metal fabrication, data communications software, hardware and medical device industries.

Salary Minimum: $40,000
Functions: Product dev., Purchasing, Mkt. research, Personnel, Systems implem., R&D, Engineering
Industries: Mfg., Medical devices, Plastics/rubber, Human resource svcs., Packaging, High tech, Software

Applied Search Assoc., Inc.
P.O. Box 1207
Dawsonville, Georgia 30534-1207
(706) 265-2530
Email: ApplySrch@stc.net

Key Contact - Specialty:
Mr. Richard B. Rockwell, Sr. - *Process, manufacturing, sales, marketing, engineering*

Description: Our specialty is direct recruiting and placement of hard to find personnel with specific backgrounds, talent and education. We produce results through experience, preparation and individualized attention to all project details.

Salary Minimum: $50,000
Functions: Generalist, Product dev., Automation, Advertising, Sales mgmt., Engineering, Int'l.
Industries: Paper, Plastics/rubber, Metal products, Machinery/Appliances, Test/measurement equip., Environmental svcs., High tech

Applied Technology Solutions Inc.
(a division of Sigma Systems Group)
151 Front St. W., Ste. 514
Toronto, Ontario M5J 2N1
Canada
(416) 369-0008
Fax: (416) 369-0199
Email: info@ats-canada.com
Web: www.ats-canada.com

Key Contact - Specialty:
Mr. Felix Bedard - *Information technology*

Description: We are an ISO 9000 registered information technology contract and full time staffing firm and a division of a multi-faceted IT consulting company specializing in systems development, LAN/WAN, telecommunications, outsourcing, offshore development and ERP solutions.

Salary Minimum: $30,000
Functions: MIS mgmt., Systems anal., Systems dev., Systems implem., Systems support, Network admin., DB admin.
Industries: Generalist, High tech, Software

Charles P. Aquavella & Assoc.
1241 Emerald Sound Blvd.
Oak Point, Texas 75068
(972) 292-2344
Fax: (972) 292-2377

Key Contact - Specialty:
Mr. Charles P. Aquavella - *Manufacturing (housing, all positions, levels), sales, retail sales*

Description: Human resource consulting and executive search in personnel, general management, all management, manufactured housing and manufacturing.

Salary Minimum: $30,000
Functions: Middle mgmt., Plant mgmt., Purchasing, Sales mgmt., Personnel, Credit, MIS mgmt.
Industries: Food/bev/tobacco, Lumber/furniture, Misc. mfg., Retail, Hospitality, Human resource svcs.

The Argus Group Corp.
249 Roehampton Ave.
Toronto, Ontario M4P 1R4
Canada
(416) 932-9321
Fax: (416) 932-9387
Email: argus@istar.ca

Key Contact - Specialty:
Mr. Alec Reed - *Sales & marketing*

Description: Like the multi-eyed monster of mythical fame, we always keep our watchful eyes out for your best interest: selecting appropriately trained people who can immediately benefit your corporation.
Functions: Senior mgmt., Advertising, Mkt. research, Mktg. mgmt., Sales mgmt., Direct mktg., IT
Industries: Generalist

Aries Search Group
9925 Haynes Bridge Rd., #200-146
Alpharetta, Georgia 30022
(770) 569-4708
Fax: (770) 569-4709
Email: cmcand6089@aol.com

Key Contact - Specialty:
Ms. Cindy McAndrew - *Medical industry, sales, sales management, marketing*

Description: We specialize in search and recruitment nationally in the medical industry. We offer twelve years of experience and strive towards a commitment to becoming partners in strategic planning with our client companies. We specialize in all levels of sales and sales management as well as marketing and product development positions.
Functions: Senior mgmt., Middle mgmt., Mkt. research, Mktg. mgmt., Sales mgmt.
Industries: Medical devices, Test/measurement equip., Software, Biotech

ARJay & Assoc.
875 Walnut St., Ste. 150
Cary, North Carolina 27511
(919) 469-5540
Fax: (919) 481-9176

Key Contact - Specialty:
Mr. Ronald T. Jones
Mr. Russell E. Miller

Description: Executive search and technical recruiting for management professionals, engineers and scientists. Specializing in electrical, automotive, appliance and aerospace industries.

Salary Minimum: $30,000
Functions: General mgmt., Mfg., Materials, Sales & mktg., R&D, Engineering
Industries: Energy/utilities, Plastics/rubber, Machinery/Appliances, Motor vehicles, Computer equip., Consumer electronics, Misc. mfg.

Branches:
2386 Clower St., Ste. A202
Snellville, Georgia 30278
(404) 979-3799
Fax: (404) 985-7696

Armor Personnel
(a division of AP Careers Inc.)
(Firm declined to update.)
181 Queen St. E.
Brampton, Ontario L6W 2B3
Canada
(905) 459-1617
Email: armor@inforamp.net

Key Contact - Specialty:
Mr. Lou Duggan - *General management*

Description: Diversified staffing services firm. Contract staff and comprehensive human resources division to complement recruitment.

Salary Minimum: $40,000
Functions: Senior mgmt., Middle mgmt., Admin. svcs., Plant mgmt., Sales mgmt., Benefits, CFO's
Industries: Generalist

R & J Arnold & Assoc., Inc.
1401 Walnut St., Ste. 302
Boulder, Colorado 80302
(303) 447-9940
Fax: (303) 447-0062
Email: r-j-arnold-assoc@worldnet.att.net

Key Contact - Specialty:
Ms. Janet N. Arnold - *Healthcare*
Mr. Robert W. Arnold - *Engineering, chemical*

Description: We have earned a very solid reputation for surfacing qualified professionals who meet our client's clinical/technical, philosophical and personality needs. Over 50% placed remain with the client over 5 years.
Functions: Senior mgmt., Middle mgmt., Physicians, Nurses, Health admin., MIS mgmt., Engineering
Industries: Generalist, Healthcare

Aronow Assoc., Inc.
6923 Fairway Lakes Drive
Boynton Beach, Florida 33437
(561) 732-6008

Key Contact - Specialty:
Mr. Lawrence E. Aronow - *Financial services*

Description: Management recruiting for the financial services industry specializing in sales, product management, strategic planning and all marketing functions. Global finance and treasury management for the corporate market.

Salary Minimum: $60,000
Functions: General mgmt., Sales & mktg., Finance
Industries: Finance

A. Artze Assoc.-Personnel Consultants
Urb Santa Maria
1908 Petunia St.
San Juan, Puerto Rico 00927-6621
(787) 751-3303

Key Contact - Specialty:
Ms. Angeles Artze - *Pharmaceutical (middle to high management), healthcare*

Description: Executive search for industry Fortune 500.
Functions: General mgmt., Mfg., Materials, HR mgmt., Finance, IT, Engineering
Industries: Textiles/apparel, Paper, Chemicals, Drugs mfg., Plastics/rubber, Computer equip., Misc. mfg.

Affiliates:
Evan Thomas Assoc.

Asheville Search & Consulting
P.O. Box 549
29 Spring Cove Court
Arden, North Carolina 28704
(828) 687-7722
Fax: (828) 687-2444
Email: Vspvincep@aol.com

Key Contact - Specialty:
Mr. Vincent Putiri - *Manufacturing, design, plant support staff*

Description: We offer client companies a partnered relationship and the expertise of its principal, who has over twenty years of management experience in both entrepreneurial and established business environments.

Salary Minimum: $25,000
Functions: Middle mgmt., Product dev., Production, Automation, Plant mgmt., R&D, Engineering
Industries: Metal products, Machinery/Appliances, Motor vehicles, Computer equip., Test/measurement equip., Misc. mfg., Aerospace

E. J. Ashton & Assoc., Ltd.
P.O. Box 1048
Lake Zurich, Illinois 60047-1048
(847) 540-9922
Fax: (847) 540-1235
Email: ejaltd@aol.com

Key Contact - Specialty:
Mr. Edward J. Ashton - *Insurance*
Mr. Gene Rowls - *Insurance*
Mr. Edmund Lipinski

Description: Executive recruiters/consultants in and for the insurance industry nationwide. Specializing in all technical and management disciplines within insurance and financial services industries.

Salary Minimum: $40,000
Functions: Middle mgmt., CFO's, Budgeting, Cash mgmt., Taxes, M&A, Risk mgmt.
Industries: Insurance

Ashton Computer Professionals, Inc.
C-15 Chesterfield Place
North Vancouver, British Columbia V6E 3V7
Canada
(604) 904-0304
Fax: (604) 904-0305
Email: acp@axionet.com
Web: www.axionet.com/acprecruit

Key Contact - Specialty:
Ms. Barbara L. Ashton - *Telecommunications, semiconductor, information technology*

Description: We work only with advanced computing and telecommunications professionals. Serve the Pacific Northwest, handling all areas of information technology, technical hardware/software development, engineering and management personnel.

Salary Minimum: $35,000
Functions: MIS mgmt., Systems anal., Systems dev., Systems support, Network admin., DB admin., Engineering
Industries: Computer equip., Test/measurement equip., Computer svcs., New media, Telecoms, High tech, Software

Ashway Ltd. Agency
295 Madison Ave., Ste. 1101
New York, New York 10017
(212) 679-3300
Fax: (212) 447-0583

Key Contact - Specialty:
Mr. Steven King - *Science & technology, insurance*
Mr. Arthur S. Harelick - *Science & technology*

Description: Specialize in executive search and contingency placements in science and technology: physics, engineering, chemistry/biology, mathematics and computer science. We also place actuaries and insurance professionals. We also are technology management consultants.

Salary Minimum: $25,000
Functions: Production, Plant mgmt., Mktg. mgmt., M&A, R&D, Engineering, Mgmt. consultants
Industries: Energy/utilities, Drugs mfg., Mgmt. consulting, Environmental svcs., Insurance, High tech, Biotech

ASI
11693 San Vicente Blvd., Ste. 363
Los Angeles, California 90049
(310) 277-3456
Fax: (310) 362-8489
Email: info@pleniverse.com
Web: www.pleniverse.com

Key Contact - Specialty:
Mr. James Beau Buck - *Start-ups*

Description: Executive search and private capital for start-ups and rapidly growing companies in technology, hospitality and consumer products.
Functions: Directors, Senior mgmt., MIS mgmt., Systems anal., Systems dev., Systems implem., Systems support
Industries: Hospitality, Entertainment, New media, Telecoms, High tech, Software

Ask Guy Tucker
4990 High Point Rd.
Atlanta, Georgia 30342
(404) 303-7177
Fax: (404) 303-0136
Email: guy@askguy.com
Web: www.askguy.com

Key Contact - Specialty:
Mr. Guy Tucker - *Advertising*

Description: An Atlanta based contact resource company specializing in advertising, headhunting, interactive media services and film production.

Salary Minimum: $30,000
Functions: Advertising, Mktg. mgmt., PR
Industries: Communications, Advertising/PR, Publishing, New media, Broadcast & Film

Asset Resource, Inc.
15 Alicante Aisle
Irvine, California 92614-5926
(949) 756-1600
Fax: (949) 756-1661
Email: fbailin@earthlink.net

Key Contact - Specialty:
Mr. Fred Bailin - *Engineering, software/hardware development, communications*
Ms. Fran Shulman - *Engineering, software/hardware development, communications*

Description: Specialization in data communications and networking industries, software and hardware development engineering. Working with start-up, emerging growth and mature companies. History of repeat business based on ability to fill requirements.

Salary Minimum: $60,000
Functions: Directors, Senior mgmt., Middle mgmt., Systems dev., Engineering
Industries: Computer equip., Telecoms, High tech, Software

Affiliates:
Lipsky Group, Inc.

Associated Recruiters
7144 N. Park Manor Drive
Milwaukee, Wisconsin 53224
(414) 353-1933
Fax: (414) 353-9418
Email: maury@execpc.com

Key Contact - Specialty:
Mr. Maurice A. Pettengill - *Corrugated packaging*

Description: Certified personnel consultant, serving the packaging industry. Primary focus is corrugated, folding cartons and packaging engineers. Over 30 years of personal experience in management, sales and consulting.

Salary Minimum: $30,000
Functions: Middle mgmt., Production, Plant mgmt., Packaging, Sales mgmt., Graphic artists
Industries: Packaging

The Associates, HR Search Executives, Inc.
2212 NW 50th St., Ste. 164
Oklahoma City, Oklahoma 73112
(405) 843-7755
Fax: (405) 843-9861
Email: Tahrsei@aol.com

Key Contact - Specialty:
Ms. Susan Estes - *Generalist, engineering*
Mr. Don McMullan - *Generalist*

Description: We are a contingency search firm founded by professionals with 20 plus years experience in the employment industry. Management and development programs available as on client site training and development.

Salary Minimum: $25,000
Functions: Production, Plant mgmt., Purchasing, Materials Plng., Finance, Engineering, Int'l.
Industries: Generalist, Food/bev/tobacco, Plastics/rubber, Metal products, Misc. mfg., Misc. financial, Aerospace

Association for Sales Force Management
6800 48th Ave. NE
Seattle, Washington 98115
(206) 527-8775
Email: scottw@asfm.com
Web: www.asfm.com

Key Contact - Specialty:
Mr. Scott Walmsley - *Sales managers (all industries), sales personnel, account managers*

Description: We specialize in recruiting sales personnel, account managers and sales management personnel with a minimum of four years experience. Our client base is generally medium sized companies with 50-300 employees.

Salary Minimum: $40,000
Functions: Advertising, Mkt. research, Mktg. mgmt., Sales mgmt., Direct mktg., Customer svc., PR
Industries: Printing, Consumer electronics, Test/measurement equip., Computer svcs., Broadcast & Film, Telecoms, High tech

Astro Executive Search Firm
11219 Muriel Ave., Ste. 418
Baton Rouge, Louisiana 70816
(504) 292-7363
Fax: (504) 292-7364
Web: astroexec@linknet.net

Key Contact - Specialty:
Ms. Annemarie T. Danielsen - *Engineering, computer science*

Description: We will strive to create high quality applicant and client company relationships through focused understanding of each party's needs and goals, effective communication and a professional level of understanding of the career fields being addressed.

Salary Minimum: $50,000
Functions: Mfg., IT, Engineering
Industries: Chemicals, Drugs mfg., Plastics/rubber, Paints/petroleum products, Computer svcs., Software, Biotech

W. R. Atchison & Assoc., Inc.
612 Pasteur Drive, Ste. 209
Freeman Bldg.
Greensboro, North Carolina 27403
(336) 855-5943

Email: watch@nr.infi.net

Key Contact - Specialty:
Mr. W. R. Atchison - *Engineering, operations, financial, human resources, materials management (professional & managerial positions)*
Ms. Ann G. Atchison - *Administrative*

Description: A specialized and creative service for over 20 years in recruiting engineering, manufacturing professionals and managerial personnel for growth and major firms in the Southeast.

Salary Minimum: $30,000
Functions: Middle mgmt., Mfg., Materials, HR mgmt., Finance, R&D, Engineering
Industries: Food/bev/tobacco, Textiles/apparel, Paper, Chemicals, Drugs mfg., Metal products, Machinery/Appliances

---

Atkinson Search & Placement, Inc.

203B W. Broadway, P.O. Box 493
Fairfield, Iowa 52556
(515) 472-3666
(800) 888-9248
Fax: (515) 472-7270
Email: asap@aatkinson.com
Web: www.aatkinson.com

Key Contact - Specialty:
Mr. Arthur Atkinson - *Software vendors, consulting firms (individual contributors, directors, VP)*

Description: We serve the software industry finding developers, marketers, sales representatives and sales managers, pre and post sales engineers and managers of development, support, marketing, sales up to the director - VP level.

Salary Minimum: $50,000
Functions: Mktg. mgmt., Sales mgmt., Systems anal., Systems dev., Systems implem., Systems support, Engineering
Industries: Computer svcs., Software

Atlantic Pacific Group

P.O. Box 4563
Laguna Beach, California 92652
(949) 376-4938
Fax: (949) 376-4855
Email: lindablakemore@sprynet.com

Key Contact - Specialty:
Ms. Linda Blakemore - *Staffing industry, human resources*

Description: Executive search for the temporary staffing industry, human resources consulting firms and corporate human resources positions. Other specialties include sales and finance professionals. Hourly consulting includes search and training.

Salary Minimum: $40,000
Functions: Middle mgmt., Plant mgmt., Health admin., Direct mktg., Personnel, Cash mgmt., Credit
Industries: Drugs mfg., Medical devices, Invest. banking, Venture cap., Hospitality, Accounting, Telecoms

---

Atlantic Search Group, Inc.

1 Liberty Sq.
Boston, Massachusetts 02109-4825
(617) 426-9700
Fax: (617) 426-9013
Email: jobs@atlanticsearch.com

Key Contact - Specialty:
Mr. John B. Beckvold
Mr. Daniel F. Jones
Ms. Gayla K. Hensley

Description: Specializing in accounting, finance, tax, auditing in all industries. All principals are experienced professional accountants and experienced in the personnel/recruiting business. Committed to arranging only quality interviews.
Functions: CFO's, Budgeting, Cash mgmt., Credit, Taxes
Industries: Generalist

Atlantic West Int'l.

1201 Raleigh Rd., Ste. F-101
Chapel Hill, North Carolina 27514
(919) 942-3080
Fax: (919) 942-0190
Email: rvawi@aol.com

Key Contact - Specialty:
Mr. Richard W. Valenti

Description: Executive search and recruitment services focused in the medical device industry for multinational corporations to small, privately held domestic firms.

Salary Minimum: $60,000
Functions: General mgmt., Mfg., Materials, Sales & mktg., Finance, R&D, Engineering
Industries: Drugs mfg., Medical devices, Pharmaceutical svcs., Biotech

Branches:
6337 S. Highland Drive, Ste. 300
Salt Lake City, Utah 84121
(801) 943-9944
Fax: (801) 943-8755
Key Contact - Specialty:
Mr. James H. Doddridge

Atomic Personnel, Inc.

P.O. Box 11244/Z4
Philadelphia, Pennsylvania 19027-0244
(215) 885-4223

Key Contact - Specialty:
Mr. Arthur L. Krasnow

Description: Professional and management level contingency recruitment for all engineering, technical and scientific fields and industries across the U.S. Staffed by experienced graduate technical professionals.

Salary Minimum: $35,000
Functions: Mfg., Production, Automation, Packaging, Sales mgmt., R&D, Engineering
Industries: Energy/utilities, Construction, Mfg., Haz. waste, Packaging, High tech

---

ATS Executive Recruitment

1425 Market Blvd., Ste. 330-A
Roswell, Georgia 30076
(770) 642-9804
Fax: (770) 643-8635
Email: rvanweelde@mindspring.com

Key Contact - Specialty:
Mr. Ron Van Weelde - *Commercial, investment banking (generalist)*

Description: Provide executive search nationally for banking positions $50,000 and up. Banking searches include capital markets, treasury, corporate finance, corporate lending, credit card, cash management and international lending.

Salary Minimum: $50,000
Functions: Cash mgmt., Credit, M&A, Risk mgmt.
Industries: Banking, Invest. banking, Brokers, Misc. financial

---

Attorney Search Global, Inc.

5445 N. Sheridan Rd.
Edgewater Plaza, Ste. 301
Chicago, Illinois 60640
(773) 271-5100
Fax: (773) 271-9011
Email: asglaw@aol.com
Web: www.attorneyrecruit.com

Key Contact - Specialty:
Ms. Lucille K. Green - *Attorney recruitment*

Description: We are specialists in attorney recruitment.

Salary Minimum: $50,000
Functions: Legal
Industries: Generalist, Energy/utilities, Mfg., Wholesale, Finance, Legal, Environmental svcs.

Attorneys at Work
(a division of Net Placement Corp.)

550 Pharr Rd., Ste. 530
Atlanta, Georgia 30305
(404) 467-0076
Fax: (404) 467-1090
Email: sales@legnetwork.com
Web: www.attorneysatwork.com

Key Contact - Specialty:
Mr. Patrick A. Arnold - *Law*
Mr. Peter Sinden - *Law*
Mr. Samuel B. Kellett, Jr. - *Law*

Description: Taking the place of a traditional search firm, we are a company that links hundreds of legal employers with thousands of individual attorneys and students confidentially via a secured website.
Functions: Attorneys
Industries: Legal

Aurora Tech Search
704 Fifth Ave. E.
Owen Sound, Ontario N4K 2R6
Canada
(519) 371-6089
(716) 631-7647
Email: jmols@log.on.ca
Web: www.ipa.com/eoffice/716-631-7647.html

Key Contact - Specialty:
Mr. Jeff Mols - *Information technology, aerospace engineering, sales and marketing*

Description: We provide professional search services for businesses in the information technology industry and in the aerospace industry. Our focus area includes Ontario, Canada and New York State. A full guarantee for our service is offered, permanent placement searches offered on contingency and retainer.

Salary Minimum: $35,000
Functions: Middle mgmt., Automation, Materials Plng., Mkt. research, Training, IT, Engineering
Industries: Computer equip., Banking, Computer svcs., Telecoms, Aerospace, High tech, Software

Cami Austin & Assoc.
P.O. Box 1005
Marion, Illinois 62959-7505
(618) 995-1608
Fax: (618) 995-1610
Email: camihunter@aol.com

Key Contact - Specialty:
Ms. Cami Austin - *Radio frequency, microwave, wireless, telecommunications engineers (all types), sales & marketing operations*

Description: Professional search consultants for management, engineering and sales/marketing talent in the electronics industry including: wireless, radio frequency, microwave, semiconductors, fiber optics, switching power supplies, instrumentation, satellite communications, cellular.

Salary Minimum: $50,000
Functions: Senior mgmt., Middle mgmt., Product dev., Mktg. mgmt., Sales mgmt., Systems anal., Engineering
Industries: Consumer electronics, Test/measurement equip., Telecoms, Aerospace, High tech

Austin - Allen Co.
8127 Walnut Grove Rd.
Cordova, Tennessee 38018
(901) 756-0900
Fax: (901) 756-0933
Email: austinrec@aol.com
Web: www.austinallen.com

Key Contact - Specialty:
Mr. C. A. Cupp - *Engineering, human resources*

Description: Broad range of assignments in engineering, manufacturing and human resources for manufacturing.

Salary Minimum: $35,000
Functions: Production, Automation, Materials Plng., Distribution, Personnel, Training, Engineering
Industries: Chemicals, Medical devices, Plastics/rubber, Machinery/Appliances, Motor vehicles, Computer equip., Misc. mfg.

Austin Michaels, Ltd., Inc.
8687 E. Via de Ventura, Ste. 303
Scottsdale, Arizona 85258
(602) 483-5000
Fax: (602) 483-6068
Email: frank@austinmichaels.com

Key Contact - Specialty:
Mr. Frank E. O'Brien - *Sales & marketing, engineering, manufacturing, high technology*
Mr. Robert R. Hebert - *Manufacturing, engineering*

Description: We offer competitive fees and by having a small active client base, we eliminate the possibility of conflict of interest.
Functions: Senior mgmt., Middle mgmt., Quality, Purchasing, Materials Plng., Mkt. research, Engineering
Industries: Computer equip., Consumer electronics, Test/measurement equip., High tech, Software

Austin Park Management Group Inc.
40 Eglinton Ave. E., Ste. 207
Toronto, Ontario M4P 3A2
Canada
(416) 488-9565
Fax: (416) 488-9601
Email: austin@web.net
Web: www.austinpark.com

Key Contact - Specialty:
Mr. Howard Prince - *Professional services (UNIX)*
Mr. Earl Gardiner - *Professional services (UNIX)*

Description: Our firm conducts searches at a variety of functional levels: management, executive and senior staff based on experience in the Unix and three tier client/server technology sectors.

Salary Minimum: $60,000
Functions: Mfg., Sales & mktg., HR mgmt., IT, Systems dev., Systems support, Specialized services
Industries: Mfg., Computer equip., Finance, Svcs., Communications, High tech, Software

Affiliates:
APX inc.

Austin, Hill & Assoc.
8483 Spring Showers Way
Ellicott City, Maryland 21043
(410) 418-4660
Fax: (410) 418-5517
Email: austin4660@aol.com

Key Contact - Specialty:
Mr. Michael G. Hill

Description: Search firm principal has extensive personal experience in sales, marketing, human resources and finance. Working searches nationally, we seek superior results for our clients.

Salary Minimum: $50,000
Functions: Generalist, General mgmt., Sales & mktg., Direct mktg., HR mgmt., Finance, IT
Industries: Generalist, Food/bev/tobacco, Soap/perfume/cosmetics, Motor vehicles, Retail, Hospitality, Human resource svcs.

Automation Technology Search
7309 Del Cielo Way
Modesto, California 95356
(209) 545-4500
Fax: (209) 545-3060
Email: atsearch@pc-intouch.com

Key Contact - Specialty:
Mr. Ralph L. Becker - *Manufacturing, engineering, software*

Description: Recruiters of managers and engineers in design and development involving s/w, h/w, firmware in the food, metals, plastics, medical and packaging industries. Specialties are mechanical, electronic, chemical, computer science engineers.

Salary Minimum: $30,000
Functions: Product dev., Production, Automation, Materials Plng., Sales mgmt., Systems implem., Engineering

Industries: Food/bev/tobacco, Metal products, Machinery/Appliances, Computer equip., Misc. mfg., Software

Branches:
P.O. Box 2152
Livermore, California 94551
(408) 897-3157
Fax: (408) 897-3010
Email: ingerice@worldnet.att.net
Key Contact - Specialty:
Ms. Inge Rice - *MIS*

AutoPeople
4 North St.
Brattleboro, Vermont 05301
(802) 257-2719
Fax: (802) 257-2769
Email: blaushild@autopeople.com
Web: www.autopeople.com

Key Contact - Specialty:
Mr. Eric Blaushild - *Automobile dealership management*

Description: Founded and managed by a former automobile dealer, our only specialty is providing management to automobile dealerships.
Functions: Senior mgmt., Middle mgmt., Sales mgmt., CFO's
Industries: Retail

Branches:
101 North Main St.
Sharon, Massachusetts 02067
(781) 793-9070
Key Contact - Specialty:
Mr. Robert B. Hershman

5050 Quorum Drive, Ste. 700
Dallas, Texas 75240
(214) 788-1988
Key Contact - Specialty:
Mr. Eric Blaushild - *Automotive dealership management*

Availability Personnel Consultants
169 S. River Rd.
Bedford, New Hampshire 03110-6936
(603) 669-4440
Fax: (603) 669-8757
Email: availability@sprintmail.com

Key Contact - Specialty:
Mr. Walter D. Kilian

Description: Contingency search specialists serving New England in all aspects of professional staffing for manufacturing and service industries from 5MM to Fortune 500 firms and their divisions.

Salary Minimum: $40,000
Functions: Product dev., Production, Plant mgmt., Quality, Purchasing, Materials Plng., Engineering
Industries: Medical devices, Plastics/rubber, Metal products

Avestruz & Assoc.
47 Bluejay
Irvine, California 92604
(949) 651-8721
Fax: (949) 559-4040
Email: avestruzassoc@home.com

Key Contact - Specialty:
Mr. Alner Avestruz - *Medical device*

Description: Specializing in the placement of senior level medical personnel in marketing, sales, administrative and biomedical engineering in the radiology, cardiology, information systems and surgery industries.

Salary Minimum: $75,000
Functions: Senior mgmt., Middle mgmt., Product dev., Allied health, Mkt. research, Mktg. mgmt., Sales mgmt.
Industries: Medical devices, High tech, Software, Biotech, Healthcare

---

Avion International Technology Inc.
6745A Century Ave.
Mississauga, Ontario L5N 7K2
Canada
(905) 812-7601
Fax: (905) 812-7606
Email: jfortin@avionintl.com
Web: www.avionintl.com

Key Contact - Specialty:
Ms. Joanne Fortin-Menendez - *Information technology*
Ms. Caroline Hartman - *Information technology*

Description: We provide contract and permanent staffing services, focusing strictly in information technology related positions in the areas of PC/LAN, WAN, as well as mid-range and mainframe environments.

Salary Minimum: $40,000
Functions: MIS mgmt., Systems anal., Systems dev., Systems implem., Systems support, Network admin., DB admin.
Industries: Mfg., Finance, Svcs., Communications, Government, High tech, Software

---

Bader Research Corp.
6 E. 45th St.
New York, New York 10017
(212) 682-4750
Fax: (212) 682-4758

Key Contact - Specialty:
Mr. Sam Bader - *Attorneys*

Description: Our 31st year as specialists in the recruitment of highly qualified attorneys for the nation's leading law firms, corporations and financial institutions. We also effect mergers and acquisitions of law firms.

Salary Minimum: $75,000
Functions: Attorneys
Industries: Legal

Keith Bagg & Assoc., Inc.
85 Richmond St. W., Ste. 700
Toronto, Ontario M5H 2C9
Canada
(416) 863-1800
Fax: (416) 350-9600
Email: info@bagg.com
Web: www.bagg.com

Key Contact - Specialty:
Mr. Keith Bagg
Ms. Mary Bagg - *Administrative*
Mr. Bruce McAlpine

Description: Our mission is to become the source of choice for our client's most valuable corporate resource, namely their employees.

Salary Minimum: $45,000
Functions: Senior mgmt., Middle mgmt., Mfg., Materials, Sales & mktg., Finance, IT
Industries: Food/bev/tobacco, Chemicals, Computer equip., Misc. financial, Communications, High tech, Software

---

Bailey Employment System Inc.
5 W Branch Rd.
Westport, Connecticut 06680-1249
(203) 227-8434
Fax: (203) 227-8151
Email: bailey51@aol.com

Key Contact - Specialty:
Mr. Sheldon Leighton - *Physicians*

Description: We have been recruiting since 1960 and in the healthcare field since 1985. We have successfully placed throughout the United States and attribute our longevity and success to our professionalism.
Functions: Physicians
Industries: Healthcare

D. W. Baird & Associates
10751 Falls Rd., Ste. 250
Baltimore, Maryland 21093
(410) 339-7670
Fax: (410) 823-0146

Key Contact - Specialty:
Mr. David W. Baird

Description: Mid-Atlantic recruiting specialists in manufacturing, marketing, technical and management personnel.

Particular areas of expertise include the chemical, coatings, plastics, mechanical and environmental industries.

Salary Minimum: $40,000
Functions: Product dev., Production, Plant mgmt., Productivity, Sales mgmt., R&D, Engineering
Industries: Paper, Chemicals, Plastics/rubber, Paints/petroleum products, Metal products, Machinery/Appliances, Environmental svcs.

Baker Scott & Co.

1259 Rte. 46
Parsippany, New Jersey 07054
(973) 263-3355
Fax: (973) 263-9255
Email: bkrscott@planet.net
Web: www.bakerscott.com

Key Contact - Specialty:
Ms. Judy Bouer
Mr. David Allen

Description: Full service executive search firm specializing in nationwide and international assignments in telecommunications, cable, broadcasting and emerging technologies across functional disciplines.

Salary Minimum: $50,000
Functions: Senior mgmt., Middle mgmt., Advertising, HR mgmt., CFO's, MIS mgmt., Int'l.
Industries: Communications, New media, Broadcast & Film, Telecoms, Software

---

Baker, Nelms & Montgomery

676 St. Clair, Ste. 2050
Chicago, Illinois 60611
(312) 397-8808
Fax: (312) 397-9631
Email: bakernelms@worldnet.att.net

Key Contact - Specialty:
Mr. William W. Baker
Ms. Sharon I. Baker
Ms. Debra Nelms

Description: A retained search firm focusing on IT and corporate strategy consulting firms and major industry clients. Positions are generally at the manager up through partner and VP levels.
Functions: Senior mgmt., Middle mgmt., MIS mgmt., Systems anal., Systems implem., DB admin., Mgmt. consultants
Industries: Banking, Invest. banking, Brokers, Non-profits, Mgmt. consulting, Telecoms, High tech

---

Baldwin & Assoc.

3975 Erie Ave.
Cincinnati, Ohio 45208-1908
(513) 272-2400
Fax: (513) 527-5929
Web: www.baldwin-assoc.com

Key Contact - Specialty:
Mr. W. Keith Baldwin - *Technical, management, CEO*
Ms. Janice F. Seymour - *Sales, manufacturing*
Mr. William W. Schrepferman - *Human resources, management*
Ms. Nancy Foster - *Finance*
Mr. Keith Powers - *Information systems, information technology, MIS*
Mr. Thomas Pharr - *Information systems, information technology, MIS*

Description: Generalists assisting greater-Cincinnati area companies to fill requirements ranging from individual contributor to executive management. We tailor our service to clients' needs with capability for project, search and ongoing retainer relationships.

Salary Minimum: $30,000
Functions: Middle mgmt., Mfg., Purchasing, Mktg. mgmt., Benefits, Systems anal., Engineering
Industries: Generalist, Mfg., Finance, Svcs., Communications, High tech, Software

---

The Bales-Waugh Group

1301 River Place Tower, Ste. 2016
Jacksonville, Florida 32207
(904) 398-9080
Fax: (904) 398-8121
Email: HdsHnted@aol.com

Key Contact - Specialty:
Ms. Sally Bales - *Medical device, international*
Mr. Chris Waugh - *Medical, international*

Description: Full service firm recruiting for all areas within company. Entry-level through executive search. The six year old international division includes 30 retained search firm partners worldwide.

Salary Minimum: $40,000
Functions: Directors, Senior mgmt., Middle mgmt., Product dev., Production, Nurses, Allied health
Industries: Drugs mfg., Medical devices, Healthcare

Carol Ball & Co.

72 St. Johns Rd.
Wilton, Connecticut 06897
(203) 762-1752
Fax: (203) 762-1753
Web: elizbrand@aol.com

Key Contact - Specialty:
Ms. Carol Ball - *Public relations, corporate communications*

Description: Specialists in communications professionals for PR agencies and corporate communications departments throughout the USA. Recruit middle, senior and top management level personnel.

Salary Minimum: $35,000
Functions: PR
Industries: Generalist, Pharmaceutical svcs., Mgmt. consulting, Advertising/PR

Branches:
88 Colgate Ave.
Wyckoff, New Jersey 07481
(201) 670-7142
Fax: (201) 670-6142
Key Contact - Specialty:
Ms. Elizabeth Brand - *Public relations, corporate communications executives*

BallResources

P.O. Box 480391
Kansas City, Missouri 64148
(816) 322-2727
Email: ronball@swbell.net

Key Contact - Specialty:
Mr. Ronald D. Ball - *Industrial sales, sales management*

Description: A no frills get the job done search service. Specializing in industrial sales and sales management. National (USA) scope.

Salary Minimum: $25,000
Functions: Mktg. mgmt., Sales mgmt.
Industries: Chemicals, Plastics/rubber, Metal products, Machinery/Appliances, Test/measurement equip., Misc. mfg., Packaging

---

The Bankers Group
(a division of Executive Directions, Inc.)

10 S. Riverside Plaza
Chicago, Illinois 60606
(312) 930-9456
Fax: (312) 930-1119

Key Contact - Specialty:
Mr. Joseph Womak - *Banking*
Mr. Peter Chappell - *Banking*

Description: Recruitment of banking professionals for investment and brokerage firms, foreign exchange, major money centers and regional banks, leasing and mortgage firms and savings and loan institutions.

Salary Minimum: $50,000
Functions: Senior mgmt., Middle mgmt., Admin. svcs., Mkt. research, Mktg. mgmt., Sales mgmt., Minorities

Industries: Banking, Invest. banking, Brokers, Misc. financial, Accounting, Human resource svcs., Insurance

The Bankers Register
500 Fifth Ave., Ste. 414
New York, New York 10110
(212) 840-0800

Key Contact - Specialty:
Mr. James Bogart - *Banking*
Ms. Vivian Richards - *Banking*

Description: Specialists in the recruitment and placement of banking personnel: commercial, corporate, international, thrift, mortgage/real estate.
Functions: Cash mgmt., Credit
Industries: Finance, Banking

Bankers Search, L.L.C.
P.O. Box 854
Madison, Connecticut 06443
(203) 245-0694
Fax: (203) 245-9567

Key Contact - Specialty:
Mr. Timothy M. Loughlin - *Banking*

Description: For over 30 years, we have been providing superior executive recruiting services throughout New England. We cater to all disciplines of banking, focusing on the placement of middle and senior management.

Salary Minimum: $60,000
Industries: Banking

Paul C. Banks Assoc.
(Firm declined to update.)
2715 Bridgegate Cove
Marietta, Georgia 30068
(770) 565-2346

Key Contact - Specialty:
Mr. Paul C. Banks - *Purchasing, materials management, logistics*

Description: Specializing in: purchasing buyers/managers/directors, subcontract administrators, materials managers, operations management, traffic and warehouse management, inventory and production control.

Salary Minimum: $40,000
Functions: Materials, Purchasing, Materials Plng., Distribution
Industries: Generalist

Barber & Assoc.
143 Knight Court, Ste. 100
Georgetown, Kentucky 40324
(502) 863-5575
Email: bcbarber@lex.infi.net

Key Contact - Specialty:
Mr. Bill C. Barber - *Automotive, seating, metal fabrication*
Mrs. Barbara R. Barber

Description: Computerized network database offers clients in excess of 50,000 candidates of all professions, varying skill and salary levels. We offer permanent and contract personnel and can respond quickly to your need.

Salary Minimum: $20,000
Functions: Product dev., Production, Automation, Quality, Productivity, Engineering
Industries: Plastics/rubber, Metal products, Machinery/Appliances, Motor vehicles, Misc. mfg.

Barclay Consultants, Inc.
16 Chestnut Court, Ste. B
Brielle, New Jersey 08730
(732) 223-1131

Key Contact - Specialty:
Mr. Jules Silverman - *Sales, sales management, technical support, technical management*
Ms. Linda Pappas - *Sales, sales management, technical support, technical management*

Description: Professional search firm staffed by individuals from the data and information processing industries. Areas of specialization are sales, marketing and technical.

Salary Minimum: $30,000
Functions: Senior mgmt., Middle mgmt., Sales mgmt., Systems dev., Systems implem., Systems support, Mgmt. consultants
Industries: Computer equip., Consumer electronics, Computer svcs., Mgmt. consulting, High tech, Software

Barnes & Assoc. Executive Search
1101 Dove St., Ste. 200
Newport Beach, California 92660
(949) 253-6750
Fax: (949) 253-6753
Email: msbarnes@ix.netcom.com
Web: www.barnesandassociates.com

Key Contact - Specialty:
Ms. Meredith Barnes Schwarz - *IT, sales, marketing, technical support*
Mr. Michael G. Larsen - *VP sales, VP marketing, product, PR*
Ms. Joan M. Bernal - *System engineers, pre-sales, post-sales*
Ms. Elaine K. Hobbins - *System engineers, data communications*

Description: 18 years of executive search experience in the high tech industry. The firm works the entire nation placing executives in the software, networking and pre-IPO companies.

Salary Minimum: $60,000
Functions: Senior mgmt., Middle mgmt., Mktg. mgmt., Sales mgmt., PR, IT, Systems implem.
Industries: Computer equip., Computer svcs., Advertising/PR, New media, Telecoms, High tech, Software

Barone Assoc.
3121 Atlantic Ave.
P.O. Box 706
Allenwood, New Jersey 08720-0706
(732) 292-0900
Fax: (732) 292-0880

Key Contact - Specialty:
Mr. L. Donald Rizzo
Mr. Noel Cram
Mr. Robert Horan

Description: A firm of industry professionals reacting to and positively affecting the human dynamics of the recruitment/search process. Significant engineering, marketing and manufacturing work in healthcare products, chemical process and manufacturing industries.

Salary Minimum: $30,000
Functions: Product dev., Production, Purchasing, Distribution, Mktg. mgmt., Sales mgmt., Engineering
Industries: Chemicals, Drugs mfg., Medical devices, Plastics/rubber, Metal products, Computer equip., Misc. mfg.

Barr Assoc.
93 S. West End Blvd., Ste. 105B
Quakertown, Pennsylvania 18951
(215) 538-9411
Fax: (215) 538-9466
Email: barr@pipeline.com

Key Contact - Specialty:
Ms. Sharon A. Barr - *Technical sales, marketing, semiconductor, telecommunications industries*
Mr. Charly Barr - *Engineering, operations, sales & marketing, semiconductor industry*
Mr. Agim Zabeli - *Semiconductor, telecommunications industries (all positions)*
Mr. Tom Ozoroski - *Semiconductor, telecommunications industries, engineering*

Description: Established specialized recruiting firm with in-depth knowledge in the semiconductor and telecommunications industries. Custom recruiting focusing on long term relationships.
Functions: Product dev., Production, Quality, Mktg. mgmt., Sales mgmt., R&D, Engineering

Industries: Computer equip., Telecoms, High tech

Barr Associates

521 Fifth Ave., 17th Floor
New York, New York 10017
(212) 867-3215
Fax: (212) 867-3144
Email: barrassociates@worldnet.att.net

Key Contact - Specialty:
Mr. Jamie Barr
Mr. Kelly Barr
Ms. Patricia Fiorentino

Description: Executive search firm specializing in senior level positions in the broker dealer and commercial banking industries. Our areas of expertise are risk management and corporate finance positions in the domestic and emerging markets.

Salary Minimum: $75,000
Functions: M&A, Risk mgmt.
Industries: Banking, Invest. banking

The Barrett Group

59 Stiles Rd., Ste. 105
Salem, New Hampshire 03079
(603) 890-1111
Fax: (603) 890-1118
Email: headhunt@iname.com
Web: http://home.ici.net/customers/barrett/barrett.htm

Key Contact - Specialty:
Mr. Bill Barrett - *Medical sales, sales management, marketing positions*
Mr. Frank Dion - *Medical*

Description: 19 years in business. 100% medical recruiting at all levels including international. Deal quite a bit with start-up medical companies.

Salary Minimum: $40,000
Functions: Directors, Senior mgmt., Middle mgmt., Mkt. research, Mktg. mgmt., Sales mgmt., CFO's
Industries: Medical devices

Barrett Partners

100 N. LaSalle St., Ste. 1420
Chicago, Illinois 60602
(312) 443-8877
Fax: (312) 443-8866
Email: questions@barrettpartners.com
Web: www.barrettpartners.com

Key Contact - Specialty:
Mr. Joseph Thielman
Mr. John L. Molitor - *Accounting, financial*
Mr. Jeffrey McNear - *Accounting & finance, engineering, technical*
Mr. Nicholas Kapetan - *Engineering, technical*

Description: Professional search consultants specializing in the placement of accounting/financial and engineering/technical candidates for permanent and contract/temporary opportunities.

Salary Minimum: $30,000
Functions: Finance, MIS mgmt., Systems dev., Systems support, Engineering
Industries: Mfg., Finance, Svcs., Communications, Insurance, High tech, Biotech

Affiliates:
Barrettemps

Barrett Rose & Lee, Inc.

330 Bay St., Ste. 520
Toronto, Ontario M5H 2S8
Canada
(416) 363-9700
Fax: (416) 363-8999
Email: info@barrettrose.com

Key Contact - Specialty:
Mr. J. Arthur Clark - *High technology vendors*
Mr. H. Peter Heinemann - *High technology vendors*

Description: A management oriented local firm focusing on information technology vendors in disciplines of information technology professionals, sales and marketing as well as finance and administration.

Salary Minimum: $60,000
Functions: Sales & mktg., Finance, MIS mgmt.
Industries: Computer equip., Computer svcs., Telecoms, High tech, Software

Aldonna Barry Personnel & Management

(Firm declined to update.)
18 King St. E, Ste. 8
Bolton, Ontario L7E 1E8
Canada
(905) 951-3434

Key Contact - Specialty:
Ms. Aldonna Kaulius-Barry - *Senior management, executives*

Description: We recruit gold. Top individuals with absolutely proven abilities and integrity are those presented. Ethics, intelligence, hands-on and team focus is bottom line.
Functions: Senior mgmt., Middle mgmt., Admin. svcs., Mktg. mgmt., Sales mgmt., Training, Int'l.
Industries: Generalist, Mfg., Drugs mfg., Plastics/rubber, Paints/petroleum products, Misc. mfg., Packaging

Bartl & Evins
(a division of Fidelity Employment Group, Inc.)

The Penthouse, 333 N. Broadway
Jericho, New York 11753
(516) 433-3333
Fax: (516) 433-2692
Email: bartl@ibm.net

Key Contact - Specialty:
Ms. Susan Evins - *CFOs*
Mr. Frank Bartl - *Controllers and accountants*

Description: Twenty years financial recruiting means that we know many CFO's and controllers. This knowledge translates into a superior resource for our clients.

Salary Minimum: $65,000
Functions: CFO's, Budgeting, Cash mgmt., Credit, Taxes, M&A
Industries: Wholesale, Retail, Finance, Entertainment, Computer svcs., Accounting, Real estate

The Barton Group, Inc.

8854 Roslyn
Livonia, Michigan 48150-3533
(734) 458-7555
Fax: (734) 458-5176
Email: bfoster@thebartongroup.com
Web: www.thebartongroup.com

Key Contact - Specialty:
Mr. Barton T. Foster - *Technical, industry, manufacturing, auto, audio*
Ms. Dianne Hamilton
Mr. Al Mirsky - *Technical, industry, manufacturing, auto, audio*

Description: We place engineers, purchasing, technical sales, marketing, management and executives in manufacturing and industry. We do retained and contingency searches. Our excellent reputation is due to commitment fulfilling client's needs.

Salary Minimum: $40,000
Functions: Directors, Senior mgmt., Middle mgmt., Product dev., Production, Plant mgmt., Quality
Industries: Lumber/furniture, Motor vehicles, Consumer electronics, Transportation

Bartz Rogers & Partners

6465 Wayzata Blvd., Ste. 777
Minneapolis, Minnesota 55426
(612) 595-8100
Fax: (612) 595-8009

Email: career@bartz-rogers.com

Key Contact - Specialty:
Mr. Douglas Bartz - *Information systems (executives & professionals)*
Mr. Scott Rogers - *Information systems (executives & professionals)*

Description: We provide our clients quality and timely search and consulting services specializing in information technology recruitment from the programmer level to the CIO.

Salary Minimum: $45,000
Functions: MIS mgmt., Systems anal., Systems dev., Systems implem., Systems support
Industries: Generalist

Bassett Laudi Partners
2 Bloor St. W., Ste. 2600, Box 4
Toronto, Ontario M4W 2G7
Canada
(416) 935-0855
Fax: (416) 935-1106
Email: careers@bassettlaudi.com
Web: www.bassettlaudi.com

Key Contact - Specialty:
Mr. Martyn Bassett - *Information technology*
Mr. Mario Laudi - *Information technology*

Description: We bring together the best human capital with the best corporations in North America. We provide Fortune 500 and Fortune 1000 companies with the research and representation they need to stay ahead in the marketplace by using leading edge technology to find the right job match quickly.

Salary Minimum: $35,000
Functions: IT, MIS mgmt., Systems anal., Systems dev., Systems implem., Systems support, DB admin.
Industries: Software

Bast & Assoc., Inc.
11726 San Vicente Blvd., Ste. 200
Los Angeles, California 90049
(310) 207-2100
Fax: (310) 207-3003
Email: bastassoc@aol.com

Key Contact - Specialty:
Mr. Larry C. Bast
Ms. Sue E. Bast

Description: Executive search for marketing/advertising management positions with consumer goods/services firms, specializing in Western United States.

Salary Minimum: $50,000
Functions: Advertising, Mkt. research, Mktg. mgmt., Direct mktg., PR
Industries: Food/bev/tobacco, Soap/perfume/cosmetics, Consumer electronics, Entertainment, New media, Broadcast & Film, Telecoms

---

L. Battalin & Co.
P.O. Box 31815
Palm Beach Gardens, Florida 33410-7815
(561) 627-0042
Fax: (561) 627-6771

Key Contact - Specialty:
Mr. Laurence H. Battalin - *Consumer packaged goods marketing*

Description: Specialize in national recruitment and placement of marketing management within the consumer packaged goods industry while pursuing the equal opportunity objectives.

Salary Minimum: $60,000
Functions: Mkt. research, Mktg. mgmt., Minorities
Industries: Food/bev/tobacco, Textiles/apparel, Soap/perfume/cosmetics

---

Bayland Assoc.
4286 Redwood Hwy., Ste. 342
San Rafael, California 94903
(415) 499-8111
Email: baylandtjk@aol.com

Key Contact - Specialty:
Mr. Thomas J. Kunkel - *Medical device, instrumentation, information management*

Description: Specializes in conducting national and local executive searches exclusively within medical manufacturing, sales and services environments. Medical diagnostic, therapeutic, instrumentation, equipment, device and service marketplaces are where we have the greatest expertise.

Salary Minimum: $70,000
Functions: General mgmt., Mfg., Mktg. mgmt., Sales mgmt., IT, R&D, Engineering
Industries: Medical devices, High tech, Software

Beacon Int'l., Inc.
8300 Boone Blvd., Ste. 500
Vienna, Virginia 22182
(703) 848-9266
Fax: (703) 713-0933
Email: lgoldbach@aol.com
Web: www.beaconsearch.com

Key Contact - Specialty:
Ms. Linda J. Goldbach - *Insurance, risk management, finance, manufacturing, media*

Description: Retained search firm specializing in middle management and senior level positions in insurance, finance, high technology and media recruiting for domestic and international clients.

Salary Minimum: $75,000
Functions: General mgmt., Senior mgmt., Middle mgmt., Sales & mktg., Finance, IT, Int'l.
Industries: Mfg., Retail, Finance, Svcs., Communications, Insurance, High tech

---

The Beardsley Group Inc.
427 Bridgeport Ave.
Shelton, Connecticut 06484
(203) 944-0050
Fax: (203) 944-0052
Email: directory@beardsleygroup.com
Web: www.beardsleygroup.com

Key Contact - Specialty:
Mr. Harry Roscoe - *Data communications, telecommunications, networking*
Ms. Joan Leone - *Data communications, telecommunications, networking*
Ms. Liz Cooper - *Data communications, telecommunications, networking*
Ms. Kathy McCormack - *Data communications, telecommunications, networking*
Ms. Noreen Upton - *Data communications, telecommunications, networking*
Ms. Adele Hoffman - *Data communications, telecommunications, networking*
Ms. Beverly Newell - *Data communications, telecommunications, networking*

Description: We are comprised of individuals who once worked in the datacommunications field who best understand the needs of the client based on personal experience.
Functions: Sales mgmt., Systems anal., Systems implem., Systems support
Industries: Computer equip., Telecoms, High tech

Beck/Eastwood Recruitment Solutions
28170 Ave. Crocker, Ste. 202
Valencia, California 91355
(805) 295-6666
Fax: (805) 295-5153
Email: beckeast@scvnet.com
Web: beckeastwood.com

Key Contact - Specialty:
Mr. Steven Beck - *Sales & marketing, information technology*
Mr. Gary Eastwood - *Sales & marketing, information technology, medical, pharmaceutical*

Description: We raise the level of commitment to satisfy our clients' needs through innovative strategic partnerships (co-venture program), expert direct recruiting and our recruiting network of over 370 offices nationwide.

Salary Minimum: $50,000
Functions: Mktg. mgmt., Sales mgmt.
Industries: Drugs mfg., Medical devices, Computer equip., Computer svcs., Telecoms, High tech, Software

Becker Personnel

6301 NW Fifth Way, Ste. 2100
Ft. Lauderdale, Florida 33309
(954) 776-5554
Fax: (954) 776-5855
Email: matthew_becker@becker-personnel.com
Web: www.becker-personnel.com

Key Contact - Specialty:
Mr. Matthew Becker - *Accounting, finance, human resources*
Mr. Dean Gross - *Accounting, finance, human resources*
Ms. Marjorie Hawke - *Accounting, finance, human resources*
Ms. Debra McCarthy - *Temporary, accounting, finance, human resources*
Ms. Veroushka MacLean - *Information technology*

Description: We analyze the specific needs of our clients and execute a customized search. We consistently seek feedback from our customers in order to continually improve the placement process.
Functions: HR mgmt., Finance, IT
Industries: Generalist

Branches:
1101 Brickell Ave., Ste. 701-S
Miami, Florida 33131
(305) 377-1110
Fax: (305) 377-9511
Email: dean-gross@becker-personnel.com
Web: www.becker-personnel.com
Key Contact - Specialty:
Mr. Dean Gross - *Accounting, finance, human resources*

Becker Project Resources, Inc.

6327 SW Capital Hwy., #215
Portland, Oregon 97201-1937
(503) 246-6500
(888) 246-6500
Fax: (503) 246-9546
Email: jsbecker@bpr.com
Web: www.bpr.com

Key Contact - Specialty:
Mr. John Becker - *Information technology, SAP*

Description: We are an information technology specialty firm focused on SAP recruiting. Candidates are placed on permanent and contract positions worldwide.

Salary Minimum: $50,000
Functions: Training, Systems anal., Systems dev., Systems implem., Systems support, Mgmt. consultants
Industries: Mfg., Banking, Aerospace, High tech, Software

Beckman & Assoc. Legal Search

Rivercenter, P.O. Box 75142
Cincinnati, Ohio 45275
(513) 651-2992
Fax: (513) 651-2240
Email: beckman@rof.net

Key Contact - Specialty:
Ms. Susan R. Beckman - *Healthcare law, corporate, litigation, tax & computer law*

Description: We work with law firms and corporations nationwide to find qualified partner and associate level candidates. We also provide searches for practice group and potential merger candidates.
Functions: Legal
Industries: Legal

Branches:
P.O. Box 8167
Aspen, Colorado 81612
(970) 920-3227
Email: charlesd@rof.net
Key Contact - Specialty:
Mr. Charles D. Fagin

Robert Beech West Inc.

383 S. Palm Caynon Dr.
Palm Canyon, California 92262
(760) 864-1380
Fax: (760) 864-1382
Email: beechinc@aol.com

Key Contact - Specialty:
Mr. Robert Beech - *Computer sales & marketing*

Description: Over 22 years placing sales and marketing managers and senior sales personnel nationally in computer hardware and software industry.

Salary Minimum: $60,000
Functions: General mgmt., Senior mgmt., Middle mgmt., Mktg. mgmt., Sales mgmt., IT, Systems support
Industries: Mfg., Computer equip., Svcs., Computer svcs., Communications, Telecoms, Software

Branches:
2551 State St.
Carlsbad, California 92008
(760) 434-6635
Email: beechinc@aol.com
Key Contact - Specialty:
Mr. Robert Beech - *Computer sales & marketing*

55 A Galli Drive
San Francisco, California 94949
(415) 884-2600
Fax: (415) 884-2684
Key Contact - Specialty:
Ms. Arleen Beech

Behrens and Company

2480 Sparks Rd.
P.O. Box 157
Easton, Washington 98925
(509) 656-0284
Fax: (509) 656-2298
Email: doc19@ix.netcom.com
Web: www.behrensco.com

Key Contact - Specialty:
Mr. Rick Behrens - *Capital machinery*

Description: Concentration on the food, pharmaceutical and packaging machinery systems industries and companies allied to those industries. Focus on locating accomplished executive management, sales and marketing and engineering professionals on a national and international basis. Search services for engineering and field technical service candidates are also offered.

Salary Minimum: $50,000
Functions: Directors, Middle mgmt., Automation, Packaging, Sales mgmt., Engineering, Int'l.
Industries: Food/bev/tobacco, Paper, Printing, Metal products, Machinery/Appliances, Misc. mfg., Packaging

Marcia Beilin, Inc.

230 Park Ave., Ste. 1530
New York, New York 10169
(212) 370-4330
Fax: (212) 370-4335

Key Contact - Specialty:
Ms. Marcia Beilin - *Attorneys (top credentialed)*

Description: Marcia Beilin, Inc. was founded in 1981 with three years of prior experience in the field. We place lawyers only, with law firms, corporations and investment banks. Our candidates come from the leading law schools or the top 10% of their classes.

Salary Minimum: $80,000
Functions: Attorneys
Industries: Legal

Belanger Partners Ltd.

20 Bluffwood Drive
Willowdale, Ontario M2H 3L6
Canada
(416) 499-9090
Fax: (416) 498-6573
Email: belanger@belangerpartners.ca
Web: www.belangerpartners.ca

Key Contact - Specialty:
Mr. Rick Belanger - *Computers, communications (vendors)*

Description: A small firm we specialize in search and recruitment for the vendor community of the computer/communications industries. Our placements and client relations endure.
Functions: General mgmt., Sales & mktg., CFO's, Systems implem., Systems support, Int'l.
Industries: Computer equip., Computer svcs., Telecoms, High tech, Software

---

Edward Bell Assoc.

50 First St., Ste. 320
San Francisco, California 94105
(415) 442-0270
Fax: (415) 442-1862
Email: ebajobs@ix.netcom.com

Key Contact - Specialty:
Mr. Edward Bell - *Accounting, finance, real estate*
Mr. Luigi Favero - *Data processing*
Ms. Janet Guardiani - *Data processing*
Ms. Ilana Brody - *Data processing*
Mr. Keith Sears - *Accounting, finance, clerical*
Mr. John Postlethwaite - *Accounting, finance, clerical*

Description: As a local recruiting firm, our recruiters have developed strong business relations with our clients. If any questions or concerns arise, our clients have immediate access to our account managers with authority to resolve all issues.
Functions: Finance, IT
Industries: Finance, Computer svcs., Accounting, Real estate, Software

Branches:
40087 Mission Blvd., #331
Fremont, California 94539
(510) 490-3516
Fax: (510) 490-3516
Key Contact - Specialty:
Mr. Michael Mitzmacher - *Accounting, finance*

Gary S. Bell Assoc., Inc.

55 Harristown Rd.
Glen Rock, New Jersey 07452
(201) 670-4900
Fax: (201) 670-4940
Email: gsbassoc@aol.com
Web: www.mindspring.com/~careerdr/garybell.htm

Key Contact - Specialty:
Mr. Gary S. Bell

Description: Our strengths lie in all facets of general management, marketing, R&D and operations. We concentrate on laboratory products and services, pharmaceuticals, medical devices and biotechnology. We can identify qualified people who can fill your specific needs.

Salary Minimum: $50,000
Functions: General mgmt., Mfg., Materials, Sales & mktg., CFO's, R&D, Engineering
Industries: Chemicals, Soap/perfume/cosmetics, Drugs mfg., Medical devices, Pharmaceutical svcs., Packaging, Biotech

---

William Bell Assoc., Inc.

605 Candlewood Commons
Howell, New Jersey 07731-2173
(732) 901-6000
Fax: (732) 901-2299
Email: WilliambellAssociates.com

Key Contact - Specialty:
Mr. Steven Neidenberg - *Cosmetics, chemical, personal care*
Mr. Ken Cerra - *Operations management, household, health & beauty aids*
Ms. Phyllis Kay - *Generalist*
Ms. Debbie Madrigal - *Generalist*

Description: Specialists in placement of cosmetic chemists and management. Additional areas include purchasing, planning, quality control, quality assurance, packaging and manufacturing.
Functions: Product dev., Production, Plant mgmt., Quality, Purchasing, Materials Plng., Packaging
Industries: Chemicals, Soap/perfume/cosmetics

Bell Oaks Co., Inc.

3390 Peachtree Rd. NE, Ste 1124
Atlanta, Georgia 30326
(404) 261-2170
Fax: (404) 261-4885
Email: careers@belloaks.com

Key Contact - Specialty:
Mr. Price P. Harding, III

Description: Performs executive searches on a retained, contingency or contract basis in the fields of finance/accounting, information technology, engineering and manufacturing/operations. Inc. 500 company with more than 7000 completed searches.

Salary Minimum: $50,000
Functions: General mgmt., Mfg., Materials, Sales & mktg., Finance, IT, Engineering
Industries: Mfg., Finance, Communications, Government, High tech, Software, Biotech

Branches:
929 Massachusetts Ave.
Cambridge, Massachusetts 02139
(617) 497-9500
Fax: (617) 497-8989
Email: belloaks@concentric.net
Key Contact - Specialty:
Mr. Gary Seligson

Bellamy & Assoc.

(Firm declined to update.)
2670 Links End, Ste. 102
Roswell, Georgia 30076
(678) 969-0775
Email: bbells@aol.com

Key Contact - Specialty:
Mr. William J. Bellamy - *High technology (all functions)*

Description: Experienced high-tech sales professionals recruiting high tech sales professionals.

Salary Minimum: $30,000
Functions: Mkt. research, Systems support
Industries: Computer svcs., High tech, Software

Benamati & Assoc.

12247 E. Iowa Drive
Aurora, Colorado 80012
(303) 671-5344
Fax: (303) 671-0450
Email: nben@worldnet.att.net

Key Contact - Specialty:
Ms. Nancy Benamati - *Engineering*

Description: Full service engineering recruiting specializing in A/E consulting, construction, manufacturing, petrochemical, and facilties.
Functions: Mfg., Engineering, Architects, Int'l.
Industries: Energy/utilities, Construction, Mfg.

J. P. Bencik Assoc.

1332 E. Fairview, Ste. 200
Rochester Hills, Michigan 48306
(248) 651-7426

Key Contact - Specialty:
Mr. James P. Bencik - *General management, engineering*

Description: Executive search/recruitment of middle management and engineering professionals for the automotive, automation, general manufacturing, related service industries (sales, engineering and management). Human resource consulting specialists.

Salary Minimum: $35,000
Functions: Generalist, Middle mgmt., Automation, Distribution, Mktg. mgmt., Cash mgmt., Systems anal.
Industries: Generalist, Plastics/rubber, Machinery/Appliances, Misc. mfg., Human resource svcs., Aerospace, Software

Richard L. Bencin & Assoc.
8553 Timber Trail
Brecksville, Ohio 44141
(440) 526-6726
Fax: (440) 546-1623

Key Contact - Specialty:
Mr. Richard L. Bencin - *Call centers (customer service & telesales)*

Description: World's first dedicated specialist in call center management/sales recruiting. Firm's president is the author of 3 industry texts and he writes for over 100 industry magazines.

Salary Minimum: $40,000
Functions: Directors, Senior mgmt., Mkt. research, Mktg. mgmt., Sales mgmt., Direct mktg., Customer svc.
Industries: Generalist

Benford & Assoc., Inc.
3000 Town Ctr., Ste. 1333
Southfield, Michigan 48075
(248) 351-0250
Fax: (248) 351-8698
Email: ben4jobs@aol.com

Key Contact - Specialty:
Mr. Edward A. Benford
Ms. Monica Debry

Description: We create a plan, detail strategy tailored for individual corporate clients. Research sources and candidates, bringing to the attention only those individuals especially suited to the particular requirements. Minority recruiting specialist.
Functions: Mfg., Product dev., Purchasing, Personnel, Budgeting, Engineering, Minorities
Industries: Food/bev/tobacco, Motor vehicles

N. L. Benke & Assoc., Inc.
956 Hanna Bldg.
Cleveland, Ohio 44115-1951
(216) 771-6822
Fax: (216) 771-3568

Key Contact - Specialty:
Mr. Norman L. Benke - *Banking, accounting, finance, information technology*

Description: We talk your language! Our recruiters have prior experience as accountants, bankers, financial or computer professionals. We do not waste your time with unqualified candidates because we know who the top performers are and where to find them.

Salary Minimum: $30,000
Functions: Materials, HR mgmt., Finance, IT, Mgmt. consultants, Minorities
Industries: Finance, Computer svcs., Accounting, Mgmt. consulting, Real estate, High tech, Software

Bennett & Associates
2732 Palo Verde
Odessa, Texas 79762
(915) 550-9096
Fax: (915) 362-3211
Email: bennettm@nwol.net
Web: virtualstaffing.com

Key Contact - Specialty:
Mr. Mark Bennett - *General management, human resources, information technology*

Description: Founded in 1954, we have placed thousands of candidates with hundreds of companies. Our range is sr. management, HR, IT, etc., in a broad range of industries.

Salary Minimum: $40,000
Functions: General mgmt., Middle mgmt., Mfg., Healthcare, HR mgmt., Finance, DB admin.
Industries: Energy/utilities, Construction, Svcs., Telecoms, High tech, Software, Healthcare

Bennett & Co. Consulting Group
2135 Manzanita Drive, #1
Oakland, California 94611
(510) 339-3175
Fax: (510) 339-2162
Email: bennettco@compuserve.com

Key Contact - Specialty:
Ms. Linda E. Bennett - *Human resources, HRIS*

Description: Specialist in HRIS consultants; technical conversion of HRIS systems; directors and management of human resources nationwide across many industries.

Salary Minimum: $65,000
Functions: HR mgmt., Benefits, Personnel, Training, Systems implem.
Industries: Human resource svcs., Software

Robert Bennett Assoc.
P.O. Box 261
Little Neck, New York 11363
(212) 949-2355
Fax: (718) 428-1714
Email: robertbennett@I-2000.com

Key Contact - Specialty:
Ms. Mary Bloom - *Lawyers*

Salary Minimum: $50,000
Functions: Mgmt. consultants, Attorneys, Int'l.
Industries: Entertainment, Insurance, Real estate

Benson Associates
280 Madison Ave., #703
New York, New York 10016
(212) 683-5962

Key Contact - Specialty:
Mr. Irwin Cohen - *Marketing, finance, human resources*
Mr. Laurence Rutkovsky - *Public accounting*

Description: Firm's principals have focused on executive recruitment for a total of 45 years.

Salary Minimum: $50,000
Functions: Middle mgmt., Advertising, Direct mktg., HR mgmt., Finance
Industries: Food/bev/tobacco, Invest. banking, Human resource svcs., Advertising/PR, Broadcast & Film

Dick Berg & Assoc.
P.O. Box 927171
San Diego, California 92192-7171
(619) 452-2745
Fax: (619) 546-8680
Email: dickberg@staffing.net
Web: www.staffing.net/dickberg.htm

Key Contact - Specialty:
Mr. Richard C. Lechtenberg - *Medical electronics, telecommunications, semiconductors*
Ms. Leda Lechtenberg - *Portuguese & Spanish speaking technical*

Description: Certified recruiter with 17 years experience in recruiting high technology engineers and technical professionals. Permanent or contract placement.

Salary Minimum: $25,000
Functions: Product dev., Customer svc., Systems anal., Systems dev., Systems implem., Engineering, Technicians
Industries: Medical devices, Computer svcs., Equip. svcs., High tech, Software, Biotech, Healthcare

Berger & Leff
One Sansome St., Ste. 2100
San Francisco, California 94104
(415) 951-4750
Fax: (415) 951-4571
Email: taxjobs@aol.com

Key Contact - Specialty:
Ms. Lisa A. Leff - *Taxation*

Description: Executive search/recruiting in tax in a variety of industries with a specialization in high technology, manufacturing and professional organizations.

Salary Minimum: $50,000
Functions: Taxes

Industries: Drugs mfg., Medical devices, Computer equip., Accounting, High tech, Software, Biotech

Bergeris & Co., Inc.
P.O. Box 341
Larchmont, New York 10538
(914) 833-0519
Fax: (914) 834-6461
Email: bergeris@aol.com

Key Contact - Specialty:
Mr. Jim Bergeris - *Investment banking, credit risk management*

Description: Executive search for sales professionals in commercial and investment banking. Special, but not exclusive, focus on credit and securities trading related areas. A truly individualized approach.

Salary Minimum: $100,000
Functions: Cash mgmt., Credit, M&A, Risk mgmt.
Industries: Finance, Banking, Invest. banking, Brokers, Venture cap., Misc. financial

Berglund Int'l. Resources, Inc.
4635 SW Frwy., Ste. 165
Houston, Texas 77027
(713) 629-4031
Fax: (713) 629-4032
Email: sharon@berglundintl.com
Web: www.berglundintl.com

Key Contact - Specialty:
Ms. Sharon Berglund - *Financial, accounting, information technology*

Description: We specialize in matching candidates to our client's needs by blending the required technical skills with communication skills, personality and interpersonal traits.

Salary Minimum: $30,000
Functions: Senior mgmt., Middle mgmt., Budgeting, Risk mgmt., Systems dev., Systems implem., Int'l.
Industries: Energy/utilities, Computer svcs.

Berkana Int'l., Inc.
18907 Forest Park Drive NE
Seattle, Washington 98155
(206) 547-3226
(206) 365-2959
Fax: (206) 547-3843
Email: sonja@headhunters.com
Web: www.headhunters.com

Key Contact - Specialty:
Ms. Sonja Carson
Mr. Paul Allen - *Converging high technology*

Salary Minimum: $50,000
Functions: Senior mgmt., Product dev., Mktg. mgmt., MIS mgmt., Systems dev., Engineering, Graphic artists
Industries: Computer equip., Venture cap., New media, Telecoms, Aerospace, High tech, Software

Berkshire Search Assoc.
P.O. Box 459
Becket, Massachusetts 01223-0459
(413) 623-8855
Fax: (413) 623-8858
Email: bsearch@bcn.net
Web: BerkshireSearch.com

Key Contact - Specialty:
Mr. Donald Munger - *Mechanical, electrical, civil, environmental engineering, HVAC design*
Barbara Markessinis - *Legal, attorneys, patent attorneys*

Description: Environmental (air pollution), hazardous waste remediation, water and waste water, hydrogeology, etc... Mechanical, electrical and civil engineers for A/E firms. HVAC, electrical, heavy, highway and general construction. Nationwide. HVAC/R sales and marketing.

Salary Minimum: $35,000
Functions: Middle mgmt., Production, Plant mgmt., Materials Plng., Mktg. mgmt., Sales mgmt., Engineering
Industries: Energy/utilities, Construction, Paper, Chemicals, Plastics/rubber, Metal products, Environmental svcs.

Berman & Larson
140 Rte. 17 N., Ste. 204
Paramus, New Jersey 07652
(800) 640-0126
(201) 262-9200
Fax: (201) 262-7060
Email: Ken@jobsbl.com
Web: www.jobsbl.com

Key Contact - Specialty:
Mr. Robert Larson - *Information systems*

Description: With over 35,000 systems professionals on file we will isolate a information systems professional to meet your needs. Candidates available for both full time and contracting.

Salary Minimum: $45,000
Functions: IT, MIS mgmt., Systems anal., Systems dev., Systems implem., Systems support

Bernhart Assoc.
2068 Greenwood Drive, #220
Owatonna, Minnesota 55060
(507) 451-4270
Fax: (507) 451-9433
Email: bgb@bernhart.com
Web: www.bernhart.com

Key Contact - Specialty:
Mr. Jerry Bernhart - *Direct Marketing*

Description: We are a nationally recognized search firm focusing exclusively in direct marketing, concentrating in database marketing, telemarketing management and statistical analysis.

Salary Minimum: $50,000
Functions: General mgmt., Sales & mktg., Mktg. mgmt., Sales mgmt., Direct mktg., IT, R&D
Industries: Mfg., Finance, Svcs., Communications, Insurance, High tech, Software

Ed Bertolas Assoc., Inc.
855 Cofair Court
Solana Beach, California 92075
(619) 259-1555
Fax: (619) 259-1155
Email: bertolas@ix.netcom.com
Web: www.ebertolasinc.com

Key Contact - Specialty:
Mr. Ed Bertolas

Description: We can recruit any medical background needed. I have placed over 25 mid and senior level managers, directors and VPs into one medical client. My knowledge and recruiting power are not limited to any one or two disciplines, but rather the main functions for a company to be successful.

Salary Minimum: $40,000
Functions: Directors, Senior mgmt., Middle mgmt., Product dev., R&D, Engineering
Industries: Medical devices, Biotech

Jack Bertram, Executive Recruiter
1405 Pine Rock Rd.
West Chester, Pennsylvania 19380-6215
(610) 431-3985

Key Contact - Specialty:
Mr. John J. Bertram - *Electro-mechanical products*

Description: Specialize in engineering with emphasis on electric motors and related products. All functions, design through manufacturing and quality.

Salary Minimum: $30,000
Functions: Middle mgmt., Product dev., Production, Automation, Plant mgmt., Quality, Productivity
Industries: Metal products, Machinery/Appliances, Motor vehicles, Misc. mfg.

Bertrand, Ross & Assoc., Inc.
6300 N. River Rd., Ste. 205
Rosemont, Illinois 60018
(847) 698-2800
Fax: (847) 698-4606

Key Contact - Specialty:
Mr. Robert F. Ross - *Sales & marketing*
Mr. Frank Davis - *Manufacturing, engineering*
Mr. Carl A. Johnson - *Electronics, high technology*
Ms. Betsy Brace - *Healthcare*

Description: Retained searches for middle management positions. Will not recruit from clients.

Salary Minimum: $50,000
Functions: General mgmt., Mfg., Healthcare, Sales & mktg., Finance, IT, Engineering
Industries: Generalist, Mfg., Svcs., Telecoms, High tech, Software, Healthcare

Affiliates:
International Management Services Inc.

Besen Assoc. Inc.
115 Rte. 46 W., Bldg. C-21
Mountain Lakes, New Jersey 07046
(973) 334-5533
Fax: (973) 334-4810
Email: besenassoc@aol.com
Web: www.besen.com

Key Contact - Specialty:
Mr. Douglas Besen - *Upper management physicians, presidents, vice presidents, diagnostic, OTC companies*

Description: Research and engineering for the pharmaceutical industry. Medical doctors, internal medicine, infectious disease, cardio/pulmonary respiratory, rheumatology, endocrinology, general and biotechnical engineers, marketing sales and manufacturing support personnel, regulatory and quality assurance control.

Salary Minimum: $55,000
Functions: Directors, Middle mgmt., Product dev., Mkt. research, Mktg. mgmt., MIS mgmt., Systems anal.
Industries: Soap/perfume/cosmetics, Computer equip., Hospitality, Pharmaceutical svcs., Telecoms, Packaging, Biotech

Affiliates:
Chemsultants Int'l.

BFW, Inc.
302 Wymberly Rd.
St. Simons Island, Georgia 31522-1708
(912) 638-0025
Fax: (912) 638-2855
Web: rbuf@thebest.net

Key Contact - Specialty:
Mr. E. Ralph Bufkin - *Investment professionals (analysts, portfolio/fund managers)*

Description: Recruitment and placement of investment professionals exclusively, including portfolio managers, CIO's, analysts, finance, compliance and marketing disciplines in buy side, sell side and industry positions.

Salary Minimum: $50,000
Industries: Finance, Invest. banking, Brokers, Venture cap., Misc. financial

BG & Assoc.
10112 Langhorne Court, Ste. B
Bethesda, Maryland 20817
(301) 365-4046
(301) 218-8173
Fax: (301) 365-0435
Email: bgajob@erols.com

Key Contact - Specialty:
Mr. Brian A. Gray - *Information technology, human resources, finance & accounting, management consultants*
Ms. Linda Cooper - *Information technology, human resources, finance & accounting, management consultants*
Ms. Phyllis Manson - *General management, materials management, minorities*

Description: We are a preferred member of Top Echelon Network, the nation's largest computerized network of independent recruiting firms. In addition to permanent recruiting, we offer clients interim professional employees.

Salary Minimum: $40,000
Functions: Mfg., Materials, HR mgmt., Finance, IT, Mgmt. consultants, Minorities
Industries: Mfg., Finance, Svcs., Computer svcs., Mgmt. consulting, Communications, Software

BGB Assoc., Inc.
P.O. Box 556
Itasca, Illinois 60143
(630) 250-8993
Fax: (630) 250-9211

Key Contact - Specialty:
Mr. Gregory J. Burchill - *Operations, logistics, marketing*
Ms. Barbara E. Burchill - *Finance, human resources*
Mr. Gary Jones - *Operations, logistics, marketing, finance*

Description: Founder has over 20 years experience in operations senior management. Round the clock access. Competitive fee structure.

Salary Minimum: $30,000
Functions: Generalist, Mfg., Materials, Sales & mktg., HR mgmt., Finance, Engineering
Industries: Food/bev/tobacco, Soap/perfume/cosmetics, Plastics/rubber, Machinery/Appliances, Motor vehicles, Computer equip., Consumer electronics

Bickerton & Gordon LLC
(a division of Bickerton & Gordon Legal Temps)
60 State St., Ste. 700
Boston, Massachusetts 02109
(617) 371-2929
Fax: (617) 371-2999
Email: bickgord@aol.com
Web: www.lawyersearch.com

Key Contact - Specialty:
Mr. Richards Gordon - *Lawyers*
Mr. Brion Bickerton - *Lawyers*

Description: Nationally recognized legal recruiters staffed by prominent lawyers. In-house searches in all disciplines. Recruit for established and start-up companies. General counsel and staff searches. Sweeping national database of candidates.

Salary Minimum: $50,000
Functions: Attorneys, Paralegals
Industries: Generalist

Binder Hospitality Group
526 Silverbrook Drive
Danville, Kentucky 40422-1076
(606) 239-0096
Fax: (606) 238-1256

Key Contact - Specialty:
Mr. Kenneth K. Binder - *Hospitality (executive & middle management)*

Description: Specializing in search and placement of mid and upper level management for hotels, restaurants and clubs. Over thirty years executive level operations experience in the hospitality industry.

Salary Minimum: $30,000
Functions: Senior mgmt., Middle mgmt., Mktg. mgmt., Sales mgmt., Personnel, CFO's, Budgeting
Industries: Hospitality

Bio-Venture Group
(a division of Robert Pencarski & Co.)
P.O. Box 50
Lincoln, Rhode Island 02865
(401) 728-0760
Fax: (401) 725-8666
Email: BioVgroup@brainiac.com

Key Contact - Specialty:
Mr. Robert Pencarski - *Biotechnology, pharmaceutical, diagnostic, technical professionals*

Description: We provide retained and contingency technical placement at all levels in biopharmaceutical, medical device, diagnostic and life science industries. R&D, hardware, software and management.
Functions: General mgmt., Product dev., Quality, IT, Systems dev., R&D, Engineering
Industries: Generalist, Mfg., Communications, Aerospace, High tech, Software, Biotech

---

BioPharmMed
550 N. Reo St., Ste. 300
Tampa, Florida 33611
(813) 287-5117
Fax: (813) 805-0502
Email: bpm@ix.netcom.com
Web: www.BioPharmMed.com

Key Contact - Specialty:
Ms. Tina Hunter Stewart - *Medical device, biotech, pharmaceuticals*

Description: We offer commitment, knowledge, experience and results in our partnership with clients ranging from start-up ventures to Fortune 500 corporations. Computer linked to over 695 search firms worldwide. Retained & contingency searches - permanent & contract placements.

Salary Minimum: $50,000
Functions: General mgmt., Mfg., Materials, HR mgmt., IT, R&D, Engineering
Industries: Drugs mfg., Medical devices, Plastics/rubber, Computer equip., Pharmaceutical svcs., High tech, Biotech

Affiliates:
MedQuest

BioTech Research Recruiters Inc.
1651 Falling Star Ave.
Westlake Village, California 91362
(818) 597-9001
Fax: (818) 597-9027

Key Contact - Specialty:
Mr. Ted Feightner - *Scientists, engineers, computer science*

Description: We specialize in finding scientists, engineers and MIS professionals for the biotech and pharmaceutical industries.

Salary Minimum: $60,000
Functions: Directors, Middle mgmt., Automation, Systems dev., Systems implem., R&D, Engineering
Industries: Drugs mfg., Medical devices, Biotech

Birch & Associes
2155 Guy St., Ste. 740
Montreal, Quebec H3H 2R9
Canada
(514) 846-1878
Fax: (514) 846-9395
Email: Protocol@total.net

Key Contact - Specialty:
Mr. Jerry Birch
Mr. Stanley Birch - *High technology*

Description: Specialists in executive recruiting and hi-tech, we carefully investigate each of our client's needs and provide them with qualified candidates who have been rigorously evaluated. An attentive after-hiring follow-up ensures that the needs of our clients and candidates have been met.
Functions: Generalist, Mfg., Sales & mktg., Finance, IT, Engineering, Mgmt. consultants
Industries: Drugs mfg., Retail, Banking, Invest. banking, Accounting, Telecoms, High tech

Affiliates:
Protocole

BJB Assoc.
1501 Crystal Drive, Ste. 1025
Arlington, Virginia 22202
(703) 413-0541
Fax: (703) 418-4467
Web: bjbrecruit.aol.com

Key Contact - Specialty:
Ms. Bobbi Bauman - *Manufacturing (high speed), consumer products, paper converting, packaging*

Description: Recruit for clients in nonwovens consumer disposable market, medical disposables, paper converters, packaging and supporting chemical and engineering firms to these industries.

Salary Minimum: $30,000
Functions: Product dev., Production, Plant mgmt., Packaging, Mkt. research, R&D, Engineering
Industries: Textiles/apparel, Paper, Printing, Chemicals, Plastics/rubber, Packaging

---

The Black Leopard
79-180 Fox Run
La Quinta, California 92253
(800) 360-4191
(760) 771-8400
Fax: (760) 771-9300
Email: TBLeopard@aol.com
Web: www.BlackLeopard.com

Key Contact - Specialty:
Mr. Jerry Kurbatoff - *Food processing, newspaper publishing*
Ms. Lauren Kurbatoff - *Food processing*

Description: Nationwide executive search to the food processing and newspaper publishing industries. Staffing junior to senior level executives in operations, engineering/maintenance, quality assurance, R&D, sales/marketing, finance and human resources.

Salary Minimum: $25,000
Functions: General mgmt., Mfg., Materials, HR mgmt., Finance, R&D, Engineering
Industries: Mfg., Human resource svcs., Publishing

Blackhawk Advantage, Inc.
1100 Irvine Blvd., Ste. 340
Tustin, California 92780
(714) 731-9400
Fax: (714) 731-8400
Email: phil@blackhawkusa.com
Web: www.blackhawkusa.com

Key Contact - Specialty:
Mr. Phil Andersen - *Financial service industry, trust, investments, audit, accounting & tax*
Ms. Phyllis Busser-Andersen - *Bank trust positions*

Description: All principals are CPA's with extensive consulting and banking experience.

Salary Minimum: $40,000
Functions: Senior mgmt., Middle mgmt., Sales mgmt., Budgeting, Taxes, MIS mgmt., Mgmt. consultants
Industries: Banking

The Blackman Kallick Search Division
300 S. Riverside Plaza, Ste. 660
Chicago, Illinois 60606
(312) 207-1040
Fax: (312) 207-1066
Web: www.bkbcpa.com/practice/hr.html

Key Contact - Specialty:
Mr. Gary M. Wolfson - *Management, investment banking, banking & finance, manufacturing, legal*

Description: Each search assignment custom designed and researched for every client. Unique client mix, dedicated staff, outstanding references. Middle management specialists. Several clients retained on annual partnership basis.

Salary Minimum: $50,000
Functions: Generalist, General mgmt., Middle mgmt., Plant mgmt., Sales & mktg., Finance, Attorneys
Industries: Generalist, Mfg., Banking, Invest. banking, Legal, Accounting, Real estate

Blair/Tech Recruiters, Inc.
77 Milltown Rd.
East Brunswick, New Jersey 08816
(732) 390-5550
Fax: (732) 390-1453

Key Contact - Specialty:
Mr. Kenneth J. Rathborne - *Chemists, chemical engineers*

Description: Exclusively broad based engineering and scientific disciplines for varied clients in the middle Atlantic and northeastern US.

Salary Minimum: $40,000
Functions: Product dev., Automation, Quality, Productivity, Packaging, R&D, Engineering
Industries: Food/bev/tobacco, Chemicals, Drugs mfg., Paints/petroleum products, Machinery/Appliances, Test/measurement equip., Packaging

Blane, Stevens & Kellogg
13456 Troon Trace Lane, Ste. 100
Jacksonville, Florida 32225
(904) 296-1910
Fax: (904) 296-1914
Email: BSK@Mediaone.net

Key Contact - Specialty:
Mr. Steven B. Highfill - *Legal*
Mr. Michael P. Draper - *Legal*
Monique S. Young - *Legal*
Sheryl Barnes - *Legal*

Description: Extremely specialized in the search for and recruitment of attorneys for in-house corporate and private law firm positions, with an emphasis on the merger or acquisition of practice groups or mid-sized firms.

Salary Minimum: $50,000
Functions: Attorneys
Industries: Legal

Branches:
3475 Lenox Rd., Ste. 665
Atlanta, Georgia 30326
(404) 233-9797
Fax: (404) 233-7878
Key Contact - Specialty:
Monique S. Young
Sheryl Barnes

Blanton & Co.
P.O. Box 94041
Birmingham, Alabama 35220-4041
(205) 836-3063
Fax: (205) 836-4189
Email: tblanton@blantonco.com

Key Contact - Specialty:
Ms. Julia Blanton
Mr. Thomas Blanton

Description: Specialists in all disciplines in the biotechnology, paper, industrial process control, medical equipment and pharmaceutical industries.

Salary Minimum: $50,000
Functions: General mgmt., Mfg., Materials, Sales & mktg., IT, R&D, Engineering
Industries: Chemicals, Drugs mfg., Medical devices, Plastics/rubber, Machinery/Appliances, Computer equip., Test/measurement equip.

BLB Consulting
110 E. 42nd St., Ste. 1309
New York, New York 10017
(212) 808-0577
Fax: (212) 338-9696
Email: hr@blbco.com
Web: www.blbco.com

Key Contact - Specialty:
Ms. Barbara L. Bartell - *Human resources*

Description: Certified personnel consultant specializing exclusively in human resource management.

Salary Minimum: $35,000
Functions: HR mgmt., Personnel
Industries: Generalist, Finance, Invest. banking, Mgmt. consulting, Communications, Insurance, High tech

David Blevins & Assoc.
1424 4th Ave., Ste. 824
Seattle, Washington 98101
(206) 521-8953
(888) JOB-EXEC
Fax: (206) 521-8963
Email: blevins@jobexec.com

Key Contact - Specialty:
Mr. David C. Blevins - *Wine & specialty beverage, hospitality, sales executives, production executives*
Mr. Paul Herbert - *Start-up ventures, real estate, food & beverage*

Description: Focus on matching job candidates with company culture. We offer a personal approach, comprehensive service and effective results. Growing small and medium-sized firms are a specialty.
Functions: Generalist, General mgmt., Mfg., Sales & mktg., Training, Finance, Mgmt. consultants
Industries: Food/bev/tobacco, Wholesale, Retail, Hospitality

The Howard C. Bloom Co.
5000 Quorum Drive, Ste. 550
Dallas, Texas 75240
(972) 385-6455
Fax: (972) 385-1006

Key Contact - Specialty:
Mr. Howard Bloom - *Attorneys*
Ms. Joyce Bloom - *Attorneys*

Description: Places attorneys for in-house and firms as well as law firm administrators and law firm P.R. and marketing specialists.

Salary Minimum: $50,000
Functions: Attorneys
Industries: Legal

Blue Chip Law Consulting, Inc.
2030 Main St., Ste. 1300
Irvine, California 92614
(714) 260-4723
Fax: (714) 260-9085
Email: jrm@bluechiplaw.com
Web: www.bluechiplaw.com

Key Contact - Specialty:
Joseph R. Manning, Jr. - *Attorneys, paralegals*

Description: We specialize in contract and career attorney placement in Southern California.
Functions: Attorneys, Paralegals
Industries: Legal

Branches:
468 N. Camden Drive, Ste. 200
Beverly Hills, California 90210
(310) 285-1744
Fax: (310) 285-1745
Email: jrm@bluechiplaw.com
Web: www.bluechiplaw.com
Key Contact - Specialty:
Ms. Catherine M. Ward - *Attorneys, paralegals*

The BMW Group, Inc.
40 Exchange Place, Ste. 700
New York, New York 10005
(212) 943-8800
Email: bmw40x@aol.com

Key Contact - Specialty:
Mr. Alan Burke - *Technical*
Mr. Michael Mantel - *Technical*
Mr. Ronald Weiss - *Technical*

Description: Full service organization specializing in the placement of information technology professionals.

Salary Minimum: $45,000
Functions: IT, MIS mgmt., Systems anal., Systems dev., Systems implem., Systems support
Industries: Banking, Invest. banking, Brokers, Venture cap., Misc. financial, High tech, Software

Bodner Inc.
372 Fifth Ave., Ste. 9K
New York, New York 10018
(212) 714-0371

Key Contact - Specialty:
Ms. Marilyn S. Bodner - *Accounting, finance*

Description: Specialize in placement of accounting and financial professionals.

Salary Minimum: $35,000
Functions: Finance, CFO's, Budgeting
Industries: Generalist

Tom Bogle & Assoc.
19200 Von Karman Ave., Ste. 400
Irvine, California 92612
(949) 622-5422
Fax: (714) 960-8605
Email: bogleassoc@aol.com

Key Contact - Specialty:
Mr. Tom Bogle - *Medical imaging, medical technologies management, sales & marketing*

Description: Confidential consulting to attract, recruit and retain outstanding sales and marketing talent for companies in the medical technology/medical device industry, leadership, staffing issues and organizational development to start-ups and Fortune 500 firms.

Salary Minimum: $100,000
Functions: Middle mgmt., Product dev., Mktg. mgmt., Sales mgmt., Personnel, M&A, Mgmt. consultants
Industries: Drugs mfg., Medical devices, Mgmt. consulting

Affiliates:
Patricia M. Bray

Mark Bolno & Assoc.
4916 35th Court E.
Bradenton, Florida 34203
(941) 751-2276
Fax: (941) 756-2100

Key Contact - Specialty:
Mr. Mark Bolno - *Food manufacturing, hotel executives*

Description: Upper management, executive and corporate recruiting and consulting.

Salary Minimum: $50,000
Functions: Senior mgmt., Middle mgmt., Product dev., Production, Plant mgmt.
Industries: Food/bev/tobacco, Hospitality

Bolton Group
P.O. Box 1566
Alturas, California 96101
(530) 233-5062
Fax: (800) 820-9115
Email: sherryj@boltongrp.com
Web: www.boltongrp.com

Key Contact - Specialty:
Ms. Sherry Junker - *Telecommunications, data communications, networking*

Description: We will cold call into companies, looking for the candidate you specify. We also network with other recruiters for a larger selection of candidates.
Functions: Directors, Middle mgmt., Product dev., Production, Systems anal., Systems dev., Engineering
Industries: New media, Broadcast & Film, Telecoms

Ann Bond Assoc. Inc.
275 West St., Ste. 304
Annapolis, Maryland 21401
(410) 280-6002

Key Contact - Specialty:
Ms. Ann F. Bond - *Sales & marketing (middle & upper management)*
Mr. Robert S. Bond - *Sales & marketing (middle & upper management)*

Description: We represent well known food manufacturers (both privately and publicly held) who seek sales and marketing managers whose customers have included: hotels, restaurants, institutions, supermarkets and food manufacturers. Our president has been specializing in this category since 1980.

Salary Minimum: $50,000
Functions: Directors, Senior mgmt., Middle mgmt., Mkt. research, Mktg. mgmt., Sales mgmt.
Industries: Food/bev/tobacco

Bonifield Assoc.
1 Eves Drive, Ste. 115
Marlton, New Jersey 08053
(609) 596-3300
Fax: (609) 596-8866
Email: info@bonifield.com
Web: www.bonifield.com

Key Contact - Specialty:
Mr. Richard L. Tyson - *Insurance*

Description: All professional consultants have experience/background in either banking or insurance. Over 20 years specializing for clients ranging from $90 billion to $2 billion of assets. Served 300+ clients.

Salary Minimum: $40,000
Functions: Generalist, General mgmt., Healthcare, Sales & mktg., Finance
Industries: Banking, Invest. banking, Misc. financial, Pharmaceutical svcs., Insurance

Affiliates:
Bonifield Associates
Len Bonifield
Clifford R. Mungal

Boone-Scaturro Assoc., Inc.
4780 Ashford Dunwoody Rd., Ste. A448
Atlanta, Georgia 30338
(770) 740-9737
Fax: (770) 475-5055
Email: femrec@aol.com

Key Contact - Specialty:
Ms. Mary Ellen Scaturro - *Physicians, executives, physician executives, mid levels, group practice administrators*
Mr. Charles C. Boone - *Executives, administrators*
Mr. Leonard Scaturro - *Financial*

Description: Flexible fee structures.

Salary Minimum: $40,000
Functions: Senior mgmt., Physicians, Health admin., Benefits, Personnel, CFO's, MIS mgmt.
Industries: Generalist, Medical devices, Pharmaceutical svcs., Accounting, Software, Healthcare

---

Bor-Maq Assoc.
1200 Golden Key Circle, Ste. 228
El Paso, Texas 79925
(915) 592-2077
Fax: (915) 595-6658
Email: bormaq@whc.net
Web: www.bormaq.com

Key Contact - Specialty:
Mr. Manny Aldana - *Executives, senior management, international*
Mr. Mario Pinedo - *Finance, accounting, MIS*
Ms. Margie Gomez - *Engineering*
Mr. Tom Walters - *Engineering*

Description: Executive search firm exclusively specializing in search and recruitment for primarily manufacturing companies operating on the US/Mexico border, in Mexico and South America.

Salary Minimum: $50,000
Functions: General mgmt., Mfg., Materials, HR mgmt., Finance, IT, Int'l.
Industries: Mfg., Plastics/rubber, Consumer electronics, Misc. mfg., Finance, Misc. financial

---

Borchert Assoc.
17430 Campbell Rd., Ste. 111
Dallas, Texas 75252
(972) 818-2801
(888) 818-2801
Fax: (972) 818-2777
Email: greg@glborchert.com
Web: www.glborchert.com

Key Contact - Specialty:
Mr. Gregory L. Borchert - *Metalcasting, foundry, automotive*

Description: 21 years experience completing mid-management through executive level assignments in the metal-casting field.

Salary Minimum: $50,000
Functions: Senior mgmt., Middle mgmt., Plant mgmt., Quality, Productivity, Engineering, Environmentalists
Industries: Metal products, Machinery/Appliances, Motor vehicles, Misc. mfg.

Born & Bicknell, Inc.
2300 Corporate Blvd. NW, Ste. 212
Boca Raton, Florida 33431
(561) 988-9880
(800) 376-2676
Fax: (561) 988-9886
Email: info@bornbicknell.com
Web: www.bornbicknell.com

Key Contact - Specialty:
Ms. Jane E. Born - *Physician*
Mr. Samuel J. Born - *Physician*

Description: We offer premium physician recruitment services which are personalized, efficient and cost effective for today's growth oriented healthcare provider organizations.
Functions: Physicians
Industries: Healthcare

Branches:
1905 Fairview St.
Ruston, Louisiana 71270
(800) 374-2676
(318) 254-8481
Fax: (318) 254-8335
Key Contact - Specialty:
Ms. Helen M. Bicknell - *Physician*

Lynn Borne & Co.
6934 Canby Ave., Ste. 109
Reseda, California 91335
(818) 881-9353
Fax: (818) 881-2796
Email: lbnet@compuserve.com
Web: www.ibnet-jobs.com

Key Contact - Specialty:
Mr. Lynn H. Borne

Description: Search and placement services involved with positions in public accounting, industry accounting, finance, marketing, manufacturing and information technology.

Salary Minimum: $40,000
Functions: Generalist, General mgmt., Mfg., Materials, Sales & mktg., Finance, IT
Industries: Generalist

Bornholdt Shivas & Friends Executive Recruiters
400 E. 87th St.
New York, New York 10128-6533
(212) 557-5252
Fax: (212) 557-5704
Email: BSANDF@aol.com
Web: www.members.aol.com/bsandf/

Key Contact - Specialty:
Mr. John Bornholdt - *Marketing, international, telecommunications, interactive advertising, software development*

Description: Global executive search firm that concentrates in packaged good marketing, telecommunications and computer software development jobs at the managerial, director, vice president and general management level. We also service interactive advertising agencies worldwide.

Salary Minimum: $60,000
Functions: Advertising, Mkt. research, Mktg. mgmt., Systems dev., Mgmt. consultants, Minorities, Int'l.
Industries: Food/bev/tobacco, Drugs mfg., Consumer electronics, Computer svcs., Advertising/PR, New media, Telecoms

---

Bos Business Consultants
4211 N. Buffalo St.
P.O. Box 533
Orchard Park, New York 14127
(716) 662-0800
Fax: (716) 662-0623
Email: bosbc@aol.com
Web: members.aol.com/BosBC/bosbc.html

Key Contact - Specialty:
Mr. John Bos - *Engineering, manufacturing, marketing*

Description: Specializes in marketing, engineering, R&D, product development, quality and manufacturing positions relating to compressors/turbines, medical devices, food, automotive components, aerospace and consumer products.

Salary Minimum: $30,000
Functions: Mfg., Mkt. research, Mktg. mgmt., Systems dev., R&D, Engineering
Industries: Mfg., Aerospace, Packaging, High tech, Software

Bosco-Hubert & Assoc.
114 S. Sixth St., Ste. 210
St. Marys, Kansas 66536
(913) 437-6754
Fax: (913) 437-6756
Email: dhohman@bosco-hubert.com
Web: www.bosco-hubert.com

Key Contact - Specialty:
Mr. Daniel G. Hohman - *Generalist*

Description: We are an executive search firm specializing in the fluid power industry. Our searches extend throughout North America and encompass management, engineering and sales functions.

Salary Minimum: $25,000
Functions: General mgmt., Mfg., Sales & mktg., Engineering
Industries: Agri/forestry/mining, Construction, Mfg., Packaging

---

Boston Professional Search, Inc.
20 Park Plaza, Ste. 637
Statler Bldg.
Boston, Massachusetts 02116
(617) 451-5900
Fax: (617) 451-3825
Email: Samuels10@aol.com

Key Contact - Specialty:
Mr. Jonathan Samuels - *Sales & marketing, accounting*
Robert DeLena - *Legal*

Description: We are industry specific, experienced recruiters, dedicated to providing confidential and professional searches. We are sensitive to our client and candidate's needs providing quality and excellence.

Salary Minimum: $40,000
Functions: Generalist, Mktg. mgmt., Sales mgmt., Budgeting, Credit, Taxes, Attorneys
Industries: Generalist, Pharmaceutical svcs., Legal, Accounting, High tech, Software, Healthcare

---

Howard Bowen Consulting
283N North Lake Blvd., Ste. 111
Altamonte Lakeside Executive Stes.
Altamonte Springs, Florida 32701
(407) 830-8854
Fax: (407) 298-0784

Key Contact - Specialty:
Mr. Howard Bowen - *Management consulting*

Description: Concentration in management consulting industry nationwide with emphasis on business/manufacturing, rapid product development technologies. Focusing on manufacturing operations, concurrent engineering, supply chain management and systems applications. ERP implementations.

Salary Minimum: $70,000
Functions: Senior mgmt., Production, Productivity, Purchasing, Materials Plng., Systems implem., Mgmt. consultants
Industries: Metal products, Motor vehicles, Mgmt. consulting, Telecoms, Aerospace, High tech, Software

Bower & Associates
P.O. Box 1206
Bedford, Texas 76095
(817) 283-2256
Fax: (817) 283-1628
Email: basearch@flash.net
Web: www.ipa.com/eoffice/817-283-2256.html

Key Contact - Specialty:
Mr. Richard Bower - *Capital equipment for printed circuit board assembly and semiconductor industries, test equipment*

Description: Search for sales management, technical support, engineering, electronics assembly capital equipment, semiconductor, PCB, SEM, test, vision, SMT, robots, software tools for factory automation, HW/SW design engineers.

Salary Minimum: $50,000
Functions: Mfg., Automation, Materials, Sales & mktg., IT, R&D, Engineering
Industries: Mfg., Computer equip., Test/measurement equip., New media, Telecoms, High tech, Software

BowersThomas
11150 W. Olympic Blvd., Ste. 805
Los Angeles, California 90064-1544
(310) 477-3244
Fax: (310) 444-1885

Key Contact - Specialty:
Ms. Pat Bowers Thomas - *Attorneys (for corporations & law firms)*

Description: Global attorney search and placement for corporations and law firms. Ethical,qualitative and insightful search services for all levels of attorneys in commercial practice areas, all have JD/LL.B and U.S. Bar.

Salary Minimum: $80,000
Functions: Attorneys
Industries: Mfg., Finance, Legal, Communications, Real estate, High tech, Biotech

Affiliates:
The Counsel Network
Frey & Sher Assoc., Inc.
The Marley Group, Ltd.
John Peebles Associates Ltd.

Bowie & Associates, Inc.
100 N. Beechwood Ave., Ste. 200
Baltimore, Maryland 21228-4927
(410) 747-1919
Email: abowie@us.net

Key Contact - Specialty:
Mr. Andrew Bowie

Description: Specialists in transportation and logistics. Clients range from small domestic firms to foreign conglomerates. Geographical scope includes all major cities throughout the U.S.

Salary Minimum: $50,000
Functions: Directors, Middle mgmt., Distribution, Sales mgmt.
Industries: Transportation

Bowman & Assoc.
1660 S. Amphlett Blvd., Ste. 245
San Mateo, California 94402
(650) 573-0188

Key Contact - Specialty:
Mr. Daniel P. Bowman - *Senior leisure time industry*
Mr. Rion J. Moran - *Leisure time industry*

Description: Staffed by senior professionals completing middle and senior level management assignments exclusively for hospitality and leisure industry employers. Primarily retained assignments, both domestic and international.

Salary Minimum: $50,000
Functions: Generalist
Industries: Hospitality, Entertainment

Bowman & Marshall, Inc.
P.O. Box 25503
Overland Park, Kansas 66225-5503
(913) 648-3332
Fax: (913) 341-9596
Email: bowmarsh@aol.com
Web: www. bowmarsh.com

Key Contact - Specialty:
Mr. Peter Grassl

Description: Search services for financial positions within the manufacturing sector.

Salary Minimum: $50,000
Functions: Finance
Industries: Energy/utilities, Construction, Mfg., Wholesale, Retail, Aerospace, Packaging

BR & Assoc.
300 Winston Drive, Ste. 3123
Cliffside Park, New Jersey 07010
(201) 886-2721
Fax: (201) 224-2993
Email: ericperl@hotmail.com

Key Contact - Specialty:
Mr. Bernard Rotsky - *Retail, information technology*
Mr. Dan Andrews - *Retail, information technology*
Mr. Eric Perl - *Management, sales & marketing*
Ms. Sally Rotsky - *Retail*

Description: Retail market: place financial, operational, administrative and MIS executives. Recruit sales and marketing professionals for energy services and telecom.

Salary Minimum: $40,000
Functions: Health admin., Sales mgmt., MIS mgmt., Systems anal., Systems dev., Systems implem., Systems support
Industries: Generalist, Energy/utilities, Retail, Telecoms

Bradford & Galt, Inc.
12400 Olive Blvd., Ste. 430
St. Louis, Missouri 63141
(314) 434-9200
Fax: (314) 434-9266
Email: kdg@bgcs.com
Web: www.bradford.com

Key Contact - Specialty:
Mr. Bradford Layton - *Information systems*
Ms. Barbara Layton

Description: Founded as search firm in 1984; expanded services to include information systems contracting/consulting temporary staffing in 1990.

Salary Minimum: $30,000
Functions: MIS mgmt., Systems anal., Systems dev., Systems implem., Systems support
Industries: Generalist

Branches:
1211 W. 22nd St., Ste. 417
Oak Brook, Illinois 60521
(708) 990-4644
Fax: (708) 990-4819
Key Contact - Specialty:
Mr. Jeff Gipson

112 State St., Ste D
Peoria, Illinois 61602
(309) 674-2000
Fax: (309) 674-8300
Key Contact - Specialty:
Ms. Susan Harvey

9200 Indian Creek Parkway, Ste. 570
Overland Park, Kansas 66210
(913) 663-1264
Fax: (913) 345-9742
Key Contact - Specialty:
Ms. Dawn McGuire

1425 Greenway Dr., Ste. 400
Irving, Texas 75038
(972) 580-8020
Fax: (972) 580-7700
Key Contact - Specialty:
Mr. Dave Fingers

Bradford Executives Int'l.
5113 Leesburg Pike, Ste. 510
Four Skyline Place
Falls Church, Virginia 22041
(703) 820-8618
Fax: (703) 820-3368

Email: bmoore@bradfordexec.com
Web: www.bradfordexec.com

Key Contact - Specialty:
Ms. Elisabeth Peebles
Mr. Brian P. Moore

Description: We are an executive search firm specializing in the recruitment of healthcare and pharmaceutical administrators, executives and physicians.
Functions: Senior mgmt., Physicians, Health admin., Sales mgmt., Benefits, CFO's, Non-profits
Industries: Energy/utilities, Drugs mfg., Medical devices, Non-profits, Pharmaceutical svcs., Mgmt. consulting, Insurance

---

Bradley & Assoc.
5341 River Bluff Curve, Ste. 116
Bloomington, Minnesota 55437
(612) 884-2607
Fax: (612) 884-2019

Key Contact - Specialty:
Mr. T. John Bradley - *Engineering*
Ms. Mary X. Bradley - *Production, research & development*

Description: One person responsible for all aspects of your search, which will be handled professionally, according to your instructions. We prefer your toughest assignments.

Salary Minimum: $35,000
Functions: Mfg., Engineering
Industries: Agri/forestry/mining, Food/bev/tobacco, Chemicals

---

M. F. Branch Assoc., Inc.
P.O. Box 18105
Asheville, North Carolina 28814
(828) 658-0055
Fax: (828) 645-9866
Email: mfbranch@aol.com
Web: www.mfbranch.com

Key Contact - Specialty:
Ms. Minnie Branch - *Advanced communications*

Description: Specialists in search for voice (wire and wireless) communication and advanced data communication networking product clients for 23 years. Positions represented include advanced R&D, marketing, product management and sales.

Salary Minimum: $60,000
Functions: Directors, Middle mgmt., Mkt. research, Mktg. mgmt., Sales mgmt., Systems dev., R&D
Industries: Telecoms, High tech, Software

Brandjes Assoc.
16 S. Calvert St., Ste. 500
Baltimore, Maryland 21202
(410) 547-6887
Fax: (410) 727-2489

Key Contact - Specialty:
Mr. Michael Brandjes - *Banking*
Ms. Suzanne Frock - *Banking*

Description: A small, very specialized financial services recruiting firm, primarily banking.

Salary Minimum: $50,000
Industries: Finance, Banking, Invest. banking, Brokers, Venture cap.

Brandt Associates
P.O. Box 79
Clarks Summit, Pennsylvania 18411-0079
(717) 563-2058
Fax: (717) 586-0764
Email: web4cape@aol.comm

Key Contact - Specialty:
Mr. William E. Brandt - *Human resource management, information systems, MIS management*

Description: Recruiting for middle and senior level management positions with a greater than average success rate. Effective and efficient!!

Salary Minimum: $50,000
Functions: Generalist, Mfg., HR mgmt., Finance, IT, MIS mgmt., Systems anal.
Industries: Generalist, Finance, Computer svcs., Accounting, Human resource svcs., Telecoms, Environmental svcs.

Branthover Assoc.
51 E. 42nd St., Ste. 500
New York, New York 10017
(212) 949-9400
Fax: (212) 949-5905
Email: branthover@aol.com

Key Contact - Specialty:
Ms. Jeanne Branthover
Ms. Lisa Amore
Ms. Judy Brenner

Description: A generalist search firm specializing in the placement of middle market (100K-300K) executives. Also offer research to clients such as organizational charts, consulting assignment, etc.

Salary Minimum: $75,000
Functions: Generalist, General mgmt., Mfg., Sales & mktg., HR mgmt., Finance, IT
Industries: Generalist, Mfg., Finance, Svcs., Communications, High tech

---

Bratland & Assoc.
5424 Brittany Drive, Ste. 150
McHenry, Illinois 60050
(815) 344-4335
Fax: (815) 344-6424
Email: bratland@sprintmail.com

Key Contact - Specialty:
Mr. A. J. Bratland - *Fiber optics, telecommunications*

Description: We are aligned with the largest network of recruiters in the U.S. Through these affiliations we have access to the databases of about 700 recruiting offices worldwide. Whether you are client or candidate we can open doors for you.
Functions: Automation, Quality, MIS mgmt.
Industries: Medical devices, Computer equip., Telecoms, High tech

---

Jerold Braun & Assoc.
P.O. Box 67C13
Century City Station
Los Angeles, California 90067
(310) 203-0515

Key Contact - Specialty:
Mr. Jerold Braun
Ms. Joyce Davis

Description: With 33 years of retail and HR experience, firm specializes in retail, telemarketing and allied fields. Also specializes in all areas of HR management.
Functions: General mgmt., Sales & mktg., Advertising, Direct mktg., Customer svc., HR mgmt., Finance
Industries: Textiles/apparel, Wholesale, Retail

Brei & Assoc., Inc.
P.O. Box 445
Marion, Iowa 52302
(319) 377-9196
Fax: (319) 377-9219
Email: rbrei@netins.net
Web: www.engsource.com

Key Contact - Specialty:
Mr. Randy Brei - *Electronics engineers, software developers*

Description: Specializing in electronic design and real-time software development engineers. Principals have a total of over 20 years experience in electronic product development and engineering management in radio, process control and avionics.

Salary Minimum: $40,000
Functions: Systems anal., Systems dev., Systems implem., R&D, Engineering
Industries: Computer equip., Consumer electronics, Telecoms, Aerospace, High tech, Software

The Bren Group

13951 N. Scottsdale Rd., Ste. 111A
Scottsdale, Arizona 85254
(602) 951-BREN
Fax: (602) 951-5881
Web: www.brengroup.com

Key Contact - Specialty:
Ms. Brenda Rowenhorst

Description: Seasoned travel professionals focusing recruitment efforts within the travel industry. Full time and temporary management and staff positions plus access to a large computer database which is maintained covering many disciplines.

Salary Minimum: $25,000
Functions: Generalist
Industries: Transportation, Hospitality, Entertainment

Brethet, Barnum & Assoc., Inc.

703 Evans Ave., Ste. 300
Etobicoke, Ontario M9C 5E9
Canada
(416) 621-4900
Fax: (416) 621-9818
Email: brethet@castlecom.net

Key Contact - Specialty:
Mr. Bob Shiley - *Biotechnology, healthcare, medical devices, medical sales, pharmaceutical*
Ms. Phyllis Chrzan - *Medical and pharmaceutical, sales and marketing*

Description: As specialists in healthcare, we are committed to excellence--in both the quality of our service and the superior people we recruit. Our reputation for integrity and responsiveness to our clients' needs is second to none. We get results!

Salary Minimum: $35,000
Functions: Directors, Senior mgmt., Middle mgmt., Sales & mktg., Mkt. research, Mktg. mgmt., Sales mgmt.
Industries: Drugs mfg., Medical devices, Pharmaceutical svcs., Biotech, Healthcare

Brett Personnel Specialists

2184 Morris Ave.
Union, New Jersey 07083
(908) 687-7772

Key Contact - Specialty:
Mr. Gene Reight

Description: Expertise in the recruitment of engineering, maintenance, manufacturing and scientific personnel within the pharmaceutical, chemical, electromechanical and consumer products industries.

Salary Minimum: $25,000
Functions: Middle mgmt., Production, Plant mgmt., Quality, Productivity, R&D, Engineering
Industries: Chemicals, Soap/perfume/cosmetics, Drugs mfg., Medical devices, Plastics/rubber, Paints/petroleum products, Leather/stone/glass/clay

Brian Assoc., Inc.

2152 81st Street, Suite 2
Brooklyn, New York 11214-2508
(718) 232-4500
Fax: (718) 232-4510
Email: brianassoc@aol.com

Key Contact - Specialty:
Mr. Brian D. Wittlin - *General management, technical, sales & marketing*
Ms. Deborah M. Rizzo - *Information technology*
Mr. Jonathan J. Braxton - *Technical product design (electronic, digital, optical)*
Ms. Jennifer L. Halding - *Information technology*

Description: Executive search for general managment, operations, product development, sales and marketing executives in technology companies focused on IS, product engineering and electronic, digital and optical technology development.

Salary Minimum: $45,000
Functions: Senior mgmt., Product dev., Mktg. mgmt., Sales mgmt., Systems dev., R&D, Engineering
Industries: Medical devices, Machinery/Appliances, Motor vehicles, Computer equip., High tech, Software

The Bridge

P.O. Box 740297
Arvada, Colorado 80006
(303) 422-1900
Fax: (303) 422-0016

Key Contact - Specialty:
Mr. Alex B. Wilcox - *Mining, environmental, chemical, construction, high technology manufacturing*

Description: We are a diversified executive search firm offering professional search services carefully targeted to the specific needs of our clients. We are the connection between you and that needed professional you have been looking for.

Salary Minimum: $30,000
Functions: General mgmt., Materials, Sales & mktg., HR mgmt., Finance, IT, Engineering
Industries: Agri/forestry/mining, Energy/utilities, Construction, Chemicals, Computer equip., Human resource svcs., High tech

Bridgecreek Personnel Agency

12792 Valley View, Ste. 202
Garden Grove, California 92645
(714) 891-1771
Fax: (714) 892-1567
Email: BFoster1@ix.netcom.com

Key Contact - Specialty:
Mr. William A. Foster - *Manufacturing, distribution management, engineering, sales, management information systems*

Description: We specialize in manufacturing and distribution, plastics, chemicals, machine tools and related industries. Positions are national and international in management, sales, engineering, related technical fields.
Functions: Generalist, Middle mgmt., Mfg., Materials, Systems dev., R&D, Engineering
Industries: Food/bev/tobacco, Plastics/rubber, Machinery/Appliances, New media, Telecoms, Environmental svcs., High tech

BridgeGate LLC

18401 Von Karman, Ste. 440
Irvine, California 92612
(949) 553-9200
Fax: (949) 852-0749
Email: info@bridgegate.com
Web: www.bridgegate.com

Key Contact - Specialty:
Mr. Dudley G. Brown - *Information technology*

Description: We have defined the strategic discipline of management search, builds high performance teams for emerging and established companies. By supporting multiple specialties within a single engagement, we provide a complete recruitment solution.

Salary Minimum: $60,000
Functions: General mgmt., Directors, Sales & mktg., HR mgmt., Finance, IT, Mgmt. consultants
Industries: Generalist

Branches:
11400 W. Olympic Blvd., #200
Los Angeles, California 90064
(310) 479-0123
Fax: (310) 477-4893
Email: info@bridgegate.com
Web: www.bridgegate.com
Key Contact - Specialty:
Mr. Kevin M. Rosenberg - *Information technology*

Brierwood Group, Inc.

3136 Hubbard Run
Ft. Wayne, Indiana 46815
(219) 486-3849
Fax: (219) 486-4254

Email: EFree52180@aol.com

Key Contact - Specialty:
Ms. Evelyn Freeman - *Plastics, medical, automotive products*

Description: Twenty years search; technical and operations positions; Japanese/German joint ventures; domestic U.S. searches; technical, sales, line management of molded plastics. Automotive, consumer, medical and industrial products.

Salary Minimum: $50,000
Functions: Product dev., Plant mgmt., Quality, Mktg. mgmt., Sales mgmt., Engineering, Int'l.
Industries: Chemicals, Medical devices, Plastics/rubber, Machinery/Appliances, Motor vehicles, Computer equip., Consumer electronics

---

Bright Search/Professional Staffing
8120 Penn Ave. S., Ste. 167
Minneapolis, Minnesota 55431
(612) 884-8111

Key Contact - Specialty:
Mr. Leo D. Bright
Ms. Sue AlJo - *Client relations*

Description: We deliver what we agree to after 20+ years our recruiting efforts usually bring success.
Functions: Middle mgmt., Production, Plant mgmt., Purchasing, Mktg. mgmt., Sales mgmt., Direct mktg.
Industries: Food/bev/tobacco, Printing, Medical devices, Plastics/rubber, Metal products, Misc. mfg.

Affiliates:
Personnel Consultants, Inc.

Bristol Assoc., Inc.
5757 W. Century Blvd., Ste. 628
Los Angeles, California 90045
(310) 670-0525
Fax: (310) 670-4075
Email: jbright@bristolassoc.com
Web: www.bristolassoc.com

Key Contact - Specialty:
Mr. James J. Bright, Jr. - *Gaming*

Description: Depth of experience and professional knowledge. Sophisticated sourcing techniques. Focused personal service. Results-oriented. Healthcare, hospitality, gaming, food manufacturing, telecommunications, marketing, accounting and finance.
Functions: General mgmt., Mfg., Healthcare, Sales & mktg., HR mgmt., Finance, IT
Industries: Food/bev/tobacco, Hospitality, Entertainment, Accounting, Advertising/PR, Telecoms, Healthcare

---

Britt Assoc., Inc.
2709 Black Rd.
Joliet, Illinois 60435
(815) 744-7200
Fax: (815) 744-7294

Key Contact - Specialty:
Mr. William E. Lichtenauer - *Distribution, materials management*

Description: Recruitment/placement of distribution and materials management professionals on a national scale. Activity is conducted with all of industrial goods and consumer products manufacturers along with wholesale and retail firms.

Salary Minimum: $35,000
Functions: Production, Purchasing, Materials Plng., Distribution, Customer svc., Systems implem.
Industries: Generalist

Broad Waverly & Assoc.
200 Broad St., P.O. Box 741
Red Bank, New Jersey 07701
(908) 741-1010
Fax: (908) 219-9644

Key Contact - Specialty:
Mr. Bill I. Saloukas - *Insurance, property & casualty*

Description: Recruitment and placement of middle to upper property and casualty insurance candidates.

Salary Minimum: $50,000
Functions: Risk mgmt.
Industries: Insurance

Broadband Resource Group
P.O. Box 639
San Juan Capistrano, California 92693
(949) 488-8855
Fax: (949) 488-8858
Email: Broadband1@aol.com
Web: www.recruitersonline.com/eoffice/714-488-8855.html

Key Contact - Specialty:
Mr. Mark Clancey - *Broadband telecommunications (executive, management, engineering, technical)*
Ms. Darcie Clancey - *Broadband telecommunications (executive, management, engineering, technical)*

Description: We specialize in broadband telecommunications positions in cable, telephony, satellite, wireless and related areas of information technology transmission and distribution. Full-Service Network Recruiter ™.

Salary Minimum: $30,000
Functions: Product dev., Mktg. mgmt., Sales mgmt., Training, Network admin., Engineering, Technicians
Industries: Construction, Test/measurement equip., Misc. mfg., Broadcast & Film, Telecoms, High tech

---

Dan B. Brockman
P.O. Box 913
Barrington, Illinois 60011
(847) 382-6015
Fax: (847) 382-6019
Email: danbrockman@sprintmail.com

Key Contact - Specialty:
Mr. Dan B. Brockman - *Safety engineers*

Description: Specialists in degreed safety engineering practitioners, industrial hygienists, ergonomists, compliance managers (OSHA, EPA and MSHA) and environmental affairs managers. Included are diplomats with CSP, CIH, CHCM, CSM certificates.

Salary Minimum: $25,000
Functions: Plant mgmt., Productivity, Environmentalists
Industries: Agri/forestry/mining, Energy/utilities, Construction, Environmental svcs., Insurance, Biotech

---

Brookman Associates
12 E. 41st St., Ste. 1400
New York, New York 10017
(212) 213-5666
Fax: (212) 683-4672

Key Contact - Specialty:
Mr. Geoffrey Brookman - *Generalist*

Description: Professional search recruitment and placement services. Over 35 years of experience in both client and provider roles. Management consulting includes all HR activities as well as market research, field analysis, etc.

Salary Minimum: $75,000
Functions: Generalist, Healthcare, Sales & mktg., HR mgmt., Finance, IT, R&D
Industries: Mfg., Food/bev/tobacco, Drugs mfg., Medical devices, Finance, Communications, Healthcare
Professional Associations: IACPR

Broward-Dobbs, Inc.
1532 Dunwoody Village Pkwy., Ste. 200
Atlanta, Georgia 30338
(770) 399-0744
Fax: (770) 395-6881

Key Contact - Specialty:
Mr. W. Luke Greene, Jr. - *Engineering, technical sales & marketing*

Description: Client oriented executive recruiting firm specializing in engineering, environmental, telecommunications, technical sales, manufacturing and real estate. Clients are national ranging from Fortune 500 to small local companies. Personal attention is our emphasis.

Salary Minimum: $35,000
Functions: Senior mgmt., Production, Plant mgmt., Materials Plng., Mktg. mgmt., Environmentalists, Architects
Industries: Energy/utilities, Paper, Chemicals, Plastics/rubber, Misc. mfg., Telecoms, Environmental svcs.

D. Brown & Assoc., Inc.

610 SW Alder, Ste. 1111
Portland, Oregon 97205
(503) 224-6860
Fax: (503) 241-8855
Email: dennus@dbrown.net
Web: www.dbrown.net

Key Contact - Specialty:
Mr. Dennis S. Brown - *Information systems, information technology, financial, healthcare*

Description: One of Oregon's largest independent search and recruitment organizations. Thirty year commitment serving national clientele in the healthcare-accounting, information systems and information technology.

Salary Minimum: $40,000
Functions: Budgeting, MIS mgmt., Systems anal., Systems dev., Systems implem., Network admin., DB admin.
Industries: High tech, Software, Healthcare

J. B. Brown & Assoc., Inc.

820 Terminal Tower
Cleveland, Ohio 44113
(216) 696-2525
Fax: (216) 696-5825
Web: www.jbbrown@stratos.net

Key Contact - Specialty:
Mr. Jeffrey B. Brown - *Banking, call center (executives)*
Mr. Dan Barnett - *Employee leasing*
Mr. Kevin O'Neill - *Call center (executives)*

Description: Multi-divisional recruiting service with national strength in the areas of banking, call center, rehab and engineering.
Functions: Middle mgmt., Plant mgmt., Sales mgmt., Customer svc., CFO's, Engineering, Minorities
Industries: Food/bev/tobacco, Medical devices, Banking, Legal, Human resource svcs., Telecoms, Insurance

Brown, Bernardy, Van Remmen, Inc.

12100 Wilshire Blvd., Ste. M-40
Los Angeles, California 90025
(310) 826-5777
Fax: (310) 820-6330
Email: BBVR@aol.com

Key Contact - Specialty:
Mr. Buzz Brown - *Advertising, marketing, sales*
Mr. Roger Van Remmen - *Advertising, marketing, sales*
Ms. Cathie Kanuit
Ms. Renee Dollaway

Description: Specializing in creative and executive personnel for all product and service industries involved with consumer marketing, direct marketing, telemarketing, public relations, advertising and sales.

Salary Minimum: $30,000
Functions: Advertising, Mkt. research, Mktg. mgmt., Sales mgmt., Direct mktg., Graphic artists
Industries: Food/bev/tobacco, Hospitality, Entertainment, Pharmaceutical svcs., Advertising/PR, Publishing, New media

Branches:
P.O. Box 247
New Hampton, New York 10958
(914) 355-7020
Fax: (914) 355-2629
Email: BBVR@aol.com

Brownstone Sales & Marketing Group, Inc.

312 S. 22nd St., Ste. C
New York, New York 10010
(212) 254-8700
Fax: (212) 254-8282
Email: jriely@b-stone.com

Key Contact - Specialty:
Mr. James A. Riely - *Sales, sales management*
Mr. Christopher K. Doyle

Description: We offer a mix of contingency and retained work for sales professionals. We are highly ethical and hard-working on behalf of the corporation and candidate. Over 50% growth in the past 4 years.

Salary Minimum: $35,000
Functions: General mgmt., Sales & mktg., Advertising, Sales mgmt., Direct mktg., IT
Industries: Misc. mfg., Entertainment, Computer svcs., Advertising/PR, Publishing, Healthcare

BRW Search

10801 Wayzata Blvd., Ste. 100
Minnetonka, Minnesota 55305
(612) 525-1698
Fax: (612) 525-1627
Email: JFrankovich@isd.net

Key Contact - Specialty:
Mr. John Frankovich - *Sales & marketing, general management, retail, e-commerce, high-tech*

Description: We work exclusively with companies that view their employees as a valuable asset and work hard not only to attract great people, but keep them. All contingency & retained placements are guaranteed for 6 months with a replacement search at no additional cost to you.

Salary Minimum: $45,000
Functions: Generalist, General mgmt., Mfg., Healthcare, Sales & mktg., HR mgmt., Finance
Industries: Generalist, Wholesale, Retail, Communications, High tech, Software, Healthcare

Bryan & Louis Research

6263 Mayfield Rd., Ste. 226
Cleveland, Ohio 44124
(440) 442-8744
Fax: (440) 442-8745

Key Contact - Specialty:
Mr. Antony R. Terlizzi - *Signage, fixtures*
Mr. R. Louis Terlizzi - *Displays, packaging*

Description: We are specialists in our chosen industries with relationships in-depth across the U.S. and Canada.

Salary Minimum: $25,000
Functions: General mgmt., Mfg., Packaging, Sales & mktg., R&D, Engineering, Graphic artists
Industries: Lumber/furniture, Printing, Chemicals, Metal products, Machinery/Appliances, Communications, Packaging

Branches:
25820 Hurlingham Rd.
Cleveland, Ohio 44122
(216) 442-8744
Fax: (216) 442-8745
Key Contact - Specialty:
Mr. Les Snider, Jr. - *Chemical, mechanical, industrial, plastics*

Bryan, Jason & Assoc. Inc.

111 Richmond St. W., Ste. 202
Toronto, Ontario M5H 2G4
Canada
(416) 867-9295
Fax: (416) 867-3067
Email: bryjasoninterlog.com

Key Contact - Specialty:
Ms. Rickie Bryan
Ms. Bonnie Jason

Salary Minimum: $25,000
Functions: Middle mgmt., Admin. svcs., Benefits, Personnel, Training, Cash mgmt., Credit
Industries: Real estate

Bryant Research

466 Old Hook Rd., Ste. 32
Emerson, New Jersey 07630
(201) 599-0590
Fax: (201) 599-2423

Web: www.trb.trb@Ix.netcom.com

Key Contact - Specialty:
Mr. Tom Bryant - *Clinical research, health outcomes*

Description: Pharmaceutical industry research and development executive recruitment. Primary emphasis on physician and executive level R&D personnel. Also biostatistics, regulatory affairs, clinical, data management and health economics/outcomes.

Salary Minimum: $80,000
Functions: Physicians, R&D
Industries: Drugs mfg., Pharmaceutical svcs., Biotech

The Buckley Group
5301 N. Federal Hwy., #265
Boca Raton, Florida 33487
(561) 241-5010
Fax: (561) 241-5019
Email: consultants@buckleygroup.com

Key Contact - Specialty:
Mr. Daniel Buckley - *High tech sales, marketing*

Description: We are known nationally as a leader in placing sales & marketing people in the high tech fields. Mainly, PCs/mainframes, telecom, datacom and software companies.

Salary Minimum: $40,000
Functions: Directors, Senior mgmt., Middle mgmt., Mktg. mgmt., Sales mgmt., Mgmt. consultants, Int'l.
Industries: Computer equip., Consumer electronics, Publishing, New media, Telecoms, High tech, Software

Branches:
140 S. Broadway, Ste. 4
Pitman, New Jersey 08071
(609) 256-1844
Fax: (609) 256-1855
Key Contact - Specialty:
Mr. Doug Webster - *High technology, sales & marketing*

15851 Dallas Pkwy. #675
Dallas, Texas 75248
(972) 490-7722
Fax: (972) 450-5890
Key Contact - Specialty:
Mr. John Kearney - *High tech sales & marketing*

Buckman/Enochs & Assoc., Inc.
1625 Bethel Rd., Ste. 202
Columbus, Ohio 43220
(614) 457-7807
Fax: (614) 457-1946
Email: s.enochs@juno.com.

Key Contact - Specialty:
Mr. Steve Enochs - *Medical sales & marketing, consumer, high technology sales & marketing*

Description: Corporate search work on national level. Specializes in medical field with emphasis on sales and marketing.

Salary Minimum: $50,000
Functions: Mkt. research, Mktg. mgmt., Sales mgmt.
Industries: Drugs mfg., Medical devices, Computer equip., High tech, Biotech, Healthcare

Branches:
316 Creekwood Drive
Bardstown, Kentucky 40004
(502) 348-1135
Fax: (502) 348-0144
Key Contact - Specialty:
Mr. Jim Buckman

J. Burke & Assoc., Inc.
2000 E. Lamar Blvd., Ste. 600
Arlington, Texas 76006
(817) 588-3024
Fax: (817) 274-6763
Web: jsburke@flash.net

Key Contact - Specialty:
Mr. Stoney Burke - *Packaging, single service*
Ms. Kaye Burke - *Food industry, packaging*
Ms. Gayle Smith - *Packaging, chemical*

Description: We have an excellent reputation and a solid network of client companies, as well as candidates; all projects are handled with confidence, speed and professionalism. References available upon request.

Salary Minimum: $35,000
Functions: Senior mgmt., Middle mgmt., Production, Plant mgmt., Mkt. research, Mktg. mgmt., Sales mgmt.
Industries: Food/bev/tobacco, Paper, Chemicals, Soap/perfume/cosmetics, Plastics/rubber, Machinery/Appliances

Burke & Assoc./The Westfield Group
1010 Washington Blvd.
Stamford, Connecticut 06901
(203) 406-2300
Fax: (203) 406-2315
Email: burkeassoc@aol.com
Web: info@burkeandassociates.com

Key Contact - Specialty:
Mr. T. Michael Burke - *Finance, operations technology*
Ms. Joanne C. Fiala - *Human resources*

Description: Our firm deals with high profile corporate clients and top business school/Big 6 CPA firm candidates.

Salary Minimum: $70,000
Functions: Senior mgmt., Mfg., Materials, Sales & mktg., HR mgmt., Finance, Mgmt. consultants
Industries: Food/bev/tobacco, Drugs mfg., Accounting, Human resource svcs., Publishing, Telecoms, Software
Professional Associations: IACPR

The Burke Group
63 Church St., Ste. 204
St. Catharines, Ontario L2R 3C4
Canada
(905) 641-3070
Fax: (905) 641-0478
Email: tbg@theburkegroup.com
Web: www.theburkegroup.com

Key Contact - Specialty:
Ms. Anne Charette - *Generalist*
Ms. Elaine Maude - *Generalist*

Description: We offer extensive HR expertise in executive recruitment, consulting, outplacement and outsourcing. We provide solutions in areas of assessment, training and development, temporary/contract staffing.
Functions: Generalist, Senior mgmt., Plant mgmt., Health admin., Training, Engineering, Mgmt. consultants
Industries: Generalist, Paper, Motor vehicles, Hospitality, Government

Burkholder & Assoc., Inc.
15400 Knoll Trail, Ste. 230
Dallas, Texas 75248-3465
(972) 960-1291
Fax: (972) 960-7078

Key Contact - Specialty:
Mr. John Burkholder - *Property & casualty insurance, human resources management*
Mr. Curtis Powell - *Property & casualty insurance*

Description: Principal, a former SVP with a major insurance carrier, directs a national search practice in insurance and human resources management. Focus is on senior professional, management and executive level positions.

Salary Minimum: $75,000
Functions: HR mgmt., Risk mgmt.
Industries: Insurance

David S. Burt Assoc.
991 Dixon Circle
Billings, Montana 59105-2209
(406) 245-9500
Fax: (406) 245-9570
Email: DBurtSerch@aol.com

Key Contact - Specialty:
Mr. David S. Burt - *Chemical (sales & marketing)*

Description: 12 years chemical industry experience nationwide-several exclusive agreements with large chemical companies. One of ten agencies the world's largest specialty chemical manufacturers utilize. Stressing quality of placements, not quantity.

Salary Minimum: $35,000
Functions: Product dev., Mkt. research, Mktg. mgmt., Sales mgmt., Engineering, Environmentalists, Int'l.
Industries: Energy/utilities, Paper, Chemicals, Plastics/rubber, Paints/ petroleum products, Test/measurement equip., Environmental svcs.

Business Partners, Inc.

1900 Land O'Lakes Blvd., Ste. 113
Lutz, Florida 33549
(813) 948-1440
Fax: (813) 948-1450
Email: bpijobs@aol.com
Web: www.businesspartnersinc.com

Key Contact - Specialty:
Mr. Joe Johnson - *Information technology (all industries)*

Description: Executive, professional and technical staffing specializing in MIS and data processing with particular emphasis on relational database, object oriented, open systems technology. Also, client requirements as requested.

Salary Minimum: $30,000
Functions: MIS mgmt., Systems anal., Systems dev., Systems implem., Systems support, DB admin., Int'l.
Industries: Generalist, Transportation, Computer svcs., New media, Telecoms, High tech, Software

International Branches:
Lampertheim

Business Solutions Worldwide, Inc.

35 Dorland Farm Court
P.O. Box 122
Skillman, New Jersey 08558-0122
(908) 904-9685
Fax: (908) 904-9685
Email: jgonedes@worldnet.att.net

Key Contact - Specialty:
Ms. Marcy L. Pollack - *Human resource management*
Ms. Ellen G. Kusnetz - *General, finance*
Mr. James T. Gonedes - *Sales & marketing*

Description: A marketing focused organization, providing solutions to businesses of all sizes, while taking the time to help all candidates.

Salary Minimum: $50,000
Functions: Generalist, General mgmt., Mfg., Materials, Sales & mktg., HR mgmt., Finance
Industries: Generalist, Mfg., Wholesale, Retail, Finance, Government, Packaging

---

Business Systems of America, Inc.

200 W. Adams St., Ste. 2015
Chicago, Illinois 60606
(312) 849-9222
Fax: (312) 849-9260
Email: recruiter@bussysam.com
Web: www.bussysam.com

Key Contact - Specialty:
Mr. Chris Edwards - *PC professionals*
Mr. Lou Costabile - *PC professionals*

Description: We provide tested, PC and LAN support personnel to Chicago's Fortune 500 companies. We discover, empower and support the career of the best technical support personnel in Chicago.

Salary Minimum: $30,000
Functions: IT, MIS mgmt., Systems anal., Systems dev., Systems implem., Systems support
Industries: Computer svcs., Human resource svcs., High tech

The Butlers Co. Insurance Recruiters

2753 State Rd. 580, Ste. 103
Clearwater, Florida 34621
(813) 725-1065
Fax: (813) 726-7125
Email: kbutler@GTE.net

Key Contact - Specialty:
Mr. Kirby B. Butler, Jr. - *Insurance (executives & upper management)*
Ms. Martha Butler - *Insurance (technical & administrative)*

Description: Insurance national search involvement, technical through executive; actuarial, accounting, financial, underwriting, loss control, marketing, claims, administrative, DP and sales. Property and casualty, life and health. Kirby Butler, CPC, previous president of Florida Assoc. (FAPS).

Salary Minimum: $30,000
Functions: Directors, Senior mgmt., Middle mgmt., Sales mgmt., Personnel, Finance, Risk mgmt.
Industries: Insurance

Butterfield & Co. Int'l., Inc.

P.O. Box 370
Koloa, Hawaii 96756-0370
(808) 742-1900
Fax: (808) 742-1926
Email: resumes@butterfield-intl.com
Web: butterfield-intl.com

Key Contact - Specialty:
Mr. N. Blair Butterfield - *Medical imaging, computing technologies*

Description: Strategic contact network for diagnostic imaging and ideal location for U.S. & Asian clients. Only firm so specialized in global recruiting industry.

Salary Minimum: $50,000
Functions: General mgmt., Sales & mktg., Mktg. mgmt., MIS mgmt., R&D, Engineering, Int'l.
Industries: Medical devices, Computer equip., High tech, Software, Healthcare

Branches:
639 Whispering Hills Rd., Ste. 327
Boone, North Carolina 28607
(704) 266-9851
Fax: (704) 266-9850
Email: cehall@boone.net
Key Contact - Specialty:
Mr. Charles Hall - *Software*

Button Group

1608 Emory Circle
Plano, Texas 75093
(972) 985-0619

Key Contact - Specialty:
Mr. David R. Button - *Facility design, engineering, construction*
Ms. Dianne Vann - *Telecommunications, manufacturing*

Description: Facilities design/build, manufacture and support including strong emphasis on managers, engineers and specialized services categories nationwide. Foods, chemicals, pharmaceuticals, telecommunications, high tech electronics.

Salary Minimum: $60,000
Functions: Directors, Senior mgmt., Mktg. mgmt., MIS mgmt., Systems implem., Engineering, Architects
Industries: Construction, Drugs mfg., Medical devices, Test/measurement equip., Telecoms, High tech, Software

---

C & H Personnel

126 White Oak Drive
Lancaster, Pennsylvania 17601
(717) 581-1380
Fax: (717) 560-1686
Email: chp@lancnews.infi.net

Key Contact - Specialty:
Mr. Jon A. Singer

Description: Serving professionals since 1975. Two CPC's on staff. Service based on the highest standards of ethics and quality.

Salary Minimum: $30,000
Functions: Mfg., Materials, HR mgmt., Finance, IT
Industries: Generalist

C and P Marketing, Ltd.

4335 Quail Ridge, Ste. 100
Enid, Oklahoma 73703
(405) 234-2211
Fax: (405) 234-7711

Key Contact - Specialty:
Mr. Paul G. Krienke - *Community banking*

Description: 16 years exclusive representation of Midwest community banks in all types of lending positions, senior loan officers and chief executives.
Functions: Middle mgmt., Cash mgmt., Credit
Industries: Agri/forestry/mining, Finance, Banking

C Assoc.

1619 G St. SE
Washington, District of Columbia 20003
(202) 518-8595
Fax: (202) 387-7033
Email: john@cassociates.com
Web: cassociates.com

Key Contact - Specialty:
Mr. John Capozzi - *UNIX, C, client/server, relational database, web development*
Ms. Susan Sieler - *UNIX, C, client/server, relational database*

Industries: Computer svcs., High tech, Software

C. R. Assoc.

P.O. Box 60998
Palo Alto, California 94306
(650) 324-9000
Fax: (650) 856-3556
Email: eagle4@webtv.net

Key Contact - Specialty:
Mr. Harold Stephenson - *Banking, finance*

Description: Established 1977, we specialize in recruiting for the banking and credit union industries in California and especially in independent banking. Also serve the small business administration field.

Salary Minimum: $30,000
Industries: Banking, Misc. financial

The C.P.R. Group

26 Park St.
Montclair, New Jersey 07042
(973) 744-0818
Fax: (973) 744-0775

Key Contact - Specialty:
Mr. Thomas Keoughan - *Toy, gift, juvenile products industries*

Description: Discreet and personal handling of worldwide recruitment of all disciplines within the toy, gift and juvenile products industries.
Functions: Senior mgmt., Product dev., Purchasing, Mkt. research, Sales mgmt., Engineering, Graphic artists
Industries: Entertainment

C.P.S., Inc.

(Firm declined to update.)
1 Westbrook Corp. Ctr., Ste. 600
Westchester, Illinois 60154
(708) 562-0001
Email: cpsjobs@aol.com

Key Contact - Specialty:
Mr. H. Douglas Christiansen
Ms. Renee Mydlach
Mr. Rich Brandeis
Ms. Cheryl Laird
Mr. Dale Graham
Mr. Pat Kilcoyne
Mr. Jim Clark
Mr. Dave Schueneman
Mr. Mark Pomerance
Mr. Tom Scalamera
Mr. Lee Romano

Description: Dynamic technical firm employing over 60 specialized recruiters. Consistently placing the top 20% of applicants nationwide. Divisionalized into 13 distinct marketplaces: engineering, sales and marketing, production supervision, etc. We do not waste anyone's time.

Salary Minimum: $25,000
Functions: Mfg., Materials, Sales & mktg., Benefits, IT, R&D, Engineering
Industries: Transportation, Misc. financial, Computer svcs., Packaging, Insurance, Software

C.T.E.W. Executive Personnel Services Inc.

409 Granville St., Ste. 1207
1207 United Kingdom Bldg.
Vancouver, British Columbia V6C 1T2
Canada
(604) 682-3218
Fax: (604) 683-3211
Email: ctew@imag.net

Key Contact - Specialty:
Mr. Alex Kahng - *Executives, finance*
Mr. Stan Dahl - *Generalist, environmental, technical*
Ms. Karen Lai - *Information technology, high technology*
Mr. Grant Sutherland - *Accounting, finance, executives*
Ms. Hayley Lace - *Sales & marketing executives*

Description: Full service search firm servicing clients with executive, managerial and supervisory recruiting assignments across all industry sectors.

Salary Minimum: $40,000
Functions: Generalist, Senior mgmt., Production, Customer svc., Budgeting, Systems anal., Mgmt. consultants
Industries: Generalist, Mfg., Misc. financial, Higher ed., Environmental svcs., High tech, Software

Branches:
335 Bay St., Ste. 638
Toronto, Ontario M5H 2R3
Canada
(416) 368-0367
Fax: (416) 368-7362
Email: ctew888@aol.com
Key Contact - Specialty:
Ms. Hayley Lau - *Executives, information technology*

C/R Associates

1231 Delaware Ave., Ste. 1
Buffalo, New York 14209
(716) 884-1734
Fax: (716) 883-0776
Email: p.cramer@cpstaffing.com

Key Contact - Specialty:
Mr. Paul J. Cramer - *Accounting, banking, finance, human resources*

Description: Specialize in accounting, banking, finance, human resources, serve upstate NY and Northwest PA directly and through membership in AAFA cover entire USA, parts of Canada and Europe.

Salary Minimum: $30,000
Functions: Benefits, Personnel, CFO's, Budgeting, Cash mgmt., Credit, Taxes
Industries: Misc. mfg., Banking, Accounting, Broadcast & Film, Healthcare

Affiliates:
Computer People

Cadillac Assoc.

100 S. Sunrise Way, Ste. 353
Palm Springs, California 92262
(760) 327-0920
Fax: (760) 322-5699
Email: cadsearch@aol.com
Web: websites.earthlink.net/~cadsearch

Key Contact - Specialty:
Mr. Dwight Hanna - *Healthcare, high technology, hospitality*

Description: Impeccable service operating with specialized account executives. Strict confidentiality and prior consent assured. Seasoned veterans as search managers.

Salary Minimum: $60,000

Functions: Production, Nurses, Allied health, Mkt. research, Mktg. mgmt., Sales mgmt., Systems dev.
Industries: Drugs mfg., Medical devices, Computer equip., High tech, Software, Biotech, Healthcare

Branches:
8033 Sunset Blvd., Ste. 5200
Los Angeles, California 90046-2427
(213) 385-9111
Fax: (619) 322-5699

CadTech Staffing Services
825-B Franklin Court
Marietta, Georgia 30067
(770) 499-1443
Fax: (770) 499-8867
Email: cadtech@mindspring.com

Key Contact - Specialty:
Mr. Daniel W. Telford - *Architects, engineers*

Description: We specialize in the placement of drafting and design professionals in the fields of architecture, engineering and manufacturing.
Functions: Production, Engineering, Architects, Graphic artists
Industries: Construction

Cahill Assoc.
P.O. Box 401, 100 Main St.
Southington, Connecticut 06489
(860) 628-3963
Fax: (860) 628-3966
Email: pmc3963@aol.com

Key Contact - Specialty:
Mr. Peter Cahill - *Technology based, engineering, marketing, manufacturing operations*

Description: Specialize in filling key management and senior staff positions for small to medium firms.

Salary Minimum: $50,000
Functions: Senior mgmt., Mfg., Materials, Mktg. mgmt., Sales mgmt., HR mgmt., Engineering
Industries: Chemicals, Medical devices, Plastics/rubber, Metal products, Misc. mfg., Aerospace, High tech

Juliette Lang Cahn Executive Search
12 Beekman Place
New York, New York 10022
(212) 371-0725
Fax: (212) 371-7251

Key Contact - Specialty:
Ms. Juliette Lang Cahn - *Extrusion, plastics*

Description: Executive search utilizing twenty years of contacts in plastics industry.

Salary Minimum: $50,000
Functions: Product dev., Production, Plant mgmt., Quality, Materials Plng., R&D, Engineering
Industries: Chemicals, Plastics/rubber

Caldwell Legal Recruiting Consultants
(Firm declined to update.)
561 Atlantic Hwy., Ste. 100
Northport, Maine 04849
(207) 338-9500

Key Contact - Specialty:
Ms. Kate Caldwell - *Intellectual property attorneys & agents (includes biotech, computer & other high tech industries)*

Description: We are a nationwide intellectual property placement service. Our clients include both law firms and the corporate sector. We place all levels of attorneys from associate to chief patent counsel positions.
Functions: Attorneys
Industries: Legal

California Management Search
(a division of R. Marsh & Associates, Inc.)
881 11th St., Ste. 117
Lakeport, California 95453
(707) 263-6000
Fax: (707) 263-6800
Email: cms@zapcom.net
Web: www.careerdomain.com/cms

Key Contact - Specialty:
Mr. Norman R. Marsh - *Insurance*

Description: We pride ourselves on prompt, courteous service to our clients. Although most of our placements are within the western states, we do offer service throughout the U.S. through the efforts of our national network.
Functions: CFO's, Risk mgmt., Network admin., DB admin.
Industries: Insurance, High tech, Healthcare

California Search Agency, Inc.
2603 Main St., Ste. 550
Irvine, California 92614-6232
(949) 475-0790
Fax: (949) 475-0796
Email: dcrane@jobagency.com
Web: www.jobagency.com

Key Contact - Specialty:
Mr. Don Crane - *Engineering, manufacturing*
Mr. Mike Baine - *Engineering, manufacturing*

Description: Technical recruiting for small, medium and large manufacturing and R&D (commercial, industrial, aerospace and military). Firms specializing in all disciplines of engineering and manufacturing personnel.

Salary Minimum: $25,000
Functions: General mgmt., Mfg., Materials, Sales & mktg., IT, R&D, Engineering
Industries: Generalist, Energy/utilities, Mfg., Aerospace, Packaging, High tech, Software

Callos Personnel Services
5083 Market St.
Corporate Center Bldg.
Youngstown, Ohio 44512
(800) 4-CALLOS
(330) 788-4001
Fax: (216) 783-3966
Email: callosassoc@worldnet.att.net

Key Contact - Specialty:
Mr. Eric Sutton
Mr. John G. Callos
Mr. Thomas Walsh

Description: Ability to access a national pool of talent and placement expertise to help you select the best possible candidate, in the right location. Experienced staff with the technical capability to perform effectively. 350+ offices, computer linked, covering USA, Canada, Europe and the Pacific Rim with specialists in nearly every career field.

Salary Minimum: $25,000
Functions: Generalist, General mgmt., Mfg., Materials, Engineering
Industries: Mfg.

Branches:
150 Springside Drive, Ste. B250
Akron, Ohio 44333
(800) 344-7091
Fax: (216) 665-4474
Email: callos@apk.net
Key Contact - Specialty:
Mr. Daniel Wismar

Cambridge Group Ltd. - Exec. Search Div.
1175 Post Rd. E.
Westport, Connecticut 06880
(203) 226-4243
Fax: (203) 226-3856
Email: cambridgegroup@internetmci.com
Web: www.cambridgegroup.com

Key Contact - Specialty:
Mr. Michael Salvagno
Mr. Alfred Judge

Description: Our thirty person staff is departmentalized to offer the highest quality service that can only come from specialization. Specialties include information systems, general management, healthcare, physicians, pharmaceutical, finance, human resources.

Salary Minimum: $80,000

Functions: General mgmt., Sales & mktg., HR mgmt., Finance, CFO's, IT, MIS mgmt.
Industries: Generalist, Textiles/apparel, Drugs mfg., Mgmt. consulting, Telecoms, Software, Healthcare

Branches:
161A John Jefferson Rd.
Williamsburg, Virginia 23185
(757) 565-1150
Fax: (757) 565-0391
Key Contact - Specialty:
Mr. Fred DiSalvo - *Search*

The Cambridge Group Ltd.
1175 Post Rd. E.
Westport, Connecticut 06880
(203) 226-4243
Fax: (203) 226-3856
Email: msalvagno@cambridgegroup.com
Web: www.cambridgegroup.com

Key Contact - Specialty:
Mr. Alfred Judge
Mr. Mike Salvagno

Description: Cambridge's seasoned staff and computerized database affords our clients the most efficient and expedient searches available. Specialties include physicians, pharmaceutical, finance, physical therapy, information systems, healthcare and general management.

Salary Minimum: $60,000
Functions: Senior mgmt., Physicians, CFO's, MIS mgmt., Systems implem., Network admin., DB admin.
Industries: Textiles/apparel, Drugs mfg., Misc. mfg., Accounting, High tech, Software, Healthcare

Branches:
161 A John Jefferson Rd.
Williamsburg, Virginia 23187
(757) 565-1150
Fax: (757) 565-0391
Email: cambridge@widomaker.com
Key Contact - Specialty:
Mr. Fred DiSalvo - *Search*

Campbell, Edgar Inc.
4388 49th St.
Delta, British Columbia V4K 2S7
Canada
(604) 946-8535
Fax: (604) 946-2384
Email: info@retailcareers.com
Web: www.retailcareers.com

Key Contact - Specialty:
Ms. Elaine Hay - *Retail executives*
Ms. Ruth Kirk - *Fashion store management, store operations*
Ms. Natalie Marin - *Store management*

Description: We are the largest recruitment firm in Canada committed to the retail industry. Placement of only highest quality personnel throughout the country. Additional services such as mystery shopping, store auditing and staff training available.

Salary Minimum: $20,000
Functions: Senior mgmt., Middle mgmt., Admin. svcs., Purchasing, Advertising, Sales mgmt., Customer svc.
Industries: Retail

Branches:
366-11215 Jasper Ave.
Edmonton, Alberta T5K 0L5
Canada
(403) 496-3530
Fax: (403) 496-3527
Web: www.retailcareers.com
Key Contact - Specialty:
Ms. Ruth Kirk - *Specialty retail store operations*

212-4940 #3 Rd.
Richmond, British Columbia V4K 2S7
Canada
(604) 273-8515
Fax: (604) 278-3005
Email: info@retailcareers.com
Web: www.retailcareers.com
Key Contact - Specialty:
Mr. Ed Wong - *Retail store operations*

CanMed Consultants Inc.
62 Queen St. S.
Mississauga, Ontario L5M 1K4
Canada
(905) 567-1080
Fax: (905) 567-1081
Email: mraheja@canmed.com
Web: www.canmed.com

Key Contact - Specialty:
Dr. Marc C. Raheja - *Healthcare sector, senior management*

Description: International consultants to executives and professionals in the healthcare sector. Services include management training, executive and professional search, locum/contract employees, management consulting, plus providing expert speakers on healthcare related topics.

Salary Minimum: $50,000
Functions: Directors, Senior mgmt., Physicians, Mktg. mgmt., Training, R&D
Industries: Drugs mfg., Higher ed., Pharmaceutical svcs.

J. P. Canon Assoc.
225 Broadway, Ste. 3602
New York, New York 10007-3001
(212) 233-3131
Fax: (212) 233-0457
Email: headhunter@iname.com
Web: www.jpcanon.com

Key Contact - Specialty:
Mr. James Rohan - *Purchasing, supply chain management*
Ms. Paula Blumenthal - *Materials, logistics management*

Description: We specialize in the nationwide recruitment of materials management, logistics, distribution, purchasing and user interface systems professionals.

Salary Minimum: $30,000
Functions: Production, Purchasing, Materials Plng., Distribution, Packaging, Systems implem., Mgmt. consultants
Industries: Generalist, Food/bev/tobacco, Paper, Soap/perfume/cosmetics, Drugs mfg., Mgmt. consulting, Packaging

The Canon Group
27936 Lost Canyon Rd.
Santa Clarita, California 91351
(805) 252-7400
Fax: (805) 252-7880
Web: www.canon search.com

Key Contact - Specialty:
Mr. Tim Grayem - *Generalist*
Ms. Cindy Ferguson - *Insurance, marketing*
Mr. Damon King - *Insurance, management*
Mr. Norm Diaz - *Insurance, education*
Ms. Laurie Jayroe - *Insurance*

Description: We are a contingency, retained or temporary executive search firm offering professional services devoted to property and casualty insurance technicians. We search nationally, but predominantly service the Los Angeles area.

Salary Minimum: $60,000
Functions: Senior mgmt., Middle mgmt., Mkt. research, Mktg. mgmt., Sales mgmt., Mgmt. consultants
Industries: Mgmt. consulting, Human resource svcs., Insurance

Cantrell & Assoc.
3121 Pleasant Court
Tallahassee, Florida 32303
(850) 531-9992
Fax: (850) 531-9962
Email: warren@staffing.net

Key Contact - Specialty:
Mr. Rick Warren

Description: Our company has developed many contacts over the years. This enriches our base and allows us to present the most qualified candidates possible in our disciplines. From engineers to broadcasters, we have the sources.

Salary Minimum: $25,000
Functions: Production, Allied health, Sales mgmt., MIS mgmt., Systems anal., Systems dev., Engineering

Industries: Paper, Chemicals, Computer svcs., Broadcast & Film, Telecoms, Software, Healthcare

Canyon Consulting, Inc.

4 Ohio St.
New Braunfels, Texas 78130
(830) 608-9199
(830) 620-5671
Email: batwood@canyoncg.com

Key Contact - Specialty:
Mr. Bob Atwood - *Manufacturing*
Mr. Paul Berry - *Quality, regulatory*

Description: The recruiters have many years of experience hiring and managing the same type professionals they now recruit. They are degreed engineers.

Salary Minimum: $50,000
Functions: Senior mgmt., Middle mgmt., Mfg., Materials, Budgeting
Industries: Medical devices, Metal products, Machinery/Appliances, Consumer electronics, Test/measurement equip., Misc. mfg.

Capital Markets Resources, Inc.
(a division of Professional Computer Resources, Inc.)

233 S. Sharon Amity, Ste. 200-A
Charlotte, North Carolina 28211
(704) 362-6727
Fax: (704) 362-4904
Email: cmrresumes@pcr.net

Key Contact - Specialty:
Mr. Patrick Hermsen - *Real estate finance & structuring, sales & trading (capital markets) portfolio manager*
Mr. T. J. Foltz - *Commercial finance, leveraged finance, derivatives & foreign exchange, investment banking*
Mr. Scott Horton - *Corporate banking, international finance, high yield risk management*

Description: We provide primarily permanent placement of professionals from Wall Street and the world's top 20 financial institutions, with First Union and Nationsbank in Charlotte, with over 100 placements since 1990.

Salary Minimum: $50,000
Functions: Sales mgmt., Budgeting, Cash mgmt., M&A, Risk mgmt., Systems anal., Systems dev.
Industries: Banking, Invest. banking, Brokers, Venture cap., Real estate, High tech, Software

Capitol Management Consulting, Inc.

114 Hopewell-Lambertville Rd.
Hopewell, New Jersey 08525
(609) 466-2822
Email: jk@capitolmgmt.com
Web: www.capitolmgmt.com

Key Contact - Specialty:
Mr. Joseph J. Kowalski

Description: Specializes in operations analysis and executive search. Particular expertise in assignments for biomedical, pharmaceutical, medical device, chemical and plastic industries. Locates, selects and evaluates candidates for middle and upper management positions.

Salary Minimum: $35,000
Functions: Generalist
Industries: Food/bev/tobacco, Paper, Printing, Chemicals, Soap/perfume/cosmetics, Drugs mfg., Biotech

Sally Caplan & Assoc.

1420 NW Gilman Blvd., Ste. 2292
Issaquah, Washington 98027
(425) 557-0015
Fax: (425) 557-0017
Email: scaplan@nwlink.com

Key Contact - Specialty:
Ms. Sally Caplan - *High technology*

Description: We specialize exclusively in high technology professionals. We recruit top performing sales, technical, marketing, consulting and management executives throughout North America.

Salary Minimum: $75,000
Functions: Directors, Senior mgmt., Middle mgmt., Mkt. research, Mktg. mgmt., Sales mgmt., Systems implem.
Industries: High tech, Software

Career +Plus

136 Riverside Drive
Old Forge, New York 13420
(315) 369-4495
Fax: (315) 369-4496
Email: careerop@telenet.net

Key Contact - Specialty:
Mr. James M. Keyser - *Optics, laser sciences, sales, engineering*

Description: We specialize in professional sales and engineering in the optics and laser science industries. Engineering includes: management, design and research. Sales include: management and field reps.

Salary Minimum: $40,000
Functions: Sales & mktg., Sales mgmt., R&D, Engineering
Industries: Mfg., Medical devices, Test/measurement equip., Aerospace

Branches:
11 N. Goodman St.
Rochester, New York 14607
(716) 271-5790
Fax: (315) 369-4496
Email: careerop@telenet.net
Key Contact - Specialty:
Mr. Aaron Brandt

Career Advisors, Inc.

6169 Miami Lakes Drive E.
Miami Lakes, Florida 33014
(305) 826-2525
Fax: (305) 827-2685
Email: rrthibault@aol.com

Key Contact - Specialty:
Mr. Raymond Thibault - *General business*

Description: Most of my assignments are close to the 6 figure mark but I continue to help $50-60,000 staff and light managers because they are the controllers, CFOs, directors and vice presidents of tomorrow.

Salary Minimum: $50,000
Functions: Generalist, General mgmt., Sales & mktg., HR mgmt., Finance, CFO's, IT
Industries: Generalist, Drugs mfg., Computer equip., Transportation, Finance, Publishing, Insurance

Career Alternatives Executive Search

1519 N. Lakeshore Drive
Harbor Springs, Michigan 49740
(616) 526-9900
Fax: (616) 526-9927
Email: pat@freeway.net

Key Contact - Specialty:
Mr. Patrick J. Burns - *Sales*

Description: An executive search firm specializing in the sales and marketing areas. Primary clients are consumer product companies.

Salary Minimum: $40,000
Functions: Distribution, Sales & mktg., Advertising, Mkt. research, Mktg. mgmt., Sales mgmt.
Industries: Food/bev/tobacco, Paper, Soap/perfume/cosmetics, Drugs mfg., Plastics/rubber, Consumer electronics, Misc. mfg.

Career Consulting Group, Inc.

1100 Summer St.
Stamford, Connecticut 06905
(203) 975-8800
Fax: (203) 975-8808
Email: ccgexecsearch.com

Key Contact - Specialty:
Mr. Gerald Kanovsky
Ms. Marlene Kanovsky

Description: Marketing specialists in market research, decision support, marketing information industry, sales promotion, direct response marketing, database modeling, brand sales analysis, product management, marketing modeling, category management, trade marketing.

Salary Minimum: $40,000
Functions: Advertising, Mkt. research, Mktg. mgmt., Sales mgmt., Direct mktg.
Industries: Food/bev/tobacco, Drugs mfg., Misc. financial, Mgmt. consulting, Publishing, New media, Broadcast & Film

---

Career Counseling Inc. (CCI)
1401 Spring Bank Drive, Bldg. C, Ste. 4
Owensboro, Kentucky 42303
(502) 686-7766
Fax: (502) 686-7772
Email: headhunter@job4u.com

Key Contact - Specialty:
Mr. Steven J. Young - *Electromechanical, chemical, mechanical engineering, store fixtures*
Ms. Paula G. Young - *Plastic, paper & pulp, converting, executive, engineering*
Mr. Randy Cain - *Sales*
Mr. Bob Randolph - *Information systems (computer), manufacturing*

Description: We are a privately owned, quality driven executive search firm that has national and international search capabilities. Professionalism, ethics and quality work are the standards this firm insists on.

Salary Minimum: $35,000
Functions: Senior mgmt., Plant mgmt., Sales mgmt., CFO's, MIS mgmt., R&D, Engineering
Industries: Generalist, Lumber/furniture, Paper, Plastics/rubber, Metal products, Motor vehicles, Computer equip.

Career Counseling Ltd. (C.C.L.)
71 Schriever Lane, Ste. 210
New City, New York 10956-3313
(914) 634-0111
(888) CCL-0021
Fax: (914) 634-0126
Email: cclsearch@aol.com

Key Contact - Specialty:
Mr. Michael Richter - *Healthcare, medical*
Ms. Heidi Hollander - *Registered nurses, physical therapists, occupational therapists, physicians assistants, nurse practitioners*
Ms. Shelly Tomkin - *Sales, pharmacy sales, research positions*

Description: A search firm specializing in healthcare. During the last 18 years we have been instrumental in the growth of many hospitals, health centers and private practices around the US. We are placing administrators, physicians, P.A., P.T., OT nurses, practitioners and other healthcare personnel.

Functions: Physicians, Nurses, Allied health, Health admin., Systems anal., Systems dev.
Industries: Pharmaceutical svcs., Computer svcs., Healthcare

Branches:
21374 Bridge View Drive
Boca Raton, Florida 33428
(561) 852-0020
Fax: (561) 852-5588
Key Contact - Specialty:
Mr. Michael Richter - *Healthcare, medical*

2304 Magnolia Court E., Ste. 308
Buffalo Grove, Illinois 60089
(847) 634-3456
Fax: (847) 634-3434
Key Contact - Specialty:
Ms. Fern Rae - *Physicians, healthcare*
Ms. Heidi Richter - *Medical, healthcare*
Ms. Heidi Hollander - *Physicians, healthcare*

Career Development Associates
6290 Harrison Drive, Ste. 4
Las Vegas, Nevada 89120
(702) 798-0744
Fax: (702) 798-0385
Email: cda1v@cda1v.com
Web: www.cda1v.com

Key Contact - Specialty:
Ms. Sharon K. Fields - *Hospitality, gaming*
Ms. Dyann Rios - *Hospitality, gaming*

Description: Personalized searches and customized placement in the gaming and hospitality industries. Our professionals have excellent contacts and relationships within this field. Above all our confidentiality is guaranteed.

Salary Minimum: $35,000
Functions: Directors, Senior mgmt., Middle mgmt., Mktg. mgmt., CFO's, MIS mgmt., Mgmt. consultants
Industries: Mfg., Hospitality, Mgmt. consulting, Law enfcmt.

Career Enterprises
5 East Main St.
Hudson, Ohio 44236-3012
(330) 656-1700
Fax: (330) 656-1234
Email: info@careerenterprises.com
Web: www.careerenterprises.com

Key Contact - Specialty:
Mr. Stuart Taylor

Description: Privately owned contingency and executive search firm. Fully automated national database including access to Internet, capable of management and senior executive level search as well as staff technical placement.

Functions: MIS mgmt., Systems anal., Systems dev., Systems implem., Systems support, Network admin., DB admin.
Industries: Generalist

Career Images
P.O. Box 1777
Palm Harbor, Florida 34682
(727) 786-9334
Fax: (727) 786-9235
Email: careerimages@tbi.net

Key Contact - Specialty:
Ms. Deborah J. Hunkins - *Environmental, safety, engineering, ergonomics, health safety*

Description: We are a national recruiting and search firm specializing in the placement of environmental health, safety and engineering professionals for all major industrial corporations.

Salary Minimum: $35,000
Functions: Quality, Nurses, HR mgmt., Engineering, Environmentalists
Industries: Generalist, Food/bev/tobacco, Paper, Chemicals, Medical devices, Plastics/rubber, Metal products

---

Career Marketing Assoc., Inc.
7100 E. Belleview Ave., Ste. 102
Greenwood Village, Colorado 80111-1634
(303) 779-8890
Fax: (303) 779-8139
Email: cma@cmagroup.com
Web: www.cmagroup.com

Key Contact - Specialty:
Mr. Jan Sather - *Engineering*
Mr. Terry Leyden - *Toxicology*
Mr. Chip Doro - *Technical sales*
Mr. Richard Steinman - *Medical device, diagnostics*
Mr. Cary Woody - *Regulatory affairs*
Mr. Gary Patton - *Software engineering, Windows*

Description: Since 1968 our only business has been to provide capable personnel to companies nationwide. Each CMA recruiter specializes in a field utilizing his or her background.

Salary Minimum: $35,000
Functions: Product dev., Production, Systems anal., Systems dev., Systems support
Industries: Computer equip., Test/measurement equip., Telecoms, High tech, Software, Biotech

---

Career Marketing Consultants, Inc.
P.O. Box 1068
Roswell, Georgia 30077-1068
(770) 587-1090
Fax: (770) 587-5070

Email: cmc4jobs@aol.com

Key Contact - Specialty:
Mr. James L. Ferrel - *High tech, HR, manufacturing management*
Ms. Bonny Brown - *Research, HR, manufacturing management*

Description: We focus on professional recruitment of executive management, manufacturing management, middle and upper level management in high technology sales and sales support, HR management and MIS executive management.

Salary Minimum: $60,000
Functions: Senior mgmt., Plant mgmt., Sales mgmt., Customer svc., HR mgmt., CFO's, MIS mgmt.
Industries: Mfg., Computer svcs., Human resource svcs., High tech, Software

---

Career Profiles
84 Pleasant St., P.O. Box 4430
Portsmouth, New Hampshire 03802
(603) 433-3355
Email: jobnexus@aol.com
Web: www.careerprofiles.net

Key Contact - Specialty:
Ms. Leanne P. Gray - *Sales*
Mr. Norman G. Gray - *Sales*

Description: We place individuals with sales, sales management and marketing backgrounds in medical, pharmaceutical, publishing and industrial sales positions. We also place professionals in other disciplines as well.
Functions: Healthcare, Nurses, Sales & mktg., Sales mgmt., Minorities
Industries: Food/bev/tobacco, Soap/perfume/cosmetics, Drugs mfg., Medical devices, Svcs., Communications, Healthcare

---

Career Search Group
1301 Seminole Blvd., Ste. 128
Largo, Florida 33770
(813) 586-2892
Fax: (813) 584-6323
Email: nhelsel247@aol.com

Key Contact - Specialty:
Mr. Tony Manatine - *Medical sales, marketing, management*

Description: Why us? We offer 18 years of professional recruiting in the medical field on a national basis, specializing in sales, sales management, marketing and product management. We offer the highest degree of professionalism, which is reflected in our closing success rate of over 75%.
Functions: Directors, Senior mgmt., Middle mgmt., Product dev., Mktg. mgmt., Sales mgmt.
Industries: Food/bev/tobacco, Drugs mfg., Medical devices, Healthcare

Affiliates:
Neal Helsel & Assoc.

Career Strategies, Inc.
3435 Wilshire Blvd., Ste. 2120
Los Angeles, California 90010
(213) 385-0440

Key Contact - Specialty:
Mr. Darin Rado
Mr. Jim King - *Financial, accounting*

Description: Flexible recruiting firm with multiple expertise. Prides itself in finding staff that will have impact on bottom line. Prestigious list of clients however open accounts from which we can recruit is plentiful.
Functions: Admin. svcs., Nurses, Customer svc., Benefits, CFO's, Attorneys, Graphic artists
Industries: Mfg., Finance, Svcs., Communications, High tech, Software, Healthcare

Branches:
2390 E. Camelback Rd. #427
Phoenix, Arizona 85016
(602) 955-5811
Key Contact - Specialty:
Mr. David Bonewell

2600 Michelson, Ste. 1560
Irvine, California 92612
(714) 251-8811
Email: occsi@aol.com
Key Contact - Specialty:
Mr. Matt McGowan

11845 W. Tower, Ste. 710
Los Angeles, California 90064
(310) 445-2727
Key Contact - Specialty:
Ms. Joann Cavarretta

21031 Ventura Blvd., Ste. 1005
Woodland Hills, California 91364
(818) 883-0440
Key Contact - Specialty:
Ms. Julie Maddox

Careerfit, Inc.
(a division of Growth & Leadership Solutions, Inc.)
2900 N. Loop W., Ste. 800
Houston, Texas 77092
(713) 688-0686
Fax: (713) 688-7526
Email: lhummel@careerfit.com
Web: www.careerfit.com

Key Contact - Specialty:
Mr. Gary L. Selman - *Senior executives*
Ms. D. Linda Hummel - *Engineering, technical*
Mr. Daniel T. Batista - *Technical, managerial*

Description: We specialize in the recruitment and placement of executive and professional talent in the energy industry.
Functions: General mgmt., Mfg., Sales & mktg., HR mgmt., Finance, IT, Engineering
Industries: Energy/utilities, Mfg., Finance, Legal, High tech, Software

---

Careers First, Inc.
305 U.S. Route 130
Cinnaminson, New Jersey 08077-3398
(609) 786-0004
Fax: (609) 786-3336
Web: www.careersfirst.com

Key Contact - Specialty:
Ms. Gail Duncan - *Computer technologists*

Description: Outsource your difficult or sensitive technical searches to a reliable, high performance, modest fee resource ready to serve your needs at all levels in information technology, computer and communications specialties.
Functions: Senior mgmt., Automation, MIS mgmt., Systems anal., Systems dev., Network admin., DB admin.
Industries: Chemicals, Computer equip., Computer svcs., New media, Telecoms, High tech, Software

Affiliates:
CEO Services, Inc.

Careers On Track
(formerly Ryerson Tabor Assoc.)
150 County Rd., Box 222
Tenafly, New Jersey 07670
(201) 894-0600
Fax: (201) 894-0563
Email: tabortrak@aol.com

Key Contact - Specialty:
Mr. Gary Tabor - *Marketing, packaged goods, marketing consulting, marketing services, data based marketing, computer software*

Description: Former packaged goods marketing professionals provide key general management, marketing and marketing service people to top product, service and consulting companies within packaged goods industries as well as to other industries where packaged goods markets have migrated.

Salary Minimum: $50,000
Functions: Middle mgmt., Advertising, Mktg. mgmt., Direct mktg.
Industries: Food/bev/tobacco, Soap/perfume/cosmetics, Drugs mfg., Equip. svcs., Mgmt. consulting, Advertising/PR, Telecoms

Careers/Inc.

1919 Banco Popular Ctr.
Hato Rey, Puerto Rico 00918
(787) 764-2298
Fax: (787) 764-2530

Key Contact - Specialty:
Mr. J. V. DeMoss - *General senior management*
Mr. Rupert R. Amy - *General senior management*

Description: Careers Incorporated, founded in 1970, is the largest recruiting firm in the Caribbean area serving all disciplines involved in outplacement and consulting. Affiliate corporation, Career Contract Services, Inc. offers contract temporaries for exempt positions. We offer executive searches for markets in Latin America.

Salary Minimum: $25,000
Functions: General mgmt., Mfg., Materials, Healthcare, Sales & mktg., HR mgmt., Finance
Industries: Construction, Mfg., Finance, Svcs., Software

Affiliates:
Career Contract Services, Inc.

The Carey Company

508-A W. Harden St.
Graham, North Carolina 27253
(336) 226-0204
Fax: (336) 226-0205
Email: careyco@careyco.com
Web: www.careyco.com

Key Contact - Specialty:
Ms. Brenda Carey - *Information technology*

Description: 15 years experience.
Functions: IT, MIS mgmt., Systems anal., Systems dev., Systems implem., Systems support
Industries: Generalist

Carion Resource Group Inc.

6790 Davand Drive, Unit #1
Mississauga, Ontario L5T 2G5
Canada
(905) 795-9187
Email: jobs@carionresource.com
Web: www.carionresource.com

Key Contact - Specialty:
Mr. Harvey Carey - *Professional management, manufacturing, distribution*

Description: Management and support staff recruiters. Career transition and outplacement services.

Salary Minimum: $20,000
Functions: Middle mgmt., Production, Automation, Plant mgmt., Sales mgmt., CFO's, Systems anal.
Industries: Food/bev/tobacco, Textiles/apparel, Plastics/rubber, Motor vehicles, Misc. mfg., Computer svcs., Telecoms

Carnegie Resources, Inc.

1100 S. Mint St., Ste. 102
Charlotte, North Carolina 28203-4034
(704) 375-7701
Fax: (704) 375-7727
Email: carnres@earthlink.net
Web: www.carnegieresources.com

Key Contact - Specialty:
Mr. Thomas Shearer - *Manufacturing, engineering*
Mr. Lee Holland - *Product development, product design*
Mr. Rick Linstead - *Plastics, metal working, machining*
Mr. Ron McDowell - *Quality, materials*

Description: Over 43 years experience in recruiting, serving the manufacturing sector.
Functions: Product dev., Automation, Quality, Productivity, Purchasing, Materials Plng., Packaging
Industries: Mfg., Chemicals, Plastics/rubber, Machinery/Appliances, Computer equip., Consumer electronics, Test/measurement equip.

Carpenter & Assoc.

8333 Douglas Ave., Ste. 875
Dallas, Texas 75225
(214) 691-6585
Fax: (214) 691-6838

Key Contact - Specialty:
Ms. Elsie Carpenter - *Advertising*

Description: In business 15 years with a nationwide clientele in retail and direct mail. We work on mid to senior level management positions, field and corporate. Contingency search firm.

Salary Minimum: $35,000
Functions: Distribution, Advertising, Benefits, MIS mgmt., Graphic artists
Industries: Retail

Carpenter Legal Search

301 Grant St., Ste. 3325
One Oxford Centre
Pittsburgh, Pennsylvania 15219-1417
(412) 255-3770
Fax: (412) 255-3780
Email: clsearch@usaor.net
Web: carpenterlegalsearch.com

Key Contact - Specialty:
Ms. Lori J. Carpenter - *Legal (attorneys only)*

Description: With over a decade of legal recruiting experience, we specialize in corporations nationwide and law firms in the Mid-West and Mid-Atlantic. Corporate searches range from general counsel to junior-level positions.
Functions: Attorneys
Industries: Legal

Carr Management Services, Inc.

Harvey Rd.
Chadds Ford, Pennsylvania 19317
(610) 358-5630
Fax: (610) 358-5696
Email: Carrms@aol.com

Key Contact - Specialty:
Dr. Denise Carr - *Research products*
Dr. James Lowry - *Clinical diagnostics*
Ms. Barbara Clos - *Clinical diagnostics*

Description: Offering recruiting services in the areas of biotechnology, biopharmaceuticals, life sciences, research products, diagnostics and healthcare. We have many years of combined experience working in the industries we serve.
Functions: General mgmt., Mfg., Sales & mktg., Mktg. mgmt., Sales mgmt., R&D, Engineering
Industries: Drugs mfg., Medical devices, Biotech

K. Carroll & Assoc.

707 Skokie Blvd., Ste. 600
Northbrook, Illinois 60062
(847) 291-4310

Key Contact - Specialty:
Ms. Kathy Carroll - *Information systems*

Description: Professional and executive search specializing in information systems.

Salary Minimum: $40,000
Functions: MIS mgmt., Systems anal., Systems dev., Systems implem., Systems support
Industries: Generalist

Carson-Thomas & Assoc.

900 Wilshire Blvd., Ste. 606
Omni Centre
Los Angeles, California 90017-4707
(213) 489-4480

Key Contact - Specialty:
Ms. Sandra Carson - *Support, management, professional information technology, accounting, human resource management*
Mr. Frank Thomas - *Finance, legal, management consulting, activity marketing*

Description: Want QK results at reasonable rates? Our multilingual pool of quality applicants reflects all skill levels-beginners/college/highly experienced. With 21 years experience in L.A. area we have the resources to locate just the right person. Many satisfied clients can attest to our high success rate.

Salary Minimum: $22,000
Functions: Generalist, General mgmt., Mfg., Healthcare, Sales & mktg., HR mgmt., CFO's
Industries: Generalist, Finance, Svcs., Communications, Insurance, Real estate, Software

Affiliates:
Personnel by Carson-Thomas
Workload Temporary Services

Carter, Lavoie Associates
5 Mechanic St.
Hope Valley, Rhode Island 02832
(401) 539-7600
Web: search@ids.net

Key Contact - Specialty:
Mr. Leo R. Lavoie - *Generalist*

Description: Placement of professionals in engineering, manufacturing, sales/ marketing, finance. Provider of outplacement services and consultations.

Salary Minimum: $30,000
Functions: Generalist, Production, Materials Plng., Sales mgmt., Personnel, IT, Engineering
Industries: Generalist, Chemicals, Drugs mfg., Plastics/rubber, High tech, Software, Healthcare

Carter McKenzie, Inc.
300 Executive Drive, Ste. 250
West Orange, New Jersey 07052
(201) 736-7100
Fax: (201) 736-9416
Email: carter@media-ware.com
Web: www media-ware.com/carter/

Key Contact - Specialty:
Mr. Richard Kilcoyne - *Information technology (middle & executive management)*
Mr. John Capo - *Senior technical staff*

Description: We are an organization whose principal function is the identification and recruitment of professional staff within the field of information systems.

Salary Minimum: $50,000
Functions: Directors, MIS mgmt., Systems anal., Systems dev., Systems implem., Systems support, Mgmt. consultants
Industries: Drugs mfg., Finance, Communications, Government, Insurance, Software, Healthcare

Affiliates:
The Livingston Consulting Group

Carter-Evdemon & Assoc.
777 S. Harbour Island Blvd., Ste. 930
1 Harbour Place
Tampa, Florida 33602
(813) 229-2220
(800) 229-HIRE (4473)
Fax: (813) 229-1294
Email: cesearch@ibm.net

Key Contact - Specialty:
Mr. Jeffrey M. Carter - *Insurance companies*
Mr. Michael S. Evdemon, II - *Insurance brokers & agencies*

Description: Contingency and retained search of insurance executives, legal, managerial and professional personnel for companies, agencies, brokers and risk managers for general industry and healthcare nationally and internationally.

Salary Minimum: $35,000
Functions: Senior mgmt., Mktg. mgmt., Sales mgmt., CFO's, Risk mgmt., MIS mgmt., Attorneys
Industries: Insurance

Carter/MacKay
777 Terrace Ave.
Hasbrouck Heights, New Jersey 07604
(201) 288-5100
Fax: (201) 288-2660
Email: info@cartermackay.com
Web: www.cartermackay.com

Key Contact - Specialty:
Mr. Bruce Green - *Healthcare (sales, sales management, marketing)*
Mr. George Villano - *Computer automation (sales, sales management, marketing)*

Description: Sales, sales management and sales support in medical, pharmaceuticals, computers and high technologies.

Salary Minimum: $40,000
Functions: Senior mgmt., Middle mgmt., Mkt. research, Mktg. mgmt., Sales mgmt., Systems implem., Systems support
Industries: Drugs mfg., Medical devices, Computer equip., Computer svcs., Software, Biotech, Healthcare

Branches:
111 Speen St.
Framingham, Massachusetts 01701
(508) 626-2240
Fax: (508) 879-2327
Key Contact - Specialty:
Mr. Mike Rowell - *Healthcare, computer automation, telecommunications, data communications, sales*

1981 Marcus Ave., Ste. 201
Lake Success, New York 11042
(516) 616-7700
Key Contact - Specialty:
Mr. Larry Orbach

2000 Regency Pkwy., Ste. 460
Cary, North Carolina 27511
(910) 380-1200
Fax: (910) 380-1267
Key Contact - Specialty:
Mr. Al Hertz - *Healthcare, computer automation, telecommunications, data communications, sales*

Carver Search Consultants
9303 E. Bullard Ave., #1
Clovis, California 93611
(209) 298-7791
Fax: (209) 298-7791
Email: mcavolina@aol.com

Key Contact - Specialty:
Mr. Michael Cavolina - *Agricultural, engineering, biotechnology*
Ms. Joan Albers - *Medical*

Description: Senior management including start up and turnaround specialists. Engineers chemical, electrical, structural and mechanical. Medical professional: chemists, toxicologists, microbiologists, pathologists and geneticists. Produce industry sales, marketing and management professionals.

Salary Minimum: $50,000
Functions: Senior mgmt., Plant mgmt., Physicians, Mktg. mgmt., CFO's, R&D, Mgmt. consultants
Industries: Agri/forestry/mining, Food/bev/ tobacco, Drugs mfg., Medical devices, Plastics/rubber, Biotech

The CARVIR Group, Inc.
P.O. Box 125
Fayetteville, Georgia 30214
(770) 460-8272
Fax: (770) 460-2216
Web: www.carvir.com

Key Contact - Specialty:
Mr. Virgil L. Fludd - *Finance, human resources, marketing*
Ms. Carolyn Kelley - *Information systems*

Description: We have worked with a broad spectrum of clients-multinational corporations, as well as start-up companies. We focus on clients in the financial services, technology, manufacturing and consumer products industries.

Salary Minimum: $40,000
Functions: Sales & mktg., HR mgmt., Finance, IT, Specialized services
Industries: Finance, Svcs., Communications, High tech

CAS Comsearch Inc.
501 Madison Ave., Ste. 406
New York, New York 10022
(212) 593-0861
Fax: (212) 755-4597

Email: 102372.3277@compuserve.com

Key Contact - Specialty:
Ms. Gail Kleinberg Koch - *Sales, marketing, new media, telecommunications*

Description: We are an executive search firm founded in 1980 specializing in the telecommunications industry, on-line information industry as well as new media.

Salary Minimum: $40,000
Functions: Senior mgmt., Mkt. research, Sales mgmt., Customer svc., Network admin., DB admin., Technicians
Industries: Entertainment, Computer svcs., New media, Telecoms, High tech, Software

---

Case Executive Search
15008 Kercheval Ave.
Grosse Pointe Park, Michigan 48230
(313) 331-6095
Fax: (313) 823-2439

Key Contact - Specialty:
Mr. David R. Case - *Engineering, manufacturing*

Description: Practice directed at automotive, aerospace and machine tool industries with focus on engineering and manufacturing disciplines. Emphasis on new plant start up consulting on manufacturing engineering and quality staffing requirements.

Salary Minimum: $30,000
Functions: Product dev., Production, Plant mgmt., Quality, Materials, HR mgmt., Engineering
Industries: Plastics/rubber, Metal products, Machinery/Appliances, Motor vehicles, Test/measurement equip., Misc. mfg.

Casey & Assoc., Inc.
3419 Westminster Ave., Ste. 222
Dallas, Texas 75205
(214) 522-1010
Fax: (214) 522-8263
Email: techjobs@ccasey.com

Key Contact - Specialty:
Ms. Carol M. Casey - *Information technology*

Description: Information technology recruiting and consulting services with an emphasis on AS/400 and client server technology. Our placements include CIOs, information systems directors, programmer/analysts, systems programmers, WEB developers, project managers. Recognized for in-depth work with both clients and candidates, resulting in a 90%+ placement rate.

Salary Minimum: $50,000
Functions: IT, MIS mgmt., Systems anal., Systems dev., Systems implem., Systems support, Network admin.
Industries: Generalist, Mfg., Retail, Svcs., High tech, Software, Healthcare

---

Cassell & Kaye
311 E. 75th St.
New York, New York 10021
(212) 585-1624
Fax: (212) 585-1625
Email: candkaye@aol.com

Key Contact - Specialty:
Ms. Shelley Kaye - *Advertising agencies (general, direct response, pharmaceutical, sales promotion)*

Description: Executive search firm specializing in advertising agencies (general, direct response, pharmaceutical and sales promotion) in all levels of account management and marketing positions for consumer products and service companies.

Salary Minimum: $25,000
Functions: Advertising, Direct mktg.
Industries: Advertising/PR

CBA Companies
2522 Back Bay Loop, Ste. 210
Costa Mesa, California 92627
(949) 548-8790
Fax: (949) 548-9240
Email: cba@primenet.com

Key Contact - Specialty:
Mr. Allen F. Joseph - *Sales, marketing, technical, software*
Ms. Patti D. Joseph - *Technical software engineers*

Description: Professional recruiters who specialize in the software and computer network companies. Partners have 30+ years experience in the software industry and 5+ years as professional recruiters.

Salary Minimum: $50,000
Functions: Mktg. mgmt., Sales mgmt., Systems dev., Systems implem., Systems support, Network admin., DB admin.
Industries: Computer svcs., Mgmt. consulting, High tech, Software

---

CCI - Career Consultants Int'l.
620 Newport Center Drive #DER
Newport Ctr., Ste. 1100
Newport Beach, California 92660
(714) 721-1166
Fax: (714) 721-8963
Email: resume@ccinetwork.com
Web: www.ccinetwork.com

Key Contact - Specialty:
Mr. George Vasu - *Accounting & finance*
Mr. Tom Meyer - *Information technology*

Description: Full service specialized staffing firm utilizing a team partnership consulting strategy where service is a top priority. We are a full service accounting and financial, information technology, engineering, sales and marketing staffing firm assisting organizations on a regional, national and international basis.

Salary Minimum: $25,000
Functions: Generalist, Sales & mktg., HR mgmt., Finance, IT, Engineering
Industries: Generalist

Malin Cederquist, Esq.
(Firm declined to update.)
240 Central Park S., Ste. 11 H
New York, New York 10019
(212) 586-9206

Key Contact - Specialty:
Ms. Malin Cederquist - *Partner, legal*

Description: Clients are a diverse group of law firms. Expertise in partner search and recruitment in most legal practice areas; also cover groups and mergers.
Functions: Attorneys
Industries: Legal

Cella Assoc.
(Firm declined to update.)
4045 Wetherburn Way, Ste. 4
Norcross, Georgia 30092
(770) 242-3040
Email: cella@cella.com
Web: www.cella.com

Key Contact - Specialty:
Mr. John E. Gorry - *Food*

Description: Largest multi-divisional, national firm specializing in food industry. Team concept; very deep contacts throughout the industry; service oriented.

Salary Minimum: $30,000
Functions: General mgmt., Senior mgmt., Distribution, Sales & mktg., HR mgmt., Finance, IT
Industries: Generalist, Food/bev/tobacco, Wholesale, Retail, Hospitality, Entertainment, Advertising/PR

Cemco, Ltd.
Two First Nat'l. Plaza, Ste. 610
Chicago, Illinois 60603
(312) 855-1500
Fax: (312) 855-1510
Email: cemcoltd.flash.net.com

Key Contact - Specialty:
Mr. Dillon Hale - *Accounting, finance, healthcare, medical*

Description: Full service national executive search firm specializing in accounting and financial services, real estate, professional medical and MIS.

Salary Minimum: $35,000
Functions: Nurses, Health admin., CFO's, Budgeting, Taxes, MIS mgmt., Systems dev.
Industries: Misc. mfg., Computer svcs., Accounting, Real estate, Healthcare

Branches:
2015 Spring Rd., #250
Oak Brook, Illinois 60521
(708) 573-5050
Fax: (708) 573-5060
Key Contact - Specialty:
Mr. Dave Gordon - *MIS, client/server, telecommunication personnel*

11469 Olive Blvd., #117
St. Louis, Missouri 63141
(314) 838-7400
Fax: (314) 838-2228
Key Contact - Specialty:
Mr. Ira Steuer - *MIS, client/server, telecommunication personnel*

The Center for Career Advancement, LLC
One Exchange Place, Ste. 1000
Jersey City, New Jersey 07302
(201) 876-1912
Fax: (201) 222-5201
Email: sharon@advanceyourcareer.com
Web: www.advanceyourcareer.com

Key Contact - Specialty:
Ms. Sharon Bussey - *Management consulting, technology, financial services, healthcare*

Description: A diversity organization which offers executive recruiting services to companies wishing to diversify and who are seeking African-Americans, Hispanics and women. We specialize in recruiting specifically these minority classes.
Functions: Cash mgmt., M&A, Systems support, DB admin., Engineering, Minorities, Attorneys
Industries: Brokers, Venture cap., Legal, Mgmt. consulting, Government, Insurance, Software

Branches:
204 E. Joppa Rd., Ste 214
Towson, Maryland 21286
(410) 769-9871
Fax: (410) 769-9872
Email: virginia@advanceyourcareer.com
Web: www.advanceyourcareer.com
Key Contact - Specialty:
Ms. Virginia L. Jenkins - *Management consulting, technology, financial services, healthcare*

Central Executive Search, Inc.
6151 Wilson Mills Rd., Ste. 240
Highland Heights, Ohio 44143
(440) 461-5400
Fax: (440) 461-8442
Email: central@acclink.com
Web: www.centraljobs.com

Key Contact - Specialty:
Mr. Gary Giallombardo
Ms. Toni Graziano
Ms. Stacey Herbert
Mr. Rodger Locher

Description: Specializing in the paper, printing, packaging and adhesives industry. Positions range from manufacturing, R&D, sales/management and marketing. Worldwide searches. Good reputation and very experienced in industries.

Salary Minimum: $30,000
Functions: Senior mgmt., Production, Plant mgmt., Mkt. research, Mktg. mgmt., Sales mgmt., R&D
Industries: Paper, Printing, Chemicals, Plastics/rubber, Paints/petroleum products, Publishing, Packaging

Century Assoc., Inc.
1420 Walnut St., Ste. 1402
Philadelphia, Pennsylvania 19102
(215) 732-4311
Fax: (215) 735-1804
Email: century1@ix.netcom.com
Web: www.centuryassociates.com

Key Contact - Specialty:
Mr. David Allen - *Vice presidents, directors of marketing, software*
Mr. Michael Hurley - *Sales, sales management, medical, pharmaceutical*

Description: We are involved in the nationwide recruitment of sales, technical and marketing professionals in the information technology and medical fields.

Salary Minimum: $60,000
Functions: Directors, Senior mgmt., Mkt. research, Mktg. mgmt., Sales mgmt., CFO's, Systems support
Industries: Pharmaceutical svcs., Mgmt. consulting, High tech, Software, Biotech

The Century Group
9800 La Cienega Blvd., Ste. 904
Inglewood, California 90301
(310) 216-2100
(800) 337-9675
Fax: (310) 216-2116
Email: century@century-group.com
Web: www.century-group.com

Key Contact - Specialty:
Mr. Harry Boxer - *Accounting & finance, controllers, CFOs*
Mr. Don Yaeger - *Accounting & finance, controllers, CFOs*
Mr. Ron Proul - *Accounting & finance, controllers, CFO's*

Description: One of L.A.'s top 15 search groups; specializes in accounting/financial searches in a broad range of industries in southern California and has a staff with over 100 years combined search experience.

Salary Minimum: $30,000
Functions: CFO's, Budgeting, Cash mgmt., Taxes, M&A
Industries: Mfg., Finance, Svcs., Communications, High tech, Software, Healthcare

Branches:
19000 MacArthur Blvd., #500
Irvine, California 92612
(714) 440-7923
Fax: (714) 440-7953
Key Contact - Specialty:
Mr. Phil Jacobson

The Century Group
8400 W. 110th St., Ste. 310
Overland Park, Kansas 66211
(913) 451-7666
Fax: (913) 451-2161
Email: cengroup@worldnet.att.net

Key Contact - Specialty:
Mr. Michael A. Jones - *Information technology, healthcare, pharmaceutical, banking, collection*

Description: We are a large firm with 15 trained consultants. We are twice listed as an INC 500 company and were the winners of the Blue Chip Enterprise Award for KS.

Salary Minimum: $30,000
Functions: Nurses, Health admin., Sales mgmt., Credit, Systems anal., Systems dev., R&D
Industries: Pharmaceutical svcs., Computer svcs., Biotech, Healthcare

Affiliates:
Century Personnel
SOS Staffing Services

CEO Consulting
P.O. Box 134
Overseas Hwy.
Islamorada, Florida 33036
(305) 853-5200
Email: Cookc@Bellsouth.com

Key Contact - Specialty:
Mr. Clifford L. Cook - *Sales, engineering, satellite, semiconductor industry*
Ms. Christine Engler - *Diversity, telecommunications, data communications*
Mr. Guillermo Acosta

Description: Focused on the technical and management needs of the communications industry worldwide. We offer over 15 years experience. To executive-level positions, we recruit top-quality candidates in engineering, sales and development for cellular, satellite, telephone and data services.
Functions: Senior mgmt., Production, Mktg. mgmt., Sales mgmt., Systems dev., Engineering, Minorities
Industries: Computer equip., Computer svcs., New media, Telecoms, High tech, Software

CFOs 2 Go
1990 N. California Blvd., Ste. 830
Walnut Creek, California 94596
(925) 945-7850
Fax: (925) 283-4458
Email: info@cfos2go.com
Web: www.cfos2go.com

Key Contact - Specialty:
Mr. Robert Weis - *Financial management executives*

Description: An executive placement/contract staffing firm specializing in placing senior financial executives with high growth companies. The firm is owned/directed by CFO's who bring knowledge and know how to the hiring process.

Salary Minimum: $50,000
Functions: CFO's, Budgeting, Cash mgmt., Credit, Taxes, M&A, Risk mgmt.
Industries: Generalist

CFR Executive Search, Inc.
175 W. Jackson Blvd., Ste. A1918
Chicago, Illinois 60604
(312) 435-0990
Fax: (312) 435-1333
Email: cfrexecsearch@msn.com
Web: www.cfrsearch.com

Key Contact - Specialty:
Mr. James Barry - *Accounting & finance*
Mr. Joseph Sexton - *Accounting & finance*

Description: We assure quality, prescreened professionals who will meet our clients' technical specifications. They will possess the appropriate management style and work ethic to fit our client's culture.

Salary Minimum: $30,000
Functions: CFO's, Budgeting, Cash mgmt., Credit, Taxes, M&A, Risk mgmt.
Industries: Mfg., Transportation, Wholesale, Retail, Misc. financial, Svcs., Insurance

Chacra, Belliveau & Assoc. Inc.
1550 DeMaisonneuve St. W., Ste. 805
Montreal, Quebec H3G 1N2
Canada
(514) 931-8801
Fax: (514) 931-1940
Email: stevenc@chacra.com

Key Contact - Specialty:
Mr. Steven Chacra - *Information technology*

Description: Specializing exclusively in the information technology/systems sector nationally and internationally. Managed and staffed by information technology and human resource professionals.

Salary Minimum: $35,000
Functions: MIS mgmt., Systems anal., Systems dev., Systems implem., Systems support, Network admin., DB admin.
Industries: Generalist

Chad Management Group
21 St. Clair Ave. E., Ste. 1000
Toronto, Ontario M4T 1L9
Canada
(416) 968-1000
Fax: (416) 968-7754
Email: jobs@chadman.com

Key Contact - Specialty:
Mr. Rick A. Chad - *Marketing, general management*
Mr. Rick Richter - *Sales*
Ms. C.A. Harrison - *Creative*
Ms. Barbara Morris - *Direct marketing, finance*
Mr. Michael Cooper - *Sales, high technology, administration*

Description: A leader in marketing and sales recruitment with long term success in identifying and delivering the top performers promptly and effectively.
Functions: General mgmt., Product dev., Materials, Sales & mktg., Finance, IT, Graphic artists
Industries: Mfg., Finance, Entertainment, Communications, High tech

Chadwell & Assoc., Inc.
P.O. Box 1028
Portage, Michigan 49081-1028
(616) 349-6381
Fax: (616) 349-6422
Email: chadwell@chadwell.com
Web: www.chadwell.com

Key Contact - Specialty:
Ms. Rebecca A. Chadwell - *Engineering, technical, engineers (quality & sales)*

Description: We follow our recruiter's code of ethics. Within it, we explain how crucial it is to follow the 3 R's of recruiting: respect, response and reliability.

Functions: Mfg., Product dev., Production, Automation, Plant mgmt., Quality, Engineering
Industries: Food/bev/tobacco, Drugs mfg., Machinery/Appliances, Packaging

Wayne S. Chamberlain & Assoc.
25835 Narbonne Ave., Ste. 280-C
Lomita, California 90717
(310) 534-4840
Fax: (310) 539-9885
Web: www.quikpage.com/W/wchamberlain/

Key Contact - Specialty:
Mr. Wayne Chamberlain - *Electronics, connectors*

Description: Over 10 years of experience specializing in technical placement. Emphasis is on electronics engineers in the connector field.

Salary Minimum: $40,000
Functions: Middle mgmt., Product dev., Automation, Plant mgmt., Quality, Mktg. mgmt., Sales mgmt.
Industries: Plastics/rubber, Computer equip., Consumer electronics, High tech

Chamberlain Assoc.
4244 Riverlook Pkwy.
Marietta, Georgia 30067
(770) 690-0085
(800) 877-9631
Fax: (770) 690-0091
Email: chamassoc@mci2000.com
Web: www.themedicalcenter.com

Key Contact - Specialty:
Ms. Inga Chamberlain - *Healthcare*

Description: We place clinical and management candidates in hospitals nationwide. We do thorough references and supply you with only the best candidates.

Salary Minimum: $50,000
Functions: Physicians, Nurses, Health admin., IT
Industries: Healthcare

Vickers Chambless Managed Search
5901-B Peachtree Dunwoody Rd., Ste. 500
The Palisades
Atlanta, Georgia 30328
(404) 365-0030
Fax: (404) 231-1351
Email: vc@vcmssearch.com
Web: www.vcmssearch.com

Key Contact - Specialty:
Mr. Vickers Chambless - *Healthcare administration (especially finance)*
Ms. Reyn Steadman - *Healthcare administration (especially finance)*
Ms. Mallory Lehn - *Healthcare administration (especially finance)*
Mr. Eric Bergeon - *Physician practice management and managed care*

Description: Executive search services exclusively in the healthcare financial and administrative areas. Financial: CFO, controller, assistant controller, reimbursement, auditors. Administrative: medical records, information systems.

Salary Minimum: $40,000
Functions: Health admin., CFO's, Taxes, M&A, Risk mgmt., MIS mgmt.
Industries: Healthcare

Elsie Chan & Assoc.
132 N. El Camino Real, Ste. 514
Encinitas, California 92024
(760) 944-9478
Fax: (760) 633-3329
Email: elsiechan@aol.com
Web: members.aol.com/elsiechan/

Key Contact - Specialty:
Ms. Elsie Chan - *Information systems, software developers*
Mr. Harold Olson, Jr.

Description: All aspects of IS, emphasizing newer technologies, search done by IS-seasoned staff. Focus on LA and Orange Counties. Nationally recognized for achievement in search. Confidentiality; credibility.

Salary Minimum: $30,000
Functions: IT
Industries: Computer svcs., High tech, Software

Chapman & Assoc.
555 Burrard St., Ste. 1065
Two Bentall Centre
Vancouver, British Columbia V7X 1M8
Canada
(604) 682-7764
Fax: (604) 682-8746
Email: resumes@chapmanassoc.com
Web: www.chapmanassoc.com

Key Contact - Specialty:
Mr. Gary W. Fumano - *Sales, marketing, finance, administration, engineering*
Mr. Bruce J. MacKenzie - *Sales, marketing, high technology, engineering*
Mr. Bryce A. Stacey - *Finance, Sales, Engineering*

Description: With more than 40 years of experience recruiting and selecting mid-level to senior personnel, our firm enjoys a proven track record for professionalism, confidentiality and success.

Functions: General mgmt., Mfg., Materials, Sales & mktg., HR mgmt., IT, Engineering
Industries: Agri/forestry/mining, Construction, Mfg., Hospitality, Communications, High tech, Software

---

The Chapman Group, Inc.
15111 N. Hayden Rd. #160-357
Scottsdale, Arizona 85260
(602) 483-8833
Fax: (602) 483-6750
Email: jeffc@thechapmangroup.com
Web: www.thechapmangroup.com

Key Contact - Specialty:
Mr. Jeff H. Chapman - *Factory automation technology*

Description: We conduct searches for mission critical individual contributors, managers and executives for factory automation technology product, software and systems companies throughout North America, Europe and Asia.

Salary Minimum: $55,000
Functions: Senior mgmt., Middle mgmt., Automation, Sales mgmt., Systems implem., Engineering
Industries: Machinery/Appliances, Test/measurement equip., Computer svcs., Mgmt. consulting, Software

---

Charet & Assoc.
P.O. Box 435
Cresskill, New Jersey 07626
(201) 894-5197
Fax: (201) 894-9095
Email: charet@compuserve.com

Key Contact - Specialty:
Ms. Sandra Charet - *Corporate communications, investor relations, PR, marketing*

Description: Small firm with sterling reputation for high level of personal attention and commitment. Service public relations, corporate communications, public affairs, investor relations and marketing for all industries worldwide.

Salary Minimum: $50,000
Functions: Mktg. mgmt., PR, Benefits
Industries: Generalist

Charles & Associates, Inc.
Chamber of Commerce Bldg., Ste. C
Kearney, Nebraska 68847
(308) 236-8891
Fax: (308) 236-8893

Key Contact - Specialty:
Mr. Charles F. Dummer - *Outdoor power equipment, lawn & garden*
Mr. Jeffry J. Dummer

Description: Specialists in the outdoor power/lawn and garden equipment industry covering sales and marketing, engineering, manufacturing, production, quality control and material handling.
Functions: Middle mgmt., Product dev., Mkt. research, Mktg. mgmt., Sales mgmt., R&D, Engineering

---

Robert L. Charon
206 Trellis Place
Richardson, Texas 75081
(972) 479-9571
Fax: (972) 479-9577
Email: bcharon@spacestar.net

Key Contact - Specialty:
Mr. Robert L. Charon

Description: Specialist in design, industrial/manufacturing and administrative functions in heavy equipment; ag equipment and metal manufacturing/fabrication industries.

Salary Minimum: $30,000
Functions: Mfg., Product dev., Production, Materials, Engineering
Industries: Metal products, Machinery/Appliances, Motor vehicles

---

Chase-Gardner Executive Search Associates, Inc.
36181 E. Lake Rd., Ste. A
Palm Harbor, Florida 34685
(813) 934-7000
Fax: (813) 934-2390
Email: cgardner@staffing.net
Web: www.staffing.net/findjobs.htm also www.chase gardner.com

Key Contact - Specialty:
Mr. Sidney Gardner - *Engineering, manufacturing support*

Description: A full service executive search and placement agency, servicing our clients and our candidates with a permanent placement division as well as a contract and temporary placement division.

Salary Minimum: $30,000
Functions: Senior mgmt., Product dev., Production, Plant mgmt., Quality, Personnel, Engineering
Industries: Medical devices, Plastics/rubber, Metal products, Machinery/Appliances, Motor vehicles, Environmental svcs., High tech

---

The Chatham Group, Ltd.
P.O. Box 614
Ridgefield, Connecticut 06877
(203) 438-9517

Key Contact - Specialty:
Dr. Arlene McSweeney - *Generalist*

Description: Generalist firm with expertise in information products, education, publishing and consumer products. Specific focus on management in operations, sales, marketing, technical service, educators, foreign nationals, publishing, etc.

Salary Minimum: $40,000
Functions: General mgmt., Mfg., Sales & mktg., HR mgmt., Finance, IT, Engineering
Industries: Generalist, Food/bev/tobacco, Higher ed., Communications, High tech, Software

---

Chatham Search Assoc., Inc.

10 Ridgedale Ave., Ste. 5
Florham Park, New Jersey 07932
(973) 301-0100
Fax: (973) 301-1771
Email: csa@chathamsearch.com
Web: www.quikpage.com/C/chatsea

Key Contact - Specialty:
Ms. Michelle Pesco - *Information technology*
Ms. Theresa Ryan-Ulyatt - *Information technology*

Description: Specialize in information system technology placements for both permanent and consulting positions. Placements are made from entry level to MIS directors. All searches are conducted with the highest level of professionalism.

Salary Minimum: $35,000
Functions: MIS mgmt., Systems dev., Systems support, Network admin., DB admin., Engineering, Technicians
Industries: Computer svcs., Communications, Telecoms, High tech, Software

---

Chelsea Resources, Inc.

18 Oneco St.
Norwich, Connecticut 06360
(860) 886-4110
Fax: (860) 886-2210
Email: pat@chelsearesources.com
Web: www.chelsearesources.com

Key Contact - Specialty:
Mr. Patrick J. Soo Hoo - *Medical devices, medical instruments, bio-materials*
Mr. Leo F. Bawza - *Medical devices, medical instruments, bio-materials*

Description: Recognized leaders in medical devices and instrumentation recruiting. Responsive and sucessful. Excels at staffing critical positions quickly. Experienced with venture start-up operations. Clients include Fortune 50 and emerging technology companies.

Salary Minimum: $50,000
Functions: General mgmt., Mfg., Product dev., Materials, Finance, R&D, Engineering
Industries: Medical devices, Plastics/rubber, High tech, Software, Biotech

---

Cheney Associates
(a division of Headway Corp. Resources)

One Laurel Sq., 3190 Whitney Ave.
Hamden, Connecticut 06518
(203) 281-3736
Fax: (203) 281-6881
Email: webmaster@cheney.com
Web: www.cheney.com

Key Contact - Specialty:
Mr. Timothy W. Cheney - *Information technology*
Mr. Michael List

Description: Contingency and retained technical search firm specializing in information technologies, engineering, manufacturing and quality assurance. Service primarily companies in the northeast region of the USA.
Functions: MIS mgmt., Systems anal., Systems dev., Systems implem., Network admin., DB admin., Engineering
Industries: Mfg., Metal products, Machinery/Appliances, Computer svcs., High tech, Software, Healthcare

---

Chesapeake Group

134 Cutspring Rd.
Stratford, Connecticut 06497
(203) 378-5070
Fax: (203) 380-1214
Email: info@chesgroup.com
Web: www.chesgroup.com

Key Contact - Specialty:
Mr. Scott Gardner - *Sales & marketing*
Mr. Keith McShane - *Finance*
Mr. Chris Messina
Mr. Steve Givens - *MIS, IT*

Description: We are an executive search firm placing sales/marketing, IT and finance professionals in emerging technology companies across the United States.
Functions: Sales & mktg., Mktg. mgmt., Sales mgmt., Finance, CFO's, IT, MIS mgmt.
Industries: Computer equip., Finance, Svcs., Computer svcs., Mgmt. consulting, High tech, Software

---

Chicago Legal Search, Ltd.

33 N. Dearborn St., Ste. 2302
Chicago, Illinois 60602-3109
(312) 251-2580
Fax: (312) 251-0223
Email: chgolegal@interaccess.com
Web: www.chicagolawjobs.com

Key Contact - Specialty:
Gary A. D'Alessio - *Legal*
Ms. Chris Percival - *Legal*
Alan J. Rubenstein - *Legal*
Shelly Remen Sibul - *Legal*

Description: Legal recruiting specialists exclusively conducting attorney search and placement for law firms, corporations, financial institutions and not-for-profit foundations primarily in the Chicago metropolitan area.
Functions: Benefits, M&A, Minorities, Attorneys
Industries: Finance, Communications, Telecoms, Insurance, Real estate, High tech, Healthcare

---

R. Christine Assoc.

Front & Orange Sts.
Media, Pennsylvania 19063
(610) 565-3310
Fax: (610) 565-3313

Key Contact - Specialty:
Mr. Rich Christine - *Engineering, manufacturing, sales, MIS personnel*

Description: We have specialized in personal one-on-one service, recruiting technical and executive professionals in the Philadelphia metropolitan tri state area. High-tech to smoke stack.

Salary Minimum: $40,000
Functions: Product dev., Production, Automation, Quality, Sales mgmt., Systems anal., Engineering
Industries: Medical devices, Metal products, Machinery/Appliances, Motor vehicles, Consumer electronics, Test/measurement equip., Misc. mfg.

Christmas, McIvor & Assoc. Inc.

33 City Centre Drive, Ste. 551
Mississauga, Ontario L5B 2N5
Canada
(905) 270-0405
Email: recruiters@globalserve.net

Key Contact - Specialty:
Mr. Jim McIvor - *Generalist, senior level*
Mr. Mike McIvor - *High tech, operations, sales*
Ms. Julie Taraso - *Temporary, contract*

Description: Temporary, contract and permanent placement service covering administrative through senior executive.
Functions: Generalist, Mfg., Materials, Sales & mktg., Finance, IT, Graphic artists
Industries: Consumer electronics, Transportation, Finance, Equip. svcs., Human resource svcs., Telecoms, High tech

Christopher and Long
15 Worthington
Maryland Heights, Missouri 63043
(314) 576-6300
(800) 800-5664
Fax: (314) 576-7740
Email: recruit@primary.net
Web: www.christopher-and-long.com

Key Contact - Specialty:
Mr. Keith A. Long - *Generalist*
Ms. Marybeth Ciancio - *Physicians*
Mr. Ray Culli - *Manufacturing, engineering*
Mr. Brian Thiemann - *Apparel, retailing, consumer goods, consumer products*
Ms. Glenda M. Ward
Mr. Bill Dubuque - *Manufacturing, engineering*

Description: Physician, executive and technical search for nationwide clients for over 25 years, all specialties and industries served.
Functions: General mgmt., Mfg., Materials, Physicians, Sales & mktg., HR mgmt., Engineering
Industries: Textiles/apparel, Plastics/rubber, Metal products, Machinery/Appliances, Motor vehicles, Retail, Healthcare

The Christopher Group
P.O. Box 20664
Raleigh, North Carolina 27619
(919) 319-3123
Fax: (919) 319-3183
Email: chrisgroup@ibm.net

Key Contact - Specialty:
Mr. J. Christopher Sprehe - *Real estate, mortgage banking, asset management, development, property management*

Description: Focus exclusively on the placement of experienced real estate professionals with corporate real estate entities, financial institutions, valuation/consulting firms, brokerage/management organizations and government agencies worldwide.

Salary Minimum: $40,000
Industries: Banking, Misc. financial, Hospitality, Real estate

Branches:
P.O. Box 11161
Shawnee Mission, Kansas 66207-0161
(913) 649-8882
Fax: (919) 319-3183

J. F. Church Associates
P.O. Box 6128
Bellevue, Washington 98008-0128
(425) 644-3278
Fax: (425) 747-1293
Email: jfchurch@scn.org

Key Contact - Specialty:
Mr. Jim Church - *Computer industry (sales, marketing, sales support in computer industry only)*

Description: Our services are designed for companies who are manufacturers and/or vendors of computer based hardware, software or services. Focal areas include sales, sales support and marketing.

Salary Minimum: $40,000
Functions: Mkt. research, Mktg. mgmt., Sales mgmt., Direct mktg., Customer svc.
Industries: Computer equip., Computer svcs., Software

The Churchill Group
1 Yonge St., Ste. 1801
Toronto, Ontario M5E 1W7
Canada
(416) 368-1358
Fax: (416) 369-0515
Email: churchil@bmts.com

Key Contact - Specialty:
Mr. Murray Fullerton - *Manufacturing*

Description: Our firm is made up of experienced managers who are familiar with the issues facing organizations today. Each of our consultants has over 20 years of recruitment experience in the manufacturing sector on an international basis.

Salary Minimum: $60,000
Functions: General mgmt., Mfg., Materials, Sales & mktg., HR mgmt., Finance, Engineering
Industries: Mfg., Food/bev/tobacco, Paper, Drugs mfg., Metal products, Computer equip., Packaging

Circlewood Search Group, Inc.
3307 E. Kilgore Rd., Ste. 2
Kalamazoo, Michigan 49001-5512
(616) 383-9520
(800) 968-9520
Fax: (616) 383-9530
Email: circlewd@net-link.net
Web: www.circlewood.com

Key Contact - Specialty:
Ms. Melissa Webb - *Healthcare, medical*

Description: Place physicians, physician assistants/nurse practitioners, PT/OT/SLP's and nurse managers in all medical specialties in all 50 states. Our recruiters are assigned on a state-by-state basis, so you'll always speak with a professional who knows the specific laws/license requirements of where the candidate will work. 24-hour phone and fax.

Salary Minimum: $40,000
Functions: Physicians, Nurses, Allied health, Health admin.
Industries: Healthcare

Circuit Search
7 Moul Drive, P.O. Box 218
Red Hook, New York 12571
(914) 758-1979
Fax: (914) 758-2367
Email: kms@webjogger.net

Key Contact - Specialty:
Mr. Kevin M. Stack - *Printed circuit board industry, CEOs, process engineers, electronic interconnect industry*

Description: Specialist recruiters in the field of electronic circuitry (printed circuits and I.C.). Also specialize in chemists and chemical engineers with applications to the electronic industry. Executive, operation, sales & marketing positions also covered within advanced electronics.

Salary Minimum: $50,000

Branches:
PO Box 447
Derry, New Hampshire 03038
(603) 421-9070
Fax: (603) 421-2367
Key Contact - Specialty:
Mr. Richard P. Saporito

CJSI-Cindy Jackson Search Int'l.
3031 Tisch Way, #700
San Jose, California 95128
(408) 247-6767
Fax: (408) 247-6677
Email: cindycjsi@aol.com

Key Contact - Specialty:
Ms. Cindy Jackson - *Sales, marketing, application engineers, electronic design automation*
Mrs. Tracy Marseline - *Software developers, electronic design automation*

Description: Together we have almost 20 years experience. Interviewing skills taught to candidates.

Salary Minimum: $50,000
Functions: Mktg. mgmt., Sales mgmt., Direct mktg., Customer svc., Engineering
Industries: High tech, Software

Claimsearch
P.O. Box 357
Ft. Bragg, California 95437
(707) 964-1795
Fax: (707) 964-1555
Email: tbayard@mcn.org

Key Contact - Specialty:
Mr. Thomas E. Bayard - *Property/casualty insurance, risk management*
Dr. Apryl Bonham - *Insurance, risk management, legal*

Description: We have been recruiting claims professionals and risk management personnel and placing them with insurance companies and major corporations for the last 18 years.

Salary Minimum: $40,000
Functions: Senior mgmt., Middle mgmt., Nurses, Risk mgmt., Attorneys
Industries: Legal, Insurance

Clanton & Co.

One City Blvd. W., Ste. 820
Orange, California 92868
(714) 978-7100
Fax: (714) 978-7103
Email: FSSEARCH@aol.com

Key Contact - Specialty:
Ms. Diane Clanton - *Food service sales management*

Description: Clanton & Company was established in 1984 by a trained psychologist to identify personality factors as well as job qualifications in placement of sales managers with food and non-food manufacturers that sell to the food service industry.

Salary Minimum: $40,000
Functions: Sales mgmt.
Industries: Food/bev/tobacco

Claremont-Branan, Inc.

1298 Rockbridge Rd., Ste. B
Stone Mountain, Georgia 30087
(770) 925-2915
Fax: (770) 925-2601
Email: cbinc@mindspring.com
Web: cbisearch.com

Key Contact - Specialty:
Mr. Phil Collins - *Architects, environmental engineers, transportation engineers, public works engineers*
Mr. Bob Bowers - *Mechanical, electrical, civil & structural engineering*

Description: Professional recruiting and search for the architecture, consulting engineering services industry. Specialist in key technical and management positions. National coverage. Member-Professional Services Management Association.

Salary Minimum: $40,000
Functions: Engineering, Architects
Industries: Construction

Howard Clark Assoc.

P.O. Box 423
Bellmawr, New Jersey 08099-0423
(609) 467-3725
Fax: (609) 467-3384
Email: hclark@dvnc.net

Key Contact - Specialty:
Mr. Howard L. Clark - *Human resources, sales & marketing, MIS, data processing, finance*
Mr. Jim Anderson - *Science, business management, engineering, product management, distribution*

Description: Recruitment of professional candidates for placement with major corporations-nationwide-contingency and search. Also involved in minority/female/disadvantaged recruitment.

Salary Minimum: $40,000
Functions: Mktg. mgmt., Benefits, Personnel, Budgeting, Systems dev., Engineering, Minorities
Industries: Energy/utilities, Food/bev/tobacco, Drugs mfg., Computer equip., Banking, Equip. svcs., Broadcast & Film

---

Toby Clark Assoc. Inc.

405 E. 54th St.
New York, New York 10022
(212) 752-5670
Fax: (212) 752-5674

Key Contact - Specialty:
Ms. Toby Clark
Ms. Sharon Davis

Description: High caliber recruitment for marketing, marketing communications, advertising and public relations for corporations and financial services companies.

Salary Minimum: $50,000
Functions: Advertising, Mktg. mgmt., PR
Industries: Misc. mfg., Misc. financial, Pharmaceutical svcs., Communications, Advertising/PR, New media

---

Clark Executive Search

135 N. Ferry Rd.
P.O. Box 560
Shelter Island, New York 11964
(516) 749-3540
Fax: (516) 749-3539
Email: clarkexsrh@aol.com

Key Contact - Specialty:
Ms. Ellen H. Clark - *Pharmaceutical, biotech*

Description: A recruiting firm that specializes in finding mid to senior executives for pharmaceutical, biotechnology and medical device companies. As niche-market specialists, we fully understand the whole drug development process from discovery to finished product.

Salary Minimum: $60,000
Functions: Directors, Middle mgmt., Product dev., Production, Plant mgmt., Quality, Purchasing
Industries: Chemicals, Drugs mfg., Medical devices, Pharmaceutical svcs., Biotech

---

The Clark Group

679 S. Lakeshore Drive
Harbor Springs, Michigan 49740
(616) 526-3210
Fax: (616) 526-3212
Email: clarkgp@freeway.net

Key Contact - Specialty:
Mr. Larry A. Clark - *Sales, sales support, marketing executives, food, health & beauty aids and general merchandise segments of the consumer product industry)*

Description: Specializing in consumer product sales positions from entry level through vice presidents; sales support positions including shelf management, category managers and trade promotion and marketing positions from assistants through directors.
Functions: Directors, Senior mgmt., Middle mgmt., Advertising, Mkt. research, Mktg. mgmt., Sales mgmt.

Clark Personnel Service, Inc.

P.O. Box 991850
Mobile, Alabama 36691-1850
(334) 342-5511
Fax: (334) 343-5588

Key Contact - Specialty:
Ms. Donna Clark - *Generalist*

Description: Full service staffing firm including professional recruiting, temporary staffing and PEO operation.
Functions: Senior mgmt., Middle mgmt., Production, Plant mgmt., Materials Plng., Sales mgmt., Engineering
Industries: Generalist, Food/bev/tobacco, Textiles/apparel, Lumber/furniture, Paper, Chemicals, Metal products

Affiliates:
Staff Leasing, Inc.

The Clayton Edward Group

146 Monroe Ctr., Ste. 1126
McKay Twr.
Grand Rapids, Michigan 49503
(616) 336-8066
Fax: (616) 336-7680

Key Contact - Specialty:
Mr. Ron Meadley

Description: Specialize in the metal stamping/forming industry on a national basis.

Salary Minimum: $40,000
Functions: Senior mgmt., Middle mgmt., Production, Plant mgmt., Sales mgmt., MIS mgmt., Engineering
Industries: Lumber/furniture, Plastics/rubber, Metal products, Machinery/

Appliances, Motor vehicles, Misc. mfg., Transportation

Clinton, Charles, Wise & Co.

931 State Rd. 434, Ste. 1201-319
Altamonte Springs, Florida 32714
(407) 682-6790
Fax: (407) 682-1697

Key Contact - Specialty:
Mr. Craig D. Wise - *Sales, computer industry*
Mr. Omari Clinton - *Sales management, computer industry*
Mr. Kamal Charles - *Medical sales, financial sales*
Ms. Annette C. Wise - *Sales*

Description: Specializing in recruiting sales, marketing and management talent in the computer, financial and healthcare industries primarily in Midwest, Southwest, Mid-Atlantic and Southeast regions of the country (USA).
Functions: Mkt. research, Mktg. mgmt., Sales mgmt., Systems implem., Systems support, Minorities
Industries: Banking, Computer svcs., High tech, Software

CMC Search Consultants

500 N. Michigan Ave., Ste. 1940
Chicago, Illinois 60611
(312) 670-5300
Fax: (312) 670-5333

Key Contact - Specialty:
Ms. Carol Marcovich - *Generalist*

Description: Specialists in the professional recruitment of middle level managers in a variety of fields: accounting, finance, sales, marketing, engineering and human resources.

Salary Minimum: $40,000
Functions: Generalist, Middle mgmt., Mfg., Sales & mktg., HR mgmt., Finance, Engineering
Industries: Generalist, Misc. mfg., Finance, Accounting, Human resource svcs., Insurance, Real estate

CMS, Inc.

500 Commercial St.
Manchester, New Hampshire 03101-1151
(603) 644-7800
Fax: (603) 644-5560
Email: stan@cms-rsi.mv.com

Key Contact - Specialty:
Mr. Stan Clayman - *Sporting goods, footwear, apparel*

Description: Prominent international specialists in sporting goods, footwear, apparel and healthcare; all specialties and disciplines.

Salary Minimum: $50,000
Functions: Senior mgmt., Production, Distribution, Health admin., Mkt. research, Sales mgmt., CFO's
Industries: Plastics/rubber, Leather/stone/glass/clay, Misc. mfg., Wholesale, Retail, Insurance, Healthcare

Affiliates:
(RSI) Re: Search Int'l.

CMS Management Services LLC
(a division of Corporate Staffing Resources)

401 E. Colfax, Ste. 401
South Bend, Indiana 46617
(219) 282-3980
Fax: (219) 282-3995
Email: cms@staffing.net
Web: www.staffing.net/cms.htm

Key Contact - Specialty:
Mr. Joseph A. Noto - *Accounting, finance*
Mr. Patrick B. Laake - *Information technology*

Description: Employment service firm specializing in financial, information systems, engineering and manufacturing professionals nationwide on a direct hire, temp-to-hire, or contract basis.

Salary Minimum: $30,000
Functions: General mgmt., Mfg., Materials, Sales & mktg., Finance, IT, Engineering
Industries: Generalist, Mfg., Svcs., Software

Branches:
5920 Castleway West Drive.,Ste. 120
Indianapolis, Indiana 46250
(317) 842-5777
Fax: (317) 577-3077
Key Contact - Specialty:
Mr. Richard Halstead - *Accounting, finance*

2717 Ward Circle, Ste. 102
Brentwood, Tennessee 37027
(615) 377-3700
Fax: (615) 377-8625
Key Contact - Specialty:
Mr. Rick Beller - *Information technology*

CMW & Associates, Inc.

122 W. Pine
Springfield, Illinois 62704
(217) 522-0452
(800) 618-8706
Fax: (217) 241-5974
Email: char@midwest.net
Web: www.cmwassoc.com

Key Contact - Specialty:
Ms. Charlene Turczyn - *Information technology*

Description: We have at least 10 years experience in our specialty field. Our clients consist of many of the Fortune 500.

Salary Minimum: $35,000
Functions: Mfg., Sales & mktg., IT, Engineering, Minorities, Architects, Technicians
Industries: Energy/utilities, Mfg., Finance, Computer svcs., Aerospace, Insurance, High tech

Branches:
711 Old Ballas Rd., Ste. 110
St. Louis, Missouri 63141
(800) 618-8706
Fax: (888) Resume1
Email: tammy@midwest.net
Key Contact - Specialty:
Ms. Charlene Turczyn

Affiliates:
Technical Resource Group

CN Associates

4040 Civic Ctr. Drive, Ste. 200
San Rafael, California 94903
(415) 883-1114
Fax: (415) 883-3321
Email: chanic@ix.netcom.com
Web: www.topechelon.com/cnassociates

Key Contact - Specialty:
Mr. Charles Nicolosi - *Software, data communications, telecommunications, sales & marketing, software developers*

Description: A small specialized executive search firm, serving the office information systems industry, encompassing sales, marketing and technical/customer support and software developers professionals. Heavy concentration, hardware/software vendors - data/telecom; San Francisco, Silicon Valley areas.

Salary Minimum: $50,000
Functions: Sales & mktg., MIS mgmt., Systems dev., Systems support, Mgmt. consultants, Architects, Technicians
Industries: Computer equip., Computer svcs., New media, Broadcast & Film, Telecoms, High tech, Software

Coast Personnel Services Ltd.

2A-3411 Shenton Rd.
Nanaimo, British Columbia V9T 2H1
Canada
(250) 758-1828
Fax: (250) 758-8244
Email: vwcoast@island.net
Web: www.island.net/~work

Key Contact - Specialty:
Mr. Vincent G. B. Willden - *Technical sales, engineering*

Description: Twelve year focus on the forest industry in western Canada - pulp & paper, sawmills, woodlands and supporting industries. Technical recruiting and consulting in western Canada.

Salary Minimum: $30,000

Functions: Generalist, General mgmt., Production, Sales mgmt., Finance, IT, Engineering
Industries: Generalist, Agri/forestry/mining, Lumber/furniture, Paper, Metal products, High tech, Software

Ann Coe & Assoc.

2033 Sherman Ave., Ste. 301
Evanston, Illinois 60201
(847) 864-0668
Fax: (847) 864-0625
Email: anncoe@aol.com
Web: www.anncoe_jobsearch.com

Key Contact - Specialty:
Ms. Ann Coe - *MIS*

Description: Professional and executive search specializing in information technology/MIS.

Salary Minimum: $40,000
Functions: MIS mgmt., Systems anal., Systems dev., Systems implem., Systems support, Network admin., DB admin.
Industries: High tech, Software

Coleman Legal Search Consultants

1535 JFK Blvd., Two Penn Ctr., Ste. 1010
Philadelphia, Pennsylvania 19102
(215) 864-2700
Fax: (215) 864-2709
Email: legalsearc@aol.com
Web: www.colemanlegal.com

Key Contact - Specialty:
Mr. Michael M. Coleman

Description: We specialize in recruiting lawyers, partners and associates for law firms and general counsels and staff attorneys for corporations in the Eastern United States. We also assist in law firm mergers and opening of satellite offices.
Functions: Attorneys
Industries: Legal

Branches:
33 Wood Ave. S., Ste. 400
Metropark Office Complex
Iselin, New Jersey 08830
(732) 603-3896
Fax: (732) 321-6562
Key Contact - Specialty:
Mr. Michael M. Coleman

Collins & Associates

10188 W. "H" Ave.
Kalamazoo, Michigan 49009
(616) 372-3275
Fax: (616) 372-3921
Email: pcollins@collins-associates.com
Web: www.collins-associates.com

Key Contact - Specialty:
Mr. Philip M. Collins - *Computers*

Description: Specializing in the west Michigan area. All areas of computers and computer professionals.

Salary Minimum: $40,000
Functions: Materials Plng., MIS mgmt., Systems anal., Systems dev., Systems implem., Systems support, Technicians
Industries: Generalist, Energy/utilities, Mfg., Retail, Finance, High tech, Software

S L Collins Assoc.

P.O. Box 472181
Charlotte, North Carolina 28247-2181
(704) 365-9889
Fax: (704) 365-9890
Email: collins@slcollins.com
Web: www.slcollins.com

Key Contact - Specialty:
Mr. Steve L. Collins - *Pharmaceutical, biotechnology*

Description: We are well known in the pharmaceutical and biotechnology industries for our professionalism, integrity and service to both client companies and candidates. Positions are throughout the United States and up to the level of senior vice president. Visit our web site for additional information including a listing of available positions.

Salary Minimum: $40,000
Functions: Generalist
Industries: Drugs mfg., Medical devices, Pharmaceutical svcs., Packaging, Biotech

Colt Systems Professional Personnel Services

1880 Century Park E., Ste. 208
Los Angeles, California 90067
(310) 277-4741
Fax: (310) 277-8317

Key Contact - Specialty:
Mr. Sheldon Arons - *Senior financial executives, MIS personnel, programmers*

Description: We work with Fortune 100-500 corporations. The firm specializes in accounting, finance and data processing placement. We provide key employees for numerous corporate entities, another specialty of the firm is confidential replacement of senior executives.
Functions: Senior mgmt., Admin. svcs., Finance, Credit, MIS mgmt., Systems anal., Systems dev.
Industries: Misc. mfg., Finance, Entertainment, Computer svcs., Telecoms, Insurance, High tech

Commercial Programming Systems, Inc.

3250 Wilshire Blvd., Ste. 1212
Los Angeles, California 90010
(213) 380-2681
Fax: (213) 389-2603
Email: cps@cpsinc.com
Web: www.cpsinc.com

Key Contact - Specialty:
Mr. Alan Strong

Description: We are Southern California's contract service of choice for information technology professionals. With offices in Los Angeles and Orange County, we provide contract, lease to hire and executive placement opportunities.
Functions: MIS mgmt., Systems anal., Systems dev., Systems implem., Systems support, Network admin., DB admin.
Industries: Motor vehicles, Finance, Entertainment, Communications, Broadcast & Film, Telecoms, Government

Branches:
7755 Center Ave., #1100
Huntington Beach, California 90010
(714) 372-2280
Fax: (714) 372-4992
Email: cattman@cpsinc.com
Web: www.cpsinc.com
Key Contact - Specialty:
Mr. Steve Catt

Affiliates:
CPS Consulting Services

Commonwealth Consultants

5064 Roswell Rd., Ste. B 101
Atlanta, Georgia 30342
(404) 256-0000

Key Contact - Specialty:
Mr. David Aiken
Mr. Tim Panetta
Mr. Marcus Mouchet

Description: Supply computer vendors and consulting firms exceptional candidates with strong computer skills. All levels in the disciplines of programmers, systems analysts, hardware/software engineers, sales, technical support and marketing.

Salary Minimum: $35,000
Functions: Sales mgmt.
Industries: High tech, Software

Comprehensive Search
(a division of Jeffrey W. Brown, Inc.)

316 S. Lewis St., Cary Bldg.
LaGrange, Georgia 30240
(706) 884-3232
Fax: (706) 884-4106
Email: compsrch@wp-lag.mindspring.com
Web: www.comp-search.com

Key Contact - Specialty:
Mr. Jeffrey W. Brown - *Built environment*
Ms. Gail W. Standard - *Built environment*
Ms. Merritt S. Shelton - *Built environment*
Ms. Gail Morin - *Built environment*
Ms. Marilyn McSweeney - *Contract furnishings*
Mr. Gordon Miller - *Information technology*

Description: Retainer, contingency, recruitment research and contract employees provided nationwide. Synergistically we also offer contract employees (we presently have them in most major U.S. cities), testing, outplacement and spousal assistance.

Salary Minimum: $30,000
Functions: Plant mgmt., Mktg. mgmt., Sales mgmt., MIS mgmt., Systems dev., Architects
Industries: Textiles/apparel, Lumber/furniture, Paints/petroleum products, Computer equip., Misc. mfg., Hospitality, Computer svcs.

CompuPro
1117 S. Milwaukee Ave., Ste. B9
Libertyville, Illinois 60048
(847) 549-8603

Key Contact - Specialty:
Mr. Douglas J. Baniqued - *Information technology*

Description: Specialists in the computer industry and related areas.

Salary Minimum: $50,000
Functions: General mgmt., Finance, MIS mgmt., Systems anal., Systems dev., Systems implem., Systems support
Industries: Computer equip., Finance, Computer svcs., Mgmt. consulting, New media, High tech, Software

---

Computer Int'l. Consultants, Inc.
1111 N. Westshore Blvd., Ste. 200B
Tampa, Florida 33607-4705
(813) 281-0505
Fax: (813) 281-0913
Email: mail@cictampa.com
Web: www.cictampa.com

Key Contact - Specialty:
Mr. Michael R. Mitchell - *Executive search in information technology*
Ms. Linda M. Mitchell - *Contract services*

Description: Recruitment experience and competence by a staff of former Fortune 500 and Big Six executives, that understand corporate structure, culture and requirements.

Salary Minimum: $50,000
Functions: MIS mgmt., Systems anal., Systems dev., Systems implem.
Industries: Energy/utilities, Transportation, Misc. financial, Computer svcs., New media, Telecoms, Software

---

Computer Network Resources, Inc.
28231 Tinajo
Mission Viejo, California 92692
(714) 951-5929
Fax: (714) 951-6013
Email: cnrkenmiller@home.com
Web: www.cnrsearch.com

Key Contact - Specialty:
Mr. Kenneth Miller - *High technology, insurance, healthcare, financial applications (sales, consulting & technical positions)*

Description: Experienced nationwide firm with unmatched insurance industry expertise in information technology. Extensive database of openings and available candidates. We do not advertise, we network on a confidential basis.

Salary Minimum: $50,000
Functions: Sales mgmt., MIS mgmt., Systems anal., Systems dev., Systems implem., Systems support, DB admin.
Industries: Computer svcs., Mgmt. consulting, Insurance, High tech, Software, Healthcare

---

Computer Personnel, Inc.
720 Olive Way, Ste. 510
Seattle, Washington 98101
(206) 985-0282
Fax: (206) 985-0283
Email: ron@cpi-seattle.com
Web: cpi-seattle.com

Key Contact - Specialty:
Mr. Ron Meints - *Information technology professionals*

Description: Practice is limited to information technology professionals including software engineers, systems programmers, product and project managers, MIS management and pre/post sales support.

Salary Minimum: $30,000
Functions: MIS mgmt., Systems anal., Systems dev., Systems implem., Systems support, Network admin., DB admin.
Industries: Generalist, Computer svcs., High tech, Software

Computer Placements Unlimited Inc.
102 Palo Alto Drive
Plainview, New York 11803
(516) 933-7707
Fax: (516) 933-7716
Email: cpu-inc@erols.com

Key Contact - Specialty:
Ms. Ada Gracin - *Information technology*
Mr. Bart Collins - *Information technology*
Dr. Lynn Collins - *Human resources*

Description: Executive search firm focusing on information technology professionls. As we have an in-house industrial psychologist we are capable of consulting our clients on staffing needs and processes and our candidates on career issues and choices.
Functions: MIS mgmt., Systems anal., Systems dev., Systems implem., Systems support, Network admin., DB admin.
Industries: Generalist

Computer Professionals Unlimited
13612 Midway Rd., Ste. 333
Dallas, Texas 75244
(972) 233-1773
Fax: (972) 233-9619
Email: zipzap@onramp.net

Key Contact - Specialty:
Mr. V. J. Zapotocky - *Network management, software engineering*
Mr. Mark Allen - *Client/server systems, MIS*

Description: Computer based product development, management, key individual contributors, software/hardware engineering, systems architecture. Information technologists, client server specialists, graphical user interface design, network engineering, network administration, telecommunication systems-voice, data, cellular.

Salary Minimum: $40,000
Functions: MIS mgmt., Systems anal., Systems dev., Systems implem., Network admin., DB admin., Engineering
Industries: Computer equip., Computer svcs., Telecoms, High tech, Software

---

Computer Recruiters, Inc.
22276 Buenaventura St.
Woodland Hills, California 91364-5006
(818) 704-7722
Fax: (818) 704-7724
Email: b.moore@usa.net
Web: tekjobs.com

Key Contact - Specialty:
Mr. Bob Moore - *Data processing*

Description: Specialists for PC (client server), Internet, data warehouse, midrange and mainframe: database administrators, programmer analysts, network administrators, systems programmers, systems engineers and managers. Full time and contract nationwide.

Salary Minimum: $35,000

Functions: MIS mgmt., Systems anal., Systems dev., Systems implem., Systems support, Network admin., DB admin.
Industries: Generalist, High tech, Software

Computer Security Placement Service

One Computer Drive, Box 204-D
Northborough, Massachusetts 01532
(508) 393-7803
Fax: (508) 393-6802
Email: ccarey@telepowercorp.com
Web: www.computersecurity.com

Key Contact - Specialty:
Mr. Cameron Carey - *Telecommunications, data security, disaster recovery planning*

Description: We understand information security problems, we're the oldest and largest executive recruiting firm specializing in information security nationwide. Our affiliate specializes in telecommunications and electrical power marketing.

Salary Minimum: $40,000
Functions: Sales mgmt., Systems implem., Systems support
Industries: Computer equip., Banking, Invest. banking, Brokers, Mgmt. consulting, New media, Telecoms

Affiliates:
Telepower Corp.

The Comwell Company, Inc.

227 Route 206
Flanders, New Jersey 07836
(973) 927-9400
Fax: (973) 927-0372
Email: comwell@aol.com
Web: www.comwellconsultants.com

Key Contact - Specialty:
Mr. John F. Sobecki
Mr. David Gavin

Description: As we help give people dignity and align their skills, abilities, values and interests with current tasks and future strategies, client organizations become more competitive, productive and profitable.

Salary Minimum: $75,000
Functions: Generalist, Directors, Senior mgmt., Middle mgmt., Mkt. research, Personnel, Training
Industries: Generalist, Chemicals, Misc. mfg., Finance, Human resource svcs., Communications, Healthcare

Concorde Search Assoc.

1 N. Broadway, Ste. 410
White Plains, New York 10601
(914) 428-0700
Fax: (914) 428-4865
Web: www.concorde.idsite.com

Key Contact - Specialty:
Ms. Anita Greenwald - *Banking, finance*

Description: We are a 100% client driven search firm. Our total thrust is fulfilling and maximizing the corporate staffing goals of our clients. We provide extra commitment and work ethic.

Salary Minimum: $25,000
Functions: HR mgmt., Finance
Industries: Finance

Concorde Staff Source Inc.

735 N. Water St., Ste. 185
Milwaukee, Wisconsin 53202
(414) 291-6180
Fax: (414) 272-3852
Email: bradbrin@execpc.com

Key Contact - Specialty:
Mr. Bradley Brin - *Healthcare, information technology, physicians*

Description: Recruiting limited to healthcare industry and information technology.
Functions: Physicians, Nurses, Allied health, Health admin., Systems dev., Systems implem., Systems support
Industries: Generalist, Healthcare

M. L. Conner

P.O. Box 660
Pierson, Florida 32180
(904) 749-0901

Key Contact - Specialty:
Mr. A. M. Oppenheimer - *Insurance*
Ms. Marlene L. Conner - *Insurance*

Description: 20+ years experience, confidentiality, personalized service by our account executives, a client base of the top insurance agencies and companies, industry-wide competitive fee structure.

Salary Minimum: $20,000
Functions: Senior mgmt., Middle mgmt., Mktg. mgmt., Sales mgmt., Customer svc., M&A
Industries: Insurance

Branches:
6600 Landings Dr., #106
Ft. Lauderdale, Florida 33319
(954) 486-7680
Key Contact - Specialty:
Ms. Toni Oppenheimer - *Insurance*

Connors, Lovell & Assoc. Inc.

4 Robert Speck Pkwy., Ste. 280
Mississauga, Ontario L4Z 1S1
Canada
(905) 566-4051
Fax: (905) 566-1038
Email: conlov@globalserve.net
Web: conlov.com

Key Contact - Specialty:
Ms. Andrée Lovell - *Generalist*
Ms. Lynn Beechey - *Generalist*
Mr. Jim Vanderleeuw - *Generalist*
Ms. Tammy Thompson - *Generalist*

Description: We are committed to performance excellence and are driven by the desire to become one of the most successful search firms in Ontario. As true generalists, we focus on relationship building and long term partnering.
Functions: Generalist, Mfg., Sales & mktg., HR mgmt., Finance, IT, Engineering
Industries: Generalist, Mfg., Finance, Svcs., Aerospace, Packaging, High tech

Branches:
22-260 Holiday Inn Drive
Cambridge, Ontario N3C 4E8
Canada
(519) 651-1004
Fax: (519) 651-2083
Email: conlov@golden.net
Web: www.conclov.com
Key Contact - Specialty:
Mr. Barry Connors

Consolidated Management Services

190 Robert Speck Pkwy., Ste. 113
Mississauga, Ontario L4Z 3K3
Canada
(905) 272-5566
Fax: (905) 272-8246

Key Contact - Specialty:
Mr. Dwight Smith
Mr. Archie Harkins

Description: CMS sets itself apart from the traditional recruiting and specialized HR providers, who have a limited variety of service offerings or the bench strength and in some cases, the required expertise to deliver the goods.
Functions: Generalist, General mgmt., Mfg., Materials, Sales & mktg., HR mgmt., Finance
Industries: Generalist, Construction, Mfg., Transportation, Finance, Svcs., Communications

The Consortium
(a division of RCM Technologies, Inc.)

1156 Ave. of the Americas
New York, New York 10036
(212) 221-1544
Fax: (212) 764-6848
Email: mail.rcmt.com
Web: www.consortiumjobs.com

Key Contact - Specialty:
Mr. Leon Kopyt

Description: We provide executive search and consulting services to the data processing, legal, tax, bank/finance, insurance and financial sales and health services communities on a retainer or contingency basis. We further supply legal, engineering and data processing temporary services.

Salary Minimum: $40,000
Functions: Allied health, Benefits, Taxes, Systems anal., Systems implem., Engineering, Attorneys
Industries: Banking, Invest. banking, Computer svcs., Insurance, High tech, Software, Healthcare

Conspectus, Inc.

222 Purchase St., Ste. 318
Rye, New York 10580
(914) 925-0600
Fax: (914) 925-0602
Email: resume@conspectusinc.com

Key Contact - Specialty:
Mr. Eric Stieglitz
Mr. John Stieglitz

Description: Specializing in security analysts, portfolio managers and investment bankers.

Salary Minimum: $70,000
Functions: Cash mgmt.
Industries: Finance, Invest. banking, Brokers, Venture cap., Misc. financial

Construct Management Services

8264 Peony Lane, Ste. 1
Maple Grove, Minnesota 55311
(612) 420-2696
Fax: (612) 420-2517
Email: RLyngen@aol.com

Key Contact - Specialty:
Mr. Robert Lyngen - *Construction, architecture*
Mr. C. J. Lyngen - *Manufacturing, plastics*
Ms. Trish Lyngen - *Manufacturing, construction, real estate/development, architecture*

Description: Staff has industry experience and professional search experience with KPMG Peat Marwick.

Salary Minimum: $40,000
Functions: Senior mgmt., Plant mgmt., Mktg. mgmt., CFO's, Engineering, Architects
Industries: Construction, Paper, Medical devices, Metal products, Computer svcs., Accounting, Insurance

Affiliates:
Davian
HR Services

Construction Search Specialists, Inc.

115 5th Ave. S., Ste.501
LaCrosse, Wisconsin 54601
(608) 784-4711
Fax: (608) 784-4904
Email: twatters@csssearch.com
Web: www.csssearch.com

Key Contact - Specialty:
Mr. Duane McClain - *Presidents, CEOs, division managers*
Ms. Tamara Watters - *Project managers, estimators*

Description: Executive search and recruiting from mid-management to upper level exclusively for construction and engineering industries. USA and international. Over 23 years of experience. Professional and confidential.

Salary Minimum: $35,000
Functions: Directors, Senior mgmt., Middle mgmt., Production, Engineering, Environmentalists, Architects
Industries: Agri/forestry/mining, Construction, Mfg., Transportation, Equip. svcs., Environmental svcs., Real estate

Consultant Recruiters

6842 N. Park Manor Drive
Milwaukee, Wisconsin 53224
(414) 358-3036
Fax: (414) 358-2660
Email: dwcornell@ibm.com

Key Contact - Specialty:
Mr. Don Cornell - *Management consulting*

Description: Management consulting and information technology consulting specialists. Over 10 years recruiting for highly regarded consulting firms. Principal is former Big 6 consultant.

Salary Minimum: $75,000
Functions: Senior mgmt., Middle mgmt., MIS mgmt., Systems anal., Systems dev., Systems implem., Mgmt. consultants
Industries: Wholesale, Finance, Svcs., Mgmt. consulting, Software

The Consulting Group of North America, Inc.

8150 Leesburg Pike, Ste. 503
Vienna, Virginia 22182
(703) 442-8500
Fax: (703) 442-3800
Email: tcg-inc@msn.com
Web: www.tcgna.com

Key Contact - Specialty:
Mr. Roman Mesina - *PeopleSoft, Oracle, SAP, BAAN*
Ms. Avery Plavin - *Client/server technology, PeopleSoft, SAP, Oracle*

Description: We are a retained technical search firm placing technical (developers, software engineers, managers and senior managers) in the high tech industry. Only those with prior systems experience need apply. Main clients include the Big 6 and private consulting consortiums.

Salary Minimum: $50,000
Functions: MIS mgmt., Systems anal., Systems dev., Systems implem., Systems support, Network admin., DB admin.
Industries: Computer svcs., Mgmt. consulting, Human resource svcs., High tech, Software

Branches:
1200 Lebanon Road
West Mifflin, Pennsylvania 15122
(412) 464-0100
Fax: (412) 464-0700
Key Contact - Specialty:
Ms. Deanna Burgman

Consulting Resource Group, Inc.

100 Galleria Pkwy., Ste. 400
Atlanta, Georgia 30339
(404) 240-5550
Fax: (404) 240-5552
Email: mailbox@crg-inc.com
Web: www.crg-inc.com

Key Contact - Specialty:
Mr. P. Andrew Robinson - *Management consultants, technology consultants*

Description: Specialize in search assignments for boutique, national and international management consulting firms. Focus on strategy, process re-engineering, technology consulting and change management.

Salary Minimum: $75,000
Functions: M&A, Systems anal., Systems dev., Systems implem., Mgmt. consultants
Industries: Energy/utilities, Banking, Accounting, Mgmt. consulting, Communications, Insurance, Healthcare

Consulting Rhonda

49 Spadina Ave., Studio B
Toronto, Ontario M5V 2J1
Canada
(416) 205-9909
Fax: (416) 977-6645
Email: rbelous@canadianfindings.com
Web: www.canadianfindings.com

Key Contact - Specialty:
Ms. Rhonda Belous

Functions: Generalist, Quality, Distribution, Advertising, Mkt. research, Personnel, Cash mgmt.
Industries: Generalist, Food/bev/tobacco, Textiles/apparel, Transportation, Advertising/PR, High tech

Consumer Search Inc.
300 W. Main St.
Northborough, Massachusetts 01532
(508) 393-8506
Fax: (508) 393-7458

Key Contact - Specialty:
Ms. Connie Musso - *OTC, HBC, sales & marketing executives*

Description: Health and beauty care, over the counter pharmaceuticals, sales and marketing executives.

Salary Minimum: $75,000
Functions: Directors, Mkt. research, Mktg. mgmt., Sales mgmt.
Industries: Pharmaceutical svcs.

Continental Research Search, Inc.
1190 Turnberry Court, Geneva National
Lake Geneva, Wisconsin 53147
(414) 245-1808
Fax: (414) 245-0873

Key Contact - Specialty:
Ms. Jill Hillner - *Healthcare, paper industry, hospitality, engineering*

Description: Generalist with additional expertise in healthcare, paper industry and the hospitality industry. Also customized research and information broker.

Salary Minimum: $50,000
Functions: Generalist, Admin. svcs., Physicians, Allied health, Health admin., Engineering
Industries: Generalist, Paper, Medical devices, Hospitality, Pharmaceutical svcs., Healthcare

Continental Search & Outplacement, Inc.
4134 E. Joppa Rd., Ste. 203
Baltimore, Maryland 21236
(410) 529-7000
Fax: (410) 529-7007
Email: recruiter@consearch.com
Web: www.comsearch.com

Key Contact - Specialty:
Mr. Daniel C. Simmons - *MIS*

Description: Our focus is on the recruitment of programmers, systems managers, DBA's, and analysts across a variety of platforms.

Salary Minimum: $40,000
Functions: MIS mgmt., Systems anal., Systems dev., Systems implem., Systems support, DB admin.
Industries: Mfg., Transportation, Retail, Finance, Telecoms, High tech, Software

Continental Search Assoc.
1249 Hill Rd. N., Ste. D
Pickerington, Ohio 43147
(614) 868-8100
Fax: (614) 868-5344
Email: callen9@idt.net

Key Contact - Specialty:
Mr. James R. Allen - *Manufacturing, scientific*

Description: Strong ethics are the guiding principle of our firm. Complete trust is of the utmost importance in relationships between recruiter and client and between recruiter and candidate.

Salary Minimum: $70,000
Functions: General mgmt., Mfg., Purchasing, Materials Plng., R&D, Engineering
Industries: Plastics/rubber, Metal products, Machinery/Appliances, Biotech

Cook Assoc. Int'l., Inc.
P.O. Box 962
Brentwood, Tennessee 37024-0962
(615) 373-8264
(615) 373-8266
Fax: (615) 371-8215
Email: CAI@bellsouth.net
Web: www.jobguide.net

Key Contact - Specialty:
Mr. Stephen G. Cook - *Engineering, technical, manufacturing management*
Ms. Anita Dixon - *Accounting, actuarial, benefits administration*
Ms. Juli C. Wells - *Manufacturing, operations management*
Ms. Sonja Canady - *Healthcare*
Mr. Greg Bell - *Manufacturing-plastics*
Mr. Gene Cook - *Healthcare, manufacturing, engineering, human resources*
Mr. Martin E. Cook - *Information technology, MIS, data processing, engineering*
Ms. Traci Bloodworth - *Accounting, administration*

Description: Staff of professionals from manufacturing, healthcare, actuarial and benefits consulting firms. Consultants in human resources and operations management. Retained and contingency search. Consulting by the hour or by contract in human resources management.

Salary Minimum: $28,000
Functions: Senior mgmt., Quality, Productivity, Allied health, Health admin., Systems anal., Systems dev.
Industries: Mfg., Medical devices, Plastics/rubber, Finance, Computer svcs., Software, Healthcare

David C. Cooper & Assoc. Financial Search
(an ACSYS company)
Five Concourse Pkwy., Ste. 2700
Atlanta, Georgia 30328
(770) 395-0014
Fax: (770) 395-6521
Email: info@acsysatlanta.com
Web: www.acsysatlanta.com

Key Contact - Specialty:
Mr. David C. Cooper - *Accounting, finance*
Ms. Patricia J. Homrich - *Accounting, finance*
Mr. Ted Justiss - *Accounting, finance*

Functions: Finance, CFO's, Budgeting, Cash mgmt., Credit, Taxes, M&A

Cooper Assoc., Inc.
6 Chester Drive, Ste. 200
Rye, New York 10580

Key Contact - Specialty:
Mr. Norman T. Cooper - *Generalist*
Ms. Lisa Clark - *Sales & marketing*

Salary Minimum: $50,000
Functions: Generalist, Mktg. mgmt., Sales mgmt.
Industries: Generalist, Computer svcs., Telecoms, High tech

Cooper Management Assoc., Inc.
177 Main St., Ste. 107
Ft. Lee, New Jersey 07024
(201) 947-5171
Fax: (201) 947-5306
Email: mcpr@aol.com

Key Contact - Specialty:
Mr. Michael Cooper - *Retail*

Description: Twenty years of national executive recruitment experience for the retail industry. Serving clients in department stores, discounters, hard and soft goods specialty chains, mail order and home centers.

Salary Minimum: $60,000
Industries: Retail

COR Management Services, Ltd.
420 Lexington Ave., Ste. 3029
New York, New York 10170
(212) 599-2640
Fax: (212) 599-3048
Email: staff@corjobs.com
Web: www.corjobs.com

Key Contact - Specialty:
Mr. Robert Olman - *Information technology, capital markets*

Description: Permanent placement, supplemental staffing, projects (outsourcing).
Functions: Systems anal., Systems dev., Systems implem., Systems support, Network admin., DB admin., Mgmt. consultants
Industries: Banking, Invest. banking, Brokers, High tech, Software

Corbin Packaging Professionals
11729 Casa Grande Drive
St. Louis, Missouri 63146-4223
(314) 993-1419

Key Contact - Specialty:
Mr. Earl Corbin - *Packaging (technical & sales)*

Description: Specialist, packaging & allied industries: process, plastics, conveying, converting. Years of personal experience and contacts within these industries justify specialization. US and Germany.

Salary Minimum: $40,000
Functions: Middle mgmt., Packaging, Mktg. mgmt., Sales mgmt., Engineering
Industries: Food/bev/tobacco, Paper, Soap/perfume/cosmetics, Drugs mfg., Plastics/rubber, Machinery/Appliances, Packaging

Cornerstone Resources, Inc.
3535 NW 58th St., Ste. 1000
Oklahoma City, Oklahoma 73112
(405) 947-3131
Fax: (405) 947-1234
Email: corstone@concentric.net
Web: www.cornerstoneresources.com

Key Contact - Specialty:
Mr. Jim Edwards - *Information technology*
Mr. Bill Franz - *Hospitality*
Mr. Mark Smith - *Healthcare*
Mr. Joe Gibeault - *Hospitality*

Description: We are international permanent, contract and temporary professional placement firm. We have specialized in the following professions: hospitality, rehabilitation medicine, information technology and physician and nursing.
Functions: Physicians, Allied health, MIS mgmt., Systems anal., Systems dev., Network admin., DB admin.
Industries: Hospitality, Computer svcs., Human resource svcs., High tech, Software, Healthcare

Branches:
6695 Peachtree Industrial Blvd., Ste. 250
Atlanta, Georgia 30360
(770) 248-0441
Fax: (770) 248-9911
Email: corstone@concentric.net
Web: www.cornerstoneresources.com
Key Contact - Specialty:
Mr. John Cary - *Healthcare*

Cornerstone Search Assoc. Inc.
7 Grove St.
Belmont, Massachusetts 02178
(800) 826-6573
(617) 489-8892
Fax: (617) 489-8893
Email: cstone1@flash.net
Web: www.flash.net/~cstone1

Key Contact - Specialty:
Mr. Richard Rosen - *Long term care, subacute, retirement housing, clinical, administrative*
Ms. Robin Feingold - *Long term care, subacute, retirement housing, clinical, administrative*
Mr. Michael Clark - *Long term care, subacute, retirement housing, clinical, administrative*

Description: We are a nationwide full service placement firm specializing in all areas of subacute, long term care and retirement housing.
Functions: Senior mgmt., Middle mgmt., Admin. svcs., Nurses, Health admin., CFO's
Industries: Healthcare

Cornwall Stockton & Co., Inc.
5930 LBJ Frwy., Ste. 400
Dallas, Texas 75240
(972) 458-7490
Fax: (972) 239-2282
Email: cscoasp@flash.net
Web: www.flash.net/~cscoasp/

Key Contact - Specialty:
Mr. Anthony S. Pirro - *Chemicals*

Description: Our 10+ years of experience offer the highest level of expertise and performance in assisting clients in satisfying their human resource needs.
Functions: Senior mgmt., Admin. svcs., Sales mgmt., Engineering, Environmentalists, Technicians
Industries: Chemicals, Paints/petroleum products, Haz. waste

Corporate Advisors, Inc.
250 NE. 27th St.
Miami, Florida 33137
(305) 573-7753
Fax: (305) 573-7929
Email: jk@corporateadvisors.com
Web: www.corporateadvisors.com

Key Contact - Specialty:
Mr. Jerry Kurtzman - *Business process improvement*

Description: We have built a unique practice focusing on the special needs of major multi-national organizations who have selected South Florida as a strategic gateway to Latin America, as well as an ideal corporate headquarters location.

Salary Minimum: $50,000
Functions: General mgmt., Materials, Sales & mktg., HR mgmt., Finance, IT, Int'l.
Industries: Generalist

Corporate Builders, Inc.
812 SW Washington, Ste. 660
Portland, Oregon 97205-3212
(503) 223-4344
Fax: (503) 221-7778

Key Contact - Specialty:
Mr. William C. Meysing
Mr. Larry E. Meysing
Mrs. Joan Johnson
Ms. LeAnn Blumenstein
Mr. Brian Legate
Ms. Cheryl Walker

Description: Dedicated to research, analysis and consistently better recruiting results. Provide all the hiring companies with a superior recruiting workbook (WIF's) that improves their hiring results.
Functions: Engineering, Mgmt. consultants
Industries: Construction

Corporate Careers, Inc.
1500 Quail St., Ste. 290
Newport Beach, California 92660
(714) 476-7007
Fax: (714) 476-9019
Email: cci3@ix.netcom.com

Key Contact - Specialty:
Ms. Dolores Cronin - *Staffing industry*

Description: Sales and marketing placement with special emphasis on temporary help and recruiting industry including branch, regional managers and area vice presidents for national, regional and local firms.

Salary Minimum: $30,000
Functions: Directors, Senior mgmt., Middle mgmt., Sales mgmt., IT
Industries: High tech, Non-classifiable industries

Branches:
50 Airport Parkway
San Jose, California 95110
(408) 451-8432
Fax: (408) 437-7777
Key Contact - Specialty:
Ms. N. Lloyd Wood - *Staffing industry*

The Corporate Connection, Ltd.
7202 Glen Forest Drive, Ste. 208
Richmond, Virginia 23226
(804) 288-8844
Web:
www.thecorporateconnectionltd@msn.com

Key Contact - Specialty:
Mr. Marshall W. Rotella - *Financial, engineering*

Description: Full service recruiting firm with clients and candidate database throughout the Southeast. Over fifty years of combined experience in contingency and search placements in the Southeast and Virginia.

Salary Minimum: $25,000
Functions: Senior mgmt., Middle mgmt., Production, Sales mgmt., CFO's, Taxes, Engineering
Industries: Generalist, Paper, Chemicals, Machinery/Appliances, Non-profits, Accounting, Human resource svcs.

Corporate Dynamix

6619 N. Scottsdale Rd.
Scottsdale, Arizona 85250
(602) 607-0040
Fax: (602) 607-0054
Email: david@cdynamix.com
Web: www.cdynamix.com

Key Contact - Specialty:
Mr. David Sterenfeld - *Sales, sales management, software, services*

Description: We specialize in the placement of sales, sales management and sales support personnel in the high tech industry.

Salary Minimum: $40,000
Functions: Directors, Senior mgmt., Middle mgmt., Mkt. research, Mktg. mgmt., Sales mgmt., Direct mktg.
Industries: High tech, Software

Branches:
222 N. Sepulveda Blvd.
Los Angeles, California 90049
(310) 662-4770
Fax: (310) 662-4771
Email: carolyn@cdynamix.com
Web: www.cdynamix.com
Key Contact - Specialty:
Ms. Carolyn Stokes - *Pre & post sales & marketing*

Affiliates:
Management Decision Systems, Inc. (MDSI)

Corporate Image Group

3145 Hickory Hill, Ste. 204
Hickory Place Office Complex
Memphis, Tennessee 38115
(901) 360-8091
Fax: (901) 360-0813
Web: www.corpimg.com

Key Contact - Specialty:
Mr. Joseph M. Knose, II - *Audit, accounting, finance, senior executives*
Mr. Barry C. Mathews - *Engineering*
Mr. John Wright - *Engineering, manufacturing, human resources*
Ms. Judy Presley-Cannon - *Engineering, manufacturing, human resources*

Description: Nationally recognized for placement successes, we are a full-service search firm with clients in Fortune 1000, Big 6 and fast growth firms. Concentration is manufacturing and distribution sectors on a national scale.

Functions: Product dev., Plant mgmt., Purchasing, Sales mgmt., Personnel, Finance, Systems anal.
Industries: Paper, Chemicals, Plastics/rubber, Metal products, Machinery/Appliances, Consumer electronics, Entertainment

Branches:
P.O. Box 669516
Marietta, Georgia 30066-0109
(770) 924-9432
Fax: (770) 924-9483
Key Contact - Specialty:
Mr. Jim Mincy - *Audit, accounting, finance, manufacturing, engineering*

Corporate Management Services

P.O. Box 16271
Pittsburgh, Pennsylvania 15220
(412) 279-1180
Fax: (412) 279-2703
Email: 102526.745@compuserve.com

Key Contact - Specialty:
Mr. Robert J. Bushee
Ms. Dorothea Crass

Description: We help client companies identify and employ qualified people.

Salary Minimum: $40,000
Functions: Senior mgmt., Middle mgmt., Plant mgmt., Quality, Purchasing, Materials Plng., Engineering
Industries: Generalist, Plastics/rubber, Metal products, Machinery/Appliances, Misc. mfg.

Corporate Plus, Ltd.

3145 Tucker-Norcross Rd., Ste. 205
Tucker, Georgia 30084
(770) 934-5101
Fax: (770) 934-5127
Email: wmcglawn@aol.com

Key Contact - Specialty:
Mr. Walter McGlawn - *Sales, human resources, MIS, engineering*
Mr. Shawn Menefee - *Sales, manufacturing, finance*

Description: Nationwide executive search and management development firm that specializes in the area of diversity staffing. We specialize in sales, human resources, MIS and engineering.

Salary Minimum: $35,000
Functions: General mgmt., Production, Distribution, Sales mgmt., HR mgmt., Systems dev., Minorities
Industries: Generalist, Food/bev/tobacco, Transportation, Hospitality, Human resource svcs., Telecoms, Insurance

---

Corporate Recruiters Ltd.

1140 W. Pender St., Ste. 490
Vancouver, British Columbia V6E 4G1
Canada
(604) 687-5993
Fax: (604) 687-2427
Email: jobs@corporate.bc.ca
Web: www.corporate.bc.ca

Key Contact - Specialty:
Mr. Bruce Edmond - *High tech sales & marketing, business development, general manager, CEO*

Description: Recruitment firm specializing in the advanced technology industries. This includes: electronic engineering (both hardware and software); information technology; sales and marketing in the high-tech/computer industry, plus specialty chemicals and technical sales to the pulp and paper industry.

Salary Minimum: $40,000
Functions: Product dev., Production, Sales mgmt., MIS mgmt., Systems anal., Systems dev., Engineering
Industries: Computer equip., Consumer electronics, High tech, Software

---

Corporate Recruiters Inc.

1107 Bethlehem Pike, Ste. 206
Flourtown, Pennsylvania 19031
(215) 233-4701
Fax: (215) 233-5603

Key Contact - Specialty:
Mr. Stephen Berlin

Description: 32 years successful recruiting for pharmaceutical industry and bio-tech.

Salary Minimum: $100,000
Functions: Directors, Senior mgmt., Physicians, R&D
Industries: Drugs mfg., Medical devices, Pharmaceutical svcs., Biotech, Healthcare

---

Corporate Resources Professional Placement

4205 Lancaster Lane N., Ste. 108
Minneapolis, Minnesota 55441-1700
(612) 550-9222
Fax: (612) 550-9657

Email: info@corpres.com
Web: www.corpres.com

Key Contact - Specialty:
Mr. Bill Lanctot - *Management, technology*
Mr. Dean Anderson - *Management, technology*

Description: Retained and contingent search for advanced electronics, mechanical and biomedical engineering management and with other related positions available. $40K and above.

Salary Minimum: $40,000
Functions: Senior mgmt., Middle mgmt., Product dev., Systems dev., Systems implem., R&D, Engineering
Industries: High tech, Software, Biotech

Corporate Resources
5381 Autumnwood Drive
Cincinnati, Ohio 45242
(513) 793-5807
Fax: (513) 793-5981
Email: ccordell@eos.net

Key Contact - Specialty:
Ms. Cindy Andrew Cordell - *Information systems, finance, human resources*

Description: Each partner/consultant has 15+ years in recruitment of technical personnel. On a national network to facilitate clients in areas of IS, engineering, healthcare, accounting and human resources. Both search and contingency.

Salary Minimum: $35,000
Functions: Materials, Personnel, Finance, IT, Engineering

Corporate Search Consultants, Inc.
509 W. Colonial Drive
Orlando, Florida 32804
(800) 800-7231
(407) 578-3888
Fax: (407) 578-5153
Email: mail@corpsearch.com
Web: www.CORPSEARCH.com

Key Contact - Specialty:
Mr. Anthony Ciaramitaro - *Mortgage, banking, treasury, tax, trust*
Mr. Paul Ciaramitaro - *Information technology, AS 400, UNIX administration, database administration, client server, data security*
Mr. Joseph Ciaramitaro - *Financial services, internal audit, capital markets, risk management, commercial banking*

Description: Specialize in information technology including midrange/database, and client/server and in financial services including internal audit, EDP audit, mortgage banking and commercial banking.

Salary Minimum: $60,000
Functions: Production, Automation, Finance, IT, Network admin., DB admin., Engineering
Industries: Mfg., Finance, Computer svcs., Accounting

Corporate Search Consultants
2901 Ohio Blvd., Ste. 253
Terre Haute, Indiana 47803
(812) 235-2992
Fax: (812) 235-3029
Email: csc1@msn.com
Web: hometown.net/csc.htm

Key Contact - Specialty:
Mr. F. Scott Myers, IV
Mr. Gregg A. Greven

Description: Leading food and beverage search firm. Also work in closely related industries. Key clients include both Fortune 500 and emerging companies. We represent the top 20% candidates in industry.

Salary Minimum: $30,000
Functions: Senior mgmt., Middle mgmt., Mfg., Materials, HR mgmt., Minorities
Industries: Food/bev/tobacco, Chemicals, Soap/perfume/cosmetics, Drugs mfg.

Corporate Search, Inc.
6800 Jericho Tnpk., Ste. 203W
Syosset, New York 11791
(516) 496-3200
Fax: (516) 496-3165
Email: clairez@corporatesearch.com
Web: corporatesearch.com

Key Contact - Specialty:
Ms. Claire Zukerman - *Accounting (public & private), finance, administration, office services, human resources, sales & marketing*

Salary Minimum: $20,000
Functions: Admin. svcs., Materials, Sales & mktg., HR mgmt., Finance, Non-profits, Paralegals
Industries: Construction, Mfg., Transportation, Banking, Svcs., Real estate, Healthcare

Corporate Select Int'l., Ltd.
401 N. Michigan Ave., Ste. 1200
Chicago, Illinois 60611
(312) 616-6672
Fax: (312) 616-6678
Email: csiltd@earthlink.net

Key Contact - Specialty:
Ms. Mayumi Cochran

Description: We specialize in recruiting professionals and support staff for companies doing business in increasingly international and multicultural environments.

Salary Minimum: $30,000
Functions: Purchasing, Sales & mktg., HR mgmt., Finance, IT, Engineering, Int'l.
Industries: Chemicals, Medical devices, Plastics/rubber, Machinery/Appliances, Motor vehicles, Computer equip., Misc. financial

Corporate Staffing Group, Inc.
P.O. Box 2497
Doylestown, Pennsylvania 18901
(215) 345-1100
Fax: (215) 345-8177
Email: cbaker@corporatestaffing.com

Key Contact - Specialty:
Mr. Charles D. Baker - *Telecommunications*
Mrs. Laurie B. Carey - *Telecommunications*

Description: Representing medium to large firms in the TC industry, private and public switching. Emphasis on general management, marketing and engineering. Significant experience in high level systems and advance software implementation for AI networks, ATM, packet, wireless PCN/PCS, SONET and internet. Current in transport and transmission and Access markets.

Salary Minimum: $50,000
Functions: Directors, Middle mgmt., Mktg. mgmt., Systems dev., Systems implem., R&D, Engineering
Industries: Computer equip., Consumer electronics, Test/measurement equip., Telecoms, High tech, Software

Corporate Suite, Ltd.
507 Merle Hay Twr.
Des Moines, Iowa 50310
(515) 278-2744
Fax: (515) 278-4177

Key Contact - Specialty:
Ms. Pat Brown - *Insurance, property and casualty*

Description: Over 20 years of actual experience in the insurance industry.

Salary Minimum: $30,000
Functions: Generalist
Industries: Insurance

Corrao, Miller, Rush & Wiesenthal
499 Park Ave., 20th Floor
New York, New York 10022
(212) 328-6180
Fax: (212) 328-6181
Email: cmrwlegal@juno.com

Key Contact - Specialty:
Ms. Laura S. Corrao
Ms. Robin S. Miller
Ms. Renee Berliner Rush
Ms. Lauren M. Wiesenthal

Description: Premier national search firm specializing exclusively in the placement of exceptional attorneys. Our client roster includes law firms, investment and commercial banking institutions and corporations worldwide. We conduct retained partner and associate searches, mergers and acquisitions of groups and firms.
Functions: Attorneys
Industries: Legal

Leonard Corwen Assoc.

P.O. Box 350453
New York, New York 11235-0008
(718) 646-7581
Fax: (718) 646-7581
Email: 73740.3614@compuserve.com

Key Contact - Specialty:
Mr. Leonard Corwen - *Corporate communications, public relations, publishing, marketing communications*
Ms. Carol Butler - *Financial, marketing, human resources*

Description: For over 25 years serving the personnel needs of companies and organizations in the recruitment and placement of corporate communications, public relations, finance, advertising, marketing and publishing personnel at all levels.

Salary Minimum: $40,000
Functions: Middle mgmt., Advertising, Mktg. mgmt., PR, Benefits, Cash mgmt., Non-profits
Industries: Printing, Misc. financial, Accounting, Human resource svcs., Communications, Advertising/PR, Publishing

Cosier & Assoc.

717 - 7th Ave. SW, Ste. 1500
Calgary, Alberta T2P 0Z3
Canada
(403) 232-8350
Fax: (403) 265-1870
Email: casierb@cadvision.com

Key Contact - Specialty:
Mr. Brian Cosier - *Engineers, geoscientists, oil & gas*
Mr. Barry Krell - *Information technology*

Description: Technical and professional recruiter to the Western Canadian oil and gas industry. Also expanding to information technology for USA utilities.
Functions: Middle mgmt., Production, Systems dev., R&D, Engineering
Industries: Energy/utilities, Paints/petroleum products

J. D. Cotter Search Inc.

2999 E. Dublin-Granville Rd.
Columbus, Ohio 43231
(614) 895-2065
Fax: (614) 895-3071
Email: jdc.search@aol.com

Key Contact - Specialty:
Mr. Joe Cotter
Mr. Dan Cotter

Description: Contingency or retained. References. Fast, thorough, guaranteed. Client list available. Peak performance and results. Others search, we find. Celebrating our 29th anniversary in commitment to excellence in search.

Salary Minimum: $40,000
Functions: Middle mgmt., Mfg., Materials, HR mgmt., Finance, IT, Engineering
Industries: Generalist, Mfg., Finance, Svcs., Environmental svcs., Software, Healthcare

CountryHouse Hotels Executive Search

619 E. High St.
P.O. Box 2429
Charlottesville, Virginia 22902
(804) 977-5029
Fax: (804) 977-5431

Key Contact - Specialty:
Mr. Grant Howlett - *Hospitality*
Mr. Steve Samuels - *Hospitality*

Description: Major client base - consists of 4 and 5 star hotels and resorts throughout the U.S. Forty years experience.

Salary Minimum: $25,000
Functions: Senior mgmt., Middle mgmt., Sales mgmt., Personnel, CFO's, Mgmt. consultants
Industries: Hospitality, Entertainment, Accounting, Human resource svcs., Advertising/PR

International Branches:
London

Trudi Cowlan

295 Madison Ave., 43rd Floor
New York, New York 10017
(212) 213-9708
Fax: (212) 213-5932
Email: tmcowlan@aol.com

Key Contact - Specialty:
Ms. Trudi Cowlan - *Advertising, media, research, account*

Description: Twenty years experience in the advertising field. All candidates are screened; we match the client with applicant.

Salary Minimum: $25,000
Functions: Senior mgmt., Middle mgmt., Advertising, Mkt. research, Direct mktg., Systems support
Industries: Entertainment, Advertising/PR, Publishing, New media, Broadcast & Film

Cox, Darrow & Owens, Inc.

6 E. Clementon Rd., Ste. E-4
Gibbsboro, New Jersey 08026
(609) 782-1300
Fax: (609) 782-7277
Email: cdo@snip.net

Key Contact - Specialty:
Mr. William R. Cox
Mr. Robert J. Darrow

Description: Professional recruiting and search service for all business functions. We serve clients in the manufacturing, process and service industries from our suburban Philadelphia location.

Salary Minimum: $40,000

Craig Affiliates, Inc.

901 Waterfall Way, Ste. 107
Richardson, Texas 75080
(972) 644-3264
Fax: (972) 644-4065
Email: craig@craigaff.com
Web: www.craigaff.com

Key Contact - Specialty:
Mr. Edward C. Nemec - *Retail, wholesale grocery, food services*

Description: Nationwide executive search specializing in placement of middle and senior level management within the retail grocery, wholesale grocery and food service distribution industries.

Salary Minimum: $50,000
Functions: Generalist, Directors, Senior mgmt., Middle mgmt., Purchasing, Distribution
Industries: Transportation, Wholesale, Retail

Affiliates:
Midwest Management, Inc.

Crane, Reed & Co., Inc.

P.O. Box 1359
Center Harbor, New Hampshire 03226
(603) 253-3000
Fax: (603) 253-3800
Email: bunting@cranereed.com

Key Contact - Specialty:
Mr. David F. Bunting - *International high technology*

Description: Ten year history of placing regional general managers, country managers, directors of sales, marketing, service, finance throughout Asia/Pacific, Europe and Latin America. Strong candidates delivered in two weeks.

Salary Minimum: $80,000
Functions: Senior mgmt., Middle mgmt., Sales & mktg., Mktg. mgmt., Sales mgmt., CFO's, Int'l.
Industries: Computer equip., Telecoms, High tech, Software

The Crawford Group
100 Colony Sq., Box 326
Atlanta, Georgia 30361
(404) 872-8500
Email: tcrawford@bellsouth.net

Key Contact - Specialty:
Mr. Tom Crawford - *Advertising agencies*

Description: We cover all areas of advertising agency and corporate marketing placement.

Salary Minimum: $35,000
Functions: Advertising, Mktg. mgmt., Direct mktg.

Creative Financial Staffing Inc.
595 Bay St., Ste. 303
P.O. Box 122
Toronto, Ontario M5G 2C2
Canada
(416) 596-7075
Fax: (416) 596-1456
Email: mbelaiche@hto.com
Web: www.cfstaffing.com

Key Contact - Specialty:
Mr. Marc Belaiche - *Accounting, financial personnel*

Description: We place temporary and permanent accounting and financial personnel at all levels. Affiliated with the chartered accounting firm of Horwath Orenstein in Toronto, we have 35 offices worldwide and are the only placement service affiliated with professional accounting firms.

Salary Minimum: $25,000
Functions: CFO's, Budgeting, Cash mgmt., Credit, Taxes
Industries: Generalist, Finance, Insurance

Affiliates:
Horwath Orenstein

Creative Financial Staffing
155 Federal St., 12th Floor
Boston, Massachusetts 02110
(617) 753-6012
Fax: (617) 753-6016
Email: casey@cfstaffing.com
Web: www.cfstaffing.com

Key Contact - Specialty:
Mr. Bruce Gobdel - *Accounting & finance*

Description: Temporary & permanent accounting & finance and IT placement service affiliated with CPA firms.
Functions: MIS mgmt., Systems anal., Systems dev., Systems implem., Systems support, Network admin., DB admin.
Industries: Generalist, Banking, Invest. banking, Brokers, Venture cap., Misc. financial, Hospitality

Branches:
Two Penn Center, Ste. 700
Philadelphia, Pennsylvania 19102
(215) 972-2374
Fax: (215) 563-4925
Key Contact - Specialty:
Mr. Daniel J. Casey - *Accounting & finance*

Creative HR Solutions
P.O. Box 1966
Stone Mountain, Georgia 30083
(404) 508-2093
Fax: (404) 508-3454
Email: jerry@atlonline.com
Web: superpages.gte.net

Key Contact - Specialty:
Mr. Jerry Gross - *Telecommunication, data communication, pre-sales, client server*
Mr. Tim Duckett - *Financial*
Mr. Solomon Tedla - *Financial, information technology, lean manufacturing*

Description: We are a multicultural organization providing services in the areas of executive/technical search, human resources management, business development, diversity training and outplacement.

Salary Minimum: $35,000
Functions: Senior mgmt., Admin. svcs., Personnel, Training, Systems anal., Systems support, Minorities
Industries: Generalist, Test/measurement equip., Hospitality, Telecoms, Defense, High tech, Software

Creative Input, Inc.
P.O. Box 1725
East Greenwich, Rhode Island 02818
(401) 885-3254
Fax: (401) 885-3349

Key Contact - Specialty:
Dr. Richard H. Brien - *Senior management, Mexico, textiles, general manufacturing*
Mr. Joe Stewart - *Mexico (all functions)*

Description: Calling ourselves Finders of Keepers is not meant as cutesy marketing. It reflects our commitment to each client to recruit individuals who (1) fit the organization's general chemistry and (2) make enduring contributions to excellence in their specific skill areas.

Salary Minimum: $40,000
Functions: General mgmt., Mfg., Materials, Sales & mktg., HR mgmt., Finance, MIS mgmt.
Industries: Generalist, Textiles/apparel, Paper, Chemicals, Plastics/rubber, Motor vehicles, Packaging

Affiliates:
Brien & Assoc. Management Consulting

CRI Professional Search
1784 Leimert Blvd.
Oakland, California 94602
(510) 531-1681
Fax: (510) 531-9599
Email: chuck@california.com

Key Contact - Specialty:
Mr. Charles W. Acridge - *Medical*

Description: Nationwide healthcare professional search specializing in the environments of: women's health (CNMs, OB/GYNs, nursing directors/managers), and managed care (case managers, managed care contracts, provider relations, risk management, UR/UM, QA).

Salary Minimum: $40,000
Functions: Directors, Senior mgmt., Middle mgmt., Physicians, Nurses, Health admin., Risk mgmt.
Industries: Insurance, Healthcare

Marlene Critchfield Co.
150 W. Gabilan St., Ste. 2
Salinas, California 95023
(408) 753-2466
Fax: (408) 753-2467

Key Contact - Specialty:
Ms. Marlene Critchfield - *Food, agriculture processing, manufacturing generalist*

Description: The reputation I have earned for commitment to excellence and etchical standards has opened the door for long-term, repeat business relationships and a national network of colleagues and associates.

Salary Minimum: $30,000
Functions: Generalist, Senior mgmt., Plant mgmt., Sales mgmt., CFO's
Industries: Agri/forestry/mining, Food/bev/tobacco

Criterion Executive Search, Inc.
5420 Bay Center Drive, Ste. 101
Tampa, Florida 33609-3469
(813) 286-2000
Fax: (813) 287-1660
Email:
CriterionExecutiveSearch@worldnet.att.net

Key Contact - Specialty:
Mr. Richard James

Description: Contingency firm consisting of professional recruiters with corporate experience in their fields. Specialties include accounting and finance, data

processing, engineering, insurance, legal, manufacturing, managed care and retailing.
Functions: Mfg., Materials, Healthcare, Finance, IT, Engineering, Minorities
Industries: Medical devices, Motor vehicles, Legal, Telecoms, Insurance, High tech, Healthcare

Cross Country Consultants, Inc.
111 Warren Rd., Ste. 4B
Hunt Valley, Maryland 21030
(410) 666-1100
Fax: (410) 666-1119

Key Contact - Specialty:
Mr. Sheldon Gottesfeld - *Engineering*

Description: Professional recruiters since 1961 specializing in engineering, manufacturing, telecommunications and sales. Engineering disciplines: electronics, chemical process, plastics, consumer products, mechanical engineering, medical and healthcare on a nationwide basis.

Salary Minimum: $30,000
Functions: Mfg., Packaging, Sales mgmt., IT, R&D, Engineering
Industries: Chemicals, Plastics/rubber, Paints/petroleum products, Machinery/Appliances, Consumer electronics, Telecoms, High tech

Crowe Chizek & Co.
340 Columbia St.
P.O. Box 11208
South Bend, Indiana 46634-0208
(219) 232-3992
(219) 236-8673
Fax: (219) 239-7878
Email: jracht@crowechizek.com
Web: www.crowechizek.com

Key Contact - Specialty:
Ms. Janet G. Racht - *Financial Institutions*
Mr. Casey Hamilton - *Manufacturing/IT*

Description: We offer expertise in searching for accounting and financial professionals, as well as technical, engineering, and executive management personnel. Our consultative approach allows us to maintain flexible methods and address precisely the client need.

Salary Minimum: $60,000
Functions: General mgmt., Mfg., Materials, HR mgmt., Finance, IT, Engineering

Jim Crumpley & Assoc.
1200 E. Woodhurst Drive, B-400
Springfield, Missouri 65804
(417) 882-7555
Fax: (417) 882-8555

Key Contact - Specialty:
Mr. Jim Crumpley - *Pharmaceutical*

Description: Retained and contingency search and placement of technical, scientific and engineering personnel for the pharmaceutical and medical device industry.

Salary Minimum: $40,000
Functions: Product dev., Production, Plant mgmt., Quality, Materials Plng., R&D, Engineering
Industries: Drugs mfg., Medical devices

CS Associates, LLC
P.O. Box 30926
Tucson, Arizona 85751-0926
(520) 327-7999
Fax: (520) 327-9489
Email: headhunter@csassoc.com
Web: www.csassoc.com

Key Contact - Specialty:
Mr. Joseph H. Connelly, III - *Consulting engineers, construction, architects*
Ms. Susan D. Connelly - *Consulting engineers, construction, architects*

Description: Recruit engineers and architects for consulting firms that design/build project. Professionals must have PE's, EIT's or NCARB registrations. Also surveyors, construction personnel, and mining.

Salary Minimum: $50,000
Functions: Engineering, Environmentalists, Architects
Industries: Agri/forestry/mining, Construction

CSA/Clinical Staffing Assoc., LLC
407 Main St., Ste. 204
Metuchen, New Jersey 08840
(732) 321-0088
Fax: (732) 321-0394
Email: main407@aol.com
Web: www.clinicalstaffing.com

Key Contact - Specialty:
Ms. Carole Ornstein - *Pharmaceutical, R&D*

Description: We are a full service organization with expertise in both the permanent and contractural staffing arena. We specialize in providing experienced clinical research professionals to the pharmaceutical and bio-tech industry.
Functions: General mgmt., Healthcare, R&D
Industries: Drugs mfg., Medical devices, Pharmaceutical svcs., Biotech

Culver Personnel Services
6610 Flanders Drive
San Diego, California 92121
(619) 587-4804
Fax: (619) 587-1185

Key Contact - Specialty:
Mr. Timothy J. Culver
Mr. Mike Hobbs
Mr. Ted Hill - *Sales, medical, pharmaceutical products*
Mr. John Weaver - *Sales, software*
Ms. Tami Sullivan - *Retail management, sales, consumer products*

Description: We are a contingency placement service with 21 offices throughout California specializing in sales, management, finance, software and biotechnology.
Functions: Middle mgmt., Mkt. research, Mktg. mgmt., Sales mgmt., Direct mktg., CFO's, MIS mgmt.
Industries: Food/bev/tobacco, Drugs mfg., Retail, Pharmaceutical svcs., Software, Biotech

Cumberland Group Inc.
608 S. Washington St., Ste. 101
Naperville, Illinois 60540
(630) 416-9494
Fax: (630) 416-3250
Email: cgii@inil.com

Key Contact - Specialty:
Mr. Jerry Vogus - *Capital equipment, metals*

Description: We provide executive search for sales, management and marketing on a nationwide basis for industrial companies. Strong emphasis on capital equipment and metals industry.

Salary Minimum: $40,000
Functions: Automation, Mktg. mgmt., Sales mgmt., Engineering
Industries: Metal products, Machinery/Appliances, Test/measurement equip., Misc. mfg., High tech

Cumberland Professional Search Inc.
1210 Churchill Drive
Gallatin, Tennessee 37066
(615) 230-5190
Fax: (615) 230-5192

Key Contact - Specialty:
Ms. Brenda Skelton - *Technical, rubber, engineering, chemical production, plant management*

Description: We are leading recruiters in the rubber industry. Work nationwide with some of the largest companies in the industry. This office is also heavily involved with plastic manufacturing, automotive.

Salary Minimum: $40,000
Functions: Middle mgmt., Production, Automation, Plant mgmt., Quality, Materials Plng., Engineering
Industries: Plastics/rubber

Frank Cuomo & Assoc., Inc.
111 Brook St.
Scarsdale, New York 10583
(914) 723-8001
Fax: (914) 472-0507

Key Contact - Specialty:
Mr. Frank Cuomo

Description: Broad range of services to include executive search and recruitment for service and manufacturing companies. Particular emphasis on sales, marketing, engineering, general management and manufacturing management.

Salary Minimum: $30,000
Functions: Senior mgmt., Plant mgmt., Mktg. mgmt., Sales mgmt., Engineering, Environmentalists, Int'l.
Industries: Energy/utilities, Construction, Metal products, Test/measurement equip., Environmental svcs., Haz. waste

---

Current Resource Group, Inc.
4555 Mansell Rd., Ste. 300
Alpharetta, Georgia 30022
(770) 645-1574
Fax: (770) 645-0874
Email: alexgrp@mindspring.com

Key Contact - Specialty:
Ms. Stacey Barkan - *Computer & technical professionals*
Mr. Vince Brannon

Description: We provide quality targeted selection of exceptional professionals with technical focus. We work closely with clients and candidates to provide placement retention.

Salary Minimum: $28,000
Functions: IT, Systems anal., Systems dev., Systems implem., Systems support, Network admin., DB admin.
Industries: Computer equip., Computer svcs., Human resource svcs., Telecoms, High tech, Software

---

The Currier-Winn Co., Inc.
P.O. Box 902
Cherry Hill, New Jersey 08003-0902
(609) 429-0710
Fax: (609) 429-8086
Email: currierwinn@mindspring.com

Key Contact - Specialty:
Mr. E. H. Bauzenberger, III - *Hardware, software, plastics, metals*

Description: Clients are only Fortune 200 firms in plastics, metal and computer hardware and software industries. We recruit for management, engineering and professional positions on a national basis. We are members of a national network for the past 12 years.

Salary Minimum: $35,000
Functions: Plant mgmt., Quality, Purchasing, Sales mgmt., Personnel, CFO's, Engineering
Industries: Food/bev/tobacco, Chemicals, Drugs mfg., Plastics/rubber, Leather/stone/glass/clay, Metal products, High tech

---

Tony Curtis & Associates
2 Sheppard Ave. E., Ste. 900
North York, Ontario M2N 5Y7
Canada
(416) 224-0500
Fax: (905) 305-1469

Key Contact - Specialty:
Mr. Tony Curtis - *Apparel (manufacturing & sales)*
Mr. Howard Curtis - *Apparel (manufacturing & sales)*

Description: With 19 years experience, we are the preeminent specialists for recruitment of the top professionals in the needle trade. Our fees are contingency based on 10% of annual salary.
Functions: General mgmt., Mfg., Production, Materials, Sales & mktg., Finance, IT
Industries: Mfg., Textiles/apparel, Leather/stone/glass/clay, Wholesale, Retail, Banking

---

Custom Resources
3141 Lorna Rd., Ste. 102
Birmingham, Alabama 35216
(205) 823-5570
Fax: (205) 823-5520
Email: Heather@customresourcesinc.com

Key Contact - Specialty:
Ms. Carolyn Campbell
Ms. Sherry Hartley

Description: Provide human resource services and products customized to meet a company's diverse needs. As human resource professionals, we offer a combination of recruiting, candidate profiling, evaluation services and human resource consulting.
Functions: Sales mgmt., Personnel, Cash mgmt., Credit, Systems dev., Engineering, Architects
Industries: Construction, Banking, Accounting, Human resource svcs., Advertising/PR, Telecoms, Insurance

---

CV Associates
56 N. Broadway
Nyack, New York 10960
(914) 353-3466
Fax: (914) 353-3405
Email: vincecv@aol.com
Web: www.targetsearch.com

Key Contact - Specialty:
Mr. Vince Quiros - *Electronics, high technology*

Description: We strive to fully understand and respect the career needs of the engineers and scientists we serve. We conduct our business according to the highest levels of integrity and professionalism.

Salary Minimum: $50,000
Functions: Mfg., Sales & mktg., R&D, Engineering
Industries: Computer equip., Consumer electronics, Test/measurement equip., Telecoms, Aerospace, High tech, Software

---

Cyberna Assoc. Ltd.
999 de Maisonneuve Blvd. W., Ste. 650
Montreal, Quebec H3A 3L4
Canada
(514) 843-8349
Fax: (514) 843-6993

Key Contact - Specialty:
Ms. Wanda Brown

Description: Recruitment and search, executive contracting, outsourcing, consulting, innovative and customized programs to meet client needs.

Salary Minimum: $50,000
Functions: Generalist
Industries: Generalist

Cybernautic Corp.
P.O. Box 3011
Newtown, Connecticut 06470
(203) 426-6576
Email: jdz1@cybernautic.com
Web: www.cybernautic.com

Key Contact - Specialty:
Mr. David Zincavage - *Information technology, finance*

Description: We specialize in recruiting mid-to-senior information technology and finance executives for national and international positions in the securities trading industry. We are a Bloomberg-approved executive search firm.

Salary Minimum: $45,000
Functions: Finance, IT, Mgmt. consultants, Int'l.
Industries: Finance, High tech, Software

Cyr Associates, Inc.

177 Worcester St., Ste. 303
Wellesley Hills, Massachusetts 02181
(781) 235-5900
Fax: (781) 239-0140
Email: cyrinc@mindspring.com
Web: www.mindspring.com/~cyrinc

Key Contact - Specialty:
Mr. Maury N. Cyr - *Consumer products, direct marketing*

Description: Recruits for client companies in consumer goods and direct marketing including consumer and business-to-business catalog. Expertise in footwear, apparel, textiles, food, giftware, arts, crafts and toys.

Salary Minimum: $40,000
Functions: Product dev., Purchasing, Distribution, Mktg. mgmt., Sales mgmt., Direct mktg., Graphic artists
Industries: Food/bev/tobacco, Textiles/apparel, Soap/perfume/cosmetics, Plastics/rubber, Consumer electronics, Wholesale, Hospitality

D & M Associates

(Firm declined to update.)
245 Cedar Blvd., Ste. 100
Pittsburgh, Pennsylvania 15228
(412) 343-4892

Key Contact - Specialty:
Mr. David Stobbe
Ms. Mickey Stobbe

Description: Specializing in marketing, advertising, banking, real estate, construction and non-profits.

Salary Minimum: $40,000
Functions: Middle mgmt., Advertising, Mktg. mgmt., Minorities, Non-profits, Graphic artists
Industries: Construction, Banking, Communications, Advertising/PR, Publishing, Government, Real estate

D.P. Specialists, Inc.

2141 Rosecrans, Ste. 5100
El Segundo, California 90245
(310) 416-9846
Fax: (310) 416-9003
Email: dps@dpsla.com

Key Contact - Specialty:
Mr. Ed Myers - *Information technology*

Description: As a full service firm recruit all levels of data processing professionals from vice presidents to programmers. Also provide consulting services to all levels specializing in new technologies.

Salary Minimum: $40,000
Functions: MIS mgmt., Systems anal., Systems dev., Systems implem., Systems support
Industries: Energy/utilities, Finance, Misc. financial, Broadcast & Film, Insurance

Charles Dahl Group, Inc.

77-13th St. NE
Minneapolis, Minnesota 55413
(612) 331-7777
Fax: (612) 331-7778
Email: cdahl@cdassoc.com
Web: www.cdassoc.com

Key Contact - Specialty:
Mr. Charles Dahl - *CIO's, CEOs, scientists, diversity, international*
Mr. Thomas Dunlap - *Engineering, MIS, sales*
Ms. Janice Kuschnov - *Engineering, MIS, sales, legal*

Description: Specialize in legal, research and development, high technologies and biotech/gene sequencing industries. Concentration in diversity.

Salary Minimum: $50,000
Functions: Directors, Sales mgmt., Systems implem., R&D, Engineering, Minorities
Industries: Medical devices, Computer equip., Legal, Packaging, High tech, Software, Biotech

Dalton Management Consultants, Ltd.

327 Grove St., Ste. 279
Jersey City, New Jersey 07302
(201) 309-2351
Fax: (201) 309-2351

Key Contact - Specialty:
Ms. Evonne Dalton - *Human resources*

Description: Executive recruiters.

Salary Minimum: $50,000
Functions: Benefits, Personnel, Training
Industries: Generalist

Damon & Assoc., Inc.

7515 Greenville Ave., Ste. 900
Dallas, Texas 75231
(214) 696-6990
Fax: (214) 696-6993
Email: ddamon2@ix.netcom.com

Key Contact - Specialty:
Mr. Richard E. Damon - *Sales, sales management*
Mr. H. M. Hailey - *Sales, sales management*

Description: Sales and sales management: medical, consumer, industrial, software and hardware, contract furniture, office products, information technology, telecommunications and LAN/WAN.

Salary Minimum: $25,000
Functions: Middle mgmt., Materials, Sales & mktg., IT, Specialized services
Industries: Generalist

The Danbrook Group, Inc.

4100 Spring Valley Rd., Ste. 700, LB-2
Dallas, Texas 75244
(972) 392-0057
Fax: (972) 386-1974
Email: dallas@danbrookgroup.com

Key Contact - Specialty:
Mr. Michael Kennedy - *Insurance*
Ms. Sandra Teter - *Accounting, finance*

Description: Specialty search firm delivering high-level client service in four major disciplines. Each department consists of a team dedicated to a targeted, professional approach to search.

Salary Minimum: $30,000
Functions: Generalist, Senior mgmt., Middle mgmt., Finance, CFO's, Budgeting, Taxes
Industries: Generalist, Finance, Accounting, Insurance

Daniel Marks Company

(Firm declined to update.)
5350 E. Livingston Ave., 2nd Floor
Columbus, Ohio 43232
(614) 863-0818
Email: danielcomp@aol.com
Web: www.danielmarks.com

Key Contact - Specialty:
Mr. Daniel M. Lowe - *Manufacturing (general management, middle management)*

Description: Retained search firm for key impact employees in manufacturing arenas. Interim contract professionals in manufacturing and engineering. Management consulting with cost reductions thru lean manufacturing techniques.

Salary Minimum: $40,000
Functions: Senior mgmt., Production, Plant mgmt., Quality, Materials Plng., Benefits, Engineering
Industries: Generalist, Food/bev/tobacco, Plastics/rubber, Metal products, Machinery/Appliances, Motor vehicles, Misc. mfg.

Affiliates:
ICON Management Services

The Danielson Group, Inc.

P.O. Box 50692
Denton, Texas 76206
(817) 383-0700
Fax: (817) 383-0800
Email: txhdhunter@centuryinter.net
Web: www.jobcoach.com

Key Contact - Specialty:
Mr. Michael A. Pajak - *Healthcare, pharmaceuticals, plastics, rubber*

Description: Twenty-five years of executive and technical search/recruitment for both retainer and contingency clients in the rubber, plastics, pharmaceuticals and healthcare industries nationwide, outplacement consulting division and professional jobcoaching.

Salary Minimum: $40,000
Functions: General mgmt., Mfg., Plant mgmt., Quality, Packaging, Allied health, Engineering
Industries: Drugs mfg., Plastics/rubber, Healthcare

Dankowski & Assoc., Inc.
6479 Stoney Ridge Rd., Ste. 200 NE
P.O. Box 39478
North Ridgeville, Ohio 44039-0478
(440) 327-8717
Fax: (440) 327-1853
Email: dankowski@aol.com

Key Contact - Specialty:
Mr. Tom Dankowski - *Human resources*

Description: Local, regional and national recruiter of human resources professionals from $40,000-$150,000. Over 25 years of experience in recruiting, 15 years as specialist in human resources recruiting.

Salary Minimum: $40,000
Functions: HR mgmt., Benefits, Personnel, Training
Industries: Generalist

Dapexs Consultants, Inc.
5320 W. Genesee St.
Camillus, New York 13031
(315) 484-9300
Fax: (315) 484-9330
Email: dapexs@servtech.com
Web: www.servtech.com/~dapexs

Key Contact - Specialty:
Mr. Peter J. Leofsky - *Computer professionals*

Description: Search and placement specialists in MIS, information technology, software engineering and finance/ accounting. We search, screen, select; present only fully qualified candidates. Our exclusive search plan is tailored to fit specific client needs.

Salary Minimum: $30,000
Functions: Materials Plng., Budgeting, MIS mgmt., Systems anal., Systems dev., Systems implem., Systems support
Industries: Generalist

DARE Personnel Inc.
275 Slater St., Ste. 900
Ottawa, Ontario K1P 5H9
Canada
(613) 238-4485
Fax: (613) 236-3754
Email: hr@daregroup.com
Web: www.daregroup.com

Key Contact - Specialty:
Ms. Jocelyne Vitanza - *Executive, information technology, engineering, human resources, financial*
Mr. Andrew Ross - *Executive, sales & marketing, human resources, operational, financial*
Ms. Rose-Marie Sherwood - *Administrative, clerical, aerospace, technical*
Mr. Denis Faubert - *Human resources consulting, job description writing, pay/ benefits, outplacement*

Description: Providing leading edge human resource and technical solutions catered to meet the specific needs of each company we service.
Functions: Senior mgmt., Admin. svcs., Personnel, Credit, Systems anal., Systems dev., Mgmt. consultants
Industries: Banking, Brokers, Human resource svcs., Publishing, New media, Government, High tech

---

Data Search Network, Inc.
21218 St. Andrews Blvd., #611
Boca Raton, Florida 33433
(561) 347-6421
Fax: (561) 347-6429
Email: careers@dsninc.com
Web: www.dsninc.com

Key Contact - Specialty:
Mr. Ken Gross - *Information systems*

Description: Information systems firm serving wide range of clients nationwide. All consultants are principals with direct involvement in the search. Over 15 years experience in information systems search.

Salary Minimum: $50,000
Functions: MIS mgmt., Systems anal., Systems dev., Systems implem., Systems support, Network admin., DB admin.
Industries: Generalist, Misc. mfg., Retail, Finance, Computer svcs., Software

Branches:
P.O. Box 305
Emerson, New Jersey 07630
(201) 967-8600
Fax: (201) 265-0207
Key Contact - Specialty:
Ms. JoAnn Skorupski - *Information systems*

Data-AxIS Corp.
5970 SW 18th St., Ste. 108
Boca Raton, Florida 33433
(561) 487-1423
Fax: (561) 487-0736
Email: info@data-axis.com
Web: www.data-axis.com

Key Contact - Specialty:
Mr. Alan Wade - *Technical*

Description: Executive search, technical recruitment and business management consulting focused on high tech corporate clients.

Salary Minimum: $50,000
Functions: Systems anal., Systems dev., Systems implem., Network admin., DB admin., R&D, Engineering
Industries: Computer equip., Consumer electronics, Computer svcs., Mgmt. consulting, New media, High tech, Software

---

The DataFinders Group, Inc.
25 E. Spring Valley Ave.
Maywood, New Jersey 07607
(201) 845-7700
Fax: (201) 845-7365
Email: postmaster@data-finders.com
Web: www.data-finders.com

Key Contact - Specialty:
Mr. Thomas J. Credidio - *Line sales, computer industry*
Mr. Peter Warns - *Sales management, computer industry*

Description: A nationwide search firm specializing in the data/tele-processing industries in sales, sales management, field support and traditional end user staff consulting/programming positions on both a permanent and temporary basis.

Salary Minimum: $25,000
Functions: Sales mgmt., MIS mgmt., Systems anal., Systems dev., Systems implem., Systems support, Mgmt. consultants
Industries: Computer equip., Computer svcs., Mgmt. consulting, Telecoms, High tech, Software

Affiliates:
DFG Staffing Consultants, Inc.

Datamatics Management Services, Inc.
330 New Brunswick Ave.
Fords, New Jersey 08863
(732) 738-9600
(732) 738-8500
Fax: (732) 738-9603
Email: nch@datamaticsinc.com
Web: datamaticsinc.com

Key Contact - Specialty:
Mr. Norman C. Heinle, Jr.
Mr. R. Kevin Heinle
Mr. R. N. Buteau - *Sales*
Dr. Harry Hanson

Description: Specialists in service related industries, general management, human resources, data processing, information systems, labor relations, training. Placement concerns center on organization fit within existing management structures, evaluating job requirements and formulation position specifications.

Salary Minimum: $40,000
Functions: Generalist, General mgmt., Sales & mktg., HR mgmt., Finance, CFO's, IT
Industries: Generalist

DataPro Personnel Consultants
13355 Noel Rd., Ste. 2001
One Galleria Twr.
Dallas, Texas 75240
(972) 661-8600
Fax: (972) 661-1309
Email: datapro@flash.net
Web: www.ipa.com/datapro

Key Contact - Specialty:
Ms. Donna Schuback - *Information technology*
Mr. Jeff Davis - *Big 6 consultants, ERP, data warehousing*
Ms. Lynn Kollaritsch - *Information technology*

Description: Since our founding in Dallas/Fort Worth in 1970, we have placed more than 4,000 individuals in information technology positions ranging from programmers to top MIS managers.

Salary Minimum: $40,000
Functions: MIS mgmt., Systems anal., Systems dev., Systems implem., Systems support, Network admin., DB admin.
Industries: Generalist

Alan N. Daum & Assoc., Inc.
6241 Riverside Drive
Dublin, Ohio 43017
(614) 793-1200
Fax: (614) 766-9644
Email: al@Adaum.com
Web: www.Adaum.com

Key Contact - Specialty:
Mr. Alan N. Daum - *Process control engineering*

Description: Over 20 years experience recruiting only process control engineers nationally. We have a database of thousands of process control engineers, nationally.

Salary Minimum: $35,000
Functions: Automation, Systems dev., Systems implem., Engineering
Industries: Food/bev/tobacco, Paper, Chemicals, Drugs mfg., Plastics/rubber, Paints/petroleum products, Mgmt. consulting

---

David Anthony Personnel Assoc., Inc.
64 E. Ridgewood Ave.
Paramus, New Jersey 07652
(201) 262-6100
Fax: (201) 262-7744
Email: dferrara@aol.com
Web: www.davidanthony.com

Key Contact - Specialty:
Mr. David K. Ferrara - *Banking, accounting, data processing*

Description: Representing an ever-expanding clientele for the metro NJ and NY region. Our domestic and foreign bank opportunities range from credit analysts to senior executive level, handling all disciplines.

Salary Minimum: $80,000
Functions: IT, MIS mgmt., Systems anal., Systems dev.
Industries: Finance, Banking, Misc. financial, High tech, Software

---

David Perry Assoc.
525 Rte. 73 S., Ste. 201
Marlton, New Jersey 08053
(609) 596-9400
Fax: (609) 596-9125
Email: dauperas@att.net
Web: DavidPerryAssoc.com

Key Contact - Specialty:
Mr. Raymond Spadaro - *Sales, marketing, general management*

Description: Mainly recruit and place candidates in the consumer packaged goods industry. In sales anyone from key account manager to VP of sales. In marketing - brand managers to general managers.

Salary Minimum: $55,000
Functions: Middle mgmt., Mkt. research, Mktg. mgmt., Sales mgmt.
Industries: Food/bev/tobacco, Textiles/apparel, Soap/perfume/cosmetics, Drugs mfg., Entertainment, Telecoms

---

Davidson, Laird & Assoc.
29260 Franklin Rd., Ste. 110
Southfield, Michigan 48034
(810) 358-2160
Fax: (810) 358-1225
Email: mlaird@rust.net

Key Contact - Specialty:
Ms. Meri Laird - *Automotive, plastics engineering*
Ms. Lori Dow - *Manufacturing*

Description: We have an excellent reputation for long term retention of our candidates with our clients. We attribute that to our team approach to matching and full service placement with our clients.

Salary Minimum: $35,000
Functions: Product dev., Production, Automation, Plant mgmt., Quality, Purchasing, Engineering
Industries: Generalist, Plastics/rubber, Motor vehicles

Allen Davis & Assoc.
P.O. Box 2007
Amherst, Massachusetts 01004-2007
(413) 253-0600
Fax: (413) 253-3535
Email: inbox@softwarejobs.com
Web: www.softwarejobs.com

Key Contact - Specialty:
Mr. Allen Davis - *IT Consulting*

Description: Permanent and contract. We reach thousands of candidates via our WWW home page which lists many of our current search assignments. Specialties include SAP, Baan, Peoplesoft, JD Edwards, Oracle applications, Data Warehousing, C++/Windows, and internet.
Functions: MIS mgmt., Systems anal., Systems dev., Systems implem., Systems support, DB admin.
Industries: Generalist, Computer svcs., Mgmt. consulting, High tech, Software

Branches:
Cambridge Business Center
432 Columbia Street, Ste. B-15
Cambridge, Massachusetts 02141
(617) 252-3343
Fax: (617) 252-3363
Key Contact - Specialty:
Mr. Daniel Canala-Parola

Davis & James, Inc.
14377 Woodlake Drive, Ste. 312
Chesterfield, Missouri 63017
(314) 205-1228
Fax: (314) 205-0086
Email: jlpdavis@inlink.com

Key Contact - Specialty:
Mr. Jerry Paetzhold - *Banking, financial institutions, financial services, securities*

Description: Specializing in search and recruiting for technical and management personnel for engineering and manufacturing positions. A second division specializes in banking and financial positions.

Salary Minimum: $35,000
Functions: Personnel, Cash mgmt., M&A
Industries: Finance, Banking, Invest. banking, Brokers

Donna Davis Assoc.

530 Main St., Ste. 4
Ft. Lee, New Jersey 07024
(201) 592-6000
Fax: (201) 592-0701

Key Contact - Specialty:
Ms. Donna Davis - *Human resources*
Ms. Leslie Martin - *Human resources*

Description: We are a national recruiting firm exclusively dedicated to placing mid and senior level human resource professionals.

Salary Minimum: $50,000
Functions: HR mgmt., Benefits, Personnel, Training
Industries: Generalist

Carolyn Davis Assoc., Inc.

701 Westchester Ave.
White Plains, New York 10604
(914) 682-7040
Fax: (914) 682-8361

Key Contact - Specialty:
Ms. Carolyn Davis - *Insurance*

Description: We specialize in the recruitment of property and casualty, life, health and pension professionals. Our commitment to excellence combined with integrity, respect for confidentiality, experience and knowledge of the insurance industry assures a successful search.
Industries: Insurance

Bert Davis Publishing Placement Consultants

425 Madison Ave., Ste. 14A
New York, New York 10017
(212) 838-4000
Email: bdavis2289@aol.com

Key Contact - Specialty:
Ms. Sally Dougan - *Book publishing*
Ms. Wendy Baker - *Magazine industry*
Mr. Larry Eidelberg - *Technology*
Ms. Linda Rascher - *Financial*

Description: A leading executive placement firm specializing in publishing, publication communication, information and electronic media fields.

Salary Minimum: $50,000
Functions: General mgmt., Senior mgmt., Product dev., Sales & mktg., Finance, IT
Industries: Advertising/PR, Publishing, New media, Software

Davis-Smith, Inc.

27656 Franklin Rd.
Southfield, Michigan 48034
(248) 354-4100
Fax: (248) 354-6702

Key Contact - Specialty:
Mr. Charles C. Corbett - *Executive*
Ms. Karen Hogan - *Medical staffing (temporary & permanent)*

Description: A full service human resources firm for the medical profession. Services include search, staffing, locum tenens and consulting.
Functions: Physicians, Nurses, Allied health, Health admin.
Industries: Healthcare

The Dayton Group, Ltd.

32 Broadway, Ste. 1212
New York, New York 10004
(212) 344-9120
Fax: (212) 344-9114
Web: www.websiteint.com/193784

Key Contact - Specialty:
Mr. Mal Stevens - *Pensions/401(K)*

Description: Our area of specialty expertise is the recruitment of 401(K) recordkeepers/DC w/wo DB from senior management levels involved in 401(K) conversion/systems implementation to plan administrators, exempt and non-exempt level.

Salary Minimum: $35,000
Functions: Directors, Middle mgmt., Admin. svcs., Benefits, Cash mgmt., Systems implem., Mgmt. consultants
Industries: Invest. banking, Brokers, Misc. financial, Mgmt. consulting, Human resource svcs., Insurance, Healthcare

---

DBC Recruiting Network

5672 Peachtree Pkwy., Ste. E
Norcross, Georgia 30092
(770) 729-0990
Fax: (770) 729-1183
Email: dbc-jobs@mindspring.com

Key Contact - Specialty:
Mrs. Debbie Brooks - *Computer sales, high technology sales*

Description: Executive recruiting in the computer industry, including sales, marketing, sales management and technical support, with a nationwide network of affiliates, including the First Interview Recruiting Network.
Functions: Senior mgmt., Middle mgmt., Sales mgmt., Systems anal., Systems dev., Systems implem., Network admin.
Industries: Computer equip., Computer svcs., Telecoms, High tech, Software

---

DBL Associates

1334 Park View Ave., Ste. 100
Manhattan Beach, California 90266
(310) 546-8121
Fax: (310) 546-8122
Email: davelong@ix.netcom.com

Key Contact - Specialty:
Mr. David B. Long - *MBAs, CPAs*

Description: Placement of CPA's, MBA's in financial, accounting, tax and MIS positions. Client base: financial services, high tech, healthcare, manufacturing, distribution and entertainment. Over fifteen years experience in Southern California.

Salary Minimum: $60,000
Functions: Senior mgmt., CFO's, Budgeting, M&A, MIS mgmt., Mgmt. consultants
Industries: Generalist, Food/bev/tobacco, Misc. mfg., Entertainment, High tech, Software, Healthcare

---

DCA Professional Search

437 Ridge Point Drive
Lewisville, Texas 75067
(972) 315-2934
Fax: (972) 315-2334
Email: DCA777@aol.com

Key Contact - Specialty:
Ms. Doris Aguirre - *Hispanic advertising & hispanic marketing*

Description: Specialization in marketing and advertising professionals dealing with the hispanic marketplace. This includes all facets of advertising such as creatives, account service, media, promotions, marketing and public relations on the client level.

Salary Minimum: $30,000
Functions: Sales & mktg., Advertising, Mktg. mgmt., PR
Industries: Generalist, Communications, Advertising/PR

Dean-Dzierzawiec Assoc.

72 W. End Ave.
Somerville, New Jersey 08876
(908) 575-0010
Fax: (908) 575-0155
Email: deanja@aol.com

Key Contact - Specialty:
Mr. James L. Dean - *Human resources, information technology*
Mr. Kenneth J. Dzierzawiec - *Human resources*

Description: Specialists in human resources/personnel.

Salary Minimum: $60,000
Functions: HR mgmt., Benefits, Personnel, Training, IT
Industries: Generalist

Debbon Recruiting Group, Inc.
P.O. Box 510323
St. Louis, Missouri 63151
(314) 846-9101
Email: DebbonGrop@aol.com

Key Contact - Specialty:
Mr. John Zipfel - *Food, pharmaceutical (staff, line management, technical positions)*

Description: Recruiting specialization since 1978 in technical, staff and line management positions for food and pharmaceutical industries has resulted in industry-wide contacts allowing for timely response to individual situations.

Salary Minimum: $30,000
Functions: Middle mgmt., Plant mgmt., Quality, Packaging, Personnel, R&D, Engineering
Industries: Food/bev/tobacco, Soap/perfume/cosmetics, Drugs mfg.

DeCaster Assoc.
1346 Wren Lane
Green Bay, Wisconsin 54313
(920) 499-6005
Fax: (920) 499-6023
Email: pdecaster@aol.com
Web: www.ipa.com/eoffice/920-499-6005.html

Key Contact - Specialty:
Mr. Paul DeCaster - *Legal, executive management*

Description: We offer professional search and recruiting services for corporation and law firms. Focused in attorneys (all practice areas) and executive management.

Salary Minimum: $75,000
Functions: Directors, Senior mgmt., Legal, Mktg. mgmt., CFO's, MIS mgmt., Attorneys
Industries: Generalist

DeCorrevont & Assoc.
233 S. Kenilworth Ave.
Oak Park, Illinois 60302
(708) 445-1199
Fax: (708) 445-0248
Email: jdecor@earthlink.net

Key Contact - Specialty:
Mr. James DeCorrevont - *High technology, software, healthcare*

Description: Recruiting and search for the healthcare: sales/marketing and tech professions.

Salary Minimum: $40,000
Functions: Health admin., Sales mgmt., Non-profits
Industries: Non-profits, Computer svcs., Insurance, Software, Healthcare

---

Deeco Int'l.
710 Aspen Heights Drive
P.O. Box 57033
Salt Lake City, Utah 84157
(801) 261-3326
Fax: (801) 261-3955
Web: deecointernationalinc@worldnet.att.net

Key Contact - Specialty:
Ms. Dee McBride - *Medical*

Description: 20 years experience in medical products marketing, sales, engineering and research.
Functions: Senior mgmt., Middle mgmt., Product dev., Mkt. research, Mktg. mgmt., Sales mgmt., R&D
Industries: Drugs mfg., Medical devices, Computer equip., Pharmaceutical svcs., High tech, Biotech, Healthcare

---

DEL Technical Services, Inc.
P.O. Box 4101
Wheaton, Illinois 60189
(630) 752-1471
Fax: (630) 752-1401
Email: deltech@mcs.com
Web: www.mcs.net/~deltech/

Key Contact - Specialty:
Ms. Dee Lalagos - *Technical, engineers, technicians, information technology*

Description: Skill match, as proven process used to match the critical success factors of your ideal candidate with over 100,000 personnel that are not in the job market.

Salary Minimum: $25,000
Functions: Production, IT, Systems dev., Systems implem., Systems support, Engineering, Technicians
Industries: Energy/utilities, Construction, Mfg., Computer svcs., Haz. waste, High tech, Software

---

Delacore Resources
101 Park Place, Ste. 205
Hutchinson, Minnesota 55350
(320) 587-4420
Fax: (320) 587-7252
Email: delacore@hutchtel.net

Key Contact - Specialty:
Mr. Verne Meyer - *Physicians, physician's assistants, nurse practitioners*

Description: Two divisions: 1.) Physician recruiting (most subspecialty areas). 2.) Allied healthcare professions.

Salary Minimum: $40,000
Functions: Physicians, Allied health
Industries: Healthcare

DeLalla - Fried Assoc.
201 E. 69th St., Ste. 4K
New York, New York 10021
(212) 879-9100
Fax: (212) 472-8963

Key Contact - Specialty:
Ms. Barbara DeLalla - *Consumer packaged goods, service industries*
Ms. Ann Fried - *Consumer packaged goods, service industries*

Description: Eighteen years of specialization in the consumer packaged goods and service industries. Provide executive talent on a full time and project consultant basis.

Salary Minimum: $50,000
Functions: Directors, Middle mgmt., Advertising, Mkt. research, Mktg. mgmt., Minorities
Industries: Food/bev/tobacco, Soap/perfume/cosmetics, Entertainment, Advertising/PR

Delta Management Group Ltd.
55 St. Clair Ave. W., Ste. 230
Toronto, Ontario M4V 2Y7
Canada
(416) 925-2005
Fax: (416) 925-8367
Email: gavin@deltamanagement.com
Web: deltamanagement.com

Key Contact - Specialty:
Mr. Gavin Pitchford - *Data networking (sales, technical, executives, marketing)*
Ms. Lynda Chalmers - *Computer/telephony integration, voice networking (sales, technical, executives, marketing)*

Description: A vertical market niche firm, we focus on the networking (data/voice) communications, software and CTI industries. Clients include most market leading vendors (sales, engineers, etc.) and large end-users (executive/technical).

Salary Minimum: $60,000
Functions: Senior mgmt., Mktg. mgmt., Sales mgmt., MIS mgmt., Systems implem., Systems support, Mgmt. consultants
Industries: Computer equip., Banking, Computer svcs., Broadcast & Film, Telecoms, High tech, Software

---

Delta Medical Search Assoc.
615 Rome-Hilliard Rd., Ste. 107
Columbus, Ohio 43228-9475
(614) 878-0550
Email: associates@deltasearch.com
Web: www.deltasearch.com

Key Contact - Specialty:
Ms. Marilyn Wallace

Description: Recruitment of physicians, nurses, licensed healthcare professionals and management personnel for hospitals, clinics and private practices. All our account executives have a medical background to better understand and service your needs.

Salary Minimum: $50,000
Functions: Physicians, Nurses, Allied health, Health admin.
Industries: Healthcare

Delta ProSearch

P.O. Box 267
Delta, Pennsylvania 17314-0267
(717) 456-7172
(800) 753-6693
Fax: (717) 456-7593
Email: deltapro@gte.net

Key Contact - Specialty:
Mr. John Banister - *Pharmacy, managed care, allied health*

Description: We are experienced healthcare professionals with a good knowledge of the industry. Our high standards emphasize quality service, choice referrals and client satisfaction. We specialize in managed care, pharmacy and other allied healthcare recruiting.

Salary Minimum: $30,000
Functions: Allied health
Industries: Healthcare

Delta Resource Group, Ltd.

P.O. Box 672642
Marietta, Georgia 30006
(770) 952-1169
Email: jharmonldelta@mindspring.com

Key Contact - Specialty:
Mr. Jerry Harmon - *Oracle, PeopleSoft, software, telecommunications, high technology*

Description: Practice focuses on information technology and telecommunications, with emphasis on computer networks, data communications and consulting (Big 6 and national firms) engaged in software implementation for a range of applications utilizing Peoplesoft and Oracle.

Salary Minimum: $45,000
Functions: HR mgmt., IT, MIS mgmt., Systems anal., Systems dev., Systems implem., Mgmt. consultants
Industries: Computer equip., Computer svcs., Telecoms, High tech, Software

---

DeMatteo Associates

P.O. Box 13955
Albany, New York 12212
(518) 356-3900
Fax: (800) 477-8205
Email: rnatodma@albany.net

Key Contact - Specialty:
Ms. Robena DeMatteo - *Sales & marketing, insurance (to include claims), loss control & underwriting, information technology*
Mr. Robert Natowitz - *Engineering, manufacturing, design, management, sales, applications engineering*
Mr. Ryan Flatt

Description: Full-service custom executive search firm. Qualified candidates in sales, engineering and management. Specialize in industrial, manufacturing, insurance markets and information technology. National searches for clients in the United States and Canada.
Functions: Generalist, Mfg., Materials, Sales & mktg., IT, Engineering
Industries: Generalist, Mfg., Svcs., Communications, Insurance, Software

---

Derek Associates, Inc.

P.O. Box 13
Mendon, Massachusetts 01756-0013
(508) 883-2289
Fax: (508) 883-2264
Email: joren@kersur.net

Key Contact - Specialty:
Mr. Joren Fishback - *Environmental*

Description: Specialize in recruiting and placing environmental professionals including geologists, hydrogeologists, industrial hygienists, environmental, chemical and air quality engineers, hazardous waste specialists, business development and technical sales professionals.

Salary Minimum: $40,000
Functions: Engineering, Environmentalists
Industries: Environmental svcs., Haz. waste

Descheneaux Recruitment Services Ltd.

#1700 - 750 W. Pender St.
Vancouver, British Columbia V6C 2T8
Canada
(604) 669-9787
Fax: (604) 688-2130

Key Contact - Specialty:
Ms. Pat Descheneaux - *Insurance*
Ms. Dawn Copeland - *Insurance*
Ms. Carolyn Quinlin - *Insurance*

Description: Serving exclusively the needs of the insurance industry providing assistance in recruiting and hiring at all levels of executive, technical, sales and support staff. We bring talent and opportunity together.
Functions: Senior mgmt., Middle mgmt., Admin. svcs., MIS mgmt., Systems anal., Systems dev., Systems implem.
Industries: Brokers, Misc. financial, Insurance

Desktop Staffing, Inc.

1904 Capri, Ste. 100
Schaumburg, Illinois 60193
(847) 352-4340
Fax: (847) 352-6441
Email: info@deskstaff.com

Key Contact - Specialty:
Ms. Cindy Caravello - *Graphic arts, editorial*

Description: Graphic arts and editorial positions for all industries and levels of positions.

Salary Minimum: $25,000
Functions: Advertising, Mktg. mgmt., Direct mktg., PR, Network admin., DB admin., Graphic artists
Industries: Misc. mfg., Advertising/PR, Publishing, Packaging, High tech, Software, Healthcare

---

Despres & Associates

(Firm declined to update.)
117 S. Cook St., Ste. 304
Barrington, Illinois 60010
(847) 382-0625
Email: rdespres@sprynet.com
Web: www.chicweb.com/despres

Key Contact - Specialty:
Mr. Raoul Despres - *Sales, sales management, general management*
Ms. Suzzett Despres - *Healthcare*

Description: We offer credibility (30 years in industry), added value and related sales/sales management consulting and/or training.
Functions: Automation, Sales mgmt., Systems implem., Systems support
Industries: Computer equip., Computer svcs., New media, Telecoms, High tech, Software, Healthcare

---

The Devlin Search Group, Inc.

451 Andover Street, Suite 170
North Andover, Massachusetts 01845
(978) 725-8000
Fax: (978) 725-8200
Email: devlinsearchgroup@usa.net
Web: www.staffing.net/dsginc.htm

Key Contact - Specialty:
Mr. Jack Devlin - *Sales, marketing, marketing communications, year 2000 related disciplines*
Mr. Greg Therizien - *Sales, marketing, marketing communications, year 2000 related disciplines*

Description: We specialize in contingency, contract and retained placement of: sales, marketing, marcom, consultants, technologists, software engineers and selling support professionals for the information systems, software, hardware industries. We offer to our clients and candidates: experience, recruiting, effective assessment and national reach.

Salary Minimum: $50,000
Functions: General mgmt., Mfg., Sales & mktg., IT, Mgmt. consultants, Technicians
Industries: Computer equip., Mgmt. consulting, Advertising/PR, Telecoms, Government, Aerospace, Software

---

Devoto & Assoc.

790 Knoll Drive
San Carlos, California 94070
(650) 593-8205
Fax: (650) 593-8206
Email: devoto-associates@worldnet.att.net

Key Contact - Specialty:
Ms. Andrea Devoto - *Software sales*

Description: Specializes in software sales professionals only.

Salary Minimum: $55,000
Functions: Sales mgmt., Direct mktg.
Industries: Software

Diamond Tax Recruiting

2 Pennsylvania Plaza, Ste. 1985
New York, New York 10121
(212) 695-4220
Fax: (212) 695-4053
Email: dtrassoc@aol.com

Key Contact - Specialty:
Mr. Steven Hunter - *Taxation, attorneys & non-attorneys*

Description: Twenty years of experience specializing within the tax profession. The largest and most comprehensive database of experienced tax professionals within the New York metropolitan area.

Salary Minimum: $50,000
Functions: Taxes
Industries: Generalist, Food/bev/tobacco, Banking, Invest. banking, Entertainment, Broadcast & Film, Insurance

---

Roger Dietsch & Assoc.

10706 107th Place, Ste. 204
Maple Grove, Minnesota 55369
(612) 424-8619

Key Contact - Specialty:
Mr. Roger A. Dietsch - *Insurance (group and individual), managed care, reinsurance, executive, marketing & sales*
Ms. Audrey D. Haugen - *Insurance (individual & group), marketing, underwriting, claim, administrative*
Mr. G. A. Crabtree - *Consumer products, general management, marketing & sales*

Description: Comprehensive knowledge of life and group insurance, managed care and specialty insurance areas such as reinsurance, special risk, direct response and other insurance specialty areas.

Salary Minimum: $60,000
Functions: Generalist, Senior mgmt., Middle mgmt., Health admin., Direct mktg., Mgmt. consultants, Int'l.
Industries: Medical devices, Machinery/Appliances, Misc. financial, Advertising/PR, Insurance, Healthcare

---

Direct Marketing Resources

2915 Providence Rd., Ste. 230
Charlotte, North Carolina 28211
(704) 365-5890
Fax: (704) 365-5892
Email: dan@dmresources.com
Web: www.dmresources.com

Key Contact - Specialty:
Mr. Dan Sullivan - *Database marketing*
Ms. Dawn Darcy - *Database marketing*
Ms. Rene Welti - *Account management*

Description: National search firm specializing exclusively in the direct marketing industry. Functional area's include database marketing, research and analysis, account management, product management and creative.

Salary Minimum: $60,000
Functions: Direct mktg., DB admin.

Direct Marketing Solutions

1972 U.S. 60E
Salem, Kentucky 42078-9365
(502) 988-4888
Fax: (502) 988-4887

Key Contact - Specialty:
Mr. Thomas A. Ingala - *Direct marketing, database marketing*

Description: Recruit and place direct marketing sales, sales support and marketing professionals nationally. Specialize in production firms: DP service bureaus, lettershops, full service firms, direct response advertising agencies and database marketing firms.

Functions: Advertising, Mktg. mgmt., Sales mgmt., Direct mktg., Customer svc.

Direct Recruiters, Inc.

24100 Chagrin Blvd., Ste. 450
Beachwood, Ohio 44122
(216) 464-5570
Fax: (216) 464-7567
Email: dri@directrecruiters.com
Web: www.directrecruiters.com

Key Contact - Specialty:
Mr. Sheldon Myeroff - *Automatic identification, data collection*
Ms. Gina Petrello-Pray - *Industrial, manufacturing software*
Mr. Michael Rossen - *Material handling, packaging*

Functions: Sales mgmt.
Industries: Mfg., Wholesale, Packaging, High tech, Software

Discovery, The Staffing Specialists, Inc.

101 W. Grand Ave., Ste. 200
Chicago, Illinois 60610
(773) 529-7361
Fax: (773) 529-7363
Email: Discovery-Gail@worldnet.att.net
Web: www.discovery-staffing.com

Key Contact - Specialty:
Ms. Gail Sanders - *Banking, finance*

Description: Specialize in 1) banking and finance, 2) real estate lending, 3) credit, collection and customer service, 4) information technology and, 5) executive and administrative support in almost every industry.
Functions: Senior mgmt., Middle mgmt., Health admin., CFO's, Credit, Risk mgmt.
Industries: Banking, Invest. banking, Brokers, Misc. financial, Mgmt. consulting, Real estate, High tech

Branches:
865 S. Figueroa, Ste. 3030
Los Angeles, California 90017
(213) 362-0755
Key Contact - Specialty:
Ms. Rita Adler - *Banking, finance*

1820 Orangewood Ave., Ste. 204
Orange, California 92668
(714) 385-8165
Key Contact - Specialty:
Ms. Cydney McFarlan - *Banking, finance*

3519 Silverside Rd., Ridgely Bldg., Ste. 102

Wilmington, Delaware 19810
(302) 477-0680
Fax: (302) 477-1236
Key Contact - Specialty:
Ms. Cindy James - *Banking, finance*

5001 LBJ Frwy., Ste. 935
Dallas, Texas 75244
(972) 726-7999
Key Contact - Specialty:
Ms. Patti Smith - *Banking, finance*

DiTech Resources
175 N. Main St.
Branford, Connecticut 06405
(203) 483-4360
Fax: (203) 483-4361
Email: DiTech@worldnet.att.net

Key Contact - Specialty:
Ms. Diane Brecciaroli - *Engineering, technical*

Description: We specialize in the placement of technical professionals. My firm is characterized by highly skilled professionalism and caring for all individuals that come in contact with us.

Salary Minimum: $40,000
Functions: Product dev., Automation, Quality, Sales mgmt., Systems dev., R&D, Engineering
Industries: Generalist, Printing, Consumer electronics, Test/measurement equip., Misc. mfg., High tech, Software

---

Diversified Consulting Services, Inc.
P.O. Box 130
Evergreen, Colorado 80437-0130
(303) 670-5482
Fax: (303) 674-3671
Email: headhnts@ix.netcom.com

Key Contact - Specialty:
Ms. Susan F. Baker - *Information technology, sales, recruiters, management*
Mr. Chet Baker - *High tech, telecommunications, internet, VAR's, networking*

Description: We are a contingency fee based technical recruiting company specializing in sales, marketing and engineering in high tech and information technology companies.

Salary Minimum: $40,000
Functions: Mfg., Sales & mktg., Mktg. mgmt., Sales mgmt., IT, MIS mgmt., Engineering
Industries: Mfg., Medical devices, Computer equip., Computer svcs., Telecoms, High tech, Biotech

---

Diversified Management Resources
1020 N. Milwaukee Ave.
Deerfield, Illinois 60015
(847) 537-5660

Key Contact - Specialty:
Mr. Frank Wolowicz - *Accounting & finance*

Description: National firm specializing in all areas of accounting, finance and financial systems development and implementation. Scope includes audit, cost, tax, reporting and analysis, treasury, general, etc. Staff level to upper management.

Salary Minimum: $40,000
Functions: Finance
Industries: Generalist

Dixie Search Assoc.
(a division of The Fill Corporation)
501 Village Trace, Bldg. 9
Marietta, Georgia 30067
(770) 850-0250
Fax: (770) 850-9295
Email: dsa@mindspring.com
Web: www.mindspring.com/~dsa/

Key Contact - Specialty:
Mr. Clifford G. Fill
Ms. Ellyn H. Fill

Description: Leading international search firm working exclusively in the food, beverage and hospitality industries. Search services are unique and broad based in all facets of the industries served.

Salary Minimum: $35,000
Functions: Middle mgmt., Production, Distribution, Sales mgmt., CFO's, R&D, Engineering
Industries: Agri/forestry/mining, Food/bev/tobacco, Transportation, Wholesale, Retail, Hospitality, Packaging

---

DNA Search, Inc.
16133 Ventura Blvd., Ste. 805
Encino, California 91436
(818) 986-6300
Fax: (818) 981-1105
Email: search@dnamedical.com
Web: www.dnamedical.com

Key Contact - Specialty:
Mr. Daniel Leevy - *Healthcare*
Ms. Sandra Smith - *Healthcare*

Description: President has 23 years of experience in search and recruitment. We specialize in clinical and management placement in the healthcare industry. Our placements are nationwide.

Salary Minimum: $50,000
Functions: Nurses, Health admin., Advertising, Mkt. research, Benefits, CFO's, Cash mgmt.
Industries: Medical devices, Hospitality, Pharmaceutical svcs., Mgmt. consulting, Human resource svcs., Healthcare
Professional Associations: IACPR

Doering & Assoc.
144 Hathaway Ave.
Freedom, California 95019-0030
(408) 728-1293
Email: LDoeringES@aol.com
Web: www.louis.doerings.com

Key Contact - Specialty:
Mr. Louis Doering - *Senior management*

Description: Specializing in fast strategic placements since 1978! Focus: high-tech, leading-edge, top performers. CPM/PERT/JIT fast-track systems.

Salary Minimum: $25,000
Functions: Generalist, Senior mgmt., Mktg. mgmt., Finance, IT, R&D, Int'l.
Industries: Generalist, Agri/forestry/mining, Mfg., Finance, Communications, High tech, Software

---

Doherty Healthcare Consultants
P.O. Box 4514
Portland, Maine 04112-4514
(207) 767-2089
Fax: (207) 767-1675
Email: dhc@maine.rr.com

Key Contact - Specialty:
Mr. Shawn Doherty - *Physicians, healthcare*
Mr. David Foster - *Physicians, healthcare*
Ms. Jennifer Corkum - *Physicians, nurses, physical therapists*

Description: We are an executive search and placement firm dedicated to the recruitment of physicians and other healthcare professionals throughout the country.

Salary Minimum: $50,000
Functions: Physicians, Nurses, Allied health, Health admin.

Don Allan Assoc., Inc.
P.O. Box 12988
La Jolla, California 92039-2988
(619) 587-4800
Fax: (619) 587-4810
Email: dasearch@ix.netcom.com

Key Contact - Specialty:
Mr. David Adler - *Technical sales management, marketing management*

Description: Executive search to the information systems, interactive/multimedia and medical/healthcare industries. Primary focus on management, marketing, sales, technical support and consulting. An unbundled approach to the entire search process.

Salary Minimum: $60,000
Functions: Directors, Senior mgmt., Middle mgmt., Sales mgmt., MIS mgmt., Systems implem., Mgmt. consultants

Industries: Computer equip., Computer svcs., Mgmt. consulting, Broadcast & Film, Telecoms, High tech, Software

J P Donnelly Assoc., Inc.

420 Lexington Ave., Ste. 300
New York, New York 10170
(212) 972-9696
Fax: (516) 868-3642

Key Contact - Specialty:
Mr. John P. Donnelly - *Computer, Wall Street*

Description: Concentration of clients represented in N.Y. metropolitan and New England areas with an emphasis on Wall Street and computer careers. Computerized applicant tracking system.

Salary Minimum: $40,000
Functions: Cash mgmt., MIS mgmt., Systems anal., Systems dev., Systems implem., Systems support, Mgmt. consultants
Industries: Finance, Banking, Invest. banking, Misc. financial, Computer svcs., High tech

Branches:
P.O. Box 403
Bellmore, New York 11710-0403
(516) 739-8620
Fax: (516) 868-3642
Key Contact - Specialty:
Mr. John P. Donnelly - *Computer, Wall Street*

The Donnelly Group-Sales Recruiters, Inc.

745 Craig Rd., Ste. 210
St. Louis, Missouri 63141
(314) 991-9191
Fax: (314) 991-8911
Email: donnellyy@aol.com

Key Contact - Specialty:
Mr. Dan Donnelly - *Sales, sales management (industrial, pharmaceutical & medical)*
Ms. Robin Holder - *Medical capital equipment, disposables*

Description: Specializes in sales and marketing positions. 1-5 years experience through national sales management levels. Very strong contacts in the Midwest with national capabilities.

Salary Minimum: $35,000
Functions: Sales mgmt.
Industries: Drugs mfg., Medical devices, Plastics/rubber, Metal products, Machinery/Appliances, Telecoms, Software

The Dorfman Group

12005 E. Mission Lane
Scottsdale, Arizona 85259
(602) 860-8820
Fax: (602) 860-0888
Email: dorfgrp@getnet.com
Web: www.getnet.com/dorfman

Key Contact - Specialty:
Mr. Michael Flamer - *Material handling, logistics, packaging equipment*

Description: In-depth knowledge of the industries served. President of MHMS. Have personal relationships with the leaders of the industry.

Salary Minimum: $55,000
Functions: Middle mgmt., Automation, Purchasing, Distribution, Sales mgmt., Systems implem., Engineering
Industries: Food/bev/tobacco, Metal products, Machinery/Appliances, Misc. mfg., Packaging

Dorst Information Services, Inc.

821 Franklin Ave., Ste. 309
Garden City, New York 11530
(516) 294-0884
Fax: (516) 747-8873
Email: dorstm@aol.com

Key Contact - Specialty:
Mr. Martin Dorst - *Consulting, software, telecommunications, hardware, professional services*

Description: Executive search/high technology, sales/technical marketing, domestic/international packages 200k-500k. Consulting, software, telco, hardware, professional services.

Salary Minimum: $100,000
Functions: Directors, Senior mgmt., Middle mgmt., Sales mgmt., MIS mgmt., Systems anal., Mgmt. consultants
Industries: New media, Telecoms, High tech, Software

The Doty Group

P.O. Box 222032
Dallas, Texas 75222-2032
(214) 660-0606
Fax: (214) 660-0707
Email: edoty@worldnet.att.net

Key Contact - Specialty:
Ms. Eleanor C. Doty - *Human resources, finance, accounting*

Description: We provide specialized executive search founded on extensive corporate management experience and successful industry - specific recruiting with major financial services and telecommunications companies.
Functions: HR mgmt., Finance, IT
Industries: Transportation, Finance, Communications, Software

Dougherty & Assoc.

2345 Ashford Drive
Chattanooga, Tennessee 37421
(423) 899-1060
Fax: (423) 855-5138
Email: bobbydoc@aol.com

Key Contact - Specialty:
Mr. Robert E. Dougherty - *Chemical sales*

Description: Specialized in sales, engineering and product management positions in specialty chemicals with over 25 years in recruiting, sales and as a hiring field manager in the water treatment industry.

Salary Minimum: $35,000
Functions: Sales mgmt., Customer svc., Engineering
Industries: Energy/utilities, Food/bev/tobacco, Textiles/apparel, Paper, Chemicals, Paints/petroleum products

Dow Consultants Int'l.

370 Lexington Ave., Ste. 1407
New York, New York 10017
(212) 953-4800
Fax: (212) 953-3611
Email: Idow@aol.com

Key Contact - Specialty:
Mr. Ian James Dow - *Commercial banking, investment banking*

Description: A contingency and retainer based search firm specializing in middle to senior level assignments in investment and commercial banking.

Salary Minimum: $75,000
Functions: M&A, Risk mgmt., Int'l.
Industries: Banking, Invest. banking

Downing & Downing, Inc.

7757 Auburn Rd., Unit 9
Concord, Ohio 44077
(440) 357-1996
Fax: (440) 357-1995
Email: info@downing-downing.com
Web: www.downing-downing.com

Key Contact - Specialty:
Mr. Gus Downing - *Loss prevention/audit*
Ms. Jacqueline Downing - *Loss prevention/audit*

Description: With over forty years of loss prevention and recruiting experience we offer the most effective network of individuals in the retail loss prevention (security) and audit industries in the nation.

Salary Minimum: $25,000
Functions: Generalist, Risk mgmt.
Industries: Retail, Law enfcmt.

Drake & Assoc.
4400 Park Newport
Newport Beach, California 92660
(714) 718-0687

Key Contact - Specialty:
Ms. Mary Ann Schuessler

Description: Confidential searches are a specialty.

Salary Minimum: $50,000
Functions: Finance, IT, Attorneys
Industries: Finance, Legal, Real estate, High tech, Software

Dreier Consulting
P.O. Box 356
10 S. Franklin Tnpk.
Ramsey, New Jersey 07446
(201) 327-1113
Fax: (201) 327-0816
Email: dreiercslt@mindspring.com
Web: www.dreierconsulting.com

Key Contact - Specialty:
Mr. John S. Dreier - *Medical (technical & marketing), telecommunications, electronics, data communications*

Description: Professional and management recruiters for high tech industries. Clients manufacture and/or distribute medical, telecommunications, instrumentation, controls, process and automation equipment. Friendly, professional staff with 40 years experience.

Salary Minimum: $40,000
Functions: Mkt. research, Mktg. mgmt., Sales mgmt., Systems dev., Network admin., Engineering, Technicians
Industries: Medical devices, Computer equip., Consumer electronics, Test/measurement equip., Telecoms, High tech, Software

Drummond Assoc., Inc.
50 Broadway, Ste. 1201
New York, New York 10004
(212) 248-1120
Fax: (212) 248-1171
Email: chetdas@aol.com

Key Contact - Specialty:
Mr. Chester A. Fienberg - *Information technology, consulting*
Mr. Donald Mochwart - *Capital markets, operations*

Description: We serve NYC Wall Street firms, money center banks and financial consulting firms. Coverage includes middle/upper positions in capital markets including quantitative analysis, corporate finance, consulting and operations.

Salary Minimum: $40,000
Functions: Admin. svcs., CFO's, Cash mgmt., MIS mgmt., Systems anal., DB admin., Mgmt. consultants
Industries: Banking, Invest. banking, Brokers, Misc. financial, Mgmt. consulting, Real estate, High tech

DRZ Medical Recruiters
6426 S. Robb Way
Littleton, Colorado 80127
(303) 933-1921
Fax: (303) 933-1921

Key Contact - Specialty:
Ms. Donna Zickerman - *Medical*

Description: National recruitment firm with experience in placement of medical and pharmaceutical sales representatives as well as management positions, with regional focus in the Rocky Mountain area. Experience in all areas of medical.
Functions: Middle mgmt., Sales mgmt., MIS mgmt.
Industries: Drugs mfg., Medical devices, Healthcare

DS&A (Doug Sears & Assoc.)
320 Corporate Way, Ste. 100
Jacksonville, Florida 32073
(904) 278-9998
(800) 553-5361
Fax: (904) 278-9995
Email: dsa@d-s-a.com
Web: www.d-s-a.com

Key Contact - Specialty:
Mr. J. Douglas Sears - *Legal*

Description: We are a full-service human resource provider offering services from recruiting to background checks, assessments, training/development, benefit transition counseling to resume scanning, tracking, retrieval and activity scheduling.
Functions: Sales mgmt., Benefits, M&A, MIS mgmt., Mgmt. consultants, Attorneys, Int'l.
Industries: Finance, Misc. financial, Computer svcs., Human resource svcs., Insurance, Software, Healthcare

Branches:
4922 Lakepark Lane
Acworth, Georgia 30100
(888) 966-8850
Fax: (770) 966-8850
Key Contact - Specialty:
Ms. Crystal Banks

Affiliates:
Creative System Solutions, Inc.

DSR-Search & Recruitment
1201 Richardson Drive, Ste. 220
Richardson, Texas 75080
(972) 680-8282
Fax: (972) 680-3202
Email: dsr@telecomsearch.com
Web: www.telecomsearch.com

Key Contact - Specialty:
Mr. David G. Crowley - *Telecommunications*
Mr. Norman Mole - *Telecommunications*

Description: Principal has over 25 years in telecommunications industry. Human resources executive with previous experience at major telecommunications design and manufacturers. Expertise in telephony based areas, engineering, mid to senior level management; switching, access, transmission systems.

Salary Minimum: $50,000
Functions: Directors, Senior mgmt., Middle mgmt., R&D, Engineering
Industries: Telecoms, High tech, Software

DuBrul Management Co.
2180 Crescent Drive
Tarrytown, New York 10591
(914) 332-8055
Fax: (914) 332-8041

Key Contact - Specialty:
Mr. Donald C. DuBrul - *Information technology, MIS*

Description: Our highly personal and confidential recruiting process emphasizes placing the best interests and needs of our client companies as well as our applicants as our primary goal resulting in long term relationships.
Functions: IT, MIS mgmt., Systems anal., Systems dev., Systems implem., Systems support, Mgmt. consultants
Industries: Generalist, Mfg., Food/bev/tobacco, Drugs mfg., Finance, Banking, Misc. financial

Dukas Assoc.
236 Payson Rd.
Belmont, Massachusetts 02178
(617) 484-9268
Fax: (617) 484-8607
Email: dukassoc@aol.com

Key Contact - Specialty:
Mr. Theodore Dukas - *Medical, biotechnology, sales, marketing, manufacturing research & development*

Description: A precise customized recruitment service specializing in senior biotech marketing and technical personnel; bi-coastal knowledge of companies, personnel and industry trends.

Salary Minimum: $50,000
Functions: Product dev., Mkt. research, Mktg. mgmt., Sales mgmt., R&D, Engineering, Int'l.

Industries: Chemicals, Drugs mfg., Medical devices, Test/measurement equip., Biotech

---

Dumont & Co.

1681 Chestnut St., Ste. 400
Vancouver, British Columbia V6J 4M6
Canada
(604) 733-8133
Fax: (604) 924-1754
Email: bdumont@retailheadhunter.com
Web: www.retailheadhunter.com

Key Contact - Specialty:
Ms. Brenda Dumont - *Senior managerial, executive, retail*
Ms. Gina Nicolaas - *Specialty store management, retail*
Ms. Judy Doutre - *Hardlines management, retail*

Description: Specialized expertise in the area of managerial and executive recruitment services strictly for the retail profession in Western Canada.

Salary Minimum: $45,000
Functions: Senior mgmt., Purchasing, Distribution
Industries: Retail

M. Dunbar & Assoc.

13607 Runney Meade
Sugar Land, Texas 77478
(281) 242-9578
(800) 728-9577
Fax: (281) 242-9578
Email: mdunbar@wordweb.org
Web: www.wordweb.org

Key Contact - Specialty:
Ms. Meg Dunbar - *Healthcare, clinical, technical, professional, administrative*

Description: As an MT (ASCP) with 16 years in medical sales and 8 years in healthcare executive search, I bring a unique qualification to each search. Medical and healthcare sales, clinical lab products and services, sales management, home healthcare sales and management, allied health, specialized nurse management.

Salary Minimum: $40,000
Functions: Senior mgmt., Middle mgmt., Nurses, Allied health, Health admin., Sales mgmt., CFO's
Industries: Healthcare

The Duncan-O'Dell Group Inc.

P.O. Box 1161
La Porte, Texas 77571
(281) 470-1881
Fax: (281) 470-1880
Email: dog1@sprintmail.com
Web: dog1@sprintmail.com

Key Contact - Specialty:
Mr. James E. Hall - *Manufacturing (electromechanical, metals, off road equipment)*

Description: 32 years of business experience. A practice that is multi-national. Available to clients 24 hours per day, 7 days per week. Offering solutions to problems.

Salary Minimum: $50,000
Functions: Middle mgmt., Product dev., Production, Purchasing, Materials Plng., Sales mgmt., Benefits
Industries: Metal products, Machinery/Appliances, Test/measurement equip., Misc. mfg., Human resource svcs.

Dunhill Staffing Systems, Inc.

150 Motor Pkwy.
Hauppauge, New York 11788-5111
(516) 952-3000
Fax: (516) 952-3500
Email: info@dunhillstaff.com
Web: www.dunhillstaff.com

Key Contact - Specialty:
Mr. Daniel Abramson
Mr. Richard W. Kean
Mr. Rich DeSantis
Mr. H. Pete Erbe

Description: A nationwide network of executive recruiting offices (more than 180 locations), specializing in many disciplines.

Salary Minimum: $25,000
Functions: Mfg., Healthcare, Sales & mktg., HR mgmt., Finance, IT, Engineering
Industries: Energy/utilities, Mfg., Transportation, Wholesale, Finance, Svcs., Communications

Branches:
2738 18th St. S.
Birmingham, Alabama 35209
(205) 877-4580
Fax: (205) 877-4590
Key Contact - Specialty:
Ms. Peggy Clark

1350 Hayes St., Ste. B-5
Benicia, California 94510
(707) 748-3000
Fax: (707) 748-3001
Key Contact - Specialty:
Mr. Patick Cacho

1777 S. Bascam Ave.
Campbell, California 95080
(408) 369-1900
Fax: (408) 369-8709
Key Contact - Specialty:
Mr. Gary Yuhara

9 Executive Circle, Ste. 240
Irvine, California 92714
(714) 474-6666
Fax: (714) 474-6674
Key Contact - Specialty:
Mr. David Vaughan

1215 N. Nevada, Ste. 1
Colorado Springs, Colorado 80903
(719) 473-7273
Fax: (719) 473-7278
Key Contact - Specialty:
Mr. Marinus Vanden Hul

P.O. Box 200637
1805 S. Bellaire St., Ste. 301
Denver, Colorado 80220-0637
(303) 757-7003
Fax: (303) 757-7774
Email: dunhill@ally.ios.com
Key Contact - Specialty:
Mr. Mike Orceyre

6909 S. Holly Circle, Ste. 305
Englewood, Colorado 80112
(303) 721-0525
Fax: (303) 721-0747
Key Contact - Specialty:
Mr. Leon Parnes
Ms. Sandy Parnes

40 Old Ridgebury Rd.
Danbury, Connecticut 06810
(203) 743-6994
(203) 830-4742
Fax: (203) 743-1902

333 E. River Drive, Ste. 403
East Hartford, Connecticut 06108
(860) 282-8800
Fax: (860) 290-4778

160 Bridge St., Ste.107
Hartfield Executive park
East Windsor, Connecticut 06088
(860) 623-4416
Fax: (860) 292-1383

270 Farmington Ave., Ste. 107
Farmington, Connecticut 06032
(860) 677-6779
Fax: (860) 676-8710

59 Elm St.
New Haven, Connecticut 06510
(203) 562-0511
Fax: (203) 562-2637
Key Contact - Specialty:
Mr. Donald Kaiser

430 Main Ave.
Norwalk, Connecticut 06851
(203) 849-8800
Fax: (203) 750-1245

850 N. Main St. Ext. Bldg.
Wallingford, Connecticut 06492
(203) 949-2000
Fax: (203) 949-2008

551-2 Wolcott St.
Waterbury, Connecticut 06705
(203) 755-9675
(203) 574-3256
Fax: (203) 597-8673

1520 Royal Palm Sq. Blvd.
Ft. Myers, Florida 33919-4993
(941) 931-0171
Fax: (941) 931-0177

Key Contact - Specialty:
Mr. Osborne Byrd

240 Crandon Blvd.
Key Biscayne, Florida 33149
(305) 365-0400
Fax: (305) 365-0251
Key Contact - Specialty:
Mr. Paul Gregg

1915 E. Bay Drive, Ste. B-3
Largo, Florida 34641-2203
(813) 585-0000
Key Contact - Specialty:
Mr. Richard Williams

670 N. Orlando Ave., Ste. 1002
Maitland, Florida 32751
(407) 599-9840
Fax: (407) 599-9845
Key Contact - Specialty:
Ms. Elaine Gregory
Mr. Ron Gregory

305 N. Pompano Beach Blvd.
Pompano Beach, Florida 33062-5118
(303) 757-7003
Fax: (303) 757-7774
Email: dunhill@ally.ios.com
Key Contact - Specialty:
Mr. Mike Orceyre

5053 Ocean Ave., Ste. 59
Sarasota, Florida 34242
(941) 349-6200
Fax: (941) 349-8866
Key Contact - Specialty:
Mr. John Olson

3340 Peachtree Rd. NE, Ste. 2570
Atlanta, Georgia 30326
(404) 261-3751
Fax: (404) 237-8361
Key Contact - Specialty:
Mr. Marvin Bearman

68 E. Wacker Place, Ste. 1200
Chicago, Illinois 60601
(312) 346-0933
Fax: (312) 346-0837
Key Contact - Specialty:
Mr. George Baker
Mr. Keith McRae

809 W. Detweiller Drive, Ste. 811
Peoria, Illinois 61615
(309) 689-2573
Fax: (309) 692-0492
Key Contact - Specialty:
Mr. Jay Morris

916 E. Main St., Ste. 114
Greenwood, Indiana 46143-1500
(317) 859-8900
Fax: (317) 859-7200
Key Contact - Specialty:
Ms. Leah Paine

3905 Vincennes Rd., Ste. 104
Indianapolis, Indiana 46268
(317) 471-0665
Fax: (317) 471-0672

7400 Shadeland, Ste. 140
Indianapolis, Indiana 46250
(317) 594-1477
Fax: (317) 594-1482

5420 Southern Ave., Ste. 103
Indianapolis, Indiana 46241
(317) 247-1775
Fax: (317) 241-4029

1233 Gilbert Court, Ste. A
Iowa City, Iowa 52240
(319) 354-1407
Fax: (319) 354-1715
Key Contact - Specialty:
Mr. Lee Stannard

3706 SW Topeka Blvd.
Topeka, Kansas 66609-1239
(913) 267-2773
Fax: (913) 267-2791
Key Contact - Specialty:
Mr. Robert Washatka

317 S. Hydraulic
Wichita, Kansas 67211
(316) 265-9541
Fax: (316) 265-2947
Key Contact - Specialty:
Mr. Harold Wood

5723 Superior Drive, Ste. B-4
Baton Rouge, Louisiana 70816-8016
(504) 291-0450
Fax: (504) 291-0452
Key Contact - Specialty:
Mr. Fritz Falcon

145 Acadian Lane
Mandeville, Louisiana 70471
(504) 845-1746
Fax: (504) 845-4118
Key Contact - Specialty:
Mr. Jerald Bailey

2920 Knight St., Ste. 140
Shreveport, Louisiana 71105-2412
(318) 861-3576
Fax: (318) 868-9872
Key Contact - Specialty:
Mr. Don Richards

7185 Columbia Gateway Drive, Ste G
Columbia, Maryland 21046
(410) 290-1515
(301) 596-2325
Fax: (410) 290-1199
Key Contact - Specialty:
Ms. Rosa Harper

414 Hungerford Drive, Ste. 252
Rockville, Maryland 20850-4125
(301) 424-0450
Fax: (301) 762-4694
Key Contact - Specialty:
Mr. Gordon Powers

138 Memorial Ave.
Century Plaza
West Springfield, Massachusetts 01089
(413) 733-5147
Fax: (413) 781-3461

1031 E. Saginaw
Lansing, Michigan 48906
(517) 487-5585
Fax: (517) 487-1129
Key Contact - Specialty:
Mr. Dennis W. Voketz

25060 Southfield Rd.
Southfield, Michigan 48075
(810) 569-3333
Fax: (810) 569-1400
Key Contact - Specialty:
Ms. Pamela Murff

206A Main St.
Festus, Missouri 63019
(314) 931-4477
(314) 931-4513
Fax: (314) 937-5930
Key Contact - Specialty:
Mr. Bob Bahr

801 E. 20th St., Ste. 1
Joplin, Missouri 64804
(417) 624-6552
Fax: (417) 624-7941
Key Contact - Specialty:
Mr. Mark Lickteig

500 Northwest Plaza, Ste. 410
St. Ann, Missouri 63074-2219
(314) 298-1617

509 Olive St., Ste. 200
St. Louis, Missouri 63101
(314) 421-5959
Fax: (314) 421-2259

1040 Kings Hwy. N., Ste. 400
Cherry Hill, New Jersey 08034-1986
(609) 667-9180
Fax: (609) 667-0064
Key Contact - Specialty:
Mr. William Emerson
Ms. Annette Emerson
Mr. Bill Emerson, Jr.
Ms. Linda Souder
Ms. Donna Erhard

303 W. Main St.
Freehold, New Jersey 07728
(732) 431-2700
Fax: (732) 431-0329
Key Contact - Specialty:
Mr. Richard Hanson - *Accounting*

105 College Rd.,E.
Princeton, New Jersey 08540
(609) 452-1222
(609) 951-0325
Fax: (609) 452-9222

233 E. Lancaster Ave.
Ardmore, New York 19003
(610) 642-2223
Fax: (610) 642-2347
Key Contact - Specialty:
Mr. Alan Trager

584 Delaware Ave.
Buffalo, New York 14202
(716) 885-3576
Fax: (716) 885-3594

Key Contact - Specialty:
Ms. Lupe J. Breen

775 Park Ave., Ste. 255
Huntington, New York 11743
(516) 421-9500
Fax: (516) 421-9700
Key Contact - Specialty:
Mr. Joe Mellilo

6175 Sunrise Highway
Massapequa, New York 11758-5341
(516) 797-1000
Fax: (516) 797-1015
Key Contact - Specialty:
Mr. Philip Missirlian
Ms. Barbara Missirlian

P.O. Box 528
Pittsford, New York 14534
(716) 377-7880
Fax: (716) 377-7972
Key Contact - Specialty:
Mr. Jack Tanner

P.O. Box 1347
Port Washington, New York 11050
(516) 883-1172
Fax: (516) 767-0526
Key Contact - Specialty:
Mr. Neville I. Newby

41 Mohegan Lane
Rye Brook, New York 10573
(914) 934-0801
Fax: (914) 934-0825
Key Contact - Specialty:
Mr. Robert J. Morris - *Information processing (sales talent)*

200 E. Arlington Blvd.
Greenville, North Carolina 27858
(919) 355-3808
Fax: (919) 355-1865
Key Contact - Specialty:
Mr. Ed Belcher

4110 Spinnacker Bay Drive
Sherrills Ford, North Carolina 28673
(704) 478-7000
Fax: (704) 478-9083
Key Contact - Specialty:
Mr. Tom Barbeau

4015 Executive Park Drive, Ste. 304
Cincinnati, Ohio 45241
(513) 769-6975
(888) 769-7975
Fax: (513) 956-5165
Key Contact - Specialty:
Ms. Judith Green

1166 Goodale Blvd., Ste. 200
Columbus, Ohio 43212
(614) 421-0111
Fax: (614) 421-0309
Key Contact - Specialty:
Mr. John W. Salzman - *Internal audit, information technology*

1500 W. Broadway
Ardmore, Oklahoma 73401
(405) 226-6710
Fax: (405) 223-5920
Key Contact - Specialty:
Mr. Larry Kalesnik

247 N. Broadway, Ste. 205
Edmond, Oklahoma 73034
(405) 341-0990
Fax: (405) 341-8400
Key Contact - Specialty:
Mr. Dennis Garton

224 Nazareth Pike, Ste. 16
Bethlehem, Pennsylvania 18017
(610) 746-5066
Fax: (610) 746-5799
Key Contact - Specialty:
Ms. Mary Jo Stofflet

96 Villa Rd.
Piedmont Ctr.
Greenville, South Carolina 29615
(864) 271-7180
Fax: (864) 271-7181
Key Contact - Specialty:
Mr. Duke Haynie

231F Hampton St.
Greenwood, South Carolina 29646
(864) 229-5251
Fax: (864) 229-6306
Key Contact - Specialty:
Mr. Hal Freese

5120 Stage Rd.
Stage Woods Office Park, #2
Memphis, Tennessee 38134
(901) 386-2500
Fax: (901) 386-2535
Key Contact - Specialty:
Mr. Eugene Rhodes

669 Airport Frwy., Ste. 310
Hurst, Texas 76053
(817) 282-8367
Fax: (817) 282-1142
Key Contact - Specialty:
Mr. Andrew Barham

3622 N. Beltine Rd.
Irving, Texas 75062
(972) 252-8367
Fax: (972) 255-9679
Key Contact - Specialty:
Mr. Jacob Joseph

110 N. Main St.
Mansfield, Texas 76063
(817) 453-4473
Fax: (817) 453-3932
Email: gkmb+prodigy.com
Web: dunhillstaff.com
Key Contact - Specialty:
Ms. Lana Morris

14514 Majestic Prince
781 Loop 337
San Antonio, Texas 78248
(210) 492-5435
Fax: (210) 492-5297
Key Contact - Specialty:
Ms. Angella Woodard

15102 Jones Maltsberger, Ste. 101
P.O. Box 700888
San Antonio, Texas 78270-0888
(210) 490-1744
Fax: (210) 490-2355
Key Contact - Specialty:
Mr. John R. Webb
Mr. Carl Gist

4828 Eastwind Rd.
Virginia Beach, Virginia 23464
(757) 495-8916
Fax: (757) 495-8923
Key Contact - Specialty:
Mr. James Naughton

P.O. Box 547
Charleston, West Virginia 25311
(304) 340-4260
Fax: (304) 340-4262
Key Contact - Specialty:
Ms. Marsha Simpkins

336 S. Jefferson St.
Green Bay, Wisconsin 54301
(920) 432-2977
Fax: (920) 432-2038
Key Contact - Specialty:
Mr. Kramer Rock

530 W. Main St.
Sun Prairie, Wisconsin 53590
(800) 645-6330
Fax: (608) 645-0169
Key Contact - Specialty:
Mr. Jim McCann

2300 N. Mayfair Rd., Ste. 220
Wauwatosa, Wisconsin 53226
(414) 771-1399
Fax: (414) 771-3920

1681 Chestnut St., Ste. 400
Vancouver, British Columbia V6J-4M6
Canada
(604) 739-0100
Fax: (604) 730-9962
Key Contact - Specialty:
Mr. Peter Hamilton

159 Albert St.
London, Ontario N6A 1L9
Canada
(519) 673-6684
Fax: (519) 673-6792
Key Contact - Specialty:
Ms. Lynn Lindsay

5650 Yonge St., Xerox Tower, Ste. 1500
North York, Ontario M2M 4G3
Canada
(905) 771-6241
Key Contact - Specialty:
Mr. Peter Pollock

Affiliates:
Associated Health Consultants

Dunhill Professional Search of San Jose

1475 S. Bascom Ave., Ste. 202
Campbell, California 95008
(408) 559-7377
Fax: (408) 559-7101
Email: dunhill@pacbell.net
Web: dunhillstaff.com/sajca.htm

Key Contact - Specialty:
Mr. Kevin A. P. Keifer - *Front end capital equipment, equipment used to make semiconductors*
Ms. Danna Keifer - *Insurance*
Ms. Maria Saso - *Components*
Ms. Shauna Ruden - *Electronics*
Mr. Andrew Trappen
Ms. Monica Burneikis - *Electronics*
Mr. David Rosner - *Electronics*

Description: We are focused on the high technology industry born in the Silicon Valley; that has spread to the manufacturing center of the world.

Salary Minimum: $25,000
Functions: Production, Materials Plng., Distribution, Mktg. mgmt., Sales mgmt., Systems dev., Engineering
Industries: Chemicals, Computer equip., Test/measurement equip., High tech, Software

Dunhill Professional Search of Oakland

3732 Mt. Diablo Blvd., Ste. 375
Lafayette, California 94549-3605
(925) 283-5300
Fax: (925) 283-5310
Email: Dunprosear@aol.com

Key Contact - Specialty:
Mr. John F. Tierney - *High tech*

Description: We work hard to find a custom fit between the position you need to fill and the person to fill it.

Salary Minimum: $30,000
Functions: General mgmt., Senior mgmt., Mfg., Materials, Mkt. research, IT, Engineering
Industries: Food/bev/tobacco, High tech

Dunhill Executive Search of Los Angeles, Inc.

4727 Wilshire Blvd., Ste. 410
Los Angeles, California 90010
(213) 931-1311
Fax: (213) 931-0565
Email: DunhilLA@aol.com
Web: www.dunhillstaff.com

Key Contact - Specialty:
Mr. Raymond R. Cech - *Environmental health & safety, real estate, sales/marketing*
Ms. Janet Justus - *Financial, accounting*
Ms. Carolyn Fair - *High technology, computer, software, hardware, sales & marketing*
Mr. Steve LePatner - *High technology, computer, software, hardware, sales & marketing*

Description: We offer you over twenty years of experience.
Functions: Senior mgmt., Middle mgmt., Product dev., Plant mgmt., Mktg. mgmt., Customer svc., Personnel
Industries: Chemicals, Consumer electronics, Retail, Computer svcs., Environmental svcs., Real estate, Software

Dunhill of San Francisco, Inc.

268 Bush St., Box 2909
San Francisco, California 94104
(415) 956-3700
Email: dunhills@pacbell.net
Web: www.dunhillstaff.com/safca.htm

Key Contact - Specialty:
Mr. George R. Curtiss - *Generalist*
Mr. Chris N. Curtiss
Mr. Michael R. Curtiss

Description: Tied in with the Dunhill Personnel System database.
Functions: Generalist, Middle mgmt., Plant mgmt., Sales mgmt., Taxes, Engineering, Environmentalists
Industries: Generalist, Chemicals, Metal products, Machinery/Appliances, Misc. mfg., Environmental svcs., High tech

Affiliates:
Dunhill Staffing Systems, Inc.

Dunhill Professional Search of Englewood, Inc.

P.O. Box 4905
Englewood, Colorado 80155
(303) 755-7466
Fax: (303) 755-7081
Email: dsengco@dunhillstaff.com

Key Contact - Specialty:
Mr. John L. Lippe - *Manufacturing, process*

Description: Specializing in engineering, quality control, production management and research and development for process industries nationwide. Recruitment primarily in food/beverage, medical device, cosmetic and pharmaceutical manufacturing.

Salary Minimum: $40,000
Functions: Production, Plant mgmt., Quality, Distribution, Packaging, R&D, Engineering
Industries: Food/bev/tobacco, Soap/perfume/cosmetics, Drugs mfg., Medical devices, Environmental svcs., Packaging

Dunhill of Ft. Collins, Inc.

2120 S. College Ave., Ste. 3
Ft. Collins, Colorado 80525
(970) 221-5630
Fax: (970) 221-5692
Email: dfc@frii.com

Key Contact - Specialty:
Mr. Jerold Lyons - *Plant engineers, manufacturing engineers*
Mr. Jack Donahue - *Semiconductor engineers*
Mr. Herb McCulla - *Trust & commercial loan officers*

Description: Privately owned and managed office. Personal attention by staff of 3 averaging 18 years recruiting experience. Access to national exchange system with 40 year record of success.

Salary Minimum: $25,000
Functions: Production, Purchasing, Credit, Engineering
Industries: Mfg., Plastics/rubber, Metal products, Computer equip., Banking, High tech, Software

Dunhill Personnel of Boulder

P.O. Box 488
Niwot, Colorado 80544
(303) 652-8370
Fax: (303) 652-8369
Email: dunbldr@aol.com

Key Contact - Specialty:
Mr. Fran Boruff - *Manufacturing, food, beverage, durable goods*
Mr. Doug Boruff - *Manufacturing, food, beverage, durable goods*

Description: Our office is an independently owned franchise, part of a large corporation consisting of 130 offices nationwide and international. Ownership of business has 40 years of experience (supervisors to vice presidents of operations) in the recruiting specialty.
Functions: Senior mgmt., Production, Plant mgmt., Quality, Productivity, Purchasing, Materials Plng.
Industries: Food/bev/tobacco, Chemicals, Drugs mfg., Transportation

Dunhill Professional Search of Miami

550 Brickell Ave., Ste. 502
Miami, Florida 33131
(305) 372-5757
Fax: (305) 372-5724
Email: staffing@dunhillmiami.com
Web: www.dunhillmiami.com

Key Contact - Specialty:
Mr. Paul J. Gregg - *Senior management, international*
Mr. Charles E. Parsons - *Senior management*
Mr. John M. Crittenden - *Sales & marketing*
Ms. Estela Ortega de Diego - *Financial Services, Sales & Marketing*
Ms. Elizabeth P. Reitzamer - *Sales & Marketing*
Ms. Cecilia Chaves-Gregg - *International*

Description: Active member of Dunhill's 200-office international network.

Salary Minimum: $75,000
Functions: Senior mgmt., Middle mgmt., Mktg. mgmt., Sales mgmt., Finance, IT, Int'l.
Industries: Generalist, Machinery/ Appliances, Computer equip., Consumer electronics, Finance, Communications, High tech

Dunhill Professional Search of Tampa
4350 W. Cypress St., Ste. 225
Tampa, Florida 33607
(813) 872-8118
Fax: (813) 872-6398
Email: dunhill@icubed.net

Key Contact - Specialty:
Mr. Donald J. Kramer - *Audit, EDP audit*
Mr. Peter Kramer - *Audit, EDP audit*
Ms. Mona Kramer

Description: Our specialties are healthcare and auditing. We recruit nurse management, hospital techs, hospital administration and finance executives and auditors both financial and EDP. We also specialize in MIS, AS400 programmers; network specialists.

Salary Minimum: $20,000
Functions: Nurses, Health admin., Systems anal., Systems dev., Systems implem., Systems support
Industries: Generalist, Accounting, Healthcare

Dunhill Search of West Atlanta
2110 Powers Ferry Rd., Ste. 110
Atlanta, Georgia 30339
(770) 952-0009
Fax: (770) 952-9422
Email: dswatlga@mindspring.com
Web: dunhillstaff.com/watga.htm

Key Contact - Specialty:
Mr. Jon Harvill - *Manufacturing*

Description: Effectively use team recruiting with closely networked 200 offices.

Salary Minimum: $30,000
Functions: General mgmt., Mfg., Plant mgmt., Materials, Purchasing, HR mgmt., Engineering
Industries: Food/bev/tobacco, Textiles/ apparel, Paper, Drugs mfg., Metal products, Motor vehicles

Dunhill Professional Search of Augusta
801 Broad St., Ste. 411
SunTrust Bank Bldg.
Augusta, Georgia 30901
(706) 722-5741

Key Contact - Specialty:
Mr. Frederick P. Gehle - *Chemical, pulp & paper, engineering (junior to mid level), process control, automation systems engineers*

Description: Close, individual attention including resume guidance, concerted marketing effort to agreed upon companies in specific geographic locations. Effort can run months to year or more.

Salary Minimum: $30,000
Functions: Production, Automation, Quality, Productivity, Engineering, Environmentalists
Industries: Lumber/furniture, Paper, Chemicals, Plastics/rubber, Paints/ petroleum products, Telecoms

Dunhill Professional Search of Hawaii
1164 Bishop St., Ste. 124
Honolulu, Hawaii 96813
(808) 524-2550
Fax: (808) 533-2196
Email: jobsrus@aloha.net
Web: dunhillstaff.com

Key Contact - Specialty:
Ms. Nadine Stollenmaier - *Accounting, engineering, technical, information systems, insurance*
Mr. James Stollenmaier
Mr. Henry Sotelo - *Engineering, technical*

Description: Permanent placement, temporary placement and professional contract staffing of experienced and qualified individuals for client companies and associations in engineering, accounting, data processing, audit, construction fields, technical and sales.

Salary Minimum: $22,000
Functions: General mgmt., Production, Sales & mktg., Finance, IT, Engineering, Int'l.
Industries: Generalist, Finance, Hospitality, Accounting, Telecoms, Insurance, High tech

Dunhill Professional Search of Rolling Meadows
5005 Newport Drive, Ste. 201
Rolling Meadows, Illinois 60008
(847) 398-3400
Fax: (847) 398-3766

Key Contact - Specialty:
Mr. Russ Kunke - *Information technology*

Description: 25 years as a hiring manager-understands technology, terminology, etc. We have a nationwide network of 200 offices.

Salary Minimum: $30,000
Functions: MIS mgmt., Systems anal., Systems dev., Systems implem., Systems support, Network admin., DB admin.
Industries: Generalist

Dunhill of Ft. Wayne, Inc.
9918 Coldwater Rd.
Ft. Wayne, Indiana 46825
(219) 489-5966
Fax: (219) 489-6120
Email: dunhill@ctlnet.com
Web: www.dunhillstaff.com/ftwin.htm

Key Contact - Specialty:
Mr. Charlie Davis - *Manufacturing plant, engineers, quality assurance*

Description: Twenty-two years experience in providing salaried individuals for manufacturing plants Specialize in the food, food packaging industry.

Salary Minimum: $30,000
Functions: Production, Automation, Plant mgmt., Quality, Productivity, Engineering
Industries: Food/bev/tobacco, Chemicals, Soap/perfume/cosmetics, Drugs mfg.

Dunhill Technical Staffing
950 N. Meridian St., Ste. 110
Indianapolis, Indiana 46204
(317) 237-7860
Fax: (317) 237-7859
Email: bpg@dunhillstaffing.com
Web: www.dunhillstaffing.com

Key Contact - Specialty:
Mr. Mark Rowe - *Information systems/ technology*
Mr. Eric Smith - *Information systems/ technology*

Description: We specialize in the placement of computer information systems professionals on a permanent as well as a contract basis.
Functions: IT, MIS mgmt., Systems anal., Systems dev., Systems implem., Systems support, Network admin.
Industries: Generalist, Mfg., Finance, Svcs., Insurance, High tech, Software

Dunhill Executive Search of Brown County

P.O. Box 1068
Nashville, Indiana 47448
(812) 988-1944

Key Contact - Specialty:
Mr. George W. Rogers - *Engineering, manufacturing)*
Ms. S. L. Rogers - *Engineering, manufacturing)*

Description: We actively participate with other Dunhill offices in the exchange of both applicants and job opportunities, which gives a greater exposure of the marketable applicant and a greater potential for us to complete a search for the manufacturer.

Salary Minimum: $30,000
Functions: Mfg., Product dev., Production, Plant mgmt., Quality, Personnel, Engineering
Industries: Metal products, Motor vehicles, Computer equip., Misc. mfg., Healthcare

Dunhill Professional Search of Greater New Orleans

3401 Ridge Lake Drive., Ste. 106
Metairie, Louisiana 70002
(504) 834-8188
Fax: (504) 834-8356
Email: dpsofno1@mail.iamerica.net
Web: dunhillstaff.com/norla.htm

Key Contact - Specialty:
Mr. Jerald W. Bailey - *Telecommunications, utilities, finance & accounting, human resources, information technology*
Mr. Quinn Jones

Description: Telecommunications, IT, gas & electric recruiting firm specializing in technical and sales oriented prescreened candidates at all levels.

Salary Minimum: $40,000
Functions: Middle mgmt., Mktg. mgmt., Sales mgmt., Personnel, MIS mgmt., Systems dev., Network admin.
Industries: Energy/utilities, Computer svcs., Telecoms, High tech, Software

Dunhill Professional Search of Byram

P.O. Box 720097
Jackson, Mississippi 39212-0097
(601) 878-9997
Fax: (601) 878-9998
Email: dsbyram@earthlink.net
Web: www.dunhillstaff.com/byrms.htm

Key Contact - Specialty:
Ms. C.J. Armstrong - *Information technology, AS400 programmers*
Mr. Don Armstrong - *Information technology, engineering*

Description: A comprehensive search in any given geographical locale that results in the finding of the most qualified applicants for our hiring officials. As well as, the most desired positions for our applicants.
Functions: Senior mgmt., MIS mgmt., Systems anal., Systems dev., Systems implem., Engineering, Int'l.
Industries: Mfg., Finance, Computer svcs., High tech, Software

Dunhill Professional Search

1350 Rusticview Drive
Ballwin, Missouri 63011
(314) 394-0602
Fax: (314) 394-2802

Key Contact - Specialty:
Mr. Don Vogel - *Aluminum*

Description: This office has over 23 years experience servicing the aluminum extrusion industry providing managers, supervisors, engineers and technical specialists throughout North America.
Functions: Mfg., Materials, Sales & mktg., HR mgmt., Engineering
Industries: Metal products

Dunhill Professional Search of Omaha, Inc.

14620 Frances Circle
Omaha, Nebraska 68144-2131
(402) 334-1233
Email: dsomane@dunhillstaff.com

Key Contact - Specialty:
Mr. Kenneth A. Jaspersen - *Banking, credit cards, trust & commercial loan officers*

Description: Specialize in credit cards, trust, commercial lending and agribusiness. We distinguish ourselves by our careful, committed, on-target, surprise-free approach to the search and recruiting business.

Salary Minimum: $25,000
Functions: CFO's, Budgeting, Credit, Risk mgmt.
Industries: Agri/forestry/mining, Banking, Misc. financial

Dunhill of Manchester Inc.

814 Elm St., Beacon Bldg.
Manchester, New Hampshire 03101
(603) 645-6330
Fax: (603) 645-0169

Key Contact - Specialty:
Mr. Jack Schoenfeld - *Finance, software, data processing*
Ms. Marian Schoenfeld - *Legal, insurance, administrative support*

Description: We specialize in finance, legal, insurance, office support, software, MIS and D.P.
Functions: Middle mgmt., Admin. svcs., CFO's, MIS mgmt., Systems dev., Systems support, Attorneys, Paralegals
Industries: Finance, Legal, Accounting, Human resource svcs., Insurance, High tech, Software

Dunhill Search of Medford

520 Stokes Rd., Ste. B-11
Medford, New Jersey 08055
(609) 953-1515
Fax: (609) 953-1551

Key Contact - Specialty:
Mr. Karl W. Fischer - *Accounting & finance, human resources*

Description: Approach is personalized and professional. Principal's background is Fortune 100 HR executive.

Salary Minimum: $30,000
Functions: Generalist, Benefits, CFO's, Budgeting, Cash mgmt., M&A, Risk mgmt.
Industries: Generalist

Dunhill Professional Search of Ramsey

393 State Rte. 202
Oakland, New Jersey 07436-2744
(201) 337-2200
Fax: (201) 337-3445

Key Contact - Specialty:
Mr. Roger Lippincott - *Sales, human resources*

Description: Since founded, the firm has placed over 400 executives. One specialty is large scale staffing expansion projects and total outsourcing of clients HR staffing needs.

Salary Minimum: $30,000
Functions: Plant mgmt., Productivity, Sales mgmt., Personnel, Training
Industries: Drugs mfg., Computer equip., Telecoms

Dunhill Staffing Systems

975 Walnut St., Ste. 260
Cary, North Carolina 27511
(919) 460-9988
(800) 783-9933
Fax: (919) 460-9931
Email: ralnc919@aol.com
Web: www.dunhillstaff.com

Key Contact - Specialty:
Mr. Jay Babson - *Contract programmers*
Ms. Lelia Babson - *Healthcare, managed care*

Description: We have placed more than two million professionals in new and challenging positions. Our national computerized network of specialists can provide you with all the information necessary to make smart career decisions.
Functions: Nurses, Allied health, Health admin., MIS mgmt., Systems anal., Systems dev., Systems implem.
Industries: Mfg., Finance, Healthcare

Dunhill Professional Search of Winston-Salem

108 1/2 S. Main St.
Kernersville, North Carolina 27284
(910) 996-2286
Fax: (910) 993-3205
Email: dpsws@worldnet.att.net
Web: dpsws.com

Key Contact - Specialty:
Mr. Bob Martineau - *Data processing, information systems*
Mr. Dan Martineau - *Data processing, information systems*
Mr. Bill Martineau - *Data processing, information systems*
Ms. Jocelyn Sharpe - *Data processing, information systems*

Description: We are cost effective-we recruit (not advertise) for candidates, qualify for your specific needs, match your corporate requirements and always check references before we present or market a candidate.

Salary Minimum: $30,000
Functions: MIS mgmt., Systems anal., Systems dev., Systems implem., Systems support
Industries: Food/bev/tobacco, Textiles/apparel, Drugs mfg., Motor vehicles, Wholesale, Banking, Telecoms

Dunhill Personnel Service of Fargo

109 1/2 Broadway
Fargo, North Dakota 58102
(701) 235-3719
(800) 473-2512
Fax: (701) 235-7092
Email: dsfargo@mail.rrnet.com
Web: dunhillstaff.com

Key Contact - Specialty:
Mr. Albert Raney - *Medical, engineering, technicians, information systems*
Mr. Kent Hochgraber - *Physicians, programmers*
Mel Van Beek - *Sales, information systems*

Description: Specializing in healthcare and engineering, information systems and physicians.

Salary Minimum: $25,000
Functions: General mgmt., Physicians, Health admin., Sales & mktg., Finance, IT, Engineering
Industries: Machinery/Appliances, Banking, Hospitality, Pharmaceutical svcs., Computer svcs., Accounting, Software

Dunhill Personnel of Northeast Tulsa, Inc.

10159 E. 11th St., Ste. 370
Tulsa, Oklahoma 74128-3054
(918) 832-8857
(800) 466-8857
Fax: (918) 832-8859

Key Contact - Specialty:
Ms. Joy M. Porrello - *Credit card industry*

Description: Firm specializes in executive search for all disciplines in the credit card industry on a national basis.

Salary Minimum: $40,000
Functions: Senior mgmt., Middle mgmt., Mktg. mgmt., Direct mktg., Customer svc., Credit, Risk mgmt.
Industries: Misc. financial

Dunhill Professional Search of Bucks-Mont., Inc.

801 W. Street Rd., Ste. 7
Feasterville, Pennsylvania 19053
(215) 357-6591
Fax: (215) 953-1612
Email: dbon@integra-net.com
Web: dunhillstaff.com/bumpa.htm

Key Contact - Specialty:
Mr. David M. Bontempo - *EDP audit, sales & marketing, financial*
Mr. Arthur C. Dettra - *Administration*
Ms. Mary F. Bontempo - *Office services*

Description: Specialize in EDP audit, accounting and sales professionals, nationwide; clerical/light industrial temporary placements in the greater Philadelphia area.

Salary Minimum: $25,000
Functions: Middle mgmt., Admin. svcs., Sales mgmt., Budgeting, MIS mgmt.
Industries: Food/bev/tobacco, Paper, Computer equip., Banking, Invest. banking, Pharmaceutical svcs., Equip. svcs.

Affiliates:
Bontemps Staffing Services

Dunhill Professional Search of Wilkes-Barre/Scranton, Inc.

15 Public Square, Ste. 212
Bicentenial Bldg.
Wilkes-Barre, Pennsylvania 18701
(717) 826-8953
Fax: (717) 821-5525
Email: dunhill@tl.infi.net

Key Contact - Specialty:
Mr. Anthony J. Desiderio - *Technical*
Ms. Janie Hendershot - *Information systems*
Ms. Donna Zehner - *Healthcare*

Description: Engineering and sales management assignments in electronics, automotive, power transmission related industries for domestic and international clients. Additional emphasis on information systems, EDP auditors, NT systems.

Salary Minimum: $40,000
Functions: Senior mgmt., Healthcare, Sales mgmt., Taxes, Network admin., DB admin., Engineering
Industries: Machinery/Appliances, Motor vehicles, Misc. financial, Computer svcs., Equip. svcs., Telecoms, Healthcare

Affiliates:
Associated Health Consultants

Dunhill Personnel of St. Andrews

16 Berry Hill Rd., Ste. 120
Interstate Ctr.
Columbia, South Carolina 29210
(803) 772-6751
Fax: (803) 798-0874
Email: DunhillSta@aol.com
Web: www.dunhillSta.com

Key Contact - Specialty:
Mr. Richard V. Bramblett - *Metalworking/automotive*
Mr. Steve Harbin - *Engineering/outdoor power, manufacturing/materials management*
Mrs. Denise McCoy
Ms. Jeanette Bramblett

Description: Our strength is specializing in the metal working areas of automotive, textile and power tools in engineering, management and sales professionals.

Salary Minimum: $30,000
Functions: Product dev., Production, Automation, Plant mgmt., Quality, Purchasing, Engineering
Industries: Metal products, Machinery/Appliances, Motor vehicles, Test/measurement equip., Misc. mfg., Aerospace

Dunhill Search of Arlington

1301 S. Bowen Rd., Ste. 370
Arlington, Texas 76013
(817) 265-2291
Fax: (817) 265-2294
Email: dunhill@flashnet.com
Web: www.dunhillsearch.com

Key Contact - Specialty:
Mr. Jon Molkentine - *Information systems audit, audit, sales, accounting*

Description: We are celebrating 20 years in the industry, specializing in accounting, audit, EDP audit, sales and engineering. We work with Fortune 500 clients as well as small to medium sized companies in Dallas/Fort Worth and throughout the U.S. We are computer linked with over 150 Dunhill offices and maintain an extensive jobs database.

Salary Minimum: $35,000
Functions: CFO's, Cash mgmt., Taxes, M&A, Risk mgmt., Systems anal., Systems dev.
Industries: Agri/forestry/mining, Mfg., Transportation, Wholesale, Retail, Svcs., Communications

Dunhill of Corpus Christi, Inc.

4455 S. Padre Island Drive, #102
Corpus Christi, Texas 78411-4417
(512) 225-2580
Fax: (512) 225-3888
Email: dfry@talentscouts.com
Web: www.talentscouts.com

Key Contact - Specialty:
Mr. Don Fry - *HVAC, engineers-design & development, manufacturing, stress & finite element analysis*

Description: President is a certified personnel consultant with 25 years experience. We specialize in all engineering functions, mostly product development and manufacturing engineering.

Salary Minimum: $25,000
Functions: Product dev., Production, R&D, Engineering
Industries: Food/bev/tobacco, Metal products, Machinery/Appliances, Computer svcs.

Dunhill Professional Search, Inc. of McAllen

P.O. Box 3114
McAllen, Texas 78502-3114
(210) 687-9531
Fax: (210) 687-9531
Email: lfsteele@juno.com

Key Contact - Specialty:
Mr. Lloyd F. Steele - *Engineers*
Ms. Dolores M. Steele - *Engineers*

Description: Specialize in line management, engineering and staff support recruiting. Manufacturing sector. National in scope via franchised offices and computerized matching of candidates and current job openings.

Salary Minimum: $30,000
Functions: Middle mgmt., Production, Automation, Plant mgmt., Quality, Engineering, Minorities
Industries: Food/bev/tobacco, Medical devices, Metal products, Machinery/Appliances, Motor vehicles, Misc. mfg., Packaging

Dunhill Search of Vermont

P.O. Box 204
Warren, Vermont 05674-0204
(802) 496-0115
Fax: (802) 496-0116

Key Contact - Specialty:
Mr. Herb Hauser - *Accounting & finance, EDP audit, auditing*
Ms. Renate Von Recklinghausen - *Accounting & finance, auditing*

Description: Contingency and retainer search for accounting/financial/EDP audit professional, 2+ years experience. Work closely with Big 6 firms for referrals as well as major MBA schools, customized searches as required.

Salary Minimum: $35,000
Functions: Middle mgmt., Budgeting, Taxes, M&A
Industries: Generalist

Dunhill Professional Search of Richmond

8100 Three Chopt Rd., Ste. 133
Richmond, Virginia 23229-4833
(804) 282-2216
Fax: (804) 282-5682

Key Contact - Specialty:
Mr. P. Frank Lassiter - *Trust officers (administration, investments)*

Description: In business for over 22 years. Part of a large franchise network.

Salary Minimum: $30,000
Functions: General mgmt., Mfg., Sales & mktg., Finance, Engineering, Int'l.
Industries: Food/bev/tobacco, Paper, Chemicals, Plastics/rubber, Machinery/Appliances, Banking

Dussick Management Assoc.

149 Durham Rd.
Madison, Connecticut 06443
(203) 245-9311
Fax: (203) 245-9570
Email: dussick@aol.com

Key Contact - Specialty:
Mr. Vince Dussick - *Marketing, sales, promotion management*
Ms. Gayle Moran - *Marketing, sales, promotion management*
Ms. Carol Kinney - *Marketing, sales, promotion management*
Mr. Mike Piccione - *Marketing, sales, promotion management*

Description: Established firm specializes in marketing/marketing research, sales, sales research and sales/consumer promotion positions with large/small Fortune 500 companies. Owners/counselors have over 40+ years of marketing and sales experience.

Salary Minimum: $60,000
Functions: Senior mgmt., Healthcare, Advertising, Mktg. mgmt., Sales mgmt., HR mgmt., Int'l.
Industries: Generalist, Food/bev/tobacco, Textiles/apparel, Soap/perfume/cosmetics, Drugs mfg., Consumer electronics, Pharmaceutical svcs.

Gwen Dycus & Assoc.

P.O. Box 1791
Bradenton, Florida 34206-1791
(941) 792-5011
Email: gwendycus@worldnet.att.net

Key Contact - Specialty:
Ms. Gwen Dycus - *Development, finance, legal, leasing, construction*
Mr. Frank Hamilton - *Development, finance, legal, leasing, construction*

Description: International service specializing in the shopping center and retail real estate fields including positions in development, leasing, finance, legal, construction, management and marketing since 1976.

Salary Minimum: $30,000
Functions: Directors, Senior mgmt., Middle mgmt., Advertising, CFO's, Attorneys, Int'l.
Industries: Construction, Advertising/PR, Real estate, Non-classifiable industries

G. L. Dykstra Assoc., Inc.

P.O. Box 8035
Holland, Michigan 49422-8035
(616) 786-9419

Key Contact - Specialty:
Mr. Gene L. Dykstra
Ms. Glenda M. Dykstra

Description: Exclusive executive search and staffing for small, expanding companies of 100 to 1,000 employees. Concentrating on all areas, however primarily manufacturing, engineering, finance and sales management.

Salary Minimum: $40,000
Functions: Product dev., Production, Quality, Productivity, Purchasing, Materials Plng., Benefits
Industries: Generalist, Plastics/rubber, Paints/petroleum products, Motor vehicles, Transportation

Dynamic Choices Inc.

36 Four Seasons Ctr., Ste. 330
Chesterfield, Missouri 63017
(314) 878-8575
Fax: (314) 878-3301

Key Contact - Specialty:
Ms. Nancy J. Riehl - *Information technology*

Description: Well-connected information technology specialist with 20 years high technology industry experience maintains network of contacts nationwide. Provides professional confidential executive search services on contingency basis.

Salary Minimum: $35,000
Functions: Sales mgmt., MIS mgmt., Systems anal., Systems dev., Systems implem., Network admin., Mgmt. consultants
Industries: Computer equip., Finance, Computer svcs., Accounting, Telecoms, High tech, Software

Dynamic Computer Consultants, Inc.

7534 E. 2nd St., Ste. 102
Scottsdale, Arizona 85251
(602) 990-8179
Fax: (602) 994-8705
Email: dynamic@netwrx.net
Web: www.netwrx.net/dynamic

Key Contact - Specialty:
Mr. Roc Rogers - *Information technology, midrange systems personnel*

Description: We provide a full range of service including: programming, analysis, project management, network support, technical writing, internet/intranet design and operations and technical support.
Functions: MIS mgmt., Systems anal., Systems dev., Systems implem., Systems support, Network admin., DB admin.
Industries: Generalist

Dynamic Search Systems, Inc.

3800 N. Wilke Rd., Ste. 485
Arlington Heights, Illinois 60004
(847) 259-3444
Fax: (847) 259-3480
Email: dyanmsys@aol.com
Web: ww.dssjobs.com

Key Contact - Specialty:
Mr. Michael J. Brindise - *MIS*

Description: Place MIS professionals including applications programmers, programmer/analysts, systems analysts, project leaders/managers, application managers/directors and technical services/systems programmers covering operating systems, telecommunications and database.

Salary Minimum: $25,000
Functions: MIS mgmt., Systems anal., Systems dev., Systems implem., Systems support
Industries: Generalist, Computer equip., Computer svcs., Telecoms, High tech, Software

Dynamic Staffing Network

2625 W. Butterfield Rd., Ste. 300 S
Oak Brook, Illinois 60521
(630) 572-9980
Fax: (630) 572-9892
Email: Bradley@dynastaff.com
Web: Dynastaff.com

Key Contact - Specialty:
Mr. Richard Bradley - *Information Systems*
Mr. George Custer - *Manufacturing, Accounting*
Mr. James Gilbert - *Engineering*

Description: We service the greater Chicago metropolitan area with recruiters that average over 7 years in the business. We strive to have our clients look forward to working with us again...and they do.
Functions: Mfg., Materials, Finance, IT, Systems anal., Systems support, Network admin.
Industries: Generalist
Professional Associations: IACPR

The E & K Group

3 McDermott Pass
Denville, New Jersey 07834
(201) 627-9312
Fax: (201) 627-7712

Key Contact - Specialty:
Mr. Frank Brescher

Description: General recruitment firm committed to total quality and providing personal control of each assignment. Managed as a confidential search successful candidates can provide significant bottom line contributions.

Salary Minimum: $47,000
Functions: Generalist, Senior mgmt., Product dev., Plant mgmt., Distribution, CFO's, R&D
Industries: Generalist

Affiliates:
J. Vincent Assoc.

E O Technical

57 North St.
Danbury, Connecticut 06810
(203) 797-2653
Fax: (203) 797-2657
Email: ausy09d@prodigy.com
Web: www.employops.com

Key Contact - Specialty:
Mr. Robert Neubauer - *Technical*

Description: We are a female owned Connecticut operation open for one purpose; to serve our clients and our applicants.
Functions: Generalist, MIS mgmt., R&D
Industries: Generalist, Plastics/rubber, Banking, Legal, Human resource svcs., Insurance, Healthcare

Branches:
2425 Post Rd., Ste. 102
Southport, Connecticut 06490
(203) 255-5403
Fax: (203) 256-1158
Key Contact - Specialty:
Mr. Gary Petroski - *Technical*

E T Search Inc.

1250 Prospect St., Ste. 101
La Jolla, California 92037-3618
(619) 459-3443
Fax: (619) 459-4147
Email: taxpros@etsearch.com
Web: www.etsearch.com

Key Contact - Specialty:
Ms. Kathleen Neuharth - *Tax*
Ms. Suzanne Curle - *Tax*

Description: Exclusive tax search, serving major corporations, public accounting firms and law firms. Search specialties include domestic, state & local and international tax.

Salary Minimum: $70,000
Functions: Taxes
Industries: Lumber/furniture, Chemicals, Retail, Entertainment, Legal, Communications, Aerospace

E.P. Int'l.

590 Madison Ave., 21st Floor
New York, New York 10022
(212) 521-4430
Email: neilepi@viconet.com
Web: www.epint.com

Key Contact - Specialty:
Mr. P. Neil Ralley - *Specialty chemicals, filtration products, international*

Description: We have the unusual capability of undertaking international searches from bases in the US, Europe and Singapore. Intensely client-focused, we have a uniquely flexible fee structure, offering clients a fixed fee based on the work involved.

Salary Minimum: $80,000
Functions: General mgmt., Senior mgmt., Middle mgmt., Sales & mktg., Mktg. mgmt., Sales mgmt., HR mgmt.
Industries: Mfg., Chemicals, Paints/petroleum products, Consumer electronics, Misc. mfg., Telecoms, High tech

Branches:
P.O. Box 211
Verona, New Jersey 07044
(973) 571-1367
Web: www.epint.com

Key Contact - Specialty:
Mr. P. Neil Ralley - *Specialty chemicals, filtration products, international*

International Branches:
London

E/Search Int'l.

2200 Mountain Rd.
P.O. Box 408
West Suffield, Connecticut 06093-0408
(860) 668-5848
(800) 300-0477
Fax: (860) 668-5125
Email: esearch@earthlink.net
Web: www.esearchintl.com

Key Contact - Specialty:
Mr. Bob Rossow - *Executives, electronic contract manufacturing*

Description: The executive search firm of the electronic contract manufacturing industry.

Salary Minimum: $90,000
Functions: Senior mgmt., Plant mgmt., Sales mgmt., CFO's, Int'l.
Industries: Medical devices, Motor vehicles, Computer equip., Consumer electronics, Test/measurement equip., Telecoms, High tech

---

EA Plus, Inc.

P.O. Box 11587
Ft. Worth, Texas 76110-9711
(800) 297-1USA
Fax: (817) 922-0528
Email: jcpeee@onramp.net
Web: www.eaplus.com

Key Contact - Specialty:
Ms. Julia Lockleer - *Healthcare, Financial services*
Mr. Jim Everett - *Manufacturing, electronics, telecommunications, healthcare*

Description: Generalist search firm specializing in executive, managerial and professional assignments. We will split fees with reciprocal arrangement on most listings.

Salary Minimum: $65,000
Functions: General mgmt., Mfg., Healthcare, HR mgmt., Finance, IT, Specialized services
Industries: Mfg., Finance, Svcs., Communications, High tech, Healthcare

---

Eagle Consulting Group Inc.

12300 Ford Rd., Ste. 150
Dallas, Texas 75234
(972) 247-0990
Fax: (972) 247-4306
Email: eaglecg@mindspring.com

Key Contact - Specialty:
Mr. William G. Mitchell - *Biopharmaceutical*

Description: Our mission is to always provide excellence in performance while assuring the highest standards of professionalism and to meld our candidate delivery systems to meet each client's expectations and corporate objectives.

Salary Minimum: $60,000
Functions: Senior mgmt., Mfg., Production, Quality, Materials Plng., R&D, Engineering
Industries: Mfg., Drugs mfg., Pharmaceutical svcs., Healthcare

---

J. M. Eagle Partners Ltd.

11514 N. Port Washington Rd., Ste. 105
Mequon, Wisconsin 53092
(414) 241-1400
Fax: (414) 241-4745
Email: jerry12@execpc.com
Web: www.exepc.com/2jerry12/

Key Contact - Specialty:
Mr. Jerry Moses

Description: A vertical approach to medical industry search. Specialization: in-depth knowledge and reputation within diagnostic imaging (radiology manufacturers).

Salary Minimum: $60,000
Functions: Generalist, General mgmt., Healthcare, Sales & mktg., IT, R&D, Engineering
Industries: Drugs mfg., Medical devices, Computer equip., High tech, Software, Biotech, Healthcare

---

Eagle Research, Inc.

373 D Rt. 46W
Fairfield, New Jersey 07004
(201) 244-0992
Fax: (201) 244-1239
Email: asbaron@aol.com
Web: www.biosys.net/eagleresearch

Key Contact - Specialty:
Ms. Annette S. Baron - *Pharmaceutical*

Description: Specializing in the pharmaceutical and biotechnology industries with an emphasis in clinical research, medical marketing and activities related to drug development.
Functions: Directors, Senior mgmt., Middle mgmt., Physicians, R&D, Int'l.
Industries: Pharmaceutical svcs., Healthcare

Eagle Search Assoc.

336 Bon Air Center, #295
Greenbrae, California 94904
(415) 398-6066
Fax: (415) 924-8996
Email: mark@eaglesearch.com
Web: www.eaglesearch.com

Key Contact - Specialty:
Mr. Mark Gideon - *High technology, sales, sales support, managers, MIS executives*

Description: Computer software applications and systems software, hardware and other high-tech vendors, workflow including imaging. Specializing in sales and technical support representatives and their management, MIS executives, CIO's, senior technology managers, business development and marketing. Currently work with many Silicon Valley firms.

Salary Minimum: $65,000
Functions: Directors, Senior mgmt., Mktg. mgmt., Sales mgmt., Customer svc., MIS mgmt., Systems support
Industries: Computer equip., Higher ed., Legal, Computer svcs., Accounting, Human resource svcs., High tech

---

EagleView, Inc.

1601 Trapelo Rd., Reservoir Place
Waltham, Massachusetts 02154
(781) 672-6000
Fax: (781) 672-6019
Email: evi@eagleview.com
Web: www.eagleview.com

Key Contact - Specialty:
Mr. Edward J. Alexander - *Sales and marketing*

Description: Recruiter that provides full-time, part-time and contact opportunities in most functions and industries.

Salary Minimum: $20,000
Functions: Middle mgmt., Mktg. mgmt., Sales mgmt., CFO's, MIS mgmt., Systems dev., Engineering
Industries: Computer equip., Misc. financial, Computer svcs., Accounting, Telecoms, High tech, Software

---

Eastern Executive Assoc.
(a division of F.X. Jones Associates)

45 Hamilton Drive E.
North Caldwell, New Jersey 07006
(973) 226-7341

Key Contact - Specialty:
Ms. Madeline G. Jones

Description: We regularly serve these industries: electronics, aerospace, pharmaceutical, consumer products, EDP.

Salary Minimum: $30,000
Functions: Engineering
Industries: Energy/utilities, Aerospace, High tech

Eastridge Infotech
(a division of The Eastridge Group)
2355 Northside Drive, Ste. 180
San Diego, California 92108
(619) 260-2085
Email: infotech@cts.com
Web: eastridge-infotech.com

Key Contact - Specialty:
Ms. Joanne Kinsey - *Information technology*
Ms. Nanci Porter - *Information technology*
Ms. Eve Hager - *Information technology*

Description: We have 160 employees in California and Nevada and annual revenues of $60 million. Our recruiting division specializes in information technology, placing individuals on both a temporary and full-time basis.

Salary Minimum: $40,000
Functions: MIS mgmt., Systems anal., Systems dev., Systems implem., Systems support, Network admin., DB admin.
Industries: Finance, High tech, Software

Branches:
311 California St., 6th Floor
San Francisco, California 94104
(415) 616-9724
Key Contact - Specialty:
Ms. Toffee Real - *Information technology*

4220 S. Maryland Pkwy.
Las Vegas, Nevada 89119
(702) 732-8859
Key Contact - Specialty:
Mr. Jim D'Amora - *Information technology*

ECG Resources, Inc.
215 N. Ocean Ave.
Patchogue, New York 11772
(516) 447-1118
Fax: (516) 447-1142
Email: DaveGlaser@ECGresources.com
Web: www.ECGresources.com

Key Contact - Specialty:
Mr. David Glaser - *Tax, trust, estates, executive financial planning*

Description: Tax, trust, estates, financial planning and employee benefits, concentrating in the financial service sector. Contingency search with retainer proficiency. Contacts include CPA's, attorneys from Big 6, law firms, corporations and financial planning professionals.

Salary Minimum: $50,000
Functions: Taxes, Attorneys
Industries: Generalist

Eckler Personnel Network
P.O. Box 549
Woodstock, Vermont 05091
(802) 457-1605
Fax: (802) 457-1606
Email: epn@sover.net
Web: www.epn1.com

Key Contact - Specialty:
Mr. Geoffrey N. Eckler - *Information systems, business software*

Description: Regionalized search and contingency placement firm specializing in all levels of business software and management information systems professionals. Servicing clients throughout the Northeastern U.S.

Salary Minimum: $50,000
Functions: MIS mgmt., Systems anal., Systems dev., Systems implem., Systems support, Network admin., DB admin.
Industries: High tech, Software

Eden & Assoc., Inc.
794 N. Valley Rd.
Paoli, Pennsylvania 19301
(610) 889-9993
Fax: (610) 889-9660
Email: brooks_eden@prodigy.com
Web: www.edenandassociates.com

Key Contact - Specialty:
Mr. Brooks D. Eden - *Senior executives*
Mr. Fred A. Nunziata - *Financial, distribution, middle management*
Mr. Earl M. Eden - *Administration*
Mr. Greg Edwards - *Middle management, retail, sales*

Description: We are a specialized national executive search and recruiting organization focusing on serving the critical hiring needs of retailers, distributors, manufacturers, brokers, hospitality trades and related consulting organizations.

Salary Minimum: $65,000
Functions: Directors, Senior mgmt., Middle mgmt., Purchasing, Distribution, CFO's, MIS mgmt.
Industries: Food/bev/tobacco, Transportation, Wholesale, Retail, Advertising/PR, Real estate

The Edge Resource Group
P.O. Box 457
Greensburg, Pennsylvania 15601
(724) 523-4795
Fax: (724) 523-5840
Email: dischoff@aol.com

Key Contact - Specialty:
Ms. Diane L. Schoff - *Generalist, information systems technology, sales & marketing, human resources, executive level management*

Description: A generalist firm working nationally with an emphasis on information technology, sales and marketing.

Salary Minimum: $50,000
Functions: Generalist, General mgmt., Mfg., Sales & mktg., HR mgmt., Finance, IT
Industries: Generalist, Mfg., Finance, Svcs., High tech, Software

EDI, Inc.
(a subsidiary of Roberts, Ryan and Bentley)
1107 Kenilworth Drive, Ste. 208
Baltimore, Maryland 21204
(410) 494-1400
Fax: (410) 321-1347

Key Contact - Specialty:
Ms. Judith A. Lambert - *Enterprise resource planning (ERP) technology*

Description: Our mission is to exceed our clients' and candidates' expectations by adhering to an internally developed search methodology that is qualitative in nature.

Salary Minimum: $50,000
Functions: MIS mgmt., Systems anal., Systems dev., Systems implem., Systems support, Mgmt. consultants
Industries: Energy/utilities, Misc. mfg., Banking, Mgmt. consulting, Insurance, Healthcare

EDI/Executive Dynamics Inc.
2 James Brite Circle
Mahwah, New Jersey 07430
(201) 327-9070
Fax: (201) 327-9071

Key Contact - Specialty:
Ms. Susan J. Wagner - *Sales & marketing*

Description: Experienced track record of placement of sales and marketing professionals in both consumer and marketing service companies. Confidential professional services.

Salary Minimum: $45,000
Functions: Generalist, Senior mgmt., Middle mgmt., Sales & mktg., Advertising, Mktg. mgmt., Sales mgmt.
Industries: Food/bev/tobacco, Soap/perfume/cosmetics, Drugs mfg., Communications, Advertising/PR, Publishing, New media

Affiliates:
Consumer Search inc./CSI

EDMS Solutions
3300 Bee Caves Rd., Ste. 650-161
Austin, Texas 78746
(512) 327-8850
Fax: (512) 328-9630
Email: apd@usa.net

Key Contact - Specialty:
Mr. Albert P. D'Andrea - *Electronic document management systems, publishing systems industry*

Description: We specialize exclusively in executive recruiting for the electronic document management and publishing systems industries.

Salary Minimum: $50,000
Functions: Sales & mktg., IT
Industries: Software

EDP Staffing Solutions, Inc.

2024 Arkansas Valley Drive, #206
Little Rock, Arkansas 72212
(501) 223-4733
Fax: (501) 223-4735
Email: headhunt@cei.net
Web: www.recruitme.com

Key Contact - Specialty:
Ms. Marjean Bean - *Data processing*
Ms. Ellen Howland

Description: Excellent reputation, combined 35+ years of experience, specialists in data processing/information technology.

Salary Minimum: $35,000
Functions: MIS mgmt., Systems anal., Systems dev., Systems implem., Systems support, Engineering
Industries: Misc. mfg., Computer svcs., Telecoms, Insurance, High tech, Software, Healthcare

---

Edwards & Assoc.

4015 Goshen Lake Drive S.
Augusta, Georgia 30906
(706) 793-3679
Fax: (706) 796-6611

Key Contact - Specialty:
Ms. Lisa Edwards - *Sales, sales management*

Description: Firm's primary focus is in sales and sales management. Secondary focus is information technology and/or medical sales. Ideal candidate profile has a business product or service background, if not industry specific.

Salary Minimum: $35,000
Functions: Senior mgmt., Middle mgmt., Sales mgmt.
Industries: Medical devices, Pharmaceutical svcs., Computer svcs., Accounting, Equip. svcs., Telecoms, Software

---

EFCO Consultants, Inc.

P.O. Box 1486
Quogue, New York 11959
(516) 653-4302
Fax: (516) 653-8278
Email: nfells@aol.com

Key Contact - Specialty:
Mr. Norman Fells - *Information systems (vendor)*

Description: Specialists in the data processing community (vendor).

Salary Minimum: $60,000
Functions: Senior mgmt., Middle mgmt., Mktg. mgmt., Sales mgmt., Systems implem., Systems support, Mgmt. consultants
Industries: Computer equip., Computer svcs., Equip. svcs., Mgmt. consulting, New media, High tech, Software

---

D. C. Egan & Assoc.

8097-B Roswell Rd.
Atlanta, Georgia 30350
(770) 673-0600
Fax: (770) 673-0609

Key Contact - Specialty:
Mr. David C. Egan - *Food processing, sanitation chemicals, engineering, automation, financial services (credit card & equipment leasing)*

Description: We focus on finding top qualified candidates for each position available in your organization. Quality not quantity of candidates is what differentiates us from other firms.

Salary Minimum: $45,000
Functions: Production, Automation, Quality, Mktg. mgmt., Sales mgmt., Credit, Risk mgmt.
Industries: Food/bev/tobacco, Chemicals, Drugs mfg., Banking, Misc. financial

---

Eggers Consulting Co., Inc.

11272 Elm St., Eggers Plaza
Omaha, Nebraska 68144-4788
(402) 333-3672
Fax: (402) 333-9759
Email: eggrs@aol.com
Web: www.eggersconsulting.com

Key Contact - Specialty:
Mr. James W. Eggers
Mr. Raymond Hamilius
Mr. J. W. Eggers
Ms. Ellen Hembertt
Ms. L. D. Miller - *Information technology*

Description: Professional search and executive recruiting firm that works regionally and nationally. Specializing in banking, data processing, insurance, retail and recruiting. Have placed candidates in client companies in all 50 states.

Salary Minimum: $25,000
Functions: Personnel, IT, MIS mgmt., Network admin., DB admin.
Industries: Retail, Banking, Computer svcs., Insurance

W. Robert Eissler & Assoc., Inc.

1610 Woodstead Court, Ste. 230
The Woodlands, Texas 77380
(281) 367-1052
Fax: (281) 292-6489
Web: www.eissler.com

Key Contact - Specialty:
Mr. W. Robert Eissler - *Valve industry, process equipment*
Mr. Keith Newman - *Telecommunications, electronics*
Mr. David White - *Plastics*
Mr. Vinny Sinisi - *Chemical industry*
Mr. Larry Patronella - *Distributed control systems, process software, instrumentation*
Ms. Marie Devaney - *Fluid power*

Description: Recruiters for nationwide senior and middle level sales, marketing and technical positions. We specialize in the valve, instrumentation, automation, manufacturing software, fluid power, chemical, plastics, filtration, medical device and pulp and paper industries.

Salary Minimum: $25,000
Functions: Product dev., Automation, Plant mgmt., Mktg. mgmt., Sales mgmt., Customer svc., Engineering
Industries: Chemicals, Drugs mfg., Medical devices, Plastics/rubber, Metal products, Test/measurement equip., Telecoms

---

The Eldridge Group, Ltd.

810 S. Waukegan Rd., Ste. 102C
Lake Forest, Illinois 60045
(847) 295-4800
Fax: (847) 295-9981

Key Contact - Specialty:
Mr. David E. Archibald - *Sales, management, consumer products*

Description: We have a strong national network dealing with the strongest recruiters in all markets. Whether they are a franchise or independent we network with the top producers.
Functions: Directors, Middle mgmt., Mktg. mgmt., Sales mgmt.
Industries: Food/bev/tobacco, Soap/perfume/cosmetics, Drugs mfg., Medical devices, Plastics/rubber, Computer equip., Misc. mfg.

Electronic Search, Inc.

3601 Algonquin Rd., Ste. 820
Rolling Meadows, Illinois 60008
(847) 506-0700
(800) 356-3501
Fax: (847) 506-9999
Email: lshepherd@electronicsearch.com
Web: www.electronicsearch.com

Key Contact - Specialty:
Ms. Linda Shepherd
Mr. Steve Eddington - *Information technology*
Mr. Al Born - *Telecommunications*
Ms. Cathy Bayer - *Customized staffing services for outsourced recruiting*

Description: We service Fortune 500 multinationals and local entrepreneurial enterprises. Track record is built on trust, long term relationships and commitment to achieving a successful conclusion to each search. Consultants are seasoned professionals. We operate a WAN system with Intranet and Internet links.
Functions: IT, MIS mgmt., Systems anal., Systems dev., Systems implem., Engineering, Int'l.
Industries: Computer equip., Misc. financial, Computer svcs., Mgmt. consulting, Telecoms, High tech, Software

Branches:
990 Highland Dr., Ste. 212-K
Solana Beach, California 92075
(619) 792-8108
Fax: (619) 792-8121
Email: jmiller@electronicsearch.com
Web: www.electronicsearch.com
Key Contact - Specialty:
Mr. John Miller - *Telecommunications*

P.O. Box 506
Bradley Beach, New Jersey 07720
(732) 775-5017
Fax: (732) 775-5035
Email: esi_inc@ix.netcom.com
Web: www.eletronicsearch.com
Key Contact - Specialty:
Mr. Tom Manni - *Telecommunications*

Elinvar
3200 Beechleaf Court, Ste. 409
Raleigh, North Carolina 27604
(919) 878-4454
Fax: (919) 878-0634
Email: info@elinvar.com
Web: www.elinvar.com

Key Contact - Specialty:
Mr. Randy Bye
Ms. Patti Gillenwater - *Accounting & finance, administrative management, legal*

Description: We are a locally-owned recruiting and consulting firm specializing in the areas of accounting/finance, legal and administrative placement for temp, temp to hire and direct hire.

Salary Minimum: $25,000
Functions: Admin. svcs., Purchasing, HR mgmt., Finance, Specialized services, Mgmt. consultants, Attorneys
Industries: Generalist, Mfg., Finance, Svcs., Insurance, Real estate, High tech

---

Elite Consultants, Inc.
976 Florida Central Pkwy., Ste. 112
Longwood, Florida 32750
(407) 831-3448
Fax: (407) 260-1347
Email: elite@totcon.com
Web: www.elite-eci.com

Key Contact - Specialty:
Ms. Janeen Cepull - *Telecommunications software/hardware development, systems engineers*
Ms. Denise Putnam - *Telecommunications software/hardware development, systems engineers*

Description: We maintain a large network of engineers and clients located throughout the U.S. and China; our resources enable us to quickly match our clients' need with the right expertise.
Functions: Systems dev., Systems implem., Systems support, Network admin., DB admin., Engineering
Industries: Telecoms, High tech, Software

Elite Medical Search
100 Crescent Centre Pkwy., Ste. 360
Tucker, Georgia 30084
(770) 908-2113
Fax: (770) 908-2203
Email: elite@elitesearch.com
Web: www.elitesearch.com

Key Contact - Specialty:
Mr. David Alexander - *Healthcare*
Mr. Ron Washburn - *Medical device*

Description: We are a priority search firm working nationally with clients including many of the Fortune 500, niche firms and healthcare providers.

Salary Minimum: $35,000
Functions: Product dev., Production, Nurses, Health admin., Systems dev., R&D, Engineering
Industries: Mfg., Medical devices, Pharmaceutical svcs., Healthcare

Affiliates:
Quality Healthcare Solutions

Gene Ellefson & Assoc. Inc.
330 Town Center Drive, Ste. 304
Dearborn, Michigan 48126-2711
(313) 982-6000
Fax: (313) 982-1277
Email: gellefson@advdata.net

Key Contact - Specialty:
Mr. Gene Ellefson - *Automotive OEM's, automotive suppliers*

Description: We work with automotive tier 1 & 2 suppliers. We primarily are involved with sales, engineering, manufacturing and accounting positions, mid-management and higher.

Salary Minimum: $50,000
Functions: General mgmt., Mfg., Sales & mktg., Finance, Engineering, Int'l.
Industries: Mfg., Plastics/rubber, Metal products, Motor vehicles, Transportation

---

Ellis & Associates
66 Queen St., Ste. 1802
Honolulu, Hawaii 96813
(808) 526-3812
Fax: (808) 523-9356
Email: jellis@aloha.net

Key Contact - Specialty:
Mr. James P. Ellis - *Information technology, telecommunications*

Description: Executive search in all functions and industries in Hawaii with much repeat business. Comprehensive search and exceptional company service delivered with a sense of urgency and integrity.

Salary Minimum: $50,000
Functions: General mgmt., Sales & mktg., Finance, IT, MIS mgmt., Systems anal., Systems implem.
Industries: Generalist, Retail, Finance, Hospitality, New media, Telecoms, Healthcare

---

Ellis Career Consultants
1090 Broadway
West Long Branch, New Jersey 07764
(732) 222-5333
Fax: (732) 222-2332

Key Contact - Specialty:
Ms. Lisa Shapiro - *Retail*

Description: Executive search organization specializing in retail industry.

Salary Minimum: $30,000
Functions: General mgmt., Materials, Sales & mktg., HR mgmt., Finance
Industries: Transportation, Wholesale, Retail, Hospitality, Entertainment, Human resource svcs.

Steve Ellis
3207 Colorado Ave., Ste. 3
Santa Monica, California 90404
(310) 829-0611
Fax: (310) 829-2024
Email: sellissrch@aol.com

Key Contact - Specialty:
Mr. Steve Ellis - *Banking, financial services*

Description: Individualized executive search exclusively to commercial and corporate banking as well as service industries; professional, ethical recruitment of top-level candidates for retainer/contingency clients.

Salary Minimum: $50,000

Functions: Senior mgmt., Middle mgmt.
Industries: Banking, Misc. financial, Hospitality

Affiliates:
The LS Group

The Ellsworth Group
270 Jay St., Ste. 151
Brooklyn, New York 11201
(212) 237-4084
Fax: (212) 855-2859
Email: Kirk@ellsworthgroup.com

Key Contact - Specialty:
Mr. Kirk Nicklas - *Marketing, communications, sales*
Mr. Rory Kelly - *Marketing, communications, sales*

Description: National executive search firm specializing in marketing, communications and sales positions across industries.

Salary Minimum: $60,000
Functions: Advertising, Mkt. research, Mktg. mgmt., Sales mgmt., Direct mktg., Customer svc., PR
Industries: Generalist, Mfg., Finance, Svcs., Communications, High tech, Healthcare

The Elmhurst Group
4120 Douglas Blvd., Ste. 306
Granite Bay, California 95746
(916) 772-6720
Fax: (916) 786-2981
Email: teg@elmhurstgroup.com

Key Contact - Specialty:
Ms. Sharon Miller - *Information technology, senior executives, PA's*

Description: Our focus is on placing hard to find executive and technical candidates. Clients interview only thoroughly screened, qualified, interested individuals who are suited to the company's goals and culture and willing to accept a fair offer of employment.
Functions: Mktg. mgmt., Sales mgmt., MIS mgmt., Systems anal., Systems dev., Systems implem., DB admin.
Industries: Printing, Medical devices, Computer equip., Telecoms, High tech, Software, Biotech

The Elsworth Group
12910 Queens Forest, Ste. B
San Antonio, Texas 78230-1539
(210) 493-7211
Fax: (210) 493-6873
Email: elsworth@txdirect.net
Web: elsworth@txdirect.net

Key Contact - Specialty:
Ms. Beverly W. O'Daniel - *Aerospace, high technology, manufacturing*
Mr. James E. O'Daniel - *Oil, chemical, manufacturing*

Description: We serve the aerospace, high technology, oil, chemical and other manufacturing industries.

Salary Minimum: $35,000
Functions: General mgmt., Mfg., Purchasing, Mktg. mgmt., Sales mgmt., R&D, Engineering
Industries: Chemicals, Plastics/rubber, Paints/petroleum products, Misc. mfg., Aerospace, High tech, Software

Mark Elzweig Co., Ltd.
101 Fifth Ave., Ste. 10A
New York, New York 10003
(212) 243-0539
Fax: (212) 243-0566
Email: elzweig@aol.com
Web: ww.elzweig.com

Key Contact - Specialty:
Mr. Mark Elzweig - *Institutional marketers, portfolio managers, retail brokers*
Ms. Nancy Miller - *Institutional marketers, portfolio managers*

Description: We recruit buyside marketers, portfolio managers and retail account executives. Our clients are money management firms and major investment banks.

Salary Minimum: $80,000
Functions: Senior mgmt., Mktg. mgmt., Sales mgmt., Cash mgmt.
Industries: Finance, Invest. banking, Brokers, Misc. financial

Emerald Legal Search
22 Eastman Ave.
Bedford, New Hampshire 03110
(603) 623-5300
Fax: (603) 623-5322
Email: judy@emeraldsearch.com
Web: www.emeraldsearch.com

Key Contact - Specialty:
Ms. Judy Mulligan - *Attorneys (intellectual property, in-house corporate counsel)*

Description: We are dedicated to the recruitment and placement of intellectual property attorneys and corporate counsel who meet the demanding requirements of companies nationwide.
Functions: Senior mgmt., Middle mgmt., Legal, Attorneys, Paralegals
Industries: Chemicals, Plastics/rubber, Paints/petroleum products, Computer equip., Legal, High tech, Software

Emerging Medical Technologies, Inc.
7502 S. Willow Circle
Englewood, Colorado 80112
(303) 322-6226
Fax: (303) 721-8173

Key Contact - Specialty:
Mr. Thomas C. Miller - *Engineering, marketing, regulatory affairs, senior management*
Ms. Karlan Emery - *Sales, regulatory affairs, MIS, product management*

Description: We serve companies and investors in the fields of medical devices, biotechnology and pharmaceuticals. Specializing in research, product development, marketing, sales, quality and regulatory affairs.

Salary Minimum: $50,000
Functions: Senior mgmt., Product dev., Quality, Mktg. mgmt., Sales mgmt., R&D, Engineering
Industries: Food/bev/tobacco, Chemicals, Drugs mfg., Medical devices, Pharmaceutical svcs., Biotech, Healthcare

Emerging Technology Search
1080 Holcomb Bridge Rd., Bldg. 200/305
Roswell, Georgia 30076
(770) 643-4994
Fax: (770) 643-4991
Email: careers@emergingtech.com
Web: www.emergingtech.com

Key Contact - Specialty:
Mr. Peter A. Lehrman - *Software, network, database engineers*
Ms. Laura M. Lehrman

Description: Flexibility and partner involvement combined with information technology staffing experience makes us a valuable resource to firms hiring software, network and database engineers.

Salary Minimum: $40,000
Functions: MIS mgmt., Systems anal., Systems dev., Systems implem., Systems support
Industries: Lumber/furniture, Misc. financial, New media, Telecoms, High tech, Software, Healthcare

Emerson & Co.
449 Pleasant Hill Rd., Ste. 313
Lilburn, Georgia 30247
(770) 564-3215

Key Contact - Specialty:
Mr. Harold C. Popham - *Generalist, manufacturing*

Description: Middle to upper management recruitment primarily in manufacturing.

Salary Minimum: $35,000
Functions: Generalist, Senior mgmt., Product dev., Plant mgmt., Distribution, Sales mgmt., R&D
Industries: Generalist, Printing, Medical devices, Misc. mfg., Transportation

Emmett Executive Search, Inc.

55 Emmett Place
Yonkers, New York 10703
(914) 966-1917
Fax: (914) 966-1859
Web: emmett.es@msn.com

Key Contact - Specialty:
Ms. Maryrose H. Mullen - *Medical, pharmaceutical, chemical, marketing & sales, technical*

Description: All consultants working with this corporation are degreed in their specialties. The president holds a masters in public relations.

Salary Minimum: $75,000
Functions: Generalist, Directors, Senior mgmt., Healthcare, Sales & mktg., R&D, Engineering
Industries: Generalist, Chemicals, Drugs mfg., Medical devices, Pharmaceutical svcs., Communications, Healthcare

Employ®

P.O. Box 2032
Media, Pennsylvania 19063
(610) 565-1573
Fax: (610) 565-1573

Key Contact - Specialty:
Ms. Sayre Dixon - *Management level*

Description: Can produce the hard to find candidate i.e.: PhD, food, microbiologist, diversity.
Functions: Generalist, Mktg. mgmt., HR mgmt., Finance, IT, R&D, Minorities
Industries: Generalist, Misc. mfg., Finance, Publishing

Employment Solutions, Inc.

(Firm declined to update.)
1422 W. Main St., Ste. 101B
Lewisville, Texas 75067
(972) 221-5566

Key Contact - Specialty:
Ms. Lynne Von Villas - *Engineering*

Description: Recruitment and placement of engineers in the chemical, petro chemical and refining industries. Contract engineers in same.
Functions: Middle mgmt., Engineering
Industries: Printing, Chemicals, Paints/petroleum products

Empowered Solutions Corp.

555 Sun Valley Drive, Ste. N-4
Roswell, Georgia 30076
(770) 645-9333
Fax: (770) 645-9339
Email: mail@empow.com
Web: www.empow.com

Key Contact - Specialty:
Mr. Todd Deutscher
Ms. Eileen R. Johnson

Description: We are a national management recruiting and professional services firm serving the customer and technology service industries.

Salary Minimum: $75,000
Functions: General mgmt., Directors, Mfg., Materials, Customer svc., IT, Mgmt. consultants
Industries: Computer equip., Computer svcs., Equip. svcs., Mgmt. consulting, High tech, Software

The Enfield Company

504 W. 24th St., Ste. 204
Austin, Texas 78705
(512) 477-4888
Email: enfieldpub@aol.com
Web: members.aol.com/enfieldco

Key Contact - Specialty:
Mr. Herbert E. Smith - *Traditional publishing, new media publishing*

Description: Specialty is with key personnel bridging the gap between traditional and new media publishing, in intrapreneurial or entreprenuerial settings; also conduct senior level searches for talented individuals within related industries.

Salary Minimum: $60,000
Functions: Generalist, Senior mgmt., Mkt. research, Mktg. mgmt., Sales mgmt., Direct mktg., Mgmt. consultants
Industries: Generalist, Entertainment, Higher ed., Mgmt. consulting, Publishing, New media, Software

Engineering & Scientific Search Assoc. (ESSA)

P.O. Box 14
Fanwood, New Jersey 07023
(908) 889-7828
Fax: (908) 889-7318

Key Contact - Specialty:
Mr. Steve Skaar
Ms. Mirlam Skaar
Mr. Edward Monahan
Ms. Marie Blabolil
Ms. Rosemarie Graziano

Description: A technically oriented search group focusing primarily on the chemical process and allied industries. Staff consists of technically degreed industry experienced personnel addressing R&D, engineering and marketing needs.

Salary Minimum: $25,000
Functions: Middle mgmt., Plant mgmt., Mkt. research, Direct mktg., R&D, Engineering
Industries: Chemicals, Drugs mfg., Medical devices, Plastics/rubber, Paints/petroleum products, Pharmaceutical svcs., Computer svcs.

Engineering Futures, LLC

70 Duval St.
P.O. Box 845
Manchester, Connecticut 06045-0845
(860) 649-7084
(860) 649-7086
Fax: (860) 649-7082

Key Contact - Specialty:
Mr. David Andrews - *Engineering, information technology, plastics*
Ms. Veronica Gomez - *Engineering, information technology*

Description: A truly exceptional search practice that achieves success through cultivating trust-based relationships with clients. We deliver results where others have failed and represent our clients with professionalism and integrity.
Functions: General mgmt., Mfg., Sales & mktg., HR mgmt., IT, R&D, Engineering
Industries: Mfg., Drugs mfg., Plastics/rubber, Aerospace, High tech, Software, Biotech

Engineering Placement Specialists

P.O. Box 416
Elcho, Wisconsin 54428
(715) 275-5322
Fax: (715) 275-5325

Key Contact - Specialty:
Ms. Lynn Sexton - *Pulp & paper*

Description: Sole proprietorship: working all disciplines of engineering, sales and marketing. Our agency works in placement and recruitment worldwide. Pulp and paper industry.

Salary Minimum: $30,000
Functions: Mfg.
Industries: Paper

Engineering Profiles

2216 E. Olive Rd., Ste. 204
Pensacola, Florida 32514
(850) 969-9991
Fax: (850) 969-9987
Email: bprice@engineeringprofiles.com
Web: www.engineeringprofiles.com

Key Contact - Specialty:
Mr. William G. Price - *Chemical industry (technical, engineering, operations)*

Description: We specialize in technical, engineering and operations professionals within the chemical process industry. Our focus is on operating companies, primarily concentrating in manufacturing operations, with plant/operations management and technical and engineering support positions as our specialty.

Salary Minimum: $40,000
Functions: Product dev., Production, Plant mgmt., R&D, Engineering
Industries: Paper, Chemicals, Paints/petroleum products

Engineering Resource Group, Inc.

Powder Mill Plaza, 101 Gibraltar Drive
Morris Plains, New Jersey 07950
(973) 490-7000
Fax: (973) 490-1957

Key Contact - Specialty:
Mr. Branko A. Terkovich
Mr. James Z. Terkovich

Description: Specialize in professional recruiting of mechanical engineers, electrical engineers, electronic engineers, software engineers and aerospace engineers. We recruit for the aerospace, electronics, industrial and defense markets.

Salary Minimum: $40,000
Functions: Engineering
Industries: Food/bev/tobacco, Drugs mfg., Plastics/rubber, Computer equip., Telecoms, Aerospace, Software

---

Ensearch Management Consultants

921 Transport Way, Ste. 29
Petaluma, California 94954
(800) 473-6776
Fax: (707) 778-1555
Email: guest@ensearch.com
Web: www.ensearch.com

Key Contact - Specialty:
Mr. Tim Mattis - *Healthcare*

Description: Service-based organization, performing customized searches using computerized database. We present a limited number of qualified candidates and boast high interview to acceptance ratios. Proven track record in filling hard to fill positions.

Salary Minimum: $40,000
Functions: Physicians, Nurses, Allied health, Health admin.
Industries: Healthcare

Environmental, Health & Safety Search Assoc.

P.O. Box 1325
Palm Harbor, Florida 34682
(813) 787-3225
Fax: (813) 787-5599
Email: ehs@ehssearch.com
Web: ehssearch.com

Key Contact - Specialty:
Mr. Randy L. Williams - *Safety, environmental, industrial hygiene*

Description: An executive search firm that specializes exclusively in recruiting safety, industrial hygiene and environmental professionals for major industrial corporations.

Salary Minimum: $40,000
Functions: Engineering, Environmentalists
Industries: Generalist, Energy/utilities, Paper, Chemicals, Motor vehicles, Computer equip., High tech

---

Essential Solutions, Inc.

2542 S. Bascom Ave., Ste. 225
Campbell, California 95008
(408) 369-9500
Fax: (408) 369-9595
Email: info@esiweb.com
Web: www.esiweb.com

Key Contact - Specialty:
Mr. Art Narita - *Engineering, sales marketing, professional*
Mr. Spencer S. Tashima - *Engineering management, individual technical contributors*
Mr. Aaron C. Woo - *Engineering, sales & marketing executives*

Description: Specializing in the placement of key contributors in management, engineering, marketing and sales for emerging communications companies. Specializing in: wireless communications, networking, internet, multi-media and system semiconductors.

Salary Minimum: $70,000
Functions: General mgmt., Mfg., Sales & mktg., Finance, IT, R&D, Engineering
Industries: Computer equip., Consumer electronics, Test/measurement equip., Finance, Communications, High tech, Software

Affiliates:
Kanektions

The Evans McDonnell Co.

16030 Mesa Verde Drive
Houston, Texas 77059
(281) 286-7711
Fax: (281) 286-9775

Key Contact - Specialty:
Mr. Patrick Evans - *Design, construction*

Description: For most of our clients, we recruit design and construction professionals at the P.M. - Director level.

Salary Minimum: $50,000
Functions: Directors, Senior mgmt., Middle mgmt., Architects
Industries: Construction, Hospitality, Real estate

Evans Transportation Search

16 The Links Rd., Ste. 312
Willowdale, Ontario M2P 1T5
Canada
(416) 224-2277

Key Contact - Specialty:
Mr. Ray Evans - *Transportation*

Description: A tireless group of headhunters totally committed to recruiting the best talent available in air, ocean and road transportation. Our focus is on emerging growth companies.

Salary Minimum: $40,000
Functions: Senior mgmt., Middle mgmt., Purchasing, Distribution, Mktg. mgmt., Sales mgmt., CFO's
Industries: Transportation

Evergreen & Co.

160 Mouse Mill Rd.
Westport, Massachusetts 02790
(800) 828-6705
Fax: (508) 636-8633
Email: maukp@staffing.net
Web: www.net-temps.com/egreen

Key Contact - Specialty:
Ms. Patricia Mauk - *Information technology*
Mr. Gary Mauk

Description: Search firm specializing in software engineering professionals and information technology managers and specialists. Providing recruiting assistance to manufacturing, financial and service industries.

Salary Minimum: $30,000
Functions: MIS mgmt., Systems anal., Systems dev., Systems implem., Systems support, Network admin., DB admin.
Industries: Generalist, Mfg., Svcs., Communications, Insurance, High tech, Software

---

Exclusive Search Consultants

26250 Euclid Ave., Ste. 805
Euclid, Ohio 44132
(216) 731-7733
(800) 731-8683
Fax: (216) 731-2096
Email: hireyounow@aol.com
Web: www.ohiocareers.com

Key Contact - Specialty:
Mr. Robert Holzheimer - *Data processing, MIS, engineering, manufacturing, materials management*

Description: Our success depends upon both satisfied applicants and clients. Client firms rely on our ability to screen and place personnel with professionalism and confidentiality.
Functions: Mfg., Materials, IT, MIS mgmt., Systems anal., Systems dev., Engineering
Industries: Generalist, Mfg., Software

Exec Tech, Inc.
101 W. Brighton Place
Mt. Prospect, Illinois 60056-1003
(847) 797-1880
Fax: (847) 797-1989
Email: exectk@aol.com
Web: www.bharris.com

Key Contact - Specialty:
Ms. Bea Harris - *Medical devices, high tech capital equipment, scientific instrumentation, biotech processes*

Description: Twenty-five years in global contingency and retained search. Interim and start-up executives and staffing specialists. Expert consulting on international distributor selection and expansion of global operations.

Salary Minimum: $75,000
Functions: Directors, Senior mgmt., Mktg. mgmt., Sales mgmt., R&D, Engineering, Int'l.
Industries: Drugs mfg., Medical devices, Biotech

Affiliates:
Medical Insights Ltd.

Execu-Tech Search Inc.
3500 W. 80th St., Ste. 20
Minneapolis, Minnesota 55431
(612) 893-6915

Key Contact - Specialty:
Mr. Marv Kaiser - *Manufacturing, engineering*
Mr. Greg Kaiser - *Engineering, computer software*

Description: 22 years experience in executive and technical candidates within the following engineering sectors: mechanical product design and the consulting engineering industry.
Functions: Production, Automation, Plant mgmt., Quality, Systems dev., Systems support, Engineering
Industries: Food/bev/tobacco, Chemicals, Drugs mfg., Metal products, Misc. mfg., Packaging, Software

---

The Execu/Search Group
675 Third Ave.
New York, New York 10017-5704
(212) 922-1001
Fax: (212) 922-0033
Email: info@execu-search.com
Web: www.execu-search.com

Key Contact - Specialty:
Mr. Edward Fleischman
Mr. Robert Fligel
Mr. Gary Grossman

Description: Recruitment of accounting, financial, controller/CFO, tax and brokerage back-office professionals. Industries serviced include financial services, communications, manufacturing, real estate and accounting firms.

Salary Minimum: $30,000
Functions: CFO's, Budgeting, Cash mgmt., Credit, Taxes, Risk mgmt.
Industries: Finance, Invest. banking, Brokers, Svcs., Accounting, Communications, Real estate

---

ExecuSource Assoc., Inc.
3232 Cobb Pkwy., Ste. 227
Atlanta, Georgia 30339
(770) 943-4254
Email: execusrc@aol.com

Key Contact - Specialty:
Mr. Melvin P. Larry - *Transportation, MIS, telecommunications*

Description: A retained search firm, dedicated to providing businesses with a cost effective, efficient and quality alternative for locating talented individuals, necessary for long-term organizational success.

Salary Minimum: $40,000
Functions: Generalist, Senior mgmt., Distribution, Sales mgmt., CFO's, MIS mgmt., Minorities
Industries: Generalist, Computer equip., Transportation, Computer svcs., Telecoms, High tech, Software

---

ExecuSource Consultants, Inc.
P.O. Box 680746
Houston, Texas 77268
(281) 257-1340
Fax: (281) 655-9685
Email: xsource@flash.net

Key Contact - Specialty:
Mr. Chris Trapani - *Telecommunications, sales, marketing, engineering, upper management*
Ms. Delores Trapani - *Telecommunications, sales, marketing*

Description: We are a contingency based firm, dedicated to building solid client relationships through integrity, service and performance. Our focus is telecommunications, with emphasis on wireless service providers and vendors.

Salary Minimum: $50,000
Functions: Senior mgmt., Middle mgmt., Product dev., Production, Mktg. mgmt., Sales mgmt., Engineering
Industries: Computer equip., Test/measurement equip., Wholesale, Communications, Telecoms, High tech, Software

---

ExecuTech
P.O. Box 2628
West Lafayette, Indiana 47906
(765) 447-0764

Key Contact - Specialty:
Mr. Thomas P. Fidelle - *Chemistry*

Description: Recruiting chemists, chemical engineers, polymer scientists and environmental engineers for R&D, product development, manufacturing, sales and marketing positions, entry level through management.

Salary Minimum: $25,000
Functions: Product dev., Mkt. research, R&D, Engineering
Industries: Textiles/apparel, Chemicals, Drugs mfg., Plastics/rubber

---

Executive Business Solutions, Inc.
P.O. Box 1589
Bothell, Washington 98041-1589
(425) 485-0660
Fax: (425) 485-3350
Email: ebs@sprynet.com
Web: www.ipa.com/eoffice/425-485-0660.html

Key Contact - Specialty:
Ms. Jeanine K. Hannas - *Software, information systems, engineering*

Description: Software development, information systems, high tech manufacturing and all types of engineering placements. We are a certified Woman-owned business, and contracting with us can be beneficial to meet minority requirements in government contracts.
Functions: Mfg., Mktg. mgmt., Sales mgmt., IT, R&D, Engineering, Technicians
Industries: Energy/utilities, Medical devices, Computer equip., Consumer electronics, Test/measurement equip., High tech, Software

---

Executive Career Search
P.O. Box 480
Lightfoot, Virginia 23090-0480
(757) 564-3013
Fax: (757) 564-1736
Email: headhunter@widomaker.com

Key Contact - Specialty:
Mr. Charles H. Sillery - *Engineering, data processing*

Description: Certified Personnel Consultant, by testing. Cover all engineering and data processing functions on a shared basis. Primary areas of recruiting all construction material industries, chemical, high tech electronics.

Salary Minimum: $35,000
Functions: Middle mgmt., Product dev., Plant mgmt., Purchasing, Systems anal., Systems dev., Engineering
Industries: Agri/forestry/mining, Chemicals, Leather/stone/glass/clay, Consumer electronics, Test/measurement equip.

Executive Connection
8221 Brecksville Rd., Bldg. 3, Ste. 2
Brecksville, Ohio 44141
(216) 838-5657
Email: econnect@staffing.net

Key Contact - Specialty:
Mr. Steven C. Brandvold - *Engineering, quality, operations*
Mr. Vincent Kirkwood - *Food*

Description: Executive/technical search firm specialists in the recruitment and placement of all disciplines in all manufacturing industries.

Salary Minimum: $30,000
Functions: Middle mgmt., Product dev., Production, Automation, Plant mgmt., Quality, R&D
Industries: Generalist, Food/bev/tobacco, Paper, Plastics/rubber, Metal products, Motor vehicles, Misc. mfg.

Executive Direction, Inc.
155 Sansome St., Ste. 400
San Francisco, California 94104
(415) 394-5500
Fax: (415) 956-5186
Email: edi@exdir.com
Web: www.exdir.com

Key Contact - Specialty:
Mr. Fred Naderi - *Executive level, IT*

Description: We specialize in placement of professionals in the areas of telecommunications, information technology and software development.

Salary Minimum: $70,000
Functions: CFO's, Systems anal., Systems dev., Systems implem., Systems support, Network admin., DB admin.
Industries: Software

Affiliates:
Executive Direction, Inc.

Executive Exchange Corp.
2517 Hwy. 35 G-103
Manasquan, New Jersey 08736
(908) 223-6655
Fax: (908) 223-1162

Key Contact - Specialty:
Ms. Elizabeth B. Glosser - *Computer related sales, recruiters, managers*

Description: Professional recruitment in computer related sales, outplacement, career counseling, contingency and retainer.

Salary Minimum: $25,000
Functions: Mktg. mgmt., Sales mgmt., Direct mktg., Personnel, Systems implem., Mgmt. consultants
Industries: Computer svcs., Mgmt. consulting, Human resource svcs.

Executive Partners Inc.
49 Welles St., Ste. 202
Glastonbury, Connecticut 06033
(860) 657-1458
Fax: (860) 657-1459
Email: execpart@execpartners.com
Web: www.execpartners.com

Key Contact - Specialty:
Ms. Holly Seymour - *Management consulting*

Description: Executive search consulting serving the management consulting industry worldwide. Special emphasis on the recruitment of IT, reengineering, strategy and operations consultants.

Salary Minimum: $85,000
Functions: Production, Purchasing, Systems anal., Systems implem., Network admin., Engineering, Mgmt. consultants
Industries: Drugs mfg., Invest. banking, Mgmt. consulting, New media, Telecoms, High tech

---

Executive Placement Services
5901-C Peachtree Dunwoody Rd., Ste. 498
Atlanta, Georgia 30328
(770) 396-9114
Fax: (770) 393-3040
Email: execplac@mindspring.com
Web: www.execplacement.com

Key Contact - Specialty:
Mr. John J. Weiss - *Middle to upper management, retail*

Description: Fourteen years of experience in recruiting and executive search. Focus is on middle and upper management in retail, hospitality and gaming industries.

Salary Minimum: $30,000
Functions: Senior mgmt., Middle mgmt.
Industries: Retail, Hospitality, Entertainment

Branches:
P.O. Box 1140
Waldorf, Maryland 20604-1140
(301) 934-5457
Fax: (301) 609-6087

Key Contact - Specialty:
Mr. John Ehman - *Retail management & executives*

Executive Placement Consultants
2700 River Rd., Ste. 107
Des Plaines, Illinois 60018
(847) 298-6445
Fax: (847) 298-8393
Email: epc@wwa.com

Key Contact - Specialty:
Mr. Michael Colman - *Finance, accounting, human resources, systems*

Description: Over 20 years of experience in finance, accounting, human resources, systems and placement of temp professional, finance and accounting temps.

Salary Minimum: $35,000
Functions: Generalist, Benefits, Personnel, Finance, CFO's, Budgeting, M&A
Industries: Generalist, Food/bev/tobacco, Transportation, Finance, Pharmaceutical svcs., Communications

---

Executive Recruiters Agency, Inc.
14 Office Park Drive, Ste. 100
P.O. Box 21810
Little Rock, Arkansas 72221-1810
(501) 224-7000
Fax: (501) 224-8534
Email: gtdowns@execrecruit.com
Web: www.execrecruit.com

Key Contact - Specialty:
Mr. Greg Downs - *Mechanical design engineers, safety engineers, managers*
Mr. Aaron Lubin

Description: We are dedicated to the delivery of staffing services of the highest quality. Our commitment is to provide our clients with extraordinary value, efficiency through the personal caring of our staff and modern technology.

Salary Minimum: $35,000
Functions: Product dev., Automation, Sales mgmt., MIS mgmt., Systems anal., Systems support, Engineering
Industries: Chemicals, Plastics/rubber, Machinery/Appliances, Motor vehicles, Computer equip., Accounting, High tech

---

Executive Recruiters Int'l.
1150 Griswold, Ste. 3000
David Stott Bldg.
Detroit, Michigan 48226-1976
(313) 961-6200
Fax: (313) 963-1826
Web: www.execrecruiters.com

Key Contact - Specialty:
Ms. Kathleen A. Sinclair - *Automotive manufacturing (international)*

Description: Technical specialists; automotive, sales, international, manufacturing, management, environmental, computer, finance, healthcare and property management specialists on staff.

Salary Minimum: $30,000
Functions: Senior mgmt., Mfg., Materials, Sales & mktg., IT, Engineering, Int'l.
Industries: Construction, Mfg., Motor vehicles, Svcs., Government, Environmental svcs., High tech

Executive Recruiters

600 108th Ave. NE, Ste. 242
Bellevue, Washington 98004
(206) 447-7404
Fax: (425) 451-8424
Email: info@execr.com

Key Contact - Specialty:
Mr. Jerry Taylor - *Software, sales & marketing, finance & accounting, product management*

Description: We are committed to developing continuing client relationships by providing excellent service. We approach each of our employer clients with the highest degree of professionalism, integrity, confidentiality, tact and urgency.

Salary Minimum: $65,000
Functions: Directors, Senior mgmt., Middle mgmt., Mfg., Sales & mktg., IT, Engineering
Industries: Computer equip., Computer svcs., New media, High tech, Software

Executive Recruiters, Inc.

813 Ondossagan Way
Madison, Wisconsin 53719-3249
(608) 833-4004
Fax: (608) 833-4774
Email: gobadger2@aol.com

Key Contact - Specialty:
Mr. Gilbert E. Ormson - *Engineering (technical, management), manufacturing (technical, management), information technology (systems analysis/programming, management)*

Description: Professional recruiting firm specializing in recruitment and placement of technical and management personnel for engineering, manufacturing and technical sales/marketing positions of manufacturing companies. Since 1979 we have matched talents with challenging opportunities.

Salary Minimum: $35,000
Functions: Middle mgmt., Product dev., Production, Plant mgmt., Systems dev., Network admin., Engineering
Industries: Plastics/rubber, Metal products, Machinery/Appliances, Computer equip., Test/measurement equip., High tech, Software

Executive Recruitment Services, Inc. (ERS, Inc.)

3210 Ennfield Lane
Duluth, Georgia 30096
(678) 584-9810
(800) 774-1517
Fax: (678) 584-9811
Email: ers@mindspring.com
Web: www.allhitech.com

Key Contact - Specialty:
Mr. Randall Shute - *High technology engineering*

Description: We specialize in high technology job searches (usually requiring a technical degree) in medical, telecommunications, semiconductor and computer industries.

Salary Minimum: $40,000
Functions: Product dev., Automation, Sales mgmt., Systems dev., Systems implem., R&D, Engineering
Industries: Mfg., Medical devices, Machinery/Appliances, Computer equip., Consumer electronics, High tech, Software

Affiliates:
Segal & Assoc.

Executive Referral Services, Inc.

8770 W. Bryn Mawr, Ste. 110
Chicago, Illinois 60631
(773) 693-6622
Fax: (773) 693-8466

Key Contact - Specialty:
Mr. Bruce Freier - *Hospitality, retail*
Mr. Mark Gray - *Restaurant, entertainment*
Ms. Monica Lanum - *Hotel industry*
Mr. Garry Chesla - *Retail, grocery*
Ms. Susanne Tabisz - *Healthcare*
Mr. Layne Marshall - *Restaurant Management*

Description: Our national network, impeccable references and complete commitment to our assignments, have resulted in our reputation as the source for recruitment within the hotel, restaurant, retail, club, gaming, entertainment, construction and real estate industries.

Salary Minimum: $25,000
Functions: Senior mgmt., Allied health, Benefits, Personnel, CFO's, Int'l.
Industries: Construction, Retail, Finance, Hospitality, Entertainment, Accounting, Real estate

Executive Registry

1200 McGill College Ave., Ste. 1910
Montreal, Quebec H3B 2L1
Canada
(514) 866-7981
Fax: (514) 866-7093
Email: donylee@ican.net

Key Contact - Specialty:
Mr. Harvey Stewart - *General management, finance, real estate*

Description: Full service management recruitment servicing the Montreal and Quebec marketplace for over thirty-five years.

Salary Minimum: $50,000
Functions: General mgmt., Mfg., Sales & mktg., HR mgmt., Finance, IT, Engineering
Industries: Generalist, Mfg., Retail, Svcs., Packaging, Real estate, High tech

Executive Resource Assoc.

1612 Bay Breeze Drive
Virginia Beach, Virginia 23454
(757) 481-6221
Fax: (757) 481-1944

Key Contact - Specialty:
Mr. Dave David - *Chemicals, plastics, agricultural chemicals, manufacturing*

Description: TEN association is a recruiting network of over 600 offices throughout U.S. and covers most professional disciplines and industries.

Salary Minimum: $45,000
Functions: Generalist, Middle mgmt., Production, Plant mgmt., Sales mgmt., R&D, Engineering
Industries: Generalist, Agri/forestry/mining, Chemicals, Plastics/rubber, Paints/petroleum products, Misc. mfg., Software

Executive Resource Inc.

553 S. Industrial Drive
P.O. Box 356
Hartland, Wisconsin 53029
(414) 369-2540
Fax: (414) 369-2558
Email: executiveresource@pitnet.net

Key Contact - Specialty:
Mr. William H. Mitton - *Accounting & finance, human resources*
Mr. Duane Strong - *Manufacturing, engineering professionals*
Mr. Peter Lamb - *Banking*

Description: A professional recruiting firm that specializes in identifying and evaluating those professionals that are in the top 20% of their field based on skill level and academic achievement.

Salary Minimum: $35,000

Functions: Mfg., Materials, HR mgmt., Finance, CFO's, Engineering
Industries: Mfg., Lumber/furniture, Paper, Medical devices, Plastics/rubber, Machinery/Appliances, Finance

---

Executive Resource Systems
P.O. Box 2992
Capistrano Beach, California 92624
(949) 248-3800
Fax: (949) 496-4407

Key Contact - Specialty:
Mr. Steve Brody - *Accounting, finance, systems, engineering, human resources*

Description: Your resource for permanent and contract placements throughout the USA. On-line with the world's largest candidate database. Over 1000 affiliate offices in all 50 states. Performance! Professionalism! Results!

Salary Minimum: $40,000
Functions: HR mgmt., Finance, CFO's, Taxes, IT, Engineering, Mgmt. consultants
Industries: Mfg., Finance, Accounting, Communications, High tech, Biotech, Healthcare

Affiliates:
Steve Brody & Assoc.

Executive Sales Search
5136 S. Drew Court
Littleton, Colorado 80123
(303) 979-4531
Fax: (303) 948-6691
Email: essearch@plinet.com
Web: www.executivesalessearch.com

Key Contact - Specialty:
Mr. Jonathan Pollack - *Sales & marketing, digital imaging, information technology*
Ms. Jeanne Chisum - *Sales & marketing, imaging, voice communications, data communications*

Description: Dedicated to the recruitment of top level sales, sales support and marketing personnel on a national basis. We specialize in the digital imaging, document processing, information technology and telecommunications fields.

Salary Minimum: $30,000
Functions: Directors, Middle mgmt., Advertising, Mkt. research, Mktg. mgmt., Sales mgmt., Direct mktg.
Industries: Computer equip., Computer svcs., Publishing, Telecoms, High tech

---

Executive Search Consultants
2108 Appaloosa Circle
Petaluma, California 94954-4654
(707) 763-0100
Email: peg@escba.com
Web: www.escba.com

Key Contact - Specialty:
Ms. Peg Iversen Grubb - *Software product development*
Ms. Kat Reed - *Software product development*

Description: We specialize in software product development primary team building for Silicon Valley start-ups. Many inter/intranet clients as well as established corporations. MS Windows, Window NT and Unix only. No MIS or IT, please.

Salary Minimum: $70,000
Functions: Directors, Senior mgmt., Middle mgmt., R&D, Engineering
Industries: High tech, Software

Executive Search Consultants, Inc.
3116 N. Federal Hwy.
Lighthouse Point, Florida 33064
(954) 783-1833
Fax: (954) 783-1890
Email: lenkurtz@mindspring.com
Web: www.insurancerecruiters.com

Key Contact - Specialty:
Mr. Leonard A. Kurtz - *Property & casualty insurance generalist*

Description: The company works within the property and casualty insurance industry with a majority of the searches for actuaries, claims professionals and underwriters with a concentration in professional liability and reinsurance.

Salary Minimum: $50,000
Functions: Senior mgmt., Middle mgmt., Mktg. mgmt., Sales mgmt., CFO's, Risk mgmt.
Industries: Misc. financial, Accounting, Insurance

Affiliates:
Larese y Asociados

Executive Search Consultants Corp.
8 S. Michigan Ave., Ste. 1205
Chicago, Illinois 60603
(312) 251-8400
Fax: (312) 251-8401

Key Contact - Specialty:
Mr. Jack Flynn - *Insurance*
Mr. William Weatherstone - *Insurance*
Ms. Sandy Kinney - *Telecommunications*
Mr. Bill Williams - *Oil, gas, electrical utilities*
Mr. Joe Marcello - *Non-profit*
Mr. Brent O'Brien - *Oil, gas, electrical utilities*

Description: Recruitment without delegation ensures high quality execution tailored to transform the ideal to tangible. Offering counsel in partnership with client, sharing observations and experience, building fidelity through commitment. Firm size affords full time and attention.

Salary Minimum: $50,000
Functions: Senior mgmt., Middle mgmt., CFO's, Cash mgmt., Risk mgmt., Mgmt. consultants, Non-profits
Industries: Energy/utilities, Broadcast & Film, Telecoms, Aerospace, Insurance

---

Executive Search Group LLC
1441 4th St., Ste. 200
Santa Monica, California 90401-3405
(310) 395-2320
(800) 677-8098
Fax: (310) 395-8078
Email: phil@esg.cc

Key Contact - Specialty:
Mr. Phil Stephenson - *Insurance, property & casualty, MIS consulting*

Description: Specialists in the property-casualty insurance field on a national level. Our working relationships encompass carrier companies, brokerage houses including reinsurance, excess, surplus and various risk management positions. Also, MIS- primarily information technology, project managers for financial services and communications.

Salary Minimum: $40,000
Functions: Senior mgmt., IT, MIS mgmt., Systems dev., Systems implem., Network admin.
Industries: Insurance

Executive Search Group, Inc.
44 Thornridge Drive
Colchester, Connecticut 06415
(860) 537-2373
Fax: (860) 537-2374
Email: exec.search.grp@snet.net

Key Contact - Specialty:
Mr. Rudy Brann - *Packaging, mechanical engineering*

Description: We are a contingency search group specializing in sales managers, general managers and engineering disciplines in packaging, automotive and HVAC environments.

Salary Minimum: $40,000
Functions: Generalist, Senior mgmt., Packaging
Industries: Svcs., Aerospace, Packaging, Non-classifiable industries

---

Executive Search Int'l.
1700 Alma Drive, Ste. 370
Plano, Texas 75075-6936
(972) 424-4714
Fax: (972) 424-5314

Email: esi370@airmail.net
Web: www.hbcesi.com

Key Contact - Specialty:
Mr. Ed Nalley - *Sales & marketing, consumer products*
Ms. Linda Rogers - *Category management-consumer products*
Ms. Ginger Nalley - *Category management-consumer products*
Mr. Jeff Nalley - *Sales & marketing, consumer products*

Description: Specialist in non-food consumer products with key focus on HBC and GM from presidents to VPs or market and field management and marketing in North America.

Salary Minimum: $40,000
Functions: Senior mgmt., Middle mgmt., Advertising, Mkt. research, Mktg. mgmt., Sales mgmt., Customer svc.
Industries: Soap/perfume/cosmetics, Drugs mfg., Medical devices

Executive Search, Ltd.

4830 Interstate Drive
Heitman Centre Tri-County
Cincinnati, Ohio 45246-1114
(513) 874-6901
Fax: (513) 870-6348
Email: executivesearch@executivesearch.net
Web: www.executivesearch.net

Key Contact - Specialty:
Mr. James J. Cimino - *COO's, CEOs (mainly manufacturing)*
Mr. Steve Storer - *Automotive, foundry (all technical & tech sales)*
Mrs. Terry Cimino - *Technical & operations (metal fab, metal machining & electronics)*
Mr. Jim Phillips - *Packaging (designers & sales)*
Mr. Don Gold - *Finance & accounting*
Mrs. Sandy Nickley - *Healthcare (providers)*
Mr. Steven Dong - *Information systems, IT, MIS, CIO's*
Mr. Joe Diersing - *Information systems, IT, MIS, CIO's*
Mr. John Detling - *Information, IT, MIS, CIO's*
Mr. John Vujeec - *Human resources, training, O.D., compensation, benefits*

Description: Seasoned account executives with extensive prior experience in manufacturing, engineering, marketing, human resources and general manufacturing, foundry, automotive, capital equipment, food, pulp/paper, IS/IT and healthcare. Also provide expert witness services.

Salary Minimum: $50,000
Functions: Senior mgmt., Plant mgmt., Purchasing, Sales mgmt., Benefits, Budgeting, Engineering
Industries: Paper, Medical devices, Plastics/rubber, Metal products, Machinery/Appliances, Consumer electronics, Packaging

Executive Search of New England, Inc.

131 Ocean St.
South Portland, Maine 04106
(207) 741-4100
Fax: (207) 741-4110
Email: najoban@nlbbs.com
Web: www.nationaljobbank.com

Key Contact - Specialty:
Mr. Robert L. Sloat - *Sales & marketing*
Mr. Robert T. Thayer - *Finance & accounting*

Description: Executive recruiting firm covering Maine, N.H. Mostly contingency, some retainer search in data processing, accounting, sales, retail, insurance, human resources, engineering, medical and pharmaceutical sales, finance and general management.

Salary Minimum: $30,000
Functions: Generalist, Middle mgmt., Plant mgmt., Physicians, Mkt. research, Benefits, CFO's
Industries: Generalist

Executive Search of America, Inc.

22700 Shore Ctr. Drive
Cleveland, Ohio 44123
(216) 261-7400
Fax: (216) 289-1635
Email: carp@execsearchamerica.com
Web: www.execsearchamerica.com

Key Contact - Specialty:
Mr. Edward Carpenter - *Wireless telecommunications, data processing, IT, engineering, & sales*

Description: Executive search $40,000 - $250,000 salary range. Key disciplines: telecommunications, wireless communications; P.C.S., cellular, paging, software/hardware engineering, AMPS, CDMA, TDMA and GSM technologies, RF engineering. Expertise in wireless recruiting.

Salary Minimum: $40,000
Functions: Senior mgmt., Sales & mktg., Sales mgmt., IT, Systems dev., Network admin., Engineering
Industries: Consumer electronics, Test/measurement equip., New media, Telecoms, Aerospace, High tech, Software

Executive Search Placements, Inc.

P.O. Box 17403
Boulder, Colorado 80308
(303) 776-0094
Fax: (303) 776-3017
Email: espinc@concentric.net
Web: www.concentric.net/~espinc

Key Contact - Specialty:
Mr. Richard Baggott - *Public finance, investment bankers*

Description: Specialist in public finance and related areas working from database in excess 100,000. Background based on municipal sales, management and recruiting experience since 1978.

Salary Minimum: $50,000
Functions: Generalist, Directors, Senior mgmt., Middle mgmt.
Industries: Invest. banking

Executive Search Plus, Inc.

401 E. Colfax Ave., Ste. 207
South Bend, Indiana 46617
(219) 232-1818
Fax: (219) 288-3838
Email: bassmannfl@aol.com
Web: execsearchplus.com

Key Contact - Specialty:
Mr. Donald G. Walker - *Manufacturing, engineering, human resources, quality, materials*
Mr. Michael Niedbalski - *Engineering, telecommunications*

Description: Executive search, outplacement and contract services in engineering, management, manufacturing, data processing and financial areas.
Functions: Mfg., Materials, HR mgmt., Finance, IT, R&D, Engineering
Industries: Generalist, Construction, Plastics/rubber, Metal products, Machinery/Appliances, Motor vehicles, Computer equip.

Executive Search Team
(a division of Staffing Matters L.L.C.)

32255 Northwestern Hwy., Ste. 190
Farmington Hills, Michigan 48334
(248) 932-9770
Fax: (248) 932-9777
Email: staffmatters@msn.com

Key Contact - Specialty:
Mr. Phillip Levin - *CEO, COO, CIO, CFO, VP-Sales*
Mr. Marv Talan - *Finance, marketing, human resources, sales*
Mr. Roger Manning - *Information technology, accounting, sales*
Ms. Barbara Hanssen - *Information technology, sales*

Description: We are a contingent fee firm specializing in upper level recruiting in the areas of general management, finance, information technology, sales, marketing and human resources

Salary Minimum: $75,000
Functions: Senior mgmt., Plant mgmt., Mkt. research, Budgeting, Systems anal., Systems dev., Mgmt. consultants
Industries: Mfg., Finance, Accounting, Mgmt. consulting, Human resource svcs., Insurance, Real estate

The Executive Source

2201 - 11th Avenue, Ste. 401
Regina, Saskatchewan S4P 0J8
Canada
(306) 359-2550
Fax: (306) 359-2555
Email: execsource@cableregina.com

Key Contact - Specialty:
Ms. Holly Hetherington
Ms. Judith Chelsom

Description: Executive search is our only business. Two senior professionals offer independence, consultation, extensive database, documentation, presentation process and guarantee.
Functions: Directors, Senior mgmt., Production, Plant mgmt., Materials, CFO's, Engineering
Industries: Energy/utilities, Metal products, Finance, Higher ed., Government, Healthcare, Non-classifiable industries

Executive Strategies, Inc.

1425 Market Blvd., Ste. 330-N7
Roswell, Georgia 30076
(770) 552-3085
Fax: (770) 643-9921
Email: esi@mindspring.com
Web: www.executivestrategiesinc.com

Key Contact - Specialty:
Mr. Holland R. Earle - *General management, information technology, nuclear power, software services*

Description: Extensive senior management experience in a multitude of industries. Understanding of internal and external recruiting processes. Work with clients through the entire process: position description, reference checking and follow up after placement. Principals are former corporate executives.

Salary Minimum: $85,000
Functions: Generalist, General mgmt., Sales & mktg., HR mgmt., IT, Mgmt. consultants
Industries: Generalist, Energy/utilities, Computer svcs., Mgmt. consulting, Human resource svcs., High tech, Software

Executive/Retail Placement Assoc.

6001 Montrose Rd., Ste. 702
Rockville, Maryland 20852
(301) 231-8150
Fax: (301) 881-2918
Email: eparpa@erols.com

Key Contact - Specialty:
Mr. Mark J. Suss - *Retail all areas*

Description: Retail industry specialists for: merchandising, operations, management, finance, distribution, loss prevention and management information systems. Personality testing, employee screening and drug testing. Employee contracting.

Salary Minimum: $35,000
Functions: General mgmt., Advertising
Industries: Retail, Advertising/PR

ExecutiveFit

526 Old Liverpool Rd., Victorian Sq.
P.O. Box 8
Syracuse, New York 13207-1512
(315) 451-5457
(315) 453-7608
Fax: (315) 461-9857
Email: executivefit@netsitesys.com
Web: www.ipa.com

Key Contact - Specialty:
Mr. Timothy J. Dermady - *Software, data communications, telecommunications, Big 6 consultants, consumer packaged goods*

Description: Emphasis on an executive's fit within the following disciplines: data communications, telecommunications, software, consumer goods and Big 6 management consulting. Product manager, project, program managers. Senior managers, director level and above in marketing disciplines. Considerable activity with internationally known management consulting firms.

Salary Minimum: $80,000
Functions: Directors, Senior mgmt., Mktg. mgmt., Training, Systems anal., Mgmt. consultants, Minorities
Industries: Food/bev/tobacco, Consumer electronics, Accounting, Human resource svcs., Advertising/PR, Telecoms, Software

Executives Worldwide, Inc.

158 NE Greenwood Ave.
Dept. KP97
Bend, Oregon 97701
(541) 385-5405
Fax: (541) 385-5407
Email: eworldwide@eworldwide.com
Web: www.eworldwide.com

Key Contact - Specialty:
Mr. Donald S. Sullivan - *Biotechnology, pharmaceuticals*
Mr. Tony Graham - *High technology, computer*
Mr. Keith Erickson - *Legal*
Mr. Cotter Ray Gould - *Executive level*

Description: National and international recruiting in: environmental engineering, biotechnical, legal: environmental and patent. High tech, data processing, telecommunications, information technology.

Salary Minimum: $45,000
Functions: Senior mgmt., IT, MIS mgmt., Systems dev., R&D, Attorneys, Int'l.
Industries: Pharmaceutical svcs., Legal, Communications, Environmental svcs., High tech, Software, Biotech

International Branches:
Lamma Island

EXETER 2100

Computer Park
P.O. Box 2120
Hampton, New Hampshire 03842
(603) 926-6712
Fax: (603) 926-0536

Key Contact - Specialty:
Mr. Bruce A. Montville - *Information technology*

Description: A retained search firm exclusively in the information systems and telecommunications disciplines. Client/server and mainframe software is a specialty. Clients are nationwide. All industries.

Salary Minimum: $50,000
Functions: MIS mgmt., Systems anal., Systems dev., Systems implem., Systems support, R&D, Engineering
Industries: Energy/utilities, Mfg., Transportation, Finance, Svcs., High tech, Software

eXsource Inc.

920 Bay Street
P.O. Box 2082
Beaufort, South Carolina 29901
(843) 525-0333
Fax: (843) 525-1073
Email: exsource@hargray.com
Web: www.exsource-inc.com

Key Contact - Specialty:
Mr. Samuel F. Domby - *Banking information systems, healthcare information systems*

Description: Specialize in information systems (MIS) recruiting for banking and healthcare industries.

Salary Minimum: $25,000

Functions: IT, MIS mgmt., Systems anal., Systems dev., Systems implem., Systems support
Industries: Finance, Banking, Misc. financial, Computer svcs., High tech, Software, Healthcare

---

F.L.A.G.
625 E. County Line Rd.
Springfield, Ohio 45502
(937) 342-0200
Fax: (937) 342-0201
Email: flag@flagsearch.com
Web: www.flagsearch.com

Key Contact - Specialty:
Mr. Tom S. Warren - *Lubricant industry*

Description: Specializing in fuel, lubricant, asphalt, grease, oil field and refinery chemicals. Research, sales/marketing and testing positions. Serving large and small firms nationwide. Proven confidential performance. References available.

Salary Minimum: $40,000
Functions: Mkt. research, Mktg. mgmt., Sales mgmt., R&D, Engineering
Industries: Energy/utilities, Chemicals, Test/measurement equip.

Fabian Assoc. Inc.
521 Fifth Ave., 17th Floor
New York, New York 10017
(212) 697-9460
Fax: (212) 697-9488
Email: jfab@erols.com

Key Contact - Specialty:
Ms. Jeanne Fabian - *Finance & quantitative analysis, direct marketing*

Description: President has extensive experience in accounting and finance, having worked for 15 years in Fortune 500 companies. She is also a CPA and MBA and has many contacts in Fortune companies as well as in the financial services industry.

Salary Minimum: $40,000
Functions: Distribution, Mktg. mgmt., Direct mktg., Budgeting, Cash mgmt., Systems dev., Mgmt. consultants
Industries: Chemicals, Misc. mfg., Invest. banking, Misc. financial, Entertainment, Insurance, Non-classifiable industries

---

FAI
P.O. Box 200248
Denver, Colorado 80220-0248
(303) 388-8486
Fax: (303) 355-4213

Key Contact - Specialty:
Mr. Gary Franklin - *Computer professionals, software*

Description: National search firm specializing in placing certified and non-certified computer professionals in positions ranging from entry level programmers to MIS directors.
Functions: Generalist, Sales & mktg., Benefits, M&A, IT
Industries: Generalist, Construction, High tech, Software

Fallstaff Search
111 Warren Rd., Ste. 4B
Hunt Valley, Maryland 21030
(410) 666-1100
Fax: (410) 666-1119
Email: bobchert@aol.com

Key Contact - Specialty:
Mr. Robert Chertkof - *Medical*

Description: Sales, sales management, marketing, nurse managers, director of nursing, utilization review, case management, director of pharmacy, managed care executives, home health, clinical trial coordinators.

Salary Minimum: $35,000
Functions: Senior mgmt., Healthcare, Nurses, Allied health, Sales mgmt., Finance, R&D
Industries: Pharmaceutical svcs., Real estate, Biotech, Healthcare

---

Fament, Inc.
17 Aldrich Rd., Ste. B
Columbus, Ohio 43214
(614) 261-0552
Fax: (614) 261-1820
Email: fament@famentinc.com
Web: www.famentinc.com

Key Contact - Specialty:
Mr. Marty Shuherk - *Insurance*

Description: Midwest's oldest insurance recruiting firm assisting companies, agencies, brokers and banks with mid to top management level personnel needs.

Salary Minimum: $75,000
Functions: Sales mgmt., Int'l.
Industries: Insurance

Dorothy W. Farnath & Assoc., Inc.
5 Pawtucket Drive
Cherry Hill, New Jersey 08003
(609) 751-1993
Fax: (609) 751-7753
Email: dwfinc@aol.com

Key Contact - Specialty:
Ms. Dorothy W. Farnath
Ms. Melissa F. Scott
Mr. Frederick R. Clemens
Ms. T. Nancy Davis

Description: Specialize in recruiting for all positions within the clinical and biotech markets. Our skills in identifying qualified candidates are enhanced by our strong technical education and expertise. Exceptional reputation, consistent ethical standards, excellent references.
Functions: Directors, Senior mgmt., Middle mgmt., Mkt. research, Mktg. mgmt., Sales mgmt., Systems dev.
Industries: Medical devices, Biotech, Healthcare

Faro Consultants Int'l.
8298-B Old Courthouse Rd.
Vienna, Virginia 22182
(703) 506-4555
Email: faro@alltech-intl.com
Web: farocons@aol.com

Key Contact - Specialty:
Mr. George Amato - *Employee benefits, human resource consultants, actuaries & attorneys*
Ms. Susan Lee Moe - *International benefits consultants*

Description: Specialized recruiting in employee benefits and human resources consulting, legal and actuarial areas. Experts at identifying consulting talent inside and outside of consulting firms.

Salary Minimum: $80,000
Functions: Health admin., Benefits, Taxes, Mgmt. consultants, Attorneys, Int'l.
Industries: Legal, Mgmt. consulting, Human resource svcs., Healthcare

---

Fast Switch, Ltd.
37 W. Bridge St., Ste. 200
Dublin, Ohio 43017
(614) 336-3690
Fax: (614) 336-3695
Email: mark_pukita@fastswitch.com

Key Contact - Specialty:
Mr. Mark Pukita - *High technology, information systems, sales*
Ms. Kimberly A. Crosby - *High technology, information systems, sales*

Description: Our principals have a minimum of 15 years of experience doing the jobs for which we perform searches. Our clients get only highly qualified candidates because of this--saving them time and expense.

Salary Minimum: $50,000
Functions: Sales & mktg., Sales mgmt., IT, MIS mgmt., Systems anal., Systems dev., Systems implem.
Industries: Generalist, Computer svcs., Mgmt. consulting, New media, Telecoms, High tech, Software

Federal Placement Services

35 Park Ave., Ste. 6M
Suffern, New York 10901
(914) 357-4577

Key Contact - Specialty:
Ms. Joan Bialkin - *Banking*

Description: Executive search exclusively for the banking and financial communities representing major banking, finance and mortgage institutions in the metropolitan Northeast.

Salary Minimum: $30,000
Functions: Senior mgmt., Middle mgmt., Advertising, Mkt. research, CFO's, Cash mgmt., Risk mgmt.
Industries: Banking, Misc. financial

James Feerst & Assoc., Inc.

Eagle Ridge Plaza, Ste. 200
6613 Eagle Ridge Drive
Tucson, Arizona 85750-0931
(520) 577-1500

Key Contact - Specialty:
Mr. James E. Feerst - *Pharmaceutical*
Ms. Judith E. Miller - *Pharmaceutical*

Description: Executive search firm specializing in the worldwide pharmaceutical, biotechnology, diagnostics and medical device fields. Broad range of functional experience. Expert in recruiting physicians. Active in the U.S., Europe and Japan.

Salary Minimum: $50,000
Functions: Product dev., Physicians, Nurses, Health admin., Mktg. mgmt., R&D, Engineering
Industries: Drugs mfg., Medical devices, Pharmaceutical svcs., Biotech, Healthcare

A. E. Feldman Assoc., Inc.

445 Northern Blvd.
Great Neck, New York 11021
(516) 719-7900
Fax: (516) 466-5122
Email: info@execrecruiter.com
Web: www.execrecruiter.com

Key Contact - Specialty:
Mr. Mitchell Feldman - *Telecommunications, information technology*
Mr. Abe Feldman - *Watches, jewelry, retailing, fashion*
Ms. Carol Schwam - *Telecommunications, information technology*
Mr. Ira Skalet - *Information technology*
Mr. Philip Schene - *Telecommunications*
Mr. Neal DerAris - *Information technology*
Ms. Claudeth Crowe - *Research*
Ms. Olga Milman - *Technical*
Mr. Michael Harris - *Technical*
Mr. Ben Wilder - *Technical*

Description: Recruitment/search firm specializing in information technology and telecommunications industries. Quick response, high-quality candidates, industry experience and insight into corporate needs account for our rapid growth and client loyalty. Placements nationwide.

Salary Minimum: $40,000
Functions: Senior mgmt., Middle mgmt., Mktg. mgmt., Sales mgmt., MIS mgmt., Systems dev., Mgmt. consultants
Industries: Retail, Computer svcs., Mgmt. consulting, New media, Telecoms, High tech, Software

Feldman Gray & Assoc. Inc.

45 St. Clair Ave. W., Ste. 700
Toronto, Ontario M4V 1K9
Canada
(416) 515-7600
Fax: (416) 515-7595

Key Contact - Specialty:
Mr. Frank Gray - *Generalist, senior management*
Mr. R.J. Donald - *Generalist, senior management*
Mr. Ron Meyers - *Generalist, senior management*
Mr. Corey Daxon - *Middle management, senior management, generalist*
Ms. Vickie Ralles - *Middle management, senior management, generalist*

Description: One of Canada's largest retainer executive search practices providing services to a broad range of industries for over 18 years.

Salary Minimum: $60,000
Functions: Generalist
Industries: Generalist

Fenzel Milar Assoc.

602 Quincy St.
Ironton, Ohio 45638
(740) 532-6409
Fax: (740) 533-0813
Email: fmil@wwd.net

Key Contact - Specialty:
Mr. John F. Milar - *Generalist*

Description: Wide variety of success; many industries, occupations.

Salary Minimum: $30,000
Functions: Middle mgmt., Production, Plant mgmt., Budgeting, Systems implem., Network admin., Engineering
Industries: Generalist, Chemicals, Metal products, Machinery/Appliances, Motor vehicles

Fergason Assoc., Inc.

1350 Lake Shore Drive, Ste. 1715
Chicago, Illinois 60610
(312) 642-6376
Fax: (312) 642-6332

Key Contact - Specialty:
Mr. Loel G. Hahn - *Senior level executives, entrepreneurs, director of manufacturing, director of operations*

Description: Our organization operates as a contingency and retainer executive search firm. We work in all industries with emphasis on the manufacturing, financial and distribution fields.

Salary Minimum: $40,000
Functions: Generalist, Directors, Senior mgmt., Middle mgmt., Admin. svcs., Production, Plant mgmt.
Industries: Generalist, Mfg., Plastics/rubber, Paints/petroleum products, Consumer electronics, Test/measurement equip., Packaging

Fergus Legal Search & Consulting, Inc.

1325 Ave. of the Americas, Ste. 2302
New York, New York 10019-6026
(212) 767-1775
Fax: (212) 315-0351
Email: colin@ferguslex.com
Web: www.ferguslex.com

Key Contact - Specialty:
Mr. Colin Fergus - *General counsel, senior counsel, partners*
Ms. Jean M. H. Fergus - *General counsel, senior counsel, partners*

Description: We are one of the largest search firms devoted exclusively to attorney recruitment. The principals, Jean & Colin Fergus, are considered experts in their field and have authored numerous articles for major national and international publications.

Salary Minimum: $100,000
Functions: Attorneys, Int'l.
Industries: Legal

Fernow Assoc.

191 Presidential Blvd., Ste. BN13
Bala Cynwyd, Pennsylvania 19004-1207
(610) 664-2281
Fax: (610) 664-2779
Email: cfernow220@aol.com
Web: members.aol.com/cfernow/home/fajobs.html

Key Contact - Specialty:
Mr. Charles S. Fernow - *Computers, information technology, engineers, scientists, electronics*
Mr. S. George Goich - *Human resources, labor relations*
Mr. Robert A. Burchell - *Engineering, scientific*

Description: Offers search and placement within the electronics, computer, aerospace, high technology, information technology and nuclear fields. Also provides outplacement for firms who are downsizing within those areas. Serves US and international.

Salary Minimum: $35,000
Functions: Mfg., Sales & mktg., HR mgmt., IT, R&D, Engineering, Int'l.
Industries: Mfg., Svcs., Communications, Defense, Aerospace, High tech, Software

---

Ferrari Search Group
16781 Chagrin Blvd., Ste. 164
Cleveland, Ohio 44120
(216) 491-1122
Fax: (216) 491-1510

Key Contact - Specialty:
Mr. S. Jay Ferrari
Ms. Kathryn Poole-Ferrari
Mr. Howard Rubin
Mr. Harvey Epstein

Description: Executive search on a proactive basis serving the financial community on a national basis. We maintain an active computerized database of executives in investment firms, banks, investment banking institutions and corporate financial executives.

Salary Minimum: $60,000
Functions: Senior mgmt., Middle mgmt., Product dev., Mktg. mgmt., Sales mgmt., Finance
Industries: Finance, Insurance

Guild Fetridge Acoustical Search, Inc.
560 White Plains Road, Suite 500
Tarrytown, New York 10591
(914) 467-7851
Fax: (914) 467-7847
Email: GFAcoustic@aol.com

Key Contact - Specialty:
Mr. Guild Fetridge - *Acoustics, vibration, noise control, HVAC, audio, audio-visual*

Description: Specialists in acoustics, vibration noise control, HVAC, audio, and audio-visual for engineering, scientific, sales and marketing functions.

Salary Minimum: $60,000
Functions: Directors, Middle mgmt., Mktg. mgmt., Sales mgmt., R&D, Engineering, Technicians
Industries: Generalist, Energy/utilities, Construction, Mfg., Environmental svcs., Aerospace, High tech

---

Jerry Fields Assoc.
(a company of the Howard-Sloan-Koller Group)
353 Lexington Ave., 11th Floor
New York, New York 10016
(212) 661-6644
Fax: (212) 557-9178
Email: hsk@hsksearch.com
Web: www.hsksearch.com

Key Contact - Specialty:
Mr. Edward R. Koller, Jr. - *General management, operations*
Mr. Philip Growick - *Creative (copy), art, graphics*
Ms. Sharon Spielman - *Marketing, advertising agencies, corporate advertising*

Description: In both the creative and account management areas, executive search and consulting for advertising and sales promotion agencies, design firms and direct companies and corporations.

Salary Minimum: $30,000
Functions: Senior mgmt., Middle mgmt., Advertising, Mktg. mgmt., Sales mgmt., PR
Industries: Advertising/PR, New media, Telecoms

Affiliates:
Tesar-Reynes, Inc.

Financial Connections Company
5008 Andrea Ave.
Annandale, Virginia 22003
(703) 425-4240
Fax: (703) 323-6919
Email: m6272@erols.com

Key Contact - Specialty:
Mr. David A. Richard - *Life insurance, securities, financial services*

Description: Founder of firm has 30+ years of management experience in the life insurance and securities fields in addition to numerous certifications in the fields (CLU, CHFC, CFP, FLMI).

Salary Minimum: $50,000
Functions: Middle mgmt., Sales mgmt., Personnel, CFO's, Cash mgmt., MIS mgmt., Attorneys
Industries: Invest. banking, Brokers, Misc. financial, Legal, Computer svcs., Accounting, Insurance

---

Financial Resource Assoc., Inc.
105 W. Orange St.
Altamonte Springs, Florida 32714
(407) 869-7000
Fax: (407) 682-7291
Email: finres@iag.net
Web: www.banking-financejobs.com

Key Contact - Specialty:
Mr. John Cannavino - *Commercial banking*
Mr. Terry L. Krick - *Mortgage banking*

Description: We are a national executive search firm specializing in the recruitment and placement of middle and senior management executives for mortgage companies, banks, savings and loans and other financial institutions throughout the country.

Salary Minimum: $40,000
Functions: Cash mgmt., Risk mgmt.
Industries: Finance, Banking, Invest. banking, Brokers, Misc. financial, Real estate

---

Financial Search Corp.
2720 Des Plaines Ave., Ste. 106
Des Plaines, Illinois 60018
(847) 297-4900
Fax: (847) 297-0294
Email: admin@financial-search.com

Key Contact - Specialty:
Mr. Robert J. Collins - *Accounting & finance*

Description: Our firm specializes in the recruitment, screening and placement of accounting and financial professionals in the $40,000 to $100,000 salary range.

Salary Minimum: $25,000
Functions: Finance, CFO's, Budgeting, Cash mgmt., Taxes
Industries: Generalist

Financialjobs.com
481 El Jina Lane
Ojai, California 93023
(805) 640-1849
Fax: (805) 640-0523
Email: mmuller@financialjobs.com
Web: www.financialjobs.com

Key Contact - Specialty:
Mr. Michael Muller - *Accounting, financial, internet, CPAs, MBAs, CMA's*

Description: Accounting and finance middle management jobs in southern California and the entire USA - from staff to financial analysts, auditors, controllers and CFO's - all jobs are listed on the internet at http://www.financialjobs.com. Please visit our site before sending us resumes.

Salary Minimum: $30,000

Functions: CFO's, Budgeting, Cash mgmt., Credit, Taxes, M&A, MIS mgmt.
Industries: Food/bev/tobacco, Machinery/ Appliances, Computer equip., Consumer electronics, Misc. mfg., Entertainment, Broadcast & Film

---

Eileen Finn & Assoc., Inc.

237 Park Ave., 21st Floor
New York, New York 10017
(212) 687-1260
Fax: (212) 551-1473
Email: efinn@sprynet.com

Key Contact - Specialty:
Ms. Eileen Finn - *Financial services, human resources*

Description: With over 17 years in the recruiting/search business we will continue to service the financial services industry with particular emphasis on human resources.

Salary Minimum: $100,000
Functions: Generalist, Middle mgmt., Mkt. research, Benefits, Personnel, Training, Int'l.
Industries: Banking, Invest. banking, Brokers, Entertainment, Mgmt. consulting, Human resource svcs.

Finn & Schneider Assoc., Inc.

1730 Rhode Island Ave. NW, Ste. 1212
Washington, District of Columbia 20036
(202) 822-8400
Fax: (202) 466-2898
Email: finnschne4@aol.com

Key Contact - Specialty:
Ms. Susan Schneider - *Attorneys*
Ms. Jacquelyn Finn - *Attorneys*

Description: Place partners and associates in all legal specialty areas. Advise on law firm mergers and opening of branch offices. Firm has a national and international referral network. Retainer and contingency search.
Functions: Attorneys
Industries: Legal

Finney-Taylor Personnel & Management Consultants Ltd.

#200, 703 6th Ave. SW
Calgary, Alberta T2P 0T9
Canada
(403) 231-2707
Email: mailbox@finney-taylor.com
Web: www.finney-taylor.com

Key Contact - Specialty:
Mr. David Skode - *Information systems*
Mr. David O'Brien - *Engineering*
Mr. Rick Marrin - *Information systems*

Description: Technical recruiting both permanent and contract in the areas of IT, engineering and accounting.

Salary Minimum: $30,000
Functions: Mktg. mgmt., Training, Finance, Taxes, IT, Engineering
Industries: Energy/utilities, Mfg., Transportation, Communications, Government, Software

---

First Search America, Inc.

P.O. Box 85
Ardmore, Tennessee 38449
(256) 423-8800
Fax: (256) 423-8801
Web: www.firstsearch@ardmore.net

Key Contact - Specialty:
Mr. Jim Fowler - *Agribusiness*

Description: We recruit and place experienced, degreed individuals in the animal health, poultry, seed and related agribusiness industries. Sales/marketing, production, research and development, technical services. Nationwide. Never a fee to applicant.

Salary Minimum: $35,000
Functions: Senior mgmt., Middle mgmt., Admin. svcs., Mfg., Mktg. mgmt., Sales mgmt., R&D
Industries: Agri/forestry/mining, Food/bev/ tobacco, Drugs mfg.

Branches:
P.O. Box 1183
Athens, Alabama 35612
(256) 216-5931
Fax: (256) 216-5932
Key Contact - Specialty:
Mr. Luke Haggard - *Poultry*

4023 Poole Valley Rd. SW
Decatur, Alabama 35603
(256) 308-0880
Fax: (256) 308-0990
Key Contact - Specialty:
Mr. Ray Johnson - *Poultry*

First Search Inc.

6584 N. Northwest Hwy., Ste. D
Chicago, Illinois 60631
(773) 774-0001
Fax: (773) 774-5571
Email: fsihunter@aol.com

Key Contact - Specialty:
Mr. Allen M. Katz
Mr. Michael R. Zarnek
Mr. Charles Szajkovics

Description: Technical recruiters servicing the telecom, cellular, PCS and wireless industry from senior executive levels in engineering, operations, sales and marketing and R&D, as well as temp-to-perm, contracting and specialty staffing.

Salary Minimum: $35,000
Functions: Middle mgmt., Mktg. mgmt., Sales mgmt., Systems anal., Systems dev., Systems implem., Engineering
Industries: Computer equip., Consumer electronics, New media, Telecoms, High tech, Software

---

Fishel HR Assoc., Inc.

5125 N. 16th St., Ste. B-125
Phoenix, Arizona 85016
(602) 266-5600
Fax: (602) 266-5656
Email: nhlt31b@prodigy.com

Key Contact - Specialty:
Mr. Richard A. Fishel - *Human resources, accounting, general management*
Mr. John L. Marshall - *Engineering, manufacturing management, data processing, MIS*

Description: 30+ years a leading, full service, contingency search firm recruiting nationwide for various industries in the areas of human resources, engineering, management, financial, DP and other professional and technical disciplines.

Salary Minimum: $45,000
Functions: Production, Plant mgmt., Benefits, Personnel, Training, CFO's, MIS mgmt.
Industries: Computer equip., Consumer electronics, Finance, Human resource svcs., Aerospace, High tech, Software

---

Jack Stuart Fisher Assoc.

P.O. Box 835
Lakewood, New Jersey 08701
(732) 367-4950
Fax: (732) 367-2012

Key Contact - Specialty:
Mr. Jack Stuart Fisher - *Pharmaceutical, biotechnology research*

Description: Full service search for scientists. Experience dealing with universities, think tanks, biotech and pharmaceutical companies. Some work in other functional areas. Increasing involvement in consulting and ventures.

Salary Minimum: $60,000
Functions: Directors, Senior mgmt., Middle mgmt., R&D, Engineering
Industries: Chemicals, Drugs mfg., Venture cap., Pharmaceutical svcs., Biotech

---

Fisher-Todd Assoc.
(a division of Winston Resources, Inc.)

535 Fifth Ave., Ste. 800A
New York, New York 10017
(212) 986-9052
Fax: (212) 682-1742

Key Contact - Specialty:
Mr. Saul Samet - *Marketing research, MIS, brand management, market analysis, general search*
Mr. Michael Aronin - *Brand management, sales promotion, communications, finance*
Mr. Ronald Franz - *Brand management, sales promotion, communications, finance*

Description: We recruit at mid to senior levels of management within functional specialties in a wide variety of industries. We build long-term relationships by bringing professionalism and expertise to the recruitment process. National/international assignments. Specialty: marketing management.

Salary Minimum: $50,000
Functions: Middle mgmt., Advertising, Mkt. research, Mktg. mgmt., Direct mktg., Int'l.
Industries: Food/bev/tobacco, Soap/perfume/cosmetics, Drugs mfg., Retail, Finance, Telecoms, Healthcare

James L. Fisk & Assoc.
1921 Buckington Drive
Chesterfield, Missouri 63017
(314) 394-5381

Key Contact - Specialty:
Mr. James L. Fisk - *Healthcare, management consultants, manufacturing, materials management, SAP consultants*

Description: All industries - specialize in SAP consultants, management consultants, manufacturing, materials management and healthcare.

Salary Minimum: $30,000
Functions: Generalist, Production, Plant mgmt., Materials Plng., Nurses, Systems implem., Mgmt. consultants
Industries: Generalist, Medical devices, Misc. mfg., Computer svcs., Mgmt. consulting, High tech, Healthcare

Susan Fletcher Attorney Employment Services
501 Grant St., 450 Union Trust Bldg.
Pittsburgh, Pennsylvania 15219
(412) 281-6609
Fax: (412) 281-2949
Email: sufletcher@aol.com

Key Contact - Specialty:
Ms. Susan Fletcher - *Attorneys (for law firms, corporations)*

Description: 15 years experience as law school placement director and legal search consultant. Will supply references from client employers and candidates placed.
Functions: Minorities, Attorneys
Industries: Energy/utilities, Mfg., Finance, Legal, Accounting, High tech, Software

Flexible Resources, Inc.
399 E. Putnam Ave.
Cos Cob, Connecticut 06807
(203) 629-3255
Fax: (203) 629-3257

Key Contact - Specialty:
Ms. Nadine Mockler - *Permanent part-time & interim management staffing*
Ms. Laurie Young - *Permanent part-time & interim management staffing*

Description: Placement of highly qualified professionals in flexible work arrangements, e.g. permanent part-time, job sharing, telecommuting and interim management staffing.
Functions: General mgmt., Purchasing, Sales & mktg., HR mgmt., Finance, IT, Mgmt. consultants
Industries: Mfg., Finance, Svcs., Communications, High tech, Software, Healthcare

Branches:
1114 Hi-Point St.
Los Angeles, California 90035
(213) 939-5048
Fax: (213) 939-2774
Key Contact - Specialty:
Mr. Roy Young - *Permanent part-time, interim management staffing*

542 Hopmeadow St., #222
Simsbury, Connecticut 06070
(203) 651-5299
Fax: (203) 651-5964
Key Contact - Specialty:
Ms. Susan Glasspiegel - *Permanent part-time & interim management staffing*
Ms. Susan Rietano-Davey - *Permanent part-time & interim management staffing*

186 Reservoir Rd.
Chestnut Hill, Massachusetts 02167
(617) 731-2729
Fax: (617) 731-2603
Key Contact - Specialty:
Ms. Suzanne Austin - *Permanent part-time & interim management staffing*
Ms. Kim Whelan - *Permanent part-time & interim management staffing*

310 Madison Ave., Ste. 1801
New York, New York 10017
(212) 697-3867
Fax: (212) 697-3877
Key Contact - Specialty:
Ms. Patricia Burns - *Finance*

Flowers & Assoc.
2100 W. Alexis
Toledo, Ohio 43613
(419) 472-6900
Fax: (419) 472-6902
Email: hdhunter@aol.com

Key Contact - Specialty:
Mr. William J. Ross - *Manufacturing, Engineering*
Mr. Marc A. Ross

Description: Over 20 years of assisting companies in their hard to fill positions. Experienced working with all levels of management with enthusiasm.

Salary Minimum: $35,000
Functions: Middle mgmt., Plant mgmt., Purchasing, Mktg. mgmt., Sales mgmt., Systems anal., Engineering
Industries: Generalist, Plastics/rubber, Metal products, Machinery/Appliances, Motor vehicles, Computer equip., High tech

David Fockler & Assoc., Inc.
25944 Paseo Estribo
Monterey, California 93940
(408) 649-6666
Fax: (408) 649-0600

Key Contact - Specialty:
Mr. David B. Fockler - *Sales & marketing management for food, consumer products, food ingredients, food equipment and HBC manufacturers*

Description: Sales and marketing management positions for food, including retail and food service and for consumer, HBC, food equipment and food ingredient manufacturers. Mid-management ($50K) to lower upper management ($150K).

Salary Minimum: $50,000
Functions: Mktg. mgmt., Sales mgmt.
Industries: Food/bev/tobacco, Soap/perfume/cosmetics

Branches:
940 S. River Rd.
Naperville, Illinois 60540
(630) 428-3194
Fax: (630) 428-3201
Key Contact - Specialty:
Mr. Steve Swan

Focus Consulting Services, Inc.
1507 S. University Dr.
Plantation, Florida 33324
(954) 476-0411
Fax: (954) 476-2685
Email: alouis@focusjobs.com
Web: www.focusjobs.com

Key Contact - Specialty:
Ms. Anne Louis

Description: Recruiter to the benefit consulting industries including actuaries, health and welfare consultants, systems and outsourcing administration.

Functions: Middle mgmt., Health admin., Benefits, Budgeting, Systems anal., Systems dev., Mgmt. consultants
Industries: Invest. banking, Computer svcs., Human resource svcs., Telecoms, Insurance, High tech, Software

Branches:
1404 Crowell Rd.
Vienna, Virginia 22182
(703) 759-1119
Fax: (703) 759-1149
Email: GJacobs@focusjobs.com
Key Contact - Specialty:
Mr. Gilbert B. Jacobs - *Systems*

Focus Executive Search

431 S. Seventh St., Ste. 2475
Minneapolis, Minnesota 55415
(612) 706-4444
Fax: (612) 783-9286
Web: focuses@aol.com

Key Contact - Specialty:
Mr. Tim McLafferty - *Food*
Mr. Tim Schultz - *Food manufacturing equipment industry*
Ms. Angela Mass - *Food service industry*
Ms. Pam Carlson
Ms. Molly Barrett

Description: Excel at partnering with food industry companies. High level of repeat business clients. Offer an understanding of the food industry for timely and successful targeted searches.

Salary Minimum: $40,000
Functions: Directors, Senior mgmt., Middle mgmt., Mfg., Product dev., Mktg. mgmt., Sales mgmt.
Industries: Food/bev/tobacco, Chemicals, Machinery/Appliances, Transportation, Biotech

Ford & Assoc., Inc.

808 Greenbay Trail
Myrtle Beach, South Carolina 29577
(843) 497-5350
Fax: (843) 497-5351
Email: fordsearch@aol.com

Key Contact - Specialty:
Mr. Travis Ford - *Textile manufacturing (line & staff positions), chemical, plastic, metal fabrication professionals*
Mrs. Merlin B. Ford - *Generalist*

Description: Specialists in confidential recruiting for textiles, chemicals, plastics and metals industry management; for engineers and staff professionals within all industries.

Salary Minimum: $35,000
Functions: Mfg., Materials, HR mgmt., Finance, Budgeting, IT, Engineering
Industries: Textiles/apparel, Chemicals, Drugs mfg., Plastics/rubber, Metal products, Machinery/Appliances, Motor vehicles

Ford & Ford

105 Chestnut St., Ste. 34
Needham, Massachusetts 02492
(781) 449-8200
Fax: (781) 444-7335
Email: seek@staffing.net

Key Contact - Specialty:
Ms. Eileen F. Ford - *Retail, distribution, information technology, financial services, direct marketing, supply chain*

Description: Retail, direct marketing, human resources. Training and development. Established in 1968. Telemarketing, information systems. Call center technology.

Salary Minimum: $50,000
Functions: Middle mgmt., Materials, Sales mgmt., Direct mktg., HR mgmt., IT, MIS mgmt.
Industries: Transportation, Wholesale, Retail, Finance, Telecoms, Insurance, Software

Forest People Int'l. Search Ltd.

1100 Melville St., 800 Sun Life Plaza
Vancouver, British Columbia V7P 3G7
Canada
(604) 669-5635
Fax: (604) 684-4972
Email: people@forestpeople.com
Web: www.forestpeople.com

Key Contact - Specialty:
Mr. Ronald J. Hogg - *Forest industry, senior management*
Mr. David Laurence - *Forest industry, forestry management, manufacturing management*
Mr. Jason McRobbie - *Forest industry, pulp & paper, panelboard management*
Mr. Bill Waschuk - *Forest industry, sawmills, remanufacturing management*

Description: Canada's largest forest industry recruiting firm. Serve over 80 client companies worldwide. Use database of 9,000 candidates and highly effective search methods.
Functions: General mgmt., Plant mgmt., Mktg. mgmt., Sales mgmt., R&D, Engineering, Int'l.
Industries: Agri/forestry/mining, Lumber/furniture, Paper

Fortuna Technologies Inc.

1270A Lawrence Station Rd., Ste. A
Sunnyvale, California 94089
(408) 541-0200
(408) 973-1529
Fax: (408) 541-0300
Email: pad@fortuna.com
Web: www.fortuna.com

Key Contact - Specialty:
Mr. Pad N. Swami - *Oracle financials, SAP, PeopleSoft, BAAN, DBA's*
Mr. T. C. Ashok - *EDA, database internals, ATM, KIVA, Netscape*
Mr. William E. Lynch - *Mainframe, CICS, DB2, COBOL, Y2K*

Description: Delivers on time under budget, with int'l. sourcing, focus on Oracle financials, SAP, BAAN, PeopleSoft, DBAs, administrators, Windows, HUI, Java, Corba, Y2K, EDA for financial, manufacturing, utilities and retail segments.

Salary Minimum: $55,000
Functions: General mgmt., MIS mgmt., Systems anal., Systems dev., Systems support, Network admin., DB admin.
Industries: Mfg., Wholesale, Finance, Svcs., Communications, Software, Biotech

Branches:
2903 Lakeridge Lane
Dunwoody, Georgia 30338
(770) 936-8411
Fax: (770) 458-7852
Email: psuri@bellsouth.net
Key Contact - Specialty:
Mr. Prem Suri - *Mainframe, Y2K, GUI*

177 Pershing Ave.
Iselin, New Jersey 08830
(908) 404-1033
Fax: (908) 404-1312
Email: fortunanj@aol.com
Key Contact - Specialty:
Mr. Sanjay Nair - *Mainframe, Y2K, SY base*

International Branches:
Aldermaston, Hyderabad

Affiliates:
Nicco Corporation
SBM, Inc.

Fortune Personnel Consultants of Huntsville, Inc.

3311 Bob Wallace Ave., Ste. 204
Huntsville, Alabama 35805
(256) 534-7282
Fax: (256) 534-7334
Email: huntfpc1@ro.com
Web: www.wayf.com/fortune.html

Key Contact - Specialty:
Mr. Bob Langford - *Operations management, manufacturing engineering, management, electronics, electromechanical industries*
Ms. Judy Langford
Mr. Pat Henry - *Electrical engineering, hardware/software*
Mr. Andrew Henshaw - *Engineers (metal industries)*
Mr. Bob Henshaw - *Operations management (metals industries), environmental engineering (all industries), safety engineering*

(all industries), human resources (all industries)
Ms. Lynn Lamb - *Purchasing & materials, P&IC (all industries)*
Mr. Matt Langford - *Accounting & finance, manufacturing & process engineers (electronics industries)*
Mr. Lindy Bell - *Plastics, rubber, distribution*
Ms. Anneta Simmons - *Test Engineering & test engineering management in electronics, marketing/business development in electronics/computer related industries*
Mr. Hal Myers - *Information technology*
Mr. Hugh Hanson - *Quality (all industries)*
Ms. Crystal Orange

Description: Full service, nationwide. Areas include general management, managers and professionals in the fields of manufacturing, materials, purchasing, quality, engineering, test and software.

Salary Minimum: $30,000
Functions: Middle mgmt., Plant mgmt., Purchasing, Benefits, CFO's, MIS mgmt., Engineering
Industries: Plastics/rubber, Motor vehicles, Computer equip., Consumer electronics, Test/measurement equip., Accounting, Software

---

F-O-R-T-U-N-E Personnel Consultants of San Diego
332 Encinitas Blvd., Ste. 200
Encinitas, California 92024
(760) 944-8980
Fax: (760) 944-0075
Email: fortune@frontiernet.net

Key Contact - Specialty:
Mr. Carmine A. Furioso - *Regulatory affairs, quality assurance, quality control, clinical research, engineering*
Ms. Donna DeRario - *Regulatory affairs, clinical research, data management*

Description: We are a national executive search firm specializing in the placement of professionals in the medical device, pharmaceutical and biotechnology fields. Also temps in software and MIS.
Functions: Directors, Senior mgmt., Middle mgmt., Product dev., Quality, CFO's
Industries: Drugs mfg., Medical devices, Pharmaceutical svcs., Biotech

---

Fortune Personnel Consultants
2615 Pacific Coast Hwy., Ste. 330
Hermosa Beach, California 90254
(310) 376-6964
Fax: (310) 376-7173
Email: beverlyhills@fpcweb.com

Key Contact - Specialty:
Mr. Marc Kasten - *Medical device, pharmaceutical, biotechnology*

Description: Technical positions in medical device, pharmaceutical and biotech industries, including engineering, research and development, manufacturing management, quality assurance, quality control and regulatory.

Salary Minimum: $50,000
Functions: Middle mgmt., Mfg., Product dev., Plant mgmt., Quality, R&D, Engineering
Industries: Drugs mfg., Medical devices, Biotech

Fortune Personnel Consultants of Colorado Springs
6165 Lehman Drive, Ste. 202
Colorado Springs, Colorado 80918
(719) 599-7353
Fax: (719) 599-7339
Email: fortune@fortunejobs.com
Web: www.fortunejobs.com

Key Contact - Specialty:
Mr. Ron Curtis - *Computer industry (sales, marketing, engineering)*

Description: Specialists in computer industry-hardware, software and graphics companies. Placing engineering, marketing, technical support and sales personnel.
Functions: Mktg. mgmt., Sales mgmt., Systems dev., Systems support, R&D, Engineering, Int'l.
Industries: Computer equip., Consumer electronics, Computer svcs., New media, Telecoms, High tech, Software

---

F-O-R-T-U-N-E Personnel Consultants of Greenwood Village
7400 E. Arapahoe Rd., Ste. 200
Greenwood Village, Colorado 80112
(303) 773-0047
Fax: (303) 773-0048
Web: www.fpcexecsearch.com

Key Contact - Specialty:
Mr. Geoff Pike - *Food & beverage processing, pharmaceutical, consumer products manufacturing*

Description: Our objective is to excel in the placement industry and to deliver results. We will consult with clients and individuals for accomplishments that are mutually beneficial. We are focused on the consumer products industry and work all manufacturing disciplines.

Salary Minimum: $40,000
Functions: Production, Plant mgmt., Quality, Purchasing, Distribution, Personnel, Engineering
Industries: Food/bev/tobacco, Soap/perfume/cosmetics, Drugs mfg.

F-O-R-T-U-N-E Personnel Consultants of Denver, Inc.
7800 S. Elati St., Ste. 319
Littleton, Colorado 80120
(303) 795-9210
Fax: (303) 795-9215
Email: jd@fpcdenver.com

Key Contact - Specialty:
Mr. Jan Dorfman - *Engineering, scientific, clinic, quality, regulatory*

Description: Our office offers consultants with over 30 years of direct experience in the technical fields and regulated industries.
Functions: Mfg., Product dev., Automation, Quality, Systems dev., R&D, Engineering
Industries: Drugs mfg., Medical devices, Biotech

F-O-R-T-U-N-E Personnel Consultants of Wilmington
191 S. Chapel St.
Newark, Delaware 19711
(302) 453-0404
Fax: (302) 453-0405
Email: hdhntrlaw@aol.com

Key Contact - Specialty:
Mr. Leonard A. Weston - *Biopharm industries (operations, manufacturing, quality, information systems, engineering management)*
Ms. Joan C. Weston - *Biopharmaceuticals industries (research & development)*

Description: Our firm was the first in the system to specialize in the biotech and pharmaceuticals industries. Now in our 12th year. Principals have advanced degrees and personal experience in their recruiting specialties. One of approximately one hundred Fortune offices nationwide.

Salary Minimum: $50,000
Functions: Directors, Senior mgmt., Production, Plant mgmt., Quality, Systems anal., R&D
Industries: Drugs mfg., Pharmaceutical svcs., Biotech

F-O-R-T-U-N-E Personnel Consultants of Tampa
2531 Landmark Drive, Ste. 207
Clearwater, Florida 33761
(813) 797-9577
Fax: (813) 791-8128

Email: fpctampa@gte.net

Key Contact - Specialty:
Mr. Ted Brill - *Purchasing, operations, manufacturing management*
Mr. Michael Brill - *Logistics, materials management*
Mr. Dan Sarver - *Quality*

Description: Our recruiters have 51 years of senior manufacturing and recruiting experience. We perform the role of hiring manager to screen candidates to bring our clients uncompromising standards of qualifications to spec.
Functions: Production, Plant mgmt., Quality, Purchasing, Materials Plng., Distribution
Industries: Medical devices, Computer equip., Transportation, Telecoms, Aerospace, Packaging, High tech

---

Fortune Personnel Consultants of Jacksonville
3000-6 Hartley Rd.
Jacksonville, Florida 32257
(904) 886-2471
Fax: (904) 886-2472
Email: fortune@fpcjax.com
Web: www.fpcjax.com

Key Contact - Specialty:
Mr. Bob Pepple - *Engineers, quality disciplines, manufacturing professionals, material handlers*

Description: We are a nationwide leader in the recruitment and placement of middle management and executive level personnel with major corporations throughout the United States. This office specializes in engineers, quality, manufacturing professionals and material handlers.

Salary Minimum: $35,000
Functions: General mgmt., Mfg., Materials, IT, Engineering
Industries: Mfg., Telecoms, Environmental svcs., Packaging, High tech, Software

---

F-O-R-T-U-N-E Personnel Consultants of Palm Beach
11211 Prosperity Farms Rd., B205
Palm Beach Gardens, Florida 33410
(561) 624-7550
Fax: (561) 624-7551
Email: resume@fortunepalmbeach.com
Web: www.fortunepalmbeach.com

Key Contact - Specialty:
Mr. Eric D. Dmytrow - *Quality (automotive & plastics manufacturing), quality executives, middle management, engineers*
Ms. Andrea Keller - *Purchasing, production & inventory control, materials management, logistics, warehousing*
Mr. John Clayton

Description: We specialize in quality and engineering professionals for the automotive and plastics industries. We also place executives in quality positions for all industries. We have specialists in the procurement, materials and logistics areas for manufacturing. We have a specialty in the medical devices and pharmaceutical industries also.

Salary Minimum: $40,000
Functions: General mgmt., Mfg., Materials, Engineering
Industries: Medical devices, Plastics/rubber, Motor vehicles, Misc. mfg., Insurance

---

F-O-R-T-U-N-E Personnel Consultants of Manatee County
923 Fourth St. W.
Palmetto, Florida 34221
(941) 729-3674
Fax: (941) 729-7927
Email: fortune@gte.net
Web: www.fpcweb.com

Key Contact - Specialty:
Mr. Jeffrey A. Sangster - *Electronic manufacturing (executive, management, technical)*

Description: Over 20 years experience as a plant manager and engineering manager in various high tech electronic manufacturing operations.

Salary Minimum: $40,000
Functions: Product dev., Automation, Plant mgmt., Quality, Purchasing, Materials Plng., Engineering
Industries: Medical devices, Computer equip., Consumer electronics, Test/ measurement equip., Computer svcs., Telecoms, High tech

---

Fortune Personnel Consultants of Sarasota Inc.
98 Sarasota Center Blvd., Ste. C
Sarasota, Florida 34240-9770
(941) 378-5262
Fax: (941) 379-9233
Email: fpcsarasota@packet.net

Key Contact - Specialty:
Mr. Arthur R. Grindlinger - *Manufacturing*

Description: Providing professionals for manufacturing companies up through the executive level. Specialists available in manufacturing operations, materials, purchasing, engineering and quality. Access to national network of recruiters.

Salary Minimum: $30,000
Functions: Product dev., Production, Plant mgmt., Quality, Purchasing, Materials Plng., Distribution
Industries: Generalist

F-O-R-T-U-N-E Personnel Consultants of Atlanta, Inc.
6525 The Corners Pkwy., Ste. 216
Norcross, Georgia 30092
(770) 246-9757
Fax: (770) 246-0526
Email: search@fpccareers.com
Web: www.fpccareers.com

Key Contact - Specialty:
Mr. James M. Deavours

Description: Executive recruitment for manufacturing, engineering, quality, validation, regulatory affairs, R&D, product development, sensory, pharmaceuticals, medical device, food, personal care, cosmetics, home care, chemicals, plastics and electronics.

Salary Minimum: $40,000
Functions: Product dev., Production, Automation, Plant mgmt., Quality, R&D, Engineering
Industries: Food/bev/tobacco, Chemicals, Soap/perfume/cosmetics, Drugs mfg., Medical devices, Plastics/rubber, Consumer electronics

Affiliates:
Alternastaff

F-O-R-T-U-N-E Personnel Consultants of Savannah, Inc.
7 E. Congress St.
Savannah, Georgia 31401
(912) 233-4556
Fax: (912) 233-8633
Email: execsearch@fortunesav.com

Key Contact - Specialty:
Mr. Clark W. Smith - *Manufacturing, operations management, human resources, quality engineering, manufacturing engineering*
Mr. Stark Sutton

Description: We place professionals in manufacturing industries focusing on the following disciplines: manufacturing/ industrial engineering, quality engineers/ managers, purchasing, human resources, materials management, operations management and Latin American positions.
Functions: Senior mgmt., Production, Quality, Purchasing, Benefits, Personnel, Int'l.
Industries: Textiles/apparel, Paper, Metal products, Machinery/Appliances, Motor vehicles, Computer equip., Consumer electronics

---

Fortune of Arlington Heights
825 E. Golf Rd., Ste. 1146
Arlington Heights, Illinois 60005
(847) 228-7205
Fax: (847) 228-7206

Email: forarlht@theramp.net

Key Contact - Specialty:
Mr. Marshall Antonio - *Automotive, quality, manufacturing (engineers, managers), purchasing, materials*

Description: Specialists in the automotive industry.

Salary Minimum: $40,000
Functions: Directors, Senior mgmt., Plant mgmt., Quality, Purchasing, PR, Engineering
Industries: Motor vehicles, Advertising/PR

Fortune Personnel Consultants of Hinsdale, IL

115 E. 1st St., Ste. 2E
Hinsdale, Illinois 60521
(630) 920-1952
Email: fpchinil@starnetinc.com

Key Contact - Specialty:
Mr. Robert J. Kalember, Jr. - *Finance & accounting management*

Description: Principal has over 20 years experience as financial professional with Fortune 50 manufacturers. Providing finance and accounting professionals for manufacturing companies up through the executive level.

Salary Minimum: $50,000
Functions: CFO's, Budgeting, Credit, Taxes, M&A, Int'l.
Industries: Generalist, Mfg., Chemicals, Medical devices, Plastics/rubber, Motor vehicles, Packaging

---

F-O-R-T-U-N-E Personnel Consultants of Southwest Indiana

909 W. Fourth St., P.O. Box 246
Mt. Vernon, Indiana 47620
(812) 838-6636
Fax: (812) 838-6648
Email: gbfort@aol.com
Web: members.aol.com/gbfort/swin.html

Key Contact - Specialty:
Mr. Al Gmutza - *Finance, accounting*
Mr. Gary Fox - *Engineers, chemists, manufacturing operations*

Description: The two principals have over 40 years combined experience in the engineering, manufacturing, materials management and financial areas in the chemical and plastics industries with four Fortune 50 companies.

Salary Minimum: $35,000
Functions: Materials, Sales & mktg., CFO's, Budgeting, IT, R&D, Engineering
Industries: Chemicals, Plastics/rubber, Paints/petroleum products, Motor vehicles, Accounting, Software

---

F-O-R-T-U-N-E Personnel Consultants of South Bend

52303 Emmons Rd., Ste. 27
South Bend, Indiana 46637
(219) 273-3188
Fax: (219) 273-3887
Email: fortune@michiana.org

Key Contact - Specialty:
Mr. Michael Petras - *Engineers, operations management, quality professionals*

Description: We focus exclusively in the automotive and plastic industries.
Functions: Middle mgmt., Product dev., Quality, Engineering
Industries: Motor vehicles

F-o-r-t-u-n-e of Owensboro, Inc.

620 Carlton Drive, Ste. 103
Owensboro, Kentucky 42303
(502) 686-7277
Fax: (502) 686-7215
Email: fortune@fpcky.com
Web: www.fpcky.com

Key Contact - Specialty:
Mr. Joe Vance - *Engineering*

Description: Specialists in manufacturing careers worldwide.
Functions: Product dev., Production, Automation, Plant mgmt., Quality, Productivity, Purchasing
Industries: Medical devices, Plastics/rubber, Metal products, Machinery/Appliances, Motor vehicles, Computer equip., Consumer electronics

---

Fortune Personnel Consultants of Topsfield

458 Boston St., Ste. 2P
Topsfield, Massachusetts 01983
(978) 887-2032
Fax: (978) 887-2336
Email: plastics@topsfpc.com
Web: www.topsfpc.com

Key Contact - Specialty:
Mr. James E. Slate - *Plastics*

Description: Nationwide recruiting for general management, engineering, operations and sales executives exclusively in the plastics industry. Each recruiter has a particular process expertise that allows very focused search capability.

Salary Minimum: $50,000
Functions: Generalist, Senior mgmt., Middle mgmt., Product dev., Plant mgmt., Sales mgmt., R&D, Engineering
Industries: Plastics/rubber

Fortune Personnel Consultants of Bloomfield, Inc.

800 W. Long Lake Rd., Ste. 220
Bloomfield Hills, Michigan 48302
(248) 642-9383
Fax: (248) 642-9575
Email: fcblmhls@ix.netcom.com

Key Contact - Specialty:
Mr. Karl Zimmermann - *Manufacturing, materials management, quality*

Description: As specialists in their industry and discipline, our search consultants possess in-depth knowledge of the business and resources available. Our searches are therefore focused, achieving results quickly and efficiently.

Salary Minimum: $40,000
Functions: Middle mgmt., Production, Plant mgmt., Quality, Purchasing, Materials Plng., Distribution
Industries: Metal products, Machinery/Appliances, Motor vehicles, Computer equip., Consumer electronics, Misc. mfg., High tech

---

F-O-R-T-U-N-E Personnel Consultants

31800 Northwestern Hwy., Ste. 207
Farmington Hills, Michigan 48334-1664
(248) 932-8870
Email: novi@fpcweb.com

Key Contact - Specialty:
Mr. Gary Snyder - *Engineers, finance*

Description: Nationally recognized in engineering, finance, manufacturing and MIS placement.

Salary Minimum: $45,000
Functions: Production, Plant mgmt., Quality, CFO's, Budgeting, Systems dev.
Industries: Plastics/rubber, Motor vehicles, Misc. mfg., Misc. financial, Computer svcs., Accounting

---

F-o-r-t-u-n-e Personnel Consultants of Detroit, Inc.

17515 W. Nine Mile Rd., Ste. 770
Southfield, Michigan 48075
(248) 557-7250
Fax: (248) 557-7260
Email: fpcdet@mich.com

Key Contact - Specialty:
Mr. Mark L. Schwartz - *Attorneys*

Description: Firm specializes in offering legal search services for law firms and corporate legal departments nationwide on a contingency and retained search basis.
Functions: Attorneys
Industries: Legal

F-O-R-T-U-N-E Personnel Consultants of Troy, Inc.

560 Kirts Blvd., Ste. 102
Troy, Michigan 48084
(248) 244-9646
Fax: (248) 244-8568
Email: troy@fpcweb.com

Key Contact - Specialty:
Mr. Michael Dubeck - *Manufacturing (executives & professionals)*
Ms. Debra Hunter - *Healthcare, executives, professionals*

Description: Personalized service, full menu of search and recruitment functions, national candidate network, thorough and creative style locates and delivers top quality executives and professionals, reputation for integrity and excellence.

Salary Minimum: $35,000
Functions: Mfg., Plant mgmt., Healthcare, Physicians, Health admin., Engineering, Specialized services
Industries: Medical devices, Plastics/rubber, Metal products, Motor vehicles, Test/measurement equip., Packaging, Healthcare

F-O-R-T-U-N-E Personnel Consultants of St. Louis-West County

(a division of CSS Enterprises, Inc.)
14377 Woodlake Drive, Ste. 101
Chesterfield, Missouri 63017
(314) 205-1818
Fax: (314) 205-1822
Email: careers@fortune-stl.com
Web: www.fortune-stl.com

Key Contact - Specialty:
Mr. Craig Schultz - *Automotive, metal fabrication, machinery, equipment*
Mrs. Sandy Schultz
Mr. Bill Compton - *plastics*

Description: We have set a distinguished standard for leadership, integrity and quality in recruitment. We provide prompt, efficient, confidential searches and present only qualified professional, management and executive candidates.
Functions: Middle mgmt., Production, Plant mgmt., Quality, Materials Plng., HR mgmt., Engineering
Industries: Plastics/rubber, Metal products, Machinery/Appliances, Motor vehicles, Computer equip., Consumer electronics, Misc. mfg.

F-O-R-T-U-N-E Search Consultants

1736 E. Sunshine, Ste. 707
Springfield, Missouri 65804
(417) 887-6737
Email: info@fortuneswmo.com
Web: www.fortuneswmo.com

Key Contact - Specialty:
Mr. Bill Belle Isle - *Manufacturing management, engineering*
Ms. Patrice Belle Isle - *Manufacturing management, engineering*

Description: Providing professionals nationwide for manufacturing firms seeking the best in executive and technical expertise. Our candidates are thoroughly screened and interviewed prior to presentation to our clients.

Salary Minimum: $36,000
Functions: General mgmt., Mfg., Materials, Finance, IT, Engineering
Industries: Medical devices, Plastics/rubber, Metal products, Machinery/Appliances, Motor vehicles, Computer equip., Test/measurement equip.

Fortune Personnel Consultants

104 E. Main St., Ste. 302
Bozeman, Montana 59715
(406) 585-1332
Fax: (406) 585-2255
Email: fortune@mcn.net

Key Contact - Specialty:
Mr. Ray Regan - *Operations management, biomedical*
Ms. Kate Regan Ciari - *Sales & marketing, engineering, medical device, pharmaceutical*

Description: Recruiting firm specializing in all disciplines within the medical device, pharmaceutical and bio-tech industries.

Salary Minimum: $30,000
Functions: Senior mgmt., Product dev., Quality, Purchasing, Mktg. mgmt., R&D, Engineering
Industries: Drugs mfg., Medical devices, Pharmaceutical svcs., Packaging

Fortune Personnel Consultants

505 W. Hollis St., Ste. 208
Nashua, New Hampshire 03062
(603) 880-4900
Fax: (603) 880-8861
Email: mail@fortunecareers.com
Web: fortunecareers.com

Key Contact - Specialty:
Mr. Norman J. Oppenheim - *Regulatory affairs*

Description: Specialists in the bio-tech, pharmaceutical and medical device industries (with special emphasis on regulatory affairs, quality assurance, clinical affairs, validation, formulations and process engineering).

Salary Minimum: $35,000
Functions: Product dev., Production, Plant mgmt., Quality
Industries: Drugs mfg., Medical devices, Biotech

F-O-R-T-U-N-E Personnel Consultants of Menlo Park, Inc.

16 Bridge St.
Metuchen, New Jersey 08840
(732) 494-6266
Fax: (732) 494-5669
Email: pprovda@castle.net

Key Contact - Specialty:
Mr. Peter Provda - *Materials management (softgoods industry), cosmetics, manufacturing, engineering*

Description: Established more than 20 years ago, this firm has been a leader in recruiting middle and upper level management personnel for growing companies in the cosmetics, pharmaceutical and chemical industries.

Salary Minimum: $35,000
Functions: Middle mgmt., Production, Purchasing, Distribution, Training, R&D, Engineering
Industries: Food/bev/tobacco, Chemicals, Soap/perfume/cosmetics, Drugs mfg., Paints/petroleum products, Packaging

F-O-R-T-U-N-E Personnel Consultants of Bergen County Inc.

350 W. Passaic St.
Rochelle Park, New Jersey 07662
(201) 843-7621
Fax: (201) 843-8189
Email: fortuneb@ix.netcom.com

Key Contact - Specialty:
Mr. Howard G. Klein - *Medical device, pharmaceutical, biotechnology, materials management, operations (all industries) & purchasing (all industries)*

Description: Specialists-tech, mid and senior level in pharmaceutical, biotech and medical device industries. Areas of specialization include QA, quality engineering, engineering, R&D, regulatory affairs, clinical affairs, QC, microbiology, scientific, manufacturing and statistics. Also specialists in mid and senior management in purchasing materials management and operations across all industries.

Salary Minimum: $40,000
Functions: Senior mgmt., Product dev., Quality, Materials, Mktg. mgmt., R&D, Engineering
Industries: Drugs mfg., Medical devices, Metal products, Computer equip., Pharmaceutical svcs., High tech, Biotech

F-O-R-T-U-N-E Personnel Consultants of Rockland County, Inc.

71 E. Eckerson Rd., Ste. A
Spring Valley, New York 10977-3014
(914) 426-3200
Fax: (914) 426-3814
Email: fpcrock@frontiernet.net

Key Contact - Specialty:
Mr. Mark H. Axelrod - *Quality assurance (manufacturing, engineering, operations, metallurgy)*

Description: Nationwide search and placement of engineers and middle managers with emphasis in quality assurance and manufacturing. Services available on a contingency as well as a retained basis. All fees are client (company) paid.

Salary Minimum: $35,000
Functions: Middle mgmt., Product dev., Plant mgmt., Quality, Productivity, Engineering
Industries: Printing, Metal products, Machinery/Appliances, Motor vehicles, Consumer electronics, Misc. mfg.

F-O-R-T-U-N-E Personnel Consultants of Charlotte

315 Main St., Ste. C
P.O. Box 460
Charlotte, North Carolina 28134-0460
(704) 889-1100
Fax: (704) 889-1109
Email: ftnchar@ix.netcom.com
Web: www.ftnchar.com

Key Contact - Specialty:
Mr. David B. Griffith - *Medical devices*
Ms. Sandra Griffith

Description: Executive recruiters specializing in the medical device, pharmaceutical and biotechnical industries. Our consultants are all degreed at the BS/masters level and have work experience in our areas of expertise.

Salary Minimum: $40,000
Functions: Product dev., Production, Plant mgmt., Quality, Mkt. research, Finance, Engineering
Industries: Medical devices, Metal products, Machinery/Appliances, Motor vehicles, Finance

Fortune Personnel Consultants of Greensboro, NC, Inc.

3831 West Market Street
Greensboro, North Carolina 27407
(336) 852-4455
Fax: (336) 852-3429
Email: billmartin@fortunegboro.com
Web: www.fortunegboro.com

Key Contact - Specialty:
Mr. Bill Martin - *Plant management, operations*
Mr. Doug Edwards - *Logistics*
Mr. Rich Bremer - *Materials*
Mr. Larry Brenowitz - *Transportation*

Description: Executive and middle management retainer/contingent recruiting in distribution, transportation, third party logistics and manufacturing (technical and administrative.)

Salary Minimum: $30,000
Functions: Production, Plant mgmt., Productivity, Purchasing, Distribution, Systems implem., Engineering
Industries: Textiles/apparel, Paper, Chemicals, Drugs mfg., Transportation, Wholesale, Retail

Fortune Personnel Consultants of Raleigh, Inc.

7521 Mourning Dove Rd., Ste. 101
Raleigh, North Carolina 27615
(919) 848-9929
Fax: (919) 848-1062
Email: info@fortune-ral.com
Web: www.fortune-ral.com

Key Contact - Specialty:
Mr. Stan Deckelbaum - *Electronics, software, hardware, ME, test, manufacturing*
Mr. Rick Deckelbaum - *Presidents, CEOs, vice presidents (all industries)*
Mr. Randy A. Cagan - *Production management, engineering, QC, ME, project*
Mr. C.C. Jay Brown - *Pulp & paper (all areas), suppliers, packaging, converting*
Mr. David L. Singer - *Purchasing*
Mr. Richard D. Gorberg - *Telecommunications, marketing, product management, wireless, CATV*

Description: With over 25 consultants specializing in a variety of disciplines, we have demonstrated that we can effectively handle all salaried staffing needs for our client firms.

Salary Minimum: $40,000
Functions: Mfg., Materials, Healthcare, Sales & mktg., HR mgmt., Finance, Engineering
Industries: Mfg., Finance, Legal, Accounting, Human resource svcs., High tech, Healthcare

F-O-R-T-U-N-E Personnel Consultants of Cincinnati

8170 Corporate Park Drive, Ste. 304
Cincinnati, Ohio 45242
(513) 469-0808
Fax: (513) 469-0824
Email: fpccin@one.net

Key Contact - Specialty:
Mr. James P. Boule - *General management, operations management, printing, packaging*
Mr. Joseph S. Fenimore - *Purchasing, logistics, materials*
Mr. James P. Pilcher - *Capital goods, machining operations*

Description: Our firm focuses only in disciplines or industries which our consultants have worked in. This provides an in-depth understanding of the clients we serve.

Salary Minimum: $40,000
Functions: Senior mgmt., Middle mgmt., Production, Plant mgmt., Quality, Purchasing, Materials Plng.
Industries: Food/bev/tobacco, Paper, Printing, Plastics/rubber, Metal products, Machinery/Appliances

F-O-R-T-U-N-E of West Portland

543 Third St., Ste. C-3
Lake Oswego, Oregon 97034
(503) 635-0994
Fax: (503) 635-1132
Email: fpcwp@frontiernet.net
Web: www.fpcwp.globalcenter.net

Key Contact - Specialty:
Mr. Mark Vague - *Packaging, plastic, pulp & paper, automotive, medical devices.*

Description: Over 20 years experience in plastics, packaging and related industries.

Salary Minimum: $50,000
Functions: Middle mgmt., Product dev., Production, Plant mgmt., Quality, Packaging, Engineering
Industries: Paper, Printing, Plastics/rubber, Machinery/Appliances, Motor vehicles, Misc. mfg., Packaging

Fortune Personnel Consultants of Allentown, Inc.

3644 Rte. 378, Unit C
Bethlehem, Pennsylvania 18018
(610) 866-1300
Fax: (610) 866-2366
Email: fpcallen@aol.com

Key Contact - Specialty:
Mr. Robert E. Graham - *High technology, computer manufacturing*
Ms. Sara L. Graham

Description: Executive recruiters of professionals for positions in high-tech/computer manufacturing companies. We handle all disciplines within typical manufacturing, development, headquarters organizations.

Salary Minimum: $40,000

Functions: Middle mgmt., Production, Packaging, Personnel, Taxes, Systems anal., R&D
Industries: Printing, Computer equip., Consumer electronics, Test/measurement equip., Human resource svcs., Aerospace, Software

Fortune Consultants of Ft. Washington

455 Pennsylvania Ave., Ste. 105
Ft. Washington, Pennsylvania 19034
(215) 542-9800
Fax: (215) 540-9312
Email: search@fffortune.com

Key Contact - Specialty:
Ms. Suzanne S. Richards - *Legal, insurance investments*

Description: Nationwide placement of attorneys and other professionals for the insurance and ivestment industries. Partnerships, associate placements and mergers in law firms. The District of Columbia office places employee benefit specialists and general attorneys.
Functions: Benefits, Attorneys
Industries: Brokers, Insurance

Branches:
8206 Leesburg Park, Ste. 304
Vienna, Virginia 22182
(703) 848-4640
Fax: (703) 848-4636
Key Contact - Specialty:
Ms. Suzanne Richards

Fortune Personnel Consultants of Anderson, Inc.

100 Miracle Mile, Ste. F
Anderson, South Carolina 29621
(864) 226-5322
Fax: (864) 225-6767
Email: results@fpcsearch.com
Web: www.fpcsearch.com

Key Contact - Specialty:
Mr. Daryl Kress - *Pharmaceutical, medical devices (professionals)*
Mr. Joe Kaiser - *Pharmaceutical, research & development, scientists*

Description: Focus on R&D through manufacturing-formulations, analytical chemistry, quality/regulatory compliance, operations, for pharmaceuticals and medical devices.

Salary Minimum: $50,000
Functions: Directors, Middle mgmt., Product dev., Plant mgmt., Quality, R&D, Engineering
Industries: Chemicals, Soap/perfume/cosmetics, Drugs mfg., Medical devices, Pharmaceutical svcs., Biotech

Affiliates:
Alternastaff

Fortune Personnel Consultants of Hilton Head

52 New Orleans Rd., Ste. 201
Hilton Head Island, South Carolina 29928
(843) 842-7221
Fax: (843) 842-7205
Email: recruit@fpchh.com

Key Contact - Specialty:
Mr. David J. Ducharme - *Medical device, quality assurance, regulatory affairs*
Mr. Lance Beehler - *Medical device, research & development, manufacturing*
Ms. Sandra Dietrich - *Purchasing, materials management, medical device, pharmaceutical, telecommunication, automotive, electronics*
Ms. Donne G. Paine - *Medical device, clinical affairs, marketing, biotechnology, pharmaceutical*

Description: We specialize in the medical device and pharmaceutical industries with our consultants being experts in their particular disciplines.
Functions: Directors, Middle mgmt., Product dev., Production, Quality, Purchasing, Mkt. research
Industries: Drugs mfg., Medical devices, Motor vehicles, Computer equip., Consumer electronics

FORTUNE Personnel Consultants of Charleston, Inc.

410 Mill St., Ste. 106
Mt. Pleasant, South Carolina 29464-4351
(843) 884-0505
Fax: (843) 849-9522
Web: fpc_chas@ix.netcom.com

Key Contact - Specialty:
Mr. Robert Spears - *Automotive manufacturing, quality, engineering*
Mr. Mike Phillips - *Manufacturing (quality & engineering)*

Description: Offering twelve plus years of solid expertise in serving automotive OEM and other manufacturers of fabricated metal, plastic and assembled parts supplying North American automobile domestic and transplant tier I and tier II operations.

Salary Minimum: $40,000
Functions: Middle mgmt., Product dev., Production, Plant mgmt., Quality, Productivity, Purchasing
Industries: Textiles/apparel, Plastics/rubber, Metal products, Machinery/Appliances, Motor vehicles

Fortune Personnel Consultants of Chattanooga Inc.

5726 Marlin Rd.
Franklin Bldg., Ste. 212
Chattanooga, Tennessee 37411-4095
(423) 855-0444
Fax: (423) 892-0083
Email: fortune@cdc.net
Web: www.fpcweb.com

Key Contact - Specialty:
Mr. David W. Dickson - *Manufacturing, consumer goods, human resources*
Ms. Brenda Hays - *Apparel (textile & related)*
Mr. William Alisbrook - *Chemical engineering, manufacturing, process & project engineering*
Mr. Kevin Marunick - *Materials, distribution logistics*

Description: We can satisfy needs nationwide through 100 other franchise offices - strong, fast-paced office dedicated to filling every job order and placing every applicant.

Salary Minimum: $25,000
Functions: Middle mgmt., Production, Plant mgmt., Purchasing, Distribution, Personnel, Engineering
Industries: Textiles/apparel, Chemicals, Plastics/rubber, Consumer electronics, Transportation, Human resource svcs., Packaging

F-O-R-T-U-N-E Consultants of Memphis

52 Timber Creek Drive, Ste. 250
Cordova, Tennessee 38018
(901) 757-5031
Fax: (901) 757-5048
Email: fpcmem@memphisonline.com

Key Contact - Specialty:
Mr. H. Gordon Taylor - *Human resources (all industries)*
Mr. Floyd Schriber - *Engineering, operations management*
Mr. Fred O'Connor - *Engineering, operations management*

Description: Specializing in management and technical searches within specific industries and disciplines. Commitment to professionalism, qualified consultants, industry/discipline specialization and confidentiality.

Salary Minimum: $40,000
Functions: Product dev., Production, Plant mgmt., Quality, HR mgmt., Engineering
Industries: Food/bev/tobacco, Paper, Soap/perfume/cosmetics, Medical devices, Plastics/rubber, Metal products, Machinery/Appliances

F-O-R-T-U-N-E Personnel Consultants of the Tri-Cities, Inc.

2700 S. Roan St., Ste. 206
Johnson City, Tennessee 37601
(423) 926-1123
Fax: (423) 926-1124

Key Contact - Specialty:
Mr. Walter E. Engel - *Engineering, manufacturing, human resources, finance, accounting, quality/reliability positions*

Description: Cost effective multi-discipline recruiting across most manufacturing industries. Firm is led by a former Fortune 50 plant manager and satisfaction is always guaranteed.

Salary Minimum: $40,000
Functions: Generalist, General mgmt., Mfg., Materials, HR mgmt., IT, Engineering
Industries: Plastics/rubber, Metal products, Machinery/Appliances, Motor vehicles, Consumer electronics, Test/measurement equip., Misc. mfg.

F-O-R-T-U-N-E Personnel Consultants of Knoxville
(a division of Fortune Franchise Corporation)

111 Center Park Drive, #1004
Knoxville, Tennessee 37922
(423) 769-9444
Fax: (423) 769-9449
Email: fortunetys@aol.com
Web: members.aol.com/fortunetys/index.htm

Key Contact - Specialty:
Mr. Ken Colbourn - *QC/QA, automotive (engineering), HVAC, plastics, medical devices*
Mr. Paul Morin - *QC/QA, automotive (engineering), HVAC, medical devices, electronics*
Mr. Robert Cutshaw - *Information technology, financial, accounting*
Ms. Becky Arrants - *Human resources professionals*

Description: Staff of industry-recognized leaders in the automotive, manufacturing and high-technology industries. Backed by 110 office network founded in 1959, our recruiters continue as a driving force in our specialties.

Salary Minimum: $40,000
Functions: Mfg., Quality, Productivity, HR mgmt., Finance, IT, Engineering
Industries: Medical devices, Plastics/rubber, Metal products, Machinery/Appliances, Motor vehicles, Misc. mfg., High tech

F-O-R-T-U-N-E Personnel of Nashville

125 Belle Forest Circle, Ste. 205
Bellevue Executive Plaza
Nashville, Tennessee 37221
(615) 662-9110
Fax: (615) 662-9140

Key Contact - Specialty:
Mr. Tom Oglesby - *Operations, engineering, quality, materials, human resources*
Ms. Peggy Oglesby - *Office manager*
Mr. Tim Schroeder - *Engineering, quality*

Description: Recruiting services manufacturing firms specializing in operational management, human resources, engineering, quality assurance, materials management and MIS.

Salary Minimum: $40,000
Functions: General mgmt., Mfg., Materials, Sales & mktg., HR mgmt., IT, Engineering
Industries: Agri/forestry/mining, Plastics/rubber, Metal products, Motor vehicles, Misc. mfg.

FORTUNE Personnel Consultants of North Dallas

1545 W. Mockingbird Lane, Ste. 1020
Dallas, Texas 75235
(214) 634-3929
(800) 618-3929
Fax: (214) 634-7741
Email: philfortun@aol.com

Key Contact - Specialty:
Mr. Philip H. Pritchett - *Medical devices, pharmaceutical, manufacturing technology*
Mr. Norman Spencer - *Medical device, pharmaceutical, manufacturing technology*

Description: We offer quick response to both client and candidate needs with 66 years combined industry experience in medical device, engineering and software.

Salary Minimum: $30,000
Functions: Product dev., Quality, Mktg. mgmt., Sales mgmt., Systems implem., R&D, Engineering
Industries: Drugs mfg., Medical devices, Plastics/rubber, Computer equip., High tech, Software, Biotech

F-O-R-T-U-N-E Personnel Consultants of Houston, Inc.

2555 Central Pkwy.
Houston, Texas 77092
(713) 680-9132
Fax: (713) 680-1737
Email: fortune@ix.netcom.com

Key Contact - Specialty:
Mr. Robert M. Shanley
Ms. Suzanne M. Shanley

Description: Firm specializes in oil and gas, petro chemical, specialty chemical and plastics processing. A new division, ALTERNASTAFF, specializes in professional temporary placement. Assignments range from specialized technical to managerial up to president of small company.

Salary Minimum: $30,000
Functions: Senior mgmt., Plant mgmt., Quality, Sales mgmt., Personnel, R&D, Engineering
Industries: Chemicals, Drugs mfg., Medical devices, Plastics/rubber, Paints/petroleum products, Metal products, Packaging

Fortune Personnel Consultants of Plano

1700 Alma, Ste. 242
Plano, Texas 75075
(972) 509-4809
Fax: (972) 516-0312
Email: fplano2@airmail.net

Key Contact - Specialty:
Ms. Katherine Greenwood - *Quality assurance, regulatory affairs, human resource, product development, engineering*

Description: We specialize in the medical device and pharmaceuticals industries.

Salary Minimum: $40,000
Functions: General mgmt., Mfg., Quality, Materials, HR mgmt., R&D, Engineering
Industries: Drugs mfg., Medical devices, Computer equip., Consumer electronics, High tech, Software, Biotech

Fortune Personnel Consultants of San Antonio, Inc.

10924 Vance Jackson, Ste. 303-K
San Antonio, Texas 78230
(210) 690-9797
Fax: (210) 696-6909
Email: fortunesat@fortunesat.com
Web: fortunesat.com

Key Contact - Specialty:
Mr. Jim Morrisey - *General management, quality reliability, regulatory affairs*
Mr. Stan Witt - *Consumer products, automation equipment*
Mr. Michael King - *Quality, manufacturing, product development*
Mr. Ken Larsen - *Product development, process development*
Mr. Denny Brubaker - *Computer manufacturing, PCB manufacturing*

Description: Since 1980, our expertise has been assisting manufacturing/engineering professionals build their careers, by recruiting and placing senior management to engineers, primarily in the medical, electronics, automotive and consumer products industries.

Salary Minimum: $30,000
Functions: Mfg., HR mgmt., IT, R&D, Engineering
Industries: Medical devices, Machinery/ Appliances, Motor vehicles, Computer equip., Consumer electronics, Test/ measurement equip., Software

Fortune Personnel Consultants of the Virginia Highlands

The Virginia Highlands
Route 1, Box 132
Millboro, Virginia 24460
(540) 925-2430
Fax: (540) 925-2434
Email: fortune@va.tds.net
Web: www.tds.net/fortune

Key Contact - Specialty:
Ms. Jean Howell - *Purchasing, materials management*

Description: Specialize in placement of middle management professionals in purchasing, materials, logistics, supplier quality.

Salary Minimum: $30,000
Functions: Middle mgmt., Production, Purchasing, Materials Plng., Distribution
Industries: Generalist, Drugs mfg., Medical devices, Plastics/rubber, Machinery/ Appliances, Motor vehicles, Consumer electronics

F-O-R-T-U-N-E Personnel Consultants of East Seattle

11661 SE 1st St., Ste. 202
Bellevue, Washington 98005
(425) 450-9665
Fax: (425) 450-0357
Email: info@fortuneseattle.com
Web: www.fortuneseattle.com

Key Contact - Specialty:
Mr. Daniel Chin - *Heavy industrial lift equipment, material handling, off-road equipment*
Ms. Penny Thomason - *Lawn & garden equipment, mobile equipment*
Ms. Becky Deschamps
Mr. Lee Wells - *Materials management, purchasing, logistics, supply chain*

Description: We are an executive search firm specializing in mobile heavy equipment, lawn and garden and electrical type processes and high tech software. We work mostly on a contingency basis and satisfaction is our guarantee.
Functions: Middle mgmt., Mfg., Materials, IT, Engineering
Industries: Machinery/Appliances, Motor vehicles, Consumer electronics, High tech, Software

Forum Personnel Inc.

(Firm declined to update.)
342 Madison Ave., Ste. 509
New York, New York 10017
(212) 687-4050
Email: sgoldstein@forumper.com

Key Contact - Specialty:
Mr. Steve Goldstein

Description: Management recruitment firm established in 1974. Areas of specialization include accounting, finance, human resources, marketing/sales and information technology. Permanent and temporary consultant placement.

Salary Minimum: $50,000
Functions: Advertising, Mkt. research, Benefits, Personnel, CFO's, Cash mgmt., MIS mgmt.
Industries: Generalist, Misc. mfg., Finance, Accounting, Communications, Advertising/PR

Foster Associates

The Livery, 209 Cooper Ave.
Upper Montclair, New Jersey 07043
(973) 746-2800

Key Contact - Specialty:
Mr. Donald J. Foster

Description: Highly personalized professional executive search; specialize in finance, capital markets, management consulting, systems, CPA's, audit tax, legal. Recruit difficult-to-find, high quality senior and middle level professional and management talent who can add real value. Efficiently completed searches save client time, resources and expense.

Salary Minimum: $45,000
Functions: Finance, CFO's, Taxes, Systems anal., Systems implem., Mgmt. consultants, Attorneys
Industries: Generalist, Finance, Invest. banking, Legal, Accounting, Mgmt. consulting, Real estate

Fought, Jameson Assoc.

55 West Monroe, Ste. 1190
Chicago, Illinois 60603
(312) 422-8260
Fax: (312) 422-8268
Email: foughtjameson@compuserve.com

Key Contact - Specialty:
Mr. Jay D. Fought - *Technical, management consulting*
Mr. Brad M. Jameson - *Technical, management consulting*

Description: We are owned and operated by two principals both having extensive system engineering and management backgrounds. Our in-depth technical knowledge enables us to quickly assess candidates' interests and potential client opportunities.
Functions: Benefits, Training, MIS mgmt., Systems anal., Systems dev., Systems implem., Systems support
Industries: Energy/utilities, Mfg., Finance, Svcs., High tech, Software, Healthcare

The Fourbes Group, Inc.

1030 St. George Ave., Ste. 300
Avenel, New Jersey 07001
(732) 855-7722
Fax: (732) 855-8406
Web: www.fourbes.com

Key Contact - Specialty:
Ms. Kathleen Burke
Mr. Robert Jay

Description: We are a minority-owned firm (2 of 3 owners are women). We go to great lengths to ensure that each deal is a good one - both for the client company and the applicant.
Functions: Middle mgmt., Admin. svcs., Production, Plant mgmt., Purchasing, Customer svc., Credit
Industries: Soap/perfume/cosmetics, Misc. mfg., Accounting, Insurance

Fox, White & Assoc.

15 Miramar Rd.
Stuart, Florida 34996
(561) 781-1844
Fax: (561) 781-2180
Email: foxwhite@ibm.net

Key Contact - Specialty:
Mr. Louis Volpe - *Marketing management, consumer packaged goods*
Ms. Evelyne F. White - *Marketing management, consumer packaged goods*

Salary Minimum: $50,000
Functions: Mkt. research, Mktg. mgmt., Sales mgmt.
Industries: Food/bev/tobacco, Soap/ perfume/cosmetics, Drugs mfg.

Branches:
379 Spahr St.
Pittsburgh, Pennsylvania 15232
(412) 363-8819
Fax: (412) 363-8909
Email: foxwhite@ibm.net
Key Contact - Specialty:
Ms. Evelyne F. White

Fox-Morris Assoc., Inc.

1617 JFK Blvd., Ste. 1850
Philadelphia, Pennsylvania 19103-1892
(215) 561-6300
Fax: (215) 561-6333

Email: philadelphia@fox-morris.com

Key Contact - Specialty:
Mr. Thomas J. Glynn - *Senior management, human resources, marketing*
Mr. Harvey Brooks - *Senior management, operations, MIS*

Description: We were founded as an executive search and recruiting firm and have since grown to become a national firm with offices coast-to-coast. We provide a full range of career transition services in addition to recruiting.

Salary Minimum: $50,000
Functions: Senior mgmt., Middle mgmt., Plant mgmt., Mktg. mgmt., MIS mgmt., Systems implem., Engineering
Industries: Generalist

Branches:
1940 W. Orangewood Ave., Ste. 207
Orange, California 92868
(714) 634-2600
Key Contact - Specialty:
Mr. William Gerard - *Sales & marketing, manufacturing, human resources, finance*

1140 Hammond Drive, Ste. I-9250
Atlanta, Georgia 30328
(770) 399-4497
Key Contact - Specialty:
Mr. Robert Smith - *Human resources, engineering, manufacturing, finance, sales & marketing*

409 Washington Ave., Ste. 1020
Baltimore, Maryland 21204
(410) 296-4500
Key Contact - Specialty:
Mr. George Simmons - *Human resources*

1050 Wall St., Ste. 310
Lyndhurst, New Jersey 07071
(201) 933-8900
Key Contact - Specialty:
Mr. Tom Hughes - *Human resources, data processing, sales & marketing*

122 E. 42nd St., Chanin Bldg.
New York, New York 10168
(212) 286-1400
Key Contact - Specialty:
Mr. Richard Zaher - *Finance, banking, investment banking, attorneys*

9140 Arrowpoint Blvd., Ste. 380
Charlotte, North Carolina 28273
(704) 522-8244
Key Contact - Specialty:
Ms. Toni Marie Reilly - *Sales & marketing, manufacturing, engineering, human resources*

4700 Rockside Rd., Ste. 640
Cleveland, Ohio 44131
(216) 524-6565
Key Contact - Specialty:
Mr. Jim Scaparotti - *Human resources, generalist, engineering*

One Gateway Ctr., 18th Floor
North Wing
Pittsburgh, Pennsylvania 15222
(412) 232-0410
Key Contact - Specialty:
Mr. Murray Leety - *Engineering, manufacturing, human resources, career transition services, advertising*

P.O. Box 10087, Calder Sq., Ste. 405
State College, Pennsylvania 16805-0087
(814) 237-2218
Key Contact - Specialty:
Mr. Dick Wilson - *Human resources*

One Lincoln Centre
5400 LBJ Frwy., Ste. 1445
Dallas, Texas 75240
(972) 404-8044
Key Contact - Specialty:
Mr. Jerry Sewell - *Human resources, engineering, executive search, technical sales*

Franchise Search, Inc.

431 Carpenter Ave.
Sea Cliff, New York 11579
(516) 671-6447
Fax: (516) 671-1989
Email: franchise_search@msn.com

Key Contact - Specialty:
Mr. Douglas T. Kushell - *Franchise, hospitality*

Description: Search company dedicated exclusively to franchising domestically and internationally. We represent only franchiser clients and we place only professional franchise management candidates in franchise sales, operations, training, marketing, legal, financial, real estate, construction and international development.

Salary Minimum: $40,000
Functions: Senior mgmt., Middle mgmt., Int'l.
Industries: Generalist, Hospitality

International Branches:
Riyadh, Sao Paulo, Taipei

Franklin Int'l. Search, Inc.

4 Franklin Commons
Framingham, Massachusetts 01702
(508) 872-1133
Fax: (508) 872-4680
Email: franintl@ziplink.net

Key Contact - Specialty:
Mr. Stanley L. Shindler - *Data storage, data communications, inter-networking, wireless, cellular communications*

Description: Recruitment of technical, sales/marketing, manufacturing and quality control personnel in the wireless, internetworking, data/telecom, semicon thin films, data storage and analytical and biomed/bio tech fields. Also extensive experience in lasers, electroptics and fiber optics.

Salary Minimum: $50,000
Functions: Senior mgmt., Product dev., Mktg. mgmt., Sales mgmt., Systems support, Engineering
Industries: Computer equip., Test/measurement equip., Telecoms, High tech, Software

Franstaff Inc.

73 S. Palm Ave., Ste. 219
Sarasota, Florida 34236
(941) 952-9555
Fax: (941) 952-9520
Email: franstaf@ix.netcom.com
Web: www.franstaff.com

Key Contact - Specialty:
Mr. James W. Dement - *Franchising*
Mr. Peter Capodice - *Franchising*
Mr. Michael Coffee - *Franchising*

Description: The largest executive search organization in franchising... and the only recruiting firm staffed with experienced franchising professionals. Providing uniquely qualified management, sales, and support staff to franchisors worldwide.

Salary Minimum: $40,000
Functions: Senior mgmt., Legal, Mktg. mgmt., HR mgmt., CFO's, MIS mgmt., Int'l.
Industries: Retail, Hospitality, Entertainment, Human resource svcs., Advertising/PR, Real estate, Non-classifiable industries

Mel Frazer Consultant

20350 Chapter Drive
Woodland Hills, California 91364-5609
(818) 703-0040
Fax: (818) 703-0049
Email: exechelp@earthlink.net

Key Contact - Specialty:
Mr. Mel Frazer - *High technology instruments, computers, software*

Description: Middle management medical device contingency search and MDs.

Salary Minimum: $50,000
Functions: Middle mgmt., Sales mgmt., MIS mgmt.
Industries: Computer equip., Consumer electronics, Test/measurement equip., High tech

Fresquez & Assoc.

405 14th St., Ste. 1040
Financial Ctr. Bldg.
Oakland, California 94612
(925) 283-0295
(510) 912-6378
Fax: (925) 283-0335
Email: efresquez@aol.com
Web: www.fresquez.com

Key Contact - Specialty:
Mr. Ernesto Fresquez - *Hispanic, bilingual professionals (Spanish)*
Ms. Jeanette Acosta

Description: Search firm that specializes in the recruitment of minority/diversity professionals, particularly strong in Hispanic community for bilingual professionals in accounting, auditing, finance, marketing, management, human resources, information systems and engineering for the US and Latin America.
Functions: Mktg. mgmt., Sales mgmt., Benefits, Personnel, Engineering, Minorities, Int'l.
Industries: Food/bev/tobacco, Retail, Hospitality, Human resource svcs., High tech, Software

Branches:
San Juan de La Cruz, 655 Col. Camino Real
Zapopan, Jalisco CP 45040
Mexico
52 3 6 19 97 82
Fax: 52 3 6 28 60 58

Affiliates:
Corporate Diversity Search

Frey & Sher Assoc., Inc.
1800 N. Kent St., Ste. 1006
Arlington, Virginia 22209-9998
(703) 524-6500
Fax: (703) 524-6578
Email: freysher@erols.com

Key Contact - Specialty:
Ms. Florence Frey - *Legal*
Ms. Eileen Sher - *Legal*

Description: Attorney search specialists placing lawyers in law firms and corporations.
Functions: Mgmt. consultants, Attorneys
Industries: Legal, Mgmt. consulting

Affiliates:
Frey, Sher & Nix

Bernard Frigon & Assoc. Inc.
1155 W. Rene-Levesque Blvd., 25th Floor
Montreal, Quebec H3B 2K4
Canada
(514) 393-8145
Fax: (514) 393-1236

Key Contact - Specialty:
Mr. Bernard Frigon - *Information technology*

Description: Our team is well known for efficient interventions based on extensive knowledge acquired through previous practical management responsibilities in the fields of information systems, management consulting as well as sales management for a major computer manufacturer.
Functions: Automation, Sales mgmt., MIS mgmt., Systems anal., Systems dev., Systems support, Mgmt. consultants
Industries: Generalist

Fristoe & Carleton, Inc.
77 Milford Drive
Hudson, Ohio 44236
(330) 655-3535
Fax: (330) 655-3585
Email: fristcarl@adjob.com

Key Contact - Specialty:
Mr. Jack Fristoe - *Advertising*
Mr. Bob Carleton

Description: Principals have in depth ad agency experience. Work outside New York and Chicago, midwest and south.

Salary Minimum: $25,000
Functions: Advertising, Mkt. research, Mktg. mgmt., Direct mktg., PR

Peter Froehlich & Co.
P.O. Box 339
Weatherford, Texas 76086
(817) 594-9991
Email: pfsearch@flash.net
Web: flash.net/~pfsearch

Key Contact - Specialty:
Mr. Peter Froehlich - *Upper management broadband communications*
Mr. Mike Pask - *Middle management CATV*
Ms. Karen Egeland
Ms. Valerie Howard
Mr. Noel Egeland - *Manufacturers (communications)*

Description: Specializing in all levels of management positions for all disciplines within the cable television and wireless communications industry. Clientele include operators and manufacturers.
Functions: Generalist, Engineering
Industries: Telecoms

The Fry Group, Inc.
369 Lexington Ave.
New York, New York 10017
(212) 557-0011
Fax: (212) 557-3449
Email: frygroup.com

Key Contact - Specialty:
Mr. John M. Fry - *Public relations, corporate communications*

Description: Public relations, corporate communications and marketing communications. Executive and middle management recruitment.

Salary Minimum: $30,000
Functions: PR
Industries: Advertising/PR

Frye/Joure & Assoc., Inc.
4515 Poplar Ave., Ste. 215
Memphis, Tennessee 38117-7506
(901) 683-7792
Fax: (901) 682-9636
Email: fja@accessus.net

Key Contact - Specialty:
Dr. Sylvia A. Joure - *Generalist*

Description: Full service human resources consulting firm with emphasis on organizational effectiveness, staffing, selection and senior level executive search. Highly successful in filling positions that are difficult to locate candidates for. Discreet.

Salary Minimum: $40,000
Functions: Generalist, Senior mgmt., Production, Distribution, Training, Engineering, Mgmt. consultants
Industries: Generalist, Machinery/ Appliances, Misc. mfg., Computer svcs., Human resource svcs., Advertising/PR, New media

Further Management Group
4938 Hampden Lane, Ste. 163
Bethesda, Maryland 20814
(301) 907-7934
Fax: (301) 907-7935
Email: further@intr.net
Web: www.furthermanagement.com

Key Contact - Specialty:
Mr. Bob McKay - *Restaurant, front-of-house management, culinary*
Mr. Clyde White - *Restaurant, front-of-house management, culinary*

Description: We are a management services firm for the hospitality industry specializing in the Boston through Washington D.C. corridor. We specialize in full service, high quality operations.

Salary Minimum: $40,000
Industries: Hospitality

Future Employment Service, Inc.
3392 Hillcrest Rd.
Dubuque, Iowa 52002
(319) 556-3040
Fax: (319) 556-3041
Email: employ@mwci.net
Web: www.careerpros.com

Key Contact - Specialty:
Mr. James C. Townsend - *Sales, marketing, engineering, finance*
Ms. Carol A. Townsend - *Data processing, manufacturing*

Description: Client driven, only seek the most highly qualified candidates.

Functions: Mfg., Plant mgmt., Sales & mktg., HR mgmt., Finance, IT, Engineering
Industries: Mfg., Human resource svcs., Communications, Biotech

Branches:
2337 Blairs Ferry Rd. NE
Cedar Rapids, Iowa 52402
(319) 378-4487
Fax: (319) 378-4489
Email: sedonacr.com
Key Contact - Specialty:
Ms. Jenny Koppes - *Accounting, sales, manufacturing, computers*

208 S. Main St.
Maquoketa, Iowa 52060
(319) 652-5699
Fax: (319) 652-4206
Key Contact - Specialty:
Ms. Judy Steiner - *Sales, manufacturing*

Futures, Inc.
1 Hampton Rd., Ste. 301
Exeter, New Hampshire 03833
(603) 775-7800
Fax: (603) 775-7900

Key Contact - Specialty:
Mr. Thomas P. Colacchio - *Food service (sales & marketing)*
Mr. Richard J. Mazzola - *Supermarkets, wholesale industry*

Description: Retail food/NAC and supermarket merchandising and operations, food service sales, retail sales and marketing in all disciplines.

Salary Minimum: $40,000
Functions: Distribution, Sales mgmt.
Industries: Food/bev/tobacco, Hospitality

G. H. Enterprises
2324 E. Turney Ave.
Phoenix, Arizona 85016-6221
(602) 955-9249
Fax: (602) 508-9666
Email: ghills@netzone.com

Key Contact - Specialty:
Mr. Glen Hills - *Engineering, sales & marketing, computers, accounting*

Description: Being a small independent recruiting firm, we provide the personal touch required by clients.

Salary Minimum: $50,000
Functions: Senior mgmt., Middle mgmt., Mfg., Production, Sales mgmt., Systems dev., Engineering
Industries: Generalist, Chemicals, Machinery/Appliances, Misc. mfg., Accounting, High tech, Software

---

The Gabriel Group
1601 Market St., 24th Floor
Philadelphia, Pennsylvania 19103
(215) 496-9990
Fax: (215) 636-0860
Web: www.GabrielGroup.com

Key Contact - Specialty:
Mr. John Turnblacer - *Senior management, CFO, human resources*
Mr. Reggie Owens - *Generalist, manufacturing, human resources*
Mr. Richard Walsh - *Manufacturing, human resources, information technology*
Mr. Warren Levy - *Sales & marketing, human resources*
Ms. Anita Maximo - *Generalist, human resources*

Description: Full service human resources and management consulting firm able to integrate search objectives with business strategies.
Functions: Generalist, General mgmt., Mfg., Sales & mktg., HR mgmt., CFO's, IT
Industries: Generalist, Mfg., Finance, Svcs., Communications, Insurance, High tech

---

Gabriele & Company
2 Emery Rd.
Bedford, Massachusetts 01730-1061
(781) 276-7999
Fax: (781) 276-7933
Email: gabriele.company@juno.com
Web: ourworld.compuserve.com/homepages/gabriele_company

Key Contact - Specialty:
Ms. Leslie Gabriele - *Manufacturing, materials*

Description: Recruiters for manufacturing and materials for the New England area.

Salary Minimum: $50,000
Functions: Mfg., Production, Plant mgmt., Quality, Materials, Materials Plng.
Industries: Medical devices, Metal products, Machinery/Appliances, Computer equip., Consumer electronics, Test/measurement equip., Misc. mfg.

Gallin Associates, Inc.
P.O. Box 1065
Safety Harbor, Florida 34695-1065
(813) 724-8303
Fax: (813) 724-8503
Web: gallin@gallinassociates.com

Key Contact - Specialty:
Mr. Lawrence Gallin - *Management, engineering*
Mr. John Fabriele - *Research & development*
Mr. Paul Stepler - *Hardware, software engineers*

Description: Specialists in technical and managerial search for the chemical process, electronics, telecommunications, computer equipment semiconductor industries.

Salary Minimum: $50,000
Functions: Mfg., Sales & mktg., IT, R&D, Engineering
Industries: Chemicals, Medical devices, Plastics/rubber, Paints/petroleum products, Computer equip., Consumer electronics, Software

Branches:
1784 Alamand Drive
Naples, Florida 34182-5017
(941) 403-9210
Fax: (941) 403-9209
Key Contact - Specialty:
Mr. Paul Stepler - *Technology, computers, data communications, telecommunications, semiconductors*

The Gammill Group, Inc.
8425 Pulsar Place, Ste. 410
Columbus, Ohio 43240
(614) 848-7726
Fax: (614) 848-7738
Email: gammill@gammillgroup.com
Web: www.gammillgroup.com

Key Contact - Specialty:
Mr. Robert A. Gammill
Mr. James Nash - *Managed care*
Mr. Mark Zeigler

Description: This firm is regarded for its service - taking a partnering approach to executive search; quality - consistently locating the best professionals and speed - agility in responding to customer's needs.

Salary Minimum: $30,000
Functions: Senior mgmt., Health admin., Mktg. mgmt., Sales mgmt., CFO's
Industries: Insurance, Healthcare

Garb & Assoc., Legal Placement
2001 Wilshire Blvd., Ste. 510
Santa Monica, California 90403
(310) 998-3388
Fax: (310) 998-3392
Email: sgarb@aol.com

Key Contact - Specialty:
Ms. Sheila Garb - *Attorneys*

Description: We place lawyers with outstanding credentials into law firms and corporations.
Functions: Attorneys
Industries: Generalist, Entertainment, Real estate, Healthcare

Garland Assoc. Int'l.

1727 State St.
Santa Barbara, California 93101-2521
(805) 687-1320
Fax: (805) 563-7441
Email: 432kabl@msn.com

Key Contact - Specialty:
Mr. R. Darryl Garland - *Executive, management, technical*

Description: Since 1979, discreet firm with focus on client service and quality. Executive, management, technical/scientific, telecommunications, microelectronics, semi-conductors, environmental services, construction, oil and gas, computers/peripherals, most others.

Salary Minimum: $100,000
Functions: Senior mgmt., MIS mgmt., Systems anal., Systems dev., Systems implem., R&D, Engineering
Industries: Computer equip., New media, Telecoms, High tech, Software

Affiliates:
KABL Ability Network

The Garvis Group, Inc.

200 Greenleaves Blvd., Ste. 4
Mandeville, Louisiana 70448
(504) 624-3594
Fax: (504) 674-9093
Email: garvis@wild.net
Web: www.wild.net/garvis/

Key Contact - Specialty:
Ms. Michele Corrao

Description: We do executive search and recruiting nationally and internationally in all industries

Salary Minimum: $65,000
Functions: General mgmt., Directors, Senior mgmt., Sales & mktg., HR mgmt., Finance, IT
Industries: Generalist, Finance, Svcs., Hospitality, Entertainment, Advertising/PR, High tech

GateSource Partners

14150-A Willard Rd., Ste. 200
Chantilly, Virginia 20151-2933
(703) 222-4069
Fax: (703) 222-4255
Email: jobs@gatesource.com
Web: www.gatesource.com

Key Contact - Specialty:
Mr. Steve Ratliff - *Information technology, telecommunications, telephony*

Description: Human resources consulting and recruiting services.

Salary Minimum: $40,000
Functions: Senior mgmt., Sales & mktg., CFO's, IT, MIS mgmt., Systems anal., Systems dev.
Industries: Computer svcs., Telecoms, High tech, Software

Gateway Group Personnel, LLC

1770 Kirby Pkwy., Ste. 216
Memphis, Tennessee 38138-7405
(901) 756-6050
Fax: (901) 756-8445
Email: gateway@gatewaypersonnel.com
Web: www.gatewaypersonnel.com

Key Contact - Specialty:
Mr. Charles G. Haddad - *Accounting, banking, audit*
Ms. Darlene R. Murphy - *Accounting, banking, audit*

Description: Contingent search with specialty in accounting, finance, auditing and banking. Serve Fortune 500 clients through closely held entities.

Salary Minimum: $25,000
Functions: CFO's, Budgeting, Cash mgmt., Credit, Taxes, M&A, Risk mgmt.
Industries: Generalist, Paper, Medical devices, Banking, Invest. banking, Entertainment, Accounting

Gateway Management Resources

(Firm declined to update.)
3025 Carmel Drive
Flossmoor, Illinois 60422
(708) 798-9330

Key Contact - Specialty:
Mr. Kye Stockwell - *Non-profit*

Description: Recruiters for non-profit organizations.
Functions: Generalist, Non-profits
Industries: Non-profits, Higher ed.

Gatti & Assoc.

266 Main St., Ste. 21
Medfield, Massachusetts 02052
(508) 359-4153
Fax: (508) 359-5902
Email: Info@GattiHR.com
Web: www.gattihr.com

Key Contact - Specialty:
Mr. Robert D. Gatti - *Human resource executives*
Ms. Judith Banker - *Human resource executives*
Mr. Richard Fleming - *Human resource executives*
Ms. Mary Bloomfield - *Human resource executives*

Description: Specialists in the placement of human resources practitioners such as generalists, employment, compensation and benefits, training and development, college relations, EEO/AA, employee/labor relations or HRIS professionals in all industries.
Functions: HR mgmt., Benefits, Personnel, Training
Industries: Generalist

Branches:
400 Cummings Park W.
Woburn, Massachusetts 01801
(617) 935-9144
Key Contact - Specialty:
Ms. Rita Allen - *Human resources, generalist*

Dianne Gauger & Assoc.

8573 Buena Tierra Place, Ste. 200
Buena Park, California 90621
(714) 522-4300
Fax: (714) 522-4338

Key Contact - Specialty:
Ms. Dianne Gauger - *High-tech, sales & marketing, management*

Description: 14 years of intense specialization focusing on the automation, industrial controls, process control and automation software markets guarantees our clients receive in-depth qualified industry knowldege and services to assure consistent and expedient results.

Salary Minimum: $50,000
Functions: Directors, Senior mgmt., Middle mgmt., Mkt. research, Mktg. mgmt., Sales mgmt., Engineering
Industries: Machinery/Appliances, Computer equip., Test/measurement equip., High tech, Software

GCO

970 W. 190th St., Ste. 600
Torrance, California 90266
(310) 523-3455
Fax: (310) 523-3456
Email: JasonKeller@Jobbrowser.com

Key Contact - Specialty:
Mr. Jason Keller - *Information Technology*

Description: We identify and represent experts in all phases of software development and support, throughout California.
Functions: MIS mgmt., Systems anal., Systems dev., Systems implem., Systems support, Network admin., DB admin.

Gelpi & Assoc.

P.O. Box 231187
Harahan, Louisiana 70183-1187
(504) 737-6086
Fax: (504) 737-6089
Email: ggelpi@juno.com

Key Contact - Specialty:
Ms. Gerry Gelpi - *Insurance, managed care*

Description: Hands-on experience in the company, agency and broker areas of insurance.

Salary Minimum: $30,000
Functions: Generalist
Industries: Insurance

Genel Associates

223 E. Thousand Oaks Blvd., Ste. 220
Thousand Oaks, California 91360
(805) 374-8737
Fax: (805) 374-8337
Email: genel@genel.com
Web: www.genel.com

Key Contact - Specialty:
Mr. George Genel - *Financial services, high technology, legal, biotechnology, entertainment, manufacturing, healthcare, actuary, insurance*

Description: We are a professional, ethical firm that understands client needs and is able to perform target searches fast with excellent results. Client servicing is our forte.

Salary Minimum: $45,000
Functions: Senior mgmt., Mfg., Sales & mktg., Finance, IT, Engineering, Specialized services
Industries: Mfg., Finance, Legal, Communications, High tech, Software, Biotech

General Engineering Tectonics

1807 Navy Drive, Ste. A
Stockton, California 95206
(209) 469-9147
Fax: (209) 469-2614
Email: getcareers@gettec.com
Web: www.gettec.com

Key Contact - Specialty:
Mr. Gary Kroll - *Research, sourcing*
Mr. Stan Flott - *Semiconductor*
Ms. Linda Kneen - *Wireless communications*
Mr. Andy Vucicevic - *Hardware design*
Mr. Marshall Matson - *Software designers*
Ms. Christina Lewis

Description: We are a recruiting and search consulting firm specializing in finding and profiling high-tech industry personnel. We find the right people at the right time.
Functions: Production, Mkt. research, MIS mgmt., Systems anal., Systems dev., Systems implem., Systems support
Industries: Computer equip., Human resource svcs., Telecoms, High tech

Genesis Personnel Service, Inc.

4503 Sunny Slope Terrace
Cincinnati, Ohio 45229
(513) 242-4111
Fax: (513) 242-4137

Key Contact - Specialty:
Ms. Delora Bennett - *Women, minorities*

Description: Fourteen years of demonstrated success in placing women and minorities with Fortune 500 companies. Company also offers consulting services for limited outplacement.

Salary Minimum: $20,000
Functions: General mgmt., Mfg., Healthcare, Sales & mktg., Finance, Engineering, Minorities
Industries: Generalist, Mfg., Transportation, Svcs., Communications, Healthcare, Non-classifiable industries

Genesis Recruiting

P.O. Box 2388
Granite Bay, California 95746
(916) 652-8615
Fax: (916) 652-8583

Key Contact - Specialty:
Mr. Jerry Kleames - *Coatings, chemicals*

Description: Recruiting chemists, scientists and engineers for laboratory, engineering, manufacturing positions in the paint, coatings, adhesives, plastics and chemical industries.

Salary Minimum: $35,000
Functions: Product dev., Production, Plant mgmt., Quality, R&D, Engineering
Industries: Printing, Chemicals, Paints/petroleum products

Genesis Research

1520 Whetstone Court
Wildwood, Missouri 63038
(314) 273-6797
Fax: (314) 273-6799
Email: genesis211@primary.net

Key Contact - Specialty:
Mr. Dennis Lasini - *Chemical refining, pulp & paper, steel, sales & marketing*

Description: National, employer fee paid, contingency search/placement firm specializing in technical sales, marketing, technical service, plant engineering and management positions in the chemical, refining, pulp and paper, steel and power generation industry.

Salary Minimum: $35,000
Functions: Product dev., Production, Plant mgmt., Mkt. research, Mktg. mgmt., Sales mgmt., Engineering
Industries: Energy/utilities, Paper, Chemicals, Plastics/rubber, Paints/petroleum products, Metal products, Misc. mfg.

Gent & Assoc.

(Firm declined to update.)
153 S. California Ave., Ste. F101
Palo Alto, California 94306
(650) 326-1129
Email: garyd2@ix.netcom.com
Web: gent-jobs.com

Key Contact - Specialty:
Mr. Gary Daugenti - *High technology, executives, middle management*

Description: We are extremely technical and understand the positions that we are doing searches for. We also understand and can identify successful executive strategists.
Functions: CFO's, MIS mgmt., Systems anal., Systems dev., Systems implem., Systems support, Mgmt. consultants

Delores F. George, C.P.C.

269 Hamilton St., #1
Worcester, Massachusetts 01604
(508) 754-3451
Fax: (508) 754-1367
Email: deloresg@ultranet.com

Key Contact - Specialty:
Ms. Delores F. George - *Information Technology*

Description: Since 1978, through meticulous search efforts, we source the very best possible talent for each specific situation and have filled positions in virtually every discipline. We are experts at our clients desire for speed plus a thorough, thoughtful survey of the market.
Functions: IT, MIS mgmt., Systems anal., Systems dev., Systems implem., Engineering
Industries: High tech, Software

C. R. Gerald & Assoc.

RR #4, Concession 6, #4189
Uxbridge, Ontario L9P 1R4
Canada
(905) 649-3831
Fax: (905) 649-3086
Email: dgerald@hotmail.com

Key Contact - Specialty:
Mr. C. Richard Gerald - *Information technology, senior executive, sales & technical management*

Description: Relative experiences in country management and software development (product & systems) enhanced by knowledge of our associates when required, have enabled our organization to relate well to client needs, make thoughtful recommendations regarding qualified personnel and fulfill the needs proposed.

Salary Minimum: $85,000
Functions: Senior mgmt., Mktg. mgmt., Sales mgmt., Training, CFO's, MIS mgmt., Systems anal.
Industries: Computer equip., Finance, Computer svcs., Mgmt. consulting, Telecoms, High tech, Software

Affiliates:
D. B. Heslip & Assoc. Inc.

J. Gernetzke & Assoc., Inc.
P.O. Box 307331
Columbus, Ohio 43230
(614) 856-1480
Fax: (614) 856-1491
Email: jgsearch@infinet.com

Key Contact - Specialty:
Mr. James Gernetzke - *Retail, generalist*
Mr. Don Jensen - *Generalist*

Description: We are dedicated to building strong relationships with our client companies enabling us to support any of their staffing needs.

Salary Minimum: $50,000
Functions: Product dev., Purchasing, Distribution, Advertising, HR mgmt., Finance, Engineering
Industries: Retail, Hospitality

GFI Professional Staffing Services
127 Washington St.
Keene, New Hampshire 03431
(603) 357-3116
Fax: (603) 357-7818
Email: sbreen@gfijobs.com
Web: gfijobs.com

Key Contact - Specialty:
Ms. Susan V. Breen - *Office administration, accounting, information technology, manufacturing, banking*

Description: We place the top 10% of talent - from entry level to the top tier of management - for a select group of corporations and businesses in New Hampshire and Vermont.

Salary Minimum: $18,000
Functions: General mgmt., Admin. svcs., Mfg., Materials, Finance, IT, Systems dev.
Industries: Printing, Medical devices, Misc. mfg., Wholesale, Accounting, Insurance

Branches:
The Vermont Bldg., P.O. Box 8144
Brattleboro, Vermont 05304
(802) 257-1146
Fax: (802) 257-1533
Key Contact - Specialty:
Ms. Suzanne Singer - *Generalist*

Affiliates:
Career Investments

John Gilbert Co.
6 N. Longspur Drive
The Woodlands, Texas 77380
(281) 363-3310
Fax: (281) 298-5152

Key Contact - Specialty:
Mr. John Gilbert - *Healthcare, consulting, MIS, finance*

Description: National healthcare executive search firm, specializing in acute care, long-term care, home health, rehab and psych.

Salary Minimum: $50,000
Functions: Directors, Nurses, Health admin., CFO's, MIS mgmt., Systems dev., Mgmt. consultants
Industries: Healthcare

Gilbert Scott Assoc., LLC
85 Tower Office Park
Woburn, Massachusetts 01801
(781) 939-5959
Fax: (781) 939-5962
Email: harry@gilbertscott.com
Web: www.gilbertscott.com

Key Contact - Specialty:
Mr. H. Harry Gilbert, Jr. - *Real estate, generalist*
Ms. Lisa A. Pais - *Real estate*

Description: Specialist in all industrial and functions relevent to the professional management of real estate and related assets.

Salary Minimum: $50,000
Functions: Generalist, Senior mgmt., Materials, CFO's, Risk mgmt., MIS mgmt.
Industries: Energy/utilities, Construction, Banking, Invest. banking, Accounting, Insurance, Real estate

---

Joe L. Giles & Assoc.
15565 Northland Drive, Room #608 W.
Southfield, Michigan 48075
(248) 569-8660
Fax: (248) 569-8663
Email: gilesjobs@bignet.net

Key Contact - Specialty:
Mr. Joe L. Giles - *Engineering, IT, IS*
Ms. Valerie Gamache - *Engineering, IT, IS*
Mr. David Atley - *IT, IS*

Description: We provide quality placements in areas that are very difficult to find, such as: PLCs and controls engineers, software and network engineers, manufacturing and quality engineers, minority and diversity candidates.
Functions: Mfg., Automation, Purchasing, IT, R&D, Engineering, Minorities
Industries: Mfg., High tech, Software, Biotech

Gillard Assoc. Legal Search
75 McNeil Way, #201
Dedham, Massachusetts 02026
(617) 329-4731
Fax: (617) 329-1357
Email: gillardlgl@aol.com

Key Contact - Specialty:
Ms. Elizabeth A. Gillard - *Attorneys*
Ms. Cheryl A. Gillard - *Attorneys, paralegals*

Description: Follow strict ethical guidelines; firm founded in 1980 to serve legal community.
Functions: Attorneys, Paralegals
Industries: Legal

Gilmore & Assoc.
P.O. Box 1124
Topanga, California 90290
(310) 455-7094
Fax: (310) 455-1693

Key Contact - Specialty:
Mr. Roger Gilmore - *Healthcare*

Description: All searches are handled personally by the owner. My 13 years as a doctor opens doors that might be closed to a layperson. Extremely ethical, reliable and confidential.

Salary Minimum: $45,000
Functions: Physicians, Nurses, Benefits, CFO's, Network admin., DB admin.
Industries: Software, Healthcare

Gimbel & Assoc.
201 NE 2nd St.
Ft. Lauderdale, Florida 33301
(954) 525-7000
Fax: (954) 525-7300
Email: gimbel@gate.net

Key Contact - Specialty:
Mr. Mike Gimbel - *Accounting, finance, consulting, information technology*

Description: Low profile, established, respected, successful firm. Excellent ability to recruit and place strong talent. President was a controller with Motorola.

Salary Minimum: $40,000
Functions: Healthcare, Finance, IT, Mgmt. consultants, Attorneys
Industries: Banking, Telecoms

Lawrence Glaser Assoc., Inc.
505 S. Lenola Rd., Ste. 202
Moorestown, New Jersey 08057
(609) 778-9500
Fax: (609) 778-4390
Email: lgainc@erols.com
Web: www.lgasearch.com

Key Contact - Specialty:
Mr. Larry Glaser - *Sales & marketing managers, grocery, consumer, confectionery, beverage products*
Ms. Lisa Wolf - *Sales & marketing managers, foodservice, institutional food products*
Ms. Christine M. Slusser - *Sales managers, HBC, non-food, consumer durable products*

Description: We offer executive recruitment for sales and marketing managers in grocery, consumer, HBC, non-food, beverage, confectionary and foodservice product/services categories.

Salary Minimum: $60,000
Functions: Sales & mktg., Mktg. mgmt., Sales mgmt.
Industries: Food/bev/tobacco, Soap/perfume/cosmetics, Computer equip., Consumer electronics, Computer svcs., Telecoms, Software

Glass & Assoc., Inc.

4571 Stephen Circle NW, Ste. 130
Canton, Ohio 44718
(330) 494-3252
Fax: (330) 494-2420
Email: glass@ezo.net
Web: www.glass-consulting.com

Key Contact - Specialty:
Mr. Henry F. Meyer
Mr. Shaun K. Donnellan

Description: Temporary executives, managers and functional staff specialists to perform specific tasks with certain time frames are provided on a test drive basis. Perform traditional executive search, selection and placement services in addition to specialized advisory and support consulting.

Salary Minimum: $100,000
Functions: Generalist
Industries: Generalist

The Glenwood Group

6428 Joliet Rd., Ste. 112
Countryside, Illinois 60525
(708) 482-3750
Fax: (708) 482-0633
Email: glenwood@glenwoodgrp.com
Web: www.glenwoodgrp.com

Key Contact - Specialty:
Mr. Frank J. Filippelli - *Engineering and manufacturing; chemicals, foods, packaging, consumer products*

Description: Searches conducted on specialized basis for engineering/manufacturing positions in the foods, consumer products, chemicals industries. Our network of contacts developed since 1974 enable us to produce results very quickly.

Salary Minimum: $40,000
Functions: Middle mgmt., Product dev., Production, Plant mgmt., Distribution, Packaging, R&D
Industries: Food/bev/tobacco, Paper, Soap/perfume/cosmetics, Drugs mfg., Medical devices, Plastics/rubber, Packaging

Global 1000 Int'l. Services

433 N. Camden Drive, 6th Floor
Beverly Hills, California 90210
(800) 965-3932
Fax: (800) 285-4554
Email: employment@global1000.com
Web: www.GLOBAL1000.com

Key Contact - Specialty:
Mr. Jeff Goldman - *Consulting, sales, information systems, healthcare, senior managers to chairman of the board*

Description: We have over 10+ years experience and 12 offices serving the world for general management, sales, marketing, healthcare, consulting, I.T., human resources and operations. We also offer contract recruiting and consulting services.
Functions: Advertising, Benefits, CFO's, IT, Engineering, Mgmt. consultants, Int'l.
Industries: Transportation, Human resource svcs., New media, Environmental svcs., Packaging, High tech, Healthcare

Global Career Services, Inc.

555 Fifth Ave. 8th Floor
New York, New York 10017-2416
(212) 599-6769
Email: info@globalcareers.com
Web: www.globalcareers.com

Key Contact - Specialty:
Mr. Frank Jones - *Generalist*
Mr. Robert McNamara - *Human resources, consulting, IT*
Ms. Bonita Jones - *Generalist, administrative*

Functions: HR mgmt., Finance, IT, Engineering, Mgmt. consultants, Graphic artists, Int'l.
Industries: Agri/forestry/mining, Mfg., Finance, Communications, Packaging, Real estate, Software

Global Consulting Group Inc.

6090 Hwy. #7 E.
Markham, Ontario L3P 3B1
Canada
(905) 472-9677
Email: info@globalrecruit.com
Web: www.globalrecruit.com

Key Contact - Specialty:
Ms. Patricia Chambers - *Information technology, high technology, executive level*
Mr. Bill Johnson - *Engineering, information technology, sales & marketing*
Ms. Libby Roberts - *Sales & marketing, high technology, generalist*
Ms. Judy Chambers - *Scientific, engineering, generalist*
Ms. Gail Buffey

Description: We are a multi-lingual recruitment firm that operates nationally and internationally with affiliated groups to service the specialized needs of clients in information technology, engineering, scientific, sales/marketing and executive search requirements.
Functions: General mgmt., Sales & mktg., Finance, IT, R&D, Engineering, Int'l.
Industries: Mfg., Finance, Communications, Environmental svcs., Insurance, High tech, Software

Global Engineers Inc.

P.O. Box 782
Bailey Island, Maine 04003
(207) 833-2800
Fax: (207) 833-0021
Email: jobs@globalengineers.com
Web: www.GlobalEngineers.com

Key Contact - Specialty:
Mr. Mark R. Nowakowski - *Biotechnology, chemical*

Description: Providing engineers for short-term and regular full-time placements nationwide.
Functions: Middle mgmt., R&D, Engineering, Mgmt. consultants
Industries: Chemicals, Drugs mfg., Medical devices, Machinery/Appliances, Computer equip., High tech, Biotech

Global Executive Search Group

230 Second Ave., 2nd Floor
Waltham, Massachusetts 02154
(781) 890-7890
Email: david.miller@sulcog.com

Key Contact - Specialty:
Mr. David Miller - *Capital markets, derivatives, Wall Street information technology*

Description: We specialize in search and placement of professionals in the disciplines of capital markets, risk management, financial engineering, derivatives and Wall Street technology.

Salary Minimum: $250,000
Functions: M&A, Risk mgmt.
Industries: Invest. banking, Brokers, Misc. financial

Global Technologies Group Inc.

4525 Hedgemore Drive, Ste. R
Charlotte, North Carolina 28209
(704) 523-9441
Fax: (704) 523-9833
Email: greg_smith@mindspring.com

Key Contact - Specialty:
Mr. Gregory K. Smith - *Data communications, telecommunications, internet, sales & management (senior level)*
Ms. Patricia Wilson - *Data communications, internet sales & support*

Description: We specialize in placing people in sales, support, management and consulting positions within the data communications, telecommunications and internet industries.

Salary Minimum: $45,000
Functions: Mktg. mgmt., Sales mgmt., Cash mgmt., MIS mgmt., Systems implem., Network admin., Mgmt. consultants
Industries: Banking, Invest. banking, Computer svcs., New media, Telecoms, High tech, Software

Global Telecommunications, Inc.

9901 IH 10 West, Ste. 800
San Antonio, Texas 78230
(210) 558-2828
Fax: (210) 558-4477
Email: globaltinc@aol.com

Key Contact - Specialty:
Mr. Robert S. Ott - *Cellular, paging, cable, long distance, call center management*

Description: We are an executive search firm serving client companies in the telecommunication industry:(ie: Cellular/PCS, long distance,messaging, CLEC's and telecommunication equipment manufacturers). Specializing in middle to upper level management opportunities within sales, marketing and customer service/call center management.

Salary Minimum: $60,000
Functions: Senior mgmt., Middle mgmt., Mkt. research, Sales mgmt., Direct mktg., Customer svc., Mgmt. consultants
Industries: Computer equip., Equip. svcs., New media, Broadcast & Film, Telecoms, High tech

The GlobalSearch Group

1900 W. Loop S., Ste. 300
Houston, Texas 77027
(713) 964-4007
Fax: (713) 964-4006

Key Contact - Specialty:
Mr. Ronald J. Hakim - *Sales, sales management, marketing*

Description: Confidential, custom-tailored, attention to detail professionalism resulting in solutions to complex recruiting problems.

Salary Minimum: $40,000
Functions: Generalist, General mgmt., Mfg., Materials, Sales & mktg., HR mgmt., Int'l.
Industries: Generalist, Mfg., Transportation, Svcs., Communications, High tech, Biotech

Affiliates:
QuestSearch

Gnodde Assoc.

128 N. Lincoln St.
Hinsdale, Illinois 60521
(630) 887-9510
Fax: (630) 887-9531
Email: gnoddeassc@msn.com

Key Contact - Specialty:
Mr. R. Dirk Gnodde - *Banking, financial services*

Description: We conduct contingency searches for banks and financial institutions. Searches are conducted in the Midwest with an emphasis on the Chicago market.

Salary Minimum: $40,000
Functions: Generalist, Cash mgmt., Risk mgmt.
Industries: Banking, Invest. banking, Misc. financial, Real estate

Godfrey Personnel, Inc.

300 W. Adams, Ste. 612
Chicago, Illinois 60606-5194
(312) 236-4455
Fax: (312) 580-6292
Email: Jim@godfreypersonnel.com
Web: www.godfreypersonnel.com

Key Contact - Specialty:
Mr. James R. Godfrey - *Insurance (technical, professional & executives)*

Description: Our specialty is recruitment/placement of insurance personnel from technical to senior management; i.e, underwriters, actuaries, claims adjusters (all lines), accounting, customer service reps, risk manager and loss control.

Salary Minimum: $25,000
Functions: CFO's, Budgeting, Cash mgmt., Risk mgmt.
Industries: Insurance

H. L. Goehring & Assoc., Inc.

3200 Wrenford St.
Dayton, Ohio 45409-1250
(513) 294-8854
Fax: (513) 294-4699

Key Contact - Specialty:
Mr. Hal Goehring - *Middle to top management (all disciplines)*

Description: We provide personalized professional executive search activities for middle to top management positions in all corporate disciplines in a wide range of industries. Management and human resource consulting.

Salary Minimum: $40,000
Functions: Senior mgmt., Plant mgmt., Distribution, Mktg. mgmt., Benefits, CFO's, Mgmt. consultants
Industries: Generalist, Printing, Metal products, Machinery/Appliances, Human resource svcs., Publishing

Barry M. Gold & Co.

2402 Michelson Drive, Ste. 225
Irvine, California 92612-1323
(949) 660-5677
Fax: (949) 660-5611
Email: bmgco@deltanet.com
Web: www.insurancerecruiting.com

Key Contact - Specialty:
Mr. Barry M. Gold - *Insurance, managed care, benefits*

Description: 25% retained insurance brokerage consultants, executive search, selection and appraisal.

Salary Minimum: $40,000
Functions: Senior mgmt., Middle mgmt., Health admin., Sales mgmt., Benefits, Risk mgmt.
Industries: Mgmt. consulting, Insurance, Healthcare

Goldbeck Recruiting Inc.

650 W. Georgia St., Ste. 1212
P.O. Box 11619
Vancouver, British Columbia V6B 4N9
Canada
(604) 684-1428
Fax: (604) 801-5712
Email: goldbeck@intouch.bc.ca
Web: www.goldbeck.com

Key Contact - Specialty:
Mr. Henry Goldbeck - *Sales & marketing, production, plant management*

Description: Individual practice with expertise in sales and marketing as well as production and plant management.

Salary Minimum: $35,000
Functions: Middle mgmt., Automation, Plant mgmt., Purchasing, Materials Plng., Mktg. mgmt., Engineering
Industries: Generalist, Agri/forestry/mining, Energy/utilities, Construction, Food/bev/tobacco, Lumber/furniture, Paper

Barry Goldberg & Assoc., Inc.
(Attorney Search & Placement)

(Firm declined to update.)
2049 Century Park E., Ste. 1100
Los Angeles, California 90067
(310) 277-5800

Key Contact - Specialty:
Mr. Barry Goldberg - *Attorneys only*

Description: Placement of partners and associates at the nations' leading law firms.

Salary Minimum: $75,000
Functions: Attorneys
Industries: Legal

Goldman+Bell, LLC

381 Park Ave. S., Ste. 1520
New York, New York 10016
(212) 685-9311
Fax: (212) 532-2740

Key Contact - Specialty:
Mr. Peter P. Bell
Ms. Elaine Goldman
Mr. Barry Piatoff

Description: Provide interim (temporary) public relations professionals to PR agencies and corporations.
Functions: PR
Industries: Textiles/apparel, Pharmaceutical svcs., Communications, Advertising/PR, New media, High tech, Healthcare

Joseph Goldring & Assoc. Inc.

31500 W. 13 Mile Rd., Ste. 200
Farmington Hills, Michigan 48334
(248) 539-2660
(800) 851-1381
Fax: (248) 539-2667
Email: jga@road.com
Web: www.jga.road.com

Key Contact - Specialty:
Mr. Joe Goldring - *CEO, COO*
Mr. Ken Jacobs - *Physicians, physician assistants*

Description: We are an independent search organization devoted to providing confidential service on a contingency basis, main areas are accounting/finance, engineering, information services and medical/healthcare.

Salary Minimum: $30,000
Functions: Generalist, Senior mgmt., Physicians, HR mgmt., Finance, IT, Engineering
Industries: Generalist, Mfg., Finance, Biotech, Healthcare

Goldstein & Co.
(a division of TeamSearch Inc.)

1700 N. Broadway, Ste. 307
Walnut Creek, California 94596
(925) 935-6360
Fax: (925) 939-7980
Email: resume@GC1.com
Web: www.GC1.com

Key Contact - Specialty:
Mr. Michael Goldstein - *Electronic publishing, high technology*
Ms. Peggy Goldstein - *Information technology*

Description: We are the largest electronic publishing, graphic arts recruiting firm in the country.
Functions: Mfg., Sales & mktg., Mkt. research, Mktg. mgmt., Sales mgmt., IT, Technicians
Industries: Printing, Computer equip., Publishing, New media, Packaging, High tech, Software

Branches:
3655 Torrance Blvd., Ste. 364
Torrance, California 90503
(310) 543-9050
Fax: (310) 543-2029
Email: gclax@yahoo.com
Web: www.gc1.com
Key Contact - Specialty:
Mr. Peter Leimpeter - *High technology, information technology*

Gomez Fregoso y Asociados

Salto del Agua #2130
Jardines del Country
Guadalajara, Jalisco CP 44210
Mexico
52 3 826 12 89
Fax: 52 3 825 14 14
Email: gomezfre@galileo.orbinet.com.mx

Key Contact - Specialty:
Mr. Miguel Gomez
Ms. Monica Vazquez

Description: Executive search consultants. Serving clients nationwide in most functions and industries.

Salary Minimum: $35,000
Functions: Generalist, Senior mgmt., Plant mgmt., Purchasing, Mktg. mgmt., Personnel, CFO's
Industries: Generalist, Food/bev/tobacco, Chemicals, Drugs mfg., Metal products, Machinery/Appliances

L. J. Gonzer Assoc.

1225 Raymond Blvd.
Newark, New Jersey 07102
(973) 624-5600
(800) 631-4218
Fax: (973) 624-7170
Email: ljga@gonzer.com
Web: www.gonzer.com

Key Contact - Specialty:
Mr. Lawrence J. Gonzer - *Engineering, technical fields, information technology*
Mr. Daniel J. Muhlfelder - *Engineering, technical fields, information technology*

Description: Professional search with concentration on corporations producing technical or engineered products. Although recruiting is done on an individual basis per each associate, the selection process is by consensus.

Salary Minimum: $25,000
Functions: Production, Systems dev., Systems support, Engineering, Mgmt. consultants, Technicians, Graphic artists
Industries: Energy/utilities, Machinery/Appliances, Mgmt. consulting, Communications, Aerospace, High tech, Software

Branches:
274 Main St.
Reading, Massachusetts 01867
(781) 942-0450
Fax: (781) 942-0164
Key Contact - Specialty:
Mr. Hank Bardol

Goodkind Assoc. Inc.

110 E. 42nd St., Ste. 1300
New York, New York 10017
(212) 378-0700
Fax: (212) 378-0780
Email: pgoodkind@aol.com

Key Contact - Specialty:
Mr. Peter Goodkind - *Generalist*
Ms. Kelly O'Hara - *Human resources, marketing*
Ms. Jennifer Stork - *Investment banking, finance*
Mr. Christopher Denney - *Marketing*
Ms. Lynn Berman - *Generalist*

Description: Middle management search firm specializing in human resources, marketing and finance/investment banking. All officers have corporate experience relevant to their specialty giving them a unique understanding of the goals and requirements of our clients.

Salary Minimum: $50,000
Functions: Middle mgmt., Sales & mktg., HR mgmt., Benefits, Personnel, Training, Finance
Industries: Finance, Invest. banking, Communications

Affiliates:
Goodkind Technical Consulting

Government Contract Solutions, Inc.

1401 Chain Bridge Rd., Ste. 303
McLean, Virginia 22101
(703) 749-2223
Fax: (703) 749-2244

Email: resume@gcsplacement.com

Key Contact - Specialty:
Ms. Nicole Geller - *Contracts, procurement, pricing personnel (federal contractors market)*
Ms. Cathy Farrell - *Contracts, procurement, pricing personnel (federal & commercial market)*

Description: GCS specializes in the temporary and permanent placement of contracts, procurement and pricing personnel. GCS recruiters and staffing consultants are all former contract and procurement professionals who know and understand the nuances of government contracting work. We place junior to executive level candidates.

Salary Minimum: $30,000
Functions: Admin. svcs., Purchasing, Budgeting, Risk mgmt., Systems implem.
Industries: Misc. financial, Defense, Haz. waste, High tech, Software

Gowdy Consultants

12059 Starcrest Drive
San Antonio, Texas 78247
(210) 499-4444
Fax: (210) 499-4676
Email: gowdy@texas.net

Key Contact - Specialty:
Ms. Olga M. Gowdy - *Sales & marketing, administrative*
Ms. Theresa Gungle - *Sales, sales management*
Mr. Lee Holder - *Management*

Description: Specializing in bilingual (Spanish speaking) candidates in all sales and marketing disciplines.
Functions: Admin. svcs., Mktg. mgmt., Customer svc., MIS mgmt., Systems support, Minorities, Int'l.
Industries: Food/bev/tobacco, Paper, Drugs mfg., Plastics/rubber, Computer equip., Pharmaceutical svcs., Accounting

Alexander Graham Assoc.

702 Hunters Lane
Mt. Laurel, New Jersey 08054
(609) 235-8052
Fax: (609) 235-1043

Key Contact - Specialty:
Mr. Alexander J. Graham - *Sales & marketing*

Description: Specialize in executive placement of sales and marketing professionals with manufacturers selling to mass merchants.

Salary Minimum: $50,000
Functions: Sales & mktg., Advertising, Mkt. research, Mktg. mgmt., Sales mgmt., Direct mktg.
Industries: Food/bev/tobacco, Textiles/apparel, Lumber/furniture, Plastics/rubber, Metal products, Consumer electronics, Misc. mfg.

Robert Grant Assoc., Inc.

44 Montgomery St., #860
San Francisco, California 94104
(415) 981-7424
Fax: (415) 981-6120
Email: rgrant@ix.netcom.com

Key Contact - Specialty:
Mr. Robert Grant

Description: Both retained and exclusive contingent searches in financial services, healthcare, consumer products, medical equipment, hi-tech marketing/sales, public agency and communications.

Salary Minimum: $50,000
Functions: Middle mgmt., Advertising, Mkt. research, Mktg. mgmt., Sales mgmt., Mgmt. consultants
Industries: Food/bev/tobacco, Drugs mfg., Communications, High tech, Software, Biotech, Healthcare

Affiliates:
RGA Assoc., Inc.

The Grant Search Group, Inc.

2275 Lakeshore Blvd. W., Ste. 514
Toronto, Ontario M8V 3Y3
Canada
(416) 252-5656
Fax: (416) 252-8511
Email: bodnaryk@ica.net

Key Contact - Specialty:
Mr. David Bodnaryk - *Marketing*

Description: We continually refresh our database by proactive screening, including personal interviews and tracking of personnel which allows us to quickly access the right candidate. Therefore, we minimize our client's resignation disruptions.

Salary Minimum: $50,000
Functions: Mkt. research, Mktg. mgmt., Direct mktg., MIS mgmt., DB admin.
Industries: Food/bev/tobacco, Chemicals, Soap/perfume/cosmetics, Drugs mfg., Plastics/rubber, Publishing, Telecoms

Grant-Franks & Assoc.

929 N. Kings Hwy.
Cherry Hill, New Jersey 08034
(609) 779-8844
Fax: (609) 779-0898

Key Contact - Specialty:
Ms. Lee Grant

Description: Focus on mid to small size firms utilizing expertise in functioning as their human resource/personnel departments. Principal is a PHR.

Salary Minimum: $25,000
Functions: Generalist, Materials, Healthcare, Sales & mktg., HR mgmt., Finance, IT
Industries: Generalist, Construction, Transportation, Finance, Packaging, Insurance

Grant/Morgan Assoc., Inc.

7316 Wisconsin Ave., Ste. 350
Bethesda, Maryland 20814
(301) 718-8888
Fax: (301) 718-9119
Email: grantmorgan.com

Key Contact - Specialty:
Mr. Mark A. Pugrant - *Management, real estate, financial services*
Ms. Kimberly D. Crowell - *Telecommunications*
Ms. M. Theresa O'Donnell - *High technology, media*

Description: Consultative search and personnel recruiting services to a variety of Fortune 1000 and rapidly growing entrepreneurial companies. Emphasis in high technology, financial services, real estate, aerospace and telecommunications industries, management level financial/accounting positions.

Salary Minimum: $50,000
Functions: Middle mgmt., HR mgmt., Finance, MIS mgmt., Network admin., Mgmt. consultants
Industries: Construction, Finance, Mgmt. consulting, Human resource svcs., Aerospace, High tech, Software

Graphic Arts Marketing Assoc., Inc.

3533 Deepwood Drive
Lambertville, Michigan 48144
(734) 854-5225
Fax: (734) 854-5224
Email: GRaphicama@aol.com

Key Contact - Specialty:
Ms. Jacqueline Crawford - *Advertising, creative*
Mr. Roger Crawford - *Advertising, marketing*

Description: Placement in advertising, merchandising, printing, public relations and marketing covering all functions from general management, sales, sales management, account executives, production, creative and media.

Salary Minimum: $30,000

Functions: Advertising, Mkt. research, Mktg. mgmt., Direct mktg., PR, Graphic artists
Industries: Printing, Communications, Advertising/PR, Publishing, New media, Broadcast & Film

Graphic Search Assoc. Inc.
P.O. Box 373
Newtown Square, Pennsylvania 19073
(610) 359-1234
Fax: (610) 353-8120
Email: GraphSrch@aol.com
Web: www.napl.org/GraphicSearch

Key Contact - Specialty:
Mr. Roger W. Linde - *Senior management*

Description: Recruiters for the graphic arts industry specializing in staff support, manufacturing, sales, marketing and general management opportunities.

Salary Minimum: $30,000
Functions: Senior mgmt., Middle mgmt., Admin. svcs., Plant mgmt., Sales mgmt., Customer svc., CFO's
Industries: Printing

Grauss & Co.
55 New Montgomery St., Ste. 503
San Francisco, California 94105
(415) 777-5656
Fax: (415) 777-5606
Email: info@grauss.com
Web: www.grauss.com

Key Contact - Specialty:
Mr. Bryan J. Grauss - *Financial, technical*
Ms. Debra M. Grauss - *Financial*

Description: Brokerage, investment banking, capital management, MIS, venture capital and technical recruiting.

Salary Minimum: $40,000
Functions: Senior mgmt., Finance, Cash mgmt., M&A, IT, MIS mgmt., Systems implem.
Industries: Finance, Banking, Invest. banking, Brokers, Venture cap., Accounting, High tech

Ben Greco Assoc., Inc.
445 S. Figueroa St., Ste. 2600
Los Angeles, California 90071
(213) 612-7766
Fax: (213) 612-7767

Key Contact - Specialty:
Mr. Ben Greco - *Generalist*

Description: Provide a personal, direct, efficient and confidential process to identify and recruit a quality executive with high performance standards who will make an immediate contribution and have long term potential for the client company.

Salary Minimum: $75,000
Functions: Generalist, CFO's, Budgeting, Cash mgmt., Taxes, M&A, Int'l.
Industries: Generalist, Retail, Entertainment, Accounting, Broadcast & Film, Real estate, High tech

Sheila Greco Assoc.
8 Mohawk Place
Amsterdam, New York 12010
(518) 843-4611
Fax: (518) 843-5498
Web: sheilagreco.com

Key Contact - Specialty:
Ms. Sheila Greco - *Generalist, professional services, tax*
Mr. Erik Voss - *Generalist, professional services, tax*

Description: We are a full service recruiting firm. We specialize in executive search and research.

Salary Minimum: $50,000
Functions: Senior mgmt., Nurses, Mkt. research, Benefits, CFO's, IT, Mgmt. consultants
Industries: Generalist, Mfg., Hospitality, Pharmaceutical svcs., Communications, Advertising/PR, High tech

R. Green & Assoc., Inc.
One South St. Clair St.
Toledo, Ohio 43602
(419) 249-2800
Fax: (419) 249-2803
Email: recruit@r-green.com
Web: www.r-green.com

Key Contact - Specialty:
Ms. Rita Green - *Generalist*
Mr. Stuart Brody - *Sales, marketing*
Ms. Tina Kern - *Accounting, human resources*
Mr. Neil Ford - *Materials/Purchasing, engineering*

Description: Our customized service is appreciated by mostly Fortune 500 manufacturing clients. Our candidate base is very select and limited to the nation's top performers. Only represent management positions.

Salary Minimum: $75,000
Functions: Middle mgmt., Production, Purchasing, Mktg. mgmt., Benefits, CFO's, Engineering
Industries: Plastics/rubber, Leather/stone/glass/clay, Motor vehicles, Misc. mfg.

Greene & Co.
5 Powderhouse Lane, P.O. Box 1025
Sherborn, Massachusetts 01770-1025
(508) 655-1210
Fax: (508) 655-2139
Email: 104736.636@compuserve.com
Web: www.greeneandco.com

Key Contact - Specialty:
Mr. Timothy G. Greene - *Banking, investment banking*

Description: Experienced search services for banking and financial executives in New England. Also handle searches for CFO/controllers for manufacturing and service companies.

Salary Minimum: $40,000
Industries: Banking, Invest. banking, Misc. financial, Equip. svcs., Real estate

Greene Personnel Consultants
1925 Broad St.
Cranston, Rhode Island 02905-3427
(401) 461-9700
Fax: (401) 461-7170

Key Contact - Specialty:
Ms. Dorcas P. Greene - *Direct marketing, market research, public relations, financial services, marketing communications*
Ms. Angela Payette - *Sales, sales promotion, market research, product & services market management, international*

Description: DB marketing, advertising, PR, product marketing, sales (consumer, business-to-business, software), financial services (pensions, trust, investment). International candidates available.

Salary Minimum: $50,000
Functions: Advertising, Mkt. research, Mktg. mgmt., Sales mgmt., Direct mktg., PR, Benefits
Industries: Food/bev/tobacco, Textiles/apparel, Soap/perfume/cosmetics, Drugs mfg., Misc. financial, Advertising/PR, New media

Greene-Levin-Snyder LLC
150 E. 58th St., 16th Floor
New York, New York 10155
(212) 752-5200
Fax: (212) 752-8245
Email: search@glslsg.com

Key Contact - Specialty:
Ms. Karin L. Greene - *Legal*
Alisa F. Levin - *Legal*
Susan Kurz Snyder - *Legal*

Description: Full service legal search firm, placing attorneys at all levels at major corporations, financial institutions and top tier law firms worldwide. The principals combine over thirty-five years of search expertise.
Functions: Legal, Attorneys
Industries: Mfg., Finance, Banking, Invest. banking, Brokers, Communications, Insurance

Greenfields Engineering Search

618 Brighton Court
Rolla, Missouri 65401
(573) 364-0020
Fax: (573) 341-9120
Email: mdoyen@rollanet.org
Web: www.rollanet.org/~mdoyen

Key Contact - Specialty:
Mr. Mike Doyen - *Engineering, manufacturing*

Description: Our firm recruits engineers and managers in the primary and fabricated metal products industry, with emphasis on metallurgical and materials engineering and techincal management. (College recruiting for metallurgical engineers nationwide.

Salary Minimum: $40,000
Functions: Mfg., Engineering
Industries: Metal products, Misc. mfg.

Greenwich Internet

8 Sound Shore Drive, Ste. 100
Greenwich, Connecticut 06830
(203) 629-5268
Fax: (203) 629-4848
Email: gvpinc@aol.com

Key Contact - Specialty:
Mr. Dan Cavicchio - *Software programmers, internet developers, intranet developers, technical sales & marketing*

Description: Contingency firm specializing in placing software professionals and internet/intranet developers. Reduced fee for entry-level searches. Will place individuals in the U.S.

Salary Minimum: $25,000
Functions: Sales & mktg., IT, MIS mgmt., Systems dev., Engineering, Technicians, Graphic artists
Industries: Computer equip., Finance, Computer svcs., Communications, New media, High tech, Software

Greenwich Search Partners, LLC

55 Old Field Point Rd.
Greenwich, Connecticut 06830
(203) 622-8133
Fax: (203) 622-7344
Email: frish@mail.snet.net

Key Contact - Specialty:
Mr. Robert Frishman - *Computer industry, sales management, marketing, consulting*
Ms. M. Susan Jones - *Computer industry, application software sales*

Description: Every individual associated with us has been a senior manager in a computer firm. We perform searches in the manner we preferred when we were hiring managers.

Salary Minimum: $75,000
Functions: Senior mgmt., Middle mgmt., Mktg. mgmt., Sales mgmt., MIS mgmt., Systems implem., Systems support
Industries: Computer equip., Computer svcs., Accounting, Mgmt. consulting, Software

Affiliates:
Irvine Search Partners

Gregory, Kyle & Assoc.

P.O. Box 901
Concord, North Carolina 28026-0901
(704) 786-1231
Email: HRGP@aol.com

Key Contact - Specialty:
Mr. Greg Picarella - *Manufacturing*

Description: With our extensive resources, including a national network of specialists with automotive manufacturing experience, we can locate the professional you are looking for in a timely manner.

Salary Minimum: $35,000
Functions: Directors, Plant mgmt., Quality, Materials, HR mgmt., Finance, Engineering
Industries: Mfg., Plastics/rubber, Leather/stone/glass/clay, Metal products, Motor vehicles, Misc. mfg., Human resource svcs.

Groenekamp & Assoc.

P.O. Box 2308
Beverly Hills, California 90213-2308
(310) 855-0119
Fax: (310) 855-0110
Email: hrwag@artnet.net
Web: www.hrwag.com

Key Contact - Specialty:
Mr. William A. Groenekamp - *Generalist*

Description: Executive search and professional staffing in broad range of industries. Also offer wide range of management consulting in human resources.

Salary Minimum: $40,000
Functions: Generalist
Industries: Generalist

J. B. Groner Executive Search, Inc.

2803B Philadelphia Pike, Ste. 101
Claymont, Delaware 19703
(302) 792-9228
Fax: (610) 497-5500
Email: groner@execjobsearch.com
Web: www.execjobsearch.com

Key Contact - Specialty:
Mr. James B. Groner - *Executive level (technical & administrative)*

Description: Specializing in senior corporate executives, financial and senior accounting executives, trade association and non-profit executives, engineering managers and executives, data processing, MIS, IT and computer managers and executives, human resources managers and executives.

Salary Minimum: $25,000
Functions: Senior mgmt., Production, Health admin., Personnel, CFO's, MIS mgmt., Engineering
Industries: Energy/utilities, Finance, Non-profits, New media, Government, High tech, Healthcare

Gros Executive Search, Inc.

155 Franklin Rd., Ste. 181
Brentwood, Tennessee 37027
(800) 283-5643
Fax: (615) 370-8512
Email: careers@plasticsjobs.com
Web: www.plasticsjobs.com

Key Contact - Specialty:
Mr. Dennis Gros - *Plastics*

Description: Serving companies and individuals as the marketplace of professional career opportunites in the plastics industry.
Functions: Senior mgmt., Middle mgmt., Product dev., Production, Plant mgmt., Productivity, Sales mgmt.
Industries: Plastics/rubber

Groupe PCA Inc.

(Firm declined to update.)
6850 Sherbrooke Est., Ste. 300
Montreal, Quebec H1N 1E1
Canada
(514) 256-8000

Key Contact - Specialty:
Mr. Pierre Chartrand - *Information systems technology*
Mr. Sylvain Hebert - *Information systems technology*

Description: Provider of choice of IT specialists in key business markets across Canada and the United States.

Salary Minimum: $30,000
Functions: Admin. svcs., Direct mktg., Personnel, MIS mgmt., Systems anal., Systems dev., Systems implem.
Industries: Svcs., Computer svcs., Accounting, Human resource svcs.

Branches:
721 SE 17th St., Ste. 200
Ft. Lauderdale, Florida 33316
(954) 463-0080
Key Contact - Specialty:
Ms. Lucie Vigneault

1 City Centre Dr., Ste. 304
Mississauga, Ontario L5B 1M2
Canada
(905) 848-2200
Key Contact - Specialty:
Mr. Felix Bedard - *Information systems technology*

Groupe Ranger Inc.

2045 Stanley St., #1400
Montreal, Quebec H3A 2V4
Canada
(514) 844-1746
Fax: (514) 844-6996
Email: ranger@odyssee.net

Key Contact - Specialty:
Mr. Jean-Jacques Ranger - *Information technology*
Ms. Lise Hebert - *Information technology*
Mr. Normand Leduc - *Generalist*
Ms. Manon Lamontagne - *Information technology*

Description: Very active in international searches for American companies established in francophone countries, by supplying French speaking outstanding MIS candidate.
Functions: Generalist, IT, MIS mgmt., Systems anal., Systems dev., Systems implem., Systems support

Affiliates:
Multi-Ressources

GSP International

90 Woodbridge Center Drive, Ste. 110
Woodbridge, New Jersey 07095
(732) 602-0100
Fax: (732) 602-0108
Email: gspintl@home.com
Web: www.gspintl.com

Key Contact - Specialty:
Mr. Edward Kaye - *Accounting & finance*
Mr. Tony Glennon - *Accounting & finance*
Mr. John Sicilia - *Accounting & finance*
Mr. Ray Pirre - *Accounting & finance*

Description: An executive search and placement firm specializing in the accounting and finance professions.
Functions: CFO's, Budgeting, Cash mgmt., Credit, Taxes, M&A, Risk mgmt.
Industries: Energy/utilities, Mfg., Finance, Svcs., Communications, Insurance, Real estate

Nadine Guber & Assoc., Inc.

575 Lexington Ave., Ste. 410
New York, New York 10022
(212) 572-9630
Fax: (212) 572-9635
Email: nadineg@aol.com

Key Contact - Specialty:
Ms. Nadine B. Guber - *Marketing and advertising*

Description: We specialize in the placement of advertising agency account management and corporate marketing management executives. Our professionals utilize their experience, extensive database and understanding of clients' cultures to identify uniquely qualified candidates.

Salary Minimum: $50,000
Functions: Advertising, Mkt. research, Mktg. mgmt., Direct mktg.
Industries: Generalist, Communications, Advertising/PR, New media, Telecoms

Michael R. Guerin Co.

16368 Avenida Suavidad
San Diego, California 92128
(619) 675-0395
Fax: (619) 675-0393
Email: mrgco1192@aol.com

Key Contact - Specialty:
Mr. Michael R. Guerin - *Software, telecommunications*

Description: Author, (RIST) recruiting, interviewing, selecting and training - used to develop three national organizations in high tech, financial service industry at a senior level. Most recent directed sales and marketing for Forbes 500 company in support of 40 million to 1.6 billion in annual sales.

Salary Minimum: $70,000
Functions: Senior mgmt., Middle mgmt., Product dev., Mktg. mgmt., Sales mgmt., Engineering
Industries: Computer equip., Test/measurement equip., Computer svcs., Equip. svcs., Telecoms, High tech, Software

The Guild Corp.

8260 Greensboro Drive, Ste. 460
McLean, Virginia 22102
(703) 761-4023
Fax: (703) 761-4024
Email: resumes@guildcorp.com
Web: guildcorp.com

Key Contact - Specialty:
Mr. Paul W. Siker - *Software product, data communications*
Mr. Michael M. Kohonoski - *Software product, data communications*
Mr. William J. Joyce - *Software product, data communications*

Description: Providing top quality, results oriented search services to the information technology, computer software, data communications, management consulting and high tech engineering marketplaces. Searches range from individual contributors to senior executives.

Salary Minimum: $50,000
Functions: MIS mgmt., Systems anal., Systems dev., Systems implem., R&D, Engineering, Mgmt. consultants
Industries: Generalist, Computer equip., Test/measurement equip., Svcs., Computer svcs., High tech, Software

The Gullgroup

5608 Canada Court
Rockwall, Texas 75087
(972) 772-0582
Fax: (972) 772-0587
Email: gullgrp@swbell.net

Key Contact - Specialty:
Mr. James A. Ryan - *Information technology executives*

Description: Over twenty years of recruiting experience concentrating in the consulting and information technology arena.

Salary Minimum: $40,000
Functions: CFO's, MIS mgmt., Systems anal., Systems dev., Systems implem., Network admin., Mgmt. consultants
Industries: Energy/utilities, Mfg., Finance, Communications, High tech, Software, Non-classifiable industries

Affiliates:
Network Recruiters

Gumbinner/Haubenstock, Inc.

509 Madison Ave., Ste. 708
New York, New York 10022
(212) 688-0129

Key Contact - Specialty:
Mr. Paul S. Gumbinner - *Advertising (agency account managers)*
Ms. Eileen Haubenstock - *Advertising (agency account managers)*

Description: Professional recruitment by advertising people for advertising people. Advertising account management from account executives to presidents. Client side advertising executives as well.

Salary Minimum: $50,000
Functions: Advertising, Direct mktg.
Industries: Advertising/PR

H R Solutions, Inc.

One Mid Rivers Mall Drive, Ste. 264
St. Peters, Missouri 63376
(314) 278-1200
Fax: (314) 970-2299
Email: hrsol@inlink.com

Key Contact - Specialty:
Mr. Robert J. Keymer - *Hospitality*
Mr. James McDaniel - *Home health*
Mr. Jason Wagenknecht - *Hospitality*

Description: Principals have combined total experience in excess of 35 years recruiting mid management and executive level candidates. Principals have prior work experience in their respective specializations.
Functions: Directors, Senior mgmt., Middle mgmt., CFO's, IT
Industries: Hospitality, Healthcare

The H. S. Group, Inc.

2611 Libal St.
Green Bay, Wisconsin 54301
(414) 432-7444
Fax: (414) 436-2966
Email: hsgroup@gbonline.com

Key Contact - Specialty:
Mr. Jock Seal - *Human resources, manufacturing, finance, accounting, food*
Mr. Chris Cegelski - *Engineers, research & development, sales & marketing, food, paper*
Mr. Jeff Lasee - *Information technology, Human resources, accounting, finance, sales*

Description: Over 32 years of experience in professional placement.

Salary Minimum: $30,000
Functions: Senior mgmt., Mfg., Materials, Sales & mktg., Benefits, Finance, IT
Industries: Mfg., Food/bev/tobacco, Paper, Finance, Accounting, Human resource svcs., Insurance

H.Q. Search, Inc.

22 E. Chicago Ave., Ste. 119
Naperville, Illinois 60563
(630) 717-5570
Fax: (630) 527-9841

Key Contact - Specialty:
Mr. Don Graham - *Financial services field*

Description: Specializing in all areas of financial services in: corporations, domestic and international banks, investment banks, venture capital, sales and trading, consulting, pension funds, money management and insurance companies.

Salary Minimum: $35,000
Functions: Finance, CFO's, Cash mgmt., Credit, M&A, Risk mgmt., Mgmt. consultants
Industries: Finance, Banking, Invest. banking, Brokers, Venture cap., Misc. financial

Stephen Haas Legal Placement

60 East 42nd St.
New York, New York 10017
(212) 661-5555
(800) 224-0750
Fax: (212) 972-1279
Web: recru2r@aol.com

Key Contact - Specialty:
Ms. Marilyn Wallberg - *Real estate, corporate*
Ms. Diane Edelman - *Litigation, trusts & estates, labor*

Description: Our recruiters offer discretion, extensive placement and counseling experience and strong relationships with partners and counsels. We are one of the oldest and most successful agencies in the field.
Functions: Attorneys
Industries: Legal

Russ Hadick & Assoc. Inc.

7100 Corporate Way, Ste. B
Centerville, Ohio 45459
(937) 439-7700
Fax: (937) 439-7705
Email: rhadick@rharecruiters.com
Web: www.rharecruiters.com

Key Contact - Specialty:
Mr. Russ Hadick - *Engineering, management*
Mr. Rob Hugsman - *Human resources, administration, finance*
Mr. Ron Toke - *Engineering*
Mr. Terry Flowers - *Programmers, database administrators*
Mr. Dick Westerfield - *Banking*
Mr. Ted O'Neill - *Manufacturing management*

Description: We interview, reference check and verify degrees before our customers ever see our clients. We've been in business 18 years. All of our people held top management positions before coming into recruiting.
Functions: General mgmt., Senior mgmt., Mfg., Materials, HR mgmt., Finance, IT
Industries: Energy/utilities, Mfg., Banking, High tech, Software

Hadley Associates, Inc.

147 Columbia Tnpk., Ste. 104
Florham Park, New Jersey 07932-2145
(973) 377-9177
Fax: (973) 377-9223
Email: tmhadley@ix.netcom.com
Web: www.netcom.com~tmhadley

Key Contact - Specialty:
Mr. Thomas M. Hadley - *Healthcare (regulatory, quality assurance, clinical affairs)*

Description: National and international search capabilities exclusively for the pharmaceutical, biotechnology, medical device and related healthcare industries. Areas of expertise include: regulatory affairs, QA/QC, clinical research, R&D, biotechnology and marketing.
Functions: R&D, Engineering, Int'l.
Industries: Drugs mfg., Medical devices, Pharmaceutical svcs., Biotech, Healthcare

Hahn & Assoc., Inc.

7026 Corporate Way, Ste. 212
Dayton, Ohio 45459
(513) 436-3141
Fax: (513) 436-3252

Key Contact - Specialty:
Mr. Kenneth R. Hahn - *Manufacturing (professionals)*

Description: Search and placement since 1971. Successful placements with over 700 different client employers. Mr. Hahn in private personnel business since 1960.
Functions: General mgmt., Mfg., Materials, HR mgmt., Finance, Engineering
Industries: Paper, Plastics/rubber, Metal products, Machinery/Appliances, Motor vehicles, Consumer electronics, Misc. mfg.

Halbrecht & Co.

10195 Main St., Ste. L
Fairfax, Virginia 22031
(703) 359-2880
Fax: (703) 359-2933
Email: tomm@halbrecht.com
Web: www.halbrecht.com

Key Contact - Specialty:
Mr. Thomas J. Maltby - *Information systems, quantitative analysts*
Mr. Alec Siegel - *Information systems, network engineers*

Description: We are proud of our reputation for assisting our clients in identifying and selecting superior business professionals dedicated to excellence rather than the merely qualified technician.

Salary Minimum: $40,000
Functions: Mkt. research, MIS mgmt., Systems anal., Systems dev., Systems implem., R&D, Mgmt. consultants
Industries: Mfg., Transportation, Svcs., Computer svcs., Mgmt. consulting, High tech, Software

Branches:
P.O. Box 324
Old Greenwich, Connecticut 06870
(203) 637-5815
Fax: (203) 637-4953
Key Contact - Specialty:
Mr. Thomas J. Kubiak - *Management consulting, marketing, quantitative analysts*
Mr. Paul Calale - *Transportation, logistics*

Robert Half Canada Inc.

181 Bay St., Ste. 820
P.O. Box 824
Toronto, Ontario M5J 2T3
Canada
(416) 350-2330
Fax: (416) 350-3573
Web: www.rhit.com

Key Contact - Specialty:
Ms. Kathryn Bolt - *Accounting, finance*

Description: Recruiters specializing in the placement of finance and accounting professionals at all levels. Three Toronto area offices. Part of Robert Half International, the world's first and leading financial staffing service.
Functions: CFO's, Budgeting, Cash mgmt., Credit, Taxes, M&A, Risk mgmt.
Industries: Generalist

Branches:
421 7th Ave. S.W., Ste. 1515
Calgary, Alberta T2P 4K9
Canada
(403) 269-5387
Fax: (403) 264-0934
Key Contact - Specialty:
Ms. Audrey MacDougall - *Finance, accounting*

10180 101st St., Ste. 1280
Edmonton, Alberta T5J 3S4
Canada
Key Contact - Specialty:
Ms. Donna Norwood

714-1055 Dunsmuir St., P.O. Box 49301
Vancouver, British Columbia V7X 1L4
Canada
(604) 685-4253
Fax: (604) 687-7533
Key Contact - Specialty:
Ms. Diana Infanti - *Finance, accounting*

1 Robert Speck Pkwy., Ste. 940
Mississauga, Ontario L4Z 3M3
Canada
(905) 273-4229
Fax: (905) 273-6217
Key Contact - Specialty:
Ms. Christine Lucy - *Finance, accounting*

5140 Yonge St., Ste. 1500
North York, Ontario M2N 6L7
Canada
(416) 226-4570
Fax: (416) 226-4498
Key Contact - Specialty:
Ms. Tami Turner - *Finance, accounting*

427 Laurier Ave. W., Ste. 1400
Ottawa, Ontario K1R 7Y2
Canada
(613) 236-4253
Fax: (613) 236-2159
Key Contact - Specialty:
Ms. Avalee Prehogan - *Finance, accounting*

1 Place Ville Marie, Ste. 2727
Montreal, Quebec H3B 4G4
Canada
(514) 875-8585
Fax: (514) 875-8066
Key Contact - Specialty:
Mr. Michel LeBoeuf - *Finance, accounting*

Don Hall & Assoc.

617 Catalina Drive
Waco, Texas 76712
(254) 772-0420
(800) 999-0420
Fax: (254) 772-1333
Email: dha@texnet.net
Web: www.millworkjobs.com

Key Contact - Specialty:
Mr. Don Hall - *Millwork, windows, doors, stairs, moldings*
Ms. Joann Hall - *Millwork*

Description: The Millwork Network, nationwide executive and management placement for manufacturers, distributors and retailers of windows, doors, stairs, moldings and related building materials. Also consulting and mergers/acquisitions.

Salary Minimum: $20,000
Functions: General mgmt., Mfg., Materials, Sales & mktg., HR mgmt., Finance, IT
Industries: Lumber/furniture, Wholesale, Retail, Advertising/PR, Haz. waste

Branches:
14711 Mimosa Lane
Tustin, California 92780
(714) 730-0745
Fax: (714) 730-0277
Key Contact - Specialty:
Mr. Jerry Sheppard - *Millwork, home centers*

3505 Spalding Terrace
Norcross, Georgia 30092
(770) 441-9071
Fax: (770) 448-8804
Key Contact - Specialty:
Mr. Emile Castanet - *Millwork, mergers, consulting*

Affiliates:
The Wittmann Group

Susan Hall Executive Search

3713 Branchwood Drive
Plano, Texas 75093
(972) 378-9378
Fax: (972) 378-9379

Key Contact - Specialty:
Ms. Susan Hall - *Advertising, marketing communications*

Description: With over 10 years experience recruiting for advertising agencies in the Dallas area, the principal has the ability to identify and recruit individuals who add value to your agency or company.

Salary Minimum: $30,000
Functions: Advertising, Mkt. research, Mktg. mgmt., PR
Industries: Advertising/PR

Hall Kinion

19925 Stevens Creek Blvd., Ste. 180
Cupertino, California 95014
(408) 863-5600
Fax: (408) 863-5707
Email: stars@hallkinion.com
Web: www.hallkinion.com

Key Contact - Specialty:
Mr. Craig Silverman - *Technical, information systems, software*
Ms. Jennifer Waldrip - *Technical, information systems, software*
Ms. Debbie Allen - *Technical, information systems, software*
Mr. Jason Hancock - *Technical, information systems, software*

Description: Hall Kinion is a leading provider of specialized information technology professionals on a contract and permanent basis operating in 21 offices in 14 major technology markets throughout the U.S. and in London

Salary Minimum: $40,000
Functions: Product dev., Systems anal., Systems dev., Systems support, Network admin., DB admin., Engineering
Industries: Computer equip., Test/measurement equip., Finance, Svcs., Computer svcs., High tech, Software

Branches:
1201 S. Alma School Rd., Ste. 4450
Bank of America Bldg.
Mesa, Arizona 85210
(602) 833-8686
(888) 833-3308
Fax: (602) 833-3877
Key Contact - Specialty:
Mr. Jared Taylor

820 Bay Ave., Ste. 136
Capitola, California 95010
(408) 462-9800
Fax: (408) 462-0148
Key Contact - Specialty:
Ms. Joyce Borland

1900 McCarthy Blvd., Ste. 420
Milpitas, California 95035
(408) 435-8367
Fax: (408) 428-6484

1804 Shoreline Blvd., Ste. 120
Mountain View, California 94043
(650) 526-1500
Fax: (650) 526-1501
Key Contact - Specialty:
Mr. Ed Blom

1700 S. El Camino Real, Ste. 108
San Mateo, California 94402
(650) 345-5600
(888) 682-6400
Fax: (650) 345-8646

5613 DTC Pkwy., Ste. 830
Englewood, Colorado 80111
(303) 741-9900
(800) 425-5764
Fax: (303) 741-9986
Key Contact - Specialty:
Mr. Aaron Mills

3030 N. Rocky Point Drive W., Ste. 400
Tampa, Florida 33607
(813) 207-0100
(800) 441-5720
Fax: (813) 207-0488
Key Contact - Specialty:
Ms. Juli Reynolds

440 S. LaSalle St., Ste. 3904
One Financial Place
Chicago, Illinois 60605
(312) 913-0111
(888) 913-0111
Fax: (312) 913-1180
Key Contact - Specialty:
Mr. Mike Rimmele

475 N. Martingale Rd., Ste. 450
Schaumburg, Illinois 60173
(847) 517-9500
(888) 459-4254
Fax: (847) 517-9400

10 Burlington Mall Rd., Ste. 250
Burlington, Massachusetts 01803
(781) 229-2225
(800) 955-4254
Fax: (781) 229-7772
Key Contact - Specialty:
Mr. Robert Misita

590 5th Ave., 18th Floor
New York, New York 10036
(212) 575-1400
(800) 963-8326
Fax: (212) 575-2640
Key Contact - Specialty:
Ms. Debbie Allen-Oberbillig

2525 Meridian Pkwy., Ste. 280
Research Triangle Park
Durham, North Carolina 27713
(919) 572-9999
(800) 365-3031
Fax: (919) 572-6550
Key Contact - Specialty:
Ms. Debbie Bush

10260 SW Greenburg Rd., Ste. 810
Portland, Oregon 97223
(503) 244-2700
(888) 302-2700
Fax: (503) 244-6522

8911 Capitol of Texas Hwy., Ste. 3310
Austin, Texas 78759-7267
(512) 349-0960
(888) 788-4231
Fax: (512) 349-0983
Key Contact - Specialty:
Ms. Beth Valkarcel

901 MoPac Expwy. S., Ste. 343
Austin, Texas 78746
(512) 306-8400
(888) 788-4254
Fax: (512) 306-8060
Key Contact - Specialty:
Ms. Beth Valkarcel

3040 Post Oak Blvd., Ste. 440
Houston, Texas 77056
(713) 622-6800
(888) 622-6889
Fax: (713) 622-6920
Key Contact - Specialty:
Mr. Rich Hamilton

60 E. South Temple, Ste. 2050
Eagle Gate Plaza
Salt Lake City, Utah 84111
(801) 322-2225
(888) 665-2225
Fax: (801) 322-2205
Key Contact - Specialty:
Mr. Brent Packer

3001 112th Ave., NE, Ste. 101
Bellevue, Washington 98004
(425) 889-5003
(800) 234-1136
Fax: (425) 889-5985
Key Contact - Specialty:
Ms. Maureen Kerber

2825 Eastlake Ave. E., Ste. 120
Seattle, Washington 98102
(206) 726-8800
(888) 270-6008
Fax: (206) 726-8833
Key Contact - Specialty:
Mr. Didi Zahariades

International Branches:
Weybridge

Hall Management Group, Inc.
736 Green St. NW
Gainesville, Georgia 30501
(770) 534-5568
Fax: (770) 534-5572
Email: billlennon@mindspring.com

Key Contact - Specialty:
Mr. Bill Lennon - *Medical device, manufacturing, pharmaceuticals, accounting, IT, HR*

Description: Over 25 years recruiting as a manufacturing placement specialist. Sunbelt and Atlantic states specialist. Extensive networking for specialty needs.

Salary Minimum: $40,000
Functions: General mgmt., Mfg., HR mgmt., Finance, IT, Engineering
Industries: Mfg., Food/bev/tobacco, Drugs mfg., Medical devices, Plastics/rubber, Machinery/Appliances, Motor vehicles

Hallman Group, Inc.
4528 West KL Ave.
Kalamazoo, Michigan 49006
(616) 353-6835
Fax: (616) 353-6845
Email: hallman@iserv.net
Web: hallmangroup.com

Key Contact - Specialty:
Ms. Nancy L. Hall - *Information technology*
Mr. Kenneth Killman - *Information technology*

Description: We are matchmakers. We prescreen and qualify thoroughly our candidates and companies. We do not advertise but work off our reputation.

Salary Minimum: $25,000
Functions: Production, Credit, Risk mgmt., Systems anal., Systems dev., Systems implem., DB admin.
Industries: Mfg.

Halo Insurance Service
P.O. Box 160272
Mobile, Alabama 36616
(334) 478-1604
Fax: (334) 478-1606
Email: halo_ins@viptx.net
Web: halo_ins@zebra.net

Key Contact - Specialty:
Mr. Thomas J. Blythe - *Insurance*

Salary Minimum: $30,000
Functions: Sales mgmt.
Industries: Insurance

Hamilton & Co.
5544 Caplestone Lane
Dublin, Ohio 43017
(614) 792-7772
Fax: (614) 792-7773
Email: ljhamco@aol.com

Key Contact - Specialty:
Ms. Lisa J. Hamilton - *Advertising, public relations, direct marketing agencies*

Description: Recruiter brings 22 years of account service and corporate agency management experience to search industry. Known for exceptionally high standards, critical talent assessment, reliable follow-through and client-candidate trust.
Functions: Senior mgmt., Middle mgmt., Advertising, Mkt. research, Mktg. mgmt., Direct mktg., PR
Industries: Communications, Advertising/PR, New media

The Hampton Group
33 Flying Point Rd.
Southampton, New York 11968
(516) 287-3330

Web: hgroup@peconic.net

Key Contact - Specialty:
Ms. Belle Lareau - *Diagnostics, biotechnology, pharmaceutical*
Mr. Gerard A. Lareau - *Genetics, biotechnology*
Ms. Valerie Remkus - *Pharmaceutical, research & development*
Ms. Bev Norindr - *Biotechnology, pharmaceutical, business development, marketing*
Ms. Janine Jolly - *Biotechnology, molecular biology, biostatistics, bioinformatics*

Description: We are an executive search firm specializing in placing middle and senior level management in the medical, pharmaceutical and biotech industries. Our knowledge of the marketplace and database profiles of candidates and companies enables us to quickly target and identify contacts which closely match specific profiles.
Functions: Directors, Senior mgmt., Product dev., Quality, Mkt. research, Mktg. mgmt., R&D
Industries: Drugs mfg., Medical devices, Biotech

The Hanna Group
8437 Mayfield Rd., Ste. 102
Chesterland, Ohio 44026
(216) 729-1255
Fax: (216) 729-1755
Email: hanna@hannagroup.com
Web: www.hannagroup.com

Key Contact - Specialty:
Mr. M. A. Jack Hanna, Jr. - *Upper level operations, finance, engineering, sales & marketing*
Mr. C. Szymanski - *Human resources, manufacturing engineering*
Ms. U. T. Hanna

Description: Mid to upper level management search in manufacturing, engineering, finance and sales/marketing. Specific expertise in commercial vehicle, construction, agricultural equipment, heavy capital equipment, automotive and allied industry.

Salary Minimum: $40,000
Functions: Senior mgmt., Mfg., Materials, Sales & mktg., HR mgmt., Finance, Engineering
Industries: Construction, Plastics/rubber, Metal products, Machinery/Appliances, Motor vehicles, Transportation, Communications

The Hanover Consulting Group
11707 Hunters Run Drive
Hunt Valley, Maryland 21030
(410) 785-1912
Fax: (410) 785-1913
Email: TGraff@thehanovergroup.net
Web: thehanovergroup.net

Key Contact - Specialty:
Mr. Thomas D. B. Graff - *Banking, trust, lending*

Description: Our reputation has been built on providing top talent for our clients at the quickest possible turnaround time. We provide comprehensive search work for the banking and the investment industries. We fill trust, investment, lending and sales positions.

Salary Minimum: $50,000
Functions: Senior mgmt., Middle mgmt., CFO's, Cash mgmt., Credit, M&A, Risk mgmt.
Industries: Finance, Banking, Invest. banking, Brokers, Venture cap.

Hansen Executive Search, Inc.
1629 S. 152nd St.
Omaha, Nebraska 68144
(402) 697-7960
Fax: (402) 697-7959

Key Contact - Specialty:
Mr. James P. Hansen - *Consumer packaged goods (sales & marketing, operations, general management)*

Description: Executive recruitment in consumer packaged goods, specializing in sales/marketing management, MIS, manufacturing and general management.

Salary Minimum: $50,000
Functions: General mgmt., Mfg., Sales & mktg., Advertising, Mkt. research, Mktg. mgmt., Sales mgmt.
Industries: Food/bev/tobacco, Paper, Soap/perfume/cosmetics, Drugs mfg., Finance, Communications

Janet Harberth & Assoc., Inc.
3350 Sweetwater Rd., #703
Lawrenceville, Georgia 30044
(770) 638-3659
Fax: (770) 638-3660

Key Contact - Specialty:
Ms. Janet Harberth - *Advertising, corporate communications*

Description: Partnered with numerous recruitment firms allows us full access to a broad array of opportunities and candidates within advertising, public relations, sales promotion and direct marketing.

Salary Minimum: $25,000
Functions: Advertising, Mkt. research, Mktg. mgmt., Direct mktg., PR
Industries: Advertising/PR, New media

Affiliates:
Hamilton & Co.
NDB Assoc., Inc.

Harbor Consultants Int'l., Inc.
P.O. Box 221616
Chantilly, Virginia 20153-1616
(703) 352-1888
Fax: (703) 385-1755

Key Contact - Specialty:
Mr. Frank Ojeda

Description: A well established and highly regarded international executive search firm with experience in most industries and all functions at the senior level with emphasis on quality and staffing consulting services.
Functions: Healthcare, HR mgmt., IT, Mgmt. consultants, Attorneys, Int'l.
Industries: Legal, Mgmt. consulting, Human resource svcs., Communications, Environmental svcs., High tech, Healthcare

Harbrowe, Inc.
222 Mamaroneck Ave., #107
White Plains, New York 10605
(914) 949-6400
Fax: (914) 949-6924

Key Contact - Specialty:
Ms. Barbara Dolphin - *Outside corporate sales*
Ms. Valerie Gehn - *Office support, middle management, inside sales*
Ms. Joanne LeBow - *Pharmaceutical, medical sales*

Description: Professional personal interviewing, testing and screening for business/industrial/pharmaceutical/medical sales, office support, middle management.
Functions: Middle mgmt., Admin. svcs., Sales mgmt., Customer svc., Benefits, Credit, Systems support
Industries: Paper, Drugs mfg., Medical devices, Misc. mfg., Transportation, Accounting, Human resource svcs.

Harcourt & Assoc.
1703 Toronto Dominion Twr.
Edmonton Centre
Edmonton, Alberta T5J 2Z1
Canada
(403) 425-5555
Fax: (403) 990-1891
Email: recruiter@harcourt.ab.ca
Web: www.harcourt.ab.ca

Key Contact - Specialty:
Ms. Judy Harcourt - *Association management, retail management*
Ms. Barbara Perkins - *IT staff, computer consulting*
Mr. Peter Harcourt - *Manufacturing*
Ms. Mimi Garbutt - *Insurance*
Mr. Don Unger - *Technical sales, sales management*

Description: We provide staff and contract recruiting services for Alberta businesses.
Functions: Senior mgmt., Mfg., Materials, Sales & mktg., Finance, IT, Engineering
Industries: Agri/forestry/mining, Energy/ utilities, Construction, Chemicals, Metal products, Computer equip., High tech

Branches:
1600 -444 5th Ave. SW
Calgary, Alberta T2P 2T8
Canada
(403) 263-5445
Fax: (403) 263-5467
Email: recruiter@harcourt.ab.ca
Web: www.harcourt.ab.ca
Key Contact - Specialty:
Ms. Debbie Johnston - *Information technology*

Hardage Group
220 N. Main
Baird-Brewer Bldg., Ste. 106
Dyersburg, Tennessee 38025-0208
(901) 285-3120
Fax: (901) 285-3414
Email: hardage@ecsis.net
Web: www.hardagegroup.com

Key Contact - Specialty:
Mr. Phillip Hardage - *Human resources, finance, engineering*
Mr. Allen Tillman - *Textiles, plastics, engineering*
Ms. Grace Phelps - *Human resources, printing, retail*

Description: Principals are seasoned human resources professionals with extensive executive recruiting experience. Primarily focused on union-free manufacturing environments in the functional areas of human resources, finance, engineering and general management.

Salary Minimum: $40,000
Functions: Middle mgmt., Production, Automation, Benefits, Personnel, Training, Engineering
Industries: Printing, Chemicals, Plastics/ rubber, Metal products, Machinery/ Appliances, Motor vehicles, Transportation

---

Robert Harkins Assoc., Inc.
P.O. Box 236, 1248 W. Main St.
Ephrata, Pennsylvania 17522
(717) 733-9664
Fax: (717) 733-9668
Email: info@harkinsassoc.com

Key Contact - Specialty:
Mr. Robert E. Harkins - *Engineering, manufacturing management, human resources*
Mr. Thomas M. Dabich - *Data processing, finance, banking*
Mr. Thomas Refi - *Technical sales/ marketing, chemical process engineering*

Description: The firm offers contingency, retained search and contract professional placement services.

Salary Minimum: $35,000
Functions: Purchasing, Sales & mktg., CFO's, MIS mgmt., Systems anal., Systems dev., Engineering
Industries: Generalist, Plastics/rubber, Metal products, Machinery/Appliances, Computer equip., Computer svcs., Accounting

---

Harmeling & Associates
3232 Governor Drive, Ste. J
San Diego, California 92122
(619) 455-6212
Fax: (619) 455-9239

Key Contact - Specialty:
Mr. Dutch Harmeling - *Retail management, leasing, marketing, development*

Description: I specialize in working with shopping center developers and retailers only.

Salary Minimum: $50,000
Industries: Retail

Harper Associates
29870 Middlebelt
Farmington Hills, Michigan 48334
(248) 932-1170
Fax: (248) 932-1214
Web: www.harper-jobs.com

Key Contact - Specialty:
Mr. Bennett Schwartz - *Hospitality*
Ms. Cindy Krainen - *Hospitality*

Description: Many search assignments underway for healthcare industry (physician recruitment, pharmacy, administration, finance, nursing, medical records). Hospitality placement specialists for hotels, restaurants, resorts, country clubs and food service industry.
Functions: Middle mgmt., Physicians, Nurses, Allied health, Health admin., Budgeting, Systems dev.
Industries: Retail, Misc. financial, Hospitality, Computer svcs., Accounting, Healthcare

---

Harper Hewes, Inc.
1473 Calkins Rd.
Pittsford, New York 14534
(716) 321-1700
Fax: (716) 321-1707
Email: hhsearch@servtech.com

Key Contact - Specialty:
Ms. Deborah Harper - *Telecommunications, computer, information systems consulting, management consulting*

Description: Particularly successful in placing key individuals who serve as agents of cultural and/or technological change. Implementation of virtual project teams allows us to successfully complete searches of any size.

Salary Minimum: $75,000
Functions: Senior mgmt., Mktg. mgmt., Sales mgmt., Systems dev., Systems implem., Mgmt. consultants
Industries: Computer equip., Computer svcs., Mgmt. consulting, Telecoms, High tech, Software

---

Harrington & O'Brien, Inc.
67 Emerald St., Ste 702
Keene, New Hampshire 03431

Key Contact - Specialty:
Mr. Christopher Patrick Harrington
Mr. Michael Joseph O'Brien

Description: General management for most industries with some concentration in the medical field.

Salary Minimum: $35,000
Functions: General mgmt., Nurses, Allied health, HR mgmt.
Industries: Generalist, Drugs mfg., Medical devices, Healthcare

---

Harris McCully Assoc., Inc.
99 Park Ave., 18th Floor
New York, New York 10016
(212) 983-1400
Fax: (212) 983-1451

Key Contact - Specialty:
Mr. Alan Harris
Mr. Ron Hamara

Description: A contingency and retainer-based search firm specializing in the placement of middle to senior level professionals. Our forte is in financial services, yet we work with diverse industries and multiple disciplines.

Salary Minimum: $75,000
Functions: General mgmt., HR mgmt., Finance, IT, Int'l.
Industries: Textiles/apparel, Banking, Invest. banking, Brokers, Venture cap., Misc. financial, Entertainment

---

Harrison Consulting Group, Inc.
21550 Oxnard St., Ste. 300
Woodland Hills, California 91367
(818) 615-2040
Fax: (818) 615-2027
Email: dhgrue@aol.com

Key Contact - Specialty:
Mr. Douglas Harrison Grue - *Tax (California only)*

Description: We place tax professionals in California for clients in private industry and large accounting firms. To discern technical and leadership skills,we meet every candidate. Our process creates a team with HR and tax professionals.

Salary Minimum: $40,000
Functions: Taxes
Industries: Generalist

Harrison Moore Inc.

7638 Pierce St.
Omaha, Nebraska 68124
(402) 391-5494
Fax: (402) 391-5381

Key Contact - Specialty:
Mr. Curt McLey - *Foundry, machining industries*

Description: Specialty in the foundry and machining industries: management, production, operations, quality, technical, sales, metallurgy, plant engineering and maintenance.
Functions: Product dev., Production, Automation, Plant mgmt., Quality, Productivity, Engineering
Industries: Metal products, Misc. mfg.

Hart & Co.

219 E. 69th St., Ste. 7H
New York, New York 10021
(212) 585-4000
Fax: (212) 585-1294
Email: gghart@aol.com

Key Contact - Specialty:
Mr. Gerry Hart - *Advertising agencies*

Description: An executive recruiting organization with focus on the consumer advertising agency and corporate communications industries. Agency positions are in account management, media and research. Clientside includes advertising and marketing specialists.

Salary Minimum: $30,000
Functions: Sales & mktg., Advertising, Mkt. research, Mktg. mgmt., Sales mgmt., Direct mktg.
Industries: Mgmt. consulting, Advertising/PR, Broadcast & Film

---

Hartman Greene & Wells

1025 Connecticut Ave., Suite 1012
Washington, District of Columbia 20036
(202) 223-7644
Fax: (301) 765-2223

Key Contact - Specialty:
Ms. Zina L. Greene - *Attorneys*

Description: With over thirty years of combined experience, our greatest strength is providing qualified candidates both expeditiously and confidentially in the legal community.
Functions: Attorneys

Phyllis Hawkins & Assoc., Inc.

5025 N. Central Ave., Ste. 611
Phoenix, Arizona 85012
(602) 263-0248
Fax: (602) 678-1564
Email: phawk@azlink.com
Web: www.azlawsearch.com

Key Contact - Specialty:
Ms. Phyllis Hawkins - *Attorneys*
Ms. Elaine Goldman - *Attorneys*
Ms. Tracy Tabler - *Attorneys*

Description: We conduct searches for law firms and corporations. Our staff has an in-depth knowledge of the legal communities in our area and substantial experience in legal recruitment.

Salary Minimum: $60,000
Functions: Attorneys
Industries: Legal

Affiliates:
Newman-Hawkins

Michael J. Hawkins, Inc.

1615 Colonial Pkwy.
Inverness, Illinois 60067-4732
(847) 705-5400
Fax: (847) 705-9065
Email: HawkinsInc@aol.com

Key Contact - Specialty:
Mr. Michael J. Hawkins - *Foodservice, food retail, food, supplies, equipment*

Description: The nation's leading executive search organization specializing in the supply segment of the food service industry. Search limited to general management, sales, marketing, engineering and manufacturing executives.

Salary Minimum: $50,000
Functions: Senior mgmt., Mfg., Product dev., Production, Mktg. mgmt., Sales mgmt., Engineering
Industries: Food/bev/tobacco, Paper, Chemicals, Plastics/rubber

---

Hayden & Assoc., Inc.

7825 Washington Ave. S., Ste. 120
Minneapolis, Minnesota 55439
(612) 941-6300
Fax: (612) 941-9602
Web: haydenassoc.com

Key Contact - Specialty:
Mr. Steve Benedict
Mr. Lowell Singerman

Description: Large progressive firm with a personal database of over 110,000 candidates. Very client service oriented with 80% of our client companies becoming repeat customers. 300 affiliates nationally.

Salary Minimum: $30,000
Functions: Mkt. research, Mktg. mgmt., Sales mgmt., CFO's, Systems anal., Systems dev., Engineering
Industries: Generalist, Computer equip., Finance, Computer svcs., Telecoms, High tech, Software

---

Haydon Legal Search

1740 Ridge Ave.
Evanston, Illinois 60201-5918
(847) 475-4222
Fax: (847) 475-0939
Email: haydonsrch@aol.com

Key Contact - Specialty:
Ms. Meredith Haydon - *Attorneys*

Description: Specializing in attorney search & placement since 1979, Meredith Haydon is recognized for providing exceptional recruiting services to major law firms and corporate legal departments in the greater Chicago area.
Functions: Attorneys
Industries: Legal

Hayman Daugherty Assoc., Inc.

5105 Old Ellis Pointe, Ste. 2000
Roswell, Georgia 30076
(800) 765-0432
Fax: (800) 782-4999
Email: info@haymandaugherty.com
Web: www.haymandaugherty.com

Key Contact - Specialty:
Ms. Kimberly J. Daugherty-Hill - *Physicians, healthcare, MIS, data processing, information technology, technical*

Description: We specialize in building relationships. Our consultants are geographically and specialty divided which allows them to enjoy a high level of expertise. We understand your needs and can help you accomplish your goals.

Salary Minimum: $30,000
Functions: Physicians, IT, MIS mgmt., Systems anal., Systems dev., Systems implem., Network admin.
Industries: Mfg., Finance, Svcs., Communications, High tech, Software, Healthcare

Affiliates:
The OutSource ReSource Corp.
Tech Management

Hazard, Young, Attea & Assoc., Ltd.

540 Frontage Rd., Ste. 3045
Northfield, Illinois 60093-1230
(847) 441-8466
Fax: (847) 441-8467

Key Contact - Specialty:
Dr. William Attea - *Schools, superintendents, administrative personnel, public*

Description: Executive search services and management consulting with special emphasis on school districts, higher education.
Functions: Senior mgmt., Middle mgmt., HR mgmt., Benefits, Personnel, Training
Industries: Higher ed., Mgmt. consulting, Non-classifiable industries

HCI Corp.

29W585 Batavia Rd.
Warrenville, Illinois 60555
(630) 393-6400
Fax: (630) 393-6864
Web: www.hci-search.com

Key Contact - Specialty:
Mr. Frank Cianchetti - *Healthcare*
Mr. Kevin Joy - *Bakery*
Ms. Lindsay Porter - *toy, consumer products, sporting goods*
Mr. Richard Smith - *Actuarial*
Mr. Wade Kawahara - *Chemical*
Ms. Brenda Schinke - *Packaging*

Description: What we offer is the ability to locate, screen and recruit the best possible candidates that fit your stringent criteria. This eliminates many of the risks involved in the hiring process along with finding the top candidates who may not be actively looking.
Functions: Senior mgmt., Production, Plant mgmt., Sales & mktg., HR mgmt., Engineering, Int'l.
Industries: Medical devices, Biotech, Healthcare

HDB Incorporated

301 Baxter Acres Drive
St. Louis, Missouri 63011-3939
(314) 391-7799
Fax: (314) 391-1224
Email: k.wolfe@hdbinc.com
Web: www.hdbinc.com

Key Contact - Specialty:
Ms. Kathryn Davis Wolfe - *SAP R-3, TRITON BaaN, Oracle, PeopleSoft, ERP*

Description: Our philosophy is simple: provide quality service to our client companies and candidates by setting standards of excellence through the commitment of our talents, expertise and resources.
Functions: MIS mgmt., Systems anal., Systems dev., Systems implem., Systems support, DB admin., Mgmt. consultants
Industries: Computer svcs., Mgmt. consulting, High tech, Software

Branches:
7515 Oxfordshire Drive
Spring, Texas 77379
(281) 370-6465
Fax: (281) 370-6476
Email: acyphers@swbell.net
Key Contact - Specialty:
Ms. Amy Cyphers

International Branches:
Shenzhen

Health Care Dimensions

335 Manitou Ave.
Manitau Springs, Colorado 80829-2537
(800) 373-3401
Fax: (719) 685-4756
Email: hcdltd@ibm.net

Key Contact - Specialty:
Ms. Christine Carter - *Long term care, subacute, retirement housing, rehabilitation*
Ms. Lisa Hazelton - *Long term care, subacute, retirement housing, rehabilitation*
Ms. Jill Howard - *Long term care, subacute, retirement housing, rehabilitation*
Ms. Nancy West - *Long term care, subacute, retirement housing, rehabilitation*

Description: We are the oldest and largest national search firm specializing in all areas of sub-acute care, long term care, rehab and retirement housing including assisted living, ancillary services and other post-acute areas.

Salary Minimum: $50,000
Functions: Senior mgmt., Middle mgmt., Health admin., Mktg. mgmt., Sales mgmt., CFO's
Industries: Healthcare

Health Care Plus, Inc.

9861 Broken Land Pkwy., Ste. 154
Columbia, Maryland 21046
(800) 348-4040
Fax: (410) 381-3875
Email: health1@erols.com
Web: www.healthcareexecutive.com

Key Contact - Specialty:
Mr. Michael Hargrave
Ms. Linda Moran
Ms. Susan Hargrave

Description: The nation's leading executive search firm serving the post acute care industry. Clients are for profit and not for profit providers of long term care, subacute care, acute rehabilitation, home healthcare and other related post acute services.

Salary Minimum: $45,000
Functions: Allied health, Health admin.
Industries: Healthcare

Health Network USA
(dba United Search Assoc.)

5902 Smoke Glass Trail
Dallas, Texas 75252
(972) 818-9393
Fax: (972) 818-9395
Email: info@unitedsearch.com
Web: www.unitedsearch.com

Key Contact - Specialty:
Mr. David J. Elliott - *Healthcare*
Ms. C. J. Elliott - *Healthcare*

Description: Placement of healthcare professionals across the USA. Clients include hospitals, clinics and other providers.

Salary Minimum: $40,000
Functions: Physicians, Nurses, Allied health, Health admin.
Industries: Healthcare

Health Search

1240 N. Lakeview Ave., Ste. 280
Anaheim, California 92807
(714) 779-7800
Fax: (714) 779-7805

Key Contact - Specialty:
Mr. Jeffrey Robbins - *Healthcare*
Mr. George Grayson - *Healthcare*
Mr. Larry Robinow - *Healthcare*
Ms. Barbara Carol - *Healthcare*
Ms. Nancy Ryan - *Healthcare*

Description: A national healthcare executive search firm placing administrative, financial and nursing executives in the hospital, home health, managed care and medical group management fields.

Salary Minimum: $75,000
Functions: Senior mgmt., Physicians, Nurses, Allied health, Health admin., CFO's, MIS mgmt.
Industries: Healthcare

Affiliates:
Peggy Shea & Assoc.

Health Search, Inc.

240 N. Rock Rd., Ste. 355
Wichita, Kansas 67206
(316) 322-8077
(800) 800-6580
Fax: (316) 322-8290
Email: vwaller@southwind.net

Key Contact - Specialty:
Ms. Victoria Waller - *Rehabilitation medicine, physical therapy, occupational therapy, speech language pathologist, physical therapy assistant*

Description: Our mission is to serve the medical community by bringing qualified employees and employers together. We offer a 6 month guarantee with our services.

Salary Minimum: $30,000
Functions: Healthcare, Nurses, Allied health
Industries: Healthcare

Healthcare Executive Recruiters, Inc.
17003 Ventura Blvd., Ste. E-1
Encino, California 91316
(818) 788-0150
Fax: (818) 788-6549
Email: SfBr17003@aol.com

Key Contact - Specialty:
Ms. Susan Fleischer - *Nursing administration, hospital executives*
Ms. Bette Rosenbaum - *Nursing, senior management*

Description: Healthcare administrators, nursing executives, nurse managers, CFO's, all senior level managers in the healthcare industry recruited to fit your individual needs.
Functions: Nurses, Health admin., HR mgmt., Finance, IT
Industries: Healthcare

Affiliates:
Professional Recruiters

Healthcare Recruiters Int'l. - Alabama
1945 Hoover Court, Ste. 205
Birmingham, Alabama 35226
(205) 979-9840
Fax: (205) 979-5879
Email: hcrala@traveller.com

Key Contact - Specialty:
Mr. Frank Y. Johnson - *Healthcare sales, marketing, physicians, management*
Mr. Sean M. Johnson - *Physicians, pharmacists, PT, OT, management*

Description: Recruit healthcare professionals in all areas; sales, marketing, physicians, field services, nursing, phyiscal therapy and pharmacy.

Salary Minimum: $35,000
Functions: General mgmt., Healthcare, Physicians, Sales & mktg., Mktg. mgmt., Sales mgmt., IT
Industries: Drugs mfg., Medical devices, Pharmaceutical svcs., Computer svcs., Software, Biotech, Healthcare

Healthcare Recruiters Int'l. Phoenix
4545 E. Shea Blvd., #209
Phoenix, Arizona 85028
(602) 494-9468
Fax: (602) 494-0220
Email: hcroaz@treknet.net
Web: hcroaz

Key Contact - Specialty:
Mr. Mike Strieker - *Managed care*
Ms. Suzanne Akre - *Pharmaceutical*
Ms. Darlene Hanson - *Home healthcare*
Ms. Stacie Brennise - *Sales, sales management*

Description: Our firm specializes in the placement of professionals strictly within the healthcare industry.

Salary Minimum: $50,000
Functions: Mfg., Healthcare, Physicians, Nurses, Health admin., Mktg. mgmt., Sales mgmt.
Industries: Medical devices, Pharmaceutical svcs., Biotech

Healthcare Recruiters Int'l. Orange County
26361 Crown Valley Pkwy., Ste. 150
Mission Viejo, California 92691
(949) 367-7888
Fax: (949) 367-7881
Email: tonyraia@earthlink.net

Key Contact - Specialty:
Ms. Carol Raia - *Medical marketing*
Mr. Tony Raia - *Medical management*

Description: National network of sales, marketing, management specializing only in healthcare.
Functions: Product dev., Production, Mkt. research, Mktg. mgmt., Sales mgmt.
Industries: Drugs mfg., Medical devices, Pharmaceutical svcs., Biotech, Healthcare

Healthcare Recruiters Int'l. - Los Angeles
15300 Ventura Blvd., Ste. 207
Sherman Oaks, California 91403
(818) 981-9510
Fax: (818) 981-9523
Email: hcrla@aol.com
Web: www.healthcarerecruiters.com

Key Contact - Specialty:
Ms. Deborah Wilson - *Medical products manufacturing (full scope)*
Ms. Rita Montgomery - *Home healthcare, pharmaceutical, biotechnology*
Mr. Glen Smith

Description: Full scope medical specialty search firm primarily involved with medical products manufacturing and service providers along with physician, etc. placement.
Functions: Generalist
Industries: Drugs mfg., Medical devices, Pharmaceutical svcs., High tech, Biotech, Healthcare

Healthcare Recruiters Int'l. Bay Area
1575 Treat Blvd., Ste. 210
Walnut Creek, California 94598
(925) 210-1530
Fax: (925) 210-1580
Email: hcrbayarea@aol.com
Web: www.hcrintl.com

Key Contact - Specialty:
Ms. Patricia Garfield - *Healthcare*

Description: One of the largest healthcare recruiting firms with 34 offices nationwide. All areas of healthcare, executive, information systems, surgery, sales, engineering, pharmaceutical, diagnostic.
Functions: General mgmt., Sales & mktg., Mkt. research, Finance, IT, R&D, Engineering
Industries: Biotech, Healthcare

Healthcare Recruiters of the Rockies, Inc.
6860 S. Yosemite Court, Ste. 200
Englewood, Colorado 80112
(303) 779-8570
Fax: (303) 779-7974
Email: hcr1@ix.netcom.com

Key Contact - Specialty:
Ms. Vicki L. Faas - *Medical device, information systems (healthcare), surgical*
Mr. Richard Moore - *Information systems (healthcare), lab, diagnostics*

Description: Experts in sourcing top quality sales, marketing, field support and clinical specialists for medical device, diagnostic, surgical, nutritional, managed care and healthcare information system industries, entry level to upper management.

Salary Minimum: $30,000
Functions: Senior mgmt., Middle mgmt., Product dev., Mktg. mgmt., Sales mgmt., Training, CFO's
Industries: Drugs mfg., Medical devices, Pharmaceutical svcs., Healthcare

Healthcare Recruiters of Indiana
11550 N. Meridian St., Ste. 210
Carmel, Indiana 46032
(317) 843-5522
Fax: (317) 843-5490
Web: www.jobsrus.com

Key Contact - Specialty:
Mr. John A. Clark
Ms. Ginny Ware
Ms. Jeannie Nigbor
Mr. Steve Baces

Description: We are all healthcare professionals who understand the needs of the industry.

Functions: Senior mgmt., Production, Nurses, Sales mgmt., CFO's, MIS mgmt., Engineering
Industries: Mfg., Chemicals, Medical devices, High tech, Software, Biotech, Healthcare

---

Healthcare Recruiters of New Orleans

3500 N. Causeway Blvd., Ste. 160
Metairie, Louisiana 70002
(504) 838-8875
Fax: (504) 838-9962
Web: www.hcrintl.com

Key Contact - Specialty:
Mr. Vic Palazola - *Healthcare*

Description: Specializing in medical sales, sales management and executive level positions in healthcare.
Functions: Senior mgmt., Middle mgmt., Sales mgmt., MIS mgmt.
Industries: Medical devices, Pharmaceutical svcs., Healthcare

---

Healthcare Recruiters of New England

100 Corporate Place, Ste. 401
Peabody, Massachusetts 01960
(978) 535-3302
Fax: (978) 535-3677
Email: hcrine@aol.com

Key Contact - Specialty:
Mr. Melvyn Robbins - *Pharmaceutical, clinical lab equipment & diagnostics*
Mr. Denis Montgomery - *Surgical cap equipment & instruments, orthopedics*

Description: Major emphasis sales, sales management, marketing, medical and pharmaceutical.

Salary Minimum: $40,000
Functions: Nurses, Allied health, Mkt. research, Mktg. mgmt., Sales mgmt., Direct mktg., Minorities
Industries: Drugs mfg., Medical devices, Software, Biotech, Healthcare, Non-classifiable industries

---

Healthcare Recruiters Int'l - Minnesota, Inc.

6442 City W. Pkwy., Ste. 303
Eden Prairie, Minnesota 55344
(612) 942-5424
Fax: (612) 942-5452
Email: syungner@juno.com
Web: www.healthcarerecruiters.com

Key Contact - Specialty:
Mr. Steven J. Yungner

Description: We place sales, sales management, marketing, executive and technical people with client companies that sell healthcare products or services.

Salary Minimum: $50,000
Functions: Directors, Senior mgmt., Middle mgmt., Sales & mktg., Mktg. mgmt., Sales mgmt., CFO's
Industries: Mfg., Drugs mfg., Medical devices, Svcs., Pharmaceutical svcs., Biotech, Healthcare

---

Healthcare Recruiters International-NY/NJ

55 Harristown Rd.
Glen Rock, New Jersey 07452
(201) 670-9800
Fax: (201) 670-1908
Email: hcrnynj@idt.net
Web: www.HealthCareRecruiters.com

Key Contact - Specialty:
Mr. Harold B. Conant - *Healthcare products, healthcare services*
Ms. Ann M. Moore - *Home healthcare, managed care*
Mr. Ronald D. Len - *Laboratory, diagnostic, pharmaceutical (sales, marketing, technical)*
Ms. Iris L. Fisher - *Sales, marketing, technical*

Description: Our mission is to help companies and medical facilities grow and succeed by providing the best professionals in the healthcare field. We are wholly dedicated to the healthcare industry.
Functions: Senior mgmt., Middle mgmt., Plant mgmt., Mkt. research, Mktg. mgmt., Sales mgmt., MIS mgmt.
Industries: Chemicals, Drugs mfg., Medical devices, Pharmaceutical svcs., Software, Biotech, Healthcare

---

Healthcare Recruiters Int'l. Philadelphia

3 Eves Drive, Ste. 303
Marlton, New Jersey 08053
(609) 596-7179
Fax: (609) 596-6895
Email: mrlucky@snip.net
Web: www.hcrintl.com

Key Contact - Specialty:
Mr. Frank Rosamilia - *High level*

Description: Executive search firm specializing in healthcare.
Functions: Senior mgmt., Nurses, Advertising, Sales mgmt., CFO's, MIS mgmt., Engineering
Industries: Drugs mfg., Computer equip., Biotech, Healthcare

Healthcare Recruiters of New York, Inc.

445 Electronics Pkwy., Ste. 208
Liverpool, New York 13088
(315) 453-4080
Fax: (315) 453-9525
Email: headhunt@servtech.com
Web: www.healthcarerecruiters.com

Key Contact - Specialty:
Mr. Dean McNitt - *Healthcare*

Description: Executive search and recruitment in the healthcare industry. Sales, marketing, HMO, managed care, home care, hospital professionals, product management, R&D and engineering.
Functions: Senior mgmt., Product dev., Healthcare, Mktg. mgmt., Sales mgmt., IT, Minorities
Industries: Drugs mfg., Medical devices, Pharmaceutical svcs., Insurance, Software, Biotech, Healthcare

---

Healthcare Recruiters Int'l. - Pittsburgh

428 Forbes Ave., Ste. 600
Lawyers Bldg.
Pittsburgh, Pennsylvania 15219
(412) 261-2244
(800) 875-5339
Fax: (412) 261-3577
Email: hcrpgh@sgi.net
Web: www.healthcarerecruiters.com/

Key Contact - Specialty:
Ms. Helen Lynch

Description: We are part of a national network of over 30 offices across the country serving the healthcare industry. Linked by our client candidate referral system database we help companies and medical facilities find the best professionals in a confidential manner.
Functions: Healthcare, Sales & mktg., R&D, Engineering, Minorities, Technicians, Int'l.
Industries: Drugs mfg., Medical devices, Pharmaceutical svcs., Insurance, Biotech, Healthcare

---

Healthcare Recruiters of Midsouth

185 S. Center St., Ste. 200
Collierville, Tennessee 38017
(901) 853-0900
Fax: (901) 853-6500
Email: jeb@wspice.com

Key Contact - Specialty:
Mr. Jeb Blanchard - *Healthcare, medical*

Description: Specializing in the healthcare industry. Pharmaceutical-sales, marketing, management, regulatory affairs, compliance. Medical-sales, marketing, management. Hospital-administration.
Functions: Nurses, Health admin.
Industries: Biotech, Healthcare

Healthcare Recruiters of Dallas

4100 Spring Valley Rd., Ste. 800
Dallas, Texas 75244
(972) 851-5470
Fax: (972) 851-5432
Email: jwhcrdallas@compuserve.com
Web: www.hcrintl.com

Key Contact - Specialty:
Mr. Jim Wimberly - *Lab, diagnostics, biotechnology, healthcare information systems*

Description: Exclusive healthcare search firm emphasizing sales and marketing opportunities.
Functions: Senior mgmt., Middle mgmt., Sales mgmt.
Industries: Medical devices, Pharmaceutical svcs., Biotech, Healthcare

Healthcare Recruiters - Northwest

550 Kirkland Way, Ste. 200
Kirkland, Washington 98033
(425) 739-2046
Fax: (425) 739-2253
Email: dcgarland@msn.com
Web: www.hcrintl.com

Key Contact - Specialty:
Mr. David C. Garland - *Healthcare*

Description: Provides customized professional and executive recruiting services to match a healthcare company's unique personnel needs with qualified candidates to build a winning team.
Functions: Senior mgmt., Middle mgmt., Product dev., Health admin., Mkt. research, Mktg. mgmt., Sales mgmt.
Industries: Pharmaceutical svcs., Software, Biotech, Healthcare

Healthcare Resources Group

3945 SE 15th St., Ste. 101
Del City, Oklahoma 73115
(405) 677-7872
Fax: (405) 672-5053
Email: dan.smith@Juno.com

Key Contact - Specialty:
Mr. Dan Smith - *Sales, healthcare non-sales*

Description: Contingency search firm specializing in the medical field of licensed and registered professionals as well as medical equipment and supplies sales and research. Other non-medical sales.
Functions: Nurses, Allied health, Sales mgmt.
Industries: Drugs mfg., Medical devices, Healthcare, Non-classifiable industries

Healthcare Search Associates

12304 Santa Monica Blvd., Ste. 220
Los Angeles, California 90025
(310) 207-0979
Fax: (310) 207-3437
Email: drscorner@aol.com

Key Contact - Specialty:
Mr. Gregorius K. Balk - *Healthcare generalist*
Mr. John Raskin - *Healthcare, managed care*
Dr. Jacquelene R. Lee - *Healthcare, hospitals*
Mr. Tony Sands - *Healthcare, nursing, home health, skilled nursing*

Description: Healthcare professionals throughout the country for managed care, hospitals skilled nursing facilities, home health and all other healthcare facilities. Listed by the LA Business Journal as the largest firm in LA county specializing in healthcare recruiting.

Salary Minimum: $50,000
Functions: Physicians, Nurses, Allied health, Health admin., Mktg. mgmt., CFO's
Industries: Healthcare

Branches:
8444 Reseda Blvd., Ste. G
Northridge, California 91324
(818) 772-9931
Fax: (818) 772-6457
Key Contact - Specialty:
Mr. John Raskin - *Healthcare*

3855 Pacific Coast Hwy., Ste. 8
Torrance, California 90505
(310) 378-9349
Fax: (310) 373-7914
Key Contact - Specialty:
Mr. Gregorius K. Balk

HealthSearch Assoc.

19632 Club House Rd., Ste. 525
Gaithersburg, Maryland 20886
(301) 258-2656
Fax: (301) 963-0250

Key Contact - Specialty:
Mr. Ted Schneider

Description: We offer recruiting services to healthcare providers, i.e. hospitals, clinics, HMOs, etc. Most searches are for clinical management and administrative positions. Physician recruitment on a retainer basis is also available.

Salary Minimum: $40,000
Functions: Physicians, Nurses, Allied health, Health admin.
Industries: Healthcare

The Healthsearch Group, Inc.

109 Croton Ave.
Ossining, New York 10562
(914) 941-6107
Fax: (914) 941-1748

Key Contact - Specialty:
Mr. Alan Gordon - *Healthcare*
Mr. Jeff Gordon - *Healthcare*

Description: We are one of the largest recruiting companies in the Northeast with a healthcare specialty. We pride ourselves on the service we provide our clients and the effectiveness of our search process.
Functions: General mgmt., Healthcare, Physicians, Nurses, Allied health, Health admin., Finance

HeartBeat Medical, Inc.

260 Madison Ave., Ste. 106
Corvallis, Oregon 97333
(541) 752-5557
Fax: (541) 752-5559
Email: hbm@heartbeatmedical.com
Web: www.heartbeatmedical.com

Key Contact - Specialty:
Mr. Scott Bailey - *Medical device (R&D, manufacturing and operations)*
Ms. Evelyn Bailey
Mr. Ed Browning - *Medical device (quality, regulatory, clinical)*
Mr. Matt Miller - *Medical device (R&D, manufacturing & operations)*

Description: Emphasis on West Coast for start-up medical device, R&D and manufacturing companies. Fundraising available.

Salary Minimum: $50,000
Functions: Middle mgmt., Product dev., Production, Quality, R&D, Engineering
Industries: Medical devices

Heartland National Medical Search

3410 Bellwood Lane
Glenview, Illinois 60025
(847) 832-1716
Fax: (847) 832-1721
Email: HLmedsrch@aol.com

Key Contact - Specialty:
Ms. Karen Winterburn - *Physicians, nurse practitioners, allied health, health administration*

Description: Specializes in recruitment and placement of healthcare professionals. Part of 180 member network of recruiters nationwide. All fees are employer-paid. Our services are free to candidates and confidential.

Salary Minimum: $40,000

Functions: Healthcare, Physicians, Nurses, Allied health, Health admin.
Industries: Pharmaceutical svcs., Insurance, Healthcare

HEC Group
911 Golf Links Rd., Ste. 207
Ancaster, Ontario L9K 1H9
Canada
(905) 648-0013
Fax: (905) 648-7016
Email: hec@hec-group.com
Web: www.hec-group.com

Key Contact - Specialty:
Mr. Paul Bennett
Mr. Robert Leek - *Technical*
Ms. Karen Clarke - *Human resources, administration, sales & marketing*

Description: International recruiters with affiliates in most major cities in North America. Major areas of expertise include manufacturing, high tech and IT positions. Present management has been with company since 1976.
Functions: General mgmt., Mfg., Sales & mktg., HR mgmt., Finance, IT, Engineering
Industries: Mfg., Plastics/rubber, Computer equip., Aerospace, High tech, Software

---

Thomas E. Hedefine Assoc.
21 Ardagh St.
Toronto, Ontario M6S 1Y2
Canada
(416) 604-9444
Fax: (416) 604-8995
Email: hedefine@sprint.ca

Key Contact - Specialty:
Mr. Thomas E. Hedefine - *Equipment finance, equipment leasing, asset based lending*
Dr. Kathleen P. Shea - *Corporate banking, finance*

Description: Provide national recruitment activities for leasing finance company's banks from line marketing, risk management and senior management positions.

Salary Minimum: $40,000
Functions: Credit, M&A, Risk mgmt.
Industries: Finance, Banking, Invest. banking, Venture cap., Misc. financial, Equip. svcs.

Hedlund Corp.
One IBM Plaza, Ste. 2618
Chicago, Illinois 60611
(312) 755-1400
Fax: (312) 755-1405
Email: hedlund@ameritech.net
Web: www.hedlundcorp.com

Key Contact - Specialty:
Mr. David Hedlund - *Information technology consultants*
Ms. Holly Burny - *Information technology consultants*
Ms. Eve Shapiro - *Information technology consultants*
Ms. Jean Wittner - *Information technology consultants*
Ms. Peggy Meller - *Information technology consultants*
Ms. Ingrid Baumgaertel - *Information technology consultants*

Description: National management search firm specialized in recruiting information technology and management consultants. Specific emphasis on client/server and software package developers.

Salary Minimum: $60,000
Functions: Mfg., Materials, Healthcare, Finance, IT, Mgmt. consultants
Industries: Finance, Communications, Insurance, Software, Healthcare

---

Jay Heino Company, LLC
7 Penn Plaza, Ste. 830
New York, New York 10001-3900
(212) 279-6780
Fax: (212) 279-6784

Key Contact - Specialty:
Mr. Jay Heino - *Tax*

Description: There are less than 12 search agencies in the United States who specialize in placing tax professionals exclusively. We anticipate becoming #1 through our determination and dedication to our clients. Give us the opportunity to show you why we excel in every area of tax for any industry.

Salary Minimum: $35,000
Functions: Middle mgmt., Taxes, M&A, Attorneys, Int'l.
Industries: Chemicals, Drugs mfg., Invest. banking, Brokers, Venture cap., Legal, Accounting

---

Helffrich Int'l.
P.O. Box 607
Safety Harbor, Florida 34695
(727) 725-5525
Email: helffrichintl@mindspring.com

Key Contact - Specialty:
Mr. Alan B. Helffrich, Jr.
Mr. Michael D. Helffrich
Ms. Henrietta Helffrich

Description: Executive search specializing in senior level: engineers and managers for the chemical, construction, engineering, metals, minerals, mining, oil and gas industries; environmental and safety professionals for all industries; international managers for all industries.

Salary Minimum: $75,000
Functions: Senior mgmt., Plant mgmt., Engineering, Environmentalists, Int'l.
Industries: Energy/utilities, Construction, Chemicals, Metal products, Environmental svcs., Non-classifiable industries

---

Heller Kil Assoc., Inc.
123 Green Heron Court
Daytona Beach, Florida 32119
(904) 761-5100
Fax: (904) 761-7206
Email: Pheller@bellsouth.net
Web: www.hellerkil.com

Key Contact - Specialty:
Mr. Phillip Heller - *Sales, marketing, general management*

Description: Executive search and professional staffing to the automotive and heavy duty truck parts/components industries specializing in sales, marketing, engineering, quality and manufacturing management to the general manager and presidential level.

Salary Minimum: $40,000
Functions: Senior mgmt., Product dev., Plant mgmt., Quality, Purchasing, Sales mgmt., Engineering
Industries: Motor vehicles, Transportation

Branches:
306 Robert Drive
Normal, Illinois 61761
(309) 454-7077
Fax: (309) 454-8227
Key Contact - Specialty:
Mr. Larry Shapiro - *Engineering, manufacturing management*

Hemingway Personnel, Inc.
1301 Dove St., Ste. 960
Newport Beach, California 92660
(949) 851-1228
Fax: (949) 253-3761
Email: lara@hemingwaypersonnel.com

Key Contact - Specialty:
Ms. Dolores Lara - *Information systems*
Mr. John Aylward - *Accounting, finance*

Description: Executive search, contract services and temporaries serving the accounting and finance, information systems and collections professions.

Salary Minimum: $35,000
Functions: Finance, CFO's, Credit, Taxes, IT, MIS mgmt., Systems dev.
Industries: Generalist

Branches:
1990 S. Bundy Drive, Ste.395
West Los Angeles, California 90025
(310) 826-0042
Fax: (310) 226-8532

Key Contact - Specialty:
Ms. Aleesa Powell - *Collectors*
Ms. Laura Casanova - *Accounting, finance*

Henrietta's Personnel & Executive Search, Inc.

One Turnberry Place, Ste. 401A
19495 Biscayne Blvd.
Aventura, Florida 33180
(305) 931-3131
Fax: (305) 937-2966

Key Contact - Specialty:
Ms. Stephanie Aral - *Banking (private, corporate, corresponding, commercial)*

Description: To our clients, candidates and corporations, we provide service with integrity.

Salary Minimum: $30,000
Functions: Engineering, Int'l.
Industries: Banking

Kay Henry, Inc.

1200 Bustleton Pike, Ste. 5
Feasterville, Pennsylvania 19053
(215) 355-1600
Fax: (215) 355-4395
Email: khinc@axs2000.net

Key Contact - Specialty:
Ms. Kay Henry - *Advertising, public relations, marketing*
Ms. Rose Gregory - *Advertising, public relations, marketing*
Ms. Shelley Miller - *Advertising, public relations, marketing*

Description: All areas of consumer and business to business advertising, public relations and marketing as they apply to agencies and corporations including direct marketing, pharmaceutical, ag chem and animal health.

Salary Minimum: $25,000
Functions: Senior mgmt., Middle mgmt., Advertising, Mktg. mgmt., Direct mktg., PR, Graphic artists
Industries: Pharmaceutical svcs., Advertising/PR, Publishing, New media

Henson Partners

P.O. Box 26658
Phoenix, Arizona 85068-6658
(602) 331-3333
Fax: (602) 331-3838
Email: jrh@hensonpartners.com
Web: www.hensonpartners.com

Key Contact - Specialty:
Mr. Jeff Henson - *Food processing, consumer products, high technology, software, computer industries*

Description: Dedicated to developing lasting relationships with our client companies through performance, integrity, and professionalism. Our specialists generate enhanced results due to their direct experience, and extensive knowledge of select industries. Search focus and expertise includes executive level assignments in a variety of functional areas for the industries listed below.

Salary Minimum: $65,000
Functions: General mgmt., Mfg., Sales & mktg., Finance, IT, R&D, Engineering
Industries: Food/bev/tobacco, Computer equip., Consumer electronics, High tech, Software

Heritage Pacific Corp.

15707 Rockfield Blvd., Ste. 217
Irvine, California 92618
(800) 927-1566
Fax: (800) 927-1501
Email: hpsearch@wans.net

Key Contact - Specialty:
Mr. Gary Draper - *Paper industry*

Description: Twenty-one years serving the paper industry exclusively.
Functions: Generalist, General mgmt., Mfg., Engineering
Industries: Paper

Heritage Search Group, Inc.

7687 Wyldwood Way, Ste. 100
Port St. Lucie, Florida 34986
(561) 489-5300
Fax: (561) 489-5301
Email: trip7687@gate.net
Web: trip7687@gate.new

Key Contact - Specialty:
Mr. Philip Tripician - *Consumer packaged goods (marketing)*

Description: Specialize in consumer packaged goods marketing and/or related fields both international and domestic. Different and unique positions. Normally small to medium sized companies. Also place high caliber people in consulting firms, small to medium, in all disciplines.

Salary Minimum: $60,000
Functions: Directors, Middle mgmt., Advertising, Mkt. research, Mktg. mgmt., Sales mgmt., Minorities
Industries: Food/bev/tobacco, Paper, Chemicals, Soap/perfume/cosmetics, Drugs mfg., Entertainment, Mgmt. consulting

Branches:
41 Dewberry Rd.
Waterbury, Connecticut 06705
(203) 757-6263
Key Contact - Specialty:
Mr. Fred Hodde - *Consumer packaged goods (marketing)*

Affiliates:
F. B. Schmidt Int'l.

J. J. Herlihy & Assoc., Inc.

9608 Donna Ave.
Northridge, California 91324
(818) 349-8211
Fax: (818) 349-8747

Key Contact - Specialty:
Mr. Jack Herlihy - *Sales management, marketing for high technology, technical positions in computer field (i.e. consulting, TCD, systems integration)*

Description: Primarily oriented toward the sales management, marketing and general management in the computer field and related industries; also active in the senior technical roles of the computer field.

Salary Minimum: $75,000
Functions: Senior mgmt., Middle mgmt., Mktg. mgmt., Sales mgmt., MIS mgmt., Systems anal., Systems implem.
Industries: Computer equip., Computer svcs., Mgmt. consulting, Human resource svcs., New media, High tech, Software

Herring & Assoc.

600 Pine Forest Dr., Ste. 130
Maumelle, Arkansas 72113
(501) 851-1234
Fax: (501) 851-7753
Email: bill.herring@worldnet.att
Web: www.herring-assoc.com

Key Contact - Specialty:
Mr. Bill Herring - *Transportation, distribution, HR, generalist*
Mr. Tony Horne - *Transportation, distribution, HR, generalist*

Description: We are a national recruiter search firm has extensive experience in the placement of executives and professionals, ranging from key supervisory positions to Vice President and President levels.
Functions: Senior mgmt., Purchasing, Materials Plng., Distribution, Sales mgmt., HR mgmt., CFO's
Industries: Agri/forestry/mining, Mfg., Food/bev/tobacco, Soap/perfume/cosmetics, Transportation, Retail, Environmental svcs.

Branches:
6539 Yale Rd.
Bartlett, Tennessee 38134
(901) 384-4873
Fax: (901) 384-4873
Key Contact - Specialty:
Ms. Jennifer Thornton

Affiliates:
Apple & Assoc.

J. D. Hersey & Assoc.

1695 Old Henderson Rd.
Columbus, Ohio 43220
(614) 459-4555
Fax: (614) 459-4544

Email: info@jdhersey.com
Web: www.jdhersey.com

Key Contact - Specialty:
Mr. Jeffrey D. Hersey - *Generalist*

Description: Conducting national searches for sales, marketing, operations and engineering executives. Industries: personal computer (including retailing, reselling, distribution, hardware manufacturing and software publishing), data and telecommunications, networking, systems integration, real estate, construction, hospitality and restaurant.

Salary Minimum: $40,000
Functions: General mgmt., Sales & mktg., Sales mgmt., Direct mktg., IT, Systems anal., Systems implem.
Industries: Construction, Computer equip., Retail, New media, Real estate, High tech, Software

Affiliates:
J. D. Hersey & Assoc.

H. Hertner Assoc., Inc.
6600 Cowpen Rd., Ste 220
Lakes Park Plaza
Miami, Florida 33014
(305) 556-8882
Fax: (305) 556-5650
Email: hhertner@bellsouth.net
Web: www.legalrecruiting.com

Key Contact - Specialty:
Mr. Herbert H. Hertner - *Legal*
Mr. David J. Block - *Legal*
Ms. Valerie J. Grandin - *Legal*
Ms. Pamela R. Hertner - *Legal*

Description: President has 27 years of recruiting expertise, together with the other consultants, work as a team to service corporation needs for in-house general counsel positions, law firms for partners, associates, mergers and legal disciplines.

Salary Minimum: $50,000
Functions: Legal, Attorneys
Industries: Legal

Robert Hess & Assoc., Inc.
35 Primrose Lane
Dillon, Colorado 80435
(970) 262-9388
Fax: (970) 262-9432
Email: robhess@robhess.com
Web: www.robhess@robhess.com

Key Contact - Specialty:
Mr. Robert W. Hess - *Real estate*

Description: National recruiters specializing in real estate.

Salary Minimum: $50,000
Functions: Senior mgmt., Middle mgmt., Mktg. mgmt., Sales mgmt., CFO's, Architects
Industries: Construction, Real estate

Hessel Assoc., Inc.
420 Lexington Ave., Ste. 300
New York, New York 10170
(212) 297-6105
Fax: (212) 682-1029
Email: haisearch@aol.com
Web: www.haisearch.com

Key Contact - Specialty:
Mr. Jeffrey J. Hessel

Description: Experienced team of personnel consultants specializing in the recruitment of financial, operations and systems professionals with particular emphasis on the financial services industries including banking, brokerage and insurance.

Salary Minimum: $50,000
Functions: Finance, CFO's, Budgeting, Cash mgmt., M&A, Risk mgmt., Mgmt. consultants
Industries: Mfg., Finance, Banking, Invest. banking, Brokers, Misc. financial, Insurance

---

Higbee Assoc., Inc.
(Firm declined to update.)
112 Rowayton Ave.
Rowayton, Connecticut 06853
(203) 853-7600
Email: rhigbee@netaxis.com
Web: www.higbeeassociates.com

Key Contact - Specialty:
Mr. R. W. Higbee - *Management consultants (principal & partner)*

Description: Retained specialist to the consulting industry at senior level; global reach; financial services, telecommunications, healthcare, insurance, pharmaceutical as it relates to strategy, operations and information technology.

Salary Minimum: $75,000
Functions: Senior mgmt., Mkt. research, Risk mgmt., MIS mgmt., Systems implem., Mgmt. consultants, Int'l.
Industries: Drugs mfg., Invest. banking, Computer svcs., Mgmt. consulting, New media, Telecoms, Real estate

---

B. W. Higgins, Inc.
6828 Alnwick Court
Indianapolis, Indiana 46220
(317) 842-6346
Fax: (317) 578-1005
Email: bwhinc@aol.com
Web: www.members.aol.com/bwhinc

Key Contact - Specialty:
Ms. Lynda Lacy-Higgins - *Insurance*
Mr. Bruce W. Higgins - *Insurance*

Description: An established and recognized national search firm dedicated to all facets of the insurance industry.

Salary Minimum: $75,000
Functions: Senior mgmt., Middle mgmt., Mkt. research, Sales mgmt., CFO's, Risk mgmt., MIS mgmt.
Industries: Insurance

High Tech Opportunities, Inc.
264B N. Broadway, Ste. 206
Salem, New Hampshire 03079
(603) 893-9486
Fax: (603) 893-9492
Email: hightech@mv.mv.com
Web: www.mv.com/hightech/

Key Contact - Specialty:
Mr. Ron Cooper - *Microelectronics, CAD/EDA, sales & marketing, applications, design*
Mr. Michael Buckley - *Microelectronics, integrated circuits, logic & CPU design, CAE software*
Mr. Robert Kierstead - *Executive, management, software, board level, hardware development*

Description: A firm specializing in recruiting in electronic design automation, semiconductor, microprocessor design and computer hardware/software professionals as well as wireless communications. Satellite, VSAT, cellular, etc.

Salary Minimum: $30,000
Functions: Engineering
Industries: Telecoms, High tech, Software

High Tech Staffing Group
1020 SW Taylor St., Ste. 720
Portland, Oregon 97205
(503) 227-2565
Fax: (503) 227-2413
Email: jobs@htsg.com
Web: www.htsg.com

Key Contact - Specialty:
Mr. Frank Michael Odia - *Data processing, software engineering*

Description: We are a professional staffing and consulting firm that serves the needs of the high tech industry in Oregon and Washington. Our services include temporary and permanent placement. Our emphasis is on the gamut of data processing software and hardware engineering personnel.
Functions: Automation, MIS mgmt., Systems anal., Systems dev., Systems implem., Systems support, Mgmt. consultants
Industries: Medical devices, Consumer electronics, Test/measurement equip., Computer svcs., Telecoms, High tech, Software

High-Tech Recruiters

30 High St., Ste. 104A
Hartford, Connecticut 06103
(860) 527-4262

Key Contact - Specialty:
Mr. Clement W. Williams

Description: Data processing, data communications, telecommunications, engineering, finance, minorities, nationwide affiliates.

Salary Minimum: $30,000
Functions: Budgeting, Cash mgmt., Systems dev., Network admin., DB admin., Engineering, Minorities
Industries: Medical devices, Finance, Computer svcs., Telecoms, Insurance, High tech, Software

Highland & Assoc.

3830 Valley Ctr. Drive, Ste. 646
Bldg. 705
San Diego, California 92130
(619) 794-1782
Fax: (619) 794-8209
Email: mhighla@aol.com

Key Contact - Specialty:
Ms. Maryjo Highland - *Real estate*

Description: We have over 13 years experience in the commercial real estate industry from East to West Coast. Specializing in real estate directors, construction, asset and property management and leasing.

Salary Minimum: $40,000
Functions: Senior mgmt., Admin. svcs.
Industries: Construction, Real estate

Highlander Search

210 W. Friendly Ave., Ste. 200
Greensboro, North Carolina 27401
(336) 333-9886
Fax: (336) 273-2309
Email: jphighlander@mindspring.com

Key Contact - Specialty:
Mr. Jeffrey M. Penley - *Furniture manufacturing, furniture retail, automotive manufacturing*

Description: 12 years in executive search, technical recruiting and outplacement consulting has yielded wide industry knowledge and understanding of modern business challanges and goals.

Salary Minimum: $50,000
Functions: General mgmt., Mfg., Materials, Sales & mktg., HR mgmt., Finance, Engineering
Industries: Lumber/furniture, Metal products, Motor vehicles, Wholesale, Retail

Affiliates:
Ariail & Assoc.

Hill & Assoc.
(a division of Melfar Intl. Inc. Corp.)

860 Via de la Paz #E-2
Pacific Palisades, California 90272
(310) 573-1261

Key Contact - Specialty:
Mr. Tom Hill - *Consumer products, sales & marketing*

Description: Extensive industry knowledge and contacts. Outstanding ability to build management teams. I am an ex-Carnation Company sales manager, with fifteen years experience in management consulting and executive search. A true specialist in the food and beverage industry.

Salary Minimum: $50,000
Functions: Mkt. research, Mktg. mgmt., Sales mgmt., PR, Int'l.
Industries: Food/bev/tobacco, Drugs mfg., Medical devices, Retail, Hospitality, Advertising/PR

Hill Allyn Assoc.

P.O. Box 15247
San Francisco, California 94115-0247
(415) 922-8797
Email: HillAllyn@AOL.com

Key Contact - Specialty:
Ms. Gayle Hill Vignet - *Generalist*

Description: Recruits for staff and management positions in San Francisco area. Certified employment specialist (CES) with graduate training in organizational consultation.

Salary Minimum: $25,000
Functions: General mgmt., Healthcare, Sales & mktg., HR mgmt., Finance, Specialized services, Int'l.
Industries: Generalist, Energy/utilities, Mfg., Retail, Finance, Svcs., Communications

The Hindman Group, Inc.

383 Diablo Rd., Ste. 100
Danville, California 94526
(800) 800-9220
Fax: (800) 241-9220
Email: thgsearch@aol.com
Web: www.thehindmangroup.com

Key Contact - Specialty:
Mr. Jeffrey J. Hindman - *Food service manufacturing & distribution*

Description: Executive search consultants to the food service distribution and manufacturing industries specializing in the recruitment of mid to top level executives. Also generalist in other.

Salary Minimum: $85,000
Functions: Generalist, Senior mgmt., Middle mgmt., Mfg., Distribution, Sales mgmt., HR mgmt.
Industries: Generalist, Food/bev/tobacco, Computer equip., Transportation, Wholesale, Hospitality, Entertainment

Branches:
71 Old Ballas Rd. Ste. 117
St. Louis, Missouri 63017
(800) 800-9220
(800) 241-9220

Hintz Associates

Box 442
Valhalla, New York 10595-1831
(914) 761-4227
Fax: (914) 948-8630
Email: geohintz@aol.com

Key Contact - Specialty:
Mr. George Hintz - *Consultants*
Mr. George Jefferies - *Sales consultants*
Ms. DeAnne Cerreta
Ms. Dorothy DiMaggio

Description: Banking, insurance; cost reduction analysts, internal/external consultants. Assignments include methods improvement and short interval scheduling consultants. EDP analysts, programming, industrial engineering. Consulting placements in US/U.K./Australia/Canada/Europe.

Salary Minimum: $25,000
Functions: Quality, Productivity, Materials Plng., Sales mgmt., Training, Systems anal., Mgmt. consultants
Industries: Medical devices, Motor vehicles, Misc. mfg., Banking, Insurance, Healthcare

Hire Authority, Inc.

26622 Woodward Ave., Ste. 103
Royal Oak, Michigan 48067-0955
(248) 542-4640
(248) 542-4316
Fax: (248) 542-4875

Key Contact - Specialty:
Ms. Mary C. Huebner - *General management, transportation, materials management*
Ms. Marcia L. Kuypers - *Human resource management*

Description: Placement firm specializing in sales and management professionals. We utilize a team partnership strategy that is quality driven. We provide clients with the highest standards of service and satisfaction.
Functions: General mgmt., Materials, Sales & mktg., HR mgmt.
Industries: Generalist, Mfg., Transportation, Human resource svcs.

Branches:
835 Mason, Ste. 180
Dearborn, Michigan 48124-2221
(313) 274-4909
Fax: (313) 274-3890
Key Contact - Specialty:
Ms. Wendy A. Dant - *General management, sales, manufacturing*

The Hiring Authority, Inc.
601 N. Lois Ave.
The Marc Bldg.
Tampa, Florida 33609
(813) 289-4400
Fax: (813) 289-3419
Email: jobs@hiringauthority.com
Web: www.hiringauthority.com

Key Contact - Specialty:
Mr. Elton Marcus
Mr. Nicholas Cokins - *Information systems, information technology*

Description: We offer technical and executive search, as well as contract technical staffing and outsourcing services.

Salary Minimum: $50,000
Functions: Senior mgmt., MIS mgmt., Systems anal., Systems dev., Systems implem., Network admin., DB admin.
Industries: Generalist, Mfg., Svcs., Communications, High tech, Software, Non-classifiable industries

Ruth Hirsch Assoc., Inc.
201 E. 66 St., Ste. 7C
New York, New York 10021
(212) 396-0200
Fax: (212) 396-0679

Key Contact - Specialty:
Ms. Ruth Hirsch - *Architecture, interior design, construction, facilities management*

Description: Boutique firm specializing in placement of registered architects, facilities, construction managers, owner's representatives and interior designers primarily in the NY Metropolitan area. Candidates are only referred after a personal meeting.

Salary Minimum: $50,000
Functions: Personnel, Architects

Hitchens & Foster, Inc.
Pines Office Ctr., 1 Pine Court
St. Louis, Missouri 63141-6076
(314) 453-0800
Fax: (314) 453-9530
Email: hfmedica@inlink.com

Key Contact - Specialty:
Mr. Rex Hermsmeyer
Mr. Robert deRoode
Mr. Rich Cornell

Description: Specializes in physician search and recruitment for healthcare centers nationwide.
Functions: Physicians, Allied health, Health admin.
Industries: Healthcare

HLR Consulting
2 South Beechwood Road
Bedford Hills, New York 10507-1712
(914) 242-7300
Fax: (914) 242-7300
Email: hlrsearch1@aol.com

Key Contact - Specialty:
Mr. Harvey Zuckerman
Ms. Linda Marie Mauriello

Description: An executive search firm offering recruitment expertise for information technology professionals throughout the New York tri-state area with state-of-the-art computerized capabilities to enhance speed and efficiency.

Salary Minimum: $50,000
Functions: IT
Industries: Finance, Svcs., Communications, Insurance, High tech, Software, Healthcare

HMO Executive Search
8910 Purdue Rd., Ste. 200
Indianapolis, Indiana 46268-1155
(317) 872-1056
Fax: (317) 879-1233
Email: hmoes@iquest.net
Web: www.hmoexecsearch.com

Key Contact - Specialty:
Mr. Richard J. Carroll - *Managed care*

Description: Established in 1985, we are a nationwide recruiting firm specializing in executive personnel placement with health maintenance organizations and other alternative delivery healthcare systems.

Salary Minimum: $40,000
Functions: Healthcare

Hobson Assoc.
P.O. Box 278
Cheshire, Connecticut 06410
(203) 272-0227
Fax: (203) 272-1237
Email: hobson@hobsonassoc.com
Web: www.hobsonassoc.com

Key Contact - Specialty:
Mr. Danny Cahill - *Engineering*
Mr. Mark Bassett - *Sales & marketing, high technology*
Mr. Vern Chanski - *Information technology*

Description: Owner is world renowned industry trainer. Aggressive, dynamic, client-oriented approach. Integrated services for broad exposure in niche areas.
Functions: Senior mgmt., Product dev., Plant mgmt., Sales mgmt., CFO's, MIS mgmt., Engineering
Industries: Plastics/rubber, Computer equip., Test/measurement equip., Computer svcs., Aerospace, High tech, Software

Affiliates:
Cahill Consulting Group

Hochman & Assoc.
1801 Ave. of the Stars, Ste. 420
Los Angeles, California 90067
(310) 552-0662
Fax: (310) 552-4650
Email: JHochman@earthlink.com

Key Contact - Specialty:
Ms. Judi Hochman - *Finance, banking, investment banking*

Description: Networking and disciplined search methodology have consistently allowed us to efficiently find and prepare the perfect match candidates to fill client needs. Extensive, hands-on experience has enhanced Ms. Hochman's ability to complete successful job placements.

Salary Minimum: $50,000
Functions: MIS mgmt., Systems anal., Systems dev., Systems implem., Systems support
Industries: Banking, Invest. banking, Brokers, Misc. financial, Computer svcs., Software

Hoffman Partnership Group Inc.
42 Huntington Court
Williamsville, New York 14221-5310
(716) 632-3379
(716) 632-1306
Fax: (716) 632-1425
Email: BDHATHPG@aol.com
Web: www.hpgrecruit.com

Key Contact - Specialty:
Mr. Bradley D. Hoffman - *Sales & marketing (in consumer packaged goods)*
Ms. Lisa M. Hoffman - *Sales & marketing (in consumer packaged goods)*

Description: We create long-term client partnerships to consistently fill opportunities in consumer packaged goods. Specialize in diversity searches (45% of placements). Expertise in category management, trade marketing, national accounts and sales management.

Salary Minimum: $50,000

Functions: Directors, Senior mgmt., Middle mgmt., Sales & mktg., Sales mgmt., Minorities
Industries: Food/bev/tobacco, Paper, Soap/perfume/cosmetics, Drugs mfg.

Hoffman Recruiters

841 Main St., Ste. 2
Walpole, Massachusetts 02081
(508) 660-2220
888-5-RECRUIT
Fax: (508) 668-5460
Email: resume@HoffmanRecruiters.com
Web: www.HoffmanRecruiters.com

Key Contact - Specialty:
Mr. Judd A. Hoffman
Mr. Mark S. Hoffman

Description: We are a national career matching service which gives candidates confidential exposure to multiple potential employers at no cost or obligation.We have created an interactive online service called e-recruit.
Functions: General mgmt., Sales & mktg., Finance, IT, Systems dev., Systems implem., Engineering
Industries: Computer equip., Finance, Computer svcs., Mgmt. consulting, Communications, High tech, Software

---

The Hogan Group

P.O. Box 15175
Cleveland, Ohio 44115
(216) 371-9705
Fax: (216) 371-9706
Email: TheHoganGp@aol.com

Key Contact - Specialty:
Ms. Ann B. Hogan - *Pharmaceutical, biotechnology, CRO companies*

Description: We are a full service recruitment firm conducting both contingency and retained searches. We specialize in placing clinical research professionals in pharmaceutical industry and related positions.

Salary Minimum: $35,000
Functions: Directors, Middle mgmt., Physicians, Nurses, Sales & mktg., R&D, Minorities
Industries: Drugs mfg., Pharmaceutical svcs., Biotech

Holden & Harlan Assoc., Inc.

P.O. Box 91
Flossmoor, Illinois 60422
(708) 799-4447
Fax: (708) 799-4461
Email: info@ActuarialRecruiting.com
Web: ActuarialRecruiting.com

Key Contact - Specialty:
Mr. Jerry Hayes - *Actuarial, property & casualty insurance*
Ms. Mara Hayes

Description: National and international recruiting actuaries for the property and casualty insurance companies, consulting and brokerage firms.
Functions: CFO's, Budgeting, M&A, Risk mgmt., MIS mgmt., Network admin., DB admin.
Industries: Insurance

Holloway Schulz & Partners

1188 W. Georgia St., Ste. 1500
Vancouver, British Columbia V6E 4A2
Canada
(604) 688-9595
Fax: (604) 688-3608
Email: holloway@recruiters.com
Web: www.holloway-schulz.com

Key Contact - Specialty:
Mr. Clive Holloway - *High technology management*
Mr. Bill Schulz - *General management*
Mr. Malcolm McGowan - *Financial/accounting management*
Ms. Heather G. Latondresse - *MIS management*
Ms. Dawn A. Longshaw - *Sales/marketing management*
Mr. Terry Dusome - *technical sales/management, manufacturing, engineering*
Mr. James Seidel - *High technology*

Description: We are a 25 year old professional recruitment and search firm with consultants specializing in various disciplines. Searches are conducted on both a contingency and retainer basis.

Salary Minimum: $40,000
Functions: General mgmt., Mfg., Materials, Sales & mktg., HR mgmt., Finance, IT
Industries: Construction, Mfg., Transportation, Finance, Svcs., High tech, Software

---

Home Health & Hospital Recruiters, Inc.

2858 Johnson Ferry Rd., Ste. 250
Marietta, Georgia 30062
(770) 993-2828
Fax: (770) 993-6448
Email: hhhr@mindspring.com
Web: www.hhhr.com

Key Contact - Specialty:
Mr. Barry P. Savransky - *Medical*
Mr. Alan Savransky - *Medical*

Description: We specialize in the recruitment of home healthcare, hospice, hospital and long term care professionals. In addition, we also do mergers and acquisitions and consulting.

Salary Minimum: $35,000
Functions: Directors, Senior mgmt., Middle mgmt., Nurses, Health admin., CFO's, M&A
Industries: Healthcare

Fred Hood & Assoc.

23801 Calabasas Rd., Ste. 2034
Calabasas, California 91302
(818) 222-6222
Fax: (818) 222-4445
Email: fredhood@earthlink.net
Web: fredhood.com

Key Contact - Specialty:
Mr. Fred L. Hood - *Sales & marketing, distribution, transportation*
Mr. John Mitchell - *Sales, finance*
Mr. Emile Bose - *Sales*

Description: We locate outstanding marketing, sales, operations, warehouse, category management and computer executives for the beverage and food industries.
Functions: Senior mgmt., Middle mgmt., Distribution, Sales mgmt., PR, Cash mgmt., MIS mgmt.
Industries: Hospitality

J. G. Hood Assoc.

599 Riverside Ave., Ste. 2 & 3
Westport, Connecticut 06880
(203) 226-1126
Fax: (203) 227-7688
Web: jghood@worldnet.att.net

Key Contact - Specialty:
Ms. Joyce G. Hood

Description: Full service search firm established in 1982, specializing in technical engineering/manufacturing, DP, financial, marketing/sales and professional. For top Fortune and private client companies, including consumer product, healthcare and pharmaceuticals.
Functions: Generalist, Mfg., Materials, HR mgmt., IT, Systems dev., Engineering
Industries: Generalist, Plastics/rubber, Machinery/Appliances, Computer equip., Misc. mfg., High tech, Software

---

Hook-Up!

323 Geary St., Ste. 613
San Francisco, California 94102
(415) 362-3573
Fax: (415) 362-3575
Email: hookup@sirius.com
Web: www.hookupjobs.com

Key Contact - Specialty:
Mr. Martin Perlmutter - *Senior management, creative, technical*
Ms. Miki Raver - *Creative personnel*

Description: We are specialists in interactive media. Our sales approach to clients is consultative; our relationship with candidates is that of talent agents. We are headhunters with heart - and vision!

Salary Minimum: $50,000
Functions: Senior mgmt., Mktg. mgmt., Sales mgmt., CFO's, MIS mgmt., Systems dev., Graphic artists
Industries: New media

Horizon Medical Search of NH

8 Grenada Circle
Nashua, New Hampshire 03062-1429
(800) 639-6611
(603) 598-6611
Fax: (603) 598-6622
Email: HorizonMed@aol.com

Key Contact - Specialty:
Mr. Joseph W. DuBois, Jr. - *Physicians, nurse practitioners, dentists, healthcare executives*
Ms. Sabine G. DuBois - *Physicians, physicians assistants*
Mr. Anthony G. DuBois - *Physicians assistants*
Mr. Scott Matteson - *Pharmacists*

Description: Specializes in assisting healthcare professionals locate practice opportunities throughout contiguous United States and Canada. All fees are employer paid-no cost to candidates. Counselors are available Monday-Saturday 9:00 a.m. to 8:00 p.m. All communications are confidential.

Salary Minimum: $50,000
Functions: Physicians, Nurses, Allied health, Health admin., IT
Industries: Healthcare

Affiliates:
Recruiters Professional Network

Horizons Unlimited

9385 Tenaya Way
Kelseyville, California 95451
(707) 277-9744
Fax: (707) 277-9040

Key Contact - Specialty:
Mr. Bruce Van Buskirk - *Chemical industry*

Description: Sales, technical service and technical positions in the chemical and petroleum industries; catalyst, process additives, fuel/lubricant additives, water treatment, adsorbants, alumina, surfactants and process simulation.
Functions: Product dev., Plant mgmt., Mkt. research, Mktg. mgmt., Sales mgmt., R&D, Engineering
Industries: Chemicals, Paints/petroleum products, Misc. mfg.

David C. Horn Executive Search

P.O. Box 720065
Dallas, Texas 75372-0065
(214) 821-3931
Fax: (214) 821-0993
Email: davidchorn@worldnet.att.net

Key Contact - Specialty:
Mr. David C. Horn - *Financial services, management, finance, information technology*

Description: Specialty search firm focusing on the financial services industry, with sub-specialties in finance, information technology management positions and related management consulting.

Salary Minimum: $60,000
Functions: General mgmt., CFO's, Cash mgmt., MIS mgmt., Systems implem., Mgmt. consultants, Int'l.
Industries: Banking, Computer svcs., Mgmt. consulting, Human resource svcs., Software

Hospitality Int'l.

23 West 73, Ste. 100
New York, New York 10023
(212) 769-8800
Fax: (212) 769-2138
Email: hospinto@erols.com

Key Contact - Specialty:
Mr. Joseph A. Radice - *Hotel, food service, restaurant executive level, contract management*
Mr. Frank Marino - *Food service, restaurant management*
Mr. Joseph Francis - *Hotels, resorts, clubs*

Description: Recruitment and placement of management and staff support for the restaurant, hotel, food service, healthcare and casino industries nationally and internationally.

Salary Minimum: $30,000
Functions: General mgmt., Sales & mktg., HR mgmt., Finance, IT, Minorities, Int'l.
Industries: Hospitality, Entertainment, Healthcare

Branches:
5214 Bast Shaw Butte Drive
Scottsdale, Arizona 85254
(602) 951-6081
Fax: (602) 596-6561
Key Contact - Specialty:
Mr. Allen Gentry - *Hotels, resorts, food service, contract management*

P.O. Box 5008
Cortland, New York 13045
(607) 756-8550
Fax: (607) 756-8620
Key Contact - Specialty:
Ms. Susan P. Stafford - *Hotels, casino management, cruise management, convention center management*

Houser, Martin, Morris

110 110th Avenue NE, Ste. 503
P.O. Box 90015
Bellevue, Washington 98009
(425) 453-2700
Fax: (425) 453-8726
Email: recruitr@houser.com
Web: www.houser.com

Key Contact - Specialty:
Mr. Robert Holert - *Information technology*
Mr. Josef Verner - *Information technology*
Mr. Craig Macdonald - *Manufacturing, human resources*
Ms. Victoria Harris - *Attorney, legal*
Ms. LuAnn Carlson - *Accounting, finance*

Description: Professional recruiting and search consultants based in the Pacific Northwest providing recruiting and search expertise in a variety of key disciplines for your company.

Salary Minimum: $40,000
Functions: Senior mgmt., Mfg., Sales mgmt., Finance, IT, Engineering, Attorneys
Industries: Generalist, Mfg., Transportation, Finance, Legal, High tech, Software

Howard-Sloan Assoc.
(a division of the Howard-Sloan-Koller Group)

353 Lexington Ave., 11th Floor
New York, New York 10016
(212) 661-5250
Fax: (212) 557-9178
Email: hsk@hsksearch.com
Web: www.hsksearch.com

Key Contact - Specialty:
Mr. Edward R. Koller, Jr. - *General management, sales & marketing*
Ms. Karen Danziger - *Editorial, creative services*

Description: A partial contingency recruiting firm in magazine, newspaper, newsletter and book publishing, including advertising sales, editorial, production, art, circulation, finance and operations; direct marketing, public relations, new media, information technology and cable.

Salary Minimum: $50,000
Functions: Senior mgmt., Middle mgmt., Advertising, Mktg. mgmt., Sales mgmt., PR
Industries: Advertising/PR, Publishing, New media, Broadcast & Film, Telecoms

Affiliates:
Jerry Fields Assoc.

Howard-Sloan Legal Search, Inc.

1140 Ave. of the Americas, Ste. 1000
New York, New York 10036
(212) 704-0444
Fax: (212) 869-7999
Email: hslegal@aol.com
Web: www.howardsloan.com

Key Contact - Specialty:
Mr. Mitchell L. Berger - *Legal*

Description: Now in our fourth decade, we are a leader in the nationwide and international recruitment of attorneys for law firms and corporations. Our company pioneered the approach of recruiters specializing in a specific area. Areas of specialization include bankruptcy, corporate, energy/environmental, intellectual property, international, labor/employment, litigation, real estate, tax/ERISA/ trusts and estates, partners and law firm mergers.
Functions: Attorneys
Industries: Legal

Affiliates:
Howard-Sloan Professional Search, Inc.

Howard/Williams Assoc.

105 S. Narcissus Ave., Ste. 806
West Palm Beach, Florida 33401-5530
(561) 833-4888
Fax: (561) 833-2343

Key Contact - Specialty:
Mr. John Williams - *Attorneys*
Mr. Richard D. Rahaim - *Attorneys*
Mr. George Howard - *Attorneys*
Ms. Susan Martin - *Paralegals, legal secretaries, administrative, clerical, accounting*

Description: Have specialized in the recruitment of lawyers, at all levels, on behalf of law firm and corporation clients within the State of Florida since 1983 (and N.Y.C. 1972-1983). Acquired local recruiting firm in 1996 that specializes in legal support e.g. paralegals, legal secretary, etc.

Salary Minimum: $60,000
Functions: Attorneys, Paralegals
Industries: Generalist, Legal, Accounting

HR Advantage, Inc.

P.O. Box 10319
Burke, Virginia 22009
(703) 978-6028
Fax: (703) 978-4029
Email: julierana@prodigy.net
Web: www.ipa.com/eoffice/703-978-6028.html

Key Contact - Specialty:
Ms. Julie B. Rana - *Telecommunications*

Description: Placement agency serving primarily the Washington, DC area. Specializes in recruiting telecommunications executives and professionals for big name telecommunications firms. Recruits in engineering, marketing, sales, finance and customer service.

Salary Minimum: $45,000
Functions: Sales & mktg., Finance, IT, Engineering
Industries: Telecoms, High tech

HR Consultants

3780 Willowmeade Drive
Snellville, Georgia 30278
(770) 985-8201
Fax: (770) 982-9063
Email: LRBishop@mindspring.com
Web: www.hrconsultants.net

Key Contact - Specialty:
Mr. Larry R. Bishop

Description: We are a client driven firm providing value added searches in PeopleSoft and Oracle placements. Other areas of emphasis are healthcare administration and telecommunications consulting. We have over 15 years experience and strive to do excellent work on a consistent basis.

Salary Minimum: $40,000
Functions: Health admin., Systems implem., Network admin., Mgmt. consultants
Industries: Mgmt. consulting, Software, Healthcare

HR Inc.

117 N. Main St.
Belmont, North Carolina 28012
(704) 825-0490
(704) 209-3102
Fax: (704) 825-0560
Email: HRIncCLT@aol.com

Key Contact - Specialty:
Ms. Glenda Spencer - *Engineering, human resources*
Mr. Leo Hageman, Jr. - *Engineering, chemicals, human resources*

Description: An outsource firm specializing in human resource management, training and development, executive search and placement. Our primary objective: to provide quality professional services customized to meet clients' specific needs.

Salary Minimum: $35,000
Functions: Mfg., Plant mgmt., Materials, Materials Plng., HR mgmt., R&D, Engineering
Industries: Generalist, Mfg., Svcs.

Hreshko Consulting Group

850 US Hwy. 1
North Brunswick, New Jersey 08902
(732) 545-9000
Fax: (732) 545-0080

Key Contact - Specialty:
Mr. Frank M. Hreshko - *Accounting, information technology*
Mr. John C. Diefenbach - *Sales & marketing, accounting*
Mr. Joseph Talarico - *Systems integration, networks*
Ms. Olga Vignuolo - *Generalist*
Mr. Michael Franklin - *Financial services*
Mr. Daniel Butler - *Information technology*
Mr. Dave Holmes - *Accounting, financial service*
Mr. Jeff Holmes - *Information technology*

Description: Our founder, F. Hreshko (former director of executive search for Ernst & Young)offers same high quality services found in the Big 6 professional environment.

Salary Minimum: $50,000
Functions: Middle mgmt., Sales & mktg., HR mgmt., Finance, IT, Systems implem., Mgmt. consultants
Industries: Mfg., Finance, Invest. banking, Computer svcs., Human resource svcs., Insurance, Software

HRI Services, Inc.

1200 E. St.
Westwood, Massachusetts 02090
(781) 251-9188
Fax: (781) 251-9189

Key Contact - Specialty:
Mr. Paul R. Tallino
Mr. Paul R. Tallino, Jr.

Description: National executive search and placement firm who specializes in the placement of professionals within the food service sales and hotel/restaurant industries. We have been specializing in the hospitality industry for over 18 years.

Salary Minimum: $30,000
Functions: Directors, Senior mgmt., Middle mgmt., Admin. svcs., CFO's, M&A
Industries: Hospitality, Entertainment

Affiliates:
HRI Services Inc. Financial Group

The HRM Group, Inc.

321 Lorna Sq.
Birmingham, Alabama 35216
(205) 978-7181
Fax: (205) 978-7616
Web: www.hrmgroup.com

Key Contact - Specialty:
Mr. Jim Taylor
Mr. Charles Wilkinson

Description: Generalist HR management firm noted for its domestic and international recruitment research services billed at an hourly rate and contingency/retained placement fees ranging between 15% and 30%. Weekly written progress reports including information on all candidates contacted. All associates possess HR degrees.

Salary Minimum: $25,000
Functions: General mgmt., Healthcare, Sales & mktg., HR mgmt., Finance, IT, Int'l.
Industries: Energy/utilities, Mfg., Finance, Communications, Insurance, High tech, Healthcare

Branches:
1500 Perimeter Corporate Park, Ste. 440
Huntsville, Alabama 35806
(205) 978-7181
Key Contact - Specialty:
Ms. Lucy Eisele

HRNI
815 Newport Rd.
Ann Arbor, Michigan 48103
(734) 663-6446
Email: jobs@jobsbyjohnson.com

Key Contact - Specialty:
Mr. John Johnson - *Big 6 Consultants, plastics*

Description: We offer retainer and contingency placement services to manufacturing, food processing, logistics and major consulting firms for all consulting areas.

Salary Minimum: $30,000
Functions: Mfg., Materials, HR mgmt., Finance, Engineering, Mgmt. consultants
Industries: Generalist, Food/bev/tobacco, Plastics/rubber, Motor vehicles, Transportation, Mgmt. consulting, Human resource svcs.

Huddleston Assoc.
4007 E. 37th St.
Tulsa, Oklahoma 74135
(918) 742-5166
Fax: (918) 744-0206
Email: lkhudd@aol.com
Web: members.aol.com/lkhudd/index.html

Key Contact - Specialty:
Ms. Linda Huddleston - *Technical*
Mr. Victor Huddleston - *Technical*
Ms. Miranda Suvak - *Technical*

Description: Executive and technical contingency search firm with experience in a variety of industries.

Salary Minimum: $40,000
Functions: Generalist
Industries: Generalist

Hudson Assoc. Inc.
P.O. Box 2502
Anderson, Indiana 46018
(765) 649-1133
Fax: (765) 649-1155
Email: hudassoc@aol.com

Key Contact - Specialty:
Mr. George A. Hudson - *Insurance*

Description: Small, highly specialized firm handling L&H and P&C insurance positions. Very active in the placement of attorneys within advanced marketing specialty area, as well as sales and marketing individuals.

Salary Minimum: $40,000
Functions: Directors, Senior mgmt., Middle mgmt., Advertising, Mkt. research, Mktg. mgmt., Sales mgmt.
Industries: Insurance

The Hudson Group
P.O. Box 263
Simsbury, Connecticut 06070
(860) 658-0245
Fax: (860) 651-0835
Email: TheHudsonG@aol.com

Key Contact - Specialty:
Mr. Paul E. Hudson - *Digital signal processing, algorithm development, radio frequency, microwave, electronic packaging*
Ms. Judy K. Hudson - *Digital design, analog design, mechanical design, software, quality assurance*

Description: Specialists in placing degreed engineering, technical, scientific professionals in hi-tech electronics (in any industry), communications, telecommunications, telephony, materials and R&D. Positions cover design, development, quality assurance/verification, R&D and manufacturing.

Salary Minimum: $35,000
Functions: Product dev., Production, Quality, Systems anal., Systems implem., R&D, Engineering
Industries: Computer equip., Consumer electronics, Telecoms, Defense, Aerospace, High tech, Software

Hughes & Assoc.
718 Oakwood Trail
Ft. Worth, Texas 76112
(817) 496-3650
Fax: (817) 429-5923
Email: kenhughes@sprintmail.com

Key Contact - Specialty:
Mr. Ken Hughes - *Insurance, managed care*

Description: Former insurance company CEO heads firm of experienced senior officers who now conduct contingency recruiting and retained search in life/health insurance and managed care industries; nationwide practice.

Salary Minimum: $50,000
Functions: Generalist
Industries: Insurance, Healthcare

Affiliates:
Search America, Inc.

Hughes & Assoc. Int'l. Inc.
3737 Government Blvd., Ste. 304B
Mobile, Alabama 36693
(334) 661-8888
Fax: (334) 661-6991
Email: TimoHughes@aol.com

Key Contact - Specialty:
Mr. Tim Hughes - *Engineers, refining, petrochemical, chemical, pulp & paper*

Description: Nationwide recruiting of engineers for Fortune 500 companies and companies who serve those companies.

Salary Minimum: $40,000
Functions: Engineering
Industries: Paper, Chemicals, Plastics/rubber, Paints/petroleum products

Hughes & Sloan, Inc.
1360 Peachtree St. NE, Ste. 1010
One Midtown Plaza
Atlanta, Georgia 30309-3214
(404) 873-3421
Fax: (404) 873-3861
Email: hslaw@mindspring.com
Web: www.hughes-sloan.com

Key Contact - Specialty:
Ms. Melba N. G. Hughes
Ms. Linda Sloan-Young
Robert Drury
Wendy A. Strassner
Ms. Tanya R. Cunningham
Ms. Gina R. Thomas
Ashley P. Langdon
Ms. Joy Nicholson
Ms. Lynda Edwards

Description: We are the largest Southeastern legal recruiting firm, placing attorneys in firms and corporations in the United States and abroad. More than half of our placements are in-house.
Functions: Attorneys
Industries: Legal

Hughes & Wilden Assoc.
3935 Old William Penn Hwy.
Murrysville, Pennsylvania 15668
(724) 733-1130

Key Contact - Specialty:
Mr. Roger Sulkowski - *Transportation, distribution, logistics*
Mr. Joseph Orlich - *Transportation, distribution, logistics*

Description: We have been in business for over 24 years.

Salary Minimum: $30,000
Functions: Purchasing, Materials Plng., Distribution
Industries: Transportation

Human Capital Resources, Inc.

424 Central Ave., 5th Floor
St. Petersburg, Florida 33701
(813) 898-0212
Fax: (813) 898-0314
Email: werlwind@aol.com
Web: www.humancap.com

Key Contact - Specialty:
Mr. Paul A. Werlin - *Financial services, financial institutions, investment programs, mutual funds, insurance*
Mr. John Donovan - *Financial institutions (investment institutions)*
Mr. Paul Heise

Description: We specialize in the need for professionals in the financial institution investment program marketplace. Our clients include banks, third-party marketing firm, product manufacturers and broker/dealers.
Functions: Senior mgmt., Middle mgmt., Mkt. research, Mktg. mgmt., Sales mgmt., Training, Mgmt. consultants
Industries: Banking, Brokers, Misc. financial, Insurance

Human Resource Bureau

P.O. Box 19793-403
Irvine, California 92623-9793
(949) 660-7966

Key Contact - Specialty:
Ms. Joyce Newberry
Mr. Pat Brogan - *Management, legal*

Description: Nationwide executive search firm dealing with management of all types earning $40K-$350K, attorneys, engineers, etc.

Salary Minimum: $60,000
Functions: Generalist, Senior mgmt., CFO's, MIS mgmt., Attorneys
Industries: Generalist, Mfg., Finance, Legal, Accounting, Advertising/PR, High tech

---

Human Resource Dimensions, Inc.

1304 W. Abram, Ste. 200
Arlington, Texas 76013
(817) 801-5100
Fax: (817) 801-9079
Email: rburgess@hrdimensions.com
Web: www.hrdimensions.com

Key Contact - Specialty:
Mr. Rick Burgess - *Call centers, telecommunications, human resources*
Ms. Felecia York - *Call centers, telecommunications, human resources, retail*
Ms. Liz Andrews
Ms. Susan Warren
Ms. Sherry Mathews
Mr. Sunny Morris

Description: By utilizing technology and team work we are able to screen and present qualified candidates within the first seven to fourteen days of a search.

Salary Minimum: $50,000
Functions: Middle mgmt., Direct mktg., Customer svc., Personnel, Training, Credit, Risk mgmt.
Industries: Generalist, Svcs., Hospitality, Pharmaceutical svcs., Human resource svcs., Telecoms

Branches:
318 W. Southside Blvd.
Independence, Missouri 64055
(816) 833-7788
Fax: (816) 833-7789
Email: kmulliken@hrdimensions.com
Key Contact - Specialty:
Mr. Ken Mulliken - *Call centers*

Human Resources Management Hawaii, Inc.

210 Ward Ave., Ste. 126
Honolulu, Hawaii 96814
(808) 536-3438
Fax: (808) 536-0352
Email: hrmhelinski@mci1.com

Key Contact - Specialty:
Mr. Mike Elinski - *Information systems, consultants, financial*

Description: Our personal careers reflect successful work experience in administration, management, engineering and MIS. We therefore can better understand your staffing needs and save you time to do what you do best.

Salary Minimum: $40,000
Functions: Generalist, Senior mgmt., HR mgmt., CFO's, IT, Engineering, Mgmt. consultants
Industries: Generalist, Banking, Computer svcs., Mgmt. consulting, Human resource svcs., Telecoms, Software

---

E. F. Humay Assoc.

P.O. Box 173 R
Fairview Village, Pennsylvania 19409-0173
(610) 275-1559
Fax: (610) 275-3485
Email: EFHumay@msn.com

Key Contact - Specialty:
Mr. Gene Humay - *Sales, marketing, parts, service, manufacturing*
Ms. Jane Humay - *Sales, marketing, parts, service, manufacturing*

Description: Recruit for manufacturers and distributors of construction and mining equipment (road, bridge, mining, etc.) in positions for sales, marketing, parts, service, engineering and all management positions.

Salary Minimum: $35,000
Functions: Senior mgmt., Plant mgmt., Mkt. research, Mktg. mgmt., Sales mgmt., Engineering, Int'l.
Industries: Agri/forestry/mining, Construction, Wholesale

Hunegnaw Executive Search

641 N. High St., Ste. 109
Columbus, Ohio 43215
(614) 228-6898
Fax: (614) 228-2866
Email: davidh@hunegnaw.com
Web: www.hunegnaw.com

Key Contact - Specialty:
Mr. David B. Hunegnaw

Description: We believe the success of a company depends on the quality of its employees. With that in mind, we recruit the very best candidates from the outside to help our clients achieve their goals.

Salary Minimum: $50,000
Functions: Directors, Senior mgmt., Mkt. research, Sales mgmt., Credit, Systems anal., Systems dev.
Industries: Generalist, Banking, Computer svcs.

Leigh Hunt & Assoc., Inc.

14 Maine St., Ste. 312, Ft. Andruss
Brunswick, Maine 04011
(207) 729-3840
Fax: (207) 729-3888
Email: LHunt@leighhunt.com
Web: www.leighhunt.com

Key Contact - Specialty:
Leigh Hunt - *Polyurethane, paints & coatings, medical devices, information technology*

Description: We maintain a database of over 2500 companies and 4000 candidates-an invaluable resource for job search, recruitment and placement. The right chemistry between candidate and company equals success. Over 12 years of experience.

Salary Minimum: $30,000

Functions: IT, MIS mgmt., Systems anal., Systems dev., Systems implem., Systems support, Network admin.
Industries: Medical devices, Plastics/rubber, Paints/petroleum products, Computer equip., Computer svcs., Software

---

Hunt Ltd.
1050 Wall St. W., Ste. 330
Lyndhurst, New Jersey 07071
(201) 438-8200
Fax: (201) 438-8372
Email: AMetz@huntltd.com
Web: www.huntltd.com

Key Contact - Specialty:
Mr. Alex Metz - *Logistics, distribution, materials management*
Mr. Donald Jacobson - *Logistics, distribution, materials management*

Description: Staff is made up of former distribution executives. Company specializes primarily in distribution/transportation opportunities nationwide.

Salary Minimum: $45,000
Functions: Senior mgmt., Middle mgmt., Materials, Purchasing, Materials Plng., Distribution
Industries: Food/bev/tobacco, Paper, Chemicals, Soap/perfume/cosmetics, Drugs mfg., Medical devices, Retail

---

Hunt Patton & Brazeal, Inc.
2250 E. 73rd St., Ste. 120
Tulsa, Oklahoma 74136
(918) 492-6910
Fax: (918) 492-7023
Email: hpb@huntpatton.com
Web: huntpatton.com

Key Contact - Specialty:
Dr. Michael Patton - *Mergers & acquisitions*
Ms. Linda Huddleston - *Generalist*

Description: Management consulting firm providing acquisition/merger related services as well as professional, executive and technical retained search services.

Salary Minimum: $55,000
Functions: Generalist, Senior mgmt., Middle mgmt., Production, Plant mgmt., Mktg. mgmt., Engineering
Industries: Generalist, Energy/utilities, Chemicals, Environmental svcs., Haz. waste, High tech, Software

Branches:
1200 17th St., Ste. 1000
Denver, Colorado 80202
(303) 572-0751
Fax: (303) 572-0752
Email: hpb@huntpatton.com
Key Contact - Specialty:
Mr. Pat Patton - *Generalist*
Mr. E. Gene Daniels
Mr. J. Tadewald
Mr. P. Burns
Mr. M. Goldman

2350 N. Sam Houston Frwy. E., Ste. 210
Houston, Texas 77032
(281) 590-8350
Fax: (281) 590-8351
Key Contact - Specialty:
Mr. Bob Buckman - *Generalist*
Mr. Ben Boujemaa - *Generalist*

Affiliates:
Patton & Associates
Peterson & Associates

Hunter Adams
537 Merwick Circle
Charlotte, North Carolina 28211
(704) 362-0830
Fax: (704) 364-5072
Web: www.hunteradams.com

Key Contact - Specialty:
Mr. Edwin Ziegler

Description: Specialization in the communications (data, voice, wireless computer telephone and internet) industry. Specifically sales, marketing and related technical support at all levels.

Salary Minimum: $50,000
Functions: Mkt. research, Mktg. mgmt., Sales mgmt., Systems implem., Systems support, Engineering, Technicians
Industries: Computer equip., Telecoms, High tech, Software

Hunter Assoc.
181 Park Ave.
West Springfield, Massachusetts 01089
(413) 737-6560
Fax: (413) 785-1295
Email: hunter@hunterworldwide.com
Web: www.hunterworldwide.com

Key Contact - Specialty:
Mr. Daniel M. Shooshan - *Engineering, administration*

Description: Our particular area of search specialization is contract/subcontract, financial and engineering professionals for domestic and expatriate assignments.

Salary Minimum: $45,000
Functions: Senior mgmt., Middle mgmt., Production, Purchasing, Sales mgmt., Engineering
Industries: Aerospace, High tech, Software

The Hunter Group, Inc.
1577 N. Woodward Ave., Ste. 211
Bloomfield Hills, Michigan 48304
(810) 645-1551
Email: skling@huntergroup.com
Web: www.huntergroup.com

Key Contact - Specialty:
Mr. James Lionas - *Senior level executive*
Mr. Steve Klingensmith - *Financial*
Ms. Sherry Muir - *Technical, automotive*

Description: Combining more than 40 years of recruiting expertise, recognized as Michigan's fastest growing executive search firm.

Salary Minimum: $75,000
Functions: Generalist, Senior mgmt., Mfg., Health admin., HR mgmt., CFO's, Engineering
Industries: Generalist, Plastics/rubber, Metal products, Machinery/Appliances, Motor vehicles, Misc. mfg., High tech

---

The Hunter Group
1605 Green Pine Court
Raleigh, North Carolina 27614
(919) 676-5900
Fax: (919) 676-8510
Email: huntergp@mindspring.com
Web: huntergrp.home.mindspring.com

Key Contact - Specialty:
Ms. Martha Lempicke - *Generalist*
Mr. Todd Lempicke - *Generalist*

Description: Locates key performers in a given industry, function or discipline quickly and discreetly. We represent some of the world's most admired employers, in a variety of locations nationwide. Diversity recruiting specialists.

Salary Minimum: $40,000
Functions: Generalist, Mfg., Sales & mktg., HR mgmt., Finance, Engineering, Minorities
Industries: Generalist, Mfg., Textiles/apparel, Machinery/Appliances, Motor vehicles, Transportation, Aerospace

---

Hunter Int'l. LLC
20 Park Plaza., Ste. 433
Boston, Massachusetts 02116
(617) 695-0509
Fax: (617) 695-0568

Key Contact - Specialty:
Mr. William M. Phillips

Description: We present finalist for senior, mid level and executive or corporate level positions involving domestic or international assignments possessing remarkable talents and energy necessary to build accomplishments while meeting difficult challenges in competitive global business environments.

Salary Minimum: $65,000

Functions: Senior mgmt., Middle mgmt., Mkt. research, Sales mgmt., CFO's, Risk mgmt., Int'l.
Industries: Paper, Chemicals, Soap/perfume/cosmetics, Drugs mfg., Medical devices, Paints/petroleum products, Machinery/Appliances

---

Hunter, Rowan & Crowe

9843 Treasure Cay Lane
Bonita Springs, Florida 34135
(941) 495-1389
Fax: (941) 992-7517
Email: crowehrc@naples.infi.net

Key Contact - Specialty:
Mr. Thomas H. Crowe - *Sales & marketing executives, general*

Description: Management consulting experience provides unique expertise for quick study and understanding of client organization culture to better match candidate styles. Proprietary network and research database.

Salary Minimum: $50,000
Functions: Generalist, Sales & mktg., Advertising, Mktg. mgmt., Direct mktg., CFO's, Engineering
Industries: Generalist, Mfg., Finance, Svcs., Communications, Packaging, High tech

Branches:
P.O. Box 456
Elkhart Lake, Wisconsin 53020-0456
(920) 467-1007
Fax: (920) 467-1244
Key Contact - Specialty:
Ms. Carol Rowan - *Research only*

Affiliates:
Innovation Consultants Int'l.

Huntington Personnel Consultants, Inc.

P.O. Box 1077
Huntington, New York 11743-0640
(516) 549-8888
Fax: (516) 549-3012
Email: jahenry@i-2000.com

Key Contact - Specialty:
Ms. Jeannette A. Henry - *Information technology, software engineering*

Description: Recruitment and placement of information technology and software engineering professionals in NYC metro area and nationwide.

Salary Minimum: $30,000
Functions: MIS mgmt., Systems anal., Systems dev., Systems implem., Systems support, Network admin., DB admin.
Industries: Generalist, Mfg., Finance, Computer svcs., New media, High tech, Software

---

Huntley Associates (Dallas), Inc.

P.O. Box 868144
Plano, Texas 75086-8144
(972) 599-0100
Fax: (972) 599-0300
Email: consult@huntley.com
Web: www.huntley.com

Key Contact - Specialty:
Mr. David E. Huntley - *SAP, PeopleSoft, Baan*
Mr. Dean R. Huntley
Mr. John Galka - *Hardware/software engineering, client/server, Mainframe, MIS, information technology*
Ms. Hanh Nguyen

Description: International corporate consultants engaged in business consulting, executive recruiting and the provision of contract consulting professionals.

Salary Minimum: $35,000
Functions: General mgmt., Mfg., IT, Engineering, Int'l.
Industries: Mfg., Computer svcs., Communications, Aerospace, High tech, Software

International Branches:
Arnersham

Affiliates:
Gevers Deynoot Management Consultants

The Hutton Group, Inc.

815 Live Oak Rd., Ste. A
Vero Beach, Florida 32963
(561) 234-7333
Fax: (561) 234-9009
Email: huttongroup@pobox.com

Key Contact - Specialty:
Ms. M. Joan Hutton - *Managed care, healthcare reengineering consultants, integrated health system executives*

Description: After 15 years as a nursing administer and educator, Joan moved into executive placement in 1977. She is active in many healthcare organizations and is a keynote speaker for professional groups nationwide.

Salary Minimum: $50,000
Functions: Health admin., CFO's, Budgeting, M&A, Risk mgmt., Systems implem., Mgmt. consultants
Industries: Healthcare

Affiliates:
Alliance Management Resources
Bill Bishop & Assoc.
Cunningham & Associates
Forbes Management Services, Inc.

Hyland Executive Search
(a division of Hyland & Company, Inc.)

5060 North 40th Street, Suite 214
Phoenix, Arizona 85018
(602) 381-1177
Fax: (602) 381-1024
Web: www.hylandbay.com

Key Contact - Specialty:
Mr. Kenneth J. Hyland - *Real estate for new home builders*
Ms. Susan L. Hyland - *Real estate for new home builders*

Description: Search for the real estate industry only. Handle all corporate positions with heavy emphasis on the home building industry and master planned communities. Also, place experienced people for marketing and sales for new home builders, including training/placement of personnel.

Salary Minimum: $20,000
Functions: Sales & mktg., Sales mgmt., Mgmt. consultants
Industries: Construction, Real estate

Affiliates:
The Hyland Bay Company, Inc.
Hyland Executive Search
National Institute of Community Management

Hyman & Assoc.

719 Sawdust Rd., #217
The Woodlands, Texas 77380
(281) 292-1969
Fax: (281) 292-1664
Email: dhyman@iwl.net
Web: www.teamhyman.com

Key Contact - Specialty:
Mr. Derry Hyman - *Human resources, operations, general management*

Description: We are committed to providing quality solutions to clients' individualized needs. We have established ourselves as a valuable resource in successfully fulfilling meeting our clients' needs in diversity recruiting.

Salary Minimum: $70,000
Functions: Senior mgmt., Middle mgmt., Distribution, Sales mgmt., HR mgmt., Mgmt. consultants, Minorities
Industries: Generalist, Mfg., Transportation, Retail, Hospitality, Mgmt. consulting, Human resource svcs.

---

i.j. & assoc., inc.

2525 S. Wadsworth Blvd., Ste. 106
Lakewood, Colorado 80227
(303) 984-2585
Email: ilarson@csn.net
Web: www.ijassoc.com

Key Contact - Specialty:
Ms. Ila Larson - *Software engineering, information systems*

Description: Presently involved in recruiting for a wide range of clients both in software development and IS technology in state-of-the-art and leading edge technology - client/server and database.

Salary Minimum: $45,000
Functions: MIS mgmt., Systems anal., Systems dev., Systems implem., Systems support, Network admin., DB admin.
Industries: Computer svcs., New media, Telecoms, Defense, Aerospace, High tech, Software

---

The Icard Group, Inc.

120 Boardman Ave., Ste. F
Traverse City, Michigan 49684
(616) 929-2196
Fax: (616) 929-3336
Email: icard@ptway.com
Web: icardgroup.com

Key Contact - Specialty:
Mr. Bob Icard, Sr. - *Automotive quality*
Mr. Robert Icard, Jr. - *Automotive quality, engineering*
Ms. Cheryl Valencia-Icard - *Automotive quality, engineering*

Description: Specialists in automotive quality. We build long term client relationships.

Salary Minimum: $30,000
Functions: Directors, Middle mgmt., Product dev., Production, Plant mgmt., Quality, Productivity
Industries: Plastics/rubber, Metal products, Motor vehicles, Test/measurement equip.

Branches:
517 1/2 Pleasant Ave.
St. Joseph, Michigan 49085
(616) 983-3100
Fax: (616) 983-3177
Key Contact - Specialty:
Mr. Rick Stobbelaar - *Plastics*

Icon Recruiters, LLC

1220 Rosecrans St., Ste. 330
San Diego, California 92106
(619) 613-1031
Fax: (619) 613-1022
Email: Icon1@san.rr.com
Web: www.crwse-ventura.com/iconrecruiters/

Key Contact - Specialty:
Mr. C. Philip Slaton - *Pharmacists, physicians*
Ms. Joanne Conedera - *Pharmacists, physicians*

Description: We specialize in the placement of pharmacists and physicians into the pharmaceutical and healthcare industries.

Salary Minimum: $50,000
Functions: Generalist, Physicians, Allied health
Industries: Drugs mfg.

IDC Executive Search Inc.

2032 W. Vina del Mar Blvd.
St. Petersburg, Florida 33706
(813) 360-1310
Fax: (813) 465-0675
Email: info@idcexec.com
Web: www.idcexec.com

Key Contact - Specialty:
Mr. Marc Granet - *Independent power, power marketing*
Ms. Danae Luffman - *Independent power, power marketing*

Description: We are a full service executive search firm with over ten years strictly in the power industry. We have the experience and contacts to match your background to the right position.

Salary Minimum: $75,000
Functions: Senior mgmt., Engineering
Industries: Energy/utilities

Impact Search & Strategies

161 Leverington Ave., Ste. 102
Philadelphia, Pennsylvania 19127
(215) 482-6881
Fax: (215) 482-7518
Email: CJDoroba@mrmanayunk.com

Key Contact - Specialty:
Mr. Scott Quitel
Ms. Robin Cook - *Marketing, market research*
Ms. Carol Doroba - *Information technology, multimedia*
Ms. Beth Lubaroff - *Office administration*
Ms. Elyse Leace - *Law*
Ms. Victoria Degges - *Information technology*

Description: Full service national search firm specializes in marketing, pharmaceuticals, information technology, multimedia, law and office administration. Permanent and temporary staffing. Partnering with clients ranging from start-up to Fortune 500 companies.
Functions: Senior mgmt., Admin. svcs., Mkt. research, MIS mgmt., Systems dev., R&D, Attorneys
Industries: Pharmaceutical svcs., Legal, Computer svcs., Accounting, Human resource svcs., High tech, Healthcare

---

Impact Source, Inc.

3750 Sweepstakes Court, Ste. 2110
Palm Harbor, Florida 34684
(727) 772-6499
Fax: (727) 772-6599
Email: impacts@gte.net

Key Contact - Specialty:
Mr. John E. Sattler - *Sales & marketing*

Description: We help companies build, maintain and upgrade their sales and marketing teams by locating and facilitating the hire of the best people possible.

Salary Minimum: $25,000
Functions: Senior mgmt., Middle mgmt., Product dev., Mkt. research, Mktg. mgmt., Sales mgmt., Engineering
Industries: Generalist, Construction, Lumber/furniture, Leather/stone/glass/clay, Metal products, Machinery/Appliances, Wholesale

---

Impact Technical Staffing
(a division of SOS Staffing Services, Inc.)

10220 SW Greenburg Rd., #540
Portland, Oregon 97223
(503) 977-1907
Fax: (503) 977-1928
Email: portland@impactstaffing.com
Web: www.impactstaffing.com

Key Contact - Specialty:
Mr. Craig Smith - *Technical*
Mr. Don Dimick - *Technical*
Mr. Kevin Ashworth - *Technical*
Ms. Krista O'Dell - *Technical*

Description: A full service company that provides the Oregon and SW Washington areas with engineering and technician talent for some of the most recognized companies in the world.
Functions: MIS mgmt., Systems anal., Systems dev., Systems implem., Systems support, Engineering, Technicians
Industries: Computer equip., Test/measurement equip., Computer svcs., High tech, Software

---

Independent Power Consultants

5065 Westheimer, Ste. 815 E.
Galleria Financial Ctr.
Houston, Texas 77056
(713) 960-1868
Fax: (713) 960-1917
Email: lahjr200@msn.com
Web: www.myweb-site.com/ipc

Key Contact - Specialty:
Mr. Luis A. Hernandez, Jr. - *Independent power & energy, worldwide*
Ms. Robyn Stewart - *Independent power & energy*

Description: Houston based firm specializing in worldwide independent power industry executive search. Assignments include positions in power marketing, business development, project development, project management, operations and asset management.

Salary Minimum: $60,000
Functions: Directors, Senior mgmt., Middle mgmt., Mktg. mgmt., Personnel, Engineering
Industries: Energy/utilities, Mgmt. consulting, Human resource svcs.

Independent Resource Systems

22122 Sherman Way, Ste. 209
Canoga Park, California 91303
(818) 999-5690
Fax: (818) 999-5691
Email: speth@irsystems.com
Web: www.irsystems.com

Key Contact - Specialty:
Mr. Don Speth - *High technology*

Description: Experience in all facets of high-tech industry from development through marketing on a national basis.

Salary Minimum: $40,000
Functions: General mgmt., Sales & mktg., IT, Network admin., DB admin., R&D, Engineering
Industries: Computer equip., Test/measurement equip., Computer svcs., Telecoms, Aerospace, High tech, Software

Industry Consultants, Inc.

5805 State Bridge Rd., Ste. G-277
Duluth, Georgia 30097
(770) 623-9400
Fax: (520) 751-7673
Email: corey@azstarnet.com

Key Contact - Specialty:
Mr. Robert Stroud - *logistics, materials management, quality engineering, industrial engineering*

Description: Engineering and quality control recruiting within the disciplines of food science, chemistry, microbiology, chemical/industrial/mechanical and electrical engineering. Primarily for food, beverage, personal care and healthcare manufacturers. Also cover fields of logistics, materials management and quality engineering.

Salary Minimum: $65,000
Functions: Product dev., Quality, Purchasing, Distribution, Systems anal., DB admin., Minorities
Industries: Food/bev/tobacco, Printing, Chemicals, Soap/perfume/cosmetics, Drugs mfg.

Branches:
9121 E. Tanque Verde Rd., Ste. 277
Tucson, Arizona 85749
(520) 751-9400
Fax: (520) 751-7673
Key Contact - Specialty:
Mr. Joe Corey - *Process engineering, maintenance management, packaging equipment engineering, environmental, chemical engineering*

Information Systems Professionals

5904 Castlebrook Drive
Raleigh, North Carolina 27604
(919) 954-9100
Fax: (919) 954-1947
Email: ispros@staffing.net
Web: www.citysearch.com/rdu/ispros

Key Contact - Specialty:
Mr. Brad Moses - *Information systems, technology, telecommunications*
Mr. Bob Williams - *Information systems, technology, telecommunications*

Description: With 50+ years MIS experience, integrity, a personal touch and nationwide affiliates, we represent top local/regional companies. Conducting searches to fill MIS positions for a broad spectrum of industries.

Salary Minimum: $20,000
Functions: MIS mgmt., Systems anal., Systems dev., Systems implem., Systems support, Network admin., DB admin.
Industries: Generalist, Energy/utilities, Finance, Computer svcs., Software, Healthcare

Information Technology Search

P.O. Box 317
Chadds Ford, Pennsylvania 19317
(610) 388-0587
Email: aitken@400search.com

Key Contact - Specialty:
Ms. Carol Aitken - *AS/400 computer professionals*

Description: AS 400 niche specialist for PA, NJ & DE. Highly technical regional and national searches for ERP implementation specialists, directors of I.T. and the staff that reports to them.

Salary Minimum: $50,000
Functions: IT, MIS mgmt., Systems anal., Systems dev., Systems implem., Network admin., DB admin.
Industries: Mfg., Chemicals, Drugs mfg., Medical devices, Plastics/rubber, Paints/petroleum products, Metal products

InfoTech Search

8700 King George Drive, Ste. 102
Dallas, Texas 75235
(214) 638-0058
Fax: (214) 638-0060
Email: haroldh@onramp.net

Key Contact - Specialty:
Mr. Harold M. Harrison - *MIS management, database administrators (all level technical skills)*

Description: Recruitment of MIS management, database administration and senior technical personnel for companies in Dallas and throughout the United States.

Salary Minimum: $60,000
Functions: Personnel, MIS mgmt., Systems anal., Systems dev., Systems implem., Systems support, Mgmt. consultants
Industries: Computer svcs., Mgmt. consulting, Human resource svcs., High tech, Software

Infovia

2050 Asilomar Drive
Oakland, California 94611
(510) 339-6201
Fax: (510) 339-1275
Email: ebhh@infovia.com
Web: www.infovia.com

Key Contact - Specialty:
Ms. Elizabeth Boyle - *Information technology*

Description: We build long term relationships with our clients and candidates by interviewing all parties. We are conversant with the latest technology trends and maintain a database of 3000+ information technology professionals located in Silicon Valley.

Salary Minimum: $50,000
Functions: MIS mgmt., Systems anal., Systems dev., Systems implem., Systems support, Network admin., DB admin.
Industries: Generalist, Mfg., Transportation, Retail, Finance, High tech, Software

Meredith Ingram, Ltd.

55 W. Goethe St., # 1227
Chicago, Illinois 60610
(312) 640-0002
Fax: (312) 640-1376
Email: Ingrammere@aol.com

Key Contact - Specialty:
Ms. Meredith Ingram - *Consumer packaging goods, sales & marketing*

Functions: Sales & mktg., Mktg. mgmt., Sales mgmt.

Innovative Healthcare Services, Inc.

3765 Wetherburn Drive
P.O. Box 1096
Clarkston, Georgia 30021
(404) 298-6490
Fax: (404) 296-2362
Email: adickey232@aol.com

Key Contact - Specialty:
Ms. Avis D. Dickey - *Healthcare*

Description: We specialize in healthcare, medical care, insurance, medical equipment, pharmaceutical and technology.

Salary Minimum: $50,000
Functions: Generalist, General mgmt., Healthcare, Sales & mktg., Finance, IT, Specialized services
Industries: Generalist, Medical devices, Misc. financial, Pharmaceutical svcs., Insurance, High tech, Healthcare

Innovative Resource Group, LLC
(a division of SIA Group)

26 Pinecrest Plaza, Ste. 160
Southern Pines, North Carolina 28387
(910) 215-8885
(910) 690-9400
Fax: (910) 215-8886
Email: rthomas@ac.net
Web: www.siasearch.com

Key Contact - Specialty:
Mr. Roger C. Thomas - *Manufacturing, business operations, distributions*

Description: We are a full service firm specializing in permanent and leased executive staffing exclusively for internal strategic planning and consulting operations within the manufacturing and service industries. Offices also in Pittsburg, PA and Atlanta, G.A.

Salary Minimum: $35,000
Functions: Generalist, General mgmt., Mfg., Materials, IT, Engineering, Mgmt. consultants
Industries: Generalist, Energy/utilities, Mfg., Finance, Svcs., Communications, Packaging

Branches:
35 Technology Parkway South, Suite 170
Norcross, Georgia 30097
(770) 279-8898
Fax: (770) 279-9110
Key Contact - Specialty:
Mr. Thomas Izzo

651 Holiday, Ste. 300
Pittsburgh, Pennsylvania 15220
(412) 561-4643
Fax: (412) 561-9091
Key Contact - Specialty:
Mr. Ken Spear

innovativestaffsearch

425 Soledad St., Ste. 200
San Antonio, Texas 78205
(210) 472-1636
Fax: (210) 472-1686
Email: iss@texas.net

Key Contact - Specialty:
Mr. Kevin J. Mero - *Pharmacy, physicians assistant, nurse practitioners*

Description: Specializing in the placement of pharmacists, physician assistants and nurse practitioners.
Functions: Physicians, Nurses, Allied health, Health admin.
Industries: Healthcare

Branches:
P.O. Box 711
Madison, Wisconsin 53701-0711
(800) 799-5339
Fax: (608) 251-6660
Key Contact - Specialty:
Mr. Kevin J. Mero - *Pharmacy, physicians assistant, nurse practitioners*

InSearch

P.O. Box 8110
Aspen, Colorado 81612
(970) 920-2221
Fax: (970) 920-6767
Email: thirsch@insearch.com
Web: www.insearch.com

Key Contact - Specialty:
Mr. Tom Hirsch - *Mechanical engineering (new product design & development),industrial design (new product design & development)*

Description: Expertise in product development/design, with special expertise in mechanical engineering in consumer and medical device. Focusing on electronics and high technology.
Functions: Product dev., Engineering
Industries: Medical devices, Computer equip., Consumer electronics, Entertainment, Telecoms, High tech, Software

The Inside Track

504 Hilltop Drive, Ste. 200
Weatherford, Texas 76086-5724
(817) 599-7094
Fax: (817) 596-0807
Email: trak1@airmail.net
Web: www.refreq.com/inside.htm

Key Contact - Specialty:
Mr. Matthew B. DiLorenzo - *High technology engineering, telecommunications, software, I & C*
Mr. Robert L. Presley - *Plastics*
Mr. Michael H. Moore - *Wireless RF, cellular managers, sales, marketing*
Mr. George N. Stokes - *Software engineers, programmers*

Description: Owner is a degreed engineer. After a successful career, his strong technical background and extensive contacts in the national and international technical arena have made him the recruiter of choice for many corporations at the cutting edge of technology.

Salary Minimum: $45,000
Functions: Senior mgmt., Middle mgmt., Plant mgmt., Mktg. mgmt., Sales mgmt., IT, Engineering
Industries: Medical devices, Consumer electronics, New media, Telecoms, Packaging, High tech, Software

Insight Consulting Co.

P.O. Box 283
East Norwich, New York 11732
(516) 624-0348
Fax: (516) 624-0349

Key Contact - Specialty:
Mr. Alfred J. Arsenault - *Healthcare, pharmaceutical*

Description: Executive search services in the pharmaceutical and healthcare industry for marketing, advertising and sales. Clients include pharmaceutical companies, their ad agencies, medical education and project houses and medical publishers. Contacts coast to coast.
Functions: Middle mgmt., Advertising, Mkt. research, Mktg. mgmt., Sales mgmt., Direct mktg., PR
Industries: Drugs mfg., Medical devices

Insight Personnel Group, Inc.

5701 Woodway, Ste. 300
Houston, Texas 77057
(713) 784-4200
Fax: (713) 784-3040
Email: insight@nol.net
Web: www.insightpersonnel.com

Key Contact - Specialty:
Mr. David P. Richards - *Computer industry, high technology*
Ms. Joni K. Richards

Description: Primarily cover Texas with emphasis on computer technology and oil & gas search/placement.

Salary Minimum: $40,000
Functions: Sales mgmt., IT, MIS mgmt., Systems anal., Systems dev., Systems implem., Systems support
Industries: Energy/utilities, Computer svcs., High tech, Software

Insurance Career Center, Inc.

1280 Blue Hills Ave.
Bloomfield, Connecticut 06002
(860) 726-9133
Fax: (860) 726-9148

Key Contact - Specialty:
Ms. Linda Kiner - *Insurance*

Description: Recruit and place experienced insurance personnel - countrywide - with a high concentration in New England - handle mainly property and casualty insurance positions.

Salary Minimum: $25,000
Functions: Senior mgmt., Middle mgmt., Personnel, Risk mgmt.
Industries: Insurance

Insurance People
(Firm declined to update.)
P.O. Box 55171
Indianapolis, Indiana 46205
(317) 253-2128

Key Contact - Specialty:
Mr. George R. McMath - *Property & casualty insurance*
Ms. Katherine Hesselgrave - *Life & health insurance*

Description: All staff members have worked in the insurance industry. George McMath is a charter member of the Central Indiana Underwriters Association.
Functions: Directors, Senior mgmt., Middle mgmt., Admin. svcs.
Industries: Insurance

Insurance Personnel Resources, Inc.
8097-B Roswell Rd.
Atlanta, Georgia 30350
(770) 730-0701
Fax: (770) 730-0703
Email: blerch@mindspring.com
Web: www.insurancepersonnel.net/

Key Contact - Specialty:
Mr. Brent Lerch - *Insurance (property & casualty, life & health)*

Description: All professional, managerial and technical jobs in the insurance and employee benefit consulting fields and healthcare.

Salary Minimum: $25,000
Functions: General mgmt., Sales & mktg., HR mgmt., Finance, IT
Industries: Insurance, Healthcare

Branches:
2076 Old Grandview Rd.
Jasper, Georgia 30143
(706) 692-7391
Fax: (706) 692-7392
Key Contact - Specialty:
Mr. John Ector - *Insurance, life, health*

209 Tremont Circle
Chapel Hill, North Carolina 27516
(919) 933-4788
Fax: (919) 933-4789
Email: jrpfeiffer@mindspring
Key Contact - Specialty:
Mr. Joseph Pfeiffer - *Insurance, healthcare*

Insurance Recruiting Specialists
115 N. Center St.
Pickerington, Ohio 43147
(614) 834-3900
Fax: (614) 834-4983
Email: irsohio@aol.com

Key Contact - Specialty:
Mr. Steve Barker - *Insurance*

Description: Specializing in the recruitment of underwriting, marketing and claims and loss control personnel in the Midwest region of the U.S. A small specialized firm which tailors the search to meet the clients needs.

Salary Minimum: $25,000
Functions: Generalist
Industries: Insurance

Insurance Search
P.O. Box 7354
The Woodlands, Texas 77387
(281) 367-0137
(281) 367-3742
Fax: (281) 367-3842
Email: rainbowjobs@pdq.net
Web: www.rainbowjobs.com

Key Contact - Specialty:
Mr. Bert Dionne - *Insurance*
Ms. Wanda Hodges - *Insurance*

Description: Property and casualty, risk management, life and health insurance positions. All levels.

Salary Minimum: $30,000
Functions: Health admin., Mktg. mgmt., Sales mgmt., Benefits, Finance, CFO's, Risk mgmt.
Industries: Insurance, Healthcare

InTech Services, Inc.
5093 Shadow Glen Court
Dunwoody, Georgia 30338
(770) 481-0920
Fax: (770) 399-9790
Email: mth@mindspring.com

Key Contact - Specialty:
Mr. Mark Hutts - *Information systems*

Description: Specialize in IS developers and consultants - candidates personally screened.

Salary Minimum: $40,000
Functions: Mkt. research, IT, MIS mgmt., Systems anal., Systems dev., Systems implem., Systems support
Industries: Generalist

Integrated Management Solutions
32 Broadway, Ste. 1200
New York, New York 10004-1609
(212) 509-7800
Fax: (212) 509-8347
Email: hspindel@intman.com

Key Contact - Specialty:
Mr. Howard Spindel - *Financial services*
Ms. Jeanine P. Kelly - *Financial services*
Mr. Michael E. Stupay - *Financial services*

Description: Serving the needs of the financial community with special emphasis on operations, accounting, regulatory, finance, sales, research and trading areas.
Functions: General mgmt., Finance, IT, Mgmt. consultants
Industries: Invest. banking, Brokers, Venture cap., Misc. financial, Accounting, Mgmt. consulting

---

Intelegra, Inc.
P.O. Box 505
Far Hills, New Jersey 07931-0505
(908) 876-5900
(908) 231-1970
Fax: (908) 231-7909
Email: jpalmer111@interactive.net
Web: www.intelegra.com

Key Contact - Specialty:
Mr. John A. Palmer - *Information technology*

Description: Provides technical help for the information technology marketplace including technical sales people, system engineers, programmers, project managers and executive consultants. All placements are guaranteed.

Salary Minimum: $45,000
Functions: Senior mgmt., Sales mgmt., MIS mgmt., Systems anal., Systems dev., Systems implem., Systems support
Industries: Computer equip., Computer svcs., Telecoms, High tech, Software

---

Intelligent Marketing Solutions, Inc.
200 Park Ave. S., Ste. 518
New York, New York 10003
(212) 420-9777
Email: LSO@notanoxymoron.com
Web: www.notanoxymoron.com

Key Contact - Specialty:
Ms. Linda Sedloff Orton - *Marketing, communications, public relations*

Description: A former in-house marketing director with 10+ years experience for leading firms in NY and London, I will find you your best marketing match.

Salary Minimum: $50,000

Functions: Legal, Sales & mktg., Advertising, Mkt. research, Mktg. mgmt., PR, Non-profits
Industries: Svcs., Non-profits, Legal, Accounting, Mgmt. consulting, Advertising/PR, New media

---

IntelliSearch

17218 Preston Rd., Ste. 400
Dallas, Texas 75252
(972) 735-3199
Fax: (972) 735-3198
Email: bjhsearch@aol.com

Key Contact - Specialty:
Mr. Bradford J. Hopson - *Mortgage banking, mortgage finance*

Description: We provide high-impact executive search services at the highest standards of honesty, integrity and professionalism.

Salary Minimum: $40,000
Functions: Senior mgmt., Middle mgmt., Admin. svcs., Mktg. mgmt., Sales mgmt., Risk mgmt.
Industries: Misc. financial

IntelliSource, inc.

P.O. Box 106
Narberth, Pennsylvania 19072
(610) 617-8873
Fax: (610) 617-8874
Email: intlsrce@bellatlantic.net

Key Contact - Specialty:
Ms. Carolyn Dougherty - *Information systems*

Description: Knowledge of and retainment by desirable, growth oriented companies within the Delaware Valley. Ability to honestly, without bias, advise candidates of strong career moves within information technology. Our clients look for strong technical knowledge along with rapid career growth.

Salary Minimum: $40,000
Functions: MIS mgmt., Systems anal., Systems dev., Systems implem., Systems support
Industries: Mfg., Finance, Pharmaceutical svcs., Mgmt. consulting, High tech, Software, Healthcare

---

Inter Regional Executive Search, Inc. (IRES, Inc.)

191 Hamburg Tnpk.
Pompton Lakes, New Jersey 07442
(201) 616-8800
Fax: (201) 616-8115
Email: IRES@erols.com
Web: www.NJcareers.com

Key Contact - Specialty:
Mr. Frank G. Risalvato - *Insurance, accounting*
Mr. Randall Johnson - *Chemistry, scientific*

Description: Nationwide, concentration in the Northeastern U.S. Featured in national publications and internationally on CNBC. Recognized for consistent track record of filling positions at management and executive levels. Call for 8 page brochure.

Salary Minimum: $50,000
Functions: Middle mgmt., Product dev., Quality, Sales mgmt., CFO's, R&D, Engineering
Industries: Chemicals, Soap/perfume/cosmetics, Drugs mfg., Medical devices, Consumer electronics, Pharmaceutical svcs., Insurance

Affiliates:
IRES Temps, Inc.

Interactive Search Assoc.

P.O. Box 1803
Southeastern, Pennsylvania 19399-1803
(610) 630-3670
Fax: (610) 630-3678
Email: jzsenior@jobswitch.com
Web: www.jobswitch.com

Key Contact - Specialty:
Mr. John P. Zerkle, Sr.

Description: Executive search firm, in business over 25 years, with account executives specializing in sales, financial, administrative, technical, insurance, EDP and healthcare areas.

Salary Minimum: $50,000
Functions: Generalist, Production, Mkt. research, Mktg. mgmt., Sales mgmt., MIS mgmt., Engineering
Industries: Chemicals, Paints/petroleum products, Machinery/Appliances, Test/measurement equip., Computer svcs., Insurance, Healthcare

---

Intercontinental Executive Group

674 Louis Drive
The Vogel Bldg.
Warminster, Pennsylvania 18974
(215) 957-9012
Fax: (215) 957-6090
Email: dgweir@aol.com
Web: dgweir.com

Key Contact - Specialty:
Mr. David G. Weir

Description: National/international practice exclusively serving the electrical power generation marketplace industries: utilities, developers, owners, operators, environmental services, legal, project finance, equipment suppliers, AE & EPC firms, etc.

Salary Minimum: $60,000
Functions: Generalist, Senior mgmt., Middle mgmt., Plant mgmt., Sales mgmt., Engineering, Int'l.
Industries: Generalist, Energy/utilities, Construction, Machinery/Appliances, Misc. mfg., Equip. svcs., Non-classifiable industries

---

Interim Accounting Professionals

200 Pringle Ave., Ste. 325
Walnut Creek, California 94596
(925) 934-7092
Fax: (925) 934-2011
Email: trishawilliams@interim.com
Web: www.interim.com\accounting

Key Contact - Specialty:
Ms. Kris Norris - *Finance, accounting*
Ms. Trish Williams - *Finance, accounting*

Description: Experienced professionals specializing in accounting and finance. Nationwide network - fully computerized.

Salary Minimum: $30,000
Functions: CFO's, Budgeting, Cash mgmt., Credit, Taxes, M&A, Risk mgmt.
Industries: Generalist, Food/bev/tobacco, Computer equip., Finance, Environmental svcs., High tech, Biotech

Branches:
18400 Von Karman Ave., Ste. 920
Irvine, California 92715
(714) 756-1028
Fax: (714) 756-1225
Key Contact - Specialty:
Mr. Mark Behrens - *Finance, accounting*

9255 Towne Center Drive, Ste. 150
San Diego, California 92121
(619) 458-9200
Fax: (619) 458-1830
Key Contact - Specialty:
Mr. Rob Burton - *Finance, accounting*

44 Montgomery St., Ste. 870
San Francisco, California 94104
(415) 391-0200
Fax: (415) 391-0280
Key Contact - Specialty:
Ms. Hillary Shor - *Finance, accounting*

181 Metro Drive, Ste. 380
San Jose, California 95110
(408) 452-1700
Fax: (408) 436-1666
Key Contact - Specialty:
Ms. Staci Taylor - *Finance, accounting*

7777 Glades Rd., Ste. 212
Boca Raton, Florida 33434
(407) 487-4800
Fax: (407) 487-3598
Key Contact - Specialty:
Mr. Andrew Pober - *Finance, accounting*

2600 Douglas Rd.
Coral Gables, Florida 33134
(305) 444-9900
Fax: (305) 444-9160
Key Contact - Specialty:
Mr. Jorge Sanchez - *Finance, accounting*

1 Financial Plaza, Ste. 1514
Ft. Lauderdale, Florida 33394
(954) 462-6979
Fax: (954) 462-6885
Key Contact - Specialty:
Mr. Mitchel Kramer - *Finance, accounting*

6710 Main St., Ste 234
Miami Lakes, Florida 33014
(305) 558-1700
Fax: (305) 558-5772
Key Contact - Specialty:
Mr. Andrew Zalman - *Finance, accounting*

130 Atlanta Financial Center N.
3353 Peachtree Rd. NE
Atlanta, Georgia 30326
(404) 364-4661
Fax: (404) 364-4650
Key Contact - Specialty:
Ms. Sandra Roberson

3630 IDS Ctr., 80 S. Eighth St.
Minneapolis, Minnesota 55402
(612) 339-7663
Fax: (612) 339-9274
Key Contact - Specialty:
Ms. Carol Miletti - *Finance, accounting*

8222 Douglas, Ste. 220
Dallas, Texas 75225
(214) 691-9471
Fax: (214) 691-8976
Key Contact - Specialty:
Mr. Curtis Ludwig

5179 Richmond Ave., Ste. 1020
Houston, Texas 77056
(713) 965-9191
Fax: (713) 629-0010
Key Contact - Specialty:
Mr. Steve Fenton - *Finance, accounting*

Interim Executive Recruiting

7000 Central Pkwy., Ste. 900
Atlanta, Georgia 30305
(770) 604-6000
Fax: (770) 604-6003
Email: mikeloftus@interim.com
Web: www.interim.com

Key Contact - Specialty:
Mr. Michael G. Loftus - *Manufacturing, logistics, engineering*

Description: We specialize in recruitment of positions in manufacturing, finance and engineering.

Salary Minimum: $30,000
Functions: Mfg., Production, Quality, Materials, HR mgmt., Finance, Engineering
Industries: Mfg., Machinery/Appliances, Motor vehicles, Misc. mfg., Retail, Finance, Telecoms

Interim Financial Solutions - Mid-Atlantic Region
(formerly A.J. Burton Group, Inc.)

120 E. Baltimore St., Ste. 2220
Baltimore, Maryland 21202
(410) 752-5244
Email: ifsbaltimore@interim.com
Web: www.interim.com

Key Contact - Specialty:
Mr. Carl A. J. Wright - *Finance & accounting*
Ms. Kimberly Cobb - *Administrative*
Mr. Brendan Courtney - *Banking, mortgage banking, technology*
Mr. Mitch Halbrich - *Finance & accounting*
Mr. Craig Walker - *Finance & accounting*

Description: Formerly A.J. Burton Group, we were acquired by Interim Services Inc. and assumed responsibility for the Mid-Atlantic region. Teaming up with them gave us access to the international resources of this rapidly growing industry leader.
Functions: General mgmt., Middle mgmt., Admin. svcs., Health admin., HR mgmt., Finance, IT
Industries: Energy/utilities, Mfg., Finance, Svcs., Real estate, High tech, Healthcare

Branches:
1625 K. St. NW. Ste. 975
Washington, District of Columbia 20006
(202) 463-4500
Key Contact - Specialty:
Mr. Mark Tootsey - *Finance & accounting*

4550 Montgomery Ave., Ste 325 N.
Bethesda, Maryland 20814
(301) 654-0082
Key Contact - Specialty:
Mr. Mark A. Tootsey - *Finance & accounting*

9891 Broken Land Pkwy., Ste. 401
Columbia, Maryland 21046
(410) 290-5755
Key Contact - Specialty:
Mr. Mitch Halbrich - *Finance & accounting*

1595 Spring Hill Rd., Ste. 220
Vienna, Virginia 22182
(703) 790-1100
Key Contact - Specialty:
Mr. Ron Sall - *Finance, accounting, technical*
Mr. Barry Goldstein - *Finance, accounting, technical*

Affiliates:
StratfordGroup

Interim Management Resources Inc.

420 Brittania Rd. E., Ste. 208
Mississauga, Ontario L4Z 3L5
Canada
(905) 507-4662
Email: quality1@idirect.com

Key Contact - Specialty:
Dr. R. J. Nicholls - *Manufacturing, engineering, finance*
Mr. D. C. Crosbie - *Manufacturing, engineering, aerospace, mining, international*
Mr. Nicholas Hogya - *Senior management*
Mr. Donald E. Gordon - *Consulting & contract employees*
Mr. Bradley Dix - *Middle management specialist*

Description: We are a human resources/career management consulting firm with extensive experience in conducting effective executive recruitment programs.

Salary Minimum: $40,000
Functions: Middle mgmt., Plant mgmt., Mkt. research, Benefits, Cash mgmt., Engineering, Int'l.
Industries: Agri/forestry/mining, Mfg., Printing, Metal products, Motor vehicles, Misc. mfg., Aerospace

Affiliates:
Northern Vocational Services

International Business Partners

221 Balliol St., Ste. 1714
Toronto, Ontario M4S 1C8
Canada
(416) 322-3324
Fax: (416) 322-3360
Email: intlbus@mail.ican.net

Key Contact - Specialty:
Mr. Les Keremelevich

Description: Our experience covers conventional assignments with small companies to major complex, and highly sophisticated projects spanning a cross-section of industries using our unique personalised approach.
Functions: Plant mgmt., Packaging, Direct mktg., Training, Risk mgmt., DB admin., Int'l.
Industries: Mfg., Finance, Communications, Environmental svcs., Packaging, Software, Healthcare

International Consulting Services, Inc.

541 Castlewood Lane
Buffalo Grove, Illinois 60089
(847) 537-1611
Fax: (847) 541-1899

Key Contact - Specialty:
Mr. Peter A. Sendler - *Engineers, physicists, computer scientists, applied mathematicians, management*

Description: Key experienced technical performers in R&D nationally with no advertising and with great consideration for corporate culture match and technology interleaving; based on 25+ years of hands on involvement.

Salary Minimum: $65,000
Functions: Senior mgmt., Middle mgmt., Sales mgmt., Systems dev., R&D, Engineering
Industries: Medical devices, Computer equip., Test/measurement equip., Telecoms, Defense, High tech, Software

International Executive Recruiters

157 W. Cedar St., Ste. B-16
Akron, Ohio 44307
(330) 376-1000
Fax: (330) 376-1936
Email: recruitus@recruitus.com
Web: www.recruitus.com

Key Contact - Specialty:
Mr. David Fitzgibbons - *Sales, marketing, information technology*
Mr. Thomas Haller - *Sales, marketing and financial*

Description: Executive placement firm specializing in the toy and consumer products industries. Client list includes numerous Fortune 500 companies. Expertise in CEO and Vice President level searches. Firm offers personal service, is aggressive, and ethical.

Salary Minimum: $45,000
Functions: Directors, Senior mgmt., Plant mgmt., Mktg. mgmt., Sales mgmt., CFO's, MIS mgmt.
Industries: Energy/utilities, Soap/perfume/cosmetics, Plastics/rubber, Misc. mfg., Banking, High tech, Software

International Management Development Corp.

6 Maplewood Drive
Bellport, New York 11713
(516) 286-1060
Fax: (516) 286-3188
Email: RonDavis77@aol.com

Key Contact - Specialty:
Mr. Ronald Davis - *Global logistics, supply chain management, total quality management, project management, engineering*

Description: We can staff, operate and manage your overseas projects with high quality, professional US, European and third country national staff.

Salary Minimum: $50,000
Functions: Mfg., Materials, Purchasing, Distribution, Engineering, Specialized services, Int'l.
Industries: Generalist, Energy/utilities, Construction, Mfg., Transportation, Svcs., Government

International Market Recruiters

1140 Ave. of the Americas, 6th Floor
New York, New York 10036
(212) 819-9100
Fax: (212) 354-9476
Email: imr@imr-recruiters.com
Web: www.imr-recruiters.com

Key Contact - Specialty:
Mr. Joseph M. Sullivan - *Financial services*

Description: We specialize in both permanent and temporary placements in the international financial service industries. We have earned a reputation for excellence in finding staff that resolve current situations, as well as becoming important decision makers for our clients.
Functions: Cash mgmt., Risk mgmt., Systems support
Industries: Banking, Invest. banking, Brokers, Misc. financial

Branches:
112 S. Tryon St.
Charlotte, North Carolina 28202
(704) 334-1044
Fax: (704) 334-1011
Key Contact - Specialty:
Mr. James Marchetti - *Financial services*

1800 John F. Kennedy Blvd.
Philadelphia, Pennsylvania 19103
(215) 981-0488
Fax: (215) 981-0988
Email: imr@imr-recruiters.com
Web: www.imr-recruiters.com
Key Contact - Specialty:
Mr. Douglas Wong - *Financial services*

International Pro Sourcing, Inc.

407 Executive Drive
Langhorne, Pennsylvania 19047
(215) 968-7666
Email: admin@prosourcing.com

Key Contact - Specialty:
Ms. Ann Harris - *Sales*
Ms. Mary Crane - *Sales*
Ms. Joan Gallagher - *Sales*
Ms. Kelly Gallagher - *Sales*

Description: We are highly ethical contingency recruiters specializing in the placement of thoroughly screened and qualified candidates in high technology, pharmaceutical and medical sales positions for top notch U.S. companies.
Functions: Mkt. research, Sales mgmt., Systems anal., Systems dev., Systems implem., Systems support, Network admin.
Industries: Pharmaceutical svcs., High tech, Software, Biotech, Healthcare

International Recruiting Services

P.O. Drawer 533976
Orlando, Florida 32853
(407) 896-9606
Fax: (407) 896-9191
Email: intlrs@aol.com

Key Contact - Specialty:
Mr. Mell D. Leonard - *Agriculture, horticulture, floriculture, and all allied industries*

Description: Although we had our start in 1950, Mell D. Leonard has been in business for 48 years and has had experience in all phases of employment, including, speaking, seminars and is legal expert on employment issues.

Salary Minimum: $35,000
Functions: General mgmt., Middle mgmt., Purchasing, Direct mktg., R&D, Environmentalists, Architects
Industries: Agri/forestry/mining, Construction, Wholesale, Retail, Hospitality, Environmental svcs., Haz. waste

International Staffing Consultants, Inc.

2010 Main St., Ste. 840
Irvine, California 92614-7224
(949) 263-5200
Fax: (949) 263-5201
Email: iscinc@iscworld.com
Web: www.iscworld.com

Key Contact - Specialty:
Mr. James R. Gettys
Mr. Ian A. Thomas

Description: Technical/professional people for most industries with emphasis on international or overseas jobs. Also human resources professionals for all industries. Also, wireless communications.

Salary Minimum: $35,000
Functions: Mfg., Sales & mktg., HR mgmt., IT, Engineering, Architects, Int'l.
Industries: Generalist, Energy/utilities, Construction, Mfg., Human resource svcs., Telecoms, High tech

International Branches:
Hampshire

International Technical Resources

725 N. AIA
Suite D-106
Jupiter, Florida 33477
(561) 743-7006
(561) 745-9551
Fax: (561) 743-3111

Email: terryitr@aol.com

Key Contact - Specialty:
Mr. Terry L. Funk - *Information technology*

Description: Two division firm, one dedicated to mid-upper level software development professionals, one division dedicated to sales, marketing, implementation professionals. Extremely confidential and thorough.

Salary Minimum: $50,000
Functions: Mkt. research, Mktg. mgmt., Sales mgmt., Systems anal., Systems dev., Systems implem., Network admin.
Industries: High tech, Software

InterNeed
2900 Weslayan, Ste. 555
Houston, Texas 77027
(713) 626-9233
Fax: (713) 626-9291
Web: www.interneed.com

Key Contact - Specialty:
Mr. David Balzen - *Sales & management*

Description: We are a full service business development service provider. Services include sales and management recruiting, marketing, advertising, market research, web site development and lead generation programs.
Functions: Advertising, Mkt. research, Mktg. mgmt., Sales mgmt., Direct mktg., PR, Graphic artists

---

Interspace Interactive, Inc.
50 E. 42nd St., Ste. 2400
New York, New York 10017
(212) 867-6661
Fax: (212) 867-6682
Email: info@interspaceinc.com
Web: www.interspaceinc.com

Key Contact - Specialty:
Mr. Bill Ellis - *Sales*

Description: Our primary focus is to identify and provide outstanding candidates for our clients. We target individuals with sales experience in advertising, financial, office products, services, information systems and telecommunications, pharmaceuticals.
Functions: Advertising, Sales mgmt., Direct mktg.
Industries: Drugs mfg., Computer equip., Banking, Advertising/PR, Publishing, Telecoms

---

Iona Partners
588 Chestnut St., Ste. 100
San Francisco, California 94133
(888) 818-IONA
Fax: (415) 576-0924
Email: mail@ionapartners.com
Web: www.ionapartners.com

Key Contact - Specialty:
Ms. Carol Haverty - *Biotechnology, pharmaceuticals*
Mr. Sean Kelly - *Semiconductor*
Mr. Pat McCutcheon - *Information technology, financial*

Description: Our slogan is, Not your average candidates, not your average search firm. This is because we attract a disproportionate number of unusually, talented, professionally accomplished individuals, particularly in science and engineering, largely because of our consultants' backgrounds and the quality of our client companies.
Functions: General mgmt., Mfg., Product dev., Sales & mktg., IT, Systems anal., R&D
Industries: Medical devices, Banking, Invest. banking, Pharmaceutical svcs., Equip. svcs., High tech, Biotech

---

IprGroup, Inc.
8097 B Roswell Rd.
Atlanta, Georgia 30350
(770) 396-7500
Fax: (770) 396-7510
Email: iprgroup@mindspring.com

Key Contact - Specialty:
Mr. Richard C. Gay - *Human resources*

Description: Focus primarily in SE but work nationally as a human resource generalist and specialist in all industries including corporate risk and safety management.

Salary Minimum: $30,000
Functions: HR mgmt., Benefits, Personnel, Training
Industries: Generalist

Joan Isbister Consultants
350 W. 20th St.
New York, New York 10011
(212) 243-8733
Fax: (212) 255-3395

Key Contact - Specialty:
Ms. Joan Isbister

Description: Graphics and printing industries specialists; professional searches in management, marketing and sales.

Salary Minimum: $30,000
Functions: Senior mgmt., Middle mgmt., Plant mgmt., Sales mgmt., Customer svc.
Industries: Printing

ISC of Atlanta, Inc.
4350 Georgetown Sq., Ste. 707
Atlanta, Georgia 30338
(770) 458-4180
Fax: (770) 458-4131
Email: iscatl@mindspring.com

Key Contact - Specialty:
Mr. Arthur Kwapisz - *Technical management, manufacturing, engineering*
Mr. William Konrad - *Accounting & finance management, sales, industrial*

Description: Successfully meeting the challenges of our changing industry while striving to do business in a friendly and fair way, we push towards gaining the respect and confidence of our clients, candidates and colleagues.

Salary Minimum: $35,000
Functions: Senior mgmt., Middle mgmt., Plant mgmt., Sales mgmt., CFO's, R&D, Engineering
Industries: Generalist, Energy/utilities, Food/bev/tobacco, Chemicals, Drugs mfg., Misc. mfg., Biotech

---

ISC of Cincinnati Inc.
130 Tri-County Pkwy., Ste. 205
Cincinnati, Ohio 45246-3235
(513) 771-4484
Fax: (513) 771-6662

Key Contact - Specialty:
Mr. David J. Poeppelmeier - *Chemicals, coatings*
Mr. Kenneth Brown - *Packaging*
Mr. Michael L. Myers - *Graphics*
Ms. Phyllis E. Smith - *Healthcare*
Mr. A.E. Putnam - *Packaging, pop*

Description: Over sixty years of experience in executive recruiting (coatings, packaging, graphics and healthcare industries).
Functions: Senior mgmt., Middle mgmt., Plant mgmt., Nurses, Health admin., Mktg. mgmt., Sales mgmt.
Industries: Mfg., Paper, Printing, Paints/petroleum products, Packaging, Healthcare

---

ISC of Houston, Inc.
16800 Imperial Valley Drive, Ste. 220
Houston, Texas 77060
(281) 847-0050
Fax: (281) 847-1357
Email: isch1@flash.net

Key Contact - Specialty:
Ms. Karen Burke - *Healthcare*
Mr. Bob Bennett - *Home building (single family/multi family)*

Description: We understand and speak the language of the home building and healthcare industry. Through our national network and superior reputation, we can complete assignments in a timely and cost effective manner.

Salary Minimum: $40,000

Functions: Directors, Senior mgmt., Middle mgmt., Purchasing, Mktg. mgmt., Sales mgmt., CFO's
Industries: Construction, Misc. financial, Accounting, Real estate, Healthcare

ISG Informatics Search Group

5045 Orbitor Drive, Bldg. 7, Ste. 200
Mississauga, Ontario L4W 4Y5
Canada
(905) 602-6085
Fax: (905) 602-6091
Email: resumes@isgjobs.com
Web: www.isgjobs.com

Key Contact - Specialty:
Mr. Frank Vrabel - *Information technology*
Mr. Paul Bottero - *Operations and development*
Mr. Vincent Michaels
Mr. Peter Baxter - *Information technology*
Ms. Andrea Guinn - *Information technology*

Description: We provide full time and contractual information technology personnel to mid to large sized companies. We place all types of IT professionals in various industries across North America.
Functions: MIS mgmt., Systems anal., Systems dev., Systems implem., Systems support, Network admin., DB admin.
Industries: Mfg., Finance, Svcs., Communications, High tech, Software, Biotech

Ann Israel & Assoc., Inc.

730 Fifth Ave., Ste. 900
New York, New York 10019
(212) 333-8730
Fax: (212) 765-4462
Email: israel@ljextra.com
Web: www.attorneysearch.com

Key Contact - Specialty:
Ms. Ann M. Israel - *Attorneys*

Description: Serving the global legal community with broad range of services to law firms and corporations including lateral placements of partners/associates, mergers/acquisitions of practice groups and management advisory services.

Salary Minimum: $100,000
Functions: Attorneys
Industries: Legal

Ives & Associates, Inc.

471 E. Broad St., Ste. 2010
Columbus, Ohio 43215
(614) 228-0202
Fax: (614) 228-0830
Email: ivesheads@worldnet.att.net

Key Contact - Specialty:
Ms. Phyllis E. Ives - *Human resources, marketing*

Description: We endeavor to form a partnership with our clients. By working together we can find that individual who will fit within our clients particular corporate culture.

Salary Minimum: $40,000
Functions: PR, HR mgmt., Finance, CFO's, IT, MIS mgmt., Systems anal.
Industries: Retail, Finance, Banking, Invest. banking, Human resource svcs., Advertising/PR, Telecoms

J & D Resources Inc.

6555 Quince Road, Ste. 425
Memphis, Tennessee 38119
(901) 753-0500
Fax: (901) 753-0550
Email: jdrmail@jdresources.com
Web: www.jdresources.com

Key Contact - Specialty:
Ms. Jill T. Herrin - *Information technology*
Mr. Danny L. McKinney - *Information technology*

Description: We present only the most qualified applicants for your review. We ensure that these individuals are interested in the opportunity you have to offer. Our overall commitment is to you - to find the people that will contribute to your success.

Salary Minimum: $25,000
Functions: MIS mgmt., Systems anal., Systems dev., Systems implem., Systems support, Network admin., DB admin.
Industries: Generalist

J. B. Linde & Assoc.

1415 Elbridge Payne Rd., Ste. 148
Chesterfield, Missouri 63017
(314) 532-8040
Fax: (314) 532-0320

Key Contact - Specialty:
Mr. Roy Kessler - *Manufacturing management, engineering*

Description: Technical, management and executive recruiting in the manufacturing arena.

Salary Minimum: $40,000
Functions: Senior mgmt., Production, Automation, Plant mgmt., Quality, Purchasing, Materials Plng.
Industries: Medical devices, Metal products, Machinery/Appliances, Motor vehicles, Computer equip., Test/measurement equip., Misc. mfg.

The J. B. Search Group

2518 Tuscany Way
Fullerton, California 92835
(714) 871-6470
Fax: (714) 871-6619
Email: j.m.declouet@aol.com

Key Contact - Specialty:
Mr. J. Michael DeClouet - *Sales, marketing, middle management, directors*

Description: We conduct targeted searches that save our clients time and money. We help our clients find professionals that make an immediate impact.

Salary Minimum: $70,000
Functions: Middle mgmt., Purchasing, Mkt. research, Mktg. mgmt., Sales mgmt., Customer svc., Minorities
Industries: Food/bev/tobacco, Textiles/apparel, Soap/perfume/cosmetics, Plastics/rubber, Paints/petroleum products, Misc. mfg., Packaging

J. Joseph & Assoc.

3809 Darrow Rd.
Stow, Ohio 44224
(330) 688-2101
Fax: (330) 688-1922
Email: jjosephs@msn.com
Web: jjosephrecruiter.com

Key Contact - Specialty:
Mr. Scott Raymont - *Sales*
Mr. Joe McGoldrick - *Sales*
Ms. Carolyn James - *Sales*

Description: Our firm specializes in field sales staffing for USA. Our clients are exclusive to us. Our focus is national.

Salary Minimum: $28,000
Functions: Generalist, Production, Advertising, Mkt. research, MIS mgmt., Systems anal., Engineering
Industries: Generalist, Paper, Printing, Medical devices, Computer equip.

J. R. Scott & Assoc., Ltd.
(a division of Esquire Personnel Services, Inc.)

One S. Wacker Drive, Ste. 1616
Chicago, Illinois 60606-4616
(312) 795-4400
Fax: (312) 795-4329
Email: esqscott@wwa.com

Key Contact - Specialty:
Mr. Joseph Trendl - *Financial, securities & banking*
Mr. Sherwin J. Fischer - *Retail brokerage*

Description: We are the executive search division of The Esquire Companies. Our consultants have a history of locating and motivating some of the most prestigious professionals in the financial services arena both on LaSalle Street and across the country including complete office staffings.
Functions: Directors, Senior mgmt., Mkt. research, Sales mgmt., Cash mgmt., M&A, Risk mgmt.

Industries: Finance, Banking, Invest. banking, Brokers, Venture cap., Misc. financial

---

J.N. Adams & Assoc., Inc.

301 S. Allen St., Ste. 103A
State College, Pennsylvania 16801
(814) 234-0670
Email: jnadams@naccess.net
Web: www.state-college.com/jnadams/

Key Contact - Specialty:
Mr. Eric M. Berg - *Quality assurance, reliability, statisticians*

Description: We are an executive recruitment firm specializing in the nationwide recruitment of quality assurance/reliability professionals and statisticians.
Functions: Quality
Industries: Medical devices, Plastics/rubber, Metal products, Motor vehicles

---

Jackley Search Consultants

Ridge Run Office Ctr.
14581 Grand Ave. S.
Burnsville, Minnesota 55306-5769
(612) 831-2344
Fax: (612) 831-9101
Email: jackl1@ix.netcom.com
Web: www.cities-online.com/jackley/

Key Contact - Specialty:
Mr. Brian D. Jackley - *Engineering, engineering management*

Description: Twelve years of experience recruiting engineers, scientists and technical managers for national manufacturing firms. Our clients are involved in researching, developing and manufacturing highly technical devices and systems.

Salary Minimum: $50,000
Functions: Product dev., Production, Automation, Plant mgmt., Quality, R&D, Engineering
Industries: Medical devices, Plastics/rubber, Machinery/Appliances, Computer equip., Test/measurement equip.

Ron Jackson & Assoc.

4405 Mall Blvd., Ste. 315, Shannon Twrs.
Union City, Georgia 30291
(770) 969-6300
Fax: (770) 969-4333
Email: RJacksonandassoc@Prodigy.net

Key Contact - Specialty:
Mr. Ron Jackson - *Generalist*

Description: Our 25 years of HR generalist experience, which included staffing at all levels, gives us the ability to provide superior service to our clients. We offer expert handling of a variety of assignments and we offer access to a broad range of diversity candidates.

Salary Minimum: $50,000
Functions: Generalist, Senior mgmt., Middle mgmt., Plant mgmt., Sales mgmt., CFO's, Minorities
Industries: Generalist, Food/bev/tobacco, Textiles/apparel, Misc. mfg., Entertainment, Accounting, Telecoms

---

Jackson & Coker

1150 Hammond Drive, Suite A-1200
Atlanta, Georgia 30328
(770) 522-1890
(800) 272-2707
Fax: (770) 730-2870
Email: recruiting@jackson-coker.com
Web: www.jackson-coker.com

Key Contact - Specialty:
Mr. Steve Sullivan - *Physician, allied health professionals*

Description: Placing physicians, allied health professionals in hospitals, group practices, HMO's and other healthcare settings nationwide in both permanent and locum tenens positions.
Functions: Healthcare, Physicians, Nurses, Allied health, Health admin.
Industries: Healthcare

Jackson Group Int'l.

650 S. Cherry St., Ste. 610
Denver, Colorado 80246
(303) 321-3844
Fax: (303) 321-3551
Email: jacksongrp@msn.com
Web: www.jacksongrp.com

Key Contact - Specialty:
Mr. George E. Jackson - *Generalist practice for executive and professional level positions*

Description: We are a firm specializing in international and domestic executive, financial, human resources, engineering, environmental and information technology searches for client companies.

Salary Minimum: $35,000
Functions: Middle mgmt., Taxes, IT, Systems dev., Engineering, Int'l.
Industries: Agri/forestry/mining, Energy/utilities, Construction, Telecoms, Environmental svcs., High tech, Software

Affiliates:
Bushell & Cornish

Jacobson Assoc.

120 S. LaSalle St., Ste. 1410
Chicago, Illinois 60603
(312) 726-1578
Fax: (312) 726-2295
Email: chicago@jacobson-associates.com
Web: www.jacobson-associates.com

Key Contact - Specialty:
Mr. David Jacobson

Description: Since 1971, we have provided a cost effective resource to insurers and healthcare providers in their pursuit of obtaining the best qualified staff, management and executive personnel.

Salary Minimum: $20,000
Functions: Generalist, Senior mgmt., Physicians, Mktg. mgmt., Benefits, CFO's, Risk mgmt.
Industries: Insurance, Healthcare

Branches:
1775 The Exchange, Ste. 240
Atlanta, Georgia 30339
(770) 952-3877
Fax: (770) 952-0061
Key Contact - Specialty:
Mr. Gregory Jacobson - *Insurance*
Mr. John Baumann - *Physicians, healthcare*

Five Neshaminy Interplex, Ste. 113
Trevose, Pennsylvania 19053
(215) 639-5860
Fax: (215) 639-8096
Key Contact - Specialty:
Mr. Nate Bass - *Insurance*

K. Jaeger & Assoc.

60 Thoreau St., Ste. 300
Concord, Massachusetts 01742-9116
(978) 369-3352
Fax: (978) 369-0757

Key Contact - Specialty:
Mr. Karl Schoellkopf - *Industrial sales & marketing*

Description: Contingency search with a difference: thorough, consultative approach ensures efficient solutions to sales, marketing, engineering line and staff searches. Clients are suppliers of mechanical and electro-mechanical products, controls and capital equipment.

Salary Minimum: $40,000
Functions: Middle mgmt., Product dev., Production, Mkt. research, Mktg. mgmt., Sales mgmt., Customer svc.
Industries: Chemicals, Plastics/rubber, Metal products, Computer equip., Test/measurement equip., Aerospace, High tech

---

Jaeger Int'l., Inc.

(Firm declined to update.)
4889 Sinclair Rd., Ste. 112
Columbus, Ohio 43229
(614) 885-0364
Email: ilcook2@aol.com
Web: jaegerint.com

Key Contact - Specialty:
Mr. Ted Langley - *Automotive, manufacturing, technology based companies (technical, professional & managerial)*

Description: Full service staffing consultant specializing in technical, professional and managerial talent for automotive, manufacturing, telecommunications, castings, machining and technology-based companies. National in scope, primary focus in east of the Mississippi.

Salary Minimum: $35,000
Functions: Automation, Plant mgmt., Quality, Purchasing, Systems anal., Systems dev., Engineering
Industries: Plastics/rubber, Machinery/Appliances, Motor vehicles, Computer equip., Misc. mfg., Telecoms, High tech

R. I. James, Inc.
325 Riverside Drive, Ste. 54
New York, New York 10025-4156
(212) 662-0203
Fax: (212) 864-9602
Web: rijames@earthlink.net

Key Contact - Specialty:
Ms. Rhoda Isaacs - *Logistics (domestic & international)*

Description: Specialists in mid to senior level placement. Our client references reflect the highest standards of excellence. Recognized by the Council of Logistics Management for professional logistics recruitment.

Salary Minimum: $40,000
Functions: Directors, Senior mgmt., Middle mgmt., Purchasing, Materials Plng., Distribution, Engineering
Industries: Mfg., Transportation, Wholesale, Retail, Mgmt. consulting

James Moore & Assoc.
90 New Montgomery St., Ste. 412
San Francisco, California 94105
(415) 392-3933
Fax: (415) 896-0931
Email: info@jamesmoore.com
Web: www.jamesmoore.com

Key Contact - Specialty:
Mr. Leslie Fenyves - *Software engineering, information technology*

Description: Our search firm has thirteen years of experience in delivering well qualified computer professionals to a diverse mix of Bay area client companies.

Salary Minimum: $45,000
Functions: MIS mgmt., Systems anal., Systems dev., Systems implem., Systems support, Network admin., DB admin.
Industries: Computer equip., Finance, Computer svcs., High tech, Software, Biotech, Healthcare

David James Search
27315 Jefferson Avenue, Suite J
Temecula, California 92590
(909) 693-2555
Fax: (909) 693-2881
Email: mail@DavidJamessearch.com
Web: www.davidjamessearch.com

Key Contact - Specialty:
Mr. David James - *Internal audit, IS audit*

Description: We do not accept searches we cannot fill and have a 100% success record with our retained clients. Our purpose is to: be in service; network people and promote self worth. We take a very sincere approach to matching chemistry and corporate culture between clients and candidates.

Salary Minimum: $50,000
Functions: General mgmt., Sales & mktg., Finance, IT, MIS mgmt., Minorities

The Jameson Group
1900 Ave. of the Stars, Ste. 200
Los Angeles, California 90067
(310) 286-0220
Fax: (310) 286-0866
Email: tjg@ix.netcom.com

Key Contact - Specialty:
Mr. John B. Jameson - *Legal (attorneys)*

Description: We specialize in attorney recruiting and placement for law firms and corporations.

Salary Minimum: $70,000
Functions: Attorneys
Industries: Legal

Jaral Consultants, Inc.
P.O. Box 498
Springfield, New Jersey 07081
(973) 564-9236
Fax: (973) 379-1275

Key Contact - Specialty:
Mr. Joseph Morgan - *Fashion industry*

Description: We specialize in placing in the following areas; fashion, including designers, production, sales and all other technical and professional specialties specific to the fashion industry. Presidents and other top executives are our primary placements.

Salary Minimum: $50,000
Functions: Directors, Senior mgmt., Product dev., Production, Sales mgmt., Graphic artists
Industries: Textiles/apparel, Wholesale, Retail

JCL & Assoc.
P.O. Box 9541
Panama City, Florida 32417
(850) 230-1888
Fax: (850) 230-0888

Key Contact - Specialty:
Ms. Judy Lee

Description: Over 30 years in private placement, national and international. Highly specialized in mens, womens, childrens knitware and intimate apparel from sales/marketing, manufacturing/sourcing, financial, product development/design.

Salary Minimum: $30,000
Functions: Senior mgmt., Product dev., Plant mgmt., Distribution, Mkt. research, Sales mgmt., CFO's
Industries: Textiles/apparel

JDC Assoc.
300 Wheeler Rd., Ste.104
Hauppauge, New York 11788
(516) 231-8581
Fax: (516) 231-8011

Key Contact - Specialty:
Ms. Lori Boyle - *Sales, accounting, office support*

Description: Professional recruiting firm committed to identifying and isolating only the top 10% proven documented performers. Their success is due to their creativity, versatility and commitment to excellence in the marketplace.
Functions: Nurses, Allied health, Sales mgmt., Customer svc., Credit, Systems support, Network admin.
Industries: Generalist, Drugs mfg., Medical devices, Accounting, Healthcare

JDG Assoc., Ltd.
1700 Research Blvd.
Rockville, Maryland 20850
(301) 340-2210
Fax: (301) 762-3117
Email: degioia@jdgsearch.com
Web: www.jdgsearch.com

Key Contact - Specialty:
Mr. Joseph DeGioia - *Management consultants*

Description: Recruiters serving the disciplines of computer sciences, electronics, telecommunications engineering, management science and association management.

Salary Minimum: $50,000
Functions: Materials Plng., MIS mgmt., Systems anal., Systems implem., R&D, Engineering, Mgmt. consultants
Industries: Non-profits, Computer svcs., Mgmt. consulting, Defense, High tech, Software, Biotech

JDH & Assoc.
1014 S. Westlake Blvd., Ste. 14159
Westlake Village, California 91361
(818) 706-8464
Fax: (818) 706-8842

Email: jhannafin@aol.com

Key Contact - Specialty:
Mr. James D. Hannafin - *Entertainment (finance, sales, marketing, information systems)*

Description: Twenty-five years of diversified experience (CFO, EVP - marketing, sales, business affairs, division GM) in the entertainment industry provides a broad database of talent from studios to post production and multi-media.

Salary Minimum: $75,000
Functions: Senior mgmt., Middle mgmt., Sales mgmt., CFO's, M&A, MIS mgmt., Engineering
Industries: Entertainment, Communications, Advertising/PR, Publishing, New media, Broadcast & Film, Telecoms

Affiliates:
Security Search & Consulting, Inc.

Jefferson-Ross Assoc. Inc.
2 Penn Ctr. Plaza, Ste. 312
Philadelphia, Pennsylvania 19102
(215) 564-5322
Fax: (215) 587-0766
Email: cwlserch@itw.com

Key Contact - Specialty:
Mr. Craig Zander - *Generalist*

Description: Executive search assignments for professional/technical and mid-management individuals in financial services, insurance, healthcare, information systems and computer services industries nationwide. Over 25 years of experience in professional recruitment and search.

Salary Minimum: $40,000
Functions: Generalist, General mgmt., Sales & mktg., Sales mgmt., HR mgmt., Finance, IT
Industries: Generalist, Finance, Computer svcs., Insurance, Software, Healthcare

---

Jeffrey Allan Co., Inc.
2775 Via De La Valle, Ste. 200
Del Mar, California 92014
(800) 886-1522
(619) 792-8666
Fax: (619) 792-8991
Email: jacsearch@aol.com
Web: jeffreyallan.com

Key Contact - Specialty:
Mr. Jeffrey Conners
Ms. Norma Conners

Description: National and international executive search firm dedicated to meeting the changing needs of its clients. Jeffrey Allan Company continues to be the search firm of choice for today's top companies.

Salary Minimum: $50,000
Functions: Senior mgmt., Distribution, Sales & mktg., HR mgmt., Finance, IT, Int'l.
Industries: Mfg., Food/bev/tobacco, Consumer electronics, Retail, Hospitality, Entertainment, Broadcast & Film

---

Jeffrey Meryl Assoc., Inc.
1115 Inman Ave., Ste. 171
Edison, New Jersey 08820
(908) 889-6459
Fax: (908) 889-8818
Email: drien@jma-jobs.com
Web: www.jma-jobs.com

Key Contact - Specialty:
Mr. David Rien - *Information systems*

Description: We specialize in the recruitment and placement of information technology professionals in New Jersey and NYC.
Functions: IT, Systems anal., Systems dev., Systems implem., Systems support, Network admin., DB admin.
Industries: Drugs mfg., Computer equip., Banking, Invest. banking, Brokers, Computer svcs., Advertising/PR

Jenex Technology Placement Inc.
#104, 1260 Hornby St.
Vancouver, British Columbia V6Z 1W2
Canada
(604) 687-3585
Fax: (604) 687-5432
Email: jobs@jenex.bc.ca
Web: www.jenex.bc.ca

Key Contact - Specialty:
Ms. Jennifer Rigal - *High technology, software*
Ms. Allison Guld - *High technology, software*

Description: We are a Vancouver-based recruiter of Western Canada's leading advanced technology professionals. Including software development, programmers, database designers, systems architects and other technical specialists in the industry.

Salary Minimum: $30,000
Functions: Systems anal., Systems dev., Systems support, Network admin., DB admin.
Industries: High tech, Software

JenKim Int'l. Ltd., Inc.
7040 W. Palmetto Park Rd., Ste. 250
Boca Raton, Florida 33433
(954) 427-6962
Fax: (954) 427-0021
Email: jnkm@aol.com

Key Contact - Specialty:
Mr. Robert W. Norton - *Computer, telecommunications*
Ms. Kim Norton - *Telecommunications*
Mrs. Jennifer Johnson - *Telecommunications*

Description: We are a highly skilled and professional recruiting/search firm providing expert advice and assistance to those professionals seeking to advance their careers in the computer or telecommunications industry.
Functions: Senior mgmt., Middle mgmt., Personnel, CFO's, Systems anal., Systems dev.
Industries: Computer svcs., Human resource svcs., Broadcast & Film, Telecoms

---

Jerome & Co.
211 Culver Blvd., Ste. R
Playa Del Rey, California 90293
(310) 305-1812

Key Contact - Specialty:
Mr. Gerald E. Jerome - *Presidents, general managers & vice presidents (manufacturing companies on the West coast)*

Description: We recruit general managers, department managers and engineers for manufacturing companies on the West Coast.

Salary Minimum: $50,000
Functions: General mgmt., Senior mgmt., Middle mgmt., Mfg., Materials, CFO's, Engineering
Industries: Mfg., Defense, Aerospace

JFW Associates, LLC
1200 Boston Post Rd., Ste. 212
P.O. Box 267
Guilford, Connecticut 06437
(203) 458-7151
Fax: (203) 458-1347
Email: jobs@jfw.com
Web: www.jfw.com

Key Contact - Specialty:
John Wilbur - *Computer professionals*
Robert Vissers

Description: Retained and contingency search for computer professionals in IT, software engineering and technical specialties, with emphasis on applications programming, database and network design, support and administration.
Functions: IT, MIS mgmt., Systems anal., Systems dev., Systems implem., Systems support
Industries: Generalist, Computer svcs., Software

JL & Co.

3020 Bridgeway, Ste. 330
Sausalito, California 94965
(415) 331-9940
Email: jlco@msn.com

Key Contact - Specialty:
Mr. Jon R. Love - *Software, internet (marketing & business development)*

Description: Exclusive focus on finding marketing and business development executives and management for software/ internet companies in Northern California. Specialty working with VC funded start-ups.

Salary Minimum: $70,000
Functions: Mkt. research, Mktg. mgmt.
Industries: New media, High tech, Software

JNB Assoc., Inc.

990 Washington St., Ste. 200
Dedham, Massachusetts 02026
(781) 407-0401
Fax: (781) 407-0407

Key Contact - Specialty:
Mr. Joseph N. Baker, Jr. - *Banking, financial (all)*

Description: Banking and financial specialists - retainer and some contingency depending on circumstances.

Salary Minimum: $50,000
Functions: Directors, Mktg. mgmt., Personnel, CFO's, Cash mgmt.
Industries: Finance, Banking, Invest. banking, Brokers, Misc. financial

Job Link, Inc.

7060 Miramar Rd., Ste. 205
San Diego, California 92121-2348
(619) 695-1100
Fax: (800) 930-5627
Email: JobLink4u@aol.com
Web: www.JobLink.net

Key Contact - Specialty:
Ms. Mary Rose Gutierrez - *High technology, manufacturing operations, executives, bilingual*
Ms. Susan Hinds - *Technical, sales & marketing*

Description: Specialize in technical, professional, managerial and sales & marketing for manufacturing, high technology industries and distribution centers specializing in bilingual maquiladora professionals-Spanish.

Salary Minimum: $65,000
Functions: General mgmt., Senior mgmt., Mfg., Sales & mktg., Finance, IT, Engineering
Industries: Mfg., Medical devices, Plastics/ rubber, Computer equip., High tech, Biotech

Job-Born Candidate Selection Bureau

399 Main St. E.
Hamilton, Ontario L8N 1J7
Canada
(905) 522-7551
Fax: (905) 522-2952
Email: jobborn@Sprint.ca

Key Contact - Specialty:
Ms. Mary Ann Warriner - *General insurance*
Mr. Bob Warriner - *Engineering, generalist*

Description: In addition to recruiting top quality personnel, we are a proactive agency, actively marketing exceptional candidates whom we have isolated and evaluated.
Functions: Generalist, Mfg., Materials, HR mgmt., Finance, IT, Engineering
Industries: Generalist, Mfg., Svcs., Aerospace, Packaging, Insurance, Non-classifiable industries

John Jay & Co.

1 Union St., Ste. 403
Portland, Maine 04101
(207) 772-6951
Fax: (207) 772-0159

Key Contact - Specialty:
Mr. Jay Hotchkiss

Description: Small, boutique firm with a very personalized approach. Offers particular expertise in human resources search and can provide H.R. consulting services as well.

Salary Minimum: $45,000
Functions: Generalist, Senior mgmt., Plant mgmt., HR mgmt., Finance, R&D, Mgmt. consultants
Industries: Generalist, Misc. mfg., Finance, Hospitality, Human resource svcs., Biotech, Healthcare

Affiliates:
Traill Assoc., Inc.

John Ryan Assoc., LLC.

450 7th Ave., Ste. 2906A
New York, New York 10123
(212) 279-5151
Fax: (212) 279-3377
Email: jnryn@aol.com

Key Contact - Specialty:
Mr. John Mark Arceri - *Data processing, client/server, brokerage, banking, Fortune 100*
Mr. Ryan Richter - *Data processing, client/ server, brokerage, banking, Fortune 100*

Description: Over 15 years experience as a resource provider to the major banks, brokerage and Fortune 500 companies. Providing local and foreign resources at highly competitive rates quickly and efficiently, in addition to full-time placement of IT professionals.

Salary Minimum: $60,000
Functions: Directors, MIS mgmt., Systems anal., Systems dev., Systems implem., Systems support, Mgmt. consultants
Industries: Banking, Invest. banking, Brokers, Computer svcs., Mgmt. consulting, Human resource svcs.

J. M. Johnson & Assoc.

2610 Schaller Drive, Ste. 2B
St. Paul, Minnesota 55119-5869
(612) 910-9918
Fax: (612) 578-7669
Email: johnsonRPN@aol.com

Key Contact - Specialty:
Ms. Justyna M. Johnson

Description: We have supplied physicians, dentists and other healthcare professionals for positions in an effective and timely manner. All positions secured through RPN-Twin Cities are employer paid.
Functions: Physicians, Nurses, Allied health, Health admin.
Industries: Healthcare

Affiliates:
Recruiters Professional Network

Johnson Assoc., Inc.

114 N. Hale St.
Wheaton, Illinois 60187
(630) 690-9200
Fax: (630) 690-9910
Email: Foodsearch@aol.com

Key Contact - Specialty:
Mr. Scott Johnson - *Foodservice distribution*

Description: We provide both broadline and specialty foodservice distributors with the best possible talent in every functional area: (senior management, sales, operations, finance, purchasing and M.I.S.). As a national specialist, our commitment to our industry is unmatched.

Salary Minimum: $60,000
Functions: Senior mgmt., Middle mgmt., Purchasing, Distribution, Sales mgmt., CFO's, MIS mgmt.
Industries: Food/bev/tobacco, Transportation, Wholesale, Retail, Hospitality, Non-classifiable industries

K. E. Johnson Assoc.

4213-187th Place SE
Issaquah, Washington 98027
(425) 747-4559

Key Contact - Specialty:
Mr. Karl Johnson - *High technology, scientific, research & development*

Description: Specializing in hi-tech industries. Electronics, computers, software, peripherals, telecommunications, instruments, semiconductors; all scientific disciplines. Executive management, sales and marketing, engineering and R&D type positions. Special client service featuring exclusive assignment.

Salary Minimum: $60,000
Functions: Generalist, Senior mgmt., Product dev., Mkt. research, Systems dev., R&D, Engineering
Industries: Generalist, Chemicals, Computer equip., Telecoms, High tech, Software, Biotech

Johnson Brown Assoc., Inc.

55 Monument Circle, Ste. 1214
Indianapolis, Indiana 46204
(317) 237-4328
Fax: (317) 237-4335
Web: danbrown@topechelon.com

Key Contact - Specialty:
Mr. Daniel P. Brown - *Automotive manufacturing (operations, engineering, quality)*
Mr. John Kimbrough Johnson - *Human resources, labor relations, accounting, finance*
Ms. Amy Reece Connelly - *Sales & marketing, customer service*
Mr. Joseph R. Williamson - *Corporate investment portfolio management*
Ms. Jean Wilfong - *Packaging industry*

Description: Responsive search firm conducting focused searches. Emphasis is on working relationships and in-depth understanding of client's operations. Specialties include industrial management, engineering, accounting, investments, human resources, sales & marketing.

Salary Minimum: $35,000
Functions: Mfg., Materials, Sales & mktg., HR mgmt., Finance, Cash mgmt., Engineering
Industries: Generalist, Mfg., Wholesale, Finance, Svcs., Communications, Packaging

The Johnson Group, Unlimited

1 World Trade Ctr., Ste. 4517
New York, New York 10048-0202
(212) 775-0036
Fax: (212) 775-0046
Email: tjgunltd@aol.com
Web: johnson-group.com

Key Contact - Specialty:
Ms. Priscilla Johnson - *Generalist*
Mr. Steve Collins - *Financial services institutions*
Mr. Hassan Shariff - *Consumer products, financial services*
Mr. Howard O. Smith - *Financial Services*
Mr. Howard Baker - *Generalist*

Description: Specializing in financial institutions and F500 corporations, we offer a wide range of career opportunities at the mid to upper management level on a global basis. Our talent bank is composed of finance, marketing, human resources, operations and IT executives.

Salary Minimum: $85,000
Functions: General mgmt., Directors, Sales & mktg., HR mgmt., Finance, MIS mgmt., Mgmt. consultants
Industries: Mfg., Finance, Communications, Insurance

Johnson, Kemper & Assoc.

10122 Ivy Gate Circle, Ste. 100
Dallas, Texas 75238
(214) 348-0880
Fax: (214) 348-0103
Email: jka@onramp.net

Key Contact - Specialty:
Mr. Paul Johnson - *Sales & marketing, computer industry*

Description: Over ten years experience placing sales, marketing candidates in the computer industry, nationwide. Including sales people, SE's, sales managers and executives, product managers, presidents. Provide unique, helpful candidate interest profiles, debriefs.

Salary Minimum: $50,000
Functions: Senior mgmt., Middle mgmt., Mkt. research, Mktg. mgmt., Sales mgmt., Direct mktg.
Industries: Computer equip., Computer svcs., Telecoms, Software

Roye Johnston Assoc., Inc.

16885 W. Bernardo Drive, Ste. 270
San Diego, California 92127
(619) 487-5200
Fax: (619) 487-5296

Key Contact - Specialty:
Ms. Roye Johnston
Mr. Brian Johnston

Description: Specialists in occupational medicine, industrial hygiene, toxicology and epidemiology, nationally and internationally.

Salary Minimum: $100,000
Functions: Physicians, Nurses
Industries: Healthcare

International Branches:
Paris

Jonathan Lawrence Assoc.

(Firm declined to update.)
103 Washington St., Ste. 354
Morristown, New Jersey 07960
(973) 285-1988

Key Contact - Specialty:
Mr. Don Singel - *Information systems*
Ms. Jo Singel - *Human resources, sales*

Description: We are highly skilled recruiters with business backgrounds in technology, human resources and sales. We apply our talent to create the best possible match between our clients and candidates.

Salary Minimum: $50,000
Functions: Sales mgmt., Personnel, MIS mgmt., Systems dev., Systems implem., Systems support, Minorities
Industries: Misc. financial, Computer svcs., High tech, Software

Jones Consulting Executive Search

6050 Peachtree Pkwy., Ste. 340-118
Norcross, Georgia 30092
(770) 497-6677
Fax: (770) 813-1212
Email: esc@mindspring.com
Web: www.escinc.com

Key Contact - Specialty:
Mr. James A. Jones - *Insurance*

Description: A focused professional team of recruiting and placement consultants endeavoring to provide an exceptional and ethical recruiting service.

Salary Minimum: $25,000
Functions: Senior mgmt., Middle mgmt., Sales mgmt., Risk mgmt.
Industries: Insurance

Joseph Chris & Assoc.

900 Rockmead Drive, Ste. 101
Kingwood, Texas 77339-2116
(281) 359-0060
Fax: (281) 359-0067
Email: joeramirez@josephchris.com
Web: www.josephchris.com

Key Contact - Specialty:
Mr. Joe Ramirez

Description: Clients are real estate and development firms, construction, architectural and engineering companies and financial institutions that provide funding to the real estate industry. Their portfolios vary and may include raw land, single family, multifamily, commercial and industrial.

Salary Minimum: $50,000

Functions: General mgmt., Senior mgmt., Middle mgmt., Finance, Specialized services, Architects, Int'l.
Industries: Construction, Accounting, Real estate

Joseph Consulting, Inc.
216 Park Ave. S.
Winter Park, Florida 32789
(407) 628-7073
Fax: (407) 628-7074
Email: joco@parkave.net
Web: www.jocoinc.com

Key Contact - Specialty:
Mr. Jerry McGee - *Information technology*

Description: We are an information-technology professional services and recruiting firm. IT professionals are supplied to clients on a contract/consulting or permanent placement basis for the purposes of providing technical information systems solutions.

Salary Minimum: $45,000
Functions: Senior mgmt., HR mgmt., Finance, IT, MIS mgmt., Systems anal., Systems dev.
Industries: Mfg., Finance, Svcs., Communications, High tech, Software, Healthcare

Joseph Michaels
120 Montgomery St., Ste. 1260
San Francisco, California 94104
(415) 434-1099
Fax: (415) 434-1165
Email: josephmike@aol.com
Web: www.JosephMichaels.com

Key Contact - Specialty:
Mr. Joe Pelayo - *Accounting, finance*
Mr. Dennis Billingsley - *Accounting, finance*

Description: The name to know in accounting. Temporary and permanent accounting placement from clerk to CFO.

Salary Minimum: $30,000
Functions: CFO's, Budgeting, Cash mgmt., Credit, Taxes, M&A, Risk mgmt.
Industries: Misc. mfg., Misc. financial, Accounting, Real estate, High tech, Software, Biotech

Joslin & Assoc., Ltd.
291 Deer Trail Court, Ste. C-3
Barrington, Illinois 60010-1773
(847) 304-1100
Fax: (847) 304-1102
Email: JoslinLtd@aol.com

Key Contact - Specialty:
Dr. Robert S. Joslin - *Pharmaceutical research & development, quality control, production*

Description: Optimizing opportunities for individuals and organizations with scientific or technical orientation in the pharmaceutical industry, including search and placement, acquisition and licensing. Extensive industry research and executive experience.

Salary Minimum: $50,000
Functions: Product dev., Production, Quality, R&D
Industries: Drugs mfg.

The Jotorok Group
4 Richmond Sq.
Providence, Rhode Island 02906
(401) 521-7989
Fax: (401) 521-7993
Email: jobs@jotorok.com
Web: www.jotorok.com

Key Contact - Specialty:
Mr. Ron Wnek - *Information technology*
Mr. Tom Leonard - *Information technology*
Mr. Joe DiMucchio - *Information technology*
Mr. Kevin Sklarski - *Information technology*

Description: We are a single source provider to the information technology industry by offering both permanent and contract staffing solutions.

Salary Minimum: $25,000
Functions: MIS mgmt., Systems anal., Systems dev., Systems implem., Systems support, Network admin., DB admin.

JPM International
26034 Acero
Mission Viejo, California 92691
(949) 699-4300
Fax: (949) 699-4333
Email: jpmintl@ix.netcom.com
Web: www.jpmintl.com

Key Contact - Specialty:
Ms. Melissa Hannigan - *Medical, healthcare*
Ms. Lesley Graham - *Telecommunications*
Ms. Judy Smith - *Hospital administration, nursing*
Mr. Mike Balsamo - *Physician*

Description: HR consulting firm specializing in the staffing/retention of all permanent employees hired into an organization. Through our program, SHARED VISION, a partnership between us and the client, we achieve a full understanding of your company's needs, corporate cultures, goals and objectives.

Salary Minimum: $35,000
Functions: Middle mgmt., Nurses, Mktg. mgmt., Sales mgmt., CFO's, R&D, Engineering
Industries: Drugs mfg., Medical devices, Test/measurement equip., Telecoms, High tech, Biotech, Healthcare

JRL Executive Recruiters
2700 Rockcreek Pkwy., Ste. 303
North Kansas City, Missouri 64117-2519
(816) 471-4022
Fax: (816) 471-8634

Key Contact - Specialty:
Mr. Larry E. Eason - *Engineering, technical, manufacturing*

Description: We are a professional search firm that recruits for technical personnel to senior-level management. The firm practice is national in scope and has worked assignments for international clients.

Salary Minimum: $25,000
Functions: General mgmt., Mfg., Materials, HR mgmt., IT, Engineering, Specialized services
Industries: Energy/utilities, Construction, Mfg., Transportation, Environmental svcs., High tech, Software

Branches:
2187 Hopkins Terrace
Duluth, Georgia 30136
(770) 446-1291
Fax: (770) 446-0402
Key Contact - Specialty:
Mr. James M. Eason - *Engineering, data processing*

JT Assoc.
89 Comstock Hill Rd.
New Canaan, Connecticut 06840
(203) 966-6311
Fax: (203) 966-8149

Key Contact - Specialty:
Mr. Joe Fazio
Ms. Mary Ellen Calderone

Description: A contingency/retainer search firm specializing in professional, technical and middle mangement for diversified client base.

Salary Minimum: $40,000
Functions: General mgmt., Middle mgmt., HR mgmt., Benefits, CFO's, Credit, IT
Industries: Energy/utilities, Chemicals, Drugs mfg., Invest. banking, Misc. financial, Computer svcs.

Julian Assoc., Inc.
162 Willard Ave.
Newington, Connecticut 06111
(860) 232-7876
Fax: (860) 232-8864

Key Contact - Specialty:
Mr. Julian Brownstein - *Advertising, public relations, direct marketing agencies*
Ms. Joan Brownstein - *Advertising, public relations, direct marketing agencies*

Description: Marketing and advertising/ public relations executive search for all industries. Agencies only.

Salary Minimum: $40,000
Functions: Advertising, Direct mktg., PR
Industries: Advertising/PR

Juno Systems, Inc.
516 Fifth Ave., 14th Floor
New York, New York 10036
(212) 354-5390
Fax: (212) 354-5391
Email: worldnet@junosytems.com
Web: www.junosystems.com

Key Contact - Specialty:
Ms. Mary J. Kuric - *Generalist*

Description: We recruit IT professionals for both domestic and overseas clients. We specialize in understanding cross-cultural issues in addition to technical competencies.
Functions: MIS mgmt., Systems anal., Systems dev., Systems implem., Systems support, Mgmt. consultants, Int'l.
Industries: Generalist, Finance, Communications, Software

International Branches:
Central Hong Kong

Just Management Services Inc.
701 Enterprise Rd. E., Ste. 805
Safety Harbor, Florida 34695
(813) 726-4000
Fax: (813) 725-4966
Email: susan@justmgt.com
Web: www.justmgt.com

Key Contact - Specialty:
Mr. Jim Just
Ms. Susan Just - *Textiles, apparel, plastics, machinery, metals, information systems, embroidery and screenprint*

Description: Broad range of consulting services to the apparel, home furnishings and textile industries, plastics, including; manufacturing consulting, '807' consulting, import sourcing, executive search, associated personnel consulting services.
Functions: General mgmt., Mfg., Materials, Sales & mktg., R&D, Engineering
Industries: Generalist, Textiles/apparel, Medical devices, Plastics/rubber, Metal products, Misc. mfg.

Branches:
1121 Chucky Pike
Jefferson City, Tennessee 37760
(423) 475-1188
Fax: (423) 471-5155
Key Contact - Specialty:
Ms. Debra Just - *Apparel, plastics*

A H Justice Search Consultants
P.O. Box 891542
Houston, Texas 77289
(281) 474-7364
Fax: (281) 228-9204
Email: justice@hal-pc.org

Key Contact - Specialty:
Mr. J. C. King - *Information technology, general manufacturing, technology sales, high technology, engineers (mechanical, electrical & chemical)*

Description: Nationwide interests in the information technology markets-including all disciplines on all platforms/ operating systems, databases, languages, applications. Several thousand current and active positions on line. Several thousand active candidates on line.

Salary Minimum: $35,000
Functions: Mfg., Sales mgmt., IT, R&D, Engineering
Industries: Energy/utilities, Mfg., Computer svcs., Telecoms, High tech, Software, Biotech

---

K & C Assoc.
290 A Oakhurst Lane
Arcadia, California 91007
(626) 446-3087
Fax: (626) 445-1961

Key Contact - Specialty:
Mr. R. G. Kuhnmuench - *Construction, mining, municipal, industrial machinery industries*

Description: Serving all middle and top management positions in the machinery industries. Also the construction, building materials, industrial, mining and municipal, concrete, sand/gravel, rock and cement industries. Domestic and international.

Salary Minimum: $30,000
Functions: General mgmt., Mfg., Materials, Sales & mktg., Finance, Engineering, Int'l.
Industries: Construction, Leather/stone/ glass/clay, Metal products, Machinery/ Appliances, Motor vehicles, Equip. svcs.

K2 Resources, L.P.
34 E. Putnam Ave., Ste. 100
Greenwich, Connecticut 06830
(203) 622-6779
Fax: (203) 622-6970
Email: k2@westnet.com

Key Contact - Specialty:
Ms. Kelly Macaluso - *New media, technology*
Ms. Kelly Gallagher - *New media, technology*

Description: Mission statement: to provide our client partners with a targeted approach to staffing which will enable them to sustain their competitive advantage and increase profitability.
Functions: Mktg. mgmt., Sales mgmt., IT, MIS mgmt., Systems anal., Systems dev., Systems implem.
Industries: Computer svcs., New media, High tech, Software

Kaas Employment Services
425 2nd St. SE, Ste. 610
Cedar Rapids, Iowa 52401
(319) 366-1731
Fax: (319) 366-1402
Email: jobs@kaas-emp.com

Key Contact - Specialty:
Ms. Linda M. Kaas - *Engineering, manufacturing*

Description: Contingency search and placement specializing in manufacturing and engineering. Nationwide placement with concentration in Iowa and Midwest.
Functions: Product dev., Automation, Packaging, IT, MIS mgmt., Systems support, Engineering
Industries: Food/bev/tobacco, Paper, Chemicals, Plastics/rubber, Machinery/ Appliances, Motor vehicles, Software

---

Kabana Corp.
49175 W. Pontiac Trail
P.O. Box 930785
Wixom, Michigan 48393-0785
(248) 926-6427
Email: kabana@mich.com
Web: www.kabana.com

Key Contact - Specialty:
Mr. Steven E. Kabanuk - *OEM automotive production parts supplier*
Mr. James Allen Kabanuk - *OEM automotive production parts supplier*

Description: Japanese language skills

Salary Minimum: $40,000
Functions: Production, Materials Plng., Sales mgmt., Training, Engineering, Minorities, Int'l.
Industries: Plastics/rubber, Motor vehicles, Computer equip., Transportation, High tech, Software

---

KABL Ability Network
(a division of Syntre Corp.)
1727 State St.
Santa Barbara, California 93101
(805) 563-2398
Email: 432kabl@msn.com
Web: www.kabl.com

Key Contact - Specialty:
Mr. Brad Naegle - *Senior management of small companies*

Description: Network of Southern California recruiters specializing in top management of small companies, especially successors of entrepreneurial founders. Both permanent and temporary.

Salary Minimum: $75,000
Functions: Directors, Senior mgmt., CFO's, MIS mgmt., Systems dev., R&D, Engineering
Industries: Computer equip., Computer svcs., Telecoms, Environmental svcs., Aerospace, High tech, Software

Kaczmar & Assoc.

10 S. Clinton St., Ste. 106
Landmark Bldg.
Doylestown, Pennsylvania 18901
(215) 230-0750
Fax: (215) 230-0752
Email: kaczmar@comcat

Key Contact - Specialty:
Mr. Michael A. Kaczmar - *Software sales executives, software consultants*

Description: We specialize in placing senior level sales and pre and post sales consulting support with primarily top 100 independent software vendors in the Mid-Atlantic and Northeast markets.
Functions: Sales mgmt.
Industries: High tech, Software

Richard Kader & Assoc.

7850 Freeway Circle, Ste. 201
Cleveland, Ohio 44130
(440) 891-1700
Fax: (440) 891-1443
Email: careers99@aol.com

Key Contact - Specialty:
Mr. Richard H. Kader - *Industrial sales & marketing*
Mr. Vern Sponseller - *Financial, accounting*
Ms. Mamie Rodd - *Telecommunications sales & marketing*
Mrs. Marlene Mason - *Computer sales (hardware & software)*
Mr. Ronald Scott - *Consumer product sales*
Mr. James Flash - *Medical sales*

Description: We handle both local and national searches in sales/marketing, medical, industrial, chemical, engineering, telecommunications, accounting and administrative.

Salary Minimum: $40,000
Functions: Senior mgmt., Mktg. mgmt., Sales mgmt., Benefits, CFO's, MIS mgmt.
Industries: Generalist

Robert Kaestner & Assoc.

3047 Flat Rock Place
Land O' Lakes, Florida 34639
(813) 996-5664
Fax: (813) 996-5934
Email: robkae@gte.net
Web: www.pacificarts.com/Kaestner

Key Contact - Specialty:
Mr. Bob Kaestner - *Office furniture, office supplies*
Ms. Pat Kaye

Description: This professional contingency and retained search firm is devoted to serving the office furniture and office supply industries at all disciplines. We cater to the search needs of manufacturers as well as dealers and distributors.

Salary Minimum: $40,000
Functions: General mgmt., Middle mgmt., Product dev., Plant mgmt., Mktg. mgmt., Sales mgmt., Graphic artists
Industries: Lumber/furniture, Wholesale

Lisa Kalus & Assoc., Inc.

26 Broadway, Ste. 400
New York, New York 10004
(212) 837-7889
Fax: (212) 837-7890

Key Contact - Specialty:
Ms. Lisa Kalus - *Construction, engineering, real estate personnel*

Description: Recruitment firm specializing in construction, engineering and real estate personnel, primarily in the New York City metropolitan area.
Functions: Engineering
Industries: Construction, Real estate

Kames & Assoc.

P.O. Box 3342
Annapolis, Maryland 21403-3342
(410) 990-0780
Fax: (410) 990-0784
Email: jobs@kames.com
Web: www.kames.com

Key Contact - Specialty:
Mr. Robert Kames

Description: Professional recruiting service specializing in high tech, engineering, telecom and software areas. Intelligence, DOD and aerospace community. TS/SCI clearances highly sought. Working level plus senior management and executive management. Salaries 50K+.

Salary Minimum: $50,000
Functions: General mgmt., Sales & mktg., IT, Systems anal., Systems dev., Network admin., DB admin.
Industries: Computer equip., Computer svcs., Telecoms, Defense, Aerospace, High tech, Software

Kane & Assoc.

2825 Wilcrest, Ste. 675
Houston, Texas 77042
(713) 977-3600
Fax: (713) 430-5512
Email: bkane@jobmenu.com
Web: www.jobmenu.com

Key Contact - Specialty:
Mr. Bernie Kane - *Financial*
Mr. Michael Kane - *Generalist*
Mr. Guy Davis - *Tax*
Mr. Jason Brien - *Geoscience*
Mr. David Booth - *Information technology*

Description: We perform searches for a variety of functions and industries. We specialize in the financial, engineering, information technology and geoscience areas. Our searches include candidates for domestic and international positions.

Salary Minimum: $30,000
Functions: Generalist, General mgmt., Mfg., Finance, IT, Engineering, Int'l.
Industries: Generalist, Energy/utilities, Mfg., Finance, Packaging, High tech, Software

Karp & Assoc.

931 State Rd. 434, Ste. 1201
Altamonte Springs, Florida 32714
(407) 292-4637
Fax: (407) 294-1695
Email: lindakarp@juno.com

Key Contact - Specialty:
Ms. Linda S. Karp - *Medical sales, marketing, management*

Description: Twelve plus years experience in medical/pharmaceutical sales, marketing and management recruiting. The owner personally has a clinical background as a registered nurse and a background in medical sales.
Functions: Senior mgmt., Middle mgmt., Product dev., Nurses, Mkt. research, Mktg. mgmt., Sales mgmt.
Industries: Food/bev/tobacco, Drugs mfg., Medical devices, Computer equip., Telecoms, Biotech, Healthcare

Karras Personnel, Inc.

2 Central Ave.
Madison, New Jersey 07940
(973) 966-6800
Email: karraspersonnel@mindspring.com

Key Contact - Specialty:
Mr. Bill Karras - *Human resources*

Description: Human resources recruiting for professionals in functions of: employment, training and organization development, human resources planning, compensation, benefits, employee relations, labor relations, affirmative action/ equal employment opportunity, safety and HRIS.

Salary Minimum: $20,000
Functions: HR mgmt., Benefits, Personnel, Training
Industries: Generalist

Kass/Abell & Assoc., Inc.
10780 Santa Monica Blvd., Ste. 200
Los Angeles, California 90025
(310) 475-4666
Fax: (310) 475-0485
Email: attyplcmnt@kass-abell.com

Key Contact - Specialty:
Mr. Peter J. Redgrove - *Attorneys*

Description: The firm handles recruiting for corporate law departments and law firms throughout California. We are networked nationwide to assist attorneys wishing to relocate.
Functions: Specialized services, Attorneys
Industries: Svcs., Legal

Katelyn Partners
3780 Tampa Rd., Ste. B-102
Oldsmar, Florida 34677
(813) 855-8043
Fax: (813) 855-0032
Email: jimw@promed.com
Web: www/mcenter.com/katelyn

Key Contact - Specialty:
Mr. James Whitehurst - *Healthcare information systems*
Mr. Edward White - *Healthcare finance*

Description: Nine years healthcare industry experience. Fixed fee contingent and retained search. Specialize in clinical, technical and executive level placements.

Salary Minimum: $40,000
Functions: Health admin., CFO's, Budgeting, Cash mgmt., MIS mgmt., Systems anal., Systems dev.
Industries: Healthcare

Melissa Katzman, Executive Search
44 Bayberry Drive
Peekskill, New York 10566
(914) 736-2901
Fax: (914) 788-9214
Email: mkatzvette@aol.com
Web: www.ecal.com

Key Contact - Specialty:
Ms. Melissa Katzman - *Information systems, finance, manufacturing*

Description: We are focused on the placement of middle management and senior executive level positions across a broad diversity of functions. Multi-national clients are Fortune 200+ in most industries.

Salary Minimum: $50,000
Functions: Materials Plng., Budgeting, M&A, Systems anal., Systems implem., Network admin., DB admin.
Industries: Generalist, High tech

Affiliates:
Estes Consulting Associates Inc.

Jim Kay & Assoc.
1111 Plaza Drive, Ste. 480
Schaumburg, Illinois 60173
(847) 330-9600
Fax: (847) 413-8106

Key Contact - Specialty:
Mr. Jim Kay - *Generalist*
Mr. Patrick Weglarz - *Technical*

Description: Cost effective, timely recruiting backed by twenty plus years of client satisfaction in both retained and contingency search assignments.

Salary Minimum: $65,000
Functions: Senior mgmt., Middle mgmt., Product dev., CFO's, Systems dev., R&D, Engineering
Industries: Generalist, Computer equip., Consumer electronics, Misc. mfg., Telecoms, High tech, Software

---

Kay Concepts, Inc.
P.O. Box 4825
Palm Harbor, Florida 34685
(813) 786-3580
(800) 879-5850
Fax: (813) 786-3358
Email: kconcept@staffing.net
Web: kayconcepts.com

Key Contact - Specialty:
Ms. Heidi Kay - *High technology engineering, manufacturing, marketing, point of sale, electronic systems*

Description: A full service firm specializing in the high-tech, manufacturing, and development of electronic systems. Clients develop product primarily to point-of-sale and point-of-service industries.
Functions: Product dev., Production, Plant mgmt., Quality, Mkt. research, Systems dev., Engineering
Industries: Medical devices, Plastics/rubber, Metal products, Computer equip., Consumer electronics, High tech, Software

---

The Kay Group of 5th Ave.
350 Fifth Ave., Ste. 2205
New York, New York 10118
(212) 947-4646
Fax: (212) 947-3472
Email: kayrecruit@worldnet.att.net

Key Contact - Specialty:
Mr. Joseph H. Kay - *Advertising agency management*
Mr. Bernard A. Feinberg - *Advertising agency management*

Description: Every candidate is interviewed in person before any evaluation is made.

Salary Minimum: $40,000
Functions: Senior mgmt., Middle mgmt., Advertising, Sales mgmt., Direct mktg., CFO's, Budgeting
Industries: Metal products, Advertising/PR, Publishing, New media

---

Keeley Consulting Inc.
120 Adelaide St. W., Ste. 2215
Toronto, Ontario M5H 1T1
Canada
(416) 363-3311
Fax: (416) 363-3309
Email: keeley@ican.net

Key Contact - Specialty:
Ms. Stephanie Brooks Keeley - *Financial services*
Mr. Timothy J. Keeley - *Financial services*
Ms. Ann H. Chamberlain - *Financial services*

Description: We are a search firm that specializes in the financial services industry.

Salary Minimum: $40,000
Functions: Mkt. research, CFO's, Budgeting, Cash mgmt., Taxes, M&A, Risk mgmt.
Industries: Finance, Banking, Invest. banking, Brokers, Venture cap., Misc. financial

---

Keena Staffing Services
147 Ridge St.
Glens Falls, New York 12801
(518) 793-9825
Fax: (518) 793-0224
Email: staff@keena.com
Web: www.keena.com/keena/index.html

Key Contact - Specialty:
Mr. Paul S. Gerarde - *Manufacturing, sales, human resources, accounting, information technology*

Description: Most of our clients are manufacturing companies. We conduct searches for all line and staff functions. We also recruit attorneys.

Salary Minimum: $50,000
Functions: Mfg., Materials, Sales & mktg., Finance, IT, Engineering, Attorneys
Industries: Mfg., Legal

Kehn & Gabor, Inc.

70 W. Streetsboro St.
Hudson, Ohio 44236
(330) 342-3786
Fax: (330) 342-3881
Email: kgi@gwis.com

Key Contact - Specialty:
Mr. Robert A. Gabor
Ms. Elizabeth R. Kehn

Description: Conduct executive search on an exclusive or retained basis for technical, management and executive personnel.
Functions: Plant mgmt., Quality, Purchasing, Materials Plng., Distribution, Systems dev., Engineering
Industries: Generalist

Kelley & Keller, Inc.

2518 Key Largo Lane
Ft. Lauderdale, Florida 33312
(954) 791-4944

Key Contact - Specialty:
Mr. Verne Kelley - *Marketing management*

Description: Management consultants doing executive search for consumer marketing management only.

Salary Minimum: $50,000
Functions: Senior mgmt., Middle mgmt., Sales & mktg., Advertising, Mkt. research, Mktg. mgmt., Direct mktg.
Industries: Food/bev/tobacco, Soap/perfume/cosmetics, Consumer electronics, Misc. mfg., Hospitality, Entertainment, Communications

Kendall & Davis Co., Inc.

11325 Concord Village Ave.
St. Louis, Missouri 63123
(314) 843-8838
Fax: (314) 843-2262
Web: www.kendallanddavis.com

Key Contact - Specialty:
Mr. James C. Kendall - *Physicians*

Description: Physician recruitment.
Functions: Physicians
Industries: Healthcare

Kenmore Executives Inc.

1 S. Ocean Blvd., Ste. 306
Boca Raton, Florida 33432
(561) 392-0700
Fax: (561) 392-4748

Key Contact - Specialty:
Mr. Lawrence D. Loprete - *Management consultants*
Ms. Marilyn Orr - *Management consultants*
Mr. Steven LoPrete - *Management consultants*

Description: Specializing in the placement of consultants experienced in the implementation of concepts supporting business re-engineering, change management, downsizing, organization restructuring, management development, total quality management and strategic planning.

Salary Minimum: $50,000
Functions: Quality, Productivity, Materials Plng., Distribution, Training, MIS mgmt., Mgmt. consultants
Industries: Generalist, Mgmt. consulting

William W. Kenney

9 Powder Horn Rd.
Norwalk, Connecticut 06850
(203) 831-8144

Key Contact - Specialty:
Mr. William Kenney - *Property, casualty insurance*

Description: Our extensive network in the insurance industry with respect to underwriting and claims facilitates timely placements. We are best known in the metro New York City region.

Salary Minimum: $30,000
Functions: Directors, Senior mgmt., Middle mgmt.
Industries: Insurance

Kennison & Assoc. Inc.

3101 Broadway, Ste. 280
Kansas City, Missouri 64111
(816) 753-4401
(800) 496-7860
Fax: (816) 753-3430
Email: careerkc@kennison.com
Web: www.kennison.com

Key Contact - Specialty:
Mr. Gary S. Fawkes - *MIS*
Ms. Victoria Kennison - *MIS*

Description: We earn the fee. Specialized and experienced. No-nonsense approach to filling your sensitive and important positions. Honesty, integrity and professionalism practiced.

Salary Minimum: $18,000
Functions: MIS mgmt., Systems anal., Systems dev., Systems implem., Systems support, Network admin., DB admin.
Industries: Generalist

Barbara Kerner Consultants

230 Park Ave., Ste. 315
New York, New York 10169
(212) 682-1100
Fax: (212) 682-1575

Key Contact - Specialty:
Ms. Barbara Kerner - *Attorneys, legal*

Description: Contingent and retainer searches on a global basis. Specialize in placement within corporations; general counsel, corporate counsel. Also law firm partners, associates and merger activity.

Salary Minimum: $50,000
Functions: Mgmt. consultants, Attorneys
Industries: Legal

Blair Kershaw Assoc., Inc.

1903 W. 8th St., Ste. 302
Erie, Pennsylvania 16505
(814) 454-5872
Fax: (814) 452-4598

Key Contact - Specialty:
Mr. Blair Kershaw - *Manufacturing, finance, engineering, management*

Description: We recruit for manufacturing, engineering, financial, medical and management people in our Tri-state area. Most work is in the $40,000-$60,000 range.

Salary Minimum: $40,000
Functions: Middle mgmt., Mfg., Product dev., Production, Quality, CFO's, Engineering
Industries: Food/bev/tobacco, Plastics/rubber, Metal products, Machinery/Appliances, Misc. mfg., Software

Key Employment

1014 Livingston Ave.
North Brunswick, New Jersey 08902
(908) 249-2454
Fax: (908) 249-2521
Email: gene_sansone@gowebway.com

Key Contact - Specialty:
Mr. Gary Silberger - *Engineering power, sales, marketing*

Description: International search and recruiting for engineering, administration, manufacturing, laboratory, technical sales and marketing. Clients include chemical, power engr., cogeneration, plastics, electrical, electro mechanical, petroleum, environmental, pulp and paper industries.

Salary Minimum: $40,000
Functions: Senior mgmt., Plant mgmt., Purchasing, Materials Plng., Mkt. research, Mktg. mgmt., Engineering
Industries: Energy/utilities, Construction, Food/bev/tobacco, Chemicals, Paints/petroleum products, Consumer electronics, Advertising/PR

Key Resources Int'l.

109 Crows Nest Dr.
Boulder Creek, California 95006
(408) 338-7686
Fax: (408) 338-0245

Email: keysource@aol.com

Key Contact - Specialty:
Mr. Dirk S. Gilson - *High technology software, computer, telecommunications, CAD/CAM, electronics*
Ms. Linda L. Gilson - *Computer, software, sales*

Description: We offer emerging technical companies industry experience and an extensive network of contacts to find key people for their organizations. Each principal has over 25 years of experience in high technology.
Functions: Directors, Middle mgmt., Sales & mktg., Sales mgmt., IT, MIS mgmt., Systems dev.
Industries: Computer equip., Computer svcs., Telecoms, High tech, Software

Keystone Consulting Group

1600 Parkwood Circle, Ste. 500
Atlanta, Georgia 30339
(770) 937-0944
Fax: (770) 937-0942
Email: keystne@mindspring.com
Web: www.mindspring.com/~keystne

Key Contact - Specialty:
Ms. Stephany Lewis

Description: Specialize in the placement of permanent and project based consulting accounting and banking professionals primarily in the Southeast.

Salary Minimum: $30,000
Functions: Middle mgmt., CFO's, Budgeting, Cash mgmt., Taxes
Industries: Banking, Invest. banking, Misc. financial, Accounting

Branches:
2100 South Bridge Pkwy. Ste. 650
Birmingham, Alabama 35209
(205) 414-1410
Fax: (205) 414-1412
Key Contact - Specialty:
Ms. Kristi Spangler

1551 Atlantic Blvd. Ste. 300
Jacksonville, Florida 32207
(904) 398-6661
Fax: (904) 398-7142
Key Contact - Specialty:
Ms. Daneene Simmeman

1600 Parkwood Circle, Ste. 500
Atlanta, Georgia 30339
(770) 937-0944
Fax: (770) 937-0942
Key Contact - Specialty:
Ms. Caryn Berack

55 W. Port Plaza, Ste. 250
St. Louis, Missouri 63146
(314) 514-9999
Fax: (314) 514-9262
Key Contact - Specialty:
Ms. Sandy Palubiak

831 East Morehead St. Ste. 540
Charlotte, North Carolina 28202
(704) 342-3832
Fax: (704) 342-3833
Key Contact - Specialty:
Ms. Krisnne Knighton

3447 Robinhood Rd. Ste. 315
Winston-Salem, North Carolina 27106
(336) 768-5221
Fax: (336) 768-7813
Key Contact - Specialty:
Ms. Marcia Staples

445 Hutchinson Ave. Ste. 800
Columbus, Ohio 43235
(614) 785-6444
Fax: (614) 785-6447
Key Contact - Specialty:
Mr. John Meller

Galleria-Tower Two 13455 Noel Rd.
Ste. 1000
Dallas, Texas 75240
(972) 778-8144
Fax: (972) 778-8143
Key Contact - Specialty:
Ms. Kim Yenhana

707 East Main St. Ste. 700
Richmond, Virginia 23219
(804) 698-7388
Fax: (804) 698-7389
Key Contact - Specialty:
Mr. Dana Sutherland

KGA Inc.

1320 Greenway Terrace, Ste. 1
Brookfield, Wisconsin 53005
(414) 786-5209
Fax: (414) 786-7961

Key Contact - Specialty:
Mr. Keith J. Gunkel - *Human resources, personnel*

Description: 22 years recruiting and placing human resources professionals exclusively. Work with major US corporations as clients on exclusive contingency and retained searches. Specializing in all facets of HR placement as well as HR generalists.

Salary Minimum: $50,000
Functions: HR mgmt., Benefits, Personnel, Training
Industries: Generalist

Ki Technologies, Inc.

1325 N. Hwy. 89, Ste. 300
Farmington, Utah 84025
(801) 544-3214
Fax: (801) 544-4030
Email: Mellos@ix.netcom.com
Web: www.ki-tech.com

Key Contact - Specialty:
Mr. James S. Mellos
Dr. Thomas Bakehorn
Mr. B. Waltz - *Telecommunications*
Ms. D. Vance - *High Technology*

Description: Elite small firm specializing in high technology engineering, marketing and technical sales professionals both management and hands on contributors; software/hardware engineers, product marketing and management. Mid-level to executive placement.

Salary Minimum: $50,000
Functions: Directors, Middle mgmt., Mktg. mgmt., Sales mgmt., Systems dev., Engineering, Int'l.
Industries: Medical devices, Computer equip., Communications, New media, Telecoms, High tech, Software

Kimmel & Associates, Inc.

25 Page Ave.
Asheville, North Carolina 28801
(828) 251-9900
Fax: (828) 251-9955
Email: kimmel@circle.net
Web: www.kimmel.com

Key Contact - Specialty:
Mr. Joe W. Kimmel - *Construction, real estate and development*

Description: Aggressive, national recruiting firm specializing in construction, real estate, development, solid waste.

Salary Minimum: $50,000
Functions: General mgmt., Purchasing, Sales & mktg., HR mgmt., Finance, CFO's, MIS mgmt.
Industries: Construction, Real estate

Kincaid Group Inc. (KGI)

16350 Blanco Rd., Ste. 117-157
San Antonio, Texas 78232
(210) 308-9221
Fax: (210) 308-9201
Email: ray@kincaidgroup.com
Web: www.kincaidgroup.com

Key Contact - Specialty:
Mr. Raymond W. Kincaid - *Physician, executive*
Mr. Tracy Estelle - *Physician, nurse*
Mr. Trevor Anderson - *Physician, nurse, ancillary*
Mr. Lee Johnson - *Nurse, ancillary, technical*

Description: We are a search consulting firm specializing in medical, technical and executive placement. We assist organizations throughout the entire process of personnel activities-from recruiting and training to termination and outplacement.
Functions: Middle mgmt., Physicians, Training, CFO's, MIS mgmt., Systems implem., Mgmt. consultants

Industries: Svcs., Mgmt. consulting, Human resource svcs., High tech, Healthcare

Branches:
1150 Bluff Forest
San Antonio, Texas 78248
(210) 479-9210
Fax: (210) 479-9233
Email: kincaid@kincaidgroup.com
Web: kincaidgroup.com
Key Contact - Specialty:
Ms. Lynn Kincaid

Kinderis & Loercher Group
9510 Turnberry Trail
Crystal Lake, Illinois 60014
(815) 459-3700
Fax: (815) 459-6314
Email: kinderis@mc.net
Web: www.kandlgroup.com

Key Contact - Specialty:
Mr. Paul Kinderis - *Insurance (professionals)*

Description: Commitment to service. Effective results through local concentration. Straight forward, no nonsense style.

Salary Minimum: $20,000
Functions: Directors, Senior mgmt., Middle mgmt., Risk mgmt., IT
Industries: Insurance

King ComputerSearch, Inc.
9221 LBJ Frwy., Ste. 208
Dallas, Texas 75243
(972) 238-1021
(800) 738-1021
Fax: (972) 699-9551
Email: post@kingsearch.com
Web: www.kingsearch.com

Key Contact - Specialty:
Ms. Sally King
Mr. Ron S. Hunt

Description: We provide top technical and management talent for technology development companies and advanced IT environments, including systems analysts, software, hardware, test engineers and managers. Full-time and strategic contracting services available.
Functions: Sales mgmt., Direct mktg., MIS mgmt., Systems dev., Systems implem., Systems support, Engineering
Industries: High tech, Software

Kirkbride Assoc., Inc.
915 118th Ave. SE, Ste. 370
Bellevue, Washington 98005
(425) 453-5256
(425) 453-5268
Fax: (206) 453-5257
Email: kirkbride@isomedia.com
Web: www.kirkbrideassoc.com

Key Contact - Specialty:
Mr. Robert Kirkbride - *Sales, engineering, technical, HVAC/R, industrial*
Mr. Richard Logie - *Sales, engineering, technical, HVAC/R, industrial*
Mr. Paul Roberts

Description: Sales and marketing, industrial, technical and HVAC. Engineering: computer and HVAC.. Management: general, sales, engineering.

Salary Minimum: $45,000
Functions: Senior mgmt., Middle mgmt., Mktg. mgmt., Sales mgmt., Engineering, Technicians
Industries: Energy/utilities, Construction, High tech

KL Consultants
7855 Blvd. E.
North Bergen, New Jersey 07047
(201) 295-0754
Fax: (201) 295-0658
Email: klresource@aol.com

Key Contact - Specialty:
Ms. Jill Krumholz - *Human resources*

Description: Specialist in recruitment and placement of mid to senior level human resources professionals nationwide.

Salary Minimum: $65,000
Functions: HR mgmt., Benefits, Personnel, Training, Mgmt. consultants, Minorities
Industries: Generalist, Mgmt. consulting, Human resource svcs.

Kleber & Assoc.
4312-29th Ave. W.
Seattle, Washington 98199
(206) 282-8880
Fax: (206) 283-2664
Email: kleber@kleber.com

Key Contact - Specialty:
Ms. Deb Kleber

Description: Experienced professionals recruiting senior field management, technical sales, implementation consultants and technical project managers. Clients range from startup software vendors to Big Six. Focus: client/server environment, industry-specific applications, storage systems.

Salary Minimum: $70,000
Functions: Materials, Sales mgmt., Systems implem., Systems support, Network admin., DB admin., Mgmt. consultants
Industries: Computer svcs., New media, High tech, Software

Affiliates:
T. M. Campbell Co.
Sally Caplan & Assoc.

Klein, Landau & Romm
1725 K St. NW, Ste. 602
Washington, District of Columbia 20006
(202) 728-0100
Fax: (202) 728-0112
Email: jurisjob@aol.com
Web: www.jurisjob.com/

Key Contact - Specialty:
Mr. Gary Ethan Klein
Mr. David Landau
Mr. Barry Romm

Description: The company is the largest legal search firm in Washington D.C. and specializes in placing attorneys with federal government expertise. The company also places temporary attorneys in Washington D.C.
Functions: Attorneys
Industries: Legal

The Kleven Group, Inc.
(a division of StaffMark/IntelliMark)
One Cranberry Hill, P.O. Box 636
Lexington, Massachusetts 02173
(781) 861-1020
Fax: (781) 861-1047
Email: kleven@kleven.com
Web: www.kleven.com

Key Contact - Specialty:
Mr. Robert Kleven - *Technical management (software)*
Ms. Maria Routh - *Software engineering, information technology*
Ms. Michele White

Description: We have four specific areas of concentration; contingency placement, retained search, temporary staffing and technical contract staffing. We strive to be the diversified staffing solutions partner of choice for our clients.

Salary Minimum: $40,000
Functions: General mgmt., Mfg., IT, MIS mgmt., Systems dev., R&D, Engineering
Industries: Mfg., New media, Telecoms, Defense, High tech, Software

KM Associates
30 Colpitts Rd.
Weston, Massachusetts 02193
(781) 899-6655
Fax: (781) 899-6444
Email: bestjobs@kmasearch.com
Web: www.kmasearch.com

Key Contact - Specialty:
Mr. Kimball L. Mason - *Management, consultants*
Mr. Christopher Mason - *Sales & marketing*

Description: Our methodology of partnership search is unique in that we charge like a contingency firm but work like a retained search firm. We meet with all our candidates as well as meet initially with clients. We specialize in the software industry, thus are knowledgeable about a client's business and can recruit the right profile quickly.

Salary Minimum: $35,000
Functions: Directors, Mkt. research, Mktg. mgmt., Sales mgmt., Direct mktg., Systems implem., Systems support
Industries: Computer svcs., High tech, Software

Joyce C. Knauff & Assoc.

P.O. Box 624
Wilmette, Illinois 60091
(847) 251-7284
Fax: (847) 251-6945
Web: jck@wwa.com

Key Contact - Specialty:
Ms. Joyce C. Knauff - *MIS*

Description: Search firm specializing in the MIS function of corporations and consulting firms.

Salary Minimum: $35,000
Functions: IT, MIS mgmt., Systems anal., Systems dev., Systems implem., Systems support, Specialized services

The Koehler Group

P.O. Box 18156
Philadelphia, Pennsylvania 19116
(215) 673-8315
Fax: (215) 673-7206

Key Contact - Specialty:
Mr. Frank R. Koehler - *Human resources, finance, marketing*

Description: National recruitment and search for mid to senior management personnel in the fields of human resources - all disciplines, finance including accounting, marketing and sales.

Salary Minimum: $45,000
Functions: HR mgmt., Benefits, Personnel, Training, CFO's, Cash mgmt., Minorities
Industries: Generalist, Mfg., Food/bev/tobacco, Finance, Svcs., Publishing, Insurance

Koerner & Assoc., Inc.

750 Old Hickory Blvd., Ste. 150
Two Brentwood Commons
Brentwood, Tennessee 37027
(615) 371-6162
Fax: (615) 371-6172
Email: koerner.assoc@nashville.com
Web: www.KoernerAssociates.com

Key Contact - Specialty:
Ms. Pam L. Koerner - *Attorneys*

Description: We specialize in the search and placement of attorneys. We take pride in our professionalism and ethical manner of doing business. We perform legal searches and work with clients on a local, regional and nationwide basis.

Salary Minimum: $50,000
Functions: Attorneys
Industries: Legal

Koll-Fairfield LLC

Executive House, Ste. 203
397 Post Rd.
Darien, Connecticut 06820
(203) 655-5001
Fax: (203) 656-2667
Email: callkoll@aol.com

Key Contact - Specialty:
Mr. Richard Champagne - *Accounting & finance*
Mr. Bruce Stalowicz - *Accounting & finance*
Mr. Arthur Tomack - *Accounting & finance*
Mr. Tom Reynolds - *Information technology*

Description: Full service boutique recruiting firm offering flexible search products to the accounting, finance and information technology communities. A firm dedicated to providing staffing solutions and quick results.

Salary Minimum: $60,000
Functions: Purchasing, Benefits, Finance, IT, Mgmt. consultants, Minorities
Industries: Generalist

Kordus Consulting Group

1470 E. Standish Place
Milwaukee, Wisconsin 53217-1958
(414) 228-7979
Fax: (414) 228-1080
Email: kchinc@aol.com

Key Contact - Specialty:
Ms. Lee Walther Kordus
Mr. Benedict N. Kordus

Description: Executive search and management consulting nationwide. Recruitment in all areas of marketing, marketing services, advertising, promotions, public relations, communications and research. Corporate and agency positions. Retainer and contingency search.

Salary Minimum: $40,000
Functions: Senior mgmt., Middle mgmt., Advertising, Mkt. research, Mktg. mgmt., Direct mktg., PR
Industries: Food/bev/tobacco, Soap/perfume/cosmetics, Communications, Advertising/PR

Michael Kosmetos & Assoc., Inc.

333 Babbitt Rd., Ste. 300
Cleveland, Ohio 44123
(216) 261-1950
Fax: (216) 261-9796

Key Contact - Specialty:
Mr. Michael Kosmetos - *Retail*

Description: Our staff is non-commissioned and we approach projects as a search team. With over 35 years of combined experience this team approach allows us to be expeditious and extremely thorough.

Salary Minimum: $35,000
Functions: Middle mgmt., Distribution
Industries: Retail

Kozlin Assoc., Inc.

9070 Main St.
Clarence, New York 14031
(716) 634-5955
Fax: (716) 626-0549

Key Contact - Specialty:
Mr. Jeffrey M. Kozlin

Description: Established in 1972-contingency recruitment and executive search serving manufacturing.

Salary Minimum: $50,000
Functions: Mfg., Materials, HR mgmt., Engineering
Industries: Food/bev/tobacco, Chemicals, Drugs mfg., Medical devices, Plastics/rubber, Metal products, Machinery/Appliances

KPA Assoc., Inc.

150 Broadway, Ste. 1900
New York, New York 10038
(212) 964-3640
(800) 226-5836
Fax: (212) 964-6959
Email: lenadams@pipeline.com

Key Contact - Specialty:
Mr. Len Adams - *Financial services*
Mr. Antonio Vittorioso

Description: Full range of services including executive search, managerial and technical staffing and consulting for financial services industries. Wage and salary surveys available as well as providing staff for consulting projects. An emphasis in start-up operations.

Salary Minimum: $25,000
Functions: Generalist, General mgmt., HR mgmt., Finance, IT, Specialized services, Int'l.
Industries: Finance, Banking, Invest. banking, Computer svcs., Accounting, Mgmt. consulting, Software

Kramer Executive Resources, Inc.
110 E. 59th St., Ste. 2500
New York, New York 10022-4082
(212) 832-1122
Email: alkram@aol.com
Web: www.kramerexec.com

Key Contact - Specialty:
Mr. Alan L. Kramer - *CFOs, controllers, accounting managers, CPAs*
Ms. Chloe Almour - *Litigation support directors, MIS directors*

Description: Our firm specializes in the recruitment of accounting, tax and financial professionals for placement in public or private accounting, controllership and finance.

Salary Minimum: $50,000
Functions: CFO's, Budgeting, Taxes, M&A, MIS mgmt., Mgmt. consultants, Non-profits
Industries: Textiles/apparel, Consumer electronics, Retail, Brokers, Entertainment, Advertising/PR, Real estate

Krautler Personnel Recruitment
P.O. Box 7946
34th Ave. NE
St. Petersburg, Florida 33734
(813) 823-2100
Fax: (813) 826-1562
Email: krautler@cftnet.com

Key Contact - Specialty:
Mr. William Krautler - *Information technology, telecommunications*
Ms. Leigh Barrett

Description: Our experience extends 20+ years in information technology/telecommunication industries as an executive recruiter, sales executive and H.R. director. Also, as a firm we are specialists in these industries having worked for AT&T/MCI as a marketing executive.

Salary Minimum: $40,000
Functions: General mgmt., Sales & mktg., IT, Engineering, Int'l.
Industries: Mfg., Communications, Telecoms, Government, Aerospace, High tech, Software

Evie Kreisler Assoc. Inc.
865 S. Figueroa, #950
Los Angeles, California 90017
(213) 622-8994
Fax: (213) 622-9660
Email: evie@ekjobs.com

Key Contact - Specialty:
Ms. Evie Kreisler - *Retail, apparel wholesale, manufacturing*

Description: Specialists-all disciplines - retail; apparel wholesale/manufacturing and consumer products. Our consultants have related industry background. We take pride in finding the perfect fit.

Salary Minimum: $50,000
Functions: Directors, Senior mgmt., Middle mgmt., Product dev., Advertising, Sales mgmt., CFO's
Industries: Textiles/apparel, Retail

Branches:
2575 Peachtree Rd., Ste. 300
Atlanta, Georgia 30305
(404) 262-0599
Fax: (404) 262-0699
Key Contact - Specialty:
Ms. Debbi Kreisler - *Retail, apparel wholesale, manufacturing*

333 N. Michigan, #818
Chicago, Illinois 60601
(312) 251-0077
Fax: (312) 251-0289
Key Contact - Specialty:
Mr. Wayne Tadda - *Retail, apparel wholesale, manufacturing*

1 West 34th St., Ste. 201
New York, New York 10001
(212) 279-8999
Fax: (212) 268-9660
Key Contact - Specialty:
Ms. Kathy Gross - *Retail, apparel wholesale, manufacturing*

2720 Stemmons Frwy., Ste. 812
Dallas, Texas 75207
(214) 631-8994
Fax: (214) 630-2343
Key Contact - Specialty:
Mr. Tony Priftis - *Retail, apparel wholesale, manufacturing*

Kresin Wingard
333 N. Michigan Ave., Ste. 622
Chicago, Illinois 60601
(312) 726-8676
Fax: (312) 726-4705

Key Contact - Specialty:
Mr. David Wingard

Description: Recruitment for art directors, sales promotion, graphic designers, creative directors, package designers, writers, print production personnel, sales and marketing executives.

Salary Minimum: $30,000
Functions: Advertising, Mkt. research, Mktg. mgmt., Direct mktg., Architects, Graphic artists
Industries: Advertising/PR, Publishing, New media, Packaging

Kressenberg Assoc.
8111 LBJ Frwy., Ste. 665
Dallas, Texas 75251
(214) 234-1491
Fax: (214) 234-1493

Key Contact - Specialty:
Ms. Sammye Jo Kressenberg - *Managed care, sales, sales management, semiconductor capital equipment, truck industry (class 6-8)*
Ms. Kay Trammell - *Generalist*

Description: We have several national corporations who use our services on an exclusive basis. We limit our assignments so that they can be successfully completed in a timely manner.

Salary Minimum: $50,000
Functions: Middle mgmt., Nurses, Health admin., Sales mgmt., Benefits, CFO's, Engineering
Industries: Generalist, Motor vehicles, Test/measurement equip., Misc. mfg., High tech, Healthcare

Todd L. Krueger & Assoc.
P.O. Box 1289
Seattle, Washington 98111
(425) 776-9247

Key Contact - Specialty:
Mr. Todd L. Krueger - *Accounting & finance, tax*

Description: Expertise assisting all size companies staff their corporate tax and accounting departments. Additionally, assist public accounting firms recruit specialized and experienced audit and tax personnel.

Salary Minimum: $25,000
Functions: CFO's, Budgeting, Cash mgmt., Taxes, Mgmt. consultants
Industries: Entertainment, Accounting, Equip. svcs., Mgmt. consulting, High tech

Kuhn Med-Tech
27128-B Paseo Espada, Ste. 623
San Juan Capistrano, California 92675
(714) 496-3500
Fax: (714) 496-1716
Email: der@kuhnmed-tech.com
Web: www.kuhnmed-tech.com

Key Contact - Specialty:
Mr. Larry A. Kuhn - *Medical device, biotechnology, start-up companies*
Mr. Otis Archie - *Biotechnology, pharmaceutical, medical device*
Ms. Linda Turner - *Medical device, mechanical, electrical, software*
Mr. John Pelegrino - *Medical device*

Description: Serving medical device and biotechnology industries. Exclusive contingency and retainers; positions secured for engineers, scientists, marketing/sales and senior management professionals for Fortune 500 companies and exciting start-up ventures.

Salary Minimum: $30,000
Functions: Senior mgmt., Product dev., Materials, Sales & mktg., CFO's, R&D, Engineering
Industries: Drugs mfg., Medical devices, Plastics/rubber, High tech, Software, Biotech, Healthcare

---

D. Kunkle & Assoc.
P.O. Box 184
Barrington, Illinois 60011
(847) 540-8651
Fax: (847) 540-8653

Key Contact - Specialty:
Ms. Denise Kunkle - *Packaging, research & development, engineering*

Description: The president has over 18 years of industry experience. Hands-on knowledge of the skills and qualifications required make her uniquely qualified to recruit technical & engineering professionals to meet your organizations needs.

Salary Minimum: $45,000
Functions: Materials, Purchasing, Packaging, R&D, Engineering
Industries: Food/bev/tobacco, Soap/perfume/cosmetics, Drugs mfg., Medical devices, Plastics/rubber, Consumer electronics, Packaging

---

Kurtz Pro-Search, Inc.
P.O. Box 4263
Warren, New Jersey 07059-0263
(908) 647-7789

Key Contact - Specialty:
Mr. Sheldon I. Kurtz - *Emerging technology, information technology, open systems, networking*

Description: Information technology, open systems, data and telecom industry specialist placing technical sales, systems and marketing professionals. Expertise in Big 6 consulting, systems integration and outsourcing permanent placement opportunitites (management to partner level positions).

Salary Minimum: $50,000
Functions: Sales mgmt., Systems anal., Systems dev., Systems implem., Systems support, Mgmt. consultants, Technicians
Industries: Computer equip., Computer svcs., Mgmt. consulting, New media, Telecoms, High tech, Software

---

Kutcher Tax Careers, Inc.
303 S. Broadway, Suite 105
Tarrytown, New York 10591-5410
(914) 366-6887
Fax: (914) 524-0441
Email: kutcher@taxcareers.com
Web: www.taxcareers.com

Key Contact - Specialty:
Mr. Howard Kutcher - *Taxation*

Description: We are a niche-oriented recruiting firm that specializes exclusively in the tax area (tax accountants and tax attorneys). Our clients are in the metro NY and Philadelphia areas (but extend thru New England and Northeast Philadelphia). Client base consists of corporations, CPA and law firms.

Salary Minimum: $35,000
Functions: Taxes
Industries: Generalist

Kutt, Inc.
2336 Canyon Blvd., #202
Boulder, Colorado 80302
(303) 440-4100
Fax: (303) 440-9582
Email: kuttinc@msn.com

Key Contact - Specialty:
Mr. David Huff - *Printing*
Mr. Greg Neighbors - *Printing*

Description: Executive search and recruitment firm serving the printing industry; all levels of positions filled.
Functions: Senior mgmt., Middle mgmt., Plant mgmt., Quality, Purchasing, Sales mgmt., Customer svc.
Industries: Printing

Kyle Assoc.
P.O. Box 603
Scarsdale, New York 10583
(914) 723-5070
Fax: (914) 723-5070

Key Contact - Specialty:
Mr. Donald Kyle - *Human resources*

Description: A small HR firm providing high quality services to client companies in areas of: recruiting and outplacement. As a small firm, we are able to deliver our services on a customized basis.

Salary Minimum: $50,000
Functions: General mgmt., HR mgmt., Finance
Industries: Finance, Banking, Invest. banking, Brokers, Human resource svcs., Insurance

---

L & K Assoc.
179 W. Broadway, Ste. 7
P.O. Box 202
Salem, New Jersey 08079
(609) 935-3070

Key Contact - Specialty:
Mr. Tom Kay
Mr. Gene Lankenau

Description: Experienced ethical technical recruiters: specializing in telecommunications and intellectual property attorneys.

Salary Minimum: $50,000
Functions: MIS mgmt., Systems dev., Systems support, Attorneys
Industries: Generalist

L & L Assoc.
1015 E. Imperial Hwy., Ste. C-9
Brea, California 92821
(714) 990-5525
Fax: (714) 990-3302
Email: agoldst259@aol.com

Key Contact - Specialty:
Mr. Alan Gold - *Technical*

Description: Contingency search specializing in supporting recruitment efforts to manufacturing companies located in southern California.

Salary Minimum: $25,000
Functions: Product dev., Production, Automation, Purchasing, Materials Plng., Distribution, Engineering
Industries: Drugs mfg., Plastics/rubber, Machinery/Appliances, Computer equip., Test/measurement equip., Aerospace, Software

---

L T M Assoc.
1112 Elizabeth
Naperville, Illinois 60540
(630) 961-3331
Fax: (630) 961-9921
Email: ltm@ntsource.com

Key Contact - Specialty:
Ms. Madeleine Ward - *Financial services, leasing*

Description: We focus on finance services and information systems industries; mid and senior level management, financial and legal counsel, leasing, information systems specialists and sales representatives in: capital equipment including rolling stock, auto, medical and computer equipment.

Salary Minimum: $50,000
Functions: Senior mgmt., Middle mgmt., Mktg. mgmt., Sales mgmt., Cash mgmt., Risk mgmt., Systems dev.

Industries: Banking, Invest. banking, Misc. financial, Computer svcs., Equip. svcs., High tech, Software

L&L Assoc. Global Search

3331 Street Rd., Ste. 110
Two Greenwood Sq.
Bensalem, Pennsylvania 19020
(215) 639-4443
Fax: (215) 639-6339

Key Contact - Specialty:
Mr. Len Faulkner
Ms. LaCarole A. Faulkner - *Sales & marketing*

Description: Exclusive (retainer)

Salary Minimum: $20,000
Functions: Directors, Plant mgmt., Mkt. research, Sales mgmt., Benefits, Cash mgmt., Minorities
Industries: Generalist, Food/bev/tobacco, Soap/perfume/cosmetics, Drugs mfg., Invest. banking, Telecoms, High tech

Lab Market Specialists

10325 South 2230 East
Sandy, Utah 84070
(801) 944-3858
Fax: (801) 944-3865

Key Contact - Specialty:
Ms. Karen Mendrala - *Laboratory sales, marketing, technical*

Description: We specialize in the laboratory marketplace. Technical representatives, lab sales and sales management, as well as product managers and marketing managers.
Functions: Sales mgmt.

Laboratory Resource Group

18 Washington St., Ste. 158
Canton, Massachusetts 02021
(781) 575-9653
Fax: (781) 575-9638

Key Contact - Specialty:
Mr. Kevin Boyce - *Scientific, technical*

Description: Specializing in scientific, technical and management positions for the biotech, pharmaceutical, chemical, environmental, food and beverage industries. Principal has considerable laboratory management experience and numerous contacts in related industries.

Salary Minimum: $30,000
Functions: Middle mgmt., Product dev., Production, Plant mgmt., Quality, Packaging, R&D
Industries: Food/bev/tobacco, Chemicals, Soap/perfume/cosmetics, Drugs mfg., Medical devices, Packaging, Biotech

The LaBorde Group

P.O. Box 36162
Los Angeles, California 90036-0162
(213) 938-9007
Fax: (213) 938-2770

Key Contact - Specialty:
Mr. John LaBorde - *Construction management, engineers, railroad, transit, highways*
Mr. Jim Kelly - *Construction management, engineers, R.R. transit, highways*
Mr. Bob Martin - *Architects*
Mr. Michael LaBorde - *Construction management, architects*

Description: Broad based executive recruiting firm since 1971 emphasizing transportation ranging from middle management to key executives earning six figures. Highway, transit, railroad and civil engineers and construction management. Also developing a large international department.

Salary Minimum: $70,000
Functions: Engineering, Architects, Int'l.
Industries: Construction, Transportation, Environmental svcs.

LaCosta & Assoc. Int'l. Inc.

6727 Flanders Drive, Ste. 108
San Diego, California 92121
(619) 457-1377
Fax: (619) 457-0971
Email: topaul@aol.com

Key Contact - Specialty:
Mr. Paul LaCosta - *Wireless, telecommunications, telephony*

Description: We offer a variety of people development and recruiting services in the telecommunications/wireless industry. We are flexible and customize our services to solve your people problems.

Salary Minimum: $25,000
Functions: Directors, Senior mgmt., Production, Mkt. research, HR mgmt., Engineering, Int'l.
Industries: Telecoms

Gregory Laka & Co.

18201 S. Morris, Ste. 400
Homewood, Illinois 60430
(708) 206-2000
Fax: (708) 206-2020
Email: glandco@aol.com

Key Contact - Specialty:
Mr. Gregory Laka

Description: Search in all areas of information technology having a retainer and a contingency division.

Salary Minimum: $50,000
Functions: MIS mgmt., Systems anal., Systems dev., Systems implem., Systems support
Industries: Computer svcs., Software

Branches:
11 E. Adams, Ste. 1000
Chicago, Illinois 60603
(312) 922-7100
Fax: (312) 922-7199
Key Contact - Specialty:
Mr. Scott Swanson

Lake Medical Associates

12 Elm St.
Gorham, Maine 04038
(207) 839-4004
Fax: (207) 839-2118
Email:
placement@lakemed.cumberland.me.us

Key Contact - Specialty:
Mr. Jack M. Schraeter - *Medical, nursing*
Mr. David A. Black - *Medical, rehabilitation*

Description: Healthcare recruiters specializing in nursing, physicians, physical therapists, physician assistants and nurse practitioners. Representing hospitals, clinics, HMO's and private practice throughout the USA.

Salary Minimum: $30,000
Functions: Allied health
Industries: Healthcare

Lam Assoc.

Eaton Sq., P.O. Box 75113
Honolulu, Hawaii 96836-0113
(808) 947-9815
Email: Lamasc1@aol.com
Web: www.gtesupersite.com/lamphysician

Key Contact - Specialty:
Ms. Pat Lambrecht - *Medical*

Description: Quality executive search for 48 contiguous states. Established 1988. National network. Manufacturing-engineers & process; computer programmers; analysts; electrical & environmental engineers. Mail resume, desired states and salary info. Confidential.

Salary Minimum: $40,000
Functions: Mfg., Physicians, Nurses, Allied health, Health admin., Engineering
Industries: Energy/utilities, Environmental svcs., Aerospace, Software, Biotech, Healthcare

Lancaster Assoc., Inc.

94 Grove St.
Somerville, New Jersey 08876
(908) 526-5440
Fax: (908) 526-1992

Key Contact - Specialty:
Ms. Barbara Swan - *Information technology*
Mr. Raymond F. Lancaster, Jr. - *Information technology*

Description: Small professional organization specializing in pre-screened candidates in all levels of applications and software systems and senior level management. Provide consultants with the right to hire.

Salary Minimum: $60,000
Functions: MIS mgmt., Systems anal., Systems dev., Systems implem., Systems support
Industries: Food/bev/tobacco, Chemicals, Misc. mfg., Pharmaceutical svcs., Computer svcs., Mgmt. consulting

E. J. Lance Management Assoc., Inc.

60 E. 42nd St., 51st Floor
New York, New York 10165
(212) 490-9600
Fax: (212) 490-7282

Key Contact - Specialty:
Ms. Elizabeth Kay - *Investment banking*
Mr. Elliot Webb - *Equity research & sales*

Description: Experienced professionals, many with MBAs. All candidates are personally screened, client names are confidential, average completion time for assignments is three to four weeks.

Salary Minimum: $40,000
Functions: Cash mgmt., M&A
Industries: Invest. banking

Landon Morgan

3350 Merrittville Hwy., Ste. 12
Thorold, Ontario L2V 4Y6
Canada
(905) 641-2476
Fax: (905) 641-2735

Key Contact - Specialty:
Mr. Don Hetherington - *Engineering, plant management, technical*
Ms. Traci Polak - *Information technology, administration*
Mr. Randy Vant - *Generalist*

Description: Primary experience in outreach recruiting. We don't work with our clients' competition. Our success rate is 95%. We are considered an extension of our clients.
Functions: Generalist, Production, Plant mgmt., Customer svc., Personnel, MIS mgmt., Engineering
Industries: Generalist, Mfg., Plastics/rubber, Misc. mfg.

The Landstone Group

295 Madison Ave., 36th Floor
New York, New York 10017
(212) 972-7300
Fax: (212) 972-7309
Email: landstone@earthlink.net
Web: www.mrnyc.com

Key Contact - Specialty:
Mr. Jeffrey A. Heath - *Consumer, wireless communication, new technology*
Mr. Mark Bradley - *Personal computers, software*
Mr. Dwight Hall - *Consumer electronics*

Description: 17 years working with hundreds of companies dealing in new and computer technology executive search. This experience allows us to offer a six week search process.

Salary Minimum: $70,000
Functions: Senior mgmt., Production, Mkt. research, Mktg. mgmt., Sales mgmt., CFO's, Int'l.
Industries: Computer equip., Consumer electronics, Computer svcs., Mgmt. consulting, New media, High tech, Software

Lange & Assoc., Inc.

107 W. Market St.
Wabash, Indiana 46992
(219) 563-7402
Fax: (219) 563-3897
Email: Langeassoc@ctlnet.com

Key Contact - Specialty:
Mr. Jim Lange - *Engineers, manufacturing managers, accountants*
Mr. Jack Lange - *Engineers (support professions), general managers*

Description: Our firm has experienced people who are expert at matching people and opportunities. We recruit all disciplines and specialize in rubber, plastics, metals and electronics.

Salary Minimum: $20,000
Functions: Middle mgmt., Mfg., Plant mgmt., Purchasing, Sales mgmt., HR mgmt., Engineering
Industries: Paper, Plastics/rubber, Metal products, Motor vehicles, Misc. mfg., Transportation, Aerospace

The Langford Search, Inc.

2025 3rd Ave. N., Ste. 301
Birmingham, Alabama 35203-3323
(205) 328-5477
Fax: (205) 328-5483
Email: tlsearch@aol.com

Key Contact - Specialty:
Mr. K. R. Dick Langford - *Finance & accounting, information technology, general management*
Ms. Ann S. Langford - *Information technology*
Mr. Michael O. Coffey - *Finance & accounting, sales & marketing*
Mr. John A. Nepovadny - *Manufacturing, materials management*

Description: We seek first to understand our client's business, then both the hard and soft skills required of a successful candidate. We present for consideration only those candidates that possess both.
Functions: Senior mgmt., Middle mgmt., CFO's, Budgeting, MIS mgmt., Systems dev., Engineering
Industries: Generalist, Mfg., Finance, Software, Healthcare

Lanken-Kimball-Therrell & Assoc.

1446 Old Virginia Court
Marietta, Georgia 30067
(770) 952-7530
Fax: (770) 952-6252
Email: lta@mindspring.com
Web: www.mindspring.com/~lta/lt&a.html

Key Contact - Specialty:
Mr. Joel Lanken - *Sales, marketing, finance, logistics*
Mr. Dex Kimball - *Sales, marketing, operations*
Mr. Wayne Saunders - *Training, human resources*
Ms. Diana Wilkins - *Transportation*
Mr. Brock Therrell - *Logistics, operations, sales*

Description: Specific knowledge of third party logistics positions and requirements. Outsource of human resource functions for business.

Salary Minimum: $50,000
Functions: General mgmt., Mfg., Materials, Sales & mktg., HR mgmt., IT, Engineering
Industries: Mfg., Transportation, Equip. svcs., Aerospace, High tech, Non-classifiable industries

Branches:
1241 Holly Tree Lane
Snellville, Georgia 30078
(770) 736-8701
Fax: (770) 736-8702
Email: lta@mindspring.com
Web: www.mindspring.com/~lta/lt&a.html
Key Contact - Specialty:
Mr. Brock Therrell - *Logistics*

LanSo Int'l., Inc.
3 Davis Drive
Armonk, New York 10504
(914) 273-8259
Fax: (914) 273-6822

Key Contact - Specialty:
Mr. Edwin Lew - *Financial services*

Description: We provide a fee-based consultant service to a diverse clientele in order to assist in their business efforts through strategic staff placements and business introductions.

Salary Minimum: $50,000
Functions: CFO's, Budgeting, Cash mgmt., Risk mgmt., Minorities
Industries: Banking, Invest. banking, Brokers, Misc. financial

Stephen Laramee & Assoc. Inc.
53 Village Centre Place, Ste. 202
Mississauga, Ontario L4Z 1V9
Canada
(905) 897-1474
Fax: (905) 566-0177
Email: slaramee@compuserve.com

Key Contact - Specialty:
Mr. Stephen Laramee

Description: Mid management to and including senior executive search for manufacturing and/or distributor based organizations.

Salary Minimum: $40,000
Functions: Senior mgmt., Product dev., Production, Plant mgmt., Mktg. mgmt., Sales mgmt., CFO's
Industries: Food/bev/tobacco, Textiles/apparel, Lumber/furniture, Paper, Chemicals, Drugs mfg., Metal products

Robert Larned Assoc., Inc.
291 Independence Blvd.
Pembroke Four, Ste. 421
Virginia Beach, Virginia 23462
(757) 671-7800
Fax: (757) 671-7718
Email: rlabob@aol.com
Web: www.rlastaffing.com

Key Contact - Specialty:
Mr. Robert T. Larned - *Engineers, military personnel*
Ms. Tammy Park - *Engineers, sales & marketing, computer professionals*

Description: We recruit nationally for top talent leaving the military (JMO's) as well as engineers for the inert gas and vacuum industries. Clients are Fortune 1000 companies.

Salary Minimum: $50,000
Functions: Mfg., Sales mgmt., IT, MIS mgmt., Engineering, Mgmt. consultants
Industries: Food/bev/tobacco, Drugs mfg., Misc. mfg., Mgmt. consulting, Telecoms, Software

Jack B. Larsen & Assoc., Inc.
334 West 8th St.
Erie, Pennsylvania 16502
(800) 239-5737
Fax: (800) 239-5736
Web: www.jblhires.com

Key Contact - Specialty:
Mr. Jack B. Larsen

Description: Full scope recruiting firm with handling permanent and/or temporary contract personnel.

Salary Minimum: $35,000
Functions: Generalist, Production, Distribution, Sales mgmt., Benefits, Systems anal., Engineering
Industries: Plastics/rubber, Metal products, Machinery/Appliances, Misc. mfg., Telecoms, High tech

Larson & Trent Assoc.
1837 Oakdale Drive
Dandridge, Tennessee 37725
(800) 352-6226
Fax: (423) 397-2222

Key Contact - Specialty:
Dr. Wendell C. Trent

Description: Physician recruitment, placement and practice appraisals.
Functions: Physicians
Industries: Healthcare

Larson, Katz & Young, Inc.
4460 Brookfield Corporate Drive, Ste. H
Chantilly, Virginia 20151
(703) 631-3881
Fax: (703) 631-3882
Email: info@lkyi.com
Web: www.lkyi.com

Key Contact - Specialty:
Ms. Marcia Hall - *Healthcare information systems*

Description: Nationwide search for healthcare systems vendors specializing in installations, support, product marketing, sales and sales management.
Functions: Nurses, Mktg. mgmt., Sales mgmt., Systems anal., Systems dev., Systems implem., Systems support
Industries: High tech, Software, Healthcare

Lascelle & Assoc. Inc.
1930 Yonge St., Ste. 1100
Toronto, Ontario M4S 1Z4
Canada
(416) 421-1940
Fax: (416) 421-9244
Email: don@objectsearch.com
Web: www.inforamp.net/~ooss

Key Contact - Specialty:
Mr. Donald Lascelle - *Object oriented, C++, visual basic, Java, smalltalk*
Ms. Lori Bechard - *Oracle, powerbuilder, mainframe*

Description: We specialize in object oriented search such as JAVA, smalltalk, C++ and gemstone.
Functions: Senior mgmt., MIS mgmt., Systems anal., Systems dev., Systems implem., Systems support, DB admin.
Industries: Misc. mfg., Transportation, Banking, Invest. banking, Brokers, High tech, Software

Madeleine Lav & Assoc.
5703 Califa Place, Ste. 333
Woodland Hills, California 91367
(805) 927-3098
Fax: (805) 927-4138
Email: mlav333

Key Contact - Specialty:
Ms. Madeleine Lav - *Retail, food service*

Description: We have placed senior executives both in corporate and in the field at the premier retail and food service companies in the country.

Salary Minimum: $35,000
Functions: Senior mgmt., Middle mgmt., Distribution, HR mgmt., Personnel, CFO's, MIS mgmt.
Industries: Retail, Hospitality, Human resource svcs.

LaVallee & Associates
4176 Sulgrave Court
Winston-Salem, North Carolina 27104
(910) 760-1911
Fax: (910) 760-9511
Email: lavallee@netunlimited.net

Key Contact - Specialty:
Mr. Michael J. LaVallee - *Information systems (professionals)*

Description: Contingency search in systems/data processing with focus on IBM mid-range and IBM mainframe systems. Special emphasis on emerging microcomputer programming and network professionals.
Functions: MIS mgmt., Systems anal., Systems dev., Systems implem., Systems support
Industries: Textiles/apparel, Chemicals, Computer svcs., Mgmt. consulting, Insurance, Software, Healthcare

Lawrence James Assoc. of Florida, Inc.

8795 W. McNab Rd., Ste. 202
Ft. Lauderdale, Florida 33321
(954) 721-6100
Fax: (954) 726-3555
Email: LawrenceJames@worldnet.ATT.net

Key Contact - Specialty:
Mr. Leonard Okyn - *Supermarket industry*

Description: An executive search firm specializing in the supermarket industry for over 20 years with relationships in the industry enabling us to identify quickly client and candidates that excel.
Functions: Generalist, Middle mgmt., Materials, Sales mgmt., HR mgmt., Cash mgmt., MIS mgmt.
Industries: Transportation, Wholesale, Retail

Branches:
One Somerset Drive, Ste. 160
Somerset, New Jersey 08873
(732) 748-1188
Fax: (732) 356-4660
Key Contact - Specialty:
Mr. Larry Hebert - *Supermarket industry*

Lawrence-Balakonis & Assoc., Inc.

Dunwoody Village, P.O. Box 888241
Atlanta, Georgia 30356-0241
(770) 587-2342
Fax: (770) 587-5002
Web: balakonisnassoc@mindspring.com

Key Contact - Specialty:
Mr. Charles L. Balakonis - *Sales, marketing, category management, trade marketing*
Mr. J. Robert Lawrence - *Senior management*

Description: Highly regarded executive search consulting firm specializing in the consumer packaged goods industry nationwide, with a primary focus on sales and marketing middle and senior level management positions in the grocery products industry.

Salary Minimum: $45,000
Functions: General mgmt., Senior mgmt., Middle mgmt., Plant mgmt., Sales & mktg., Mktg. mgmt., Sales mgmt.
Industries: Food/bev/tobacco, Paper, Soap/perfume/cosmetics, Drugs mfg., Misc. mfg.

The Lawson Group, Inc.

17 Pope Ave. Executive Park Rd., Ste. 3
P.O. Box 7491
Hilton Head Island, South Carolina 29938
(803) 842-4949
Fax: (803) 842-7650
Email: email@lawsongroup.com
Web: www.lawsongroup.com

Key Contact - Specialty:
Mr. James W. Lawson - *Pulp & paper*
Ms. Mary Bjong - *Pulp & paper industry*
Mr. Gregory A. Estes - *Converting*

Description: We believe the American industry is past the need for good people, today the best people are needed. Through our methods of locating and screening people, we are dedicated to that end. We understand the importance of making the right fit for both company and individual.

Salary Minimum: $40,000
Functions: General mgmt., HR mgmt., Finance, IT
Industries: Paper, Printing, Packaging

LCC Companies

7975 N. Hayden Rd., Ste. D-290
Scottsdale, Arizona 85258
(602) 483-5660
Fax: (602) 922-0234
Email: lcc@primenet.com

Key Contact - Specialty:
Mr. Ray Weinhold - *Information technology*
Ms. Jean Weinhold - *Information technology*

Description: We recruit computer/data processing professionals at all levels. For software companies, we look for developers, marketing and sales. For computer users, we look for programmers, project managers, network integrators and MIS directors.

Salary Minimum: $40,000
Functions: MIS mgmt., Systems anal., Systems dev., Systems implem., Systems support, Engineering, Technicians
Industries: Telecoms, Aerospace, High tech, Software

LCS, Inc.

(Firm declined to update.)
1104 S. Mays, Ste. 116
Round Rock, Texas 78664
(512) 255-5518
Email: tmakhani@lcsjobs.com
Web: www.lcs.jobs

Key Contact - Specialty:
Mr. Thukbir Makhani - *Technical, engineers, programmers*
Mr. Mark Spinn - *Software engineers, other specialists*
Mr. Richard Weil - *Software engineers, other specialists*
Mr. Jon Gilliam - *Technical, engineers*

Description: We locate, prequalify, screen and place engineers and other highly skilled technical people with various client companies engaged in the high tech industry.

Salary Minimum: $20,000
Functions: Product dev., MIS mgmt., Systems anal., Systems dev., Systems implem., Systems support, Engineering
Industries: Computer equip., Consumer electronics, Computer svcs., New media, Telecoms, High tech, Software

Leader Institute, Inc.

340 Interstate N. Pkwy., Ste 250
Atlanta, Georgia 30339
(770) 984-2700
Fax: (770) 984-2990
Email: leaderins@aol.com
Web: www.peoplestaff.com

Key Contact - Specialty:
Mr. Richard Zabor - *PeopleSoft, systems applications, data processing, oracle, object oriented programming*
Ms. Yvonne Perkins - *PeopleSoft, systems applications, data processing, oracle, object oriented programming*
Mr. Ben Vlahos - *PeopleSoft, systems applications, data processing, oracle, object oriented programming*
Mr. Doug Hulme - *PeopleSoft, systems applications, data processing, oracle, object oriented programming*
Mr. Barry Geiman - *PeopleSoft, systems applications, data processing, oracle, object oriented programming*

Description: Information technology specialists applying search techniques to the Peoplesoft, SAP, ORACLE and object oriented markets.CIO Search in the Peoplesoft, SAP, Oracle markets.

Salary Minimum: $40,000
Functions: Senior mgmt., IT, MIS mgmt., Systems anal., Systems dev., Systems implem., Systems support
Industries: Generalist, Mfg., Retail, Finance, Svcs., Communications, Software

Leader Network

241 Harding Court
York, Pennsylvania 17403
(717) 845-6927
Fax: (717) 854-7079

Key Contact - Specialty:
Ms. D. June Leader - *Executive, technical, aluminum, steel*

Description: Total experience- 15 years. Self employed- 6 years. Contingency search- executive, technical, aluminum and steel industries- nationally.
Functions: Senior mgmt., Middle mgmt., Production, Automation, Sales mgmt., CFO's, Engineering
Industries: Metal products

Affiliates:
Locus Inc.

Leader Resources Group
165 Emerald Drive
McDonough, Georgia 30253-5514
(770) 954-0684
Fax: (770) 957-5927
Email: lstep8455@aol.com

Key Contact - Specialty:
Mr. Ken Stephens - *Legal, financial, human resources*
Ms. Teresa Stephens - *Computer positions*

Description: Generalist firm specializing in computer, legal, human resources and financial positions. Experienced in sensitive search situations. Recruiters are thoroughly trained personnel professionals.

Salary Minimum: $30,000
Functions: Middle mgmt., HR mgmt., Finance, Risk mgmt., Systems anal., Systems dev., Attorneys
Industries: Generalist, Finance, Legal, Computer svcs., Accounting, Insurance, Non-classifiable industries

Lear & Assoc., Inc.
505 Park Ave. N., Ste. 201
Winter Park, Florida 32789
(407) 645-4611
Fax: (407) 740-8816
Email: Roger@Learsearch.com
Web: learsearch.com

Key Contact - Specialty:
Mr. Roger R. Lear - *Actuarial, claims, underwriting*
Ms. Pamela R. Ramey - *Underwriting & claims, reinsurance underwriting, HO, executive level positions*
Mr. Mark Svetic - *Underwriting, claims (managers, vice presidents)*

Description: Our clients utilize us as a branch office to fill any insurance appointment. We are able to identify top candidates quickly, matching only candidates that precisely fit your position description. We will not waste your time.

Salary Minimum: $33,000
Functions: HR mgmt., CFO's, Risk mgmt., MIS mgmt.
Industries: Hospitality, Insurance, Healthcare

Reynolds Lebus Assoc.
P.O. Box 9177
Scottsdale, Arizona 85252
(602) 946-6929
Email: lebus@ix.netcom.com
Web: www.rlebus.com

Key Contact - Specialty:
Mr. Reynolds Lebus

Description: Gift and toy product development and marketing, home healthcare, medical devices engineering, SAP, software, EDP auditors

Salary Minimum: $35,000
Functions: Product dev., Health admin., Cash mgmt., Systems dev., Systems implem., DB admin., Engineering
Industries: Medical devices, Machinery/ Appliances, Insurance, Software, Healthcare

Lechner & Assoc., Inc.
7737 Holiday Drive
Sarasota, Florida 34231
(941) 923-3671
Fax: (941) 923-3675
Email: lechner@q-net.net

Key Contact - Specialty:
Dr. David B. Lechner
Mr. David Barnhart - *Environmental engineer consulting management*
Mr. Jim Szesny - *Information technology*
Mr. Richard Maggs - *Insurance executives*

Description: Technical management - primarily retainer (60%), contingency (40%), medical devices, food R&D, insurance, environmental consulting, venture capital before IPO.

Salary Minimum: $70,000
Functions: Senior mgmt., Middle mgmt., Product dev., Mktg. mgmt., Sales mgmt., M&A, Int'l.
Industries: Food/bev/tobacco, Medical devices, Venture cap., Haz. waste, Insurance

Lectra Search
3660 Keswick Dr., Ste. 1050
Atlanta, Georgia 30341
(770) 234-9121
Fax: (770) 457-9436
Email: ExSearch@aol.com

Key Contact - Specialty:
Mr. H. O. Catherman - *Sales & marketing, electrical*

Description: Founded in 1981, contingency search firm specializing in senior management sales and marketing within the electrical industry.

Salary Minimum: $50,000
Functions: Mktg. mgmt., Sales mgmt.
Industries: Energy/utilities

Albert G. Lee Assoc.
106 Greenwood Ave.
Rumford, Rhode Island 02916
(401) 434-7614

Key Contact - Specialty:
Mr. Albert G. Lee - *Technical, pharmaceutical, research & development, other areas listed*

Description: Practice specializing in technical; engineering, biotech, medical, pharmaceutical, clinical and MIS; marketing: consumer, retail and industrial; finance: banking, real estate, accounting, taxes; and human resources: benefits, compensation and employee relations.

Salary Minimum: $60,000
Functions: Middle mgmt., Production, Mktg. mgmt., Budgeting, MIS mgmt., R&D, Engineering
Industries: Generalist, Drugs mfg., Computer equip., Retail, Pharmaceutical svcs., High tech, Biotech

Ricci Lee Assoc., Inc.
100 Spear St., Ste. 1810
San Francisco, California 94105
(415) 247-2980
Fax: (415) 247-2985
Email: carol@riccilee.com

Key Contact - Specialty:
Ms. Carol Ricci Lee - *Marketing, marketing communications, public relations, advertising*

Description: Executive search for marketing and advertising professionals.

Salary Minimum: $50,000
Functions: Advertising, Mkt. research, Mktg. mgmt., Direct mktg., PR
Industries: Computer equip., Consumer electronics, Advertising/PR, Publishing, New media, Telecoms

Vincent Lee Assoc.
91 Fallon Ave.
Elmont, New York 11003-3605
(516) 775-8551

Key Contact - Specialty:
Mr. Vincent Lee - *Generalist*
Mr. Brian Lee - *Generalist*
Ms. Sheryl Baxter - *Generalist*
Ms. Linda Monte - *Generalist*
Ms. Kathy Esposito - *Generalist*

Description: Emphasis on accounting, banking, finance, marketing, insurance (property/casualty) and human resources professionals executive search through vice president.

Salary Minimum: $25,000
Functions: Generalist, Sales & mktg., HR mgmt., Finance, IT, Systems support
Industries: Generalist, Finance, Banking, Brokers, Computer svcs., Accounting, Insurance

Lee Management Group Inc.
P.O. Box 2426
Vineland, New Jersey 08362
(609) 455-9511
Fax: (609) 455-9441

Key Contact - Specialty:
Ms. Barbara Lee - *Apparel (manufacturing)*

Description: Apparel industry specialists, who understand from a corporate perspective a company's needs from product design through production and distribution. Just as you build quality into garments, we build quality into service.

Salary Minimum: $30,000
Functions: General mgmt., Mfg., Materials, Engineering, Int'l.
Industries: Textiles/apparel

Leeds and Leeds
116 Wilson Pike, Ste. 205
Brentwood, Tennessee 37027
(615) 371-1119
Fax: (615) 371-1225
Email: info@leedsandleeds.com
Web: www.leedsandleeds.com

Key Contact - Specialty:
Mr. Gerald I. Leeds - *Insurance organizations*

Description: We provide professional and efficient service to life insurance, health insurance and managed care organizations, assisting with their recruiting needs.

Salary Minimum: $40,000
Functions: Senior mgmt., Middle mgmt., Sales & mktg., Benefits, CFO's, Cash mgmt., Risk mgmt.
Industries: Misc. financial, Insurance

Legal Network Inc.
2151 Michelson Drive, Ste. 135
Irvine, California 92715
(714) 752-8800
Fax: (714) 752-9126
Email: legalnet@pacbell.net
Web: legalnetwork.cc

Key Contact - Specialty:
Ms. Carole Wampole - *Legal*
Mr. Daniel Wampole - *Legal*

Description: Our national network of candidates provides a valuable resource for most law-related search requests.
Functions: Legal, Customer svc., Systems support, Network admin., Attorneys, Paralegals
Industries: Legal, Human resource svcs.

Legal Search Assoc.
6701 W. 64th St., Ste. 210
Overland Park, Kansas 66202
(913) 722-3500
Fax: (913) 362-4864
Email: lsa@JDHunter.com
Web: www.JDHunter.com

Key Contact - Specialty:
Dr. Terry W. Bashor - *Attorneys*

Description: We recruit experienced, qualified and highly specialized attorneys for law firms and corporations in the United States with a focus on the Kansas City, St. Louis, Denver and Chicago metropolitan areas.

Salary Minimum: $30,000
Functions: Attorneys
Industries: Legal

Leith & Assoc., Inc.
24500 Center Ridge Rd., Ste. 325
Westlake, Ohio 44145
(440) 808-1130
Fax: (440) 808-1140
Email: manager@leithnet.com
Web: www.leithnet.com

Key Contact - Specialty:
Ms. Louisa Szewczuk

Description: The three prongs or cornerstones in our logo are: the client (prospective employers); the candidate (potential employees) and the consultant. This is our triangle team. We consider our clients as partners and treat our candidates like the professionals they are. We are the link that secures the partnership.

Salary Minimum: $30,000
Functions: Middle mgmt., Production, Materials Plng., Distribution, Mktg. mgmt., Sales mgmt., Personnel
Industries: Textiles/apparel, Chemicals, Computer equip., Test/measurement equip., Transportation, Software

Affiliates:
Garrick Hall & Assoc.

Lending Personnel Services
2938 S. Daimler St., Ste. 102
Santa Ana, California 92705
(714) 250-8133
Fax: (714) 250-7180
Email: carla@lpsjobs.com
Web: www.lpsjobs.com

Key Contact - Specialty:
Ms. Carla Bloch - *Mortgage banking, savings & loans, title, escrow, real estate*

Description: Specialists in executive, managerial and staffing placements nationally and locally in mortgage, finance, banking, real estate, development, escrow, insurance, title, high technology, manufacturing, staffing and human resources.

Salary Minimum: $25,000
Functions: Generalist, General mgmt., Middle mgmt., Sales & mktg., HR mgmt., Finance, IT
Industries: Generalist, Finance, Computer svcs., Human resource svcs., Insurance, Real estate, High tech

F. P. Lennon Assoc.
300 Berwyn Park, Ste. 202
Berwyn, Pennsylvania 19312
(610) 407-0300
(888) 536-6667
Fax: (610) 407-0533
Web: www.fplennon.com

Key Contact - Specialty:
Mr. Frank P. Lennon - *ERP Software Search sales & consulting*

Description: We are recognized as the industry leader in software recruiting within the SAP software world.

Salary Minimum: $80,000
Functions: Directors, Sales mgmt., IT, MIS mgmt., Systems anal., Systems dev., Systems implem.
Industries: Computer svcs., Software

Branches:
1701 W. Hillsboro Blvd., Ste. 103
Deerfield Beach, Florida 33442
(954) 418-9900
Fax: (954) 418-0556
Key Contact - Specialty:
Mr. Larry Cadwell - *Software, ERP*

6525 The Corners Parkway, Ste. 400
Norcross, Georgia 30092
(770) 729-6920
Fax: (770) 729-6921
Key Contact - Specialty:
Mr. Steve Litras - *Software, ERP*

Leslie Kavanagh Assoc., Inc.
505 Fifth Ave., Ste. 1300
New York, New York 10017
(212) 661-0670
Fax: (212) 599-8316
Email: lkaedge@aol.com

Key Contact - Specialty:
Mr. Will Pleva - *Strategic procurement, global logistics, operations*

Description: Executive search firm specializing in human resources, strategic procurement, global logistics and operations and information technology.

Salary Minimum: $60,000
Functions: Senior mgmt., Purchasing, Distribution, Benefits, Training, MIS mgmt., Systems implem.

Industries: Generalist, Food/bev/tobacco, Drugs mfg., Computer equip., Misc. mfg., Invest. banking, Software

Hal Levy & Assoc.

275 Madison Ave., 18th Floor
New York, New York 10016
(212) 686-4444
Fax: (212) 686-7072
Email: hal@hallevy.com
Web: www.hallevy.com

Key Contact - Specialty:
Mr. Hal Levy - *Advertising direct response*
Ms. Eve Levy - *Advertising direct response*

Description: We are an executive search firm specializing in advertising direct response. We place people in direct marketing, advertising, and new media.

Salary Minimum: $25,000
Functions: Advertising, Mktg. mgmt., Direct mktg., Graphic artists
Industries: Advertising/PR, Publishing, New media

Lewis Consulting Service

1810 St. Andrews Circle
Elgin, Illinois 60123
(847) 289-9059
Fax: (847) 289-7814
Email: dlewis1588@aol.com

Key Contact - Specialty:
Mr. Donnie Lewis - *Information technology*

Description: Specializing in on-and off-site contract recruiting and contingency searches in the information technology field.

Salary Minimum: $35,000
Functions: Systems anal., Systems dev., Systems implem., Systems support, Network admin., DB admin.
Industries: Printing, Paints/petroleum products, Misc. financial, Computer svcs., Human resource svcs., Healthcare

Lexington Software Inc.

555 Fifth Ave., 17th Floor
New York, New York 10017
(212) 376-7386
Fax: (212) 316-2278
Email: lexingtn@panix.com
Web: www.lextn.com

Key Contact - Specialty:
Mr. John B. Rountree, III - *Derivatives technologies, risk management systems, trading desk analytics, quantitative methods, artificial intelligence*

Description: We are an executive search organization serving the financial services industry specializing in derivatives technologies, quantitative methods and risk management. Candidates are pre-qualified in information technology and quantitative disciplines by members of the firm who have substantial working experience in these areas.

Salary Minimum: $75,000
Functions: Risk mgmt., MIS mgmt., Systems anal., Systems dev., Systems implem., Systems support, R&D
Industries: Finance, Computer svcs., High tech, Software

LG Brand, Inc.

6701 Democracy Blvd., Ste. 300
Bethesda, Maryland 20817
(301) 762-2977
Fax: (301) 294-5187
Email: lfinkle@lgbrand.com

Key Contact - Specialty:
Ms. Linda Finkle - *Information technology*

Description: We are a contingency placement firm with over 13 years of experience in the Washington metropolitan area. Our firm has been very successful in locating and evaluating some of the most talented information systems professionals in the Washington market.

Salary Minimum: $50,000
Functions: MIS mgmt., Systems anal., Systems dev., Systems implem., Systems support
Industries: Pharmaceutical svcs., Legal, Computer svcs., Accounting, Telecoms, High tech, Software

The Libra Group Inc.

115 New Canaan Ave., Ste. 700
Norwalk, Connecticut 06850
(203) 849-1409
Fax: (203) 849-1409
Email: libragroup@worldnet.att.net
Web: www.bworks.com/libragroup

Key Contact - Specialty:
Mr. Robert R. Saracen - *Television broadcast, management, sales*

Description: Over forty years local broadcast experience with radio/TV stations and national TV representatives. Extensive national broadcast contacts for placement ranging from high performance AE to CEO's. Integrity!

Salary Minimum: $50,000
Functions: Senior mgmt., Middle mgmt., Admin. svcs., Advertising, Sales mgmt.
Industries: Communications, Advertising/PR, Broadcast & Film

The Libra Group

801 E. Morehead St., Ste. 110
Charlotte, North Carolina 28202
(704) 334-0476
Fax: (704) 334-7186
Email: LibraGP@aol.com
Web: www.libragp@aol.com

Key Contact - Specialty:
Grazell R. Howard - *Diversity*
Mr. Frank G. Chester - *Human resources, software engineering*

Description: We are an African American search firm that specializes in diversity. We have 100 percent success at placing middle to upper level managers.

Salary Minimum: $45,000
Functions: General mgmt., Mfg., HR mgmt., Finance, IT, Engineering, Minorities
Industries: Generalist, Mfg., Finance, Svcs., Government, Packaging, Software

Pat Licata & Assoc.

103 Quarter Path
Cary, North Carolina 27511
(919) 859-0511
Fax: (919) 859-0830
Email: pat_licata_associates@msn.com

Key Contact - Specialty:
Ms. Pat Licata - *Medical, pharmaceutical (sales, management, product, trainers, etc.)*

Description: Specialist in med/pharm sales and sales management on a national level with abilities to recruit trainers, product and commitment to diversity recruiting. National award winning office - First Interview.

Salary Minimum: $35,000
Functions: Directors, Middle mgmt., Mkt. research, Mktg. mgmt., Sales mgmt., Training, Minorities
Industries: Drugs mfg., Medical devices, Pharmaceutical svcs., Healthcare

Howard Lieberman & Assoc., Inc.

311 First Ave. N., Ste. 503
Minneapolis, Minnesota 55401
(612) 338-2432
Fax: (612) 332-8860
Email: hla503@aol.com
Web: member.aol.com/hlassist/hla.html

Key Contact - Specialty:
Mr. Howard Lieberman - *Attorneys*
Ms. Nancy Nelson - *Attorneys*

Description: We are the only twin cities based full service national legal search firm, placing full time attorneys exclusively.
Functions: Attorneys
Industries: Legal

LifeWork, Inc.
5525 MacArthur Blvd., Ste. 525, L.B. 60
Irving, Texas 75038
(972) 550-8447
Fax: (972) 550-8640
Web: www.lifeworkinc.com

Key Contact - Specialty:
Mr. Scott Stratton - *Junior military offices*

Description: We are a woman owned business, specializing in personnel consulting and placements of military and civilian experienced candidates throughout the United States.

Salary Minimum: $30,000
Functions: Middle mgmt., Mfg., Materials, Sales & mktg., IT, Engineering, Minorities
Industries: Energy/utilities, Mfg., Transportation, Aerospace, Packaging, High tech, Software

Lifter & Assoc.
10918 Lurline Ave.
Chatsworth, California 91311-1637
(818) 998-0283
Fax: (818) 341-7979
Email: lifters@worldnet.att.net

Key Contact - Specialty:
Ms. Barbara Lifter - *Information technology*
Mr. Jay Lifter - *Information technology*

Description: Started in the search business in 1973 with emphasis on ethical performance. Tenacity in locating qualified candidates; reference checks; salary negotiations as desired by client. Personal involvement in all searches.

Salary Minimum: $40,000
Functions: MIS mgmt., Systems anal., Systems dev., Systems implem., Systems support, Network admin., Mgmt. consultants
Industries: Generalist, Mfg., Banking, Computer svcs., Mgmt. consulting, Insurance, Software

Lois L. Lindauer Searches
20 Park Plaza, Ste. 609
Boston, Massachusetts 02116
(617) 542-1335
Fax: (617) 542-2665
Email: LoisLind@aol.com

Key Contact - Specialty:
Ms. Lois L. Lindauer - *Non-profit management, fundraising, management*
Ms. Ruth Roy - *Non-profit management, fundraising, management*

Description: We perform contingency search, which combines the exclusivity and focus of retained search with the flexibility of a contingency fee structure.

Salary Minimum: $40,000
Functions: Senior mgmt., Middle mgmt., Sales mgmt., Non-profits

J. H. Lindell & Co.
560 1st St. E.
Sonoma, California 95476
(707) 935-1771
Fax: (707) 935-9596
Email: jhlindellco@earthlink.net

Key Contact - Specialty:
Mr. John H. Lindell
Ms. Leslie S. Lindell

Description: We specialize in executive and managerial recruitment and selection exclusively within the real estate development, construction and home building industries.

Salary Minimum: $50,000
Functions: General mgmt., Purchasing, Mkt. research, Mktg. mgmt., Sales mgmt., CFO's, Engineering
Industries: Construction, Real estate

Branches:
2212 Dupont Drive, Ste. U
Irvine, California 92612
(949) 252-1771
(949) 252-0774
Fax: (949) 252-1176
Key Contact - Specialty:
Mr. James D. Stevens
Ms. Donna Hoover

Linden Group, Inc.
6408 Honegger Drive, Ste. B
Charlotte, North Carolina 28211
(704) 367-0309
Fax: (704) 365-9883
Email: lindengroup@sprintmail.com

Key Contact - Specialty:
Mr. Bruce G. Lindal - *Automotive industry, food processing*

Description: Specializations include: food processing, automotive and medical devices. Disciplines include: production managers, plant managers, quality managers and engineers, plant engineers, general managers, R&D managers and vice presidents.

Salary Minimum: $40,000
Functions: Senior mgmt., Middle mgmt., Product dev., Production, Plant mgmt., Quality, Materials Plng.
Industries: Food/bev/tobacco, Metal products, Motor vehicles

Ginger Lindsey & Assoc., Inc.
8600 N. MacArthur Blvd., Ste. 114-180
Irving, Texas 75063
(972) 304-1089
Fax: (972) 304-0983
Email: glindsey@airmail.net

Key Contact - Specialty:
Ms. Ginger Lindsey - *Market research, competitive intelligence*

Description: Specialize in mid to senior level placements nationwide in market research with an emphasis on the high tech, telecommunications, financial services and packaged goods industries.

Salary Minimum: $35,000
Functions: Mkt. research
Industries: Food/bev/tobacco, Computer equip., Consumer electronics, Advertising/PR, High tech

Lineal Recruiting Services
46 Copper Kettle Rd.
Trumbull, Connecticut 06611
(203) 386-1091
Fax: (203) 386-9788
Email: lisalineal@lineal.com
Web: www.lineal.com

Key Contact - Specialty:
Ms. Lisa Lineal - *Electro-mechanical systems & service personnel*

Description: Technical placement of sales, service, management and hourlys exclusively in the electrical power and rotating apparatus industry, emphasizing service and repair of motors, controls, switchgear, transformers, drives, etc. Nationwide, company-paid fees.
Functions: Plant mgmt., Sales mgmt., Customer svc., Engineering, Technicians
Industries: Energy/utilities, Machinery/Appliances, Motor vehicles, Test/measurement equip., Misc. mfg., Svcs., Equip. svcs.

LJ Networking, Inc.
22454 Republican Ave.
Smithsburg, Maryland 21783
(800) 679-2110
Email: ljnetworking@erols.com

Key Contact - Specialty:
Ms. Lisa M. Johnson - *Physicians*

Description: Providing nationwide recruitment/placement of physicians in all specialties of healthcare settings. Our strong network of recruiters and resources supports our commitment to locating candidates perfectly suited for our clients.
Functions: Healthcare, Physicians, Minorities
Industries: Healthcare

Lloyd Prescott Assoc., Inc.
4902 Eisenhower Blvd., Ste. 185
Tampa, Florida 33634
(813) 881-1110
Fax: (813) 889-8458

Email: headhunt@earthlink.net
Web: www.lloydprescott.com

Key Contact - Specialty:
Mr. Sheldon M. Ginsberg - *Senior management*
Mr. Manuel F. Gordon - *Senior management*

Description: Generalist firm providing nationwide executive and professional search. Specializing in senior management, healthcare, legal, insurance, high tech, sales/marketing, finance/banking, manufacturing, consultants, food industry. Offering our clients the best and the brightest candidates in their field.

Salary Minimum: $70,000
Functions: Senior mgmt., Middle mgmt., Legal, Health admin., Sales mgmt., MIS mgmt., Engineering
Industries: Generalist, Food/bev/tobacco, Drugs mfg., Computer equip., Legal, Advertising/PR, Healthcare

Branches:
8753 Yates Drive, Ste. 200
Westminster, Colorado 80030
(303) 301-2651
Key Contact - Specialty:
Mr. William D. Ray - *Senior management*

7000 Central Pkwy. Ste. 1700
Atlanta, Georgia 30328
(770) 821-5330
Key Contact - Specialty:
Mr. Gene R. Kash - *Senior Management*

500 N. Michigan Ave., Suite 300
Chicago, Illinois 60611
(312) 396-4154
(708) 532-5447
Key Contact - Specialty:
Mr. Thomas J. Dato - *Senior management*
Mr. Daniel P. Barus - *Senior management*

509 Olive St., Ste. 600
St. Louis, Missouri 63101
(314) 259-4152
Key Contact - Specialty:
Mr. Christopher P. Otto - *Senior management*

300 Vanderbilt Motor Pkwy., Ste. 200
Hauppauge, New York 11788
(516) 439-6836
Key Contact - Specialty:
Mr. Gino Comparetto - *Senior management*

4210 W. Ridge Rd.
Rochester, New York 14626
(716) 225-2350
Key Contact - Specialty:
Mr. Steven M. Eisele - *Senior Management*

1373 E. Morehead #27
Charlotte, North Carolina 28204-2979
(704) 372-3463
Key Contact - Specialty:
Mr. Ronald N. Jackson - *Senior Management*

94 Northwoods Blvd.
Columbus, Ohio 43235
(614) 847-8205
Key Contact - Specialty:
Mr. Alan L. Gabriel - *Senior management*

Two Gateway Ctr., Ste. 620
Pittsburgh, Pennsylvania 15222-1402
(412) 355-2373
Key Contact - Specialty:
Mr. Richard F. Getzug - *Senior management*

International Branches:
Copenhagen

Lloyd Staffing
445 Broadhollow Rd.
Melville, New York 11747
(516) 777-7600
Fax: (516) 777-7626
Web: lloydstaffinghq.com

Key Contact - Specialty:
Mr. Merrill Banks

Description: National retained search and contingency placement with almost 30 years experience in many specialties, providing access to the highest quality candidates and positions. Industry leader in business products and computer fields.

Salary Minimum: $50,000
Functions: Sales & mktg., Finance, IT, Graphic artists
Industries: Finance, Communications, Real estate, High tech, Software, Biotech

LMB Assoc.
1468 Sunnyside Ave.
Highland Park, Illinois 60035
(847) 831-5990
Fax: (847) 831-5991
Email: lmb@xnet.com
Web: www.xnet.com/~lmb

Key Contact - Specialty:
Ms. Lorena M. Blonsky - *Information systems*

Description: Professional and executive search specializing in information systems.

Salary Minimum: $30,000
Functions: IT, MIS mgmt., Systems anal., Systems dev., Systems implem., Systems support
Industries: Generalist

Locus Inc.
P.O. Box 930
New Haven, West Virginia 25265-0930
(304) 882-2483
Fax: (304) 882-2217

Key Contact - Specialty:
Ms. Nancy Wainwright - *Technical, engineers, managers*

Description: Recruit to specific openings emphasizing quality over quantity. Like to work directly with engineering managers and personnel to ensure all requirements are considered.

Salary Minimum: $20,000
Functions: Generalist, Middle mgmt., Mfg., Engineering
Industries: Metal products, Machinery/Appliances, Motor vehicles, Misc. mfg., Aerospace

Affiliates:
Hetfield & Elliot, Inc
L. A. Neal & Assoc.

Loderman & Costello
(a division of Healthcare Executive Resources, Inc.)
3939 Roswell Rd. NE, Ste. 100
Marietta, Georgia 30062
(770) 977-3020
Fax: (770) 977-6549
Email: lowdermn@frontiernet.net
Web:

Key Contact - Specialty:
Mr. William Lowderman - *Healthcare executives, hospitals, HMOs, physician groups*

Description: Expanded, flexible and creative search arrangements in healthcare executive recruiting. Strong emphasis in all areas of nursing management, finance and information systems.

Salary Minimum: $50,000
Functions: Senior mgmt., Nurses, Health admin., CFO's, MIS mgmt.
Industries: Healthcare

Affiliates:
Career Continuation, Inc.

Logic Assoc., Inc.
67 Wall St., Ste. 2411
New York, New York 10005
(212) 227-8000
Fax: (212) 766-0188
Email:
logic.riskmgmt.recruiters@worldnet.att.net
Web: www.logicassociates.com

Key Contact - Specialty:
Mr. Bill Perry
Mr. Barry Citron
Mr. Abe Altschule
Mr. John Gallo

Description: Regarded as the national leader in corporate insurance/risk management recruiting.

Salary Minimum: $50,000
Functions: Directors, Senior mgmt., Middle mgmt., Health admin., Benefits, Budgeting, Risk mgmt.
Industries: Generalist, Food/bev/tobacco, Drugs mfg., Retail, Broadcast & Film, Insurance, Healthcare

Logix, Inc.
1601 Trapelo Rd.
Waltham, Massachusetts 02154
(781) 890-0500
Fax: (781) 890-3535
Email: logix@logixinc.com
Web: www.logixinc.com

Key Contact - Specialty:
Mr. David M. Zell - *Computer professionals*

Description: Rated #1 in New England for the 4th consecutive year. Our seasoned consulting staff is highly specialized in the search and selection of computer professionals ensuring maximum results in a quick, effective, professional manner.

Salary Minimum: $80,000
Functions: MIS mgmt., Systems anal., Systems dev., Systems implem., Systems support, R&D, Engineering
Industries: Finance, Computer svcs., New media, Broadcast & Film, Telecoms, High tech, Software

Branches:
1111 Bayhill Drive, Ste. 280
San Bruno, California 94066
(650) 827-0100
Fax: (650) 827-0155
Email: logixwest@logixinc.com
Key Contact - Specialty:
Mr. David M. Zell - *Computer professionals*

Logue & Rice Inc.
(a division of Accustaff, Inc.)
8000 Towers Crescent Drive, Ste. 650
Vienna, Virginia 22182-2700
(703) 761-4261
Fax: (703) 761-4248
Email: loguerice@aol.com

Key Contact - Specialty:
Mr. Raymond D. Rice
Mr. Kenneth F. Logue

Description: Executive and management search in Washington, D.C. area. Provide contingent and retained services for corporate and non-profit clients. Full range from executives to professionals leaving Big Six accounting firms.

Salary Minimum: $35,000
Functions: Generalist, General mgmt., HR mgmt., Finance, IT, Mgmt. consultants
Industries: Generalist, Finance, Mgmt. consulting, Telecoms, High tech, Software, Biotech

London & Company
360 Lexington Ave., Ste. 1902
New York, New York 10017
(212) 599-2200
Fax: (212) 599-2014

Key Contact - Specialty:
Ms. Anne London - *Attorneys*

Description: Premier executive search firm placing attorneys in corporations and law firms. National and international search capabilities and strong record of achievement by a team of experienced consultants. Integrity, service and professionalism are our hallmarks.

Salary Minimum: $70,000
Functions: Attorneys

London Executive Consultants Inc.
380 Wellington St., Ste. 1420
London, Ontario N6A 5B5
Canada
(519) 434-9167
Fax: (519) 434-6318
Email: lec.oem@odyssey.on.ca
Web: www.oemsearch.com

Key Contact - Specialty:
Mr. Paul Nelson - *Technical, manufacturing management, engineering*

Salary Minimum: $40,000
Functions: Mfg., Materials, Sales & mktg., HR mgmt., Finance, IT, Engineering
Industries: Mfg., Transportation, Environmental svcs., Aerospace, Packaging

Affiliates:
Kitchener Executive Consultants
Toronto Executive Consultants

Longo Associates
4040 Civic Ctr. Drive, Ste. 200
San Rafael, California 94903-4150
(415) 472-1400
Email: rlongo@longo.com
Web: www.longo.com

Key Contact - Specialty:
Mr. Roger Longo - *Technical positions*

Description: A firm with vision, state of the art computer based technology, professional approach and successful track record. See web page for background.
Functions: Generalist, Senior mgmt., Quality, Mkt. research, Systems implem., R&D, Engineering
Industries: Computer equip., High tech, Software

Lord & Albus Co.
10314 Sweetwood Drive
Houston, Texas 77070
(281) 955-5673
Web: www.hypercon.com/albus

Key Contact - Specialty:
Mr. John P. Albus - *Manufacturing*

Description: Personalized approach to each search assignment, we will assist in defining the clients needs, coordinate all interviewing, reference checks, salary negotiations-serve as an extension of your company EEO employer.

Salary Minimum: $35,000
Functions: General mgmt., Mfg., Materials, HR mgmt., IT, R&D, Engineering
Industries: Generalist, Mfg., Packaging, High tech, Software, Biotech

Louis Search Group, Inc.
13 Gavel Rd.
Sayreville, New Jersey 08872
(732) 257-3373
Fax: (732) 257-1393
Email: jobs4u@earthlink.com

Key Contact - Specialty:
Mr. Gregory Louis - *Sales, sales management, exhibit, trade show*

Description: Executive search and placement of superior sales and sales management talent for all industries. Experts in the exhibit/trade show industry, all disciplines. 20 years experience in recruiting and training sales superstars.

Salary Minimum: $20,000
Functions: Advertising, Mktg. mgmt., Direct mktg., Customer svc., PR, Architects, Graphic artists
Industries: Wholesale, Finance, Svcs., Communications, Packaging, Software, Healthcare

Scott Love Assoc., Inc.
8300 E. Dixileta Dr. #258
Scottsdale, Arizona 85262
(602) 473-9088
Fax: (602) 473-9089
Email: recruit@neta.com
Web: www.scottlove.com

Key Contact - Specialty:
Mr. Scott T. Love - *Construction*

Description: Specific and focused efforts recruiting exceptional management talent for building contractors and subcontractors.

Salary Minimum: $55,000
Functions: Senior mgmt., Middle mgmt.
Industries: Construction

Bruce Lowery & Assoc.
P.O. Box 166
Ada, Michigan 49301-0166
(616) 676-3500
Fax: (616) 676-3516

Key Contact - Specialty:
Mr. Bruce N. Lowery - *CEOs, COOs, CFOs, sales, manufacturing management*

Description: Search firm serving mid-western United States specializing in middle and upper administrative, finance, sales, marketing, engineering, manufacturing and general management positions.

Salary Minimum: $50,000
Functions: General mgmt., Admin. svcs., Mfg., Materials, Sales & mktg., HR mgmt., Finance
Industries: Mfg., Svcs., Government, Environmental svcs.

Lucas Assoc.

3384 Peachtree Rd., Ste. 730
Atlanta, Georgia 30326
(404) 239-5625
Fax: (404) 239-5694
Email: cdemartino@lucasgroupcareers.com
Web: www.lucasassoc.com

Key Contact - Specialty:
Ms. Cathy deMartino - *Chemical, consumer, services, medical, computer, telecommunications*
Mr. Tom McGee - *Chemical, consumer, services, medical, computer*

Description: 40 executive recruiters nationally, each an expert in top sales management, marketing, manufacturing management talent and in their specific niche marketplace.

Salary Minimum: $50,000
Functions: General mgmt., Mfg., Materials, Sales & mktg., Engineering
Industries: Food/bev/tobacco, Chemicals, Medical devices, Finance, Communications, Packaging, High tech

Branches:
2600 Michelson Drive, Ste. 1550
Irvine, California 92612
(714) 833-2013
Fax: (714) 660-0126
Key Contact - Specialty:
Mr. Tony Tommarello - *Food service, distribution, computer, services, medical*

5300 Memorial, Ste. 270
Houston, Texas 77007
(713) 864-7733
Fax: (713) 864-7887
Key Contact - Specialty:
Mr. Larry Austin - *Packaging, wireless communications, software services, services, construction*

Lucas Group

2 Burke Lane, Ste. 110
Syosset, New York 11791
(516) 338-1144
Fax: (516) 338-6777

Key Contact - Specialty:
Mr. Al Weiner - *Senior operations, manufacturing management, materials management, purchasing, quality assurance*

Salary Minimum: $50,000
Functions: Middle mgmt., Quality, Purchasing, Distribution, Benefits, R&D, Engineering
Industries: Medical devices, Computer equip., Consumer electronics, Test/measurement equip., Human resource svcs., Aerospace, High tech

---

Ludwig & Assoc., Inc.

800 Bay Laurel Court
Chesapeake, Virginia 23320
(757) 547-5900
Fax: (757) 547-9670
Email: raludwig@erols.com
Web: www.ludwig-recruit.com

Key Contact - Specialty:
Mr. Bob Ludwig - *Sales & marketing, consumer products*

Description: The key principal has 14 years of experience as a sales manager in the consumer products industry. The firm specializes in placing sales and marketing professionals with major consumer product companies.

Salary Minimum: $50,000
Functions: Senior mgmt., Middle mgmt., Advertising, Mkt. research, Mktg. mgmt., Sales mgmt., Customer svc.
Industries: Food/bev/tobacco, Soap/perfume/cosmetics, Entertainment

---

Lutz Associates

9 Stephen St.
Manchester, Connecticut 06040
(860) 647-9338
Fax: (860) 647-7918

Key Contact - Specialty:
Mr. Allen Lutz - *Engineering*

Description: Executive search and placement: engineering, scientists, manufacturing and marketing nationwide. Specializing in consumer products, medical devices, electronics, rotating machinery, office equipment, CAD/CAM, CIM and AI.

Salary Minimum: $35,000
Functions: Mfg., Materials, Mktg. mgmt., IT, R&D, Engineering, Graphic artists
Industries: Medical devices, Metal products, Machinery/Appliances, Consumer electronics, Telecoms, High tech, Software

---

Lybrook Assoc., Inc.

P.O. Box 572
Newport, Rhode Island 02840
(401) 683-6990
Fax: (401) 683-6355
Email: chemistry@lybrook.com
Web: lybrook.com

Key Contact - Specialty:
Ms. Karen Lybrook - *Chemistry, senior positions, scientists, managers, executives*
Mr. Christian Lybrook - *Sales & marketing, quality control, chemical engineering*
Mr. David Lybrook - *Plastics, coatings, biotechnology, pharmaceuticals, chemical engineering*

Description: Chemistry specialists. Recruiting R&D/production/process chemists, engineers, technical sales/marketing and related scientists and managers: analytical, specialty chemicals, biotechnology, polymers, paper, plastics, organic, pharmaceutical, QA/QC, coatings, instrumentation, food, etc.- BS, MS and PhD levels nationwide.

Salary Minimum: $30,000
Functions: General mgmt., Product dev., Production, Quality, Sales mgmt., R&D, Engineering
Industries: Mfg., Paper, Chemicals, Drugs mfg., Plastics/rubber, Paints/petroleum products, Biotech

---

Lynne Palmer Executive Recruitment, Inc.

342 Madison Ave., Ste. 1430
New York, New York 10173
(212) 883-0203
Fax: (212) 883-0149
Email: lynnepalmer@worldnet.att.net

Key Contact - Specialty:
Ms. Susan Gordon

Description: We handle entry to senior level positions in the communications/publishing industry. Our nationwide client base includes magazine, book, public relations and multimedia companies.
Functions: General mgmt., Sales & mktg., HR mgmt., Finance, IT
Industries: Human resource svcs., Communications, Advertising/PR, Publishing, New media

Branches:
4107 Pebblebrook Drive
Bloomington, Minnesota 55437
(612) 835-9043
Fax: (612) 832-9298
Email: southbmzb@aol.com
Key Contact - Specialty:
Ms. Mary Southwell

Lynx, Inc.

420 Bedford St., Ste. 200
Lexington, Massachusetts 02173
(617) 274-6400
Fax: (617) 274-6300
Email: discover@lynxinc.com
Web: www.lynxinc.com

Key Contact - Specialty:
Mr. Philip J. Hurd - *Accounting & finance*
Ms. Sophia Navickas - *Software*

Description: Specialized high-quality contingency placement. Our concentrations are in software technology, information technology and accounting/finance.
Functions: Finance, IT, Systems dev., Systems implem., Systems support, Network admin., DB admin.
Industries: Mfg., Finance, Svcs., Computer svcs., Insurance, High tech, Software

---

Lyons & Assoc., Inc.
7815 Loch Glen Drive
Crystal Lake, Illinois 60014-3317
(815) 477-9292
Fax: (815) 477-9296

Key Contact - Specialty:
Mr. Kent T. Lyons - *Graphic arts (middle & senior management)*

Description: With a staff extensively experienced in the graphics arts industry, we provide detailed, thorough service to the printing and allied industries.

Salary Minimum: $45,000
Functions: Senior mgmt., Middle mgmt., Production, Plant mgmt., Quality, Sales mgmt., Direct mktg.
Industries: Printing, New media, Packaging

M H Executive Search Group
P.O. Box 868068
Plano, Texas 75086-8068
(972) 578-1511
Email: mhgroup@gte.net
Web: home1.gte.net/mhgroup/index.htm

Key Contact - Specialty:
Mr. Mike Hochwalt - *Packaging, sales & marketing, flexographics*
Mr. Lee Walt - *BSME's, marketing managers, ISO 9000, quality managers, industrial marketplace*

Description: We recruit qualified individuals in the packaging and graphics industries in sales, marketing, plant and management personnel. Located in the Dallas area, we have been recruiting nationally since 1978. Multinational.

Salary Minimum: $35,000
Functions: Plant mgmt., Quality, Packaging, Mktg. mgmt., Sales mgmt., R&D, Engineering
Industries: Paper, Plastics/rubber, Packaging

M. K. & Assoc.
309 E. Brady St.
Butler, Pennsylvania 16001
(724) 285-7474
Fax: (724) 285-8339

Key Contact - Specialty:
Mr. John G. Mossman - *Food*
Ms. Maureen Knowlson - *Food*

Description: From the benchtop to the plant floor to the boardroom, the people of the food industry are our business. Let's work together to design a personalized strategy for your search.
Functions: Middle mgmt., Product dev., Plant mgmt., Quality, Sales mgmt., R&D, Engineering
Industries: Food/bev/tobacco

M.C. Executive Search
3461 Castro Valley Blvd.
Castro Valley, California 94546
(800) 875-7969
Fax: (510) 538-5585
Email: getetdone@aol.com

Key Contact - Specialty:
Mr. Mike Cornelison - *Manufacturing, consumer, food, products*
Ms. Pat Dowell - *Manufacturing, financial*

Description: 13 years experience placing technical and administrative positions within the manufacturing, consumer, metal fabrication, pulp & paper, machinery and keyword manufacturing.
Functions: Product dev., Production, Automation, HR mgmt., CFO's, Budgeting, Engineering
Industries: Food/bev/tobacco, Soap/perfume/cosmetics, Plastics/rubber, Paints/petroleum products, Metal products, Machinery/Appliances, Packaging

---

Carol Maden Group
2019 Cunningham Drive, Ste. 218
Hampton, Virginia 23666
(757) 827-9010
Fax: (757) 827-9081
Email: Cmaden@hroads.net

Key Contact - Specialty:
Ms. Carol Maden
Ms. Patricia Fridley - *Information technology*
Ms. Janet Smitter - *Engineering*
Mr. Michael Mahoney - *Sales & marketing*

Description: We offer 26 years seasoned experience in all aspects of the employment arena. Our staff conducts a customized tailored search with highly skilled professional recruiters leading the way. We are accurate, detailed and thorough in their recruitment endeavors.
Functions: Directors, Customer svc., PR, Systems implem., Systems support, Network admin., DB admin.
Industries: Mfg., Pharmaceutical svcs., Accounting

Madison Executive Search, Inc.
4 Birch Pkwy.
Sparta, New Jersey 07871
(973) 729-5520
Fax: (973) 729-9920
Email: mcgroup@planet.net

Key Contact - Specialty:
Mr. Bill Kay

Description: Specialization in the search for telecommunication professionals, is our key competitive advantage. Telecommunications is our area of specialization and core area of focus. Positions include: sales, marketing, general administrative management, operational and technical.

Salary Minimum: $40,000
Functions: General mgmt., Directors, Senior mgmt., Middle mgmt., Sales & mktg., Sales mgmt., IT
Industries: Communications, Broadcast & Film, Telecoms, High tech, Software

---

Magellan Int'l., L.P.
24 Greenway Plaza, Ste. 1110
Houston, Texas 77046-2401
(713) 439-7485
Fax: (713) 439-7489
Email: smt@milp.com
Web: magellanintl.com

Key Contact - Specialty:
Mr. Steven M. Tatar - *Auditing (financial & IT), management consulting*
Mr. Michael C. Craig - *Management consulting*
Mr. Timothy W. Johnson - *Management consulting*
Mr. Jonathan H. Phillips - *Management consulting*
Mr. Charlie W. Waldron
Mr. Norton H. Berlin

Description: We specialize in enhancing our clients business by providing the highest caliber candidates. We also give equal, if not greater, attention to the individual needs of all of our candidates.

Salary Minimum: $100,000
Functions: Senior mgmt., CFO's, Risk mgmt., Systems implem., Engineering, Mgmt. consultants, Attorneys
Industries: Energy/utilities, Mfg., Chemicals, Invest. banking, Pharmaceutical svcs., Mgmt. consulting, High tech

---

Magnum Search
1000 E. Golfhurst Ave.
Mt. Prospect, Illinois 60056
(847) 577-0007

Key Contact - Specialty:
Mr. Arthur N. Kristufek

Description: Over 30 years HR management level experience with emphasis in search and recruiting for the metal fabrication & electronics industries.

Salary Minimum: $35,000
Functions: Generalist, Mfg., Materials, Sales & mktg., HR mgmt., Personnel, Mgmt. consultants
Industries: Generalist, Paper, Plastics/ rubber, Metal products, Machinery/ Appliances, Consumer electronics, Law enfcmt.

Maiola & Co.

12900 Lake Ave., Ste. PH29
Cleveland, Ohio 44107
(216) 521-0011
Fax: (216) 521-0064

Key Contact - Specialty:
Ms. Diana E. Maiola - *Printing, graphic arts*
Ms. Carol M. Pulito - *Printing, graphic arts*

Description: We are highly specialized industry experts who form a very cohesive, experienced team which is capable of servicing the entire executive search, marketing and management consulting needs of a corporation.

Salary Minimum: $30,000
Industries: Printing

Affiliates:
Dr. Angelo C. Valenti Ph.D.

Major, Hagen & Africa

500 Washington St.
San Francisco, California 94111
(415) 956-1010
Fax: (415) 398-2425
Email: info@mhasearch.com
Web: www.mhasearch.com

Key Contact - Specialty:
Mr. Robert A. Major, Jr. - *Attorneys*
Ms. Martha Fay Africa - *Attorneys*
Mr. Charles J. Fanning, Jr. - *Attorneys*
Ms. Kimberly Fullerton - *Attorneys*
Ms. Anna Marie Armstrong - *Attorneys*
Mr. Scott M. Dubin - *Attorneys*
Ms. Amy L. Keyser - *Attorneys*

Description: Exclusively attorney search and placement of partners, associates, corporate counsel. Provides legal search services to law firms and corporations, nationally and internationally, through five domestic offices and correspondent offices in London and Hong Kong.
Functions: Attorneys
Industries: Legal

Branches:
310 University Ave., Ste. 201
Palo Alto, California 94301
(650) 853-1010
Fax: (650) 833-6949
Email: WJEscher@aol.com
Key Contact - Specialty:
Mr. W. Jon Escher - *Attorneys*
Ms. Julie Qureshi - *Attorneys*

1355 Peachtree St., Ste. 1125
Atlanta, Georgia 30309
(404) 875-1070
Fax: (404) 875-1090
Email: mhageorgia@aol.com
Key Contact - Specialty:
Mr. Wesley Q. Dobbs - *Attorneys*
Ms. Catherine P. Butts - *Attorneys*

35 E. Wacker Drive, Ste. 2150
Chicago, Illinois 60601
(312) 372-1010
Fax: (312) 372-1696
Email: mhachi@aol.com
Key Contact - Specialty:
Ms. Laura J. Hagen - *Attorneys*
Ms. Miriam J. Frank - *Attorneys*
Ms. Lydia S. Marti - *Attorneys*
Mr. Quentin D. Calkins - *Attorneys*
Ms. Susan J. Mitchell - *Attorneys*
Ms. Jillian Jester - *Attorneys*
Mr. James Oberlander - *Attorneys*

570 Lexington Ave., 26th Floor
New York, New York 10022
(212) 421-1011
Fax: (212) 421-1042
Email: jal@mhany.com
Key Contact - Specialty:
Ms. June Eichbaum - *Attorneys*
Mr. Jonathan Lindsey - *Attorneys*
Ms. Janet Markoff - *Attorneys*
Mr. Philip Bradford - *Attorneys*
Ms. Connie Kam - *Attorneys*
Ms. Allison Ross - *Attorneys*
Ms. Leslie Gold - *Attorneys*
Ms. Laura Segal - *Attorneys*
Ms. Helen Griffin - *Attorneys*

Affiliates:
Hughes-Castell Ltd.

Major Legal Services, Inc.

1111 Chester Ave.
510 Park Plaza
Cleveland, Ohio 44114
(216) 579-9782
Fax: (216) 579-1662
Web: www.lawplacement.com

Key Contact - Specialty:
Mr. Dennis J. Foster - *Legal (attorneys, paralegals, support staff)*
Ms. Deborah L. Peters - *Legal (attorneys, paralegals, support staff)*
Ms. Kathryn Lenz - *Legal (attorneys, paralegals, support staff)*
Ms. Lesley Kinkopf - *Legal (attorneys, paralegals, support staff)*
Ms. Susan Lippens - *Legal (attorneys, paralegals, support staff)*

Description: Specialists in temporary and permanent recruiting of attorneys, paralegals, secretaries and other support staff since 1989. Client base: Ohio law firms and corporate legal departments.
Functions: Nurses, Personnel, Mgmt. consultants, Attorneys, Paralegals
Industries: Legal, Computer svcs., Mgmt. consulting, Human resource svcs.

Major Search
(a division of Major Consultants, Inc.)

500 N. Franklin Tnpk., Ste. 17
Ramsey, New Jersey 07446
(201) 934-9666
Fax: (201) 818-0339
Web: www.majorinc.com

Key Contact - Specialty:
Mr. Lou Ordini - *Management, professional, executive*
Mr. Cas Kaffke - *Management, professional, executive*
Ms. Pam Ericson - *Management, professional, executive*

Description: Combine professional recruiting with hands on consulting services in all human resource and labor relations areas. Services include: arbitration, benefit analyses, compensation plans, contract negotiations, policy development and staffing.

Salary Minimum: $25,000
Functions: Generalist, General mgmt., Mfg., HR mgmt., Engineering
Industries: Generalist

The Mallard Group

3322 Oak Borough
Ft. Wayne, Indiana 46804
(219) 436-3970
Fax: (219) 436-7012
Email: mallard04@sprynet.com

Key Contact - Specialty:
Mr. Robert Hoffman
Ms. Linda Hoffman

Description: Domestic and international recruitment of professionals in the appliance and HVAC/R industries, including suppliers to those industries.

Salary Minimum: $30,000
Functions: Product dev., Production, Plant mgmt., Quality, Purchasing, Mktg. mgmt., Sales mgmt.
Industries: Metal products, Machinery/ Appliances, Consumer electronics

Managed Care Consultants

11461 N. 109th Way
Scottsdale, Arizona 85259
(602) 391-2992
Fax: (602) 391-9781

Email: info@mgdcare.com
Web: www.mdgcare.com

Key Contact - Specialty:
Mr. Albert M. Anderer - *Managed care*

Description: We recruit in healthcare, specifically managed care, recruiting for executive, middle management and specialist positions in all functional areas of managed care. Our areas of expertise are operations, administration, marketing, sales, finance, medical management, member services, provider relations, contracting and claims.
Functions: General mgmt., Healthcare, Sales & mktg., HR mgmt., Finance, IT
Industries: Healthcare

Branches:
8260 E. Raintree Drive
Scottsdale, Arizona 85260
(602) 998-7914
Fax: (602) 998-5574
Email: info@mgdcare.com
Web: www.mgdcare.com
Key Contact - Specialty:
Ms. Peggy Breadon - *Managed care*

Managed Care Resources
P.O. Box 3004
Coppell, Texas 75019
(972) 304-7979
Fax: (972) 304-7980
Email: mcr2000@gte.net

Key Contact - Specialty:
Mr. Thomas L. Sheehan - *Managed healthcare*
Ms. Susan C. Bowman - *Managed healthcare*
Ms. Shirley Knauf - *Managed healthcare*

Description: We specialize in the recruitment and placement of professionals in the managed healthcare industry.

Salary Minimum: $30,000
Functions: Directors, Middle mgmt., Health admin., Mktg. mgmt., Sales mgmt., Customer svc., Benefits
Industries: Insurance, Healthcare

Management Advisors Int'l., Inc.
P.O. Box 3708
Hickory, North Carolina 28603
(704) 324-5772
Fax: (704) 324-4831
Email: bcastell@maisearch.com
Web: maisearch.com

Key Contact - Specialty:
Mr. William J. Castell, Jr. - *Mortgage banking*

Description: We are a management consulting firm specializing in executive search/professional placement for the mortgage banking, commercial banking, thrift, real estate finance, healthcare, data processing, accounting, international business industries worldwide.

Salary Minimum: $50,000
Functions: Sales & mktg., Mktg. mgmt., Sales mgmt., Finance, CFO's, Cash mgmt., Int'l.
Industries: Construction, Finance, Banking, Brokers, Real estate, Biotech, Healthcare

Branches:
4600 Park Rd., Ste. 400
Charlotte, North Carolina 28209
(704) 521-9595
Fax: (704) 527-6616
Key Contact - Specialty:
Ms. Ginia M. Polyzos - *Mortgage banking, corporate banking, healthcare, accounting, finance, sales*

Management Assoc.
2700 Augustine Drive, Ste. 255
Santa Clara, California 95054
(408) 727-4717
(408) 727-4970
Fax: (408) 727-2544
Email: staffing@mgmtassoc.com
Web: www.dice.com/ma

Key Contact - Specialty:
Mr. Howard Goldman

Description: Specializes in R&D engineering and MIS professionals. We are a mature, ethical company that has learned to listen to both the clients and candidates needs.

Salary Minimum: $40,000
Functions: Sales & mktg., IT, R&D
Industries: Computer equip., High tech

Management Assoc.
(a division of the Systech Organization, Inc.)
9735 Magledt Rd.
Baltimore, Maryland 21234-1818
(410) 665-6033
Fax: (410) 665-8843
Email: aasoma@aol.com

Key Contact - Specialty:
Mr. Walter J. Sistek - *Global generalist*
Mr. George Hankins - *Financial services*
Ms. Beverly Hartman - *Human resource director, healthcare*
Ms. Joyce Ralph Herman - *Marketing, advertising*
Mr. Craig Joseph - *High technology, biotechnology*
Mr. William McFaul - *Generalist*
Ms. Catherine E. Meehling - *University*

Description: Practice concentrates on senior management appointments across wide spectrum of industry including banking, financial services and insurance.

Salary Minimum: $50,000
Functions: Senior mgmt., Physicians, Advertising, Benefits, CFO's, MIS mgmt., Int'l.
Industries: Generalist, Finance, Human resource svcs., Communications, High tech, Biotech, Healthcare

Affiliates:
First Advisory Services Int'l., Inc.

Management Association Network
P.O. Box 1055
Milwaukee, Wisconsin 53201-1055
(414) 456-0731
Fax: (414) 456-0732
Email: man@execpc.com

Key Contact - Specialty:
Mr. Michael A. Noonan - *Manufacturing*

Description: National certified MBE/NA search firm conducts searches in manufacturing and information management systems industries.

Salary Minimum: $30,000
Functions: Mfg., Purchasing, HR mgmt., IT, Engineering, Specialized services, Minorities
Industries: Generalist, Mfg., Metal products, Computer equip., Aerospace, Packaging, Software

---

Management Consultants Corporate Recruiters
8912 E. Pinnacle Peak Rd., Ste. 281
Scottsdale, Arizona 85255
(800) 813-8258
Fax: (800) 838-6757
Web: exsearch@sprynet.com

Key Contact - Specialty:
Mr. John Costas

Description: We are a national company specializing in sales and sales management positions within the graphic arts/printing industry. Areas of focus are commercial, book, publication (magazine), catalog, insert, packaging, technical and documentation printing.

Salary Minimum: $40,000
Functions: Sales mgmt.
Industries: Printing

Management Decision Systems, Inc. (MDSI)
466 Kinderkamack Rd.
Oradell, New Jersey 07649
(201) 986-1200
Fax: (201) 986-1210
Email: amymdsi@ix.netcom.com
Web: www.mdsisearch.com

Key Contact - Specialty:
Mr. Brian Mahoney - *Computer software (sales, sales management, technical support)*
Mr. Angelo Messina - *Computer software (sales, sales management, technical support)*
Mr. Richard Deakmann - *Computer software (sales, sales management, technical support)*
Mr. Victor Delray - *Computer software (sales, sales management, technical support)*

Description: Data processing sales specialists. Sales, sales management, pre-sales positions within the computer vendor community.

Salary Minimum: $50,000
Functions: Sales mgmt., Systems anal.
Industries: Computer svcs., High tech, Software

Affiliates:
Corporate Dynamix

Management One Consultants

1200 Bay St., Ste. 501
Toronto, Ontario M5R 2A5
Canada
(416) 961-6100
Fax: (416) 961-7018

Key Contact - Specialty:
Mr. Frank Edelberg - *Marketing, sales, finance*
Ms. Dana Stewart - *Marketing*

Description: Our strength is developing long-term relationships with top-notch clients and candidates. You always deal with the partners. Our clients are represented by us in the marketplace in the most professional manner.

Salary Minimum: $60,000
Functions: Senior mgmt., Mkt. research, Mktg. mgmt., Sales mgmt., Direct mktg., CFO's, Mgmt. consultants
Industries: Food/bev/tobacco, Soap/perfume/cosmetics, Consumer electronics, Banking, Advertising/PR, Telecoms, Insurance

---

Management Recruiters International, Inc. (MRI)
(a subsidiary of CDI Corp.)

200 Public Sq., 31st Floor
Cleveland, Ohio 44114-2301
(216) 696-1122
Fax: (216) 696-3221
Email: abs@mrinet.com
Web: www.mrinet.com

Key Contact - Specialty:
Mr. Allen B. Salikof
Mr. Alan R. Schonberg
Mr. William E. Aglinsky
Mr. Robert A. Angell
Mr. David Oberting
Mr. Robert Gandal
Mr. Donald L. Goldman
Mr. David L. Marth
Mr. Marc L. Blessing
Mr. Jerry R. Hill
Mr. Gary P. Williams
Mr. Vincent J. Webb
Mr. Doug Young

Description: Search and recruitment - mid to senior management and professional. Also provides interim staffing, outplacement, outsourcing, assessment programs and international capability and video-conferencing services. Full range of staffing services.

Salary Minimum: $45,000
Functions: Generalist
Industries: Generalist

Branches:
200 Clinton Ave. W., Ste. 802
AmSouth Ctr.
Huntsville, Alabama 35801-4933
(205) 536-7572
Fax: (205) 536-7589
Email: mrnalabama@aol.com
Key Contact - Specialty:
Ms. Renate Banks

215 Fidalgo Ave., Ste. 101
Kenai, Alaska 99611-7798
(907) 283-5633
Fax: (907) 283-6460
Email: alaska!manager@mrinet.com
Key Contact - Specialty:
Ms. Jeannine Morse
Mr. Aaron Morse

235 N. Freeport Drive, Ste. 6
Nogales, Arizona 85621-2423
(520) 281-9440
Fax: (520) 287-3789
Key Contact - Specialty:
Mr. Joseph Garcia

6900 E. Camelback Rd., Ste. 935
Bank of America Bldg.
Scottsdale, Arizona 85251
(602) 941-1515
Fax: (602) 941-1430
Email: scott!manager@mrinet.com
Key Contact - Specialty:
Mr. Dick A. Govig
Mr. Todd Govig

P.O. Box 758
Paragould, Arkansas 72451
(501) 236-1800
Fax: (501) 236-1142
Key Contact - Specialty:
Mr. Mark S. Woodruff

102 N. First Street
Rogers, Arkansas 72756-4511
(501) 621-0706
Fax: (501) 621-9753
Email: rogers!manager@mrinet.com
Key Contact - Specialty:
Mr. Al McEwen

Stonebridge Prof. Village
15 Williamsburg Lane, Ste. A
Chico, California 95926-2225
(916) 892-9898
Fax: (916) 892-8668
Email: mrchico!manager@mrinet.com
Key Contact - Specialty:
Mr. Barry Barsuglia

150 Clovis Ave., Ste. 104
Clovis, California 93612
(209) 297-5900
Fax: (209) 297-5919
Email: nfresno!manager@mrinet.com
Key Contact - Specialty:
Ms. Kay Lemon

100 Corporate Pointe, Ste. 380
Culver City, California 90230
(310) 670-3040
Fax: (310) 670-2981
Email: culver!manager@mrinet.com

1724 Picasso, Ste. E
Davis, California 95616-0547
(530) 297-5400
Fax: (530) 297-5401
Key Contact - Specialty:
Mr. Dave Kushan

2222 Francisco Drive, Ste. 430
El Dorado Hills, California 95762
(916) 939-9780
Fax: (916) 939-9785
Email: manager@eldorado.mrinet.com
Key Contact - Specialty:
Mr. Stan Gardner

16027 Ventura Blvd., Ste. 320
Encino, California 91436-2740
(818) 906-3155
Fax: (818) 906-0642
Email: consult@mri-la.com
Key Contact - Specialty:
Mr. David Greenfader

3100 Mowry Ave., Ste. 206
Fremont, California 94538-1509
(510) 505-5125
Fax: (510) 505-5123
Email: mrfrmt@ix.netcom.com
Key Contact - Specialty:
Mr. Jim L. Anderson

P.O. Box 1998
Glendora, California 91741-1998
(818) 963-4503
Fax: (818) 857-7468
Email: mrglendora@msn.com
Key Contact - Specialty:
Mr. Matt J. Albanese

11925 Wilshire Blvd., Ste. 211
Los Angeles, California 90025
(310) 473-0803
Fax: (310) 473-3523
Key Contact - Specialty:
Mr. Richard F. Roberts

15405 Los Gatos Blvd., Ste. 203
Los Gatos, California 95032-2500
(408) 358-8707
Fax: (408) 358-0307
Key Contact - Specialty:
Mr. Kenneth W. Keegan
Ms. Elizabeth A. Dickerson
Ms. Kira lee Keegan

869 El Camino Real
Menlo Park, California 94025-4807
(650) 617-9440
Fax: (650) 617-9445
Email: ktn@menlo.mrinet.com
Key Contact - Specialty:
Mr. Bruce Solomon

Quintana Plaza
365 Quintana Rd., Ste. D
Morro Bay, California 93442-2000
(805) 772-1964
Fax: (805) 772-1946
Email: mrmorro!manager@mrinet.com
Key Contact - Specialty:
Mr. Ron Glaza

480 Roland Way, Ste. 103
Oakland, California 94621-2065
(510) 635-7901
Fax: (510) 562-7237
Email: mrsc@dnai.com
Key Contact - Specialty:
Mr. Tom S. Thrower

One City Blvd. W., Ste. 710
Orange, California 92868
(714) 978-0500
Fax: (714) 978-8064
Email: orange!manager@mrinet.com
Key Contact - Specialty:
Mr. Russell M. Muller

Embarcadero Corp Center
2479 E. Bayshore Rd., Ste. 701
Palo Alto, California 94303-3207
(650) 852-0667
Fax: (650) 852-0618
Email: hanako@paloalto.mrinet.com
Key Contact - Specialty:
Mr. Hanako Yanagi

575 Price St., Ste. 313
Pismo Beach, California 93449-2553
(805) 773-2816
Fax: (805) 773-2819
Key Contact - Specialty:
Ms. Mary Gilbert
Mr. Keith A. Gilbert

367 Civic Drive, Ste. 7
Pleasant Hill, California 94523
(925) 602-4600
Fax: (925) 602-4602
Email: plsnthil!manager@mrinet.com
Key Contact - Specialty:
Mr. Jeff L. Cundick

9455 Ridgehaven Court, Ste. 100
San Diego, California 92123-1647
(619) 565-6600
Fax: (619) 565-4937
Email: sandiego!manager@mrinet.com
Key Contact - Specialty:
Mr. Harvey J. Baron - *General management*

Montgomery Sq.
208 W. Main St., Ste. 10
Visalia, California 93291-6262
(209) 741-7900
Fax: (209) 741-7909
Email: recruit@theworks.com
Key Contact - Specialty:
Mr. Jim Ely

P.O. Box 4657
Boulder, Colorado 80306-4657
(303) 447-9900
Fax: (303) 447-9536
Email: sharon@mrboulder.com
Key Contact - Specialty:
Ms. Sharon W. Hunter

P.O. Box 2279
Boulder, Colorado 80306
(303) 447-9940
Fax: (303) 447-0062
Key Contact - Specialty:
Ms. Janet N. Arnold

10 Boulder Crescent, Ste. 302 B
Colorado Springs, Colorado 80903
(719) 389-0600
Fax: (719) 635-2207
Key Contact - Specialty:
Mr. Bud O. Reynolds

1888 Sherman St.
Sherman Plaza, Ste. 600
Denver, Colorado 80203-1159
(303) 832-5250
Fax: (303) 832-5211
Email: mridenver@mridenver.com
Key Contact - Specialty:
Mr. John Kirschner

Cobblestone Plaza, Ste. 210
13275 E. Fremont Place
Englewood, Colorado 80112-3909
(303) 649-9895
Fax: (303) 649-1523
Email: manager@hilands.mrinet.com
Key Contact - Specialty:
Mr. Darryl C. Shaw

2922 Evergreen Pkwy., Ste. 307
Evergreen, Colorado 80439
(303) 670-2002
Fax: (303) 670-2005
Key Contact - Specialty:
Ms. Vicki A. Neumann
Mr. Pete Neumann

12600 W. Colfax Ave., Ste. C-440
Lakewood, Colorado 80215-3736
(303) 233-8600
Fax: (303) 233-8479
Email: goldhill!manager@mrinet.com
Key Contact - Specialty:
Mr. Rodney D. Bonner

8771 Wolff Court, Ste. 125
Westminster, Colorado 80030-3683
(303) 650-8870
Fax: (303) 650-8871
Email: webmaster@mrwestminster.com
Key Contact - Specialty:
Ms. Gloria Kellerhals

P.O. Box 5936
Woodland Park, Colorado 80866
(719) 686-1026
Fax: (719) 686-1027
Email: woodprk!manager@mrinet.com
Key Contact - Specialty:
Mr. Steve Johnson

2139 Silas Deane Hwy.
Rocky Hill, Connecticut 06067-2336
(860) 563-1268
Fax: (860) 563-2305
Email: mrhtfds@aol.com
Key Contact - Specialty:
Mr. Roger C. Schultz

196 Danbury Rd.
Wilton, Connecticut 06897
(203) 834-7819
Fax: (203) 834-7829
Email: wilton!manager@mrinet.com
Key Contact - Specialty:
Mr. Paul M. Pascale

57 Danbury Rd.
Wilton, Connecticut 06897-4439
(203) 834-1111
Fax: (203) 834-2686
Email: norwalk!manager@mrinet.com
Key Contact - Specialty:
Mr. Robert C. Schmidt

6544 N. U.S. Hwy. 41N.
Ste. 204 B
Apollo Beach, Florida 33572-1706
(813) 645-6239
Fax: (813) 645-8678
Email: mri@icubed.net
Key Contact - Specialty:
Mr. Bill Handley

710 Oakfield Drive, Ste. 207
Brandon, Florida 33511
(813) 689-4249
Fax: (813) 689-4349
Email: mribarto@gte.net
Key Contact - Specialty:
Mr. Dave Titus

11041 Minneapolis Drive
Cooper City, Florida 33026
(954) 442-6102
Fax: (941) 442-6103
Email: jop@gate.net
Key Contact - Specialty:
Mr. James O'Pray

2121 Ponce De Leon Blvd., Ste. 940
Coral Gables, Florida 33134
(305) 444-1200
Fax: (305) 444-2266

Email: coralgab!manager@mrinet.com
Key Contact - Specialty:
Mr. James K. Weber

Congress Park Executive Ctr.
220 Congress PK Drive, Ste. 245
Delray Beach, Florida 33445
(561) 243-8883
Fax: (561) 243-1622
Email: mrimed.com
Key Contact - Specialty:
Mr. Joe S. Mullings

1700 E. Las Olas Blvd., Penthouse 5
Ft. Lauderdale, Florida 33301
(954) 525-0355
Fax: (954) 525-0353
Email: palmbch!manager@mrinet.com
Key Contact - Specialty:
Mr. Tom K. Johasky

1500 NW 49th St., Ste. 500
Ft. Lauderdale, Florida 33309
(954) 776-4477
Fax: (954) 776-4488
Key Contact - Specialty:
Mr. Joel Dickstein

3840-1 Williamsburg Park Blvd.
Jacksonville, Florida 32257-5586
(904) 448-5200
Fax: (904) 448-1418
Email: jakvlsth!manager@mrinet.com
Key Contact - Specialty:
Mr. Charles A. Hansen - *Metals technology*

3810-1 Williamsburg Park Blvd.
Jacksonville, Florida 32257-5584
(904) 737-5151
Fax: (904) 737-5152
Email: rle@julcrk.mrinet.com
Key Contact - Specialty:
Mr. Bob Eicher
Ms. Donna Eicher

3332 NE Sugar Hill Ave.
Jensen Beach, Florida 34957-3723
(561) 334-8633
Fax: (561) 334-4145
Email: jensen!dwl@mrinet.com
Key Contact - Specialty:
Mr. Douglas W. Lane

1001 N. US Hwy. 1
Haas Bldg., Ste. 204
Jupiter, Florida 33477
(561) 743-7772
Fax: (561) 743-8115
Email: jupiter!manager@mrinet.com
Key Contact - Specialty:
Mr. Ronald A. Ellis

2600 Maitland Ctr. Pkwy., Ste. 295
Maitland, Florida 32751-7227
(407) 660-0089
Fax: (407) 660-2066
Key Contact - Specialty:
Ms. Arlene Brown
Mr. Tom Brown

5652-B Hwy. 90
Milton, Florida 32583
(850) 626-3303
Fax: (850) 626-3448
Email: srmri@aol.com
Key Contact - Specialty:
Mr. John E. Brand
Ms. Karen M. Brand

1300 Third St. S., Ste. 301-A
Naples, Florida 34102
(941) 261-8800
Fax: (941) 261-7551
Email: naples!manager@mrinet.com
Key Contact - Specialty:
Mr. Dan R. Ressler

1542 Kingsley Ave., Ste. 137
Orangepark, Florida 32073-4547
(904) 264-5644
Fax: (904) 264-5966
Key Contact - Specialty:
Mr. Regis Lageman

8030 Peters Rd., Ste. D104
Plantation, Florida 33324-4038
(954) 916-1890
Fax: (954) 916-1891
Email: manager@plantatn.mrinet.com
Key Contact - Specialty:
Mr. Miles Sturgis

685 Royal Palm Beach Blvd., Ste. 103-B
Royal Palm Beach, Florida 33411
(561) 793-8400
Fax: (561) 793-8471
Email: roylpalm!manager@mrinet.com
Key Contact - Specialty:
Mr. Ron Bizick

7737 Holiday Drive
Sarasota, Florida 34231
(941) 923-3671
Fax: (941) 923-3675
Key Contact - Specialty:
Mr. David B. Lechner

9500 Koger Blvd., Ste. 203
St. Petersburg, Florida 33702
(813) 577-2116
Fax: (813) 576-5594
Email: mristpete@aol.com
Key Contact - Specialty:
Mr. Robert P. Raffin

4020 Park St., Lighthouse Point
St. Petersburg, Florida 33709-4034
(813) 345-8811
Fax: (813) 345-5148
Key Contact - Specialty:
Ms. Jean Hand

1406 Hays St., Ste. 7
Tallahassee, Florida 32301-2843
(904) 656-8444
Fax: (904) 942-2793
Email: tallahas!manager@mrinet.com
Key Contact - Specialty:
Ms. Kitte H. Carter

2909 Bay to Bay Blvd., Ste. 302
Tampa, Florida 33629
(813) 831-7611
Fax: (813) 831-6966
Key Contact - Specialty:
Mr. Rudy E. Koletic

500 N. Westshore Blvd., Ste. 540
Tampa, Florida 33609
(813) 281-2353
Fax: (813) 281-0622
Email: tampa!manager@mrinet.com
Key Contact - Specialty:
Mr. Peter W. Wolfe

400 N. Ashley Drive, Ste. 2010
Tampa, Florida 33602-4300
(813) 229-0545
Fax: (813) 229-0785
Email: manager@bayside.mrinet.com
Key Contact - Specialty:
Mr. Larry J. Scofield
Ms. Nancy A. Scofield

3802 Ehrlich Rd., Ste. 101
Tampa, Florida 33624-2300
(813) 265-8789
Fax: (813) 265-8902
Email: carow@gte.net
Key Contact - Specialty:
Mr. James A. Carow

230 S. New York Ave., Ste. 200
Winter Park, Florida 32789-4236
(407) 629-2424
Fax: (407) 629-6424
Email: manager@wintrprk.mrinet.com
Key Contact - Specialty:
Ms. Stacy L. Gulden

1080 Cambridge Sq., Ste. C
Alpharetta, Georgia 30004-1878
(770) 619-0060
Fax: (770) 619-0061
Email: barillas@alpha.mrinet.com
Key Contact - Specialty:
Mr. Nick Barillas

2814 New Spring Rd., Ste. 217
Atlanta, Georgia 30339
(770) 436-3464
Fax: (770) 436-7969
Email: mri@mindspring.com
Key Contact - Specialty:
Mr. David P. Borel
Mr. Doug C. Malcolm

2625 Cumberland Pkwy., Ste. 485
Atlanta, Georgia 30339-3911
(770) 433-8330
Fax: (770) 433-1701
Email: officemgr@mrinet-atlanta.com
Key Contact - Specialty:
Mr. Richard G. Holland

P.O. Box 18636
Atlanta, Georgia 31126-0636
(404) 874-3636
Fax: (404) 874-0221
Key Contact - Specialty:
Mr. Eugene E. Houchins, Jr.

230 Peachtree St. NW, Ste. 1515
Atlanta, Georgia 30303-1513
(770) 221-1021
Fax: (770) 221-0121
Key Contact - Specialty:
Mr. Tom Jayroe

415 E. Walnut Ave., Ste. 314
Dalton, Georgia 30721-4406
(706) 226-8550
Fax: (706) 226-8353
Email: dalton!manager@mrinet.com
Key Contact - Specialty:
Mr. Donald W. Webb
Ms. Verna F. Webb

2470 Windy Hill Rd., Ste. 461
Marietta, Georgia 30067
(770) 955-6445
Fax: (770) 955-6446
Email: manager@windyhil.mrinet.com
Key Contact - Specialty:
Mr. Ron Hollis

2840 Johnson Ferry NE, Ste. 15 O
Marietta, Georgia 30062
(770) 643-9990
Fax: (770) 643-0818
Key Contact - Specialty:
Mr. Lawrence J. Dougherty

118 S. Second Ave.
McRae, Georgia 31055-1539
(912) 868-5001
Fax: (912) 868-6603
Key Contact - Specialty:
Mr. Ron Graves

406 Line Creek Rd., Ste. B
Peachtree City, Georgia 30269
(770) 486-0603
Fax: (770) 631-7684
Email: mrias@mindspring.com
Key Contact - Specialty:
Mr. Ronald L. Wise

916 Main St., Ste. 2000
P.O. Box 1455
Perry, Georgia 31069
(912) 988-4444
Fax: (912) 988-4445
Email: twentz@msn.com
Key Contact - Specialty:
Mr. Terry M. Wentz

920 Holcomb Bridge Rd., Ste. 450
Roswell, Georgia 30076-1974
(770) 649-8778
Fax: (770) 649-8197
Email: mriin@mindspring.com
Key Contact - Specialty:
Mr. Randolph L. Nugent

1626 Frederica Rd., Ste. 203
St. Simons Island, Georgia 31522-2509
(912) 634-2390
Fax: (912) 634-2391
Email: lorene@darlentel.net
Key Contact - Specialty:
Ms. Lorene M. Ledingham

9465 Main St., Ste. 210
Woodstock, Georgia 30188-3700
(770) 592-9550
Fax: (770) 924-6206
Email: woodstck!manager@mrinet.com
Key Contact - Specialty:
Mr. Doug O. Ralston

94 Kamehameha Ave.
Hilo, Hawaii 96720
(808) 935-0425
Fax: (808) 935-2238
Email: mrhilo@aloha.net
Key Contact - Specialty:
Mr. Paul W. Reagan

64-1061 Manalahoa Hwy.
Waimea Town Plaza, #10
Kamuela, Hawaii 96743
(808) 885-7503
Fax: (808) 885-6338
Key Contact - Specialty:
Ms. Amy Cody-Quinn

Route 3
Box 138 A, Sunset Drive
Albion, Illinois 62806
(618) 445-2333
Fax: (618) 445-3664
Email: tcc@wworld.com
Key Contact - Specialty:
Ms. Lois Christensen
Mr. Tom Christensen

Arlington Heights Office Ctr.
3413-A N. Kennicot Ave.
Arlington Heights, Illinois 60004
(847) 590-8880
Fax: (847) 590-0847
Email: steve.briody@internetmci.com
Key Contact - Specialty:
Mr. Steve Briody

1740 Bell School Rd., Point East
Cherry Valley, Illinois 61016-9337
(815) 399-1942
Fax: (815) 399-2750
Email: dmcmri@aol.com
Key Contact - Specialty:
Mr. D. Michael Carter

Sears Tower, Ste. 4810
233 S. Wacker Drive
Chicago, Illinois 60606
(312) 706-1500
Fax: (312) 706-1508
Email: chicodt!manager@mrinet.com
Key Contact - Specialty:
Ms. Glenda A. Baranski
Mr. David J. Baranski

1400 E. Touhy Ave., Ste. 160
Des Plaines, Illinois 60018-3374
(847) 297-7102
Fax: (847) 297-8477
Email: jobs@mr-ohare.com
Key Contact - Specialty:
Mr. Richard A. Kurz
Mr. Ward Larkin

472 N. McLean Blvd., Ste. 201
Elgin, Illinois 60123
(847) 697-2201
Fax: (847) 697-0622
Email: mrelgin@mrelgin.com
Key Contact - Specialty:
Mr. Ron C. Reeves

1007 Church St., Ste. 302
Evanston, Illinois 60201-5902
(847) 866-8050
Fax: (847) 866-8577
Email: manager@evanston.mrinet.com
Key Contact - Specialty:
Mr. Hilmon Sorey, Jr.

19350 S. Harlem Ave., Ste. 203
Frankfort, Illinois 60423
(815) 464-5992
Fax: (815) 464-5982
Email: manager@willcnty.mrinet.com
Key Contact - Specialty:
Mr. Bob Bauer

1921 St. Johns Ave., Ste. 220
Highland Park, Illinois 60035-3520
(847) 681-2144
Fax: (847) 681-2140
Key Contact - Specialty:
Ms. Gayle Galloway
Ms. Sally Salzer

2711 W. 183rd St., Ste. 303
Homewood, Illinois 60430-2951
(708) 922-3397
Fax: (708) 922-3370
Email: manager@chicagos.mrinet.com
Key Contact - Specialty:
Mr. Darrell L. Bewsey

83 W. Main St., Ste. 200
Lake Zurich, Illinois 60047-2398
(847) 550-1300
Fax: (847) 550-1314
Email: gary@mrchicago.com
Key Contact - Specialty:
Mr. Gary Bozza

13522 W. Choctaw Trail
Lockport, Illinois 60441
(708) 361-8778
Fax: (708) 361-9728
Email: chisw!manager@mrinet.com
Key Contact - Specialty:
Mr. Victor J. Persico

1405 Lafayette Ave.
P.O. Box 461
Mattoon, Illinois 61938
(217) 235-9393
Fax: (217) 235-9396
Key Contact - Specialty:
Mr. David W. Tolle

479 Business Ctr. Drive, Ste. 104
Kensington Ctr.
Mt. Prospect, Illinois 60056-6037
(847) 298-8780
Fax: (847) 298-8781
Email: prospect!manager@mrinet.com
Key Contact - Specialty:
Mr. Tom A. Diduca

564 S. Washington St., Ste. 203
Naperville, Illinois 60540
(630) 305-0200
Fax: (630) 305-0273
Email: mrchicagofw@ameritech.net
Key Contact - Specialty:
Ms. Sherri Chaifetz
Mr. Marc Chaifetz

211 Landmark Drive, Ste. E-1
Normal, Illinois 61761
(309) 452-1844
Fax: (309) 452-0403
Email: mrbloom@mrbloomington.com
Key Contact - Specialty:
Mr. Alan Snedden

211 Waukegan Rd., Ste. 104
Northfield, Illinois 60093-2745
(847) 501-3881
Fax: (847) 501-3889
Email: manager@glenview.mrinet.com
Key Contact - Specialty:
Mr. Fred Brooks

4507 N. Sterling Ave., Ste. 303
Peoria, Illinois 61615
(309) 681-6774
Fax: (309) 681-6775
Email: manager@peoria.mrinet.com
Key Contact - Specialty:
Mr. Walt Deehring
Mr. Rod Smith

502 E. Southline Rd., Ste. 2C
Tuscola, Illinois 61953
(217) 253-6358
Fax: (217) 253-6360
Key Contact - Specialty:
Mr. Kenneth C. Williams
Mr. Gary Campbell

Ameriana Bank Bldg.
99 S. Dan Jones Rd., Ste. 200
Avon, Indiana 46168-9771
(317) 272-5454
Fax: (317) 272-5440
Email: avon!manager@mrinet.com
Key Contact - Specialty:
Mr. Bert E. Miller
Ms. Laura Gonzalez-Miller

P.O. Box 2234
Columbus, Indiana 47201
(812) 372-5500
Fax: (812) 372-8292
Email: columin!manager@mrinet.com
Key Contact - Specialty:
Mr. J. Michael Percifield

101 Court St., Ste. 209
Riverside 1
Evansville, Indiana 47708
(812) 464-9155
Fax: (812) 422-6718
Key Contact - Specialty:
Ms. Marjorie L. Caldemeyer

4011 W. Jefferson Blvd.
Ft. Wayne, Indiana 46804-6853
(219) 459-1123
Fax: (219) 459-1091
Email: ftwayne!manager@mrinet.com
Key Contact - Specialty:
Ms. Myra Rudin
Mr. Harold Rudin

2519 E. Main St., Ste. 101
Forest Park Bldg.
Richmond, Indiana 47374-5864
(765) 935-3356
Fax: (765) 935-3417
Key Contact - Specialty:
Mr. Rande L. Martin

2435 Kimberly Rd., Penthouse
Alpine Centre S.
Bettendorf, Iowa 52722
(319) 359-3503
Fax: (319) 359-1681
Email: mriqc@aol.com
Key Contact - Specialty:
Mr. Jerry C. Herrmann

P.O. Box 247
Centerville, Iowa 52544-0247
(515) 437-1115
Fax: (515) 437-1116
Email: mrictv@aol.com
Key Contact - Specialty:
Mr. Dick Hovey

806 Fifth St., Ste. 209
Fifth St. Business Ctr.
Coralville, Iowa 52241
(319) 354-4320
Fax: (319) 354-6183
Email: manager@mriowa.mrinet.com
Key Contact - Specialty:
Mr. John Sims

1312 Fourth St. SW, Ste. 102
Westside Offices
Mason City, Iowa 50401
(515) 424-1680
Fax: (515) 424-6868
Email: mrimc@willowtree.com
Key Contact - Specialty:
Ms. Cheryl L. Plagge

P.O. Box 5020
Ft. Scott, Kansas 66701
(316) 223-3133
Fax: (316) 223-3733
Email: mrscott!manager@mrinet.com
Key Contact - Specialty:
Mr. Michael Del Chiaro
Mr. James Stark

7600 W. 110th, Ste. 204
Overland Park, Kansas 66210
(913) 663-2323
Fax: (913) 663-2424
Email: leawood!manager@mrinet.com
Key Contact - Specialty:
Ms. Kathleen S. Howard
Mr. Brian E. Howard

9401 Indian Creek Pkwy., Ste. 920
Corporate Woods Bldg. 40
Overland Park, Kansas 66210-2098
(913) 661-9300
Fax: (913) 661-9030
Email: ovrland!manager@mrinet.com
Key Contact - Specialty:
Mr. Danny Buda, Jr.

8100 E. 22nd St. N.
Bldg. 1500, Ste. B
Wichita, Kansas 67226
(316) 682-8239
Fax: (316) 682-8132
Email: wichita!manager@mrinet.com
Key Contact - Specialty:
Mr. Marvin Reimer

2350 Sterlington Rd.
Alumni Office Park
Lexington, Kentucky 40502
(606) 273-5665
Fax: (606) 273-9106
Email: len4jobs@ix.netcom.com
Key Contact - Specialty:
Mr. Kent T. Simpson

4360 Brownsboro Rd., Ste. 240
Louisville, Kentucky 40207
(502) 897-0333
Fax: (502) 897-0496
Email: info@angel-group.com
Key Contact - Specialty:
Mr. Steven R. Angel - *Central Region*

1203 Mt. Eden Rd., Ste. 1
Shelbyville, Kentucky 40065-8822
(502) 633-6100
Fax: (502) 647-3300
Email: shlbyvil!manager@mrinet.com
Key Contact - Specialty:
Mr. Barney O. Barnett

P.O. Box 6605
3527 Ridgelake Drive
Metairie, Louisiana 70009
(504) 831-7333
Fax: (504) 838-9009
Email: neworl!manager@mrinet.com
Key Contact - Specialty:
Mr. Edward N. Ameen
Mr. Paul M. Luce

920 Pierremont, Ste. 112
Shreveport, Louisiana 71106-8794
(318) 865-8411
Fax: (318) 861-3411
Key Contact - Specialty:
Mr. Charles Magee
Ms. Gerri Magee

106 Village Sq., Ste. 2
Slidell, Louisiana 70458
(504) 847-1900
Fax: (504) 847-1984
Email: Mrislidell@aol.com
Key Contact - Specialty:
Mr. Jack L. Pecot

2083 West St., Ste. 5A
Annapolis, Maryland 21401-3030
(410) 841-6600
Fax: (410) 841-6600
Key Contact - Specialty:
Mr. John Czajkowski

201 N. Charles St., Ste. 2208
Baltimore, Maryland 21201-4102
(410) 385-0300
Fax: (410) 385-0330
Email: baltcty!manager@mrinet.com
Key Contact - Specialty:
Mr. Ron E. D'Angelo

5606 Ridgefield Rd.
Bethesda, Maryland 20816
(301) 654-9282
Fax: (301) 320-1877
Key Contact - Specialty:
Mr. Michael C. Prentiss

Dorsey Hall Professional Park
5044 Dorsey Hall Drive, Ste. 204
Ellicott City, Maryland 21043-7739
(410) 884-1363
Fax: (410) 884-1369
Email: mriellic@erols.com
Key Contact - Specialty:
Mr. Danny Bell
Ms. Cathy Bell

201 International Circle, Ste. 180
Hunt Valley, Maryland 21031
(410) 785-6313
Fax: (410) 785-6314
Email: mrihuntvalley@msn.com
Key Contact - Specialty:
Mr. David E. Wise

132 E. Main St., Ste. 300
Salisbury, Maryland 21801-4921
(410) 548-4473
Fax: (410) 548-4487
Key Contact - Specialty:
Mr. Fred J. Puente

607 Boylston St., Ste. 700
Boston, Massachusetts 02116
(617) 262-5050
Fax: (617) 421-9630
Email: mriboston@aol.com
Key Contact - Specialty:
Mr. Jack J. Nehiley

607 Boylston St., Ste. 603
Boston, Massachusetts 02116
(617) 262-5050
Fax: (617) 859-9917
Key Contact - Specialty:
Mr. Jack Mohan
Mr. Art Greenfield

639 Granite St.
Braintree, Massachusetts 02184
(781) 848-1666
Fax: (781) 843-8916
Key Contact - Specialty:
Mr. Stephen W. Morse

1500 Main St., Ste. 1822
Bay Bank Tower
Springfield, Massachusetts 01115
(413) 781-1550
Fax: (413) 731-6566
Key Contact - Specialty:
Mr. Jack Mohan

2000 W. Park Drive
Westborough Office Park
Westborough, Massachusetts 01581-3901
(508) 366-9900
Fax: (508) 898-9982
Key Contact - Specialty:
Ms. Irene Garrity

3600 Green Court, Ste. 100
Ann Arbor, Michigan 48105
(313) 769-1720
Fax: (313) 769-0035
Email: annarbor@concentric.net
Key Contact - Specialty:
Mr. Sam N. Sarafa

401 Old Kent Bank Bldg.
Battle Creek, Michigan 49017
(616) 968-5440
Fax: (616) 968-5443
Email: rgm@calhoun.mrinet.com
Key Contact - Specialty:
Mr. Mark Maire
Ms. Renee Maire

146 Monroe Ctr., Ste. 1126
McKay Tower
Grand Rapids, Michigan 49503
(616) 336-8484
Fax: (616) 336-7680
Key Contact - Specialty:
Mr. Ronald J. Meadley

400 N. 136th Ave., Ste. 6, Bldg. 200
Holland, Michigan 49424-1830
(616) 396-2620
Fax: (616) 396-9465
Email: mri@macatawa.com
Key Contact - Specialty:
Mr. Robert E. Bakker

2491 Cedar Park Drive
Holt, Michigan 48842-2184
(517) 694-1153
Fax: (517) 694-6502
Email: lansing!manager@mrinet.com
Key Contact - Specialty:
Ms. Priscilla J. Peterson
Mr. John A. Peterson

7190 W. Houghton Lake Drive, Ste. 109
Houghton Lake, Michigan 48629
(517) 422-5700
Fax: (517) 422-5738
Key Contact - Specialty:
Mr. Jack L. Harris
Ms. Vicki M. Harris

4021 W. Main St., Ste. 200
Briarwood Valley Office Plaza
Kalamazoo, Michigan 49007-2746
(616) 381-1153
Fax: (616) 381-8031
Email: kalamaz!manager@mrinet.com
Key Contact - Specialty:
Mr. Cy Tessin

302 S. Water St.
Marine City, Michigan 48039-1689
(810) 765-3480
Fax: (810) 765-3420
Email: stclair!manager@mrinet.com
Key Contact - Specialty:
Mr. Bob Bommarito

124 N. Division
Traverse City, Michigan 49684
(616) 947-8000
(616) 968-5959
Fax: (616) 922-9481
Email: mrtc@traverse.com
Key Contact - Specialty:
Ms. Mary J. Barker
Mr. Tony R. Richardson

550 Stephenson Hwy., Ste. 407
Troy, Michigan 48083-1152
(810) 585-4200
Fax: (810) 597-0492
Email: troy!manager@mrinet.com
Key Contact - Specialty:
Mr. Ed J. Moeller

7964 Univeristy Ave. NE
Fridley, Minnesota 55432
(612) 784-4199
Fax: (612) 717-7378
Key Contact - Specialty:
Mr. Al Johnson

6600 France Ave. S., Ste. 620
Minneapolis, Minnesota 55435
(612) 925-6141
Fax: (612) 925-4422
Email: mrminna!manager@mrinet.com
Key Contact - Specialty:
Ms. Carrie Schoenwetter

1530 Greenview Drive, Ste. 122
Rochester, Minnesota 55902
(507) 536-0350
Fax: (507) 536-0349
Key Contact - Specialty:
Mr. Bill E. Risma

206 Scott St.
Shakopee, Minnesota 55379
(612) 496-2552
Fax: (612) 445-3446
Email: manager@shakopee.mrinet.com
Key Contact - Specialty:
Mr. Michael Brown

7650 Currell Blvd., Ste. 240
Woodbury, Minnesota 55125
(651) 730-7668
Fax: (651) 730-7191
Email: mrwoodbury@aol.com
Key Contact - Specialty:
Mr. David W. Kriesel - *General manufacturing, construction engineering*
Mr. Michael L. Fox - *Informational services, finance, insurance*
Ms. Judy A. Olson - *Human resources, administration, sales & marketing*

1755 Lelia Drive, Ste. 102
Jackson, Mississippi 39216
(601) 366-4488
Fax: (601) 366-4699
Email: jmmri@worldnet.att.net
Key Contact - Specialty:
Mr. J. W. Gardner

102 W. 5th St.
Long Beach, Mississippi 39560-6029
(228) 863-8606
Fax: (228) 863-8604
Key Contact - Specialty:
Mr. Gene Lowery

P.O. Box 1197
Camdenton, Missouri 65020-9004
(573) 346-4833
Fax: (573) 346-1705
Email: careers@iland.net
Key Contact - Specialty:
Mr. Robert D. Hodgson
Ms. Judy H. Hodgson

200 Fabricator Drive
Meramec Valley Ctr.
Fenton, Missouri 63026
(314) 349-4455
Fax: (314) 326-4207
Key Contact - Specialty:
Mr. Edward Travis
Mr. Glenwood Alley

712 Broadway, Ste. 500
Soho Office Ctr.
Kansas City, Missouri 64105
(816) 221-2377
Fax: (816) 221-7164
Key Contact - Specialty:
Ms. Eileen Mason
Mr. Steve Orr

1101 Edgewater Pointe Blvd.
Lake St. Louis, Missouri 63367-2906
(314) 625-1780
Fax: (314) 625-1788
Email: lakestlouis!manager@mrinet.com
Key Contact - Specialty:
Mr. Terry Bacigalupo

Hwy. 5, Southport Bldg.
P.O. Box 1509
Laurie, Missouri 65038-1509
(573) 374-9338
Fax: (573) 374-7745
Email: jlc@advertisnet.com
Key Contact - Specialty:
Ms. Janet Cartella
Mr. Mike Cartella

14615 Manchester Rd., Ste. 202
Manchester, Missouri 63011-3790
(314) 391-3777
Fax: (314) 391-3444
Email: manager@chstrfld.mrinet.com
Key Contact - Specialty:
Mr. Carl D. Travis

1807 E. Edgewood
The Edgewood, Ste. B
Springfield, Missouri 65804
(417) 882-6220
Fax: (417) 882-7855
Key Contact - Specialty:
Ms. Arlyn B. Rudolph

11701 Borman Drive, Ste. 250
St. Louis, Missouri 63146
(314) 991-4355
Fax: (314) 991-9586
Email: slwestport@aol.com
Key Contact - Specialty:
Mr. Phil L. Bertsch

3301 Rider Trail S., Ste. 100
St. Louis, Missouri 63045-1309
(314) 344-0959
Fax: (314) 298-7706
Email: phoene@mricorp.mrinet.com
Key Contact - Specialty:
Mr. Patrick Hoene

210 Gateway, Ste. 434
Greentree Court
Lincoln, Nebraska 68505-2438
(402) 467-5534
Fax: (402) 467-1150
Email: lincoln!manager@mrinet.com
Key Contact - Specialty:
Mr. Bill J. Elam

109 S. 2nd
Norfolk, Nebraska 68701-5327
(402) 379-8212
Fax: (402) 379-8210
Email: mrinrflk@aol.com
Key Contact - Specialty:
Mr. Dan R. Ankeney

7171 W. Mercy Rd., Ste. 252
Omaha, Nebraska 68106-2696
(402) 397-8320
Fax: (402) 397-6322
Email: omaha!manager@mrinet.com
Key Contact - Specialty:
Mr. Les V. Zanotti
Mr. Gary Adams

Copper Point, 4530 S. Eastern, Ste. A-12
Las Vegas, Nevada 89119-6181
(702) 733-1818
Fax: (702) 733-0102
Email: mrlv@mrlasvegas.com
Key Contact - Specialty:
Mr. Joel Lalonde

810 S. Durango Drive, Ste. 102
Las Vegas, Nevada 89128
(702) 243-8189
Fax: (702) 243-8190
Email: rpn@sumerlin.mrinet.com
Key Contact - Specialty:
Mr. Raymond P. Nolan

116-C S. River Rd.
Cold Stream Office Park
Bedford, New Hampshire 03110-2131
(603) 669-9800
Fax: (603) 623-8609
Key Contact - Specialty:
Mr. Michael Bacon

10 Anderson Rd., Ste. 7
Bernardsville, New Jersey 07924-2319
(908) 204-0070
Fax: (908) 204-9716
Key Contact - Specialty:
Mr. Marlon W. O'Brien
Ms. Debbie A. O'Brien

1170 Rte. 22 E.
Bridgewater, New Jersey 08807-1786
(908) 725-2595
Fax: (908) 725-0439
Key Contact - Specialty:
Mr. Barry S. Smith

440 County Rd. 513, Ste. 207
Califon, New Jersey 07830
(908) 832-6455
Fax: (908) 832-6525
Key Contact - Specialty:
Ms. Sarah J. Rodgers

1040 N. Kings Hwy., Ste. 705
Executive House
Cherry Hill, New Jersey 08034-1908
(609) 667-3381
Fax: (609) 667-3724
Key Contact - Specialty:
Mr. Scott W. Ziluck

186 Princeton-Highstown Rd.
Cranbury, New Jersey 08512-1939
(609) 897-0055
Fax: (609) 897-0099
Email: manager@windsor.mrinet.com
Key Contact - Specialty:
Mr. Robert Walling

19 Tanner St.
Haddonfield, New Jersey 08033
(609) 428-2233
Fax: (609) 428-7733
Email: haddon!manager@mrinet.com
Key Contact - Specialty:
Mr. Roy P. Kelly

276 Main St., 2nd Floor
Metuchen, New Jersey 08840-2429
(732) 767-1025
Fax: (732) 767-1218
Email: edison!manager@mrinet.com
Key Contact - Specialty:
Mr. Frank Noorani

24 Lackawanna Plaza
Millburn, New Jersey 07041
(973) 379-4020
Fax: (973) 379-2699
Email: mrshort!manager@mrinet.com
Key Contact - Specialty:
Mr. Marty Nicoll

1104 Springfield Ave.
Mountainside Crossing
Mountainside, New Jersey 07092
(908) 789-9400
Fax: (908) 789-8845
Email: mriunion@aol.com
Key Contact - Specialty:
Mr. Jim L. Malfetti
Ms. Rosemary Malfetti

750 Hamburg Tnpk., Ste. 203
Pompton Lakes, New Jersey 07442-1418
(201) 831-7778
Fax: (201) 831-0233
Key Contact - Specialty:
Mr. David Zawicki

210 W. Front St., Ste. 102
Red Bank, New Jersey 07701-0871
(908) 530-0600
Fax: (908) 747-4076
Email: redbacnk!manager@mrinet.com
Key Contact - Specialty:
Mr. Mike A. Unger

191 Woodport Rd., Ste. 201
Sparta, New Jersey 07871-2641
(973) 729-1888
Fax: (973) 729-1620
Email: recruiter@retailplacement.com
Key Contact - Specialty:
Mr. Lance M. Incitti

4 Waterloo Rd.
Waterloo Executive Plaza
Stanhope, New Jersey 07874
(973) 691-2020
Fax: (973) 691-0728
Email: arthur@recruiter.com
Key Contact - Specialty:
Mr. Arthur Young - *Data processing*
Ms. Janet Joyce

The Commons, Ste. 180
121 Highway 36
West Long Branch, New Jersey
07764-1436
(732) 222-6686
Fax: (732) 222-5339
Email: manager@monmouth.mrinet.com
Key Contact - Specialty:
Mr. Robert E. Goehring

2500 Louisiana Blvd. NE, Ste. 506
Albuquerque, New Mexico 87110-4319
(505) 346-4700
Fax: (505) 346-4701
Email: albuq!tjs@mrinet.com
Key Contact - Specialty:
Mr. Tom J. Schneider

1850 Old Pecos Trail, Ste. H
Santa Fe, New Mexico 87505-4760
(505) 982-5445
Fax: (505) 982-7170
Email: manager@santafe.mrinet.com
Key Contact - Specialty:
Mr. Bill Miller

Four Executive Park Drive
Stuyvesant Plaza
Albany, New York 12203-3707
(518) 438-7722
Fax: (518) 438-0948
Email: MRIAlbany@aol.com
Key Contact - Specialty:
Mr. Bob T. Mulcahey

435 New Karner Rd.
Albany, New York 12205-3833
(518) 464-1461
Fax: (518) 464-1464
Email: colonie!manager@mrinet.com
Key Contact - Specialty:
Mr. Bob Kayajian

33 Walt Whitman Rd., Ste. 107
Huntington Station, New York 11746-3627
(516) 385-0633
Fax: (516) 385-0759
Key Contact - Specialty:
Mr. Bob Levitt

P.O. Box 218, 2 Church St.
Madrid, New York 13660
(315) 322-0222
Fax: (315) 322-0220
Email: stlawrnc!manager@mrinet.com
Key Contact - Specialty:
Mr. Nicky Scott

295 Madison Ave., 36th Floor
New York, New York 10017
(212) 972-7300
Fax: (212) 972-7309
Email: admin@mrnyc.mrinet.com
Key Contact - Specialty:
Mr. Jeffrey A. Heath

225 Main St., Ste. 204
Northport, New York 11768
(516) 261-0400
Fax: (516) 261-8575
Email: northprt!manager@mrinet.com
Key Contact - Specialty:
Mr. Sebastian F. Livolsi

16 Main St. W., Ste. 225
Powers Bldg.
Rochester, New York 14614-1601
(716) 454-2440
Fax: (716) 454-4092
Email: roch-ny!manager@mrinet.com
Key Contact - Specialty:
Mr. Jerry Annesi

1721 Black River Blvd., Ste. 205 B
Executive Bldg.
Rome, New York 13440-2425
(315) 339-6342
Fax: (315) 339-6415
Key Contact - Specialty:
Mr. Bob Mosca

1721 Black River Blvd., Ste. 205
Executive Bldg.
Rome, New York 13440
(315) 339-6342
Fax: (315) 339-6415
Key Contact - Specialty:
Mr. Carl Tardugno

Flying Point Office Park, #207
33 Flying Point Rd.
Southampton, New York 11968-5244
(516) 287-5030
Fax: (516) 287-5610
Key Contact - Specialty:
Mr. Jerry A. Lareau
Ms. Belle Lareau
Mr. Bill O. Jose

P.O. Box 386
Stone Ridge, New York 12484-0386
(914) 339-1300
Fax: (914) 339-1443
Key Contact - Specialty:
Mr. Robert A. Mackenzie

10 Main St., Ste. 202
Whitesboro, New York 13492
(315) 768-3322
Fax: (315) 768-4349
Email: www.mrmv@dreamscape.com
Key Contact - Specialty:
Mr. Michael Maurizio

104 E. College Ave.
P.O. Box 1405
Boiling Springs, North Carolina
28017-1405
(704) 434-0211
Fax: (704) 434-0274
Email: shelby!manager@mrinet.com
Key Contact - Specialty:
Mr. Lee S. Sherrill
Mr. Dave G. Holland

P.O. Box 699
Bunn, North Carolina 27508
(919) 269-6612
Fax: (919) 269-6676
Email: rockymtn!manager@mrinet.com
Key Contact - Specialty:
Mr. Dan P. Cone

800 Eastowne Drive, Ste. 103
Chapel Hill, North Carolina 27514-2215
(919) 408-3311
Fax: (919) 408-3225
Email: mrchaphl@gte.net
Key Contact - Specialty:
Mr. Rice Day

5701 Westpark Drive, Ste. 110
Charlotte, North Carolina 28217
(704) 525-9270
Fax: (704) 527-0070
Email: mrichlt@aol.com
Key Contact - Specialty:
Ms. Bobbi Brown

One Pine Brook Plaza, Ste. 110
9101 Southern Pine Blvd.
Charlotte, North Carolina 28273
(704) 523-3377
Fax: (704) 523-1965
Email: westchar!manager@mrinet.com
Key Contact - Specialty:
Mr. Dave W. Oberting

2101 Sardis Rd. N., Ste. 205
Charlotte, North Carolina 28227
(704) 849-9200
Fax: (704) 849-9207
Email: mrchareast@internetmci.com
Key Contact - Specialty:
Mr. Frank A. Quinn
Ms. Peggy Quinn

660 Westinghouse Blvd., Ste. 108
Charlotte, North Carolina 28273-6303
(704) 588-9300
Fax: (704) 588-6001
Email: charsw!manager@mrinet.com
Key Contact - Specialty:
Mr. Wallace Means

19501 Hwy. 73 W. #20
Cornelius, North Carolina 28031
(704) 896-1916
Fax: (704) 896-1923
Email: davidson!manager@mrinet.com
Key Contact - Specialty:
Mr. Sam G. Hawfield, III

P.O. Box 395
Cove City, North Carolina 28523
(919) 633-1900
Fax: (919) 633-3121
Email: newbern!manager@mrinet.com
Key Contact - Specialty:
Mr. Fred Eatman

Pine Ridge Office Park, Ste. 203
6011 Fayetteville Rd.
Durham, North Carolina 27713-8547
(919) 572-2292
Fax: (919) 572-6556
Email: manager@tripark.mrinet.com
Key Contact - Specialty:
Mr. Robert Bradley

5102 Chapel Hill-Durham Blvd., Ste. 112
Durham, North Carolina 27707
(919) 489-6521
Fax: (919) 493-4611
Email: durham!manager@mrinet.com
Key Contact - Specialty:
Mr. Steve Knauss

P.O. Box 5330
Emerald Isle, North Carolina 28594
(919) 354-7600
Fax: (919) 354-7700
Email: emerald!manager@mrinet.com
Key Contact - Specialty:
Mr. James Liles

111 NW Railroad St.
Enfield, North Carolina 27823-1334
(919) 445-4251
Fax: (919) 445-4253
Email: search@interpath.com
Key Contact - Specialty:
Ms. Maria P. Snook
Mr. Marvin G. Snook

324 W. Wendover, Ste. 230
Greensboro, North Carolina 27408
(910) 378-1818
Fax: (910) 378-0129
Email: greens!manager@mrinet.com
Key Contact - Specialty:
Mr. Mitch Oakley, Jr.
Mr. Terry D. Stout

835 Highland Ave. SE
Hickory, North Carolina 28602-1140
(828) 324-2020
Fax: (828) 324-6895
Email: mri@interbiz.net
Key Contact - Specialty:
Mr. Scott Volz
Mr. Bill Gaillard

P.O. Box 6077
Hickory, North Carolina 28603
(704) 495-8233
Fax: (704) 495-7431
Email: bethlhm!manager@mrinet.com
Key Contact - Specialty:
Mr. Byron L. King

110 Scott
High Point, North Carolina 27262-7832
(910) 869-1200
Fax: (910) 869-1566
Email: highpnt!manager@mrinet.com
Key Contact - Specialty:
Mr. Steve Smith
Ms. Gin-Nie Smith

P.O. Box 8
Louisburg, North Carolina 27549-0008
(919) 496-2153
Fax: (919) 496-1417
Email: louisbrg!manager@mrinet.com
Key Contact - Specialty:
Mr. Darrell L. Perry, Jr.

108 S. Market St., Ste. D
Madison, North Carolina 27025-2124
(336) 427-6153
Fax: (336) 427-6154
Email: mrrock@vnet.net
Key Contact - Specialty:
Mr. Gerald Summerlin

P.O. Box 2902
Matthews, North Carolina 28106
(704) 841-8850
Fax: (704) 841-8854
Email: charsth!manager@mrinet.com
Key Contact - Specialty:
Mr. David K. Camp

322 E. Center Ave.
Mooresville, North Carolina 28115
(704) 664-4997
Fax: (704) 664-0841
Key Contact - Specialty:
Mr. Hugh L. Sykes

P.O. Box 4834
Pinehurst, North Carolina 28374
(910) 695-3300
Fax: (910) 695-0540
Email: paprwork@ac.net
Key Contact - Specialty:
Mr. Doug Wright
Ms. Anne B. Wright

120 N. Franklin
Bldg. J, Ste. 101
Rocky Mount, North Carolina 27804-5448
(919) 446-3456
Fax: (919) 446-3556
Email: rockywst!manager@mrinet.com
Key Contact - Specialty:
Mr. Danny J. Sewell

P.O. Box 2464
Shelby, North Carolina 28151
(704) 480-7889
Fax: (704) 480-7890
Key Contact - Specialty:
Mr. Rex Whicker
Mr. L. J. Smith

211 South Ctr., Ste. 305
City Center
Statesville, North Carolina 28677
(704) 871-9890
Fax: (704) 873-2143
Email: manager@statsvil.mrinet.com
Key Contact - Specialty:
Mr. Neil F. Coleman

1442 Military Cutoff Rd., Ste. 25
Wilmington, North Carolina 28403
(910) 256-1056
Fax: (910) 256-1057
Email: mri@wilmingtongroup.com
Key Contact - Specialty:
Mr. Kirk Sears

Office Atrium Bldg., Ste. 118
3505 Royalton Rd.
Broadview Heights, Ohio 44147-2998
(440) 546-3898
Fax: (440) 546-5351
Email: manager@brecksvl.mrinet.com
Key Contact - Specialty:
Ms. Edna J. Anter

P.O. Box 178
Brunswick, Ohio 44212-0178
(330) 273-4300
Fax: (330) 273-2862
Email: contactMRI@aol.com
Key Contact - Specialty:
Mr. Robert A. Boal

36 E. Fourth St., Ste. 800
Bartlett
Cincinnati, Ohio 45202-2451
(513) 651-5500
Fax: (513) 651-3298
Email: mrcinci!manager@mrinet.com
Key Contact - Specialty:
Mr. Tony P. D'Eramo
Mr. Joe McCullough

7530 Lucerne Drive, Ste. 303
Islander Park Two
Cleveland, Ohio 44130
(440) 243-5151
Fax: (440) 243-4868
Email: cleveair!manager@mrinet.com
Key Contact - Specialty:
Mr. Bob Gandee
Mr. Jeff Dipaolo

200 Public Sq., 30th Floor
Cleveland, Ohio 44114
(216) 696-4411
Fax: (216) 696-4609
Key Contact - Specialty:
Mr. Mike Case
Mr. Kevin E. Peterson

9700 Rockside Rd., Ste. 490
Cleveland, Ohio 44125-6264
(216) 642-5788
Fax: (216) 642-5933
Key Contact - Specialty:
Mr. Paul F. Montigny
Mr. Robert E. Jacobson

555 S. Front St. Ste. 100
Columbus, Ohio 43215
(614) 252-6200
Fax: (614) 252-4744
Key Contact - Specialty:
Mr. Gerry Harris
Mr. Todd Williams
Mr. John R. Zambito

6025 Dixie Hwy., Ste. 200
Fairfield, Ohio 45014-4253
(513) 682-4020
Fax: (513) 682-4030
Key Contact - Specialty:
Mr. Joseph J. Bierschwal

410 W. Sandusky St., Ste. 2
Findlay, Ohio 45840-3222
(419) 425-1000
Fax: (419) 425-1075
Key Contact - Specialty:
Mr. Grant Russel

P.O. Box 31495
Independence, Ohio 44131-0495
(216) 621-5522
Fax: (216) 621-5740
Email: s.quill@csuonio.edu
Key Contact - Specialty:
Ms. Monica Rio

2200 Wales Rd. NW
Massillon, Ohio 44646
(330) 834-0600
Fax: (330) 834-0601
Key Contact - Specialty:
Mr. David Reliford

6140 Parkland Blvd., Ste. 120
Mayfield Heights, Ohio 44124-4187
(216) 646-9898
Fax: (216) 646-9897
Email: manager@mayfield.mrinet.com
Key Contact - Specialty:
Mr. Randy Pinato

Mt. Vernon Bldg., Ste. 100
6690 Beta Drive
Mayfield Village, Ohio 44143
(440) 684-6150
Fax: (440) 684-6153
Email: mrlake@acclink.com
Key Contact - Specialty:
Mr. Terry R. Wesley

1054 N. University Blvd.
N. Towne Professional Plaza
Middletown, Ohio 45042-3300
(513) 420-1800
Fax: (513) 420-0009
Email: middle!manager@mrinet.com
Key Contact - Specialty:
Mr. George A. Plotner

34100 Ctr. Ridge Rd., Ste. 110
Liberty Ctr.
North Ridgeville, Ohio 44039-3220
(440) 327-2800
Fax: (440) 327-6991
Email: poejo@ix.netcom.com
Key Contact - Specialty:
Mr. James P. Spellacy

3942 N. Hampton Drive
Powell, Ohio 43065
(614) 792-8285
Fax: (614) 792-8265
Email: manager@delcty.mrinet.com
Key Contact - Specialty:
Mr. Greg Watkins
Mr. Chris Watkins

23611 Chagrin Blvd., Ste. 380
Chagrin Plaza E.
Shaker Heights, Ohio 44122
(216) 292-1072
Fax: (216) 292-1053
Email: shaker!cmj@mrinet.com
Key Contact - Specialty:
Ms. Cindy Johnston

P.O. Box 39361
Solon, Ohio 44139-2911
(216) 248-7300
Fax: (216) 248-1832
Email: clese!manager@mrinet.com
Key Contact - Specialty:
Ms. Kim M. Barnett

1320 E. 9th, Ste. 3
Edmond, Oklahoma 73034-5709
(405) 348-5550
Fax: (405) 348-8808
Email: edmond!manager@mrinet.com
Key Contact - Specialty:
Mr. Craig S. Lyman

Western Twr., Ste. 207E
5350 S. Western Ave.
Oklahoma City, Oklahoma 73109
(405) 634-8200
Fax: (405) 634-8207
Email: oksouth!manager@mrinet.com
Key Contact - Specialty:
Ms. Julie Eazle
Mr. J. Terry

5801 E. 41st St., Ste. 440
Tulsa, Oklahoma 74135-5614
(918) 663-6744
Fax: (918) 663-1783
Email: tulsa!manager@mrinet.com
Key Contact - Specialty:
Mr. Anthony A. Wolters
Mr. Bill Wetterman

61419 S. Hwy. 97, Ste. V
Bend, Oregon 97702-2103
(541) 383-8550
Fax: (541) 383-8599
Email: mrbend@bendnet.com
Key Contact - Specialty:
Mr. Manney C. Lopez

2020 Lloyd Ctr.
Portland, Oregon 97232-1376
(503) 287-8701
Fax: (503) 282-4380
Email: portland!manager@mrinet.com
Key Contact - Specialty:
Mr. Larry P. Engelgau
Ms. Elvita B. Engelgau

2141 Downyflake Lane
Allentown, Pennsylvania 18103-4774
(610) 797-8863
Fax: (610) 797-8873
Email: alentwn!manager@mrinet.com
Key Contact - Specialty:
Mr. Gary Filko

790 Penllyn Pike, Ste. 206
Blue Bell, Pennsylvania 19422
(215) 654-7182
Fax: (215) 654-7192
Email: mrbluebell@aol.com
Key Contact - Specialty:
Mr. Jeff Garrison

P.O. Box 803
Broomall, Pennsylvania 19008
(610) 359-9100
Fax: (610) 359-9107
Email: manager@broomall.mrinet.com
Key Contact - Specialty:
Mr. Joseph M. Poach, Sr.
Ms. Shauna L. Poach

21 State Ave., Ste. 103
Carlisle, Pennsylvania 17013-3216
(717) 249-2626
Fax: (717) 249-4843
Email: mri@epix.net
Key Contact - Specialty:
Mr. Bert Wendeln

P.O. Box 648
Chinchilla, Pennsylvania 18410-0648
(717) 587-9909
Fax: (717) 587-9910
Email: scranton!manager@mrinet.com
Key Contact - Specialty:
Ms. Sheila Kochmer
Mr. Victor Kochmer

428 Pennsylvania Ave., 2nd Floor
Ft. Washington, Pennsylvania 19034-3408
(215) 793-9444
Fax: (215) 793-9451
Email: manager@montco.mrinet.com
Key Contact - Specialty:
Ms. Mark Teichman

3901 N. Front, Ste. 1 A
Harrisburg, Pennsylvania 17110-1536
(717) 238-3995
Fax: (717) 238-4311
Email: mrHbg@aol.com
Key Contact - Specialty:
Mr. Bill Milo

2233 Dutch Gold Drive
Lancaster, Pennsylvania 17601-1997
(717) 397-6444
Fax: (717) 397-6662
Email: mroflanc@lancnews.infi.net
Key Contact - Specialty:
Mr. Thomas L. Rodebaugh, Jr.
Ms. Karen Rodebaugh

The Farm Complex, Box 220-64B
Montoursville, Pennsylvania 17754
(717) 368-2277
Fax: (717) 368-7586

Key Contact - Specialty:
Mr. Wally A. Helt

161 Leverington Ave., Ste. 102
Philadelphia, Pennsylvania 19127
(215) 482-6881
Fax: (215) 482-7518
Email: manayunk!manager@mrinet.com
Key Contact - Specialty:
Mr. Scott M. Quitel

325 Chestnut St., Ste. 1106
Constitution Place
Philadelphia, Pennsylvania 19106
(215) 829-1900
Fax: (215) 829-1919
Key Contact - Specialty:
Mr. Thomas A. Lucas

300 Weyman Plaza, Ste. 200
Pittsburgh, Pennsylvania 15236
(412) 885-5222
Fax: (412) 885-5512
Email: mrpitsth@aol.com
Key Contact - Specialty:
Mr. Andy J. Hallam
Mr. Paul R. Rossman

2589 Washington Rd., Ste. 435
Pittsburgh, Pennsylvania 15241
(412) 831-7290
Fax: (412) 831-7298
Key Contact - Specialty:
Ms. Sallie Gallagher
Mr. Jim Gallagher
Mr. Mark M. Wawrzeniak

110 Fort Couch Rd., 3rd Floor
Pittsburgh, Pennsylvania 15241-1030
(412) 833-5833
Fax: (412) 833-6225
Email: ericdean@ix.netcom.com
Key Contact - Specialty:
Mr. Eric W. Dean, Jr.

4840 McKnight Rd.
Pittsburgh, Pennsylvania 15237-3413
(412) 364-0282
Fax: (412) 364-7992
Key Contact - Specialty:
Ms. Patricia L. Holupka
Mr. Gary F. Holupka

800 Perry Hwy., Ste. 2
Pittsburgh, Pennsylvania 15229-1128
(412) 635-3001
Fax: (412) 635-3002
Key Contact - Specialty:
Mr. Thomas D. Moore

4 Park Plaza
Reading, Pennsylvania 19610
(610) 375-1500
Fax: (610) 375-1504
Email: mriread@bellatlantic.net
Web: www.mirreading.com
Key Contact - Specialty:
Mr. Jeff Burridge

1035 Boyce Rd., Ste. 120
Boyce Plaza One
Upper St. Clair, Pennsylvania 15241
(412) 257-9585
Fax: (412) 257-9586
Key Contact - Specialty:
Mr. Jack N. Uhl

678 Louis Drive
Warminster, Pennsylvania 18974
(215) 675-6440
Fax: (215) 675-1446
Email: buckscty!manager@mrinet.com
Key Contact - Specialty:
Mr. Michael Mashack
Mr. Ted M. Mashack

1815 Schadt Ave., Ste. 4
Peachtree Office Plaza
Whitehall, Pennsylvania 18052-3761
(610) 740-9200
Fax: (610) 740-9224
Email: lehigh!manager@mrinet.com
Key Contact - Specialty:
Mr. Denny P. Farkas

101 Dyer St., Ste. 5-A
Providence, Rhode Island 02903-3904
(401) 274-2810
Fax: (401) 274-6440
Key Contact - Specialty:
Mr. Stephen W. Morse

P.O. Box 2874
Anderson, South Carolina 29622
(864) 225-1258
Fax: (864) 225-2332
Email: mrand@carol.net
Key Contact - Specialty:
Mr. Rod Pagan

180 Meeting St., Ste. 210
Charleston, South Carolina 29401
(803) 973-3500
Fax: (803) 973-3513
Email: mgmtrecrui@aol.com
Key Contact - Specialty:
Mr. L. S. Carper

4 Carriage Lane, Ste. 301
Charleston, South Carolina 29407
(843) 556-6461
Fax: (843) 556-4803
Email: rlbjr@internetmci.com
Key Contact - Specialty:
Mr. Robert L. Bean, Jr.

2800 Bush River Rd., Ste. 4
Columbia, South Carolina 29210-5698
(803) 772-0300
Fax: (803) 772-4600
Email: mrlexsc@discovery.com
Key Contact - Specialty:
Ms. Debbie Hall
Mr. Roger Hall

P.O. Box 50785
Columbia, South Carolina 29250
(803) 254-1334
Fax: (803) 254-1527
Email: mrcola@scsn.net
Key Contact - Specialty:
Mr. Robert Keen, Jr.

2711 Middleburg Drive, Ste. 313-A
Columbia, South Carolina 29204-2413
(803) 758-5920
Fax: (803) 758-5921
Email: manager@forest.mrinet.com
Key Contact - Specialty:
Mr. Bill Duncan

201 Old Boiling Springs Rd., Ste. D
Pelham Links Professional Park
Greer, South Carolina 29650-4227
(864) 987-9258
Fax: (864) 987-9358
Email: greer!manager@mrinet.com
Key Contact - Specialty:
Mr. Mark Fagan

1051 Johnnie Dodds Blvd., Ste. B
Mt. Pleasant, South Carolina 29464
(803) 856-0544
Fax: (803) 856-0547
Email: mtpleas!manager@mrinet.com
Key Contact - Specialty:
Mr. James L. Dooley

2037 St. Matthews Rd.
Orangeburg, South Carolina 29118
(803) 531-4101
Fax: (803) 536-3714
Email: orangbrg!manager@mrinet.com
Key Contact - Specialty:
Mr. Dick B. Crawford
Mr. Ed Chewning, Jr.

113 Court St.
Pickens, South Carolina 29671-2372
(864) 878-1113
Fax: (864) 878-1410
Email: mripickens@mindspring.com
Key Contact - Specialty:
Mr. Ed Parris, Jr.

1925 Ebenezer Rd.
Rock Hill, South Carolina 29732-1068
(803) 324-5181
Fax: (803) 324-3431
Key Contact - Specialty:
Mr. Herman D. Smith, Jr.

2811 Reidville Rd., Ste. 16
W. Oak Square
Spartanburg, South Carolina 29301-5650
(864) 587-1045
Fax: (864) 587-1048
Email: it@mriglobal.com
Key Contact - Specialty:
Mr. Chip Harrington

1675 N. Main St., Ste. B
Summerville, South Carolina 29483
(803) 821-1119
Fax: (803) 821-1117
Email: manager@sumrvil.mrinet.com
Key Contact - Specialty:
Mr. Norm Moran

7003 Chadwick Drive, Ste. 331
The Bristol Bldg.
Brentwood, Tennessee 37027-5232
(615) 373-1111
Fax: (615) 373-0988
Key Contact - Specialty:
Mr. Andrew B. Foster

5211 Hwy. 153, Ste. H
Plaza 153 Bldg.
Chattanooga, Tennessee 37343
(423) 877-4040
Fax: (423) 877-4466
Key Contact - Specialty:
Mr. Chub Ensminger

780 Walnut Knoll Lane, Ste. 1
Cordova, Tennessee 38018-6300
(901) 432-1674
Fax: (901) 432-2674
Key Contact - Specialty:
Mr. Eddy Hatcher

904 Sunset Drive, Ste. 9B
Johnson City, Tennessee 37604-3674
(423) 952-0900
Fax: (423) 952-0999
Email: mri@tricon.net
Key Contact - Specialty:
Mr. Keith Dawson
Ms. Vikki Sitter

9050 Executive Park Drive, Ste. 16
Knoxville, Tennessee 37923-4693
(423) 694-1628
Fax: (423) 691-5282
Key Contact - Specialty:
Mr. James O. Kline

530 Hwy. 321 N., Ste. 303
Lenoir City, Tennessee 37771-8914
(423) 986-3000
Fax: (423) 986-0874
Key Contact - Specialty:
Mr. Ray S. Strobo

5158 Stage Rd., Ste. 130
Memphis, Tennessee 38134-3164
(901) 888-2580
Fax: (901) 888-2581
Email: manager@bartlett.mrinet.com
Key Contact - Specialty:
Mr. George A. Harants

P.O. Box 4094
Murfreesboro, Tennessee 37133-4094
(615) 890-7623
Fax: (615) 890-9511
Key Contact - Specialty:
Mr. Tom G. Hyde

5959 W. Loop S., Ste. 380
Bellaire, Texas 77401
(713) 665-6660
Fax: (713) 665-3551
Web: mri-bellaire.com
Key Contact - Specialty:
Ms. Peggy Drown

2625 N. Josey Lane, Ste. 302
Carrollton, Texas 75007-5546
(972) 446-2254
Fax: (972) 446-6718
Email: dxf@adisn.mrinet.com
Key Contact - Specialty:
Mr. Dan Finch
Ms. Dianne Finch

13101 Preston Rd., Ste. 560
Dallas, Texas 75240
(972) 788-1515
Fax: (972) 701-8242
Email: dallas!manager@mrinet.com
Key Contact - Specialty:
Mr. Robert Lineback
Ms. Pam Lineback

13747 Montfort, Ste. 337
Dallas, Texas 75240-4460
(972) 788-9288
Fax: (972) 788-9298
Key Contact - Specialty:
Mr. Hal Daugherty
Ms. Judy Daugherty

15400 Knoll Trail, Ste. 230
Dallas, Texas 75248-3465
(972) 960-1291
Fax: (972) 960-7078
Key Contact - Specialty:
Mr. John Burkholder

6006 N. Mesa St., Ste. 408
El Paso, Texas 79912-4623
(915) 833-8211
Fax: (915) 833-8254
Email: manager@elpaso.mrinet.com
Key Contact - Specialty:
Ms. Cindy L. Capanna
Ms. Victoria A. Lummus

6666 Harwin Plaza, Ste. 460
Houston, Texas 77036
(713) 334-9292
Fax: (713) 334-9299
Email: houstsw!manager@mrinet.com
Key Contact - Specialty:
Mr. Terry Bechtold

2200 Space Park Drive, Ste. 420
Houston, Texas 77058-3663
(281) 335-0363
Fax: (281) 335-0362
Email: mricl@aol.com
Key Contact - Specialty:
Mr. Len Bird

14745 Memorial Drive, Ste. 20
Houston, Texas 77079
(281) 497-1444
Fax: (281) 497-7571
Email: mrhoustmem@aol.com
Key Contact - Specialty:
Mr. Ben Cooksey

1333 Corporate Drive, Ste. 211
Irving, Texas 75038
(972) 550-2424
Fax: (972) 550-3965
Email: broll@onramp.net
Key Contact - Specialty:
Mr. Bill Roll

4201 Wingren Drive, Ste. 200
Irving, Texas 75062
(972) 717-4402
Fax: (972) 717-4502
Email: mriworld@onramp.net
Key Contact - Specialty:
Mr. Bill Easton

8445 Freeport Pkwy., Ste. 330
Irving, Texas 75063
(972) 929-2222
Fax: (972) 929-2223
Email: jobs@ISTS.com
Key Contact - Specialty:
Mr. Eric K. Jacobson

North Park Executive Center
713 W. Wadley, Ste. L-110
Midland, Texas 79705-5351
(915) 682-3646
Fax: (915) 682-3979
Key Contact - Specialty:
Ms. Pam Hale
Mr. Don Hale

494 S. Seguin
New Braunfels, Texas 78130-7938
(830) 629-6290
Fax: (830) 629-6364
Key Contact - Specialty:
Mr. Jim K. Rice

555 Republic Drive
Executive Ctr., Ste. 200
Plano, Texas 75074
(972) 516-4227
Fax: (972) 422-9138
Email: plano-e!manager@mrinet.com
Key Contact - Specialty:
Ms. Diane Appleton
Mr. Dana L. McRoberts

2301 N. Central Expwy., Ste. 250
Plano, Texas 75075
(972) 422-3311
Fax: (972) 422-4001
Email: prstn-pk!manager@mrinet.com
Key Contact - Specialty:
Mr. Don C. Jacob

7550 Interstate Hwy. 10 W., Ste. 1230
San Antonio, Texas 78229
(210) 525-1800
Fax: (210) 525-9633
Email: sanantnw!manager@mrinet.com
Key Contact - Specialty:
Mr. Sam Goicoechea
Ms. Lydia Goicoechea

4100 Piedras Drive E., Ste. 204
San Antonio, Texas 78228-1426
(210) 733-1074
Fax: (210) 733-1173
Email: sananxrd!manager@mrinet.com
Key Contact - Specialty:
Mr. Gil C. Jimenez

50 Shadow Ridge, Ste. 103
P.O. Box 680337
Park City, Utah 84068-0337
(801) 647-5670
Fax: (801) 647-3958

Email: parkcty!manager@mrinet.com
Key Contact - Specialty:
Mr. Gregory C. Esty
Ms. Janet S. Esty

1933 N. 1120 W.
Provo, Utah 84604
(801) 375-0777
Fax: (801) 375-5757
Email: provo!manager@mrinet.com
Key Contact - Specialty:
Mr. Larry J. Massung

187 St. Paul St., Ste. 4
Burlington, Vermont 05401-4689
(802) 865-0541
Fax: (802) 865-3664
Email: burlvt!manager@mrinet.com
Key Contact - Specialty:
Mr. Alan Nyhan

2114 Angus Rd., Ste. 235
Charlottesville, Virginia 22901-2768
(804) 293-0800
Fax: (804) 293-0813
Email: jrm@charvil.mrinet.com
Key Contact - Specialty:
Mr. Jim Metzgar

11211 Waples Mill Rd., Ste. 205
Fairfax, Virginia 22030-7406
(703) 383-0099
Fax: (703) 383-0309
Email: mreston2@erols.com
Key Contact - Specialty:
Mr. Chris Garcia
Ms. Linda Garcia

2511 Memorial Ave., Ste. 202
Memorial Professional Bldg.
Lynchburg, Virginia 24501
(804) 528-1611
Fax: (804) 528-1617
Key Contact - Specialty:
Mr. C. David Blue

212 Starling Ave., Ste. 201
Martinsville, Virginia 24112-3844
(540) 632-2355
Fax: (540) 632-0153
Email: martin!whg@mrinet.com
Key Contact - Specialty:
Mr. Herschel Gurley

2 E. Church St., 3rd Floor
P.O. Box 107
Martinsville, Virginia 24114-0107
(540) 638-2000
Fax: (540) 638-2008
Email: henry!manager@mrinet.com
Key Contact - Specialty:
Mr. John C. Matthews

6849 Old Dominion Drive, Ste. 225
McLean, Virginia 22101
(703) 442-4842
Fax: (703) 356-8251
Email: mclean!manager@mrinet.com
Key Contact - Specialty:
Mr. Howard H. Reitkopp
Ms. Ellen Reitkopp

2944 Hunter Mill Rd., Ste. 204
Oakton, Virginia 22124-1761
(703) 319-0206
Fax: (703) 319-0213
Email: manager@oakton.mrinet.com
Key Contact - Specialty:
Mr. Paul Rogers

6620 W. Broad St., Ste. 406
Brookfield Bldg.
Richmond, Virginia 23230
(804) 285-2071
Fax: (804) 282-4990
Email: mririch@erols.com
Key Contact - Specialty:
Mr. Jay S. Schwartz

8134 Old Keene Mill Rd., Ste. 303
Springfield, Virginia 22152-1849
(703) 912-5600
Fax: (703) 912-6888
Key Contact - Specialty:
Mr. John Rosenberg

1577 Wilroy Rd., Ste. 101
River Creek Executive Ctr.
Suffolk, Virginia 23434
(804) 538-1519
Fax: (804) 538-2010
Key Contact - Specialty:
Mr. Neil P. McNulty

4092 Foxwood Drive, Ste. 102
Virginia Beach, Virginia 23462-5259
(757) 474-2752
Fax: (757) 474-9367
Email: mrrico!manager@mrinet.com
Key Contact - Specialty:
Mr. James F. Murphey

10900 NE Fourth St., Ste. 1450
Skyline Tower
Bellevue, Washington 98004
(206) 462-5104
Fax: (206) 462-1614
Key Contact - Specialty:
Mr. Issac Menda

1727 E. Marine View Drive, Ste. B
Everett, Washington 98201
(425) 303-0335
Fax: (425) 303-0495
Email: everett!manager@mrinet.com
Key Contact - Specialty:
Mr. John McElroy

2709 Jahn Ave. NW, #H-11
Gig Harbor, Washington 98335
(206) 858-9991
Fax: (206) 858-5140
Key Contact - Specialty:
Mr. Dennis R. Johnson

6124 Motor Ave. SW
Lakewood, Washington 98499-1529
(253) 582-8488
Fax: (253) 582-8526
Email: adminnw@careers-nw.com
Key Contact - Specialty:
Mr. Len Holmes

9725 SE 36th St., Ste. 312
Globe Bldg.
Mercer Island, Washington 98040-3896
(206) 232-0204
Fax: (206) 232-6172
Email: jim@mrmi.com
Key Contact - Specialty:
Mr. James J. Dykeman

2633-A Parkmount Lane SW, Ste. B
Olympia, Washington 98502
(360) 357-9996
Fax: (360) 357-9998
Email: manager@olympia.mrinet.com
Key Contact - Specialty:
Mr. Jim J. Pitchford

16040 Christensen Rd.
Ste. 316, Bldg. #1
Seattle, Washington 98188
(206) 242-7484
Fax: (206) 248-5005
Email: seasouth!manager@mrinet.com
Key Contact - Specialty:
Mr. Marc L. Goyette

535 Dock St., Ste. 111
Tacoma, Washington 98402-4614
(206) 572-7542
Fax: (206) 572-7872
Email: ntacom@ix.netcom.com
Key Contact - Specialty:
Mr. Bill E. Saylor

703 Broadway St., Ste. 695
Vancouver, Washington 98660
(360) 695-4688
Fax: (360) 695-4384
Email: jpoloni@teleport.com
Key Contact - Specialty:
Mr. James A. Poloni

1587 E. Washington St.
Charleston, West Virginia 25311-2505
(304) 344-5632
Fax: (304) 344-5639
Key Contact - Specialty:
Mr. Anthony P. Oliverio

1714 Mileground, Ste. 200
Morgantown, West Virginia 26505
(304) 284-8500
Fax: (304) 284-8985
Key Contact - Specialty:
Mr. Ray Wood
Ms. Vicki Adams

1711 Woolsey St., Ste. D.
Delavan, Wisconsin 53115-2020
(414) 728-8886
Fax: (414) 728-8894
Email: manager@delavan.mrinet.com
Key Contact - Specialty:
Mr. Dean Sanderson

W175 N11163 Stonewood Drive
Germantown, Wisconsin 53022
(414) 252-8810
Fax: (414) 252-8812
Key Contact - Specialty:
Ms. Diana Popp

444 S. Adams St., Ste. 1
Cadillac Sq.
Green Bay, Wisconsin 54301
(920) 437-4353
Fax: (920) 437-0647
Email: mrigb@mrijobs.com
Key Contact - Specialty:
Mr. Garland E. Ross

5307 S. 92nd St., Ste. 125
Valley View Ctr.
Hales Corners, Wisconsin 53130
(414) 529-8020
Fax: (414) 529-8028
Email: milwsth!manager@mrinet.com
Key Contact - Specialty:
Mr. John J. Henkel
Mr. Thomas E. Hurt

202 Village Walk Lane, Ste. A
Johnson Creek, Wisconsin 53038-9526
(920) 699-4010
Fax: (920) 699-4015
Key Contact - Specialty:
Mr. Dave Trepton

609A N. Main St.
Lodi, Wisconsin 53555-1232
(608) 592-2151
Fax: (608) 592-2133
Key Contact - Specialty:
Mr. Merle Morack

12201 W. Burleigh St., Ste. 7
Milwaukee, Wisconsin 53222
(414) 453-9500
Fax: (414) 453-9508
Key Contact - Specialty:
Mr. Robert Janecek

8338 Corporate Drive, Ste. 300
Racine, Wisconsin 53406
(414) 886-8000
Fax: (414) 886-7260
Email: racine!manager@mrinet.com
Key Contact - Specialty:
Mr. Thomas E. Hurt
Mr. John J. Henkel

Av. Domingo Diez 1589
Ste. 121
Cuernavaca Moreios, Mexico 62250
Mexico
52 73 114045
Fax: 52 73 114046
Email: mrimex@mrimex.com
Key Contact - Specialty:
Mr. Jens Hagedorn
Mr. Carlos Kingwergs

Alborada 124, Ste. 801
Parques Del Pedregal
Mexico City, Mexico C.P. 14010
Mexico
52 5 606 8202
Fax: 52 5 606 8569
Email: mexicocity@mrimexico.com
Key Contact - Specialty:
Mr. Sergio Albores Dumas

Affiliates:
The Delta Group
Humana Int'l. Group PLC
Karamik Management Consultants
Lynn Bichler Human Resources
Morgan & Banks
H. Neumann Int'l.
The Renwick Group
Sales Staffers Int'l. Inc.
Simon Franco Recursos Humanos
Unico Search

Management Recruiters of Birmingham

P.O. Box 381626
Birmingham, Alabama 35238
(205) 408-0767
Fax: (205) 408-0848

Key Contact - Specialty:
Mr. Cleve A. Park - *Metals, engineers*

Functions: Senior mgmt., Middle mgmt., Mfg., Plant mgmt., Quality, Systems dev., Engineering
Industries: Mfg., Food/bev/tobacco, Paper, Chemicals, Metal products

---

Management Recruiters of Birmingham, Inc.

100 Carnoustie N.
Birmingham, Alabama 35242
(205) 408-0855
Fax: (205) 408-0848

Key Contact - Specialty:
Mr. Cleve A. Park - *Accounting, human resources, manufacturing*

Description: Satisfying your critical demand for people...the resource that ultimately determines an organization's profitability.
Functions: CFO's, Budgeting, M&A, MIS mgmt., Systems dev., Systems implem., Engineering
Industries: Textiles/apparel, Metal products, Machinery/Appliances, Computer svcs., Accounting, Human resource svcs., Insurance

---

Management Recruiters of Birmingham-South, Inc.

1210 Lake Forest Circle
Birmingham, Alabama 35244-1302
(205) 444-9116
Fax: (205) 444-9227
Email: brmsouth!cem@mrinet.com
Web: www.mrinet.com

Key Contact - Specialty:
Mr. Charles E. Martin - *Generalist, banking, finance*
Ms. Patricia Martin - *Medical*

Description: Maximum professional search through the largest candidate resume computerized database in the world. Outplacement services (Career Pathways), temporary professional services (Interexec), #1 videoconferencing network (Conferview) in USA. Multiple countries worldwide.

Salary Minimum: $25,000
Functions: General mgmt., Mfg., Materials, Sales & mktg., Finance, IT, Engineering
Industries: Generalist, Misc. mfg., Banking, Brokers, Packaging, High tech, Software

---

Management Recruiters of Decatur, LLC

401 Lee St. NE, Ste. 301
Decatur, Alabama 35601-1908
(256) 341-0140
Fax: (256) 341-0041

Key Contact - Specialty:
Mr. William M. May - *Pulp & paper, plastics, packaging*

Description: National retained and contingency executive search firm specializing in the paper, plastic and packaging industries.

Salary Minimum: $40,000
Functions: Senior mgmt., Middle mgmt., Plant mgmt., Packaging, Mktg. mgmt., Sales mgmt., Engineering
Industries: Paper, Printing, Plastics/rubber, Misc. mfg., Packaging

---

Management Recruiters of Mobile Co., Inc.

3263 Demetropolis Rd., Ste. 6C
Mobile, Alabama 36693
(334) 602-0104
Fax: (334) 661-0065
Email: rcbrock@zebra.net

Key Contact - Specialty:
Mr. Rufus C. Brock

Description: Specializing in nursing management, data processing professionals. Chemical industry specialists.

Salary Minimum: $18,000
Functions: Production, Nurses, Health admin., Systems dev., Systems support, Engineering
Industries: Chemicals, Metal products, Machinery/Appliances, Misc. mfg., Healthcare, Non-classifiable industries

---

Management Recruiters of Sedona

105 Roadrunner Drive, Ste. 5
Sedona, Arizona 86336
(520) 282-8990
Fax: (520) 282-8977
Email: mrsedona@sedona.net

Key Contact - Specialty:
Mr. Phillip T. Howe - *Aviation, aerospace*

Description: We are the largest and most respected search and staffing company in the world; nobody else comes close. Our office specializes in aviation, and aerospace.
Functions: General mgmt., Materials, Sales & mktg., Technicians
Industries: Transportation, Aerospace

Management Recruiters Tucson-Foothills, Inc.

6262 N. Swan Rd.
Skyline Plaza, Ste. 125
Tucson, Arizona 85718
(520) 529-6818
Fax: (520) 529-6877
Email: lorian@mrihitech.com
Web: www.mrihitech.com

Key Contact - Specialty:
Ms. Lorian E. Roethlein - *Semi conductor manufacturing*
Mr. John Roethlein - *Semi conductor manufacturing*

Description: We provide executive search services throught the United States to both candidates and businesses, specializing in high tech manufacturing positions. We can also provide city-to-city interviewing by videoconferencing.
Functions: Senior mgmt., Product dev., Mktg. mgmt., Sales mgmt., MIS mgmt., Engineering
Industries: Computer equip., Consumer electronics, Test/measurement equip., High tech

---

Management Recruiters of Tucson

310 S. Williams Boulevard, Ste. 300
Tucson, Arizona 85711
(520) 745-2270
Fax: (520) 745-2820
Email: careers@mroftucson.com
Web: www.mroftucson.com

Key Contact - Specialty:
Mr. Jack DeJong - *Agriculture, pork production*
Mr. Herb Garman - *Agriculture, wire & cable*

Description: We are a part of MRI, the number one executive search organization in the world. Last year our 700 offices completed 35,000 successful searches.

Salary Minimum: $35,000
Functions: Production, Mkt. research, Mktg. mgmt., Sales mgmt., MIS mgmt., Systems anal., Systems dev.
Industries: Agri/forestry/mining, Misc. mfg., Computer svcs., Telecoms, Software

---

Management Recruiters of Little Rock

1701 Centerview Drive
Redding Bldg., Ste. 314
Little Rock, Arkansas 72211-4313
(501) 224-0801
Fax: (501) 224-0798
Email: litrock!ltr@mrinet.com

Key Contact - Specialty:
Mr. Earl R. Hall - *Food & beverage outside sales*
Mr. Noel K. Hall

Description: We are a contingency search firm working for client companies. These clients pay our service fee for locating mid to upper level managers; generally earning 35K & up.

Salary Minimum: $30,000
Functions: Production, Plant mgmt., Quality, Nurses, Sales mgmt., MIS mgmt., Systems dev.
Industries: Food/bev/tobacco, Plastics/rubber, Metal products, Motor vehicles, Wholesale, Computer svcs., Healthcare

---

Management Recruiters of Aptos

15 Seascape Village, #15
Aptos, California 95003
(408) 688-5200
Fax: (408) 688-5267
Email: cathyhenderson@msn.com
Web: www.mriconstruction.com

Key Contact - Specialty:
Ms. Cathy Henderson - *Construction, development*

Description: Consistently ranks in top 5% of all recruiters nationwide. Offers value added services including video conferencing, relocation guidance, 401K assistance and discounts on moving expenses.
Functions: Directors, Senior mgmt., Middle mgmt., M&A, Engineering
Industries: Construction, Real estate

Management Recruiters of San Luis Obispo

7360 El Camino Real, Ste. A
Atascadero, California 93422
(805) 462-8044
Fax: (805) 462-8047
Web: www.recruiter@healthcare-exec.com

Key Contact - Specialty:
Mr. Ralph Bunker - *Pharmaceutical, biotechnology, research & development, regulatory, compliance*

Description: Specialize in the placement of pharmaceutical/biotech industry positions in research and development, regulatory, compliance, clinical, pre-clinical and toxicology.

Salary Minimum: $50,000
Functions: Directors, Senior mgmt., Middle mgmt., Mkt. research, Mktg. mgmt., Sales mgmt., R&D
Industries: Drugs mfg., Medical devices

Management Recruiters of Berkeley

2150 Shattuck Ave., Ste. 704
Berkeley, California 94704-1306
(510) 486-8100
Fax: (510) 486-8189
Email: rhoward@mri-berkeley.com
Web: www.mri-berkeley.com

Key Contact - Specialty:
Mr. Richard H. Howard - *Banking*

Description: Account executives work an industry discipline. Best source for knowing the hidden job market.

Salary Minimum: $50,000
Functions: Middle mgmt., Materials, Health admin., Cash mgmt., Risk mgmt., Engineering, Environmentalists
Industries: Transportation, Finance, Banking, Misc. financial, Environmental svcs., Healthcare

---

Management Recruiters Peninsula

111 Anza Blvd., Ste. 109
Burlingame, California 94010
(650) 548-4800
Fax: (650) 548-4805

Key Contact - Specialty:
Mr. Don Hirschbein - *Pharmaceutical, medical sales*
Mr. Michael Shaffer - *Consumer products, food & beverage*
Ms. Crystal Parsons - *Manufacturing*

Description: Large (12 recruiters) firm with many specialists. Office ranks in top 10% world's largest executive search company.

Salary Minimum: $30,000
Functions: General mgmt., Mfg., Healthcare, Sales & mktg., IT, R&D, Engineering
Industries: Construction, Food/bev/tobacco, Wholesale, Equip. svcs., Telecoms, Environmental svcs., High tech

Management Recruiters of Clovis

150 Clovis Ave., Ste. 205
Clovis, California 93612-1152
(209) 299-7992
Fax: (209) 299-2167
Email: food@ix.netcom.com
Web: www.mrinet.com

Key Contact - Specialty:
Mr. Gary Hendrickson - *Food & beverage processing*

Description: We are the world's largest search firm with 750 offices, over 4000 account executives, a nationwide database and cost-saving services unequalled by all others.

Salary Minimum: $30,000
Functions: Directors, Middle mgmt., Distribution, Packaging, Benefits, Systems dev., Engineering
Industries: Food/bev/tobacco, Misc. mfg.

Management Recruiters Dana Point

24681 La Plaza Drive, Ste. 280
Dana Point, California 92629
(949) 443-2800
Fax: (949) 443-2806
Email: careers@home.net
Web: mridp.com

Key Contact - Specialty:
Mr. Ed L. Provost - *Transportation, logistics, warehouse distribution*
Mr. Todd Provost - *Transportation, logistics, warehouse distribution*

Description: We specialize in placing candidates in a wide range of professions. If you have a placement need, take advantage of our innovative staffing solutions.

Salary Minimum: $35,000
Functions: Senior mgmt., Distribution, Sales mgmt., CFO's, MIS mgmt., Systems dev., Environmentalists
Industries: Transportation, Broadcast & Film, Telecoms, Environmental svcs., Software

Management Recruiters of Emeryville

2354 Powell St., Ste. A
Emeryville, California 94608
(510) 658-1405
Email: emery!mah@mrinet.com
Web: www.biotech-jobs.com

Key Contact - Specialty:
Mr. Mark Hoffman - *Biotechnology, pharmaceuticals, medical device*

Description: Our specialty is in the biotech industry in the areas of research and development.

Salary Minimum: $50,000
Functions: Middle mgmt., Product dev., Automation
Industries: Drugs mfg., Medical devices, Pharmaceutical svcs., Biotech

Management Recruiters of Fresno

114 E. Shaw, Ste. 207
Fresno, California 93710
(209) 432-3700
Fax: (209) 432-9937
Email: ron@mri-fresno.com
Web: www.mri-fresno.com

Key Contact - Specialty:
Mr. Ron L. Johnson - *Sales, managed care, pharmaceuticals*
Ms. Tina Sarantino - *Food, engineering*
Mrs. Donna Johnson
Ms. Joy Huitt
Ms. T. J. Wisdom - *Construction, highways & hospitals*
Ms. Rachel Sinclair - *Building products, branch managers*
Ms. Catherine Latona - *Hydraulic manufacturers*
Mr. Scott Diorio - *MIS, software engineers, programmers*
Ms. Jennifer Elizondo - *Pharmaceutical sales, finance, insurance sales*
Mr. Roland Tamayo - *Electrical engineering, MIS, channel sales*
Ms. Maureen McCarthy - *IS programmers, insurance*
Ms. Olga Smirnoff - *IS programmers, transportation, warehousing*
Ms. Anna Hammond

Description: 1990 MRI office of the year. Had MRI rookie of the year 1989 and 1990. 20 years in business. Specializing mostly in engineering and hospital management. Also construction, telecommunications, accounting, plastics, food, data processing, information systems, electronics, pharmaceuticals, managed care, insurance, warehousing, and transportation.
Functions: Purchasing, Distribution, Benefits, Training, CFO's, MIS mgmt., Network admin.

Management Recruiters of Grass Valley

350 Crown Point Circle, Ste. 125
Grass Valley, California 95945
(530) 273-0200
Fax: (530) 273-0364
Email: ridge@mriretailsearch
Web: www.mriretailsearch.com

Key Contact - Specialty:
Mr. Ridge Eagan - *Retail*
Ms. Karen Eagan - *Retail*

Salary Minimum: $25,000
Industries: Retail

Management Recruiters of Laguna Hills

23461 S. Pointe Drive, Ste. 390
Laguna Hills, California 92653
(949) 768-9112
Fax: (949) 768-6135
Email: t2jaguar@aol.com

Key Contact - Specialty:
Mr. Thomas J. Toole - *Automotive aftermarket, multi unit retail, general management, executives*
Ms. Mary Toole - *Sales, sales management, marketing management*

Description: National specialists in automotive aftermarket, retail, marketing, executive, chemical industry, finance, telecommunications, apparel, electronics, architecture, construction. Fully computerized, branch offices in 600 cities.

Salary Minimum: $50,000
Functions: Senior mgmt., Mfg., Materials, Sales & mktg., HR mgmt., Finance, Engineering
Industries: Construction, Chemicals, Retail, Finance, Hospitality, Telecoms, Real estate

Management Recruiters of Northern California

591 Redwood Hwy., Ste. 2225
Mill Valley, California 94941
(415) 383-7044
Fax: (415) 383-1426
Email: ecw@millval.mrinet.com
Web: www.mrimvca.com

Key Contact - Specialty:
Mr. Eric Wheel - *World wide web, virtual reality, educational software*

Description: 15+ years experience in high tech recruiting. Individual specialists in functions/industries listed. Nationwide network of 500 offices. Our specialty is fast response to urgent needs.

Salary Minimum: $50,000
Functions: Senior mgmt., Middle mgmt., Product dev., Production, Mktg. mgmt., Sales mgmt., Engineering
Industries: Medical devices, Computer equip., Consumer electronics, New media, Telecoms, High tech, Software

Management Recruiters of Monterey

494 Alvarado St., Ste. F
Monterey, California 93940-2717
(408) 649-0737
Fax: (408) 649-0253
Web: mrmtry@redshift.com

Key Contact - Specialty:
Mr. Richard J. Kashinsky - *Healthcare (specifically surgical and emergency services, directors, managers, specialists)*

Description: A search firm specializing in surgical and emergency nursing management with clients nationwide.

Salary Minimum: $40,000
Functions: Nurses, Health admin.
Industries: Healthcare

Management Recruiters of Sonoma

765 Baywood Drive, Ste. 225
Petaluma, California 94954
(707) 769-2955
Fax: (707) 769-2966
Email: recruit@iscweb.com

Key Contact - Specialty:
Mr. Roland Chamberland - *Construction, engineering, mechanical trades, electrical contracting, architects*

Description: Recruiting for commercial construction, HVAC, mechanical and electrical subcontracting trades, architecture & engineering professionals.

Salary Minimum: $50,000
Functions: Senior mgmt., Middle mgmt., Mktg. mgmt., Sales mgmt., Engineering, Architects, Technicians
Industries: Construction

Management Recruiters of Pleasanton

4125 Mohr Ave., Ste. M
Pleasanton, California 94566-4740
(925) 462-8579
Fax: (925) 462-0208
Email: mricareers@eirthlink.net
Web: mricareers.com

Key Contact - Specialty:
Mr. Michael T. Machi - *Plastics, wire & cable, finance & accounting*

Description: Presidents club office, established client base, confidential contingency and retained search.

Salary Minimum: $40,000
Functions: Product dev., Production, Quality, Distribution, CFO's, Budgeting, Systems anal.
Industries: Medical devices, Plastics/rubber, Misc. mfg., Misc. financial, Entertainment, High tech, Software

Management Recruiters, Inland Empire Agency

19 E. Citrus Ave., Ste. 201
Redlands, California 92373
(909) 335-2055
Fax: (909) 792-4194
Email: mrredlands@aol.com

Key Contact - Specialty:
Mr. Maurice R. Meyers - *Construction, engineering*

Description: Single source human resource service to serve our clients with recruiting for permanent positions, executive temporary placement and outplacement. Fast, efficient, cost effective utilization of our 600 offices nationwide network.

Salary Minimum: $40,000
Functions: Senior mgmt., Middle mgmt., Distribution, Sales mgmt., Personnel, CFO's, Architects
Industries: Construction, Transportation, Accounting, Human resource svcs.

Management Recruiters of Roseville

3001 Douglas Blvd., Ste. 230
Roseville, California 95661
(916) 781-8110
Fax: (916) 781-6719
Email: mri@mriexec.com
Web: www.mriexec.com

Key Contact - Specialty:
Mr. David Sanders - *Computer software, computer hardware, information technology, multimedia, interactive entertainment*

Description: Our team of professionals is your single source for worldwide high technology recruiting of executive, technical, sales and marketing people. Additionally, we provide candidate selection tools and relocation services along with international videoconferencing.

Salary Minimum: $50,000
Functions: Senior mgmt., Mktg. mgmt., Sales mgmt., CFO's, IT
Industries: Computer equip., New media, Broadcast & Film, Telecoms, High tech, Software, Healthcare

Management Recruiters of Sacramento North

2316 Bell Executive Lane, Ste. 100
Sacramento, California 95825
(916) 565-2700
Fax: (916) 565-2828
Email: mrsacnorth@aol.com
Web: www.mrsacramento.com

Key Contact - Specialty:
Mr. Karl Dinse - *Building materials manufacturing*
Ms. Elizabeth Dinse - *Human resource management, accounting*

Description: We have a military recruiting department which recruits recently departing military personnel including professional engineers and junior military officers. Videoconferencing interviews and tapes nationally and internationally.

Salary Minimum: $50,000
Functions: Mfg., Sales & mktg., HR mgmt., Finance, IT, Engineering, Int'l.
Industries: Agri/forestry/mining, Energy/utilities, Construction, Mfg., Finance, Svcs., Software

Management Recruiters Inc. of Silicon Valley

2055 Gateway Place, Ste. 420
San Jose, California 95110
(408) 453-9999
Fax: (408) 452-8510
Email: jrosica@mrisanjose.com
Web: www.mrisanjose.com

Key Contact - Specialty:
Mr. John Rosica - *High technology, Silicon Valley companies or Silicon Valley type companies (in other parts of U.S. & world)*

Description: We are in Silicon Valley and specialize in computer and electronic industry, systems engineering and IS and IT consulting. Also semiconductor, semiconductor capital equipment industries.

Salary Minimum: $50,000
Functions: General mgmt., Middle mgmt., Product dev., Mkt. research, Mktg. mgmt., Sales mgmt., IT
Industries: Computer equip., Consumer electronics, Test/measurement equip., Computer svcs., Mgmt. consulting, High tech, Software

Management Recruiters of Colorado Springs

13 S. Tejon, Ste. 501
Colorado Springs, Colorado 80903
(719) 575-0500
Fax: (719) 575-0505
Email: info@cosprings.com

Key Contact - Specialty:
Mr. Mark Merriman - *Energy*
Mr. Jack Merriman - *Energy*

Description: Contingency search, working both regionally and nationally with an emphasis on technical positions in the following areas: utilities, data processing, environment and safety, healthcare and food.

Functions: Product dev., Production, Plant mgmt., Sales mgmt., Systems dev., Systems implem., Engineering
Industries: Energy/utilities, Food/bev/tobacco, Plastics/rubber, Machinery/Appliances, Computer equip., Computer svcs., High tech

Management Recruiters of Colorado, Inc.

9350 E. Arapahoe Rd., Ste. 480
Englewood, Colorado 80112
(303) 799-8188
Fax: (303) 799-0711
Email: kmili@aol.com

Key Contact - Specialty:
Mr. Kent Milius - *Senior management, healthcare, food & beverage, managed care, mining*

Description: 2 years executive recruiting experience. Principals have conducted searches over a vast range of industries and positions.

Salary Minimum: $20,000
Functions: Mfg., Physicians, Nurses, Allied health, Health admin., Sales & mktg.
Industries: Generalist, Agri/forestry/mining, Food/bev/tobacco, Insurance, Healthcare

Management Recruiters of Franktown

2195 N. Hwy. 83, Ste. 17
Franktown, Colorado 80116
(303) 660-0766
Fax: (303) 660-0065
Email: info@jobs-search.com
Web: www.jobs-search.com

Key Contact - Specialty:
Mr. David Empey - *Information technology, management, technical*
Mr. James Harlan - *Telecommunications, sales & marketing*
Ms. Marcie Norman - *Computer software & hardware, management, technical*
Mr. Lee Rudolph - *Telecommunications, wireless, networking*
Mr. Wes Cropp - *Telecommunication, data communications, telephony*

Description: Focus areas include enterprise software and systems development companies, technology start-up companies and telecommunication networking/solutions providers for the voice, data, fax, wireless, multimedia industries.

Salary Minimum: $50,000
Functions: Directors, Senior mgmt., Product dev., Sales & mktg., IT, Engineering
Industries: Computer equip., Consumer electronics, Computer svcs., Communications, High tech, Software

Management Recruiters of Middlesex

154 West St., Bldg. 3, Unit C
Cromwell, Connecticut 06416-2425
(860) 635-0612
Fax: (860) 632-5939
Email: midlsex!manager@mrinet.com
Web: www.mrinet.com

Key Contact - Specialty:
Mr. Leslie C. Cole - *Executive sales, marketing, management, management consulting*

Description: Individualized recruitment firm, placing and recruiting on a national basis. Mid management level positions and up.
Functions: Senior mgmt., Middle mgmt., Mkt. research, Mktg. mgmt., Sales mgmt., Mgmt. consultants
Industries: Chemicals, Soap/perfume/cosmetics, Drugs mfg., Paints/petroleum products, Misc. mfg., Misc. financial, Mgmt. consulting

Management Recruiters of Colchester

155 Sycamore St.
Glastonbury, Connecticut 06033
(860) 652-8660
Fax: (860) 652-8740

Key Contact - Specialty:
Mr. Michael Gionta - *LAN, WAN*

Description: Our 600 office network reduces relocation costs. Provide relocation services at no charge to clients (i.e. cost of living differentials, tour of area). Specialize in computer networking LAN/WAN sales/marketing.

Salary Minimum: $40,000
Functions: Sales mgmt.
Industries: Computer equip., Test/measurement equip., Computer svcs., Telecoms, Software

Management Recruiters of Milford Inc.

61 Cherry St.
Milford, Connecticut 06460-3414
(203) 876-8755
Fax: (203) 877-1281

Key Contact - Specialty:
Ms. Sandra Stratman - *Biotechnology, pharmaceutical, diagnostics*
Ms. Sandra Campbell - *Pharmaceutical, analytical, capital equipment, chemical*

Description: Specialists in executive, R&D and operations management recruiting.

Salary Minimum: $50,000
Functions: Senior mgmt., Middle mgmt., Product dev., Packaging, Sales mgmt., R&D, Engineering
Industries: Food/bev/tobacco, Chemicals, Medical devices, Computer equip., Pharmaceutical svcs., High tech, Biotech

Management Recruiters of Winsted, Inc.

P.O. Box 1017
140 Willow St., Ste. 6
Winsted, Connecticut 06098-1017
(860) 738-5035
Fax: (860) 738-5039
Email: mriwin@snet.net

Key Contact - Specialty:
Mr. Jack Bourque - *Technical, engineering, sales, administration*
Mr. John Zaharek
Mr. Rodney Bouchard - *Internet, client server, LAN, WAN, UNIX*

Description: Specialists who provide intelligent staffing solutions in: wireless/wire/cable/connectors especially with converging communications systems (45+ combined years).

Salary Minimum: $35,000
Functions: Senior mgmt., Production, Plant mgmt., Materials Plng., Sales mgmt., IT, Engineering
Industries: Construction, Metal products, Computer equip., Consumer electronics, Telecoms, Software

Management Recruiters of Altamonte

498 Palm Springs Drive, Ste. 100
Altamonte Springs, Florida 32701
(407) 260-0039
Fax: (407) 260-0255
Email: johnedw@ix.netcom.com

Key Contact - Specialty:
Mr. John Edward Clark - *Telecommunications, technical*
Mr. Jud Pahls - *Insurance, top secret clearance positions*

Description: President spent 12 years with AT&T-Bell Labs.

Salary Minimum: $30,000
Functions: Middle mgmt., Sales & mktg., IT, R&D, Engineering, Technicians, Int'l.
Industries: Communications, Telecoms, Defense, Aerospace, Real estate, High tech, Software

Management Recruiters of Boca Raton

370 W. Camino Gardens Blvd., Ste. 200
Boca Raton, Florida 33432
(561) 393-3991
(800) 886-3991
Fax: (561) 393-3992
Email: MRBoca@MRBoca.com
Web: MRBoca.com

Key Contact - Specialty:
Mr. Ernie Labadie - *Chemicals*

Description: Technical specialists for the chemicals industry. Range of expertise covers sales to production. Key consideration given to the plastics industry.
Functions: Senior mgmt., Middle mgmt., Product dev., Production, Plant mgmt., R&D, Engineering
Industries: Chemicals, Plastics/rubber, Human resource svcs.

Management Recruiters of Bonita Springs, Inc.

9240 Bonita Beach Rd., Ste. 3307
Bonita Springs, Florida 34135
(941) 495-7885
Fax: (941) 495-7686
Email: gfs@bonitasp.mrinet.com

Key Contact - Specialty:
Mr. Gary F. Shearer - *Engineering, electric and gas utility industries, management consulting, pulp and paper, forest products*

Description: A professional recruitment group genuinely interested in people, not numbers. Our employer clients can expect nothing less than sincere, accurate and thorough searches resulting in genuinely qualified candidates.

Salary Minimum: $65,000
Functions: Senior mgmt., Middle mgmt., Mfg., M&A, Engineering, Mgmt. consultants, Int'l.
Industries: Energy/utilities, Construction, Paper, Chemicals, Mgmt. consulting, Telecoms

Management Recruiters of Anna Maria Island

3655 Cortez Rd. W., Ste. 90
Bradenton, Florida 34210-3147
(941) 756-3001
Fax: (941) 756-0027
Email: Mriflorida@aol.com

Key Contact - Specialty:
Mr. R. Rush Oster - *Food, pharmaceutical, medical, paper and steel*

Description: Highly specialized in placement to the technical areas of healthcare and food ingredient and consumer product manufacturing including product development, R&D, production and technical sales/marketing.

Salary Minimum: $40,000
Functions: Product dev., Production, Mkt. research, Sales mgmt., CFO's, Mgmt. consultants
Industries: Food/bev/tobacco, Printing, Drugs mfg., Metal products, Pharmaceutical svcs., Healthcare

Management Recruiters of Clearwater

1305 S. Michigan Ave.
P.O. Box 7711
Clearwater, Florida 34618
(813) 791-3277

Key Contact - Specialty:
Ms. Helen Gleason - *Packaging, manufacturing, sales*

Description: Specialists: packaging (manufacturing and sales), corrugated boxes, flexible, thermoformed, injection molded and paper containers - medical - all disciplines - administration, engineers, physicians, etc.
Functions: Plant mgmt., Quality, Health admin., Sales mgmt., Finance, Systems dev.
Industries: Paper, Printing, Plastics/rubber, Computer svcs., Accounting, Packaging, Healthcare

Management Recruiters of Ft. Myers, FL.

3606 Evans Ave.
Ft. Myers, Florida 33901
(941) 939-2223
Fax: (941) 939-2742
Email: mricorp!chb@mrinet.com

Key Contact - Specialty:
Mr. R. J. Lynge - *Building materials, manufacturing*
Mr. Calvin Beals - *Bank & trust officers (nationally)*
Ms. Doris Anderson

Description: Specializing in manufacturing, building materials, banking, trust. Also management consulting, contingency and retainer. Open to working with good offices in related fields. Also executive temps and outplacement.

Salary Minimum: $50,000
Functions: Senior mgmt., Product dev., Production, Plant mgmt., Quality, Sales mgmt., CFO's
Industries: Construction, Lumber/furniture, Paper, Plastics/rubber, Banking, Invest. banking, Misc. financial

Management Recruiters of Melbourne, Inc.

134 Fifth Ave., Ste. 208
Indialantic, Florida 32903
(407) 951-7644
Fax: (407) 951-4235
Email: mr@mrirecruiter.com
Web: www.mrirecruiter.com

Key Contact - Specialty:
Mr. Lawrence K. Cinco - *Manager*
Ms. Sue K. Cinco - *Mobile equipment*

Description: A tenured team of 4 people in the MIS dept. specifically=IBM MidRANGE case tools- SYNON and relational database, ORACLE recruiting. Availability for conferview, video conferencing interviewing. Cost of living and relocation specialty teams to aid the new hire move to the area.
Functions: Product dev., Plant mgmt., Systems anal., Systems dev., Network admin., DB admin., Engineering
Industries: Metal products, Machinery/Appliances, Motor vehicles, Misc. financial, Equip. svcs., Broadcast & Film, Telecoms

Management Recruiters, Inc.

12708 San Jose Blvd., Ste. 1A
Jacksonville, Florida 32223
(904) 260-4444
Fax: (904) 260-4666
Email: packmann@southeast.net
Web: www.mrijax.com

Key Contact - Specialty:
Mr. Robert Lee - *Packaging, railroad supply*
Mrs. Barbara A. Lee - *General sales, administration, accounting, telecommunications*

Description: Search firm specializing in industrial sales/marketing/engineering and especially packaging/capital equipment and rail transportation industries. Some administration/accounting/CEO's in same marketplaces. Entry to upper level negotiations/positioning.

Salary Minimum: $35,000
Functions: General mgmt., Mfg., Automation, Sales & mktg., Sales mgmt., CFO's, Engineering
Industries: Machinery/Appliances, Motor vehicles, Computer equip., Transportation, Telecoms, Packaging, High tech

Management Recruiters of Miami-North

815 NW 57th Ave., Ste. 110
Miami, Florida 33126
(305) 264-4212
Fax: (305) 264-4251
Email: mrmiami@netrox.net
Web: www.mrmiami.com

Key Contact - Specialty:
Mr. Del Diaz - *General management, engineering*

Description: Specializing in confidential search and recruiting assignments for executives, managers and professionals in manufacturing, engineering, administration, sales, data processing and international trade.
Functions: Generalist, General mgmt., Mfg., Sales & mktg., Finance, Engineering, Int'l.
Industries: Generalist, Energy/utilities, Construction, Mfg., Finance, High tech, Software

---

Management Recruiters of Lake Co., Inc.

1117 N. Donnelly St.
Mt. Dora, Florida 32757
(352) 383-7101
Fax: (352) 383-7103

Key Contact - Specialty:
Mr. Roger M. Holloway - *Plastics*

Description: Manufacturing specialists-production, engineering, management, quality control, technical and sales. Particular emphasis in plastics, food processing, transportation equipment, medical manufacturing, pharmaceuticals, chemicals.

Salary Minimum: $25,000
Functions: Middle mgmt., Product dev., Production, Plant mgmt., Quality, Engineering, Technicians
Industries: Food/bev/tobacco, Chemicals, Soap/perfume/cosmetics, Drugs mfg., Metal products, Motor vehicles

---

Management Recruiters of Northern Palm Beaches

8895 N. Military Trail, Ste. 301B
Palm Beach Gardens, Florida 33410
(561) 622-8110
Fax: (561) 622-8440
Email: mrinpb@earthlink.net

Key Contact - Specialty:
Mr. James R. Kissel - *Advertising, sales promotion, public relations*
Mr. Larry Marini - *Advertising creative*
Mr. Brian J. Kissel - *Public relations*

Description: Our mission - discreet executive searches in marketing communications (advertising, promotion, public relations) for corporate and agency clients on a nationwide basis.

Salary Minimum: $50,000
Functions: Senior mgmt., Advertising, Mkt. research, Mktg. mgmt., Direct mktg., PR, Graphic artists
Industries: Entertainment, Advertising/PR, Publishing, New media, Broadcast & Film

---

Management Recruiters of Pensacola

603 E. Government St.
Pensacola, Florida 32501
(850) 434-6500
Fax: (850) 434-9911
Email: kirk@mriplastics.com
Web: www.mriplastics.com

Key Contact - Specialty:
Mr. Ken Kirchgessner - *Paper, plastic industries (management, sales), technical*
Mr. Jim Clark - *Plastic industry*

Description: Upper level sales, technical and operations management recruitment in paper and plastics industries since 1981.

Salary Minimum: $40,000
Functions: Product dev., Production, Plant mgmt., Productivity, Packaging, Sales mgmt., R&D
Industries: Paper, Printing, Plastics/rubber

Management Recruiters of Plant City, Inc.

117 W. Alexander St., Ste. 303
Plant City, Florida 33566
(813) 754-6340
Fax: (813) 754-7557
Web: davezaring@msn.com

Key Contact - Specialty:
Mr. David Zaring - *Pharmaceuticals, biotechnology, chemists, scientists*
Ms. Judy Zaring - *Human resources, finance*

Description: Specialists in the recruitment and placement of chemists, pharmaceutical and biotech scientists and chemical engineers.
Functions: R&D
Industries: Chemicals, Drugs mfg., Medical devices, Plastics/rubber, Pharmaceutical svcs., High tech, Biotech

---

Management Recruiters of St. Lucie County, Inc.

756 SE Port St. Lucie Blvd.
Port St. Lucie, Florida 34984
(561) 871-1100
Fax: (561) 871-0702
Email: larryb@mriretail.com
Web: www.mriretail.com

Key Contact - Specialty:
Mr. Larry J. Breault - *Retail technology industry*

Description: Sales and marketing representatives, management, executives, technical support, consultants, CEO's. Specialty-retail computer industry products and financial services (eg. credit/debit/smart card systems). Technology products and services for retail merchants.

Salary Minimum: $50,000
Functions: Senior mgmt., Mktg. mgmt., Sales mgmt., Customer svc., MIS mgmt., Systems implem., Int'l.
Industries: Retail, Hospitality, Entertainment, Computer svcs., Mgmt. consulting, New media, Software

---

Management Recruiters of St. Augustine

2225 State Rd., Ste. B-3A
St. Augustine, Florida 32084
(904) 461-0116
Email: cliff@cwbard.com
Web: www.cwbard.com

Key Contact - Specialty:
Mr. Cliff Bard - *Consulting, banking, finance, human resources*
Ms. Ann Bard - *Mortgage banking, ERP project managers*
Mr. Justin Bard - *Information technology, communications*

Description: Global search and placement firm providing a complete range of executive search services for management consulting, banking, financial services, telecommunications and information technology industries.

Salary Minimum: $50,000
Functions: Senior mgmt., Middle mgmt., Personnel, CFO's, Cash mgmt., Systems implem., Mgmt. consultants
Industries: Banking, Invest. banking, Brokers, Accounting, Mgmt. consulting, Human resource svcs., Telecoms

---

Management Recruiters of Tampa North

4012 Gunn Hwy., Ste. 140
Tampa, Florida 33624-4724
(813) 264-7165
Fax: (813) 968-6450
Web: www.mrtampanorth.com

Key Contact - Specialty:
Mr. Gary King - *Healthcare*
Ms. Gail King - *Insurance, Telecommunications*

Description: National executive search firm specializing in healthcare, managed care, insurance, and information technology.

Salary Minimum: $40,000
Functions: General mgmt., Healthcare, Health admin., Sales & mktg., HR mgmt., Benefits, IT
Industries: Medical devices, Computer svcs., Telecoms, Insurance, High tech, Software, Healthcare

Management Recruiters of Venice, Inc.
996B Laguna Drive
P.O. Box 1328
Venice, Florida 34284-1328
(800) 685-5653
Fax: (800) 559-5822
Email: mrvenice@gte.net

Key Contact - Specialty:
Mr. Walter W. Taylor - *Information technology*
Ms. Winifred C. Taylor - *General manufacturing*

Description: Provide value added recruiting services on a nationwide basis for quality minded corporations and candidates.

Salary Minimum: $40,000
Functions: Production, Materials Plng., Sales mgmt., MIS mgmt., Systems anal., R&D, Engineering
Industries: Metal products, Computer equip., Computer svcs., Telecoms, High tech, Software

Management Recruiters of Vero Beach
1991 19th Place
Vero Beach, Florida 32960
(561) 778-4343
Fax: (561) 778-2688
Email: headhunters@bigfoot.com

Key Contact - Specialty:
Mr. David A. Peterson - *Building products*
Ms. Diana K. Peterson - *Building products*

Description: We have been the leader in permanent placement in the building industry for 20 years. We meet our commitment to clients.
Functions: General mgmt., Directors, Senior mgmt., Middle mgmt., Plant mgmt., Sales mgmt., Engineering
Industries: Construction, Mfg., Chemicals, Paints/petroleum products, Leather/stone/glass/clay, Metal products, Misc. mfg.

Management Recruiters of North Fulton
21 N. Main St., Ste. 204
Alpharetta, Georgia 30004
(770) 664-5512
Fax: (770) 664-5046
Email: chartcon@ix.netcom.com

Key Contact - Specialty:
Mr. John K. Harvey - *Food & beverage packaging, building products*

Description: Specialize in packaging/systems, software/high tech, pulp and paper, building products and logistics industries, primarily new product development, sales, finance, marketing, operations management and engineering disciplines.

Salary Minimum: $50,000
Functions: Generalist, Distribution, Packaging, Sales & mktg., CFO's, Engineering, Int'l.
Industries: Generalist, Food/bev/tobacco, Lumber/furniture, Paper, Packaging, High tech, Software

Management Recruiters of Atlanta
5901-C Peachtree Dunwoody Rd., Ste. 370
Atlanta, Georgia 30328
(770) 394-1300
Fax: (770) 698-9384
Email: atlanta!1wc@mrinet.com
Web: www.mri-atlanta.com

Key Contact - Specialty:
Mr. Larry Cooper - *Pharmaceuticals, medical, telecommunications*
Mr. Phil Schechter - *Advertising*
Mr. Jeff Jones - *Data processing, information systems (sales & technical)*
Mr. Michael Robinson - *Data processing, information systems (sales & technical)*

Description: Only MRI provides the people, the products, the services and the technologies to help organizations like yours meet every human resource need.
Functions: Middle mgmt., Plant mgmt., Distribution, Mkt. research, Credit, Systems dev., Graphic artists
Industries: Transportation, Finance, Hospitality, Pharmaceutical svcs., Advertising/PR

Management Recruiters of Columbus, Inc.
233 12th St., Ste. 818-A
Columbus, Georgia 31901-2449
(706) 571-9611
Fax: (706) 571-3288
Email: michael@mricolumbusga.com
Web: www.mricolumbusga.com

Key Contact - Specialty:
Mr. Michael L. Silverstein - *Information systems, data processing*

Description: We specialize in DP recruiting for mainframe, midrange and mini environments including LAN/WAN connectivity. Positions range from programmers through MIS directors as well as systems network specialists.
Functions: Product dev., Production, MIS mgmt., Systems anal., Systems dev., Systems implem., Engineering
Industries: Textiles/apparel, Metal products, Machinery/Appliances, Banking, Misc. financial, Insurance, Healthcare

Management Recruiters of Forsyth County
600 Peachtree Pkwy., Ste. 108
Cumming, Georgia 30131-6822
(770) 889-5250
Fax: (770) 889-5257
Email: mriforsy@msn.com

Key Contact - Specialty:
Mr. Dan Barrett - *MIS, construction, logistics*

Description: A staff of professional account executives with senior management experience at some of nation's leading corporations. We speak your language. We've been there.

Salary Minimum: $40,000
Functions: Generalist, Mfg., Materials, Sales & mktg., MIS mgmt., Engineering
Industries: Construction, Retail, Computer svcs., Equip. svcs., Mgmt. consulting, High tech, Software

Management Recruiters of Duluth
3700 Crestwood Pkwy., Ste. 320
Duluth, Georgia 30136
(770) 925-2266
Fax: (770) 925-1090
Email: mri.atlanta@internetmci.com

Key Contact - Specialty:
Mr. David Riggs

Description: Dedicated to improve our clients' bottom line through customized staffing solutions.

Salary Minimum: $60,000
Functions: Directors, Senior mgmt., Middle mgmt., Packaging, Credit, Risk mgmt., R&D
Industries: Drugs mfg., Banking, Invest. banking, Misc. financial, Equip. svcs., Packaging, Biotech

Management Recruiters of Atlanta West, Inc.
685 Thornton Way
Lithia Springs, Georgia 30122
(770) 948-5560
Fax: (770) 948-5762
Email: mri@writeme.com

Key Contact - Specialty:
Mr. Gene Brown - *Consumer goods, sales, management, marketing management*
Mr. Steven W. Kendall

Description: We have the largest network of offices and recruiters to provide more job opportunities and quality candidates.

Salary Minimum: $50,000
Functions: Senior mgmt., Middle mgmt., Plant mgmt., Packaging, Mktg. mgmt., Sales mgmt.

Industries: Food/bev/tobacco, Soap/perfume/cosmetics, Drugs mfg., Plastics/rubber, Packaging

Management Recruiters of Marietta, Inc.

274 N. Marietta Parkway NE, Ste. C
Marietta, Georgia 30060-1456
(770) 423-1443
Fax: (770) 423-1303
Email: jkirby@mindspring.com

Key Contact - Specialty:
Mr. James E. Kirby - *Management consulting (all disciplines)*

Description: Principals and account executives are former senior executives with direct experience in hiring decisions. Our client companies frequently cite this factor as distinguishing the professionalism of our firm from others in the search industry.

Salary Minimum: $40,000
Functions: General mgmt., Mfg., Materials, HR mgmt., Finance, IT, Mgmt. consultants
Industries: Generalist, Mfg., Transportation, Mgmt. consulting, Aerospace, High tech, Software

Management Recruiters of Atlanta NE

5390 Peachtree Industrial Blvd., Ste. 200
Norcross, Georgia 30071-1593
(770) 825-0003
Fax: (770) 825-0302

Key Contact - Specialty:
Mr. Richard L. Rivard - *Property & casualty insurance*
Mr. Dwight McMillan - *High technology, telecommunications*
Ms. Cheryl Barry - *HVAL controls/engineering and sales, p/c insurance*

Description: Mid to upper level executive search/recruitment; permanent and interim placement, management consulting and video conferencing. Specializing in the P&C insurance, high technology/telecommunications and HVAC engineering/sales.

Salary Minimum: $50,000
Functions: Senior mgmt., Middle mgmt., Mktg. mgmt., Sales mgmt., Risk mgmt., Engineering, Int'l.
Industries: Energy/utilities, Computer equip., Telecoms, Insurance, High tech, Software

Management Recruiters of Atlanta North, Inc.

30 Woodstock St.
Roswell, Georgia 30075-3546
(770) 998-1555
Fax: (770) 998-1561
Email: atlnrth!aek@mrinet.com

Key Contact - Specialty:
Mr. Arthur Katz - *Generalist, healthcare, manufacturing*

Description: Over 15 years executive search. A top 10% office in the largest search and recruiting firm in the world. Particular strength in healthcare and manufacturing, nationally and internationally.

Salary Minimum: $35,000
Functions: Senior mgmt., Automation, Plant mgmt., Nurses, Systems dev., Systems implem., Engineering
Industries: Generalist, Food/bev/tobacco, Chemicals, Soap/perfume/cosmetics, Drugs mfg., Leather/stone/glass/clay, Healthcare

Management Recruiters of Sandy Springs

6100 Lake Forrest Drive, Ste. 230
Sandy Springs, Georgia 30328-3835
(404) 252-1983
Fax: (404) 252-1984
Email: mrisandy@msn.com

Key Contact - Specialty:
Mr. Bob Brown - *Wood products, building products*
Ms. Joan Parker - *Wood products*

Description: Specializing in the wood products industry: I have over 30 years of experience and contacts in the industry, serving at upper level sales, marketing, administrative and operational positions in regional, national and some international communities.

Salary Minimum: $60,000
Functions: General mgmt., Mfg., Materials, Sales & mktg., HR mgmt., Engineering
Industries: Lumber/furniture

Management Recruiters of Savannah

2431 Habersham St., 2nd Floor
P.O. Box 22548
Savannah, Georgia 31401
(912) 232-0132
Fax: (912) 232-0136
Email: savmri@internetmci.com
Web: MRINET.com

Key Contact - Specialty:
Mr. Ron McElhaney - *Chemicals, plastics*
Mr. Ron McElhaney, Jr. - *Chemicals, plastics*
Mr. Patrick Razuri - *Health, safety, environmental*

Description: Our clients give us high praise for the thorough work we do in prescreening candidates. Saving a client's time and our expertise in making a match are our highest priorities.

Salary Minimum: $30,000
Functions: Senior mgmt., Production, Plant mgmt., HR mgmt., Systems implem., R&D, Engineering
Industries: Chemicals, Drugs mfg., Plastics/rubber, Computer equip., Telecoms, Environmental svcs.

Management Recruiters - Towne Lake

120 N. Medical Pkwy.
Bldg. 200, Ste. 200
Woodstock, Georgia 30189
(770) 592-1111
Fax: (770) 592-5557
Email: smonahan@mindspring.com

Key Contact - Specialty:
Mr. Stephen C. Monahan - *Financial services*

Description: My 20 years as a senior officer in the financial services industry brings a depth and diversity of knowledge for the search process to be efficient and of the highest quality.

Salary Minimum: $75,000
Functions: General mgmt., Senior mgmt., Middle mgmt., Mktg. mgmt., Sales mgmt., Credit, Int'l.
Industries: Finance, Banking, Misc. financial

Management Recruiters of Boise

290 Bobwhite Court, Ste. 220
Boise, Idaho 83706-3966
(208) 336-6770
Fax: (208) 336-2499
Email: mrsteph@micron.net
Web: www.mrboise.com

Key Contact - Specialty:
Mr. Craig R. Alexander - *Food processing*
Mr. Greg Arndt - *Mining, industrial minerals*
Mr. Chris Walhof - *Petroleum refining, petrochemical*
Mr. John Jocke - *Computer manufacturing, component manufacturing*
Ms. Carrie Austin

Salary Minimum: $45,000
Functions: Product dev., Plant mgmt., Quality, Mktg. mgmt., Sales mgmt., Engineering

Industries: Agri/forestry/mining, Energy/utilities, Food/bev/tobacco, Chemicals, Paints/petroleum products, Computer equip., Packaging

Management Recruiters of Sun Valley

180 E. 7th St., Lower Level
P.O. Box 599
Ketchum, Idaho 83340-0599
(208) 726-8005
Fax: (208) 726-7591
Email: mrsunval@svsearch

Key Contact - Specialty:
Mr. Tom Lampl - *Equipment (rotating)*

Description: We are industry specific recruiting only in the rotating equipment industries, pumps, compressors, turbines, seals and mixers with four recruiters doing all positions within the industries.

Salary Minimum: $35,000
Functions: Senior mgmt., Middle mgmt., Product dev., Production, Plant mgmt., Mktg. mgmt., Sales mgmt.
Industries: Machinery/Appliances

Management Recruiters of Chicago West

600 N. Commons Drive, Ste. 101
Aurora, Illinois 60504
(630) 851-4164
Fax: (630) 851-4184
Email: pstray@interaccess.com
Web: www.mrichicagojobs.com

Key Contact - Specialty:
Mr. Larry Strayhorn - *Information technology*
Ms. Patricia Strayhorn - *Information technology*
Ms. Nancy Faso - *Information technology*

Description: We deliver innovative as well as state-of-the-art strategies that meet ever-changing technological advances. Motivated to accommodate all those who seek our expertise, we continually strive to recognize each client individually in order to meet their specific needs.

Salary Minimum: $30,000
Functions: Sales mgmt., Risk mgmt., MIS mgmt., Systems anal., Systems dev., Systems support, DB admin.
Industries: Generalist, Mfg., Retail, Finance, Svcs., High tech, Software

Management Recruiters of Barrington

406 N. Hough St.
Barrington, Illinois 60010
(847) 382-5544
Fax: (847) 382-5591
Email: mri.barring@internetmci.com
Web: www.mribarrington.com

Key Contact - Specialty:
Mr. Gary T. Polvere - *HVAC, building automation systems, refrigeration, energy services*
Mr. Jon Difatta - *HVAC, building automation systems, refrigeration, energy services*
Mr. Jim Van Eaton - *Consulting engineering*

Description: Retained and contingency search firm, focused primarily on professionals in the HVAC, refrigeration, building automation systems and energy services industries. Including technical, sales, upper and middle management.

Salary Minimum: $29,000
Functions: Senior mgmt., Product dev., Plant mgmt., Mkt. research, Mktg. mgmt., Sales mgmt., Engineering
Industries: Energy/utilities, Construction, Metal products, Machinery/Appliances

Management Recruiters of Batavia

28 S. Water St., Ste. 201
Batavia, Illinois 60510
(630) 406-8003
Fax: (630) 406-8321
Web: Joe_Val@msn.com

Key Contact - Specialty:
Mr. Joseph Valente - *Information technology*

Functions: General mgmt., IT, MIS mgmt., Systems implem., Systems support, Network admin., DB admin.
Industries: Generalist

Management Recruiters of Lake Forest, IL

191 E. Deerpath, Ste. 302
Lake Forest, Illinois 60045
(847) 604-9000
Fax: (847) 604-9020
Email: mrlakfor@i-netdirect.net

Key Contact - Specialty:
Mr. Harry J. Cunneff - *Medical device, biotechnology, regulatory, quality, clinical, engineering, manufacturing*
Mr. Charlie Berg - *Medical device, marketing, product management, sales managers, engineering, quality*
Ms. Lauren Welch - *Engineering, clinical operations, regulatory*

Description: Our office has some 30 years experience in the medical device industry; of the 725 MRI offices we are one of the top producing offices in medical device placement. We have been in business for 5 years.

Salary Minimum: $50,000
Functions: Directors, Senior mgmt., Middle mgmt., Quality, Mkt. research, Mktg. mgmt., R&D
Industries: Generalist, Medical devices

Management Recruiters of Chicago-North Shore

3400 Dundee Rd., Ste. 340
Northbrook, Illinois 60062
(847) 509-9000
Fax: (847) 509-9010

Key Contact - Specialty:
Mr. Mark Rafferty - *Electrical, electronics, sales & marketing*
Mr. Steve Fried - *Sales & marketing (intangibles-business to business services)*
Mr. Dennis Kotloski - *Capitol equipment, sales & marketing, technical*

Functions: Mfg., Production, Automation, Packaging, IT, MIS mgmt., Int'l.
Industries: Food/bev/tobacco, Lumber/furniture, Machinery/Appliances, Test/measurement equip., Retail, Banking, Computer svcs.

Management Recruiters of Springfield, Inc.

124 E. Laurel St., Ste. B
Springfield, Illinois 62704
(217) 544-2051
Fax: (217) 544-2055
Email: mri@famvid.com
Web: www2.famvid.com/mri

Key Contact - Specialty:
Mr. Mark A. Cobb - *Senior management, marketing, engineering*
Ms. Lynn A. Cobb - *Pharmaceutical, biotechnology*

Description: Your company's needs are our top concern. We put our professional reputation on the line to search and recruit the top talent within your industry to meet your staffing requirements.

Salary Minimum: $25,000
Functions: Senior mgmt., Product dev., Production, Quality, Materials, R&D, Engineering
Industries: Generalist, Chemicals, Drugs mfg., Medical devices, Misc. mfg., Pharmaceutical svcs., Biotech

Management Recruiters of St. Charles

10 E. State Ave., Ste. 201
St. Charles, Illinois 60174-1940
(630) 377-6466
Fax: (630) 377-6642
Email: mrichgo@ix.netcom.com

Key Contact - Specialty:
Mr. Daniel C. Lasse - *Human resources, accounting*

Description: Firm specialty is manufacturing positions in the Midwest.

Salary Minimum: $40,000
Functions: Mfg., Sales mgmt., HR mgmt., Finance
Industries: Mfg., Food/bev/tobacco, Chemicals, Soap/perfume/cosmetics, Plastics/rubber, Metal products

---

Management Recruiters of Indianapolis-North

11611 N. Meridian St., Ste. 220
Carmel, Indiana 46032
(317) 582-0202
Fax: (317) 582-0303
Email: mrindy@mrindianapolis.com

Key Contact - Specialty:
Mr. George V. Ceryak - *Executive sales*

Description: 30 years of outstanding success meeting corporate America's total staffing needs. This outstanding firm is lead by George Ceryak, 30 years with MRI and winner of the prestigious office of the decade award for the 80's.
Functions: Senior mgmt., Production, Mkt. research, Sales mgmt., Cash mgmt., Systems anal., Systems dev.
Industries: Agri/forestry/mining, Chemicals, Machinery/Appliances, Finance, Computer svcs., Software, Healthcare

---

Management Recruiters of Indianapolis

8200 Haverstick Rd., Ste. 240
Indianapolis, Indiana 46240
(317) 257-5411
Fax: (317) 259-6886
Email: resume@mriindy.com
Web: www.mriindy.com

Key Contact - Specialty:
Mr. William A. Kuntz - *Manufacturing, human resources, accounting, information technology, general management*

Description: Our office has served hundreds of client companies. Collectively possessing 180+ years of recruiting experience, our team of 31 recruiters filled over 650 positions last year alone.
Functions: Senior mgmt., Mfg., Materials, Sales & mktg., HR mgmt., Finance, IT
Industries: Lumber/furniture, Printing, Metal products, Misc. mfg., Finance, Telecoms, Packaging

---

Management Recruiters - Indianapolis

3905 Vincennes Rd., Ste. 301
Indianapolis, Indiana 46268
(317) 228-3300
Fax: (317) 228-9939

Key Contact - Specialty:
Ms. Brenda Patterson - *General manufacturing, telecommunications*
Mr. Mike Eickhoff - *Insurance*
Ms. Laura Duncan - *Telecommunications*
Mr. Dennis Butler
Ms. Kelly Garrett - *Software sales*
Ms. Marilyn Licht - *Telecommunications*
Ms. Jean Connor - *Computers*
Mr. Keda Sikora - *Computers*
Mr. Steve Skillern - *Computers*
Ms. Linda Handy - *Computers*
Ms. Angelique Boyle - *Computers*
Mr. Terry Wilkin - *Insurance*
Mr. Andy Rutledge - *Insurance*
Ms. Jane Blair - *Sales & marketing*
Ms. Amy Brugh - *Finance & accounting*

Description: With 600 offices, and nearly 3,000 search and recruitment specialists, we are the largest company of our kind by far. With sales topping $225 million, + 22,000 placements each year, no other search and recruitment company comes close to us in size or capabilities.
Functions: Senior mgmt., Middle mgmt., Sales & mktg., Mktg. mgmt., Sales mgmt., Finance, IT
Industries: Finance, Hospitality, Telecoms, Insurance, Software

---

Management Recruiters of Noblesville, Inc.

15209 Herriman Blvd.
Noblesville, Indiana 46060
(317) 773-4323
Fax: (317) 773-9744
Email: mri@iquest.net

Key Contact - Specialty:
Mr. H. Peter Isenberg - *Technical sales, engineering*

Description: Contingency recruiting primarily engineers, supervisors, managers and VPs, in general manufacturing, technical sales engineers, sales management. Regional based basics within 250 miles of Indianapolis, Indiana.

Salary Minimum: $40,000
Functions: Production, Plant mgmt., Quality, Materials Plng., Sales mgmt., Systems dev., Engineering
Industries: Plastics/rubber, Metal products, Machinery/Appliances, Motor vehicles, Misc. mfg., Packaging

---

Management Recruiters of South Bend

1001 Hickory Rd., Ste. 7A
South Bend, Indiana 46615
(219) 234-6380
Fax: (219) 234-6377

Key Contact - Specialty:
Mr. R. William Shaw - *Manufacturing, engineering, research & development, sales & marketing, information technology*

Description: $35,000 annually is minimum.

Salary Minimum: $35,000
Functions: Mfg., Materials, Sales & mktg., HR mgmt., IT, R&D, Engineering
Industries: Mfg., Transportation, Wholesale, Communications, Packaging, Biotech

---

Management Recruiters of Spencer

589 Hwy. 71 S.
P.O. Box 840
Arnolds Park, Iowa 51331
(712) 332-2011
Fax: (712) 332-2051
Email: mrspencr@ncn.net

Key Contact - Specialty:
Mr. Brad Dach - *General manufacturing, agriculture*

Description: We specialize in general manufacturing and food manufacturing positions; ie engineering, operations, administration, data processing. We offer pre-interview services and total relocation service and counseling.
Functions: Product dev., Production, Automation, Quality, Systems anal., Systems dev., Engineering
Industries: Agri/forestry/mining, Food/bev/tobacco, Metal products, Machinery/Appliances, Motor vehicles, Misc. mfg., Software

---

Management Recruiters-Cedar Rapids, Inc.

150 First Ave. NE, Ste. 400
Brenton Financial Ctr.
Cedar Rapids, Iowa 52401-1126
(319) 366-8441
Fax: (319) 366-1103
Email: info@mricr.com

Key Contact - Specialty:
Ms. Cindy Lyness - *Sales & marketing, management, administration support*
Ms. Marlene Miller - *Accounting, PC support*
Ms. Sara Henton - *Food processing, engineering*
Ms. Bobbiette Wachuku - *Programmers, analysts, UNIX, AS400*
Ms. Becky Kindig - *Customer service, sales, clerical*
Ms. Heather Ross - *Sales & marketing, management*
Ms. Sarah Fare - *Software trainers, PC support, programmers*

Description: Number one contingency search firm in the world. Sets the pace and example for the entire recruiting industry, known worldwide for quality of performance. Also active in contract and flexible staffing.

Salary Minimum: $25,000
Functions: Middle mgmt., Admin. svcs., Sales mgmt., Customer svc., Systems dev., Systems support, Network admin.
Industries: Food/bev/tobacco, Computer svcs., Accounting, Telecoms, Insurance, Software

---

Management Recruiters of Des Moines

7400 University, Ste. D
Des Moines, Iowa 50325-1336
(515) 224-9142
Fax: (515) 224-7187
Email: mridsm@netins.net
Web: www.mrdsm.com

Key Contact - Specialty:
Mr. Michael Vermillion - *Telecommunications*
Mr. Russ Tessman - *Information technology*
Ms. Janette Weber - *Telecommunications*
Mr. Ken Dickerson - *Information technology*
Mr. Jim Roth - *Insurance, financial services*
Mr. Jeff Simmerman

Description: We are the largest executive search firm in the Midwest focusing exclusively on telecommunications.
Functions: Senior mgmt., Mktg. mgmt., Sales mgmt., CFO's, MIS mgmt., Systems anal., Engineering
Industries: Energy/utilities, Medical devices, Computer equip., Consumer electronics, Insurance, High tech, Software

---

Management Recruiters of Fairfield

106 W. Lowe
Fairfield, Iowa 52556
(515) 469-5811
Fax: (515) 469-6012
Email: mgmtrec@fairfield.com

Key Contact - Specialty:
Mr. Mark Soth - *Human resources*
Ms. Maureen Boehm - *Information technology*

Description: Experienced, professional staff dedicated to middle and upper management contingency placement in information technology and human resources functions.

Salary Minimum: $40,000
Functions: General mgmt., HR mgmt., MIS mgmt., Systems anal., Systems dev., Systems implem., Systems support
Industries: Generalist, Food/bev/tobacco, Lumber/furniture, Chemicals, Computer equip., Misc. mfg., Telecoms

---

Management Recruiters of Siouxland

4617 Morningside Ave.
Sioux City, Iowa 51106-2943
(712) 276-8454
Fax: (712) 276-8453
Email: mrisc@pionet.net

Key Contact - Specialty:
Mr. James A. Rupert - *Finance, banking, general manufacturing*
Ms. Helen G. Hurley - *Foods*
Ms. Patty Grace - *Metal building (manufacturing & construction)*

Description: Complete search, reference checks, personality profiles.

Salary Minimum: $30,000
Functions: Production, Quality, Mktg. mgmt., Sales mgmt., HR mgmt., Finance, Engineering
Industries: Agri/forestry/mining, Construction, Metal products, Machinery/Appliances, Misc. mfg., Invest. banking, Brokers

---

Management Recruiters of Williamsburg

600 Court St., P.O. Box 1136
Williamsburg, Iowa 52361-1136
(319) 668-2881
Fax: (319) 668-1404
Email: william!jjl@mrinet.com

Key Contact - Specialty:
Mr. John J. Lehnst - *Agriculture*
Ms. Sharon Thomas - *Agriculture*
Ms. Lori Stecker - *Finance*

Description: Agricultural specialists with an emphasis on agronomic, vegetable and farm seed industries in all aspects of management, sales and research.
Functions: Senior mgmt., Middle mgmt., Advertising, Mkt. research, Sales mgmt., CFO's, Cash mgmt.
Industries: Agri/forestry/mining, Finance

Management Recruiters of Topeka, Inc.

3400 SW Van Buren
Topeka, Kansas 66611
(785) 267-5430
Fax: (785) 267-0513

Key Contact - Specialty:
Mr. Kirk Hawkins

Description: We recruit primarily in healthcare: specifically (nurse managers, nurse practitioners and physician assistants), general manufacturing (e.g. engineers), accounting/finance and agriculture.

Salary Minimum: $25,000
Functions: Generalist
Industries: Agri/forestry/mining, Metal products, Accounting, Healthcare

---

Management Recruiters of Warren County, KY

546 Park St., Ste. 100
Fairview Park Plaza
Bowling Green, Kentucky 42101
(502) 782-3820
Fax: (502) 782-3985
Web: www.grimeslegal.com

Key Contact - Specialty:
Mr. G. D. Grimes
Ms. Nancy C. Grimes
Mr. Richard D. Grimes

Description: We recruit and place attorneys only as a legal search and placement agency.
Functions: Attorneys
Industries: Legal

Management Recruiters of Danville

105 Citation Drive, Ste. A
Danville, Kentucky 40422-9200
(606) 236-0505
Fax: (606) 236-0488
Email: mriky@searnet.com
Web: www.mriky.com

Key Contact - Specialty:
Mr. Michael W. Smith - *General manufacturing*

Description: Specialize in electrical, mechanical, process and quality engineers and departmental managers in general metalworking.

Salary Minimum: $30,000
Functions: Generalist, Product dev., Production, Automation, Plant mgmt., Quality, Engineering
Industries: Generalist, Plastics/rubber, Metal products, Machinery/Appliances, Motor vehicles, Test/measurement equip., Transportation

---

Management Recruiters of Richmond

213 St. George St., Ste. B
Richmond, Kentucky 40475-2323
(606) 624-3535
Fax: (606) 624-3539
Email: mri@iclub.org
Web: www.cinetwork.com/international/mri.html

Key Contact - Specialty:
Mr. Ron S. Lawson

Description: Recruiting specialists serving Kentucky and surrounding states.
Functions: Product dev., Production, Automation, Plant mgmt., Quality, Productivity

Industries: Plastics/rubber, Leather/stone/glass/clay, Motor vehicles

Management Recruiters of Monroe, Inc.

1401 Hudson Lane, Ste. 135
Monroe, Louisiana 71201-2184
(318) 322-2200
Fax: (318) 322-4745
Email: mrmonroe@iamerica.net

Key Contact - Specialty:
Mr. Bruce Hursey - *General manufacturing*

Description: We offer prompt response in slating candidates for key positions, discount moving rates and special mortgage program if relocation is desired/required. Additional services include outplacement, executive temporary placement and personality profiling.

Salary Minimum: $30,000
Functions: Mfg., Production, Plant mgmt., Mktg. mgmt., Sales mgmt., HR mgmt., Engineering
Industries: Lumber/furniture, Paper, Plastics/rubber, Metal products, Machinery/Appliances, Motor vehicles, Misc. mfg.

Management Recruiters of Columbia

5550 Sterrett Place, Ste. 314
K&M Lakefront N.
Columbia, Maryland 21044
(410) 715-1141
(800) 267-1226
Fax: (410) 715-1145
Email: mricolum@erols.com
Web: www.mriplastic-packaging.com

Key Contact - Specialty:
Mr. Randolph Reyes - *Plastic manufacturing, product development, product design, CAD systems, packaging*
Ms. Mark Villee - *Plastic processing, shift supervisors, processing injection, extrusion, blow molding*
Mr. Anthony Grant - *Plastic processing, engineers, manufacturing engineers, injection, tooling*
Ms. Vicky Wonderfund - *Polymers, pharmaceutical, food & beverage*
Ms. Renee Reyes - *Packaging, films, rigid, thermoforming, corrugated, cosmetic*

Description: We are the pre-eminent plastic recruitment firm in the nation. We provide plastic manufacturing folks the best way to optimize their job search while remaining discrete and safe. Our industries include automotive, medical, consumer, industrial and technology. Packaging, cosmetic, food and beverage, connector among others.

Salary Minimum: $35,000
Functions: Mfg., Product dev., Production, Automation, Plant mgmt., Quality, Engineering
Industries: Mfg., Soap/perfume/cosmetics, Drugs mfg., Medical devices, Plastics/rubber, Machinery/Appliances, Packaging

Management Recruiters of Frederick, Inc.

4 East St.
Frederick, Maryland 21701
(301) 663-0600
Fax: (301) 663-0454

Key Contact - Specialty:
Mrs. Pat Webb

Description: Specialize in working with any company, any level, within the healthcare, pharmaceutical and medical equipment industries, informations systems and administrative areas.
Functions: Senior mgmt., Admin. svcs., Health admin., Sales mgmt., MIS mgmt., Systems support
Industries: Drugs mfg., Medical devices, Hospitality, Pharmaceutical svcs., Accounting, Software, Healthcare

Management Recruiters of the Baltimore Washington Corridor

7240 Parkway Drive, Ste. 150
Hanover, Maryland 21076
(410) 712-0770
Fax: (410) 712-0510
Email: baltwash!lxs@mrinet.com
Web: www.mrinet.com

Key Contact - Specialty:
Mr. Lee Stubberfield - *Senior management, medical device manufacturing, healthcare, home healthcare, sales & marketing*
Ms. Jodie Ballou - *Engineering, research & development, management, medical device manufacturing, plastics*
Ms. Jeannette Olesen - *Engineering, management, sales, specialty machinery, C&C machinery*
Ms. Rhoda Gale - *Engineering, senior management, sales, research & development, management*
Mr. J. Jay Tinker - *Engineering, management, senior management, sales, sales management*
Mr. Dan Gawitt - *Information systems, information technology, software, management, graphics*
Ms. Toni Stroud - *Information systems, information technology, software, sales, management*
Ms. Ellen Worthing - *Chemical industry, engineering, research & development, management, sales*

Description: Complete search/placement, permanent/interim in telecommunications, healthcare, engineering, manufacturing, medical device, process industries, chemicals, filtration, specialty machinery, electronics, security electronics, sales, management, research & development, healthcare, information systems, software, sales/marketing, finance, management. Adjacent to Baltimore/Washington International Airport. Videoconferencing network to 400 US/international cities available for private use.
Functions: General mgmt., Mfg., Healthcare, Sales & mktg., IT, R&D, Engineering
Industries: Food/bev/tobacco, Chemicals, Medical devices, Machinery/Appliances, Telecoms, High tech, Software

Management Recruiters of Rockville

3750 University Blvd.
Kensington, Maryland 20895
(301) 949-6226
Fax: (301) 949-6603
Email: ramdak@earthlink.net
Web: www.rockvillerecruiter.com

Key Contact - Specialty:
Mr. Robert Moore - *Retail, distribution, warehousing, industrial engineering*
Ms. Penny Richards-Davy - *Retail merchandise planning & buying*

Functions: Middle mgmt., Plant mgmt., Distribution, HR mgmt., IT, Engineering, Minorities
Industries: Generalist, Textiles/apparel, Retail, Human resource svcs.

Management Recruiters of Washington, DC Inc.

1100 Wayne Ave., Ste. 1080
Silver Spring, Maryland 20910
(301) 589-5400
Email: mrwashdc@aol.com
Web: www.MRIwashington.com

Key Contact - Specialty:
Mr. Frank S. Black, Jr. - *Marketing, marketing research*
Ms. Marilyn Staley
Ms. Barbara Silver - *Managed care*
Mr. Robert Fodge - *Energy*
Mr. Stuart Meyers - *Managed care (behavioral)*
Ms. Deborah Bandzerewicz - *Tax accounting*

Description: Specialize in the industries of marketing, managed care and healthcare, engineering, biotechnology and pharmaceuticals, accounting and finance, marketing research, and information technology.

Functions: Healthcare, Health admin., Mkt. research, Taxes, IT, Engineering
Industries: Pharmaceutical svcs., Accounting, High tech, Biotech, Healthcare

---

Management Recruiters of Baltimore

9515 Deereco Rd., Ste. 900
Timonium, Maryland 21093
(410) 252-6616
Fax: (410) 252-7076
Email: kendmr@erols.com
Web: mrbaltimore.com

Key Contact - Specialty:
Mr. Kenneth R. Davis
Ms. Linda A. Burton

Description: We are the world's largest professional search organization specializing in managerial, sales and professional talent. As part of a national organization, we serve firms of all types and sizes through the expertise and efforts of over 750 affiliated offices.
Functions: Production, Plant mgmt., Packaging, IT, Systems anal., Systems dev., Engineering
Industries: Mfg., Food/bev/tobacco, Chemicals, Plastics/rubber, Telecoms, Packaging, High tech

---

Management Recruiters of Birmingham

30700 Telegraph Rd., Ste. 3650
Bingham Farms, Michigan 48025-4527
(248) 647-7766
Fax: (248) 647-9722
Email: mri@bignet.net
Web: www.recruiters-mri.com

Key Contact - Specialty:
Mr. Brian Binke - *Information technology*
Ms. Elle McCowan - *Automotive engineering, management*

Description: We partner with our clients to bring them the finest talent in the nation.

Salary Minimum: $40,000
Functions: Senior mgmt., Middle mgmt., Mfg., Sales & mktg., IT, MIS mgmt., Engineering
Industries: Construction, Motor vehicles, Computer equip., New media, Telecoms, Insurance, Software

---

Management Recruiters of Southeastern Michigan

115 N. Main St.
P.O. Box 3
Blissfield, Michigan 49228-0003
(517) 486-2167
Fax: (517) 486-2324
Email: recruit@cass.net
Web: www.cass.net/recruit/

Key Contact - Specialty:
Ms. Mary W. Snellbaker - *Manufacturing, engineering*

Description: Always looking for production and engineering candidates with metal or plastics background. Have positions available throughout the U.S. If you have these qualifications, please send your resume in confidence.
Functions: Mfg., Quality, Materials, HR mgmt., Finance, Engineering
Industries: Plastics/rubber, Metal products, Motor vehicles, Packaging

---

Management Recruiters of Dearborn, Inc.

3 Parklane Blvd., Ste. 1224
Parklane Towers West
Dearborn, Michigan 48126
(313) 336-6650
Fax: (313) 336-7436

Key Contact - Specialty:
Mr. William J. Tripp

Description: Over twenty years in the confidential recruitment and placement of middle management and professionals in most functional disciplines. M/R Nat'l. Office of the year-1987; Compu-Search Division-Nat'l Office of the year-1989.

Salary Minimum: $25,000
Functions: Middle mgmt., Mfg., Materials, Sales mgmt., Finance, IT, Engineering
Industries: Chemicals, Plastics/rubber, Metal products, Machinery/Appliances, Motor vehicles, Misc. mfg., Computer svcs.

Management Recruiters of Detroit & Farmington Hills

300 River Place, Ste. 5350
Detroit, Michigan 48207
(313) 568-4200
Email: mri@aol.com

Key Contact - Specialty:
Ms. Debra Lawson - *Human resources, administrative, accounting*

Description: Largest permanent placement firm in the world with the best trained recruiters and largest network/database available. Locally owned franchise for over 14 years.
Functions: Admin. svcs., Customer svc., HR mgmt., Benefits, Personnel, Finance, Mgmt. consultants
Industries: Generalist

Management Recruiters - Flint

G-5524 S. Saginaw Rd.
Flint, Michigan 48507
(810) 695-0120

Key Contact - Specialty:
Mr. Dave Reed - *Technical, metal stamping, machining, plastics, electro-mechanical*
Mr. Rick Reed

Description: We are one of 700 franchised offices of Management Recruiters and we rely on corporate national advertising: Wall Street Journal and major radio stations along with news releases sent to all local media.

Salary Minimum: $25,000
Functions: Product dev., Production, Automation, Plant mgmt., Quality, Productivity, Technicians
Industries: Generalist, Plastics/rubber, Metal products, Machinery/Appliances, Motor vehicles, Test/measurement equip., Misc. mfg.

Management Recruiters of Livonia

37677 Professional Ctr. Drive
Ste. 100C
Livonia, Michigan 48154-1138
(313) 953-9590
Fax: (313) 953-0566

Key Contact - Specialty:
Mr. Don Eden - *Technical, administrative management*
Ms. Judy Somershoe - *Technical*

Description: We find and place professional and technical persons with employers needing permanent or temporary employees with specific skills and qualifications. We also provide outplacement and relocation assistance.

Salary Minimum: $30,000
Functions: Product dev., Production, Automation, Quality, Materials, Finance, Engineering
Industries: Plastics/rubber, Metal products, Machinery/Appliances, Motor vehicles, Test/measurement equip., Misc. mfg., Insurance

---

Management Recruiters of Muskegon

3145 Henry St., Ste. 203
Muskegon, Michigan 49441
(616) 755-6486
Fax: (616) 759-8041
Email: mrmuskegon@aol.com

Key Contact - Specialty:
Mr. John R. Mitchell, Jr. - *Generalist*

Description: Our account executives know your business. We are industry specialists with a combined total of 40 years of recruiting expertise and are qualified to handle the most difficult assignments.
Functions: Middle mgmt., Production, Plant mgmt., Purchasing, Mktg. mgmt., CFO's, Engineering

Industries: Lumber/furniture, Plastics/rubber, Metal products, Motor vehicles, Misc. mfg., Accounting, Human resource svcs.

Management Recruiters of North Oakland County, Inc.

2530 S. Rochester Rd.
Rochester Hills, Michigan 48307-4441
(248) 299-1900
Fax: (248) 299-5681
Email: mrnocmi@mrnoc.com

Key Contact - Specialty:
Mr. Mark Angott - *Banking*

Description: Dedicated to helping our clients address their professional staffing needs. We are part of the largest contingency search firm in the United States with over 600 offices nationwide conducting searches throughout the United States and Europe.

Salary Minimum: $25,000
Functions: Production, Plant mgmt., Health admin., HR mgmt., Finance, IT, Engineering
Industries: Generalist, Metal products, Motor vehicles, Banking, Computer svcs., Human resource svcs., Healthcare

---

Management Recruiters of Bloomington

4200 W. Old Shakopee Rd., Ste. 200
Bloomington, Minnesota 55437
(612) 948-0280
Fax: (612) 948-1045
Email: mrbloomington@internetmci.com
Web: www.mrinet.com

Key Contact - Specialty:
Mr. Dale Gustafson

Description: Confidential search in telecommunications, information technology, engineering and employee benefits/insurance; superior personal service.

Salary Minimum: $30,000
Functions: Sales & mktg., Benefits, IT, Engineering
Industries: Mfg., Finance, Svcs., Telecoms, Insurance, High tech, Software

---

Management Recruiters of Chanhassen

80 W. 78th St., Ste. 230
Chanhassen Office Complex
Chanhassen, Minnesota 55317
(612) 937-9693
Fax: (612) 937-9697
Email: manager@mrchan.com
Web: www.mrchan.com

Key Contact - Specialty:
Mr. John Ho - *Information systems, software development, telecommunications*

Description: Office run by former executive in the field of information systems and software development. We also offer video conferencing, temporary staffing, outplacement services and are part of largest search firm in the world.

Salary Minimum: $30,000
Functions: Product dev., Production, MIS mgmt., Systems anal., Systems dev., Systems support, Engineering
Industries: Generalist, Misc. mfg., Finance, Computer svcs., Communications, High tech, Software

---

Management Recruiters of Rochester

1903 S. Broadway
Rochester, Minnesota 55904
(507) 282-2400
Fax: (507) 282-1308
Email: mrrocmn@ismidwest.com
Web: www.ismidwest.com

Key Contact - Specialty:
Mr. Robert Vierkant - *Information systems (Upper Midwest)*
Ms. Nona E. Vierkant
Mr. John Harris - *Information systems (Upper Midwest)*
Ms. Char Tansey - *Information systems (Upper Midwest)*
Ms. Jane Glomski - *Information systems (Upper Midwest)*

Description: We specialize in information systems in the Upper Midwest including all IS titles and most common technologies.
Functions: MIS mgmt., Systems anal., Systems dev., Systems implem., Systems support, Network admin., DB admin.
Industries: Generalist

Management Recruiters of Winona

157 W. 3rd St., Ste. 100
Winona, Minnesota 55987
(507) 452-2700
Fax: (507) 452-2722
Email: mrwinona@rconnect.com
Web: telecomcareer.com

Key Contact - Specialty:
Mr. James Crigler - *Telecommunications*

Description: We provide staffing exclusively for telecommunications companies and are uniquely qualified to select and present candidates of the highest quality because of extensive hands-on experience in the telecommunications industry.

Salary Minimum: $25,000
Functions: General mgmt., Senior mgmt., Middle mgmt., Sales & mktg., CFO's
Industries: Telecoms

Management Recruiters of Woodbury

7650 Currell Blvd., Ste. 240
Woodbury, Minnesota 55125
(651) 730-7668
Fax: (651) 730-7191
Email: mrwoodbury@aol.com

Key Contact - Specialty:
Mr. David W. Kriesel - *General manufacturing, construction engineering*
Mr. Michael L. Fox - *Informational services, finance, insurance*
Ms. Judy A. Olson - *Human resources, administration, sales & marketing*

Description: We customize confidential searches to your company's strategic business plan. Our team of professional recruiters specialize in specific career disciplines, covering the full spectrum of your staffing requirements.

Salary Minimum: $30,000
Functions: General mgmt., Mfg., Materials, Sales & mktg., HR mgmt., Finance, IT
Industries: Generalist, Mfg., Finance, Packaging, Insurance, Software, Non-classifiable industries

---

Management Recruiters of Rankin Co.

2506 Lakeland Drive, Ste. 408
Jackson, Mississippi 39208
(601) 936-7900
Fax: (601) 936-9004

Key Contact - Specialty:
Mr. Mike Van Wick - *Food operations, engineering, technical*

Description: Specializing in manufacturing for all mid-management and professional areas. Emphasis in engineering and technical for food, automotive and consumer goods, metal fabrication.

Salary Minimum: $50,000
Functions: Directors, Senior mgmt., Middle mgmt., Product dev., Production, Plant mgmt., Quality
Industries: Food/bev/tobacco, Metal products, Motor vehicles, Telecoms

---

Management Recruiters of Cass County, NE

12635 S. Izard St.
Omaha, Nebraska 68154
(402) 498-8981
Fax: (402) 445-9736

Email: efisher@tconl.com

Key Contact - Specialty:
Mr. Earl Fisher - *Energy, electric, power, natural gas*

Description: Ph.D. level account executives with 20 years of technical and management experience. Focus on non regulatory areas of the electric utility and natural gas industries emphasizing wholesale and retail sales and marketing, energy traders, risk management and individuals in asset acquisition and development.

Salary Minimum: $60,000
Functions: Legal, Mkt. research, Mktg. mgmt., Sales mgmt., Risk mgmt., Engineering
Industries: Energy/utilities, Misc. financial, Legal

Management Recruiters of Reno
1025 Ridgeview Drive, Ste. 100
Reno, Nevada 89509-6321
(702) 826-5243
Fax: (702) 826-8329

Key Contact - Specialty:
Mr. Ed Trapp - *Sales & marketing*

Description: Specialties are insurance (actuaries and marketing), general manufacturing, industrial sales. All national desks.

Salary Minimum: $30,000
Functions: Production, Plant mgmt., Quality, Sales mgmt., IT, MIS mgmt., Engineering
Industries: Agri/forestry/mining, Food/bev/tobacco, Chemicals, Plastics/rubber, Misc. mfg., Insurance, Software

---

Management Recruiters of Lake Tahoe, NV
P.O. Box 4766
Stateline, Nevada 89449
(702) 588-7388
Fax: (702) 588-7380
Email: recruit@sierra.net

Key Contact - Specialty:
Mr. Jim Cargill - *Retail, gaming, construction*
Mr. David C. Bailey - *Transportation, distribution*
Mr. Jeff Skiba - *Information services, information technology*

Description: Specialists in retail corporate, gaming, construction, transportation and info services, from technical through CEO. Interim and permanent, nationwide, references available.

Salary Minimum: $40,000
Functions: Directors, Senior mgmt., Middle mgmt., Distribution, MIS mgmt., Systems dev., DB admin.
Industries: Construction, Transportation, Retail, Hospitality, High tech, Software

---

Management Recruiters of Bay Head
106 Bridge Ave., Bay Head Commons
Bay Head, New Jersey 08742
(732) 714-1300
Fax: (732) 714-1311
Email: recruiter@mrielectrical.com
Web: www.mrielectrical.com

Key Contact - Specialty:
Mr. Robert P. Ceresi - *Electrical electronics computer automation*
Ms. Carole Ceresi - *Electrical electronics computer automation*

Description: Our firm specializes in all jobs (except clerical) in: electrical, electronics, factory automation, process controls, hardware, software and services. Sales, marketing, engineering, manufacturing, service and management.

Salary Minimum: $35,000
Functions: Product dev., Automation, Mktg. mgmt., Sales mgmt., Systems dev., Systems implem., Engineering
Industries: Machinery/Appliances, Computer equip., Test/measurement equip., Wholesale, High tech, Software

---

Management Recruiters of Orange County, N.Y., Inc.
16 Birch Run Ave.
Denville, New Jersey 07834
(973) 625-4822
Fax: (973) 625-8117
Email: cac@Intercall.net

Key Contact - Specialty:
Ms. Carolyn A. Chermak - *Generalist*

Description: Confidential, honest, professionals. We are committed to the pursuit of excellence with integrity and standards that put us ahead of our competitors.
Functions: Generalist, General mgmt., Mfg., Sales & mktg., IT, Engineering, Specialized services
Industries: Generalist, Construction, Mfg., Transportation, Environmental svcs., High tech, Software

---

Management Recruiters of Morris County, NJ
17 Hanover Rd., Ste. 450
Florham Park, New Jersey 07932
(973) 593-0400
Fax: (973) 593-0150
Email: mrimc@aol.com
Web: mrinet.com/data

Key Contact - Specialty:
Mr. Wayne T. Young - *Internetworking, data communications, sales, sales management, technical support*
Ms. Susan M. Young - *Marketing, data systems, data communications, telecommunications, business development*

Description: Building remote sales teams for clients nationwide. Building specialty groups - mergers and acquisitions, product managers, marketing groups, large projects. Sales, marketing and technical positions in the data, telecommunications and data systems industries.

Salary Minimum: $60,000
Functions: Sales & mktg., IT, Int'l.
Industries: Computer equip., Test/measurement equip., Computer svcs., Telecoms, High tech

---

Management Recruiters of North Warren Inc.
1298 Rte. 519 American House Annex
Box 244
Hope, New Jersey 07844-0244
(908) 459-5798
Fax: (908) 459-4672
Email: mrinw@planet.net

Key Contact - Specialty:
Mr. Henry F. Magnusen - *Human resources change agents, mechanical engineers*

Description: Specialists in finding mechanical engineers, human resources generalists and compensation and benefits experts.
Functions: General mgmt., Mfg., HR mgmt., Benefits, Engineering, Int'l.
Industries: Generalist, Medical devices, Metal products, Machinery/Appliances, Motor vehicles, Misc. mfg., Human resource svcs.

Management Recruiters of Medford, N.J.
520 Stokes Rd., Bldg. B-6
Medford, New Jersey 08055
(609) 654-9109
Fax: (609) 654-9166
Email: mrinet@recom.com
Web: pages.recom.com/~mrinet

Key Contact - Specialty:
Mr. Norman Talbot - *Technical recruitment*
Mr. Matt Talbot

Description: Nationwide search for engineering/technical/administrative personnel. All disciplines for middle to upper management. Serving pharmaceutical, chemical, manufacturing, electronic, petro/chem, construction and all related industries.

Salary Minimum: $50,000

Functions: Senior mgmt., Middle mgmt., Plant mgmt., Purchasing, Distribution, Sales mgmt., Engineering
Industries: Construction, Chemicals, Drugs mfg., Medical devices, Consumer electronics, High tech, Biotech

Management Recruiters of Bordentown

1200 S. Church St.
Village II, Ste. 20
Mt. Laurel, New Jersey 08054
(609) 727-0005
Fax: (609) 727-3444

Key Contact - Specialty:
Mr. Randy R. Ruschak - *Management consulting, energy, utilities*
Ms. Christine Buchanan - *Property & casualty claims, underwriting, product management*

Description: Search for management consulting firms for utility industry: utilities and energy firms, insurance-P&C claim and underwriting.

Salary Minimum: $45,000
Functions: Middle mgmt., Mgmt. consultants
Industries: Energy/utilities, Insurance

Management Recruiters of New Providence

150 Floral Ave.
New Providence, New Jersey 07974-1511
(908) 771-0600
Fax: (908) 771-0779
Email: mrinp@aol.com
Web: www.mrinp.com

Key Contact - Specialty:
Mr. Andrew S. Miller - *Consumer products, information technology*

Description: Part of largest executive search firm in the world. New services include interim executive placement and video conferencing to produce superior results.

Salary Minimum: $40,000
Functions: General mgmt., Sales & mktg., Credit, Risk mgmt., IT, R&D, Engineering
Industries: Food/bev/tobacco, Soap/perfume/cosmetics, Drugs mfg., Entertainment, High tech, Software, Biotech

Affiliates:
Brainworks

Management Recruiters of Middlesex County NJ

984 Rte. 9, Ste. 3
Parlin, New Jersey 08859
(732) 727-8300
Fax: (732) 727-9523

Key Contact - Specialty:
Mr. Herbert Hardbrod - *Pharmaceutical advertising & marketing*

Description: Thirty years experience in pharmaceuticals, healthcare. Advertising and marketing positions are our specialty.
Functions: Advertising, Mktg. mgmt.
Industries: Drugs mfg., Pharmaceutical svcs., Advertising/PR

Management Recruiters of Princeton

1230 Parkway Ave., Ste. 102
West Trenton, New Jersey 08628
(609) 882-8388
Fax: (609) 882-4862

Key Contact - Specialty:
Mr. Robert J. Bodnar - *Energy, management consulting*
Ms. Beverly H. Bodnar

Description: Provides professional consultative services at senior executive levels regarding strategic and tactical planning interpretation into quantitative and qualitative human resource requirements to achieve goals as part of the executive search services.

Salary Minimum: $50,000
Functions: Senior mgmt., Middle mgmt., Sales & mktg., Finance, IT, Engineering, Mgmt. consultants
Industries: Energy/utilities, Finance, Banking, Invest. banking, Mgmt. consulting, High tech, Biotech

Management Recruiters of The Sandias

10400 Academy NE, Ste. 204
Albuquerque, New Mexico 87111
(505) 292-9800
Fax: (505) 292-9810
Email: don@mrisandias.com
Web: www.mrisandias.com

Key Contact - Specialty:
Mr. Don Ancona

Description: Our firm specializes in the placement of information systems and software development professionals.

Salary Minimum: $50,000
Functions: MIS mgmt., Systems anal., Systems dev., Systems implem., Systems support, Network admin., DB admin.
Industries: Mfg., Finance, Svcs., Communications, Aerospace, High tech, Software

Management Recruiters of Broome County, Inc.

One Marine Midland Plaza, Ste. 603
Binghamton, New York 13901-3216
(607) 722-2243
Fax: (607) 722-2456
Email: bamabc@aol.com
Web: www.therecruiters.com

Key Contact - Specialty:
Mr. Robert H. Clingan - *Engineering, information technology, general manufacturing, sales & marketing (technical)*
Mr. Mark J. Wallace - *Quality, finance*

Description: We are functional experts, professionally trained in the art of search and recruitment. We are solution oriented and understand the problems, needs and expectations of your functional executives and organizations.

Salary Minimum: $40,000
Functions: General mgmt., Mfg., Budgeting, IT, Engineering
Industries: Consumer electronics, Misc. mfg., Higher ed., Aerospace, Packaging, High tech, Software

Management Recruiters of Great Neck

98 Cutter Mill Rd., Ste. 234 S.
Great Neck, New York 11021-3006
(516) 482-4000
Fax: (516) 482-5772
Email: head.hunter@usa.net.com

Key Contact - Specialty:
Mr. Stuart Kaufman - *Real estate, legal, environmental, consulting*

Description: Principal of firm is a former lawyer, investment banker and real estate consultant and developer. Highly selective in client base.

Salary Minimum: $50,000
Functions: Legal, Cash mgmt., Risk mgmt., Mgmt. consultants, Attorneys
Industries: Energy/utilities, Invest. banking, Legal, Accounting, Mgmt. consulting, Haz. waste

Management Recruiters of Upper Westchester

118 N. Bedford Rd., Ste. 103
Mt. Kisco, New York 10549-9998
(914) 241-2788
Fax: (914) 241-2783
Email: northprt!manager@mrinet.com

Key Contact - Specialty:
Mr. Vern D. Nepple - *Food, beverage*
Ms. Rosemarie Nepple - *Food, beverage*

Description: Our office specializes totally in the food/beverage industry and our expertise is sales and sales management.

We limit the number of searches we accept so we can offer our clients an uncompromised level of commitment to their needs.

Salary Minimum: $50,000
Functions: Directors, Senior mgmt., Middle mgmt., Plant mgmt., Sales mgmt.

Management Recruiters of Gramercy, Inc.

200 Park Ave. S., Ste. 1510
New York, New York 10003
(212) 505-5530
Fax: (212) 505-6240
Email: manhattn!sds@mrinet.com

Key Contact - Specialty:
Mr. Stephen D. Schwartz - *Advertising (agency & corporate),marketing (agency & corporate)*
Mr. James K. Harragan - *Publishing, consumer sales, telemarketing*
Mr. Joseph Altschuler - *Marketing (corporate)*

Description: Consumate professionals, committed to the pursuit of excellence with uncompromising integrity, these are the standards which set us apart from the crowd.
Functions: Advertising, Mkt. research, Mktg. mgmt., Sales mgmt., Direct mktg., Customer svc., PR
Industries: Communications, Advertising/PR, Publishing, New media, Broadcast & Film, Telecoms, Healthcare

---

Management Recruiters of Manhattan on Broadway

1650 Broadway, Ste. 410
New York, New York 10019
(212) 974-7676
Fax: (212) 974-8585
Email: mronbroadway@usa.pipeline.com
Web: www.mrusa.com

Key Contact - Specialty:
Mr. Richard Cohen - *Banking, credit card, investment banking, marketing, risk analysts*

Description: Part of the largest and most successful executive search and recruitment organizations offering permanent and interim staffing solutions as well as outplacement and video conferencing services.

Salary Minimum: $40,000
Functions: Directors, Middle mgmt., Mktg. mgmt., Direct mktg., Cash mgmt., Credit, Risk mgmt.
Industries: Generalist, Banking, Invest. banking, Brokers, Venture cap., Misc. financial

---

Management Recruiters of Woodbury Inc.

100 Crossways Park W., Ste. 208
Woodbury, New York 11797
(516) 364-9290
Fax: (516) 364-4478
Email: mrcareers@mrcareers.com
Web: mrcareers.com

Key Contact - Specialty:
Mr. William Jose - *Pharmaceutical consumer products*
Mr. Warren Kornfeld - *Information technology*

Description: Specialize in placing middle and senior management personnel in pharmaceutical, medical device, data processing, banking and financial positions.

Salary Minimum: $35,000
Functions: Physicians, Mktg. mgmt., Sales mgmt., Systems anal., Systems dev., R&D
Industries: Drugs mfg., Medical devices, Consumer electronics, Pharmaceutical svcs., Computer svcs., Insurance, Software

---

Management Recruiters of Asheville, Inc.

53 Arlington St.
Asheville, North Carolina 28801
(828) 258-9646
Fax: (828) 252-0866
Email: PRumson@internetmci.com

Key Contact - Specialty:
Mr. Paul M. Rumson - *Engineering*
Ms. Barbara A. Rumson - *Engineering*
Mr. Paul Michael Rumson - *Hospitality*

Description: Search and recruitment specialists for upper and middle management professionals.

Salary Minimum: $25,000
Functions: Product dev., Automation, Plant mgmt., Quality, Purchasing, Engineering, Int'l.
Industries: Drugs mfg., Medical devices, Plastics/rubber, Metal products, Machinery/Appliances, Motor vehicles, Hospitality

---

Management Recruiters of Burlington

336 Holly Hill Lane
Burlington, North Carolina 27215
(336) 584-1444
Fax: (336) 584-9754
Email: burlnc!manager@mrinet.com

Key Contact - Specialty:
Mr. Dick Pike - *Paper & film converting, chemicals, plastics*

Description: Providing technical, production, sales and marketing resources to clients in the specialty materials (i.e. chemicals, plastics, rubber, polymers) and the web processing (i.e. paper, film, tape, label, converting) industries.

Salary Minimum: $30,000
Functions: Product dev., Plant mgmt., Quality, Mktg. mgmt., Sales mgmt., R&D, Engineering
Industries: Paper, Printing, Chemicals, Plastics/rubber

Management Recruiters of Cedar Mountain

P.O. Box 629
Cedar Mountain, North Carolina 28718
(704) 884-4118
Fax: (704) 884-3512
Email: mrischoff@citcom.net

Key Contact - Specialty:
Mr. Frank J. Schoff - *Networking, telecommunications technologies*

Description: Proven track record recruiting networking and telecommunications professionals. Principal has 20 years Fortune 500 network management experience. Recruits both technical and managerial professionals for clients nationwide.

Salary Minimum: $50,000
Functions: MIS mgmt., Systems anal., Mgmt. consultants
Industries: Energy/utilities, Finance, Svcs., Telecoms, Insurance

---

Management Recruiters of Fayetteville

951 S. McPherson Church Rd., Ste. 105
Fayetteville, North Carolina 28303
(910) 483-2555
Fax: (910) 483-6524
Email: mrifaync@worldnet.att.net
Web: home.att.net/~mrifaync/

Key Contact - Specialty:
Mr. John R. Semmes - *General manufacturing*

Description: We specialize in key account development in all areas of manufacturing operations: engineering, quality, design, electrical, mechanical, financial, human resources, management--in various industries including appliances, motors, electronics and automotives.

Salary Minimum: $30,000
Functions: Product dev., Production, Plant mgmt., Quality, Materials, HR mgmt., Engineering
Industries: Generalist, Mfg., Metal products, Machinery/Appliances, Motor vehicles, Telecoms

Management Recruiters of Gastonia
1501 S. York Rd.
Gastonia, North Carolina 28052-6137
(704) 868-8080
Fax: (704) 868-8160
Email: mriscgas@vnet.net
Web: www.jobs-careers.com/mri/south.html

Key Contact - Specialty:
Mr. Chuck Deal

Description: Over 27 years experience. References provided. We do not accept assignments if we aren't going to devote full attention to them.
Functions: Mktg. mgmt., Sales mgmt., Engineering, Environmentalists
Industries: Construction, Environmental svcs.

Management Recruiters of Charlotte - North, Inc.
103 Commerce Ctr. Drive, Ste. 102
Huntersville, North Carolina 28078
(704) 947-0660
Fax: (704) 947-0705
Email: mrcharnrth@aol.com

Key Contact - Specialty:
Mr. Lawrence Duke - *Human resources, management consulting*

Description: Our firm specializes in human resource and management consulting executive search. Key functional areas include compensation, human resource systems, human resource strategy, change management and IT.
Functions: HR mgmt., Benefits, Training, MIS mgmt., Systems dev., Systems support, Mgmt. consultants
Industries: Generalist

Management Recruiters - Kannapolis
305 S. Main St.
Kannapolis, North Carolina 28081
(704) 938-6144
Fax: (704) 938-3480
Email: computerjobs@ctc.net
Web: www.computer-jobs-careers.com

Key Contact - Specialty:
Mr. T. H. Whitley - *Information systems*

Description: Offering a full range of recruiting services for information systems staff. Highly successful in recruiting either an entire development team or one top notch CIO.
Functions: Automation, MIS mgmt., Systems anal., Systems dev., Systems implem., Systems support, Mgmt. consultants
Industries: Generalist

Management Recruiters of Kinston
2852 Hull Rd.
P.O. Box 219
Kinston, North Carolina 28502-0219
(919) 527-9191
Fax: (919) 527-3625

Key Contact - Specialty:
Mr. Bill E. Thomas

Description: Nine account executives and manager with over 80 years combined experience in recruiting engineering, manufacturing, healthcare professionals and managers.

Salary Minimum: $30,000
Functions: Middle mgmt., Production, Automation, Quality, Nurses, HR mgmt., Engineering
Industries: Paper, Machinery/Appliances, Motor vehicles, Computer equip., Consumer electronics, Test/measurement equip., Healthcare

Management Recruiters of Mt. Airy
231 N. Main St.
Mt. Airy, North Carolina 27030-3809
(910) 719-2250
Fax: (910) 719-2350
Email: mrmtairy@advi.net

Key Contact - Specialty:
Mr. Donald F. Hackett - *Manufacturing (metals, plastics), including automotive*

Description: Specialist in metals and plastic manufacturing including engineering, plant management, planning, Q.C. Primarily in Southeast USA.

Salary Minimum: $40,000
Functions: Senior mgmt., Middle mgmt., Product dev., Production, Plant mgmt., Quality, Engineering
Industries: Plastics/rubber, Machinery/Appliances, Motor vehicles, Computer equip., Consumer electronics, Misc. mfg., Human resource svcs.

Management Recruiters of Raleigh
5509 Creedmoor Rd., Ste. 206
Raleigh, North Carolina 27612
(919) 781-0400
Fax: (919) 881-0117
Web: www.mrinet.com

Key Contact - Specialty:
Mr. Wade Stanley - *Manufacturing, technical, R&D, sales, engineering*

Description: Member of the President's gold club of MRI which includes only the top 25% of all offices. Established national search firm with specialty by industry.

Salary Minimum: $30,000
Functions: Production, Automation, Plant mgmt., Quality, Sales mgmt., R&D, Engineering
Industries: Textiles/apparel, Chemicals, Plastics/rubber, Leather/stone/glass/clay, Machinery/Appliances, Motor vehicles, Misc. mfg.

Management Recruiters of Rocky Mount - Southwest
Franklin Sq., Ste. J
P.O. Box 4139
Rocky Mount, North Carolina 27803-4139
(252) 442-8000
Fax: (252) 442-9000
Email: mri@web-point.com
Web: mrinet.com

Key Contact - Specialty:
Mr. Bob Manning - *Food*
Mr. Dave Weddell - *Food*
Ms. Sherry Strickland -

Description: Food industry and general manufacturing specialists.
Functions: Middle mgmt., Product dev., Quality, Mkt. research, Sales mgmt., R&D, Engineering
Industries: Agri/forestry/mining, Food/bev/tobacco, Hospitality, Aerospace

Management Recruiters of Boone
3657 Valle Circle, P.O. Box 691
Valle Crucis, North Carolina 28691
(828) 963-5111
Fax: (828) 963-5161
Email: mrboone@appstate.campus.mci.net

Key Contact - Specialty:
Mr. Donald L. Driscoll - *Data processing*
Mr. Matthew Murray - *Data processing*
Ms. Lynn D. Simmons - *Data Processing*
Mr. Dan Norris - *Data Processing*
Ms. Kristine Cornett - *Data Processing*
Mr. John Peet - *Data Processing*
Ms. Candace Randell - *Data Processing*

Description: Specialize in providing the health information systems industry with sales and technical talent. We provide sales, marketing and technical talent for vendors and healthcare providers.
Functions: Sales mgmt., MIS mgmt., Systems anal., Systems dev., Systems implem., Network admin., DB admin.
Industries: Software, Healthcare

Management Recruiters of Wilmington
4024 Oleander Drive, Ste. 1-B
Oleander Office Park
Wilmington, North Carolina 28403
(910) 791-2999
Fax: (910) 791-3099
Email: hlb@internectmci.com

Key Contact - Specialty:
Harry L. Bargholz - *Human resource management*

Description: Each account executive is grounded in two fundamentals: professional and recruiting a specific industry group which is his/her desk specialty.

Salary Minimum: $30,000
Functions: General mgmt., Plant mgmt., HR mgmt., Benefits, Personnel, Training
Industries: Misc. mfg., Svcs., Mgmt. consulting, Human resource svcs.

Management Recruiters of Winston-Salem
P.O. Box 17054
Winston-Salem, North Carolina 27116
(336) 723-0484
Fax: (336) 723-0841
Email: mriwinsal@aol.com
Web: www.mrinet.com

Key Contact - Specialty:
Mr. Mike Jones - *Materials management, logistics*
Ms. Judy Jones - *Finance & accounting, human resources*
Mr. Ken White - *Chemical, environment, health & safety*
Ms. Freda Weitzel - *Food industry*

Salary Minimum: $30,000
Functions: Middle mgmt., Mfg., Materials, HR mgmt., CFO's, R&D, Engineering
Industries: Food/bev/tobacco, Chemicals, Soap/perfume/cosmetics, Plastics/rubber, Metal products, Machinery/Appliances, Transportation

Management Recruiters of Akron
1900 W. Market St.
Akron, Ohio 44313-6927
(330) 867-2900
Fax: (330) 867-3830
Email: mrecruit@neo.lrun.com

Key Contact - Specialty:
Mr. Thomas J. Gerst - *Rubber, plastics*

Description: Specialists in rubber and plastic for 23 years.
Functions: Senior mgmt., Product dev., Production, Automation, Plant mgmt., Productivity, Sales mgmt.
Industries: Plastics/rubber

Management Recruiters of Cincinnati/Sharonville, Inc.
4050 Executive Park Drive, Ste. 125
Cincinnati, Ohio 45241-2020
(513) 769-4747
Fax: (513) 769-0471
Email: cincishr!manager@mrinet.com
Web: www.mrinet.com/cincinnati

Key Contact - Specialty:
Mr. William E. O'Reilly - *Packaging, paper, plastic, chemical, building products, construction*

Description: National retained/contingency executive search firm specializing in general management, manufacturing, engineering, finance/accounting and sales/marketing in paper, packaging, chemical and plastic industries. Nation's largest search firm 400 offices.

Salary Minimum: $40,000
Functions: Plant mgmt., Quality, Packaging, Mktg. mgmt., Sales mgmt., Engineering, Graphic artists
Industries: Construction, Lumber/furniture, Paper, Printing, Chemicals, Plastics/rubber, Packaging

Management Recruiters of Cleveland
812 Huron Rd. E., Ste. 760
Cleveland, Ohio 44115-1126
(216) 436-2436
Fax: (216) 436-2441
Email: 76351.2662@compuserve.com
Web: www.mrihvac.com

Key Contact - Specialty:
Mr. Gary Gardiner - *HVAC, sales engineering, mechanical contracting*

Description: Executive recruiters working on retained and contingency searches for sales and technical engineering positions.

Salary Minimum: $50,000
Functions: Middle mgmt., Production, Automation, Mktg. mgmt., Sales mgmt., Engineering
Industries: Generalist, Energy/utilities, Construction, Mfg., Machinery/Appliances, Svcs., Environmental svcs.

Management Recruiters of Cleveland
20600 Chagrin Blvd., Ste. 703
Cleveland, Ohio 44122
(216) 561-6776
Fax: (216) 561-2393
Email: mticleve@aol.com

Key Contact - Specialty:
Mr. Robert Gandee

Description: Full service; contingency and retainer search, temporary executives, national video interviewing network. Heavy experience in multi-opening national projects and team approach to staffing.
Functions: Generalist, Plant mgmt., Health admin., Sales & mktg., CFO's, IT
Industries: Food/bev/tobacco, Lumber/furniture, Printing, Finance, Equip. svcs., Insurance, Healthcare

Branches:
7550 Lucerne Drive
Cleveland, Ohio 44130
(216) 243-5151
Fax: (216) 243-4868
Key Contact - Specialty:
Mr. Jeff DiPaolo

Management Recruiters of Columbus
1900 E. Dublin-Granville Rd., Ste. 110B
Columbus, Ohio 43229-3374
(614) 794-3200
Fax: (614) 794-3233
Email: mrcmanager@mricolumbus.com
Web: www.mricolumbus.com

Key Contact - Specialty:
Mr. Richard Stoltz - *Information systems*

Salary Minimum: $20,000
Functions: Middle mgmt., Mfg., Materials, HR mgmt., IT, Engineering
Industries: Construction, Plastics/rubber, Transportation, Broadcast & Film, Software

Management Recruiters of Dayton, Inc.
333 W. First St., Ste. 304
Dayton, Ohio 45402
(937) 228-8271
Fax: (937) 228-2620
Email: mrdayton@msn.com
Web: mridayton.com

Key Contact - Specialty:
Mr. Jeffrey M. Noble
Dr. Gerald R. Kotler - *Engineering*

Description: We are a franchisee of the largest professional placement service in the world. Dr. Kotler was named Management Recruiters International account executive of the decade for the 80's.
Functions: Mfg., Materials, Healthcare, Sales & mktg., IT, Engineering
Industries: Mfg., Plastics/rubber, Metal products, Machinery/Appliances, Motor vehicles, Misc. mfg., Healthcare

Management Recruiters of Mentor, Inc.
8039 Broadmoor Rd., Ste. 20
Mentor, Ohio 44060
(440) 946-2355

Key Contact - Specialty:
Mr. Ronald Sterling - *Banking*
Ms. Cheryl Sterling - *Banking*

Description: We focus on permanent placement in the banking industry.

Salary Minimum: $30,000
Functions: Senior mgmt., Middle mgmt., Mkt. research, Mktg. mgmt., Sales mgmt., HR mgmt., Cash mgmt.
Industries: Banking

Management Recruiters - North Canton, Inc.
7300 Whipple Ave. NW
P.O. Box 2970
North Canton, Ohio 44720
(216) 497-0122
Fax: (216) 497-9730
Email: mrnc@compuserve.com
Web: www.mrnc.com

Key Contact - Specialty:
Ms. Shirley R. Bascom - *MIS*

Description: MIS

Salary Minimum: $25,000
Functions: MIS mgmt., Systems anal., Systems dev., Systems implem., Systems support, Network admin., DB admin.
Industries: Energy/utilities, Mfg., Transportation, Finance, Svcs.

Management Recruiters of Sidney
113 N. Ohio Ave., Ste. 400
The Ohio Bldg.
Sidney, Ohio 45365-2749
(937) 497-7080
Fax: (937) 497-7061
Email: kuniacke@aol.com

Key Contact - Specialty:
Mr. Keith J. Uniacke - *Food industry*
Ms. Diane Milanese - *Food industry*

Description: Our 25 years experience in the food industry offers an insider's perspective beneficial to your company by focusing on your total company needs relative to personality, company atmosphere and skill sets.

Salary Minimum: $45,000
Functions: Senior mgmt., Middle mgmt., Plant mgmt., Mkt. research, Mktg. mgmt., Sales mgmt.
Industries: Generalist, Food/bev/tobacco

Management Recruiters of Northwest Ohio, Inc.
3450 W. Central Ave., Ste. 360
Toledo, Ohio 43606
(419) 537-1100
Fax: (419) 537-8730
Email: nwest!gkf@mrinet.com
Web: www.superrecruiter.com

Key Contact - Specialty:
Mr. Gary Fruchtman - *Steel, pipe & tube, steel products, automotive, food plastics, IS/IT, administration, finance and accounting*

Description: Full service, emphasizing technical, data processing, financial, marketing and sales, primarily for manufacturing clients. Part of 600 office national network for United States and Canada.

Salary Minimum: $35,000
Functions: Generalist, Production, Direct mktg., Finance, MIS mgmt., Systems dev., Engineering
Industries: Generalist, Leather/stone/glass/clay, Metal products, Motor vehicles, Misc. mfg., Accounting, Software

Management Recruiters of Youngstown
8090 Market St., Ste. 2
Youngstown, Ohio 44512
(330) 726-6656
Fax: (330) 726-0199
Web: mrcsy@msn.com

Key Contact - Specialty:
Mr. Donald A. Somers - *Information systems*

Description: Experienced executive recruiting firm specializing in MIS, LAN/WAN, client server as well as engineering, sales and manufacturing.

Salary Minimum: $25,000
Functions: MIS mgmt., Systems anal., Systems dev., Systems implem., Systems support, Network admin., DB admin.
Industries: Generalist, Finance, Banking, Telecoms, High tech, Software, Healthcare

Management Recruiters of Oklahoma City
3441 W. Memorial Rd., Ste. 4
Oklahoma City, Oklahoma 73134-7000
(405) 752-8848
Fax: (405) 752-8783
Web: gary@mriokc.com

Key Contact - Specialty:
Mr. Gary P. Roy

Description: 1996 office of the year in SW region. President & Gold Club (top 5% in MRI).

Salary Minimum: $30,000
Functions: Middle mgmt., Mktg. mgmt., Sales mgmt., Cash mgmt., M&A, IT, Mgmt. consultants
Industries: Misc. financial, Hospitality, Telecoms, Software, Healthcare

Management Recruiters of Bethlehem, PA
1414 Millard St., Ste. 102
Bethlehem, Pennsylvania 18018-2632
(610) 974-9770
Fax: (610) 974-9775

Key Contact - Specialty:
Mr. Fred R. Meyer - *Food, chemicals, logistics, insurance, marketing*
Ms. Gayle A. McGeehan - *Food, chemicals, logistics, insurance, marketing, general manufacturing, pharmaceutical*

Description: Our office specializes in recruiting for all areas of the food industry. We find the best candidates for our clients. We also specialize in logistics, chemicals and insurance. Sales and marketing national and global.
Functions: Product dev., Production, Plant mgmt., Distribution, Mkt. research, Sales mgmt., Int'l.
Industries: Food/bev/tobacco, Chemicals, Drugs mfg., Machinery/Appliances, Computer svcs., Real estate, Biotech

Management Recruiters of Easton, PA
6 S. Third St., Ste. 304
Easton Ctr. Sq.
Easton, Pennsylvania 18042
(610) 258-0490
Fax: (610) 258-0676
Email: recruitment@mripa.com
Web: www.mripa.com

Key Contact - Specialty:
Mr. Max S. Kush - *Information technology, quality*

Description: Information technology professionals and manufacturing industry specialists offering a full range of staffing solutions. Services include permanent, interim and outplacement staffing, nationwide videoconferencing capability and personality testing.
Functions: General mgmt., Mfg., Quality, Materials, IT, Systems dev., Engineering
Industries: Mfg., Machinery/Appliances, Computer equip., Consumer electronics, Misc. mfg., High tech, Software

Management Recruiters of Lionville, Inc.

64 Uwchlan Ave., Ste. 272
Exton, Pennsylvania 19341-1203
(610) 363-6651
Fax: (610) 524-9153
Email: mri@worldaxes.com
Web: www.jobs-careers.com/mri/Lionville.html

Key Contact - Specialty:
Mr. J. F. Lynch - *Sales & marketing (general), telecommunications, insurance*
Ms. A. F. VanDolah - *Communications, high technology, biotechnology, biopharmaceutical*

Description: We are a retained technical search firm placing technical (developers, software engineers, managers and senior managers) in the high tech industry. Only those with prior systems experience need apply. Main clients include the Big 6 and private consulting consortiums.

Salary Minimum: $40,000
Functions: Senior mgmt., Middle mgmt., Mkt. research, Mktg. mgmt., Sales mgmt., Training, Risk mgmt.
Industries: Drugs mfg., Misc. financial, Pharmaceutical svcs., Telecoms, Insurance, Biotech, Non-classifiable industries

Management Recruiters of Valley Forge

65 Valley Stream Pkwy., Ste. 320
Malvern, Pennsylvania 19355
(610) 993-0070
Fax: (610) 993-0071
Email: mrvf@msn.com
Web: www.mrvalleyforge.com

Key Contact - Specialty:
Ms. Ina Lentz - *Metals industries*
Mr. James Lentz - *Metals industries*

Description: Our principals have a combined 40+ years of industry experience making us uniquely qualified to meet any needs you may have. This is aided by our affiliation with MRI and the 750 offices nationwide.

Salary Minimum: $40,000
Functions: Middle mgmt., Production, Plant mgmt., Quality, Productivity, IT, Engineering
Industries: Food/bev/tobacco, Metal products, Machinery/Appliances, Test/measurement equip., Misc. mfg., Hospitality

Management Recruiters of McMurray, Inc.

115 Hidden Valley Rd.
McMurray, Pennsylvania 15317
(724) 942-4100
Fax: (724) 942-4111
Email: mcmurray!mef@mrinet.com
Web: www.chemicaljobs.com

Key Contact - Specialty:
Mr. Michael Fosnot - *Chemicals, technical*

Description: One of the top offices within the Management Recruiters system for recruiting technical talent within the chemically related fields. Place BS/MS/PhD level chemists and chemical engineers up to the V.P. level.
Functions: Mfg., Product dev., Production, Plant mgmt., Quality, Productivity, R&D
Industries: Chemicals, Soap/perfume/cosmetics, Drugs mfg., Medical devices, Plastics/rubber, Paints/petroleum products

Management Recruiters of Westmoreland County, Inc.

3925 Reed Blvd., Ste. 200
Murrysville, Pennsylvania 15668-1848
(724) 325-4011
Fax: (724) 325-1760
Email: mriwc@mriwc.com
Web: www.mriwc.com

Key Contact - Specialty:
Mr. Frank Williamson - *Chemical industry*

Description: Chemical industry: sales, marketing, technical support and chemists. Managed care: utilization/quality management, marketing, finance, operations, provider networking, medical directors, medical services and related areas.

Salary Minimum: $30,000
Functions: Product dev., Physicians, Nurses, Health admin., Mktg. mgmt., Sales mgmt., R&D
Industries: Paper, Chemicals, Soap/perfume/cosmetics, Plastics/rubber, Paints/petroleum products, Healthcare

Management Recruiters of Delaware County

7 St. Albans Circle
Newtown Square, Pennsylvania 19073
(610) 356-8360
Fax: (610) 356-8731
Email: mr@op.net

Key Contact - Specialty:
Mr. Sandy Bishop - *Factory automation controls (electric & process, sales, marketing, & technical support)*

Description: Our market focus is the electrical equipment, process instrument and controls segments. We place sales, marketing and technical service professionals and middle managers.

Salary Minimum: $50,000
Functions: Middle mgmt., Automation, Mkt. research, Mktg. mgmt., Sales mgmt., Int'l.
Industries: Mfg., High tech, Software

Management Recruiters of Cherry Hill

2005 Market St., Ste. 555
One Commerce Sq.
Philadelphia, Pennsylvania 19103
(215) 567-1448
Fax: (215) 567-2153
Email: mrch@mriphiladelphia.com
Web: www.mriphiladelphia.com

Key Contact - Specialty:
Ms. Kaye Salikof
Mr. David Campeas

Description: Recruits technical and professional personnel on a national and international basis; specializing in operations, sales & marketing, logistics and consulting with upper level searches in human resources, customer service and information technology.
Functions: General mgmt., Materials, HR mgmt., IT, Engineering, Specialized services
Industries: Mfg., Transportation, Retail, Finance, Entertainment, Mgmt. consulting, Human resource svcs.

Management Recruiters of Pittsburgh

112 Washington Place, Ste. 1400
2 Chatham Ctr.
Pittsburgh, Pennsylvania 15219-3423
(412) 566-2100
Fax: (412) 566-2229
Email: lconnell@mricorp.mrinet.com
Web: lconnell@mricorp.mrinet.com

Key Contact - Specialty:
Ms. Laura Connelly - *Telecommunications*

Description: Executive search firm specializing in financial services, information technology, telecommunications and managed care.
Functions: Health admin., Sales mgmt., Cash mgmt., MIS mgmt., Systems anal., Systems dev., Systems support
Industries: Banking, Invest. banking, Computer svcs., Telecoms, High tech, Software, Healthcare

Management Recruiters of Pittsburgh-North, Inc.

435 Broad St., P.O. Box 69
Sewickley, Pennsylvania 15143
(412) 741-5805
Fax: (412) 741-3801
Email: mri@city-net.com
Web: www.htinfo.com/mrimrpittsburghnorth.htm

Key Contact - Specialty:
Mr. Richard Lampl
Ms. Joni Lampl - *MIS*

Description: Specialties: data processing, medical (DR), medical device sales, medical administration (HMO).

Salary Minimum: $30,000
Functions: Physicians, Health admin., MIS mgmt., Systems anal., Systems dev., Systems implem., Systems support
Industries: Medical devices, Healthcare

Management Recruiters of West Chester, Inc.

129 Willowbrook Lane
West Chester, Pennsylvania 19382
(610) 436-6556
Fax: (610) 436-6545
Email: rmeitz@dplus.net

Key Contact - Specialty:
Mr. Robert Meitz - *Chemical industry*

Description: Provide free total relocation service and counseling, reduced moving costs and a preferred mortgage program for clients. Also provide financial planning services for new employees.

Salary Minimum: $40,000
Functions: Production, Mkt. research, Sales mgmt., R&D, Engineering
Industries: Food/bev/tobacco, Paper, Chemicals, Soap/perfume/cosmetics, Drugs mfg., Plastics/rubber, Paints/petroleum products

Management Recruiters of Puerto Rico

#289 Piñero Ave., Ste. 200
San Juan, Puerto Rico 00925
(787) 766-4020
Fax: (787) 763-0870
Email: mripr@coqui.net
Web: www.mrinet.com

Key Contact - Specialty:
Mr. Carlos R. Rodriguez

Description: Specializing in: 1. Bi-lingual, bi-cultural talent for Puerto Rico, the Caribbean and Latin America. 2. Proven performers for both management and staff positions. 3. Motivated candidates who realistically will accept your offer if selected.

Salary Minimum: $15,000
Functions: Production, Materials Plng., Mktg. mgmt., Sales mgmt., Budgeting, Systems dev., Engineering
Industries: Food/bev/tobacco, Chemicals, Drugs mfg., Metal products, Consumer electronics, Wholesale, Banking

Management Recruiters of Aiken

P.O. Box 730
Aiken, South Carolina 29802
(803) 648-1361
Fax: (803) 642-5114
Email: aiken!mkk@mrinet.com

Key Contact - Specialty:
Mr. Michael Hardwick - *Glass manufacturing*

Description: Fee paid, national specialists in utilities, primary metals, computers, automotive, appliance and electrical components, glass-ceramics, plastics, textiles, building materials.

Salary Minimum: $30,000
Functions: Senior mgmt., Middle mgmt., Automation, Plant mgmt., Quality, R&D, Engineering
Industries: Energy/utilities, Textiles/apparel, Plastics/rubber, Leather/stone/glass/clay, Metal products, Motor vehicles, Computer svcs.

Management Recruiters of Florence

1224 W. Evans St.
Florence, South Carolina 29501-3322
(843) 664-1112
Fax: (843) 673-2701
Email: citas@earthlink.net

Key Contact - Specialty:
Mr. Alan Feimster - *World class manufacturing*

Description: We identify, recruit and deliver manufacturing and manufacturing support managers, executives and technical professionals for clients who are or want to become world class manufacturers.

Salary Minimum: $20,000
Functions: Mfg., Materials, HR mgmt., Budgeting, IT, R&D, Engineering
Industries: Mfg., Packaging

Management Recruiters of Greenville

330 Pelham Rd., Ste. 109-B
Greenville, South Carolina 29615
(864) 370-1341
Fax: (864) 370-9633
Web: www.htinfo.com/mriscGreenville.htm

Key Contact - Specialty:
Mr. M.D. Searboro - *Industrial, electrical, automation*

Description: The search and recruiting specialists - 400 offices.
Functions: Middle mgmt.
Industries: Mfg.

Management Recruiters of Myrtle Beach, Inc.

1500 Hwy. 17 N.,Ste. 308
Myrtle Beach, South Carolina 29575
(843) 477-8800
Web: www.jobquestsite.com

Key Contact - Specialty:
Mr. Mark E. Lewis - *Food & beverage operations, manufacturing*

Description: We provide a superior recruiting service for corporate clients to aid in their growth and to provide candidates with the most rewarding career opportunities in their pursuit of excellence.

Salary Minimum: $40,000
Functions: Production, Plant mgmt., Physicians, Health admin., Mktg. mgmt., Engineering
Industries: Food/bev/tobacco, Plastics/rubber, Leather/stone/glass/clay, Motor vehicles, Consumer electronics, Misc. mfg., Healthcare

Management Recruiters of North Charleston

4975 Lacross Rd., Ste. 311
North Charleston, South Carolina 29406-6525
(843) 744-5888
Fax: (843) 744-4666
Email: mrncharles@earthlink

Key Contact - Specialty:
Mr. Ray Fountain - *Manufacturing, healthcare management, industrial sales, distribution, information technology*
Mr. Kurt Schenck - *Banking and financial management*

Description: As part of a network of over 700 offices, we bring together top quality candidates and top flight employers.

Salary Minimum: $30,000
Functions: Mfg., Materials, Healthcare, Sales & mktg., Finance, IT, Engineering
Industries: Mfg., Wholesale, Finance, Communications, Aerospace, Software, Healthcare

Management Recruiters of Georgetown

4111 Hwy. 17 N., Litchfield Executive Ctr.
Pawleys Island, South Carolina 29585
(843) 235-2323
Fax: (843) 235-9078

Key Contact - Specialty:
Mr. Scott Knowles - *Insurance, finance (general), information (general)*
Ms. Joan Roby - *Information systems*

Description: Specializes in middle to senior level management positions for clients in insurance and managed care, or other industries requiring operations, finance, information systems professionals.

Salary Minimum: $40,000
Functions: Directors, Senior mgmt., Middle mgmt., Healthcare, Sales & mktg., Finance, IT
Industries: Generalist, Drugs mfg., Medical devices, Pharmaceutical svcs., Computer svcs., Insurance, Healthcare

Management Recruiters of Travelers Rest, Inc.

907 N. Main St.
P.O. Box 639
Travelers Rest, South Carolina 29690-0639
(864) 834-0643
Fax: (864) 834-0275
Email: mrtrmgr@aol.com

Key Contact - Specialty:
Mr. Guy W. Carter - *General manufacturing, information systems*

Description: Will be one of 1,000 offices by year 2000 that are fully computerized with inter-office referral, executive search profile program, video conferencing centers, and MRILink a custom designed information technology program that optimzes information and communication flow within each office, between Management Recruiters offices, and between individual offices and the business world.

Salary Minimum: $30,000
Functions: Production, Plant mgmt., MIS mgmt., Systems anal., Systems implem., Network admin., DB admin.
Industries: Textiles/apparel, Lumber/furniture, Paper, Chemicals, Drugs mfg., Plastics/rubber, Computer equip.

Management Recruiters of Sioux Falls, LLP

2600 S. Minnesota Ave., Ste. 202
Sioux Falls, South Dakota 57105
(605) 334-9291
Fax: (605) 334-9826
Email: mr605@sd.cybernex.net

Key Contact - Specialty:
Mr. David J. Good - *Agriculture*
Mr. Robert B. Good - *Banking & related*

Description: Permanent & interim search and placement; executive, professional, management, technical, sales/marketing.

Salary Minimum: $25,000
Functions: General mgmt., Mfg., Sales & mktg., Finance, IT, R&D, Engineering
Industries: Agri/forestry/mining, Construction, Mfg., Finance, Insurance, High tech, Software

Management Recruiters of Chattanooga-Brainerd, Inc.

7010 Lee Hwy., Ste. 216
Chattanooga, Tennessee 37421
(423) 894-5500
Fax: (423) 894-1177
Email: mrichatt@internetmci.com
Web: www.mrichattanooga.com

Key Contact - Specialty:
Mr. Bill Cooper - *General manufacturing, technical, chemical, medical, pharmaceutical*

Description: Full service recruitment, outplacement and video-conference center both retained and contingency search. Specialties include: technical, management, medical and pharmaceutical sales/marketing and information systems.

Salary Minimum: $30,000
Functions: Mfg., Production, Plant mgmt., Materials, Sales & mktg., IT, Systems dev.
Industries: Chemicals, Drugs mfg., Metal products, Misc. mfg., Computer svcs., Software, Healthcare

Management Recruiters of Columbia, Tennessee

1117 Trotwood Ave., Ste. 201
Columbia, Tennessee 38401-3033
(931) 388-5586
Fax: (931) 380-0615
Email: mritn@usit.net
Web: www.mritn.com

Key Contact - Specialty:
Mr. Douglas Holt - *Automotive manufacturing & related processes in KY & TN*
Ms. Marianne Stevick - *Automotive manufacturing & related processes in KY & TN*

Description: We specialize in manufacturing and quality assurance engineers and managers for the automotive and appliance industries. We concentrate on companies in Tennessee and Kentucky and surrounding southeastern states.

Salary Minimum: $25,000
Functions: Middle mgmt., Plant mgmt., Productivity, Purchasing, Materials Plng., Benefits, Training
Industries: Mfg., Plastics/rubber, Metal products, Machinery/Appliances, Motor vehicles

Management Recruiters of Franklin, Inc.

236 Public Sq., Ste. 201
Franklin, Tennessee 37064-2520
(615) 791-4391
Fax: (615) 791-4769

Key Contact - Specialty:
Mr. Roger H. Marriott - *Printing industry (sales, sales management, technical)*
Ms. Gloria A. Marriott - *Printing industry (sales, sales management, technical)*

Description: One of approximately 600 offices of the world's largest contingency search and recruitment organization. This office specializes in the printing industry.

Salary Minimum: $35,000
Functions: Senior mgmt., Middle mgmt., Production, Plant mgmt., Distribution, Sales mgmt., Customer svc.
Industries: Printing

Management Recruiters The Delta Group, Inc.

5050 Poplar Ave.
White Station Twr., Ste. 1103
Memphis, Tennessee 38157
(901) 844-8000
Fax: (901) 844-8001
Email: mrtdg@accessus.net
Web: www.mrinet.com

Key Contact - Specialty:
Mr. Raymond F. Wojcik - *Consumer products, sales & marketing*
Mr. Jeff Paddock - *Banking, financial services*
Mr. Don Frease - *Engineering, information technology*

Description: We specialize in banking and financial services, engineering, information technology, marketing and sales professionals.

Salary Minimum: $60,000
Functions: Senior mgmt., Middle mgmt., Production, Mktg. mgmt., Sales mgmt., Cash mgmt., Engineering
Industries: Food/bev/tobacco, Soap/perfume/cosmetics, Drugs mfg., Medical devices, Computer equip., Banking, Invest. banking

Management Recruiters of Memphis, TN

5495 Winchester Rd., Ste. 5
Memphis, Tennessee 38115
(901) 794-3130
(901) 794-3137
Fax: (901) 794-5671

Key Contact - Specialty:
Mr. Wally Watson - *Logistics Management*

Description: Search and recruiting specialists. Affiliate of the world's largest search firm---700 offices nationwide.
Functions: Generalist
Industries: Generalist

Management Recruiters of Arlington

1001 W. Randol Mill Rd.
Arlington, Texas 76012
(817) 469-6161
Fax: (817) 462-9155
Email: mri@topcareers.com
Web: www.topcareers.com

Key Contact - Specialty:
Mr. Robert J. Stoessel

Description: Consistent leading mid size MR office in Southwest, specializing in placing engineering, oil & gas, electronic, manufacturing, environmental, chemical, plastics, printing, packaging, telecommunications and graphic arts professionals nationally.

Salary Minimum: $35,000
Functions: Senior mgmt., Middle mgmt., Product dev., Production, Automation, Plant mgmt., Engineering
Industries: Energy/utilities, Paper, Printing, Metal products, Misc. mfg., Packaging, High tech

Management Recruiters of Austin

1250 Capital of Texas Hwy.
3 Cielo Ctr., Ste. 650
Austin, Texas 78746
(512) 327-8292
Fax: (512) 327-3901
Email: dfrazier@mriaustin.com

Key Contact - Specialty:
Ms. Donna Frazier

Description: We are one of the top ten offices within the Management Recruiters system of 750 offices, the largest search firm in the nation.

Salary Minimum: $40,000
Functions: Mfg., Healthcare, Allied health, Sales & mktg., Advertising, IT, R&D
Industries: Mfg., Computer svcs., Advertising/PR, High tech, Software, Biotech, Healthcare

Management Recruiters of North West Austin

P.O. Box 27258
Austin, Texas 78755-2258
(512) 338-0880
Fax: (512) 338-0481

Key Contact - Specialty:
Ms. Lorraine Keller - *Technical*

Description: Our experience as industry managers makes us uniquely qualified to find the individual you are looking for who is not looking for you.

Salary Minimum: $30,000
Functions: Product dev., Production, R&D, Engineering
Industries: Chemicals, Drugs mfg., Plastics/rubber, Packaging

Management Recruiters Dallas North (MRDN)

15150 Preston Rd., Ste. 300
Dallas, Texas 75248
(972) 991-4500
Fax: (972) 991-6226
Email: gbuntrock@sprynet.com

Key Contact - Specialty:
Mr. George Buntrock - *Distribution/logistics*

Description: We offer a project approach using project coordinators, computerized database and access to the Internet. Value added services include video interviewing, relocation assistance with discounts, various testing and background investigation services.
Functions: Middle mgmt., Materials Plng., Distribution, Sales mgmt., Systems dev., Engineering
Industries: Misc. mfg., Transportation, Wholesale, Retail, Telecoms

Management Recruiters of LBJ Park/Dallas

3003 LBJ Frwy., Ste. 220E
Dallas, Texas 75234-7771
(972) 488-1133
Fax: (972) 488-1099
Email: mrdfw.airmail.net
Web: www.mrinet.com

Key Contact - Specialty:
Mr. Ray Vlasek - *Technical*

Description: My background includes 18 years experience in electronics companies based in personnel management and training.

Salary Minimum: $40,000
Functions: Product dev., Production, Quality, Productivity, Packaging, Systems dev., Engineering
Industries: Machinery/Appliances, Computer equip., Consumer electronics, Test/measurement equip., Telecoms, High tech, Software

Management Recruiters - Friendswood

317 S. Friendswood Drive
Friendswood, Texas 77546
(713) 996-0008
Fax: (713) 996-5449

Key Contact - Specialty:
Mr. Louis Bellview - *Chemicals, food processing*
Ms. Sibyl Bellview - *Healthcare*

Description: Specializing in the placement of technical, professional and management personnel in the food processing, healthcare and petrochemical industries.
Functions: Middle mgmt., Production, Plant mgmt., Nurses, Allied health, Health admin., Engineering
Industries: Food/bev/tobacco, Chemicals, Soap/perfume/cosmetics, Drugs mfg., Human resource svcs., Packaging, Healthcare

Management Recruiters of Champions

3934 W. FM 1960, Ste. 105
Houston, Texas 77068
(281) 580-6020
Fax: (281) 580-6029
Email: mrichamp@swbell.net
Web: mrichampions.com

Key Contact - Specialty:
Mr. Gary K. Akin - *General manufacturing*
Ms. Nicola Akin
Mr. James Barkley - *Benefits administration*

Description: Providing nationwide permanent placement, interim executive and outplacement services to clients needing candidates in sales, manufacturing, engineering design and employee benefits consulting.

Salary Minimum: $35,000
Functions: Middle mgmt., Production, Benefits
Industries: Food/bev/tobacco, Drugs mfg., Machinery/Appliances, Misc. financial, Mgmt. consulting, Packaging

Management Recruiters of Houston

1360 Post Oak Blvd., Ste. 2110
Houston, Texas 77056
(713) 850-9850
(800) 878-0995
Fax: (713) 850-1429
Email: mri.houston@internetmci.com
Web: www.mrhouston.com

Key Contact - Specialty:
Mr. Rich Bolls - *Sales management, executives*

Description: Retained and contingency search - healthcare, engineering, manufacturing, financial, information services, sales and marketing, middle management and senior management, medical and pharmaceutical sales, retail.
Functions: Senior mgmt., Production, Allied health, Health admin., CFO's, MIS mgmt., Engineering
Industries: Energy/utilities, Chemicals, Retail, Invest. banking, Pharmaceutical svcs., Accounting, Healthcare

---

Management Recruiters of Houston-Northeast
1412-A Stonehollow Drive
Kingwood, Texas 77339
(281) 359-7940
Fax: (281) 359-7947
Email: gatelin@nol.net
Web: mrilingate.com

Key Contact - Specialty:
Ms. Linda Copeland - *Forest products*
Mr. Gates Copeland - *Forest products*
Ms. Jamie Myers - *Forest products*

Salary Minimum: $40,000
Functions: Directors, Senior mgmt., Middle mgmt.
Industries: Agri/forestry/mining, Lumber/furniture, Paper, Motor vehicles, Insurance

---

Management Recruiters of Lewisville
1660 S. Stemmons, Ste. 460
Brookhollow N.
Lewisville, Texas 75067
(972) 434-9612
Fax: (972) 221-0268

Key Contact - Specialty:
Ms. Desni C. Kramer

Salary Minimum: $45,000

Management Recruiters of Lubbock
#22 Briercroft Office Park, Ste. 14
Lubbock, Texas 79412
(806) 749-2345
Fax: (806) 749-3456

Key Contact - Specialty:
Mr. Lester Warren - *Hospital professionals*
Mrs. Deborah Warren - *Telecommunications*

Description: Medical: technical, nursing, administrative. Engineer: telecommunications.

Salary Minimum: $28,000
Functions: Production, Plant mgmt., Physicians, Nurses, Allied health, Health admin.
Industries: Consumer electronics, Telecoms, Healthcare

Management Recruiters of Round Rock
301 Hesters Crossing, Ste. 110
Round Rock, Texas 78681
(512) 310-1918
Fax: (512) 310-8318
Email: jomanly@msn.com

Key Contact - Specialty:
Ms. Jodi Hohlstein - *Electrical, electro-mechanical controls, automation and robotics*
Mr. Jeff Hohlstein - *Automated industrial controls*
Ms. Jo Manly - *Automated industrial controls*
Ms. Karrie Richardson - *General manufacturing*
Mr. Daniel Schuhmacher - *Industrial automation equipment, robotics*

Description: Highly focused professional recruitment team specializing in the permanent placement of professionals within commercial, industrial and residential products in refrigeration and heating industries. Additionally, we focus on industrial and commercial controls, residential and commercial cooking products and recreational equipment used for camping and backpacking.
Functions: Middle mgmt., Product dev., Production, Automation, Sales mgmt., Engineering, Minorities
Industries: Food/bev/tobacco, Plastics/rubber, Metal products, Machinery/Appliances, Consumer electronics, Misc. mfg.

Management Recruiters of San Antonio
8700 Crownhill, Ste. 701
San Antonio, Texas 78209
(210) 829-8666
Fax: (210) 822-2218
Email: sananton!manager@mrinet.com
Web: mrisatx@swbell.net

Key Contact - Specialty:
Mr. James L. Cornfoot - *Manufacturing (1st & 2nd Tier automotive)*
Ms. Denise Carrigan - *Food industry, senior management, marketing, operations*

Description: Additional client services include reduced rate moves, reduced rate mortgages, refinancing and closing costs, video conference network for interviewing (all financial services available to clients and candidates placed by us).

Salary Minimum: $60,000
Functions: Senior mgmt., Middle mgmt., Production, Plant mgmt., Quality, Sales mgmt., Finance
Industries: Food/bev/tobacco, Metal products, Machinery/Appliances, Motor vehicles

---

Management Recruiters of San Antonio - North
12500 San Pedro Ave., Ste. 450
San Antonio, Texas 78216-2858
(210) 495-2725
Fax: (210) 495-2726
Email: mri-recruitem@msn.com
Web: www.mrinet.com/

Key Contact - Specialty:
Mr. Randall W. Spencer - *Insurance, managed care, healthcare*

Description: The MRI global network targets, recruits and delivers high impact talent for our clients' critical needs. Our mission is to be the world's preferred and pre-eminent provider of staffing solutions.

Salary Minimum: $40,000
Functions: General mgmt., Directors, Middle mgmt., Healthcare, Health admin., Sales mgmt., Customer svc.
Industries: Finance, Svcs., Insurance, Healthcare

Management Recruiters of San Marcos
165 S. Guadalupe, Ste. 150
San Marcos, Texas 78666-5531
(512) 392-3838
Fax: (512) 392-3133
Email: sanmarc!manager@mrinet.com

Key Contact - Specialty:
Dr. Charles D. Berry - *Agricultural chemical seed, biotechnology, research & development, sales & marketing*
Ms. Judy Aswell - *Consumer products, licensing, design, sales & marketing, merchandising*
Mr. Ken Guidroz - *Banking*
Mr. Craig Walton - *Telecommunications, information technology*

Description: Offering over 40 years experience to assist with opportunities and growth. Our office specializes in all aspects of agriculture, banking, consumer products and telecommunications.

Salary Minimum: $35,000
Functions: Sales & mktg., Sales mgmt., Systems dev.
Industries: Agri/forestry/mining, Banking, Telecoms, Biotech

Management Recruiters of Sugar Land Inc.

10707 Corporate Drive, Ste. 120
The Churchill Bldg.
Stafford, Texas 77477-4001
(281) 240-0220
Fax: (281) 240-0880
Email: gandeejr@flash.net

Key Contact - Specialty:
Mr. John R. Gandee - *Lumber, plywood, millwork*
Ms. Joan C. Gandee - *Lumber, plywood, millworks, pulp & paper*
Mr. Don Hayes - *Lumber, plywood, millworks*
Mr. Mark Lauber - *Information technology*
Mr. Brad Gandee -

Description: We are an executive search firm (80% contingency-20% retainer) working mainly in the following areas: lumber/plywood and manufacturing wood products, expanding into pulp and paper.

Salary Minimum: $30,000
Functions: General mgmt., Mfg., Materials, Sales & mktg., HR mgmt., IT, Engineering
Industries: Generalist, Lumber/furniture, Paper

Management Recruiters Int'l.-The Woodlands

1610 Woodstead Court, Ste. 495
The Woodlands, Texas 77380-3404
(281) 363-9494
Fax: (281) 292-7795
Email: mri@infohwy.com

Key Contact - Specialty:
Ms. Lynette Baker - *Telecommunications*
Mr. Caren Krochenski - *Telecommunications*

Description: We have a combined background of engineering and management experience, with an extensive network of contacts with major players in the telecommunications industry. We are very active in the area of wireless infrastructure development, system development and business development, both vendors and carriers.

Salary Minimum: $72,000
Functions: Directors, Senior mgmt., Production, Mkt. research, Mktg. mgmt., MIS mgmt., R&D
Industries: Energy/utilities, Communications, New media, Broadcast & Film, Telecoms, High tech

Management Recruiters of Ogden

533 26th St., Ste. 203 B
Ogden, Utah 84401
(801) 621-1777
Fax: (801) 621-1788
Email: recruiter@mrogden.com

Key Contact - Specialty:
Mr. Jerry Manning - *General manufacturing, technical, quality*
Mr. Ray Baker - *General manufacturing, HVAC, quality*
Mr. Vandy Butler - *Wireless communication*
Mr. Reg Burnaugh - *Chemical*

Description: Permanent and contract placement of technical and manufacturing individuals on a nationwide basis. Emphasis in HVAC, electric heat, appliance, trucks and tractors, power tools, wireless communication design, installation and sales, commercial, industrial and agricultural chemicals.

Salary Minimum: $30,000
Functions: Senior mgmt., Middle mgmt., Product dev., Production, Plant mgmt., Quality, Engineering
Industries: Chemicals, Metal products, Machinery/Appliances, Misc. mfg., Telecoms

Management Recruiters of Salt Lake City

6600 S. 1100 E., Ste. 520
Salt Lake City, Utah 84121-2400
(801) 264-9800
Fax: (801) 264-9807
Email: dirk@mrislc.com
Web: www.mrislc.com

Key Contact - Specialty:
Mr. Dirk A. Cotterell - *Information technology*

Description: We are industry experts in the niches we serve. Additionally we emphasize matching corporate culture with individual personality and chemistry. We use computer-assisted personality assessment tools and face to face video conference interviewing to ensure success.

Salary Minimum: $60,000
Functions: Quality, Health admin., Sales & mktg., Mkt. research, Finance, IT
Industries: Mfg., High tech, Software, Healthcare

Management Recruiters of Arlington

5001-A Lee Hwy., Ste. 102
Arlington, Virginia 22207-2538
(703) 276-1135
Fax: (703) 276-1138
Email: mriarl@erols.com
Web: www.htinfo.com/mriarlva.htm

Key Contact - Specialty:
Mr. Jerry Donovan - *Telecommunications, sales & marketing, human resources*

Description: We specialize in the information technology industry handling both sales and marketing and technical positions in telecommunications, software, hardware, systems engineering, network and technical support.

Salary Minimum: $40,000
Functions: Mktg. mgmt., Sales mgmt., Benefits, Training, Systems anal., Systems dev., Systems implem.
Industries: Computer equip., Human resource svcs., New media, Telecoms, Software

Management Recruiters of Fairfax, VA

4400 Fair Lakes Court, Ste. 103
Fairfax, Virginia 22033
(703) 222-8220
Fax: (703) 222-8229
Email: fairfax!tae@mrinet.com

Key Contact - Specialty:
Mr. Tony Ehrenzeller - *Insurance, technology*

Description: Part of 600 office system, both permanent and temporary management placement. 150 site video conferencing capabilities as well as international video sites. Comprehensive staffing capabilities from clerical through executive.
Functions: Sales mgmt., Systems implem.
Industries: Drugs mfg., Pharmaceutical svcs., Telecoms, Insurance, High tech

Management Recruiters - Piedmont

108 Crofton Place, Ste. 1
Palmyra, Virginia 22963
(804) 591-1028
(800) 976-1972
Fax: (804) 591-1139

Key Contact - Specialty:
Ms. Rebecca Leinen - *Pharmaceutical, sales & marketing*

Description: We provide domestic and international recruitment services within the pharmaceutical and industrial industries in three key areas: permanent placement, flexible staffing and ancillary staffing services.
Functions: Advertising, Mkt. research, Mktg. mgmt., Sales mgmt., Customer svc.
Industries: Drugs mfg., Medical devices, Pharmaceutical svcs., Healthcare

Management Recruiters of Roanoke
1960 Electric Rd., Ste. B
Roanoke, Virginia 24018
(540) 989-1676
Fax: (540) 989-7556

Key Contact - Specialty:
Mr. Paul S. Sharp - *Chemical industry, sales, technical*
Mr. Keith Zillifro - *Chemical industry, sales, technical*

Description: Paper chemical sales, technical service and marketing specialist with 15 years recruiting experience in industry. Paint and coatings specialist has 25 years industry experience.
Functions: Senior mgmt., Middle mgmt., Sales mgmt., R&D
Industries: Paper, Chemicals, Paints/petroleum products

Management Recruiters of Loudoun County South
45571 Shepard Drive
Sterling, Virginia 20164-4409
(703) 430-3700
Fax: (703) 430-7997

Key Contact - Specialty:
Mr. Jerry Gilmore - *Chemical process industry, engineering disciplines*
Ms. Pamela Nix Gilmore - *Chemical process industry, manufacturing, engineering disciplines*

Description: Complete human resources services provider: permanent and interim placement; outplacement assistance; management consulting; financial, travel and relocation services offered to client companies.

Salary Minimum: $45,000
Functions: Production, Automation, Plant mgmt., Systems implem., Engineering, Minorities, Environmentalists
Industries: Chemicals, Drugs mfg., Plastics/rubber, Paints/petroleum products, Misc. mfg., Computer svcs., High tech

Affiliates:
Trinity Capital Corporation

Management Recruiters of Lynnwood
19109 36th Ave. W., Ste. 100
Alderwood Business Ctr.
Lynnwood, Washington 98036-5767
(206) 778-1212
Fax: (206) 778-7840
Email: lynwood!manager@mrinet.com
Web: www.mri-lynnwood.com

Key Contact - Specialty:
Mr. Bud Naff - *Environmental, civil engineering, construction*

Description: Contingency search firm specializing in the recruitment and placement of professionals in the environmental consulting, engineering, construction and chemical industries.

Salary Minimum: $30,000
Functions: Directors, Senior mgmt., Middle mgmt., Health admin., Engineering, Environmentalists
Industries: Construction, Environmental svcs., Haz. waste

Management Recruiters of Seattle
2510 Fairview Ave. E.
Seattle, Washington 98102-3216
(206) 328-0936
Fax: (206) 328-3256
Email: ix.netcom.com

Key Contact - Specialty:
Mr. Dan Jilka - *Engineering*
Ms. Ronda Clark - *Engineering*
Ms. Jamie Owen - *Sales & marketing*

Description: We have 11 professionals who specialize in the high-tech, electronics, software, health and managed care, engineering, food, beverage, industrial, consumer products, marketing, retail.
Functions: Senior mgmt., Product dev., Plant mgmt., Health admin., Mktg. mgmt., R&D, Engineering
Industries: Food/bev/tobacco, Medical devices, Aerospace, High tech, Software, Biotech, Healthcare

Management Recruiters of Spokane
W. 316 Boone Ave., Ste. 370
Spokane, Washington 99201
(509) 324-3333
Fax: (509) 324-3334

Key Contact - Specialty:
Mr. Dale Gilliam - *Banking, administration*
Mr. Doug Yackel - *Technology*

Description: Executive search specializing in the medical, banking information systems, food, biotechnology and telecommunications industries.
Functions: General mgmt., Mfg., Healthcare, Sales & mktg., Finance, IT, R&D
Industries: Food/bev/tobacco, Banking, Telecoms, High tech, Software, Biotech, Healthcare

Management Recruiters of Kanawha Valley, LLC
3983 Teays Valley Rd.
Mt. Vernon Plaza, Ste. 200 C
Hurricane, West Virginia 25526
(304) 757-4399
Fax: (304) 757-4398
Email: mrikanawhavalley@citynet.net

Key Contact - Specialty:
Mr. Harry Ray, Jr. - *Energy (natural & electrical) services, power marketing, power trading*
Ms. Stephanie Glandon - *Energy services sales, marketing & engineering, HVAC*

Description: With a concentration in the deregulated energy industry, our office has both a good understanding of the constantly changing energy marketplace as well as a good recruiting base for finding highly qualified candidates.
Functions: Directors, Senior mgmt., Middle mgmt., Mkt. research, Sales mgmt., Risk mgmt., Engineering
Industries: Energy/utilities

Management Recruiters of Appleton
911 N. Lynndale Drive
Appleton, Wisconsin 54914
(920) 731-5221
Fax: (920) 731-9427
Email: appleton!manager@mrinet.com

Key Contact - Specialty:
Mr. Russell V. Hanson

Description: Offer the full range of placement services. Senior executive through all levels of technical, administrative, sales search. Executive, professional, sales search in the paper, plastic, general manufacturing and MIS specialties.

Salary Minimum: $30,000
Functions: Senior mgmt., Middle mgmt., Mfg., Plant mgmt., Materials, Sales mgmt., IT
Industries: Energy/utilities, Construction, Paper, Plastics/rubber, Machinery/Appliances, Misc. mfg., Computer svcs.

Management Recruiters of Milwaukee-West
13000 W. Bluemound Rd.
Elm Grove, Wisconsin 53122
(414) 797-7500
Fax: (414) 797-7515
Email: mrmilw@aol.com
Web: www.execpc.com/~mrmilw

Key Contact - Specialty:
Mr. William C. Healy - *Generalist*
Mr. Peder Medtlie - *Information technology*

Description: Nationwide management recruiting affiliation, specializing in middle management and professional people. Most industries and services.

Salary Minimum: $35,000
Functions: Senior mgmt., Middle mgmt., Quality, IT, Engineering

Industries: Generalist, Drugs mfg., Metal products, Machinery/Appliances, Motor vehicles, Accounting, High tech

Management Recruiters of Janesville, Inc.

20 E. Milwaukee St., Ste. 304
Janesville, Wisconsin 53545
(608) 752-2125
Fax: (608) 752-2903

Key Contact - Specialty:
Mr. Carroll V. Smith - *General manufacturing*

Description: Strong recruiting experience in automotive, ISO 9000 and executive management. Value added services include outplacement, video conferencing and contract executive placement. Established division in managed care sales and operations.
Functions: Senior mgmt., Middle mgmt., Plant mgmt., Quality, Materials Plng., Sales mgmt., CFO's
Industries: Plastics/rubber, Metal products, Machinery/Appliances, Motor vehicles, Misc. mfg., Insurance, Healthcare

Management Recruiters of Madison, Inc.

1800 Parmenter St., Ste. 200
Middleton, Wisconsin 53562-3137
(608) 831-1717
Fax: (608) 831-8188
Email: mrmad@itis.com

Key Contact - Specialty:
Ms. Patricia A. Capanna - *Telecommunications, engineering, engineering management, sales, outdoor sports*

Description: Executive recruiters for engineering, engineering management and manufacturing positions in the outdoor sports and recreational vehicles and in the telecommunications industry in the US and worldwide.

Salary Minimum: $40,000
Functions: Product dev., Production, Purchasing, Sales mgmt., Engineering, Specialized services
Industries: Machinery/Appliances, Motor vehicles, Misc. mfg., Telecoms

Management Recruiters of Milwaukee-North

601 E. Henry Clay
Milwaukee, Wisconsin 53217-5646
(414) 963-2520
Fax: (414) 963-2539
Email: mr/sc@mri-execsearch.com
Web: www.recruiters-jobs.com

Key Contact - Specialty:
Mr. Timothy M. Lawler, III - *International, manufacturing*
Mr. Ron Sloane - *Architects, construction, design, management, real estate*
Mr. Nick Curran - *Manufacturing, operations*
Mr. Bob Meissner - *International sales & marketing, export, credit, financial, Latin America*

Description: Recruitment of professionals, managers and executives. Office is in top 5% of MR/SC offices nationwide-President's Gold Club Award. 84% of our business is repeat business.
Functions: General mgmt., Mfg., Materials, Sales & mktg., Finance, Engineering, Int'l.
Industries: Generalist, Construction, Metal products, Machinery/Appliances, Motor vehicles, Misc. mfg., Telecoms

Management Recruiters of Milwaukee - Downtown

735 N. Water, Ste. 1228
Milwaukee, Wisconsin 53202
(414) 226-2420
Fax: (414) 226-2421
Email: mrimke@execpc.com
Web: www.mrimilwaukee.com

Key Contact - Specialty:
Mr. Douglas Lane - *Telecommunications, software, hardware*
Mr. Steve Tewes - *Sales & marketing*
Ms. Theresa Davis - *Accounting & finance*
Ms. Susan Fitzpatrick - *Technology, consulting*
Mr. Donald W. Butler - *Financial services, information technology*
Ms. jody Herbst - *Financial services*
Ms. Elaine Dickson - *Marketing and sales*

Salary Minimum: $40,000
Functions: Senior mgmt., Mfg., Mktg. mgmt., Sales mgmt., Finance, IT, Mgmt. consultants
Industries: Banking, Accounting, Mgmt. consulting, New media, Telecoms, High tech, Software

Management Recruiters of Stevens Point, Inc.

DuBay Professional Centre
1117W County Rd. DB
Mosinee, Wisconsin 54455
(715) 341-4900
Fax: (715) 341-4992
Email: mri@coredcs.com

Key Contact - Specialty:
Mr. Bradford L. Barick - *Commercial insurance, safety*
Ms. Linda R. Barick - *MIS, application software sales & support*
Mr. Paul M. Marshall - *Telecommunications*

Description: We are the world's largest contingency search firm. We pre-screen, pre-qualify, reference check and pre-sell your opportunity to prospective candidates. Value added services include the largest recruiting database, relocation, travel, financial mortage, Interim Executive and ConferView.

Salary Minimum: $50,000
Functions: General mgmt., Sales mgmt., Risk mgmt., MIS mgmt., Systems dev., Systems implem., Systems support
Industries: Computer equip., Computer svcs., Telecoms, Environmental svcs., Insurance, Software

Management Recruiters of Wausau, LLC

3309 Terrace Court
Wausau, Wisconsin 54401-3952
(715) 842-1750
Fax: (715) 842-1741
Email: mriwausau@pcpros.net

Key Contact - Specialty:
Ms. Laurie Prochnow - *MIS managers, programmers, project leaders, LAN managers*
Mr. Max Hawkins - *Information systems, AS400, MIS managers, programmers*
Ms. Kay Babicky - *Programmers, analysts, operators*
Ms. Irene Gruszecki - *Programmers, MIS managers, technical support*

Description: We are the #1 search firm in the US. We have a nationwide database of employers who have positions available and recruit candidates for these positions.
Functions: MIS mgmt., Systems anal., Systems dev., Systems implem., Systems support, Mgmt. consultants, Technicians
Industries: Generalist

Management Recruiters of Cheyenne

1008 E. 21st St.
Cheyenne, Wyoming 82001
(307) 635-8731
Fax: (307) 635-6653

Key Contact - Specialty:
Mr. Verle Meister - *Manufacturing, software engineering*

Description: Contingency search with four people working coast to coast in manufacturing and electronics.
Functions: Mfg., IT
Industries: Metal products, Machinery/Appliances, Motor vehicles, Computer equip., Consumer electronics, High tech, Software

Management Resource Assoc., Inc.

P.O. Box 3266
Boca Raton, Florida 33427
(561) 852-5650
Fax: (561) 852-5656
Email: mraboca@ix.netcom.com
Web: www.netcom.com/~mraboca/SEARCH.html

Key Contact - Specialty:
Mr. Gerald Schneiderman - *Finance & accounting*
Ms. Sheila Schneiderman - *Human resources, general management*

Description: A dynamic middle to upper management, management search firm, specializing in the high-tech industry and financial institutions, with access to local, national and international resources and twenty-five years corporate management/search experience.

Salary Minimum: $50,000
Functions: General mgmt., Mfg., Sales & mktg., HR mgmt., Finance, IT, Int'l.
Industries: Generalist, Mfg., Finance, High tech, Software

Management Resource Group, Ltd.

2805 Eastern Ave., Ste. 102
Davenport, Iowa 52803
(319) 323-3333
Fax: (319) 323-0767
Email: mrgltd319@aol.com

Key Contact - Specialty:
Mr. Daniel H. Portes

Description: We are a multi-office human resource consulting firm dedicated to increasing organizational effectiveness through creative and customized approaches to the identification, selection, development and transition of people.

Salary Minimum: $50,000
Functions: Senior mgmt., Middle mgmt., Admin. svcs., HR mgmt., CFO's, Cash mgmt., Non-profits
Industries: Generalist, Finance, Banking, Brokers, Misc. financial, Non-profits

Management Resource Group

8609 Lyndale Ave. S., Ste. 205
Minneapolis, Minnesota 55420
(612) 888-4599
Fax: (612) 888-4701

Key Contact - Specialty:
Mr. Michael S. Northrop - *Sales, sales management (telecommunications & software), consumer*
Mr. K. Michael Rowe - *Sales, sales management, dealer financial services*

Description: We represent telecom, software and financial institutions across the country. Our emphasis is in sales and sales management. Both principals serve on the board of directors for their state association.

Salary Minimum: $35,000
Functions: Middle mgmt., Sales mgmt., Credit
Industries: Food/bev/tobacco, Banking, Misc. financial, Telecoms, Software

Management Resource Group, Inc.

77 Bleecker St., Ste. 124
New York, New York 10012
(212) 475-5327

Key Contact - Specialty:
Mr. Matthew J. DeLuca - *Sports entertainment, television, live events, merchandise/licensing, publishing & printing, electronic media*

Description: All positions for sports entertainment and banking except system/DP. Human resources/personnel/training and development - all industries.

Salary Minimum: $40,000
Functions: Mktg. mgmt., Systems support, Graphic artists
Industries: Entertainment, Human resource svcs., Publishing, New media

Management Resources

7611 Hwy. 180 E.
Mineral Wells, Texas 76067
(940) 325-8455
Fax: (940) 325-8520
Email: jim@managementresources.com
Web: www.managementresources.com

Key Contact - Specialty:
Mr. James W. Heineman - *Managed care*
Mr. Gary Morris

Description: We were founded on the premise that lasting business relationships are built through mutual trust and respect. We are committed to a philosophy of maintaining a true partnership with our clients.

Salary Minimum: $50,000
Functions: Senior mgmt., Physicians, Nurses, Health admin., Mktg. mgmt., Sales mgmt., CFO's
Industries: Healthcare

Management Search Assoc., Inc.

P.O. Box 888849
Atlanta, Georgia 30356
(770) 300-0775
Fax: (770) 300-9965

Key Contact - Specialty:
Ms. Jean W. Hyman - *RN's, management level nurses, financial, administrative management, hospitals*

Description: Total of 10 years of production in healthcare field. Specializing in hospital administrative management, nursing management, home health nurses, clinical nurse specialists and nurse practitioners.

Salary Minimum: $35,000
Functions: Directors, Senior mgmt., Middle mgmt., Physicians, Nurses, Allied health, Health admin.
Industries: Healthcare

Management Search Int'l.

P.O. Box 51355
Irvine, California 92619
(949) 831-8353
Fax: (949) 831-9614
Email: sjsawyer@pacbell.net
Web: sjsawyer@pacbell.net

Key Contact - Specialty:
Mr. Scott J. Sawyer - *CPAs & MBAs, fraud investigators, MIS/DP*
Mr. Jess J. Lee - *CPAs & MBAs, finance & accounting, MIS/DP, MIS/Business consultants, project managers, financial analysts & management., CPA/Operational & EDP audit*

Description: We are a low volume, highly personalized full service firm offering search on a contingent or retainer basis. National and international. Finance, operations, litigation support CPA/MBA, audit, tax, accounting, general management, MIS, Sr. business analysts & systems consultants, project mgmt. & MIS sales and marketing.

Salary Minimum: $45,000
Functions: Mfg., HR mgmt., Finance, IT, Systems implem., Systems support, Mgmt. consultants
Industries: Generalist, Energy/utilities, Mfg., Finance, Svcs., Communications, Aerospace

Management Search, Inc.

117 S. Cook St., Ste. 201
Barrington, Illinois 60010
(847) 304-1775
Fax: (847) 304-8948
Email: steflink@ix.netcom.com

Key Contact - Specialty:
Mr. Stefan Levy - *Insurance, venture capital, internet*

Description: Fast, effective recruitment services. Strategic networking to provide internet and communications companies with targeted executives, capital, strategic-alliance and merger/acquisition opportunities.

Salary Minimum: $70,000
Functions: Senior mgmt., Sales mgmt., M&A, IT, MIS mgmt., Network admin., DB admin.
Industries: Venture cap., Computer svcs., New media, Telecoms, Insurance, High tech, Software

Management Search, Inc.

6051 N. Brookline, Ste. 125
Oklahoma City, Oklahoma 73112
(405) 842-3173
Fax: (405) 842-3173
Email: dorwig.juno.com

Key Contact - Specialty:
Mr. David L. Orwig - *Agriculture*

Description: Agriculture research and technical service positions, both agronomic and livestock. Agriculture sales and sales management positions.

Salary Minimum: $25,000
Functions: Middle mgmt., Mkt. research, Sales mgmt., R&D
Industries: Agri/forestry/mining

Management Solutions, Inc.

(Firm declined to update.)
99 Almaden Blvd., Ste. 600
San Jose, California 95113
(408) 292-6600
Web: www.mgmtsolutions.com

Key Contact - Specialty:
Mr. Richard Williams - *Finance, human resources*
Mr. Richard Giorgetti - *Finance*
Ms. Aggie Potter - *Finance*
Mr. Neil Glatzer - *Finance*
Mr. Randy Merrell - *Finance, human resources*
Mr. David Arnold - *Interim finance, human resources*

Description: Provide management search services in San Francisco Bay area. Largest specialized finance and accounting placement firm in Bay area. All our placement staff have finance or human resource backgrounds.

Salary Minimum: $35,000
Functions: Personnel, CFO's, Budgeting, Credit, Taxes, MIS mgmt., Systems implem.
Industries: Computer equip., Test/ measurement equip., Computer svcs., Accounting, High tech, Software, Biotech

Management Solutions, Inc.

320 180th Ave NE
Bellevue, Washington 98004
(425) 646-6300
Fax: (425) 643-6411
Email: marvsmith@msn.com
Web: www.prcsearch.com/pcs

Key Contact - Specialty:
Mr. Marvin E. Smith - *Finance, accounting, human resources*
Mr. Darren M. Casey - *Finance, accounting, human resources*
Ms. Ashlee Anderson - *Interim finance & accounting*
Ms. Vicki Campbell - *Finance, accounting, human resources*
Mr. Bill Parfitt - *Information technology, engineering*
Ms. Jan Parfitt - *Interim information technology*

Description: Practice consists of middle/ senior level management recruitment. Serve manufacturing, high technology, public accounting and industrial clients. Recruit accounting/financial and human resource professionals. In addition, we serve the information technology and engineering marketplace.

Salary Minimum: $50,000
Functions: Materials, Sales & mktg., HR mgmt., Finance, IT, R&D, Engineering
Industries: Mfg., Finance, Svcs., Aerospace, High tech, Software, Biotech

Mancini Technical Recruiting

P.O. Box 2183
Arlington, Virginia 22202
(703) 521-2183
Fax: (703) 920-0166
Email: debbie@m-t-r.com
Web: www.m-t-r.com

Key Contact - Specialty:
Ms. Deborah Mancini - *High technology, software*

Description: We are an executive search firm specializing in the technical industry. We are headquartered in Arlington, VA and place applicants within positions across the US and Canada.

Salary Minimum: $35,000
Functions: IT, Systems anal., Systems dev., Systems implem., Systems support, Network admin., DB admin.
Industries: Computer svcs., High tech, Software

Mangieri/Solutions LLC

177 Main St.
Monroe, Connecticut 06468
(203) 452-2313
Fax: (203) 452-2317
Email: cmang@aol.com

Key Contact - Specialty:
Mr. Chris Mangieri - *Direct marketing*

Description: Major specialty: direct marketing.

Salary Minimum: $50,000
Functions: Advertising, Mkt. research, Mktg. mgmt., Direct mktg., Customer svc., Training, MIS mgmt.
Industries: High tech, Software, Healthcare

Mankuta Gallagher & Assoc., Inc.

8333 W. McNab, Ste. 231
Tamarac, Florida 33321
(954) 720-9645
Fax: (954) 720-5813
Email: stanley@satelnet.org

Key Contact - Specialty:
Dr. Michael Gallagher - *Pharmaceutical, biotechnology, information systems*

Description: We are a client driven firm specializing in biotechnology, information systems, engineering, software and telecommunications. We have over 30 years of combined experience and strive to do excellent work on a consistent basis. We offer a total quality guarantee.

Salary Minimum: $45,000
Functions: Product dev., Quality, Systems anal., Systems dev., Systems implem., R&D, Engineering
Industries: Drugs mfg., Pharmaceutical svcs., Mgmt. consulting, High tech, Software, Biotech, Healthcare

Manning Lloyd Assoc. Ltd.

53 N. Park Ave., Ste. 50
Rockville Centre, New York 11570
(516) 678-9700
Fax: (516) 678-9763

Key Contact - Specialty:
Ms. Dianne Manning - *Compensation & benefit professionals*

Description: Boutique specializing in search for compensation and benefits professionals for domestic and international positions; both corporate and consulting.

Salary Minimum: $40,000
Functions: Benefits, Mgmt. consultants, Minorities, Int'l.
Industries: Generalist, Human resource svcs.

ManTech Consulting

469 7th Ave., 5th Floor
New York, New York 10018
(212) 560-5408
Fax: (212) 560-5708
Email: jsabrin@mecnet.com
Web: www.mecnet.com

Key Contact - Specialty:
Mr. Joe Sabrin - *CIO's, information systems management, sales & sales management, systems development/programming, systems integration/implementation*

Description: Over thirty years experience in NYC/NJ/CT in search and placement of information technology people with the Fortune 1000 companies.

Salary Minimum: $40,000
Functions: Sales mgmt., Training, MIS mgmt., Systems anal., Systems dev., Systems implem., Systems support
Industries: Generalist, Invest. banking, High tech, Software

The Marathon Group
P.O. Box 2901
Ponte Vedra Beach, Florida 32004-2901
(904) 273-9300
Fax: (904) 273-9077
Email: fokeefe@bellsouth.net

Key Contact - Specialty:
Mr. Frank O'Keefe - *Sales & marketing, chemicals, process equipment*

Description: Sales and marketing search in chemicals and equipment for pulp and paper, water and waste treatment, metal working, refineries, graphics, packaging and process controls.

Salary Minimum: $40,000
Functions: Senior mgmt., Middle mgmt., Product dev., Mkt. research, Mktg. mgmt., Sales mgmt., Customer svc.
Industries: Paper, Plastics/rubber, Paints/petroleum products, Metal products, Test/measurement equip., Haz. waste, Packaging

Branches:
2320 S. 3rd St., Ste. 8
Jacksonville Beach, Florida 32250
(904) 270-2121
Fax: (904) 270-2120
Key Contact - Specialty:
Mr. Michael Moore - *Sales & marketing, labels & graphics*

4456 Karls Gate Drive
Marietta, Georgia 30068
(770) 971-7198
Fax: (770) 971-5751
Key Contact - Specialty:
Mr. Dale Champion - *Sales & marketing, process controls & packaging*

MARBL Consultants, Inc.
11270 W. Park Place, Ste. 270
Milwaukee, Wisconsin 53224-3624
(414) 359-5627
Fax: (414) 359-5620
Email: marblcons@aero.net

Key Contact - Specialty:
Mr. Allan G. Adzima - *Engineering, manufacturing, materials, purchasing, logistics*
Mr. Dennis J. Pradarelli - *Data processing, MIS, finance, accounting*
Ms. Diane Pruitt - *Generalist*
Mr. Jerry Peterson - *Human resources, materials, purchasing, logistics*

Description: Client-driven organization committed to successfully completing a project in a timely manner. We are dedicated to excellence in 5 major areas: manufacturing, engineering, materials, purchasing, logistics, data processing and human resources.

Salary Minimum: $40,000
Functions: General mgmt., Mfg., Materials, HR mgmt., Finance, IT, Engineering
Industries: Generalist, Plastics/rubber, Machinery/Appliances, Motor vehicles, Misc. mfg., Computer svcs., Software

---

Marc-Allen Assoc., Inc.
7770 W. Oakland Park Blvd., Ste. 280
Ft. Lauderdale, Florida 33351
(954) 572-3771
Fax: (954) 748-6583
Email: mikepowell@usa.net

Key Contact - Specialty:
Mr. Mike Powell - *Retail, general management, accounting, finance*
Ms. Kathy Rupar

Description: We utilize nationwide search resources, including a state-of-the-art database and extensive retailing and management networks. We provide a 90 day unconditional candidate replacement guarantee.

Salary Minimum: $40,000
Functions: Senior mgmt., Middle mgmt., Mktg. mgmt., Sales mgmt., HR mgmt., Training, Finance
Industries: Generalist, Retail

Marcus & Assoc.
358 Saw Mill River Rd.
Millwood Business Ctr.
Millwood, New York 10546
(914) 941-7100
Fax: (914) 941-8629

Key Contact - Specialty:
Mr. Alvin B. Marcus - *Senior management*
Ms. Catherine McKenna - *Human resources, finance*
Mr. Dean Kaplan - *Research & development*
Ms. Marlene Rudnick - *Regulatory affairs, quality assurance*
Mr. Keith Kline - *MIS*
Mr. Greg Flanagan - *Marketing & sales*
Ms. Denise Clements - *Clinical research*
Ms. Bonnie Sacarny - *Research & development*
Mr. Dan Hoye - *Research & development*

Description: General firm with special expertise in searches for research and development, manufacturing, marketing and corporate staff personnel in the pharmaceutical, biotechnology and consumer healthcare industries.

Salary Minimum: $60,000
Functions: Generalist, Mfg., Physicians, Mktg. mgmt., HR mgmt., Finance, R&D
Industries: Generalist, Soap/perfume/cosmetics, Drugs mfg., Pharmaceutical svcs., Biotech, Healthcare

---

Marentz & Co.
P.O. Box 7374
The Woodlands, Texas 77380
(281) 847-1584
Fax: (281) 847-1587
Web: marentzco@aol.com

Key Contact - Specialty:
Mr. Frank Marentez - *Technical, telecommunications, banking, energy*
Mr. Richard Ramirez - *Banking, energy, engineering*
Ms. Lily Campos - *Healthcare*
Mr. Larry Rodriguez - *Energy, engineering*

Description: The ability to generate viable candidates from selected databases, industry networks and referrals allow our search consultants to provide the type of service demanded by the client. The firm offers flexible financial options for our search services and can be tailored to the needs of the client.

Salary Minimum: $60,000
Functions: Sales mgmt., CFO's, Cash mgmt., Taxes, Systems anal., Systems dev., Engineering
Industries: Energy/utilities, Finance, Hospitality, Accounting, Real estate, Software, Healthcare

---

Margolin Consultants, Inc.
350 Fifth Ave., Ste. 2819
New York, New York 10118
(212) 268-1940
Fax: (212) 268-2695

Key Contact - Specialty:
Mr. Efraim Margolin - *Management*

Description: Executive search, product development, market research, mergers and acquisitions, venture capital and joint venture.

Salary Minimum: $50,000
Functions: Middle mgmt., Product dev., Production, Automation, Plant mgmt., Sales mgmt., Engineering
Industries: Lumber/furniture, Plastics/rubber, Metal products, Machinery/Appliances, Telecoms, Packaging, High tech

---

Mark Christian & Assoc., Inc.
5844 E. Marconi Ave.
Scottsdale, Arizona 85254
(602) 494-9522
Fax: (602) 953-8991

Email: mchrisassc@aol.com

Key Contact - Specialty:
Mr. Gary Alexander - *Computer industry, management, sales*
Ms. Myra Alexander - *Computer industry, sales, technical*

Description: We offer the information systems industry a recruiting service to find key people for their organization. Each principal has over 20 years of experience in the information systems industry. Our extensive network of contacts is utilized in all recruiting activity.

Salary Minimum: $60,000
Functions: Senior mgmt., Middle mgmt., Sales mgmt., Systems dev., Systems support
Industries: Computer equip., Computer svcs., Telecoms, Software

Affiliates:
Key Resources International

Mark III Personnel, Inc.
4801 E. Independence Blvd., Ste. 604
Charlotte, North Carolina 28212-5403
(704) 535-5883

Key Contact - Specialty:
Mr. Lindsay Allen, Jr. - *Engineering (all disciplines), research & development, chemists, technical specialties, environmental, material/logistics management*

Description: All professional and managerial positions. Focus areas are engineers, chemists for process industries, manufacturing, materials/logistics management, environmental. Contingency and retained; minimum salary $40K.

Salary Minimum: $40,000
Functions: Production, Plant mgmt., Materials, HR mgmt., R&D, Engineering
Industries: Textiles/apparel, Paper, Chemicals, Plastics/rubber, Human resource svcs., Environmental svcs.

Markent Personnel, Inc.
722 Wisconsin Ave., Box 328
Wisconsin Dells, Wisconsin 53965
(608) 254-6233
Fax: (608) 254-4064
Email: markent@midplains.net

Key Contact - Specialty:
Mr. Thomas L. Udulutch - *Engineering*
Mr. Mark Udulutch - *Engineering*

Description: 100 mailings a week to alumni of Wisconsin engineering schools. Permanent recruiting engineering and manufacturing/process management. Immigration attorney on staff. Contracting of technical and management temporaries. Certified public accountant on staff.

Salary Minimum: $30,000
Functions: Middle mgmt., Mfg., Materials, Sales & mktg., Finance, IT, Engineering
Industries: Food/bev/tobacco, Paper, Plastics/rubber, Metal products, Machinery/Appliances, Motor vehicles, Consumer electronics

Branches:
201 75th St. N.
Brooklyn Park, Minnesota 55444
(612) 561-6812
Fax: (612) 561-6908
Email: hjebens@bright.net
Key Contact - Specialty:
Mr. Harry Jebens - *Safety engineering, sanitary engineering*

W6407 20th St.
Necedah, Wisconsin 54646
(608) 565-2101
Fax: (608) 565-6920
Key Contact - Specialty:
Mr. Dave Arnold - *Engineering*

Market Niche Consulting
3002 E. Weldon Ave.
Phoenix, Arizona 85016
(602) 955-8230
Fax: (602) 955-3599
Email: rsamp@amug.org

Key Contact - Specialty:
Mr. Ron Sampson - *Information systems technology*

Description: Management information systems with emphasis on bankcard and/or credit card processing and software development. Heavy emphasis on users of pay systems products.

Salary Minimum: $50,000
Functions: Credit, IT, MIS mgmt., Systems anal., Systems dev., Systems implem.
Industries: Computer equip., Misc. financial, Computer svcs., High tech, Software

Marketing & Sales Resources, Inc.
14000 Military Trail
Delray Beach, Florida 33484
(561) 637-7711
Fax: (561) 637-7555
Web: www.msresources@mindspring.com

Key Contact - Specialty:
Mr. Alan H. Gross - *Marketing & sales management*
Mr. Robert C. Kleinman

Description: Uniquely specialized in the recruitment of mid and senior level marketing and sales management executives within the consumer, industrial, chemicals, plastics and service industries.

Salary Minimum: $60,000
Functions: Senior mgmt., Middle mgmt., Advertising, Mkt. research, Mktg. mgmt., Sales mgmt., Int'l.
Industries: Construction, Chemicals, Soap/perfume/cosmetics, Plastics/rubber, Machinery/Appliances, Test/measurement equip., Misc. mfg.

Marketing Consultants
3015 N. Shepard Ave.
Milwaukee, Wisconsin 53211-3437
(414) 962-6611
Fax: (414) 962-6623
Email: csmolizer@execpc.com

Key Contact - Specialty:
Ms. Carole E. Smolizer - *Marketing*

Description: Specializing in the search and placement of candidates in the fields of consumer marketing management, advertising, sales promotion and market research.

Salary Minimum: $40,000
Functions: Advertising, Mkt. research, Mktg. mgmt., Minorities, Int'l.
Industries: Food/bev/tobacco, Paper, Soap/perfume/cosmetics

Marketing Recruiters, Inc.
P.O. Box 4098
Asheboro, North Carolina 27204
(336) 626-4009
Fax: (336) 626-5116

Key Contact - Specialty:
Mr. Rass Bagley - *Medical sales*

Description: We specialize in finding and placing sales and marketing professionals. Our area of expertise lies within the medical industry.

Salary Minimum: $30,000
Functions: Sales mgmt.
Industries: Medical devices

Marketing Resources
P.O. Box 463, 18 North Rd.
Chelmsford, Massachusetts 01824
(978) 256-8001
Email: resomark@medjobs.com
Web: www.medjobs.com

Key Contact - Specialty:
Mr. Joseph D. Sheedy - *Medical products, medical services*

Description: Executive search and placement services for marketing managers or specialists with focus on medical technologies. Segments are medical-surgical, clinical chemistry, patient monitoring, cardiovascular, medical computer and medical device companies.

Salary Minimum: $70,000

Functions: Directors, Senior mgmt., Mkt. research, Mktg. mgmt., Sales mgmt., R&D, Engineering
Industries: Drugs mfg., Medical devices, Test/measurement equip., Pharmaceutical svcs., Software, Biotech, Healthcare

---

Marketing Search Inc.

7207 Wooster Pike
Cincinnati, Ohio 45227
(513) 561-1603
Fax: (513) 561-1303
Email: awb@fuse.net

Key Contact - Specialty:
Ms. Anne Williams Badanes - *Consumer marketing*

Description: 15 years experience in national; mid to senior level; specializing in marketing/advertising; consumer focus.

Salary Minimum: $60,000
Functions: Advertising, Mkt. research, Mktg. mgmt., Sales mgmt., Direct mktg.
Industries: Food/bev/tobacco, Soap/perfume/cosmetics, Drugs mfg., Misc. financial, Advertising/PR, Telecoms

Affiliates:
Satterfield & Assoc., Inc.

Marketing/Public Relations Research Recruiting

8 Norwalk Ave.
Westport, Connecticut 06880
(203) 226-6738
Fax: (203) 226-7172

Key Contact - Specialty:
Mr. Ben V. Luden - *Marketing, public relations research*

Description: Succeeding over 10 years' diversified marketing and research work at General Electric, A.C. Nilesen, Opinion Research and Yankelovich, I offer clients an active, successful, competitively-priced recruiting service in marketing and P.R. research.

Salary Minimum: $50,000
Functions: Mkt. research
Industries: Finance, Svcs., Communications, Advertising/PR

MarketPro, Inc.

2211 Newmarket Pkwy., Ste. 154
Marietta, Georgia 30067
(770) 951-9181
(888) MRKT-PRO
Fax: (770) 612-8941
Email: mktpro@mindspring.com
Web: www.marketproinc.com

Key Contact - Specialty:
Ms. Melissa M. Haggard - *Marketing*

Description: We specialize in the contract placement and recruitment of marketing professionals.
Functions: Advertising, Mkt. research, Mktg. mgmt., Sales mgmt., Direct mktg., Customer svc., PR
Industries: Generalist

Affiliates:
MarketPro, Inc.

Marley Group Ltd.

245 Fifth Ave.
New York, New York 10016
(212) 779-1500
Fax: (212) 779-1740
Email: marleylaw@aol.com

Key Contact - Specialty:
Ms. Hazel S. Kandall
Mr. Richard Kirschner
Ms. Fran Weber - *Intellectual property*
Ms. Esther Koslow
Ms. Nancy A. Klein
Mr. Tierney E. O'Hearn
Mr. John Parker

Description: Attorney placement: associates, partners, in-house counsel, groups & mergers.

Salary Minimum: $60,000
Functions: Attorneys
Industries: Generalist

Marsar & Co., Inc.

(Firm declined to update.)
4830 W. Kennedy Blvd., Ste. 830
Tampa, Florida 33609
(813) 286-3766

Key Contact - Specialty:
Mr. Kevin P. Marsar - *Accounting, finance, treasury, human resources, information technology*
Mr. Stephen G. Christie - *Accounting, finance, treasury, human resources, information technology*

Description: 50+ years cummulative recruiting experience in West Central Florida covering all of Florida. Mature, high integrity, honest service to clients and candidates (=future clients), efficient, serious and competent.

Salary Minimum: $50,000
Functions: Benefits, Personnel, CFO's, Cash mgmt., M&A, MIS mgmt., Systems dev.
Industries: Generalist, Misc. mfg., Retail, Accounting, Telecoms, Software, Healthcare

---

Karen Marshall Assoc.

6304 Deep Creek Drive
Prospect, Kentucky 40059
(502) 228-0800

Key Contact - Specialty:
Ms. Karen Marshall - *MIS*
Mr. Dennis Marshall

Description: Recruiter, search and placement of MIS professionals and executives since 1983.

Salary Minimum: $30,000
Functions: MIS mgmt., Systems anal., Systems dev., Systems implem., Systems support, Network admin., DB admin.
Industries: Generalist, Mfg., New media, Broadcast & Film, Telecoms, High tech, Biotech

---

Marshall-Alan Assoc., Inc.

5 W. 37th St., 8th Floor
New York, New York 10018
(212) 382-2440
Fax: (212) 764-5411

Key Contact - Specialty:
Mr. Alan Massarsky - *Hospitality*
Ms. Joan Steinberg - *Hospitality*

Description: Executive search organization specializing in the hospitality industry.

Salary Minimum: $50,000
Functions: Senior mgmt., Middle mgmt., Purchasing, Sales mgmt., Training, CFO's, MIS mgmt.
Industries: Hospitality, Entertainment

Marsteller Wilcox Assoc.

799 Roosevelt Rd., Bldg. 3, Ste. 108
Glen Ellyn, Illinois 60137
(630) 790-4300
(630) 790-4394
Fax: (630) 790-4495
Email: mark@mwaltd.com
Web: mwaltd.com

Key Contact - Specialty:
Mr. Mark Wilcox - *Engineering, operations management*
Ms. Linda Marsteller - *Paper & pulp*
Ms. Carol Ranberg - *Printing, inks*
Ms. Surette Joseph - *Engineering, operations management*
Mr. Dan Grant - *Contract employment*
Mr. Steve Robinson - *Automotive, general manufacturing*

Salary Minimum: $45,000
Functions: General mgmt., Mfg., Materials, Sales & mktg., Finance, R&D, Engineering
Industries: Paper, Chemicals, Paints/petroleum products, Motor vehicles, Transportation, Wholesale, Human resource svcs.

Martin Grant Assoc. Inc., Insurance Personnel

65 Franklin St.
Boston, Massachusetts 02110
(617) 357-5380
Fax: (617) 482-6581
Email: martingrant@msn.com

Key Contact - Specialty:
Mr. Barry Davis - *Insurance*
Ms. Diana Gazzolo - *Insurance*

Description: We are Boston's oldest leading insurance placement firm specializing in all levels of property/casualty, life/health/pension and risk management placement.

Salary Minimum: $20,000
Industries: Insurance

The Martwick Group, Inc.

4380 SW Macadam Ave., Ste. 575
Portland, Oregon 97201
(503) 223-7060
Fax: (503) 223-1645
Email: gail@martwick.com

Key Contact - Specialty:
Ms. Gail Martwick

Description: Full service executive search firm. President has twelve years of successful executive recruitment for Pacific NW clients in high technology, manufacturing, data processing, medical electronics, consumer products, telecommunications.

Salary Minimum: $50,000
Functions: Mfg., Materials, Sales & mktg., IT, Engineering
Industries: Medical devices, Computer equip., Test/measurement equip., Telecoms, High tech, Software

Marvel Consultants, Inc. (a division of Century Business Services, Inc.)

28601 Chagrin Blvd., Ste. 470
Cleveland, Ohio 44122
(216) 292-2855
Fax: (216) 292-7207
Email: marvel@cyberdrive.net
Web: www.marvelcons.com

Key Contact - Specialty:
Mr. Marvin B. Basil - *Generalist*
Mr. Lester Tavens - *Sales & marketing*
Mr. John Sowers - *Information technology*

Description: Each recruiter is a niche market specialist with tenures ranging up to 25 years, recruiting on a vertical market basis.
Functions: General mgmt., Mfg., Healthcare, Sales & mktg., Finance, IT, Engineering
Industries: Generalist, Plastics/rubber, Machinery/Appliances, Test/measurement equip., Finance, Software, Healthcare

Richard L. Mather & Assoc.

P.O. Box 1183
Glastonbury, Connecticut 06033
(860) 633-8130

Key Contact - Specialty:
Mr. Richard L. Mather

Description: Specializing in manufacturing, engineering and corp./div. management recruiting for computer, energy, water, environmental, utility, information systems and other technical industries.

Salary Minimum: $40,000
Functions: Middle mgmt., Plant mgmt., Materials Plng., Mktg. mgmt., CFO's, MIS mgmt., Engineering
Industries: Energy/utilities, Plastics/rubber, Computer equip., Broadcast & Film, Telecoms, High tech, Biotech

Mathey Services

15170 Bethany Rd.
Sycamore, Illinois 60178
(815) 895-3846
Fax: (815) 895-1046

Key Contact - Specialty:
Ms. Joyce Mathey - *Plastics*

Description: Executive recruiting, searching, screening and placement services provided to clients in the plastics, packaging and chemical industries. Specializing in the fields of sales and marketing, research and development and management and manufacturing, nationwide.

Salary Minimum: $30,000
Functions: General mgmt., Product dev., Productivity, Mktg. mgmt., Sales mgmt., R&D, Engineering
Industries: Chemicals, Plastics/rubber

Matrix Consultants, Inc.

P.O. Box 986
Wrightsville Beach, North Carolina 28480
(910) 256-8080
Fax: (910) 256-9500
Email: ojwomble@worldnet.att.net

Key Contact - Specialty:
Mr. O. J. Womble - *Food ingredients*
Mr. Joe Marion - *Chemicals, allied products*
Mr. Bill Jordan - *Chemicals, allied products*
Ms. Rebecca Charles - *Food ingredients, food service*

Description: Specialize in recruiting and conducting searches in the food ingredient industry. Positions in research, sales and marketing to vice president and presidents for the largest companies in the industry.

Salary Minimum: $50,000
Functions: Directors, Senior mgmt., Middle mgmt., Product dev., Mktg. mgmt., Sales mgmt.
Industries: Food/bev/tobacco, Chemicals, Biotech

Matthews & Stephens Assoc., Inc.

1344 Silas Deane Hwy., Ste. 303
Rocky Hill, Connecticut 06067
(860) 258-1995
Fax: (860) 258-1998
Email: sbaskowski@matthews-stephens.com

Key Contact - Specialty:
Mr. Stephen A. Baskowski - *Finance & accounting*
Mr. Stephen W. Harvey - *Healthcare*
Mr. David Phillips - *Retail, accounting, MIS*
Ms. Mary Wilson - *Insurance*
Mr. Terry Gustafson - *Insurance*

Description: National practice with unique customized approach and alternatives. Extremely personalized seasoned staff that listens to you then develops a search plan. We specialize in healthcare administration, insurance, financial accounting, engineering, and call centers.

Salary Minimum: $50,000
Functions: Generalist, Health admin., Finance, CFO's, IT, Engineering
Industries: Insurance, Healthcare

The Matthews Group, Inc.

440 West St., Ste. 7N
Ft. Lee, New Jersey 07024
(201) 585-2211
Fax: (201) 585-2214

Key Contact - Specialty:
Ms. Alyce Matthews - *Sales, marketing, consumer products*

Description: We place sales, marketing and category management professionals to the consumer products industry, nationwide and at all levels of expertise.
Functions: Generalist, Senior mgmt., Middle mgmt., Mkt. research, Mktg. mgmt., Sales mgmt., Systems implem.
Industries: Food/bev/tobacco, Hospitality

Matthews Professional Employment Specialists, Inc.

321 Grand Ave.
Waukegan, Illinois 60085
(847) 244-6500
Web: skdixon@sprynet.com

Key Contact - Specialty:
Ms. Susan K. Dixon

Description: Contingency professional/ technical and support staff search and placement.

Branches:
311 E. Park Ave.
Libertyville, Illinois 60048
(847) 367-1117
Key Contact - Specialty:
Ms. Pauline Server

505 N. Wolf Rd.
Wheeling, Illinois 60090
(847) 215-0060
Key Contact - Specialty:
Mr. Paul Pirocanac

G. P. Mattocks & Associates
5015 Country Club Dr. N.
Wilson, North Carolina 27896-9123
(252) 399-0589
Fax: (252) 291-8467
Email: gpmattocks@bbnp.com
Web: www.ipa.com/eoffice/800-754-8129.html

Key Contact - Specialty:
Mr. Paul Mattocks - *Rubber, plastics, metal (technical & management)*

Description: We are a privately owned and operated search firm that works exclusively for our client companies. In addition to searching, recruiting, screening and qualifying candidates, we can tailor to their needs.

Salary Minimum: $35,000
Functions: Middle mgmt., Product dev., Plant mgmt., Quality, Productivity, Purchasing, Engineering
Industries: Plastics/rubber, Metal products

Maximum Management Corp.
230 Park Ave., Ste. 635
New York, New York 10169
(212) 867-4646
Fax: (212) 682-4882
Email: mmc@maxmanhr.com

Key Contact - Specialty:
Ms. Melissa Brophy - *Human resources*
Ms. Nancy Shield - *Human resources*

Description: A human resource consulting firm providing custom solutions to recruiting problems. We specialize in interim human resource services, search for human resource professionals, from entry level to executive.
Functions: Benefits, Personnel, Training
Industries: Generalist
Professional Associations: IACPR

Paul May & Assoc.
8 S. Michigan Ave., Ste. 2700
Chicago, Illinois 60606
(312) 649-8400
Fax: (312) 649-8999
Email: pma4jobs@computer-jobs.com
Web: www.computer-jobs.com

Key Contact - Specialty:
Mr. Paul May - *Technical information systems*

Description: Recruiting specialist for the Chicago land area. We specialize in information system professionals and software sales professionals at all levels.
Functions: IT, MIS mgmt., Systems anal., Systems dev., Systems implem., Network admin., DB admin.

Mayhall Search Group, Inc.
4410 Executive Blvd., Ste. 1A
Ft. Wayne, Indiana 46808
(219) 484-7770
Fax: (219) 482-9397
Email: dale@mayhall.com
Web: dale@mayhall.com

Key Contact - Specialty:
Mr. Dale Mayhall - *Engineering, sales*
Mr. Bob Harvey - *Manufacturing, quality control*
Mr. Bill Elrick - *Sales, engineering*
Ms. Jennifer Hammrick - *MIS*
Mr. Tom Howell - *Manufacturing*
Ms. Kathy Clawson - *Finance*

Description: Salaries from $50,000 to $150,000 in all major disciplines. We have done business with the majority of Fortune 500 companies.

Salary Minimum: $30,000
Functions: Senior mgmt., Plant mgmt., Materials Plng., Mktg. mgmt., Personnel, Credit, Systems dev.
Industries: Mfg., Plastics/rubber, Metal products, Consumer electronics, Finance, High tech, Software

MB Inc. Executive Search
505 Fifth Ave.
New York, New York 10017
(212) 661-4937
Fax: (212) 661-4939
Email: info@mbincexec.com
Web: www.mbincexec.com

Key Contact - Specialty:
Mr. Alan M. Levine - *Senior marketing, sales executives, general management, financial management*

Description: A national executive staffing resource for marketing, sales, financial and general management disciplines serving corporate and agency clients - consumer and industrial. Interim executive services to the marketing, sales and financial communities.

Salary Minimum: $50,000
Functions: Senior mgmt., Middle mgmt., Advertising, Mkt. research, Mktg. mgmt., Sales mgmt., PR
Industries: Generalist, Food/bev/tobacco, Textiles/apparel, Svcs., Pharmaceutical svcs., Mgmt. consulting, Advertising/PR

Affiliates:
MB - Interim Executive Services

Tom McCall Executive Search
20180 Governors Hwy., Ste. 100
Olympia Fields, Illinois 60461
(708) 747-5707
Email: tmccall@interaccess.com
Web: www.tmccall.com/

Key Contact - Specialty:
Ms. Jodi Stein - *Metal industries*
Mr. Tom McCall - *Metal & plastics industries*
Ms. Beverly Schoeling - *Metal industries*

Description: Consulting and recruiting for manufacturers and distributors of specialty fastener and electromechanical hardware products throughout the country as well as internationally. Salaries from $30,000 to $150,000 plus. Publishers of "Fastener People News."

Salary Minimum: $30,000
Functions: General mgmt., Mfg., Materials, Sales & mktg., HR mgmt., R&D, Engineering
Industries: Plastics/rubber, Machinery/ Appliances, Aerospace

McCarthy Assoc. National BancSearch, LLC
2727 Prytania St., Ste. 6, at The Rink
New Orleans, Louisiana 70130
(504) 897-6688
Fax: (504) 891-0102
Email: info@nationalbanksearch.com
Web: nationalbanksearch.com

Key Contact - Specialty:
Mr. Richard McCarthy - *Bank marketing, retail, commercial*
Mr. Bud Creech - *Bank, commercial lending, accounting, finance*
Ms. Molly Mahoney - *General banking*

Description: With integrity, credibility, utmost confidentiality, we identify, profile, present only top notch candidates matched to the needs of client companies and serve as invaluable liaison during the sensitive hiring process.
Functions: General mgmt., Sales & mktg., Finance
Industries: Finance, Banking, Invest. banking, Communications

The McCormick Group
4024 Plank Rd.
Fredericksburg, Virginia 22407-4800
(540) 786-9777
Fax: (540) 786-9355

Key Contact - Specialty:
Mr. William J. McCormick - *Generalist*
Mr. Brian D. McCormick - *Generalist*
Mr. W. Lyles Carr, III - *Legal*

Description: Established in Washington, D.C. in 1974 to become the most effective executive search service in America: offices in D.C., Boston and Kansas City provide national coverage.

Salary Minimum: $50,000
Functions: Mktg. mgmt., Sales mgmt., Benefits, Systems anal., Systems dev., Mgmt. consultants, Attorneys
Industries: Legal, Computer svcs., Mgmt. consulting, Communications, Insurance, High tech, Software

Branches:
20 Walnut St., Ste. 308
Wellesley Hills, Massachusetts 02181
(617) 239-1233
Fax: (617) 237-1054
Key Contact - Specialty:
Mr. Skip Hillen

1400 Wilson Blvd.
Arlington, Virginia 22209
(703) 841-1700
Fax: (703) 524-2689
Key Contact - Specialty:
Mr. Brian D. McCormick

McCormick Search Inc.
1111 Plaza Drive, Ste. 520
Schaumburg, Illinois 60173
(847) 755-9834
Fax: (847) 755-9835
Email: itopport@aol.com
Web: www.xnet.com/~itopport

Key Contact - Specialty:
Mr. Jim McCormick - *Information technology (executives), managers, senior technical professionals, information technology executive consultants*

Description: We are dedicated to helping our clients attain competitive advantage by recruiting best-in-class computer systems executives, managerial and technical candidates. We help you attract and retain people you need to get ahead and stay ahead.

Salary Minimum: $100,000
Functions: Sales mgmt., MIS mgmt., Mgmt. consultants
Industries: Software

McCoy Ltd.
3705 Beacon Ave., Ste. 200
Fremont, California 94538-1413
(510) 745-7700
Fax: (510) 745-8663
Email: bob@mccoyltd.com
Web: www.mccoyltd.com

Key Contact - Specialty:
Mr. Bob Walker - *Hardware, software*
Mr. John R. McNally - *Software, hardware*
Mr. Eric Baxley - *Software*
Mr. Benjamin Dicicco - *Telecommunications*

Description: We are a full service executive search firm specializing in all facets of hardware, software and MIS for the high tech industry.

Salary Minimum: $35,000
Functions: General mgmt., Mfg., Quality, Sales & mktg., IT, Systems dev., Engineering
Industries: Computer equip., Computer svcs., High tech, Software

Branches:
22916 Lyons Ave., Ste. 1C
Newhall, California 91321
(805) 287-9262
Fax: (805) 287-4412
Email: james@mccoyltd.com
Key Contact - Specialty:
Mr. James Brandle - *Hardware, software*

616 Stevens Ave., Ste. B
Solana Beach, California 92075
(619) 350-1117
Fax: (619) 350-1158
Email: daniel@mccoyltd.com
Key Contact - Specialty:
Mr. Daniel P. Loftus - *Hardware, software*

The Paul McDaniel Co.
P.O. Box 381672
Memphis, Tennessee 38183
(901) 757-9220
Fax: (901) 758-1111

Key Contact - Specialty:
Mr. Paul McDaniel - *Supermarket, wholesale grocery distributors, food service distributors*

Description: Over 20 years successfully recruiting for companies in categories previously listed. Excellent industry reputation.
Functions: General mgmt., Middle mgmt., Materials, Distribution, HR mgmt., Benefits, Training
Industries: Transportation, Wholesale, Retail

Earl L. McDermid & Assoc.
P.O. Box 6202
Buffalo Grove, Illinois 60089
(847) 541-9066
Fax: (847) 537-5381

Key Contact - Specialty:
Mr. Earl McDermid - *Food service*
Mr. W. John McGinnis - *Food service*

Description: A specialized executive search firm working in the business and industry, vending, healthcare, schools, colleges, food/equipment manufacturers and distributors segments of the hospitality industry.

Salary Minimum: $25,000
Functions: Generalist
Industries: Food/bev/tobacco, Hospitality, Entertainment

McDowell & Co., Recruiters
6116 N. Central Expwy #200
Dallas, Texas 75206
(214) 373-0045
Fax: (214) 373-0059
Email: jmc21@flash.net
Web: www.mcdowell-co.com

Key Contact - Specialty:
Mr. John McDowell - *Data communications, telecommunications, networking, information technology, computer software*

Description: We strive to provide our clients a quality not quantity approach in todays fast paced business environment. Time is the most valuable asset that we offer.
Functions: Sales mgmt., MIS mgmt., Systems implem., Systems support, Network admin., DB admin., Engineering
Industries: Hospitality, Computer svcs., Telecoms, High tech, Software

McInturff & Assoc., Inc.
209 G West Central St.
Natick, Massachusetts 01760
(781) 237-0220
Fax: (508) 653-1418
Email: bob@mcinturff.com

Key Contact - Specialty:
Mr. Robert E. McInturff - *Materials, manufacturing, logistics*

Description: Over twenty years as specialists in materials and manufacturing management. Our firm staffed by professionals who bring in-depth knowledge to your unique requirements.

Salary Minimum: $50,000
Functions: Product dev., Production, Plant mgmt., Quality, Purchasing, Materials Plng., Distribution
Industries: Food/bev/tobacco, Paper, Chemicals, Medical devices, Machinery/Appliances, Consumer electronics, Misc. mfg.

McIntyre Management Resources
1030 Upper James St., Ste. 301
Hamilton, Ontario L9C 6X6
Canada
(905) 574-6765
Fax: (905) 574-5025
Email: info@mcintyremgmt.com
Web: www.mcintyremgmt.com

Key Contact - Specialty:
Ms. Marlene McIntyre - *Information technology, executives all markets*

Description: Best known for partnering with clients, establishing in depth, long term relationships. Relationships may be by industry specialty or position/equipment specialty.

Salary Minimum: $40,000
Functions: Senior mgmt., Product dev., Production, Purchasing, Training, CFO's, MIS mgmt.
Industries: Construction, Food/bev/tobacco, Textiles/apparel, Lumber/furniture, Wholesale, Hospitality, Entertainment

---

McKavis Assoc.
2315 Caringa Way, Ste. 52
Carlsbad, California 92009
(760) 931-1292
(800) 800-0046
Fax: (760) 931-0016
Web: www.quikpage.com/A/adelmc

Key Contact - Specialty:
Ms. Adel McKavis - *Occupational medicine, managed care*
Ms. Margaret Pirnack - *Occupational medicine, managed care*
Mr. Bruce Cuthbert - *Administration, managed care*

Description: Executive recruiting in the field of occupational medicine and managed care. Working with corporations, clinics and hospitals placing physicians, physician assistants, nurse practitioners and COHNs within the field of occupational medicine.
Functions: Physicians, Nurses, Health admin.
Industries: Healthcare

McKee Cyber Search
P.O. Box 1751
Pascagoula, Mississippi 39568
(228) 497-1845
Email:
mckeecybersearch@mindspring.com
Web: www.mckeesearch.com

Key Contact - Specialty:
Mr. Edward F. McKee - *High technology product sales, engineering design, programmers, systems analysts*

Description: Search for design engineers and sales persons (limited to high technology products).

Salary Minimum: $75,000
Functions: Product dev., Production, Sales mgmt., Systems anal., Systems dev., Systems implem., Network admin.
Industries: Energy/utilities, Mfg., Communications, Environmental svcs., Aerospace, High tech, Software

---

The McKinnon Management Group Inc.
5160 Yonge St., Ste. 700
North York, Ontario M2N 6L9
Canada
(416) 250-6763
Fax: (416) 250-6916
Email: info@mckinnon.com
Web: www.mckinnon.com

Key Contact - Specialty:
Mr. Greg McKinnon - *Sales & marketing*
Mr. Cyril Plummer - *Financial*
Mr. Chris Bradshaw - *High technology*

Description: Executive search firm focusing on leading edge business enterprise placing sales, marketing and healthcare professionals throughout North America.
Functions: Senior mgmt., Mktg. mgmt., Direct mktg., Cash mgmt., Risk mgmt., Systems dev., Systems support
Industries: Printing, Finance, Publishing, Telecoms, Packaging, High tech, Healthcare

---

William K. McLaughlin Assoc., Inc.
P.O. Box 10308
Rochester, New York 14610-0308
(716) 442-3094
Fax: (716) 442-8587
Email: information@wkmclaughlin.com
Web: www.wkmclaughlin.com

Key Contact - Specialty:
Mr. William K. McLaughlin - *Patent attorney*
Mr. John F. McLaughlin - *Patent attorney*

Description: We have assisted patent attorneys in finding positions with the leading law firms and corporations throughout the United States.

Salary Minimum: $60,000
Functions: Attorneys
Industries: Legal

Branches:
705 North St.
Boulder, Colorado 80304
(303) 545-0014
Fax: (303) 545-0207
Key Contact - Specialty:
Ms. Patricia A. McLaughlin - *Patent attorney*

Dan P. McLean Assoc., Inc.
RR 4
Tottenham, Ontario L0G 1W0
Canada
(905) 880-4724
Fax: (905) 880-2651
Email: dmclean284@aol.com

Key Contact - Specialty:
Mr. Dan P. McLean - *High technology (programmer analysts to presidents)*
Ms. Luella McLean - *High technology (programmer analysts to presidents)*
Mr. Bob Springstein - *High technology (programmer analysts to presidents)*
Mrs. Paula Dermott - *High technology (programmer analysts to presidents)*
Mr. Roy Willcocks - *High technology (programmer analysts to presidents)*

Description: Formed to provide professional services including executive search, lease-a-professional and sales/ management consulting to high technology companies - programmer analysts to presidents.

Salary Minimum: $40,000
Functions: Directors, Senior mgmt., Middle mgmt., Mktg. mgmt., Sales mgmt., IT, Engineering
Industries: Computer equip., Test/ measurement equip., Finance, Computer svcs., Mgmt. consulting, High tech, Software

Affiliates:
XY Corp. Inc.

McPherson Square Assoc., Inc.
1025 Connecticut Ave. NW, Ste. 1012
Washington, District of Columbia 20036
(202) 737-8777
Fax: (202) 364-0066

Key Contact - Specialty:
Mr. Ronald G. Russell - *Attorney placement*

Description: Specializing in placement of partners and groups with law firms and law firm mergers. Corporate legal placement.

Salary Minimum: $140,000
Functions: Attorneys
Industries: Legal

McRoberts & Assoc.
36437 South Reserve Circle
Avon, Ohio 44011
(440) 934-4742
Fax: (440) 934-4742

Key Contact - Specialty:
Mr. C. F. McRoberts - *Engineering*

Description: Generalists with emphasis on technical searches. We have proven to our clients that we can fill those difficult assignments.

Salary Minimum: $40,000
Functions: Generalist
Industries: Generalist

Joseph J. McTaggart
5710 Arapaho Drive
San Jose, California 95123-3202
(408) 226-3203
Email: mct@sirius.com

Key Contact - Specialty:
Mr. Joseph J. McTaggart - *Upper level management & supporting staff*

Description: Solo practitioner. 100% search. No time limit guarantee. Candidate is guaranteed to earn you a profit or I replace. Specialty: general manager and supporting high level staff. Serving a potpourri of industries throughout the USA.

Salary Minimum: $100,000
Functions: Directors, Senior mgmt., Middle mgmt., Advertising, Engineering
Industries: Generalist, Computer equip., Consumer electronics, Communications, Advertising/PR, New media

MDR & Associates
11 Ontur Lane
Hot Springs Village, Arkansas 71909
(501) 915-0244
(800) 264-9701
Fax: (501) 915-0240
Email: MRobinson@hsnp.com

Key Contact - Specialty:
Mr. Mel Robinson - *Manufacturing, engineering, hospitality, industrial, real estate*

Description: We are very client oriented...we try to walk the extra mile to find the exact person described by the client. By doing this we have developed a very good client list. Companies call us when they have a search. We treat both clients and candidates with equal respect.

Salary Minimum: $45,000
Functions: IT, Engineering
Industries: Hospitality

MDR Associates, Inc.
9485 Sunset Drive, Ste. A270
Miami, Florida 33173
(305) 271-9213
Fax: (305) 274-1053
Email: mdrsearch.com
Web: www.mdrsearch.com

Key Contact - Specialty:
Ms. Judith E. Berger
Mr. Stephen G. Schoen

Description: A retainer firm specializing in the recruitment of physicians, physician managers and executives for the healthcare industry. Practice emphasis on medical groups, single and multispecialty groups, HMO's and hospitals, nationwide.

Salary Minimum: $80,000
Functions: Physicians, Nurses, Health admin.
Industries: Healthcare

Branches:
12774 Flat Meadow Lane
Herndon, Virginia 22071
(703) 620-9475
Key Contact - Specialty:
Mr. Michael E. Kurtz

Med Exec Int'l.
100 N. Brand Blvd., Ste. 306-8
Glendale, California 90213
(818) 552-2036
Fax: (818) 552-2475
Email: rosechristopher@sprintmail.com
Web: www.medexecintl.com

Key Contact - Specialty:
Ms. Rosemarie Christopher - *Technical, medical device, pharmaceutical*

Description: We provide customized search services to clients from the medical device and pharmaceutical industries who entrust their searches for regulatory affairs, clinical research and quality professionals to our care.
Functions: Directors, Senior mgmt., Middle mgmt., Plant mgmt., Quality, MIS mgmt.
Industries: Medical devices, Pharmaceutical svcs., Biotech

Med-Ex Services
5000 Rockside Rd., #100
Independence, Ohio 44131
(216) 573-1130
Fax: (216) 573-0727
Email: med-ex@stratos.net

Key Contact - Specialty:
Ms. Karin E. Deffler - *Medical (clerical & clinical)*

Description: Permanent and temporary medical/healthcare staffing with hospitals, clinics, doctors, dentists, labs, MCOs, PPOs, HMOs and more. If it's healthcare-related we will fill the position.
Functions: Healthcare, Physicians, Nurses, Allied health, Health admin., Mkt. research, Sales mgmt.
Industries: Healthcare

Branches:
445 Griswold Rd., #C
Elyria, Ohio 44035
(440) 324-6000
Fax: (440) 324-6003
Key Contact - Specialty:
Mr. Naz Nour

Medfall Inc.
6150 Valley Way, Ste. 207
Niagara Falls, Ontario L2E 1Y3
Canada
(905) 357-6644
Fax: (905) 357-2601
Email: mstoll@niagara.com

Key Contact - Specialty:
Dr. Patrick Gibney - *Physician, healthcare executives*
Ms. Joan Stoll - *Physician, healthcare executives*

Description: All of our consultants are medical professionals with a unique understanding of the goals and requirements of our clients. Our objective, evidence based search and screening process ensures quality and compatibility.

Salary Minimum: $80,000
Functions: Healthcare, Physicians, Health admin.
Industries: Healthcare

Media Recruiting Group, Inc.
One Bridge St., Ste. P2
Irvington, New York 10533
(914) 591-5511
Fax: (914) 591-8911
Email: steve@mediarecruitinggroup.com
Web: mediarecruitinggroup.com

Key Contact - Specialty:
Ms. Risa Goldberg - *Magazine publishing, ad sales, marketing, promotion*
Mr. Steve Goldberg - *Magazine publishing, circulation, consumer marketing, database marketing, new media, direct marketing, continuity*

Description: We recruit for companies in the magazine publishing and direct marketing industries. As a former advertising sales manager and chief financial officer, we have built our firm on sending candidates appropriate to each clients' specific needs for positions primarily on the business side of the masthead.

Salary Minimum: $30,000
Functions: Senior mgmt., Advertising, Mktg. mgmt., Sales mgmt., Direct mktg., PR, Finance
Industries: Entertainment, Communications, Advertising/PR, Publishing, New media, Broadcast & Film

MediaCOM Talent Group
155 Elysium St., Ste. 200
Wrentham, Massachusetts 02093
(508) 384-3682
Fax: (508) 384-3956

Email: talent@earthlink.net

Key Contact - Specialty:
Mr. Joseph Curry - *Multimedia, internet, software, biotech, telecommunications*
Mr. Wilfrid Ertaud - *Multimedia, internet, software, telecommunications*

Salary Minimum: $40,000
Functions: General mgmt., IT, R&D, Engineering, Graphic artists
Industries: New media, Telecoms, High tech, Software, Biotech

Medical Executive Recruiters
1220 Melody Lane, Ste. 106
Roseville, California 95678
(916) 786-8615
Fax: (916) 786-8609
Email: medexec@pacbell.net

Key Contact - Specialty:
Mr. John Cunningham - *Medical, software*
Ms. Kandi Williams - *Medical, biotechnology, biopharmaceutical*

Description: Our firm specializes in recruiting qualified sales, marketing and management candidates for the medical and technology industries nationwide.

Salary Minimum: $50,000
Functions: Mkt. research, Mktg. mgmt., Sales mgmt.
Industries: Medical devices, Software, Biotech, Healthcare

Medical Executive Search Assoc., Inc.
3250 N. Riverbend Circle E.
Tucson, Arizona 85750
(888) 884-2550
(520) 885-2552
Fax: (520) 885-2542
Email: wlp@mesaworldwide.com
Web: www.mesaworldwide.com

Key Contact - Specialty:
Mr. William L. Piatkiewicz - *Medical devices, biotech, pharmaceuticals*
Mrs. Mary Lou Piatkiewicz - *Medical devices, biotech, pharmaceuticals*

Description: Fourteen years of recruitment in the medical device industry, representing over several thousand contacts within that industry.

Salary Minimum: $30,000
Functions: General mgmt., Mfg., Product dev., Materials, Sales & mktg., R&D, Engineering
Industries: Drugs mfg., Medical devices, Plastics/rubber, Test/measurement equip., High tech, Biotech, Healthcare

Medical Innovations
605 Village Lane, P.O. Box 224
Orient, New York 11957
(516) 323-3899
(516) 477-0338
Fax: (516) 477-0337
Web: medinnov@aol.com

Key Contact - Specialty:
Ms. Carol Martin - *Medical sales, management, marketing, product development*

Description: Our specialty is placement in reputable healthcare manufacturers whose products are considered cutting edge technology. This is achieved only in an ethical, professional and compassionate process.

Salary Minimum: $60,000
Functions: Advertising, Mkt. research, Mktg. mgmt., Sales mgmt.
Industries: Drugs mfg., Medical devices, Computer equip., Pharmaceutical svcs., Computer svcs.

Medical Recruiters Exchange
980 W. Paseo del Cilantro
Green Valley, Arizona 85614
(520) 648-5612
Fax: (520) 648-5409
Web: azchaz@webtv.net

Key Contact - Specialty:
Mr. Charles L. Gaudette - *Physicians, nurses, senior administrators*

Description: Recruiting physican specialties: int., FP, OB/Gyn, ped., gas., ger. and others. All nurse specialties. Senior administrators only (no entry level).

Salary Minimum: $30,000
Functions: Physicians, Nurses, Allied health, Health admin., Mgmt. consultants
Industries: Mgmt. consulting, Healthcare

Medical Recruiters Inc.
12400 Olive Blvd., Ste. 555
St. Louis, Missouri 63141
(314) 275-4466
Fax: (314) 523-4566

Key Contact - Specialty:
Heidi Oberman - *Medical sales, sales management, RNs, clinical, consumer sales*
Denise Wottowa - *Medical sales, sales management, RNs, clinical, consumer sales*

Description: Specialists in medical sales and sales management placement.
Functions: Middle mgmt., Nurses, Sales mgmt., Minorities
Industries: Food/bev/tobacco, Paper, Drugs mfg., Medical devices, Computer equip., Pharmaceutical svcs., Healthcare

Medical Search of America, Inc.
P.O. Box 1716
Duluth, Georgia 30096
(770) 232-0530
(800) 523-1351
Fax: (770) 232-0610

Key Contact - Specialty:
Mr. Charles R. Sikes - *Physicians, administrative, allied health*
Ms. Laurie L. Sikes - *Physicians, allied health*

Description: Multi-faceted national healthcare search firm specializing in placement of medical professionals.
Functions: Healthcare, Physicians, Nurses, Allied health, Health admin.
Industries: Healthcare

Medicorp, Inc.
1000 Lake St. Louis Blvd., Ste. 223
Lake St. Louis, Missouri 63367
(314) 625-8700
Fax: (314) 625-8711
Email: jack@medicorpinc.com
Web: www.medicorpinc.com

Key Contact - Specialty:
Mr. Jack Johnson - *Physicians*
Ms. Madison Grace - *Physicians*

Description: An established professional contingency physician and mid level placement firm with a diverse worldwide clientele offering full time and locums placement. Everyone of our consultants are specialists in their field.

Salary Minimum: $90,000
Functions: Physicians, Nurses, Health admin., Personnel
Industries: Human resource svcs., Healthcare

The Medley Group
6351 Wilshire Blvd., Ste. 206
Los Angeles, California 90048
(323) 651-3252
Fax: (323) 651-3151
Email: jmedleygrp@aol.com
Web: members.aol.com/jmedleygrp/company.htm

Key Contact - Specialty:
Mr. Jerry Medley - *Diversity, sales, marketing, finance & accounting*

Description: We are a general practice executive search firm with expertise in diversity recruitment, sales, marketing, accounting and finance.

Salary Minimum: $80,000
Functions: Generalist, Senior mgmt., Mktg. mgmt., Sales mgmt., HR mgmt., Finance, CFO's

Industries: Energy/utilities, Invest. banking, Entertainment, Accounting, Communications, Broadcast & Film

MedPro Personnel, Inc.
1955 Cliff Valley Way, Ste. 116
Atlanta, Georgia 30329
(404) 633-8280
Fax: (404) 633-9856
Email: med.pro@mindspring.com

Key Contact - Specialty:
Ms. Marilyn Feingold - *Medical*

Description: We place medical personnel in hospitals, clinics and physician practices. We work with clerical and clinical staff in permanent, temp to hire and permanent positions.
Functions: Nurses, Health admin.
Industries: Healthcare

MedQuest Assoc.
9250 E. Costilla Ave., Ste. 600
Englewood, Colorado 80112
(303) 790-2009
Fax: (303) 790-2021
Email: cannfitz@aol.com

Key Contact - Specialty:
Ms. Judy Stiles - *Medical devices*

Description: Recruitment of sales, sales management, product management, engineering/research and development, marketing management. General management in medical product industries.

Salary Minimum: $30,000
Functions: Production, Quality, Packaging, Mkt. research, Sales mgmt., R&D, Engineering
Industries: Drugs mfg., Medical devices, Pharmaceutical svcs., Biotech

MedSearch Resources, Inc.
6503 N. Military Trail, Ste. 806
Boca Raton, Florida 33496
(561) 995-6803
Fax: (561) 995-0104

Key Contact - Specialty:
Mr. Douglas I. Glick - *Executives, CEO, COO, vice presidents, CFO, Physicians*
Ms. Francine C. Kaye - *General management, allied health, administration, information technology*

Description: Executive and professional search firm specializing in the healthcare industry. Our clients include hospitals, HMO's, managed care organizations, pharmaceutical and biotechnology companies, physician practice management companies and healthcare suppliers.

Salary Minimum: $50,000
Functions: Directors, Senior mgmt., Middle mgmt., Allied health, Health admin., CFO's, MIS mgmt.
Industries: Generalist, Drugs mfg., Medical devices, Pharmaceutical svcs., Biotech, Healthcare

Medserve & Assoc. Inc.
20 St. Andrews Rd.
Severna Park, Maryland 21146
(888) Staffer
(410) 729-4155
Fax: (410) 987-0793
Email: medserve1@aol.com
Web: www.medserve.net

Key Contact - Specialty:
Mr. Sal Eren - *Physicians, allied health*

Description: Healthcare staffing specialist - both nationwide and international staffing.
Functions: Physicians, Nurses, Allied health
Industries: Human resource svcs., Healthcare

MedXec USA, Inc.
1701 W. Hillsboro Blvd., Ste. 102
Deerfield Beach, Florida 33442
(954) 360-9980
Fax: (954) 425-0975
Email: medxecusa@mindspring.com
Web: www.medxecusa.com

Key Contact - Specialty:
Mr. Richard L. Myers - *Home healthcare senior executives*
Mr. Gregory L. Greenland - *Medical staffing companies senior executives*
Ms. Dana L. Lihan - *Home healthcare, clinical, QA executives*
Ms. Marilyn Handler - *Medical staffing companies, clinical managers*

Description: Full service contingent recruiting firm exclusively serving the home healthcare and ambulatory industries.

Salary Minimum: $30,000
Functions: General mgmt., Healthcare, Sales & mktg., HR mgmt., Finance, IT
Industries: Healthcare

Branches:
111 S. Broad St., #206
Lancaster, Ohio 43130
(740) 681-9920
Fax: (740) 681-9935
Email: tempxecusa@fairfieldi
Web: www.tempexecusa.com
Key Contact - Specialty:
Mr. Kyle A. Smith - *Healthcare financial executives*

Mee Derby & Co.
1522 K St. NW, Ste. 704
Washington, District of Columbia 20005
(202) 842-8442
(800) 597-8442
Fax: (202) 842-1900
Email: meederby@msn.com

Key Contact - Specialty:
Ms. Robin Mee - *Staffing industry*

Description: We specialize in placing recruiters, sales and management professionals in the staffing industry, staffing includes: outsourcing, IT services, administrative support and professional services.
Functions: Senior mgmt., Middle mgmt., Sales mgmt., HR mgmt.
Industries: Computer svcs., Human resource svcs.

Affiliates:
Jill Balick
Irene Nichols

Mehta Consulting
438 Rte. 35 N., Ste. 1306
Mantoloking, New Jersey 08738
(732) 793-0108
Fax: (732) 793-9599
Email: nkmehta@aol.com

Key Contact - Specialty:
Mr. Narinder K. Mehta - *Credit risk management, collection operations, sales*

Description: We are managed by a seasoned professional in the credit industry. We specialize in credit risk management, collection operations, and sales positions in the credit industry.

Salary Minimum: $50,000
Functions: Sales mgmt., Credit, Risk mgmt., Systems support
Industries: Finance, Banking, Invest. banking, Brokers, Telecoms

Juan Menefee & Assoc.
503 S. Oak Park Ave., Ste. 206
Oak Park, Illinois 60304
(708) 848-7722
Email: jmenefee@jmarecruiter.com
Web: www.jmarecruiter.com

Key Contact - Specialty:
Mr. Juan F. Menefee

Description: We are a minority owned and operated full service search firm. We specialize in the recruitment of minority professionals.

Salary Minimum: $35,000
Functions: Generalist, Directors, Advertising, Sales mgmt., Personnel, Engineering, Minorities

Industries: Energy/utilities, Food/bev/tobacco, Finance, Communications, High tech, Healthcare

Mengel & McDonald Ltd.

360 W. Erie St., Ste. B
Chicago, Illinois 60610
(312) 266-0581

Key Contact - Specialty:
Mr. Thomas W. McDonald - *Advertising, marketing*

Description: National executive search specializing in senior-level advertising professionals. Consulting and outplacement on a project basis. Both account and creative agency professionals.

Salary Minimum: $50,000
Functions: Generalist, Senior mgmt., Advertising, Direct mktg., Mgmt. consultants, Graphic artists
Industries: Generalist, Advertising/PR, New media, Broadcast & Film

J. M. Meredith & Assoc. Inc.

2240 N. Rodeo Gulch Rd.
Soquel, California 95073
(408) 479-7522
Fax: (408) 479-7529
Email: imjmm@aol.com

Key Contact - Specialty:
Mr. Ira Alan Marks - *High technology, semiconductor, capital equipment, electron beam*

Description: Twenty year old firm. Executive search in all areas of hi-tech. We will be happy to supply a list of references.

Salary Minimum: $80,000
Functions: Directors, Senior mgmt., Middle mgmt., Sales mgmt., Systems dev., R&D, Engineering
Industries: Chemicals, Medical devices, Computer equip., Test/measurement equip., Aerospace, High tech, Software

Meridian Legal Search/Legal Temps

25 W. 43rd St., Ste. 700
New York, New York 10036
(212) 354-9300
Fax: (212) 921-1127
Email: MeridianLW@aol.com

Key Contact - Specialty:
Joel Berger - *Attorneys, permanent and temporary*

Description: Attorney recruitment organization (founded 1936)-corporate law firm, not-for-profit clients. Discreet representation of clients on a contingent or retainer basis. Computerized research and targeted recruiting of credentialed and high achieving attorney candidates at all levels.

Salary Minimum: $50,000
Functions: Attorneys
Industries: Energy/utilities, Construction, Food/bev/tobacco, Textiles/apparel, Lumber/furniture, Paper

Affiliates:
Bellon & Assoc., Inc.
Sandler & Lashaw Legal Search, Inc.

Meridian Resources

1425 E. Dublin-Granville Rd., Ste. 216
Columbus, Ohio 43229
(614) 846-3124
Fax: (614) 846-3197
Email: meridianr@aol.com

Key Contact - Specialty:
Mr. Jon Joffe - *Healthcare*
Mr. Brad McLaughlin - *Healthcare, finance*

Description: We specialize in mid to senior level positions working primarily with physician groups, hospitals, practice management companies and health maintenance organizations. This firm is nationally known in the healthcare community for quick response and courteous service.

Salary Minimum: $60,000
Functions: Healthcare, Health admin., Finance, CFO's, Budgeting, Cash mgmt., Risk mgmt.

Merit Professional Search, Inc.

P.O. Box 10
Ardmore, Tennessee 38449
(615) 427-8850
Fax: (615) 427-8847

Key Contact - Specialty:
Mr. Jim Smitherman - *Meat, poultry, food (further processed)*
Mr. Ronald Daffala - *Meat, poultry, food (further processed)*

Description: We work with all the major companies in the meat/poultry and food related industries. Place people in management, operations, accounting, safety, personnel, R&D, quality control, sanitation, marketing, sales, engineering and maintenance.

Salary Minimum: $20,000
Functions: Senior mgmt., Middle mgmt., Production, Plant mgmt., Quality, Purchasing, Packaging
Industries: Food/bev/tobacco

Merlin Int'l. Inc.

P.O. Box 313
Ramsey, New Jersey 07446
(201) 825-7220
Fax: (201) 825-1043
Email: merlint@att.net
Web: merlint.com

Key Contact - Specialty:
Mr. V. James Cinquina, Jr. - *Physicians*
Mr. Alan Fitzpatrick - *Medical advertising, marketing, business development*

Description: Highly specialized firm. Devoted exclusively to all pharmaceutical and biotechnology, research and development. Clinical research physicians and staff. Pharmaceutical marketing and advertising services, domestic and international.

Salary Minimum: $50,000
Functions: Physicians, Advertising, Mkt. research, Direct mktg., R&D
Industries: Drugs mfg., Pharmaceutical svcs., Advertising/PR, Healthcare

Merrick & Moore
(a division of Borton Wallace Co.)

P.O. Box 8816
Asheville, North Carolina 28814
(704) 258-1831
Fax: (704) 251-0989
Email: merrickmoore@juno.com

Key Contact - Specialty:
Mr. Murray B. Parker

Description: Contingency firm emphasizing direct recruiting within paper, nonwovens and supplier fields utilizing database materials developed since 1978.

Salary Minimum: $40,000
Functions: Product dev., Automation, Packaging, HR mgmt., Finance, R&D, Engineering
Industries: Food/bev/tobacco, Paper, Chemicals, Finance, Packaging

Branches:
2450 Pelican Court, 101Q
Clearwater, Florida 33762
(813) 572-9359
Key Contact - Specialty:
Mr. Don Lewis
Nancy Lewis

MES Search Co.

4526 Chelton Court SE
Smyrna, Georgia 30080-6901
(770) 437-8222
Fax: (770) 805-0679
Email: messearch@mindspring.com
Web: messearch.home.mindspring.com

Key Contact - Specialty:
Mr. James O. Cox - *Manufacturing, industrial services, high technology*

Description: Search services for manufacturing, industrial services and high technology. Positions filled include upper and middle level management, staff and individual level producers in engineering and sales and other significant level achievers.

Salary Minimum: $40,000

Functions: Generalist, Senior mgmt., Middle mgmt., Mfg., Sales & mktg., R&D, Engineering
Industries: Generalist, Mfg., Telecoms, High tech, Biotech

MESA International

7777 Greenback Lane, Ste. 100A
Citrus Heights, California 95610
(916) 729-7700
Fax: (916) 729-1135
Email: mesa@mesaint.com
Web: mesaint.com

Key Contact - Specialty:
Mr. Ken McCollum - *Rigid & flexible packaging, capital machinery, international manufacturing*
Mr. Ron Krenz - *Corrugated & paperboard packaging, flexible packaging*
Ms. Meri Masters - *Computer information technology*
Mr. Jim L. Dixon - *Computer hardware, software engineering*

Description: A full service firm with a well-established record of mid and senior level search assignment completions. Clients include: Reynolds Metals, Sonoco, Boise Cascade, Hunt Wesson, IBM, Intel, Levi Strauss, Best Buy, Disney Stores.

Salary Minimum: $35,000
Functions: General mgmt., Mfg., Sales & mktg., IT, R&D, Engineering, Int'l.
Industries: Food/bev/tobacco, Textiles/apparel, Metal products, Retail, Entertainment, Packaging, High tech

Branches:
679 E. Harbor Drive, Ste. L
P.O. Box 969
Warrenton, Oregon 97146
(800) 291-7830
(503) 861-9878
Fax: (503) 861-9893
Email: rbe@seasurf.net
Key Contact - Specialty:
Mr. Bruce Ericksen - *Senior retail, entertainment, inventory management & replenishment*
Ms. Linda Ericksen - *Retail (merchants, senior buying positions)*
Mr. Chris Womack - *Retail, information systems*

MetroVantage Personnel Systems

30101 Town Center Drive, Ste. 140
Laguna Niguel, California 92677
(949) 249-8885
Fax: (949) 249-8886
Email: info@metrovantage.com
Web: www.metrovantage.com

Key Contact - Specialty:
Mr. Benson D. Garfinkle - *Technical, technical management, sales*
Ms. Gayle Garren - *Temp, contract*
Mr. Robin Marsh - *Technical*
Mr. Bryan Roberts - *Technical*
Mr. Mark Carlson - *Sales*

Description: Specialize in high technology direct and temporary staffing.

Salary Minimum: $35,000
Functions: Middle mgmt., Product dev., Production, Automation, Quality, Sales mgmt.
Industries: High tech, Software

---

mfg/Search, Inc.

220 W. Colfax Ave., Ste. 600
South Bend, Indiana 46601
(219) 282-2547
Fax: (219) 232-0982
Email: mfgsearch@sprintmail.com
Web: www.mfgsearch.com

Key Contact - Specialty:
Mr. Howard Mueller - *Manufacturing*
Ms. Judith VanEs - *Manufacturing*
Ms. Christine Cuenca - *Manufacturing*
Ms. Lisa Watson - *Manufacturing*

Description: We are a retained fee search firm which provides a full range of key employees to its north American manufacturing clients.

Salary Minimum: $60,000
Functions: Generalist, General mgmt., Mfg., Sales & mktg., HR mgmt., Finance, Engineering
Industries: Mfg.

Branches:
3040 Charlevoix Drive SE, Ste. 101
Grand Rapids, Michigan 49546
(616) 285-4075
Key Contact - Specialty:
Mr. Stephen Hickel - *Manufacturing*

39111 W. Six Mile Rd.
Livonia, Michigan 48152
(734) 591-2331
Key Contact - Specialty:
Mr. Larry Voelker - *Manufacturing*

4027 Colonel Glenn Hwy., Ste. 400
Dayton, Ohio 45431
(937) 427-9705
Key Contact - Specialty:
Mr. William A. Zielazny - *Manufacturing*

MGA Executive Search

3000 Gulf to Bay Blvd., Ste. 503
Clearwater, Florida 33759
(813) 791-7890
(800) MGA-GRAY
Fax: (813) 724-8039
Email: clearwater@mgagray.com
Web: www.mgagray.com

Key Contact - Specialty:
Ms. Peggy Kivler

Description: Our mission is to provide timely, high quality and cost effective contingency search services when undertaking nationwide MIS technical and managerial recruiting assignments for our clients.

Salary Minimum: $55,000
Functions: MIS mgmt., Systems anal., Systems dev., Systems implem., Systems support
Industries: Energy/utilities, Misc. mfg., Finance, Aerospace, Insurance, High tech, Healthcare

---

Michael James & Co.

501 W. Main St.
St. Charles, Illinois 60174
(630) 351-6500
Fax: (630) 351-6573
Email: mjandco@enteract.com

Key Contact - Specialty:
Mr. Michael Anton - *Sales & management, technical contracting, information technology, engineering*

Description: We give retained search service on a contingent basis. We complete 87% of our searches in 40 days or less.

Salary Minimum: $50,000
Functions: Middle mgmt., Production, Sales mgmt., IT, Engineering
Industries: Drugs mfg., Medical devices

Michael Thomas, Inc.

100 Old Wilson Bridge Rd., Ste. 207
Worthington, Ohio 43085
(614) 846-0926
Fax: (614) 847-5633

Key Contact - Specialty:
Mr. Thomas Joswick - *Information technology*
Mr. Michael Beckerat - *Information technology*

Description: Central Ohio's oldest and largest specialist in information technology recruiting.

Salary Minimum: $30,000
Functions: MIS mgmt., Systems anal., Systems dev., Systems implem., Systems support, Network admin., DB admin.
Industries: Energy/utilities, Banking, Misc. financial, Computer svcs., Insurance, High tech, Software

---

Michael Wayne Recruiters

1491 Ridge Rd.
Highland Park, Illinois 60035
(847) 831-9344
Fax: (847) 831-9352

Email: mwrecruit@aol.com

Key Contact - Specialty:
Mr. Irwin Goldman - *Wholesale & retail food companies*

Description: Full range of services; preferred client status; national contacts in retail, food service, manufacturing and wholesale food segments.

Salary Minimum: $25,000
Functions: Middle mgmt., Purchasing, Distribution, Sales mgmt., Personnel
Industries: Food/bev/tobacco, Motor vehicles, Wholesale, Hospitality, Accounting, Human resource svcs.

Michael/Merrill

P.O. Box 7509
Shawnee Mission, Kansas 66207
(913) 383-9497
(800) 748-8177
Fax: (913) 383-2962

Key Contact - Specialty:
Mr. Wilson M. Liggett - *Generalist*

Description: A full service search firm.

Salary Minimum: $25,000
Functions: Production, Packaging, Sales mgmt., HR mgmt., MIS mgmt., Systems implem., Systems support
Industries: Food/bev/tobacco, Human resource svcs.

Michaels & Moere

P.O. Box 48
Jackson, Wisconsin 53037
(414) 338-6670
Fax: (414) 338-7923
Email: mnmgroup@hnet.net
Web: hnet.net/~mnmgroup

Key Contact - Specialty:
Mr. Michael R. Smith - *Operations, manufacturing, engineering, materials*
Ms. Linda A. Moere - *Sales, marketing*

Description: We offer a highly personalized and cooperative approach to the search process. We are very cost conscious and work in partnership with our clients to control recruiting costs while delivering timely service.

Salary Minimum: $50,000
Functions: General mgmt., Mfg., Materials, Sales & mktg., HR mgmt., Engineering
Industries: Lumber/furniture, Plastics/rubber, Metal products, Machinery/Appliances, Computer equip., Consumer electronics, Misc. mfg.

Lou Michaels Assoc., Inc.

1230 E. Columbia Ave.
Battle Creek, Michigan 49017
(616) 965-1486
Fax: (616) 965-2232

Key Contact - Specialty:
Mr. Lou Michaels - *Machining, foundry, diecast*
Ms. Brenda Nanney - *Metal stamp, metal fab, quality*
Mr. Randy Michaels - *Foundry*
Mr. Jerry Nanney - *Sales, accounting, program management*
Mr. Bill Roth - *Plastics, rubber*

Description: Engineering and industrial management personnel/manufacturing industries, automotive, plastics, foundry, die cast, metal working, aerospace, electronics, machining, metal fabrication, stamping, primary metals, medical plastics and automotive plastics.

Salary Minimum: $35,000
Functions: General mgmt., Mfg., Quality, Materials, HR mgmt., Finance, Engineering
Industries: Mfg., Medical devices, Plastics/rubber, Metal products, Motor vehicles, Misc. mfg.

E. J. Michaels, Ltd.

2 Madison Avenue, Ste. 201
Larchmont, New York 10538
(914) 833-1700
Fax: (914) 833-1711
Email: ejmsearch@aol.com
Web: www.ejmichaels.com

Key Contact - Specialty:
Phillip E. Jacobs - *Physicians, healthcare*

Description: Physician recruiting for hospitals, HMOs, general practices, corporate needs, pharmaceutical firms, individual practices. Recruiting for domestic and int'l. pharmaceutical firms.
Functions: Physicians, Nurses, Health admin., Systems anal., Mgmt. consultants, Non-profits
Industries: Pharmaceutical svcs., Mgmt. consulting, Healthcare

---

Micro Staff Solutions, Inc.

4004 Beltline Road, Ste. 210
Dallas, Texas 75244-2328
(972) 934-0272
Fax: (972) 788-1928
Email: mbsparks@mstaff.com
Web: www.mstaff.com

Key Contact - Specialty:
Ms. Michele Benum Sparks - *Data processing, telecommunications, sales, information technology*
Ms. Gina Lawrence - *Data processing, sales, telecommunications, information technology*

Description: An executive search firm that specializes in the placement of high tech professionals in a variety of industries. We place in both permanent and contract positions.

Salary Minimum: $30,000
Functions: Middle mgmt., Admin. svcs., Sales mgmt., MIS mgmt., Systems anal., Systems dev., Mgmt. consultants

---

Midas Management

191 Post Rd. W., Ste. 70
Westport, Connecticut 06880
(203) 221-2626
Fax: (203) 454-3959
Email: elaineb@midasmgt.com

Key Contact - Specialty:
Mr. Joel Berger - *Computer software & hardware sales management, sales representatives, information technology professionals*

Description: We have always specialized in the placement of all levels of sales, sales support and executives in the computer software and hardware industry.

Salary Minimum: $70,000
Functions: MIS mgmt., Systems anal., Systems dev., Systems implem., Systems support, Mgmt. consultants
Industries: Computer svcs., Mgmt. consulting, Software

Midland Consultants
(a division of Century Business Services)

4311 Ridge Rd.
Brooklyn, Ohio 44144
(216) 398-9330
Fax: (216) 398-0879
Email: midland@bright.net
Web: www.midlandconsultants.com

Key Contact - Specialty:
Mr. David J. Sgro - *Rubber, plastics, adhesives*

Description: Servicing the entire rubber, plastic, adhesive and packaging industries from sales through technical staffing. Specialties also include information systems and metal chip cutting.
Functions: General mgmt., Mfg., Materials, Sales & mktg., IT, R&D, Engineering
Industries: Printing, Chemicals, Plastics/rubber, Paints/petroleum products, Metal products, Computer svcs., Packaging

---

Miller & Assoc.

201 E. Kennedy Blvd., Ste. 1400
Tampa, Florida 33602
(813) 224-9658
Fax: (813) 221-7491

Key Contact - Specialty:
Ms. Dixie Miller - *Attorneys*

Description: We specialize exclusively in legal search, assisting law firms and corporations in associate, partner and in-house corporate placements.
Industries: Legal

Miller + Miller

P.O. Box 3088
Kirkland, Washington 98083
(425) 822-3145
Fax: (425) 827-9194
Web: millmill@worldnet.att.net

Key Contact - Specialty:
Ms. Shirley Miller - *Biotechnology, medical-related*

Description: Placement of executives, managers in all functions and technical specialists in companies that develop and support pharmaceutical, biotechnology and medical device products. We take great pride in providing value-added, confidential service.

Salary Minimum: $50,000
Functions: Senior mgmt., Middle mgmt., Product dev., Quality, Mkt. research, HR mgmt., R&D
Industries: Drugs mfg., Medical devices, Biotech

Susan C. Miller Assoc., Inc.

1090 Vermont Ave. NW, Ste. 800
Washington, District of Columbia 20005
(202) 408-6880
Fax: (202) 898-1915

Key Contact - Specialty:
Ms. Susan C. Miller - *Attorneys*
Ms. Anne Minor - *Attorneys*
Mr. Jared Sher - *Attorneys*

Description: We are the oldest, non-franchised, legal recruiting firm in Washington and one of the most established in the country. The firm received accolades in both the 1982 and 1988 AmLaw annual survey of the nation's leading legal recruiters.
Functions: Attorneys
Industries: Legal

Miller Denver

P.O. Box 340
Castle Rock, Colorado 80104-0340
(303) 688-6630
Fax: (303) 688-4334

Key Contact - Specialty:
Mr. Eric L. Miller - *Engineering, manufacturing*

Description: Manufacturing specialists recruiting engineers and technical management professionals for positions located in Colorado, the Rocky Mountain States and the Western U.S. since 1974.

Salary Minimum: $40,000
Functions: Mfg., Materials, IT, R&D, Engineering
Industries: Medical devices, Metal products, Machinery/Appliances, Computer equip., Consumer electronics, Test/measurement equip., Software

---

Miller-Hall HRISearch

50 Woodlawn Ave.
New Rochelle, New York 10804
(914) 834-9697
Fax: (914) 833-2353
Email: hrisearch@aol.com

Key Contact - Specialty:
Mr. Marc S. Miller - *Human resource information systems*

Description: We are the only nationwide search firm exclusively focused on HRIS (human resource information system) mid to high level positions. We will price your HRIS position using industry benchmarks, prepare your job description or job specifications and present pre-screened qualified candidates.

Salary Minimum: $50,000
Functions: Personnel, Systems anal., Mgmt. consultants
Industries: Generalist

Branches:
4533 McArthur Blvd., Ste. 571
Newport Beach, California 92660
(714) 831-1727
Fax: (714) 831-0860
Key Contact - Specialty:
Mr. Larry D. Hall - *Human resource information systems*

Miller/Davis & Assoc., Inc.

60 E. 42nd St., Ste. 1440
New York, New York 10165
(212) 682-8144
Fax: (212) 682-8218
Email: millerdavis@msn.com
Web: www.millerdavisny.com

Key Contact - Specialty:
Ms. Suzanne M. Johnson - *Corporate banking & corporate finance*

Description: Specialists in corporate banking/finance positions, analyst/associate to senior management; credit/lending in structured/project/public finance, international, Fortune 500, middle market, etc., in the New York metropolitan area.

Salary Minimum: $50,000
Functions: M&A
Industries: Finance, Banking, Invest. banking, Misc. financial, Real estate

---

Danette Milne Corporate Search Inc.

4981 Hwy. 7 E., Unit 12A, Ste. 205
Markham, Ontario L3R 1N1
Canada
(416) 410-1814
Fax: (905) 426-2552
Email: dmcs@sprint.ca

Key Contact - Specialty:
Ms. Danette Milne - *Human resources, sales, engineering, finance*
Ms. Carole Milne - *Administration, engineering*
Ms. Evette Milne - *Support, sales*

Salary Minimum: $30,000
Functions: Generalist, Production, Materials Plng., Sales mgmt., Personnel, Budgeting, Systems anal.
Industries: Generalist

Milrod Assoc.

22 Riverside Drive
Princeton, New Jersey 08540
(609) 683-8787
Fax: (609) 683-8221

Key Contact - Specialty:
Ms. Jane Milrod - *Direct response marketing*
Ms. Pat Graham - *Database marketing*
Ms. Rene Constant - *Financial services and publishing*

Description: National direct marketing search specialists for over ten years. Client categories include financial services (credit card & investment products), publishing, continuity, catalogue and packaged goods. We place direct response product managers, direct response agency account managers and database quantitative/analytic executives.

Salary Minimum: $40,000
Functions: Advertising, Mkt. research, Mktg. mgmt., Direct mktg.
Industries: Communications, Advertising/PR, Publishing, New media, Broadcast & Film, Telecoms

---

MIS Computer Professionals, Inc.

5104 Foxridge Drive, Ste. 1A
Mission, Kansas 66202
(913) 384-3056
Fax: (913) 384-9516
Email: ncapps@cpnotes.com
Web: cpnotes.com

Key Contact - Specialty:
Mr. Norm Capps - *SAP, lotus notes, telephony, client/server, BaaN*
Ms. Linda Capps - *Legacy systems*
Ms. Dixie Lee Bell - *Oracle, UNIX, software developers, telephony, client/server*
Mr. Murray Anderson - *SAP*

Description: We specialize in data processing placements nationwide and internationally. Opportunities for permanent opening and contract assignments. Emphasis in software developers, database administrators, software implementators, programmer/analysts and systems/programmers. Specialists in SAP, BaaN, Oracle, telephony, PeopleSoft, BPR, package implementators, Year2000.

Salary Minimum: $50,000
Functions: MIS mgmt., Systems anal., Systems dev., Systems implem., Systems support, Network admin., DB admin.
Industries: Misc. financial, Computer svcs., Mgmt. consulting, Telecoms, High tech, Software

---

Paul Misarti Inc.

327 Kilburn Rd. S.
Garden City, New York 11530-5311
(516) 486-1497
Fax: (516) 538-3132

Key Contact - Specialty:
Mr. Paul R. Misarti - *Banking, securities, information technology managers*

Description: Over 175 search assignments have been completed in the field of information technology. These positions have been in executive management, project management, product management, applications development, systems engineering, technical support, marketing and consulting.

Salary Minimum: $75,000
Functions: Cash mgmt., Risk mgmt., MIS mgmt., Systems anal., Systems dev., Systems implem., Systems support
Industries: Computer equip., Banking, Invest. banking, Brokers, Mgmt. consulting, Human resource svcs., Software

---

Mitchell Martin Inc.

80 Wall St., Ste. 1215
New York, New York 10005
(212) 943-1404
Fax: (212) 328-0964
Email: RD@MitchellMartin.com

Key Contact - Specialty:
Mr. Gene Holtzman - *Information technology*

Description: We are a full service information technology organization servicing the contract and permanent staffing needs of our clients throughout the tri-state area. We also provide various healthcare providers with PTs, OTs and STs on a contract and permanent basis.
Functions: Allied health, Systems anal., Systems dev., Systems implem., Systems support, Network admin., DB admin.
Industries: Drugs mfg., Banking, Invest. banking, Brokers, Advertising/PR, Insurance, Healthcare

---

MJF Assoc.

49 Northford Rd., P.O. Box 132
Wallingford, Connecticut 06492
(203) 284-9878
Fax: (203) 284-9871
Email: mjf@imcinternet.net
Web: www.imcinternet.net/mjf

Key Contact - Specialty:
Mr. Matt Furman - *Sales, marketing, engineering, professional/technical requirement*

Description: Professional and technical search and placement firm. Clients are nationwide. Accent is industrial, hi-tech, electronic, computer, mechanical, electrical, with sales, marketing, management, engineering disciplines.
Functions: Senior mgmt., Product dev., Mktg. mgmt., Sales mgmt., IT, Engineering, Int'l.
Industries: Generalist, Machinery/ Appliances, Computer equip., Misc. mfg., Equip. svcs., Telecoms, High tech

---

MLA Resources, Inc.

P.O. Box 35115
Tulsa, Oklahoma 74153-0115
(918) 665-2774
Fax: (918) 665-2996
Email: mlayling@ix.netcom.com
Web: members.aol.com/mlayling

Key Contact - Specialty:
Mr. Michael L. Ayling - *Upstream oil & gas*

Description: Executive and technical recruitment worldwide for the upstream oil and gas industry.
Functions: Systems dev., Engineering, Int'l.
Industries: Energy/utilities

Modis
(formerly Technical Software Solutions, Inc.)

7901 Sandy Spring Rd., Ste. 505
Laurel, Maryland 20707
(301) 369-0040
(888) 369-0040
Fax: (301) 369-0045
Web: www.modisit.com

Key Contact - Specialty:
Mr. Scott Whiteford - *Information technology*
Mr. James Rollins

Description: Our clients are Fortune 100 companies needing technically skilled professionals for short-term assignments or full-time placement. Our databases store thousands of resumes ensuring the right person is at our fingertips.
Functions: MIS mgmt., Systems anal., Systems dev., Systems implem., Systems support, Engineering
Industries: Telecoms, High tech, Software

Mogul Consultants, Inc.

380 N. Broadway
Jericho, New York 11753
(516) 822-4363
Fax: (516) 822-4364
Email: Gmogul@aol.com

Key Contact - Specialty:
Mr. Gene Mogul - *Telecommunications, MIS*

Description: Executive search and recruitment for major users of telecommunications, communications equipment manufacturers, communications carriers and telecommunications consultants companies for managerial, technical and marketing/sales positions.

Salary Minimum: $40,000
Functions: Mktg. mgmt., Sales mgmt., MIS mgmt., Systems dev., Systems implem., Systems support, Network admin.
Industries: Computer equip., Banking, Invest. banking, Brokers, Computer svcs., Telecoms, Software

---

Diedre Moire Corp., Inc.

(Firm declined to update.)
510 Horizon Ctr.
Robbinsville, New Jersey 08691
(609) 584-9000
Email: teamdiedre@aol.com

Key Contact - Specialty:
Mr. Stephen M. Reuning
Mr. Todd Kostrub
Mr. Gregory Foss
Mr. Stephen Casano
Mr. Laurenc Chiaravallo
Ms. Cynthia Angelini
Mr. Hank Sikorski
Mr. Robert Scarcele
Mr. Tom Erickson

Description: Retainer quality search without the retainer. We have successfully concluded over 2000 searches nationwide. We love searching for those highly technical professionals which others shy away from.
Functions: Senior mgmt., R&D, Engineering
Industries: Drugs mfg., Medical devices, Biotech

Molecular Solutions, Inc.

412 Carolina Blvd.
Isle of Palms, South Carolina 29451-2113
(843) 886-8775
Fax: (843) 886-5924
Email: arichon@awod.com
Web: www.netsci.org/companies/Molsol/

Key Contact - Specialty:
Mr. Allen Richon - *R&D scientists*
Ms. Merry Ambos - *R&D scientists*

Description: With over twenty years experience in pharmaceutical research, we are the only executive search firm which can leverage technical expertise and industry contacts to effectively locate qualified computational scientists.

Salary Minimum: $60,000
Functions: Directors, Senior mgmt., Middle mgmt., MIS mgmt., Systems dev., DB admin., R&D
Industries: Pharmaceutical svcs., Biotech

Affiliates:
Osiris Consultants

Monarch Technology Management LLC

1860 Dublin Blvd., Ste. B
Colorado Springs, Colorado 80918
(719) 533-0920
Fax: (719) 533-0970
Email: monarch@monarchtech.com
Web: www.monarchtech.com

Key Contact - Specialty:
Mr. Richard P. Nashleanas - *Data processing*

Description: We specialize in both direct hire and contract positions related to MVS and OS/390 technologies, including systems programming, configuration management (such as Endevor or ChangeMan), data base administration, and senior applications (such as COBOL and PL/I) programming and analysis.

Salary Minimum: $30,000
Functions: IT, MIS mgmt., Systems anal., Systems dev., Systems implem., Systems support, DB admin.
Industries: Generalist, High tech, Software

The Montgomery Group, Inc.

P.O. Box 30791
Knoxville, Tennessee 37930-0791
(423) 693-0325
Fax: (423) 691-1900
Email: tmg@tmgincknox.com
Web: www.tmgincknox.com

Key Contact - Specialty:
Mr. Larry Suchomski - *Agribusiness, food industry management, sales, operations*

Description: We serve as consultants to agri-business and the food industry on a worldwide basis. Emphasis on recruiting the right person for the position. We have industry experience.

Salary Minimum: $35,000
Functions: Senior mgmt., Plant mgmt., Distribution, Mktg. mgmt., Personnel, CFO's, R&D
Industries: Agri/forestry/mining, Food/bev/tobacco

Affiliates:
Agriexecutive Registry
Bob Beare
Stephen Brennen
Marion Hammarlund
Rollie Hendrickson
Jack Hough
Anthony J. Koss
Robert Mackin
Walt Montgomery
Fred Nordstrom
Eileen O'Brien
C. G. Rick Richert
Ron Stout
Larry Suchomski
Bruce Symonds

Montgomery Resources, Inc.

555 Montgomery St., Ste. 1650
San Francisco, California 94111
(415) 956-4242
Fax: (415) 274-4133
Email: montres.com
Web: www.montres.com

Key Contact - Specialty:
Mr. Roger A. Lee
Mr. Thomas K. McAteer

Description: Recruitment of finance and accounting professionals for middle-management positions.

Salary Minimum: $35,000
Functions: Finance, CFO's, Budgeting, Cash mgmt., Credit, Taxes, M&A
Industries: Food/bev/tobacco, Finance, Hospitality, Communications, High tech, Software

Montgomery, Thomason & Assoc.

53 Village Centre Place, Ste. 203
Mississauga, Ontario L4Z 1V9
Canada
(905) 896-7103
Fax: (905) 566-0177
Email: thomason@compuserve.com

Key Contact - Specialty:
Mr. Ronald Thomason - *Technical, production, research, engineering*
Ms. Nancy Thomason - *Technical, sales & marketing*

Description: We recruit technical people who enjoy working in sales, marketing, research engineering and production.

Salary Minimum: $50,000
Functions: Middle mgmt., Production, Plant mgmt., Mktg. mgmt., Sales mgmt., R&D, Engineering
Industries: Chemicals, Plastics/rubber, Paints/petroleum products, Misc. mfg., Environmental svcs.

C. A. Moore & Assoc., Inc.

15500 Wayzata Blvd., Ste. 803C
Wayzata, Minnesota 55391
(612) 473-0990
Fax: (612) 473-7080
Email: camoore@mn.uswest.net

Key Contact - Specialty:
Ms. Connie Moore - *Insurance, risk management, financial services, generalist, direct marketing*

Description: Principal has been in search business since 1967; our firm has experience that few others have. Strong network of contacts. We take the time to do the job well - even when working on a contingent search.

Salary Minimum: $50,000
Functions: Middle mgmt., Direct mktg., Risk mgmt.
Industries: Generalist, Misc. financial, Accounting, Insurance

Larry Moore & Assoc.

12815 Corte Cordillera
Salinas, California 93908
(408) 484-6127
Fax: (408) 484-6133
Email: larrymoore@redshift.com

Key Contact - Specialty:
Mr. Larry W. Moore - *Information systems*

Description: I have been recruiting information system professionals since 1979 with emphasis in Northern California.
Functions: IT, Systems anal., Systems dev., Systems implem., Systems support, Network admin., DB admin.
Industries: Generalist, Mfg., Transportation, Finance, Computer svcs., High tech, Software

The Moran Group

1317 Alpine Court
Wheeling, Illinois 60090
(847) 215-0770
Fax: (847) 215-1177
Email: mo5ochi@aol.com

Key Contact - Specialty:
Ms. Maureen Tague - *Retail executives*
Mr. Evan J. Lysaght - *Leasing (equipment leasing)*

Description: Two main specialties: retail executives and leasing industry (equipment leasing).

Salary Minimum: $30,000
Functions: Sales mgmt., Customer svc.
Industries: Textiles/apparel, Retail, Equip. svcs.

Tina Morbitzer & Assoc.
668 N. Orlando Ave., Ste. 105
Maitland, Florida 32751
(407) 539-1000
Fax: (407) 539-0328
Email: morbitzr@ix.netcom.com

Key Contact - Specialty:
Ms. Tina Morbitzer - *Shopping centers, commercial real estate*

Description: Specialize in recruitment of real estate executives for shopping centers and commercial property; leasing representatives, property managers, marketing/advertising directors throughout Continental U.S.

Salary Minimum: $20,000
Functions: Senior mgmt., Middle mgmt., Advertising, PR
Industries: Real estate

Mordue, Allen, Roberts, Bonney Ltd.
P.O. Box 450
Gig Harbor, Washington 98335
(206) 851-5355
Fax: (206) 851-7969
Email: mordue@halcyon.com

Key Contact - Specialty:
Mr. Michael J. Mordue - *Software, high technology*
Ms. Sheila A. Schultz - *High technology (engineers, managers)*

Description: Recruiting and placement for engineers, managers, directors, vice presidents specializing in the software, electronic and other high tech industries. Nationwide services with special recognition to Rockies and Pacific Northwest.

Salary Minimum: $40,000
Functions: MIS mgmt., Systems anal., Systems dev., Systems implem., Systems support, R&D, Engineering
Industries: Medical devices, Computer equip., Test/measurement equip., High tech, Software

Morency Assoc.
301 Newbury St., #242
Danvers, Massachusetts 01923
(978) 750-4460
Fax: (978) 750-4465
Email: mmorency@aol.com

Key Contact - Specialty:
Ms. Marcia Morency - *Sales & marketing management*

Description: Providing very personal search and recruitment services to national and international companies.

Salary Minimum: $30,000
Functions: Mkt. research, Mktg. mgmt., Sales mgmt., Direct mktg., Systems dev., Systems implem.
Industries: Printing, Computer equip., Computer svcs., Telecoms, High tech

Morgan & Assoc.
P.O. Box 379
Granby, Massachusetts 01033
(413) 467-9156
Fax: (413) 467-3003
Email: morgan.assoc@the-spa.com

Key Contact - Specialty:
Ms. Diane R. Morgan - *Automation*
Mr. Arthur Klebba - *Engineers (electrical, software), automation*

Description: We were founded in 1981 and have specialized in the manufacturing automation field including both mechanical and electronic automation companies.

Salary Minimum: $35,000
Functions: Product dev., Production, Automation, Productivity, Systems anal., Systems implem.
Industries: Metal products, Machinery/Appliances, Computer equip., Test/measurement equip., Misc. mfg., High tech, Software

Morgan Hunter Corp.
6800 College Blvd., Ste. 550
Overland Park, Kansas 66211
(913) 491-3434
Fax: (913) 344-0703
Email: mhunter@qni.com
Web: www.morganhunter.com

Key Contact - Specialty:
Mr. Jerry Hellebusch - *Accounting, finance, insurance, risk management, MIS*

Description: Specialized contingency/retainer search firm.

Salary Minimum: $30,000
Functions: HR mgmt., Finance, CFO's, Cash mgmt., Risk mgmt., IT, Systems anal.
Industries: Generalist, Mfg., Finance, Svcs., Communications, Insurance, High tech

Affiliates:
Signature Staffing Corp.

Morgan Stampfl, Inc.
6 W. 32nd St., Ste. 901
New York, New York 10001
(212) 643-7165
Fax: (212) 643-7111

Key Contact - Specialty:
Mr. David G. Morgan - *Capital markets, corporate finance*
Mr. Eric Stampfl

Description: An executive search firm specializing in middle and senior level assignments in investment and commercial banking.

Salary Minimum: $50,000
Functions: Cash mgmt., M&A, Risk mgmt.
Industries: Banking, Invest. banking

The Morgan/Geoffries Group
21755 Ventura Blvd., Ste. 305
Woodland Hills, California 91364
(818) 704-1100

Key Contact - Specialty:
Mr. J. Lawrence Pepin - *Automation systems*

Description: Multi-functional executive search focusing upon the factory automation and independent power production industries since 1977, offering a milestone based fee disbursal system which ties remuneration to performance.

Salary Minimum: $60,000
Functions: Directors, Senior mgmt., Middle mgmt., Automation, Mktg. mgmt., Sales mgmt., Cash mgmt.
Industries: Energy/utilities, Metal products, Machinery/Appliances, Motor vehicles, Computer equip., Test/measurement equip., Misc. mfg.

Morgenstern Int'l., Inc.
2200 NW Corporate Blvd., Ste. 308
Boca Raton, Florida 33431
(561) 994-5070
Fax: (561) 994-9339
Email: morgenstern@attorney-search.com
Web: www.attorney-search.com

Key Contact - Specialty:
Richard L. Morgenstern - *Attorney (partner level)*
Herrick A. Zeefe - *Attorney (partner level)*
Ms. Phyllis S. Nevins

Description: Firm's prestigious client base regularly engages it to conduct searches for strategic/senior level acquisitions. References impeccable and integrity outstanding. Firm has outstanding reputation for being thorough and appropriately aggressive.
Functions: Directors, Senior mgmt., Attorneys
Industries: Legal

Branches:
123 W. Torrance Blvd., Ste. 105
Pier Plaza
Redondo Beach, California 90277
(310) 318-9000
Fax: (310) 318-1156
Key Contact - Specialty:
Richard L. Morgenstern - *Legal (partner level)*

527 Third Ave., P.O. Box 201
New York, New York 10016
(212) 779-1711
Fax: (212) 889-8946
Key Contact - Specialty:
Ms. Lauren H. Rubin - *Legal (partners & associates)*

The Morley Group
8910 Purdue Rd., Ste. 670
Indianapolis, Indiana 46268
(317) 879-4770
Fax: (317) 879-4787
Email: morleygroup@worldnet.att.net
Web: www.occ.com/morley

Key Contact - Specialty:
Mr. Michael A. Morley
Ms. Sharon M. Dunn - *Engineering*

Description: Over 200 years experience.

Salary Minimum: $25,000
Functions: Plant mgmt., Quality, Allied health, Budgeting, Systems anal., Systems dev., Engineering
Industries: Motor vehicles, Computer svcs., Accounting, Telecoms, Healthcare

The Morris Group
P.O. Box 188
Bryn Mawr, Pennsylvania 19010
(610) 520-0100

Key Contact - Specialty:
Mr. Paul T. Morris

Description: Broad national contacts-especially strong in H/R, clinical research, manufacturing, sales and marketing. Three recruiters specialize in pharmaceutical industry R&D (MD, PHO, RN). Also, pharmaceutical product management and CRA's.

Salary Minimum: $40,000
Functions: Mkt. research, Mktg. mgmt., Sales mgmt., Benefits, Personnel, Training
Industries: Generalist, Human resource svcs.

Mortgage & Financial Personnel Services
(International Mortgage Global Systems, Inc.)
23564 Clabasas Rd., #104
Calabasas, California 91302
(818) 591-8367
Fax: (818) 591-8033
Web: www.imeg.com/mfps

Key Contact - Specialty:
Mr. Robert Sherman - *Mortgage banking*
Ms. Debra Snowden - *Mortgage banking*
Ms. Susan Sherman - *Mortgage banking*

Description: We bring the best of the work force in banking and mortgage lending to the companies that highly value their employees and maintain a never ending search for proven professionals.

Salary Minimum: $25,000
Functions: CFO's, Credit
Industries: Banking, Human resource svcs., Real estate

Mortgage Search Network
(a division of COSI, Inc.)
955 W. Chandler Blvd., Ste. 15
Chandler, Arizona 85224
(602) 812-8086
Fax: (602) 812-8415
Email: efrost7993@aol.com

Key Contact - Specialty:
Mr. Edward W. Frost - *Mortgage, securities*
Ms. Christy L. Rank - *Mortgage loan processors, underwriters, branch managers*

Description: We specialize in top producing mortgage loan originators and all other production related positions and also fixed income sales people and analysts for the securities industry. However, mortgage activities really limit our current exposure to securities.

Salary Minimum: $36,000
Functions: Senior mgmt., Middle mgmt., Sales mgmt., CFO's, Int'l.
Industries: Energy/utilities, Finance, Brokers, Misc. financial

Affiliates:
Career Search Consultants
Lipter Associates
J. Love Associates

Robert T. Morton Assoc., Inc.
35 Fields Pond Road
Weston, Massachusetts 02193
(781) 899-4904
Fax: (781) 899-6514
Email: rtmorton@aol.com

Key Contact - Specialty:
Mr. Robert T. Morton - *High technology*
Ms. Nancy J. Morton - *High technology*

Description: Main focus is placement in a multiplicity of high technology product areas; software and hardware, including all levels of engineering, marketing, sales and manufacturing.
Functions: Mkt. research, Mktg. mgmt., Sales mgmt., Systems anal., Systems dev., Engineering
Industries: Medical devices, Computer equip., Mgmt. consulting, Telecoms, Defense, High tech, Software

MRF Enterprises, Inc.
25020 Blanco Rd., Ste. 150-105
San Antonio, Texas 78258-5511
(800) 645-4516
(830) 438-2995
Fax: (830) 438-2883
Web: janerupp@usa.net

Key Contact - Specialty:
Ms. Jane M. Rupp - *Information technology*

Description: Fifteen years of success based on personalized service that is responsive to the individual needs of client companies.
Functions: IT, MIS mgmt., Systems anal., Systems dev., Systems implem., Systems support
Industries: High tech, Software

MRI, The Sequel Group, LLC
6950 E. Belleview Ave., Ste. 102
Englewood, Colorado 80111
(303) 267-0600
Fax: (303) 267-9400
Email: mrdtc@rmi.net
Web: www.sequelgroup.com

Key Contact - Specialty:
Mr. Robert Heisser - *Software, hardware, system integration, upper level management, individual contributor*

Description: We provide services individualized to our clients (hardware, software, systems integration, telecommunications companies). These services include executive search and related project consulting and on-site service.
Functions: Directors, Senior mgmt., Middle mgmt., Sales mgmt., MIS mgmt., Mgmt. consultants
Industries: High tech, Software

MSI Int'l.
245 Peachtree Ctr. Ave. NE
2500 Marquis One Twr.
Atlanta, Georgia 30303
(404) 659-5050
Fax: (404) 659-7139

Key Contact - Specialty:
Mr. Eric J. Lindberg - *CEOs*

Description: Recruitment in the healthcare fields including physicians, data processing, manufacturing, financial services, sales and marketing.

Salary Minimum: $40,000
Functions: Physicians, Nurses, Allied health, CFO's, MIS mgmt., Systems dev., Engineering
Industries: Construction, Finance, Banking, Invest. banking, Brokers, High tech, Healthcare

Branches:
1050 Crown Pointe Pkwy., Ste. 100
Atlanta, Georgia 30338
(770) 394-2494
Fax: (770) 394-2251
Key Contact - Specialty:
Mr. Jim Watson - *Banking, healthcare, technology*

245 Peachtree Center Ave.
Atlanta, Georgia 30303
(404) 659-5236
Key Contact - Specialty:
Mr. Carlos Hagler - *Locum tenens*

6151 Powers Ferry Rd., Ste. 540
Atlanta, Georgia 30339
(770) 850-6465
Fax: (770) 850-6468
Key Contact - Specialty:
Mr. James Murphy - *Information technology*

Premier Plaza
1900 N. 18th St., Ste. 306
Monroe, Louisiana 71201
(318) 324-0406
Fax: (318) 329-8188
Key Contact - Specialty:
Ms. Laurelle Williams - *Healthcare*

701 Poydras St.
One Shell Square, Ste. 3880
New Orleans, Louisiana 70139
(504) 522-6700
Fax: (504) 522-1998
Key Contact - Specialty:
Mr. David Dietz - *Physicians*

408 Independence Twr.
4801 Independence Blvd.
Charlotte, North Carolina 28212
(704) 535-6610
Key Contact - Specialty:
Mr. Emery Hill - *Generalist*

5215 N. O'Connor Blvd.
1875 Williams Sq. Central Twr.
Irving, Texas 75039
(972) 869-3939
Fax: (972) 869-0085
Key Contact - Specialty:
Mr. Larry Klos - *Healthcare, banking*

1801 Robert Fulton Drive, Ste. 400
Reston, Virginia 22091
(703) 758-6757
Fax: (703) 758-6749
Key Contact - Specialty:
Mr. Walt Brod - *Healthcare, information technology*

International Branches:
Limassol, London, Valetta

Mulcahy Co.
535 High Bluff Drive
Grafton, Wisconsin 53024
(414) 375-2356
Fax: (414) 375-3031
Email: pat@axisnet.net

Key Contact - Specialty:
Mr. Patrick Mulcahy - *Information technology, software, electrical, mechanical engineering*

Description: We specialize in working closely with our client companies to conduct in-depth searches in order to identify and recruit highly qualified talent in the engineering and quality fields.

Salary Minimum: $24,000
Functions: Product dev., Production, Automation, Systems dev., Network admin., DB admin., Engineering
Industries: Paper, Chemicals, Plastics/rubber, Metal products, Machinery/Appliances, Motor vehicles, Computer equip.

Multisearch Recruiters
10350 N. Ballico Ave.
P.O. Box 309
Ballico, California 95303
(209) 634-5814
Fax: (209) 634-2648

Key Contact - Specialty:
Mr. Dennis Gallagher - *Manufacturing (executive & technical)*

Description: Executive and technical search firm emphasizing the plastics, building materials and transportation manufacturing industries, nationwide. Growing niche in confidential replacements.

Salary Minimum: $50,000
Functions: General mgmt., Production, Plant mgmt., Quality, Productivity, HR mgmt., Engineering
Industries: Mfg., Textiles/apparel, Lumber/furniture, Plastics/rubber, Metal products, Motor vehicles, Misc. mfg.

Kenneth Murphy & Assoc.
5112 Prince St., The Mitchell House
Halifax, Nova Scotia B3J 1L3
Canada
(902) 425-4495
Fax: (902) 425-6691
Email: kmurphy@ns.sympatico.ca

Key Contact - Specialty:
Mr. Ken Murphy - *Information technology professionals*
Ms. Karin Dobson

Description: We specialize in recruitment of information technology professionals and executive search.

Salary Minimum: $40,000
Functions: Generalist, General mgmt., Sales & mktg., Finance, IT
Industries: Generalist, High tech

The Murray Group
711 N. County Line Rd.
Hinsdale, Illinois 60521-2407
(630) 769-1390
(630) 769-0990
Fax: (630) 769-9696
Email: murrayfeld@aol.com

Key Contact - Specialty:
Mr. Patrick Murray - *Blow molding, injection molding, plastics*
Ms. Jeanette M. Murray - *Food*

Description: Seasoned business/recruitment professionals recognized for quality, integrity and confidentiality. Industry-focused with plastics and food divisions; most functions, most levels, nationwide. Full/customized service.

Salary Minimum: $30,000
Functions: Senior mgmt., Middle mgmt., Plant mgmt., Quality, Mktg. mgmt., Sales mgmt., R&D
Industries: Food/bev/tobacco, Plastics/rubber, Packaging

Musick & Assoc.
2812 Vista Mar Drive
Malibu, California 90265
(310) 456-8252
Fax: (310) 456-5783
Email:
stevem@professionalplacement.com
Web: www.professionalplacement.com

Key Contact - Specialty:
Mr. Stephen Musick - *Accounting, finance, tax, audit, marketing operations*
Ms. Diana Musick - *Accounting, finance, tax, audit, operations*

Description: Contingency and retained firm specializing in accounting, finance, IT consulting, operations, business process re-engineering, marketing and general management.

Salary Minimum: $25,000
Functions: Generalist, General mgmt., Mfg., Sales & mktg., HR mgmt., Finance, Mgmt. consultants
Industries: Generalist, Mfg., Svcs., Communications, Insurance, Real estate, High tech

The MVP Group
150 Broadway, Ste. 2100
New York, New York 10038
(212) 571-1830
Fax: (212) 393-1048
Email: mvpgroup@compuserve.com

Key Contact - Specialty:
Ms. Eileen Finn
Mr. Joe Valenti

Description: Our approach is to know our clients, most of whom have worked with the firm for years. The key to a successful search is to identify the specifications and understand the company culture in conjunction with managing the candidate process.
Functions: Benefits, Training, CFO's, Credit, Systems anal., Systems implem., Minorities
Industries: Finance, Banking, Invest. banking, Brokers

Myers Career Assoc., Inc.

P.O. Box 600950
San Diego, California 92160
(619) 644-1088
Fax: (619) 644-1098
Email: jobs@myerscareer.com
Web: www.myerscareer.com

Key Contact - Specialty:
Ms. Bonnie Myers - *Multimedia, internet, entertainment*

Description: We are a multimedia & Internet search firm. We assist companies in the field and find qualified employee's with minimal amount of effort.

Salary Minimum: $100,000
Functions: Directors, Senior mgmt., Middle mgmt., Mktg. mgmt., Systems dev., Graphic artists
Industries: New media, High tech, Software

N.A.P. Executive Services (Canada) Inc.

1912A Ave. Rd., #2
Toronto, Ontario M5M 4A1
Canada
(416) 787-8896
Fax: (416) 787-5228
Email: nap_exec@yahoo.com

Key Contact - Specialty:
Mr. Steve Rothstein - *Apparel, textiles, retail*

Description: We specialize in recruiting at all levels within the apparel and textiles industries both at wholesale and retail. Our recruiters all have industry experience.

Salary Minimum: $40,000
Functions: General mgmt., Mfg., Materials, Sales & mktg., Graphic artists
Industries: Textiles/apparel, Retail

Branches:
1200 McGill College #1910
Montreal, Quebec H3B 2LI
Canada
(514) 866-7981
Fax: (514) 866-7093
Key Contact - Specialty:
Ms. Janet Presser

1230 Docteur Penfield, Ste. 904
Montreal, Quebec H3G IB5
Canada
(514) 866-0751
Fax: (514) 284-7419
Key Contact - Specialty:
Ms. Janet Presser - *Apparel, textiles, retail*

Nachman Biomedical

50 Church St.
Cambridge, Massachusetts 02138
(617) 492-8911
Fax: (617) 492-7822
Email: nachman@channel1.com

Key Contact - Specialty:
Mr. Philip S. Nachman - *Medical products*

Description: Medical industry specialists: medical device, medical electronics, instrumentation, biotechnology, pharmaceuticals. VP's through industry experienced individual contributors skilled in R&D, scale-up, manufacturing, marketing, regulatory affairs, quality assurance.

Salary Minimum: $50,000
Functions: Senior mgmt., Middle mgmt., Product dev., Quality, Mktg. mgmt., R&D, Engineering
Industries: Drugs mfg., Medical devices, Biotech

Affiliates:
Medical Innovations
S. Tyler Sullivan & Assoc.

Nason & Nason

501 Brickell Key Drive, Ste. 203
Miami, Florida 33131
(305) 379-9400
Fax: (305) 372-9959
Email: nason@bellsouth.net

Key Contact - Specialty:
Mr. Dennis H. Nason - *Banking, finance*
Ms. Nayda Nason-Robson - *Banking, finance*
Mr. John M. Porges - *Banking*

Description: Specialized in banking, brokerage and other financial services, separate division addresses healthcare and pharmaceuticals.

Salary Minimum: $50,000
Functions: Senior mgmt., Middle mgmt., Health admin., CFO's, Cash mgmt., Risk mgmt., IT
Industries: Finance, Banking, Invest. banking, Brokers, Legal, Computer svcs., Accounting

Branches:
251 Royal Palm Way, Ste. 301 C
Palm Beach, Florida 33480
(561) 653-9996
Fax: (561) 653-9926
Email: dpinto18@aol.com
Key Contact - Specialty:
Mr. David Pinto

NaTek Corp.

27 Summerfield Lane
Saratoga Springs, New York 12866
(518) 583-0456
Email: m.dillon@natek.com
Web: www.natek.com

Key Contact - Specialty:
Mr. Mark E. Dillon - *Energy, power, pulp & paper, manufacturing*
Mr. Ed Hoffman

Description: Our reputation comes from quality work, confidentiality and ethical practices. We offer experienced professionals and quality opportunities. We are not a resume house.

Salary Minimum: $40,000
Functions: Middle mgmt., Mfg., Automation, Plant mgmt., Materials, Sales mgmt., Engineering
Industries: Energy/utilities, Construction, Mfg., Paper, Plastics/rubber, Machinery/Appliances, Misc. mfg.

National Affirmative Action Career Network, Inc.

4255 S. Buckley Rd., Ste. 299
Aurora, Colorado 80013
(303) 699-8599
Fax: (303) 699-8525

Key Contact - Specialty:
Mr. Calvin Booker - *Accounting, communications, sales, marketing*

Description: Specialize in recruiting minority and women degreed professionals.
Functions: Middle mgmt., Mkt. research, Mktg. mgmt., HR mgmt., Finance, Minorities, Environmentalists
Industries: Invest. banking, Misc. financial, Accounting, Human resource svcs., Telecoms, Haz. waste, Insurance

National Bank & Finance Executive Search

550 W. Vista Way, Ste. 107
Vista, California 92083
(760) 630-3400
Fax: (760) 630-2001
Email: exerecruit@aol.com
Web: www.bankfinancerecruiters.com

Key Contact - Specialty:
Mr. Wayne Wedderien - *Banking, finance*
Ms. Bobbie Back - *Banking, finance*
Mr. Ron McPherson - *Banking, finance*

Description: Banking and finance executive recruiters, mid to executive level positions on a nationwide basis.

Salary Minimum: $40,000
Functions: Senior mgmt., Mktg. mgmt., Benefits, CFO's, Credit, Risk mgmt., Int'l.

Industries: Banking, Invest. banking, Venture cap., Misc. financial, High tech

---

National Career Search

789 E. Acoma Drive, Ste. 208
Scottsdale, Arizona 85260
(602) 905-0755
Fax: (602) 905-0751

Key Contact - Specialty:
Mr. Ben Krawetz - *Healthcare*
Mr. Roy Myers - *Healthcare*

Description: We specifically specialize in home healthcare, home infusion, home medical equipment, hospice, medical supply and medical device industries. We work on clinical, operational, sales and financial positions.
Functions: Senior mgmt., Middle mgmt., Nurses, Health admin., Sales & mktg., Sales mgmt., Finance
Industries: Healthcare

National Computerized Employment Service, Inc.

2014 W. 8th St.
Erie, Pennsylvania 16505
(814) 454-3874
Fax: (814) 454-8097
Email: nces@erie.net

Key Contact - Specialty:
Mr. Joseph W. Beck - *Plastics*

Description: Twenty-five years of distinguished personnel recruitment/ assessment experience. References available. Plastics industry our specialty.
Functions: Middle mgmt., Automation, Plant mgmt., Materials Plng., Budgeting, Systems dev., Engineering
Industries: Medical devices, Plastics/rubber, Metal products, Motor vehicles, Computer equip., Computer svcs., Packaging

---

National Corporate Consultants, Inc.

409 E. Cook Rd.
Ft. Wayne, Indiana 46825
(219) 489-0900
Fax: (219) 489-2699

Key Contact - Specialty:
Mr. James E. Corya
Mr. Steve Frey
Mr. Jack Lange
Mr. John Hursh - *Technical & plant managers*

Description: Industry experienced executive search consultants supported by research staff dedicated to assisting client organizations in identifying, qualifying and attracting managerial and professional talent.

Salary Minimum: $35,000
Functions: General mgmt., Mfg., Materials, HR mgmt., Finance, IT, Engineering
Industries: Mfg., Svcs., Aerospace, High tech

National Executive

3200 Dufferin St., Ste. 305
Toronto, Ontario M6A 3B2
Canada
(416) 256-0300
Fax: (416) 256-0035
Email: natlexec@inforamp.net
Web: www.national-executive.com

Key Contact - Specialty:
Mr. Don Cormier - *Electronic, software engineering*
Mr. Peter Ferrante - *Information technology*

Description: Can offer a current salary survey at our website.

Salary Minimum: $35,000
Functions: MIS mgmt., Systems anal., Systems dev., Systems implem., Systems support, R&D, Engineering
Industries: Computer equip., Retail, Computer svcs., Broadcast & Film, Telecoms, High tech, Software

---

National Field Service Corp.

162 Orange Ave., National Bldg.
Suffern, New York 10901
(914) 368-1600
Fax: (914) 368-1989
Email: nfsco@aol.com
Web: www.nfsco.com

Key Contact - Specialty:
Mr. Richard W. Avazian - *Communications technicians, right of way, information technology*
Mr. Robert M. Hayward - *Electrical technicians, gas inspectors, communications technicians*
Ms. Margaret M. Forman - *Communications technicians, administration, data processing*
Ms. Mary Ann Avazian - *Administration, clerical*
Mr. Floyd Cole - *Pipeline, oil & gas, engineers, technicians*

Description: Search or provide temporaries - flexible fees; specializing in communications and data processing.
Functions: MIS mgmt., Systems anal., Systems dev., Systems implem., Systems support, Engineering, Mgmt. consultants
Industries: Computer equip., Brokers, Computer svcs., Mgmt. consulting, Broadcast & Film, Telecoms, Government

---

National Metal Services Corp.

P.O. Box 39
Dyer, Indiana 46311-0039
(219) 322-4664
Fax: (219) 322-2957

Key Contact - Specialty:
Mr. John V. Penrod - *Metals*
Mr. William A. McGinnis - *Engineering, process control*
Ms. Eleanor Woods - *Secretarial, administrative*

Description: 31 years of recruiting experience for the fully integrated steels companies, mini-mills, foundries, die casters, forging companies, mining, equipment manufacturers, steel service centers, engineering firms, automotive and farm equipment manufacturers.
Functions: Middle mgmt., Plant mgmt., Purchasing, Sales mgmt., Budgeting, IT, Engineering
Industries: Construction, Mfg., Metal products, Machinery/Appliances, Test/ measurement equip., Haz. waste

---

National Recruiters

P.O. Box 2090
Ardmore, Oklahoma 73402
(800) 776-6285
Fax: (580) 561-6600
Email: national@natrec.com
Web: www.natrec.com

Key Contact - Specialty:
Ms. Lynn Tackett - *Software*

Description: Nationwide search firm for executive, managerial and professionals serving clients in recruiting and consulting within: communications: voice & data, cellular, PCS, wireless, telecommunications, marketing and sales.

Salary Minimum: $60,000
Functions: General mgmt., Sales & mktg., IT, R&D, Engineering, Mgmt. consultants
Industries: Mgmt. consulting, New media, Broadcast & Film, Telecoms, High tech, Software

---

National Recruiting Service

1832 Hart St., P.O. Box 218
Dyer, Indiana 46311
(219) 865-2373
Fax: (219) 865-2375
Email: stanhen@jorsm.com

Key Contact - Specialty:
Mr. Stanley M. Hendricks, II - *Tubular products, metals, management, technical, sales*
Mr. Dennis M. Toms - *Plastics, management, technical, sales*

Description: Exclusive search and contingency recruiters for the steel tubular products, basic metal and plastics industries. Specializing in management, technical and sales positions on a national basis.

Salary Minimum: $30,000
Functions: Senior mgmt., Middle mgmt., Plant mgmt., Quality, Mktg. mgmt., Sales mgmt., Engineering
Industries: Plastics/rubber, Metal products

National Register Columbus Inc.

2700 E. Dublin Granville Rd., Ste. 555
Columbus, Ohio 43231
(614) 890-1200
Fax: (614) 890-1259
Web: www.nrcols.com

Key Contact - Specialty:
Mr. David Molnar - *Sales, sales management*

Description: Broad market sales search: Telecom, EDP software/hardware/ services, medical/pharmaceutical, industrial, office products, publishing, banking.
Functions: Sales mgmt.
Industries: Generalist, Banking, Computer svcs., Telecoms, High tech, Software, Healthcare

National Search Assoc.

2035 Corte del Nogal, Ste. 100
Carlsbad, California 92009
(760) 431-1115
Fax: (760) 431-0660
Email: pelnsa@adnc.com
Web: nsasearch@adnc.com

Key Contact - Specialty:
Mr. Philip Peluso - *Pharmaceutical, biotechnology*
Mr. Richard Cimicata - *Pharmaceutical, biotechnology*

Description: Executive search for pharmaceutical biotech, biomedical, software development and telecommunications industries. Clients range from start-up companies to Fortune 500 corporations. Exceptional references provided.

Salary Minimum: $50,000
Functions: Product dev., Automation, MIS mgmt., Systems anal., Systems dev., R&D, Engineering
Industries: Drugs mfg., Medical devices, Computer equip., High tech, Software, Biotech

National Search, Inc.®

2816 University Drive
Coral Springs Trade Ctr.
Coral Springs, Florida 33065
(800) 935-4355
Fax: (954) 755-7913
Email: natlsrch@aol.com
Web: www.national-search.com

Key Contact - Specialty:
Mr. Ivan Schere - *Insurance*
Ms. Nanci Gould - *Healthcare*

Description: Established nationwide recruiting organization specializing in the healthcare and insurance industries, providing cost-effective, location-specific, retained search performance, on a contingency basis.

Salary Minimum: $30,000
Functions: Nurses, Allied health, Health admin., Sales mgmt., CFO's, Risk mgmt., Mgmt. consultants
Industries: Invest. banking, Pharmaceutical svcs., Human resource svcs., Insurance, Healthcare

Nationwide Personnel Placement, Inc.

P.O. Box 206
Loveland, Ohio 45140
(513) 677-1998
Fax: (513) 683-9163
Email: moose-kopko@msn.com
Web: www.angelfire.com/biz/personnel/index.html

Key Contact - Specialty:
Mr. K. Michael Gowetski - *Technical*

Description: Over 30 years of industrial experience in 9 different firms, including 3 Fortune 500 firms and over 8 years in the recruiting business, therefore I know both sides of the recruiting and placement business.

Salary Minimum: $20,000
Functions: General mgmt., Mfg., Materials, Sales & mktg., HR mgmt., IT, Engineering
Industries: Mfg., Medical devices, Motor vehicles, Computer equip., Telecoms, High tech, Software

Nationwide Personnel Recruiting & Consulting, Inc.

20834 SW Martinazzi Ave.
Tualatin, Oregon 97062-9327
(503) 692-4925
Fax: (503) 692-6764
Web: www.barbara-nprc.com

Key Contact - Specialty:
Ms. Barbara Bodle
Mr. Darryl Bodle

Description: Executive search specialists serving the industrial marketplace in process control, chemical, environmental, automation, MMI, quality, sales, mid to upper level management.

Salary Minimum: $60,000
Functions: Directors, Senior mgmt., Middle mgmt., Production, Quality, Sales mgmt., Engineering
Industries: Generalist, Energy/utilities, Chemicals, Test/measurement equip., Misc. mfg., High tech, Software

NaviSearch

3982 Cherokee Trail, Ste. 120
Suwanee, Georgia 30024-0964
(770) 831-1303
Fax: (770) 831-1308
Email: search@navisearch.com
Web: www.navisearch.com

Key Contact - Specialty:
Mr. Gary Lowy
Mr. Scott Penn

Description: We are a full service consulting firm that develops strategic, long-term partnerships with both clients and companies.
Functions: Generalist, General mgmt., Mfg., Quality, Materials, R&D, Engineering
Industries: Generalist, Mfg., Chemicals, Medical devices, Pharmaceutical svcs., Packaging, Biotech

NCC Executive Search Consultants

1300 B Santa Barbara St., Ste. B
Santa Barbara, California 93101
(800) 622-0431
Fax: (805) 966-9857
Email: ncc@west.net

Key Contact - Specialty:
Mr. Gary Kravetz
Ms. Jo Anne Cracknell - *Research & development, clinical, pharmaceutical, regulatory, quality*
Ms. Rachel Monset - *Financial, sales, administrative*
Mr. Ted Cabugos - *Benefits consultants, healthcare actuaries*
Ms. Laura Mihalka - *Engineering, software, technical support*
Ms. Jennifer Veblan - *High technology, software, engineering, software management*

Description: Full placement service in administrative and technical disciplines with emphasis on national executive search, specializing in upper and mid-management in healthcare, biotechnology, pharmaceutical, medical devices, engineering, software, sales and finance.
Functions: Generalist, General mgmt., Mfg., Finance, IT, R&D, Engineering
Industries: Generalist, Drugs mfg., Medical devices, Computer equip., High tech, Software, Biotech

Branches:
1655 Mesa Verde Avenue
Ventura, California 93003
(805) 639-2022
Fax: (805) 639-2015

Email: vpncc@west.net
Key Contact - Specialty:
Ms. Monica Rivera - *Engineering, software, technical support*
Ms. Alicia Montijo - *Sales, administrative, accounting*

Affiliates:
Santa Barbara Placement

NDB Assoc., Inc.
RR 2, Box 2276 @ Great Oak Drive
Village of the Eagles
East Stroudsburg, Pennsylvania
18301-9642
(717) 476-6650
(717) 476-6686
Fax: (717) 476-6691
Email: ndbassoc@ptd.net

Key Contact - Specialty:
Ms. Nancy Dolan-Brady - *Advertising & marketing*

Description: Our focus is cross disciplinary, integrated communications management within the advertising and marketing sectors. Agency and individual service grounded in professionalism, integrity, and discretion. Personally managed by the directors with 20 years of agency account management and corporate product marketing experience.

Salary Minimum: $40,000
Functions: Sales & mktg., Advertising, Mkt. research, Mktg. mgmt., Direct mktg., PR, Graphic artists
Industries: Communications, Advertising/PR, Publishing, New media

Don Neal & Assoc.
404 W. Main
Stroud, Oklahoma 74079
(918) 968-2568
Fax: (918) 968-2121
Email: dneal@brightok.net

Key Contact - Specialty:
Mr. Don Neal - *Loan administration, credit & compliance, commercial underwriting, risk analysis, managed assets*
Ms. Donna Curry - *Loan administration, credit & compliance, commercial underwriting, risk analysis, managed assets*

Description: National and international search in the areas of loan administration, credit analysis compliance and accounting in banking and finance.

Salary Minimum: $45,000
Functions: Credit, M&A, Risk mgmt.
Industries: Banking

The NEIS Corp., Inc.
13565 Eagle Ridge Drive, Ste. 1112
Ft. Myers, Florida 33912
(941) 561-0428
Fax: (941) 561-6605
Email: neiscorp@worldnet.att.net

Key Contact - Specialty:
Mr. Kevin Mielcarek - *Telecommunications*

Description: National search for professionals in healthcare, environmental, chemical, manufacturing, information technology and construction. Positions include middle to upper management, sales and marketing, engineering, professional scientists and computer programmers.

Salary Minimum: $25,000
Functions: Product dev., Plant mgmt., Sales mgmt., Systems dev., R&D, Engineering, Environmentalists
Industries: Chemicals, Broadcast & Film, Telecoms, Environmental svcs., Haz. waste, High tech, Healthcare

Beverly Nelson & Assoc. Inc.
3727 Camino Del Rio S., Ste. 200
San Diego, California 92108
(619) 613-1000
Fax: (619) 613-1001

Key Contact - Specialty:
Ms. Beverly M. Nelson - *Property & casualty insurance*

Description: Executive search firm specializing in the placement of management and technical personnel in the property/casualty insurance area.

Salary Minimum: $25,000
Industries: Insurance

Len Nelson & Assoc., Inc.
P.O. Box 690570
San Antonio, Texas 78269-0570
(210) 690-9191

Key Contact - Specialty:
Mr. Len Nelson - *Manufacturing (all types), hardware, software, electronics, telecommunications*

Description: Work with other affiliates across the United States. Can market people in any location they prefer.

Salary Minimum: $30,000
Functions: Product dev., Production, Automation, Quality, Systems anal., Systems dev., Systems implem.
Industries: Medical devices, Plastics/rubber, Motor vehicles, Computer equip., Consumer electronics, High tech, Software

The Network Corporate Search Personnel Inc.
500 - 4th Ave. SW, Ste. 1515
Altius Centre
Calgary, Alberta T2P 2V6
Canada
(403) 262-6630
Fax: (403) 262-5150
Email: network@cadvision.com

Key Contact - Specialty:
Ms. Pat Riddell - *Information technology*
Ms. Kim McKay - *Insurance*

Description: A talented group of dynamic recruiters committed to servicing the marketplace in a professional manner.

Salary Minimum: $40,000
Functions: IT, Systems anal., Systems dev., Systems implem., Network admin., DB admin.
Industries: Energy/utilities, Insurance, High tech, Software

Networking Unlimited of NH, Inc.
67 W. Surry Rd., P.O. Box 802
Keene, New Hampshire 03431
(603) 357-1918
Fax: (603) 352-2627

Key Contact - Specialty:
Mr. Denis R. Dubois - *Medical, information systems*

Description: We are an executive search firm specializing in the placement of healthcare and information services professionals on a permanent, temporary and locum tenen basis.

Salary Minimum: $50,000
Functions: Admin. svcs., IT, MIS mgmt., Systems anal., Systems implem.
Industries: Pharmaceutical svcs., Computer svcs., High tech, Software, Healthcare

Branches:
1810 SW 51st Terrace
Plantation, Florida 33317
(305) 792-3767
Fax: (305) 797-7367
Key Contact - Specialty:
Ms. Kristina Fabian - *Medical*

New Dawn Employment Search
3705 Faberge Way
Sacramento, California 95826
(916) 362-4572
Fax: (916) 363-8011
Email: noliveros@aol.com

Key Contact - Specialty:
Ms. Nancy P. Oliveros - *Medical, allied health, dental, executive, generalist*

Description: Now accepting a limited number of new clients. We provide high quality medical professionals and busi-

ness executives at a reasonable fee. We emphasize customer service by giving your company the personal attention you deserve.
Functions: Generalist, General mgmt., Healthcare, Physicians, Nurses, Allied health, Health admin.
Industries: Generalist, Svcs., Hospitality, Real estate, Healthcare

New Dimensions in Technology, Inc.

Seaside Office Bldg., Ste. 101
74 Atlantic Ave.
Marblehead, Massachusetts 01945
(781) 639-0866
Fax: (781) 639-0863
Email: bk@ndt.com
Web: www.ndt.com

Key Contact - Specialty:
Ms. Beverly A. Kahn - *Software, internet, intranet, consulting, multimedia*

Description: Specialize in middle and senior level professionals for positions in software/hardware, IT, internet/intranet, consulting, multimedia, consumer electronics, support services and product marketing.

Salary Minimum: $45,000
Functions: Senior mgmt., Mkt. research, Mktg. mgmt., MIS mgmt., Systems implem., R&D, Engineering
Industries: Mgmt. consulting, New media, Telecoms, Insurance, High tech, Software, Healthcare

New Directions, Inc.

1127 Wheaton Oaks Court
P.O. Box 88
Wheaton, Illinois 60189
(630) 462-1840
Fax: (630) 462-1862
Email: newdirections@worldnet.att.net
Web: home.att.net/~newdirections/

Key Contact - Specialty:
Mr. Dale A. Frank
Mr. John M. Morton
Mr. Richard L. Santarelli
Mr. Richard B. Schlifke
Mr. Douglas W. Scott
Mr. Tim Sezonov

Description: We specialize in middle and upper management searches with primarily Fortune 500 manufacturing firms. Disciplines include: manufacturing operations, materials, purchasing, quality, human resources, engineering, sales, marketing, finance, facilities, manufacturing engineering, information technology.

Salary Minimum: $70,000
Functions: General mgmt., Mfg., Materials, Sales & mktg., HR mgmt., Finance, IT
Industries: Plastics/rubber, Metal products, Machinery/Appliances, Motor vehicles, Computer equip., Consumer electronics, Test/measurement equip.

New Venture Development, Inc.

596 Canyon Vista Drive
The Du Ket Bldg.
Thousand Oaks, California 91320
(805) 498-8506
Fax: (805) 498-2735
Email: duketnvd@gte.net
Web: homel.gte.net/dukenvd/

Key Contact - Specialty:
Mr. David R. Du Ket - *Telecommunications, electronics, aerospace*
Ms. Holly V. Du Ket - *RF microwave amplifier development engineers, VSAT modem*
Mr. Tim Aspell - *Test engineers, systems engineers, software development engineers*
Mr. Vernon S. Kendle - *RF microwave design engineers, OA reliability engineers, software test*

Description: We are known (by industry leaders) for our quite-low-key searches that install confindence and invite candor in the candidates. Our high degree of integrity assures that each individual candidate will have positive feelings about your company after the search has concluded.
Functions: Senior mgmt., Quality, Materials Plng., Sales mgmt., M&A, Mgmt. consultants, Minorities
Industries: Medical devices, Test/ measurement equip., Venture cap., Telecoms, Defense, Aerospace, High tech

Affiliates:
Contract Advisory Search

Newcomb-Desmond & Assoc., Inc.

73 Powhatton Drive
Milford, Ohio 45150
(513) 831-9522
Fax: (513) 831-9557
Email: mdesmond@fuse.net

Key Contact - Specialty:
Mr. Mike Desmond - *MIS, technology*

Description: Aggressive national recruiting firm, broad client base, all resumes welcome. Specialists in engineering, sales and marketing, manufacturing, data processing, executive management, banking, accounting and finance and human resources.

Salary Minimum: $30,000
Functions: Middle mgmt., Sales & mktg., Mktg. mgmt., Sales mgmt., HR mgmt., IT, Engineering
Industries: Mfg., Computer svcs., Human resource svcs., Insurance, High tech, Software

Newman-Johnson-King, Inc.

P.O. Box 58345
Houston, Texas 77258
(281) 474-7422
Fax: (281) 474-9382
Email: jking@hal-pc.org

Key Contact - Specialty:
Mr. Jack King - *Engineering, sales, information technologists*
Ms. Liz King - *Information technology (professionals, programmer analysts, developers)*

Description: A 40 year history of ethical, professional, effective service to nationwide firms and candidates. A full range of vocations, industry backgrounds and special backgrounds can usually be presented as needed on short notice on a contingent fee or contract basis.

Salary Minimum: $40,000
Functions: Mfg., Sales mgmt., IT, R&D, Engineering
Industries: Energy/utilities, Mfg., Computer svcs., Telecoms, Packaging, Software, Biotech

Newport Management

100 E. Hartsdale Ave.
Hartsdale, New York 10530
(914) 725-5244
Fax: (914) 725-7158
Email: newport.com@worldnet.att.net.

Key Contact - Specialty:
Mr. Kenneth Zeif - *Computer software sales, computer hardware sales, computer networking sales*

Description: Specialize in sales, sales management, marketing and technical support in computer hardware, software and networking.

Salary Minimum: $50,000
Functions: Mkt. research, Mktg. mgmt., Sales mgmt., Systems support
Industries: Computer equip., Computer svcs., Software

Newport Strategic Search LLC

23141 Verdugo Drive, Ste. 204
Laguna Hills, California 92653
(949) 851-1589
Fax: (949) 851-1198
Email: nsearch@sprynet.com
Web: www.newportsearch.com

Key Contact - Specialty:
Mr. John Fitzpatrick - *Telecommunications, finance, entertainment, high technology*

Description: Intense specialty in the telecommunications industry, working all functions including technical.

Salary Minimum: $40,000

Functions: Senior mgmt., Middle mgmt., Sales mgmt., Systems implem., Engineering, Mgmt. consultants, Technicians
Industries: Mgmt. consulting, Telecoms

Next Step Recruiting
3130 La Selva Drive, Ste. 105
San Mateo, California 94403
(650) 577-8000
Fax: (650) 577-9000
Email: info@4nextstep.com
Web: www.4nextstep.com

Key Contact - Specialty:
Mr. Jeffrey Spangler - *Business services, contract furniture, outsourcing*
Mr. Glenn S. Davis - *Software, consulting, outsourcing, sales*

Description: Close proximity to San Francisco airport. Onsite interview facilities. Videoconferencing.

Salary Minimum: $40,000
Functions: Mktg. mgmt., Sales mgmt., Personnel, Systems dev., Systems implem., Mgmt. consultants, Graphic artists
Industries: Retail, Computer svcs., Accounting, Mgmt. consulting, Human resource svcs., High tech, Software

NHA Plastics Recruiters
211 S. Lakeshore Blvd.
Howey in the Hills, Florida 34737
(888) 365-9708
Fax: (888) 365-9707
Email: Greg@Bittner.net
Web: www.nha-recruiters.com

Key Contact - Specialty:
Ms. Susan E. Bittner - *Plastics machinery*
Mr. Greg Bittner - *Plastics processing, plastics machinery*

Description: Specializing in sales, operating, design and maintenance personnel in primarily injection, extrusion and blowmolding machinery manufacturers. Extensive contacts at the highest levels of the industry.
Functions: Senior mgmt., Product dev., Production, Sales mgmt., Systems anal., Engineering, Technicians
Industries: Plastics/rubber

Marc Nichols Assoc., Inc.
205 Lexington Ave., 9th Floor
New York, New York 10016
(212) 725-1750
Fax: (212) 686-6073
Email: mna.com

Key Contact - Specialty:
Mr. Marc Nichols - *Generalist*
Mr. Bill Moore - *Generalist*

Description: 15 specialists; 2 generalists; large research staff; departments: legal, banking, investments, capital and emerging markets, MIS, accounting, EDP audit, marketing, sales, HR, compliance, telecommunications, Web development and tax.

Salary Minimum: $60,000
Functions: Sales & mktg., Finance, Cash mgmt., Risk mgmt., IT, Mgmt. consultants, Int'l.
Industries: Banking, Invest. banking, Misc. financial, Entertainment, Computer svcs., Accounting, Mgmt. consulting

P. J. Nicholson & Assoc.
1301 W. 22nd St., Ste. 604
Oakbrook, Illinois 60521
(630) 574-0555
Fax: (630) 574-0559

Key Contact - Specialty:
Mr. Philip J. Nicholson - *Finance, operations, general management*

Description: We are a custom firm that specializes in financial, operations and general management.

Salary Minimum: $70,000
Functions: Generalist, Senior mgmt., Product dev., Mktg. mgmt., CFO's, M&A, Minorities
Industries: Generalist, Chemicals, Medical devices, Metal products, Misc. mfg., Aerospace, High tech

Nino Recruiting & Staffing, Inc.
P.O. Box 781393
San Antonio, Texas 78278-1393
(210) 696-6900
Fax: (210) 696-7152
Email: r-nino@callnino.com
Web: www.callnino.com

Key Contact - Specialty:
Mr. Reyes Nino, Jr.

Description: Temporary and permanent placement services for physical, occupational and speech therapy, medical doctors and physician assistants.
Functions: Directors, Middle mgmt., Physicians, Allied health, Sales mgmt., PR
Industries: Healthcare

Ira Z. Nitzberg
#60
Granite Springs, New York 10527
(914) 245-9070
Fax: (914) 245-3743
Web: irazn@idt.net

Key Contact - Specialty:
Mr. Ira Z. Nitzberg - *Information technology, executive management*
Ms. Shelly Heller - *Information technology, medical*

Description: Recruitment of data processing, healthcare and medical professionals in management, development and implementation in both the user and vendor environments. In the vendor environment we also place sales, marketing and support personnel.
Functions: Middle mgmt., Physicians, Mktg. mgmt., MIS mgmt., Systems anal., Systems dev., Mgmt. consultants
Industries: Drugs mfg., Computer equip., Computer svcs., Mgmt. consulting, Software, Healthcare

J. L. Nixon Consulting
Route 2, Box 380-E
Celeste, Texas 75423-9776
(903) 568-4111
Fax: (903) 568-4114
Email: jnixon@jlnixon.com
Web: www.jlnixon.com

Key Contact - Specialty:
Mr. Jeffrey L. Nixon - *Insurance, managed care*

Description: Certified Personnel Consultant. Member of the 3 largest insurance recruiting networks. Serving North America in all areas of insurance and managed care.

Salary Minimum: $45,000
Functions: Senior mgmt., Middle mgmt., Health admin., Mktg. mgmt., Sales mgmt., Risk mgmt., Mgmt. consultants
Industries: Insurance, Healthcare

Branches:
3 N. 311 Emroy Ave.
Elmhurst, Illinois 60126
(630) 833-0821
Fax: (630) 833-0887
Key Contact - Specialty:
Ms. Debbie Goff

3832 Townbluff Drive
Plano, Texas 75023
(972) 867-0801
Fax: (972) 867-1801
Key Contact - Specialty:
Mr. Rudy Varney - *Insurance, managed care*

NJ Solutions
9082 Rhodesia Drive, S-201
Huntington Beach, California 92646
(714) 963-9913
Fax: (714) 892-1567
Email: njsolutn@gte.net

Key Contact - Specialty:
Mr. Gail Johnston - *Chemical sales, oil refining, chemists, environmental*

Description: Principal is a degreed chemist with 20+ years experience in the petroleum industry with a background in research & development, sales and operations. The executive search and placement business has been active for 7 years with related industries.

Salary Minimum: $35,000
Functions: Sales mgmt., R&D, Engineering
Industries: Chemicals, Paints/petroleum products

Noble & Assoc., Inc.

420 Madison Ave., Ste. 803
New York, New York 10017
(212) 838-7020
Fax: (212) 838-7344
Email: nobleinc@inch.com

Key Contact - Specialty:
Mr. Donald Noble
Mr. James Brink
Ms. Elayne Rosen

Description: Marketing, advertising and corporate communications to include direct marketing, product management, sports marketing research, advertising account management, sales promotion, creative, new business, media database marketing, general administration of marketing oriented company, international.

Salary Minimum: $50,000
Functions: Senior mgmt., Advertising, Mktg. mgmt., Direct mktg., Int'l.
Industries: Generalist, Food/bev/tobacco, Entertainment, Advertising/PR, New media

The Noebel Search Group, Inc.

15851 Dallas Pkwy., Ste. 600
Dallas, Texas 75248
(972) 855-7350
Fax: (972) 371-5741
Email: trnoebel@swbell.net
Web: Noebelsearch.com

Key Contact - Specialty:
Mr. Todd R. Noebel - *Finance, veterinary pathology*

Description: We offer shared risk performance based guarantees on all engaged/retained searches. We use Focused Flexibility ™ to satisfy our clients' critical staffing needs. Provide search services for financial professionals in all fields and veterinary pathologists (involved in biomedical research).

Salary Minimum: $60,000
Functions: Middle mgmt., HR mgmt., Benefits, CFO's, Budgeting, Taxes, R&D
Industries: Generalist, Drugs mfg., Biotech

The Nolan Group

100 Pringle Ave., Ste. 250
Walnut Creek, California 94596
(925) 938-6700
Fax: (925) 938-7740

Key Contact - Specialty:
Ms. Nancy C. Nolan - *Finance & accounting*
Mr. Thomas P. Nolan - *Finance & accounting*

Description: Executive search and consulting for accounting and finance professionals. Concentration at the controller, CFO, VP level.

Salary Minimum: $60,000
Functions: Senior mgmt., Middle mgmt., CFO's, Budgeting, Cash mgmt., M&A
Industries: Energy/utilities, Computer equip., Legal, Accounting, Real estate, High tech, Healthcare

Noll Human Resource Services

12905 W. Dodge Rd.
Omaha, Nebraska 68154
(402) 334-9200
Fax: (402) 334-7333
Email: nollinc@aol.com
Web: www.noll-inc.com

Key Contact - Specialty:
Mr. William T. Noll - *Generalist, information systems, logistics*

Description: We are the right way to find the right people because we have only experienced recruiters who perform a thorough credentialing process on every candidate placed. Large IS department.
Functions: Mfg., Distribution, Healthcare, Sales mgmt., CFO's, MIS mgmt., Systems anal.
Industries: Generalist, Misc. mfg., Retail, Insurance, High tech, Software, Healthcare

Branches:
55 Westport Plaza, Ste. 575
St. Louis, Missouri 63146
(314) 542-9200
Fax: (314) 542-0400
Key Contact - Specialty:
Mr. William Mueller - *IS, manufacturing, engineering and operations, sales and marketing*

5720 LBJ Frwy., Ste. 610
Bankers Commercial Life Bldg.
Dallas, Texas 75240
(972) 392-2900
Fax: (972) 934-3600
Key Contact - Specialty:
Mr. Perry Smith - *Information services, logistics, environmental*

Norgate Technology, Inc.

170 Old Country Road, Suite 311
Mineola, New York 11501
(516) 248-0444
Fax: (516) 248-0488
Email: info@norgate.com
Web: www.norgate.com

Key Contact - Specialty:
Mr. Lawrence J. Cohen - *Client/server technologies*

Description: Technical search and recruiting of programmers and systems administrators specializing in client/server technologies. Unix, Windows NT, MS-Windows, object oriented technology, C++, Smalltalk, RDBMS and the Internet.

Salary Minimum: $35,000
Functions: MIS mgmt., Systems anal., Systems dev., Systems implem., Systems support
Industries: Finance, High tech, Software

The Norland Group

1164 El Camino Real
San Carlos, California 95070
(650) 610-8070
Fax: (650) 610-8077
Email: career@norlandgroup.com
Web: www.norlandgroup.com

Key Contact - Specialty:
Ms. Jackie Sladky

Description: M/WBE firm specializing in searching for highly-skilled technical candidates. We offer both contract workers and regular, full-time placement.

Salary Minimum: $30,000
Functions: IT, MIS mgmt., Systems anal., Systems dev., Systems implem., Systems support, Mgmt. consultants
Industries: Mfg., Finance, Government, Insurance, High tech, Software, Non-classifiable industries

The Normyle/Erstling Health Search Group

350 W. Passaic St.
Rochelle Park, New Jersey 07662
(201) 843-6009
Fax: (201) 843-2060

Key Contact - Specialty:
Mr. Charles D. Kreps - *Medical, healthcare*

Description: Founded by former vice presidents and long time sales managers for the healthcare and medical industries. We specialize in sales, sales management, marketing and operations. Professional, confidential,... connected.

Salary Minimum: $30,000

Functions: Senior mgmt., Middle mgmt., Quality, Nurses, Mkt. research, Mktg. mgmt., Sales mgmt.
Industries: Drugs mfg., Medical devices, Test/measurement equip., Pharmaceutical svcs., Insurance, Biotech, Healthcare

Norrell Financial Staffing

3535 Piedmont Rd. NE, Bldg. 14
Atlanta, Georgia 30305
(800) 519-8448
Fax: (404) 240-3012
Email: nfshq@aol.com
Web: norrell.com

Key Contact - Specialty:
Mr. Jeff Watkins - *Accounting, finance*
Mr. Craig Ross - *Accounting, finance*
Mr. Pat Layhee - *Accounting, finance*

Description: We are a strategic workforce management firm which specializes in integrating a client's business strategy with a workforce strategy, particularly in accounting/finance organizations. We offer temporary, temp-to-hire, client-hire, managed staffing and outsourcing solutions.
Functions: CFO's, Budgeting, Cash mgmt., Credit, Taxes, M&A
Industries: Misc. mfg., Transportation, Misc. financial, Accounting, Mgmt. consulting, High tech

Branches:
4350 E. Camelback Rd., Ste. 220G
Phoenix, Arizona 85018
(602) 952-5004
Fax: (602) 952-5121
Key Contact - Specialty:
Ms. Kathryn Tobin - *Accounting, finance*

940 S. Coast Drive, Ste. 100
Costa Mesa, California 92626
(714) 850-9711
Fax: (714) 850-0914
Key Contact - Specialty:
Ms. Bridgette Wade - *Accounting, finance*

600 Corporate Pointe, Ste. 1050
Culver City, California 90230
(310) 348-8559
Fax: (310) 348-9270
Key Contact - Specialty:
Mr. Courtney Douglas - *Accounting, finance*

4500 Cherry Creek S. Drive, Ste. 1050
Denver, Colorado 80246-1535
(303) 740-7000
Fax: (303) 729-1155
Key Contact - Specialty:
Ms. Elaine Holt - *Accounting, finance*

1815 Griffin Rd., Ste. 105
Dania, Florida 33004
(954) 927-4047
Fax: (954) 954-4263
Key Contact - Specialty:
Ms. Sue Treney - *Accounting, finance*

668 N. Orlando Ave., Ste. 1009
Maitland, Florida 32751
(407) 647-8117
Fax: (407) 647-5449
Key Contact - Specialty:
Ms. Charla Wilkinson - *Accounting, finance*

1040 Crown Pointe Pkwy., Ste. 150
Atlanta, Georgia 30338
(770) 512-8987
Fax: (770) 512-8998
Key Contact - Specialty:
Ms. Suzie Negus - *Accounting & finance*

35 E. Wacker Drive, Ste. 1545
Chicago, Illinois 60601
(312) 460-0417
Fax: (312) 460-0319
Key Contact - Specialty:
Ms. Tammy Mand - *Accounting, finance*

One Gateway Ctr., Ste. 700
Newark, New Jersey 07102
(973) 824-2229
Fax: (973) 733-2796
Key Contact - Specialty:
Mr. Ken Serviss

6100 Fairview Rd., Ste. 650
Charlotte, North Carolina 28210
(704) 643-2921
Fax: (704) 554-0881
Key Contact - Specialty:
Mr. Jason Heller - *Accounting, finance*

3200 Beechleaf Court, Ste. 301
Raleigh, North Carolina 27604
(919) 850-0009
Fax: (919) 850-0818
Key Contact - Specialty:
Mr. Charlie Petrucci

610 Freedom Business Ctr., Ste. 104
King of Prussia, Pennsylvania 19406
(610) 768-5820
Fax: (610) 768-7065
Key Contact - Specialty:
Ms. Donita Burns - *Accounting, finance*

1500 Market St., Ste. 26 W.
Philadelphia, Pennsylvania 19102
(215) 575-1175
Fax: (215) 563-6090
Key Contact - Specialty:
Ms. Kris Froelich - *Accounting, finance*

155 Westminster St., Ste. 1250
Providence, Rhode Island 02903
(401) 272-1200
Fax: (401) 272-1201
Key Contact - Specialty:
Mr. Justin McAloon

50 N. Front St., Ste. 103
Memphis, Tennessee 38103
(901) 529-9337
Fax: (901) 527-0973
Key Contact - Specialty:
Mr. Andy Bell - *Accounting, finance*

6117 Richmond Ave.
Houston, Texas 77057
(713) 784-4226
Fax: (713) 784-6658
Key Contact - Specialty:
Ms. Nancy Secrist

5605 N. MacArthur Blvd., Ste. 350
Irving, Texas 75038
(972) 580-7571
Fax: (972) 751-1591
Key Contact - Specialty:
Ms. Paula Denn - *Accounting, finance*

10700 Parkridge Blvd., Ste. 420
Reston, Virginia 22091
(703) 860-6710
Fax: (703) 860-3078
Key Contact - Specialty:
Ms. Kim Hayek - *Accounting/finance*

John B. Norris & Assoc., Inc.

P.O. Box 2068
Westminster, Maryland 21158
(410) 876-5550
Fax: (410) 876-5551

Key Contact - Specialty:
Mr. John B. Norris - *Food (all management levels)*

Description: A commitment to provide an acceptable candidate within 4-6 working days after placing a job order.

Salary Minimum: $20,000
Functions: Senior mgmt., Middle mgmt., Production, Distribution, Sales mgmt., CFO's, Mgmt. consultants
Industries: Food/bev/tobacco, Drugs mfg., Wholesale, Retail, Pharmaceutical svcs., Mgmt. consulting, Packaging

Ronald Norris & Assoc.

8457 E. Prairie Rd.
Skokie, Illinois 60076
(847) 679-6074

Key Contact - Specialty:
Mr. Ronald Norris - *Commercial finance, leasing*

Description: Over 30 years of concentration in equipment finance/leasing and asset base lending and bank commercial lending.

Salary Minimum: $25,000
Functions: Middle mgmt., Sales mgmt., Credit
Industries: Banking, Equip. svcs.

Norris Agency

6112 Oakcrest Rd.
Dallas, Texas 75248
(972) 701-0110
(888) 327-6971
Fax: (972) 701-0613

Email: headhunt@waymark.net

Key Contact - Specialty:
Ms. Cathy A. Norris - *Food, beverage industry*

Description: Certified personnel consultant working nationwide. Executive searches within the food and beverage industry.

Salary Minimum: $40,000
Functions: Directors, Product dev., Packaging, R&D, Engineering
Industries: Food/bev/tobacco

NorTech Resources
321 Delaware Ave.
Delmar, New York 12054
(518) 475-9700
Fax: (518) 475-0981
Email: NTRES@aol.com

Key Contact - Specialty:
Mr. Michael T. Fahey - *Chemical industry*

Description: Serving suppliers to the adhesives, coatings, radiation curing fine chemicals and thermoset polymer industries via contingency and retained searches for chemists, technical managers, technical service and technically trained marketing people.

Salary Minimum: $45,000
Functions: Middle mgmt., Product dev., Mktg. mgmt., Sales mgmt., R&D, Engineering
Industries: Chemicals, Plastics/rubber, Paints/petroleum products, Communications, Haz. waste

North Coast Meridian
Main St.
P.O. Box 640
Pine Bush, New York 12566
(914) 744-3061
Fax: (914) 744-3961
Email: nrcoastm@frontiernet.net

Key Contact - Specialty:
Mr. Charles F. Thomaschek - *Engineering, manufacturing*

Description: Nationwide technical recruiters specializing in manufacturing and industrial engineering, related disciplines. Operations, materials management, quality assurance, related. Contingency and retained search.

Salary Minimum: $35,000
Functions: Product dev., Production, Quality, Purchasing, Distribution, Engineering, Technicians
Industries: Chemicals, Plastics/rubber, Metal products, Machinery/Appliances, Motor vehicles, Computer equip., Consumer electronics

The North Peak Group
812 Huron Rd., #315
The Caxton Bldg.
Cleveland, Ohio 44115
(216) 621-1070
Fax: (216) 621-0825
Email: mbruns6108@aol.com

Key Contact - Specialty:
Mr. Matthew Bruns - *MIS, environmental*

Description: A national search firm concentrating in (but not limited to) information technology, data processing, environmental and engineering industries. Based in Cleveland, we are affiliated with a group of the best search professionals nationwide.

Salary Minimum: $40,000
Functions: Senior mgmt., MIS mgmt., Systems anal., Systems dev., Network admin., DB admin., Engineering
Industries: Mfg., Finance, Computer svcs., Communications, Environmental svcs., High tech, Software

Northland Employment Services Inc.
10801 Wayzata Blvd., #325
Minneapolis, Minnesota 55343
(612) 541-1060
Fax: (612) 595-9878
Email: northland@iso.net
Web: jobsmn.com

Key Contact - Specialty:
Mr. David R. Gavin - *Technical, engineering, data processing*

Description: Specialist in information systems, programming and systems analysts. Multi disciplined engineering placement in a broad range of technical fields.
Functions: Quality, Productivity, Materials Plng., Systems implem., Systems support, R&D, Engineering
Industries: Computer svcs., High tech, Software, Biotech

NorthStar Technologies, Inc.
15 Maiden Lane, Ste. 803
New York, New York 10038-4003
(212) 267-4100
Email: recruit@northstar.com
Web: www.northstar.com

Key Contact - Specialty:
Mr. Paul Wilson - *Information technology*
Mr. Nick Khan - *Information technology*
Mr. Khurshed F. Birdie - *Information technology*
Mr. John Vande Woude - *Information technology*

Description: We are a technology company, not just a recruiting firm. Besides our first-class recruiting practice, we also specialize in re-engineering, world wide web/internet development, mission-critical application development, management consulting and systems integration.

Salary Minimum: $100,000
Functions: MIS mgmt., Systems anal., Systems dev., Systems implem., DB admin., Mgmt. consultants, Graphic artists
Industries: Banking, Invest. banking, Brokers, Mgmt. consulting, New media, High tech, Software

Norton & Assoc.
7 Michigan Ave.
Dundee, Illinois 60118
(847) 428-9255
Email: qwst53@prodigy.com

Key Contact - Specialty:
Mr. Greg Norton - *Microelectronics*

Description: Specialists in advanced technologies and microelectronics.

Salary Minimum: $30,000
Functions: Directors, Senior mgmt., Product dev., Automation, Productivity, Systems dev., Engineering
Industries: Chemicals, Computer equip., Consumer electronics, Test/measurement equip., Aerospace, High tech, Software

NPS of Atlanta, Inc.
(Firm declined to update.)
750 Hammond Drive, Bldg. 15
Atlanta, Georgia 30328
(404) 843-3758
Email: lynn@npsstaffing.com

Key Contact - Specialty:
Mr. Richard Niermann
Mr. Richard T. Cline
Ms. Lynn Kennedy
Ms. Mae Simpson
Ms. Tricia Mathes

Description: A full service staffing organization specializing in the placement of accounting/financial, administrative/ office support, information technology and teleserving positions for temporary, temp-to-hire, contract and permanent placement.
Functions: Admin. svcs., Direct mktg., Customer svc., Cash mgmt., Credit, Systems anal., Systems dev.

NRI Staffing Resources
1899 L St. NW, Ste. 300
Washington, District of Columbia 20036
(202) 466-2160
Fax: (202) 466-6593

Email: nri@nri-staffing.com
Web: www.nri-staffing.com

Key Contact - Specialty:
Mr. Robert M. McClimans
Mr. Robert D. Mulberger

Description: With 50 recruiters in 6 offices, we operate in 4 disciplines in the Metropolitan Washington, D.C. area. Disciplines include accounting and finance, legal office services, healthcare. We also provide temporary staffing services in all 4 disciplines.

Salary Minimum: $25,000
Functions: Directors, Healthcare, Personnel, Finance, Attorneys, Paralegals
Industries: Legal, Accounting, Human resource svcs., Healthcare

Affiliates:
NRI Accounting Resources
NRI Healthcare
NRI Legal Resources

Nuance Personnel Search, Inc.

103 Woodstream Rd.
Mooresville, North Carolina 28115
(704) 663-5831
Fax: (704) 633-5869
Web: LynnNPS@msn.com

Key Contact - Specialty:
Ms. Lynn Green - *Property & casualty insurance*

Description: 18 years of contingency search experience. Specializing in: commercial property and casualty insurance. Technical to mid-management. National networking offers unlimited resources for candidates and career opportunities nationwide.

Salary Minimum: $30,000
Industries: Insurance

Nyborg•Dow Assoc., Inc.

12781 Woodlake Rd.
Grass Valley, California 95949
(530) 477-7817
Fax: (530) 477-0745
Email: marilyn@nydow.com

Key Contact - Specialty:
Ms. Marilyn Nyborg - *Hardware engineers, software engineers*
Mr. Steven Russell - *Hardware, software*

Description: Specializing in hardware and software design engineers and management. Working with a variety of start-ups and larger companies in Silicon Valley. Multimedia, telecom, internet and process or development.
Functions: Directors, Middle mgmt.
Industries: High tech, Software

NYCOR Search, Inc.

4930 W. 77th St., Ste. 300
Minneapolis, Minnesota 55435
(612) 831-6444
Email: jobs@nycor.com
Web: www.nycor.com

Key Contact - Specialty:
Mr. John Nymark

Description: Unique combination of search and contract/consulting services provides our clients with versatile and creative solutions to hiring problems. Over 40 years experience recruiting for our national base of clients.

Salary Minimum: $40,000
Functions: Directors, Senior mgmt., Product dev., Systems anal., Systems dev., DB admin., Engineering
Industries: Computer equip., Misc. mfg., Computer svcs., Telecoms, Defense, High tech, Software

O'Brien and Roof

6812 Caine Rd.
Columbus, Ohio 43235-4233
(614) 766-8500
Fax: (614) 766-8505
Email: obrienroof@iwaynet.net

Key Contact - Specialty:
Ms. Lindy O'Brien - *Generalist*
Mr. Howard Roof - *Generalist*

Description: Generalist firm whose principals offer 25+ years of recruiting experience. Searches conducted on either a contingency or retainer basis. Over 75% of search assignments comes from satisfied clients.

Salary Minimum: $40,000
Functions: Generalist, General mgmt., Sales & mktg., HR mgmt., Finance
Industries: Generalist, Construction, Mfg., Retail, Hospitality, Advertising/PR, Real estate

O'Connell Group Inc.

475 Danbury Rd
Wilton, Connecticut 06897
(203) 834-2900
Fax: (203) 834-2728
Email: search@oconnellgroup.com
Web: www.oconnellgroup.com

Key Contact - Specialty:
Mr. Brian M. O'Connell - *Marketing, marketing research*

Description: Experts in consumer marketing discipline and marketing research in all industries selling primarily to end consumer.

Salary Minimum: $70,000
Functions: Sales & mktg., Mkt. research, Mktg. mgmt.
Industries: Food/bev/tobacco, Paper, Soap/perfume/cosmetics, Drugs mfg., Computer equip., Entertainment, Telecoms

John R. O'Connor & Assoc.

111 W. Jackson Blvd., Ste. 1300
Chicago, Illinois 60604
(312) 939-1392

Key Contact - Specialty:
Mr. John R. O'Connor - *Engineers, architects, environmental scientists*

Description: Engineering recruiters specializing in the placement of civil, structural, environmental, mechanical (HVAC) and electrical engineers. Infrastructure design and construction inspection. Highways, bridges, airports, treatment plants.

Salary Minimum: $35,000
Functions: Engineering, Environmentalists, Architects
Industries: Construction, Motor vehicles, Transportation, Environmental svcs.

Affiliates:
Bryant Assoc., Inc.
Kennedy & Co.

O'Connor Resources

5090 Richmond Ave., Ste. 333
Houston, Texas 77056
(713) 529-5744
Fax: (713) 529-5040
Email: health2000@earthlink.net

Key Contact - Specialty:
Mr. Rod O'Connor

Description: Nationally respected in managed care development, marketing, operations, MIS; joint ventures with providers, vendors, insurers, corporations. Expert in re-organization, mergers, downsizing and management succession.

Salary Minimum: $80,000
Functions: Senior mgmt., Middle mgmt., Health admin., Mktg. mgmt., Sales mgmt., MIS mgmt., Systems implem.
Industries: Drugs mfg., Venture cap., Mgmt. consulting, New media, Telecoms, Insurance, Healthcare

O'Keefe & Assoc.

3420 Executive Ctr. Drive, Ste. 114
Austin, Texas 78731
(512) 343-1134
(888) 343-1134
Fax: (512) 343-0142
Email: resumes@okeefeassociates.com
Web: www.okeefeassociates.com

Key Contact - Specialty:
Mr. John P. O'Keefe - *High technology management, software development, data processing, hardware engineering*

Description: Austin's high tech headhunters. We specialize in advanced technologies; OOP, Windows, NT, Multiplatform Unix, Java, Oracle and Powerbuilder. We strive to keep on the cutting edge of new technologies.
Functions: MIS mgmt., Systems anal., Systems dev., Systems implem., Systems support, Network admin., DB admin.
Industries: Computer svcs., Telecoms, High tech, Software

Branches:
P.O. Box 633
Jasper, Arkansas 72641
(501) 446-2137
Fax: (501) 446-2129
Email: resumes@okeefeassociates.com
Key Contact - Specialty:
Mr. Ian O'Keefe - *Software, hardware, engineers, MIS professionals*

O'Neill Group
P.O. Box 172
Lake Hopatcong, New Jersey 07849
(973) 663-5753
Fax: (973) 663-5301
Email: sheila@planet.net
Web: www.crln.com/oneill

Key Contact - Specialty:
Ms. Sheila Manning - *Executive level management, human resources*

Description: We are an international executive search firm specializing in placement of senior management and supporting staff functions.

Salary Minimum: $70,000
Functions: Middle mgmt., HR mgmt., CFO's, Systems anal., Mgmt. consultants, Minorities, Int'l.
Industries: Generalist, Mfg., Drugs mfg., Communications, Aerospace, High tech, Healthcare

O'Sullivan Search Inc.
2300 Yonge St., Ste. 401
Box 2427
Toronto, Ontario M4P 1E4
Canada
(416) 481-2992
Fax: (416) 481-3424

Key Contact - Specialty:
Ms. Kathleen O'Sullivan - *Insurance*

Description: Our mission statement: to put the right person in the right place at the right time.

Salary Minimum: $22,000
Functions: Generalist, Admin. svcs., Customer svc., Personnel, Budgeting, Credit, Engineering
Industries: Generalist, Invest. banking, Misc. financial, Accounting, Insurance

Object Resources Int'l., Inc.
14 Cresthill Place
Stamford, Connecticut 06902-8038
(203) 325-1919
Fax: (203) 977-8670
Email: Kstraat@discovernet.net

Key Contact - Specialty:
Mr. Kent L. Straat
Ms. Donna Miller

Description: In object oriented (OO) and distributed computing only, conduct searches for: CIO's, project leaders, Chief Architects, Dir OO products, division managers and senior designers.

Salary Minimum: $70,000
Functions: IT, Mgmt. consultants
Industries: Generalist

Odell & Assoc., Inc.
12700 Park Central Place, Ste. 1404
Dallas, Texas 75251
(972) 458-7900
Fax: (972) 233-1215
Email: odell@odellrecruits.com
Web: www.odellrecruits.com

Key Contact - Specialty:
Mr. Steve N. Odell
Mr. Robert D. Dralle - *Data processing, information technology*

Description: 23 year old multi-specialty firm. The company is consistently highly rated from "Dallas Morning News" and "Dallas/Fort Worth Business Journal." Their recruiting consultants are awarded top honors at personnel awards programs.

Salary Minimum: $30,000
Functions: Physicians, Nurses, Benefits, CFO's, MIS mgmt., Systems anal., Attorneys
Industries: Misc. mfg., Legal, Computer svcs., Telecoms, High tech, Software, Healthcare

OEI, Inc.
P.O. Box 22
Basking Ridge, New Jersey 07920
(908) 647-4774
Fax: (908) 647-4774
Email: njoei@aol.com

Key Contact - Specialty:
Mr. Eugene F. Kenny
Ms. Mary R. Kenny
Mr. Michael Helmer

Description: The firm services clients in the architectural, engineering, planning environmental and construction fields. We focus in the placement of personnel in all major disciplines involved with the planning, design, engineering and construction of private and public facilities.

Salary Minimum: $55,000
Functions: Sales mgmt., Engineering, Environmentalists, Architects
Industries: Energy/utilities, Transportation, Environmental svcs., Haz. waste

Olympian Recruitment, Ltd.
26 Whippoorwill Rd. E.
Armonk, New York 10504-1415
(914) 273-4643
(914) 273-4645
Email: olympian@csnet.net

Key Contact - Specialty:
Mr. Stuart M. Hopard - *Commercial banking, investment banking, credit risk, market risk, global capital markets*

Description: We are an executive search firm which has been in business 30 years. Our major clients are brokers/dealers, commercial and investment banks.

Salary Minimum: $60,000
Functions: Budgeting, Risk mgmt.
Industries: Banking, Invest. banking, Brokers, Entertainment

Omega Search, Inc.
4425 Randolph Rd., Ste. 319
Charlotte, North Carolina 28211
(704) 364-8875
Fax: (704) 364-9290

Key Contact - Specialty:
Mr. Jeffrey M. Turk - *Generalist*

Description: With over 18 years executive recruitment experience, we are dedicated to being thorough and accomplishment-oriented as well as providing outstanding customer service throughout North America.

Salary Minimum: $30,000
Functions: Mfg., Materials, Benefits, Finance, Taxes, Engineering, Attorneys
Industries: Food/bev/tobacco, Textiles/apparel, Printing, Medical devices, Machinery/Appliances, Computer equip., Packaging

Omega Systems, LLC
1206 Laskin Rd., Ste. 201
Virginia Beach, Virginia 23454
(757) 437-1800
Fax: (757) 437-7737
Email: omegadanl@aol.com

Key Contact - Specialty:
Mr. Daniel Lear - *Sales, marketing, service, engineering, high technology*

Description: Identify highest quality sales, marketing, engineering and service candidates for technical and high tech markets by capitalizing on indepth industry knowledge and practical experience as former senior executive.

Salary Minimum: $40,000
Functions: Senior mgmt., Middle mgmt., Production, Mkt. research, Mktg. mgmt., Sales mgmt., Engineering
Industries: Chemicals, Metal products, Computer equip., Test/measurement equip., Misc. mfg., High tech, Software

Omni Search, Inc.
31225 La Baya Drive, Ste. 100
Westlake Village, California 91362
(818) 707-4500
Fax: (818) 707-4528

Key Contact - Specialty:
Mr. Lory Goldstein

Description: We are a nationwide recruiting firm specializing in long-term care administrators, directors of nursing, nurse consultants and upper level management personnel. We recognize your most urgent and consistent needs for quality staffing.
Functions: Nurses, Health admin.
Industries: Healthcare

Omnisearch Assoc.
1291 E. Hillsdale Blvd., Ste. 304-A
Foster City, California 94404
(650) 574-6090
Fax: (650) 574-4109
Email: searchxprt@aol.com

Key Contact - Specialty:
Mr. David Scardifield - *High technology (engineering, support, sales)*

Description: Particularly qualified to recruit for product sales, pre/post sales applications engineers, field service, technical support, training, systems administration, hardware and software development engineers, also accounting and finance professionals.

Salary Minimum: $40,000
Functions: Sales mgmt., HR mgmt., CFO's, Cash mgmt., Systems support, DB admin., Technicians
Industries: Computer svcs., Accounting, High tech, Software

OmniSearch, Inc.
3442 Eastlake Rd., Ste. 308
Palm Harbor, Florida 34685
(813) 789-4442
Fax: (813) 787-7743
Email: omni@the-salesnet
Web: www.the-salesnet.com

Key Contact - Specialty:
Mr. Samuel Moyer - *Sales & marketing*
Ms. Laurene F. Moyer - *Sales & marketing*

Description: Excellent, documented experience in sales force expansion projects and marketing experience from product and brand manager to marketing director.

Salary Minimum: $40,000
Functions: Mktg. mgmt., Sales mgmt.
Industries: Food/bev/tobacco, Soap/perfume/cosmetics, Drugs mfg., Medical devices

Open Concepts
P.O. Box 4554
San Clemente, California 92674-4554
(714) 369-7231
Fax: (714) 369-5631
Email: openconcep@aol.com

Key Contact - Specialty:
Ms. Linda McClosky - *Manufacturing (cross functional)*
Mr. John McClosky - *Manufacturing (cross functional)*
Mr. Evan McClosky - *Manufacturing (cross functional)*

Description: We are a professional search and recruiting firm focused in manufacturing industries. We accept cross functional assignments for management and selected technical positions.

Salary Minimum: $50,000
Functions: General mgmt., Mfg., Materials, Sales & mktg., Finance, IT, Engineering
Industries: Mfg., Wholesale, Communications, Aerospace, High tech, Software

The Options Group, Inc.
(Firm declined to update.)
121 E. 18th St.
New York, New York 10003
(212) 982-0900
Email: technop@ix.netcom.com

Key Contact - Specialty:
Mr. Praveen Bhutani
Mr. Michael Karp - *Financial services*
Mr. Bob Reed - *Financial services*

Description: We are the foremost boutique recruitment firm in global derivative sales, trading, research and technology, with coverage for every exchange-traded product in every major international market.

Salary Minimum: $100,000
Functions: Cash mgmt., MIS mgmt., Systems anal., Systems implem., Systems support, Attorneys, Int'l.
Industries: Finance, Banking, Invest. banking, Brokers, Misc. financial, Legal

Orion Int'l. Consulting Group, Inc.
5511 Capital Ctr., Ste. 216
Raleigh, North Carolina 27606
(919) 851-3309
Fax: (919) 851-0129
Email: orionrdu@aol.com
Web: www.orion-careernetwork.com

Key Contact - Specialty:
Mr. Jim Tully - *Generalist, transition (military to civilian)*
Mr. Bill Laughlin
Mr. Randy Nelson - *Permanent non-exempt technicians, generalist, transition (military to civilian)*

Description: Former military service members specializing in identifying the best talent leaving the services for career opportunities with leading companies. Recruiting and transitional placement for most functions domestic and overseas.

Salary Minimum: $36,000
Functions: Production, Materials Plng., Nurses, Sales mgmt., Personnel, CFO's, MIS mgmt.
Industries: Construction, Drugs mfg., Plastics/rubber, Misc. mfg., Misc. financial, Aerospace, Healthcare

Branches:
9325 Sky Park Court, Ste. 120
San Diego, California 92123
(619) 715-1501
Fax: (619) 715-1510
Key Contact - Specialty:
Mr. Tim Isacco

601 Van Ness Ave., Ste. E3830
San Francisco, California 94102
(800) 336-7466
Fax: (512) 327-7111
Key Contact - Specialty:
Mr. Mike Starich

3562 Pahoa Ave.
Honolulu, Hawaii 96816
(808) 739-0468
Key Contact - Specialty:
Ms. Susan Moynihan

8394 Theodolite Drive, Ste. 411
Baldwinsville, New York 13027
(315) 652-1820
Fax: (315) 652-1046
Key Contact - Specialty:
Mr. Greg Wilcox

5412 Courseview Drive, Ste. 220
Mason, Ohio 45040
(513) 459-8311
Fax: (513) 459-9087
Key Contact - Specialty:
Mr. Jim Hayes - *Generalist, engineering*

5412 Courseview Drive, Ste. 220A
Mason, Ohio 45040
(513) 459-8311
Fax: (513) 459-9097

Key Contact - Specialty:
Mr. L. J. Hirnikel - *Permanent non-exempt technicians*

1250 Capital of Texas Hwy. S.
Bldg. 1, #270
Austin, Texas 78746
(512) 327-7111
Fax: (512) 327-4286
Key Contact - Specialty:
Mr. Steve Casey - *Generalist, transition (military to civilian)*

4525 South Blvd., Ste. 201
Virginia Beach, Virginia 23462
(757) 518-2970
Fax: (757) 518-2980
Key Contact - Specialty:
Mr. Mike Erickson

4423 Point Fusdick Drive NW, Ste. 303
Gig Harbor, Washington 98335
(253) 853-6925
Key Contact - Specialty:
Mr. David Derr

Affiliates:
Medical Transition Group

Ortman Recruiting Int'l.

1101 Sylvan Ave., Ste. B-20
Modesto, California 95350
(209) 529-5051
Fax: (209) 529-5054
Email: jimortman@aol.com

Key Contact - Specialty:
Mr. Jim Ortman - *Biotechnology, pharmaceutical, high purity water, waste water, pumps*

Description: Number one recruiting agency in the world for high purity water/waste water systems and related components.

Salary Minimum: $30,000
Functions: Senior mgmt., Middle mgmt., Production, Mktg. mgmt., Sales mgmt., Engineering, Int'l.
Industries: Chemicals, Medical devices, Machinery/Appliances, Environmental svcs., High tech, Biotech, Non-classifiable industries

---

OSAGUI S.A. de C.V.

(Firm declined to update.)
Aguascalientes No. 199-601
Col. Hipodromo Condesa
Mexico City, Mexico DF 06170
Mexico
52 5 584 0288

Key Contact - Specialty:
Ms. Angelina Aguirrezabal - *Sales, management*
Mr. Armando de La Hoz Ramirez - *Systems, accounting & finance, production*

Description: Most complete personnel service in Mexico, with expertise recruiting executives at all levels, for more than 15 years.

Salary Minimum: $30,000
Functions: Generalist
Industries: Generalist

Affiliates:
A la Carte Int'l., Inc.

K. Ossow & Co.

160 E. 48th St.
New York, New York 10017
(212) 753-5873

Key Contact - Specialty:
Ms. Kitty Ossow - *Marketing, advertising*

Description: Executive search specialists in advertising and marketing.

Salary Minimum: $50,000
Functions: Advertising, Mkt. research
Industries: Food/bev/tobacco, Drugs mfg., Advertising/PR

The Oxbridge Group, Ltd.

1735 Market St., 43rd Floor
Philadelphia, Pennsylvania 19103
(215) 567-8800
Fax: (215) 567-8815
Email: info@oxbridgegroup.com

Key Contact - Specialty:
Ms. Nina E. Swift - *Investment banking, financial services, merchant banking*
Ms. Marty Brady - *Investment banking, financial services, merchant banking*

Description: We target investment banks, venture capital and private equity firms where we place people from the analyst to managing director both domestically and internationally.

Salary Minimum: $50,000
Functions: M&A
Industries: Invest. banking, Venture cap., Misc. financial

Branches:
21 Custom House St.
Boston, Massachusetts 02110
(617) 946-9600
Fax: (617) 946-9605
Key Contact - Specialty:
Ms. Karen Jostrom - *Portfolio manager, research analysts*
Mr. Christopher Welles
Ms. Laura B. Mauck
Ms. Laura K. Morgan

150 E. 52nd St., 23rd Floor
New York, New York 10022
(212) 980-0800
Fax: (212) 888-6062
Key Contact - Specialty:
Ms. Ann Kraftson - *Investment banking, merchant banking*
Ms. Tamara Totah - *Investment banking, merchant banking*

The Oxford Group

17250 Knoll Trail, #1601
Dallas, Texas 75248
(972) 248-8400
Fax: (972) 248-1480
Email: oxford@onramp.net

Key Contact - Specialty:
Mr. David Jackson

Description: Specialists in computer, healthcare, chemical, electronics and packaging industries. For retained and contingency for management, sales and marketing positions. Also, special division providing consulting services and sources for mergers acquisitions.
Functions: Senior mgmt., Sales mgmt., PR, M&A, MIS mgmt., Network admin., Mgmt. consultants
Industries: Test/measurement equip., Human resource svcs., Telecoms, Aerospace, High tech, Software, Healthcare

---

The P & L Group

366 N. Broadway, Ste. 312
Jericho, New York 11753
(516) 938-7337
Fax: (516) 939-2490
Email: p-1-group@worldnet.att.net

Key Contact - Specialty:
Mr. Hyman Livingston - *General management, manufacturing, materials management, marketing, quality assurance*
Mr. James Panos - *Procurement*

Description: Most placements in manufacturing, materials management, purchasing, quality assurance, marketing, human resources and user-oriented systems. Considerable success in start-ups and venture-capital funded operations.

Salary Minimum: $50,000
Functions: General mgmt., Mfg., Materials, Purchasing, Distribution, Mktg. mgmt., MIS mgmt.
Industries: Generalist, High tech

P R Management Consultants, Inc.

601 Ewing St., C-5
Princeton, New Jersey 08540
(609) 921-6565
Email: findena6565@aol.com

Key Contact - Specialty:
Mr. Jerrold Koenig - *General technical, marketing management (many industries)*

Description: Specialists in recruiting in the following areas: biomedical division-disposables, devices and instrumentation; clinical division-regulatory affairs, clinical trials and data processing support; international division-seeks foreign nationals for management positions in Europe.

Salary Minimum: $50,000
Functions: Senior mgmt., Product dev., Plant mgmt., Mktg. mgmt., R&D, Engineering, Int'l.
Industries: Textiles/apparel, Drugs mfg., Medical devices, Plastics/rubber, Packaging, Biotech, Healthcare

Pacific Advisory Service, Inc.

200 W. Madison St., Ste. 630
Chicago, Illinois 60606
(312) 407-6770
Fax: (312) 407-6773

Key Contact - Specialty:
Mr. Hideki Terada

Description: Specialize in recruiting (1) Asian professionals for U.S. multinational corporations and (2) American executives and professionals for Japanese banks and corporations in the Midwest.

Salary Minimum: $30,000
Functions: Senior mgmt., Middle mgmt., Product dev., Production, Plant mgmt., Purchasing, Sales mgmt.
Industries: Medical devices, Plastics/rubber, Machinery/Appliances, Motor vehicles, Misc. mfg., Accounting, Healthcare

Pacific Coast Recruiting

1579 Farmers Lane, Ste. 342
Santa Rosa, California 95405
(707) 541-7070
Fax: (707) 541-0230
Email: careers@pacificsearch.com
Web: www.pacificsearch.com

Key Contact - Specialty:
Mr. Robert Abbott - *Engineering, manufacturing, operations (consumer products), quality control, quality assurance*
Ms. Barbara Rahmn

Description: For over twenty years providing top manufacturing firms with exceptional talent in a wide variety of intermediate, senior and management level positions.

Salary Minimum: $40,000
Functions: Generalist, Middle mgmt., Product dev., Production, Plant mgmt., Quality, Materials Plng.
Industries: Food/bev/tobacco, Chemicals, Soap/perfume/cosmetics, Drugs mfg., Medical devices, Plastics/rubber, Machinery/Appliances

Pacific Coast Recruiters

65 W-1 Division #144
Eugene, Oregon 97404
(541) 345-6866
Fax: (541) 345-0547
Email: pcr1@ibm.net
Web: www.pacificcoastrecruiters.com

Key Contact - Specialty:
Mr. David L. B. Watson - *Insurance (property, casualty, worker's compensation), risk management, underwriting, claims, sales & marketing*

Description: We are a search firm which specializes in all aspects of the insurance industry with an emphasis on property/casualty and worker's compensation. Specialty market: West Coast, Pacific Northwest and nationwide.

Salary Minimum: $30,000
Functions: Generalist, Senior mgmt., Middle mgmt., Mktg. mgmt., Sales mgmt., Risk mgmt.
Industries: Insurance

Pacific Crossing

2900 Bristol St., Ste. B301
Costa Mesa, California 92626
(714) 668-3838
Fax: (714) 668-0290
Email: mrcm@ix.netcom.com
Web: www.pacificcrossing.com

Key Contact - Specialty:
Mr. Walt Johnson - *High technology hardware, software, engineering, MIS*
Mr. Richard Nelson - *High technology hardware, software, engineering, MIS*

Description: Specializing in computer related technologies, with a focus in software and systems development and support. Major geographical focus in Northern California (San Francisco Bay area and Silicon Valley).
Functions: Middle mgmt., Mktg. mgmt., Sales mgmt., MIS mgmt., Systems anal., Systems dev., Systems support
Industries: Computer equip., Computer svcs., New media, Telecoms, High tech, Software

Pacific Finance Search, Inc.

18101 Von Karman Ave., Ste. 350
Irvine, California 92612
(949) 251-6501
Fax: (949) 251-6517
Email: herbertk@pacificfg.com
Web: pacfin@pacificfg.com

Key Contact - Specialty:
Mr. Kevin Herbert - *Accounting, finance*
Mr. George Merrick - *Accounting, finance*
Mr. John Dyer - *Accounting, finance*
Mr. Pete Shelley

Description: We consist of recruiters who specialize in placing accounting and finance professionals. All recruiters are previous Big 6 CPAs or controllers. Our geographic focus is Southern California.

Salary Minimum: $30,000
Functions: Finance, Budgeting, Taxes
Industries: Construction, Mfg., Svcs., Real estate, High tech, Software, Healthcare

Pacific Search Group, Inc.

10100 Santa Monica Blvd., #700
Los Angeles, California 90067-4011
(310) 286-6921
(310) 712-0770
Fax: (310) 712-0777
Email: nicker@sure.net

Key Contact - Specialty:
Mr. Nick Roberts - *Accounting & financial personnel, COOs, CEOs, MIS*

Description: Specialists in recruiting executives, consultants, CPA's and other financial personnel for public accounting and industry.

Salary Minimum: $35,000
Functions: Senior mgmt., Finance, CFO's, Taxes, M&A, MIS mgmt., Systems anal.
Industries: Generalist, Wholesale, Retail, Svcs., Entertainment, Communications, Healthcare

Packaging Personnel Co., Ltd.

1485 Avondale Dr., P.O. Box 12495
Green Bay, Wisconsin 54307-2495
(920) 498-8657
Fax: (920) 499-9512
Email: dtaylor@ppcltd.com
Web: www.ppcltd.com

Key Contact - Specialty:
Mr. Dick Taylor - *Packaging machinery*
Ms. Robin Huettl - *Packaging machinery*

Description: We recruit exclusively for the packaging industry. Serving two markets: the packaged goods industry recruiting packaging engineers and project engineers; the packaging machinery industry recruiting management, engineering, sales and service personnel.

Salary Minimum: $30,000
Functions: Senior mgmt., Middle mgmt., Production, Plant mgmt., Packaging, Sales mgmt., Engineering
Industries: Mfg., Textiles/apparel, Soap/perfume/cosmetics, Paints/petroleum products, Computer equip., Misc. mfg., Packaging

Branches:
W 1405 Beach Court
Oostburg, Wisconsin 53070-1620
(920) 564-6361
Email: PackStaf@aol.com
Web: www.ppcltd.com

Key Contact - Specialty:
Mr. Walter Ellis - *Packaged goods*

T. Page & Assoc.
1017 RR 620 S., Ste. 102
Austin, Texas 78734
(512) 263-5377
Fax: (512) 263-5783
Email: T.Page@flash.net
Web: www.flash.net/~tpage

Key Contact - Specialty:
Ms. Theresa Page - *Distribution, logistics/ supply chain consulting*
Ms. Yvonne Jones - *Manufacturing engineering*
Ms. Janet Rodriguez - *Distribution operations*

Functions: Production, Purchasing, Materials Plng., Distribution, Systems implem., Engineering
Industries: Food/bev/tobacco, Paper, Drugs mfg., Computer equip., Consumer electronics, Misc. mfg., Retail

Janou Pakter, Inc.
5 W. 19th St., Ste. 6
New York, New York 10011
(212) 989-1288
Fax: (212) 989-9079
Email: info@jpakter.com

Key Contact - Specialty:
Ms. Janou Pakter
Mr. Jerry Tavin
Ms. Vicki Martin - *Business development*

Description: Consulting, contingency and retainer executive recruiting and design consultants to the publishing, corporate and advertising industries on an international basis (i.e. art direction, creative direction, graphic design, copy, marketing, account management, marketing).

Salary Minimum: $30,000
Functions: Advertising, Mkt. research, PR, Architects, Graphic artists, Int'l.
Industries: Advertising/PR, Publishing, New media, Broadcast & Film

Paladin Group, Inc.
1722 14th St., Ste. 210
Boulder, Colorado 80302-6346
(303) 442-2210
(800) 944-2806
Fax: (303) 442-2027
Email: paladin@paladinsearch.com
Web: www.paladinsearch.com

Key Contact - Specialty:
Mr. Ted Osborn - *Sales & marketing, project management, consulting, information technology*

Description: We provide contingency and retained search services. Our consultants have extensive corporate backgrounds in sales, marketing, human resources and operations management...a key partner for your Colorado presence.

Salary Minimum: $60,000
Functions: General mgmt., Sales & mktg., IT
Industries: Computer svcs., New media, Telecoms, High tech, Software

Arthur Pann Assoc., Inc.
701 Westchester Ave., Ste. 3A1
White Plains, New York 10604
(914) 686-0700
Fax: (914) 686-0788
Email: apannassoc@aol.com

Key Contact - Specialty:
Mr. Arthur J. Pann - *Finance & accounting, tax, information technology, sales, human resources*

Description: We are committed to identifying only the most qualified individuals and helping to reduce your cost per hire. A confidential approach to recruiting serving the New York Metropolitan area.

Salary Minimum: $50,000
Functions: Finance, CFO's, Budgeting, Cash mgmt., IT, Network admin., DB admin.
Industries: Food/bev/tobacco, Soap/ perfume/cosmetics, Banking, Misc. financial, Entertainment, Accounting, Telecoms

Florence Pape Legal Search, Inc.
1208 Washington St.
Hoboken, New Jersey 07030
(201) 798-0200
Fax: (201) 798-9088

Key Contact - Specialty:
Ms. Florence Pape - *Legal*

Description: Placement of attorneys nationally in law firms or corporations.

Salary Minimum: $60,000
Functions: Attorneys
Industries: Legal

Paper Industry Recruitment (P.I.R.)
36 Main St.
Gorham, Maine 04038
(207) 839-2633
Fax: (207) 839-2634
Email: pir@gwi.net
Web: www.ccsme.com/pir/

Key Contact - Specialty:
Mr. Maynard G. Charron - *Pulp, paper, recycling*

Description: Unique exclusive contingency plan. For $1,500 client gets exclusive search service with freedom to call off search. We do top level searches for low up front fee. 22 years in paper industry recruiting.

Salary Minimum: $55,000
Functions: Senior mgmt., Product dev., Plant mgmt., Quality, Sales mgmt., HR mgmt., Engineering
Industries: Paper

Paragon Recruiting Officials Inc.
2000 W. Henderson Rd., Ste. 350
Columbus, Ohio 43220
(614) 442-8900
Fax: (614) 457-1211
Email: Procopio1@aol.com

Key Contact - Specialty:
Mr. Vince Procopio - *Information systems*

Description: My main specialty is high level consultants acting as project managers or team leaders in data warehousing, client server, Y2K, SAP and networking.

Salary Minimum: $60,000
Functions: MIS mgmt., Systems anal., Systems dev., Systems implem., Systems support, Network admin., DB admin.

Carol Park
819 Walnut, Ste. 412
Kansas City, Missouri 64106
(816) 421-1326
Fax: (816) 421-8226
Email: cpark@gvi.net
Web: http.nbn-jobs.com/mbrpages/ prkwebpg.html

Key Contact - Specialty:
Ms. Carol Park - *Banking*

Description: Bank recruiter since 1979.

Salary Minimum: $45,000
Industries: Banking

The Park Group & Assoc., Inc.
1511 Ritchie Hwy., Plaza One
Ste. 205
Arnold, Maryland 21012
(410) 974-0360
Fax: (410) 349-1869
Email: info@tpgassociates.com
Web: www.tpgassociates.com

Key Contact - Specialty:
Ms. Lise Perunovich - *Healthcare, financial services*
Ms. Katherine Ryan - *Healthcare*
Ms. Michele Sheiko - *Technology*
Mr. Robert P. Pratz - *Financial services*
Mr. RJ (Kip) Conville - *Health care*

Description: Specialize in healthcare, insurance, banking and technology. Services include executive search and management consulting in the healthcare and banking industry.

Salary Minimum: $60,000
Functions: General mgmt., Healthcare, Sales & mktg., HR mgmt., Finance, IT, Specialized services
Industries: Generalist, Finance, Svcs., Insurance, High tech, Software, Healthcare

---

Parker & Lynch
260 California St., Ste. 400
San Francisco, California 94111
(415) 956-6700
Fax: (415) 956-5642
Email: mparker@parkerlynch.com
Web: www.parkerlynch.com

Key Contact - Specialty:
Mr. Montie Parker - *Finance & accounting*

Description: We locate finance and accounting professionals for clients throughout the San Francisco Bay area. The firm's geographic and functional specialization provides our clients and candidates with an unparalled network of resources.
Functions: Finance, CFO's, Budgeting, Credit, Taxes, M&A

Branches:
1250 Aviation Ave. Ste. 240
San Jose, California 95110
(408) 298-6700
Fax: (408) 298-5642
Email: mbelochi@parkerlynch.com
Web: www.parkerlynch.com
Key Contact - Specialty:
Mr. Michael Belochi - *Finance & accounting*

Parker, McFadden & Assoc.
1581 Phoenix Blvd., Ste. 3
Atlanta, Georgia 30349
(770) 991-0873
Fax: (770) 996-2455
Web: www.parker-mcfadden.com

Key Contact - Specialty:
Mr. Kenneth Parker
Mr. James McFadden

Description: We recruit at the middle and senior management levels in all disciplines in metalworking manufacturing industries.

Salary Minimum: $40,000
Functions: General mgmt., Mfg., Production, Plant mgmt., Materials, Purchasing, Engineering
Industries: Metal products, Machinery/ Appliances, Motor vehicles, Misc. mfg., Aerospace

---

Parker Page Group
12550 Biscayne Blvd., Ste. 321
Miami, Florida 33181
(305) 892-2822
Fax: (305) 892-2880

Key Contact - Specialty:
Mr. Harry Harfenist - *Hospitality, medical, banking, finance, engineering*

Description: Seventeen years in business-upper level management; resorts and country clubs, hotels, restaurants, specialty, gaming and entertainment, also medical, banking, finance, engineering, environmental services and human resource directors. Also, interim executive placements.

Salary Minimum: $40,000
Functions: Directors, Senior mgmt., Health admin., Personnel, CFO's, MIS mgmt., Engineering
Industries: Banking, Hospitality, Entertainment, Mgmt. consulting, Human resource svcs., High tech, Healthcare

Branches:
7658 Bellerive
Houston, Texas 77036
(713) 785-4283
Key Contact - Specialty:
Ms. Sandra De Riviera - *Finance, engineering, hospitality*

Parker-Worthington, Inc.
15851 Dallas Pkwy., Ste. 500
Dallas, Texas 75248
(972) 855-7300
Fax: (972) 855-7301
Email: parker7@flash.net

Key Contact - Specialty:
Ms. Susan Parker - *Software sales*

Description: Female owned, efficient performance company committed to business practices and ethics that create value for our clients and our candidates. We represent many positions that include company equity.
Functions: Mktg. mgmt., Sales mgmt.
Industries: New media, Software

Branches:
13300 Old Blanco Rd., Ste. 307
San Antonio, Texas 78216
(210) 479-9911
Fax: (210) 524-7755
Key Contact - Specialty:
Ms. Susan Parker - *Software sales*

Largent Parks & Partners
12770 Coit Rd., Ste. 900
Dallas, Texas 75251
(972) 980-0047
Fax: (972) 980-0090

Key Contact - Specialty:
Mr. Akira Wilson - *International marketing, freight-forwarding*
Ms. Cynthia LaBarge-Wilson - *Telecommunications, credit*
Ms. Jane Mangiafico - *Mortgage, credit*
Mr. Bill Stynetski - *Construction, engineering*
Ms. Beth Wolchansky - *Insurance*

Description: We conduct retained search and contingency recruiting nationwide.

Salary Minimum: $30,000
Functions: Purchasing, Nurses, Direct mktg., Credit, MIS mgmt., Engineering, Mgmt. consultants
Industries: Generalist, Transportation, Finance, Pharmaceutical svcs., Mgmt. consulting, Telecoms, Insurance

Affiliates:
LaBarge & Assoc.

Parsons, Anderson & Gee, Inc.
44 Georgetown Lane
Fairport, New York 14450
(716) 223-3770
Fax: (716) 223-8536
Email: info@parandge.com
Web: www.parandge.com

Key Contact - Specialty:
Mr. Arthur J. Fandel - *Generalist*

Description: Principals have worked for Fortune 10 companies as well as for small organizations and have all been responsible for internal recruitment. Additionally, all are experienced in competency based interviewing. 15 years in recruiting.

Salary Minimum: $35,000
Functions: Generalist, HR mgmt., Benefits, Personnel, Training
Industries: Generalist, Mfg., Communications, Environmental svcs., Packaging

---

Partners in Recruiting
6260 E. Riverside Blvd., Ste. 325
Rockford, Illinois 61111
(815) 885-2028
Fax: (815) 885-2048
Email: partnersir@aol.com
Web: partnersir@worldnet.att.net

Key Contact - Specialty:
Ms. Diann Helnore - *Technical, industrial manufacturing, engineering, mechanical, electrical, electronic and chemical*
Mr. Kim Helnore - *Quality control, materials management, production, logistics, inspection*
Mr. Douglas Helnore - *Banking, finance, food service*
Ms. Dawn Wenzel - *Education, human resources, service industries*
Ms. Linda Coughlin - *Project management, database management, direct marketing, computer related*

Description: As a business partner, we work with your agenda and strive to complete assignments in the shortest possible time. We identify, recruit, screen, interview and background check qualified, interested candidates saving you time and money.

Salary Minimum: $45,000
Functions: General mgmt., Mfg., Materials, HR mgmt., Finance, IT, Engineering
Industries: Food/bev/tobacco, Chemicals, Medical devices, Plastics/rubber, Metal products, Machinery/Appliances, Computer equip.

The Partners, LLC

(Firm declined to update.)
970 W. 190th St., Ste. 600
Torrance, California 90502-1000
(310) 225-2900
Email: PartnersC@aol.com
Web: jobbrowser.com

Key Contact - Specialty:
Mr. Harry Greenwood - *Computer industry*
Ms. Lina Fafard - *Computer industry*
Ms. Erika Schlarmann - *Computer industry*

Description: We recommend professionals who thrive on challenge and keep their expertise current. These are achievers, dedicated to the industry and excellence. We represent the cream of the crop.

Salary Minimum: $30,000
Functions: IT, MIS mgmt., Systems anal., Systems dev., Systems implem., Systems support
Industries: Computer svcs., High tech, Software

Affiliates:
The Munro Organization

Partners Resource Group

4350 N. Fairfax Drive, Ste. 510
Arlington, Virginia 22203
(703) 351-7600
Fax: (703) 351-7639
Email: partnersdc@aol.com
Web: www.partnerstaff.com

Key Contact - Specialty:
Mr. John A. Voigt - *Temporary staffing*
Mr. John G. Olenick - *Accounting & finance*

Description: Permanent and temporary placement of accounting, finance and systems professionals.
Functions: Senior mgmt., CFO's, Budgeting, Cash mgmt., Credit, Taxes, M&A
Industries: Generalist, Accounting, New media, Broadcast & Film, Telecoms, High tech, Healthcare

Branches:
250 W. Pratt St.
Baltimore, Maryland 21201
(410) 244-5250
Fax: (410) 244-5240
Key Contact - Specialty:
Ms. Megan Kenny - *Accounting & finance*

Rick Pascal & Assoc., Inc.

P.O. Box 543, Dept. K
Fair Lawn, New Jersey 07410
(201) 791-9541
Fax: (201) 791-1861
Email: rpascal@cyberwar.com

Key Contact - Specialty:
Mr. Rick Pascal - *Packaging industry*

Description: Management and engineering professionals in package design, development, production, quality, testing, materials evaluation and purchasing for the cosmetics, consumer, household, HBA, pharmaceutical, chemicals, food and plastics industries.

Salary Minimum: $50,000
Functions: Packaging
Industries: Food/bev/tobacco, Chemicals, Soap/perfume/cosmetics, Drugs mfg., Medical devices, Plastics/rubber, Packaging

Pascale & LaMorte, LLC

500 Summer St., Ste. 303
Stamford, Connecticut 06901
(203) 358-8155
Fax: (203) 969-3990
Email: pascale@earthlink.net
Web: www.pascale-lamorte.com

Key Contact - Specialty:
Mr. Ron Pascale - *Finance, accounting, information technology*
Mr. Brian A. LaMorte - *Corporate finance, accounting and tax*

Description: Financial, accounting and information technology recruitment for middle managers through executive management.

Salary Minimum: $40,000
Functions: CFO's, Budgeting, Cash mgmt., Taxes, M&A, MIS mgmt., Systems anal.

Pasona Canada, Inc.

55 University Ave., Ste. 305
Toronto, Ontario M5J 2H7
Canada
(416) 867-1162
Fax: (416) 867-1369
Email: pasonajh@echo-on.net
Web: www.pasona.co.jp

Key Contact - Specialty:
Ms. Joy Haywood - *Japanese & English bilingual (Sr & Jr)*
Ms. Fumie Wada - *Japanese & English bilingual (Sr & Jr)*
Ms. Sayoko Onizuka - *Japanese & English bilingual (Sr & Jr)*

Description: We specialize in placing individuals into Japan related organizations. We provide bilingual and unilingual staff from entry level to senior management to such firms.
Functions: General mgmt., Mfg., Materials, Sales & mktg., IT, Engineering, Int'l.
Industries: Generalist, Mfg., Motor vehicles, Wholesale, Finance, Accounting, Software

Networks:
Pasona Group Global Network

Pathfinders

5554 Reseda Blvd., #201
Tarzana, California 91356-2200
(818) 758-8383
Fax: (818) 758-8382
Email: adaboy@aol.com

Key Contact - Specialty:
Mr. Adam Silbar

Description: Specializes in placement of nursing executives. Nationwide applications. Over 30 years combined experience.

Salary Minimum: $35,000
Functions: Directors, Nurses
Industries: Healthcare

Pathfinders Int'l.

(Firm declined to update.)
1248 Marseille Court
Rochester Hills, Michigan 48307
(248) 650-9062
(800) 447-0340
Email: pathfind21@aol.com

Key Contact - Specialty:
Ms. Sheila M. Beiter - *Medical, physicians, PA, NP, OT*

Description: We supply healthcare professionals in a cost effective manner. All our fees are on an employer paid basis. We are ready to meet your staffing needs.

Salary Minimum: $50,000
Functions: Healthcare, Physicians, Nurses, Allied health, Health admin.

Affiliates:
Recruiters Professional Network

Pathway Executive Search, Inc.

60 E. 42nd St., Ste. 405
Lincoln Bldg.
New York, New York 10165
(212) 557-2650
Fax: (212) 682-1743
Email: jberger@pesearch.com
Web: pesearch.com

Key Contact - Specialty:
Mr. Jay Berger - *Systems & technology (computer related)*
Ms. Barbara Grossman

Description: Specialized trained professionals with industry/market expertise can either fully manage your staffing and recruitment function or can consult to your in-house management to maximize efficient and effective searches.
Functions: Directors, Senior mgmt., MIS mgmt., Systems anal., Systems dev., Systems implem., Systems support
Industries: Generalist, Food/bev/tobacco, Drugs mfg., Brokers, Mgmt. consulting, Publishing, New media

Pathways Int'l.

1280 Blue Hills Ave.
Bloomfield, Connecticut 06002
(860) 243-5785
Fax: (860) 243-5796

Key Contact - Specialty:
Ms. Joan Cooper Burnett - *Minority*

Description: We are a minority owned executive recruiting firm specializing in assisting clients in building, expanding and retaining a diverse workforce.

Salary Minimum: $50,000
Functions: Generalist, General mgmt., Mfg., Purchasing, Sales & mktg., HR mgmt., Minorities
Industries: Energy/utilities, Mfg., Finance, Broadcast & Film, Insurance

The Patience Motivation Belief Group, Inc.

1971 Sandcreek Dr.
Atlanta, Georgia 30331
(404) 349-3210
Fax: (404) 349-7170
Email: pmbelief@aol.com
Web: www.pmbelief.com

Key Contact - Specialty:
Mr. Patrick M. Bradshaw - *Human resources, banking & finance, information technology*
Mr. Edward L. Bailey - *Sales & marketing, food & beverage, information technology*

Description: Based on experience and extensive research, we provide an in-depth knowledge of the targeted industry and career opportunity. We fulfill our ethical and professional commitment to the client.

Salary Minimum: $35,000
Functions: General mgmt., Sales & mktg., HR mgmt., Finance, IT, Engineering, Minorities
Industries: Finance, Hospitality, Pharmaceutical svcs., Human resource svcs., Telecoms, Non-classifiable industries

Patrice & Assoc.

(Firm declined to update.)
396 Riverside Drive
Pasadena, Maryland 21122
(410) 360-6511

Key Contact - Specialty:
Ms. Patrice Rice - *Restaurant management*

Description: Represent 63 major corporate chains offering nationwide career opportunities in areas of fast food, full service and casual dining.

Salary Minimum: $24,000
Functions: Middle mgmt., Personnel
Industries: Hospitality, Entertainment

Patriot Assoc.

125 Strafford Ave., Ste. 300
Wayne, Pennsylvania 19087
(610) 687-7770
Fax: (610) 975-4512
Email: tompatriot@aol.com
Web: members.aol.com/tompatriot

Key Contact - Specialty:
Mr. Thomas Meltser - *Pharmaceutical, healthcare*

Description: Firm specializes in pharmaceutical/healthcare. Principal was a recruitment manager for a major pharmaceutical firm. Has strong contacts throughout the industry. Knows and understands the lingo.

Salary Minimum: $25,000
Functions: Physicians, Nurses, Mkt. research, Mktg. mgmt., Sales mgmt., Systems dev., R&D
Industries: Drugs mfg., Medical devices, Pharmaceutical svcs., Software, Biotech, Healthcare

Joel H. Paul & Assoc., Inc.

352 Seventh Ave., Ste. 810
New York, New York 10001-5012
(212) 564-6500
Fax: (212) 868-2671
Email: jhpaul@idt.net

Key Contact - Specialty:
Mr. Joel H. Paul - *Non-profit executives, education, culture, healthcare, philanthropy*
Ms. Lillian Amcis
Ms. Myra Mogilner
Mr. Don Adelman

Description: Executive search firm specializing in identifying executives, fundraisers, directors, educators, etc. for non-profit organizations nationally.

Salary Minimum: $50,000
Functions: Directors, Senior mgmt., Middle mgmt., Health admin., HR mgmt., CFO's, Non-profits

Paules Associates

3231 La Loma Place
Fullerton, California 92835
(714) 738-3518

Key Contact - Specialty:
Mr. Paul E. Paules - *Laboratory & process instruments for analysis & control*

Description: Professional personnel recruitment service specializing in sales, marketing, engineering and service personnel placements for the analytical chemistry, scientific, medical and process instrumentation fields.

Salary Minimum: $25,000
Functions: Middle mgmt., Product dev., Sales mgmt., Customer svc., R&D, Engineering
Industries: Energy/utilities, Medical devices, Test/measurement equip., High tech, Biotech

PC Assoc.

2682 S. Holman St.
Lakewood, Colorado 80228
(303) 986-4111
Fax: (303) 986-8996

Key Contact - Specialty:
Mr. Paul T. Cochlan - *Engineering*

Description: Focus on high technology industries for executive and technical recruiting, specialist in engineering, sales and marketing.

Salary Minimum: $35,000
Functions: Middle mgmt., Product dev., Mkt. research, Systems dev., R&D, Engineering, Environmentalists
Industries: Generalist, Agri/forestry/mining, Chemicals, Drugs mfg., Medical devices, Environmental svcs., High tech

Peak Search Assoc.

330 Bay St., Ste. 901
Toronto, Ontario M5H 2S8
Canada
(416) 214-1777
Fax: (416) 214-1767
Email: peakinc@netcom.ca

Key Contact - Specialty:
Mr. Robert Baron - *Real estate, construction, insurance, accounting, financial services*

Description: Our consultants apply industry experience to the searches in their area of specialty.

Salary Minimum: $50,000
Functions: General mgmt., Sales & mktg., Finance, IT, Architects
Industries: Construction, Finance, Svcs., Insurance, Real estate, High tech, Software

Pearce & Assoc.

9116 Cypress Green Drive, Ste. 201
Jacksonville, Florida 32207
(904) 739-1736
Fax: (904) 739-1746
Email: fpearce@jax-inter.net

Key Contact - Specialty:
Mr. Frank Pearce - *Management*
Ms. Lois Pearce - *Sales & marketing*
Ms. Helen T. Lombardi - *Sales support*

Description: We recruit sales professionals in the staffing industry, IT-related products and services, telecommunications and executive search.
Functions: Senior mgmt., Sales mgmt., Direct mktg., Customer svc.
Industries: Generalist, Construction, Computer svcs., Telecoms

Pearson & Assoc., Inc.

7400 E. McDonald Drive
Scottsdale, Arizona 85251
(602) 953-9783
Fax: (602) 996-1261
Email: chuck@pearson-assoc.com
Web: www.pearson-assoc.com

Key Contact - Specialty:
Mr. Chuck Pearson - *Flat panel displays, executive management high tech*
Ms. Erika Feinberg - *High tech, vertical industries, enterprise software*

Description: We recruit key individuals for clients who trust our vast experience, nationwide network of contacts, our imagination, perserverance, speed and discretion.

Salary Minimum: $75,000
Functions: Directors, Senior mgmt., Nurses, Allied health, Health admin., R&D, Engineering
Industries: Agri/forestry/mining, Paper, Consumer electronics, Transportation, Communications, New media, Healthcare

Peden & Assoc.

2000 Broadway
Redwood City, California 94063
(650) 367-1181
Fax: (650) 367-7525
Email: apeden@pedenassoc.com
Web: www.pedenassoc.com

Key Contact - Specialty:
Ms. Ann Peden - *High technology, software development & marketing, start-ups*

Description: Specialize in building software development and technical marketing teams for newly funded start-up companies located in Silicon Valley.

Salary Minimum: $60,000
Functions: Mktg. mgmt., Systems dev., R&D, Engineering
Industries: High tech, Software

M. A. Pelle Assoc., Inc.

P.O. Box 476
Huntington, New York 11743
(516) 385-8925
Fax: (516) 271-6499

Key Contact - Specialty:
Mr. Michael A. Pelle - *Technical staffing*

Description: Executive search, technical high technology staffing, human resource management consulting - HRM audits, legal compliance issues, compensation, training and development and workplace issues.

Salary Minimum: $50,000
Functions: General mgmt., Mfg., Sales & mktg., Finance, IT, R&D, Engineering
Industries: Computer equip., Misc. mfg., Computer svcs., Defense, Aerospace, High tech, Software

Pennington Consulting Group

65 S. Main St., Bldg. B
Pennington, New Jersey 08534
(609) 737-8500
Fax: (609) 737-8576
Email: RBW5725@aol.com
Web: www.penningtonconsulting.com

Key Contact - Specialty:
Mr. Robert B. White
Ms. Elizabeth Ludlow
Ms. Trish Ambrosio
Ms. Karen Britt

Description: Executive search and consulting firm specializing in wireless communications services.
Functions: HR mgmt., Personnel
Industries: Mgmt. consulting, Human resource svcs., Telecoms

The Pennmor Group

25 Chestnut St., Ste. 107
Haddonfield, New Jersey 08033
(609) 354-1414
Fax: (609) 354-7660
Email: ttrasatti@pennmor.com

Key Contact - Specialty:
Mr. Anthony Trasatti - *Finance, accounting, human resources, operations management, marketing*
Mr. Andrew Cullen - *Finance, accounting, human resources, customer service management, marketing*

Description: Experts in discreet one-on-one recruiting process. Specialty areas include all functions in human resources, finance, operations, accounting and senior management. Known for our professional approach to clients and candidates and our long term client relationships.

Salary Minimum: $50,000
Functions: General mgmt., Sales & mktg., Mktg. mgmt., Customer svc., HR mgmt., Personnel, Finance
Industries: Finance, Brokers, Svcs., Accounting, Human resource svcs., Communications, Insurance

PeopleSource Inc.

9200 Old Katy Rd.
Houston, Texas 77055
(713) 935-3300
Email: peopleso@swbell.net

Key Contact - Specialty:
Mr. Bill Sonne - *Geosciences, programmers, MIS professionals, finance & accounting, energy*

Functions: Sales & mktg., Finance, IT, MIS mgmt., Systems anal., Systems dev., Engineering
Industries: Energy/utilities, Mfg., Misc. financial, Accounting, Human resource svcs., High tech, Software

PERC, Ltd.

P.O. Box 15327
Phoenix, Arizona 85060-5327
(800) 874-7246
(602) 553-9896
Fax: (602) 553-9897
Email: gordonstoa@aol.com

Key Contact - Specialty:
Mr. Gordon Stoa - *Food, agriculture, manufacturing*
Ms. Jackie Stoa - *Administration, office management*

Description: Change is constant. We offer strategic partnership in your search for qualified and competent candidates.

Salary Minimum: $25,000
Functions: Directors, Senior mgmt., Middle mgmt., Production, Plant mgmt., Productivity, Distribution
Industries: Agri/forestry/mining, Energy/utilities, Food/bev/tobacco, Drugs mfg., Motor vehicles, Misc. mfg., Transportation

---

Perez & Assoc.
3344 Hollywood
Dearborn, Michigan 48124
(313) 359-3811
Fax: (313) 359-3812
Email: perezassoc@aol.com

Key Contact - Specialty:
Ms. Gale Perez

Salary Minimum: $30,000
Functions: Advertising, Mkt. research, Mktg. mgmt., Direct mktg., PR
Industries: Advertising/PR

Perfect Search, Inc.
1801 Clint Moore Rd., Ste. 109
Boca Raton, Florida 33487
(561) 995-7533
Fax: (561) 995-7477
Email: perfsearch@aol.com

Key Contact - Specialty:
Ms. Robin D. Callicott - *Healthcare sales, management, marketing*

Description: We work on behalf of client companies to recruit sales, sales management and marketing talent for medical, pharmaceutical and biotech manufacturers. We also place executive and director level individuals within healthcare providers and consulting firms.

Salary Minimum: $35,000
Functions: Health admin., Mktg. mgmt., Sales mgmt., Training
Industries: Biotech, Healthcare

Performance Resources, Inc.
Three Regency Plaza, Ste. 117
Providence, Rhode Island 02903
(401) 854-2410
Fax: (401) 854-2305
Email: perres1@intap.net

Key Contact - Specialty:
Mr. Kevin R. O'Neill - *Generalist, senior management, plant operations*

Description: Handle full range of industries. Specialty practice includes Mid-senior operations and finance for consumer packaged goods area.
Functions: Generalist, Senior mgmt., Middle mgmt., Plant mgmt., Distribution, Sales mgmt., CFO's
Industries: Generalist, Food/bev/tobacco, Paper, Printing, Soap/perfume/cosmetics, Drugs mfg., Medical devices

Branches:
88 Columbia Ave.
Jamestown, Rhode Island 02835
(401) 423-7421
Fax: (401) 423-9865
Email: perres1@netsense.net
Key Contact - Specialty:
Ms. Chantel Byrd - *Generalist*

Affiliates:
Robert Graham Assoc.

PERI Corp/Professional Executive Recruiters, Inc.
1701 Gateway Blvd., Ste. 419
Richardson, Texas 75080-3627
(972) 235-3984
Fax: (972) 437-2017
Email: peri@airmail.net

Key Contact - Specialty:
Mr. Ken Roberts

Description: Over 22 years in recruiting mid to executive level personnel in the construction industry nationally and internationally.
Functions: Senior mgmt., Middle mgmt., CFO's, Risk mgmt., MIS mgmt., Engineering, Int'l.
Industries: Construction, Environmental svcs.

Perry • Newton Assoc.
P.O. Box 1158
Rockville, Maryland 20849
(301) 340-3360
Fax: (301) 340-3080
Email: pna@idt.net
Web: perrynewton.com

Key Contact - Specialty:
Mr. Dick Perry
Ms. Marje Newton

Description: Critical positions to fill? When you require high achieving candidates with proven track records, contact us. We'll get the job done. Retail search and placement, exclusively.

Salary Minimum: $40,000
Functions: Senior mgmt., Middle mgmt., Direct mktg., Benefits, CFO's, Budgeting, MIS mgmt.
Industries: Retail

Fred Perry Assoc.
P.O. Box 680487
Houston, Texas 77268
(281) 350-2809
Fax: (281) 350-2894

Key Contact - Specialty:
Mr. Fred Perry - *Engineering, consulting*

Description: 15 years experience recruiting nationally for the nation's leading consulting engineering firms specializing in environmental and infrastructure.

Functions: Senior mgmt., Middle mgmt., Admin. svcs., Engineering, Environmentalists, Int'l.
Industries: Construction, Telecoms, Environmental svcs., Haz. waste

---

Perry Search Assoc.
1443 Main St., Ste. 120-C
Napa, California 94559
(707) 259-4851
Fax: (707) 259-4852
Email: perysearch@aol.com

Key Contact - Specialty:
Mr. Marcus Perry

Description: A professional search firm with particular expertise in the datacommunications/telecommunications/computer networking industries. Specializing in sales, sales support, product marketing, hardware and software engineering personnel.

Salary Minimum: $40,000
Functions: Mkt. research, Sales mgmt., Systems anal., Systems dev., Systems implem., Systems support, Engineering
Industries: Computer equip., Computer svcs., New media, Telecoms, High tech, Software

---

PersoNet, Inc.
2445 Hollywood Blvd.
Hollywood, Florida 33168
(954) 647-3706
Fax: (954) 927-1500
Email: Info@PersoNet.com
Web: www.PersoNet.com

Key Contact - Specialty:
Mr. McReginald H. Denis - *Executive, management*
Mr. Alain M. Guerrier - *Executive, technical*
Ms. Lori Lane-Dodge - *Management*

Description: We are a full-service employment firm that specializes in executive, temporary, contract and permanent placements. We are designed to aid companies and professionals succeed in today's economy. We are the extended arm and heartbeat to the communities and industries.

Salary Minimum: $45,000
Functions: Generalist, General mgmt., Mfg., Materials, Sales & mktg., HR mgmt., Finance
Industries: Generalist, Mfg., Finance, Svcs., Communications, Packaging, High tech

---

Personnel Alliance Group
569 Abbington Drive
East Windsor, New Jersey 08520
(609) 443-5761
Fax: (609) 443-6926

Email: abrownpage@compuserv.com

Key Contact - Specialty:
Mr. Alan V. Brown - *Finance & accounting, sales, sales management, MIS management, environmental services*

Description: Specializing in identifying professionals who excel in their profession.

Salary Minimum: $30,000
Functions: Training, Finance, MIS mgmt., Systems anal., Systems dev., Systems implem., Systems support
Industries: Construction, Textiles/apparel, Computer svcs., Accounting, Environmental svcs., Real estate, Software

Personnel Assoc.
23 Maracay
San Clemente, California 92672-6050
(949) 492-0030
Email: margecraw@aol.com

Key Contact - Specialty:
Ms. Marjorie Crawford - *Publishing*
Mr. Edward Wells - *Publishing*

Description: Searches conducted in most areas of publishing; specialize in acquisitions editorial and in sales/marketing for medical, college publishing and professional and reference.

Salary Minimum: $25,000
Functions: Sales mgmt., Direct mktg., Minorities
Industries: Higher ed., Publishing, New media, Software

Personnel Assoc.
140 McIntyre Rd.
Cherryville, North Carolina 28021
(704) 445-0080
Fax: (704) 445-0081
Email: perassoc@shelby.net

Key Contact - Specialty:
Mr. Cliff Neighbors - *Generalist*
Ms. Betty Neighbors - *Generalist*
Ms. Chasity Tindall - *Generalist*

Description: Executive search firm with expertise in minority recruitment serving the business professional through our nationwide network. Our Charlotte office has 30 years experience in supporting operations, manufacturing, engineering and quality professionals.

Salary Minimum: $40,000
Functions: General mgmt., Mfg., Materials, Sales & mktg., HR mgmt., IT, Engineering
Industries: Generalist, Mfg., Finance, Communications, Environmental svcs., Packaging, High tech

Personnel Assoc. Inc.
731 James St., Ste. 209
Syracuse, New York 13203
(315) 422-0070
Fax: (315) 474-7293
Email: pbaskin@ix.netcom.com

Key Contact - Specialty:
Mr. Peter J. Baskin - *Insurance*

Description: Nationwide recruiting of property/casualty and life/health professionals. We specialize in branch level management positions. Over 100 affiliated offices.

Salary Minimum: $45,000
Industries: Insurance

Personnel Consultants
14042 NE 8th, #201B
Bellevue, Washington 98007
(425) 641-0657
Fax: (425) 641-0657
Email: buzy73a@prodigy.net

Key Contact - Specialty:
Mr. Larry L. Dykes - *Insurance*

Description: 25+ years experience insurance only. Education: MBA and J.D. Geographic specialty Washington, Oregon, Idaho and Alaska.

Salary Minimum: $35,000
Functions: Generalist
Industries: Insurance

Personnel, Inc.
917 Merchants Walk, Ste. D
Huntsville, Alabama 35801
(256) 536-4431
Fax: (256) 539-0583

Key Contact - Specialty:
Mr. Bill Breen - *Executive, management, engineering*

Description: Have belonged to two major networks - presently work with 34 agencies 50/50 who met through networks. Engineering and manufacturing firms in the South is the appeal.

Salary Minimum: $35,000
Functions: Senior mgmt., Middle mgmt., Production, Materials, HR mgmt., IT, Engineering
Industries: Mfg., Computer equip., Misc. mfg., Telecoms, Aerospace, High tech, Software

Personnel Incorporated
604 Locust St., Ste. 516
Des Moines, Iowa 50309-3720
(515) 243-7687
Web: pincjt@ix.netcom.com

Key Contact - Specialty:
Mr. Jack T. Textor - *Generalist*

Description: Full service personnel consulting firm. We have expertise in the areas of executive search, placements, psychological testing, outplacements, management consulting and have been in business over 35 years. Resumes will not be processed unless salary requirements are included.
Functions: Generalist, Production, Plant mgmt., Systems anal., Systems dev., Engineering
Industries: Generalist, Food/bev/tobacco, Misc. mfg., Computer svcs., High tech, Software, Healthcare

Personnel Management Group
300-209 Notre Dame Ave.
Winnipeg, Manitoba R3B 1M9
Canada
(204) 982-1100
Fax: (204) 943-9535
Email: recruiter@pmg.mb.ca
Web: pmg.mb.ca

Key Contact - Specialty:
Ms. Yvonne Baert - *Systems, engineering, accounting, manufacturing*
Mr. Robert A. Baert - *Special projects, construction (large scale hires, call centers, etc.)*
Ms. Cynthia Wharton - *Transportation, logistics, distributions*

Description: Over 20 years experience in technical, management and transportation/logistics recruiting. Intimate knowledge of the Manitoba market in systems, engineering, accounting and logistics. Cooperate with other Canadian recruiters, particularly in Western Canada. High profile in Winnipeg in systems area.

Salary Minimum: $40,000
Functions: Middle mgmt., Quality, Materials Plng., Distribution, CFO's, IT, Engineering
Industries: Mfg., Transportation, Computer svcs., Accounting, Aerospace, High tech, Software

The Personnel Network, Inc.
1246 Lake Murray Blvd.
P.O. Box 1426
Irmo, South Carolina 29063
(803) 781-2087
Fax: (803) 732-7986

Key Contact - Specialty:
Mr. Charles L. Larsen - *Environmental, public administration*
Mr. C. Lars Larsen - *Engineering, generalist*
Mr. James K. Larsen - *Industrial*
Ms. Merlyne T. Larsen - *Medical*
Mr. Stephen G. Harrell - *Government, public administration, law enforcement & detention*

Description: Management and professional staff recruited confidentially in all areas of: manufacturing, public administration, marketing, hospitality, engineering, industrial, healthcare and environmental. Fax service on resumes for instant results.

Salary Minimum: $25,000
Functions: Generalist, Senior mgmt., Middle mgmt., Production, Allied health, Engineering, Environmentalists
Industries: Generalist, Textiles/apparel, Hospitality, Human resource svcs., Government, Environmental svcs., Healthcare

Branches:
1722 Seabrook Ave.
Cary, North Carolina 27511
(919) 469-5900
Key Contact - Specialty:
Ms. Jan Brooks - *Generalist*

P.O. Box 1813
Murrells Inlet, South Carolina 29576
(803) 651-0950
Key Contact - Specialty:
Ms. Allison Jennings - *Hospitality*

Personnel Resources Organization
121 S. Broad St., Ste. 1030
The North American Bldg.
Philadelphia, Pennsylvania 19107
(215) 735-7500
Email: lawpros@aol.com
Web: www.lawpro.com

Key Contact - Specialty:
Mr. Lawrence Cesare
Ms. Joan Cesare
Ms. Lelia G. Beakey

Description: Mid-Atlantic states legal community experts offering search and counselling expertise to partner level attorneys and law firms.
Functions: Attorneys
Industries: Legal

Personnel Solutions
P.O. Box 32963
Phoenix, Arizona 85064
(602) 946-0999
Fax: (602) 990-2045
Email: RSpargo525@aol.com
Web: www.PersonnelSols.com

Key Contact - Specialty:
Mr. Rick Spargo - *Medical sales, pharmaceutical sales*

Description: Recruit sales and sales management nationally and in the Southwest specializing in the medical, pharmaceutical, biotech, disposable and device markets.
Functions: Sales mgmt.
Industries: Drugs mfg., Medical devices

Personnel Tangent Inc.
4141 Sherbrooke Ouest, Ste. 650
Westmount, Quebec H3Z 1B8
Canada
(514) 932-9686
Fax: (514) 933-9192
Email: tangent@colba.net

Key Contact - Specialty:
Mr. Thierry Dagneau - *Engineering, technical*
Mr. David Browne

Description: Province of Quebec specialist.
Functions: Directors, Middle mgmt., Automation, Plant mgmt., Productivity, Engineering, Technicians
Industries: Energy/utilities, Mfg., Transportation, Environmental svcs., Aerospace, Packaging

Personnel Unlimited/Executive Search
25 W. Nora
Spokane, Washington 99205
(509) 326-8880
Fax: (509) 326-0112
Email: puinc@iea.com

Key Contact - Specialty:
Mr. Gary P. Desgrosellier - *All upper level management disciplines*
Mr. Shawn Desgrosellier - *Accounting disciplines (all up to CFO)*

Description: Local firm with national exposure in all areas of employment. Serving Spokane and the entire United States for over 20 years, with many very satisfied national client companies.

Salary Minimum: $60,000
Functions: General mgmt., Mfg., Materials, Sales & mktg., HR mgmt., Finance, IT
Industries: Generalist, Mfg., Svcs., Communications, High tech, Software, Healthcare

J. R. Peterman Assoc., Inc.
1250 Waterbury Rd.
Stowe, Vermont 05672
(802) 253-6304
Fax: (802) 253-6314
Email: peterman@pwshift.com
Web: www.pwshift.com/peterman

Key Contact - Specialty:
Mr. James R. Peterman - *Life & health insurance, pensions*

Description: Specializes in life and health insurance especially group and pension. Provides both contingency and retained search service on a national basis. Specialties include executives, underwriters, actuaries, sales, accountants, contract analysts, marketers and administrators.

Salary Minimum: $50,000
Functions: Senior mgmt., Middle mgmt., Admin. svcs., Sales mgmt., Systems dev., Int'l.
Industries: Insurance

Petro Staff Int'l.
444 - 5th Ave. SW, Ste. 1250
Calgary, Alberta T2P 2T8
Canada
(403) 266-8988
Fax: (403) 262-1310
Email: petrostf@tcel.com
Web: www.tcel.com/~petrostf

Key Contact - Specialty:
Mr. Iqbal E. Ali
Ms. T. Ali
Ms. L. Switzer
Mr. C. Thomas
Mr. R. Tunis

Description: We specialize in recruitment of professionals for international oil and gas companies as well as petroleum specialists. We also recruit IS and IT professionals, as well as medical personnel.
Functions: General mgmt., Healthcare, HR mgmt., Finance, IT, Engineering, Int'l.
Industries: Energy/utilities, Misc. mfg., Aerospace, High tech, Software, Healthcare

Petruzzi Assoc.
P.O. Box 141
Scotch Plains, New Jersey 07076
(908) 754-1940
Fax: (908) 754-1941
Email: petruzzi@juno.com

Key Contact - Specialty:
Mr. Vincent J. Petruzzi - *Manufacturing, engineering, scientific*

Description: In search of excellence of hard to find individuals in the areas of manufacturing, packaging, engineering and marketing. Primarily in the medical device, pharmaceutical, chemical and plastics industry.

Salary Minimum: $40,000
Functions: General mgmt., Mfg., Materials, Mktg. mgmt., Sales mgmt., R&D, Engineering
Industries: Chemicals, Soap/perfume/cosmetics, Drugs mfg., Medical devices, Plastics/rubber, Paints/petroleum products, Packaging

Robert E. Pfaendler & Assoc., Inc.
12380 SW Main St.
Tigard, Oregon 97223
(503) 968-7777
Fax: (503) 620-8881

Email: rpfaenler@aol.com

Key Contact - Specialty:
Mr. Robert E. Pfaendler - *Banking*

Description: Only the highest code of professional and ethical standards. Guaranteed placements.

Salary Minimum: $40,000
Functions: CFO's, MIS mgmt.
Industries: Banking, Invest. banking, Misc. financial, Hospitality, Entertainment

---

Pharmaceutical Search Professionals, Inc.
311 N. Sumneytown Pike, Ste. 1A
North Wales, Pennsylvania 19454
(215) 699-1900
Fax: (215) 699-9189
Email: pspi@pharmaceutical-search.com
Web: www.pharmaceutical-search.com

Key Contact - Specialty:
Mr. Tony M. Fischetti - *Senior level executives*
Mr. John D. Wuko - *MDs, PhDs, directors, CEOs, vice presidents*
Mr. David Graham - *MDs, PhDs, associate directors, CEOs, clinical research*
Mr. Jean Boutin - *MDs, PhDs, associate directors, CEOs, clinical research*

Description: We have earned an unprecedented reputation for placing M.D., Ph.D. and MBA level executives. Our clientele consists of the top 50 pharmaceutical, biotech and medical device companies.
Functions: Directors, Senior mgmt., Middle mgmt., Physicians, CFO's, Minorities
Industries: Pharmaceutical svcs., Biotech

PHD Conseil en Ressources Humaines Inc.
1, Place Ville-Marie, Ste. 2821
Montreal, Quebec H3B 4R4
Canada
(514) 861-7100
Fax: (514) 879-3281
Email: phdelisle@videotron.ca

Key Contact - Specialty:
Mr. Pierre H. Delisle - *Information technology*

Description: Selection and recruitment of executives and seasoned professionals in information technology and information technology sales.

Salary Minimum: $70,000
Functions: Sales mgmt., IT, MIS mgmt., Systems anal., Systems implem., Systems support, Mgmt. consultants
Industries: Computer svcs., Mgmt. consulting, New media, Telecoms, Aerospace, High tech, Software

---

Phelps Personnel Assoc., Inc.
P.O. Box 4177
Greenville, South Carolina 29608
(864) 232-8139
Fax: (864) 271-1426
Email: rp55@aol.com
Web: www.burtchy.com/phelpspersonnel

Key Contact - Specialty:
Mr. Ronald A. Phelps - *Engineering*

Description: 22 years recruiting for southeastern manufacturing clients. Always fee-paid, permanent, engineering, technical, $35K to $90K. Automotive products, film, plastics, electro-mechanical products.
Functions: Product dev., Production, Plant mgmt., Quality, Purchasing, HR mgmt., Engineering
Industries: Chemicals, Plastics/rubber, Metal products, Machinery/Appliances, Motor vehicles, Computer equip., Consumer electronics

---

Phillips Assoc.
P.O. Box 83-2020
Delray Beach, Florida 33483
(561) 272-2120

Key Contact - Specialty:
Ms. Veronica Phillips - *Communications*

Description: National executive search-specialty in telecommunications and advertising in all related fields.

Salary Minimum: $20,000
Functions: Advertising, Benefits, Credit, Systems implem., Network admin., DB admin., Mgmt. consultants
Industries: Computer equip., Computer svcs., Advertising/PR, New media, Broadcast & Film, Telecoms, High tech

---

Phillips Int'l., Inc.
P.O. Box 6613
Greenville, South Carolina 29606
(864) 297-0000
Fax: (864) 297-0114
Email: search@phillipsintl.com
Web: www.phillipsintl.com

Key Contact - Specialty:
Mr. Walter Phillips - *Apparel, textile, information technology, automation, packaging*

Description: Provide executive search services for client companies ranging from presidents through sales and manufacturing to engineers in the apparel/textile industries and in industrial automation, the packaging industry and related manufacturing, as well as provide people for the MIS/IT field.

Salary Minimum: $40,000
Functions: General mgmt., Mfg., Materials, Sales & mktg., HR mgmt., Finance, IT
Industries: Textiles/apparel, Machinery/Appliances, Telecoms, Packaging

---

Phillips Personnel/Search
1675 Broadway, Ste. 2410
Denver, Colorado 80202
(303) 893-1850
Fax: (303) 893-0639
Email: phillipsp@worldnet.ATT.net

Key Contact - Specialty:
Mr. Phil Heinschel - *Telecommunications, distribution, CEOs of small to medium size companies, general managers*

Description: Contingency and retained search - banking/finance, sales/marketing, engineering, production, general management, telecommunications, EDP.

Salary Minimum: $45,000
Functions: Senior mgmt., Production, Distribution, Sales & mktg., HR mgmt., Finance, IT
Industries: Misc. financial, Computer svcs., Accounting, New media, Telecoms, High tech, Software

---

Phillips Resource Group
330 Pelham Rd.
P.O. Box 5664
Greenville, South Carolina 29606
(864) 271-6350
Fax: (864) 271-8499
Email: prgroup@globalvision.net

Key Contact - Specialty:
Mr. Sam B. Phillips, Jr. - *Textile industries (executive level)*
Mr. Albert M. Hicks - *Technical industries (all levels, all functions)*
Ms. Jennifer L. Doyle - *Outplacement (all levels, all functions)*
Mr. Peter Brooks - *Information technology (all levels, all functions)*
Ms. Jane Green - *Information technology (all levels, mid-range IBM)*
Ms. Priscilla Harrison - *Information technology (all levels)*
Ms. Jane Ko - *Information technology (all levels)*
Ms. Judy Stenhouse - *Information technology (all levels, all functions)*
Ms. Kelly Hardesty - *Information technology (all levels, all functions)*
Ms. Karen Bradford - *Engineering, manufacturing*
Mr. Crawford Chavons - *Engineering, manufacturing, textiles*

Description: Industry specialists, former officer level managers, offer a high degree of client consciousness and business understanding supporting organization planning as well as executive search for all management and staff levels.

Salary Minimum: $30,000
Functions: General mgmt., Mfg., Sales & mktg., Finance, IT, R&D, Engineering
Industries: Textiles/apparel, Paper, Chemicals, Plastics/rubber, Machinery/Appliances, Misc. mfg., Banking

Branches:
8720 Red Oak Blvd.
Charlotte, North Carolina 28217
(704) 523-6505
Fax: (704) 523-7115
Key Contact - Specialty:
Mr. Joel McIntyre - *Manufacturing, textiles (all functions)*
Mr. Pierce Sawyer - *Manufacturing, textiles*
Mr. Mike Plunkett - *Manufacturing, textiles*
Mr. Dick Jordan - *Information technology (all levels, all functions)*

Wendover Office Park
3402H W. Wendover Ave.
Greensboro, North Carolina 27407
(336) 292-1414
Key Contact - Specialty:
Ms. Bobby Kidd - *Information technology (all levels, all functions)*

Philo & Associates
2024 Eagle Glen Rd., Ste. A
Alpharetta, Georgia 30202
(770) 993-0550
Fax: (770) 993-0551

Key Contact - Specialty:
Mr. Dave Philo - *Food & beverage manufacturing*

Description: An executive search firm specializing in beverage industry, middle and upper management positions covering all disciplines within the liquid packaging arena.

Salary Minimum: $40,000
Functions: Production, Plant mgmt., Quality, Distribution, Packaging, CFO's, Engineering
Industries: Food/bev/tobacco

Phoenix BioSearch, Inc.
P.O. Box 6157
West Caldwell, New Jersey 07007-6157
(973) 812-2666
Fax: (973) 812-2727

Key Contact - Specialty:
Ms. E. A. Stephenson

Description: Confidential retained and exclusive contingency searches for scientific, engineering, marketing, business development, licensing, regulatory affairs, mid-to-high level executives in pharmaceutical, biotechnology and closely related industries.

Salary Minimum: $70,000
Functions: Product dev., Mktg. mgmt., R&D, Engineering
Industries: Drugs mfg., Biotech

Phoenix Partners, Inc.
5605 Glenridge Drive, Ste. 460
Two Premier Plaza
Atlanta, Georgia 30342
(404) 250-1133
Fax: (404) 252-2006
Email: hitech@phoenixpartners.com
Web: www.phoenixpartners.com

Key Contact - Specialty:
Mr. Robert A. Martin - *Computer hardware & software sales*

Description: Executive search firm specializing in serving the high technology industry worldwide. Clients include software, hardware and consulting companies who are seeking sales, support and consulting professionals.

Salary Minimum: $60,000
Functions: Directors, Senior mgmt., Mkt. research, Mktg. mgmt., Sales mgmt., Customer svc.
Industries: Computer equip., Computer svcs., High tech, Software

Physician Associates
Eaton Sq., P.O. Box 75113
Honolulu, Hawaii 96836-0113
(808) 947-9815
Email: Lamasc1@aol.com
Web: www.gtesupersite.com/lamphysician

Key Contact - Specialty:
Ms. Pat Lam - *Medical*

Description: We provide quality physician search services to Hawaii and mainland clients. Our staff of professional recruiters specializes in searching for physicians, physician assistants, pharmacists and physical therapists. Employer fee paid.

Salary Minimum: $40,000
Functions: Mfg., Physicians, Nurses, Health admin., Systems dev.
Industries: Biotech, Healthcare

Physician Recruiting Services, Inc.
1001 Craig Rd., Ste. 330
St. Louis, Missouri 63146
(800) 872-2106
(314) 872-2181
Fax: (314) 569-9874

Key Contact - Specialty:
Mr. Manny DeFranco - *Physicians*
Mr. Chuck McMillan - *Physicians*

Description: Our contingency firm provides a virtually risk free service to physicians, hospitals, medical groups, etc. assisting in matching physician staffing needs with appropriate candidates, sourced on a nationwide basis.

Functions: Physicians
Industries: Healthcare

Physicians Search®, Inc.
1224 E. Katella Ave., Ste. 202
Orange, California 92867-5045
(714) 288-8350
(800) 748-6320
Fax: (714) 288-8345
Email: info@physicianssearch.com
Web: www.physicianssearch.com

Key Contact - Specialty:
Mr. Clifford W. Rauch
Mr. Carl W. Rauch
Mr. Blaine T. Baird
Ms. Dorothy E. Romo
Mr. William G. LeBoeuf

Description: Established, reputable physician search and practice brokerage firm serving clients in the healthcare industry. As professionals we are licensed in both fields.

Salary Minimum: $50,000
Functions: Senior mgmt., Physicians, Nurses, Allied health, Health admin., M&A
Industries: Human resource svcs., Real estate, Healthcare

PIC Executive Search
1165 Northchase Pkwy., 4th Floor
Marietta, Georgia 30067
(770) 850-0100
Fax: (770) 850-0102
Email: acrawford@picworld.com
Web: www.picworld.com

Key Contact - Specialty:
Mr. Arlen Crawford - *Generalist*
Mr. Skip Berry - *Power, energy*
Mr. Matt Pellitier - *Power, energy*
Mr. Kevin Morris - *Power, energy*
Mr. Jack McClain - *Petrochemical, refining*
Mr. Steve Laufersweiler - *Telecommunications*

Description: We combine our industry specific consulting expertise with a tenured recruiting staff, broad industry networks and experience in a wide variety of industries.
Functions: Generalist, General mgmt., Mfg., Sales & mktg., Finance, Engineering, Int'l.
Industries: Generalist, Energy/utilities, Construction, Chemicals, Drugs mfg., Brokers, Telecoms

International Branches:
La Carlota City

Gregory D. Pickens
303 Riva Ridge, Box 1
Wylie, Texas 75098
(972) 437-3775

Email: pickens1@airmail.net

Key Contact - Specialty:
Mr. Gregory D. Pickens - *Manufacturing engineers, information technology, systems analysis & design, software development, database administration*

Description: We specialize in true search. Each of my staff is trained in cold call recruiting--our candidates are different than the product from a resume matching service.

Salary Minimum: $40,000
Functions: Product dev., Production, Plant mgmt., Quality, Productivity, Packaging, Engineering
Industries: Generalist, Plastics/rubber, Metal products, Test/measurement equip., Misc. mfg.

Pierce & Assoc.

19800 MacArthur Blvd., Ste. 300
Irvine, California 92612-2424
(714) 224-3885
Fax: (714) 224-3887
Email: resume@piercesearch.com
Web: www.piercesearch.com

Key Contact - Specialty:
Mr. Matthew J. Pierce - *CFOs, senior financial executives*
Ms. Sharon S. Pierce - *Marketing, planning, finance management*
Mr. Marty Foxman - *Human resources, finance*

Description: We are a highly successful, independently owned executive search firm specializing in placing talented financial executives and managers for our corporate clients.

Salary Minimum: $75,000
Functions: Senior mgmt., Benefits, CFO's, Cash mgmt., Taxes, M&A, Risk mgmt.
Industries: Generalist, Medical devices, Test/measurement equip., High tech, Software, Biotech, Healthcare

Pinnacle Executive Group Inc.

705 NE Lake Pointe Drive
Lees Summit, Missouri 64064
(816) 350-7028
Fax: (816) 350-7007
Email: scott@pinnaclexec.com
Web: www.pinnaclexec.com

Key Contact - Specialty:
Mr. Scott Eckley
Ms. Barbara Eckley

Description: We utilize progressive recruitment methods to secure candidates that meet the challenges of major transition and accelerating change found in corporate America today. Identifying chemistry, acumen and drive = success.

Salary Minimum: $30,000
Functions: Senior mgmt., Middle mgmt., Cash mgmt., M&A, Risk mgmt., Systems anal., Systems dev.
Industries: Generalist, Energy/utilities, Computer equip., Invest. banking, Brokers, Venture cap., High tech

Pinnacle Group Int'l.

P.O. Box 5690
Carefree, Arizona 85377
(602) 488-4490
(888) 208-8714
Fax: (602) 488-5009

Key Contact - Specialty:
Mr. Stephen F. Flynn - *Investment banking*
Ms. Joanne T. Flynn - *Investment banking*

Description: Executive recruitment firm specializing in investment banking at the analyst, associate and vice president levels.

Salary Minimum: $50,000
Functions: M&A
Industries: Invest. banking, Venture cap.

Branches:
130 Water St.
New York, New York 10005
(212) 968-1200
Fax: (212) 825-4915
Key Contact - Specialty:
Mr. Joseph Logan

The Pinnacle Source, Inc.

4600 S. Ulster St., Ste. 975
Denver, Colorado 80237
(303) 796-9900
Fax: (303) 796-9901
Email: pinnacle@rml.net
Web: www.pinnaclesource.com

Key Contact - Specialty:
Mr. Jordan A. Greenberg - *Information systems, sales, marketing, technical*

Description: Our unique approach to executive recruitment is supported by twenty-five years of successful executive search and management experience. Our client companies are high technology industry leaders as well as Colorado owned and operated start-up firms.

Salary Minimum: $55,000
Functions: Mkt. research, Mktg. mgmt., Sales mgmt., Direct mktg., MIS mgmt., Systems implem., Systems support
Industries: Computer equip., Computer svcs., Mgmt. consulting, New media, Broadcast & Film, High tech, Software

Pioneer Consulting Group

4201 Wilshire Blvd., Ste. 409
Los Angeles, California 90010
(213) 938-4260
Fax: (213) 938-1861
Email: pcg@wcis.com

Key Contact - Specialty:
Mr. Glen Chung
Ms. Helen Choi
Mr. Justin Jung
Mr. Brandon Kim
Mr. Jay Lee

Description: Our unique expertises provide qualified Korean-Americans who are exceptionally competent and loyal.

Salary Minimum: $35,000
Functions: General mgmt., Mfg., Finance, IT, R&D, Int'l.
Industries: Generalist, Mfg., Finance, Aerospace, High tech, Software, Biotech

Pioneer Executive Consultants

936 The East Mall, Ste. 201
Etobicoke, Ontario M9B 6J9
Canada
(416) 620-5563
Fax: (416) 620-5648
Email: Bradex2@ibm.net

Key Contact - Specialty:
Mr. Ed Gres - *Chemical, paint, adhesives*
Mr. Paul Sinclair - *Chemical, paint, adhesives*

Description: Full recruitment services to the chemical/paint/adhesives and ink industries in positions from general management, plant management, R&D, quality, engineering, sales and services.

Salary Minimum: $40,000
Functions: General mgmt., Product dev., Materials, Sales & mktg., Finance, R&D, Engineering

Pioneer Placement, Inc.

P.O. Box 434
Westfield, Massachusetts 01086
(413) 568-2442
Fax: (413) 568-2444
Email: pionplac@vgernet.net

Key Contact - Specialty:
Mr. Nathan Rosenthal - *Insurance*

Description: Client companies receive the experience of a seasoned recruiter with national exposure; yet the personal touch of the individual.
Functions: Generalist
Industries: Insurance

Pittleman & Assoc.

641 Lexington Ave., Ste. 2750
New York, New York 10022
(212) 319-2929
Fax: (212) 319-0199

Key Contact - Specialty:
Steven Pittleman - *Law firms, management consulting*
Linda Pittleman - *Corporations, investment banks, commercial banks*

Description: We are staffed entirely by attorneys. We have a sterling reputation for integrity and place with clients from the Fortune 50 to small, specialized boutiques.

Salary Minimum: $75,000
Functions: Attorneys
Industries: Invest. banking, Entertainment, Legal, Mgmt. consulting, Human resource svcs., Telecoms, Insurance

---

PKS Assoc., Inc.
(Firm declined to update.)
1928 Victory Hwy.
Coventry, Rhode Island 02816
(401) 397-6154
Email: paul@pksassociates.com
Web: pksassociates.com

Key Contact - Specialty:
Mr. Paul L. Spremulli - *Technical, manufacturing, engineering, IS*

Description: Our recruiters specialize in numerous technical disciplines. They are recognized experts in their recruiting specialty. Our goal is to form long lasting partnerships.

Salary Minimum: $30,000
Functions: IT, MIS mgmt., Systems anal., Systems dev., Systems implem., Engineering
Industries: Machinery/Appliances, Computer equip., Misc. mfg., Computer svcs., High tech, Software

---

PLA, Inc.
993 Lenox Drive, Ste. 200
Princeton Pike Corporate Ctr.
Lawrenceville, New Jersey 08648
(609) 844-7575
Fax: (609) 844-7637
Email: lipton1@worldnet.att.net

Key Contact - Specialty:
Mr. Steve Fippinger - *Marketing, advertising*
Ms. Stephanie Fippinger - *Marketing, advertising*

Description: We are a boutique search firm in business for 17 years, specializing in marketing, advertising and sales promotion executives. We work equally on the client and agency sides. The thrust of our business is in the food and beverage category, but also includes the interactive, retail and packaged goods areas.

Salary Minimum: $45,000
Functions: Advertising, Mkt. research, Mktg. mgmt., Sales mgmt., Direct mktg., PR
Industries: Food/bev/tobacco, Soap/perfume/cosmetics, Drugs mfg., Motor vehicles, Computer equip.

Branches:
9720 Pine Trail Court
Lake Worth, Florida 33467
(561) 966-4688
Fax: (561) 966-3583
Key Contact - Specialty:
Ms. Pat Lipton - *Marketing, advertising*

Place Mart Personnel Service
5 Elm Row
New Brunswick, New Jersey 08901
(732) 247-8844
(800) 394-7522
Fax: (732) 247-8973
Email: placemart@tapnet.net
Web: www.placemart.com

Key Contact - Specialty:
Mr. William R. Kuhl - *Biostatistics, drug information, clinical research & development*
Mr. David Winarsky

Description: Technical recruiting in clinical research data processing, statistics, records management and operations for the medical product research and development industry.

Salary Minimum: $20,000
Functions: Product dev., Physicians, Nurses, IT, Systems anal., Systems dev., R&D
Industries: Drugs mfg., Medical devices, Pharmaceutical svcs., Computer svcs., Biotech

---

Placement Solutions
W270 S3979 Heather Drive
Waukesha, Wisconsin 53188
(414) 542-2250
Fax: (414) 542-7373
Email: msshort@execpc.com
Web: www.execpc.com/placement_solns

Key Contact - Specialty:
Ms. Mary Sue Short - *Accounting*

Description: Accounting and information systems audit are specialties. All industries/businesses. Levels range from CFO down to $40K in salary.

Salary Minimum: $40,000
Functions: CFO's, Budgeting, Cash mgmt., Credit, Taxes, M&A, Minorities
Industries: Paper, Chemicals, Plastics/rubber, Metal products, Finance, Accounting, Broadcast & Film

---

Placement Testart Inc.
(Firm declined to update.)
5252 Boul. de Maisonneuve Ouest, Ste. 309
Montreal, Quebec H4A 3S5
Canada
(514) 489-8484
Email: testart@vir.com
Web: www.testart.com

Key Contact - Specialty:
Ms. Marion Testart - *High technology, computers, electronics*

Description: Specializing in software, hardware, communications, network, computer engineering, quality assurance and other hi-tech professional jobs. World-renowned companies.
Functions: IT, Systems anal., Systems dev., Systems implem., Systems support, R&D, Engineering
Industries: Drugs mfg., Medical devices, Communications, Telecoms, Aerospace, High tech, Software

---

Placements by Jesse Reid Assoc., Inc.
152 1/2 E. 63rd St.
New York, New York 10021
(212) 355-1300
Fax: (212) 355-1648

Key Contact - Specialty:
Ms. Georgia M. Petry - *Advertising, sales, management, marketing management*
Ms. Michele Deutschman - *Advertising, sales, marketing, research*

Description: A boutique firm offering timely, discreet, personal service to media clients using our extensive, compreshensive database, on-going research and face-to-face interviews.
Functions: Sales & mktg., Advertising, Mktg. mgmt., Sales mgmt., Direct mktg.
Industries: Publishing, New media

PMJ & Assoc.
(Firm declined to update.)
110 Richmond St. E., Ste. 211
Toronto, Ontario M5C 1P1
Canada
(416) 364-9997

Key Contact - Specialty:
Mr. Allen Fink - *Accounting, finance, investments, taxation*
Ms. Miriam Frankel - *Bi-lingual, insurance, credit*

Description: Twenty years experience and specializing in one geographic area along with our expertise in accounting/finance, insurance and bilingualism enables us to have proper understanding of today's market.
Functions: Middle mgmt., Budgeting, Cash mgmt., Credit, Taxes, M&A
Industries: Generalist, Mfg., Food/bev/tobacco, Finance, Packaging, Insurance, High tech

The Polen Group
1445 Washington Road
Washington, Pennsylvania 15301
(724) 225-9500
Fax: (724) 225-8907
Email: jpolen@polengroup.com
Web: www.polengroup.com

Key Contact - Specialty:
Mr. Jerry B. Polen

Description: We utilize a team approach to recruiting. Our least experienced recruiter has over 10 years with us.
Functions: General mgmt., Mfg., Materials, Sales & mktg., IT, R&D, Engineering
Industries: Mfg., Chemicals, Plastics/rubber, Aerospace, Packaging, High tech, Software

Bob Poline Assoc. Inc.
12625 High Bluff Drive, Ste. 114
San Diego, California 92130-2053
(619) 481-3700
Fax: (619) 481-5187
Email: BPAinc3@aol.com

Key Contact - Specialty:
Mr. Bob Poline - *Shopping centers*

Description: We make a total commitment to excellence in the executive search process. We treasure our reputation and recognition for professional service, performance and client satisfaction. We've stayed consistent since 1979.

Salary Minimum: $50,000
Functions: Senior mgmt., Middle mgmt., Legal, Mktg. mgmt., CFO's, Specialized services, Architects
Industries: Construction, Retail, Svcs., Legal, Accounting, Human resource svcs., Real estate

Branches:
7 Ascot Manor
Atlanta, Georgia 30327
(770) 955-9306
Fax: (770) 988-0175
Email: rpoline@atlcom.net
Key Contact - Specialty:
Mr. Rich Poline - *Shopping center industry*

Affiliates:
Delta Crown Corp.

The Pollack Group
176 Bronson Ave., Pollack Place
Ottawa, Ontario K1R 6H4
Canada
(613) 238-2233
Fax: (613) 238-4407
Email: tpg@pollackgroup.com
Web: www.pollackgroup.com

Key Contact - Specialty:
Mr. Paul Pollack - *Executive sales*
Mr. Etienne Malouin - *Information technology (contract)*
Mr. Charles Durning - *Sales high technology*
Mr. Brian McKenna - *Information technology (contract/permanent)*
Mr. Andrew McLean - *High technology sales, support*
Ms. Jennifer Hay - *Software, information technology*
Mr. Dan Murphy - *Software, information technology*

Description: Being in the center of high technology in Canada (Ottawa), the nation's capital, we have been supplying top prospects to Canada's best high technology companies and all federal government departments.

Salary Minimum: $40,000
Functions: Mktg. mgmt., Sales mgmt., Systems anal., Systems dev., Systems implem., Systems support, Engineering
Industries: Computer equip., Computer svcs., Human resource svcs., Aerospace, High tech, Software, Healthcare

Polytechnical Consultants, Inc.
7213 W. Breen
Niles, Illinois 60714
(847) 470-9000

Key Contact - Specialty:
Mr. Walt Zimmer - *Engineering*

Description: Search, recruiting and placement firm. Activity includes all technical/engineering markets, at all professional levels.

Salary Minimum: $25,000
Functions: Product dev., Production, Automation, Plant mgmt., Quality, Engineering
Industries: Medical devices, Plastics/rubber, Metal products, Machinery/Appliances, Consumer electronics, Test/measurement equip., Misc. mfg.

Al Ponaman Company, Inc.
10041-5 Larwin Ave.
Chatsworth, California 91311-7406
(818) 993-9100
Fax: (818) 993-9412
Email: info@banking-careers.com
Web: www.banking-careers.com

Key Contact - Specialty:
Mr. Albert L. Ponaman - *Banking, credit unions*

Description: Over a decade of confidential searches for major and independent banks and credit unions. Largest network of banks and professional bankers and credit union professionals.

Salary Minimum: $25,000
Functions: Senior mgmt., Middle mgmt., Advertising, HR mgmt., CFO's, MIS mgmt.
Industries: Banking, Misc. financial

Don V. Poole & Assoc., Inc.
7700 S. Glencoe Way
Littleton, Colorado 80122
(303) 721-6644
Web: dvpoole@ibm.net

Key Contact - Specialty:
Mr. Don V. Poole - *Semiconductor equipment, telecommunications, sales, product management, marketing management*

Description: Specialists in the telecommunications and semiconductor equipment industries placing executives and middle management sales and marketing professionals.

Salary Minimum: $60,000
Functions: Senior mgmt., Admin. svcs., Product dev., Mkt. research, Sales mgmt., CFO's, Int'l.
Industries: Computer equip., Test/measurement equip., Misc. mfg., Telecoms, High tech

Porter & Assoc., Inc.
(dba PR Assoc.)
P.O. Box 6217
Destin, Florida 32541
(850) 654-9300
Web: pranan@gnt.net

Key Contact - Specialty:
Ms. Nancy Porter - *Retail*

Description: Nationwide retail search and recruitment for corporate and field executives. Expertise includes merchandising, advertising, product development, planning and distribution, human resources, finance, MIS, operations and field management positions.

Salary Minimum: $50,000
Functions: General mgmt., Product dev., Advertising, HR mgmt., Finance, MIS mgmt., Graphic artists
Industries: Retail

Jack Porter Assoc., Inc.
24119 SE 18th Place
Issaquah, Washington 98029-1808
(425) 392-9252
Fax: (425) 391-9107

Key Contact - Specialty:
Mr. Jack Porter - *Generalist*

Description: Placement of engineers, scientists, manufacturing and sales professionals on a national basis at all levels in all industries. Also have opportunities for VP, GM, CFO, MIS, SW, DP and administrative professionals.

Salary Minimum: $30,000
Functions: Generalist, Production, Plant mgmt., Sales mgmt., MIS mgmt., R&D, Engineering
Industries: Generalist, Agri/forestry/mining, Energy/utilities, Food/bev/tobacco, Misc. mfg., Aerospace, Software

---

Power Recruiting Group

4833 Twin Valley Drive
Austin, Texas 78731
(512) 420-0767
Fax: (512) 420-8032
Email: MEdwards@PowerRecruiting.com
Web: www.powerrecruiting.com

Key Contact - Specialty:
Mr. J. Michael Edwards - *Energy & utilities*
Ms. Bonny Block - *Energy & utilities*

Description: President has more than ten years of energy industry experience. Founded to specialize exclusively in this industry.
Functions: General mgmt., Sales & mktg., Finance, Int'l.
Industries: Energy/utilities

Affiliates:
Independent Power Consultant

Power Search

2235 Ridge Rd., Ste. 102
Rockwall, Texas 75087
(972) 772-5577
Fax: (972) 772-0051
Email: tom@tommoon.com

Key Contact - Specialty:
Mr. Thomas A. Moon - *High technology software*

Description: Executive retained search. Recruiting for high tech software - sales and executive management.

Salary Minimum: $65,000
Functions: Mktg. mgmt., Sales mgmt.
Industries: High tech, Software

Robert Powers & Assoc.

P.O. Box 1085
Placentia, California 92670
(714) 524-7279

Key Contact - Specialty:
Mr. Robert Powers - *Restaurant, specialty retail, hospitality*
Ms. Susan Powers - *Restaurant, specialty retail, hospitality*

Description: Specialists in the restaurant, hospitality and specialty retail industries. Cover line, staff and executive management positions.

Salary Minimum: $25,000
Functions: Senior mgmt., Middle mgmt., Mkt. research, Personnel, Training, CFO's, Risk mgmt.
Industries: Food/bev/tobacco, Retail, Finance, Hospitality, Accounting, Human resource svcs., Advertising/PR

Norman Powers Assoc., Inc.

P.O. Box 3221
Framingham, Massachusetts 01705-3221
(508) 877-2025
Fax: (508) 877-0541
Email: normpowers@aol.com
Web: quikpage.com/n/npa/

Key Contact - Specialty:
Mr. Norman S. Powers - *Electronics, hardware, software, manufacturing, marketing*
Ms. Rebecca Powers Haberman - *Software, internet, marketing*

Description: Electronics, hi-tech and computer industry-military, commercial and industrial professional placement since 1964. Disciplines include: technical, BSEE, BSME, computer science; manufacturing-technical, management, material control, technical sales/marketing.

Salary Minimum: $25,000
Functions: Production, Mkt. research, Systems dev., Network admin., R&D, Engineering
Industries: Medical devices, Computer equip., Consumer electronics, Test/measurement equip., High tech, Software

---

PPS Information Systems Staffing

1420 E. Joppa Rd.
Towson, Maryland 21286
(410) 823-5630
Fax: (410) 821-9423
Email: headhunter@ppsinfo.com
Web: www.ppsinfo.com

Key Contact - Specialty:
Mr. Neal Fisher - *Network engineering, telecommunications*

Description: Native of area - principle on premise.

Salary Minimum: $20,000
Functions: IT, MIS mgmt., Systems anal., Systems dev., Systems implem., Systems support, DB admin.
Industries: Computer svcs., Telecoms, High tech, Software

Practice Dynamics, Inc.

11222 Richmond, Ste. 125
Houston, Texas 77082
(281) 531-0911
Fax: (281) 531-9014
Email: PDI@practice_dynamics.com

Key Contact - Specialty:
Ms. Karen M. Lovett - *Physicians*
Mr. John S. Harrison - *Physicians*

Description: All physician specialties in the South, Southeast, Mid-Atlantic, Southwest and Midwest. National expertise in ORS, ONC, URO, RHU. Also recruit mid-level practitioners and have over 10 years experience in medical practice appraisals.
Functions: Physicians
Industries: Healthcare

P. G. Prager Search Assoc., Ltd.

1461 Franklin Ave.
Garden City, New York 11530
(516) 294-4400
Fax: (516) 294-4443
Email: pgprager@worldnet.att.net
Web: www.pgprager.com

Key Contact - Specialty:
Mr. Paul Gershon Prager - *Legal, financial, insurance, marketing, management*

Description: One of Long Island's top recruitment firms specializing in legal, financial, insurance and general management - personalized service - no candidate referred without a personal interview. Substantial guarantee.
Functions: Senior mgmt., Admin. svcs., Mktg. mgmt., Personnel, CFO's, Taxes, Attorneys, Paralegals
Industries: Generalist, Misc. mfg., Wholesale, Finance, Legal, Human resource svcs., Insurance

---

The Prairie Group

1 Westbrook Corp. Ctr., Ste. 300
Westchester, Illinois 60154
(708) 449-7710
Fax: (708) 449-7708

Key Contact - Specialty:
Mr. James Kick - *Finance, marketing, consulting*
Mr. Romero Manzo - *Human resources*
Mr. Mark Scott - *Human resources*

Description: Top candidates for blue chip clients in all disciplines of HR, corporate finance and consulting. Emphasis on candidates that have demonstrated the ability to add value. Frequently selected to recruit outstanding diversity candidates due to our extensive network in minority communities.

Salary Minimum: $50,000
Functions: Mktg. mgmt., Benefits, Personnel, Training, Budgeting, M&A, Mgmt. consultants
Industries: Food/bev/tobacco, Chemicals, Metal products, Motor vehicles, Finance, Invest. banking, Mgmt. consulting

Precision Executive Search

1767 S. Sycamore St.
Mesa, Arizona 85202
(602) 456-3400
Fax: (602) 456-4718
Email: scjones@goodnet.com
Web: www.pesjobs.com

Key Contact - Specialty:
Mr. Geoffrey J. Jones - *Advertising, publishing, generalist*

Description: We are a privately held international search firm that specializes in locating and placing only the top performing professionals in rewarding careers within our client organizations.

Salary Minimum: $45,000
Functions: Generalist, Senior mgmt., Advertising, Mkt. research, Sales mgmt., CFO's, Graphic artists
Industries: Generalist, Mfg., Accounting, Advertising/PR, Publishing, New media, Software

Preferred Placement, Inc.

305 Madison Ave., Ste. 4700
New York, New York 10165
(212) 697-0888
Fax: (212) 983-1588

Key Contact - Specialty:
Anne Angowitz
Stuart Angowitz

Description: We place attorneys in in-house, non-legal positions and unique law firm opportunities. Fields have included management consulting, banking, investment banking, media, industrial manufacturing, leveraged leasing, chemicals, consumer products, pharmaceuticals and communications.
Functions: Generalist, Legal, M&A, Risk mgmt., Mgmt. consultants, Attorneys, Int'l.
Industries: Generalist, Mfg., Finance, Legal, Communications, Real estate

Preferred Professional Recruiters

P.O. Box 8747
6659 Embassy Court
Maumee, Ohio 43537
(419) 865-2406
Fax: (419) 865-2409
Email: Neilgreebe@aol.com
Web: www.placethenation.com/preferredprofessional

Key Contact - Specialty:
Mr. Neil Greebe - *Manufacturing, generalist*

Description: We specialize in accounting, computer/data processing, engineering, management personnel, sales and marketing, executives, technical and production supervisors in manufacturing.

Salary Minimum: $40,000
Functions: Product dev., Production, Purchasing, Sales mgmt., Benefits, CFO's, MIS mgmt.
Industries: Mfg., Chemicals, Plastics/rubber, Metal products, Transportation, Environmental svcs., Software

Preferred Professional Recruiters
(a division of Zingaro & Co.)

4200 Green Cliffs Rd.
Austin, Texas 78746
(512) 327-7275
Fax: (512) 327-1774
Email: search@pprecruiters.com
Web: www.pprecruiters.com

Key Contact - Specialty:
Ms. Ramona Rohrer
Mr. Joe Zingaro

Description: An executive search firm specializing in the search and selection of middle and senior management for the healthcare industry, including: pharmaceuticals, devices, diagnostics and venture/biotechnology

Salary Minimum: $50,000
Functions: General mgmt., Mfg., Healthcare, Sales & mktg., Finance, IT, R&D
Industries: Drugs mfg., Medical devices, Pharmaceutical svcs., Biotech, Healthcare

Premier Business Advisors

700 S. Chester Rd., Ste. 1
Swarthmore, Pennsylvania 19081
(610) 544-7030
Fax: (610) 544-6166
Email: jpacini@csi.com

Key Contact - Specialty:
Mr. Joseph Pacini - *Pharmaceutical, biotechnology*

Description: We are a boutique firm offering personalized, client oriented service. We cultivate long-term relationships with client companies and candidates in the pharmaceutical and biotechnology industries.

Salary Minimum: $100,000
Functions: Physicians, R&D
Industries: Drugs mfg., Pharmaceutical svcs., Biotech, Healthcare

Premier Healthcare Recruiters, Inc.

5 Woodbury Lane, Ste. B
Dearborn, Michigan 48120
(313) 441-6450
Fax: (313) 441-6460
Email: dianalynn4@aol.com

Key Contact - Specialty:
Ms. Diana L. Watson - *Physicians, physicians assistants, nurse practitioners, administrative physicians, physical therapists*

Description: Professional recruiting of physicians for both clinical and administrative positions on a contingency basis. Other areas of involvement include recruitment of nurse practitioners, physician assistants and physical therapists.

Salary Minimum: $100,000
Functions: Physicians, Health admin.
Industries: Healthcare

Premier Recruiting Group
(a division of Michigan Consulting Group)

3037 Benjamin
Royal Oak, Michigan 48073
(248) 549-7178
Fax: (248) 549-7178

Key Contact - Specialty:
Mr. David E. Southworth - *Officers, senior management, engineers, manufacturing managers in stamping, metal forming*
Mr. Rich Krezo - *Senior & middle management, engineers, manufacturing, sales, quality control (stamping & metal forming)*
Mr. Jun Tanaka - *Pacific Rim manufacturing*
Mr. Pedro Salinas - *Mexico, Central/South America manufacturing*
Ms. Dusty Miglio - *Sales & marketing management*
Ms. Kathy Palazzolo - *Manufacturing engineers, quality control management & engineers, engineers, manufacturing management*
Mr. Jack Lynch - *Senior, operations, manufacturing management, sales management, engineers (Vietnam, China, Asia)*

Description: General practice recruiting. Consultants providing ISO-9000 certified services for Fortune 500 plastics industry, automotive suppliers, metal forming, stamping, general manufacturing, consumer products, sheet metal, tool and die client needs.

Salary Minimum: $50,000
Functions: Senior mgmt., Middle mgmt., Mfg., Sales & mktg., HR mgmt., Finance, Engineering
Industries: Generalist, Lumber/furniture, Plastics/rubber, Metal products, Machinery/Appliances, Motor vehicles, Misc. mfg.

Affiliates:
Charles Day & Assoc.

Premier Search Group
P.O. Box 972
Greencastle, Indiana 46135-0972
(800) 694-8502
Fax: (765) 653-3039
Email: premier_search@juno.com

Key Contact - Specialty:
Mr. Joseph E. Boone, Jr. - *Quality control, information systems*
Ms. Lesa Greathouse - *Information systems*
Ms. Amber Bryan - *Data processing*
Ms. Deborah Daum - *Quality control*

Description: Recruiting firm that specializes in the search and placement of degreed professionals in quality control, engineering, human resources, manufacturing, marketing and data processing.

Salary Minimum: $40,000
Functions: General mgmt., Quality, IT
Industries: Food/bev/tobacco, Plastics/rubber, Metal products, Machinery/Appliances, Motor vehicles, Packaging, Software

Branches:
1137 E. Indiana Court
Decatur, Illinois 62521
(217) 425-9762
Fax: (217) 422-5315
Key Contact - Specialty:
Ms. Mary Paul - *Information systems*
Ms. Ashley Brown - *Information systems*

Affiliates:
Mechanics Unlimited, Inc.

The Premier Staffing Group
345 N. Market St., Ste. 208
Wooster, Ohio 44691
(330) 263-1300
Fax: (330) 263-9258
Email: thepremstf@aol.com
Web: www.premierstaff.com

Key Contact - Specialty:
Mr. James A. Babcock - *General management, engineering, operations, contract staffing*

Description: Professional search in management, engineering, finance and operations for manufacturing companies making parts for automotive or metal parts manufacturing. Also executive and hourly contract staffing for factory and clerical engineering.

Salary Minimum: $40,000
Functions: Generalist, Product dev., Production, Plant mgmt., Quality, CFO's, Engineering
Industries: Generalist, Lumber/furniture, Plastics/rubber, Metal products, Machinery/Appliances, Motor vehicles, Finance

Branches:
4932 Everhard Rd. NW
Canton, Ohio 44718
(330) 499-8677
Fax: (330) 499-8779
Email: premcanton@aol.com
Key Contact - Specialty:
Ms. Vicki Burns

2321 Second St.
Cuyahoga Falls, Ohio 44221
(330) 926-1890
Fax: (330) 926-1894
Email: premfallss@aol.com
Key Contact - Specialty:
Ms. Joy Wozny

458 Glessner
Mansfield, Ohio 44903
(419) 522-2789
Fax: (419) 522-5849
Email: premmansf@aol.com
Key Contact - Specialty:
Ms. Bonnie Thomas

14 Erie St. S.
Massillon, Ohio 44646
(330) 832-4300
Email: premmass@aol.com
Key Contact - Specialty:
Ms. Vicki Burns

1 Park Centre, Ste. 104
Wadsworth, Ohio 44281
(330) 334-4911
Email: premwads@aol.com
Key Contact - Specialty:
Ms. Joy Wozny

Prescott Legal Search, Inc.
3900 Essex Lane, Ste. 200
Houston, Texas 77027
(713) 439-0911
Fax: (713) 439-1317
Email: prescott@prescottlegal.com
Web: www.prescottlegal.com

Key Contact - Specialty:
Mr. Larry W. Prescott - *Lawyers*
Ms. Lauren Eaton Prescott - *Lawyers*
Ms. Susan Pye - *Temporary lawyers*
Ms. Tonda Hyde - *Paralegals*

Description: Founded in 1981; the only Texas recruiting firm to receive the highest possible ratings by employers in The American Lawyer's two most recent national surveys of legal recruiters; and the only Texas legal recruiting firm with offices in the state's three principal legal markets: Austin, Dallas, and Houston.

Salary Minimum: $55,000
Functions: Attorneys, Paralegals
Industries: Energy/utilities, Construction, Mfg., Finance, Svcs., Real estate, High tech

Branches:
106 E. Sixth St., Ste. 800
Austin, Texas 78701
(512) 322-5363
Fax: (512) 322-5364
Key Contact - Specialty:
Mr. Eric Van Zandt - *Lawyers*
Ms. Barbara L. Mayfield - *Lawyers*

3102 Oak Lawn Ave., Ste. 700
Dallas, Texas 75219
(214) 210-2930
Fax: (214) 210-2989
Key Contact - Specialty:
Ms. Anita S. Worth - *Lawyers*
Ms. Maria Dickson Parigi - *Lawyers*

Presley Consultants, Inc.
812 Third St.
Norco, California 91760
(909) 734-2237
Fax: (909) 734-1775
Email: presleyinc@aol.com
Web: www.apci.net/~presleyv

Key Contact - Specialty:
Mr. Philip E. Presley - *Operations, sales (all positions $60K up)*
Ms. Linda C. Presley - *Operations, administration (all positions $50K up)*
Mr. Jason T. Presley - *Food & beverage, operations*

Description: Executive search, recruitment specifically in the hospitality and healthcare (administration) industries; exclusively client retained and primarily contingency; will conduct and have conducted retained search assignments.

Salary Minimum: $50,000
Functions: Generalist, Middle mgmt., Nurses, Sales mgmt., Personnel, CFO's, MIS mgmt.
Industries: Hospitality, Healthcare

Branches:
1815 Wyoming Ave.
Billings, Montana 59102
(406) 652-4961
Fax: (406) 652-4523
Key Contact - Specialty:
Mr. Jason T. Presley - *Operations, sales & marketing, food & beverage*

Prestige Inc.
P.O. Box 421
Reedsburg, Wisconsin 53959
(608) 524-4032
Fax: (608) 524-8577
Email: Prestige@jvlnet.com

Key Contact - Specialty:
Mr. James A. Sammons - *Consumer products (all positions)*

Description: Industry specialization affords us the opportunity to know the language, methods and personnel before we begin a search, eliminating many of the risks involved in the hiring process.

Salary Minimum: $50,000
Functions: Generalist
Industries: Food/bev/tobacco, Lumber/furniture, Transportation, Wholesale, Retail, Hospitality, Healthcare

Branches:
P.O. Box 105
LaValle, Wisconsin 53941
(608) 985-8410
Key Contact - Specialty:
Mr. Marc Douglas - *Retail*

Price & Assoc., Inc.
5660 Indian River Rd., Ste. 126
Virginia Beach, Virginia 23464
(757) 366-0330
Fax: (757) 366-3124
Email: vprice@earthlink.net
Web: worldrecruiting.com

Key Contact - Specialty:
Ms. Velinda Hodge Price - *Sales, sales management, engineering, executive level, technicians*

Description: We were built on the need for a recruitment firm offering civilized headhunting and a commitment to excellence in the people they assist. The belief in the principles of commitment and accountability are the two characteristics that defines the firm's reputation and success.
Functions: Directors, Senior mgmt., Mktg. mgmt., Sales mgmt., Personnel, Systems dev., Engineering
Industries: Computer equip., Test/measurement equip., Computer svcs., Human resource svcs., Broadcast & Film, Telecoms, Software

Alan J. Price Assoc., Inc.
300 Front St., Ste. 507
Pawtucket, Rhode Island 02860-1054
(401) 728-8499
Fax: (401) 728-8857
Email: career1@gte.net

Key Contact - Specialty:
Mr. Alan J. Price - *Technology*
Ms. Lynn M. Price - *Marketing, sales administration*

Description: A full service recruiting firm serving both retained and contingent functions.

Salary Minimum: $35,000
Functions: Senior mgmt., Middle mgmt., Mkt. research, Mktg. mgmt., MIS mgmt., Engineering
Industries: Metal products, Computer equip., Consumer electronics, Telecoms, Aerospace, High tech, Software

Primary Care Service Corp.
4180 Fairgreen Drive
Marietta, Georgia 30068-4108
(770) 565-1191
Fax: (770) 565-7749
Email: pcsc@mindspring.com
Web: www.mindspring.com/~pcsc

Key Contact - Specialty:
Mr. Stephen P. Shasteen - *Physicians*
Ms. Martha F. Shasteen - *Physicians, long term care insurance*

Description: The principle of our business: truth & fairness.

Salary Minimum: $85,000
Functions: Physicians, Sales mgmt.
Industries: Insurance, Healthcare

Prime Management Group Inc.
365 Queens Ave.
London, Ontario N6B 1X5
Canada
(519) 672-7710
Fax: (519) 672-5155
Email: Prime@sympatico.ca
Web: www3.sympatico.ca/prime

Key Contact - Specialty:
Ms. Kimberley Chesney
Ms. Anita Baroness

Description: We are a human resources firm specializing in the recruitment of professionals for both management and non-management positions. Servicing London, Southwestern Ontario, Canada, US and overseas, it encompasses multiple areas of search and recruitment.
Functions: Generalist, Senior mgmt., Product dev., Purchasing, Mkt. research, Benefits, CFO's, MIS mgmt.
Industries: Plastics/rubber, Motor vehicles, Banking, Accounting, Human resource svcs., New media, Biotech

Branches:
260 Holiday Inn Drive
Cambridge, Ontario N3C 4E8
Canada
(519) 220-0310
Fax: (519) 220-0327
Email: prime2@sympatico.ca
Web: ww3.sympatico.ca/prime
Key Contact - Specialty:
Ms. Juliette Hunter

Prime Resource Assoc.
P.O. Box 490
Brookfield, Wisconsin 53008-0490
(414) 860-1260
Fax: (414) 860-1264
Email: prime@tcccom.net

Key Contact - Specialty:
Mr. Paul J. Schneider - *Engineering, technical, manufacturing*

Description: We excel at identifying the clients' needs as to technical requirements and target market, then identify and qualify all candidates for technical match and personal interest prior to submittal.
Functions: Mfg., Product dev., Production, Automation, Plant mgmt., Quality, Engineering
Industries: Mfg., Metal products, Machinery/Appliances, Motor vehicles, Packaging, High tech, Software

Prime Search
P.O. Box 472024
Charlotte, North Carolina 28247
(704) 846-5204
Fax: (704) 846-2486

Key Contact - Specialty:
Mr. Mike Peskosky - *Medical sales, pharmaceutical sales, sales management, marketing*

Description: Firm specializing in medical and pharmaceutical sales, sales management and marketing, recruiting and search.
Functions: Senior mgmt., Middle mgmt., Mktg. mgmt., Sales mgmt.
Industries: Drugs mfg., Medical devices

Princeton Executive Search
P.O. Box 7373
Princeton, New Jersey 08543-7373
(609) 584-1100
Fax: (609) 584-1141

Key Contact - Specialty:
Mr. Andrew B. Barkocy - *Accounting, human resources, engineering, information systems*

Description: Executive search and placement. Management level and supporting staff. High specialty in accounting, finance, banking, human resources, engineering and information systems.

Salary Minimum: $25,000
Functions: Generalist, HR mgmt., Finance, IT, Engineering
Industries: Generalist, Chemicals, Computer equip., Computer svcs., Accounting, Human resource svcs., High tech

Priority Executive Search
14317 Ravenwood Lane
Tampa, Florida 33618
(813) 961-8074
Fax: (813) 962-6027
Email: prioriti@ix.netcom.com

Key Contact - Specialty:
Mr. Rolf H. Kausch - *Medical, healthcare*
Ms. Beatriz J. Oliveira - *General management, insurance*

Description: Healthcare (administration, nursing, therapy, pharmacy; insurance risk management, benefits, compensation, actuarial), MO's, PPO's, TPL's, managed care.

Salary Minimum: $20,000
Functions: Senior mgmt., Physicians, Nurses, Allied health, Health admin., Benefits, Risk mgmt.
Industries: Generalist, Pharmaceutical svcs., Insurance, Healthcare

PRO, Inc./Professional Recruiting Offices, Inc.

9191 Towne Centre Drive, Ste. 102
San Diego, California 92122
(619) 587-1313
Fax: (619) 587-2090
Email: proinc@profrec.com
Web: proinc@profrec.com

Key Contact - Specialty:
Mr. Mark J. Schneekluth

Description: Nationwide executive search specialists in the healthcare, managed care, employee benefits and banking industries.

Salary Minimum: $40,000
Functions: Senior mgmt., Physicians, Sales mgmt., Risk mgmt., Systems dev., Mgmt. consultants
Industries: Computer svcs., Mgmt. consulting, Human resource svcs., Insurance, Healthcare

Pro Tec Technical Services

2255 Sheppard Ave. E., Ste. W 414
Willowdale, Ontario M2J 4Y1
Canada
(416) 496-8595
Fax: (416) 496-8729
Email: protec@protec-tech.com
Web: www.protec-tech.com

Key Contact - Specialty:
Mr. John J. Chrobak - *Engineering*
Mr. Reg Baraniuk - *Engineering, professional*
Mr. Iain Purvis - *Information technology*

Description: Global project staffing service in the enginnering, professional, information technology, environmental and manufacturing sectors.
Functions: General mgmt., Mfg., Healthcare, HR mgmt., IT, R&D, Engineering
Industries: Agri/forestry/mining, Energy/utilities, Construction, Mfg., Environmental svcs., High tech, Software

Pro-Tech Search, Inc.

116 W. Walnut St.
Chatham, Illinois 62629
(217) 483-3565
Fax: (217) 483-2146
Web: www.pro-techsearch.com

Key Contact - Specialty:
Mr. Karl McCoy - *Information technology*
Ms. Sharon Brust - *Information technology*
Ms. Janet Bascom - *Information technology*
Mr. Jonathan Pierce - *Information technology*

Salary Minimum: $30,000
Functions: IT, MIS mgmt., Systems anal., Systems dev., Systems implem., Network admin., DB admin.
Industries: Energy/utilities, Mfg., Finance, Svcs., Insurance, High tech, Software

Affiliates:
Pro-Tech Search of Florida

Probe Technology

P.O. Box 60521
King of Prussia, Pennsylvania 19406
(610) 337-8544
Fax: (610) 337-8068
Email: probetfb@aol.com
Web: www.busdir.com/probetech/

Key Contact - Specialty:
Mr. Thomas F. Belletieri - *Generalist*
Ms. Nancy Belletieri - *Generalist*

Description: Individualized service specializing in engineering, manufacturing and manufacturing support and sales/marketing. Many services offered with unique fee arrangements and creative approaches to recruiting.

Salary Minimum: $40,000
Functions: General mgmt., Mfg., Materials, Sales & mktg., Engineering
Industries: Chemicals, Medical devices, Metal products, Machinery/Appliances, Computer equip., Test/measurement equip., High tech

Probus Executive Search

4962 El Camino Real, Ste. 126
Los Altos, California 94022
(650) 960-3750
Fax: (650) 960-0331

Key Contact - Specialty:
Mr. Jack McNeal - *Accounting & finance*
Ms. Paulette Clements - *Accounting & finance*

Description: Finance and accounting professionals for manufacturing and other technology industries.

Salary Minimum: $40,000
Functions: CFO's, Budgeting, Cash mgmt., Credit, M&A, Risk mgmt.
Industries: High tech, Software, Biotech

Procom

2323 Yonge St., Ste. 605
Toronto, Ontario M4P 2C9
Canada
(416) 483-7999
Email: frank177@procom.ca
Web: www.procom.ca

Key Contact - Specialty:
Mr. Frank McCrea - *IT*

Description: We are one of the leading providers of full time and contract computer personnel in North America with over 100 clients in industries such as banking, automotive and software manufacturing, telecommunications, retail, insurance, transportation and oil refining.

Salary Minimum: $45,000
Functions: MIS mgmt., Systems anal., Systems dev., Systems implem., Systems support, Network admin., DB admin.
Industries: Transportation, Banking, Computer svcs., Mgmt. consulting, Insurance, High tech, Software

Branches:
1400 Fashion Island Blvd., Ste. 304
San Mateo, California 94404
(650) 358-0394
Web: www.procomservices.com
Key Contact - Specialty:
Mr. Jeremy Kmet

1117 Perlmeter Ctr. W., Ste. 500 E.
Atlanta, Georgia 30338
(770) 399-8838
Web: www.procomservices.com
Key Contact - Specialty:
Mr. Dave Long

3201 Yorktown Ave., Ste. 113
Durham, North Carolina 27713
(919) 572-6745
(800) 394-1840
Web: www.procomservices.com
Key Contact - Specialty:
Mr. Richard Kvring

801 E. Campbell Rd., Ste. 110
Richardson, Texas 75081-1890
(972) 234-6055
Web: www.procomservices.com
Key Contact - Specialty:
Mr. Neil King

250 - 6th Ave. SW, Ste. 1200
Bow Valley Sq. IV
Calgary, Alberta T2P 3H7
Canada
(403) 571-7241
(403) 571-7242
Key Contact - Specialty:
Ms. Sally Drysdale

102 Bank St., Ste. 204
Ottawa, Ontario K1P 5N4
Canada
(613) 566-4591
Web: www.procom.ca

Key Contact - Specialty:
Mr. Keith Carter

4480 Cote de Liesse, Ste. 110
Ville Mont Royal, Quebec H4N 2R1
Canada
(514) 731-7224
Key Contact - Specialty:
Mr. Joe Kurbe

Procurement Resources
1500 Delaware Court
P.O. Box 778
Finksburg, Maryland 21048
(410) 840-3692
Fax: (410) 840-3692
Email: procres@aol.com
Web: members.aol.com/ProcRes/index.html

Key Contact - Specialty:
Mr. John L. Cousins - *Purchasing, materials management, logistics, distribution*

Description: Specializing in the recruitment of purchasing, transportation and materials personnel capable of meeting today's challenges in supply chain management, global sourcing and quality criteria.

Salary Minimum: $40,000
Functions: Middle mgmt., Production, Materials, Purchasing, Materials Plng., Distribution
Industries: Energy/utilities, Construction, Mfg., Food/bev/tobacco, Paper, Metal products, Transportation

---

Professional Careers, Inc.
P.O. Box 53629
1310 Radford Rd., Ste. 2
Fayetteville, North Carolina 28305
(910) 323-3987
Fax: (910) 323-1819
Email: vicki@procareer.com
Web: www.procareer.com

Key Contact - Specialty:
Ms. Vicki Hayes Sturgill - *Information systems*

Description: Specialize in information systems and technology positions in the Southeast. Target development of clients for long term business relationship. We guarantee the professionals we place.

Salary Minimum: $40,000
Functions: MIS mgmt., Systems anal., Systems dev., Systems implem., Network admin., DB admin.

Professional Consulting Network, Inc.
595 Market St., Ste. 1400
San Francisco, California 94105-2821
(415) 777-4321
Email: hbartesch@pcntsf.com
Web: www.pcntsf.com

Key Contact - Specialty:
Mr. Heinz Bartesch - *MIS, software engineering*
Mr. Peter Jozwik
Mr. Jim Schneider

Description: Recruit for full time contract positions. Employ consultants or represent independent contractor for temporary consulting assignments in data processing/software engineering assignments.

Salary Minimum: $45,000
Functions: MIS mgmt., Systems anal., Systems dev., Systems implem., Systems support
Industries: High tech

Professional Employment Group
(Firm declined to update.)
P.O. Box 43668
Baltimore, Maryland 21236
(410) 679-1775
Email: pegroup@baltimore.net

Key Contact - Specialty:
Mr. John Schaefer - *Engineering, software*

Description: Managed by a former technical executive with over 20 years industry experience. This ensures a clear understanding of client company needs and candidate qualifications.

Salary Minimum: $30,000
Functions: Product dev., Production, Purchasing, Sales mgmt., MIS mgmt., Systems anal., Engineering
Industries: Mfg., Metal products, Machinery/Appliances, Computer svcs., Aerospace, High tech, Software

---

Professional Engineering Technical Personnel Consultants
8504 Ragan Rd.
Apex, North Carolina 27502
(919) 387-0070
Fax: (919) 387-0070

Key Contact - Specialty:
Mr. Richard B. Huffman - *Power/industrial electronics*

Description: Retained and contingency search provided for all disciplines and levels within the power electronics, industrial, motion, sensor and electronic industries.

Salary Minimum: $35,000
Functions: General mgmt., Product dev., Production, Automation, Quality, Systems dev., Engineering
Industries: Machinery/Appliances, Computer equip., Consumer electronics, Test/measurement equip., Misc. mfg., High tech, Software

---

Professional Healthcare Search & Consultants, Inc.
14144 Central Ave., Ste. A
Chino, California 91710
(909) 902-0769
Fax: (909) 902-0869
Email: phs@prohealthcaresearch.com
Web: www.prohealthcaresearch.com

Key Contact - Specialty:
Mr. Eden Dankowski - *Home health & hospital administrators, management*
Mr. Michael Gale - *Home health & hospital administrators, management*
Ms. Anissa Yorba - *Home health & hospital administrators, management*

Description: An executive search firm specializing in all aspects of hospital administration, home health administration, executive nursing, nursing management and business development with a separate division in healthcare management consulting.
Functions: Nurses, Health admin.
Industries: Healthcare

Professional Personnel Services
710 E. Kimberly Rd.
Davenport, Iowa 52807
(319) 388-4751
(319) 359-1751
Fax: (319) 388-4756
Web: shetler.james@mcleodusa.net

Key Contact - Specialty:
Mr. James W. Shetler - *Engineering disciplines, general management*
Ms. Patricia A. Shetler - *General management*

Description: Over twenty years experience. Heavy emphasis on industrial/manufacturing clients. Full personal attention to all candidates. No networks. No floating of resumes. Disclosure shared prior to referral.

Salary Minimum: $50,000
Functions: Senior mgmt., Middle mgmt., Production, Plant mgmt., Quality, Purchasing, Engineering
Industries: Mfg., Metal products, Machinery/Appliances, Motor vehicles, Computer equip., Consumer electronics, Misc. mfg.

Affiliates:
All Staff Human Resources

Professional Personnel Consultants, Inc.

28200 Orchard Lake Rd., Ste. 100
Farmington Hills, Michigan 48334
(248) 737-5860
Fax: (248) 737-5886
Email: ppcinc@ameritech.net

Key Contact - Specialty:
Mr. Dan Mistura - *Generalist*

Description: We specialize in recruiting, technical, professional and management in accounting, marketing, engineering, technical, manufacturing, information technology, healthcare.
Functions: General mgmt., Mfg., Healthcare, HR mgmt., Finance, IT, Engineering
Industries: Metal products, Motor vehicles, Banking, Computer svcs., Environmental svcs., High tech, Healthcare

Professional Persons Career Services

2970 E. Pleasant Ave.
Eden, New York 14057
(716) 992-9106
Fax: (716) 992-3732
Email: lmmaul@professionalpersons.com
Web: professionalpersons.com

Key Contact - Specialty:
Ms. Lisa M. Maul - *Project management professionals*

Description: An executive search firm that specializes in project management personnel. We support many fields at all levels for the engineering, construction and production industries.
Functions: General mgmt., Mfg., Materials, Sales & mktg., Budgeting, IT, Engineering
Industries: Energy/utilities, Construction, Mfg., Finance, Communications, Environmental svcs., High tech

Professional Placement Assoc., Inc.

14 Rye Ridge Plaza
Rye Brook, New York 10573
(914) 251-1000
Fax: (914) 251-1055

Key Contact - Specialty:
Ms. Laura J. Schachter - *Healthcare, medical*

Description: We are a high-quality firm in operation since 1974, with a focused expertise in the healthcare field. We render a highly personalized, intensive cost effective service.

Salary Minimum: $50,000
Functions: Physicians, Nurses, Health admin., MIS mgmt., Systems implem., Network admin., DB admin.
Industries: Healthcare

Professional Recruiting Network

1611 S. Pacific Coast Hwy., #207
Redondo Beach, California 90277
(310) 543-2991
Fax: (310) 543-4991
Email: prnet1@aol.com
Web: www.prnsearch.com

Key Contact - Specialty:
Mr. Scott Grillo - *Medical devices, sales & marketing*

Description: We are a full-service recruiting firm specializing in placing sales and sales management professionals in the medical device industry. Fees are employer paid and contingency-based.
Functions: Mkt. research, Mktg. mgmt., Sales mgmt.
Industries: Medical devices

Professional Recruiting Consultants, Inc.

3617-A Silverside Rd.
Wilmington, Delaware 19810
(302) 479-9550
Fax: (302) 479-9560
Email: Roger@staffing.net
Web: www.ipa.com/prcinc

Key Contact - Specialty:
Mr. Roger Malatesta - *Engineering, information technology, management, HR, purchasing*

Description: We are engaged in the business of identifying and recruiting qualified personnel for a variety of technical and non-technical disciplines at both the management and staff levels.
Functions: General mgmt., Directors, Senior mgmt., Middle mgmt., Mfg., Sales & mktg., IT
Industries: Energy/utilities, Mfg., Chemicals, Drugs mfg., Medical devices, Telecoms, Software

Professional Recruiting Consultants

7985 Meadow Rush Loop
Sarasota, Florida 34238
(941) 925-3759
Fax: (941) 921-7524
Email: prc@staffing.net
Web: www.staffing.net/prcjobs.htm

Key Contact - Specialty:
Mr. Tom McDermitt - *Semiconductor industry*

Description: Specialist in placing engineering, marketing, sales and technical support professionals in emerging technologies (ATE, CAE, cellular, LAN, multimedia, semiconductor). I formerly worked in EE design, marketing and sales.

Salary Minimum: $30,000
Functions: Product dev., Production, Quality, Mktg. mgmt., Sales mgmt.
Industries: Computer equip., Consumer electronics, Test/measurement equip., High tech, Software

Professional Recruiters Inc.

17641 Kettering Trail, Ste. 100
Lakeville, Minnesota 55044
(612) 892-3700
Fax: (612) 892-3711
Email: headhunt@primenet.com
Web: ProfessionalRecruiters.com

Key Contact - Specialty:
Mr. Robert Reinitz - *Electrical, electronic, high technology, sales & marketing, sales & marketing management*

Description: Very strong track record of success recruiting technically oriented sales, marketing and sales/marketing management talent primarily for the industrial electrical, electronic, hi-tech equipment markets. Recruiting since 1984. National market.

Salary Minimum: $40,000
Functions: Sales & mktg., Mkt. research, Mktg. mgmt., Sales mgmt.
Industries: Machinery/Appliances, Computer equip., Test/measurement equip., High tech

Professional Recruiters, Inc.

P.O. Box 4
Bala Cynwyd, Pennsylvania 19004
(610) 667-9355
Fax: (610) 667-5333

Key Contact - Specialty:
Ms. Joan Kool - *Healthcare, management, sales, marketing, consulting*
Mr. Stephen Lenobel - *Healthcare, management, sales, marketing, consulting*

Description: National searches primarily for companies in healthcare with cutting edge technology.
Functions: Senior mgmt., Middle mgmt., Mktg. mgmt., Sales mgmt.
Industries: Healthcare

Professional Recruiters

220 East 3900 South #9
Salt Lake City, Utah 84107
(801) 268-9940
Fax: (801) 268-9825
Email: recruitr@icw.com
Web: www.recruitersslc.com

Key Contact - Specialty:
Ms. Lora Lea Mock - *Technology*
Ms. Clair Simpson - *Medical*
Ms. Diana Viescas - *Medical*
Ms. Franci Eisenborg - *Technology*
Ms. Lynda Moore - *Technology*
Mr. Dave Kooyman - *Technology*
Ms. Nancy Bell - *Technology*
Mr. Brad Brian - *Technology*
Mr. Waylon Brian - *Technology*
Mr. Ron Mason - *Sales*

Description: We are dedicated to addressing the need for quality placement services. As professionals, we concentrate on the placement requirements of businesses and refer only those individuals who are specifically qualified.

Salary Minimum: $50,000
Functions: Middle mgmt., Mktg. mgmt., Sales mgmt., MIS mgmt., Systems anal., Systems dev., Systems implem.
Industries: Computer equip., Misc. mfg., Computer svcs., High tech, Software

Affiliates:
Temporary Resources

Professional Resource Group, Inc.

P.O. Box 1007
Muncie, Indiana 47308
(765) 281-1000
Fax: (765) 281-1001
Email: jbozell@iquest.net
Web: www.nursequest.com

Key Contact - Specialty:
Ms. Jeanna Bozell - *Nursing management, nurse executives, advanced practice nurses*

Description: President is RN, has experienced clinical arena.

Salary Minimum: $40,000
Functions: Nurses

Professional Resources

44 Omni Court
New City, New York 10956
(914) 638-4296
Fax: (914) 638-4323
Email: irwin@mail.creativeonline.com

Key Contact - Specialty:
Mr. Irwin J. Feigenbaum - *Retailing*

Description: Retail specialists; involved in department stores, discount stores, jewelry and specialty retailing. Covering all areas of merchandising operations, and corporate staff functions. Specializing in emerging new retail concepts.

Salary Minimum: $40,000
Functions: Senior mgmt., Admin. svcs., Benefits, Training
Industries: Textiles/apparel, Retail, Brokers, Human resource svcs.

Professional Resources

7030 S. Yale, Ste. 300
Tulsa, Oklahoma 74136
(918) 481-0088
Fax: (918) 481-1332
Email: john@taxjobs.com
Web: www.taxjobs.com

Key Contact - Specialty:
Mr. John W. Cowling - *Taxation*

Description: We are an nationally-focused executive search firm specializing in the placement of tax professionals.
Functions: Taxes
Industries: Generalist, Energy/utilities, Mfg., Wholesale, Retail, Finance, Svcs.

The Professional Sales Search Co., Inc.

3417 Harborview Drive
Gig Harbor, Washington 98335
(253) 851-3528
Fax: (253) 858-6588
Email: execadmin@psscinc.com
Web: www.psscinc.com

Key Contact - Specialty:
Mr. Douglas R. Letts - *Sales personnel*
Ms. Lene M. Knight - *Sales personnel*

Description: We provide quality, national sales personnel staffing, executive search and sales management consulting services for corporate America.

Salary Minimum: $30,000
Functions: Directors, Senior mgmt., Middle mgmt., Sales mgmt., Direct mktg., Training, Mgmt. consultants
Industries: Medical devices, Computer equip., Transportation, Equip. svcs., High tech, Software, Healthcare

Professional Search Assoc.

1818 W. Chapman Ave., Ste. D
Orange, California 92868-2614
(714) 978-9866
Fax: (714) 978-9868

Key Contact - Specialty:
Ms. Mary K. Dowell - *Accounting, finance, MIS, marketing, operations*

Description: Focus on your specified needs, identify resources, screen for fit, coordinate and schedule interviews, debrief after each interview, verify information and references, facilitate knowledgeable decision making and assure offer structured for acceptance.

Salary Minimum: $30,000
Functions: Generalist, General mgmt., Mfg., Sales & mktg., HR mgmt., Finance, MIS mgmt.
Industries: Generalist, Food/bev/tobacco, Misc. mfg., Finance, Hospitality, Accounting, Human resource svcs.

Professional Search, Inc.

7909 S. Monaco Court
Englewood, Colorado 80112
(303) 694-1210
Fax: (303) 290-0311

Key Contact - Specialty:
Mr. Lawrence M. Jock - *Generalist*

Description: A professional approach and expert applicant selection for positions resulting in quality placements, thus eliminating costly interviewing for employers.

Salary Minimum: $30,000
Functions: Generalist, Engineering
Industries: Generalist, Finance, Hospitality, Communications, Environmental svcs., High tech, Software

Professional Search Centre, Ltd.

1450 E. American Lane, #1875
Schaumburg, Illinois 60173
(847) 330-3250
Fax: (847) 330-3255
Email: jerryh@psc-usa.com
Web: www.psc-usa.com

Key Contact - Specialty:
Mr. Jerry S. Hirschel - *Information technology professionals*

Description: Specializing in the midrange environments, we take time to learn an applicant's goals/needs before you interview them, assuring an excellent fit and fulfilling your hiring needs by providing experienced quality professionals.

Salary Minimum: $25,000
Functions: MIS mgmt., Systems anal., Systems dev., Systems implem., Systems support
Industries: Computer svcs., Human resource svcs., Software

Affiliates:
PSC Consulting Services, Ltd.

Professional Search Consultants

210 Meidinger Twr.
Louisville, Kentucky 40202
(502) 583-1530
Fax: (502) 587-6960

Key Contact - Specialty:
Mr. Andrew J. Payton - *Generalist*

Description: Committed to conducting high quality national searches for organizations based in Kentucky, Indiana, Tennessee, West Virginia and Southern Ohio. Senior positions in law, finance, HR, sales and marketing and IS.

Salary Minimum: $50,000

Functions: Generalist
Industries: Generalist

Professional Search, Inc. Int'l.

1526 Kentucky
Amarillo, Texas 79102
(806) 359-0335
Fax: (806) 353-0000
Email: prorecruit@aol.com

Key Contact - Specialty:
Ms. Sandra McCartt - *Healthcare, MIS, sales*
Ms. Sabrina Scott - *Petroleum engineers, mechanical engineers*
Mr. E. J. McCartt, IV - *Big 6 public accounting O & G accountants*

Description: President is a working recruiter specializing in accounting, data processing, engineering and medical professionals.

Salary Minimum: $20,000
Functions: Healthcare, Finance, IT, Systems anal., Systems dev., Network admin., DB admin.
Industries: Generalist

Professional Search Consultants (PSC)

3050 Post Oak Blvd., Ste. 1615
Houston, Texas 77056
(713) 960-9215
Fax: (713) 960-1172
Email: recruit@psctech.com

Key Contact - Specialty:
Mr. L. Malek - *Engineering, information technology, accounting, finance*

Description: Use direct approach, knowledgeable industry sources and contacts. Early successful completings, providing services worldwide, 23 years experience. Formal executive searches on a contingency basis.

Salary Minimum: $30,000
Functions: Automation, Finance, MIS mgmt., Systems anal., Systems implem., Systems support, Engineering
Industries: Generalist, Energy/utilities, Construction, Mfg., Computer equip., High tech, Software

Affiliates:
Premier Professional Recruitment

Professional Support Inc.

501 John James Audubon Pkwy., Ste. 402
One Towne Centre
West Amherst, New York 14228
(716) 688-0235
Fax: (716) 688-0239
Email: buffalo@psi4jobs.com
Web: www.psi4jobs.com

Key Contact - Specialty:
Mr. Paul H. Eastmer - *IS, accounting*
Mr. Gregory Eastmer - *IS, SAP*

Description: Executive recruiting (retainer search), in accounting and data processing, disciplines; contract and rent-to-own programs, temporary clerical & DP operational services; contract data processing (project) services, individual and group outplacement services, training programs, facilities planning and disaster recovery services.

Salary Minimum: $30,000
Functions: Senior mgmt., Personnel, Budgeting, M&A, Systems dev., Systems implem., Mgmt. consultants
Industries: Generalist, Metal products, Computer svcs., Mgmt. consulting, High tech, Software

Branches:
500 Helendale Rd., Ste. 190
Rochester, New York 14609
(716) 654-7800
Fax: (716) 654-9265
Key Contact - Specialty:
Mr. Edward Sandusky - *DP, IS*

8221 Brecksville Rd., 3-107
Brecksville, Ohio 44141
(216) 526-7650
Fax: (216) 526-6612
Key Contact - Specialty:
Mr. Richard Beldon - *DP, IS*

Professionals in Recruiting Co.

1028 Cresthaven Rd., Ste. 202
Memphis, Tennessee 38119
(901) 685-2042
Fax: (901) 685-2729

Key Contact - Specialty:
Mr. James O. Murrell - *Managed healthcare, healthcare, insurance*
Ms. Maxine W. Murrell - *Medical directors*

Description: Any accepted search is handled in a confidential, ethical and professional manner with a vigorous and knowledgeable effort that promotes the client company and a mutually beneficial union with a candidate. We are strong in searches for medical directors in managed healthcare.

Salary Minimum: $40,000
Functions: Senior mgmt., Physicians, Nurses, Health admin., CFO's, MIS mgmt.
Industries: Insurance, Healthcare

Professions, Inc.

4665 Cornell Rd., Ste. 255
Cincinnati, Ohio 45241
(513) 530-0909
Fax: (513) 530-0916
Email: recruiters@professionsinc.com
Web: www.professionsinc.com

Key Contact - Specialty:
Ms. Karen Kranak - *Sales & marketing*
Mr. Carl Coco, Jr. - *Sales, paper, packaging*
Mr. Samuel N. Cohen - *Generalist*
Mr. Philip Gross - *Sales, paper, packaging*
Ms. Kim Valmore - *Sales, paper, packaging*

Description: 25-year-old search and recruiting firm based in Cincinnati, Ohio. Our strength is our intensity and commitment to increase our clients' competitive advantage by recruiting the highest caliber professionals.

Salary Minimum: $40,000
Functions: Generalist, General mgmt., Mfg., Materials, Sales & mktg., HR mgmt., Engineering
Industries: Generalist, Paper, Printing, Packaging

ProFinders, Inc.

P.O. Box 124
Orlando, Florida 32802-0124
(407) 650-4923
(407) 521-9186
Fax: (407) 650-4924
Email: sheri@profinders.com
Web: www.profinders.com

Key Contact - Specialty:
Ms. Sheri Mitchell - *Sales, marketing, operations*
Mr. Eric Jackson - *Sales, marketing, operations*

Description: Specializing in the recruitment of sales, marketing and operations in central Florida.

Salary Minimum: $25,000
Functions: Directors, Senior mgmt., Middle mgmt., Mktg. mgmt., Sales mgmt., Customer svc., PR
Industries: Generalist, Hospitality, Entertainment, Pharmaceutical svcs., Computer svcs., Mgmt. consulting, Human resource svcs.

Profit Pros, Inc.

23945 Calabasas Rd., #203
Calabasas, California 91302
(818) 222-4872
Web: profitpros@msn.com

Key Contact - Specialty:
Mr. David L. Gaffney

Description: 25 years of executive search experience at senior and middle management levels in both retained and contingency divisions committed to quality performance and results.

Salary Minimum: $40,000
Functions: Generalist, General mgmt., Sales & mktg., HR mgmt., Finance, IT
Industries: Construction, Finance, Hospitality, Entertainment, Accounting, Communications, Real estate

ProLink

5040 Netherwood Rd.
Rocky Mount, North Carolina 27803
(252) 443-2259
Fax: (252) 443-2976
Email: prolink@earthlink.net
Web: www.projobs.com

Key Contact - Specialty:
Mr. Don Gladwell - *Information technology*

Description: Christian business linking highly professional and ethical people with highly professional and ethical companies serving the information technology industry nationwide.

Salary Minimum: $25,000
Functions: IT
Industries: Generalist

ProNet, Inc.

3200 Glen Royal Rd., Ste. 100
Raleigh, North Carolina 27612
(919) 782-2760
Fax: (919) 782-2987
Email: dicks@ProNetNC.com

Key Contact - Specialty:
Mr. Dick Starling - *Computer hardware, software vendors, communications vendors*

Description: Recruiting in the data processing and data communication industry nationwide since 1980, providing qualified candidates in a timely manner. Principals have held national sales and marketing positions with Fortune 500 companies.

Salary Minimum: $35,000
Functions: Mkt. research, Mktg. mgmt., Sales mgmt., CFO's, MIS mgmt., Systems anal., Systems dev.
Industries: Computer equip., Telecoms, Software

Proquest Inc.

505 Pettigru St.
Greenville, South Carolina 29601
(864) 239-0237
Fax: (864) 239-0293
Email: proquest@mindspring.com
Web: www.proquest.net

Key Contact - Specialty:
Mr. Donald L. Powell - *Senior management, medical products, manufacturing operations, regulatory affairs, QA/QC*

Description: Specialists in pharmaceutical, biotechnology and medical devices/ equipment segments of the healthcare products industry. Emphasis on regulatory affairs, QA/QC, engineering, medical/clinical affairs, R&D and manufacturing.

Salary Minimum: $50,000
Functions: Directors, Middle mgmt., Product dev., Quality, R&D, Engineering
Industries: Drugs mfg., Medical devices, Biotech

ProSearch Recruiting

2899 Agoura Rd., Ste. 142
Westlake Village, California 91361
(818) 597-0300
Fax: (818) 865-0974
Email: sjcurtis@aol.com

Key Contact - Specialty:
Ms. Susan J. Curtis - *Publishing, internet, events, sales management, top management*
Mr. Brad Munson - *Publishing, internet marketing, circulation, editorial*

Description: Specializing in high tech print publishing, events and the internet. We cover sales, marketing, editorial, operations and top management. Our 20+ years of publishing gives you the insight and candidates you need!

Salary Minimum: $50,000
Functions: General mgmt., Advertising, Mkt. research, Mktg. mgmt., Sales mgmt., Direct mktg., IT
Industries: Advertising/PR, Publishing, New media, High tech

ProSearch, Inc.

70 Center Street, 3rd Floor
Portland, Maine 04112
(207) 775-7600
Email: psi@ime.net
Web: www.psicareers.com

Key Contact - Specialty:
Mr. Edward S. McKersie - *Sales, marketing, accounting, finance, information technology*

Description: Small, high quality firm dedicated to high ethics and confidentiality. Owner has over ten years in the search and staffing industry. We strive to develop strong relationships with client companies in an effort to match company culture and management styles.

Salary Minimum: $25,000
Functions: Mkt. research, Mktg. mgmt., Sales mgmt., Direct mktg., HR mgmt., Finance, IT
Industries: Insurance

Branches:
4 Courthouse Lane, Ste. 12
Chelmsford, Massachusetts 01824
(978) 454-1100
Key Contact - Specialty:
Mr. Frank Kearney

ProSearch, Inc.

29017 Chardon Rd., #220
Willoughby Hills, Ohio 44092
(440) 585-9099
Fax: (440) 585-8030
Email: c.wayne@ProSearchRecruiters.com
Web: ProSearchRecruiters.com

Key Contact - Specialty:
Mr. Cary S. Wayne - *Accounting, tax*

Description: Specialists in accounting/ finance, engineering/manufacturing, sales/marketing, data processing/MIS, operations management, general management, corporate and firm attorney's.

Salary Minimum: $40,000
Functions: Middle mgmt., Quality, Materials Plng., Sales mgmt., CFO's, Taxes, Attorneys
Industries: Printing, Plastics/rubber, Machinery/Appliances, Legal, Accounting, Packaging, High tech

ProSearch, Inc.

610 W. Germantown Pike, Ste. 120
Plymouth Meeting, Pennsylvania
19462-1050
(610) 834-8260
Fax: (610) 834-8010
Web: www.prosearchinc.com

Key Contact - Specialty:
Ms. Suzanne F. Fairlie - *MIS, client/server, data warehousing, system architect, application directors*

Description: Specialize in placing information systems professionals for Fortune 500's in Mid Atlantic area. Known for professionally interviewing/screening all candidates and arranging interviews only where appropriate for your requirements. Positions: DBA's, programmers, system architects, data modelers, business analysts, CIO's. Member of Pinnacle-honorary of Nation's Top 50 recruiters.

Salary Minimum: $45,000
Functions: IT, MIS mgmt., Systems dev., Systems implem., Network admin., DB admin., Minorities
Industries: Drugs mfg., Aerospace, High tech, Healthcare

Prospective Personnel Service, Inc.

P.O. Box 702432
Tulsa, Oklahoma 74170-2432
(918) 425-1700
Fax: (918) 524-5246
Email: BankRcrtr@aol.com

Key Contact - Specialty:
Ms. Linda Kinney - *Banking*

Description: Certified Personnel Consultant, 20 years experience, specialization in professional level banking positions. Solo operator with strong networking connections. Permanent positions.
Industries: Banking

ProStar Systems, Inc.

P.O. Box 842
Dunkirk, Maryland 20754
(301) 812-0871
Fax: (301) 855-5853
Email: prostar@crosslink.net

Key Contact - Specialty:
Mr. Ronald G. Shepherd

Description: President has spent over 30 years in the computer industry, prior to starting his recruiting firm.
Functions: Sales mgmt., MIS mgmt., Systems anal., Systems dev., Systems implem., Systems support, Mgmt. consultants
Industries: Generalist

ProTech Nationwide Staffing, Inc.

505 Fifth Ave., Ste. 1100
New York, New York 10017
(212) 557-1000
Fax: (212) 557-5020
Email: protechnyc@erols.com
Web: www.protechjobs.com

Key Contact - Specialty:
Mr. H. R. Brakel - *Technical, manufacturing, engineering, scientists, FDA/GMP/EPA regulated industries*

Description: A nationwide service which draws highly qualified candidates from all parts of the US. We refer only carefully selected, pre-qualified, pre-motivated candidates. Specialization assures our quality.

Salary Minimum: $40,000
Functions: Product dev., Automation, Quality, Distribution, Packaging, Engineering
Industries: Food/bev/tobacco, Chemicals, Soap/perfume/cosmetics, Drugs mfg., Packaging, Biotech

Protocol Inc.

300 N. Lake Ave., Ste. 208
Pasadena, California 91101-4106
(626) 449-2214
Fax: (626) 577-0484
Email: pas@protocolagency.com
Web: www.protocolagency.com

Key Contact - Specialty:
Mr. Robert W. Sparks - *Executive management*
Ms. Kelly J. Lucas - *Accountants, managers*

Description: Search and selection firm specializing in contingency and retained placement of accounting, financial, mid-range programmers, medical, human resources, middle and upper level management professionals.

Salary Minimum: $30,000
Functions: Senior mgmt., Allied health, Customer svc., Training, CFO's, Network admin., DB admin.
Industries: Generalist, Mfg., Finance, Accounting, Haz. waste, Real estate, Healthcare

Branches:
650 Hampshire Blvd., Ste. 100
Westlake Village, California 91361
(805) 371-0069
Fax: (805) 371-0048
Email: wlv@protocolagency.com
Key Contact - Specialty:
Mr. Chris Salcido - *Programmers (AS400 & client servers), network specialists (AS400 & client servers)*

Proven Edge

12616 Springbrook Drive, Ste. D
San Diego, California 92128
(619) 679-1705
Fax: (619) 679-1705

Key Contact - Specialty:
Mr. Walter Gold - *Middle management, professional, technical*

Description: A recruiting firm dedicated to adhering to the highest level of ethics, respecting the confidentiality of the client and the candidate while searching the corporate maze for either one.

Salary Minimum: $60,000
Functions: Middle mgmt., Product dev., Production, Mktg. mgmt., Sales mgmt., Cash mgmt., R&D
Industries: Printing, Chemicals, Drugs mfg., Plastics/rubber, Paints/petroleum products, Advertising/PR, Publishing

Pryor & Associates

90 New Montgomery St., Ste. 401
San Francisco, California 94105
(415) 908-1388
Fax: (415) 908-1383
Email: pryor@2extreme.net

Key Contact - Specialty:
Ms. Jo-Ann Pryor - *Insurance (all areas)*
Ms. Kathy Florence - *Insurance (all areas)*

Description: Provides specialized search and recruitment services for the insurance industry - management, administrative, finance, systems, underwriting, loss control, marketing/sales, claims, risk management, producers, account servicers and technical/clerical.

Salary Minimum: $30,000
Functions: Benefits, Risk mgmt.
Industries: Insurance

Affiliates:
Bennett-Pryor Temporaries

PSD Group, Inc.

595 Market St., Ste. 2430
San Francisco, California 94105
(415) 882-0220
Fax: (415) 882-0559
Email: general@psdsf.com
Web: www.psd.co.uk

Key Contact - Specialty:
Mr. Robert Graham-Bryce - *Communications*
Ms. Rachel Hollands - *Semiconductors*
Mr. David Holton - *Communications*
Ms. Rui Zheng - *Semiconductors*
Ms. Lisa Suchesk - *Communications*

Description: 350 specialist consultants provide world class executive search and selection recruitment service from 8 office centers, research and conference facilities in Europe, Asia Pacific and USA.

Salary Minimum: $60,000
Functions: General mgmt., Mfg., Materials, Sales & mktg., IT, Engineering, Int'l.
Industries: Computer equip., Consumer electronics, Test/measurement equip., Broadcast & Film, Telecoms, Packaging, High tech

International Branches:
London

PSP Agency

188 Montague St.
Brooklyn, New York 11201
(718) 596-3786
(718) 596-9155
Fax: (718) 596-9157
Email: pspagenc@aol.com

Key Contact - Specialty:
Mr. Frank Burwell, Jr. - *Sales & marketing*
Mr. Arnold D. Harvey - *Telecommunications*
Mr. James McFadden - *Engineers, sales computer software & hardware*

Description: Targeting sales, marketing and finance.

Salary Minimum: $40,000
Functions: Middle mgmt., Production, Systems anal., Systems dev., Systems support, Network admin., Engineering
Industries: Paints/petroleum products, Consumer electronics, Test/measurement equip., Telecoms, High tech, Software, Biotech

QD Legal

55 Adelaide St. E., Ste. 200
Toronto, Ontario M4L 2Z9
Canada
(416) 955-4783
Fax: (416) 955-0428
Email: qdlegal@ica.net
Web: www.qdgroup.com

Key Contact - Specialty:
Mr. Jonathan Marsden
Ms. Lorene Nagata
Mr. Christopher Pang

Description: Specialist Canada-wide legal recruitment firm working on a contingency and retained basis for law firms, corporations and financial institutions.
Functions: Legal, Attorneys
Industries: Generalist

Affiliates:
The Counsel Network

Quality Consulting Group, Inc.

104 S. Main St., Ste. 513
Fond Du Lac, Wisconsin 54935
(920) 923-1900
Fax: (920) 923-1993
Email: qcg@tcccom.net
Web: www.dice.dlinc.com/qcg

Key Contact - Specialty:
Ms. Mary Gerlach - *Information systems, SAP, PeopleSoft*
Ms. Celeste Christ - *Information systems, SAP, PeopleSoft*

Description: Tenured recruiters providing a high quality of service and maintaining high ethical standards. We belong to a network of recruiters and offer our personal guaranty.
Functions: MIS mgmt., Systems anal., Systems dev., Systems implem., Systems support, Network admin., DB admin.
Industries: Misc. mfg., Computer svcs., High tech, Software

Quality Control Recruiters

61 Bradley St.
P.O. Box 1900
Bristol, Connecticut 06011-1900
(860) 582-0003
Fax: (860) 585-7395

Key Contact - Specialty:
Mr. Charles V. Urban - *Quality, reliability*

Description: We provide recruiting services in quality, reliability and regulatory affairs for businesses nationwide. The firm is uniquely composed of professionals with managerial and hands-on experience in quality from a variety of industries. Also provides consulting and training services.
Functions: Senior mgmt., Production, Plant mgmt., Quality, Packaging, Engineering, Mgmt. consultants
Industries: Food/bev/tobacco, Paper, Medical devices, Plastics/rubber, Paints/petroleum products, Metal products, Motor vehicles

Quality Search

1100 S. Calumet Rd.
Chesterton, Indiana 46304
(219) 926-8202
Fax: (219) 926-3834
Email: quality@staffing.net
Web: www.niia.net/biz/quality

Key Contact - Specialty:
Mr. James L. Jeselnick

Description: We place/recruit technical/engineering personnel for most manufacturing related firms. Our specialization is packaging engineers, quality control and manufacturing management.

Salary Minimum: $40,000
Functions: Plant mgmt., Packaging, Engineering
Industries: Food/bev/tobacco, Chemicals, Soap/perfume/cosmetics, Drugs mfg., Medical devices, Paints/petroleum products, Consumer electronics

Branches:
P.O. Box 1622
Show Low, Arizona 85902
(520) 532-7333
Fax: (520) 532-7334
Key Contact - Specialty:
Mr. John Lowery

P.O. Box 9382
Wyoming, Michigan 49509
(616) 538-2117
Fax: (616) 538-2156
Key Contact - Specialty:
Ms. Suzanne Fisher

Quality Search Inc.

P.O. Box 752294
Dayton, Ohio 45475-2294
(937) 439-0744
Fax: (937) 439-0766
Email: qualitysearch@sprintmail.com
Web: www.qualitysearch.com

Key Contact - Specialty:
Mr. Robert J. Johnson - *Technical careers, engineering, sales, management*

Description: Sharply focused in serving individuals with technical backgrounds: i.e. engineers, scientists, computer specialists, finance, chemists and sales; in automotive, telecommunications, information technology, medical, aerospace, hydraulics, pneumatics, rubber and plastics.

Salary Minimum: $30,000
Functions: Product dev., Automation, Quality, Sales mgmt., Budgeting, Systems anal., Engineering
Industries: Medical devices, Plastics/rubber, Computer equip., Telecoms, Aerospace, High tech, Software

Quantum EDP Recruiting Services

2000 Ave. McGill College, Bureau 1800
Montreal, Quebec H3A 3H3
Canada
(514) 842-5555
Fax: (514) 849-8846

Key Contact - Specialty:
Mr. Louis Camus - *Information technology*

Description: Recruitment firm specializing in the placement of IT and technology professionals. We are Canada's largest, privately-held recruiting firm.
Functions: MIS mgmt., Systems anal., Systems dev., Systems implem., Systems support, Network admin., DB admin.
Industries: Energy/utilities, Mfg., Retail, Finance, Communications, High tech, Software

Branches:
420 Lexington Ave., Ste. 2221
New York, New York 10170
(212) 972-1313
Fax: (212) 983-7087
Key Contact - Specialty:
Mr. Tony Pittarelli

659 Queen St., Ste. 1
Fredericton, New Brunswick E3B 1A6
Canada
(506) 459-1166
Fax: (506) 451-8911
Key Contact - Specialty:
Ms. Cynthia Miles

50 O'Connor St., Ste. 1410
Ottawa, Ontario K1P 6L2
Canada
(613) 237-8888
Fax: (613) 230-7711
Key Contact - Specialty:
Mr. Terry Scullion
Mr. Pierre Quinn

55 University Ave., Ste. 950
Toronto, Ontario M5J 2H7
Canada
(416) 366-3660
Fax: (416) 366-4362
Key Contact - Specialty:
Ms. Christine Wall

888 St. Jean St., Ste. 510
Quebec, Quebec G1R 5H6
Canada
(418) 522-4064
Fax: (418) 522-8522
Key Contact - Specialty:
Ms. Cynthia Miles

Affiliates:
Silverside

The Quantum Group

133 Watchung Ave.
Upper Montclair, New Jersey 07043
(973) 509-2229
Fax: (973) 509-2173

Email: quantum@viconet.com
Web: quantum-group.com

Key Contact - Specialty:
Ms. Dawn Schlesinger - *Telecommunications (sales, management, operations)*
Mr. Michael Schlesinger
Ms. Jean Anne McMahon

Description: We are a professional recruiting organization specializing in telecommunications sales, sales management and operations employment opportunities. We only work with experienced telecommunications professionals.

Salary Minimum: $40,000
Functions: Directors, Senior mgmt., Middle mgmt., Sales mgmt., Technicians
Industries: Telecoms

Branches:
638 Clinton Ave.
Haddonfield, New Jersey 08033
(609) 216-1133
Key Contact - Specialty:
Ms. Jean Anne McMalton

Quest Enterprises, Ltd.
112 W. Liberty Drive
Wheaton, Illinois 60187-5124
(630) 588-8400
Fax: (630) 588-0675
Email: admin@questent.com
Web: www.questent.com

Key Contact - Specialty:
Mr. Richard W. Honquest - *Information technology*
Ms. Darcy Zulpo - *Information technology*
Mr. Rich Moss - *Information technology*
Mr. Joseph W. Kennedy, IV - *Information technology*

Description: Due to the industry experience of our entire staff and strong client relationships, we successfully fill over 80 percent of our available positions with a 98 percent retention ratio.
Functions: MIS mgmt., Systems anal., Systems dev., Systems implem., Systems support, Network admin., DB admin.
Industries: High tech, Software

The Quest Organization
11 Pennsylvania Plaza, Ste. 935
New York, New York 10001
(212) 971-0033
Fax: (212) 971-6256
Email: mrosenbl@questorg.com

Key Contact - Specialty:
Mr. Michael F. Rosenblatt - *Finance, accounting, tax, human resources, operations*

Description: We function is an extension of our client management. We have CPA's with CFO experience in public companies on our staff and we provide personalized high quality business consulting along with every search assignment.
Functions: HR mgmt., CFO's, Cash mgmt., Taxes, M&A, MIS mgmt., Mgmt. consultants
Industries: Invest. banking, Brokers, Entertainment, Accounting, Broadcast & Film, Real estate

---

Quest Worldwide Executive Search Corp.
1650 S. Pacific Coast Hwy., Ste. 209
Redondo Beach, California 90277
(800) 395-2220
Fax: (310) 316-6601
Email: careers@questworldwide.com
Web: www.questworldwide.com

Key Contact - Specialty:
Mr. Victor Gamboa - *Technology, management consulting*

Description: We are a leading information technology search firm with a proven record of successful relationships with major corporations and top management consulting firms throughout the United States and Europe.
Functions: Senior mgmt., IT, Systems anal., Systems dev., Systems implem.
Industries: High tech, Software

Questor Consultants, Inc.
2515 N. Broad St.
Colmar, Pennsylvania 18915
(215) 997-9262
Fax: (215) 997-9226
Email: qtor@cynet.net
Web: www.qtor.com

Key Contact - Specialty:
Mr. Sal Bevivino - *Property & casualty insurance claims, bond underwriting*

Description: P/C insurance industry specialists. Heavily specializing in claims and underwriting on a national basis.

Salary Minimum: $35,000
Functions: Nurses, Risk mgmt., Minorities, Attorneys
Industries: Insurance, Healthcare

QuestPro, Inc.
5580 Peterson Lane, Ste. 190
Dallas, Texas 75240
(972) 960-1305
Fax: (972) 960-1357
Email: questpro@gte.net
Web: www.questpro.com

Key Contact - Specialty:
Ms. Lauren Levinson - *Insurance, property, casualty, commercial lines underwriting, claims*
Mr. Trey Hugley - *Insurance, property, casualty, commercial lines underwriting, claims*

Description: We handle local and nationwide searches for commercial lines insurance positions from entry level to the executive officers in claims, underwriting, loss control, risk management, managed care/healthcare, professional liability and marketing. We do have experience with personal lines searches as well.

Salary Minimum: $30,000
Functions: Directors, Senior mgmt., Middle mgmt., Admin. svcs., Mktg. mgmt., Risk mgmt., Int'l.
Industries: Insurance

Quiring Assoc., Inc.
7321 Shadeland Station Way, #150
Indianapolis, Indiana 46256
(317) 841-7575
Fax: (317) 577-8240
Email: quiring@iquest.net
Web: www.iquest.net/quiring

Key Contact - Specialty:
Ms. Patti L. Quiring - *Data processing, human resources, medical*

Description: Member of both Indiana and Indianapolis Chambers of Commerce; Better Business Bureau; debt-free; extremely favorable credit history; strategic alliances in split fee situations.
Functions: General mgmt., Mfg., Physicians, Sales & mktg., HR mgmt., IT, Engineering
Industries: Energy/utilities, Medical devices, Finance, Computer svcs., Human resource svcs., Software, Healthcare

---

Quirk-Corporon & Assoc., Inc.
P.O. Box 93386
Milwaukee, Wisconsin 53203-0386
(414) 224-9399
(414) 271-8711
Fax: (414) 224-9472
Email: cecorporon@aol.com

Key Contact - Specialty:
Mr. Charles E. Corporon - *Insurance, financial*
Ms. Therese M. Quirk - *Insurance, financial*

Description: Recruit at executive level for major insurance companies and national brokers. Principals spent more than 25 years in the insurance business and twenty years in placement.
Functions: Mktg. mgmt., Sales mgmt., Customer svc.
Industries: Banking, Accounting, Insurance, Healthcare

R & K Associates, Inc.
1296 W. Stacey Lane
Tempe, Arizona 85284
(602) 961-2983
Fax: (602) 940-5190

Email: kreicha@aol.com

Key Contact - Specialty:
Mr. Karl J. Reichardt - *Semiconductors, personal computers, miscellaneous high technology*

Description: Specializing in high technology, the firm offers a cost effective alternative and short cycle times for searches. Experience handling large ramp ups is a key ingredient of experience and expertise.

Salary Minimum: $45,000
Functions: Mktg. mgmt., Sales mgmt., R&D, Engineering
Industries: Computer equip., Test/measurement equip., High tech, Software

Branches:
20822 Cactus Loop
San Antonio, Texas 78258
(210) 497-2998
Fax: (210) 497-2999
Key Contact - Specialty:
Mr. Robert Belsjoe - *Semiconductors, personal computers, miscellaneous high technology*

R. C. Services
1565 W. Main St., Ste. 208
Lewisville, Texas 75067-3397
(972) 355-1928
Fax: (972) 355-1843
Email: calvin4alaska@webtv.net

Key Contact - Specialty:
Mr. Gordon L. Collier - *Engineering, construction with heavy emphasis for oil, gas, mining, petrochemical*

Description: Work exclusively in the construction and engineering areas associated with chemical, petrochemical, refinery and cogeneration. Gordon L. Collier previously director, construction manpower for Fluor Constructors.

Salary Minimum: $30,000
Functions: Senior mgmt., Middle mgmt., Admin. svcs., Purchasing, Mktg. mgmt., Engineering, Int'l.
Industries: Energy/utilities, Construction, Haz. waste

R. J. Associates
30 Glenn St.
White Plains, New York 10603
(914) 946-0278
Fax: (914) 946-2019
Email: rjassociates@e-mail.msn.com

Key Contact - Specialty:
Mr. Richard Birnbaum - *Senior management, human resources, finance, operations, general management*

Description: Complete staffing service for major corporate clients with consultants specializing by discipline.

Salary Minimum: $75,000
Functions: Senior mgmt., Mfg., Materials, Mktg. mgmt., HR mgmt., Finance, IT
Industries: Generalist, Food/bev/tobacco, Soap/perfume/cosmetics, Medical devices, Entertainment, Publishing, Telecoms

R.A.N. Assoc., Inc.
140 Public Sq., Ste. 804
Cleveland, Ohio 44114
(216) 696-6699

Key Contact - Specialty:
Mr. Norman A. Thomas
Mr. Bill Hicks

Description: Full service operation, including professional staffing, executive search and specialist in E.E.O. and female consulting.

Salary Minimum: $30,000
Functions: Production, Purchasing, Nurses, Benefits, Budgeting, Engineering, Minorities
Industries: Energy/utilities, Chemicals, Banking, Hospitality, Computer svcs., Haz. waste, Software

R2 Services, LLC
2300 N. Barrington Rd., Ste. 315
Hoffman Estates, Illinois 60195
(847) 854-1000
Fax: (847) 490-1050
Email: info@r2services.com
Web: www.r2services.com

Key Contact - Specialty:
Mr. Randall E. Smith - *Software engineering, sales, management*
Mr. Rory J. Patchin - *Software engineering, sales, management*

Description: We specialize in development, sales and management positions associated with real-time embedded systems software development. Our staff is comprised of engineers with real-world experience.
Functions: Middle mgmt., Sales mgmt., Systems anal., Systems dev., R&D, Engineering, Minorities
Industries: Medical devices, Computer equip., Consumer electronics, Telecoms, Aerospace, High tech, Software

Railey & Assoc.
5102 Westerham Place
Houston, Texas 77069
(281) 444-4346

Key Contact - Specialty:
Mr. J. Larry Railey - *Legal*

Description: Established in 1978. Legal only. Nationwide--all industries and law firms. All practice levels especially mid and upper echelons: associates, partners, legal administrators, attorneys, general counsel. Law firm mergers.

Salary Minimum: $75,000
Functions: Attorneys
Industries: Energy/utilities, Construction, Misc. mfg., Transportation, Svcs., High tech

Ramm Search
(a division of Labor-Management Services)
Old Walt Whitman Rd.
P.O. Box 1426
Melville, New York 11747
(516) 643-7687
Email: rammsrch@aol.com

Key Contact - Specialty:
Mr. Kenneth Migdol - *General management*

Salary Minimum: $75,000
Functions: Generalist, General mgmt., Mfg., Sales & mktg., HR mgmt., Finance, IT

Ramming & Assoc., Inc.
3 Thackery Lane
Cherry Hill, New Jersey 08003-1925
(609) 428-7172
Fax: (609) 428-7173
Email: georger@dvnc.net

Key Contact - Specialty:
Mr. George Ramming

Description: Most industries. Extensive Internet recruiting experience.

Salary Minimum: $50,000
Functions: Middle mgmt., Mfg., Healthcare, HR mgmt., Finance, R&D, Engineering
Industries: Generalist, Mfg., Finance, Packaging, High tech, Healthcare

Rand Thompson Executive Search Consultants
261 Madison Ave.
New York, New York 10016
(212) 972-0090
Email: rtconsultg@aol.com

Key Contact - Specialty:
Mr. John Kelly - *Accounting, finance, Wall St.*
Mr. Harold Kost - *Generalist*
Mr. Robert Pisano - *Insurance*

Description: We have grown and maintained relationships with many firms rated #1 in their respective industries. Currently 75% of search assignments are completed with individuals referred by satisfied applicants.

Salary Minimum: $75,000

Functions: Generalist, Senior mgmt., Direct mktg., Personnel, CFO's, Systems dev., Int'l.
Industries: Generalist, Finance, Invest. banking, Brokers, Computer svcs., Human resource svcs., Insurance

Rand-Curtis Resources
10611 N. Indian Wells Drive
Fountain Hills, Arizona 85268
(602) 837-2100
Fax: (602) 837-9415
Email: randcurtis@aol.com

Key Contact - Specialty:
Ms. Judy Kopulos - *Restaurants*

Description: 20+ years experience in recruiting mid to upper level management for major restaurant companies, quick service and full service. We offer integrity, experience and industry knowledge. We recruit for all functions within the industry.

Salary Minimum: $45,000
Functions: Directors, Senior mgmt., Middle mgmt., Personnel
Industries: Retail, Svcs., Hospitality

Lea Randolph & Assoc., Inc.
10210 N. Central Expwy., Ste. 216
Dallas, Texas 75231
(214) 987-4415
Email: leagary@it.netcom.com

Key Contact - Specialty:
Ms. Lea Randolph - *General business, healthcare*
Mr. Troy Randolph - *Accounting, finance, general business*

Description: Professional recruiters specializing in mid to upper management positions in healthcare, finance/accounting and general business including sales.
Functions: Middle mgmt., Nurses, Health admin., Sales mgmt., Customer svc., Taxes, Risk mgmt.
Industries: Generalist, Finance, Accounting, Healthcare

J. E. Ranta Assoc.
112 Washington St.
Marblehead, Massachusetts 01945
(781) 639-0788
Fax: (781) 631-9828
Email: eranta@erols.com
Web: www.southpawcorp.com/ranta

Key Contact - Specialty:
Mr. Ed Ranta - *Computer software, call center management, telecommunications*

Description: Firm has placed over 700 individuals across several industry segments. Candidate pool has been developed through contacts throughout the United States and an affiliation with over thirty other firms.

Salary Minimum: $60,000
Functions: Customer svc., MIS mgmt., Systems anal., Systems dev., Systems implem., Network admin., DB admin.
Industries: Generalist, Computer svcs., New media, Telecoms, High tech, Software

Harold L. Rapp Assoc.
80 Hemlock Drive
Roslyn, New York 11576-2303
(516) 625-4341
Fax: (516) 625-4517
Email: hlrassoc@aol.com

Key Contact - Specialty:
Mr. Harold L. Rapp - *Jewelry industry (executives)*

Description: Recruitment of executives for the jewelry industry, whose earnings capacity exceeds $40,000. Searches performed for wholesalers, importers and manufacturers of jewelry and watches, as well as for retail jewelry organizations.

Salary Minimum: $40,000
Functions: Senior mgmt., Middle mgmt., Product dev., Plant mgmt., Mktg. mgmt., Sales mgmt., Customer svc.
Industries: Mgmt. consulting, Non-classifiable industries

Vera L. Rast Partners Inc.
1 S. Wacker Drive, Ste. 3890
Chicago, Illinois 60606
(312) 629-0339
Fax: (312) 629-0347

Key Contact - Specialty:
Ms. Vera L. Rast - *Legal*
Mr. Alex Trent - *Legal*
Ms. Suzanne English Jones - *Legal*

Description: Legal search for corporate law departments, law firms and patent/intellectual property practice groups.
Functions: Attorneys
Industries: Legal

Joanne E. Ratner Search
10 E. 39th St., Ste. 514
New York, New York 10016
(212) 683-1975
Fax: (212) 683-4682
Email: ratner@ix.netcom.com

Key Contact - Specialty:
Ms. Joanne E. Ratner - *Finance, marketing, accounting*

Description: Minority (female) owned boutique firm specializing in finance, accounting and marketing positions.

Salary Minimum: $50,000
Functions: Mkt. research, CFO's, M&A, Risk mgmt., MIS mgmt., Mgmt. consultants, Minorities
Industries: Food/bev/tobacco, Banking, Invest. banking, Misc. financial, Advertising/PR, Broadcast & Film, Non-classifiable industries

Affiliates:
The Meredith Group

Ray & Assoc., Inc.
4403 First Ave. SE, Ste. 407
Cedar Rapids, Iowa 52402-3221
(319) 393-3115
Fax: (319) 393-4931

Key Contact - Specialty:
Mr. Gary L. Ray - *Superintendents (school districts)*
Dr. Robert Decker - *Superintendents (school districts)*

Description: We are a national firm specializing in school personnel matters. We have been recruiting and placing school superintendents, principals and municipal administrators for 20 years. Our professional search team and our services are unmatched but our fees are competitive.
Functions: HR mgmt., Personnel, Mgmt. consultants, Minorities

Raymond Karsan Assoc.
170 S. Warner Rd., Ste. 110
Wayne, Pennsylvania 19087
(610) 971-9171
Fax: (610) 971-9181
Email: raykar@raymondkarsan.com
Web: www.raymondkarsan.com

Key Contact - Specialty:
Mr. Nooruddin S. Karsan
Mrs. Elba Rivera-Lopez - *Insurance*
Mr. Sean Lynch - *Insurance*
Mr. Richard P. Ongirski - *Insurance*
Mr. P. Grant Parker - *Insurance*
Mr. Robert B. Srolis - *Insurance*
Mr. Donald Volk - *Insurance*

Description: Organization primarily consists of individuals with appropriate technical backgrounds who have become search consultants.
Functions: Senior mgmt., Production, Sales mgmt., Benefits, CFO's, MIS mgmt., Engineering
Industries: Chemicals, Drugs mfg., Pharmaceutical svcs., Insurance, High tech, Biotech, Healthcare

Branches:
35-20th Court
Hermosa Beach, California 90254
(310) 798-5079
Fax: (310) 798-5279
Key Contact - Specialty:
Ms. Suzanne Jenne

350 Indiana St., Ste. 800
Golden, Colorado 80401
(303) 273-5800
Fax: (303) 273-0500
Key Contact - Specialty:
Mr. J. Scott Croasdale - *Temporary staffing*

1303 Hightower Trail
Northridge Pavilion #4, Ste. 170
Dunwoody, Georgia 30350
(770) 998-9360
Fax: (770) 998-2874
Key Contact - Specialty:
Mr. Craig Twiste

2340 River Rd., Ste. 414
Des Plaines, Illinois 60018
(847) 297-8000
Fax: (847) 297-8006
Key Contact - Specialty:
Mr. Andy Perler
Mr. Rick Sondhi - *Industrial/business services, engineering, not for profit, manufacturing*
Mr. Ted Zemper

7976-A Old Georgetown Rd.
Bethesda, Maryland 20814
(301) 652-0070
Fax: (301) 656-2843
Key Contact - Specialty:
Mr. Larry Williams

53 Commercial Wharf
Boston, Massachusetts 02110
(617) 227-2999
Fax: (617) 227-3171
Key Contact - Specialty:
Mrs. Anita Sakuru - *Information technology, IS, ERP, contract solutions*

18 Commerce Way, 7th Floor
Woburn, Massachusetts 01801
(781) 932-0400
Fax: (781) 932-0895
Key Contact - Specialty:
Mr. Vincent Albergato - *Insurance, legal, benefits consulting*
Mr. Angelo Buono - *High technology*
Mr. William Docker - *Information technology*
Mr. Donald Marshall
Mr. John Sacerdote
Mr. Raghu Sakuru
Mr. Dick Swanson

6200 S. 58th St.
Lincoln, Nebraska 68516
(402) 434-2660
Fax: (402) 434-2661
Key Contact - Specialty:
Mr. Bill Erickson
Mr. Troy Kanter
Mr. Shawn Sterling

8 Dixon Ave.
Concord, New Hampshire 03301
(603) 226-6677
Fax: (603) 226-6688
Key Contact - Specialty:
Mr. Barry Raymond

180 S. St.
Murray Hill, New Jersey 07974
(908) 665-1900
Fax: (908) 665-1905
Key Contact - Specialty:
Mrs. Jill Gualtieri
Mr. Greg Gunther
Mr. Christopher Lawton
Mr. Donald Tompkins

388 Wall St.
Princeton, New Jersey 08540
(609) 252-0999
Fax: (609) 252-9733
Key Contact - Specialty:
Ms. Natalie Brooks - *Human resources*
Mr. Elliot Clark - *Pharmaceutical*
Mr. Kevin Kruse

522 E. Genessee St.
Fayetteville, New York 13066
(315) 637-4600
Fax: (315) 637-4170
Key Contact - Specialty:
Mr. S. Graham Atkinson - *Temporary staffing*

11 Penn Plaza, Ste. 320
New York, New York 10001
(212) 268-7555
Fax: (212) 268-7373
Key Contact - Specialty:
Mr. P. Grant Parker
Ms. Courtney Dittmann

983 Old Eagle School Rd., Ste. 605
Wayne, Pennsylvania 19087
(610) 971-6400
Fax: (610) 971-6410
Key Contact - Specialty:
Mr. Jeff Anderson - *Temporary staffing*
Mr. Kevin Brown - *Information technology executives*
Mr. Tom Dimke - *Pharmaceutical, biotechnology*
Mr. Kevin Hudson - *Chemical manufacturing*
Mr. Angus Lamb - *Insurance*
Mr. George Scott - *Pharmaceutical, biotechnology*

638 Aldebaran St.
El Fenix Bldg., Ste. HQ
San Juan, Puerto Rico 00920
(787) 774-8865
Fax: (787) 783-9011
Key Contact - Specialty:
Mr. Juan Padilla
Mr. Jose Resto

1010 Lamar St., Ste. 310
Houston, Texas 77381
(713) 652-5739
Fax: (713) 652-5732
Key Contact - Specialty:
Mr. Kevin Hudson

6 Journeys End
The Woodlands, Texas 77381
(409) 321-2006
Fax: (409) 321-2754
Key Contact - Specialty:
Mr. Randy Miller

1500 N. Beauregard St., Ste. 110
Alexandria, Virginia 22311
(703) 845-1114
Fax: (703) 845-1011
Key Contact - Specialty:
Mr. Michael Prencipe - *Network, telecommunications*

3170 Kincross Circle
Herndon, Virginia 22071
(703) 742-9716
Fax: (703) 742-9266
Key Contact - Specialty:
Mr. Sandy Rodgers

7124 Applewood Drive
Madison, Wisconsin 53719
(608) 833-7549
Fax: (608) 833-9497
Key Contact - Specialty:
Mr. Doug Leslie

International Branches:
Hammersmith, Hyderabad

Raymond Thomas & Assoc.

407 Wekiva Springs Rd., Ste. 221
Longwood, Florida 32779
(407) 774-8300
Fax: (407) 774-7604

Key Contact - Specialty:
Mr. Ray Huegel - *Factory automation, machine tools*
Mr. Mike Garland - *Factory automation, machine tools*

Description: 34 years of experience in metal working industries along with 19 years experience in executive recruiting specializing, worldwide with machine tool and related factory automation OEM's as well as users. Extensive network in mid-upper to upper levels of management.

Salary Minimum: $60,000
Functions: Senior mgmt., Middle mgmt., Product dev., Production, Plant mgmt., Sales mgmt., Engineering
Industries: Metal products, Machinery/Appliances, Misc. mfg.

Razzino-Claymore Assoc.

277 Fairfield Rd., Ste. 332
Fairfield, New Jersey 07004
(973) 882-3388
Fax: (973) 882-2764

Key Contact - Specialty:
Ms. Janelle Razzino - *Finance, accounting, information technology, audit*
Mr. Robert Casillo - *Financial audit-systems*

Description: A boutique search firm offering the foremost in executive recruiting with a personal touch.

Salary Minimum: $35,000

Functions: CFO's, Budgeting, M&A, Risk mgmt., MIS mgmt., Systems implem., Mgmt. consultants
Industries: Food/bev/tobacco, Drugs mfg., Medical devices, Banking, Entertainment, Accounting, Telecoms

---

RBW Assoc. Inc.
30352 Lassen Lane
Junction City, Oregon 97448
(541) 688-9212
Fax: (541) 688-9312
Email: rbwassoc@cyberis.net
Web: www.rbwassoc.com

Key Contact - Specialty:
Mr. Ray B. Wheeler - *Pulp & paper industry professionals*

Description: Professional recruiting for industries top 10% talent - management, technical, engineering/maintenance, administrative and sales.

Salary Minimum: $30,000
Functions: Senior mgmt., Middle mgmt., Mfg., HR mgmt., Finance, IT, Engineering
Industries: Paper, Chemicals, Misc. mfg., Packaging, High tech

Branches:
204 San Mateo Drive
Hot Springs Village, Arkansas 71913
(501) 525-3579
Fax: (501) 525-3579
Key Contact - Specialty:
Ms. Eutha Corder - *Lumber, wood, furniture & fixtures, paper & allied industry, high technology*

RCI Employment Solutions
1655 Palm Beach Lakes Blvd., Ste. 600
West Palm Beach, Florida 33401
(561) 686-6800
Fax: (561) 686-8043
Email: recruiter@bestjobsusa.com
Web: www.bestjobsusa.com

Key Contact - Specialty:
Mr. Mike Corriero
Mr. Michael Moore - *Sales, sales management*

Description: Source, screen, qualify, recruit: we offer internet recruiting, a candidate database of 300,000, a client base of 125,000 corporations nationwide and niche advertising sources including Employment Review.
Functions: Middle mgmt., Sales mgmt.
Industries: Printing, Computer equip., Consumer electronics, Hospitality, Non-profits, Pharmaceutical svcs., High tech

Affiliates:
Employment Review

Re-Mark Assoc. Inc.
P.O. Box 215
Aberdeen, New Jersey 07747-0215
(732) 583-5100
Fax: (732) 583-5301
Email: futrgar8@worldnet.att.net

Key Contact - Specialty:
Mr. Gary Leffer - *High technology*
Mr. Philip Kase - *High technology, medical*

Description: Retained search, contingency search and enhanced candidate searches limited to staffing senior management, marketing, sales, engineering and purchasing personnel for the semiconductor, electronics, optical, fiber optics and chemical industries.

Salary Minimum: $40,000
Functions: General mgmt., Mfg., Healthcare, Sales & mktg., IT, R&D, Engineering
Industries: Mfg., Communications, Aerospace, High tech, Biotech

---

Real Estate Executive Search, Inc.
P.O. Box 40
Santa Rosa, California 95402-0040
(707) 833-6141
(707) 525-4591
Fax: (707) 525-4595

Key Contact - Specialty:
Mr. J. A. Havens - *Management*
Ms. Louise McDonald - *Real estate (all functions)*

Description: Twenty five years of service to the real estate and finance community.

Salary Minimum: $40,000
Functions: Finance, Cash mgmt.
Industries: Banking, Misc. financial, Insurance, Real estate

Reality Group
P. O. Box 2675
Broken Arrow, Oklahoma 74013-2675
(918) 451-4057
Fax: (918) 451-4743

Key Contact - Specialty:
Mr. Larry Sims - *Safety, health, environmental*

Description: The intricacies of hiring top talent requires a highly trained, competent and certified staff. Our staff is headed by an internationally renowned speaker and trainer who in the last 15 years has trained literally thousands of recruiters worldwide.

Salary Minimum: $25,000
Functions: Middle mgmt., Engineering, Environmentalists
Industries: Paper, Chemicals, Plastics/rubber

Recruit Xpress
P.O. Box 934
Bellaire, Texas 77402-0934
(713) 666-1001
Fax: (713) 666-9993

Key Contact - Specialty:
Mr. Howard Frankel - *Software & hardware engineering managers*
Ms. Marcia Frankel - *Software & hardware engineers*

Description: We represent engineers and managers who improve the performance and profitability of their employers.

Salary Minimum: $50,000
Functions: Senior mgmt., Middle mgmt., Product dev., Mktg. mgmt., Sales mgmt., MIS mgmt., Engineering
Industries: Computer equip., Consumer electronics, Computer svcs., New media, Telecoms, High tech, Software

---

Recruiters Professional Network - Fairview
28435 Quince Rd.
Fairview, Missouri 64842
(417) 632-4395
Email: medfind@juno.com

Key Contact - Specialty:
Mrs. Vickie Dent - *Medical (all specialties)*

Salary Minimum: $50,000
Functions: Physicians, Nurses, Allied health, Health admin.
Industries: Healthcare

Recruiting Assoc. of Amarillo
P.O. Box 8473
Amarillo, Texas 79114
(806) 353-9548
Fax: (806) 353-9540
Email: mikedr@arn.net

Key Contact - Specialty:
Mr. Michael Rokey

Description: Professional recruiting and staffing service, both permanent and contract nationwide affiliations, reasonable fees.
Functions: Systems anal., Systems dev., Systems implem., Engineering
Industries: Chemicals, Plastics/rubber, Metal products, Machinery/Appliances, Misc. mfg., Software

---

Recruiting Options, Inc.
1375 Northview Ave.
Atlanta, Georgia 30306
(404) 874-1003
Fax: (404) 249-9108

Email: m.sq-roi@worldnet.att.net

Key Contact - Specialty:
Ms. Martha Eskew - *Advertising, public relations, marketing communications, account service, media*

Description: ROI offers national caliber service without the high cost of a national retained search firm. Unbundling the components means a program can be tailored to meet your hiring goals, time frame and budget.

Salary Minimum: $50,000
Functions: Advertising, Mkt. research, Mktg. mgmt., Direct mktg., PR, Graphic artists
Industries: Advertising/PR, New media

Recruiting Resources Int'l.

1125 Lindero Canyon Rd., Ste. A 8238
Westlake Village, California 91362
(818) 597-1818
Fax: (818) 597-1919
Email: hh1@gte.net

Key Contact - Specialty:
Mr. Bruce A. Dean - *Electronic information content & systems*

Description: We provide sales & marketing professionals to companies selling information to corporate and academic customers.
Functions: Mkt. research, Mktg. mgmt., Sales mgmt.
Industries: Higher ed., Pharmaceutical svcs., Publishing, New media, High tech, Software

Recruiting Services Group, Inc.

5743 Nanjack Circle
Memphis, Tennessee 38115
(901) 367-0778
Fax: (901) 367-0868
Email: rsghunt@memphisonline.com
Web: www.rsghunt.com

Key Contact - Specialty:
Ms. Whitney Hodges - *Distribution, operations, manufacturing management*
Ms. Kerry Finley - *MIS, accounting*

Description: We are an independent search firm specializing in serving manufacturing and industrial corporations. We focus on finding the best possible career match for both client and individual.

Salary Minimum: $45,000
Functions: Mfg., Materials, Sales & mktg., HR mgmt., Budgeting, MIS mgmt., Engineering
Industries: Mfg., Plastics/rubber, Machinery/Appliances, Motor vehicles, Computer equip., Consumer electronics, Transportation

Recruiting Specialists

300 Providence Hwy., Ste. M-5
P.O. Box 572
Dedham, Massachusetts 02027
(617) 329-5850
Fax: (617) 329-5840

Key Contact - Specialty:
Ms. Cindy Laughlin - *Retail, specialty hardlines, softlines, off-price*
Mr. Wayne Penwell - *Retail, mass merchandising, hardlines*
Ms. Tracy Wolcott - *Retail, food, hospitality*
Mr. Rob Bowerman - *Retail (home office, store level, home fashions)*
Ms. Nancy Martirano - *All retail*
Mr. Daniel Durica - *Off price retail*
Ms. Rhonda Dresner - *Food and hospitality*

Description: We attribute our success to our ability to develop a feel for the style of a company and the unique needs of the specific position. We find not only qualified candidates-but the best candidates! We work with you through the interview process and continue after the hire is made until you are fully satisfied.

Salary Minimum: $25,000
Functions: Directors, Senior mgmt., Middle mgmt.
Industries: Retail, Hospitality

Branches:
7210 Hull St. Rd., Ste. 204
Richmond, Virginia 23235
(804) 276-9008
Fax: (804) 276-9066

Affiliates:
Retail Executive Placement Services
Retail Placement Associates

Recruiting/Solutions

5655 Lindero Canyon Rd., Ste. 521
Westlake Village, California 91362
(818) 597-8310
Fax: (818) 597-8323
Email: hh1@gte.net

Key Contact - Specialty:
Mr. Joel Rice - *Consumer products & services*
Mr. Bruce Dean - *Information technology*

Description: We are known for our ability to perform quickly for our clients. We will recruit and screen 3 to 5 qualified and interested candidates within 7 working days!
Functions: Senior mgmt., Middle mgmt., Mkt. research, Mktg. mgmt., Sales mgmt.
Industries: Food/bev/tobacco, Lumber/furniture, Paper, Soap/perfume/cosmetics, Computer svcs., New media, Software

The Recruitment Group, Inc.
(a division of Snelling Personnel)

P.O. Box 410
Williamsville, New York 14231
(716) 631-8960
Fax: (716) 631-8964
Email: robf@buffnet.net
Web: www.personnelsearch.com

Key Contact - Specialty:
Mr. Robert F. Palumbo - *Manufacturing, construction, packaging, sales & marketing*
Mr. David Ryan - *Manufacturing, motion controls, sales & marketing*

Description: Emphasis is on making quality placements. We prefer making smaller numbers of exceptional placements to large numbers of mediocre ones. Most of our orders are exclusives. Most of our clients are repeat customers.

Salary Minimum: $30,000
Functions: Middle mgmt., Automation, Materials Plng., Mktg. mgmt., M&A, Systems dev., Engineering
Industries: Construction, Mfg., Hospitality, Environmental svcs., Aerospace, Packaging, Software

Recruitment Resources

One City Blvd. W., Ste. 820
Orange, California 92868
(714) 978-7383
Fax: (714) 978-7386
Email: rmross@pacbell.net

Key Contact - Specialty:
Ms. Ruthie M. Ross - *Pharmaceutical, medical sales*

Description: We are an executive search firm that specializes in the placement of medical, pharmaceutical sales and sales management.
Functions: Healthcare, Sales mgmt.
Industries: Drugs mfg., Medical devices, Pharmaceutical svcs.

Recruitment Specialists, Inc.

1412 E. Joppa Rd.
Towson, Maryland 21286
(410) 825-6186
Fax: (410) 821-8211
Email: erols@recruit1.com

Key Contact - Specialty:
Ms. Roxanne Giannerini - *Healthcare*

Description: A nurse owned and operated firm with 15+ years of experience recruiting mid-level and senior executives for national healthcare organizations. Specialties: managed care organizations, healthcare systems, home health and sales management.

Salary Minimum: $45,000

Functions: Senior mgmt., Nurses, Allied health, Health admin., Sales mgmt., Personnel, MIS mgmt.
Industries: Healthcare

Mary Rector & Assoc., Inc.
40 S. Prospect, Ste. 200
Roselle, Illinois 60172
(630) 894-5060
Fax: (630) 894-5607
Web: www.mrector.com

Key Contact - Specialty:
Ms. Mary Rector-Gable - *Health & beauty aids*

Description: Our firm specializes in placing mid and senior level management professionals specializing in sales, marketing, operations and general management for the haircare industry.

Salary Minimum: $50,000
Functions: Directors, Senior mgmt., Mkt. research, Mktg. mgmt., Sales mgmt., PR, Training
Industries: Food/bev/tobacco, Textiles/apparel, Soap/perfume/cosmetics, Drugs mfg., Retail, Communications, Advertising/PR

P. J. Reda & Assoc., Inc.
1955 Cliff Valley Way, Ste. 117
Atlanta, Georgia 30329
(404) 325-8812
Fax: (404) 325-8850
Email: predainc@atl.mindspring.com

Key Contact - Specialty:
Ms. Pat Reda - *Restaurant, hospitality, hotels, country clubs*

Description: Executive search firm specializing in any level of restaurant and hotel operations management. Entry level through CEO. Anywhere in the U.S.

Salary Minimum: $30,000
Functions: General mgmt., Directors, Middle mgmt.
Industries: Hospitality, Human resource svcs.

Redell Search, Inc.
P.O. Box 25067
Chicago, Illinois 60625
(773) 271-4449
Fax: (773) 271-9689
Email: redell@ix.netcom.com
Web: pw1.netcom.com/~redell/search.html

Key Contact - Specialty:
Mr. John Redell - *Information systems*

Description: We specialize in doing recruitment for major consulting firms, software developers and hardware vendors.

Functions: Sales mgmt., IT, MIS mgmt., Systems anal., Systems dev., Systems implem., Systems support
Industries: Generalist, High tech, Software

Cedric L. Reese Inc.
P.O. Box 8573
Fresno, California 93747-8573
(209) 261-9566
Email: creeseqs@ix.netcom.com
Web: www.ipa.com

Key Contact - Specialty:
Mr. Cedric Reese

Description: Central California recruiters specializing in accounting, engineering and computer programming. We seek to establish a long-term, high-quality strategic relationship with our clients.
Functions: Senior mgmt., Middle mgmt., Mfg., Distribution, Finance, IT, Engineering
Industries: Agri/forestry/mining, Construction, Mfg., Svcs., Software

---

Reeve & Assoc.
700 Canal St.
Stamford, Connecticut 06902
(203) 328-3726
Fax: (203) 968-2818
Email: philreeve@snet.net

Key Contact - Specialty:
Mr. Philip Reeve - *Marketing*

Description: We are a full service contingency search firm providing professional and personalized service. Our main geographical focus is the Northeast and Westcoast but also conduct nationwide searches.

Salary Minimum: $35,000
Functions: Mkt. research, Mktg. mgmt., Direct mktg.
Industries: Computer equip., Finance, Invest. banking, Advertising/PR, New media, High tech, Healthcare

---

The Regency Group, Ltd.
256 N. 115th St., Ste. 1
Omaha, Nebraska 68154-2521
(402) 334-7255
Fax: (402) 334-7148
Email: info@regencygroup.com
Web: www.regencygroup.com

Key Contact - Specialty:
Mr. Dan J. Barrow - *Information systems, telecommunications*

Description: Information systems and telecommunications specialists. Performance oriented search and recruiting firm. Capable of providing companies in a variety of industries with the latest technologies via performance driven business people with strong IS/Telecom backgrounds. Contracting services available.

Salary Minimum: $30,000
Functions: MIS mgmt., Systems anal., Systems dev., Systems implem., Systems support
Industries: Computer svcs., Telecoms, High tech, Software

Reid Ellis Assoc. Inc.
2910 S. Sheridan Way
Oakville, Ontario L6J 7J8
Canada
(905) 829-9394
Fax: (905) 829-3045

Key Contact - Specialty:
Ms. Gail Skewes - *Intermediate management, senior management, engineering, manufacturing, technical applications*

Description: A small highly confidential firm, providing exceptional personalized service.

Salary Minimum: $50,000
Functions: General mgmt., Mfg., Materials, HR mgmt., Finance, IT, Engineering
Industries: Paper, Printing, Plastics/rubber, Motor vehicles, Misc. mfg., Packaging, High tech

---

Reinecke & Assoc.
P.O. Box 1141
Secaucus, New Jersey 07094
(201) 865-5935
Fax: (201) 865-6081

Key Contact - Specialty:
Mr. Robert Schumann - *Transportation, logistics executives*
Mr. G. Reinecke - *General management*

Description: Specializing in transportation executives.

Salary Minimum: $35,000
Functions: Middle mgmt., Distribution, Sales mgmt., CFO's, Credit, M&A, Int'l.
Industries: Transportation, Accounting, Mgmt. consulting

Branches:
PO Box 1305
4621 Green Meadows Ave.
Torrance, California 90505
(310) 378-1332
Fax: (310) 366-5823
Key Contact - Specialty:
Ms. Ellen C. Campbell

11732 Brookside Dr.
Palos Park, Illinois 60464
(708) 671-0188
Fax: (708) 671-0190
Key Contact - Specialty:
Ms. Cynthia Y. Allen

International Branches:
Basel, Hamburg, Matosinhos, Milan, Penn, Rotterdam

RemTech Business Solutions, Inc.

21894 Farmington Rd.
Farmington, Michigan 48336
(248) 426-6212
Fax: (248) 426-6216
Email: lrembisz@remtech-solutions.com
Web: www.remtech-solutions.com

Key Contact - Specialty:
Ms. Laura Rembisz - *Information systems*
Mr. Waldemar Raczkowski

Description: We are a woman owned information systems firm that offers temporary and permanent employees to businesses. A careful technical screening and personality analysis ensures high quality employees to match client specifications.
Functions: MIS mgmt., Systems anal., Systems dev., Systems implem., Systems support, Network admin., DB admin.
Industries: Computer svcs., High tech

The Renaissance Network

2 Oliver St., 8th Floor
Boston, Massachusetts 02109
(617) 946-2222
Fax: (617) 946-2220
Email: Recruiting@Ren-Network.com
Web: www.Ren-Network.com

Key Contact - Specialty:
Ms. Lisa Sacchetti - *Information technology, software engineering, IT consulting*

Description: We realize the importance of talented/skilled personnel to the success of an organization. We work closely with clients to develop focused job descriptions and carefully select and prescreen candidates before submitting them for consideration.
Functions: MIS mgmt., Systems anal., Systems dev., Systems implem., Systems support, DB admin., Engineering
Industries: Computer svcs., Telecoms, High tech, Software

RepFinders USA

(Firm declined to update.)
341 Farnum Rd.
Media, Pennsylvania 19063-1605
(610) 566-6542

Key Contact - Specialty:
Mr. Warren B. Hughes

Description: We locate, screen and help to attract the best independent manufacturers' sales rep agencies for manufacturers by geographic territory in the United States and throughout the world.
Industries: Generalist

Research Personnel Consultants

335 Bay St., Ste. 810
Toronto, Ontario M5H 2R3
Canada
(416) 726-8000
Fax: (905) 272-3900
Email: respers@interlog.com

Key Contact - Specialty:
Mr. Rob Capel - *Database, marketing, market research*

Description: Twelve years experience in market research gives me a unique understanding of the talents necessary for success. The interconnected disciplines of database, marketing and market research are my specialty.
Functions: Senior mgmt., Middle mgmt., Mkt. research, Mktg. mgmt., Mgmt. consultants, Int'l.
Industries: Food/bev/tobacco, Banking, Pharmaceutical svcs., Telecoms, Insurance, Non-classifiable industries

Resource Management Group

(Firm declined to update.)
177 Broad St., 14th Floor
Stamford, Connecticut 06901
(203) 961-7000

Key Contact - Specialty:
Mr. Denis LaPolice - *Finance*

Description: Our firm specializes in the recruitment of finance and accounting professionals. We have attracted numerous Fortune 500 companies, financial service organizations, public and privately held businesses and emerging entrepreneurial organizations. Our network of clients provides us with growing opportunities.

Salary Minimum: $50,000
Functions: CFO's, Budgeting, Cash mgmt., Credit, Taxes, M&A, Risk mgmt.
Industries: Generalist, Mfg., Finance, Svcs., Communications, Real estate, High tech

Resource Networking Inc. (dba Pergal & Co.)

6802 Madison Ave.
Indianapolis, Indiana 46227
(800) 373-5229
Fax: (317) 786-9199
Email: rnii@aol.com

Key Contact - Specialty:
Mr. Donald Pergal - *Technical upper management*

Description: Wide range of industry experience engineering through operations; metal fabrication, automotive, medical electronics staffing and consulting.

Salary Minimum: $70,000
Functions: Senior mgmt., Product dev., Personnel, CFO's, IT, R&D, Engineering
Industries: Plastics/rubber, Machinery/Appliances, Motor vehicles, Computer equip., High tech, Software, Biotech

Resource Recruiting

547 Amherst St., 4th Floor
Nashua, New Hampshire 03063
(603) 595-2822
Fax: (603) 886-1822

Key Contact - Specialty:
Mr. Alan C. Etlinger - *Accounting, finance, MIS, operations management*
Mr. Robert C. Harrington - *Accounting, finance, MIS*

Description: The company is staffed with individuals experienced not only in recruiting, but with substantial experience in the disciplines they service. Our consultants conduct searches from staff level to senior management.
Functions: General mgmt., Materials, Sales & mktg., Finance, IT, Engineering
Industries: Generalist

Affiliates:
Resource I. T. Group, Inc.

Resource Services, Inc.

20 Crossways Park N.
Woodbury, New York 11797
(516) 496-4100
Fax: (516) 496-4110
Email: jt@resourceservices.com
Web: www.resourceservices.com

Key Contact - Specialty:
Mr. Joseph Trainor
Ms. Mary Ann Trainor

Description: Executive search firm with nationwide affiliations specializing in the placement of information technology and communication professionals.

Salary Minimum: $50,000
Functions: IT, MIS mgmt., Systems dev., Systems implem., Systems support, Network admin., DB admin.
Industries: Generalist, Food/bev/tobacco, Banking, Svcs., Communications, New media, Software

Response Staffing Services

23 E. 39th St.
New York, New York 10016
(212) 983-8870
Fax: (212) 983-9492
Web: www.responsestaffing.com

Key Contact - Specialty:
Mr. Allen Gutterman - *Banking*
Mr. Edward Caligiuri - *Securities, healthcare*
Mr. Barry Cohen - *Accounting & finance, insurance, information systems*

Description: We are one of New York's top 10 specialty recruiting and temporary placement firms. We are committed to locating candidates perfectly suited for the positions our clients list with us.
Functions: Health admin., Mktg. mgmt., Personnel, Budgeting, Cash mgmt., Systems implem., Systems support
Industries: Finance, Banking, Invest. banking, Accounting, Insurance, Real estate

---

L. J. Reszotko & Assoc.
(Firm declined to update.)
1609 Greenwood Drive
Mt. Prospect, Illinois 60056
(847) 803-0888

Key Contact - Specialty:
Mr. Leonard J. Reszotko

Description: An enterprise firm focusing on strategic management positions within the corporate and SBU locations. These positions are in the areas of finance, engineering, marketing, financial and operations management. The technical disciplines that we seek are in finance, accounting, engineering and marketing.

Salary Minimum: $60,000
Functions: General mgmt., Mfg., Materials, Mkt. research, Finance, MIS mgmt., Engineering
Industries: Generalist

Retail Connection, Inc.
271 Rte. 46 W., Ste. D105
Fairfield Commons
Fairfield, New Jersey 07004
(201) 882-6662
Fax: (201) 575-5858
Email: cthaller@aol.com

Key Contact - Specialty:
Ms. Carole Thaller - *Retail*

Description: Specialize in permanent placements through active recruitment and referrals for all areas of the retail industry including store/field management positions as well as corporate merchandising and operations positions.

Salary Minimum: $25,000
Functions: Middle mgmt.
Industries: Retail

Retail Executive Search
4620 N. State Rd. 7, Ste. 212
Ft. Lauderdale, Florida 33319
(954) 731-2300
(800) 771-7130
Fax: (954) 733-0642

Key Contact - Specialty:
Mr. Manuel Kaye - *Retail*

Description: In the search field since 1980- all consultants are former retail professionals. Strong ethics oriented professional organization. Same management since inception of business.
Functions: Generalist
Industries: Retail

The Retail Network
161 Forbes Rd., Ste. 104
Braintree, Massachusetts 02184
(781) 380-8830
Fax: (781) 380-7656
Email: retail@retailnetwork.com
Web: www.retailnetwork.com

Key Contact - Specialty:
Mr. Luke Roberts - *Buyers, assistant buyers, planners, store managers (regional & district)*
Mr. Gary Belastock - *Buyers, assistant buyers, planners, merchandisers, store managers (regional & district)*

Description: We deal with general merchandise retailers. We fill both store management and corporate positions on a nationwide basis. However, our strength is New England and the Middle Atlantic states.
Functions: Directors, Senior mgmt., Middle mgmt., Distribution, Benefits, Training, CFO's
Industries: Retail

Retail Recruiters
2189 Silas Deane Hwy.
Rocky Hill, Connecticut 06067
(860) 721-9550
Fax: (860) 257-8813

Key Contact - Specialty:
Mr. Nathan Friedman - *Retail management*

Description: We specialize in the placement of retail personnel for the specialty, department and discount store industry.
Industries: Retail

Retail Recruiters/Spectrum Consultants, Inc.
111 Presidential Blvd., Ste. 105
Bala Pointe
Bala Cynwyd, Pennsylvania 19004
(610) 667-6565
Fax: (610) 667-5323

Key Contact - Specialty:
Ms. Shirlee J. Berman - *Retail, healthcare, medical*

Description: Consultants are specialists in areas of retail, medical/healthcare. Well-known for our effectiveness in the search process.
Functions: General mgmt., Mfg., Materials, Healthcare, Sales & mktg., HR mgmt., Finance
Industries: Mfg., Textiles/apparel, Retail, Svcs., Human resource svcs., Communications, Healthcare

---

Retis Assoc., Inc.
950 Milwaukee Ave., Ste. 321
Glenview, Illinois 60025
(847) 803-8830
Fax: (847) 803-8862
Email: RETIS321@aol.com

Key Contact - Specialty:
Ms. Lillian Retis - *Healthcare*

Description: Professional, effective recruitment services for healthcare executives and physicians. Successful nationwide placement at reasonable fees to clients.
Functions: Physicians, Nurses, Allied health, Health admin., MIS mgmt.
Industries: Healthcare

RGE
2106-D Gallows Rd.
Vienna, Virginia 22182
(703) 917-0573
Fax: (703) 917-0634
Email: rge@rgeconsulting.com
Web: www.rgeconsulting.com

Key Contact - Specialty:
Mr. Robert G. Epstein - *Information technology, accounting & finance, telecommunications*

Description: Permanent placement, temporary and consulting placement, retained search, executive recruiting in information technology, accounting and finance, telecommunications and financial service specialty.

Salary Minimum: $30,000
Functions: CFO's, Taxes, MIS mgmt., Systems anal., Systems dev., Systems implem., Systems support

---

RHAssoc. Inc.
10103 Switzer
Overland Park, Kansas 66212
(913) 438-8433
Email: rhassociates@topechelon.com
Web: www.qni.com/~pmgrha

Key Contact - Specialty:
Mr. Russell Hacker - *IT*
Mr. Clifford Westhoff - *IT*

Description: Technical staffing solutions search firm based in Kansas City region servicing clients in region and across the US. Searches conducted for IT professionals at all levels across all industries.
Functions: MIS mgmt., Systems anal., Systems dev., Systems implem., Systems support, Network admin., DB admin.

RHI Consulting
(a division of Robert Half Int'l.)
1100 Wilson Blvd., Ste. 900
Arlington, Virginia 22209
(703) 243-4001
Fax: (703) 465-0600
Email: dcrhic@aol.com
Web: www.rhic.com

Key Contact - Specialty:
Mr. Donald M. Ramsey - *Information technology*

Description: Specializes in information systems personnel placement for commercial companies. Clients include financial institutions, insurance companies, telecommunications firms and other commercial interests; throughout the Washington metropolitan area.
Functions: MIS mgmt., Systems anal., Systems dev., Systems implem., Systems support
Industries: Retail, Finance, Computer svcs., Communications, Insurance, Healthcare

---

RHS Assoc.
(an IntelliMark company)
1 Perimeter Park S., Ste. 400 N
Birmingham, Alabama 35243
(205) 969-1099
Fax: (205) 970-0583
Email: rhs@rhsinc.com
Web: www.IntelliMark-IT.com

Key Contact - Specialty:
Mr. Allan J. Lebow - *Executive level (all industries)*
Mr. Mark Jones
Mr. Bill Munn - *Information technology*

Description: Management and professional search, contingency or retained, information systems specialists. Information systems contract programming and consulting.

Salary Minimum: $40,000
Functions: Directors, CFO's, MIS mgmt., Systems anal., Systems dev., Systems implem., Systems support
Industries: Computer svcs., Accounting, Mgmt. consulting, Insurance, High tech, Software, Healthcare

Branches:
1341 Mehearg Rd.
Wetumpka, Alabama 36092
(334) 567-6010
Key Contact - Specialty:
Mr. Edwin Watkins

Jeff Rich Assoc.
67 Walnut Ave., Ste. 303
Clark, New Jersey 07066
(908) 574-3888
Fax: (908) 574-1424

Key Contact - Specialty:
Mr. Richard A. Thunberg - *Accounting, finance, tax, audit*

Description: We develop a long lasting relationship with our clients which enables us to better understand the culture of each company and the personality of the management involved in the selection process for new employees.

Salary Minimum: $30,000
Functions: CFO's, Budgeting, Cash mgmt., Credit, Taxes, M&A, Risk mgmt.
Industries: Generalist

Richard, Wayne & Roberts
24 Greenway Plaza, Ste. 1304
Houston, Texas 77046
(713) 629-6681
Fax: (713) 623-2740
Email: dickweiss@rwr.com

Key Contact - Specialty:
Mr. Dick Weiss - *General management*
Mr. Neal Hirsch - *Accounting*
Ms. Alexis Cannon - *Accounting*
Mr. Mark Dremely - *Real estate, construction*
Ms. Ruth Schlanger - *Legal*
Ms. Amy Adams - *Healthcare accounting*

Description: We approach each recruiting assignment with a minimum 3 member team, designating one recruiter as the principal contact for the client. Our mission is to be recognized as the leading recruiting firm in the industries and disciplines we serve.

Salary Minimum: $40,000
Functions: Mfg., Healthcare, HR mgmt., Finance, IT, Engineering, Attorneys
Industries: Energy/utilities, Construction, Chemicals, Finance, Telecoms, High tech, Healthcare

Branches:
4625 S. Wendler Drive, Ste. 111
Tempe, Arizona 85282
(602) 431-8570
Fax: (602) 431-9473
Key Contact - Specialty:
Mr. Mike Coltrane - *Telecommunications*

Richard Wright Co.
P.O. Box 127
Canton Center, Connecticut 06020
(203) 693-1822
Fax: (203) 693-9400
Email: wright@esslink.com

Key Contact - Specialty:
Mr. Richard Eickenhorst - *Property & casualty (underwriting & claims), alternative risk*

Description: Recruitment of property and casualty underwriters and claims personnel. Heavily involved with environmental claims, alternative risk underwriting and program business.

Salary Minimum: $40,000
Functions: Senior mgmt., Middle mgmt., Risk mgmt.
Industries: Insurance

The Richards Group
1608 Walnut St., Ste. 1702
Philadelphia, Pennsylvania 19103
(215) 735-9450
Fax: (215) 735-9430

Key Contact - Specialty:
Mr. Larry Winitsky

Description: Personalized approach to every search, including face-to-face meeting with every client. Other consultative services offered to every client.
Functions: Healthcare, Sales & mktg., HR mgmt., Finance, IT
Industries: Mfg., Retail, Finance, Svcs., Communications, Insurance, Healthcare

---

Terry Richards
36 Public Sq.
Willoughby, Ohio 44094
(216) 918-1800
Fax: (216) 975-1499
Email: trcpcrec@apk.net

Key Contact - Specialty:
Mr. Terry Richards - *Generalist, manufacturing, distribution*

Description: A generalist approach and a quality assured recruiting methodology have proven to be effective in a wide variety of searches.

Salary Minimum: $75,000
Functions: Senior mgmt., Middle mgmt., Plant mgmt., Quality, Materials Plng., Distribution, Sales mgmt.
Industries: Metal products, Machinery/Appliances, Motor vehicles, Computer equip., Consumer electronics, Misc. mfg., Wholesale

---

W. F. Richer Assoc., Inc.
50 Deerfield Lane S.
Pleasantville, New York 10570-1840
(212) 682-4000

Key Contact - Specialty:
Mr. William F. Richer - *Information technology (distributed computing, client/server*

technology, global telecommunications), risk management, internet development
Ms. Joyce Eidenberg Richer - *Information technology (distributed computing, client/server technology, global telecommunications), risk management, internet development*

Description: The firm specializes in advanced and emerging technologies including: client/server computing, workstation development, product development, financial analytics and Internet development.

Salary Minimum: $75,000
Functions: IT, MIS mgmt., Systems anal., Systems dev., Systems implem., Systems support, Mgmt. consultants
Industries: Communications, New media, High tech, Software

Jack Richman & Assoc.

P.O. Box 25412
Tamarac, Florida 33320
(305) 940-0721
Fax: (954) 389-9572
Email: jrafl@aol.com
Web: www.misjobs.com/jra

Key Contact - Specialty:
Mr. Jack Richman - *Information systems technology, telecommunications, client/server*
Ms. Gloria Newman - *Mid-range, client/server, information systems technology*

Description: Our firm specializes exclusively in the computer industry. Positions range from $30,000 to $100,000 plus. We handle South Florida and work nationally as well. We have a lot of clients that are looking for Spanish speaking as well.

Salary Minimum: $40,000
Functions: MIS mgmt., Systems anal., Systems dev., Systems implem., Systems support, Network admin., Mgmt. consultants
Industries: High tech

Richmond Assoc.

9 Pioneer St.
Cooperstown, New York 13326
(607) 547-9236
Fax: (607) 547-7456
Web: www.jhulse@msn.com

Key Contact - Specialty:
Ms. Jeanne Hulse - *Information systems professionals (sales & pre-sales)*

Description: We specialize in searching for and placing sales professionals and technical sales support professionals in software and hardware sales positions nationwide.

Salary Minimum: $65,000
Functions: Sales mgmt., Systems dev., Systems implem., Systems support, Network admin., DB admin.
Industries: High tech, Software

Ridgefield Search Int'l.

224 Barlow Mountain Rd.
Ridgefield, Connecticut 06877
(203) 438-8000

Key Contact - Specialty:
Mr. Ralph Bailey - *International managers (middle, upper level)*

Description: 20 years search and recruitment international management talent for Fortune 1500 manufacturer clients. Emphasis: country managers, marketing sales, finance, plant and MIS directors. Geography: Latin America, Asia, Middle East and Eastern Europe. Jobs USA based or overseas.

Salary Minimum: $75,000
Functions: Int'l.

Right/McKee Consulting Group

1221 Lamar St., Ste. 1175
4 Houston Ctr.
Houston, Texas 77010
(713) 659-8383
Fax: (713) 739-8056
Email: RMG-SG@worldnet.att.net

Key Contact - Specialty:
Mr. H. S. Skip Griffin
Mr. David Brandenburg
Mr. C. David Meadows - *Legal, energy (exploration & production), engineering (process, engineering & construction), general/professional, executive*

Description: We provide high quality, cost effective staffing services to client companies and individuals alike. Our professional staff is composed of experienced human resources professionals equipped with the latest recruiting techniques.

Salary Minimum: $45,000
Functions: General mgmt., Mfg., Materials, HR mgmt., Finance, IT, Engineering
Industries: Energy/utilities, Mfg., Finance, Svcs., High tech, Software, Healthcare

Riley Cole

P.O. Box 10635
Oakland, California 94610
(510) 428-2022
Fax: (510) 428-2072

Key Contact - Specialty:
Mr. Jim Riley - *Retail, consumer packaged goods, sales & marketing*
Mr. Don Cole - *Manufacturing management, engineering, quality assurance, research & development*

Description: Over thirty-five years of successful, in-depth recruiting experience. Competitive knowledge, organizational design understanding as well as proven integrity and discretion allow us to individualize each search assignment.

Salary Minimum: $30,000
Functions: Product dev., Packaging, Advertising, Personnel, CFO's, R&D, Engineering
Industries: Generalist, Food/bev/tobacco, Soap/perfume/cosmetics, Drugs mfg., Machinery/Appliances, Wholesale, Retail

Ritech Management Inc.

255 W. 23rd St., #3CW
New York, New York 10011-2314
(212) 620-1780
Web: www.rtmgt@msn.com

Key Contact - Specialty:
Mr. Ben Michaels - *PC/LAN/WAN engineers, computer (support specialists), PC programmers*

Description: Placement of PC programmers, PC support people, PC technicians/local and wide area network systems engineers, administrators, managers and technical support reps.

Salary Minimum: $40,000
Functions: Systems anal., Systems dev., Systems implem., Systems support, Network admin., DB admin.
Industries: High tech, Software

Ritt-Ritt & Assoc., Inc.

1350 E. Touhy Ave., #210W
Des Plaines, Illinois 60018
(847) 827-7771
Fax: (847) 827-9776

Key Contact - Specialty:
Mr. Arthur Ritt - *Food, hospitality*

Description: One of the oldest and most respected placement firms in the country specializing in only the food and hospitality industry. Guided by the president with over 30 years of experience and a previous background coming from the hospitality industry.

Salary Minimum: $25,000
Functions: Senior mgmt., Middle mgmt., Personnel, Training, CFO's, Int'l.
Industries: Hospitality, Entertainment, Accounting, Human resource svcs., Advertising/PR, Healthcare, Non-classifiable industries

Ritta Professional Search Inc.
6 Automation Lane
Albany, New York 12205
(518) 458-7340
Fax: (518) 458-7017

Key Contact - Specialty:
Mr. Arthur E. Hansen - *Engineering (research & development)*
Mr. James P. Salfi - *Telecommunications (cellular)*
Mr. Robert Mallinson - *Environmental, health, safety*

Description: Specialize in metallurgical, mechanical and electrical engineering for R&D. Also environmental/safety engineering and technical cellular telephone requirements. Strong gas/steam turbine client base. National coverage.

Salary Minimum: $50,000
Functions: Middle mgmt., Mktg. mgmt., Systems dev., Network admin., R&D, Engineering, Environmentalists
Industries: Machinery/Appliances, Test/measurement equip., Computer svcs., Telecoms, Environmental svcs., High tech, Software

River Region Personnel, Inc.
1537 Metairie Rd., Ste. D
Metairie, Louisiana 70005
(504) 831-4746
Fax: (504) 831-9916
Email: czamjahn@aol.com

Key Contact - Specialty:
Mr. Charles J. Zamjahn - *Chemical, refining, plastics, manufacturing, expanded foam packaging*

Description: Thirty years of experience in serving national process industry employers. Previous chemical industry HR positions with Monsanto Co. and American Cyanamid.

Salary Minimum: $50,000
Functions: Plant mgmt., Quality, Packaging, HR mgmt., Engineering
Industries: Paper, Chemicals, Plastics/rubber, Environmental svcs., Packaging

Rivera Legal Search, Inc.
P.O. Box 63343
Los Angeles, California 90063
(213) 780-0000
Fax: (213) 780-0388
Email: jdhuntr@pacbell.net

Key Contact - Specialty:
Mr. Al Rivera - *Legal*

Description: RLS recruits and places attorneys at all levels of experience. Clients include major law firms and corporations worldwide.

Salary Minimum: $70,000
Functions: Legal
Industries: Legal

The Riverbend Group
36 Four Seasons Ctr., Ste. 343
Chesterfield, Missouri 63017
(314) 579-9729
Fax: (314) 469-8592
Email: info@trgonline.com
Web: www.trgonline.com

Key Contact - Specialty:
Mr. John Sroka - *Information systems professionals*
Ms. Sue Thieme - *Information systems professionals*
Ms. Lynn Craig - *Information systems professionals*

Description: We specialize in solving your relational database hiring problems! Our candidates are career-minded professionals with relational database development, tools and techniques expertise.

Salary Minimum: $50,000
Functions: IT, MIS mgmt., Systems anal., Systems dev., Systems implem., Systems support, DB admin.
Industries: Generalist

RJ Associates
23730 Canzonet St.
Woodland Hills, California 91367
(818) 715-7121
Fax: (818) 715-9438
Email: rja23730@ix.netcom.com

Key Contact - Specialty:
Ms. Judith Fischer - *Accounting, finance, information technology (middle, upper management)*
Mr. Ronald Fischer - *Accounting, finance, information technology (middle, upper management)*

Description: Providing highly personalized professional search services within a wide array of industries for positions from CEO to financial analyst, from CIO to controller. Because we engage in a limited number of searches, we focus our full attention on each assignment. We are the names on the front door.

Salary Minimum: $60,000
Functions: Senior mgmt., Middle mgmt., CFO's, Budgeting, Cash mgmt., M&A, MIS mgmt.
Industries: Generalist

RML Assoc.
1201 Madison Ave.
Warren, Pennsylvania 16365
(814) 726-1671
Fax: (814) 723-8828
Email: boblr@hotmail.com

Key Contact - Specialty:
Mr. Robert L. Larson

Description: We are a consulting and recruiting firm with over 50 years combined experience. We offer companies unique solutions to their needs.

Salary Minimum: $20,000
Functions: Generalist, Middle mgmt., Mfg., Materials, Engineering
Industries: Generalist, Lumber/furniture, Plastics/rubber, Metal products, Machinery/Appliances, Motor vehicles, Misc. mfg.

Roberson & Co.
10752 N. 89th Place, Ste. 202
Scottsdale, Arizona 85260
(602) 391-3200
Fax: (602) 391-3543
Email: baytoven@msn.com

Key Contact - Specialty:
Mr. Stephen D. Silvas - *Generalist*

Description: Founded in 1967 a full service firm affiliates with over a 375 member network, computer linked nationally and internationally. Capable of the most specialized kinds of searches.

Salary Minimum: $40,000
Functions: General mgmt., Mfg., Materials, Healthcare, Sales & mktg., IT, Engineering
Industries: Generalist, Mfg., Svcs., Communications, High tech, Software, Healthcare

Robert Shields & Assoc.
1560 W. Bay Area Blvd., Ste. 200
Friendswood, Texas 77546
(281) 488-7961
(281) 679-1500
Fax: (281) 486-1496
Email: gfblack@itjobs.org
Web: www.itjobs.org

Key Contact - Specialty:
Mr. George Black - *Information technology*
Mr. Richard Gross - *Information technology*
Ms. Jani Clemons - *Midrange technology*

Description: Specialists in data processing and engineering positions nationally and overseas.
Functions: MIS mgmt., Systems anal., Systems dev., Systems implem., Systems support, Network admin., DB admin.
Industries: Generalist

Branches:
2470 Gray Falls, Ste. 260
Houston, Texas 77077
(281) 679-1500
Fax: (281) 679-1508

Key Contact - Specialty:
Ms. Betsy Hollis

Robert William James & Assoc.
(a division of Express Personnel Services)
621 SW Morrison, Ste. 500
Portland, Oregon 97205
(503) 224-5505
Fax: (503) 241-8877
Email: research@express-rwj.com
Web: www.monster.com/rwj

Key Contact - Specialty:
Ms. Lynette Duggan
Mr. William H. Stoller

Description: Personnel search firm providing comprehensive human resource consulting services to emerging growth Northwest companies.
Functions: General mgmt., Mfg., Materials, Sales & mktg., HR mgmt., Finance, IT
Industries: Mfg., Wholesale, Finance, Svcs., Communications, High tech, Software

Branches:
9029 Soquel Ave., Ste. D
Santa Cruz, California 95062
(408) 462-4115
(408) 462-4979
Fax: (408) 462-0557
Email: laurenrwj@aol.com
Key Contact - Specialty:
Ms. Lauren Anderson

924 Clocktower Drive
Springfield, Illinois 62704
(217) 787-6010
Fax: (217) 787-6235
Key Contact - Specialty:
Mr. G. L. Matthews

812 S. Elm St.
Owatonna, Minnesota 55060
(507) 451-9396
(888) 451-9396
Fax: (507) 455-0271
Email: bkl3@aol.com
Key Contact - Specialty:
Ms. Jane Starman

2518 N. Broadway
Rochester, Minnesota 55906
(507) 285-9270
Fax: (507) 529-9419
Email: djvrwj@sprynet.com
Key Contact - Specialty:
Ms. Sheryl Tasler

2741Miamisburg-Centerville Rd.
Mad River Station, Ste. 217
Dayton, Ohio 45414
(937) 438-4932
Fax: (937) 435-8931
Email: rwj@erinet.com
Key Contact - Specialty:
Mr. Dick Kortjohn

2200 N. Limestone St. Ste. 116
Springfield, Ohio 45503
(937) 399-8560
Fax: (937) 399-2961
Email: jerryc@exps.usa.com
Key Contact - Specialty:
Mr. Rick Mosholder

5909 NW Expwy., Ste. 110
Oklahoma City, Oklahoma 73132
(405) 720-4616
Fax: (405) 720-4681
Email: rwjjob19@icon.net
Key Contact - Specialty:
Ms. Shirley Webb

901 NW Carlon Ave., Ste. 3
Bend, Oregon 97701
(541) 330-1585
Fax: (541) 330-5037
Email: hhunter@teleport.com
Key Contact - Specialty:
Ms. Connie Worrell

645 Main St.
Springfield, Oregon 97477
(541) 988-1138
Fax: (503) 988-1129
Email: pmurphy@rwjoregon.com
Key Contact - Specialty:
Ms. Pat Murphy

50 Queen St.
Ste. 704, The Commerce House
Kitchener, Ontario N2H 6P4
Canada
(519) 578-9030
Fax: (519) 578-1121
Email: express-rwj@sympatico.ca
Key Contact - Specialty:
Ms. Jane Vickers

150 Dufferin Ave.
Ste. 604, Richmond Court
London, Ontario N6A 5N6
Canada
(519) 672-2RWJ
Fax: (519) 672-7694
Email: rwj@wwdc.com
Key Contact - Specialty:
Ms. Jane Vickers

International Branches:
Basingstoke, Moscow

Robertson & Assoc.
10 S. Riverside Plaza
Chicago, Illinois 60606
(312) 930-1958
Fax: (312) 930-1119

Key Contact - Specialty:
Mr. Peter C. Chappell - *Finance, treasury*

Description: Dedicated to the selection of professional executives for industry and commerce. Our 23rd year of serving clients nationwide from mid America.

Salary Minimum: $70,000
Functions: Directors, Senior mgmt., Middle mgmt., Mktg. mgmt., Finance
Industries: Finance, Accounting, Equip. svcs., Insurance

V. Robinson & Co., Inc.
1044 Main St., Ste. 600
Kansas City, Missouri 64105
(816) 421-4944
Fax: (816) 421-3559
Email: vrinc@aol.com

Key Contact - Specialty:
Ms. Verneda Robinson - *Utilities, sales & marketing, management*
Mr. William Miller - *Information systems, information technology, engineering, sales & marketing*

Description: We contract with organizations to help fill personnel positions with highly qualified professionals. Additionally, we provide counseling and advice during the interviewing and hiring process.

Salary Minimum: $25,000
Functions: General mgmt., Mfg., Sales & mktg., HR mgmt., IT, Engineering
Industries: Energy/utilities

Branches:
726 Armstrong Ave., Ste. 200
Kansas City, Kansas 66101
(913) 371-1192
Fax: (913) 371-1179
Email: vrinc@aol.com
Key Contact - Specialty:
Ms. Verneda Robinson - *Utilities, sales & marketing, management*

The Robinson Group, D.A., Ltd.
800 E. Northwest Hwy., Ste. 809
Palatine, Illinois 60067
(847) 359-0990
Email: Robgrp@aol.com

Key Contact - Specialty:
Mr. Donald Alan Robinson - *Public accounting (focus on Big 6)*

Description: Big 6 public accounting.

Salary Minimum: $55,000
Functions: Senior mgmt., Middle mgmt.
Industries: Accounting

Robinson-Robinson & Assoc., Inc.
9977 Valley View Rd., Ste. 300
Eden Prairie, Minnesota 55344
(612) 942-8938
Fax: (612) 941-7064
Email: Rob2Rob@aol.com

Key Contact - Specialty:
Mr. Sam Robinson - *Generalist*
Ms. Bunny Robinson - *Generalist*

Description: We are a search firm specializing in the recruitment and placement of diversity candidates for management and professional positions.

Salary Minimum: $50,000
Functions: Generalist, General mgmt., HR mgmt., Finance, R&D, Engineering, Minorities
Industries: Generalist, Mfg., Finance, Aerospace, High tech, Healthcare

---

Rockwood Assoc.

1202 Lexington, Ste. 153
New York, New York 10028
(212) 744-0905
Fax: (212) 744-1260
Email: rocksearch@aol.com

Key Contact - Specialty:
Mr. Charles R. Bamford

Description: Functions: sales, trading, finance, investment analytics and operations. Industries: natural gas marketers, refiners, utilities, bank/broker capital markets groups and commodity firms. Products: oil, gas, electricity, commodities, financial futures and derivatives.

Salary Minimum: $50,000
Functions: Sales mgmt., Risk mgmt., Mgmt. consultants
Industries: Energy/utilities, Banking, Invest. banking, Brokers

---

Rocky Mountain Recruiters, Inc.

1801 Broadway, Ste. 810
Denver, Colorado 80202
(303) 296-2000
Fax: (303) 296-2223
Email: Miket@rmrecruiters.com
Web: www.rmrecruiters.com

Key Contact - Specialty:
Mr. Michael Turner - *Accounting & finance*

Description: Colorado's oldest specialty recruiting firm,specializing in placing accounting and financial professionals.

Salary Minimum: $30,000
Functions: CFO's, Budgeting, Cash mgmt., Credit, Taxes, M&A
Industries: Generalist, Agri/forestry/mining, Mfg., Finance, Svcs., Communications, Biotech

Affiliates:
Temporary Accounting Personnel, Inc.

J. P. Roddy Consultants

258 S. Third St., Ste. 101
Philadelphia, Pennsylvania 19106
(215) 923-6770
Fax: (215) 923-6773
Email: jproddy@aol.com

Key Contact - Specialty:
Mr. Jack P. Roddy - *Automotive, plastics*

Description: Positions at corporate technical centers and corporate headquarters of automotive divisions of Fortune 500 companies. Also, key positions at plant facilities such as general manager, plant manager, quality manager, materials, manufacturing and industrial engineering.

Salary Minimum: $40,000
Functions: Middle mgmt., Production, Automation, Quality, Materials Plng., R&D, Engineering
Industries: Chemicals, Plastics/rubber, Motor vehicles

J. Rodgers & Associates

608 S. Washington St., Ste. 101
Naperville, Illinois 60540
(630) 961-9143
Fax: (630) 961-3545
Email: rbakken@gte.net
Web: jrodgers.bakken.com

Key Contact - Specialty:
Mr. Roger Bakken - *Office products, high technology, computer hardware & software, sales & marketing*

Description: Serving the high-tech industry sales and marketing.

Salary Minimum: $30,000
Functions: Middle mgmt., Sales & mktg., Mkt. research, Mktg. mgmt., Sales mgmt., Technicians
Industries: Computer equip.

Rodgers, Ramsey, Inc.

3401 Louisiana, Ste. 240
Houston, Texas 77002
(713) 529-7010
Fax: (713) 529-2209
Email: careers@rodgers-ramsey.com
Web: www.rodgers-ramsey.com

Key Contact - Specialty:
Ms. Gayle Rodgers - *Employee benefits*

Description: Provide recruiting service of the employee benefit professional for insurance companies, benefit consultants, managed care organizations and financial services firms on a national basis.

Salary Minimum: $48,000
Functions: Senior mgmt., Health admin., Mktg. mgmt., Sales mgmt., Direct mktg., Benefits, Training
Industries: Misc. financial, Insurance, Healthcare

R. A. Rodriguez & Assoc., Inc.

10935 Ben Crenshaw, Ste. 210
El Paso, Texas 79935
(915) 598-5028
Fax: (915) 598-5150
Email: rarjobs@flash.net

Key Contact - Specialty:
Mr. Fred Smithson - *Manufacturing, international*
Ms. Raquel Rodriguez Smithson - *Manufacturing, international*

Description: Search staff comprises experienced engineering and manufacturing managers. Exceptional experience in placing bi/multilingual managers/engineers in key national/international positions with top 100 corporations. Confidentiality guaranteed.

Salary Minimum: $50,000
Functions: Mfg., Plant mgmt., Materials, HR mgmt., Finance, Engineering, Int'l.
Industries: Generalist, Medical devices, Plastics/rubber, Machinery/Appliances, Misc. mfg., Computer svcs., Telecoms

---

Craig Roe & Assoc., LLC

3711 Ashley Way, Ste. A
Owings Mills, Maryland 21117
(410) 654-6636
Fax: (410) 654-6630
Email: croeassoc@aol.com

Key Contact - Specialty:
Ms. Sylvia A. Roe - *Sales & marketing, healthcare, medical, biotechnology, pharmaceutical*
Mr. Craig T. Roe - *Sales & marketing, food, beverage, consumer goods, food broker*

Description: We assist clients in locating the best sales talent in the marketplace. We match a candidate's experience, ability and work ethic to the requirements and culture of our client companies.

Salary Minimum: $25,000
Functions: General mgmt., Directors, Senior mgmt., Middle mgmt., Mktg. mgmt., Sales mgmt., Mgmt. consultants
Industries: Mfg., Food/bev/tobacco, Drugs mfg., Medical devices, Mgmt. consulting, Biotech, Healthcare

---

Roevin Technical People

1200 Lambton Mall Rd.
Sarnia, Ontario N7S 5R6
Canada
(519) 541-0070
Fax: (519) 541-0031
Email: roevin@ebtech.net

Key Contact - Specialty:
Mr. Steve Thomson

Functions: Mfg., Physicians, Nurses, IT, R&D, Engineering, Int'l.

Industries: Generalist, Construction, Mfg., Aerospace, High tech, Healthcare

The Rogan Group, Inc.
2900 Bristol H-204
Costa Mesa, California 92626
(714) 546-2206
Fax: (714) 546-1005
Email: roglev@aol.com
Web: www.rogangroup.com

Key Contact - Specialty:
Mr. Daniel Rogan - *Insurance (property, casualty & group), brokerage, mergers, acquisitions*
Mr. John McGraw - *Insurance (property & casualty, brokerage)*
Ms. Susan Higgins - *Insurance (company sector), brokerage, mergers, acquisitions*

Description: Recruiting firm specializing in the risk and insurance management recruiting field. 30+ years of insurance experience in addition to search background. Specialty area would include insurance brokerage production and management positions. Search assignments come from all areas of U.S..

Salary Minimum: $50,000
Functions: Middle mgmt., Health admin., Sales & mktg., Sales mgmt., CFO's, M&A, MIS mgmt.
Industries: Banking, Misc. financial, Insurance, Healthcare

Affiliates:
Entrust Insurance Staffing

Rogish Assoc., Inc.
615 Copeland Mill Rd., Ste. 1F
Westerville, Ohio 43081
(614) 899-2525
Fax: (614) 899-2524
Email: rogishinc@aol.com

Key Contact - Specialty:
Mr. Nick Rogish - *Healthcare, health insurance (sales), life insurance (sales)*
Ms. Julie Osborne - *Healthcare, long term care, clinical managers*
Ms. Betsy McCammon - *Long term care managers*

Description: Our mission is to establish long term relationships with our client organizations and candidates by combining the elements necessary to complete the search assignment in the most professional manner.

Salary Minimum: $35,000
Functions: Healthcare, Nurses, Health admin., Sales & mktg., Benefits, Finance, CFO's
Industries: Svcs., Pharmaceutical svcs., Mgmt. consulting, Human resource svcs., Insurance, Healthcare

Roll International
5580 Harvest Hill Rd., Ste. 1009
Dallas, Texas 75230
(972) 239-3800
Fax: (972) 239-2858
Email: rolli@dhc.net
Web: www.dhc.net/~rolli

Key Contact - Specialty:
Mr. M. A. Roll - *IS, finance, international*

Description: USA and International information systems recruiters specializing in SAP, BaaN, Oracle, PeopleSoft, and UNIX. People make a world of difference.

Salary Minimum: $30,000
Functions: IT, MIS mgmt., Systems anal., Systems implem., Network admin., DB admin., Int'l.
Industries: Generalist, Energy/utilities, Mfg., Finance, Svcs., High tech, Healthcare

Branches:
Lic. Arturo Monjaras Soto
Benjamin Franklin No. 47
Mexico City, Mexico DF 06140
Mexico

Rollins & Assoc.
4010 Watson Plaza Drive, Ste. 105
Lakewood, California 90712
(562) 421-6649
Fax: (562) 421-8918

Key Contact - Specialty:
Ms. Joan E. Rollins - *International trade & transportation*

Description: Import and/or export searches including international sales/marketing, traffic management and support staff, bilingual employees and servicing customs brokerages, freight forwarders and carriers. Searches conducted in North America and Far East.

Salary Minimum: $25,000
Functions: Senior mgmt., Middle mgmt., Admin. svcs., Purchasing, Distribution, Sales mgmt., Customer svc.
Industries: Food/bev/tobacco, Textiles/apparel, Soap/perfume/cosmetics, Drugs mfg., Computer equip., Transportation, Wholesale

Rollins Search Group, Inc.
216 Parkway 575
Woodstock, Georgia 30188
(770) 516-6042
Fax: (770) 516-0068
Email: jr@rollinssearch.com
Web: www.rollinssearch.com

Key Contact - Specialty:
Mr. Jay M. Rollins - *Actuarial & insurance information systems*

Description: Strong nationwide networking relationships among other recruiters and recruiting firms gives us the unique ability to expand the base of qualified applicants to fill your specific opening. This allows us to reach a wider range of the most qualified candidates in a very time efficient manner.

Salary Minimum: $30,000
Industries: Insurance, Software

Romac Int'l. - San Francisco
180 Montgomery St., Ste. 1860
San Francisco, California 94104
(415) 228-4500
Fax: (415) 788-8777
Web: www.romacintl.com

Key Contact - Specialty:
Mr. John McLaughlin - *MIS*
Mr. Steve Reiter - *Accounting, finance,*

Description: We provide search and placement services specializing in accounting, finance and MIS. Our consultants have strong technical backgrounds, including certification as CPA's & CIA's. Eighty-five offices nationwide and four locations in the Bay area. In MIS, we place programmers, analysts, systems administrators and project managers.
Functions: Budgeting, Cash mgmt., Taxes, MIS mgmt., Systems anal., Systems dev., Systems implem.
Industries: Generalist

Branches:
2055 Gateway Place, Ste. 415
San Jose, California 95110
(408) 437-2440
Fax: (408) 437-7534
Key Contact - Specialty:
Mr. Kent Gray - *Accounting & finance, information technology, contracting*

Romac Int'l.
3 Ravinia Drive, Ste. 1460
Atlanta, Georgia 30346
(770) 604-3880
Fax: (770) 604-3870
Web: www.romacintl.com

Key Contact - Specialty:
Mr. Michael V. Zaremski

Description: Permanent and temporary placement of accounting, financial and information systems professionals.
Functions: Finance, CFO's, Budgeting, IT
Industries: Generalist, Mfg., Svcs., Communications, High tech, Software

Romac Int'l.
20 N. Wacker Drive, Ste. 1360
Chicago, Illinois 60606
(312) 263-0902
Fax: (312) 263-3023
Web: www.romacintl.com

Key Contact - Specialty:
Mr. Lloyd R. Singer - *Accounting, finance, financial services, banking*

Description: We are a specialty firm specializing in banking, accounting and financial placements. 60% professional accounting/financial temps, 40% executive search.

Salary Minimum: $30,000
Functions: Finance, CFO's, Budgeting, Cash mgmt., Credit, Taxes, M&A
Industries: Generalist, Mfg., Finance, Svcs., Communications, Real estate, High tech

---

Romac Int'l.

603 Stanwix St.
Pittsburgh, Pennsylvania 15222
(412) 209-2400
Fax: (412) 209-2423
Email: dwagner@romac.com
Web: www.romacintl.com

Key Contact - Specialty:
Ms. Deborah Wagner

Description: Over thirty years of experience, devoted exclusively to financial recruitment has given our firm the unique capability to effectively provide the personnel on all levels, including CFO's, controllers, treasurers, accountants and operations management.
Functions: Middle mgmt., Health admin., Personnel, CFO's, Budgeting, Taxes, MIS mgmt.
Industries: Finance, Accounting

Romac Int'l., Inc.

120 W. Hyde Park Place, Ste. 150
Tampa, Florida 33606
(813) 251-1700
Fax: (813) 254-9640
Web: www.romacintl.com

Key Contact - Specialty:
Mr. David L. Dunkel
Mr. James D. Swartz
Mr. Howard W. Sutter
Mr. Thomas M. Calcaterra
Mr. Brian C. Cuddy

Description: Specialize in search: accounting/finance, banking, information technology, HR, healthcare, life insurance, manufacturing services, pharmaceutical research; contract: information technology, healthcare, pharmaceutical research; temporaries: accounting/finance, bookkeeping professionals.

Salary Minimum: $15,000
Functions: Mfg., Healthcare, HR mgmt., Finance, IT, Engineering
Industries: Motor vehicles, Pharmaceutical svcs., Accounting, Healthcare

Branches:
5343 N. 16th St., Ste. 270
Phoenix, Arizona 85016
(602) 230-0220
Key Contact - Specialty:
Mr. Charlie Balchumas

879 W. 190th St., Ste. 300
Gardena, California 90248
(310) 323-0900
Key Contact - Specialty:
Mr. John Spencer

2603 Main St., Ste. 1100
Irvine, California 92614
(714) 660-1666
Key Contact - Specialty:
Mr. Robert Gennawey

2029 Century Park E., Ste. 1350
Los Angeles, California 90067
(310) 284-8800
Key Contact - Specialty:
Mr. John Spencer

5020 Campus Drive
Newport Beach, California 92660
(714) 263-1212
Fax: (714) 263-1122
Key Contact - Specialty:
Mr. Todd Hall

3 Lagoon Drive, Ste. 155
Redwood City, California 94065
(650) 628-1850
Fax: (650) 628-1855
Key Contact - Specialty:
Ms. Michelle Pletkin

4510 Executive Drive, Ste. 200
San Diego, California 92121
(619) 552-0300
Key Contact - Specialty:
Mr. Ingram Losner

425 California St., Ste. 1200
San Francisco, California 94104
(415) 434-2410
Key Contact - Specialty:
Ms. Mary Anderson

101 Metro Drive, Ste. 680
San Jose, California 95110
(408) 437-2440
Fax: (408) 437-7534
Key Contact - Specialty:
Ms. Teresa Hester - *Accounting, finance, banking*

2107 N. First St., Ste. 530
San Jose, California 95131
(408) 436-0111
Fax: (408) 436-1842
Key Contact - Specialty:
Mr. Bob Tansill

15260 Ventura Blvd., Ste. 380
Sherman Oaks, California 91403
(818) 905-1500
Key Contact - Specialty:
Mr. Paul Ratajczak

1290 Oakmead Pkwy., Ste. 318
Sunnyvale, California 94086
(408) 738-8440

1350 Treat Blvd., Ste. 150
Walnut Creek, California 94595
(510) 951-1260
Fax: (510) 951-1299
Key Contact - Specialty:
Ms. Shannon Leal
Ms. Jennifer Miller

7730 E. Belleview Ave, Ste. 302
Englewood, Colorado 80111
(303) 773-3700
Key Contact - Specialty:
Mr. Brad Francis

111 Founders Plaza, Ste. 1501
East Hartford, Connecticut 06108
(860) 528-0300
Key Contact - Specialty:
Mr. Ray Turner

One Corporate Drive, Ste. 215
Shelton, Connecticut 06484
(203) 944-9001
Key Contact - Specialty:
Mr. Ray Turner

1111 19th St. NW, Ste. 620
Washington, District of Columbia 20036
(202) 223-6000
Key Contact - Specialty:
Mr. Paul Villella

500 W. Cypress Creek Rd., Ste. 200
Ft. Lauderdale, Florida 33309
(954) 928-0800
(305) 949-7762
Fax: (954) 771-7649
Key Contact - Specialty:
Mr. Rich Raniere
Ms. Cherie Hess
Mr. Dick Bramel

701 W. Cypress Creek Rd., Ste. 202
Ft. Lauderdale, Florida 33309
(954) 771-0777
Key Contact - Specialty:
Mr. Ed Crawford

15600 NW 67th Ave., Ste. 210
Miami Lakes, Florida 33014
(305) 556-8000
Key Contact - Specialty:
Mr. Ed Crawford

5979 NW 151st St., Ste. 200
Miami Lakes, Florida 33014
(305) 507-3460
Fax: (305) 819-6774
Key Contact - Specialty:
Mr. Rich Raniere - *Accounting, finance, information technology*

111 N. Orange Ave., Ste. 1150
Orlando, Florida 32801
(407) 843-0765
Fax: (407) 841-8857

Key Contact - Specialty:
Mr. Thomas Gresosky
Mr. Dan Rodriguez
Mr. Randy Ferrell

4200 W. Cypress St., Ste. 101
Tampa, Florida 33607
(813) 879-2221
Key Contact - Specialty:
Mr. Ed Crawford

400 N. Tampa St., Ste. 1200
Tampa, Florida 33602
(813) 307-2002
(813) 307-2025
Fax: (813) 225-1422
Key Contact - Specialty:
Mr. Ray Morganti - *Emerging technologies*

120 W. Hyde Park Place, Ste. 200
Tampa, Florida 33606
(813) 258-8855
Fax: (813) 251-2493
Key Contact - Specialty:
Ms. Gail A. Griffey
Mr. Dan Perlman - *Pharmaceuticals, healthcare*
Ms. Evelyn Vlock
Ms. Kristin Ellis
Mr. Joe Liberatore
Mr. Kevin Hudson
Ms. Cindy Marvin

4170 Ashford Dunwoody Rd., Ste. 285
Atlanta, Georgia 30319
(404) 255-2045
Key Contact - Specialty:
Mr. Tom Freeh

2100 Powers Ferry Rd., Ste. 110
Atlanta, Georgia 30339
(770) 481-4500
Fax: (770) 859-0688
Key Contact - Specialty:
Ms. Megan Kiburz
Ms. Tracy Dickerhoff
Ms. Eileen Paris

150 S. Wacker Drive, Ste. 400
Chicago, Illinois 60606
(312) 346-7000
Key Contact - Specialty:
Mr. Bob Clawson
Mr. Lloyd Singer

2211 S. York Rd., Ste. 310
Oak Brook, Illinois 60521
(630) 575-2100
Fax: (630) 575-0829
Key Contact - Specialty:
Mr. Scott Johnsen

3701 W. Algonquin Rd., Ste. 380
Rolling Meadows, Illinois 60008
(847) 392-0244
Key Contact - Specialty:
Mr. Bob Clawson

111 Monument Circle, Ste. 3930
Indianapolis, Indiana 46204
(317) 631-2900
Key Contact - Specialty:
Mr. Randy Emerson

7155 Shadeland Station, Ste. 145
Indianapolis, Indiana 46256
(317) 585-4000
Key Contact - Specialty:
Mr. Randy Emerson

10300 W. 103rd St., Ste. 101
Overland Park, Kansas 66214
(913) 888-8885
Key Contact - Specialty:
Mr. Kyle Tilley

4965 U.S. Hwy. 42, Ste. 2900
Louisville, Kentucky 40222
(502) 339-2900
(800) 682-9784
Fax: (502) 339-2888
Key Contact - Specialty:
Mr. Sam Smith - *Information technology*
Ms. Stacey Watson

National City Twr., Ste. 2850
Louisville, Kentucky 40202
(502) 581-9900
Key Contact - Specialty:
Ms. Kathy Mattingly

120 E. Baltimore St., Ste. 1950
Baltimore, Maryland 21202
(410) 727-4050
Key Contact - Specialty:
Mr. Paul Villella

155 Federal St., 10th Floor
Boston, Massachusetts 02110
(617) 423-3200
Key Contact - Specialty:
Mr. Steve McMahan

133 Federal St., Ste. 300
Boston, Massachusetts 02110
(617) 350-0945
Fax: (617) 542-8570
Key Contact - Specialty:
Ms. Mary Loftus
Mr. Paul Norton
Mr. Kevin Westerberg
Mr. David Rutter
Ms. Betsy Boucher
Mr. John Granger

8 New England Executive Park
Burlington, Massachusetts 01803
(781) 270-4441
Fax: (781) 270-4443
Key Contact - Specialty:
Mr. Phil Psaceas
Mr. Richard Wise

20 Burlington Mall Rd., Ste. 305
Burlington, Massachusetts 01803
(781) 272-5000
Key Contact - Specialty:
Mr. Steve McMahan

1500 W. Park Drive, Ste. 390
Westborough, Massachusetts 01581
(508) 366-2600
Key Contact - Specialty:
Mr. Steve McMahan

161 Ottawa NW, Ste. 409D
Grand Rapids, Michigan 49503
(616) 459-3600
Key Contact - Specialty:
Mr. Michael Trewhella

2000 Town Ctr., Ste. 850
Southfield, Michigan 48075
(248) 352-6520
Key Contact - Specialty:
Mr. Michael Trewhella

8500 Normandale Lake Blvd., Ste. 2160
Bloomington, Minnesota 55437
(612) 835-4177
Key Contact - Specialty:
Mr. Walt Kennedy

333 S. 7th St., Ste. 1470
Minneapolis, Minnesota 55402
(612) 288-9777
Fax: (612) 288-9705
Key Contact - Specialty:
Mr. Ronald Dressen - *Accounting, finance*

220 S. 6th St., Ste. 810
Pillsbury Center S. Bldg.
Minneapolis, Minnesota 55402
(612) 332-6460
Key Contact - Specialty:
Mr. Walt Kennedy

One CityPlace Drive, Ste. 170
St. Louis, Missouri 63141
(314) 432-4500
Key Contact - Specialty:
Mr. Jack Deck

1601 E. Flamingo Rd., Ste. 18
Las Vegas, Nevada 89119
(702) 796-9676
Key Contact - Specialty:
Mr. John Spencer

71 Spit Brook Rd., Ste. 305
Nashua, New Hampshire 03060
(603) 888-1700
Key Contact - Specialty:
Mr. Steve McMahan

15 Essex Rd., Ste. 201
Paramus, New Jersey 07652
(201) 843-2020
Key Contact - Specialty:
Mr. Joe Eiseman

1 Gatehall Drive, 3rd Floor
Parsippany, New Jersey 08540
(973) 267-3222
Key Contact - Specialty:
Mr. Joe Eiseman

5 Independence Way
Princeton, New Jersey 08540
(609) 452-7277
Key Contact - Specialty:
Mr. Joe Eiseman

100 Woodbridge Ctr. Drive, Ste. 101
Woodbridge, New Jersey 07095
(732) 283-9510
Key Contact - Specialty:
Mr. Joe Eiseman

60 E. 42nd St., 27th Floor
New York, New York 10165
(212) 883-7300
Key Contact - Specialty:
Mr. Joe Eiseman

3 Gannett Drive, Ste. 316
White Plains, New York 10604
(914) 251-9500
Key Contact - Specialty:
Mr. Joe Eiseman

201 N. Tryon St., Ste. 2660
Charlotte, North Carolina 28202
(704) 333-8311
Key Contact - Specialty:
Mr. Timothy Kessler

2290 Florence Ave.
Cincinnati, Ohio 45306
(513) 221-6877
Key Contact - Specialty:
Mr. Bruce Rockwell

525 Vine St., Ste. 2250
Cincinnati, Ohio 45202
(513) 651-3303
Key Contact - Specialty:
Mr. Bruce Rockwell

1105 Schrock Rd., Ste. 510
Columbus, Ohio 43229
(614) 846-3311
Key Contact - Specialty:
Mr. Chuck Rothenbush

One South Main St., Ste. 1440
Dayton, Ohio 45402
(937) 461-4660
Key Contact - Specialty:
Mr. Bruce Rockwell

2 S. Patterson
Dayton, Ohio 45402
(937) 220-9799
Key Contact - Specialty:
Mr. Bruce Rockwell

3 Summit Park Drive, Ste. 550
Independence, Ohio 44131
(216) 328-5900
Key Contact - Specialty:
Mr. Wiley Farler

10220 SW Greenburg Rd., Ste. 625
Portland, Oregon 97223
(503) 768-4546
Key Contact - Specialty:
Mr. Eric Carlson

150 S. Warner Rd., Ste. 238
King of Prussia, Pennsylvania 19406
(610) 341-1960
Key Contact - Specialty:
Mr. Emil Occhiboi

1500 Market St.
12th Floor, East Twr.
Philadelphia, Pennsylvania 19103
(215) 246-3484
Key Contact - Specialty:
Mr. Ed Mega
Mr. Tamzen Harrington
Ms. Patricia Lord
Mr. Jonathan Reiff
Mr. Norman McMahon

1760 Market St., 12th Floor
Philadelphia, Pennsylvania 19103
(215) 665-1717
Key Contact - Specialty:
Mr. Emil Occhiboi

Foster Plaza VI
681 Anderson Drive, 2nd Floor
Pittsburgh, Pennsylvania 15220
(412) 928-8300
Key Contact - Specialty:
Mr. Wiley Farler

8701 N. Mopac, Ste. 455
Austin, Texas 78759
(512) 345-7473
Key Contact - Specialty:
Mr. Mike Varrichio

5429 LBJ Frwy., Ste. 275
Dallas, Texas 75240
(972) 387-1600
Key Contact - Specialty:
Mr. Mike Varrichio

12770 Coit Rd., Ste. 128
Dallas, Texas 75251
(972) 934-2111
Fax: (972) 934-2332
Key Contact - Specialty:
Mr. John Randolph
Mr. Wayne Wlodawsky - *Finance, accounting, information technology*
Ms. Ginny Cochran - *Accounting, finance, information technology*

801 Cherry St., Ste. 1025
Ft. Worth, Texas 76102
(817) 338-9300
Key Contact - Specialty:
Mr. Mike Varrichio

5177 Richmond Ave., Ste. 1080
Houston, Texas 77056
(713) 622-3711
Fax: (713) 622-3778
Key Contact - Specialty:
Ms. Kathy Riley
Mr. Robert Carey

520 Post Oak Blvd., Ste. 700
Houston, Texas 77027
(713) 439-1077
Key Contact - Specialty:
Mr. Dan Luce

505 E. 200 S., Ste. 300
Salt Lake City, Utah 84102
(801) 328-0011
Key Contact - Specialty:
Mr. Rik Yerzik

11240 Waples Mill Rd., Ste. 301
Fairfax, Virginia 22030
(703) 293-9704
(888) 427-3462
Fax: (703) 293-9715
Key Contact - Specialty:
Mr. Andy MacLean
Ms. Candace Solhjou

8045 Leesburg Pike, 2nd Floor
Vienna, Virginia 22182
(703) 790-5610
Key Contact - Specialty:
Mr. Paul F. Villella

500 108th Ave. NE, Ste. 1780
Bellevue, Washington 98004
(425) 454-6400
Key Contact - Specialty:
Mr. Eric Carlson

1233 N. Mayfair Rd., Ste. 300
Milwaukee, Wisconsin 53226
(414) 475-7200
Key Contact - Specialty:
Mr. Dave Youngberg

255 Consumers Rd., Ste. 404
North York, Ontario M2J 1R4
Canada
(416) 495-1551
Key Contact - Specialty:
Mr. John Talio

Romano McAvoy Assoc., Inc.

872 Jericho Tnpk.
St. James, New York 11780
(516) 265-7878
Fax: (516) 265-1252
Email: rma@li.net

Key Contact - Specialty:
Mr. Joseph C. Romano - *Human resources, sales & marketing, finance, public relations*
Mr. Edward P. McAvoy - *Technical software, programming*

Description: Networked with other quality and responsive recruiting firms with extensive job listing database. Service national firms as well as Long Island key firms.

Salary Minimum: $40,000
Functions: Production, Quality, Purchasing, Advertising, PR, Benefits, Systems dev.
Industries: Computer equip., Consumer electronics, Aerospace, High tech, Software

---

Romeo-Hudgins & Assoc., Ltd.

200 Lake Drive E., Ste. 206
Woodlake Falls Corporate Park
Cherry Hill, New Jersey 08002
(609) 482-7840
Fax: (609) 486-0387

Email: promeo@msn.com

Key Contact - Specialty:
Mr. Paul C. Romeo - *Pharmaceutical, biotechnology, genetic engineering, medical devices & instruments*

Description: Executive search for pharmaceutical and biotechnology industries covering all disciplines.

Salary Minimum: $60,000
Functions: Product dev., Quality, Physicians, Mktg. mgmt., IT, Systems dev., Engineering
Industries: Drugs mfg., Medical devices, Biotech

Emery A. Rose & Assoc.
5916 Armour Loop SE
Olympia, Washington 98513
(360) 413-9300
Fax: (360) 413-9400

Key Contact - Specialty:
Mr. Emery Rose - *Generalist*

Description: Executive recruiting and marketing consulting in aerospace-defense, electronics and telecommunications industries specializing in marketing-sales, engineering, executive and technical professionals.

Salary Minimum: $30,000
Functions: Generalist, Senior mgmt., Sales mgmt., MIS mgmt., Systems dev., R&D, Engineering
Industries: Generalist, Mgmt. consulting, Telecoms, Defense, Aerospace, High tech, Software

---

The Rose Search Group, Inc.
6616 Fishers Farm Lane, Ste. A-2
Charlotte, North Carolina 28277-0319
(704) 543-3150
Fax: (704) 543-3146
Email: rosesearchgroup@healthcare.org
Web: www.health-medicalcareers.com

Key Contact - Specialty:
Mr. Jim Rosenberger - *Healthcare*

Description: Clinical and support management positions throughout the healthcare industry including physician placement management, managed care, PHO/MSO, long term care and hospitals.

Salary Minimum: $50,000
Functions: Physicians, Nurses, Allied health, Health admin.
Industries: Healthcare

Rosenfeld & Co., Inc.
25900 Greenfield Rd., Ste. 236
Oak Park, Michigan 48237
(248) 968-3210
Fax: (248) 968-2908
Email: mail@rosenfeldco.com
Web: www.rosenfeldco.com

Key Contact - Specialty:
Mr. Martin J. Rosenfeld - *Attorneys, law firm managers*
Ms. Sheri B. Katzman - *Attorneys, support staff*

Description: We are an international executive search firm specializing in attorneys and law firm management searches for private firms and corporations.

Salary Minimum: $70,000
Functions: Senior mgmt., Admin. svcs., Legal, CFO's, MIS mgmt., Attorneys
Industries: Legal

Ross Personnel Consultants, Inc.
161 East Ave., Ste. 105
Norwalk, Connecticut 06851
(203) 866-2033

Key Contact - Specialty:
Mr. Anthony J. Barca - *Sales & marketing*
Mr. Philip M. Young - *Computers, PC's, peripherals, networks, software*
Ms. Tracy A. Howlett - *Copiers, PC's, peripherals, networks, software*

Description: An executive search and recruiting firm specializing in sales, marketing, systems, training, field engineering and general management in the computer, telecommunications and copier industries.

Salary Minimum: $40,000
Functions: Mkt. research, Mktg. mgmt., Sales mgmt., Systems anal., Systems dev., Systems implem., Systems support
Industries: Computer equip., Consumer electronics, Computer svcs., Equip. svcs., Telecoms, High tech, Software

---

Rossi & Assoc. Inc.
1500 W. Georgia St., Ste. 1400
Vancouver, British Columbia V6G 2Z6
Canada
(604) 683-3755
Fax: (604) 683-3721
Web: Rossi@bc.sympatico.ca

Key Contact - Specialty:
Ms. Donna Rossi - *Sales and marketing in the business-to-business industries*

Description: 18 years of sales recruitment in the business to business area - senior management to sales teams.

Salary Minimum: $30,000
Functions: General mgmt., Mfg., Sales & mktg.
Industries: Paper, Printing, Equip. svcs., Communications, Telecoms, Environmental svcs., High tech

---

The Rossi Search Group
608 Northlawn Drive
Lancaster, Pennsylvania 17603
(717) 396-9111
Fax: (717) 396-9786
Email: rosco@redrose.net
Web: www.redrose.net/rosco

Key Contact - Specialty:
Mr. Alfred F. Rossi - *Technology managers, directors, vice presidents, chemical professionals*
Ms. Doris Reitz - *Engineers*
Ms. Jeanne Cleary - *MIS, software, computer hardware professionals*

Description: Focus is on engineering, scientific software, computer hardware and manufacturing professionals, with concentration in polymers, plastics and packaging. Retained search is provided for senior technical managers at $100M and above.

Salary Minimum: $50,000
Functions: Senior mgmt., Middle mgmt., Product dev., Plant mgmt., IT, R&D, Engineering
Industries: Paper, Chemicals, Plastics/rubber, Machinery/Appliances, Computer equip., Misc. mfg., Packaging

---

Roster Inc.
6333 Constitution Drive
Ft. Wayne, Indiana 46804
(219) 436-6330
Fax: (219) 432-7126
Email: roster1@gte.net

Key Contact - Specialty:
Mr. Steve Trimarchi
Mr. John King
Mr. Dennis Payne
Mr. Glenn W. Johnson

Description: We are extremely automated and research driven. To assure constant quality, we use and teach the Position Matrix ™ which is a tool described in the book Identifying, Placing, and Evaluating Employees.
Functions: Generalist, General mgmt., Mfg., HR mgmt., Finance
Industries: Generalist, Mfg., Finance, Svcs.
Professional Associations: IACPR

Patricia Roth Int'l.
2682 NE 135th St.
North Miami, Florida 33181
(305) 940-9130
Fax: (305) 940-8572
Email: rothint2@aol.com

Key Contact - Specialty:
Ms. Patricia Roth - *Construction equipment, mining equipment, engines*

Description: Our twenty-four years of experience in providing highly qualified personnel for the manufacturers and dealers throughout the world enables our client to place the responsibility of locating their new employee in our hands.
Functions: Senior mgmt., Middle mgmt., Mktg. mgmt., Sales mgmt., CFO's, Engineering, Int'l.

Roth Young of Tampa

5201 W. Kennedy Blvd., Ste. 506
Tampa, Florida 33609
(813) 289-6556
Fax: (813) 289-9118
Email: rytampa@gte.net
Web: www.rothyoungoftampabay.com

Key Contact - Specialty:
Mr. P. Barry Cushing - *Supermarkets*
Mr. Fran Maun - *Food sales, food manufacturing*

Description: Currently the only Roth Young office in the Southeast, offering national Roth Young interchange service.

Salary Minimum: $20,000
Functions: Middle mgmt., Productivity, Physicians, Allied health, Sales mgmt., Training, MIS mgmt.
Industries: Food/bev/tobacco, Hospitality

Roth Young of Chicago

35 Hanson Rd.
Algonquin, Illinois 60102
(847) 458-8808
Fax: (847) 458-8810
Email: stevef@mcs.com

Key Contact - Specialty:
Mr. James Babka - *General management, marketing, marketing research, sales, production & engineering (food & healthcare)*

Description: Specialists in hotels, restaurants, clubs, resorts, retailers (softlines, hardlines), food manufacturers, sales/marketing, operations, engineering, research and development and healthcare.

Salary Minimum: $22,000
Functions: Senior mgmt., Middle mgmt., Plant mgmt., Mkt. research, Mktg. mgmt., Sales mgmt., R&D
Industries: Food/bev/tobacco, Soap/perfume/cosmetics, Drugs mfg., Wholesale, Retail, Hospitality, Healthcare

---

Roth Young Personnel Services of Washington, DC

15718 Cherry Blossom Ln.
North Potomac, Maryland 20878
(301) 527-9522
Fax: (301) 330-4299
Email: foodjobs@rothyoung.com
Web: www.rothyoung.com

Key Contact - Specialty:
Mr. Jeffrey B. Landsman - *Food service distribution*

Description: Consultative recruitment services. Expertise in all areas within the foodservice distribution industry. Distributors & manufacturers alike. Retained & contingency.

Salary Minimum: $40,000
Functions: General mgmt., Materials, Distribution, Sales & mktg., HR mgmt., Finance, MIS mgmt.
Industries: Food/bev/tobacco, Wholesale, Hospitality

Affiliates:
Winston Personnel Inc.

Roth Young Personnel Service of Detroit, Inc.

31275 Northwestern Hwy., Ste. 116
Farmington Hills, Michigan 48334
(248) 626-6033
Fax: (248) 626-7079

Key Contact - Specialty:
Mr. Samuel Skeegan

Description: Executive recruitment specializing in the food, drug, medical and retail industries.

Salary Minimum: $60,000
Functions: Plant mgmt., Quality, Distribution, Mkt. research, R&D, Engineering, Int'l.
Industries: Food/bev/tobacco, Chemicals, Drugs mfg., Retail, Hospitality, Pharmaceutical svcs., Healthcare

---

Roth Young Executive Recruiters

4620 W. 77th St., #290
Minneapolis, Minnesota 55435
(612) 831-6655
Fax: (612) 831-7413

Key Contact - Specialty:
Mr. Donald B. Spahr - *Retail, supermarkets*

Description: We are a nationwide recruiting service with offices coast to coast, placing mid to upper management positions in all facets of the hospitality, food and retail industries; food, pharmaceutical and consumer sales; and physical and occupational therapists.
Functions: General mgmt., Mfg., Allied health, Sales & mktg., HR mgmt., R&D, Engineering
Industries: Food/bev/tobacco, Misc. mfg., Wholesale, Retail, Hospitality, Packaging, Healthcare

---

Roth Young of Pittsburgh

3087 Carson St.
Murrysville, Pennsylvania 15668
(412) 733-5900
Fax: (412) 733-0183
Email: leo@usaor.net

Key Contact - Specialty:
Mr. Len Di Naples - *Healthcare, executives*

Description: Specialists in healthcare, supermarket and hospitality industries. Healthcare placements include: physicians, physical therapists, occupational therapists, nurse practioners and physicians assistants.

Salary Minimum: $25,000
Functions: Middle mgmt., Physicians, Allied health, Advertising
Industries: Food/bev/tobacco, Wholesale, Retail, Mgmt. consulting, Human resource svcs., Healthcare

---

Roth Young Executive Search

11999 Katy Frwy., Ste. 490
Houston, Texas 77079
(281) 368-8550
Fax: (281) 368-8560
Web: www.ryhouston@aol.com

Key Contact - Specialty:
Ms. Elaine Gladstone - *Consumer goods (marketing & sales)*
Mr. Robert Gladstone - *Institutional food service, distribution*
Mr. Ray Schorejs - *Supermarkets, retail, wholesale consumer products*
Mr. Athur Gladstone - *Pharmaceuticals*
Mr. Robert O'Dell - *Retail*
Mr. Brian Claybaugh - *Restaurant, hotel*
Mr. Brian Pearson - *Food manufacturing*

Description: Principal has 30 years experience recruiting with Roth Young. Staff is highly experienced with a remarkable history of success.

Salary Minimum: $30,000
Functions: General mgmt., Mfg., Materials, Sales & mktg., HR mgmt., Finance, IT
Industries: Generalist, Mfg., Transportation, Wholesale, Retail, Svcs., Communications

---

Roth Young Seattle

305 - 111th Ave. NE
Bellevue, Washington 98004
(425) 455-2141
Fax: (425) 455-0067
Email: rydws@aol.com
Web: RothYoungSeattle.com

Key Contact - Specialty:
Mr. David Salzberg - *Sales, manufacturing, hospitality, food*

Description: We have a keen understanding of our recruiting specialists. We develop a mutual respect with our client companies. Many of our clients have long standing relationships with our organization.

Salary Minimum: $40,000
Functions: Plant mgmt., Mktg. mgmt., Sales mgmt., Finance
Industries: Food/bev/tobacco, Misc. mfg., Hospitality

Roth Young Executive Search of Milwaukee
5215 N. Ironwood Rd., Ste. 201
Milwaukee, Wisconsin 53217
(414) 962-7684
Fax: (414) 962-6261
Email: rothyong@execpc.com
Web: www.execpc.com/~rothyong

Key Contact - Specialty:
Mr. Thomas E. Brenneman - *Food (General management, manufacturing, technologies)*
Ms. Kay S. Boxer - *Food manufacturing*
Mr. Robert W. Alstrin - *Food (sales & marketing)*

Description: To successfully match our clients' management staffing needs with our candidates' career aspirations...exclusively in the food industry.

Salary Minimum: $50,000
Functions: General mgmt., Mfg., Materials, Sales & mktg., HR mgmt., R&D, Engineering
Industries: Food/bev/tobacco

Rothrock Associates, Inc.
P.O. Box 698
Cary, North Carolina 27512-0698
(919) 460-0070
Fax: (919) 460-6472
Email: rainc@raijobs.com
Web: www.raijobs.com

Key Contact - Specialty:
Mr. T. Hardy Rothrock, Jr.

Description: Nationwide searches for purchasing, materials, manufacturing and quality engineers, electronics, RF/voice/data communications, computer software programmers/engineers, electromechanical and metals industries. Human resources professionals.

Salary Minimum: $40,000
Functions: Mfg., Materials, HR mgmt., Engineering
Industries: Metal products, Computer equip., Consumer electronics, High tech

---

Rowland Assoc.
7840 Madison Ave., Ste. 185
Fair Oaks, California 95628
(916) 965-8833
Fax: (916) 962-2938

Key Contact - Specialty:
Mr. John R. Rowland - *Engineering, hardware, software, manufacturing*

Description: We are a full service search firm. When we perform a search, a team leader (focal point) is established with a team to support the team leader.

Salary Minimum: $50,000
Functions: Plant mgmt., Materials Plng., Benefits, Budgeting, MIS mgmt., Systems anal., Engineering
Industries: Construction, Food/bev/tobacco, Lumber/furniture, Chemicals, Medical devices, Leather/stone/glass/clay, Metal products

---

Rowland Mountain & Assoc.
4E Executive Park, Ste. 100
Atlanta, Georgia 30329
(404) 325-2189
Fax: (404) 321-1842
Email: Russ_Mountain@rmasales.com
Web: www.rmasales.com

Key Contact - Specialty:
Mr. Russell D. Mountain

Functions: Middle mgmt., Mktg. mgmt., Sales mgmt., Mgmt. consultants
Industries: Chemicals, Plastics/rubber, Misc. mfg., Pharmaceutical svcs., Telecoms, High tech, Software

---

Royal Assoc.
14011 Ventura Blvd., Ste. 214-W
Sherman Oaks, California 91423
(818) 981-1080
Fax: (818) 981-1338
Email: consultants@royalstaff.com
Web: www.royalstaff.com

Key Contact - Specialty:
Ms. Judith L. Rothman - *Accounting, financial*
Dr. Jacquelene Lee - *Healthcare*

Description: We have the capability, resources and experienced staff to successfully fill requirements for quality personnel. A state-of-the-art industry-specific search and retrieval system allows access to all employers stored in the database.

Salary Minimum: $45,000
Functions: Generalist, Directors, Senior mgmt., Physicians, Nurses, HR mgmt., Finance
Industries: Construction, Invest. banking, Human resource svcs., New media, Broadcast & Film, Real estate, Healthcare

Branches:
3625 Thousand Oaks Blvd.
Westlake Village, California 91362
(805) 373-9909
Fax: (805) 494-4365
Email: consultants@royalstaff.com
Web: www.royalstaff.com
Key Contact - Specialty:
Ms. Barbara Koenig - *Generalist, travel, stock brokerage, administrative*

RTE Search
25 Executive Twrs.
P.O. Box 161
Gibbsboro, New Jersey 08026-0161
(609) 772-9642

Key Contact - Specialty:
Mr. Robert English - *Engineering, manufacturing, quality control, sanitation, research & development*

Description: Specialize in R&D (exploratory, analytical, product development, technical services), manufacturing (production, quality control, sanitation, maintenance, distribution) and engineering for the food and beverage industries.

Salary Minimum: $30,000
Functions: Production, Automation, Plant mgmt., Quality, Productivity, Distribution, R&D
Industries: Food/bev/tobacco

Branches:
711 Regency Twr., P.O. Box 29668
Richmond, Virginia 23242
(804) 750-2088
Key Contact - Specialty:
Mr. Robert English - *Engineering, manufacturing, quality control, sanitation, research & development*

The Rubicon Group
7553 E. Santa Catalina
Scottsdale, Arizona 85255
(602) 515-9225
Fax: (602) 515-9213
Email: judyjacobs@aol.com

Key Contact - Specialty:
Mr. Martin Jacobs - *Administrative*
Ms. Judith Jacobs - *General management*

Description: Confidential search for attorneys, electronic engineering and actuaries. National and international search. Physician specialists. Administrative nurses. Financial estate planners.

Salary Minimum: $40,000
Functions: Middle mgmt., Nurses, Health admin., Mktg. mgmt., Cash mgmt., Mgmt. consultants, Attorneys
Industries: Energy/utilities, Misc. financial, Legal, Telecoms, Insurance, High tech, Healthcare

The Rubinic Consulting Group
1592 Jupiter Ave.
Hilliard, Ohio 43026
(614) 529-8350
Fax: (614) 529-8350
Email:
RubinicConsulting@compuserve.com

Key Contact - Specialty:
Mr. Michael Rubinic - *Management consulting, information technology*
Ms. Roxanna Rubinic - *Information technology*
Mr. Larry Matteson - *Project management*

Description: We are a specialized firm committed to placing high quality consultants with our exceptional corporate clients. With our limited overhead, we are able to provide extremely competitive compensation rates.

Salary Minimum: $30,000
Functions: IT, MIS mgmt., Systems anal., Systems dev., Systems implem., Systems support, Mgmt. consultants
Industries: Mfg., Finance, Computer svcs., Mgmt. consulting, Insurance, Software, Healthcare

Affiliates:
Contract Programming Resources

Ruderfer & Co., Inc.
908 Pompton Ave., Ste. A-2
Cedar Grove, New Jersey 07009
(973) 857-2400
Fax: (973) 857-4343

Key Contact - Specialty:
Mr. Irwin A. Ruderfer - *Regulatory affairs*
Ms. Nan Kanoff
Mr. Richard Levy
Ms. Bonnie Roseman
Mr. Harold Tapler - *Technical, R&D, quality*
Dr. Louise Greenberg - *Clinical research-pharmacy*

Description: Nationwide healthcare search consultants specializing in the biopharmaceutical industry. The matching of company and person is our constant goal and we excel in sourcing qualified candidates whose personality/chemistry and education/experience are on target.

Salary Minimum: $50,000
Functions: Mfg., Healthcare, Sales & mktg., HR mgmt., Finance, MIS mgmt., R&D
Industries: Chemicals, Drugs mfg., Medical devices, Accounting, Human resource svcs., Advertising/PR, Biotech

Susan Rudich
20 E. 9th St.
New York, New York 10003
(212) 228-8126
(212) 989-7891
Fax: (212) 228-2905

Key Contact - Specialty:
Ms. Susan Rudich - *Creative textiles*

Description: Over 35 years experience, lecturer, advisor art schools and associations. Former New York state sole textile placement specialist.
Functions: Product dev., Graphic artists
Industries: Textiles/apparel

Louis Rudzinsky Assoc., Inc.
P.O. Box 640
Lexington, Massachusetts 02173
(781) 862-6727
Fax: (781) 862-6868
Email: lra@lra.com
Web: www.lra.com

Key Contact - Specialty:
Mr. Howard Rudzinsky - *Photonics, optics, imaging, sold state/semiconductor*
Mr. Jeff Rudzinsky - *Hardware, software, systems, test engineers (Commercial/DOD)*
Mr. Mark Joyce - *Hardware, software, mechanical, electrical*

Description: Established in 1968-serving technology companies in optics, electronics, electro-optics, fiber optics, software, systems, solid state devices and instrumentation. Covering engineering, R&D, marketing, sales and general management, nationwide.

Salary Minimum: $40,000
Functions: Product dev., Production, Systems anal., Systems dev., Systems implem., R&D, Engineering
Industries: Printing, Medical devices, Computer equip., Test/measurement equip., Aerospace, High tech, Software

J. D. Ruhmann & Assoc.
P.O. Box 942
St. Charles, Missouri 63301
(314) 723-2200
(800) 366-9061
Fax: (314) 723-0440
Email: jdruhmann@ruhmann.com
Web: www.ruhmann.com

Key Contact - Specialty:
Mr. John D. Ruhmann - *Management & scientific contributors to the biotechnology & genetic engineering field*

Description: Specialists in life sciences, including scientific management and group staffing. Experience in start-up and high growth companies and difficult placements.

Salary Minimum: $50,000
Functions: Directors, Senior mgmt., Middle mgmt., R&D
Industries: Drugs mfg., Medical devices, Biotech

Russillo/Gardner/Spolsino
30 Rowes Wharf, Ste. 310
Boston, Massachusetts 02210
(617) 345-0700
Fax: (617) 951-2986
Email: russillo@idt.net
Web: www.investechsearch.com/

Key Contact - Specialty:
Mr. Thomas P. Russillo - *Insurance, reinsurance, risk management, risk financing*
Mr. Richard E. Gardner - *Information technology for the financial industries, software engineering*
Mr. Robert J. Spolsino - *Insurance, reinsurance, risk management*

Description: Sixteen years serving insurance/risk management/risk financing/employee benefits and information technology/software engineering industries. All the firm's consultants have substantial experience in the fields they represent.

Salary Minimum: $90,000
Functions: Senior mgmt., Middle mgmt., Cash mgmt., Risk mgmt., IT, Int'l.
Industries: Finance, Invest. banking, Brokers, Misc. financial, Insurance, Software

K. Russo Assoc. Inc.
151 Railroad Ave., 1st Floor
Greenwich, Connecticut 06830
(203) 552-0100
Fax: (203) 552-0865

Key Contact - Specialty:
Ms. Karen Russo - *Human resources, public relations*
Ms. Toni Mahr - *Human resources, public relations*
Ms. Nancy Morgan - *Human resources, public relations*
Ms. Noreen Haggerty - *Human resources, public relations*

Description: We are a specialist firm focusing on executive search for the human resource and public relations arena. The firm also offers career transition programs and competency modeling.

Salary Minimum: $35,000
Functions: PR, HR mgmt., Benefits, Personnel, Training
Industries: Mfg., Food/bev/tobacco, Finance, Entertainment, Human resource svcs., Communications, Advertising/PR

The Ryan Charles Group, Inc.
2151 W. Hillsboro Blvd., Ste. 203
Deerfield Beach, Florida 33442
(954) 421-9112
Fax: (954) 428-4940
Email: ryanc@icanect.net
Web: www.ipcc.com/market/ryancharles

Key Contact - Specialty:
Mr. Norman D. St. Jean - *Generalist*
Mr. Bruce Leib - *Generalist*
Ms. Joan Harris - *Generalist*

Description: A creative nationwide recruiting firm that provides personalized, results oriented service to a select group of client companies. Committed to excellence and results.

Salary Minimum: $40,000
Functions: Senior mgmt., Mktg. mgmt., HR mgmt., CFO's, MIS mgmt., Engineering, Int'l.
Industries: Generalist, Medical devices, Plastics/rubber, Metal products, Machinery/Appliances, Misc. mfg., High tech

Branches:
2021 Midwest Rd., Ste. 300
Oak Brook, Illinois 60521
(773) 233-9111
Key Contact - Specialty:
Mr. N. St. Jean

Ryan, Miller & Assoc.
4601 Wilshire Blvd., Ste. 225
Los Angeles, California 90010
(213) 938-4768
Fax: (213) 857-7009
Email: ryan_miller@compuserve.com
Web: www.aafa.com

Key Contact - Specialty:
Mr. Lee Ryan - *Generalist, CPAs, MBAs*
Mr. Michael O'Connell - *Generalist, CPAs, MBAs*

Description: An executive search firm specializing in the recruitment of accounting, banking and financial professionals within the salary ranges of $50,000 to $500,000 at the local, national and international level.

Salary Minimum: $50,000
Functions: Finance, CFO's, Budgeting, Cash mgmt., Taxes, M&A
Industries: Generalist, Misc. mfg., Finance, Svcs., Entertainment, Communications, Software

Branches:
790 E. Colorado Blvd., #506
Pasadena, California 91101
(818) 568-3100
Fax: (818) 568-3772
Key Contact - Specialty:
Mr. Roger Miller - *Banking, corporate finance, investment banking*

Affiliates:
Temporary Accounting Professionals

Ryan-Allen & Assoc., Inc.
732 Devon Court
San Diego, California 92109
(619) 576-0737
Fax: (619) 488-2621

Key Contact - Specialty:
Ms. Sheila R. Hawley

Description: Specialize in the recruitment of professionals in accounting, banking, finance and human resources.
Functions: Advertising, Direct mktg., Benefits, Training, Finance, CFO's, Credit
Industries: Mfg., Drugs mfg., Medical devices, Finance, Banking, High tech, Software

Rylan Forbes Consulting Group, Inc.
(a division of ACSYS Inc.)
102 Campus Drive
Princeton, New Jersey 08540
(609) 419-0600
Fax: (609) 419-0737
Email: joes@rylanforbes.com
Web: www.acsysinc.com

Key Contact - Specialty:
Mr. Joseph K. Stauffer - *Accounting & finance*

Description: Nearly two decades of assisting Fortune 500 companies to emerging businesses with all accounting/ finance needs. All consultants are CPA's with extensive work experience. Provides retained level service on a contingency fee basis.

Salary Minimum: $35,000
Functions: Personnel, CFO's, Budgeting, Cash mgmt., Credit, Taxes, M&A
Industries: Chemicals, Drugs mfg., Computer equip., Invest. banking, Pharmaceutical svcs., Telecoms, High tech

Branches:
1760 Market St., 7th Floor
Philadelphia, Pennsylvania 19103
(215) 851-8900
Fax: (215) 851-8903
Key Contact - Specialty:
Mr. Craig Worton - *Accounting & finance*

Ryman, Bell, Green & Michaels, Inc.
6200 Savoy, Ste. 1100
Houston, Texas 77036
(713) 784-0565
Fax: (713) 953-1152

Key Contact - Specialty:
Mr. Phil Forman
Mr. David Broadway

Description: National and international search firm representing Fortune 5000 and law firms of all sizes.

Salary Minimum: $50,000
Functions: Legal, Sales mgmt., Direct mktg., M&A, Attorneys
Industries: Banking, Invest. banking, Brokers, Legal, Advertising/PR

R. L. Rystrom & Assoc., Inc.
11325 172nd St. W., Ste. 325B
Lakeville, Minnesota 55044
(612) 898-3140
Fax: (612) 898-1352
Email: rystrom@primenet.com
Web: www.rystrom.com

Key Contact - Specialty:
Mr. R. L. Rystrom - *Computer hardware, software, data communication, computer services*

Description: The upper Midwest premier placement specialist. Our clients range from regional startups to Fortune 200 companies who have needed to hire computer hardware/software and datacom sales and support candidates.

Salary Minimum: $45,000
Functions: Middle mgmt., Mkt. research, Mktg. mgmt.
Industries: Computer equip., Test/ measurement equip., Mgmt. consulting, High tech, Software

S-H-S Int'l. of Cherry Hill
929 N. Kings Highway
Cherry Hill, New Jersey 08034
(609) 779-9030
Fax: (609) 779-0898

Key Contact - Specialty:
Mr. Louis Kennedy - *Technical*

Description: Firm provides recruiting services on a contingency basis. Specialization is engineering/technical and manufacturing. Clients are mid-sized organizations. Utilizes database candidate system. Established over 19 years and members of NAPS.

Salary Minimum: $25,000
Functions: Mfg., Engineering
Industries: Food/bev/tobacco, Paper, Medical devices, Paints/petroleum products, Metal products, Machinery/ Appliances, Misc. mfg.

S-H-S TechStaff
1124 Rte. 315
Wilkes-Barre, Pennsylvania 18702
(717) 825-3411
Fax: (717) 825-7790
Email: shs@csrlink.net
Web: www.microserve.net/~crd/ shstechstaff

Key Contact - Specialty:
Mr. Charles Davenport - *Information technology, accounting*
Mr. Nicholas J. Michalisin, Jr. - *Information technology, engineering*
Ms. Jackie Hemmings - *Accounting, information technology, general administration*
Mr. Michael McAnney - *Information technology, human resources*
Mr. Pat Tomeo - *Environmental engineers, facilities management*

Description: Offering professional recruiting services for direct hire and contract professionals. Emphasis on information technology.

Salary Minimum: $35,000
Functions: Middle mgmt., Budgeting, Systems anal., Systems implem., Systems support, Network admin., DB admin.
Industries: Mfg., Food/bev/tobacco, Plastics/rubber, Computer svcs., Accounting, Haz. waste, High tech

---

S. C. Int'l., Ltd.
1430 Branding Lane, #119
Downers Grove, Illinois 60515
(630) 963-3033
Fax: (630) 963-3170
Email: rollins@scinternational.com
Web: www.scinternational.com

Key Contact - Specialty:
Mr. Scott Rollins - *Actuaries*

Description: Specialists in insurance and employee benefits recruitment: actuaries, claims, underwriting, benefits consultants. Additionally healthcare professionals.

Salary Minimum: $30,000
Functions: HR mgmt.
Industries: Human resource svcs., Insurance, Healthcare

S. P. Assoc., Inc.
5970 Fairview Rd., Ste. 512
Charlotte, North Carolina 28210
(704) 643-7250
Fax: (704) 643-1249
Email: spassociates@mindspring.com

Key Contact - Specialty:
Mr. A. J. Edahl
Mr. Gabe C. Hill, III - *Textiles, non-wovens*

Description: All functions only in following industries: textile and fibers, non-wovens, pulp and paper mills, packaging, high exotic metals, pharmaceutical, banking and data processing. Plastics.

Salary Minimum: $30,000
Functions: Middle mgmt., Product dev., Production, Plant mgmt., CFO's, Systems dev., R&D
Industries: Textiles/apparel, Paper, Printing, Drugs mfg., Plastics/rubber, Metal products, Computer svcs.

S.C.S. & Assoc.
P.O. Box 2294
Chapel Hill, North Carolina 27515
(919) 932-6700
Fax: (919) 932-6900
Email: steve@scs-associates.com
Web: www.scs-associates.com

Key Contact - Specialty:
Mr. Steve Soltan - *Printing*

Description: I have a background of over 25 years in graphic arts; I am in my 13th year of successfully recruiting executives in the printing industry. We have an office in New York working in information technology.

Salary Minimum: $30,000
Functions: Senior mgmt., Middle mgmt., Plant mgmt., Sales mgmt., Direct mktg., Customer svc., IT
Industries: Printing, Computer svcs., Packaging, High tech, Software

Branches:
234 Fifth Ave., 3rd Floor
New York, New York 10001
(212) 213-5514
Fax: (212) 213-2712
Key Contact - Specialty:
Mr. Brian Barsher

S.D.P. Contract Recruiters
P.O. Box 82
Tennent, New Jersey 07763
(732) 446-0383

Key Contact - Specialty:
Mr. Stephen D. Porada - *Building products (manufacturing, engineering, sales & administration), pharmaceuticals (sales)*

Description: Highly personalized management recruiting and consulting service having a client base of manufacturing industries specializing in building products.

Salary Minimum: $35,000
Functions: Product dev., Production, Automation, Plant mgmt., Packaging, Sales mgmt., Engineering
Industries: Generalist, Paper, Drugs mfg., Packaging

Saber Group, Inc.
5300 Hollister, Ste. 100
Houston, Texas 77040
(713) 462-6900
Fax: (713) 462-8600
Email: sabergp@flash.net

Key Contact - Specialty:
Mr. Steven E. LeMay
Mr. Michael C. Scharringhausen - *Manufacturing*
Mr. Mark Neuweiler - *Construction, engineering*

Description: Specializing in technical, high technology, manufacturers, engineering, construction, sealants, adhesives, coatings, plastics and rubber. Middle to upper level management for specified industries.

Salary Minimum: $45,000
Functions: Senior mgmt., Middle mgmt., Plant mgmt., Quality, Mktg. mgmt., Sales mgmt., CFO's
Industries: Construction, Paper, Plastics/rubber

R. S. Sadow Assoc.
24 Heather Drive
Somerset, New Jersey 08873
(732) 545-4550
Fax: (732) 545-0797
Email: rssadow@aol.com

Key Contact - Specialty:
Mr. Raymond Sadow - *Accounting, information technology*

Description: Operates as a contingency search office. Unsolicited resumes accepted. Appointment required.

Salary Minimum: $30,000
Functions: General mgmt., Mfg., Materials, Finance, IT, R&D, Engineering
Industries: Mfg., Wholesale, Accounting, Publishing, Aerospace, High tech, Software

---

Sage Employment Recruiters
127 E. Windsor Ave.
Elkhart, Indiana 46514
(219) 264-1126
Fax: (219) 264-1128

Key Contact - Specialty:
Mr. Frank Alvey - *Industries with wheels, marine, supplier companies*
Mr. John McGuire - *Recreational vehicle, van conversions*
Mr. Bill Hudson - *Manufactured housing & related suppliers*
Ms. Ella Schaeffer

Description: Industries with wheels, manufactured housing, marine, recreation vehicles, van conversion, truck/trailer body and the supply companies for these industries. Effective, discreet approach gets assignment accomplished in weeks not months. Recognized for confidentiality.

Salary Minimum: $40,000

Functions: General mgmt., Mfg., Materials, Sales mgmt., Finance, IT, Mgmt. consultants
Industries: Metal products, Motor vehicles

Sales & Management Search, Inc.

10 S. Riverside Plaza
Chicago, Illinois 60606
(312) 930-1111
Fax: (312) 930-1119

Key Contact - Specialty:
Mr. Peter Chappell

Description: Our 20th year of mid and senior level recruitment for industrial, commercial and consumer companies. Sales, marketing, manufacturing, operations and executive management.

Salary Minimum: $50,000
Functions: Senior mgmt., Middle mgmt., Sales mgmt., Personnel, CFO's, Cash mgmt.
Industries: Generalist, Banking, Invest. banking, Misc. financial, Accounting, Human resource svcs., Insurance

Sales & Marketing Search, Inc.

100 Cummings Ctr., Ste. 453H
Beverly, Massachusetts 01915
(978) 921-8282
Email: sms@shore.net
Web: www.smsearch.com

Key Contact - Specialty:
Mr. Russell L. Smith
Ms. Betsy Gaudreau
Ms. Lisa Ettlinger
Ms. Daryl-Lynn Michaud
Ms. Claire Richards
Mr. Michael Jalbert

Description: We recruit exclusively in the sales and marketing disciplines for emerging high technology companies on a contingency or retained basis.

Salary Minimum: $50,000
Functions: Advertising, Mkt. research, Mktg. mgmt., Sales mgmt., Direct mktg., Customer svc., PR
Industries: Computer equip., Test/measurement equip., Computer svcs., Telecoms, High tech, Software

Affiliates:
GS Consultants Limited

Sales Advantage

6301 NW Fifth Way, Ste. 2100
Ft. Lauderdale, Florida 33309
(954) 351-9461
Fax: (954) 776-5855
Email: amy_hammer@salesadvantage.com
Web: www.salesadvantage.com

Key Contact - Specialty:
Ms. Amy Hammer - *Sales & marketing*
Mr. Matthew Kaufman - *Sales & marketing*
Ms. Kim Baker - *Sales & marketing*

Description: We target professionals in the top 20% of their respective fields to ensure that your company hires the candidate with the most positive impact on your bottom line.
Functions: Sales & mktg.
Industries: Generalist

Sales Consultants

200 Public Sq., 31st Floor
Cleveland, Ohio 44114-2301
(216) 696-1122
Fax: (216) 696-3221
Email: als@mrinet.com
Web: www.mrinet.com

Key Contact - Specialty:
Mr. Alan R. Schonberg
Mr. William E. Aglinsky
Mr. Robert A. Angell
Mr. Dave Oberting
Mr. Robert Gandal
Mr. Donald L. Goldman
Mr. Marc L. Blessing
Mr. Jerry R. Hill
Mr. Gary P. Williams
Mr. Vincent J. Webb
Mr. Doug Young

Description: 150 offices providing a complete range of recruitment and human resource services for sales, sales management and marketing professionals, including: permanent placement on both a contingency and retainer basis; interim staffing; videoconferencing and outplacement.

Salary Minimum: $30,000
Functions: Generalist
Industries: Generalist

Branches:
6343-B Airport Blvd., Ste. 3
Mobile, Alabama 36608-3163
(334) 342-8811
Fax: (334) 342-8817
Email: rebrock@zebra.net
Key Contact - Specialty:
Mr. Gerald Grovenstein

4300 N. Miller Rd., Ste. 241
Scottsdale, Arizona 85281
(602) 424-7958
Fax: (602) 424-3960
Email: manager@scottsdl.mrinet.com
Key Contact - Specialty:
Mr. Bob Lasker

6994 El Camino Real, Ste. 208
Carlsbad, California 92009
(760) 438-7771
Fax: (760) 438-7335
Email: norcty!manager@mrinet.com
Key Contact - Specialty:
Mr. Jim A. Yager
Mr. Jerry Harris

100 Corporate Pointe, Ste. 380
Culver City, California 90230
(310) 670-3040
Fax: (310) 670-2981
Email: mrila@internetmci.com
Key Contact - Specialty:
Mr. Mike Bryant

16027 Ventura Blvd., Ste. 320
Encino, California 91436-2740
(818) 906-3155
Fax: (818) 906-0642
Key Contact - Specialty:
Mr. David Greenfader

5715 N. West Ave., Ste. 101
Fresno, California 93711
(209) 432-3700
Fax: (209) 432-9937
Email: fresno!ron@mrinet.com
Key Contact - Specialty:
Mr. Ron L. Johnson

2081 Business Ctr. Drive, Ste. 290
Irvine, California 92612-1117
(714) 474-9222
Fax: (714) 474-8222
Email: manager@irvine.mrinet.com
Key Contact - Specialty:
Mr. Mark Tabbert

One City Blvd. W., Ste. 710
Orange, California 92868
(714) 978-0500
Fax: (714) 978-8064
Key Contact - Specialty:
Mr. Russ Miller

74 W. Neal St., Ste. 200
Pleasanton, California 94566-6632
(510) 461-6980
Fax: (510) 461-6986
Email: scpleas!manager@mrinet.com
Key Contact - Specialty:
Mr. David G. Gaulden

9455 Ridgehaven Court, Ste. 100
San Diego, California 92123-1647
(619) 565-6600
Fax: (619) 565-4937
Key Contact - Specialty:
Mr. Harvey J. Baron

6540 Lusk Blvd., Ste. C254
San Diego, California 92121-2782
(619) 450-6006
Fax: (619) 450-6007
Email: MRILaJolla@aol.com
Key Contact - Specialty:
Mr. Joseph P. Quinn

5655 Lindero Canyon Rd., Ste. 423
Westlake Village, California 91362
(818) 889-9926
Fax: (818) 889-3556
Key Contact - Specialty:
Mr. Donald A. Vezina

6395 Gunpark Drive, Ste. R
Boulder, Colorado 80301-3390
(303) 527-1440
Fax: (303) 527-1449
Key Contact - Specialty:
Mr. Bob Gills

12477 W. Cedar Avenue, Ste. 202
Lakewood, Colorado 80228
(303) 988-1011
Fax: (303) 988-1699
Email: manager@sclkwood.mrinet.com
Key Contact - Specialty:
Mr. Michael McNamara

326 W. Main St., Ste. 202
Milford, Connecticut 06460
(203) 876-4949
Fax: (203) 876-4959
Key Contact - Specialty:
Mr. Ronald L. Fink
Ms. Sarah S. Fink

2139 Silas Deane Hwy., Ste. 206A
Rocky Hill, Connecticut 06067
(860) 563-5171
Fax: (860) 563-2305
Email: schtfd@aol.com
Key Contact - Specialty:
Mr. Frederick O. Raley

196 Danbury Rd.
Wilton, Connecticut 06897-4029
(203) 761-1288
Fax: (203) 761-1258
Key Contact - Specialty:
Mr. Andy Pratt

1111 Third Ave. W., Ste. 130
Bradenton, Florida 34205-7834
(941) 708-3838
Fax: (941) 708-3939
Key Contact - Specialty:
Mr. Steve Denson

9122 58th Drive E.
Bradenton, Florida 34202-9187
(941) 756-7765
Fax: (941) 756-7313
Email: jpitz@gte.net
Key Contact - Specialty:
Ms. Judy A. Pitz

1320 S. Dixie, Ste. 941
Coral Gables, Florida 33146
(305) 666-5991
Fax: (305) 666-5994
Email: dmccar1021@aol.com
Key Contact - Specialty:
Mr. Dennis McCarthy

9900 W. Sample Rd., Ste. 407
Coral Springs, Florida 33065-4436
(954) 340-8000
Fax: (954) 340-8300
Email: coralsp!fxb@mrinet.com
Key Contact - Specialty:
Mr. Frank Braile, Jr.

9471 Baymeadows Rd., Ste. 204
Baymeadows Place
Jacksonville, Florida 32256
(904) 737-5770
Fax: (904) 737-7927
Email: scjacks@bellsouth.net
Key Contact - Specialty:
Mr. Scott Sheridan

2600 Maitland Ctr. Pkwy., Ste. 295
Maitland, Florida 32751
(407) 660-0089
Fax: (407) 660-2066
Email: scorlan!manager@mrinet.com
Key Contact - Specialty:
Mr. Thomas Brown
Ms. Arlene Brown

11983 Tamiami Trail N., Ste. 112
Naples, Florida 34110
(941) 437-6395
Fax: (941) 437-6399
Email: scnaple!manager@mrinet.com
Key Contact - Specialty:
Mr. Virgil L. Metcalf

1343 Main St., Ste. 600
Sarasota, Florida 34236
(941) 365-5151
Fax: (941) 365-1869
Email: sarasota!manager@mrinet.com
Key Contact - Specialty:
Ms. Rose Castellano-Mattran
Mr. Donald A. Mattran

500 N. Westshore Blvd., Ste. 530
Tampa, Florida 33609
(813) 289-9355
Fax: (813) 282-3449
Email: sctampa!manager@mrinet.com
Key Contact - Specialty:
Mr. Dan Smith

275 - 104th Avenue
Treasure Island, Florida 33706
(813) 367-8787
Fax: (813) 367-8532
Key Contact - Specialty:
Mr. William R. Garrett

314 Maxwell Rd., Ste. 600
Alpharetta, Georgia 30004
(770) 569-9511
Fax: (770) 569-0477
Email: alpharet!manager@mrinet.com
Key Contact - Specialty:
Mr. Bob E. Neely

8800 Roswell Rd., Ste. 248
Atlanta, Georgia 30350
(770) 992-9200
Fax: (770) 992-1501
Email: nates@internetmci.com
Key Contact - Specialty:
Mr. Nate Schemo

5901-C Peachtree-Dunwoody Rd., Ste. 370
Atlanta, Georgia 30328-5342
(770) 394-1300
Fax: (770) 698-9384
Key Contact - Specialty:
Mr. Larry W. Cooper

2840 Johnson Ferry Rd. NE, Ste. 150
Marietta, Georgia 30062
(770) 643-9990
Fax: (770) 643-0818
Key Contact - Specialty:
Mr. Larry J. Dougherty

P.O. Box 1746
Richmond Hill, Georgia 31324-1746
(912) 756-5060
Fax: (912) 756-5070
Email: scrich!manager@mrinet.com
Key Contact - Specialty:
Mr. David A. Pearl

290 Bobwhite Court, Ste. 220
Park Ctr.
Boise, Idaho 83706-3966
(208) 336-6770
Fax: (208) 336-2499
Key Contact - Specialty:
Mr. Craig A. Alexander

3413-A N. Kennicott Ave.
Arlington Heights Office Ctr.
Arlington Heights, Illinois 60004
(847) 590-8880
Fax: (847) 590-0847
Key Contact - Specialty:
Mr. Steve Briody

707 N. East St., Ste 4
Bloomington, Illinois 61701
(309) 829-6000
Fax: (309) 827-3023
Email: scbloom@scbloomington.com
Key Contact - Specialty:
Ms. Lyn M. Edwards
Mr. Jack O. Edwards

815 W. Van Buren, Ste. 430
Chicago, Illinois 60607
(312) 733-4700
Fax: (312) 733-9769
Email: manager@chidwtn.mrinet.com
Key Contact - Specialty:
Mr. Jack W. Downing

1540 E. Dundee Rd., Ste. 245
Palatine, Illinois 60067-8321
(847) 202-0202
Fax: (847) 202-0200
Key Contact - Specialty:
Mr. Brian M. Roberts

101 Court St., Ste. 207
Riverside 1
Evansville, Indiana 47708
(812) 464-5400
Fax: (812) 422-6718
Key Contact - Specialty:
Ms. Marjorie L. Caldemeyer

Omni Centre, Ste. 36
300 W. Broadway
Council Bluffs, Iowa 51503-9030
(712) 325-6884
Fax: (712) 325-6691
Key Contact - Specialty:
Mr. Jim Finocchiaro

9401 Indian Creek Pkwy., Ste. 920
Corporate Woods Bldg. 40
Overland Park, Kansas 66210-2098
(913) 661-9200
Fax: (913) 661-9030
Key Contact - Specialty:
Mr. Danny Buda
Mr. Bob Belcher

8100 E. 22nd St. N.
Bldg. 1500, Ste. B
Wichita, Kansas 67226
(316) 682-2636
Fax: (316) 682-8132
Key Contact - Specialty:
Mr. Marvin Reimer

3138 Custer Drive, Ste. 220
Lexington, Kentucky 40517-4064
(606) 245-8228
Fax: (606) 245-9590
Email: manager@blugrass.mrinet.com
Key Contact - Specialty:
Mr. Darrell B. Barber

501 Darby Creek Rd., Unit 15
Lexington, Kentucky 40509-1606
(606) 263-1197
Fax: (606) 263-1290
Email: sclex@uky.campus.mci.net
Key Contact - Specialty:
Mr. Tim J. Bosworth

4360 Brownsboro, Ste. 240
Louisville, Kentucky 40207
(502) 897-0333
Fax: (502) 897-0496
Email: info@angel-group.com
Key Contact - Specialty:
Mr. Steve Angel

1605 Murray St., Ste. 229
Alexandria, Louisiana 71301-6876
(318) 561-2882
Fax: (318) 531-2883
Email: manager@alxndria.mrinet.com
Key Contact - Specialty:
Mr. Markay Dunn

Acadia Trace Ste. 707
2237 S. Acadian Thruway
Baton Rouge, Louisiana 70808
(504) 928-2212
Fax: (504) 928-1109
Email: batroug!manager@mrinet.com
Key Contact - Specialty:
Mr. Gregory L. Fell

609 Mariner's Plaza
Mandeville, Louisiana 70448
(504) 727-3232
Fax: (504) 727-3230
Key Contact - Specialty:
Mr. Dan L. Ripp

3527 Ridgelake Drive
P.O. Box 6605
Metairie, Louisiana 70009
(504) 831-7333
Fax: (504) 838-9009
Key Contact - Specialty:
Mr. Edward N. Ameen
Mr. Paul M. Luce

575 S. Charles St., Ste. 401
Baltimore, Maryland 21201
(410) 727-5750
Fax: (410) 727-1253
Email: baltimor!tcr@mrinet.com
Key Contact - Specialty:
Mr. Steven R. Braun

10320 Little Patuxent Pkwy., Ste. 511
Columbia, Maryland 21044-3346
(410) 992-4900
Fax: (410) 992-4905
Key Contact - Specialty:
Mr. David S. Rubin

7515 Annapolis Rd., Ste. 304
Hyattsville, Maryland 20784
(301) 731-4200
Key Contact - Specialty:
Mr. Thomas F. Hummel

300 Brickstone Sq., 9th Floor
Andover, Massachusetts 01810
(978) 475-5500
Fax: (978) 470-8180
Email: scbost!manager@mrinet.com
Key Contact - Specialty:
Mr. Robert G. Stockard

P.O. Box 420
Sagamore Beach, Massachusetts
02562-0420
(508) 888-8704
Fax: (508) 888-9265
Email: capecod!manager@mrinet.com
Key Contact - Specialty:
Mr. Edward T. Cahan

2860 Carpenter Rd., Ste. 300
Sparrow Wood Office Ctr.
Ann Arbor, Michigan 48108-1193
(313) 971-4900
Fax: (313) 971-5332
Key Contact - Specialty:
Ms. Barbara A. Watson

W. 4111 Andover, Ste. 120
Bloomfield Hills, Michigan 48302-1911
(248) 594-0880
Fax: (248) 594-5993
Email: bloomfld!smk@mrinet.com
Key Contact - Specialty:
Mr. Gerry Anger
Mr. Tom Kilkenney

Grand Blanc N. Park, Bldg. D
10801 S. Saginaw St., Ste. G
Grand Blanc, Michigan 48439-8126
(810) 603-0452
Fax: (810) 603-0751
Email: scgenes!manager@mrinet.com
Key Contact - Specialty:
Ms. Rebecca R. Leinen

11460 Highland Rd.
Hartland, Michigan 48353-2710
(810) 632-6587
Fax: (810) 632-6591
Email: hartland!manager@mrinet.com
Key Contact - Specialty:
Mr. John Ragnoli

5340 Holiday Terrace
Kalamazoo, Michigan 49009-2122
(616) 372-8007
Fax: (616) 372-8388
Email: sckalamazoo@kalamazoo.net
Key Contact - Specialty:
Mr. Mark Bielecki

912 Centennial Way, Ste. 340
Lansing, Michigan 48917
(517) 323-4404
Fax: (517) 323-8083
Email: jeffyeager@voyager.net
Key Contact - Specialty:
Mr. Jeffrey A. Yeager

29777 Telegraph Rd., Ste. 2260
Southfield, Michigan 48034
(248) 352-9200
Fax: (248) 352-9374
Email: detroit!manager@mrinet.com
Key Contact - Specialty:
Mr. Thomas J. Hoy

124 N. Division St., Ste. D-3
Traverse City, Michigan 49684-2263
(616) 935-4000
Fax: (616) 935-4505
Email: sctc@traverse.com
Key Contact - Specialty:
Mr. E. J. Eckert, III

550 Stephenson Hwy., Ste. 407
Troy, Michigan 48083-1152
(248) 585-4200
Fax: (248) 597-0492
Key Contact - Specialty:
Mr. Ed Moeller

7550 France Ave. S., Ste. 180
Minneapolis, Minnesota 55435
(612) 830-1420
Fax: (612) 893-9254
Email: scminna!manager@mrinet.com
Key Contact - Specialty:
Mr. Jack Hardesty

100 S. Fuller St., Ste. 240
Shakopee, Minnesota 55379-1319
(612) 496-3030
Fax: (612) 496-1425
Email: mhs@chaska.mrinet.com
Key Contact - Specialty:
Mr. Michael Smith

3301 Rider Trail S., Ste. 100
St. Louis, Missouri 63045-1309
(314) 344-0900
Fax: (314) 298-7706
Email: stlouec!manager@mrinet.com
Key Contact - Specialty:
Mr. Patrick Hoene

1106 Hooksett Rd.
Hooksett, New Hampshire 03106
(603) 626-8400
Fax: (603) 626-1288
Key Contact - Specialty:
Mr. John J. Cote

Bldg. A, Ste. 205
271 Rte. 46 W.
Fairfield, New Jersey 07004
(973) 227-8292
Fax: (973) 575-4901
Email: sciessex@aol.com
Key Contact - Specialty:
Ms. Debbie Seminerio
Mr. Charles Seminerio

200 Munsonhurst Rd., Ste. 103
Franklin, New Jersey 07416
(201) 209-1957
Fax: (201) 209-0720
Email: scf@crystal.palace.net
Key Contact - Specialty:
Mr. Leslie Agius

1 Bethany Rd. & Rte. 35
Bldg. 1, Ste. 20
Hazlet, New Jersey 07730-1659
(732) 739-4334
Fax: (732) 739-2990
Key Contact - Specialty:
Mr. Eric Gonzalez

2 Hudson Place, Baker Bldg.
Hoboken, New Jersey 07030-5502
(201) 659-5205
Fax: (201) 659-5009
Email: schc@msn.com
Key Contact - Specialty:
Mr. Richard K. Sinay

355 Eisenhower Pkwy., Ste. 212
Livingston, New Jersey 07039-1017
(973) 597-1870
Fax: (973) 597-1871
Email: manager@livngstn.mrinet.com
Key Contact - Specialty:
Mr. Sheldon Wohl

2516 Hwy. 35
Manasquan, New Jersey 08736
(732) 223-0300
Fax: (732) 223-0450
Key Contact - Specialty:
Mr. Mark R. Daly

P.O. Box 871
210 W. Front St., Ste. 102
Red Bank, New Jersey 07701-0871
(732) 530-0600
Fax: (732) 747-4076
Email: monmoth!manager@mrinet.com
Key Contact - Specialty:
Mr. Mike A. Unger

376 Rte. 15, Ste. 200
Sparta, New Jersey 07871
(973) 579-5555
Fax: (973) 579-2220
Email: scsparta@nac.net
Key Contact - Specialty:
Mr. Harvey C. Bass

86 Summit Ave.
Summit, New Jersey 07901
(908) 522-0700
Fax: (908) 522-0785
Key Contact - Specialty:
Mr. Remus J. Klimaski

#2 San Rafael
Albuquerque, New Mexico 87122
(505) 797-7300
Fax: (505) 797-7337
Email: mri-sc-alb@worldnet.att.net
Key Contact - Specialty:
Mr. J. Terry

8555 Main St., Ste. 308
Baptist Life Bldg.
Buffalo, New York 14221-7456
(716) 631-3100
Fax: (716) 631-3140
Email: buffalo!manager@mrinet.com
Key Contact - Specialty:
Mr. Robert E. Artis

5750 Commons Park
P.O. Box 727
Dewitt, New York 13214
(315) 449-0244
Fax: (315) 449-0911
Key Contact - Specialty:
Mr. Richard D. Nassar

33 Walt Whitman Rd., Ste. 107
Huntington Station, New York 11746-3627
(516) 385-0633
Fax: (516) 385-0759
Email: suffolk!manager@mrinet.com
Key Contact - Specialty:
Mr. Bob Levitt

363 Hempstead Ave.
Malverne, New York 11565-1297
(516) 599-5824
Fax: (516) 599-2066
Email: nassau!manager@mrinet.com
Key Contact - Specialty:
Mr. James F. Jacobs

48 S. Service Rd., Ste. 100
Melville, New York 11747
(516) 777-2710
Fax: (516) 777-2714
Email: melvill!manager@mrinet.com
Key Contact - Specialty:
Mr. Harris J. Cohen

16 W. Main St.
Powers Bldg., Ste. 225
Rochester, New York 14614-1601
(716) 454-6650
Fax: (716) 454-4092
Key Contact - Specialty:
Mr. Jerry Annesi

4500 Cameron Valley Pkwy., Ste. 210
Charlotte, North Carolina 28211-3552
(704) 365-6466
Fax: (704) 365-4144
Email: manager@charlot.mrinet.com
Key Contact - Specialty:
Mr. Thomas Near

5701 Westpark Drive, Ste. 110
Charlotte, North Carolina 28217
(704) 525-9270
Fax: (704) 527-0070
Email: charlott!admin@mrinet.com
Web: www.mrinet.com
Key Contact - Specialty:
Mr. Bobby Brown

2554 Lewisville-Clemmons Rd., Ste. 302
First Citizens Bank
Clemmons, North Carolina 27012-8749
(336) 766-4750
Fax: (336) 766-4751
Email: manager@clemmons.mrinet.com
Key Contact - Specialty:
Mr. Wes McCracken

254 Church St. NE
Concord, North Carolina 28025-4737
(704) 786-0700
Fax: (704) 782-1356
Email: concord!manager@mrinet.com
Key Contact - Specialty:
Mr. A. B. Pearson - *Telecommunications, sales & marketing*
Ms. Anna Lee Pearson - *Information technology, telecommunications, sales & marketing*

218-2 Swing Rd.
Greensboro, North Carolina 27409
(336) 854-3931
Fax: (336) 854-3932
Email: manager@scgreen.mrinet.com
Key Contact - Specialty:
Mr. Bruce P. Barnes

175 Northpoint Ave., Ste. 106
High Point, North Carolina 27262-7724
(910) 869-8700
Fax: (910) 869-8719
Email: highptw!jrs@mrinet.com
Key Contact - Specialty:
Mr. James Stowers

2411 Penny Rd., Ste. 101
High Point, North Carolina 27265
(336) 883-4433
Fax: (336) 884-4433
Email: SCIHP@hpe.infi.net
Key Contact - Specialty:
Mr. Tom Bunton, III
Mr. Pervis Greene

1348 Westgate Ctr. Drive, Ste. 209
Winston-Salem, North Carolina 27103
(336) 659-1777
Fax: (336) 768-8431
Email: drhjr@earthlink.net
Key Contact - Specialty:
Mr. Donald R. Hicks, Jr.

3505 Royalton Rd., Ste. 170
Broadview Heights, Ohio 44147
(216) 546-9154
Fax: (216) 546-9389
Email: broadvue!manager@mrinet.com
Key Contact - Specialty:
Mr. Brian Doherty

Islander Park Two
7530 Lucerne Drive, Ste. 303
Cleveland, Ohio 44130
(440) 243-5151
Fax: (440) 243-4868

Key Contact - Specialty:
Mr. Jeff Dipaolo
Mr. Bob Gandee - *Central Region*

20600 Chagrin Blvd., Ste. 703
Tower E.
Cleveland, Ohio 44122
(216) 561-6776
Fax: (216) 561-2393
Key Contact - Specialty:
Mr. Bob Gandee

555 S. Front St., Ste. 100
Columbus, Ohio 43215
(614) 252-6200
Fax: (614) 252-4744
Key Contact - Specialty:
Mr. Gerry E. Harris
Mr. Todd Williams
Mr. John Zambito

West First Plaza, Ste. 515
333 W. First St.
Dayton, Ohio 45402
(937) 228-8271
Fax: (937) 228-2620
Key Contact - Specialty:
Mr. Jerry R. Kotler
Mr. Jeffrey M. Noble

34100 Ctr. Ridge Rd.
Liberty Ctr., Ste. 110
North Ridgeville, Ohio 44039-3220
(440) 327-2800
Fax: (440) 327-6991
Key Contact - Specialty:
Mr. James P. Spellacy

Chagrin Plaza E.
23611 Chagrin Blvd., Ste. 380
Shaker Heights, Ohio 44122
(216) 292-1072
Fax: (216) 292-1053
Key Contact - Specialty:
Mr. Tom Johnston

5600 Monroe St., Ste. 206 B
Sylvania, Ohio 43560-2731
(419) 882-5088
Fax: (419) 882-4119
Email: manager@sctoledo.mrinet.com
Key Contact - Specialty:
Mr. Dick Hite
Ms. Lynn Hite

6525 N. Meridian, Ste. 212
Oklahoma City, Oklahoma 73116
(405) 721-6400
Fax: (405) 728-6716
Key Contact - Specialty:
Ms. Darla Salisbury

5801 E. 41st St., Ste. 440
Tulsa, Oklahoma 74135-5614
(918) 663-6744
Fax: (918) 663-1783
Key Contact - Specialty:
Mr. Tony A. Wolters

925 NW Wall St., Ste. B NW
Bend, Oregon 97701-2021
(541) 382-9779
Fax: (541) 382-9772
Key Contact - Specialty:
Mr. Rob Schluter

2020 Lloyd Ctr.
Portland, Oregon 97232-1376
(503) 287-8701
Fax: (503) 282-4380
Key Contact - Specialty:
Mr. Larry Engelgau
Ms. Elvita Engelgau

831 Baldwin St.
Pittsburgh, Pennsylvania 15234
(412) 740-7931
Fax: (412) 561-5457
Key Contact - Specialty:
Mr. Ralph Viviano

603 Lakeside Drive
Southampton, Pennsylvania 18966
(215) 364-7559
Fax: (215) 364-7579
Email: sthhamp!manager@mrinet.com
Key Contact - Specialty:
Ms. Dee McCafferty
Mr. George McCafferty

912 Main St., Ste. 301
Stroudsburg, Pennsylvania 18360-1641
(717) 421-3911
Fax: (717) 421-4225
Email: mrisc@noln.com
Key Contact - Specialty:
Mr. Geoff J. Pitcher
Ms. Nancy J. Pitcher

454B W. Coleman Blvd.
Mt. Pleasant, South Carolina 29464
(803) 849-8080
Fax: (803) 849-7070
Email: pleasant!manager@mrinet.com
Key Contact - Specialty:
Ms. Kay H. Rigter
Mr. Joe D. Rigter

402 Old Trolley Rd., Ste. 207
Briarwood Executive Ctr.
Summerville, South Carolina 29483
(803) 851-7773
Fax: (803) 851-7774
Key Contact - Specialty:
Mr. John G. Dick

7003 Chadwick Drive, Ste. 331
Brentwood, Tennessee 37027-5232
(615) 373-1111
Fax: (615) 373-0988
Key Contact - Specialty:
Mr. Jack Sells

6139 Preservation Drive
Chattanooga, Tennessee 37416
(423) 892-5770
Fax: (423) 892-4708
Email: chat!manager@mrinet.com
Key Contact - Specialty:
Mr. Denton M. Neal

7010 Lee Hwy., Ste. 216
Chattanooga, Tennessee 37421
(423) 894-5500
Fax: (423) 894-1177
Email: mrichatt@internetmci.com
Key Contact - Specialty:
Mr. Bill Cooper

P.O. Box 38328
Memphis, Tennessee 38183-0328
(901) 751-1995
Fax: (901) 751-9903
Email: info@SalesHunter.com
Web: www.allhitech.com
Key Contact - Specialty:
Mr. Wayne Williams

6600 South 1100 E., Ste. 430
UFG & G Bldg.
Salt Lake City, Utah 84121-2400
(801) 263-2400
Fax: (801) 263-2477
Email: scslc@earthlink.net
Key Contact - Specialty:
Mr. Robert L. Hawks

6620 W. Broad St., Ste. 406
Brookfield Bldg.
Richmond, Virginia 23230-1781
(804) 285-2071
Fax: (804) 282-4990
Key Contact - Specialty:
Mr. Jay S. Schwartz

4092 Foxwood Drive, Ste. 102
Virginia Beach, Virginia 23462-4237
(757) 474-2752
Fax: (757) 474-9367
Email: mrrico!manager@mrinet.com
Key Contact - Specialty:
Mr. James F. Murphey

444 S. Adams St., Cadillac Square
Green Bay, Wisconsin 54301
(414) 437-4353
Fax: (414) 437-0647
Key Contact - Specialty:
Mr. Garland E. Ross

8338 Corporate Drive, Ste. 300
Racine, Wisconsin 53406
(414) 886-8000
Fax: (414) 886-7260
Key Contact - Specialty:
Mr. Thomas E. Hurt
Mr. John J. Henkel
Ms. Ellen L. Jante

Affiliates:
Humana Int'l. Group PLC
Karamik Management Consultants
Lynn Bichler Human Resources
Morgan & Banks
H. Neumann Int'l.
The Renwick Group
Sales Staffers Int'l.
Simon Franco Recursos Humanos
Unico Search

Sales Consultants of Birmingham

100 Carnoustie N.
Birmingham, Alabama 35242
(205) 408-0844
Fax: (205) 408-0848

Key Contact - Specialty:
Mr. Cleve A. Park - *Engineering*

Description: Our objective is to satisfy the critical demand for people...the resource that ultimately determines an organization's profitability.
Functions: Materials Plng., Health admin., Sales mgmt., Personnel, Finance, IT, Environmentalists
Industries: Food/bev/tobacco, Lumber/furniture, Chemicals, Drugs mfg., Plastics/rubber, Machinery/Appliances, Human resource svcs.

Sales Consultants of Daphne

P.O. Box 2784
184 Fairway Drive
Daphne, Alabama 36526
(334) 625-0200
Fax: (334) 625-0203

Key Contact - Specialty:
Mrs. Janet Luckey
Mr. Horace Luckey - *Industrial sales*

Description: We are a franchise of Management Recruiters International specializing in recruiting and placing sales marketing and management talent in the industrial arena with an emphasis on the valve, bearings and power transmission fields for the OEM and distribution markets.
Functions: Middle mgmt., Product dev., Plant mgmt., Mktg. mgmt., Sales mgmt., Engineering, Technicians
Industries: Plastics/rubber, Metal products, Machinery/Appliances

---

Sales Consultants of Scottsdale, Inc.

4300 N. Miller Rd., #110
Scottsdale, Arizona 85251
(602) 946-1609
Fax: (602) 946-6718

Key Contact - Specialty:
Mr. Albert Britten - *Sales & marketing, sales management, vice president sales*

Description: We are part of a 600 office (MRI) nationwide recruiting organization. Fortune 100-500 companies are our clients. We place from sales reps up to executive VP's and CEO'S.

Salary Minimum: $25,000
Functions: Senior mgmt., Mktg. mgmt., Sales mgmt., MIS mgmt.
Industries: Food/bev/tobacco, Drugs mfg., Medical devices, Computer equip., Telecoms, Healthcare

---

Sales Consultants of Northwest Arkansas, Inc.

One W. Mountain, Executive Square
Fayetteville, Arkansas 72701
(501) 521-9700
Fax: (501) 521-9770

Key Contact - Specialty:
Mr. Denver Wilson - *Equipment leasing, technology, franchising*

Description: Targets top sales and marketing talent for client companies nationwide.
Functions: Senior mgmt., Mktg. mgmt., Sales mgmt.
Industries: Misc. financial, Computer svcs., Equip. svcs., High tech, Software

---

Sales Consultants Peninsula, Inc.

111 Anza Blvd., Ste. 109
Burlingame, California 94010
(650) 548-4800
Fax: (650) 548-4805
Web: www.mricaliforniasf.com

Key Contact - Specialty:
Mr. Donald Hirschbein - *Medical*
Mr. Michael T. Shaffer - *Consumer*
Ms. Crystal Parsons - *Intangibles*

Description: Consistently ranked in top 5% of 700 office recruiting firm. 1991 & 1993 ranked #1 on West Coast. In 1994, 1995, 1996 and 1997 ranked #2.

Salary Minimum: $30,000
Functions: Middle mgmt., Nurses, Sales mgmt., Personnel, Training, MIS mgmt., Mgmt. consultants
Industries: Food/bev/tobacco, Chemicals, Medical devices, Computer equip., Accounting, Mgmt. consulting, Haz. waste

---

Sales Consultants of Chico

55 Independence Circle, Ste. 108
Chico, California 95973
(530) 892-8880
Fax: (530) 896-5480
Email: manager@chico.mrinet.com
Web: www.medicaljobs.net

Key Contact - Specialty:
Mr. K. L. Johnson - *Medical sales, marketing, research & development*
Ms. Carol Johnson - *Medical sales*

Description: We specialize in placing and recruiting sales and marketing people in the medical arena for Northern California, West Coast, national.
Functions: Senior mgmt., Middle mgmt., Product dev., Production, Materials Plng., Mkt. research, Sales mgmt.
Industries: Drugs mfg., Medical devices, Pharmaceutical svcs., Biotech

---

Sales Consultants Int'l. of Oakland

480 Roland Way, Ste. 103
Oakland, California 94621-2065
(510) 569-6231
Fax: (510) 562-7237
Email: mrsc@dnai.com
Web: www.scsanfran.com

Key Contact - Specialty:
Mr. Tom Thrower - *Medical*

Description: We work all markets in sales, sales management, marketing, food, medical and computers, chemical, biotech, agriculture, auto, consumer, electronic, environmental, health, home care, industrial and telecommunications.
Functions: Senior mgmt., Product dev., Purchasing, Healthcare, Sales & mktg., IT, Engineering
Industries: Communications, Packaging, High tech, Software, Biotech, Healthcare

---

Sales Consultants of Sacramento

4320 Auburn Blvd., Ste. 2100
Sacramento, California 95841
(916) 481-7000
Fax: (916) 481-7099
Email: scsac@earthlink.net

Key Contact - Specialty:
Mr. Ron Whitney - *Industrial, building products, computers, agriculture*

Description: We are a franchisee of MRI, the country's largest recruiter of sales and sales management personnel with more than 160 offices serving every business market. Using this network of recruiters we can locate the most highly trained candidate.

Salary Minimum: $30,000
Functions: Sales mgmt.
Industries: Agri/forestry/mining, Machinery/Appliances, Test/measurement equip., Computer svcs., Publishing, Packaging, Healthcare

---

Sales Consultants of Silicon Valley

2055 Gateway Place, Ste. 420
San Jose, California 95110
(408) 453-9999
Fax: (408) 452-8510
Email: jrosica@mrisanjose.com
Web: www.mrisanjose.com

Key Contact - Specialty:
Mr. John Rosica - *High technology*

Description: We are in Silicon Valley and specialize in computer and electronic industry, systems engineering, IS and IT consulting plus semiconductor, semiconductor capital equipment industries.

Salary Minimum: $50,000
Functions: Directors, Middle mgmt., Product dev., Mkt. research, Mktg. mgmt., Sales mgmt., Systems implem.
Industries: Computer equip., Consumer electronics, Test/measurement equip., Computer svcs., Mgmt. consulting, High tech, Software

---

Sales Consultants of Denver

13111 E. Briarwood Ave., Ste. 350
Englewood, Colorado 80112
(303) 706-0123
Fax: (303) 706-0204
Web: www.htinfo.com/mriscEnglewood.htm

Key Contact - Specialty:
Ms. Ronnette Cowlishaw - *Telecommunications, data communications*

Description: Our firm specializes in placing sales, engineering and management professionals worldwide for more than 100 clients. During the past year, we successfully placed more than 300 candidates.
Functions: Product dev., Sales mgmt., MIS mgmt., Systems anal., Systems implem., Engineering
Industries: Construction, Communications, Insurance, High tech, Software, Healthcare

---

Sales Consultants of Danbury

75 Glen Rd., River Ste.
Sandy Hook, Connecticut 06482
(203) 270-0700
Fax: (203) 270-6288
Email: mri.scdanbury@snet.net
Web: www.mri.com

Key Contact - Specialty:
Mr. Bob Smith

Description: We specialize in telecommunications, sales, engineering, marketing and operations professionals.

Salary Minimum: $50,000
Functions: Senior mgmt., Middle mgmt., Mktg. mgmt., Sales mgmt., Systems implem., Network admin., Engineering
Industries: Telecoms, High tech, Software

Sales Consultants of Stamford-Darien

111 Prospect St., Ste. 410
Stamford, Connecticut 06901
(203) 327-3270
Fax: (203) 327-6578
Email: scstamford@aol.com

Key Contact - Specialty:
Mr. James M. Burt - *Training & human resource consulting industry*

Description: The firm's principal has twenty years experience as trainer, business developer and general manager in the training and HR consulting industry - outstanding knowledge of the market and functions.

Salary Minimum: $70,000
Functions: Mktg. mgmt., Sales mgmt., Training, Mgmt. consultants
Industries: Mgmt. consulting, Human resource svcs., New media

---

Sales Consultants of Boca Raton, Inc.

4800 N. Federal Hwy., Ste. 104D
Boca Raton, Florida 33431
(561) 393-9998
Fax: (561) 393-9984
Email: scboca@gate.net
Web: www.htinfo.com/mriscbocaraton.htm

Key Contact - Specialty:
Mr. Juergen E. Buller - *Consumer products*

Salary Minimum: $60,000
Functions: Advertising, Mkt. research, Mktg. mgmt., Sales mgmt., Direct mktg., Customer svc., PR
Industries: Drugs mfg., Medical devices, Plastics/rubber, Communications, New media, Telecoms, Biotech

---

Sales Consultants of Ft. Lauderdale, Inc.

100 W. Cypress Creek Rd., Ste. 965
Ft. Lauderdale, Florida 33309
(954) 772-5100
Fax: (954) 772-0777
Web: www.mrscsfla@aol.com

Key Contact - Specialty:
Mr. Jeffrey A. Taylor - *Medical, sales, sales management, executive*
Mr. Greg Peterson - *Food & beverage, data processing, sales management, executive*

Description: Sales, sales management, marketing and executive placement, throughout the SE region. Specializing in the medical, data processing, corporate financial, services and spirits industries. Packaging-corrugated. Folding carton.

Salary Minimum: $30,000
Functions: Senior mgmt., Middle mgmt., Plant mgmt., Packaging, Mkt. research, Sales mgmt.
Industries: Food/bev/tobacco, Medical devices, Finance, Svcs., Communications, Packaging, High tech

---

Sales Consultants of Ft. Myers, Inc.

12734 Kenwood Lane, Ste. 48
Ft. Myers, Florida 33907
(941) 278-4997
Fax: (941) 278-1380
Email: teharris@pipeline.com

Key Contact - Specialty:
Mr. Thomas E. Harris - *Telecommunications, information technology*
Ms. Ana Luisa Baez - *Telecommunications, information technology*
Mr. T. J. Harris - *Telecommunications, information technology*

Description: Value added services include performance guarantees, relo assistance, interim and project staffing, outplacement. We can fill your telecom and information technology management needs - sales, marketing, operations and technical at any level.

Salary Minimum: $30,000
Functions: Directors, Senior mgmt., Middle mgmt., Mkt. research, CFO's, MIS mgmt., Engineering
Industries: Telecoms, High tech

Affiliates:
Global Human Resources

Sales Consultants of Tampa North, Inc.

4012 Gunn Hwy., Ste. 140
Tampa, Florida 33624
(813) 264-7165
Fax: (813) 968-6450
Web: www.mrtampanorth.com

Key Contact - Specialty:
Mr. Gary King - *Telecommunications*

Description: We specialize in the executive placement of sales and marketing professionals specific industries include communications and high technology positions.

Salary Minimum: $40,000
Functions: Sales & mktg., Sales mgmt.
Industries: Telecoms, High tech, Software

Sales Consultants of Savannah, GA

2431 Habersham St.
Savannah, Georgia 31401
(912) 232-0132
Fax: (912) 232-0136

Key Contact - Specialty:
Mr. Cal Bridgett - *Packaging, printing*
Ms. Gloria Bridgett - *Graphics*

Description: Professional contingency search firm: locate and place professional sales people with our client companies in the packaging/printing and graphics industries.
Functions: Mkt. research, Mktg. mgmt., Sales mgmt., Direct mktg., Customer svc., Graphic artists
Industries: Paper, Printing, Publishing, Packaging

Sales Consultants of Cherokee
275 Parkway 575, Ste. 203
Woodstock, Georgia 30188
(770) 517-2660
Fax: (770) 517-2661
Email: mgr@scchero.mrinet.com

Key Contact - Specialty:
Mr. Brett M. Stevens - *Software, consulting*
Mr. Bart Heres - *Logistics*

Description: We are a full service search firm and specialize in logistics and supply chain software.

Salary Minimum: $40,000
Functions: Directors, Senior mgmt., Middle mgmt., Materials, Mgmt. consultants
Industries: Misc. mfg., Transportation, Software

Sales Consultants of Honolulu
810 Richards St., Ste. 800
Honolulu, Hawaii 96813
(808) 533-3282
Fax: (808) 599-4760
Email: schon@lava.net
Web: www.sacbiz.com/sc.honolulu

Key Contact - Specialty:
Mr. James A. Morse
Mr. Don Bishop

Description: We place sales, sales support marketing and sales management for USA and Pacific Rim and are very strong in the Hawaiian marketplace.

Salary Minimum: $30,000
Functions: Sales & mktg., Mkt. research, Mktg. mgmt., Sales mgmt., IT, Systems support, Int'l.
Industries: Printing, Medical devices, Computer equip., Hospitality, Telecoms, Environmental svcs., Software

Sales Consultants of Barrington
18-4 E. Dundee Rd., Ste. 202
Barrington, Illinois 60010
(847) 277-1150
Fax: (847) 277-1160
Email: scbaring@starnetinc.com

Key Contact - Specialty:
Mr. Curtis L. Baer - *Software, sales, pre-sales, post-sales, marketing*

Description: Place pre-sales, sales, post-sales and marketing talent at all levels on a national basis with technology companies (software, computer hardware, telecommunications, internet). Also place engineers with manufacturing companies.
Functions: General mgmt., Senior mgmt., Sales & mktg., Mktg. mgmt., Sales mgmt., IT, Engineering
Industries: Computer equip., Mgmt. consulting, Communications, New media, Telecoms, High tech, Software

Sales Consultants
3400 Dundee Rd., Ste. 340
Northbrook, Illinois 60062
(847) 509-9000
Fax: (847) 509-9010
Email: mrichicago@earthlink.net

Key Contact - Specialty:
Mr. Steven L. Fried - *Sales & marketing management*

Description: Midwest corporate office for the world's largest recruiting agency. 705 offices in system, giving us access to more candidates than other firms.
Functions: Senior mgmt., Mktg. mgmt., Sales mgmt., Direct mktg., Cash mgmt., MIS mgmt., Mgmt. consultants
Industries: Generalist, Finance, Svcs., Legal, Computer svcs., Communications, Software

Sales Consultants of Chicago South
6420 W. 127th St., Ste. 209
Palos Heights, Illinois 60463
(708) 371-9677
Fax: (708) 371-9678
Email: scstaff@card-recruiter.com
Web: www.card-recruiter.com

Key Contact - Specialty:
Ms. Judy Collins - *Credit cards, consumer finance*
Ms. Susan Stephens - *Risk management, information systems analysis*
Ms. Mary Sullivan - *Sales and marketing*

Description: We specialize in the credit card and consumer finance industries, sales, sales management, marketing, operations, risk and legal.

Salary Minimum: $30,000
Functions: Senior mgmt., Middle mgmt., Mkt. research, Mktg. mgmt., Sales mgmt., Credit, Risk mgmt.
Industries: Misc. financial, Accounting, New media

Sales Consultants of Western McHenry County
6601 Main Street
P.O. Box 425
Union, Illinois 60180
(815) 923-2500
Email: scwmc@mc.net
Web: www.scwmc.com

Key Contact - Specialty:
Mr. Daniel M. Grant - *Software, senior management, sales & marketing*
Mr. Jeffrey M. Wilson - *Healthcare software industry (vendors), senior management, sales & marketing, installation & support*
Mr. Greg Ammirati - *Software industry (vendors), senior management, sales & marketing*

Description: We provide nationwide search and recruitment for the software vendor industry. Our principals possess over 60 man years experience within this industry in Senior Management capacities prior to creating this executive search practice.
Functions: Senior mgmt., Mktg. mgmt., Sales mgmt., CFO's, MIS mgmt., Systems implem.
Industries: Computer svcs., Software, Healthcare

Sales Consultants of Indianapolis-North
11611 N. Meridian St., Ste. 220
Carmel, Indiana 46032
(317) 582-0202
Fax: (317) 582-0303
Email: mrindy@mrindianapolis.com
Web: www.mrindianapolis.com

Key Contact - Specialty:
Mr. George V. Ceryak - *Executive sales*

Description: 30 years of outstanding success in identifying top talent and meeting corporate America's total staffing needs. This outstanding firm is lead by Mr. George Ceryak, 30 years with MRI and winner of the prestigious office of the decade award for the 80's.
Functions: Senior mgmt., Mfg., Sales & mktg., Mkt. research, Finance, IT, R&D
Industries: Agri/forestry/mining, Mfg., Chemicals, Finance, Computer svcs., High tech, Software

Sales Consultants of Indianapolis
8200 Haverstick Rd., Ste. 240
Indianapolis, Indiana 46240
(317) 257-5411
Fax: (317) 259-6886
Email: resume@mriindy.com
Web: www.mriindy.com

Key Contact - Specialty:
Mr. William A. Kuntz - *Sales, sales management, marketing*

Description: Our office has served hundreds of client companies. Collectively possessing 180+ years of recruiting experience, our team of 31 recruiters filled over 650 positions last year alone.
Functions: Advertising, Mkt. research, Mktg. mgmt., Sales mgmt., Direct mktg., Customer svc., PR
Industries: Mfg., Wholesale, Finance, Pharmaceutical svcs., Packaging, High tech, Healthcare

Sales Consultants of Bangor, Inc.

12 Acme Rd., Ste. 104
Brewer, Maine 04412-1546
(207) 989-3889
Fax: (207) 989-3679

Key Contact - Specialty:
Mr. Neil K. Ashton - *Banking, finance, telecommunications, human resources*
Ms. Patsy A. Rutkauskas - *Healthcare, pharmaceuticals, biotechnology*

Description: We work very closely with our client companies to truly solve their staffing problems by introducing top candidates to their opportunity.

Salary Minimum: $30,000
Functions: Senior mgmt., Middle mgmt., Healthcare, Sales & mktg., HR mgmt., Finance, Graphic artists
Industries: Paper, Drugs mfg., Finance, Svcs., Communications, Biotech, Healthcare

Sales Consultants of Rockville, MD

51 Monroe St., Ste. 1405
Rockville, Maryland 20850
(301) 610-7300
Fax: (301) 610-0100
Email: info@scisuccess.com
Web: www.scisuccess.com

Key Contact - Specialty:
Mr. Brian Hoffman - *Telecommunications, data communications*

Description: 700 offices - 340 videoconferencing worldwide. Executive recruiting firm specializing in recruiting for the IT fields.

Salary Minimum: $40,000
Functions: Senior mgmt., Middle mgmt., Mktg. mgmt., Sales mgmt., MIS mgmt., Systems implem.
Industries: Computer equip., Computer svcs., Mgmt. consulting, Telecoms, High tech, Software

Sales Consultants of Baltimore

9515 Deereco Rd., Ste. 900
Timonium, Maryland 21093
(410) 252-6616
Fax: (410) 252-7076
Email: kendmr@erols.com
Web: mrbaltimore.com

Key Contact - Specialty:
Mr. Kenneth R. Davis
Ms. Linda A. Burton

Description: We are the world's largest professional search organization specializing in managerial, sales and professional talent. As part of a national organization, we serve firms of all types and sizes through the expertise and efforts of over 750 affiliated offices.
Functions: Production, Plant mgmt., Sales mgmt., MIS mgmt., Systems anal., Systems dev., Engineering
Industries: Food/bev/tobacco, Lumber/furniture, Medical devices, Plastics/rubber, Test/measurement equip., Packaging, High tech

Sales Consultants of Brockton, Inc.

567 Pleasant St., Ste. 8
Brockton, Massachusetts 02401
(508) 587-2030
Fax: (508) 587-9261

Key Contact - Specialty:
Mr. Milton M. Feinson - *Generalist*

Description: Largest company in U.S.A. specializing in sales and marketing with 150 offices nationally.
Functions: Advertising, Mkt. research, Mktg. mgmt., Sales mgmt.
Industries: Food/bev/tobacco, Drugs mfg., Medical devices

Sales Consultants - Bristol County

272 Chauncy St.
Mansfield, Massachusetts 02048
(508) 339-1924
Fax: (508) 261-0348

Key Contact - Specialty:
Mr. Jim Noyes - *Marketing, sales, general management, chemical suppliers, electronics*

Description: We fill sales, marketing and related management and support positions nationally with companies that supply chemicals, piece parts and materials for the electronic, aerospace and high-tech industries.
Functions: Senior mgmt., Middle mgmt., Advertising, Mkt. research, Mktg. mgmt., Sales mgmt., Direct mktg.
Industries: Chemicals, Plastics/rubber, Paints/petroleum products

Sales Consultants of Wellesley, Inc.

888 Worcester St., Ste. 95
Wellesley, Massachusetts 02482-3717
(781) 235-7700
Fax: (781) 237-7207
Email: scwellesley@scwellesley.com
Web: scwellesley.com

Key Contact - Specialty:
Mr. Arthur J. Durante - *special projects*

Description: We specialize in the placement and recruitment of sales, marketing and sales management talent.
Functions: Advertising, Mkt. research, Mktg. mgmt., Sales mgmt., Direct mktg., Customer svc., Int'l.
Industries: Chemicals, Drugs mfg., Finance, Computer svcs., Broadcast & Film, Insurance, High tech

Sales Consultants of Auburn Hills

2701 University Drive, Ste. 205
Auburn Hills, Michigan 48326-2565
(248) 373-7177
(800) 699-7446
Fax: (248) 373-7759
Email: scah@www.scauburnhills.com
Web: sc auburnhills.com

Key Contact - Specialty:
Mr. Boe E. Embrey - *Sales & marketing*

Description: Offer exceptional candidates for regional sales and marketing positions in medical, general industrial, automotive, telecommunications, consumer products, building products and the IS/IT industries.
Functions: Sales & mktg., Sales mgmt., Engineering
Industries: Generalist, Mfg., Svcs., Environmental svcs., Healthcare

Sales Consultants of Birmingham

30700 Telegraph Rd., Ste. 3650
Bingham Farms, Michigan 48025-4527
(248) 647-7766
Fax: (248) 647-9722

Key Contact - Specialty:
Mr. Brian Binke - *Information technology*
Ms. Elle Binke - *Engineering and management*

Description: We partner with our clients to bring them the finest talent in the nation.

Salary Minimum: $40,000
Functions: Senior mgmt., Middle mgmt., Sales & mktg., Sales mgmt., IT, MIS mgmt., Network admin.
Industries: Construction, Mfg., Motor vehicles, Communications, New media, Insurance, Software

Sales Consultants of Farmington Hills

30445 Northwestern Hwy., Ste. 360
Farmington Hills, Michigan 48334-3102
(248) 626-6600
Fax: (248) 626-7542

Key Contact - Specialty:
Mr. Mark Gilbert - *Motors, drives, controls (automation)*
Mr. Harvey Gersin - *Controls, instrumentation, machinery*

Description: Contingency recruiting for executives, marketing and sales and engineers for industries in and related to factory automation, machine builders, cutting tools, material handling, electronics/electrical, controls, instrumentation and plastics/rubber.
Functions: Middle mgmt., Product dev., Automation, Mktg. mgmt., Sales mgmt., Systems anal., Engineering
Industries: Food/bev/tobacco, Machinery/Appliances, Computer equip., Misc. mfg., Wholesale, Telecoms, High tech

Sales Consultants of Grand Rapids

900 E. Paris Ave. SE, Ste. 301
Grand Rapids, Michigan 49546
(616) 940-3900
Fax: (616) 940-3041

Key Contact - Specialty:
Mr. David L. Underwood - *Furniture*

Description: A division of Management Recruiters International, recognized as the world's premier sales search firm and the largest, most progressive firm devoted solely to the placement of sales, marketing and management professionals.
Functions: Directors, Senior mgmt., Middle mgmt., Advertising, Mkt. research, Mktg. mgmt., Sales mgmt.
Industries: Generalist, Mfg., Finance, Svcs., Communications, Packaging, Software

Sales Consultants of Laurel Park, Inc.

17177 N. Laurel Park Drive, Ste. 256
Livonia, Michigan 48152
(734) 542-9099
Fax: (734) 542-9098
Email: sclaurelpark.mri@internetmci.com

Key Contact - Specialty:
Mr. Chris Arnold - *Sales & marketing management*

Description: We offer client firms in-depth working knowledge of the foodservice industry. Specifically related to manufacturers of food items, equipment and supply for sales, marketing and engineering candidates at all levels.

Salary Minimum: $60,000
Functions: Senior mgmt., Middle mgmt., Product dev., Mkt. research, Mktg. mgmt., Sales mgmt., Engineering
Industries: Food/bev/tobacco, Paper, Chemicals, Plastics/rubber, Invest. banking, Hospitality, Packaging

Sales Consultants of Omaha, Inc.

3568 Dodge St.
Omaha, Nebraska 68131-3210
(402) 342-7300
Fax: (402) 342-7100
Email: jeff@top.net

Key Contact - Specialty:
Mr. Francis O. Boggus - *Legal specialist*
Mr. Mark K. Brodersen - *Telecommunications*
Mr. Rick Covalciuc - *Printing, labeling, graphics, pre-press*
Ms. Paula DiMauro - *Computer hardware, software marketing services*
Ms. Kris Dostal - *Agriculture*
Mr. Randy Jackson - *Medical*
Mr. Robert Smith - *Environmental engineering, construction services*
Mr. Duane Vosika - *Industrial, chemical, plastics*
Mr. Kirk Reeder - *Financial, stock brokers*
Mr. James Ingalise - *Construction material sales*

Functions: Senior mgmt., Sales mgmt., Mgmt. consultants, Environmentalists, Technicians, Attorneys, Graphic artists
Industries: Agri/forestry/mining, Printing, Medical devices, Plastics/rubber, Computer equip., Legal, Telecoms

Sales Consultants of Nashua-Manchester

6 Medallion Ctr.
Greeley St. & Rte. 3
Merrimack, New Hampshire 03054
(603) 424-3282
Fax: (603) 424-3286

Key Contact - Specialty:
Mr. Sheldon S. Baron - *Sales, banking, employee benefits, insurance*

Description: We specialize in recruiting and placing sales, sales management, marketing, banking and insurance people in permanent and temporary positions. Our staff is expertly trained and each is well versed in the industries they represent, enabling them to talk your language and understand your needs.

Salary Minimum: $15,000
Functions: Middle mgmt., Advertising, Mkt. research, Mktg. mgmt., Sales mgmt., Direct mktg., Customer svc.
Industries: Mfg., Computer equip., Banking, Misc. financial, Insurance, High tech, Software

Sales Consultants Bridgewater, Inc.

1170 Rte. 22 E.
Bridgewater, New Jersey 08807
(908) 725-2595
Fax: (908) 725-0439
Email: mrbridge@bellatlantic.net
Web: mrbridgewater.com

Key Contact - Specialty:
Mr. Barry Smith - *Banking*

Description: Part of a network of over 750 offices in the U.S. and Canada, offering executive recruitment and interim executive placement using cutting edge technology.
Functions: Middle mgmt., Admin. svcs., Distribution, Sales mgmt., Customer svc., IT, Systems dev.
Industries: Transportation, Finance, Misc. financial, Equip. svcs., Insurance, High tech, Software

Sales Consultants of Cherry Hill

800 N. Kings Hwy, Ste. 402
Cherry Hill, New Jersey 08034-1511
(609) 779-9100
Fax: (609) 779-9193

Key Contact - Specialty:
Mr. Jere Chambers - *Consumer products, industrial sales*
Mr. Gene Grim - *Technical services, business services, business equipment*

Description: Our office places sales and sales management professionals in many industries nationwide.

Salary Minimum: $30,000
Functions: Generalist, Middle mgmt., Advertising, Mktg. mgmt., Sales mgmt., Customer svc., Systems implem.
Industries: Mfg., Transportation, Misc. financial, Svcs., Communications, Telecoms, Insurance

Sales Consultants of Northern Jersey, Inc.

139 Harristown Rd.
Glen Rock, New Jersey 07452
(201) 651-9200
Fax: (201) 651-1320
Web: scglenrk@mrinet.com

Key Contact - Specialty:
Mr. William Soodsma - *Sales & marketing*

Description: We specialize in finding sales, sales management and marketing professionals with proven track records of success.
Functions: Generalist, Senior mgmt., Advertising, Mkt. research, Mktg. mgmt., Sales mgmt.
Industries: Generalist

Sales Consultants of Morris County, Inc.

364 Parsippany Rd., Ste. 8B
Parsippany, New Jersey 07054
(973) 887-3838
Fax: (973) 887-2304
Email: scmorris@marketing-sales.com
Web: www.marketing-sales.com

Key Contact - Specialty:
Mr. Ernest Bivona - *Sales & marketing*

Description: Specializes in sales and sales management and secondarily in marketing; we further specialize in market niches related to telecommunications, services, chemicals, process equipment and healthcare related products. Staff tenure includes consultants with 19 years experience.

Salary Minimum: $20,000
Functions: Advertising, Mkt. research, Mktg. mgmt., Sales mgmt., Direct mktg., Customer svc., PR
Industries: Food/bev/tobacco, Chemicals, Drugs mfg., Machinery/Appliances, Test/measurement equip., Insurance, Software

---

Sales Consultants of Middlesex County, Inc.

242 Old New Brunswick Rd., Ste. 340
Piscataway, New Jersey 08854-3754
(732) 981-8008

Key Contact - Specialty:
Mr. James K. Malloy - *Packaging*

Description: Our office specializes in the packaging industry from plastics, paper, film, etc. We do mainly sales and sales management, marketing, general management and corporate level positions in packaging.

Salary Minimum: $30,000
Functions: Senior mgmt., Plant mgmt., Mktg. mgmt., Sales mgmt., Graphic artists
Industries: Paper, Printing, Soap/perfume/cosmetics, Plastics/rubber

---

Sales Consultants of Princeton, Inc.

1230 Parkway Ave., Ste. 102
West Trenton, New Jersey 08628-3007
(609) 882-8388
Fax: (609) 882-4862

Key Contact - Specialty:
Mr. Robert J. Bodnar - *Energy, utilities*
Ms. Beverly H. Bodnar

Description: Professional management consulting firm specializing in executive search - organized by divisions to address specific client needs. Management consulting services available to compliment the client's executive search needs. Specialize in interpreting strategic and tactical plans into H/R requirements - both quantitative and qualitative.

Salary Minimum: $50,000
Functions: Senior mgmt., Packaging, Sales mgmt., CFO's, Cash mgmt., Mgmt. consultants, Int'l.
Industries: Energy/utilities, Paper, Finance, Mgmt. consulting, Environmental svcs., Packaging, Biotech

---

Sales Consultants of Westchester-South, Inc.

Nine Skyline Drive
Hawthorne, New York 10532-2190
(914) 592-1290
Fax: (914) 592-1258

Key Contact - Specialty:
Mr. Robert J. Penney - *Consumer products, packaging*
Ms. Ruth Vogel

Description: 20 years in business. National search in functions of sales, marketing, management and related areas i.e. sales and/or marketing support. Network of 750 offices worldwide. Call us for further clarification of specific industries and areas of specialization.

Salary Minimum: $40,000
Functions: Generalist, Senior mgmt., Middle mgmt., Packaging, Sales & mktg., IT, Int'l.
Industries: Generalist, Construction, Food/bev/tobacco, Lumber/furniture, Printing, Communications, Packaging

---

Sales Consultants of Raleigh-Durham-RTP

107 Edinburgh S., Ste. 210
Cary, North Carolina 27511
(919) 460-9595
Fax: (919) 460-0642
Email: mriscrdu@intrex.net
Web: www.htinfo.com/mriscrdu.htm

Key Contact - Specialty:
Mr. David C. Bunce - *Information technology*

Description: Office specialties: medical/pharmaceutical, packaging industry, industrial, instrumentation, insurance and advertising-nationally, all technical sales.

Salary Minimum: $30,000
Functions: Senior mgmt., Middle mgmt., Mktg. mgmt., Sales mgmt., MIS mgmt., Systems implem., Systems support
Industries: Medical devices, Machinery/Appliances, Computer equip., Test/measurement equip., Telecoms, High tech, Software

---

Sales Consultants of Cincinnati

11311 Cornell Park Drive, #404
Cincinnati, Ohio 45242-1831
(513) 639-3000
Fax: (513) 639-3001
Email: lstone@mricorp.mrinet.com
Web: www.mrinet.com

Key Contact - Specialty:
Ms. Laura Stone - *Retail (executive level)*

Description: We are a total human resource service organization providing staffing solutions to companies throughout the world.

Salary Minimum: $25,000
Functions: Sales mgmt., Customer svc., Engineering, Mgmt. consultants
Industries: Food/bev/tobacco, Chemicals, Retail, Software, Healthcare

---

Sales Consultants of Harrisburg

702 Lisburn Rd.
Camp Hill, Pennsylvania 17011
(717) 731-8550
Fax: (717) 731-8729
Email: salescon@interramp.com

Key Contact - Specialty:
Mr. Thomas M. Waite - *Emerging communications technologies*

Description: Entire office specializes in voice/data/video technologies in the executive, sales, or marketing job titles.
Functions: General mgmt., Sales & mktg., IT
Industries: High tech

Sales Consultants of Butler County

217 Executive Drive, Ste. 102
Cranberry Township, Pennsylvania 16066
(724) 772-2000
Fax: (724) 772-2088
Email: scbc@nauticom.com

Key Contact - Specialty:
Mr. Alfred Tarquinio - *Telecommunications*

Description: Provider of permanent placement within the communications industry including voice, video, data, wireless sectors and the information technology industry including hardware and software companies.
Functions: Sales mgmt.

Industries: Telecoms

Sales Consultants of Chester County, PA

5 Frame Ave., Ste. 101
Frame Ave. Business Complex
Malvern, Pennsylvania 19355
(610) 695-8420
Fax: (610) 695-8442
Email: chester!mwh@mrinet.com

Key Contact - Specialty:
Mr. Mark W. Hetzel - *All industries*
Mr. Ben W. Hetzel - *Pharmaceutical, medical*
Ms. Terrie Hetzel

Description: Executive recruiters; sales and marketing; all industries.
Functions: Advertising, Mkt. research, Mktg. mgmt., Sales mgmt., Direct mktg., Customer svc., PR
Industries: Generalist

Sales Consultants of Newtown, Inc.

301 S. State St.
Newtown, Pennsylvania 18940-1997
(215) 579-2450
Fax: (215) 579-2458
Email: jplappert@scnewtown.com
Web: www.scnewtown.com

Key Contact - Specialty:
Mr. James F. Plappert - *Group insurance, telecommunications*

Description: Specialists in sales, sales management and general management recruiting in the: (1) group life, disability, health, managed care and pension/retirement insurance industry;and (2) telecommunications and data communications industry.

Salary Minimum: $30,000
Functions: Senior mgmt., Middle mgmt., Advertising, Mktg. mgmt., Sales mgmt., Customer svc.
Industries: Telecoms, Insurance, High tech

Sales Consultants of Pittsburgh

112 Washington Place
Two Chatham Ctr., Ste. 1480
Pittsburgh, Pennsylvania 15219
(412) 566-2200
Fax: (412) 566-2222
Email: pjones@mricorp.mrinet.com

Key Contact - Specialty:
Ms. PJ Jones - *Intangibles, business services*

Description: Contingency search firm specializing in sales: consumer, medical, services, data processing, insurance, chemical and industrial. Non-sales: banking, advertising, insurance, medical and data processing.

Salary Minimum: $48,000
Functions: Product dev., Purchasing, Physicians, Sales & mktg., IT, Engineering, Mgmt. consultants
Industries: Chemicals, Drugs mfg., Medical devices, Plastics/rubber, Metal products, Pharmaceutical svcs., Healthcare

Sales Consultants King of Prussia

992 Old Eagle School Rd., Ste. 913
Wayne, Pennsylvania 19087-1803
(610) 989-8500
Fax: (610) 989-8501
Email: pdlevitt@careerking.com
Web: www.careerking.com

Key Contact - Specialty:
Mr. Peter Levitt - *Telecommunications, data, cable, software*

Description: Focused and personalized attention providing confidential services to our clients. Our targeted and methodical approach ensures our client's objectives are met in a timely fashion.

Salary Minimum: $55,000
Functions: Middle mgmt., Mfg., Materials, Sales mgmt., IT, Engineering, Int'l.
Industries: Computer equip., Computer svcs., New media, Broadcast & Film, Telecoms, High tech, Software

Sales Consultants of Rhode Island, Inc.

Office Commons 95, 349 Centerville Rd.
Warwick, Rhode Island 02886
(401) 737-3200
Fax: (401) 737-4322
Email: slscnsltnt@aol.com

Key Contact - Specialty:
Mr. Peter C. Cotton - *Sales, sales management, marketing*

Description: Sales, sales management and marketing search and recruitment. InterExec (temporary professionals); ConferView videoconferencing services; Career Pathways (outplacement programs); Sales Staffers (temporary sales placement and outsourcing). Local, regional, national.

Salary Minimum: $25,000
Functions: Senior mgmt., Middle mgmt., Mkt. research, Mktg. mgmt., Sales mgmt., Customer svc.
Industries: Generalist

Sales Consultants of Greenville, Inc.

330 Pelham Rd., Ste. 109-B
Greenville, South Carolina 29615
(864) 370-1341

Key Contact - Specialty:
Mr. R. C. Brennecke

Description: Finding and placing sales, sales management and marketing talent is our only business. 750 offices nationally.
Functions: Sales mgmt.
Industries: Chemicals, Machinery/Appliances, High tech, Software

Sales Consultants of Orangeburg

1117 Doyle St. NE
P.O. Box 1578
Orangeburg, South Carolina 29116-1578
(803) 536-4601
Fax: (803) 536-4401

Key Contact - Specialty:
Mr. Richard Jackson - *Industrial sales & marketing*
Ms. Carolyn Jackson - *Industrial sales & marketing*

Description: Specialists in sales, sales management and marketing professionals. Industry concentrations: electronics, electrical, industrial controls, instrumentation, industrial supplies. Additional services: outplacement, executive temporary placement, relocation, video teleconferencing.

Salary Minimum: $25,000
Functions: Senior mgmt., Middle mgmt., Product dev., Production, Automation, Sales mgmt., Engineering
Industries: Metal products, Machinery/Appliances, Computer equip., Test/measurement equip., Misc. mfg., High tech

Sales Consultants of Austin, Inc.

106 E. 6th St., Ste. 430
The Littlefield Bldg.
Austin, Texas 78701-3696
(512) 476-3555
Fax: (512) 476-1331

Key Contact - Specialty:
Mr. C. Jay Middlebrook - *Electronic security*
Ms. Linda Middlebrook - *Medical device*

Description: Executive contingency search. Industry specialization covers airport architectural and design both national and international. Staff features over thirty years combined total recruiting experience. We get the job done!

Functions: Physicians, Mkt. research, Sales mgmt., IT, MIS mgmt., Systems dev., Mgmt. consultants
Industries: Medical devices, Computer svcs., Mgmt. consulting, Telecoms, High tech, Biotech, Healthcare

---

Sales Consultants of Dallas

3010 LBJ Frwy., Ste. 1470
Dallas, Texas 75234
(972) 488-9191
Fax: (972) 488-9090

Key Contact - Specialty:
Mr. Mark B. Rednick
Mr. Brian Gilbert - *Sales, service industry*
Mr. Ed Hamel - *Sales, building materials*
Mr. Paul Shehan - *Sales & management, graphics/packaging*
Ms. Holli Gibson - *Information technology*
Ms. Victoria Collins - *Sales & management, chemical industry*
Mr. Robert Adams - *Sales & management, food service industry*
Mr. Mike Addison - *Sales & management, industrial products*

Description: 30 years in professional sales and sales management staffing.
Functions: Mktg. mgmt., Sales mgmt., Customer svc.
Industries: Food/bev/tobacco, Medical devices, Leather/stone/glass/clay, Machinery/Appliances, Misc. mfg., Hospitality, Software

Branches:
5075 Westheimer #790
Houston, Texas 77056
(713) 627-0880

Sales Consultants of Houston

5075 Westheimer, Ste. 790
Galleria II
Houston, Texas 77056
(713) 627-0880
Fax: (713) 622-7285
Email: jimd@schouston.com
Web: www.schouston.com

Key Contact - Specialty:
Mr. Jim DeForest
Mr. Mark Rednick

Description: Single source human resources services which include: permanent placement, interim executives, sales blitz management, videoconferencing, outplacement and relocation assistance.

Salary Minimum: $30,000
Functions: Senior mgmt., Mfg., Sales & mktg., Benefits, Training, IT, Int'l.
Industries: Mfg., Chemicals, Pharmaceutical svcs., Law enfcmt., Publishing, Telecoms, Packaging, High tech

---

Sales Consultants of Appleton

2144 W. Spencer St.
Appleton, Wisconsin 54914
(920) 830-2575
Fax: (920) 830-2585
Email: scapple@aol.com

Key Contact - Specialty:
Mr. E. Graeme Harvey - *Food & beverage marketing*

Description: Permanent and interim executive staffing along with a variety of ancillary services that are designed to help client companies control the hiring process costs.

Salary Minimum: $35,000
Functions: Production, Mkt. research, Mktg. mgmt., Sales mgmt., Direct mktg., Customer svc., Engineering
Industries: Food/bev/tobacco, Paper, Chemicals, Medical devices, Packaging

---

Sales Consultants of Milwaukee

1333 W. Towne Square Rd.
Mequon, Wisconsin 53092-5047
(414) 404-1400
Fax: (414) 404-1414
Email: mr/sc@mri-execsearch.com
Web: www.recruiters-jobs.com

Key Contact - Specialty:
Mr. James Luzar - *Sales & marketing, management*
Mr. Tim Lawler - *International, manufacturing*
Mr. Bruce Webster - *Telecommunications, information systems, sales & marketing*
Ms. Beth Culbertson - *Sales & marketing, industrial, healthcare*
Ms. Debbie Matras - *Industrial, medical, sales & marketing*

Description: Recruitment of sales and marketing professionals, managers and executives and project-based sales staffing. Office is in top 5% of MR/SC offices nationwide. President's Gold Club Award. 1996 Office of the Year.
Functions: Sales & mktg., Advertising, Mkt. research, Mktg. mgmt., Sales mgmt., Direct mktg., Customer svc.
Industries: Printing, Plastics/rubber, Metal products, Machinery/Appliances, Misc. mfg., Computer svcs., Telecoms

---

Sales Consultants of Madison

1818 Parmenter St., Ste. 202
Middleton, Wisconsin 53562-3182
(608) 836-5566
Fax: (608) 836-1906
Email: schultzy@mailbag.com
Web: www.mrinet.com

Key Contact - Specialty:
Mr. William A. Schultz - *Computer graphics, digital video, applications software*

Description: Specialize in territory sales, sales management and general management recruitment for growth corporations.

Salary Minimum: $30,000
Functions: Mktg. mgmt., Sales mgmt., Direct mktg.
Industries: Computer equip., Computer svcs., New media, Broadcast & Film, Insurance, High tech, Software

---

Sales Executives, Inc.

755 W. Big Beaver Rd., Ste. 2107
Top of Troy Bldg.
Troy, Michigan 48084
(248) 362-1900
Fax: (248) 362-0253
Web: www.salesexecutives.com

Key Contact - Specialty:
Mr. Dale E. Statson - *Medical*
Mr. William Rabe - *Graphics*

Description: Specializing in sales, marketing and sales management.

Salary Minimum: $40,000
Functions: Sales mgmt.
Industries: Food/bev/tobacco, Medical devices, Computer equip., Computer svcs., Telecoms, High tech, Software

---

Sales Management Resources

24040 Camino Del Avion, Ste. A177
Monarch Beach, California 92629-4014
(949) 248-9429
Fax: (949) 248-8567
Email: smr@smrcareer.com
Web: www.smrcareer.com

Key Contact - Specialty:
Mr. Clancy Salway - *Sales & marketing, consumer products company clients*

Description: Southern California-based executive search firm which provides retained and contingency recruiting and consulting services to U.S. corporate consumer products industry clients. Specializes in mid-senior level sales and marketing management positions.

Salary Minimum: $50,000
Functions: Directors, Senior mgmt., Middle mgmt., Advertising, Mkt. research, Mktg. mgmt., Sales mgmt.
Industries: Food/bev/tobacco, Textiles/apparel, Paper, Soap/perfume/cosmetics, Drugs mfg., Plastics/rubber, Misc. mfg.

Branches:
535 Jackson St.
Pasadena, California 91104
(626) 398-6604
Fax: (626) 398-6603

Key Contact - Specialty:
Mr. Michael Carrillo

Sales Professionals Personnel Services

595 Market St., Ste. 2500
San Francisco, California 94105
(415) 543-2828

Key Contact - Specialty:
Mr. Sheldon Israel - *Sales, sales management, marketing management*

Description: Placement of sales, sales management and marketing management personnel.

Salary Minimum: $30,000
Functions: Mktg. mgmt., Sales mgmt.
Industries: Generalist

Sales Recruiters of Oklahoma City

6803 S. Western Ave., Ste. 305
Oklahoma City, Oklahoma 73139
(405) 848-1536
Fax: (405) 636-1561
Email: salesrec@telepath.com
Web: www.telepath.com/salesrec/

Key Contact - Specialty:
Mr. J. R. Rimele - *Medical, industrial, pharmaceutical, sales*
Mr. Glen Johnson - *Sales, medical*
Mr. Greg Johnson - *Sales, medical*

Description: We are a search firm specializing in outside sales.
Functions: Sales & mktg., Mktg. mgmt., Sales mgmt.
Industries: Construction, Medical devices, Pharmaceutical svcs., High tech

Sales Recruiting Network

344 Mason Rd.
Tarentum, Pennsylvania 15084
(724) 226-9900
Fax: (724) 226-2299
Email: cain@salsgiver.com

Key Contact - Specialty:
Mr. Douglas Cain - *Sales, consumer, industrial, food service*

Description: Primary recruiting area: sales positions, sales management positions in consumer, food service and industrial; U.S. and Canada opportunities.

Salary Minimum: $35,000
Functions: Sales mgmt.
Industries: Food/bev/tobacco, Paper, Chemicals, Soap/perfume/cosmetics, Drugs mfg.

Sales Search

17 Goodwill Ave.
Toronto, Ontario M3H 1V5
Canada
(416) 636-3660
Fax: (416) 638-9997

Key Contact - Specialty:
Mr. Bob Glassberg - *Sales, marketing & related management*

Description: With 25 years of specialized expertise, we are known for saving valuable time and effort in providing only ballpark candidates for sales, sales management and marketing positions.
Functions: Sales & mktg.
Industries: Mfg., Wholesale, Computer svcs., Equip. svcs., Telecoms, Packaging, Software

Sales Search Specialist

2408 Happy Hollow Rd.
Glenview, Illinois 60025-1115
(847) 564-1595
Fax: (847) 564-1597

Key Contact - Specialty:
Ms. Darlene Fidlow
Mr. Elliott Fidlow - *Consumer products (sales & marketing)*

Description: We only work on sales and marketing middle management base from $40,000 - $125,000. We pride ourselves on quality people.
Functions: Mkt. research, Mktg. mgmt., Sales mgmt., Customer svc., Int'l.
Industries: Food/bev/tobacco, Paper, Soap/perfume/cosmetics, Drugs mfg., Paints/petroleum products, Hospitality

Sales Solutions

P.O. Box 3557
Walnut Creek, California 94598
(925) 932-8900
Fax: (925) 935-3530
Email: salessol@ccnet.com

Key Contact - Specialty:
Mr. Bill Schmeh - *Sales & marketing*
Ms. Sandy Schmeh - *Sales*

Description: Specializes in the placement of professionals in sales and marketing, nationwide. Primary focus: chemical and plastics industries.

Salary Minimum: $45,000
Functions: Mkt. research, Mktg. mgmt., Sales mgmt., Customer svc., Int'l.
Industries: Chemicals, Plastics/rubber, Paints/petroleum products, Machinery/Appliances, High tech

A. N. Salloway Executive Search & Consulting, L.L.C.

176 Federal St., 5th Floor
Boston, Massachusetts 02110
(617) 428-0703
Fax: (617) 428-0707

Key Contact - Specialty:
Mr. Andrew N. Salloway - *Mutual fund operations, sales & marketing, client relations, communications*

Description: My practice is completely dedicated to the financial services industry, with emphasis toware mutal fund companies. I have ten years experience in various operations management, marketing and sales positions.

Salary Minimum: $35,000
Functions: Directors, Senior mgmt., Middle mgmt., Mktg. mgmt., Sales mgmt., Direct mktg., Customer svc.
Industries: Finance, Misc. financial, Svcs., Mgmt. consulting, Communications, Telecoms, Insurance

Affiliates:
Marchiel & Assoc., Inc.

Sampson Medical Search

22330 Hawthorne Blvd., Ste. 207
Torrance, California 90505-2536
(310) 791-1744
Fax: (310) 791-0684
Email: sampsonmed@aol.com

Key Contact - Specialty:
Ms. Judie Sampson - *Pharmaceutical, biotechnology, device, biostatistics*
Mr. Robert P. Sutton
Ms. Kellie Sampson - *Pharmaceutical, biotechnology, device*
Ms. Shannon Kelly Hall - *Biostatistics, data analysts, MIS, information*
Mr. Mark Johnson - *Pharmaceutical, biotechnology, device*

Description: We provide superior recruitment services to organizations at all levels. We have developed the most sophisticated computerized software system in the industry that enables us to produce immediate results.

Salary Minimum: $45,000
Functions: Senior mgmt., Health admin., Sales mgmt., Personnel, MIS mgmt., Systems dev., DB admin.
Industries: Drugs mfg., Medical devices, Pharmaceutical svcs., Computer svcs., Human resource svcs., Healthcare

Branches:
13200 W. Monte Vista Drive
Goodyear, Arizona 85338
(602) 935-5993
Fax: (602) 935-5993
Key Contact - Specialty:
Mr. Robert Bauer - *Pharmaceutical, biotechnology, device*

George D. Sandel Assoc.
P.O. Box 588
Waltham, Massachusetts 02254
(617) 558-7770
Fax: (617) 558-7771
Web: www.irsxgdsa@erols.com

Key Contact - Specialty:
Mr. Ivan R. Samuels - *High technology*

Description: Search and placement since 1958. Technical professionals and mid to upper management - computer, electronics, optics, defense and hospitals.
Functions: Middle mgmt., Health admin., Mktg. mgmt., MIS mgmt., Systems dev., R&D, Engineering
Industries: Medical devices, Computer equip., Aerospace, High tech, Software, Biotech, Healthcare

Sanders Management Assoc., Inc.
300 Lanidex Plaza
Parsippany, New Jersey 07054
(973) 887-3232
Fax: (973) 887-0099
Email: sma1@sandersinc.com

Key Contact - Specialty:
Mr. Roy Sanders
Mr. Jason Sanders
Mr. Mal Lazinsk

Description: We have been placing information technology executives for over twelve years. Our experience conducting retained searches for corporate IT executives is complemented by a particular specialty building management consulting and professional services organizations at senior levels.

Salary Minimum: $100,000
Functions: IT, MIS mgmt., Systems anal., Systems dev., Systems implem., Systems support, Mgmt. consultants
Industries: Mfg., Finance, Svcs., Communications, Insurance, High tech, Healthcare

Sanford Rose Assoc.
3737 Embassy Pkwy., Ste. 200
Akron, Ohio 44333
(330) 670-9797
(800) 731-7724
Fax: (330) 670-9798
Email: sraintl@aol.com
Web: www.sanfordrose.com

Key Contact - Specialty:
Mr. George R. Snider, Jr.
Mr. Douglas R. Eilertson

Description: Franchisor of executive recruiting offices working on retainer and contingency basis. Each office is owned and operated by an individual who has had significant operations management experience.

Salary Minimum: $40,000
Functions: Senior mgmt., Middle mgmt., Product dev., Physicians, Advertising, Engineering, Int'l.
Industries: Printing, Drugs mfg., Medical devices, Legal, Insurance, High tech, Software

Sanford Rose Assoc. - Fairhope
22787 U.S. Hwy. 98
Fairhope, Alabama 36532
(334) 928-7072
Fax: (334) 928-7738
Email: srafairhop@aol.com

Key Contact - Specialty:
Mr. Paul Marquez - *Commercial printing, business forms, direct mail, labels*

Description: 27 years hands on industry experience, in sales, marketing and production management in all aspects of print industry.

Salary Minimum: $40,000
Functions: Senior mgmt., Plant mgmt., Advertising, Mkt. research, Mktg. mgmt., Sales mgmt., Direct mktg.
Industries: Mfg., Printing, Publishing

Sanford Rose Assoc. - Mobile
4321 Downtowner Loop N., Ste. 201
Mobile, Alabama 36609
(334) 414-5551
Fax: (334) 414-5141
Email: pressjack@aol.com

Key Contact - Specialty:
Mr. Noel Jackson - *Food manufacturing & distribution, chemical manufacturing*

Description: Custom recruiting services in all disciplines of food, as well as chemical, petroleum, pharmaceutical, polymer and coatings manufacturing.

Salary Minimum: $40,000
Functions: General mgmt., Mfg., Materials, Sales & mktg., HR mgmt., Finance, IT
Industries: Food/bev/tobacco, Chemicals, Drugs mfg., Paints/petroleum products, Hospitality, High tech, Software

Sanford Rose Assoc. - Laguna Beach
580 Broadway, Ste. 218
Laguna Beach, California 92651
(949) 497-5728
Fax: (949) 497-4086
Email: bdudley@sralaguna.com
Web: www.sralaguna.com

Key Contact - Specialty:
Mr. Robert R. Dudley - *Information technology*

Description: Specialized custom recruiting of technical and managerial talent for industrial clients nationwide.

Salary Minimum: $50,000
Functions: IT, MIS mgmt., Systems anal., Systems dev., Systems implem., Systems support
Industries: Generalist, Mfg., Svcs., High tech, Software, Healthcare

Sanford Rose Assoc. - Santa Ana
2030 E. 4th St., Ste. 140
Santa Ana, California 92704
(714) 558-1622
Fax: (714) 558-3739
Email: kendres544@aol.com
Web: www.sanfordrose.com

Key Contact - Specialty:
Mr. Charles McCarthy

Description: Office specializing in all disciplines for the machine tool industry (automated systems, welding systems, robotics, manufacturing, laser technology, etc.)
Functions: Product dev., Production, Automation, Plant mgmt., Sales mgmt., MIS mgmt., Systems anal.
Industries: Metal products, Machinery/Appliances, Motor vehicles, Test/measurement equip., Misc. mfg.

Sanford Rose Assoc. - Santa Barbara
748 Dos Hermanos Rd.
Santa Barbara, California 93111
(805) 966-1846
Email: jmyatt@silcom.com

Key Contact - Specialty:
Mr. James S. Myatt, Jr. - *Technical personnel for microprocessor based electronic industries*
Mr. Francis Crusit - *MIS, information services*

Description: A management professional with extensive background in corporate management of high technology industries, both aerospace and commercial.

Salary Minimum: $50,000
Functions: Senior mgmt., Middle mgmt., Automation, Mktg. mgmt., Sales mgmt., MIS mgmt., Engineering
Industries: Generalist, Medical devices, Computer equip., Consumer electronics, Test/measurement equip., Telecoms, High tech

Sanford Rose Assoc. - Sunnyvale

(Firm declined to update.)
753 E. El Camino Real, Ste. A
Sunnyvale, California 94087
(408) 730-5833
Email: sra@ix.netcom.com

Key Contact - Specialty:
Mr. Patrick Spragge - *Semiconductor industry*

Description: Semiconductor, multimedia, software engineering positions.

Salary Minimum: $45,000

Sanford Rose Assoc. - Anaheim

9471 Florence Circle
Villa Park, California 92861
(714) 998-4290
Fax: (714) 998-4291
Email: sraanh@earthlink.net
Web: www.sanfordrose.com

Key Contact - Specialty:
Ms. Theresa Ku - *Data communications, telecommunications, semiconductors*

Description: Office specializing in all disciplines for the high-tech industries (data communications, telecommunications, wireless, semiconductors, electronics, etc.).

Salary Minimum: $60,000
Functions: MIS mgmt., Systems dev., Engineering
Industries: High tech, Software

Sanford Rose Assoc. - Clearwater

2623 McCormick Drive, Ste. 104
Clearwater, Florida 33759-1041
(813) 796-2201
Fax: (813) 669-2942
Email: search104@aol.com

Key Contact - Specialty:
Mr. Kenneth R. Monroe, Jr. - *Pharmaceuticals, medical equipment, medical devices*

Description: Managing Director has 30 years in pharmaceutical, nutritional and home medical equipment industries. Strong orientation in marketing, sales, manufacturing, research and development, quality assurance and finance. Associate has 25 years in pharmaceutical logistics and materials management.

Salary Minimum: $80,000
Functions: Senior mgmt., Middle mgmt., Product dev., Plant mgmt., Quality, Mkt. research, Mktg. mgmt.
Industries: Soap/perfume/cosmetics, Drugs mfg., Medical devices, Venture cap., Pharmaceutical svcs., Biotech, Healthcare

Sanford Rose Assoc. - Norcross

9650 Ventana Way, Ste. 204
Alpharetta, Georgia 30022
(770) 232-9900
Fax: (770) 232-1933
Email: sranorcross@mindspring.com

Key Contact - Specialty:
Mr. Donald R. Patrick - *General, sales & marketing management, staff positions*
Ms. Janet L. Patrick - *Research*
Mr. Tom Robinson - *Information technology*
Ms. Robyn Owens - *Sales/marketing/ advertising*

Description: Ethical search services with an emphasis on custom recruiting in the telecommunications marketplace. Technical, information technology, sales/marketing and general/senior management our specialty.

Salary Minimum: $50,000
Functions: Senior mgmt., Middle mgmt., Mktg. mgmt., Sales mgmt., Systems anal., Systems dev., Systems implem.
Industries: Mgmt. consulting, Advertising/ PR, New media, Telecoms, High tech, Software

Sanford Rose Assoc. - Athens

2500 W. Broad St., Ste. 106
Athens, Georgia 30606
(706) 548-3942
Fax: (706) 548-3786
Email: sraathens@aol.com

Key Contact - Specialty:
Mr. Art Weiner - *Engineering, technical, operations management*
Ms. Arlene Weiner - *Accounting, materials, technical management*
Mr. Ken Weiner - *Engineering, operations (key & management people)*

Description: Custom recruiting for key manufacturing plant positions and division/staff management, QA, DP, accounting, materials and engineers including, plant/IE/design/mfg/project/ product.

Salary Minimum: $40,000
Functions: Middle mgmt., Production, Plant mgmt., Quality, Purchasing, Budgeting, Engineering
Industries: Medical devices, Plastics/rubber, Metal products, Machinery/Appliances, Motor vehicles, Aerospace, Packaging

Sanford Rose Assoc. - Atlanta North

1580 Warsaw Rd., Ste. 101
Roswell, Georgia 30076
(770) 643-4510
Fax: (770) 643-2554
Email: dwburnette@banksearchsouth.com
Web: www.banksearchsouth.com

Key Contact - Specialty:
Mr. Dennis W. Burnette - *Senior management (in banks)*

Description: Former bank president and chairman of Georgia Bankers Association is managing director. Consultants for banking positions.
Functions: Directors, Senior mgmt., Middle mgmt.
Industries: Banking, Misc. financial

Sanford Rose Assoc. - Chicago

233 E. Erie St., Ste. 410
Chicago, Illinois 60611
(312) 787-7171
Fax: (312) 787-7190
Web: VicRobertson@prodigy.net

Key Contact - Specialty:
Mr. R. Vic Robertson - *Medical device*

Description: Executive search and professional recruiting for mid to upper level executives.

Salary Minimum: $60,000
Functions: General mgmt., Mfg., Sales & mktg., IT, R&D, Engineering
Industries: Mfg., Drugs mfg., Medical devices, Invest. banking, Packaging, Biotech

Sanford Rose Assoc. - Effingham

444 S. Willow, Ste. 11
Effingham, Illinois 62401
(217) 342-3911
Fax: (217) 347-7111

Key Contact - Specialty:
Mr. Robert A. St. Denis - *Printing*
Mr. Albert I. Hemenway - *Printing*
Mrs. Sherry A. St. Denis

Description: Experience and in-depth knowledge about printing (30 years) and recruiting (11 years) and active participation with printing related organizations like R&E council & PIA. Therefore efficient searches are conducted resulting in timely placements.

Salary Minimum: $30,000
Functions: Directors, Senior mgmt., Middle mgmt., Admin. svcs., Plant mgmt., Distribution, Sales mgmt.
Industries: Printing

Sanford Rose Assoc. - Orland Park

9405 W. Bormet Drive, Ste. One
Mokena, Illinois 60448
(708) 479-4854
(708) 479-4954
Fax: (708) 479-4750
Email: sraop1@aol.com

Key Contact - Specialty:
Mr. J. Michael Kane - *Materials management all industries*

Description: Executive search and professional recruiting for mid to upper level positions.

Salary Minimum: $75,000
Functions: General mgmt., Mfg., Materials, Sales & mktg., HR mgmt., IT
Industries: Mfg., Transportation, Wholesale, Retail, Svcs., Packaging

Sanford Rose Assoc. - Rockford

416 E. State Street
Rockford, Illinois 61104-1012
(815) 964-4080
Fax: (815) 964-3917
Web: www.sanfordrose.com

Key Contact - Specialty:
Mr. Dennis M. Wallace - *Tooling engineers*

Description: Contingency search: tooling engineers for stamping, plastic and metal cutting industries. Clients are manufacturers utilizing highspeed equipment, automation, robotics, automated or semi-automated welding processes and high speed CNC machining. Recent efforts have also included Industrial Sales positions.

Salary Minimum: $30,000
Functions: Production, Automation, Quality, Productivity, Packaging, Sales mgmt., Systems implem.
Industries: Soap/perfume/cosmetics, Plastics/rubber, Metal products, Machinery/Appliances, Motor vehicles, Misc. mfg., Packaging

Sanford Rose Assoc. - Oak Brook

944 Adare Drive
Wheaton, Illinois 60187
(630) 574-9405

Key Contact - Specialty:
Mr. James Keogh - *Banking, financial services*

Salary Minimum: $40,000
Functions: Cash mgmt., Credit, M&A
Industries: Banking, Invest. banking, Venture cap., Misc. financial

Sanford Rose Assoc. - Carmel, IN

650 E. Carmel Drive, Ste. 450
Carmel, Indiana 46032
(317) 848-9987
Fax: (317) 848-9979
Email: sracarmel@aol.com
Web: www.sanfordrose.com/Carmel

Key Contact - Specialty:
Mr. Michael A. Nichipor - *Insurance, healthcare*

Description: Recruiting staff has over 23 years of broad based executive management experience within the insurance industry..

Salary Minimum: $35,000
Functions: General mgmt., Senior mgmt., Healthcare, IT, MIS mgmt.
Industries: Insurance, Healthcare

Sanford Rose Assoc. - Evansville

7088 Stonebridge Rd., P.O. Box 1106
Newburgh, Indiana 47629-1106
(812) 853-9325
Fax: (812) 853-1953
Email: kforbes@aol.com
Web: sanfordrose.com

Key Contact - Specialty:
Mr. Kenneth P. Forbes - *Graphic arts, printing, advertising*
Ms. Kay Koob Forbes - *Advertising, media, market research*

Description: Executive search and professional staffing in a broad range of industries with special emphasis in printing, advertising, marketing and sales.

Salary Minimum: $25,000
Functions: Generalist, Admin. svcs., Advertising, Mktg. mgmt., Direct mktg., PR
Industries: Generalist, Printing, Communications, Advertising/PR

Sanford Rose Assoc. - Cedar Rapids

3343 Southgate Court, Ste. 205
Cedar Rapids, Iowa 52404
(319) 286-2969
Fax: (319) 286-2971
Email: scr12@aol.com

Key Contact - Specialty:
Mr. Michael Fleming - *Industrial products, all disciplines*

Description: Strong track record in selecting quality candidates in sales management, finance and engineering.

Salary Minimum: $50,000
Functions: Generalist, General mgmt., Production, Materials Plng., Advertising, Personnel, Engineering
Industries: Generalist, Construction, Leather/stone/glass/clay, Motor vehicles, Transportation, Aerospace, Packaging

Sanford Rose Assoc. - Louisville

2100 Gardiner Lane, Ste. 107
Nolan Bldg.
Louisville, Kentucky 40205
(502) 451-4444
Fax: (502) 459-8377
Email: sralky@aol.com

Key Contact - Specialty:
Mr. Joel S. Lerner - *Medical device, pharmaceuticals, biotechnology, engineering*

Description: We are recognized as a leading recruiter of executive and highly skilled technical personnel. We have served the recruiting needs of business and industry since 1959.

Salary Minimum: $45,000
Functions: Production, Quality, Productivity, Health admin., IT, R&D, Engineering
Industries: Drugs mfg., Medical devices, Retail, Hospitality, Pharmaceutical svcs., Biotech, Healthcare

Sanford Rose Assoc. - Columbia, MD

10630 Little Patuxent Pkwy., Ste. 309
Columbia, Maryland 21044
(301) 596-4000
Fax: (301) 596-4001
Email: sracolummd@aol.com

Key Contact - Specialty:
Mr. Howard I. Gostin - *Medical device, biotechnology, pharmaceutical (executive, managerial & technical)*

Description: Our 27 years previous industrial experience in R&D, engineering management and manufacturing in the medical device and chemical fields ensures that client needs are understood and met.

Salary Minimum: $50,000
Functions: Middle mgmt., Product dev., Automation, Plant mgmt., Quality, R&D, Engineering
Industries: Chemicals, Drugs mfg., Medical devices, Biotech

Sanford Rose Assoc. - Rockville

51 Monroe St., Ste. 1211
Rockville, Maryland 20850
(301) 762-1800
Fax: (301) 762-3688

Email: srarkv@aol.com
Web: sanfordrose.com

Key Contact - Specialty:
Mr. Eric J. Heybroek - *Food, paper, chemical*

Description: Custom recruiting for middle and upper level positions in supply chain management, engineering and manufacturing nationwide.

Salary Minimum: $50,000
Functions: General mgmt., Mfg., Production, Materials, Sales & mktg., HR mgmt., Engineering
Industries: Food/bev/tobacco, Paper, Printing, Chemicals, Paints/petroleum products, Transportation, Packaging

Sanford Rose Assoc. - Rochester

1000 W. University Drive, Ste. 203
Rochester, Michigan 48307
(248) 608-9005
Fax: (248) 608-9010
Email: srarmi@customnet.net

Key Contact - Specialty:
Mr. William J. Gongloff, Jr.

Description: Executive search and professional recruiting for mid to upper level executives.
Functions: Directors, Middle mgmt., Production, Plant mgmt., Quality, Purchasing, MIS mgmt.
Industries: Printing, Drugs mfg., Medical devices, Motor vehicles, Pharmaceutical svcs., Human resource svcs., Biotech

Sanford Rose Assoc. - Lake St. Louis

1000 Lake St. Louis Blvd., Ste. 250
Lake St. Louis, Missouri 63367
(888) 258-9082
(314) 625-3124
Fax: (314) 625-6034
Email: emitch2611@aol.com

Key Contact - Specialty:
Mr. Mitch Ellis - *Marketing & sales executives, telecommunications, wireless*
Mr. James Ellis - *Marketing & sales executives, telecommunications, wireless*
Ms. Mary Ellis

Description: We specialize in finding marketing and sales executives in the telecommunications and wireless industries.

Salary Minimum: $75,000
Functions: Directors, Middle mgmt., Mkt. research, Mktg. mgmt., Sales mgmt., Direct mktg.
Industries: Telecoms

Sanford Rose Assoc. - Springfield

5407 E. Riverview St.
Springfield, Missouri 65809
(417) 887-0484
Fax: (417) 887-4644
Email: ngarfar@aol.com

Key Contact - Specialty:
Mr. Gary Farrar - *MIS management, MIS project management, call center management*
Ms. Carolyn Farrar - *MIS management, MIS project management, call center management*

Description: Specialists in MIS management (CIO, director, application development, project management) and call center management.

Salary Minimum: $60,000
Functions: Senior mgmt., Middle mgmt., Customer svc., MIS mgmt.
Industries: Computer svcs., Telecoms, High tech, Software

Sanford Rose Assoc. - Flemington

12 Minneakoning Rd., Ste. 4
Flemington, New Jersey 08822-5729
(908) 788-8523
(908) 788-1788
Fax: (908) 788-7847
Email: sraflem@aol.com
Web: www.sraflem.com

Key Contact - Specialty:
Mr. Gary D. Bertsch - *Engineering, executive management, manufacturing*

Description: Conducts retained and contingent searches for the metals industry and general manufacturing at all levels.
Functions: General mgmt., Product dev., Production, Automation, Quality, Engineering
Industries: Aerospace

Sanford Rose Assoc. - Amherst, NY

5500 Main St., Ste. 340
Williamsville, New York 14221
(716) 626-2265
Fax: (716) 626-4997
Email: sraamh@localnet.com
Web: www.golnet.com/sraamh

Key Contact - Specialty:
Mr. Dinesh V. Parekh - *Automotive executives*
Ms. Jennifer Chazen - *Information technology*

Description: Contingency and retainer searches for the Big Three, transplants, and their Tier I & II suppliers. We also conduct searches for petrochemical and information technology companies. Customized searches for technical and managerial staff is conducted globally.

Salary Minimum: $50,000
Functions: Middle mgmt., Production, Quality, Sales mgmt., IT, R&D, Engineering
Industries: Energy/utilities, Mfg., Chemicals, Plastics/rubber, Motor vehicles, Computer svcs., High tech

Sanford Rose Assoc. - Charlotte

P.O. Box 13490
Charlotte, North Carolina 28270
(704) 366-0730
Fax: (704) 365-0620
Email: jdownssra@aol.com
Web: www.sra-charlotte.com

Key Contact - Specialty:
Mr. James L. Downs - *Information technology*
Mr. James J. Clegg - *Information technology*
Ms. Diann C. Downs
Mr. Jerry A. Johnson - *Information technology*
Mr. Bob Bruton - *Information technology*
Mr. James Lee - *Information technology*
Ms. Shannan Hearne - *Information technology*
Ms. Gretchen Demarest - *Information technology*
Mr. John McCarter - *Information technology*
Mr. Steve Kane
Mr. Martin Vahn

Description: Industry experience by all consultants in information services gives us a unique ability to meet the needs of our clients.

Salary Minimum: $50,000
Functions: MIS mgmt., Systems anal., Systems dev., Systems implem., Systems support
Industries: Computer equip., Computer svcs., Mgmt. consulting, Human resource svcs., Telecoms, High tech, Software

Sanford Rose Assoc. - Gastonia

3816-21 S. New Hope Rd., Ste. 21
Gastonia, North Carolina 28056-8439
(704) 824-0895
Fax: (704) 824-0995
Email: sragaston@aol.com
Web: www.sanfordrose.com/gastonia

Key Contact - Specialty:
Mr. Frederick D. Halek - *Fabricated steel construction*

Description: Engineering and technical recruitment for the metalworking industry. Placements nationally. Member NAPS; NCAPS.

Salary Minimum: $40,000
Functions: Senior mgmt., Middle mgmt., Production, Plant mgmt., Quality, Purchasing, Sales mgmt.
Industries: Metal products, Motor vehicles, Mgmt. consulting, Human resource svcs.

Sanford Rose Assoc. - Burlington, NC

Main Street Square, Suite 202-J
Graham, North Carolina 27253
(910) 229-1800
Fax: (910) 229-1844
Email: sraburlnc@aol.com

Key Contact - Specialty:
Mr. Ronald R. Roach - *Plant management, operations*
Mr. John P. Kensinger - *Materials, purchasing, quality*
Mr. Eugene A. Minso - *Program management, engineering*
Ms. Janet L. Roach

Description: We offer expertise recruitment in world class manufacturing environments with all recruiters having manufacturing experience in their respective disciplines.

Salary Minimum: $40,000
Functions: Senior mgmt., Automation, Plant mgmt., Materials Plng., Mktg. mgmt., MIS mgmt., Engineering
Industries: Mfg., Plastics/rubber, Metal products, Machinery/Appliances, Motor vehicles, Aerospace, High tech

---

Sanford Rose Assoc. - Greensboro

3405H W. Wendover Ave.
Greensboro, North Carolina 27407
(336) 852-3003
(336) 852-3058
Fax: (336) 852-3039
Email: sragnc@aol.com

Key Contact - Specialty:
Mr. Robert J. Harrington - *Middle manager, executive level*

Description: Specialists in the printing, prime and bar code label converting, forms manufacturing, pressure sensitive adhesive coating/laminating, office products, packaging, digital printing, direct mail, and automatic identification hardware, software and supplies companies.

Salary Minimum: $40,000
Functions: Senior mgmt., Middle mgmt., Production, Plant mgmt., Purchasing, Mktg. mgmt., Sales mgmt.
Industries: Lumber/furniture, Paper, Printing, Chemicals, Paints/petroleum products, Computer equip., Packaging

---

Sanford Rose Assoc. - Akron

265 South Main St., Ste. 200
Akron, Ohio 44308
(330) 762-6211
Fax: (330) 762-6161
Email: sra4oc@bright.net
Web: sanfordroseoc.com

Key Contact - Specialty:
Mr. Sanford M. Rose

Description: A national and international recruiting firm with offices from coast to coast.

Salary Minimum: $30,000
Functions: Plant mgmt., Sales mgmt., Systems anal., Engineering
Industries: Mfg., Plastics/rubber, Metal products, Computer equip., Consumer electronics, Computer svcs., Aerospace

---

Sanford Rose Assoc. - Youngstown

545 N. Broad St., Ste. 2
Canfield, Ohio 44406-9204
(330) 533-9270
Fax: (330) 533-9272
Email: ellisor@aol.com

Key Contact - Specialty:
Mr. Richard H. Ellison - *Information technology*

Description: We are information systems recruiters.

Salary Minimum: $30,000
Functions: MIS mgmt., Systems anal., Systems dev., Systems implem., Systems support, Network admin., DB admin.
Industries: Generalist

Branches:
909 S. Main St., Ste. C
Wake Forest, North Carolina 27587-9277
(919) 556-8797
Fax: (919) 556-9021
Key Contact - Specialty:
Ms. Linda Davis - *Information systems*

Sanford Rose Assoc. - Canton

4450 Belden Village St. NW, Ste. 209
Canton, Ohio 44718
(330) 649-9100
Fax: (330) 649-9101
Email: sracanton@aol.com

Key Contact - Specialty:
Mr. William Kuehnling - *Managerial, engineering, manufacturing*

Description: Custom recruiting for middle and upper level positions in management and engineering. Focus is on manufacturing industries, primarily automotive oem and aftermarket.

Salary Minimum: $45,000
Functions: General mgmt., Mfg., Materials, HR mgmt., Engineering
Industries: Mfg., Plastics/rubber, Leather/stone/glass/clay, Metal products, Machinery/Appliances, Motor vehicles, Test/measurement equip.

Sanford Rose Assoc. - Euclid

26250 Euclid Ave., Ste. 211
Euclid, Ohio 44132
(216) 731-0005
Fax: (216) 731-0007
Email: sraeuclid@aol.com

Key Contact - Specialty:
Mr. Ralph Orkin - *Information systems*
Ms. Sheilah Orkin - *Information systems*

Description: Concentration in information systems across all industries.

Salary Minimum: $30,000
Functions: IT, Systems anal., Systems dev., Systems implem., Systems support, Network admin., DB admin.
Industries: Generalist, Mfg., Computer svcs., New media, Telecoms, Insurance, Software

---

Sanford Rose Assoc. - Fairlawn

3040 W. Market St.
Fairlawn, Ohio 44333
(330) 865-4545
Fax: (330) 865-4544
Email: dlcreeger@aol.com

Key Contact - Specialty:
Mr. David Creeger - *Chemicals, plastics, rubber*
Ms. Ann Duke - *Chemicals, plastics*

Description: Chemicals, plastics, rubber, and allied trades for marketing, sales, general management and technical/engineering functions. 30+ years in chemical industry.

Salary Minimum: $50,000
Functions: General mgmt., Product dev., Production, Sales & mktg., Mktg. mgmt., Sales mgmt., R&D
Industries: Mfg., Chemicals, Soap/perfume/cosmetics, Drugs mfg., Plastics/rubber, Paints/petroleum products, Biotech

---

Sanford Rose Assoc. - Columbus North

130 Wetherby Lane, Ste. 101
Westerville, Ohio 43081
(614) 523-1663
(800) 560-4984
Fax: (614) 523-1689
Email: www.htinfo.com/sracols/
Web: www.htinfo.com/sracols/

Key Contact - Specialty:
Mr. Bill Earhart - *Information systems technology*
Mr. Glen Gardner - *Information systems technology*

Description: Executive search firm. Appointment requested; unsolicited resumes accepted. Work on national as well as local openings. Specializes in the areas of: MIS/EDP; computer hardware and software; software engineering.
Functions: MIS mgmt., Systems anal., Systems dev., Systems implem., Systems support, Network admin., DB admin.
Industries: Generalist

Sanford Rose Assoc. - Portland

10200 SW Eastridge, Ste. 200
Portland, Oregon 97225
(503) 297-9191
Fax: (503) 297-3528
Email: srapdx@aol.com

Key Contact - Specialty:
Mr. Jack D. Stiles - *Semiconductor*
Mr. Timothy W. Stiles - *Food processing*

Description: Serving the following industries: food processing, semiconductor, mass storage, software and hardware.

Salary Minimum: $40,000
Functions: Middle mgmt., Product dev., Plant mgmt., Quality, Distribution, Packaging, Sales mgmt.
Industries: Food/bev/tobacco, High tech, Software

Sanford Rose Assoc. - Doylestown

5230 Old York Rd., Ste. 2
P.O. Box 1017
Buckingham, Pennsylvania 18912-1017
(215) 794-5570
Fax: (215) 794-5672
Email: rmesradtp@aol.com

Key Contact - Specialty:
Mr. Robert M. Eisert - *Power generation equipment manufacturers (all disciplines)*

Description: Executive recruitment of a full range of professionals in power generation and industrial equipment.

Salary Minimum: $30,000
Functions: Production, Plant mgmt., Quality, Purchasing, Materials Plng., Sales mgmt., Engineering
Industries: Energy/utilities, Chemicals, Metal products, Machinery/Appliances, Test/measurement equip., Misc. mfg., Aerospace

Sanford Rose Assoc. - Philadelphia North

130 Almshouse Rd., Suite 107A
Richboro, Pennsylvania 18954
(215) 953-7433
Fax: (215) 953-7449
Email: sraphily@ix.netcom.com

Key Contact - Specialty:
Mr. Steven M. Frazier - *General management, marketing, engineering, MIS*
Ms. Shannon M. Kapral - *Banking, financial services*

Description: Clients are assured of high quality, value added recruiting services designed to foster long term strategic relationships. We provide our services responsively even in a client's most difficult circumstances.

Salary Minimum: $40,000
Functions: Senior mgmt., Middle mgmt., Product dev., Mkt. research, Mktg. mgmt., Cash mgmt., IT
Industries: Paper, Printing, Computer equip., Banking, Computer svcs., New media, Software

Sanford Rose Assoc. - Pittsburgh North

3500 Brooktree Center, Ste. 220
Wexford, Pennsylvania 15090
(724) 934-2261
Fax: (724) 934-1948
Email: DHayden@Execnet.net

Key Contact - Specialty:
Mr. Dale Hayden - *Banking, financial services, MIS, human resources*

Description: Executive search and professional recruiting services for middle and upper level positions.

Salary Minimum: $50,000
Functions: Senior mgmt., Mkt. research, Direct mktg., Training, CFO's, MIS mgmt., Mgmt. consultants
Industries: Banking, Invest. banking, Misc. financial, Svcs.

Sanford Rose Assoc. - Columbia

4458 Augusta Rd., Bldg. One, Ste. C
Lexington, South Carolina 29072
(803) 957-7300
Fax: (803) 957-7380
Email: sracolasc@aol.com
Web: SanfordRose.com@aol.com

Key Contact - Specialty:
Mr. Paul Morgan - *Medical device, pharmaceutical*

Description: Executive search firm involved in recruitment and placement within the medical device manufacturing, pharmaceutical and grocery products industries.
Salary Minimum: $40,000
Functions: Senior mgmt., Product dev., Health admin., Mkt. research, Systems dev., R&D, Engineering
Industries: Food/bev/tobacco, Drugs mfg., Medical devices, Pharmaceutical svcs., Computer svcs., Biotech, Healthcare

Sanford Rose Assoc. - Nashville

9000 Church St. E., Ste. 100
Brentwood, Tennessee 37027
(615) 346-3000
Fax: (615) 346-3003

Key Contact - Specialty:
Mr. Terry Tringle - *Graphic arts, marketing, market research*

Description: Sales, professional and executive searches in the printing, publishing, direct mail and graphic arts supply industries.
Functions: Senior mgmt., Middle mgmt., Plant mgmt., Mktg. mgmt., Sales mgmt., CFO's
Industries: Paper, Printing, Publishing

Sanford Rose Assoc. - Austin

4210 Spicewood Springs Rd., Ste. 211
Austin, Texas 78759
(512) 418-8444
Fax: (512) 418-8441
Email: sraaustin@aol.com

Key Contact - Specialty:
Mr. Stephen M. Sackmary - *Manufacturing operations (executive, managerial, technical professionals)*
Ms. Marcia T. Sackmary
Ms. Andrez M. Jankinson

Description: Staff has significant field experience in the designated industry sectors and key positions. Focus on electronics, automotive, automation, aerospace.

Salary Minimum: $60,000
Functions: Senior mgmt., Middle mgmt., Production, Automation, Plant mgmt., Quality, Productivity
Industries: Machinery/Appliances, Motor vehicles, Computer equip., Test/measurement equip., Aerospace, High tech

Sanford Rose Assoc. - Salt Lake City

8941 Upper Lando Lane
Park City, Utah 84098
(435) 647-9755
Fax: (435) 647-9069
Email: srautah@sprynet.com
Web: sanfordrose.com

Key Contact - Specialty:
Mr. Rodger A. Lee - *Sporting goods, consumer goods, toys and recreational products*
Ms. Amy T. Lee - *Sporting goods, consumer goods*
Ms. Cheryl Wink - *Information technology*

Description: Professional custom recruiting services for consumer products firms with a special focus in the sporting goods, recreational products, toys and other consumer products industries. Executive, marketing, sales, manufacturing and engineering disciplines. Also specialize in IT and financial services.

Salary Minimum: $50,000
Functions: Senior mgmt., Middle mgmt., Mfg., Advertising, Mkt. research, Finance, IT
Industries: Food/bev/tobacco, Soap/perfume/cosmetics, Drugs mfg., Plastics/rubber, Computer equip., Consumer electronics, Computer svcs.

Sanford Rose Assoc. - Port Washington

117 N. Milwaukee St.
Port Washington, Wisconsin 53074
(414) 268-1750
Fax: (414) 268-1753
Email: SRA PW@aol.com
Web: www.sanfordrose.com//pwi

Key Contact - Specialty:
Mr. Michael D. Eskra - *Transition management, battery*

Description: Conducts retained and contingent searches for general manufacturing, automotive, battery, telecommunications and steel industries for technical, sales and management positions.

Salary Minimum: $50,000
Functions: Senior mgmt., Production, Plant mgmt., Quality, Productivity, R&D, Engineering
Industries: Construction, Chemicals, Plastics/rubber, Metal products, Motor vehicles, Telecoms, High tech

Santangelo Consultants Inc.

60 E. 42nd St., Ste. 1333
New York, New York 10165
(212) 867-6664

Key Contact - Specialty:
Mr. Richard Santangelo - *Management consulting*

Description: Our clients are prestigious management consulting firms. Emphasis on information systems, process redesign, operations improvement, healthcare, banking, brokerage, insurance, finance, management accounting, strategic planning, inventory planning and control systems.

Salary Minimum: $60,000
Functions: Productivity, Healthcare, HR mgmt., Finance, IT, Systems implem., Mgmt. consultants
Industries: Banking, Misc. financial, Pharmaceutical svcs., Mgmt. consulting, Communications, Software, Healthcare

Sarver & Carruth Assoc.

3927 N. 1st St.
Durant, Oklahoma 74701
(580) 931-0472
Fax: (580) 931-0473
Email: cjsarver@simplynet.net

Key Contact - Specialty:
Ms. Catherine J. Sarver - *Engineering*

Description: An executive and technical recruitment firm dedicated to providing excellent service both to client companies and candidates.

Salary Minimum: $40,000
Functions: Senior mgmt., Middle mgmt., Product dev., Systems implem., R&D, Engineering
Industries: Computer equip., Test/measurement equip., Telecoms, High tech

Savalli & Assoc., Inc.

24 Hiawatha Drive
Battle Creek, Michigan 49015
(616) 968-5100
Fax: (616) 968-0102
Email: Savallicom@AOL.com

Key Contact - Specialty:
Mr. Frank Savalli - *Brand management, marketing research, consumer promotions*

Description: We are an executive recruiting firm specializing in positions in brand management, market research, promotions management in consumer packaged goods companies.

Salary Minimum: $50,000
Functions: Advertising, Mkt. research, Mktg. mgmt., R&D, Int'l.
Industries: Food/bev/tobacco, Paper, Soap/perfume/cosmetics, Drugs mfg., Medical devices, Retail, Advertising/PR

Saviar, Inc.

4110 N. Scottsdale Rd., #380
Scottsdale, Arizona 85251
(602) 946-9944
(315) 443-4460
Fax: (602) 946-9955
Email: saviar@emi.com
Web: www.saviar.com

Key Contact - Specialty:
Mr. Dominick M. Natdone, II

Description: Specializes in the recruitment and placement of senior management, sales and technical professionals. Industries include high technology, computer services, telecommunications and new media (Internet/multimedia).

Salary Minimum: $50,000
Functions: Senior mgmt., Sales mgmt., CFO's, Systems anal., Systems dev., Systems implem., Graphic artists
Industries: Hospitality, Entertainment, Computer svcs., New media, Telecoms, High tech, Software

Schattle & Duquette

1130 Ten Rod Rd., B-207
North Kingstown, Rhode Island 02852
(401) 739-0500
Fax: (401) 295-8564
Email: sdexsearch@aol.com

Key Contact - Specialty:
Mr. Donald J. Schattle
Mr. Edmond J. Duquette

Description: Search and placement firm specializing in manufacturing, finance, engineering and information systems and technology.

Salary Minimum: $50,000
Functions: General mgmt., Mfg., Materials, Sales & mktg., Finance, IT, Engineering
Industries: Generalist, Mfg., Chemicals, Finance, Banking, Venture cap., High tech

The Schatz Company

13620 Barrett Office Drive, Ste. 101 G
St. Louis, Missouri 63021
(314) 966-8699
Fax: (314) 966-5499

Key Contact - Specialty:
Mr. William G. Schatz, Jr. - *Operations, manufacturing, general management*

Description: 100% concentration of the search and placement of middle to senior level executives in manufacturing operations.

Salary Minimum: $70,000
Functions: Senior mgmt., Plant mgmt., Quality, Materials Plng., Mkt. research, Personnel, CFO's

Industries: Chemicals, Metal products, Machinery/Appliances, Motor vehicles, Misc. mfg., Misc. financial, Human resource svcs.

Schenck & Assoc. SC

P.O. Box 1739
Appleton, Wisconsin 54913
(414) 731-8111
Fax: (414) 731-8037
Email: sassochr@athenet.net

Key Contact - Specialty:
Mr. Patrick J. Egan

Description: Management search consultants providing professionalism, ethical and long lasting relationships, confidentiality, thoroughness and commitment to success through service.

Salary Minimum: $35,000
Functions: Senior mgmt., Plant mgmt., Purchasing, Materials Plng., CFO's, Budgeting, Engineering
Industries: Generalist, Paper, Metal products, Banking, Accounting, Packaging, Healthcare

---

Schick Professional Search, Inc.

11440 Market St.
P.O. Box 326
North Lima, Ohio 44452
(330) 549-3961
Fax: (330) 549-3963
Email: schicksps@aol.com

Key Contact - Specialty:
Mr. Rex Schick - *Technical (motors & motor control), hardware & software engineers*
Mr. Jon Schick - *Technical (consumer & automotive products)*

Description: Specialize in recruiting engineers for motors, electromechanical, electronic, consumer and automotive positions in design, manufacturing and sales and marketing.

Salary Minimum: $35,000
Functions: Product dev., Automation, Mkt. research, Mktg. mgmt., Sales mgmt., Engineering
Industries: Metal products, Machinery/ Appliances, Motor vehicles, Consumer electronics, Misc. mfg., Transportation

---

A.D. Schiff & Assoc., Ltd.

869 Creek Bend Drive
Vernon Hills, Illinois 60061
(847) 821-9220
Fax: (847) 821-9298
Email: adschiff@theramp.net

Key Contact - Specialty:
Ms. Arlene D. Schiff - *Medical, sales & marketing, management*

Description: We specialize in the healthcare industry. We have over 20 years experience in the medical profession. We are search and recruitment consultants in any area of healthcare, sales & marketing, executive, physician, management.
Functions: Senior mgmt., Middle mgmt., Physicians, Health admin., Mkt. research, Mktg. mgmt., Sales mgmt.
Industries: Drugs mfg., Medical devices, Pharmaceutical svcs., Biotech, Healthcare

---

Schlatter & Assoc.

388 Market St., Ste. 400
San Francisco, California 94111
(415) 433-8100
Fax: (415) 421-4176

Key Contact - Specialty:
Mr. Craig Schlatter - *Finance, accounting, systems*

Description: Firm is 15 years old. Specialization in CFO, controller, financial and accounting management positions.

Salary Minimum: $75,000
Functions: Middle mgmt., CFO's, Budgeting, Cash mgmt., M&A, MIS mgmt.
Industries: Mfg., Finance, Svcs., Real estate, High tech, Software, Biotech

---

Schoales & Assoc. Inc.

145 King St. W., Ste. 1000
Toronto, Ontario M5H 1J8
Canada
(416) 863-9978
Fax: (416) 491-1223

Key Contact - Specialty:
Mr. Michael Schoales - *Financial services, brokerage senior*
Ms. Gloria Schoales - *Senior administrative*

Description: Schoales & Associates was formed in 1984. We specialize in recruiting sales and marketing and administrative individuals primarily interstcok brokerage industry.
Functions: Senior mgmt., Sales & mktg., Sales mgmt., CFO's, M&A
Industries: Generalist, Invest. banking, Brokers, Government

Schulenburg & Assoc.

3232 Cobb Pkwy., Ste. 183
Atlanta, Georgia 30339
(770) 745-4206
(888) 248-2116
Fax: (770) 745-4205
Email: neil@schulenburg-assoc.com
Web: www.schulenburg-assoc.com

Key Contact - Specialty:
Mr. Neil P. Schulenburg - *Information systems*

Description: Professional search services and information services.
Functions: MIS mgmt., Systems anal., Systems dev., Systems implem., Systems support, Network admin., DB admin.
Industries: Finance, Banking, Invest. banking, Brokers, Insurance, Software, Healthcare

---

G. L. Schwartz & Assoc., Inc.

9040 Martin Rd.
Roswell, Georgia 30076
(770) 552-3140
Fax: (770) 552-3145
Email: glsa@aol.com

Key Contact - Specialty:
Mr. Gary L. Schwartz - *Medical, healthcare*
Ms. Beth O. Schwartz - *Medical, healthcare*

Description: Specialization in the management, operations and administration side of healthcare.
Functions: Senior mgmt., Middle mgmt., Healthcare, Health admin., Mkt. research, Mktg. mgmt., Sales mgmt.
Industries: Svcs., Healthcare

Scientific Solutions, Inc.

7417 Steeplechase Court
Saline, Michigan 48176
(734) 944-6666
Fax: (734) 944-6667
Email: spaterson@scisolve.com
Web: www.scisolve.com

Key Contact - Specialty:
Ms. Sharon Paterson - *Coatings, plastics, technical, management*
Mr. David Paterson - *Coatings, plastics, technical, management*

Description: The Managing Director has several years of experience in marketing and sales in the coatings and plastics industry, working primarily with the Big 3 automotive companies and their suppliers.

Salary Minimum: $65,000
Functions: Directors, Product dev., Plant mgmt., Mktg. mgmt., Sales mgmt., R&D, Engineering
Industries: Chemicals, Plastics/rubber, Paints/petroleum products, Motor vehicles

---

Devin Scott Assoc.

2125 Center Ave., Ste. 402
Ft. Lee, New Jersey 07024
(201) 346-0331
Fax: (201) 346-0338

Key Contact - Specialty:
Mr. Rocco M. Fedele - *Hospitality (restaurants only), restaurants*

Description: Strongest nationwide contacts for operational management and all staff support departments for the hospitality industry.

Salary Minimum: $50,000
Functions: Directors, Senior mgmt., Advertising, Mkt. research, Personnel
Industries: Hospitality

Robert Scott Assoc.

P.O. Box 486
Rancocas, New Jersey 08073-0486
(609) 835-2224
Fax: (609) 835-1933
Email: robert_scott@mindspring.com

Key Contact - Specialty:
Mr. Bob Scott - *Operations, engineering, manufacturing management*

Description: Helping companies recruit the finest technically trained professionals in research, engineering, operations and maintenance for over 25 years.

Salary Minimum: $40,000
Functions: Mfg., Materials, HR mgmt., IT, R&D, Engineering, Mgmt. consultants
Industries: Mfg., Chemicals, Drugs mfg., Medical devices, Plastics/rubber, High tech, Software

Scott Douglas Inc.

16968 Obsidian Drive, Ste. 101
Ramona, California 92065-6839
(760) 788-5560
Fax: (760) 788-5506
Email: 74737.141@compuserve.com
Web: mike49@ix.netcom.com

Key Contact - Specialty:
Mr. Michael F. Magic - *Insurance actuaries, medical doctors, benefits executives*

Description: Boutique firm specializing in actuarial/managed care/finance and marketing professionals. Provides research, account management and candidate screening, profiles and other services.

Salary Minimum: $50,000
Functions: Physicians
Industries: Insurance, Healthcare

Scott Sibley Assoc.

24 Bent Oak Trail
Fairport, New York 14450
(716) 425-1300
Fax: (716) 325-5923

Key Contact - Specialty:
Mr. Scott S. McElhearn - *Medical*

Description: Understanding our clients business and dedication to their success is our strength. We provide highly motivated, qualified career oriented candidates in whom we take a personal interest.

Salary Minimum: $25,000
Functions: Middle mgmt., Physicians, Nurses, Allied health, Health admin., Sales mgmt., Engineering
Industries: Misc. mfg., Banking, Higher ed., Human resource svcs., High tech, Software, Healthcare

Branches:
215 Alexander St.
Rochester, New York 14607
(716) 232-2020
Fax: (716) 325-5923
Key Contact - Specialty:
Mr. Scott S. McElhearn - *Medical*

Scott-Thaler Assoc. Agency, Inc.

86 Brookhollow Drive
Santa Ana, California 92705
(714) 966-1671
(800) YOU-1JOB
Fax: (714) 755-7101

Key Contact - Specialty:
Mr. Brian D. Thaler - *Apparel, textile, distribution services, logistics, retail*

Description: We offer extensive, specialized industry experience and a distinctively personalized approach to recruiting, in order to meet the immediate needs of the client and to establish a productive long-term relationship.

Salary Minimum: $30,000
Functions: Senior mgmt., Middle mgmt., Plant mgmt., Purchasing, Materials Plng., Distribution, Packaging
Industries: Food/bev/tobacco, Textiles/apparel, Drugs mfg., Misc. mfg., Transportation, Retail, Mgmt. consulting

Scott-Wayne Assoc., Inc.
(a division of Personnel Group of America)

425 Boylston St., 4th Floor
Boston, Massachusetts 02116
(617) 587-3000
Fax: (617) 587-3030
Email: swa@gte.net

Key Contact - Specialty:
Mr. R. Steven Dow - *Accounting & finance*

Description: Specialists in the search and placement of accounting, financial and temporary personnel for over twenty-five years.

Salary Minimum: $50,000
Functions: Finance
Industries: Generalist, Mfg., Finance, Svcs., High tech, Software, Biotech

Search & Recruit Int'l.

4455 South Blvd.
Virginia Beach, Virginia 23452
(757) 490-3151
Fax: (757) 497-6503
Web: www.searchandrecruit.com

Key Contact - Specialty:
Mr. R. P. Brittingham - *Technical*

Description: Recruiting at all levels of high technology, skilled technicians, engineers and professional management people. Specialties in engineers, techs, environmental, manufacturing, nuclear and software. Financial (all types) medical device manufacturing and heavy industrial sales.

Salary Minimum: $25,000
Functions: Product dev., Automation, Plant mgmt., Packaging, Network admin., Technicians
Industries: Energy/utilities, Mfg., Computer svcs., Telecoms, Defense, Aerospace, High tech

The Search America Group Inc.

18511 Heritage Trail
Strongsville, Ohio 44136
(440) 572-0450
Fax: (440) 572-2000
Email: searchamerica@newco.com
Web: www.searchamericagroup.com

Key Contact - Specialty:
Mr. Thomas J. Snow - *Sales, marketing, general management*
Mr. Eric Sted - *Sales, marketing, general management*
Mr. Steve Keefe - *Sales, marketing, general management*

Description: We service manufacturers' needs for key management executive (mid level and above) in the consumer and industrial marketplaces throughout North, Central and South America.
Functions: General mgmt., Sales & mktg., Advertising, Mkt. research, Mktg. mgmt., Sales mgmt., Int'l.
Industries: Agri/forestry/mining, Mfg., Wholesale, Retail, Mgmt. consulting, Human resource svcs., Communications

Search America, Inc.

678 Burmont Rd., Ste. 600-K
Drexel Hill, Pennsylvania 19026
(610) 259-2800
Fax: (610) 259-6110

Key Contact - Specialty:
Mr. Thomas V. Giacoponello - *Market research, management consulting*

Description: Our recruiters have extensive training in the behavioral aspects, sensitivity and art of recruiting. Our goal is to partner with our clients by increasing trust, loyalty and continued mutual success.

Salary Minimum: $60,000
Functions: Mkt. research, Mktg. mgmt., Mgmt. consultants
Industries: Banking, Invest. banking, Brokers, Misc. financial, Pharmaceutical svcs., Mgmt. consulting, Healthcare

Affiliates:
Advent Management International, Ltd.

Search America, Inc.

720 Washington St., Yale Bldg.
Hanover, Massachusetts 02339
(781) 826-0317
Email: resumes@search-america.com

Key Contact - Specialty:
Mr. Steve Lombardo - *Technology professionals, management consultants, implementation consultants specializing in supply chain (retail, distribution & warehouse management), data warehousing & database marketing processes & systems*

Description: We provide our candidates access to our clients in professional services, product development and retail/consumer products organizations nationwide.

Salary Minimum: $65,000
Functions: IT, MIS mgmt., Systems anal., Systems dev., Systems implem., DB admin., Mgmt. consultants
Industries: Retail, Computer svcs., Mgmt. consulting, High tech, Software

Search Assoc.

P.O. Box 131 R
Eastwood, Kentucky 40018-0131
(502) 245-2928
Fax: (502) 245-2923
Email: search@metaljobs.net
Web: metaljobs.net

Key Contact - Specialty:
Mr. Bill Johnstone - *Primary metals*
Ms. Glenda Dixon - *Primary metals*

Description: All aspects of steel, aluminum, copper and other primary metal industries: engineers, plant management, QA staff, metallurgists. All types of processes: casting, melting, rolling, extrusion, etc.
Functions: Middle mgmt., Production, Plant mgmt., Quality, Productivity, Engineering
Industries: Metal products

Search Assoc., Inc.

5900 Sepulveda
Sherman Oaks, California 91411
(818) 988-5600
Fax: (818) 787-0110
Email: mail@swjobs.com

Key Contact - Specialty:
Mr. Lee Woodward - *Programming, software*
Mr. Bernard Sharf - *Multimedia*

Description: Contingency and retainer-major emphasis in IS, direct marketing, real estate and development, electronics, semiconductor, multimedia, telecommunications, legal, and software. We also place professionals on a contract and temporary basis.

Salary Minimum: $40,000
Functions: Healthcare, Direct mktg., IT, Systems anal., Systems dev., Engineering, Graphic artists
Industries: Computer equip., Consumer electronics, Broadcast & Film, Telecoms, High tech, Software, Healthcare

Search Assoc., Inc.

18 Bank St.
Summit, New Jersey 07901
(908) 277-6818
Fax: (908) 273-9256

Key Contact - Specialty:
Ms. Trina R. Lawson - *Public relations, sales promotion, administrative*
Mr. George A. Richner - *Finance, sales, marketing, general management*

Description: Positions: senior/middle management and administrative. Disciplines: all. Industries served: information technology, financial, distribution, engineering sciences, retail, hospitality and service institutions.

Salary Minimum: $20,000
Functions: General mgmt., Mfg., Materials, Sales & mktg., Finance, IT, Specialized services, Int'l.
Industries: Mfg., Finance, Svcs., Communications, Insurance, High tech, Software

Branches:
4 John Henry Drive
Montville, New Jersey 07045
(973) 316-9321
Key Contact - Specialty:
Mr. E. Joseph Rotter - *Information technology*

Search Bureau Int'l.

P.O. Box 377608
Chicago, Illinois 60637
(708) 210-1834
Fax: (708) 210-1834

Key Contact - Specialty:
Mr. Reginald M. Hudson - *Accounting & finance*

Description: We are a group of professionals who specialize in the areas of accounting, finance, engineering, human resource management, data processing, marketing. Also provide outplacement service to Fortune 500 companies.

Salary Minimum: $50,000
Functions: General mgmt., Mfg., Sales & mktg., HR mgmt., Finance, IT, Specialized services
Industries: Finance, Communications, Real estate

Search By Design

P.O. Box 3316
Lake Havasu City, Arizona 86405
(520) 855-2121

Key Contact - Specialty:
Mr. Dayton VanSlyke - *Building products, home improvement, fixtures, furniture*

Description: Wood and building products, kitchen cabinets, windows, doors, stone fixtures, architectural wood work, furniture (RTA, residential, office), millwork and related. Very heavy into confidential replacements nationwide.

Salary Minimum: $50,000
Functions: General mgmt., Mfg., Materials, Sales & mktg., IT, R&D, Engineering
Industries: Lumber/furniture, Paper

The Search Center Inc.

1155 Dairy Ashford, Ste. 404
Houston, Texas 77079-3011
(713) 589-8303
Fax: (713) 589-8425

Key Contact - Specialty:
Ms. Susan M. Magnani - *Energy market/trades*

Description: Specialized in oil, natural gas, petrochemical, chemical and plastics industries. Focus on professional sales, trading and senior executive management positions. Strong emphasis in energy derivatives and trade finance.

Salary Minimum: $60,000
Functions: Mktg. mgmt., Cash mgmt., Risk mgmt., Int'l.
Industries: Energy/utilities, Invest. banking, Brokers

International Branches:
Saipan

The Search Committee

8 Westbury Rd.
Lutherville, Maryland 21093
(888) 732-6752
(410) 825-7811
Fax: (410) 825-9035
Web: www.erols.com/secor

Key Contact - Specialty:
Mr. David B. Secor - *Medical (managed care), healthcare, payors, providers, pharmaceuticals*

Description: Having spent my adult life working in the medical industry I can assure you that I will supply you with a tailored fit, not a generic solution.

Salary Minimum: $65,000
Functions: Directors, Senior mgmt., Physicians, Health admin., Sales mgmt., CFO's, MIS mgmt.
Industries: Drugs mfg., Insurance, Healthcare

Branches:
34503 Pennell Circle
Tallahassee, Florida 32310
(850) 575-7658
Fax: (850) 575-7658
Key Contact - Specialty:
Mr. Kosta Kostadinova - *Information technology*

Affiliates:
Don Flint

Search Consultants, Inc.
1 E. Ridgewood Ave.
Paramus, New Jersey 07652
(201) 444-1770
Fax: (201) 444-2530

Key Contact - Specialty:
Mr. Walter Perog - *Human resources*

Description: Looking for guaranteed satisfaction in hiring a HR executive? For the record: 25 years of success in the NJ/NY/CT region; a very efficient and timely hiring process; virtually no relo costs.

Salary Minimum: $65,000
Functions: HR mgmt., Benefits, Personnel, Training
Industries: Generalist

Search Consultants Int'l., Inc.
4545 Post Oak Place, Ste. 208
Houston, Texas 77027
(713) 622-9188
Fax: (713) 622-9186
Email: info@searchconsultants.com
Web: www.searchconsultants.com

Key Contact - Specialty:
Mr. S. Joseph Baker - *Energy industry, cement industry (engineering support, executive management)*
Mr. Michael Brentari - *Independent power industry (IPP), business development, engineering positions, energy industry, energy traders*
Mr. Richard Fiore - *Environmental engineers & safety professionals, scientists (corporations, environmental engineering consulting companies)*
Mr. Steve McAleavy - *Energy industry, gas & electric traders, marketers, power marketing managers & executives*
Mr. Lon McAllister - *Contract environmental engineering, contract geophysical professionals (oil & gas exploration & production industry)*
Ms. Judith M. Baker

Description: Extensive experience in mid and senior management executive search, with technical expertise in power marketing and trading, the energy industry (natural gas and electricity), manufacturing (chemicals & cement), environmental health and safety and independent power/cogeneration (IPP).

Salary Minimum: $50,000
Functions: General mgmt., Production, Plant mgmt., Sales & mktg., Engineering, Environmentalists, Int'l.
Industries: Energy/utilities, Chemicals, Paints/petroleum products, Leather/stone/glass/clay, Wholesale, Environmental svcs., Haz. waste

---

Search Consultants, LLC
10400 Little Patuxent Pkwy., Ste. 210
Columbia, Maryland 21044
(410) 715-0900
Fax: (410) 715-1137
Email: contact@searchalliance.com
Web: www.search-consultants.com

Key Contact - Specialty:
Ms. Paula Houck

Description: One of the largest executive search firms in the DC metro area. We specialize in senior information systems, accounting and finance positions.
Functions: CFO's, Budgeting, Cash mgmt., MIS mgmt., Systems anal., Systems dev., R&D
Industries: Mfg., Finance, Svcs., Communications, High tech, Biotech, Healthcare
Professional Associations: IACPR

Branches:
1430 Spring Hill Rd.
McLean, Virginia 22102
(703) 288-0900
Fax: (703) 288-0500
Email: searchva@searchalliance.com
Web: www.searchalliance.com
Key Contact - Specialty:
Ms. Elizabeth Hope - *IT*

Search Dynamics, Inc.
9420 W. Foster Ave., Ste. 208
Chicago, Illinois 60656
(773) 992-3900
Fax: (773) 992-2133
Email: apostle@enteract.com

Key Contact - Specialty:
Mr. George Apostle
Mr. James C. Pappas

Description: Incorporated in 1972, we have four recruiters, with 8-20 years experience. We specialize in technical, engineering and management, concentrating in the Mid-West.

Salary Minimum: $30,000

Search Enterprises, Inc.
12358 Wiles Rd.
Coral Springs, Florida 33076
(954) 755-3121
Fax: (954) 755-1094
Email: sesi@searchenterprises.com
Web: searchenterprises.com

Key Contact - Specialty:
Mr. Frank Polacek - *Engineers*

Description: Specialists in the recruitment of engineering, manufacturing management and maintenance professionals. Serve mainly the chemical process, food, pharmaceutical, plastics and paper industries.

Salary Minimum: $40,000
Functions: Automation, Plant mgmt., Engineering
Industries: Food/bev/tobacco, Chemicals, Soap/perfume/cosmetics, Drugs mfg., Paints/petroleum products, Biotech

---

Search Group
1328 Sierra Alta Way
Los Angeles, California 90069
(310) 550-0292
Fax: (310) 275-7972
Email: yardenak@aol.com

Key Contact - Specialty:
Ms. Yardena Keren - *Engineering & periphery (marketing, management, consulting)*

Description: Employer paid executive search/tech recruitment firm, specializing in engineering.

Salary Minimum: $35,000
Functions: Production, Systems anal., Systems dev., Systems implem., Systems support, R&D, Mgmt. consultants
Industries: Computer equip., Test/measurement equip., Computer svcs., Mgmt. consulting, New media, Broadcast & Film, Telecoms

---

The Search Group
9405 Hickory Limb
Columbia, Maryland 21045
(410) 381-3940
Fax: (410) 381-5264
Email: hruska@clark.net

Key Contact - Specialty:
Mr. Thomas Hruska - *Insurance (property/casualty)*

Description: We are a search practice working exclusively with the insurance industry. During the past twenty-eight

years we have completed assignments for some of the top companies and brokers in the country.
Functions: General mgmt., Mkt. research, Sales mgmt., Customer svc., Risk mgmt.
Industries: Insurance

Search Masters, USA
4598 Hamlets Grove
Sarasota, Florida 34235
(941) 351-7307
Fax: (941) 351-5416

Key Contact - Specialty:
Mr. Alex Stevenson - *Sales, sales management, marketing, medical, biomedical*
Ms. Robyn Lynne - *Medical, labs, research, sales & marketing*

Description: Specialize placing sales & marketing talent in the medical diagnostics, hospital equipment, doctor office clinics and commercial and research labs.

Salary Minimum: $50,000
Functions: Sales & mktg., Mktg. mgmt., Sales mgmt.
Industries: Drugs mfg., Medical devices, Test/measurement equip., Pharmaceutical svcs., Biotech, Healthcare

The Search Network
5755 Oberlin Drive, Ste. 312
San Diego, California 92121
(619) 535-0015
Email: snet@pacbell.net

Key Contact - Specialty:
Ms. Kaaren Liz Henderson - *High technology*

Description: By placing excellent technical professionals, we have built strong lasting relationships with top hi-tech firms in San Diego. We find the best position to suit your needs. Confidentiality guaranteed.

Salary Minimum: $30,000
Functions: Middle mgmt., Product dev., Production, Quality, Engineering
Industries: Medical devices, Computer equip., Consumer electronics, New media, Telecoms, High tech, Software

Search North America, Inc.
P.O. Box 357707
Sunriver, Oregon 97707
(503) 222-6461
Fax: (503) 227-2804
Email: carlj@teleport.com
Web: www.teleport.com/~carlj

Key Contact - Specialty:
Mr. Carl Jansen - *Forest products, pulp & paper & related industries*

Description: To improve future performance of our client companies in the forest products, pulp and paper, environmental and power generation industries through the location and placement of result-oriented candidates.

Salary Minimum: $45,000
Functions: Generalist, Senior mgmt., Mfg., Finance, R&D, Engineering, Int'l.
Industries: Agri/forestry/mining, Energy/utilities, Lumber/furniture, Paper, Transportation

Search Northwest Assoc.
10117 SE Sunnyside Rd., Ste. #F727
Clackamas, Oregon 97015
(503) 654-1487
Fax: (503) 654-9110
Email: dljansen@msn.com

Key Contact - Specialty:
Mr. Douglas L. Jansen - *Foundries, metal (fabrication, finishing)*
Mr. Hank Scrivines - *Chemical processing*

Description: We are a contingency and retainer search firm with nationwide clients. Client base includes many Fortune 500 companies.

Salary Minimum: $30,000
Functions: Product dev., Production, Automation, Plant mgmt., Quality, Productivity, Packaging
Industries: Chemicals, Metal products, Machinery/Appliances, Computer equip., Misc. mfg., Telecoms, Packaging

Search Plus Int'l.-Ohio
1440 Snow Rd., Ste. 322C
Rockside Plaza
Cleveland, Ohio 44134
(216) 485-5770
(216) 485-5771
Fax: (216) 485-5773
Email: osp@apk.net

Key Contact - Specialty:
Mr. Bill Wood - *Industrial, manufacturing, sales & marketing, engineering, executives*

Description: Our firm has over 10 years experience in automotive, aerospace, plastics and other manufacturing areas. Specializing in executives, engineers, quality, human resources, purchasing, sales and other administrative areas.

Salary Minimum: $25,000
Functions: Senior mgmt., Packaging, Mktg. mgmt., HR mgmt., Finance, Engineering, Minorities
Industries: Generalist, Plastics/rubber, Motor vehicles, Misc. mfg., Computer svcs., Haz. waste, Aerospace

Affiliates:
MAS International Plus, Ltd.
Michigan Search Plus

Search Solutions Inc.
7200 Redwood Blvd., Ste. 401
Novato, California 94945
(415) 898-1800
Fax: (415) 898-2439
Email: searchsi@searchsolutions.com
Web: www.searchsolutions.com

Key Contact - Specialty:
Mr. Mark Robbins - *ORACLE, SAP, Peoplesoft & BAAN software implementation consultants & managers*

Description: We specialize in the full-time placement of software implementation consultants who work with and implement ORACLE, SAP, Peoplesoft and BAAN software.

Salary Minimum: $60,000
Functions: Directors, Middle mgmt., MIS mgmt., Systems anal., Systems support, DB admin., Mgmt. consultants
Industries: Computer svcs., Mgmt. consulting, Human resource svcs., High tech, Software

Search South, Inc.
1000 Quintard Ave., Ste. 409
P.O. Box 2224
Anniston, Alabama 36202
(205) 237-1868
Fax: (205) 237-1850
Email: ssiyoung@aol.com

Key Contact - Specialty:
Mr. Arthur L. Young - *Accounting, manufacturing, distribution, multimedia*
Mr. Derek Raulerson - *Manufacturing, CD audio, CD ROM, distribution*
Mr. Jamie Holland

Description: We conduct confidential searches for client companies and represent candidates professionally and confidentially. Candidates are never presented to clients without their permission. All candidates are placed in our confidential database.

Salary Minimum: $30,000
Functions: Generalist, Middle mgmt., Production, Plant mgmt., Distribution, CFO's. Engineering
Industries: Generalist, Chemicals, Plastics/rubber, Metal products, Machinery/Appliances, Misc. mfg., New media

Search West, Inc.
2049 Century Park E., Ste. 650
Los Angeles, California 90067
(310) 284-8888
Fax: (310) 284-3409
Email: corphq@searchwest.com

Key Contact - Specialty:
Mr. Robert A. Cowan
Mr. Lawrence G. Cowan
Mr. Michael Schulman

Description: 30 years in California. 60 industry specialists recruiting executives and professionals in sales, marketing, finance, administration, engineering, manufacturing, information technologies, direct mail, retailing, insurance, health, real estate, high tech and financial services.

Salary Minimum: $40,000
Functions: Generalist
Industries: Generalist

Branches:
2151 Convention Center Way, Ste. 121B
Ontario, California 91764-5421
(909) 937-0100
Fax: (909) 937-0101
Key Contact - Specialty:
Mr. Nate Reddicks

750 The City Drive S., Ste. 100
Orange, California 92668-4940
(714) 748-0400
Fax: (714) 748-8973
Key Contact - Specialty:
Ms. Merrilyn Spicer

100 Pine St., Ste. 2500
San Francisco, California 94111-5203
(415) 788-1770
Fax: (415) 989-7706
Key Contact - Specialty:
Ms. Ellen Williams

340 N. Westlake Blvd., Ste. 200
Westlake Village, California 91362-3761
(805) 496-6811
Fax: (805) 496-9431
Key Contact - Specialty:
Mr. Mike Begun

SearchCorp

1801 Clint Moore Rd., Ste. 200
Boca Raton, Florida 33487
(561) 988-0587
Fax: (561) 988-8796
Email: recruiters@searchcorp.com
Web: www.searchcorp.com

Key Contact - Specialty:
Mr. Rafael E. Hernandez - *General management, finance, international*

Description: Our innovative on-line recruiting company concentrates on using the latest in technology and recruiting techniques as well as offering business consulting with our proprietary Growth Process System (GPS).

Salary Minimum: $75,000
Functions: Generalist, General mgmt., Sales & mktg., HR mgmt., Finance, IT, Int'l.
Industries: Food/bev/tobacco, Retail, Finance, Svcs., Communications, High tech, Software

SearchCorp International
(a division of Baldwin Staffing Group)

550 - 17th Avenue SW
Calgary, Alberta T2S 0B1
Canada
(403) 228-1999
Fax: (403) 228-5533

Key Contact - Specialty:
Mr. Stephen Baldwin - *Law (lawyers), financial, management*
Mr. Ian Brown - *Information technology*

Description: More than a decade in business, we have a reputation for quick, efficient service of a confidential nature. Niche markets in Canada, U.S. and abroad include information technology professionals, lawyers, CAs, sales and management.

Salary Minimum: $30,000
Functions: Senior mgmt., Middle mgmt., Sales mgmt., CFO's, MIS mgmt., Systems dev., Systems implem.
Industries: Generalist, Construction, Finance, Brokers, Mgmt. consulting, High tech, Software

Searchline Services, Inc.

5847 Broadview Rd.
Cleveland, Ohio 44134
(216) 749-2820
Fax: (216) 749-2821
Email: search@searchlinejobs.com
Web: www.search@searchlinejobs.com

Key Contact - Specialty:
Mr. Jeffrey M. Tomko - *Accounting & finance, information systems*
Mr. William E. Puckett - *Accounting & finance, information systems*

Description: Through our nationwide network, established client base and other search resources, we quickly conduct full scale, targeted searches. We find you the top permanent, temporary or contract professionals on either a local or nationwide scale.

Salary Minimum: $90,000
Functions: General mgmt., Finance, IT
Industries: Mfg., Wholesale, Retail, Finance, Insurance, High tech, Software

SearchOne, Inc.

11300 Rodney Parham, Ste. 222
Little Rock, Arkansas 72212
(501) 801-9675
Email: vickie@searchoneinc.com

Key Contact - Specialty:
Ms. Vickie H. Siebenmorgen
Mr. John Siebenmorgen

Description: We specialize in manufacturing and other technical service industries. Most specific to information systems, materials, distribution, food industry and engineering.

Salary Minimum: $40,000
Functions: General mgmt., Mfg., Materials, IT, Engineering
Industries: Mfg., Transportation, Finance, Aerospace, Packaging, High tech, Software

Searchworks, Inc.

3111 University Drive, Ste. 725
Coral Springs, Florida 33065
(954) 340-1000
Fax: (305) 340-1002
Email: searchworks@msn.com

Key Contact - Specialty:
Ms. Kim Schindel - *Healthcare, insurance (life & health, property & casualty, medical), pharmaceutical, software*

Description: We have an outstanding reputation for our expertise in the healthcare and insurance industries. Our reputation has been built upon service, perseverance and above all performance. Research intensive.

Salary Minimum: $50,000
Functions: Product dev., Physicians, Systems anal., Systems dev., Systems implem., R&D, Engineering
Industries: Drugs mfg., Pharmaceutical svcs., Accounting, Insurance, Software, Biotech, Healthcare

Sears & Associates

16776 Bernardo Center Drive, Ste. 110B
San Diego, California 92128
(619) 673-7000
Fax: (619) 487-3037

Key Contact - Specialty:
Mr. Jerry Sears - *Attorneys*

Description: Recruits senior attorneys for both law firms and in-house (corporate) positions.

Salary Minimum: $80,000
Functions: Attorneys
Industries: Generalist

Seco & Zetto Assoc., Inc.

P.O. Box 225
Harrington Park, New Jersey 07640
(201) 784-0674

Key Contact - Specialty:
Mr. William M. Seco - *Management*
Ms. Kathryn Zetto - *Management*

Description: Specialists in keeping abreast of sudden or sensitive industry changes while exhibiting exceptionally rapid response time.

Salary Minimum: $75,000
Functions: Senior mgmt., Middle mgmt., Sales mgmt., MIS mgmt., Systems anal., Systems dev., Systems implem.
Industries: Generalist, Computer svcs., Mgmt. consulting, New media, High tech, Software

Segal & Assoc.

P.O. Box 95431
Atlanta, Georgia 30347
(404) 728-1400
Fax: (404) 728-1400
Email: sgl@atl.mindspring.com
Web: www.allhitech.com

Key Contact - Specialty:
Ms. Sheila Segal - *Engineering, high technology*

Description: High technology and engineering specialists with resources including a sophisticated web site, a technology company database, extensive contacts and a software system designed to integrate job orders, resumes and skills.

Salary Minimum: $40,000
Functions: Production, Automation, Mkt. research, Systems anal., Systems support, R&D, Engineering
Industries: Medical devices, Plastics/rubber, Machinery/Appliances, Computer equip., Telecoms, High tech, Software

Affiliates:
Executive Recruiting Services

Select Services

37 W. 222 Rte. 64, Ste. 130
St. Charles, Illinois 60175
(630) 587-1050
Fax: (630) 587-1060
Email: Selectserv@Yahoo.com

Key Contact - Specialty:
Mr. Joseph Mills - *Manufacturing management*

Description: We are a hybrid of contingency and retained search firms. Our objectivity for the client, our flexibility, terms and professionalism will enable a firm to consider us as a preferred provider of recruiting needs.

Salary Minimum: $50,000
Functions: General mgmt., Mfg., Materials, Sales mgmt., HR mgmt., Finance, Engineering
Industries: Plastics/rubber, Metal products, Machinery/Appliances, Motor vehicles, Consumer electronics, Misc. mfg., Human resource svcs.

Selected Executives, Inc.

76 Winn St.
Woburn, Massachusetts 01801
(781) 933-1500
Fax: (781) 933-4145

Key Contact - Specialty:
Mr. Lee R. Sanborn, Jr.
Mr. Jackson A. Brookins
Ms. K. Jane Lewis
Ms. Suzanne S. Martin
Mr. Kenneth T. Dinklage

Description: Our firm welcomes every opportunity to demonstrate that diversity candidates can be found to fill senior positions in every professional area. More than 25 years experience specializing in minority and women professionals.

Salary Minimum: $40,000
Functions: Generalist
Industries: Generalist

Selectis Corp.

2350 Devon Ave., Ste. 114
Des Plaines, Illinois 60018
(847) 298-6100
Email: selectis@selectis.com
Web: www.selectis.com/selectis

Key Contact - Specialty:
Mr. Frank Lutostanski - *Senior management, information technology*

Description: Provides high quality recruitment services for growing organizations with specialized, time critical job openings. Extensive research, recruiter expertise and urgency involved in each search-dedicated recruiter program.

Salary Minimum: $40,000
Functions: Senior mgmt., Production, Sales mgmt., CFO's, Systems anal., Systems dev., Engineering
Industries: Plastics/rubber, Motor vehicles, Computer equip., Telecoms, Insurance, High tech, Software

Selective Management Services, Inc.

P.O. Box 17008
Sarasota, Florida 34276-0008
(941) 923-7114

Key Contact - Specialty:
Mr. Alan M. Schwartz - *Packaging, paper, corrugated box industry*
Mr. Mark D. Steel - *Packaging, paper, corrugated box industry*

Description: Recruiters, executive search and management consultants specializing in packaging and allied industries: corrugated, folding cartons, paper, pharmaceuticals, plastics and printing.

Salary Minimum: $35,000
Functions: Senior mgmt., Plant mgmt., Packaging, Mktg. mgmt., Sales mgmt., CFO's, MIS mgmt.
Industries: Generalist, Paper, Printing, Drugs mfg., Misc. mfg., Packaging

Selective Recruiting Assoc., Inc.

3290 W. North Territorial Rd.
Ann Arbor, Michigan 48105-9224
(734) 994-5632
Fax: (734) 996-8181
Email: recruiter@selective.com
Web: www.selective.com

Key Contact - Specialty:
Mr. Dave Calhoun - *Engineering management*
Ms. Gilda Bone - *Engineering*

Description: Serving the automotive industry in the Great Lakes Region. Specializing in management positions in engineering and manufacturing.

Salary Minimum: $40,000
Functions: Middle mgmt., Product dev., Production, Plant mgmt., Quality, Distribution, Engineering
Industries: Plastics/rubber, Metal products, Machinery/Appliances, Motor vehicles, Misc. mfg., Transportation

Selective Search Associates
(a division of MJZ Enterprises, Inc.)

1206 N. Main St., Ste. 112
North Canton, Ohio 44720
(330) 494-5584
Fax: (330) 494-8911
Email: ssa@jobman.com
Web: www.jobman.com

Key Contact - Specialty:
Mr. Michael E. Ziarko - *Information technology, electronic commerce, software*
Ms. Jacqueline R. Ziarko - *Doctors, medical professionals*

Description: Primary area of specialization is the recruitment and placement of information systems/information technology and software engineering personnel.

Salary Minimum: $35,000
Functions: Physicians, Nurses, Systems anal., Systems dev., Systems implem., Network admin., DB admin.
Industries: Food/bev/tobacco, Medical devices, Plastics/rubber, Metal products, Machinery/Appliances, Computer equip., Misc. mfg.

Selective Staffing
4905 N. West Ave., Ste. 115
Fresno, California 93705
(209) 227-9159
(209) 227-9100
Fax: (209) 227-2950

Key Contact - Specialty:
Ms. Jane Small

Description: Company started May 1987. Owners in recruiting total of ten years. Specialty is insurance recruiting.

Salary Minimum: $25,000
Functions: Mfg., Healthcare, Sales & mktg., Sales mgmt., HR mgmt., Finance, Attorneys
Industries: Insurance, Software, Healthcare

Selig Executive Search
P.O. Box 160
Laconia, New Hampshire 03247-0160
(603) 527-0111
Fax: (603) 527-2597

Key Contact - Specialty:
Mr. Robert J. Selig - *Footwear, apparel (all disciplines), manufacturing, finance, distribution*

Description: Former CEO's who have restructured manufacturing companies, we provide the insights needed to help structure the management team, then we identify, recruit and reference strong groups of viable candidates. We help to prepare an offer which we then negotiate for our clients.

Salary Minimum: $50,000
Functions: Senior mgmt., Middle mgmt., Plant mgmt., Quality, Purchasing, Distribution, Sales mgmt.
Industries: Textiles/apparel, Plastics/rubber, Leather/stone/glass/clay, Misc. mfg.

Seltzer Fontaine Beckwith
2999 Overland Ave., Ste. 203
Los Angeles, California 90064
(310) 839-6000
Fax: (310) 839-4408
Email: sfbsearch@aol.com
Web: www.sfbsearch.com

Key Contact - Specialty:
Ms. Valerie A. Fontaine - *Law*
Ms. Madeleine E. Seltzer - *Law*
Ms. Randy Beckwith - *Law*
Ms. Roberta Kass - *Law*

Description: Principals each have over 15 years search experience and three of the four are former practicing attorneys. Firm places individuals and groups of attorneys of all specialties with local, regional, national and international law firms and corporations.
Functions: Attorneys
Industries: Legal

Setford-Shaw-Najarian Assoc.
(a division of Transaction Information Systems, Inc.)
115 Broadway, 20th Floor
New York, New York 10006
(212) 962-1500
Fax: (212) 962-1543
Email: tis@tisny.com
Web: www.tisny.com

Key Contact - Specialty:
Mr. George Setford - *Technology professionals*

Description: We bring extensive IT experience to the business of searching for talented individuals and placing them within corporations. Clients include the most prestigious banking, investment, insurance, software development, entertainment and management consulting firms in NY/NJ/Boston and Dallas.
Functions: MIS mgmt., Systems anal., Systems dev., Systems implem., Systems support
Industries: Finance, Entertainment, Communications, New media, Insurance

SFB Legal Search
150 E. 58th St., 39th Floor
New York, New York 10155
(212) 688-1128
Fax: (212) 688-1169
Email: stacylegal@aol.com

Key Contact - Specialty:
Ms. Stacia Foster Blake - *Corporations*

Description: Specialize in corporation placements throughout the United States and abroad, with substantial success in diversity positions. Principals have 33 combined years of experience, plus two part-time recruiters.

Salary Minimum: $75,000
Functions: Attorneys
Industries: Medical devices, Computer equip., Banking, Brokers, Pharmaceutical svcs., Publishing, Telecoms

Branches:
670 White Plains Rd.
Scarsdale, New York 10583
(914) 251-0900
Fax: (914) 251-0819
Key Contact - Specialty:
Ms. Joan Blum Simon

Sharp Placement Professionals, Inc.
55 Post Ave., Ste. 202
Westbury, New York 11590
(516) 876-9222
Fax: (516) 876-9080
Email: don@sharpsearch.com
Web: www.sharpsearch.com

Key Contact - Specialty:
Mr. Donald Levine - *High level technical marketing, engineering, management*

Description: We specialize in filling those difficult positions which fall between full-service retained search and general agency contingency search. We will work out a customized program to fill your recruitment needs.

Salary Minimum: $60,000
Functions: Senior mgmt., Product dev., Mktg. mgmt., Sales mgmt., IT, R&D, Engineering
Industries: Medical devices, Computer equip., Test/measurement equip., New media, Telecoms, High tech, Software

Sharrow & Assoc., Inc.
24735 Van Dyke
Center Line, Michigan 48015
(810) 759-6910
(219) 665-1261
Fax: (810) 759-6914
Email: sharrow@rust.net
Web: www.steuben.net/asla.html

Key Contact - Specialty:
Ms. Beth S. Sharrow - *Engineering, data processing, paints & coatings, manufacturing, patent attorneys*

Description: Physician recruitment, national.
Functions: Senior mgmt., Product dev., HR mgmt., Systems dev., DB admin., Engineering, Attorneys
Industries: Construction, Plastics/rubber, Motor vehicles, Legal, Computer svcs., Real estate

Branches:
110 N. Public Sq., Ste. 2-2
Angola, Indiana 46703
(219) 665-1261
Fax: (219) 665-1343
Email: david@access.digex.net
Key Contact - Specialty:
Mr. David MacTadyen - *Construction builders, developers, heavy construction, mobile & modular manufacturers*

8100 Burlington Pike, Ste. 336
Florence, Kentucky 41042
(606) 282-0111
Fax: (606) 282-0916
Email: sharrowflo@aol.com
Key Contact - Specialty:
Mr. Steve Stoll - *Architecture, construction, real estate, property management, engineering*

Affiliates:
Physician Resource Network, Inc.

John Shell Assoc., Inc.
115 Atrium Way, Ste. 122
Columbia, South Carolina 29224
(803) 788-6619
Fax: (803) 788-1758

Email: shellacc@aol.com
Web: www.aafa.com

Key Contact - Specialty:
Mr. John C. Shell, III - *Accounting, finance*
Ms. Kay H. Mayes - *Accounting, finance, bookkeeping*

Description: South Carolina's specialists in accounting and financial placement.
Functions: Finance
Industries: Generalist

Shell Technology Group
1106 Walnut St., Ste. 200
San Luis Obispo, California 93401
(805) 786-2996
Fax: (805) 786-2998
Email: msanders@shelltechgroup.com
Web: www.shelltechgroup.com

Key Contact - Specialty:
Ms. Marlaine Sanders - *Information systems, networking*

Description: We offer professional search and placement services in Information Technology, Networking, Communications and Systems Integration. We were formed to focus specifically on the expanding technical staffing needs throughout California and the U.S.

Salary Minimum: $40,000
Functions: MIS mgmt., Systems anal., Systems dev., Systems implem., Systems support, Network admin., DB admin.
Industries: Computer svcs., New media, Telecoms, High tech, Software

Sherbrooke Assoc., Inc.
727 Raritan Rd., Ste. 202B
Clark, New Jersey 07066
(908) 382-5505
Fax: (908) 382-0052

Key Contact - Specialty:
Mr. William M. Levy - *Engineering, operations, sales & marketing*
Mr. James D. Scanlon - *Human resources, engineering, operations*

Description: Recruiting generalists with a Northeast customer base; strengths in both cosmetic, food and pharmaceutical and in high technology firms.

Salary Minimum: $40,000
Functions: Generalist
Industries: Generalist

Sherriff & Assoc.
10983 Granada Lane, Ste. 202
Overland Park, Kansas 66211
(913) 451-2112
Fax: (913) 451-3931
Email: sherriff@att.net

Key Contact - Specialty:
Mr. William W. Sherriff - *Physicians, executive healthcare, allied healthcare*
Ms. Julie A. Sherriff - *Physicians, executive healthcare*
Ms. Stephanie Cassandras - *Physicians*

Description: Fourteen years of quality, ethical physician search, physician executive placement, sourcing and pre-credentialing services. Past-president, National Association of Physician Recruiters (NAPR); current chair, NAPR Ethics Committee.
Functions: Healthcare, Physicians, Allied health, Health admin.
Industries: Healthcare

Affiliates:
Freeman-Daniel Co.

Shey-Harding Assoc. Inc.
39406 Narcissus Way
Palm Desert, California 92211-5088
(760) 345-0688
Fax: (760) 360-2625
Email: Shey-Harding@email.msn.com
Web: www.shey-harding.com

Key Contact - Specialty:
Ms. Deborah Shey-Harding - *Transportation, logistics*
Mr. Michael W. Harding - *Transportation, logistics*

Description: We specialize in recruiting for the transportation/logistics industries. We have an extensive database of expert, professional candidates and will conduct worldwide confidential searches to supply the best and brightest.
Functions: Senior mgmt., Middle mgmt., Distribution, Mktg. mgmt., Sales mgmt., Personnel, CFO's
Industries: Transportation, Accounting, Mgmt. consulting, Human resource svcs., Haz. waste, High tech

Shiell Personnel
2040 N. Causeway Blvd.
Mandeville, Louisiana 70471
(504) 674-1616
Fax: (504) 674-1611

Key Contact - Specialty:
Mr. Donald M. Shiell - *Medical equipment, pharmaceutical sales*

Description: We specialize in medical and pharmaceutical sales. Member First Interview, a computerized network of over 200 offices domestic and international..
Functions: Middle mgmt., Sales mgmt., Minorities, Int'l.
Industries: Pharmaceutical svcs., Healthcare

Shifrin-Fischer Group, Inc.
409 North Ave. E.
Cranford, New Jersey 07016-2437
(908) 931-1000
Fax: (908) 931-1009
Email: sfginc@ix.netcom.com

Key Contact - Specialty:
Mr. Brad Shifrin - *Sales & marketing*

Salary Minimum: $50,000
Functions: Advertising, Mkt. research, Mktg. mgmt., Sales mgmt., Direct mktg., Cash mgmt., Minorities

Shiloh Careers Int'l., Inc.
7105 Peach Court, Ste. 102
P.O. Box 831
Brentwood, Tennessee 37024-0831
(615) 373-3090
Fax: (615) 373-3480
Email: mawd@mindspring.com

Key Contact - Specialty:
Ms. Mary Ann Webber - *Property & casualty insurance*

Description: Successfully recruiting in the insurance industry since 1979. Mostly property and casualty-90%; life and health-10%.
Functions: Personnel
Industries: Insurance

SHS of Allentown
1401 N. Cedar Crest Blvd., Ste. 56
Allentown, Pennsylvania 18104-2399
(610) 437-5551
Fax: (610) 437-1027

Key Contact - Specialty:
Mr. David Mostow

Description: Nationwide coverage of the minerals, explosives, crushed stone, construction materials, battery and chemical industries.

Salary Minimum: $25,000
Functions: Senior mgmt., Middle mgmt., Production, Plant mgmt., Quality, Purchasing, Sales mgmt.
Industries: Construction, Chemicals, Leather/stone/glass/clay, Machinery/Appliances, Motor vehicles

Branches:
PO Box 6868
Louisville, Kentucky 40206-0868
(502) 897-7666
Fax: (502) 897-7668
Key Contact - Specialty:
Mr. Donald R. Beltz

Shupack & Michaels Inc.
27 Monmouth Drive, Ste. 277
East Northport, New York 11731
(516) 757-4559
Fax: (516) 757-3880

Email: jshupack@aol.com

Key Contact - Specialty:
Mr. Joseph Shupack - *Consulting, architectural engineering firms*
Ms. Ellen Michaels - *Consulting, architectural engineering firms*

Description: Contingency and retainer recruitment and placement of engineers at all levels for consulting, and A/E firms-mechanical/hvac, electrical, civil, etc. Domestic and international.
Functions: Senior mgmt., Middle mgmt., Engineering, Architects, Technicians
Industries: Energy/utilities, Construction, Transportation, Pharmaceutical svcs., High tech

---

Peter Siegel & Co.
P.O. Box 218
Needham, Massachusetts 02492
(781) 455-9057
Fax: (781) 455-6246

Key Contact - Specialty:
Mr. Peter A. Siegel - *Retail executives, direct marketing executives*

Description: A candor, a personality and an expertise that sources prospective employees to complement the diverse corporate cultures of clients represented.

Salary Minimum: $40,000
Functions: Senior mgmt., Middle mgmt., Product dev., Distribution, Direct mktg., Cash mgmt., MIS mgmt.
Industries: Textiles/apparel, Wholesale, Retail

Siger & Assoc., LLC
966 Westover Rd.
Stamford, Connecticut 06902
(203) 348-0976

Key Contact - Specialty:
Mr. J. Raymond Milo - *Financial services*

Description: Specialists in executive recruitment for the financial services industry. Areas include: portfolio management, mergers & acquisitions, capital markets, derivative products, sales, trading, research, structured and project finance and emerging markets.

Salary Minimum: $75,000
Functions: Senior mgmt., Healthcare, Finance, CFO's, Risk mgmt., IT, Mgmt. consultants
Industries: Finance, Banking, Invest. banking, Mgmt. consulting, Telecoms, High tech, Healthcare

---

SignatureSoft Inc.
1270 Morena Blvd.
San Diego, California 92110
(619) 276-1539
(800) 999-8829
Fax: (619) 276-1754
Email: bob@signaturesoft.com
Web: www.signaturesoft.com

Key Contact - Specialty:
Mr. Bob DeGrasse - *Software/hardware engineering, communications, networking*

Description: We are a full-service professional search firm, specializing in the high-tech, communications and networking industries in California. Software and hardware engineering is our main focus.

Salary Minimum: $35,000
Functions: Engineering
Industries: Communications, High tech, Software

Marvin L. Silcott & Assoc., Inc.
7557 Rambler Rd., Ste. 1336
Dallas, Texas 75231
(214) 369-7802
Fax: (214) 369-7875

Key Contact - Specialty:
Mr. Marvin L. Silcott - *Generalist*

Description: We specialize in executives, corporate, patent and litigation attorneys, partnerships, financial, engineering, geological and scientists. We recruit nationally and internationally. Salary $60,000 up.

Salary Minimum: $60,000
Functions: General mgmt., Mfg., HR mgmt., Finance, R&D, Engineering, Attorneys
Industries: Generalist, Energy/utilities, Construction, Mfg., Finance, Svcs., High tech

---

The Silicon Network
40 King St. W., Ste. 4900
Scotia Plaza
Toronto, Ontario M5H 4A2
Canada
(416) 777-6746
Fax: (416) 777-6748
Email: recom@total.net

Key Contact - Specialty:
Mr. Michael Fernandez - *Engineering, data communications*
Mr. Rolph Laresen - *Engineering, data communications, telecommunications*
Mr. Walter Wimmer - *Engineering, data communications, telecommunications*
Mr. Kevin McGinty - *Engineering, data communications, telecommunications*
Mr. Darryl Calder - *Engineering, data communications, telecommunications*

Description: We are a professional recruitment firm specializing in full time and contract placement of individuals in the data, telecommunications industry. Professionalism and confidentiality are the cornerstone of our business philosophy.
Functions: Systems anal., Systems dev., Systems implem., Systems support, Network admin., Engineering, Technicians
Industries: Computer equip., Computer svcs., High tech, Software

---

Sill Technical Assoc., Inc.
5250 Simpson Ferry Rd., Ste. 410
Mechanicsburg, Pennsylvania 17055
(717) 691-6730
Fax: (717) 691-6873

Key Contact - Specialty:
Mr. Darrell E. Sill - *Engineering*

Description: The manager/owner is a graduate engineer (BSME) with 13 years of recruiting/placement experience. The manager practiced engineering for 15 years before opening this employment service.

Salary Minimum: $30,000
Functions: Middle mgmt., Product dev., Production, Quality, Purchasing, Materials Plng., Engineering
Industries: Paper, Plastics/rubber, Metal products, Machinery/Appliances, Motor vehicles, Consumer electronics, Test/measurement equip.

Silver Associates
11925 Wilshire Blvd., Ste. 317
Los Angeles, California 90025
(310) 312-4820
Fax: (310) 312-1294
Email: silverassc@aol.com

Key Contact - Specialty:
Ms. Susan Silver - *Entertainment (finance, accounting, systems)*

Description: Executive search finance, strategic planning, accounting, tax, audit, MIS, sales/marketing, EDP audit, consulting, human resources, administration in entertainment, distribution, interactive multimedia, etc. Principals have over 30 years combined search industry experience.

Salary Minimum: $30,000
Functions: General mgmt., Sales & mktg., HR mgmt., Finance, IT, Mgmt. consultants, Int'l.
Industries: Generalist, Svcs., Entertainment, Accounting, Mgmt. consulting, Communications, High tech

SilverSands Int'l.
759 Bear Creek Circle
Winter Springs, Florida 32708
(407) 365-8854
Fax: (407) 366-2609
Email: jmulvey@ss4jobs.com

Key Contact - Specialty:
Mr. James E. Mulvey - *Software (sales, marketing, technical support, project management, Imp Cons.)*

Description: Executive search services to computer software companies who market their products to high technology companies. Executive levels from middle management and higher, including CEO and president positions.

Salary Minimum: $50,000
Functions: Middle mgmt., Mktg. mgmt., Sales mgmt., Systems implem., Systems support
Industries: Software

Branches:
573 Pebble Hill Rd.
Doylestown, Pennsylvania 18901
(215) 489-9857
Fax: (215) 489-9858
Key Contact - Specialty:
Mr. Scott Mulvey

Affiliates:
Sinclair & Co. Inc.

The Simmons Group
951-2 Old County Rd., Ste. 136
Belmont, California 94002
(650) 592-3775
Fax: (650) 598-9671

Key Contact - Specialty:
Mr. Noel A. Simmons - *High technology*

Description: With over 20 years experience in human resources management and administration, assist small and medium sized companies with all aspects of the human resources function. Executive recruiting limited to high technology industries.

Salary Minimum: $50,000
Functions: Generalist
Industries: Computer equip., Test/measurement equip., Mgmt. consulting, Human resource svcs., High tech, Software

D. W. Simpson & Co.
625 N. Michigan Ave., 21st Floor
Chicago, Illinois 60611
(312) 654-5220
Fax: (312) 951-8386
Email: actuaries@aol.com
Web: www.dwsimpson.com

Key Contact - Specialty:
Ms. Patricia Jacobsen - *Actuarial*
Ms. Sandra Steffke - *Actuarial*
Mr. David Simpson - *Actuarial*

Description: Serving the actuarial profession nationwide and at all levels from student to fellow. We use a straight forward approach to meet the objectives of client companies and candidates.
Industries: Insurance, Non-classifiable industries

Simpson Associates
106 Central Park S., Ste. 3B
Trump Parc
New York, New York 10019
(212) 767-0006
Fax: (212) 767-0660
Email: simpsonassociates@msn.com
Web: simpson-associates.com

Key Contact - Specialty:
Ms. Terre Simpson - *Retailing, catalogues, wholesale manufacturing (softlines & hardlines)*

Description: Middle/senior executives for retail, apparel manufacturing and direct mail industry.

Salary Minimum: $70,000
Functions: Product dev., Advertising, Mkt. research, Sales mgmt., Direct mktg., Finance, IT
Industries: Textiles/apparel, Lumber/furniture, Wholesale, Retail

Singleton & Assoc.
P.O. Box 127
Lynchburg, Virginia 24505-0127
(804) 385-6926
Fax: (804) 385-7445
Email: foundryjob@aol.com

Key Contact - Specialty:
Mr. Steven L. Singleton - *Iron, steel, foundry management*
Ms. Karen Sue Mayberry - *Iron, steel, foundry management*

Description: We are the only executive recruiting firm in the metal casting industry specializing in high production, ISO and QS 9002 automotive foundries.

Salary Minimum: $40,000
Functions: Senior mgmt., Product dev., Production, Plant mgmt., Quality, Purchasing, Sales mgmt.
Industries: Metal products, Motor vehicles, Aerospace

Affiliates:
Borchert Assoc.

SKB Enterprises
28-30 34th St., Ste. 4C
Long Island City, New York 11103
(718) 728-5046
Fax: (718) 728-4995

Key Contact - Specialty:
Ms. Sandra Booth - *Software developers, technology sales & support marketing (specifically for software companies)*

Description: Not limited to any particular industry. Clients include financial, manufacturing, software development, etc. Specializing in the software development industry.

Salary Minimum: $55,000
Functions: Mktg. mgmt., Sales mgmt., Customer svc., CFO's, Systems dev., Systems implem., Minorities
Industries: High tech, Software

Skipping Stone Inc.
120 Beulah Rd. NE, Ste. 201
Vienna, Virginia 22180
(703) 938-8001
Fax: (703) 938-8010
Email: nrgsvcs@gte.net
Web: www.skippingstone.com

Key Contact - Specialty:
Mr. Robert C. Fodge - *Energy*

Description: Comprehensive search and recruitment for IPP's, ESCO's, gas and electric companies. Focused on development, finance, marketing &sales and information technology disciplines. Also provides industry research studies on trends and compensation.

Salary Minimum: $80,000
Functions: General mgmt., Sales & mktg., CFO's, Risk mgmt., IT, Engineering, Mgmt. consultants
Industries: Energy/utilities, Invest. banking, Brokers, Misc. financial, Telecoms, Software

Branches:
15710 JFK Blvd., Ste. 315
Houston, Texas 77032
(281) 987-8166
Fax: (281) 987-8266
Email: mrgsvcs@gte.net
Web: www.skippingstone.com
Key Contact - Specialty:
Ms. Traci Rasmussen - *Energy*

Skupsky & Assoc.
5600 S. Quebec St., Ste. C-250
Greenwood Village, Colorado 80111
(303) 290-9480
Fax: (303) 290-9481

Email:
Bandaids_skupskyassociates@compuserve.com

Key Contact - Specialty:
Ms. Lorraine Skupsky - *Physicians*

Description: Dedicated to recruitment of physicians throughout the Rocky Mountain Region by assessing individually specific needs. First and only company in Colorado devoted to this type of consultation - expert witness on employment issues in medical field.
Functions: Physicians, Mgmt. consultants
Industries: Healthcare

Sloan & Assoc., Inc.
1769 Jamestown Rd.
Williamsburg, Virginia 23185-2324
(757) 220-1111
Fax: (757) 220-1694

Key Contact - Specialty:
Mr. Michael D. Sloan - *Consumer packaged goods*
Ms. Shelly Wren - *Consumer packaged goods*
Mr. John H. Holland - *Consumer packaged goods*
Ms. Sam Morton - *Consumer packaged goods*
Mr. Robert A. Richards, Jr. - *Consumer packaged goods*

Description: Specialize in consumer packaged goods industry. Emphasis on sales and marketing, mid and upper level management positions. Subspecialized by geography allows ultimate market penetration. Employment law, testing and assessment and compensation services are also available.

Salary Minimum: $50,000
Functions: Senior mgmt., Mkt. research, Mktg. mgmt., Sales mgmt.
Industries: Food/bev/tobacco, Retail, Human resource svcs.

Tom Sloan & Assoc., Inc.
1530 Utah St., P.O. Box 50
Watertown, Wisconsin 53094
(920) 261-8890
Fax: (920) 261-6357
Email: sloan@gdinet.com

Key Contact - Specialty:
Mr. Tom Sloan - *Food manufacturing, engineering*
Ms. Terri Sherman - *Food ingredients, research & development, technical support, sales*

Description: Food industry specialization, R&D, production management, engineering, sales/marketing. Industries: meat, dairy, canning/freezing, milling, baking candy, fat/oils, beverage, food ingredient, snack foods, animal feed and supplements.

Salary Minimum: $25,000
Functions: General mgmt., Product dev., Materials, Sales & mktg., HR mgmt., R&D, Engineering
Industries: Food/bev/tobacco

J. L. Small Assoc.
3201 Lorna Rd.
Birmingham, Alabama 35216
(205) 823-4545
Fax: (205) 824-1430

Key Contact - Specialty:
Mr. Jim Small - *Engineers, accountants, manufacturing*

Description: Engineering, accounting, manufacturing, human resources, generalist.

Salary Minimum: $30,000
Functions: Generalist, Senior mgmt., Mfg., HR mgmt., Finance, IT
Industries: Generalist, Mfg., Paper, Chemicals, Misc. mfg., Accounting, Human resource svcs.

Smartsource Inc.
500 Ygnacio Valley Rd., Ste. 390
Walnut Creek, California 94596
(510) 935-4200
Fax: (510) 935-0645
Email: smartsrce@aol.com
Web: smartsourceinc.com

Key Contact - Specialty:
Ms. Patricia Taylor - *Information systems (PC, LAN, WAN), telecommunications, data center operations*
Ms. Dee Dee Melmet - *Information technology*

Description: We are a statewide MWBE certified computer services firm specializing in PC/LAN/WAN, telecommunications (voice, data), data center operations and information systems for our Fortune 500 clients. A full service firm offering project staffing and contingency search.
Functions: MIS mgmt., Systems anal., Systems dev., Systems implem., Systems support, Network admin., Technicians
Industries: Generalist, Computer svcs.

Branches:
3100 Zinfandel Drive, Ste. 200
Rancho Cordova, California 95670
(916) 631-1999
Fax: (916) 631-1994
Email: smartrc@aol.com

Smith & Assoc.
3826 Monteith Drive, Ste. 300
Los Angeles, California 90043
(213) 295-8198
Fax: (213) 293-9825
Email: darrell@searchsmith.com

Key Contact - Specialty:
Mr. Darrell G. Smith

Description: Executive search/management consultants. The firm's practice is established primarily along functional lines with special emphasis on mid to senior management positions in sales, marketing, operations and general management.

Salary Minimum: $50,000
Functions: Middle mgmt., Advertising, Mktg. mgmt., Sales mgmt., Finance, Network admin., Minorities
Industries: Generalist, Food/bev/tobacco, Soap/perfume/cosmetics, Computer equip., Retail, Finance

Affiliates:
Schnebel & Assoc.

Smith & Assoc.
P.O. Box 829
Brandon, Florida 33509
(813) 689-2611
Fax: (813) 651-5446

Key Contact - Specialty:
Ms. Sylvia Smith - *Manufacturing*

Description: Nationwide placements - all company paid fees - all areas of manufacturing, engineering, environmental, chemical, quality, power generation, buyers, data processing, and all metals & plastics industries, etc.
Functions: Automation, Quality, Purchasing, Benefits, DB admin., Engineering, Environmentalists
Industries: Generalist, Plastics/rubber, Metal products, Motor vehicles, Consumer electronics, Human resource svcs., Environmental svcs.

James F. Smith & Assoc.
4651 Roswell Rd. NE, Ste. B102
Atlanta, Georgia 30342
(404) 256-6408
Fax: (404) 256-6408

Key Contact - Specialty:
Dr. James F. Smith

Description: Consulting psychologists who provide executive search/recruiting services to their corporate clients.

Salary Minimum: $45,000
Functions: Generalist, Senior mgmt., Middle mgmt., Plant mgmt., Sales mgmt., Mgmt. consultants, Int'l.

Industries: Generalist, Metal products, Misc. mfg., Retail, Hospitality, Mgmt. consulting, Defense

Peter A. Smith & Assoc.

3182 Riverbend Ave., Ste. 100
Eugene, Oregon 97408
(541) 302-8100
Fax: (541) 302-6570

Key Contact - Specialty:
Mr. Peter A. Smith - *Hospitality*

Description: Corporate and property level hospitality management and sales executives. 25+ years experience as sales director, VP-Sales & Marketing, GM and VP-Operations. Emphasis on GM and sales positions, nationally. Major hotel companies as clients.

Salary Minimum: $50,000
Industries: Hospitality

Ralph Smith & Assoc.

540 Frontage Rd., Ste. 3335
Northfield, Illinois 60093
(847) 441-0900
Fax: (847) 441-0902

Key Contact - Specialty:
Mr. Ralph E. Smith - *Generalist*

Description: General search practice, all functional areas, most industries including manufacturing, services firms, packaged goods, consumer products, advertising and public relations. Specialize in Chicago area clients and candidates.

Salary Minimum: $50,000
Functions: Generalist, Middle mgmt., Plant mgmt., Advertising, Mktg. mgmt., Sales mgmt., Cash mgmt.
Industries: Generalist, Food/bev/tobacco, Soap/perfume/cosmetics, Machinery/Appliances, Advertising/PR, Packaging

Smith Assoc.

204 S. Third St.
Fairfield, Iowa 52556
(515) 472-8252
Fax: (515) 472-7274
Email: kensmith@lisco.com

Key Contact - Specialty:
Mr. Ken Smith - *Management information systems*

Description: Contingency-based MIS search firm, specializing in Iowa and the San Francisco Bay area. Providing small firm individual attention to detail for each search. All searches are conducted with the highest level of experience, professionalism, honesty and integrity.

Salary Minimum: $25,000
Functions: MIS mgmt., Systems anal., Systems dev., Systems implem., Systems support, Network admin., DB admin.

G. L. Smith Assoc.

55 Fair Drive
Southern California College Bldg.
Costa Mesa, California 92626
(714) 556-5702
Fax: (714) 966-5460
Email: glsmith@sccu.edu

Key Contact - Specialty:
Mr. Gregory L. Smith - *Senior management*

Description: Principal does the search himself and you get a candidate finding strategy that works! Other consulting services include executive coaching, career counseling, corporate strategy and marketing strategy.

Salary Minimum: $80,000
Functions: Senior mgmt., Mktg. mgmt., Sales mgmt., CFO's, MIS mgmt.
Industries: Generalist, Energy/utilities, Mfg., Svcs., Environmental svcs., High tech

J. Harrington Smith Assoc.

P.O. Box 90065
Indianapolis, Indiana 46290
(317) 251-0678
Fax: (317) 251-1138

Key Contact - Specialty:
Mr. James H. Smith - *Mining*

Description: Human resource consultant to management.

Salary Minimum: $60,000
Functions: Engineering, Mgmt. consultants, Environmentalists
Industries: Agri/forestry/mining, Paper, Human resource svcs.

The Smith Group, Inc.

7200 Airlie Place
Wilmington, North Carolina 28405
(910) 792-1135
Fax: (910) 792-1101
Email: info@smithsearch.com
Web: www.ipa.com/chaser/

Key Contact - Specialty:
Mr. Charles Smith

Description: Highly specialized in the recruitment of sales, engineering and management individuals for the high technology manufacturing and commercial electronics industry.

Salary Minimum: $45,000
Functions: Production, Automation, Quality, Mkt. research, Sales mgmt., R&D, Engineering
Industries: Energy/utilities, Machinery/Appliances, Test/measurement equip., Misc. mfg., Broadcast & Film, Telecoms, High tech

Affiliates:
Vick & Assoc.

Smith Hanley Assoc., Inc.

99 Park Ave.
New York, New York 10016
(212) 687-9696
Fax: (212) 818-9067
Email: brants@smihan.com
Web: www.smithhanley.com

Key Contact - Specialty:
Mr. Brant R. Smith

Description: Retained and contingency recruitment concentrating on work in investment research, market research, fixed income analysis, corporate finance, technical services for financial service, consumer product, consulting firms, advertising agencies, insurance and risk management.

Salary Minimum: $50,000
Functions: Distribution, Mkt. research, Direct mktg., Cash mgmt., M&A, Risk mgmt., Mgmt. consultants
Industries: Drugs mfg., Finance, Pharmaceutical svcs., Accounting, Mgmt. consulting, Advertising/PR, Insurance

Branches:
107 John St.
Southport, Connecticut 06490
(203) 319-4300
Fax: (203) 319-4320
Key Contact - Specialty:
Mr. Andrew Davis - *Risk management, insurance*
Ms. Jacqueline Paige - *Marketing services*

191 Broad St., Ste. 314
Athens, Georgia 30601
(706) 353-2255
Key Contact - Specialty:
Ms. Natalie Washburn - *International equities*

200 W. Madison, Ste. 480
Chicago, Illinois 60606
(312) 629-2400
Key Contact - Specialty:
Ms. Linda Burtch - *Marketing services*

125 Strafford Ave., Ste. 300
Wayne, Pennsylvania 19087
(610) 975-4435
Key Contact - Specialty:
Mr. Dave Carpenter - *Statisticians*

Smith Professional Search

600 S. Adams Rd., Ste. 210
Birmingham, Michigan 48009-6863
(248) 540-8580
Fax: (248) 540-2136

Email: spsearch@msn.com

Key Contact - Specialty:
Ms. Susan P. Smith - *Human resources*

Description: Our emphasis is on quality service and the highest level of professionalism in the recruiting business. Our goal is to make the search process efficient, timely and to provide superior service.

Salary Minimum: $40,000
Functions: Benefits, Personnel, Training
Industries: Generalist

Smith's Fifth Avenue

17 E. 45th St., Ste. 406
New York, New York 10017
(212) 682-5300
Fax: (212) 599-6114

Key Contact - Specialty:
Mr. Arthur Teicher - *Marketing research*
Ms. Vivian Werner - *Marketing research*

Description: Executive recruitment in consumer market research, strategic, account planning, syndicated research, qualitative and quantitative research, competitive intelligence.

Salary Minimum: $40,000
Functions: Advertising, Mkt. research
Industries: Food/bev/tobacco, Communications, Advertising/PR, Publishing, New media, Broadcast & Film, Telecoms

---

Smith, Brown & Jones

P.O. Box 6513
Shawnee Mission, Kansas 66206
(816) 531-4770
Fax: (816) 531-5010
Email: dlsmith@streek.com
Web: www.streek.com/SBJ/

Key Contact - Specialty:
Mr. Donald L. Smith - *Food, agribusiness*
Mr. Bob Brown - *Financial*
Ms. Sally Smith - *Engineers*

Description: Contingency search. The only food and agribusiness recruiter in U.S. that is in the Pinnacle Organization (the top 60 billing recruiters in the U.S.).
Functions: Generalist, Production, Physicians, Mktg. mgmt., CFO's, R&D, Int'l.
Industries: Generalist, Mfg., Finance, Legal, Environmental svcs., Packaging, Biotech

Branches:
4100 Bel Air Lane
Naples, Florida 34103
(941) 263-2548
Fax: (941) 263-4323
Key Contact - Specialty:
Mr. Don Smith, II - *Retail, real estate*

Smythe Masterson & Judd, Inc.

380 Lexington Ave., Ste. 3908
New York, New York 10168
(212) 286-0003
Fax: (212) 599-6217
Email: smythemasterson.com

Key Contact - Specialty:
Mr. Mark D. J. Henley

Description: We are one of the nation's oldest, most established legal search firms. We engage in partner and associate placements, firm mergers and practice group acquisitions. The firm also represents major companies and financial institutions.

Salary Minimum: $90,000
Functions: Attorneys
Industries: Generalist, Finance, Hospitality, Legal, Communications

---

Snelling & Snelling, Inc.

6555 NW 9th Ave., Ste. 203
Ft. Lauderdale, Florida 33309
(954) 771-0090
(800) 393-0090
Fax: (954) 771-8583
Email: sneling@icanect.net
Web: www.snelling.com/ftlauderdale

Key Contact - Specialty:
Mr. K. Jerry Phillips - *Generalist*
Ms. Suzanne Upham - *Construction management*
Mr. Arthur Pollan - *Marine industry*
Mr. John Gildersleeve - *Sales, sales management*
Ms. Vicki Hutchinson - *Dental*

Description: A professional recruitment service with recruiting specialists in construction management placement. Dental placement and sales/marketing placement. All fees are employer paid. National placement.
Functions: Generalist, General mgmt., Mfg., Healthcare, Sales & mktg., Sales mgmt., Engineering
Industries: Generalist, Construction, Mfg., Wholesale, Svcs., Communications, Software

---

Snelling Search

1813 University Drive, Ste. 201
Huntsville, Alabama 35801
(800) 239-1410
(256) 382-3000
Fax: (888) 562-6683
Email: HeadHuntEm@aol.com
Web: www.snelling.com/huntsville

Key Contact - Specialty:
Mr. Joseph Putman - *Technical, sales, engineering*
Mr. David Brown - *MIS, data processing*
Mr. Dan Scrivens - *Engineering, technical, MIS*
Mr. Dave Deerwester - *Healthcare, medical*
Ms. April Carni - *Sales & marketing*
Ms. Jill Byrne - *Electronic sales*

Description: Regarded as one of the premier recruiting firms in the Southeastern United States. In business for over 22 years doing national searches and recruiting.

Salary Minimum: $30,000
Functions: Senior mgmt., Automation, Healthcare, Advertising, CFO's, MIS mgmt., Engineering
Industries: Mfg., Food/bev/tobacco, Wholesale, Retail, High tech, Software, Healthcare

---

Snelling Search - Transportation Division

104 E. Central, P.O. Box 1627
Bentonville, Arkansas 72712
(501) 271-0505
Fax: (501) 271-0707
Web: sneltran@nwa.quick.com

Key Contact - Specialty:
Mr. Howard Harlson - *Transportation*
Mr. Tom Bailey - *Transportation*

Description: Professionally trained staff with executive level experience in transportation industry. We know trucking!

Salary Minimum: $37,500
Functions: Senior mgmt., Middle mgmt., Sales mgmt., Benefits, Personnel, Risk mgmt., Systems anal.
Industries: Transportation

Snelling Search

2201 5th Ave., Ste. 5
Moline, Illinois 61265
(309) 797-1101
Fax: (309) 797-7099
Email: snelling@netexpress.net
Web: www.snellingmoline.com

Key Contact - Specialty:
Mr. James V. Roeder

Description: A staff of experienced, nationally recognized recruiters conduct searches in the areas of engineering, information technology, sales and marketing, purchasing and office services.
Functions: Mfg., Materials, Sales & mktg., IT
Industries: Generalist

Snelling Search

900 Jorie Blvd., Ste. 10
Oak Brook, Illinois 60523
(630) 571-1717
Fax: (630) 571-1719
Email: dyer@interaccess.com

Key Contact - Specialty:
Mr. Mark Dyer

Salary Minimum: $25,000
Functions: General mgmt., Mfg., Materials, Sales & mktg., HR mgmt., Finance
Industries: Generalist

Snelling Search
(a division of The Williamson Group)

1500 Louisville Ave., Ste. 103
Monroe, Louisiana 71201
(318) 387-0099
Fax: (318) 361-0386
Email: meddept@iamerica.net
Web: www.snelling.com/monroe

Key Contact - Specialty:
Mr. Gil Johnson - *Senior level management*

Description: Largest Snelling office, 13 branches, 42 recruiters, nationwide clients. Specialist in assisting executives, sales management in alternative careers in the employment industry. 28 years in business.

Salary Minimum: $50,000
Functions: Plant mgmt., Quality, Physicians, Personnel, CFO's, Systems anal., Systems dev.
Industries: Chemicals, Metal products, Motor vehicles, Finance, Banking, Computer svcs., Healthcare

Snelling Search Recruiters

5838 Faringdon Place, Ste. 1
Raleigh, North Carolina 27609
(919) 876-0660
Fax: (919) 876-0355
Email: recruit@interpath.com
Web: www.recruit-search.com

Key Contact - Specialty:
Mr. Robert J. Helfenbein, Sr. - *Generalist, MIS*
Mr. Gale Burns - *High technology, software & hardware design, software & hardware development, software & hardware applications*
Ms. Cheryl Liles - *Sales, marketing*
Ms. Mimi Phillips - *Hospitality, medical, office services, accounting, administration*

Description: We are a contingency recruiting headhunting firm. We are company driven and work in high technology, engineering, technical, sales, medical, IS/IT, administrative, accounting and office services disciplines.

Salary Minimum: $20,000
Functions: Generalist, Mfg., Healthcare, Sales & mktg., Finance, IT, Engineering
Industries: Generalist, Mfg., Svcs., Telecoms, High tech, Software, Healthcare

C. Snow & Assoc.

1 Yonge St., Ste. 1801
Toronto, Ontario M4L 3K4
Canada
(416) 465-8735
Fax: (416) 369-0515

Key Contact - Specialty:
Ms. Christine Snow - *Financial accounting, marketing, telecommunications*

Description: With over 20 years experience in the recruitment industry, we provide service of the highest integrity to professionals.

Salary Minimum: $50,000
Functions: Middle mgmt., Mkt. research, Mktg. mgmt., Finance
Industries: Food/bev/tobacco, Computer equip., Misc. financial, Telecoms, High tech, Software

Andrea Sobel & Assoc., Inc.

8033 Sunset Blvd. #151
Los Angeles, California 90046
(213) 650-2996
Fax: (213) 654-3486
Email: andrea8087@aol.com

Key Contact - Specialty:
Ms. Andrea Sobel - *Information services*

Description: 16 years experience matching data processing professionals (client/server, PC support, networking, mainframe) to a variety of clients including entertainment, healthcare, banking.
Functions: Systems anal., Systems dev., Systems implem., Systems support
Industries: Generalist, Banking, Entertainment, Healthcare

Sofco

33 Rector St., Ste. 703
New York, New York 10006
(212) 495-0080
Fax: (212) 495-9826
Email: sofco495@aol.com

Key Contact - Specialty:
Mr. Sy Morse - *Information technology*
Mr. Author Rose - *Information technology sales & recruiting*
Ms. Carmen Vegas - *Recruiters, sales people, programmers and systems analysts*

Description: Our niche, market is providing recruiters and sales people to IT consulting firms. Our technical database has great depth of skills and years.
Functions: IT, MIS mgmt., Systems anal., Systems dev., Systems support
Industries: High tech

Softrix, Inc.

P.O. Box 937
Dayton, New Jersey 08810
(732) 274-0073
Fax: (732) 274-0162
Email: hrd@softrix.com
Web: www.softrix.com

Key Contact - Specialty:
Ms. Amritha Raj - *Programmers, MIS, networking*
Mr. Raj Sajankila - *Engineers, programmers, project managers, computers, electronics*

Description: Technologists with extensive experience in high-tech, data processing, MIS, telecom, datacommunications, electronics and computer industries. This means that requirements are more quickly understood and the efficiency with which the proper candidate is found is radically increased.

Salary Minimum: $40,000
Functions: MIS mgmt., Systems anal., Systems dev., Systems implem., Network admin., DB admin., Engineering
Industries: Computer equip., Computer svcs., Telecoms, High tech, Software

Affiliates:
Reliance Computers (P) Ltd.

SoftSearch Inc.

P.O. Box 8416
Turnersville, New Jersey 08012
(609) 218-1000
Fax: (609) 218-9600
Email: infot@jobpros.com
Web: www.jobpros.com

Key Contact - Specialty:
Mr. Joseph Chelston - *Information systems*

Description: We specialize in the recruitment and placement of information systems professionals as well as senior level management.
Functions: MIS mgmt., Systems anal., Systems dev., Systems support, Network admin., DB admin.
Industries: High tech

Software Engineering Solutions, Inc.

914 N. Rengstorff Ave.
Mountain View, California 94043
(650) 969-0141
Fax: (650) 969-0177
Email: grace@sesinc.com
Web: www.sesinc.com

Key Contact - Specialty:
Ms. Grace Law - *Network engineers, UNIX system administration, technical writers, device driver developers*
Mr. Brandon Perry - *Senior level software engineers, systems developers, UNIX systems administration, senior technical writers (network)*
Ms. Marlena Mygatt - *Technical support, software engineers, OA engineers, UNIX/ network system administration, compiler developers*

Description: Provides high quality consulting, project management, contract staffing and placement services in Silicon Valley. Specialties include networking, network management, Unix system administration, systems engineer, device driver developers and technical writers.
Functions: MIS mgmt., Systems anal., Systems dev., Systems support, Network admin., DB admin., Engineering
Industries: Computer equip., Misc. financial, Computer svcs., High tech, Software

Software Resource Consultants

P.O. Box 38118
Memphis, Tennessee 38183
(901) 759-7225
(800) 756-8040
Fax: (901) 759-1721
Email: src1@bellsouth.net

Key Contact - Specialty:
Ms. Pinakini Sheth - *Wireless communications, telecommunications*

Description: Specialized recruiting for IT, telecommunication industry and wireless technology. Middle to senior management, programmers, analysts, engineers, development managers, business managers. Nationwide search. Work closely with hiring organization to develop recruiting plan.

Salary Minimum: $50,000
Functions: General mgmt., Product dev., Sales & mktg., IT, R&D, Engineering, Mgmt. consultants
Industries: Computer equip., Computer svcs., Mgmt. consulting, Telecoms, Aerospace, High tech, Software

Robert Sollman & Assoc.

747 Crepe Myrtle Circle
Apopka, Florida 32712-2651
(407) 880-4196
Fax: (407) 880-4396
Email: rsollman@aol.com

Key Contact - Specialty:
Mr. Robert Sollman - *Generalist*

Description: General executive recruiting with emphasis on consulting, engineering and accounting/finance searches.
Functions: Generalist, Benefits, CFO's, Taxes, MIS mgmt., Engineering, Mgmt. consultants
Industries: Generalist, Misc. mfg., Accounting, Mgmt. consulting, Aerospace, High tech, Software

Affiliates:
Biddle Assoc., Inc.

Phyllis Solomon Executive Search, Inc.

120 Sylvan Ave.
Englewood Cliffs, New Jersey 07632
(201) 947-8600
Fax: (201) 947-9894
Email: mail@solomonsearch.com
Web: solomonsearch.com

Key Contact - Specialty:
Ms. Phyllis Solomon - *Pharmaceutical, marketing, advertising, account management, medical education, domestic and international*

Description: Expertise with pharmaceuticals. We gear ourselves to isolate the top talent in the industry. We pride ourselves on an unparalleled record of customer satisfaction.

Salary Minimum: $90,000
Functions: Physicians, Advertising, Mkt. research, Mktg. mgmt., Direct mktg., PR
Industries: Advertising/PR

Somerset Group, Inc.

39 Sherman Court
Fairfield, Connecticut 06430
(203) 255-3232
Fax: (203) 255-5143
Email: somersetgi@aol.com
Web: www.somersetgroup.com

Key Contact - Specialty:
Mr. Richard Brenner - *Marketing research*
Mr. Gregory King - *Marketing research*

Description: Specialize in custom and syndicated marketing research. Clients consist of corporations, research suppliers and consulting firms. Industries include consumer packaged goods, pharmaceuticals, telecommunications, financial services, high tech, business to business and healthcare.

Salary Minimum: $50,000
Functions: Mkt. research
Industries: Food/bev/tobacco, Soap/ perfume/cosmetics, Drugs mfg., Computer equip., High tech

Southern Chemical & Plastics Search

759 Omaha Drive, Ste. 100
Norcross, Georgia 30093-4921
(770) 921-7693
Fax: (770) 923-6873
Email: chemrecrut@aol.com

Key Contact - Specialty:
Mr. Allan Hytowitz - *Chemical intermediates*
Mr. Jim Allen - *Plastic resins*

Description: Our thorough and confidential searches within an industry enable us to process qualified individuals who meet the specific needs of the client.

Salary Minimum: $30,000
Functions: Senior mgmt., Middle mgmt., Product dev., Mkt. research, Mktg. mgmt., Sales mgmt.
Industries: Paper, Chemicals, Plastics/ rubber, Paints/petroleum products, Packaging, High tech

Branches:
7849 Wilton Crescent Circle
University Park, Florida 34201
(941) 351-2789
Fax: (941) 351-4726
Key Contact - Specialty:
Mr. Tom Edwards - *Packaging*

21 Eastbrook Bend, Ste. 210
Peachtree City, Georgia 30269
(770) 486-3393
Fax: (770) 486-3394
Key Contact - Specialty:
Mr. Gary Corcoran - *Electrical, electronics*

Southern Recruiters & Consultants, Inc.

P.O. Box 2745
Aiken, South Carolina 29802
(803) 648-7834
Fax: (803) 642-2770
Email: recruiters@scescape.net
Web: southernrecruiters.com

Key Contact - Specialty:
Mr. Ray Fehrenbach - *Human resources, design engineers, health, safety, environmental*
Ms. Amy Snyder - *Metalworking (technical & operations), finishing*
Mr. Chris Bethmann - *Ceramics, plastics, materials management & logistics, accounting & finance*
Mr. Bill Irwin - *Pharmaceutical (technical & operations), wood products, chemicals, food, plant engineering*
Mr. Jeff Terry - *Electrical engineers, electronics engineers, manufacturing management, quality control*
Ms. Monika Dailey - *Information technology, hardware engineers, software engineers*

Description: Award winning firm dedicated to professional, ethical and long term service for our candidates and client companies.

Salary Minimum: $25,000
Functions: Product dev., Packaging, Personnel, Systems anal., R&D, Engineering, Minorities
Industries: Soap/perfume/cosmetics, Plastics/rubber, Metal products, Computer equip., Consumer electronics, Environmental svcs., Packaging

Southport Int'l. Assoc. Inc.

146 Via d'Este, Ste. 1005
Delray Beach, Florida 33445
(561) 393-6320
Fax: (561) 750-6808
Email: kittst@ibm.net

Key Contact - Specialty:
Ms. Kit Stelika - *Telecommunications, data communications, systems integration*

Description: Executive search services worldwide (telecommunications, data communications and information systems) director level and above. Strong client base in leading edge technologies in systems integration consulting and international communications.

Salary Minimum: $50,000
Functions: Mkt. research, Sales mgmt., MIS mgmt., Systems anal., Systems dev., Systems implem., Systems support
Industries: Computer equip., Consumer electronics, Computer svcs., Telecoms, High tech, Software

Southwest Search & Consulting, Inc.

4500 S. Lakeshore Drive, Ste. 520
Tempe, Arizona 85282
(602) 838-0333
Fax: (602) 838-0368
Email: azjobs@azjobs.com
Web: www.azjobs.com

Key Contact - Specialty:
Ms. Marilyn McDannel

Description: Largest recruiting firm in Phoenix area specializing exclusively in information systems. All five recruiters are tenured, with at least ten years experience each. Client base includes top fifty companies in Arizona.

Salary Minimum: $40,000
Functions: MIS mgmt., Systems anal., Systems dev., Systems implem., Systems support, Network admin., DB admin.

Southwest Selective Search, Inc.

1600 Airport Frwy., Ste. 328
Bedford, Texas 76022
(817) 540-6195
Fax: (817) 267-2240
Email: swsearch@flash.net
Web: flash.net/~swsearch.

Key Contact - Specialty:
Mr. Paul Neir - *Property & casualty insurance*
Ms. Karla Neir - *Property & casualty insurance*

Description: Our staff comes from the industries we serve. We take the time to fully understand your company and personnel needs to serve you better.

Salary Minimum: $25,000
Functions: Finance, Risk mgmt.
Industries: Insurance

Southwestern Professional Services

2451 Atrium Way
Nashville, Tennessee 37214
(615) 391-2617
Fax: (615) 231-4000
Email: dstaats@southwestern.com

Key Contact - Specialty:
Dr. Carl R. Roberts - *Sales & marketing*
Mr. Greg Boucher - *Sales & marketing*
Mr. Tom Truitt - *Management consultants*

Description: We recruit executive, middle management and contract labor for Fortune 100 companies and small private firms, nationally and internationally. The contract labor is for technical personnel in telecommunications.
Functions: Sales mgmt., CFO's, Budgeting, Systems dev., Systems support, Engineering, Mgmt. consultants
Industries: Equip. svcs., Publishing, Telecoms, Insurance, Real estate, High tech, Healthcare

Branches:
9485 Regency Sq. Blvd., #110
Jacksonville, Florida 32225
(904) 725-9200
Fax: (904) 723-3434
Key Contact - Specialty:
Mr. Mark Langley - *Sales*

1604 Hilltop Executive Ctr., Ste. 320
Virginia Beach, Virginia 23451
(757) 428-2660
Fax: (757) 428-0394
Key Contact - Specialty:
Mr. John Rachels - *Sales, sales management, internal medicine, family physicians*

Sparks, McDonough & Assoc., Inc.

1001 Craig Rd., Ste. 330
St. Louis, Missouri 63146
(314) 872-2166
Fax: (314) 872-2167
Email: rtsparks@aol.com

Key Contact - Specialty:
Mr. R. Thomas Sparks, Jr. - *High technology, telecommunications*

Description: A leading mid-western executive recruiting firm specializing in hardware, software, networking, internet, long distance, wireless and PBX placements of sales, management and technical positions.

Salary Minimum: $60,000
Functions: Senior mgmt., Middle mgmt., Sales mgmt., IT, Mgmt. consultants
Industries: Computer equip., Computer svcs., New media, Telecoms, High tech, Software

SPC Symcox Personnel Consultants

(Firm declined to update.)
13750 US 281 N., Ste. 510,
Camino Real Bank
San Antonio, Texas 78232
(210) 494-6674
Email: spc@onramp.net
Web: www.symcox.com

Key Contact - Specialty:
Mr. Jim Symcox - *Information technology, finance & accounting, materials management*

Description: We provide a full range of professional search, recruiting and placement services with consultants specializing in exclusive concentrations of various disciplines and industries.

Salary Minimum: $40,000
Functions: Mfg., Materials, Sales & mktg., Finance, IT
Industries: Wholesale, Retail, Computer svcs., Accounting, Telecoms, High tech, Software

Spear-Izzo Assoc., LLC
(a division of SIA Group)

651 Holiday Drive, Ste. 300
Foster Plaza, Bldg. Five
Pittsburgh, Pennsylvania 15220-2740
(412) 928-3290
Fax: (412) 561-9091
Email: info@siasearch.com
Web: www.siasearch.com

Key Contact - Specialty:
Mr. Kenneth T. Spear - *Generalist*
Mr. J. Randall Lheureau - *Generalist*
Mr. Thomas S. O. Pasquale - *Generalist*
Mr. Donald Wesley - *Generalist*

Description: Specialists for 26 years in serving the recruiting needs of the management consulting industry. Also provide experienced consultants and technical managers (permanent/interim) for general business and internal consulting positions.

Salary Minimum: $30,000
Functions: Generalist, Production, Productivity, Materials, Finance, IT, Mgmt. consultants
Industries: Generalist, Mfg., Drugs mfg., Motor vehicles, Mgmt. consulting, Insurance, Healthcare

Branches:
35 Technology Pkwy. S., Ste. 170
Norcross, Georgia 30092
(770) 613-5312
Fax: (770) 279-9110
Key Contact - Specialty:
Mr. Thomas M. Izzo - *Generalist*

Specialized Search Assoc.
15200 Jog Road, Ste. 201
Delray Beach, Florida 33446
(561) 499-3711
Fax: (561) 499-3770

Key Contact - Specialty:
Mr. Leonard Morris - *Engineering (construction industry)*

Description: Since 1969 specializing in construction and consulting engineering placements. Perform all functions of retainer firm on a contingency basis. Do no advertising. Strictly search. Excellent references.

Salary Minimum: $60,000
Functions: Senior mgmt., Middle mgmt., Mktg. mgmt., Sales mgmt., Engineering, Architects, Int'l.
Industries: Construction, Environmental svcs., Haz. waste

Specialty Employment Services, Inc.
910 Big Horn Circle
Alpharetta, Georgia 30202
(770) 442-5401
Fax: (770) 442-8317
Email: sesijobs@mindspring.com
Web: www.sesijobs.com

Key Contact - Specialty:
Mr. Michael Siegel - *Sales, marketing, technical (chemical industry)*
Ms. Karen Cheng - *Engineering, research & development (chemical industry)*

Description: We provide the employment solutions to better your organization. We evaluate your needs and develop a specific search assignment marketing plan and present only pre-screened candidates that meet your objectives.

Salary Minimum: $40,000
Functions: Sales & mktg., R&D, Engineering
Industries: Paper, Chemicals, Plastics/rubber, Paints/petroleum products, Leather/stone/glass/clay, Telecoms, High tech

Spectra International LLC
3200 N. Hayden Rd., Ste. 210
Scottsdale, Arizona 85251
(602) 481-0411
Fax: (602) 481-0525
Email: spectra@indirect.com
Web: www.indirect.com/www/spectra

Key Contact - Specialty:
Ms. Sybil Goldberg - *High technology (data-communications, semiconductor industries), retail management, grocery management, sales & marketing (high technology), MIS (contract or direct hire)*

Description: Comprehensive human resource services including search and placement (contingent and retained, domestic and international), executive temporaries, contracting, payrolling, temp-to-hire, temporary service and professional employer services (staff leasing and out-sourcing).
Functions: Sales mgmt., Benefits, IT, MIS mgmt., Systems support, Network admin., Engineering
Industries: Retail, Finance, Human resource svcs., Packaging, High tech, Software

SpectraWest
38193 Martha Ave.
Fremont, California 94536
(510) 791-1700
Fax: (510) 791-1700
Email: fred@spectrawest.com
Web: www.spectrawest.com

Key Contact - Specialty:
Mr. Fred Arredondo - *Computer hardware, software engineers*

Description: Recruit engineering directors, managers and senior project engineers with specialties in developing computer networks, databases, graphics and operating systems. Seek minimum four years technical development experience with technical degree.

Salary Minimum: $60,000
Functions: Systems dev., Engineering
Industries: Computer equip., Telecoms, High tech, Software

SpencerSearch, Inc.
5230 Hazel Rd.
Evergreen, Colorado 80439
(303) 670-3241
Fax: (303) 670-3275

Key Contact - Specialty:
Mr. Dan R. Spencer - *Semiconductor*

Description: Our firm has over thirty years of executive search experience in the semiconductor industry. Why do our clients hire us? We get the job done.

Salary Minimum: $75,000
Functions: Middle mgmt., Automation, Quality, Sales mgmt., Customer svc., Engineering, Minorities
Industries: Computer equip., High tech

Branches:
6104 Brookhollow Drive
Plano, Texas 75093
(972) 378-0280
Key Contact - Specialty:
Mr. Edmund Amara - *Semiconductor*

Kenn Spinrad Inc.
3925 Perkiomen Ave.
Reading, Pennsylvania 19606
(610) 779-0944
Fax: (610) 779-8338
Email: kspinrad@ptd.net
Web: www/elecsp.com/kspin/kspin.htm

Key Contact - Specialty:
Ms. Sharon Spinrad - *Apparel (manufacturing)*
Mr. Kenn Spinrad - *Home fashions (manufacturing)*
Mr. Robert Margolin - *Textile (manufacturing)*
Mr. James Thorpe - *Data processing, engineering*

Description: We offer complete confidentiality, personal, professional service. We present qualified candidates in the fields of apparel and home fashion manufacturing, textiles, engineering and data processing. We have been in business since 1967.
Functions: Senior mgmt., Middle mgmt., Production, Plant mgmt., Purchasing, Materials Plng., MIS mgmt.
Industries: Textiles/apparel, Metal products, Machinery/Appliances, Computer svcs., Human resource svcs., High tech, Software

Sprout/Standish, Inc.
82 Palomino Lane, Ste. 503
Bedford, New Hampshire 03110
(603) 622-0700
Fax: (603) 622-4172
Email: ssi@printquest.com
Web: www.printquest.com

Key Contact - Specialty:
Mr. David A. Clark - *Printing, pre-press, multimedia communication, sales, manufacturing*

Description: A highly specialized firm dedicated to serving the printing, publishing, packaging, and multimedia industry-only. Vertically and horizontally integrated so as to allow complete coverage including high profile sales executives, mid-management and top spots in the GAM top 100. Discreet.

Salary Minimum: $60,000
Functions: Senior mgmt., Middle mgmt., Production, Plant mgmt., Packaging, Sales mgmt., Customer svc.
Industries: Printing, Publishing, New media, Packaging

Squires Resources Inc.

146 Victoria St. W., 3rd Floor
P.O. Box 775
Alliston, Ontario L9R 1V9
Canada
(705) 435-0921
Fax: (705) 435-1213
Email: fsquires@bconnex.net

Key Contact - Specialty:
Mr. Frank Squires - *Information systems, accounting*
Ms. Mary Cicci - *Information systems*
Ms. Sandy Poitras - *Information systems*

Description: We offer a unique insight into career opportunities available for IT and accounting professionals particularly in Bermuda, secondaries in Cayman and Bahamas.

Salary Minimum: $40,000
Functions: Sales mgmt., Systems anal., Systems dev., Systems implem., Systems support, Network admin., DB admin.
Industries: Retail, Finance, Computer svcs., Accounting, New media, Insurance, Software

SR Wilson, Inc.

520 Mendocino Ave., Ste. 200
Santa Rosa, California 95401
(707) 571-5990
Fax: (707) 571-1755

Key Contact - Specialty:
Mr. Stoney Wilson - *Environmental, litigation, intellectual property & patent attorneys*
Ms. Pamela J. Wilson - *Patent, intellectual property*

Description: Historically strong in legal search nationally for law firms and corporations. About 60% of legal search is for law firms.

Salary Minimum: $45,000
Functions: Legal, Engineering, Attorneys
Industries: Energy/utilities, Mfg., Transportation, Legal, Communications, Environmental svcs., High tech

Staff Extension Int'l.

13612 Midway, Ste. 103
Dallas, Texas 75244
(972) 991-4737
Fax: (972) 991-5325
Email: dallas@staffext.com
Web: www.staffext.com

Key Contact - Specialty:
Mr. Jack R. Williams - *Executive, human resources*
Mr. Dick Steffensrud - *Executive, human resources, sales & marketing, financial*

Description: Experienced in providing corporations with customized executive search services, contract placements, human resources and executive staffing.

Salary Minimum: $30,000
Functions: Generalist, Senior mgmt., Mktg. mgmt., Sales mgmt., Benefits, Training, CFO's
Industries: Generalist

Branches:
3300 S. Gessner, Ste. 251
Houston, Texas 77063
(713) 786-8696
Fax: (713) 786-5131
Email: houston@staffext.com
Key Contact - Specialty:
Mr. Robert Tann - *Executive, operations, human resources, sales & marketing*

Staff Resources, Inc.

P.O. Box 4557
130 E. Main St.
Rock Hill, South Carolina 29732-6557
(803) 366-0500
Fax: (803) 366-1021
Email: staffres@cetlink.net
Web: www.srijobs.com

Key Contact - Specialty:
Mr. Dick Jordan - *Manufacturing, human resources, quality, finance, materials, purchasing, engineering*
Mr. Farris R. Briggs - *Sales & marketing, finance, information systems, operations, human resources, pharmaceuticals*
Ms. Carol Dodd - *Research, outplacement*
Mr. Douglas Cunningham - *Human resources, accounting distribution, automotive, electronics, safety, comp & benefits*

Description: We specialize in manufacturing and all functions that support a manufacturing facility. Most all of our clients are Fortune 500 firms and are located all over the country. Many of our clients are located in the Southeast and have excellent benefits and relocation packages.

Salary Minimum: $25,000
Functions: Mfg., Materials, Sales & mktg., HR mgmt., Finance, IT, Engineering
Industries: Generalist, Mfg., Food/bev/tobacco, Machinery/Appliances, Finance, Computer svcs., Human resource svcs.

Staffing Edge, Inc.

1001 Office Park Rd., Ste. 320
West Des Moines, Iowa 50265-2567
(515) 224-0446
Fax: (515) 224-6599
Email: dsm@staffingedge.com
Web: www.staffingedge.com

Key Contact - Specialty:
Mr. Dennis Leininger - *Information technology, engineering, accounting, banking, finance, sales, insurance*
Mr. Ed James
Mr. Mark Schaul
Mr. Mark DeneDale

Description: Specialists in mid to upper level management positions; insurance, accounting, engineering, banking, D.P. and sales.

Salary Minimum: $20,000
Functions: General mgmt., Mfg., Sales & mktg., HR mgmt., Finance, IT, Engineering
Industries: Mfg., Finance, Svcs., Communications, Insurance, High tech

Branches:
2200 N. Central, Ste. 300
Phoenix, Arizona 85004
(602) 257-8100
Fax: (602) 253-6300
Email: phoenix@staffingedge.com
Web: www.staffingedge.com
Key Contact - Specialty:
Mr. John Henderson - *Accounting, office clerical, information technology, engineering, legal*

7790 E. Arapahoe, Ste. 260
Angelwood, Colorado 80112
(303) 221-6900
Fax: (303) 221-4900
Email: denver@staffingedge.com
Web: www.staffingedge.com
Key Contact - Specialty:
Mr. Aaron Smith - *Accounting, office clerical, legal, banking, information technology*

4220 Shawnee Mission Pkwy., Ste. 101B
Fairway, Kansas 66205
(913) 722-4200
Fax: (913) 722-4813
Email: kc@staffingedge.com
Web: www.staffingedge.com
Key Contact - Specialty:
Mr. Jay Arnold - *Accounting, office clerical, information technology, engineering, legal*

2911 Turtle Creek, Ste. 300
Dallas, Texas 75219
(214) 523-9088
Email: dallas@staffingedge.com
Web: www.staffingedge.com

Key Contact - Specialty:
Ms. Mimi Dykes

12655 N. Central Expwy., Ste. 310
Dallas, Texas 75243
(972) 991-3330
Fax: (972) 991-4003
Email: dallas@staffingedge.com
Web: www.staffingedge.com
Key Contact - Specialty:
Ms. Mimi Dykes - *Accounting, office clerical, information technology, engineering, sales*

512 Main St., Ste. 401
Ft. Worth, Texas 76102
(817) 810-9488
Fax: (817) 810-9729
Key Contact - Specialty:
Ms. Rebecca Winters

5601 Bridge St., Ste. 408
Ft. Worth, Texas 76112
(817) 446-8966
Fax: (817) 446-8965
Email: ftworth@staffingedge.com
Web: www.staffingedge.com
Key Contact - Specialty:
Ms. Rebecca Winters
Ms. Mimi Dykes

1001 Texas Ave., Ste. 310
Houston, Texas 77002
(713) 776-3600
Fax: (713) 236-8346
Key Contact - Specialty:
Darb Zoldos

4544 Post Oak Place, Ste. 375
Houston, Texas 77027
(713) 622-5300
Fax: (713) 622-4600
Key Contact - Specialty:
Darb Zoldos

800 W. Airport Frwy., Ste. 712
Irving, Texas 75062
(972) 554-0003
Fax: (972) 579-5514
Email: dallas@staffingedge.com
Web: www.staffingedge.com
Key Contact - Specialty:
Ms. Mimi Dykes

7411 John Smith Drive, Ste. 110
San Antonio, Texas 78229
(210) 614-1400
Fax: (210) 614-1953
Key Contact - Specialty:
Mr. Duane Fousie

Affiliates:
Academy Training & Placement
PN Financial Recruiting

C. J. Stafford & Assoc.

2323 Yonge St., Ste. 501
Toronto, Ontario M4P 2C9
Canada
(416) 484-1960
Fax: (416) 484-0626
Email: cjstaff@idirect.com

Key Contact - Specialty:
Mr. Chris Stafford - *Mining, metals*
Mr. John Pauling - *Financial, executive senior management*
Mr. Nat Scott - *Open pit mining, underground mining*
Mr. Rhys Goodall - *Metallurgical, mineral processing, maintenance, mechanical*
Mr. Charles Sharpe - *Construction, building, utilities, civil engineering*

Description: Industry focused specialists in search and selection for international mining and metals companies and those service industries associated with them.

Salary Minimum: $50,000
Functions: Directors, Senior mgmt., IT, Engineering, Environmentalists, Int'l.
Industries: Agri/forestry/mining, Energy/utilities, Construction, Brokers, Entertainment, Computer svcs.

StaffWriters Plus

80 Austin Blvd.
Commack, New York 11725
(516) 543-1111
Fax: (516) 864-2891
Email: info@staffwriters.com
Web: www.staffwriters.com

Key Contact - Specialty:
Mr. George Grokas - *Writers, editors*

Description: We offer access to the country's best writers and editors in more than 50 highly specialized areas. We offer temporary and permanent.
Functions: Generalist, Advertising, Direct mktg., PR, Training, Systems support, Graphic artists
Industries: Computer equip., Misc. financial, Pharmaceutical svcs., Advertising/PR, New media, High tech, Software

Affiliates:
Invision, LLC

Stanewick, Hart & Assoc., Inc.

7829 Briarcreek Rd.
Tallahassee, Florida 32312-3661
(850) 893-7849

Key Contact - Specialty:
Mr. David Hunter - *Data processing, Big 6 accounting/consulting firms*
Mr. B. David Stanewick - *Data processing, logistics industry, power generation utility companies*

Description: In-depth recruiting and search in technical development for the logistics and telecommunications industry. Technical programmers through management. Management mostly by search and Southeast U.S. preferably.

Salary Minimum: $30,000
Functions: Directors, Distribution, Systems anal., Systems implem., Network admin., DB admin., Mgmt. consultants
Industries: Transportation, Computer svcs., Mgmt. consulting, High tech, Software, Non-classifiable industries

The Stanton Group, Inc.

830 W. Main St., Ste. 365
Lake Zurich, Illinois 60047
(847) 540-1183
Fax: (847) 540-1154
Email: keister@stantongp.com
Web: www.stantongp.com/

Key Contact - Specialty:
Mr. John Keister - *Software engineering*
Ms. Beth Keister - *Software quality*

Description: Our small size enables us to offer excellent personal service to both clients and candidates. We are proud that our clients are among the leaders in software technologies.

Salary Minimum: $80,000
Functions: IT, MIS mgmt., Systems dev., Systems implem., Systems support, R&D, Engineering
Industries: Motor vehicles, Computer equip., Consumer electronics, Telecoms, High tech, Software

Star Search Consultants

211 Consumers Rd., Ste. 300
Willowdale, Ontario M2J 4G8
Canada
(416) 491-4440
Fax: (416) 491-4451
Email: star@searchstar.com
Web: searchstar.com

Key Contact - Specialty:
Mr. John P. Weiss - *Sales & marketing, engineering, technical, finance, administration*

Description: One stop recruitment center since 1974.We recruit on assignments on a contingency basis up to 70K, over that we serve our employer/clients on an executive search basis.
Functions: General mgmt., Mfg., Materials, Sales & mktg., Finance, R&D, Engineering
Industries: Generalist, Mfg., Transportation, Aerospace, Packaging, Insurance, High tech

Starbridge Group Inc.

10201 Lee Hwy., Ste. 480
Fairfax, Virginia 22030
(703) 691-3900
Fax: (703) 691-3999

Key Contact - Specialty:
Mr. David S. Kurke - *Training, consulting, multimedia*

Description: Industry segmented specialization in order to provide added value and expertise to our clients. We aggressively deliver on our commitments to our clients with high integrity and professionalism. We specialize in permanent and project based placement at mid-level to senior level professionals.
Functions: Senior mgmt., Middle mgmt., Sales mgmt., Training, Systems anal., Systems implem., Mgmt. consultants
Industries: Higher ed., Computer svcs., Accounting, Mgmt. consulting, Human resource svcs., New media

---

STAT Search

7 Colby Court, Ste. 4-204
Bedford, New Hampshire 03110
(603) 666-5500
Fax: (603) 623-5322
Email: hunter@statsearch.com
Web: www.statsearch.com

Key Contact - Specialty:
Ms. Dale Poklemba - *Healthcare*
Ms. Jill Mooney - *Healthcare*
Ms. Susan Goehring - *Healthcare*

Description: We conduct nationwide searches. We have satisfied clients across the country. We specialize in healthcare search for payors and providers. We listen to your needs and provide well screened candidates in an efficient and timely manner. These candidates are not only able to do your job, but want to do it and will enjoy your corporate culture.

Salary Minimum: $50,000
Functions: Senior mgmt., Middle mgmt., Health admin., Mktg. mgmt., Sales mgmt., CFO's, MIS mgmt.
Industries: Pharmaceutical svcs., Insurance, Healthcare

Branches:
13817 N. W. 22nd St.
Sunrise, Florida 33323-5303
(954) 835-2415
Fax: (954) 835-2420
Email: careerko1@aol.com
Key Contact - Specialty:
Ms. Karen Ostarticki-Sanchez - *Healthcare*

290 Turnpike Rd., #148
Westborough, Massachusetts 01581
(508) 898-2510
(800) 892-2651
Fax: (508) 898-2585
Email: rozmartin@sprynet.com
Key Contact - Specialty:
Ms. Roz Martin - *Healthcare*

Steinbach & Co.

6 Dana Rd.
Maynard, Massachusetts 01754
(508) 897-8661
Fax: (508) 897-8661
Email: hrconsult@usa.net

Key Contact - Specialty:
Mr. David M. Steinbach - *MIS, scientific software, hardware technologists, managers*

Description: 20 years recruiting and search experience. Source software and hardware technologists, consultants and managers. Very comfortable in MPP, OOP, multimedia, RT, Internet/www, DB, OPSYS, Windows, MIS, ASIC, investment, insurance and financial.

Salary Minimum: $40,000
Functions: MIS mgmt., Systems anal., Systems dev., Systems implem., Systems support, R&D, Engineering
Industries: New media, Broadcast & Film, Telecoms, High tech, Software

---

Steinfield & Assoc.

2626 Cole Ave., Ste. 400
Dallas, Texas 75204
(214) 220-0535
Fax: (214) 665-9535
Email: steinfield@airmail.net

Key Contact - Specialty:
Mr. David Steinfield - *Finance, accounting, treasury, audit, human resources*

Description: We are an executive search firm specializing in the placement of finance, accounting, treasury, audit and human resources professionals.

Salary Minimum: $70,000
Functions: HR mgmt., CFO's, Budgeting, Cash mgmt., Taxes, M&A, Mgmt. consultants
Industries: Mfg., Retail, Finance, Accounting, Mgmt. consulting, Human resource svcs., High tech

---

The Stelton Group, Inc.

904 Oak Tree Rd., Ste. A
South Plainfield, New Jersey 07080
(908) 757-9888
Fax: (908) 757-3179
Email: abrestic@bellatlantic.net
Web: silo.com/stelton/stelton.htm

Key Contact - Specialty:
Mr. Al Lewis - *Engineering, plastic, medical devices*
Mr. C. Ace Plyley, Jr. - *Human resources, finance, marketing & sales*
Ms. Cindy L. Slusser - *Scientific, Information technology*

Description: Industry specific recruiting of professional and executive candidates for all industries.
Functions: Product dev., Plant mgmt., Purchasing, Mktg. mgmt., Systems dev., R&D, Engineering
Industries: Food/bev/tobacco, Soap/perfume/cosmetics, Metal products, Machinery/Appliances, Misc. mfg., Packaging, Biotech

---

Peter Sterling & Co.

One Riverway, Ste. 1700
Houston, Texas 77056
(713) 840-6363
Fax: (713) 622-1937

Key Contact - Specialty:
Mr. Peter D. Sterling

Description: Former banker specializing in recruitment for financial institutions.

Salary Minimum: $40,000
Functions: Generalist, Credit, M&A, Risk mgmt.
Industries: Energy/utilities, Banking, Invest. banking

Sterling Int'l. Management Recruitment, Ltd. Inc.

P.O. Box 18201
Greensboro, North Carolina 27410
(336) 218-0339
Fax: (336) 218-5116

Key Contact - Specialty:
Ms. Joanna Williams Campbell - *Generalist*
Ms. K. J. Campbell - *Staff*
Mr. J. S. Campbell - *Staff*

Description: Achieving excellence through quality people we provide a full candidate consolidated file to the hiring company prior to on-site interviewing.

Salary Minimum: $45,000
Functions: Senior mgmt., Distribution, Training, Taxes, MIS mgmt., Systems dev., Engineering
Industries: Textiles/apparel, Metal products, Machinery/Appliances, Computer equip., Consumer electronics, Software, Biotech

---

Daniel Stern & Assoc.

211 N. Whitfield St.
The Medical Ctr. E.
Pittsburgh, Pennsylvania 15206
(412) 363-9700
Fax: (412) 363-8267
Email: dsa@danielstern.com
Web: www.danielstern.com

Key Contact - Specialty:
Mr. Daniel Stern - *Physician specialties (all)*

Description: Twenty-five years of specialized physician recruiting and consulting services including practice set-up and enhancement, maximizing revenues, practice sales and acquisitions, contract development, negotiations and billing services.

Salary Minimum: $75,000
Functions: Physicians, Health admin.

Industries: Higher ed., Mgmt. consulting, Human resource svcs., Healthcare

Steven Douglas Assoc.

3040 Universal Blvd., Ste. 190
Weston, Florida 33331
(954) 385-8595
(305) 381-8100
Fax: (954) 385-1414
Email: sabrina@stevendouglas.com
Web: stevendouglas.com

Key Contact - Specialty:
Mr. Mark Sadovnick - *Generalist*
Mr. Steve Sadaka - *Generalist*

Description: Commitment to proactively search - identify and most importantly, attract - the best qualified individual for the client's positions.
Functions: Senior mgmt., Mktg. mgmt., CFO's, Budgeting, Taxes, M&A, MIS mgmt.
Industries: Invest. banking, Computer svcs., Accounting, Human resource svcs., Real estate, Healthcare

Steven Michaels & Assoc.

One Penn Plaza, Ste. 1421
New York, New York 10119
(212) 736-9300
Fax: (212) 563-4444
Email: SMAnyc@aol.com

Key Contact - Specialty:
Ms. Linda Liebman

Description: Executive search firm staffing the temporary, permanent, contract technical and home healthcare industries, mid and upper management levels nationally. Also sales industry within service related products, Wall Street, capital markets and stock brokers.

Salary Minimum: $50,000
Functions: Middle mgmt., Sales mgmt., Cash mgmt., M&A
Industries: Banking, Invest. banking, Brokers, Venture cap.

Ron Stevens & Assoc., Inc.

4501 Galloway Blvd.
Bradenton, Florida 34210-2949
(800) 458-1611
Fax: (800) 458-1611
Web: rsa-inc@worldnet.att.net

Key Contact - Specialty:
Mr. Ron Stevens - *Technical sales & service*

Description: A contingency search firm concentrating in the areas of chemical process, pulp and paper, petro-chemical, utilities, retail trade, plastics & metals.

Salary Minimum: $35,000
Functions: Product dev., Production, Plant mgmt., Mkt. research, Sales mgmt., R&D, Engineering
Industries: Energy/utilities, Paper, Chemicals, Plastics/rubber, Paints/petroleum products, Metal products, Environmental svcs.

Stevens Assoc.

65 Forest St., Ste. 3
Marshfield, Massachusetts 02050-2818
(617) 834-0800
Email: stevassc@erols.com

Key Contact - Specialty:
Mr. Wayne J. Stevens - *High technology, marketing & sales*

Description: Software computer and allied high tech industry specialist. Primarily focusing on senior levels of marketing, sales, consultants, executive management and technical support personnel.

Salary Minimum: $60,000
Functions: Advertising, Mkt. research, Mktg. mgmt., Sales mgmt., Direct mktg., PR, Systems support
Industries: Computer equip., Test/measurement equip., Computer svcs., New media, Telecoms, High tech, Software

The Stevens Group

(Firm declined to update.)
Warner Ctr. Plaza, P.O. Box 367
Woodland Hills, California 91365
(818) 712-0242

Key Contact - Specialty:
Ms. Martha Stevens

Description: Boutique practice committed to excellence and building long-term client and candidate relationships. All new business results from referrals. Proud of reputation of integrity and honesty. Publish ultimate job-seekers guide of the 90's, "Get Yourself Acquired!"

Salary Minimum: $40,000
Functions: General mgmt., Sales & mktg., HR mgmt., Finance, IT, Mgmt. consultants, Int'l.
Industries: Generalist

Stevens, Valentine & McKeever

300 Kings Highway E., Ste. 008
Haddonfield, New Jersey 08033
(609) 795-7222
Fax: (609) 795-3351
Web: svmsrch@worldnet.att.net

Key Contact - Specialty:
Mr. Leonard W. Stevens - *Diversified financial services*

Description: Responsive, consultative search and assessment for all functions within the insurance and diversified financial service industry, internationally.

Salary Minimum: $60,000
Functions: Generalist
Industries: Finance, Mgmt. consulting, Human resource svcs., Insurance

Stewart Assoc.

245 Butler Ave., The Executive Offices
Lancaster, Pennsylvania 17601
(717) 299-9242
Fax: (717) 299-4879

Key Contact - Specialty:
Mr. Walter S. Poyck - *Manufacturing*

Description: Broad range of recruiting services for the high tech, commercial and defense sectors of the economy. Specializing in engineering and manufacturing management.

Salary Minimum: $35,000
Functions: Product dev., Production, Automation, Plant mgmt., Quality, Productivity, Purchasing
Industries: Printing, Drugs mfg., Medical devices, Plastics/rubber, Metal products, Machinery/Appliances, Misc. mfg.

The Stewart Group

201 ATP Tour Blvd., Ste. 130
P.O. Box 2588
Ponte Vedra Beach, Florida 32004-2588
(904) 285-6622
Fax: (904) 285-0076
Email: stewgrp@cybermax-net
Web: www.stewartgroup.net

Key Contact - Specialty:
Mr. James H. Stewart - *Pharmaceutical sales, marketing, clinical, medical, regulatory*
Mr. Gary S. Jurenovich - *Sales, pharmaceutical, medical, industrial*
Ms. Diane C. Kinney - *Hospital administrators, managed care, organizations (MCO's)*
Mr. Chuck Crossman - *MIS, engineering, clinical research, pharmaceutical, business development*
Mr. Paul Venditti - *Telecommunications, computer/telephone integration*

Description: Pharmaceutical and medical in all departments. Mid to senior level searches in most industries. Hospital and physician practice and executive. MIS and related areas, engineering and telecommunications.
Functions: Generalist, Senior mgmt., Healthcare, Sales & mktg., Finance, IT, R&D
Industries: Finance, Hospitality, Pharmaceutical svcs., Communications, High tech, Biotech, Healthcare

Stewart/Greene & Co. of The Triad, Inc.

5504 Stonebridge Rd.
Pleasant Garden, North Carolina 27313
(336) 674-5345
Fax: (336) 674-5937
Email: billgreene@worldnet.att.net
Web: www.stewartgreene.com

Key Contact - Specialty:
Mr. William Greene - *Generalist, furniture, wood products*
Mr. John Ibsen - *Generalist, furniture, wood products*
Ms. Ginny Brown - *Front line supervisors, plant supervisors*
Ms. Sharon Greene - *Interim management, outplacement, contract services*

Description: We are an executive and management search firm specializing in the furniture and wood products industries. Other services include interim management, outplacement services and contract services.

Salary Minimum: $25,000
Functions: General mgmt., Mfg., Materials, Sales & mktg., HR mgmt., Finance, Engineering
Industries: Agri/forestry/mining, Textiles/apparel, Lumber/furniture, Paints/petroleum products, Wholesale, Mgmt. consulting, Human resource svcs.

Branches:
P.O. Box 847
Hickory, North Carolina 28603
(828) 322-4544
Fax: (828) 322-4545
Email: sqhkky@wave.net
Key Contact - Specialty:
Mr. Tom Stewart - *Generalist, furniture, wood products*

Affiliates:
Renaissance Resources, LLC

Stone & Youngblood

304 Newbury St., Ste. 210
Boston, Massachusetts 02115
(781) 647-0070
Fax: (781) 647-0460
Email: stoneyoungblood@hotmail.com

Key Contact - Specialty:
Mr. Stephen Sarkis

Description: Consultants best known for executive searches conducted for clients in media, communications, advertising, public relations, sales and marketing. Affiliated with offices coast to coast.
Functions: General mgmt., Advertising, Mktg. mgmt., Sales mgmt., Direct mktg., PR, HR mgmt.
Industries: Svcs., Advertising/PR, Publishing, New media, Broadcast & Film, Telecoms, Software

Affiliates:
TargetSearch

Stone Assoc. LLC

25600 N. Woodward Ave., Ste. 214
Royal Oak, Michigan 48067
(248) 548-0445
Fax: (248) 548-1102
Email: stoltd@home.com

Key Contact - Specialty:
Mr. Richard Stone - *Accounting, finance, banking, public accounting*
Mr. Marc Van Gyseghem - *Controllers, accounting manager, analyst*

Description: We are an executive search firm that specializes in accounting, finance and information systems. Company pays fee.

Salary Minimum: $30,000
Functions: CFO's, Budgeting, Cash mgmt., Credit, Taxes, M&A, Risk mgmt.
Industries: Mfg., Banking, Invest. banking, Svcs., Insurance, Real estate, High tech

Stone Enterprises Ltd.

645 N. Michigan Ave., Ste. 800
Chicago, Illinois 60611
(773) 404-9300
(312) 836-0470
Fax: (773) 404-9388
Email: Hire2000@aol.com

Key Contact - Specialty:
Ms. Susan L. Stone - *Software, hardware, telecommunications, manufacturing, distribution, accounting*

Description: Successful, Chicago-based boutique firm providing a quality-conscious, results-oriented service catering to long-term client relationships. Assist Fortune 500, Big 6, software development, telecom and medium-sized manufacturing and distribution firms in positions ranging from $40,000.

Salary Minimum: $40,000
Functions: General mgmt., Mfg., Materials, Finance, IT, Engineering, Int'l.
Industries: Generalist, Mfg., Transportation, Finance, Computer svcs., High tech, Software

DM Stone Personnel Services

100 Bush St., Ste. 650
San Francisco, California 94104
(415) 391-5151
Fax: (415) 391-5536
Email: mailbox@dmstone.com
Web: www.dmstone.com

Key Contact - Specialty:
Mr. Dave M. Stone - *Accounting & finance direct hire & temporaries*

Description: A financial services specialist, serving clients in banking, brokerage, insurance, investment banking and asset management. Providing temporary, temp-to-hire and direct hire placement, from entry level to executive management.
Functions: Admin. svcs., Legal, Sales mgmt., Customer svc., Budgeting, Cash mgmt., Paralegals
Industries: Banking, Invest. banking, Brokers, Venture cap., Misc. financial, Legal, Accounting

Branches:
333 Cobalt Way, Ste. 107
Sunnyvale, California 94086
(408) 774-6774
Fax: (408) 774-6777
Email: mailbox@dmstone.com
Web: www.dmstone.com
Key Contact - Specialty:
Mr. Tim Wenzel - *Accounting & finance*

Affiliates:
Accountancies

The Stonebridge Group
(an affiliate of Management Recruiters Int'l.)

3901 N. Front, Ste. 1A
Harrisburg, Pennsylvania 17110-1536
(717) 238-3995
Fax: (717) 238-4311
Email: mr-harrisburg@juno.com
Web: www.mrinet.com

Key Contact - Specialty:
Mr. William P. Milo - *Insurance*
Mr. Dade Royer - *Healthcare and long term care*
Ms. Nancy Richey - *Security, fire protection, building control*

Description: Capabilities include nationwide searches, permanent and interim staffing; filling single or multiple openings. Worldwide services available. Videoconferencing facilities available.

Salary Minimum: $50,000
Functions: Senior mgmt., Middle mgmt., Sales & mktg., Sales mgmt., Finance
Industries: Computer equip., Test/measurement equip., Insurance, Healthcare

Stoneburner Assoc., Inc.

10000 W. 75th St., Ste. 102
King's Cove
Shawnee Mission, Kansas 66204
(913) 432-0055
Fax: (913) 432-0056

Key Contact - Specialty:
Mr. Dwight T. Stoneburner - *Technical*

Description: Executive search or contingency placement in a wide variety of industries. Emphasis on high tech firms and professionals. Nationwide recruiting activity. 90 day pro-rated guarantee.

Salary Minimum: $35,000
Functions: Production, Plant mgmt., Quality, Purchasing, Systems dev., R&D, Engineering
Industries: Chemicals, Medical devices, Plastics/rubber, Paints/petroleum products, High tech, Software, Biotech

Affiliates:
Inter-City Personnel Assoc., Inc.
Professional Recruiters, Inc.

Storfer & Assoc.

1200 Broadway, Ste. 7D
New York, New York 10001
(212) 689-2713
Fax: (212) 532-6519
Email: storf@aol.com

Key Contact - Specialty:
Mr. Herbert F. Storfer - *Cosmetics & fragrance industry, packaging industry*
Mr. Paul D. Storfer - *Pharmaceutical, human resources*

Description: A highly professional, specialized executive search firm offering focused, personalized service for major companies in the cosmetics, healthcare, food and packaging industries. Established in 1970.

Salary Minimum: $50,000
Functions: Quality, Purchasing, Materials Plng., Packaging, Mktg. mgmt., Sales mgmt., MIS mgmt.
Industries: Food/bev/tobacco, Soap/perfume/cosmetics, Drugs mfg., Plastics/rubber, Packaging

Strategic Alliance Network, Ltd.

10901 Reed Hartman Hwy., Ste. 217
Cincinnati, Ohio 45242
(513) 792-2800
Fax: (513) 791-9162
Email: alliance@eos.net

Key Contact - Specialty:
Ms. Gina R. Brown - *Accounting & finance*
Ms. Theresa L. Oldfield - *Information technologies*

Description: Our experienced staff of certified personnel consultants is dedicated to providing thouroughly screened, quality candidates that are carefully matched to meet our client's employment needs.
Functions: CFO's, Budgeting, Taxes, MIS mgmt., Systems anal., Systems dev., Systems implem.
Industries: Computer equip., Misc. financial, Computer svcs., Accounting, Software

Strategic Assoc., Inc.

13915 Burnet Rd., Ste. 300
Austin, Texas 78728
(512) 218-8222
Fax: (512) 218-8102
Email: sai@strategicassociates.com

Key Contact - Specialty:
Mr. Michael L. Goldman - *Manufacturing consulting, logistics consulting*
Mr. Greg Coleman - *Logistics & distribution, materials management*
Mr. Ralph Cyphers - *High technology, consulting*
Ms. Carrie Beaton - *Manufacturing operations*
Ms. Amy Tutchings - *Purchasing*

Description: Specializing in manufacturing operations, materials management, purchasing, distribution, manufacturing systems and technologies and manufacturing consulting professionals nationwide. Clients are among broad cross-section of industries and major consulting practices.

Salary Minimum: $65,000
Functions: Plant mgmt., Productivity, Purchasing, Distribution, Systems implem., Engineering, Mgmt. consultants
Industries: Mfg., Food/bev/tobacco, Computer equip., Consumer electronics, Misc. mfg., Mgmt. consulting, High tech

Strategic Resources Biotechnology & Medical Group

6210 146th Place SE
Bellevue, Washington 98006-4337
(425) 688-9807
Fax: (425) 747-4274
Email: info@srbmg.com
Web: www.srbmg.com

Key Contact - Specialty:
Ms. Rena Roberts Bouchard - *Pharmaceuticals, biotechnology, medical devices*

Description: Nationwide executive search firm specializing in recruiting for biotechnology, medical, pharmaceutical industries. Typical candidates have 3-5 years of relevant industry experience. Sales, product managers, director to vice president level.

Salary Minimum: $80,000
Functions: Directors, Senior mgmt., Middle mgmt., Mkt. research, Mktg. mgmt., Sales mgmt., HR mgmt.
Industries: Drugs mfg., Medical devices, Pharmaceutical svcs., Human resource svcs., Biotech, Healthcare

Strategic Resources

1607 116th Ave. NE, Ste. 104
Bellevue, Washington 98004
(425) 688-1151
Fax: (425) 688-1272
Email: info@strategicresources.com
Web: www.strategicresources.com

Key Contact - Specialty:
Mr. Philip Kagan - *Agricultural, food science*
Mr. Ted Warren - *Advertising, public relations*
Mr. Mike Esler - *Security, facilities management*
Mr. Dick Trueb - *Consumer products*
Mr. Roberto Martinez - *Ethnic marketing*
Ms. Carie Vennetti - *Apparel, retailing*
Mr. Mark Zender - *Sports, sporting goods*
Ms. Melanie Hamilton - *International executive management*
Mr. Stephen Furst - *Executive management, operations*

Description: We are a principals only executive search firm specializing in advertising, animal health and nutrition, apparel, communications, consumer products sales and marketing, facilities management/logistics, food science/technology, international executive management, marketing, media, operations management, retailing, security, and sports/sporting goods.

Salary Minimum: $50,000
Functions: General mgmt., Product dev., Plant mgmt., Packaging, Sales & mktg., R&D, Int'l.
Industries: Agri/forestry/mining, Textiles/apparel, Wholesale, Retail, Law enfcmt., Communications

Strategic Search, LLC

47 Finca, Ste. 100
San Clemente, California 92672
(949) 369-8545
Fax: (949) 369-8546
Email: info@strategicsearch.com
Web: www.top-tier.com

Key Contact - Specialty:
Mr. Glenn M. Fox - *Strategic planning, corporate finance, consulting*
Ms. Deborah D. Lefier - *Marketing*

Description: Our candidate profile: top-school MBA with 2-12 years of progressive work experience from top-tier, A companies and consulting firms.

Salary Minimum: $100,000
Functions: Senior mgmt., Mktg. mgmt., Cash mgmt., M&A, Mgmt. consultants
Industries: Mfg., Food/bev/tobacco, Hospitality, Communications, High tech

Strategic Technologies, Inc.
2183 Buckingham Rd., Ste. 232
Richardson, Texas 75081
(972) 490-9192
Web: sandi1@mail.airmail.net

Key Contact - Specialty:
Ms. Sandi M. Taylor - *Plastics, composites*

Description: Specialize in the plastics and composites industries; clients include materials manufacturers, compounders, molders and fabricators. Domestic and international clientele; full range including sales and marketing, product development, manufacturing, operations and materials management, R&D, engineering, process engineering, etc.

Salary Minimum: $40,000
Functions: General mgmt., Mfg., Sales & mktg., HR mgmt., R&D, Engineering, Int'l.
Industries: Plastics/rubber

Stratin Assoc.
242 Old New Brunswick Rd., Ste. 100
Piscataway, New Jersey 08854
(908) 562-9337
Fax: (908) 562-9448

Key Contact - Specialty:
Mr. Andrew Borkin
Ms. Lisa Gold - *Banking & financial services*

Description: A full service human resource consulting firm specializing in the placement of mid and lower level management positions.

Salary Minimum: $25,000
Functions: Generalist, Middle mgmt., Mfg., Sales & mktg., HR mgmt., Finance, IT
Industries: Generalist, Paper, Soap/perfume/cosmetics, Misc. mfg., Banking, Misc. financial, Insurance

Strauss Personnel Service
Investment Building, Ste. 1105
239 Fourth Ave.
Pittsburgh, Pennsylvania 15222
(412) 281-8235
Fax: (412) 281-9417
Email: jeff@ihire.com
Web: www.ihire.com

Key Contact - Specialty:
Mr. T. Jeff McGraw
Mr. Jay K. Jarrell
Mr. Chuck Conner - *Accounting, finance, sales*
Ms. Nancy Rexroad - *Sales, accounting, finance*
Ms. Cathy Stackhouse - *Administrative*

Description: 45 years of experience providing small to medium sized companies talented professional and management level personnel. Searches are conducted on a local level or nationwide from a Pittsburgh base utilizing NPA affiliates.

Functions: Admin. svcs., Sales & mktg., Direct mktg., Finance, Mgmt. consultants
Industries: Energy/utilities, Mfg., Finance, Accounting, Mgmt. consulting, High tech

Success Seekers Connection
3339 Tiki Drive
Holiday, Florida 34691-3262
(813) 934-9222
Fax: (813) 938-8166

Key Contact - Specialty:
Mr. Peter Louis Peters - *Marketing & sales, MIS, information technology, software engineers, manufacturing*

Description: Experiences since 1955 mandate an honest/candid relationship with both the success seeker and the potential employer-client. As such, I practice personalized, confidential executive search and placement of achievers.

Salary Minimum: $25,000
Functions: Generalist, Senior mgmt., Production, Materials Plng., Personnel, IT, Engineering
Industries: Drugs mfg., Computer equip., Banking, Advertising/PR, Aerospace, Insurance

Sudina Search, Inc.
375 W. Padonia Rd., Ste. 235
The Atrium
Timonium, Maryland 21093
(410) 252-6900
Fax: (410) 252-8033
Email: resume@sudinasearch.com
Web: www.sudinasearch.com

Key Contact - Specialty:
Mr. Chuck Sudina - *Information systems, accounting, finance, healthcare*

Description: Concentrating in the accounting and information systems areas, we are one of Baltimore's largest search firms. Established in 1983, we currently have a staff of 14 recruiters and specialize in $40-120,000 level positions.

Salary Minimum: $40,000
Functions: Healthcare, Finance, IT
Industries: Finance, Computer svcs., Accounting, High tech, Software, Healthcare

Summerfield Assoc., Inc.
6555 Quince Rd., Ste. 311
The Koger Ctr.
Memphis, Tennessee 38119
(901) 753-7068
Fax: (901) 753-8947
Email: dsummerfield@summerfield.net
Web: www.summerfield.net

Key Contact - Specialty:
Ms. Dotty Summerfield-Beall - *Human resources, information systems, logistics*

Description: Principals bring 40+ years combined experience in recruiting and consulting services. Consistently establish solid rapport with client companies by meeting their business goals and objectives. Recognized top producer in field.

Salary Minimum: $35,000
Functions: Purchasing, HR mgmt., MIS mgmt., Systems anal., Systems dev., Attorneys
Industries: Generalist, Lumber/furniture, Paper, Printing, Hospitality, Telecoms

The Summit Group
860 Hampshire Rd., Ste. W
Thousand Oaks, California 91361
(805) 449-1323
Fax: (805) 449-1326
Email: sumgroup@earthlink.net

Key Contact - Specialty:
Mr. Larry Ross - *Software engineering, software quality assurance, programming, telecommunications, information technology marketing,*

Description: Executive search/information technology recruiting, specializing in software engineering, programmers and information services/MIS placement, software quality assurance and technical marketing.

Salary Minimum: $30,000
Functions: Directors, Senior mgmt., MIS mgmt., Systems dev., Systems implem., Network admin., DB admin.
Industries: Computer svcs., Mgmt. consulting, Publishing, Telecoms, High tech, Software

Summit Search Specialists
(a division of Ashford Resources, Inc.)
14825 St. Mary's Lane, #275
Houston, Texas 77079
(281) 497-5840
Fax: (281) 497-5841
Email: summit@phoenix.net
Web: www.phoenix.net/~summit

Key Contact - Specialty:
Mr. David S. Bunce - *Property & casualty insurance*

Description: Over 21 years specializing in the placement of quality insurance professionals. Nationwide in scope and affiliated with two national recruiting organizations.

Salary Minimum: $50,000

Functions: Senior mgmt., Middle mgmt., Product dev., CFO's, Risk mgmt., MIS mgmt.
Industries: Insurance

Ron Sunshine & Assoc.
20 N. Wacker Drive, Ste. 1731
Chicago, Illinois 60606
(312) 558-5502
Fax: (312) 558-9770
Email: rlsunshine@aol.com

Key Contact - Specialty:
Mr. Ron Sunshine - *Manufacturing, engineering*
Mr. Scott Frazier - *Broadcast, cable communications*
Ms. Barbara Blake - *Food, executive temp*

Description: Placement of middle and upper management in all fields of manufacturing and engineering-metals, plastics and consumer goods.

Salary Minimum: $50,000
Functions: Senior mgmt., Middle mgmt., Production, Plant mgmt., Quality, Purchasing, Materials Plng.
Industries: Medical devices, Plastics/rubber, Metal products, Machinery/Appliances, Motor vehicles, Entertainment, Broadcast & Film

---

Survival Systems Staffing, Inc.
2149 Portola Rd.
Ventura, California 93003
(805) 650-8888
Fax: (805) 650-8976
Email: email@survivalsystems.com
Web: www.survivalsystems.com

Key Contact - Specialty:
Mr. Dennis Nickerson - *Engineers & CEOs (high level technology searches)*
Ms. Jeanette Nickerson
Ms. Sandy Schreiber - *Electronic power conversion (retained only)*

Description: We are a national leading, award winning, high technology electronics search firm with skills ranging from engineers and managers of engineering, operations, manufacturing, quality, sales and marketing, CFOs and CEOs. Our areas of expertise include power conversion, motors, drives, semiconductors, electric vehicle, magnetics, lighting, batteries, information control technology, utility and telecommunications.

Salary Minimum: $50,000
Functions: Senior mgmt., Product dev., Quality, Mktg. mgmt., Sales mgmt., Systems anal., Engineering
Industries: Energy/utilities, Computer equip., Test/measurement equip., Broadcast & Film, Telecoms, Aerospace, High tech

Professional Associations: IACPR

Swift & Assoc.
71 Carleton St.
Portland, Maine 04102
(207) 773-0330
Fax: (207) 773-7445
Email: cswift@swiftassociates.com
Web: www.swiftassociates.com

Key Contact - Specialty:
Ms. Catherine Swift - *General business including marketing, finance, advertising, design as well as law*

Description: 20 years' experience successfully directing and implementing executive search strategies in the legal, investment, manufacturing and retail professions. Formerly president of Maine's first legal search firm and served as Cole Haan's first in-house search professional.
Functions: Generalist, Middle mgmt., Purchasing, Customer svc., CFO's
Industries: Mfg., Leather/stone/glass/clay, Retail, New media

---

Synagent Inc.
130 Slater St., Ste. 750
Ottawa, Ontario K1P 6E2
Canada
(613) 832-1122
Email: john.bickerstaff@synagent.com
Web: www.synagent.com

Key Contact - Specialty:
Mr. John Bickerstaff - *Inventory finance, equipment leasing, vehicle leasing*
Ms. Tiziana Pelusi - *Insurance*

Description: Recruit sales and credit personnel for financial services companies specialized in inventory finance and equipment leasing in North America.

Salary Minimum: $50,000
Functions: Mktg. mgmt., Sales mgmt., Credit, M&A, Risk mgmt.
Industries: Finance, Banking, Misc. financial

Affiliates:
Ambridge Management Corp.

Synergistech Communications
1824 Byron Ave.
San Mateo, California 94401-3404
(650) 344-2141
Fax: (650) 344-5664
Email: pubpros@synergistech.com
Web: www.synergistech.com

Key Contact - Specialty:
Mr. Andrew Davis - *Technical writing (software development)*
Ms. Alice Gallagher - *Marketing communications (software development)*
Ms. Jessica Hart - *Staff placements*

Description: We recruit staff and contract technical writers, editors, trainers, web content creators and desktop publishers for San Francisco Bay area software companies. We charge low commissions and offer the highest rates.

Salary Minimum: $40,000
Functions: Systems anal., Systems dev., Systems implem., Network admin., DB admin., Engineering, Graphic artists
Industries: Computer svcs., Publishing, New media, Telecoms, High tech, Software, Biotech

---

Synergy 2000
1899 L Street NW, Ste.500
Washington, District of Columbia 20036
(202) 452-1227
Fax: (202) 452-1229
Email: densyn2000@aol.com

Key Contact - Specialty:
Mr. Denman Hamilton - *High technology, diversity recruiting, finance, senior management*

Description: Specialists in high technology, healthcare, legal, public relations, financial and diversity recruiting. Clients include major high technology, consulting, banks, telecommunication and healthcare institutions.

Salary Minimum: $60,000
Functions: Senior mgmt., Finance, IT, MIS mgmt., Systems anal., Systems implem., Minorities
Industries: Finance, Mgmt. consulting, Defense, High tech, Software, Healthcare

---

Synergy Solutions, Ltd.
P.O. Box 28328
Bellingham, Washington 98228-0328
(360) 988-2066
Fax: (360) 988-0316
Email: synergy@becksolutions.com
Web: www.becksolutions.com

Key Contact - Specialty:
Mr. Larry Beck - *Executive, high technology, materials, purchasing, senior level*
Mr. Mitch Tlustos - *Entry to mid-level*

Description: We specialize in purchasing, materials, Big 6 consulting, supply chain, automotive design engineers, information technology, microwave technology, RF, high technology and EDA (PCB, FPGA, ASIC) professionals at all levels with clients in California, Oregon, Washington, Nebraska, Maryland,Georgia, Ohio, Tennessee, Texas, Toronto and offshore opportunities for tandem systems programmers.

Salary Minimum: $40,000
Functions: Purchasing, Systems anal., Systems dev., Systems implem., Network admin., DB admin., Engineering

Industries: Motor vehicles, Test/ measurement equip., Computer svcs., Mgmt. consulting, Aerospace, High tech, Software

Synergy Systems

(Firm declined to update.)
40 Sheppard Ave. W., Ste. 507
North York, Ontario M2N 6K9
Canada
(416) 590-1969

Key Contact - Specialty:
Mr. Bruce Cowan - *Computer vendor, end-user market*
Mr. John Hall - *Computer vendor, end-user market*
Mr. Tony Graham - *End-user market*

Description: Senior recruiters who know the computer vendor and end-user computing environment in eastern Canada both permanent and contract. Quick, discreet, professional service is our credo.

Salary Minimum: $40,000
Functions: Advertising, Mktg. mgmt., Direct mktg., PR, MIS mgmt., Systems dev., Systems support
Industries: High tech, Software

System 1 Search

3021 Citrus Circle, Ste. 230
Walnut Creek, California 94598
(925) 932-8801
Fax: (925) 932-3651
Email: system1@ccnet.com
Web: www.system1search.com

Key Contact - Specialty:
Mr. David Doyle - *Technical, engineers, production, quality*

Description: Special emphasis on Bay area candidates due to the high cost of relocations. We offer a total of 20 years in the search industry. We conduct searches in all Western states.
Functions: Production, Plant mgmt., Materials Plng., R&D, Engineering
Industries: Chemicals, Drugs mfg., Computer equip., High tech, Software, Biotech

Systems Careers

211 Sutter St., Ste. 607
San Francisco, California 94108
(415) 434-4770
Fax: (415) 434-1529
Email: Wayne_Sarchett@msn.com

Key Contact - Specialty:
Mr. A. Wayne Sarchett - *Software, consulting*

Description: Broad range of executive placement services in the computing industry in systems development, software engineering, technical marketing, customer support, QA management, consulting, hardware and software vendor professionals.

Salary Minimum: $80,000
Functions: Mkt. research, Mktg. mgmt., Systems dev., Systems implem., Engineering, Mgmt. consultants
Industries: Computer svcs., Mgmt. consulting, New media, High tech, Software

Systems One Ltd.

1100 E. Woodfield Rd.
Schaumburg, Illinois 60173
(847) 619-9300
Fax: (847) 619-0071
Email: recruitsos@aol.com

Key Contact - Specialty:
Mr. Edward V. Hildy - *Information technology, human resources*

Description: We offer effective information technology and human resources recruiting services to our corporate clients enabling them to pursue their strategic corporate goals.

Salary Minimum: $60,000
Functions: HR mgmt., Finance, MIS mgmt., Systems anal., Systems dev., Systems implem., Systems support
Industries: Generalist, Finance, Computer svcs., Accounting, Human resource svcs., Software

Affiliates:
The Raleigh Warwick Group

Systems Personnel, Inc.

256 Stonehenge Drive
Orchard Park, New York 14127
(716) 677-2667
Fax: (716) 677-0658
Email: compro@pce.net
Web: www.systemspersonnel.com

Key Contact - Specialty:
Mr. Jim Cipriani, Jr. - *Computer*
Mr. Jim Cipriani, Sr. - *Computer*

Description: Is a firm that provides computer staffing on a direct or temporary basis. We strive to differentiate ourselves by providing value added computer services and by thoroughly understanding our clients' needs.
Functions: MIS mgmt., Systems anal., Systems dev., Systems implem., Systems support, Network admin., DB admin.
Industries: Computer equip., Banking, Computer svcs., Broadcast & Film, Telecoms, High tech, Software

Systems Research Group

162 S. Rancho Santa Fe Rd., Ste. B-80
Encinitas, California 92024
(760) 436-1575
Fax: (760) 634-3614
Email: jobs@systemsresearchgroup.com
Web: www.systemsresearchgroup.com

Key Contact - Specialty:
Mr. Stephen Gebler - *High tech executives, sales & marketing*
Mr. Earl Pinger - *CAD, CAM, CAE, high technology*
Ms. Lola Jordeth - *PDM, EDM, ERP*

Description: Specializes in CAD, CAM, CAE, rapid prototyping, product data management and other computer applications. Plastics technology and industrial automation. Sales, marketing, application engineering and customer support.

Salary Minimum: $60,000
Functions: Directors, Senior mgmt., Middle mgmt., Mkt. research, Mktg. mgmt., Sales mgmt., Systems implem.
Industries: Plastics/rubber, High tech, Software

Systems Research Group

231 W. Fourth St., #607A
Cincinnati, Ohio 45202
(513) 381-2222
Fax: (513) 381-2204
Email: srg@fuse.net

Key Contact - Specialty:
Mr. James Cole - *Architect, engineering, construction*
Mr. Bryn Lewis - *Architect*

Description: We recruit top talent in the U. S., Latin America, Europe and the Pacific Rim. Clients include some of the best design and construction firms internationally.
Functions: Engineering, Architects
Industries: Construction

Systems Research Inc. (SRI)

1051 Perimeter Drive, Ste. 1075
Schaumburg, Illinois 60173
(847) 330-1222
Fax: (847) 330-1411
Email: sriinc1@aol.com
Web: www.systemsresearchinc.com

Key Contact - Specialty:
Mr. Dan Kuesis - *Technical, engineering, manufacturing, materials*
Mr. Frank Agnello - *Technical, engineering, manufacturing, materials*
Mr. Rich Kane - *Technical, engineering, manufacturing, materials*
Mr. Art Hurley - *Technical, engineering, manufacturing, materials*
Ms. Carol Miller - *Finance & accounting*

Description: Our programs offer you complete confidentiality and the satisfaction of knowing you are effectively managing the difficult recruitment process by delegating the effort to qualified professionals trained in and solely responsible for its successful outcome.

Salary Minimum: $40,000
Functions: Mfg., Materials, Finance, IT, Engineering, Architects, Technicians
Industries: Mfg., Finance, Computer svcs., Aerospace, High tech, Software

Affiliates:
SRI Technologies, Inc.

Systems Search
2366 Bradshire Court
Arlington Heights, Illinois 60004
(847) 577-0595
Fax: (847) 632-0224
Email: ed@sysearch.com
Web: www.sysearch.com

Key Contact - Specialty:
Mr. Edward Nathan - *Information technology*

Description: Concentrate on client satisfaction which has developed our reputation for excellence. We screen, interview and evaluate candidates and clients, to make sure you're getting the service and results you expect.

Salary Minimum: $30,000
Functions: IT, MIS mgmt., Systems anal., Systems dev., Systems support, Network admin., DB admin.
Industries: Misc. mfg., Finance, Computer svcs., Insurance, High tech, Software, Healthcare

---

Systems Search Group, Inc.
16507-E Northcross Drive
Huntersville, North Carolina 28078
(704) 895-8440
Fax: (704) 895-8441
Email: ssgnc@ibm.net

Key Contact - Specialty:
Ms. Eileen Brady - *Information systems*

Description: Information systems search and placement of operational, analysts/programmers, systems programmers, administrators and management professionals in the Southeast region of the US, predominantly in North Carolina, targeting industry leading, Fortune 500 companies.
Functions: MIS mgmt., Systems anal., Systems dev., Systems implem., Systems support
Industries: Mgmt. consulting, Human resource svcs., High tech

---

T E M Assoc.
P.O. Box 5243
De Pere, Wisconsin 54115
(920) 339-8055
Fax: (920) 339-6177
Email: mccracken@execpc.com

Key Contact - Specialty:
Ms. Terri McCracken - *Pulp, paper, converting industry, consumer products*

Description: Specialize in the paper and forest products areas, as well as related industries and consumer products. Nationwide focus with special attention to Midwest region.

Salary Minimum: $40,000
Functions: Production, Plant mgmt., Materials, Sales & mktg., Mkt. research, HR mgmt., Engineering
Industries: Paper, Chemicals, Soap/perfume/cosmetics, Machinery/Appliances, Packaging

---

T. H. Hunter, Inc.
526 Nicollet Mall, Ste. 310
Minneapolis, Minnesota 55402
(612) 339-0530
Fax: (612) 339-1937
Email: mconroy@thhunter.com

Key Contact - Specialty:
Mr. Martin Conroy - *Generalist*
Mr. Robert Beller - *Generalist*

Description: A downtown Minneapolis generalist firm with a national practice specializing in client oriented custom tailored searches, focusing on active recruiting of the best possible candidates.
Functions: Generalist, General mgmt., Sales & mktg., HR mgmt., Finance, Credit, IT
Industries: Generalist, Finance, Computer svcs., Accounting, Telecoms, Software, Healthcare

---

Roy Talman & Assoc.
150 South Wacker Drive, Suite 2250
Chicago, Illinois 60606
(312) 425-1300
Fax: (312) 425-0100
Email: resume@roy-talman.com
Web: www.roy-talman.com

Key Contact - Specialty:
Mr. Ilya Talman - *Information technology, software*
Mr. Hal Klegman

Description: Retained and contingency technology search firm. Specialist in software and related information technology. All positions are for Chicago area employers.

Salary Minimum: $35,000
Functions: Risk mgmt., MIS mgmt., Systems anal., Systems dev., Systems implem., Systems support, Mgmt. consultants
Industries: Brokers, Misc. financial, Computer svcs., Mgmt. consulting, High tech, Software

---

S. Tanner & Assoc. Inc.
700 Dorval Drive, Ste. 503
Oakville Corporate Centre
Oakville, Ontario L6K 3V3
Canada
(905) 339-2233
Fax: (905) 339-2230
Email: stanner@globalserve.net
Web: www.globalserve.net/~stanner

Key Contact - Specialty:
Mr. Steve Tanner - *Engineering, operations management, logistics*
Ms. Joanne Tanner - *Engineering, operations management, logistics*
Mr. Brian J. Connors - *Engineering, operations management, logistics*

Description: Quality is never an accident. It is always the result of high intentions, sincere effort, intelligent direction and skillful execution; it represents the wise choice of many alternatives.

Salary Minimum: $35,000
Functions: Generalist, Middle mgmt., Production, Quality, Purchasing, Packaging, Engineering
Industries: Generalist, Food/bev/tobacco, Printing, Drugs mfg., Plastics/rubber, Misc. mfg., Packaging

---

Tarbex
4545 Connecticut Ave. NW, Ste. 326
Washington, District of Columbia 20008-6009
(202) 244-9258
Email: seniorrecruiter@tarbex.com
Web: www.tarbex.com

Key Contact - Specialty:
Ms. Parul Bhandari - *Generalist, information technology, consulting*

Description: We conduct highly selective searches in a timely and cost effective manner for healthcare, telecom, major national, international, regional and boutique consulting firms using personalized and customized partnership approach.

Salary Minimum: $40,000
Functions: General mgmt., Healthcare, Sales & mktg., Finance, IT, Systems implem., Mgmt. consultants
Industries: Finance, Mgmt. consulting, Communications, Telecoms, High tech, Software, Healthcare

Target Search, Inc.
Station Sq. One, Ste. 204
Paoli, Pennsylvania 19301
(610) 889-2000
Fax: (610) 889-2424

Key Contact - Specialty:
Mr. Paul S. Berry
Ms. Pat Toomey

Description: Client driven - innovative - flexible services - 40 years of industry - related field management experience. 10 years successful recruiting in food and contract management, healthcare and restaurants.

Salary Minimum: $35,000
Functions: Directors, Senior mgmt., Middle mgmt., Sales mgmt., Personnel, Engineering, Minorities
Industries: Retail, Hospitality, Entertainment, Environmental svcs.

M. L. Tawney & Assoc.
P.O. Box 630573
Houston, Texas 77263-0573
(713) 784-9163
Email: mtawney@ix.netcom.com

Key Contact - Specialty:
Mr. Mel Tawney - *ERP package based solutions*

Description: Executive search, on an international basis. Associates in Western Europe, Far East, Central and South America and Australia.

Salary Minimum: $50,000
Functions: General mgmt., Mfg., Materials, Sales & mktg., IT, Engineering, Mgmt. consultants
Industries: Generalist, Energy/utilities, Chemicals, Computer equip., Computer svcs., Mgmt. consulting, Software

Tax Network Resources, Inc.
19 Hanover Place, Ste. 257
Hicksville, New York 11801
(516) 777-7167
Fax: (516) 752-8553
Email: TaxNetwork@aol.com

Key Contact - Specialty:
Mr. Mike Marino - *Public accounting (all areas), audit & tax, internal audit, corporate tax*

Description: Specialize in tax, accounting, audit and consulting in NYC metro, Philadelphia and Hartford areas. President has hands-on experience after working for CPA firms in audit/tax/accounting departments.

Salary Minimum: $25,000
Functions: Generalist, HR mgmt., Finance, Taxes, IT, Specialized services, Mgmt. consultants
Industries: Generalist, Finance, Banking, Svcs., Accounting, Insurance, Healthcare

Branches:
60 E. 42nd St., Ste. 746
New York, New York 10165
(212) 983-3030
Key Contact - Specialty:
Mr. Mike Marino

Peter R. Taylor Assoc., Inc.
43 Orchard Drive
East Williston, New York 11596
(516) 742-9292
Fax: (516) 742-9296

Key Contact - Specialty:
Mr. Peter R. Taylor - *Retail real estate*

Description: Corporate real estate executive search, retail chains, financial institutions, developers, industrial corporations.

Salary Minimum: $50,000
Industries: Real estate

TBC, Inc.
2437 La Cross Court
Lexington, Kentucky 40514
(606) 296-2491
Fax: (606) 296-4356
Email: bogueco@mindspring.com
Web: www.bogueco.com

Key Contact - Specialty:
Mr. Randall L. Bogue - *Telecommunications, software, sales & marketing, general management*
Mr. Kevin Maher - *Telecommunications, internet, marketing, engineering management*
Mr. Phill Gunning - *E-commerce, internet, utilities, sales & marketing, general*

Salary Minimum: $60,000
Functions: Senior mgmt., Middle mgmt., Mkt. research, Mktg. mgmt., M&A, Systems implem., Network admin.
Industries: Energy/utilities, Test/measurement equip., Computer svcs., Mgmt. consulting, New media, Telecoms, Software

TCM Enterprises
57 W. Timonium Rd., Ste. 310
Timonium, Maryland 21093
(410) 561-5244
Fax: (410) 561-5248
Email: tmcpoyle@erols.com

Key Contact - Specialty:
Mr. Thomas C. McPoyle, Jr. - *Engineers, scientists*

Description: Defense electronics, material scientists, meteorologists, shock physicists, chemical and environmental specialties, intelligent vehicle highway systems people and experts in marketing and accounting/finance.
Functions: General mgmt., Materials, Sales & mktg., Finance, IT, R&D, Engineering
Industries: Mfg., Transportation, Defense, Environmental svcs., Aerospace, High tech, Software

TE, Inc.
1919 Midwest Rd.
Oak Brook, Illinois 60521
(630) 325-8627
Fax: (630) 325-8630
Email: info_te@teinc.com
Web: www.teinc.com

Key Contact - Specialty:
Mr. Eric K. Schuller - *Generalist*
Ms. Bonita Mae - *Generalist*

Description: We have the philosophy of catering to the client needs and to determine the most effective candidate for the position. Our management consulting group caters to the middle tier of management.

Salary Minimum: $35,000
Functions: Production, Mkt. research, MIS mgmt., Systems anal., Systems dev., Systems implem., Systems support
Industries: Generalist

Team One Partners, Inc.
3901 Roswell Rd. NE, Ste. 205
Marietta, Georgia 30062
(770) 579-3877
Fax: (770) 579-3994
Email: teamone@ibm.net

Key Contact - Specialty:
Mr. Robb Robley
Mr. Tom Arnette

Description: When we tackle a search, we dedicate a team to completely canvasse the applicable industries, disciplines and geographies. Our canvassing process quickly provides a comprehensive look at the top performers, how they rank among their peers and how to attract them to your team.
Functions: Senior mgmt., Middle mgmt., Mfg., Sales mgmt., Finance, IT
Industries: Agri/forestry/mining, Energy/utilities, Food/bev/tobacco, Paper, Chemicals, Hospitality, Healthcare

TeamBuilders
3081 Holcomb Bridge Rd., Ste. A1
Norcross, Georgia 30071
(770) 416-0996
Fax: (770) 416-0894
Email: teambldr@mindspring.com
Web: www.teambuilder.com

Key Contact - Specialty:
Mr. Buz Mayo - *Information systems management; systems networking*

Description: We serve employers by understanding technology as it relates to business. We locate people who demonstrate, by their attitude and experience, their commitment to an integrity-based work ethic.
Functions: MIS mgmt., Systems anal., Systems dev., Systems implem., Systems support
Industries: Legal, Computer svcs., Accounting, Telecoms, High tech, Software

Teamsearch, Inc.

27600 Farmington Rd., Ste. 108
Farmington Hills, Michigan 48334
(248) 553-9881
Fax: (248) 553-9883
Email: passons@bignet.net

Key Contact - Specialty:
Mr. Steven A. Passon - *Automation machinery, machine tool, special machinery*

Description: A nationwide network of service to the assembly and automation equipment and metal working machine and equipment industries.

Salary Minimum: $35,000
Functions: Product dev., Production, Automation, Plant mgmt., Productivity, Purchasing, Engineering
Industries: Metal products, Machinery/ Appliances, Motor vehicles, Test/ measurement equip., Misc. mfg.

Tech 2000

P.O. Box 2099
Valrico, Florida 33595-2099
(813) 643-0600
Fax: (813) 643-0700
Email: tech2000@worldnet.att.net

Key Contact - Specialty:
Mr. Arthur J. Arcand - *MIS, telecommunications*
Ms. Roberta Jones - *MIS, telecommunications*

Description: We provide a respected, unique service-permanent MIS/telecommunications placement only and only in the state of Florida-by two acknowledged technical recruiting leaders.

Salary Minimum: $40,000
Functions: IT, Systems anal., Systems dev., Systems implem.
Industries: Generalist, Computer svcs., Accounting, New media, Telecoms, High tech, Software

Tech Connector Group

2899 Agoura Rd., Ste. 252
Westlake Village, California 91361
(805) 496-3994
Fax: (805) 496-5515
Email: search@techconnector.com
Web: www.techconnector.com

Key Contact - Specialty:
Ms. Priscilla Jacobson - *Telecommunications, data communications*

Description: We are a dynamic, proactive team dedicated to providing employers and candidates with a superior match. We carefully and diligently match your requirements and the career objectives of our candidates.
Functions: Mkt. research, MIS mgmt., Systems anal., Systems dev., Systems implem., Systems support, Engineering
Industries: Computer equip., Telecoms, High tech, Software

Tech Consulting

50 S. Belcher Rd., Ste. 113
Clearwater, Florida 34625
(813) 443-5335
Fax: (813) 446-4183
Email: tc4mb@aol.com

Key Contact - Specialty:
Mr. Mark Bavli - *Telecommunications engineering*

Description: Recruiting for Fortune 100 and subsidiaries in areas of computers, telecommunications - only - engineering and marketing-in computers/ telecommunications.

Salary Minimum: $40,000
Functions: Mkt. research, Mktg. mgmt., Systems anal., Systems dev., R&D, Engineering
Industries: Computer equip., Computer svcs., Telecoms, High tech, Software

Tech Search

2015 Bridgeway, Ste. 301
Sausalito, California 94965
(415) 332-1282
Fax: (415) 332-1285
Email: resume@jobsight.com
Web: www.jobsight.com

Key Contact - Specialty:
Mr. Roger M. King - *Senior level management*

Description: We specialize in staffing technology companies in both the US and Europe.

Salary Minimum: $50,000
Functions: Senior mgmt., Middle mgmt., MIS mgmt., Systems dev., Systems implem., Network admin., Int'l.
Industries: Computer equip., Consumer electronics, Computer svcs., Telecoms, High tech, Software

Tech-Net

(Firm declined to update.)
4223 Timberglen, Ste. 450
Dallas, Texas 75287
(972) 934-3000
Email: technet@onramp.net
Web: rampages.onramp.net/~technet

Key Contact - Specialty:
Mr. Christopher Cole - *Technical, sales, sales support, consultants*
Ms. Laurie Sprouse - *PeopleSoft, MIS*

Description: We specialize in matching experienced technical professionals for sales, engineering, software or Unix based business solution positions. Candidates must have excellent presentation and communication skills.
Functions: Automation, Mktg. mgmt., Benefits, Cash mgmt., IT, R&D, Engineering
Industries: Computer equip., Test/ measurement equip., Computer svcs., Human resource svcs., Aerospace, High tech, Software
Professional Associations: IACPR

Techaid Inc.

5165 Queen Mary Rd., Ste. 401
Montreal, Quebec H3W 1X7
Canada
(514) 482-6790
(800) 341-6790
Fax: (514) 482-0324
Email: info@techaid.ca
Web: www.techaid.ca

Key Contact - Specialty:
Mr. William F. Allen

Description: We recruit and provide experienced technical staff on a temporary or permanent basis. We are the longest established technical personnel agency in Quebec with over 1200 customers in 35 years.
Functions: Mfg., Materials, Sales & mktg., IT, Engineering, Technicians, Int'l.
Industries: Energy/utilities, Construction, Mfg., New media, Telecoms, High tech, Software

Technical Connections, Inc.

11400 Olympic Blvd., Ste. 700
Los Angeles, California 90064
(310) 479-8830
Fax: (310) 445-8726
Email:
hmackinnon@technicalconnections.com
Web: www.technicalconnections.com

Key Contact - Specialty:
Ms. Helen MacKinnon - *Computer science, information technology professionals*
Mr. Peter MacKinnon

Description: Largest S. California firm specializing strictly in computer systems professionals including MIS, software development and management consulting. Staffed by computer professionals, we conduct face-to-face interviews with all candidates.

Salary Minimum: $35,000
Functions: MIS mgmt., Systems anal., Systems dev., Systems implem., Systems support, Network admin., DB admin.
Industries: Non-classifiable industries

Technical Employment Consultants
308 Lakeside Drive
Southampton, Pennsylvania 18966
(215) 396-1503
Fax: (215) 396-1501
Email: teccarl@aol.com

Key Contact - Specialty:
Mr. Carl Richards - *Engineering, quality, manufacturing, electrical design software*
Mr. Lou Schwartz - *Engineering, quality, manufacturing, electrical design software*
Mrs. Cindy Brookes - *Engineering, quality, manufacturing, electrical design software*
Mrs. Pat Swanson

Description: Represents clients on a national basis including overseas assignments. We specialize in both the defense and commercial sectors with an emphasis in software, aerospace, avionics, plastics, power, accounting and finance.

Salary Minimum: $25,000
Functions: Production, Quality, IT, Engineering
Industries: Mfg., Plastics/rubber, Computer equip., Aerospace, High tech, Software, Biotech

Technical Recruiting Consultants
(Firm declined to update.)
1100 W. Northwest Hwy., Ste. 208
Mt. Prospect, Illinois 60056
(847) 394-1101

Key Contact - Specialty:
Mr. Dick Latimer - *MIS, engineering, manufacturing*

Description: Specialists in information systems, engineering and manufacturing positions.
Functions: MIS mgmt., Systems anal., Systems dev., Systems implem., Systems support

Technical Recruiting Services
9769 Chaucer Court
Pickerington, Ohio 43147
(614) 837-6556
Fax: (614) 837-0800
Web: nicklang@compute/net.com

Key Contact - Specialty:
Mr. Nick Lang - *Metals, materials*

Description: Client-oriented firm placing sales, marketing, senior level management and technical personnel with companies in the metals, materials, chemical, power transmission and healthcare industries. Permanent and contract placement.

Salary Minimum: $35,000
Functions: Generalist, Senior mgmt., Plant mgmt., Quality, Mktg. mgmt., Sales mgmt.
Industries: Generalist, Metal products, Aerospace

Technical Resource Assoc.
P.O. Box 1269
Hendersonville, Tennessee 37077
(615) 824-1444
Fax: (615) 824-7696

Key Contact - Specialty:
Mr. Richard D. Holtz - *Engineering, technical, scientists, management*

Description: Technical and management search in all areas of advanced materials development, research, mfg., processing, sales and marketing. Materials expertise include: engineered plastics, composites, metallics, medical plastics and ceramics. Forensic engineers.

Salary Minimum: $32,000
Functions: Product dev., Production, Plant mgmt., Quality, Mktg. mgmt., Sales mgmt., Engineering
Industries: Chemicals, Medical devices, Plastics/rubber, Metal products, Machinery/Appliances, Motor vehicles, Aerospace

Technical Search Assoc.
20325 Center Ridge Rd., Ste. 622
Westgate Plaza
Rocky River, Ohio 44116
(440) 356-0880
Fax: (440) 356-9036

Key Contact - Specialty:
Mr. John M. Brunschwig - *Engineering*

Description: Specializing in electrical, mechanical and manufacturing engineers in the electronics, automotive and aerospace industries. Also perform specialized searches per client requirements.

Salary Minimum: $40,000
Functions: Engineering
Industries: Motor vehicles, Computer equip., Consumer electronics, Aerospace, High tech, Software

Technical Staffing Solutions
16775 Addison Rd., Ste. 240
Dallas, Texas 75248
(972) 248-0700
Fax: (972) 248-1175
Email: don@technicalstaffing.com
Web: www.technicalstaffing.com

Key Contact - Specialty:
Mr. Don J. Fink - *Chemical industry*

Description: Recruit process, project, production, process control and environmental engineers for the chemical, petrochemical and petroleum refining industries on a regular employment or contractual employment basis.

Salary Minimum: $40,000
Functions: Product dev., Automation, Quality, Productivity, Systems anal., Systems dev., Engineering
Industries: Chemicals, High tech

Technifind Int'l.
5959 Gateway W., Ste. 601
El Paso, Texas 79925
(915) 775-1176
Fax: (915) 778-9314
Email: info@technifind.com
Web: www.technifind.com

Key Contact - Specialty:
Mr. Tim Vida
Mr. Bruce Steiner

Description: Extensive network established throughout north, south and central America. Very familiar with demographics in various markets and industries. Most clients in Fortune 500 list.

Salary Minimum: $50,000
Functions: General mgmt., Mfg., Materials, Sales & mktg., Finance, Engineering, Int'l.
Industries: Energy/utilities, Mfg., Environmental svcs., Packaging, High tech, Software

TechNix Inc.
1 Caines Ave.
North York, Ontario M2M 1G1
Canada
(416) 250-9195
Fax: (416) 250-0256
Email: technix@inforamp.net

Key Contact - Specialty:
Mr. Ted Nixon - *High tech vendors*

Description: Specialists in recruiting sales, marketing, pre & post sales, senior architects and executive management for technology vendors.

Salary Minimum: $60,000
Functions: Senior mgmt., Mktg. mgmt., Sales mgmt., Direct mktg., PR, MIS mgmt., Mgmt. consultants
Industries: Computer equip., Computer svcs., Mgmt. consulting, Advertising/PR, High tech, Software

Techno-Trac Systems, Inc.

251 Central Park W.
New York, New York 10024
(212) 769-8722
Fax: (212) 873-1596

Key Contact - Specialty:
Mr. Mort Trachtenberg - *Information technology professionals*

Description: NY/metropolitan based information technology search firm. President's 20+ years experience in the field yields broad client base, especially brokerage, banking and financial. Supportive candidate relationship, programmers through senior executives.

Salary Minimum: $25,000
Functions: MIS mgmt., Systems anal., Systems dev., Systems implem., Systems support, Network admin., DB admin.
Industries: Finance, Banking, Invest. banking, Brokers, Computer svcs., High tech, Software

Technology Consultants Int'l.

6965 El Camino Real, Ste. 105
Carlsbad, California 92009
(760) 436-8400
Fax: (760) 436-8900
Email: tom@techconsultants.com
Web: www.techconsultants.com

Key Contact - Specialty:
Mr. Thomas Conway

Description: We serve the computer hardware and software vendor community whose applications consist of scientific, engineering, manufacturing, intranet and enterprise wide business applications. The positions we place are in the areas of executive management, sales, marketing, support and development.

Salary Minimum: $50,000
Functions: Product dev., Automation, Purchasing, Materials Plng., Sales mgmt., Systems implem., Engineering
Industries: High tech, Software

Branches:
9134 Union Cemetery Rd., Ste. 212
Cincinnati, Ohio 45249
(513) 489-2327
Fax: (513) 489-3038
Key Contact - Specialty:
Mr. Ed Neenan

Technology Search Int'l.

25 Metro Drive, Ste. 238
San Jose, California 95110
(408) 437-9500
Fax: (408) 437-1033
Email: info@tsearch.com
Web: www.tsearch.com

Key Contact - Specialty:
Mr. Steve Dyson - *Client/server, www, distributed systems, database*
Mr. Alan Shapiro - *Operating systems, management*
Mr. Chris Dangerfield - *Consulting, operating systems, client/server*
Mr. Don Sirey - *Database, operating systems, marketing*

Description: We specialize in software development, in particular hands-on developers in the operating systems, client/server, distributed systems, database and www spaces.
Functions: Directors, Sales mgmt., Systems anal., Systems support, R&D, Engineering, Architects
Industries: Computer equip., Computer svcs., New media, High tech, Software

Techsearch Services Inc.

46 Wickford Place
Madison, Connecticut 06443
(203) 318-1100
Fax: (203) 318-8800
Email: dtaft@snet.net
Web: www.techsearchservices.com

Key Contact - Specialty:
Mr. David G. Taft

Description: Executive recruitment of information/financial services professionals and traders for major investment companies/commercial banks. Emphasis on financial services community. Particular expertise in the more analytical systems and business analysis. Fixed income, equities and derivatives.

Salary Minimum: $50,000
Functions: Risk mgmt., MIS mgmt., Systems anal., Systems dev., Systems implem., Mgmt. consultants
Industries: Banking, Invest. banking, Brokers, Misc. financial

Techstaff Inc.

(Firm declined to update.)
11270 W. Park Place, Ste. 111
Milwaukee, Wisconsin 53224
(414) 359-4444
Email: recruiter@techstaff.com
Web: www.techstaff.com

Key Contact - Specialty:
Mr. Thomas Montgomery - *Generalist, technical*
Ms. Susan Metzger - *Generalist, technical*

Description: We specialize in the recruitment and placement of engineering and technical personnel.

Salary Minimum: $35,000
Functions: Mfg., Materials, HR mgmt., Finance, IT, Engineering, Specialized services
Industries: Medical devices, Plastics/rubber, Metal products, Machinery/Appliances, Consumer electronics, Misc. mfg., Software

Branches:
3900 E. Camelback Rd., Ste. 108
Phoenix, Arizona 85018
(602) 955-6464
Key Contact - Specialty:
Mr. James Meyers

500 Esplanade Dr., Ste. 1200
Oxnard, California 93030
(805) 485-7456
Key Contact - Specialty:
Mr. Mike Moran

1200 W. Hillcrest Dr., Ste. 201
Thousand Oaks, California 91320
(805) 376-2250
Key Contact - Specialty:
Ms. Sue Duffy

1100 N. Florida Ave.
P.O. Box 172126
Tampa, Florida 33602
(813) 221-1222
Key Contact - Specialty:
Ms. Gale Porter

9801 W. Higgins Rd., Ste. 580
Rosemont, Illinois 60018
(847) 692-3090
Key Contact - Specialty:
Mr. Steve Bauer

2828-18th St., Ste. 2
Bettendorf, Iowa 52722
(319) 355-4400
Key Contact - Specialty:
Mr. Steve Nord

4829 E. Beltline Ave., NE
Grand Rapids, Michigan 49525
(616) 361-0033
Key Contact - Specialty:
Mr. Bill Gansser

2670 S. Ashland Ave., #206
Green Bay, Wisconsin 54304
(920) 498-9870
Key Contact - Specialty:
Mr. Chris Kahn
Mr. R. J. Kahn

Affiliates:
Pacific Coast Staffing

Tecmark Associates Inc.

P.O. Box 545
Port Washington, New York 11050
(516) 883-6336
(212) 947-6027
Fax: (516) 883-6388
Email: info@tecmark.com
Web: tecmark.com

Key Contact - Specialty:
Mr. Donald R. Valentine - *Electronic high technology industry*
Mr. Bradford M. Kennedy - *Electronic high technology industry*

Description: Electronic industry worldwide executive, managerial and professional search for all technology/market sensitive positions from president/CEO on through R&D, development, hard & software design engineering, manufacturing, sales, marketing, support for semiconductors, computers, instrumentation, EDA, ATE, CIM, etc.

Salary Minimum: $40,000
Functions: General mgmt., Mfg., Sales & mktg., IT, R&D, Engineering, Technicians
Industries: Medical devices, Machinery/Appliances, Computer equip., Consumer electronics, Test/measurement equip., High tech

Branches:
10675 S. DeAnza Blvd., #4
Cupertino, California 95014-4449
(408) 446-4672
Key Contact - Specialty:
Mr. Charles R. Wilkenson - *Electronic industry technical, professional & management*

1253 Worcester Rd., Ste. 302
Framingham, Massachusetts 01701-5250
(978) 897-4454
Key Contact - Specialty:
Mr. Robert T. McLean - *Electronic industry technical, professional & management*

Teknon Employment Resources, Inc.

17 S. Saint Clair St., Ste. 300
Dayton, Ohio 45402-2137
(937) 222-5300
Fax: (937) 222-6311
Email: teknon@csi.com

Key Contact - Specialty:
Mr. Raymond B. Gooch
Mr. William M. Gaffney - *Telecommunications, sales & marketing*
Mr. Joseph S. Murawski - *Engineering*

Description: We provide targeted contingency search within the telecommunications and engineering disciplines while providing access to top talent in all disciplines through network affiliations with search firms throughout the US.

Salary Minimum: $50,000
Functions: General mgmt., Directors, Senior mgmt., Mfg., Sales & mktg., Engineering
Industries: Mfg., Plastics/rubber, Machinery/Appliances, Motor vehicles, Consumer electronics, High tech, Software

Tekworx, Inc.

2250 E. 73rd St., Ste. 120A
Tulsa, Oklahoma 74136
(918) 492-3350
Fax: (918) 492-7023
Email: tekworx@huntpatton.com
Web: huntpatton.com

Key Contact - Specialty:
Mr. M. Pat Patton - *Generalist*
Ms. Linda Huddleston - *Generalist*

Description: Recruiting specialists executive, professional, technical engineering, environmental, construction, oil and gas, petroleum, chemical, computer, medical and laboratory.

Salary Minimum: $25,000
Functions: Senior mgmt., Middle mgmt., Production, Plant mgmt., Purchasing, Mktg. mgmt., Engineering
Industries: Generalist, Construction, Chemicals, Environmental svcs., Haz. waste, High tech, Software

Branches:
1200 Seventeenth St., Ste. 1000
Denver, Colorado 80202
(303) 572-0751
Fax: (303) 572-0752
Email: tekworx@huntpatton.com
Key Contact - Specialty:
Mr. Pat Patton - *Generalist*
Mr. James Jadewald - *Generalist*

2350 N. Sam Houston Pkwy. E., Ste. 210
Houston, Texas 77032
(281) 590-8356
Fax: (281) 590-8351
Email: tekworx@huntpatton.com
Key Contact - Specialty:
Mr. Patrick Burns - *Generalist*

Tele-Media Int'l. Inc.

14 S. Bryn Mawr Ave., Ste. 209
Bryn Mawr, Pennsylvania 19010
(610) 527-5957
Fax: (610) 527-5927
Email: tmi@inet.net
Web: www.tmidirect.com

Key Contact - Specialty:
Mr. William R. DePhillipo - *Telecommunications, information technology*

Description: We are a contingent search firm concentrating on mutually beneficial opportunities for our contracted telecommunication companies and prospective candidates looking for a positive career move. We are a direct link to the permanent job market.

Salary Minimum: $35,000
Functions: Senior mgmt., Middle mgmt., Sales mgmt., Direct mktg., Customer svc., IT, Technicians

Affiliates:
Executive Management Recruiters

Tele-Solutions of Arizona, Inc.

8655 E. Via De Ventura, Ste. F-127
Scottsdale, Arizona 85258
(602) 483-1300
Fax: (602) 483-7221
Email: tele-sol@primenet.com
Web: www.primenet.com/~tele-501

Key Contact - Specialty:
Ms. Carole Wichansky - *Software, telecommunications, engineering*
Ms. Janice Robertson - *Hardware, telecommunications, engineering*
Ms. Barbara McCain - *Cellular, wireless*
Ms. Cheryl Perea - *Information technology*

Description: We are a full service national engineering search firm. Degreed engineers with 2 years minimum industry experience up to the Director of Engineering.

Salary Minimum: $60,000
Functions: Systems anal., Systems dev., Systems implem., Systems support, Network admin., DB admin., Engineering
Industries: Communications, High tech, Software

Telecom Connections, Inc.

2102 Lakeway Blvd.
Austin, Texas 78734
(512) 261-3290
Fax: (512) 261-3278
Email: gorr1@compuserve.com
Web: gorr1@compuserve.com

Key Contact - Specialty:
Mr. George H. Orr - *Wireless telecommunications*

Description: Specializing in placements of middle management through executive level in wireless telecommunications companies (PCS, cellular, messaging).

Salary Minimum: $50,000
Functions: General mgmt., Sales & mktg., HR mgmt., Finance, IT, Engineering
Industries: Telecoms

Telecom Executive Group
(a division of Hagarty Associates)
4 Greentree Ctr., Ste. 403
Marlton, New Jersey 08053
(609) 985-5368
Fax: (609) 985-7496
Email: RickdeRose@msn.com
Web: www.telecomexecutive.com

Key Contact - Specialty:
Mr. Rick DeRose - *Telecommunications, sales, management*

Description: We offer sales, middle management and executive recruiting for telecommunications companies. Our focus is on carriers, CLECS, ISP's and networking companies as start-ups or existing companies.

Salary Minimum: $75,000
Functions: Directors, Senior mgmt., Middle mgmt., Mktg. mgmt., Sales mgmt., Customer svc.
Industries: New media, Broadcast & Film, Telecoms

Branches:
11 Penn Plaza, 5th Floor
New York, New York 10001
(212) 946-2894
Fax: (212) 946-2895
Email: marciyacker@msn.com
Key Contact - Specialty:
Ms. Marci Yacker Nigro - *Telecommunications, sales, management*

8537 Acadia Drive
Sagamore Hills, Ohio 44067
(216) 328-2123
Key Contact - Specialty:
Ms. Carol Barker

8000 Towers Crescent Drive, Ste. 1350
Vienna, Virginia 22182
(703) 847-3675
Key Contact - Specialty:
Ms. Katy O'Brien

Telecom Recruiters, Inc.
12531 Lt. Nichols Rd., Ste. 100
Fairfax, Virginia 22033
(703) 620-4096
Fax: (703) 620-2973
Email: ztif@erols.com
Web: www.telecom-recruiters.com

Key Contact - Specialty:
Mr. Thomas L. Fitzgerald - *Telecommunications, technical*
Mr. Matthew A. Fitzgerald - *Telecommunications, marketing & sales*

Description: We specialize in providing telecommunications professionals to service providers for landline, wireless and call centers.

Salary Minimum: $40,000
Functions: Directors, Mkt. research, Sales mgmt., Customer svc., IT, Systems anal., Engineering
Industries: Communications, Telecoms

Telem Adhesive Search Corp.
P.O. Box 656
Owings Mills, Maryland 21117
(410) 356-6200
Fax: (410) 356-5189
Email: Peter@adhesivesearch.com
Web: www.adhesivesearch.com

Key Contact - Specialty:
Mr. Peter B. Telem - *Adhesives, polymers, coatings, medical devices, film converting*

Description: We are widely recognized as one of the nation's preeminent search firms, satisfying the personnel needs of the adhesives, sealant and coating industries.

Salary Minimum: $50,000
Functions: Senior mgmt., Middle mgmt., Plant mgmt., Quality, Mktg. mgmt., Sales mgmt., R&D
Industries: Paper, Chemicals, Drugs mfg., Medical devices, Plastics/rubber, Paints/petroleum products

TeleManagement Search
114 E. 32nd St., Ste. 1231
New York, New York 10016
(212) 684-3500
(312) 527-1166
Fax: (212) 696-1287
Email: telemgnt@pipeline.com
Web: www.tmrecruiters.com

Key Contact - Specialty:
Ms. Connie Caroli - *Telemarketing, call center management*

Description: National executive search firm dedicated to recruiting professional managerial inbound, outbound and customer service personnel. Recruit at all management levels including presidents, vice presidents, directors and managers.

Salary Minimum: $40,000
Functions: Direct mktg., Customer svc.
Industries: Energy/utilities, Banking, Entertainment, Telecoms, Insurance, High tech, Healthcare

Telequest Communications, Inc.
P.O. Box 94
Mahwah, New Jersey 07430
(914) 357-2212
(914) 639-0006
Fax: (914) 369-8724
Web: www.telequestcom.com

Key Contact - Specialty:
Mr. Thomas Bartchak - *Telecommunications*
Ms. Ellen Dansky - *Telecommunications*

Description: We are a telecommunications search firm specializing in all areas of telecommunications including voice, data and local and wide area networks. We place candidates at all levels.
Functions: MIS mgmt., Systems anal., Systems implem., Systems support, Network admin.
Industries: Generalist, Telecoms

Tell/Com Recruiters
306 Corporate Drive E.
Langhorne, Pennsylvania 19047
(215) 860-4100
Fax: (215) 968-6680
Email: dyoung@tellcom.com
Web: www.tellcom.com

Key Contact - Specialty:
Mr. Dennis F. Young - *Telecommunications*

Description: We specialize in placements in the telecommunications industry in sales, engineering and management within voice processing, ACD, CDR, long distance, predictive dialing and video conferencing as well as with leading interconnects and manufacturers of PBX and KEY systems.

Salary Minimum: $50,000
Functions: Mkt. research, Mktg. mgmt., Sales mgmt.
Industries: Telecoms, High tech, Software

Templeton & Assoc.
10 S. Fifth St., Ste. 990
Minneapolis, Minnesota 55402
(612) 334-8900
Fax: (612) 334-8905

Key Contact - Specialty:
Ms. Denise Templeton - *Legal*
Mr. R. Patrick Maxwell - *Legal*
Ms. Renee Hammes-Briggs - *Legal*

Description: We specialize in providing legal staffing services to top law firms and corporate legal departments throughout the country.
Functions: Training, Systems support, Attorneys
Industries: Legal

Branches:
One E. Wacker Drive, Ste. 3130
Chicago, Illinois 60601
(312) 644-8400
Fax: (312) 644-8700
Key Contact - Specialty:
Ms. Jill Pace

15 S. 5th St., Ste. 1000
Minneapolis, Minnesota 55402
(612) 332-8079
Fax: (612) 332-6690

Key Contact - Specialty:
Ms. Susan Melrose

The TGA Company

P.O. Box 331121
Ft. Worth, Texas 76163
(817) 370-0865
Fax: (817) 292-6451

Key Contact - Specialty:
Mr. Thomas R. Green - *Finance*
Ms. Carolyn M. Byrne - *Finance, MIS*

Description: Contingency and retained search for financial executives - all industries.

Salary Minimum: $30,000
Functions: CFO's, Budgeting, Taxes, Risk mgmt., Systems implem., Systems support, Mgmt. consultants
Industries: Chemicals, Drugs mfg., Medical devices, Metal products, Machinery/ Appliances, Misc. mfg., Accounting

---

Thomas & Assoc. of Michigan

16283 Red Arrow Highway, P.O. Box 366
Union Pier, Michigan 49129
(616) 469-5760
Email: tzonka@harborcountry.com
Web: www.career-change.com

Key Contact - Specialty:
Mr. Thomas J. Zonka - *Executive, engineering, manufacturing, MIS, sales & marketing*

Description: Computerized nationwide affiliation with over 680 recruiting firms. Permanent - contract - outplacement.

Salary Minimum: $30,000
Functions: Generalist, General mgmt., Materials, Sales & mktg., HR mgmt., IT, Engineering
Industries: Generalist, Mfg., Environmental svcs., Packaging, High tech, Software

---

Thomas Lyle & Co.

16 S. Bothwell
Palatine, Illinois 60067
(847) 991-5050
Fax: (847) 991-5095
Email: tlc@ameritech.net

Key Contact - Specialty:
Mr. Lyle Stenfors - *Generalist*
Mr. Thomas G. Beamer - *Medical sales, sales management*
Mr. Russell Riendeau - *Sales, sales management*

Description: Our retained business specialty is in the packaging and chemical areas. We also do assorted other industry retained searches.
Functions: Generalist, Senior mgmt., Middle mgmt., Packaging, Sales mgmt., Int'l.
Industries: Generalist, Misc. financial, Hospitality, Telecoms, Packaging, Healthcare

---

Thomas, Whelan Assoc., Inc.

P.O. Box 40237
Washington, District of Columbia
20016-2523
(202) 966-3960
Fax: (202) 966-3970
Email: twahunt@aol.com

Key Contact - Specialty:
Ms. Cheryl Molliver Ross - *Finance, accounting, systems, mid-management, senior level*

Description: Specializing in the recruitment and placement of mid-management and senior level accounting, finance and systems professionals in the Baltimore/ Washington/Virginia area.

Salary Minimum: $35,000
Functions: CFO's, Budgeting, Cash mgmt., Taxes, M&A, Systems implem., Mgmt. consultants
Industries: Banking, Invest. banking, Accounting, Mgmt. consulting, Publishing, New media, Telecoms

---

Judy Thompson & Assoc., Inc.

3727 Camino Del Rio S., Ste. 200
San Diego, California 92108
(619) 281-2626
Email: judysearch@aol.com

Key Contact - Specialty:
Ms. Judy Thompson - *Accounting & finance (professionals, degreed, experienced)*

Description: Specialist in recruiting experienced degreed accounting/financial professionals for all industries in San Diego (excluding lending and operations for financial institutions and financial sales).

Salary Minimum: $35,000
Functions: CFO's, Budgeting, Cash mgmt., Credit, Taxes, M&A
Industries: Generalist, Accounting

Affiliates:
Ryan Allen & Associates

Thompson Assoc.

4747 Hopyard Rd., Ste. 100
Pleasanton, California 94588
(925) 462-7478
Fax: (925) 462-5445
Email: dennis@thompson.net
Web: thompson.net

Key Contact - Specialty:
Mr. Dennis Thompson - *Executive sales/ sales management - software only*

Description: 20 years experience in executive sales/sales management. VP marketing, VP sales, Director sales, account executives - software only.

Salary Minimum: $50,000
Functions: Senior mgmt., Sales & mktg., Mktg. mgmt., Sales mgmt.
Industries: Software

Thomson, Sponar & Adams, Inc.

10116 36th Ave. Court SW, Ste. 200
Lakewood, Washington 98499
(253) 588-1216
Fax: (253) 588-2528
Email: tsa@frugal.com
Web: www.aaa-mall.com/tsa/

Key Contact - Specialty:
Mr. Frank S. Adams - *High energy physics, applied superconductivity, electronics, instrumentation*

Description: We specialize in solutions for firms needing quality people and top quality people looking for exceptional opportunities, in the fields of superconductivity, high energy physics, cryogenics, electronics and instrumentation.
Functions: Middle mgmt., Production, Quality, Mkt. research, Mktg. mgmt., R&D, Engineering
Industries: Energy/utilities, Chemicals, Medical devices, Computer equip., Test/ measurement equip., Aerospace, High tech

---

Thor, Inc.

3601 Aviation Blvd., #2700
Manhattan Beach, California 90266
(310) 727-1777
Fax: (310) 727-1770
Email: ThorSB@msn.com

Key Contact - Specialty:
Mr. Terry Thormodsgaard - *Information technology*
Mr. Robert Fischer

Description: Business approach focus: increasing sales, reducing costs and making business life easier through offering the following unique added value concepts: conversion/migration/ upgrade computer and software trainers: outsourcing, fractional headcount budgeting. Contract programming.
Functions: Customer svc., Training, Finance, Credit, MIS mgmt., Systems dev., Systems support
Industries: Generalist, Finance, Hospitality, Entertainment, Computer svcs., Communications

The Tidewater Group Inc.
115 Main St.
Monroe, Connecticut 06468
(203) 459-2500
Fax: (203) 459-8373
Email: tide@nutmeg.net
Web: www.tidewater.org

Key Contact - Specialty:
Mr. John Kalas

Description: We are recruiters working nationally for a diversified clientele. We have 30 years recruiting nationally.

Salary Minimum: $40,000
Functions: Generalist, Purchasing, Distribution, Packaging, CFO's, R&D, Engineering
Industries: Generalist, Food/bev/tobacco, Chemicals, Soap/perfume/cosmetics, Drugs mfg., Aerospace, Healthcare

Fred C. Tippel & Assoc.
105 Shawnee Drive
Marietta, Ohio 45750
(740) 374-3288
Fax: (740) 374-3294
Email: tipcruit@juno.com

Key Contact - Specialty:
Mr. Fred C. Tippel - *Plastics, resins, compounds, coated fabrics, packaging, films, injection molding, paper, printing*

Description: Custom search for professionals with technical, engineering and management background in plastics and paper, films and coated fabrics, resins and compounds, extrusions, injection molding, packaging, coating, printing and paper.

Salary Minimum: $35,000
Functions: Middle mgmt., Product dev., Production, Plant mgmt., Productivity, R&D, Engineering
Industries: Textiles/apparel, Paper, Printing, Chemicals, Medical devices, Plastics/rubber, Packaging

Tittemore Cowan Assoc.
300, 400 - 5 Ave. SW
Calgary, Alberta T2P 0L6
Canada
(403) 263-4110
Fax: (403) 264-9218

Key Contact - Specialty:
Mr. Gordon Cowan - *Executives, professionals*
Mr. Jim Tittlemore - *Service, non-profit (executives & professionals)*

Description: Uncompromising quality searches for organizations in both public and private as well as profit and not-for-profit sectors, e.g., executive directors, presidents, vice presidents, finance, operations as well as professionals.

Salary Minimum: $35,000
Functions: Senior mgmt., Middle mgmt., Sales mgmt., Benefits, CFO's, Taxes, Engineering
Industries: Generalist, Agri/forestry/mining, Energy/utilities, Motor vehicles, Misc. mfg., Invest. banking, Human resource svcs.

Tomlinson Assoc. Inc.
401 N. Michigan Ave., Ste. 1200
Chicago, Illinois 60611
(312) 840-8250

Key Contact - Specialty:
Ms. Betsy Tomlinson - *Market research, marketing consulting*

Description: Boutique retainer firm offering highly personalized service for reasonable fees. Specialize in market research. Clients include Fortune 100 manufacturers and smaller privately held firms in market research, advertising and management consulting.

Salary Minimum: $60,000
Functions: Mkt. research, Personnel
Industries: Svcs., High tech

Tondorf & Assoc. Inc.
52 Accord Park Drive
Norwell, Massachusetts 02061
(781) 871-8895
Fax: (781) 871-8896
Email: tondorfasc@aol.com

Key Contact - Specialty:
Mr. Paul Tondorf, Jr.
Ms. Jane Pimental

Description: Executive search and recruiting firm which specializes in the consumer products and healthcare industry. Specializes in category management and trade marketing positions, leading to future sales management positions.

Salary Minimum: $60,000
Functions: Middle mgmt., Sales mgmt.
Industries: Food/bev/tobacco, Soap/perfume/cosmetics, Drugs mfg., Medical devices, Pharmaceutical svcs.

Top Gun Group, Inc.
220 E. Flamingo Rd., Ste. 121
Las Vegas, Nevada 89109
(702) 894-9191

Key Contact - Specialty:
Mr. Richard L. Bayer - *Sales, marketing*

Description: 80% of activity is candidate representation. Sales executives or personnel must be exceptional. I do not throw people into some database.

Salary Minimum: $75,000
Functions: Senior mgmt., Mktg. mgmt., Sales mgmt.
Industries: Generalist, Food/bev/tobacco, Soap/perfume/cosmetics, Misc. mfg., Hospitality, Entertainment

Topaz Int'l., Inc., Attorney Search
383 Northfield Ave.
West Orange, New Jersey 07052
(973) 669-7300
Fax: (973) 669-9811
Email: topazlegal@aol.com
Web: www.TopAttorneys.com

Key Contact - Specialty:
Ms. Ronni L. Gaines - *Attorneys*
Mr. Stewart Michaels - *Attorneys, consulting*
Pamela S. Cohen - *Attorneys*

Description: Confidential permanent/temporary attorney search for law firms and corporations, all disciplines, all levels; law firm mergers and establishing new practice areas and branch offices; creating/expanding in-house legal departments; legal consulting services.

Salary Minimum: $50,000
Functions: Senior mgmt., Minorities, Attorneys, Paralegals, Int'l.
Industries: Generalist, Legal

Affiliates:
Topaz Legal Minority Network
Topaz Legal Solutions

The Touchstone Group
340 Main St., Ste. 775
Worcester, Massachusetts 01608
(508) 795-0769
Fax: (508) 798-0671
Email: vozekas@msn.com
Web: touchstonegroup.com

Key Contact - Specialty:
Mr. James P. Vozekas - *Sales, marketing*
Ms. Connie Palmer - *Sales support, marketing communication*

Description: Dedicated to assisting emerging high technology firms in finding talented sales and marketing professionals at a reasonable cost.

Salary Minimum: $40,000
Functions: Advertising, Mkt. research, Mktg. mgmt., Sales mgmt., Direct mktg., Customer svc., PR
Industries: Computer equip., Consumer electronics, Test/measurement equip., Computer svcs., Telecoms, High tech, Software

Affiliates:
Sales & Marketing Search, Inc.

TPG & Assoc.

10619 Burgoyne Rd.
Houston, Texas 77042
(713) 781-2010
Fax: (713) 785-0507
Email: porter@staffing.net

Key Contact - Specialty:
Ms. Mary C. Porter
Mr. James H. Porter

Description: Oil and gas exploration, production, refining and marketing, power generation, environmental, aerospace and biotech. Also R & D, administrative, computer staff related to the above industries. Some contractors.

Salary Minimum: $40,000
Functions: Senior mgmt., Middle mgmt., IT, R&D, Engineering, Int'l.
Industries: Energy/utilities, Defense, Haz. waste, Aerospace, High tech, Software, Biotech

TPS Staffing Solutions

15552 Herriman Blvd.
Noblesville, Indiana 46060
(317) 770-7601
Fax: (317) 770-7603
Email: blackshelton@prodigy.net

Key Contact - Specialty:
Mr. Dean A. Black - *Executive management, human resources*
Ms. Michelle Soltwedel - *Administrative management*

Description: Full range of long-term, short-term, temporary and permanent placement in addition to human resources consulting.
Functions: Generalist, Senior mgmt., Plant mgmt., Purchasing, Mktg. mgmt., Personnel, Cash mgmt.
Industries: Generalist, Mfg., Retail, Finance, Svcs., Communications, Insurance

Affiliates:
Temporary Personnel Services

Jay Tracey Assoc. Inc.

P.O. Box 30
Bridgewater, Vermont 05034
(802) 672-3000
Fax: (802) 672-3033
Email: search1@aol.com
Web: amsquare.com/america/search1.html

Key Contact - Specialty:
Mr. Jay E. Tracey - *Plastics, automation, PLC, SCADA, drives, software, vision, semiconductor test equipment*
Mr. Mark H. Auriema - *Industrial controls, automation, PLC, SCADA, drives, software, vision*

Description: Work with sales, engineering, marketing, service technicians for the drives, process control (DCS), PLC, industrial controls, factory automation and converting industry. Also work with all disciplines in the plastic extrusion and blow molding industry.

Salary Minimum: $35,000
Functions: Senior mgmt., Middle mgmt., Automation, Mkt. research, Mktg. mgmt., Sales mgmt., Engineering, Technicians
Industries: Paper, Printing, Plastics/rubber, Metal products, Machinery/Appliances, Computer equip., High tech, Software

Trainor/Frank & Assoc. Inc.

16550 W. Lisbon Rd., P.O. Box 850
Menomonee Falls, Wisconsin 53052
(414) 783-7900
Fax: (414) 783-5006
Email: tsacsi@execpc.com
Web: www.tsacsi.com

Key Contact - Specialty:
Mr. James F. Trainor - *Engineering, technical*
Mr. Joel Frank

Description: Technical recruiting firm with a focus on the hard to find engineers. Skilled staff with extensive knowledge in manufacturing operations. We understand your openings.

Salary Minimum: $35,000
Functions: Mfg., Production, Automation, Quality, HR mgmt., IT, Engineering
Industries: Medical devices, Plastics/rubber, Metal products, Machinery/Appliances, Motor vehicles, Computer equip., Test/measurement equip.

Affiliates:
Contract Services Inc.
SITE Personnel
Transition Division

Trambley the Recruiter

5353 Wyoming Blvd. NE, Ste. 8
Albuquerque, New Mexico 87109-3132
(505) 821-5440
Fax: (505) 821-8509

Key Contact - Specialty:
Mr. J. Brian Trambley - *Engineering, manufacturing*

Description: Specialist in design and development personnel for the off road equipment industries including hydraulics, mechanical, structural and electronic controls, engineers and engineering managers.
Functions: Mfg., Materials, R&D, Engineering
Industries: Metal products, Machinery/Appliances, Motor vehicles, Test/measurement equip., Misc. mfg.

Trans-United Consultants Ltd.

3228 S. Service Rd., Ste. 110
Burlington, Ontario L7N 3H8
Canada
(905) 632-7176
Fax: (905) 632-5777
Email: tuc@netaccess.on.ca
Web: www.netaccess.on.ca/~tuc

Key Contact - Specialty:
Mr. Brian L. de Lottinville - *Engineering, computer personnel*
Mr. John L. Train - *Engineering, computer personnel*

Description: We provide contract and permanent personnel to business and industry. We have over 20,000 computerized applicant files to service our clients.
Functions: Product dev., Production, Automation, Purchasing, MIS mgmt., Systems anal., Engineering
Industries: Mfg., Environmental svcs., Aerospace, Packaging, High tech, Software

Transportation Recruiting Services, Inc.

5719 Hwy. 25, Ste. 106E, Box 5
Brandon, Mississippi 39042
(601) 992-7900
Fax: (601) 992-7999
Web: AUTOHEADHUNTER.COM

Key Contact - Specialty:
Mr. Dave Bradshaw
Ms. Traci Carpenter - *Automotive engineering*

Description: Transportation manufacturers' and major component suppliers' search specialists for management, engineering and manufacturing professionals. National/international, retained and contingency recruiting services.

Salary Minimum: $35,000
Functions: General mgmt., Mfg., Product dev., Materials, Sales & mktg., HR mgmt., Engineering
Industries: Motor vehicles

Travel Executive Search
(a division of Workstyles, Inc.)

5 Rose Ave.
Great Neck, New York 11021
(516) 829-8829
Web: tesintl@aol.com

Key Contact - Specialty:
Ms. Karen Rubin - *Travel, tourism, hospitality, transportation*

Description: Executive recruitment specialists for the travel industry: airlines, car rentals, motorcoach, tours, corporate travel, hotel and resorts, retail, incentives, conventions and meetings, cruise companies and tourist offices; import and export; international; sports and entertainment.

Salary Minimum: $30,000
Functions: Generalist, General mgmt., Sales & mktg., HR mgmt., Finance, IT, Int'l.
Industries: Transportation, Hospitality, Entertainment, Non-profits, Advertising/ PR, New media, Broadcast & Film

Affiliates:
TES Int'l.

Travel Personnel

1525 Joseph St.
Cincinnati, Ohio 45237
(513) 641-3885
(800) 790-0588
Fax: (513) 641-3995

Key Contact - Specialty:
Mr. Chris O'Malley - *Travel, tourism*

Description: Travel industry search firm serving staffing needs of tour operators, airlines, cruise lines, travel agencies, travel management firms, CVB's, adventure travel, guides and expedition leaders.

Salary Minimum: $20,000
Functions: Senior mgmt., Middle mgmt., Mktg. mgmt., Sales mgmt.
Industries: Transportation, Hospitality, Entertainment, Non-profits, Advertising/ PR

Traynor Confidential, Ltd.

P.O. Box 189
Pittsford, New York 14534
(716) 387-0383
Fax: (716) 387-0384
Email: recruiter@traynor.com
Web: www.traynor.com

Key Contact - Specialty:
Mr. Thomas H. Traynor - *Accounting & finance, information systems, software engineering, construction, real estate*

Description: Recognized leader in upstate New York in filling mid-level staff positions, heavy emphasis (but not limited to) accounting/finance, software engineering and management information systems. Client base primarily medium size, $1 million and up.

Salary Minimum: $25,000
Functions: Mfg., Materials, Sales & mktg., Finance, IT, Engineering, Minorities
Industries: Construction, Mfg., Finance, Svcs., Communications, Real estate, High tech

Triad Consultants, Inc.

P.O. Box 717
West Caldwell, New Jersey 07007-0717
(973) 890-1655
Fax: (973) 890-9201

Key Contact - Specialty:
Mr. Jack Daudt - *Benefits, compensation*

Description: Focused solely on benefits and compensation positions to $200K, we offer corporations and consulting firms the thoroughness and attention of retained search without advanced payment.

Salary Minimum: $50,000
Functions: Benefits, Mgmt. consultants, Non-profits
Industries: Banking, Human resource svcs., Insurance

Triad Technology Group

10200 SW Greenburg Rd., Ste. 350
Portland, Oregon 97223
(503) 293-9547
(503) 293-9545
Fax: (503) 293-9546
Email: triadjob@triadtechnology.com
Web: www.triadtechnology.com

Key Contact - Specialty:
Mr. Bruno C. Amicci - *Information technology*

Description: We are a Pacific northwest based information technology recruiting and contracting firm founded to provide a wide range of systems development and software engineering services including programming, relational database management system design, development and implementation and system integration.

Salary Minimum: $45,000
Functions: IT, MIS mgmt., Systems anal., Systems dev., Systems implem., Systems support, DB admin.
Industries: Generalist, High tech, Software

Triangle Assoc.

P.O. Box 506
Warrington, Pennsylvania 18976
(215) 343-3702
Fax: (215) 343-3703

Key Contact - Specialty:
Mr. Stephen R. Ostroff - *Engineers, management*

Description: Recruiters of engineering and technical management talent for the process and manufacturing industries. Specialties - chemical engineers, manufacturing/industrial engineers, engineering management.

Salary Minimum: $30,000
Functions: Product dev., Production, Plant mgmt., R&D, Engineering
Industries: Chemicals, Soap/perfume/ cosmetics, Drugs mfg., Medical devices, Plastics/rubber, Paints/petroleum products

Trillium Human Resources Inc.

R.R. No. 3
Ayr, Ontario N0B 1E0
Canada
(519) 632-8423
(800) 335-9668
Fax: (519) 632-8364
Email: thr@easynet.on.ca
Web: www.easynet.on.ca/~thr

Key Contact - Specialty:
Ms. Beryl Collingwood - *Speech language pathologists, physicians*
Ms. Sabina Dinino - *Registered nurses, physical therapists, occupational therapists*
Ms. Lorri Talbot - *Registered nurses, physical therapists, occupational therapists*

Description: Quality personal service providing quality placements full assistance with licensing and immigration.
Functions: Healthcare, Physicians, Nurses, Allied health, Int'l.
Industries: Healthcare

Affiliates:
Boles & Company

TriStaff Group

4350 Executive Drive, Ste. 100
San Diego, California 92121
(619) 453-1331
Fax: (619) 453-6022
Email: tristaff@tristaff.com
Web: www.tristaff.com

Key Contact - Specialty:
Mr. Gary van Eik - *Managed healthcare*
Mr. Richard Papike - *Newspaper, publishing, media*
Ms. Amy Moser - *Software engineering, information technology*

Description: We utilize resources that are untapped by conventional recruiting methods. We focus our efforts on top performers who may not be actively seeking a new position or answering employment ads.
Functions: Senior mgmt., Physicians, Health admin., CFO's, Systems anal., Systems dev., Engineering
Industries: Computer equip., Computer svcs., Mgmt. consulting, Publishing, Broadcast & Film, Healthcare

Branches:
19782 MacArthur Blvd., #305
Irvine, California 92612
(714) 477-9414
Fax: (714) 477-9417
Email: staff@tristaff.com
Key Contact - Specialty:
Mr. Trever Neves - *Software consultants*

TRS Staffing Solutions Inc.
(a subsidiary of Fluor Corporation)

(Firm declined to update.)
144 Merchant St., Ste. 210
Cincinnati, Ohio 45246
(513) 326-3400
Email: trscincinnati@worldnet.att.net
Web: www.trsstaffingsolutions.com

Key Contact - Specialty:
Ms. Jamie Levine - *Chemical process engineers, packaging engineers, electrical engineers, structural engineers*
Ms. Trina Koers - *Project controls, information systems, information technology*

Description: We are a total staffing resource providing technical and professional support to our clients.

Salary Minimum: $25,000
Functions: Production, Automation, Materials Plng., Packaging, Budgeting, Engineering, Architects
Industries: Construction, Food/bev/tobacco, Paper, Chemicals, Soap/perfume/cosmetics, Drugs mfg., Packaging

The Truman Agency
13200 Crossroads Pkwy. N., Ste. 470
City of Industry, California 91746
(562) 980-1233
Fax: (562) 908-1238
Email: bob@trumanagency.com
Web: www.trumanagency.com

Key Contact - Specialty:
Mr. Robert P. Truman - *Manufacturing*

Description: Confidential management recruiting serving the manufacturing sector. Strengths in engineering, plant management, sales, accounting, MIS.

Salary Minimum: $30,000
Functions: Quality, Distribution, Customer svc., HR mgmt., CFO's, IT, Engineering
Industries: Food/bev/tobacco, Printing, Chemicals, Metal products, Machinery/Appliances, Misc. mfg., Packaging

TSC Management Services Group, Inc.
P.O. Box 384
Barrington, Illinois 60011
(847) 381-0167
Fax: (847) 381-2169
Email: tscmgtserv@aol.com

Key Contact - Specialty:
Mr. Robert G. Stanton - *Executive levels, management levels*
Mr. Grant Stanton - *Arcade games, computer games*
Mr. R. J. Wagner - *Electronics*

Description: Established 1968 as The Stanton Company, well known specialists in technical-manufacturing. Practice predominantly Midwestern. Subspecialty: gaming -- coin-operated, home systems and wagering (all areas/professions). Worldwide.

Salary Minimum: $35,000
Functions: Generalist, Senior mgmt., Middle mgmt., Quality, R&D, Engineering, Graphic artists
Industries: Consumer electronics, Misc. mfg., Entertainment, New media, Broadcast & Film, High tech, Software

Affiliates:
TSC: Temporary Help Group, Inc.

TSI Group/TSI Staffing Services
5045 Orbitor Drive, Bldg. 8, Ste. 400
Mississauga, Ontario L4W 4Y4
Canada
(905) 629-3701
Fax: (905) 629-0799
Email: tsigroup@inforamp.net
Web: www.tsigroup.com

Key Contact - Specialty:
Ms. Pamela Ruebusch
Ms. Stacy Agnos

Description: We are a recruitment firm specializing in providing human resource solutions in supply chain management. We have the proven expertise and extensive network to source logistics and transportation professionals.

Salary Minimum: $20,000
Functions: General mgmt., Production, Materials, Distribution, Sales mgmt., Customer svc., MIS mgmt.
Industries: Mfg., Transportation, Non-classifiable industries

TSS Consulting, Ltd.
2525 E. Camelback Rd., Ste. 560
Phoenix, Arizona 85016
(602) 955-7000
Fax: (602) 957-3948
Email: recruit@tss-consulting.com
Web: www.tss-consulting.com

Key Contact - Specialty:
Mr. John R. McDonald - *High technology, electronics*

Description: High technology/executive recruitment firm with concentration in CAD/CAE, system software, semiconductor, government electronics, artificial intelligence and associated executive functions.

Salary Minimum: $70,000
Functions: Systems dev., Systems implem., R&D, Engineering
Industries: Computer equip., Test/measurement equip., Aerospace, High tech

TTG/Sterling Services
4727 Wilshire Blvd., Ste. 400
Los Angeles, California 90010
(213) 857-1700
Fax: (213) 936-6721
Web: www.ttg-consult.com

Key Contact - Specialty:
Mr. David Bowman - *General management, entertainment*
Mr. Bret Willbanks - *Healthcare, financial services, technology, information technology*

Description: A full service human resource consulting and recruitment firm, speciaizing in healthcare, accounting/finance, information tech, entertainment, general management.

Salary Minimum: $50,000
Functions: Generalist, General mgmt., Healthcare, Sales mgmt., HR mgmt., Finance, IT
Industries: Food/bev/tobacco, Retail, Hospitality, Computer svcs., Accounting, Broadcast & Film, Healthcare

U.S. Search
712 W. Broad St., Ste. 3
Falls Church, Virginia 22046
(703) 448-1900
Fax: (703) 448-1907
Email: ahsearch@aol.com
Web: us-search.com

Key Contact - Specialty:
Mr. Arnie Hiller - *Plastics, ceramics, composite materials, plastics processing, plastics equipment*

Description: Industry-specialized recruitment and search firm with more than 16 years of timely, discrete and effective service to our clients in all phases of the plastics and specialty materials industries.

Salary Minimum: $50,000
Functions: Senior mgmt., Product dev., Purchasing, Mktg. mgmt., Sales mgmt., R&D, Engineering
Industries: Paper, Chemicals, Plastics/rubber, Paints/petroleum products, Leather/stone/glass/clay, Machinery/Appliances, Packaging

UniQuest Int'l., Inc.
4350 W. Cypress St., Ste. 450
Tampa, Florida 33607
(813) 879-1222
Fax: (813) 879-1317

Email: uniquest@worldnet.att.net

Key Contact - Specialty:
Mr. Anthony F. Valone - *Healthcare, insurance, legal*
Ms. Judith Valone - *Legal, healthcare, finance*
Mr. Mike Venekotter - *Healthcare, long-term care, managed care*
Mr. Michael Valone - *Healthcare, physicians*
Ms. Debra J. Price - *Engineering (ASIC/RF)*

Description: Our consultants specialize by industry and function, staying abreast of the latest developments and trends. They focus on locating and tracking the top performers within their specialty.

Salary Minimum: $50,000
Functions: General mgmt., Healthcare, HR mgmt., Finance, MIS mgmt., Engineering, Attorneys
Industries: Generalist, Computer equip., Legal, Accounting, Insurance, Software, Healthcare

Unisearch Search & Recruiting Inc.

790 The City Drive S., Ste. 150
Orange, California 92868
(714) 748-0700

Key Contact - Specialty:
Mr. James L. Rose - *Electronics*
Ms. Patricia Ergas - *Accounting, finance*

Description: Executive and high tech search in healthcare, finance, plastics, electronics, banking, legal, construction, food technology, each account executive specializes in a particular field.
Functions: Legal, Mfg., Healthcare, Finance, IT, Engineering, Attorneys
Industries: Construction, Mfg., Plastics/rubber, Computer equip., Banking, High tech, Healthcare

Branches:
P.O. Box 810
Lake Havasu City, Arizona 86405-0810
(520) 680-6077
Key Contact - Specialty:
Mr. Jim Enrico - *Plastics*

United Personnel Services

1331 Main St.
Springfield, Massachusetts 01103
(413) 736-0800
Fax: (413) 747-9021
Email: uniteds@tiac.net
Web: www.unitedpersonnel.com

Key Contact - Specialty:
Ms. Patricia Canavan - *General*

Description: Offering full service temporary help and temp-to-hire situations and permanent professional placements.
Functions: Admin. svcs., Health admin., Sales mgmt., Customer svc., Personnel, IT
Industries: Generalist, Energy/utilities, Mfg., Finance, Insurance, High tech, Software

Branches:
99 Pratt St.
Hartford, Connecticut 06103-1614
(860) 560-8009
Fax: (860) 560-8099
Key Contact - Specialty:
Ms. Laura Conley

250 Northampton St.
Easthampton, Massachusetts 01027-1046
(413) 527-7445
Fax: (413) 527-7494
Key Contact - Specialty:
Ms. Amber Black

Unlimited Staffing Solutions, Inc.

4111 Andover, Ste. 140
Bloomfield Hills, Michigan 48302
(248) 258-5111
Fax: (248) 258-8895
Email: ussi1@flash.net
Web: unlimitedstaffing.com

Key Contact - Specialty:
Ms. Caleene Jones Newman - *Technical*

Description: Temporary/contract staffing, employee leasing
Functions: Generalist, Mfg., Materials, HR mgmt., Finance, IT, Engineering
Industries: Generalist, Mfg., Transportation, Finance, Svcs., High tech

Branches:
1161 Murfreesboro Rd.
Nashville, Tennessee 75075
(615) 366-0721
Fax: (615) 366-0754
Email: ussi@mindspring.com
Key Contact - Specialty:
Ms. Barbara Thomas

The Urban Placement Service

602 Sawyer St., Ste. 460
Houston, Texas 77007-7510
(713) 880-2211
Fax: (713) 880-5577
Email: urbanplacement@msn.com
Web: urbanplacement.com

Key Contact - Specialty:
Mr. Willie S. Bright - *Diversity generalist*
Mr. Develous A. Bright - *Diversity generalist*

Description: Professional search-minority recruitment; accounting/finance, engineering, marketing/sales, production/logistics and human resources.

Salary Minimum: $35,000
Functions: Generalist, Mfg., Sales & mktg., HR mgmt., Finance, Engineering, Minorities
Industries: Generalist, Mfg., Finance, Svcs., Aerospace, Healthcare

USA Medical Placement Inc.

3604 Date Palm
McAllen, Texas 78501
(210) 631-3540
Fax: (210) 686-3540

Key Contact - Specialty:
Ms. Patricia Tracy - *Medical healthcare*

Description: A medical search firm, administration, nursing, physicians and hospital administration contingency. We treat each hospital or candidate with individual consideration and do a search for that specific individual in regard to degree abilities whether client or candidate.

Salary Minimum: $50,000
Functions: Physicians, Nurses, Health admin.

V.I.P. Resources, Inc.

350 Fifth Ave., Ste. 3304
Empire State Bldg.
New York, New York 10118-0069
(212) 344-2100

Key Contact - Specialty:
Mr. Joe Gross - *Employee benefits*

Description: We are a specialized firm that provides professional, confidential search and recruitment services in compensation and employee benefits. Areas of specialty include group and retirement benefits, health and managed care, communication and all aspects of compensation.
Functions: Benefits
Industries: Human resource svcs., Healthcare

Valentine & Assoc.

One Woodfield Lake, Ste. 117
Schaumburg, Illinois 60173-5921
(847) 605-8090

Key Contact - Specialty:
Ms. Linda S. Valentine - *Materials management*
Mr. James P. Valentine

Description: Small firm operated by former practitioners working solely in materials, purchasing, ship/receiving, distribution, manufacturing systems and production/inventory control arena in Midwest.

Salary Minimum: $25,000
Functions: Production, Purchasing, Materials Plng., Distribution, Packaging, Systems implem.
Industries: Mfg., Transportation, Software

Vaughan & Co.
9 Executive Circle, Ste. 240
Irvine, California 92614
(949) 623-3300
(949) 474-6666
Fax: (949) 623-3333
Email:
recruiters@vaughanandcompany.com
Web: www.vaughanandcompany.com

Key Contact - Specialty:
Mr. David B. Vaughan - *Industrial, aviation, sales, marketing, engineering*
Ms. Julie Raab - *High technology, industrial, manufacturing, engineering*

Description: 200 associated Dunhill offices throughout US and Canada. Professional service, sales, marketing, management, industrial, aviation, medical, engineering, high technology electronics, information systems.

Salary Minimum: $50,000
Functions: Mfg., Plant mgmt., Quality, Materials, Sales & mktg., Mktg. mgmt., Sales mgmt.
Industries: Plastics/rubber, Metal products, Machinery/Appliances, Computer equip., Misc. mfg., Aerospace, High tech

Venpro Consulting Inc.
37 Rainbow Creekway
North York, Ontario M2K 2T9
Canada
(416) 223-3341
Fax: (416) 223-3345
Email: venpro@idirect.com

Key Contact - Specialty:
Mr. Brian H. Campbell - *Sales, sales support, consultants, marketing for vendors in computer hardware, software, and systems integration)*

Description: Working exclusively with Canada's computer vendors for over a decade, our mission is to recruit high quality professionals in the following job functions: sales, pre-sales support, tele-sales, telemarketing, consulting and sales/marketing management.
Functions: Mktg. mgmt., Sales mgmt., Direct mktg.
Industries: High tech, Software

Vento Assoc.
11130 Kingston Pike, Ste. 1-405
Knoxville, Tennessee 37922
(423) 777-3900
Fax: (423) 777-3904
Email: jvento@vento.com
Web: www.vento.com

Key Contact - Specialty:
Mr. Joseph P. Vento - *High technology, software applications*

Description: Specializing in technical applications, with an emphasis on CEO, president, vp, gm, sales management, marketing, sales, application engineering, pre & post sales, consulting and implementation positions for the application software & service markets.

Salary Minimum: $40,000
Functions: Automation, Mktg. mgmt., Sales mgmt., Systems implem.
Industries: Medical devices, Computer equip., Test/measurement equip., High tech, Software

Vezan Assoc.
P.O. Box 270753
West Hartford, Connecticut 06127-0753
(860) 521-8848

Key Contact - Specialty:
Mr. Henry D. Vezan - *Healthcare*

Description: We now offer, on a contingency basis, the high level of selectivity, which this firm practiced during thirty years of intensive search assignments, normally on retainer.

Salary Minimum: $40,000
Functions: Physicians, Nurses, Allied health, Health admin., HR mgmt.
Industries: Pharmaceutical svcs., Human resource svcs., Biotech, Healthcare

Victor White Int'l.
23332 Mill Creek Drive, Ste. 120
Laguna Hills, California 92653
(949) 380-4800
Fax: (949) 380-7477
Email: vic@victorwhite.com
Web: www.victorwhite.com

Key Contact - Specialty:
Mr. Victor Chapa - *Medical*
Ms. Kate Maurina

Description: Resource management firm that develops early stage technologies and infrastructure building through strategic recruitment of senior staff. Emphasis on R&D, regulatory, quality, COO, CFO, VP sales, marketing, president and CEO's

Salary Minimum: $125,000
Functions: Directors, Senior mgmt., Middle mgmt., Quality, IT, R&D, Engineering
Industries: Drugs mfg., Medical devices, Venture cap., Pharmaceutical svcs., Mgmt. consulting, Biotech, Healthcare

Villasenor & Assoc.
6546 San Vicente Blvd.
Los Angeles, California 90048
(213) 936-4880
Fax: (213) 936-8066
Email: thefourvs

Key Contact - Specialty:
Mr. Hector Villasenor
Ms. Carole Howard

Description: Specialize in placement of attorneys in law firms and corporations; ability to successfully match job description with qualified high caliber candidates; EO consulting firm and certified WMBE.

Salary Minimum: $75,000
Functions: Attorneys
Industries: Legal

C. J. Vincent Assoc., LLC
2000 Century Plaza
Columbia, Maryland 21044
(410) 997-8590
Fax: (410) 997-1608
Email: cucuzzella@aol.com

Key Contact - Specialty:
Mr. Vincent J. Cucuzzella - *Computer system & software sales & marketing*
Mr. John S. Cook - *Computer system & software sales & marketing*

Description: Professional recruitment for sales and marketing in the computer industry based on prior sales management experience in the computer system field.

Salary Minimum: $40,000
Functions: Mkt. research, Mktg. mgmt., Sales mgmt.
Industries: Computer equip., Test/measurement equip., Computer svcs., High tech, Software

Vincenty & Co.
6059 Frantz Rd, Ste. 203
Dublin, Ohio 43017
(614) 792-2100
(888) 745-6689
Fax: (614) 792-1442
Email: lmvco@aol.com

Key Contact - Specialty:
Ms. Lorraine Vincenty - *Financial services (stockbrokers, analysts, fixed income, equity, branch managers)*

Description: Nationally retained/contained search firm providing search expertise in various fields and industries, utilizing innovative search techniques and ethical methodologies.

Salary Minimum: $70,000
Functions: Admin. svcs., Plant mgmt., Packaging, Sales mgmt., Training, Cash mgmt., MIS mgmt.
Industries: Generalist, Mfg., Finance, Invest. banking, Brokers, Misc. financial, Insurance

Vintage Resources, Inc.
11 E 44th St., Ste. 708
New York, New York 10017
(212) 867-1001
Fax: (212) 490-9277

Key Contact - Specialty:
Mr. Perry Fishman
Ms. Judy Fishman

Description: Clients seeking a cost efficient, personalized approach from a select staff of recruitment professionals serving the advertising/direct marketing industries are encouraged to call us.
Functions: Middle mgmt., Sales & mktg., Advertising, Mkt. research, Direct mktg.
Industries: Communications, Advertising/PR, Publishing, New media, Broadcast & Film, Telecoms

Vogel Assoc.
P.O. Box 269R
Huntingdon Valley, Pennsylvania 19006-0269
(215) 938-1700
Fax: (215) 938-1789

Key Contact - Specialty:
Mr. Michael S. Vogel - *Human resources*

Description: Professional recruiting and search specializing exclusively in all areas of human resources: employment, training, MD/OD, compensation, benefits, labor and employee relations, EEO/AA, HRIS, etc. Client and candidate bases are national.

Salary Minimum: $40,000
Functions: Benefits, Personnel, Training
Industries: Generalist

Beverly von Winckler & Assoc.
123 W. Madison, Ste. 205
Chicago, Illinois 60602
(312) 332-6283
(312) 332-6262
Fax: (312) 332-6284
Email: lhazan@aol.com

Key Contact - Specialty:
Ms. Lynn Hazan - *Communications, marketing, consulting*

Description: Specialties include communications, marketing, consulting for agencies, corporations, suppliers. Concentration in Chicago and Midwest. Form career long associations with both clients and candidates. Provide one year guarantee on placements.
Functions: Sales & mktg., Advertising, Direct mktg., PR, Benefits, Mgmt. consultants, Graphic artists
Industries: Finance, Mgmt. consulting, Human resource svcs., Communications, High tech, Software, Healthcare

VZ Int'l., Inc.
7411 E. 6th Ave., Ste. 205
Scottsdale, Arizona 85251
(602) 946-1907
Fax: (602) 946-3005
Email: vzintl1@ix.netcom.com

Key Contact - Specialty:
Mr. William Van Zanten - *Semiconductor executives, technical, sales & marketing*
Mr. Jerry Farro - *Semiconductor executives, technical, sales & marketing*

Description: We service the semiconductor market, conducting executive searches on an international basis for process engineers, general management, sales, marketing, engineering and field service personnel.

Salary Minimum: $60,000
Functions: Middle mgmt., Production, Plant mgmt., Productivity, Mktg. mgmt., Sales mgmt., CFO's
Industries: High tech

Branches:
748 Ivers Lane
Warminster, Pennsylvania 18974
(215) 773-9055
Fax: (215) 773-9054
Email: r.keyser@msn.com
Key Contact - Specialty:
Mr. Rich Keyser - *Semiconductor*

W. P. Assoc.
4020 Jones Ave., Ste. 108
Riverside, California 92505
(909) 687-1927

Key Contact - Specialty:
Mr. William D. Piper - *Medical device, pharmaceutical*

Description: Principal has 20 years of experience working in medical device and pharmaceutical companies and 10 years working as a recruiter (contingency and retained) and placing regulatory, quality engineering and executives at all levels.

Salary Minimum: $50,000
Functions: Directors, Senior mgmt., Middle mgmt., Production, Quality, Mktg. mgmt., Sales mgmt.
Industries: Soap/perfume/cosmetics, Drugs mfg., Medical devices, Plastics/rubber, Pharmaceutical svcs., Biotech

The Wabash Group
3480 Kossuth, Ste. 9
P.O. Box 5753
Lafayette, Indiana 47905
(765) 448-4887
Fax: (765) 448-1599
Email: wabash_group@msn.com

Key Contact - Specialty:
Mr. Earl Richter - *Engineering, management, human resources*
Mr. Mike Johnson - *Industrial safety, environmental*
Ms. Helen Hunter - *Engineering*

Description: We proudly serve the industrial markets of the Great Lakes region. The firm has experienced 200% revenue growth the last two years.

Salary Minimum: $30,000
Functions: General mgmt., Mfg., Materials, HR mgmt., Finance, IT, Engineering
Industries: Mfg., Plastics/rubber, Metal products, Motor vehicles, Misc. mfg., Computer svcs., Software

Wachendorfer & Assoc.
13047 Chandler Drive, #100
Dallas, Texas 75243
(972) 783-0999
Fax: (972) 783-0995
Email: wachendorfer@worldnet.att.net

Key Contact - Specialty:
Ms. Nancy Wachendorfer - *Research & development, engineers, QC, food industry*
Mr. Tom Wachendorfer - *Sales & marketing, production management, food industry*
Ms. Lauren Mitchell - *Plant management, QC, food industry*
Ms. Adrienne McKinney - *Plant management, engineers, food industry*

Description: We specialize in placements for the food and food ingredient industries. We work closely with both the candidate and company to insure a good match. All recruiters are CPCs.

Salary Minimum: $40,000
Functions: Directors, Senior mgmt., Product dev., Plant mgmt., Quality, Sales mgmt., Engineering
Industries: Food/bev/tobacco

Gordon Wahls Executive Search
P.O. Box 905
Media, Pennsylvania 19063-0905
(610) 565-0800
Fax: (610) 565-1698
Email: gwahls@prodigy.com

Key Contact - Specialty:
Mr. Thomas F. Glancey, Jr. - *Printing, publishing, packaging*

Description: We specialize in newspaper publishing, printing, graphic arts, labels, folding carton and corrugated paper industries. Most searches in the $50,000 to $150,000 range. Our professional staff includes twenty consultants.

Salary Minimum: $30,000

Functions: Production, Plant mgmt., Packaging, Sales mgmt., Direct mktg., Customer svc., Graphic artists
Industries: Paper, Printing, Publishing, Packaging

Waldorf Associates, Inc.

11400 W. Olympic Blvd., 2nd Floor
Los Angeles, California 90064-1507
(310) 445-8886
Fax: (310) 445-8810
Email: info@waldorfsearch.com
Web: waldorfsearch.com

Key Contact - Specialty:
Michael Waldorf - *Law, partners, associates, law firm practice groups, mergers*

Description: Attorney search and placement, California and nationally. Partners, associates, law firm mergers, specialty practice groups, branch office development; in-house and corporate law department attorney staffing.
Functions: Attorneys
Industries: Legal

Kelly Walker Assoc.

949 Forest Grove Drive
Dallas, Texas 75218
(214) 320-3006
Fax: (214) 324-5105
Web: www.kellywalker.com

Key Contact - Specialty:
Mr. Kelly Walker - *Construction, mining industrial, governmental, public utility (manufacturers, dealers, equipment, fleets)*
Mr. Jack Mears - *Construction, mining, trucking (manufacturers, dealers, equipment, fleets)*

Description: Manufacturers and distributors of construction and mining equipment and fleets which use heavy equipment utilize our specialized knowledge of this industry to recruit world class managers.

Salary Minimum: $40,000
Functions: Senior mgmt., Middle mgmt., Distribution, Mktg. mgmt., Sales mgmt., Training, Technicians
Industries: Agri/forestry/mining, Energy/utilities, Construction, Machinery/Appliances, Wholesale, Equip. svcs., Government

---

Walker Personnel, Inc.

3000 26th St., Ste. A
Metairie, Louisiana 70002
(504) 831-4767

Key Contact - Specialty:
Ms. Linda G. Walker - *Property & casualty insurance*

Description: Specializing in property/casualty insurance placement. Fee paid only. National contacts.
Industries: Insurance

K. K. Walker Professional Recruitment

P.O. Box 1588
Fair Oaks, California 95628
(916) 863-6363
Fax: (916) 863-3224
Email: kkwalker@ns.net

Key Contact - Specialty:
Ms. Karen K. Walker - *Healthcare*

Description: All areas of healthcare-clinical, administrative-hospital and non-hospital. Special attention to laboratory, nursing, home health.
Functions: Senior mgmt., Physicians, Nurses, Allied health, Health admin., Sales mgmt.
Industries: Healthcare

B. D. Wallace & Assoc.

217 Georgetown Rd.
Annapolis, Maryland 21403
(410) 268-2024
Fax: (410) 267-8374
Email: dick@bdwallace.com
Web: www.bdwallace.com

Key Contact - Specialty:
Mr. Dick Duval - *Sales, sales management, technical, systems integration*
Ms. Barbara Heacock - *IT systems development, analysis, design, programming integration*

Description: An executive search firm specializing in information technology. Our commitment is to provide the best qualified candidate to match our client's requirements in a professional, ethical and timely manner.
Functions: Sales mgmt., Direct mktg., Customer svc., Systems dev., Systems implem., Systems support, Network admin.
Industries: Computer equip., Computer svcs., Advertising/PR, New media, Telecoms, High tech, Software

---

Wallace Assoc.

49 Leavenworth St., Ste. 200
P.O. Box 11294
Waterbury, Connecticut 06703
(203) 879-2011
Fax: (203) 879-2407
Email: walstaff@world.std.com
Web: world.std.com/~walstaff

Key Contact - Specialty:
Mr. Gregory Gordon - *Engineering*

Description: Personal consulting expertise to clients throughout the U.S. with concentration in engineering and manufacturing support disciplines, up to and including the executive level.

Salary Minimum: $40,000
Functions: Generalist, General mgmt., Production, Automation, Quality, Systems dev., Engineering
Industries: Generalist, Medical devices, Plastics/rubber, Metal products, Machinery/Appliances, High tech, Software

---

Wallace Assoc.

57 Pearl St.
Amesbury, Massachusetts 01913
(508) 388-6191
Fax: (508) 388-8445
Email: bgWallace@aol.com

Key Contact - Specialty:
Mr. Bruce Georgian

Description: General management consulting, technology consulting, technology sales and marketing-specifically internet technology, interactive technology, electronic commerce.

Salary Minimum: $75,000
Functions: Mkt. research, Mktg. mgmt., Sales mgmt., Mgmt. consultants
Industries: New media, High tech

The Wallace Law Registry

43 Woodland St., Ste. 400
Hartford, Connecticut 06105
(800) 248-4LAW
Fax: (860) 549-8794

Key Contact - Specialty:
Ms. Kathryn Hynes

Description: We are a full service placement agency engaged in the permanent placement of attorneys, general/senior counsel, partnership search and the temporary and permanent placement of associates, in-house counsel, legal administrators and paralegals.
Functions: Attorneys
Industries: Legal

Gerald Walsh & Co. Inc.

10th Floor, Barrington Twr., Scotia Sq.
P.O. Box 2166
Halifax, Nova Scotia B3J 3C4
Canada
(902) 421-1676
Fax: (902) 425-1108
Email: gwalsh@fox.nstn.ca

Key Contact - Specialty:
Mr. Gerald Walsh
Mr. Scott Miller
Ms. Patty Sypher

Description: Our firm specializes in the recruitment of middle to senior level managers and professionals.

Salary Minimum: $30,000

Functions: Generalist, General mgmt., Mfg., Sales & mktg., HR mgmt., Finance, Engineering
Industries: Generalist

Branches:
361 Victoria St., Ste. 203
Fredericton, New Brunswick E3B 1W5
Canada
(506) 455-2420
Fax: (506) 455-2421
Key Contact - Specialty:
Mr. Paul Masterson

Linda Walter & Associes

291 Montee Sagala
Ile Perrot, Quebec J7V 3C8
Canada
(514) 425-7000
Fax: (514) 425-6170

Key Contact - Specialty:
Ms. Linda Walter

Description: More than 20 years experience. Selective screening customized to company's needs.
Functions: Mfg., Materials, Sales & mktg., HR mgmt., Finance, IT, Engineering
Industries: Generalist, Mfg., Transportation, Wholesale, Retail, Finance, Aerospace

Karen Wanger & Assoc., Inc.

707 Skokie Blvd., Ste. 600
Northbrook, Illinois 60062
(847) 291-4333
Fax: (847) 831-1860
Email: karkarr1@aol.com

Key Contact - Specialty:
Ms. Karen Wanger - *Insurance, generalist*

Description: Search consulting and recruiting in most industries with specialization in the insurance sector.

Salary Minimum: $40,000
Functions: Generalist, Personnel
Industries: Generalist, Insurance

Ward Assoc.

145 Wellington St. W., Ste. 210
Toronto, Ontario M5J 1H8
Canada
(416) 293-1660
(800) 668-8215
Fax: (416) 593-1661
Email: candidates@ward-associates.com
Web: www.ward-associates.com

Key Contact - Specialty:
Mr. Peter Ward - *Information technology, high technology*

Description: We specialize in information technology and high tech staffing, placement and recruitment.
Functions: Directors, Mkt. research, Sales mgmt., Systems anal., Systems implem., R&D, Mgmt. consultants

Branches:
328 Somerset St. W.
Ottawa, Ontario K2P 0J9
Canada
(613) 233-9273
Fax: (613) 233-9658
Email: ottawa@ward-associates.com
Web: www.ward-associates.com
Key Contact - Specialty:
Mr. Kevin O'Rourke - *Information technology, high technology*

2000 Peel St., Ste. 680
Montreal, Quebec H3A 2W5
Canada
(514) 848-9361
Fax: (514) 848-6376
Email: montreal@ward-associates.com
Web: www.ward-associates.com
Key Contact - Specialty:
Mr. Kevin O'Rourke - *Information technology, high technology*

Martha Ward Executive Search, Inc.

4 Laurel Hill Lane, P.O. Box 2759
Amagansett, New York 11930-2759
(516) 267-3730
Fax: (516) 267-6335
Email: marketing@marthaward.com
Web: www.marthaward.com

Key Contact - Specialty:
Ms. Martha Ward - *Marketing, marketing services (market research & sales promotion)*
Mr. Paul Poutouves - *Advertising, sales*

Description: 30 years specializing in successful national consumer products-marketing, advertising, telecomunications and sales recruitment with Fortune 500 companies.

Salary Minimum: $60,000
Functions: Directors, Senior mgmt., Middle mgmt., Mkt. research, Mktg. mgmt., Sales mgmt., Direct mktg.
Industries: Generalist, Food/bev/tobacco, Textiles/apparel, Soap/perfume/cosmetics, Drugs mfg., Advertising/PR, Telecoms

Ward-Hoffman & Assoc.

2020 Lakewood Drive, Ste. 312
Coeur d'Alene, Idaho 83814
(208) 667-6095
Fax: (208) 765-8377
Email: allward@nidlink.com

Key Contact - Specialty:
Mr. Al L. Ward - *Construction, engineering, mining*
Ms. Gayle E. Ward - *Medical, sales*

Description: Worldwide recruiting experience.

Salary Minimum: $30,000
Functions: Senior mgmt., Plant mgmt., Mkt. research, MIS mgmt., DB admin., Engineering, Environmentalists
Industries: Agri/forestry/mining, Energy/utilities, Construction, Mfg., Food/bev/tobacco, Environmental svcs., Software

C. D. Warner & Assoc.

12 Davenport Drive
Downingtown, Pennsylvania 19335
(610) 458-8335
Fax: (610) 458-0498
Email: DougWarner@cdwarner.com
Web: cdwarner.com

Key Contact - Specialty:
Mr. C. Douglas Warner - *Information technology, executive management*
Ms. Susan C. Warner - *Executive financial managers*

Description: Executive search firm specializing in information technology and high tech computing focusing on management (all levels), marketing, sales and technical professionals. North America and European geographical territory.
Functions: Directors, Senior mgmt., Middle mgmt., Mktg. mgmt., Sales mgmt., MIS mgmt., Mgmt. consultants
Industries: Computer svcs., Mgmt. consulting, Telecoms, High tech, Software

Branches:
1605 Creston Drive
Forest Hill, Maryland 21050
(410) 420-1613
Fax: (410) 420-1614
Email: HeatherFinley@mindspring.com
Key Contact - Specialty:
Ms. Heather Finley

Affiliates:
Bay Resource Group
B. D. Wallace & Assoc.

Warner & Assoc., Inc.

101 E. College Ave.
Westerville, Ohio 43081
(614) 891-9003

Key Contact - Specialty:
Mr. Thomas P. Warner - *Manufacturing, industrial clients*

Description: Well-established, owner-managed firm offering customized and personal response to the needs of our clients. Specialist within most functional areas of manufacturing management. Guaranteed success in recruitment.

Salary Minimum: $40,000
Functions: Directors, Senior mgmt., Middle mgmt., Mfg., Materials, HR mgmt., Engineering
Industries: Mfg., Plastics/rubber, Metal products, Machinery/Appliances, Motor vehicles, Computer equip., Consumer electronics

Warren Executive Services

P.O. Box 1517
Lilburn, Georgia 30048
(770) 381-1175
Fax: (770) 279-7865
Email: rwarren103@aol.com
Web: www.mindspring.com/~wesco/

Key Contact - Specialty:
Mr. Robert L. Warren
Ms. Wanda Chappelle

Description: Recruiters for manufacturing industries, with emphasis on manufacturing support, personnel, automation, plant engineering and logistical support.

Salary Minimum: $20,000
Functions: Product dev., Production, Purchasing, Materials Plng., Benefits, MIS mgmt., Engineering
Industries: Medical devices, Plastics/rubber, Motor vehicles, Consumer electronics, Aerospace, High tech, Software

Warren, Morris & Madison, Ltd.

2190 Carmel Valley Rd.
Del Mar, California 92014-3766
(619) 481-3388
Fax: (619) 481-6221
Email: info@wmmltd.com
Web: www.wmmltd.com

Key Contact - Specialty:
Mr. Charles C. Morris - *Cable television, multimedia, wireless communications, international*

Description: We have made indispensable contributions to the telecommunications industries. To help our clients capitalize on converging technologies, we've attracted industry-experienced executives to head each of our individual divisions.

Salary Minimum: $75,000
Functions: Generalist, Directors, Advertising, CFO's, MIS mgmt., Engineering, Int'l.
Industries: Communications, Advertising/PR, New media, Broadcast & Film, Telecoms, High tech

Branches:
44 Newmarket Road, 3rd Floor
Durham, New Hampshire 03824
(603) 868-6200
Fax: (603) 868-5061
Email: jcapra@wmmltd.com
Key Contact - Specialty:
Mr. Jamie V. Capra - *Cable television, advertising sales, manufacturing*
Mr. Corwyn J. Scott - *Cable television, advertising sales, manufacturing*

132 Chapel St.
Portsmouth, New Hampshire 03801
(603) 431-7929
Fax: (603) 431-3460
Email: jarnold@wmmltd.com
Key Contact - Specialty:
Mr. Scott C. Warren - *International, multimedia, cable television, wireless, competitive telephone*
Mr. David J. Higgins - *Multimedia*

4108 Holly Rd.
Virginia Beach, Virginia 23451
(757) 425-9950
Fax: (757) 425-9936
Email: dmadison@wmmltd.com
Key Contact - Specialty:
Mr. T. Dean Madison - *International, telephony, multimedia*

Affiliates:
Bull Thompson International

Wasserman Assoc. Inc.

604 Sunspot Rd.
Reisterstown, Maryland 21136
(410) 517-0060
Fax: (410) 517-0080
Email: swass@erols.com

Key Contact - Specialty:
Mr. Stan Wasserman - *Consumer product sales & category management, trade marketing*

Description: Over 22 years specializing in consumer product sales and marketing, emphasis on food, drug, beverage and general merchandise/non-food areas. First level manager to VP-sales and marketing, also trade marketing managers, category managers and sales planning managers.

Salary Minimum: $50,000
Functions: Sales mgmt.
Industries: Food/bev/tobacco, Paper, Soap/perfume/cosmetics, Drugs mfg., Plastics/rubber, Consumer electronics

Waterford Executive Group Ltd.

1 N. 141 County Farm Rd., Ste. 220 D
Winfield, Illinois 60190
(630) 690-0055
Fax: (630) 690-5533
Email: waterfrd@wwa.com

Key Contact - Specialty:
Mr. Patrick J. Atkinson - *Compensation consultants, organizational effectiveness, organizational development, change management, human resources*
Mr. Sean O'Neill - *Pension & benefits consultants, actuaries, health & welfare consultants, benefits systems, outsourcing*
Mr. Ted Tomei - *Compensation consultants, organizational effectiveness, organizational development, change management, health & welfare*

Description: Our firm will fulfill our clients needs via retainer or contingency arrangements with a highly personalized and focused approach, mainly in compensation and benefits consulting industry and corporate HR.

Salary Minimum: $40,000
Functions: Benefits, Mgmt. consultants
Industries: Mgmt. consulting, Human resource svcs., Healthcare

Watring & Assoc., Inc.

316 W. Roosevelt Rd., Ste. 10A
Wheaton, Illinois 60187
(630) 690-2707
Fax: (630) 690-2243
Email: BAWatring@aol.com

Key Contact - Specialty:
Ms. Bernie Watring - *Medical sales, medical marketing management to CEO's at medical corporations clinical specialists, RN's*

Description: Placement of all medical sales marketing, management, engineering, including R&D, quality control; also dealer sales forces and clinical applications specialists, for U.S. and international.
Functions: Senior mgmt., Middle mgmt., Nurses, Mkt. research, Mktg. mgmt., Sales mgmt., Int'l.
Industries: Drugs mfg., Medical devices, Pharmaceutical svcs., Biotech

Branches:
19932 Cato Circle
Huntington Beach, California 92646
(714) 964-8874
Fax: (714) 964-9774
Key Contact - Specialty:
Ms. Kris Byer

Wayne Assoc., Inc.

2628 Barrett St.
Virginia Beach, Virginia 23452
(757) 340-0555
Fax: (757) 340-0826
Email: wai@infi.net

Key Contact - Specialty:
Mr. Robert W. Cozzens

Description: We have over 20 years experience working with top chemical companies placing entry-level to presidents.

Salary Minimum: $50,000
Functions: Packaging, Mkt. research, Mktg. mgmt., Sales mgmt., Engineering
Industries: Paper, Chemicals, Plastics/rubber, Paints/petroleum products

The Wayne Group, Ltd.

84 William St., 15th Floor
New York, New York 10038
(212) 668-1414
Fax: (212) 668-0963

Email: sam@waynegroup.com
Web: www.waynegroup.com

Key Contact - Specialty:
Mr. Samuel Schwimmer - *Information technology professionals*

Description: We serve the information systems analysis of the financial investments industry by focusing on technology/information systems selection and placement. We fulfill clients' consulting and full-time needs at both the senior and technical level. Our success lies in our ability to provide the proper match by melding the nature and character of the company, the candidates' skills and interest and cultures involved.

Salary Minimum: $75,000
Functions: Senior mgmt., Purchasing, Personnel, MIS mgmt., Systems anal., Systems implem., Systems support
Industries: Finance, Invest. banking, Venture cap., Mgmt. consulting, Human resource svcs., Insurance, Software

---

Weatherby Healthcare
25 Van Zant St.
Norwalk, Connecticut 06855
(203) 866-1144
Fax: (203) 853-3154
Email: lstewart@whcmail.com
Web: whofirst.com

Key Contact - Specialty:
Mr. Joseph Pendergast
Mr. Lawrence D. Stewart

Description: Healthcare executive search and physician recruitment.
Functions: Physicians, Health admin.
Industries: Healthcare

Branches:
3230 W. Commercial Blvd., Ste. 240
Ft. Lauderdale, Florida 33309
(954) 730-3340
Key Contact - Specialty:
Mr. Michael Pendergast

9701 W. Higgins Rd.
Rosemont, Illinois 60018
(847) 384-9500
Key Contact - Specialty:
Mr. Don Babchick

Affiliates:
Weatherby Locums, Inc.

Wegner & Assoc.
11270 W. Park Place, Ste. 310
One Park Plaza
Milwaukee, Wisconsin 53224
(414) 359-2333
Fax: (414) 359-2325
Email: wegner310@aol.com

Key Contact - Specialty:
Mr. Carl Wegner - *Financial, general management*
Mr. Bob Schultz - *MIS, information systems*

Description: Specializing in upper and middle management recruiting with particular emphasis in general management, financial, accounting and the MIS areas. Also do extensive staff level recruiting in the accounting and MIS areas.

Salary Minimum: $30,000
Functions: Middle mgmt., Plant mgmt., Purchasing, Sales & mktg., HR mgmt., Finance, IT
Industries: Generalist, Machinery/ Appliances, Transportation, Finance, Accounting, Real estate, Healthcare

---

Lee Weil Assoc., Inc.
205 W. Wacker Drive, Ste. 901
Chicago, Illinois 60606
(312) 578-0828
Fax: (312) 578-0829
Email: leeweil@mcs.com

Key Contact - Specialty:
Ms. Lee Weil - *Classical brand marketing, market research, advertising account planning, account management*

Description: Classical brand marketing, market research, account planning and account management (advertising); national and international clients; trained, experienced researchers and recruiters. Goal: results!

Salary Minimum: $50,000
Functions: Directors, Senior mgmt., Middle mgmt., Advertising, Mkt. research, Mktg. mgmt.
Industries: Food/bev/tobacco, Motor vehicles, Entertainment, Mgmt. consulting, Advertising/PR, Telecoms, High tech

Branches:
2740 San Juan Lane
Costa Mesa, California 92626
(714) 545-6515
Fax: (714) 545-7215
Email: robin_haggard@msn.com
Key Contact - Specialty:
Ms. Robin Haggard

David Weinfeld Group
6512 Six Forks Rd., Ste. 603B
Raleigh, North Carolina 27615
(919) 676-7828
Fax: (919) 676-7399
Email: email@weinfeldgroup.com
Web: www.weinfeldgroup.com

Key Contact - Specialty:
Mr. David C. Weinfeld - *Telecommunications, computers, software, data communications, CATV, IT, Technology Consultants*
Mr. Drew Karkow - *Telecommunications, computers, software, data communications, CATV*
Ms. Angelle Marcantel
Ms. Susan Schmidt - *Telecommunications, computers, software, data communications, CATV, IT, technology consulting*

Description: Customized recruitment of key executives in sales, marketing, engineering and management consultants in the telecommunications, data com, cable TV, broadcasting, networking and other related applications including consulting functions and software applications.

Salary Minimum: $45,000
Functions: Middle mgmt., Product dev., Sales mgmt., Systems dev., Systems implem., R&D, Engineering
Industries: Computer equip., Test/ measurement equip., Computer svcs., Broadcast & Film, Telecoms, Software

---

Weinman & Assoc.
7110 E. McDonald Drive, Ste. B-6
Scottsdale, Arizona 85253
(602) 483-2132
Fax: (602) 922-9248
Email: mweinman@primenet.com

Key Contact - Specialty:
Ms. Mary Weinman - *Hospitality*
Ms. Robin Duncan - *Hospitality*
Ms. Lynn Mizel - *Legal, attorneys, paralegals*
Ms. Patti Sussman - *MIS, accounting, real estate, construction*

Description: Full service executive search firm.
Functions: General mgmt., IT, MIS mgmt., Specialized services, Attorneys, Paralegals
Industries: Construction, Svcs., Hospitality

Weinpel Search, Inc.
P.O. Box 248
Hamburg Tnpk.
Riverdale, New Jersey 07457
(201) 628-0858
Fax: (201) 694-7319
Email: cweinpel@aol.com

Key Contact - Specialty:
Mr. Charles J. Weinpel - *Engineering, science, software (all levels)*

Description: Specialize in search recruitment for executives and world class specialists for high technology industries.
Functions: Middle mgmt., Production, Plant mgmt., Mktg. mgmt., Systems anal., R&D, Engineering
Industries: Consumer electronics, Defense, Aerospace, High tech, Software

C. Weiss Assoc., Inc.

60 W. 57th St.
New York, New York 10019
(212) 581-4040
Email: cwpiss1301@aol.com

Key Contact - Specialty:
Ms. Cathy Weiss - *Consumer bank marketing, residential mortgage sales and marketing, direct marketing, database management*

Description: Specialty in domestic and international recruiting for consumer financial services. Excellent research department, capable of handling unique assignments. Mortgage banking expertise, both retail and wholesale.

Salary Minimum: $40,000
Functions: Advertising, Mkt. research, Mktg. mgmt., Direct mktg., MIS mgmt., DB admin.
Industries: Finance, Banking, Misc. financial

Weliver & Assoc.

5340 Plymouth Rd., Ste. 108
Ann Arbor, Michigan 48105
(734) 913-0070
Fax: (734) 913-0079
Email: edweliver@worldnet.att.net

Key Contact - Specialty:
Mr. Edward A. Weliver - *Information technology, human resources, engineers*
Ms. Billie S. Weliver

Description: We have consultants who specialize in systems mainframe, midrange and PC in Southeast Michigan, Arkansas and Massachusetts. Ranging from entry to CIO in all environments. We work in all peripheral areas; i.e. finance, sales, training and engineers. We interface in the total US.
Functions: Personnel, MIS mgmt., Systems anal., Systems dev., Systems implem., Systems support, Network admin.
Industries: Generalist, New media

Affiliates:
Express Personnel

Henry Welker & Assoc.

P.O. Box 530846
Livonia, Michigan 48153-0846
(734) 953-4900
Fax: (734) 953-5918
Email: welkerh@aol.com

Key Contact - Specialty:
Mr. Henry A. Welker - *EDP, engineering, sales (technical)*

Description: Specialists in Management, IT, IS, HR ,Engineering,Sales.

Salary Minimum: $40,000
Functions: Mfg., Purchasing, Sales mgmt., HR mgmt., IT, Engineering, Mgmt. consultants
Industries: Generalist, Energy/utilities, Mfg., Transportation, Computer svcs., High tech, Software

Wellington Thomas Ltd.

6544 U.S. Hwy. 41 N., Ste. 209
Apollo Beach, Florida 33572
(800) 779-1233
Fax: (888) 363-7704

Key Contact - Specialty:
Ms. Jean M. De Mange - *Healthcare, medical, nursing, regulatory, clinical & managed care*

Description: Premier national search firm serving the healthcare marketplace. Our reputation for integrity and work ethic is our bond. Our emphasis is in clinical, operational, business development and administrative positions from staff to vice president level.

Salary Minimum: $40,000
Functions: Senior mgmt., Middle mgmt., Admin. svcs., Healthcare, Nurses, Health admin., Mgmt. consultants
Industries: Healthcare

Wells, Bradley & Assoc., Inc.

520 Lake Elmo Ave. N.
Lake Elmo, Minnesota 55042-9703
(651) 731-9202
Fax: (651) 436-1485
Email: wellsbradley@sprintmail.com

Key Contact - Specialty:
Ms. Gillis Lindberg - *Banking, credit card*

Description: Executive search concentrating in banking, commercial banking, credit card, smart card, foreign exchange and investment management.

Salary Minimum: $50,000
Functions: Senior mgmt., Mkt. research, Sales mgmt., Budgeting, Credit, Systems anal., Int'l.
Industries: Banking

R. A. Wells Co.

107 N. Lakeside Drive
Kennesaw, Georgia 30144
(770) 424-8493
Fax: (770) 424-8545
Email: rawco@mindspring.com

Key Contact - Specialty:
Mr. Robert A. Wells - *Plastics*

Description: Our firm specializes in conducting search activity for clients in the plastic packaging industry throughout the world market.

Salary Minimum: $45,000
Functions: Senior mgmt., Product dev., Automation, Plant mgmt., Packaging, Mktg. mgmt., Sales mgmt.
Industries: Chemicals, Plastics/rubber, Packaging, High tech

Welzig, Lowe & Assoc.

761 W. Birch Court
Louisville, Colorado 80027
(303) 666-4195

Key Contact - Specialty:
Mr. Frank E. Welzig - *Generalist, high technology*

Description: Specialize in management and senior engineers for fast-growth companies in all industries.

Salary Minimum: $60,000
Functions: Generalist, MIS mgmt., R&D, Engineering, Int'l.
Industries: Generalist, Software

Werbin Assoc. Executive Search, Inc.

140 Riverside Drive, 10N
New York, New York 10024
(212) 799-6111

Key Contact - Specialty:
Ms. Susan Werbin - *Information technology, operations & market research, finance*

Description: Oriented towards assisting the computer, research, finance and management science professionals, technical management-all levels.
Functions: Mfg., Materials, Mkt. research, Direct mktg., Finance, IT, Engineering
Industries: Computer equip., Finance, Computer svcs., Mgmt. consulting, Communications, High tech, Software

West & Assoc.

2511 W. Schaumburg Rd., Ste. 335
Schaumburg, Illinois 60194-3887
(847) 885-4880
Fax: (847) 885-4889
Email: hunter4880@aol.com

Key Contact - Specialty:
Mr. Al West - *Manufacturing, machine tools*

Description: 12 years experience serving the machine tool industry. Specializing in field service engineers, application engineers, CNC programmers, design engineers and management and sales personnel.
Functions: Senior mgmt., Middle mgmt., Automation, Plant mgmt., Sales mgmt., Engineering, Technicians
Industries: Metal products, Machinery/ Appliances, Motor vehicles, Test/ measurement equip., Misc. mfg.

West Coast Recruiting
290 E. Verdugo Ave., Ste. 204
Burbank, California 91502
(818) 556-6056
Fax: (818) 556-6102
Email: lprec.aol.com

Key Contact - Specialty:
Ms. Tracy A. Coleman - *Loss prevention, security*
Mr. Steven B. Nini - *Loss prevention & security*
Mr. Michael Duff - *Human resources*

Description: We specialize in executive search and placement of the nations' foremost loss prevention and security professionals within the retail and manufacturing industries of North America.

Salary Minimum: $35,000
Functions: General mgmt., HR mgmt., Risk mgmt.
Industries: Misc. mfg., Retail, Law enfcmt., High tech

Western Technical Resources
451 Los Gatos Blvd., Ste. 102
Los Gatos, California 95032
(408) 358-8533
(800) 600-5351
Fax: (408) 358-8535
Email: wtr@wtrusa.com
Web: www.wtrusa.com

Key Contact - Specialty:
Mr. Bruce Weinstein - *High technology engineering, information sciences*

Description: Worldwide contingent and temporary placement limited to the engineering and computer disciplines.

Salary Minimum: $45,000
Functions: General mgmt., Mfg., Mktg. mgmt., IT, R&D, Engineering
Industries: New media, Telecoms, Aerospace, High tech, Software, Biotech

The Westfield Group
1010 Washington Blvd.
Stamford, Connecticut 06901
(203) 406-2300
Fax: (203) 406-2315

Key Contact - Specialty:
Ms. Joanne C. Fiala - *Human resources, MIS, accounting, finance*

Description: Contingency and retained search firm specializing in human resources, MIS, accounting and finance. Fortune 500 client base, national client base, salaries range from $50,000 to $150,000.

Salary Minimum: $50,000
Functions: Benefits, Personnel, Training, Budgeting, Cash mgmt., Systems anal., Mgmt. consultants
Industries: Generalist

Westfields Int'l., Inc.
P.O. Box 356
Bemus Point, New York 14712
(716) 386-0303
Email: westflds@cecomet.net
Web: westflds@epix.net

Key Contact - Specialty:
Mr. Bruce A. Boje - *Pharmaceutical, biotech, information systems, engineering and management*

Description: We are a full service executive search firm offering over a decade of experience in medium to high level searches. Highly experienced in handling quick turnaround situations with professionalism.
Functions: Generalist, General mgmt., Mfg., Materials, Healthcare, IT, R&D
Industries: Drugs mfg., Pharmaceutical svcs., Biotech

WestPacific National Search, Inc.
23421 S. Pointe Drive, Ste. 270
Laguna Hills, California 92653
(949) 830-8780
Email: wstpac@ix.netcom.com
Web: westpacific.com

Key Contact - Specialty:
Mr. Glenn Burnett - *Insurance, healthcare, managed care*

Description: National and international capability with dedicated research team, extensive contacts within the growing managed care, physician practice management and ancillary healthcare service and product companies. Network connected-internet capability.

Salary Minimum: $60,000
Functions: Directors, Physicians, Sales & mktg., Finance, IT, R&D, Engineering
Industries: Drugs mfg., Medical devices, Misc. financial, Insurance, High tech, Biotech, Healthcare

Weterrings & Agnew, Inc.
925 Midtown Twr.
Rochester, New York 14604
(716) 454-3888
Fax: (716) 454-5998
Email: info@weterrings.com
Web: www.weterrings.com

Key Contact - Specialty:
Ms. Elaine McKenna - *Finance, administration, human resources, banking, general management*
Mr. Richard F. Corey - *Engineering, manufacturing, software development, MIS*
Mr. Thomas H. Quinn - *Sales, sales management, marketing*

Description: Providing professional recruitment services in all functional areas and across virtually all industry lines contingent and retained search.

Salary Minimum: $30,000
Functions: Product dev., Mkt. research, Benefits, CFO's, MIS mgmt., R&D, Engineering
Industries: Generalist

The Whitaker Companies
(Firm declined to update.)
820 Gessner, Ste. 1400
Houston, Texas 77024
(713) 465-1500
Email: twc@whitakercos.com
Web: www.whitakercos.com

Key Contact - Specialty:
Mr. Bruce Whitaker
Dr. Linda Bruce - *Physicians*
Ms. Carol Dibb Wenom - *Engineering*
Ms. Bonnie Lyons - *Information technology professionals*

Description: Search division recruits physicians, engineers, middle and upper managers for chemical and refining industries and legal placement (attorneys and paralegals). Temporary professional placement of physicians, engineers and information systems professionals.

Salary Minimum: $40,000
Functions: Physicians, Systems dev., Engineering, Attorneys, Paralegals
Industries: Chemicals, Plastics/rubber, Legal, Computer svcs., Environmental svcs., Software, Healthcare

White, Roberts & Stratton, Inc.
444 N. Michigan Ave., Ste. 2940
Chicago, Illinois 60611
(312) 644-5554
Fax: (312) 644-4853

Key Contact - Specialty:
Mr. Marc P. White
Mr. William F. Stratton
Mr. Warren H. Roberts

Description: Our primary objective is to locate, evaluate and select prospective candidates in accordance with your specifications. We are also very capable in assisting in search assignments that address cultural diversity.

Salary Minimum: $75,000

Functions: General mgmt., Mfg., Sales & mktg., HR mgmt., Finance, Engineering, Minorities
Industries: Generalist, Food/bev/tobacco, Soap/perfume/cosmetics, Medical devices, Misc. mfg., Entertainment, Accounting

Whitehead & Assoc., Inc.

330 Palisades Drive
Lake Ozark, Missouri 65049
(573) 365-2112
Fax: (573) 365-4224
Email: white330@usmo.com

Key Contact - Specialty:
Mr. Robert S. Whitehead - *Software engineers, hardware engineers, manufacturing, engineering*
Ms. Elizabeth S. Whitehead - *MIS management, systems analysis & design, software development*

Description: Machine design/mechanical/electro-mechanical/electronic for manufacturing and industry. All engineering disciplines. Human resource management. Sales and marketing. Automotive engineering for Big 3, Tier I and Tier II; job shops.
Functions: General mgmt., Mfg., Materials, Sales & mktg., HR mgmt., Systems dev., Engineering
Industries: Printing, Metal products, Machinery/Appliances, Motor vehicles, Computer equip., Consumer electronics, Test/measurement equip.

The Whitney Group

3605 Sandy Plains Rd., Ste. 240-163
Marietta, Georgia 30066
(770) 592-1840
Fax: (770) 592-2012
Email: JewGenie@aol.com

Key Contact - Specialty:
Mr. Paul Komorner - *Sales, sales management, marketing management*

Description: Have been a recruiter for the past 22 years, specializing in all areas of industrial sales, sales, management and marketing.

Salary Minimum: $30,000
Functions: Senior mgmt., Middle mgmt., Mktg. mgmt., Sales mgmt.
Industries: Plastics/rubber, Metal products, Machinery/Appliances, Test/measurement equip., Misc. mfg., Accounting, Packaging

Whitney Smith Co.

500 Throckmorton, Ste. 1820
Ft. Worth, Texas 76102
(817) 877-4120
Fax: (817) 877-3846

Key Contact - Specialty:
Mr. David W. Farmer - *Banking, general management, human resources*

Description: Specialize in recruiting and placement of professionals in banking, savings and loans and credit unions. Also place human resource professionals, accountants, attorneys and engineers.

Salary Minimum: $30,000
Functions: Senior mgmt., Middle mgmt., Plant mgmt., Health admin., Benefits, Personnel, CFO's
Industries: Chemicals, Banking, Misc. financial, Hospitality, Accounting, Human resource svcs., Healthcare

Whittaker & Assoc., Inc.

2675 Cumberland Pkwy., Ste. 263
Atlanta, Georgia 30339
(770) 434-3779
Fax: (770) 431-0213

Key Contact - Specialty:
Ms. Millie A. Boatman
Mr. Arnold G. Whittaker - *Ingredients, pet food & related areas*
Mr. Brad Winkler - *Bakery & ingredient & related areas*
Mr. Harry Stanley - *Dairy, beverage & related areas*
Mr. Jeff Howell - *Meat, poultry, pet food, seafood & related*

Description: Specializes in the search and placement of managerial, supervisory and executive level positions within the food industry nationwide with emphasis on dairy, meat, poultry, bakery and related products.

Salary Minimum: $30,000
Functions: Senior mgmt., Middle mgmt., Plant mgmt., Quality, Sales mgmt., R&D, Engineering
Industries: Food/bev/tobacco

The Whittaker Group

1000 S. Old Woodward, Ste. 105/22
Birmingham, Michigan 48009
(248) 489-3900
Fax: (248) 489-1419

Key Contact - Specialty:
Ms. Michelle A. Whittaker-Jhaveri - *Healthcare, managed care*

Description: National healthcare and managed care executive search and outplacement specialists.

Salary Minimum: $60,000
Functions: Physicians, Nurses, Health admin., Training, CFO's, Budgeting, Cash mgmt.
Industries: Pharmaceutical svcs., Healthcare

Wilder & Assoc.

24 S. Old Glebe Rd., Ste. 104
Arlington, Virginia 22204
(703) 521-6429
(703) 521-3020
Fax: (703) 521-3212
Email: WilderJobs@aol.com

Key Contact - Specialty:
Mr. Bruce Wilder - *Generalist*
Ms. Diane Wilder - *Administrative*
Mr. James Rallerty - *Finance & accounting*

Description: Administrative, financial and technical search firm.
Functions: Generalist, General mgmt., Sales & mktg., HR mgmt., Finance, IT, Specialized services
Industries: Generalist, Banking, Computer svcs., Accounting, Telecoms, High tech, Software

Branches:
287 Old Bethel Rd.
Edinburg, Virginia 22824
(540) 984-4964
(540) 984-3242
Key Contact - Specialty:
Ms. Diana Wilder

Joel H. Wilensky Assoc., Inc.

22 Union Ave.
P.O. Box 155
Sudbury, Massachusetts 01776
(978) 443-5176
Fax: (978) 443-3009

Key Contact - Specialty:
Mr. Joel H. Wilensky - *Retail chains*

Description: One person contingency recruiting firm specializing in retail chain placement. Specific emphasis on corporate or home office placement i.e. finance, data processing, etc.

Salary Minimum: $70,000
Functions: CFO's, MIS mgmt., Systems dev.
Industries: Retail

Wilkinson SoftSearch, Inc.

10613 Moore St., Ste. 210
Fairfax, Virginia 22030-3911
(703) 352-1795
Fax: (703) 352-1797
Email: jobs@softsearch.net
Web: www.softsearch.net

Key Contact - Specialty:
Mr. Kurt A. Wilkinson - *Information technology*

Description: As a trusted recruiting resource in the Information Technology field, we represent premier Management Consulting firms, leading edge Software Vendors, and progressive Fortune 1000 companies throughout the U.S.

Salary Minimum: $70,000
Functions: MIS mgmt., Systems anal., Systems dev., Systems implem., DB admin., Mgmt. consultants
Industries: Computer svcs., Mgmt. consulting, High tech, Software

Branches:
2010 Corporate Ridge, Ste. 175
McLean, Virginia 22102-7838
(703) 352-1795
Fax: (703) 352-1797
Key Contact - Specialty:
Ms. Ann Trego Wilkinson - *Information technology*

William-Johns Co., Inc.
14081 Yorba, Ste. 202
The Allan Bldg.
Tustin, California 92780
(714) 544-1222
Fax: (714) 544-6555

Key Contact - Specialty:
Mr. William J. Kresich - *Hospitality*
Mr. William Thomas III - *Hospitality*
Ms. Renate Mettler - *Hospitality*
Ms. Carmen Anne Collier - *Hospitality*

Description: Four full-time recruiters with an accumulated history of 100 years of experience in the hospitality industry who have spent 50 of those 100 years in the search industry.

Salary Minimum: $75,000
Functions: Directors, Senior mgmt., Healthcare, Sales & mktg., Advertising, Personnel, Training
Industries: Drugs mfg., Medical devices, Hospitality, Pharmaceutical svcs., Healthcare

Dick Williams & Assoc.
5776 Stoneridge Mall Rd., Ste. 136
Pleasanton, California 94588
(925) 468-0304
Fax: (925) 468-0306
Email: info@dwasearch.com
Web: www.dwasearch.com

Key Contact - Specialty:
Mr. Dick Williams - *Semiconductor, process equipment, sales, engineers, information technology*
Mr. Rob Albertson - *Information technology, software, networking, security*
Mr. Kenn Giles - *Semiconductor, process equipment, sales*
Mr. Ray Mussato - *Information technology, software, networking, security*

Description: Dynamic, responsive, effective recruitment of high quality semiconductor, chemical and electronics sales/marketing executives, process engineers and managers in the semiconductor, processing equipment, hi-tech fields, software and networking (LAN, WAN Internet).

Salary Minimum: $60,000
Functions: Sales & mktg., IT, MIS mgmt., Systems anal., Systems dev., Systems support, Engineering
Industries: New media, High tech, Software

John R. Williams & Assoc., Inc.

2102 N. Elm St., Ste. H-6
Greensboro, North Carolina 27408
(910) 279-8800

Key Contact - Specialty:
Mr. John R. Williams - *Manufacturing management executives*

Description: Confidential executive search and placement services specializing in manufacturing industries with particular emphasis on textiles, furniture, chemicals and related supporting companies. Corporate, division and plant levels.

Salary Minimum: $50,000
Functions: Generalist, Middle mgmt., Production, Plant mgmt., Purchasing, HR mgmt., Finance
Industries: Textiles/apparel, Lumber/furniture, Chemicals, Drugs mfg., Plastics/rubber, Misc. mfg., Environmental svcs.

John Williams & Assoc.
401 W. Pecan St., Ste. 2A
Pflugerville, Texas 78660
(512) 990-9750
Fax: (512) 990-7807
Email: williams@gyro.net

Key Contact - Specialty:
Mr. John G. Williams - *Manufacturing, engineering, food industry*
Ms. Victoria Deyeaux - *Quality assurance*

Description: A full service executive recruiting firm specializing in manufacturing operations, engineering, quality assurance and distribution/logistics, disciplines within the consumer food and beverage industries(both retained and exclusive contingency searches.)

Salary Minimum: $40,000
Functions: Middle mgmt., Plant mgmt., Quality, Distribution, Engineering, Mgmt. consultants, Minorities
Industries: Food/bev/tobacco, Soap/perfume/cosmetics, Drugs mfg.

Williams & Delmore, Inc.
1800 Violet Hill Lane, Ste. 210
Raleigh, North Carolina 27610
(919) 217-0060
Fax: (919) 217-2801
Email: hilles@wdinc.net
Web: www.wdinc.net

Key Contact - Specialty:
Mr. Jeffrey W. Hilles - *Wireless telecommunications*

Description: Confidential and ethical placement of engineering and sales professionals in the Wireless Telecommunications industry.

Salary Minimum: $60,000
Functions: Mkt. research, Mktg. mgmt., Sales mgmt., Systems anal., Systems dev., Systems implem., Engineering
Industries: Telecoms, High tech, Software

Williams Recruiting, Inc.
16336 NE 81st St.
Williams Ctr.
Redmond, Washington 98052-3811
(425) 869-7775
Fax: (425) 869-1849
Email: williamsrecruiting@imailbox.com

Key Contact - Specialty:
Ms. Gail Williams
Mr. David Kloppman

Description: Specialized knowledge of technical and management talent in pharmaceutical, biopharmaceuticals. Experience in building teams in diversified areas: R&D, manufacturing and process development/regulatory and clinical, quality, engineering, marketing and business development.
Functions: Directors, Product dev., Quality, Packaging, Mktg. mgmt., R&D, Engineering
Industries: Drugs mfg., Medical devices, Pharmaceutical svcs., Biotech

Williamsburg Group
385 Cranbury Rd., Ste. 3
East Brunswick, New Jersey 08816
(732) 651-0404
Fax: (732) 651-8615
Email: wgileen@aol.com

Key Contact - Specialty:
Ms. Eileen Levine - *Technical, manufacturing*

Description: Our reputation for success is built on pride, ethics, integrity and quality of service to our clients. Save valuable time and money by speaking to only our best candidates. We are a service, providing company information and candidate information nationwide.
Functions: Product dev., Production, Plant mgmt., Quality, Purchasing, Packaging, Graphic artists
Industries: Chemicals, Soap/perfume/cosmetics, Drugs mfg., Medical devices, Plastics/rubber, Metal products, Misc. mfg.

Willmott & Assoc.
922 Waltham St., Ste. 103
Lexington, Massachusetts 02173
(781) 863-5400
Fax: (781) 863-8000
Email: Willmott@Willmott.com

Key Contact - Specialty:
Mr. D. Clark Willmott - *Human resources*
Mr. David Tomaras - *Compensation, benefits, human resource information system professionals*
Ms. Francine Sparks - *Human resources*
Mr. Daniel J. Meagher - *Contract human resources*

Description: We are a human resource consulting firm specializing in the search and placement of human resource professionals both permanent and temporary.

Salary Minimum: $30,000
Functions: HR mgmt., Benefits, Personnel, Training
Industries: Generalist

Branches:
175 Federal St.
Boston, Massachusetts 02110
(617) 728-0990
Fax: (617) 728-4477
Key Contact - Specialty:
Ms. Joanne A. Lynch

95 Sockanosset Rd., Unit 107
Cranston, Rhode Island 02920
(401) 943-5556
Fax: (401) 943-5575
Key Contact - Specialty:
Mr. David Zito

The Wilmington Group
1442 Military Cutoff Rd., #25
Wilmington, North Carolina 28403
(910) 256-1056
Fax: (910) 256-1057
Email: mri@willmingtongroup.com
Web: www.willmingtongroup.com

Key Contact - Specialty:
Mr. Richard G. Sears - *General manufacturing, automotive*
Mr. Kirk P. Sears - *Engineering, technical sales, information technology*

Description: Our mission is to be a high integrity executive search and recruiting organization, national in scope, who specializes in placing top professionals for world class manufacturing organizations.

Salary Minimum: $20,000
Functions: Directors, Automation, Packaging, Mktg. mgmt., HR mgmt., MIS mgmt., DB admin.
Industries: Paper, Printing, Plastics/rubber, Metal products, Machinery/Appliances, Motor vehicles, Telecoms

Affiliates:
Management Recruiters of Atlanta-Acworth

Wilson & Assoc. Int'l. Inc.
2451 McMullen Booth Rd., Ste. 301
Clearwater, Florida 34619
(813) 796-4955
Fax: (813) 796-4014
Email: ww@wilsonandassociates.com
Web: www.wilsonandassociates.com

Key Contact - Specialty:
Mr. Wayne Wilson - *Apparel executives, international, home furnishings, textiles, auto*

Description: A search firm that specializes in the apparel, home furnishings, footwear, auto and textiles manufacturing areas, with consultants who specialize in executive management, engineering, middle management, MIS, product development design.
Functions: Directors, Product dev., Quality, Distribution, MIS mgmt., Engineering, Int'l.
Industries: Textiles/apparel, Retail

Affiliates:
Source I, Inc.

Wilson McLeran, Inc.
25 Lyon St.
New Haven, Connecticut 06511
(800) 562-9646
Fax: (203) 562-5546
Email: bobwilson@job-bridge.com
Web: www.job-bridge.com

Key Contact - Specialty:
Mr. Robert F. Wilson - *Publishing, new media*
Ms. Martha Buchanan - *Museums, galleries, music, arts*

Description: Fees charged for successful searches only. Replacements found at no additional cost for hires terminated within 60 days of start date (except for reductions in force).

Salary Minimum: $35,000
Functions: Senior mgmt., Purchasing, Mkt. research, Customer svc., Benefits, Systems anal., Systems implem.
Industries: Non-profits, Publishing, New media

Affiliates:
J. L. Krug & Assoc., Inc.

Wilson Personnel, Inc.
134 Montford Ave.
Asheville, North Carolina 28801-2130
(828) 258-3900
Fax: (828) 258-3902

Key Contact - Specialty:
Mr. Charles K. Wilson
Mr. Kenneth Schapira - *Engineering, technical management*

Description: 30 years in the recruitment and placement of engineers, technical and manufacturing management professionals. Nationwide. Specialists in serving the manufacturing industries.

Salary Minimum: $35,000
Functions: Middle mgmt., Product dev., Automation, Plant mgmt., Purchasing, HR mgmt., Engineering
Industries: Soap/perfume/cosmetics, Medical devices, Plastics/rubber, Metal products, Machinery/Appliances, Computer equip., Misc. mfg.

Wilson-Douglas-Jordan
70 W. Madison, Ste. 1400
Chicago, Illinois 60602
(312) 782-0286
Fax: (312) 214-3424
Email: wdjinc@aol.com

Key Contact - Specialty:
Mr. John T. Wilson - *Management consulting, information technology*

Description: Provide executive and professional search for the information technology industry. Particular specialization given to client/server and object-oriented technologies. Target market: Fortune 200 and management consulting firms.

Salary Minimum: $40,000
Functions: Directors, Sales mgmt., MIS mgmt., Systems anal., Systems dev., DB admin., Mgmt. consultants
Industries: Computer svcs., Mgmt. consulting, New media, Telecoms, High tech, Software

Windsor Consultants, Inc.
13201 NW Frwy., Ste. 704
Houston, Texas 77040-6025
(713) 460-0586
(212) 563-4275
Fax: (713) 460-0945

Key Contact - Specialty:
Mr. Daniel Narsh - *Legal, intellectual property*
Mr. Carlton Porter - *Healthcare*
Mr. Bruce Litvin - *Legal, general practice*
Mr. William Fraser - *Outside sales, computer, general*
Ms. Kitty Seabaugh - *Restaurant management*

Description: Top team of recruiters. Highly successful in all areas of healthcare, legal, sales and hospitality. Flexible rates.
Functions: Middle mgmt., Nurses, Health admin., Sales mgmt., CFO's, Attorneys
Industries: Hospitality, Pharmaceutical svcs., Legal, Computer svcs., Mgmt. consulting, Healthcare

Winfield Assoc., Inc.

53 Winter St.
Weymouth, Massachusetts 02188
(781) 337-1010
Fax: (781) 335-0089

Key Contact - Specialty:
Mr. Carl W. Siegel - *Medical product manufacturers*

Description: Provides recruiting services for personnel in sales, marketing, general management, technical disciplines and regulatory affairs. The industries served are limited to manufacturers of medical and biotechnical products.

Salary Minimum: $40,000
Functions: Middle mgmt., Product dev., Quality, Mktg. mgmt., Sales mgmt., R&D, Engineering
Industries: Drugs mfg., Medical devices, Biotech

Wing Tips & Pumps, Inc.

P.O. Box 99580
Troy, Michigan 48099
(248) 641-0980
Fax: (248) 641-0895

Key Contact - Specialty:
Mr. Verba Lee Edwards - *Engineering, manufacturing, data processing, finance, sales*

Description: A minority-owned executive search corporation emphasizing world class service to corporate America. We place candidates in all areas from $20,000 to $300,000.

Salary Minimum: $20,000
Functions: Plant mgmt., Purchasing, Sales mgmt., Benefits, Cash mgmt., Systems dev., Engineering
Industries: Generalist, Plastics/rubber, Motor vehicles, Banking, Environmental svcs., Packaging, Software

The Winn Group, Inc.

501 Lawrence Ave.
Lawrence, Kansas 66049
(785) 842-7111
(913) 843-6001
Fax: (785) 842-6333
Email: jim@winngrp.com

Key Contact - Specialty:
Mr. James G. Winn - *Property & casualty actuaries*
Mrs. Pamela A. Heath - *Property & casualty actuaries*
Mr. Thomas A. Heath - *Property & casualty actuaries*

Description: A sharply focused and selective recruiting practice limited exclusively to property and casualty actuaries, U.S. and U.K. trained, for domestic and international positions.

Salary Minimum: $50,000
Industries: Insurance

Winston & Green

225 W. Washington #525
Chicago, Illinois 60606
(312) 201-9777
Fax: (312) 201-9781
Web: wglaw@megsinet.net

Key Contact - Specialty:
Mr. Larry A. Green - *Attorneys (in house & small to medium law firms), minorities*

Description: Specialties include general counsel, senior corporate counsel and staff attorneys for corporations and law firms of all sizes. Law firm mergers and acquisitions. Also, conduct marketing and research studies for law firms.

Salary Minimum: $50,000
Functions: Benefits, Minorities, Attorneys

Winter, Wyman & Co.

950 Winter St., Ste. 3100
Waltham, Massachusetts 02154-1294
(781) 890-7000
Fax: (781) 890-3266
Email: global@winterwyman.com
Web: www.winterwyman.com

Key Contact - Specialty:
Mr. Kevin Steele - *Accounting, finance, software engineering, computer sales & marketing, information technology*

Description: One of New England's largest professional placement firms, staffed by consultants experienced in their specialty field.

Salary Minimum: $35,000
Functions: Mktg. mgmt., Sales mgmt., Personnel, CFO's, Budgeting, MIS mgmt., Systems anal.
Industries: Computer equip., Finance, Computer svcs., Mgmt. consulting, High tech, Software

Branches:
1100 Circle 75 Pkwy., Ste. 800
Atlanta, Georgia 30339
(770) 933-1525
Fax: (770) 933-1526
Key Contact - Specialty:
Mr. Greg McConnell - *Information technology*

101 Federal St., 27th Floor
Boston, Massachusetts 02110
(617) 542-5000
Fax: (617) 542-5000

Key Contact - Specialty:
Mr. Mark Gleckman - *Accounting, finance*

Affiliates:
Winter, Wyman Contract Services

The Witt Group

P.O. Box 521281
Longwood, Florida 32752-1281
(407) 324-4137
Fax: (407) 322-5172

Key Contact - Specialty:
Mr. Gerald E. Witt - *Chemical industry, technical, sales & marketing*

Description: Technical placements in the chemical industry. Over 25 years experience, results-oriented. Excellent ratio of offers to interviews. Guaranteed satisfaction.

Salary Minimum: $50,000
Functions: Mfg., Product dev., Plant mgmt., Quality, Sales & mktg., R&D, Engineering
Industries: Chemicals, Soap/perfume/cosmetics, Drugs mfg., Plastics/rubber, Paints/petroleum products, Biotech

WMD inc.

P.O.Box 321
Pittstown, New Jersey 08867
(908) 735-2471
Fax: (908) 735-4556

Key Contact - Specialty:
Mr. Wayne Donelon - *Power, main drivers (turbines, diesels, boilers), air quality*

Description: Worldwide recruiter with 28 years of experience within the areas of search. Understands both sides, from the company's viewpoint and the candidate's viewpoint.

Salary Minimum: $50,000
Functions: Senior mgmt., Plant mgmt., Materials Plng., Sales mgmt., Personnel, Engineering, Int'l.
Industries: Energy/utilities, Machinery/Appliances

Susan L. Wonderling Recruiting

P.O. Box 35
Irvine, Pennsylvania 16329
(814) 563-3522
Fax: (814) 563-4502
Email: susan@allegany.com
Web: wonderling.com

Key Contact - Specialty:
Ms. Susan Wonderling - *Manufacturing, engineering*

Description: Engineering and manufacturing, specialty areas: mechanical, metallurgical, automotive, quality, machines and machining, managers and engineers, general manufacturing.

Salary Minimum: $22,000
Functions: Middle mgmt., Product dev., Production, Automation, Quality, Productivity, Engineering
Industries: Generalist, Plastics/rubber, Metal products, Machinery/Appliances, Motor vehicles, Test/measurement equip., Misc. mfg.

Louise Wood & Assoc.

90 Park Ave., Ste. 1700
New York, New York 10016
(212) 751-0325
Fax: (212) 750-6712
Email: louisewood@worldnet.att.net

Key Contact - Specialty:
Ms. Louise Wood - *Direct marketing*

Description: Concentration in direct marketing recruitment nationwide with an emphasis on recruiting creative and marketing professionals.

Salary Minimum: $75,000
Functions: Advertising, Mktg. mgmt., Direct mktg.
Industries: Misc. financial, Pharmaceutical svcs., Advertising/PR, Publishing, New media, Telecoms, Healthcare

Wood & Assoc./Executive Search Consultants

17 Escalle Lane
Larkspur, California 94939
(415) 927-3112
Fax: (415) 927-3117
Email: mwood51319@aol.com

Key Contact - Specialty:
Mr. Milo Wood

Description: Specializing in the placement of engineering and healthcare professionals, management personnel.

Salary Minimum: $50,000
Functions: General mgmt., Middle mgmt., Healthcare, Health admin., Engineering
Industries: Energy/utilities, Construction, Environmental svcs., High tech, Healthcare

Wood West & Partners Inc.

1281 W. Georgia St., Ste. 502
Vancouver, British Columbia V6E 3J7
Canada
(604) 682-3141
(604) 688-3787
Fax: (604) 688-5749
Email: search@wood-west.com
Web: www.wood-west.com

Key Contact - Specialty:
Mr. Fred West - *Engineering, information technology, telecommunications, construction, manufacturing*
Mr. Ron Wood - *Information technology, telecommunications, marketing & sales*
Mr. Cliff Tang - *Information technology, telecommunications, marketing & sales*
Mr. Don Sturgess - *Pulp & paper, mining, resource industries*

Description: Executive search and recruitment for specialists, managers, marketing & sales in information technology, engineering, telecommunications, construction.

Salary Minimum: $35,000
Functions: General mgmt., Mfg., Materials, Sales & mktg., IT, R&D, Engineering
Industries: Agri/forestry/mining, Construction, Mfg., Communications, Environmental svcs., High tech, Software

Woodmoor Group

325 2nd St.
P.O. Box 1383
Monument, Colorado 80132
(719) 488-8589
Fax: (719) 488-9043
Email: woodmoor@usa.net
Web: www.woodmoor.com

Key Contact - Specialty:
Mr. Ray N. Bedingfield - *Manufacturing*
Mr. Brian McQuiddy - *Manufacturing*
Mr. Lee Williams - *Oil & gas*
Dr. Michael Bremer - *Chemicals*

Description: Experienced, energetic and tenacious, we conduct comprehensive searches with professionalism, always mindful that we are an extension of your company. We consider it a point of honor to complete every search assigned to us.

Salary Minimum: $60,000
Functions: Mfg., Materials, Sales & mktg., HR mgmt., Finance, R&D, Engineering
Industries: Generalist

Jim Woodson & Assoc., Inc.

1080 River Oaks Drive, Ste. B-102
Jackson, Mississippi 39208
(601) 936-4037
Fax: (601) 936-4041
Email: Jwood0335@aol.com

Key Contact - Specialty:
Mr. Jim Woodson - *Generalist*

Description: Recruit heavily in engineering/manufacturing to include metal fab, high volume assembly, machined products, consumer appliances, consumer electronics, automotive, electric motors and environmental. Also actively recruit accounting/financial people.

Salary Minimum: $25,000
Functions: Product dev., Production, Automation, Plant mgmt., Quality, Purchasing, Engineering
Industries: Medical devices, Plastics/rubber, Metal products, Machinery/Appliances, Motor vehicles, Computer equip., Consumer electronics

Working Relationships, Inc.

1405 Lilac Drive N., Ste. 150
Minneapolis, Minnesota 55422
(612) 546-2999
Fax: (612) 546-2898
Email: hwalch@workingrelationships.com
Web: www.wrinc.com

Key Contact - Specialty:
Mr. Russ Lilienthal - *Generalist*
Mr. Hutch Walch - *Generalist*

Description: We are a unique company assisting companies nationwide with management placement at all levels and then performance coaching and management motivational seminars for clients.

Salary Minimum: $45,000
Functions: General mgmt., Mfg., Materials, Sales & mktg., HR mgmt., Finance, Specialized services
Industries: Construction, Retail, Finance, Svcs., Communications, Environmental svcs., Real estate

Worlco Computer Resources, Inc.

997 Old Eagle School Rd., Ste. 219
Wayne, Pennsylvania 19087-1706
(610) 293-9070
Fax: (610) 293-1027
Email: parisi@worlco.com
Web: www.worlco.com

Key Contact - Specialty:
Mr. Frank Parisi - *Computer, communications (data)*

Description: Provides full range of recruiting, executive search and personnel consulting services relating to computer professionals and executives in Philadelphia area marketplace; the leading organization of its kind. Also places consultants and undertakes project professional service assignments.

Salary Minimum: $25,000
Functions: Mkt. research, Mktg. mgmt., Sales mgmt., MIS mgmt., Systems anal., Systems implem., Systems support
Industries: Computer svcs., Software

Branches:
901 Route 38
Cherry Hill, New Jersey 08002
(609) 665-4700
Fax: (609) 665-4700

Email: hughes@worlco.com
Key Contact - Specialty:
Mr. Robert J. Hughes

World Search
4130 Linden Ave., Ste. 125
Dayton, Ohio 45432
(937) 254-9071
Fax: (937) 254-0229
Email: world@erinet.com

Key Contact - Specialty:
Mr. Robert Bannister
Ms. Sherry Bannister
Mr. Thomas A. Baehl - *Engineering, production management, HVAC*

Description: Contingency and retained search, with emphasis in the engineering, production management.

Salary Minimum: $40,000
Functions: Product dev., Automation, Productivity, Sales mgmt., Systems anal., Systems implem., Engineering
Industries: Plastics/rubber, Metal products, Computer equip., Transportation, Aerospace

Worldwide Medical Services
617 S. State St.
Ukiah, California 95482
(707) 468-9301
Fax: (707) 462-5208
Email: locumnet@wwmedical.com
Web: www.wwmedical.com

Key Contact - Specialty:
Mr. John Paju

Description: Worldwide medical recruits and places physicians, nurse anesthetists, medical administrators and executives both permanent and temporary.
Functions: Senior mgmt., Physicians, Nurses, Health admin., CFO's, M&A, MIS mgmt.
Industries: Misc. financial, Computer svcs., Accounting, Human resource svcs., Healthcare

The Worth Group
35 Technology Pkwy. S., Ste. 170
Norcross, Georgia 30092
(770) 613-5353
Fax: (770) 613-5354
Email: theworthgroup@mindspring.com

Key Contact - Specialty:
Mr. Brett Buckwald - *Telecommunications*

Description: We place high level sales, sales management and marketing positions nationally in the telecommunications industry.
Functions: Senior mgmt., Sales mgmt.
Industries: Telecoms

Branches:
295 Madison Ave., Ste. 1030
New York, New York 10017
(212) 986-9630
Fax: (212) 953-3665
Key Contact - Specialty:
Mr. Al Rosenblum - *Telecommunications*

Jay Wren & Assoc.
6355 Riverside Blvd., Ste. P
Sacramento, California 95831
(916) 394-2920
Fax: (916) 424-8192
Email: jaywren@aol.com

Key Contact - Specialty:
Mr. Jay Wren - *Consumer packaged goods region sales*

Description: Have placed sales managers, sales support managers, product and brand managers with over 50 major consumer package goods companies and package goods promotional, service and information companies.

Salary Minimum: $50,000
Functions: Sales mgmt.
Industries: Paper, Soap/perfume/cosmetics, Drugs mfg.

The Wright Group
9217 Frenchman's Way
Dallas, Texas 75220
(214) 351-1115
Fax: (214) 902-9569
Email: jayj6@airmail.net

Key Contact - Specialty:
Ms. Jay Wright - *Marketing research, target base, marketing science executives*

Description: Nationwide executive search specializing in the placement of marketing research professionals, marketing science, database, and targeting marketing professionals.

Salary Minimum: $30,000
Functions: Directors, Senior mgmt., Middle mgmt.

Branches:
7429 Wentwood
Dallas, Texas 75225
(214) 373-0660
Fax: (214) 373-0675
Key Contact - Specialty:
Ms. Leslie A. Root - *Marketing research, target base, marketing science executives*

Bob Wright Recruiting, Inc.
56 DeForest Rd.
Wilton, Connecticut 06897-1907
(203) 762-9046
Fax: (203) 762-5807

Key Contact - Specialty:
Mr. J. Robert Wright - *Sales, marketing, general management*

Description: Principal has worked in direct marketing, sales promotion and business information industries since 1969.

Salary Minimum: $40,000
Functions: Senior mgmt., Middle mgmt., Advertising, Mkt. research, Mktg. mgmt., Sales mgmt., Direct mktg.
Industries: Generalist, Printing, Svcs., Non-profits, Mgmt. consulting, Advertising/PR, Publishing

John Wylie Assoc., Inc.
1727 E. 71st St.
Tulsa, Oklahoma 74136
(918) 496-2100
Fax: (918) 496-2101

Key Contact - Specialty:
Mr. John L. Wylie - *Manufacturing managerial, technical, chemical processing (managers, engineers)*

Description: Professional, technical and managerial recruitment in the Southwest, principally for the petroleum/chemical processing and manufacturing industries. Have over 25 years of corporate recruiting experience.

Salary Minimum: $25,000
Functions: General mgmt., Mfg., Materials, HR mgmt., IT, Engineering
Industries: Energy/utilities, Mfg., Environmental svcs., High tech, Software

Dennis Wynn Assoc., Inc.
P.O. Box 7100
St. Petersburg, Florida 33734-7100
(813) 823-2042

Key Contact - Specialty:
Mr. Dennis N. Wynn
Ms. Jean Wynn

Description: Information systems recruitment specialist.

Salary Minimum: $20,000
Functions: MIS mgmt., Systems anal., Systems dev., Systems implem., Systems support
Industries: Computer svcs., Software

The Yaiser Group
904 Riverview Drive
Brielle, New Jersey 08730-1635
(908) 528-0443
Email: dickyaiser@worldnet.att.net

Key Contact - Specialty:
Mr. Richard A. Yaiser - *Pharmaceutical*
Mr. Tom Coghan - *Pharmaceutical*

Description: We are ethical, on target and waste neither our time nor yours in our efforts to identify proper candidates based upon your specifications.

Salary Minimum: $40,000

Functions: Directors, Middle mgmt., Product dev., Quality, Training, R&D
Industries: Drugs mfg.

Yankee Hospitality Search
406 Farmington Ave.
Farmington, Connecticut 06032
(860) 738-1900
(508) 620-5375
Fax: (860) 738-4972
Email: info@yankeehospitality.com
Web: www.yankeehospitality.com

Key Contact - Specialty:
Mr. Dan Tolman
Mr. Joseph Cresci
Mr. Mark Austin
Mr. Allen Bellview

Description: Executive and middle management for the restaurant and hotel industries.

Salary Minimum: $35,000
Functions: Senior mgmt., Middle mgmt., Mktg. mgmt., Sales mgmt., HR mgmt., Training, Finance
Industries: Hospitality, Entertainment

Branches:
945 Concord St.
Framingham, Massachusetts 01072
(508) 620-5375
Key Contact - Specialty:
Mr. Joseph Cresci

The York Group
3958 Rambla Orienta
Malibu, California 90265
(310) 317-8568
Fax: (310) 317-8570
Email: karen@yorkgroup.com
Web: yorkgroup.com/york

Key Contact - Specialty:
Ms. Karen York - *Healthcare marketing, healthcare advertising*
Ms. Diane Geiser - *Healthcare marketing, healthcare advertising*

Description: Serving the healthcare industry and their marketing/communications needs.
Functions: Healthcare, Health admin., Advertising, Mkt. research, Sales mgmt., PR, Graphic artists
Industries: Drugs mfg., Medical devices, Pharmaceutical svcs., Advertising/PR

The Yorkshire Group, Ltd.
182 W. Central St.
Natick, Massachusetts 01760
(508) 653-1222
Fax: (508) 653-2631

Key Contact - Specialty:
Mr. Michael P. Tornesello
Mr. David O. McGavern

Description: Insurance recruiting and consulting constitutes the majority of the company business. Searching for mergers and acquisitions in the insurance industry has been added. Management assessment and testing round out company services.

Salary Minimum: $50,000
Functions: Senior mgmt., Middle mgmt., Mktg. mgmt., Sales mgmt., HR mgmt., Finance, MIS mgmt.
Industries: Insurance

Yormak & Assoc.
3780 Kilroy Airport Way, Ste. 200
Long Beach, California 90806
(562) 988-6555
Fax: (562) 988-6566
Email: syormak@aol.com

Key Contact - Specialty:
Mr. Stuart I. Yormak - *Accounting & finance*

Description: Southern California based recruitment firm serving the public accounting industry - including the Big 6, local and regional CPA firms - as well as private industry companies. We focus on placing qualified accounting and finance professionals in full-time regular positions.

Salary Minimum: $30,000
Functions: CFO's, Budgeting, Cash mgmt., Credit, Taxes
Industries: Finance, Hospitality, Entertainment, Broadcast & Film, Real estate, Software, Healthcare

Bill Young & Assoc.
367 Saddleback Knoll
Nellysford, Virginia 22958
(703) 573-0200
Email: byoung@billyoung.com
Web: www.billyoung.com

Key Contact - Specialty:
Mr. William H. Young - *Information systems, telecommunications*

Description: Retained permanent and tempperm executives for information systems, telecomms professionals. Placements are local Washington, DC metro area. Principals have over 25 years corporate hi-tech experience.

Salary Minimum: $70,000
Functions: MIS mgmt., Systems anal., Systems dev., Systems implem., Systems support, Network admin., DB admin.
Industries: Computer svcs., Telecoms, High tech, Software

Affiliates:
Crawford & Assoc.
Rectrix Consulting & Co.

Youngblood Assoc.
131 Fourth Ave. W., Ste. 222
Hendersonville, North Carolina 28792
(800) 545-9123
Fax: (828) 698-3272
Email: youngbloodas@ioa.com

Key Contact - Specialty:
Mr. Robert S. Youngblood - *Investment management, banking*
Ms. Noelle Bauer - *Invesetment management, banking*

Description: President is a recognized leader in recruiting for the investment management industry. For over nine years, he has been successfully placing analysts, portfolio managers, marketers and traders throughout the United States.

Salary Minimum: $50,000
Functions: Senior mgmt., Middle mgmt., Mkt. research, Sales mgmt., Customer svc., Cash mgmt., Int'l.
Industries: Banking, Invest. banking, Misc. financial

Your Advantage Staffing Consultants Inc.
218 Boida Ave., #3
Ayr, Ontario N0B 1E0
Canada
(519) 623-4576
(888) 213-3375
Fax: (519) 623-3892
Email: advantagestaffing@sympatico.ca
Web: www3.sympatico.ca/advantagestaffing

Key Contact - Specialty:
Ms. Lori Van Opstal - *Transportation*

Description: We offer significant expertise in the recruitment and selection of staff for the transportation industry.
Functions: Generalist
Industries: Transportation

Affiliates:
Anderson & Assoc.

Yours In Travel Personnel Agency, Inc.
12 W. 37 St., 5th Floor
New York, New York 10018
(212) 697-7855
Web: www.yoursintravel.com

Key Contact - Specialty:
Mr. P. Jason King - *Travel industry*

Description: Largest recruitment firm specializing solely in the travel industry. Contingency and retained searches - worldwide - fully automated. For travel industry experienced only.

Salary Minimum: $50,000
Functions: Directors, Senior mgmt., Middle mgmt., Mktg. mgmt., CFO's, MIS mgmt.

Industries: Hospitality, Entertainment

Branches:
301 Rte. 17 N., Ste. 800
Rutherford, New Jersey 07070
(201) 438-3500
Key Contact - Specialty:
Ms. Robyn Hering - *Travel industry*

2111 Wilson Blvd., Ste. 700
Arlington, Virginia 22201
(703) 527-5777
Key Contact - Specialty:
Ms. Jeanie Kurzrok - *Travel industry*

Zaccaria Int'l.

Brook 35 Park, Bldg. A
2130 Hwy. 35
Sea Girt, New Jersey 08750
(732) 282-1203
Fax: (732) 282-1204
Email: retailjob@aol.com
Web: www.retailjob.com

Key Contact - Specialty:
Ms. Fran Zaccaria - *Retail*
Mr. Jack Zaccaria - *Retail, recruitment research*

Description: Specialists in the retail industry. Three main staffing services are offered: executive search, recruitment research (executive search on an hourly basis) and contract staffing, interim services.
Functions: Directors, Middle mgmt., Product dev., Direct mktg., Personnel, MIS mgmt., Mgmt. consultants
Industries: Retail

Zackrison Assoc., Inc.

P.O. Box 1808
Dunnellon, Florida 34430
(352) 489-2215
Email: zackl@mfi.net

Key Contact - Specialty:
Mr. Walter Zackrison - *Pharmaceutical, biotechnological*

Description: Executive recruiting firm which specializes in pharmaceutical and biotech search in clinical and medical affairs, research and development, finance, manufacturing and executive officers.

Salary Minimum: $60,000
Functions: Physicians, R&D
Industries: Drugs mfg., Pharmaceutical svcs., Biotech

Zeiger Assoc. L.L.C.

4766 Park Granada Blvd., Ste. 211
Calabasas, California 91302
(818) 222-0052
Fax: (818) 222-0232
Email: S.Zeiger147@aol.com

Key Contact - Specialty:
Mr. Stephen A. Zeiger - *Hard disk drive executives, engineers, VP, directors, ASIC*
Mr. David Barkin Zeiger - *ASIC, hard disk drive, semiconductor*

Description: Design, project, program, engineering including A&D, test, software, hardware, computer hard disk development, S.C.S.I. engineering and management. Specialists in disk drive executives and executive technical management (ie: president, CEO, COO, etc.).

Salary Minimum: $45,000
Functions: Generalist, Directors, Senior mgmt., Middle mgmt., MIS mgmt., R&D, Engineering
Industries: Generalist, Computer equip., Consumer electronics, Computer svcs., Telecoms, High tech, Software

Zen Zen Int'l. Inc.

3421 Portage Ave., Ste. 530
Winnipeg, Manitoba R3K 2C9
Canada
(204) 837-7943
Fax: (204) 837-4646
Email: zenzenmy@mb.sympatico.ca

Key Contact - Specialty:
Mr. Michael Yakimishyn - *Information technology, engineering, accounting, sales & marketing, human resources*

Description: Specialists in recruitment and placement of information technology professionals.
Functions: General mgmt., Mfg., Materials, Sales & mktg., HR mgmt., Finance, IT
Industries: Motor vehicles, Misc. financial, Accounting, Human resource svcs., Advertising/PR, Aerospace, Software

Affiliates:
The Mancomit Group

Zenner Consulting Group

75 E. Wacker Drive, Ste. 3000
Chicago, Illinois 60601
(312) 849-3800
Fax: (312) 849-3600
Email: zenconsult@msn.com
Web: www.zennerconsulting.com

Key Contact - Specialty:
Teri E. Zenner - *Lawyers*

Description: We are comprised of five attorneys who practiced law at premier national firms. Our recruiters graduated from the following law schools: Northwestern, the University of Chicago, Boalt Hall School of Law (Berkeley), the University of Wisconsin, and Loyola University.
Functions: Attorneys
Industries: Legal

Helen Ziegler & Assoc., Inc.

180 Dundas St. W., Ste. 2403
Toronto, Ontario M5G 1Z8
Canada
(416) 977-6941
(800) 387-4616
Fax: (416) 977-6128
Email: hza@hziegler.com
Web: www.hziegler.com

Key Contact - Specialty:
Ms. Helen Ziegler - *Doctors, administrators*

Description: We specialize in identifying hard-to-get candidates for challenging assignments and assessing their suitability for the given assignment.

Salary Minimum: $38,000
Functions: Healthcare, Personnel, CFO's, Risk mgmt., IT, R&D, Int'l.
Industries: High tech, Healthcare

P. D. Zier Assoc.

14 Ascolese Rd.
Trumbull, Connecticut 06611
(203) 452-0078
Fax: (203) 261-2051

Key Contact - Specialty:
Ms. Patricia D. Zier - *High technology, information systems*

Description: Professional, experienced, knowlegeable and successful high technology recruiters.

Salary Minimum: $35,000
Functions: IT, MIS mgmt., Systems anal., Systems dev., Systems implem., Systems support
Industries: Generalist, Computer svcs., Telecoms, High tech, Software

Chuck Zimering Advertising Recruitment (CZAR)

170 W. End Ave., Ste. 11G
New York, New York 10023
(212) 724-7904
Fax: (212) 724-7163

Key Contact - Specialty:
Mr. Chuck Zimering - *Media, account (general & direct advertising agencies)*

Description: I specialize in recruiting for general and direct advertising agencies, mostly in New York City. My area of expertise is media and account work.

Salary Minimum: $30,000
Functions: Advertising
Industries: Advertising/PR

Zona & Assoc., Inc.

26 Broadway, Ste. 400
New York, New York 10004
(212) 837-7878
Fax: (212) 837-7879
Email: 102151.3146@compuserve.com
Web: HZona@compuserve.com

Key Contact - Specialty:
Mr. Henry F. Zona

Description: Our role is to act as an appropriate representative of your company, support your search process, not become the focus of it, make the best use of the time of everyone involved and provide your search efforts with not just paper, but perspective.

Salary Minimum: $65,000
Functions: General mgmt., Sales & mktg., HR mgmt., Finance, IT, Specialized services, Int'l.
Industries: Finance, Misc. financial, Mgmt. consulting, Human resource svcs., Insurance, Healthcare

Indexes

Index by Functions

Firms with (R) are from the Retainer Section, which begins on page 1.
Firms with (C) are from the Contingency Section, which begins on page 231.

Basis of Functions Classification

The kernel of this coding system was developed by several parties including Jerome H. Fuchs, Glenn Van Doren and Kennedy Information.

00.0 **GENERALIST**

01.0 **GENERAL MANAGEMENT**
01.1 Directors
01.2 Senior management *(e.g. CEO, COO, President, General Manager)*
01.3 Middle management
01.4 Administrative services
01.5 Legal

02.0 **MANUFACTURING**
02.1 Product development
02.2 Production engineering, planning, scheduling & control
02.3 Automation, robotics
02.4 Plant management
02.5 Quality
02.6 Productivity

03.0 **MATERIALS MANAGEMENT**
03.1 Purchasing, inventory management
03.2 Materials & requirement planning
03.3 Physical distribution, traffic & transportation, logistics
03.4 Packaging

04.0 **MEDICAL/HEALTHCARE**
04.1 Physicians
04.2 Nurses
04.3 Allied health *(e.g. chiropractors, therapists, psychologists)*
04.4 Administration

05.0 **SALES & MARKETING**
05.1 Advertising, sales promotion
05.2 Marketing & product research
05.3 Marketing management
05.4 Sales & sales management
05.5 Direct mail, marketing, telemarketing
05.6 Customer service
05.7 Public relations

06.0 **HUMAN RESOURCE MANAGEMENT**
06.1 Benefits, compensation planning
06.2 Personnel selection, placement & records
06.3 Training

07.0 **FINANCE & ACCOUNTING**
07.1 CFO's
07.2 Budgeting, cost controls
07.3 Cash management, financing & management of funds, portfolios
07.4 Credit & collection
07.5 Taxes
07.6 Mergers & acquisitions
07.7 Risk management

08.0 **INFORMATION TECHNOLOGY**
08.1 MIS management *(e.g. CIO, VP-MIS)*
08.2 Systems analysis & design
08.3 Software development
08.4 Systems integration/implementation
08.5 Support
08.6 Network administration
08.7 Database administration

09.0 **RESEARCH & DEVELOPMENT/ SCIENTISTS**

10.0 **ENGINEERING**

11.0 **SPECIALIZED SERVICES**
11.1 Management consultants
11.2 Minorities
11.3 Fund raisers & other non-profit services
11.4 Environmentalists
11.5 Architects
11.6 Technicians
11.7 Attorneys
11.8 Graphic artists, designers
11.9 Paralegals

12.0 **INTERNATIONAL**

00.0 Generalist

A. D. & Assoc. Executive Search, Inc. (C), GA, *231*
Abbott Associates (R), CA, *1*
Abécassis Conseil (R), QE, *1*
B. J. Abrams & Assoc. Inc. (C), IL, *233*
Accelerated Data Decision, Inc. (C), NJ, *233*
Access Assoc. Inc. (C), MD, *233*
Accountants On Call (C), FL, *237*
Advanced Executive Resources (R), MI, *2*
Advice Personnel Inc. (C), NY, *241*
Ahrensdorf & Assoc. (R), PA, *2*
Alaska Executive Search, Inc. (C), AK, *243*
The Alexander Group (R), NJ, *3*
The Alice Groves Co., Inc. (C), CT, *244*
Allen Evans Assoc. (R), NY, *4*
Allen, Wayne & Co. LLC (C), WI, *245*
Allen/Associates (R), OH, *4*
Tom Allison Assoc. (C), NM, *245*
Altec/HRC (C), MI, *246*
AM & G Certified Public Accountants & Consultants (R), IL, *4*
Peter W. Ambler Co. (R), TX, *5*
American Executive Search (C), FL, *247*
Ames & Ames (R), CA, *5*
Amherst Human Resource Group, Ltd. (C), IL, *249*
Amrop International (R), MX, *5*
Anderson & Associates (R), NC, *5*
Anderson & Schwab, Inc. (R), NY, *5*
Angus Employment Ltd. (C), ON, *250*
Applied Search Assoc., Inc. (C), GA, *252*
Argus National, Inc. (R), CT, *6*
ARI Int'l. (R), CA, *6*
William B. Arnold Assoc., Inc. (R), CO, *7*
Patrick Arnone & Assoc. Inc. (R), VA, *7*
Atlanta Executive Partners, Inc. (R), MA, *8*
A. M. Auster Associates (R), FL, *9*
Austin, Hill & Assoc. (C), MD, *256*
The Badger Group (R), CA, *10*
Baeder Kalinski Int'l. Group, Inc. (R), NH, *10*
The Baer Group (R), OH, *10*
Baldwin Associates, LLC (R), CT, *10*
The Baldwin Group (R), IL, *10*
Ballos & Co., Inc. (R), NJ, *10*
Barger & Sargeant, Inc. (R), NH, *11*
J. W. Barleycorn, Renard & Assoc., Inc. (R), OH, *11*
Barnes Development Group, LLC (R), WI, *11*
Barrington Hart, Inc. (R), IL, *12*
Barton Assoc., Inc. (R), TX, *12*
Martin H. Bauman Assoc., Inc. (R), NY, *13*
Neail Behringer Consultants Inc. (R), NY, *15*
J. P. Bencik Assoc. (C), MI, *263*
BEST/World Assoc. Inc. (R), TX, *16*
BGB Assoc., Inc. (C), IL, *266*
Birch & Associes (C), QE, *267*
The Blackman Kallick Search Division (C), IL, *267*
Blackshaw, Olmstead, Lynch & Koenig (R), GA, *18*
Blake/Hansen Ltd. (R), FL, *18*
David Blevins & Assoc. (C), WA, *268*
Blum & Co. (R), WI, *19*
Boardroom Consultants/Kenny Kindler Tholke (R), NY, *19*
Boettcher Assoc. (R), WI, *19*
Bonifield Assoc. (C), NJ, *269*
John C. Boone & Co. (R), IL, *19*
Lynn Borne & Co. (C), CA, *270*
Bosland Gray Assoc. (R), NJ, *20*
Boston Professional Search, Inc. (C), MA, *270*
BowdenGlobal, Ltd. (R), OH, *20*
Bowman & Assoc. (C), CA, *271*
Boyden (R), NY, *20*
The Brand Co., Inc. (R), FL, *22*
Brandt Associates (C), PA, *272*
Branthover Assoc. (C), NY, *272*
The Bren Group (C), AZ, *273*
Brentwood Int'l. (R), CA, *23*
Bridgecreek Personnel Agency (C), CA, *273*
The Broadmoor Group, L.L.C. (R), TX, *23*
Brookman Associates (C), NY, *274*
Brush Creek Partners (R), MO, *24*
BRW Search (C), MN, *275*
Charles Buck & Assoc., Inc. (R), NY, *24*
Bullis & Co., Inc. (R), CA, *25*
The Burke Group (C), ON, *276*
Burke, O'Brien & Bishop Assoc., Inc. (R), NJ, *25*
Joseph R. Burns & Assoc., Inc. (R), NJ, *25*
Business Solutions Worldwide, Inc. (C), NJ, *277*
Byron Leonard Int'l., Inc. (R), CA, *25*
C.T.E.W. Executive Personnel Services Inc. (C), BC, *278*
Robert Caldwell & Assoc. (R), CA, *26*
The Caldwell Partners Amrop International (R), ON, *26*
Lee Calhoon & Co., Inc. (R), PA, *26*
Callos Personnel Services (C), OH, *279*
Cambridge Management Planning (R), ON, *27*
Cameron Consulting Group (R), CA, *27*
Canadian Career Partners (R), AB, *27*
Canny, Bowen Inc. (R), NY, *27*
Capital Consulting Group, Inc. (R), MD, *28*
Capitol Management Consulting, Inc. (C), NJ, *281*
Capstone Consulting, Inc. (R), IL, *29*
Career Advisors, Inc. (C), FL, *281*
Career Specialists, Inc. (R), WA, *29*
Carlsen Resources, Inc. (R), CO, *29*
Carlson & Czeswik (R), MN, *30*
Carris, Jackowitz Assoc. (R), NY, *30*
Carson-Thomas & Assoc. (C), CA, *284*
Carter, Lavoie Associates (C), RI, *285*
Cary & Assoc. (R), FL, *31*
Catalyx Group (R), NY, *31*
CCI - Career Consultants Int'l. (C), CA, *286*
Joseph Chandler & Assoc., Inc. (R), IL, *33*
A. D. Check Assoc., Inc. (R), PA, *33*
The Cherbonnier Group, Inc. (R), TX, *33*
Chicago Research Group, Inc. (R), NC, *33*
Chrisman & Co. Inc. (R), CA, *33*
Christian & Timbers, Inc. (R), OH, *34*
Christmas, McIvor & Assoc. Inc. (C), ON, *290*
Cizek Assoc., Inc. (R), AZ, *35*
Clarey & Andrews, Inc. (R), IL, *35*
Richard Clarke Assoc., Inc. (R), NY, *36*
CMC Search Consultants (C), IL, *293*
Coast Personnel Services Ltd. (C), BC, *293*
Dean M. Coe Assoc. (R), MA, *37*
Cole, Warren & Long, Inc. (R), PA, *37*
Coleman Lew & Assoc., Inc. (R), NC, *37*
S L Collins Assoc. (C), NC, *294*
Colucci, Blendow & Johnson (R), CA, *38*
Columbia Consulting Group (R), MD, *38*
The Comwell Company, Inc. (C), NJ, *296*
Conard Associates, Inc. (R), NH, *39*
Connors, Lovell & Assoc. Inc. (C), ON, *296*
Consolidated Management Services (C), ON, *296*
Consulpro (R), ON, *39*
Consulting Rhonda (C), ON, *297*
Continental Research Search, Inc. (C), WI, *298*
Cook Assoc.,® Inc. (R), IL, *40*
The Cooke Group (R), WI, *40*
Cooper Assoc., Inc., Inc. (C), NY, *298*
The Cooper Executive Search Group Inc. (R), WI, *41*
Corporate Leadership Strategies, Inc. (R), NH, *41*
The Corporate Source Group, Inc. (R), MA, *41*
Corporate Suite, Ltd. (C), IA, *301*
The Corrigan Group (R), CA, *42*
Corso, Mizgala + French (R), ON, *42*
Courtright & Assoc., Inc. (R), PA, *42*
Craig Affiliates, Inc. (C), TX, *302*
The Cris Group, Inc. (R), NY, *42*
Marlene Critchfield Co. (C), CA, *303*
Crowder & Company (R), MI, *43*
Curran Partners, Inc. (R), CT, *44*
The Curtiss Group International (R), FL, *44*
Cusack Consulting (R), NY, *44*
The Custer Group, Inc. (R), TN, *44*
Cyberna Assoc. Ltd. (C), QE, *305*
Cypress Int'l., Inc. (R), FL, *45*
The Danbrook Group, Inc. (C), TX, *306*
Alan Darling Consulting (R), VT, *46*
Datamatics Management Services, Inc. (C), NJ, *307*
Davies, Park (R), AB, *46*
Davis & Company (R), CA, *47*
Joseph A. Davis Consultants, Inc. (R), NY, *47*
Bert Davis Executive Search, Inc. (R), NY, *47*
Dean-MacDonald (R), OH, *47*
Delphi Systems, Ltd. (R), MO, *48*
DeMatteo Associates (C), NY, *311*
Derhak Ireland & Partners Ltd. (R), ON, *48*
DHR Int'l., Inc. (R), IL, *49*
Roger Dietsch & Assoc. (C), MN, *312*
DiMarchi Partners (R), CO, *51*
J. Dinerstein & Co., Inc. (R), NY, *51*
Robert W. Dingman Co., Inc. (R), CA, *52*
Dinte Resources, Inc. (R), VA, *52*
Diversified Search, Inc. (R), PA, *52*
Doering & Assoc. (C), CA, *313*
Doleman Enterprises (R), VA, *53*
Downing & Downing, Inc. (C), OH, *314*
Drinkwater & Assoc. (R), MA, *54*
Dunhill of San Francisco, Inc. (C), CA, *319*
Dunhill Search of Medford (C), NJ, *321*

Dunn Associates (R), PA, *55*
The E & K Group (C), NJ, *324*
E O Technical (C), CT, *324*
J. M. Eagle Partners Ltd. (C), WI, *325*
Eastman & Beaudine, Inc. (R), TX, *56*
EBA Group (R), NJ, *56*
The Edge Resource Group (C), PA, *326*
EDI/Executive Dynamics Inc. (C), NJ, *326*
Bruce Edwards & Associates, Inc. (R), NC, *56*
EFL Assoc. (R), KS, *57*
EFL Int'l. (R), AZ, *57*
Egan & Assoc. (R), WI, *57*
Egan Search Group (R), NY, *57*
Richard A. Eisner & Co., LLP (R), NY, *57*
Elite Resources Group (R), OH, *58*
Emerson & Co. (C), GA, *329*
Emmett Executive Search, Inc. (C), NY, *330*
Empire International (R), PA, *59*
Employ® (C), PA, *330*
The Enfield Company (C), TX, *330*
The Enns Partners Inc. (R), ON, *59*
The Enterprise Group (R), MA, *60*
Mary R. Erickson & Assoc. (R), MN, *60*
Erlanger Assoc. (R), CT, *60*
ExecuQuest, Inc. (R), MI, *61*
ExecuSource Assoc., Inc. (C), GA, *332*
Executech (R), OH, *62*
Executive Alliance (R), MA, *62*
Executive Directions (R), OH, *62*
Executive Manning Corp. (R), FL, *63*
Executive Placement Consultants (C), IL, *333*
Executive Resource Assoc. (C), VA, *334*
Executive Search Consultants (R), CA, *63*
Executive Search Group, Inc. (C), CT, *335*
Executive Search Inc. (R), MN, *63*
Executive Search Int'l./Transearch (R), MA, *63*
Executive Search of New England, Inc. (C), ME, *336*
Executive Search Placements, Inc. (C), CO, *336*
Executive Strategies, Inc. (C), GA, *337*
Raymond L. Extract & Assoc. (R), CA, *64*
Fagan & Company (R), PA, *64*
FAI (C), CO, *338*
Leon A. Farley Assoc. (R), CA, *65*
James Farris Assoc. (R), OK, *65*
FCI, Inc. (R), NJ, *65*
Feldman Gray & Assoc. Inc. (C), ON, *339*
Fenwick Partners (R), MA, *66*
Fergason Assoc., Inc. (C), IL, *339*
Ferneborg & Assoc., Inc. (R), CA, *66*
Eileen Finn & Assoc., Inc. (C), NY, *341*
First Advisory Services Int'l., Inc. (R), MD, *67*
First Union Executive Search (R), NC, *67*
The Fisher Group (R), AB, *67*
James L. Fisk & Assoc. (C), MO, *342*
J. G. Flynn & Assoc. Inc. (R), BC, *69*
Flynn, Hannock, Inc. (R), CT, *69*
L. W. Foote Co. (R), WA, *69*
Fortune Personnel Consultants of Topsfield (C), MA, *346*
F-O-R-T-U-N-E Personnel Consultants of the Tri-Cities, Inc. (C), TN, *350*
Foster Partners (R), NY, *70*
Foy, Schneid & Daniel, Inc. (R), NY, *71*
Francis & Assoc. (R), IA, *71*
P. N. French Assoc., Inc. (R), MA, *72*
Peter Froehlich & Co. (C), TX, *353*
Frye/Joure & Assoc., Inc. (C), TN, *353*
Furlong Search, Inc. (R), CA, *72*
C. F. Furr & Co. (R), NC, *72*
The Gabriel Group (C), PA, *354*
Gahan Assoc. (R), NY, *73*
Jay Gaines & Company, Inc. (R), NY, *73*
W. N. Garbarini & Assoc. (R), NJ, *74*
Gateway Management Resources (C), IL, *355*
Gaudry, Shink, Levasseur (R), QE, *75*
Geddes & Rubin Management Inc. (R), ON, *76*
Gelpi & Assoc. (C), LA, *355*
Genesis Consulting Partners (R), PA, *76*
Gibson & Co., Inc. (R), WI, *76*
Gilbert Scott Assoc., LLC (C), MA, *357*
Gilbert Tweed Assoc. Inc. (R), NY, *76*
Gilreath Weatherby Inc. (R), MA, *77*
Glass & Assoc., Inc. (C), OH, *358*
Global Employer's Network, Inc. (R), TX, *77*
Global Research Partnership Inc. (R), NY, *78*
The GlobalSearch Group (C), TX, *359*
Gnodde Assoc. (C), IL, *359*
The Gobbell Co. (R), CA, *78*
Robert G. Godfrey Assoc. Ltd. (R), IL, *78*
Joseph Goldring & Assoc. Inc. (C), MI, *360*
David Gomez & Assoc., Inc. (R), IL, *79*
Gomez Fregoso y Asociados (C), JAL, *360*
Goodrich & Sherwood Assoc., Inc. (R), NY, *79*
Goodwin & Co. (R), DC, *80*
Gould, McCoy & Chadick, Inc. (R), NY, *80*
Robert Graham Assoc. (R), RI, *81*
Grant Cooper & Assoc., Inc. (R), MO, *81*
Grant-Franks & Assoc. (C), NJ, *361*
Ben Greco Assoc., Inc. (C), CA, *362*
Greenhaven & Assoc., Inc. (R), NY, *81*
Gregory Michaels & Assoc., Inc. (R), IL, *82*
Groenekamp & Assoc. (C), CA, *363*
Grossberg & Assoc. (R), IL, *82*
Groupe Ranger Inc. (C), QE, *364*
Grover & Assoc. (R), OH, *82*
William Guy & Assoc., Inc. (R), CA, *84*
Habelmann & Assoc. (R), MI, *84*
Haddad Assoc. (R), FL, *84*
M. A. Haggith Consultants Ltd. (R), ON, *84*
Hale Assoc. (R), IL, *84*
The Halyburton Co., Inc. (R), NC, *85*
Hamilton-Chase & Assoc., Inc. (R), MA, *85*
R. C. Handel Assoc. Inc. (R), CT, *85*
Harcor Quest & Assoc. (R), OH, *86*
Hartsfield Group, Inc. (R), GA, *87*
William E. Hay & Co. (R), IL, *88*
Hayman & Co. (R), TX, *88*
Headden Assoc. (R), WA, *88*
Healthcare Recruiters Int'l. - Los Angeles (C), CA, *372*
Hedman & Assoc. (R), TX, *89*
Heidrick & Struggles, Inc. (R), IL, *90*
The Heidrick Partners, Inc. (R), IL, *90*
Heinze & Assoc. Inc. (R), MN, *91*
Heller Assoc., Ltd. (R), IL, *91*
Hergenrather & Co. (R), WA, *92*
Heritage Pacific Corp. (C), CA, *376*
The Herrmann Group Ltd. (R), ON, *92*
The Hetzel Group, Inc. (R), IL, *92*
HG & Assoc. (R), IL, *93*
Higgins Assoc., Inc. (R), IL, *93*
The Hindman Co. (R), KY, *94*
The Hindman Group, Inc. (C), CA, *378*
Hite Executive Search (R), OH, *94*
Hockett Associates, Inc. (R), CA, *94*
Hodge-Cronin & Assoc., Inc. (R), IL, *94*
Richard D. Holbrook Assoc. (R), MA, *94*
Holland Rusk & Assoc. (R), IL, *95*
The Hollins Group, Inc. (R), IL, *95*
Holohan Group, Ltd. (R), MO, *95*
J. G. Hood Assoc. (C), CT, *380*
Horton Int'l. Inc. (R), NY, *96*
Howe & Assoc. (R), PA, *97*
HRS, Inc. (R), PA, *97*
Huddleston Assoc. (C), OK, *383*
Hughes & Assoc. (C), TX, *383*
Human Resource Bureau (C), CA, *384*
The Human Resource Consulting Group, Inc. (R), CO, *98*
Human Resources Management Hawaii, Inc. (C), HI, *384*
Human Resources Personnel Agency (R), AR, *99*
Hunt & Howe Inc. (R), NY, *99*
The Hunt Co. (R), NY, *99*
Hunt Patton & Brazeal, Inc. (C), OK, *385*
The Hunter Group, Inc. (C), MI, *385*
The Hunter Group (C), NC, *385*
Hunter Int'l., Inc. (R), CT, *100*
Hunter, Rowan & Crowe (C), FL, *386*
Hyde Danforth & Co. (R), TX, *100*
Icon Recruiters, LLC (C), CA, *387*
IMA Search, Inc. (R), NY, *101*
John Imber Assoc., Ltd. (R), IL, *101*
Innovative Healthcare Services, Inc. (C), GA, *389*
Innovative Resource Group, LLC (C), NC, *389*
Innovative Search Group, Inc. (R), GA, *102*
Insurance Recruiting Specialists (C), OH, *390*
Interactive Search Assoc. (C), PA, *391*
Intercontinental Executive Group (C), PA, *391*
International Management Advisors, Inc. (R), NY, *103*
Jeffrey Irving Assoc., Inc. (R), VA, *104*
Isaacson, Miller (R), MA, *104*
J. Joseph & Assoc. (C), OH, *395*
J. Robert Scott (R), MA, *104*
J.B.A. Assoc. (R), WA, *104*
Ron Jackson & Assoc. (C), GA, *396*
Jacobs & Co. (R), CT, *105*
Jacobson Assoc. (C), IL, *396*
Jakobs & Assoc. Int'l. (R), NY, *105*
January Management Group (R), OH, *105*
JDavid Assoc., Inc. (R), CT, *105*
Jefferson-Ross Assoc. Inc. (C), PA, *398*
Jender & Company (R), IL, *105*
Job-Born Candidate Selection Bureau (C), ON, *399*

John & Powers, Inc. (R), MO, *106*
John Jay & Co. (C), ME, *399*
John H. Johnson & Assoc., Inc. (R), IL, *106*
Johnson & Company (R), CT, *107*
K. E. Johnson Assoc. (C), WA, *399*
Jordon & Jordon, Inc. (R), PA, *108*
Judd Associates (R), NJ, *109*
Kane & Assoc. (C), TX, *403*
Kanzer Assoc., Inc. (R), IL, *109*
Gary Kaplan & Assoc. (R), CA, *109*
Martin Kartin & Co., Inc. (R), NY, *110*
A.T. Kearney Executive Search (R), IL, *111*
Kelly Associates (R), PA, *112*
Kent & Assoc. (R), OH, *113*
Daniel J. Kerstein, Consultant to Management (R), CO, *114*
Kincannon & Reed (R), VA, *114*
Kingsley Allen Partners Inc. (R), ON, *114*
Richard Kinser & Assoc. (R), NY, *115*
Kiradjieff & Goode, Inc. (R), MA, *115*
Kirby Assoc. (R), PA, *115*
The Kleinstein Group, Inc. (R), NJ, *116*
KPA Assoc., Inc. (C), NY, *408*
KPMG Executive Search (R), ON, *119*
Krauthamer & Assoc. (R), MD, *120*
Kreutz Consulting Group, Inc. (R), IL, *121*
Krueger Assoc. (R), IL, *121*
John Kurosky & Assoc. (R), CA, *122*
L. Patrick Group (R), NJ, *122*
Rene LaFlamme & Associes (R), QE, *122*
LAI Ward Howell (R), NY, *122*
Lamon + Stuart + Michaels Inc. (R), ON, *124*
Landon Morgan (C), ON, *412*
Jack B. Larsen & Assoc., Inc. (C), PA, *413*
Larsen, Whitney, Blecksmith & Zilliacus, Inc. (R), CA, *125*
Larson Assoc. (R), CA, *125*
Michael Latas & Assoc., Inc. (R), MO, *125*
Latham International, Ltd. (R), NJ, *126*
Lauer, Sbarbaro Assoc., EMA Partners Int'l. (R), IL, *126*
Lautz, Grotte, Engler & Swimley (R), CA, *126*
Lawrence James Assoc. of Florida, Inc. (C), FL, *414*
Lawrence-Leiter & Co. (R), KS, *126*
W. R. Lawry, Inc. (R), CT, *126*
Vincent Lee Assoc. (C), NY, *415*
Lekan & Assoc., Inc. (R), OH, *128*
Lending Personnel Services (C), CA, *416*
Lewis Companies Inc. (R), ON, *129*
Lindsey & Co., Inc. (R), CT, *129*
Litchfield & Willis, Inc. (R), TX, *130*
Lloyd Associates (R), GA, *130*
Lloyd Prescott & Churchill, Inc. (R), FL, *130*
Locus Inc. (C), WV, *419*
J. P. Logan & Co., Inc. (R), NY, *131*
The Logan Group, Inc. (R), MO, *131*
Logue & Rice Inc. (C), VA, *420*
Longo Associates (C), CA, *420*
J. S. Lord & Company, Inc. (R), MA, *131*
The John Lucht Consultancy Inc. (R), NY, *131*
Charles Luntz & Assoc., Inc. (R), MO, *132*
Lynch Miller Moore Partners, Inc. (R), IL, *132*
Lyons Assoc. (R), NY, *132*
The Macdonald Group, Inc. (R), NJ, *133*
The Madeira Group (R), PA, *133*
Magnum Search (C), IL, *422*
Maiorino & Weston Assoc., Inc. (R), CT, *134*
Major Search (C), NJ, *423*
Management Recruiters International, Inc. (MRI) (C), OH, *425*
Management Recruiters of Miami-North (C), FL, *443*
Management Recruiters of North Fulton (C), GA, *445*
Management Recruiters of Forsyth County (C), GA, *445*
Management Recruiters of Danville (C), KY, *449*
Management Recruiters of Topeka, Inc. (C), KS, *449*
Management Recruiters of Orange County, N.Y., Inc. (C), NJ, *453*
Management Recruiters of Cleveland (C), OH, *457*
Management Recruiters of Northwest Ohio, Inc. (C), OH, *458*
Management Recruiters of Memphis, TN (C), TN, *462*
Management Resources Int'l. (R), NY, *135*
Mannard & Assoc., Inc. (R), IL, *135*
Marcus & Assoc. (C), NY, *469*
Mark Stanley & Co./EMA Partners International (R), FL, *136*
The Marshall Group (R), IL, *137*
Maschal/Connors Inc. (R), NJ, *137*
Massey-Horton Int'l. (R), ON, *138*
Louis Thomas Masterson & Co. (R), OH, *138*
Matte Consulting Group Inc. (R), QE, *138*
Matthews & Stephens Assoc., Inc. (C), CT, *472*
The Matthews Group, Inc. (C), NJ, *472*
Maxecon Executive Search Consultants (R), FL, *138*
The Mazzitelli Group, Ltd. (R), MN, *139*
The McAulay Firm (R), NC, *139*
McCartan Assoc. (R), NJ, *139*
K. E. McCarthy & Assoc. (R), CA, *139*
McCormack & Farrow (R), CA, *140*
Earl L. McDermid & Assoc. (C), IL, *474*
McDonald, Long & Assoc., Inc. (R), NY, *140*
G. E. McFarland & Co. (R), GA, *140*
Clarence E. McFeely, Inc. (R), IL, *141*
McNichol Assoc. (R), PA, *142*
McRoberts & Assoc. (C), OH, *475*
Meder & Assoc., Inc. (R), IL, *142*
The Medley Group (C), CA, *477*
Melancon & Co. (R), TX, *143*
Juan Menefee & Assoc. (C), IL, *478*
Mengel & McDonald Ltd. (C), IL, *479*
MES Search Co. (C), GA, *479*
Messett Assoc., Inc. (R), FL, *143*
META/MAT, Ltd. (R), NJ, *144*
mfg/Search, Inc. (C), IN, *480*
Million & Assoc., Inc. (R), OH, *144*
Danette Milne Corporate Search Inc. (C), ON, *482*
Milo Research (R), NY, *145*
Mirtz Morice, Inc. (R), CT, *145*
MIXTEC Group (R), CA, *145*
Moffitt Int'l., Inc. (R), NC, *146*
Moriarty/Fox, Inc. (R), IL, *147*
Morris & Berger (R), CA, *147*
Morton, McCorkle & Assoc. Inc. (R), MO, *147*
MPA Executive Search Inc. (R), QE, *148*
Mullen Assoc., Inc. (R), NC, *148*
P. J. Murphy & Assoc., Inc. (R), WI, *150*
Kenneth Murphy & Assoc. (C), NS, *487*
Murphy Partners Int'l. (R), IL, *150*
Musick & Assoc. (C), CA, *487*
Nagler, Robins & Poe, Inc. (R), MA, *150*
National Restaurant Search, Inc. (R), GA, *150*
NaviSearch (C), GA, *490*
NCC Executive Search Consultants (C), CA, *490*
New Dawn Employment Search (C), CA, *491*
Newell Assoc. (R), NY, *151*
Nicholaou & Co. (R), IL, *151*
Nichols Brown Int'l. (R), NY, *151*
P. J. Nicholson & Assoc. (C), IL, *493*
Nordeman Grimm, Inc. (R), NY, *152*
Norman Broadbent Int'l., Inc. (R), NY, *152*
North American Recruiters, Inc. (R), MN, *153*
Nuessle, Kurdziel & Weiss, Inc. (R), PA, *153*
O'Brien and Roof (C), OH, *497*
O'Callaghan Honey/Ray & Berndtson Inc. (R), AB, *153*
O'Rourke Companies, Inc. (R), TX, *154*
O'Shea, Divine & Co., Inc. (R), CA, *154*
O'Sullivan Search Inc. (C), ON, *498*
O'Toole & Company, Inc. (R), IL, *154*
Oberlander & Co., Inc. (R), IL, *155*
The Odessa Group (R), CA, *155*
The Ogdon Partnership (R), NY, *155*
Organization Consulting Ltd. (R), ON, *157*
Orion Consulting, Inc. (R), NJ, *157*
OSAGUI S.A. de C.V. (C), MX, *500*
Ott & Hansen, Inc. (R), CA, *157*
Ovca Assoc. Inc. (R), KY, *157*
LaMonte Owens, Inc. (R), PA, *157*
Pacific Coast Recruiting (C), CA, *501*
Pacific Coast Recruiters (C), OR, *501*
Page-Wheatcroft & Co., Ltd. (R), TX, *158*
J. Palacios & Assoc., Inc. (R), PR, *158*
R. Parker & Assoc., Inc. (R), NY, *159*
Parsons, Anderson & Gee, Inc. (C), NY, *503*
Parsons Assoc. Inc. (R), IL, *159*
Partridge Assoc., Inc. (R), MA, *160*
Pathways Int'l. (C), CT, *505*
Pawlik/Dorman Partners (R), IL, *161*
The Penn Partners, Inc. (R), PA, *162*
People Management Mid-South, LLC (R), TN, *162*
People Management Northeast, Inc. (R), CT, *162*
Performance Resources, Inc. (C), RI, *507*
The Perkins Group (R), NC, *162*
R. H. Perry & Assoc., Inc. (R), DC, *162*
Perry-D'Amico & Assoc. (R), CA, *162*
Barry Persky & Co., Inc. (R), CT, *163*

PersoNet, Inc. (C), FL, *507*
Personnel Consultants (C), WA, *508*
Personnel Incorporated (C), IA, *508*
The Personnel Network, Inc. (C), SC, *508*
Petrie Partners, Inc. (R), FL, *163*
PIC Executive Search (C), GA, *511*
Pinsker and Company, Inc. (R), CA, *164*
Pioneer Placement, Inc. (C), MA, *512*
DNPitchon Assoc. (R), NJ, *165*
Poirier, Hoevel & Co. (R), CA, *166*
Polson & Co., Inc. (R), MN, *166*
Jack Porter Assoc., Inc. (C), WA, *514*
Prairie Resource Group, Inc. (R), IL, *166*
Elan Pratzer & Partners Inc. (R), ON, *167*
Precision Executive Search (C), AZ, *516*
Preferred Placement, Inc. (C), NY, *516*
The Premier Staffing Group (C), OH, *517*
Presley Consultants, Inc. (C), CA, *517*
Prestige Inc. (C), WI, *517*
Preston-Hunter, Inc. (R), IL, *167*
Prime Management Group Inc. (C), ON, *518*
Princeton Executive Search (C), NJ, *518*
Princeton Search Partners, Inc. (R), NJ, *169*
Prior/Martech Assoc., Inc. (R), WA, *169*
Professional Research Services, Inc. (R), IL, *169*
Professional Search (R), MI, *169*
Professional Search Assoc. (C), CA, *522*
Professional Search, Inc. (C), CO, *522*
Professional Search Consultants (C), KY, *522*
Professions, Inc. (C), OH, *523*
Profit Pros, Inc. (C), CA, *523*
QVS Int'l. (R), GA, *170*
R M Associates (R), OH, *171*
Radosevic Assoc. (R), CA, *171*
Ramm Search (C), NY, *528*
Rand Assoc. (R), ME, *171*
Rand Thompson Executive Search Consultants (C), NY, *528*
Ray & Berndtson (R), TX, *171*
Ray & Berndtson/Lovas Stanley (R), ON, *172*
Reece & Mruk Partners/EMA Partners Int'l. (R), MA, *173*
Reese Assoc. (R), PA, *174*
The Regis Group, Ltd. (R), GA, *174*
Michael James Reid & Co. (R), CA, *174*
Rein & Co., Inc. (R), NJ, *174*
Resolve Assoc. Int'l. (R), FL, *175*
Resources for Management (R), PA, *175*
Retail Executive Search (C), FL, *535*
Retained Search Assoc. (R), NC, *176*
The Revere Assoc., Inc. (R), OH, *176*
S. Reyman & Assoc., Ltd. (R), IL, *176*
Russell Reynolds Assoc., Inc. (R), NY, *176*
RIC Corp. (R), FL, *177*
Marshall Rice Assoc. (R), RI, *177*
Rieser & Assoc., Inc. (R), MO, *178*
RMA Search (R), TN, *179*
RML Assoc. (C), PA, *538*
Robert Lowell Int'l. (R), TX, *179*
Robertson-Surrette Ltd. (R), NS, *179*
Robinson-Robinson & Assoc., Inc. (C), MN, *539*
Robison & Associates (R), NC, *180*
Rodzik & Assoc., Inc. (R), NC, *180*
Rollo Assoc. (R), CA, *181*
Emery A. Rose & Assoc. (C), WA, *545*
Roster Inc. (C), IN, *545*
Rovner Gerner & Assoc. (R), CA, *182*
Royal Assoc. (C), CA, *547*
Ruppert Comann Assoc., Inc. (R), CO, *182*
Rurak & Assoc., Inc (R), DC, *182*
W. A. Rutledge & Assoc. (R), CT, *183*
The S C Group LLC (R), NY, *183*
The Sager Co. (R), OH, *183*
Sales Consultants (C), OH, *551*
Sales Consultants of Cherry Hill (C), NJ, *560*
Sales Consultants of Northern Jersey, Inc. (C), NJ, *560*
Sales Consultants of Westchester-South, Inc. (C), NY, *561*
Salzmann Gay Assoc., Inc. (R), PA, *184*
Sanford Rose Assoc. - Lake Forest (R), IL, *184*
Sanford Rose Assoc. - Cedar Rapids (C), IA, *567*
Sanford Rose Assoc. - Evansville (C), IN, *567*
Sathe & Associates, Inc. (R), MN, *184*
Schuyler, Baker & Parker, Inc. (R), GA, *185*
Schwab-Carrese Assoc., Inc. Executive Search (R), NC, *185*
Search Excellence (R), CA, *186*
Search Group Inc. (R), AB, *186*
Search North America, Inc. (C), OR, *576*
Search South, Inc. (C), AL, *576*
Search West, Inc. (C), CA, *576*
SearchCorp (C), FL, *577*
Seiden Krieger Assoc., Inc. (R), NY, *188*
Seitchik Corwin & Seitchik Inc. (R), CA, *188*
Selected Executives, Inc. (C), MA, *578*
Senior Careers (R), NY, *188*
Sensible Solutions, Inc. (R), IL, *188*
Shepherd Bueschel & Provus, Inc. (R), IL, *189*
Sherbrooke Assoc., Inc. (C), NJ, *580*
Sherwood Lehman Massucco, Inc. (R), CA, *189*
Michael Shirley Assoc. Inc. (R), KS, *190*
Shoemaker & Assoc. (R), GA, *190*
E. L. Shore & Assoc. (R), ON, *190*
Shore Asociados Ejecutivos, S. A. de C.V. (R), MX, *190*
The Shorr Group (R), IL, *190*
M. Shulman, Inc. (R), CA, *191*
John Sibbald Assoc., Inc. (R), MO, *191*
The Simmons Group (C), CA, *582*
J. L. Small Assoc. (C), AL, *583*
James F. Smith & Assoc. (C), GA, *583*
Ralph Smith & Assoc. (C), IL, *584*
Howard W. Smith Assoc. (R), CT, *193*
Smith James Group, Inc. (R), GA, *194*
H. C. Smith Ltd. (R), OH, *194*
Smith, Roth & Squires (R), NY, *194*
Smith Search, S.C. (R), MX, *194*
Smith, Brown & Jones (C), KS, *585*
Snelling & Snelling, Inc. (C), FL, *585*
Snelling Search Recruiters (C), NC, *586*
Sockwell & Assoc. (R), NC, *194*
Robert Sollman & Assoc. (C), FL, *587*
Solomon-Page Healthcare Group (R), NY, *195*
Soltis Management Services (R), PA, *195*
Stephen M. Sonis Assoc. (R), MA, *195*
Spear-Izzo Assoc., LLC (C), PA, *588*
Special Markets Group, Inc. (R), GA, *195*
Specialty Consultants Inc. (R), PA, *195*
SpencerStuart (R), NY, *196*
Spilman & Assoc. (R), TX, *197*
Splaine & Assoc., Inc. (R), CA, *198*
Springer Souder & Assoc. L.L.C. (R), IL, *198*
SSA Executive Search Int'l. (R), AZ, *198*
Staff Extension Int'l. (C), TX, *590*
StaffWriters Plus (C), NY, *591*
Staub, Warmbold & Assoc., Inc. (R), NY, *199*
Stephens Assoc. Ltd., Inc. (R), OH, *200*
Peter Sterling & Co. (C), TX, *592*
The Stevens Group (R), TX, *200*
Stevens, Valentine & McKeever (C), NJ, *593*
The Stewart Group (C), FL, *593*
Stewart, Stein & Scott, Ltd. (R), MN, *200*
Strategic Executives, Inc. (R), CT, *202*
StratfordGroup (R), OH, *203*
W. R. Strathmann Assoc. (R), NY, *203*
Stratin Assoc. (C), NJ, *596*
Straube Associates (R), MA, *203*
J. Stroll Assoc., Inc. (R), CT, *203*
Stroman Int'l., Inc. (R), CO, *204*
Success Seekers Connection (C), FL, *596*
Joe Sullivan & Assoc., Inc. (R), NY, *204*
Summit Group Int'l., Inc. (R), GA, *204*
Sweeney Harbert & Mummert, Inc. (R), FL, *205*
Swift & Assoc. (C), ME, *597*
T. H. Hunter, Inc. (C), MN, *599*
S. Tanner & Assoc. Inc. (C), ON, *599*
Tarnow Int'l. (R), NJ, *206*
TASA International (R), NY, *206*
Tax Network Resources, Inc. (C), NY, *600*
The TBI Group (R), PA, *207*
Technical Recruiting Services (C), OH, *602*
TEMCO-The Executive Management Consulting Organization (R), WI, *208*
Thomas & Assoc. of Michigan (C), MI, *606*
Thomas Lyle & Co. (C), IL, *606*
Thomas Mangum Co. (R), CA, *208*
Richard Thompson Assoc., Inc. (R), MN, *209*
Thorne, Brieger Assoc., Inc. (R), NY, *209*
The Tidewater Group Inc. (C), CT, *607*
TNS Partners, Inc. (R), TX, *209*
TPS Staffing Solutions (C), IN, *608*
Trac One (R), NJ, *210*
Travel Executive Search (C), NY, *608*
TRH Assoc., Inc. (R), NY, *210*
Tryon & Heideman, LLC (R), MO, *211*
TSC Management Services Group, Inc. (C), IL, *610*
Tschudin Inc. (R), NJ, *211*
TTG/Sterling Services (C), CA, *610*
Tucker Assoc. (R), NJ, *211*
Tuttle Venture Group, Inc. (R), TX, *212*
Unlimited Staffing Solutions, Inc. (C), MI, *611*
The Urban Placement Service (C), TX, *611*
Van Dyke Assoc. (R), IL, *212*
Van Leeuwen Assoc. (R), CA, *213*

VanMaldegiam Assoc., Inc. (R), IL, *213*
Verkamp-Joyce Assoc., Inc. (R), IL, *213*
Claude Vezina, Conseil en recherche de cadres inc. (R), QE, *213*
Villareal & Assoc., Inc. (R), OK, *214*
Vlcek & Company, Inc. (R), CA, *214*
Fred Wackerle, Inc. (R), IL, *214*
Robert H. Wadsworth & Assoc., Inc. (R), AZ, *214*
Wallace Assoc. (C), CT, *614*
Wallace Management Co. (R), TN, *215*
Gerald Walsh & Co. Inc. (C), NS, *614*
Karen Wanger & Assoc., Inc. (C), IL, *615*
Warren, Morris & Madison, Ltd. (C), CA, *616*
Warring & Assoc. (R), CA, *215*
Scott Watson & Assoc., Inc. (R), FL, *216*
Webb, Johnson Assoc., Inc. (R), NY, *216*
Weinstein & Co. (R), MA, *217*
D. L. Weiss & Assoc. (R), CA, *217*
Welzig, Lowe & Assoc. (C), CO, *618*
The Wentworth Co., Inc. (R), CA, *217*
Jude M. Werra & Assoc. (R), WI, *218*
West & West (R), CA, *218*
Westfields Int'l., Inc. (C), NY, *619*
The Westminster Group, Inc. (R), RI, *218*
Weston Consultants, Inc. (R), MA, *219*
Wheeler, Moore & Elam Co. (R), TX, *219*
Whitbeck & Assoc. (R), MN, *219*
Wilder & Assoc. (C), VA, *620*
Wilder, Gammel Partners, Ltd. (R), CA, *220*
Wilkinson & Ives (R), CA, *221*
John R. Williams & Assoc., Inc. (C), NC, *621*
Williams Executive Search, Inc. (R), MN, *221*
Williams, Roth & Krueger, Inc. (R), IL, *221*
Wilson Assoc. Inc. (R), NS, *222*
The Windham Group (R), OH, *222*
Windsor International (R), GA, *222*
Wojdula & Assoc., Ltd. (R), WI, *223*
S. R. Wolman Assoc., Inc. (R), NY, *224*
Wood, Franchot Inc. (R), MN, *224*
Woodworth Int'l. Group (R), OR, *224*
Wyatt & Jaffe (R), MN, *225*
Wyndham Mills Int'l., Inc. (R), GA, *225*
Xavier Associates, Inc. (R), MA, *226*
Your Advantage Staffing Consultants Inc. (C), ON, *626*
Egon Zehnder Int'l. Inc. (R), NY, *227*
Zeiger Assoc. L.L.C. (C), CA, *627*
Zurick, Davis & Co., Inc. (R), MA, *227*

01.0 General management

A First Resource (C), NC, *231*
A la Carte Int'l., Inc. (R), VA, *1*
A Permanent Success Employment Services (C), CA, *231*
A-K-A (Anita Kaufmann Assoc.) (C), NY, *231*
A-L Assoc., Inc. (R), NY, *1*
A. D. & Assoc. Executive Search, Inc. (C), GA, *231*
A.J. & Assoc. (C), FL, *232*
A.K.S. Assoc., Ltd. (R), MA, *1*
A.L.S. Group (C), NJ, *232*
Abbott Associates (R), CA, *1*
The Abbott Group, Inc. (R), MD, *1*
Abeln, Magy & Assoc., Inc. (R), MN, *1*
Cathy Abelson Legal Search (C), PA, *232*
ACC Technical Services (C), OH, *233*
ACCESS Technology (C), CA, *234*
Accountants Executive Search (C), PA, *234*
Accounting Personnel & Engineering Personnel Consultants (C), LA, *238*
Ackerman Johnson Inc. (C), TX, *238*
Action Executive Personnel Consulting Inc. (C), ON, *239*
Action Management Corp. (C), MI, *239*
Adams & Assoc. Int'l. (R), IL, *1*
G. Adams Partners (R), IL, *2*
The Addison Consulting Group (C), NJ, *239*
Adirect Recruiting Corp. (C), ON, *240*
Adler Management, Inc. (R), NJ, *2*
ADR Accounting Management Recruiters (C), ON, *240*
Advanced Corporate Search (C), CA, *240*
Advanced Executive Resources (R), MI, *2*
Advancement Recruiting Services (C), OH, *241*
Advancement, Inc. (C), IL, *241*
Advantage Partners, Inc. (R), OH, *2*
Advice Personnel Inc. (C), NY, *241*
The Advisory Group, Inc. (R), CA, *2*
Affinity Executive Search (C), FL, *241*
Aggressive Corporation (C), IL, *242*
AGRI-associates (C), MO, *242*
Agri-Personnel (C), GA, *242*
Agri-Tech Personnel, Inc. (C), MO, *242*
Agriesti & Assoc. (C), CA, *243*
Ahrensdorf & Assoc. (R), PA, *2*
J. R. Akin & Co. (R), MA, *2*
Albrecht & Assoc., Executive Search Consultants (C), TX, *243*
Alexander Enterprises, Inc. (C), PA, *243*
The Alexander Group (R), TX, *3*
The Alexander Group (R), NJ, *3*
The Alfus Group (R), NY, *3*
Allard Associates (C), CA, *244*
D. S. Allen Assoc. (C), NJ, *244*
David Allen Assoc. (R), NJ, *3*
Allen Austin Lowe & Powers (R), TX, *3*
Allen Evans Assoc. (R), NY, *4*
Allen, Wayne & Co. LLC (C), WI, *245*
Allen/Associates (R), OH, *4*
Allerton Heneghan & O'Neill (R), IL, *4*
Alliance Executive Search, Inc. (R), MA, *4*
Allied Search, Inc. (C), CA, *245*
Tom Allison Assoc. (C), NM, *245*
Alpha Resource Group, Inc. (C), TX, *246*
Alpha Search (C), FL, *246*
Altec/HRC (C), MI, *246*
AM & G Certified Public Accountants & Consultants (R), IL, *4*
Amato & Assoc., Inc. (C), CA, *246*
Amato & Associates Insurance Recruiters (C), PA, *247*
Peter W. Ambler Co. (R), TX, *5*
American Executive Management, Inc. (R), MA, *5*
American Heritage Group, Inc. (C), MI, *247*
American Services Group (C), IL, *248*
AmeriPro Search, Inc. (C), NC, *248*
AmeriResource Group Inc. (C), OK, *248*
Ames Assoc. Inc. (C), MD, *249*
Amherst Human Resource Group, Ltd. (C), IL, *249*
AMS Int'l. (R), VA, *5*
Anderson & Schwab, Inc. (R), NY, *5*
Anderson Bradshaw Assoc., Inc. (R), TX, *6*
Andrews & Wald Group (C), FL, *250*
Tryg R. Angell, Ltd. (C), CT, *250*
Angus Employment Ltd. (C), ON, *250*
Fred Anthony Assoc. (C), WI, *251*
Anthony Michael & Co. (C), MA, *251*
APA Employment Agency Inc. (C), OR, *251*
APA Search, Inc. (R), NY, *6*
David Aplin & Assoc. (C), AB, *251*
Applied Resources (C), MA, *252*
Charles P. Aquavella & Assoc. (C), TX, *252*
Argonaut Partners, LLC (R), CA, *6*
The Argus Group Corp. (C), ON, *252*
Argus National, Inc. (R), CT, *6*
Ariail & Assoc. (R), NC, *7*
Ariel Recruitment Assoc. (R), NY, *7*
Aries Search Group (C), GA, *252*
ARJay & Assoc. (C), NC, *252*
Armitage Associates Ltd. (R), ON, *7*
Armor Personnel (C), ON, *253*
J. S. Armstrong & Assoc., Inc. (R), CA, *7*
R & J Arnold & Assoc., Inc. (C), CO, *253*
Patrick Arnone & Assoc. Inc. (R), VA, *7*
Aronow Assoc., Inc. (C), FL, *253*
Artgo, Inc. (R), OH, *7*
A. Artze Assoc.-Personnel Consultants (C), PR, *253*
Asheville Search & Consulting (C), NC, *253*
Ashford Management Group, Inc. (R), GA, *7*
Ashlar-Stone Management Consultants Inc. (R), ON, *8*
E. J. Ashton & Assoc., Ltd. (C), IL, *253*
Ashworth Consultants, Inc. (R), MA, *8*
ASI (C), CA, *254*
Asset Resource, Inc. (C), CA, *254*
Associated Recruiters (C), WI, *254*
Association Executive Resources Group (R), MD, *8*
AST/BRYANT (R), CT, *8*
W. R. Atchison & Assoc., Inc. (C), NC, *254*
Atlanta Executive Partners, Inc. (R), MA, *8*
Atlantic Pacific Group (C), CA, *255*
Atlantic West Int'l. (C), NC, *255*
Attorney Search Global, Inc. (C), IL, *255*
Aubin Int'l. Inc. (R), MA, *8*
Auerbach Associates, Inc. (R), MA, *9*
Aurora Tech Search (C), ON, *256*
A. M. Auster Associates (R), FL, *9*
Cami Austin & Assoc. (C), IL, *256*
Austin Group Int'l./Marlar Int'l. (R), TX, *9*
Austin Michaels, Ltd., Inc. (C), AZ, *256*
Austin, Hill & Assoc. (C), MD, *256*
AutoPeople (C), VT, *257*
Avalon Health Group, Inc. (R), NY, *9*
Avery Assoc. (R), CA, *9*
Avestruz & Assoc. (C), CA, *257*
Avondale Search Int'l., Inc. (R), FL, *9*
The Badger Group (R), CA, *10*

Baeder Kalinski Int'l. Group, Inc. (R), NH, *10*
The Baer Group (R), OH, *10*
Keith Bagg & Assoc., Inc. (C), ON, *257*
Baker Scott & Co. (C), NJ, *258*
Baker, Nelms & Montgomery (C), IL, *258*
Baldwin & Assoc. (C), OH, *258*
Baldwin Associates, LLC (R), CT, *10*
The Bales-Waugh Group (C), FL, *258*
Allen Ballach Assoc. Inc. (R), ON, *10*
Ballantyne & Assoc. (R), CA, *10*
Ballos & Co., Inc. (R), NJ, *10*
James Bangert & Assoc., Inc. (R), MN, *11*
The Bankers Group (C), IL, *258*
The Barack Group, Inc. (R), NY, *11*
Barclay Consultants, Inc. (C), NJ, *259*
Barger & Sargeant, Inc. (R), NH, *11*
J. W. Barleycorn, Renard & Assoc., Inc. (R), OH, *11*
Barnes & Assoc. Executive Search (C), CA, *259*
Barnes Development Group, LLC (R), WI, *11*
Fred A. Barnette & Assoc. (R), NC, *11*
Barone-O'Hara Assoc., Inc. (R), NJ, *11*
The Barrett Group (C), NH, *260*
Barrett Hospitality Search (R), CA, *12*
Barrington Hart, Inc. (R), IL, *12*
Nathan Barry Assoc., Inc. (R), MA, *12*
Aldonna Barry Personnel & Management (C), ON, *260*
Barth Smith Company (R), IL, *12*
Bartholdi & Co., Inc. (R), CO, *12*
Barton Assoc., Inc. (R), TX, *12*
The Barton Group, Inc. (C), MI, *260*
Bason Associates (R), OH, *13*
Battalia Winston Int'l./The Euram Consultants Group (R), NY, *13*
R. Gaines Baty Assoc., Inc. (R), TX, *13*
Martin H. Bauman Assoc., Inc. (R), NY, *13*
The Bauman Group (R), CA, *14*
Bayland Assoc. (C), CA, *261*
BayResearch Group, Inc. (R), IL, *14*
BCG Search, Inc. (R), FL, *14*
Beacon Int'l., Inc. (C), VA, *261*
The Beam Group (R), PA, *14*
Becker, Norton & Co. (R), PA, *14*
Beckman & Assoc. Legal Search (C), OH, *262*
The Bedford Consulting Group Inc. (R), ON, *14*
The Bedford Group (R), RI, *15*
Robert Beech West Inc. (C), CA, *262*
Behavioral Science Assoc., Inc. (R), AZ, *15*
Behrens and Company (C), WA, *262*
Neail Behringer Consultants Inc. (R), NY, *15*
Belanger Partners Ltd. (C), ON, *262*
Gary S. Bell Assoc., Inc. (C), NJ, *263*
Bell Oaks Co., Inc. (C), GA, *263*
Bell Wishingrad Partners Inc. (R), NY, *15*
Joy Reed Belt Search Consultants, Inc. (R), OK, *15*
Bench Int'l. Search, Inc. (R), CA, *15*
J. P. Bencik Assoc. (C), MI, *263*
Richard L. Bencin & Assoc. (C), OH, *264*
Bender Executive Search Management Consulting (R), NY, *16*
Bennett & Associates (C), TX, *264*
The Bennett Group, Inc. (R), IN, *16*
Bennett Search & Consulting Co. (R), FL, *16*
Benson Associates (C), NY, *264*
C. Berger And Company (R), IL, *16*
Berglund Int'l. Resources, Inc. (C), TX, *265*
Berkana Int'l., Inc. (C), WA, *265*
Berkhemer/Clayton, Inc. (R), CA, *16*
Berkshire Search Assoc. (C), MA, *265*
Bernhart Assoc. (C), MN, *265*
Ed Bertolas Assoc., Inc. (C), CA, *265*
Jack Bertram, Executive Recruiter (C), PA, *265*
Bertrand, Ross & Assoc., Inc. (C), IL, *266*
Besen Assoc. Inc. (C), NJ, *266*
Best, Coleman & Co., Inc., Inc. (R), MA, *16*
BEST/World Assoc. Inc. (R), TX, *16*
Bialla & Assoc. Inc. (R), CA, *17*
Billington & Assoc. (R), CA, *17*
Binder Hospitality Group (C), KY, *266*
Bio-Venture Group (C), RI, *266*
BioPharmMed (C), FL, *267*
BioQuest Inc. (R), CA, *17*
BioTech Research Recruiters Inc. (C), CA, *267*
Deborah Bishop & Assoc. (R), CA, *17*
Bishop Partners (R), NY, *17*
The Black Leopard (C), CA, *267*
Blackhawk Advantage, Inc. (C), CA, *267*
The Blackman Kallick Search Division (C), IL, *267*
J: Blakslee Int'l., Ltd. (R), CA, *18*
Blaney Executive Search (R), MA, *18*
Blanton & Co. (C), AL, *268*
Blau Mancino Schroeder (R), NJ, *18*
David Blevins & Assoc. (C), WA, *268*
Block & Assoc. (R), CA, *18*
D. R. Blood & Assoc. (R), AZ, *18*
Blum & Co. (R), WI, *19*
Boardroom Consultants/Kenny Kindler Tholke (R), NY, *19*
Boettcher Assoc. (R), WI, *19*
Tom Bogle & Assoc. (C), CA, *269*
Mark Bolno & Assoc. (C), FL, *269*
Bolton Group (C), CA, *269*
Ann Bond Assoc. Inc. (C), MD, *269*
Bonifield Assoc. (C), NJ, *269*
Boone-Scaturro Assoc., Inc. (C), GA, *269*
Bor-Maq Assoc. (C), TX, *269*
Borchert Assoc. (C), TX, *269*
Lynn Borne & Co. (C), CA, *270*
The Borton Wallace Co. (R), NC, *19*
Bosco-Hubert & Assoc. (C), KS, *270*
Boulware & Assoc. Inc. (R), IL, *20*
Bowden & Co., Inc. (R), OH, *20*
BowdenGlobal, Ltd. (R), OH, *20*
Howard Bowen Consulting (C), FL, *270*
Bowie & Associates, Inc. (C), MD, *271*
Boyden (R), NY, *20*
Boyle/Ogata Executive Search (R), CA, *21*
The Bradbury Management Group, Inc. (R), CA, *21*
Bradford Executives Int'l. (C), VA, *271*
M. F. Branch Assoc., Inc. (C), NC, *272*
The Brand Co., Inc. (R), FL, *22*
Brandywine Consulting Group (R), PA, *22*
Brandywine Management Group (R), MD, *22*
Brandywine Retained Ventures, Inc. (R), CT, *22*
Branthover Assoc. (C), NY, *272*
Brault & Assoc., Ltd. (R), VA, *22*
Jerold Braun & Assoc. (C), CA, *272*
Bredeson Executive Recruitment, LLC (R), TX, *22*
The Brentwood Group Ltd. (R), OR, *23*
Brentwood Int'l. (R), CA, *23*
Brethet, Barnum & Assoc., Inc. (C), ON, *273*
Brett Personnel Specialists (C), NJ, *273*
Brian Assoc., Inc. (C), NY, *273*
Briant Assoc., Inc. (R), IL, *23*
The Bridge (C), CO, *273*
Bridgecreek Personnel Agency (C), CA, *273*
BridgeGate LLC (C), CA, *273*
Brigade, Inc. (R), CA, *23*
Bright Search/Professional Staffing (C), MN, *274*
Brindisi Search (R), MD, *23*
Brissenden, McFarland, Fuccella & Reynolds, Inc. (R), NJ, *23*
Bristol Assoc., Inc. (C), CA, *274*
Brooke Chase Assoc., Inc. (R), IL, *24*
Bernard E. Brooks & Assoc., Inc. (R), SC, *24*
Broward-Dobbs, Inc. (C), GA, *274*
J. B. Brown & Assoc., Inc. (C), OH, *275*
Brown Venture Assoc. (R), CA, *24*
Brownstone Sales & Marketing Group, Inc. (C), NY, *275*
Brush Creek Partners (R), MO, *24*
BRW Search (C), MN, *275*
Bryan & Louis Research (C), OH, *275*
Bryan, Jason & Assoc. Inc. (C), ON, *275*
BT&A, LLC (R), CT, *24*
Charles Buck & Assoc., Inc. (R), NY, *24*
The Buckley Group (C), FL, *276*
Bullis & Co., Inc. (R), CA, *25*
J. Burke & Assoc., Inc. (C), TX, *276*
Burke & Assoc./The Westfield Group (C), CT, *276*
The Burke Group (C), ON, *276*
J. Burkey Assoc. (R), NJ, *25*
Joseph R. Burns & Assoc., Inc. (R), NJ, *25*
Busch International (R), CA, *25*
Business Solutions Worldwide, Inc. (C), NJ, *277*
The Butlers Co. Insurance Recruiters (C), FL, *277*
Butterfield & Co. Int'l., Inc. (C), HI, *277*
Button Group (C), TX, *277*
Buzhardt Assoc. (R), MS, *25*
Byron Leonard Int'l., Inc. (R), CA, *25*
C and P Marketing, Ltd. (C), OK, *278*
C. M. Management Services, Inc. (R), KY, *26*
C. P. Consulting (R), PA, *26*
The C.P.R. Group (C), NJ, *278*
C.T.E.W. Executive Personnel Services Inc. (C), BC, *278*
Cahill Assoc. (C), CT, *279*
Caliber Associates (R), PA, *27*
California Search Agency, Inc. (C), CA, *279*
Callan Assoc., Ltd. (R), IL, *27*
Callos Personnel Services (C), OH, *279*

Cambridge Group Ltd. - Exec. Search Div. (C), CT, *279*
The Cambridge Group Ltd. (C), CT, *280*
Cambridge Management Planning (R), ON, *27*
Campa & Assoc. (R), ON, *27*
Campbell, Edgar Inc. (C), BC, *280*
Canadian Career Partners (R), AB, *27*
CanMed Consultants Inc. (C), ON, *280*
Canny, Bowen Inc. (R), NY, *27*
The Canon Group (C), CA, *280*
Canyon Consulting, Inc. (C), TX, *281*
Capital Consulting & Research, Inc. (R), CT, *28*
Capital Consulting Group, Inc. (R), MD, *28*
Sally Caplan & Assoc. (C), WA, *281*
Caplan Assoc., Inc. (R), NJ, *28*
The Caplan-Taylor Group (R), CA, *28*
Caprio & Assoc. Inc. (R), IL, *29*
Capstone Consulting, Inc. (R), IL, *29*
Capstone Inc. (R), NY, *29*
Career Advisors, Inc. (C), FL, *281*
Career Consultants (R), IN, *29*
Career Counseling Inc. (CCI) (C), KY, *282*
Career Development Associates (C), NV, *282*
Career Marketing Consultants, Inc. (C), GA, *282*
Career Search Group (C), FL, *283*
Career Specialists, Inc. (R), WA, *29*
Career Strategies, Inc. (C), CA, *283*
Careerfit, Inc. (C), TX, *283*
Careers First, Inc. (C), NJ, *283*
Careers On Track (C), NJ, *283*
Careers Plus (R), CA, *29*
Careers/Inc. (C), PR, *284*
Carion Resource Group Inc. (C), ON, *284*
Carlson & Czeswik (R), MN, *30*
The Carlyle Group, Ltd. (R), IL, *30*
Carnegie Partners, Inc. (R), IL, *30*
Carpenter Assoc., Inc. (R), IL, *30*
Carpenter, Shackleton & Company (R), IL, *30*
Carr Management Services, Inc. (C), PA, *284*
Carson-Thomas & Assoc. (C), CA, *284*
Carter McKenzie, Inc. (C), NJ, *285*
Carter-Evdemon & Assoc. (C), FL, *285*
Carter/MacKay (C), NJ, *285*
Caruso & Assoc., Inc. (R), FL, *31*
Carver Search Consultants (C), CA, *285*
Cary & Assoc. (R), FL, *31*
CAS Comsearch Inc. (C), NY, *285*
Rosemary Cass Ltd. (R), CT, *31*
The Cassie Group (R), NJ, *31*
Catalyx Group (R), NY, *31*
Michael J. Cavanagh & Assoc. Inc. (R), ON, *31*
Caywood Partners, Ltd. (R), CA, *32*
CEC Associates (R), MA, *32*
Cejka Healthcare Executive Search Services (CHESS) (R), MO, *32*
Cella Assoc. (C), GA, *286*
Cendea Connection Int'l. (R), TX, *32*
Central Executive Search, Inc. (C), OH, *287*
Century Assoc., Inc. (C), PA, *287*
CEO Consulting (C), FL, *287*
cFour Partners (R), CA, *32*
Chad Management Group (C), ON, *288*
Wayne S. Chamberlain & Assoc. (C), CA, *288*
David Chambers & Assoc., Inc. (R), CT, *32*
Chanko-Ward, Ltd. (R), NY, *33*
Chapman & Assoc. (C), BC, *289*
The Chapman Group, Inc. (C), AZ, *289*
Charles & Associates, Inc. (C), NE, *289*
Chase Partners (R), ON, *33*
Chase-Gardner Executive Search Associates, Inc. (C), FL, *289*
The Chatham Group, Ltd. (C), CT, *289*
A. D. Check Assoc., Inc. (R), PA, *33*
Chelsea Resources, Inc. (C), CT, *290*
Christenson Hutchison McDowell, LLC (R), NJ, *34*
Christian & Timbers, Inc. (R), OH, *34*
Christopher and Long (C), MO, *291*
William J. Christopher Assoc., Inc. (R), PA, *34*
Christopher-Westmont & Assoc., Inc. (R), OH, *34*
Churchill & Affiliates, Inc. (R), PA, *35*
M. A. Churchill & Assoc., Inc. (R), PA, *35*
The Churchill Group (C), ON, *291*
Cizek Assoc., Inc. (R), AZ, *35*
CJA-The Adler Group, Inc. (R), CA, *35*
Claimsearch (C), CA, *291*
Arlene Clapp, Ltd. (R), MN, *35*
Clarey & Andrews, Inc. (R), IL, *35*
Clarey/Napier Int'l., L.C. (R), TX, *35*
Clark Executive Search (C), NY, *292*
The Clark Group (C), MI, *292*
Ken Clark Int'l. (R), NJ, *36*
Clark Personnel Service, Inc. (C), AL, *292*
Clayman & Co. (R), MA, *36*
The Clayton Edward Group (C), MI, *292*
CMC Search Consultants (C), IL, *293*
CMS, Inc. (C), NH, *293*
CMS Management Services LLC (C), IN, *293*
Coast Personnel Services Ltd. (C), BC, *293*
Coastal Int'l., Inc. (R), MA, *36*
COBA Executive Search (R), CO, *36*
Cochran, Cochran & Yale, Inc. (R), NY, *36*
Coe & Co. Int'l. Inc./EMA Partners Int'l. (R), AB, *37*
Dean M. Coe Assoc. (R), MA, *37*
The Coelyn Group (R), CA, *37*
Cole, Warren & Long, Inc. (R), PA, *37*
J. Kevin Coleman & Assoc., Inc. (R), CA, *37*
Coleman Lew & Assoc., Inc. (R), NC, *37*
Colt Systems Professional Personnel Services (C), CA, *294*
Colton Bernard Inc. (R), CA, *37*
Compass Group Ltd. (R), MI, *38*
CompuPro (C), IL, *295*
Computer Professionals (R), IL, *38*
The Comwell Company, Inc. (C), NJ, *296*
Conard Associates, Inc. (R), NH, *39*
Conasa de Mexico, S.C. (R), MX, *39*
Conex Inc./InterSearch (R), NY, *39*
Robert Connelly & Assoc., Inc. (R), MN, *39*
M. L. Conner (C), FL, *296*
Conroy Partners Ltd. (R), AB, *39*
Consolidated Management Services (C), ON, *296*
Construct Management Services (C), MN, *297*
Construction Search Specialists, Inc. (C), WI, *297*
Consulpro (R), ON, *39*
Consultant Recruiters (C), WI, *297*
Consumer Search Inc. (C), MA, *298*
Continental Research Search, Inc. (C), WI, *298*
Continental Search Assoc. (C), OH, *298*
Conway & Assoc. (R), IL, *40*
Philip Conway Management (R), IL, *40*
Cook Assoc. Int'l., Inc. (C), TN, *298*
Cook Assoc.,® Inc. (R), IL, *40*
The Cooke Group (R), WI, *40*
Corbin Packaging Professionals (C), MO, *299*
Cornell Group Int'l. Consulting, Inc. (R), NY, *41*
Cornerstone Search Assoc. Inc. (C), MA, *299*
Cornwall Stockton & Co., Inc. (C), TX, *299*
Corporate Advisors, Inc. (C), FL, *299*
The Corporate Advisory Group (R), NJ, *41*
Corporate Careers, Inc. (C), CA, *299*
The Corporate Connection, Ltd. (C), VA, *299*
Corporate Dynamix (C), AZ, *300*
Corporate Environment Ltd. (R), IL, *41*
Corporate Leadership Strategies, Inc. (R), NH, *41*
Corporate Management Services (C), PA, *300*
Corporate Plus, Ltd. (C), GA, *300*
Corporate Recruiters Inc. (C), PA, *300*
Corporate Resources Professional Placement (C), MN, *300*
Corporate Search Consultants (C), IN, *301*
Corporate Search, Inc. (C), NY, *301*
The Corporate Source Group, Inc. (R), MA, *41*
Corporate Staffing Group, Inc. (C), PA, *301*
Leonard Corwen Assoc. (C), NY, *302*
Cosier & Assoc. (C), AB, *302*
J. D. Cotter Search Inc. (C), OH, *302*
CountryHouse Hotels Executive Search (C), VA, *302*
Cowell & Associates, Ltd. (R), IL, *42*
Cowin Assoc. (R), NY, *42*
Trudi Cowlan (C), NY, *302*
Craig Affiliates, Inc. (C), TX, *302*
Crane, Reed & Co., Inc. (C), NH, *302*
Creative HR Solutions (C), GA, *303*
Creative Input, Inc. (C), RI, *303*
Creative Management Strategies, Ltd. (R), NY, *42*
Creative-Leadership, Inc. (R), CA, *42*
CRI Professional Search (C), CA, *303*
The Cris Group, Inc. (R), NY, *42*
Crispi, Wagner & Co., Inc. (R), NY, *43*
Crist Partners, Ltd. (R), IL, *43*
Marlene Critchfield Co. (C), CA, *303*
Crowder & Company (R), MI, *43*
Crowe Chizek & Co. (C), IN, *304*
Crown Advisors, Inc. (R), PA, *43*
CSA/Clinical Staffing Assoc., LLC (C), NJ, *304*

CTR (R), CA, *43*
Culver Personnel Services (C), CA, *304*
Cumberland Professional Search Inc. (C), TN, *304*
Frank Cuomo & Assoc., Inc. (C), NY, *305*
Curran Partners, Inc. (R), CT, *44*
Tony Curtis & Associates (C), ON, *305*
The Curtiss Group International (R), FL, *44*
Cusack Consulting (R), NY, *44*
The Custer Group, Inc. (R), TN, *44*
Cyntal Int'l. Ltd. (R), NY, *44*
Cypress Int'l., Inc. (R), FL, *45*
D & M Associates (C), PA, *306*
D.A.I Human Resources Consultants (R), QE, *45*
D.A.L. Associates, Inc. (R), CT, *45*
Daggett & Kvistad (R), CA, *45*
Charles Dahl Group, Inc. (C), MN, *306*
Dahl-Morrow Int'l. (R), VA, *45*
The Dalley Hewitt Co. (R), GA, *45*
Damon & Assoc., Inc. (C), TX, *306*
The Danbrook Group, Inc. (C), TX, *306*
Daniel Marks Company (C), OH, *306*
Alfred Daniels & Assoc., Inc. (R), CA, *46*
The Danielson Group, Inc. (C), TX, *306*
DARE Personnel Inc. (C), ON, *307*
Alan Darling Consulting (R), VT, *46*
The Dartmouth Group (R), NY, *46*
Datamatics Management Services, Inc. (C), NJ, *307*
Daubenspeck & Associates, Ltd. (R), IL, *46*
David Perry Assoc. (C), NJ, *308*
Davies, Park (R), AB, *46*
Joseph A. Davis Consultants, Inc. (R), NY, *47*
Bert Davis Executive Search, Inc. (R), NY, *47*
Bert Davis Publishing Placement Consultants (C), NY, *309*
The Dayton Group, Ltd. (C), NY, *309*
DBC Recruiting Network (C), GA, *309*
DBL Associates (C), CA, *309*
Dean-MacDonald (R), OH, *47*
Debbon Recruiting Group, Inc. (C), MO, *310*
DeCaster Assoc. (C), WI, *310*
Deeco Int'l. (C), UT, *310*
Defrain Mayer (R), KS, *48*
DeLalla - Fried Assoc. (C), NY, *310*
Thorndike Deland Assoc. LLC (R), NY, *48*
Delta Management Group Ltd. (C), ON, *310*
Delta Services (R), TX, *48*
Derhak Ireland & Partners Ltd. (R), ON, *48*
Descheneaux Recruitment Services Ltd. (C), BC, *311*
Development Resource Group (R), NY, *48*
Development Search Specialists (R), MN, *49*
The Devlin Search Group, Inc. (C), MA, *311*
Rob Dey Executive Search (R), FL, *49*
Dieckmann & Assoc., Ltd. (R), IL, *51*
DieckMueller Group (R), WI, *51*
The Diestel Group (R), UT, *51*
Roger Dietsch & Assoc. (C), MN, *312*
DiMarchi Partners (R), CO, *51*
J. Dinerstein & Co., Inc. (R), NY, *51*
Robert W. Dingman Co., Inc. (R), CA, *52*
Dinte Resources, Inc. (R), VA, *52*
Discovery, The Staffing Specialists, Inc. (C), IL, *312*
Dise & Co. (R), OH, *52*
R. J. Dishaw & Assoc. (R), TX, *52*
Diversified Health Search (R), PA, *52*
Diversified Search, Inc. (R), PA, *52*
Dixie Search Assoc. (C), GA, *313*
DLB Assoc. (R), NY, *53*
DLG Assoc., Inc. (R), NC, *53*
Doering & Assoc. (C), CA, *313*
L. J. Doherty & Assoc. (R), MA, *53*
Doherty Int'l., Inc. (R), IL, *53*
The Domann Organization (R), CA, *53*
Dominguez-Metz & Assoc. (R), CA, *53*
Domres Professional Search (R), WI, *53*
Don Allan Assoc., Inc. (C), CA, *313*
Donahue/Bales Assoc. (R), IL, *54*
Donini Assoc. (R), VA, *54*
The Dorfman Group (C), AZ, *314*
Dorst Information Services, Inc. (C), NY, *314*
CS Dowling Executive Services (R), NJ, *54*
Drinkwater & Assoc. (R), MA, *54*
Dromeshauser Assoc. (R), MA, *55*
Drummond Assoc., Inc. (C), NY, *315*
DRZ Medical Recruiters (C), CO, *315*
DSR-Search & Recruitment (C), TX, *315*
J. H. Dugan & Assoc., Inc. (R), CA, *55*
Dumont & Co. (C), BC, *316*
M. Dunbar & Assoc. (C), TX, *316*
The Duncan-O'Dell Group Inc. (C), TX, *316*
Dunhill Professional Search of Miami (C), FL, *319*
Dunhill Executive Search of Los Angeles, Inc. (C), CA, *319*
Dunhill of San Francisco, Inc. (C), CA, *319*
Dunhill Personnel of Boulder (C), CO, *319*
Dunhill Professional Search of Oakland (C), CA, *319*
Dunhill Search of West Atlanta (C), GA, *320*
Dunhill Professional Search of Hawaii (C), HI, *320*
Dunhill of Manchester Inc. (C), NH, *321*
Dunhill Professional Search of Greater New Orleans (C), LA, *321*
Dunhill Professional Search of Byram (C), MS, *321*
Dunhill Personnel Service of Fargo (C), ND, *322*
Dunhill Personnel of Northeast Tulsa, Inc. (C), OK, *322*
Dunhill Professional Search of Bucks-Mont., Inc. (C), PA, *322*
Dunhill Professional Search of Wilkes-Barre/Scranton, Inc. (C), PA, *322*
Dunhill Professional Search, Inc. of McAllen (C), TX, *323*
Dunhill Professional Search of Richmond (C), VA, *323*
Dunhill Search of Vermont (C), VT, *323*
Dunlap & Sullivan Assoc. (R), MI, *55*
C. A. Durakis Assoc., Inc. (R), MD, *55*
Dussick Management Assoc. (C), CT, *323*
Donald F. Dvorak & Co. (R), IL, *55*
Dwyer Consulting Group, Inc. (R), WV, *56*
Gwen Dycus & Assoc. (C), FL, *323*
Dynamic Synergy Corp. (R), CA, *56*
The E & K Group (C), NJ, *324*
E.P. Int'l. (C), NY, *324*
E/Search Int'l. (C), CT, *325*
EA Plus, Inc. (C), TX, *325*
Eagle Consulting Group Inc. (C), TX, *325*
J. M. Eagle Partners Ltd. (C), WI, *325*
Eagle Research, Inc. (C), NJ, *325*
Eagle Search Assoc. (C), CA, *325*
EagleView, Inc. (C), MA, *325*
Earley Kielty & Assoc., Inc. (R), NY, *56*
Early Cochran & Olson (R), IL, *56*
Eastbourne Assoc. Inc. (R), NY, *56*
Eastman & Beaudine, Inc. (R), TX, *56*
EBA Group (R), NJ, *56*
Eden & Assoc., Inc. (C), PA, *326*
The Edge Resource Group (C), PA, *326*
EDI/Executive Dynamics Inc. (C), NJ, *326*
Edwards & Assoc. (C), GA, *327*
Bruce Edwards & Associates, Inc. (R), NC, *56*
EFCO Consultants, Inc. (C), NY, *327*
Effective Search, Inc. (R), IL, *57*
EGM Consulting, Inc. (R), FL, *57*
Richard A. Eisner & Co., LLP (R), NY, *57*
William J. Elam & Assoc. (R), NE, *58*
The Eldridge Group, Ltd. (C), IL, *327*
Elinvar (C), NC, *328*
Yves Elkas Inc. (R), QE, *58*
Gene Ellefson & Assoc. Inc. (C), MI, *328*
Elliot Assoc. Inc. (R), NY, *58*
H. J. Elliot, Inc. (R), IL, *58*
The Elliott Company (R), MA, *58*
Ellis & Associates (C), HI, *328*
Ellis Career Consultants (C), NJ, *328*
Steve Ellis (C), CA, *328*
David M. Ellner Assoc. (R), NY, *59*
The Elsworth Group (C), TX, *329*
Elwell & Assoc., Inc. (R), MI, *59*
Mark Elzweig Co., Ltd. (C), NY, *329*
Emerald Legal Search (C), NH, *329*
Emerging Medical Technologies, Inc. (C), CO, *329*
Emerson & Co. (C), GA, *329*
Emmett Executive Search, Inc. (C), NY, *330*
EMN/Witt/Kieffer (R), MA, *59*
Empire International (R), PA, *59*
Employment Solutions, Inc. (C), TX, *330*
Empowered Solutions Corp. (C), GA, *330*
The Energists (R), TX, *59*
The Enfield Company (C), TX, *330*
Engineering & Scientific Search Assoc. (ESSA) (C), NJ, *330*
Engineering Futures, LLC (C), CT, *330*
ENI (R), CT, *59*
The Enterprise Group (R), MA, *60*
Epsen, Fuller & Assoc., LLC (R), NJ, *60*
Erlanger Assoc. (R), CT, *60*
Erwin Assoc. (R), IL, *60*
ESA (R), CT, *60*
ESS (Executive Search Services) (R), CA, *61*
Essential Solutions, Inc. (C), CA, *331*
Ethos Consulting, Inc. (R), CA, *61*
ETI Search Int'l. (R), GA, *61*
The Evans McDonnell Co. (C), TX, *331*
The Evans Search Group (R), CT, *61*
Evans Transportation Search (C), ON, *331*

Excalibur Human Resources, Inc. (R), NJ, *61*
Exec Tech, Inc. (C), IL, *332*
ExeConnex, LLC (R), GA, *61*
ExecuGroup, Inc. (R), MS, *61*
ExecuQuest, Inc. (R), MI, *61*
ExecuSource Assoc., Inc. (C), GA, *332*
ExecuSource Consultants, Inc. (C), TX, *332*
Executech (R), OH, *62*
Executive Access Inc. (R), NY, *62*
Executive Alliance (R), MA, *62*
Executive Career Search (C), VA, *332*
Executive Careers (R), CA, *62*
Executive Connection (C), OH, *333*
Executive Dimensions (R), NY, *62*
Executive Directions (R), OH, *62*
The Executive Group, Inc. (R), CA, *62*
Executive Manning Corp. (R), FL, *63*
Executive Placement Services (C), GA, *333*
Executive Recruiters Int'l. (C), MI, *333*
Executive Recruiters, Inc. (C), WI, *334*
Executive Recruiters (C), WA, *334*
Executive Recruitment Specialists, Inc. (R), NC, *63*
Executive Referral Services, Inc. (C), IL, *334*
Executive Registry (C), QE, *334*
Executive Resource Assoc. (C), VA, *334*
Executive Sales Search (C), CO, *335*
Executive Search Consultants (R), CA, *63*
Executive Search Consultants International, Inc. (R), NY, *63*
Executive Search Consultants, Inc. (C), FL, *335*
Executive Search Consultants (C), CA, *335*
Executive Search Consultants Corp. (C), IL, *335*
Executive Search Group LLC (C), CA, *335*
Executive Search Group, Inc. (C), CT, *335*
Executive Search Int'l./Transearch (R), MA, *63*
Executive Search Int'l. (C), TX, *335*
Executive Search, Ltd. (C), OH, *336*
Executive Search of America, Inc. (C), OH, *336*
Executive Search of New England, Inc. (C), ME, *336*
Executive Search Partners (R), NY, *63*
Executive Search Placements, Inc. (C), CO, *336*
Executive Search Team (C), MI, *336*
Executive Solutions (R), MN, *64*
The Executive Source (C), SA, *337*
Executive Strategies, Inc. (C), GA, *337*
The Executive Tree (R), FL, *64*
Executive/Retail Placement Assoc. (C), MD, *337*
ExecutiveFit (C), NY, *337*
Executives Worldwide, Inc. (C), OR, *337*
Raymond L. Extract & Assoc. (R), CA, *64*
Eyler Assoc., Inc. (R), IA, *64*
Fagan & Company (R), PA, *64*
Fairfaxx Corp. (R), CT, *64*
Fairfield Int'l. Resources (R), NY, *65*
Paul Falcone Assoc. (R), NJ, *65*
Fallstaff Search (C), MD, *338*
Family-Business Roundtable, Inc. (R), AZ, *65*
Leon A. Farley Assoc. (R), CA, *65*
Dorothy W. Farnath & Assoc., Inc. (C), NJ, *338*
The Fawcett Group (R), MA, *65*
Federal Placement Services (C), NY, *339*
A. E. Feldman Assoc., Inc. (C), NY, *339*
Fell & Nicholson Technology Resources (R), CA, *65*
Fenwick Partners (R), MA, *66*
Fenzel Milar Assoc. (C), OH, *339*
Fergason Assoc., Inc. (C), IL, *339*
Ferneborg & Assoc., Inc. (R), CA, *66*
Ferrari Search Group (C), OH, *340*
Guild Fetridge Acoustical Search, Inc. (C), NY, *340*
Fidelity Search Group, Inc. (R), PA, *66*
Jerry Fields Assoc. (C), NY, *340*
Financial Connections Company (C), VA, *340*
Financial Plus Management Solutions Inc. (R), ON, *66*
Neil Fink Assoc. (R), CA, *66*
Eileen Finn & Assoc., Inc. (C), NY, *341*
Finnegan & Assoc. (R), CA, *67*
First Advisory Services Int'l., Inc. (R), MD, *67*
First Choice Search (R), WA, *67*
First Search America, Inc. (C), TN, *341*
First Search Inc. (C), IL, *341*
First Union Executive Search (R), NC, *67*
Howard Fischer Assoc. Int'l., Inc. (R), PA, *67*
Fisher & Assoc. (R), CA, *67*
Jack Stuart Fisher Assoc. (C), NJ, *341*
The Fisher Group (R), AB, *67*
Fisher Personnel Management Services (R), CA, *68*
Fisher-Todd Assoc. (C), NY, *341*
A. G. Fishkin & Assoc., Inc. (R), MD, *68*
FitzGibbon & Assoc. (R), PA, *68*
The Flagship Group (R), MA, *68*
Robert M. Flanagan & Assoc., Ltd. (R), NY, *68*
Flexible Resources, Inc. (C), CT, *342*
Flowers & Assoc. (C), OH, *342*
J. G. Flynn & Assoc. Inc. (R), BC, *69*
Flynn, Hannock, Inc. (R), CT, *69*
Focus Consulting Services, Inc. (C), FL, *342*
Focus Executive Search (C), MN, *343*
The Forbes Group (R), GA, *69*
Ford & Ford (C), MA, *343*
The Ford Group, Inc. (R), PA, *69*
Forest People Int'l. Search Ltd. (C), BC, *343*
Forray Assoc., Inc. (R), NY, *70*
Fortuna Technologies Inc. (C), CA, *343*
F-O-R-T-U-N-E Personnel Consultants of Boise (R), ID, *70*
Fortune Group Int'l., Inc. (R), PA, *70*
Fortune Personnel Consultants of Huntsville, Inc. (C), AL, *343*
F-O-R-T-U-N-E Personnel Consultants of Wilmington (C), DE, *344*
Fortune Personnel Consultants (C), CA, *344*
F-O-R-T-U-N-E Personnel Consultants of San Diego (C), CA, *344*
F-O-R-T-U-N-E Personnel Consultants of Palm Beach (C), FL, *345*
F-O-R-T-U-N-E Personnel Consultants of Savannah, Inc. (C), GA, *345*
Fortune Personnel Consultants of Jacksonville (C), FL, *345*
Fortune of Arlington Heights (C), IL, *345*
Fortune Personnel Consultants of Bloomfield, Inc. (C), MI, *346*
F-O-R-T-U-N-E Personnel Consultants of South Bend (C), IN, *346*
Fortune Personnel Consultants of Topsfield (C), MA, *346*
F-O-R-T-U-N-E Personnel Consultants of St. Louis-West County (C), MO, *347*
F-O-R-T-U-N-E Personnel Consultants of Menlo Park, Inc. (C), NJ, *347*
Fortune Personnel Consultants (C), MT, *347*
F-O-R-T-U-N-E Search Consultants (C), MO, *347*
F-O-R-T-U-N-E Personnel Consultants of Bergen County Inc. (C), NJ, *347*
F-O-R-T-U-N-E of West Portland (C), OR, *348*
F-O-R-T-U-N-E Personnel Consultants of Rockland County, Inc. (C), NY, *348*
Fortune Personnel Consultants of Allentown, Inc. (C), PA, *348*
F-O-R-T-U-N-E Personnel Consultants of Cincinnati (C), OH, *348*
Fortune Personnel Consultants of Hilton Head (C), SC, *349*
FORTUNE Personnel Consultants of Charleston, Inc. (C), SC, *349*
Fortune Personnel Consultants of Chattanooga Inc. (C), TN, *349*
Fortune Personnel Consultants of Anderson, Inc. (C), SC, *349*
F-O-R-T-U-N-E Personnel Consultants of Houston, Inc. (C), TX, *350*
F-O-R-T-U-N-E Personnel of Nashville (C), TN, *350*
Fortune Personnel Consultants of Plano (C), TX, *350*
F-O-R-T-U-N-E Personnel Consultants of the Tri-Cities, Inc. (C), TN, *350*
F-O-R-T-U-N-E Personnel Consultants of East Seattle (C), WA, *351*
Fortune Personnel Consultants of the Virginia Highlands (C), VA, *351*
Foster Partners (R), NY, *70*
The Fourbes Group, Inc. (C), NJ, *351*
Fox-Morris Assoc., Inc. (C), PA, *351*
Foy, Schneid & Daniel, Inc. (R), NY, *71*
Franchise Recruiters Ltd. (R), IL, *71*
Franchise Search, Inc. (C), NY, *352*
Franklin Allen Consultants, Ltd. (R), NY, *71*
Franklin Int'l. Search, Inc. (C), MA, *352*
The Franklin Search Group, Inc./Medzilla (R), WA, *71*
Franstaff Inc. (C), FL, *352*
KS Frary & Assoc. (R), MA, *71*
Mel Frazer Consultant (C), CA, *352*
P. N. French Assoc., Inc. (R), MA, *72*
Gerald Frisch Assoc., Inc. (R), NY, *72*
Frye/Joure & Assoc., Inc. (C), TN, *353*
C. F. Furr & Co. (R), NC, *72*

The Furst Group, Inc. (R), IL, *72*
Furst Group/MPI (R), IL, *72*
G. H. Enterprises (C), AZ, *354*
GAAP Inc. (R), QE, *73*
The Gabriel Group (C), PA, *354*
Gaffney Management Consultants (R), IL, *73*
Gahan Assoc. (R), NY, *73*
Gaines & Assoc. Int'l., Inc. (R), IL, *73*
Jay Gaines & Company, Inc. (R), NY, *73*
Gaming Consultants, Inc. (R), LA, *74*
The Gammill Group, Inc. (C), OH, *354*
Gans, Gans & Assoc., Inc. (R), FL, *74*
W. N. Garbarini & Assoc. (R), NJ, *74*
Gardiner, Townsend & Assoc. (R), NY, *74*
Gardner-Ross Assoc., Inc. (R), NY, *74*
Garland Assoc. Int'l. (C), CA, *355*
The Garms Group (R), IL, *74*
Garrett Assoc. Inc. (R), GA, *75*
The Garrison Organization (R), IA, *75*
Garrison-Randall, Inc. (R), CA, *75*
The Garvis Group, Inc. (C), LA, *355*
GateSource Partners (C), VA, *355*
Dianne Gauger & Assoc. (C), CA, *355*
Geddes & Rubin Management Inc. (R), ON, *76*
Genel Associates (C), CA, *356*
Genesis Consulting Partners (R), PA, *76*
Genesis Personnel Service, Inc. (C), OH, *356*
Geneva Group Int'l. (R), CA, *76*
C. R. Gerald & Assoc. (C), ON, *356*
GFI Professional Staffing Services (C), NH, *357*
Gielow Assoc., Inc. (R), WI, *76*
Gilbert & Van Campen Int'l. (R), NY, *76*
John Gilbert Co. (C), TX, *357*
Gilbert Scott Assoc., LLC (C), MA, *357*
Gilbert Tweed Assoc. Inc. (R), NY, *76*
Howard Gilmore & Assoc. (R), OH, *77*
Gilreath Weatherby Inc. (R), MA, *77*
The Glazin Group (R), BC, *77*
J. P. Gleason Assoc., Inc. (R), IL, *77*
The Glenwood Group (C), IL, *358*
Glines Assoc., Inc. (R), IL, *77*
Global Consulting Group Inc. (C), ON, *358*
Global Data Services, Inc. (R), NY, *77*
Global Employer's Network, Inc. (R), TX, *77*
Global Engineers Inc. (C), ME, *358*
Global HealthCare Partners (R), IL, *78*
Global Research Partnership Inc. (R), NY, *78*
Global Resources Group (R), CA, *78*
Global Telecommunications, Inc. (C), TX, *359*
The GlobalSearch Group (C), TX, *359*
F. Gloss Int'l. (R), VA, *78*
Glou Int'l., Inc. (R), MA, *78*
The Tracy Glover Co. (R), TX, *78*
The Gobbell Co. (R), CA, *78*
Robert G. Godfrey Assoc. Ltd. (R), IL, *78*
H. L. Goehring & Assoc., Inc. (C), OH, *359*
Barry M. Gold & Co. (C), CA, *359*
Goldbeck Recruiting Inc. (C), BC, *359*
Joseph Goldring & Assoc. Inc. (C), MI, *360*
Fred J. Goldsmith Assoc. (R), CA, *79*
David Gomez & Assoc., Inc. (R), IL, *79*
Gomez Fregoso y Asociados (C), JAL, *360*
Goodkind Assoc. Inc. (C), NY, *360*
The Goodman Group (R), CA, *79*
Goodrich & Sherwood Assoc., Inc. (R), NY, *79*
Goodwin & Co. (R), DC, *80*
Gossage Regan Assoc. (R), NY, *80*
Gould, McCoy & Chadick, Inc. (R), NY, *80*
The Governance Group, Inc. (R), NJ, *80*
Government Contract Solutions, Inc. (C), VA, *360*
Gowdy Consultants (C), TX, *361*
Graham & Co. (R), NJ, *80*
Robert Graham Assoc. (R), RI, *81*
Granger, Counts & Assoc. (R), OH, *81*
Robert Grant Assoc., Inc. (C), CA, *361*
Grant Cooper & Assoc., Inc. (R), MO, *81*
Grant/Morgan Assoc., Inc. (C), MD, *361*
Grantham & Co., Inc. (R), NC, *81*
Graphic Search Assoc. Inc. (C), PA, *362*
Grauss & Co. (C), CA, *362*
Annie Gray Assoc., Inc. (R), MO, *81*
Sheila Greco Assoc. (C), NY, *362*
R. Green & Assoc., Inc. (C), OH, *362*
Greene-Levin-Snyder LLC (C), NY, *362*
Greenwich Search Partners, LLC (C), CT, *363*
Greger/Peterson Assoc., Inc. (R), CA, *81*
Gregory, Kyle & Assoc. (C), NC, *363*
Griffith & Werner, Inc. (R), FL, *82*
J. B. Groner Executive Search, Inc. (C), DE, *363*
Gros Executive Search, Inc. (C), TN, *363*
Groupe PCA Inc. (C), QE, *363*
Groussman & Assoc., Inc. (R), TX, *82*
Grover & Assoc. (R), OH, *82*
Growth Consultants of America (R), MI, *82*
Growth Strategies, Inc. (R), FL, *83*
David E. Grumney Co. Inc. (R), WA, *83*
GSW Consulting Group, Inc. (R), CA, *83*
Michael R. Guerin Co. (C), CA, *364*
Wolf Gugler & Assoc. Ltd. (R), ON, *83*
Gundersen Partners, L.L.C. (R), NY, *83*
Gustin Partners, Ltd. (R), MA, *83*
William Guy & Assoc., Inc. (R), CA, *84*
GWS Partners (R), IL, *84*
H R Solutions, Inc. (C), MO, *365*
The H. S. Group, Inc. (C), WI, *365*
Habelmann & Assoc. (R), MI, *84*
Haddad Assoc. (R), FL, *84*
Russ Hadick & Assoc. Inc. (C), OH, *365*
M. A. Haggith Consultants Ltd. (R), ON, *84*
Hahn & Assoc., Inc. (C), OH, *365*
Halbrecht Lieberman Assoc., Inc. (R), CT, *84*
Hale Assoc. (R), IL, *84*
K. C. Hale, Inc. (R), CT, *85*
Haley Associates (R), CA, *85*
Don Hall & Assoc. (C), TX, *366*
Hall Management Group, Inc. (C), GA, *367*
The Halyburton Co., Inc. (R), NC, *85*
Hamilton & Co. (C), OH, *367*
The Hamilton Group (R), MD, *85*
The Hampton Group (C), NY, *367*
R. C. Handel Assoc. Inc. (R), CT, *85*
W. L. Handler & Assoc. (R), GA, *85*
Hands-on Broadcast (R), NY, *86*
Handy HRM (R), NY, *86*
Hanley & Assoc. (R), FL, *86*
The Hanna Group (C), OH, *368*
The Hanover Consulting Group (C), MD, *368*
Hansen Executive Search, Inc. (C), NE, *368*
Harbrowe, Inc. (C), NY, *368*
Harcor Quest & Assoc. (R), OH, *86*
Harcourt & Assoc. (C), AB, *368*
Harcourt Group Ltd. (R), OH, *86*
Hardage Group (C), TN, *369*
Hardison & Company (R), TX, *86*
Harper Associates (C), MI, *369*
Harper Hewes, Inc. (C), NY, *369*
Harrington & O'Brien, Inc. (C), NH, *369*
The Harris Consulting Corp. (R), MB, *87*
Harris Heery & Assoc., Inc. (R), CT, *87*
Harris McCully Assoc., Inc. (C), NY, *369*
Hartman & Barnette (R), VA, *87*
Hartsfield Group, Inc. (R), GA, *87*
Harvard Group Int'l. (R), GA, *87*
Harvey Hohauser & Assoc., LLC (R), MI, *87*
Bruce W. Haupt Assoc. (R), DC, *88*
Michael J. Hawkins, Inc. (C), IL, *370*
William E. Hay & Co. (R), IL, *88*
Hayden Group, Inc. (R), MA, *88*
The Haystack Group, Inc. (R), ME, *88*
Hazard, Young, Attea & Assoc., Ltd. (C), IL, *371*
Hazlett Associates (R), IL, *88*
HCI Corp. (C), IL, *371*
Headden Assoc. (R), WA, *88*
Healey Executive Search, Inc. (R), MN, *88*
Health Care Dimensions (C), CO, *371*
Health Industry Consultants, Inc. (R), CO, *89*
Health Search (C), CA, *371*
Healthcare Management Resources, Inc. (R), GA, *89*
Healthcare Recruiters of the Rockies, Inc. (C), CO, *372*
Healthcare Recruiters Int'l. Bay Area (C), CA, *372*
Healthcare Recruiters of Indiana (C), IN, *372*
Healthcare Recruiters Int'l. - Alabama (C), AL, *372*
Healthcare Recruiters Int'l - Minnesota, Inc. (C), MN, *373*
Healthcare Recruiters International-NY/NJ (C), NJ, *373*
Healthcare Recruiters of New Orleans (C), LA, *373*
Healthcare Recruiters of New York, Inc. (C), NY, *373*
Healthcare Recruiters Int'l. Philadelphia (C), NJ, *373*
Healthcare Recruiters - Northwest (C), WA, *374*
Healthcare Recruiters of Dallas (C), TX, *374*
The Healthsearch Group, Inc. (C), NY, *374*
F. P. Healy & Co., Inc. (R), NY, *89*
HeartBeat Medical, Inc. (C), OR, *374*
Heath/Norton Assoc., Inc. (R), NY, *89*
R. W. Hebel Assoc. (R), TX, *89*
HEC Group (C), ON, *375*

Hechkoff/Work Executive Search Inc. (R), NY, *89*
Heffelfinger Assoc., Inc. (R), MA, *89*
The Heidrick Partners, Inc. (R), IL, *90*
Jay Heino Company, LLC (C), NY, *375*
Heinze & Assoc. Inc. (R), MN, *91*
Helbling & Assoc., Inc. (R), PA, *91*
Helfer Executive Consultants (R), TN, *91*
Helffrich Int'l. (C), FL, *375*
Heller Assoc., Ltd. (R), IL, *91*
Heller Kil Assoc., Inc. (C), FL, *375*
G. W. Henn & Co. (R), OH, *91*
Bruce Henry Assoc. Inc. (R), CA, *91*
Kay Henry, Inc. (C), PA, *376*
The Hensge Co. (R), IL, *91*
Henson Partners (C), AZ, *376*
Herbeck Kline & Assoc. (R), IL, *92*
Hergenrather & Co. (R), WA, *92*
Heritage Pacific Corp. (C), CA, *376*
Heritage Search Group, Inc. (C), FL, *376*
J. J. Herlihy & Assoc., Inc. (C), CA, *376*
Hermann & Westmore (R), CA, *92*
A. Herndon & Assoc., Inc. (R), TX, *92*
Herrerias & Assoc. (R), CA, *92*
Herring & Assoc. (C), AR, *376*
The Herrmann Group Ltd. (R), ON, *92*
J. D. Hersey & Assoc. (C), OH, *376*
H. Hertner Assoc., Inc. (C), FL, *377*
Stanley Herz & Co. (R), NY, *92*
Robert Hess & Assoc., Inc. (C), CO, *377*
The Hetzel Group, Inc. (R), IL, *92*
Higbee Assoc., Inc. (C), CT, *377*
Higdon Prince Inc. (R), NY, *93*
Higgins Assoc., Inc. (R), IL, *93*
B. W. Higgins, Inc. (C), IN, *377*
Highland & Assoc. (C), CA, *378*
Highland Search Group, L.L.C. (R), NY, *93*
Highlander Search (C), NC, *378*
Higley, Hall & Co., Inc. (R), MA, *93*
Hill Allyn Assoc. (C), CA, *378*
Frank P. Hill (R), MX, *93*
The Hindman Co. (R), KY, *94*
The Hindman Group, Inc. (C), CA, *378*
Hire Authority, Inc. (C), MI, *378*
The Hiring Authority, Inc. (C), FL, *379*
Hite Executive Search (R), OH, *94*
Hobson Assoc. (C), CT, *379*
Hockett Associates, Inc. (R), CA, *94*
Hodge-Cronin & Assoc., Inc. (R), IL, *94*
Hoffman Partnership Group Inc. (C), NY, *379*
Hoffman Recruiters (C), MA, *380*
The Hogan Group (C), OH, *380*
Hoglund & Assoc., Inc. (R), IL, *94*
Holland & Assoc., Inc. (R), MI, *94*
Holland Rusk & Assoc. (R), IL, *95*
The Hollins Group, Inc. (R), IL, *95*
Holloway Schulz & Partners (C), BC, *380*
Holohan Group, Ltd. (R), MO, *95*
Home Health & Hospital Recruiters, Inc. (C), GA, *380*
Fred Hood & Assoc. (C), CA, *380*
Hook-Up! (C), CA, *380*
David C. Horn Executive Search (C), TX, *381*
Hornberger Management Company (R), DE, *95*
Horton Int'l. Inc. (R), NY, *96*
Hospitality Executive Search, Inc. (R), MA, *96*
Hospitality Int'l. (C), NY, *381*
Houser, Martin, Morris (C), WA, *381*
Houtz•Strawn & Arnold, Inc. (R), TX, *96*
William C. Houze & Co. (R), CA, *96*
Randall Howard & Assoc., Inc. (R), TN, *96*
Howard-Sloan Assoc. (C), NY, *381*
The Howard-Sloan-Koller Group (R), NY, *97*
Howe & Assoc. (R), PA, *97*
Robert Howe & Assoc. (R), GA, *97*
HRCS (R), CA, *97*
Hreshko Consulting Group (C), NJ, *382*
HRI Services, Inc. (C), MA, *382*
The HRM Group, Inc. (C), AL, *382*
HRS, Inc. (R), PA, *97*
Hudson Assoc. Inc. (C), IN, *383*
E. A. Hughes & Co., Inc. (R), NY, *98*
Hughes & Company (R), VA, *98*
Human Capital Resources, Inc. (C), FL, *384*
Human Resource Bureau (C), CA, *384*
The Human Resource Department Ltd. (R), OH, *98*
Human Resource Dimensions, Inc. (C), TX, *384*
The Human Resource Group, Inc. (R), OH, *98*
Human Resource Solutions (R), TX, *98*
Human Resource Technologies, Inc. (R), IL, *99*
Human Resources Management Hawaii, Inc. (C), HI, *384*
E. F. Humay Assoc. (C), PA, *384*
Hunegnaw Executive Search (C), OH, *384*
Hunt & Howe Inc. (R), NY, *99*
The Hunt Co. (R), NY, *99*
The Hunt Group, Inc. (R), NC, *99*
Hunt Ltd. (C), NJ, *385*
Hunt Patton & Brazeal, Inc. (C), OK, *385*
Hunter Assoc. (C), MA, *385*
Hunter Douglas Group, Inc. (R), IL, *99*
The Hunter Group, Inc. (C), MI, *385*
Hunter Int'l., Inc. (R), CT, *100*
Hunter Int'l. LLC (C), MA, *385*
Huntley Associates (Dallas), Inc. (C), TX, *386*
Huntress Real Estate Executive Search (R), MO, *100*
W. Hutt Management Resources Ltd. (R), ON, *100*
Hutton Merrill & Assoc. (R), CA, *100*
HVS Executive Search (R), NY, *100*
The Hyde Group, Inc. (R), CT, *101*
Hyman & Assoc. (C), TX, *386*
The Icard Group, Inc. (C), MI, *387*
IDC Executive Search Inc. (C), FL, *387*
IM Independent Management Recruiters (R), TN, *101*
The IMC Group of Companies (R), NY, *101*
Impact Search & Strategies (C), PA, *387*
Impact Source, Inc. (C), FL, *387*
Independent Power Consultants (C), TX, *387*
Independent Resource Systems (C), CA, *388*
Innovative Healthcare Services, Inc. (C), GA, *389*
Innovative Partnerships (R), CA, *101*
Innovative Resource Group, LLC (C), NC, *389*
The Inside Track (C), TX, *389*
Insight Consulting Co. (C), NY, *389*
Insurance Career Center, Inc. (C), CT, *389*
Insurance People (C), IN, *390*
Insurance Personnel Resources, Inc. (C), GA, *390*
Intech Summit Group, Inc. (R), CA, *102*
Integrated Management Solutions (C), NY, *390*
Integrated Search Solutions Group, LLC (ISSG) (R), NY, *102*
Intelegra, Inc. (C), NJ, *390*
InteliSearch, Inc. (R), CT, *102*
Intelligent Marketing Solutions, Inc. (C), NY, *390*
IntelliSearch (C), TX, *391*
Inter Regional Executive Search, Inc. (IRES, Inc.) (C), NJ, *391*
Interactive Search Network (R), CA, *102*
Intercontinental Executive Group (C), PA, *391*
Interim Financial Solutions - Mid-Atlantic Region (C), MD, *392*
Interim Management Resources Inc. (C), ON, *392*
International Consulting Services, Inc. (C), IL, *392*
International Executive Recruiters (C), OH, *393*
International Management Services Inc. (R), IL, *102*
International Management Advisors, Inc. (R), NY, *103*
International Recruiting Services (C), FL, *393*
Interquest, Inc. (R), NY, *103*
Iona Partners (C), CA, *394*
IR Search (R), CA, *103*
Jeffrey Irving Assoc., Inc. (R), VA, *104*
Isaacson, Miller (R), MA, *104*
Joan Isbister Consultants (C), NY, *394*
ISC of Atlanta, Inc. (C), GA, *394*
ISC of Cincinnati Inc. (C), OH, *394*
ISC of Houston, Inc. (C), TX, *394*
J. B. Linde & Assoc. (C), MO, *395*
The J. B. Search Group (C), CA, *395*
J. Nicholas Arthur (R), MA, *104*
J. R. Scott & Assoc., Ltd. (C), IL, *395*
J.D.G. y Asociados, S.A. de C.V. (R), SO, *104*
Ron Jackson & Assoc. (C), GA, *396*
Jackson Group Int'l. (C), CO, *396*
Jacobson Assoc. (C), IL, *396*
K. Jaeger & Assoc. (C), MA, *396*
JAG Group (R), MO, *105*
Jakobs & Assoc. Int'l. (R), NY, *105*
Pendleton James Assoc., Inc. (R), NY, *105*
R. I. James, Inc. (C), NY, *397*
David James Search (C), CA, *397*
Jaral Consultants, Inc. (C), NJ, *397*
JCL & Assoc. (C), FL, *397*
JDH & Assoc. (C), CA, *397*
Jefferson-Ross Assoc. Inc. (C), PA, *398*
Jeffrey Allan Co., Inc. (C), CA, *398*

JenKim Int'l. Ltd., Inc. (C), FL, *398*
Jerome & Co. (C), CA, *398*
JG Consultants, Inc. (R), TX, *106*
JLI-Boston (R), MA, *106*
JM & Company (R), PA, *106*
JNB Assoc., Inc. (C), MA, *399*
Job Link, Inc. (C), CA, *399*
John Jay & Co. (C), ME, *399*
John Ryan Assoc., LLC. (C), NY, *399*
John H. Johnson & Assoc., Inc. (R), IL, *106*
Johnson & Assoc., Inc. (R), CA, *106*
Johnson & Company (R), CT, *107*
Ronald S. Johnson Assoc., Inc. (R), CA, *107*
Johnson Assoc., Inc. (C), IL, *399*
K. E. Johnson Assoc. (C), WA, *399*
The Johnson Group, Unlimited (C), NY, *400*
Johnson, Kemper & Assoc. (C), TX, *400*
Johnson Smith & Knisely (R), NY, *107*
Jonas, Walters & Assoc., Inc. (R), WI, *107*
The Jonathan Stevens Group, Inc. (R), NJ, *108*
Jones and Jones (R), OR, *108*
Jones Consulting Executive Search (C), GA, *400*
Jordan-Sitter Assoc. (R), TX, *108*
Jordon & Jordon, Inc. (R), PA, *108*
J. M. Joseph Assoc. (R), NJ, *109*
Joseph Chris & Assoc. (C), TX, *400*
Joseph Consulting, Inc. (C), FL, *401*
JPM International (C), CA, *401*
JRL Executive Recruiters (C), MO, *401*
JSG Group Management Consultants (R), ON, *109*
JT Assoc. (C), CT, *401*
Judd Associates (R), NJ, *109*
Just Management Services Inc. (C), FL, *402*
K & C Assoc. (C), CA, *402*
KABL Ability Network (C), CA, *402*
Richard Kader & Assoc. (C), OH, *403*
Robert Kaestner & Assoc. (C), FL, *403*
Kames & Assoc. (C), MD, *403*
Kane & Assoc. (C), TX, *403*
Gary Kaplan & Assoc. (R), CA, *109*
Kaplan & Assoc., Inc. (R), PA, *109*
Karp & Assoc. (C), FL, *403*
Allan Karson Assoc., Inc. (R), NJ, *110*
Martin Kartin & Co., Inc. (R), NY, *110*
Chris Kauffman & Company (R), GA, *110*
Kaufman Assoc. (R), CA, *110*
Jim Kay & Assoc. (C), IL, *404*
The Kay Group of 5th Ave. (C), NY, *404*
Kazan International, Inc. (R), NJ, *110*
Keane Assoc. (R), MA, *110*
A.T. Kearney Executive Search (R), IL, *111*
Thomas A. Kelley & Assoc. (R), CA, *112*
Kelley & Keller, Inc. (C), FL, *405*
S. D. Kelly & Assoc., Inc. (R), MA, *112*
Kennedy & Co. (R), IL, *112*
The Kennett Group, Inc. (R), PA, *112*
William W. Kenney (C), CT, *405*
Kensington Int'l., Inc. (R), IL, *113*
Kent & Assoc. (R), OH, *113*
Kenzer Corp. (R), NY, *113*
Blair Kershaw Assoc., Inc. (C), PA, *405*
Kershner & Co. (R), DC, *113*
Michael L. Ketner & Assoc., Inc. (R), PA, *114*
Key Employment (C), NJ, *405*
Key Resources Int'l. (C), CA, *405*
Keystone Consulting Group (C), GA, *406*
Ki Technologies, Inc. (C), UT, *406*
Kimmel & Associates, Inc. (C), NC, *406*
Kincaid Group Inc. (KGI) (C), TX, *406*
Kinderis & Loercher Group (C), IL, *407*
Kingsbury • Wax • Bova (R), MA, *114*
The Kingsley Group (R), CA, *114*
Kingsley Quinn/USA (R), NJ, *115*
Richard Kinser & Assoc. (R), NY, *115*
Kip Williams, Inc. (R), NY, *115*
Kiradjieff & Goode, Inc. (R), MA, *115*
Kirby Assoc. (R), PA, *115*
Kirkbride Assoc., Inc. (C), WA, *407*
Kittleman & Assoc.,LLC (R), IL, *115*
The Kleinstein Group, Inc. (R), NJ, *116*
Raymond J. Klemmer & Assoc. (R), NY, *116*
The Kleven Group, Inc. - Executive Search Division (R), MA, *116*
The Kleven Group, Inc. (C), MA, *407*
KM Associates (C), MA, *407*
Knapp Consultants (R), CT, *116*
Koehler & Co. (R), WI, *116*
Lee Koehn Assoc., Inc. (R), OR, *116*
T. J. Koellhoffer & Assoc. (R), NJ, *116*
Fred Koffler Assoc. (R), NY, *116*
Koltnow & Company (R), NY, *117*
Koontz, Jeffries & Assoc., Inc. (R), FL, *117*
Kopplin Search, Inc. (R), CA, *117*
Korban Associates (R), PA, *117*
Kordus Consulting Group (C), WI, *408*
Koren, Rogers Assoc. Inc. (R), NY, *117*
Korn/Ferry Int'l. (R), NY, *117*
Kors Montgomery Int'l. (R), TX, *118*
Michael Kosmetos & Assoc., Inc. (C), OH, *408*
Kossuth & Assoc., Inc. (R), WA, *119*
Kostmayer Assoc., Inc. (R), MD, *119*
The J. Kovach Group (R), PA, *119*
KPA Assoc., Inc. (C), NY, *408*
Katherine R. Kraemer (R), CA, *120*
C. R. Krafski & Assoc., Inc. (R), IL, *120*
Krakower Group, Inc. (R), CA, *120*
J. Krauss Assoc. (R), FL, *120*
Krautler Personnel Recruitment (C), FL, *409*
Evie Kreisler Assoc. Inc. (C), CA, *409*
Kremple & Meade, Inc. (R), CA, *120*
Kremple Consulting Group (R), CA, *120*
Kressenberg Assoc. (C), TX, *409*
D. A. Kreuter Assoc., Inc. (R), PA, *121*
Kreutz Consulting Group, Inc. (R), IL, *121*
John Kuhn & Assoc., Inc. (R), WI, *121*
Kuhn Med-Tech (C), CA, *409*
Paul Kull & Co. (R), NJ, *121*
Kulper & Co., L.L.C. (R), NJ, *121*
Kunzer Assoc., Ltd. (R), IL, *121*
John Kurosky & Assoc. (R), CA, *122*
Kutt, Inc. (C), CO, *410*
Kyle Assoc. (C), NY, *410*
L T M Assoc. (C), IL, *410*
L&L Assoc. Global Search (C), PA, *411*
L. Patrick Group (R), NJ, *122*
Marvin Laba & Assoc. (R), CA, *122*
Laboratory Resource Group (C), MA, *411*
LaCosta & Assoc. Int'l. Inc. (C), CA, *411*
Rene LaFlamme & Associes (R), QE, *122*
Lamay Assoc., Inc. (R), CT, *124*
The Landstone Group (C), NY, *412*
Lange & Assoc., Inc. (C), IN, *412*
The Langford Search, Inc. (C), AL, *412*
Langley & Associates, Inc. (Executive Search Consultants) (R), CO, *124*
Lanken-Kimball-Therrell & Assoc. (C), GA, *412*
Lawrence L. Lapham, Inc. (R), NY, *124*
Stephen Laramee & Assoc. Inc. (C), ON, *413*
Larkin & Co. (R), CA, *124*
R. H. Larsen & Assoc., Inc. (R), FL, *125*
Larsen Int'l., Inc. (R), TX, *125*
Larsen, Whitney, Blecksmith & Zilliacus, Inc. (R), CA, *125*
Larson Assoc. (R), CA, *125*
Lascelle & Assoc. Inc. (C), ON, *413*
Lasher Assoc. (R), FL, *125*
Michael Latas & Assoc., Inc. (R), MO, *125*
Latham International, Ltd. (R), NJ, *126*
Lauer, Sbarbaro Assoc., EMA Partners Int'l. (R), IL, *126*
Lautz, Grotte, Engler & Swimley (R), CA, *126*
Madeleine Lav & Assoc. (C), CA, *413*
Lawrence James Assoc. of Florida, Inc. (C), FL, *414*
Lawrence-Balakonis & Assoc., Inc. (C), GA, *414*
Lawrence-Leiter & Co. (R), KS, *126*
W. R. Lawry, Inc. (R), CT, *126*
The Lawson Group, Inc. (C), SC, *414*
Layne-Mendez & Co. (R), TX, *127*
Leader Institute, Inc. (C), GA, *414*
Leader Network (C), PA, *414*
Leader Resources Group (C), GA, *415*
Leader Search Inc. (R), AB, *127*
Leaders-Trust Int'l./Carce y Asociados, S.C. (R), MX, *127*
The Lear Group, Inc. (R), OH, *127*
Lechner & Assoc., Inc. (C), FL, *415*
Ledbetter/Davidson Int'l., Inc. (R), NY, *127*
Albert G. Lee Assoc. (C), RI, *415*
The Conrad Lee Co. Inc. (R), FL, *127*
Lee Management Group Inc. (C), NJ, *416*
Leeds and Leeds (C), TN, *416*
Legal Network Inc. (C), CA, *416*
V. J. Lehman & Assoc., Inc. (R), CO, *127*
Leith & Assoc., Inc. (C), OH, *416*
Lekan & Assoc., Inc. (R), OH, *128*
Lemming/LeVan, Inc. (R), GA, *128*
Lending Personnel Services (C), CA, *416*
F. P. Lennon Assoc. (C), PA, *416*
AG Lennox & Assoc. (R), AB, *128*
Jacques LePage Executive Search Inc. (R), QE, *128*
Leslie Kavanagh Assoc., Inc. (C), NY, *416*
J. E. Lessner Assoc., Inc. (R), MI, *128*
Levin & Company, Inc. (R), MA, *128*
Alan Levine Assoc. (R), MA, *129*
Michael Levine Search Consultants (R), NY, *129*
Lewis & Blank Int'l. (R), CA, *129*
Lewis Companies Inc. (R), ON, *129*
The Libra Group Inc. (C), CT, *417*

The Libra Group (C), NC, *417*
Pat Licata & Assoc. (C), NC, *417*
LifeWork, Inc. (C), TX, *418*
Lois L. Lindauer Searches (C), MA, *418*
J. H. Lindell & Co. (C), CA, *418*
Linden Group, Inc. (C), NC, *418*
Lipsky Group, Inc. (R), CA, *129*
Lipson & Co. (R), CA, *130*
Lipton Assoc., Inc. (R), NY, *130*
Livingston, Robert & Co. (R), CT, *130*
Lloyd Associates (R), GA, *130*
Lloyd Prescott & Churchill, Inc. (R), FL, *130*
Lloyd Prescott Assoc., Inc. (C), FL, *418*
Locke & Assoc. (R), NC, *131*
Locus Inc. (C), WV, *419*
Loderman & Costello (C), GA, *419*
Loewenstein & Assoc., Inc. (R), TX, *131*
The Logan Group, Inc. (R), MO, *131*
Logic Assoc., Inc. (C), NY, *419*
Logue & Rice Inc. (C), VA, *420*
Longo Associates (C), CA, *420*
Longshore + Simmons (R), PA, *131*
Lord & Albus Co. (C), TX, *420*
Scott Love Assoc., Inc. (C), AZ, *420*
Bruce Lowery & Assoc. (C), MI, *420*
Lucas Assoc. (C), GA, *421*
Lucas Group (C), NY, *421*
The John Lucht Consultancy Inc. (R), NY, *131*
Ludwig & Assoc., Inc. (C), VA, *421*
Charles Luntz & Assoc., Inc. (R), MO, *132*
Lybrook Assoc., Inc. (C), RI, *421*
P. J. Lynch Assoc. (R), CT, *132*
Lynch Miller Moore Partners, Inc. (R), IL, *132*
Lynne Palmer Executive Recruitment, Inc. (C), NY, *421*
Lyons & Assoc., Inc. (C), IL, *422*
Lyons Pruitt Int'l. (R), PA, *132*
M. K. & Assoc. (C), PA, *422*
M/J/A Partners (R), IL, *133*
The Mackenzie Group (R), MD, *133*
MacNaughton Assoc. (R), CA, *133*
Maczkov-Biosciences, Inc. (R), CA, *133*
Carol Maden Group (C), VA, *422*
Madison Executive Search, Inc. (C), NJ, *422*
The Madison Group (R), NY, *133*
Magellan Int'l., L.P. (C), TX, *422*
Maglio & Co., Inc. (R), WI, *134*
Maiorino & Weston Assoc., Inc. (R), CT, *134*
Major Search (C), NJ, *423*
Managed Care Consultants (C), AZ, *423*
Managed Care Resources (C), TX, *424*
Management & Human Resources (R), MA, *134*
Management Alliance Group, Inc. (R), NJ, *134*
Management Assoc. (C), MD, *424*
Management Dimensions Ltd. (R), ON, *134*
Management One Consultants (C), ON, *425*
Management Recruiters of Nassau, Inc. (R), NY, *134*
Management Recruiters of Birmingham-South, Inc. (C), AL, *438*
Management Recruiters of Birmingham (C), AL, *438*
Management Recruiters of Sedona (C), AZ, *438*
Management Recruiters of Decatur, LLC (C), AL, *438*
Management Recruiters of San Luis Obispo (C), CA, *439*
Management Recruiters Tucson-Foothills, Inc. (C), AZ, *439*
Management Recruiters of Aptos (C), CA, *439*
Management Recruiters Peninsula (C), CA, *439*
Management Recruiters of Berkeley (C), CA, *439*
Management Recruiters of Clovis (C), CA, *440*
Management Recruiters of Emeryville (C), CA, *440*
Management Recruiters of Northern California (C), CA, *440*
Management Recruiters of Laguna Hills (C), CA, *440*
Management Recruiters Dana Point (C), CA, *440*
Management Recruiters, Inland Empire Agency (C), CA, *441*
Management Recruiters of Roseville (C), CA, *441*
Management Recruiters of Sonoma (C), CA, *441*
Management Recruiters Inc. of Silicon Valley (C), CA, *441*
Management Recruiters of Winsted, Inc. (C), CT, *442*
Management Recruiters of Franktown (C), CO, *442*
Management Recruiters of Middlesex (C), CT, *442*
Management Recruiters of Altamonte (C), FL, *442*
Management Recruiters of Milford Inc. (C), CT, *442*
Management Recruiters of Ft. Myers, FL. (C), FL, *443*
Management Recruiters of Bonita Springs, Inc. (C), FL, *443*
Management Recruiters of Boca Raton (C), FL, *443*
Management Recruiters of Miami-North (C), FL, *443*
Management Recruiters, Inc. (C), FL, *443*
Management Recruiters of St. Lucie County, Inc. (C), FL, *444*
Management Recruiters of Lake Co., Inc. (C), FL, *444*
Management Recruiters of Tampa North (C), FL, *444*
Management Recruiters of Northern Palm Beaches (C), FL, *444*
Management Recruiters of St. Augustine (C), FL, *444*
Management Recruiters of Duluth (C), GA, *445*
Management Recruiters of Atlanta West, Inc. (C), GA, *445*
Management Recruiters of Atlanta (C), GA, *445*
Management Recruiters of Vero Beach (C), FL, *445*
Management Recruiters of Atlanta North, Inc. (C), GA, *446*
Management Recruiters of Savannah (C), GA, *446*
Management Recruiters of Sandy Springs (C), GA, *446*
Management Recruiters of Atlanta NE (C), GA, *446*
Management Recruiters of Marietta, Inc. (C), GA, *446*
Management Recruiters - Towne Lake (C), GA, *446*
Management Recruiters of Lake Forest, IL (C), IL, *447*
Management Recruiters of Springfield, Inc. (C), IL, *447*
Management Recruiters of Barrington (C), IL, *447*
Management Recruiters of Sun Valley (C), ID, *447*
Management Recruiters of Batavia (C), IL, *447*
Management Recruiters of Indianapolis (C), IN, *448*
Management Recruiters of Indianapolis-North (C), IN, *448*
Management Recruiters-Cedar Rapids, Inc. (C), IA, *448*
Management Recruiters - Indianapolis (C), IN, *448*
Management Recruiters of Des Moines (C), IA, *449*
Management Recruiters of Fairfield (C), IA, *449*
Management Recruiters of Williamsburg (C), IA, *449*
Management Recruiters of Rockville (C), MD, *450*
Management Recruiters of Frederick, Inc. (C), MD, *450*
Management Recruiters of the Baltimore Washington Corridor (C), MD, *450*
Management Recruiters of Muskegon (C), MI, *451*
Management Recruiters of Birmingham (C), MI, *451*
Management Recruiters of Detroit & Farmington Hills (C), MI, *451*
Management Recruiters of Dearborn, Inc. (C), MI, *451*
Management Recruiters of Winona (C), MN, *452*
Management Recruiters of Woodbury (C), MN, *452*
Management Recruiters of Cass County, NE (C), NE, *452*
Management Recruiters of Rankin Co. (C), MS, *452*
Management Recruiters of Lake Tahoe, NV (C), NV, *453*
Management Recruiters of Medford, N.J. (C), NJ, *453*
Management Recruiters of Orange County, N.Y., Inc. (C), NJ, *453*
Management Recruiters of North Warren Inc. (C), NJ, *453*

Management Recruiters of Princeton (C), NJ, *454*
Management Recruiters of Upper Westchester (C), NY, *454*
Management Recruiters of New Providence (C), NJ, *454*
Management Recruiters of Bordentown (C), NJ, *454*
Management Recruiters of Great Neck (C), NY, *454*
Management Recruiters of Broome County, Inc. (C), NY, *454*
Management Recruiters of Manhattan on Broadway (C), NY, *455*
Management Recruiters of Rocky Mount - Southwest (C), NC, *456*
Management Recruiters of Mt. Airy (C), NC, *456*
Management Recruiters of Kinston (C), NC, *456*
Management Recruiters of Wilmington (C), NC, *457*
Management Recruiters of Winston-Salem (C), NC, *457*
Management Recruiters of Akron (C), OH, *457*
Management Recruiters of Columbus (C), OH, *457*
Management Recruiters of Cleveland (C), OH, *457*
Management Recruiters of Oklahoma City (C), OK, *458*
Management Recruiters of Easton, PA (C), PA, *458*
Management Recruiters of Sidney (C), OH, *458*
Management Recruiters of Mentor, Inc. (C), OH, *458*
Management Recruiters of Cherry Hill (C), PA, *459*
Management Recruiters of Lionville, Inc. (C), PA, *459*
Management Recruiters of Valley Forge (C), PA, *459*
Management Recruiters of Delaware County (C), PA, *459*
Management Recruiters of Greenville (C), SC, *460*
Management Recruiters of Aiken (C), SC, *460*
Management Recruiters The Delta Group, Inc. (C), TN, *461*
Management Recruiters of Sioux Falls, LLP (C), SD, *461*
Management Recruiters of Georgetown (C), SC, *461*
Management Recruiters of Franklin, Inc. (C), TN, *461*
Management Recruiters of Columbia, Tennessee (C), TN, *461*
Management Recruiters Dallas North (MRDN) (C), TX, *462*
Management Recruiters of Houston (C), TX, *462*
Management Recruiters of Champions (C), TX, *462*
Management Recruiters of Arlington (C), TX, *462*
Management Recruiters - Friendswood (C), TX, *462*
Management Recruiters of Houston-Northeast (C), TX, *463*
Management Recruiters of San Antonio (C), TX, *463*
Management Recruiters of San Antonio - North (C), TX, *463*
Management Recruiters of Round Rock (C), TX, *463*
Management Recruiters of Ogden (C), UT, *464*
Management Recruiters Int'l.-The Woodlands (C), TX, *464*
Management Recruiters of Sugar Land Inc. (C), TX, *464*
Management Recruiters of Milwaukee-West (C), WI, *465*
Management Recruiters of Kanawha Valley, LLC (C), WV, *465*
Management Recruiters of Seattle (C), WA, *465*
Management Recruiters of Spokane (C), WA, *465*
Management Recruiters of Roanoke (C), VA, *465*
Management Recruiters of Lynnwood (C), WA, *465*
Management Recruiters of Appleton (C), WI, *465*
Management Recruiters of Milwaukee-North (C), WI, *466*
Management Recruiters of Stevens Point, Inc. (C), WI, *466*
Management Recruiters of Janesville, Inc. (C), WI, *466*
Management Recruiters of Milwaukee - Downtown (C), WI, *466*
Management Resource Assoc., Inc. (C), FL, *467*
Management Resource Group, Ltd. (C), IA, *467*
Management Resource Group (C), MN, *467*
Management Resources (C), TX, *467*
Management Search Assoc., Inc. (C), GA, *467*
Management Search, Inc. (C), IL, *467*
Management Search, Inc. (C), OK, *468*
Management Search of R.I. Inc. (R), RI, *135*
Mannard & Assoc., Inc. (R), IL, *135*
F. L. Mannix & Co. (R), MA, *135*
Manuso, Alexander & Associates, Inc. (R), NY, *135*
The Marathon Group (C), FL, *469*
MARBL Consultants, Inc. (C), WI, *469*
Marc-Allen Assoc., Inc. (C), FL, *469*
Margolin Consultants, Inc. (C), NY, *469*
J. L. Mark Assoc., Inc. (R), CO, *135*
Mark Christian & Assoc., Inc. (C), AZ, *469*
Mark Stanley & Co./EMA Partners International (R), FL, *136*
Markent Personnel, Inc. (C), WI, *470*
Marketing & Sales Resources, Inc. (C), FL, *470*
Marketing Resources (C), MA, *470*
Paula Marks Inc. (R), NY, *136*
Brad Marks Int'l. (R), CA, *136*
The Marlow Group (R), MA, *136*
The Maroon Group (R), CT, *136*
Marra Peters & Partners (R), NJ, *136*
Marshall-Alan Assoc., Inc. (C), NY, *471*
Marsteller Wilcox Assoc. (C), IL, *471*
Donovan Martin & Assoc. (R), CA, *137*
J. Martin & Assoc. (R), CA, *137*
George R. Martin (R), PA, *137*
The Martin Group (R), CA, *137*
Martin Partners, L.L.C. (R), IL, *137*
Marvel Consultants, Inc. (C), OH, *472*
Massey-Horton Int'l. (R), ON, *138*
Louis Thomas Masterson & Co. (R), OH, *138*
Richard L. Mather & Assoc. (C), CT, *472*
Mathey Services (C), IL, *472*
Matrix Consultants, Inc. (C), NC, *472*
Matté & Company, Inc. (R), CT, *138*
Matte Consulting Group Inc. (R), QE, *138*
The Matthews Group, Inc. (C), NJ, *472*
G. P. Mattocks & Associates (C), NC, *473*
Maxecon Executive Search Consultants (R), FL, *138*
K. Maxin & Assoc. (R), PA, *139*
Mary L. Mayer, Ltd. (R), MN, *139*
The Mayes Group, Ltd. (R), PA, *139*
Mayhall Search Group, Inc. (C), IN, *473*
The Mazzitelli Group, Ltd. (R), MN, *139*
MB Inc. Executive Search (C), NY, *473*
McBride Assoc., Inc. (R), DC, *139*
Tom McCall Executive Search (C), IL, *473*
McCann, Choi & Associates, LLC (R), NY, *139*
K. E. McCarthy & Assoc. (R), CA, *139*
McCarthy Assoc. National BancSearch, LLC (C), LA, *473*
McCooe & Assoc., Inc. (R), NJ, *140*
McCormack & Assoc. (R), CA, *140*
McCormack & Farrow (R), CA, *140*
McCoy Ltd. (C), CA, *474*
McCray, Shriver, Eckdahl & Assoc., Inc. (R), CA, *140*
The Paul McDaniel Co. (C), TN, *474*
McDonald Assoc. Int'l. (R), IL, *140*
Clarence E. McFeely, Inc. (R), IL, *141*
Robert E. McGrath & Assoc. (R), CT, *141*
McGrath & Assoc., Inc. (R), NJ, *141*
McHale & Assoc. (R), WA, *141*
McIntyre Assoc. (R), CT, *141*
McIntyre Management Resources (C), ON, *474*
McKeen & Company (R), TX, *141*
McKinley•Arend Int'l. (R), TX, *141*
The McKinnon Management Group Inc. (C), ON, *475*
Dan P. McLean Assoc., Inc. (C), ON, *475*
McManners Assoc., Inc. (R), CA, *142*
McNichol Assoc. (R), PA, *142*
Jon McRae & Associates, Inc. (R), GA, *142*
MCS Assoc. (R), CA, *142*
Joseph J. McTaggart (C), CA, *476*
James Mead & Co. (R), CT, *142*
Med Exec Int'l. (C), CA, *476*
Meder & Assoc., Inc. (R), IL, *142*
Media Management Resources, Inc. (R), CO, *142*
Media Recruiting Group, Inc. (C), NY, *476*
MediaCOM Talent Group (C), MA, *476*

Medical Executive Search Assoc., Inc. (C), AZ, *477*
Medical Recruiters Inc. (C), MO, *477*
The Medley Group (C), CA, *477*
MedSearch Resources, Inc. (C), FL, *478*
MedXec USA, Inc. (C), FL, *478*
Mee Derby & Co. (C), DC, *478*
Melancon & Co. (R), TX, *143*
Juan Menefee & Assoc. (C), IL, *478*
Meng, Finseth & Assoc., Inc. (R), CA, *143*
Mengel & McDonald Ltd. (C), IL, *479*
Mercedes & Co., Inc. (R), MA, *143*
The Mercer Group, Inc. (R), NM, *143*
J. M. Meredith & Assoc. Inc. (C), CA, *479*
Merit Professional Search, Inc. (C), TN, *479*
MES Search Co. (C), GA, *479*
MESA, Inc. (R), CO, *143*
MESA International (C), CA, *480*
Messett Assoc., Inc. (R), FL, *143*
META/MAT, Ltd. (R), NJ, *144*
MetroVantage Personnel Systems (C), CA, *480*
Walter Meyer & Assoc. (R), NY, *144*
Meyer Assoc., Inc. (R), GA, *144*
mfg/Search, Inc. (C), IN, *480*
Michael Assoc. (R), IL, *144*
Michael James & Co. (C), IL, *480*
Michael Wayne Recruiters (C), IL, *480*
Michaels & Moere (C), WI, *481*
Lou Michaels Assoc., Inc. (C), MI, *481*
Michigan Consulting Group (R), MI, *144*
Micro Staff Solutions, Inc. (C), TX, *481*
Midland Consultants (C), OH, *481*
Millennium Search Group, Inc. (R), CA, *144*
Miller + Miller (C), WA, *482*
Milo Research (R), NY, *145*
Herbert Mines Assoc., Inc. (R), NY, *145*
Mirtz Morice, Inc. (R), CT, *145*
MIXTEC Group (R), CA, *145*
MJF Assoc. (C), CT, *483*
MK & Assoc. (R), CA, *146*
Moffitt Int'l., Inc. (R), NC, *146*
Diedre Moire Corp., Inc. (C), NJ, *483*
Molecular Solutions, Inc. (C), SC, *483*
Molloy Partners (R), NY, *146*
Oscar Montaño, Inc. (R), CA, *146*
Montenido Assoc. (R), CA, *146*
The Montgomery Group, Inc. (C), TN, *484*
Montgomery West (R), CA, *146*
Montgomery, Thomason & Assoc. (C), ON, *484*
C. A. Moore & Assoc., Inc. (C), MN, *484*
Moore Research Assoc. (R), NJ, *147*
Tina Morbitzer & Assoc. (C), FL, *485*
Morgan Int'l., Inc. (R), IL, *147*
Morgan Samuels Co. (R), CA, *147*
The Morgan/Geoffries Group (C), CA, *485*
Morgan/Webber, Inc. (R), NY, *147*
Morgenstern Int'l., Inc. (C), FL, *485*
Morris & Berger (R), CA, *147*
Mortgage Search Network (C), AZ, *486*
Morton, McCorkle & Assoc. Inc. (R), MO, *147*
MRI, The Sequel Group, LLC (C), CO, *486*
Mruk & E.M.A. Partners (R), NY, *148*
MTA Partners (R), TX, *148*
Mullen Assoc., Inc. (R), NC, *148*
Pamela L. Mulligan, Inc. (R), NH, *149*
The Mulshine Co., Inc. (R), NJ, *149*
The Mulshine Company, Ltd. (R), NY, *149*
Multi Processing, Inc. (R), NH, *149*
Multisearch Recruiters (C), CA, *487*
R. F. Mulvaney & Assoc., Inc. (R), MO, *149*
Jennifer Munro & Partners, Inc. (R), SC, *149*
Munroe, Curry & Bond Assoc. (R), NJ, *149*
P. J. Murphy & Assoc., Inc. (R), WI, *150*
Kenneth Murphy & Assoc. (C), NS, *487*
The Murray Group (C), IL, *487*
Musick & Assoc. (C), CA, *487*
Mycoff & Assoc. (R), CO, *150*
Myers Career Assoc., Inc. (C), CA, *488*
DDJ Myers, Ltd. (R), AZ, *150*
N.A.P. Executive Services (Canada) Inc. (C), ON, *488*
Nachman Biomedical (C), MA, *488*
Nadzam, Lusk, Horgan & Assoc., Inc. (R), CA, *150*
Nason & Nason (C), FL, *488*
NaTek Corp. (C), NY, *488*
National Affirmative Action Career Network, Inc. (C), CO, *488*
National Bank & Finance Executive Search (C), CA, *488*
National Career Search (C), AZ, *489*
National Computerized Employment Service, Inc. (C), PA, *489*
National Corporate Consultants, Inc. (C), IN, *489*
National Metal Services Corp. (C), IN, *489*
National Recruiters (C), OK, *489*
National Recruiting Service (C), IN, *489*
National Search, Inc. (R), NC, *150*
Nationwide Personnel Recruiting & Consulting, Inc. (C), OR, *490*
Nationwide Personnel Placement, Inc. (C), OH, *490*
NaviSearch (C), GA, *490*
NCC Executive Search Consultants (C), CA, *490*
The Neil Michael Group, Inc./Global Partners (R), NY, *151*
J. Fielding Nelson & Assoc., Inc. (R), UT, *151*
Networking Unlimited of NH, Inc. (C), NH, *491*
New Dawn Employment Search (C), CA, *491*
New Dimensions in Technology, Inc. (C), MA, *492*
New Directions, Inc. (C), IL, *492*
New Venture Development, Inc. (C), CA, *492*
New World Healthcare Solutions, Inc. (R), NY, *151*
Newcomb-Desmond & Assoc., Inc. (C), OH, *492*
Newell Assoc. (R), NY, *151*
Newport Strategic Search LLC (C), CA, *492*
NHA Plastics Recruiters (C), FL, *493*
Nicholaou & Co. (R), IL, *151*
Nichols & Company (R), CO, *151*
P. J. Nicholson & Assoc. (C), IL, *493*
The Niemond Corp. (R), CA, *152*
Nino Recruiting & Staffing, Inc. (C), TX, *493*
Ira Z. Nitzberg (C), NY, *493*
J. L. Nixon Consulting (C), TX, *493*
NMC & Kay Int'l. (R), CO, *152*
Noble & Assoc., Inc. (C), NY, *494*
The Noebel Search Group, Inc. (C), TX, *494*
The Nolan Group (C), CA, *494*
W. D. Nolte & Company (R), CT, *152*
Nordeman Grimm, Inc. (R), NY, *152*
Paul Winston Norman & Assoc. (R), IL, *152*
Norman Broadbent Int'l., Inc. (R), NY, *152*
The Normyle/Erstling Health Search Group (C), NJ, *494*
John B. Norris & Assoc., Inc. (C), MD, *495*
Ronald Norris & Assoc. (C), IL, *495*
Norris Agency (C), TX, *495*
NorTech Resources (C), NY, *496*
North American Recruiters, Inc. (R), MN, *153*
The North Peak Group (C), OH, *496*
Northern Consultants Inc. (R), ME, *153*
Norton & Assoc. (C), IL, *496*
NPS of Atlanta, Inc. (C), GA, *496*
NRI Staffing Resources (C), DC, *496*
Nuessle, Kurdziel & Weiss, Inc. (R), PA, *153*
Nyborg•Dow Assoc., Inc. (C), CA, *497*
NYCOR Search, Inc. (C), MN, *497*
O'Brien & Bell (R), OH, *153*
O'Brien and Roof (C), OH, *497*
O'Brien Consulting Services (R), MA, *153*
O'Callaghan Honey/Ray & Berndtson Inc. (R), AB, *153*
O'Connor, O'Connor, Lordi, Ltd. (R), PA, *154*
O'Connor Resources (C), TX, *497*
O'Keefe & Assoc., Inc. (R), CT, *154*
O'Neill Group (C), NJ, *498*
O'Rourke Companies, Inc. (R), TX, *154*
O'Shea, Divine & Co., Inc. (R), CA, *154*
O'Sullivan Search Inc. (C), ON, *498*
Dennis P. O'Toole & Assoc. Inc. (R), NY, *154*
O'Toole & Company, Inc. (R), IL, *154*
Oak Assoc. (R), CA, *155*
Ober & Company (R), CA, *155*
Oberlander & Co., Inc. (R), IL, *155*
The Odessa Group (R), CA, *155*
The Ogdon Partnership (R), NY, *155*
The Oldani Group (R), WA, *155*
Oliver & Rozner Assoc., Inc. (R), NY, *155*
Ollinger Partners (R), MA, *156*
Olsen/Clark (R), WA, *156*
Omega Systems, LLC (C), VA, *498*
The Onstott Group (R), MA, *156*
Open Concepts (C), CA, *499*
Opportunity Resources, Inc. (R), NY, *156*
Organization Consulting Ltd. (R), ON, *157*
Organization Resources Inc. (R), MA, *157*
Ortman Recruiting Int'l. (C), CA, *500*
Ott & Hansen, Inc. (R), CA, *157*
Robert Ottke Assoc. (R), CA, *157*
Overton Consulting (R), WI, *157*
LaMonte Owens, Inc. (R), PA, *157*
The Oxford Group (C), TX, *500*
The P & L Group (C), NY, *500*

P R Management Consultants, Inc. (C), NJ, *500*
P.A.R. Assoc., Inc. (R), MA, *158*
P.R.H. Management, Inc. (R), CT, *158*
Pacific Advisory Service, Inc. (C), IL, *501*
Pacific Coast Recruiting (C), CA, *501*
Pacific Coast Recruiters (C), OR, *501*
Pacific Crossing (C), CA, *501*
Pacific Search Group, Inc. (C), CA, *501*
Packaging Personnel Co., Ltd. (C), WI, *501*
Page-Wheatcroft & Co., Ltd. (R), TX, *158*
Paladin Group, Inc. (C), CO, *502*
Kirk Palmer & Assoc., Inc. (R), NY, *158*
Pamenter, Pamenter, Brezer & Deganis Ltd. (R), ON, *159*
Paper Industry Recruitment (P.I.R.) (C), ME, *502*
The PAR Group - Paul A. Reaume, Ltd. (R), IL, *159*
Parenica & Co. (R), NC, *159*
Jim Parham & Assoc., Inc. (R), FL, *159*
Frank Parillo & Assoc. (R), CA, *159*
The Park Group & Assoc., Inc. (C), MD, *502*
D. P. Parker & Assoc., Inc. (R), MA, *159*
Parker, McFadden & Assoc. (C), GA, *503*
Parker Page Group (C), FL, *503*
Michael W. Parres & Assoc. (R), MI, *159*
Parsons Assoc. Inc. (R), IL, *159*
Partners Executive Search Consultants Inc. (R), ON, *160*
Partners In Human Resources Int'l., Inc. (R), NY, *160*
Partners in Recruiting (C), IL, *503*
Partners Resource Group (C), VA, *504*
The Partnership Group (R), NJ, *160*
Partnervision Consulting Group Inc. (R), ON, *160*
Partridge Assoc., Inc. (R), MA, *160*
Carolyn Smith Paschal Int'l. (R), CA, *160*
Pasona Canada, Inc. (C), ON, *504*
Pathfinders (C), CA, *504*
Pathway Executive Search, Inc. (C), NY, *505*
Pathways Int'l. (C), CT, *505*
The Patience Motivation Belief Group, Inc. (C), GA, *505*
Patrice & Assoc. (C), MD, *505*
Joel H. Paul & Assoc., Inc. (C), NY, *505*
Paules Associates (C), CA, *505*
Pawlik/Dorman Partners (R), IL, *161*
PC Assoc. (C), CO, *505*
PCD Partners (R), PA, *161*
Peachtree Executive Search (R), GA, *161*
Peak Search Assoc. (C), ON, *506*
Pearce & Assoc. (C), FL, *506*
Pearson & Assoc., Inc. (C), AZ, *506*
Pearson, Caldwell & Farnsworth (R), CA, *161*
Peck & Assoc., Ltd. (R), WI, *161*
Peeney Assoc., Inc. (R), NJ, *161*
Paul S. Pelland, P.C. (R), SC, *161*
M. A. Pelle Assoc., Inc. (C), NY, *506*
The Penn Partners, Inc. (R), PA, *162*
The Pennmor Group (C), NJ, *506*
People Management Mid-South, LLC (R), TN, *162*
People Management Northeast, Inc. (R), CT, *162*
PERC, Ltd. (C), AZ, *506*
Performance Resources, Inc. (C), RI, *507*
PERI Corp/Professional Executive Recruiters, Inc. (C), TX, *507*
The Perkins Group (R), NC, *162*
Perry • Newton Assoc. (C), MD, *507*
Fred Perry Assoc. (C), TX, *507*
Perry-Martel Int'l., Inc. (R), ON, *163*
Barry Persky & Co., Inc. (R), CT, *163*
PersoNet, Inc. (C), FL, *507*
Personnel Assoc. (C), NC, *508*
The Personnel Group, Inc. (R), MN, *163*
Personnel, Inc. (C), AL, *508*
Personnel Management Group (C), MB, *508*
The Personnel Network, Inc. (C), SC, *508*
Personnel Tangent Inc. (C), QE, *509*
Personnel Unlimited/Executive Search (C), WA, *509*
J. R. Peterman Assoc., Inc. (C), VT, *509*
Alec Peters Assoc. Inc./DLR (R), GA, *163*
Richard Peterson & Assoc., Inc. (R), GA, *163*
Petrie Partners, Inc. (R), FL, *163*
Petro Staff Int'l. (C), AB, *509*
Petruzzi Assoc. (C), NJ, *509*
Peyser Assoc., Inc. (R), FL, *163*
Pharmaceutical Recruiters, Inc. (R), NY, *163*
Pharmaceutical Search Professionals, Inc. (C), PA, *510*
Phase II Management (R), CT, *164*
J. R. Phillip & Assoc., Inc. (R), CA, *164*
Phillips & Assoc. (R), MA, *164*
Phillips Int'l., Inc. (C), SC, *510*
Phillips Personnel/Search (C), CO, *510*
Phillips Resource Group (C), SC, *510*
Phoenix Partners, Inc. (C), GA, *511*
Phoenix Search (R), MX, *164*
Physician Executive Management Center (R), FL, *164*
Physicians Search®, Inc. (C), CA, *511*
PIC Executive Search (C), GA, *511*
Pierce & Assoc. (C), CA, *512*
Pierce & Crow (R), CA, *164*
Pinnacle Executive Group Inc. (C), MO, *512*
Pinsker and Company, Inc. (R), CA, *164*
Pioneer Consulting Group (C), CA, *512*
Pioneer Executive Consultants (C), ON, *512*
DNPitchon Assoc. (R), NJ, *165*
Plemmons Assoc., Inc. (R), GA, *165*
Rene Plessner Assoc., Inc. (R), NY, *165*
R. L. Plimpton Assoc., Inc. (R), CO, *165*
Yves Plouffe & Assoc. (R), QE, *165*
Plummer & Assoc., Inc. (R), CT, *166*
PMJ & Assoc. (C), ON, *513*
Poirier, Hoevel & Co. (R), CA, *166*
The Polen Group (C), PA, *514*
Ray Polhill & Assoc. (R), NC, *166*
Bob Poline Assoc. Inc. (C), CA, *514*
Polson & Co., Inc. (R), MN, *166*
Al Ponaman Company, Inc. (C), CA, *514*
Don V. Poole & Assoc., Inc. (C), CO, *514*
Porter & Assoc., Inc. (C), FL, *514*
David Powell, Inc. (R), CA, *166*
Power Recruiting Group (C), TX, *515*
Robert Powers & Assoc. (C), CA, *515*
Powers Consultants, Inc. (R), MO, *166*
P. G. Prager Search Assoc., Ltd. (C), NY, *515*
Prairie Resource Group, Inc. (R), IL, *166*
Elan Pratzer & Partners Inc. (R), ON, *167*
PRAXIS Partners (R), VA, *167*
Precision Executive Search (C), AZ, *516*
Predictor Systems Corp. (R), CA, *167*
Preferred Placement, Inc. (C), NY, *516*
Preferred Professional Recruiters (C), TX, *516*
George Preger & Associates Inc. (R), ON, *167*
Premier Recruiting Group (C), MI, *516*
Premier Search Group (C), IN, *517*
Preng & Assoc., Inc. (R), TX, *167*
Presley Consultants, Inc. (C), CA, *517*
Preston & Co. (R), NJ, *167*
Preston-Hunter, Inc. (R), IL, *167*
Prestonwood Assoc. (R), MA, *168*
Price & Assoc., Inc. (C), VA, *518*
Alan J. Price Assoc., Inc. (C), RI, *518*
PricewaterhouseCoopers Executive Search (R), ON, *168*
PricewaterhouseCoopers Executive Search (R), MX, *168*
Prichard Kymen Inc. (R), AB, *168*
The Primary Group, Inc. (R), FL, *168*
Prime Management Group Inc. (C), ON, *518*
Prime Search (C), NC, *518*
Primus Assoc., L.C. (R), TX, *169*
Princeton Search Partners, Inc. (R), NJ, *169*
Prior/Martech Assoc., Inc. (R), WA, *169*
Priority Executive Search (C), FL, *518*
PRO, Inc./Professional Recruiting Offices, Inc. (C), CA, *519*
Pro Tec Technical Services (C), ON, *519*
Probe Technology (C), PA, *519*
Procurement Resources (C), MD, *520*
Professional Engineering Technical Personnel Consultants (C), NC, *520*
Professional Personnel Services (C), IA, *520*
Professional Personnel Consultants, Inc. (C), MI, *521*
Professional Persons Career Services (C), NY, *521*
Professional Recruiters, Inc. (C), PA, *521*
Professional Recruiters (C), UT, *521*
Professional Recruiting Consultants, Inc. (C), DE, *521*
Professional Resources (C), NY, *522*
The Professional Sales Search Co., Inc. (C), WA, *522*
Professional Search Assoc. (C), CA, *522*
Professional Selection Services (R), GA, *169*
Professional Support Inc. (C), NY, *523*
Professional Team Search, Inc. (R), AZ, *169*
Professionals in Recruiting Co. (C), TN, *523*
Professions, Inc. (C), OH, *523*
ProFinders, Inc. (C), FL, *523*
Profit Pros, Inc. (C), CA, *523*
Proquest Inc. (C), SC, *524*
ProSearch Recruiting (C), CA, *524*
ProSearch, Inc. (C), OH, *524*

Protocol Inc. (C), CA, *525*
Proven Edge (C), CA, *525*
PSD Group, Inc. (C), CA, *525*
PSP Agency (C), NY, *525*
QD Legal (C), ON, *525*
Quality Control Recruiters (C), CT, *526*
The Quantum Group (C), NJ, *526*
Quantum Int'l., Ltd. (R), FL, *170*
Quest Worldwide Executive Search Corp. (C), CA, *527*
QuestPro, Inc. (C), TX, *527*
Quetico Corp. (R), TX, *170*
L. J. Quinn & Assoc., Inc. (R), CA, *170*
Quiring Assoc., Inc. (C), IN, *527*
QVS Int'l. (R), GA, *170*
R & L Assoc., Ltd. (R), NY, *170*
R M Associates (R), OH, *171*
R. C. Services (C), TX, *528*
R. J. Associates (C), NY, *528*
R/K International Inc. (R), CT, *171*
R2 Services, LLC (C), IL, *528*
Raines Int'l. Inc. (R), NY, *171*
Ramm Search (C), NY, *528*
Ramming & Assoc., Inc. (C), NJ, *528*
Rand Assoc. (R), ME, *171*
Rand Thompson Executive Search Consultants (C), NY, *528*
Rand-Curtis Resources (C), AZ, *529*
Lea Randolph & Assoc., Inc. (C), TX, *529*
The Rankin Group, Ltd. (R), WI, *171*
The Ransford Group (R), TX, *171*
Harold L. Rapp Assoc. (C), NY, *529*
Ray & Berndtson/Laurendeau Labrecque (R), QE, *172*
Ray & Berndtson/Lovas Stanley (R), ON, *172*
Ray & Berndtson/Tanton Mitchell (R), BC, *173*
Raymond Karsan Assoc. (C), PA, *529*
Raymond Thomas & Assoc. (C), FL, *530*
RBW Assoc. Inc. (C), OR, *531*
RCE Assoc. (R), NJ, *173*
RCI Employment Solutions (C), FL, *531*
Re-Mark Assoc. Inc. (C), NJ, *531*
Reality Group (C), OK, *531*
Recruit Xpress (C), TX, *531*
Recruiting Specialists (C), MA, *532*
Recruiting/Solutions (C), CA, *532*
The Recruitment Group, Inc. (C), NY, *532*
Recruitment Specialists, Inc. (C), MD, *532*
Mary Rector & Assoc., Inc. (C), IL, *533*
P. J. Reda & Assoc., Inc. (C), GA, *533*
Redden-Shaffer Group (R), CA, *173*
Reece & Mruk Partners/EMA Partners Int'l. (R), MA, *173*
Reeder & Assoc., Ltd. (R), GA, *173*
Cedric L. Reese Inc. (C), CA, *533*
The Regis Group, Ltd. (R), GA, *174*
Michael James Reid & Co. (R), CA, *174*
Reid Ellis Assoc. Inc. (C), ON, *533*
Reifel & Assoc. (R), IL, *174*
Rein & Co., Inc. (R), NJ, *174*
Reinecke & Assoc. (C), NJ, *533*
The Douglas Reiter Co., Inc. (R), OR, *174*
Renaissance Resources, LLC (R), VA, *174*
Research Personnel Consultants (C), ON, *534*
Reserve Technology Institute (R), TX, *175*
The Resource Group (R), NJ, *175*
The Resource Group (R), CT, *175*
Resource Inc. (R), MA, *175*
Resource Networking Inc. (C), IN, *534*
Resource Perspectives, Inc. (R), CA, *175*
Resource Recruiting (C), NH, *534*
Resources for Management (R), PA, *175*
L. J. Reszotko & Assoc. (C), IL, *535*
Retail Connection, Inc. (C), NJ, *535*
The Retail Network (C), MA, *535*
Retail Recruiters/Spectrum Consultants, Inc. (C), PA, *535*
S. Reyman & Assoc., Ltd. (R), IL, *176*
Russell Reynolds Assoc., Inc. (R), NY, *176*
Reynolds Consulting Int'l. (R), ON, *177*
RHS Assoc. (C), AL, *536*
RIC Corp. (R), FL, *177*
Marshall Rice Assoc. (R), RI, *177*
Rice Cohen Int'l. (R), PA, *178*
Richard Wright Co. (C), CT, *536*
Richards Assoc., Inc. (R), NY, *178*
Terry Richards (C), OH, *536*
Riddle & McGrath LLC (R), GA, *178*
Ridenour & Assoc. (R), IL, *178*
Rieser & Assoc., Inc. (R), MO, *178*
Right/McKee Consulting Group (C), TX, *537*
Riotto-Jones Assoc. (R), NY, *178*
Ritt-Ritt & Assoc., Inc. (C), IL, *537*
Ritta Professional Search Inc. (C), NY, *538*
Rivera Legal Search, Inc. (C), CA, *538*
RJ Associates (C), CA, *538*
RJN Consulting (R), NY, *179*
RLM Assoc., Ltd. (R), NY, *179*
RML Assoc. (C), PA, *538*
Roberson & Co. (C), AZ, *538*
Robert William James & Assoc. (C), OR, *539*
Norman Roberts & Assoc., Inc. (R), CA, *179*
Roberts Ryan & Bentley, Inc. (R), MD, *179*
Robertson & Assoc. (C), IL, *539*
V. Robinson & Co., Inc. (C), MO, *539*
Bruce Robinson Assoc. (R), NJ, *180*
The Robinson Group, D.A., Ltd. (C), IL, *539*
Robinson, Fraser Group Ltd. (R), ON, *180*
Robinson-Robinson & Assoc., Inc. (C), MN, *539*
Robison Humphreys & Assoc., Inc. (R), ON, *180*
Robsham & Assoc., Inc. (R), MA, *180*
J. P. Roddy Consultants (C), PA, *540*
J. Rodgers & Associates (C), IL, *540*
Rodgers, Ramsey, Inc. (C), TX, *540*
Craig Roe & Assoc., LLC (C), MD, *540*
The Rogan Group, Inc. (C), CA, *541*
Rogers - McManamon Executive Search (R), CA, *180*
ROI International, Inc. (R), WA, *181*
Rolland Ressources Humaines Inc. (R), QE, *181*
Rollins & Assoc. (C), CA, *541*
Rollo Assoc. (R), CA, *181*
Romac Int'l. (C), PA, *542*
Rooney Assoc., Inc. (R), IL, *181*
Ropella & Assoc. (R), FL, *181*
Ropes Associates, Inc. (R), FL, *182*
Emery A. Rose & Assoc. (C), WA, *545*
Rosenfeld & Co., Inc. (C), MI, *545*
Rossi & Assoc. Inc. (C), BC, *545*
The Rossi Search Group (C), PA, *545*
Roster Inc. (C), IN, *545*
Patricia Roth Int'l. (C), FL, *545*
Roth Young of Chicago (C), IL, *546*
Roth Young Executive Search (C), TX, *546*
Roth Young Executive Recruiters (C), MN, *546*
Roth Young of Pittsburgh (C), PA, *546*
Roth Young of Tampa (C), FL, *546*
Roth Young Personnel Services of Washington, DC (C), MD, *546*
Roth Young Executive Search of Milwaukee (C), WI, *547*
Rovner & Assoc., Inc. (R), IL, *182*
Rovner Gerner & Assoc. (R), CA, *182*
Rowland Mountain & Assoc. (C), GA, *547*
Royal Assoc. (C), CA, *547*
RSMR, Inc. (R), IL, *182*
The Rubicon Group (C), AZ, *547*
J. D. Ruhmann & Assoc. (C), MO, *548*
Ruppert Comann Assoc., Inc. (R), CO, *182*
Rusher, Loscavio & LoPresto (R), CA, *183*
Rushmore • Judge Inc. (R), ON, *183*
Russillo/Gardner/Spolsino (C), MA, *548*
Rust & Assoc., Inc. (R), IL, *183*
W. A. Rutledge & Assoc. (R), CT, *183*
The Ryan Charles Group, Inc. (C), FL, *548*
Ryman, Bell, Green & Michaels, Inc. (C), TX, *549*
R. L. Rystrom & Assoc., Inc. (C), MN, *549*
S-H-S TechStaff (C), PA, *549*
S. P. Assoc., Inc. (C), NC, *550*
S.C.S. & Assoc. (C), NC, *550*
Saber Group, Inc. (C), TX, *550*
R. S. Sadow Assoc. (C), NJ, *550*
Sage Employment Recruiters (C), IN, *550*
Sales & Management Search, Inc. (C), IL, *551*
Sales Builders, Inc. (R), VA, *183*
Sales Consultants Int'l. of Oakland (C), CA, *556*
Sales Consultants of Scottsdale, Inc. (C), AZ, *556*
Sales Consultants Peninsula, Inc. (C), CA, *556*
Sales Consultants of Silicon Valley (C), CA, *556*
Sales Consultants of Chico (C), CA, *556*
Sales Consultants of Daphne (C), AL, *556*
Sales Consultants of Northwest Arkansas, Inc. (C), AR, *556*
Sales Consultants of Ft. Lauderdale, Inc. (C), FL, *557*
Sales Consultants of Ft. Myers, Inc. (C), FL, *557*
Sales Consultants of Danbury (C), CT, *557*
Sales Consultants of Chicago South (C), IL, *558*
Sales Consultants of Western McHenry County (C), IL, *558*
Sales Consultants (C), IL, *558*
Sales Consultants of Cherokee (C), GA, *558*
Sales Consultants of Barrington (C), IL, *558*
Sales Consultants of Indianapolis-North (C), IN, *558*

Sales Consultants of Rockville, MD (C), MD, *559*
Sales Consultants - Bristol County (C), MA, *559*
Sales Consultants of Bangor, Inc. (C), ME, *559*
Sales Consultants of Birmingham (C), MI, *559*
Sales Consultants of Nashua-Manchester (C), NH, *560*
Sales Consultants of Farmington Hills (C), MI, *560*
Sales Consultants of Grand Rapids (C), MI, *560*
Sales Consultants of Laurel Park, Inc. (C), MI, *560*
Sales Consultants of Omaha, Inc. (C), NE, *560*
Sales Consultants of Northern Jersey, Inc. (C), NJ, *560*
Sales Consultants of Cherry Hill (C), NJ, *560*
Sales Consultants Bridgewater, Inc. (C), NJ, *560*
Sales Consultants of Raleigh-Durham-RTP (C), NC, *561*
Sales Consultants of Harrisburg (C), PA, *561*
Sales Consultants of Middlesex County, Inc. (C), NJ, *561*
Sales Consultants of Westchester-South, Inc. (C), NY, *561*
Sales Consultants of Princeton, Inc. (C), NJ, *561*
Sales Consultants of Newtown, Inc. (C), PA, *562*
Sales Consultants of Rhode Island, Inc. (C), RI, *562*
Sales Consultants King of Prussia (C), PA, *562*
Sales Consultants of Orangeburg (C), SC, *562*
Sales Consultants of Houston (C), TX, *563*
Sales Management Resources (C), CA, *563*
A. N. Salloway Executive Search & Consulting, L.L.C. (C), MA, *564*
Salveson Stetson Group, Inc. (R), PA, *184*
Salzmann Gay Assoc., Inc. (R), PA, *184*
Sampson Medical Search (C), CA, *564*
George D. Sandel Assoc. (C), MA, *565*
Sanford Rose Assoc. - Lake Forest (R), IL, *184*
Sanford Rose Assoc. (C), OH, *565*
Sanford Rose Assoc. - Mobile (C), AL, *565*
Sanford Rose Assoc. - Fairhope (C), AL, *565*
Sanford Rose Assoc. - Santa Barbara (C), CA, *565*
Sanford Rose Assoc. - Clearwater (C), FL, *566*
Sanford Rose Assoc. - Atlanta North (C), GA, *566*
Sanford Rose Assoc. - Effingham (C), IL, *566*
Sanford Rose Assoc. - Norcross (C), GA, *566*
Sanford Rose Assoc. - Athens (C), GA, *566*
Sanford Rose Assoc. - Chicago (C), IL, *566*
Sanford Rose Assoc. - Columbia, MD (C), MD, *567*
Sanford Rose Assoc. - Orland Park (C), IL, *567*
Sanford Rose Assoc. - Cedar Rapids (C), IA, *567*
Sanford Rose Assoc. - Rockville (C), MD, *567*
Sanford Rose Assoc. - Carmel, IN (C), IN, *567*
Sanford Rose Assoc. - Evansville (C), IN, *567*
Sanford Rose Assoc. - Springfield (C), MO, *568*
Sanford Rose Assoc. - Lake St. Louis (C), MO, *568*
Sanford Rose Assoc. - Amherst, NY (C), NY, *568*
Sanford Rose Assoc. - Rochester (C), MI, *568*
Sanford Rose Assoc. - Gastonia (C), NC, *568*
Sanford Rose Assoc. - Flemington (C), NJ, *568*
Sanford Rose Assoc. - Canton (C), OH, *569*
Sanford Rose Assoc. - Greensboro (C), NC, *569*
Sanford Rose Assoc. - Burlington, NC (C), NC, *569*
Sanford Rose Assoc. - Fairlawn (C), OH, *569*
Sanford Rose Assoc. - Philadelphia North (C), PA, *570*
Sanford Rose Assoc. - Austin (C), TX, *570*
Sanford Rose Assoc. - Nashville (C), TN, *570*
Sanford Rose Assoc. - Columbia (C), SC, *570*
Sanford Rose Assoc. - Portland (C), OR, *570*
Sanford Rose Assoc. - Pittsburgh North (C), PA, *570*
Sanford Rose Assoc. - Salt Lake City (C), UT, *571*
Sanford Rose Assoc. - Port Washington (C), WI, *571*
Sarver & Carruth Assoc. (C), OK, *571*
Sathe & Associates, Inc. (R), MN, *184*
Satterfield & Assoc., Inc. (R), OH, *184*
Saviar, Inc. (C), AZ, *571*
Savoy Partners, Ltd. (R), DC, *184*
David Saxner & Assoc., Inc. (DSA, Inc.) (R), IL, *185*
Schall Executive Search Partners (R), MN, *185*
Schattle & Duquette (C), RI, *571*
The Schatz Company (C), MO, *571*
Schenck & Assoc. SC (C), WI, *572*
A.D. Schiff & Assoc., Ltd. (C), IL, *572*
Schlatter & Assoc. (C), CA, *572*
F. B. Schmidt Int'l. (R), CA, *185*
Schneider, Hill & Spangler, Inc. (R), PA, *185*
Schoales & Assoc. Inc. (C), ON, *572*
Schuyler Assoc., Ltd. (R), GA, *185*
G. L. Schwartz & Assoc., Inc. (C), GA, *572*
Schweichler Assoc., Inc. (R), CA, *186*
Scientific Solutions, Inc. (C), MI, *572*
Devin Scott Assoc. (C), NJ, *572*
Scott Executive Search, Inc. (R), NY, *186*
Scott Sibley Assoc. (C), NY, *573*
Scott-Thaler Assoc. Agency, Inc. (C), CA, *573*
Search Advisors Int'l. Corp. (R), FL, *186*
The Search Alliance, Inc. (R), FL, *186*
The Search America Group Inc. (C), OH, *573*
Search Assoc. (C), KY, *574*
Search Assoc., Inc. (C), NJ, *574*
Search Bureau Int'l. (C), IL, *574*
Search By Design (C), AZ, *574*
The Search Committee (C), MD, *574*
The Search Company (R), ON, *186*
Search Consultants Int'l., Inc. (C), TX, *575*
Search Group Inc. (R), AB, *186*
The Search Group (C), MD, *575*
Search Innovations, Inc. (R), PA, *187*
Search Int'l. (R), MA, *187*
Search Masters Int'l. (R), AZ, *187*
The Search Network (C), CA, *576*
Search North America, Inc. (C), OR, *576*
Search Plus Int'l.-Ohio (C), OH, *576*
Search Research Assoc., Inc. (R), MA, *187*
Search Solutions Inc. (C), CA, *576*
Search South, Inc. (C), AL, *576*
SearchCorp (C), FL, *577*
SearchCorp International (C), AB, *577*
Searchforce, Inc. (R), FL, *187*
Searchline Services, Inc. (C), OH, *577*
SearchOne, Inc. (C), AR, *577*
Seco & Zetto Assoc., Inc. (C), NJ, *577*
Secura/Burnett Partners (R), CA, *187*
Sedlar & Miners (R), NY, *188*
Seiden Krieger Assoc., Inc. (R), NY, *188*
Select Services (C), IL, *578*
Selectis Corp. (C), IL, *578*
Selective Management Services, Inc. (C), FL, *578*
Selective Recruiting Assoc., Inc. (C), MI, *578*
Selig Executive Search (C), NH, *579*
Sensible Solutions, Inc. (R), IL, *188*
Sevcor Int'l., Inc. (R), IL, *188*
Shannahan & Co., Inc. (R), CA, *189*
Sharp Placement Professionals, Inc. (C), NY, *579*
Sharrow & Assoc., Inc. (C), MI, *579*
M. B. Shattuck & Assoc., Inc. (R), CA, *189*
Peggy Shea & Assoc. (R), CA, *189*
Shepherd Bueschel & Provus, Inc. (R), IL, *189*
Shey-Harding Assoc. Inc. (C), CA, *580*
Shiell Personnel (C), LA, *580*
Shinn & Assoc. (R), CA, *189*
Michael Shirley Assoc. Inc. (R), KS, *190*
Shoemaker & Assoc. (R), GA, *190*
E. L. Shore & Assoc. (R), ON, *190*
Shore Asociados Ejecutivos, S. A. de C.V. (R), MX, *190*
The Shorr Group (R), IL, *190*
The Shotland Group (R), CA, *190*
SHS of Allentown (C), PA, *580*
M. Shulman, Inc. (R), CA, *191*
Shupack & Michaels Inc. (C), NY, *580*
John Sibbald Assoc., Inc. (R), MO, *191*
Larry Siegel & Assoc. (R), WA, *191*
Peter Siegel & Co. (C), MA, *581*
Siger & Assoc., LLC (C), CT, *581*

Marvin L. Silcott & Assoc., Inc. (C), TX, *581*
Sill Technical Assoc., Inc. (C), PA, *581*
L. A. Silver Assoc., Inc. (R), MA, *191*
Silver Associates (C), CA, *581*
SilverSands Int'l. (C), FL, *582*
Daniel A. Silverstein Assoc. Inc. (R), FL, *191*
D. J. Simpson Assoc. Inc. (R), ON, *191*
Singleton & Assoc. (C), VA, *582*
Sink, Walker, Boltrus Int'l. (R), MA, *192*
Skipping Stone Inc. (C), VA, *582*
Ruth Sklar Assoc., Inc. (RSA Executive Search) (R), NY, *192*
Skott/Edwards Consultants (R), NY, *192*
Slayton Int'l., Inc. (R), IL, *192*
Tom Sloan & Assoc., Inc. (C), WI, *583*
Sloan & Assoc., Inc. (C), VA, *583*
J. L. Small Assoc. (C), AL, *583*
Christopher Smallhorn Executive Recruiting, Inc. (R), MA, *193*
Smith & Assoc. (C), CA, *583*
James F. Smith & Assoc. (C), GA, *583*
Ralph Smith & Assoc. (C), IL, *584*
Smith & Laue Search (R), OR, *193*
Smith & Sawyer, Inc. (R), NY, *193*
Smith & Syberg, Inc. (R), IN, *193*
G. L. Smith Assoc. (C), CA, *584*
Herman Smith Executive Initiatives Inc. (R), ON, *193*
Smith, Roth & Squires (R), NY, *194*
Smith Search, S.C. (R), MX, *194*
A. William Smyth, Inc. (R), CA, *194*
Snelling & Snelling, Inc. (C), FL, *585*
Snelling Search (C), AL, *585*
Snelling Search - Transportation Division (C), AR, *585*
Snelling Search (C), IL, *586*
C. Snow & Assoc. (C), ON, *586*
Snyder & Co. (R), CT, *194*
Sockwell & Assoc. (R), NC, *194*
Software Resource Consultants (C), TN, *587*
Solomon-Page Healthcare Group (R), NY, *195*
Soltis Management Services (R), PA, *195*
Solutions Group (R), AL, *195*
Souder & Assoc. (R), VA, *195*
Southern Chemical & Plastics Search (C), GA, *587*
Southern Research Services (R), FL, *195*
Sparks, McDonough & Assoc., Inc. (C), MO, *588*
Special Markets Group, Inc. (R), GA, *195*
Specialized Search Assoc. (C), FL, *589*
Spectrum Consultants (R), CA, *196*
SpencerSearch, Inc. (C), CO, *589*
SpencerStuart (R), NY, *196*
Spilman & Assoc. (R), TX, *197*
Kenn Spinrad Inc. (C), PA, *589*
Splaine & Assoc., Inc. (R), CA, *198*
Sports Group Int'l. (R), NC, *198*
Spriggs & Co., Inc. (R), IL, *198*
M. H. Springer & Assoc. (R), CA, *198*
Springer Souder & Assoc. L.L.C. (R), IL, *198*
Sprout/Standish, Inc. (C), NH, *589*
SR Wilson, Inc. (C), CA, *590*
SSA Executive Search Int'l. (R), AZ, *198*
Staff Extension Int'l. (C), TX, *590*
Staffing Edge, Inc. (C), IA, *590*
C. J. Stafford & Assoc. (C), ON, *591*
Stafford Consulting Group (R), CA, *198*
Stanewick, Hart & Assoc., Inc. (C), FL, *591*
Stanton Chase Int'l. (R), MD, *198*
Star Search Consultants (C), ON, *591*
Starbridge Group Inc. (C), VA, *591*
The Stark Wilton Group (R), MI, *199*
STAT Search (C), NH, *592*
Steeple Resources & Consulting (R), NJ, *199*
Stentiford & Berardi Assoc. Ltd. (R), NY, *199*
Sterling Int'l. Management Recruitment, Ltd. Inc. (C), NC, *592*
Michael Stern Assoc., Inc./Euram (R), ON, *200*
Steven Douglas Assoc. (C), FL, *593*
Steven Michaels & Assoc. (C), NY, *593*
The Stevens Group (C), CA, *593*
The Stevenson Group, Inc. (N.J.) (R), NJ, *200*
The Stewart Group (C), FL, *593*
Stewart, Stein & Scott, Ltd. (R), MN, *200*
Stewart/Greene & Co. of The Triad, Inc. (C), NC, *594*
Stewart/Laurence Assoc., Inc. (R), NJ, *201*
Charles Stickler Assoc. (R), PA, *201*
Linford E. Stiles & Assoc., L.L.C. (R), NH, *201*
Stillinger & Assoc. (R), CA, *201*
STM Assoc. (R), UT, *201*
Allan Stolee Inc. (R), FL, *201*
Stone & Youngblood (C), MA, *594*
Stone Enterprises Ltd. (C), IL, *594*
Stone, Murphy & Olson (R), MN, *201*
DM Stone Personnel Services (C), CA, *594*
The Stonebridge Group (C), PA, *594*
Stoopen Asociados, S.C./EMA Partners Int'l. (R), MX, *202*
Straight & Co. (R), GA, *202*
Mark Stranberg & Assoc. Inc. (R), MA, *202*
Strategic Advancement Inc. (R), NJ, *202*
Strategic Alternatives (R), CA, *202*
Strategic Executives, Inc. (R), CT, *202*
Strategic Resources (C), WA, *595*
Strategic Resources Biotechnology & Medical Group (C), WA, *595*
Strategic Search, LLC (C), CA, *595*
Strategic Technologies, Inc. (C), TX, *596*
StratfordGroup (R), OH, *203*
W. R. Strathmann Assoc. (R), NY, *203*
Stratin Assoc. (C), NJ, *596*
Straube Associates (R), MA, *203*
Strauss Personnel Service (C), PA, *596*
Stroman Int'l., Inc. (R), CO, *204*
Success Seekers Connection (C), FL, *596*
Sullivan & Assoc. (R), MI, *204*
Joe Sullivan & Assoc., Inc. (R), NY, *204*
Sullivan & Company (R), NY, *204*
Summit Group Int'l., Inc. (R), GA, *204*
The Summit Group (C), CA, *596*
Summit Search Specialists (C), TX, *596*
Ron Sunshine & Assoc. (C), IL, *597*
Survival Systems Staffing, Inc. (C), CA, *597*
Swartz & Assoc., Inc. (R), AZ, *204*
Swift & Assoc. (C), ME, *597*
Synapse Human Resource Consulting Group (R), TX, *205*
Synergistics Assoc. Ltd. (R), IL, *205*
Synergy 2000 (C), DC, *597*
The Synergy Organization (R), PA, *205*
Systems Research Group (C), CA, *598*
T. H. Hunter, Inc. (C), MN, *599*
Tabb & Assoc. (R), OH, *205*
Tactical Alternatives (R), CA, *205*
The Talon Group (R), TX, *205*
Martin Stevens Tamaren & Assoc., Inc. (R), CA, *206*
S. Tanner & Assoc. Inc. (C), ON, *599*
Tanner & Assoc., Inc. (R), TX, *206*
Tarbex (C), DC, *599*
Target Search, Inc. (C), PA, *600*
Tarnow Int'l. (R), NJ, *206*
Tate & Assoc., Inc. (R), NJ, *207*
M. L. Tawney & Assoc. (C), TX, *600*
Carl J. Taylor & Co. (R), TX, *207*
Taylor Winfield (R), TX, *207*
TBC, Inc. (C), KY, *600*
The TBI Group (R), PA, *207*
TCM Enterprises (C), MD, *600*
Team One Partners, Inc. (C), GA, *600*
Tech Search (C), CA, *601*
TechFind, Inc. (R), MA, *207*
Technical Recruiting Services (C), OH, *602*
Technifind Int'l. (C), TX, *602*
TechNix Inc. (C), ON, *602*
The Technology Group (R), IL, *208*
Technology Management Partners (R), CA, *208*
Technology Search Int'l. (C), CA, *603*
Tecmark Associates Inc. (C), NY, *604*
Teknon Employment Resources, Inc. (C), OH, *604*
Tekworx, Inc. (C), OK, *604*
Tele-Media Int'l. Inc. (C), PA, *604*
Telecom Connections, Inc. (C), TX, *604*
Telecom Executive Group (C), NJ, *605*
Telecom Recruiters, Inc. (C), VA, *605*
Telem Adhesive Search Corp. (C), MD, *605*
Telford, Adams & Alexander (R), CA, *208*
Thomas & Assoc. of Michigan (C), MI, *606*
Thomas Lyle & Co. (C), IL, *606*
Thomas Mangum Co. (R), CA, *208*
Thomas Resource Group (R), CA, *209*
Thompson Assoc. (C), CA, *606*
Richard Thompson Assoc., Inc. (R), MN, *209*
Thomson, Sponar & Adams, Inc. (C), WA, *606*
Thorne, Brieger Assoc., Inc. (R), NY, *209*
Tierney Assoc., Inc. (R), PA, *209*
Fred C. Tippel & Assoc. (C), OH, *607*
Tirocchi, Wright, Inc. (R), CA, *209*
Tittemore Cowan Assoc. (C), AB, *607*
TNS Partners, Inc. (R), TX, *209*
Tondorf & Assoc. Inc. (C), MA, *607*
Top Gun Group, Inc. (C), NV, *607*
Topaz Int'l., Inc., Attorney Search (C), NJ, *607*
TPG & Assoc. (C), TX, *608*
TPS Staffing Solutions (C), IN, *608*

Jay Tracey Assoc. Inc. (C), VT, *608*
Transportation Recruiting Services, Inc. (C), MS, *608*
Travel Executive Search (C), NY, *608*
Travel Personnel (C), OH, *609*
Travis & Co., Inc. (R), MA, *210*
TriStaff Group (C), CA, *609*
Triumph Consulting, Inc. (R), IA, *210*
Trout & Assoc. Inc. (R), UT, *211*
Trowbridge & Co., Inc. (R), MA, *211*
Tryon & Heideman, LLC (R), MO, *211*
TSC Management Services Group, Inc. (C), IL, *610*
Tschudin Inc. (R), NJ, *211*
TSI Group/TSI Staffing Services (C), ON, *610*
TSW Assoc., LLC (R), CT, *211*
TTG/Sterling Services (C), CA, *610*
W. G. Tucker & Assoc. (R), PA, *211*
Tucker Assoc. (R), NJ, *211*
The Thomas Tucker Co. (R), CA, *211*
Tuft & Assoc., Inc. (R), IL, *212*
Tully/Woodmansee Int'l. Inc. (R), FL, *212*
U.S. Search (C), VA, *610*
The Ultimate Source (R), CA, *212*
UniQuest Int'l., Inc. (C), FL, *610*
Unisearch Search & Recruiting Inc. (C), CA, *611*
United Personnel Services (C), MA, *611*
Van Dyke Assoc. (R), IL, *212*
Peter Van Leer & Assoc. (R), MN, *213*
Van Leeuwen Assoc. (R), CA, *213*
VanMaldegiam Assoc., Inc. (R), IL, *213*
VanReypen Enterprises, Ltd. (R), NY, *213*
Venture Resources, Inc. (R), CA, *213*
Verkamp-Joyce Assoc., Inc. (R), IL, *213*
The Verriez Group Inc. (R), ON, *213*
Victor White Int'l. (C), CA, *612*
Vincenty & Co. (C), OH, *612*
Vintage Resources, Inc. (C), NY, *613*
Vlcek & Company, Inc. (R), CA, *214*
Voigt Assoc. (R), IL, *214*
VZ Int'l., Inc. (C), AZ, *613*
W. P. Assoc. (C), CA, *613*
The Wabash Group (C), IN, *613*
Wachendorfer & Assoc. (C), TX, *613*
Fred Wackerle, Inc. (R), IL, *214*
Wakefield Talabisco Int'l. (R), NY, *214*
Kelly Walker Assoc. (C), TX, *614*
Walker Group, Inc. (R), MN, *215*
K. K. Walker Professional Recruitment (C), CA, *614*
Wallace Assoc. (C), CT, *614*
Wallace Management Co. (R), TN, *215*
Gerald Walsh & Co. Inc. (C), NS, *614*
Deborah Snow Walsh, Inc. (R), IL, *215*
Lee H. Walton & Assoc. (R), NY, *215*
Ward Assoc. (C), ON, *615*
Martha Ward Executive Search, Inc. (C), NY, *615*
The Ward Group (R), MA, *215*
Ward Liebelt Assoc. Inc. (R), CT, *215*
Ward-Hoffman & Assoc. (C), ID, *615*
C. D. Warner & Assoc. (C), PA, *615*
Warner & Assoc., Inc. (C), OH, *615*
Warren, Morris & Madison, Ltd. (C), CA, *616*
Warring & Assoc. (R), CA, *215*
The Washington Firm, Ltd. (R), WA, *216*
R. J. Watkins & Co., Ltd. (R), CA, *216*
Watring & Assoc., Inc. (C), IL, *616*
Scott Watson & Assoc., Inc. (R), FL, *216*
Watson Int'l., Inc. (R), NY, *216*
Waveland Int'l. (R), IL, *216*
The Wayne Group, Ltd. (C), NY, *616*
Webb, Johnson Assoc., Inc. (R), NY, *216*
Weber Executive Search (R), NY, *216*
S. B. Webster & Associates (R), MA, *217*
Wegner & Assoc. (C), WI, *617*
Lee Weil Assoc., Inc. (C), IL, *617*
David Weinfeld Group (C), NC, *617*
Weinman & Assoc. (C), AZ, *617*
Weinpel Search, Inc. (C), NJ, *617*
Weinstein & Co. (R), MA, *217*
S. E. Weinstein Co. (R), IL, *217*
The Wellesley Group, Inc. (R), IL, *217*
Wellington Management Group (R), PA, *217*
Wellington Thomas Ltd. (C), FL, *618*
Wells, Bradley & Assoc., Inc. (C), MN, *618*
R. A. Wells Co. (C), GA, *618*
Jude M. Werra & Assoc. (R), WI, *218*
Wesley Brown & Bartle Co., Inc. (R), NY, *218*
West & Assoc. (C), IL, *618*
West Coast Recruiting (C), CA, *619*
Western Management Consultants (R), BC, *218*
Western Technical Resources (C), CA, *619*
Westfields Int'l., Inc. (C), NY, *619*
WestPacific National Search, Inc. (C), CA, *619*
Wheeler Assoc. (R), CT, *219*
White, Roberts & Stratton, Inc. (C), IL, *619*
Whitehead & Assoc., Inc. (C), MO, *620*
The Whitney Group (C), GA, *620*
Whitney Smith Co. (C), TX, *620*
Whittaker & Assoc., Inc. (C), GA, *620*
Whittlesey & Assoc., Inc. (R), PA, *220*
The Whyte Group, Inc. (R), MD, *220*
Daniel Wier & Assoc. (R), CA, *220*
Wilcox Bertoux & Miller (R), CA, *220*
Wilcoxen, Blackwell, Niven & Assoc. (R), FL, *220*
Wilder & Assoc. (C), VA, *620*
The Wilkie Group Int'l. (R), ON, *220*
Wilkinson & Ives (R), CA, *221*
William-Johns Co., Inc. (C), CA, *621*
John R. Williams & Assoc., Inc. (C), NC, *621*
John Williams & Assoc. (C), TX, *621*
Williams Executive Search, Inc. (R), MN, *221*
Williams Recruiting, Inc. (C), WA, *621*
Williams, Roth & Krueger, Inc. (R), IL, *221*
William Willis Worldwide Inc. (R), CT, *221*
The Wilmington Group (C), NC, *622*
Wilson & Assoc. Int'l. Inc. (C), FL, *622*
Wilson McLeran, Inc. (C), CT, *622*
Wilson Personnel, Inc. (C), NC, *622*
Wilson-Douglas-Jordan (C), IL, *622*
The Winchester Group (R), CA, *222*
The Windham Group (R), OH, *222*
Windsor Consultants, Inc. (C), TX, *622*
Windsor International (R), GA, *222*
Winfield Assoc., Inc. (C), MA, *623*
Winguth, Grant & Donahue (R), CA, *222*
Winston Search, Inc. (R), MD, *222*
Winthrop Partners, Inc. (R), NY, *222*
Wisnewski & Assoc. (R), CA, *223*
Witt/Kieffer, Ford, Hadelman & Lloyd (R), IL, *223*
WMD inc. (C), NJ, *623*
Wojdula & Assoc., Ltd. (R), WI, *223*
S. R. Wolman Assoc., Inc. (R), NY, *224*
Susan L. Wonderling Recruiting (C), PA, *623*
Wood & Assoc./Executive Search Consultants (C), CA, *624*
M. Wood Company (R), IL, *224*
Wood, Franchot Inc. (R), MN, *224*
Wood West & Partners Inc. (C), BC, *624*
Wood-Glavin, Inc. (R), KS, *224*
The Woodstone Consulting Company, Inc. (R), CO, *224*
Woodworth Int'l. Group (R), OR, *224*
Working Relationships, Inc. (C), MN, *624*
Worldwide Medical Services (C), CA, *625*
The Worth Group (C), GA, *625*
Dick Wray & Consultants, Inc. (R), CA, *225*
The Wright Group (C), TX, *625*
Bob Wright Recruiting, Inc. (C), CT, *625*
WTW Assoc., Inc. (R), NY, *225*
R. S. Wyatt Assoc., Inc. (R), TX, *225*
John Wylie Assoc., Inc. (C), OK, *625*
Wyndham Mills Int'l., Inc. (R), GA, *225*
The Yaiser Group (C), NJ, *625*
Yankee Hospitality Search (C), CT, *626*
Yelverton Executive Search (R), CA, *226*
The Yorkshire Group, Ltd. (C), MA, *626*
Youngblood Assoc. (C), NC, *626*
Yours In Travel Personnel Agency, Inc. (C), NY, *626*
Steven Yungerberg Assoc., Inc. (R), MN, *226*
Yungner & Bormann (R), MN, *226*
Zaccaria Int'l. (C), NJ, *627*
The Zammataro Company (R), OH, *226*
ZanExec L.L.C. (R), VA, *226*
The Zarkin Group, Inc. (R), NY, *226*
Zeiger Assoc. L.L.C. (C), CA, *627*
Zen Zen Int'l. Inc. (C), MB, *627*
Zingaro & Company (R), TX, *227*
Michael D. Zinn & Assoc., Inc. (R), NJ, *227*
Zona & Assoc., Inc. (C), NY, *628*
Zurick, Davis & Co., Inc. (R), MA, *227*
Zwell Int'l. (R), IL, *228*

01.1 Directors

A la Carte Int'l., Inc. (R), VA, *1*
Action Executive Personnel Consulting Inc. (C), ON, *239*
G. Adams Partners (R), IL, *2*
Advancement, Inc. (C), IL, *241*
Advantage Partners, Inc. (R), OH, *2*
Albrecht & Assoc., Executive Search Consultants (C), TX, *243*
Alexander Enterprises, Inc. (C), PA, *243*
D. S. Allen Assoc. (C), NJ, *244*
Allen/Associates (R), OH, *4*
Alpha Resource Group, Inc. (C), TX, *246*

Anderson & Schwab, Inc. (R), NY, *5*
Anthony Michael & Co. (C), MA, *251*
Argonaut Partners, LLC (R), CA, *6*
Armitage Associates Ltd. (R), ON, *7*
Patrick Arnone & Assoc. Inc. (R), VA, *7*
Ashford Management Group, Inc. (R), GA, *7*
ASI (C), CA, *254*
Asset Resource, Inc. (C), CA, *254*
Aubin Int'l. Inc. (R), MA, *8*
The Badger Group (R), CA, *10*
Baeder Kalinski Int'l. Group, Inc. (R), NH, *10*
The Bales-Waugh Group (C), FL, *258*
The Barack Group, Inc. (R), NY, *11*
Barger & Sargeant, Inc. (R), NH, *11*
The Barrett Group (C), NH, *260*
Nathan Barry Assoc., Inc. (R), MA, *12*
Barth Smith Company (R), IL, *12*
The Barton Group, Inc. (C), MI, *260*
Battalia Winston Int'l./The Euram Consultants Group (R), NY, *13*
BayResearch Group, Inc. (R), IL, *14*
BCG Search, Inc. (R), FL, *14*
Behrens and Company (C), WA, *262*
Bench Int'l. Search, Inc. (R), CA, *15*
Richard L. Bencin & Assoc. (C), OH, *264*
Bennett Search & Consulting Co. (R), FL, *16*
Berkhemer/Clayton, Inc. (R), CA, *16*
Ed Bertolas Assoc., Inc. (C), CA, *265*
Besen Assoc. Inc. (C), NJ, *266*
Bialla & Assoc. Inc. (R), CA, *17*
BioQuest Inc. (R), CA, *17*
BioTech Research Recruiters Inc. (C), CA, *267*
Deborah Bishop & Assoc. (R), CA, *17*
J: Blakslee Int'l., Ltd. (R), CA, *18*
Blau Mancino Schroeder (R), NJ, *18*
Block & Assoc. (R), CA, *18*
Boardroom Consultants/Kenny Kindler Tholke (R), NY, *19*
Bolton Group (C), CA, *269*
Ann Bond Assoc. Inc. (C), MD, *269*
Bowie & Associates, Inc. (C), MD, *271*
Boyden (R), NY, *20*
M. F. Branch Assoc., Inc. (C), NC, *272*
Brandywine Consulting Group (R), PA, *22*
Brandywine Retained Ventures, Inc. (R), CT, *22*
Brault & Assoc., Ltd. (R), VA, *22*
The Brentwood Group Ltd. (R), OR, *23*
Brethet, Barnum & Assoc., Inc. (C), ON, *273*
BridgeGate LLC (C), CA, *273*
The Buckley Group (C), FL, *276*
J. Burkey Assoc. (R), NJ, *25*
The Butlers Co. Insurance Recruiters (C), FL, *277*
Button Group (C), TX, *277*
C. P. Consulting (R), PA, *26*
CanMed Consultants Inc. (C), ON, *280*
Canny, Bowen Inc. (R), NY, *27*
Capital Consulting Group, Inc. (R), MD, *28*
Sally Caplan & Assoc. (C), WA, *281*
Caplan Assoc., Inc. (R), NJ, *28*
Career Development Associates (C), NV, *282*
Career Search Group (C), FL, *283*
Career Specialists, Inc. (R), WA, *29*
Carter McKenzie, Inc. (C), NJ, *285*
Catalyx Group (R), NY, *31*
Caywood Partners, Ltd. (R), CA, *32*
Cejka Healthcare Executive Search Services (CHESS) (R), MO, *32*
Century Assoc., Inc. (C), PA, *287*
David Chambers & Assoc., Inc. (R), CT, *32*
Christian & Timbers, Inc. (R), OH, *34*
Arlene Clapp, Ltd. (R), MN, *35*
Clark Executive Search (C), NY, *292*
The Clark Group (C), MI, *292*
Clayman & Co. (R), MA, *36*
Coastal Int'l., Inc. (R), MA, *36*
Cochran, Cochran & Yale, Inc. (R), NY, *36*
The Coelyn Group (R), CA, *37*
Colton Bernard Inc. (R), CA, *37*
Computer Professionals (R), IL, *38*
The Comwell Company, Inc. (C), NJ, *296*
Construction Search Specialists, Inc. (C), WI, *297*
Consumer Search Inc. (C), MA, *298*
Cornell Group Int'l. Consulting, Inc. (R), NY, *41*
Corporate Careers, Inc. (C), CA, *299*
Corporate Dynamix (C), AZ, *300*
Corporate Recruiters Inc. (C), PA, *300*
Corporate Staffing Group, Inc. (C), PA, *301*
Craig Affiliates, Inc. (C), TX, *302*
CRI Professional Search (C), CA, *303*
Crispi, Wagner & Co., Inc. (R), NY, *43*
Crist Partners, Ltd. (R), IL, *43*
The Curtiss Group International (R), FL, *44*
Cypress Int'l., Inc. (R), FL, *45*
Charles Dahl Group, Inc. (C), MN, *306*
The Dayton Group, Ltd. (C), NY, *309*
DeCaster Assoc. (C), WI, *310*
DeLalla - Fried Assoc. (C), NY, *310*
Development Resource Group (R), NY, *48*
Diversified Search, Inc. (R), PA, *52*
Don Allan Assoc., Inc. (C), CA, *313*
Dorst Information Services, Inc. (C), NY, *314*
CS Dowling Executive Services (R), NJ, *54*
Dromeshauser Assoc. (R), MA, *55*
DSR-Search & Recruitment (C), TX, *315*
Donald F. Dvorak & Co. (R), IL, *55*
Dwyer Consulting Group, Inc. (R), WV, *56*
Gwen Dycus & Assoc. (C), FL, *323*
Dynamic Synergy Corp. (R), CA, *56*
Eagle Research, Inc. (C), NJ, *325*
Eagle Search Assoc. (C), CA, *325*
Eastman & Beaudine, Inc. (R), TX, *56*
Eden & Assoc., Inc. (C), PA, *326*
The Eldridge Group, Ltd. (C), IL, *327*
Elliot Assoc. Inc. (R), NY, *58*
Emmett Executive Search, Inc. (C), NY, *330*
Empowered Solutions Corp. (C), GA, *330*
The Enterprise Group (R), MA, *60*
ESA (R), CT, *60*
The Evans McDonnell Co. (C), TX, *331*
Exec Tech, Inc. (C), IL, *332*
ExeConnex, LLC (R), GA, *61*
Executive Dimensions (R), NY, *62*
Executive Recruiters (C), WA, *334*
Executive Sales Search (C), CO, *335*
Executive Search Consultants (R), CA, *63*
Executive Search Consultants (C), CA, *335*
Executive Search Placements, Inc. (C), CO, *336*
The Executive Source (C), SA, *337*
ExecutiveFit (C), NY, *337*
Fagan & Company (R), PA, *64*
Paul Falcone Assoc. (R), NJ, *65*
Leon A. Farley Assoc. (R), CA, *65*
Dorothy W. Farnath & Assoc., Inc. (C), NJ, *338*
Fell & Nicholson Technology Resources (R), CA, *65*
Fenwick Partners (R), MA, *66*
Fergason Assoc., Inc. (C), IL, *339*
Guild Fetridge Acoustical Search, Inc. (C), NY, *340*
Howard Fischer Assoc. Int'l., Inc. (R), PA, *67*
Fisher & Assoc. (R), CA, *67*
Jack Stuart Fisher Assoc. (C), NJ, *341*
Focus Executive Search (C), MN, *343*
Forray Assoc., Inc. (R), NY, *70*
F-O-R-T-U-N-E Personnel Consultants of Boise (R), ID, *70*
F-O-R-T-U-N-E Personnel Consultants of Wilmington (C), DE, *344*
F-O-R-T-U-N-E Personnel Consultants of San Diego (C), CA, *344*
Fortune of Arlington Heights (C), IL, *345*
Fortune Personnel Consultants of Hilton Head (C), SC, *349*
Fortune Personnel Consultants of Anderson, Inc. (C), SC, *349*
Foster Partners (R), NY, *70*
Franchise Recruiters Ltd. (R), IL, *71*
The Franklin Search Group, Inc./Medzilla (R), WA, *71*
GAAP Inc. (R), QE, *73*
Gaines & Assoc. Int'l., Inc. (R), IL, *73*
The Garvis Group, Inc. (C), LA, *355*
Dianne Gauger & Assoc. (C), CA, *355*
Geneva Group Int'l. (R), CA, *76*
John Gilbert Co. (C), TX, *357*
Gilbert Tweed Assoc. Inc. (R), NY, *76*
Global Resources Group (R), CA, *78*
Glou Int'l., Inc. (R), MA, *78*
The Tracy Glover Co. (R), TX, *78*
David Gomez & Assoc., Inc. (R), IL, *79*
Goodrich & Sherwood Assoc., Inc. (R), NY, *79*
Gossage Regan Assoc. (R), NY, *80*
Gould, McCoy & Chadick, Inc. (R), NY, *80*
Annie Gray Assoc., Inc. (R), MO, *81*
Gregory, Kyle & Assoc. (C), NC, *363*
Grover & Assoc. (R), OH, *82*
GSW Consulting Group, Inc. (R), CA, *83*
William Guy & Assoc., Inc. (R), CA, *84*
GWS Partners (R), IL, *84*
H R Solutions, Inc. (C), MO, *365*
M. A. Haggith Consultants Ltd. (R), ON, *84*
K. C. Hale, Inc. (R), CT, *85*
The Hamilton Group (R), MD, *85*
The Hampton Group (C), NY, *367*
Hands-on Broadcast (R), NY, *86*
Handy HRM (R), NY, *86*
Hardison & Company (R), TX, *86*
Hartman & Barnette (R), VA, *87*

Bruce W. Haupt Assoc. (R), DC, *88*
Hayden Group, Inc. (R), MA, *88*
The Haystack Group, Inc. (R), ME, *88*
Healey Executive Search, Inc. (R), MN, *88*
Health Industry Consultants, Inc. (R), CO, *89*
Healthcare Recruiters Int'l - Minnesota, Inc. (C), MN, *373*
Hechkoff/Work Executive Search Inc. (R), NY, *89*
The Heidrick Partners, Inc. (R), IL, *90*
Heller Assoc., Ltd. (R), IL, *91*
Heritage Search Group, Inc. (C), FL, *376*
Hermann & Westmore (R), CA, *92*
A. Herndon & Assoc., Inc. (R), TX, *92*
Herrerias & Assoc. (R), CA, *92*
Higgins Assoc., Inc. (R), IL, *93*
Highland Search Group, L.L.C. (R), NY, *93*
Higley, Hall & Co., Inc. (R), MA, *93*
Hoffman Partnership Group Inc. (C), NY, *379*
The Hogan Group (C), OH, *380*
Holland Rusk & Assoc. (R), IL, *95*
Home Health & Hospital Recruiters, Inc. (C), GA, *380*
Hornberger Management Company (R), DE, *95*
Hospitality Executive Search, Inc. (R), MA, *96*
HRI Services, Inc. (C), MA, *382*
Hudson Assoc. Inc. (C), IN, *383*
E. A. Hughes & Co., Inc. (R), NY, *98*
Hughes & Company (R), VA, *98*
Human Resource Solutions (R), TX, *98*
Hunegnaw Executive Search (C), OH, *384*
The Hunt Co. (R), NY, *99*
HVS Executive Search (R), NY, *100*
The Icard Group, Inc. (C), MI, *387*
IM Independent Management Recruiters (R), TN, *101*
The IMC Group of Companies (R), NY, *101*
Independent Power Consultants (C), TX, *387*
Insurance People (C), IN, *390*
Integrated Search Solutions Group, LLC (ISSG) (R), NY, *102*
International Executive Recruiters (C), OH, *393*
Interquest, Inc. (R), NY, *103*
IR Search (R), CA, *103*
Isaacson, Miller (R), MA, *104*
ISC of Houston, Inc. (C), TX, *394*
J. R. Scott & Assoc., Ltd. (C), IL, *395*
Jakobs & Assoc. Int'l. (R), NY, *105*
Pendleton James Assoc., Inc. (R), NY, *105*
R. I. James, Inc. (C), NY, *397*
Jaral Consultants, Inc. (C), NJ, *397*
JNB Assoc., Inc. (C), MA, *399*
John Ryan Assoc., LLC. (C), NY, *399*
The Johnson Group, Unlimited (C), NY, *400*
KABL Ability Network (C), CA, *402*
A.T. Kearney Executive Search (R), IL, *111*
Kennedy & Co. (R), IL, *112*
The Kennett Group, Inc. (R), PA, *112*
William W. Kenney (C), CT, *405*
Kenzer Corp. (R), NY, *113*
Kershner & Co. (R), DC, *113*
Michael L. Ketner & Assoc., Inc. (R), PA, *114*
Key Resources Int'l. (C), CA, *405*
Ki Technologies, Inc. (C), UT, *406*
Kinderis & Loercher Group (C), IL, *407*
Richard Kinser & Assoc. (R), NY, *115*
KM Associates (C), MA, *407*
Korn/Ferry Int'l. (R), NY, *117*
The J. Kovach Group (R), PA, *119*
Katherine R. Kraemer (R), CA, *120*
J. Krauss Assoc. (R), FL, *120*
Evie Kreisler Assoc. Inc. (C), CA, *409*
Kremple & Meade, Inc. (R), CA, *120*
L&L Assoc. Global Search (C), PA, *411*
LaCosta & Assoc. Int'l. Inc. (C), CA, *411*
Langley & Associates, Inc. (Executive Search Consultants) (R), CO, *124*
Lautz, Grotte, Engler & Swimley (R), CA, *126*
Leaders-Trust Int'l./Carce y Asociados, S.C. (R), MX, *127*
Ledbetter/Davidson Int'l., Inc. (R), NY, *127*
Lemming/LeVan, Inc. (R), GA, *128*
F. P. Lennon Assoc. (C), PA, *416*
Levin & Company, Inc. (R), MA, *128*
Lewis & Blank Int'l. (R), CA, *129*
Pat Licata & Assoc. (C), NC, *417*
Lipson & Co. (R), CA, *130*
Logic Assoc., Inc. (C), NY, *419*
Longshore + Simmons (R), PA, *131*
The John Lucht Consultancy Inc. (R), NY, *131*
The Mackenzie Group (R), MD, *133*
Maczkov-Biosciences, Inc. (R), CA, *133*
Carol Maden Group (C), VA, *422*
Madison Executive Search, Inc. (C), NJ, *422*
Managed Care Resources (C), TX, *424*
Management Recruiters of San Luis Obispo (C), CA, *439*
Management Recruiters of Aptos (C), CA, *439*
Management Recruiters of Clovis (C), CA, *440*
Management Recruiters of Franktown (C), CO, *442*
Management Recruiters of Duluth (C), GA, *445*
Management Recruiters of Vero Beach (C), FL, *445*
Management Recruiters of Lake Forest, IL (C), IL, *447*
Management Recruiters of Rankin Co. (C), MS, *452*
Management Recruiters of Lake Tahoe, NV (C), NV, *453*
Management Recruiters of Upper Westchester (C), NY, *454*
Management Recruiters of Manhattan on Broadway (C), NY, *455*
Management Recruiters of Georgetown (C), SC, *461*
Management Recruiters of Houston-Northeast (C), TX, *463*
Management Recruiters of San Antonio - North (C), TX, *463*
Management Recruiters Int'l.-The Woodlands (C), TX, *464*
Management Recruiters of Kanawha Valley, LLC (C), WV, *465*
Management Recruiters of Lynnwood (C), WA, *465*
Management Search Assoc., Inc. (C), GA, *467*
Manuso, Alexander & Associates, Inc. (R), NY, *135*
Marketing Resources (C), MA, *470*
Paula Marks Inc. (R), NY, *136*
J. Martin & Assoc. (R), CA, *137*
Matrix Consultants, Inc. (C), NC, *472*
McBride Assoc., Inc. (R), DC, *139*
McCormack & Assoc. (R), CA, *140*
Clarence E. McFeely, Inc. (R), IL, *141*
McIntyre Assoc. (R), CT, *141*
Dan P. McLean Assoc., Inc. (C), ON, *475*
Joseph J. McTaggart (C), CA, *476*
James Mead & Co. (R), CT, *142*
Med Exec Int'l. (C), CA, *476*
MedSearch Resources, Inc. (C), FL, *478*
Juan Menefee & Assoc. (C), IL, *478*
J. M. Meredith & Assoc. Inc. (C), CA, *479*
META/MAT, Ltd. (R), NJ, *144*
Millennium Search Group, Inc. (R), CA, *144*
Herbert Mines Assoc., Inc. (R), NY, *145*
MIXTEC Group (R), CA, *145*
MK & Assoc. (R), CA, *146*
Molecular Solutions, Inc. (C), SC, *483*
Molloy Partners (R), NY, *146*
Morgan Int'l., Inc. (R), IL, *147*
The Morgan/Geoffries Group (C), CA, *485*
Morgenstern Int'l., Inc. (C), FL, *485*
Morris & Berger (R), CA, *147*
MRI, The Sequel Group, LLC (C), CO, *486*
Mruk & E.M.A. Partners (R), NY, *148*
MTA Partners (R), TX, *148*
Multi Processing, Inc. (R), NH, *149*
Munroe, Curry & Bond Assoc. (R), NJ, *149*
P. J. Murphy & Assoc., Inc. (R), WI, *150*
Myers Career Assoc., Inc. (C), CA, *488*
Nationwide Personnel Recruiting & Consulting, Inc. (C), OR, *490*
The Neil Michael Group, Inc./Global Partners (R), NY, *151*
Nichols & Company (R), CO, *151*
Nino Recruiting & Staffing, Inc. (C), TX, *493*
Nordeman Grimm, Inc. (R), NY, *152*
Norman Broadbent Int'l., Inc. (R), NY, *152*
Norris Agency (C), TX, *495*
Norton & Assoc. (C), IL, *496*
NRI Staffing Resources (C), DC, *496*
Nyborg•Dow Assoc., Inc. (C), CA, *497*
NYCOR Search, Inc. (C), MN, *497*
O'Brien Consulting Services (R), MA, *153*
The Odessa Group (R), CA, *155*
The Ogdon Partnership (R), NY, *155*
The Oldani Group (R), WA, *155*
Olsen/Clark (R), WA, *156*
P.A.R. Assoc., Inc. (R), MA, *158*
Jim Parham & Assoc., Inc. (R), FL, *159*
Parker Page Group (C), FL, *503*
Pathfinders (C), CA, *504*
Pathway Executive Search, Inc. (C), NY, *505*

Joel H. Paul & Assoc., Inc. (C), NY, *505*
PCD Partners (R), PA, *161*
Pearson & Assoc., Inc. (C), AZ, *506*
Pearson, Caldwell & Farnsworth (R), CA, *161*
Peck & Assoc., Ltd. (R), WI, *161*
PERC, Ltd. (C), AZ, *506*
Personnel Tangent Inc. (C), QE, *509*
Pharmaceutical Recruiters, Inc. (R), NY, *163*
Pharmaceutical Search Professionals, Inc. (C), PA, *510*
Phillips & Assoc. (R), MA, *164*
Phoenix Partners, Inc. (C), GA, *511*
Phoenix Search (R), MX, *164*
Pinsker and Company, Inc. (R), CA, *164*
Plummer & Assoc., Inc. (R), CT, *166*
PRAXIS Partners (R), VA, *167*
George Preger & Associates Inc. (R), ON, *167*
Preng & Assoc., Inc. (R), TX, *167*
Prestonwood Assoc. (R), MA, *168*
Price & Assoc., Inc. (C), VA, *518*
Primus Assoc., L.C. (R), TX, *169*
Professional Recruiting Consultants, Inc. (C), DE, *521*
The Professional Sales Search Co., Inc. (C), WA, *522*
ProFinders, Inc. (C), FL, *523*
Proquest Inc. (C), SC, *524*
The Quantum Group (C), NJ, *526*
QuestPro, Inc. (C), TX, *527*
L. J. Quinn & Assoc., Inc. (R), CA, *170*
Rand-Curtis Resources (C), AZ, *529*
The Ransford Group (R), TX, *171*
Recruiting Specialists (C), MA, *532*
Mary Rector & Assoc., Inc. (C), IL, *533*
P. J. Reda & Assoc., Inc. (C), GA, *533*
Rein & Co., Inc. (R), NJ, *174*
The Douglas Reiter Co., Inc. (R), OR, *174*
The Resource Group (R), CT, *175*
The Retail Network (C), MA, *535*
Russell Reynolds Assoc., Inc. (R), NY, *176*
RHS Assoc. (C), AL, *536*
Rice Cohen Int'l. (R), PA, *178*
Roberts Ryan & Bentley, Inc. (R), MD, *179*
Robertson & Assoc. (C), IL, *539*
Robinson, Fraser Group Ltd. (R), ON, *180*
Craig Roe & Assoc., LLC (C), MD, *540*
Rogers - McManamon Executive Search (R), CA, *180*
ROI International, Inc. (R), WA, *181*
Rollo Assoc. (R), CA, *181*
Ropella & Assoc. (R), FL, *181*
Royal Assoc. (C), CA, *547*
J. D. Ruhmann & Assoc. (C), MO, *548*
Rusher, Loscavio & LoPresto (R), CA, *183*
Sales Consultants of Silicon Valley (C), CA, *556*
Sales Consultants of Ft. Myers, Inc. (C), FL, *557*
Sales Consultants of Cherokee (C), GA, *558*
Sales Consultants of Grand Rapids (C), MI, *560*
Sales Management Resources (C), CA, *563*
A. N. Salloway Executive Search & Consulting, L.L.C. (C), MA, *564*
Sanford Rose Assoc. - Effingham (C), IL, *566*
Sanford Rose Assoc. - Atlanta North (C), GA, *566*
Sanford Rose Assoc. - Lake St. Louis (C), MO, *568*
Sanford Rose Assoc. - Rochester (C), MI, *568*
Schneider, Hill & Spangler, Inc. (R), PA, *185*
Scientific Solutions, Inc. (C), MI, *572*
Devin Scott Assoc. (C), NJ, *572*
The Search Committee (C), MD, *574*
Search Masters Int'l. (R), AZ, *187*
Search Solutions Inc. (C), CA, *576*
Secura/Burnett Partners (R), CA, *187*
Seiden Krieger Assoc., Inc. (R), NY, *188*
Shepherd Bueschel & Provus, Inc. (R), IL, *189*
M. Shulman, Inc. (R), CA, *191*
Daniel A. Silverstein Assoc. Inc. (R), FL, *191*
D. J. Simpson Assoc. Inc. (R), ON, *191*
Christopher Smallhorn Executive Recruiting, Inc. (R), MA, *193*
Smith & Laue Search (R), OR, *193*
Smith & Sawyer, Inc. (R), NY, *193*
Smith Search, S.C. (R), MX, *194*
SpencerStuart (R), NY, *196*
SSA Executive Search Int'l. (R), AZ, *198*
C. J. Stafford & Assoc. (C), ON, *591*
Stanewick, Hart & Assoc., Inc. (C), FL, *591*
Stanton Chase Int'l. (R), MD, *198*
Mark Stranberg & Assoc. Inc. (R), MA, *202*
Strategic Resources Biotechnology & Medical Group (C), WA, *595*
W. R. Strathmann Assoc. (R), NY, *203*
The Summit Group (C), CA, *596*
Swartz & Assoc., Inc. (R), AZ, *204*
The Synergy Organization (R), PA, *205*
Systems Research Group (C), CA, *598*
Tactical Alternatives (R), CA, *205*
The Talon Group (R), TX, *205*
Target Search, Inc. (C), PA, *600*
Taylor Winfield (R), TX, *207*
TechFind, Inc. (R), MA, *207*
Technology Search Int'l. (C), CA, *603*
Teknon Employment Resources, Inc. (C), OH, *604*
Telecom Executive Group (C), NJ, *605*
Telecom Recruiters, Inc. (C), VA, *605*
Thomas Resource Group (R), CA, *209*
TSW Assoc., LLC (R), CT, *211*
Tully/Woodmansee Int'l. Inc. (R), FL, *212*
Venture Resources, Inc. (R), CA, *213*
Victor White Int'l. (C), CA, *612*
W. P. Assoc. (C), CA, *613*
Wachendorfer & Assoc. (C), TX, *613*
Fred Wackerle, Inc. (R), IL, *214*
Walker Group, Inc. (R), MN, *215*
Ward Assoc. (C), ON, *615*
Martha Ward Executive Search, Inc. (C), NY, *615*
Ward Liebelt Assoc. Inc. (R), CT, *215*
C. D. Warner & Assoc. (C), PA, *615*
Warner & Assoc., Inc. (C), OH, *615*
Warren, Morris & Madison, Ltd. (C), CA, *616*
Warring & Assoc. (R), CA, *215*
R. J. Watkins & Co., Ltd. (R), CA, *216*
Lee Weil Assoc., Inc. (C), IL, *617*
The Wellesley Group, Inc. (R), IL, *217*
Wesley Brown & Bartle Co., Inc. (R), NY, *218*
Western Management Consultants (R), BC, *218*
WestPacific National Search, Inc. (C), CA, *619*
Wheeler Assoc. (R), CT, *219*
Daniel Wier & Assoc. (R), CA, *220*
Wilcoxen, Blackwell, Niven & Assoc. (R), FL, *220*
Wilkinson & Ives (R), CA, *221*
William-Johns Co., Inc. (C), CA, *621*
Williams Recruiting, Inc. (C), WA, *621*
Williams, Roth & Krueger, Inc. (R), IL, *221*
William Willis Worldwide Inc. (R), CT, *221*
The Wilmington Group (C), NC, *622*
Wilson & Assoc. Int'l. Inc. (C), FL, *622*
Wilson-Douglas-Jordan (C), IL, *622*
The Wright Group (C), TX, *625*
The Yaiser Group (C), NJ, *625*
Yours In Travel Personnel Agency, Inc. (C), NY, *626*
Zaccaria Int'l. (C), NJ, *627*
Zeiger Assoc. L.L.C. (C), CA, *627*
Zurick, Davis & Co., Inc. (R), MA, *227*
Zwell Int'l. (R), IL, *228*

01.2 Senior management (e.g. CEO, COO, President, General Manager)

A la Carte Int'l., Inc. (R), VA, *1*
A.J. & Assoc. (C), FL, *232*
A.K.S. Assoc., Ltd. (R), MA, *1*
Abbott Associates (R), CA, *1*
The Abbott Group, Inc. (R), MD, *1*
Ackerman Johnson Inc. (C), TX, *238*
Action Management Corp. (C), MI, *239*
G. Adams Partners (R), IL, *2*
Adler Management, Inc. (R), NJ, *2*
Advanced Corporate Search (C), CA, *240*
Advancement Recruiting Services (C), OH, *241*
Advantage Partners, Inc. (R), OH, *2*
Advice Personnel Inc. (C), NY, *241*
Affinity Executive Search (C), FL, *241*
Agri-Tech Personnel, Inc. (C), MO, *242*
Ahrensdorf & Assoc. (R), PA, *2*
J. R. Akin & Co. (R), MA, *2*
Albrecht & Assoc., Executive Search Consultants (C), TX, *243*
Alexander Enterprises, Inc. (C), PA, *243*
The Alfus Group (R), NY, *3*
Allard Associates (C), CA, *244*
D. S. Allen Assoc. (C), NJ, *244*
Allen Evans Assoc. (R), NY, *4*
Allen, Wayne & Co. LLC (C), WI, *245*
Allen/Associates (R), OH, *4*
Allerton Heneghan & O'Neill (R), IL, *4*
Alliance Executive Search, Inc. (R), MA, *4*

Tom Allison Assoc. (C), NM, *245*
Alpha Resource Group, Inc. (C), TX, *246*
Alpha Search (C), FL, *246*
AM & G Certified Public Accountants & Consultants (R), IL, *4*
Amato & Assoc., Inc. (C), CA, *246*
Peter W. Ambler Co. (R), TX, *5*
American Executive Management, Inc. (R), MA, *5*
Ames Assoc. Inc. (C), MD, *249*
Amherst Human Resource Group, Ltd. (C), IL, *249*
AMS Int'l. (R), VA, *5*
Anderson & Schwab, Inc. (R), NY, *5*
Anderson Bradshaw Assoc., Inc. (R), TX, *6*
Andrews & Wald Group (C), FL, *250*
Tryg R. Angell, Ltd. (C), CT, *250*
Angus Employment Ltd. (C), ON, *250*
Anthony Michael & Co. (C), MA, *251*
APA Search, Inc. (R), NY, *6*
Applied Resources (C), MA, *252*
The Argus Group Corp. (C), ON, *252*
Argus National, Inc. (R), CT, *6*
Ariail & Assoc. (R), NC, *7*
Ariel Recruitment Assoc. (R), NY, *7*
Aries Search Group (C), GA, *252*
Armitage Associates Ltd. (R), ON, *7*
Armor Personnel (C), ON, *253*
J. S. Armstrong & Assoc., Inc. (R), CA, *7*
R & J Arnold & Assoc., Inc. (C), CO, *253*
Patrick Arnone & Assoc. Inc. (R), VA, *7*
Artgo, Inc. (R), OH, *7*
Ashford Management Group, Inc. (R), GA, *7*
Ashworth Consultants, Inc. (R), MA, *8*
ASI (C), CA, *254*
Asset Resource, Inc. (C), CA, *254*
Association Executive Resources Group (R), MD, *8*
AST/BRYANT (R), CT, *8*
Aubin Int'l. Inc. (R), MA, *8*
Auerbach Associates, Inc. (R), MA, *9*
A. M. Auster Associates (R), FL, *9*
Cami Austin & Assoc. (C), IL, *256*
Austin Group Int'l./Marlar Int'l. (R), TX, *9*
Austin Michaels, Ltd., Inc. (C), AZ, *256*
AutoPeople (C), VT, *257*
Avalon Health Group, Inc. (R), NY, *9*
Avestruz & Assoc. (C), CA, *257*
The Badger Group (R), CA, *10*
Baeder Kalinski Int'l. Group, Inc. (R), NH, *10*
Keith Bagg & Assoc., Inc. (C), ON, *257*
Baker Scott & Co. (C), NJ, *258*
Baker, Nelms & Montgomery (C), IL, *258*
Baldwin Associates, LLC (R), CT, *10*
The Bales-Waugh Group (C), FL, *258*
Allen Ballach Assoc. Inc. (R), ON, *10*
The Bankers Group (C), IL, *258*
The Barack Group, Inc. (R), NY, *11*
Barclay Consultants, Inc. (C), NJ, *259*
Barger & Sargeant, Inc. (R), NH, *11*
J. W. Barleycorn, Renard & Assoc., Inc. (R), OH, *11*
Barnes & Assoc. Executive Search (C), CA, *259*
Barone-O'Hara Assoc., Inc. (R), NJ, *11*
The Barrett Group (C), NH, *260*
Barrett Hospitality Search (R), CA, *12*
Nathan Barry Assoc., Inc. (R), MA, *12*
Aldonna Barry Personnel & Management (C), ON, *260*
Barth Smith Company (R), IL, *12*
Bartholdi & Co., Inc. (R), CO, *12*
The Barton Group, Inc. (C), MI, *260*
Battalia Winston Int'l./The Euram Consultants Group (R), NY, *13*
Martin H. Bauman Assoc., Inc. (R), NY, *13*
BCG Search, Inc. (R), FL, *14*
Beacon Int'l., Inc. (C), VA, *261*
The Beam Group (R), PA, *14*
Becker, Norton & Co. (R), PA, *14*
The Bedford Consulting Group Inc. (R), ON, *14*
Robert Beech West Inc. (C), CA, *262*
Behavioral Science Assoc., Inc. (R), AZ, *15*
Neail Behringer Consultants Inc. (R), NY, *15*
Bell Wishingrad Partners Inc. (R), NY, *15*
Bench Int'l. Search, Inc. (R), CA, *15*
Richard L. Bencin & Assoc. (C), OH, *264*
Bender Executive Search Management Consulting (R), NY, *16*
The Bennett Group, Inc. (R), IN, *16*
Bennett Search & Consulting Co. (R), FL, *16*
Berglund Int'l. Resources, Inc. (C), TX, *265*
Berkana Int'l., Inc. (C), WA, *265*
Berkhemer/Clayton, Inc. (R), CA, *16*
Ed Bertolas Assoc., Inc. (C), CA, *265*
Best, Coleman & Co., Inc. (R), MA, *16*
Bialla & Assoc. Inc. (R), CA, *17*
Billington & Assoc. (R), CA, *17*
Binder Hospitality Group (C), KY, *266*
BioQuest Inc. (R), CA, *17*
Deborah Bishop & Assoc. (R), CA, *17*
Bishop Partners (R), NY, *17*
Blackhawk Advantage, Inc. (C), CA, *267*
J: Blakslee Int'l., Ltd. (R), CA, *18*
Blaney Executive Search (R), MA, *18*
Blau Mancino Schroeder (R), NJ, *18*
Block & Assoc. (R), CA, *18*
D. R. Blood & Assoc. (R), AZ, *18*
Blum & Co. (R), WI, *19*
Boardroom Consultants/Kenny Kindler Tholke (R), NY, *19*
Mark Bolno & Assoc. (C), FL, *269*
Ann Bond Assoc. Inc. (C), MD, *269*
Boone-Scaturro Assoc., Inc. (C), GA, *269*
Borchert Assoc. (C), TX, *269*
Bowden & Co., Inc. (R), OH, *20*
BowdenGlobal, Ltd. (R), OH, *20*
Howard Bowen Consulting (C), FL, *270*
Boyden (R), NY, *20*
Boyle/Ogata Executive Search (R), CA, *21*
Bradford Executives Int'l. (C), VA, *271*
The Brand Co., Inc. (R), FL, *22*
Brandywine Consulting Group (R), PA, *22*
Brandywine Management Group (R), MD, *22*
Brandywine Retained Ventures, Inc. (R), CT, *22*
Brault & Assoc., Ltd. (R), VA, *22*
The Brentwood Group Ltd. (R), OR, *23*
Brethet, Barnum & Assoc., Inc. (C), ON, *273*
Brian Assoc., Inc. (C), NY, *273*
Brindisi Search (R), MD, *23*
Brooke Chase Assoc., Inc. (R), IL, *24*
Bernard E. Brooks & Assoc., Inc. (R), SC, *24*
Broward-Dobbs, Inc. (C), GA, *274*
Brown Venture Assoc. (R), CA, *24*
Brush Creek Partners (R), MO, *24*
Charles Buck & Assoc., Inc. (R), NY, *24*
The Buckley Group (C), FL, *276*
Bullis & Co., Inc. (R), CA, *25*
J. Burke & Assoc., Inc. (C), TX, *276*
Burke & Assoc./The Westfield Group (C), CT, *276*
The Burke Group (C), ON, *276*
Joseph R. Burns & Assoc., Inc. (R), NJ, *25*
Busch International (R), CA, *25*
The Butlers Co. Insurance Recruiters (C), FL, *277*
Button Group (C), TX, *277*
Byron Leonard Int'l., Inc. (R), CA, *25*
C. M. Management Services, Inc. (R), KY, *26*
The C.P.R. Group (C), NJ, *278*
C.T.E.W. Executive Personnel Services Inc. (C), BC, *278*
Cahill Assoc. (C), CT, *279*
Caliber Associates (R), PA, *27*
The Cambridge Group Ltd. (C), CT, *280*
Cambridge Management Planning (R), ON, *27*
Campbell, Edgar Inc. (C), BC, *280*
Canadian Career Partners (R), AB, *27*
CanMed Consultants Inc. (C), ON, *280*
Canny, Bowen Inc. (R), NY, *27*
The Canon Group (C), CA, *280*
Canyon Consulting, Inc. (C), TX, *281*
Capital Consulting & Research, Inc. (R), CT, *28*
Sally Caplan & Assoc. (C), WA, *281*
Caplan Assoc., Inc. (R), NJ, *28*
Caprio & Assoc. Inc. (R), IL, *29*
Capstone Consulting, Inc. (R), IL, *29*
Capstone Inc. (R), NY, *29*
Career Consultants (R), IN, *29*
Career Counseling Inc. (CCI) (C), KY, *282*
Career Development Associates (C), NV, *282*
Career Marketing Consultants, Inc. (C), GA, *282*
Career Search Group (C), FL, *283*
Career Specialists, Inc. (R), WA, *29*
Careers First, Inc. (C), NJ, *283*
Careers Plus (R), CA, *29*
Carlson & Czeswik (R), MN, *30*
Carpenter Assoc., Inc. (R), IL, *30*
Carter-Evdemon & Assoc. (C), FL, *285*
Carter/MacKay (C), NJ, *285*
Caruso & Assoc., Inc. (R), FL, *31*
Carver Search Consultants (C), CA, *285*
Cary & Assoc. (R), FL, *31*
CAS Comsearch Inc. (C), NY, *285*
Catalyx Group (R), NY, *31*
Michael J. Cavanagh & Assoc. Inc. (R), ON, *31*
CEC Associates (R), MA, *32*
Cejka Healthcare Executive Search Services (CHESS) (R), MO, *32*
Cella Assoc. (C), GA, *286*
Central Executive Search, Inc. (C), OH, *287*

Century Assoc., Inc. (C), PA, *287*
CEO Consulting (C), FL, *287*
David Chambers & Assoc., Inc. (R), CT, *32*
Chanko-Ward, Ltd. (R), NY, *33*
The Chapman Group, Inc. (C), AZ, *289*
Chase Partners (R), ON, *33*
Chase-Gardner Executive Search Associates, Inc. (C), FL, *289*
A. D. Check Assoc., Inc. (R), PA, *33*
Christenson Hutchison McDowell, LLC (R), NJ, *34*
Christian & Timbers, Inc. (R), OH, *34*
William J. Christopher Assoc., Inc. (R), PA, *34*
Churchill & Affiliates, Inc. (R), PA, *35*
CJA-The Adler Group, Inc. (R), CA, *35*
Claimsearch (C), CA, *291*
Arlene Clapp, Ltd. (R), MN, *35*
Clarey/Napier Int'l., L.C. (R), TX, *35*
The Clark Group (C), MI, *292*
Clark Personnel Service, Inc. (C), AL, *292*
Clayman & Co. (R), MA, *36*
The Clayton Edward Group (C), MI, *292*
CMS, Inc. (C), NH, *293*
Coastal Int'l., Inc. (R), MA, *36*
Cochran, Cochran & Yale, Inc. (R), NY, *36*
Coe & Co. Int'l. Inc./EMA Partners Int'l. (R), AB, *37*
Dean M. Coe Assoc. (R), MA, *37*
The Coelyn Group (R), CA, *37*
Cole, Warren & Long, Inc. (R), PA, *37*
Coleman Lew & Assoc., Inc. (R), NC, *37*
Colt Systems Professional Personnel Services (C), CA, *294*
Colton Bernard Inc. (R), CA, *37*
Compass Group Ltd. (R), MI, *38*
Computer Professionals (R), IL, *38*
The Comwell Company, Inc. (C), NJ, *296*
Conard Associates, Inc. (R), NH, *39*
Conex Inc./InterSearch (R), NY, *39*
Robert Connelly & Assoc., Inc. (R), MN, *39*
M. L. Conner (C), FL, *296*
Conroy Partners Ltd. (R), AB, *39*
Construct Management Services (C), MN, *297*
Construction Search Specialists, Inc. (C), WI, *297*
Consultant Recruiters (C), WI, *297*
Philip Conway Management (R), IL, *40*
Cook Assoc. Int'l., Inc. (C), TN, *298*
Cook Assoc.,® Inc. (R), IL, *40*
The Cooke Group (R), WI, *40*
Cornell Group Int'l. Consulting, Inc. (R), NY, *41*
Cornerstone Search Assoc. Inc. (C), MA, *299*
Cornwall Stockton & Co., Inc. (C), TX, *299*
The Corporate Advisory Group (R), NJ, *41*
Corporate Careers, Inc. (C), CA, *299*
The Corporate Connection, Ltd. (C), VA, *299*
Corporate Dynamix (C), AZ, *300*
Corporate Environment Ltd. (R), IL, *41*
Corporate Leadership Strategies, Inc. (R), NH, *41*
Corporate Management Services (C), PA, *300*
Corporate Recruiters Inc. (C), PA, *300*
Corporate Resources Professional Placement (C), MN, *300*
Corporate Search Consultants (C), IN, *301*
The Corporate Source Group, Inc. (R), MA, *41*
CountryHouse Hotels Executive Search (C), VA, *302*
Cowell & Associates, Ltd. (R), IL, *42*
Trudi Cowlan (C), NY, *302*
Craig Affiliates, Inc. (C), TX, *302*
Crane, Reed & Co., Inc. (C), NH, *302*
Creative HR Solutions (C), GA, *303*
Creative Management Strategies, Ltd. (R), NY, *42*
CRI Professional Search (C), CA, *303*
Crist Partners, Ltd. (R), IL, *43*
Marlene Critchfield Co. (C), CA, *303*
Crown Advisors, Inc. (R), PA, *43*
CTR (R), CA, *43*
Frank Cuomo & Assoc., Inc. (C), NY, *305*
Curran Partners, Inc. (R), CT, *44*
The Curtiss Group International (R), FL, *44*
Cyntal Int'l. Ltd. (R), NY, *44*
Cypress Int'l., Inc. (R), FL, *45*
D.A.I Human Resources Consultants (R), QE, *45*
Daggett & Kvistad (R), CA, *45*
Dahl-Morrow Int'l. (R), VA, *45*
The Dalley Hewitt Co. (R), GA, *45*
The Danbrook Group, Inc. (C), TX, *306*
Daniel Marks Company (C), OH, *306*
Alfred Daniels & Assoc., Inc. (R), CA, *46*
DARE Personnel Inc. (C), ON, *307*
The Dartmouth Group (R), NY, *46*
Daubenspeck & Associates, Ltd. (R), IL, *46*
Davies, Park (R), AB, *46*
Bert Davis Publishing Placement Consultants (C), NY, *309*
DBC Recruiting Network (C), GA, *309*
DBL Associates (C), CA, *309*
DeCaster Assoc. (C), WI, *310*
Deeco Int'l. (C), UT, *310*
Defrain Mayer (R), KS, *48*
Thorndike Deland Assoc. LLC (R), NY, *48*
Delta Management Group Ltd. (C), ON, *310*
Descheneaux Recruitment Services Ltd. (C), BC, *311*
Development Resource Group (R), NY, *48*
Development Search Specialists (R), MN, *49*
Rob Dey Executive Search (R), FL, *49*
Dieckmann & Assoc., Ltd. (R), IL, *51*
DieckMueller Group (R), WI, *51*
The Diestel Group (R), UT, *51*
Roger Dietsch & Assoc. (C), MN, *312*
DiMarchi Partners (R), CO, *51*
J. Dinerstein & Co., Inc. (R), NY, *51*
Robert W. Dingman Co., Inc. (R), CA, *52*
Dinte Resources, Inc. (R), VA, *52*
Discovery, The Staffing Specialists, Inc. (C), IL, *312*
Diversified Health Search (R), PA, *52*
Diversified Search, Inc. (R), PA, *52*
DLG Assoc., Inc. (R), NC, *53*
Doering & Assoc. (C), CA, *313*
Don Allan Assoc., Inc. (C), CA, *313*
Dorst Information Services, Inc. (C), NY, *314*
CS Dowling Executive Services (R), NJ, *54*
Drinkwater & Assoc. (R), MA, *54*
Dromeshauser Assoc. (R), MA, *55*
DSR-Search & Recruitment (C), TX, *315*
Dumont & Co. (C), BC, *316*
M. Dunbar & Assoc. (C), TX, *316*
Dunhill Professional Search of Miami (C), FL, *319*
Dunhill Executive Search of Los Angeles, Inc. (C), CA, *319*
Dunhill Personnel of Boulder (C), CO, *319*
Dunhill Professional Search of Oakland (C), CA, *319*
Dunhill Professional Search of Byram (C), MS, *321*
Dunhill Personnel of Northeast Tulsa, Inc. (C), OK, *322*
Dunhill Professional Search of Wilkes-Barre/Scranton, Inc. (C), PA, *322*
C. A. Durakis Assoc., Inc. (R), MD, *55*
Dussick Management Assoc. (C), CT, *323*
Donald F. Dvorak & Co. (R), IL, *55*
Dwyer Consulting Group, Inc. (R), WV, *56*
Gwen Dycus & Assoc. (C), FL, *323*
Dynamic Synergy Corp. (R), CA, *56*
The E & K Group (C), NJ, *324*
E.P. Int'l. (C), NY, *324*
E/Search Int'l. (C), CT, *325*
Eagle Consulting Group Inc. (C), TX, *325*
Eagle Research, Inc. (C), NJ, *325*
Eagle Search Assoc. (C), CA, *325*
Eastbourne Assoc. Inc. (R), NY, *56*
Eastman & Beaudine, Inc. (R), TX, *56*
EBA Group (R), NJ, *56*
Eden & Assoc., Inc. (C), PA, *326*
EDI/Executive Dynamics Inc. (C), NJ, *326*
Edwards & Assoc. (C), GA, *327*
EFCO Consultants, Inc. (C), NY, *327*
EGM Consulting, Inc. (R), FL, *57*
William J. Elam & Assoc. (R), NE, *58*
Elliot Assoc. Inc. (R), NY, *58*
Steve Ellis (C), CA, *328*
David M. Ellner Assoc. (R), NY, *59*
Elwell & Assoc., Inc. (R), MI, *59*
Mark Elzweig Co., Ltd. (C), NY, *329*
Emerald Legal Search (C), NH, *329*
Emerging Medical Technologies, Inc. (C), CO, *329*
Emerson & Co. (C), GA, *329*
Emmett Executive Search, Inc. (C), NY, *330*
EMN/Witt/Kieffer (R), MA, *59*
Empire International (R), PA, *59*
The Energists (R), TX, *59*
The Enfield Company (C), TX, *330*
The Enterprise Group (R), MA, *60*
Epsen, Fuller & Assoc., LLC (R), NJ, *60*
Erlanger Assoc. (R), CT, *60*
ESA (R), CT, *60*
ESS (Executive Search Services) (R), CA, *61*
ETI Search Int'l. (R), GA, *61*
The Evans McDonnell Co. (C), TX, *331*
The Evans Search Group (R), CT, *61*
Evans Transportation Search (C), ON, *331*
Exec Tech, Inc. (C), IL, *332*
ExecuSource Assoc., Inc. (C), GA, *332*

ExecuSource Consultants, Inc. (C), TX, *332*
Executech (R), OH, *62*
Executive Access Inc. (R), NY, *62*
Executive Alliance (R), MA, *62*
Executive Careers (R), CA, *62*
Executive Dimensions (R), NY, *62*
Executive Directions (R), OH, *62*
Executive Manning Corp. (R), FL, *63*
Executive Placement Services (C), GA, *333*
Executive Recruiters Int'l. (C), MI, *333*
Executive Recruiters (C), WA, *334*
Executive Recruitment Specialists, Inc. (R), NC, *63*
Executive Referral Services, Inc. (C), IL, *334*
Executive Search Consultants (R), CA, *63*
Executive Search Consultants, Inc. (C), FL, *335*
Executive Search Consultants (C), CA, *335*
Executive Search Consultants Corp. (C), IL, *335*
Executive Search Group LLC (C), CA, *335*
Executive Search Group, Inc. (C), CT, *335*
Executive Search Int'l. (C), TX, *335*
Executive Search, Ltd. (C), OH, *336*
Executive Search of America, Inc. (C), OH, *336*
Executive Search Partners (R), NY, *63*
Executive Search Placements, Inc. (C), CO, *336*
Executive Search Team (C), MI, *336*
Executive Solutions (R), MN, *64*
The Executive Source (C), SA, *337*
The Executive Tree (R), FL, *64*
ExecutiveFit (C), NY, *337*
Executives Worldwide, Inc. (C), OR, *337*
Raymond L. Extract & Assoc. (R), CA, *64*
Eyler Assoc., Inc. (R), IA, *64*
Fagan & Company (R), PA, *64*
Fairfaxx Corp. (R), CT, *64*
Fairfield Int'l. Resources (R), NY, *65*
Fallstaff Search (C), MD, *338*
Family-Business Roundtable, Inc. (R), AZ, *65*
Leon A. Farley Assoc. (R), CA, *65*
Dorothy W. Farnath & Assoc., Inc. (C), NJ, *338*
The Fawcett Group (R), MA, *65*
Federal Placement Services (C), NY, *339*
A. E. Feldman Assoc., Inc. (C), NY, *339*
Fell & Nicholson Technology Resources (R), CA, *65*
Fenwick Partners (R), MA, *66*
Fergason Assoc., Inc. (C), IL, *339*
Ferrari Search Group (C), OH, *340*
Fidelity Search Group, Inc. (R), PA, *66*
Jerry Fields Assoc. (C), NY, *340*
First Advisory Services Int'l., Inc. (R), MD, *67*
First Search America, Inc. (C), TN, *341*
Howard Fischer Assoc. Int'l., Inc. (R), PA, *67*
Fisher & Assoc. (R), CA, *67*
Jack Stuart Fisher Assoc. (C), NJ, *341*
The Fisher Group (R), AB, *67*
FitzGibbon & Assoc. (R), PA, *68*
Flynn, Hannock, Inc. (R), CT, *69*
Focus Executive Search (C), MN, *343*
The Forbes Group (R), GA, *69*
The Ford Group, Inc. (R), PA, *69*
Forray Assoc., Inc. (R), NY, *70*
F-O-R-T-U-N-E Personnel Consultants of Boise (R), ID, *70*
Fortune Group Int'l., Inc. (R), PA, *70*
F-O-R-T-U-N-E Personnel Consultants of Wilmington (C), DE, *344*
F-O-R-T-U-N-E Personnel Consultants of San Diego (C), CA, *344*
F-O-R-T-U-N-E Personnel Consultants of Savannah, Inc. (C), GA, *345*
Fortune of Arlington Heights (C), IL, *345*
Fortune Personnel Consultants of Topsfield (C), MA, *346*
Fortune Personnel Consultants (C), MT, *347*
F-O-R-T-U-N-E Personnel Consultants of Bergen County Inc. (C), NJ, *347*
F-O-R-T-U-N-E Personnel Consultants of Cincinnati (C), OH, *348*
F-O-R-T-U-N-E Personnel Consultants of Houston, Inc. (C), TX, *350*
Foster Partners (R), NY, *70*
Fox-Morris Assoc., Inc. (C), PA, *351*
Foy, Schneid & Daniel, Inc. (R), NY, *71*
Franchise Recruiters Ltd. (R), IL, *71*
Franchise Search, Inc. (C), NY, *352*
Franklin Allen Consultants, Ltd. (R), NY, *71*
Franklin Int'l. Search, Inc. (C), MA, *352*
The Franklin Search Group, Inc./Medzilla (R), WA, *71*
Franstaff Inc. (C), FL, *352*
KS Frary & Assoc. (R), MA, *71*
P. N. French Assoc., Inc. (R), MA, *72*
Gerald Frisch Assoc., Inc. (R), NY, *72*
Frye/Joure & Assoc., Inc. (C), TN, *353*
The Furst Group, Inc. (R), IL, *72*
Furst Group/MPI (R), IL, *72*
G. H. Enterprises (C), AZ, *354*
GAAP Inc. (R), QE, *73*
Gaines & Assoc. Int'l., Inc. (R), IL, *73*
Jay Gaines & Company, Inc. (R), NY, *73*
Gaming Consultants, Inc. (R), LA, *74*
The Gammill Group, Inc. (C), OH, *354*
Gans, Gans & Assoc., Inc. (R), FL, *74*
W. N. Garbarini & Assoc. (R), NJ, *74*
Gardiner, Townsend & Assoc. (R), NY, *74*
Garland Assoc. Int'l. (C), CA, *355*
Garrett Assoc. Inc. (R), GA, *75*
Garrison-Randall, Inc. (R), CA, *75*
The Garvis Group, Inc. (C), LA, *355*
GateSource Partners (C), VA, *355*
Dianne Gauger & Assoc. (C), CA, *355*
Genel Associates (C), CA, *356*
Genesis Consulting Partners (R), PA, *76*
Geneva Group Int'l. (R), CA, *76*
C. R. Gerald & Assoc. (C), ON, *356*
Gielow Assoc., Inc. (R), WI, *76*
Gilbert & Van Campen Int'l. (R), NY, *76*
Gilbert Scott Assoc., LLC (C), MA, *357*
Gilbert Tweed Assoc. Inc. (R), NY, *76*
Gilreath Weatherby Inc. (R), MA, *77*
Global Resources Group (R), CA, *78*
Global Telecommunications, Inc. (C), TX, *359*
F. Gloss Int'l. (R), VA, *78*
Glou Int'l., Inc. (R), MA, *78*
The Tracy Glover Co. (R), TX, *78*
The Gobbell Co. (R), CA, *78*
Robert G. Godfrey Assoc. Ltd. (R), IL, *78*
H. L. Goehring & Assoc., Inc. (C), OH, *359*
Barry M. Gold & Co. (C), CA, *359*
Joseph Goldring & Assoc. Inc. (C), MI, *360*
Fred J. Goldsmith Assoc. (R), CA, *79*
David Gomez & Assoc., Inc. (R), IL, *79*
Gomez Fregoso y Asociados (C), JAL, *360*
The Goodman Group (R), CA, *79*
Goodrich & Sherwood Assoc., Inc. (R), NY, *79*
Goodwin & Co. (R), DC, *80*
Gossage Regan Assoc. (R), NY, *80*
Gould, McCoy & Chadick, Inc. (R), NY, *80*
The Governance Group, Inc. (R), NJ, *80*
Robert Graham Assoc. (R), RI, *81*
Granger, Counts & Assoc. (R), OH, *81*
Grant Cooper & Assoc., Inc. (R), MO, *81*
Grantham & Co., Inc. (R), NC, *81*
Graphic Search Assoc. Inc. (C), PA, *362*
Grauss & Co. (C), CA, *362*
Annie Gray Assoc., Inc. (R), MO, *81*
Sheila Greco Assoc. (C), NY, *362*
Greenwich Search Partners, LLC (C), CT, *363*
Greger/Peterson Assoc., Inc. (R), CA, *81*
Griffith & Werner, Inc. (R), FL, *82*
J. B. Groner Executive Search, Inc. (C), DE, *363*
Gros Executive Search, Inc. (C), TN, *363*
Groussman & Assoc., Inc. (R), TX, *82*
Grover & Assoc. (R), OH, *82*
Growth Consultants of America (R), MI, *82*
Growth Strategies, Inc. (R), FL, *83*
David E. Grumney Co. Inc. (R), WA, *83*
GSW Consulting Group, Inc. (R), CA, *83*
Michael R. Guerin Co. (C), CA, *364*
Gundersen Partners, L.L.C. (R), NY, *83*
Gustin Partners, Ltd. (R), MA, *83*
William Guy & Assoc., Inc. (R), CA, *84*
GWS Partners (R), IL, *84*
H R Solutions, Inc. (C), MO, *365*
The H. S. Group, Inc. (C), WI, *365*
Haddad Assoc. (R), FL, *84*
Russ Hadick & Assoc. Inc. (C), OH, *365*
M. A. Haggith Consultants Ltd. (R), ON, *84*
Halbrecht Lieberman Assoc., Inc. (R), CT, *84*
Hale Assoc. (R), IL, *84*
K. C. Hale, Inc. (R), CT, *85*
Haley Associates (R), CA, *85*
The Halyburton Co., Inc. (R), NC, *85*
Hamilton & Co. (C), OH, *367*
The Hamilton Group (R), MD, *85*
The Hampton Group (C), NY, *367*
R. C. Handel Assoc. Inc. (R), CT, *85*
Handy HRM (R), NY, *86*
The Hanna Group (C), OH, *368*
The Hanover Consulting Group (C), MD, *368*
Harcourt & Assoc. (C), AB, *368*
Hardison & Company (R), TX, *86*
Harper Hewes, Inc. (C), NY, *369*
The Harris Consulting Corp. (R), MB, *87*
Harris Heery & Assoc., Inc. (R), CT, *87*
Hartman & Barnette (R), VA, *87*

Hartsfield Group, Inc. (R), GA, *87*
Michael J. Hawkins, Inc. (C), IL, *370*
William E. Hay & Co. (R), IL, *88*
Hayden Group, Inc. (R), MA, *88*
Hazard, Young, Attea & Assoc., Ltd. (C), IL, *371*
HCI Corp. (C), IL, *371*
Headden Assoc. (R), WA, *88*
Healey Executive Search, Inc. (R), MN, *88*
Health Care Dimensions (C), CO, *371*
Health Industry Consultants, Inc. (R), CO, *89*
Health Search (C), CA, *371*
Healthcare Management Resources, Inc. (R), GA, *89*
Healthcare Recruiters of the Rockies, Inc. (C), CO, *372*
Healthcare Recruiters of Indiana (C), IN, *372*
Healthcare Recruiters Int'l - Minnesota, Inc. (C), MN, *373*
Healthcare Recruiters International-NY/NJ (C), NJ, *373*
Healthcare Recruiters of New Orleans (C), LA, *373*
Healthcare Recruiters of New York, Inc. (C), NY, *373*
Healthcare Recruiters Int'l. Philadelphia (C), NJ, *373*
Healthcare Recruiters - Northwest (C), WA, *374*
Healthcare Recruiters of Dallas (C), TX, *374*
F. P. Healy & Co., Inc. (R), NY, *89*
Heath/Norton Assoc., Inc. (R), NY, *89*
R. W. Hebel Assoc. (R), TX, *89*
Hechkoff/Work Executive Search Inc. (R), NY, *89*
The Heidrick Partners, Inc. (R), IL, *90*
Heinze & Assoc. Inc. (R), MN, *91*
Helbling & Assoc., Inc. (R), PA, *91*
Helffrich Int'l. (C), FL, *375*
Heller Assoc., Ltd. (R), IL, *91*
Heller Kil Assoc., Inc. (C), FL, *375*
G. W. Henn & Co. (R), OH, *91*
Bruce Henry Assoc. Inc. (R), CA, *91*
Kay Henry, Inc. (C), PA, *376*
The Hensge Co. (R), IL, *91*
J. J. Herlihy & Assoc., Inc. (C), CA, *376*
Hermann & Westmore (R), CA, *92*
A. Herndon & Assoc., Inc. (R), TX, *92*
Herring & Assoc. (C), AR, *376*
The Herrmann Group Ltd. (R), ON, *92*
Stanley Herz & Co. (R), NY, *92*
Robert Hess & Assoc., Inc. (C), CO, *377*
The Hetzel Group, Inc. (R), IL, *92*
Higbee Assoc., Inc. (C), CT, *377*
Higdon Prince Inc. (R), NY, *93*
B. W. Higgins, Inc. (C), IN, *377*
Highland & Assoc. (C), CA, *378*
Highland Search Group, L.L.C. (R), NY, *93*
Higley, Hall & Co., Inc. (R), MA, *93*
The Hindman Co. (R), KY, *94*
The Hindman Group, Inc. (C), CA, *378*
The Hiring Authority, Inc. (C), FL, *379*
Hobson Assoc. (C), CT, *379*
Hockett Associates, Inc. (R), CA, *94*
Hodge-Cronin & Assoc., Inc. (R), IL, *94*
Hoffman Partnership Group Inc. (C), NY, *379*
Hoglund & Assoc., Inc. (R), IL, *94*
Holland & Assoc., Inc. (R), MI, *94*
Holland Rusk & Assoc. (R), IL, *95*
Home Health & Hospital Recruiters, Inc. (C), GA, *380*
Fred Hood & Assoc. (C), CA, *380*
Hook-Up! (C), CA, *380*
Hornberger Management Company (R), DE, *95*
Horton Int'l. Inc. (R), NY, *96*
Hospitality Executive Search, Inc. (R), MA, *96*
Houser, Martin, Morris (C), WA, *381*
Houtz•Strawn & Arnold, Inc. (R), TX, *96*
Howard-Sloan Assoc. (C), NY, *381*
The Howard-Sloan-Koller Group (R), NY, *97*
Howe & Assoc. (R), PA, *97*
HRI Services, Inc. (C), MA, *382*
Hudson Assoc. Inc. (C), IN, *383*
E. A. Hughes & Co., Inc. (R), NY, *98*
Hughes & Company (R), VA, *98*
Human Capital Resources, Inc. (C), FL, *384*
Human Resource Bureau (C), CA, *384*
Human Resource Solutions (R), TX, *98*
Human Resources Management Hawaii, Inc. (C), HI, *384*
E. F. Humay Assoc. (C), PA, *384*
Hunegnaw Executive Search (C), OH, *384*
Hunt & Howe Inc. (R), NY, *99*
The Hunt Co. (R), NY, *99*
Hunt Ltd. (C), NJ, *385*
Hunt Patton & Brazeal, Inc. (C), OK, *385*
Hunter Assoc. (C), MA, *385*
The Hunter Group, Inc. (C), MI, *385*
Hunter Int'l., Inc. (R), CT, *100*
Hunter Int'l. LLC (C), MA, *385*
Huntress Real Estate Executive Search (R), MO, *100*
HVS Executive Search (R), NY, *100*
The Hyde Group, Inc. (R), CT, *101*
Hyman & Assoc. (C), TX, *386*
IDC Executive Search Inc. (C), FL, *387*
The IMC Group of Companies (R), NY, *101*
Impact Search & Strategies (C), PA, *387*
Impact Source, Inc. (C), FL, *387*
Independent Power Consultants (C), TX, *387*
Innovative Partnerships (R), CA, *101*
The Inside Track (C), TX, *389*
Insurance Career Center, Inc. (C), CT, *389*
Insurance People (C), IN, *390*
Intech Summit Group, Inc. (R), CA, *102*
Integrated Search Solutions Group, LLC (ISSG) (R), NY, *102*
Intelegra, Inc. (C), NJ, *390*
InteliSearch, Inc. (R), CT, *102*
IntelliSearch (C), TX, *391*
Intercontinental Executive Group (C), PA, *391*
International Consulting Services, Inc. (C), IL, *392*
International Executive Recruiters (C), OH, *393*
International Management Advisors, Inc. (R), NY, *103*
Interquest, Inc. (R), NY, *103*
IR Search (R), CA, *103*
Isaacson, Miller (R), MA, *104*
Joan Isbister Consultants (C), NY, *394*
ISC of Atlanta, Inc. (C), GA, *394*
ISC of Cincinnati Inc. (C), OH, *394*
ISC of Houston, Inc. (C), TX, *394*
J. B. Linde & Assoc. (C), MO, *395*
J. Nicholas Arthur (R), MA, *104*
J. R. Scott & Assoc., Ltd. (C), IL, *395*
Ron Jackson & Assoc. (C), GA, *396*
Jacobson Assoc. (C), IL, *396*
JAG Group (R), MO, *105*
Pendleton James Assoc., Inc. (R), NY, *105*
R. I. James, Inc. (C), NY, *397*
Jaral Consultants, Inc. (C), NJ, *397*
JCL & Assoc. (C), FL, *397*
JDH & Assoc. (C), CA, *397*
Jeffrey Allan Co., Inc. (C), CA, *398*
JenKim Int'l. Ltd., Inc. (C), FL, *398*
Jerome & Co. (C), CA, *398*
JG Consultants, Inc. (R), TX, *106*
JM & Company (R), PA, *106*
Job Link, Inc. (C), CA, *399*
John Jay & Co. (C), ME, *399*
Johnson & Assoc., Inc. (R), CA, *106*
Johnson & Company (R), CT, *107*
Ronald S. Johnson Assoc., Inc. (R), CA, *107*
Johnson Assoc., Inc. (C), IL, *399*
K. E. Johnson Assoc. (C), WA, *399*
Johnson, Kemper & Assoc. (C), TX, *400*
The Jonathan Stevens Group, Inc. (R), NJ, *108*
Jones and Jones (R), OR, *108*
Jones Consulting Executive Search (C), GA, *400*
Jordan-Sitter Assoc. (R), TX, *108*
J. M. Joseph Assoc. (R), NJ, *109*
Joseph Chris & Assoc. (C), TX, *400*
Joseph Consulting, Inc. (C), FL, *401*
Judd Associates (R), NJ, *109*
KABL Ability Network (C), CA, *402*
Richard Kader & Assoc. (C), OH, *403*
Gary Kaplan & Assoc. (R), CA, *109*
Kaplan & Assoc., Inc. (R), PA, *109*
Karp & Assoc. (C), FL, *403*
Allan Karson Assoc., Inc. (R), NJ, *110*
Martin Kartin & Co., Inc. (R), NY, *110*
Chris Kauffman & Company (R), GA, *110*
Kaufman Assoc. (R), CA, *110*
Jim Kay & Assoc. (C), IL, *404*
The Kay Group of 5th Ave. (C), NY, *404*
Keane Assoc. (R), MA, *110*
A.T. Kearney Executive Search (R), IL, *111*
Thomas A. Kelley & Assoc. (R), CA, *112*
Kelley & Keller, Inc. (C), FL, *405*
S. D. Kelly & Assoc., Inc. (R), MA, *112*
Kennedy & Co. (R), IL, *112*
The Kennett Group, Inc. (R), PA, *112*
William W. Kenney (C), CT, *405*
Kensington Int'l., Inc. (R), IL, *113*
Kent & Assoc. (R), OH, *113*
Kenzer Corp. (R), NY, *113*
Kershner & Co. (R), DC, *113*

Michael L. Ketner & Assoc., Inc. (R), PA, *114*
Key Employment (C), NJ, *405*
Kinderis & Loercher Group (C), IL, *407*
Kingsbury • Wax • Bova (R), MA, *114*
Richard Kinser & Assoc. (R), NY, *115*
Kirby Assoc. (R), PA, *115*
Kirkbride Assoc., Inc. (C), WA, *407*
Kittleman & Assoc.,LLC (R), IL, *115*
The Kleinstein Group, Inc. (R), NJ, *116*
The Kleven Group, Inc. - Executive Search Division (R), MA, *116*
Koehler & Co. (R), WI, *116*
Lee Koehn Assoc., Inc. (R), OR, *116*
T. J. Koellhoffer & Assoc. (R), NJ, *116*
Fred Koffler Assoc. (R), NY, *116*
Koltnow & Company (R), NY, *117*
Kopplin Search, Inc. (R), CA, *117*
Kordus Consulting Group (C), WI, *408*
Koren, Rogers Assoc. Inc. (R), NY, *117*
Korn/Ferry Int'l. (R), NY, *117*
Kors Montgomery Int'l. (R), TX, *118*
Kostmayer Assoc., Inc. (R), MD, *119*
The J. Kovach Group (R), PA, *119*
Katherine R. Kraemer (R), CA, *120*
C. R. Krafski & Assoc., Inc. (R), IL, *120*
J. Krauss Assoc. (R), FL, *120*
Evie Kreisler Assoc. Inc. (C), CA, *409*
Kremple & Meade, Inc. (R), CA, *120*
Kremple Consulting Group (R), CA, *120*
D. A. Kreuter Assoc., Inc. (R), PA, *121*
Kuhn Med-Tech (C), CA, *409*
Paul Kull & Co. (R), NJ, *121*
Kulper & Co., L.L.C. (R), NJ, *121*
Kutt, Inc. (C), CO, *410*
L T M Assoc. (C), IL, *410*
L. Patrick Group (R), NJ, *122*
Marvin Laba & Assoc. (R), CA, *122*
LaCosta & Assoc. Int'l. Inc. (C), CA, *411*
Lamay Assoc., Inc. (R), CT, *124*
The Landstone Group (C), NY, *412*
The Langford Search, Inc. (C), AL, *412*
Langley & Associates, Inc. (Executive Search Consultants) (R), CO, *124*
Lawrence L. Lapham, Inc. (R), NY, *124*
Stephen Laramee & Assoc. Inc. (C), ON, *413*
Larkin & Co. (R), CA, *124*
Larsen Int'l., Inc. (R), TX, *125*
Larsen, Whitney, Blecksmith & Zilliacus, Inc. (R), CA, *125*
Larson Assoc. (R), CA, *125*
Lascelle & Assoc. Inc. (C), ON, *413*
Michael Latas & Assoc., Inc. (R), MO, *125*
Lautz, Grotte, Engler & Swimley (R), CA, *126*
Madeleine Lav & Assoc. (C), CA, *413*
Lawrence-Balakonis & Assoc., Inc. (C), GA, *414*
Lawrence-Leiter & Co. (R), KS, *126*
Leader Institute, Inc. (C), GA, *414*
Leader Network (C), PA, *414*
The Lear Group, Inc. (R), OH, *127*
Lechner & Assoc., Inc. (C), FL, *415*
Ledbetter/Davidson Int'l., Inc. (R), NY, *127*
Leeds and Leeds (C), TN, *416*
Leslie Kavanagh Assoc., Inc. (C), NY, *416*
Levin & Company, Inc. (R), MA, *128*
Michael Levine Search Consultants (R), NY, *129*
Lewis & Blank Int'l. (R), CA, *129*
The Libra Group Inc. (C), CT, *417*
Lois L. Lindauer Searches (C), MA, *418*
Linden Group, Inc. (C), NC, *418*
Lipsky Group, Inc. (R), CA, *129*
Lipson & Co. (R), CA, *130*
Livingston, Robert & Co. (R), CT, *130*
Lloyd Associates (R), GA, *130*
Lloyd Prescott & Churchill, Inc. (R), FL, *130*
Lloyd Prescott Assoc., Inc. (C), FL, *418*
Locke & Assoc. (R), NC, *131*
Loderman & Costello (C), GA, *419*
Loewenstein & Assoc., Inc. (R), TX, *131*
The Logan Group, Inc. (R), MO, *131*
Logic Assoc., Inc. (C), NY, *419*
Longo Associates (C), CA, *420*
Longshore + Simmons (R), PA, *131*
Scott Love Assoc., Inc. (C), AZ, *420*
The John Lucht Consultancy Inc. (R), NY, *131*
Ludwig & Assoc., Inc. (C), VA, *421*
P. J. Lynch Assoc. (R), CT, *132*
Lynch Miller Moore Partners, Inc. (R), IL, *132*
Lyons & Assoc., Inc. (C), IL, *422*
Lyons Pruitt Int'l. (R), PA, *132*
M/J/A Partners (R), IL, *133*
The Mackenzie Group (R), MD, *133*
MacNaughton Assoc. (R), CA, *133*
Maczkov-Biosciences, Inc. (R), CA, *133*
Madison Executive Search, Inc. (C), NJ, *422*
Magellan Int'l., L.P. (C), TX, *422*
Management Alliance Group, Inc. (R), NJ, *134*
Management Assoc. (C), MD, *424*
Management Dimensions Ltd. (R), ON, *134*
Management One Consultants (C), ON, *425*
Management Recruiters of Nassau, Inc. (R), NY, *134*
Management Recruiters of Birmingham (C), AL, *438*
Management Recruiters of Decatur, LLC (C), AL, *438*
Management Recruiters of San Luis Obispo (C), CA, *439*
Management Recruiters Tucson-Foothills, Inc. (C), AZ, *439*
Management Recruiters of Aptos (C), CA, *439*
Management Recruiters of Northern California (C), CA, *440*
Management Recruiters of Laguna Hills (C), CA, *440*
Management Recruiters Dana Point (C), CA, *440*
Management Recruiters, Inland Empire Agency (C), CA, *441*
Management Recruiters of Roseville (C), CA, *441*
Management Recruiters of Sonoma (C), CA, *441*
Management Recruiters of Winsted, Inc. (C), CT, *442*
Management Recruiters of Franktown (C), CO, *442*
Management Recruiters of Middlesex (C), CT, *442*
Management Recruiters of Milford Inc. (C), CT, *442*
Management Recruiters of Ft. Myers, FL. (C), FL, *443*
Management Recruiters of Bonita Springs, Inc. (C), FL, *443*
Management Recruiters of Boca Raton (C), FL, *443*
Management Recruiters of St. Lucie County, Inc. (C), FL, *444*
Management Recruiters of Northern Palm Beaches (C), FL, *444*
Management Recruiters of St. Augustine (C), FL, *444*
Management Recruiters of Duluth (C), GA, *445*
Management Recruiters of Atlanta West, Inc. (C), GA, *445*
Management Recruiters of Vero Beach (C), FL, *445*
Management Recruiters of Savannah (C), GA, *446*
Management Recruiters of Atlanta North, Inc. (C), GA, *446*
Management Recruiters of Atlanta NE (C), GA, *446*
Management Recruiters - Towne Lake (C), GA, *446*
Management Recruiters of Lake Forest, IL (C), IL, *447*
Management Recruiters of Springfield, Inc. (C), IL, *447*
Management Recruiters of Barrington (C), IL, *447*
Management Recruiters of Sun Valley (C), ID, *447*
Management Recruiters of Indianapolis (C), IN, *448*
Management Recruiters of Indianapolis-North (C), IN, *448*
Management Recruiters - Indianapolis (C), IN, *448*
Management Recruiters of Des Moines (C), IA, *449*
Management Recruiters of Williamsburg (C), IA, *449*
Management Recruiters of Frederick, Inc. (C), MD, *450*
Management Recruiters of Birmingham (C), MI, *451*
Management Recruiters of Winona (C), MN, *452*
Management Recruiters of Rankin Co. (C), MS, *452*
Management Recruiters of Lake Tahoe, NV (C), NV, *453*
Management Recruiters of Medford, N.J. (C), NJ, *453*
Management Recruiters of Princeton (C), NJ, *454*
Management Recruiters of Upper Westchester (C), NY, *454*
Management Recruiters of Mt. Airy (C), NC, *456*

Management Recruiters of Akron (C), OH, *457*
Management Recruiters of Sidney (C), OH, *458*
Management Recruiters of Mentor, Inc. (C), OH, *458*
Management Recruiters of Lionville, Inc. (C), PA, *459*
Management Recruiters of Aiken (C), SC, *460*
Management Recruiters The Delta Group, Inc. (C), TN, *461*
Management Recruiters of Georgetown (C), SC, *461*
Management Recruiters of Franklin, Inc. (C), TN, *461*
Management Recruiters of Houston (C), TX, *462*
Management Recruiters of Arlington (C), TX, *462*
Management Recruiters of Houston-Northeast (C), TX, *463*
Management Recruiters of San Antonio (C), TX, *463*
Management Recruiters of Ogden (C), UT, *464*
Management Recruiters Int'l.-The Woodlands (C), TX, *464*
Management Recruiters of Milwaukee-West (C), WI, *465*
Management Recruiters of Kanawha Valley, LLC (C), WV, *465*
Management Recruiters of Seattle (C), WA, *465*
Management Recruiters of Lynnwood (C), WA, *465*
Management Recruiters of Roanoke (C), VA, *465*
Management Recruiters of Appleton (C), WI, *465*
Management Recruiters of Janesville, Inc. (C), WI, *466*
Management Recruiters of Milwaukee - Downtown (C), WI, *466*
Management Resource Group, Ltd. (C), IA, *467*
Management Resources (C), TX, *467*
Management Search Assoc., Inc. (C), GA, *467*
Management Search, Inc. (C), IL, *467*
Management Search of R.I. Inc. (R), RI, *135*
Mannard & Assoc., Inc. (R), IL, *135*
F. L. Mannix & Co. (R), MA, *135*
Manuso, Alexander & Associates, Inc. (R), NY, *135*
The Marathon Group (C), FL, *469*
Marc-Allen Assoc., Inc. (C), FL, *469*
Mark Christian & Assoc., Inc. (C), AZ, *469*
Mark Stanley & Co./EMA Partners International (R), FL, *136*
Marketing & Sales Resources, Inc. (C), FL, *470*
Marketing Resources (C), MA, *470*
The Marlow Group (R), MA, *136*
Marshall-Alan Assoc., Inc. (C), NY, *471*
Donovan Martin & Assoc. (R), CA, *137*
J. Martin & Assoc. (R), CA, *137*
Martin Partners, L.L.C. (R), IL, *137*
Massey-Horton Int'l. (R), ON, *138*
Louis Thomas Masterson & Co. (R), OH, *138*
Matrix Consultants, Inc. (C), NC, *472*
The Matthews Group, Inc. (C), NJ, *472*
Maxecon Executive Search Consultants (R), FL, *138*
K. Maxin & Assoc. (R), PA, *139*
Mary L. Mayer, Ltd. (R), MN, *139*
The Mayes Group, Ltd. (R), PA, *139*
Mayhall Search Group, Inc. (C), IN, *473*
MB Inc. Executive Search (C), NY, *473*
McCann, Choi & Associates, LLC (R), NY, *139*
K. E. McCarthy & Assoc. (R), CA, *139*
McCooe & Assoc., Inc. (R), NJ, *140*
McCormack & Assoc. (R), CA, *140*
McCray, Shriver, Eckdahl & Assoc., Inc. (R), CA, *140*
McDonald Assoc. Int'l. (R), IL, *140*
Clarence E. McFeely, Inc. (R), IL, *141*
Robert E. McGrath & Assoc. (R), CT, *141*
McHale & Assoc. (R), WA, *141*
McIntyre Assoc. (R), CT, *141*
McIntyre Management Resources (C), ON, *474*
McKinley•Arend Int'l. (R), TX, *141*
The McKinnon Management Group Inc. (C), ON, *475*
Dan P. McLean Assoc., Inc. (C), ON, *475*
McNichol Assoc. (R), PA, *142*
Jon McRae & Associates, Inc. (R), GA, *142*
MCS Assoc. (R), CA, *142*
Joseph J. McTaggart (C), CA, *476*
James Mead & Co. (R), CT, *142*
Med Exec Int'l. (C), CA, *476*
Meder & Assoc., Inc. (R), IL, *142*
Media Management Resources, Inc. (R), CO, *142*
Media Recruiting Group, Inc. (C), NY, *476*
The Medley Group (C), CA, *477*
MedSearch Resources, Inc. (C), FL, *478*
Mee Derby & Co. (C), DC, *478*
Meng, Finseth & Assoc., Inc. (R), CA, *143*
Mengel & McDonald Ltd. (C), IL, *479*
The Mercer Group, Inc. (R), NM, *143*
J. M. Meredith & Assoc. Inc. (C), CA, *479*
Merit Professional Search, Inc. (C), TN, *479*
MES Search Co. (C), GA, *479*
MESA, Inc. (R), CO, *143*
Messett Assoc., Inc. (R), FL, *143*
META/MAT, Ltd. (R), NJ, *144*
Walter Meyer & Assoc. (R), NY, *144*
Meyer Assoc., Inc. (R), GA, *144*
Michigan Consulting Group (R), MI, *144*
Millennium Search Group, Inc. (R), CA, *144*
Miller + Miller (C), WA, *482*
Herbert Mines Assoc., Inc. (R), NY, *145*
Mirtz Morice, Inc. (R), CT, *145*
MIXTEC Group (R), CA, *145*
MJF Assoc. (C), CT, *483*
MK & Assoc. (R), CA, *146*
Moffitt Int'l., Inc. (R), NC, *146*
Diedre Moire Corp., Inc. (C), NJ, *483*
Molecular Solutions, Inc. (C), SC, *483*
Molloy Partners (R), NY, *146*
Oscar Montaño, Inc. (R), CA, *146*
Montenido Assoc. (R), CA, *146*
The Montgomery Group, Inc. (C), TN, *484*
Tina Morbitzer & Assoc. (C), FL, *485*
Morgan Samuels Co. (R), CA, *147*
The Morgan/Geoffries Group (C), CA, *485*
Morgenstern Int'l., Inc. (C), FL, *485*
Morris & Berger (R), CA, *147*
Mortgage Search Network (C), AZ, *486*
Morton, McCorkle & Assoc. Inc. (R), MO, *147*
MRI, The Sequel Group, LLC (C), CO, *486*
MTA Partners (R), TX, *148*
Pamela L. Mulligan, Inc. (R), NH, *149*
The Mulshine Company, Ltd. (R), NY, *149*
Multi Processing, Inc. (R), NH, *149*
R. F. Mulvaney & Assoc., Inc. (R), MO, *149*
Jennifer Munro & Partners, Inc. (R), SC, *149*
Munroe, Curry & Bond Assoc. (R), NJ, *149*
P. J. Murphy & Assoc., Inc. (R), WI, *150*
The Murray Group (C), IL, *487*
Mycoff & Assoc. (R), CO, *150*
Myers Career Assoc., Inc. (C), CA, *488*
DDJ Myers, Ltd. (R), AZ, *150*
Nachman Biomedical (C), MA, *488*
Nason & Nason (C), FL, *488*
National Bank & Finance Executive Search (C), CA, *488*
National Career Search (C), AZ, *489*
National Recruiting Service (C), IN, *489*
Nationwide Personnel Recruiting & Consulting, Inc. (C), OR, *490*
The Neil Michael Group, Inc./Global Partners (R), NY, *151*
J. Fielding Nelson & Assoc., Inc. (R), UT, *151*
New Dimensions in Technology, Inc. (C), MA, *492*
New Venture Development, Inc. (C), CA, *492*
New World Healthcare Solutions, Inc. (R), NY, *151*
Newell Assoc. (R), NY, *151*
Newport Strategic Search LLC (C), CA, *492*
NHA Plastics Recruiters (C), FL, *493*
Nichols & Company (R), CO, *151*
P. J. Nicholson & Assoc. (C), IL, *493*
J. L. Nixon Consulting (C), TX, *493*
Noble & Assoc., Inc. (C), NY, *494*
The Nolan Group (C), CA, *494*
Nordeman Grimm, Inc. (R), NY, *152*
Paul Winston Norman & Assoc. (R), IL, *152*
Norman Broadbent Int'l., Inc. (R), NY, *152*
The Normyle/Erstling Health Search Group (C), NJ, *494*
John B. Norris & Assoc., Inc. (C), MD, *495*
North American Recruiters, Inc. (R), MN, *153*
The North Peak Group (C), OH, *496*
Northern Consultants Inc. (R), ME, *153*
Norton & Assoc. (C), IL, *496*
NYCOR Search, Inc. (C), MN, *497*
O'Brien & Bell (R), OH, *153*
O'Brien Consulting Services (R), MA, *153*
O'Callaghan Honey/Ray & Berndtson Inc. (R), AB, *153*

O'Connor, O'Connor, Lordi, Ltd. (R), PA, *154*
O'Connor Resources (C), TX, *497*
O'Rourke Companies, Inc. (R), TX, *154*
Dennis P. O'Toole & Assoc. Inc. (R), NY, *154*
O'Toole & Company, Inc. (R), IL, *154*
Oak Assoc. (R), CA, *155*
The Odessa Group (R), CA, *155*
The Ogdon Partnership (R), NY, *155*
The Oldani Group (R), WA, *155*
Oliver & Rozner Assoc., Inc. (R), NY, *155*
Ollinger Partners (R), MA, *156*
Olsen/Clark (R), WA, *156*
Omega Systems, LLC (C), VA, *498*
The Onstott Group (R), MA, *156*
Opportunity Resources, Inc. (R), NY, *156*
Ortman Recruiting Int'l. (C), CA, *500*
Robert Ottke Assoc. (R), CA, *157*
Overton Consulting (R), WI, *157*
The Oxford Group (C), TX, *500*
P R Management Consultants, Inc. (C), NJ, *500*
P.A.R. Assoc., Inc. (R), MA, *158*
P.R.H. Management, Inc. (R), CT, *158*
Pacific Advisory Service, Inc. (C), IL, *501*
Pacific Coast Recruiters (C), OR, *501*
Pacific Search Group, Inc. (C), CA, *501*
Packaging Personnel Co., Ltd. (C), WI, *501*
Page-Wheatcroft & Co., Ltd. (R), TX, *158*
Pamenter, Pamenter, Brezer & Deganis Ltd. (R), ON, *159*
Paper Industry Recruitment (P.I.R.) (C), ME, *502*
The PAR Group - Paul A. Reaume, Ltd. (R), IL, *159*
Parenica & Co. (R), NC, *159*
Jim Parham & Assoc., Inc. (R), FL, *159*
Frank Parillo & Assoc. (R), CA, *159*
D. P. Parker & Assoc., Inc. (R), MA, *159*
Parker Page Group (C), FL, *503*
Michael W. Parres & Assoc. (R), MI, *159*
Parsons Assoc. Inc. (R), IL, *159*
Partners Resource Group (C), VA, *504*
Partridge Assoc., Inc. (R), MA, *160*
Carolyn Smith Paschal Int'l. (R), CA, *160*
Pathway Executive Search, Inc. (C), NY, *505*
Joel H. Paul & Assoc., Inc. (C), NY, *505*
Pawlik/Dorman Partners (R), IL, *161*
PCD Partners (R), PA, *161*
Peachtree Executive Search (R), GA, *161*
Pearce & Assoc. (C), FL, *506*
Pearson & Assoc., Inc. (C), AZ, *506*
Pearson, Caldwell & Farnsworth (R), CA, *161*
Peck & Assoc., Ltd. (R), WI, *161*
Paul S. Pelland, P.C. (R), SC, *161*
The Penn Partners, Inc. (R), PA, *162*
PERC, Ltd. (C), AZ, *506*
Performance Resources, Inc. (C), RI, *507*
PERI Corp/Professional Executive Recruiters, Inc. (C), TX, *507*
Perry • Newton Assoc. (C), MD, *507*
Fred Perry Assoc. (C), TX, *507*
Perry-Martel Int'l., Inc. (R), ON, *163*
Barry Persky & Co., Inc. (R), CT, *163*
Personnel, Inc. (C), AL, *508*
The Personnel Network, Inc. (C), SC, *508*
J. R. Peterman Assoc., Inc. (C), VT, *509*
Richard Peterson & Assoc., Inc. (R), GA, *163*
Petrie Partners, Inc. (R), FL, *163*
Peyser Assoc., Inc. (R), FL, *163*
Pharmaceutical Recruiters, Inc. (R), NY, *163*
Pharmaceutical Search Professionals, Inc. (C), PA, *510*
Phase II Management (R), CT, *164*
J. R. Phillip & Assoc., Inc. (R), CA, *164*
Phillips Personnel/Search (C), CO, *510*
Phoenix Partners, Inc. (C), GA, *511*
Phoenix Search (R), MX, *164*
Physician Executive Management Center (R), FL, *164*
Physicians Search®, Inc. (C), CA, *511*
Pierce & Assoc. (C), CA, *512*
Pierce & Crow (R), CA, *164*
Pinnacle Executive Group Inc. (C), MO, *512*
Pinsker and Company, Inc. (R), CA, *164*
DNPitchon Assoc. (R), NJ, *165*
Plemmons Assoc., Inc. (R), GA, *165*
Plummer & Assoc., Inc. (R), CT, *166*
Poirier, Hoevel & Co. (R), CA, *166*
Ray Polhill & Assoc. (R), NC, *166*
Bob Poline Assoc. Inc. (C), CA, *514*
Al Ponaman Company, Inc. (C), CA, *514*
Don V. Poole & Assoc., Inc. (C), CO, *514*
David Powell, Inc. (R), CA, *166*
Robert Powers & Assoc. (C), CA, *515*
Powers Consultants, Inc. (R), MO, *166*
P. G. Prager Search Assoc., Ltd. (C), NY, *515*
Elan Pratzer & Partners Inc. (R), ON, *167*
PRAXIS Partners (R), VA, *167*
Precision Executive Search (C), AZ, *516*
Predictor Systems Corp. (R), CA, *167*
George Preger & Associates Inc. (R), ON, *167*
Premier Recruiting Group (C), MI, *516*
Preng & Assoc., Inc. (R), TX, *167*
Preston & Co. (R), NJ, *167*
Prestonwood Assoc. (R), MA, *168*
Price & Assoc., Inc. (C), VA, *518*
Alan J. Price Assoc., Inc. (C), RI, *518*
PricewaterhouseCoopers Executive Search (R), ON, *168*
Prichard Kymen Inc. (R), AB, *168*
The Primary Group, Inc. (R), FL, *168*
Prime Management Group Inc. (C), ON, *518*
Prime Search (C), NC, *518*
Primus Assoc., L.C. (R), TX, *169*
Princeton Search Partners, Inc. (R), NJ, *169*
Prior/Martech Assoc., Inc. (R), WA, *169*
Priority Executive Search (C), FL, *518*
PRO, Inc./Professional Recruiting Offices, Inc. (C), CA, *519*
Professional Personnel Services (C), IA, *520*
Professional Recruiters, Inc. (C), PA, *521*
Professional Recruiting Consultants, Inc. (C), DE, *521*
Professional Resources (C), NY, *522*
The Professional Sales Search Co., Inc. (C), WA, *522*
Professional Support Inc. (C), NY, *523*
Professional Team Search, Inc. (R), AZ, *169*
Professionals in Recruiting Co. (C), TN, *523*
ProFinders, Inc. (C), FL, *523*
Protocol Inc. (C), CA, *525*
Quality Control Recruiters (C), CT, *526*
The Quantum Group (C), NJ, *526*
Quantum Int'l., Ltd. (R), FL, *170*
Quest Worldwide Executive Search Corp. (C), CA, *527*
QuestPro, Inc. (C), TX, *527*
R & L Assoc., Ltd. (R), NY, *170*
R. C. Services (C), TX, *528*
R. J. Associates (C), NY, *528*
Rand Assoc. (R), ME, *171*
Rand Thompson Executive Search Consultants (C), NY, *528*
Rand-Curtis Resources (C), AZ, *529*
The Rankin Group, Ltd. (R), WI, *171*
The Ransford Group (R), TX, *171*
Harold L. Rapp Assoc. (C), NY, *529*
Ray & Berndtson/Lovas Stanley (R), ON, *172*
Ray & Berndtson/Tanton Mitchell (R), BC, *173*
Raymond Karsan Assoc. (C), PA, *529*
Raymond Thomas & Assoc. (C), FL, *530*
RBW Assoc. Inc. (C), OR, *531*
Recruit Xpress (C), TX, *531*
Recruiting Specialists (C), MA, *532*
Recruiting/Solutions (C), CA, *532*
Recruitment Specialists, Inc. (C), MD, *532*
Mary Rector & Assoc., Inc. (C), IL, *533*
Reeder & Assoc., Ltd. (R), GA, *173*
Cedric L. Reese Inc. (C), CA, *533*
Michael James Reid & Co. (R), CA, *174*
Rein & Co., Inc. (R), NJ, *174*
The Douglas Reiter Co., Inc. (R), OR, *174*
Research Personnel Consultants (C), ON, *534*
Reserve Technology Institute (R), TX, *175*
The Resource Group (R), NJ, *175*
The Resource Group (R), CT, *175*
Resource Inc. (R), MA, *175*
Resource Networking Inc. (C), IN, *534*
Resource Perspectives, Inc. (R), CA, *175*
Resources for Management (R), PA, *175*
The Retail Network (C), MA, *535*
S. Reyman & Assoc., Ltd. (R), IL, *176*
Russell Reynolds Assoc., Inc. (R), NY, *176*
Reynolds Consulting Int'l. (R), ON, *177*
RIC Corp. (R), FL, *177*
Marshall Rice Assoc. (R), RI, *177*
Rice Cohen Int'l. (R), PA, *178*
Richard Wright Co. (C), CT, *536*
Richards Assoc., Inc. (R), NY, *178*
Terry Richards (C), OH, *536*
Riddle & McGrath LLC (R), GA, *178*
Ridenour & Assoc. (R), IL, *178*
Rieser & Assoc., Inc. (R), MO, *178*
Riotto-Jones Assoc. (R), NY, *178*
Ritt-Ritt & Assoc., Inc. (C), IL, *537*
RJ Associates (C), CA, *538*
RJN Consulting (R), NY, *179*
RLM Assoc., Ltd. (R), NY, *179*
Norman Roberts & Assoc., Inc. (R), CA, *179*
Robertson & Assoc. (C), IL, *539*

The Robinson Group, D.A., Ltd. (C), IL, *539*
Robinson, Fraser Group Ltd. (R), ON, *180*
Robison Humphreys & Assoc., Inc. (R), ON, *180*
Rodgers, Ramsey, Inc. (C), TX, *540*
Craig Roe & Assoc., LLC (C), MD, *540*
ROI International, Inc. (R), WA, *181*
Rollins & Assoc. (C), CA, *541*
Rollo Assoc. (R), CA, *181*
Rooney Assoc., Inc. (R), IL, *181*
Ropella & Assoc. (R), FL, *181*
Ropes Associates, Inc. (R), FL, *182*
Emery A. Rose & Assoc. (C), WA, *545*
Rosenfeld & Co., Inc. (C), MI, *545*
The Rossi Search Group (C), PA, *545*
Patricia Roth Int'l. (C), FL, *545*
Roth Young of Chicago (C), IL, *546*
Royal Assoc. (C), CA, *547*
J. D. Ruhmann & Assoc. (C), MO, *548*
Ruppert Comann Assoc., Inc. (R), CO, *182*
Rusher, Loscavio & LoPresto (R), CA, *183*
Rushmore • Judge Inc. (R), ON, *183*
Russillo/Gardner/Spolsino (C), MA, *548*
Rust & Assoc., Inc. (R), IL, *183*
W. A. Rutledge & Assoc. (R), CT, *183*
The Ryan Charles Group, Inc. (C), FL, *548*
S.C.S. & Assoc. (C), NC, *550*
Saber Group, Inc. (C), TX, *550*
Sales & Management Search, Inc. (C), IL, *551*
Sales Builders, Inc. (R), VA, *183*
Sales Consultants Int'l. of Oakland (C), CA, *556*
Sales Consultants of Scottsdale, Inc. (C), AZ, *556*
Sales Consultants of Chico (C), CA, *556*
Sales Consultants of Northwest Arkansas, Inc. (C), AR, *556*
Sales Consultants of Ft. Lauderdale, Inc. (C), FL, *557*
Sales Consultants of Ft. Myers, Inc. (C), FL, *557*
Sales Consultants of Danbury (C), CT, *557*
Sales Consultants of Chicago South (C), IL, *558*
Sales Consultants of Western McHenry County (C), IL, *558*
Sales Consultants (C), IL, *558*
Sales Consultants of Cherokee (C), GA, *558*
Sales Consultants of Barrington (C), IL, *558*
Sales Consultants of Indianapolis-North (C), IN, *558*
Sales Consultants of Rockville, MD (C), MD, *559*
Sales Consultants - Bristol County (C), MA, *559*
Sales Consultants of Bangor, Inc. (C), ME, *559*
Sales Consultants of Birmingham (C), MI, *559*
Sales Consultants of Grand Rapids (C), MI, *560*
Sales Consultants of Laurel Park, Inc. (C), MI, *560*
Sales Consultants of Omaha, Inc. (C), NE, *560*
Sales Consultants of Northern Jersey, Inc. (C), NJ, *560*
Sales Consultants of Raleigh-Durham-RTP (C), NC, *561*
Sales Consultants of Middlesex County, Inc. (C), NJ, *561*
Sales Consultants of Princeton, Inc. (C), NJ, *561*
Sales Consultants of Westchester-South, Inc. (C), NY, *561*
Sales Consultants of Newtown, Inc. (C), PA, *562*
Sales Consultants of Rhode Island, Inc. (C), RI, *562*
Sales Consultants of Orangeburg (C), SC, *562*
Sales Consultants of Houston (C), TX, *563*
Sales Management Resources (C), CA, *563*
A. N. Salloway Executive Search & Consulting, L.L.C. (C), MA, *564*
Salzmann Gay Assoc., Inc. (R), PA, *184*
Sampson Medical Search (C), CA, *564*
Sanford Rose Assoc. (C), OH, *565*
Sanford Rose Assoc. - Santa Barbara (C), CA, *565*
Sanford Rose Assoc. - Fairhope (C), AL, *565*
Sanford Rose Assoc. - Clearwater (C), FL, *566*
Sanford Rose Assoc. - Atlanta North (C), GA, *566*
Sanford Rose Assoc. - Effingham (C), IL, *566*
Sanford Rose Assoc. - Norcross (C), GA, *566*
Sanford Rose Assoc. - Carmel, IN (C), IN, *567*
Sanford Rose Assoc. - Springfield (C), MO, *568*
Sanford Rose Assoc. - Gastonia (C), NC, *568*
Sanford Rose Assoc. - Burlington, NC (C), NC, *569*
Sanford Rose Assoc. - Greensboro (C), NC, *569*
Sanford Rose Assoc. - Philadelphia North (C), PA, *570*
Sanford Rose Assoc. - Austin (C), TX, *570*
Sanford Rose Assoc. - Nashville (C), TN, *570*
Sanford Rose Assoc. - Columbia (C), SC, *570*
Sanford Rose Assoc. - Pittsburgh North (C), PA, *570*
Sanford Rose Assoc. - Salt Lake City (C), UT, *571*
Sanford Rose Assoc. - Port Washington (C), WI, *571*
Sarver & Carruth Assoc. (C), OK, *571*
Satterfield & Assoc., Inc. (R), OH, *184*
Saviar, Inc. (C), AZ, *571*
David Saxner & Assoc., Inc. (DSA, Inc.) (R), IL, *185*
Schall Executive Search Partners (R), MN, *185*
The Schatz Company (C), MO, *571*
Schenck & Assoc. SC (C), WI, *572*
A.D. Schiff & Assoc., Ltd. (C), IL, *572*
F. B. Schmidt Int'l. (R), CA, *185*
Schneider, Hill & Spangler, Inc. (R), PA, *185*
Schoales & Assoc. Inc. (C), ON, *572*
G. L. Schwartz & Assoc., Inc. (C), GA, *572*
Schweichler Assoc., Inc. (R), CA, *186*
Devin Scott Assoc. (C), NJ, *572*
Scott Executive Search, Inc. (R), NY, *186*
Scott-Thaler Assoc. Agency, Inc. (C), CA, *573*
The Search Committee (C), MD, *574*
The Search Company (R), ON, *186*
Search Group Inc. (R), AB, *186*
Search Masters Int'l. (R), AZ, *187*
Search North America, Inc. (C), OR, *576*
Search Plus Int'l.-Ohio (C), OH, *576*
SearchCorp International (C), AB, *577*
Searchforce, Inc. (R), FL, *187*
Seco & Zetto Assoc., Inc. (C), NJ, *577*
Secura/Burnett Partners (R), CA, *187*
Seiden Krieger Assoc., Inc. (R), NY, *188*
Selectis Corp. (C), IL, *578*
Selective Management Services, Inc. (C), FL, *578*
Selig Executive Search (C), NH, *579*
Sensible Solutions, Inc. (R), IL, *188*
Shannahan & Co., Inc. (R), CA, *189*
Sharp Placement Professionals, Inc. (C), NY, *579*
Sharrow & Assoc., Inc. (C), MI, *579*
Peggy Shea & Assoc. (R), CA, *189*
Shepherd Bueschel & Provus, Inc. (R), IL, *189*
Shey-Harding Assoc. Inc. (C), CA, *580*
Michael Shirley Assoc. Inc. (R), KS, *190*
Shoemaker & Assoc. (R), GA, *190*
E. L. Shore & Assoc. (R), ON, *190*
The Shotland Group (R), CA, *190*
SHS of Allentown (C), PA, *580*
M. Shulman, Inc. (R), CA, *191*
Shupack & Michaels Inc. (C), NY, *580*
Larry Siegel & Assoc. (R), WA, *191*
Peter Siegel & Co. (C), MA, *581*
Siger & Assoc., LLC (C), CT, *581*
Daniel A. Silverstein Assoc. Inc. (R), FL, *191*
D. J. Simpson Assoc. Inc. (R), ON, *191*
Singleton & Assoc. (C), VA, *582*
Ruth Sklar Assoc., Inc. (RSA Executive Search) (R), NY, *192*
Sloan & Assoc., Inc. (C), VA, *583*
J. L. Small Assoc. (C), AL, *583*
Christopher Smallhorn Executive Recruiting, Inc. (R), MA, *193*
James F. Smith & Assoc. (C), GA, *583*
Smith & Laue Search (R), OR, *193*
Smith & Sawyer, Inc. (R), NY, *193*
Smith & Syberg, Inc. (R), IN, *193*
G. L. Smith Assoc. (C), CA, *584*
Herman Smith Executive Initiatives Inc. (R), ON, *193*
Snelling Search (C), AL, *585*
Snelling Search - Transportation Division (C), AR, *585*
Sockwell & Assoc. (R), NC, *194*
Solomon-Page Healthcare Group (R), NY, *195*
Soltis Management Services (R), PA, *195*
Southern Chemical & Plastics Search (C), GA, *587*

Southern Research Services (R), FL, 195
Sparks, McDonough & Assoc., Inc. (C), MO, 588
Special Markets Group, Inc. (R), GA, 195
Specialized Search Assoc. (C), FL, 589
Spectrum Consultants (R), CA, 196
SpencerStuart (R), NY, 196
Kenn Spinrad Inc. (C), PA, 589
Sports Group Int'l. (R), NC, 198
Spriggs & Co., Inc. (R), IL, 198
M. H. Springer & Assoc. (R), CA, 198
Springer Souder & Assoc. L.L.C. (R), IL, 198
Sprout/Standish, Inc. (C), NH, 589
Staff Extension Int'l. (C), TX, 590
C. J. Stafford & Assoc. (C), ON, 591
Stafford Consulting Group (R), CA, 198
Stanton Chase Int'l. (R), MD, 198
Starbridge Group Inc. (C), VA, 591
The Stark Wilton Group (R), MI, 199
STAT Search (C), NH, 592
Steeple Resources & Consulting (R), NJ, 199
Stentiford & Berardi Assoc. Ltd. (R), NY, 199
Sterling Int'l. Management Recruitment, Ltd. Inc. (C), NC, 592
Michael Stern Assoc., Inc./Euram (R), ON, 200
Steven Douglas Assoc. (C), FL, 593
The Stevenson Group, Inc. (N.J.) (R), NJ, 200
The Stewart Group (C), FL, 593
Stewart, Stein & Scott, Ltd. (R), MN, 200
Stewart/Laurence Assoc., Inc. (R), NJ, 201
Linford E. Stiles & Assoc., L.L.C. (R), NH, 201
The Stonebridge Group (C), PA, 594
Stoopen Asociados, S.C./EMA Partners Int'l. (R), MX, 202
Straight & Co. (R), GA, 202
Mark Stranberg & Assoc. Inc. (R), MA, 202
Strategic Alternatives (R), CA, 202
Strategic Executives, Inc. (R), CT, 202
Strategic Resources Biotechnology & Medical Group (C), WA, 595
Strategic Search, LLC (C), CA, 595
StratfordGroup (R), OH, 203
W. R. Strathmann Assoc. (R), NY, 203
Straube Associates (R), MA, 203
Stroman Int'l., Inc. (R), CO, 204
Success Seekers Connection (C), FL, 596
Sullivan & Assoc. (R), MI, 204
Joe Sullivan & Assoc., Inc. (R), NY, 204
Sullivan & Company (R), NY, 204
The Summit Group (C), CA, 596
Summit Search Specialists (C), TX, 596
Ron Sunshine & Assoc. (C), IL, 597
Survival Systems Staffing, Inc. (C), CA, 597
Swartz & Assoc., Inc. (R), AZ, 204
Synapse Human Resource Consulting Group (R), TX, 205
Synergy 2000 (C), DC, 597
The Synergy Organization (R), PA, 205
Systems Research Group (C), CA, 598
The Talon Group (R), TX, 205
Martin Stevens Tamaren & Assoc., Inc. (R), CA, 206
Tanner & Assoc., Inc. (R), TX, 206
Target Search, Inc. (C), PA, 600
Tate & Assoc., Inc. (R), NJ, 207
Taylor Winfield (R), TX, 207
TBC, Inc. (C), KY, 600
The TBI Group (R), PA, 207
Team One Partners, Inc. (C), GA, 600
Tech Search (C), CA, 601
TechFind, Inc. (R), MA, 207
Technical Recruiting Services (C), OH, 602
TechNix Inc. (C), ON, 602
The Technology Group (R), IL, 208
Technology Management Partners (R), CA, 208
Teknon Employment Resources, Inc. (C), OH, 604
Tekworx, Inc. (C), OK, 604
Tele-Media Int'l. Inc. (C), PA, 604
Telecom Executive Group (C), NJ, 605
Telem Adhesive Search Corp. (C), MD, 605
Telford, Adams & Alexander (R), CA, 208
Thomas Lyle & Co. (C), IL, 606
Thomas Mangum Co. (R), CA, 208
Thomas Resource Group (R), CA, 209
Thompson Assoc. (C), CA, 606
Richard Thompson Assoc., Inc. (R), MN, 209
Tittemore Cowan Assoc. (C), AB, 607
Top Gun Group, Inc. (C), NV, 607
Topaz Int'l., Inc., Attorney Search (C), NJ, 607
TPG & Assoc. (C), TX, 608
TPS Staffing Solutions (C), IN, 608
Jay Tracey Assoc. Inc. (C), VT, 608
Travel Personnel (C), OH, 609
Travis & Co., Inc. (R), MA, 210
TriStaff Group (C), CA, 609
Triumph Consulting, Inc. (R), IA, 210
Trout & Assoc. Inc. (R), UT, 211
Tryon & Heideman, LLC (R), MO, 211
TSC Management Services Group, Inc. (C), IL, 610
Tschudin Inc. (R), NJ, 211
TSW Assoc., LLC (R), CT, 211
Tucker Assoc. (R), NJ, 211
The Thomas Tucker Co. (R), CA, 211
Tuft & Assoc., Inc. (R), IL, 212
Tully/Woodmansee Int'l. Inc. (R), FL, 212
U.S. Search (C), VA, 610
The Ultimate Source (R), CA, 212
Van Dyke Assoc. (R), IL, 212
Peter Van Leer & Assoc. (R), MN, 213
Van Leeuwen Assoc. (R), CA, 213
VanMaldegiam Assoc., Inc. (R), IL, 213
VanReypen Enterprises, Ltd. (R), NY, 213
Venture Resources, Inc. (R), CA, 213
Victor White Int'l. (C), CA, 612
Vlcek & Company, Inc. (R), CA, 214
W. P. Assoc. (C), CA, 613
Wachendorfer & Assoc. (C), TX, 613
Fred Wackerle, Inc. (R), IL, 214
Wakefield Talabisco Int'l. (R), NY, 214
Kelly Walker Assoc. (C), TX, 614
Walker Group, Inc. (R), MN, 215
K. K. Walker Professional Recruitment (C), CA, 614
Martha Ward Executive Search, Inc. (C), NY, 615
The Ward Group (R), MA, 215
Ward Liebelt Assoc. Inc. (R), CT, 215
Ward-Hoffman & Assoc. (C), ID, 615
C. D. Warner & Assoc. (C), PA, 615
Warner & Assoc., Inc. (C), OH, 615
Warring & Assoc. (R), CA, 215
R. J. Watkins & Co., Ltd. (R), CA, 216
Watring & Assoc., Inc. (C), IL, 616
Scott Watson & Assoc., Inc. (R), FL, 216
The Wayne Group, Ltd. (C), NY, 616
Lee Weil Assoc., Inc. (C), IL, 617
S. E. Weinstein Co. (R), IL, 217
The Wellesley Group, Inc. (R), IL, 217
Wellington Management Group (R), PA, 217
Wellington Thomas Ltd. (C), FL, 618
Wells, Bradley & Assoc., Inc. (C), MN, 618
R. A. Wells Co. (C), GA, 618
Jude M. Werra & Assoc. (R), WI, 218
West & Assoc. (C), IL, 618
Western Management Consultants (R), BC, 218
Wheeler Assoc. (R), CT, 219
The Whitney Group (C), GA, 620
Whitney Smith Co. (C), TX, 620
Whittaker & Assoc., Inc. (C), GA, 620
The Whyte Group, Inc. (R), MD, 220
Daniel Wier & Assoc. (R), CA, 220
Wilcox Bertoux & Miller (R), CA, 220
Wilcoxen, Blackwell, Niven & Assoc. (R), FL, 220
The Wilkie Group Int'l. (R), ON, 220
Wilkinson & Ives (R), CA, 221
William-Johns Co., Inc. (C), CA, 621
Williams Executive Search, Inc. (R), MN, 221
Williams, Roth & Krueger, Inc. (R), IL, 221
William Willis Worldwide Inc. (R), CT, 221
Wilson McLeran, Inc. (C), CT, 622
The Winchester Group (R), CA, 222
The Windham Group (R), OH, 222
Winguth, Grant & Donahue (R), CA, 222
Winston Search, Inc. (R), MD, 222
Witt/Kieffer, Ford, Hadelman & Lloyd (R), IL, 223
WMD inc. (C), NJ, 623
S. R. Wolman Assoc., Inc. (R), NY, 224
M. Wood Company (R), IL, 224
Wood-Glavin, Inc. (R), KS, 224
Worldwide Medical Services (C), CA, 625
The Worth Group (C), GA, 625
Dick Wray & Consultants, Inc. (R), CA, 225
The Wright Group (C), TX, 625
Bob Wright Recruiting, Inc. (C), CT, 625
R. S. Wyatt Assoc., Inc. (R), TX, 225
Yankee Hospitality Search (C), CT, 626
Yelverton Executive Search (R), CA, 226
The Yorkshire Group, Ltd. (C), MA, 626
Youngblood Assoc. (C), NC, 626
Yours In Travel Personnel Agency, Inc. (C), NY, 626
Steven Yungerberg Assoc., Inc. (R), MN, 226

Yungner & Bormann (R), MN, *226*
ZanExec L.L.C. (R), VA, *226*
Zeiger Assoc. L.L.C. (C), CA, *627*
Michael D. Zinn & Assoc., Inc. (R), NJ, *227*
Zurick, Davis & Co., Inc. (R), MA, *227*
Zwell Int'l. (R), IL, *228*

01.3 Middle management

A First Resource (C), NC, *231*
A la Carte Int'l., Inc. (R), VA, *1*
A Permanent Success Employment Services (C), CA, *231*
A.J. & Assoc. (C), FL, *232*
A.K.S. Assoc., Ltd. (R), MA, *1*
ACC Technical Services (C), OH, *233*
ACCESS Technology (C), CA, *234*
Accountants Executive Search (C), PA, *234*
Ackerman Johnson Inc. (C), TX, *238*
Action Management Corp. (C), MI, *239*
G. Adams Partners (R), IL, *2*
Adirect Recruiting Corp. (C), ON, *240*
Adler Management, Inc. (R), NJ, *2*
ADR Accounting Management Recruiters (C), ON, *240*
Agri-Tech Personnel, Inc. (C), MO, *242*
Agriesti & Assoc. (C), CA, *243*
Albrecht & Assoc., Executive Search Consultants (C), TX, *243*
Alexander Enterprises, Inc. (C), PA, *243*
Allen, Wayne & Co. LLC (C), WI, *245*
Tom Allison Assoc. (C), NM, *245*
Alpha Resource Group, Inc. (C), TX, *246*
Alpha Search (C), FL, *246*
Altec/HRC (C), MI, *246*
Amato & Assoc., Inc. (C), CA, *246*
Amato & Associates Insurance Recruiters (C), PA, *247*
American Executive Management, Inc. (R), MA, *5*
Ames Assoc. Inc. (C), MD, *249*
Anderson Bradshaw Assoc., Inc. (R), TX, *6*
Andrews & Wald Group (C), FL, *250*
Fred Anthony Assoc. (C), WI, *251*
APA Search, Inc. (R), NY, *6*
Charles P. Aquavella & Assoc. (C), TX, *252*
Aries Search Group (C), GA, *252*
Armor Personnel (C), ON, *253*
R & J Arnold & Assoc., Inc. (C), CO, *253*
Asheville Search & Consulting (C), NC, *253*
E. J. Ashton & Assoc., Ltd. (C), IL, *253*
Ashworth Consultants, Inc. (R), MA, *8*
Asset Resource, Inc. (C), CA, *254*
Associated Recruiters (C), WI, *254*
Association Executive Resources Group (R), MD, *8*
W. R. Atchison & Assoc., Inc. (C), NC, *254*
Atlantic Pacific Group (C), CA, *255*
Auerbach Associates, Inc. (R), MA, *9*
Aurora Tech Search (C), ON, *256*
Cami Austin & Assoc. (C), IL, *256*
Austin Group Int'l./Marlar Int'l. (R), TX, *9*
Austin Michaels, Ltd., Inc. (C), AZ, *256*
AutoPeople (C), VT, *257*
Avestruz & Assoc. (C), CA, *257*
Keith Bagg & Assoc., Inc. (C), ON, *257*
Baker Scott & Co. (C), NJ, *258*
Baker, Nelms & Montgomery (C), IL, *258*
Baldwin & Assoc. (C), OH, *258*
The Bales-Waugh Group (C), FL, *258*
Ballantyne & Assoc. (R), CA, *10*
The Bankers Group (C), IL, *258*
The Barack Group, Inc. (R), NY, *11*
Barclay Consultants, Inc. (C), NJ, *259*
Barnes & Assoc. Executive Search (C), CA, *259*
The Barrett Group (C), NH, *260*
Barrett Hospitality Search (R), CA, *12*
Barrington Hart, Inc. (R), IL, *12*
Aldonna Barry Personnel & Management (C), ON, *260*
The Barton Group, Inc. (C), MI, *260*
The Bauman Group (R), CA, *14*
Beacon Int'l., Inc. (C), VA, *261*
The Bedford Consulting Group Inc. (R), ON, *14*
The Bedford Group (R), RI, *15*
Robert Beech West Inc. (C), CA, *262*
Behavioral Science Assoc., Inc. (R), AZ, *15*
Behrens and Company (C), WA, *262*
Joy Reed Belt Search Consultants, Inc. (R), OK, *15*
Bench Int'l. Search, Inc. (R), CA, *15*
J. P. Bencik Assoc. (C), MI, *263*
Bender Executive Search Management Consulting (R), NY, *16*
Bennett & Associates (C), TX, *264*
The Bennett Group, Inc. (R), IN, *16*
Benson Associates (C), NY, *264*
Berglund Int'l. Resources, Inc. (C), TX, *265*
Berkshire Search Assoc. (C), MA, *265*
Ed Bertolas Assoc., Inc. (C), CA, *265*
Jack Bertram, Executive Recruiter (C), PA, *265*
Besen Assoc. Inc. (C), NJ, *266*
Bialla & Assoc. Inc. (R), CA, *17*
Billington & Assoc. (R), CA, *17*
Binder Hospitality Group (C), KY, *266*
BioQuest Inc. (R), CA, *17*
BioTech Research Recruiters Inc. (C), CA, *267*
Blackhawk Advantage, Inc. (C), CA, *267*
The Blackman Kallick Search Division (C), IL, *267*
Blau Mancino Schroeder (R), NJ, *18*
Block & Assoc. (R), CA, *18*
Blum & Co. (R), WI, *19*
Tom Bogle & Assoc. (C), CA, *269*
Mark Bolno & Assoc. (C), FL, *269*
Bolton Group (C), CA, *269*
Ann Bond Assoc. Inc. (C), MD, *269*
Borchert Assoc. (C), TX, *269*
The Borton Wallace Co. (R), NC, *19*
Bowden & Co., Inc. (R), OH, *20*
BowdenGlobal, Ltd. (R), OH, *20*
Bowie & Associates, Inc. (C), MD, *271*
M. F. Branch Assoc., Inc. (C), NC, *272*
Brandywine Consulting Group (R), PA, *22*
Brandywine Retained Ventures, Inc. (R), CT, *22*
The Brentwood Group Ltd. (R), OR, *23*
Brethet, Barnum & Assoc., Inc. (C), ON, *273*
Brett Personnel Specialists (C), NJ, *273*
Bridgecreek Personnel Agency (C), CA, *273*
Bright Search/Professional Staffing (C), MN, *274*
Brooke Chase Assoc., Inc. (R), IL, *24*
J. B. Brown & Assoc., Inc. (C), OH, *275*
Bryan, Jason & Assoc. Inc. (C), ON, *275*
The Buckley Group (C), FL, *276*
J. Burke & Assoc., Inc. (C), TX, *276*
J. Burkey Assoc. (R), NJ, *25*
The Butlers Co. Insurance Recruiters (C), FL, *277*
C and P Marketing, Ltd. (C), OK, *278*
Caliber Associates (R), PA, *27*
Campbell, Edgar Inc. (C), BC, *280*
Canny, Bowen Inc. (R), NY, *27*
The Canon Group (C), CA, *280*
Canyon Consulting, Inc. (C), TX, *281*
Sally Caplan & Assoc. (C), WA, *281*
Caplan Assoc., Inc. (R), NJ, *28*
Capstone Consulting, Inc. (R), IL, *29*
Career Consultants (R), IN, *29*
Career Development Associates (C), NV, *282*
Career Search Group (C), FL, *283*
Careers On Track (C), NJ, *283*
Carion Resource Group Inc. (C), ON, *284*
Carlson & Czeswik (R), MN, *30*
The Carlyle Group, Ltd. (R), IL, *30*
Carter/MacKay (C), NJ, *285*
Cary & Assoc. (R), FL, *31*
Caywood Partners, Ltd. (R), CA, *32*
CEC Associates (R), MA, *32*
Cejka Healthcare Executive Search Services (CHESS) (R), MO, *32*
Wayne S. Chamberlain & Assoc. (C), CA, *288*
The Chapman Group, Inc. (C), AZ, *289*
Charles & Associates, Inc. (C), NE, *289*
A. D. Check Assoc., Inc. (R), PA, *33*
William J. Christopher Assoc., Inc. (R), PA, *34*
Christopher-Westmont & Assoc., Inc. (R), OH, *34*
Claimsearch (C), CA, *291*
Arlene Clapp, Ltd. (R), MN, *35*
Clark Executive Search (C), NY, *292*
The Clark Group (C), MI, *292*
Clark Personnel Service, Inc. (C), AL, *292*
The Clayton Edward Group (C), MI, *292*
CMC Search Consultants (C), IL, *293*
Coastal Int'l., Inc. (R), MA, *36*
The Coelyn Group (R), CA, *37*
Computer Professionals (R), IL, *38*
The Comwell Company, Inc. (C), NJ, *296*
Conex Inc./InterSearch (R), NY, *39*
M. L. Conner (C), FL, *296*
Construction Search Specialists, Inc. (C), WI, *297*
Consultant Recruiters (C), WI, *297*
Conway & Assoc. (R), IL, *40*
Philip Conway Management (R), IL, *40*
The Cooke Group (R), WI, *40*
Corbin Packaging Professionals (C), MO, *299*
Cornerstone Search Assoc. Inc. (C), MA, *299*
Corporate Careers, Inc. (C), CA, *299*

The Corporate Connection, Ltd. (C), VA, *299*
Corporate Dynamix (C), AZ, *300*
Corporate Management Services (C), PA, *300*
Corporate Resources Professional Placement (C), MN, *300*
Corporate Search Consultants (C), IN, *301*
Corporate Staffing Group, Inc. (C), PA, *301*
Leonard Corwen Assoc. (C), NY, *302*
Cosier & Assoc. (C), AB, *302*
J. D. Cotter Search Inc. (C), OH, *302*
CountryHouse Hotels Executive Search (C), VA, *302*
Cowin Assoc. (R), NY, *42*
Trudi Cowlan (C), NY, *302*
Craig Affiliates, Inc. (C), TX, *302*
Crane, Reed & Co., Inc. (C), NH, *302*
Creative-Leadership, Inc. (R), CA, *42*
CRI Professional Search (C), CA, *303*
Crown Advisors, Inc. (R), PA, *43*
CTR (R), CA, *43*
Culver Personnel Services (C), CA, *304*
Cumberland Professional Search Inc. (C), TN, *304*
The Curtiss Group International (R), FL, *44*
Cyntal Int'l. Ltd. (R), NY, *44*
D & M Associates (C), PA, *306*
D.A.I Human Resources Consultants (R), QE, *45*
Damon & Assoc., Inc. (C), TX, *306*
The Danbrook Group, Inc. (C), TX, *306*
Alfred Daniels & Assoc., Inc. (R), CA, *46*
David Perry Assoc. (C), NJ, *308*
Bert Davis Executive Search, Inc. (R), NY, *47*
The Dayton Group, Ltd. (C), NY, *309*
DBC Recruiting Network (C), GA, *309*
Debbon Recruiting Group, Inc. (C), MO, *310*
Deeco Int'l. (C), UT, *310*
DeLalla - Fried Assoc. (C), NY, *310*
Descheneaux Recruitment Services Ltd. (C), BC, *311*
Dieckmann & Assoc., Ltd. (R), IL, *51*
The Diestel Group (R), UT, *51*
Roger Dietsch & Assoc. (C), MN, *312*
Robert W. Dingman Co., Inc. (R), CA, *52*
Discovery, The Staffing Specialists, Inc. (C), IL, *312*
Dise & Co. (R), OH, *52*
Diversified Search, Inc. (R), PA, *52*
Dixie Search Assoc. (C), GA, *313*
DLG Assoc., Inc. (R), NC, *53*
Doherty Int'l., Inc. (R), IL, *53*
Domres Professional Search (R), WI, *53*
Don Allan Assoc., Inc. (C), CA, *313*
The Dorfman Group (C), AZ, *314*
Dorst Information Services, Inc. (C), NY, *314*
Drinkwater & Assoc. (R), MA, *54*
Dromeshauser Assoc. (R), MA, *55*
DRZ Medical Recruiters (C), CO, *315*
DSR-Search & Recruitment (C), TX, *315*
M. Dunbar & Assoc. (C), TX, *316*
The Duncan-O'Dell Group Inc. (C), TX, *316*
Dunhill Professional Search of Miami (C), FL, *319*
Dunhill Executive Search of Los Angeles, Inc. (C), CA, *319*
Dunhill of San Francisco, Inc. (C), CA, *319*
Dunhill of Manchester Inc. (C), NH, *321*
Dunhill Professional Search of Greater New Orleans (C), LA, *321*
Dunhill Personnel of Northeast Tulsa, Inc. (C), OK, *322*
Dunhill Professional Search of Bucks-Mont., Inc. (C), PA, *322*
Dunhill Professional Search, Inc. of McAllen (C), TX, *323*
Dunhill Search of Vermont (C), VT, *323*
Gwen Dycus & Assoc. (C), FL, *323*
E.P. Int'l. (C), NY, *324*
Eagle Research, Inc. (C), NJ, *325*
EagleView, Inc. (C), MA, *325*
Eden & Assoc., Inc. (C), PA, *326*
EDI/Executive Dynamics Inc. (C), NJ, *326*
Edwards & Assoc. (C), GA, *327*
Bruce Edwards & Associates, Inc. (R), NC, *56*
EFCO Consultants, Inc. (C), NY, *327*
The Eldridge Group, Ltd. (C), IL, *327*
Elliot Assoc. Inc. (R), NY, *58*
H. J. Elliot, Inc. (R), IL, *58*
Steve Ellis (C), CA, *328*
Emerald Legal Search (C), NH, *329*
Employment Solutions, Inc. (C), TX, *330*
The Energists (R), TX, *59*
Engineering & Scientific Search Assoc. (ESSA) (C), NJ, *330*
ENI (R), CT, *59*
The Enterprise Group (R), MA, *60*
Epsen, Fuller & Assoc., LLC (R), NJ, *60*
Erwin Assoc. (R), IL, *60*
ESS (Executive Search Services) (R), CA, *61*
ETI Search Int'l. (R), GA, *61*
The Evans McDonnell Co. (C), TX, *331*
Evans Transportation Search (C), ON, *331*
ExeConnex, LLC (R), GA, *61*
ExecuSource Consultants, Inc. (C), TX, *332*
Executive Access Inc. (R), NY, *62*
Executive Career Search (C), VA, *332*
Executive Connection (C), OH, *333*
The Executive Group, Inc. (R), CA, *62*
Executive Placement Services (C), GA, *333*
Executive Recruiters, Inc. (C), WI, *334*
Executive Recruiters (C), WA, *334*
Executive Resource Assoc. (C), VA, *334*
Executive Sales Search (C), CO, *335*
Executive Search Consultants (R), CA, *63*
Executive Search Consultants, Inc. (C), FL, *335*
Executive Search Consultants (C), CA, *335*
Executive Search Consultants Corp. (C), IL, *335*
Executive Search Int'l. (C), TX, *335*
Executive Search of New England, Inc. (C), ME, *336*
Executive Search Partners (R), NY, *63*
Executive Search Placements, Inc. (C), CO, *336*
Executive Solutions (R), MN, *64*
Dorothy W. Farnath & Assoc., Inc. (C), NJ, *338*
Federal Placement Services (C), NY, *339*
A. E. Feldman Assoc., Inc. (C), NY, *339*
Fenzel Milar Assoc. (C), OH, *339*
Fergason Assoc., Inc. (C), IL, *339*
Ferrari Search Group (C), OH, *340*
Guild Fetridge Acoustical Search, Inc. (C), NY, *340*
Fidelity Search Group, Inc. (R), PA, *66*
Jerry Fields Assoc. (C), NY, *340*
Financial Connections Company (C), VA, *340*
Eileen Finn & Assoc., Inc. (C), NY, *341*
First Choice Search (R), WA, *67*
First Search America, Inc. (C), TN, *341*
First Search Inc. (C), IL, *341*
First Union Executive Search (R), NC, *67*
Fisher & Assoc. (R), CA, *67*
Jack Stuart Fisher Assoc. (C), NJ, *341*
Fisher-Todd Assoc. (C), NY, *341*
FitzGibbon & Assoc. (R), PA, *68*
Flowers & Assoc. (C), OH, *342*
Flynn, Hannock, Inc. (R), CT, *69*
Focus Consulting Services, Inc. (C), FL, *342*
Focus Executive Search (C), MN, *343*
Ford & Ford (C), MA, *343*
Forray Assoc., Inc. (R), NY, *70*
Fortune Group Int'l., Inc. (R), PA, *70*
Fortune Personnel Consultants of Huntsville, Inc. (C), AL, *343*
F-O-R-T-U-N-E Personnel Consultants of San Diego (C), CA, *344*
Fortune Personnel Consultants (C), CA, *344*
Fortune Personnel Consultants of Bloomfield, Inc. (C), MI, *346*
F-O-R-T-U-N-E Personnel Consultants of South Bend (C), IN, *346*
Fortune Personnel Consultants of Topsfield (C), MA, *346*
F-O-R-T-U-N-E Personnel Consultants of St. Louis-West County (C), MO, *347*
F-O-R-T-U-N-E Personnel Consultants of Menlo Park, Inc. (C), NJ, *347*
F-O-R-T-U-N-E of West Portland (C), OR, *348*
F-O-R-T-U-N-E Personnel Consultants of Rockland County, Inc. (C), NY, *348*
Fortune Personnel Consultants of Allentown, Inc. (C), PA, *348*
F-O-R-T-U-N-E Personnel Consultants of Cincinnati (C), OH, *348*
Fortune Personnel Consultants of Hilton Head (C), SC, *349*
Fortune Personnel Consultants of Chattanooga Inc. (C), TN, *349*
FORTUNE Personnel Consultants of Charleston, Inc. (C), SC, *349*
Fortune Personnel Consultants of Anderson, Inc. (C), SC, *349*
F-O-R-T-U-N-E Personnel Consultants of East Seattle (C), WA, *351*
Fortune Personnel Consultants of the Virginia Highlands (C), VA, *351*
Foster Partners (R), NY, *70*
The Fourbes Group, Inc. (C), NJ, *351*
Fox-Morris Assoc., Inc. (C), PA, *351*

Franchise Recruiters Ltd. (R), IL, *71*
Franchise Search, Inc. (C), NY, *352*
Franklin Allen Consultants, Ltd. (R), NY, *71*
The Franklin Search Group, Inc./Medzilla (R), WA, *71*
Mel Frazer Consultant (C), CA, *352*
C. F. Furr & Co. (R), NC, *72*
G. H. Enterprises (C), AZ, *354*
Gahan Assoc. (R), NY, *73*
Gardner-Ross Assoc., Inc. (R), NY, *74*
The Garrison Organization (R), IA, *75*
Garrison-Randall, Inc. (R), CA, *75*
Dianne Gauger & Assoc. (C), CA, *355*
Gielow Assoc., Inc. (R), WI, *76*
Howard Gilmore & Assoc. (R), OH, 77
Gilreath Weatherby Inc. (R), MA, *77*
The Glenwood Group (C), IL, *358*
Global Engineers Inc. (C), ME, *358*
Global Telecommunications, Inc. (C), TX, *359*
Robert G. Godfrey Assoc. Ltd. (R), IL, *78*
Barry M. Gold & Co. (C), CA, *359*
Goldbeck Recruiting Inc. (C), BC, *359*
Goodkind Assoc. Inc. (C), NY, *360*
The Goodman Group (R), CA, *79*
Gossage Regan Assoc. (R), NY, *80*
Graham & Co. (R), NJ, *80*
Robert Grant Assoc., Inc. (C), CA, *361*
Grant/Morgan Assoc., Inc. (C), MD, *361*
Graphic Search Assoc. Inc. (C), PA, *362*
R. Green & Assoc., Inc. (C), OH, *362*
Greenwich Search Partners, LLC (C), CT, *363*
Gros Executive Search, Inc. (C), TN, *363*
Groussman & Assoc., Inc. (R), TX, *82*
David E. Grumney Co. Inc. (R), WA, *83*
Michael R. Guerin Co. (C), CA, *364*
Wolf Gugler & Assoc. Ltd. (R), ON, *83*
H R Solutions, Inc. (C), MO, *365*
M. A. Haggith Consultants Ltd. (R), ON, *84*
Hamilton & Co. (C), OH, *367*
R. C. Handel Assoc. Inc. (R), CT, *85*
Hands-on Broadcast (R), NY, *86*
The Hanover Consulting Group (C), MD, *368*
Harbrowe, Inc. (C), NY, *368*
Hardage Group (C), TN, *369*
Harper Associates (C), MI, *369*
The Harris Consulting Corp. (R), MB, *87*
Harris Heery & Assoc., Inc. (R), CT, *87*
William E. Hay & Co. (R), IL, *88*
Hazard, Young, Attea & Assoc., Ltd. (C), IL, *371*
Headden Assoc. (R), WA, *88*
Health Care Dimensions (C), CO, *371*
Healthcare Recruiters of the Rockies, Inc. (C), CO, *372*
Healthcare Recruiters Int'l - Minnesota, Inc. (C), MN, *373*
Healthcare Recruiters International-NY/NJ (C), NJ, *373*
Healthcare Recruiters of New Orleans (C), LA, *373*
Healthcare Recruiters - Northwest (C), WA, *374*
Healthcare Recruiters of Dallas (C), TX, *374*
HeartBeat Medical, Inc. (C), OR, *374*
Heath/Norton Assoc., Inc. (R), NY, *89*
Hechkoff/Work Executive Search Inc. (R), NY, *89*
Jay Heino Company, LLC (C), NY, *375*
Helbling & Assoc., Inc. (R), PA, *91*
Heller Assoc., Ltd. (R), IL, *91*
Bruce Henry Assoc. Inc. (R), CA, *91*
Kay Henry, Inc. (C), PA, *376*
Heritage Search Group, Inc. (C), FL, *376*
J. J. Herlihy & Assoc., Inc. (C), CA, *376*
A. Herndon & Assoc., Inc. (R), TX, *92*
Robert Hess & Assoc., Inc. (C), CO, *377*
B. W. Higgins, Inc. (C), IN, *377*
Higley, Hall & Co., Inc. (R), MA, *93*
The Hindman Group, Inc. (C), CA, *378*
Hoffman Partnership Group Inc. (C), NY, *379*
The Hogan Group (C), OH, *380*
Home Health & Hospital Recruiters, Inc. (C), GA, *380*
Fred Hood & Assoc. (C), CA, *380*
Hornberger Management Company (R), DE, *95*
Howard-Sloan Assoc. (C), NY, *381*
The Howard-Sloan-Koller Group (R), NY, *97*
Hreshko Consulting Group (C), NJ, *382*
HRI Services, Inc. (C), MA, *382*
Hudson Assoc. Inc. (C), IN, *383*
Hughes & Company (R), VA, *98*
Human Capital Resources, Inc. (C), FL, *384*
Human Resource Dimensions, Inc. (C), TX, *384*
Human Resource Solutions (R), TX, *98*
Hunt Ltd. (C), NJ, *385*
Hunt Patton & Brazeal, Inc. (C), OK, *385*
Hunter Assoc. (C), MA, *385*
Hunter Douglas Group, Inc. (R), IL, *99*
Hunter Int'l., Inc. (R), CT, *100*
Hunter Int'l. LLC (C), MA, *385*
Huntress Real Estate Executive Search (R), MO, *100*
HVS Executive Search (R), NY, *100*
Hyman & Assoc. (C), TX, *386*
The Icard Group, Inc. (C), MI, *387*
Impact Source, Inc. (C), FL, *387*
Independent Power Consultants (C), TX, *387*
Innovative Partnerships (R), CA, *101*
The Inside Track (C), TX, *389*
Insight Consulting Co. (C), NY, *389*
Insurance Career Center, Inc. (C), CT, *389*
Insurance People (C), IN, *390*
IntelliSearch (C), TX, *391*
Inter Regional Executive Search, Inc. (IRES, Inc.) (C), NJ, *391*
Interactive Search Network (R), CA, *102*
Intercontinental Executive Group (C), PA, *391*
Interim Financial Solutions - Mid-Atlantic Region (C), MD, *392*
Interim Management Resources Inc. (C), ON, *392*
International Consulting Services, Inc. (C), IL, *392*
International Recruiting Services (C), FL, *393*
IR Search (R), CA, *103*
Isaacson, Miller (R), MA, *104*
Joan Isbister Consultants (C), NY, *394*
ISC of Atlanta, Inc. (C), GA, *394*
ISC of Cincinnati Inc. (C), OH, *394*
ISC of Houston, Inc. (C), TX, *394*
The J. B. Search Group (C), CA, *395*
Ron Jackson & Assoc. (C), GA, *396*
Jackson Group Int'l. (C), CO, *396*
K. Jaeger & Assoc. (C), MA, *396*
R. I. James, Inc. (C), NY, *397*
JDH & Assoc. (C), CA, *397*
JenKim Int'l. Ltd., Inc. (C), FL, *398*
Jerome & Co. (C), CA, *398*
JM & Company (R), PA, *106*
Johnson & Assoc., Inc. (R), CA, *106*
Johnson Assoc., Inc. (C), IL, *399*
Johnson, Kemper & Assoc. (C), TX, *400*
Jones Consulting Executive Search (C), GA, *400*
Jordan-Sitter Assoc. (R), TX, *108*
Joseph Chris & Assoc. (C), TX, *400*
JPM International (C), CA, *401*
JSG Group Management Consultants (R), ON, *109*
JT Assoc. (C), CT, *401*
Robert Kaestner & Assoc. (C), FL, *403*
Karp & Assoc. (C), FL, *403*
Kaufman Assoc. (R), CA, *110*
Jim Kay & Assoc. (C), IL, *404*
The Kay Group of 5th Ave. (C), NY, *404*
A.T. Kearney Executive Search (R), IL, *111*
Kelley & Keller, Inc. (C), FL, *405*
William W. Kenney (C), CT, *405*
Kensington Int'l., Inc. (R), IL, *113*
Blair Kershaw Assoc., Inc. (C), PA, *405*
Kershner & Co. (R), DC, *113*
Michael L. Ketner & Assoc., Inc. (R), PA, *114*
Key Resources Int'l. (C), CA, *405*
Keystone Consulting Group (C), GA, *406*
Ki Technologies, Inc. (C), UT, *406*
Kincaid Group Inc. (KGI) (C), TX, *406*
Kinderis & Loercher Group (C), IL, *407*
Kingsbury • Wax • Bova (R), MA, *114*
Kirkbride Assoc., Inc. (C), WA, *407*
The Kleven Group, Inc. - Executive Search Division (R), MA, *116*
Koltnow & Company (R), NY, *117*
Kopplin Search, Inc. (R), CA, *117*
Kordus Consulting Group (C), WI, *408*
Michael Kosmetos & Assoc., Inc. (C), OH, *408*
Kostmayer Assoc., Inc. (R), MD, *119*
The J. Kovach Group (R), PA, *119*
C. R. Krafski & Assoc., Inc. (R), IL, *120*
J. Krauss Assoc. (R), FL, *120*
Evie Kreisler Assoc. Inc. (C), CA, *409*
Kremple Consulting Group (R), CA, *120*
Kressenberg Assoc. (C), TX, *409*
John Kuhn & Assoc., Inc. (R), WI, *121*
Kutt, Inc. (C), CO, *410*
L T M Assoc. (C), IL, *410*
L. Patrick Group (R), NJ, *122*
Laboratory Resource Group (C), MA, *411*
Lamay Assoc., Inc. (R), CT, *124*
Lange & Assoc., Inc. (C), IN, *412*
The Langford Search, Inc. (C), AL, *412*

Larsen, Whitney, Blecksmith & Zilliacus, Inc. (R), CA, *125*
Larson Assoc. (R), CA, *125*
Michael Latas & Assoc., Inc. (R), MO, *125*
Latham International, Ltd. (R), NJ, *126*
Madeleine Lav & Assoc. (C), CA, *413*
Lawrence James Assoc. of Florida, Inc. (C), FL, *414*
Lawrence-Balakonis & Assoc., Inc. (C), GA, *414*
W. R. Lawry, Inc. (R), CT, *126*
Leader Network (C), PA, *414*
Leader Resources Group (C), GA, *415*
Lechner & Assoc., Inc. (C), FL, *415*
Ledbetter/Davidson Int'l., Inc. (R), NY, *127*
Albert G. Lee Assoc. (C), RI, *415*
Leeds and Leeds (C), TN, *416*
Leith & Assoc., Inc. (C), OH, *416*
Lending Personnel Services (C), CA, *416*
Michael Levine Search Consultants (R), NY, *129*
The Libra Group Inc. (C), CT, *417*
Pat Licata & Assoc. (C), NC, *417*
LifeWork, Inc. (C), TX, *418*
Lois L. Lindauer Searches (C), MA, *418*
Linden Group, Inc. (C), NC, *418*
Lipsky Group, Inc. (R), CA, *129*
Lloyd Associates (R), GA, *130*
Lloyd Prescott Assoc., Inc. (C), FL, *418*
Locus Inc. (C), WV, *419*
Logic Assoc., Inc. (C), NY, *419*
Scott Love Assoc., Inc. (C), AZ, *420*
Lucas Group (C), NY, *421*
Ludwig & Assoc., Inc. (C), VA, *421*
Lyons & Assoc., Inc. (C), IL, *422*
M. K. & Assoc. (C), PA, *422*
The Mackenzie Group (R), MD, *133*
Madison Executive Search, Inc. (C), NJ, *422*
Managed Care Resources (C), TX, *424*
Management Dimensions Ltd. (R), ON, *134*
Management Recruiters of Nassau, Inc. (R), NY, *134*
Management Recruiters of Birmingham (C), AL, *438*
Management Recruiters of Decatur, LLC (C), AL, *438*
Management Recruiters of San Luis Obispo (C), CA, *439*
Management Recruiters of Aptos (C), CA, *439*
Management Recruiters of Berkeley (C), CA, *439*
Management Recruiters of Clovis (C), CA, *440*
Management Recruiters of Emeryville (C), CA, *440*
Management Recruiters of Northern California (C), CA, *440*
Management Recruiters, Inland Empire Agency (C), CA, *441*
Management Recruiters of Sonoma (C), CA, *441*
Management Recruiters Inc. of Silicon Valley (C), CA, *441*
Management Recruiters of Middlesex (C), CT, *442*
Management Recruiters of Altamonte (C), FL, *442*
Management Recruiters of Milford Inc. (C), CT, *442*
Management Recruiters of Bonita Springs, Inc. (C), FL, *443*
Management Recruiters of Boca Raton (C), FL, *443*
Management Recruiters of Lake Co., Inc. (C), FL, *444*
Management Recruiters of St. Augustine (C), FL, *444*
Management Recruiters of Duluth (C), GA, *445*
Management Recruiters of Atlanta West, Inc. (C), GA, *445*
Management Recruiters of Atlanta (C), GA, *445*
Management Recruiters of Vero Beach (C), FL, *445*
Management Recruiters of Atlanta NE (C), GA, *446*
Management Recruiters - Towne Lake (C), GA, *446*
Management Recruiters of Lake Forest, IL (C), IL, *447*
Management Recruiters of Sun Valley (C), ID, *447*
Management Recruiters-Cedar Rapids, Inc. (C), IA, *448*
Management Recruiters - Indianapolis (C), IN, *448*
Management Recruiters of Williamsburg (C), IA, *449*
Management Recruiters of Rockville (C), MD, *450*
Management Recruiters of Muskegon (C), MI, *451*
Management Recruiters of Birmingham (C), MI, *451*
Management Recruiters of Dearborn, Inc. (C), MI, *451*
Management Recruiters of Winona (C), MN, *452*
Management Recruiters of Rankin Co. (C), MS, *452*
Management Recruiters of Lake Tahoe, NV (C), NV, *453*
Management Recruiters of Medford, N.J. (C), NJ, *453*
Management Recruiters of Princeton (C), NJ, *454*
Management Recruiters of Upper Westchester (C), NY, *454*
Management Recruiters of Bordentown (C), NJ, *454*
Management Recruiters of Manhattan on Broadway (C), NY, *455*
Management Recruiters of Rocky Mount - Southwest (C), NC, *456*
Management Recruiters of Kinston (C), NC, *456*
Management Recruiters of Mt. Airy (C), NC, *456*
Management Recruiters of Winston-Salem (C), NC, *457*
Management Recruiters of Columbus (C), OH, *457*
Management Recruiters of Cleveland (C), OH, *457*
Management Recruiters of Oklahoma City (C), OK, *458*
Management Recruiters of Sidney (C), OH, *458*
Management Recruiters of Mentor, Inc. (C), OH, *458*
Management Recruiters of Lionville, Inc. (C), PA, *459*
Management Recruiters of Valley Forge (C), PA, *459*
Management Recruiters of Delaware County (C), PA, *459*
Management Recruiters of Greenville (C), SC, *460*
Management Recruiters of Aiken (C), SC, *460*
Management Recruiters The Delta Group, Inc. (C), TN, *461*
Management Recruiters of Georgetown (C), SC, *461*
Management Recruiters of Franklin, Inc. (C), TN, *461*
Management Recruiters of Columbia, Tennessee (C), TN, *461*
Management Recruiters Dallas North (MRDN) (C), TX, *462*
Management Recruiters of Champions (C), TX, *462*
Management Recruiters of Arlington (C), TX, *462*
Management Recruiters - Friendswood (C), TX, *462*
Management Recruiters of Houston-Northeast (C), TX, *463*
Management Recruiters of San Antonio (C), TX, *463*
Management Recruiters of San Antonio - North (C), TX, *463*
Management Recruiters of Round Rock (C), TX, *463*
Management Recruiters of Ogden (C), UT, *464*
Management Recruiters of Milwaukee-West (C), WI, *465*
Management Recruiters of Kanawha Valley, LLC (C), WV, *465*
Management Recruiters of Lynnwood (C), WA, *465*
Management Recruiters of Roanoke (C), VA, *465*
Management Recruiters of Appleton (C), WI, *465*
Management Recruiters of Janesville, Inc. (C), WI, *466*
Management Resource Group, Ltd. (C), IA, *467*
Management Resource Group (C), MN, *467*
Management Search Assoc., Inc. (C), GA, *467*
Management Search, Inc. (C), OK, *468*
Management Search of R.I. Inc. (R), RI, *135*
The Marathon Group (C), FL, *469*
Marc-Allen Assoc., Inc. (C), FL, *469*
Margolin Consultants, Inc. (C), NY, *469*
Mark Christian & Assoc., Inc. (C), AZ, *469*

Markent Personnel, Inc. (C), WI, *470*
Marketing & Sales Resources, Inc. (C), FL, *470*
Marshall-Alan Assoc., Inc. (C), NY, *471*
J. Martin & Assoc. (R), CA, *137*
George R. Martin (R), PA, *137*
Richard L. Mather & Assoc. (C), CT, *472*
Matrix Consultants, Inc. (C), NC, *472*
The Matthews Group, Inc. (C), NJ, *472*
G. P. Mattocks & Associates (C), NC, *473*
Maxecon Executive Search Consultants (R), FL, *138*
K. Maxin & Assoc. (R), PA, *139*
MB Inc. Executive Search (C), NY, *473*
K. E. McCarthy & Assoc. (R), CA, *139*
The Paul McDaniel Co. (C), TN, *474*
Robert E. McGrath & Assoc. (R), CT, *141*
Dan P. McLean Assoc., Inc. (C), ON, *475*
McNichol Assoc. (R), PA, *142*
MCS Assoc. (R), CA, *142*
Joseph J. McTaggart (C), CA, *476*
James Mead & Co. (R), CT, *142*
Med Exec Int'l. (C), CA, *476*
Medical Recruiters Inc. (C), MO, *477*
MedSearch Resources, Inc. (C), FL, *478*
Mee Derby & Co. (C), DC, *478*
Mercedes & Co., Inc. (R), MA, *143*
J. M. Meredith & Assoc. Inc. (C), CA, *479*
Merit Professional Search, Inc. (C), TN, *479*
MES Search Co. (C), GA, *479*
MetroVantage Personnel Systems (C), CA, *480*
Walter Meyer & Assoc. (R), NY, *144*
Meyer Assoc., Inc. (R), GA, *144*
Michael Assoc. (R), IL, *144*
Michael James & Co. (C), IL, *480*
Michael Wayne Recruiters (C), IL, *480*
Micro Staff Solutions, Inc. (C), TX, *481*
Miller + Miller (C), WA, *482*
Milo Research (R), NY, *145*
MK & Assoc. (R), CA, *146*
Molecular Solutions, Inc. (C), SC, *483*
Montgomery, Thomason & Assoc. (C), ON, *484*
C. A. Moore & Assoc., Inc. (C), MN, *484*
Tina Morbitzer & Assoc. (C), FL, *485*
The Morgan/Geoffries Group (C), CA, *485*
Morris & Berger (R), CA, *147*
Mortgage Search Network (C), AZ, *486*
MRI, The Sequel Group, LLC (C), CO, *486*
MTA Partners (R), TX, *148*
The Mulshine Company, Ltd. (R), NY, *149*
R. F. Mulvaney & Assoc., Inc. (R), MO, *149*
Jennifer Munro & Partners, Inc. (R), SC, *149*
Munroe, Curry & Bond Assoc. (R), NJ, *149*
The Murray Group (C), IL, *487*
Mycoff & Assoc. (R), CO, *150*
Myers Career Assoc., Inc. (C), CA, *488*
Nachman Biomedical (C), MA, *488*
Nason & Nason (C), FL, *488*
NaTek Corp. (C), NY, *488*
National Affirmative Action Career Network, Inc. (C), CO, *488*
National Career Search (C), AZ, *489*
National Computerized Employment Service, Inc. (C), PA, *489*
National Metal Services Corp. (C), IN, *489*
National Recruiting Service (C), IN, *489*
Nationwide Personnel Recruiting & Consulting, Inc. (C), OR, *490*
J. Fielding Nelson & Assoc., Inc. (R), UT, *151*
Newcomb-Desmond & Assoc., Inc. (C), OH, *492*
Newport Strategic Search LLC (C), CA, *492*
The Niemond Corp. (R), CA, *152*
Nino Recruiting & Staffing, Inc. (C), TX, *493*
Ira Z. Nitzberg (C), NY, *493*
J. L. Nixon Consulting (C), TX, *493*
The Noebel Search Group, Inc. (C), TX, *494*
The Nolan Group (C), CA, *494*
Paul Winston Norman & Assoc. (R), IL, *152*
Norman Broadbent Int'l., Inc. (R), NY, *152*
The Normyle/Erstling Health Search Group (C), NJ, *494*
John B. Norris & Assoc., Inc. (C), MD, *495*
Ronald Norris & Assoc. (C), IL, *495*
NorTech Resources (C), NY, *496*
North American Recruiters, Inc. (R), MN, *153*
Nyborg•Dow Assoc., Inc. (C), CA, *497*
O'Brien Consulting Services (R), MA, *153*
O'Connor Resources (C), TX, *497*
O'Neill Group (C), NJ, *498*
O'Rourke Companies, Inc. (R), TX, *154*
Dennis P. O'Toole & Assoc. Inc. (R), NY, *154*
O'Toole & Company, Inc. (R), IL, *154*
Omega Systems, LLC (C), VA, *498*
Ortman Recruiting Int'l. (C), CA, *500*
Pacific Advisory Service, Inc. (C), IL, *501*
Pacific Coast Recruiting (C), CA, *501*
Pacific Coast Recruiters (C), OR, *501*
Pacific Crossing (C), CA, *501*
Packaging Personnel Co., Ltd. (C), WI, *501*
Pamenter, Pamenter, Brezer & Deganis Ltd. (R), ON, *159*
The PAR Group - Paul A. Reaume, Ltd. (R), IL, *159*
Jim Parham & Assoc., Inc. (R), FL, *159*
Frank Parillo & Assoc. (R), CA, *159*
Michael W. Parres & Assoc. (R), MI, *159*
Parsons Assoc. Inc. (R), IL, *159*
Partners Executive Search Consultants Inc. (R), ON, *160*
The Partnership Group (R), NJ, *160*
Partnervision Consulting Group Inc. (R), ON, *160*
Partridge Assoc., Inc. (R), MA, *160*
Patrice & Assoc. (C), MD, *505*
Joel H. Paul & Assoc., Inc. (C), NY, *505*
Paules Associates (C), CA, *505*
Pawlik/Dorman Partners (R), IL, *161*
PC Assoc. (C), CO, *505*
Paul S. Pelland, P.C. (R), SC, *161*
The Penn Partners, Inc. (R), PA, *162*
PERC, Ltd. (C), AZ, *506*
Performance Resources, Inc. (C), RI, *507*
PERI Corp/Professional Executive Recruiters, Inc. (C), TX, *507*
Perry • Newton Assoc. (C), MD, *507*
Fred Perry Assoc. (C), TX, *507*
Personnel, Inc. (C), AL, *508*
Personnel Management Group (C), MB, *508*
The Personnel Network, Inc. (C), SC, *508*
Personnel Tangent Inc. (C), QE, *509*
J. R. Peterman Assoc., Inc. (C), VT, *509*
Richard Peterson & Assoc., Inc. (R), GA, *163*
Petrie Partners, Inc. (R), FL, *163*
Pharmaceutical Recruiters, Inc. (R), NY, *163*
Pharmaceutical Search Professionals, Inc. (C), PA, *510*
Phase II Management (R), CT, *164*
Phillips & Assoc. (R), MA, *164*
Pinnacle Executive Group Inc. (C), MO, *512*
Pinsker and Company, Inc. (R), CA, *164*
DNPitchon Assoc. (R), NJ, *165*
Plemmons Assoc., Inc. (R), GA, *165*
R. L. Plimpton Assoc., Inc. (R), CO, *165*
Plummer & Assoc., Inc. (R), CT, *166*
PMJ & Assoc. (C), ON, *513*
Ray Polhill & Assoc. (R), NC, *166*
Bob Poline Assoc. Inc. (C), CA, *514*
Al Ponaman Company, Inc. (C), CA, *514*
Robert Powers & Assoc. (C), CA, *515*
Predictor Systems Corp. (R), CA, *167*
Premier Recruiting Group (C), MI, *516*
Preng & Assoc., Inc. (R), TX, *167*
Presley Consultants, Inc. (C), CA, *517*
Preston & Co. (R), NJ, *167*
Alan J. Price Assoc., Inc. (C), RI, *518*
PricewaterhouseCoopers Executive Search (R), ON, *168*
Prime Search (C), NC, *518*
Primus Assoc., L.C. (R), TX, *169*
Princeton Search Partners, Inc. (R), NJ, *169*
Procurement Resources (C), MD, *520*
Professional Personnel Services (C), IA, *520*
Professional Recruiters, Inc. (C), PA, *521*
Professional Recruiters (C), UT, *521*
Professional Recruiting Consultants, Inc. (C), DE, *521*
The Professional Sales Search Co., Inc. (C), WA, *522*
Professional Selection Services (R), GA, *169*
ProFinders, Inc. (C), FL, *523*
Proquest Inc. (C), SC, *524*
ProSearch, Inc. (C), OH, *524*
Proven Edge (C), CA, *525*
PSP Agency (C), NY, *525*
The Quantum Group (C), NJ, *526*
Quantum Int'l., Ltd. (R), FL, *170*
QuestPro, Inc. (C), TX, *527*
R & L Assoc., Ltd. (R), NY, *170*
R M Associates (R), OH, *171*
R. C. Services (C), TX, *528*
R2 Services, LLC (C), IL, *528*
Ramming & Assoc., Inc. (C), NJ, *528*
Rand Assoc. (R), ME, *171*
Rand-Curtis Resources (C), AZ, *529*
Lea Randolph & Assoc., Inc. (C), TX, *529*
The Rankin Group, Ltd. (R), WI, *171*
Harold L. Rapp Assoc. (C), NY, *529*

Ray & Berndtson/Tanton Mitchell (R), BC, *173*
Raymond Thomas & Assoc. (C), FL, *530*
RBW Assoc. Inc. (C), OR, *531*
RCI Employment Solutions (C), FL, *531*
Reality Group (C), OK, *531*
Recruit Xpress (C), TX, *531*
Recruiting Specialists (C), MA, *532*
Recruiting/Solutions (C), CA, *532*
The Recruitment Group, Inc. (C), NY, *532*
P. J. Reda & Assoc., Inc. (C), GA, *533*
Cedric L. Reese Inc. (C), CA, *533*
Reinecke & Assoc. (C), NJ, *533*
The Douglas Reiter Co., Inc. (R), OR, *174*
Research Personnel Consultants (C), ON, *534*
The Resource Group (R), NJ, *175*
The Resource Group (R), CT, *175*
Retail Connection, Inc. (C), NJ, *535*
The Retail Network (C), MA, *535*
RIC Corp. (R), FL, *177*
Richard Wright Co. (C), CT, *536*
Richards Assoc., Inc. (R), NY, *178*
Terry Richards (C), OH, *536*
Riotto-Jones Assoc. (R), NY, *178*
Ritt-Ritt & Assoc., Inc. (C), IL, *537*
Ritta Professional Search Inc. (C), NY, *538*
RJ Associates (C), CA, *538*
RJN Consulting (R), NY, *179*
RLM Assoc., Ltd. (R), NY, *179*
RML Assoc. (C), PA, *538*
Robertson & Assoc. (C), IL, *539*
The Robinson Group, D.A., Ltd. (C), IL, *539*
Robison Humphreys & Assoc., Inc. (R), ON, *180*
J. P. Roddy Consultants (C), PA, *540*
J. Rodgers & Associates (C), IL, *540*
Craig Roe & Assoc., LLC (C), MD, *540*
The Rogan Group, Inc. (C), CA, *541*
Rogers - McManamon Executive Search (R), CA, *180*
Rollins & Assoc. (C), CA, *541*
Romac Int'l. (C), PA, *542*
Rooney Assoc., Inc. (R), IL, *181*
Ropella & Assoc. (R), FL, *181*
Ropes Associates, Inc. (R), FL, *182*
The Rossi Search Group (C), PA, *545*
Patricia Roth Int'l. (C), FL, *545*
Roth Young of Chicago (C), IL, *546*
Roth Young of Pittsburgh (C), PA, *546*
Roth Young of Tampa (C), FL, *546*
Rovner & Assoc., Inc. (R), IL, *182*
Rowland Mountain & Assoc. (C), GA, *547*
The Rubicon Group (C), AZ, *547*
J. D. Ruhmann & Assoc. (C), MO, *548*
Ruppert Comann Assoc., Inc. (R), CO, *182*
Russillo/Gardner/Spolsino (C), MA, *548*
Rust & Assoc., Inc. (R), IL, *183*
W. A. Rutledge & Assoc. (R), CT, *183*
R. L. Rystrom & Assoc., Inc. (C), MN, *549*
S-H-S TechStaff (C), PA, *549*
S. P. Assoc., Inc. (C), NC, *550*
S.C.S. & Assoc. (C), NC, *550*
Saber Group, Inc. (C), TX, *550*
Sales & Management Search, Inc. (C), IL, *551*
Sales Consultants Peninsula, Inc. (C), CA, *556*
Sales Consultants of Silicon Valley (C), CA, *556*
Sales Consultants of Chico (C), CA, *556*
Sales Consultants of Daphne (C), AL, *556*
Sales Consultants of Ft. Lauderdale, Inc. (C), FL, *557*
Sales Consultants of Ft. Myers, Inc. (C), FL, *557*
Sales Consultants of Danbury (C), CT, *557*
Sales Consultants of Chicago South (C), IL, *558*
Sales Consultants of Cherokee (C), GA, *558*
Sales Consultants of Rockville, MD (C), MD, *559*
Sales Consultants - Bristol County (C), MA, *559*
Sales Consultants of Bangor, Inc. (C), ME, *559*
Sales Consultants of Birmingham (C), MI, *559*
Sales Consultants of Farmington Hills (C), MI, *560*
Sales Consultants of Nashua-Manchester (C), NH, *560*
Sales Consultants of Grand Rapids (C), MI, *560*
Sales Consultants of Laurel Park, Inc. (C), MI, *560*
Sales Consultants of Cherry Hill (C), NJ, *560*
Sales Consultants Bridgewater, Inc. (C), NJ, *560*
Sales Consultants of Raleigh-Durham-RTP (C), NC, *561*
Sales Consultants of Westchester-South, Inc. (C), NY, *561*
Sales Consultants of Newtown, Inc. (C), PA, *562*
Sales Consultants of Rhode Island, Inc. (C), RI, *562*
Sales Consultants King of Prussia (C), PA, *562*
Sales Consultants of Orangeburg (C), SC, *562*
Sales Management Resources (C), CA, *563*
A. N. Salloway Executive Search & Consulting, L.L.C. (C), MA, *564*
George D. Sandel Assoc. (C), MA, *565*
Sanford Rose Assoc. (C), OH, *565*
Sanford Rose Assoc. - Santa Barbara (C), CA, *565*
Sanford Rose Assoc. - Clearwater (C), FL, *566*
Sanford Rose Assoc. - Effingham (C), IL, *566*
Sanford Rose Assoc. - Atlanta North (C), GA, *566*
Sanford Rose Assoc. - Athens (C), GA, *566*
Sanford Rose Assoc. - Norcross (C), GA, *566*
Sanford Rose Assoc. - Columbia, MD (C), MD, *567*
Sanford Rose Assoc. - Springfield (C), MO, *568*
Sanford Rose Assoc. - Lake St. Louis (C), MO, *568*
Sanford Rose Assoc. - Amherst, NY (C), NY, *568*
Sanford Rose Assoc. - Rochester (C), MI, *568*
Sanford Rose Assoc. - Gastonia (C), NC, *568*
Sanford Rose Assoc. - Greensboro (C), NC, *569*
Sanford Rose Assoc. - Philadelphia North (C), PA, *570*
Sanford Rose Assoc. - Austin (C), TX, *570*
Sanford Rose Assoc. - Nashville (C), TN, *570*
Sanford Rose Assoc. - Portland (C), OR, *570*
Sanford Rose Assoc. - Salt Lake City (C), UT, *571*
Sarver & Carruth Assoc. (C), OK, *571*
David Saxner & Assoc., Inc. (DSA, Inc.) (R), IL, *185*
A.D. Schiff & Assoc., Ltd. (C), IL, *572*
Schlatter & Assoc. (C), CA, *572*
G. L. Schwartz & Assoc., Inc. (C), GA, *572*
Scott Sibley Assoc. (C), NY, *573*
Scott-Thaler Assoc. Agency, Inc. (C), CA, *573*
Search Assoc. (C), KY, *574*
The Search Company (R), ON, *186*
Search Innovations, Inc. (R), PA, *187*
Search Int'l. (R), MA, *187*
The Search Network (C), CA, *576*
Search Research Assoc., Inc. (R), MA, *187*
Search Solutions Inc. (C), CA, *576*
Search South, Inc. (C), AL, *576*
SearchCorp International (C), AB, *577*
Searchforce, Inc. (R), FL, *187*
Seco & Zetto Assoc., Inc. (C), NJ, *577*
Seiden Krieger Assoc., Inc. (R), NY, *188*
Selective Recruiting Assoc., Inc. (C), MI, *578*
Selig Executive Search (C), NH, *579*
Sevcor Int'l., Inc. (R), IL, *188*
Shannahan & Co., Inc. (R), CA, *189*
Peggy Shea & Assoc. (R), CA, *189*
Shey-Harding Assoc. Inc. (C), CA, *580*
Shiell Personnel (C), LA, *580*
E. L. Shore & Assoc. (R), ON, *190*
The Shotland Group (R), CA, *190*
SHS of Allentown (C), PA, *580*
Shupack & Michaels Inc. (C), NY, *580*
Peter Siegel & Co. (C), MA, *581*
Sill Technical Assoc., Inc. (C), PA, *581*
SilverSands Int'l. (C), FL, *582*
Smith & Assoc. (C), CA, *583*
James F. Smith & Assoc. (C), GA, *583*
Ralph Smith & Assoc. (C), IL, *584*
Smith & Laue Search (R), OR, *193*
Smith & Syberg, Inc. (R), IN, *193*
Herman Smith Executive Initiatives Inc. (R), ON, *193*
Snelling Search - Transportation Division (C), AR, *585*
C. Snow & Assoc. (C), ON, *586*
Solomon-Page Healthcare Group (R), NY, *195*
Southern Chemical & Plastics Search (C), GA, *587*
Southern Research Services (R), FL, *195*
Sparks, McDonough & Assoc., Inc. (C), MO, *588*
Specialized Search Assoc. (C), FL, *589*

SpencerSearch, Inc. (C), CO, *589*
SpencerStuart (R), NY, *196*
Kenn Spinrad Inc. (C), PA, *589*
Sports Group Int'l. (R), NC, *198*
Sprout/Standish, Inc. (C), NH, *589*
Stafford Consulting Group (R), CA, *198*
Stanton Chase Int'l. (R), MD, *198*
Starbridge Group Inc. (C), VA, *591*
STAT Search (C), NH, *592*
Steeple Resources & Consulting (R), NJ, *199*
Stentiford & Berardi Assoc. Ltd. (R), NY, *199*
Steven Michaels & Assoc. (C), NY, *593*
The Stevenson Group, Inc. (N.J.) (R), NJ, *200*
Stewart/Laurence Assoc., Inc. (R), NJ, *201*
The Stonebridge Group (C), PA, *594*
Straight & Co. (R), GA, *202*
Strategic Advancement Inc. (R), NJ, *202*
Strategic Resources Biotechnology & Medical Group (C), WA, *595*
Stratin Assoc. (C), NJ, *596*
Summit Group Int'l., Inc. (R), GA, *204*
Summit Search Specialists (C), TX, *596*
Ron Sunshine & Assoc. (C), IL, *597*
Swift & Assoc. (C), ME, *597*
Synergistics Assoc. Ltd. (R), IL, *205*
Systems Research Group (C), CA, *598*
The Talon Group (R), TX, *205*
S. Tanner & Assoc. Inc. (C), ON, *599*
Tanner & Assoc., Inc. (R), TX, *206*
Target Search, Inc. (C), PA, *600*
TBC, Inc. (C), KY, *600*
The TBI Group (R), PA, *207*
Team One Partners, Inc. (C), GA, *600*
Tech Search (C), CA, *601*
TechFind, Inc. (R), MA, *207*
The Technology Group (R), IL, *208*
Technology Management Partners (R), CA, *208*
Tekworx, Inc. (C), OK, *604*
Tele-Media Int'l. Inc. (C), PA, *604*
Telecom Executive Group (C), NJ, *605*
Telem Adhesive Search Corp. (C), MD, *605*
Telford, Adams & Alexander (R), CA, *208*
Thomas Lyle & Co. (C), IL, *606*
Thomson, Sponar & Adams, Inc. (C), WA, *606*
Fred C. Tippel & Assoc. (C), OH, *607*
Tittemore Cowan Assoc. (C), AB, *607*
Tondorf & Assoc. Inc. (C), MA, *607*
TPG & Assoc. (C), TX, *608*
Jay Tracey Assoc. Inc. (C), VT, *608*
Travel Personnel (C), OH, *609*
TSC Management Services Group, Inc. (C), IL, *610*
Tschudin Inc. (R), NJ, *211*
Tuft & Assoc., Inc. (R), IL, *212*
Van Dyke Assoc. (R), IL, *212*
VanReypen Enterprises, Ltd. (R), NY, *213*
Victor White Int'l. (C), CA, *612*
Vintage Resources, Inc. (C), NY, *613*
Voigt Assoc. (R), IL, *214*
VZ Int'l., Inc. (C), AZ, *613*
W. P. Assoc. (C), CA, *613*
Wakefield Talabisco Int'l. (R), NY, *214*
Kelly Walker Assoc. (C), TX, *614*
Walker Group, Inc. (R), MN, *215*
Lee H. Walton & Assoc. (R), NY, *215*
Martha Ward Executive Search, Inc. (C), NY, *615*
C. D. Warner & Assoc. (C), PA, *615*
Warner & Assoc., Inc. (C), OH, *615*
Watring & Assoc., Inc. (C), IL, *616*
S. B. Webster & Associates (R), MA, *217*
Wegner & Assoc. (C), WI, *617*
Lee Weil Assoc., Inc. (C), IL, *617*
David Weinfeld Group (C), NC, *617*
Weinpel Search, Inc. (C), NJ, *617*
The Wellesley Group, Inc. (R), IL, *217*
Wellington Thomas Ltd. (C), FL, *618*
Wesley Brown & Bartle Co., Inc. (R), NY, *218*
West & Assoc. (C), IL, *618*
Western Management Consultants (R), BC, *218*
The Whitney Group (C), GA, *620*
Whitney Smith Co. (C), TX, *620*
Whittaker & Assoc., Inc. (C), GA, *620*
The Whyte Group, Inc. (R), MD, *220*
Wilcox Bertoux & Miller (R), CA, *220*
Wilcoxen, Blackwell, Niven & Assoc. (R), FL, *220*
John R. Williams & Assoc., Inc. (C), NC, *621*
John Williams & Assoc. (C), TX, *621*
Williams, Roth & Krueger, Inc. (R), IL, *221*
Wilson Personnel, Inc. (C), NC, *622*
Windsor Consultants, Inc. (C), TX, *622*
Winfield Assoc., Inc. (C), MA, *623*
Winthrop Partners, Inc. (R), NY, *222*
Susan L. Wonderling Recruiting (C), PA, *623*
Wood & Assoc./Executive Search Consultants (C), CA, *624*
M. Wood Company (R), IL, *224*
Wood-Glavin, Inc. (R), KS, *224*
The Woodstone Consulting Company, Inc. (R), CO, *224*
Dick Wray & Consultants, Inc. (R), CA, *225*
The Wright Group (C), TX, *625*
Bob Wright Recruiting, Inc. (C), CT, *625*
WTW Assoc., Inc. (R), NY, *225*
R. S. Wyatt Assoc., Inc. (R), TX, *225*
The Yaiser Group (C), NJ, *625*
Yankee Hospitality Search (C), CT, *626*
The Yorkshire Group, Ltd. (C), MA, *626*
Youngblood Assoc. (C), NC, *626*
Yours In Travel Personnel Agency, Inc. (C), NY, *626*
Zaccaria Int'l. (C), NJ, *627*
ZanExec L.L.C. (R), VA, *226*
Zeiger Assoc. L.L.C. (C), CA, *627*
Michael D. Zinn & Assoc., Inc. (R), NJ, *227*
Zurick, Davis & Co., Inc. (R), MA, *227*
Zwell Int'l. (R), IL, *228*

01.4 Administrative services

A.K.S. Assoc., Ltd. (R), MA, *1*
ADR Accounting Management Recruiters (C), ON, *240*
Advice Personnel Inc. (C), NY, *241*
Alpha Search (C), FL, *246*
American Heritage Group, Inc. (C), MI, *247*
Ames Assoc. Inc. (C), MD, *249*
APA Employment Agency Inc. (C), OR, *251*
Armor Personnel (C), ON, *253*
The Bankers Group (C), IL, *258*
Aldonna Barry Personnel & Management (C), ON, *260*
Battalia Winston Int'l./The Euram Consultants Group (R), NY, *13*
C. Berger And Company (R), IL, *16*
Bryan, Jason & Assoc. Inc. (C), ON, *275*
Campbell, Edgar Inc. (C), BC, *280*
Career Strategies, Inc. (C), CA, *283*
Colt Systems Professional Personnel Services (C), CA, *294*
Continental Research Search, Inc. (C), WI, *298*
Cornerstone Search Assoc. Inc. (C), MA, *299*
Cornwall Stockton & Co., Inc. (C), TX, *299*
Corporate Search, Inc. (C), NY, *301*
Creative HR Solutions (C), GA, *303*
DARE Personnel Inc. (C), ON, *307*
The Dayton Group, Ltd. (C), NY, *309*
Descheneaux Recruitment Services Ltd. (C), BC, *311*
Diversified Health Search (R), PA, *52*
Diversified Search, Inc. (R), PA, *52*
Drummond Assoc., Inc. (C), NY, *315*
Dunhill of Manchester Inc. (C), NH, *321*
Dunhill Professional Search of Bucks-Mont., Inc. (C), PA, *322*
Elinvar (C), NC, *328*
Executive Search Consultants (R), CA, *63*
Fergason Assoc., Inc. (C), IL, *339*
First Search America, Inc. (C), TN, *341*
Foster Partners (R), NY, *70*
The Fourbes Group, Inc. (C), NJ, *351*
GFI Professional Staffing Services (C), NH, *357*
The Gobbell Co. (R), CA, *78*
Government Contract Solutions, Inc. (C), VA, *360*
Gowdy Consultants (C), TX, *361*
Graphic Search Assoc. Inc. (C), PA, *362*
Groupe PCA Inc. (C), QE, *363*
Harbrowe, Inc. (C), NY, *368*
Highland & Assoc. (C), CA, *378*
HRI Services, Inc. (C), MA, *382*
The Hyde Group, Inc. (R), CT, *101*
Impact Search & Strategies (C), PA, *387*
Insurance People (C), IN, *390*
IntelliSearch (C), TX, *391*
Interim Financial Solutions - Mid-Atlantic Region (C), MD, *392*
Isaacson, Miller (R), MA, *104*
A.T. Kearney Executive Search (R), IL, *111*
Michael L. Ketner & Assoc., Inc. (R), PA, *114*
The Libra Group Inc. (C), CT, *417*
Bruce Lowery & Assoc. (C), MI, *420*
Management Recruiters-Cedar Rapids, Inc. (C), IA, *448*

Management Recruiters of Frederick, Inc. (C), MD, *450*
Management Recruiters of Detroit & Farmington Hills (C), MI, *451*
Management Resource Group, Ltd. (C), IA, *467*
MCS Assoc. (R), CA, *142*
Micro Staff Solutions, Inc. (C), TX, *481*
Herbert Mines Assoc., Inc. (R), NY, *145*
Networking Unlimited of NH, Inc. (C), NH, *491*
Nordeman Grimm, Inc. (R), NY, *152*
NPS of Atlanta, Inc. (C), GA, *496*
O'Sullivan Search Inc. (C), ON, *498*
LaMonte Owens, Inc. (R), PA, *157*
PCD Partners (R), PA, *161*
Fred Perry Assoc. (C), TX, *507*
J. R. Peterman Assoc., Inc. (C), VT, *509*
Don V. Poole & Assoc., Inc. (C), CO, *514*
P. G. Prager Search Assoc., Ltd. (C), NY, *515*
Professional Resources (C), NY, *522*
QuestPro, Inc. (C), TX, *527*
R. C. Services (C), TX, *528*
Ray & Berndtson/Tanton Mitchell (R), BC, *173*
Rollins & Assoc. (C), CA, *541*
Rosenfeld & Co., Inc. (C), MI, *545*
Sales Consultants Bridgewater, Inc. (C), NJ, *560*
Sanford Rose Assoc. - Effingham (C), IL, *566*
Sanford Rose Assoc. - Evansville (C), IN, *567*
SpencerStuart (R), NY, *196*
Stafford Consulting Group (R), CA, *198*
DM Stone Personnel Services (C), CA, *594*
Strauss Personnel Service (C), PA, *596*
The TBI Group (R), PA, *207*
United Personnel Services (C), MA, *611*
VanReypen Enterprises, Ltd. (R), NY, *213*
Vincenty & Co. (C), OH, *612*
Wellington Thomas Ltd. (C), FL, *618*

01.5 Legal

A-K-A (Anita Kaufmann Assoc.) (C), NY, *231*
Cathy Abelson Legal Search (C), PA, *232*
Attorney Search Global, Inc. (C), IL, *255*
A. M. Auster Associates (R), FL, *9*
Battalia Winston Int'l./The Euram Consultants Group (R), NY, *13*
Beckman & Assoc. Legal Search (C), OH, *262*
Bredeson Executive Recruitment, LLC (R), TX, *22*
DeCaster Assoc. (C), WI, *310*
Early Cochran & Olson (R), IL, *56*
Emerald Legal Search (C), NH, *329*
Franstaff Inc. (C), FL, *352*
Greene-Levin-Snyder LLC (C), NY, *362*
Bruce W. Haupt Assoc. (R), DC, *88*
H. Hertner Assoc., Inc. (C), FL, *377*
Intelligent Marketing Solutions, Inc. (C), NY, *390*
Interquest, Inc. (R), NY, *103*
A.T. Kearney Executive Search (R), IL, *111*
Legal Network Inc. (C), CA, *416*
Lipton Assoc., Inc. (R), NY, *130*
Lloyd Prescott Assoc., Inc. (C), FL, *418*
Management Recruiters of Cass County, NE (C), NE, *452*
Management Recruiters of Great Neck (C), NY, *454*
Page-Wheatcroft & Co., Ltd. (R), TX, *158*
Bob Poline Assoc. Inc. (C), CA, *514*
Preferred Placement, Inc. (C), NY, *516*
QD Legal (C), ON, *525*
Russell Reynolds Assoc., Inc. (R), NY, *176*
Rivera Legal Search, Inc. (C), CA, *538*
Rosenfeld & Co., Inc. (C), MI, *545*
Ryman, Bell, Green & Michaels, Inc. (C), TX, *549*
SR Wilson, Inc. (C), CA, *590*
DM Stone Personnel Services (C), CA, *594*
Unisearch Search & Recruiting Inc. (C), CA, *611*

02.0 Manufacturing

The 500 Granary Inc. (C), ON, *231*
A First Resource (C), NC, *231*
A la Carte Int'l., Inc. (R), VA, *1*
A Permanent Success Employment Services (C), CA, *231*
A.M.C.R., Inc. (C), OH, *232*
Abbott Associates (R), CA, *1*
The Abbott Group, Inc. (R), MD, *1*
Abécassis Conseil (R), QE, *1*
Abeln, Magy & Assoc., Inc. (R), MN, *1*
B. J. Abrams & Assoc. Inc. (C), IL, *233*
ACC Technical Services (C), OH, *233*
Access Assoc. Inc. (C), MD, *233*
ACCESS Technology (C), CA, *234*
Action Management Corp. (C), MI, *239*
Adams & Assoc. Int'l. (R), IL, *1*
The Addison Consulting Group (C), NJ, *239*
Adirect Recruiting Corp. (C), ON, *240*
Advanced Executive Resources (R), MI, *2*
Advanced Recruitment, Inc. (C), TN, *240*
Advancement Recruiting Services (C), OH, *241*
Advancement, Inc. (C), IL, *241*
The Advisory Group, Inc. (R), CA, *2*
AES Search (C), NJ, *241*
Affinity Executive Search (C), FL, *241*
Aggressive Corporation (C), IL, *242*
Agra Placements, Ltd. (C), IA, *242*
AGRI-associates (C), MO, *242*
Agri-Tech Personnel, Inc. (C), MO, *242*
Ahrensdorf & Assoc. (R), PA, *2*
J. R. Akin & Co. (R), MA, *2*
Albrecht & Assoc., Executive Search Consultants (C), TX, *243*
Alexander Enterprises, Inc. (C), PA, *243*
The Alexander Group (R), NJ, *3*
David Allen Assoc. (R), NJ, *3*
Allen Austin Lowe & Powers (R), TX, *3*
Allen, Wayne & Co. LLC (C), WI, *245*
Allen-Jeffers Assoc. (C), CA, *245*
Allen/Associates (R), OH, *4*
Allerton Heneghan & O'Neill (R), IL, *4*
Alliance Executive Search, Inc. (R), MA, *4*
Tom Allison Assoc. (C), NM, *245*
Alpha Executive Search (C), AL, *245*
The Altco Group (C), NJ, *246*
Altec/HRC (C), MI, *246*
ALW Research Int'l. (R), NJ, *4*
Peter W. Ambler Co. (R), TX, *5*
American Executive Search (C), FL, *247*
American Heritage Group, Inc. (C), MI, *247*
American Professional Search, Inc. (C), TN, *248*
American Resources Corp. (C), IL, *248*
American Services Group (C), IL, *248*
AmeriPro Search, Inc. (C), NC, *248*
AmeriResource Group Inc. (C), OK, *248*
Ames & Ames (R), CA, *5*
Ames-O'Neill Assoc., Inc. (C), NY, *249*
Amherst Human Resource Group, Ltd. (C), IL, *249*
AMS Int'l. (R), VA, *5*
Analytic Recruiting, Inc. (C), NY, *249*
Anderson Bradshaw Assoc., Inc. (R), TX, *6*
Anderson Industrial Assoc., Inc. (C), GA, *250*
Andre David & Assoc., Inc. (R), TX, *6*
Andrews & Wald Group (C), FL, *250*
Angel Group Int'l. (C), KY, *250*
Tryg R. Angell, Ltd. (C), CT, *250*
Angus Employment Ltd. (C), ON, *250*
The Angus Group, Ltd. (C), OH, *251*
Ansara, Bickford & Fiske (C), MA, *251*
APA Search, Inc. (R), NY, *6*
David Aplin & Assoc. (C), AB, *251*
Applied Resources, Inc. (C), MN, *252*
Applied Search Assoc., Inc. (C), GA, *252*
Charles P. Aquavella & Assoc. (C), TX, *252*
Argus National, Inc. (R), CT, *6*
Ariail & Assoc. (R), NC, *7*
Ariel Recruitment Assoc. (R), NY, *7*
ARJay & Assoc. (C), NC, *252*
Armor Personnel (C), ON, *253*
Artgo, Inc. (R), OH, *7*
A. Artze Assoc.-Personnel Consultants (C), PR, *253*
Asheville Search & Consulting (C), NC, *253*
Ashford Management Group, Inc. (R), GA, *7*
Ashlar-Stone Management Consultants Inc. (R), ON, *8*
Ashway Ltd. Agency (C), NY, *253*
Associated Recruiters (C), WI, *254*
The Associates, HR Search Executives, Inc. (C), OK, *254*
Astro Executive Search Firm (C), LA, *254*
W. R. Atchison & Assoc., Inc. (C), NC, *254*
Atlanta Executive Partners, Inc. (R), MA, *8*
Atlantic Pacific Group (C), CA, *255*
Atlantic West Int'l. (C), NC, *255*
Atomic Personnel, Inc. (C), PA, *255*
Aurora Tech Search (C), ON, *256*
A. M. Auster Associates (R), FL, *9*
Cami Austin & Assoc. (C), IL, *256*
Austin - Allen Co. (C), TN, *256*
Austin Michaels, Ltd., Inc. (C), AZ, *256*
Austin Park Management Group Inc. (C), ON, *256*
Austin-McGregor Int'l. (R), TX, *9*

Automation Technology Search (C), CA, *256*
Availability Personnel Consultants (C), NH, *257*
Avestruz & Assoc. (C), CA, *257*
The Baer Group (R), OH, *10*
Keith Bagg & Assoc., Inc. (C), ON, *257*
D. W. Baird & Associates (C), MD, *257*
Baldwin & Assoc. (C), OH, *258*
The Bales-Waugh Group (C), FL, *258*
Allen Ballach Assoc. Inc. (R), ON, *10*
Ballos & Co., Inc. (R), NJ, *10*
James Bangert & Assoc., Inc. (R), MN, *11*
Barber & Assoc. (C), KY, *259*
Barger & Sargeant, Inc. (R), NH, *11*
J. W. Barleycorn, Renard & Assoc., Inc. (R), OH, *11*
Barnes Development Group, LLC (R), WI, *11*
Fred A. Barnette & Assoc. (R), NC, *11*
Barone Assoc. (C), NJ, *259*
Barone-O'Hara Assoc., Inc. (R), NJ, *11*
Barr Assoc. (C), PA, *259*
Barrington Hart, Inc. (R), IL, *12*
Nathan Barry Assoc., Inc. (R), MA, *12*
The Barton Group, Inc. (C), MI, *260*
Bason Associates (R), OH, *13*
Battalia Winston Int'l./The Euram Consultants Group (R), NY, *13*
Martin H. Bauman Assoc., Inc. (R), NY, *13*
Bayland Assoc. (C), CA, *261*
BayResearch Group, Inc. (R), IL, *14*
Beach Executive Search Inc. (R), FL, *14*
The Beam Group (R), PA, *14*
Becker, Norton & Co. (R), PA, *14*
The Bedford Group (R), RI, *15*
Behrens and Company (C), WA, *262*
Gary S. Bell Assoc., Inc. (C), NJ, *263*
William Bell Assoc., Inc. (C), NJ, *263*
Bell Oaks Co., Inc. (C), GA, *263*
Benamati & Assoc. (C), CO, *263*
J. P. Bencik Assoc. (C), MI, *263*
Benford & Assoc., Inc. (C), MI, *264*
Bennett & Associates (C), TX, *264*
The Bennett Group, Inc. (R), IN, *16*
Dick Berg & Assoc. (C), CA, *264*
Berkana Int'l., Inc. (C), WA, *265*
Berkshire Search Assoc. (C), MA, *265*
Ed Bertolas Assoc., Inc. (C), CA, *265*
Jack Bertram, Executive Recruiter (C), PA, *265*
Bertrand, Ross & Assoc., Inc. (C), IL, *266*
Besen Assoc. Inc. (C), NJ, *266*
BG & Assoc. (C), MD, *266*
BGB Assoc., Inc. (C), IL, *266*
Paul J. Biestek Assoc., Inc. (R), IL, *17*
Bio-Venture Group (C), RI, *266*
Biomedical Search Consultants (R), CT, *17*
BioPharmMed (C), FL, *267*
BioTech Research Recruiters Inc. (C), CA, *267*
Birch & Associes (C), QE, *267*
Deborah Bishop & Assoc. (R), CA, *17*
BJB Assoc. (C), VA, *267*
The Black Leopard (C), CA, *267*
The Blackman Kallick Search Division (C), IL, *267*
Blair/Tech Recruiters, Inc. (C), NJ, *268*
J: Blakslee Int'l., Ltd. (R), CA, *18*
Blaney Executive Search (R), MA, *18*
Blanton & Co. (C), AL, *268*
Blau Mancino Schroeder (R), NJ, *18*
David Blevins & Assoc. (C), WA, *268*
D. R. Blood & Assoc. (R), AZ, *18*
Boettcher Assoc. (R), WI, *19*
Tom Bogle & Assoc. (C), CA, *269*
Mark Bolno & Assoc. (C), FL, *269*
Bolton Group (C), CA, *269*
Bor-Maq Assoc. (C), TX, *269*
Borchert Assoc. (C), TX, *269*
Lynn Borne & Co. (C), CA, *270*
The Borton Wallace Co. (R), NC, *19*
Bos Business Consultants (C), NY, *270*
Bosco-Hubert & Assoc. (C), KS, *270*
Bowden & Co., Inc. (R), OH, *20*
BowdenGlobal, Ltd. (R), OH, *20*
Howard Bowen Consulting (C), FL, *270*
Bower & Associates (C), TX, *271*
Boyden (R), NY, *20*
Boyle/Ogata Executive Search (R), CA, *21*
The Bradbury Management Group, Inc. (R), CA, *21*
Bradley & Assoc. (C), MN, *272*
The Brand Co., Inc. (R), FL, *22*
Brandt Associates (C), PA, *272*
Brandywine Consulting Group (R), PA, *22*
Brandywine Management Group (R), MD, *22*
Brandywine Retained Ventures, Inc. (R), CT, *22*
Branthover Assoc. (C), NY, *272*
Bratland & Assoc. (C), IL, *272*
The Brentwood Group Ltd. (R), OR, *23*
Brett Personnel Specialists (C), NJ, *273*
Brian Assoc., Inc. (C), NY, *273*
Briant Assoc., Inc. (R), IL, *23*
Bridgecreek Personnel Agency (C), CA, *273*
Brierwood Group, Inc. (C), IN, *273*
Brigade, Inc. (R), CA, *23*
Bright Search/Professional Staffing (C), MN, *274*
Brissenden, McFarland, Fuccella & Reynolds, Inc. (R), NJ, *23*
Bristol Assoc., Inc. (C), CA, *274*
Britt Assoc., Inc. (C), IL, *274*
Broadband Resource Group (C), CA, *274*
Dan B. Brockman (C), IL, *274*
Brooke Chase Assoc., Inc. (R), IL, *24*
Bernard E. Brooks & Assoc., Inc. (R), SC, *24*
Broward-Dobbs, Inc. (C), GA, *274*
J. B. Brown & Assoc., Inc. (C), OH, *275*
BRW Search (C), MN, *275*
Bryan & Louis Research (C), OH, *275*
Bullis & Co., Inc. (R), CA, *25*
The Burgess Group-Corporate Recruiters Int'l., Inc. (R), NY, *25*
J. Burke & Assoc., Inc. (C), TX, *276*
Burke & Assoc./The Westfield Group (C), CT, *276*
The Burke Group (C), ON, *276*
J. Burkey Assoc. (R), NJ, *25*
Joseph R. Burns & Assoc., Inc. (R), NJ, *25*
David S. Burt Assoc. (C), MT, *276*
Business Solutions Worldwide, Inc. (C), NJ, *277*
Buzhardt Assoc. (R), MS, *25*
Byron Leonard Int'l., Inc. (R), CA, *25*
C & H Personnel (C), PA, *277*
C. M. Management Services, Inc. (R), KY, *26*
The C.P.R. Group (C), NJ, *278*
C.P.S., Inc. (C), IL, *278*
C.T.E.W. Executive Personnel Services Inc. (C), BC, *278*
Cadillac Assoc. (C), CA, *278*
CadTech Staffing Services (C), GA, *279*
Cahill Assoc. (C), CT, *279*
Juliette Lang Cahn Executive Search (C), NY, *279*
Caliber Associates (R), PA, *27*
California Search Agency, Inc. (C), CA, *279*
Callos Personnel Services (C), OH, *279*
Cambridge Management Planning (R), ON, *27*
Campa & Assoc. (R), ON, *27*
Canadian Career Partners (R), AB, *27*
Canny, Bowen Inc. (R), NY, *27*
J. P. Canon Assoc. (C), NY, *280*
Cantrell & Assoc. (C), FL, *280*
Canyon Consulting, Inc. (C), TX, *281*
The Caplan-Taylor Group (R), CA, *28*
Caprio & Assoc. Inc. (R), IL, *29*
Capstone Consulting, Inc. (R), IL, *29*
Capstone Inc. (R), NY, *29*
Career Consultants (R), IN, *29*
Career Counseling Inc. (CCI) (C), KY, *282*
Career Images (C), FL, *282*
Career Marketing Assoc., Inc. (C), CO, *282*
Career Marketing Consultants, Inc. (C), GA, *282*
Career Search Group (C), FL, *283*
Career Specialists, Inc. (R), WA, *29*
Careerfit, Inc. (C), TX, *283*
Careers First, Inc. (C), NJ, *283*
Careers/Inc. (C), PR, *284*
Carion Resource Group Inc. (C), ON, *284*
Carlson & Czeswik (R), MN, *30*
Carnegie Partners, Inc. (R), IL, *30*
Carnegie Resources, Inc. (C), NC, *284*
Carpenter, Shackleton & Company (R), IL, *30*
Carr Management Services, Inc. (C), PA, *284*
Carson-Thomas & Assoc. (C), CA, *284*
Carter, Lavoie Associates (C), RI, *285*
Carver Search Consultants (C), CA, *285*
Case Executive Search (C), MI, *286*
Rosemary Cass Ltd. (R), CT, *31*
The Cassie Group (R), NJ, *31*
Michael J. Cavanagh & Assoc. Inc. (R), ON, *31*
Cendea Connection Int'l. (R), TX, *32*
Central Executive Search, Inc. (C), OH, *287*
CEO Consulting (C), FL, *287*
cFour Partners (R), CA, *32*
Chad Management Group (C), ON, *288*
Chadwell & Assoc., Inc. (C), MI, *288*
Wayne S. Chamberlain & Assoc. (C), CA, *288*
David Chambers & Assoc., Inc. (R), CT, *32*
Chapman & Assoc. (C), BC, *289*
The Chapman Group, Inc. (C), AZ, *289*
Charles & Associates, Inc. (C), NE, *289*

Robert L. Charon (C), TX, *289*
Chase-Gardner Executive Search Associates, Inc. (C), FL, *289*
The Chatham Group, Ltd. (C), CT, *289*
A. D. Check Assoc., Inc. (R), PA, *33*
Chelsea Resources, Inc. (C), CT, *290*
The Cherbonnier Group, Inc. (R), TX, *33*
Christenson Hutchison McDowell, LLC (R), NJ, *34*
R. Christine Assoc. (C), PA, *290*
Christmas, McIvor & Assoc. Inc. (C), ON, *290*
Christopher and Long (C), MO, *291*
William J. Christopher Assoc., Inc. (R), PA, *34*
Christopher-Westmont & Assoc., Inc. (R), OH, *34*
The Churchill Group (C), ON, *291*
Cizek Assoc., Inc. (R), AZ, *35*
CJA-The Adler Group, Inc. (R), CA, *35*
Clarey & Andrews, Inc. (R), IL, *35*
Clark Executive Search (C), NY, *292*
Ken Clark Int'l. (R), NJ, *36*
Clark Personnel Service, Inc. (C), AL, *292*
The Clayton Edward Group (C), MI, *292*
CMC Search Consultants (C), IL, *293*
CMS, Inc. (C), NH, *293*
CMS Management Services LLC (C), IN, *293*
CMW & Associates, Inc. (C), IL, *293*
Coast Personnel Services Ltd. (C), BC, *293*
COBA Executive Search (R), CO, *36*
Cochran, Cochran & Yale, Inc. (R), NY, *36*
Coe & Co. Int'l. Inc./EMA Partners Int'l. (R), AB, *37*
Cole, Warren & Long, Inc. (R), PA, *37*
J. Kevin Coleman & Assoc., Inc. (R), CA, *37*
Coleman Lew & Assoc., Inc. (R), NC, *37*
Columbia Consulting Group (R), MD, *38*
Compass Group Ltd. (R), MI, *38*
Comprehensive Search (C), GA, *294*
Conard Associates, Inc. (R), NH, *39*
Conasa de Mexico, S.C. (R), MX, *39*
Connors, Lovell & Assoc. Inc. (C), ON, *296*
Consolidated Management Services (C), ON, *296*
Construct Management Services (C), MN, *297*
Construction Search Specialists, Inc. (C), WI, *297*
Consulting Rhonda (C), ON, *297*
Continental Search Assoc. (C), OH, *298*
Philip Conway Management (R), IL, *40*
Cook Assoc. Int'l., Inc. (C), TN, *298*
P. G. Cook Assoc. (R), TN, *40*
Cook Assoc.,® Inc. (R), IL, *40*
The Cooke Group (R), WI, *40*
Cornell Group Int'l. Consulting, Inc. (R), NY, *41*
The Corporate Advisory Group (R), NJ, *41*
The Corporate Connection, Ltd. (C), VA, *299*
Corporate Environment Ltd. (R), IL, *41*
Corporate Image Group (C), TN, *300*
Corporate Management Services (C), PA, *300*
Corporate Plus, Ltd. (C), GA, *300*
Corporate Recruiters Ltd. (C), BC, *300*
Corporate Resources Professional Placement (C), MN, *300*
Corporate Search Consultants (C), IN, *301*
Corporate Search Consultants, Inc. (C), FL, *301*
Cosier & Assoc. (C), AB, *302*
J. D. Cotter Search Inc. (C), OH, *302*
Cowin Assoc. (R), NY, *42*
Creative Input, Inc. (C), RI, *303*
Creative-Leadership, Inc. (R), CA, *42*
Marlene Critchfield Co. (C), CA, *303*
Criterion Executive Search, Inc. (C), FL, *303*
Cross Country Consultants, Inc. (C), MD, *304*
Crowder & Company (R), MI, *43*
Crowe Chizek & Co. (C), IN, *304*
Timothy D. Crowe, Jr. (R), MA, *43*
Jim Crumpley & Assoc. (C), MO, *304*
CTR (R), CA, *43*
Cumberland Group Inc. (C), IL, *304*
Cumberland Professional Search Inc. (C), TN, *304*
Frank Cuomo & Assoc., Inc. (C), NY, *305*
The Currier-Winn Co., Inc. (C), NJ, *305*
Curry, Telleri Group, Inc. (R), NJ, *44*
Tony Curtis & Associates (C), ON, *305*
Cusack Consulting (R), NY, *44*
The Custer Group, Inc. (R), TN, *44*
CV Associates (C), NY, *305*
Cyntal Int'l. Ltd. (R), NY, *44*
Cypress Int'l., Inc. (R), FL, *45*
Cyr Associates, Inc. (C), MA, *306*
D.A.L. Associates, Inc. (R), CT, *45*
D.R. Assoc. (R), CA, *45*
The Dalley Hewitt Co. (R), GA, *45*
Daniel Marks Company (C), OH, *306*
The Danielson Group, Inc. (C), TX, *306*
Alan Darling Consulting (R), VT, *46*
The Dartmouth Group (R), NY, *46*
Alan N. Daum & Assoc., Inc. (C), OH, *308*
Davidson, Laird & Assoc. (C), MI, *308*
Alan Davis & Assoc. Inc. (R), QE, *47*
Bert Davis Executive Search, Inc. (R), NY, *47*
Bert Davis Publishing Placement Consultants (C), NY, *309*
Dean-MacDonald (R), OH, *47*
Debbon Recruiting Group, Inc. (C), MO, *310*
Deeco Int'l. (C), UT, *310*
Defrain Mayer (R), KS, *48*
DEL Technical Services, Inc. (C), IL, *310*
DeMatteo Associates (C), NY, *311*
Derhak Ireland & Partners Ltd. (R), ON, *48*
Despres & Associates (C), IL, *311*
The Devlin Search Group, Inc. (C), MA, *311*
DieckMueller Group (R), WI, *51*
The Diestel Group (R), UT, *51*
Dise & Co. (R), OH, *52*
R. J. Dishaw & Assoc. (R), TX, *52*
DiTech Resources (C), CT, *313*
Diversified Consulting Services, Inc. (C), CO, *313*
Dixie Search Assoc. (C), GA, *313*
Doherty Int'l., Inc. (R), IL, *53*
The Domann Organization (R), CA, *53*
Dominguez-Metz & Assoc. (R), CA, *53*
Domres Professional Search (R), WI, *53*
Donahue/Bales Assoc. (R), IL, *54*
The Dorfman Group (C), AZ, *314*
Robert Drexler Assoc., Inc. (R), NJ, *54*
J. H. Dugan & Assoc., Inc. (R), CA, *55*
Dukas Assoc. (C), MA, *315*
The Duncan-O'Dell Group Inc. (C), TX, *316*
Dunhill Staffing Systems, Inc. (C), NY, *316*
Dunhill Executive Search of Los Angeles, Inc. (C), CA, *319*
Dunhill of San Francisco, Inc. (C), CA, *319*
Dunhill Personnel of Boulder (C), CO, *319*
Dunhill Professional Search of Englewood, Inc. (C), CO, *319*
Dunhill of Ft. Collins, Inc. (C), CO, *319*
Dunhill Professional Search of San Jose (C), CA, *319*
Dunhill Professional Search of Oakland (C), CA, *319*
Dunhill of Ft. Wayne, Inc. (C), IN, *320*
Dunhill Search of West Atlanta (C), GA, *320*
Dunhill Professional Search of Augusta (C), GA, *320*
Dunhill Professional Search of Hawaii (C), HI, *320*
Dunhill Executive Search of Brown County (C), IN, *321*
Dunhill Professional Search (C), MO, *321*
Dunhill Professional Search of Ramsey (C), NJ, *321*
Dunhill Personnel of St. Andrews (C), SC, *322*
Dunhill Professional Search, Inc. of McAllen (C), TX, *323*
Dunhill of Corpus Christi, Inc. (C), TX, *323*
Dunhill Professional Search of Richmond (C), VA, *323*
Dunlap & Sullivan Assoc. (R), MI, *55*
Dunn Associates (R), PA, *55*
Donald F. Dvorak & Co. (R), IL, *55*
G. L. Dykstra Assoc., Inc. (C), MI, *323*
Dynamic Staffing Network (C), IL, *324*
The E & K Group (C), NJ, *324*
E/Search Int'l. (C), CT, *325*
EA Plus, Inc. (C), TX, *325*
Eagle Consulting Group Inc. (C), TX, *325*
EBA Group (R), NJ, *56*
The Edge Resource Group (C), PA, *326*
Bruce Edwards & Associates, Inc. (R), NC, *56*
Effective Search, Inc. (R), IL, *57*
D. C. Egan & Assoc. (C), GA, *327*
EGM Consulting, Inc. (R), FL, *57*
W. Robert Eissler & Assoc., Inc. (C), TX, *327*
William J. Elam & Assoc. (R), NE, *58*
Elite Medical Search (C), GA, *328*
Elite Resources Group (R), OH, *58*
Yves Elkas Inc. (R), QE, *58*
Gene Ellefson & Assoc. Inc. (C), MI, *328*
The Elliott Company (R), MA, *58*
The Elsworth Group (C), TX, *329*
Elwell & Assoc., Inc. (R), MI, *59*

Emerging Medical Technologies, Inc. (C), CO, *329*
Emerson & Co. (C), GA, *329*
Empowered Solutions Corp. (C), GA, *330*
Engineering & Scientific Search Assoc. (ESSA) (C), NJ, *330*
Engineering Futures, LLC (C), CT, *330*
Engineering Placement Specialists (C), WI, *330*
Engineering Profiles (C), FL, *330*
Epsen, Fuller & Assoc., LLC (R), NJ, *60*
Erlanger Assoc. (R), CT, *60*
Erwin Assoc. (R), IL, *60*
ESS (Executive Search Services) (R), CA, *61*
Essential Solutions, Inc. (C), CA, *331*
Excalibur Human Resources, Inc. (R), NJ, *61*
Exclusive Search Consultants (C), OH, *331*
ExeConnex, LLC (R), GA, *61*
Execu-Tech Search Inc. (C), MN, *332*
ExecuQuest, Inc. (R), MI, *61*
ExecuSource Consultants, Inc. (C), TX, *332*
Executech (R), OH, *62*
ExecuTech (C), IN, *332*
Executive Business Solutions, Inc. (C), WA, *332*
Executive Career Search (C), VA, *332*
Executive Connection (C), OH, *333*
Executive Directions (R), OH, *62*
Executive Manning Corp. (R), FL, *63*
Executive Partners Inc. (C), CT, *333*
Executive Recruiters Int'l. (C), MI, *333*
Executive Recruiters Agency, Inc. (C), AR, *333*
Executive Recruiters, Inc. (C), WI, *334*
Executive Recruiters (C), WA, *334*
Executive Recruitment Services, Inc. (ERS, Inc.) (C), GA, *334*
Executive Registry (C), QE, *334*
Executive Resource Assoc. (C), VA, *334*
Executive Resource Group, Inc. (R), ME, *63*
Executive Resource Inc. (C), WI, *334*
Executive Search Int'l./Transearch (R), MA, *63*
Executive Search, Ltd. (C), OH, *336*
Executive Search of New England, Inc. (C), ME, *336*
Executive Search Plus, Inc. (C), IN, *336*
Executive Search Team (C), MI, *336*
The Executive Source (C), SA, *337*
The Executive Tree (R), FL, *64*
Eyler Assoc., Inc. (R), IA, *64*
Fagan & Company (R), PA, *64*
Fairfaxx Corp. (R), CT, *64*
Fairfield Int'l. Resources (R), NY, *65*
James Feerst & Assoc., Inc. (C), AZ, *339*
Fenwick Partners (R), MA, *66*
Fenzel Milar Assoc. (C), OH, *339*
Fergason Assoc., Inc. (C), IL, *339*
Ferneborg & Assoc., Inc. (R), CA, *66*
Fernow Assoc. (C), PA, *339*
Ferrari Search Group (C), OH, *340*
Neil Fink Assoc. (R), CA, *66*
Finnegan & Assoc. (R), CA, *67*
First Choice Search (R), WA, *67*
First Search America, Inc. (C), TN, *341*
Fishel HR Assoc., Inc. (C), AZ, *341*
The Fisher Group (R), AB, *67*
Fisher Personnel Management Services (R), CA, *68*
James L. Fisk & Assoc. (C), MO, *342*
Robert M. Flanagan & Assoc., Ltd. (R), NY, *68*
Flowers & Assoc. (C), OH, *342*
J. G. Flynn & Assoc. Inc. (R), BC, *69*
Focus Executive Search (C), MN, *343*
Fogec Consultants, Inc. (R), WI, *69*
Ford & Assoc., Inc. (C), SC, *343*
Forest People Int'l. Search Ltd. (C), BC, *343*
F-O-R-T-U-N-E Personnel Consultants of Boise (R), ID, *70*
Fortune Group Int'l., Inc. (R), PA, *70*
Fortune Personnel Consultants of Huntsville, Inc. (C), AL, *343*
F-O-R-T-U-N-E Personnel Consultants of Denver, Inc. (C), CO, *344*
F-O-R-T-U-N-E Personnel Consultants of Tampa (C), FL, *344*
F-O-R-T-U-N-E Personnel Consultants of Wilmington (C), DE, *344*
F-O-R-T-U-N-E Personnel Consultants of San Diego (C), CA, *344*
Fortune Personnel Consultants (C), CA, *344*
F-O-R-T-U-N-E Personnel Consultants of Greenwood Village (C), CO, *344*
F-O-R-T-U-N-E Personnel Consultants of Manatee County (C), FL, *345*
F-O-R-T-U-N-E Personnel Consultants of Palm Beach (C), FL, *345*
F-O-R-T-U-N-E Personnel Consultants of Savannah, Inc. (C), GA, *345*
Fortune Personnel Consultants of Jacksonville (C), FL, *345*
Fortune Personnel Consultants of Sarasota Inc. (C), FL, *345*
F-O-R-T-U-N-E Personnel Consultants of Atlanta, Inc. (C), GA, *345*
Fortune of Arlington Heights (C), IL, *345*
F-O-R-T-U-N-E Personnel Consultants (C), MI, *346*
Fortune Personnel Consultants of Bloomfield, Inc. (C), MI, *346*
F-o-r-t-u-n-e of Owensboro, Inc. (C), KY, *346*
F-O-R-T-U-N-E Personnel Consultants of South Bend (C), IN, *346*
Fortune Personnel Consultants of Topsfield (C), MA, *346*
Fortune Personnel Consultants (C), NH, *347*
F-O-R-T-U-N-E Personnel Consultants of St. Louis-West County (C), MO, *347*
F-O-R-T-U-N-E Personnel Consultants of Troy, Inc. (C), MI, *347*
F-O-R-T-U-N-E Personnel Consultants of Menlo Park, Inc. (C), NJ, *347*
Fortune Personnel Consultants (C), MT, *347*
F-O-R-T-U-N-E Search Consultants (C), MO, *347*
F-O-R-T-U-N-E Personnel Consultants of Bergen County Inc. (C), NJ, *347*
F-O-R-T-U-N-E of West Portland (C), OR, *348*
F-O-R-T-U-N-E Personnel Consultants of Rockland County, Inc. (C), NY, *348*
Fortune Personnel Consultants of Allentown, Inc. (C), PA, *348*
F-O-R-T-U-N-E Personnel Consultants of Charlotte (C), NC, *348*
F-O-R-T-U-N-E Personnel Consultants of Cincinnati (C), OH, *348*
Fortune Personnel Consultants of Raleigh, Inc. (C), NC, *348*
Fortune Personnel Consultants of Greensboro, NC, Inc. (C), NC, *348*
Fortune Personnel Consultants of Hilton Head (C), SC, *349*
F-O-R-T-U-N-E Consultants of Memphis (C), TN, *349*
Fortune Personnel Consultants of Chattanooga Inc. (C), TN, *349*
FORTUNE Personnel Consultants of Charleston, Inc. (C), SC, *349*
Fortune Personnel Consultants of Anderson, Inc. (C), SC, *349*
F-O-R-T-U-N-E Personnel Consultants of Houston, Inc. (C), TX, *350*
F-O-R-T-U-N-E Personnel Consultants of Knoxville (C), TN, *350*
Fortune Personnel Consultants of San Antonio, Inc. (C), TX, *350*
F-O-R-T-U-N-E Personnel of Nashville (C), TN, *350*
FORTUNE Personnel Consultants of North Dallas (C), TX, *350*
Fortune Personnel Consultants of Plano (C), TX, *350*
F-O-R-T-U-N-E Personnel Consultants of the Tri-Cities, Inc. (C), TN, *350*
F-O-R-T-U-N-E Personnel Consultants of East Seattle (C), WA, *351*
Fortune Personnel Consultants of the Virginia Highlands (C), VA, *351*
Foster Partners (R), NY, *70*
The Fourbes Group, Inc. (C), NJ, *351*
Fox-Morris Assoc., Inc. (C), PA, *351*
Foy, Schneid & Daniel, Inc. (R), NY, *71*
Franklin Int'l. Search, Inc. (C), MA, *352*
KS Frary & Assoc. (R), MA, *71*
Friedman Eisenstein Raemer & Schwartz, LLP (R), IL, *72*
Bernard Frigon & Assoc. Inc. (C), QE, *353*
Frye/Joure & Assoc., Inc. (C), TN, *353*
The Furst Group, Inc. (R), IL, *72*
Future Employment Service, Inc. (C), IA, *353*
G. H. Enterprises (C), AZ, *354*
GAAP Inc. (R), QE, *73*
The Gabriel Group (C), PA, *354*
Gabriele & Company (C), MA, *354*
Gaffney Management Consultants (R), IL, *73*
Gaines & Assoc. Int'l., Inc. (R), IL, *73*
Gallin Associates, Inc. (C), FL, *354*
Gardner-Ross Assoc., Inc. (R), NY, *74*
The Garms Group (R), IL, *74*
The Garret Group (R), NJ, *75*
Gaudry, Shink, Levasseur (R), QE, *75*
Geddes & Rubin Management Inc. (R), ON, *76*

Genel Associates (C), CA, *356*
General Engineering Tectonics (C), CA, *356*
Genesis Personnel Service, Inc. (C), OH, *356*
Genesis Recruiting (C), CA, *356*
Genesis Research (C), MO, *356*
J. Gernetzke & Assoc., Inc. (C), OH, *357*
GFI Professional Staffing Services (C), NH, *357*
Gilbert Tweed Assoc. Inc. (R), NY, *76*
Joe L. Giles & Assoc. (C), MI, *357*
Gilreath Weatherby Inc. (R), MA, *77*
The Glazin Group (R), BC, *77*
J. P. Gleason Assoc., Inc. (R), IL, *77*
The Glenwood Group (C), IL, *358*
Glines Assoc., Inc. (R), IL, *77*
Global Employer's Network, Inc. (R), TX, *77*
Global Research Partnership Inc. (R), NY, *78*
The GlobalSearch Group (C), TX, *359*
Robert G. Godfrey Assoc. Ltd. (R), IL, *78*
H. L. Goehring & Assoc., Inc. (C), OH, *359*
Goldbeck Recruiting Inc. (C), BC, *359*
Fred J. Goldsmith Assoc. (R), CA, *79*
Goldstein & Co. (C), CA, *360*
Gomez Fregoso y Asociados (C), JAL, *360*
L. J. Gonzer Assoc. (C), NJ, *360*
Goodrich & Sherwood Assoc., Inc. (R), NY, *79*
Gordon/Tyler (R), PA, *80*
The Governance Group, Inc. (R), NJ, *80*
Graham & Co. (R), NJ, *80*
Granger, Counts & Assoc. (R), OH, *81*
Grant Cooper & Assoc., Inc. (R), MO, *81*
Graphic Search Assoc. Inc. (C), PA, *362*
Annie Gray Assoc., Inc. (R), MO, *81*
R. Green & Assoc., Inc. (C), OH, *362*
Greenfields Engineering Search (C), MO, *363*
Gregory, Kyle & Assoc. (C), NC, *363*
Griffith & Werner, Inc. (R), FL, *82*
J. B. Groner Executive Search, Inc. (C), DE, *363*
Gros Executive Search, Inc. (C), TN, *363*
Grossberg & Assoc. (R), IL, *82*
Groton Planning Group (R), ME, *82*
Grover & Assoc. (R), OH, *82*
David E. Grumney Co. Inc. (R), WA, *83*
Michael R. Guerin Co. (C), CA, *364*
Wolf Gugler & Assoc. Ltd. (R), ON, *83*
The H. S. Group, Inc. (C), WI, *365*
Habelmann & Assoc. (R), MI, *84*
Russ Hadick & Assoc. Inc. (C), OH, *365*
Hahn & Assoc., Inc. (C), OH, *365*
Don Hall & Assoc. (C), TX, *366*
Hall Kinion (C), CA, *366*
Hall Management Group, Inc. (C), GA, *367*
Hallman Group, Inc. (C), MI, *367*
The Hamilton Group (R), MD, *85*
The Hampton Group (C), NY, *367*
R. C. Handel Assoc. Inc. (R), CT, *85*
W. L. Handler & Assoc. (R), GA, *85*
The Hanna Group (C), OH, *368*
Hansen Executive Search, Inc. (C), NE, *368*
Harcor Quest & Assoc. (R), OH, *86*
Harcourt & Assoc. (C), AB, *368*
Harcourt Group Ltd. (R), OH, *86*
Hardage Group (C), TN, *369*
The Harris Consulting Corp. (R), MB, *87*
Harrison Moore Inc. (C), NE, *370*
Hartman & Barnette (R), VA, *87*
Harvard Group Int'l. (R), GA, *87*
Harvey Hohauser & Assoc., LLC (R), MI, *87*
The Hawkins Co. (R), CA, *88*
Michael J. Hawkins, Inc. (C), IL, *370*
William E. Hay & Co. (R), IL, *88*
The Haystack Group, Inc. (R), ME, *88*
HCI Corp. (C), IL, *371*
Healey Executive Search, Inc. (R), MN, *88*
Health Industry Consultants, Inc. (R), CO, *89*
Healthcare Management Resources, Inc. (R), GA, *89*
Healthcare Recruiters Int'l. Phoenix (C), AZ, *372*
Healthcare Recruiters of the Rockies, Inc. (C), CO, *372*
Healthcare Recruiters of Indiana (C), IN, *372*
Healthcare Recruiters Int'l. Orange County (C), CA, *372*
Healthcare Recruiters International-NY/NJ (C), NJ, *373*
Healthcare Recruiters of New York, Inc. (C), NY, *373*
Healthcare Recruiters - Northwest (C), WA, *374*
F. P. Healy & Co., Inc. (R), NY, *89*
HeartBeat Medical, Inc. (C), OR, *374*
Heath/Norton Assoc., Inc. (R), NY, *89*
R. W. Hebel Assoc. (R), TX, *89*
HEC Group (C), ON, *375*
Hedlund Corp. (C), IL, *375*
Heffelfinger Assoc., Inc. (R), MA, *89*
Heinze & Assoc. Inc. (R), MN, *91*
Helfer Executive Consultants (R), TN, *91*
Helffrich Int'l. (C), FL, *375*
Heller Assoc., Ltd. (R), IL, *91*
Heller Kil Assoc., Inc. (C), FL, *375*
The Hensge Co. (R), IL, *91*
Henson Partners (C), AZ, *376*
Herbeck Kline & Assoc. (R), IL, *92*
Hergenrather & Co. (R), WA, *92*
Heritage Pacific Corp. (C), CA, *376*
Stanley Herz & Co. (R), NY, *92*
High Tech Staffing Group (C), OR, *377*
Highlander Search (C), NC, *378*
Frank P. Hill (R), MX, *93*
The Hindman Co. (R), KY, *94*
The Hindman Group, Inc. (C), CA, *378*
Hintz Associates (C), NY, *378*
Hite Executive Search (R), OH, *94*
Hobson Assoc. (C), CT, *379*
Hockett Associates, Inc. (R), CA, *94*
Hodge-Cronin & Assoc., Inc. (R), IL, *94*
Hoglund & Assoc., Inc. (R), IL, *94*
Holland Rusk & Assoc. (R), IL, *95*
Hollander Horizon Int'l. (R), CA, *95*
Holloway Schulz & Partners (C), BC, *380*
Holohan Group, Ltd. (R), MO, *95*
J. G. Hood Assoc. (C), CT, *380*
Horizons Unlimited (C), CA, *381*
Horton Int'l. Inc. (R), NY, *96*
Hospitality Executive Search, Inc. (R), MA, *96*
Houser, Martin, Morris (C), WA, *381*
Houtz•Strawn & Arnold, Inc. (R), TX, *96*
William C. Houze & Co. (R), CA, *96*
Randall Howard & Assoc., Inc. (R), TN, *96*
Howe & Assoc. (R), PA, *97*
Robert Howe & Assoc. (R), GA, *97*
HR Inc. (C), NC, *382*
HRCS (R), CA, *97*
HRNI (C), MI, *383*
HRS, Inc. (R), PA, *97*
The Hudson Group (C), CT, *383*
Huff Assoc. (R), NJ, *98*
E. A. Hughes & Co., Inc. (R), NY, *98*
The Human Resource Department Ltd. (R), OH, *98*
The Human Resource Group, Inc. (R), OH, *98*
Human Resource Technologies, Inc. (R), IL, *99*
Human Resources Personnel Agency (R), AR, *99*
E. F. Humay Assoc. (C), PA, *384*
The Hunt Group, Inc. (R), NC, *99*
Hunt Patton & Brazeal, Inc. (C), OK, *385*
Hunter Assoc. (C), MA, *385*
The Hunter Group, Inc. (C), MI, *385*
The Hunter Group (C), NC, *385*
Huntley Associates (Dallas), Inc. (C), TX, *386*
W. Hutt Management Resources Ltd. (R), ON, *100*
Hutton Merrill & Assoc. (R), CA, *100*
Hyde Danforth & Co. (R), TX, *100*
The Icard Group, Inc. (C), MI, *387*
Impact Source, Inc. (C), FL, *387*
Industry Consultants, Inc. (C), GA, *388*
Innovative Resource Group, LLC (C), NC, *389*
InSearch (C), CO, *389*
The Inside Track (C), TX, *389*
Inter Regional Executive Search, Inc. (IRES, Inc.) (C), NJ, *391*
Interactive Search Assoc. (C), PA, *391*
Interactive Search Network (R), CA, *102*
Intercontinental Executive Group (C), PA, *391*
Interim Executive Recruiting (C), GA, *392*
Interim Management Resources Inc. (C), ON, *392*
International Business Partners (C), ON, *392*
International Executive Recruiters (C), OH, *393*
International Management Services Inc. (R), IL, *102*
International Management Development Corp. (C), NY, *393*
International Research Group (R), CA, *103*
International Staffing Consultants, Inc. (C), CA, *393*
Iona Partners (C), CA, *394*
Joan Isbister Consultants (C), NY, *394*
ISC of Atlanta, Inc. (C), GA, *394*
ISC of Cincinnati Inc. (C), OH, *394*
J. B. Linde & Assoc. (C), MO, *395*
J. Joseph & Assoc. (C), OH, *395*

J.D.G. y Asociados, S.A. de C.V. (R), SO, *104*
J.N. Adams & Assoc., Inc. (C), PA, *396*
Jackley Search Consultants (C), MN, *396*
Ron Jackson & Assoc. (C), GA, *396*
K. Jaeger & Assoc. (C), MA, *396*
Jaeger Int'l., Inc. (C), OH, *396*
JAG Group (R), MO, *105*
Jakobs & Assoc. Int'l. (R), NY, *105*
January Management Group (R), OH, *105*
Jaral Consultants, Inc. (C), NJ, *397*
JCL & Assoc. (C), FL, *397*
Jender & Company (R), IL, *105*
Jerome & Co. (C), CA, *398*
JG Consultants, Inc. (R), TX, *106*
JLI-Boston (R), MA, *106*
JM & Company (R), PA, *106*
Job Link, Inc. (C), CA, *399*
Job-Born Candidate Selection Bureau (C), ON, *399*
John Jay & Co. (C), ME, *399*
John H. Johnson & Assoc., Inc. (R), IL, *106*
L. J. Johnson & Co. (R), MI, *106*
Ronald S. Johnson Assoc., Inc. (R), CA, *107*
K. E. Johnson Assoc. (C), WA, *399*
Johnson Brown Assoc., Inc. (C), IN, *400*
Johnson Smith & Knisely (R), NY, *107*
Jonas, Walters & Assoc., Inc. (R), WI, *107*
The Jonathan Stevens Group, Inc. (R), NJ, *108*
Jordan-Sitter Assoc. (R), TX, *108*
J. M. Joseph Assoc. (R), NJ, *109*
Joslin & Assoc., Ltd. (C), IL, *401*
JRL Executive Recruiters (C), MO, *401*
JSG Group Management Consultants (R), ON, *109*
Just Management Services Inc. (C), FL, *402*
A H Justice Search Consultants (C), TX, *402*
K & C Assoc. (C), CA, *402*
Kaas Employment Services (C), IA, *402*
Kabana Corp. (C), MI, *402*
Robert Kaestner & Assoc. (C), FL, *403*
Kane & Assoc. (C), TX, *403*
Kanzer Assoc., Inc. (R), IL, *109*
Karp & Assoc. (C), FL, *403*
Martin Kartin & Co., Inc. (R), NY, *110*
Jim Kay & Assoc. (C), IL, *404*
Kay Concepts, Inc. (C), FL, *404*
Kazan International, Inc. (R), NJ, *110*
A.T. Kearney Executive Search (R), IL, *111*
Keena Staffing Services (C), NY, *404*
Kehn & Gabor, Inc. (C), OH, *405*
S. D. Kelly & Assoc., Inc. (R), MA, *112*
Kelly Associates (R), PA, *112*
Kenmore Executives Inc. (C), FL, *405*
Kensington Int'l., Inc. (R), IL, *113*
Kenzer Corp. (R), NY, *113*
Blair Kershaw Assoc., Inc. (C), PA, *405*
Key Employment (C), NJ, *405*
Kingsbury • Wax • Bova (R), MA, *114*
Kingsley Quinn/USA (R), NJ, *115*
Richard Kinser & Assoc. (R), NY, *115*
Kiradjieff & Goode, Inc. (R), MA, *115*
Kirby Assoc. (R), PA, *115*
Raymond J. Klemmer & Assoc. (R), NY, *116*
The Kleven Group, Inc. (C), MA, *407*
Knapp Consultants (R), CT, *116*
Koehler & Co. (R), WI, *116*
Lee Koehn Assoc., Inc. (R), OR, *116*
T. J. Koellhoffer & Assoc. (R), NJ, *116*
Fred Koffler Assoc. (R), NY, *116*
Koltnow & Company (R), NY, *117*
Koontz, Jeffries & Assoc., Inc. (R), FL, *117*
Korban Associates (R), PA, *117*
Korn/Ferry Int'l. (R), NY, *117*
Kossuth & Assoc., Inc. (R), WA, *119*
Kozlin Assoc., Inc. (C), NY, *408*
J. Krauss Assoc. (R), FL, *120*
Evie Kreisler Assoc. Inc. (C), CA, *409*
Kremple & Meade, Inc. (R), CA, *120*
Kreutz Consulting Group, Inc. (R), IL, *121*
Krueger Assoc. (R), IL, *121*
John Kuhn & Assoc., Inc. (R), WI, *121*
Kuhn Med-Tech (C), CA, *409*
Paul Kull & Co. (R), NJ, *121*
Kulper & Co., L.L.C. (R), NJ, *121*
Kunzer Assoc., Ltd. (R), IL, *121*
John Kurosky & Assoc. (R), CA, *122*
Kutt, Inc. (C), CO, *410*
L & L Assoc. (C), CA, *410*
L O R (R), NJ, *122*
L&L Assoc. Global Search (C), PA, *411*
L. Patrick Group (R), NJ, *122*
Marvin Laba & Assoc. (R), CA, *122*
Laboratory Resource Group (C), MA, *411*
LaCosta & Assoc. Int'l. Inc. (C), CA, *411*
Rene LaFlamme & Associes (R), QE, *122*
Lam Assoc. (C), HI, *411*
Lamon + Stuart + Michaels Inc. (R), ON, *124*
Landon Morgan (C), ON, *412*
The Landstone Group (C), NY, *412*
Lange & Assoc., Inc. (C), IN, *412*
Lanken-Kimball-Therrell & Assoc. (C), GA, *412*
Stephen Laramee & Assoc. Inc. (C), ON, *413*
Robert Larned Assoc., Inc. (C), VA, *413*
R. H. Larsen & Assoc., Inc. (R), FL, *125*
Jack B. Larsen & Assoc., Inc. (C), PA, *413*
Lasher Assoc. (R), FL, *125*
Lauer, Sbarbaro Assoc., EMA Partners Int'l. (R), IL, *126*
Lawrence-Balakonis & Assoc., Inc. (C), GA, *414*
Lawrence-Leiter & Co. (R), KS, *126*
W. R. Lawry, Inc. (R), CT, *126*
LCS, Inc. (C), TX, *414*
Leader Network (C), PA, *414*
Leader Search Inc. (R), AB, *127*
Leaders-Trust Int'l./Carce y Asociados, S.C. (R), MX, *127*
The Lear Group, Inc. (R), OH, *127*
Reynolds Lebus Assoc. (C), AZ, *415*
Lechner & Assoc., Inc. (C), FL, *415*
Albert G. Lee Assoc. (C), RI, *415*
Lee Management Group Inc. (C), NJ, *416*
V. J. Lehman & Assoc., Inc. (R), CO, *127*
Lehman McLeskey (R), TX, *128*
Leith & Assoc., Inc. (C), OH, *416*
Lemming/LeVan, Inc. (R), GA, *128*
Jacques LePage Executive Search Inc. (R), QE, *128*
J. E. Lessner Assoc., Inc. (R), MI, *128*
The Levton Group Inc. (R), ON, *129*
Lewis & Blank Int'l. (R), CA, *129*
Lewis Companies Inc. (R), ON, *129*
The Libra Group (C), NC, *417*
LifeWork, Inc. (C), TX, *418*
Linden Group, Inc. (C), NC, *418*
Lineal Recruiting Services (C), CT, *418*
Livingston, Robert & Co. (R), CT, *130*
Lloyd Prescott & Churchill, Inc. (R), FL, *130*
Locke & Assoc. (R), NC, *131*
Locus Inc. (C), WV, *419*
Loewenstein & Assoc., Inc. (R), TX, *131*
London Executive Consultants Inc. (C), ON, *420*
Longo Associates (C), CA, *420*
Lord & Albus Co. (C), TX, *420*
J. S. Lord & Company, Inc. (R), MA, *131*
Bruce Lowery & Assoc. (C), MI, *420*
Lucas Assoc. (C), GA, *421*
Lucas Group (C), NY, *421*
Charles Luntz & Assoc., Inc. (R), MO, *132*
Lutz Associates (C), CT, *421*
Lybrook Assoc., Inc. (C), RI, *421*
P. J. Lynch Assoc. (R), CT, *132*
Lynch Miller Moore Partners, Inc. (R), IL, *132*
Lyons & Assoc., Inc. (C), IL, *422*
Lyons Pruitt Int'l. (R), PA, *132*
M H Executive Search Group (C), TX, *422*
M. K. & Assoc. (C), PA, *422*
M.C. Executive Search (C), CA, *422*
MacNaughton Assoc. (R), CA, *133*
Maczkov-Biosciences, Inc. (R), CA, *133*
The Madison Group (R), NY, *133*
Maglio & Co., Inc. (R), WI, *134*
Magnum Search (C), IL, *422*
Maiorino & Weston Assoc., Inc. (R), CT, *134*
Major Search (C), NJ, *423*
The Mallard Group (C), IN, *423*
Management Association Network (C), WI, *424*
Management Catalysts (R), NJ, *134*
Management Recruiters of Birmingham-South, Inc. (C), AL, *438*
Management Recruiters of Mobile Co., Inc. (C), AL, *438*
Management Recruiters of Birmingham (C), AL, *438*
Management Recruiters of Decatur, LLC (C), AL, *438*
Management Recruiters of Tucson (C), AZ, *439*
Management Recruiters Tucson-Foothills, Inc. (C), AZ, *439*
Management Recruiters of Little Rock (C), AR, *439*
Management Recruiters Peninsula (C), CA, *439*
Management Recruiters of Emeryville (C), CA, *440*
Management Recruiters of Northern California (C), CA, *440*
Management Recruiters of Laguna Hills (C), CA, *440*

Management Recruiters of Colorado Springs (C), CO, *441*
Management Recruiters of Pleasanton (C), CA, *441*
Management Recruiters of Sacramento North (C), CA, *441*
Management Recruiters Inc. of Silicon Valley (C), CA, *441*
Management Recruiters of Winsted, Inc. (C), CT, *442*
Management Recruiters of Colorado, Inc. (C), CO, *442*
Management Recruiters of Franktown (C), CO, *442*
Management Recruiters of Milford Inc. (C), CT, *442*
Management Recruiters of Bonita Springs, Inc. (C), FL, *443*
Management Recruiters of Ft. Myers, FL. (C), FL, *443*
Management Recruiters of Boca Raton (C), FL, *443*
Management Recruiters of Clearwater (C), FL, *443*
Management Recruiters of Anna Maria Island (C), FL, *443*
Management Recruiters of Miami-North (C), FL, *443*
Management Recruiters, Inc. (C), FL, *443*
Management Recruiters of Melbourne, Inc. (C), FL, *443*
Management Recruiters of Pensacola (C), FL, *444*
Management Recruiters of Lake Co., Inc. (C), FL, *444*
Management Recruiters of Forsyth County (C), GA, *445*
Management Recruiters of Atlanta West, Inc. (C), GA, *445*
Management Recruiters of Venice, Inc. (C), FL, *445*
Management Recruiters of Columbus, Inc. (C), GA, *445*
Management Recruiters of Atlanta (C), GA, *445*
Management Recruiters of Vero Beach (C), FL, *445*
Management Recruiters of Savannah (C), GA, *446*
Management Recruiters of Atlanta North, Inc. (C), GA, *446*
Management Recruiters of Sandy Springs (C), GA, *446*
Management Recruiters of Marietta, Inc. (C), GA, *446*
Management Recruiters of Boise (C), ID, *446*
Management Recruiters of St. Charles (C), IL, *447*
Management Recruiters of Lake Forest, IL (C), IL, *447*
Management Recruiters of Springfield, Inc. (C), IL, *447*
Management Recruiters of Barrington (C), IL, *447*
Management Recruiters of Sun Valley (C), ID, *447*
Management Recruiters of Chicago-North Shore (C), IL, *447*
Management Recruiters of Noblesville, Inc. (C), IN, *448*
Management Recruiters of Spencer (C), IA, *448*
Management Recruiters of Indianapolis (C), IN, *448*
Management Recruiters of South Bend (C), IN, *448*
Management Recruiters of Indianapolis-North (C), IN, *448*
Management Recruiters of Danville (C), KY, *449*
Management Recruiters of Richmond (C), KY, *449*
Management Recruiters of Siouxland (C), IA, *449*
Management Recruiters of Columbia (C), MD, *450*
Management Recruiters of Rockville (C), MD, *450*
Management Recruiters of the Baltimore Washington Corridor (C), MD, *450*
Management Recruiters of Monroe, Inc. (C), LA, *450*
Management Recruiters of Muskegon (C), MI, *451*
Management Recruiters of Livonia (C), MI, *451*
Management Recruiters of Birmingham (C), MI, *451*
Management Recruiters of Baltimore (C), MD, *451*
Management Recruiters - Flint (C), MI, *451*
Management Recruiters of Southeastern Michigan (C), MI, *451*
Management Recruiters of Dearborn, Inc. (C), MI, *451*
Management Recruiters of Woodbury (C), MN, *452*
Management Recruiters of Chanhassen (C), MN, *452*
Management Recruiters of Rankin Co. (C), MS, *452*
Management Recruiters of North Oakland County, Inc. (C), MI, *452*
Management Recruiters of Bay Head (C), NJ, *453*
Management Recruiters of Medford, N.J. (C), NJ, *453*
Management Recruiters of North Warren Inc. (C), NJ, *453*
Management Recruiters of Orange County, N.Y., Inc. (C), NJ, *453*
Management Recruiters of Reno (C), NV, *453*
Management Recruiters of Upper Westchester (C), NY, *454*
Management Recruiters of Broome County, Inc. (C), NY, *454*
Management Recruiters of Fayetteville (C), NC, *455*
Management Recruiters of Burlington (C), NC, *455*
Management Recruiters of Asheville, Inc. (C), NC, *455*
Management Recruiters of Rocky Mount - Southwest (C), NC, *456*
Management Recruiters of Kinston (C), NC, *456*
Management Recruiters - Kannapolis (C), NC, *456*
Management Recruiters of Mt. Airy (C), NC, *456*
Management Recruiters of Raleigh (C), NC, *456*
Management Recruiters of Wilmington (C), NC, *457*
Management Recruiters of Akron (C), OH, *457*
Management Recruiters of Winston-Salem (C), NC, *457*
Management Recruiters of Dayton, Inc. (C), OH, *457*
Management Recruiters of Columbus (C), OH, *457*
Management Recruiters of Cleveland (C), OH, *457*
Management Recruiters of Cincinnati/Sharonville, Inc. (C), OH, *457*
Management Recruiters of Cleveland (C), OH, *457*
Management Recruiters of Easton, PA (C), PA, *458*
Management Recruiters of Sidney (C), OH, *458*
Management Recruiters of Northwest Ohio, Inc. (C), OH, *458*
Management Recruiters of Bethlehem, PA (C), PA, *458*
Management Recruiters of McMurray, Inc. (C), PA, *459*
Management Recruiters of Valley Forge (C), PA, *459*
Management Recruiters of Westmoreland County, Inc. (C), PA, *459*
Management Recruiters of Delaware County (C), PA, *459*
Management Recruiters of Puerto Rico (C), PR, *460*
Management Recruiters of North Charleston (C), SC, *460*
Management Recruiters of Myrtle Beach, Inc. (C), SC, *460*
Management Recruiters of Florence (C), SC, *460*
Management Recruiters of West Chester, Inc. (C), PA, *460*
Management Recruiters of Aiken (C), SC, *460*
Management Recruiters The Delta Group, Inc. (C), TN, *461*
Management Recruiters of Chattanooga-Brainerd, Inc. (C), TN, *461*
Management Recruiters of Sioux Falls, LLP (C), SD, *461*
Management Recruiters of Travelers Rest, Inc. (C), SC, *461*
Management Recruiters of Franklin, Inc. (C), TN, *461*
Management Recruiters of Columbia, Tennessee (C), TN, *461*
Management Recruiters of North West Austin (C), TX, *462*
Management Recruiters of Houston (C), TX, *462*
Management Recruiters of Champions (C), TX, *462*

Management Recruiters of Austin (C), TX, *462*
Management Recruiters of Arlington (C), TX, *462*
Management Recruiters of LBJ Park/Dallas (C), TX, *462*
Management Recruiters - Friendswood (C), TX, *462*
Management Recruiters of San Antonio (C), TX, *463*
Management Recruiters of Lubbock (C), TX, *463*
Management Recruiters of Round Rock (C), TX, *463*
Management Recruiters of Salt Lake City (C), UT, *464*
Management Recruiters of Ogden (C), UT, *464*
Management Recruiters of Sugar Land Inc. (C), TX, *464*
Management Recruiters Int'l.-The Woodlands (C), TX, *464*
Management Recruiters of Milwaukee-West (C), WI, *465*
Management Recruiters of Loudoun County South (C), VA, *465*
Management Recruiters of Seattle (C), WA, *465*
Management Recruiters of Spokane (C), WA, *465*
Management Recruiters of Appleton (C), WI, *465*
Management Recruiters of Milwaukee-North (C), WI, *466*
Management Recruiters of Madison, Inc. (C), WI, *466*
Management Recruiters of Janesville, Inc. (C), WI, *466*
Management Recruiters of Milwaukee - Downtown (C), WI, *466*
Management Recruiters of Cheyenne (C), WY, *466*
Management Resource Assoc., Inc. (C), FL, *467*
Management Search Int'l. (C), CA, *467*
Management Search of R.I. Inc. (R), RI, *135*
Mankuta Gallagher & Assoc., Inc. (C), FL, *468*
Mannard & Assoc., Inc. (R), IL, *135*
Manuso, Alexander & Associates, Inc. (R), NY, *135*
The Marathon Group (C), FL, *469*
MARBL Consultants, Inc. (C), WI, *469*
Marcus & Assoc. (C), NY, *469*
Margolin Consultants, Inc. (C), NY, *469*
Mark III Personnel, Inc. (C), NC, *470*
Markent Personnel, Inc. (C), WI, *470*
Paula Marks Inc. (R), NY, *136*
The Maroon Group (R), CT, *136*
Marra Peters & Partners (R), NJ, *136*
Marsteller Wilcox Assoc. (C), IL, *471*
George R. Martin (R), PA, *137*
The Martin Group (R), CA, *137*
Martin Partners, L.L.C. (R), IL, *137*
The Martwick Group, Inc. (C), OR, *472*
Marvel Consultants, Inc. (C), OH, *472*
Massey-Horton Int'l. (R), ON, *138*
Louis Thomas Masterson & Co. (R), OH, *138*
Richard L. Mather & Assoc. (C), CT, *472*
Mathey Services (C), IL, *472*
Matrix Consultants, Inc. (C), NC, *472*
Matté & Company, Inc. (R), CT, *138*
Matte Consulting Group Inc. (R), QE, *138*
G. P. Mattocks & Associates (C), NC, *473*
Mayhall Search Group, Inc. (C), IN, *473*
The Mazzitelli Group, Ltd. (R), MN, *139*
Tom McCall Executive Search (C), IL, *473*
McCooe & Assoc., Inc. (R), NJ, *140*
McCormack & Farrow (R), CA, *140*
McCoy Ltd. (C), CA, *474*
McCray, Shriver, Eckdahl & Assoc., Inc. (R), CA, *140*
McDonald Assoc. Int'l. (R), IL, *140*
McDonald, Long & Assoc., Inc. (R), NY, *140*
Robert E. McGrath & Assoc. (R), CT, *141*
McGrath & Assoc., Inc. (R), NJ, *141*
McInturff & Assoc., Inc. (C), MA, *474*
McIntyre Management Resources (C), ON, *474*
McKee Cyber Search (C), MS, *475*
McKeen & Company (R), TX, *141*
McKinley•Arend Int'l. (R), TX, *141*
McManners Assoc., Inc. (R), CA, *142*
Med Exec Int'l. (C), CA, *476*
Meder & Assoc., Inc. (R), IL, *142*
Medical Executive Search Assoc., Inc. (C), AZ, *477*
MedQuest Assoc. (C), CO, *478*
Melancon & Co. (R), TX, *143*
Mercedes & Co., Inc. (R), MA, *143*
Merit Professional Search, Inc. (C), TN, *479*
Merrick & Moore (C), NC, *479*
MES Search Co. (C), GA, *479*
MESA, Inc. (R), CO, *143*
MESA International (C), CA, *480*
MetroVantage Personnel Systems (C), CA, *480*
Walter Meyer & Assoc. (R), NY, *144*
Meyer Assoc., Inc. (R), GA, *144*
mfg/Search, Inc. (C), IN, *480*
Michael Assoc. (R), IL, *144*
Michael James & Co. (C), IL, *480*
Michael/Merrill (C), KS, *481*
Michaels & Moere (C), WI, *481*
Lou Michaels Assoc., Inc. (C), MI, *481*
Michigan Consulting Group (R), MI, *144*
Midland Consultants (C), OH, *481*
Miller + Miller (C), WA, *482*
Miller Denver (C), CO, *482*
Danette Milne Corporate Search Inc. (C), ON, *482*
Herbert Mines Assoc., Inc. (R), NY, *145*
MIXTEC Group (R), CA, *145*
MJF Assoc. (C), CT, *483*
The Montgomery Group, Inc. (C), TN, *484*
Montgomery, Thomason & Assoc. (C), ON, *484*
Moore Research Assoc. (R), NJ, *147*
Morgan & Assoc. (C), MA, *485*
Morgan Int'l., Inc. (R), IL, *147*
The Morgan/Geoffries Group (C), CA, *485*
Morgan/Webber, Inc. (R), NY, *147*
The Morley Group (C), IN, *486*
Morton, McCorkle & Assoc. Inc. (R), MO, *147*
MPA Executive Search Inc. (R), QE, *148*
Mruk & E.M.A. Partners (R), NY, *148*
Mulcahy Co. (C), WI, *487*
Mullen Assoc., Inc. (R), NC, *148*
The Mulshine Co., Inc. (R), NJ, *149*
The Mulshine Company, Ltd. (R), NY, *149*
Multisearch Recruiters (C), CA, *487*
R. F. Mulvaney & Assoc., Inc. (R), MO, *149*
Jennifer Munro & Partners, Inc. (R), SC, *149*
Munroe, Curry & Bond Assoc. (R), NJ, *149*
The Murray Group (C), IL, *487*
Musick & Assoc. (C), CA, *487*
N.A.P. Executive Services (Canada) Inc. (C), ON, *488*
Nachman Biomedical (C), MA, *488*
Nadzam, Lusk, Horgan & Assoc., Inc. (R), CA, *150*
NaTek Corp. (C), NY, *488*
National Computerized Employment Service, Inc. (C), PA, *489*
National Corporate Consultants, Inc. (C), IN, *489*
National Metal Services Corp. (C), IN, *489*
National Recruiting Service (C), IN, *489*
National Search Assoc. (C), CA, *490*
National Search, Inc. (R), NC, *150*
Nationwide Personnel Recruiting & Consulting, Inc. (C), OR, *490*
Nationwide Personnel Placement, Inc. (C), OH, *490*
NaviSearch (C), GA, *490*
NCC Executive Search Consultants (C), CA, *490*
The Neil Michael Group, Inc./Global Partners (R), NY, *151*
The NEIS Corp., Inc. (C), FL, *491*
J. Fielding Nelson & Assoc., Inc. (R), UT, *151*
Len Nelson & Assoc., Inc. (C), TX, *491*
New Directions, Inc. (C), IL, *492*
New Venture Development, Inc. (C), CA, *492*
Newman-Johnson-King, Inc. (C), TX, *492*
NHA Plastics Recruiters (C), FL, *493*
Nicholaou & Co. (R), IL, *151*
Nichols & Company (R), CO, *151*
P. J. Nicholson & Assoc. (C), IL, *493*
The Niemond Corp. (R), CA, *152*
NMC & Kay Int'l. (R), CO, *152*
Noll Human Resource Services (C), NE, *494*
W. D. Nolte & Company (R), CT, *152*
Norman Broadbent Int'l., Inc. (R), NY, *152*
The Normyle/Erstling Health Search Group (C), NJ, *494*
John B. Norris & Assoc., Inc. (C), MD, *495*
Norris Agency (C), TX, *495*
NorTech Resources (C), NY, *496*
North American Recruiters, Inc. (R), MN, *153*
North Coast Meridian (C), NY, *496*
Northern Consultants Inc. (R), ME, *153*
Northland Employment Services Inc. (C), MN, *496*
Norton & Assoc. (C), IL, *496*

Nuessle, Kurdziel & Weiss, Inc. (R), PA, *153*
NYCOR Search, Inc. (C), MN, *497*
O'Brien & Bell (R), OH, *153*
O'Connor, O'Connor, Lordi, Ltd. (R), PA, *154*
O'Keefe & Assoc., Inc. (R), CT, *154*
O'Rourke Companies, Inc. (R), TX, *154*
O'Shea, Divine & Co., Inc. (R), CA, *154*
Ober & Company (R), CA, *155*
Oberlander & Co., Inc. (R), IL, *155*
The Odessa Group (R), CA, *155*
Oliver & Rozner Assoc., Inc. (R), NY, *155*
Olsen/Clark (R), WA, *156*
Omega Search, Inc. (C), NC, *498*
Omega Systems, LLC (C), VA, *498*
The Onstott Group (R), MA, *156*
Open Concepts (C), CA, *499*
Organization Consulting Ltd. (R), ON, *157*
Organization Resources Inc. (R), MA, *157*
Orion Int'l. Consulting Group, Inc. (C), NC, *499*
Ortman Recruiting Int'l. (C), CA, *500*
Ott & Hansen, Inc. (R), CA, *157*
LaMonte Owens, Inc. (R), PA, *157*
The P & L Group (C), NY, *500*
P R Management Consultants, Inc. (C), NJ, *500*
Pacific Advisory Service, Inc. (C), IL, *501*
Pacific Coast Recruiting (C), CA, *501*
Packaging Personnel Co., Ltd. (C), WI, *501*
T. Page & Assoc. (C), TX, *502*
The Pailin Group Professional Search Consultants (R), TX, *158*
Kirk Palmer & Assoc., Inc. (R), NY, *158*
Paper Industry Recruitment (P.I.R.) (C), ME, *502*
Frank Parillo & Assoc. (R), CA, *159*
R. Parker & Assoc., Inc. (R), NY, *159*
D. P. Parker & Assoc., Inc. (R), MA, *159*
Parker, McFadden & Assoc. (C), GA, *503*
Michael W. Parres & Assoc. (R), MI, *159*
Parsons Assoc. Inc. (R), IL, *159*
Partners In Human Resources Int'l., Inc. (R), NY, *160*
Partners in Recruiting (C), IL, *503*
The Partnership Group (R), NJ, *160*
Pasona Canada, Inc. (C), ON, *504*
Pathways Int'l. (C), CT, *505*
Paules Associates (C), CA, *505*
PC Assoc. (C), CO, *505*
Peachtree Executive Search (R), GA, *161*
Peck & Assoc., Ltd. (R), WI, *161*
Peeney Assoc., Inc. (R), NJ, *161*
Paul S. Pelland, P.C. (R), SC, *161*
M. A. Pelle Assoc., Inc. (C), NY, *506*
People Management Mid-South, LLC (R), TN, *162*
People Management Northeast, Inc. (R), CT, *162*
PERC, Ltd. (C), AZ, *506*
Performance Resources, Inc. (C), RI, *507*
The Perkins Group (R), NC, *162*
Perry-D'Amico & Assoc. (R), CA, *162*
Barry Persky & Co., Inc. (R), CT, *163*
PersoNet, Inc. (C), FL, *507*
Personnel Assoc. (C), NC, *508*
The Personnel Group, Inc. (R), MN, *163*
Personnel, Inc. (C), AL, *508*
Personnel Incorporated (C), IA, *508*
Personnel Management Group (C), MB, *508*
The Personnel Network, Inc. (C), SC, *508*
Personnel Tangent Inc. (C), QE, *509*
Personnel Unlimited/Executive Search (C), WA, *509*
Petruzzi Assoc. (C), NJ, *509*
Peyser Assoc., Inc. (R), FL, *163*
Pharmaceutical Recruiters, Inc. (R), NY, *163*
Phase II Management (R), CT, *164*
Phelps Personnel Assoc., Inc. (C), SC, *510*
J. R. Phillip & Assoc., Inc. (R), CA, *164*
Phillips Int'l., Inc. (C), SC, *510*
Phillips Personnel/Search (C), CO, *510*
Phillips Resource Group (C), SC, *510*
Philo & Associates (C), GA, *511*
Phoenix BioSearch, Inc. (C), NJ, *511*
Physician Associates (C), HI, *511*
PIC Executive Search (C), GA, *511*
Gregory D. Pickens (C), TX, *511*
Pioneer Consulting Group (C), CA, *512*
Pioneer Executive Consultants (C), ON, *512*
Place Mart Personnel Service (C), NJ, *513*
Rene Plessner Assoc., Inc. (R), NY, *165*
R. L. Plimpton Assoc., Inc. (R), CO, *165*
Yves Plouffe & Assoc. (R), QE, *165*
The Polen Group (C), PA, *514*
Ray Polhill & Assoc. (R), NC, *166*
Polson & Co., Inc. (R), MN, *166*
Polytechnical Consultants, Inc. (C), IL, *514*
Don V. Poole & Assoc., Inc. (C), CO, *514*
Porter & Assoc., Inc. (C), FL, *514*
Jack Porter Assoc., Inc. (C), WA, *514*
David Powell, Inc. (R), CA, *166*
Norman Powers Assoc., Inc. (C), MA, *515*
Prairie Resource Group, Inc. (R), IL, *166*
Elan Pratzer & Partners Inc. (R), ON, *167*
PRAXIS Partners (R), VA, *167*
Predictor Systems Corp. (R), CA, *167*
Preferred Professional Recruiters (C), OH, *516*
Preferred Professional Recruiters (C), TX, *516*
George Preger & Associates Inc. (R), ON, *167*
Premier Recruiting Group (C), MI, *516*
Premier Search Group (C), IN, *517*
The Premier Staffing Group (C), OH, *517*
Preston-Hunter, Inc. (R), IL, *167*
PricewaterhouseCoopers Executive Search (R), ON, *168*
PricewaterhouseCoopers Executive Search (R), MX, *168*
Prichard Kymen Inc. (R), AB, *168*
Prime Management Group Inc. (C), ON, *518*
Prime Resource Assoc. (C), WI, *518*
Pro Tec Technical Services (C), ON, *519*
Probe Technology (C), PA, *519*
Procurement Resources (C), MD, *520*
Professional Employment Group (C), MD, *520*
Professional Engineering Technical Personnel Consultants (C), NC, *520*
Professional Personnel Services (C), IA, *520*
Professional Personnel Consultants, Inc. (C), MI, *521*
Professional Persons Career Services (C), NY, *521*
Professional Recruiting Consultants (C), FL, *521*
Professional Recruiting Consultants, Inc. (C), DE, *521*
Professional Research Services, Inc. (R), IL, *169*
Professional Search (R), MI, *169*
Professional Search Assoc. (C), CA, *522*
Professional Search Consultants (PSC) (C), TX, *523*
Professions, Inc. (C), OH, *523*
Proquest Inc. (C), SC, *524*
ProSearch, Inc. (C), OH, *524*
ProTech Nationwide Staffing, Inc. (C), NY, *525*
Proven Edge (C), CA, *525*
PSD Group, Inc. (C), CA, *525*
PSP Agency (C), NY, *525*
Quality Control Recruiters (C), CT, *526*
Quality Search (C), IN, *526*
Quality Search Inc. (C), OH, *526*
Quiring Assoc., Inc. (C), IN, *527*
QVS Int'l. (R), GA, *170*
R M Associates (R), OH, *171*
R. J. Associates (C), NY, *528*
R.A.N. Assoc., Inc. (C), OH, *528*
R/K International Inc. (R), CT, *171*
Raines Int'l. Inc. (R), NY, *171*
Ramm Search (C), NY, *528*
Ramming & Assoc., Inc. (C), NJ, *528*
Rand Assoc. (R), ME, *171*
Harold L. Rapp Assoc. (C), NY, *529*
Ray & Berndtson/Laurendeau Labrecque (R), QE, *172*
Ray & Berndtson/Lovas Stanley (R), ON, *172*
Raymond Karsan Assoc. (C), PA, *529*
Raymond Thomas & Assoc. (C), FL, *530*
RBW Assoc. Inc. (C), OR, *531*
RCE Assoc. (R), NJ, *173*
Re-Mark Assoc. Inc. (C), NJ, *531*
Recruit Xpress (C), TX, *531*
Recruiting Services Group, Inc. (C), TN, *532*
The Recruitment Group, Inc. (C), NY, *532*
Redden-Shaffer Group (R), CA, *173*
Reece & Mruk Partners/EMA Partners Int'l. (R), MA, *173*
Cedric L. Reese Inc. (C), CA, *533*
The Regis Group, Ltd. (R), GA, *174*
Reid Ellis Assoc. Inc. (C), ON, *533*
Reifel & Assoc. (R), IL, *174*
The Remington Group (R), IL, *174*
Renaissance Resources, LLC (R), VA, *174*
Resource Inc. (R), MA, *175*
Resource Networking Inc. (C), IN, *534*
Resource Perspectives, Inc. (R), CA, *175*
Resources for Management (R), PA, *175*
L. J. Reszotko & Assoc. (C), IL, *535*
Retail Recruiters/Spectrum Consultants, Inc. (C), PA, *535*
Retained Search Assoc. (R), NC, *176*
The Revere Assoc., Inc. (R), OH, *176*
Russell Reynolds Assoc., Inc. (R), NY, *176*
Rice Cohen Int'l. (R), PA, *178*

Richard, Wayne & Roberts (C), TX, *536*
Terry Richards (C), OH, *536*
Riddle & McGrath LLC (R), GA, *178*
Right/McKee Consulting Group (C), TX, *537*
Riley Cole (C), CA, *537*
River Region Personnel, Inc. (C), LA, *538*
RJN Consulting (R), NY, *179*
RML Assoc. (C), PA, *538*
Roberson & Co. (C), AZ, *538*
Robert William James & Assoc. (C), OR, *539*
V. Robinson & Co., Inc. (C), MO, *539*
Bruce Robinson Assoc. (R), NJ, *180*
Robison & Associates (R), NC, *180*
J. P. Roddy Consultants (C), PA, *540*
R. A. Rodriguez & Assoc., Inc. (C), TX, *540*
Rodzik & Assoc., Inc. (R), NC, *180*
Roevin Technical People (C), ON, *540*
ROI Assoc. (R), NY, *180*
Rolland Ressources Humaines Inc. (R), QE, *181*
Romac Int'l., Inc. (C), FL, *542*
Romano McAvoy Assoc., Inc. (C), NY, *544*
Romeo-Hudgins & Assoc., Ltd. (C), NJ, *544*
Rossi & Assoc. Inc. (C), BC, *545*
The Rossi Search Group (C), PA, *545*
Roster Inc. (C), IN, *545*
Roth Young of Chicago (C), IL, *546*
Roth Young Executive Recruiters (C), MN, *546*
Roth Young Executive Search (C), TX, *546*
Roth Young Personnel Service of Detroit, Inc. (C), MI, *546*
Roth Young Seattle (C), WA, *546*
Roth Young of Tampa (C), FL, *546*
Roth Young Executive Search of Milwaukee (C), WI, *547*
Rothrock Associates, Inc. (C), NC, *547*
Rovner Gerner & Assoc. (R), CA, *182*
Rowland Assoc. (C), CA, *547*
RSMR, Inc. (R), IL, *182*
RTE Search (C), NJ, *547*
Ruderfer & Co., Inc. (C), NJ, *548*
Susan Rudich (C), NY, *548*
Louis Rudzinsky Assoc., Inc. (C), MA, *548*
Rushmore • Judge Inc. (R), ON, *183*
S-H-S Int'l. of Cherry Hill (C), NJ, *549*
S. P. Assoc., Inc. (C), NC, *550*
S.C.S. & Assoc. (C), NC, *550*
S.D.P. Contract Recruiters (C), NJ, *550*
Saber Group, Inc. (C), TX, *550*
R. S. Sadow Assoc. (C), NJ, *550*
Sage Employment Recruiters (C), IN, *550*
Sales Consultants Int'l. of Oakland (C), CA, *556*
Sales Consultants of Silicon Valley (C), CA, *556*
Sales Consultants of Chico (C), CA, *556*
Sales Consultants of Daphne (C), AL, *556*
Sales Consultants of Ft. Lauderdale, Inc. (C), FL, *557*
Sales Consultants of Denver (C), CO, *557*
Sales Consultants of Indianapolis-North (C), IN, *558*
Sales Consultants of Baltimore (C), MD, *559*
Sales Consultants of Farmington Hills (C), MI, *560*
Sales Consultants of Laurel Park, Inc. (C), MI, *560*
Sales Consultants of Middlesex County, Inc. (C), NJ, *561*
Sales Consultants of Pittsburgh (C), PA, *562*
Sales Consultants King of Prussia (C), PA, *562*
Sales Consultants of Orangeburg (C), SC, *562*
Sales Consultants of Houston (C), TX, *563*
Sales Consultants of Appleton (C), WI, *563*
Salveson Stetson Group, Inc. (R), PA, *184*
Sanford Rose Assoc. - Lake Forest (R), IL, *184*
Sanford Rose Assoc. - Santa Ana (C), CA, *565*
Sanford Rose Assoc. (C), OH, *565*
Sanford Rose Assoc. - Mobile (C), AL, *565*
Sanford Rose Assoc. - Fairhope (C), AL, *565*
Sanford Rose Assoc. - Santa Barbara (C), CA, *565*
Sanford Rose Assoc. - Clearwater (C), FL, *566*
Sanford Rose Assoc. - Effingham (C), IL, *566*
Sanford Rose Assoc. - Athens (C), GA, *566*
Sanford Rose Assoc. - Chicago (C), IL, *566*
Sanford Rose Assoc. - Columbia, MD (C), MD, *567*
Sanford Rose Assoc. - Rockford (C), IL, *567*
Sanford Rose Assoc. - Orland Park (C), IL, *567*
Sanford Rose Assoc. - Cedar Rapids (C), IA, *567*
Sanford Rose Assoc. - Rockville (C), MD, *567*
Sanford Rose Assoc. - Louisville (C), KY, *567*
Sanford Rose Assoc. - Amherst, NY (C), NY, *568*
Sanford Rose Assoc. - Rochester (C), MI, *568*
Sanford Rose Assoc. - Gastonia (C), NC, *568*
Sanford Rose Assoc. - Flemington (C), NJ, *568*
Sanford Rose Assoc. - Canton (C), OH, *569*
Sanford Rose Assoc. - Burlington, NC (C), NC, *569*
Sanford Rose Assoc. - Greensboro (C), NC, *569*
Sanford Rose Assoc. - Akron (C), OH, *569*
Sanford Rose Assoc. - Fairlawn (C), OH, *569*
Sanford Rose Assoc. - Philadelphia North (C), PA, *570*
Sanford Rose Assoc. - Austin (C), TX, *570*
Sanford Rose Assoc. - Nashville (C), TN, *570*
Sanford Rose Assoc. - Columbia (C), SC, *570*
Sanford Rose Assoc. - Doylestown (C), PA, *570*
Sanford Rose Assoc. - Portland (C), OR, *570*
Sanford Rose Assoc. - Salt Lake City (C), UT, *571*
Sanford Rose Assoc. - Port Washington (C), WI, *571*
Santangelo Consultants Inc. (C), NY, *571*
Sarver & Carruth Assoc. (C), OK, *571*
Sathe & Associates, Inc. (R), MN, *184*
Schattle & Duquette (C), RI, *571*
The Schatz Company (C), MO, *571*
Schenck & Assoc. SC (C), WI, *572*
Schick Professional Search, Inc. (C), OH, *572*
Scientific Solutions, Inc. (C), MI, *572*
Robert Scott Assoc. (C), NJ, *573*
Scott Executive Search, Inc. (R), NY, *186*
Scott-Thaler Assoc. Agency, Inc. (C), CA, *573*
Search & Recruit Int'l. (C), VA, *573*
Search Advisors Int'l. Corp. (R), FL, *186*
Search Assoc. (C), KY, *574*
Search Assoc., Inc. (C), NJ, *574*
Search Bureau Int'l. (C), IL, *574*
Search By Design (C), AZ, *574*
Search Consultants Int'l., Inc. (C), TX, *575*
Search Enterprises, Inc. (C), FL, *575*
Search Group (C), CA, *575*
Search Group Inc. (R), AB, *186*
Search Masters Int'l. (R), AZ, *187*
The Search Network (C), CA, *576*
Search North America, Inc. (C), OR, *576*
Search Northwest Assoc. (C), OR, *576*
Search South, Inc. (C), AL, *576*
Searchforce, Inc. (R), FL, *187*
SearchOne, Inc. (C), AR, *577*
Searchworks, Inc. (C), FL, *577*
Segal & Assoc. (C), GA, *578*
Select Services (C), IL, *578*
Selectis Corp. (C), IL, *578*
Selective Management Services, Inc. (C), FL, *578*
Selective Recruiting Assoc., Inc. (C), MI, *578*
Selective Staffing (C), CA, *579*
Selig Executive Search (C), NH, *579*
Sensible Solutions, Inc. (R), IL, *188*
Sharp Placement Professionals, Inc. (C), NY, *579*
Sharrow & Assoc., Inc. (C), MI, *579*
M. B. Shattuck & Assoc., Inc. (R), CA, *189*
Sherwood Lehman Massucco, Inc. (R), CA, *189*
Shinn & Assoc. (R), CA, *189*
Shoemaker & Assoc. (R), GA, *190*
The Shorr Group (R), IL, *190*
SHS of Allentown (C), PA, *580*
John Sibbald Assoc., Inc. (R), MO, *191*
Larry Siegel & Assoc. (R), WA, *191*
Peter Siegel & Co. (C), MA, *581*
RitaSue Siegel Resources, Inc. (R), NY, *191*
Marvin L. Silcott & Assoc., Inc. (C), TX, *581*
Sill Technical Assoc., Inc. (C), PA, *581*
L. A. Silver Assoc., Inc. (R), MA, *191*
D. J. Simpson Assoc. Inc. (R), ON, *191*

Simpson Associates (C), NY, *582*
Sinclair & Co., Inc. (R), MA, *192*
Singleton & Assoc. (C), VA, *582*
Sink, Walker, Boltrus Int'l. (R), MA, *192*
Skott/Edwards Consultants (R), NY, *192*
Slayton Int'l., Inc. (R), IL, *192*
Tom Sloan & Assoc., Inc. (C), WI, *583*
J. L. Small Assoc. (C), AL, *583*
Smith & Assoc. (C), FL, *583*
James F. Smith & Assoc. (C), GA, *583*
Ralph Smith & Assoc. (C), IL, *584*
Smith & Syberg, Inc. (R), IN, *193*
Herman Smith Executive Initiatives Inc. (R), ON, *193*
The Smith Group, Inc. (C), NC, *584*
Smith James Group, Inc. (R), GA, *194*
Smith, Roth & Squires (R), NY, *194*
Smith Search, S.C. (R), MX, *194*
Smith, Brown & Jones (C), KS, *585*
Snelling & Snelling, Inc. (C), FL, *585*
Snelling Search (C), AL, *585*
Snelling Search (C), IL, *585*
Snelling Search (C), LA, *586*
Snelling Search (C), IL, *586*
Snelling Search Recruiters (C), NC, *586*
Snyder & Co. (R), CT, *194*
Soderlund Assoc. Inc. (R), OH, *194*
Software Resource Consultants (C), TN, *587*
Soltis Management Services (R), PA, *195*
Solutions Group (R), AL, *195*
Souder & Assoc. (R), VA, *195*
Southern Chemical & Plastics Search (C), GA, *587*
Southern Recruiters & Consultants, Inc. (C), SC, *587*
Southern Research Services (R), FL, *195*
SPC Symcox Personnel Consultants (C), TX, *588*
Spear-Izzo Assoc., LLC (C), PA, *588*
Spectrum Consultants (R), CA, *196*
SpencerSearch, Inc. (C), CO, *589*
SpencerStuart (R), NY, *196*
Kenn Spinrad Inc. (C), PA, *589*
Splaine & Assoc., Inc. (R), CA, *198*
Sports Group Int'l. (R), NC, *198*
Spriggs & Co., Inc. (R), IL, *198*
Sprout/Standish, Inc. (C), NH, *589*
Staff Resources, Inc. (C), SC, *590*
Staffing Edge, Inc. (C), IA, *590*
Stanton Chase Int'l. (R), MD, *198*
Star Search Consultants (C), ON, *591*
The Stelton Group, Inc. (C), NJ, *592*
Michael Stern Assoc., Inc./Euram (R), ON, *200*
Ron Stevens & Assoc., Inc. (C), FL, *593*
Stewart Assoc. (C), PA, *593*
Stewart/Greene & Co. of The Triad, Inc. (C), NC, *594*
Charles Stickler Assoc. (R), PA, *201*
Linford E. Stiles & Assoc., L.L.C. (R), NH, *201*
STM Assoc. (R), UT, *201*
Allan Stolee Inc. (R), FL, *201*
Stone Enterprises Ltd. (C), IL, *594*
Stone, Murphy & Olson (R), MN, *201*
Stoneburner Assoc., Inc. (C), KS, *594*
Stoopen Asociados, S.C./EMA Partners Int'l. (R), MX, *202*
Storfer & Assoc. (C), NY, *595*
Strategic Advancement Inc. (R), NJ, *202*
Strategic Assoc., Inc. (C), TX, *595*
Strategic Resources (C), WA, *595*
Strategic Search Corp. (R), IL, *202*
Strategic Technologies, Inc. (C), TX, *596*
StratfordGroup (R), OH, *203*
Stratin Assoc. (C), NJ, *596*
Straube Associates (R), MA, *203*
Success Seekers Connection (C), FL, *596*
Sullivan & Assoc. (R), MI, *204*
Summit Executive Search Consultants, Inc. (R), FL, *204*
Summit Group Int'l., Inc. (R), GA, *204*
Summit Search Specialists (C), TX, *596*
Ron Sunshine & Assoc. (C), IL, *597*
Survival Systems Staffing, Inc. (C), CA, *597*
System 1 Search (C), CA, *598*
Systems Research Inc. (SRI) (C), IL, *598*
T E M Assoc. (C), WI, *599*
Tabb & Assoc. (R), OH, *205*
Tactical Alternatives (R), CA, *205*
S. Tanner & Assoc. Inc. (C), ON, *599*
Tanner & Assoc., Inc. (R), TX, *206*
Tarnow Int'l. (R), NJ, *206*
Tate & Assoc., Inc. (R), NJ, *207*
M. L. Tawney & Assoc. (C), TX, *600*
TE, Inc. (C), IL, *600*
Team One Partners, Inc. (C), GA, *600*
Teamsearch, Inc. (C), MI, *601*
Tech-Net (C), TX, *601*
Techaid Inc. (C), QE, *601*
TechFind, Inc. (R), MA, *207*
Technical Employment Consultants (C), PA, *602*
Technical Recruiting Services (C), OH, *602*
Technical Resource Assoc. (C), TN, *602*
Technical Skills Consulting Inc. (R), ON, *207*
Technical Staffing Solutions (C), TX, *602*
Technifind Int'l. (C), TX, *602*
Technology Consultants Int'l. (C), CA, *603*
The Technology Group (R), IL, *208*
Techstaff Inc. (C), WI, *603*
Tecmark Associates Inc. (C), NY, *604*
Teknon Employment Resources, Inc. (C), OH, *604*
Tekworx, Inc. (C), OK, *604*
Telem Adhesive Search Corp. (C), MD, *605*
Thomas Mangum Co. (R), CA, *208*
Richard Thompson Assoc., Inc. (R), MN, *209*
Thomson, Sponar & Adams, Inc. (C), WA, *606*
Thorne, Brieger Assoc., Inc. (R), NY, *209*
Tierney Assoc., Inc. (R), PA, *209*
Fred C. Tippel & Assoc. (C), OH, *607*
Tirocchi, Wright, Inc. (R), CA, *209*
TNS Partners, Inc. (R), TX, *209*
TPS Staffing Solutions (C), IN, *608*
Jay Tracey Assoc. Inc. (C), VT, *608*
Trainor/Frank & Assoc. Inc. (C), WI, *608*
Trambley the Recruiter (C), NM, *608*
Trans-United Consultants Ltd. (C), ON, *608*
Transportation Recruiting Services, Inc. (C), MS, *608*
Travis & Co., Inc. (R), MA, *210*
Traynor Confidential, Ltd. (C), NY, *609*
Triangle Assoc. (C), PA, *609*
Triumph Consulting, Inc. (R), IA, *210*
Trowbridge & Co., Inc. (R), MA, *211*
TRS Staffing Solutions Inc. (C), OH, *610*
The Truman Agency (C), CA, *610*
TSC Management Services Group, Inc. (C), IL, *610*
Tschudin Inc. (R), NJ, *211*
TSI Group/TSI Staffing Services (C), ON, *610*
The Thomas Tucker Co. (R), CA, *211*
U.S. Search (C), VA, *610*
Unisearch Search & Recruiting Inc. (C), CA, *611*
Unlimited Staffing Solutions, Inc. (C), MI, *611*
The Urban Placement Service (C), TX, *611*
Valentine & Assoc. (C), IL, *611*
VanMaldegiam Assoc., Inc. (R), IL, *213*
Vaughan & Co. (C), CA, *612*
Vento Assoc. (C), TN, *612*
Verkamp-Joyce Assoc., Inc. (R), IL, *213*
Victor White Int'l. (C), CA, *612*
Vincenty & Co. (C), OH, *612*
Vlcek & Company, Inc. (R), CA, *214*
Voigt Assoc. (R), IL, *214*
VZ Int'l., Inc. (C), AZ, *613*
W. P. Assoc. (C), CA, *613*
The Wabash Group (C), IN, *613*
Wachendorfer & Assoc. (C), TX, *613*
Gordon Wahls Executive Search (C), PA, *613*
Wallace Assoc. (C), CT, *614*
Gerald Walsh & Co. Inc. (C), NS, *614*
Linda Walter & Associes (C), QE, *615*
Ward-Hoffman & Assoc. (C), ID, *615*
Warner & Assoc., Inc. (C), OH, *615*
Warren Executive Services (C), GA, *616*
R. J. Watkins & Co., Ltd. (R), CA, *216*
Waveland Int'l. (R), IL, *216*
Webb, Johnson Assoc., Inc. (R), NY, *216*
Weber Executive Search (R), NY, *216*
S. B. Webster & Associates (R), MA, *217*
Wegner & Assoc. (C), WI, *617*
David Weinfeld Group (C), NC, *617*
Weinpel Search, Inc. (C), NJ, *617*
S. E. Weinstein Co. (R), IL, *217*
Henry Welker & Assoc. (C), MI, *618*
R. A. Wells Co. (C), GA, *618*
Werbin Assoc. Executive Search, Inc. (C), NY, *618*
Jude M. Werra & Assoc. (R), WI, *218*
Wesley Brown & Bartle Co., Inc. (R), NY, *218*
West & Assoc. (C), IL, *618*
West & West (R), CA, *218*
Western Technical Resources (C), CA, *619*
Westfields Int'l., Inc. (C), NY, *619*
Weterrings & Agnew, Inc. (C), NY, *619*
White, Roberts & Stratton, Inc. (C), IL, *619*
Whitehead & Assoc., Inc. (C), MO, *620*
Arch S. Whitehead Assoc. Inc. (ASWA) (R), NY, *219*
Whitney Smith Co. (C), TX, *620*
Whittaker & Assoc., Inc. (C), GA, *620*
Whittlesey & Assoc., Inc. (R), PA, *220*
Daniel Wier & Assoc. (R), CA, *220*

Wilcox Bertoux & Miller (R), CA, *220*
Wilkinson & Ives (R), CA, *221*
John R. Williams & Assoc., Inc. (C), NC, *621*
John Williams & Assoc. (C), TX, *621*
Williams Recruiting, Inc. (C), WA, *621*
Williamsburg Group (C), NJ, *621*
Willis & Assoc. (R), OH, *221*
The Wilmington Group (C), NC, *622*
Wilson & Assoc. Int'l. Inc. (C), FL, *622*
Wilson Personnel, Inc. (C), NC, *622*
The Winchester Group (R), CA, *222*
Winfield Assoc., Inc. (C), MA, *623*
Wing Tips & Pumps, Inc. (C), MI, *623*
Winguth, Grant & Donahue (R), CA, *222*
Winston Search, Inc. (R), MD, *222*
Winthrop Partners, Inc. (R), NY, *222*
The Witt Group (C), FL, *623*
WMD inc. (C), NJ, *623*
Wojdula & Assoc., Ltd. (R), WI, *223*
S. R. Wolman Assoc., Inc. (R), NY, *224*
Susan L. Wonderling Recruiting (C), PA, *623*
Wood, Franchot Inc. (R), MN, *224*
Wood West & Partners Inc. (C), BC, *624*
Woodmoor Group (C), CO, *624*
Jim Woodson & Assoc., Inc. (C), MS, *624*
Woodworth Int'l. Group (R), OR, *224*
Working Relationships, Inc. (C), MN, *624*
World Search (C), OH, *625*
WTW Assoc., Inc. (R), NY, *225*
John Wylie Assoc., Inc. (C), OK, *625*
Wyndham Mills Int'l., Inc. (R), GA, *225*
Xagas & Assoc. (R), IL, *226*
The Yaiser Group (C), NJ, *625*
Yungner & Bormann (R), MN, *226*
Zaccaria Int'l. (C), NJ, *627*
The Zammataro Company (R), OH, *226*
The Zarkin Group, Inc. (R), NY, *226*
Zen Zen Int'l. Inc. (C), MB, *627*
Zingaro & Company (R), TX, *227*
Zwell Int'l. (R), IL, *228*

02.1 Product development

A la Carte Int'l., Inc. (R), VA, *1*
The Abbott Group, Inc. (R), MD, *1*
ACC Technical Services (C), OH, *233*
Access Assoc. Inc. (C), MD, *233*
ACCESS Technology (C), CA, *234*
The Addison Consulting Group (C), NJ, *239*
Advanced Recruitment, Inc. (C), TN, *240*
Advancement Recruiting Services (C), OH, *241*
Advancement, Inc. (C), IL, *241*
Affinity Executive Search (C), FL, *241*
AGRI-associates (C), MO, *242*
Alexander Enterprises, Inc. (C), PA, *243*
David Allen Assoc. (R), NJ, *3*
Alpha Executive Search (C), AL, *245*
The Altco Group (C), NJ, *246*
Anderson Industrial Assoc., Inc. (C), GA, *250*
Tryg R. Angell, Ltd. (C), CT, *250*
Angus Employment Ltd. (C), ON, *250*
Applied Resources, Inc. (C), MN, *252*
Applied Search Assoc., Inc. (C), GA, *252*
Argus National, Inc. (R), CT, *6*
Ariel Recruitment Assoc. (R), NY, *7*
Asheville Search & Consulting (C), NC, *253*
Ashford Management Group, Inc. (R), GA, *7*
Cami Austin & Assoc. (C), IL, *256*
Automation Technology Search (C), CA, *256*
Availability Personnel Consultants (C), NH, *257*
Avestruz & Assoc. (C), CA, *257*
D. W. Baird & Associates (C), MD, *257*
The Bales-Waugh Group (C), FL, *258*
Barber & Assoc. (C), KY, *259*
Barone Assoc. (C), NJ, *259*
Barone-O'Hara Assoc., Inc. (R), NJ, *11*
Barr Assoc. (C), PA, *259*
The Barton Group, Inc. (C), MI, *260*
Battalia Winston Int'l./The Euram Consultants Group (R), NY, *13*
BayResearch Group, Inc. (R), IL, *14*
The Bedford Group (R), RI, *15*
William Bell Assoc., Inc. (C), NJ, *263*
Benford & Assoc., Inc. (C), MI, *264*
Dick Berg & Assoc. (C), CA, *264*
Berkana Int'l., Inc. (C), WA, *265*
Ed Bertolas Assoc., Inc. (C), CA, *265*
Jack Bertram, Executive Recruiter (C), PA, *265*
Besen Assoc. Inc. (C), NJ, *266*
Bio-Venture Group (C), RI, *266*
BJB Assoc. (C), VA, *267*
Blair/Tech Recruiters, Inc. (C), NJ, *268*
J: Blakslee Int'l., Ltd. (R), CA, *18*
Blaney Executive Search (R), MA, *18*
Blau Mancino Schroeder (R), NJ, *18*
Tom Bogle & Assoc. (C), CA, *269*
Mark Bolno & Assoc. (C), FL, *269*
Bolton Group (C), CA, *269*
BowdenGlobal, Ltd. (R), OH, *20*
The Brentwood Group Ltd. (R), OR, *23*
Brian Assoc., Inc. (C), NY, *273*
Brierwood Group, Inc. (C), IN, *273*
Broadband Resource Group (C), CA, *274*
J. Burkey Assoc. (R), NJ, *25*
David S. Burt Assoc. (C), MT, *276*
Byron Leonard Int'l., Inc. (R), CA, *25*
The C.P.R. Group (C), NJ, *278*
Juliette Lang Cahn Executive Search (C), NY, *279*
Caliber Associates (R), PA, *27*
Career Marketing Assoc., Inc. (C), CO, *282*
Career Search Group (C), FL, *283*
Carnegie Resources, Inc. (C), NC, *284*
Case Executive Search (C), MI, *286*
Chad Management Group (C), ON, *288*
Chadwell & Assoc., Inc. (C), MI, *288*
Wayne S. Chamberlain & Assoc. (C), CA, *288*
Charles & Associates, Inc. (C), NE, *289*
Robert L. Charon (C), TX, *289*
Chase-Gardner Executive Search Associates, Inc. (C), FL, *289*
Chelsea Resources, Inc. (C), CT, *290*
The Cherbonnier Group, Inc. (R), TX, *33*
R. Christine Assoc. (C), PA, *290*
Clark Executive Search (C), NY, *292*
Corporate Image Group (C), TN, *300*
Corporate Recruiters Ltd. (C), BC, *300*
Corporate Resources Professional Placement (C), MN, *300*
Cowin Assoc. (R), NY, *42*
Jim Crumpley & Assoc. (C), MO, *304*
CTR (R), CA, *43*
Cyr Associates, Inc. (C), MA, *306*
Davidson, Laird & Assoc. (C), MI, *308*
Bert Davis Executive Search, Inc. (R), NY, *47*
Bert Davis Publishing Placement Consultants (C), NY, *309*
Deeco Int'l. (C), UT, *310*
DiTech Resources (C), CT, *313*
Dominguez-Metz & Assoc. (R), CA, *53*
Robert Drexler Assoc., Inc. (R), NJ, *54*
Dukas Assoc. (C), MA, *315*
The Duncan-O'Dell Group Inc. (C), TX, *316*
Dunhill Executive Search of Los Angeles, Inc. (C), CA, *319*
Dunhill Executive Search of Brown County (C), IN, *321*
Dunhill Personnel of St. Andrews (C), SC, *322*
Dunhill of Corpus Christi, Inc. (C), TX, *323*
G. L. Dykstra Assoc., Inc. (C), MI, *323*
The E & K Group (C), NJ, *324*
W. Robert Eissler & Assoc., Inc. (C), TX, *327*
Elite Medical Search (C), GA, *328*
Emerging Medical Technologies, Inc. (C), CO, *329*
Emerson & Co. (C), GA, *329*
Engineering Profiles (C), FL, *330*
Epsen, Fuller & Assoc., LLC (R), NJ, *60*
Erwin Assoc. (R), IL, *60*
ExeConnex, LLC (R), GA, *61*
ExecuSource Consultants, Inc. (C), TX, *332*
ExecuTech (C), IN, *332*
Executive Career Search (C), VA, *332*
Executive Connection (C), OH, *333*
Executive Directions (R), OH, *62*
Executive Recruiters Agency, Inc. (C), AR, *333*
Executive Recruiters, Inc. (C), WI, *334*
Executive Recruitment Services, Inc. (ERS, Inc.) (C), GA, *334*
Eyler Assoc., Inc. (R), IA, *64*
Fairfield Int'l. Resources (R), NY, *65*
James Feerst & Assoc., Inc. (C), AZ, *339*
Fenwick Partners (R), MA, *66*
Ferrari Search Group (C), OH, *340*
Neil Fink Assoc. (R), CA, *66*
First Choice Search (R), WA, *67*
Focus Executive Search (C), MN, *343*
F-O-R-T-U-N-E Personnel Consultants of Denver, Inc. (C), CO, *344*
Fortune Personnel Consultants (C), CA, *344*
F-O-R-T-U-N-E Personnel Consultants of San Diego (C), CA, *344*
F-O-R-T-U-N-E Personnel Consultants of Manatee County (C), FL, *345*
Fortune Personnel Consultants of Sarasota Inc. (C), FL, *345*
F-O-R-T-U-N-E Personnel Consultants of Atlanta, Inc. (C), GA, *345*

F-o-r-t-u-n-e of Owensboro, Inc. (C), KY, *346*
F-O-R-T-U-N-E Personnel Consultants of South Bend (C), IN, *346*
Fortune Personnel Consultants of Topsfield (C), MA, *346*
Fortune Personnel Consultants (C), NH, *347*
Fortune Personnel Consultants (C), MT, *347*
F-O-R-T-U-N-E Personnel Consultants of Bergen County Inc. (C), NJ, *347*
F-O-R-T-U-N-E of West Portland (C), OR, *348*
F-O-R-T-U-N-E Personnel Consultants of Rockland County, Inc. (C), NY, *348*
F-O-R-T-U-N-E Personnel Consultants of Charlotte (C), NC, *348*
Fortune Personnel Consultants of Hilton Head (C), SC, *349*
F-O-R-T-U-N-E Consultants of Memphis (C), TN, *349*
FORTUNE Personnel Consultants of Charleston, Inc. (C), SC, *349*
Fortune Personnel Consultants of Anderson, Inc. (C), SC, *349*
FORTUNE Personnel Consultants of North Dallas (C), TX, *350*
Foster Partners (R), NY, *70*
Franklin Int'l. Search, Inc. (C), MA, *352*
The Garret Group (R), NJ, *75*
Genesis Recruiting (C), CA, *356*
Genesis Research (C), MO, *356*
J. Gernetzke & Assoc., Inc. (C), OH, *357*
The Glenwood Group (C), IL, *358*
Goodrich & Sherwood Assoc., Inc. (R), NY, *79*
Gordon/Tyler (R), PA, *80*
Gros Executive Search, Inc. (C), TN, *363*
Groton Planning Group (R), ME, *82*
Michael R. Guerin Co. (C), CA, *364*
Hall Kinion (C), CA, *366*
The Hampton Group (C), NY, *367*
Harrison Moore Inc. (C), NE, *370*
The Hawkins Co. (R), CA, *88*
Michael J. Hawkins, Inc. (C), IL, *370*
The Haystack Group, Inc. (R), ME, *88*
Healthcare Management Resources, Inc. (R), GA, *89*
Healthcare Recruiters of the Rockies, Inc. (C), CO, *372*
Healthcare Recruiters Int'l. Orange County (C), CA, *372*
Healthcare Recruiters of New York, Inc. (C), NY, *373*
Healthcare Recruiters - Northwest (C), WA, *374*
HeartBeat Medical, Inc. (C), OR, *374*
R. W. Hebel Assoc. (R), TX, *89*
Heller Assoc., Ltd. (R), IL, *91*
Heller Kil Assoc., Inc. (C), FL, *375*
Hobson Assoc. (C), CT, *379*
Hockett Associates, Inc. (R), CA, *94*
Hoglund & Assoc., Inc. (R), IL, *94*
Horizons Unlimited (C), CA, *381*
Hospitality Executive Search, Inc. (R), MA, *96*
Houtz•Strawn & Arnold, Inc. (R), TX, *96*
Howe & Assoc. (R), PA, *97*
The Hudson Group (C), CT, *383*
E. A. Hughes & Co., Inc. (R), NY, *98*
The Icard Group, Inc. (C), MI, *387*
Impact Source, Inc. (C), FL, *387*
Industry Consultants, Inc. (C), GA, *388*
InSearch (C), CO, *389*
Inter Regional Executive Search, Inc. (IRES, Inc.) (C), NJ, *391*
Interactive Search Network (R), CA, *102*
Iona Partners (C), CA, *394*
Jackley Search Consultants (C), MN, *396*
K. Jaeger & Assoc. (C), MA, *396*
Jaral Consultants, Inc. (C), NJ, *397*
JCL & Assoc. (C), FL, *397*
JG Consultants, Inc. (R), TX, *106*
Ronald S. Johnson Assoc., Inc. (R), CA, *107*
K. E. Johnson Assoc. (C), WA, *399*
The Jonathan Stevens Group, Inc. (R), NJ, *108*
Joslin & Assoc., Ltd. (C), IL, *401*
Kaas Employment Services (C), IA, *402*
Robert Kaestner & Assoc. (C), FL, *403*
Karp & Assoc. (C), FL, *403*
Jim Kay & Assoc. (C), IL, *404*
Kay Concepts, Inc. (C), FL, *404*
A.T. Kearney Executive Search (R), IL, *111*
Kenzer Corp. (R), NY, *113*
Blair Kershaw Assoc., Inc. (C), PA, *405*
Koltnow & Company (R), NY, *117*
Evie Kreisler Assoc. Inc. (C), CA, *409*
Kuhn Med-Tech (C), CA, *409*
Paul Kull & Co. (R), NJ, *121*
L & L Assoc. (C), CA, *410*
Marvin Laba & Assoc. (R), CA, *122*
Laboratory Resource Group (C), MA, *411*
Stephen Laramee & Assoc. Inc. (C), ON, *413*
W. R. Lawry, Inc. (R), CT, *126*
LCS, Inc. (C), TX, *414*
Reynolds Lebus Assoc. (C), AZ, *415*
Lechner & Assoc., Inc. (C), FL, *415*
Lemming/LeVan, Inc. (R), GA, *128*
Lewis & Blank Int'l. (R), CA, *129*
Linden Group, Inc. (C), NC, *418*
Lybrook Assoc., Inc. (C), RI, *421*
M. K. & Assoc. (C), PA, *422*
M.C. Executive Search (C), CA, *422*
The Mallard Group (C), IN, *423*
Management Catalysts (R), NJ, *134*
Management Recruiters Tucson-Foothills, Inc. (C), AZ, *439*
Management Recruiters of Emeryville (C), CA, *440*
Management Recruiters of Northern California (C), CA, *440*
Management Recruiters of Colorado Springs (C), CO, *441*
Management Recruiters of Pleasanton (C), CA, *441*
Management Recruiters Inc. of Silicon Valley (C), CA, *441*
Management Recruiters of Franktown (C), CO, *442*
Management Recruiters of Milford Inc. (C), CT, *442*
Management Recruiters of Ft. Myers, FL. (C), FL, *443*
Management Recruiters of Anna Maria Island (C), FL, *443*
Management Recruiters of Boca Raton (C), FL, *443*
Management Recruiters of Melbourne, Inc. (C), FL, *443*
Management Recruiters of Pensacola (C), FL, *444*
Management Recruiters of Lake Co., Inc. (C), FL, *444*
Management Recruiters of Columbus, Inc. (C), GA, *445*
Management Recruiters of Boise (C), ID, *446*
Management Recruiters of Springfield, Inc. (C), IL, *447*
Management Recruiters of Barrington (C), IL, *447*
Management Recruiters of Sun Valley (C), ID, *447*
Management Recruiters of Spencer (C), IA, *448*
Management Recruiters of Danville (C), KY, *449*
Management Recruiters of Richmond (C), KY, *449*
Management Recruiters of Columbia (C), MD, *450*
Management Recruiters of Livonia (C), MI, *451*
Management Recruiters - Flint (C), MI, *451*
Management Recruiters of Rankin Co. (C), MS, *452*
Management Recruiters of Chanhassen (C), MN, *452*
Management Recruiters of Bay Head (C), NJ, *453*
Management Recruiters of Fayetteville (C), NC, *455*
Management Recruiters of Burlington (C), NC, *455*
Management Recruiters of Asheville, Inc. (C), NC, *455*
Management Recruiters of Rocky Mount - Southwest (C), NC, *456*
Management Recruiters of Mt. Airy (C), NC, *456*
Management Recruiters of Akron (C), OH, *457*
Management Recruiters of Bethlehem, PA (C), PA, *458*
Management Recruiters of McMurray, Inc. (C), PA, *459*
Management Recruiters of Westmoreland County, Inc. (C), PA, *459*
Management Recruiters of North West Austin (C), TX, *462*
Management Recruiters of Arlington (C), TX, *462*
Management Recruiters of LBJ Park/Dallas (C), TX, *462*
Management Recruiters of Round Rock (C), TX, *463*
Management Recruiters of Ogden (C), UT, *464*
Management Recruiters of Seattle (C), WA, *465*
Management Recruiters of Madison, Inc. (C), WI, *466*

Mankuta Gallagher & Assoc., Inc. (C), FL, *468*
The Marathon Group (C), FL, *469*
Margolin Consultants, Inc. (C), NY, *469*
Paula Marks Inc. (R), NY, *136*
Mathey Services (C), IL, *472*
Matrix Consultants, Inc. (C), NC, *472*
G. P. Mattocks & Associates (C), NC, *473*
McCray, Shriver, Eckdahl & Assoc., Inc. (R), CA, *140*
McInturff & Assoc., Inc. (C), MA, *474*
McIntyre Management Resources (C), ON, *474*
McKee Cyber Search (C), MS, *475*
Medical Executive Search Assoc., Inc. (C), AZ, *477*
Merrick & Moore (C), NC, *479*
MetroVantage Personnel Systems (C), CA, *480*
Michael Assoc. (R), IL, *144*
Miller + Miller (C), WA, *482*
Herbert Mines Assoc., Inc. (R), NY, *145*
MJF Assoc. (C), CT, *483*
Morgan & Assoc. (C), MA, *485*
Mulcahy Co. (C), WI, *487*
The Mulshine Company, Ltd. (R), NY, *149*
Munroe, Curry & Bond Assoc. (R), NJ, *149*
Nachman Biomedical (C), MA, *488*
National Search Assoc. (C), CA, *490*
The Neil Michael Group, Inc./Global Partners (R), NY, *151*
The NEIS Corp., Inc. (C), FL, *491*
J. Fielding Nelson & Assoc., Inc. (R), UT, *151*
Len Nelson & Assoc., Inc. (C), TX, *491*
NHA Plastics Recruiters (C), FL, *493*
P. J. Nicholson & Assoc. (C), IL, *493*
Norman Broadbent Int'l., Inc. (R), NY, *152*
Norris Agency (C), TX, *495*
NorTech Resources (C), NY, *496*
North Coast Meridian (C), NY, *496*
Norton & Assoc. (C), IL, *496*
NYCOR Search, Inc. (C), MN, *497*
P R Management Consultants, Inc. (C), NJ, *500*
Pacific Advisory Service, Inc. (C), IL, *501*
Pacific Coast Recruiting (C), CA, *501*
Kirk Palmer & Assoc., Inc. (R), NY, *158*
Paper Industry Recruitment (P.I.R.) (C), ME, *502*
Frank Parillo & Assoc. (R), CA, *159*
R. Parker & Assoc., Inc. (R), NY, *159*
D. P. Parker & Assoc., Inc. (R), MA, *159*
Paules Associates (C), CA, *505*
PC Assoc. (C), CO, *505*
Peck & Assoc., Ltd. (R), WI, *161*
Barry Persky & Co., Inc. (R), CT, *163*
Pharmaceutical Recruiters, Inc. (R), NY, *163*
Phelps Personnel Assoc., Inc. (C), SC, *510*
J. R. Phillip & Assoc., Inc. (R), CA, *164*
Phoenix BioSearch, Inc. (C), NJ, *511*
Gregory D. Pickens (C), TX, *511*
Pioneer Executive Consultants (C), ON, *512*
Place Mart Personnel Service (C), NJ, *513*
Polytechnical Consultants, Inc. (C), IL, *514*
Don V. Poole & Assoc., Inc. (C), CO, *514*
Porter & Assoc., Inc. (C), FL, *514*
Elan Pratzer & Partners Inc. (R), ON, *167*
Predictor Systems Corp. (R), CA, *167*
Preferred Professional Recruiters (C), OH, *516*
The Premier Staffing Group (C), OH, *517*
Prime Management Group Inc. (C), ON, *518*
Prime Resource Assoc. (C), WI, *518*
Professional Employment Group (C), MD, *520*
Professional Engineering Technical Personnel Consultants (C), NC, *520*
Professional Recruiting Consultants (C), FL, *521*
Proquest Inc. (C), SC, *524*
ProTech Nationwide Staffing, Inc. (C), NY, *525*
Proven Edge (C), CA, *525*
Quality Search Inc. (C), OH, *526*
Harold L. Rapp Assoc. (C), NY, *529*
Ray & Berndtson/Lovas Stanley (R), ON, *172*
Raymond Thomas & Assoc. (C), FL, *530*
Recruit Xpress (C), TX, *531*
The Remington Group (R), IL, *174*
Resource Networking Inc. (C), IN, *534*
Resource Perspectives, Inc. (R), CA, *175*
The Revere Assoc., Inc. (R), OH, *176*
Riley Cole (C), CA, *537*
Romeo-Hudgins & Assoc., Ltd. (C), NJ, *544*
The Rossi Search Group (C), PA, *545*
Susan Rudich (C), NY, *548*
Louis Rudzinsky Assoc., Inc. (C), MA, *548*
S. P. Assoc., Inc. (C), NC, *550*
S.D.P. Contract Recruiters (C), NJ, *550*
Sales Consultants Int'l. of Oakland (C), CA, *556*
Sales Consultants of Silicon Valley (C), CA, *556*
Sales Consultants of Chico (C), CA, *556*
Sales Consultants of Daphne (C), AL, *556*
Sales Consultants of Denver (C), CO, *557*
Sales Consultants of Farmington Hills (C), MI, *560*
Sales Consultants of Laurel Park, Inc. (C), MI, *560*
Sales Consultants of Pittsburgh (C), PA, *562*
Sales Consultants of Orangeburg (C), SC, *562*
Sanford Rose Assoc. - Santa Ana (C), CA, *565*
Sanford Rose Assoc. (C), OH, *565*
Sanford Rose Assoc. - Clearwater (C), FL, *566*
Sanford Rose Assoc. - Columbia, MD (C), MD, *567*
Sanford Rose Assoc. - Flemington (C), NJ, *568*
Sanford Rose Assoc. - Fairlawn (C), OH, *569*
Sanford Rose Assoc. - Philadelphia North (C), PA, *570*
Sanford Rose Assoc. - Columbia (C), SC, *570*
Sanford Rose Assoc. - Portland (C), OR, *570*
Sarver & Carruth Assoc. (C), OK, *571*
Schick Professional Search, Inc. (C), OH, *572*
Scientific Solutions, Inc. (C), MI, *572*
Scott Executive Search, Inc. (R), NY, *186*
Search & Recruit Int'l. (C), VA, *573*
The Search Network (C), CA, *576*
Search Northwest Assoc. (C), OR, *576*
Searchforce, Inc. (R), FL, *187*
Searchworks, Inc. (C), FL, *577*
Selective Recruiting Assoc., Inc. (C), MI, *578*
Sharp Placement Professionals, Inc. (C), NY, *579*
Sharrow & Assoc., Inc. (C), MI, *579*
Peter Siegel & Co. (C), MA, *581*
RitaSue Siegel Resources, Inc. (R), NY, *191*
Sill Technical Assoc., Inc. (C), PA, *581*
Simpson Associates (C), NY, *582*
Singleton & Assoc. (C), VA, *582*
Tom Sloan & Assoc., Inc. (C), WI, *583*
Smith & Syberg, Inc. (R), IN, *193*
Software Resource Consultants (C), TN, *587*
Southern Chemical & Plastics Search (C), GA, *587*
Southern Recruiters & Consultants, Inc. (C), SC, *587*
Spectrum Consultants (R), CA, *196*
SpencerStuart (R), NY, *196*
Sports Group Int'l. (R), NC, *198*
Spriggs & Co., Inc. (R), IL, *198*
Stanton Chase Int'l. (R), MD, *198*
The Stelton Group, Inc. (C), NJ, *592*
Ron Stevens & Assoc., Inc. (C), FL, *593*
Stewart Assoc. (C), PA, *593*
Strategic Resources (C), WA, *595*
Strategic Search Corp. (R), IL, *202*
Straube Associates (R), MA, *203*
Summit Search Specialists (C), TX, *596*
Survival Systems Staffing, Inc. (C), CA, *597*
Tanner & Assoc., Inc. (R), TX, *206*
Tate & Assoc., Inc. (R), NJ, *207*
Teamsearch, Inc. (C), MI, *601*
TechFind, Inc. (R), MA, *207*
Technical Resource Assoc. (C), TN, *602*
Technical Skills Consulting Inc. (R), ON, *207*
Technical Staffing Solutions (C), TX, *602*
Technology Consultants Int'l. (C), CA, *603*
The Technology Group (R), IL, *208*
Fred C. Tippel & Assoc. (C), OH, *607*
Trans-United Consultants Ltd. (C), ON, *608*
Transportation Recruiting Services, Inc. (C), MS, *608*
Triangle Assoc. (C), PA, *609*
U.S. Search (C), VA, *610*
Voigt Assoc. (R), IL, *214*
Wachendorfer & Assoc. (C), TX, *613*
Warren Executive Services (C), GA, *616*
R. J. Watkins & Co., Ltd. (R), CA, *216*
David Weinfeld Group (C), NC, *617*
R. A. Wells Co. (C), GA, *618*
Weterrings & Agnew, Inc. (C), NY, *619*
Williams Recruiting, Inc. (C), WA, *621*
Williamsburg Group (C), NJ, *621*
Wilson & Assoc. Int'l. Inc. (C), FL, *622*

Wilson Personnel, Inc. (C), NC, *622*
Winfield Assoc., Inc. (C), MA, *623*
The Witt Group (C), FL, *623*
Susan L. Wonderling Recruiting (C), PA, *623*
Jim Woodson & Assoc., Inc. (C), MS, *624*
World Search (C), OH, *625*
The Yaiser Group (C), NJ, *625*
Yungner & Bormann (R), MN, *226*
Zaccaria Int'l. (C), NJ, *627*

02.2 Production engineering, planning, scheduling & control

A.M.C.R., Inc. (C), OH, *232*
ACC Technical Services (C), OH, *233*
Advanced Recruitment, Inc. (C), TN, *240*
Advancement Recruiting Services (C), OH, *241*
Agri-Tech Personnel, Inc. (C), MO, *242*
Allen, Wayne & Co. LLC (C), WI, *245*
Tom Allison Assoc. (C), NM, *245*
Alpha Executive Search (C), AL, *245*
American Resources Corp. (C), IL, *248*
Analytic Recruiting, Inc. (C), NY, *249*
Angel Group Int'l. (C), KY, *250*
Ansara, Bickford & Fiske (C), MA, *251*
Artgo, Inc. (R), OH, *7*
Asheville Search & Consulting (C), NC, *253*
Ashway Ltd. Agency (C), NY, *253*
Associated Recruiters (C), WI, *254*
The Associates, HR Search Executives, Inc. (C), OK, *254*
Atomic Personnel, Inc. (C), PA, *255*
Austin - Allen Co. (C), TN, *256*
Automation Technology Search (C), CA, *256*
Availability Personnel Consultants (C), NH, *257*
D. W. Baird & Associates (C), MD, *257*
The Bales-Waugh Group (C), FL, *258*
Allen Ballach Assoc. Inc. (R), ON, *10*
Barber & Assoc. (C), KY, *259*
Barone Assoc. (C), NJ, *259*
Barr Assoc. (C), PA, *259*
Barrington Hart, Inc. (R), IL, *12*
The Barton Group, Inc. (C), MI, *260*
Battalia Winston Int'l./The Euram Consultants Group (R), NY, *13*
Becker, Norton & Co. (R), PA, *14*
The Bedford Group (R), RI, *15*
William Bell Assoc., Inc. (C), NJ, *263*
The Bennett Group, Inc. (R), IN, *16*
Berkshire Search Assoc. (C), MA, *265*
Jack Bertram, Executive Recruiter (C), PA, *265*
Biomedical Search Consultants (R), CT, *17*
BJB Assoc. (C), VA, *267*
D. R. Blood & Assoc. (R), AZ, *18*
Mark Bolno & Assoc. (C), FL, *269*
Bolton Group (C), CA, *269*
Howard Bowen Consulting (C), FL, *270*
Brandywine Consulting Group (R), PA, *22*
Brandywine Management Group (R), MD, *22*
Brandywine Retained Ventures, Inc. (R), CT, *22*
Brett Personnel Specialists (C), NJ, *273*
Bright Search/Professional Staffing (C), MN, *274*
Britt Assoc., Inc. (C), IL, *274*
Broward-Dobbs, Inc. (C), GA, *274*
The Burgess Group-Corporate Recruiters Int'l., Inc. (R), NY, *25*
J. Burke & Assoc., Inc. (C), TX, *276*
C.T.E.W. Executive Personnel Services Inc. (C), BC, *278*
Cadillac Assoc. (C), CA, *278*
CadTech Staffing Services (C), GA, *279*
Juliette Lang Cahn Executive Search (C), NY, *279*
Canny, Bowen Inc. (R), NY, *27*
J. P. Canon Assoc. (C), NY, *280*
Cantrell & Assoc. (C), FL, *280*
Career Marketing Assoc., Inc. (C), CO, *282*
Carion Resource Group Inc. (C), ON, *284*
Carter, Lavoie Associates (C), RI, *285*
Case Executive Search (C), MI, *286*
Central Executive Search, Inc. (C), OH, *287*
CEO Consulting (C), FL, *287*
Chadwell & Assoc., Inc. (C), MI, *288*
Robert L. Charon (C), TX, *289*
Chase-Gardner Executive Search Associates, Inc. (C), FL, *289*
R. Christine Assoc. (C), PA, *290*
Clark Executive Search (C), NY, *292*
Clark Personnel Service, Inc. (C), AL, *292*
The Clayton Edward Group (C), MI, *292*
CMS, Inc. (C), NH, *293*
Coast Personnel Services Ltd. (C), BC, *293*
Cochran, Cochran & Yale, Inc. (R), NY, *36*
Coleman Lew & Assoc., Inc. (R), NC, *37*
Construction Search Specialists, Inc. (C), WI, *297*
The Corporate Connection, Ltd. (C), VA, *299*
Corporate Plus, Ltd. (C), GA, *300*
Corporate Recruiters Ltd. (C), BC, *300*
Corporate Search Consultants, Inc. (C), FL, *301*
Cosier & Assoc. (C), AB, *302*
Cowin Assoc. (R), NY, *42*
Jim Crumpley & Assoc. (C), MO, *304*
Cumberland Professional Search Inc. (C), TN, *304*
Tony Curtis & Associates (C), ON, *305*
Daniel Marks Company (C), OH, *306*
Davidson, Laird & Assoc. (C), MI, *308*
DEL Technical Services, Inc. (C), IL, *310*
Dixie Search Assoc. (C), GA, *313*
Domres Professional Search (R), WI, *53*
The Duncan-O'Dell Group Inc. (C), TX, *316*
Dunhill Personnel of Boulder (C), CO, *319*
Dunhill of Ft. Collins, Inc. (C), CO, *319*
Dunhill Professional Search of Englewood, Inc. (C), CO, *319*
Dunhill Professional Search of San Jose (C), CA, *319*
Dunhill of Ft. Wayne, Inc. (C), IN, *320*
Dunhill Professional Search of Augusta (C), GA, *320*
Dunhill Professional Search of Hawaii (C), HI, *320*
Dunhill Executive Search of Brown County (C), IN, *321*
Dunhill Personnel of St. Andrews (C), SC, *322*
Dunhill Professional Search, Inc. of McAllen (C), TX, *323*
Dunhill of Corpus Christi, Inc. (C), TX, *323*
Donald F. Dvorak & Co. (R), IL, *55*
G. L. Dykstra Assoc., Inc. (C), MI, *323*
Eagle Consulting Group Inc. (C), TX, *325*
EBA Group (R), NJ, *56*
D. C. Egan & Assoc. (C), GA, *327*
Elite Medical Search (C), GA, *328*
Elite Resources Group (R), OH, *58*
Engineering Profiles (C), FL, *330*
ExeConnex, LLC (R), GA, *61*
Execu-Tech Search Inc. (C), MN, *332*
ExecuSource Consultants, Inc. (C), TX, *332*
Executive Connection (C), OH, *333*
Executive Directions (R), OH, *62*
Executive Manning Corp. (R), FL, *63*
Executive Partners Inc. (C), CT, *333*
Executive Recruiters, Inc. (C), WI, *334*
Executive Resource Assoc. (C), VA, *334*
The Executive Source (C), SA, *337*
Fairfaxx Corp. (R), CT, *64*
Fenwick Partners (R), MA, *66*
Fenzel Milar Assoc. (C), OH, *339*
Fergason Assoc., Inc. (C), IL, *339*
Fishel HR Assoc., Inc. (C), AZ, *341*
James L. Fisk & Assoc. (C), MO, *342*
Fortune Group Int'l., Inc. (R), PA, *70*
F-O-R-T-U-N-E Personnel Consultants of Tampa (C), FL, *344*
F-O-R-T-U-N-E Personnel Consultants of Wilmington (C), DE, *344*
F-O-R-T-U-N-E Personnel Consultants of Greenwood Village (C), CO, *344*
F-O-R-T-U-N-E Personnel Consultants of Savannah, Inc. (C), GA, *345*
Fortune Personnel Consultants of Sarasota Inc. (C), FL, *345*
F-O-R-T-U-N-E Personnel Consultants of Atlanta, Inc. (C), GA, *345*
F-O-R-T-U-N-E Personnel Consultants (C), MI, *346*
Fortune Personnel Consultants of Bloomfield, Inc. (C), MI, *346*
F-o-r-t-u-n-e of Owensboro, Inc. (C), KY, *346*
Fortune Personnel Consultants (C), NH, *347*
F-O-R-T-U-N-E Personnel Consultants of St. Louis-West County (C), MO, *347*
F-O-R-T-U-N-E Personnel Consultants of Menlo Park, Inc. (C), NJ, *347*
F-O-R-T-U-N-E of West Portland (C), OR, *348*
Fortune Personnel Consultants of Allentown, Inc. (C), PA, *348*
F-O-R-T-U-N-E Personnel Consultants of Cincinnati (C), OH, *348*
F-O-R-T-U-N-E Personnel Consultants of Charlotte (C), NC, *348*

Fortune Personnel Consultants of Greensboro, NC, Inc. (C), NC, *348*
F-O-R-T-U-N-E Consultants of Memphis (C), TN, *349*
Fortune Personnel Consultants of Hilton Head (C), SC, *349*
FORTUNE Personnel Consultants of Charleston, Inc. (C), SC, *349*
Fortune Personnel Consultants of Chattanooga Inc. (C), TN, *349*
Fortune Personnel Consultants of the Virginia Highlands (C), VA, *351*
Foster Partners (R), NY, *70*
The Fourbes Group, Inc. (C), NJ, *351*
Frye/Joure & Assoc., Inc. (C), TN, *353*
G. H. Enterprises (C), AZ, *354*
Gabriele & Company (C), MA, *354*
Gaines & Assoc. Int'l., Inc. (R), IL, *73*
The Garret Group (R), NJ, *75*
General Engineering Tectonics (C), CA, *356*
Genesis Recruiting (C), CA, *356*
Genesis Research (C), MO, *356*
The Glenwood Group (C), IL, *358*
Robert G. Godfrey Assoc. Ltd. (R), IL, *78*
L. J. Gonzer Assoc. (C), NJ, *360*
The Governance Group, Inc. (R), NJ, *80*
Graham & Co. (R), NJ, *80*
R. Green & Assoc., Inc. (C), OH, *362*
J. B. Groner Executive Search, Inc. (C), DE, *363*
Gros Executive Search, Inc. (C), TN, *363*
Hallman Group, Inc. (C), MI, *367*
Hardage Group (C), TN, *369*
Harrison Moore Inc. (C), NE, *370*
The Hawkins Co. (R), CA, *88*
Michael J. Hawkins, Inc. (C), IL, *370*
HCI Corp. (C), IL, *371*
Healthcare Recruiters of Indiana (C), IN, *372*
Healthcare Recruiters Int'l. Orange County (C), CA, *372*
HeartBeat Medical, Inc. (C), OR, *374*
The Hudson Group (C), CT, *383*
The Hunt Group, Inc. (R), NC, *99*
Hunt Patton & Brazeal, Inc. (C), OK, *385*
Hunter Assoc. (C), MA, *385*
The Icard Group, Inc. (C), MI, *387*
Interactive Search Assoc. (C), PA, *391*
Interim Executive Recruiting (C), GA, *392*
J. B. Linde & Assoc. (C), MO, *395*
J. Joseph & Assoc. (C), OH, *395*
Jackley Search Consultants (C), MN, *396*
K. Jaeger & Assoc. (C), MA, *396*
JAG Group (R), MO, *105*
Jaral Consultants, Inc. (C), NJ, *397*
Joslin & Assoc., Ltd. (C), IL, *401*
Kabana Corp. (C), MI, *402*
Kay Concepts, Inc. (C), FL, *404*
A.T. Kearney Executive Search (R), IL, *111*
Blair Kershaw Assoc., Inc. (C), PA, *405*
J. Krauss Assoc. (R), FL, *120*
L & L Assoc. (C), CA, *410*
Laboratory Resource Group (C), MA, *411*
LaCosta & Assoc. Int'l. Inc. (C), CA, *411*
Landon Morgan (C), ON, *412*
The Landstone Group (C), NY, *412*
Stephen Laramee & Assoc. Inc. (C), ON, *413*
Jack B. Larsen & Assoc., Inc. (C), PA, *413*
Leader Network (C), PA, *414*
Albert G. Lee Assoc. (C), RI, *415*
Leith & Assoc., Inc. (C), OH, *416*
Linden Group, Inc. (C), NC, *418*
Loewenstein & Assoc., Inc. (R), TX, *131*
Lybrook Assoc., Inc. (C), RI, *421*
Lyons & Assoc., Inc. (C), IL, *422*
Lyons Pruitt Int'l. (R), PA, *132*
M.C. Executive Search (C), CA, *422*
The Mallard Group (C), IN, *423*
Management Recruiters of Mobile Co., Inc. (C), AL, *438*
Management Recruiters of Tucson (C), AZ, *439*
Management Recruiters of Little Rock (C), AR, *439*
Management Recruiters of Northern California (C), CA, *440*
Management Recruiters of Colorado Springs (C), CO, *441*
Management Recruiters of Pleasanton (C), CA, *441*
Management Recruiters of Winsted, Inc. (C), CT, *442*
Management Recruiters of Ft. Myers, FL. (C), FL, *443*
Management Recruiters of Anna Maria Island (C), FL, *443*
Management Recruiters of Boca Raton (C), FL, *443*
Management Recruiters of Pensacola (C), FL, *444*
Management Recruiters of Lake Co., Inc. (C), FL, *444*
Management Recruiters of Columbus, Inc. (C), GA, *445*
Management Recruiters of Venice, Inc. (C), FL, *445*
Management Recruiters of Savannah (C), GA, *446*
Management Recruiters of Springfield, Inc. (C), IL, *447*
Management Recruiters of Sun Valley (C), ID, *447*
Management Recruiters of Chicago-North Shore (C), IL, *447*
Management Recruiters of Noblesville, Inc. (C), IN, *448*
Management Recruiters of Spencer (C), IA, *448*
Management Recruiters of Indianapolis-North (C), IN, *448*
Management Recruiters of Danville (C), KY, *449*
Management Recruiters of Richmond (C), KY, *449*
Management Recruiters of Siouxland (C), IA, *449*
Management Recruiters of Columbia (C), MD, *450*
Management Recruiters of Monroe, Inc. (C), LA, *450*
Management Recruiters of Muskegon (C), MI, *451*
Management Recruiters of Livonia (C), MI, *451*
Management Recruiters of Baltimore (C), MD, *451*
Management Recruiters - Flint (C), MI, *451*
Management Recruiters of Rankin Co. (C), MS, *452*
Management Recruiters of Chanhassen (C), MN, *452*
Management Recruiters of North Oakland County, Inc. (C), MI, *452*
Management Recruiters of Reno (C), NV, *453*
Management Recruiters of Fayetteville (C), NC, *455*
Management Recruiters of Kinston (C), NC, *456*
Management Recruiters of Mt. Airy (C), NC, *456*
Management Recruiters of Raleigh (C), NC, *456*
Management Recruiters of Akron (C), OH, *457*
Management Recruiters of Cleveland (C), OH, *457*
Management Recruiters of Bethlehem, PA (C), PA, *458*
Management Recruiters of Northwest Ohio, Inc. (C), OH, *458*
Management Recruiters of McMurray, Inc. (C), PA, *459*
Management Recruiters of Valley Forge (C), PA, *459*
Management Recruiters of Puerto Rico (C), PR, *460*
Management Recruiters of Myrtle Beach, Inc. (C), SC, *460*
Management Recruiters of West Chester, Inc. (C), PA, *460*
Management Recruiters The Delta Group, Inc. (C), TN, *461*
Management Recruiters of Chattanooga-Brainerd, Inc. (C), TN, *461*
Management Recruiters of Travelers Rest, Inc. (C), SC, *461*
Management Recruiters of Franklin, Inc. (C), TN, *461*
Management Recruiters of North West Austin (C), TX, *462*
Management Recruiters of Houston (C), TX, *462*
Management Recruiters of Champions (C), TX, *462*
Management Recruiters of Arlington (C), TX, *462*
Management Recruiters of LBJ Park/Dallas (C), TX, *462*
Management Recruiters - Friendswood (C), TX, *462*
Management Recruiters of San Antonio (C), TX, *463*
Management Recruiters of Lubbock (C), TX, *463*
Management Recruiters of Round Rock (C), TX, *463*
Management Recruiters of Ogden (C), UT, *464*
Management Recruiters Int'l.-The Woodlands (C), TX, *464*
Management Recruiters of Loudoun County South (C), VA, *465*

Management Recruiters of Madison, Inc. (C), WI, *466*
Margolin Consultants, Inc. (C), NY, *469*
Mark III Personnel, Inc. (C), NC, *470*
Robert E. McGrath & Assoc. (R), CT, *141*
McInturff & Assoc., Inc. (C), MA, *474*
McIntyre Management Resources (C), ON, *474*
McKee Cyber Search (C), MS, *475*
Meder & Assoc., Inc. (R), IL, *142*
MedQuest Assoc. (C), CO, *478*
Mercedes & Co., Inc. (R), MA, *143*
Merit Professional Search, Inc. (C), TN, *479*
MetroVantage Personnel Systems (C), CA, *480*
Michael Assoc. (R), IL, *144*
Michael James & Co. (C), IL, *480*
Michael/Merrill (C), KS, *481*
Danette Milne Corporate Search Inc. (C), ON, *482*
Herbert Mines Assoc., Inc. (R), NY, *145*
MIXTEC Group (R), CA, *145*
Montgomery, Thomason & Assoc. (C), ON, *484*
Morgan & Assoc. (C), MA, *485*
Morgan Int'l., Inc. (R), IL, *147*
MPA Executive Search Inc. (R), QE, *148*
Mulcahy Co. (C), WI, *487*
Multisearch Recruiters (C), CA, *487*
Nationwide Personnel Recruiting & Consulting, Inc. (C), OR, *490*
Len Nelson & Assoc., Inc. (C), TX, *491*
NHA Plastics Recruiters (C), FL, *493*
Norman Broadbent Int'l., Inc. (R), NY, *152*
John B. Norris & Assoc., Inc. (C), MD, *495*
North Coast Meridian (C), NY, *496*
The Odessa Group (R), CA, *155*
Omega Systems, LLC (C), VA, *498*
Orion Int'l. Consulting Group, Inc. (C), NC, *499*
Ortman Recruiting Int'l. (C), CA, *500*
LaMonte Owens, Inc. (R), PA, *157*
Pacific Advisory Service, Inc. (C), IL, *501*
Pacific Coast Recruiting (C), CA, *501*
Packaging Personnel Co., Ltd. (C), WI, *501*
T. Page & Assoc. (C), TX, *502*
Frank Parillo & Assoc. (R), CA, *159*
Parker, McFadden & Assoc. (C), GA, *503*
PERC, Ltd. (C), AZ, *506*
Personnel, Inc. (C), AL, *508*
Personnel Incorporated (C), IA, *508*
The Personnel Network, Inc. (C), SC, *508*
Phelps Personnel Assoc., Inc. (C), SC, *510*
Phillips Personnel/Search (C), CO, *510*
Philo & Associates (C), GA, *511*
Gregory D. Pickens (C), TX, *511*
Polytechnical Consultants, Inc. (C), IL, *514*
Jack Porter Assoc., Inc. (C), WA, *514*
Norman Powers Assoc., Inc. (C), MA, *515*
Preferred Professional Recruiters (C), OH, *516*
The Premier Staffing Group (C), OH, *517*
Prichard Kymen Inc. (R), AB, *168*
Prime Resource Assoc. (C), WI, *518*
Procurement Resources (C), MD, *520*
Professional Employment Group (C), MD, *520*
Professional Engineering Technical Personnel Consultants (C), NC, *520*
Professional Personnel Services (C), IA, *520*
Professional Recruiting Consultants (C), FL, *521*
Proven Edge (C), CA, *525*
PSP Agency (C), NY, *525*
Quality Control Recruiters (C), CT, *526*
R.A.N. Assoc., Inc. (C), OH, *528*
Raymond Karsan Assoc. (C), PA, *529*
Raymond Thomas & Assoc. (C), FL, *530*
J. P. Roddy Consultants (C), PA, *540*
Romano McAvoy Assoc., Inc. (C), NY, *544*
RTE Search (C), NJ, *547*
Louis Rudzinsky Assoc., Inc. (C), MA, *548*
S. P. Assoc., Inc. (C), NC, *550*
S.D.P. Contract Recruiters (C), NJ, *550*
Sales Consultants of Chico (C), CA, *556*
Sales Consultants of Baltimore (C), MD, *559*
Sales Consultants of Orangeburg (C), SC, *562*
Sales Consultants of Appleton (C), WI, *563*
Sanford Rose Assoc. - Santa Ana (C), CA, *565*
Sanford Rose Assoc. - Athens (C), GA, *566*
Sanford Rose Assoc. - Rockford (C), IL, *567*
Sanford Rose Assoc. - Cedar Rapids (C), IA, *567*
Sanford Rose Assoc. - Rockville (C), MD, *567*
Sanford Rose Assoc. - Louisville (C), KY, *567*
Sanford Rose Assoc. - Amherst, NY (C), NY, *568*
Sanford Rose Assoc. - Rochester (C), MI, *568*
Sanford Rose Assoc. - Gastonia (C), NC, *568*
Sanford Rose Assoc. - Flemington (C), NJ, *568*
Sanford Rose Assoc. - Greensboro (C), NC, *569*
Sanford Rose Assoc. - Fairlawn (C), OH, *569*
Sanford Rose Assoc. - Austin (C), TX, *570*
Sanford Rose Assoc. - Doylestown (C), PA, *570*
Sanford Rose Assoc. - Port Washington (C), WI, *571*
Scott Executive Search, Inc. (R), NY, *186*
Search Assoc. (C), KY, *574*
Search Consultants Int'l., Inc. (C), TX, *575*
Search Group (C), CA, *575*
The Search Network (C), CA, *576*
Search Northwest Assoc. (C), OR, *576*
Search South, Inc. (C), AL, *576*
Segal & Assoc. (C), GA, *578*
Selectis Corp. (C), IL, *578*
Selective Recruiting Assoc., Inc. (C), MI, *578*
SHS of Allentown (C), PA, *580*
Sill Technical Assoc., Inc. (C), PA, *581*
Singleton & Assoc. (C), VA, *582*
The Smith Group, Inc. (C), NC, *584*
Smith, Brown & Jones (C), KS, *585*
Spear-Izzo Assoc., LLC (C), PA, *588*
SpencerStuart (R), NY, *196*
Kenn Spinrad Inc. (C), PA, *589*
Sprout/Standish, Inc. (C), NH, *589*
Stanton Chase Int'l. (R), MD, *198*
Ron Stevens & Assoc., Inc. (C), FL, *593*
Stewart Assoc. (C), PA, *593*
Linford E. Stiles & Assoc., L.L.C. (R), NH, *201*
Stoneburner Assoc., Inc. (C), KS, *594*
Strategic Search Corp. (R), IL, *202*
Success Seekers Connection (C), FL, *596*
Sullivan & Assoc. (R), MI, *204*
Summit Executive Search Consultants, Inc. (R), FL, *204*
Ron Sunshine & Assoc. (C), IL, *597*
System 1 Search (C), CA, *598*
T E M Assoc. (C), WI, *599*
Tactical Alternatives (R), CA, *205*
S. Tanner & Assoc. Inc. (C), ON, *599*
TE, Inc. (C), IL, *600*
Teamsearch, Inc. (C), MI, *601*
Technical Employment Consultants (C), PA, *602*
Technical Resource Assoc. (C), TN, *602*
Tekworx, Inc. (C), OK, *604*
Thomson, Sponar & Adams, Inc. (C), WA, *606*
Fred C. Tippel & Assoc. (C), OH, *607*
Trainor/Frank & Assoc. Inc. (C), WI, *608*
Trans-United Consultants Ltd. (C), ON, *608*
Triangle Assoc. (C), PA, *609*
TRS Staffing Solutions Inc. (C), OH, *610*
TSI Group/TSI Staffing Services (C), ON, *610*
The Thomas Tucker Co. (R), CA, *211*
Valentine & Assoc. (C), IL, *611*
VZ Int'l., Inc. (C), AZ, *613*
W. P. Assoc. (C), CA, *613*
Gordon Wahls Executive Search (C), PA, *613*
Wallace Assoc. (C), CT, *614*
Warren Executive Services (C), GA, *616*
Weinpel Search, Inc. (C), NJ, *617*
S. E. Weinstein Co. (R), IL, *217*
John R. Williams & Assoc., Inc. (C), NC, *621*
Williamsburg Group (C), NJ, *621*
The Winchester Group (R), CA, *222*
Susan L. Wonderling Recruiting (C), PA, *623*
Jim Woodson & Assoc., Inc. (C), MS, *624*
WTW Assoc., Inc. (R), NY, *225*

02.3 Automation, robotics

ACC Technical Services (C), OH, *233*
Access Assoc. Inc. (C), MD, *233*
ACCESS Technology (C), CA, *234*
Advanced Recruitment, Inc. (C), TN, *240*
Advancement Recruiting Services (C), OH, *241*
Allen-Jeffers Assoc. (C), CA, *245*
Anderson Industrial Assoc., Inc. (C), GA, *250*
Ansara, Bickford & Fiske (C), MA, *251*
Applied Search Assoc., Inc. (C), GA, *252*

Asheville Search & Consulting (C), NC, *253*
Atomic Personnel, Inc. (C), PA, *255*
Aurora Tech Search (C), ON, *256*
Austin - Allen Co. (C), TN, *256*
Automation Technology Search (C), CA, *256*
Barber & Assoc. (C), KY, *259*
Battalia Winston Int'l./The Euram Consultants Group (R), NY, *13*
Behrens and Company (C), WA, *262*
J. P. Bencik Assoc. (C), MI, *263*
Jack Bertram, Executive Recruiter (C), PA, *265*
BioTech Research Recruiters Inc. (C), CA, *267*
Blair/Tech Recruiters, Inc. (C), NJ, *268*
Bower & Associates (C), TX, *271*
Bratland & Assoc. (C), IL, *272*
Capstone Inc. (R), NY, *29*
Career Consultants (R), IN, *29*
Careers First, Inc. (C), NJ, *283*
Carion Resource Group Inc. (C), ON, *284*
Carnegie Resources, Inc. (C), NC, *284*
Chadwell & Assoc., Inc. (C), MI, *288*
Wayne S. Chamberlain & Assoc. (C), CA, *288*
The Chapman Group, Inc. (C), AZ, *289*
R. Christine Assoc. (C), PA, *290*
P. G. Cook Assoc. (R), TN, *40*
Corporate Search Consultants, Inc. (C), FL, *301*
Cumberland Group Inc. (C), IL, *304*
Cumberland Professional Search Inc. (C), TN, *304*
Cypress Int'l., Inc. (R), FL, *45*
Alan N. Daum & Assoc., Inc. (C), OH, *308*
Davidson, Laird & Assoc. (C), MI, *308*
Despres & Associates (C), IL, *311*
DiTech Resources (C), CT, *313*
The Dorfman Group (C), AZ, *314*
Robert Drexler Assoc., Inc. (R), NJ, *54*
Dunhill of Ft. Wayne, Inc. (C), IN, *320*
Dunhill Professional Search of Augusta (C), GA, *320*
Dunhill Personnel of St. Andrews (C), SC, *322*
Dunhill Professional Search, Inc. of McAllen (C), TX, *323*
D. C. Egan & Assoc. (C), GA, *327*
W. Robert Eissler & Assoc., Inc. (C), TX, *327*
Erwin Assoc. (R), IL, *60*
Execu-Tech Search Inc. (C), MN, *332*
Executive Connection (C), OH, *333*
Executive Recruiters Agency, Inc. (C), AR, *333*
Executive Recruitment Services, Inc. (ERS, Inc.) (C), GA, *334*
Fenwick Partners (R), MA, *66*
F-O-R-T-U-N-E Personnel Consultants of Boise (R), ID, *70*
F-O-R-T-U-N-E Personnel Consultants of Denver, Inc. (C), CO, *344*
F-O-R-T-U-N-E Personnel Consultants of Manatee County (C), FL, *345*
F-O-R-T-U-N-E Personnel Consultants of Atlanta, Inc. (C), GA, *345*
F-o-r-t-u-n-e of Owensboro, Inc. (C), KY, *346*
Foster Partners (R), NY, *70*
Bernard Frigon & Assoc. Inc. (C), QE, *353*
Joe L. Giles & Assoc. (C), MI, *357*
Goldbeck Recruiting Inc. (C), BC, *359*
Hardage Group (C), TN, *369*
Harrison Moore Inc. (C), NE, *370*
High Tech Staffing Group (C), OR, *377*
Hodge-Cronin & Assoc., Inc. (R), IL, *94*
Human Resources Personnel Agency (R), AR, *99*
J. B. Linde & Assoc. (C), MO, *395*
Jackley Search Consultants (C), MN, *396*
Jaeger Int'l., Inc. (C), OH, *396*
Kaas Employment Services (C), IA, *402*
A.T. Kearney Executive Search (R), IL, *111*
S. D. Kelly & Assoc., Inc. (R), MA, *112*
L & L Assoc. (C), CA, *410*
Leader Network (C), PA, *414*
Loewenstein & Assoc., Inc. (R), TX, *131*
M.C. Executive Search (C), CA, *422*
Management Recruiters of Emeryville (C), CA, *440*
Management Recruiters, Inc. (C), FL, *443*
Management Recruiters of Atlanta North, Inc. (C), GA, *446*
Management Recruiters of Chicago-North Shore (C), IL, *447*
Management Recruiters of Spencer (C), IA, *448*
Management Recruiters of Danville (C), KY, *449*
Management Recruiters of Richmond (C), KY, *449*
Management Recruiters of Columbia (C), MD, *450*
Management Recruiters of Livonia (C), MI, *451*
Management Recruiters - Flint (C), MI, *451*
Management Recruiters of Bay Head (C), NJ, *453*
Management Recruiters of Asheville, Inc. (C), NC, *455*
Management Recruiters - Kannapolis (C), NC, *456*
Management Recruiters of Kinston (C), NC, *456*
Management Recruiters of Raleigh (C), NC, *456*
Management Recruiters of Akron (C), OH, *457*
Management Recruiters of Cleveland (C), OH, *457*
Management Recruiters of Delaware County (C), PA, *459*
Management Recruiters of Aiken (C), SC, *460*
Management Recruiters of Arlington (C), TX, *462*
Management Recruiters of Round Rock (C), TX, *463*
Management Recruiters of Loudoun County South (C), VA, *465*
Margolin Consultants, Inc. (C), NY, *469*
Merrick & Moore (C), NC, *479*
MetroVantage Personnel Systems (C), CA, *480*
Morgan & Assoc. (C), MA, *485*
The Morgan/Geoffries Group (C), CA, *485*
Mulcahy Co. (C), WI, *487*
The Mulshine Company, Ltd. (R), NY, *149*
Munroe, Curry & Bond Assoc. (R), NJ, *149*
NaTek Corp. (C), NY, *488*
National Computerized Employment Service, Inc. (C), PA, *489*
National Search Assoc. (C), CA, *490*
Len Nelson & Assoc., Inc. (C), TX, *491*
Norman Broadbent Int'l., Inc. (R), NY, *152*
Norton & Assoc. (C), IL, *496*
D. P. Parker & Assoc., Inc. (R), MA, *159*
Personnel Tangent Inc. (C), QE, *509*
Peyser Assoc., Inc. (R), FL, *163*
R. L. Plimpton Assoc., Inc. (R), CO, *165*
Polytechnical Consultants, Inc. (C), IL, *514*
Prime Resource Assoc. (C), WI, *518*
Professional Engineering Technical Personnel Consultants (C), NC, *520*
Professional Search Consultants (PSC) (C), TX, *523*
ProTech Nationwide Staffing, Inc. (C), NY, *525*
Quality Search Inc. (C), OH, *526*
The Recruitment Group, Inc. (C), NY, *532*
J. P. Roddy Consultants (C), PA, *540*
RTE Search (C), NJ, *547*
S.D.P. Contract Recruiters (C), NJ, *550*
Sales Consultants of Farmington Hills (C), MI, *560*
Sales Consultants of Orangeburg (C), SC, *562*
Sanford Rose Assoc. - Santa Ana (C), CA, *565*
Sanford Rose Assoc. - Santa Barbara (C), CA, *565*
Sanford Rose Assoc. - Columbia, MD (C), MD, *567*
Sanford Rose Assoc. - Rockford (C), IL, *567*
Sanford Rose Assoc. - Flemington (C), NJ, *568*
Sanford Rose Assoc. - Burlington, NC (C), NC, *569*
Sanford Rose Assoc. - Austin (C), TX, *570*
Schick Professional Search, Inc. (C), OH, *572*
Search & Recruit Int'l. (C), VA, *573*
Search Enterprises, Inc. (C), FL, *575*
Search Northwest Assoc. (C), OR, *576*
Segal & Assoc. (C), GA, *578*
Smith & Assoc. (C), FL, *583*
The Smith Group, Inc. (C), NC, *584*
Snelling Search (C), AL, *585*
SpencerSearch, Inc. (C), CO, *589*
SpencerStuart (R), NY, *196*
Stanton Chase Int'l. (R), MD, *198*
Stewart Assoc. (C), PA, *593*
Strategic Search Corp. (R), IL, *202*
Summit Executive Search Consultants, Inc. (R), FL, *204*
Teamsearch, Inc. (C), MI, *601*
Tech-Net (C), TX, *601*
Technical Staffing Solutions (C), TX, *602*
Technology Consultants Int'l. (C), CA, *603*
Jay Tracey Assoc. Inc. (C), VT, *608*
Trainor/Frank & Assoc. Inc. (C), WI, *608*

Trans-United Consultants Ltd. (C), ON, *608*
TRS Staffing Solutions Inc. (C), OH, *610*
Vento Assoc. (C), TN, *612*
Wallace Assoc. (C), CT, *614*
R. A. Wells Co. (C), GA, *618*
West & Assoc. (C), IL, *618*
Arch S. Whitehead Assoc. Inc. (ASWA) (R), NY, *219*
The Wilmington Group (C), NC, *622*
Wilson Personnel, Inc. (C), NC, *622*
Susan L. Wonderling Recruiting (C), PA, *623*
Jim Woodson & Assoc., Inc. (C), MS, *624*
World Search (C), OH, *625*
Xagas & Assoc. (R), IL, *226*

02.4 Plant management

A First Resource (C), NC, *231*
A.M.C.R., Inc. (C), OH, *232*
ACC Technical Services (C), OH, *233*
Action Management Corp. (C), MI, *239*
Advanced Recruitment, Inc. (C), TN, *240*
Agri-Tech Personnel, Inc. (C), MO, *242*
Ahrensdorf & Assoc. (R), PA, *2*
J. R. Akin & Co. (R), MA, *2*
Allen-Jeffers Assoc. (C), CA, *245*
Allerton Heneghan & O'Neill (R), IL, *4*
Alpha Executive Search (C), AL, *245*
The Altco Group (C), NJ, *246*
Peter W. Ambler Co. (R), TX, *5*
American Heritage Group, Inc. (C), MI, *247*
American Resources Corp. (C), IL, *248*
Amherst Human Resource Group, Ltd. (C), IL, *249*
Anderson Bradshaw Assoc., Inc. (R), TX, *6*
Andre David & Assoc., Inc. (R), TX, *6*
Andrews & Wald Group (C), FL, *250*
Tryg R. Angell, Ltd. (C), CT, *250*
The Angus Group, Ltd. (C), OH, *251*
Ansara, Bickford & Fiske (C), MA, *251*
Charles P. Aquavella & Assoc. (C), TX, *252*
Argus National, Inc. (R), CT, *6*
Ariail & Assoc. (R), NC, *7*
Armor Personnel (C), ON, *253*
Asheville Search & Consulting (C), NC, *253*
Ashway Ltd. Agency (C), NY, *253*
Associated Recruiters (C), WI, *254*
The Associates, HR Search Executives, Inc. (C), OK, *254*
Atlantic Pacific Group (C), CA, *255*
Availability Personnel Consultants (C), NH, *257*
D. W. Baird & Associates (C), MD, *257*
Barger & Sargeant, Inc. (R), NH, *11*
J. W. Barleycorn, Renard & Assoc., Inc. (R), OH, *11*
Barone-O'Hara Assoc., Inc. (R), NJ, *11*
The Barton Group, Inc. (C), MI, *260*
Battalia Winston Int'l./The Euram Consultants Group (R), NY, *13*
William Bell Assoc., Inc. (C), NJ, *263*
Berkshire Search Assoc. (C), MA, *265*
Jack Bertram, Executive Recruiter (C), PA, *265*
Biomedical Search Consultants (R), CT, *17*
BJB Assoc. (C), VA, *267*
The Blackman Kallick Search Division (C), IL, *267*
Mark Bolno & Assoc. (C), FL, *269*
Borchert Assoc. (C), TX, *269*
Boyden (R), NY, *20*
The Brand Co., Inc. (R), FL, *22*
Brandywine Consulting Group (R), PA, *22*
Brandywine Management Group (R), MD, *22*
The Brentwood Group Ltd. (R), OR, *23*
Brett Personnel Specialists (C), NJ, *273*
Brierwood Group, Inc. (C), IN, *273*
Bright Search/Professional Staffing (C), MN, *274*
Dan B. Brockman (C), IL, *274*
Brooke Chase Assoc., Inc. (R), IL, *24*
Bernard E. Brooks & Assoc., Inc. (R), SC, *24*
Broward-Dobbs, Inc. (C), GA, *274*
J. B. Brown & Assoc., Inc. (C), OH, *275*
Bullis & Co., Inc. (R), CA, *25*
J. Burke & Assoc., Inc. (C), TX, *276*
The Burke Group (C), ON, *276*
Joseph R. Burns & Assoc., Inc. (R), NJ, *25*
Juliette Lang Cahn Executive Search (C), NY, *279*
Caliber Associates (R), PA, *27*
Cambridge Management Planning (R), ON, *27*
Campa & Assoc. (R), ON, *27*
Caprio & Assoc. Inc. (R), IL, *29*
Career Counseling Inc. (CCI) (C), KY, *282*
Career Marketing Consultants, Inc. (C), GA, *282*
Carion Resource Group Inc. (C), ON, *284*
Carlson & Czeswik (R), MN, *30*
Carver Search Consultants (C), CA, *285*
Case Executive Search (C), MI, *286*
Michael J. Cavanagh & Assoc. Inc. (R), ON, *31*
Central Executive Search, Inc. (C), OH, *287*
Chadwell & Assoc., Inc. (C), MI, *288*
Wayne S. Chamberlain & Assoc. (C), CA, *288*
Chase-Gardner Executive Search Associates, Inc. (C), FL, *289*
A. D. Check Assoc., Inc. (R), PA, *33*
William J. Christopher Assoc., Inc. (R), PA, *34*
CJA-The Adler Group, Inc. (R), CA, *35*
Clark Executive Search (C), NY, *292*
Clark Personnel Service, Inc. (C), AL, *292*
The Clayton Edward Group (C), MI, *292*
Coe & Co. Int'l. Inc./EMA Partners Int'l. (R), AB, *37*
Comprehensive Search (C), GA, *294*
Conard Associates, Inc. (R), NH, *39*
Construct Management Services (C), MN, *297*
Philip Conway Management (R), IL, *40*
Cook Assoc.,® Inc. (R), IL, *40*
Corporate Image Group (C), TN, *300*
Corporate Management Services (C), PA, *300*
Creative-Leadership, Inc. (R), CA, *42*
Marlene Critchfield Co. (C), CA, *303*
Timothy D. Crowe, Jr. (R), MA, *43*
Jim Crumpley & Assoc. (C), MO, *304*
Cumberland Professional Search Inc. (C), TN, *304*
Frank Cuomo & Assoc., Inc. (C), NY, *305*
The Currier-Winn Co., Inc. (C), NJ, *305*
Daniel Marks Company (C), OH, *306*
The Danielson Group, Inc. (C), TX, *306*
Davidson, Laird & Assoc. (C), MI, *308*
Debbon Recruiting Group, Inc. (C), MO, *310*
Defrain Mayer (R), KS, *48*
DieckMueller Group (R), WI, *51*
Dise & Co. (R), OH, *52*
Doherty Int'l., Inc. (R), IL, *53*
Robert Drexler Assoc., Inc. (R), NJ, *54*
Dunhill Executive Search of Los Angeles, Inc. (C), CA, *319*
Dunhill of San Francisco, Inc. (C), CA, *319*
Dunhill Personnel of Boulder (C), CO, *319*
Dunhill Professional Search of Englewood, Inc. (C), CO, *319*
Dunhill of Ft. Wayne, Inc. (C), IN, *320*
Dunhill Search of West Atlanta (C), GA, *320*
Dunhill Executive Search of Brown County (C), IN, *321*
Dunhill Professional Search of Ramsey (C), NJ, *321*
Dunhill Personnel of St. Andrews (C), SC, *322*
Dunhill Professional Search, Inc. of McAllen (C), TX, *323*
The E & K Group (C), NJ, *324*
E/Search Int'l. (C), CT, *325*
W. Robert Eissler & Assoc., Inc. (C), TX, *327*
William J. Elam & Assoc. (R), NE, *58*
Emerson & Co. (C), GA, *329*
Engineering & Scientific Search Assoc. (ESSA) (C), NJ, *330*
Engineering Profiles (C), FL, *330*
Erlanger Assoc. (R), CT, *60*
ESS (Executive Search Services) (R), CA, *61*
Execu-Tech Search Inc. (C), MN, *332*
Executive Career Search (C), VA, *332*
Executive Connection (C), OH, *333*
Executive Directions (R), OH, *62*
Executive Recruiters, Inc. (C), WI, *334*
Executive Resource Assoc. (C), VA, *334*
Executive Resource Group, Inc. (R), ME, *63*
Executive Search, Ltd. (C), OH, *336*
Executive Search of New England, Inc. (C), ME, *336*
Executive Search Team (C), MI, *336*
The Executive Source (C), SA, *337*
Eyler Assoc., Inc. (R), IA, *64*
Fagan & Company (R), PA, *64*
Fenzel Milar Assoc. (C), OH, *339*
Fergason Assoc., Inc. (C), IL, *339*
First Choice Search (R), WA, *67*
Fishel HR Assoc., Inc. (C), AZ, *341*
The Fisher Group (R), AB, *67*
James L. Fisk & Assoc. (C), MO, *342*
Flowers & Assoc. (C), OH, *342*
Forest People Int'l. Search Ltd. (C), BC, *343*

F-O-R-T-U-N-E Personnel Consultants of Boise (R), ID, *70*
Fortune Personnel Consultants of Huntsville, Inc. (C), AL, *343*
F-O-R-T-U-N-E Personnel Consultants of Tampa (C), FL, *344*
F-O-R-T-U-N-E Personnel Consultants of Wilmington (C), DE, *344*
Fortune Personnel Consultants (C), CA, *344*
F-O-R-T-U-N-E Personnel Consultants of Greenwood Village (C), CO, *344*
F-O-R-T-U-N-E Personnel Consultants of Manatee County (C), FL, *345*
Fortune Personnel Consultants of Sarasota Inc. (C), FL, *345*
Fortune of Arlington Heights (C), IL, *345*
F-O-R-T-U-N-E Personnel Consultants of Atlanta, Inc. (C), GA, *345*
F-O-R-T-U-N-E Personnel Consultants (C), MI, *346*
Fortune Personnel Consultants of Bloomfield, Inc. (C), MI, *346*
F-o-r-t-u-n-e of Owensboro, Inc. (C), KY, *346*
Fortune Personnel Consultants of Topsfield (C), MA, *346*
Fortune Personnel Consultants (C), NH, *347*
F-O-R-T-U-N-E Personnel Consultants of St. Louis-West County (C), MO, *347*
F-O-R-T-U-N-E Personnel Consultants of Troy, Inc. (C), MI, *347*
F-O-R-T-U-N-E of West Portland (C), OR, *348*
F-O-R-T-U-N-E Personnel Consultants of Rockland County, Inc. (C), NY, *348*
F-O-R-T-U-N-E Personnel Consultants of Charlotte (C), NC, *348*
F-O-R-T-U-N-E Personnel Consultants of Cincinnati (C), OH, *348*
Fortune Personnel Consultants of Greensboro, NC, Inc. (C), NC, *348*
F-O-R-T-U-N-E Consultants of Memphis (C), TN, *349*
FORTUNE Personnel Consultants of Charleston, Inc. (C), SC, *349*
Fortune Personnel Consultants of Chattanooga Inc. (C), TN, *349*
Fortune Personnel Consultants of Anderson, Inc. (C), SC, *349*
F-O-R-T-U-N-E Personnel Consultants of Houston, Inc. (C), TX, *350*
Foster Partners (R), NY, *70*
The Fourbes Group, Inc. (C), NJ, *351*
Fox-Morris Assoc., Inc. (C), PA, *351*
Foy, Schneid & Daniel, Inc. (R), NY, *71*
KS Frary & Assoc. (R), MA, *71*
Friedman Eisenstein Raemer & Schwartz, LLP (R), IL, *72*
Future Employment Service, Inc. (C), IA, *353*
GAAP Inc. (R), QE, *73*
Gabriele & Company (C), MA, *354*
Gardner-Ross Assoc., Inc. (R), NY, *74*
The Garret Group (R), NJ, *75*
Genesis Recruiting (C), CA, *356*
Genesis Research (C), MO, *356*
Gilbert Tweed Assoc. Inc. (R), NY, *76*
Gilreath Weatherby Inc. (R), MA, *77*
The Glenwood Group (C), IL, *358*
H. L. Goehring & Assoc., Inc. (C), OH, *359*
Goldbeck Recruiting Inc. (C), BC, *359*
Gomez Fregoso y Asociados (C), JAL, *360*
Goodrich & Sherwood Assoc., Inc. (R), NY, *79*
Graham & Co. (R), NJ, *80*
Granger, Counts & Assoc. (R), OH, *81*
Graphic Search Assoc. Inc. (C), PA, *362*
Gregory, Kyle & Assoc. (C), NC, *363*
Griffith & Werner, Inc. (R), FL, *82*
Gros Executive Search, Inc. (C), TN, *363*
Grover & Assoc. (R), OH, *82*
David E. Grumney Co. Inc. (R), WA, *83*
The Harris Consulting Corp. (R), MB, *87*
Harrison Moore Inc. (C), NE, *370*
William E. Hay & Co. (R), IL, *88*
HCI Corp. (C), IL, *371*
Healey Executive Search, Inc. (R), MN, *88*
Healthcare Recruiters International-NY/NJ (C), NJ, *373*
F. P. Healy & Co., Inc. (R), NY, *89*
Heath/Norton Assoc., Inc. (R), NY, *89*
Heinze & Assoc. Inc. (R), MN, *91*
Helffrich Int'l. (C), FL, *375*
Heller Kil Assoc., Inc. (C), FL, *375*
Stanley Herz & Co. (R), NY, *92*
Frank P. Hill (R), MX, *93*
The Hindman Co. (R), KY, *94*
Hobson Assoc. (C), CT, *379*
Hodge-Cronin & Assoc., Inc. (R), IL, *94*
Hollander Horizon Int'l. (R), CA, *95*
Horizons Unlimited (C), CA, *381*
HR Inc. (C), NC, *382*
E. F. Humay Assoc. (C), PA, *384*
The Hunt Group, Inc. (R), NC, *99*
Hunt Patton & Brazeal, Inc. (C), OK, *385*
The Icard Group, Inc. (C), MI, *387*
The Inside Track (C), TX, *389*
Intercontinental Executive Group (C), PA, *391*
Interim Management Resources Inc. (C), ON, *392*
International Business Partners (C), ON, *392*
International Executive Recruiters (C), OH, *393*
Joan Isbister Consultants (C), NY, *394*
ISC of Atlanta, Inc. (C), GA, *394*
ISC of Cincinnati Inc. (C), OH, *394*
J. B. Linde & Assoc. (C), MO, *395*
Jackley Search Consultants (C), MN, *396*
Ron Jackson & Assoc. (C), GA, *396*
Jaeger Int'l., Inc. (C), OH, *396*
JCL & Assoc. (C), FL, *397*
JM & Company (R), PA, *106*
John Jay & Co. (C), ME, *399*
Robert Kaestner & Assoc. (C), FL, *403*
Kay Concepts, Inc. (C), FL, *404*
A.T. Kearney Executive Search (R), IL, *111*
Kehn & Gabor, Inc. (C), OH, *405*
Kensington Int'l., Inc. (R), IL, *113*
Key Employment (C), NJ, *405*
Kingsbury • Wax • Bova (R), MA, *114*
Richard Kinser & Assoc. (R), NY, *115*
Kirby Assoc. (R), PA, *115*
J. Krauss Assoc. (R), FL, *120*
Kremple & Meade, Inc. (R), CA, *120*
Kutt, Inc. (C), CO, *410*
L&L Assoc. Global Search (C), PA, *411*
Laboratory Resource Group (C), MA, *411*
Landon Morgan (C), ON, *412*
Lange & Assoc., Inc. (C), IN, *412*
Stephen Laramee & Assoc. Inc. (C), ON, *413*
Lawrence-Balakonis & Assoc., Inc. (C), GA, *414*
Lawrence-Leiter & Co. (R), KS, *126*
W. R. Lawry, Inc. (R), CT, *126*
Leaders-Trust Int'l./Carce y Asociados, S.C. (R), MX, *127*
Lehman McLeskey (R), TX, *128*
The Levton Group Inc. (R), ON, *129*
Linden Group, Inc. (C), NC, *418*
Lineal Recruiting Services (C), CT, *418*
Locke & Assoc. (R), NC, *131*
Lyons & Assoc., Inc. (C), IL, *422*
M H Executive Search Group (C), TX, *422*
M. K. & Assoc. (C), PA, *422*
MacNaughton Assoc. (R), CA, *133*
Maczkov-Biosciences, Inc. (R), CA, *133*
The Mallard Group (C), IN, *423*
Management Recruiters of Birmingham (C), AL, *438*
Management Recruiters of Decatur, LLC (C), AL, *438*
Management Recruiters of Little Rock (C), AR, *439*
Management Recruiters of Colorado Springs (C), CO, *441*
Management Recruiters of Winsted, Inc. (C), CT, *442*
Management Recruiters of Ft. Myers, FL. (C), FL, *443*
Management Recruiters of Clearwater (C), FL, *443*
Management Recruiters of Boca Raton (C), FL, *443*
Management Recruiters of Melbourne, Inc. (C), FL, *443*
Management Recruiters of Pensacola (C), FL, *444*
Management Recruiters of Lake Co., Inc. (C), FL, *444*
Management Recruiters of Atlanta West, Inc. (C), GA, *445*
Management Recruiters of Atlanta (C), GA, *445*
Management Recruiters of Vero Beach (C), FL, *445*
Management Recruiters of Savannah (C), GA, *446*
Management Recruiters of Atlanta North, Inc. (C), GA, *446*
Management Recruiters of Boise (C), ID, *446*
Management Recruiters of Barrington (C), IL, *447*
Management Recruiters of Sun Valley (C), ID, *447*
Management Recruiters of Noblesville, Inc. (C), IN, *448*
Management Recruiters of Danville (C), KY, *449*
Management Recruiters of Richmond (C), KY, *449*

Management Recruiters of Columbia (C), MD, *450*
Management Recruiters of Rockville (C), MD, *450*
Management Recruiters of Monroe, Inc. (C), LA, *450*
Management Recruiters of Muskegon (C), MI, *451*
Management Recruiters of Baltimore (C), MD, *451*
Management Recruiters - Flint (C), MI, *451*
Management Recruiters of Rankin Co. (C), MS, *452*
Management Recruiters of North Oakland County, Inc. (C), MI, *452*
Management Recruiters of Medford, N.J. (C), NJ, *453*
Management Recruiters of Reno (C), NV, *453*
Management Recruiters of Upper Westchester (C), NY, *454*
Management Recruiters of Burlington (C), NC, *455*
Management Recruiters of Fayetteville (C), NC, *455*
Management Recruiters of Asheville, Inc. (C), NC, *455*
Management Recruiters of Mt. Airy (C), NC, *456*
Management Recruiters of Raleigh (C), NC, *456*
Management Recruiters of Wilmington (C), NC, *457*
Management Recruiters of Akron (C), OH, *457*
Management Recruiters of Cleveland (C), OH, *457*
Management Recruiters of Cincinnati/ Sharonville, Inc. (C), OH, *457*
Management Recruiters of Bethlehem, PA (C), PA, *458*
Management Recruiters of Sidney (C), OH, *458*
Management Recruiters of McMurray, Inc. (C), PA, *459*
Management Recruiters of Valley Forge (C), PA, *459*
Management Recruiters of Myrtle Beach, Inc. (C), SC, *460*
Management Recruiters of Aiken (C), SC, *460*
Management Recruiters of Chattanooga-Brainerd, Inc. (C), TN, *461*
Management Recruiters of Travelers Rest, Inc. (C), SC, *461*
Management Recruiters of Franklin, Inc. (C), TN, *461*
Management Recruiters of Columbia, Tennessee (C), TN, *461*
Management Recruiters of Arlington (C), TX, *462*
Management Recruiters - Friendswood (C), TX, *462*
Management Recruiters of Lubbock (C), TX, *463*
Management Recruiters of San Antonio (C), TX, *463*
Management Recruiters of Ogden (C), UT, *464*
Management Recruiters of Loudoun County South (C), VA, *465*
Management Recruiters of Seattle (C), WA, *465*
Management Recruiters of Appleton (C), WI, *465*
Management Recruiters of Janesville, Inc. (C), WI, *466*
Mannard & Assoc., Inc. (R), IL, *135*
Manuso, Alexander & Associates, Inc. (R), NY, *135*
Margolin Consultants, Inc. (C), NY, *469*
Mark III Personnel, Inc. (C), NC, *470*
George R. Martin (R), PA, *137*
Massey-Horton Int'l. (R), ON, *138*
Richard L. Mather & Assoc. (C), CT, *472*
G. P. Mattocks & Associates (C), NC, *473*
Mayhall Search Group, Inc. (C), IN, *473*
McCooe & Assoc., Inc. (R), NJ, *140*
McCray, Shriver, Eckdahl & Assoc., Inc. (R), CA, *140*
Robert E. McGrath & Assoc. (R), CT, *141*
McInturff & Assoc., Inc. (C), MA, *474*
McKinley•Arend Int'l. (R), TX, *141*
Med Exec Int'l. (C), CA, *476*
Merit Professional Search, Inc. (C), TN, *479*
Meyer Assoc., Inc. (R), GA, *144*
Herbert Mines Assoc., Inc. (R), NY, *145*
The Montgomery Group, Inc. (C), TN, *484*
Montgomery, Thomason & Assoc. (C), ON, *484*
The Morley Group (C), IN, *486*
Morton, McCorkle & Assoc. Inc. (R), MO, *147*
Mruk & E.M.A. Partners (R), NY, *148*
Multisearch Recruiters (C), CA, *487*
R. F. Mulvaney & Assoc., Inc. (R), MO, *149*
Jennifer Munro & Partners, Inc. (R), SC, *149*
The Murray Group (C), IL, *487*
NaTek Corp. (C), NY, *488*
National Computerized Employment Service, Inc. (C), PA, *489*
National Metal Services Corp. (C), IN, *489*
National Recruiting Service (C), IN, *489*
The NEIS Corp., Inc. (C), FL, *491*
The Niemond Corp. (R), CA, *152*
Norman Broadbent Int'l., Inc. (R), NY, *152*
North American Recruiters, Inc. (R), MN, *153*
Northern Consultants Inc. (R), ME, *153*
O'Brien & Bell (R), OH, *153*
O'Connor, O'Connor, Lordi, Ltd. (R), PA, *154*
O'Rourke Companies, Inc. (R), TX, *154*
The Odessa Group (R), CA, *155*
Oliver & Rozner Assoc., Inc. (R), NY, *155*
Olsen/Clark (R), WA, *156*
P R Management Consultants, Inc. (C), NJ, *500*
Pacific Advisory Service, Inc. (C), IL, *501*
Pacific Coast Recruiting (C), CA, *501*
Packaging Personnel Co., Ltd. (C), WI, *501*
The Pailin Group Professional Search Consultants (R), TX, *158*
Paper Industry Recruitment (P.I.R.) (C), ME, *502*
D. P. Parker & Assoc., Inc. (R), MA, *159*
Parker, McFadden & Assoc. (C), GA, *503*
Michael W. Parres & Assoc. (R), MI, *159*
Parsons Assoc. Inc. (R), IL, *159*
The Partnership Group (R), NJ, *160*
Peachtree Executive Search (R), GA, *161*
Paul S. Pelland, P.C. (R), SC, *161*
PERC, Ltd. (C), AZ, *506*
Performance Resources, Inc. (C), RI, *507*
Personnel Incorporated (C), IA, *508*
Personnel Tangent Inc. (C), QE, *509*
Pharmaceutical Recruiters, Inc. (R), NY, *163*
Phelps Personnel Assoc., Inc. (C), SC, *510*
Philo & Associates (C), GA, *511*
Gregory D. Pickens (C), TX, *511*
Polytechnical Consultants, Inc. (C), IL, *514*
Jack Porter Assoc., Inc. (C), WA, *514*
PRAXIS Partners (R), VA, *167*
George Preger & Associates Inc. (R), ON, *167*
The Premier Staffing Group (C), OH, *517*
PricewaterhouseCoopers Executive Search (R), ON, *168*
Prime Resource Assoc. (C), WI, *518*
Professional Personnel Services (C), IA, *520*
Quality Control Recruiters (C), CT, *526*
Quality Search (C), IN, *526*
R M Associates (R), OH, *171*
Rand Assoc. (R), ME, *171*
Harold L. Rapp Assoc. (C), NY, *529*
Raymond Thomas & Assoc. (C), FL, *530*
RCE Assoc. (R), NJ, *173*
Reifel & Assoc. (R), IL, *174*
Resource Inc. (R), MA, *175*
Resource Perspectives, Inc. (R), CA, *175*
Resources for Management (R), PA, *175*
The Revere Assoc., Inc. (R), OH, *176*
Terry Richards (C), OH, *536*
River Region Personnel, Inc. (C), LA, *538*
RJN Consulting (R), NY, *179*
R. A. Rodriguez & Assoc., Inc. (C), TX, *540*
ROI Assoc. (R), NY, *180*
The Rossi Search Group (C), PA, *545*
Roth Young of Chicago (C), IL, *546*
Roth Young Personnel Service of Detroit, Inc. (C), MI, *546*
Roth Young Seattle (C), WA, *546*
Rowland Assoc. (C), CA, *547*
RTE Search (C), NJ, *547*
Rushmore • Judge Inc. (R), ON, *183*
S. P. Assoc., Inc. (C), NC, *550*
S.C.S. & Assoc. (C), NC, *550*
S.D.P. Contract Recruiters (C), NJ, *550*
Saber Group, Inc. (C), TX, *550*
Sales Consultants of Daphne (C), AL, *556*
Sales Consultants of Ft. Lauderdale, Inc. (C), FL, *557*
Sales Consultants of Baltimore (C), MD, *559*
Sales Consultants of Middlesex County, Inc. (C), NJ, *561*
Sanford Rose Assoc. - Santa Ana (C), CA, *565*
Sanford Rose Assoc. - Fairhope (C), AL, *565*

Sanford Rose Assoc. - Clearwater (C), FL, 566
Sanford Rose Assoc. - Effingham (C), IL, 566
Sanford Rose Assoc. - Athens (C), GA, 566
Sanford Rose Assoc. - Columbia, MD (C), MD, 567
Sanford Rose Assoc. - Rochester (C), MI, 568
Sanford Rose Assoc. - Gastonia (C), NC, 568
Sanford Rose Assoc. - Greensboro (C), NC, 569
Sanford Rose Assoc. - Burlington, NC (C), NC, 569
Sanford Rose Assoc. - Akron (C), OH, 569
Sanford Rose Assoc. - Austin (C), TX, 570
Sanford Rose Assoc. - Nashville (C), TN, 570
Sanford Rose Assoc. - Doylestown (C), PA, 570
Sanford Rose Assoc. - Portland (C), OR, 570
Sanford Rose Assoc. - Port Washington (C), WI, 571
The Schatz Company (C), MO, 571
Schenck & Assoc. SC (C), WI, 572
Scientific Solutions, Inc. (C), MI, 572
Scott Executive Search, Inc. (R), NY, 186
Scott-Thaler Assoc. Agency, Inc. (C), CA, 573
Search & Recruit Int'l. (C), VA, 573
Search Assoc. (C), KY, 574
Search Consultants Int'l., Inc. (C), TX, 575
Search Enterprises, Inc. (C), FL, 575
Search Masters Int'l. (R), AZ, 187
Search Northwest Assoc. (C), OR, 576
Search South, Inc. (C), AL, 576
Selective Management Services, Inc. (C), FL, 578
Selective Recruiting Assoc., Inc. (C), MI, 578
Selig Executive Search (C), NH, 579
Shoemaker & Assoc. (R), GA, 190
SHS of Allentown (C), PA, 580
D. J. Simpson Assoc. Inc. (R), ON, 191
Singleton & Assoc. (C), VA, 582
James F. Smith & Assoc. (C), GA, 583
Ralph Smith & Assoc. (C), IL, 584
Smith & Syberg, Inc. (R), IN, 193
Smith Search, S.C. (R), MX, 194
Snelling Search (C), LA, 586
Soltis Management Services (R), PA, 195
Southern Research Services (R), FL, 195
SpencerStuart (R), NY, 196
Kenn Spinrad Inc. (C), PA, 589
Sprout/Standish, Inc. (C), NH, 589
Stanton Chase Int'l. (R), MD, 198
The Stelton Group, Inc. (C), NJ, 592
Ron Stevens & Assoc., Inc. (C), FL, 593
Stewart Assoc. (C), PA, 593
Linford E. Stiles & Assoc., L.L.C. (R), NH, 201
Stoneburner Assoc., Inc. (C), KS, 594
Stoopen Asociados, S.C./EMA Partners Int'l. (R), MX, 202
Strategic Assoc., Inc. (C), TX, 595
Strategic Resources (C), WA, 595
Strategic Search Corp. (R), IL, 202
StratfordGroup (R), OH, 203
Ron Sunshine & Assoc. (C), IL, 597
System 1 Search (C), CA, 598
T E M Assoc. (C), WI, 599
Teamsearch, Inc. (C), MI, 601
Technical Recruiting Services (C), OH, 602
Technical Resource Assoc. (C), TN, 602
Tekworx, Inc. (C), OK, 604
Telem Adhesive Search Corp. (C), MD, 605
Fred C. Tippel & Assoc. (C), OH, 607
TPS Staffing Solutions (C), IN, 608
Travis & Co., Inc. (R), MA, 210
Triangle Assoc. (C), PA, 609
Triumph Consulting, Inc. (R), IA, 210
Tschudin Inc. (R), NJ, 211
Vaughan & Co. (C), CA, 612
Vincenty & Co. (C), OH, 612
Voigt Assoc. (R), IL, 214
VZ Int'l., Inc. (C), AZ, 613
Wachendorfer & Assoc. (C), TX, 613
Gordon Wahls Executive Search (C), PA, 613
Ward-Hoffman & Assoc. (C), ID, 615
Waveland Int'l. (R), IL, 216
Wegner & Assoc. (C), WI, 617
Weinpel Search, Inc. (C), NJ, 617
R. A. Wells Co. (C), GA, 618
Wesley Brown & Bartle Co., Inc. (R), NY, 218
West & Assoc. (C), IL, 618
West & West (R), CA, 218
Whitney Smith Co. (C), TX, 620
Whittaker & Assoc., Inc. (C), GA, 620
Wilcox Bertoux & Miller (R), CA, 220
John R. Williams & Assoc., Inc. (C), NC, 621
John Williams & Assoc. (C), TX, 621
Williamsburg Group (C), NJ, 621
Wilson Personnel, Inc. (C), NC, 622
Wing Tips & Pumps, Inc. (C), MI, 623
Winston Search, Inc. (R), MD, 222
Winthrop Partners, Inc. (R), NY, 222
The Witt Group (C), FL, 623
WMD inc. (C), NJ, 623
S. R. Wolman Assoc., Inc. (R), NY, 224
Jim Woodson & Assoc., Inc. (C), MS, 624
Xagas & Assoc. (R), IL, 226
Zwell Int'l. (R), IL, 228

02.5 Quality

The Addison Consulting Group (C), NJ, 239
Advanced Recruitment, Inc. (C), TN, 240
Advancement Recruiting Services (C), OH, 241
AGRI-associates (C), MO, 242
Alpha Executive Search (C), AL, 245
The Altco Group (C), NJ, 246
American Professional Search, Inc. (C), TN, 248
Anderson Industrial Assoc., Inc. (C), GA, 250
Austin Michaels, Ltd., Inc. (C), AZ, 256
Availability Personnel Consultants (C), NH, 257
Barber & Assoc. (C), KY, 259
Barr Assoc. (C), PA, 259
The Barton Group, Inc. (C), MI, 260
Battalia Winston Int'l./The Euram Consultants Group (R), NY, 13
The Bedford Group (R), RI, 15
William Bell Assoc., Inc. (C), NJ, 263
Jack Bertram, Executive Recruiter (C), PA, 265
Bio-Venture Group (C), RI, 266
Blair/Tech Recruiters, Inc. (C), NJ, 268
Borchert Assoc. (C), TX, 269
Boyden (R), NY, 20
Bratland & Assoc. (C), IL, 272
Brett Personnel Specialists (C), NJ, 273
Brierwood Group, Inc. (C), IN, 273
Brooke Chase Assoc., Inc. (R), IL, 24
Juliette Lang Cahn Executive Search (C), NY, 279
Canny, Bowen Inc. (R), NY, 27
Career Images (C), FL, 282
Carnegie Resources, Inc. (C), NC, 284
Case Executive Search (C), MI, 286
Chadwell & Assoc., Inc. (C), MI, 288
Wayne S. Chamberlain & Assoc. (C), CA, 288
Chase-Gardner Executive Search Associates, Inc. (C), FL, 289
R. Christine Assoc. (C), PA, 290
William J. Christopher Assoc., Inc. (R), PA, 34
Christopher-Westmont & Assoc., Inc. (R), OH, 34
Clark Executive Search (C), NY, 292
Consulting Rhonda (C), ON, 297
Philip Conway Management (R), IL, 40
Cook Assoc. Int'l., Inc. (C), TN, 298
Cornell Group Int'l. Consulting, Inc. (R), NY, 41
Corporate Management Services (C), PA, 300
Creative-Leadership, Inc. (R), CA, 42
Jim Crumpley & Assoc. (C), MO, 304
Cumberland Professional Search Inc. (C), TN, 304
The Currier-Winn Co., Inc. (C), NJ, 305
Daniel Marks Company (C), OH, 306
The Danielson Group, Inc. (C), TX, 306
Davidson, Laird & Assoc. (C), MI, 308
Debbon Recruiting Group, Inc. (C), MO, 310
DiTech Resources (C), CT, 313
Dunhill Personnel of Boulder (C), CO, 319
Dunhill Professional Search of Englewood, Inc. (C), CO, 319
Dunhill of Ft. Wayne, Inc. (C), IN, 320
Dunhill Professional Search of Augusta (C), GA, 320
Dunhill Executive Search of Brown County (C), IN, 321
Dunhill Personnel of St. Andrews (C), SC, 322
Dunhill Professional Search, Inc. of McAllen (C), TX, 323
G. L. Dykstra Assoc., Inc. (C), MI, 323
Eagle Consulting Group Inc. (C), TX, 325
D. C. Egan & Assoc. (C), GA, 327
EGM Consulting, Inc. (R), FL, 57
Emerging Medical Technologies, Inc. (C), CO, 329
Execu-Tech Search Inc. (C), MN, 332

Executive Connection (C), OH, *333*
Executive Directions (R), OH, *62*
First Choice Search (R), WA, *67*
Fogec Consultants, Inc. (R), WI, *69*
F-O-R-T-U-N-E Personnel Consultants of Denver, Inc. (C), CO, *344*
F-O-R-T-U-N-E Personnel Consultants of Tampa (C), FL, *344*
F-O-R-T-U-N-E Personnel Consultants of Wilmington (C), DE, *344*
F-O-R-T-U-N-E Personnel Consultants of San Diego (C), CA, *344*
Fortune Personnel Consultants (C), CA, *344*
F-O-R-T-U-N-E Personnel Consultants of Greenwood Village (C), CO, *344*
F-O-R-T-U-N-E Personnel Consultants of Manatee County (C), FL, *345*
F-O-R-T-U-N-E Personnel Consultants of Savannah, Inc. (C), GA, *345*
Fortune Personnel Consultants of Sarasota Inc. (C), FL, *345*
F-O-R-T-U-N-E Personnel Consultants of Atlanta, Inc. (C), GA, *345*
Fortune of Arlington Heights (C), IL, *345*
F-O-R-T-U-N-E Personnel Consultants (C), MI, *346*
Fortune Personnel Consultants of Bloomfield, Inc. (C), MI, *346*
F-o-r-t-u-n-e of Owensboro, Inc. (C), KY, *346*
F-O-R-T-U-N-E Personnel Consultants of South Bend (C), IN, *346*
Fortune Personnel Consultants (C), NH, *347*
F-O-R-T-U-N-E Personnel Consultants of St. Louis-West County (C), MO, *347*
Fortune Personnel Consultants (C), MT, *347*
F-O-R-T-U-N-E Personnel Consultants of Bergen County Inc. (C), NJ, *347*
F-O-R-T-U-N-E of West Portland (C), OR, *348*
F-O-R-T-U-N-E Personnel Consultants of Rockland County, Inc. (C), NY, *348*
F-O-R-T-U-N-E Personnel Consultants of Charlotte (C), NC, *348*
F-O-R-T-U-N-E Personnel Consultants of Cincinnati (C), OH, *348*
Fortune Personnel Consultants of Hilton Head (C), SC, *349*
F-O-R-T-U-N-E Consultants of Memphis (C), TN, *349*
FORTUNE Personnel Consultants of Charleston, Inc. (C), SC, *349*
Fortune Personnel Consultants of Anderson, Inc. (C), SC, *349*
F-O-R-T-U-N-E Personnel Consultants of Houston, Inc. (C), TX, *350*
F-O-R-T-U-N-E Personnel Consultants of Knoxville (C), TN, *350*
FORTUNE Personnel Consultants of North Dallas (C), TX, *350*
Fortune Personnel Consultants of Plano (C), TX, *350*
Foster Partners (R), NY, *70*
Gabriele & Company (C), MA, *354*
The Garret Group (R), NJ, *75*
Genesis Recruiting (C), CA, *356*
Gilbert Tweed Assoc. Inc. (R), NY, *76*
Fred J. Goldsmith Assoc. (R), CA, *79*
Graham & Co. (R), NJ, *80*
Gregory, Kyle & Assoc. (C), NC, *363*
The Hampton Group (C), NY, *367*
Harrison Moore Inc. (C), NE, *370*
HeartBeat Medical, Inc. (C), OR, *374*
Heath/Norton Assoc., Inc. (R), NY, *89*
Heller Kil Assoc., Inc. (C), FL, *375*
Hintz Associates (C), NY, *378*
Hollander Horizon Int'l. (R), CA, *95*
The Hudson Group (C), CT, *383*
The Icard Group, Inc. (C), MI, *387*
Industry Consultants, Inc. (C), GA, *388*
Inter Regional Executive Search, Inc. (IRES, Inc.) (C), NJ, *391*
Interim Executive Recruiting (C), GA, *392*
J. B. Linde & Assoc. (C), MO, *395*
J.N. Adams & Assoc., Inc. (C), PA, *396*
Jackley Search Consultants (C), MN, *396*
Jaeger Int'l., Inc. (C), OH, *396*
Joslin & Assoc., Ltd. (C), IL, *401*
Kanzer Assoc., Inc. (R), IL, *109*
Kay Concepts, Inc. (C), FL, *404*
A.T. Kearney Executive Search (R), IL, *111*
Kehn & Gabor, Inc. (C), OH, *405*
Kenmore Executives Inc. (C), FL, *405*
Blair Kershaw Assoc., Inc. (C), PA, *405*
Kulper & Co., L.L.C. (R), NJ, *121*
Kutt, Inc. (C), CO, *410*
Laboratory Resource Group (C), MA, *411*
W. R. Lawry, Inc. (R), CT, *126*
The Lear Group, Inc. (R), OH, *127*
Linden Group, Inc. (C), NC, *418*
Longo Associates (C), CA, *420*
Lucas Group (C), NY, *421*
Lybrook Assoc., Inc. (C), RI, *421*
Lyons & Assoc., Inc. (C), IL, *422*
M H Executive Search Group (C), TX, *422*
M. K. & Assoc. (C), PA, *422*
The Mallard Group (C), IN, *423*
Management Catalysts (R), NJ, *134*
Management Recruiters of Birmingham (C), AL, *438*
Management Recruiters of Little Rock (C), AR, *439*
Management Recruiters of Pleasanton (C), CA, *441*
Management Recruiters of Ft. Myers, FL. (C), FL, *443*
Management Recruiters of Clearwater (C), FL, *443*
Management Recruiters of Lake Co., Inc. (C), FL, *444*
Management Recruiters of Boise (C), ID, *446*
Management Recruiters of Lake Forest, IL (C), IL, *447*
Management Recruiters of Springfield, Inc. (C), IL, *447*
Management Recruiters of Noblesville, Inc. (C), IN, *448*
Management Recruiters of Spencer (C), IA, *448*
Management Recruiters of Danville (C), KY, *449*
Management Recruiters of Richmond (C), KY, *449*
Management Recruiters of Siouxland (C), IA, *449*
Management Recruiters of Columbia (C), MD, *450*
Management Recruiters of Livonia (C), MI, *451*
Management Recruiters - Flint (C), MI, *451*
Management Recruiters of Southeastern Michigan (C), MI, *451*
Management Recruiters of Rankin Co. (C), MS, *452*
Management Recruiters of Reno (C), NV, *453*
Management Recruiters of Fayetteville (C), NC, *455*
Management Recruiters of Burlington (C), NC, *455*
Management Recruiters of Asheville, Inc. (C), NC, *455*
Management Recruiters of Rocky Mount - Southwest (C), NC, *456*
Management Recruiters of Kinston (C), NC, *456*
Management Recruiters of Mt. Airy (C), NC, *456*
Management Recruiters of Raleigh (C), NC, *456*
Management Recruiters of Cincinnati/Sharonville, Inc. (C), OH, *457*
Management Recruiters of Easton, PA (C), PA, *458*
Management Recruiters of McMurray, Inc. (C), PA, *459*
Management Recruiters of Valley Forge (C), PA, *459*
Management Recruiters of Aiken (C), SC, *460*
Management Recruiters of LBJ Park/Dallas (C), TX, *462*
Management Recruiters of San Antonio (C), TX, *463*
Management Recruiters of Salt Lake City (C), UT, *464*
Management Recruiters of Ogden (C), UT, *464*
Management Recruiters of Milwaukee-West (C), WI, *465*
Management Recruiters of Janesville, Inc. (C), WI, *466*
Mankuta Gallagher & Assoc., Inc. (C), FL, *468*
George R. Martin (R), PA, *137*
G. P. Mattocks & Associates (C), NC, *473*
McCoy Ltd. (C), CA, *474*
McInturff & Assoc., Inc. (C), MA, *474*
Med Exec Int'l. (C), CA, *476*
MedQuest Assoc. (C), CO, *478*
Merit Professional Search, Inc. (C), TN, *479*
MetroVantage Personnel Systems (C), CA, *480*
Walter Meyer & Assoc. (R), NY, *144*
Lou Michaels Assoc., Inc. (C), MI, *481*
Miller + Miller (C), WA, *482*
Herbert Mines Assoc., Inc. (R), NY, *145*
The Morley Group (C), IN, *486*
Multisearch Recruiters (C), CA, *487*
The Murray Group (C), IL, *487*
Nachman Biomedical (C), MA, *488*

National Recruiting Service (C), IN, *489*
Nationwide Personnel Recruiting & Consulting, Inc. (C), OR, *490*
NaviSearch (C), GA, *490*
Len Nelson & Assoc., Inc. (C), TX, *491*
New Venture Development, Inc. (C), CA, *492*
Norman Broadbent Int'l., Inc. (R), NY, *152*
The Normyle/Erstling Health Search Group (C), NJ, *494*
North Coast Meridian (C), NY, *496*
Northland Employment Services Inc. (C), MN, *496*
Pacific Coast Recruiting (C), CA, *501*
Paper Industry Recruitment (P.I.R.) (C), ME, *502*
Paul S. Pelland, P.C. (R), SC, *161*
Personnel Management Group (C), MB, *508*
Phelps Personnel Assoc., Inc. (C), SC, *510*
Philo & Associates (C), GA, *511*
Gregory D. Pickens (C), TX, *511*
Polytechnical Consultants, Inc. (C), IL, *514*
Premier Search Group (C), IN, *517*
The Premier Staffing Group (C), OH, *517*
Prime Resource Assoc. (C), WI, *518*
Professional Engineering Technical Personnel Consultants (C), NC, *520*
Professional Personnel Services (C), IA, *520*
Professional Recruiting Consultants (C), FL, *521*
Proquest Inc. (C), SC, *524*
ProSearch, Inc. (C), OH, *524*
ProTech Nationwide Staffing, Inc. (C), NY, *525*
Quality Control Recruiters (C), CT, *526*
Quality Search Inc. (C), OH, *526*
Resource Inc. (R), MA, *175*
Terry Richards (C), OH, *536*
River Region Personnel, Inc. (C), LA, *538*
J. P. Roddy Consultants (C), PA, *540*
ROI Assoc. (R), NY, *180*
Romano McAvoy Assoc., Inc. (C), NY, *544*
Romeo-Hudgins & Assoc., Ltd. (C), NJ, *544*
Roth Young Personnel Service of Detroit, Inc. (C), MI, *546*
RTE Search (C), NJ, *547*
Saber Group, Inc. (C), TX, *550*
Sanford Rose Assoc. - Clearwater (C), FL, *566*
Sanford Rose Assoc. - Athens (C), GA, *566*
Sanford Rose Assoc. - Columbia, MD (C), MD, *567*
Sanford Rose Assoc. - Rockford (C), IL, *567*
Sanford Rose Assoc. - Louisville (C), KY, *567*
Sanford Rose Assoc. - Amherst, NY (C), NY, *568*
Sanford Rose Assoc. - Rochester (C), MI, *568*
Sanford Rose Assoc. - Gastonia (C), NC, *568*
Sanford Rose Assoc. - Flemington (C), NJ, *568*
Sanford Rose Assoc. - Austin (C), TX, *570*
Sanford Rose Assoc. - Doylestown (C), PA, *570*
Sanford Rose Assoc. - Portland (C), OR, *570*
Sanford Rose Assoc. - Port Washington (C), WI, *571*
The Schatz Company (C), MO, *571*
Search Assoc. (C), KY, *574*
The Search Network (C), CA, *576*
Search Northwest Assoc. (C), OR, *576*
Selective Recruiting Assoc., Inc. (C), MI, *578*
Selig Executive Search (C), NH, *579*
SHS of Allentown (C), PA, *580*
Sill Technical Assoc., Inc. (C), PA, *581*
Singleton & Assoc. (C), VA, *582*
Smith & Assoc. (C), FL, *583*
The Smith Group, Inc. (C), NC, *584*
Snelling Search (C), LA, *586*
Spectrum Consultants (R), CA, *196*
SpencerSearch, Inc. (C), CO, *589*
SpencerStuart (R), NY, *196*
Stanton Chase Int'l. (R), MD, *198*
Stewart Assoc. (C), PA, *593*
Stoneburner Assoc., Inc. (C), KS, *594*
Storfer & Assoc. (C), NY, *595*
Strategic Search Corp. (R), IL, *202*
Summit Executive Search Consultants, Inc. (R), FL, *204*
Ron Sunshine & Assoc. (C), IL, *597*
Survival Systems Staffing, Inc. (C), CA, *597*
S. Tanner & Assoc. Inc. (C), ON, *599*
Technical Employment Consultants (C), PA, *602*
Technical Recruiting Services (C), OH, *602*
Technical Resource Assoc. (C), TN, *602*
Technical Staffing Solutions (C), TX, *602*
Telem Adhesive Search Corp. (C), MD, *605*
Thomson, Sponar & Adams, Inc. (C), WA, *606*
Trainor/Frank & Assoc. Inc. (C), WI, *608*
The Truman Agency (C), CA, *610*
TSC Management Services Group, Inc. (C), IL, *610*
Vaughan & Co. (C), CA, *612*
Victor White Int'l. (C), CA, *612*
Voigt Assoc. (R), IL, *214*
W. P. Assoc. (C), CA, *613*
Wachendorfer & Assoc. (C), TX, *613*
Wallace Assoc. (C), CT, *614*
S. B. Webster & Associates (R), MA, *217*
Whittaker & Assoc., Inc. (C), GA, *620*
John Williams & Assoc. (C), TX, *621*
Williams Recruiting, Inc. (C), WA, *621*
Williamsburg Group (C), NJ, *621*
Wilson & Assoc. Int'l. Inc. (C), FL, *622*
Winfield Assoc., Inc. (C), MA, *623*
The Witt Group (C), FL, *623*
Susan L. Wonderling Recruiting (C), PA, *623*
Jim Woodson & Assoc., Inc. (C), MS, *624*
Xagas & Assoc. (R), IL, *226*
The Yaiser Group (C), NJ, *625*

02.6 Productivity

David Allen Assoc. (R), NJ, *3*
American Professional Search, Inc. (C), TN, *248*
Anderson Industrial Assoc., Inc. (C), GA, *250*
D. W. Baird & Associates (C), MD, *257*
Barber & Assoc. (C), KY, *259*
The Bennett Group, Inc. (R), IN, *16*
Jack Bertram, Executive Recruiter (C), PA, *265*
Biomedical Search Consultants (R), CT, *17*
Blair/Tech Recruiters, Inc. (C), NJ, *268*
Borchert Assoc. (C), TX, *269*
Howard Bowen Consulting (C), FL, *270*
Brett Personnel Specialists (C), NJ, *273*
Dan B. Brockman (C), IL, *274*
Carnegie Resources, Inc. (C), NC, *284*
Cook Assoc. Int'l., Inc. (C), TN, *298*
Dunhill Personnel of Boulder (C), CO, *319*
Dunhill of Ft. Wayne, Inc. (C), IN, *320*
Dunhill Professional Search of Augusta (C), GA, *320*
Dunhill Professional Search of Ramsey (C), NJ, *321*
G. L. Dykstra Assoc., Inc. (C), MI, *323*
Fenwick Partners (R), MA, *66*
F-o-r-t-u-n-e of Owensboro, Inc. (C), KY, *346*
F-O-R-T-U-N-E Personnel Consultants of Rockland County, Inc. (C), NY, *348*
Fortune Personnel Consultants of Greensboro, NC, Inc. (C), NC, *348*
FORTUNE Personnel Consultants of Charleston, Inc. (C), SC, *349*
F-O-R-T-U-N-E Personnel Consultants of Knoxville (C), TN, *350*
Foster Partners (R), NY, *70*
Gilbert Tweed Assoc. Inc. (R), NY, *76*
Gros Executive Search, Inc. (C), TN, *363*
Harrison Moore Inc. (C), NE, *370*
Hintz Associates (C), NY, *378*
Human Resources Personnel Agency (R), AR, *99*
The Icard Group, Inc. (C), MI, *387*
JSG Group Management Consultants (R), ON, *109*
A.T. Kearney Executive Search (R), IL, *111*
Kenmore Executives Inc. (C), FL, *405*
John Kuhn & Assoc., Inc. (R), WI, *121*
Management Recruiters of Pensacola (C), FL, *444*
Management Recruiters of Richmond (C), KY, *449*
Management Recruiters - Flint (C), MI, *451*
Management Recruiters of Akron (C), OH, *457*
Management Recruiters of McMurray, Inc. (C), PA, *459*
Management Recruiters of Valley Forge (C), PA, *459*
Management Recruiters of Columbia, Tennessee (C), TN, *461*
Management Recruiters of LBJ Park/Dallas (C), TX, *462*
Mathey Services (C), IL, *472*
G. P. Mattocks & Associates (C), NC, *473*
McDonald Assoc. Int'l. (R), IL, *140*
Walter Meyer & Assoc. (R), NY, *144*
Herbert Mines Assoc., Inc. (R), NY, *145*

Morgan & Assoc. (C), MA, *485*
Multisearch Recruiters (C), CA, *487*
Norman Broadbent Int'l., Inc. (R), NY, *152*
Northland Employment Services Inc. (C), MN, *496*
Norton & Assoc. (C), IL, *496*
PERC, Ltd. (C), AZ, *506*
Personnel Tangent Inc. (C), QE, *509*
Gregory D. Pickens (C), TX, *511*
Roth Young of Tampa (C), FL, *546*
RTE Search (C), NJ, *547*
Sanford Rose Assoc. - Rockford (C), IL, *567*
Sanford Rose Assoc. - Louisville (C), KY, *567*
Sanford Rose Assoc. - Austin (C), TX, *570*
Sanford Rose Assoc. - Port Washington (C), WI, *571*
Santangelo Consultants Inc. (C), NY, *571*
Search Assoc. (C), KY, *574*
Search Northwest Assoc. (C), OR, *576*
Spear-Izzo Assoc., LLC (C), PA, *588*
SpencerStuart (R), NY, *196*
Stanton Chase Int'l. (R), MD, *198*
Stewart Assoc. (C), PA, *593*
Strategic Assoc., Inc. (C), TX, *595*
Teamsearch, Inc. (C), MI, *601*
Technical Staffing Solutions (C), TX, *602*
Fred C. Tippel & Assoc. (C), OH, *607*
VZ Int'l., Inc. (C), AZ, *613*
Susan L. Wonderling Recruiting (C), PA, *623*
World Search (C), OH, *625*
Xagas & Assoc. (R), IL, *226*

03.0 Materials management

The 500 Granary Inc. (C), ON, *231*
A.M.C.R., Inc. (C), OH, *232*
The Abbott Group, Inc. (R), MD, *1*
Abécassis Conseil (R), QE, *1*
Abeln, Magy & Assoc., Inc. (R), MN, *1*
B. J. Abrams & Assoc. Inc. (C), IL, *233*
Accelerated Data Decision, Inc. (C), NJ, *233*
Access/Resources, Inc. (C), MA, *234*
Accountants Executive Search (C), CT, *234*
Ackerman Johnson Inc. (C), TX, *238*
Adirect Recruiting Corp. (C), ON, *240*
Advanced Executive Resources (R), MI, *2*
The Advisory Group, Inc. (R), CA, *2*
Aggressive Corporation (C), IL, *242*
Agra Placements, Ltd. (C), IA, *242*
AGRI-associates (C), MO, *242*
Tom Allison Assoc. (C), NM, *245*
Alpha Executive Search (C), AL, *245*
Alpha Search (C), FL, *246*
The Altco Group (C), NJ, *246*
Altec/HRC (C), MI, *246*
ALW Research Int'l. (R), NJ, *4*
Alynco, Inc. (C), AR, *246*
Peter W. Ambler Co. (R), TX, *5*
American Heritage Group, Inc. (C), MI, *247*
American Logistics Consultants, Inc. (C), IL, *247*
American Professional Search, Inc. (C), TN, *248*
American Services Group (C), IL, *248*
AmeriPro Search, Inc. (C), NC, *248*
Ames-O'Neill Assoc., Inc. (C), NY, *249*
Anderson Industrial Assoc., Inc. (C), GA, *250*
Anderson Network Group (C), OH, *250*
Angel Group Int'l. (C), KY, *250*
Ansara, Bickford & Fiske (C), MA, *251*
Applied Resources, Inc. (C), MN, *252*
Charles P. Aquavella & Assoc. (C), TX, *252*
ARJay & Assoc. (C), NC, *252*
Artgo, Inc. (R), OH, *7*
A. Artze Assoc.-Personnel Consultants (C), PR, *253*
The Ascher Group (R), NJ, *7*
Ashlar-Stone Management Consultants Inc. (R), ON, *8*
Associated Recruiters (C), WI, *254*
The Associates, HR Search Executives, Inc. (C), OK, *254*
W. R. Atchison & Assoc., Inc. (C), NC, *254*
Atlantic West Int'l. (C), NC, *255*
Atomic Personnel, Inc. (C), PA, *255*
Aurora Tech Search (C), ON, *256*
Austin - Allen Co. (C), TN, *256*
Austin Michaels, Ltd., Inc. (C), AZ, *256*
Austin-McGregor Int'l. (R), TX, *9*
Automation Technology Search (C), CA, *256*
Availability Personnel Consultants (C), NH, *257*
Avery Assoc. (R), CA, *9*
Avondale Search Int'l., Inc. (R), FL, *9*
Keith Bagg & Assoc., Inc. (C), ON, *257*
Baldwin & Assoc. (C), OH, *258*
Ballos & Co., Inc. (R), NJ, *10*
James Bangert & Assoc., Inc. (R), MN, *11*
Paul C. Banks Assoc. (C), GA, *259*
Fred A. Barnette & Assoc. (R), NC, *11*
Barone Assoc. (C), NJ, *259*
Barth Smith Company (R), IL, *12*
Battalia Winston Int'l./The Euram Consultants Group (R), NY, *13*
R. Gaines Baty Assoc., Inc. (R), TX, *13*
Martin H. Bauman Assoc., Inc. (R), NY, *13*
Behrens and Company (C), WA, *262*
Gary S. Bell Assoc., Inc. (C), NJ, *263*
William Bell Assoc., Inc. (C), NJ, *263*
Bell Oaks Co., Inc. (C), GA, *263*
J. P. Bencik Assoc. (C), MI, *263*
Benford & Assoc., Inc. (C), MI, *264*
N. L. Benke & Assoc., Inc. (C), OH, *264*
C. Berger And Company (R), IL, *16*
Berkshire Search Assoc. (C), MA, *265*
BG & Assoc. (C), MD, *266*
BGB Assoc., Inc. (C), IL, *266*
Paul J. Biestek Assoc., Inc. (R), IL, *17*
Billington & Assoc. (R), CA, *17*
Biomedical Search Consultants (R), CT, *17*
BioPharmMed (C), FL, *267*
BJB Assoc. (C), VA, *267*
The Black Leopard (C), CA, *267*
Blair/Tech Recruiters, Inc. (C), NJ, *268*
Blanton & Co. (C), AL, *268*
D. R. Blood & Assoc. (R), AZ, *18*
Boettcher Assoc. (R), WI, *19*
Bor-Maq Assoc. (C), TX, *269*
Lynn Borne & Co. (C), CA, *270*
The Borton Wallace Co. (R), NC, *19*
Bosland Gray Assoc. (R), NJ, *20*
Howard Bowen Consulting (C), FL, *270*
Bower & Associates (C), TX, *271*
Bowie & Associates, Inc. (C), MD, *271*
Boyden (R), NY, *20*
Brandywine Management Group (R), MD, *22*
Bredeson Executive Recruitment, LLC (R), TX, *22*
Briant Assoc., Inc. (R), IL, *23*
The Bridge (C), CO, *273*
Bridgecreek Personnel Agency (C), CA, *273*
Bright Search/Professional Staffing (C), MN, *274*
Britt Assoc., Inc. (C), IL, *274*
Broward-Dobbs, Inc. (C), GA, *274*
Bryan & Louis Research (C), OH, *275*
Burke & Assoc./The Westfield Group (C), CT, *276*
Business Solutions Worldwide, Inc. (C), NJ, *277*
C & H Personnel (C), PA, *277*
C. M. Management Services, Inc. (R), KY, *26*
The C.P.R. Group (C), NJ, *278*
C.P.S., Inc. (C), IL, *278*
Cahill Assoc. (C), CT, *279*
Juliette Lang Cahn Executive Search (C), NY, *279*
California Search Agency, Inc. (C), CA, *279*
Callan Assoc., Ltd. (R), IL, *27*
Callos Personnel Services (C), OH, *279*
Campa & Assoc. (R), ON, *27*
Campbell, Edgar Inc. (C), BC, *280*
J. P. Canon Assoc. (C), NY, *280*
Canyon Consulting, Inc. (C), TX, *281*
Caprio & Assoc. Inc. (R), IL, *29*
Career Alternatives Executive Search (C), MI, *281*
Careers/Inc. (C), PR, *284*
Carnegie Partners, Inc. (R), IL, *30*
Carnegie Resources, Inc. (C), NC, *284*
Carpenter & Assoc. (C), TX, *284*
Carrington & Carrington, Ltd. (R), IL, *30*
Carter, Lavoie Associates (C), RI, *285*
Cary & Assoc. (R), FL, *31*
Case Executive Search (C), MI, *286*
Michael J. Cavanagh & Assoc. Inc. (R), ON, *31*
Cella Assoc. (C), GA, *286*
Cendea Connection Int'l. (R), TX, *32*
Chad Management Group (C), ON, *288*
Chapman & Assoc. (C), BC, *289*
Robert L. Charon (C), TX, *289*
Chelsea Resources, Inc. (C), CT, *290*
Christmas, McIvor & Assoc. Inc. (C), ON, *290*
Christopher and Long (C), MO, *291*
Christopher-Westmont & Assoc., Inc. (R), OH, *34*
The Churchill Group (C), ON, *291*
CJA-The Adler Group, Inc. (R), CA, *35*
Clark Executive Search (C), NY, *292*
Ken Clark Int'l. (R), NJ, *36*
Clark Personnel Service, Inc. (C), AL, *292*
CMS, Inc. (C), NH, *293*

CMS Management Services LLC (C), IN, *293*
Cochran, Cochran & Yale, Inc. (R), NY, *36*
Coleman Lew & Assoc., Inc. (R), NC, *37*
Collins & Associates (C), MI, *294*
Compass Group Ltd. (R), MI, *38*
Conasa de Mexico, S.C. (R), MX, *39*
Consolidated Management Services (C), ON, *296*
Consulting Rhonda (C), ON, *297*
Continental Search Assoc. (C), OH, *298*
P. G. Cook Assoc. (R), TN, *40*
Corbin Packaging Professionals (C), MO, *299*
Corporate Advisors, Inc. (C), FL, *299*
The Corporate Advisory Group (R), NJ, *41*
Corporate Environment Ltd. (R), IL, *41*
Corporate Image Group (C), TN, *300*
Corporate Management Services (C), PA, *300*
Corporate Plus, Ltd. (C), GA, *300*
Corporate Resources (C), OH, *301*
Corporate Search Consultants (C), IN, *301*
Corporate Search, Inc. (C), NY, *301*
Corporate Select Int'l., Ltd. (C), IL, *301*
J. D. Cotter Search Inc. (C), OH, *302*
Craig Affiliates, Inc. (C), TX, *302*
Creative Input, Inc. (C), RI, *303*
Criterion Executive Search, Inc. (C), FL, *303*
Cross Country Consultants, Inc. (C), MD, *304*
Crowe Chizek & Co. (C), IN, *304*
Timothy D. Crowe, Jr. (R), MA, *43*
Jim Crumpley & Assoc. (C), MO, *304*
Cumberland Professional Search Inc. (C), TN, *304*
The Currier-Winn Co., Inc. (C), NJ, *305*
Curry, Telleri Group, Inc. (R), NJ, *44*
Tony Curtis & Associates (C), ON, *305*
Cusack Consulting (R), NY, *44*
Cyr Associates, Inc. (C), MA, *306*
Daggett & Kvistad (R), CA, *45*
Damon & Assoc., Inc. (C), TX, *306*
Daniel Marks Company (C), OH, *306*
The Danielson Group, Inc. (C), TX, *306*
Dapexs Consultants, Inc. (C), NY, *307*
The Dartmouth Group (R), NY, *46*
Daubenspeck & Associates, Ltd. (R), IL, *46*
Davidson, Laird & Assoc. (C), MI, *308*
Dean-MacDonald (R), OH, *47*
Debbon Recruiting Group, Inc. (C), MO, *310*
DeMatteo Associates (C), NY, *311*
R. J. Dishaw & Assoc. (R), TX, *52*
Diversified Health Search (R), PA, *52*
Diversified Search, Inc. (R), PA, *52*
Dixie Search Assoc. (C), GA, *313*
Doherty Int'l., Inc. (R), IL, *53*
Dominguez-Metz & Assoc. (R), CA, *53*
Domres Professional Search (R), WI, *53*
The Dorfman Group (C), AZ, *314*
J. H. Dugan & Assoc., Inc. (R), CA, *55*
Dumont & Co. (C), BC, *316*
The Duncan-O'Dell Group Inc. (C), TX, *316*
Dunhill Personnel of Boulder (C), CO, *319*
Dunhill of Ft. Collins, Inc. (C), CO, *319*
Dunhill Professional Search of Englewood, Inc. (C), CO, *319*
Dunhill Professional Search of Oakland (C), CA, *319*
Dunhill Professional Search of San Jose (C), CA, *319*
Dunhill Search of West Atlanta (C), GA, *320*
Dunhill Professional Search (C), MO, *321*
Dunhill Personnel of St. Andrews (C), SC, *322*
Dunn Associates (R), PA, *55*
G. L. Dykstra Assoc., Inc. (C), MI, *323*
Dynamic Staffing Network (C), IL, *324*
The E & K Group (C), NJ, *324*
Eagle Consulting Group Inc. (C), TX, *325*
EBA Group (R), NJ, *56*
Eden & Assoc., Inc. (C), PA, *326*
Effective Search, Inc. (R), IL, *57*
Elinvar (C), NC, *328*
Elite Resources Group (R), OH, *58*
Yves Elkas Inc. (R), QE, *58*
Ellis Career Consultants (C), NJ, *328*
The Elsworth Group (C), TX, *329*
Elwell & Assoc., Inc. (R), MI, *59*
Emerson & Co. (C), GA, *329*
Empowered Solutions Corp. (C), GA, *330*
Epsen, Fuller & Assoc., LLC (R), NJ, *60*
Erwin Assoc. (R), IL, *60*
Evans Transportation Search (C), ON, *331*
Exclusive Search Consultants (C), OH, *331*
ExecuSource Assoc., Inc. (C), GA, *332*
Executive Career Search (C), VA, *332*
Executive Manning Corp. (R), FL, *63*
Executive Partners Inc. (C), CT, *333*
Executive Recruiters Int'l. (C), MI, *333*
Executive Resource Inc. (C), WI, *334*
Executive Search Consultants International, Inc. (R), NY, *63*
Executive Search Group, Inc. (C), CT, *335*
Executive Search Int'l./Transearch (R), MA, *63*
Executive Search, Ltd. (C), OH, *336*
Executive Search Plus, Inc. (C), IN, *336*
The Executive Source (C), SA, *337*
Fabian Assoc. Inc. (C), NY, *338*
Fairfaxx Corp. (R), CT, *64*
Fairfield Int'l. Resources (R), NY, *65*
Paul Falcone Assoc. (R), NJ, *65*
Fisher Personnel Management Services (R), CA, *68*
James L. Fisk & Assoc. (C), MO, *342*
FitzGibbon & Assoc. (R), PA, *68*
Robert M. Flanagan & Assoc., Ltd. (R), NY, *68*
Flexible Resources, Inc. (C), CT, *342*
Flowers & Assoc. (C), OH, *342*
Ford & Assoc., Inc. (C), SC, *343*
Ford & Ford (C), MA, *343*
Fortune Personnel Consultants of Huntsville, Inc. (C), AL, *343*
F-O-R-T-U-N-E Personnel Consultants of Tampa (C), FL, *344*
F-O-R-T-U-N-E Personnel Consultants of Greenwood Village (C), CO, *344*
F-O-R-T-U-N-E Personnel Consultants of Manatee County (C), FL, *345*
F-O-R-T-U-N-E Personnel Consultants of Palm Beach (C), FL, *345*
F-O-R-T-U-N-E Personnel Consultants of Savannah, Inc. (C), GA, *345*
Fortune Personnel Consultants of Jacksonville (C), FL, *345*
Fortune Personnel Consultants of Sarasota Inc. (C), FL, *345*
Fortune of Arlington Heights (C), IL, *345*
Fortune Personnel Consultants of Bloomfield, Inc. (C), MI, *346*
F-o-r-t-u-n-e of Owensboro, Inc. (C), KY, *346*
F-O-R-T-U-N-E Personnel Consultants of Southwest Indiana (C), IN, *346*
F-O-R-T-U-N-E Personnel Consultants of St. Louis-West County (C), MO, *347*
F-O-R-T-U-N-E Personnel Consultants of Menlo Park, Inc. (C), NJ, *347*
Fortune Personnel Consultants (C), MT, *347*
F-O-R-T-U-N-E Search Consultants (C), MO, *347*
F-O-R-T-U-N-E Personnel Consultants of Bergen County Inc. (C), NJ, *347*
F-O-R-T-U-N-E of West Portland (C), OR, *348*
Fortune Personnel Consultants of Allentown, Inc. (C), PA, *348*
F-O-R-T-U-N-E Personnel Consultants of Cincinnati (C), OH, *348*
Fortune Personnel Consultants of Raleigh, Inc. (C), NC, *348*
Fortune Personnel Consultants of Greensboro, NC, Inc. (C), NC, *348*
Fortune Personnel Consultants of Hilton Head (C), SC, *349*
FORTUNE Personnel Consultants of Charleston, Inc. (C), SC, *349*
Fortune Personnel Consultants of Chattanooga Inc. (C), TN, *349*
F-O-R-T-U-N-E Personnel of Nashville (C), TN, *350*
Fortune Personnel Consultants of Plano (C), TX, *350*
F-O-R-T-U-N-E Personnel Consultants of the Tri-Cities, Inc. (C), TN, *350*
F-O-R-T-U-N-E Personnel Consultants of East Seattle (C), WA, *351*
Fortune Personnel Consultants of the Virginia Highlands (C), VA, *351*
Foster Partners (R), NY, *70*
The Fourbes Group, Inc. (C), NJ, *351*
Foy, Schneid & Daniel, Inc. (R), NY, *71*
P. N. French Assoc., Inc. (R), MA, *72*
Frye/Joure & Assoc., Inc. (C), TN, *353*
The Furst Group, Inc. (R), IL, *72*
Futures, Inc. (C), NH, *354*
GAAP Inc. (R), QE, *73*
Gabriele & Company (C), MA, *354*
Gaffney Management Consultants (R), IL, *73*
Gaming Consultants, Inc. (R), LA, *74*
Gaudry, Shink, Levasseur (R), QE, *75*
J. Gernetzke & Assoc., Inc. (C), OH, *357*
GFI Professional Staffing Services (C), NH, *357*
Gilbert & Van Campen Int'l. (R), NY, *76*
Gilbert Scott Assoc., LLC (C), MA, *357*
Gilbert Tweed Assoc. Inc. (R), NY, *76*
Joe L. Giles & Assoc. (C), MI, *357*

The Glenwood Group (C), IL, *358*
Glines Assoc., Inc. (R), IL, *77*
The GlobalSearch Group (C), TX, *359*
H. L. Goehring & Assoc., Inc. (C), OH, *359*
Goldbeck Recruiting Inc. (C), BC, *359*
Fred J. Goldsmith Assoc. (R), CA, *79*
Gomez Fregoso y Asociados (C), JAL, *360*
Goodrich & Sherwood Assoc., Inc. (R), NY, *79*
Government Contract Solutions, Inc. (C), VA, *360*
Graham & Co. (R), NJ, *80*
Granger, Counts & Assoc. (R), OH, *81*
Grant-Franks & Assoc. (C), NJ, *361*
Grantham & Co., Inc. (R), NC, *81*
R. Green & Assoc., Inc. (C), OH, *362*
Gregory, Kyle & Assoc. (C), NC, *363*
Griffith & Werner, Inc. (R), FL, *82*
Grossberg & Assoc. (R), IL, *82*
Groton Planning Group (R), ME, *82*
Wolf Gugler & Assoc. Ltd. (R), ON, *83*
GWS Partners (R), IL, *84*
The H. S. Group, Inc. (C), WI, *365*
Russ Hadick & Assoc. Inc. (C), OH, *365*
Hahn & Assoc., Inc. (C), OH, *365*
Don Hall & Assoc. (C), TX, *366*
W. L. Handler & Assoc. (R), GA, *85*
The Hanna Group (C), OH, *368*
Harcor Quest & Assoc. (R), OH, *86*
Harcourt & Assoc. (C), AB, *368*
Harcourt Group Ltd. (R), OH, *86*
Robert Harkins Assoc., Inc. (C), PA, *369*
The Harris Consulting Corp. (R), MB, *87*
Harvard Group Int'l. (R), GA, *87*
Heath/Norton Assoc., Inc. (R), NY, *89*
Hedlund Corp. (C), IL, *375*
The Heidrick Partners, Inc. (R), IL, *90*
Helfer Executive Consultants (R), TN, *91*
Heller Kil Assoc., Inc. (C), FL, *375*
The Hensge Co. (R), IL, *91*
Herring & Assoc. (C), AR, *376*
Highland Search Group, L.L.C. (R), NY, *93*
Highlander Search (C), NC, *378*
Frank P. Hill (R), MX, *93*
The Hindman Group, Inc. (C), CA, *378*
Hintz Associates (C), NY, *378*
Hire Authority, Inc. (C), MI, *378*
Holland & Assoc., Inc. (R), MI, *94*
Holloway Schulz & Partners (C), BC, *380*
Fred Hood & Assoc. (C), CA, *380*
J. G. Hood Assoc. (C), CT, *380*
William C. Houze & Co. (R), CA, *96*
Howe & Assoc. (R), PA, *97*
Robert Howe & Assoc. (R), GA, *97*
HR Inc. (C), NC, *382*
HRNI (C), MI, *383*
Hughes & Wilden Assoc. (C), PA, *383*
The Human Resource Group, Inc. (R), OH, *98*
Human Resources Personnel Agency (R), AR, *99*
The Hunt Group, Inc. (R), NC, *99*
Hunt Ltd. (C), NJ, *385*
Hunter Assoc. (C), MA, *385*
W. Hutt Management Resources Ltd. (R), ON, *100*
Hyman & Assoc. (C), TX, *386*
Industry Consultants, Inc. (C), GA, *388*
Innovative Resource Group, LLC (C), NC, *389*
Interim Executive Recruiting (C), GA, *392*
International Business Partners (C), ON, *392*
International Management Development Corp. (C), NY, *393*
International Recruiting Services (C), FL, *393*
ISC of Houston, Inc. (C), TX, *394*
J. B. Linde & Assoc. (C), MO, *395*
The J. B. Search Group (C), CA, *395*
J.D.G. y Asociados, S.A. de C.V. (R), SO, *104*
Jaeger Int'l., Inc. (C), OH, *396*
R. I. James, Inc. (C), NY, *397*
January Management Group (R), OH, *105*
JCL & Assoc. (C), FL, *397*
JDG Assoc., Ltd. (C), MD, *397*
Jeffrey Allan Co., Inc. (C), CA, *398*
Jender & Company (R), IL, *105*
Jerome & Co. (C), CA, *398*
JLI-Boston (R), MA, *106*
JM & Company (R), PA, *106*
Job-Born Candidate Selection Bureau (C), ON, *399*
L. J. Johnson & Co. (R), MI, *106*
Johnson Assoc., Inc. (C), IL, *399*
Johnson Brown Assoc., Inc. (C), IN, *400*
Jonas, Walters & Assoc., Inc. (R), WI, *107*
JRL Executive Recruiters (C), MO, *401*
Just Management Services Inc. (C), FL, *402*
K & C Assoc. (C), CA, *402*
Kaas Employment Services (C), IA, *402*
Kabana Corp. (C), MI, *402*
Martin Kartin & Co., Inc. (R), NY, *110*
Melissa Katzman, Executive Search (C), NY, *404*
A.T. Kearney Executive Search (R), IL, *111*
Keena Staffing Services (C), NY, *404*
Kehn & Gabor, Inc. (C), OH, *405*
S. D. Kelly & Assoc., Inc. (R), MA, *112*
Kelly Associates (R), PA, *112*
Kenmore Executives Inc. (C), FL, *405*
David Warwick Kennedy & Assoc. (R), BC, *112*
Kenzer Corp. (R), NY, *113*
Key Employment (C), NJ, *405*
Kimmel & Associates, Inc. (C), NC, *406*
The Kingsley Group (R), CA, *114*
Kirby Assoc. (R), PA, *115*
Kleber & Assoc. (C), WA, *407*
Knapp Consultants (R), CT, *116*
Koehler & Co. (R), WI, *116*
Fred Koffler Assoc. (R), NY, *116*
Koll-Fairfield LLC (C), CT, *408*
Korn/Ferry Int'l. (R), NY, *117*
Michael Kosmetos & Assoc., Inc. (C), OH, *408*
Kossuth & Assoc., Inc. (R), WA, *119*
Kozlin Assoc., Inc. (C), NY, *408*
John Kuhn & Assoc., Inc. (R), WI, *121*
Kuhn Med-Tech (C), CA, *409*
D. Kunkle & Assoc. (C), IL, *410*
Kutt, Inc. (C), CO, *410*
L & L Assoc. (C), CA, *410*
L. Patrick Group (R), NJ, *122*
Marvin Laba & Assoc. (R), CA, *122*
Laboratory Resource Group (C), MA, *411*
Lamon + Stuart + Michaels Inc. (R), ON, *124*
Lange & Assoc., Inc. (C), IN, *412*
Lanken-Kimball-Therrell & Assoc. (C), GA, *412*
R. H. Larsen & Assoc., Inc. (R), FL, *125*
Jack B. Larsen & Assoc., Inc. (C), PA, *413*
Madeleine Lav & Assoc. (C), CA, *413*
Lawrence James Assoc. of Florida, Inc. (C), FL, *414*
Leader Search Inc. (R), AB, *127*
The Lear Group, Inc. (R), OH, *127*
The Conrad Lee Co. Inc. (R), FL, *127*
Lee Management Group Inc. (C), NJ, *416*
V. J. Lehman & Assoc., Inc. (R), CO, *127*
Leith & Assoc., Inc. (C), OH, *416*
Lekan & Assoc., Inc. (R), OH, *128*
Lemming/LeVan, Inc. (R), GA, *128*
Jacques LePage Executive Search Inc. (R), QE, *128*
Leslie Kavanagh Assoc., Inc. (C), NY, *416*
J. E. Lessner Assoc., Inc. (R), MI, *128*
Lewis Companies Inc. (R), ON, *129*
LifeWork, Inc. (C), TX, *418*
J. H. Lindell & Co. (C), CA, *418*
Linden Group, Inc. (C), NC, *418*
Livingston, Robert & Co. (R), CT, *130*
Logistics Management Resources, Inc. (R), NY, *131*
London Executive Consultants Inc. (C), ON, *420*
Lord & Albus Co. (C), TX, *420*
Bruce Lowery & Assoc. (C), MI, *420*
Lucas Assoc. (C), GA, *421*
Lucas Group (C), NY, *421*
Lutz Associates (C), CT, *421*
M H Executive Search Group (C), TX, *422*
M/J/A Partners (R), IL, *133*
Maglio & Co., Inc. (R), WI, *134*
Magnum Search (C), IL, *422*
The Mallard Group (C), IN, *423*
Management Alliance Group, Inc. (R), NJ, *134*
Management Association Network (C), WI, *424*
Management Catalysts (R), NJ, *134*
Management Recruiters of Birmingham-South, Inc. (C), AL, *438*
Management Recruiters of Sedona (C), AZ, *438*
Management Recruiters of Decatur, LLC (C), AL, *438*
Management Recruiters of Berkeley (C), CA, *439*
Management Recruiters of Fresno (C), CA, *440*
Management Recruiters of Clovis (C), CA, *440*
Management Recruiters of Laguna Hills (C), CA, *440*
Management Recruiters Dana Point (C), CA, *440*
Management Recruiters, Inland Empire Agency (C), CA, *441*
Management Recruiters of Pleasanton (C), CA, *441*

Management Recruiters of Winsted, Inc. (C), CT, *442*
Management Recruiters of Milford Inc. (C), CT, *442*
Management Recruiters of Pensacola (C), FL, *444*
Management Recruiters of Duluth (C), GA, *445*
Management Recruiters of North Fulton (C), GA, *445*
Management Recruiters of Forsyth County (C), GA, *445*
Management Recruiters of Atlanta West, Inc. (C), GA, *445*
Management Recruiters of Venice, Inc. (C), FL, *445*
Management Recruiters of Atlanta (C), GA, *445*
Management Recruiters of Sandy Springs (C), GA, *446*
Management Recruiters of Marietta, Inc. (C), GA, *446*
Management Recruiters of Springfield, Inc. (C), IL, *447*
Management Recruiters of Chicago-North Shore (C), IL, *447*
Management Recruiters of Noblesville, Inc. (C), IN, *448*
Management Recruiters of Indianapolis (C), IN, *448*
Management Recruiters of South Bend (C), IN, *448*
Management Recruiters of Rockville (C), MD, *450*
Management Recruiters of Muskegon (C), MI, *451*
Management Recruiters of Livonia (C), MI, *451*
Management Recruiters of Baltimore (C), MD, *451*
Management Recruiters of Southeastern Michigan (C), MI, *451*
Management Recruiters of Dearborn, Inc. (C), MI, *451*
Management Recruiters of Woodbury (C), MN, *452*
Management Recruiters of Lake Tahoe, NV (C), NV, *453*
Management Recruiters of Medford, N.J. (C), NJ, *453*
Management Recruiters of Fayetteville (C), NC, *455*
Management Recruiters of Asheville, Inc. (C), NC, *455*
Management Recruiters of Winston-Salem (C), NC, *457*
Management Recruiters of Dayton, Inc. (C), OH, *457*
Management Recruiters of Columbus (C), OH, *457*
Management Recruiters of Cincinnati/Sharonville, Inc. (C), OH, *457*
Management Recruiters of Easton, PA (C), PA, *458*
Management Recruiters of Bethlehem, PA (C), PA, *458*
Management Recruiters of Cherry Hill (C), PA, *459*
Management Recruiters of Puerto Rico (C), PR, *460*
Management Recruiters of North Charleston (C), SC, *460*
Management Recruiters of Florence (C), SC, *460*
Management Recruiters of Chattanooga-Brainerd, Inc. (C), TN, *461*
Management Recruiters of Franklin, Inc. (C), TN, *461*
Management Recruiters of Columbia, Tennessee (C), TN, *461*
Management Recruiters Dallas North (MRDN) (C), TX, *462*
Management Recruiters of LBJ Park/Dallas (C), TX, *462*
Management Recruiters of Sugar Land Inc. (C), TX, *464*
Management Recruiters of Appleton (C), WI, *465*
Management Recruiters of Milwaukee-North (C), WI, *466*
Management Recruiters of Madison, Inc. (C), WI, *466*
Management Recruiters of Janesville, Inc. (C), WI, *466*
Management Solutions, Inc. (C), WA, *468*
MARBL Consultants, Inc. (C), WI, *469*
Mark III Personnel, Inc. (C), NC, *470*
Markent Personnel, Inc. (C), WI, *470*
Paula Marks Inc. (R), NY, *136*
Marshall-Alan Assoc., Inc. (C), NY, *471*
Marsteller Wilcox Assoc. (C), IL, *471*
The Martin Group (R), CA, *137*
The Martwick Group, Inc. (C), OR, *472*
Richard L. Mather & Assoc. (C), CT, *472*
Matté & Company, Inc. (R), CT, *138*
G. P. Mattocks & Associates (C), NC, *473*
Mayhall Search Group, Inc. (C), IN, *473*
Tom McCall Executive Search (C), IL, *473*
McCooe & Assoc., Inc. (R), NJ, *140*
The Paul McDaniel Co. (C), TN, *474*
Robert E. McGrath & Assoc. (R), CT, *141*
McInturff & Assoc., Inc. (C), MA, *474*
McIntyre Management Resources (C), ON, *474*
Medical Executive Search Assoc., Inc. (C), AZ, *477*
MedQuest Assoc. (C), CO, *478*
Merit Professional Search, Inc. (C), TN, *479*
Merrick & Moore (C), NC, *479*
MESA, Inc. (R), CO, *143*
META/MAT, Ltd. (R), NJ, *144*
Walter Meyer & Assoc. (R), NY, *144*
Michael Assoc. (R), IL, *144*
Michael Wayne Recruiters (C), IL, *480*
Michael/Merrill (C), KS, *481*
Michaels & Moere (C), WI, *481*
Lou Michaels Assoc., Inc. (C), MI, *481*
Midland Consultants (C), OH, *481*
Miller Denver (C), CO, *482*
Danette Milne Corporate Search Inc. (C), ON, *482*
The Montgomery Group, Inc. (C), TN, *484*
Moore Research Assoc. (R), NJ, *147*
Morgan Int'l., Inc. (R), IL, *147*
Morton, McCorkle & Assoc. Inc. (R), MO, *147*
MPA Executive Search Inc. (R), QE, *148*
The Mulshine Co., Inc. (R), NJ, *149*
The Mulshine Company, Ltd. (R), NY, *149*
Murphy Partners Int'l. (R), IL, *150*
N.A.P. Executive Services (Canada) Inc. (C), ON, *488*
NaTek Corp. (C), NY, *488*
National Computerized Employment Service, Inc. (C), PA, *489*
National Corporate Consultants, Inc. (C), IN, *489*
National Metal Services Corp. (C), IN, *489*
Nationwide Personnel Placement, Inc. (C), OH, *490*
NaviSearch (C), GA, *490*
NDI Services (R), MI, *151*
New Directions, Inc. (C), IL, *492*
New Venture Development, Inc. (C), CA, *492*
The Niemond Corp. (R), CA, *152*
NMC & Kay Int'l. (R), CO, *152*
Noll Human Resource Services (C), NE, *494*
W. D. Nolte & Company (R), CT, *152*
Norman Broadbent Int'l., Inc. (R), NY, *152*
John B. Norris & Assoc., Inc. (C), MD, *495*
Norris Agency (C), TX, *495*
North American Recruiters, Inc. (R), MN, *153*
North Coast Meridian (C), NY, *496*
Northland Employment Services Inc. (C), MN, *496*
Nuessle, Kurdziel & Weiss, Inc. (R), PA, *153*
O'Brien & Bell (R), OH, *153*
O'Connor, O'Connor, Lordi, Ltd. (R), PA, *154*
O'Keefe & Assoc., Inc. (R), CT, *154*
Dennis P. O'Toole & Assoc. Inc. (R), NY, *154*
Oliver & Rozner Assoc., Inc. (R), NY, *155*
Omega Search, Inc. (C), NC, *498*
Open Concepts (C), CA, *499*
Organization Resources Inc. (R), MA, *157*
Orion Int'l. Consulting Group, Inc. (C), NC, *499*
Overton Consulting (R), WI, *157*
LaMonte Owens, Inc. (R), PA, *157*
The P & L Group (C), NY, *500*
Pacific Advisory Service, Inc. (C), IL, *501*
Pacific Coast Recruiting (C), CA, *501*
Packaging Personnel Co., Ltd. (C), WI, *501*
T. Page & Assoc. (C), TX, *502*
The Pailin Group Professional Search Consultants (R), TX, *158*
Kirk Palmer & Assoc., Inc. (R), NY, *158*
Jim Parham & Assoc., Inc. (R), FL, *159*
Parker, McFadden & Assoc. (C), GA, *503*
Largent Parks & Partners (C), TX, *503*
Michael W. Parres & Assoc. (R), MI, *159*
Partners in Recruiting (C), IL, *503*
Rick Pascal & Assoc., Inc. (C), NJ, *504*
Pasona Canada, Inc. (C), ON, *504*
Pathways Int'l. (C), CT, *505*
PERC, Ltd. (C), AZ, *506*
Performance Resources, Inc. (C), RI, *507*
The Perkins Group (R), NC, *162*
PersoNet, Inc. (C), FL, *507*
Personnel Assoc. (C), NC, *508*

Personnel, Inc. (C), AL, *508*
Personnel Management Group (C), MB, *508*
Personnel Unlimited/Executive Search (C), WA, *509*
Petrie Partners, Inc. (R), FL, *163*
Petruzzi Assoc. (C), NJ, *509*
Phase II Management (R), CT, *164*
Phelps Personnel Assoc., Inc. (C), SC, *510*
Phillips Int'l., Inc. (C), SC, *510*
Phillips Personnel/Search (C), CO, *510*
Philo & Associates (C), GA, *511*
Gregory D. Pickens (C), TX, *511*
Pinton Forrest & Madden/EMA Partners Int'l. (R), BC, *165*
Pioneer Executive Consultants (C), ON, *512*
R. L. Plimpton Assoc., Inc. (R), CO, *165*
The Polen Group (C), PA, *514*
Preferred Professional Recruiters (C), OH, *516*
PricewaterhouseCoopers Executive Search (R), MX, *168*
Prichard Kymen Inc. (R), AB, *168*
Prime Management Group Inc. (C), ON, *518*
Probe Technology (C), PA, *519*
Procurement Resources (C), MD, *520*
Professional Employment Group (C), MD, *520*
Professional Personnel Services (C), IA, *520*
Professional Persons Career Services (C), NY, *521*
Professional Research Services, Inc. (R), IL, *169*
Professions, Inc. (C), OH, *523*
ProSearch, Inc. (C), OH, *524*
ProTech Nationwide Staffing, Inc. (C), NY, *525*
PSD Group, Inc. (C), CA, *525*
Quality Control Recruiters (C), CT, *526*
Quality Search (C), IN, *526*
R M Associates (R), OH, *171*
R. C. Services (C), TX, *528*
R. J. Associates (C), NY, *528*
R.A.N. Assoc., Inc. (C), OH, *528*
R/K International Inc. (R), CT, *171*
Raines Int'l. Inc. (R), NY, *171*
Rand Assoc. (R), ME, *171*
Recruiting Services Group, Inc. (C), TN, *532*
The Recruitment Group, Inc. (C), NY, *532*
Cedric L. Reese Inc. (C), CA, *533*
The Regis Group, Ltd. (R), GA, *174*
Reid Ellis Assoc. Inc. (C), ON, *533*
Reinecke & Assoc. (C), NJ, *533*
Renaissance Resources, LLC (R), VA, *174*
Resource Inc. (R), MA, *175*
Resource Recruiting (C), NH, *534*
L. J. Reszotko & Assoc. (C), IL, *535*
The Retail Network (C), MA, *535*
Retail Recruiters/Spectrum Consultants, Inc. (C), PA, *535*
S. Reyman & Assoc., Ltd. (R), IL, *176*
Russell Reynolds Assoc., Inc. (R), NY, *176*
Reynolds Consulting Int'l. (R), ON, *177*
RIC Corp. (R), FL, *177*
Terry Richards (C), OH, *536*
Riddle & McGrath LLC (R), GA, *178*
Right/McKee Consulting Group (C), TX, *537*
Riley Cole (C), CA, *537*
River Region Personnel, Inc. (C), LA, *538*
RML Assoc. (C), PA, *538*
Roberson & Co. (C), AZ, *538*
Robert William James & Assoc. (C), OR, *539*
J. P. Roddy Consultants (C), PA, *540*
R. A. Rodriguez & Assoc., Inc. (C), TX, *540*
ROI Assoc. (R), NY, *180*
Rolland Ressources Humaines Inc. (R), QE, *181*
Rollins & Assoc. (C), CA, *541*
Romano McAvoy Assoc., Inc. (C), NY, *544*
Roth Young Executive Search (C), TX, *546*
Roth Young Personnel Service of Detroit, Inc. (C), MI, *546*
Roth Young Personnel Services of Washington, DC (C), MD, *546*
Roth Young Executive Search of Milwaukee (C), WI, *547*
Rothrock Associates, Inc. (C), NC, *547*
Rowland Assoc. (C), CA, *547*
RSMR, Inc. (R), IL, *182*
RTE Search (C), NJ, *547*
Rushmore • Judge Inc. (R), ON, *183*
S.D.P. Contract Recruiters (C), NJ, *550*
R. S. Sadow Assoc. (C), NJ, *550*
Sage Employment Recruiters (C), IN, *550*
Sales Consultants of Birmingham (C), AL, *555*
Sales Consultants Int'l. of Oakland (C), CA, *556*
Sales Consultants of Chico (C), CA, *556*
Sales Consultants of Ft. Lauderdale, Inc. (C), FL, *557*
Sales Consultants of Cherokee (C), GA, *558*
Sales Consultants Bridgewater, Inc. (C), NJ, *560*
Sales Consultants of Westchester-South, Inc. (C), NY, *561*
Sales Consultants of Princeton, Inc. (C), NJ, *561*
Sales Consultants of Pittsburgh (C), PA, *562*
Sales Consultants King of Prussia (C), PA, *562*
Salveson Stetson Group, Inc. (R), PA, *184*
Sanford Rose Assoc. - Mobile (C), AL, *565*
Sanford Rose Assoc. - Effingham (C), IL, *566*
Sanford Rose Assoc. - Athens (C), GA, *566*
Sanford Rose Assoc. - Rockford (C), IL, *567*
Sanford Rose Assoc. - Orland Park (C), IL, *567*
Sanford Rose Assoc. - Cedar Rapids (C), IA, *567*
Sanford Rose Assoc. - Rockville (C), MD, *567*
Sanford Rose Assoc. - Rochester (C), MI, *568*
Sanford Rose Assoc. - Gastonia (C), NC, *568*
Sanford Rose Assoc. - Burlington, NC (C), NC, *569*
Sanford Rose Assoc. - Canton (C), OH, *569*
Sanford Rose Assoc. - Greensboro (C), NC, *569*
Sanford Rose Assoc. - Doylestown (C), PA, *570*
Sanford Rose Assoc. - Portland (C), OR, *570*
Schall Executive Search Partners (R), MN, *185*
Schattle & Duquette (C), RI, *571*
The Schatz Company (C), MO, *571*
Schenck & Assoc. SC (C), WI, *572*
Robert Scott Assoc. (C), NJ, *573*
Scott Executive Search, Inc. (R), NY, *186*
Scott-Thaler Assoc. Agency, Inc. (C), CA, *573*
Search & Recruit Int'l. (C), VA, *573*
Search Assoc., Inc. (C), NJ, *574*
Search By Design (C), AZ, *574*
Search Northwest Assoc. (C), OR, *576*
Search Plus Int'l.-Ohio (C), OH, *576*
Search South, Inc. (C), AL, *576*
SearchOne, Inc. (C), AR, *577*
Select Services (C), IL, *578*
Selective Management Services, Inc. (C), FL, *578*
Selective Recruiting Assoc., Inc. (C), MI, *578*
Selig Executive Search (C), NH, *579*
M. B. Shattuck & Assoc., Inc. (R), CA, *189*
Sherwood Lehman Massucco, Inc. (R), CA, *189*
Shey-Harding Assoc. Inc. (C), CA, *580*
Shinn & Assoc. (R), CA, *189*
E. L. Shore & Assoc. (R), ON, *190*
Shore Asociados Ejecutivos, S. A. de C.V. (R), MX, *190*
The Shotland Group (R), CA, *190*
SHS of Allentown (C), PA, *580*
Larry Siegel & Assoc. (R), WA, *191*
Peter Siegel & Co. (C), MA, *581*
Sill Technical Assoc., Inc. (C), PA, *581*
Singleton & Assoc. (C), VA, *582*
Tom Sloan & Assoc., Inc. (C), WI, *583*
Smith & Assoc. (C), FL, *583*
Smith & Laue Search (R), OR, *193*
Smith & Syberg, Inc. (R), IN, *193*
Smith Hanley Assoc., Inc. (C), NY, *584*
Smith James Group, Inc. (R), GA, *194*
Snelling Search (C), IL, *585*
Snelling Search (C), IL, *586*
Soderlund Assoc. Inc. (R), OH, *194*
Solutions Group (R), AL, *195*
Stephen M. Sonis Assoc. (R), MA, *195*
Southern Recruiters & Consultants, Inc. (C), SC, *587*
SPC Symcox Personnel Consultants (C), TX, *588*
Spear-Izzo Assoc., LLC (C), PA, *588*
SpencerStuart (R), NY, *196*
Kenn Spinrad Inc. (C), PA, *589*
Sprout/Standish, Inc. (C), NH, *589*
Staff Resources, Inc. (C), SC, *590*
Stanewick, Hart & Assoc., Inc. (C), FL, *591*
Stanton Chase Int'l. (R), MD, *198*
Star Search Consultants (C), ON, *591*

Steeple Resources & Consulting (R), NJ, *199*
The Stelton Group, Inc. (C), NJ, *592*
Sterling Int'l. Management Recruitment, Ltd. Inc. (C), NC, *592*
Stewart Assoc. (C), PA, *593*
Stewart/Greene & Co. of The Triad, Inc. (C), NC, *594*
Charles Stickler Assoc. (R), PA, *201*
Linford E. Stiles & Assoc., L.L.C. (R), NH, *201*
STM Assoc. (R), UT, *201*
Allan Stolee Inc. (R), FL, *201*
Stone Enterprises Ltd. (C), IL, *594*
Stoneburner Assoc., Inc. (C), KS, *594*
Stoopen Asociados, S.C./EMA Partners Int'l. (R), MX, *202*
Storfer & Assoc. (C), NY, *595*
Strategic Advancement Inc. (R), NJ, *202*
Strategic Assoc., Inc. (C), TX, *595*
Strategic Resources (C), WA, *595*
Success Seekers Connection (C), FL, *596*
Summerfield Assoc., Inc. (C), TN, *596*
Summit Executive Search Consultants, Inc. (R), FL, *204*
Summit Group Int'l., Inc. (R), GA, *204*
Ron Sunshine & Assoc. (C), IL, *597*
Swift & Assoc. (C), ME, *597*
Synergy Solutions, Ltd. (C), WA, *597*
System 1 Search (C), CA, *598*
Systems Research Inc. (SRI) (C), IL, *598*
T E M Assoc. (C), WI, *599*
S. Tanner & Assoc. Inc. (C), ON, *599*
M. L. Tawney & Assoc. (C), TX, *600*
The TBI Group (R), PA, *207*
TCM Enterprises (C), MD, *600*
Teamsearch, Inc. (C), MI, *601*
Techaid Inc. (C), QE, *601*
Technical Skills Consulting Inc. (R), ON, *207*
Technifind Int'l. (C), TX, *602*
Technology Consultants Int'l. (C), CA, *603*
Techstaff Inc. (C), WI, *603*
Tekworx, Inc. (C), OK, *604*
Telford, Adams & Alexander (R), CA, *208*
Thomas & Assoc. of Michigan (C), MI, *606*
Thomas Lyle & Co. (C), IL, *606*
Thomas Mangum Co. (R), CA, *208*
Thorne, Brieger Assoc., Inc. (R), NY, *209*
The Tidewater Group Inc. (C), CT, *607*
Tierney Assoc., Inc. (R), PA, *209*
Tirocchi, Wright, Inc. (R), CA, *209*
TNS Partners, Inc. (R), TX, *209*
TPS Staffing Solutions (C), IN, *608*
Trambley the Recruiter (C), NM, *608*
Trans-United Consultants Ltd. (C), ON, *608*
Transportation Recruiting Services, Inc. (C), MS, *608*
Traynor Confidential, Ltd. (C), NY, *609*
TRS Staffing Solutions Inc. (C), OH, *610*
The Truman Agency (C), CA, *610*
TSI Group/TSI Staffing Services (C), ON, *610*
W. G. Tucker & Assoc. (R), PA, *211*
U.S. Search (C), VA, *610*
Unlimited Staffing Solutions, Inc. (C), MI, *611*
Valentine & Assoc. (C), IL, *611*
VanMaldegiam Assoc., Inc. (R), IL, *213*
Vaughan & Co. (C), CA, *612*
Verkamp-Joyce Assoc., Inc. (R), IL, *213*
Vincenty & Co. (C), OH, *612*
The Wabash Group (C), IN, *613*
Gordon Wahls Executive Search (C), PA, *613*
Kelly Walker Assoc. (C), TX, *614*
Linda Walter & Associes (C), QE, *615*
Warner & Assoc., Inc. (C), OH, *615*
Warren Executive Services (C), GA, *616*
Waveland Int'l. (R), IL, *216*
Wayne Assoc., Inc. (C), VA, *616*
The Wayne Group, Ltd. (C), NY, *616*
S. B. Webster & Associates (R), MA, *217*
Wegner & Assoc. (C), WI, *617*
Henry Welker & Assoc. (C), MI, *618*
Wellington Management Group (R), PA, *217*
R. A. Wells Co. (C), GA, *618*
Werbin Assoc. Executive Search, Inc. (C), NY, *618*
Westfields Int'l., Inc. (C), NY, *619*
Whitehead & Assoc., Inc. (C), MO, *620*
John R. Williams & Assoc., Inc. (C), NC, *621*
John Williams & Assoc. (C), TX, *621*
Williams Recruiting, Inc. (C), WA, *621*
Williamsburg Group (C), NJ, *621*
Willis & Assoc. (R), OH, *221*
The Wilmington Group (C), NC, *622*
Wilson & Assoc. Int'l. Inc. (C), FL, *622*
Wilson McLeran, Inc. (C), CT, *622*
Wilson Personnel, Inc. (C), NC, *622*
The Winchester Group (R), CA, *222*
The Windham Group (R), OH, *222*
Wing Tips & Pumps, Inc. (C), MI, *623*
WMD inc. (C), NJ, *623*
Wojdula & Assoc., Ltd. (R), WI, *223*
S. R. Wolman Assoc., Inc. (R), NY, *224*
Wood West & Partners Inc. (C), BC, *624*
Woodmoor Group (C), CO, *624*
Bruce G. Woods Executive Search (R), TX, *224*
Jim Woodson & Assoc., Inc. (C), MS, *624*
The Woodstone Consulting Company, Inc. (R), CO, *224*
Working Relationships, Inc. (C), MN, *624*
R. S. Wyatt Assoc., Inc. (R), TX, *225*
John Wylie Assoc., Inc. (C), OK, *625*
Xagas & Assoc. (R), IL, *226*
The Zammataro Company (R), OH, *226*
The Zarkin Group, Inc. (R), NY, *226*
Zen Zen Int'l. Inc. (C), MB, *627*

03.1 Purchasing, inventory management

A.M.C.R., Inc. (C), OH, *232*
Accelerated Data Decision, Inc. (C), NJ, *233*
Access/Resources, Inc. (C), MA, *234*
Accountants Executive Search (C), CT, *234*
AGRI-associates (C), MO, *242*
Tom Allison Assoc. (C), NM, *245*
Alpha Executive Search (C), AL, *245*
Alpha Search (C), FL, *246*
Peter W. Ambler Co. (R), TX, *5*
American Logistics Consultants, Inc. (C), IL, *247*
Anderson Industrial Assoc., Inc. (C), GA, *250*
Applied Resources, Inc. (C), MN, *252*
Charles P. Aquavella & Assoc. (C), TX, *252*
Artgo, Inc. (R), OH, *7*
The Ascher Group (R), NJ, *7*
The Associates, HR Search Executives, Inc. (C), OK, *254*
Austin Michaels, Ltd., Inc. (C), AZ, *256*
Availability Personnel Consultants (C), NH, *257*
Baldwin & Assoc. (C), OH, *258*
Paul C. Banks Assoc. (C), GA, *259*
Barone Assoc. (C), NJ, *259*
Battalia Winston Int'l./The Euram Consultants Group (R), NY, *13*
William Bell Assoc., Inc. (C), NJ, *263*
Benford & Assoc., Inc. (C), MI, *264*
C. Berger And Company (R), IL, *16*
Billington & Assoc. (R), CA, *17*
Biomedical Search Consultants (R), CT, *17*
Howard Bowen Consulting (C), FL, *270*
Bright Search/Professional Staffing (C), MN, *274*
Britt Assoc., Inc. (C), IL, *274*
C. M. Management Services, Inc. (R), KY, *26*
The C.P.R. Group (C), NJ, *278*
Campbell, Edgar Inc. (C), BC, *280*
J. P. Canon Assoc. (C), NY, *280*
Carnegie Resources, Inc. (C), NC, *284*
Michael J. Cavanagh & Assoc. Inc. (R), ON, *31*
CJA-The Adler Group, Inc. (R), CA, *35*
Clark Executive Search (C), NY, *292*
Continental Search Assoc. (C), OH, *298*
Corporate Environment Ltd. (R), IL, *41*
Corporate Image Group (C), TN, *300*
Corporate Management Services (C), PA, *300*
Corporate Select Int'l., Ltd. (C), IL, *301*
Craig Affiliates, Inc. (C), TX, *302*
Timothy D. Crowe, Jr. (R), MA, *43*
The Currier-Winn Co., Inc. (C), NJ, *305*
Cyr Associates, Inc. (C), MA, *306*
Daggett & Kvistad (R), CA, *45*
Davidson, Laird & Assoc. (C), MI, *308*
Diversified Search, Inc. (R), PA, *52*
Domres Professional Search (R), WI, *53*
The Dorfman Group (C), AZ, *314*
Dumont & Co. (C), BC, *316*
The Duncan-O'Dell Group Inc. (C), TX, *316*
Dunhill Personnel of Boulder (C), CO, *319*
Dunhill of Ft. Collins, Inc. (C), CO, *319*
Dunhill Search of West Atlanta (C), GA, *320*
Dunhill Personnel of St. Andrews (C), SC, *322*
G. L. Dykstra Assoc., Inc. (C), MI, *323*
EBA Group (R), NJ, *56*
Eden & Assoc., Inc. (C), PA, *326*
Elinvar (C), NC, *328*
Elite Resources Group (R), OH, *58*
The Elsworth Group (C), TX, *329*

Evans Transportation Search (C), ON, *331*
Executive Career Search (C), VA, *332*
Executive Partners Inc. (C), CT, *333*
Executive Search, Ltd. (C), OH, *336*
Fairfield Int'l. Resources (R), NY, *65*
Flexible Resources, Inc. (C), CT, *342*
Flowers & Assoc. (C), OH, *342*
Fortune Personnel Consultants of Huntsville, Inc. (C), AL, *343*
F-O-R-T-U-N-E Personnel Consultants of Tampa (C), FL, *344*
F-O-R-T-U-N-E Personnel Consultants of Greenwood Village (C), CO, *344*
F-O-R-T-U-N-E Personnel Consultants of Manatee County (C), FL, *345*
F-O-R-T-U-N-E Personnel Consultants of Savannah, Inc. (C), GA, *345*
Fortune Personnel Consultants of Sarasota Inc. (C), FL, *345*
Fortune of Arlington Heights (C), IL, *345*
Fortune Personnel Consultants of Bloomfield, Inc. (C), MI, *346*
F-o-r-t-u-n-e of Owensboro, Inc. (C), KY, *346*
F-O-R-T-U-N-E Personnel Consultants of Menlo Park, Inc. (C), NJ, *347*
Fortune Personnel Consultants (C), MT, *347*
F-O-R-T-U-N-E Personnel Consultants of Cincinnati (C), OH, *348*
Fortune Personnel Consultants of Greensboro, NC, Inc. (C), NC, *348*
Fortune Personnel Consultants of Hilton Head (C), SC, *349*
Fortune Personnel Consultants of Chattanooga Inc. (C), TN, *349*
FORTUNE Personnel Consultants of Charleston, Inc. (C), SC, *349*
Fortune Personnel Consultants of the Virginia Highlands (C), VA, *351*
Foster Partners (R), NY, *70*
The Fourbes Group, Inc. (C), NJ, *351*
P. N. French Assoc., Inc. (R), MA, *72*
Gaming Consultants, Inc. (R), LA, *74*
J. Gernetzke & Assoc., Inc. (C), OH, *357*
Joe L. Giles & Assoc. (C), MI, *357*
Goldbeck Recruiting Inc. (C), BC, *359*
Gomez Fregoso y Asociados (C), JAL, *360*
Government Contract Solutions, Inc. (C), VA, *360*
Graham & Co. (R), NJ, *80*
Grantham & Co., Inc. (R), NC, *81*
R. Green & Assoc., Inc. (C), OH, *362*
Wolf Gugler & Assoc. Ltd. (R), ON, *83*
Robert Harkins Assoc., Inc. (C), PA, *369*
Heath/Norton Assoc., Inc. (R), NY, *89*
The Heidrick Partners, Inc. (R), IL, *90*
Heller Kil Assoc., Inc. (C), FL, *375*
Herring & Assoc. (C), AR, *376*
Highland Search Group, L.L.C. (R), NY, *93*
Holland & Assoc., Inc. (R), MI, *94*
Hughes & Wilden Assoc. (C), PA, *383*
Hunt Ltd. (C), NJ, *385*
Hunter Assoc. (C), MA, *385*
Industry Consultants, Inc. (C), GA, *388*
International Management Development Corp. (C), NY, *393*
International Recruiting Services (C), FL, *393*
ISC of Houston, Inc. (C), TX, *394*
J. B. Linde & Assoc. (C), MO, *395*
The J. B. Search Group (C), CA, *395*
Jaeger Int'l., Inc. (C), OH, *396*
R. I. James, Inc. (C), NY, *397*
Johnson Assoc., Inc. (C), IL, *399*
A.T. Kearney Executive Search (R), IL, *111*
Kehn & Gabor, Inc. (C), OH, *405*
David Warwick Kennedy & Assoc. (R), BC, *112*
Kenzer Corp. (R), NY, *113*
Key Employment (C), NJ, *405*
Kimmel & Associates, Inc. (C), NC, *406*
Koll-Fairfield LLC (C), CT, *408*
D. Kunkle & Assoc. (C), IL, *410*
Kutt, Inc. (C), CO, *410*
L & L Assoc. (C), CA, *410*
Marvin Laba & Assoc. (R), CA, *122*
Lange & Assoc., Inc. (C), IN, *412*
The Lear Group, Inc. (R), OH, *127*
Lemming/LeVan, Inc. (R), GA, *128*
Leslie Kavanagh Assoc., Inc. (C), NY, *416*
J. H. Lindell & Co. (C), CA, *418*
Livingston, Robert & Co. (R), CT, *130*
Logistics Management Resources, Inc. (R), NY, *131*
Lucas Group (C), NY, *421*
The Mallard Group (C), IN, *423*
Management Association Network (C), WI, *424*
Management Recruiters of Fresno (C), CA, *440*
Management Recruiters of Muskegon (C), MI, *451*
Management Recruiters of Medford, N.J. (C), NJ, *453*
Management Recruiters of Asheville, Inc. (C), NC, *455*
Management Recruiters of Columbia, Tennessee (C), TN, *461*
Management Recruiters of Madison, Inc. (C), WI, *466*
Marshall-Alan Assoc., Inc. (C), NY, *471*
G. P. Mattocks & Associates (C), NC, *473*
McInturff & Assoc., Inc. (C), MA, *474*
McIntyre Management Resources (C), ON, *474*
Merit Professional Search, Inc. (C), TN, *479*
META/MAT, Ltd. (R), NJ, *144*
Michael Assoc. (R), IL, *144*
Michael Wayne Recruiters (C), IL, *480*
Morgan Int'l., Inc. (R), IL, *147*
National Metal Services Corp. (C), IN, *489*
NDI Services (R), MI, *151*
Norman Broadbent Int'l., Inc. (R), NY, *152*
North Coast Meridian (C), NY, *496*
Dennis P. O'Toole & Assoc. Inc. (R), NY, *154*
The P & L Group (C), NY, *500*
Pacific Advisory Service, Inc. (C), IL, *501*
T. Page & Assoc. (C), TX, *502*
The Pailin Group Professional Search Consultants (R), TX, *158*
Kirk Palmer & Assoc., Inc. (R), NY, *158*
Parker, McFadden & Assoc. (C), GA, *503*
Largent Parks & Partners (C), TX, *503*
Pathways Int'l. (C), CT, *505*
Phelps Personnel Assoc., Inc. (C), SC, *510*
Pinton Forrest & Madden/EMA Partners Int'l. (R), BC, *165*
Preferred Professional Recruiters (C), OH, *516*
Prime Management Group Inc. (C), ON, *518*
Procurement Resources (C), MD, *520*
Professional Employment Group (C), MD, *520*
Professional Personnel Services (C), IA, *520*
R. C. Services (C), TX, *528*
R.A.N. Assoc., Inc. (C), OH, *528*
Resource Inc. (R), MA, *175*
Reynolds Consulting Int'l. (R), ON, *177*
ROI Assoc. (R), NY, *180*
Rollins & Assoc. (C), CA, *541*
Romano McAvoy Assoc., Inc. (C), NY, *544*
Sales Consultants Int'l. of Oakland (C), CA, *556*
Sales Consultants of Pittsburgh (C), PA, *562*
Sanford Rose Assoc. - Athens (C), GA, *566*
Sanford Rose Assoc. - Rochester (C), MI, *568*
Sanford Rose Assoc. - Gastonia (C), NC, *568*
Sanford Rose Assoc. - Greensboro (C), NC, *569*
Sanford Rose Assoc. - Doylestown (C), PA, *570*
Schenck & Assoc. SC (C), WI, *572*
Scott Executive Search, Inc. (R), NY, *186*
Scott-Thaler Assoc. Agency, Inc. (C), CA, *573*
Selig Executive Search (C), NH, *579*
SHS of Allentown (C), PA, *580*
Sill Technical Assoc., Inc. (C), PA, *581*
Singleton & Assoc. (C), VA, *582*
Smith & Assoc. (C), FL, *583*
SpencerStuart (R), NY, *196*
Kenn Spinrad Inc. (C), PA, *589*
Stanton Chase Int'l. (R), MD, *198*
Steeple Resources & Consulting (R), NJ, *199*
The Stelton Group, Inc. (C), NJ, *592*
Stewart Assoc. (C), PA, *593*
Linford E. Stiles & Assoc., L.L.C. (R), NH, *201*
Stoneburner Assoc., Inc. (C), KS, *594*
Storfer & Assoc. (C), NY, *595*
Strategic Assoc., Inc. (C), TX, *595*
Summerfield Assoc., Inc. (C), TN, *596*
Summit Executive Search Consultants, Inc. (R), FL, *204*
Ron Sunshine & Assoc. (C), IL, *597*
Swift & Assoc. (C), ME, *597*
Synergy Solutions, Ltd. (C), WA, *597*
S. Tanner & Assoc. Inc. (C), ON, *599*
Teamsearch, Inc. (C), MI, *601*
Technical Skills Consulting Inc. (R), ON, *207*
Technology Consultants Int'l. (C), CA, *603*
Tekworx, Inc. (C), OK, *604*
The Tidewater Group Inc. (C), CT, *607*

TPS Staffing Solutions (C), IN, *608*
Trans-United Consultants Ltd. (C), ON, *608*
U.S. Search (C), VA, *610*
Valentine & Assoc. (C), IL, *611*
Warren Executive Services (C), GA, *616*
The Wayne Group, Ltd. (C), NY, *616*
Wegner & Assoc. (C), WI, *617*
Henry Welker & Assoc. (C), MI, *618*
Wellington Management Group (R), PA, *217*
John R. Williams & Assoc., Inc. (C), NC, *621*
Williamsburg Group (C), NJ, *621*
Wilson McLeran, Inc. (C), CT, *622*
Wilson Personnel, Inc. (C), NC, *622*
Wing Tips & Pumps, Inc. (C), MI, *623*
S. R. Wolman Assoc., Inc. (R), NY, *224*
Jim Woodson & Assoc., Inc. (C), MS, *624*
The Woodstone Consulting Company, Inc. (R), CO, *224*

03.2 Materials & requirement planning

The Abbott Group, Inc. (R), MD, *1*
American Heritage Group, Inc. (C), MI, *247*
American Logistics Consultants, Inc. (C), IL, *247*
Ansara, Bickford & Fiske (C), MA, *251*
The Associates, HR Search Executives, Inc. (C), OK, *254*
Aurora Tech Search (C), ON, *256*
Austin - Allen Co. (C), TN, *256*
Austin Michaels, Ltd., Inc. (C), AZ, *256*
Automation Technology Search (C), CA, *256*
Availability Personnel Consultants (C), NH, *257*
Paul C. Banks Assoc. (C), GA, *259*
Battalia Winston Int'l./The Euram Consultants Group (R), NY, *13*
William Bell Assoc., Inc. (C), NJ, *263*
Berkshire Search Assoc. (C), MA, *265*
D. R. Blood & Assoc. (R), AZ, *18*
Howard Bowen Consulting (C), FL, *270*
Britt Assoc., Inc. (C), IL, *274*
Broward-Dobbs, Inc. (C), GA, *274*
Juliette Lang Cahn Executive Search (C), NY, *279*
J. P. Canon Assoc. (C), NY, *280*
Carnegie Resources, Inc. (C), NC, *284*
Carter, Lavoie Associates (C), RI, *285*
Christopher-Westmont & Assoc., Inc. (R), OH, *34*
CJA-The Adler Group, Inc. (R), CA, *35*
Clark Personnel Service, Inc. (C), AL, *292*
Cochran, Cochran & Yale, Inc. (R), NY, *36*
Collins & Associates (C), MI, *294*
Continental Search Assoc. (C), OH, *298*
P. G. Cook Assoc. (R), TN, *40*
Corporate Management Services (C), PA, *300*
Jim Crumpley & Assoc. (C), MO, *304*
Cumberland Professional Search Inc. (C), TN, *304*
Daggett & Kvistad (R), CA, *45*
Daniel Marks Company (C), OH, *306*
Dapexs Consultants, Inc. (C), NY, *307*
Diversified Search, Inc. (R), PA, *52*
The Duncan-O'Dell Group Inc. (C), TX, *316*
Dunhill Personnel of Boulder (C), CO, *319*
Dunhill Professional Search of San Jose (C), CA, *319*
G. L. Dykstra Assoc., Inc. (C), MI, *323*
Eagle Consulting Group Inc. (C), TX, *325*
Elite Resources Group (R), OH, *58*
Erwin Assoc. (R), IL, *60*
Executive Manning Corp. (R), FL, *63*
Fairfield Int'l. Resources (R), NY, *65*
James L. Fisk & Assoc. (C), MO, *342*
F-O-R-T-U-N-E Personnel Consultants of Tampa (C), FL, *344*
F-O-R-T-U-N-E Personnel Consultants of Manatee County (C), FL, *345*
Fortune Personnel Consultants of Sarasota Inc. (C), FL, *345*
Fortune Personnel Consultants of Bloomfield, Inc. (C), MI, *346*
F-O-R-T-U-N-E Personnel Consultants of St. Louis-West County (C), MO, *347*
F-O-R-T-U-N-E Personnel Consultants of Cincinnati (C), OH, *348*
Fortune Personnel Consultants of the Virginia Highlands (C), VA, *351*
Foster Partners (R), NY, *70*
Gabriele & Company (C), MA, *354*
Goldbeck Recruiting Inc. (C), BC, *359*
Graham & Co. (R), NJ, *80*
Granger, Counts & Assoc. (R), OH, *81*
Griffith & Werner, Inc. (R), FL, *82*
Groton Planning Group (R), ME, *82*
Wolf Gugler & Assoc. Ltd. (R), ON, *83*
The Harris Consulting Corp. (R), MB, *87*
Herring & Assoc. (C), AR, *376*
Hintz Associates (C), NY, *378*
HR Inc. (C), NC, *382*
Hughes & Wilden Assoc. (C), PA, *383*
Hunt Ltd. (C), NJ, *385*
J. B. Linde & Assoc. (C), MO, *395*
R. I. James, Inc. (C), NY, *397*
JDG Assoc., Ltd. (C), MD, *397*
Kabana Corp. (C), MI, *402*
Melissa Katzman, Executive Search (C), NY, *404*
A.T. Kearney Executive Search (R), IL, *111*
Kehn & Gabor, Inc. (C), OH, *405*
Kenmore Executives Inc. (C), FL, *405*
Key Employment (C), NJ, *405*
John Kuhn & Assoc., Inc. (R), WI, *121*
L & L Assoc. (C), CA, *410*
Leith & Assoc., Inc. (C), OH, *416*
Linden Group, Inc. (C), NC, *418*
M/J/A Partners (R), IL, *133*
Management Recruiters of Winsted, Inc. (C), CT, *442*
Management Recruiters of Venice, Inc. (C), FL, *445*
Management Recruiters of Noblesville, Inc. (C), IN, *448*
Management Recruiters of Puerto Rico (C), PR, *460*
Management Recruiters of Columbia, Tennessee (C), TN, *461*
Management Recruiters Dallas North (MRDN) (C), TX, *462*
Management Recruiters of Janesville, Inc. (C), WI, *466*
Richard L. Mather & Assoc. (C), CT, *472*
Mayhall Search Group, Inc. (C), IN, *473*
McInturff & Assoc., Inc. (C), MA, *474*
Walter Meyer & Assoc. (R), NY, *144*
Michael Assoc. (R), IL, *144*
Danette Milne Corporate Search Inc. (C), ON, *482*
National Computerized Employment Service, Inc. (C), PA, *489*
New Venture Development, Inc. (C), CA, *492*
Northland Employment Services Inc. (C), MN, *496*
Oliver & Rozner Assoc., Inc. (R), NY, *155*
Orion Int'l. Consulting Group, Inc. (C), NC, *499*
Pacific Coast Recruiting (C), CA, *501*
T. Page & Assoc. (C), TX, *502*
Personnel Management Group (C), MB, *508*
Pinton Forrest & Madden/EMA Partners Int'l. (R), BC, *165*
Procurement Resources (C), MD, *520*
ProSearch, Inc. (C), OH, *524*
Rand Assoc. (R), ME, *171*
The Recruitment Group, Inc. (C), NY, *532*
Terry Richards (C), OH, *536*
J. P. Roddy Consultants (C), PA, *540*
ROI Assoc. (R), NY, *180*
Rowland Assoc. (C), CA, *547*
Sales Consultants of Birmingham (C), AL, *555*
Sales Consultants of Chico (C), CA, *556*
Sanford Rose Assoc. - Cedar Rapids (C), IA, *567*
Sanford Rose Assoc. - Burlington, NC (C), NC, *569*
Sanford Rose Assoc. - Doylestown (C), PA, *570*
The Schatz Company (C), MO, *571*
Schenck & Assoc. SC (C), WI, *572*
Scott-Thaler Assoc. Agency, Inc. (C), CA, *573*
The Shotland Group (R), CA, *190*
Sill Technical Assoc., Inc. (C), PA, *581*
SpencerStuart (R), NY, *196*
Kenn Spinrad Inc. (C), PA, *589*
Steeple Resources & Consulting (R), NJ, *199*
Stoopen Asociados, S.C./EMA Partners Int'l. (R), MX, *202*
Storfer & Assoc. (C), NY, *595*
Success Seekers Connection (C), FL, *596*
Summit Executive Search Consultants, Inc. (R), FL, *204*
Ron Sunshine & Assoc. (C), IL, *597*
System 1 Search (C), CA, *598*
Technology Consultants Int'l. (C), CA, *603*
Telford, Adams & Alexander (R), CA, *208*
TRS Staffing Solutions Inc. (C), OH, *610*
Valentine & Assoc. (C), IL, *611*
Warren Executive Services (C), GA, *616*
S. B. Webster & Associates (R), MA, *217*
WMD inc. (C), NJ, *623*
Xagas & Assoc. (R), IL, *226*

03.3 Physical distribution, traffic & transportation, logistics

Ackerman Johnson Inc. (C), TX, *238*
Alpha Search (C), FL, *246*
Alynco, Inc. (C), AR, *246*
American Logistics Consultants, Inc. (C), IL, *247*
American Professional Search, Inc. (C), TN, *248*
Anderson Network Group (C), OH, *250*
Angel Group Int'l. (C), KY, *250*
Ansara, Bickford & Fiske (C), MA, *251*
The Ascher Group (R), NJ, *7*
Austin - Allen Co. (C), TN, *256*
Avondale Search Int'l., Inc. (R), FL, *9*
Paul C. Banks Assoc. (C), GA, *259*
Barone Assoc. (C), NJ, *259*
Battalia Winston Int'l./The Euram Consultants Group (R), NY, *13*
R. Gaines Baty Assoc., Inc. (R), TX, *13*
Martin H. Bauman Assoc., Inc. (R), NY, *13*
J. P. Bencik Assoc. (C), MI, *263*
D. R. Blood & Assoc. (R), AZ, *18*
Bosland Gray Assoc. (R), NJ, *20*
Bowie & Associates, Inc. (C), MD, *271*
Boyden (R), NY, *20*
Britt Assoc., Inc. (C), IL, *274*
J. P. Canon Assoc. (C), NY, *280*
Career Alternatives Executive Search (C), MI, *281*
Carpenter & Assoc. (C), TX, *284*
Cary & Assoc. (R), FL, *31*
Cella Assoc. (C), GA, *286*
CMS, Inc. (C), NH, *293*
Coleman Lew & Assoc., Inc. (R), NC, *37*
Consulting Rhonda (C), ON, *297*
Corporate Plus, Ltd. (C), GA, *300*
Craig Affiliates, Inc. (C), TX, *302*
Cyr Associates, Inc. (C), MA, *306*
Daubenspeck & Associates, Ltd. (R), IL, *46*
Dixie Search Assoc. (C), GA, *313*
Dominguez-Metz & Assoc. (R), CA, *53*
The Dorfman Group (C), AZ, *314*
Dumont & Co. (C), BC, *316*
Dunhill Professional Search of Englewood, Inc. (C), CO, *319*
Dunhill Professional Search of San Jose (C), CA, *319*
The E & K Group (C), NJ, *324*
Eden & Assoc., Inc. (C), PA, *326*
Elite Resources Group (R), OH, *58*
Emerson & Co. (C), GA, *329*
Epsen, Fuller & Assoc., LLC (R), NJ, *60*
Evans Transportation Search (C), ON, *331*
ExecuSource Assoc., Inc. (C), GA, *332*
Fabian Assoc. Inc. (C), NY, *338*
Fairfaxx Corp. (R), CT, *64*
Paul Falcone Assoc. (R), NJ, *65*
FitzGibbon & Assoc. (R), PA, *68*
F-O-R-T-U-N-E Personnel Consultants of Tampa (C), FL, *344*
F-O-R-T-U-N-E Personnel Consultants of Greenwood Village (C), CO, *344*
Fortune Personnel Consultants of Sarasota Inc. (C), FL, *345*
Fortune Personnel Consultants of Bloomfield, Inc. (C), MI, *346*
F-O-R-T-U-N-E Personnel Consultants of Menlo Park, Inc. (C), NJ, *347*
Fortune Personnel Consultants of Greensboro, NC, Inc. (C), NC, *348*
Fortune Personnel Consultants of Chattanooga Inc. (C), TN, *349*
Fortune Personnel Consultants of the Virginia Highlands (C), VA, *351*
Foster Partners (R), NY, *70*
Foy, Schneid & Daniel, Inc. (R), NY, *71*
Frye/Joure & Assoc., Inc. (C), TN, *353*
Futures, Inc. (C), NH, *354*
GAAP Inc. (R), QE, *73*
J. Gernetzke & Assoc., Inc. (C), OH, *357*
The Glenwood Group (C), IL, *358*
H. L. Goehring & Assoc., Inc. (C), OH, *359*
Fred J. Goldsmith Assoc. (R), CA, *79*
Groton Planning Group (R), ME, *82*
Wolf Gugler & Assoc. Ltd. (R), ON, *83*
Herring & Assoc. (C), AR, *376*
The Hindman Group, Inc. (C), CA, *378*
Fred Hood & Assoc. (C), CA, *380*
Hughes & Wilden Assoc. (C), PA, *383*
Hunt Ltd. (C), NJ, *385*
Hyman & Assoc. (C), TX, *386*
Industry Consultants, Inc. (C), GA, *388*
International Management Development Corp. (C), NY, *393*
R. I. James, Inc. (C), NY, *397*
JCL & Assoc. (C), FL, *397*
Jeffrey Allan Co., Inc. (C), CA, *398*
L. J. Johnson & Co. (R), MI, *106*
Johnson Assoc., Inc. (C), IL, *399*
A.T. Kearney Executive Search (R), IL, *111*
Kehn & Gabor, Inc. (C), OH, *405*
Kenmore Executives Inc. (C), FL, *405*
David Warwick Kennedy & Assoc. (R), BC, *112*
Kenzer Corp. (R), NY, *113*
The Kingsley Group (R), CA, *114*
Kirby Assoc. (R), PA, *115*
Michael Kosmetos & Assoc., Inc. (C), OH, *408*
L & L Assoc. (C), CA, *410*
Jack B. Larsen & Assoc., Inc. (C), PA, *413*
Madeleine Lav & Assoc. (C), CA, *413*
Leith & Assoc., Inc. (C), OH, *416*
Leslie Kavanagh Assoc., Inc. (C), NY, *416*
Logistics Management Resources, Inc. (R), NY, *131*
Lucas Group (C), NY, *421*
Management Recruiters of Fresno (C), CA, *440*
Management Recruiters of Clovis (C), CA, *440*
Management Recruiters Dana Point (C), CA, *440*
Management Recruiters, Inland Empire Agency (C), CA, *441*
Management Recruiters of Pleasanton (C), CA, *441*
Management Recruiters of North Fulton (C), GA, *445*
Management Recruiters of Atlanta (C), GA, *445*
Management Recruiters of Rockville (C), MD, *450*
Management Recruiters of Lake Tahoe, NV (C), NV, *453*
Management Recruiters of Medford, N.J. (C), NJ, *453*
Management Recruiters of Bethlehem, PA (C), PA, *458*
Management Recruiters of Franklin, Inc. (C), TN, *461*
Management Recruiters Dallas North (MRDN) (C), TX, *462*
Paula Marks Inc. (R), NY, *136*
Matté & Company, Inc. (R), CT, *138*
McCooe & Assoc., Inc. (R), NJ, *140*
The Paul McDaniel Co. (C), TN, *474*
McInturff & Assoc., Inc. (C), MA, *474*
Michael Wayne Recruiters (C), IL, *480*
The Montgomery Group, Inc. (C), TN, *484*
MPA Executive Search Inc. (R), QE, *148*
Murphy Partners Int'l. (R), IL, *150*
Noll Human Resource Services (C), NE, *494*
John B. Norris & Assoc., Inc. (C), MD, *495*
North Coast Meridian (C), NY, *496*
Nuessle, Kurdziel & Weiss, Inc. (R), PA, *153*
O'Brien & Bell (R), OH, *153*
LaMonte Owens, Inc. (R), PA, *157*
The P & L Group (C), NY, *500*
T. Page & Assoc. (C), TX, *502*
Jim Parham & Assoc., Inc. (R), FL, *159*
Michael W. Parres & Assoc. (R), MI, *159*
PERC, Ltd. (C), AZ, *506*
Performance Resources, Inc. (C), RI, *507*
Personnel Management Group (C), MB, *508*
Petrie Partners, Inc. (R), FL, *163*
Phillips Personnel/Search (C), CO, *510*
Philo & Associates (C), GA, *511*
R. L. Plimpton Assoc., Inc. (R), CO, *165*
Prichard Kymen Inc. (R), AB, *168*
Procurement Resources (C), MD, *520*
ProTech Nationwide Staffing, Inc. (C), NY, *525*
R M Associates (R), OH, *171*
Cedric L. Reese Inc. (C), CA, *533*
Reinecke & Assoc. (C), NJ, *533*
Resource Inc. (R), MA, *175*
The Retail Network (C), MA, *535*
S. Reyman & Assoc., Ltd. (R), IL, *176*
RIC Corp. (R), FL, *177*
Terry Richards (C), OH, *536*
Riddle & McGrath LLC (R), GA, *178*
Rollins & Assoc. (C), CA, *541*
Roth Young Personnel Service of Detroit, Inc. (C), MI, *546*
Roth Young Personnel Services of Washington, DC (C), MD, *546*
RTE Search (C), NJ, *547*
Rushmore • Judge Inc. (R), ON, *183*
Sales Consultants Bridgewater, Inc. (C), NJ, *560*
Sanford Rose Assoc. - Effingham (C), IL, *566*
Sanford Rose Assoc. - Portland (C), OR, *570*
Schall Executive Search Partners (R), MN, *185*

Scott-Thaler Assoc. Agency, Inc. (C), CA, *573*
Search South, Inc. (C), AL, *576*
Selective Recruiting Assoc., Inc. (C), MI, *578*
Selig Executive Search (C), NH, *579*
Shey-Harding Assoc. Inc. (C), CA, *580*
E. L. Shore & Assoc. (R), ON, *190*
The Shotland Group (R), CA, *190*
Peter Siegel & Co. (C), MA, *581*
Smith Hanley Assoc., Inc. (C), NY, *584*
SpencerStuart (R), NY, *196*
Stanewick, Hart & Assoc., Inc. (C), FL, *591*
Stanton Chase Int'l. (R), MD, *198*
Sterling Int'l. Management Recruitment, Ltd. Inc. (C), NC, *592*
Strategic Assoc., Inc. (C), TX, *595*
Summit Group Int'l., Inc. (R), GA, *204*
The TBI Group (R), PA, *207*
The Tidewater Group Inc. (C), CT, *607*
The Truman Agency (C), CA, *610*
TSI Group/TSI Staffing Services (C), ON, *610*
Valentine & Assoc. (C), IL, *611*
Kelly Walker Assoc. (C), TX, *614*
John Williams & Assoc. (C), TX, *621*
Wilson & Assoc. Int'l. Inc. (C), FL, *622*
The Winchester Group (R), CA, *222*
The Woodstone Consulting Company, Inc. (R), CO, *224*
R. S. Wyatt Assoc., Inc. (R), TX, *225*
The Zammataro Company (R), OH, *226*

03.4 Packaging

AGRI-associates (C), MO, *242*
The Altco Group (C), NJ, *246*
American Logistics Consultants, Inc. (C), IL, *247*
American Professional Search, Inc. (C), TN, *248*
Anderson Industrial Assoc., Inc. (C), GA, *250*
Ansara, Bickford & Fiske (C), MA, *251*
Associated Recruiters (C), WI, *254*
Atomic Personnel, Inc. (C), PA, *255*
Behrens and Company (C), WA, *262*
William Bell Assoc., Inc. (C), NJ, *263*
Biomedical Search Consultants (R), CT, *17*
BJB Assoc. (C), VA, *267*
Blair/Tech Recruiters, Inc. (C), NJ, *268*
D. R. Blood & Assoc. (R), AZ, *18*
Boyden (R), NY, *20*
Brandywine Management Group (R), MD, *22*
Bryan & Louis Research (C), OH, *275*
J. P. Canon Assoc. (C), NY, *280*
Caprio & Assoc. Inc. (R), IL, *29*
Carnegie Resources, Inc. (C), NC, *284*
Corbin Packaging Professionals (C), MO, *299*
Cross Country Consultants, Inc. (C), MD, *304*
The Danielson Group, Inc. (C), TX, *306*
Debbon Recruiting Group, Inc. (C), MO, *310*
J. H. Dugan & Assoc., Inc. (R), CA, *55*
Dunhill Professional Search of Englewood, Inc. (C), CO, *319*
Executive Search Group, Inc. (C), CT, *335*
F-O-R-T-U-N-E of West Portland (C), OR, *348*
Fortune Personnel Consultants of Allentown, Inc. (C), PA, *348*
Foster Partners (R), NY, *70*
Gilbert Tweed Assoc. Inc. (R), NY, *76*
The Glenwood Group (C), IL, *358*
Goodrich & Sherwood Assoc., Inc. (R), NY, *79*
Howe & Assoc. (R), PA, *97*
Human Resources Personnel Agency (R), AR, *99*
International Business Partners (C), ON, *392*
JLI-Boston (R), MA, *106*
JM & Company (R), PA, *106*
Kaas Employment Services (C), IA, *402*
A.T. Kearney Executive Search (R), IL, *111*
D. Kunkle & Assoc. (C), IL, *410*
Laboratory Resource Group (C), MA, *411*
M H Executive Search Group (C), TX, *422*
Management Catalysts (R), NJ, *134*
Management Recruiters of Decatur, LLC (C), AL, *438*
Management Recruiters of Clovis (C), CA, *440*
Management Recruiters of Milford Inc. (C), CT, *442*
Management Recruiters of Pensacola (C), FL, *444*
Management Recruiters of Duluth (C), GA, *445*
Management Recruiters of North Fulton (C), GA, *445*
Management Recruiters of Atlanta West, Inc. (C), GA, *445*
Management Recruiters of Chicago-North Shore (C), IL, *447*
Management Recruiters of Baitimore (C), MD, *451*
Management Recruiters of Cincinnati/ Sharonville, Inc. (C), OH, *457*
Management Recruiters of LBJ Park/Dallas (C), TX, *462*
Robert E. McGrath & Assoc. (R), CT, *141*
MedQuest Assoc. (C), CO, *478*
Merit Professional Search, Inc. (C), TN, *479*
Merrick & Moore (C), NC, *479*
Michael/Merrill (C), KS, *481*
The Mulshine Company, Ltd. (R), NY, *149*
Norris Agency (C), TX, *495*
Packaging Personnel Co., Ltd. (C), WI, *501*
Rick Pascal & Assoc., Inc. (C), NJ, *504*
Philo & Associates (C), GA, *511*
Gregory D. Pickens (C), TX, *511*
ProTech Nationwide Staffing, Inc. (C), NY, *525*
Quality Control Recruiters (C), CT, *526*
Quality Search (C), IN, *526*
Riley Cole (C), CA, *537*
River Region Personnel, Inc. (C), LA, *538*
S.D.P. Contract Recruiters (C), NJ, *550*
Sales Consultants of Ft. Lauderdale, Inc. (C), FL, *557*
Sales Consultants of Princeton, Inc. (C), NJ, *561*
Sales Consultants of Westchester-South, Inc. (C), NY, *561*
Sanford Rose Assoc. - Rockford (C), IL, *567*
Sanford Rose Assoc. - Portland (C), OR, *570*
Scott-Thaler Assoc. Agency, Inc. (C), CA, *573*
Search & Recruit Int'l. (C), VA, *573*
Search Northwest Assoc. (C), OR, *576*
Search Plus Int'l.-Ohio (C), OH, *576*
Selective Management Services, Inc. (C), FL, *578*
Smith & Laue Search (R), OR, *193*
Southern Recruiters & Consultants, Inc. (C), SC, *587*
SpencerStuart (R), NY, *196*
Sprout/Standish, Inc. (C), NH, *589*
Storfer & Assoc. (C), NY, *595*
Strategic Resources (C), WA, *595*
S. Tanner & Assoc. Inc. (C), ON, *599*
Thomas Lyle & Co. (C), IL, *606*
The Tidewater Group Inc. (C), CT, *607*
TRS Staffing Solutions Inc. (C), OH, *610*
Valentine & Assoc. (C), IL, *611*
Vincenty & Co. (C), OH, *612*
Gordon Wahls Executive Search (C), PA, *613*
Wayne Assoc., Inc. (C), VA, *616*
R. A. Wells Co. (C), GA, *618*
Williams Recruiting, Inc. (C), WA, *621*
Williamsburg Group (C), NJ, *621*
The Wilmington Group (C), NC, *622*

04.0 Medical/healthcare

A.K.S. Assoc., Ltd. (R), MA, *1*
Abeln, Magy & Assoc., Inc. (R), MN, *1*
B. J. Abrams & Assoc. Inc. (C), IL, *233*
ACC Consultants, Inc. (C), NM, *233*
Acuity Medical Recruitment (C), MS, *239*
Adept Tech Recruiting, Inc. (C), NY, *240*
ADR Accounting Management Recruiters (C), ON, *240*
Advancement Recruiting Services (C), OH, *241*
AES Search (C), NJ, *241*
J. R. Akin & Co. (R), MA, *2*
Albrecht & Assoc., Executive Search Consultants (C), TX, *243*
Alexander Enterprises, Inc. (C), PA, *243*
The Alfus Group (R), NY, *3*
Jay Allen & Assoc. (C), FL, *244*
Allhands Placement Consultants (C), IN, *245*
Alliance Search Management Inc. (R), TX, *4*
AMD & Associates (C), GA, *247*
American Executive Search (C), FL, *247*
American Group Practice, Inc. (R), NY, *5*
American Medical Consultants, Inc. (C), FL, *247*
American Medical Recruiters (C), CO, *248*
American Medical Recruiting Co. Inc. (C), MS, *248*
AmeriResource Group Inc. (C), OK, *248*

Amherst Human Resource Group, Ltd. (C), IL, *249*
Anderson & Associates (R), NC, *5*
R & J Arnold & Assoc., Inc. (C), CO, *253*
Aster Search Group (R), NY, *8*
Atlantic Pacific Group (C), CA, *255*
Auerbach Associates, Inc. (R), MA, *9*
Austin-McGregor Int'l. (R), TX, *9*
Avestruz & Assoc. (C), CA, *257*
The Baer Group (R), OH, *10*
Bailey Employment System Inc. (C), CT, *257*
The Bales-Waugh Group (C), FL, *258*
J. W. Barleycorn, Renard & Assoc., Inc. (R), OH, *11*
Barnes Development Group, LLC (R), WI, *11*
Fred A. Barnette & Assoc. (R), NC, *11*
Battalia Winston Int'l./The Euram Consultants Group (R), NY, *13*
The Bauman Group (R), CA, *14*
BCG Search, Inc. (R), FL, *14*
Neail Behringer Consultants Inc. (R), NY, *15*
Joy Reed Belt Search Consultants, Inc. (R), OK, *15*
Bennett & Associates (C), TX, *264*
Bertrand, Ross & Assoc., Inc. (C), IL, *266*
Billington & Assoc. (R), CA, *17*
Bonifield Assoc. (C), NJ, *269*
Boone-Scaturro Assoc., Inc. (C), GA, *269*
Born & Bicknell, Inc. (C), FL, *270*
Boulware & Assoc. Inc. (R), IL, *20*
Boyden (R), NY, *20*
Boyle/Ogata Executive Search (R), CA, *21*
BR & Assoc. (C), NJ, *271*
Bradford Executives Int'l. (C), VA, *271*
Brandywine Management Group (R), MD, *22*
Bristol Assoc., Inc. (C), CA, *274*
Brookman Associates (C), NY, *274*
Bernard E. Brooks & Assoc., Inc. (R), SC, *24*
BRW Search (C), MN, *275*
Bryant Research (C), NJ, *275*
The Burke Group (C), ON, *276*
Joseph R. Burns & Assoc., Inc. (R), NJ, *25*
Cadillac Assoc. (C), CA, *278*
Caliber Associates (R), PA, *27*
The Cambridge Group Ltd. (C), CT, *280*
CanMed Consultants Inc. (C), ON, *280*
Cantrell & Assoc. (C), FL, *280*
Career Counseling Ltd. (C.C.L.) (C), NY, *282*
Career Images (C), FL, *282*
Career Profiles (C), NH, *283*
Career Strategies, Inc. (C), CA, *283*
Careers/Inc. (C), PR, *284*
Carrington & Carrington, Ltd. (R), IL, *30*
Carson-Thomas & Assoc. (C), CA, *284*
Carver Search Consultants (C), CA, *285*
CEC Associates (R), MA, *32*
Cejka Healthcare Executive Search Services (CHESS) (R), MO, *32*
Cemco, Ltd. (C), IL, *286*
The Century Group (C), KS, *287*
Chamberlain Assoc. (C), GA, *288*
Vickers Chambless Managed Search (C), GA, *288*
Christian & Timbers, Inc. (R), OH, *34*
Christopher and Long (C), MO, *291*
Circlewood Search Group, Inc. (C), MI, *291*
Claimsearch (C), CA, *291*
CMS, Inc. (C), NH, *293*
Columbia Consulting Group (R), MD, *38*
Concorde Staff Source Inc. (C), WI, *296*
The Consortium (C), NY, *296*
Continental Research Search, Inc. (C), WI, *298*
Cook Assoc. Int'l., Inc. (C), TN, *298*
P. G. Cook Assoc. (R), TN, *40*
Cornerstone Resources, Inc. (C), OK, *299*
Cornerstone Search Assoc. Inc. (C), MA, *299*
Corporate Leadership Strategies, Inc. (R), NH, *41*
Corporate Recruiters Inc. (C), PA, *300*
Creative Management Strategies, Ltd. (R), NY, *42*
CRI Professional Search (C), CA, *303*
Criterion Executive Search, Inc. (C), FL, *303*
CSA/Clinical Staffing Assoc., LLC (C), NJ, *304*
The Custer Group, Inc. (R), TN, *44*
Cypress Int'l., Inc. (R), FL, *45*
The Danielson Group, Inc. (C), TX, *306*
Alan Darling Consulting (R), VT, *46*
Daudlin, De Beaupre & Co., Inc. (R), MI, *46*
Davies, Park (R), AB, *46*
Davis-Smith, Inc. (C), MI, *309*
DeCorrevont & Assoc. (C), IL, *310*
Delacore Resources (C), MN, *310*
Delta Medical Search Assoc. (C), OH, *310*
Delta ProSearch (C), PA, *311*
Derhak Ireland & Partners Ltd. (R), ON, *48*
Development Resource Group (R), NY, *48*
Rob Dey Executive Search (R), FL, *49*
Roger Dietsch & Assoc. (C), MN, *312*
Discovery, The Staffing Specialists, Inc. (C), IL, *312*
Diversified Health Search (R), PA, *52*
Diversified Search, Inc. (R), PA, *52*
DNA Search, Inc. (C), CA, *313*
Doherty Healthcare Consultants (C), ME, *313*
The Domann Organization (R), CA, *53*
Donini Assoc. (R), VA, *54*
Dotson & Assoc. (R), NY, *54*
Drew Assoc. Int'l. (R), NJ, *54*
M. Dunbar & Assoc. (C), TX, *316*
Dunhill Staffing Systems, Inc. (C), NY, *316*
Dunhill Professional Search of Tampa (C), FL, *320*
Dunhill Staffing Systems (C), NC, *321*
Dunhill Personnel Service of Fargo (C), ND, *322*
Dunhill Professional Search of Wilkes-Barre/Scranton, Inc. (C), PA, *322*
Dussick Management Assoc. (C), CT, *323*
EA Plus, Inc. (C), TX, *325*
J. M. Eagle Partners Ltd. (C), WI, *325*
Eagle Research, Inc. (C), NJ, *325*
EGM Consulting, Inc. (R), FL, *57*
William J. Elam & Assoc. (R), NE, *58*
Elite Medical Search (C), GA, *328*
Emmett Executive Search, Inc. (C), NY, *330*
EMN/Witt/Kieffer (R), MA, *59*
ENI (R), CT, *59*
Ensearch Management Consultants (C), CA, *331*
Entelechy Group Ltd. (R), MD, *59*
Executive Careers (R), CA, *62*
Executive Dimensions (R), NY, *62*
The Executive Group, Inc. (R), CA, *62*
Executive Manning Corp. (R), FL, *63*
Executive Recruitment Specialists, Inc. (R), NC, *63*
Executive Referral Services, Inc. (C), IL, *334*
Executive Search of New England, Inc. (C), ME, *336*
Executive Solutions (R), MN, *64*
Eyler Assoc., Inc. (R), IA, *64*
Fagan & Company (R), PA, *64*
Fallstaff Search (C), MD, *338*
Faro Consultants Int'l. (C), VA, *338*
James Feerst & Assoc., Inc. (C), AZ, *339*
First Advisory Services Int'l., Inc. (R), MD, *67*
James L. Fisk & Assoc. (C), MO, *342*
Fitzgerald Associates (R), MA, *68*
Focus Consulting Services, Inc. (C), FL, *342*
Foley Proctor Yoskowitz (R), NJ, *69*
F-O-R-T-U-N-E Personnel Consultants of Troy, Inc. (C), MI, *347*
Fortune Personnel Consultants of Raleigh, Inc. (C), NC, *348*
Foster Partners (R), NY, *70*
Franklin Allen Consultants, Ltd. (R), NY, *71*
The Franklin Search Group, Inc./Medzilla (R), WA, *71*
Furst Group/MPI (R), IL, *72*
Gable Healthcare Group, Inc. (R), FL, *73*
The Gammill Group, Inc. (C), OH, *354*
Gardner-Ross Assoc., Inc. (R), NY, *74*
Garrett Assoc. Inc. (R), GA, *75*
Garrison-Randall, Inc. (R), CA, *75*
Genesis Personnel Service, Inc. (C), OH, *356*
Gielow Assoc., Inc. (R), WI, *76*
John Gilbert Co. (C), TX, *357*
Gilbert Tweed Assoc. Inc. (R), NY, *76*
Gilmore & Assoc. (C), CA, *357*
Gimbel & Assoc. (C), FL, *357*
Global HealthCare Partners (R), IL, *78*
Global Resources Group (R), CA, *78*
Robert G. Godfrey Assoc. Ltd. (R), IL, *78*
Barry M. Gold & Co. (C), CA, *359*
Joseph Goldring & Assoc. Inc. (C), MI, *360*
Robert Graham Assoc. (R), RI, *81*
Grant-Franks & Assoc. (C), NJ, *361*
Sheila Greco Assoc. (C), NY, *362*
J. B. Groner Executive Search, Inc. (C), DE, *363*
Growth Consultants of America (R), MI, *82*
Guidry & East Healthcare Search Consultants (R), TX, *83*
Habelmann & Assoc. (R), MI, *84*
Hanley & Assoc. (R), FL, *86*
Harbor Consultants Int'l., Inc. (C), VA, *368*

Harper Associates (C), MI, *369*
Harrington & O'Brien, Inc. (C), NH, *369*
Bruce W. Haupt Assoc. (R), DC, *88*
Hayman Daugherty Assoc., Inc. (C), GA, *370*
Health Care Dimensions (C), CO, *371*
Health Care Plus, Inc. (C), MD, *371*
Health Network USA (C), TX, *371*
Health Search (C), CA, *371*
Health Search, Inc. (C), KS, *371*
Healthcare Executive Recruiters, Inc. (C), CA, *372*
Healthcare Recruiters Int'l. Phoenix (C), AZ, *372*
Healthcare Recruiters Int'l. - Alabama (C), AL, *372*
Healthcare Recruiters of Indiana (C), IN, *372*
Healthcare Recruiters of New England (C), MA, *373*
Healthcare Recruiters of New York, Inc. (C), NY, *373*
Healthcare Recruiters of Midsouth (C), TN, *373*
Healthcare Recruiters Int'l. Philadelphia (C), NJ, *373*
Healthcare Recruiters Int'l. - Pittsburgh (C), PA, *373*
Healthcare Recruiters - Northwest (C), WA, *374*
Healthcare Resources Group (C), OK, *374*
Healthcare Search Associates (C), CA, *374*
HealthSearch Assoc. (C), MD, *374*
The Healthsearch Group, Inc. (C), NY, *374*
Heartland National Medical Search (C), IL, *374*
Hedlund Corp. (C), IL, *375*
Bruce Henry Assoc. Inc. (R), CA, *91*
Hersher Assoc., Ltd. (R), IL, *92*
Hill Allyn Assoc. (C), CA, *378*
Hitchens & Foster, Inc. (C), MO, *379*
HMO Executive Search (C), IN, *379*
The Hogan Group (C), OH, *380*
Holland & Assoc., Inc. (R), MI, *94*
The Hollins Group, Inc. (R), IL, *95*
Home Health & Hospital Recruiters, Inc. (C), GA, *380*
Horizon Medical Search of NH (C), NH, *381*
HR Consultants (C), GA, *382*
HRCS (R), CA, *97*
The HRM Group, Inc. (C), AL, *382*
Huff Assoc. (R), NJ, *98*
Hunter Douglas Group, Inc. (R), IL, *99*
The Hunter Group, Inc. (C), MI, *385*
The Hutton Group, Inc. (C), FL, *386*
Icon Recruiters, LLC (C), CA, *387*
IM Independent Management Recruiters (R), TN, *101*
IMA Search, Inc. (R), NY, *101*
Ingram & Aydelotte, Inc. (R), NY, *101*
Innovative Healthcare Services, Inc. (C), GA, *389*
Innovative Partnerships (R), CA, *101*
innovativestaffsearch (C), TX, *389*
Insurance Search (C), TX, *390*
Intech Summit Group, Inc. (R), CA, *102*
Interim Financial Solutions - Mid-Atlantic Region (C), MD, *392*
International Management Services Inc. (R), IL, *102*
Isaacson, Miller (R), MA, *104*
ISC of Cincinnati Inc. (C), OH, *394*
Jackson & Coker (C), GA, *396*
Jacobson Assoc. (C), IL, *396*
JAG Group (R), MO, *105*
JDC Assoc. (C), NY, *397*
J. M. Johnson & Assoc. (C), MN, *399*
Roye Johnston Assoc., Inc. (C), CA, *400*
Jonas, Walters & Assoc., Inc. (R), WI, *107*
Jordon & Jordon, Inc. (R), PA, *108*
JPM International (C), CA, *401*
Judd Associates (R), NJ, *109*
Karp & Assoc. (C), FL, *403*
Katelyn Partners (C), FL, *404*
Kaye/Bassman Int'l. Corp. (R), TX, *110*
A.T. Kearney Executive Search (R), IL, *111*
Kendall & Davis Co., Inc. (C), MO, *405*
Kent & Assoc. (R), OH, *113*
Kincaid Group Inc. (KGI) (C), TX, *406*
Kingsley Quinn/USA (R), NJ, *115*
Kittleman & Assoc.,LLC (R), IL, *115*
Lee Koehn Assoc., Inc. (R), OR, *116*
Koontz, Jeffries & Assoc., Inc. (R), FL, *117*
Korban Associates (R), PA, *117*
Korn/Ferry Int'l. (R), NY, *117*
The J. Kovach Group (R), PA, *119*
Kressenberg Assoc. (C), TX, *409*
Rene LaFlamme & Associes (R), QE, *122*
Lake Medical Associates (C), ME, *411*
Lam Assoc. (C), HI, *411*
Lawrence L. Lapham, Inc. (R), NY, *124*
Larson & Trent Assoc. (C), TN, *413*
Larson, Katz & Young, Inc. (C), VA, *413*
Lauer, Sbarbaro Assoc., EMA Partners Int'l. (R), IL, *126*
Reynolds Lebus Assoc. (C), AZ, *415*
AG Lennox & Assoc. (R), AB, *128*
Levison Search Assoc. (R), CA, *129*
Lewis & Blank Int'l. (R), CA, *129*
LJ Networking, Inc. (C), MD, *418*
Lloyd Prescott & Churchill, Inc. (R), FL, *130*
Lloyd Prescott Assoc., Inc. (C), FL, *418*
Loderman & Costello (C), GA, *419*
Logic Assoc., Inc. (C), NY, *419*
Longshore + Simmons (R), PA, *131*
Maczkov-Biosciences, Inc. (R), CA, *133*
Major Legal Services, Inc. (C), OH, *423*
Managed Care Consultants (C), AZ, *423*
Managed Care Resources (C), TX, *424*
Management & Human Resources (R), MA, *134*
Management Assoc. (C), MD, *424*
Management Recruiters of Mobile Co., Inc. (C), AL, *438*
Management Recruiters of Little Rock (C), AR, *439*
Management Recruiters Peninsula (C), CA, *439*
Management Recruiters of Berkeley (C), CA, *439*
Management Recruiters of Monterey (C), CA, *441*
Management Recruiters of Colorado, Inc. (C), CO, *442*
Management Recruiters of Clearwater (C), FL, *443*
Management Recruiters of Tampa North (C), FL, *444*
Management Recruiters of Atlanta North, Inc. (C), GA, *446*
Management Recruiters of Washington, DC Inc. (C), MD, *450*
Management Recruiters of Frederick, Inc. (C), MD, *450*
Management Recruiters of the Baltimore Washington Corridor (C), MD, *450*
Management Recruiters of North Oakland County, Inc. (C), MI, *452*
Management Recruiters of Woodbury Inc. (C), NY, *455*
Management Recruiters of Kinston (C), NC, *456*
Management Recruiters of Dayton, Inc. (C), OH, *457*
Management Recruiters of Cleveland (C), OH, *457*
Management Recruiters of Westmoreland County, Inc. (C), PA, *459*
Management Recruiters of Pittsburgh (C), PA, *459*
Management Recruiters of Pittsburgh-North, Inc. (C), PA, *460*
Management Recruiters of Myrtle Beach, Inc. (C), SC, *460*
Management Recruiters of North Charleston (C), SC, *460*
Management Recruiters of Georgetown (C), SC, *461*
Management Recruiters of Houston (C), TX, *462*
Management Recruiters of Austin (C), TX, *462*
Management Recruiters - Friendswood (C), TX, *462*
Management Recruiters of Lubbock (C), TX, *463*
Management Recruiters of San Antonio - North (C), TX, *463*
Management Recruiters of Salt Lake City (C), UT, *464*
Management Recruiters of Seattle (C), WA, *465*
Management Recruiters of Spokane (C), WA, *465*
Management Recruiters of Lynnwood (C), WA, *465*
Management Resources (C), TX, *467*
Management Search Assoc., Inc. (C), GA, *467*
Manuso, Alexander & Associates, Inc. (R), NY, *135*
Marcus & Assoc. (C), NY, *469*
J. L. Mark Assoc., Inc. (R), CO, *135*
Marvel Consultants, Inc. (C), OH, *472*
Louis Thomas Masterson & Co. (R), OH, *138*
Matte Consulting Group Inc. (R), QE, *138*
Matthews & Stephens Assoc., Inc. (C), CT, *472*
The Mayes Group, Ltd. (R), PA, *139*
McHale & Assoc. (R), WA, *141*
McKavis Assoc. (C), CA, *475*
McManners Assoc., Inc. (R), CA, *142*

MDR Associates, Inc. (C), FL, *476*
Med-Ex Services (C), OH, *476*
Meder & Assoc., Inc. (R), IL, *142*
Medfall Inc. (C), ON, *476*
Medical Recruiters Exchange (C), AZ, *477*
Medical Recruiters Inc. (C), MO, *477*
Medical Search of America, Inc. (C), GA, *477*
Medicorp, Inc. (C), MO, *477*
MedPro Personnel, Inc. (C), GA, *478*
MedSearch Resources, Inc. (C), FL, *478*
Medserve & Assoc. Inc. (C), MD, *478*
MedXec USA, Inc. (C), FL, *478*
Martin H. Meisel Assoc., Inc. (R), NY, *143*
Meng, Finseth & Assoc., Inc. (R), CA, *143*
Meridian Resources (C), OH, *479*
Merlin Int'l. Inc. (C), NJ, *479*
E. J. Michaels, Ltd. (C), NY, *481*
Mitchell Martin Inc. (C), NY, *483*
Moffitt Int'l., Inc. (R), NC, *146*
Moore Research Assoc. (R), NJ, *147*
Morgan Int'l., Inc. (R), IL, *147*
Morgan Samuels Co. (R), CA, *147*
The Morley Group (C), IN, *486*
Mruk & E.M.A. Partners (R), NY, *148*
MSA Executive Search (R), MO, *148*
MSI Int'l. (C), GA, *486*
Pamela L. Mulligan, Inc. (R), NH, *149*
R. F. Mulvaney & Assoc., Inc. (R), MO, *149*
P. J. Murphy & Assoc., Inc. (R), WI, *150*
Nason & Nason (C), FL, *488*
National Career Search (C), AZ, *489*
National Search, Inc.r (C), FL, *490*
NDI Services (R), MI, *151*
New Dawn Employment Search (C), CA, *491*
New World Healthcare Solutions, Inc. (R), NY, *151*
Newell Assoc. (R), NY, *151*
Nino Recruiting & Staffing, Inc. (C), TX, *493*
Ira Z. Nitzberg (C), NY, *493*
J. L. Nixon Consulting (C), TX, *493*
Noll Human Resource Services (C), NE, *494*
Paul Winston Norman & Assoc. (R), IL, *152*
Norman Broadbent Int'l., Inc. (R), NY, *152*
The Normyle/Erstling Health Search Group (C), NJ, *494*
NRI Staffing Resources (C), DC, *496*
Nursing Technomics (R), PA, *153*
O'Connor Resources (C), TX, *497*
Ober & Company (R), CA, *155*
Odell & Assoc., Inc. (C), TX, *498*
The Oldani Group (R), WA, *155*
Omni Search, Inc. (C), CA, *499*
Organization Resources Inc. (R), MA, *157*
Orion Int'l. Consulting Group, Inc. (C), NC, *499*
Robert Ottke Assoc. (R), CA, *157*
P.A.R. Assoc., Inc. (R), MA, *158*
The Park Group & Assoc., Inc. (C), MD, *502*
Parker Page Group (C), FL, *503*
Largent Parks & Partners (C), TX, *503*
The Partnership Group (R), NJ, *160*
Pathfinders (C), CA, *504*
Pathfinders Int'l. (C), MI, *504*
Patriot Assoc. (C), PA, *505*
Joel H. Paul & Assoc., Inc. (C), NY, *505*
PCD Partners (R), PA, *161*
Pearson & Assoc., Inc. (C), AZ, *506*
People Management Mid-South, LLC (R), TN, *162*
Perfect Search, Inc. (C), FL, *507*
The Personnel Group, Inc. (R), MN, *163*
The Personnel Network, Inc. (C), SC, *508*
Petro Staff Int'l. (C), AB, *509*
Pharmaceutical Search Professionals, Inc. (C), PA, *510*
Phillips & Assoc. (R), MA, *164*
Physician Associates (C), HI, *511*
Physician Executive Management Center (R), FL, *164*
Physician Recruiting Services, Inc. (C), MO, *511*
Physicians Search®, Inc. (C), CA, *511*
Picard Int'l., Ltd. (R), NY, *164*
Place Mart Personnel Service (C), NJ, *513*
Plante & Moran, LLP (R), MI, *165*
Plemmons Assoc., Inc. (R), GA, *165*
Practice Dynamics, Inc. (C), TX, *515*
Preferred Professional Recruiters (C), TX, *516*
Premier Business Advisors (C), PA, *516*
Premier Healthcare Recruiters, Inc. (C), MI, *516*
Presley Consultants, Inc. (C), CA, *517*
PricewaterhouseCoopers Executive Search (R), ON, *168*
Prichard Kymen Inc. (R), AB, *168*
Primary Care Service Corp. (C), GA, *518*
Princeton Search Partners, Inc. (R), NJ, *169*
Prior/Martech Assoc., Inc. (R), WA, *169*
Priority Executive Search (C), FL, *518*
PRO, Inc./Professional Recruiting Offices, Inc. (C), CA, *519*
Pro Tec Technical Services (C), ON, *519*
Professional Healthcare Search & Consultants, Inc. (C), CA, *520*
Professional Personnel Consultants, Inc. (C), MI, *521*
Professional Placement Assoc., Inc. (C), NY, *521*
Professional Research Services, Inc. (R), IL, *169*
Professional Resource Group, Inc. (C), IN, *522*
Professional Search, Inc. Int'l. (C), TX, *523*
Professional Selection Services (R), GA, *169*
Professionals in Recruiting Co. (C), TN, *523*
Protocol Inc. (C), CA, *525*
Questor Consultants, Inc. (C), PA, *527*
Quetico Corp. (R), TX, *170*
Quigley Assoc. (R), MD, *170*
L. J. Quinn & Assoc., Inc. (R), CA, *170*
Quiring Assoc., Inc. (C), IN, *527*
R.A.N. Assoc., Inc. (C), OH, *528*
Ramming & Assoc., Inc. (C), NJ, *528*
Lea Randolph & Assoc., Inc. (C), TX, *529*
Ray & Berndtson/Tanton Mitchell (R), BC, *173*
Re-Mark Assoc. Inc. (C), NJ, *531*
Recruiters Professional Network - Fairview (C), MO, *531*
Recruitment Resources (C), CA, *532*
Recruitment Specialists, Inc. (C), MD, *532*
Reece & Mruk Partners/EMA Partners Int'l. (R), MA, *173*
Reeder & Assoc., Ltd. (R), GA, *173*
Response Staffing Services (C), NY, *534*
Retail Recruiters/Spectrum Consultants, Inc. (C), PA, *535*
Retis Assoc., Inc. (C), IL, *535*
Russell Reynolds Assoc., Inc. (R), NY, *176*
Reynolds Partners (R), NY, *177*
Marshall Rice Assoc. (R), RI, *177*
Rice Cohen Int'l. (R), PA, *178*
Richard, Wayne & Roberts (C), TX, *536*
The Richards Group (C), PA, *536*
Roberson & Co. (C), AZ, *538*
Norman Roberts & Assoc., Inc. (R), CA, *179*
Bruce Robinson Assoc. (R), NJ, *180*
Rodgers, Ramsey, Inc. (C), TX, *540*
Roevin Technical People (C), ON, *540*
The Rogan Group, Inc. (C), CA, *541*
Rogish Assoc., Inc. (C), OH, *541*
Rollo Assoc. (R), CA, *181*
Romac Int'l. (C), PA, *542*
Romac Int'l., Inc. (C), FL, *542*
Romeo-Hudgins & Assoc., Ltd. (C), NJ, *544*
The Rose Search Group, Inc. (C), NC, *545*
Roth Young Executive Recruiters (C), MN, *546*
Roth Young of Pittsburgh (C), PA, *546*
Roth Young of Tampa (C), FL, *546*
David Rowe & Assoc., Inc. (R), IL, *182*
Royal Assoc. (C), CA, *547*
The Rubicon Group (C), AZ, *547*
Ruderfer & Co., Inc. (C), NJ, *548*
Rushmore • Judge Inc. (R), ON, *183*
Sales Consultants of Birmingham (C), AL, *555*
Sales Consultants Int'l. of Oakland (C), CA, *556*
Sales Consultants Peninsula, Inc. (C), CA, *556*
Sales Consultants of Bangor, Inc. (C), ME, *559*
Sales Consultants of Austin, Inc. (C), TX, *562*
Sales Consultants of Pittsburgh (C), PA, *562*
Sampson Medical Search (C), CA, *564*
George D. Sandel Assoc. (C), MA, *565*
Sanford Rose Assoc. (C), OH, *565*
Sanford Rose Assoc. - Carmel, IN (C), IN, *567*
Sanford Rose Assoc. - Louisville (C), KY, *567*
Sanford Rose Assoc. - Columbia (C), SC, *570*
Santangelo Consultants Inc. (C), NY, *571*
A.D. Schiff & Assoc., Ltd. (C), IL, *572*
Schuyler Assoc., Ltd. (R), GA, *185*
G. L. Schwartz & Assoc., Inc. (C), GA, *572*
Scott Douglas Inc. (C), CA, *573*
Scott Sibley Assoc. (C), NY, *573*
Search Assoc., Inc. (C), CA, *574*
The Search Committee (C), MD, *574*

Search Research Assoc., Inc. (R), MA, *187*
Searchworks, Inc. (C), FL, *577*
Selective Search Associates (C), OH, *578*
Selective Staffing (C), CA, *579*
Peggy Shea & Assoc. (R), CA, *189*
Sherriff & Assoc. (C), KS, *580*
Michael Shirley Assoc. Inc. (R), KS, *190*
Siger & Assoc., LLC (C), CT, *581*
Skott/Edwards Consultants (R), NY, *192*
Skupsky & Assoc. (C), CO, *582*
Christopher Smallhorn Executive Recruiting, Inc. (R), MA, *193*
Howard W. Smith Assoc. (R), CT, *193*
Smith, Brown & Jones (C), KS, *585*
Snelling & Snelling, Inc. (C), FL, *585*
Snelling Search (C), AL, *585*
Snelling Search (C), LA, *586*
Snelling Search Recruiters (C), NC, *586*
Snyder & Co. (R), CT, *194*
Sockwell & Assoc. (R), NC, *194*
Phyllis Solomon Executive Search, Inc. (C), NJ, *587*
Solomon-Page Healthcare Group (R), NY, *195*
Solutions Group (R), AL, *195*
SpencerStuart (R), NY, *196*
Stanton Chase Int'l. (R), MD, *198*
STAT Search (C), NH, *592*
Daniel Stern & Assoc. (C), PA, *592*
Michael Stern Assoc., Inc./Euram (R), ON, *200*
The Stewart Group (C), FL, *593*
Stewart, Stein & Scott, Ltd. (R), MN, *200*
Sudina Search, Inc. (C), MD, *596*
Sullivan & Assoc. (R), MI, *204*
Synapse Human Resource Consulting Group (R), TX, *205*
The Synergy Organization (R), PA, *205*
Tarbex (C), DC, *599*
TechFind, Inc. (R), MA, *207*
Telford, Adams & Alexander (R), CA, *208*
Trillium Human Resources Inc. (C), ON, *609*
TriStaff Group (C), CA, *609*
Triumph Consulting, Inc. (R), IA, *210*
Trowbridge & Co., Inc. (R), MA, *211*
TTG/Sterling Services (C), CA, *610*
W. G. Tucker & Assoc. (R), PA, *211*
The Thomas Tucker Co. (R), CA, *211*
Tuft & Assoc., Inc. (R), IL, *212*
Tyler & Company (R), GA, *212*
UniQuest Int'l., Inc. (C), FL, *610*
Unisearch Search & Recruiting Inc. (C), CA, *611*
United Personnel Services (C), MA, *611*
USA Medical Placement Inc. (C), TX, *611*
Van Dyke Assoc. (R), IL, *212*
Vezan Assoc. (C), CT, *612*
K. K. Walker Professional Recruitment (C), CA, *614*
Warring & Assoc. (R), CA, *215*
Watring & Assoc., Inc. (C), IL, *616*
Weatherby Healthcare (C), CT, *617*
Wellington Management Group (R), PA, *217*
Wellington Thomas Ltd. (C), FL, *618*
Westfields Int'l., Inc. (C), NY, *619*
WestPacific National Search, Inc. (C), CA, *619*
The Whitaker Companies (C), TX, *619*
Whitney Smith Co. (C), TX, *620*
The Whittaker Group (C), MI, *620*
The Whyte Group, Inc. (R), MD, *220*
Wilcox Bertoux & Miller (R), CA, *220*
Walter K. Wilkins & Co. (R), NJ, *221*
William-Johns Co., Inc. (C), CA, *621*
Willis & Assoc. (R), OH, *221*
The Winchester Group (R), CA, *222*
Windsor Consultants, Inc. (C), TX, *622*
Winthrop Partners, Inc. (R), NY, *222*
Witt/Kieffer, Ford, Hadelman & Lloyd (R), IL, *223*
Wood & Assoc./Executive Search Consultants (C), CA, *624*
Bruce G. Woods Executive Search (R), TX, *224*
Worldwide Medical Services (C), CA, *625*
The York Group (C), CA, *626*
Zackrison Assoc., Inc. (C), FL, *627*
Helen Ziegler & Assoc., Inc. (C), ON, *627*
Zingaro & Company (R), TX, *227*
Zurick, Davis & Co., Inc. (R), MA, *227*

04.1 Physicians

Acuity Medical Recruitment (C), MS, *239*
Advancement Recruiting Services (C), OH, *241*
Alexander Enterprises, Inc. (C), PA, *243*
Jay Allen & Assoc. (C), FL, *244*
Allhands Placement Consultants (C), IN, *245*
American Group Practice, Inc. (R), NY, *5*
American Medical Consultants, Inc. (C), FL, *247*
American Medical Recruiting Co. Inc. (C), MS, *248*
Anderson & Associates (R), NC, *5*
R & J Arnold & Assoc., Inc. (C), CO, *253*
Bailey Employment System Inc. (C), CT, *257*
The Bauman Group (R), CA, *14*
Boone-Scaturro Assoc., Inc. (C), GA, *269*
Born & Bicknell, Inc. (C), FL, *270*
Bradford Executives Int'l. (C), VA, *271*
Bryant Research (C), NJ, *275*
Caliber Associates (R), PA, *27*
The Cambridge Group Ltd. (C), CT, *280*
CanMed Consultants Inc. (C), ON, *280*
Career Counseling Ltd. (C.C.L.) (C), NY, *282*
Carver Search Consultants (C), CA, *285*
Cejka Healthcare Executive Search Services (CHESS) (R), MO, *32*
Chamberlain Assoc. (C), GA, *288*
Christopher and Long (C), MO, *291*
Circlewood Search Group, Inc. (C), MI, *291*
Concorde Staff Source Inc. (C), WI, *296*
Continental Research Search, Inc. (C), WI, *298*
Cornerstone Resources, Inc. (C), OK, *299*
Corporate Recruiters Inc. (C), PA, *300*
Creative Management Strategies, Ltd. (R), NY, *42*
CRI Professional Search (C), CA, *303*
Cypress Int'l., Inc. (R), FL, *45*
Daudlin, De Beaupre & Co., Inc. (R), MI, *46*
Davies, Park (R), AB, *46*
Davis-Smith, Inc. (C), MI, *309*
Delacore Resources (C), MN, *310*
Delta Medical Search Assoc. (C), OH, *310*
Rob Dey Executive Search (R), FL, *49*
Diversified Health Search (R), PA, *52*
Diversified Search, Inc. (R), PA, *52*
Doherty Healthcare Consultants (C), ME, *313*
Drew Assoc. Int'l. (R), NJ, *54*
Dunhill Personnel Service of Fargo (C), ND, *322*
Eagle Research, Inc. (C), NJ, *325*
EGM Consulting, Inc. (R), FL, *57*
Ensearch Management Consultants (C), CA, *331*
The Executive Group, Inc. (R), CA, *62*
Executive Search of New England, Inc. (C), ME, *336*
James Feerst & Assoc., Inc. (C), AZ, *339*
First Advisory Services Int'l., Inc. (R), MD, *67*
Foley Proctor Yoskowitz (R), NJ, *69*
F-O-R-T-U-N-E Personnel Consultants of Troy, Inc. (C), MI, *347*
Foster Partners (R), NY, *70*
The Franklin Search Group, Inc./Medzilla (R), WA, *71*
Furst Group/MPI (R), IL, *72*
Gable Healthcare Group, Inc. (R), FL, *73*
Gielow Assoc., Inc. (R), WI, *76*
Gilbert Tweed Assoc. Inc. (R), NY, *76*
Gilmore & Assoc. (C), CA, *357*
Global Resources Group (R), CA, *78*
Joseph Goldring & Assoc. Inc. (C), MI, *360*
Growth Consultants of America (R), MI, *82*
Guidry & East Healthcare Search Consultants (R), TX, *83*
Harper Associates (C), MI, *369*
Bruce W. Haupt Assoc. (R), DC, *88*
Hayman Daugherty Assoc., Inc. (C), GA, *370*
Health Network USA (C), TX, *371*
Health Search (C), CA, *371*
Healthcare Recruiters Int'l. Phoenix (C), AZ, *372*
Healthcare Recruiters Int'l. - Alabama (C), AL, *372*
Healthcare Search Associates (C), CA, *374*
HealthSearch Assoc. (C), MD, *374*
The Healthsearch Group, Inc. (C), NY, *374*
Heartland National Medical Search (C), IL, *374*
Bruce Henry Assoc. Inc. (R), CA, *91*
Hitchens & Foster, Inc. (C), MO, *379*
The Hogan Group (C), OH, *380*
Horizon Medical Search of NH (C), NH, *381*
Huff Assoc. (R), NJ, *98*
Hunter Douglas Group, Inc. (R), IL, *99*
Icon Recruiters, LLC (C), CA, *387*
IM Independent Management Recruiters (R), TN, *101*
innovativestaffsearch (C), TX, *389*
Isaacson, Miller (R), MA, *104*
Jackson & Coker (C), GA, *396*
Jacobson Assoc. (C), IL, *396*

J. M. Johnson & Assoc. (C), MN, *399*
Roye Johnston Assoc., Inc. (C), CA, *400*
A.T. Kearney Executive Search (R), IL, *111*
Kendall & Davis Co., Inc. (C), MO, *405*
Kincaid Group Inc. (KGI) (C), TX, *406*
Korn/Ferry Int'l. (R), NY, *117*
The J. Kovach Group (R), PA, *119*
Lam Assoc. (C), HI, *411*
Larson & Trent Assoc. (C), TN, *413*
Levison Search Assoc. (R), CA, *129*
LJ Networking, Inc. (C), MD, *418*
Longshore + Simmons (R), PA, *131*
Maczkov-Biosciences, Inc. (R), CA, *133*
Management Assoc. (C), MD, *424*
Management Recruiters of Colorado, Inc. (C), CO, *442*
Management Recruiters of Woodbury Inc. (C), NY, *455*
Management Recruiters of Westmoreland County, Inc. (C), PA, *459*
Management Recruiters of Pittsburgh-North, Inc. (C), PA, *460*
Management Recruiters of Myrtle Beach, Inc. (C), SC, *460*
Management Recruiters of Lubbock (C), TX, *463*
Management Resources (C), TX, *467*
Management Search Assoc., Inc. (C), GA, *467*
Manuso, Alexander & Associates, Inc. (R), NY, *135*
Marcus & Assoc. (C), NY, *469*
Louis Thomas Masterson & Co. (R), OH, *138*
The Mayes Group, Ltd. (R), PA, *139*
McKavis Assoc. (C), CA, *475*
MDR Associates, Inc. (C), FL, *476*
Med-Ex Services (C), OH, *476*
Medfall Inc. (C), ON, *476*
Medical Recruiters Exchange (C), AZ, *477*
Medical Search of America, Inc. (C), GA, *477*
Medicorp, Inc. (C), MO, *477*
Medserve & Assoc. Inc. (C), MD, *478*
Martin H. Meisel Assoc., Inc. (R), NY, *143*
Meng, Finseth & Assoc., Inc. (R), CA, *143*
Merlin Int'l. Inc. (C), NJ, *479*
E. J. Michaels, Ltd. (C), NY, *481*
Moffitt Int'l., Inc. (R), NC, *146*
Morgan Int'l., Inc. (R), IL, *147*
MSI Int'l. (C), GA, *486*
P. J. Murphy & Assoc., Inc. (R), WI, *150*
New Dawn Employment Search (C), CA, *491*
Nino Recruiting & Staffing, Inc. (C), TX, *493*
Ira Z. Nitzberg (C), NY, *493*
Norman Broadbent Int'l., Inc. (R), NY, *152*
Odell & Assoc., Inc. (C), TX, *498*
Robert Ottke Assoc. (R), CA, *157*
Pathfinders Int'l. (C), MI, *504*
Patriot Assoc. (C), PA, *505*
PCD Partners (R), PA, *161*
Pharmaceutical Search Professionals, Inc. (C), PA, *510*
Physician Associates (C), HI, *511*
Physician Executive Management Center (R), FL, *164*
Physician Recruiting Services, Inc. (C), MO, *511*
Physicians Search®, Inc. (C), CA, *511*
Place Mart Personnel Service (C), NJ, *513*
Plemmons Assoc., Inc. (R), GA, *165*
Practice Dynamics, Inc. (C), TX, *515*
Premier Business Advisors (C), PA, *516*
Premier Healthcare Recruiters, Inc. (C), MI, *516*
Primary Care Service Corp. (C), GA, *518*
Priority Executive Search (C), FL, *518*
PRO, Inc./Professional Recruiting Offices, Inc. (C), CA, *519*
Professional Placement Assoc., Inc. (C), NY, *521*
Professionals in Recruiting Co. (C), TN, *523*
Quigley Assoc. (R), MD, *170*
Quiring Assoc., Inc. (C), IN, *527*
Recruiters Professional Network - Fairview (C), MO, *531*
Reeder & Assoc., Ltd. (R), GA, *173*
Retis Assoc., Inc. (C), IL, *535*
Roevin Technical People (C), ON, *540*
Romeo-Hudgins & Assoc., Ltd. (C), NJ, *544*
The Rose Search Group, Inc. (C), NC, *545*
Roth Young of Pittsburgh (C), PA, *546*
Roth Young of Tampa (C), FL, *546*
David Rowe & Assoc., Inc. (R), IL, *182*
Royal Assoc. (C), CA, *547*
Sales Consultants of Austin, Inc. (C), TX, *562*
Sales Consultants of Pittsburgh (C), PA, *562*
Sanford Rose Assoc. (C), OH, *565*
A.D. Schiff & Assoc., Ltd. (C), IL, *572*
Scott Douglas Inc. (C), CA, *573*
Scott Sibley Assoc. (C), NY, *573*
The Search Committee (C), MD, *574*
Searchworks, Inc. (C), FL, *577*
Selective Search Associates (C), OH, *578*
Sherriff & Assoc. (C), KS, *580*
Skupsky & Assoc. (C), CO, *582*
Smith, Brown & Jones (C), KS, *585*
Snelling Search (C), LA, *586*
Phyllis Solomon Executive Search, Inc. (C), NJ, *587*
Solomon-Page Healthcare Group (R), NY, *195*
SpencerStuart (R), NY, *196*
Stanton Chase Int'l. (R), MD, *198*
Daniel Stern & Assoc. (C), PA, *592*
Trillium Human Resources Inc. (C), ON, *609*
TriStaff Group (C), CA, *609*
USA Medical Placement Inc. (C), TX, *611*
Vezan Assoc. (C), CT, *612*
K. K. Walker Professional Recruitment (C), CA, *614*
Warring & Assoc. (R), CA, *215*
Weatherby Healthcare (C), CT, *617*
WestPacific National Search, Inc. (C), CA, *619*
The Whitaker Companies (C), TX, *619*
The Whittaker Group (C), MI, *620*
Walter K. Wilkins & Co. (R), NJ, *221*
The Winchester Group (R), CA, *222*
Witt/Kieffer, Ford, Hadelman & Lloyd (R), IL, *223*
Worldwide Medical Services (C), CA, *625*
Zackrison Assoc., Inc. (C), FL, *627*
Zurick, Davis & Co., Inc. (R), MA, *227*

04.2 Nurses

Adept Tech Recruiting, Inc. (C), NY, *240*
Alliance Search Management Inc. (R), TX, *4*
American Group Practice, Inc. (R), NY, *5*
American Medical Consultants, Inc. (C), FL, *247*
American Medical Recruiters (C), CO, *248*
American Medical Recruiting Co. Inc. (C), MS, *248*
R & J Arnold & Assoc., Inc. (C), CO, *253*
The Bales-Waugh Group (C), FL, *258*
Cadillac Assoc. (C), CA, *278*
Career Counseling Ltd. (C.C.L.) (C), NY, *282*
Career Images (C), FL, *282*
Career Profiles (C), NH, *283*
Career Strategies, Inc. (C), CA, *283*
CEC Associates (R), MA, *32*
Cemco, Ltd. (C), IL, *286*
The Century Group (C), KS, *287*
Chamberlain Assoc. (C), GA, *288*
Circlewood Search Group, Inc. (C), MI, *291*
Claimsearch (C), CA, *291*
Concorde Staff Source Inc. (C), WI, *296*
Cornerstone Search Assoc. Inc. (C), MA, *299*
CRI Professional Search (C), CA, *303*
Daudlin, De Beaupre & Co., Inc. (R), MI, *46*
Davis-Smith, Inc. (C), MI, *309*
Delta Medical Search Assoc. (C), OH, *310*
Diversified Search, Inc. (R), PA, *52*
DNA Search, Inc. (C), CA, *313*
Doherty Healthcare Consultants (C), ME, *313*
M. Dunbar & Assoc. (C), TX, *316*
Dunhill Professional Search of Tampa (C), FL, *320*
Dunhill Staffing Systems (C), NC, *321*
William J. Elam & Assoc. (R), NE, *58*
Elite Medical Search (C), GA, *328*
Ensearch Management Consultants (C), CA, *331*
Executive Recruitment Specialists, Inc. (R), NC, *63*
Fallstaff Search (C), MD, *338*
James Feerst & Assoc., Inc. (C), AZ, *339*
James L. Fisk & Assoc. (C), MO, *342*
Foley Proctor Yoskowitz (R), NJ, *69*
Foster Partners (R), NY, *70*
The Franklin Search Group, Inc./Medzilla (R), WA, *71*
Gable Healthcare Group, Inc. (R), FL, *73*
Garrett Assoc. Inc. (R), GA, *75*
Garrison-Randall, Inc. (R), CA, *75*
John Gilbert Co. (C), TX, *357*
Gilmore & Assoc. (C), CA, *357*
Sheila Greco Assoc. (C), NY, *362*
Growth Consultants of America (R), MI, *82*

Guidry & East Healthcare Search Consultants (R), TX, *83*
Harper Associates (C), MI, *369*
Harrington & O'Brien, Inc. (C), NH, *369*
Health Network USA (C), TX, *371*
Health Search (C), CA, *371*
Health Search, Inc. (C), KS, *371*
Healthcare Executive Recruiters, Inc. (C), CA, *372*
Healthcare Recruiters Int'l. Phoenix (C), AZ, *372*
Healthcare Recruiters of Indiana (C), IN, *372*
Healthcare Recruiters of New England (C), MA, *373*
Healthcare Recruiters of Midsouth (C), TN, *373*
Healthcare Recruiters Int'l. Philadelphia (C), NJ, *373*
Healthcare Resources Group (C), OK, *374*
Healthcare Search Associates (C), CA, *374*
HealthSearch Assoc. (C), MD, *374*
The Healthsearch Group, Inc. (C), NY, *374*
Heartland National Medical Search (C), IL, *374*
Bruce Henry Assoc. Inc. (R), CA, *91*
The Hogan Group (C), OH, *380*
Home Health & Hospital Recruiters, Inc. (C), GA, *380*
Horizon Medical Search of NH (C), NH, *381*
Hunter Douglas Group, Inc. (R), IL, *99*
innovativestaffsearch (C), TX, *389*
Isaacson, Miller (R), MA, *104*
ISC of Cincinnati Inc. (C), OH, *394*
Jackson & Coker (C), GA, *396*
JDC Assoc. (C), NY, *397*
J. M. Johnson & Assoc. (C), MN, *399*
Roye Johnston Assoc., Inc. (C), CA, *400*
JPM International (C), CA, *401*
Karp & Assoc. (C), FL, *403*
A.T. Kearney Executive Search (R), IL, *111*
Kressenberg Assoc. (C), TX, *409*
Lam Assoc. (C), HI, *411*
Larson, Katz & Young, Inc. (C), VA, *413*
Loderman & Costello (C), GA, *419*
Major Legal Services, Inc. (C), OH, *423*
Management Recruiters of Mobile Co., Inc. (C), AL, *438*
Management Recruiters of Little Rock (C), AR, *439*
Management Recruiters of Monterey (C), CA, *441*
Management Recruiters of Colorado, Inc. (C), CO, *442*
Management Recruiters of Atlanta North, Inc. (C), GA, *446*
Management Recruiters of Kinston (C), NC, *456*
Management Recruiters of Westmoreland County, Inc. (C), PA, *459*
Management Recruiters - Friendswood (C), TX, *462*
Management Recruiters of Lubbock (C), TX, *463*
Management Resources (C), TX, *467*
Management Search Assoc., Inc. (C), GA, *467*
The Mayes Group, Ltd. (R), PA, *139*
McKavis Assoc. (C), CA, *475*
MDR Associates, Inc. (C), FL, *476*
Med-Ex Services (C), OH, *476*
Medical Recruiters Exchange (C), AZ, *477*
Medical Recruiters Inc. (C), MO, *477*
Medical Search of America, Inc. (C), GA, *477*
Medicorp, Inc. (C), MO, *477*
MedPro Personnel, Inc. (C), GA, *478*
Medserve & Assoc. Inc. (C), MD, *478*
Martin H. Meisel Assoc., Inc. (R), NY, *143*
E. J. Michaels, Ltd. (C), NY, *481*
MSI Int'l. (C), GA, *486*
Pamela L. Mulligan, Inc. (R), NH, *149*
National Career Search (C), AZ, *489*
National Search, Inc.r (C), FL, *490*
New Dawn Employment Search (C), CA, *491*
Norman Broadbent Int'l., Inc. (R), NY, *152*
The Normyle/Erstling Health Search Group (C), NJ, *494*
Nursing Technomics (R), PA, *153*
Odell & Assoc., Inc. (C), TX, *498*
Omni Search, Inc. (C), CA, *499*
Orion Int'l. Consulting Group, Inc. (C), NC, *499*
Robert Ottke Assoc. (R), CA, *157*
Largent Parks & Partners (C), TX, *503*
Pathfinders (C), CA, *504*
Pathfinders Int'l. (C), MI, *504*
Patriot Assoc. (C), PA, *505*
Pearson & Assoc., Inc. (C), AZ, *506*
Physician Associates (C), HI, *511*
Physicians Search®, Inc. (C), CA, *511*
Place Mart Personnel Service (C), NJ, *513*
Presley Consultants, Inc. (C), CA, *517*
Priority Executive Search (C), FL, *518*
Professional Healthcare Search & Consultants, Inc. (C), CA, *520*
Professional Placement Assoc., Inc. (C), NY, *521*
Professional Resource Group, Inc. (C), IN, *522*
Professionals in Recruiting Co. (C), TN, *523*
Questor Consultants, Inc. (C), PA, *527*
R.A.N. Assoc., Inc. (C), OH, *528*
Lea Randolph & Assoc., Inc. (C), TX, *529*
Recruiters Professional Network - Fairview (C), MO, *531*
Recruitment Specialists, Inc. (C), MD, *532*
Retis Assoc., Inc. (C), IL, *535*
Roevin Technical People (C), ON, *540*
Rogish Assoc., Inc. (C), OH, *541*
The Rose Search Group, Inc. (C), NC, *545*
David Rowe & Assoc., Inc. (R), IL, *182*
Royal Assoc. (C), CA, *547*
The Rubicon Group (C), AZ, *547*
Sales Consultants Peninsula, Inc. (C), CA, *556*
Scott Sibley Assoc. (C), NY, *573*
Selective Search Associates (C), OH, *578*
Peggy Shea & Assoc. (R), CA, *189*
Solomon-Page Healthcare Group (R), NY, *195*
SpencerStuart (R), NY, *196*
Stanton Chase Int'l. (R), MD, *198*
The Synergy Organization (R), PA, *205*
TechFind, Inc. (R), MA, *207*
Trillium Human Resources Inc. (C), ON, *609*
Tuft & Assoc., Inc. (R), IL, *212*
USA Medical Placement Inc. (C), TX, *611*
Vezan Assoc. (C), CT, *612*
K. K. Walker Professional Recruitment (C), CA, *614*
Watring & Assoc., Inc. (C), IL, *616*
Wellington Thomas Ltd. (C), FL, *618*
The Whittaker Group (C), MI, *620*
Windsor Consultants, Inc. (C), TX, *622*
Witt/Kieffer, Ford, Hadelman & Lloyd (R), IL, *223*
Worldwide Medical Services (C), CA, *625*

04.3 Allied health (e.g. chiropractors, therapists, psychologists)

ACC Consultants, Inc. (C), NM, *233*
Adept Tech Recruiting, Inc. (C), NY, *240*
Alliance Search Management Inc. (R), TX, *4*
American Executive Search (C), FL, *247*
American Group Practice, Inc. (R), NY, *5*
American Medical Consultants, Inc. (C), FL, *247*
American Medical Recruiters (C), CO, *248*
Anderson & Associates (R), NC, *5*
Avestruz & Assoc. (C), CA, *257*
The Bales-Waugh Group (C), FL, *258*
Cadillac Assoc. (C), CA, *278*
Cantrell & Assoc. (C), FL, *280*
Career Counseling Ltd. (C.C.L.) (C), NY, *282*
Circlewood Search Group, Inc. (C), MI, *291*
Concorde Staff Source Inc. (C), WI, *296*
The Consortium (C), NY, *296*
Continental Research Search, Inc. (C), WI, *298*
Cook Assoc. Int'l., Inc. (C), TN, *298*
Cornerstone Resources, Inc. (C), OK, *299*
Cypress Int'l., Inc. (R), FL, *45*
The Danielson Group, Inc. (C), TX, *306*
Daudlin, De Beaupre & Co., Inc. (R), MI, *46*
Davis-Smith, Inc. (C), MI, *309*
Delacore Resources (C), MN, *310*
Delta Medical Search Assoc. (C), OH, *310*
Delta ProSearch (C), PA, *311*
Doherty Healthcare Consultants (C), ME, *313*
M. Dunbar & Assoc. (C), TX, *316*
Dunhill Staffing Systems (C), NC, *321*
Ensearch Management Consultants (C), CA, *331*
Executive Recruitment Specialists, Inc. (R), NC, *63*
Executive Referral Services, Inc. (C), IL, *334*
Fallstaff Search (C), MD, *338*
Foley Proctor Yoskowitz (R), NJ, *69*
Foster Partners (R), NY, *70*
Gable Healthcare Group, Inc. (R), FL, *73*
Gielow Assoc., Inc. (R), WI, *76*

Guidry & East Healthcare Search Consultants (R), TX, *83*
Harper Associates (C), MI, *369*
Harrington & O'Brien, Inc. (C), NH, *369*
Health Care Plus, Inc. (C), MD, *371*
Health Network USA (C), TX, *371*
Health Search (C), CA, *371*
Health Search, Inc. (C), KS, *371*
Healthcare Recruiters of New England (C), MA, *373*
Healthcare Resources Group (C), OK, *374*
Healthcare Search Associates (C), CA, *374*
HealthSearch Assoc. (C), MD, *374*
The Healthsearch Group, Inc. (C), NY, *374*
Heartland National Medical Search (C), IL, *374*
Hitchens & Foster, Inc. (C), MO, *379*
Horizon Medical Search of NH (C), NH, *381*
Hunter Douglas Group, Inc. (R), IL, *99*
Icon Recruiters, LLC (C), CA, *387*
innovativestaffsearch (C), TX, *389*
Isaacson, Miller (R), MA, *104*
Jackson & Coker (C), GA, *396*
JDC Assoc. (C), NY, *397*
J. M. Johnson & Assoc. (C), MN, *399*
A.T. Kearney Executive Search (R), IL, *111*
Lake Medical Associates (C), ME, *411*
Lam Assoc. (C), HI, *411*
Management Recruiters of Colorado, Inc. (C), CO, *442*
Management Recruiters of Houston (C), TX, *462*
Management Recruiters of Austin (C), TX, *462*
Management Recruiters - Friendswood (C), TX, *462*
Management Recruiters of Lubbock (C), TX, *463*
Management Search Assoc., Inc. (C), GA, *467*
Med-Ex Services (C), OH, *476*
Medical Recruiters Exchange (C), AZ, *477*
Medical Search of America, Inc. (C), GA, *477*
MedSearch Resources, Inc. (C), FL, *478*
Medserve & Assoc. Inc. (C), MD, *478*
Martin H. Meisel Assoc., Inc. (R), NY, *143*
Mitchell Martin Inc. (C), NY, *483*
Morgan Samuels Co. (R), CA, *147*
The Morley Group (C), IN, *486*
MSI Int'l. (C), GA, *486*
National Search, Inc.r (C), FL, *490*
New Dawn Employment Search (C), CA, *491*
Nino Recruiting & Staffing, Inc. (C), TX, *493*
Norman Broadbent Int'l., Inc. (R), NY, *152*
Pathfinders Int'l. (C), MI, *504*
Pearson & Assoc., Inc. (C), AZ, *506*
The Personnel Network, Inc. (C), SC, *508*
Physicians Search®, Inc. (C), CA, *511*
Plante & Moran, LLP (R), MI, *165*
Prichard Kymen Inc. (R), AB, *168*
Priority Executive Search (C), FL, *518*
Protocol Inc. (C), CA, *525*
Recruiters Professional Network - Fairview (C), MO, *531*
Recruitment Specialists, Inc. (C), MD, *532*
Retis Assoc., Inc. (C), IL, *535*
The Rose Search Group, Inc. (C), NC, *545*
Roth Young Executive Recruiters (C), MN, *546*
Roth Young of Pittsburgh (C), PA, *546*
Roth Young of Tampa (C), FL, *546*
Scott Sibley Assoc. (C), NY, *573*
Peggy Shea & Assoc. (R), CA, *189*
Sherriff & Assoc. (C), KS, *580*
SpencerStuart (R), NY, *196*
The Synergy Organization (R), PA, *205*
Trillium Human Resources Inc. (C), ON, *609*
Vezan Assoc. (C), CT, *612*
K. K. Walker Professional Recruitment (C), CA, *614*
Zurick, Davis & Co., Inc. (R), MA, *227*

04.4 Administration

A.K.S. Assoc., Ltd. (R), MA, *1*
ACC Consultants, Inc. (C), NM, *233*
ADR Accounting Management Recruiters (C), ON, *240*
J. R. Akin & Co. (R), MA, *2*
Albrecht & Assoc., Executive Search Consultants (C), TX, *243*
Jay Allen & Assoc. (C), FL, *244*
Alliance Search Management Inc. (R), TX, *4*
AMD & Associates (C), GA, *247*
American Group Practice, Inc. (R), NY, *5*
American Medical Consultants, Inc. (C), FL, *247*
American Medical Recruiters (C), CO, *248*
American Medical Recruiting Co. Inc. (C), MS, *248*
Amherst Human Resource Group, Ltd. (C), IL, *249*
Anderson & Associates (R), NC, *5*
R & J Arnold & Assoc., Inc. (C), CO, *253*
Aster Search Group (R), NY, *8*
Atlantic Pacific Group (C), CA, *255*
Auerbach Associates, Inc. (R), MA, *9*
J. W. Barleycorn, Renard & Assoc., Inc. (R), OH, *11*
Barnes Development Group, LLC (R), WI, *11*
Battalia Winston Int'l./The Euram Consultants Group (R), NY, *13*
BCG Search, Inc. (R), FL, *14*
Neail Behringer Consultants Inc. (R), NY, *15*
Joy Reed Belt Search Consultants, Inc. (R), OK, *15*
Billington & Assoc. (R), CA, *17*
Boone-Scaturro Assoc., Inc. (C), GA, *269*
Boulware & Assoc. Inc. (R), IL, *20*
Boyden (R), NY, *20*
BR & Assoc. (C), NJ, *271*
Bradford Executives Int'l. (C), VA, *271*
Bernard E. Brooks & Assoc., Inc. (R), SC, *24*
The Burke Group (C), ON, *276*
Joseph R. Burns & Assoc., Inc. (R), NJ, *25*
Career Counseling Ltd. (C.C.L.) (C), NY, *282*
CEC Associates (R), MA, *32*
Cejka Healthcare Executive Search Services (CHESS) (R), MO, *32*
Cemco, Ltd. (C), IL, *286*
The Century Group (C), KS, *287*
Chamberlain Assoc. (C), GA, *288*
Vickers Chambless Managed Search (C), GA, *288*
Christian & Timbers, Inc. (R), OH, *34*
Circlewood Search Group, Inc. (C), MI, *291*
CMS, Inc. (C), NH, *293*
Concorde Staff Source Inc. (C), WI, *296*
Continental Research Search, Inc. (C), WI, *298*
Cook Assoc. Int'l., Inc. (C), TN, *298*
P. G. Cook Assoc. (R), TN, *40*
Cornerstone Search Assoc. Inc. (C), MA, *299*
Creative Management Strategies, Ltd. (R), NY, *42*
CRI Professional Search (C), CA, *303*
Cypress Int'l., Inc. (R), FL, *45*
Alan Darling Consulting (R), VT, *46*
Daudlin, De Beaupre & Co., Inc. (R), MI, *46*
Davies, Park (R), AB, *46*
Davis-Smith, Inc. (C), MI, *309*
DeCorrevont & Assoc. (C), IL, *310*
Delta Medical Search Assoc. (C), OH, *310*
Development Resource Group (R), NY, *48*
Roger Dietsch & Assoc. (C), MN, *312*
Discovery, The Staffing Specialists, Inc. (C), IL, *312*
Diversified Search, Inc. (R), PA, *52*
DNA Search, Inc. (C), CA, *313*
Doherty Healthcare Consultants (C), ME, *313*
Dotson & Assoc. (R), NY, *54*
Drew Assoc. Int'l. (R), NJ, *54*
M. Dunbar & Assoc. (C), TX, *316*
Dunhill Professional Search of Tampa (C), FL, *320*
Dunhill Staffing Systems (C), NC, *321*
Dunhill Personnel Service of Fargo (C), ND, *322*
William J. Elam & Assoc. (R), NE, *58*
Elite Medical Search (C), GA, *328*
EMN/Witt/Kieffer (R), MA, *59*
ENI (R), CT, *59*
Ensearch Management Consultants (C), CA, *331*
Executive Careers (R), CA, *62*
Executive Dimensions (R), NY, *62*
Executive Manning Corp. (R), FL, *63*
Executive Solutions (R), MN, *64*
Eyler Assoc., Inc. (R), IA, *64*
Fagan & Company (R), PA, *64*
Faro Consultants Int'l. (C), VA, *338*
James Feerst & Assoc., Inc. (C), AZ, *339*
Focus Consulting Services, Inc. (C), FL, *342*
Foley Proctor Yoskowitz (R), NJ, *69*
F-O-R-T-U-N-E Personnel Consultants of Troy, Inc. (C), MI, *347*
Foster Partners (R), NY, *70*
Franklin Allen Consultants, Ltd. (R), NY, *71*
Furst Group/MPI (R), IL, *72*
Gable Healthcare Group, Inc. (R), FL, *73*

The Gammill Group, Inc. (C), OH, *354*
Gardner-Ross Assoc., Inc. (R), NY, *74*
Garrett Assoc. Inc. (R), GA, *75*
Garrison-Randall, Inc. (R), CA, *75*
Gielow Assoc., Inc. (R), WI, *76*
John Gilbert Co. (C), TX, *357*
Global Resources Group (R), CA, *78*
Robert G. Godfrey Assoc. Ltd. (R), IL, *78*
Barry M. Gold & Co. (C), CA, *359*
Robert Graham Assoc. (R), RI, *81*
J. B. Groner Executive Search, Inc. (C), DE, *363*
Growth Consultants of America (R), MI, *82*
Guidry & East Healthcare Search Consultants (R), TX, *83*
Hanley & Assoc. (R), FL, *86*
Harper Associates (C), MI, *369*
Health Care Dimensions (C), CO, *371*
Health Care Plus, Inc. (C), MD, *371*
Health Network USA (C), TX, *371*
Health Search (C), CA, *371*
Healthcare Executive Recruiters, Inc. (C), CA, *372*
Healthcare Recruiters Int'l. Phoenix (C), AZ, *372*
Healthcare Recruiters of Midsouth (C), TN, *373*
Healthcare Recruiters - Northwest (C), WA, *374*
Healthcare Search Associates (C), CA, *374*
HealthSearch Assoc. (C), MD, *374*
The Healthsearch Group, Inc. (C), NY, *374*
Heartland National Medical Search (C), IL, *374*
Hersher Assoc., Ltd. (R), IL, *92*
Hitchens & Foster, Inc. (C), MO, *379*
Home Health & Hospital Recruiters, Inc. (C), GA, *380*
Horizon Medical Search of NH (C), NH, *381*
HR Consultants (C), GA, *382*
Hunter Douglas Group, Inc. (R), IL, *99*
The Hunter Group, Inc. (C), MI, *385*
The Hutton Group, Inc. (C), FL, *386*
IM Independent Management Recruiters (R), TN, *101*
IMA Search, Inc. (R), NY, *101*
Ingram & Aydelotte, Inc. (R), NY, *101*
Innovative Partnerships (R), CA, *101*
innovativestaffsearch (C), TX, *389*
Insurance Search (C), TX, *390*
Intech Summit Group, Inc. (R), CA, *102*
Interim Financial Solutions - Mid-Atlantic Region (C), MD, *392*
Isaacson, Miller (R), MA, *104*
ISC of Cincinnati Inc. (C), OH, *394*
Jackson & Coker (C), GA, *396*
J. M. Johnson & Assoc. (C), MN, *399*
Judd Associates (R), NJ, *109*
Katelyn Partners (C), FL, *404*
A.T. Kearney Executive Search (R), IL, *111*
Kittleman & Assoc.,LLC (R), IL, *115*
Lee Koehn Assoc., Inc. (R), OR, *116*
Korn/Ferry Int'l. (R), NY, *117*
The J. Kovach Group (R), PA, *119*
Kressenberg Assoc. (C), TX, *409*
Lam Assoc. (C), HI, *411*
Lawrence L. Lapham, Inc. (R), NY, *124*
Reynolds Lebus Assoc. (C), AZ, *415*
Levison Search Assoc. (R), CA, *129*
Lewis & Blank Int'l. (R), CA, *129*
Lloyd Prescott Assoc., Inc. (C), FL, *418*
Loderman & Costello (C), GA, *419*
Logic Assoc., Inc. (C), NY, *419*
Longshore + Simmons (R), PA, *131*
Managed Care Resources (C), TX, *424*
Management & Human Resources (R), MA, *134*
Management Recruiters of Mobile Co., Inc. (C), AL, *438*
Management Recruiters of Berkeley (C), CA, *439*
Management Recruiters of Monterey (C), CA, *441*
Management Recruiters of Colorado, Inc. (C), CO, *442*
Management Recruiters of Clearwater (C), FL, *443*
Management Recruiters of Tampa North (C), FL, *444*
Management Recruiters of Washington, DC Inc. (C), MD, *450*
Management Recruiters of Frederick, Inc. (C), MD, *450*
Management Recruiters of North Oakland County, Inc. (C), MI, *452*
Management Recruiters of Cleveland (C), OH, *457*
Management Recruiters of Westmoreland County, Inc. (C), PA, *459*
Management Recruiters of Pittsburgh (C), PA, *459*
Management Recruiters of Pittsburgh-North, Inc. (C), PA, *460*
Management Recruiters of Myrtle Beach, Inc. (C), SC, *460*
Management Recruiters of Houston (C), TX, *462*
Management Recruiters - Friendswood (C), TX, *462*
Management Recruiters of Lubbock (C), TX, *463*
Management Recruiters of San Antonio - North (C), TX, *463*
Management Recruiters of Salt Lake City (C), UT, *464*
Management Recruiters of Seattle (C), WA, *465*
Management Recruiters of Lynnwood (C), WA, *465*
Management Resources (C), TX, *467*
Management Search Assoc., Inc. (C), GA, *467*
Louis Thomas Masterson & Co. (R), OH, *138*
Matthews & Stephens Assoc., Inc. (C), CT, *472*
The Mayes Group, Ltd. (R), PA, *139*
McHale & Assoc. (R), WA, *141*
McKavis Assoc. (C), CA, *475*
MDR Associates, Inc. (C), FL, *476*
Med-Ex Services (C), OH, *476*
Meder & Assoc., Inc. (R), IL, *142*
Medfall Inc. (C), ON, *476*
Medical Recruiters Exchange (C), AZ, *477*
Medical Search of America, Inc. (C), GA, *477*
Medicorp, Inc. (C), MO, *477*
MedPro Personnel, Inc. (C), GA, *478*
MedSearch Resources, Inc. (C), FL, *478*
Meridian Resources (C), OH, *479*
E. J. Michaels, Ltd. (C), NY, *481*
Mruk & E.M.A. Partners (R), NY, *148*
MSA Executive Search (R), MO, *148*
R. F. Mulvaney & Assoc., Inc. (R), MO, *149*
Nason & Nason (C), FL, *488*
National Career Search (C), AZ, *489*
National Search, Inc.r (C), FL, *490*
NDI Services (R), MI, *151*
New Dawn Employment Search (C), CA, *491*
New World Healthcare Solutions, Inc. (R), NY, *151*
Newell Assoc. (R), NY, *151*
J. L. Nixon Consulting (C), TX, *493*
Paul Winston Norman & Assoc. (R), IL, *152*
Norman Broadbent Int'l., Inc. (R), NY, *152*
O'Connor Resources (C), TX, *497*
The Oldani Group (R), WA, *155*
Omni Search, Inc. (C), CA, *499*
Robert Ottke Assoc. (R), CA, *157*
P.A.R. Assoc., Inc. (R), MA, *158*
Parker Page Group (C), FL, *503*
The Partnership Group (R), NJ, *160*
Pathfinders Int'l. (C), MI, *504*
Joel H. Paul & Assoc., Inc. (C), NY, *505*
PCD Partners (R), PA, *161*
Pearson & Assoc., Inc. (C), AZ, *506*
People Management Mid-South, LLC (R), TN, *162*
Perfect Search, Inc. (C), FL, *507*
Phillips & Assoc. (R), MA, *164*
Physician Associates (C), HI, *511*
Physicians Search®, Inc. (C), CA, *511*
Picard Int'l., Ltd. (R), NY, *164*
Plemmons Assoc., Inc. (R), GA, *165*
Premier Healthcare Recruiters, Inc. (C), MI, *516*
PricewaterhouseCoopers Executive Search (R), ON, *168*
Princeton Search Partners, Inc. (R), NJ, *169*
Prior/Martech Assoc., Inc. (R), WA, *169*
Priority Executive Search (C), FL, *518*
Professional Healthcare Search & Consultants, Inc. (C), CA, *520*
Professional Placement Assoc., Inc. (C), NY, *521*
Professionals in Recruiting Co. (C), TN, *523*
Quetico Corp. (R), TX, *170*
Quigley Assoc. (R), MD, *170*
L. J. Quinn & Assoc., Inc. (R), CA, *170*
Lea Randolph & Assoc., Inc. (C), TX, *529*
Ray & Berndtson/Tanton Mitchell (R), BC, *173*
Recruiters Professional Network - Fairview (C), MO, *531*
Recruitment Specialists, Inc. (C), MD, *532*
Reeder & Assoc., Ltd. (R), GA, *173*
Response Staffing Services (C), NY, *534*
Retis Assoc., Inc. (C), IL, *535*
Russell Reynolds Assoc., Inc. (R), NY, *176*
Marshall Rice Assoc. (R), RI, *177*

Norman Roberts & Assoc., Inc. (R), CA, *179*
Rodgers, Ramsey, Inc. (C), TX, *540*
The Rogan Group, Inc. (C), CA, *541*
Rogish Assoc., Inc. (C), OH, *541*
Romac Int'l. (C), PA, *542*
The Rose Search Group, Inc. (C), NC, *545*
David Rowe & Assoc., Inc. (R), IL, *182*
The Rubicon Group (C), AZ, *547*
Rushmore • Judge Inc. (R), ON, *183*
Sales Consultants of Birmingham (C), AL, *555*
Sampson Medical Search (C), CA, *564*
George D. Sandel Assoc. (C), MA, *565*
Sanford Rose Assoc. - Louisville (C), KY, *567*
Sanford Rose Assoc. - Columbia (C), SC, *570*
A.D. Schiff & Assoc., Ltd. (C), IL, *572*
G. L. Schwartz & Assoc., Inc. (C), GA, *572*
Scott Sibley Assoc. (C), NY, *573*
The Search Committee (C), MD, *574*
Search Research Assoc., Inc. (R), MA, *187*
Peggy Shea & Assoc. (R), CA, *189*
Sherriff & Assoc. (C), KS, *580*
Michael Shirley Assoc. Inc. (R), KS, *190*
Howard W. Smith Assoc. (R), CT, *193*
Sockwell & Assoc. (R), NC, *194*
Solutions Group (R), AL, *195*
SpencerStuart (R), NY, *196*
Stanton Chase Int'l. (R), MD, *198*
STAT Search (C), NH, *592*
Daniel Stern & Assoc. (C), PA, *592*
Stewart, Stein & Scott, Ltd. (R), MN, *200*
Sullivan & Assoc. (R), MI, *204*
The Synergy Organization (R), PA, *205*
Telford, Adams & Alexander (R), CA, *208*
TriStaff Group (C), CA, *609*
Triumph Consulting, Inc. (R), IA, *210*
W. G. Tucker & Assoc. (R), PA, *211*
The Thomas Tucker Co. (R), CA, *211*
Tuft & Assoc., Inc. (R), IL, *212*
Tyler & Company (R), GA, *212*
United Personnel Services (C), MA, *611*
USA Medical Placement Inc. (C), TX, *611*
Van Dyke Assoc. (R), IL, *212*
Vezan Assoc. (C), CT, *612*
K. K. Walker Professional Recruitment (C), CA, *614*
Weatherby Healthcare (C), CT, *617*
Wellington Management Group (R), PA, *217*
Wellington Thomas Ltd. (C), FL, *618*
Whitney Smith Co. (C), TX, *620*
The Whittaker Group (C), MI, *620*
Wilcox Bertoux & Miller (R), CA, *220*
Walter K. Wilkins & Co. (R), NJ, *221*
Windsor Consultants, Inc. (C), TX, *622*
Winthrop Partners, Inc. (R), NY, *222*
Wood & Assoc./Executive Search Consultants (C), CA, *624*
Worldwide Medical Services (C), CA, *625*
The York Group (C), CA, *626*
Zurick, Davis & Co., Inc. (R), MA, *227*

05.0 Sales & marketing

The 500 Granary Inc. (C), ON, *231*
A C Personnel Services, Inc. (C), OK, *231*
A la Carte Int'l., Inc. (R), VA, *1*
A Permanent Success Employment Services (C), CA, *231*
A. D. & Assoc. Executive Search, Inc. (C), GA, *231*
A.J. & Assoc. (C), FL, *232*
A.L.S. Group (C), NJ, *232*
Abbott Associates (R), CA, *1*
The Abbott Group, Inc. (R), MD, *1*
Abécassis Conseil (R), QE, *1*
Abeln, Magy & Assoc., Inc. (R), MN, *1*
Abraham & London Ltd. (C), CT, *232*
B. J. Abrams & Assoc. Inc. (C), IL, *233*
Accelerated Data Decision, Inc. (C), NJ, *233*
ACCESS Technology (C), CA, *234*
Access/Resources, Inc. (C), MA, *234*
Ackerman Johnson Inc. (C), TX, *238*
ACSYS Resources, Inc. (C), DE, *238*
Action Executive Personnel Consulting Inc. (C), ON, *239*
Action Management Corp. (C), MI, *239*
Arthur Adams & Assoc. (C), OH, *239*
Adams & Assoc. Int'l. (R), IL, *1*
The Addison Consulting Group (C), NJ, *239*
Adirect Recruiting Corp. (C), ON, *240*
Adler Management, Inc. (R), NJ, *2*
ADR Accounting Management Recruiters (C), ON, *240*
Advanced Corporate Search (C), CA, *240*
Advanced Executive Resources (R), MI, *2*
Advancement, Inc. (C), IL, *241*
Advantage Partners, Inc. (R), OH, *2*
Advisors' Search Group, Inc. (C), NY, *241*
The Advisory Group, Inc. (R), CA, *2*
AES Search (C), NJ, *241*
Affinity Executive Search (C), FL, *241*
Affordable Executive Recruiters (C), CA, *241*
Aggressive Corporation (C), IL, *242*
Agra Placements, Ltd. (C), IA, *242*
AGRI-associates (C), MO, *242*
Agri-Personnel (C), GA, *242*
Agriesti & Assoc. (C), CA, *243*
Ahrensdorf & Assoc. (R), PA, *2*
AKH Executive Search (C), OR, *243*
J. R. Akin & Co. (R), MA, *2*
Alexander & Co. (C), CA, *243*
Alexander Associates (R), NJ, *2*
The Alexander Group (R), NJ, *3*
The Alfus Group (R), NY, *3*
Allard Associates (C), CA, *244*
Allen & Assoc. (C), NV, *244*
D. S. Allen Assoc. (C), NJ, *244*
David Allen Assoc. (R), NJ, *3*
Allen Austin Lowe & Powers (R), TX, *3*
Allen Evans Assoc. (R), NY, *4*
Allen, Wayne & Co. LLC (C), WI, *245*
Allen-Jeffers Assoc. (C), CA, *245*
Allen/Associates (R), OH, *4*
Allerton Heneghan & O'Neill (R), IL, *4*
Alliance Executive Search, Inc. (R), MA, *4*
Tom Allison Assoc. (C), NM, *245*
Allstaff, Inc. (C), IL, *245*
Alpha Executive Search (C), AL, *245*
Alpha Resource Group, Inc. (C), TX, *246*
Alpha Resources (C), IL, *246*
Alpha Search (C), FL, *246*
Altec/HRC (C), MI, *246*
The Alternatives Group, Inc. (C), TX, *246*
Amato & Assoc., Inc. (C), CA, *246*
Amato & Associates Insurance Recruiters (C), PA, *247*
Peter W. Ambler Co. (R), TX, *5*
AMD & Associates (C), GA, *247*
American Executive Management, Inc. (R), MA, *5*
American Executive Search (C), FL, *247*
American Heritage Group, Inc. (C), MI, *247*
American Resources Corp. (C), IL, *248*
American Services Group (C), IL, *248*
AmeriPro Search, Inc. (C), NC, *248*
Ames & Ames (R), CA, *5*
Ames-O'Neill Assoc., Inc. (C), NY, *249*
Amherst Human Resource Group, Ltd. (C), IL, *249*
Amherst Personnel Group Inc. (C), NY, *249*
Aminex Corp. (C), MA, *249*
Analytic Recruiting, Inc. (C), NY, *249*
Andre David & Assoc., Inc. (R), TX, *6*
Andrews & Wald Group (C), FL, *250*
Angel Group Int'l. (C), KY, *250*
Tryg R. Angell, Ltd. (C), CT, *250*
Angus Employment Ltd. (C), ON, *250*
The Angus Group, Ltd. (C), OH, *251*
Fred Anthony Assoc. (C), WI, *251*
Anthony Michael & Co. (C), MA, *251*
APA Employment Agency Inc. (C), OR, *251*
APA Search, Inc. (R), NY, *6*
David Aplin & Assoc. (C), AB, *251*
Applied Resources (C), MA, *252*
Applied Resources, Inc. (C), MN, *252*
Applied Search Assoc., Inc. (C), GA, *252*
Charles P. Aquavella & Assoc. (C), TX, *252*
Argonaut Partners, LLC (R), CA, *6*
The Argus Group Corp. (C), ON, *252*
Argus National, Inc. (R), CT, *6*
Ariail & Assoc. (R), NC, *7*
Ariel Recruitment Assoc. (R), NY, *7*
Aries Search Group (C), GA, *252*
ARJay & Assoc. (C), NC, *252*
Armor Personnel (C), ON, *253*
J. S. Armstrong & Assoc., Inc. (R), CA, *7*
Patrick Arnone & Assoc. Inc. (R), VA, *7*
Aronow Assoc., Inc. (C), FL, *253*
Ashford Management Group, Inc. (R), GA, *7*
Ashlar-Stone Management Consultants Inc. (R), ON, *8*
Ashway Ltd. Agency (C), NY, *253*
Ask Guy Tucker (C), GA, *254*
Associated Recruiters (C), WI, *254*
Association for Sales Force Management (C), WA, *254*
Atkinson Search & Placement, Inc. (C), IA, *255*
Atlanta Executive Partners, Inc. (R), MA, *8*
Atlantic Pacific Group (C), CA, *255*
Atlantic West Int'l. (C), NC, *255*
Atomic Personnel, Inc. (C), PA, *255*
Aubin Int'l. Inc. (R), MA, *8*
Aurora Tech Search (C), ON, *256*
Cami Austin & Assoc. (C), IL, *256*

Austin Group Int'l./Marlar Int'l. (R), TX, *9*
Austin Michaels, Ltd., Inc. (C), AZ, *256*
Austin Park Management Group Inc. (C), ON, *256*
Austin, Hill & Assoc. (C), MD, *256*
Austin-McGregor Int'l. (R), TX, *9*
Automation Technology Search (C), CA, *256*
AutoPeople (C), VT, *257*
Avalon Health Group, Inc. (R), NY, *9*
Avery Assoc. (R), CA, *9*
Avestruz & Assoc. (C), CA, *257*
Avondale Search Int'l., Inc. (R), FL, *9*
The Badger Group (R), CA, *10*
Keith Bagg & Assoc., Inc. (C), ON, *257*
D. W. Baird & Associates (C), MD, *257*
Baker Scott & Co. (C), NJ, *258*
Baldwin & Assoc. (C), OH, *258*
Baldwin Associates, LLC (R), CT, *10*
Carol Ball & Co. (C), CT, *258*
Allen Ballach Assoc. Inc. (R), ON, *10*
Ballantyne & Assoc. (R), CA, *10*
Ballos & Co., Inc. (R), NJ, *10*
BallResources (C), MO, *258*
James Bangert & Assoc., Inc. (R), MN, *11*
The Bankers Group (C), IL, *258*
The Barack Group, Inc. (R), NY, *11*
Barclay Consultants, Inc. (C), NJ, *259*
Barger & Sargeant, Inc. (R), NH, *11*
J. W. Barleycorn, Renard & Assoc., Inc. (R), OH, *11*
Barnes & Assoc. Executive Search (C), CA, *259*
Barnes Development Group, LLC (R), WI, *11*
Fred A. Barnette & Assoc. (R), NC, *11*
Barone Assoc. (C), NJ, *259*
Barone-O'Hara Assoc., Inc. (R), NJ, *11*
Barr Assoc. (C), PA, *259*
The Barrett Group (C), NH, *260*
Barrett Hospitality Search (R), CA, *12*
Barrett Rose & Lee, Inc. (C), ON, *260*
Barrington Hart, Inc. (R), IL, *12*
Nathan Barry Assoc., Inc. (R), MA, *12*
Aldonna Barry Personnel & Management (C), ON, *260*
Barth Smith Company (R), IL, *12*
Bartholdi & Co., Inc. (R), CO, *12*
Barton Assoc., Inc. (R), TX, *12*
Bason Associates (R), OH, *13*
Bast & Assoc., Inc. (C), CA, *261*
Battalia Winston Int'l./The Euram Consultants Group (R), NY, *13*
L. Battalin & Co. (C), FL, *261*
R. Gaines Baty Assoc., Inc. (R), TX, *13*
Martin H. Bauman Assoc., Inc. (R), NY, *13*
The Bauman Group (R), CA, *14*
Bayland Assoc. (C), CA, *261*
Beach Executive Search Inc. (R), FL, *14*
Beacon Int'l., Inc. (C), VA, *261*
The Beam Group (R), PA, *14*
The Beardsley Group Inc. (C), CT, *261*
Beck/Eastwood Recruitment Solutions (C), CA, *261*
Becker, Norton & Co. (R), PA, *14*
The Bedford Consulting Group Inc. (R), ON, *14*
The Bedford Group (R), RI, *15*
Robert Beech West Inc. (C), CA, *262*
Behavioral Science Assoc., Inc. (R), AZ, *15*
Behrens and Company (C), WA, *262*
Neail Behringer Consultants Inc. (R), NY, *15*
Belanger Partners Ltd. (C), ON, *262*
Gary S. Bell Assoc., Inc. (C), NJ, *263*
Bell Oaks Co., Inc. (C), GA, *263*
Bell Wishingrad Partners Inc. (R), NY, *15*
Bellamy & Assoc. (C), GA, *263*
Joy Reed Belt Search Consultants, Inc. (R), OK, *15*
Bench Int'l. Search, Inc. (R), CA, *15*
J. P. Bencik Assoc. (C), MI, *263*
Richard L. Bencin & Assoc. (C), OH, *264*
Bender Executive Search Management Consulting (R), NY, *16*
Bennett Search & Consulting Co. (R), FL, *16*
Benson Associates (C), NY, *264*
Dick Berg & Assoc. (C), CA, *264*
Berkana Int'l., Inc. (C), WA, *265*
Berkhemer/Clayton, Inc. (R), CA, *16*
Berkshire Search Assoc. (C), MA, *265*
Bernhart Assoc. (C), MN, *265*
Bertrand, Ross & Assoc., Inc. (C), IL, *266*
Besen Assoc. Inc. (C), NJ, *266*
Best, Coleman & Co., Inc. (R), MA, *16*
BGB Assoc., Inc. (C), IL, *266*
Bialla & Assoc. Inc. (R), CA, *17*
Paul J. Biestek Assoc., Inc. (R), IL, *17*
Binder Hospitality Group (C), KY, *266*
BioQuest Inc. (R), CA, *17*
Birch & Associes (C), QE, *267*
Deborah Bishop & Assoc. (R), CA, *17*
Bishop Partners (R), NY, *17*
BJB Assoc. (C), VA, *267*
Blackhawk Advantage, Inc. (C), CA, *267*
The Blackman Kallick Search Division (C), IL, *267*
J: Blakslee Int'l., Ltd. (R), CA, *18*
Blaney Executive Search (R), MA, *18*
Blanton & Co. (C), AL, *268*
Blau Mancino Schroeder (R), NJ, *18*
David Blevins & Assoc. (C), WA, *268*
Block & Assoc. (R), CA, *18*
Boettcher Assoc. (R), WI, *19*
Tom Bogle & Assoc. (C), CA, *269*
Ann Bond Assoc. Inc. (C), MD, *269*
Bonell Ryan Inc. (R), NY, *19*
Bonifield Assoc. (C), NJ, *269*
Bonnell Assoc. Ltd. (R), CT, *19*
Lynn Borne & Co. (C), CA, *270*
Bornholdt Shivas & Friends Executive Recruiters (C), NY, *270*
The Borton Wallace Co. (R), NC, *19*
Bos Business Consultants (C), NY, *270*
Bosch & Assoc., LLC (R), CT, *19*
Bosco-Hubert & Assoc. (C), KS, *270*
Bosland Gray Assoc. (R), NJ, *20*
Boston Professional Search, Inc. (C), MA, *270*
Boulware & Assoc. Inc. (R), IL, *20*
Bowden & Co., Inc. (R), OH, *20*
BowdenGlobal, Ltd. (R), OH, *20*
Bower & Associates (C), TX, *271*
Bowie & Associates, Inc. (C), MD, *271*
Boyden (R), NY, *20*
Boyle/Ogata Executive Search (R), CA, *21*
BR & Assoc. (C), NJ, *271*
The Bradbury Management Group, Inc. (R), CA, *21*
Bradford Executives Int'l. (C), VA, *271*
M. F. Branch Assoc., Inc. (C), NC, *272*
The Brand Co., Inc. (R), FL, *22*
Brandywine Consulting Group (R), PA, *22*
Brandywine Management Group (R), MD, *22*
Brandywine Retained Ventures, Inc. (R), CT, *22*
Branthover Assoc. (C), NY, *272*
Brault & Assoc., Ltd. (R), VA, *22*
Jerold Braun & Assoc. (C), CA, *272*
The Brentwood Group, Inc. (R), NJ, *22*
The Brentwood Group Ltd. (R), OR, *23*
Brentwood Int'l. (R), CA, *23*
Brethet, Barnum & Assoc., Inc. (C), ON, *273*
Brian Assoc., Inc. (C), NY, *273*
Briant Assoc., Inc. (R), IL, *23*
The Bridge (C), CO, *273*
BridgeGate LLC (C), CA, *273*
Brierwood Group, Inc. (C), IN, *273*
Brigade, Inc. (R), CA, *23*
Bright Search/Professional Staffing (C), MN, *274*
Brissenden, McFarland, Fuccella & Reynolds, Inc. (R), NJ, *23*
Bristol Assoc., Inc. (C), CA, *274*
Britt Assoc., Inc. (C), IL, *274*
Broadband Resource Group (C), CA, *274*
Brooke Chase Assoc., Inc. (R), IL, *24*
Brookman Associates (C), NY, *274*
Broward-Dobbs, Inc. (C), GA, *274*
J. B. Brown & Assoc., Inc. (C), OH, *275*
Brown, Bernardy, Van Remmen, Inc. (C), CA, *275*
Brown Venture Assoc. (R), CA, *24*
Brownstone Sales & Marketing Group, Inc. (C), NY, *275*
Brush Creek Partners (R), MO, *24*
BRW Search (C), MN, *275*
Bryan & Louis Research (C), OH, *275*
BT&A, LLC (R), CT, *24*
Charles Buck & Assoc., Inc. (R), NY, *24*
The Buckley Group (C), FL, *276*
Buckman/Enochs & Assoc., Inc. (C), OH, *276*
The Burgess Group-Corporate Recruiters Int'l., Inc. (R), NY, *25*
J. Burke & Assoc., Inc. (C), TX, *276*
Burke & Assoc./The Westfield Group (C), CT, *276*
J. Burkey Assoc. (R), NJ, *25*
Joseph R. Burns & Assoc., Inc. (R), NJ, *25*
David S. Burt Assoc. (C), MT, *276*
Business Solutions Worldwide, Inc. (C), NJ, *277*
The Butlers Co. Insurance Recruiters (C), FL, *277*
Butterfield & Co. Int'l., Inc. (C), HI, *277*
Button Group (C), TX, *277*
Buzhardt Assoc. (R), MS, *25*
Byron Leonard Int'l., Inc. (R), CA, *25*
C. M. Management Services, Inc. (R), KY, *26*
C. P. Consulting (R), PA, *26*
The C.P.R. Group (C), NJ, *278*
C.P.S., Inc. (C), IL, *278*

C.T.E.W. Executive Personnel Services Inc. (C), BC, *278*
Cadillac Assoc. (C), CA, *278*
Cahill Assoc. (C), CT, *279*
Caliber Associates (R), PA, *27*
California Search Agency, Inc. (C), CA, *279*
Callan Assoc., Ltd. (R), IL, *27*
Cambridge Group Ltd. - Exec. Search Div. (C), CT, *279*
Cambridge Management Planning (R), ON, *27*
Campa & Assoc. (R), ON, *27*
T. M. Campbell Co. (R), WA, *27*
Campbell, Edgar Inc. (C), BC, *280*
Canadian Career Partners (R), AB, *27*
CanMed Consultants Inc. (C), ON, *280*
Canny, Bowen Inc. (R), NY, *27*
The Canon Group (C), CA, *280*
The Cantor Concern, Inc. (R), NY, *28*
Cantrell & Assoc. (C), FL, *280*
Capital Consulting & Research, Inc. (R), CT, *28*
Capital Consulting Group, Inc. (R), MD, *28*
Capital Markets Resources, Inc. (C), NC, *281*
Sally Caplan & Assoc. (C), WA, *281*
Caplan Assoc., Inc. (R), NJ, *28*
The Caplan-Taylor Group (R), CA, *28*
Caprio & Assoc. Inc. (R), IL, *29*
Capstone Consulting, Inc. (R), IL, *29*
Capstone Inc. (R), NY, *29*
Cardwell Enterprises Inc. (R), IL, *29*
Career +Plus (C), NY, *281*
Career Advisors, Inc. (C), FL, *281*
Career Alternatives Executive Search (C), MI, *281*
Career Consultants (R), IN, *29*
Career Consulting Group, Inc. (C), CT, *281*
Career Counseling Inc. (CCI) (C), KY, *282*
Career Development Associates (C), NV, *282*
Career Marketing Consultants, Inc. (C), GA, *282*
Career Profiles (C), NH, *283*
Career Search Group (C), FL, *283*
Career Strategies, Inc. (C), CA, *283*
Careerfit, Inc. (C), TX, *283*
Careers On Track (C), NJ, *283*
Careers Plus (R), CA, *29*
Careers/Inc. (C), PR, *284*
Carion Resource Group Inc. (C), ON, *284*
Carlsen Resources, Inc. (R), CO, *29*
Carlson & Czeswik (R), MN, *30*
Carnegie Partners, Inc. (R), IL, *30*
Carpenter & Assoc. (C), TX, *284*
Carpenter Assoc., Inc. (R), IL, *30*
Carpenter, Shackleton & Company (R), IL, *30*
Carr Management Services, Inc. (C), PA, *284*
Carrington & Carrington, Ltd. (R), IL, *30*
Carson-Thomas & Assoc. (C), CA, *284*
Carter, Lavoie Associates (C), RI, *285*
Carter-Evdemon & Assoc. (C), FL, *285*
Carter/MacKay (C), NJ, *285*
Caruso & Assoc., Inc. (R), FL, *31*
Caruthers & Co., L.L.C. (R), CT, *31*
Carver Search Consultants (C), CA, *285*
The CARVIR Group, Inc. (C), GA, *285*
Cary & Assoc. (R), FL, *31*
CAS Comsearch Inc. (C), NY, *285*
Rosemary Cass Ltd. (R), CT, *31*
Cassell & Kaye (C), NY, *286*
The Cassie Group (R), NJ, *31*
Michael J. Cavanagh & Assoc. Inc. (R), ON, *31*
Caywood Partners, Ltd. (R), CA, *32*
CBA Companies (C), CA, *286*
CCI - Career Consultants Int'l. (C), CA, *286*
CEC Associates (R), MA, *32*
Cella Assoc. (C), GA, *286*
Cendea Connection Int'l. (R), TX, *32*
Central Executive Search, Inc. (C), OH, *287*
Century Assoc., Inc. (C), PA, *287*
The Century Group (C), KS, *287*
CEO Consulting (C), FL, *287*
cFour Partners (R), CA, *32*
Chad Management Group (C), ON, *288*
Chaloner Assoc. (R), MA, *32*
Wayne S. Chamberlain & Assoc. (C), CA, *288*
Chapman & Assoc. (C), BC, *289*
The Chapman Group, Inc. (C), AZ, *289*
Charet & Assoc. (C), NJ, *289*
Charles & Associates, Inc. (C), NE, *289*
The Chatham Group, Ltd. (C), CT, *289*
A. D. Check Assoc., Inc. (R), PA, *33*
Chesapeake Group (C), CT, *290*
Christenson Hutchison McDowell, LLC (R), NJ, *34*
Christian & Timbers, Inc. (R), OH, *34*
R. Christine Assoc. (C), PA, *290*
Christmas, McIvor & Assoc. Inc. (C), ON, *290*
Christopher and Long (C), MO, *291*
William J. Christopher Assoc., Inc. (R), PA, *34*
Christopher-Westmont & Assoc., Inc. (R), OH, *34*
J. F. Church Associates (C), WA, *291*
Churchill & Affiliates, Inc. (R), PA, *35*
M. A. Churchill & Assoc., Inc. (R), PA, *35*
The Churchill Group (C), ON, *291*
Cizek Assoc., Inc. (R), AZ, *35*
CJA-The Adler Group, Inc. (R), CA, *35*
CJSI-Cindy Jackson Search Int'l. (C), CA, *291*
Clanton & Co. (C), CA, *292*
Arlene Clapp, Ltd. (R), MN, *35*
Clarey & Andrews, Inc. (R), IL, *35*
Howard Clark Assoc. (C), NJ, *292*
Toby Clark Assoc. Inc. (C), NY, *292*
The Clark Group (C), MI, *292*
Ken Clark Int'l. (R), NJ, *36*
Clark Personnel Service, Inc. (C), AL, *292*
Clayman & Co. (R), MA, *36*
The Clayton Edward Group (C), MI, *292*
Clinton, Charles, Wise & Co. (C), FL, *293*
CMC Search Consultants (C), IL, *293*
CMS, Inc. (C), NH, *293*
CMS Management Services LLC (C), IN, *293*
CMW & Associates, Inc. (C), IL, *293*
CN Associates (C), CA, *293*
Coast Personnel Services Ltd. (C), BC, *293*
Coastal Int'l., Inc. (R), MA, *36*
COBA Executive Search (R), CO, *36*
Coe & Co. Int'l. Inc./EMA Partners Int'l. (R), AB, *37*
Cole, Warren & Long, Inc. (R), PA, *37*
Coleman Lew & Assoc., Inc. (R), NC, *37*
Colton Bernard Inc. (R), CA, *37*
Columbia Consulting Group (R), MD, *38*
Commonwealth Consultants (C), GA, *294*
Compass Group Ltd. (R), MI, *38*
Comprehensive Search (C), GA, *294*
Computer Network Resources, Inc. (C), CA, *295*
Computer Security Placement Service (C), MA, *296*
The Comwell Company, Inc. (C), NJ, *296*
Conard Associates, Inc. (R), NH, *39*
Conasa de Mexico, S.C. (R), MX, *39*
Conex Inc./InterSearch (R), NY, *39*
Robert Connelly & Assoc., Inc. (R), MN, *39*
M. L. Conner (C), FL, *296*
Connors, Lovell & Assoc. Inc. (C), ON, *296*
Conroy Partners Ltd. (R), AB, *39*
Consolidated Management Services (C), ON, *296*
Construct Management Services (C), MN, *297*
Consulpro (R), ON, *39*
Consulting Rhonda (C), ON, *297*
Consumer Search Inc. (C), MA, *298*
Conway & Assoc. (R), IL, *40*
Philip Conway Management (R), IL, *40*
Cook Assoc.,® Inc. (R), IL, *40*
The Cooke Group (R), WI, *40*
Cooper Assoc., Inc. (C), NY, *298*
Corbin Packaging Professionals (C), MO, *299*
Cornwall Stockton & Co., Inc. (C), TX, *299*
Corporate Advisors, Inc. (C), FL, *299*
The Corporate Advisory Group (R), NJ, *41*
Corporate Careers, Inc. (C), CA, *299*
The Corporate Connection, Ltd. (C), VA, *299*
Corporate Dynamix (C), AZ, *300*
Corporate Environment Ltd. (R), IL, *41*
Corporate Image Group (C), TN, *300*
Corporate Plus, Ltd. (C), GA, *300*
Corporate Recruiters Ltd. (C), BC, *300*
Corporate Search, Inc. (C), NY, *301*
Corporate Select Int'l., Ltd. (C), IL, *301*
Corporate Staffing Group, Inc. (C), PA, *301*
Leonard Corwen Assoc. (C), NY, *302*
CountryHouse Hotels Executive Search (C), VA, *302*
Cowell & Associates, Ltd. (R), IL, *42*
Cowin Assoc. (R), NY, *42*
Trudi Cowlan (C), NY, *302*
Crane, Reed & Co., Inc. (C), NH, *302*
The Crawford Group (C), GA, *303*
Creative Input, Inc. (C), RI, *303*
Creative Management Strategies, Ltd. (R), NY, *42*
Creative-Leadership, Inc. (R), CA, *42*
The Cris Group, Inc. (R), NY, *42*
Crist Partners, Ltd. (R), IL, *43*

Marlene Critchfield Co. (C), CA, *303*
Cross Country Consultants, Inc. (C), MD, *304*
Crowder & Company (R), MI, *43*
Timothy D. Crowe, Jr. (R), MA, *43*
Culver Personnel Services (C), CA, *304*
Cumberland Group Inc. (C), IL, *304*
Frank Cuomo & Assoc., Inc. (C), NY, *305*
Curran Partners, Inc. (R), CT, *44*
The Currier-Winn Co., Inc. (C), NJ, *305*
Curry, Telleri Group, Inc. (R), NJ, *44*
Tony Curtis & Associates (C), ON, *305*
Judith Cushman & Assoc. (R), WA, *44*
The Custer Group, Inc. (R), TN, *44*
Custom Resources (C), AL, *305*
CV Associates (C), NY, *305*
Cyntal Int'l. Ltd. (R), NY, *44*
Cypress Int'l., Inc. (R), FL, *45*
Cyr Associates, Inc. (C), MA, *306*
D & M Associates (C), PA, *306*
D.A.I Human Resources Consultants (R), QE, *45*
D.A.L. Associates, Inc. (R), CT, *45*
Daggett & Kvistad (R), CA, *45*
Charles Dahl Group, Inc. (C), MN, *306*
Dahl-Morrow Int'l. (R), VA, *45*
The Dalley Hewitt Co. (R), GA, *45*
Damon & Assoc., Inc. (C), TX, *306*
Alfred Daniels & Assoc., Inc. (R), CA, *46*
Alan Darling Consulting (R), VT, *46*
The Dartmouth Group (R), NY, *46*
The DataFinders Group, Inc. (C), NJ, *307*
Datamatics Management Services, Inc. (C), NJ, *307*
David Perry Assoc. (C), NJ, *308*
Alan Davis & Assoc. Inc. (R), QE, *47*
Joseph A. Davis Consultants, Inc. (R), NY, *47*
Bert Davis Executive Search, Inc. (R), NY, *47*
Bert Davis Publishing Placement Consultants (C), NY, *309*
DBC Recruiting Network (C), GA, *309*
DCA Professional Search (C), TX, *309*
Dean-MacDonald (R), OH, *47*
DeCaster Assoc. (C), WI, *310*
DeCorrevont & Assoc. (C), IL, *310*
Deeco Int'l. (C), UT, *310*
Defrain Mayer (R), KS, *48*
DeLalla - Fried Assoc. (C), NY, *310*
Thorndike Deland Assoc. LLC (R), NY, *48*
Delta Management Group Ltd. (C), ON, *310*
Delta Services (R), TX, *48*
DeMatteo Associates (C), NY, *311*
Derhak Ireland & Partners Ltd. (R), ON, *48*
Desktop Staffing, Inc. (C), IL, *311*
Despres & Associates (C), IL, *311*
The Devlin Search Group, Inc. (C), MA, *311*
Devoto & Assoc. (C), CA, *312*
The Diestel Group (R), UT, *51*
Roger Dietsch & Assoc. (C), MN, *312*
DiMarchi Partners (R), CO, *51*
J. Dinerstein & Co., Inc. (R), NY, *51*
Robert W. Dingman Co., Inc. (R), CA, *52*
Dinte Resources, Inc. (R), VA, *52*
Direct Marketing Resources (C), NC, *312*
Direct Marketing Solutions (C), KY, *312*
Direct Recruiters, Inc. (C), OH, *312*
Dise & Co. (R), OH, *52*
R. J. Dishaw & Assoc. (R), TX, *52*
DiTech Resources (C), CT, *313*
Diversified Consulting Services, Inc. (C), CO, *313*
Diversified Search, Inc. (R), PA, *52*
Dixie Search Assoc. (C), GA, *313*
DLB Assoc. (R), NY, *53*
DLG Assoc., Inc. (R), NC, *53*
DNA Search, Inc. (C), CA, *313*
Doering & Assoc. (C), CA, *313*
L. J. Doherty & Assoc. (R), MA, *53*
Doherty Int'l., Inc. (R), IL, *53*
Doleman Enterprises (R), VA, *53*
Dominguez-Metz & Assoc. (R), CA, *53*
Domres Professional Search (R), WI, *53*
Don Allan Assoc., Inc. (C), CA, *313*
Donahue/Bales Assoc. (R), IL, *54*
Donini Assoc. (R), VA, *54*
The Donnelly Group-Sales Recruiters, Inc. (C), MO, *314*
The Dorfman Group (C), AZ, *314*
Dorst Information Services, Inc. (C), NY, *314*
Dotson & Assoc. (R), NY, *54*
Dougherty & Assoc. (C), TN, *314*
Douglas-Allen, Inc. (R), MA, *54*
CS Dowling Executive Services (R), NJ, *54*
Dreier Consulting (C), NJ, *315*
Drew Assoc. Int'l. (R), NJ, *54*
Drinkwater & Assoc. (R), MA, *54*
Dromeshauser Assoc. (R), MA, *55*
DRZ Medical Recruiters (C), CO, *315*
DS&A (Doug Sears & Assoc.) (C), FL, *315*
J. H. Dugan & Assoc., Inc. (R), CA, *55*
Dukas Assoc. (C), MA, *315*
M. Dunbar & Assoc. (C), TX, *316*
The Duncan-O'Dell Group Inc. (C), TX, *316*
Dunhill Staffing Systems, Inc. (C), NY, *316*
Dunhill Professional Search of Miami (C), FL, *319*
Dunhill Executive Search of Los Angeles, Inc. (C), CA, *319*
Dunhill of San Francisco, Inc. (C), CA, *319*
Dunhill Professional Search of San Jose (C), CA, *319*
Dunhill Professional Search of Oakland (C), CA, *319*
Dunhill Professional Search of Hawaii (C), HI, *320*
Dunhill Professional Search of Greater New Orleans (C), LA, *321*
Dunhill Professional Search (C), MO, *321*
Dunhill Professional Search of Ramsey (C), NJ, *321*
Dunhill Personnel Service of Fargo (C), ND, *322*
Dunhill Personnel of Northeast Tulsa, Inc. (C), OK, *322*
Dunhill Professional Search of Wilkes-Barre/Scranton, Inc. (C), PA, *322*
Dunhill Professional Search of Bucks-Mont., Inc. (C), PA, *322*
Dunhill Professional Search of Richmond (C), VA, *323*
Dunlap & Sullivan Assoc. (R), MI, *55*
Dunn Associates (R), PA, *55*
C. A. Durakis Assoc., Inc. (R), MD, *55*
Dussick Management Assoc. (C), CT, *323*
Gwen Dycus & Assoc. (C), FL, *323*
Dynamic Choices Inc. (C), MO, *323*
Dynamic Synergy Corp. (R), CA, *56*
E.P. Int'l. (C), NY, *324*
E/Search Int'l. (C), CT, *325*
J. M. Eagle Partners Ltd. (C), WI, *325*
Eagle Search Assoc. (C), CA, *325*
EagleView, Inc. (C), MA, *325*
Earley Kielty & Assoc., Inc. (R), NY, *56*
Eastbourne Assoc. Inc. (R), NY, *56*
Eastman & Beaudine, Inc. (R), TX, *56*
The Edge Resource Group (C), PA, *326*
EDI/Executive Dynamics Inc. (C), NJ, *326*
EDMS Solutions (C), TX, *326*
Edwards & Assoc. (C), GA, *327*
Bruce Edwards & Associates, Inc. (R), NC, *56*
EFCO Consultants, Inc. (C), NY, *327*
Effective Search, Inc. (R), IL, *57*
D. C. Egan & Assoc. (C), GA, *327*
EGM Consulting, Inc. (R), FL, *57*
Richard A. Eisner & Co., LLP (R), NY, *57*
W. Robert Eissler & Assoc., Inc. (C), TX, *327*
William J. Elam & Assoc. (R), NE, *58*
The Eldridge Group, Ltd. (C), IL, *327*
Yves Elkas Inc. (R), QE, *58*
Gene Ellefson & Assoc. Inc. (C), MI, *328*
Elliot Assoc. Inc. (R), NY, *58*
H. J. Elliot, Inc. (R), IL, *58*
The Elliott Company (R), MA, *58*
Ellis & Associates (C), HI, *328*
Ellis Career Consultants (C), NJ, *328*
David M. Ellner Assoc. (R), NY, *59*
The Ellsworth Group (C), NY, *329*
The Elmhurst Group (C), CA, *329*
The Elsworth Group (C), TX, *329*
Elwell & Assoc., Inc. (R), MI, *59*
Mark Elzweig Co., Ltd. (C), NY, *329*
Emerging Medical Technologies, Inc. (C), CO, *329*
Emerson & Co. (C), GA, *329*
Emmett Executive Search, Inc. (C), NY, *330*
Empire International (R), PA, *59*
Employ® (C), PA, *330*
Empowered Solutions Corp. (C), GA, *330*
The Enfield Company (C), TX, *330*
Engineering & Scientific Search Assoc. (ESSA) (C), NJ, *330*
Engineering Futures, LLC (C), CT, *330*
ENI (R), CT, *59*
Epsen, Fuller & Assoc., LLC (R), NJ, *60*
Erlanger Assoc. (R), CT, *60*
Erwin Assoc. (R), IL, *60*
ESA (R), CT, *60*
ESS (Executive Search Services) (R), CA, *61*
Essential Solutions, Inc. (C), CA, *331*
Ethos Consulting, Inc. (R), CA, *61*
ETI Search Int'l. (R), GA, *61*
The Evans Search Group (R), CT, *61*
Evans Transportation Search (C), ON, *331*
Excalibur Human Resources, Inc. (R), NJ, *61*
Exec Tech, Inc. (C), IL, *332*

ExecuGroup, Inc. (R), MS, *61*
ExecuQuest, Inc. (R), MI, *61*
ExecuSource Assoc., Inc. (C), GA, *332*
ExecuSource Consultants, Inc. (C), TX, *332*
Executech (R), OH, *62*
ExecuTech (C), IN, *332*
Executive Alliance (R), MA, *62*
Executive Business Solutions, Inc. (C), WA, *332*
Executive Careers (R), CA, *62*
Executive Directions (R), OH, *62*
Executive Exchange Corp. (C), NJ, *333*
The Executive Group, Inc. (R), CA, *62*
Executive Recruiters Int'l. (C), MI, *333*
Executive Recruiters Agency, Inc. (C), AR, *333*
Executive Recruiters (C), WA, *334*
Executive Recruitment Services, Inc. (ERS, Inc.) (C), GA, *334*
Executive Registry (C), QE, *334*
Executive Resource Assoc. (C), VA, *334*
Executive Resource Group, Inc. (R), ME, *63*
Executive Sales Search (C), CO, *335*
Executive Search Consultants International, Inc. (R), NY, *63*
Executive Search Consultants, Inc. (C), FL, *335*
Executive Search Int'l./Transearch (R), MA, *63*
Executive Search Int'l. (C), TX, *335*
Executive Search, Ltd. (C), OH, *336*
Executive Search of America, Inc. (C), OH, *336*
Executive Search of New England, Inc. (C), ME, *336*
Executive Search Partners (R), NY, *63*
Executive Search Team (C), MI, *336*
Executive Strategies, Inc. (C), GA, *337*
The Executive Tree (R), FL, *64*
Executive/Retail Placement Assoc. (C), MD, *337*
ExecutiveFit (C), NY, *337*
Raymond L. Extract & Assoc. (R), CA, *64*
F.L.A.G. (C), OH, *338*
Fabian Assoc. Inc. (C), NY, *338*
FAI (C), CO, *338*
Fairfaxx Corp. (R), CT, *64*
Fairfield Int'l. Resources (R), NY, *65*
Paul Falcone Assoc. (R), NJ, *65*
Fallstaff Search (C), MD, *338*
Fament, Inc. (C), OH, *338*
Leon A. Farley Assoc. (R), CA, *65*
Dorothy W. Farnath & Assoc., Inc. (C), NJ, *338*
Fast Switch, Ltd. (C), OH, *338*
The Fawcett Group (R), MA, *65*
Federal Placement Services (C), NY, *339*
James Feerst & Assoc., Inc. (C), AZ, *339*
A. E. Feldman Assoc., Inc. (C), NY, *339*
Fell & Nicholson Technology Resources (R), CA, *65*
Fenwick Partners (R), MA, *66*
Ferneborg & Assoc., Inc. (R), CA, *66*
Fernow Assoc. (C), PA, *339*
Ferrari Search Group (C), OH, *340*
Guild Fetridge Acoustical Search, Inc. (C), NY, *340*
Jerry Fields Assoc. (C), NY, *340*
Financial Connections Company (C), VA, *340*
Financial Plus Management Solutions Inc. (R), ON, *66*
Neil Fink Assoc. (R), CA, *66*
Eileen Finn & Assoc., Inc. (C), NY, *341*
Finnegan & Assoc. (R), CA, *67*
Finney-Taylor Personnel & Management Consultants Ltd. (C), AB, *341*
First Search America, Inc. (C), TN, *341*
First Search Inc. (C), IL, *341*
First Union Executive Search (R), NC, *67*
Howard Fischer Assoc. Int'l., Inc. (R), PA, *67*
Fisher & Assoc. (R), CA, *67*
The Fisher Group (R), AB, *67*
Fisher Personnel Management Services (R), CA, *68*
Fisher-Todd Assoc. (C), NY, *341*
A. G. Fishkin & Assoc., Inc. (R), MD, *68*
FitzGibbon & Assoc. (R), PA, *68*
The Flagship Group (R), MA, *68*
Robert M. Flanagan & Assoc., Ltd. (R), NY, *68*
Flesher & Assoc., Inc. (R), CA, *68*
Flexible Resources, Inc. (C), CT, *342*
Flowers & Assoc. (C), OH, *342*
Flynn, Hannock, Inc. (R), CT, *69*
David Fockler & Assoc., Inc. (C), CA, *342*
Focus Executive Search (C), MN, *343*
Ford & Ford (C), MA, *343*
Forest People Int'l. Search Ltd. (C), BC, *343*
Forray Assoc., Inc. (R), NY, *70*
Fortune Group Int'l., Inc. (R), PA, *70*
Fortune Personnel Consultants of Colorado Springs (C), CO, *344*
Fortune of Arlington Heights (C), IL, *345*
Fortune Personnel Consultants of Topsfield (C), MA, *346*
F-O-R-T-U-N-E Personnel Consultants of Southwest Indiana (C), IN, *346*
Fortune Personnel Consultants (C), MT, *347*
F-O-R-T-U-N-E Personnel Consultants of Bergen County Inc. (C), NJ, *347*
F-O-R-T-U-N-E Personnel Consultants of Charlotte (C), NC, *348*
Fortune Personnel Consultants of Raleigh, Inc. (C), NC, *348*
Fortune Personnel Consultants of Hilton Head (C), SC, *349*
F-O-R-T-U-N-E Personnel Consultants of Houston, Inc. (C), TX, *350*
F-O-R-T-U-N-E Personnel of Nashville (C), TN, *350*
FORTUNE Personnel Consultants of North Dallas (C), TX, *350*
Forum Personnel Inc. (C), NY, *351*
Foster Partners (R), NY, *70*
The Fourbes Group, Inc. (C), NJ, *351*
Fox, White & Assoc. (C), FL, *351*
Fox-Morris Assoc., Inc. (C), PA, *351*
Foy, Schneid & Daniel, Inc. (R), NY, *71*
Franchise Recruiters Ltd. (R), IL, *71*
Neil Frank & Co. (R), CA, *71*
Franklin Allen Consultants, Ltd. (R), NY, *71*
Franklin Int'l. Search, Inc. (C), MA, *352*
The Franklin Search Group, Inc./Medzilla (R), WA, *71*
Franstaff Inc. (C), FL, *352*
KS Frary & Assoc. (R), MA, *71*
Mel Frazer Consultant (C), CA, *352*
Fresquez & Assoc. (C), CA, *352*
Friedman Eisenstein Raemer & Schwartz, LLP (R), IL, *72*
Bernard Frigon & Assoc. Inc. (C), QE, *353*
Gerald Frisch Assoc., Inc. (R), NY, *72*
Fristoe & Carleton, Inc. (C), OH, *353*
The Fry Group, Inc. (C), NY, *353*
C. F. Furr & Co. (R), NC, *72*
The Furst Group, Inc. (R), IL, *72*
Furst Group/MPI (R), IL, *72*
Future Employment Service, Inc. (C), IA, *353*
Futures, Inc. (C), NH, *354*
G. H. Enterprises (C), AZ, *354*
GAAP Inc. (R), QE, *73*
The Gabriel Group (C), PA, *354*
Gaffney Management Consultants (R), IL, *73*
Gahan Assoc. (R), NY, *73*
Gaines & Assoc. Int'l., Inc. (R), IL, *73*
Jay Gaines & Company, Inc. (R), NY, *73*
Gallin Associates, Inc. (C), FL, *354*
Gaming Consultants, Inc. (R), LA, *74*
The Gammill Group, Inc. (C), OH, *354*
W. N. Garbarini & Assoc. (R), NJ, *74*
Gardiner, Townsend & Assoc. (R), NY, *74*
Gardner-Ross Assoc., Inc. (R), NY, *74*
Dick Garland Consultants (R), NY, *74*
The Garms Group (R), IL, *74*
The Garrison Organization (R), IA, *75*
The Garvis Group, Inc. (C), LA, *355*
GateSource Partners (C), VA, *355*
Gaudry, Shink, Levasseur (R), QE, *75*
Dianne Gauger & Assoc. (C), CA, *355*
Geddes & Rubin Management Inc. (R), ON, *76*
Genel Associates (C), CA, *356*
General Engineering Tectonics (C), CA, *356*
Genesis Consulting Partners (R), PA, *76*
Genesis Personnel Service, Inc. (C), OH, *356*
Genesis Research (C), MO, *356*
C. R. Gerald & Assoc. (C), ON, *356*
J. Gernetzke & Assoc., Inc. (C), OH, *357*
GES Services, Inc. (R), NY, *76*
Gilbert & Van Campen Int'l. (R), NY, *76*
Gilbert Tweed Assoc. Inc. (R), NY, *76*
Howard Gilmore & Assoc. (R), OH, *77*
Gilreath Weatherby Inc. (R), MA, *77*
Lawrence Glaser Assoc., Inc. (C), NJ, *357*
The Glazin Group (R), BC, *77*
J. P. Gleason Assoc., Inc. (R), IL, *77*
Glines Assoc., Inc. (R), IL, *77*
Global 1000 Int'l. Services (C), CA, *358*
Global Consulting Group Inc. (C), ON, *358*
Global Data Services, Inc. (R), NY, *77*
Global HealthCare Partners (R), IL, *78*
Global Research Partnership Inc. (R), NY, *78*
Global Resources Group (R), CA, *78*
Global Technologies Group Inc. (C), NC, *359*

Global Telecommunications, Inc. (C), TX, *359*
The GlobalSearch Group (C), TX, *359*
F. Gloss Int'l. (R), VA, *78*
Glou Int'l., Inc. (R), MA, *78*
H. L. Goehring & Assoc., Inc. (C), OH, *359*
Barry M. Gold & Co. (C), CA, *359*
Goldbeck Recruiting Inc. (C), BC, *359*
The Goldman Group Inc. (R), NY, *79*
Goldman+Bell, LLC (C), NY, *360*
Fred J. Goldsmith Assoc. (R), CA, *79*
Goldstein & Co. (C), CA, *360*
David Gomez & Assoc., Inc. (R), IL, *79*
Gomez Fregoso y Asociados (C), JAL, *360*
Goodkind Assoc. Inc. (C), NY, *360*
The Goodman Group (R), CA, *79*
Goodrich & Sherwood Assoc., Inc. (R), NY, *79*
Goodwin & Co. (R), DC, *80*
Gould, McCoy & Chadick, Inc. (R), NY, *80*
The Governance Group, Inc. (R), NJ, *80*
Gowdy Consultants (C), TX, *361*
Alexander Graham Assoc. (C), NJ, *361*
Robert Graham Assoc. (R), RI, *81*
Granger, Counts & Assoc. (R), OH, *81*
Robert Grant Assoc., Inc. (C), CA, *361*
Grant Cooper & Assoc., Inc. (R), MO, *81*
The Grant Search Group, Inc. (C), ON, *361*
Grant-Franks & Assoc. (C), NJ, *361*
Grantham & Co., Inc. (R), NC, *81*
Graphic Arts Marketing Assoc., Inc. (C), MI, *361*
Graphic Search Assoc. Inc. (C), PA, *362*
Sheila Greco Assoc. (C), NY, *362*
R. Green & Assoc., Inc. (C), OH, *362*
Greene Personnel Consultants (C), RI, *362*
Greenhaven & Assoc., Inc. (R), NY, *81*
Greenwich Internet (C), CT, *363*
Greenwich Search Partners, LLC (C), CT, *363*
Greger/Peterson Assoc., Inc. (R), CA, *81*
Griffith & Werner, Inc. (R), FL, *82*
Gros Executive Search, Inc. (C), TN, *363*
Grossberg & Assoc. (R), IL, *82*
Groton Planning Group (R), ME, *82*
Groupe PCA Inc. (C), QE, *363*
Groussman & Assoc., Inc. (R), TX, *82*
Grover & Assoc. (R), OH, *82*
Growth Consultants of America (R), MI, *82*
Growth Strategies, Inc. (R), FL, *83*
David E. Grumney Co. Inc. (R), WA, *83*
GSW Consulting Group, Inc. (R), CA, *83*
Nadine Guber & Assoc., Inc. (C), NY, *364*
Michael R. Guerin Co. (C), CA, *364*
Wolf Gugler & Assoc. Ltd. (R), ON, *83*
Guidarelli Assoc., Inc. (R), MI, *83*
Guidry & East Healthcare Search Consultants (R), TX, *83*
Gumbinner/Haubenstock, Inc. (C), NY, *364*
Gundersen Partners, L.L.C. (R), NY, *83*
Gustin Partners, Ltd. (R), MA, *83*
The H. S. Group, Inc. (C), WI, *365*
Haddad Assoc. (R), FL, *84*
Halbrecht & Co. (C), VA, *365*
Hale Assoc. (R), IL, *84*
K. C. Hale, Inc. (R), CT, *85*
Haley Associates (R), CA, *85*
Don Hall & Assoc. (C), TX, *366*
Michael J. Hall & Co. (R), WA, *85*
Susan Hall Executive Search (C), TX, *366*
Halo Insurance Service (C), AL, *367*
Hamilton & Co. (C), OH, *367*
The Hamilton Group (R), MD, *85*
The Hampton Group (C), NY, *367*
R. C. Handel Assoc. Inc. (R), CT, *85*
W. L. Handler & Assoc. (R), GA, *85*
Hands-on Broadcast (R), NY, *86*
Handy HRM (R), NY, *86*
Hanley & Assoc. (R), FL, *86*
The Hanna Group (C), OH, *368*
Hansen Executive Search, Inc. (C), NE, *368*
Janet Harberth & Assoc., Inc. (C), GA, *368*
Harbrowe, Inc. (C), NY, *368*
Harcourt & Assoc. (C), AB, *368*
Harcourt Group Ltd. (R), OH, *86*
Hardison & Company (R), TX, *86*
Robert Harkins Assoc., Inc. (C), PA, *369*
Harper Hewes, Inc. (C), NY, *369*
The Harris Consulting Corp. (R), MB, *87*
Harris Heery & Assoc., Inc. (R), CT, *87*
Hart & Co. (C), NY, *370*
Hartman & Barnette (R), VA, *87*
Hartsfield Group, Inc. (R), GA, *87*
Harvard Group Int'l. (R), GA, *87*
Harvey Hohauser & Assoc., LLC (R), MI, *87*
The Hawkins Co. (R), CA, *88*
Michael J. Hawkins, Inc. (C), IL, *370*
William E. Hay & Co. (R), IL, *88*
Hayden & Assoc., Inc. (C), MN, *370*
Hayden Group, Inc. (R), MA, *88*
The Haystack Group, Inc. (R), ME, *88*
Hazlett Associates (R), IL, *88*
HCI Corp. (C), IL, *371*
Headden Assoc. (R), WA, *88*
Healey Executive Search, Inc. (R), MN, *88*
Health Care Dimensions (C), CO, *371*
Health Industry Consultants, Inc. (R), CO, *89*
Healthcare Management Resources, Inc. (R), GA, *89*
Healthcare Recruiters Int'l. Phoenix (C), AZ, *372*
Healthcare Recruiters of the Rockies, Inc. (C), CO, *372*
Healthcare Recruiters Int'l. Bay Area (C), CA, *372*
Healthcare Recruiters of Indiana (C), IN, *372*
Healthcare Recruiters Int'l. - Alabama (C), AL, *372*
Healthcare Recruiters Int'l. Orange County (C), CA, *372*
Healthcare Recruiters Int'l - Minnesota, Inc. (C), MN, *373*
Healthcare Recruiters International-NY/NJ (C), NJ, *373*
Healthcare Recruiters of New England (C), MA, *373*
Healthcare Recruiters of New Orleans (C), LA, *373*
Healthcare Recruiters of New York, Inc. (C), NY, *373*
Healthcare Recruiters Int'l. Philadelphia (C), NJ, *373*
Healthcare Recruiters Int'l. - Pittsburgh (C), PA, *373*
Healthcare Recruiters - Northwest (C), WA, *374*
Healthcare Recruiters of Dallas (C), TX, *374*
Healthcare Resources Group (C), OK, *374*
Healthcare Search Associates (C), CA, *374*
F. P. Healy & Co., Inc. (R), NY, *89*
Heath/Norton Assoc., Inc. (R), NY, *89*
R. W. Hebel Assoc. (R), TX, *89*
HEC Group (C), ON, *375*
Hechkoff/Work Executive Search Inc. (R), NY, *89*
Heffelfinger Assoc., Inc. (R), MA, *89*
The Heidrick Partners, Inc. (R), IL, *90*
Heinze & Assoc. Inc. (R), MN, *91*
Helbling & Assoc., Inc. (R), PA, *91*
Helfer Executive Consultants (R), TN, *91*
Heller Assoc., Ltd. (R), IL, *91*
Heller Kil Assoc., Inc. (C), FL, *375*
The Helms Int'l. Group (R), VA, *91*
G. W. Henn & Co. (R), OH, *91*
Bruce Henry Assoc. Inc. (R), CA, *91*
Kay Henry, Inc. (C), PA, *376*
The Hensge Co. (R), IL, *91*
Henson Partners (C), AZ, *376*
Herbeck Kline & Assoc. (R), IL, *92*
Hergenrather & Co. (R), WA, *92*
Heritage Search Group, Inc. (C), FL, *376*
J. J. Herlihy & Assoc., Inc. (C), CA, *376*
A. Herndon & Assoc., Inc. (R), TX, *92*
Herrerias & Assoc. (R), CA, *92*
Herring & Assoc. (C), AR, *376*
The Herrmann Group Ltd. (R), ON, *92*
J. D. Hersey & Assoc. (C), OH, *376*
Hersher Assoc., Ltd. (R), IL, *92*
Stanley Herz & Co. (R), NY, *92*
Robert Hess & Assoc., Inc. (C), CO, *377*
The Hetzel Group, Inc. (R), IL, *92*
Heyman Assoc., Inc. (R), NY, *93*
Higbee Assoc., Inc. (C), CT, *377*
Higdon Prince Inc. (R), NY, *93*
Higgins Assoc., Inc. (R), IL, *93*
B. W. Higgins, Inc. (C), IN, *377*
Highlander Search (C), NC, *378*
Hill & Assoc. (C), CA, *378*
Hill Allyn Assoc. (C), CA, *378*
Frank P. Hill (R), MX, *93*
The Hindman Co. (R), KY, *94*
The Hindman Group, Inc. (C), CA, *378*
Hintz Associates (C), NY, *378*
Hire Authority, Inc. (C), MI, *378*
Hite Executive Search (R), OH, *94*
Hobson Assoc. (C), CT, *379*
Hockett Associates, Inc. (R), CA, *94*
Hodge-Cronin & Assoc., Inc. (R), IL, *94*
Hoffman Partnership Group Inc. (C), NY, *379*
Hoffman Recruiters (C), MA, *380*
The Hogan Group (C), OH, *380*
Hoglund & Assoc., Inc. (R), IL, *94*
Holland & Assoc., Inc. (R), MI, *94*
Holland Rusk & Assoc. (R), IL, *95*
The Hollins Group, Inc. (R), IL, *95*
Holloway Schulz & Partners (C), BC, *380*
Holohan Group, Ltd. (R), MO, *95*
Fred Hood & Assoc. (C), CA, *380*
Hook-Up! (C), CA, *380*

Horizons Unlimited (C), CA, *381*
Hornberger Management Company (R), DE, *95*
Horton Int'l. Inc. (R), NY, *96*
Hospitality Int'l. (C), NY, *381*
Houser, Martin, Morris (C), WA, *381*
Houtz•Strawn & Arnold, Inc. (R), TX, *96*
William C. Houze & Co. (R), CA, *96*
Howard-Sloan Assoc. (C), NY, *381*
The Howard-Sloan-Koller Group (R), NY, *97*
Howe & Assoc. (R), PA, *97*
Robert Howe & Assoc. (R), GA, *97*
HR Advantage, Inc. (C), VA, *382*
HRCS (R), CA, *97*
Hreshko Consulting Group (C), NJ, *382*
The HRM Group, Inc. (C), AL, *382*
HRS, Inc. (R), PA, *97*
Arnold Huberman Assoc., Inc. (R), NY, *97*
Hudson Assoc. Inc. (C), IN, *383*
Huff Assoc. (R), NJ, *98*
E. A. Hughes & Co., Inc. (R), NY, *98*
Hughes & Company (R), VA, *98*
Human Capital Resources, Inc. (C), FL, *384*
Human Resource Dimensions, Inc. (C), TX, *384*
The Human Resource Group, Inc. (R), OH, *98*
Human Resource Technologies, Inc. (R), IL, *99*
E. F. Humay Assoc. (C), PA, *384*
Hunegnaw Executive Search (C), OH, *384*
Hunt Patton & Brazeal, Inc. (C), OK, *385*
Hunter Adams (C), NC, *385*
Hunter Assoc. (C), MA, *385*
The Hunter Group (C), NC, *385*
Hunter Int'l., Inc. (R), CT, *100*
Hunter Int'l. LLC (C), MA, *385*
Hunter, Rowan & Crowe (C), FL, *386*
Huntress Real Estate Executive Search (R), MO, *100*
W. Hutt Management Resources Ltd. (R), ON, *100*
Hutton Merrill & Assoc. (R), CA, *100*
HVS Executive Search (R), NY, *100*
Hyde Danforth & Co. (R), TX, *100*
The Hyde Group, Inc. (R), CT, *101*
Hyland Executive Search (C), AZ, *386*
Hyman & Assoc. (C), TX, *386*
IMA Search, Inc. (R), NY, *101*
The IMC Group of Companies (R), NY, *101*
Impact Search & Strategies (C), PA, *387*
Impact Source, Inc. (C), FL, *387*
Independent Power Consultants (C), TX, *387*
Independent Resource Systems (C), CA, *388*
Ingram & Aydelotte, Inc. (R), NY, *101*
Meredith Ingram, Ltd. (C), IL, *388*
Innovative Healthcare Services, Inc. (C), GA, *389*
Innovative Partnerships (R), CA, *101*
The Inside Track (C), TX, *389*
Insight Consulting Co. (C), NY, *389*
Insight Personnel Group, Inc. (C), TX, *389*
Insurance Personnel Resources, Inc. (C), GA, *390*
Insurance Search (C), TX, *390*
InTech Services, Inc. (C), GA, *390*
Integrated Search Solutions Group, LLC (ISSG) (R), NY, *102*
Integrity Search, Inc. (R), PA, *102*
Intelegra, Inc. (C), NJ, *390*
InteliSearch, Inc. (R), CT, *102*
Intelligent Marketing Solutions, Inc. (C), NY, *390*
IntelliSearch (C), TX, *391*
Inter Regional Executive Search, Inc. (IRES, Inc.) (C), NJ, *391*
Interactive Search Assoc. (C), PA, *391*
Interactive Search Network (R), CA, *102*
Intercontinental Executive Group (C), PA, *391*
Interim Management Resources Inc. (C), ON, *392*
International Business Partners (C), ON, *392*
International Consulting Services, Inc. (C), IL, *392*
International Executive Recruiters (C), OH, *393*
International Management Services Inc. (R), IL, *102*
International Management Advisors, Inc. (R), NY, *103*
International Pro Sourcing, Inc. (C), PA, *393*
International Recruiting Services (C), FL, *393*
International Research Group (R), CA, *103*
International Staffing Consultants, Inc. (C), CA, *393*
International Technical Resources (C), FL, *393*
InterNeed (C), TX, *394*
Interspace Interactive, Inc. (C), NY, *394*
Iona Partners (C), CA, *394*
IR Search (R), CA, *103*
Jeffrey Irving Assoc., Inc. (R), VA, *104*
Isaacson, Miller (R), MA, *104*
Joan Isbister Consultants (C), NY, *394*
ISC of Atlanta, Inc. (C), GA, *394*
ISC of Cincinnati Inc. (C), OH, *394*
ISC of Houston, Inc. (C), TX, *394*
Ives & Associates, Inc. (C), OH, *395*
The J. B. Search Group (C), CA, *395*
J. Joseph & Assoc. (C), OH, *395*
J. Nicholas Arthur (R), MA, *104*
J. R. Scott & Assoc., Ltd. (C), IL, *395*
J.D.G. y Asociados, S.A. de C.V. (R), SO, *104*
Ron Jackson & Assoc. (C), GA, *396*
Jackson Resources (R), TX, *105*
Jacobs & Co. (R), CT, *105*
Jacobson Assoc. (C), IL, *396*
K. Jaeger & Assoc. (C), MA, *396*
JAG Group (R), MO, *105*
Jakobs & Assoc. Int'l. (R), NY, *105*
Pendleton James Assoc., Inc. (R), NY, *105*
David James Search (C), CA, *397*
Jaral Consultants, Inc. (C), NJ, *397*
JCL & Assoc. (C), FL, *397*
JDC Assoc. (C), NY, *397*
JDH & Assoc. (C), CA, *397*
Jefferson-Ross Assoc. Inc. (C), PA, *398*
Jeffrey Allan Co., Inc. (C), CA, *398*
Jender & Company (R), IL, *105*
JG Consultants, Inc. (R), TX, *106*
JL & Co. (C), CA, *399*
JLI-Boston (R), MA, *106*
JM & Company (R), PA, *106*
JNB Assoc., Inc. (C), MA, *399*
Job Link, Inc. (C), CA, *399*
John H. Johnson & Assoc., Inc. (R), IL, *106*
Johnson & Assoc., Inc. (R), CA, *106*
Johnson & Company (R), CT, *107*
Ronald S. Johnson Assoc., Inc. (R), CA, *107*
Johnson Assoc., Inc. (C), IL, *399*
K. E. Johnson Assoc. (C), WA, *399*
Johnson Brown Assoc., Inc. (C), IN, *400*
The Johnson Group, Unlimited (C), NY, *400*
Johnson, Kemper & Assoc. (C), TX, *400*
Johnson Smith & Knisely (R), NY, *107*
Jonas, Walters & Assoc., Inc. (R), WI, *107*
Jonathan Lawrence Assoc. (C), NJ, *400*
The Jonathan Stevens Group, Inc. (R), NJ, *108*
Jones and Jones (R), OR, *108*
Jones Consulting Executive Search (C), GA, *400*
Jordan-Sitter Assoc. (R), TX, *108*
Jordon & Jordon, Inc. (R), PA, *108*
J. M. Joseph Assoc. (R), NJ, *109*
JPM International (C), CA, *401*
JSG Group Management Consultants (R), ON, *109*
Judd Associates (R), NJ, *109*
Julian Assoc., Inc. (C), CT, *401*
Just Management Services Inc. (C), FL, *402*
A H Justice Search Consultants (C), TX, *402*
K & C Assoc. (C), CA, *402*
K2 Resources, L.P. (C), CT, *402*
Kabana Corp. (C), MI, *402*
Kacevich, Lewis & Brown, Inc. (R), MA, *109*
Kaczmar & Assoc. (C), PA, *403*
Richard Kader & Assoc. (C), OH, *403*
Robert Kaestner & Assoc. (C), FL, *403*
Kames & Assoc. (C), MD, *403*
Kanzer Assoc., Inc. (R), IL, *109*
Gary Kaplan & Assoc. (R), CA, *109*
Kaplan & Assoc., Inc. (R), PA, *109*
Karel & Co. (R), CA, *109*
Karp & Assoc. (C), FL, *403*
Allan Karson Assoc., Inc. (R), NJ, *110*
Martin Kartin & Co., Inc. (R), NY, *110*
Kaufman Assoc. (R), CA, *110*
Kay Concepts, Inc. (C), FL, *404*
The Kay Group of 5th Ave. (C), NY, *404*
Kaye/Bassman Int'l. Corp. (R), TX, *110*
Kazan International, Inc. (R), NJ, *110*
Keane Assoc. (R), MA, *110*
A.T. Kearney Executive Search (R), IL, *111*
Keeley Consulting Inc. (C), ON, *404*
Keena Staffing Services (C), NY, *404*
The Keith-Murray Partnership (R), ON, *112*
Kelley & Keller, Inc. (C), FL, *405*
S. D. Kelly & Assoc., Inc. (R), MA, *112*

Kensington Int'l., Inc. (R), IL, *113*
Kent & Assoc. (R), OH, *113*
Kenzer Corp. (R), NY, *113*
Daniel J. Kerstein, Consultant to Management (R), CO, *114*
Michael L. Ketner & Assoc., Inc. (R), PA, *114*
Key Employment (C), NJ, *405*
Key Resources Int'l. (C), CA, *405*
Ki Technologies, Inc. (C), UT, *406*
Kiley, Owen & McGovern, Inc. (R), NJ, *114*
Kimmel & Associates, Inc. (C), NC, *406*
King ComputerSearch, Inc. (C), TX, *407*
Kingsbury • Wax • Bova (R), MA, *114*
The Kingsley Group (R), CA, *114*
Kingsley Quinn/USA (R), NJ, *115*
The Kinlin Co., Inc. (R), MA, *115*
Richard Kinser & Assoc. (R), NY, *115*
Kip Williams, Inc. (R), NY, *115*
Kiradjieff & Goode, Inc. (R), MA, *115*
Kirkbride Assoc., Inc. (C), WA, *407*
Kittleman & Assoc.,LLC (R), IL, *115*
Kleber & Assoc. (C), WA, *407*
Raymond J. Klemmer & Assoc. (R), NY, *116*
KM Associates (C), MA, *407*
Knapp Consultants (R), CT, *116*
Koehler & Co. (R), WI, *116*
Lee Koehn Assoc., Inc. (R), OR, *116*
T. J. Koellhoffer & Assoc. (R), NJ, *116*
Fred Koffler Assoc. (R), NY, *116*
Koltnow & Company (R), NY, *117*
Koontz, Jeffries & Assoc., Inc. (R), FL, *117*
Kopplin Search, Inc. (R), CA, *117*
Korban Associates (R), PA, *117*
Kordus Consulting Group (C), WI, *408*
Korn/Ferry Int'l. (R), NY, *117*
Kors Montgomery Int'l. (R), TX, *118*
Kossuth & Assoc., Inc. (R), WA, *119*
Kostmayer Assoc., Inc. (R), MD, *119*
Katherine R. Kraemer (R), CA, *120*
Krakower Group, Inc. (R), CA, *120*
J. Krauss Assoc. (R), FL, *120*
Krautler Personnel Recruitment (C), FL, *409*
Evie Kreisler Assoc. Inc. (C), CA, *409*
Kremple & Meade, Inc. (R), CA, *120*
Kremple Consulting Group (R), CA, *120*
Kresin Wingard (C), IL, *409*
Kressenberg Assoc. (C), TX, *409*
D. A. Kreuter Assoc., Inc. (R), PA, *121*
Kreutz Consulting Group, Inc. (R), IL, *121*
Krueger Assoc. (R), IL, *121*
John Kuhn & Assoc., Inc. (R), WI, *121*
Kuhn Med-Tech (C), CA, *409*
Paul Kull & Co. (R), NJ, *121*
Kunzer Assoc., Ltd. (R), IL, *121*
John Kurosky & Assoc. (R), CA, *122*
Kurtz Pro-Search, Inc. (C), NJ, *410*
Kutt, Inc. (C), CO, *410*
L O R (R), NJ, *122*
L T M Assoc. (C), IL, *410*
L&L Assoc. Global Search (C), PA, *411*
Lab Market Specialists (C), UT, *411*
Marvin Laba & Assoc. (R), CA, *122*
LaCosta & Assoc. Int'l. Inc. (C), CA, *411*
Rene LaFlamme & Associes (R), QE, *122*
Lamay Assoc., Inc. (R), CT, *124*
Lamon + Stuart + Michaels Inc. (R), ON, *124*
Landon Morgan (C), ON, *412*
The Landstone Group (C), NY, *412*
Lange & Assoc., Inc. (C), IN, *412*
Lanken-Kimball-Therrell & Assoc. (C), GA, *412*
Lawrence L. Lapham, Inc. (R), NY, *124*
Stephen Laramee & Assoc. Inc. (C), ON, *413*
Larkin & Co. (R), CA, *124*
Robert Larned Assoc., Inc. (C), VA, *413*
R. H. Larsen & Assoc., Inc. (R), FL, *125*
Jack B. Larsen & Assoc., Inc. (C), PA, *413*
Larson Assoc. (R), CA, *125*
Larson, Katz & Young, Inc. (C), VA, *413*
Lasher Assoc. (R), FL, *125*
Latham International, Ltd. (R), NJ, *126*
Lauer, Sbarbaro Assoc., EMA Partners Int'l. (R), IL, *126*
Lautz, Grotte, Engler & Swimley (R), CA, *126*
Lawrence James Assoc. of Florida, Inc. (C), FL, *414*
Lawrence-Balakonis & Assoc., Inc. (C), GA, *414*
Lawrence-Leiter & Co. (R), KS, *126*
Leader Network (C), PA, *414*
Leader Search Inc. (R), AB, *127*
Leaders-Trust Int'l./Carce y Asociados, S.C. (R), MX, *127*
The Lear Group, Inc. (R), OH, *127*
Lechner & Assoc., Inc. (C), FL, *415*
Lectra Search (C), GA, *415*
Ledbetter/Davidson Int'l., Inc. (R), NY, *127*
Albert G. Lee Assoc. (C), RI, *415*
Ricci Lee Assoc., Inc. (C), CA, *415*
Vincent Lee Assoc. (C), NY, *415*
The Conrad Lee Co. Inc. (R), FL, *127*
Leeds and Leeds (C), TN, *416*
Legal Network Inc. (C), CA, *416*
V. J. Lehman & Assoc., Inc. (R), CO, *127*
Lehman McLeskey (R), TX, *128*
Leith & Assoc., Inc. (C), OH, *416*
Lekan & Assoc., Inc. (R), OH, *128*
Lemming/LeVan, Inc. (R), GA, *128*
Lending Personnel Services (C), CA, *416*
F. P. Lennon Assoc. (C), PA, *416*
AG Lennox & Assoc. (R), AB, *128*
Jacques LePage Executive Search Inc. (R), QE, *128*
J. E. Lessner Assoc., Inc. (R), MI, *128*
Alan Levine Assoc. (R), MA, *129*
Michael Levine Search Consultants (R), NY, *129*
The Levton Group Inc. (R), ON, *129*
Hal Levy & Assoc. (C), NY, *417*
Lewis & Blank Int'l. (R), CA, *129*
Lewis Companies Inc. (R), ON, *129*
The Libra Group Inc. (C), CT, *417*
Pat Licata & Assoc. (C), NC, *417*
LifeWork, Inc. (C), TX, *418*
Lois L. Lindauer Searches (C), MA, *418*
J. H. Lindell & Co. (C), CA, *418*
Ginger Lindsey & Assoc., Inc. (C), TX, *418*
Lineal Recruiting Services (C), CT, *418*
Lipsky Group, Inc. (R), CA, *129*
Lipson & Co. (R), CA, *130*
Lloyd Prescott Assoc., Inc. (C), FL, *418*
Lloyd Staffing (C), NY, *419*
Locke & Assoc. (R), NC, *131*
Loewenstein & Assoc., Inc. (R), TX, *131*
The Logan Group, Inc. (R), MO, *131*
Logistics Management Resources, Inc. (R), NY, *131*
London Executive Consultants Inc. (C), ON, *420*
Longo Associates (C), CA, *420*
J. S. Lord & Company, Inc. (R), MA, *131*
Louis Search Group, Inc. (C), NJ, *420*
Bruce Lowery & Assoc. (C), MI, *420*
Lucas Assoc. (C), GA, *421*
The John Lucht Consultancy Inc. (R), NY, *131*
Ludwig & Assoc., Inc. (C), VA, *421*
Charles Luntz & Assoc., Inc. (R), MO, *132*
Lutz Associates (C), CT, *421*
Lybrook Assoc., Inc. (C), RI, *421*
P. J. Lynch Assoc. (R), CT, *132*
Lynch Miller Moore Partners, Inc. (R), IL, *132*
Lynne Palmer Executive Recruitment, Inc. (C), NY, *421*
Lyons & Assoc., Inc. (C), IL, *422*
Lyons Pruitt Int'l. (R), PA, *132*
M H Executive Search Group (C), TX, *422*
M. K. & Assoc. (C), PA, *422*
M/J/A Partners (R), IL, *133*
The Mackenzie Group (R), MD, *133*
MacNaughton Assoc. (R), CA, *133*
Maczkov-Biosciences, Inc. (R), CA, *133*
Carol Maden Group (C), VA, *422*
Madison Executive Search, Inc. (C), NJ, *422*
The Madison Group (R), NY, *133*
Madison MacArthur Inc. (R), ON, *133*
Maglio & Co., Inc. (R), WI, *134*
Magnum Search (C), IL, *422*
The Mallard Group (C), IN, *423*
Managed Care Consultants (C), AZ, *423*
Managed Care Resources (C), TX, *424*
Management & Human Resources (R), MA, *134*
Management Advisors Int'l., Inc. (C), NC, *424*
Management Alliance Group, Inc. (R), NJ, *134*
Management Assoc. (C), MD, *424*
Management Assoc. (C), CA, *424*
Management Consultants Corporate Recruiters (C), AZ, *424*
Management Decision Systems, Inc. (MDSI) (C), NJ, *424*
Management Dimensions Ltd. (R), ON, *134*
Management One Consultants (C), ON, *425*
Management Recruiters of Nassau, Inc. (R), NY, *134*
Management Recruiters of Birmingham-South, Inc. (C), AL, *438*
Management Recruiters of Sedona (C), AZ, *438*
Management Recruiters of Decatur, LLC (C), AL, *438*
Management Recruiters of Tucson (C), AZ, *439*

Management Recruiters Tucson-Foothills, Inc. (C), AZ, *439*
Management Recruiters of Little Rock (C), AR, *439*
Management Recruiters of San Luis Obispo (C), CA, *439*
Management Recruiters Peninsula (C), CA, *439*
Management Recruiters of Northern California (C), CA, *440*
Management Recruiters of Laguna Hills (C), CA, *440*
Management Recruiters Dana Point (C), CA, *440*
Management Recruiters, Inland Empire Agency (C), CA, *441*
Management Recruiters of Colorado Springs (C), CO, *441*
Management Recruiters of Roseville (C), CA, *441*
Management Recruiters of Sonoma (C), CA, *441*
Management Recruiters of Sacramento North (C), CA, *441*
Management Recruiters Inc. of Silicon Valley (C), CA, *441*
Management Recruiters of Winsted, Inc. (C), CT, *442*
Management Recruiters of Colorado, Inc. (C), CO, *442*
Management Recruiters of Franktown (C), CO, *442*
Management Recruiters of Middlesex (C), CT, *442*
Management Recruiters of Colchester (C), CT, *442*
Management Recruiters of Altamonte (C), FL, *442*
Management Recruiters of Milford Inc. (C), CT, *442*
Management Recruiters of Ft. Myers, FL. (C), FL, *443*
Management Recruiters of Clearwater (C), FL, *443*
Management Recruiters of Anna Maria Island (C), FL, *443*
Management Recruiters, Inc. (C), FL, *443*
Management Recruiters of Miami-North (C), FL, *443*
Management Recruiters of St. Lucie County, Inc. (C), FL, *444*
Management Recruiters of Pensacola (C), FL, *444*
Management Recruiters of Tampa North (C), FL, *444*
Management Recruiters of Northern Palm Beaches (C), FL, *444*
Management Recruiters of North Fulton (C), GA, *445*
Management Recruiters of Forsyth County (C), GA, *445*
Management Recruiters of Atlanta West, Inc. (C), GA, *445*
Management Recruiters of Venice, Inc. (C), FL, *445*
Management Recruiters of Atlanta (C), GA, *445*
Management Recruiters of Vero Beach (C), FL, *445*
Management Recruiters of Sandy Springs (C), GA, *446*
Management Recruiters of Atlanta NE (C), GA, *446*
Management Recruiters - Towne Lake (C), GA, *446*
Management Recruiters of Boise (C), ID, *446*
Management Recruiters of St. Charles (C), IL, *447*
Management Recruiters of Lake Forest, IL (C), IL, *447*
Management Recruiters of Barrington (C), IL, *447*
Management Recruiters of Sun Valley (C), ID, *447*
Management Recruiters of Chicago West (C), IL, *447*
Management Recruiters of Noblesville, Inc. (C), IN, *448*
Management Recruiters of Indianapolis (C), IN, *448*
Management Recruiters of South Bend (C), IN, *448*
Management Recruiters of Indianapolis-North (C), IN, *448*
Management Recruiters-Cedar Rapids, Inc. (C), IA, *448*
Management Recruiters - Indianapolis (C), IN, *448*
Management Recruiters of Des Moines (C), IA, *449*
Management Recruiters of Williamsburg (C), IA, *449*
Management Recruiters of Siouxland (C), IA, *449*
Management Recruiters of Frederick, Inc. (C), MD, *450*
Management Recruiters of Washington, DC Inc. (C), MD, *450*
Management Recruiters of the Baltimore Washington Corridor (C), MD, *450*
Management Recruiters of Monroe, Inc. (C), LA, *450*
Management Recruiters of Muskegon (C), MI, *451*
Management Recruiters of Birmingham (C), MI, *451*
Management Recruiters of Detroit & Farmington Hills (C), MI, *451*
Management Recruiters of Dearborn, Inc. (C), MI, *451*
Management Recruiters of Winona (C), MN, *452*
Management Recruiters of Woodbury (C), MN, *452*
Management Recruiters of Cass County, NE (C), NE, *452*
Management Recruiters of Bloomington (C), MN, *452*
Management Recruiters of Bay Head (C), NJ, *453*
Management Recruiters of Morris County, NJ (C), NJ, *453*
Management Recruiters of Medford, N.J. (C), NJ, *453*
Management Recruiters of Orange County, N.Y., Inc. (C), NJ, *453*
Management Recruiters of Reno (C), NV, *453*
Management Recruiters of Princeton (C), NJ, *454*
Management Recruiters of Middlesex County NJ (C), NJ, *454*
Management Recruiters of Upper Westchester (C), NY, *454*
Management Recruiters of New Providence (C), NJ, *454*
Management Recruiters of Gramercy, Inc. (C), NY, *455*
Management Recruiters of Manhattan on Broadway (C), NY, *455*
Management Recruiters of Burlington (C), NC, *455*
Management Recruiters of Woodbury Inc. (C), NY, *455*
Management Recruiters of Rocky Mount - Southwest (C), NC, *456*
Management Recruiters of Raleigh (C), NC, *456*
Management Recruiters of Boone (C), NC, *456*
Management Recruiters of Gastonia (C), NC, *456*
Management Recruiters of Akron (C), OH, *457*
Management Recruiters of Dayton, Inc. (C), OH, *457*
Management Recruiters of Cincinnati/ Sharonville, Inc. (C), OH, *457*
Management Recruiters of Cleveland (C), OH, *457*
Management Recruiters of Cleveland (C), OH, *457*
Management Recruiters of Oklahoma City (C), OK, *458*
Management Recruiters of Sidney (C), OH, *458*
Management Recruiters of Mentor, Inc. (C), OH, *458*
Management Recruiters of Northwest Ohio, Inc. (C), OH, *458*
Management Recruiters of Bethlehem, PA (C), PA, *458*
Management Recruiters of Lionville, Inc. (C), PA, *459*
Management Recruiters of Westmoreland County, Inc. (C), PA, *459*
Management Recruiters of Delaware County (C), PA, *459*
Management Recruiters of Pittsburgh (C), PA, *459*
Management Recruiters of Puerto Rico (C), PR, *460*
Management Recruiters of North Charleston (C), SC, *460*
Management Recruiters of Myrtle Beach, Inc. (C), SC, *460*
Management Recruiters of West Chester, Inc. (C), PA, *460*
Management Recruiters The Delta Group, Inc. (C), TN, *461*
Management Recruiters of Sioux Falls, LLP (C), SD, *461*
Management Recruiters of Chattanooga-Brainerd, Inc. (C), TN, *461*

Management Recruiters of Franklin, Inc. (C), TN, *461*
Management Recruiters of Georgetown (C), SC, *461*
Management Recruiters Dallas North (MRDN) (C), TX, *462*
Management Recruiters of Austin (C), TX, *462*
Management Recruiters of San Antonio (C), TX, *463*
Management Recruiters of San Marcos (C), TX, *463*
Management Recruiters of San Antonio - North (C), TX, *463*
Management Recruiters of Round Rock (C), TX, *463*
Management Recruiters of Salt Lake City (C), UT, *464*
Management Recruiters of Fairfax, VA (C), VA, *464*
Management Recruiters of Arlington (C), VA, *464*
Management Recruiters of Sugar Land Inc. (C), TX, *464*
Management Recruiters Int'l.-The Woodlands (C), TX, *464*
Management Recruiters - Piedmont (C), VA, *464*
Management Recruiters of Kanawha Valley, LLC (C), WV, *465*
Management Recruiters of Seattle (C), WA, *465*
Management Recruiters of Spokane (C), WA, *465*
Management Recruiters of Roanoke (C), VA, *465*
Management Recruiters of Appleton (C), WI, *465*
Management Recruiters of Milwaukee-North (C), WI, *466*
Management Recruiters of Stevens Point, Inc. (C), WI, *466*
Management Recruiters of Madison, Inc. (C), WI, *466*
Management Recruiters of Milwaukee - Downtown (C), WI, *466*
Management Recruiters of Janesville, Inc. (C), WI, *466*
Management Resource Assoc., Inc. (C), FL, *467*
Management Resource Group, Inc. (C), NY, *467*
Management Resource Group (C), MN, *467*
Management Resources (C), TX, *467*
Management Search, Inc. (C), IL, *467*
Management Search, Inc. (C), OK, *468*
Management Search of R.I. Inc. (R), RI, *135*
Management Solutions, Inc. (C), WA, *468*
Mangieri/Solutions LLC (C), CT, *468*
Mannard & Assoc., Inc. (R), IL, *135*
F. L. Mannix & Co. (R), MA, *135*
ManTech Consulting (C), NY, *468*
Manuso, Alexander & Associates, Inc. (R), NY, *135*
The Marathon Group (C), FL, *469*
Marc-Allen Assoc., Inc. (C), FL, *469*
Marcus & Assoc. (C), NY, *469*
Marentz & Co. (C), TX, *469*
Margolin Consultants, Inc. (C), NY, *469*
J. L. Mark Assoc., Inc. (R), CO, *135*
Mark Christian & Assoc., Inc. (C), AZ, *469*
Mark Stanley & Co./EMA Partners International (R), FL, *136*
Markent Personnel, Inc. (C), WI, *470*
Marketing & Sales Resources, Inc. (C), FL, *470*
Marketing Consultants (C), WI, *470*
Marketing Recruiters, Inc. (C), NC, *470*
Marketing Resources (C), MA, *470*
Marketing Search Inc. (C), OH, *471*
Marketing/Public Relations Research Recruiting (C), CT, *471*
MarketPro, Inc. (C), GA, *471*
Paula Marks Inc. (R), NY, *136*
Brad Marks Int'l. (R), CA, *136*
The Marlow Group (R), MA, *136*
The Maroon Group (R), CT, *136*
Marra Peters & Partners (R), NJ, *136*
Marshall Consultants, Inc. (R), NY, *137*
Marshall-Alan Assoc., Inc. (C), NY, *471*
Marsteller Wilcox Assoc. (C), IL, *471*
Donovan Martin & Assoc. (R), CA, *137*
J. Martin & Assoc. (R), CA, *137*
George R. Martin (R), PA, *137*
Martin Partners, L.L.C. (R), IL, *137*
The Martwick Group, Inc. (C), OR, *472*
Marvel Consultants, Inc. (C), OH, *472*
Massey-Horton Int'l. (R), ON, *138*
Richard L. Mather & Assoc. (C), CT, *472*
Mathey Services (C), IL, *472*
Matrix Consultants, Inc. (C), NC, *472*
Matte Consulting Group Inc. (R), QE, *138*
The Matthews Group, Inc. (C), NJ, *472*
Maxecon Executive Search Consultants (R), FL, *138*
K. Maxin & Assoc. (R), PA, *139*
The Mayes Group, Ltd. (R), PA, *139*
Mayhall Search Group, Inc. (C), IN, *473*
The Mazzitelli Group, Ltd. (R), MN, *139*
MB Inc. Executive Search (C), NY, *473*
McBride Assoc., Inc. (R), DC, *139*
Tom McCall Executive Search (C), IL, *473*
McCarthy Assoc. National BancSearch, LLC (C), LA, *473*
McCormack & Farrow (R), CA, *140*
The McCormick Group (C), VA, *473*
McCormick Search Inc. (C), IL, *474*
McCoy Ltd. (C), CA, *474*
McCray, Shriver, Eckdahl & Assoc., Inc. (R), CA, *140*
McDonald Assoc. Int'l. (R), IL, *140*
McDonald, Long & Assoc., Inc. (R), NY, *140*
McDowell & Co., Recruiters (C), TX, *474*
Robert E. McGrath & Assoc. (R), CT, *141*
McGrath & Assoc., Inc. (R), NJ, *141*
McIntyre Assoc. (R), CT, *141*
McKee Cyber Search (C), MS, *475*
McKinley•Arend Int'l. (R), TX, *141*
The McKinnon Management Group Inc. (C), ON, *475*
Dan P. McLean Assoc., Inc. (C), ON, *475*
McManners Assoc., Inc. (R), CA, *142*
Joseph J. McTaggart (C), CA, *476*
James Mead & Co. (R), CT, *142*
Meads & Assoc. (R), FL, *142*
Med-Ex Services (C), OH, *476*
Meder & Assoc., Inc. (R), IL, *142*
Media Recruiting Group, Inc. (C), NY, *476*
Medical Executive Recruiters (C), CA, *477*
Medical Executive Search Assoc., Inc. (C), AZ, *477*
Medical Innovations (C), NY, *477*
Medical Recruiters Inc. (C), MO, *477*
The Medley Group (C), CA, *477*
MedQuest Assoc. (C), CO, *478*
MedXec USA, Inc. (C), FL, *478*
Mee Derby & Co. (C), DC, *478*
Mehta Consulting (C), NJ, *478*
Melancon & Co. (R), TX, *143*
Juan Menefee & Assoc. (C), IL, *478*
Meng, Finseth & Assoc., Inc. (R), CA, *143*
Mengel & McDonald Ltd. (C), IL, *479*
Mercedes & Co., Inc. (R), MA, *143*
J. M. Meredith & Assoc. Inc. (C), CA, *479*
Merlin Int'l. Inc. (C), NJ, *479*
MES Search Co. (C), GA, *479*
MESA, Inc. (R), CO, *143*
MESA International (C), CA, *480*
Messett Assoc., Inc. (R), FL, *143*
MetroVantage Personnel Systems (C), CA, *480*
Walter Meyer & Assoc. (R), NY, *144*
Meyer Assoc., Inc. (R), GA, *144*
mfg/Search, Inc. (C), IN, *480*
Michael James & Co. (C), IL, *480*
Michael Wayne Recruiters (C), IL, *480*
Michael/Merrill (C), KS, *481*
Michaels & Moere (C), WI, *481*
Michigan Consulting Group (R), MI, *144*
Micro Staff Solutions, Inc. (C), TX, *481*
Midland Consultants (C), OH, *481*
Miller + Miller (C), WA, *482*
Danette Milne Corporate Search Inc. (C), ON, *482*
Milo Research (R), NY, *145*
Milrod Assoc. (C), NJ, *482*
Herbert Mines Assoc., Inc. (R), NY, *145*
Mirtz Morice, Inc. (R), CT, *145*
Laurie Mitchell & Co., Inc. (R), OH, *145*
MIXTEC Group (R), CA, *145*
MJF Assoc. (C), CT, *483*
Mogul Consultants, Inc. (C), NY, *483*
Molloy Partners (R), NY, *146*
Oscar Montaño, Inc. (R), CA, *146*
Montenido Assoc. (R), CA, *146*
The Montgomery Group, Inc. (C), TN, *484*
Montgomery West (R), CA, *146*
Montgomery, Thomason & Assoc. (C), ON, *484*
C. A. Moore & Assoc., Inc. (C), MN, *484*
Thomas R. Moore Executive Search (R), TX, *146*
Moore Research Assoc. (R), NJ, *147*
The Moran Group (C), IL, *484*
Tina Morbitzer & Assoc. (C), FL, *485*
Morency Assoc. (C), MA, *485*
Morgan Int'l., Inc. (R), IL, *147*
Morgan Samuels Co. (R), CA, *147*
The Morgan/Geoffries Group (C), CA, *485*
Morgan/Webber, Inc. (R), NY, *147*
Morris & Berger (R), CA, *147*
The Morris Group (C), PA, *486*
Mortgage Search Network (C), AZ, *486*

Robert T. Morton Assoc., Inc. (C), MA, *486*
Moyer, Sherwood Assoc., Inc. (R), NY, *148*
MPA Executive Search Inc. (R), QE, *148*
MRI, The Sequel Group, LLC (C), CO, *486*
Mruk & E.M.A. Partners (R), NY, *148*
MTA Partners (R), TX, *148*
Mullen Assoc., Inc. (R), NC, *148*
Pamela L. Mulligan, Inc. (R), NH, *149*
The Mulshine Co., Inc. (R), NJ, *149*
Multi Processing, Inc. (R), NH, *149*
Jennifer Munro & Partners, Inc. (R), SC, *149*
P. J. Murphy & Assoc., Inc. (R), WI, *150*
Kenneth Murphy & Assoc. (C), NS, *487*
Murphy Partners Int'l. (R), IL, *150*
The Murray Group (C), IL, *487*
Musick & Assoc. (C), CA, *487*
Mycoff & Assoc. (R), CO, *150*
Myers Career Assoc., Inc. (C), CA, *488*
N.A.P. Executive Services (Canada) Inc. (C), ON, *488*
Nachman Biomedical (C), MA, *488*
Nadzam, Lusk, Horgan & Assoc., Inc. (R), CA, *150*
NaTek Corp. (C), NY, *488*
National Affirmative Action Career Network, Inc. (C), CO, *488*
National Bank & Finance Executive Search (C), CA, *488*
National Career Search (C), AZ, *489*
National Metal Services Corp. (C), IN, *489*
National Recruiters (C), OK, *489*
National Recruiting Service (C), IN, *489*
National Register Columbus Inc. (C), OH, *490*
National Search, Inc. (R), NC, *150*
National Search, Inc.r (C), FL, *490*
Nationwide Personnel Recruiting & Consulting, Inc. (C), OR, *490*
Nationwide Personnel Placement, Inc. (C), OH, *490*
NDB Assoc., Inc. (C), PA, *491*
The Neil Michael Group, Inc./Global Partners (R), NY, *151*
The NEIS Corp., Inc. (C), FL, *491*
J. Fielding Nelson & Assoc., Inc. (R), UT, *151*
New Dimensions in Technology, Inc. (C), MA, *492*
New Directions, Inc. (C), IL, *492*
New Venture Development, Inc. (C), CA, *492*
New World Healthcare Solutions, Inc. (R), NY, *151*
Newcomb-Desmond & Assoc., Inc. (C), OH, *492*
Newman-Johnson-King, Inc. (C), TX, *492*
Newport Management (C), NY, *492*
Newport Strategic Search LLC (C), CA, *492*
Next Step Recruiting (C), CA, *493*
NHA Plastics Recruiters (C), FL, *493*
Nicholaou & Co. (R), IL, *151*
Marc Nichols Assoc., Inc. (C), NY, *493*
P. J. Nicholson & Assoc. (C), IL, *493*
The Niemond Corp. (R), CA, *152*
Nino Recruiting & Staffing, Inc. (C), TX, *493*
Ira Z. Nitzberg (C), NY, *493*
J. L. Nixon Consulting (C), TX, *493*
NJ Solutions (C), CA, *493*
Noble & Assoc., Inc. (C), NY, *494*
Noll Human Resource Services (C), NE, *494*
W. D. Nolte & Company (R), CT, *152*
Nordeman Grimm, Inc. (R), NY, *152*
Paul Winston Norman & Assoc. (R), IL, *152*
Norman Broadbent Int'l., Inc. (R), NY, *152*
The Normyle/Erstling Health Search Group (C), NJ, *494*
John B. Norris & Assoc., Inc. (C), MD, *495*
Ronald Norris & Assoc. (C), IL, *495*
NorTech Resources (C), NY, *496*
North American Recruiters, Inc. (R), MN, *153*
Northern Consultants Inc. (R), ME, *153*
NPS of Atlanta, Inc. (C), GA, *496*
Nuessle, Kurdziel & Weiss, Inc. (R), PA, *153*
O'Brien & Bell (R), OH, *153*
O'Brien and Roof (C), OH, *497*
O'Brien Consulting Services (R), MA, *153*
O'Connell Group Inc. (C), CT, *497*
O'Connor, O'Connor, Lordi, Ltd. (R), PA, *154*
O'Connor Resources (C), TX, *497*
O'Keefe & Assoc., Inc. (R), CT, *154*
O'Neill & Co. (R), CT, *154*
O'Shea, Divine & Co., Inc. (R), CA, *154*
O'Sullivan Search Inc. (C), ON, *498*
Dennis P. O'Toole & Assoc. Inc. (R), NY, *154*
O'Toole & Company, Inc. (R), IL, *154*
Oak Assoc. (R), CA, *155*
Ober & Company (R), CA, *155*
Oberlander & Co., Inc. (R), IL, *155*
OEI, Inc. (C), NJ, *498*
The Ogdon Partnership (R), NY, *155*
The Oldani Group (R), WA, *155*
Oliver & Rozner Assoc., Inc. (R), NY, *155*
Ollinger Partners (R), MA, *156*
Olsen/Clark (R), WA, *156*
Omega Systems, LLC (C), VA, *498*
Omnisearch Assoc. (C), CA, *499*
OmniSearch, Inc. (C), FL, *499*
The Onstott Group (R), MA, *156*
Opalka Dixon Consultants to Management (R), VA, *156*
Open Concepts (C), CA, *499*
Oppedisano & Co., Inc. (R), NY, *156*
Opus Marketing (R), CA, *156*
Organization Consulting Ltd. (R), ON, *157*
Organization Resources Inc. (R), MA, *157*
Orion Int'l. Consulting Group, Inc. (C), NC, *499*
Ortman Recruiting Int'l. (C), CA, *500*
K. Ossow & Co. (C), NY, *500*
Ott & Hansen, Inc. (R), CA, *157*
Overton Consulting (R), WI, *157*
LaMonte Owens, Inc. (R), PA, *157*
The Oxford Group (C), TX, *500*
The P & L Group (C), NY, *500*
P R Management Consultants, Inc. (C), NJ, *500*
P.A.R. Assoc., Inc. (R), MA, *158*
P.R.H. Management, Inc. (R), CT, *158*
Pacific Advisory Service, Inc. (C), IL, *501*
Pacific Coast Recruiters (C), OR, *501*
Pacific Crossing (C), CA, *501*
Packaging Personnel Co., Ltd. (C), WI, *501*
Page-Wheatcroft & Co., Ltd. (R), TX, *158*
The Pailin Group Professional Search Consultants (R), TX, *158*
Janou Pakter, Inc. (C), NY, *502*
Paladin Group, Inc. (C), CO, *502*
Kirk Palmer & Assoc., Inc. (R), NY, *158*
Pamenter, Pamenter, Brezer & Deganis Ltd. (R), ON, *159*
Paper Industry Recruitment (P.I.R.) (C), ME, *502*
Frank Parillo & Assoc. (R), CA, *159*
The Park Group & Assoc., Inc. (C), MD, *502*
R. Parker & Assoc., Inc. (R), NY, *159*
D. P. Parker & Assoc., Inc. (R), MA, *159*
Parker-Worthington, Inc. (C), TX, *503*
Largent Parks & Partners (C), TX, *503*
Michael W. Parres & Assoc. (R), MI, *159*
Parsons Assoc. Inc. (R), IL, *159*
Partners Executive Search Consultants Inc. (R), ON, *160*
Partners In Human Resources Int'l., Inc. (R), NY, *160*
The Partnership Group (R), NJ, *160*
Partridge Assoc., Inc. (R), MA, *160*
Carolyn Smith Paschal Int'l. (R), CA, *160*
Pasona Canada, Inc. (C), ON, *504*
Pathways Int'l. (C), CT, *505*
The Patience Motivation Belief Group, Inc. (C), GA, *505*
Patriot Assoc. (C), PA, *505*
Paul-Tittle Assoc., Inc. (R), VA, *161*
Paules Associates (C), CA, *505*
Pawlik/Dorman Partners (R), IL, *161*
PC Assoc. (C), CO, *505*
Peachtree Executive Search (R), GA, *161*
Peak Search Assoc. (C), ON, *506*
Pearce & Assoc. (C), FL, *506*
Pearson, Caldwell & Farnsworth (R), CA, *161*
Peden & Assoc. (C), CA, *506*
Peeney Assoc., Inc. (R), NJ, *161*
Paul S. Pelland, P.C. (R), SC, *161*
M. A. Pelle Assoc., Inc. (C), NY, *506*
The Penn Partners, Inc. (R), PA, *162*
The Pennmor Group (C), NJ, *506*
People Management Northeast, Inc. (R), CT, *162*
PeopleSource Inc. (C), TX, *506*
Perez & Assoc. (C), MI, *507*
Perfect Search, Inc. (C), FL, *507*
Performance Resources, Inc. (C), RI, *507*
The Perkins Group (R), NC, *162*
Perry • Newton Assoc. (C), MD, *507*
Perry Search Assoc. (C), CA, *507*
Perry-D'Amico & Assoc. (R), CA, *162*
Perry-Martel Int'l., Inc. (R), ON, *163*
Barry Persky & Co., Inc. (R), CT, *163*
PersoNet, Inc. (C), FL, *507*
Personnel Assoc. (C), NC, *508*
Personnel Assoc. (C), CA, *508*
The Personnel Group, Inc. (R), MN, *163*
Personnel Solutions (C), AZ, *509*

Personnel Unlimited/Executive Search (C), WA, *509*
J. R. Peterman Assoc., Inc. (C), VT, *509*
Alec Peters Assoc. Inc./DLR (R), GA, *163*
Richard Peterson & Assoc., Inc. (R), GA, *163*
Petruzzi Assoc. (C), NJ, *509*
Peyser Assoc., Inc. (R), FL, *163*
Pharmaceutical Recruiters, Inc. (R), NY, *163*
Phase II Management (R), CT, *164*
PHD Conseil en Ressources Humaines Inc. (C), QE, *510*
J. R. Phillip & Assoc., Inc. (R), CA, *164*
Phillips & Assoc. (R), MA, *164*
Phillips Assoc. (C), FL, *510*
Phillips Int'l., Inc. (C), SC, *510*
Phillips Personnel/Search (C), CO, *510*
Phillips Resource Group (C), SC, *510*
Phoenix BioSearch, Inc. (C), NJ, *511*
Phoenix Partners, Inc. (C), GA, *511*
Phoenix Search (R), MX, *164*
PIC Executive Search (C), GA, *511*
Pierce & Crow (R), CA, *164*
The Pinnacle Source, Inc. (C), CO, *512*
Pinton Forrest & Madden/EMA Partners Int'l. (R), BC, *165*
Pioneer Executive Consultants (C), ON, *512*
DNPitchon Assoc. (R), NJ, *165*
PLA, Inc. (C), NJ, *513*
Placements by Jesse Reid Assoc., Inc. (C), NY, *513*
Plante & Moran, LLP (R), MI, *165*
Rene Plessner Assoc., Inc. (R), NY, *165*
R. L. Plimpton Assoc., Inc. (R), CO, *165*
Yves Plouffe & Assoc. (R), QE, *165*
Plummer & Assoc., Inc. (R), CT, *166*
Poirier, Hoevel & Co. (R), CA, *166*
The Polen Group (C), PA, *514*
Ray Polhill & Assoc. (R), NC, *166*
Bob Poline Assoc. Inc. (C), CA, *514*
The Pollack Group (C), ON, *514*
Polson & Co., Inc. (R), MN, *166*
Al Ponaman Company, Inc. (C), CA, *514*
Don V. Poole & Assoc., Inc. (C), CO, *514*
Porter & Assoc., Inc. (C), FL, *514*
Jack Porter Assoc., Inc. (C), WA, *514*
David Powell, Inc. (R), CA, *166*
Power Recruiting Group (C), TX, *515*
Power Search (C), TX, *515*
Robert Powers & Assoc. (C), CA, *515*
Norman Powers Assoc., Inc. (C), MA, *515*
Powers Consultants, Inc. (R), MO, *166*
P. G. Prager Search Assoc., Ltd. (C), NY, *515*
The Prairie Group (C), IL, *515*
Elan Pratzer & Partners Inc. (R), ON, *167*
PRAXIS Partners (R), VA, *167*
Precision Executive Search (C), AZ, *516*
Preferred Professional Recruiters (C), OH, *516*
Preferred Professional Recruiters (C), TX, *516*
George Preger & Associates Inc. (R), ON, *167*
Premier Recruiting Group (C), MI, *516*
Presley Consultants, Inc. (C), CA, *517*
Preston & Co. (R), NJ, *167*
Preston-Hunter, Inc. (R), IL, *167*
Prestonwood Assoc. (R), MA, *168*
Price & Assoc., Inc. (C), VA, *518*
Alan J. Price Assoc., Inc. (C), RI, *518*
PricewaterhouseCoopers Executive Search (R), ON, *168*
PricewaterhouseCoopers Executive Search (R), MX, *168*
Prichard Kymen Inc. (R), AB, *168*
Primary Care Service Corp. (C), GA, *518*
The Primary Group, Inc. (R), FL, *168*
Prime Management Group Inc. (C), ON, *518*
Prime Search (C), NC, *518*
Primus Assoc., L.C. (R), TX, *169*
Princeton Search Partners, Inc. (R), NJ, *169*
PRO, Inc./Professional Recruiting Offices, Inc. (C), CA, *519*
Probe Technology (C), PA, *519*
Professional Employment Group (C), MD, *520*
Professional Persons Career Services (C), NY, *521*
Professional Recruiting Consultants (C), FL, *521*
Professional Recruiters Inc. (C), MN, *521*
Professional Recruiting Network (C), CA, *521*
Professional Recruiters, Inc. (C), PA, *521*
Professional Recruiters (C), UT, *521*
Professional Recruiting Consultants, Inc. (C), DE, *521*
Professional Research Services, Inc. (R), IL, *169*
The Professional Sales Search Co., Inc. (C), WA, *522*
Professional Search (R), MI, *169*
Professional Search Assoc. (C), CA, *522*
Professional Selection Services (R), GA, *169*
Professions, Inc. (C), OH, *523*
ProFinders, Inc. (C), FL, *523*
Profit Pros, Inc. (C), CA, *523*
ProNet, Inc. (C), NC, *524*
ProSearch Recruiting (C), CA, *524*
ProSearch, Inc. (C), ME, *524*
ProSearch, Inc. (C), OH, *524*
ProStar Systems, Inc. (C), MD, *525*
Protocol Inc. (C), CA, *525*
Proven Edge (C), CA, *525*
PSD Group, Inc. (C), CA, *525*
Quality Search Inc. (C), OH, *526*
The Quantum Group (C), NJ, *526*
Quantum Int'l., Ltd. (R), FL, *170*
QuestPro, Inc. (C), TX, *527*
L. J. Quinn & Assoc., Inc. (R), CA, *170*
Quiring Assoc., Inc. (C), IN, *527*
Quirk-Corporon & Assoc., Inc. (C), WI, *527*
QVS Int'l. (R), GA, *170*
R & K Associates, Inc. (C), AZ, *527*
R & L Assoc., Ltd. (R), NY, *170*
R M Associates (R), OH, *171*
R. C. Services (C), TX, *528*
R. J. Associates (C), NY, *528*
R/K International Inc. (R), CT, *171*
R2 Services, LLC (C), IL, *528*
Raines Int'l. Inc. (R), NY, *171*
Ramm Search (C), NY, *528*
Rand Assoc. (R), ME, *171*
Rand Thompson Executive Search Consultants (C), NY, *528*
Lea Randolph & Assoc., Inc. (C), TX, *529*
The Rankin Group, Ltd. (R), WI, *171*
The Ransford Group (R), TX, *171*
J. E. Ranta Assoc. (C), MA, *529*
Harold L. Rapp Assoc. (C), NY, *529*
Joanne E. Ratner Search (C), NY, *529*
Ray & Berndtson/Laurendeau Labrecque (R), QE, *172*
Ray & Berndtson/Lovas Stanley (R), ON, *172*
Raymond Karsan Assoc. (C), PA, *529*
Raymond Thomas & Assoc. (C), FL, *530*
RCE Assoc. (R), NJ, *173*
RCI Employment Solutions (C), FL, *531*
Re-Mark Assoc. Inc. (C), NJ, *531*
Recruit Xpress (C), TX, *531*
Recruiting Options, Inc. (C), GA, *531*
Recruiting Resources Int'l. (C), CA, *532*
Recruiting Services Group, Inc. (C), TN, *532*
Recruiting/Solutions (C), CA, *532*
The Recruitment Group, Inc. (C), NY, *532*
Recruitment Resources (C), CA, *532*
Recruitment Specialists, Inc. (C), MD, *532*
Mary Rector & Assoc., Inc. (C), IL, *533*
Redden & McGrath Assoc., Inc. (R), NY, *173*
Redden-Shaffer Group (R), CA, *173*
Redell Search, Inc. (C), IL, *533*
Redwood Partners Ltd. (R), NY, *173*
Reece & Mruk Partners/EMA Partners Int'l. (R), MA, *173*
Reeder & Assoc., Ltd. (R), GA, *173*
Reeve & Assoc. (C), CT, *533*
The Regis Group, Ltd. (R), GA, *174*
Reifel & Assoc. (R), IL, *174*
Reinecke & Assoc. (C), NJ, *533*
The Remington Group (R), IL, *174*
Renaissance Resources, LLC (R), VA, *174*
The Repovich-Reynolds Group (TRRG, Inc.) (R), CA, *175*
Research Personnel Consultants (C), ON, *534*
Reserve Technology Institute (R), TX, *175*
The Resource Group (R), NJ, *175*
The Resource Group (R), CT, *175*
Resource Inc. (R), MA, *175*
Resource Perspectives, Inc. (R), CA, *175*
Resource Recruiting (C), NH, *534*
Resources for Management (R), PA, *175*
Response Staffing Services (C), NY, *534*
L. J. Reszotko & Assoc. (C), IL, *535*
Retail Recruiters/Spectrum Consultants, Inc. (C), PA, *535*
The Revere Assoc., Inc. (R), OH, *176*
S. Reyman & Assoc., Ltd. (R), IL, *176*
Russell Reynolds Assoc., Inc. (R), NY, *176*
Reynolds Consulting Int'l. (R), ON, *177*
Reynolds Partners (R), NY, *177*
RIC Corp. (R), FL, *177*
Rice Cohen Int'l. (R), PA, *178*
Richards Assoc., Inc. (R), NY, *178*
The Richards Group (C), PA, *536*
Terry Richards (C), OH, *536*
Richmond Assoc. (C), NY, *537*
Riddle & McGrath LLC (R), GA, *178*

Ridenour & Assoc. (R), IL, *178*
Rieser & Assoc., Inc. (R), MO, *178*
Riley Cole (C), CA, *537*
Riotto-Jones Assoc. (R), NY, *178*
Ritta Professional Search Inc. (C), NY, *538*
RJN Consulting (R), NY, *179*
Roberson & Co. (C), AZ, *538*
Robert William James & Assoc. (C), OR, *539*
Roberts Ryan & Bentley, Inc. (R), MD, *179*
Robertson & Assoc. (C), IL, *539*
V. Robinson & Co., Inc. (C), MO, *539*
Bruce Robinson Assoc. (R), NJ, *180*
Robison & Associates (R), NC, *180*
Robison Humphreys & Assoc., Inc. (R), ON, *180*
Robsham & Assoc., Inc. (R), MA, *180*
Rockwood Assoc. (C), NY, *540*
J. Rodgers & Associates (C), IL, *540*
Rodgers, Ramsey, Inc. (C), TX, *540*
Rodzik & Assoc., Inc. (R), NC, *180*
Craig Roe & Assoc., LLC (C), MD, *540*
The Rogan Group, Inc. (C), CA, *541*
Rogers - McManamon Executive Search (R), CA, *180*
Rogish Assoc., Inc. (C), OH, *541*
ROI International, Inc. (R), WA, *181*
Rojek Marketing Group, Inc. (R), OH, *181*
Rolland Ressources Humaines Inc. (R), QE, *181*
Rollins & Assoc. (C), CA, *541*
Rollo Assoc. (R), CA, *181*
Romano McAvoy Assoc., Inc. (C), NY, *544*
Romeo-Hudgins & Assoc., Ltd. (C), NJ, *544*
Rooney Assoc., Inc. (R), IL, *181*
Ropella & Assoc. (R), FL, *181*
Ropes Associates, Inc. (R), FL, *182*
Emery A. Rose & Assoc. (C), WA, *545*
Ross Personnel Consultants, Inc. (C), CT, *545*
Rossi & Assoc. Inc. (C), BC, *545*
Patricia Roth Int'l. (C), FL, *545*
Roth Young of Chicago (C), IL, *546*
Roth Young Executive Search (C), TX, *546*
Roth Young Personnel Service of Detroit, Inc. (C), MI, *546*
Roth Young Executive Recruiters (C), MN, *546*
Roth Young of Pittsburgh (C), PA, *546*
Roth Young Seattle (C), WA, *546*
Roth Young of Tampa (C), FL, *546*
Roth Young Personnel Services of Washington, DC (C), MD, *546*
Roth Young Executive Search of Milwaukee (C), WI, *547*
Rovner & Assoc., Inc. (R), IL, *182*
Rovner Gerner & Assoc. (R), CA, *182*
Rowland Mountain & Assoc. (C), GA, *547*
RSMR, Inc. (R), IL, *182*
The Rubicon Group (C), AZ, *547*
Ruderfer & Co., Inc. (C), NJ, *548*
K. Russo Assoc. Inc. (C), CT, *548*
Rust & Assoc., Inc. (R), IL, *183*
The Ryan Charles Group, Inc. (C), FL, *548*
Ryan-Allen & Assoc., Inc. (C), CA, *549*
Ryman, Bell, Green & Michaels, Inc. (C), TX, *549*
R. L. Rystrom & Assoc., Inc. (C), MN, *549*
S.C.S. & Assoc. (C), NC, *550*
S.D.P. Contract Recruiters (C), NJ, *550*
Saber Group, Inc. (C), TX, *550*
Sage Employment Recruiters (C), IN, *550*
Sales & Management Search, Inc. (C), IL, *551*
Sales & Marketing Search, Inc. (C), MA, *551*
Sales Advantage (C), FL, *551*
Sales Builders, Inc. (R), VA, *183*
Sales Consultants of Birmingham (C), AL, *555*
Sales Consultants Int'l. of Oakland (C), CA, *556*
Sales Consultants Peninsula, Inc. (C), CA, *556*
Sales Consultants of Sacramento (C), CA, *556*
Sales Consultants of Scottsdale, Inc. (C), AZ, *556*
Sales Consultants of Silicon Valley (C), CA, *556*
Sales Consultants of Chico (C), CA, *556*
Sales Consultants of Daphne (C), AL, *556*
Sales Consultants of Northwest Arkansas, Inc. (C), AR, *556*
Sales Consultants of Ft. Lauderdale, Inc. (C), FL, *557*
Sales Consultants of Savannah, GA (C), GA, *557*
Sales Consultants of Stamford-Darien (C), CT, *557*
Sales Consultants of Boca Raton, Inc. (C), FL, *557*
Sales Consultants of Ft. Myers, Inc. (C), FL, *557*
Sales Consultants of Danbury (C), CT, *557*
Sales Consultants of Denver (C), CO, *557*
Sales Consultants of Tampa North, Inc. (C), FL, *557*
Sales Consultants of Western McHenry County (C), IL, *558*
Sales Consultants (C), IL, *558*
Sales Consultants of Chicago South (C), IL, *558*
Sales Consultants of Indianapolis (C), IN, *558*
Sales Consultants of Honolulu (C), HI, *558*
Sales Consultants of Barrington (C), IL, *558*
Sales Consultants of Indianapolis-North (C), IN, *558*
Sales Consultants of Baltimore (C), MD, *559*
Sales Consultants of Rockville, MD (C), MD, *559*
Sales Consultants of Auburn Hills (C), MI, *559*
Sales Consultants - Bristol County (C), MA, *559*
Sales Consultants of Wellesley, Inc. (C), MA, *559*
Sales Consultants of Brockton, Inc. (C), MA, *559*
Sales Consultants of Bangor, Inc. (C), ME, *559*
Sales Consultants of Birmingham (C), MI, *559*
Sales Consultants of Farmington Hills (C), MI, *560*
Sales Consultants of Nashua-Manchester (C), NH, *560*
Sales Consultants of Grand Rapids (C), MI, *560*
Sales Consultants of Laurel Park, Inc. (C), MI, *560*
Sales Consultants of Omaha, Inc. (C), NE, *560*
Sales Consultants of Cherry Hill (C), NJ, *560*
Sales Consultants of Northern Jersey, Inc. (C), NJ, *560*
Sales Consultants Bridgewater, Inc. (C), NJ, *560*
Sales Consultants of Raleigh-Durham-RTP (C), NC, *561*
Sales Consultants of Harrisburg (C), PA, *561*
Sales Consultants of Cincinnati (C), OH, *561*
Sales Consultants of Butler County (C), PA, *561*
Sales Consultants of Middlesex County, Inc. (C), NJ, *561*
Sales Consultants of Princeton, Inc. (C), NJ, *561*
Sales Consultants of Westchester-South, Inc. (C), NY, *561*
Sales Consultants of Morris County, Inc. (C), NJ, *561*
Sales Consultants of Newtown, Inc. (C), PA, *562*
Sales Consultants of Austin, Inc. (C), TX, *562*
Sales Consultants of Chester County, PA (C), PA, *562*
Sales Consultants of Pittsburgh (C), PA, *562*
Sales Consultants of Rhode Island, Inc. (C), RI, *562*
Sales Consultants of Greenville, Inc. (C), SC, *562*
Sales Consultants King of Prussia (C), PA, *562*
Sales Consultants of Orangeburg (C), SC, *562*
Sales Consultants of Madison (C), WI, *563*
Sales Consultants of Milwaukee (C), WI, *563*
Sales Consultants of Houston (C), TX, *563*
Sales Consultants of Appleton (C), WI, *563*
Sales Consultants of Dallas (C), TX, *563*
Sales Executives, Inc. (C), MI, *563*
Sales Management Resources (C), CA, *563*
Sales Professionals Personnel Services (C), CA, *564*
Sales Recruiters of Oklahoma City (C), OK, *564*
Sales Recruiting Network (C), PA, *564*
Sales Search (C), ON, *564*
Sales Search Specialist (C), IL, *564*
Sales Solutions (C), CA, *564*
A. N. Salloway Executive Search & Consulting, L.L.C. (C), MA, *564*
Salveson Stetson Group, Inc. (R), PA, *184*
Salzmann Gay Assoc., Inc. (R), PA, *184*
Sampson Medical Search (C), CA, *564*

George D. Sandel Assoc. (C), MA, *565*
Sanford Rose Assoc. - Lake Forest (R), IL, *184*
Sanford Rose Assoc. - Santa Ana (C), CA, *565*
Sanford Rose Assoc. (C), OH, *565*
Sanford Rose Assoc. - Mobile (C), AL, *565*
Sanford Rose Assoc. - Santa Barbara (C), CA, *565*
Sanford Rose Assoc. - Fairhope (C), AL, *565*
Sanford Rose Assoc. - Clearwater (C), FL, *566*
Sanford Rose Assoc. - Effingham (C), IL, *566*
Sanford Rose Assoc. - Norcross (C), GA, *566*
Sanford Rose Assoc. - Chicago (C), IL, *566*
Sanford Rose Assoc. - Rockford (C), IL, *567*
Sanford Rose Assoc. - Orland Park (C), IL, *567*
Sanford Rose Assoc. - Cedar Rapids (C), IA, *567*
Sanford Rose Assoc. - Rockville (C), MD, *567*
Sanford Rose Assoc. - Evansville (C), IN, *567*
Sanford Rose Assoc. - Springfield (C), MO, *568*
Sanford Rose Assoc. - Lake St. Louis (C), MO, *568*
Sanford Rose Assoc. - Amherst, NY (C), NY, *568*
Sanford Rose Assoc. - Gastonia (C), NC, *568*
Sanford Rose Assoc. - Burlington, NC (C), NC, *569*
Sanford Rose Assoc. - Greensboro (C), NC, *569*
Sanford Rose Assoc. - Akron (C), OH, *569*
Sanford Rose Assoc. - Fairlawn (C), OH, *569*
Sanford Rose Assoc. - Philadelphia North (C), PA, *570*
Sanford Rose Assoc. - Nashville (C), TN, *570*
Sanford Rose Assoc. - Columbia (C), SC, *570*
Sanford Rose Assoc. - Doylestown (C), PA, *570*
Sanford Rose Assoc. - Portland (C), OR, *570*
Sanford Rose Assoc. - Pittsburgh North (C), PA, *570*
Sanford Rose Assoc. - Salt Lake City (C), UT, *571*
Sathe & Associates, Inc. (R), MN, *184*
Satterfield & Assoc., Inc. (R), OH, *184*
Savalli & Assoc., Inc. (C), MI, *571*
Saviar, Inc. (C), AZ, *571*
Savoy Partners, Ltd. (R), DC, *184*
David Saxner & Assoc., Inc. (DSA, Inc.) (R), IL, *185*
Schall Executive Search Partners (R), MN, *185*
Schattle & Duquette (C), RI, *571*
The Schatz Company (C), MO, *571*
Schick Professional Search, Inc. (C), OH, *572*
A.D. Schiff & Assoc., Ltd. (C), IL, *572*
F. B. Schmidt Int'l. (R), CA, *185*
Schneider, Hill & Spangler, Inc. (R), PA, *185*
Schoales & Assoc. Inc. (C), ON, *572*
Schuyler Assoc., Ltd. (R), GA, *185*
G. L. Schwartz & Assoc., Inc. (C), GA, *572*
Schweichler Assoc., Inc. (R), CA, *186*
Scientific Solutions, Inc. (C), MI, *572*
Devin Scott Assoc. (C), NJ, *572*
Scott Executive Search, Inc. (R), NY, *186*
Scott Sibley Assoc. (C), NY, *573*
Search Advisors Int'l. Corp. (R), FL, *186*
The Search Alliance, Inc. (R), FL, *186*
The Search America Group Inc. (C), OH, *573*
Search America, Inc. (C), PA, *573*
Search Assoc., Inc. (C), NJ, *574*
Search Assoc., Inc. (C), CA, *574*
Search Bureau Int'l. (C), IL, *574*
Search By Design (C), AZ, *574*
The Search Center Inc. (C), TX, *574*
The Search Committee (C), MD, *574*
The Search Company (R), ON, *186*
Search Consultants Int'l., Inc. (C), TX, *575*
The Search Group (C), MD, *575*
Search Innovations, Inc. (R), PA, *187*
Search Int'l. (R), MA, *187*
Search Masters Int'l. (R), AZ, *187*
Search Masters, USA (C), FL, *576*
Search Plus Int'l.-Ohio (C), OH, *576*
Search Research Assoc., Inc. (R), MA, *187*
SearchCom, Inc. (R), TX, *187*
SearchCorp (C), FL, *577*
SearchCorp International (C), AB, *577*
Seco & Zetto Assoc., Inc. (C), NJ, *577*
Sedlar & Miners (R), NY, *188*
Segal & Assoc. (C), GA, *578*
Seiden Krieger Assoc., Inc. (R), NY, *188*
Select Services (C), IL, *578*
Selectis Corp. (C), IL, *578*
Selective Management Services, Inc. (C), FL, *578*
Selective Staffing (C), CA, *579*
Selig Executive Search (C), NH, *579*
Shannahan & Co., Inc. (R), CA, *189*
Sharp Placement Professionals, Inc. (C), NY, *579*
M. B. Shattuck & Assoc., Inc. (R), CA, *189*
Shepherd Bueschel & Provus, Inc. (R), IL, *189*
Sherwood Lehman Massucco, Inc. (R), CA, *189*
Shey-Harding Assoc. Inc. (C), CA, *580*
Shiell Personnel (C), LA, *580*
Shifrin-Fischer Group, Inc. (C), NJ, *580*
Shinn & Assoc. (R), CA, *189*
Michael Shirley Assoc. Inc. (R), KS, *190*
Shoemaker & Assoc. (R), GA, *190*
Shore Asociados Ejecutivos, S. A. de C.V. (R), MX, *190*
The Shotland Group (R), CA, *190*
SHS of Allentown (C), PA, *580*
John Sibbald Assoc., Inc. (R), MO, *191*
Larry Siegel & Assoc. (R), WA, *191*
Peter Siegel & Co. (C), MA, *581*
RitaSue Siegel Resources, Inc. (R), NY, *191*
L. A. Silver Assoc., Inc. (R), MA, *191*
Silver Associates (C), CA, *581*
SilverSands Int'l. (C), FL, *582*
D. J. Simpson Assoc. Inc. (R), ON, *191*
Simpson Associates (C), NY, *582*
Sinclair & Co., Inc. (R), MA, *192*
Singleton & Assoc. (C), VA, *582*
Sink, Walker, Boltrus Int'l. (R), MA, *192*
SKB Enterprises (C), NY, *582*
Skipping Stone Inc. (C), VA, *582*
Ruth Sklar Assoc., Inc. (RSA Executive Search) (R), NY, *192*
Skott/Edwards Consultants (R), NY, *192*
Slayton Int'l., Inc. (R), IL, *192*
Tom Sloan & Assoc., Inc. (C), WI, *583*
Sloan & Assoc., Inc. (C), VA, *583*
Christopher Smallhorn Executive Recruiting, Inc. (R), MA, *193*
Smith & Assoc. (C), CA, *583*
James F. Smith & Assoc. (C), GA, *583*
Ralph Smith & Assoc. (C), IL, *584*
Smith & Laue Search (R), OR, *193*
Smith & Sawyer, Inc. (R), NY, *193*
G. L. Smith Assoc. (C), CA, *584*
Herman Smith Executive Initiatives Inc. (R), ON, *193*
The Smith Group, Inc. (C), NC, *584*
Smith Hanley Assoc., Inc. (C), NY, *584*
Smith James Group, Inc. (R), GA, *194*
Smith, Roth & Squires (R), NY, *194*
Smith Search, S.C. (R), MX, *194*
Smith's Fifth Avenue (C), NY, *585*
Smith, Brown & Jones (C), KS, *585*
A. William Smyth, Inc. (R), CA, *194*
Snelling & Snelling, Inc. (C), FL, *585*
Snelling Search (C), AL, *585*
Snelling Search (C), IL, *585*
Snelling Search - Transportation Division (C), AR, *585*
Snelling Search (C), IL, *586*
Snelling Search Recruiters (C), NC, *586*
C. Snow & Assoc. (C), ON, *586*
Snyder & Co. (R), CT, *194*
Sockwell & Assoc. (R), NC, *194*
Soderlund Assoc. Inc. (R), OH, *194*
Software Resource Consultants (C), TN, *587*
Phyllis Solomon Executive Search, Inc. (C), NJ, *587*
Solomon-Page Healthcare Group (R), NY, *195*
Soltis Management Services (R), PA, *195*
Somerset Group, Inc. (C), CT, *587*
Stephen M. Sonis Assoc. (R), MA, *195*
Souder & Assoc. (R), VA, *195*
Southern Chemical & Plastics Search (C), GA, *587*
Southport Int'l. Assoc. Inc. (C), FL, *588*
Southwestern Professional Services (C), TN, *588*
Sparks, McDonough & Assoc., Inc. (C), MO, *588*
SPC Symcox Personnel Consultants (C), TX, *588*
Special Markets Group, Inc. (R), GA, *195*
Specialized Search Assoc. (C), FL, *589*

Specialty Employment Services, Inc. (C), GA, *589*
Spectra International LLC (C), AZ, *589*
Spectrum Consultants (R), CA, *196*
SpencerSearch, Inc. (C), CO, *589*
SpencerStuart (R), NY, *196*
The Spiegel Group (R), MA, *197*
Sports Group Int'l. (R), NC, *198*
Spriggs & Co., Inc. (R), IL, *198*
Springer Souder & Assoc. L.L.C. (R), IL, *198*
Sprout/Standish, Inc. (C), NH, *589*
Squires Resources Inc. (C), ON, *590*
Staff Extension Int'l. (C), TX, *590*
Staff Resources, Inc. (C), SC, *590*
Staffing Edge, Inc. (C), IA, *590*
Stafford Consulting Group (R), CA, *198*
StaffWriters Plus (C), NY, *591*
Stanton Chase Int'l. (R), MD, *198*
Star Search Consultants (C), ON, *591*
Starbridge Group Inc. (C), VA, *591*
The Stark Wilton Group (R), MI, *199*
STAT Search (C), NH, *592*
Steeple Resources & Consulting (R), NJ, *199*
The Stelton Group, Inc. (C), NJ, *592*
Stentiford & Berardi Assoc. Ltd. (R), NY, *199*
Michael Stern Assoc., Inc./Euram (R), ON, *200*
Steven Douglas Assoc. (C), FL, *593*
Steven Michaels & Assoc. (C), NY, *593*
Ron Stevens & Assoc., Inc. (C), FL, *593*
Stevens Assoc. (C), MA, *593*
The Stevens Group (C), CA, *593*
The Stevenson Group, Inc. (N.J.) (R), NJ, *200*
The Stewart Group (C), FL, *593*
Stewart, Stein & Scott, Ltd. (R), MN, *200*
Stewart/Greene & Co. of The Triad, Inc. (C), NC, *594*
Stewart/Laurence Assoc., Inc. (R), NJ, *201*
Charles Stickler Assoc. (R), PA, *201*
Stillinger & Assoc. (R), CA, *201*
Allan Stolee Inc. (R), FL, *201*
Stone & Youngblood (C), MA, *594*
Stone, Murphy & Olson (R), MN, *201*
DM Stone Personnel Services (C), CA, *594*
The Stonebridge Group (C), PA, *594*
Stoopen Asociados, S.C./EMA Partners Int'l. (R), MX, *202*
Storfer & Assoc. (C), NY, *595*
Straight & Co. (R), GA, *202*
Mark Stranberg & Assoc. Inc. (R), MA, *202*
Strategic Advancement Inc. (R), NJ, *202*
Strategic Alternatives (R), CA, *202*
Strategic Executives, Inc. (R), CT, *202*
Strategic Resources (C), WA, *595*
Strategic Resources Biotechnology & Medical Group (C), WA, *595*
Strategic Search, LLC (C), CA, *595*
Strategic Technologies, Inc. (C), TX, *596*
StratfordGroup (R), OH, *203*
Stratin Assoc. (C), NJ, *596*
Straube Associates (R), MA, *203*
Strauss Personnel Service (C), PA, *596*
Stroman Int'l., Inc. (R), CO, *204*
Sullivan & Assoc. (R), MI, *204*
Joe Sullivan & Assoc., Inc. (R), NY, *204*
Summit Group Int'l., Inc. (R), GA, *204*
Survival Systems Staffing, Inc. (C), CA, *597*
Swift & Assoc. (C), ME, *597*
Synagent Inc. (C), ON, *597*
Synapse Human Resource Consulting Group (R), TX, *205*
Synergy Systems (C), ON, *598*
Systems Careers (C), CA, *598*
Systems Research Group (C), CA, *598*
T E M Assoc. (C), WI, *599*
T. H. Hunter, Inc. (C), MN, *599*
Tabb & Assoc. (R), OH, *205*
Tactical Alternatives (R), CA, *205*
The Talley Group (R), VA, *205*
The Talon Group (R), TX, *205*
Martin Stevens Tamaren & Assoc., Inc. (R), CA, *206*
Tanner & Assoc., Inc. (R), TX, *206*
Tarbex (C), DC, *599*
Target Search, Inc. (C), PA, *600*
Tarnow Int'l. (R), NJ, *206*
Tate & Assoc., Inc. (R), NJ, *207*
M. L. Tawney & Assoc. (C), TX, *600*
Taylor Winfield (R), TX, *207*
TBC, Inc. (C), KY, *600*
The TBI Group (R), PA, *207*
TCM Enterprises (C), MD, *600*
TE, Inc. (C), IL, *600*
Team One Partners, Inc. (C), GA, *600*
Tech Connector Group (C), CA, *601*
Tech Consulting (C), FL, *601*
Tech-Net (C), TX, *601*
Techaid Inc. (C), QE, *601*
Technical Recruiting Services (C), OH, *602*
Technical Resource Assoc. (C), TN, *602*
Technical Skills Consulting Inc. (R), ON, *207*
Technifind Int'l. (C), TX, *602*
TechNix Inc. (C), ON, *602*
Technology Consultants Int'l. (C), CA, *603*
The Technology Group (R), IL, *208*
Technology Management Partners (R), CA, *208*
Technology Search Int'l. (C), CA, *603*
Tecmark Associates Inc. (C), NY, *604*
Teknon Employment Resources, Inc. (C), OH, *604*
Tekworx, Inc. (C), OK, *604*
Tele-Media Int'l. Inc. (C), PA, *604*
Telecom Connections, Inc. (C), TX, *604*
Telecom Executive Group (C), NJ, *605*
Telecom Recruiters, Inc. (C), VA, *605*
Telem Adhesive Search Corp. (C), MD, *605*
TeleManagement Search (C), NY, *605*
Telford, Adams & Alexander (R), CA, *208*
Tell/Com Recruiters (C), PA, *605*
Tennyson Advisors (R), NY, *208*
Tesar-Reynes, Inc. (R), IL, *208*
Thomas & Assoc. of Michigan (C), MI, *606*
Thomas Lyle & Co. (C), IL, *606*
Thomas Mangum Co. (R), CA, *208*
Thomas Resource Group (R), CA, *209*
Thompson Assoc. (C), CA, *606*
Thomson, Sponar & Adams, Inc. (C), WA, *606*
Thor, Inc. (C), CA, *606*
Tierney Assoc., Inc. (R), PA, *209*
Tirocchi, Wright, Inc. (R), CA, *209*
Tittemore Cowan Assoc. (C), AB, *607*
Tomlinson Assoc. Inc. (C), IL, *607*
Tondorf & Assoc. Inc. (C), MA, *607*
Top Gun Group, Inc. (C), NV, *607*
The Touchstone Group (C), MA, *607*
TPS Staffing Solutions (C), IN, *608*
Jay Tracey Assoc. Inc. (C), VT, *608*
Transportation Recruiting Services, Inc. (C), MS, *608*
Travaille Executive Search (R), DC, *210*
Travel Executive Search (C), NY, *608*
Travel Personnel (C), OH, *609*
Travis & Co., Inc. (R), MA, *210*
Traynor Confidential, Ltd. (C), NY, *609*
Trebor Weldon Lawrence, Inc. (R), NY, *210*
Triumph Consulting, Inc. (R), IA, *210*
Trowbridge & Co., Inc. (R), MA, *211*
The Truman Agency (C), CA, *610*
Tschudin Inc. (R), NJ, *211*
TSI Group/TSI Staffing Services (C), ON, *610*
TSW Assoc., LLC (R), CT, *211*
TTG/Sterling Services (C), CA, *610*
W. G. Tucker & Assoc. (R), PA, *211*
Tucker Assoc. (R), NJ, *211*
Tully/Woodmansee Int'l. Inc. (R), FL, *212*
U.S. Search (C), VA, *610*
The Ultimate Source (R), CA, *212*
United Personnel Services (C), MA, *611*
The Urban Placement Service (C), TX, *611*
Peter Van Leer & Assoc. (R), MN, *213*
VanMaldegiam Assoc., Inc. (R), IL, *213*
VanReypen Enterprises, Ltd. (R), NY, *213*
Vaughan & Co. (C), CA, *612*
Venpro Consulting Inc. (C), ON, *612*
Vento Assoc. (C), TN, *612*
Venture Resources, Inc. (R), CA, *213*
Verkamp-Joyce Assoc., Inc. (R), IL, *213*
The Verriez Group Inc. (R), ON, *213*
Vick & Assoc. (R), TX, *214*
C. J. Vincent Assoc., LLC (C), MD, *612*
Vincenty & Co. (C), OH, *612*
Vintage Resources, Inc. (C), NY, *613*
The Viscusi Group, Inc. (R), NY, *214*
Vlcek & Company, Inc. (R), CA, *214*
Voigt Assoc. (R), IL, *214*
Beverly von Winckler & Assoc. (C), IL, *613*
VZ Int'l., Inc. (C), AZ, *613*
W. P. Assoc. (C), CA, *613*
Wachendorfer & Assoc. (C), TX, *613*
Gordon Wahls Executive Search (C), PA, *613*
Wakefield Talabisco Int'l. (R), NY, *214*
Kelly Walker Assoc. (C), TX, *614*
Walker Group, Inc. (R), MN, *215*
K. K. Walker Professional Recruitment (C), CA, *614*
B. D. Wallace & Assoc. (C), MD, *614*
Wallace Assoc. (C), MA, *614*
Wallace Management Co. (R), TN, *215*
Gerald Walsh & Co. Inc. (C), NS, *614*
J. D. Walsh & Co. (R), CT, *215*
Deborah Snow Walsh, Inc. (R), IL, *215*
Linda Walter & Associes (C), QE, *615*

Lee H. Walton & Assoc. (R), NY, *215*
Ward Assoc. (C), ON, *615*
Martha Ward Executive Search, Inc. (C), NY, *615*
The Ward Group (R), MA, *215*
Ward Liebelt Assoc. Inc. (R), CT, *215*
Ward-Hoffman & Assoc. (C), ID, *615*
C. D. Warner & Assoc. (C), PA, *615*
Warren, Morris & Madison, Ltd. (C), CA, *616*
The Washington Firm, Ltd. (R), WA, *216*
Wasserman Assoc. Inc. (C), MD, *616*
R. J. Watkins & Co., Ltd. (R), CA, *216*
Watring & Assoc., Inc. (C), IL, *616*
Scott Watson & Assoc., Inc. (R), FL, *216*
Watson Int'l., Inc. (R), NY, *216*
Waveland Int'l. (R), IL, *216*
Wayne Assoc., Inc. (C), VA, *616*
Webb, Johnson Assoc., Inc. (R), NY, *216*
Weber Executive Search (R), NY, *216*
S. B. Webster & Associates (R), MA, *217*
Wegner & Assoc. (C), WI, *617*
Lee Weil Assoc., Inc. (C), IL, *617*
David Weinfeld Group (C), NC, *617*
Weinpel Search, Inc. (C), NJ, *617*
Weinstein & Co. (R), MA, *217*
S. E. Weinstein Co. (R), IL, *217*
C. Weiss Assoc., Inc. (C), NY, *618*
Henry Welker & Assoc. (C), MI, *618*
The Wellesley Group, Inc. (R), IL, *217*
Wellington Management Group (R), PA, *217*
Wells, Bradley & Assoc., Inc. (C), MN, *618*
R. A. Wells Co. (C), GA, *618*
Werbin Assoc. Executive Search, Inc. (C), NY, *618*
Jude M. Werra & Assoc. (R), WI, *218*
Wesley Brown & Bartle Co., Inc. (R), NY, *218*
West & Assoc. (C), IL, *618*
West & West (R), CA, *218*
Western Management Consultants (R), BC, *218*
Western Technical Resources (C), CA, *619*
WestPacific National Search, Inc. (C), CA, *619*
Weterrings & Agnew, Inc. (C), NY, *619*
Wheeler Assoc. (R), CT, *219*
Wheelless Group (R), IL, *219*
White, Roberts & Stratton, Inc. (C), IL, *619*
Whitehead & Assoc., Inc. (C), MO, *620*
The Whitney Group (C), GA, *620*
Whittaker & Assoc., Inc. (C), GA, *620*
Whittlesey & Assoc., Inc. (R), PA, *220*
The Whyte Group, Inc. (R), MD, *220*
Daniel Wier & Assoc. (R), CA, *220*
Wilcoxen, Blackwell, Niven & Assoc. (R), FL, *220*
Wilder & Assoc. (C), VA, *620*
The Wilkie Group Int'l. (R), ON, *220*
Wilkinson & Ives (R), CA, *221*
William-Johns Co., Inc. (C), CA, *621*
Dick Williams & Assoc. (C), CA, *621*
Williams & Delmore, Inc. (C), NC, *621*
Williams Recruiting, Inc. (C), WA, *621*
William Willis Worldwide Inc. (R), CT, *221*
N. Willner & Co., Inc. (R), NJ, *221*
Wills Consulting Assoc. Inc. (R), CT, *221*
The Wilmington Group (C), NC, *622*
Wilson McLeran, Inc. (C), CT, *622*
Wilson-Douglas-Jordan (C), IL, *622*
The Winchester Group (R), CA, *222*
The Windham Group (R), OH, *222*
Windsor Consultants, Inc. (C), TX, *622*
Windsor International (R), GA, *222*
Winfield Assoc., Inc. (C), MA, *623*
Wing Tips & Pumps, Inc. (C), MI, *623*
Winguth, Grant & Donahue (R), CA, *222*
Winston Search, Inc. (R), MD, *222*
Winter, Wyman & Co. (C), MA, *623*
Winthrop Partners, Inc. (R), NY, *222*
Wisnewski & Assoc. (R), CA, *223*
The Witt Group (C), FL, *623*
Witt/Kieffer, Ford, Hadelman & Lloyd (R), IL, *223*
WMD inc. (C), NJ, *623*
Wojdula & Assoc., Ltd. (R), WI, *223*
S. R. Wolman Assoc., Inc. (R), NY, *224*
Louise Wood & Assoc. (C), NY, *624*
M. Wood Company (R), IL, *224*
Wood, Franchot Inc. (R), MN, *224*
Wood West & Partners Inc. (C), BC, *624*
Wood-Glavin, Inc. (R), KS, *224*
Woodmoor Group (C), CO, *624*
The Woodstone Consulting Company, Inc. (R), CO, *224*
Woodworth Int'l. Group (R), OR, *224*
Working Relationships, Inc. (C), MN, *624*
Worlco Computer Resources, Inc. (C), PA, *624*
World Search (C), OH, *625*
The Worth Group (C), GA, *625*
Dick Wray & Consultants, Inc. (R), CA, *225*
Jay Wren & Assoc. (C), CA, *625*
Bob Wright Recruiting, Inc. (C), CT, *625*
WTW Assoc., Inc. (R), NY, *225*
R. S. Wyatt Assoc., Inc. (R), TX, *225*
Wyndham Mills Int'l., Inc. (R), GA, *225*
Yankee Hospitality Search (C), CT, *626*
Yelverton Executive Search (R), CA, *226*
The York Group (C), CA, *626*
The Yorkshire Group, Ltd. (C), MA, *626*
Youngblood Assoc. (C), NC, *626*
Yours In Travel Personnel Agency, Inc. (C), NY, *626*
Steven Yungerberg Assoc., Inc. (R), MN, *226*
Yungner & Bormann (R), MN, *226*
Zaccaria Int'l. (C), NJ, *627*
The Zammataro Company (R), OH, *226*
ZanExec L.L.C. (R), VA, *226*
The Zarkin Group, Inc. (R), NY, *226*
Zen Zen Int'l. Inc. (C), MB, *627*
Chuck Zimering Advertising Recruitment (CZAR) (C), NY, *627*
Zingaro & Company (R), TX, *227*
Michael D. Zinn & Assoc., Inc. (R), NJ, *227*
Zona & Assoc., Inc. (C), NY, *628*
Zweig White & Assoc., Inc. (R), MA, *228*

05.1 Advertising, sales promotion

AKH Executive Search (C), OR, *243*
Alexander & Co. (C), CA, *243*
David Allen Assoc. (R), NJ, *3*
Amherst Personnel Group Inc. (C), NY, *249*
Applied Search Assoc., Inc. (C), GA, *252*
The Argus Group Corp. (C), ON, *252*
Ask Guy Tucker (C), GA, *254*
Association for Sales Force Management (C), WA, *254*
Baker Scott & Co. (C), NJ, *258*
Ballantyne & Assoc. (R), CA, *10*
The Barack Group, Inc. (R), NY, *11*
Bast & Assoc., Inc. (C), CA, *261*
Joy Reed Belt Search Consultants, Inc. (R), OK, *15*
Bender Executive Search Management Consulting (R), NY, *16*
Benson Associates (C), NY, *264*
Bonell Ryan Inc. (R), NY, *19*
Bornholdt Shivas & Friends Executive Recruiters (C), NY, *270*
Jerold Braun & Assoc. (C), CA, *272*
Brown, Bernardy, Van Remmen, Inc. (C), CA, *275*
Brownstone Sales & Marketing Group, Inc. (C), NY, *275*
Campbell, Edgar Inc. (C), BC, *280*
Capital Consulting Group, Inc. (R), MD, *28*
Caprio & Assoc. Inc. (R), IL, *29*
Cardwell Enterprises Inc. (R), IL, *29*
Career Alternatives Executive Search (C), MI, *281*
Career Consulting Group, Inc. (C), CT, *281*
Careers On Track (C), NJ, *283*
Carpenter & Assoc. (C), TX, *284*
Carpenter Assoc., Inc. (R), IL, *30*
Caruthers & Co., L.L.C. (R), CT, *31*
Cassell & Kaye (C), NY, *286*
Chaloner Assoc. (R), MA, *32*
Churchill & Affiliates, Inc. (R), PA, *35*
Toby Clark Assoc. Inc. (C), NY, *292*
The Clark Group (C), MI, *292*
Consulting Rhonda (C), ON, *297*
Leonard Corwen Assoc. (C), NY, *302*
Trudi Cowlan (C), NY, *302*
The Crawford Group (C), GA, *303*
D & M Associates (C), PA, *306*
D.A.I Human Resources Consultants (R), QE, *45*
DCA Professional Search (C), TX, *309*
DeLalla - Fried Assoc. (C), NY, *310*
Desktop Staffing, Inc. (C), IL, *311*
J. Dinerstein & Co., Inc. (R), NY, *51*
Direct Marketing Solutions (C), KY, *312*
Diversified Search, Inc. (R), PA, *52*
DLB Assoc. (R), NY, *53*
DNA Search, Inc. (C), CA, *313*
Dotson & Assoc. (R), NY, *54*
C. A. Durakis Assoc., Inc. (R), MD, *55*
Dussick Management Assoc. (C), CT, *323*
Gwen Dycus & Assoc. (C), FL, *323*
EDI/Executive Dynamics Inc. (C), NJ, *326*
The Ellsworth Group (C), NY, *329*
Executive Resource Group, Inc. (R), ME, *63*

Executive Sales Search (C), CO, *335*
Executive Search Int'l. (C), TX, *335*
Executive/Retail Placement Assoc. (C), MD, *337*
Federal Placement Services (C), NY, *339*
Jerry Fields Assoc. (C), NY, *340*
Fisher-Todd Assoc. (C), NY, *341*
Forum Personnel Inc. (C), NY, *351*
Foster Partners (R), NY, *70*
Fristoe & Carleton, Inc. (C), OH, *353*
Gaming Consultants, Inc. (R), LA, *74*
J. Gernetzke & Assoc., Inc. (C), OH, *357*
Global 1000 Int'l. Services (C), CA, *358*
Alexander Graham Assoc. (C), NJ, *361*
Robert Grant Assoc., Inc. (C), CA, *361*
Graphic Arts Marketing Assoc., Inc. (C), MI, *361*
Greene Personnel Consultants (C), RI, *362*
Growth Consultants of America (R), MI, *82*
Nadine Guber & Assoc., Inc. (C), NY, *364*
Gumbinner/Haubenstock, Inc. (C), NY, *364*
Gundersen Partners, L.L.C. (R), NY, *83*
Susan Hall Executive Search (C), TX, *366*
Hamilton & Co. (C), OH, *367*
Hansen Executive Search, Inc. (C), NE, *368*
Janet Harberth & Assoc., Inc. (C), GA, *368*
Hart & Co. (C), NY, *370*
Healthcare Recruiters Int'l. Philadelphia (C), NJ, *373*
Kay Henry, Inc. (C), PA, *376*
Heritage Search Group, Inc. (C), FL, *376*
Howard-Sloan Assoc. (C), NY, *381*
The Howard-Sloan-Koller Group (R), NY, *97*
Hudson Assoc. Inc. (C), IN, *383*
Hunter, Rowan & Crowe (C), FL, *386*
Insight Consulting Co. (C), NY, *389*
InteliSearch, Inc. (R), CT, *102*
Intelligent Marketing Solutions, Inc. (C), NY, *390*
Interactive Search Network (R), CA, *102*
InterNeed (C), TX, *394*
Interspace Interactive, Inc. (C), NY, *394*
J. Joseph & Assoc. (C), OH, *395*
Julian Assoc., Inc. (C), CT, *401*
Kanzer Assoc., Inc. (R), IL, *109*
The Kay Group of 5th Ave. (C), NY, *404*
A.T. Kearney Executive Search (R), IL, *111*
The Keith-Murray Partnership (R), ON, *112*
Kelley & Keller, Inc. (C), FL, *405*
Kenzer Corp. (R), NY, *113*
Kordus Consulting Group (C), WI, *408*
Kostmayer Assoc., Inc. (R), MD, *119*
Evie Kreisler Assoc. Inc. (C), CA, *409*
Kresin Wingard (C), IL, *409*
Ricci Lee Assoc., Inc. (C), CA, *415*
Lemming/LeVan, Inc. (R), GA, *128*
Michael Levine Search Consultants (R), NY, *129*
Hal Levy & Assoc. (C), NY, *417*
The Libra Group Inc. (C), CT, *417*
Louis Search Group, Inc. (C), NJ, *420*
Ludwig & Assoc., Inc. (C), VA, *421*
Madison MacArthur Inc. (R), ON, *133*
Management Assoc. (C), MD, *424*
Management Recruiters of Northern Palm Beaches (C), FL, *444*
Management Recruiters of Williamsburg (C), IA, *449*
Management Recruiters of Middlesex County NJ (C), NJ, *454*
Management Recruiters of Gramercy, Inc. (C), NY, *455*
Management Recruiters of Austin (C), TX, *462*
Management Recruiters - Piedmont (C), VA, *464*
Mangieri/Solutions LLC (C), CT, *468*
Marketing & Sales Resources, Inc. (C), FL, *470*
Marketing Consultants (C), WI, *470*
Marketing Search Inc. (C), OH, *471*
MarketPro, Inc. (C), GA, *471*
Marshall Consultants, Inc. (R), NY, *137*
MB Inc. Executive Search (C), NY, *473*
Joseph J. McTaggart (C), CA, *476*
James Mead & Co. (R), CT, *142*
Meads & Assoc. (R), FL, *142*
Media Recruiting Group, Inc. (C), NY, *476*
Medical Innovations (C), NY, *477*
Juan Menefee & Assoc. (C), IL, *478*
Mengel & McDonald Ltd. (C), IL, *479*
Merlin Int'l. Inc. (C), NJ, *479*
Milrod Assoc. (C), NJ, *482*
Herbert Mines Assoc., Inc. (R), NY, *145*
Laurie Mitchell & Co., Inc. (R), OH, *145*
Tina Morbitzer & Assoc. (C), FL, *485*
NDB Assoc., Inc. (C), PA, *491*
Noble & Assoc., Inc. (C), NY, *494*
Nordeman Grimm, Inc. (R), NY, *152*
Norman Broadbent Int'l., Inc. (R), NY, *152*
O'Neill & Co. (R), CT, *154*
Ollinger Partners (R), MA, *156*
K. Ossow & Co. (C), NY, *500*
The Pailin Group Professional Search Consultants (R), TX, *158*
Janou Pakter, Inc. (C), NY, *502*
R. Parker & Assoc., Inc. (R), NY, *159*
Partners Executive Search Consultants Inc. (R), ON, *160*
Perez & Assoc. (C), MI, *507*
Phillips Assoc. (C), FL, *510*
PLA, Inc. (C), NJ, *513*
Placements by Jesse Reid Assoc., Inc. (C), NY, *513*
Rene Plessner Assoc., Inc. (R), NY, *165*
Plummer & Assoc., Inc. (R), CT, *166*
Al Ponaman Company, Inc. (C), CA, *514*
Porter & Assoc., Inc. (C), FL, *514*
Precision Executive Search (C), AZ, *516*
ProSearch Recruiting (C), CA, *524*
Recruiting Options, Inc. (C), GA, *531*
Redwood Partners Ltd. (R), NY, *173*
The Remington Group (R), IL, *174*
The Repovich-Reynolds Group (TRRG, Inc.) (R), CA, *175*
Russell Reynolds Assoc., Inc. (R), NY, *176*
Richards Assoc., Inc. (R), NY, *178*
Ridenour & Assoc. (R), IL, *178*
Riley Cole (C), CA, *537*
Roberts Ryan & Bentley, Inc. (R), MD, *179*
Robison Humphreys & Assoc., Inc. (R), ON, *180*
Rojek Marketing Group, Inc. (R), OH, *181*
Romano McAvoy Assoc., Inc. (C), NY, *544*
Roth Young of Pittsburgh (C), PA, *546*
Ryan-Allen & Assoc., Inc. (C), CA, *549*
Sales & Marketing Search, Inc. (C), MA, *551*
Sales Consultants of Boca Raton, Inc. (C), FL, *557*
Sales Consultants of Indianapolis (C), IN, *558*
Sales Consultants - Bristol County (C), MA, *559*
Sales Consultants of Wellesley, Inc. (C), MA, *559*
Sales Consultants of Brockton, Inc. (C), MA, *559*
Sales Consultants of Nashua-Manchester (C), NH, *560*
Sales Consultants of Grand Rapids (C), MI, *560*
Sales Consultants of Northern Jersey, Inc. (C), NJ, *560*
Sales Consultants of Cherry Hill (C), NJ, *560*
Sales Consultants of Morris County, Inc. (C), NJ, *561*
Sales Consultants of Newtown, Inc. (C), PA, *562*
Sales Consultants of Chester County, PA (C), PA, *562*
Sales Consultants of Milwaukee (C), WI, *563*
Sales Management Resources (C), CA, *563*
Sanford Rose Assoc. (C), OH, *565*
Sanford Rose Assoc. - Fairhope (C), AL, *565*
Sanford Rose Assoc. - Cedar Rapids (C), IA, *567*
Sanford Rose Assoc. - Evansville (C), IN, *567*
Sanford Rose Assoc. - Salt Lake City (C), UT, *571*
Savalli & Assoc., Inc. (C), MI, *571*
F. B. Schmidt Int'l. (R), CA, *185*
Devin Scott Assoc. (C), NJ, *572*
The Search America Group Inc. (C), OH, *573*
The Search Company (R), ON, *186*
SearchCom, Inc. (R), TX, *187*
Shifrin-Fischer Group, Inc. (C), NJ, *580*
RitaSue Siegel Resources, Inc. (R), NY, *191*
Simpson Associates (C), NY, *582*
Smith & Assoc. (C), CA, *583*
Ralph Smith & Assoc. (C), IL, *584*
Smith's Fifth Avenue (C), NY, *585*
Snelling Search (C), AL, *585*
Phyllis Solomon Executive Search, Inc. (C), NJ, *587*
SpencerStuart (R), NY, *196*
StaffWriters Plus (C), NY, *591*
Stentiford & Berardi Assoc. Ltd. (R), NY, *199*
Stevens Assoc. (C), MA, *593*
Stone & Youngblood (C), MA, *594*
Synergy Systems (C), ON, *598*
Tesar-Reynes, Inc. (R), IL, *208*
The Touchstone Group (C), MA, *607*

Trebor Weldon Lawrence, Inc. (R), NY, *210*
Vintage Resources, Inc. (C), NY, *613*
Beverly von Winckler & Assoc. (C), IL, *613*
The Ward Group (R), MA, *215*
Ward Liebelt Assoc. Inc. (R), CT, *215*
Warren, Morris & Madison, Ltd. (C), CA, *616*
Lee Weil Assoc., Inc. (C), IL, *617*
C. Weiss Assoc., Inc. (C), NY, *618*
Wilcoxen, Blackwell, Niven & Assoc. (R), FL, *220*
William-Johns Co., Inc. (C), CA, *621*
N. Willner & Co., Inc. (R), NJ, *221*
Wills Consulting Assoc. Inc. (R), CT, *221*
Louise Wood & Assoc. (C), NY, *624*
Bob Wright Recruiting, Inc. (C), CT, *625*
R. S. Wyatt Assoc., Inc. (R), TX, *225*
The York Group (C), CA, *626*
Chuck Zimering Advertising Recruitment (CZAR) (C), NY, *627*

05.2 Marketing & product research

A la Carte Int'l., Inc. (R), VA, *1*
A.J. & Assoc. (C), FL, *232*
Abraham & London Ltd. (C), CT, *232*
Access/Resources, Inc. (C), MA, *234*
ACSYS Resources, Inc. (C), DE, *238*
Advanced Corporate Search (C), CA, *240*
Advancement, Inc. (C), IL, *241*
Agriesti & Assoc. (C), CA, *243*
Alexander & Co. (C), CA, *243*
Amato & Associates Insurance Recruiters (C), PA, *247*
AMD & Associates (C), GA, *247*
Aminex Corp. (C), MA, *249*
Analytic Recruiting, Inc. (C), NY, *249*
Tryg R. Angell, Ltd. (C), CT, *250*
Fred Anthony Assoc. (C), WI, *251*
Applied Resources, Inc. (C), MN, *252*
The Argus Group Corp. (C), ON, *252*
Aries Search Group (C), GA, *252*
Association for Sales Force Management (C), WA, *254*
Aurora Tech Search (C), ON, *256*
Austin Group Int'l./Marlar Int'l. (R), TX, *9*
Austin Michaels, Ltd., Inc. (C), AZ, *256*
Avestruz & Assoc. (C), CA, *257*
Ballantyne & Assoc. (R), CA, *10*
The Bankers Group (C), IL, *258*
Barone-O'Hara Assoc., Inc. (R), NJ, *11*
The Barrett Group (C), NH, *260*
Bast & Assoc., Inc. (C), CA, *261*
L. Battalin & Co. (C), FL, *261*
The Bauman Group (R), CA, *14*
The Bedford Group (R), RI, *15*
Bellamy & Assoc. (C), GA, *263*
Bench Int'l. Search, Inc. (R), CA, *15*
Richard L. Bencin & Assoc. (C), OH, *264*
Bender Executive Search Management Consulting (R), NY, *16*
Besen Assoc. Inc. (C), NJ, *266*
Best, Coleman & Co., Inc. (R), MA, *16*
BJB Assoc. (C), VA, *267*
Blaney Executive Search (R), MA, *18*
Ann Bond Assoc. Inc. (C), MD, *269*
Bornholdt Shivas & Friends Executive Recruiters (C), NY, *270*
Bos Business Consultants (C), NY, *270*
Bosch & Assoc., LLC (R), CT, *19*
M. F. Branch Assoc., Inc. (C), NC, *272*
Brethet, Barnum & Assoc., Inc. (C), ON, *273*
Brooke Chase Assoc., Inc. (R), IL, *24*
Brown, Bernardy, Van Remmen, Inc. (C), CA, *275*
Charles Buck & Assoc., Inc. (R), NY, *24*
Buckman/Enochs & Assoc., Inc. (C), OH, *276*
J. Burke & Assoc., Inc. (C), TX, *276*
J. Burkey Assoc. (R), NJ, *25*
David S. Burt Assoc. (C), MT, *276*
Byron Leonard Int'l., Inc. (R), CA, *25*
The C.P.R. Group (C), NJ, *278*
Cadillac Assoc. (C), CA, *278*
The Canon Group (C), CA, *280*
Sally Caplan & Assoc. (C), WA, *281*
Career Alternatives Executive Search (C), MI, *281*
Career Consulting Group, Inc. (C), CT, *281*
Careers Plus (R), CA, *29*
Carpenter Assoc., Inc. (R), IL, *30*
Carter/MacKay (C), NJ, *285*
Caruthers & Co., L.L.C. (R), CT, *31*
CAS Comsearch Inc. (C), NY, *285*
Caywood Partners, Ltd. (R), CA, *32*
Central Executive Search, Inc. (C), OH, *287*
Century Assoc., Inc. (C), PA, *287*
Chaloner Assoc. (R), MA, *32*
Charles & Associates, Inc. (C), NE, *289*
J. F. Church Associates (C), WA, *291*
Churchill & Affiliates, Inc. (R), PA, *35*
CJA-The Adler Group, Inc. (R), CA, *35*
The Clark Group (C), MI, *292*
Clayman & Co. (R), MA, *36*
Clinton, Charles, Wise & Co. (C), FL, *293*
CMS, Inc. (C), NH, *293*
Coastal Int'l., Inc. (R), MA, *36*
The Comwell Company, Inc. (C), NJ, *296*
Robert Connelly & Assoc., Inc. (R), MN, *39*
Consulting Rhonda (C), ON, *297*
Consumer Search Inc. (C), MA, *298*
Corporate Dynamix (C), AZ, *300*
Trudi Cowlan (C), NY, *302*
Culver Personnel Services (C), CA, *304*
D.A.I Human Resources Consultants (R), QE, *45*
David Perry Assoc. (C), NJ, *308*
Deeco Int'l. (C), UT, *310*
DeLalla - Fried Assoc. (C), NY, *310*
Thorndike Deland Assoc. LLC (R), NY, *48*
Diversified Search, Inc. (R), PA, *52*
DLG Assoc., Inc. (R), NC, *53*
DNA Search, Inc. (C), CA, *313*
Doherty Int'l., Inc. (R), IL, *53*
Domres Professional Search (R), WI, *53*
Dotson & Assoc. (R), NY, *54*
Douglas-Allen, Inc. (R), MA, *54*
Dreier Consulting (C), NJ, *315*
Drew Assoc. Int'l. (R), NJ, *54*
Dukas Assoc. (C), MA, *315*
Dunhill Professional Search of Oakland (C), CA, *319*
Eastbourne Assoc. Inc. (R), NY, *56*
EGM Consulting, Inc. (R), FL, *57*
The Ellsworth Group (C), NY, *329*
The Enfield Company (C), TX, *330*
Engineering & Scientific Search Assoc. (ESSA) (C), NJ, *330*
ExecuTech (C), IN, *332*
The Executive Group, Inc. (R), CA, *62*
Executive Resource Group, Inc. (R), ME, *63*
Executive Sales Search (C), CO, *335*
Executive Search Int'l. (C), TX, *335*
Executive Search of New England, Inc. (C), ME, *336*
Executive Search Team (C), MI, *336*
F.L.A.G. (C), OH, *338*
Fairfield Int'l. Resources (R), NY, *65*
Dorothy W. Farnath & Assoc., Inc. (C), NJ, *338*
Federal Placement Services (C), NY, *339*
Fenwick Partners (R), MA, *66*
Eileen Finn & Assoc., Inc. (C), NY, *341*
Fisher & Assoc. (R), CA, *67*
Fisher-Todd Assoc. (C), NY, *341*
Forray Assoc., Inc. (R), NY, *70*
F-O-R-T-U-N-E Personnel Consultants of Charlotte (C), NC, *348*
Fortune Personnel Consultants of Hilton Head (C), SC, *349*
Forum Personnel Inc. (C), NY, *351*
Foster Partners (R), NY, *70*
Fox, White & Assoc. (C), FL, *351*
Foy, Schneid & Daniel, Inc. (R), NY, *71*
Fristoe & Carleton, Inc. (C), OH, *353*
Gardiner, Townsend & Assoc. (R), NY, *74*
Dianne Gauger & Assoc. (C), CA, *355*
General Engineering Tectonics (C), CA, *356*
Genesis Research (C), MO, *356*
Global Telecommunications, Inc. (C), TX, *359*
Goldstein & Co. (C), CA, *360*
Goodrich & Sherwood Assoc., Inc. (R), NY, *79*
Alexander Graham Assoc. (C), NJ, *361*
Robert Grant Assoc., Inc. (C), CA, *361*
The Grant Search Group, Inc. (C), ON, *361*
Grantham & Co., Inc. (R), NC, *81*
Graphic Arts Marketing Assoc., Inc. (C), MI, *361*
Sheila Greco Assoc. (C), NY, *362*
Greene Personnel Consultants (C), RI, *362*
Groton Planning Group (R), ME, *82*
Nadine Guber & Assoc., Inc. (C), NY, *364*
Guidry & East Healthcare Search Consultants (R), TX, *83*
Halbrecht & Co. (C), VA, *365*
K. C. Hale, Inc. (R), CT, *85*
Susan Hall Executive Search (C), TX, *366*
Hamilton & Co. (C), OH, *367*
The Hampton Group (C), NY, *367*
Hansen Executive Search, Inc. (C), NE, *368*
Janet Harberth & Assoc., Inc. (C), GA, *368*
Harris Heery & Assoc., Inc. (R), CT, *87*
Hart & Co. (C), NY, *370*
The Hawkins Co. (R), CA, *88*

Hayden & Assoc., Inc. (C), MN, *370*
The Haystack Group, Inc. (R), ME, *88*
Hazlett Associates (R), IL, *88*
Healthcare Recruiters Int'l. Bay Area (C), CA, *372*
Healthcare Recruiters Int'l. Orange County (C), CA, *372*
Healthcare Recruiters International-NY/NJ (C), NJ, *373*
Healthcare Recruiters of New England (C), MA, *373*
Healthcare Recruiters - Northwest (C), WA, *374*
Heath/Norton Assoc., Inc. (R), NY, *89*
R. W. Hebel Assoc. (R), TX, *89*
Heritage Search Group, Inc. (C), FL, *376*
The Herrmann Group Ltd. (R), ON, *92*
Higbee Assoc., Inc. (C), CT, *377*
B. W. Higgins, Inc. (C), IN, *377*
Hill & Assoc. (C), CA, *378*
Horizons Unlimited (C), CA, *381*
Hudson Assoc. Inc. (C), IN, *383*
E. A. Hughes & Co., Inc. (R), NY, *98*
Human Capital Resources, Inc. (C), FL, *384*
E. F. Humay Assoc. (C), PA, *384*
Hunegnaw Executive Search (C), OH, *384*
Hunter Adams (C), NC, *385*
Hunter Int'l. LLC (C), MA, *385*
Impact Search & Strategies (C), PA, *387*
Impact Source, Inc. (C), FL, *387*
Insight Consulting Co. (C), NY, *389*
InTech Services, Inc. (C), GA, *390*
Integrity Search, Inc. (R), PA, *102*
InteliSearch, Inc. (R), CT, *102*
Intelligent Marketing Solutions, Inc. (C), NY, *390*
Interactive Search Assoc. (C), PA, *391*
Interim Management Resources Inc. (C), ON, *392*
International Pro Sourcing, Inc. (C), PA, *393*
International Technical Resources (C), FL, *393*
InterNeed (C), TX, *394*
Isaacson, Miller (R), MA, *104*
The J. B. Search Group (C), CA, *395*
J. Joseph & Assoc. (C), OH, *395*
J. R. Scott & Assoc., Ltd. (C), IL, *395*
K. Jaeger & Assoc. (C), MA, *396*
JCL & Assoc. (C), FL, *397*
JL & Co. (C), CA, *399*
Johnson & Assoc., Inc. (R), CA, *106*
K. E. Johnson Assoc. (C), WA, *399*
Johnson, Kemper & Assoc. (C), TX, *400*
Karp & Assoc. (C), FL, *403*
Allan Karson Assoc., Inc. (R), NJ, *110*
Kaufman Assoc. (R), CA, *110*
Kay Concepts, Inc. (C), FL, *404*
A.T. Kearney Executive Search (R), IL, *111*
Keeley Consulting Inc. (C), ON, *404*
Kelley & Keller, Inc. (C), FL, *405*
Kenzer Corp. (R), NY, *113*
Key Employment (C), NJ, *405*
Kiley, Owen & McGovern, Inc. (R), NJ, *114*
KM Associates (C), MA, *407*
Koltnow & Company (R), NY, *117*
Kordus Consulting Group (C), WI, *408*
Kresin Wingard (C), IL, *409*
L&L Assoc. Global Search (C), PA, *411*
LaCosta & Assoc. Int'l. Inc. (C), CA, *411*
The Landstone Group (C), NY, *412*
Ricci Lee Assoc., Inc. (C), CA, *415*
Michael Levine Search Consultants (R), NY, *129*
Lewis & Blank Int'l. (R), CA, *129*
Pat Licata & Assoc. (C), NC, *417*
J. H. Lindell & Co. (C), CA, *418*
Ginger Lindsey & Assoc., Inc. (C), TX, *418*
Lipson & Co. (R), CA, *130*
The Logan Group, Inc. (R), MO, *131*
Longo Associates (C), CA, *420*
Ludwig & Assoc., Inc. (C), VA, *421*
Madison MacArthur Inc. (R), ON, *133*
Management One Consultants (C), ON, *425*
Management Recruiters of Tucson (C), AZ, *439*
Management Recruiters of San Luis Obispo (C), CA, *439*
Management Recruiters Inc. of Silicon Valley (C), CA, *441*
Management Recruiters of Middlesex (C), CT, *442*
Management Recruiters of Anna Maria Island (C), FL, *443*
Management Recruiters of Northern Palm Beaches (C), FL, *444*
Management Recruiters of Atlanta (C), GA, *445*
Management Recruiters of Lake Forest, IL (C), IL, *447*
Management Recruiters of Barrington (C), IL, *447*
Management Recruiters of Indianapolis-North (C), IN, *448*
Management Recruiters of Williamsburg (C), IA, *449*
Management Recruiters of Washington, DC Inc. (C), MD, *450*
Management Recruiters of Cass County, NE (C), NE, *452*
Management Recruiters of Gramercy, Inc. (C), NY, *455*
Management Recruiters of Rocky Mount - Southwest (C), NC, *456*
Management Recruiters of Bethlehem, PA (C), PA, *458*
Management Recruiters of Sidney (C), OH, *458*
Management Recruiters of Mentor, Inc. (C), OH, *458*
Management Recruiters of Lionville, Inc. (C), PA, *459*
Management Recruiters of Delaware County (C), PA, *459*
Management Recruiters of West Chester, Inc. (C), PA, *460*
Management Recruiters of Salt Lake City (C), UT, *464*
Management Recruiters Int'l.-The Woodlands (C), TX, *464*
Management Recruiters - Piedmont (C), VA, *464*
Management Recruiters of Kanawha Valley, LLC (C), WV, *465*
Management Search, Inc. (C), OK, *468*
Mangieri/Solutions LLC (C), CT, *468*
Manuso, Alexander & Associates, Inc. (R), NY, *135*
The Marathon Group (C), FL, *469*
Marketing & Sales Resources, Inc. (C), FL, *470*
Marketing Consultants (C), WI, *470*
Marketing Resources (C), MA, *470*
Marketing Search Inc. (C), OH, *471*
Marketing/Public Relations Research Recruiting (C), CT, *471*
MarketPro, Inc. (C), GA, *471*
George R. Martin (R), PA, *137*
The Matthews Group, Inc. (C), NJ, *472*
MB Inc. Executive Search (C), NY, *473*
McIntyre Assoc. (R), CT, *141*
McKinley•Arend Int'l. (R), TX, *141*
James Mead & Co. (R), CT, *142*
Med-Ex Services (C), OH, *476*
Medical Executive Recruiters (C), CA, *477*
Medical Innovations (C), NY, *477*
MedQuest Assoc. (C), CO, *478*
Meng, Finseth & Assoc., Inc. (R), CA, *143*
Mercedes & Co., Inc. (R), MA, *143*
Merlin Int'l. Inc. (C), NJ, *479*
Miller + Miller (C), WA, *482*
Milrod Assoc. (C), NJ, *482*
Herbert Mines Assoc., Inc. (R), NY, *145*
Laurie Mitchell & Co., Inc. (R), OH, *145*
Morency Assoc. (C), MA, *485*
The Morris Group (C), PA, *486*
Robert T. Morton Assoc., Inc. (C), MA, *486*
National Affirmative Action Career Network, Inc. (C), CO, *488*
NDB Assoc., Inc. (C), PA, *491*
New Dimensions in Technology, Inc. (C), MA, *492*
Newport Management (C), NY, *492*
Norman Broadbent Int'l., Inc. (R), NY, *152*
The Normyle/Erstling Health Search Group (C), NJ, *494*
O'Connell Group Inc. (C), CT, *497*
O'Neill & Co. (R), CT, *154*
Omega Systems, LLC (C), VA, *498*
K. Ossow & Co. (C), NY, *500*
Janou Pakter, Inc. (C), NY, *502*
R. Parker & Assoc., Inc. (R), NY, *159*
Partners Executive Search Consultants Inc. (R), ON, *160*
Partridge Assoc., Inc. (R), MA, *160*
Patriot Assoc. (C), PA, *505*
PC Assoc. (C), CO, *505*
Perez & Assoc. (C), MI, *507*
Perry Search Assoc. (C), CA, *507*
Peyser Assoc., Inc. (R), FL, *163*
Pharmaceutical Recruiters, Inc. (R), NY, *163*
Phoenix Partners, Inc. (C), GA, *511*
The Pinnacle Source, Inc. (C), CO, *512*
PLA, Inc. (C), NJ, *513*
Don V. Poole & Assoc., Inc. (C), CO, *514*
Robert Powers & Assoc. (C), CA, *515*
Norman Powers Assoc., Inc. (C), MA, *515*
Precision Executive Search (C), AZ, *516*
Prestonwood Assoc. (R), MA, *168*
Alan J. Price Assoc., Inc. (C), RI, *518*
The Primary Group, Inc. (R), FL, *168*

Prime Management Group Inc. (C), ON, *518*
Professional Recruiters Inc. (C), MN, *521*
Professional Recruiting Network (C), CA, *521*
ProNet, Inc. (C), NC, *524*
ProSearch Recruiting (C), CA, *524*
ProSearch, Inc. (C), ME, *524*
Joanne E. Ratner Search (C), NY, *529*
Recruiting Options, Inc. (C), GA, *531*
Recruiting Resources Int'l. (C), CA, *532*
Recruiting/Solutions (C), CA, *532*
Mary Rector & Assoc., Inc. (C), IL, *533*
Redden & McGrath Assoc., Inc. (R), NY, *173*
Reeve & Assoc. (C), CT, *533*
The Remington Group (R), IL, *174*
The Repovich-Reynolds Group (TRRG, Inc.) (R), CA, *175*
Research Personnel Consultants (C), ON, *534*
The Resource Group (R), CT, *175*
Resource Perspectives, Inc. (R), CA, *175*
L. J. Reszotko & Assoc. (C), IL, *535*
The Revere Assoc., Inc. (R), OH, *176*
Russell Reynolds Assoc., Inc. (R), NY, *176*
Rice Cohen Int'l. (R), PA, *178*
Richards Assoc., Inc. (R), NY, *178*
Riotto-Jones Assoc. (R), NY, *178*
RJN Consulting (R), NY, *179*
J. Rodgers & Associates (C), IL, *540*
Rogers - McManamon Executive Search (R), CA, *180*
Rojek Marketing Group, Inc. (R), OH, *181*
Ropella & Assoc. (R), FL, *181*
Ross Personnel Consultants, Inc. (C), CT, *545*
Roth Young of Chicago (C), IL, *546*
Roth Young Personnel Service of Detroit, Inc. (C), MI, *546*
Rust & Assoc., Inc. (R), IL, *183*
R. L. Rystrom & Assoc., Inc. (C), MN, *549*
Sales & Marketing Search, Inc. (C), MA, *551*
Sales Builders, Inc. (R), VA, *183*
Sales Consultants of Silicon Valley (C), CA, *556*
Sales Consultants of Chico (C), CA, *556*
Sales Consultants of Ft. Lauderdale, Inc. (C), FL, *557*
Sales Consultants of Savannah, GA (C), GA, *557*
Sales Consultants of Boca Raton, Inc. (C), FL, *557*
Sales Consultants of Ft. Myers, Inc. (C), FL, *557*
Sales Consultants of Chicago South (C), IL, *558*
Sales Consultants of Indianapolis (C), IN, *558*
Sales Consultants of Honolulu (C), HI, *558*
Sales Consultants of Indianapolis-North (C), IN, *558*
Sales Consultants - Bristol County (C), MA, *559*
Sales Consultants of Wellesley, Inc. (C), MA, *559*
Sales Consultants of Brockton, Inc. (C), MA, *559*
Sales Consultants of Nashua-Manchester (C), NH, *560*
Sales Consultants of Grand Rapids (C), MI, *560*
Sales Consultants of Laurel Park, Inc. (C), MI, *560*
Sales Consultants of Northern Jersey, Inc. (C), NJ, *560*
Sales Consultants of Morris County, Inc. (C), NJ, *561*
Sales Consultants of Austin, Inc. (C), TX, *562*
Sales Consultants of Chester County, PA (C), PA, *562*
Sales Consultants of Rhode Island, Inc. (C), RI, *562*
Sales Consultants of Milwaukee (C), WI, *563*
Sales Consultants of Appleton (C), WI, *563*
Sales Management Resources (C), CA, *563*
Sales Search Specialist (C), IL, *564*
Sales Solutions (C), CA, *564*
Sanford Rose Assoc. - Fairhope (C), AL, *565*
Sanford Rose Assoc. - Clearwater (C), FL, *566*
Sanford Rose Assoc. - Lake St. Louis (C), MO, *568*
Sanford Rose Assoc. - Philadelphia North (C), PA, *570*
Sanford Rose Assoc. - Columbia (C), SC, *570*
Sanford Rose Assoc. - Pittsburgh North (C), PA, *570*
Sanford Rose Assoc. - Salt Lake City (C), UT, *571*
Savalli & Assoc., Inc. (C), MI, *571*
The Schatz Company (C), MO, *571*
Schick Professional Search, Inc. (C), OH, *572*
A.D. Schiff & Assoc., Ltd. (C), IL, *572*
F. B. Schmidt Int'l. (R), CA, *185*
G. L. Schwartz & Assoc., Inc. (C), GA, *572*
Devin Scott Assoc. (C), NJ, *572*
The Search America Group Inc. (C), OH, *573*
Search America, Inc. (C), PA, *573*
The Search Company (R), ON, *186*
The Search Group (C), MD, *575*
SearchCom, Inc. (R), TX, *187*
Segal & Assoc. (C), GA, *578*
Shannahan & Co., Inc. (R), CA, *189*
Shifrin-Fischer Group, Inc. (C), NJ, *580*
Simpson Associates (C), NY, *582*
Sloan & Assoc., Inc. (C), VA, *583*
Smith & Laue Search (R), OR, *193*
The Smith Group, Inc. (C), NC, *584*
Smith Hanley Assoc., Inc. (C), NY, *584*
Smith's Fifth Avenue (C), NY, *585*
C. Snow & Assoc. (C), ON, *586*
Phyllis Solomon Executive Search, Inc. (C), NJ, *587*
Somerset Group, Inc. (C), CT, *587*
Southern Chemical & Plastics Search (C), GA, *587*
Southport Int'l. Assoc. Inc. (C), FL, *588*
SpencerStuart (R), NY, *196*
Sports Group Int'l. (R), NC, *198*
Spriggs & Co., Inc. (R), IL, *198*
The Stark Wilton Group (R), MI, *199*
Ron Stevens & Assoc., Inc. (C), FL, *593*
Stevens Assoc. (C), MA, *593*
Strategic Alternatives (R), CA, *202*
Strategic Resources Biotechnology & Medical Group (C), WA, *595*
Systems Careers (C), CA, *598*
Systems Research Group (C), CA, *598*
T E M Assoc. (C), WI, *599*
TBC, Inc. (C), KY, *600*
TE, Inc. (C), IL, *600*
Tech Connector Group (C), CA, *601*
Tech Consulting (C), FL, *601*
Technical Skills Consulting Inc. (R), ON, *207*
Technology Management Partners (R), CA, *208*
Telecom Recruiters, Inc. (C), VA, *605*
Tell/Com Recruiters (C), PA, *605*
Thomson, Sponar & Adams, Inc. (C), WA, *606*
Tomlinson Assoc. Inc. (C), IL, *607*
The Touchstone Group (C), MA, *607*
Jay Tracey Assoc. Inc. (C), VT, *608*
TSW Assoc., LLC (R), CT, *211*
The Ultimate Source (R), CA, *212*
C. J. Vincent Assoc., LLC (C), MD, *612*
Vintage Resources, Inc. (C), NY, *613*
Wallace Assoc. (C), MA, *614*
Ward Assoc. (C), ON, *615*
Martha Ward Executive Search, Inc. (C), NY, *615*
The Ward Group (R), MA, *215*
Ward Liebelt Assoc. Inc. (R), CT, *215*
Ward-Hoffman & Assoc. (C), ID, *615*
R. J. Watkins & Co., Ltd. (R), CA, *216*
Watring & Assoc., Inc. (C), IL, *616*
Wayne Assoc., Inc. (C), VA, *616*
Lee Weil Assoc., Inc. (C), IL, *617*
C. Weiss Assoc., Inc. (C), NY, *618*
The Wellesley Group, Inc. (R), IL, *217*
Wells, Bradley & Assoc., Inc. (C), MN, *618*
Werbin Assoc. Executive Search, Inc. (C), NY, *618*
West & West (R), CA, *218*
Weterrings & Agnew, Inc. (C), NY, *619*
Williams & Delmore, Inc. (C), NC, *621*
N. Willner & Co., Inc. (R), NJ, *221*
Wills Consulting Assoc. Inc. (R), CT, *221*
Wilson McLeran, Inc. (C), CT, *622*
Wood-Glavin, Inc. (R), KS, *224*
The Woodstone Consulting Company, Inc. (R), CO, *224*
Worlco Computer Resources, Inc. (C), PA, *624*
Bob Wright Recruiting, Inc. (C), CT, *625*
The York Group (C), CA, *626*
Youngblood Assoc. (C), NC, *626*
Steven Yungerberg Assoc., Inc. (R), MN, *226*
Yungner & Bormann (R), MN, *226*

05.3 Marketing management

A.J. & Assoc. (C), FL, *232*
The Abbott Group, Inc. (R), MD, *1*
Abraham & London Ltd. (C), CT, *232*
ACCESS Technology (C), CA, *234*

Ackerman Johnson Inc. (C), TX, *238*
Action Executive Personnel Consulting Inc. (C), ON, *239*
Adler Management, Inc. (R), NJ, *2*
Advanced Corporate Search (C), CA, *240*
Advancement, Inc. (C), IL, *241*
Advantage Partners, Inc. (R), OH, *2*
Advisors' Search Group, Inc. (C), NY, *241*
Affinity Executive Search (C), FL, *241*
Agriesti & Assoc. (C), CA, *243*
Ahrensdorf & Assoc. (R), PA, *2*
Alexander & Co. (C), CA, *243*
Allard Associates (C), CA, *244*
Allen & Assoc. (C), NV, *244*
D. S. Allen Assoc. (C), NJ, *244*
Allen Evans Assoc. (R), NY, *4*
Allen-Jeffers Assoc. (C), CA, *245*
Allen/Associates (R), OH, *4*
Allerton Heneghan & O'Neill (R), IL, *4*
Allstaff, Inc. (C), IL, *245*
Alpha Resources (C), IL, *246*
Amato & Assoc., Inc. (C), CA, *246*
AMD & Associates (C), GA, *247*
Amherst Personnel Group Inc. (C), NY, *249*
Aminex Corp. (C), MA, *249*
Andre David & Assoc., Inc. (R), TX, *6*
Andrews & Wald Group (C), FL, *250*
Angus Employment Ltd. (C), ON, *250*
The Angus Group, Ltd. (C), OH, *251*
Fred Anthony Assoc. (C), WI, *251*
Anthony Michael & Co. (C), MA, *251*
Argonaut Partners, LLC (R), CA, *6*
The Argus Group Corp. (C), ON, *252*
Argus National, Inc. (R), CT, *6*
Aries Search Group (C), GA, *252*
J. S. Armstrong & Assoc., Inc. (R), CA, *7*
Ashway Ltd. Agency (C), NY, *253*
Ask Guy Tucker (C), GA, *254*
Association for Sales Force Management (C), WA, *254*
Atkinson Search & Placement, Inc. (C), IA, *255*
Aubin Int'l. Inc. (R), MA, *8*
Cami Austin & Assoc. (C), IL, *256*
Austin Group Int'l./Marlar Int'l. (R), TX, *9*
Avestruz & Assoc. (C), CA, *257*
The Badger Group (R), CA, *10*
Baldwin & Assoc. (C), OH, *258*
Ballantyne & Assoc. (R), CA, *10*
BallResources (C), MO, *258*
The Bankers Group (C), IL, *258*
The Barack Group, Inc. (R), NY, *11*
Barger & Sargeant, Inc. (R), NH, *11*
Barnes & Assoc. Executive Search (C), CA, *259*
Barone Assoc. (C), NJ, *259*
Barone-O'Hara Assoc., Inc. (R), NJ, *11*
Barr Assoc. (C), PA, *259*
The Barrett Group (C), NH, *260*
Barrett Hospitality Search (R), CA, *12*
Aldonna Barry Personnel & Management (C), ON, *260*
Bartholdi & Co., Inc. (R), CO, *12*
Barton Assoc., Inc. (R), TX, *12*
Bast & Assoc., Inc. (C), CA, *261*
Battalia Winston Int'l./The Euram Consultants Group (R), NY, *13*
L. Battalin & Co. (C), FL, *261*
The Bauman Group (R), CA, *14*
Bayland Assoc. (C), CA, *261*
The Beam Group (R), PA, *14*
Beck/Eastwood Recruitment Solutions (C), CA, *261*
The Bedford Consulting Group Inc. (R), ON, *14*
The Bedford Group (R), RI, *15*
Robert Beech West Inc. (C), CA, *262*
Behavioral Science Assoc., Inc. (R), AZ, *15*
Bell Wishingrad Partners Inc. (R), NY, *15*
J. P. Bencik Assoc. (C), MI, *263*
Richard L. Bencin & Assoc. (C), OH, *264*
Bender Executive Search Management Consulting (R), NY, *16*
Berkana Int'l., Inc. (C), WA, *265*
Berkhemer/Clayton, Inc. (R), CA, *16*
Berkshire Search Assoc. (C), MA, *265*
Bernhart Assoc. (C), MN, *265*
Besen Assoc. Inc. (C), NJ, *266*
Best, Coleman & Co., Inc. (R), MA, *16*
Bialla & Assoc. Inc. (R), CA, *17*
Binder Hospitality Group (C), KY, *266*
BioQuest Inc. (R), CA, *17*
J: Blakslee Int'l., Ltd. (R), CA, *18*
Blau Mancino Schroeder (R), NJ, *18*
Block & Assoc. (R), CA, *18*
Tom Bogle & Assoc. (C), CA, *269*
Ann Bond Assoc. Inc. (C), MD, *269*
Bonell Ryan Inc. (R), NY, *19*
Bornholdt Shivas & Friends Executive Recruiters (C), NY, *270*
Bos Business Consultants (C), NY, *270*
Bosch & Assoc., LLC (R), CT, *19*
Bosland Gray Assoc. (R), NJ, *20*
Boston Professional Search, Inc. (C), MA, *270*
BowdenGlobal, Ltd. (R), OH, *20*
Boyden (R), NY, *20*
M. F. Branch Assoc., Inc. (C), NC, *272*
The Brand Co., Inc. (R), FL, *22*
Brandywine Consulting Group (R), PA, *22*
The Brentwood Group, Inc. (R), NJ, *22*
The Brentwood Group Ltd. (R), OR, *23*
Brethet, Barnum & Assoc., Inc. (C), ON, *273*
Brian Assoc., Inc. (C), NY, *273*
Brierwood Group, Inc. (C), IN, *273*
Bright Search/Professional Staffing (C), MN, *274*
Broadband Resource Group (C), CA, *274*
Brooke Chase Assoc., Inc. (R), IL, *24*
Broward-Dobbs, Inc. (C), GA, *274*
Brown, Bernardy, Van Remmen, Inc. (C), CA, *275*
Brown Venture Assoc. (R), CA, *24*
Charles Buck & Assoc., Inc. (R), NY, *24*
The Buckley Group (C), FL, *276*
Buckman/Enochs & Assoc., Inc. (C), OH, *276*
The Burgess Group-Corporate Recruiters Int'l., Inc. (R), NY, *25*
J. Burke & Assoc., Inc. (C), TX, *276*
J. Burkey Assoc. (R), NJ, *25*
Joseph R. Burns & Assoc., Inc. (R), NJ, *25*
David S. Burt Assoc. (C), MT, *276*
Butterfield & Co. Int'l., Inc. (C), HI, *277*
Button Group (C), TX, *277*
Byron Leonard Int'l., Inc. (R), CA, *25*
C. M. Management Services, Inc. (R), KY, *26*
C. P. Consulting (R), PA, *26*
Cadillac Assoc. (C), CA, *278*
Cahill Assoc. (C), CT, *279*
Caliber Associates (R), PA, *27*
CanMed Consultants Inc. (C), ON, *280*
Canny, Bowen Inc. (R), NY, *27*
The Canon Group (C), CA, *280*
Sally Caplan & Assoc. (C), WA, *281*
Career Alternatives Executive Search (C), MI, *281*
Career Consulting Group, Inc. (C), CT, *281*
Career Development Associates (C), NV, *282*
Career Search Group (C), FL, *283*
Careers On Track (C), NJ, *283*
Careers Plus (R), CA, *29*
Carlsen Resources, Inc. (R), CO, *29*
Carlson & Czeswik (R), MN, *30*
Carpenter Assoc., Inc. (R), IL, *30*
Carr Management Services, Inc. (C), PA, *284*
Carter-Evdemon & Assoc. (C), FL, *285*
Carter/MacKay (C), NJ, *285*
Caruso & Assoc., Inc. (R), FL, *31*
Caruthers & Co., L.L.C. (R), CT, *31*
Carver Search Consultants (C), CA, *285*
Michael J. Cavanagh & Assoc. Inc. (R), ON, *31*
Caywood Partners, Ltd. (R), CA, *32*
CBA Companies (C), CA, *286*
Central Executive Search, Inc. (C), OH, *287*
Century Assoc., Inc. (C), PA, *287*
CEO Consulting (C), FL, *287*
Chaloner Assoc. (R), MA, *32*
Wayne S. Chamberlain & Assoc. (C), CA, *288*
Charet & Assoc. (C), NJ, *289*
Charles & Associates, Inc. (C), NE, *289*
A. D. Check Assoc., Inc. (R), PA, *33*
Chesapeake Group (C), CT, *290*
Christian & Timbers, Inc. (R), OH, *34*
J. F. Church Associates (C), WA, *291*
CJSI-Cindy Jackson Search Int'l. (C), CA, *291*
Howard Clark Assoc. (C), NJ, *292*
Toby Clark Assoc. Inc. (C), NY, *292*
The Clark Group (C), MI, *292*
Clayman & Co. (R), MA, *36*
Clinton, Charles, Wise & Co. (C), FL, *293*
Coastal Int'l., Inc. (R), MA, *36*
Coleman Lew & Assoc., Inc. (R), NC, *37*
Colton Bernard Inc. (R), CA, *37*
Comprehensive Search (C), GA, *294*
Conex Inc./InterSearch (R), NY, *39*
Robert Connelly & Assoc., Inc. (R), MN, *39*
M. L. Conner (C), FL, *296*
Conroy Partners Ltd. (R), AB, *39*
Construct Management Services (C), MN, *297*
Consumer Search Inc. (C), MA, *298*
Cook Assoc.,® Inc. (R), IL, *40*
The Cooke Group (R), WI, *40*
Cooper Assoc., Inc. (C), NY, *298*
Corbin Packaging Professionals (C), MO, *299*

The Corporate Advisory Group (R), NJ, *41*
Corporate Dynamix (C), AZ, *300*
Corporate Staffing Group, Inc. (C), PA, *301*
Leonard Corwen Assoc. (C), NY, *302*
Cowell & Associates, Ltd. (R), IL, *42*
Cowin Assoc. (R), NY, *42*
Crane, Reed & Co., Inc. (C), NH, *302*
The Crawford Group (C), GA, *303*
Crist Partners, Ltd. (R), IL, *43*
Timothy D. Crowe, Jr. (R), MA, *43*
Culver Personnel Services (C), CA, *304*
Cumberland Group Inc. (C), IL, *304*
Frank Cuomo & Assoc., Inc. (C), NY, *305*
Curran Partners, Inc. (R), CT, *44*
Cyr Associates, Inc. (C), MA, *306*
D & M Associates (C), PA, *306*
D.A.I Human Resources Consultants (R), QE, *45*
Daggett & Kvistad (R), CA, *45*
Dahl-Morrow Int'l. (R), VA, *45*
The Dalley Hewitt Co. (R), GA, *45*
Alfred Daniels & Assoc., Inc. (R), CA, *46*
David Perry Assoc. (C), NJ, *308*
DCA Professional Search (C), TX, *309*
DeCaster Assoc. (C), WI, *310*
Deeco Int'l. (C), UT, *310*
Defrain Mayer (R), KS, *48*
DeLalla - Fried Assoc. (C), NY, *310*
Thorndike Deland Assoc. LLC (R), NY, *48*
Delta Management Group Ltd. (C), ON, *310*
Desktop Staffing, Inc. (C), IL, *311*
The Diestel Group (R), UT, *51*
DiMarchi Partners (R), CO, *51*
J. Dinerstein & Co., Inc. (R), NY, *51*
Robert W. Dingman Co., Inc. (R), CA, *52*
Direct Marketing Solutions (C), KY, *312*
Dise & Co. (R), OH, *52*
Diversified Consulting Services, Inc. (C), CO, *313*
Diversified Search, Inc. (R), PA, *52*
DLB Assoc. (R), NY, *53*
Doering & Assoc. (C), CA, *313*
Doherty Int'l., Inc. (R), IL, *53*
Dotson & Assoc. (R), NY, *54*
CS Dowling Executive Services (R), NJ, *54*
Dreier Consulting (C), NJ, *315*
Dromeshauser Assoc. (R), MA, *55*
Dukas Assoc. (C), MA, *315*
Dunhill Professional Search of Miami (C), FL, *319*
Dunhill Executive Search of Los Angeles, Inc. (C), CA, *319*
Dunhill Professional Search of San Jose (C), CA, *319*
Dunhill Professional Search of Greater New Orleans (C), LA, *321*
Dunhill Personnel of Northeast Tulsa, Inc. (C), OK, *322*
C. A. Durakis Assoc., Inc. (R), MD, *55*
Dussick Management Assoc. (C), CT, *323*
Dynamic Synergy Corp. (R), CA, *56*
E.P. Int'l. (C), NY, *324*
Eagle Search Assoc. (C), CA, *325*
EagleView, Inc. (C), MA, *325*
Eastman & Beaudine, Inc. (R), TX, *56*
EDI/Executive Dynamics Inc. (C), NJ, *326*
EFCO Consultants, Inc. (C), NY, *327*
D. C. Egan & Assoc. (C), GA, *327*
EGM Consulting, Inc. (R), FL, *57*
Richard A. Eisner & Co., LLP (R), NY, *57*
W. Robert Eissler & Assoc., Inc. (C), TX, *327*
William J. Elam & Assoc. (R), NE, *58*
The Eldridge Group, Ltd. (C), IL, *327*
David M. Ellner Assoc. (R), NY, *59*
The Ellsworth Group (C), NY, *329*
The Elmhurst Group (C), CA, *329*
The Elsworth Group (C), TX, *329*
Mark Elzweig Co., Ltd. (C), NY, *329*
Emerging Medical Technologies, Inc. (C), CO, *329*
Employ® (C), PA, *330*
The Enfield Company (C), TX, *330*
ENI (R), CT, *59*
Erlanger Assoc. (R), CT, *60*
ESA (R), CT, *60*
ETI Search Int'l. (R), GA, *61*
The Evans Search Group (R), CT, *61*
Evans Transportation Search (C), ON, *331*
Exec Tech, Inc. (C), IL, *332*
ExecuGroup, Inc. (R), MS, *61*
ExecuSource Consultants, Inc. (C), TX, *332*
Executive Business Solutions, Inc. (C), WA, *332*
Executive Exchange Corp. (C), NJ, *333*
Executive Sales Search (C), CO, *335*
Executive Search Consultants, Inc. (C), FL, *335*
Executive Search Int'l. (C), TX, *335*
Executive Search Partners (R), NY, *63*
ExecutiveFit (C), NY, *337*
F.L.A.G. (C), OH, *338*
Fabian Assoc. Inc. (C), NY, *338*
Paul Falcone Assoc. (R), NJ, *65*
Leon A. Farley Assoc. (R), CA, *65*
Dorothy W. Farnath & Assoc., Inc. (C), NJ, *338*
James Feerst & Assoc., Inc. (C), AZ, *339*
A. E. Feldman Assoc., Inc. (C), NY, *339*
Fell & Nicholson Technology Resources (R), CA, *65*
Fenwick Partners (R), MA, *66*
Ferrari Search Group (C), OH, *340*
Guild Fetridge Acoustical Search, Inc. (C), NY, *340*
Jerry Fields Assoc. (C), NY, *340*
Neil Fink Assoc. (R), CA, *66*
Finney-Taylor Personnel & Management Consultants Ltd. (C), AB, *341*
First Search America, Inc. (C), TN, *341*
First Search Inc. (C), IL, *341*
First Union Executive Search (R), NC, *67*
Howard Fischer Assoc. Int'l., Inc. (R), PA, *67*
Fisher & Assoc. (R), CA, *67*
Fisher-Todd Assoc. (C), NY, *341*
A. G. Fishkin & Assoc., Inc. (R), MD, *68*
Flowers & Assoc. (C), OH, *342*
Flynn, Hannock, Inc. (R), CT, *69*
David Fockler & Assoc., Inc. (C), CA, *342*
Focus Executive Search (C), MN, *343*
Forest People Int'l. Search Ltd. (C), BC, *343*
Forray Assoc., Inc. (R), NY, *70*
Fortune Personnel Consultants of Colorado Springs (C), CO, *344*
Fortune Personnel Consultants (C), MT, *347*
F-O-R-T-U-N-E Personnel Consultants of Bergen County Inc. (C), NJ, *347*
FORTUNE Personnel Consultants of North Dallas (C), TX, *350*
Foster Partners (R), NY, *70*
Fox, White & Assoc. (C), FL, *351*
Fox-Morris Assoc., Inc. (C), PA, *351*
Franklin Allen Consultants, Ltd. (R), NY, *71*
Franklin Int'l. Search, Inc. (C), MA, *352*
The Franklin Search Group, Inc./Medzilla (R), WA, *71*
Franstaff Inc. (C), FL, *352*
KS Frary & Assoc. (R), MA, *71*
Fresquez & Assoc. (C), CA, *352*
Gerald Frisch Assoc., Inc. (R), NY, *72*
Fristoe & Carleton, Inc. (C), OH, *353*
GAAP Inc. (R), QE, *73*
Gaines & Assoc. Int'l., Inc. (R), IL, *73*
Gaming Consultants, Inc. (R), LA, *74*
The Gammill Group, Inc. (C), OH, *354*
W. N. Garbarini & Assoc. (R), NJ, *74*
Dianne Gauger & Assoc. (C), CA, *355*
Genesis Research (C), MO, *356*
C. R. Gerald & Assoc. (C), ON, *356*
Gilbert Tweed Assoc. Inc. (R), NY, *76*
Howard Gilmore & Assoc. (R), OH, *77*
Gilreath Weatherby Inc. (R), MA, *77*
Lawrence Glaser Assoc., Inc. (C), NJ, *357*
Global Resources Group (R), CA, *78*
Global Technologies Group Inc. (C), NC, *359*
F. Gloss Int'l. (R), VA, *78*
Glou Int'l., Inc. (R), MA, *78*
H. L. Goehring & Assoc., Inc. (C), OH, *359*
Goldbeck Recruiting Inc. (C), BC, *359*
Goldstein & Co. (C), CA, *360*
Gomez Fregoso y Asociados (C), JAL, *360*
The Goodman Group (R), CA, *79*
Goodrich & Sherwood Assoc., Inc. (R), NY, *79*
Gould, McCoy & Chadick, Inc. (R), NY, *80*
The Governance Group, Inc. (R), NJ, *80*
Gowdy Consultants (C), TX, *361*
Alexander Graham Assoc. (C), NJ, *361*
Robert Graham Assoc. (R), RI, *81*
Granger, Counts & Assoc. (R), OH, *81*
Robert Grant Assoc., Inc. (C), CA, *361*
The Grant Search Group, Inc. (C), ON, *361*
Graphic Arts Marketing Assoc., Inc. (C), MI, *361*
R. Green & Assoc., Inc. (C), OH, *362*
Greene Personnel Consultants (C), RI, *362*
Greenwich Search Partners, LLC (C), CT, *363*
Greger/Peterson Assoc., Inc. (R), CA, *81*
Griffith & Werner, Inc. (R), FL, *82*
Groton Planning Group (R), ME, *82*
Growth Strategies, Inc. (R), FL, *83*
David E. Grumney Co. Inc. (R), WA, *83*
GSW Consulting Group, Inc. (R), CA, *83*
Nadine Guber & Assoc., Inc. (C), NY, *364*
Michael R. Guerin Co. (C), CA, *364*
Guidarelli Assoc., Inc. (R), MI, *83*

Gundersen Partners, L.L.C. (R), NY, *83*
Gustin Partners, Ltd. (R), MA, *83*
Haddad Assoc. (R), FL, *84*
Hale Assoc. (R), IL, *84*
Haley Associates (R), CA, *85*
Michael J. Hall & Co. (R), WA, *85*
Susan Hall Executive Search (C), TX, *366*
Hamilton & Co. (C), OH, *367*
The Hampton Group (C), NY, *367*
Hands-on Broadcast (R), NY, *86*
Handy HRM (R), NY, *86*
Hansen Executive Search, Inc. (C), NE, *368*
Janet Harberth & Assoc., Inc. (C), GA, *368*
Hardison & Company (R), TX, *86*
Harper Hewes, Inc. (C), NY, *369*
Harris Heery & Assoc., Inc. (R), CT, *87*
Hart & Co. (C), NY, *370*
Michael J. Hawkins, Inc. (C), IL, *370*
William E. Hay & Co. (R), IL, *88*
Hayden & Assoc., Inc. (C), MN, *370*
The Haystack Group, Inc. (R), ME, *88*
Hazlett Associates (R), IL, *88*
Headden Assoc. (R), WA, *88*
Healey Executive Search, Inc. (R), MN, *88*
Health Care Dimensions (C), CO, *371*
Healthcare Recruiters Int'l. Phoenix (C), AZ, *372*
Healthcare Recruiters of the Rockies, Inc. (C), CO, *372*
Healthcare Recruiters Int'l. - Alabama (C), AL, *372*
Healthcare Recruiters Int'l. Orange County (C), CA, *372*
Healthcare Recruiters Int'l - Minnesota, Inc. (C), MN, *373*
Healthcare Recruiters International-NY/NJ (C), NJ, *373*
Healthcare Recruiters of New England (C), MA, *373*
Healthcare Recruiters of New York, Inc. (C), NY, *373*
Healthcare Recruiters - Northwest (C), WA, *374*
Healthcare Search Associates (C), CA, *374*
F. P. Healy & Co., Inc. (R), NY, *89*
Heath/Norton Assoc., Inc. (R), NY, *89*
Hechkoff/Work Executive Search Inc. (R), NY, *89*
The Heidrick Partners, Inc. (R), IL, *90*
Heinze & Assoc. Inc. (R), MN, *91*
Helbling & Assoc., Inc. (R), PA, *91*
The Helms Int'l. Group (R), VA, *91*
G. W. Henn & Co. (R), OH, *91*
Bruce Henry Assoc. Inc. (R), CA, *91*
Kay Henry, Inc. (C), PA, *376*
Heritage Search Group, Inc. (C), FL, *376*
J. J. Herlihy & Assoc., Inc. (C), CA, *376*
Hersher Assoc., Ltd. (R), IL, *92*
Stanley Herz & Co. (R), NY, *92*
Robert Hess & Assoc., Inc. (C), CO, *377*
Higdon Prince Inc. (R), NY, *93*
Hill & Assoc. (C), CA, *378*
The Hindman Co. (R), KY, *94*
Hockett Associates, Inc. (R), CA, *94*
Hodge-Cronin & Assoc., Inc. (R), IL, *94*
Hoglund & Assoc., Inc. (R), IL, *94*
Holland & Assoc., Inc. (R), MI, *94*
Hook-Up! (C), CA, *380*
Horizons Unlimited (C), CA, *381*
Houtz•Strawn & Arnold, Inc. (R), TX, *96*
Howard-Sloan Assoc. (C), NY, *381*
Howe & Assoc. (R), PA, *97*
Hudson Assoc. Inc. (C), IN, *383*
E. A. Hughes & Co., Inc. (R), NY, *98*
Hughes & Company (R), VA, *98*
Human Capital Resources, Inc. (C), FL, *384*
E. F. Humay Assoc. (C), PA, *384*
Hunt Patton & Brazeal, Inc. (C), OK, *385*
Hunter Adams (C), NC, *385*
Hunter, Rowan & Crowe (C), FL, *386*
HVS Executive Search (R), NY, *100*
The Hyde Group, Inc. (R), CT, *101*
IMA Search, Inc. (R), NY, *101*
The IMC Group of Companies (R), NY, *101*
Impact Source, Inc. (C), FL, *387*
Independent Power Consultants (C), TX, *387*
Meredith Ingram, Ltd. (C), IL, *388*
Innovative Partnerships (R), CA, *101*
The Inside Track (C), TX, *389*
Insight Consulting Co. (C), NY, *389*
Insurance Search (C), TX, *390*
Integrated Search Solutions Group, LLC (ISSG) (R), NY, *102*
Integrity Search, Inc. (R), PA, *102*
Intelligent Marketing Solutions, Inc. (C), NY, *390*
IntelliSearch (C), TX, *391*
Interactive Search Assoc. (C), PA, *391*
International Executive Recruiters (C), OH, *393*
International Management Advisors, Inc. (R), NY, *103*
International Research Group (R), CA, *103*
International Technical Resources (C), FL, *393*
InterNeed (C), TX, *394*
IR Search (R), CA, *103*
Isaacson, Miller (R), MA, *104*
ISC of Cincinnati Inc. (C), OH, *394*
ISC of Houston, Inc. (C), TX, *394*
The J. B. Search Group (C), CA, *395*
J. Nicholas Arthur (R), MA, *104*
Jacobson Assoc. (C), IL, *396*
K. Jaeger & Assoc. (C), MA, *396*
JAG Group (R), MO, *105*
JL & Co. (C), CA, *399*
JM & Company (R), PA, *106*
JNB Assoc., Inc. (C), MA, *399*
Johnson & Company (R), CT, *107*
Ronald S. Johnson Assoc., Inc. (R), CA, *107*
Johnson, Kemper & Assoc. (C), TX, *400*
Jones and Jones (R), OR, *108*
J. M. Joseph Assoc. (R), NJ, *109*
JPM International (C), CA, *401*
Judd Associates (R), NJ, *109*
K2 Resources, L.P. (C), CT, *402*
Kacevich, Lewis & Brown, Inc. (R), MA, *109*
Richard Kader & Assoc. (C), OH, *403*
Robert Kaestner & Assoc. (C), FL, *403*
Kaplan & Assoc., Inc. (R), PA, *109*
Karp & Assoc. (C), FL, *403*
Allan Karson Assoc., Inc. (R), NJ, *110*
A.T. Kearney Executive Search (R), IL, *111*
The Keith-Murray Partnership (R), ON, *112*
Kelley & Keller, Inc. (C), FL, *405*
Kensington Int'l., Inc. (R), IL, *113*
Kenzer Corp. (R), NY, *113*
Key Employment (C), NJ, *405*
Ki Technologies, Inc. (C), UT, *406*
Kiley, Owen & McGovern, Inc. (R), NJ, *114*
The Kinlin Co., Inc. (R), MA, *115*
Richard Kinser & Assoc. (R), NY, *115*
Kirkbride Assoc., Inc. (C), WA, *407*
Kittleman & Assoc.,LLC (R), IL, *115*
KM Associates (C), MA, *407*
T. J. Koellhoffer & Assoc. (R), NJ, *116*
Kopplin Search, Inc. (R), CA, *117*
Kordus Consulting Group (C), WI, *408*
Kors Montgomery Int'l. (R), TX, *118*
Kostmayer Assoc., Inc. (R), MD, *119*
J. Krauss Assoc. (R), FL, *120*
Kremple & Meade, Inc. (R), CA, *120*
Kremple Consulting Group (R), CA, *120*
Kresin Wingard (C), IL, *409*
Paul Kull & Co. (R), NJ, *121*
L T M Assoc. (C), IL, *410*
The Landstone Group (C), NY, *412*
Lawrence L. Lapham, Inc. (R), NY, *124*
Stephen Laramee & Assoc. Inc. (C), ON, *413*
Larkin & Co. (R), CA, *124*
Larson Assoc. (R), CA, *125*
Larson, Katz & Young, Inc. (C), VA, *413*
Lawrence-Balakonis & Assoc., Inc. (C), GA, *414*
Lawrence-Leiter & Co. (R), KS, *126*
Leaders-Trust Int'l./Carce y Asociados, S.C. (R), MX, *127*
Lechner & Assoc., Inc. (C), FL, *415*
Lectra Search (C), GA, *415*
Albert G. Lee Assoc. (C), RI, *415*
Ricci Lee Assoc., Inc. (C), CA, *415*
Lehman McLeskey (R), TX, *128*
Leith & Assoc., Inc. (C), OH, *416*
Hal Levy & Assoc. (C), NY, *417*
Pat Licata & Assoc. (C), NC, *417*
J. H. Lindell & Co. (C), CA, *418*
Lipsky Group, Inc. (R), CA, *129*
Lipson & Co. (R), CA, *130*
The Logan Group, Inc. (R), MO, *131*
Louis Search Group, Inc. (C), NJ, *420*
The John Lucht Consultancy Inc. (R), NY, *131*
Ludwig & Assoc., Inc. (C), VA, *421*
Lutz Associates (C), CT, *421*
P. J. Lynch Assoc. (R), CT, *132*
M H Executive Search Group (C), TX, *422*
The Mackenzie Group (R), MD, *133*
Maczkov-Biosciences, Inc. (R), CA, *133*
Madison MacArthur Inc. (R), ON, *133*
The Mallard Group (C), IN, *423*
Managed Care Resources (C), TX, *424*
Management Advisors Int'l., Inc. (C), NC, *424*
Management Dimensions Ltd. (R), ON, *134*
Management One Consultants (C), ON, *425*

Management Recruiters of Decatur, LLC (C), AL, *438*
Management Recruiters of Tucson (C), AZ, *439*
Management Recruiters Tucson-Foothills, Inc. (C), AZ, *439*
Management Recruiters of San Luis Obispo (C), CA, *439*
Management Recruiters of Northern California (C), CA, *440*
Management Recruiters of Roseville (C), CA, *441*
Management Recruiters of Sonoma (C), CA, *441*
Management Recruiters Inc. of Silicon Valley (C), CA, *441*
Management Recruiters of Middlesex (C), CT, *442*
Management Recruiters of St. Lucie County, Inc. (C), FL, *444*
Management Recruiters of Northern Palm Beaches (C), FL, *444*
Management Recruiters of Atlanta West, Inc. (C), GA, *445*
Management Recruiters of Atlanta NE (C), GA, *446*
Management Recruiters - Towne Lake (C), GA, *446*
Management Recruiters of Boise (C), ID, *446*
Management Recruiters of Lake Forest, IL (C), IL, *447*
Management Recruiters of Barrington (C), IL, *447*
Management Recruiters of Sun Valley (C), ID, *447*
Management Recruiters - Indianapolis (C), IN, *448*
Management Recruiters of Des Moines (C), IA, *449*
Management Recruiters of Siouxland (C), IA, *449*
Management Recruiters of Monroe, Inc. (C), LA, *450*
Management Recruiters of Muskegon (C), MI, *451*
Management Recruiters of Cass County, NE (C), NE, *452*
Management Recruiters of Bay Head (C), NJ, *453*
Management Recruiters of Middlesex County NJ (C), NJ, *454*
Management Recruiters of Gramercy, Inc. (C), NY, *455*
Management Recruiters of Manhattan on Broadway (C), NY, *455*
Management Recruiters of Burlington (C), NC, *455*
Management Recruiters of Woodbury Inc. (C), NY, *455*
Management Recruiters of Gastonia (C), NC, *456*
Management Recruiters of Cincinnati/Sharonville, Inc. (C), OH, *457*
Management Recruiters of Cleveland (C), OH, *457*
Management Recruiters of Oklahoma City (C), OK, *458*
Management Recruiters of Sidney (C), OH, *458*
Management Recruiters of Mentor, Inc. (C), OH, *458*
Management Recruiters of Lionville, Inc. (C), PA, *459*
Management Recruiters of Westmoreland County, Inc. (C), PA, *459*
Management Recruiters of Delaware County (C), PA, *459*
Management Recruiters of Puerto Rico (C), PR, *460*
Management Recruiters of Myrtle Beach, Inc. (C), SC, *460*
Management Recruiters The Delta Group, Inc. (C), TN, *461*
Management Recruiters of Arlington (C), VA, *464*
Management Recruiters Int'l.-The Woodlands (C), TX, *464*
Management Recruiters - Piedmont (C), VA, *464*
Management Recruiters of Seattle (C), WA, *465*
Management Recruiters of Milwaukee - Downtown (C), WI, *466*
Management Resource Group, Inc. (C), NY, *467*
Management Resources (C), TX, *467*
Mangieri/Solutions LLC (C), CT, *468*
The Marathon Group (C), FL, *469*
Marc-Allen Assoc., Inc. (C), FL, *469*
Marcus & Assoc. (C), NY, *469*
Marketing & Sales Resources, Inc. (C), FL, *470*
Marketing Consultants (C), WI, *470*
Marketing Resources (C), MA, *470*
Marketing Search Inc. (C), OH, *471*
MarketPro, Inc. (C), GA, *471*
The Marlow Group (R), MA, *136*
Marshall Consultants, Inc. (R), NY, *137*
Donovan Martin & Assoc. (R), CA, *137*
J. Martin & Assoc. (R), CA, *137*
George R. Martin (R), PA, *137*
Richard L. Mather & Assoc. (C), CT, *472*
Mathey Services (C), IL, *472*
Matrix Consultants, Inc. (C), NC, *472*
The Matthews Group, Inc. (C), NJ, *472*
Maxecon Executive Search Consultants (R), FL, *138*
K. Maxin & Assoc. (R), PA, *139*
Mayhall Search Group, Inc. (C), IN, *473*
MB Inc. Executive Search (C), NY, *473*
The McCormick Group (C), VA, *473*
McCray, Shriver, Eckdahl & Assoc., Inc. (R), CA, *140*
McDonald Assoc. Int'l. (R), IL, *140*
Robert E. McGrath & Assoc. (R), CT, *141*
The McKinnon Management Group Inc. (C), ON, *475*
Dan P. McLean Assoc., Inc. (C), ON, *475*
James Mead & Co. (R), CT, *142*
Meder & Assoc., Inc. (R), IL, *142*
Media Recruiting Group, Inc. (C), NY, *476*
Medical Executive Recruiters (C), CA, *477*
Medical Innovations (C), NY, *477*
The Medley Group (C), CA, *477*
Melancon & Co. (R), TX, *143*
MESA, Inc. (R), CO, *143*
Meyer Assoc., Inc. (R), GA, *144*
Milrod Assoc. (C), NJ, *482*
Herbert Mines Assoc., Inc. (R), NY, *145*
Mirtz Morice, Inc. (R), CT, *145*
Laurie Mitchell & Co., Inc. (R), OH, *145*
MIXTEC Group (R), CA, *145*
MJF Assoc. (C), CT, *483*
Mogul Consultants, Inc. (C), NY, *483*
Montenido Assoc. (R), CA, *146*
The Montgomery Group, Inc. (C), TN, *484*
Montgomery, Thomason & Assoc. (C), ON, *484*
Morency Assoc. (C), MA, *485*
The Morgan/Geoffries Group (C), CA, *485*
Morris & Berger (R), CA, *147*
The Morris Group (C), PA, *486*
Robert T. Morton Assoc., Inc. (C), MA, *486*
Mruk & E.M.A. Partners (R), NY, *148*
MTA Partners (R), TX, *148*
Pamela L. Mulligan, Inc. (R), NH, *149*
Multi Processing, Inc. (R), NH, *149*
Jennifer Munro & Partners, Inc. (R), SC, *149*
Murphy Partners Int'l. (R), IL, *150*
The Murray Group (C), IL, *487*
Mycoff & Assoc. (R), CO, *150*
Myers Career Assoc., Inc. (C), CA, *488*
Nachman Biomedical (C), MA, *488*
National Affirmative Action Career Network, Inc. (C), CO, *488*
National Bank & Finance Executive Search (C), CA, *488*
National Recruiting Service (C), IN, *489*
NDB Assoc., Inc. (C), PA, *491*
The Neil Michael Group, Inc./Global Partners (R), NY, *151*
New Dimensions in Technology, Inc. (C), MA, *492*
Newcomb-Desmond & Assoc., Inc. (C), OH, *492*
Newport Management (C), NY, *492*
Next Step Recruiting (C), CA, *493*
P. J. Nicholson & Assoc. (C), IL, *493*
The Niemond Corp. (R), CA, *152*
Ira Z. Nitzberg (C), NY, *493*
J. L. Nixon Consulting (C), TX, *493*
Noble & Assoc., Inc. (C), NY, *494*
Nordeman Grimm, Inc. (R), NY, *152*
Norman Broadbent Int'l., Inc. (R), NY, *152*
The Normyle/Erstling Health Search Group (C), NJ, *494*
NorTech Resources (C), NY, *496*
Northern Consultants Inc. (R), ME, *153*
O'Brien & Bell (R), OH, *153*
O'Connell Group Inc. (C), CT, *497*
O'Connor, O'Connor, Lordi, Ltd. (R), PA, *154*
O'Connor Resources (C), TX, *497*
Dennis P. O'Toole & Assoc. Inc. (R), NY, *154*
Oak Assoc. (R), CA, *155*
The Oldani Group (R), WA, *155*
Oliver & Rozner Assoc., Inc. (R), NY, *155*
Olsen/Clark (R), WA, *156*
Omega Systems, LLC (C), VA, *498*
OmniSearch, Inc. (C), FL, *499*
Ortman Recruiting Int'l. (C), CA, *500*
Overton Consulting (R), WI, *157*

The P & L Group (C), NY, *500*
P R Management Consultants, Inc. (C), NJ, *500*
P.A.R. Assoc., Inc. (R), MA, *158*
P.R.H. Management, Inc. (R), CT, *158*
Pacific Coast Recruiters (C), OR, *501*
Pacific Crossing (C), CA, *501*
Page-Wheatcroft & Co., Ltd. (R), TX, *158*
Pamenter, Pamenter, Brezer & Deganis Ltd. (R), ON, *159*
Frank Parillo & Assoc. (R), CA, *159*
R. Parker & Assoc., Inc. (R), NY, *159*
D. P. Parker & Assoc., Inc. (R), MA, *159*
Parker-Worthington, Inc. (C), TX, *503*
Partners Executive Search Consultants Inc. (R), ON, *160*
The Partnership Group (R), NJ, *160*
Partridge Assoc., Inc. (R), MA, *160*
Patriot Assoc. (C), PA, *505*
Paul-Tittle Assoc., Inc. (R), VA, *161*
Peachtree Executive Search (R), GA, *161*
Pearson, Caldwell & Farnsworth (R), CA, *161*
Peden & Assoc. (C), CA, *506*
Paul S. Pelland, P.C. (R), SC, *161*
The Pennmor Group (C), NJ, *506*
Perez & Assoc. (C), MI, *507*
Perfect Search, Inc. (C), FL, *507*
Barry Persky & Co., Inc. (R), CT, *163*
Richard Peterson & Assoc., Inc. (R), GA, *163*
Petruzzi Assoc. (C), NJ, *509*
Pharmaceutical Recruiters, Inc. (R), NY, *163*
J. R. Phillip & Assoc., Inc. (R), CA, *164*
Phoenix BioSearch, Inc. (C), NJ, *511*
Phoenix Partners, Inc. (C), GA, *511*
Phoenix Search (R), MX, *164*
Pierce & Crow (R), CA, *164*
The Pinnacle Source, Inc. (C), CO, *512*
Pinton Forrest & Madden/EMA Partners Int'l. (R), BC, *165*
DNPitchon Assoc. (R), NJ, *165*
PLA, Inc. (C), NJ, *513*
Placements by Jesse Reid Assoc., Inc. (C), NY, *513*
Rene Plessner Assoc., Inc. (R), NY, *165*
R. L. Plimpton Assoc., Inc. (R), CO, *165*
Poirier, Hoevel & Co. (R), CA, *166*
Ray Polhill & Assoc. (R), NC, *166*
Bob Poline Assoc. Inc. (C), CA, *514*
The Pollack Group (C), ON, *514*
Power Search (C), TX, *515*
P. G. Prager Search Assoc., Ltd. (C), NY, *515*
The Prairie Group (C), IL, *515*
Elan Pratzer & Partners Inc. (R), ON, *167*
Preston & Co. (R), NJ, *167*
Price & Assoc., Inc. (C), VA, *518*
Alan J. Price Assoc., Inc. (C), RI, *518*
Prichard Kymen Inc. (R), AB, *168*
The Primary Group, Inc. (R), FL, *168*
Prime Search (C), NC, *518*
Professional Recruiters Inc. (C), MN, *521*
Professional Recruiting Consultants (C), FL, *521*
Professional Recruiting Network (C), CA, *521*
Professional Recruiters, Inc. (C), PA, *521*
Professional Recruiters (C), UT, *521*
ProFinders, Inc. (C), FL, *523*
ProNet, Inc. (C), NC, *524*
ProSearch Recruiting (C), CA, *524*
ProSearch, Inc. (C), ME, *524*
Proven Edge (C), CA, *525*
Quantum Int'l., Ltd. (R), FL, *170*
QuestPro, Inc. (C), TX, *527*
L. J. Quinn & Assoc., Inc. (R), CA, *170*
Quirk-Corporon & Assoc., Inc. (C), WI, *527*
R & K Associates, Inc. (C), AZ, *527*
R. C. Services (C), TX, *528*
R. J. Associates (C), NY, *528*
Rand Assoc. (R), ME, *171*
The Rankin Group, Ltd. (R), WI, *171*
The Ransford Group (R), TX, *171*
Harold L. Rapp Assoc. (C), NY, *529*
RCE Assoc. (R), NJ, *173*
Recruit Xpress (C), TX, *531*
Recruiting Options, Inc. (C), GA, *531*
Recruiting Resources Int'l. (C), CA, *532*
Recruiting/Solutions (C), CA, *532*
The Recruitment Group, Inc. (C), NY, *532*
Mary Rector & Assoc., Inc. (C), IL, *533*
Redden & McGrath Assoc., Inc. (R), NY, *173*
Redwood Partners Ltd. (R), NY, *173*
Reeder & Assoc., Ltd. (R), GA, *173*
Reeve & Assoc. (C), CT, *533*
Reifel & Assoc. (R), IL, *174*
The Remington Group (R), IL, *174*
The Repovich-Reynolds Group (TRRG, Inc.) (R), CA, *175*
Research Personnel Consultants (C), ON, *534*
The Resource Group (R), NJ, *175*
The Resource Group (R), CT, *175*
Resource Perspectives, Inc. (R), CA, *175*
Resources for Management (R), PA, *175*
Response Staffing Services (C), NY, *534*
The Revere Assoc., Inc. (R), OH, *176*
S. Reyman & Assoc., Ltd. (R), IL, *176*
Russell Reynolds Assoc., Inc. (R), NY, *176*
Reynolds Consulting Int'l. (R), ON, *177*
Reynolds Partners (R), NY, *177*
RIC Corp. (R), FL, *177*
Rice Cohen Int'l. (R), PA, *178*
Richards Assoc., Inc. (R), NY, *178*
Rieser & Assoc., Inc. (R), MO, *178*
Riotto-Jones Assoc. (R), NY, *178*
Ritta Professional Search Inc. (C), NY, *538*
RJN Consulting (R), NY, *179*
Robertson & Assoc. (C), IL, *539*
Robison Humphreys & Assoc., Inc. (R), ON, *180*
J. Rodgers & Associates (C), IL, *540*
Rodgers, Ramsey, Inc. (C), TX, *540*
Craig Roe & Assoc., LLC (C), MD, *540*
Rogers - McManamon Executive Search (R), CA, *180*
ROI International, Inc. (R), WA, *181*
Rojek Marketing Group, Inc. (R), OH, *181*
Romeo-Hudgins & Assoc., Ltd. (C), NJ, *544*
Rooney Assoc., Inc. (R), IL, *181*
Ropella & Assoc. (R), FL, *181*
Ropes Associates, Inc. (R), FL, *182*
Ross Personnel Consultants, Inc. (C), CT, *545*
Patricia Roth Int'l. (C), FL, *545*
Roth Young of Chicago (C), IL, *546*
Roth Young Seattle (C), WA, *546*
Rovner & Assoc., Inc. (R), IL, *182*
Rowland Mountain & Assoc. (C), GA, *547*
The Rubicon Group (C), AZ, *547*
Rust & Assoc., Inc. (R), IL, *183*
The Ryan Charles Group, Inc. (C), FL, *548*
R. L. Rystrom & Assoc., Inc. (C), MN, *549*
Saber Group, Inc. (C), TX, *550*
Sales & Marketing Search, Inc. (C), MA, *551*
Sales Builders, Inc. (R), VA, *183*
Sales Consultants of Scottsdale, Inc. (C), AZ, *556*
Sales Consultants of Silicon Valley (C), CA, *556*
Sales Consultants of Daphne (C), AL, *556*
Sales Consultants of Northwest Arkansas, Inc. (C), AR, *556*
Sales Consultants of Savannah, GA (C), GA, *557*
Sales Consultants of Stamford-Darien (C), CT, *557*
Sales Consultants of Boca Raton, Inc. (C), FL, *557*
Sales Consultants of Danbury (C), CT, *557*
Sales Consultants of Indianapolis (C), IN, *558*
Sales Consultants of Western McHenry County (C), IL, *558*
Sales Consultants of Chicago South (C), IL, *558*
Sales Consultants (C), IL, *558*
Sales Consultants of Honolulu (C), HI, *558*
Sales Consultants of Barrington (C), IL, *558*
Sales Consultants of Rockville, MD (C), MD, *559*
Sales Consultants - Bristol County (C), MA, *559*
Sales Consultants of Wellesley, Inc. (C), MA, *559*
Sales Consultants of Brockton, Inc. (C), MA, *559*
Sales Consultants of Nashua-Manchester (C), NH, *560*
Sales Consultants of Farmington Hills (C), MI, *560*
Sales Consultants of Grand Rapids (C), MI, *560*
Sales Consultants of Laurel Park, Inc. (C), MI, *560*
Sales Consultants of Cherry Hill (C), NJ, *560*
Sales Consultants of Northern Jersey, Inc. (C), NJ, *560*
Sales Consultants of Raleigh-Durham-RTP (C), NC, *561*
Sales Consultants of Middlesex County, Inc. (C), NJ, *561*
Sales Consultants of Morris County, Inc. (C), NJ, *561*
Sales Consultants of Newtown, Inc. (C), PA, *562*
Sales Consultants of Chester County, PA (C), PA, *562*

Sales Consultants of Rhode Island, Inc. (C), RI, *562*
Sales Consultants of Madison (C), WI, *563*
Sales Consultants of Milwaukee (C), WI, *563*
Sales Consultants of Dallas (C), TX, *563*
Sales Consultants of Appleton (C), WI, *563*
Sales Management Resources (C), CA, *563*
Sales Professionals Personnel Services (C), CA, *564*
Sales Recruiters of Oklahoma City (C), OK, *564*
Sales Search Specialist (C), IL, *564*
Sales Solutions (C), CA, *564*
A. N. Salloway Executive Search & Consulting, L.L.C. (C), MA, *564*
George D. Sandel Assoc. (C), MA, *565*
Sanford Rose Assoc. - Santa Barbara (C), CA, *565*
Sanford Rose Assoc. - Fairhope (C), AL, *565*
Sanford Rose Assoc. - Clearwater (C), FL, *566*
Sanford Rose Assoc. - Norcross (C), GA, *566*
Sanford Rose Assoc. - Evansville (C), IN, *567*
Sanford Rose Assoc. - Lake St. Louis (C), MO, *568*
Sanford Rose Assoc. - Greensboro (C), NC, *569*
Sanford Rose Assoc. - Burlington, NC (C), NC, *569*
Sanford Rose Assoc. - Fairlawn (C), OH, *569*
Sanford Rose Assoc. - Philadelphia North (C), PA, *570*
Sanford Rose Assoc. - Nashville (C), TN, *570*
Satterfield & Assoc., Inc. (R), OH, *184*
Savalli & Assoc., Inc. (C), MI, *571*
David Saxner & Assoc., Inc. (DSA, Inc.) (R), IL, *185*
Schall Executive Search Partners (R), MN, *185*
Schick Professional Search, Inc. (C), OH, *572*
A.D. Schiff & Assoc., Ltd. (C), IL, *572*
F. B. Schmidt Int'l. (R), CA, *185*
G. L. Schwartz & Assoc., Inc. (C), GA, *572*
Schweichler Assoc., Inc. (R), CA, *186*
Scientific Solutions, Inc. (C), MI, *572*
Scott Executive Search, Inc. (R), NY, *186*
The Search America Group Inc. (C), OH, *573*
Search America, Inc. (C), PA, *573*
The Search Center Inc. (C), TX, *574*
Search Innovations, Inc. (R), PA, *187*
Search Masters Int'l. (R), AZ, *187*
Search Masters, USA (C), FL, *576*
Search Plus Int'l.-Ohio (C), OH, *576*
Search Research Assoc., Inc. (R), MA, *187*
SearchCom, Inc. (R), TX, *187*
Seiden Krieger Assoc., Inc. (R), NY, *188*
Selective Management Services, Inc. (C), FL, *578*
Shannahan & Co., Inc. (R), CA, *189*
Sharp Placement Professionals, Inc. (C), NY, *579*
Shey-Harding Assoc. Inc. (C), CA, *580*
Shifrin-Fischer Group, Inc. (C), NJ, *580*
Michael Shirley Assoc. Inc. (R), KS, *190*
Shoemaker & Assoc. (R), GA, *190*
RitaSue Siegel Resources, Inc. (R), NY, *191*
SilverSands Int'l. (C), FL, *582*
D. J. Simpson Assoc. Inc. (R), ON, *191*
Sinclair & Co., Inc. (R), MA, *192*
SKB Enterprises (C), NY, *582*
Ruth Sklar Assoc., Inc. (RSA Executive Search) (R), NY, *192*
Sloan & Assoc., Inc. (C), VA, *583*
Christopher Smallhorn Executive Recruiting, Inc. (R), MA, *193*
Smith & Assoc. (C), CA, *583*
Ralph Smith & Assoc. (C), IL, *584*
Smith & Sawyer, Inc. (R), NY, *193*
G. L. Smith Assoc. (C), CA, *584*
Smith Search, S.C. (R), MX, *194*
Smith, Brown & Jones (C), KS, *585*
C. Snow & Assoc. (C), ON, *586*
Sockwell & Assoc. (R), NC, *194*
Phyllis Solomon Executive Search, Inc. (C), NJ, *587*
Solomon-Page Healthcare Group (R), NY, *195*
Stephen M. Sonis Assoc. (R), MA, *195*
Southern Chemical & Plastics Search (C), GA, *587*
Special Markets Group, Inc. (R), GA, *195*
Specialized Search Assoc. (C), FL, *589*
Spectrum Consultants (R), CA, *196*
SpencerStuart (R), NY, *196*
The Spiegel Group (R), MA, *197*
Sports Group Int'l. (R), NC, *198*
Springer Souder & Assoc. L.L.C. (R), IL, *198*
Staff Extension Int'l. (C), TX, *590*
Stanton Chase Int'l. (R), MD, *198*
The Stark Wilton Group (R), MI, *199*
STAT Search (C), NH, *592*
The Stelton Group, Inc. (C), NJ, *592*
Stentiford & Berardi Assoc. Ltd. (R), NY, *199*
Steven Douglas Assoc. (C), FL, *593*
Stevens Assoc. (C), MA, *593*
The Stevenson Group, Inc. (N.J.) (R), NJ, *200*
Stewart, Stein & Scott, Ltd. (R), MN, *200*
Stewart/Laurence Assoc., Inc. (R), NJ, *201*
Stone & Youngblood (C), MA, *594*
Storfer & Assoc. (C), NY, *595*
Straight & Co. (R), GA, *202*
Mark Stranberg & Assoc. Inc. (R), MA, *202*
Strategic Advancement Inc. (R), NJ, *202*
Strategic Executives, Inc. (R), CT, *202*
Strategic Resources Biotechnology & Medical Group (C), WA, *595*
Strategic Search, LLC (C), CA, *595*
Straube Associates (R), MA, *203*
Stroman Int'l., Inc. (R), CO, *204*
Survival Systems Staffing, Inc. (C), CA, *597*
Synagent Inc. (C), ON, *597*
Synergy Systems (C), ON, *598*
Systems Careers (C), CA, *598*
Systems Research Group (C), CA, *598*
Tactical Alternatives (R), CA, *205*
Martin Stevens Tamaren & Assoc., Inc. (R), CA, *206*
Tanner & Assoc., Inc. (R), TX, *206*
Tate & Assoc., Inc. (R), NJ, *207*
Taylor Winfield (R), TX, *207*
TBC, Inc. (C), KY, *600*
Tech Consulting (C), FL, *601*
Tech-Net (C), TX, *601*
Technical Recruiting Services (C), OH, *602*
Technical Resource Assoc. (C), TN, *602*
TechNix Inc. (C), ON, *602*
The Technology Group (R), IL, *208*
Tekworx, Inc. (C), OK, *604*
Telecom Executive Group (C), NJ, *605*
Telem Adhesive Search Corp. (C), MD, *605*
Telford, Adams & Alexander (R), CA, *208*
Tell/Com Recruiters (C), PA, *605*
Tesar-Reynes, Inc. (R), IL, *208*
Thomas Resource Group (R), CA, *209*
Thompson Assoc. (C), CA, *606*
Thomson, Sponar & Adams, Inc. (C), WA, *606*
Tierney Assoc., Inc. (R), PA, *209*
Top Gun Group, Inc. (C), NV, *607*
The Touchstone Group (C), MA, *607*
TPS Staffing Solutions (C), IN, *608*
Jay Tracey Assoc. Inc. (C), VT, *608*
Travel Personnel (C), OH, *609*
Travis & Co., Inc. (R), MA, *210*
Trebor Weldon Lawrence, Inc. (R), NY, *210*
Triumph Consulting, Inc. (R), IA, *210*
Tschudin Inc. (R), NJ, *211*
U.S. Search (C), VA, *610*
VanMaldegiam Assoc., Inc. (R), IL, *213*
VanReypen Enterprises, Ltd. (R), NY, *213*
Vaughan & Co. (C), CA, *612*
Venpro Consulting Inc. (C), ON, *612*
Vento Assoc. (C), TN, *612*
Venture Resources, Inc. (R), CA, *213*
C. J. Vincent Assoc., LLC (C), MD, *612*
Voigt Assoc. (R), IL, *214*
VZ Int'l., Inc. (C), AZ, *613*
W. P. Assoc. (C), CA, *613*
Wakefield Talabisco Int'l. (R), NY, *214*
Kelly Walker Assoc. (C), TX, *614*
Walker Group, Inc. (R), MN, *215*
Wallace Assoc. (C), MA, *614*
Martha Ward Executive Search, Inc. (C), NY, *615*
The Ward Group (R), MA, *215*
Ward Liebelt Assoc. Inc. (R), CT, *215*
C. D. Warner & Assoc. (C), PA, *615*
Watring & Assoc., Inc. (C), IL, *616*
Scott Watson & Assoc., Inc. (R), FL, *216*
Wayne Assoc., Inc. (C), VA, *616*
Lee Weil Assoc., Inc. (C), IL, *617*
Weinpel Search, Inc. (C), NJ, *617*
S. E. Weinstein Co. (R), IL, *217*
C. Weiss Assoc., Inc. (C), NY, *618*
Wellington Management Group (R), PA, *217*
R. A. Wells Co. (C), GA, *618*
Wesley Brown & Bartle Co., Inc. (R), NY, *218*
Western Technical Resources (C), CA, *619*
Wheeler Assoc. (R), CT, *219*

(R) = Retainer; (C) = Contingency

The Whitney Group (C), GA, 620
The Whyte Group, Inc. (R), MD, 220
The Wilkie Group Int'l. (R), ON, 220
Williams & Delmore, Inc. (C), NC, 621
Williams Recruiting, Inc. (C), WA, 621
William Willis Worldwide Inc. (R), CT, 221
N. Willner & Co., Inc. (R), NJ, 221
Wills Consulting Assoc. Inc. (R), CT, 221
The Wilmington Group (C), NC, 622
The Winchester Group (R), CA, 222
Winfield Assoc., Inc. (C), MA, 623
Winter, Wyman & Co. (C), MA, 623
Winthrop Partners, Inc. (R), NY, 222
Witt/Kieffer, Ford, Hadelman & Lloyd (R), IL, 223
S. R. Wolman Assoc., Inc. (R), NY, 224
Louise Wood & Assoc. (C), NY, 624
M. Wood Company (R), IL, 224
Wood-Glavin, Inc. (R), KS, 224
Worlco Computer Resources, Inc. (C), PA, 624
Dick Wray & Consultants, Inc. (R), CA, 225
Bob Wright Recruiting, Inc. (C), CT, 625
WTW Assoc., Inc. (R), NY, 225
Yankee Hospitality Search (C), CT, 626
Yelverton Executive Search (R), CA, 226
The Yorkshire Group, Ltd. (C), MA, 626
Yours In Travel Personnel Agency, Inc. (C), NY, 626
ZanExec L.L.C. (R), VA, 226
Zweig White & Assoc., Inc. (R), MA, 228

05.4 Sales & sales management

A la Carte Int'l., Inc. (R), VA, 1
A.J. & Assoc. (C), FL, 232
Abraham & London Ltd. (C), CT, 232
Accelerated Data Decision, Inc. (C), NJ, 233
ACCESS Technology (C), CA, 234
Ackerman Johnson Inc. (C), TX, 238
Action Management Corp. (C), MI, 239
Arthur Adams & Assoc. (C), OH, 239
Adler Management, Inc. (R), NJ, 2
Advanced Corporate Search (C), CA, 240
Advancement, Inc. (C), IL, 241
Affinity Executive Search (C), FL, 241
Affordable Executive Recruiters (C), CA, 241
AGRI-associates (C), MO, 242
Agriesti & Assoc. (C), CA, 243
Ahrensdorf & Assoc. (R), PA, 2
J. R. Akin & Co. (R), MA, 2
Allen & Assoc. (C), NV, 244
D. S. Allen Assoc. (C), NJ, 244
Allen, Wayne & Co. LLC (C), WI, 245
Allen-Jeffers Assoc. (C), CA, 245
Tom Allison Assoc. (C), NM, 245
Alpha Executive Search (C), AL, 245
Alpha Resource Group, Inc. (C), TX, 246
Alpha Resources (C), IL, 246
Alpha Search (C), FL, 246
Altec/HRC (C), MI, 246
The Alternatives Group, Inc. (C), TX, 246
Amato & Assoc., Inc. (C), CA, 246
Amato & Associates Insurance Recruiters (C), PA, 247
Peter W. Ambler Co. (R), TX, 5
AMD & Associates (C), GA, 247
Amherst Personnel Group Inc. (C), NY, 249
Aminex Corp. (C), MA, 249
Andrews & Wald Group (C), FL, 250
Angel Group Int'l. (C), KY, 250
Tryg R. Angell, Ltd. (C), CT, 250
The Angus Group, Ltd. (C), OH, 251
Fred Anthony Assoc. (C), WI, 251
Anthony Michael & Co. (C), MA, 251
Applied Resources (C), MA, 252
Applied Search Assoc., Inc. (C), GA, 252
Charles P. Aquavella & Assoc. (C), TX, 252
The Argus Group Corp. (C), ON, 252
Ariail & Assoc. (R), NC, 7
Ariel Recruitment Assoc. (R), NY, 7
Aries Search Group (C), GA, 252
Armor Personnel (C), ON, 253
J. S. Armstrong & Assoc., Inc. (R), CA, 7
Associated Recruiters (C), WI, 254
Association for Sales Force Management (C), WA, 254
Atkinson Search & Placement, Inc. (C), IA, 255
Atomic Personnel, Inc. (C), PA, 255
Aubin Int'l. Inc. (R), MA, 8
Cami Austin & Assoc. (C), IL, 256
Austin Group Int'l./Marlar Int'l. (R), TX, 9
Automation Technology Search (C), CA, 256
AutoPeople (C), VT, 257
Avestruz & Assoc. (C), CA, 257
The Badger Group (R), CA, 10
D. W. Baird & Associates (C), MD, 257
Allen Ballach Assoc. Inc. (R), ON, 10
BallResources (C), MO, 258
The Bankers Group (C), IL, 258
Barclay Consultants, Inc. (C), NJ, 259
J. W. Barleycorn, Renard & Assoc., Inc. (R), OH, 11
Barnes & Assoc. Executive Search (C), CA, 259
Barone Assoc. (C), NJ, 259
Barone-O'Hara Assoc., Inc. (R), NJ, 11
Barr Assoc. (C), PA, 259
The Barrett Group (C), NH, 260
Barrett Hospitality Search (R), CA, 12
Aldonna Barry Personnel & Management (C), ON, 260
Bartholdi & Co., Inc. (R), CO, 12
Battalia Winston Int'l./The Euram Consultants Group (R), NY, 13
R. Gaines Baty Assoc., Inc. (R), TX, 13
The Bauman Group (R), CA, 14
Bayland Assoc. (C), CA, 261
The Beardsley Group Inc. (C), CT, 261
Beck/Eastwood Recruitment Solutions (C), CA, 261
Becker, Norton & Co. (R), PA, 14
The Bedford Consulting Group Inc. (R), ON, 14
Robert Beech West Inc. (C), CA, 262
Behrens and Company (C), WA, 262
Bell Wishingrad Partners Inc. (R), NY, 15
Richard L. Bencin & Assoc. (C), OH, 264
Bender Executive Search Management Consulting (R), NY, 16
Berkshire Search Assoc. (C), MA, 265
Bernhart Assoc. (C), MN, 265
Best, Coleman & Co., Inc. (R), MA, 16
Paul J. Biestek Assoc., Inc. (R), IL, 17
Binder Hospitality Group (C), KY, 266
BioQuest Inc. (R), CA, 17
Blackhawk Advantage, Inc. (C), CA, 267
Block & Assoc. (R), CA, 18
Tom Bogle & Assoc. (C), CA, 269
Ann Bond Assoc. Inc. (C), MD, 269
Bosch & Assoc., LLC (R), CT, 19
Bosland Gray Assoc. (R), NJ, 20
Boston Professional Search, Inc. (C), MA, 270
Bowie & Associates, Inc. (C), MD, 271
Boyden (R), NY, 20
BR & Assoc. (C), NJ, 271
Bradford Executives Int'l. (C), VA, 271
M. F. Branch Assoc., Inc. (C), NC, 272
The Brand Co., Inc. (R), FL, 22
Brandywine Consulting Group (R), PA, 22
Brandywine Retained Ventures, Inc. (R), CT, 22
Brethet, Barnum & Assoc., Inc. (C), ON, 273
Brian Assoc., Inc. (C), NY, 273
Brierwood Group, Inc. (C), IN, 273
Bright Search/Professional Staffing (C), MN, 274
Broadband Resource Group (C), CA, 274
Brooke Chase Assoc., Inc. (R), IL, 24
J. B. Brown & Assoc., Inc. (C), OH, 275
Brown, Bernardy, Van Remmen, Inc. (C), CA, 275
Brown Venture Assoc. (R), CA, 24
Brownstone Sales & Marketing Group, Inc. (C), NY, 275
Charles Buck & Assoc., Inc. (R), NY, 24
The Buckley Group (C), FL, 276
Buckman/Enochs & Assoc., Inc. (C), OH, 276
The Burgess Group-Corporate Recruiters Int'l., Inc. (R), NY, 25
J. Burke & Assoc., Inc. (C), TX, 276
David S. Burt Assoc. (C), MT, 276
The Butlers Co. Insurance Recruiters (C), FL, 277
The C.P.R. Group (C), NJ, 278
Cadillac Assoc. (C), CA, 278
Cahill Assoc. (C), CT, 279
Cambridge Management Planning (R), ON, 27
Campbell, Edgar Inc. (C), BC, 280
Canadian Career Partners (R), AB, 27
The Canon Group (C), CA, 280
Cantrell & Assoc. (C), FL, 280
Capital Consulting & Research, Inc. (R), CT, 28
Capital Markets Resources, Inc. (C), NC, 281
Sally Caplan & Assoc. (C), WA, 281
Caprio & Assoc. Inc. (R), IL, 29
Capstone Consulting, Inc. (R), IL, 29
Career +Plus (C), NY, 281
Career Alternatives Executive Search (C), MI, 281
Career Consultants (R), IN, 29

Career Consulting Group, Inc. (C), CT, *281*
Career Counseling Inc. (CCI) (C), KY, *282*
Career Marketing Consultants, Inc. (C), GA, *282*
Career Profiles (C), NH, *283*
Career Search Group (C), FL, *283*
Careers Plus (R), CA, *29*
Carion Resource Group Inc. (C), ON, *284*
Carr Management Services, Inc. (C), PA, *284*
Carter, Lavoie Associates (C), RI, *285*
Carter-Evdemon & Assoc. (C), FL, *285*
Carter/MacKay (C), NJ, *285*
Caruso & Assoc., Inc. (R), FL, *31*
Cary & Assoc. (R), FL, *31*
CAS Comsearch Inc. (C), NY, *285*
Michael J. Cavanagh & Assoc. Inc. (R), ON, *31*
CBA Companies (C), CA, *286*
CEC Associates (R), MA, *32*
Central Executive Search, Inc. (C), OH, *287*
Century Assoc., Inc. (C), PA, *287*
The Century Group (C), KS, *287*
CEO Consulting (C), FL, *287*
Wayne S. Chamberlain & Assoc. (C), CA, *288*
The Chapman Group, Inc. (C), AZ, *289*
Charles & Associates, Inc. (C), NE, *289*
A. D. Check Assoc., Inc. (R), PA, *33*
Chesapeake Group (C), CT, *290*
Christian & Timbers, Inc. (R), OH, *34*
R. Christine Assoc. (C), PA, *290*
William J. Christopher Assoc., Inc. (R), PA, *34*
Christopher-Westmont & Assoc., Inc. (R), OH, *34*
J. F. Church Associates (C), WA, *291*
CJA-The Adler Group, Inc. (R), CA, *35*
CJSI-Cindy Jackson Search Int'l. (C), CA, *291*
Clanton & Co. (C), CA, *292*
Arlene Clapp, Ltd. (R), MN, *35*
The Clark Group (C), MI, *292*
Clark Personnel Service, Inc. (C), AL, *292*
Clayman & Co. (R), MA, *36*
The Clayton Edward Group (C), MI, *292*
Clinton, Charles, Wise & Co. (C), FL, *293*
CMS, Inc. (C), NH, *293*
Coast Personnel Services Ltd. (C), BC, *293*
Coastal Int'l., Inc. (R), MA, *36*
Commonwealth Consultants (C), GA, *294*
Comprehensive Search (C), GA, *294*
Computer Network Resources, Inc. (C), CA, *295*
Computer Security Placement Service (C), MA, *296*
Conard Associates, Inc. (R), NH, *39*
Conex Inc./InterSearch (R), NY, *39*
M. L. Conner (C), FL, *296*
Consulpro (R), ON, *39*
Consumer Search Inc. (C), MA, *298*
Conway & Assoc. (R), IL, *40*
Philip Conway Management (R), IL, *40*
The Cooke Group (R), WI, *40*
Cooper Assoc., Inc. (C), NY, *298*
Corbin Packaging Professionals (C), MO, *299*
Cornwall Stockton & Co., Inc. (C), TX, *299*
Corporate Careers, Inc. (C), CA, *299*
The Corporate Connection, Ltd. (C), VA, *299*
Corporate Dynamix (C), AZ, *300*
Corporate Environment Ltd. (R), IL, *41*
Corporate Image Group (C), TN, *300*
Corporate Plus, Ltd. (C), GA, *300*
Corporate Recruiters Ltd. (C), BC, *300*
CountryHouse Hotels Executive Search (C), VA, *302*
Crane, Reed & Co., Inc. (C), NH, *302*
Creative Management Strategies, Ltd. (R), NY, *42*
Creative-Leadership, Inc. (R), CA, *42*
Marlene Critchfield Co. (C), CA, *303*
Cross Country Consultants, Inc. (C), MD, *304*
Timothy D. Crowe, Jr. (R), MA, *43*
Culver Personnel Services (C), CA, *304*
Cumberland Group Inc. (C), IL, *304*
Frank Cuomo & Assoc., Inc. (C), NY, *305*
Curran Partners, Inc. (R), CT, *44*
The Currier-Winn Co., Inc. (C), NJ, *305*
Custom Resources (C), AL, *305*
Cyr Associates, Inc. (C), MA, *306*
D.A.I Human Resources Consultants (R), QE, *45*
Charles Dahl Group, Inc. (C), MN, *306*
Dahl-Morrow Int'l. (R), VA, *45*
The Dalley Hewitt Co. (R), GA, *45*
Alfred Daniels & Assoc., Inc. (R), CA, *46*
The DataFinders Group, Inc. (C), NJ, *307*
David Perry Assoc. (C), NJ, *308*
DBC Recruiting Network (C), GA, *309*
DeCorrevont & Assoc. (C), IL, *310*
Deeco Int'l. (C), UT, *310*
Thorndike Deland Assoc. LLC (R), NY, *48*
Delta Management Group Ltd. (C), ON, *310*
Despres & Associates (C), IL, *311*
Devoto & Assoc. (C), CA, *312*
DiMarchi Partners (R), CO, *51*
Robert W. Dingman Co., Inc. (R), CA, *52*
Direct Marketing Solutions (C), KY, *312*
Direct Recruiters, Inc. (C), OH, *312*
DiTech Resources (C), CT, *313*
Diversified Consulting Services, Inc. (C), CO, *313*
Diversified Search, Inc. (R), PA, *52*
Dixie Search Assoc. (C), GA, *313*
Don Allan Assoc., Inc. (C), CA, *313*
The Donnelly Group-Sales Recruiters, Inc. (C), MO, *314*
The Dorfman Group (C), AZ, *314*
Dorst Information Services, Inc. (C), NY, *314*
Dotson & Assoc. (R), NY, *54*
Dougherty & Assoc. (C), TN, *314*
Douglas-Allen, Inc. (R), MA, *54*
CS Dowling Executive Services (R), NJ, *54*
Dreier Consulting (C), NJ, *315*
Drew Assoc. Int'l. (R), NJ, *54*
Dromeshauser Assoc. (R), MA, *55*
DRZ Medical Recruiters (C), CO, *315*
DS&A (Doug Sears & Assoc.) (C), FL, *315*
Dukas Assoc. (C), MA, *315*
M. Dunbar & Assoc. (C), TX, *316*
The Duncan-O'Dell Group Inc. (C), TX, *316*
Dunhill Professional Search of Miami (C), FL, *319*
Dunhill of San Francisco, Inc. (C), CA, *319*
Dunhill Professional Search of San Jose (C), CA, *319*
Dunhill Professional Search of Greater New Orleans (C), LA, *321*
Dunhill Professional Search of Ramsey (C), NJ, *321*
Dunhill Professional Search of Bucks-Mont., Inc. (C), PA, *322*
Dunhill Professional Search of Wilkes-Barre/Scranton, Inc. (C), PA, *322*
C. A. Durakis Assoc., Inc. (R), MD, *55*
Dussick Management Assoc. (C), CT, *323*
Dynamic Choices Inc. (C), MO, *323*
E.P. Int'l. (C), NY, *324*
E/Search Int'l. (C), CT, *325*
Eagle Search Assoc. (C), CA, *325*
EagleView, Inc. (C), MA, *325*
Eastman & Beaudine, Inc. (R), TX, *56*
EDI/Executive Dynamics Inc. (C), NJ, *326*
Edwards & Assoc. (C), GA, *327*
Bruce Edwards & Associates, Inc. (R), NC, *56*
EFCO Consultants, Inc. (C), NY, *327*
D. C. Egan & Assoc. (C), GA, *327*
W. Robert Eissler & Assoc., Inc. (C), TX, *327*
The Eldridge Group, Ltd. (C), IL, *327*
H. J. Elliot, Inc. (R), IL, *58*
The Ellsworth Group (C), NY, *329*
The Elmhurst Group (C), CA, *329*
The Elsworth Group (C), TX, *329*
Mark Elzweig Co., Ltd. (C), NY, *329*
Emerging Medical Technologies, Inc. (C), CO, *329*
Emerson & Co. (C), GA, *329*
Empire International (R), PA, *59*
The Enfield Company (C), TX, *330*
ENI (R), CT, *59*
Erwin Assoc. (R), IL, *60*
ESS (Executive Search Services) (R), CA, *61*
ETI Search Int'l. (R), GA, *61*
Evans Transportation Search (C), ON, *331*
Exec Tech, Inc. (C), IL, *332*
ExecuGroup, Inc. (R), MS, *61*
ExecuSource Assoc., Inc. (C), GA, *332*
ExecuSource Consultants, Inc. (C), TX, *332*
Executech (R), OH, *62*
Executive Business Solutions, Inc. (C), WA, *332*
Executive Directions (R), OH, *62*
Executive Exchange Corp. (C), NJ, *333*
Executive Recruiters Agency, Inc. (C), AR, *333*
Executive Recruitment Services, Inc. (ERS, Inc.) (C), GA, *334*
Executive Resource Assoc. (C), VA, *334*
Executive Sales Search (C), CO, *335*
Executive Search Consultants, Inc. (C), FL, *335*
Executive Search Int'l. (C), TX, *335*
Executive Search, Ltd. (C), OH, *336*

Executive Search of America, Inc. (C), OH, *336*
Executive Search Partners (R), NY, *63*
F.L.A.G. (C), OH, *338*
Fairfaxx Corp. (R), CT, *64*
Fairfield Int'l. Resources (R), NY, *65*
Paul Falcone Assoc. (R), NJ, *65*
Fallstaff Search (C), MD, *338*
Fament, Inc. (C), OH, *338*
Dorothy W. Farnath & Assoc., Inc. (C), NJ, *338*
Fast Switch, Ltd. (C), OH, *338*
A. E. Feldman Assoc., Inc. (C), NY, *339*
Fell & Nicholson Technology Resources (R), CA, *65*
Fenwick Partners (R), MA, *66*
Ferrari Search Group (C), OH, *340*
Guild Fetridge Acoustical Search, Inc. (C), NY, *340*
Jerry Fields Assoc. (C), NY, *340*
Financial Connections Company (C), VA, *340*
Neil Fink Assoc. (R), CA, *66*
First Search America, Inc. (C), TN, *341*
First Search Inc. (C), IL, *341*
Howard Fischer Assoc. Int'l., Inc. (R), PA, *67*
Fisher & Assoc. (R), CA, *67*
The Fisher Group (R), AB, *67*
A. G. Fishkin & Assoc., Inc. (R), MD, *68*
Flowers & Assoc. (C), OH, *342*
David Fockler & Assoc., Inc. (C), CA, *342*
Focus Executive Search (C), MN, *343*
Ford & Ford (C), MA, *343*
Forest People Int'l. Search Ltd. (C), BC, *343*
Fortune Personnel Consultants of Colorado Springs (C), CO, *344*
Fortune Personnel Consultants of Topsfield (C), MA, *346*
F-O-R-T-U-N-E Personnel Consultants of Houston, Inc. (C), TX, *350*
FORTUNE Personnel Consultants of North Dallas (C), TX, *350*
Foster Partners (R), NY, *70*
Fox, White & Assoc. (C), FL, *351*
Franchise Recruiters Ltd. (R), IL, *71*
Franklin Int'l. Search, Inc. (C), MA, *352*
KS Frary & Assoc. (R), MA, *71*
Mel Frazer Consultant (C), CA, *352*
Fresquez & Assoc. (C), CA, *352*
Friedman Eisenstein Raemer & Schwartz, LLP (R), IL, *72*
Bernard Frigon & Assoc. Inc. (C), QE, *353*
C. F. Furr & Co. (R), NC, *72*
The Furst Group, Inc. (R), IL, *72*
Futures, Inc. (C), NH, *354*
G. H. Enterprises (C), AZ, *354*
The Gammill Group, Inc. (C), OH, *354*
W. N. Garbarini & Assoc. (R), NJ, *74*
Dick Garland Consultants (R), NY, *74*
The Garrison Organization (R), IA, *75*
Dianne Gauger & Assoc. (C), CA, *355*
Genesis Research (C), MO, *356*
C. R. Gerald & Assoc. (C), ON, *356*
GES Services, Inc. (R), NY, *76*
Gilbert Tweed Assoc. Inc. (R), NY, *76*
Howard Gilmore & Assoc. (R), OH, *77*
Gilreath Weatherby Inc. (R), MA, *77*
Lawrence Glaser Assoc., Inc. (C), NJ, *357*
Global Resources Group (R), CA, *78*
Global Technologies Group Inc. (C), NC, *359*
Global Telecommunications, Inc. (C), TX, *359*
F. Gloss Int'l. (R), VA, *78*
Barry M. Gold & Co. (C), CA, *359*
Fred J. Goldsmith Assoc. (R), CA, *79*
Goldstein & Co. (C), CA, *360*
The Goodman Group (R), CA, *79*
Goodrich & Sherwood Assoc., Inc. (R), NY, *79*
Alexander Graham Assoc. (C), NJ, *361*
Robert Grant Assoc., Inc. (C), CA, *361*
Graphic Search Assoc. Inc. (C), PA, *362*
Greene Personnel Consultants (C), RI, *362*
Greenhaven & Assoc., Inc. (R), NY, *81*
Greenwich Search Partners, LLC (C), CT, *363*
Greger/Peterson Assoc., Inc. (R), CA, *81*
Gros Executive Search, Inc. (C), TN, *363*
Groton Planning Group (R), ME, *82*
Groussman & Assoc., Inc. (R), TX, *82*
Growth Consultants of America (R), MI, *82*
Growth Strategies, Inc. (R), FL, *83*
David E. Grumney Co. Inc. (R), WA, *83*
GSW Consulting Group, Inc. (R), CA, *83*
Michael R. Guerin Co. (C), CA, *364*
Gundersen Partners, L.L.C. (R), NY, *83*
Gustin Partners, Ltd. (R), MA, *83*
Hale Assoc. (R), IL, *84*
K. C. Hale, Inc. (R), CT, *85*
Haley Associates (R), CA, *85*
Halo Insurance Service (C), AL, *367*
Hansen Executive Search, Inc. (C), NE, *368*
Harbrowe, Inc. (C), NY, *368*
Harper Hewes, Inc. (C), NY, *369*
The Harris Consulting Corp. (R), MB, *87*
Hart & Co. (C), NY, *370*
The Hawkins Co. (R), CA, *88*
Michael J. Hawkins, Inc. (C), IL, *370*
Hayden & Assoc., Inc. (C), MN, *370*
Hayden Group, Inc. (R), MA, *88*
The Haystack Group, Inc. (R), ME, *88*
Hazlett Associates (R), IL, *88*
Health Care Dimensions (C), CO, *371*
Healthcare Management Resources, Inc. (R), GA, *89*
Healthcare Recruiters Int'l. Phoenix (C), AZ, *372*
Healthcare Recruiters of the Rockies, Inc. (C), CO, *372*
Healthcare Recruiters of Indiana (C), IN, *372*
Healthcare Recruiters Int'l. - Alabama (C), AL, *372*
Healthcare Recruiters Int'l. Orange County (C), CA, *372*
Healthcare Recruiters Int'l - Minnesota, Inc. (C), MN, *373*
Healthcare Recruiters International-NY/NJ (C), NJ, *373*
Healthcare Recruiters of New England (C), MA, *373*
Healthcare Recruiters of New Orleans (C), LA, *373*
Healthcare Recruiters of New York, Inc. (C), NY, *373*
Healthcare Recruiters Int'l. Philadelphia (C), NJ, *373*
Healthcare Recruiters - Northwest (C), WA, *374*
Healthcare Recruiters of Dallas (C), TX, *374*
Healthcare Resources Group (C), OK, *374*
Heath/Norton Assoc., Inc. (R), NY, *89*
The Heidrick Partners, Inc. (R), IL, *90*
Heinze & Assoc. Inc. (R), MN, *91*
Heller Assoc., Ltd. (R), IL, *91*
Heller Kil Assoc., Inc. (C), FL, *375*
G. W. Henn & Co. (R), OH, *91*
Heritage Search Group, Inc. (C), FL, *376*
J. J. Herlihy & Assoc., Inc. (C), CA, *376*
Herring & Assoc. (C), AR, *376*
J. D. Hersey & Assoc. (C), OH, *376*
Hersher Assoc., Ltd. (R), IL, *92*
Robert Hess & Assoc., Inc. (C), CO, *377*
The Hetzel Group, Inc. (R), IL, *92*
Higdon Prince Inc. (R), NY, *93*
B. W. Higgins, Inc. (C), IN, *377*
Hill & Assoc. (C), CA, *378*
The Hindman Co. (R), KY, *94*
The Hindman Group, Inc. (C), CA, *378*
Hintz Associates (C), NY, *378*
Hobson Assoc. (C), CT, *379*
Hockett Associates, Inc. (R), CA, *94*
Hodge-Cronin & Assoc., Inc. (R), IL, *94*
Hoffman Partnership Group Inc. (C), NY, *379*
Hoglund & Assoc., Inc. (R), IL, *94*
Holland & Assoc., Inc. (R), MI, *94*
Fred Hood & Assoc. (C), CA, *380*
Hook-Up! (C), CA, *380*
Horizons Unlimited (C), CA, *381*
Hornberger Management Company (R), DE, *95*
Houser, Martin, Morris (C), WA, *381*
Houtz•Strawn & Arnold, Inc. (R), TX, *96*
Howard-Sloan Assoc. (C), NY, *381*
The Howard-Sloan-Koller Group (R), NY, *97*
Hudson Assoc. Inc. (C), IN, *383*
E. A. Hughes & Co., Inc. (R), NY, *98*
Hughes & Company (R), VA, *98*
Human Capital Resources, Inc. (C), FL, *384*
E. F. Humay Assoc. (C), PA, *384*
Hunegnaw Executive Search (C), OH, *384*
Hunter Adams (C), NC, *385*
Hunter Assoc. (C), MA, *385*
Hunter Int'l. LLC (C), MA, *385*
Hyland Executive Search (C), AZ, *386*
Hyman & Assoc. (C), TX, *386*
The IMC Group of Companies (R), NY, *101*
Impact Source, Inc. (C), FL, *387*
Meredith Ingram, Ltd. (C), IL, *388*
The Inside Track (C), TX, *389*
Insight Consulting Co. (C), NY, *389*
Insight Personnel Group, Inc. (C), TX, *389*
Insurance Search (C), TX, *390*
Integrated Search Solutions Group, LLC (ISSG) (R), NY, *102*
Intelegra, Inc. (C), NJ, *390*
IntelliSearch (C), TX, *391*

Inter Regional Executive Search, Inc. (IRES, Inc.) (C), NJ, *391*
Interactive Search Assoc. (C), PA, *391*
Intercontinental Executive Group (C), PA, *391*
International Consulting Services, Inc. (C), IL, *392*
International Executive Recruiters (C), OH, *393*
International Pro Sourcing, Inc. (C), PA, *393*
International Technical Resources (C), FL, *393*
InterNeed (C), TX, *394*
Interspace Interactive, Inc. (C), NY, *394*
IR Search (R), CA, *103*
Isaacson, Miller (R), MA, *104*
Joan Isbister Consultants (C), NY, *394*
ISC of Atlanta, Inc. (C), GA, *394*
ISC of Cincinnati Inc. (C), OH, *394*
ISC of Houston, Inc. (C), TX, *394*
The J. B. Search Group (C), CA, *395*
J. Nicholas Arthur (R), MA, *104*
J. R. Scott & Assoc., Ltd. (C), IL, *395*
Ron Jackson & Assoc. (C), GA, *396*
K. Jaeger & Assoc. (C), MA, *396*
Pendleton James Assoc., Inc. (R), NY, *105*
Jaral Consultants, Inc. (C), NJ, *397*
JCL & Assoc. (C), FL, *397*
JDC Assoc. (C), NY, *397*
JDH & Assoc. (C), CA, *397*
Jefferson-Ross Assoc. Inc. (C), PA, *398*
JG Consultants, Inc. (R), TX, *106*
JM & Company (R), PA, *106*
Johnson & Assoc., Inc. (R), CA, *106*
Johnson & Company (R), CT, *107*
Ronald S. Johnson Assoc., Inc. (R), CA, *107*
Johnson Assoc., Inc. (C), IL, *399*
Johnson, Kemper & Assoc. (C), TX, *400*
Jonathan Lawrence Assoc. (C), NJ, *400*
Jones and Jones (R), OR, *108*
Jones Consulting Executive Search (C), GA, *400*
J. M. Joseph Assoc. (R), NJ, *109*
JPM International (C), CA, *401*
A H Justice Search Consultants (C), TX, *402*
K2 Resources, L.P. (C), CT, *402*
Kabana Corp. (C), MI, *402*
Kacevich, Lewis & Brown, Inc. (R), MA, *109*
Kaczmar & Assoc. (C), PA, *403*
Richard Kader & Assoc. (C), OH, *403*
Robert Kaestner & Assoc. (C), FL, *403*
Kaplan & Assoc., Inc. (R), PA, *109*
Karp & Assoc. (C), FL, *403*
Kaufman Assoc. (R), CA, *110*
The Kay Group of 5th Ave. (C), NY, *404*
Keane Assoc. (R), MA, *110*
A.T. Kearney Executive Search (R), IL, *111*
Kensington Int'l., Inc. (R), IL, *113*
Kenzer Corp. (R), NY, *113*
Michael L. Ketner & Assoc., Inc. (R), PA, *114*
Key Resources Int'l. (C), CA, *405*
Ki Technologies, Inc. (C), UT, *406*
Kiley, Owen & McGovern, Inc. (R), NJ, *114*
King ComputerSearch, Inc. (C), TX, *407*
Kingsbury • Wax • Bova (R), MA, *114*
The Kinlin Co., Inc. (R), MA, *115*
Kirkbride Assoc., Inc. (C), WA, *407*
Kleber & Assoc. (C), WA, *407*
KM Associates (C), MA, *407*
Lee Koehn Assoc., Inc. (R), OR, *116*
Koltnow & Company (R), NY, *117*
Kors Montgomery Int'l. (R), TX, *118*
Kostmayer Assoc., Inc. (R), MD, *119*
J. Krauss Assoc. (R), FL, *120*
Evie Kreisler Assoc. Inc. (C), CA, *409*
Kressenberg Assoc. (C), TX, *409*
John Kuhn & Assoc., Inc. (R), WI, *121*
Paul Kull & Co. (R), NJ, *121*
Kurtz Pro-Search, Inc. (C), NJ, *410*
Kutt, Inc. (C), CO, *410*
L O R (R), NJ, *122*
L T M Assoc. (C), IL, *410*
L&L Assoc. Global Search (C), PA, *411*
Lab Market Specialists (C), UT, *411*
Marvin Laba & Assoc. (R), CA, *122*
The Landstone Group (C), NY, *412*
Lange & Assoc., Inc. (C), IN, *412*
Stephen Laramee & Assoc. Inc. (C), ON, *413*
Larkin & Co. (R), CA, *124*
Robert Larned Assoc., Inc. (C), VA, *413*
Jack B. Larsen & Assoc., Inc. (C), PA, *413*
Larson Assoc. (R), CA, *125*
Larson, Katz & Young, Inc. (C), VA, *413*
Lawrence James Assoc. of Florida, Inc. (C), FL, *414*
Lawrence-Balakonis & Assoc., Inc. (C), GA, *414*
Leader Network (C), PA, *414*
The Lear Group, Inc. (R), OH, *127*
Lechner & Assoc., Inc. (C), FL, *415*
Lectra Search (C), GA, *415*
Ledbetter/Davidson Int'l., Inc. (R), NY, *127*
Lehman McLeskey (R), TX, *128*
Leith & Assoc., Inc. (C), OH, *416*
F. P. Lennon Assoc. (C), PA, *416*
The Levton Group Inc. (R), ON, *129*
The Libra Group Inc. (C), CT, *417*
Pat Licata & Assoc. (C), NC, *417*
Lois L. Lindauer Searches (C), MA, *418*
J. H. Lindell & Co. (C), CA, *418*
Lineal Recruiting Services (C), CT, *418*
Lipsky Group, Inc. (R), CA, *129*
Lloyd Prescott Assoc., Inc. (C), FL, *418*
Locke & Assoc. (R), NC, *131*
Loewenstein & Assoc., Inc. (R), TX, *131*
Ludwig & Assoc., Inc. (C), VA, *421*
Lybrook Assoc., Inc. (C), RI, *421*
Lyons & Assoc., Inc. (C), IL, *422*
Lyons Pruitt Int'l. (R), PA, *132*
M H Executive Search Group (C), TX, *422*
M. K. & Assoc. (C), PA, *422*
The Mackenzie Group (R), MD, *133*
MacNaughton Assoc. (R), CA, *133*
Madison Executive Search, Inc. (C), NJ, *422*
Madison MacArthur Inc. (R), ON, *133*
The Mallard Group (C), IN, *423*
Managed Care Resources (C), TX, *424*
Management Advisors Int'l., Inc. (C), NC, *424*
Management Consultants Corporate Recruiters (C), AZ, *424*
Management Decision Systems, Inc. (MDSI) (C), NJ, *424*
Management Dimensions Ltd. (R), ON, *134*
Management One Consultants (C), ON, *425*
Management Recruiters of Nassau, Inc. (R), NY, *134*
Management Recruiters of Decatur, LLC (C), AL, *438*
Management Recruiters of Tucson (C), AZ, *439*
Management Recruiters of San Luis Obispo (C), CA, *439*
Management Recruiters of Little Rock (C), AR, *439*
Management Recruiters Tucson-Foothills, Inc. (C), AZ, *439*
Management Recruiters of Northern California (C), CA, *440*
Management Recruiters Dana Point (C), CA, *440*
Management Recruiters, Inland Empire Agency (C), CA, *441*
Management Recruiters of Colorado Springs (C), CO, *441*
Management Recruiters of Roseville (C), CA, *441*
Management Recruiters of Sonoma (C), CA, *441*
Management Recruiters Inc. of Silicon Valley (C), CA, *441*
Management Recruiters of Winsted, Inc. (C), CT, *442*
Management Recruiters of Middlesex (C), CT, *442*
Management Recruiters of Colchester (C), CT, *442*
Management Recruiters of Milford Inc. (C), CT, *442*
Management Recruiters of Ft. Myers, FL. (C), FL, *443*
Management Recruiters of Clearwater (C), FL, *443*
Management Recruiters of Anna Maria Island (C), FL, *443*
Management Recruiters, Inc. (C), FL, *443*
Management Recruiters of St. Lucie County, Inc. (C), FL, *444*
Management Recruiters of Pensacola (C), FL, *444*
Management Recruiters of Atlanta West, Inc. (C), GA, *445*
Management Recruiters of Venice, Inc. (C), FL, *445*
Management Recruiters of Vero Beach (C), FL, *445*
Management Recruiters of Atlanta NE (C), GA, *446*
Management Recruiters of Boise (C), ID, *446*
Management Recruiters - Towne Lake (C), GA, *446*
Management Recruiters of St. Charles (C), IL, *447*

Management Recruiters of Barrington (C), IL, *447*
Management Recruiters of Sun Valley (C), ID, *447*
Management Recruiters of Chicago West (C), IL, *447*
Management Recruiters of Noblesville, Inc. (C), IN, *448*
Management Recruiters of Indianapolis-North (C), IN, *448*
Management Recruiters - Indianapolis (C), IN, *448*
Management Recruiters-Cedar Rapids, Inc. (C), IA, *448*
Management Recruiters of Des Moines (C), IA, *449*
Management Recruiters of Williamsburg (C), IA, *449*
Management Recruiters of Siouxland (C), IA, *449*
Management Recruiters of Frederick, Inc. (C), MD, *450*
Management Recruiters of Monroe, Inc. (C), LA, *450*
Management Recruiters of Dearborn, Inc. (C), MI, *451*
Management Recruiters of Cass County, NE (C), NE, *452*
Management Recruiters of Bay Head (C), NJ, *453*
Management Recruiters of Medford, N.J. (C), NJ, *453*
Management Recruiters of Reno (C), NV, *453*
Management Recruiters of Upper Westchester (C), NY, *454*
Management Recruiters of Gramercy, Inc. (C), NY, *455*
Management Recruiters of Burlington (C), NC, *455*
Management Recruiters of Woodbury Inc. (C), NY, *455*
Management Recruiters of Rocky Mount - Southwest (C), NC, *456*
Management Recruiters of Boone (C), NC, *456*
Management Recruiters of Raleigh (C), NC, *456*
Management Recruiters of Gastonia (C), NC, *456*
Management Recruiters of Akron (C), OH, *457*
Management Recruiters of Cincinnati/Sharonville, Inc. (C), OH, *457*
Management Recruiters of Cleveland (C), OH, *457*
Management Recruiters of Oklahoma City (C), OK, *458*
Management Recruiters of Bethlehem, PA (C), PA, *458*
Management Recruiters of Sidney (C), OH, *458*
Management Recruiters of Mentor, Inc. (C), OH, *458*
Management Recruiters of Lionville, Inc. (C), PA, *459*
Management Recruiters of Delaware County (C), PA, *459*
Management Recruiters of Westmoreland County, Inc. (C), PA, *459*
Management Recruiters of Pittsburgh (C), PA, *459*
Management Recruiters of Puerto Rico (C), PR, *460*
Management Recruiters of West Chester, Inc. (C), PA, *460*
Management Recruiters The Delta Group, Inc. (C), TN, *461*
Management Recruiters of Franklin, Inc. (C), TN, *461*
Management Recruiters Dallas North (MRDN) (C), TX, *462*
Management Recruiters of San Antonio (C), TX, *463*
Management Recruiters of San Marcos (C), TX, *463*
Management Recruiters of San Antonio - North (C), TX, *463*
Management Recruiters of Round Rock (C), TX, *463*
Management Recruiters of Fairfax, VA (C), VA, *464*
Management Recruiters of Arlington (C), VA, *464*
Management Recruiters - Piedmont (C), VA, *464*
Management Recruiters of Kanawha Valley, LLC (C), WV, *465*
Management Recruiters of Roanoke (C), VA, *465*
Management Recruiters of Appleton (C), WI, *465*
Management Recruiters of Stevens Point, Inc. (C), WI, *466*
Management Recruiters of Madison, Inc. (C), WI, *466*
Management Recruiters of Milwaukee - Downtown (C), WI, *466*
Management Recruiters of Janesville, Inc. (C), WI, *466*
Management Resource Group (C), MN, *467*
Management Resources (C), TX, *467*
Management Search, Inc. (C), IL, *467*
Management Search, Inc. (C), OK, *468*
Management Search of R.I. Inc. (R), RI, *135*
F. L. Mannix & Co. (R), MA, *135*
ManTech Consulting (C), NY, *468*
The Marathon Group (C), FL, *469*
Marc-Allen Assoc., Inc. (C), FL, *469*
Marentz & Co. (C), TX, *469*
Margolin Consultants, Inc. (C), NY, *469*
Mark Christian & Assoc., Inc. (C), AZ, *469*
Mark Stanley & Co./EMA Partners International (R), FL, *136*
Marketing & Sales Resources, Inc. (C), FL, *470*
Marketing Recruiters, Inc. (C), NC, *470*
Marketing Resources (C), MA, *470*
Marketing Search Inc. (C), OH, *471*
MarketPro, Inc. (C), GA, *471*
The Marlow Group (R), MA, *136*
Marshall-Alan Assoc., Inc. (C), NY, *471*
Donovan Martin & Assoc. (R), CA, *137*
J. Martin & Assoc. (R), CA, *137*
Massey-Horton Int'l. (R), ON, *138*
Mathey Services (C), IL, *472*
Matrix Consultants, Inc. (C), NC, *472*
The Matthews Group, Inc. (C), NJ, *472*
Maxecon Executive Search Consultants (R), FL, *138*
The Mayes Group, Ltd. (R), PA, *139*
MB Inc. Executive Search (C), NY, *473*
The McCormick Group (C), VA, *473*
McCormick Search Inc. (C), IL, *474*
McCray, Shriver, Eckdahl & Assoc., Inc. (R), CA, *140*
McDowell & Co., Recruiters (C), TX, *474*
McIntyre Assoc. (R), CT, *141*
McKee Cyber Search (C), MS, *475*
Dan P. McLean Assoc., Inc. (C), ON, *475*
James Mead & Co. (R), CT, *142*
Med-Ex Services (C), OH, *476*
Media Recruiting Group, Inc. (C), NY, *476*
Medical Executive Recruiters (C), CA, *477*
Medical Innovations (C), NY, *477*
Medical Recruiters Inc. (C), MO, *477*
The Medley Group (C), CA, *477*
MedQuest Assoc. (C), CO, *478*
Mee Derby & Co. (C), DC, *478*
Mehta Consulting (C), NJ, *478*
Juan Menefee & Assoc. (C), IL, *478*
J. M. Meredith & Assoc. Inc. (C), CA, *479*
MetroVantage Personnel Systems (C), CA, *480*
Walter Meyer & Assoc. (R), NY, *144*
Michael James & Co. (C), IL, *480*
Michael Wayne Recruiters (C), IL, *480*
Michael/Merrill (C), KS, *481*
Micro Staff Solutions, Inc. (C), TX, *481*
Danette Milne Corporate Search Inc. (C), ON, *482*
Milo Research (R), NY, *145*
Herbert Mines Assoc., Inc. (R), NY, *145*
MIXTEC Group (R), CA, *145*
MJF Assoc. (C), CT, *483*
Mogul Consultants, Inc. (C), NY, *483*
Molloy Partners (R), NY, *146*
Oscar Montaño, Inc. (R), CA, *146*
Montenido Assoc. (R), CA, *146*
Montgomery, Thomason & Assoc. (C), ON, *484*
The Moran Group (C), IL, *484*
Morency Assoc. (C), MA, *485*
Morgan Int'l., Inc. (R), IL, *147*
The Morgan/Geoffries Group (C), CA, *485*
The Morris Group (C), PA, *486*
Mortgage Search Network (C), AZ, *486*
Robert T. Morton Assoc., Inc. (C), MA, *486*
MPA Executive Search Inc. (R), QE, *148*
MRI, The Sequel Group, LLC (C), CO, *486*
MTA Partners (R), TX, *148*
Pamela L. Mulligan, Inc. (R), NH, *149*
Multi Processing, Inc. (R), NH, *149*
Jennifer Munro & Partners, Inc. (R), SC, *149*
The Murray Group (C), IL, *487*
NaTek Corp. (C), NY, *488*
National Career Search (C), AZ, *489*
National Metal Services Corp. (C), IN, *489*
National Recruiting Service (C), IN, *489*
National Register Columbus Inc. (C), OH, *490*
National Search, Inc.r (C), FL, *490*

Nationwide Personnel Recruiting & Consulting, Inc. (C), OR, *490*
The Neil Michael Group, Inc./Global Partners (R), NY, *151*
The NEIS Corp., Inc. (C), FL, *491*
J. Fielding Nelson & Assoc., Inc. (R), UT, *151*
New Venture Development, Inc. (C), CA, *492*
New World Healthcare Solutions, Inc. (R), NY, *151*
Newcomb-Desmond & Assoc., Inc. (C), OH, *492*
Newman-Johnson-King, Inc. (C), TX, *492*
Newport Management (C), NY, *492*
Newport Strategic Search LLC (C), CA, *492*
Next Step Recruiting (C), CA, *493*
NHA Plastics Recruiters (C), FL, *493*
Nino Recruiting & Staffing, Inc. (C), TX, *493*
J. L. Nixon Consulting (C), TX, *493*
NJ Solutions (C), CA, *493*
Noll Human Resource Services (C), NE, *494*
Nordeman Grimm, Inc. (R), NY, *152*
Paul Winston Norman & Assoc. (R), IL, *152*
Norman Broadbent Int'l., Inc. (R), NY, *152*
The Normyle/Erstling Health Search Group (C), NJ, *494*
John B. Norris & Assoc., Inc. (C), MD, *495*
Ronald Norris & Assoc. (C), IL, *495*
NorTech Resources (C), NY, *496*
North American Recruiters, Inc. (R), MN, *153*
Northern Consultants Inc. (R), ME, *153*
O'Brien & Bell (R), OH, *153*
O'Connor, O'Connor, Lordi, Ltd. (R), PA, *154*
O'Connor Resources (C), TX, *497*
Dennis P. O'Toole & Assoc. Inc. (R), NY, *154*
O'Toole & Company, Inc. (R), IL, *154*
Oak Assoc. (R), CA, *155*
OEI, Inc. (C), NJ, *498*
The Ogdon Partnership (R), NY, *155*
Olsen/Clark (R), WA, *156*
Omega Systems, LLC (C), VA, *498*
Omnisearch Assoc. (C), CA, *499*
OmniSearch, Inc. (C), FL, *499*
Oppedisano & Co., Inc. (R), NY, *156*
Opus Marketing (R), CA, *156*
Orion Int'l. Consulting Group, Inc. (C), NC, *499*
Ortman Recruiting Int'l. (C), CA, *500*
LaMonte Owens, Inc. (R), PA, *157*
The Oxford Group (C), TX, *500*
P.R.H. Management, Inc. (R), CT, *158*
Pacific Advisory Service, Inc. (C), IL, *501*
Pacific Coast Recruiters (C), OR, *501*
Pacific Crossing (C), CA, *501*
Packaging Personnel Co., Ltd. (C), WI, *501*
Paper Industry Recruitment (P.I.R.) (C), ME, *502*
Frank Parillo & Assoc. (R), CA, *159*
R. Parker & Assoc., Inc. (R), NY, *159*
Parker-Worthington, Inc. (C), TX, *503*
Michael W. Parres & Assoc. (R), MI, *159*
Parsons Assoc. Inc. (R), IL, *159*
Partners Executive Search Consultants Inc. (R), ON, *160*
Patriot Assoc. (C), PA, *505*
Paules Associates (C), CA, *505*
Peachtree Executive Search (R), GA, *161*
Pearce & Assoc. (C), FL, *506*
Pearson, Caldwell & Farnsworth (R), CA, *161*
Perfect Search, Inc. (C), FL, *507*
Performance Resources, Inc. (C), RI, *507*
Perry Search Assoc. (C), CA, *507*
Perry-Martel Int'l., Inc. (R), ON, *163*
Personnel Assoc. (C), CA, *508*
Personnel Solutions (C), AZ, *509*
J. R. Peterman Assoc., Inc. (C), VT, *509*
Petruzzi Assoc. (C), NJ, *509*
PHD Conseil en Ressources Humaines Inc. (C), QE, *510*
Phillips & Assoc. (R), MA, *164*
Phoenix Partners, Inc. (C), GA, *511*
Phoenix Search (R), MX, *164*
Pierce & Crow (R), CA, *164*
The Pinnacle Source, Inc. (C), CO, *512*
Pinton Forrest & Madden/EMA Partners Int'l. (R), BC, *165*
PLA, Inc. (C), NJ, *513*
Placements by Jesse Reid Assoc., Inc. (C), NY, *513*
Rene Plessner Assoc., Inc. (R), NY, *165*
Ray Polhill & Assoc. (R), NC, *166*
The Pollack Group (C), ON, *514*
Don V. Poole & Assoc., Inc. (C), CO, *514*
Jack Porter Assoc., Inc. (C), WA, *514*
Power Search (C), TX, *515*
Powers Consultants, Inc. (R), MO, *166*
PRAXIS Partners (R), VA, *167*
Precision Executive Search (C), AZ, *516*
Preferred Professional Recruiters (C), OH, *516*
George Preger & Associates Inc. (R), ON, *167*
Presley Consultants, Inc. (C), CA, *517*
Preston & Co. (R), NJ, *167*
Prestonwood Assoc. (R), MA, *168*
Price & Assoc., Inc. (C), VA, *518*
Primary Care Service Corp. (C), GA, *518*
The Primary Group, Inc. (R), FL, *168*
Prime Search (C), NC, *518*
Primus Assoc., L.C. (R), TX, *169*
PRO, Inc./Professional Recruiting Offices, Inc. (C), CA, *519*
Professional Employment Group (C), MD, *520*
Professional Recruiting Consultants (C), FL, *521*
Professional Recruiters Inc. (C), MN, *521*
Professional Recruiting Network (C), CA, *521*
Professional Recruiters, Inc. (C), PA, *521*
Professional Recruiters (C), UT, *521*
The Professional Sales Search Co., Inc. (C), WA, *522*
ProFinders, Inc. (C), FL, *523*
ProNet, Inc. (C), NC, *524*
ProSearch Recruiting (C), CA, *524*
ProSearch, Inc. (C), ME, *524*
ProSearch, Inc. (C), OH, *524*
ProStar Systems, Inc. (C), MD, *525*
Proven Edge (C), CA, *525*
Quality Search Inc. (C), OH, *526*
The Quantum Group (C), NJ, *526*
Quirk-Corporon & Assoc., Inc. (C), WI, *527*
R & K Associates, Inc. (C), AZ, *527*
R & L Assoc., Ltd. (R), NY, *170*
R M Associates (R), OH, *171*
R2 Services, LLC (C), IL, *528*
Lea Randolph & Assoc., Inc. (C), TX, *529*
The Rankin Group, Ltd. (R), WI, *171*
Harold L. Rapp Assoc. (C), NY, *529*
Ray & Berndtson/Lovas Stanley (R), ON, *172*
Raymond Karsan Assoc. (C), PA, *529*
Raymond Thomas & Assoc. (C), FL, *530*
RCE Assoc. (R), NJ, *173*
RCI Employment Solutions (C), FL, *531*
Recruit Xpress (C), TX, *531*
Recruiting Resources Int'l. (C), CA, *532*
Recruiting/Solutions (C), CA, *532*
Recruitment Resources (C), CA, *532*
Recruitment Specialists, Inc. (C), MD, *532*
Mary Rector & Assoc., Inc. (C), IL, *533*
Redell Search, Inc. (C), IL, *533*
Redwood Partners Ltd. (R), NY, *173*
Reinecke & Assoc. (C), NJ, *533*
The Remington Group (R), IL, *174*
Reserve Technology Institute (R), TX, *175*
The Resource Group (R), NJ, *175*
Resource Inc. (R), MA, *175*
Resources for Management (R), PA, *175*
The Revere Assoc., Inc. (R), OH, *176*
Russell Reynolds Assoc., Inc. (R), NY, *176*
Rice Cohen Int'l. (R), PA, *178*
Terry Richards (C), OH, *536*
Richmond Assoc. (C), NY, *537*
Ridenour & Assoc. (R), IL, *178*
Riotto-Jones Assoc. (R), NY, *178*
RJN Consulting (R), NY, *179*
Robison Humphreys & Assoc., Inc. (R), ON, *180*
Rockwood Assoc. (C), NY, *540*
J. Rodgers & Associates (C), IL, *540*
Rodgers, Ramsey, Inc. (C), TX, *540*
Craig Roe & Assoc., LLC (C), MD, *540*
The Rogan Group, Inc. (C), CA, *541*
ROI International, Inc. (R), WA, *181*
Rollins & Assoc. (C), CA, *541*
Rooney Assoc., Inc. (R), IL, *181*
Ropella & Assoc. (R), FL, *181*
Ropes Associates, Inc. (R), FL, *182*
Emery A. Rose & Assoc. (C), WA, *545*
Ross Personnel Consultants, Inc. (C), CT, *545*
Patricia Roth Int'l. (C), FL, *545*
Roth Young of Chicago (C), IL, *546*
Roth Young of Tampa (C), FL, *546*
Roth Young Seattle (C), WA, *546*
Rovner & Assoc., Inc. (R), IL, *182*
Rowland Mountain & Assoc. (C), GA, *547*
RSMR, Inc. (R), IL, *182*
Rust & Assoc., Inc. (R), IL, *183*
Ryman, Bell, Green & Michaels, Inc. (C), TX, *549*
S.C.S. & Assoc. (C), NC, *550*
S.D.P. Contract Recruiters (C), NJ, *550*
Saber Group, Inc. (C), TX, *550*
Sage Employment Recruiters (C), IN, *550*

Sales & Management Search, Inc. (C), IL, *551*
Sales & Marketing Search, Inc. (C), MA, *551*
Sales Builders, Inc. (R), VA, *183*
Sales Consultants of Birmingham (C), AL, *555*
Sales Consultants Peninsula, Inc. (C), CA, *556*
Sales Consultants of Scottsdale, Inc. (C), AZ, *556*
Sales Consultants of Sacramento (C), CA, *556*
Sales Consultants of Silicon Valley (C), CA, *556*
Sales Consultants of Chico (C), CA, *556*
Sales Consultants of Daphne (C), AL, *556*
Sales Consultants of Northwest Arkansas, Inc. (C), AR, *556*
Sales Consultants of Ft. Lauderdale, Inc. (C), FL, *557*
Sales Consultants of Savannah, GA (C), GA, *557*
Sales Consultants of Stamford-Darien (C), CT, *557*
Sales Consultants of Boca Raton, Inc. (C), FL, *557*
Sales Consultants of Danbury (C), CT, *557*
Sales Consultants of Denver (C), CO, *557*
Sales Consultants of Tampa North, Inc. (C), FL, *557*
Sales Consultants of Chicago South (C), IL, *558*
Sales Consultants of Indianapolis (C), IN, *558*
Sales Consultants (C), IL, *558*
Sales Consultants of Western McHenry County (C), IL, *558*
Sales Consultants of Honolulu (C), HI, *558*
Sales Consultants of Barrington (C), IL, *558*
Sales Consultants of Baltimore (C), MD, *559*
Sales Consultants of Rockville, MD (C), MD, *559*
Sales Consultants of Auburn Hills (C), MI, *559*
Sales Consultants of Wellesley, Inc. (C), MA, *559*
Sales Consultants - Bristol County (C), MA, *559*
Sales Consultants of Brockton, Inc. (C), MA, *559*
Sales Consultants of Birmingham (C), MI, *559*
Sales Consultants of Farmington Hills (C), MI, *560*
Sales Consultants of Nashua-Manchester (C), NH, *560*
Sales Consultants of Grand Rapids (C), MI, *560*
Sales Consultants of Laurel Park, Inc. (C), MI, *560*
Sales Consultants of Omaha, Inc. (C), NE, *560*
Sales Consultants Bridgewater, Inc. (C), NJ, *560*
Sales Consultants of Cherry Hill (C), NJ, *560*
Sales Consultants of Northern Jersey, Inc. (C), NJ, *560*
Sales Consultants of Raleigh-Durham-RTP (C), NC, *561*
Sales Consultants of Cincinnati (C), OH, *561*
Sales Consultants of Butler County (C), PA, *561*
Sales Consultants of Middlesex County, Inc. (C), NJ, *561*
Sales Consultants of Princeton, Inc. (C), NJ, *561*
Sales Consultants of Morris County, Inc. (C), NJ, *561*
Sales Consultants of Newtown, Inc. (C), PA, *562*
Sales Consultants of Austin, Inc. (C), TX, *562*
Sales Consultants of Chester County, PA (C), PA, *562*
Sales Consultants of Rhode Island, Inc. (C), RI, *562*
Sales Consultants of Greenville, Inc. (C), SC, *562*
Sales Consultants King of Prussia (C), PA, *562*
Sales Consultants of Orangeburg (C), SC, *562*
Sales Consultants of Madison (C), WI, *563*
Sales Consultants of Milwaukee (C), WI, *563*
Sales Consultants of Dallas (C), TX, *563*
Sales Consultants of Appleton (C), WI, *563*
Sales Executives, Inc. (C), MI, *563*
Sales Management Resources (C), CA, *563*
Sales Professionals Personnel Services (C), CA, *564*
Sales Recruiters of Oklahoma City (C), OK, *564*
Sales Recruiting Network (C), PA, *564*
Sales Search Specialist (C), IL, *564*
Sales Solutions (C), CA, *564*
A. N. Salloway Executive Search & Consulting, L.L.C. (C), MA, *564*
Sampson Medical Search (C), CA, *564*
Sanford Rose Assoc. - Santa Ana (C), CA, *565*
Sanford Rose Assoc. - Fairhope (C), AL, *565*
Sanford Rose Assoc. - Santa Barbara (C), CA, *565*
Sanford Rose Assoc. - Effingham (C), IL, *566*
Sanford Rose Assoc. - Norcross (C), GA, *566*
Sanford Rose Assoc. - Rockford (C), IL, *567*
Sanford Rose Assoc. - Lake St. Louis (C), MO, *568*
Sanford Rose Assoc. - Amherst, NY (C), NY, *568*
Sanford Rose Assoc. - Gastonia (C), NC, *568*
Sanford Rose Assoc. - Greensboro (C), NC, *569*
Sanford Rose Assoc. - Akron (C), OH, *569*
Sanford Rose Assoc. - Fairlawn (C), OH, *569*
Sanford Rose Assoc. - Nashville (C), TN, *570*
Sanford Rose Assoc. - Doylestown (C), PA, *570*
Sanford Rose Assoc. - Portland (C), OR, *570*
Satterfield & Assoc., Inc. (R), OH, *184*
Saviar, Inc. (C), AZ, *571*
Schall Executive Search Partners (R), MN, *185*
Schick Professional Search, Inc. (C), OH, *572*
A.D. Schiff & Assoc., Ltd. (C), IL, *572*
F. B. Schmidt Int'l. (R), CA, *185*
Schoales & Assoc. Inc. (C), ON, *572*
G. L. Schwartz & Assoc., Inc. (C), GA, *572*
Schweichler Assoc., Inc. (R), CA, *186*
Scientific Solutions, Inc. (C), MI, *572*
Scott Sibley Assoc. (C), NY, *573*
The Search America Group Inc. (C), OH, *573*
The Search Committee (C), MD, *574*
The Search Group (C), MD, *575*
Search Int'l. (R), MA, *187*
Search Masters Int'l. (R), AZ, *187*
Search Masters, USA (C), FL, *576*
SearchCorp International (C), AB, *577*
Seco & Zetto Assoc., Inc. (C), NJ, *577*
Select Services (C), IL, *578*
Selectis Corp. (C), IL, *578*
Selective Management Services, Inc. (C), FL, *578*
Selective Staffing (C), CA, *579*
Selig Executive Search (C), NH, *579*
Shannahan & Co., Inc. (R), CA, *189*
Sharp Placement Professionals, Inc. (C), NY, *579*
Shepherd Bueschel & Provus, Inc. (R), IL, *189*
Shey-Harding Assoc. Inc. (C), CA, *580*
Shiell Personnel (C), LA, *580*
Shifrin-Fischer Group, Inc. (C), NJ, *580*
Michael Shirley Assoc. Inc. (R), KS, *190*
Shoemaker & Assoc. (R), GA, *190*
The Shotland Group (R), CA, *190*
SHS of Allentown (C), PA, *580*
SilverSands Int'l. (C), FL, *582*
D. J. Simpson Assoc. Inc. (R), ON, *191*
Simpson Associates (C), NY, *582*
Singleton & Assoc. (C), VA, *582*
SKB Enterprises (C), NY, *582*
Ruth Sklar Assoc., Inc. (RSA Executive Search) (R), NY, *192*
Sloan & Assoc., Inc. (C), VA, *583*
Smith & Assoc. (C), CA, *583*
James F. Smith & Assoc. (C), GA, *583*
Ralph Smith & Assoc. (C), IL, *584*
G. L. Smith Assoc. (C), CA, *584*
The Smith Group, Inc. (C), NC, *584*
Snelling & Snelling, Inc. (C), FL, *585*
Snelling Search - Transportation Division (C), AR, *585*
Soltis Management Services (R), PA, *195*
Southern Chemical & Plastics Search (C), GA, *587*
Southport Int'l. Assoc. Inc. (C), FL, *588*
Southwestern Professional Services (C), TN, *588*

Sparks, McDonough & Assoc., Inc. (C), MO, *588*
Special Markets Group, Inc. (R), GA, *195*
Specialized Search Assoc. (C), FL, *589*
Spectra International LLC (C), AZ, *589*
Spectrum Consultants (R), CA, *196*
SpencerSearch, Inc. (C), CO, *589*
SpencerStuart (R), NY, *196*
The Spiegel Group (R), MA, *197*
Sports Group Int'l. (R), NC, *198*
Spriggs & Co., Inc. (R), IL, *198*
Sprout/Standish, Inc. (C), NH, *589*
Squires Resources Inc. (C), ON, *590*
Staff Extension Int'l. (C), TX, *590*
Stafford Consulting Group (R), CA, *198*
Stanton Chase Int'l. (R), MD, *198*
Starbridge Group Inc. (C), VA, *591*
STAT Search (C), NH, *592*
Steeple Resources & Consulting (R), NJ, *199*
Stentiford & Berardi Assoc. Ltd. (R), NY, *199*
Steven Michaels & Assoc. (C), NY, *593*
Ron Stevens & Assoc., Inc. (C), FL, *593*
Stevens Assoc. (C), MA, *593*
Stewart/Laurence Assoc., Inc. (R), NJ, *201*
Stone & Youngblood (C), MA, *594*
DM Stone Personnel Services (C), CA, *594*
The Stonebridge Group (C), PA, *594*
Storfer & Assoc. (C), NY, *595*
Straight & Co. (R), GA, *202*
Mark Stranberg & Assoc. Inc. (R), MA, *202*
Strategic Advancement Inc. (R), NJ, *202*
Strategic Resources Biotechnology & Medical Group (C), WA, *595*
StratfordGroup (R), OH, *203*
Sullivan & Assoc. (R), MI, *204*
Summit Group Int'l., Inc. (R), GA, *204*
Survival Systems Staffing, Inc. (C), CA, *597*
Synagent Inc. (C), ON, *597*
Systems Research Group (C), CA, *598*
Tactical Alternatives (R), CA, *205*
Martin Stevens Tamaren & Assoc., Inc. (R), CA, *206*
Tanner & Assoc., Inc. (R), TX, *206*
Target Search, Inc. (C), PA, *600*
The TBI Group (R), PA, *207*
Team One Partners, Inc. (C), GA, *600*
Technical Recruiting Services (C), OH, *602*
Technical Resource Assoc. (C), TN, *602*
TechNix Inc. (C), ON, *602*
Technology Consultants Int'l. (C), CA, *603*
The Technology Group (R), IL, *208*
Technology Management Partners (R), CA, *208*
Technology Search Int'l. (C), CA, *603*
Tele-Media Int'l. Inc. (C), PA, *604*
Telecom Executive Group (C), NJ, *605*
Telecom Recruiters, Inc. (C), VA, *605*
Telem Adhesive Search Corp. (C), MD, *605*
Tell/Com Recruiters (C), PA, *605*
Tennyson Advisors (R), NY, *208*
Thomas Lyle & Co. (C), IL, *606*
Thomas Resource Group (R), CA, *209*
Thompson Assoc. (C), CA, *606*
Tierney Assoc., Inc. (R), PA, *209*
Tittemore Cowan Assoc. (C), AB, *607*
Tondorf & Assoc. Inc. (C), MA, *607*
Top Gun Group, Inc. (C), NV, *607*
The Touchstone Group (C), MA, *607*
Jay Tracey Assoc. Inc. (C), VT, *608*
Travel Personnel (C), OH, *609*
Travis & Co., Inc. (R), MA, *210*
Trebor Weldon Lawrence, Inc. (R), NY, *210*
Tschudin Inc. (R), NJ, *211*
TSI Group/TSI Staffing Services (C), ON, *610*
TTG/Sterling Services (C), CA, *610*
U.S. Search (C), VA, *610*
The Ultimate Source (R), CA, *212*
United Personnel Services (C), MA, *611*
VanReypen Enterprises, Ltd. (R), NY, *213*
Vaughan & Co. (C), CA, *612*
Venpro Consulting Inc. (C), ON, *612*
Vento Assoc. (C), TN, *612*
Venture Resources, Inc. (R), CA, *213*
C. J. Vincent Assoc., LLC (C), MD, *612*
Vincenty & Co. (C), OH, *612*
The Viscusi Group, Inc. (R), NY, *214*
VZ Int'l., Inc. (C), AZ, *613*
W. P. Assoc. (C), CA, *613*
Wachendorfer & Assoc. (C), TX, *613*
Gordon Wahls Executive Search (C), PA, *613*
Kelly Walker Assoc. (C), TX, *614*
Walker Group, Inc. (R), MN, *215*
K. K. Walker Professional Recruitment (C), CA, *614*
B. D. Wallace & Assoc. (C), MD, *614*
Wallace Assoc. (C), MA, *614*
J. D. Walsh & Co. (R), CT, *215*
Ward Assoc. (C), ON, *615*
Martha Ward Executive Search, Inc. (C), NY, *615*
C. D. Warner & Assoc. (C), PA, *615*
Wasserman Assoc. Inc. (C), MD, *616*
Watring & Assoc., Inc. (C), IL, *616*
Wayne Assoc., Inc. (C), VA, *616*
S. B. Webster & Associates (R), MA, *217*
David Weinfeld Group (C), NC, *617*
Henry Welker & Assoc. (C), MI, *618*
The Wellesley Group, Inc. (R), IL, *217*
Wells, Bradley & Assoc., Inc. (C), MN, *618*
R. A. Wells Co. (C), GA, *618*
West & Assoc. (C), IL, *618*
The Whitney Group (C), GA, *620*
Whittaker & Assoc., Inc. (C), GA, *620*
The Whyte Group, Inc. (R), MD, *220*
The Wilkie Group Int'l. (R), ON, *220*
Williams & Delmore, Inc. (C), NC, *621*
N. Willner & Co., Inc. (R), NJ, *221*
Wilson-Douglas-Jordan (C), IL, *622*
Windsor Consultants, Inc. (C), TX, *622*
Winfield Assoc., Inc. (C), MA, *623*
Wing Tips & Pumps, Inc. (C), MI, *623*
Winston Search, Inc. (R), MD, *222*
Winter, Wyman & Co. (C), MA, *623*
WMD inc. (C), NJ, *623*
S. R. Wolman Assoc., Inc. (R), NY, *224*
Worlco Computer Resources, Inc. (C), PA, *624*
World Search (C), OH, *625*
The Worth Group (C), GA, *625*
Jay Wren & Assoc. (C), CA, *625*
Bob Wright Recruiting, Inc. (C), CT, *625*
Yankee Hospitality Search (C), CT, *626*
Yelverton Executive Search (R), CA, *226*
The York Group (C), CA, *626*
The Yorkshire Group, Ltd. (C), MA, *626*
Youngblood Assoc. (C), NC, *626*
Yungner & Bormann (R), MN, *226*
Michael D. Zinn & Assoc., Inc. (R), NJ, *227*

05.5 Direct mail, marketing, telemarketing

A C Personnel Services, Inc. (C), OK, *231*
Affinity Executive Search (C), FL, *241*
Affordable Executive Recruiters (C), CA, *241*
AKH Executive Search (C), OR, *243*
Alexander & Co. (C), CA, *243*
Allard Associates (C), CA, *244*
Amato & Associates Insurance Recruiters (C), PA, *247*
American Heritage Group, Inc. (C), MI, *247*
Analytic Recruiting, Inc. (C), NY, *249*
The Argus Group Corp. (C), ON, *252*
Ariel Recruitment Assoc. (R), NY, *7*
Ashford Management Group, Inc. (R), GA, *7*
Association for Sales Force Management (C), WA, *254*
Atlantic Pacific Group (C), CA, *255*
Austin Group Int'l./Marlar Int'l. (R), TX, *9*
Austin, Hill & Assoc. (C), MD, *256*
Barger & Sargeant, Inc. (R), NH, *11*
Bast & Assoc., Inc. (C), CA, *261*
The Beam Group (R), PA, *14*
Richard L. Bencin & Assoc. (C), OH, *264*
Bender Executive Search Management Consulting (R), NY, *16*
Benson Associates (C), NY, *264*
Bernhart Assoc. (C), MN, *265*
Bialla & Assoc. Inc. (R), CA, *17*
Bonell Ryan Inc. (R), NY, *19*
Bosch & Assoc., LLC (R), CT, *19*
Boyden (R), NY, *20*
Jerold Braun & Assoc. (C), CA, *272*
The Brentwood Group, Inc. (R), NJ, *22*
Bright Search/Professional Staffing (C), MN, *274*
Brown, Bernardy, Van Remmen, Inc. (C), CA, *275*
Brownstone Sales & Marketing Group, Inc. (C), NY, *275*
Canny, Bowen Inc. (R), NY, *27*
Caprio & Assoc. Inc. (R), IL, *29*
Career Consulting Group, Inc. (C), CT, *281*
Careers On Track (C), NJ, *283*
Carpenter Assoc., Inc. (R), IL, *30*
Caruthers & Co., L.L.C. (R), CT, *31*
Cassell & Kaye (C), NY, *286*
Chaloner Assoc. (R), MA, *32*
William J. Christopher Assoc., Inc. (R), PA, *34*
J. F. Church Associates (C), WA, *291*
CJSI-Cindy Jackson Search Int'l. (C), CA, *291*

Conway & Assoc. (R), IL, *40*
Corporate Dynamix (C), AZ, *300*
Trudi Cowlan (C), NY, *302*
The Crawford Group (C), GA, *303*
Culver Personnel Services (C), CA, *304*
Cyr Associates, Inc. (C), MA, *306*
Thorndike Deland Assoc. LLC (R), NY, *48*
Desktop Staffing, Inc. (C), IL, *311*
Devoto & Assoc. (C), CA, *312*
Roger Dietsch & Assoc. (C), MN, *312*
Direct Marketing Resources (C), NC, *312*
Direct Marketing Solutions (C), KY, *312*
Diversified Search, Inc. (R), PA, *52*
DLB Assoc. (R), NY, *53*
Dotson & Assoc. (R), NY, *54*
Dunhill Personnel of Northeast Tulsa, Inc. (C), OK, *322*
Eastbourne Assoc. Inc. (R), NY, *56*
The Ellsworth Group (C), NY, *329*
The Enfield Company (C), TX, *330*
Engineering & Scientific Search Assoc. (ESSA) (C), NJ, *330*
Executive Careers (R), CA, *62*
Executive Exchange Corp. (C), NJ, *333*
Executive Sales Search (C), CO, *335*
Fabian Assoc. Inc. (C), NY, *338*
Fenwick Partners (R), MA, *66*
First Union Executive Search (R), NC, *67*
Fisher-Todd Assoc. (C), NY, *341*
FitzGibbon & Assoc. (R), PA, *68*
Ford & Ford (C), MA, *343*
Foster Partners (R), NY, *70*
Fristoe & Carleton, Inc. (C), OH, *353*
Gahan Assoc. (R), NY, *73*
Gardner-Ross Assoc., Inc. (R), NY, *74*
Gilbert Tweed Assoc. Inc. (R), NY, *76*
Global Telecommunications, Inc. (C), TX, *359*
Alexander Graham Assoc. (C), NJ, *361*
The Grant Search Group, Inc. (C), ON, *361*
Graphic Arts Marketing Assoc., Inc. (C), MI, *361*
Greene Personnel Consultants (C), RI, *362*
Greenhaven & Assoc., Inc. (R), NY, *81*
Groupe PCA Inc. (C), QE, *363*
David E. Grumney Co. Inc. (R), WA, *83*
Nadine Guber & Assoc., Inc. (C), NY, *364*
Gumbinner/Haubenstock, Inc. (C), NY, *364*
Gundersen Partners, L.L.C. (R), NY, *83*
Haddad Assoc. (R), FL, *84*
Hamilton & Co. (C), OH, *367*
Janet Harberth & Assoc., Inc. (C), GA, *368*
Harris Heery & Assoc., Inc. (R), CT, *87*
Hart & Co. (C), NY, *370*
Hazlett Associates (R), IL, *88*
Healthcare Recruiters of New England (C), MA, *373*
F. P. Healy & Co., Inc. (R), NY, *89*
Kay Henry, Inc. (C), PA, *376*
J. D. Hersey & Assoc. (C), OH, *376*
E. A. Hughes & Co., Inc. (R), NY, *98*
Human Resource Dimensions, Inc. (C), TX, *384*
Hunter, Rowan & Crowe (C), FL, *386*
Insight Consulting Co. (C), NY, *389*
International Business Partners (C), ON, *392*
International Recruiting Services (C), FL, *393*
InterNeed (C), TX, *394*
Interspace Interactive, Inc. (C), NY, *394*
J. Nicholas Arthur (R), MA, *104*
Johnson & Company (R), CT, *107*
Johnson, Kemper & Assoc. (C), TX, *400*
The Jonathan Stevens Group, Inc. (R), NJ, *108*
Julian Assoc., Inc. (C), CT, *401*
The Kay Group of 5th Ave. (C), NY, *404*
A.T. Kearney Executive Search (R), IL, *111*
The Keith-Murray Partnership (R), ON, *112*
Kelley & Keller, Inc. (C), FL, *405*
Kent & Assoc. (R), OH, *113*
Kenzer Corp. (R), NY, *113*
King ComputerSearch, Inc. (C), TX, *407*
Kingsbury • Wax • Bova (R), MA, *114*
KM Associates (C), MA, *407*
Kordus Consulting Group (C), WI, *408*
Kresin Wingard (C), IL, *409*
Lawrence L. Lapham, Inc. (R), NY, *124*
Ricci Lee Assoc., Inc. (C), CA, *415*
Hal Levy & Assoc. (C), NY, *417*
Louis Search Group, Inc. (C), NJ, *420*
Lyons & Assoc., Inc. (C), IL, *422*
M/J/A Partners (R), IL, *133*
Madison MacArthur Inc. (R), ON, *133*
Management One Consultants (C), ON, *425*
Management Recruiters of Northern Palm Beaches (C), FL, *444*
Management Recruiters of Gramercy, Inc. (C), NY, *455*
Management Recruiters of Manhattan on Broadway (C), NY, *455*
Management Recruiters of Northwest Ohio, Inc. (C), OH, *458*
Mangieri/Solutions LLC (C), CT, *468*
Marketing Search Inc. (C), OH, *471*
MarketPro, Inc. (C), GA, *471*
The Marlow Group (R), MA, *136*
The McKinnon Management Group Inc. (C), ON, *475*
Media Recruiting Group, Inc. (C), NY, *476*
Mengel & McDonald Ltd. (C), IL, *479*
Merlin Int'l. Inc. (C), NJ, *479*
Milo Research (R), NY, *145*
Milrod Assoc. (C), NJ, *482*
Herbert Mines Assoc., Inc. (R), NY, *145*
Laurie Mitchell & Co., Inc. (R), OH, *145*
C. A. Moore & Assoc., Inc. (C), MN, *484*
Thomas R. Moore Executive Search (R), TX, *146*
Morency Assoc. (C), MA, *485*
NDB Assoc., Inc. (C), PA, *491*
Noble & Assoc., Inc. (C), NY, *494*
Nordeman Grimm, Inc. (R), NY, *152*
Norman Broadbent Int'l., Inc. (R), NY, *152*
NPS of Atlanta, Inc. (C), GA, *496*
The Ogdon Partnership (R), NY, *155*
Opalka Dixon Consultants to Management (R), VA, *156*
R. Parker & Assoc., Inc. (R), NY, *159*
Largent Parks & Partners (C), TX, *503*
Partners Executive Search Consultants Inc. (R), ON, *160*
Pearce & Assoc. (C), FL, *506*
Perez & Assoc. (C), MI, *507*
Perry • Newton Assoc. (C), MD, *507*
Personnel Assoc. (C), CA, *508*
The Pinnacle Source, Inc. (C), CO, *512*
PLA, Inc. (C), NJ, *513*
Placements by Jesse Reid Assoc., Inc. (C), NY, *513*
Princeton Search Partners, Inc. (R), NJ, *169*
The Professional Sales Search Co., Inc. (C), WA, *522*
ProSearch Recruiting (C), CA, *524*
ProSearch, Inc. (C), ME, *524*
Rand Thompson Executive Search Consultants (C), NY, *528*
Recruiting Options, Inc. (C), GA, *531*
Redden & McGrath Assoc., Inc. (R), NY, *173*
Reeve & Assoc. (C), CT, *533*
The Resource Group (R), CT, *175*
Russell Reynolds Assoc., Inc. (R), NY, *176*
Rice Cohen Int'l. (R), PA, *178*
Ridenour & Assoc. (R), IL, *178*
Rodgers, Ramsey, Inc. (C), TX, *540*
Ryan-Allen & Assoc., Inc. (C), CA, *549*
Ryman, Bell, Green & Michaels, Inc. (C), TX, *549*
S.C.S. & Assoc. (C), NC, *550*
Sales & Marketing Search, Inc. (C), MA, *551*
Sales Builders, Inc. (R), VA, *183*
Sales Consultants of Savannah, GA (C), GA, *557*
Sales Consultants of Boca Raton, Inc. (C), FL, *557*
Sales Consultants of Indianapolis (C), IN, *558*
Sales Consultants (C), IL, *558*
Sales Consultants - Bristol County (C), MA, *559*
Sales Consultants of Wellesley, Inc. (C), MA, *559*
Sales Consultants of Nashua-Manchester (C), NH, *560*
Sales Consultants of Morris County, Inc. (C), NJ, *561*
Sales Consultants of Chester County, PA (C), PA, *562*
Sales Consultants of Madison (C), WI, *563*
Sales Consultants of Milwaukee (C), WI, *563*
Sales Consultants of Appleton (C), WI, *563*
A. N. Salloway Executive Search & Consulting, L.L.C. (C), MA, *564*
Salzmann Gay Assoc., Inc. (R), PA, *184*
Sanford Rose Assoc. - Fairhope (C), AL, *565*
Sanford Rose Assoc. - Evansville (C), IN, *567*
Sanford Rose Assoc. - Lake St. Louis (C), MO, *568*
Sanford Rose Assoc. - Pittsburgh North (C), PA, *570*
F. B. Schmidt Int'l. (R), CA, *185*
Schweichler Assoc., Inc. (R), CA, *186*
Search Assoc., Inc. (C), CA, *574*
Search Innovations, Inc. (R), PA, *187*
SearchCom, Inc. (R), TX, *187*
Sedlar & Miners (R), NY, *188*
Shifrin-Fischer Group, Inc. (C), NJ, *580*
Peter Siegel & Co. (C), MA, *581*
Simpson Associates (C), NY, *582*

Smith Hanley Assoc., Inc. (C), NY, *584*
Phyllis Solomon Executive Search, Inc. (C), NJ, *587*
Stephen M. Sonis Assoc. (R), MA, *195*
SpencerStuart (R), NY, *196*
Stafford Consulting Group (R), CA, *198*
StaffWriters Plus (C), NY, *591*
Stentiford & Berardi Assoc. Ltd. (R), NY, *199*
Stevens Assoc. (C), MA, *593*
Stone & Youngblood (C), MA, *594*
Strauss Personnel Service (C), PA, *596*
Synergy Systems (C), ON, *598*
TechNix Inc. (C), ON, *602*
Tele-Media Int'l. Inc. (C), PA, *604*
TeleManagement Search (C), NY, *605*
Tesar-Reynes, Inc. (R), IL, *208*
Thomas Resource Group (R), CA, *209*
The Touchstone Group (C), MA, *607*
Trebor Weldon Lawrence, Inc. (R), NY, *210*
Peter Van Leer & Assoc. (R), MN, *213*
VanReypen Enterprises, Ltd. (R), NY, *213*
Venpro Consulting Inc. (C), ON, *612*
Vintage Resources, Inc. (C), NY, *613*
Beverly von Winckler & Assoc. (C), IL, *613*
Gordon Wahls Executive Search (C), PA, *613*
Wakefield Talabisco Int'l. (R), NY, *214*
B. D. Wallace & Assoc. (C), MD, *614*
Martha Ward Executive Search, Inc. (C), NY, *615*
The Ward Group (R), MA, *215*
Ward Liebelt Assoc. Inc. (R), CT, *215*
C. Weiss Assoc., Inc. (C), NY, *618*
Werbin Assoc. Executive Search, Inc. (C), NY, *618*
Wheelless Group (R), IL, *219*
Louise Wood & Assoc. (C), NY, *624*
Bob Wright Recruiting, Inc. (C), CT, *625*
R. S. Wyatt Assoc., Inc. (R), TX, *225*
Zaccaria Int'l. (C), NJ, *627*

05.6 Customer service

ACSYS Resources, Inc. (C), DE, *238*
ADR Accounting Management Recruiters (C), ON, *240*
Amato & Associates Insurance Recruiters (C), PA, *247*
Aminex Corp. (C), MA, *249*
APA Employment Agency Inc. (C), OR, *251*
Association for Sales Force Management (C), WA, *254*
Richard L. Bencin & Assoc. (C), OH, *264*
Dick Berg & Assoc. (C), CA, *264*
Bonell Ryan Inc. (R), NY, *19*
Jerold Braun & Assoc. (C), CA, *272*
Britt Assoc., Inc. (C), IL, *274*
J. B. Brown & Assoc., Inc. (C), OH, *275*
C.T.E.W. Executive Personnel Services Inc. (C), BC, *278*
Campbell, Edgar Inc. (C), BC, *280*
Career Marketing Consultants, Inc. (C), GA, *282*
Career Strategies, Inc. (C), CA, *283*
Caruthers & Co., L.L.C. (R), CT, *31*
CAS Comsearch Inc. (C), NY, *285*
J. F. Church Associates (C), WA, *291*
CJSI-Cindy Jackson Search Int'l. (C), CA, *291*
Coe & Co. Int'l. Inc./EMA Partners Int'l. (R), AB, *37*
M. L. Conner (C), FL, *296*
Daggett & Kvistad (R), CA, *45*
Direct Marketing Solutions (C), KY, *312*
Diversified Search, Inc. (R), PA, *52*
Dougherty & Assoc. (C), TN, *314*
Dunhill Executive Search of Los Angeles, Inc. (C), CA, *319*
Dunhill Personnel of Northeast Tulsa, Inc. (C), OK, *322*
Eagle Search Assoc. (C), CA, *325*
Eastbourne Assoc. Inc. (R), NY, *56*
W. Robert Eissler & Assoc., Inc. (C), TX, *327*
The Ellsworth Group (C), NY, *329*
Empowered Solutions Corp. (C), GA, *330*
Executive Search Int'l. (C), TX, *335*
Fenwick Partners (R), MA, *66*
FitzGibbon & Assoc. (R), PA, *68*
Foster Partners (R), NY, *70*
The Fourbes Group, Inc. (C), NJ, *351*
Gerald Frisch Assoc., Inc. (R), NY, *72*
Global Telecommunications, Inc. (C), TX, *359*
Gowdy Consultants (C), TX, *361*
Graphic Search Assoc. Inc. (C), PA, *362*
Harbrowe, Inc. (C), NY, *368*
Human Resource Dimensions, Inc. (C), TX, *384*
Joan Isbister Consultants (C), NY, *394*
The J. B. Search Group (C), CA, *395*
K. Jaeger & Assoc. (C), MA, *396*
JDC Assoc. (C), NY, *397*
JSG Group Management Consultants (R), ON, *109*
A.T. Kearney Executive Search (R), IL, *111*
Kenzer Corp. (R), NY, *113*
Kiley, Owen & McGovern, Inc. (R), NJ, *114*
Kutt, Inc. (C), CO, *410*
Landon Morgan (C), ON, *412*
Legal Network Inc. (C), CA, *416*
Lineal Recruiting Services (C), CT, *418*
Lipsky Group, Inc. (R), CA, *129*
Logistics Management Resources, Inc. (R), NY, *131*
Louis Search Group, Inc. (C), NJ, *420*
Ludwig & Assoc., Inc. (C), VA, *421*
Carol Maden Group (C), VA, *422*
Madison MacArthur Inc. (R), ON, *133*
Managed Care Resources (C), TX, *424*
Management Recruiters of St. Lucie County, Inc. (C), FL, *444*
Management Recruiters-Cedar Rapids, Inc. (C), IA, *448*
Management Recruiters of Detroit & Farmington Hills (C), MI, *451*
Management Recruiters of Gramercy, Inc. (C), NY, *455*
Management Recruiters of Franklin, Inc. (C), TN, *461*
Management Recruiters of San Antonio - North (C), TX, *463*
Management Recruiters - Piedmont (C), VA, *464*
Mangieri/Solutions LLC (C), CT, *468*
The Marathon Group (C), FL, *469*
MarketPro, Inc. (C), GA, *471*
The Moran Group (C), IL, *484*
NPS of Atlanta, Inc. (C), GA, *496*
O'Sullivan Search Inc. (C), ON, *498*
Paul-Tittle Assoc., Inc. (R), VA, *161*
Paules Associates (C), CA, *505*
Pearce & Assoc. (C), FL, *506*
The Pennmor Group (C), NJ, *506*
Phoenix Partners, Inc. (C), GA, *511*
Plante & Moran, LLP (R), MI, *165*
Ray Polhill & Assoc. (R), NC, *166*
ProFinders, Inc. (C), FL, *523*
Protocol Inc. (C), CA, *525*
Quirk-Corporon & Assoc., Inc. (C), WI, *527*
Lea Randolph & Assoc., Inc. (C), TX, *529*
J. E. Ranta Assoc. (C), MA, *529*
Harold L. Rapp Assoc. (C), NY, *529*
Redden & McGrath Assoc., Inc. (R), NY, *173*
The Resource Group (R), CT, *175*
Russell Reynolds Assoc., Inc. (R), NY, *176*
Rollins & Assoc. (C), CA, *541*
S.C.S. & Assoc. (C), NC, *550*
Sales & Marketing Search, Inc. (C), MA, *551*
Sales Builders, Inc. (R), VA, *183*
Sales Consultants of Savannah, GA (C), GA, *557*
Sales Consultants of Boca Raton, Inc. (C), FL, *557*
Sales Consultants of Indianapolis (C), IN, *558*
Sales Consultants of Wellesley, Inc. (C), MA, *559*
Sales Consultants of Nashua-Manchester (C), NH, *560*
Sales Consultants of Cherry Hill (C), NJ, *560*
Sales Consultants Bridgewater, Inc. (C), NJ, *560*
Sales Consultants of Cincinnati (C), OH, *561*
Sales Consultants of Morris County, Inc. (C), NJ, *561*
Sales Consultants of Newtown, Inc. (C), PA, *562*
Sales Consultants of Chester County, PA (C), PA, *562*
Sales Consultants of Rhode Island, Inc. (C), RI, *562*
Sales Consultants of Milwaukee (C), WI, *563*
Sales Consultants of Dallas (C), TX, *563*
Sales Consultants of Appleton (C), WI, *563*
Sales Search Specialist (C), IL, *564*
Sales Solutions (C), CA, *564*
A. N. Salloway Executive Search & Consulting, L.L.C. (C), MA, *564*
Sanford Rose Assoc. - Springfield (C), MO, *568*
Schweichler Assoc., Inc. (R), CA, *186*
The Search Group (C), MD, *575*
SKB Enterprises (C), NY, *582*
SpencerSearch, Inc. (C), CO, *589*

SpencerStuart (R), NY, *196*
The Spiegel Group (R), MA, *197*
Sprout/Standish, Inc. (C), NH, *589*
DM Stone Personnel Services (C), CA, *594*
Swift & Assoc. (C), ME, *597*
Tele-Media Int'l. Inc. (C), PA, *604*
Telecom Executive Group (C), NJ, *605*
Telecom Recruiters, Inc. (C), VA, *605*
TeleManagement Search (C), NY, *605*
Thor, Inc. (C), CA, *606*
The Touchstone Group (C), MA, *607*
The Truman Agency (C), CA, *610*
TSI Group/TSI Staffing Services (C), ON, *610*
United Personnel Services (C), MA, *611*
Gordon Wahls Executive Search (C), PA, *613*
B. D. Wallace & Assoc. (C), MD, *614*
Wilcoxen, Blackwell, Niven & Assoc. (R), FL, *220*
Wilson McLeran, Inc. (C), CT, *622*
Youngblood Assoc. (C), NC, *626*

05.7 Public relations

AKH Executive Search (C), OR, *243*
Alexander & Co. (C), CA, *243*
Ask Guy Tucker (C), GA, *254*
Association for Sales Force Management (C), WA, *254*
Carol Ball & Co. (C), CT, *258*
Barnes & Assoc. Executive Search (C), CA, *259*
Bast & Assoc., Inc. (C), CA, *261*
Battalia Winston Int'l./The Euram Consultants Group (R), NY, *13*
Berkhemer/Clayton, Inc. (R), CA, *16*
Bosch & Assoc., LLC (R), CT, *19*
Boyden (R), NY, *20*
Canny, Bowen Inc. (R), NY, *27*
The Cantor Concern, Inc. (R), NY, *28*
Cardwell Enterprises Inc. (R), IL, *29*
Caruthers & Co., L.L.C. (R), CT, *31*
Caywood Partners, Ltd. (R), CA, *32*
Chaloner Assoc. (R), MA, *32*
Charet & Assoc. (C), NJ, *289*
Churchill & Affiliates, Inc. (R), PA, *35*
Toby Clark Assoc. Inc. (C), NY, *292*
Clayman & Co. (R), MA, *36*
Consulpro (R), ON, *39*
Leonard Corwen Assoc. (C), NY, *302*
Judith Cushman & Assoc. (R), WA, *44*
Bert Davis Executive Search, Inc. (R), NY, *47*
DCA Professional Search (C), TX, *309*
Desktop Staffing, Inc. (C), IL, *311*
J. Dinerstein & Co., Inc. (R), NY, *51*
Diversified Search, Inc. (R), PA, *52*
DLB Assoc. (R), NY, *53*
The Ellsworth Group (C), NY, *329*
The Evans Search Group (R), CT, *61*
Fenwick Partners (R), MA, *66*
Jerry Fields Assoc. (C), NY, *340*
Flesher & Assoc., Inc. (R), CA, *68*
Fortune of Arlington Heights (C), IL, *345*
Foster Partners (R), NY, *70*
Neil Frank & Co. (R), CA, *71*
Gerald Frisch Assoc., Inc. (R), NY, *72*
Fristoe & Carleton, Inc. (C), OH, *353*
The Fry Group, Inc. (C), NY, *353*
Glou Int'l., Inc. (R), MA, *78*
The Goldman Group Inc. (R), NY, *79*
Goldman+Bell, LLC (C), NY, *360*
Goodwin & Co. (R), DC, *80*
Graphic Arts Marketing Assoc., Inc. (C), MI, *361*
Greene Personnel Consultants (C), RI, *362*
Susan Hall Executive Search (C), TX, *366*
Hamilton & Co. (C), OH, *367*
Handy HRM (R), NY, *86*
Janet Harberth & Assoc., Inc. (C), GA, *368*
Kay Henry, Inc. (C), PA, *376*
Heyman Assoc., Inc. (R), NY, *93*
Hill & Assoc. (C), CA, *378*
Fred Hood & Assoc. (C), CA, *380*
Howard-Sloan Assoc. (C), NY, *381*
The Howard-Sloan-Koller Group (R), NY, *97*
Arnold Huberman Assoc., Inc. (R), NY, *97*
The Hyde Group, Inc. (R), CT, *101*
Innovative Partnerships (R), CA, *101*
Insight Consulting Co. (C), NY, *389*
Integrity Search, Inc. (R), PA, *102*
Intelligent Marketing Solutions, Inc. (C), NY, *390*
InterNeed (C), TX, *394*
Isaacson, Miller (R), MA, *104*
Ives & Associates, Inc. (C), OH, *395*
Julian Assoc., Inc. (C), CT, *401*
Karel & Co. (R), CA, *109*
A.T. Kearney Executive Search (R), IL, *111*
The Keith-Murray Partnership (R), ON, *112*
Kenzer Corp. (R), NY, *113*
Richard Kinser & Assoc. (R), NY, *115*
Kittleman & Assoc.,LLC (R), IL, *115*
Kordus Consulting Group (C), WI, *408*
Ricci Lee Assoc., Inc. (C), CA, *415*
Michael Levine Search Consultants (R), NY, *129*
Louis Search Group, Inc. (C), NJ, *420*
Carol Maden Group (C), VA, *422*
Madison MacArthur Inc. (R), ON, *133*
Management Recruiters of Northern Palm Beaches (C), FL, *444*
Management Recruiters of Gramercy, Inc. (C), NY, *455*
MarketPro, Inc. (C), GA, *471*
Marshall Consultants, Inc. (R), NY, *137*
MB Inc. Executive Search (C), NY, *473*
McBride Assoc., Inc. (R), DC, *139*
Meads & Assoc. (R), FL, *142*
Media Recruiting Group, Inc. (C), NY, *476*
Herbert Mines Assoc., Inc. (R), NY, *145*
Laurie Mitchell & Co., Inc. (R), OH, *145*
Tina Morbitzer & Assoc. (C), FL, *485*
Moyer, Sherwood Assoc., Inc. (R), NY, *148*
NDB Assoc., Inc. (C), PA, *491*
Nino Recruiting & Staffing, Inc. (C), TX, *493*
Nordeman Grimm, Inc. (R), NY, *152*
Norman Broadbent Int'l., Inc. (R), NY, *152*
The Oxford Group (C), TX, *500*
Janou Pakter, Inc. (C), NY, *502*
Pamenter, Pamenter, Brezer & Deganis Ltd. (R), ON, *159*
Carolyn Smith Paschal Int'l. (R), CA, *160*
Perez & Assoc. (C), MI, *507*
Perry-Martel Int'l., Inc. (R), ON, *163*
PLA, Inc. (C), NJ, *513*
Rene Plessner Assoc., Inc. (R), NY, *165*
Prestonwood Assoc. (R), MA, *168*
ProFinders, Inc. (C), FL, *523*
Recruiting Options, Inc. (C), GA, *531*
Mary Rector & Assoc., Inc. (C), IL, *533*
The Repovich-Reynolds Group (TRRG, Inc.) (R), CA, *175*
Russell Reynolds Assoc., Inc. (R), NY, *176*
Richards Assoc., Inc. (R), NY, *178*
RJN Consulting (R), NY, *179*
Rojek Marketing Group, Inc. (R), OH, *181*
Romano McAvoy Assoc., Inc. (C), NY, *544*
K. Russo Assoc. Inc. (C), CT, *548*
Sales & Marketing Search, Inc. (C), MA, *551*
Sales Consultants of Boca Raton, Inc. (C), FL, *557*
Sales Consultants of Indianapolis (C), IN, *558*
Sales Consultants of Morris County, Inc. (C), NJ, *561*
Sales Consultants of Chester County, PA (C), PA, *562*
Sanford Rose Assoc. - Evansville (C), IN, *567*
The Search Company (R), ON, *186*
SearchCom, Inc. (R), TX, *187*
Phyllis Solomon Executive Search, Inc. (C), NJ, *587*
SpencerStuart (R), NY, *196*
Sports Group Int'l. (R), NC, *198*
StaffWriters Plus (C), NY, *591*
Stevens Assoc. (C), MA, *593*
Stone & Youngblood (C), MA, *594*
Synergy Systems (C), ON, *598*
TechNix Inc. (C), ON, *602*
Tesar-Reynes, Inc. (R), IL, *208*
The Touchstone Group (C), MA, *607*
Travaille Executive Search (R), DC, *210*
Beverly von Winckler & Assoc. (C), IL, *613*
The Ward Group (R), MA, *215*
Wesley Brown & Bartle Co., Inc. (R), NY, *218*
Wheelless Group (R), IL, *219*
Wills Consulting Assoc. Inc. (R), CT, *221*
The York Group (C), CA, *626*

06.0 Human resource management

The 500 Granary Inc. (C), ON, *231*
A Permanent Success Employment Services (C), CA, *231*
A. D. & Assoc. Executive Search, Inc. (C), GA, *231*
Abbott Associates (R), CA, *1*
The Abbott Group, Inc. (R), MD, *1*
Abécassis Conseil (R), QE, *1*
Abeln, Magy & Assoc., Inc. (R), MN, *1*
B. J. Abrams & Assoc. Inc. (C), IL, *233*
Accelerated Data Decision, Inc. (C), NJ, *233*

Access Assoc. Inc. (C), MD, *233*
Access/Resources, Inc. (C), MA, *234*
Accounting Personnel & Engineering Personnel Consultants (C), LA, *238*
ACSYS Resources, Inc. (C), DE, *238*
Action Management Corp. (C), MI, *239*
Adirect Recruiting Corp. (C), ON, *240*
Advantage Partners, Inc. (R), OH, *2*
Affordable Executive Recruiters (C), CA, *241*
Aggressive Corporation (C), IL, *242*
Agri-Personnel (C), GA, *242*
Ahrensdorf & Assoc. (R), PA, *2*
J. R. Akin & Co. (R), MA, *2*
The Alexander Group (R), TX, *3*
Alexander Ross & Co. (R), NY, *3*
The Alfus Group (R), NY, *3*
Frank E. Allen & Assoc. (C), NJ, *244*
D. S. Allen Assoc. (C), NJ, *244*
Allen Austin Lowe & Powers (R), TX, *3*
Allerton Heneghan & O'Neill (R), IL, *4*
Alliance Executive Search, Inc. (R), MA, *4*
Allied Search, Inc. (C), CA, *245*
Tom Allison Assoc. (C), NM, *245*
Alpha Resource Group, Inc. (C), TX, *246*
Altec/HRC (C), MI, *246*
ALW Research Int'l. (R), NJ, *4*
American Executive Management, Inc. (R), MA, *5*
American Heritage Group, Inc. (C), MI, *247*
American Resources Corp. (C), IL, *248*
AmeriResource Group Inc. (C), OK, *248*
Aminex Corp. (C), MA, *249*
AMS Int'l. (R), VA, *5*
Anderson Bradshaw Assoc., Inc. (R), TX, *6*
Anderson Network Group (C), OH, *250*
Andre David & Assoc., Inc. (R), TX, *6*
The Andre Group, Inc. (R), PA, *6*
Angel Group Int'l. (C), KY, *250*
Tryg R. Angell, Ltd. (C), CT, *250*
The Angus Group, Ltd. (C), OH, *251*
APA Employment Agency Inc. (C), OR, *251*
David Aplin & Assoc. (C), AB, *251*
R. W. Apple & Assoc. (C), NJ, *251*
Applied Resources, Inc. (C), MN, *252*
Charles P. Aquavella & Assoc. (C), TX, *252*
Argonaut Partners, LLC (R), CA, *6*
Ariel Recruitment Assoc. (R), NY, *7*
Armor Personnel (C), ON, *253*
A. Artze Assoc.-Personnel Consultants (C), PR, *253*
The Ascher Group (R), NJ, *7*
Ashford Management Group, Inc. (R), GA, *7*
Ashlar-Stone Management Consultants Inc. (R), ON, *8*
Ashworth Consultants, Inc. (R), MA, *8*
W. R. Atchison & Assoc., Inc. (C), NC, *254*
Atlantic Pacific Group (C), CA, *255*
Aurora Tech Search (C), ON, *256*
A. M. Auster Associates (R), FL, *9*
Austin - Allen Co. (C), TN, *256*
Austin Park Management Group Inc. (C), ON, *256*
Austin, Hill & Assoc. (C), MD, *256*
Avery Assoc. (R), CA, *9*
The Ayers Group, Inc. (R), NY, *9*
The Baer Group (R), OH, *10*
Baker Scott & Co. (C), NJ, *258*
Baldwin & Assoc. (C), OH, *258*
James Bangert & Assoc., Inc. (R), MN, *11*
Barnes Development Group, LLC (R), WI, *11*
Barrett Hospitality Search (R), CA, *12*
Aldonna Barry Personnel & Management (C), ON, *260*
Barton Assoc., Inc. (R), TX, *12*
Bason Associates (R), OH, *13*
Battalia Winston Int'l./The Euram Consultants Group (R), NY, *13*
Martin H. Bauman Assoc., Inc. (R), NY, *13*
BayResearch Group, Inc. (R), IL, *14*
Beach Executive Search Inc. (R), FL, *14*
Becker, Norton & Co. (R), PA, *14*
Becker Personnel (C), FL, *262*
Becker Project Resources, Inc. (C), OR, *262*
The Bedford Consulting Group Inc. (R), ON, *14*
Behavioral Science Assoc., Inc. (R), AZ, *15*
Joy Reed Belt Search Consultants, Inc. (R), OK, *15*
Benford & Assoc., Inc. (C), MI, *264*
N. L. Benke & Assoc., Inc. (C), OH, *264*
Bennett & Associates (C), TX, *264*
Bennett & Co. Consulting Group (C), CA, *264*
Benson Associates (C), NY, *264*
C. Berger And Company (R), IL, *16*
BG & Assoc. (C), MD, *266*
BGB Assoc., Inc. (C), IL, *266*
Binder Hospitality Group (C), KY, *266*
BioPharmMed (C), FL, *267*
Bishop Partners (R), NY, *17*
The Black Leopard (C), CA, *267*
BLB Consulting (C), NY, *268*
David Blevins & Assoc. (C), WA, *268*
Boettcher Assoc. (R), WI, *19*
Tom Bogle & Assoc. (C), CA, *269*
Bonnell Assoc. Ltd. (R), CT, *19*
Boone-Scaturro Assoc., Inc. (C), GA, *269*
Bor-Maq Assoc. (C), TX, *269*
Bosch & Assoc., LLC (R), CT, *19*
Boulware & Assoc. Inc. (R), IL, *20*
Bowden & Co., Inc. (R), OH, *20*
Boyden (R), NY, *20*
Boyle/Ogata Executive Search (R), CA, *21*
The Bradbury Management Group, Inc. (R), CA, *21*
Bradford Executives Int'l. (C), VA, *271*
The Brand Co., Inc. (R), FL, *22*
Brandt Associates (C), PA, *272*
Brandywine Management Group (R), MD, *22*
Brandywine Retained Ventures, Inc. (R), CT, *22*
Branthover Assoc. (C), NY, *272*
Jerold Braun & Assoc. (C), CA, *272*
The Brentwood Group, Inc. (R), NJ, *22*
Brentwood Int'l. (R), CA, *23*
The Bridge (C), CO, *273*
BridgeGate LLC (C), CA, *273*
Brigade, Inc. (R), CA, *23*
Brindisi Search (R), MD, *23*
Brissenden, McFarland, Fuccella & Reynolds, Inc. (R), NJ, *23*
Bristol Assoc., Inc. (C), CA, *274*
Broadband Resource Group (C), CA, *274*
Brookman Associates (C), NY, *274*
Brush Creek Partners (R), MO, *24*
BRW Search (C), MN, *275*
Bryan, Jason & Assoc. Inc. (C), ON, *275*
Brystol Cove Assoc. (R), CA, *24*
Burke & Assoc./The Westfield Group (C), CT, *276*
The Burke Group (C), ON, *276*
Burkholder & Assoc., Inc. (C), TX, *276*
Business Solutions Worldwide, Inc. (C), NJ, *277*
The Butlers Co. Insurance Recruiters (C), FL, *277*
Butterfass, Pepe & MacCallan Inc. (R), NJ, *25*
Buzhardt Assoc. (R), MS, *25*
C & H Personnel (C), PA, *277*
C. M. Management Services, Inc. (R), KY, *26*
C. P. Consulting (R), PA, *26*
C.P.S., Inc. (C), IL, *278*
C/R Associates (C), NY, *278*
Cahill Assoc. (C), CT, *279*
Callan Assoc., Ltd. (R), IL, *27*
Cambridge Group Ltd. - Exec. Search Div. (C), CT, *279*
T. M. Campbell Co. (R), WA, *27*
CanMed Consultants Inc. (C), ON, *280*
Canny, Bowen Inc. (R), NY, *27*
Capital Consulting Group, Inc. (R), MD, *28*
The Caplan-Taylor Group (R), CA, *28*
Capstone Consulting, Inc. (R), IL, *29*
Career Advisors, Inc. (C), FL, *281*
Career Images (C), FL, *282*
Career Marketing Consultants, Inc. (C), GA, *282*
Career Strategies, Inc. (C), CA, *283*
Careerfit, Inc. (C), TX, *283*
Careers/Inc. (C), PR, *284*
Carlsen Resources, Inc. (R), CO, *29*
The Carlyle Group, Ltd. (R), IL, *30*
Carnegie Partners, Inc. (R), IL, *30*
Carpenter & Assoc. (C), TX, *284*
Carpenter, Shackleton & Company (R), IL, *30*
Carrington & Carrington, Ltd. (R), IL, *30*
Carson-Thomas & Assoc. (C), CA, *284*
Carter, Lavoie Associates (C), RI, *285*
The CARVIR Group, Inc. (C), GA, *285*
Case Executive Search (C), MI, *286*
Rosemary Cass Ltd. (R), CT, *31*
The Cassie Group (R), NJ, *31*
CCI - Career Consultants Int'l. (C), CA, *286*
Cella Assoc. (C), GA, *286*
cFour Partners (R), CA, *32*
David Chambers & Assoc., Inc. (R), CT, *32*
Chapman & Assoc. (C), BC, *289*
Charet & Assoc. (C), NJ, *289*
Chase-Gardner Executive Search Associates, Inc. (C), FL, *289*
The Chatham Group, Ltd. (C), CT, *289*
Chicago Legal Search, Ltd. (C), IL, *290*
Christenson Hutchison McDowell, LLC (R), NJ, *34*

Christopher and Long (C), MO, *291*
William J. Christopher Assoc., Inc. (R), PA, *34*
The Churchill Group (C), ON, *291*
Cizek Assoc., Inc. (R), AZ, *35*
Clarey & Andrews, Inc. (R), IL, *35*
Clarey/Napier Int'l., L.C. (R), TX, *35*
Howard Clark Assoc. (C), NJ, *292*
CMC Search Consultants (C), IL, *293*
Coe & Co. Int'l. Inc./EMA Partners Int'l. (R), AB, *37*
Cole, Warren & Long, Inc. (R), PA, *37*
J. Kevin Coleman & Assoc., Inc. (R), CA, *37*
The Colton Partnership, Inc. (R), NY, *38*
Columbia Consulting Group (R), MD, *38*
The Comwell Company, Inc. (C), NJ, *296*
Conasa de Mexico, S.C. (R), MX, *39*
Concorde Search Assoc. (C), NY, *296*
Connors, Lovell & Assoc. Inc. (C), ON, *296*
Consolidated Management Services (C), ON, *296*
The Consortium (C), NY, *296*
Consulting Rhonda (C), ON, *297*
Conway & Assoc. (R), IL, *40*
Philip Conway Management (R), IL, *40*
P. G. Cook Assoc. (R), TN, *40*
Corporate Advisors, Inc. (C), FL, *299*
The Corporate Advisory Group (R), NJ, *41*
Corporate Image Group (C), TN, *300*
Corporate Leadership Strategies, Inc. (R), NH, *41*
Corporate Plus, Ltd. (C), GA, *300*
Corporate Resources (C), OH, *301*
Corporate Search Consultants (C), IN, *301*
Corporate Search, Inc. (C), NY, *301*
Corporate Select Int'l., Ltd. (C), IL, *301*
Leonard Corwen Assoc. (C), NY, *302*
J. D. Cotter Search Inc. (C), OH, *302*
CountryHouse Hotels Executive Search (C), VA, *302*
Creative HR Solutions (C), GA, *303*
Creative Input, Inc. (C), RI, *303*
Creative-Leadership, Inc. (R), CA, *42*
The Cris Group, Inc. (R), NY, *42*
Crowder & Company (R), MI, *43*
Crowe Chizek & Co. (C), IN, *304*
The Currier-Winn Co., Inc. (C), NJ, *305*
Curry, Telleri Group, Inc. (R), NJ, *44*
Cusack Consulting (R), NY, *44*
Custom Resources (C), AL, *305*
Cyntal Int'l. Ltd. (R), NY, *44*
Cypress Int'l., Inc. (R), FL, *45*
D.A.L. Associates, Inc. (R), CT, *45*
The Dalley Hewitt Co. (R), GA, *45*
Dalton Management Consultants, Ltd. (C), NJ, *306*
Daniel Marks Company (C), OH, *306*
Dankowski & Assoc., Inc. (C), OH, *307*
DARE Personnel Inc. (C), ON, *307*
The Dartmouth Group (R), NY, *46*
Datamatics Management Services, Inc. (C), NJ, *307*
Daubenspeck & Associates, Ltd. (R), IL, *46*
Davies, Park (R), AB, *46*
Alan Davis & Assoc. Inc. (R), QE, *47*
Davis & James, Inc. (C), MO, *308*
Donna Davis Assoc. (C), NJ, *309*
Joseph A. Davis Consultants, Inc. (R), NY, *47*
The Dayton Group, Ltd. (C), NY, *309*
Dean-Dzierzawiec Assoc. (C), NJ, *309*
Dean-MacDonald (R), OH, *47*
Debbon Recruiting Group, Inc. (C), MO, *310*
Defrain Mayer (R), KS, *48*
Delta Resource Group, Ltd. (C), GA, *311*
Rob Dey Executive Search (R), FL, *49*
DieckMueller Group (R), WI, *51*
The Diestel Group (R), UT, *51*
J. Dinerstein & Co., Inc. (R), NY, *51*
Dinte Resources, Inc. (R), VA, *52*
Dise & Co. (R), OH, *52*
Diversified Health Search (R), PA, *52*
Diversified Search, Inc. (R), PA, *52*
DNA Search, Inc. (C), CA, *313*
Doherty Int'l., Inc. (R), IL, *53*
Doleman Enterprises (R), VA, *53*
Dominguez-Metz & Assoc. (R), CA, *53*
Donahue/Bales Assoc. (R), IL, *54*
Donini Assoc. (R), VA, *54*
The Doty Group (C), TX, *314*
DS&A (Doug Sears & Assoc.) (C), FL, *315*
The Duncan-O'Dell Group Inc. (C), TX, *316*
Dunhill Staffing Systems, Inc. (C), NY, *316*
Dunhill Executive Search of Los Angeles, Inc. (C), CA, *319*
Dunhill Search of West Atlanta (C), GA, *320*
Dunhill Executive Search of Brown County (C), IN, *321*
Dunhill Professional Search of Greater New Orleans (C), LA, *321*
Dunhill Professional Search (C), MO, *321*
Dunhill Professional Search of Ramsey (C), NJ, *321*
Dunhill Search of Medford (C), NJ, *321*
Dunlap & Sullivan Assoc. (R), MI, *55*
Dussick Management Assoc. (C), CT, *323*
G. L. Dykstra Assoc., Inc. (C), MI, *323*
E.P. Int'l. (C), NY, *324*
EA Plus, Inc. (C), TX, *325*
Earley Kielty & Assoc., Inc. (R), NY, *56*
The Edge Resource Group (C), PA, *326*
Effective Search, Inc. (R), IL, *57*
Eggers Consulting Co., Inc. (C), NE, *327*
Richard A. Eisner & Co., LLP (R), NY, *57*
Elinvar (C), NC, *328*
Yves Elkas Inc. (R), QE, *58*
Elliot Assoc. Inc. (R), NY, *58*
H. J. Elliot, Inc. (R), IL, *58*
The Elliott Company (R), MA, *58*
Ellis Career Consultants (C), NJ, *328*
Elwell & Assoc., Inc. (R), MI, *59*
Employ® (C), PA, *330*
Engineering Futures, LLC (C), CT, *330*
Ethos Consulting, Inc. (R), CA, *61*
ETI Search Int'l. (R), GA, *61*
Excalibur Human Resources, Inc. (R), NJ, *61*
ExecuGroup, Inc. (R), MS, *61*
ExecuQuest, Inc. (R), MI, *61*
Executech (R), OH, *62*
Executive Access Inc. (R), NY, *62*
Executive Careers (R), CA, *62*
Executive Dimensions (R), NY, *62*
Executive Exchange Corp. (C), NJ, *333*
The Executive Group, Inc. (R), CA, *62*
Executive Placement Consultants (C), IL, *333*
Executive Referral Services, Inc. (C), IL, *334*
Executive Registry (C), QE, *334*
Executive Resource Group, Inc. (R), ME, *63*
Executive Resource Inc. (C), WI, *334*
Executive Resource Systems (C), CA, *335*
Executive Search, Ltd. (C), OH, *336*
Executive Search of New England, Inc. (C), ME, *336*
Executive Search Partners (R), NY, *63*
Executive Search Plus, Inc. (C), IN, *336*
Executive Solutions (R), MN, *64*
The Executive Source Inc. (R), NY, *64*
Executive Strategies, Inc. (C), GA, *337*
The Executive Tree (R), FL, *64*
ExecutiveFit (C), NY, *337*
Raymond L. Extract & Assoc. (R), CA, *64*
FAI (C), CO, *338*
Paul Falcone Assoc. (R), NJ, *65*
Faro Consultants Int'l. (C), VA, *338*
The Fawcett Group (R), MA, *65*
Fenwick Partners (R), MA, *66*
Ferneborg & Assoc., Inc. (R), CA, *66*
Fernow Assoc. (C), PA, *339*
Fidelity Search Group, Inc. (R), PA, *66*
Financial Connections Company (C), VA, *340*
Financial Plus Management Solutions Inc. (R), ON, *66*
Eileen Finn & Assoc., Inc. (C), NY, *341*
Finney-Taylor Personnel & Management Consultants Ltd. (C), AB, *341*
First Choice Search (R), WA, *67*
Howard Fischer Assoc. Int'l., Inc. (R), PA, *67*
Fishel HR Assoc., Inc. (C), AZ, *341*
The Flagship Group (R), MA, *68*
Robert M. Flanagan & Assoc., Ltd. (R), NY, *68*
Flexible Resources, Inc. (C), CT, *342*
J. G. Flynn & Assoc. Inc. (R), BC, *69*
Flynn, Hannock, Inc. (R), CT, *69*
Focus Consulting Services, Inc. (C), FL, *342*
Fogec Consultants, Inc. (R), WI, *69*
Ford & Assoc., Inc. (C), SC, *343*
Ford & Ford (C), MA, *343*
The Ford Group, Inc. (R), PA, *69*
F-O-R-T-U-N-E Personnel Consultants of Boise (R), ID, *70*
Fortune Personnel Consultants of Huntsville, Inc. (C), AL, *343*
F-O-R-T-U-N-E Personnel Consultants of Greenwood Village (C), CO, *344*
F-O-R-T-U-N-E Personnel Consultants of Savannah, Inc. (C), GA, *345*
F-O-R-T-U-N-E Personnel Consultants of St. Louis-West County (C), MO, *347*
F-O-R-T-U-N-E Personnel Consultants of Menlo Park, Inc. (C), NJ, *347*
Fortune Personnel Consultants of Allentown, Inc. (C), PA, *348*

Fortune Personnel Consultants of Raleigh, Inc. (C), NC, *348*
F-O-R-T-U-N-E Consultants of Memphis (C), TN, *349*
Fortune Personnel Consultants of Chattanooga Inc. (C), TN, *349*
Fortune Consultants of Ft. Washington (C), PA, *349*
F-O-R-T-U-N-E Personnel Consultants of Houston, Inc. (C), TX, *350*
F-O-R-T-U-N-E Personnel Consultants of Knoxville (C), TN, *350*
Fortune Personnel Consultants of San Antonio, Inc. (C), TX, *350*
F-O-R-T-U-N-E Personnel of Nashville (C), TN, *350*
Fortune Personnel Consultants of Plano (C), TX, *350*
F-O-R-T-U-N-E Personnel Consultants of the Tri-Cities, Inc. (C), TN, *350*
Forum Personnel Inc. (C), NY, *351*
Foster Partners (R), NY, *70*
Fought, Jameson Assoc. (C), IL, *351*
Foy, Schneid & Daniel, Inc. (R), NY, *71*
Franstaff Inc. (C), FL, *352*
Fresquez & Assoc. (C), CA, *352*
Friedman Eisenstein Raemer & Schwartz, LLP (R), IL, *72*
Frye/Joure & Assoc., Inc. (C), TN, *353*
C. F. Furr & Co. (R), NC, *72*
The Furst Group, Inc. (R), IL, *72*
Furst Group/MPI (R), IL, *72*
Future Employment Service, Inc. (C), IA, *353*
The Gabriel Group (C), PA, *354*
Gaffney Management Consultants (R), IL, *73*
Gahan Assoc. (R), NY, *73*
Jay Gaines & Company, Inc. (R), NY, *73*
Gaming Consultants, Inc. (R), LA, *74*
Garrison-Randall, Inc. (R), CA, *75*
The Garvis Group, Inc. (C), LA, *355*
Gatti & Assoc. (C), MA, *355*
Gaudry, Shink, Levasseur (R), QE, *75*
Geddes & Rubin Management Inc. (R), ON, *76*
C. R. Gerald & Assoc. (C), ON, *356*
J. Gernetzke & Assoc., Inc. (C), OH, *357*
Gielow Assoc., Inc. (R), WI, *76*
Gilbert & Van Campen Int'l. (R), NY, *76*
Gilmore & Assoc. (C), CA, *357*
Howard Gilmore & Assoc. (R), OH, *77*
The Glazin Group (R), BC, *77*
J. P. Gleason Assoc., Inc. (R), IL, *77*
Global 1000 Int'l. Services (C), CA, *358*
Global Career Services, Inc. (C), NY, *358*
Global HealthCare Partners (R), IL, *78*
The GlobalSearch Group (C), TX, *359*
The Gobbell Co. (R), CA, *78*
Robert G. Godfrey Assoc. Ltd. (R), IL, *78*
H. L. Goehring & Assoc., Inc. (C), OH, *359*
Barry M. Gold & Co. (C), CA, *359*
Joseph Goldring & Assoc. Inc. (C), MI, *360*
Fred J. Goldsmith Assoc. (R), CA, *79*
Gomez Fregoso y Asociados (C), JAL, *360*
Goodkind Assoc. Inc. (C), NY, *360*
Goodrich & Sherwood Assoc., Inc. (R), NY, *79*
Gould, McCoy & Chadick, Inc. (R), NY, *80*
The Governance Group, Inc. (R), NJ, *80*
Granger, Counts & Assoc. (R), OH, *81*
Grant Cooper & Assoc., Inc. (R), MO, *81*
Grant-Franks & Assoc. (C), NJ, *361*
Grant/Morgan Assoc., Inc. (C), MD, *361*
Grantham & Co., Inc. (R), NC, *81*
Sheila Greco Assoc. (C), NY, *362*
R. Green & Assoc., Inc. (C), OH, *362*
Greene Personnel Consultants (C), RI, *362*
Gregory, Kyle & Assoc. (C), NC, *363*
Griffith & Werner, Inc. (R), FL, *82*
J. B. Groner Executive Search, Inc. (C), DE, *363*
Grossberg & Assoc. (R), IL, *82*
Groupe PCA Inc. (C), QE, *363*
Wolf Gugler & Assoc. Ltd. (R), ON, *83*
Guidry & East Healthcare Search Consultants (R), TX, *83*
GWS Partners (R), IL, *84*
The H. S. Group, Inc. (C), WI, *365*
Habelmann & Assoc. (R), MI, *84*
Russ Hadick & Assoc. Inc. (C), OH, *365*
Hahn & Assoc., Inc. (C), OH, *365*
Don Hall & Assoc. (C), TX, *366*
Hall Management Group, Inc. (C), GA, *367*
R. C. Handel Assoc. Inc. (R), CT, *85*
W. L. Handler & Assoc. (R), GA, *85*
Handy HRM (R), NY, *86*
The Hanna Group (C), OH, *368*
Harbor Consultants Int'l., Inc. (C), VA, *368*
Harbrowe, Inc. (C), NY, *368*
Harcourt Group Ltd. (R), OH, *86*
Hardage Group (C), TN, *369*
Harrington & O'Brien, Inc. (C), NH, *369*
The Harris Consulting Corp. (R), MB, *87*
Harris McCully Assoc., Inc. (C), NY, *369*
Harvard Group Int'l. (R), GA, *87*
Harvey Hohauser & Assoc., LLC (R), MI, *87*
Hazard, Young, Attea & Assoc., Ltd. (C), IL, *371*
HCI Corp. (C), IL, *371*
Healey Executive Search, Inc. (R), MN, *88*
Healthcare Executive Recruiters, Inc. (C), CA, *372*
Healthcare Recruiters of the Rockies, Inc. (C), CO, *372*
HEC Group (C), ON, *375*
Helbling & Assoc., Inc. (R), PA, *91*
Helfer Executive Consultants (R), TN, *91*
The Helms Int'l. Group (R), VA, *91*
The Hensge Co. (R), IL, *91*
Herbeck Kline & Assoc. (R), IL, *92*
Hergenrather & Co. (R), WA, *92*
Herrerias & Assoc. (R), CA, *92*
Herring & Assoc. (C), AR, *376*
The Herrmann Group Ltd. (R), ON, *92*
Higdon Prince Inc. (R), NY, *93*
Highland Search Group, L.L.C. (R), NY, *93*
Highlander Search (C), NC, *378*
Hill Allyn Assoc. (C), CA, *378*
Frank P. Hill (R), MX, *93*
The Hindman Group, Inc. (C), CA, *378*
Hintz Associates (C), NY, *378*
Hire Authority, Inc. (C), MI, *378*
Ruth Hirsch Assoc., Inc. (C), NY, *379*
Hodge-Cronin & Assoc., Inc. (R), IL, *94*
Hoglund & Assoc., Inc. (R), IL, *94*
The Hollins Group, Inc. (R), IL, *95*
Holloway Schulz & Partners (C), BC, *380*
J. G. Hood Assoc. (C), CT, *380*
Horton Int'l. Inc. (R), NY, *96*
Hospitality Executive Search, Inc. (R), MA, *96*
Hospitality Int'l. (C), NY, *381*
William C. Houze & Co. (R), CA, *96*
Randall Howard & Assoc., Inc. (R), TN, *96*
Robert Howe & Assoc. (R), GA, *97*
HR Inc. (C), NC, *382*
HRCS (R), CA, *97*
HRD Consultants, Inc. (R), NJ, *97*
Hreshko Consulting Group (C), NJ, *382*
The HRM Group, Inc. (C), AL, *382*
HRNI (C), MI, *383*
Human Capital Resources, Inc. (C), FL, *384*
The Human Resource Department Ltd. (R), OH, *98*
Human Resource Dimensions, Inc. (C), TX, *384*
The Human Resource Group, Inc. (R), OH, *98*
Human Resource Solutions (R), TX, *98*
Human Resource Technologies, Inc. (R), IL, *99*
Human Resources Management Hawaii, Inc. (C), HI, *384*
Human Resources Personnel Agency (R), AR, *99*
The Hunter Group, Inc. (C), MI, *385*
The Hunter Group (C), NC, *385*
Hunter Int'l., Inc. (R), CT, *100*
W. Hutt Management Resources Ltd. (R), ON, *100*
Hyde Danforth & Co. (R), TX, *100*
The Hyde Group, Inc. (R), CT, *101*
Hyman & Assoc. (C), TX, *386*
Independent Power Consultants (C), TX, *387*
InfoTech Search (C), TX, *388*
Ingram & Aydelotte, Inc. (R), NY, *101*
Insurance Career Center, Inc. (C), CT, *389*
Insurance Personnel Resources, Inc. (C), GA, *390*
Insurance Search (C), TX, *390*
Intech Summit Group, Inc. (R), CA, *102*
Integrated Search Solutions Group, LLC (ISSG) (R), NY, *102*
Integrity Search, Inc. (R), PA, *102*
InteliSearch, Inc. (R), CT, *102*
Interactive Search Network (R), CA, *102*
Interim Executive Recruiting (C), GA, *392*
Interim Financial Solutions - Mid-Atlantic Region (C), MD, *392*
Interim Management Resources Inc. (C), ON, *392*
International Business Partners (C), ON, *392*
International Management Advisors, Inc. (R), NY, *103*
International Staffing Consultants, Inc. (C), CA, *393*
Intersource, Ltd. (R), GA, *103*
IPR, Inc. (R), VA, *103*
IprGroup, Inc. (C), GA, *394*

Jeffrey Irving Assoc., Inc. (R), VA, *104*
Isaacson, Miller (R), MA, *104*
Ives & Associates, Inc. (C), OH, *395*
J.B.A. Assoc. (R), WA, *104*
J.D.G. y Asociados, S.A. de C.V. (R), SO, *104*
Jacobson Assoc. (C), IL, *396*
Jakobs & Assoc. Int'l. (R), NY, *105*
Jefferson-Ross Assoc. Inc. (C), PA, *398*
Jeffrey Allan Co., Inc. (C), CA, *398*
JenKim Int'l. Ltd., Inc. (C), FL, *398*
JNB Assoc., Inc. (C), MA, *399*
Job-Born Candidate Selection Bureau (C), ON, *399*
John Jay & Co. (C), ME, *399*
John H. Johnson & Assoc., Inc. (R), IL, *106*
L. J. Johnson & Co. (R), MI, *106*
Johnson Brown Assoc., Inc. (C), IN, *400*
The Johnson Group, Unlimited (C), NY, *400*
Johnson Smith & Knisely (R), NY, *107*
Jonas, Walters & Assoc., Inc. (R), WI, *107*
Jonathan Lawrence Assoc. (C), NJ, *400*
Jones and Jones (R), OR, *108*
Jordon & Jordon, Inc. (R), PA, *108*
J. M. Joseph Assoc. (R), NJ, *109*
Joseph Consulting, Inc. (C), FL, *401*
JRL Executive Recruiters (C), MO, *401*
JT Assoc. (C), CT, *401*
Kabana Corp. (C), MI, *402*
Richard Kader & Assoc. (C), OH, *403*
Kanzer Assoc., Inc. (R), IL, *109*
Gary Kaplan & Assoc. (R), CA, *109*
Kaplan & Assoc., Inc. (R), PA, *109*
Karel & Co. (R), CA, *109*
Karras Personnel, Inc. (C), NJ, *403*
A.T. Kearney Executive Search (R), IL, *111*
The Keith-Murray Partnership (R), ON, *112*
Kelly Assoc. (R), WI, *112*
Kelly Associates (R), PA, *112*
Kenmore Executives Inc. (C), FL, *405*
Kenzer Corp. (R), NY, *113*
KGA Inc. (C), WI, *406*
Kimmel & Associates, Inc. (C), NC, *406*
Kincaid Group Inc. (KGI) (C), TX, *406*
The Kingsley Group (R), CA, *114*
Kip Williams, Inc. (R), NY, *115*
Kiradjieff & Goode, Inc. (R), MA, *115*
Kirby Assoc. (R), PA, *115*
KL Consultants (C), NJ, *407*
Raymond J. Klemmer & Assoc. (R), NY, *116*
Koehler & Co. (R), WI, *116*
The Koehler Group (C), PA, *408*
Koll-Fairfield LLC (C), CT, *408*
Koontz, Jeffries & Assoc., Inc. (R), FL, *117*
Korn/Ferry Int'l. (R), NY, *117*
Kossuth & Assoc., Inc. (R), WA, *119*
Kozlin Assoc., Inc. (C), NY, *408*
KPA Assoc., Inc. (C), NY, *408*
Kremple Consulting Group (R), CA, *120*
Kressenberg Assoc. (C), TX, *409*
Krueger Assoc. (R), IL, *121*
John Kuhn & Assoc., Inc. (R), WI, *121*
Kulper & Co., L.L.C. (R), NJ, *121*
Kunzer Assoc., Ltd. (R), IL, *121*
Kyle Assoc. (C), NY, *410*
L O R (R), NJ, *122*
L&L Assoc. Global Search (C), PA, *411*
Marvin Laba & Assoc. (R), CA, *122*
LaCosta & Assoc. Int'l. Inc. (C), CA, *411*
Rene LaFlamme & Associes (R), QE, *122*
Landon Morgan (C), ON, *412*
Lange & Assoc., Inc. (C), IN, *412*
Lanken-Kimball-Therrell & Assoc. (C), GA, *412*
Larkin & Co. (R), CA, *124*
R. H. Larsen & Assoc., Inc. (R), FL, *125*
Jack B. Larsen & Assoc., Inc. (C), PA, *413*
Larsen, Whitney, Blecksmith & Zilliacus, Inc. (R), CA, *125*
Madeleine Lav & Assoc. (C), CA, *413*
Lawrence James Assoc. of Florida, Inc. (C), FL, *414*
The Lawson Group, Inc. (C), SC, *414*
Leader Resources Group (C), GA, *415*
Leaders-Trust Int'l./Carce y Asociados, S.C. (R), MX, *127*
Lear & Assoc., Inc. (C), FL, *415*
Vincent Lee Assoc. (C), NY, *415*
The Conrad Lee Co. Inc. (R), FL, *127*
Leeds and Leeds (C), TN, *416*
V. J. Lehman & Assoc., Inc. (R), CO, *127*
Leith & Assoc., Inc. (C), OH, *416*
Lekan & Assoc., Inc. (R), OH, *128*
Lemming/LeVan, Inc. (R), GA, *128*
Lending Personnel Services (C), CA, *416*
AG Lennox & Assoc. (R), AB, *128*
Jacques LePage Executive Search Inc. (R), QE, *128*
Leslie Kavanagh Assoc., Inc. (C), NY, *416*
Alan Levine Assoc. (R), MA, *129*
The Levton Group Inc. (R), ON, *129*
Lewis Companies Inc. (R), ON, *129*
The Libra Group (C), NC, *417*
Pat Licata & Assoc. (C), NC, *417*
Livingston, Robert & Co. (R), CT, *130*
Locke & Assoc. (R), NC, *131*
Logic Assoc., Inc. (C), NY, *419*
Logue & Rice Inc. (C), VA, *420*
London Executive Consultants Inc. (C), ON, *420*
Lord & Albus Co. (C), TX, *420*
Bruce Lowery & Assoc. (C), MI, *420*
Lucas Group (C), NY, *421*
The John Lucht Consultancy Inc. (R), NY, *131*
Fran Luisi Assoc. (R), NJ, *132*
Charles Luntz & Assoc., Inc. (R), MO, *132*
Lynch Miller Moore Partners, Inc. (R), IL, *132*
Lynne Palmer Executive Recruitment, Inc. (C), NY, *421*
M.C. Executive Search (C), CA, *422*
M/J/A Partners (R), IL, *133*
MacNaughton Assoc. (R), CA, *133*
Maglio & Co., Inc. (R), WI, *134*
Magnum Search (C), IL, *422*
Maiorino & Weston Assoc., Inc. (R), CT, *134*
Major Legal Services, Inc. (C), OH, *423*
Major Search (C), NJ, *423*
Managed Care Consultants (C), AZ, *423*
Managed Care Resources (C), TX, *424*
Management & Human Resources (R), MA, *134*
Management Assoc. (C), MD, *424*
Management Association Network (C), WI, *424*
Management Recruiters of Clovis (C), CA, *440*
Management Recruiters of Fresno (C), CA, *440*
Management Recruiters of Laguna Hills (C), CA, *440*
Management Recruiters, Inland Empire Agency (C), CA, *441*
Management Recruiters of Sacramento North (C), CA, *441*
Management Recruiters of Tampa North (C), FL, *444*
Management Recruiters of St. Augustine (C), FL, *444*
Management Recruiters of Savannah (C), GA, *446*
Management Recruiters of Sandy Springs (C), GA, *446*
Management Recruiters of Marietta, Inc. (C), GA, *446*
Management Recruiters of St. Charles (C), IL, *447*
Management Recruiters of Indianapolis (C), IN, *448*
Management Recruiters of South Bend (C), IN, *448*
Management Recruiters of Fairfield (C), IA, *449*
Management Recruiters of Siouxland (C), IA, *449*
Management Recruiters of Rockville (C), MD, *450*
Management Recruiters of Monroe, Inc. (C), LA, *450*
Management Recruiters of Southeastern Michigan (C), MI, *451*
Management Recruiters of Detroit & Farmington Hills (C), MI, *451*
Management Recruiters of Woodbury (C), MN, *452*
Management Recruiters of North Oakland County, Inc. (C), MI, *452*
Management Recruiters of Bloomington (C), MN, *452*
Management Recruiters of North Warren Inc. (C), NJ, *453*
Management Recruiters of Fayetteville (C), NC, *455*
Management Recruiters of Kinston (C), NC, *456*
Management Recruiters of Charlotte - North, Inc. (C), NC, *456*
Management Recruiters of Wilmington (C), NC, *457*
Management Recruiters of Winston-Salem (C), NC, *457*
Management Recruiters of Columbus (C), OH, *457*
Management Recruiters of Mentor, Inc. (C), OH, *458*
Management Recruiters of Lionville, Inc. (C), PA, *459*
Management Recruiters of Cherry Hill (C), PA, *459*

Management Recruiters of Florence (C), SC, *460*
Management Recruiters of Columbia, Tennessee (C), TN, *461*
Management Recruiters of Champions (C), TX, *462*
Management Recruiters of Arlington (C), VA, *464*
Management Recruiters of Sugar Land Inc. (C), TX, *464*
Management Resource Assoc., Inc. (C), FL, *467*
Management Resource Group, Ltd. (C), IA, *467*
Management Search Int'l. (C), CA, *467*
Management Solutions, Inc. (C), WA, *468*
Management Solutions, Inc. (C), CA, *468*
Mangieri/Solutions LLC (C), CT, *468*
Mannard & Assoc., Inc. (R), IL, *135*
Manning Lloyd Assoc. Ltd. (C), NY, *468*
ManTech Consulting (C), NY, *468*
MARBL Consultants, Inc. (C), WI, *469*
Marc-Allen Assoc., Inc. (C), FL, *469*
Marcus & Assoc. (C), NY, *469*
J. L. Mark Assoc., Inc. (R), CO, *135*
Mark III Personnel, Inc. (C), NC, *470*
Paula Marks Inc. (R), NY, *136*
Brad Marks Int'l. (R), CA, *136*
The Maroon Group (R), CT, *136*
Marra Peters & Partners (R), NJ, *136*
Marsar & Co., Inc. (C), FL, *471*
Marshall-Alan Assoc., Inc. (C), NY, *471*
The Martin Group (R), CA, *137*
Louis Thomas Masterson & Co. (R), OH, *138*
Matté & Company, Inc. (R), CT, *138*
Maximum Management Corp. (C), NY, *473*
Mary L. Mayer, Ltd. (R), MN, *139*
Mayhall Search Group, Inc. (C), IN, *473*
The Mazzitelli Group, Ltd. (R), MN, *139*
McBride Assoc., Inc. (R), DC, *139*
Tom McCall Executive Search (C), IL, *473*
The McCormick Group (C), VA, *473*
The Paul McDaniel Co. (C), TN, *474*
McDonald Assoc. Int'l. (R), IL, *140*
McGrath & Assoc., Inc. (R), NJ, *141*
McIntyre Management Resources (C), ON, *474*
MCS Assoc. (R), CA, *142*
Medicorp, Inc. (C), MO, *477*
The Medley Group (C), CA, *477*
MedXec USA, Inc. (C), FL, *478*
Mee Derby & Co. (C), DC, *478*
Martin H. Meisel Assoc., Inc. (R), NY, *143*
Melancon & Co. (R), TX, *143*
Juan Menefee & Assoc. (C), IL, *478*
Meng, Finseth & Assoc., Inc. (R), CA, *143*
The Mercer Group, Inc. (R), NM, *143*
Merrick & Moore (C), NC, *479*
MESA, Inc. (R), CO, *143*
Messett Assoc., Inc. (R), FL, *143*
mfg/Search, Inc. (C), IN, *480*
Michael Wayne Recruiters (C), IL, *480*
Michael/Merrill (C), KS, *481*
Michaels & Moere (C), WI, *481*
Lou Michaels Assoc., Inc. (C), MI, *481*
Millennium Search Group, Inc. (R), CA, *144*
Miller + Miller (C), WA, *482*
Miller-Hall HRISearch (C), NY, *482*
Danette Milne Corporate Search Inc. (C), ON, *482*
Milo Research (R), NY, *145*
Herbert Mines Assoc., Inc. (R), NY, *145*
Mirtz Morice, Inc. (R), CT, *145*
Mitchell/Wolfson, Assoc. (R), IL, *145*
Moffitt Int'l., Inc. (R), NC, *146*
Molloy Partners (R), NY, *146*
The Montgomery Group, Inc. (C), TN, *484*
Montgomery West (R), CA, *146*
Morgan Hunter Corp. (C), KS, *485*
Morgan Samuels Co. (R), CA, *147*
Morgan/Webber, Inc. (R), NY, *147*
The Morris Group (C), PA, *486*
MPA Executive Search Inc. (R), QE, *148*
Multisearch Recruiters (C), CA, *487*
P. J. Murphy & Assoc., Inc. (R), WI, *150*
Murphy Partners Int'l. (R), IL, *150*
Musick & Assoc. (C), CA, *487*
The MVP Group (C), NY, *487*
DDJ Myers, Ltd. (R), AZ, *150*
Nadzam, Lusk, Horgan & Assoc., Inc. (R), CA, *150*
National Affirmative Action Career Network, Inc. (C), CO, *488*
National Bank & Finance Executive Search (C), CA, *488*
National Corporate Consultants, Inc. (C), IN, *489*
Nationwide Personnel Placement, Inc. (C), OH, *490*
New Directions, Inc. (C), IL, *492*
Newcomb-Desmond & Assoc., Inc. (C), OH, *492*
Next Step Recruiting (C), CA, *493*
Nichols Brown Int'l. (R), NY, *151*
The Niemond Corp. (R), CA, *152*
The Noebel Search Group, Inc. (C), TX, *494*
Nordeman Grimm, Inc. (R), NY, *152*
Norman Broadbent Int'l., Inc. (R), NY, *152*
NPF Assoc. Ltd. Inc. (R), FL, *153*
NRI Staffing Resources (C), DC, *496*
Nursing Technomics (R), PA, *153*
O'Brien and Roof (C), OH, *497*
O'Brien Consulting Services (R), MA, *153*
O'Keefe & Assoc., Inc. (R), CT, *154*
O'Neill Group (C), NJ, *498*
O'Rourke Companies, Inc. (R), TX, *154*
O'Sullivan Search Inc. (C), ON, *498*
Dennis P. O'Toole & Assoc. Inc. (R), NY, *154*
Ober & Company (R), CA, *155*
Oberlander & Co., Inc. (R), IL, *155*
Odell & Assoc., Inc. (C), TX, *498*
Oliver & Rozner Assoc., Inc. (R), NY, *155*
Ollinger Partners (R), MA, *156*
Olsen/Clark (R), WA, *156*
Omega Search, Inc. (C), NC, *498*
Omnisearch Assoc. (C), CA, *499*
The Onstott Group (R), MA, *156*
Organization Consulting Ltd. (R), ON, *157*
Orion Int'l. Consulting Group, Inc. (C), NC, *499*
Ott & Hansen, Inc. (R), CA, *157*
Overton Consulting (R), WI, *157*
The Pailin Group Professional Search Consultants (R), TX, *158*
Kirk Palmer & Assoc., Inc. (R), NY, *158*
Pamenter, Pamenter, Brezer & Deganis Ltd. (R), ON, *159*
Paper Industry Recruitment (P.I.R.) (C), ME, *502*
Parenica & Co. (R), NC, *159*
The Park Group & Assoc., Inc. (C), MD, *502*
Parker Page Group (C), FL, *503*
Parsons, Anderson & Gee, Inc. (C), NY, *503*
Partners in Recruiting (C), IL, *503*
The Partnership Group (R), NJ, *160*
Partnervision Consulting Group Inc. (R), ON, *160*
Pathways Int'l. (C), CT, *505*
The Patience Motivation Belief Group, Inc. (C), GA, *505*
Patrice & Assoc. (C), MD, *505*
Joel H. Paul & Assoc., Inc. (C), NY, *505*
Pawlik/Dorman Partners (R), IL, *161*
Peck & Assoc., Ltd. (R), WI, *161*
Peeney Assoc., Inc. (R), NJ, *161*
Penn Associates (R), PA, *161*
The Penn Partners, Inc. (R), PA, *162*
Pennington Consulting Group (C), NJ, *506*
The Pennmor Group (C), NJ, *506*
People Management Northeast, Inc. (R), CT, *162*
Perfect Search, Inc. (C), FL, *507*
Perry • Newton Assoc. (C), MD, *507*
Perry-D'Amico & Assoc. (R), CA, *162*
PersoNet, Inc. (C), FL, *507*
Personnel Alliance Group (C), NJ, *507*
Personnel Assoc. (C), NC, *508*
The Personnel Group, Inc. (R), MN, *163*
Personnel, Inc. (C), AL, *508*
Personnel Unlimited/Executive Search (C), WA, *509*
Alec Peters Assoc. Inc./DLR (R), GA, *163*
Richard Peterson & Assoc., Inc. (R), GA, *163*
Petrie Partners, Inc. (R), FL, *163*
Petro Staff Int'l. (C), AB, *509*
Phelps Personnel Assoc., Inc. (C), SC, *510*
Phillips Assoc. (C), FL, *510*
Phillips Int'l., Inc. (C), SC, *510*
Phillips Personnel/Search (C), CO, *510*
Pierce & Assoc. (C), CA, *512*
DNPitchon Assoc. (R), NJ, *165*
Plante & Moran, LLP (R), MI, *165*
Yves Plouffe & Assoc. (R), QE, *165*
Polson & Co., Inc. (R), MN, *166*
Al Ponaman Company, Inc. (C), CA, *514*
Porter & Assoc., Inc. (C), FL, *514*
David Powell, Inc. (R), CA, *166*
Robert Powers & Assoc. (C), CA, *515*
P. G. Prager Search Assoc., Ltd. (C), NY, *515*
The Prairie Group (C), IL, *515*
PRAXIS Partners (R), VA, *167*
Preferred Professional Recruiters (C), OH, *516*
Premier Recruiting Group (C), MI, *516*
Presley Consultants, Inc. (C), CA, *517*
Price & Assoc., Inc. (C), VA, *518*

PricewaterhouseCoopers Executive Search (R), MX, *168*
Prichard Kymen Inc. (R), AB, *168*
Prime Management Group Inc. (C), ON, *518*
Princeton Executive Search (C), NJ, *518*
Priority Executive Search (C), FL, *518*
Pro Tec Technical Services (C), ON, *519*
Professional Personnel Consultants, Inc. (C), MI, *521*
Professional Resources (C), NY, *522*
The Professional Sales Search Co., Inc. (C), WA, *522*
Professional Search (R), MI, *169*
Professional Search Assoc. (C), CA, *522*
Professional Selection Services (R), GA, *169*
Professional Support Inc. (C), NY, *523*
Professions, Inc. (C), OH, *523*
Profit Pros, Inc. (C), CA, *523*
ProSearch, Inc. (C), ME, *524*
Protocol Inc. (C), CA, *525*
Pryor & Associates (C), CA, *525*
The Quest Organization (C), NY, *527*
Quetico Corp. (R), TX, *170*
Quigley Assoc. (R), MD, *170*
L. J. Quinn & Assoc., Inc. (R), CA, *170*
Quiring Assoc., Inc. (C), IN, *527*
R & L Assoc., Ltd. (R), NY, *170*
R. J. Associates (C), NY, *528*
R.A.N. Assoc., Inc. (C), OH, *528*
R/K International Inc. (R), CT, *171*
Ramm Search (C), NY, *528*
Ramming & Assoc., Inc. (C), NJ, *528*
Rand Thompson Executive Search Consultants (C), NY, *528*
Rand-Curtis Resources (C), AZ, *529*
Ray & Assoc., Inc. (C), IA, *529*
Ray & Berndtson/Lovas Stanley (R), ON, *172*
Raymond Karsan Assoc. (C), PA, *529*
RBW Assoc. Inc. (C), OR, *531*
Recruiting Services Group, Inc. (C), TN, *532*
Recruitment Specialists, Inc. (C), MD, *532*
Mary Rector & Assoc., Inc. (C), IL, *533*
Redden & McGrath Assoc., Inc. (R), NY, *173*
Redden-Shaffer Group (R), CA, *173*
Reeder & Assoc., Ltd. (R), GA, *173*
Michael James Reid & Co. (R), CA, *174*
Reid Ellis Assoc. Inc. (C), ON, *533*
Resource Networking Inc. (C), IN, *534*
Response Staffing Services (C), NY, *534*
The Retail Network (C), MA, *535*
Retail Recruiters/Spectrum Consultants, Inc. (C), PA, *535*
Retained Search Assoc. (R), NC, *176*
S. Reyman & Assoc., Ltd. (R), IL, *176*
Russell Reynolds Assoc., Inc. (R), NY, *176*
Reynolds Partners (R), NY, *177*
Rice Cohen Int'l. (R), PA, *178*
Richard, Wayne & Roberts (C), TX, *536*
The Richards Group (C), PA, *536*
Riddle & McGrath LLC (R), GA, *178*
Right/McKee Consulting Group (C), TX, *537*
Riley Cole (C), CA, *537*
Ritt-Ritt & Assoc., Inc. (C), IL, *537*
River Region Personnel, Inc. (C), LA, *538*
RLM Assoc., Ltd. (R), NY, *179*
Robert William James & Assoc. (C), OR, *539*
Norman Roberts & Assoc., Inc. (R), CA, *179*
Roberts Ryan & Bentley, Inc. (R), MD, *179*
V. Robinson & Co., Inc. (C), MO, *539*
Bruce Robinson Assoc. (R), NJ, *180*
Robinson-Robinson & Assoc., Inc. (C), MN, *539*
Rodgers, Ramsey, Inc. (C), TX, *540*
R. A. Rodriguez & Assoc., Inc. (C), TX, *540*
Rodzik & Assoc., Inc. (R), NC, *180*
Rogish Assoc., Inc. (C), OH, *541*
Rolland Ressources Humaines Inc. (R), QE, *181*
Romac Int'l. (C), PA, *542*
Romac Int'l., Inc. (C), FL, *542*
Romano McAvoy Assoc., Inc. (C), NY, *544*
Roster Inc. (C), IN, *545*
Roth Young Executive Search (C), TX, *546*
Roth Young Executive Recruiters (C), MN, *546*
Roth Young of Tampa (C), FL, *546*
Roth Young Personnel Services of Washington, DC (C), MD, *546*
Roth Young Executive Search of Milwaukee (C), WI, *547*
Rothrock Associates, Inc. (C), NC, *547*
Rovner & Assoc., Inc. (R), IL, *182*
Rovner Gerner & Assoc. (R), CA, *182*
Rowland Assoc. (C), CA, *547*
Royal Assoc. (C), CA, *547*
Ruderfer & Co., Inc. (C), NJ, *548*
Rusher, Loscavio & LoPresto (R), CA, *183*
K. Russo Assoc. Inc. (C), CT, *548*
The Ryan Charles Group, Inc. (C), FL, *548*
Ryan-Allen & Assoc., Inc. (C), CA, *549*
Rylan Forbes Consulting Group, Inc. (C), NJ, *549*
S. C. Int'l., Ltd. (C), IL, *550*
Sales & Management Search, Inc. (C), IL, *551*
Sales Consultants of Birmingham (C), AL, *555*
Sales Consultants Peninsula, Inc. (C), CA, *556*
Sales Consultants of Stamford-Darien (C), CT, *557*
Sales Consultants of Bangor, Inc. (C), ME, *559*
Sales Consultants of Houston (C), TX, *563*
Salveson Stetson Group, Inc. (R), PA, *184*
Sampson Medical Search (C), CA, *564*
Sanford Rose Assoc. - Mobile (C), AL, *565*
Sanford Rose Assoc. - Orland Park (C), IL, *567*
Sanford Rose Assoc. - Cedar Rapids (C), IA, *567*
Sanford Rose Assoc. - Rockville (C), MD, *567*
Sanford Rose Assoc. - Canton (C), OH, *569*
Sanford Rose Assoc. - Pittsburgh North (C), PA, *570*
Santangelo Consultants Inc. (C), NY, *571*
Allan Sarn Assoc., Inc. (R), NY, *184*
Savoy Partners, Ltd. (R), DC, *184*
Schall Executive Search Partners (R), MN, *185*
The Schatz Company (C), MO, *571*
Schneider, Hill & Spangler, Inc. (R), PA, *185*
Devin Scott Assoc. (C), NJ, *572*
Robert Scott Assoc. (C), NJ, *573*
Scott Executive Search, Inc. (R), NY, *186*
Search Advisors Int'l. Corp. (R), FL, *186*
The Search Alliance, Inc. (R), FL, *186*
Search Bureau Int'l. (C), IL, *574*
Search Consultants, Inc. (C), NJ, *575*
Search Innovations, Inc. (R), PA, *187*
Search Plus Int'l.-Ohio (C), OH, *576*
Search Research Assoc., Inc. (R), MA, *187*
SearchCorp (C), FL, *577*
Secura/Burnett Partners (R), CA, *187*
Select Services (C), IL, *578*
Selective Staffing (C), CA, *579*
Sharrow & Assoc., Inc. (C), MI, *579*
M. B. Shattuck & Assoc., Inc. (R), CA, *189*
Shepherd Bueschel & Provus, Inc. (R), IL, *189*
Sheridan Search (R), IL, *189*
Sherwood Lehman Massucco, Inc. (R), CA, *189*
Shey-Harding Assoc. Inc. (C), CA, *580*
Shiloh Careers Int'l., Inc. (C), TN, *580*
E. L. Shore & Assoc. (R), ON, *190*
Shore Asociados Ejecutivos, S. A. de C.V. (R), MX, *190*
The Shorr Group (R), IL, *190*
John Sibbald Assoc., Inc. (R), MO, *191*
Larry Siegel & Assoc. (R), WA, *191*
Marvin L. Silcott & Assoc., Inc. (C), TX, *581*
Silver Associates (C), CA, *581*
Slayton Int'l., Inc. (R), IL, *192*
Tom Sloan & Assoc., Inc. (C), WI, *583*
J. L. Small Assoc. (C), AL, *583*
Smith & Assoc. (C), FL, *583*
Smith & Syberg, Inc. (R), IN, *193*
Abbott Smith Assoc., Inc. (R), NY, *193*
Herman Smith Executive Initiatives Inc. (R), ON, *193*
Smith James Group, Inc. (R), GA, *194*
Smith Professional Search (C), MI, *584*
Snelling Search - Transportation Division (C), AR, *585*
Snelling Search (C), LA, *586*
Snelling Search (C), IL, *586*
Snyder & Co. (R), CT, *194*
Soderlund Assoc. Inc. (R), OH, *194*
Robert Sollman & Assoc. (C), FL, *587*
Solutions Group (R), AL, *195*
Stephen M. Sonis Assoc. (R), MA, *195*
Souder & Assoc. (R), VA, *195*
Southern Recruiters & Consultants, Inc. (C), SC, *587*
Southern Research Services (R), FL, *195*
Spectra International LLC (C), AZ, *589*
SpencerStuart (R), NY, *196*
Spilman & Assoc. (R), TX, *197*
Staff Extension Int'l. (C), TX, *590*
Staff Resources, Inc. (C), SC, *590*
Staffing Edge, Inc. (C), IA, *590*
StaffWriters Plus (C), NY, *591*
Starbridge Group Inc. (C), VA, *591*

Steinfield & Assoc. (C), TX, *592*
Sterling Int'l. Management Recruitment, Ltd. Inc. (C), NC, *592*
Michael Stern Assoc., Inc./Euram (R), ON, *200*
The Stevens Group (C), CA, *593*
Stewart, Stein & Scott, Ltd. (R), MN, *200*
Stewart/Greene & Co. of The Triad, Inc. (C), NC, *594*
Stillinger & Assoc. (R), CA, *201*
STM Assoc. (R), UT, *201*
Stone & Youngblood (C), MA, *594*
Stone, Murphy & Olson (R), MN, *201*
Stoopen Asociados, S.C./EMA Partners Int'l. (R), MX, *202*
Strategic Advancement Inc. (R), NJ, *202*
Strategic Resources Biotechnology & Medical Group (C), WA, *595*
Strategic Technologies, Inc. (C), TX, *596*
StratfordGroup (R), OH, *203*
Stratin Assoc. (C), NJ, *596*
Straube Associates (R), MA, *203*
Stroman Int'l., Inc. (R), CO, *204*
Success Seekers Connection (C), FL, *596*
Sullivan & Assoc. (R), MI, *204*
Joe Sullivan & Assoc., Inc. (R), NY, *204*
Summerfield Assoc., Inc. (C), TN, *596*
Summit Group Int'l., Inc. (R), GA, *204*
Synapse Human Resource Consulting Group (R), TX, *205*
Systems One Ltd. (C), IL, *598*
T E M Assoc. (C), WI, *599*
T. H. Hunter, Inc. (C), MN, *599*
Tabb & Assoc. (R), OH, *205*
The Talley Group (R), VA, *205*
The Talon Group (R), TX, *205*
Target Search, Inc. (C), PA, *600*
Tarnow Int'l. (R), NJ, *206*
Tax Network Resources, Inc. (C), NY, *600*
The TBI Group (R), PA, *207*
Tech-Net (C), TX, *601*
Techstaff Inc. (C), WI, *603*
Telecom Connections, Inc. (C), TX, *604*
Templeton & Assoc. (C), MN, *605*
Thomas & Assoc. of Michigan (C), MI, *606*
Thomas Resource Group (R), CA, *209*
Richard Thompson Assoc., Inc. (R), MN, *209*
Thor, Inc. (C), CA, *606*
Thorne, Brieger Assoc., Inc. (R), NY, *209*
Tirocchi, Wright, Inc. (R), CA, *209*
Tittemore Cowan Assoc. (C), AB, *607*
TNS Partners, Inc. (R), TX, *209*
Tomlinson Assoc. Inc. (C), IL, *607*
Tower Consultants, Ltd. (R), PA, *209*
TPS Staffing Solutions (C), IN, *608*
Trainor/Frank & Assoc. Inc. (C), WI, *608*
Transportation Recruiting Services, Inc. (C), MS, *608*
Travel Executive Search (C), NY, *608*
Van Treadaway Assoc., Inc. (R), GA, *210*
TRH Assoc., Inc. (R), NY, *210*
Triad Consultants, Inc. (C), NJ, *609*
Triumph Consulting, Inc. (R), IA, *210*
The Truman Agency (C), CA, *610*
Tryon & Heideman, LLC (R), MO, *211*
TTG/Sterling Services (C), CA, *610*
W. G. Tucker & Assoc. (R), PA, *211*
Tully/Woodmansee Int'l. Inc. (R), FL, *212*
UniQuest Int'l., Inc. (C), FL, *610*
United Personnel Services (C), MA, *611*
Unlimited Staffing Solutions, Inc. (C), MI, *611*
The Urban Placement Service (C), TX, *611*
V.I.P. Resources, Inc. (C), NY, *611*
Van Dyke Assoc. (R), IL, *212*
VanMaldegiam Assoc., Inc. (R), IL, *213*
The Verriez Group Inc. (R), ON, *213*
Vezan Assoc. (C), CT, *612*
Vincenty & Co. (C), OH, *612*
Vlcek & Company, Inc. (R), CA, *214*
Vogel Assoc. (C), PA, *613*
Beverly von Winckler & Assoc. (C), IL, *613*
The Wabash Group (C), IN, *613*
Wakefield Talabisco Int'l. (R), NY, *214*
Kelly Walker Assoc. (C), TX, *614*
Wallace Management Co. (R), TN, *215*
Gerald Walsh & Co. Inc. (C), NS, *614*
Linda Walter & Associes (C), QE, *615*
Lee H. Walton & Assoc. (R), NY, *215*
Karen Wanger & Assoc., Inc. (C), IL, *615*
Warner & Assoc., Inc. (C), OH, *615*
Warren Executive Services (C), GA, *616*
The Washington Firm, Ltd. (R), WA, *216*
Waterford Executive Group Ltd. (C), IL, *616*
Waveland Int'l. (R), IL, *216*
The Wayne Group, Ltd. (C), NY, *616*
Weber Executive Search (R), NY, *216*
Wegner & Assoc. (C), WI, *617*
Weinstein & Co. (R), MA, *217*
Weliver & Assoc. (C), MI, *618*
Henry Welker & Assoc. (C), MI, *618*
Jude M. Werra & Assoc. (R), WI, *218*
West & West (R), CA, *218*
West Coast Recruiting (C), CA, *619*
Western Management Consultants (R), BC, *218*
The Westfield Group (C), CT, *619*
Weterrings & Agnew, Inc. (C), NY, *619*
S. J. Wexler Assoc., Inc. (R), NY, *219*
Wheeler Assoc. (R), CT, *219*
White, Roberts & Stratton, Inc. (C), IL, *619*
Whitehead & Assoc., Inc. (C), MO, *620*
Whitney Smith Co. (C), TX, *620*
The Whittaker Group (C), MI, *620*
Whittlesey & Assoc., Inc. (R), PA, *220*
The Whyte Group, Inc. (R), MD, *220*
Daniel Wier & Assoc. (R), CA, *220*
Wilder & Assoc. (C), VA, *620*
Wilder, Gammel Partners, Ltd. (R), CA, *220*
William-Johns Co., Inc. (C), CA, *621*
John R. Williams & Assoc., Inc. (C), NC, *621*
Willis & Assoc. (R), OH, *221*
William Willis Worldwide Inc. (R), CT, *221*
Willmott & Assoc. (C), MA, *622*
The Wilmington Group (C), NC, *622*
Wilson McLeran, Inc. (C), CT, *622*
Wilson Personnel, Inc. (C), NC, *622*
The Windham Group (R), OH, *222*
Wing Tips & Pumps, Inc. (C), MI, *623*
Winguth, Grant & Donahue (R), CA, *222*
Winston & Green (C), IL, *623*
Winter, Wyman & Co. (C), MA, *623*
Winthrop Partners, Inc. (R), NY, *222*
Wisnewski & Assoc. (R), CA, *223*
WMD inc. (C), NJ, *623*
Wojdula & Assoc., Ltd. (R), WI, *223*
D. S. Wolf Assoc., Inc. (R), NY, *223*
Wood-Glavin, Inc. (R), KS, *224*
Woodmoor Group (C), CO, *624*
The Woodstone Consulting Company, Inc. (R), CO, *224*
Working Relationships, Inc. (C), MN, *624*
WTW Assoc., Inc. (R), NY, *225*
R. S. Wyatt Assoc., Inc. (R), TX, *225*
John Wylie Assoc., Inc. (C), OK, *625*
The Yaiser Group (C), NJ, *625*
Yankee Hospitality Search (C), CT, *626*
The Yorkshire Group, Ltd. (C), MA, *626*
Steven Yungerberg Assoc., Inc. (R), MN, *226*
Zaccaria Int'l. (C), NJ, *627*
The Zammataro Company (R), OH, *226*
The Zarkin Group, Inc. (R), NY, *226*
Zen Zen Int'l. Inc. (C), MB, *627*
Helen Ziegler & Assoc., Inc. (C), ON, *627*
Michael D. Zinn & Assoc., Inc. (R), NJ, *227*
Zona & Assoc., Inc. (C), NY, *628*

06.1 Benefits, compensation planning

The Abbott Group, Inc. (R), MD, *1*
Access Assoc. Inc. (C), MD, *233*
Access/Resources, Inc. (C), MA, *234*
Alexander Ross & Co. (R), NY, *3*
Tom Allison Assoc. (C), NM, *245*
Aminex Corp. (C), MA, *249*
Anderson Network Group (C), OH, *250*
Andre David & Assoc., Inc. (R), TX, *6*
The Andre Group, Inc. (R), PA, *6*
Angel Group Int'l. (C), KY, *250*
Tryg R. Angell, Ltd. (C), CT, *250*
R. W. Apple & Assoc. (C), NJ, *251*
Armor Personnel (C), ON, *253*
The Ascher Group (R), NJ, *7*
Ashford Management Group, Inc. (R), GA, *7*
Ashworth Consultants, Inc. (R), MA, *8*
A. M. Auster Associates (R), FL, *9*
Avery Assoc. (R), CA, *9*
Baldwin & Assoc. (C), OH, *258*
Battalia Winston Int'l./The Euram Consultants Group (R), NY, *13*
Becker, Norton & Co. (R), PA, *14*
Behavioral Science Assoc., Inc. (R), AZ, *15*
Joy Reed Belt Search Consultants, Inc. (R), OK, *15*
Bennett & Co. Consulting Group (C), CA, *264*
Boone-Scaturro Assoc., Inc. (C), GA, *269*
Bradford Executives Int'l. (C), VA, *271*
Brindisi Search (R), MD, *23*
Bryan, Jason & Assoc. Inc. (C), ON, *275*
Brystol Cove Assoc. (R), CA, *24*
C. P. Consulting (R), PA, *26*
C.P.S., Inc. (C), IL, *278*
C/R Associates (C), NY, *278*
Canny, Bowen Inc. (R), NY, *27*

Capital Consulting Group, Inc. (R), MD, *28*
Career Strategies, Inc. (C), CA, *283*
Carpenter & Assoc. (C), TX, *284*
Charet & Assoc. (C), NJ, *289*
Chicago Legal Search, Ltd. (C), IL, *290*
Howard Clark Assoc. (C), NJ, *292*
Coe & Co. Int'l. Inc./EMA Partners Int'l. (R), AB, *37*
The Consortium (C), NY, *296*
Conway & Assoc. (R), IL, *40*
P. G. Cook Assoc. (R), TN, *40*
Leonard Corwen Assoc. (C), NY, *302*
The Cris Group, Inc. (R), NY, *42*
Cypress Int'l., Inc. (R), FL, *45*
Dalton Management Consultants, Ltd. (C), NJ, *306*
Daniel Marks Company (C), OH, *306*
Dankowski & Assoc., Inc. (C), OH, *307*
Donna Davis Assoc. (C), NJ, *309*
The Dayton Group, Ltd. (C), NY, *309*
Dean-Dzierzawiec Assoc. (C), NJ, *309*
Diversified Search, Inc. (R), PA, *52*
DNA Search, Inc. (C), CA, *313*
DS&A (Doug Sears & Assoc.) (C), FL, *315*
The Duncan-O'Dell Group Inc. (C), TX, *316*
Dunhill Search of Medford (C), NJ, *321*
G. L. Dykstra Assoc., Inc. (C), MI, *323*
H. J. Elliot, Inc. (R), IL, *58*
Executech (R), OH, *62*
The Executive Group, Inc. (R), CA, *62*
Executive Placement Consultants (C), IL, *333*
Executive Referral Services, Inc. (C), IL, *334*
Executive Resource Group, Inc. (R), ME, *63*
Executive Search, Ltd. (C), OH, *336*
Executive Search of New England, Inc. (C), ME, *336*
Executive Search Partners (R), NY, *63*
The Executive Source Inc. (R), NY, *64*
FAI (C), CO, *338*
Faro Consultants Int'l. (C), VA, *338*
Fenwick Partners (R), MA, *66*
Eileen Finn & Assoc., Inc. (C), NY, *341*
Fishel HR Assoc., Inc. (C), AZ, *341*
Flynn, Hannock, Inc. (R), CT, *69*
Focus Consulting Services, Inc. (C), FL, *342*
Fogec Consultants, Inc. (R), WI, *69*
Fortune Personnel Consultants of Huntsville, Inc. (C), AL, *343*
F-O-R-T-U-N-E Personnel Consultants of Savannah, Inc. (C), GA, *345*
Fortune Consultants of Ft. Washington (C), PA, *349*
Forum Personnel Inc. (C), NY, *351*
Foster Partners (R), NY, *70*
Fought, Jameson Assoc. (C), IL, *351*
Fresquez & Assoc. (C), CA, *352*
C. F. Furr & Co. (R), NC, *72*
Gaming Consultants, Inc. (R), LA, *74*
Gatti & Assoc. (C), MA, *355*
Gilbert & Van Campen Int'l. (R), NY, *76*
Gilmore & Assoc. (C), CA, *357*
Global 1000 Int'l. Services (C), CA, *358*
H. L. Goehring & Assoc., Inc. (C), OH, *359*
Barry M. Gold & Co. (C), CA, *359*
Fred J. Goldsmith Assoc. (R), CA, *79*
Goodkind Assoc. Inc. (C), NY, *360*
Goodrich & Sherwood Assoc., Inc. (R), NY, *79*
Gould, McCoy & Chadick, Inc. (R), NY, *80*
The Governance Group, Inc. (R), NJ, *80*
Grantham & Co., Inc. (R), NC, *81*
Sheila Greco Assoc. (C), NY, *362*
R. Green & Assoc., Inc. (C), OH, *362*
Greene Personnel Consultants (C), RI, *362*
GWS Partners (R), IL, *84*
The H. S. Group, Inc. (C), WI, *365*
Harbrowe, Inc. (C), NY, *368*
Hardage Group (C), TN, *369*
Hazard, Young, Attea & Assoc., Ltd. (C), IL, *371*
Healey Executive Search, Inc. (R), MN, *88*
Hodge-Cronin & Assoc., Inc. (R), IL, *94*
HRD Consultants, Inc. (R), NJ, *97*
The Human Resource Department Ltd. (R), OH, *98*
Human Resource Solutions (R), TX, *98*
Human Resources Personnel Agency (R), AR, *99*
Insurance Search (C), TX, *390*
Integrity Search, Inc. (R), PA, *102*
InteliSearch, Inc. (R), CT, *102*
Interim Management Resources Inc. (C), ON, *392*
Intersource, Ltd. (R), GA, *103*
IprGroup, Inc. (C), GA, *394*
Isaacson, Miller (R), MA, *104*
Jacobson Assoc. (C), IL, *396*
Jakobs & Assoc. Int'l. (R), NY, *105*
JT Assoc. (C), CT, *401*
Richard Kader & Assoc. (C), OH, *403*
Kanzer Assoc., Inc. (R), IL, *109*
Karel & Co. (R), CA, *109*
Karras Personnel, Inc. (C), NJ, *403*
A.T. Kearney Executive Search (R), IL, *111*
KGA Inc. (C), WI, *406*
Kirby Assoc. (R), PA, *115*
KL Consultants (C), NJ, *407*
The Koehler Group (C), PA, *408*
Koll-Fairfield LLC (C), CT, *408*
Kressenberg Assoc. (C), TX, *409*
L&L Assoc. Global Search (C), PA, *411*
Jack B. Larsen & Assoc., Inc. (C), PA, *413*
Leeds and Leeds (C), TN, *416*
Lemming/LeVan, Inc. (R), GA, *128*
Leslie Kavanagh Assoc., Inc. (C), NY, *416*
Locke & Assoc. (R), NC, *131*
Logic Assoc., Inc. (C), NY, *419*
Lucas Group (C), NY, *421*
Fran Luisi Assoc. (R), NJ, *132*
Managed Care Resources (C), TX, *424*
Management Assoc. (C), MD, *424*
Management Recruiters of Fresno (C), CA, *440*
Management Recruiters of Clovis (C), CA, *440*
Management Recruiters of Tampa North (C), FL, *444*
Management Recruiters of Detroit & Farmington Hills (C), MI, *451*
Management Recruiters of Bloomington (C), MN, *452*
Management Recruiters of North Warren Inc. (C), NJ, *453*
Management Recruiters of Charlotte - North, Inc. (C), NC, *456*
Management Recruiters of Wilmington (C), NC, *457*
Management Recruiters of Columbia, Tennessee (C), TN, *461*
Management Recruiters of Champions (C), TX, *462*
Management Recruiters of Arlington (C), VA, *464*
Manning Lloyd Assoc. Ltd. (C), NY, *468*
Marsar & Co., Inc. (C), FL, *471*
Maximum Management Corp. (C), NY, *473*
Mary L. Mayer, Ltd. (R), MN, *139*
The McCormick Group (C), VA, *473*
The Paul McDaniel Co. (C), TN, *474*
McDonald Assoc. Int'l. (R), IL, *140*
MCS Assoc. (R), CA, *142*
Martin H. Meisel Assoc., Inc. (R), NY, *143*
Mitchell/Wolfson, Assoc. (R), IL, *145*
The Morris Group (C), PA, *486*
The MVP Group (C), NY, *487*
National Bank & Finance Executive Search (C), CA, *488*
The Noebel Search Group, Inc. (C), TX, *494*
Norman Broadbent Int'l., Inc. (R), NY, *152*
NPF Assoc. Ltd. Inc. (R), FL, *153*
Odell & Assoc., Inc. (C), TX, *498*
Ollinger Partners (R), MA, *156*
Omega Search, Inc. (C), NC, *498*
Parsons, Anderson & Gee, Inc. (C), NY, *503*
The Partnership Group (R), NJ, *160*
Peck & Assoc., Ltd. (R), WI, *161*
Penn Associates (R), PA, *161*
Perry • Newton Assoc. (C), MD, *507*
Richard Peterson & Assoc., Inc. (R), GA, *163*
Phillips Assoc. (C), FL, *510*
Pierce & Assoc. (C), CA, *512*
The Prairie Group (C), IL, *515*
Preferred Professional Recruiters (C), OH, *516*
Prime Management Group Inc. (C), ON, *518*
Priority Executive Search (C), FL, *518*
Professional Resources (C), NY, *522*
Pryor & Associates (C), CA, *525*
R.A.N. Assoc., Inc. (C), OH, *528*
Ray & Berndtson/Lovas Stanley (R), ON, *172*
Raymond Karsan Assoc. (C), PA, *529*
Michael James Reid & Co. (R), CA, *174*
The Retail Network (C), MA, *535*
Russell Reynolds Assoc., Inc. (R), NY, *176*
Rice Cohen Int'l. (R), PA, *178*
Rodgers, Ramsey, Inc. (C), TX, *540*
Rogish Assoc., Inc. (C), OH, *541*
Romano McAvoy Assoc., Inc. (C), NY, *544*
Rowland Assoc. (C), CA, *547*
Rusher, Loscavio & LoPresto (R), CA, *183*
K. Russo Assoc. Inc. (C), CT, *548*
Ryan-Allen & Assoc., Inc. (C), CA, *549*
Sales Consultants of Houston (C), TX, *563*

Schall Executive Search Partners (R), MN, *185*
Search Consultants, Inc. (C), NJ, *575*
Search Innovations, Inc. (R), PA, *187*
Sheridan Search (R), IL, *189*
Smith & Assoc. (C), FL, *583*
Abbott Smith Assoc., Inc. (R), NY, *193*
Smith Professional Search (C), MI, *584*
Snelling Search - Transportation Division (C), AR, *585*
Robert Sollman & Assoc. (C), FL, *587*
Spectra International LLC (C), AZ, *589*
SpencerStuart (R), NY, *196*
Staff Extension Int'l. (C), TX, *590*
StratfordGroup (R), OH, *203*
Sullivan & Assoc. (R), MI, *204*
The Talley Group (R), VA, *205*
Tech-Net (C), TX, *601*
Tittemore Cowan Assoc. (C), AB, *607*
Tower Consultants, Ltd. (R), PA, *209*
Triad Consultants, Inc. (C), NJ, *609*
V.I.P. Resources, Inc. (C), NY, *611*
Vogel Assoc. (C), PA, *613*
Beverly von Winckler & Assoc. (C), IL, *613*
Warren Executive Services (C), GA, *616*
Waterford Executive Group Ltd. (C), IL, *616*
The Westfield Group (C), CT, *619*
Weterrings & Agnew, Inc. (C), NY, *619*
Whitney Smith Co. (C), TX, *620*
Willmott & Assoc. (C), MA, *622*
Wilson McLeran, Inc. (C), CT, *622*
Wing Tips & Pumps, Inc. (C), MI, *623*
Winston & Green (C), IL, *623*
Steven Yungerberg Assoc., Inc. (R), MN, *226*

06.2 Personnel selection, placement & records

Accelerated Data Decision, Inc. (C), NJ, *233*
Action Management Corp. (C), MI, *239*
Affordable Executive Recruiters (C), CA, *241*
Alexander Ross & Co. (R), NY, *3*
Alpha Resource Group, Inc. (C), TX, *246*
American Heritage Group, Inc. (C), MI, *247*
Aminex Corp. (C), MA, *249*
Andre David & Assoc., Inc. (R), TX, *6*
The Andre Group, Inc. (R), PA, *6*
APA Employment Agency Inc. (C), OR, *251*
R. W. Apple & Assoc. (C), NJ, *251*
Applied Resources, Inc. (C), MN, *252*
Charles P. Aquavella & Assoc. (C), TX, *252*
Atlantic Pacific Group (C), CA, *255*
Austin - Allen Co. (C), TN, *256*
Avery Assoc. (R), CA, *9*
The Ayers Group, Inc. (R), NY, *9*
Battalia Winston Int'l./The Euram Consultants Group (R), NY, *13*
The Bedford Consulting Group Inc. (R), ON, *14*
Benford & Assoc., Inc. (C), MI, *264*
Bennett & Co. Consulting Group (C), CA, *264*
C. Berger And Company (R), IL, *16*
Binder Hospitality Group (C), KY, *266*
BLB Consulting (C), NY, *268*
Tom Bogle & Assoc. (C), CA, *269*
Boone-Scaturro Assoc., Inc. (C), GA, *269*
Brindisi Search (R), MD, *23*
Bryan, Jason & Assoc. Inc. (C), ON, *275*
The Butlers Co. Insurance Recruiters (C), FL, *277*
C. P. Consulting (R), PA, *26*
C/R Associates (C), NY, *278*
Canny, Bowen Inc. (R), NY, *27*
Carlsen Resources, Inc. (R), CO, *29*
The Carlyle Group, Ltd. (R), IL, *30*
Carter, Lavoie Associates (C), RI, *285*
Chase-Gardner Executive Search Associates, Inc. (C), FL, *289*
William J. Christopher Assoc., Inc. (R), PA, *34*
Howard Clark Assoc. (C), NJ, *292*
The Comwell Company, Inc. (C), NJ, *296*
Consulting Rhonda (C), ON, *297*
Conway & Assoc. (R), IL, *40*
Philip Conway Management (R), IL, *40*
Corporate Image Group (C), TN, *300*
Corporate Leadership Strategies, Inc. (R), NH, *41*
Corporate Resources (C), OH, *301*
CountryHouse Hotels Executive Search (C), VA, *302*
Creative HR Solutions (C), GA, *303*
Creative-Leadership, Inc. (R), CA, *42*
The Currier-Winn Co., Inc. (C), NJ, *305*
Custom Resources (C), AL, *305*
Cypress Int'l., Inc. (R), FL, *45*
The Dalley Hewitt Co. (R), GA, *45*
Dalton Management Consultants, Ltd. (C), NJ, *306*
Dankowski & Assoc., Inc. (C), OH, *307*
DARE Personnel Inc. (C), ON, *307*
Daubenspeck & Associates, Ltd. (R), IL, *46*
Davis & James, Inc. (C), MO, *308*
Donna Davis Assoc. (C), NJ, *309*
Dean-Dzierzawiec Assoc. (C), NJ, *309*
Debbon Recruiting Group, Inc. (C), MO, *310*
Diversified Search, Inc. (R), PA, *52*
Dunhill Executive Search of Los Angeles, Inc. (C), CA, *319*
Dunhill Executive Search of Brown County (C), IN, *321*
Dunhill Professional Search of Greater New Orleans (C), LA, *321*
Dunhill Professional Search of Ramsey (C), NJ, *321*
Eggers Consulting Co., Inc. (C), NE, *327*
Executive Access Inc. (R), NY, *62*
Executive Exchange Corp. (C), NJ, *333*
Executive Placement Consultants (C), IL, *333*
Executive Referral Services, Inc. (C), IL, *334*
The Executive Source Inc. (R), NY, *64*
Fenwick Partners (R), MA, *66*
Financial Connections Company (C), VA, *340*
Eileen Finn & Assoc., Inc. (C), NY, *341*
Fishel HR Assoc., Inc. (C), AZ, *341*
Fogec Consultants, Inc. (R), WI, *69*
F-O-R-T-U-N-E Personnel Consultants of Greenwood Village (C), CO, *344*
F-O-R-T-U-N-E Personnel Consultants of Savannah, Inc. (C), GA, *345*
Fortune Personnel Consultants of Allentown, Inc. (C), PA, *348*
Fortune Personnel Consultants of Chattanooga Inc. (C), TN, *349*
F-O-R-T-U-N-E Personnel Consultants of Houston, Inc. (C), TX, *350*
Forum Personnel Inc. (C), NY, *351*
Foster Partners (R), NY, *70*
Fresquez & Assoc. (C), CA, *352*
Gatti & Assoc. (C), MA, *355*
Gielow Assoc., Inc. (R), WI, *76*
Gomez Fregoso y Asociados (C), JAL, *360*
Goodkind Assoc. Inc. (C), NY, *360*
Goodrich & Sherwood Assoc., Inc. (R), NY, *79*
Gould, McCoy & Chadick, Inc. (R), NY, *80*
Granger, Counts & Assoc. (R), OH, *81*
Grantham & Co., Inc. (R), NC, *81*
J. B. Groner Executive Search, Inc. (C), DE, *363*
Groupe PCA Inc. (C), QE, *363*
Hardage Group (C), TN, *369*
The Harris Consulting Corp. (R), MB, *87*
Hazard, Young, Attea & Assoc., Ltd. (C), IL, *371*
Helbling & Assoc., Inc. (R), PA, *91*
The Herrmann Group Ltd. (R), ON, *92*
Ruth Hirsch Assoc., Inc. (C), NY, *379*
Hoglund & Assoc., Inc. (R), IL, *94*
HRD Consultants, Inc. (R), NJ, *97*
The Human Resource Department Ltd. (R), OH, *98*
Human Resource Dimensions, Inc. (C), TX, *384*
Human Resource Solutions (R), TX, *98*
Independent Power Consultants (C), TX, *387*
InfoTech Search (C), TX, *388*
Insurance Career Center, Inc. (C), CT, *389*
Integrated Search Solutions Group, LLC (ISSG) (R), NY, *102*
InteliSearch, Inc. (R), CT, *102*
Intersource, Ltd. (R), GA, *103*
IprGroup, Inc. (C), GA, *394*
Isaacson, Miller (R), MA, *104*
J.B.A. Assoc. (R), WA, *104*
JenKim Int'l. Ltd., Inc. (C), FL, *398*
JNB Assoc., Inc. (C), MA, *399*
Jonathan Lawrence Assoc. (C), NJ, *400*
J. M. Joseph Assoc. (R), NJ, *109*
Karras Personnel, Inc. (C), NJ, *403*
A.T. Kearney Executive Search (R), IL, *111*
Kelly Assoc. (R), WI, *112*
Kenzer Corp. (R), NY, *113*
KGA Inc. (C), WI, *406*
Kirby Assoc. (R), PA, *115*
KL Consultants (C), NJ, *407*
The Koehler Group (C), PA, *408*
Marvin Laba & Assoc. (R), CA, *122*
Landon Morgan (C), ON, *412*
Madeleine Lav & Assoc. (C), CA, *413*

Leith & Assoc., Inc. (C), OH, *416*
Fran Luisi Assoc. (R), NJ, *132*
Magnum Search (C), IL, *422*
Major Legal Services, Inc. (C), OH, *423*
Management Recruiters, Inland Empire Agency (C), CA, *441*
Management Recruiters of St. Augustine (C), FL, *444*
Management Recruiters of Detroit & Farmington Hills (C), MI, *451*
Management Recruiters of Wilmington (C), NC, *457*
Management Solutions, Inc. (C), CA, *468*
Marsar & Co., Inc. (C), FL, *471*
Maximum Management Corp. (C), NY, *473*
Mayhall Search Group, Inc. (C), IN, *473*
Medicorp, Inc. (C), MO, *477*
Martin H. Meisel Assoc., Inc. (R), NY, *143*
Juan Menefee & Assoc. (C), IL, *478*
The Mercer Group, Inc. (R), NM, *143*
Michael Wayne Recruiters (C), IL, *480*
Millennium Search Group, Inc. (R), CA, *144*
Miller-Hall HRISearch (C), NY, *482*
Danette Milne Corporate Search Inc. (C), ON, *482*
Mirtz Morice, Inc. (R), CT, *145*
The Montgomery Group, Inc. (C), TN, *484*
The Morris Group (C), PA, *486*
MPA Executive Search Inc. (R), QE, *148*
Next Step Recruiting (C), CA, *493*
Norman Broadbent Int'l., Inc. (R), NY, *152*
NPF Assoc. Ltd. Inc. (R), FL, *153*
NRI Staffing Resources (C), DC, *496*
O'Sullivan Search Inc. (C), ON, *498*
Ollinger Partners (R), MA, *156*
Orion Int'l. Consulting Group, Inc. (C), NC, *499*
The Pailin Group Professional Search Consultants (R), TX, *158*
Parker Page Group (C), FL, *503*
Parsons, Anderson & Gee, Inc. (C), NY, *503*
Patrice & Assoc. (C), MD, *505*
Penn Associates (R), PA, *161*
Pennington Consulting Group (C), NJ, *506*
The Pennmor Group (C), NJ, *506*
Richard Peterson & Assoc., Inc. (R), GA, *163*
Petrie Partners, Inc. (R), FL, *163*
Robert Powers & Assoc. (C), CA, *515*
P. G. Prager Search Assoc., Ltd. (C), NY, *515*
The Prairie Group (C), IL, *515*
Presley Consultants, Inc. (C), CA, *517*
Price & Assoc., Inc. (C), VA, *518*
Professional Support Inc. (C), NY, *523*
L. J. Quinn & Assoc., Inc. (R), CA, *170*
Rand Thompson Executive Search Consultants (C), NY, *528*
Rand-Curtis Resources (C), AZ, *529*
Ray & Assoc., Inc. (C), IA, *529*
Recruitment Specialists, Inc. (C), MD, *532*
Michael James Reid & Co. (R), CA, *174*
Resource Networking Inc. (C), IN, *534*
Response Staffing Services (C), NY, *534*
S. Reyman & Assoc., Ltd. (R), IL, *176*
Riley Cole (C), CA, *537*
Ritt-Ritt & Assoc., Inc. (C), IL, *537*
RLM Assoc., Ltd. (R), NY, *179*
Roberts Ryan & Bentley, Inc. (R), MD, *179*
Romac Int'l. (C), PA, *542*
K. Russo Assoc. Inc. (C), CT, *548*
Rylan Forbes Consulting Group, Inc. (C), NJ, *549*
Sales & Management Search, Inc. (C), IL, *551*
Sales Consultants of Birmingham (C), AL, *555*
Sales Consultants Peninsula, Inc. (C), CA, *556*
Sampson Medical Search (C), CA, *564*
Sanford Rose Assoc. - Cedar Rapids (C), IA, *567*
The Schatz Company (C), MO, *571*
Devin Scott Assoc. (C), NJ, *572*
Scott Executive Search, Inc. (R), NY, *186*
Search Consultants, Inc. (C), NJ, *575*
Search Innovations, Inc. (R), PA, *187*
Search Research Assoc., Inc. (R), MA, *187*
Secura/Burnett Partners (R), CA, *187*
Sheridan Search (R), IL, *189*
Shey-Harding Assoc. Inc. (C), CA, *580*
Shiloh Careers Int'l., Inc. (C), TN, *580*
Abbott Smith Assoc., Inc. (R), NY, *193*
Smith Professional Search (C), MI, *584*
Snelling Search - Transportation Division (C), AR, *585*
Snelling Search (C), LA, *586*
Southern Recruiters & Consultants, Inc. (C), SC, *587*
Southern Research Services (R), FL, *195*
SpencerStuart (R), NY, *196*
Straube Associates (R), MA, *203*
Success Seekers Connection (C), FL, *596*
The Talley Group (R), VA, *205*
Target Search, Inc. (C), PA, *600*
Tomlinson Assoc. Inc. (C), IL, *607*
Tower Consultants, Ltd. (R), PA, *209*
TPS Staffing Solutions (C), IN, *608*
Van Treadaway Assoc., Inc. (R), GA, *210*
United Personnel Services (C), MA, *611*
Vogel Assoc. (C), PA, *613*
Wakefield Talabisco Int'l. (R), NY, *214*
Karen Wanger & Assoc., Inc. (C), IL, *615*
The Wayne Group, Ltd. (C), NY, *616*
Weliver & Assoc. (C), MI, *618*
West & West (R), CA, *218*
The Westfield Group (C), CT, *619*
Whitney Smith Co. (C), TX, *620*
William-Johns Co., Inc. (C), CA, *621*
Willmott & Assoc. (C), MA, *622*
Winter, Wyman & Co. (C), MA, *623*
Winthrop Partners, Inc. (R), NY, *222*
WMD inc. (C), NJ, *623*
The Woodstone Consulting Company, Inc. (R), CO, *224*
Zaccaria Int'l. (C), NJ, *627*
Helen Ziegler & Assoc., Inc. (C), ON, *627*

06.3 Training

Alexander Ross & Co. (R), NY, *3*
Allerton Heneghan & O'Neill (R), IL, *4*
APA Employment Agency Inc. (C), OR, *251*
Argonaut Partners, LLC (R), CA, *6*
Ariel Recruitment Assoc. (R), NY, *7*
The Ascher Group (R), NJ, *7*
Aurora Tech Search (C), ON, *256*
Austin - Allen Co. (C), TN, *256*
Avery Assoc. (R), CA, *9*
The Ayers Group, Inc. (R), NY, *9*
Aldonna Barry Personnel & Management (C), ON, *260*
Becker Project Resources, Inc. (C), OR, *262*
Bennett & Co. Consulting Group (C), CA, *264*
David Blevins & Assoc. (C), WA, *268*
Brindisi Search (R), MD, *23*
Broadband Resource Group (C), CA, *274*
Bryan, Jason & Assoc. Inc. (C), ON, *275*
Brystol Cove Assoc. (R), CA, *24*
The Burke Group (C), ON, *276*
C. P. Consulting (R), PA, *26*
CanMed Consultants Inc. (C), ON, *280*
The Carlyle Group, Ltd. (R), IL, *30*
The Comwell Company, Inc. (C), NJ, *296*
Creative HR Solutions (C), GA, *303*
Cypress Int'l., Inc. (R), FL, *45*
Dalton Management Consultants, Ltd. (C), NJ, *306*
Dankowski & Assoc., Inc. (C), OH, *307*
Donna Davis Assoc. (C), NJ, *309*
Dean-Dzierzawiec Assoc. (C), NJ, *309*
Dise & Co. (R), OH, *52*
Diversified Search, Inc. (R), PA, *52*
Dunhill Professional Search of Ramsey (C), NJ, *321*
The Executive Source Inc. (R), NY, *64*
ExecutiveFit (C), NY, *337*
Fenwick Partners (R), MA, *66*
Eileen Finn & Assoc., Inc. (C), NY, *341*
Finney-Taylor Personnel & Management Consultants Ltd. (C), AB, *341*
First Choice Search (R), WA, *67*
Fishel HR Assoc., Inc. (C), AZ, *341*
Flynn, Hannock, Inc. (R), CT, *69*
F-O-R-T-U-N-E Personnel Consultants of Menlo Park, Inc. (C), NJ, *347*
Foster Partners (R), NY, *70*
Fought, Jameson Assoc. (C), IL, *351*
Frye/Joure & Assoc., Inc. (C), TN, *353*
Gatti & Assoc. (C), MA, *355*
C. R. Gerald & Assoc. (C), ON, *356*
Howard Gilmore & Assoc. (R), OH, *77*
Goodkind Assoc. Inc. (C), NY, *360*
Gould, McCoy & Chadick, Inc. (R), NY, *80*
Hardage Group (C), TN, *369*
Hazard, Young, Attea & Assoc., Ltd. (C), IL, *371*
Healthcare Recruiters of the Rockies, Inc. (C), CO, *372*
The Helms Int'l. Group (R), VA, *91*
Hintz Associates (C), NY, *378*
Hospitality Executive Search, Inc. (R), MA, *96*
HRD Consultants, Inc. (R), NJ, *97*
Human Capital Resources, Inc. (C), FL, *384*
The Human Resource Department Ltd. (R), OH, *98*
Human Resource Dimensions, Inc. (C), TX, *384*

Human Resource Solutions (R), TX, *98*
The Hyde Group, Inc. (R), CT, *101*
International Business Partners (C), ON, *392*
Intersource, Ltd. (R), GA, *103*
IprGroup, Inc. (C), GA, *394*
Isaacson, Miller (R), MA, *104*
Jones and Jones (R), OR, *108*
Kabana Corp. (C), MI, *402*
Karras Personnel, Inc. (C), NJ, *403*
A.T. Kearney Executive Search (R), IL, *111*
Kenmore Executives Inc. (C), FL, *405*
KGA Inc. (C), WI, *406*
Kincaid Group Inc. (KGI) (C), TX, *406*
KL Consultants (C), NJ, *407*
The Koehler Group (C), PA, *408*
John Kuhn & Assoc., Inc. (R), WI, *121*
Kulper & Co., L.L.C. (R), NJ, *121*
Leslie Kavanagh Assoc., Inc. (C), NY, *416*
Pat Licata & Assoc. (C), NC, *417*
Fran Luisi Assoc. (R), NJ, *132*
MacNaughton Assoc. (R), CA, *133*
Management Recruiters of Fresno (C), CA, *440*
Management Recruiters of Charlotte - North, Inc. (C), NC, *456*
Management Recruiters of Wilmington (C), NC, *457*
Management Recruiters of Lionville, Inc. (C), PA, *459*
Management Recruiters of Columbia, Tennessee (C), TN, *461*
Management Recruiters of Arlington (C), VA, *464*
Mangieri/Solutions LLC (C), CT, *468*
ManTech Consulting (C), NY, *468*
Marc-Allen Assoc., Inc. (C), FL, *469*
Marshall-Alan Assoc., Inc. (C), NY, *471*
Maximum Management Corp. (C), NY, *473*
The Paul McDaniel Co. (C), TN, *474*
McIntyre Management Resources (C), ON, *474*
The Morris Group (C), PA, *486*
The MVP Group (C), NY, *487*
Norman Broadbent Int'l., Inc. (R), NY, *152*
NPF Assoc. Ltd. Inc. (R), FL, *153*
Nursing Technomics (R), PA, *153*
O'Rourke Companies, Inc. (R), TX, *154*
Parsons, Anderson & Gee, Inc. (C), NY, *503*
Penn Associates (R), PA, *161*
Perfect Search, Inc. (C), FL, *507*
Personnel Alliance Group (C), NJ, *507*
Petrie Partners, Inc. (R), FL, *163*
Plante & Moran, LLP (R), MI, *165*
Robert Powers & Assoc. (C), CA, *515*
The Prairie Group (C), IL, *515*
Professional Resources (C), NY, *522*
The Professional Sales Search Co., Inc. (C), WA, *522*
Protocol Inc. (C), CA, *525*
R & L Assoc., Ltd. (R), NY, *170*
Mary Rector & Assoc., Inc. (C), IL, *533*
Michael James Reid & Co. (R), CA, *174*
The Retail Network (C), MA, *535*
Rice Cohen Int'l. (R), PA, *178*
Ritt-Ritt & Assoc., Inc. (C), IL, *537*
Rodgers, Ramsey, Inc. (C), TX, *540*
Roth Young of Tampa (C), FL, *546*
K. Russo Assoc. Inc. (C), CT, *548*
Ryan-Allen & Assoc., Inc. (C), CA, *549*
Sales Consultants Peninsula, Inc. (C), CA, *556*
Sales Consultants of Stamford-Darien (C), CT, *557*
Sales Consultants of Houston (C), TX, *563*
Sanford Rose Assoc. - Pittsburgh North (C), PA, *570*
Search Consultants, Inc. (C), NJ, *575*
Search Innovations, Inc. (R), PA, *187*
Sheridan Search (R), IL, *189*
Abbott Smith Assoc., Inc. (R), NY, *193*
Smith Professional Search (C), MI, *584*
SpencerStuart (R), NY, *196*
Staff Extension Int'l. (C), TX, *590*
StaffWriters Plus (C), NY, *591*
Starbridge Group Inc. (C), VA, *591*
Sterling Int'l. Management Recruitment, Ltd. Inc. (C), NC, *592*
The Talley Group (R), VA, *205*
Templeton & Assoc. (C), MN, *605*
Thor, Inc. (C), CA, *606*
Tower Consultants, Ltd. (R), PA, *209*
Vincenty & Co. (C), OH, *612*
Vogel Assoc. (C), PA, *613*
Kelly Walker Assoc. (C), TX, *614*
The Westfield Group (C), CT, *619*
The Whittaker Group (C), MI, *620*
William-Johns Co., Inc. (C), CA, *621*
Willmott & Assoc. (C), MA, *622*
R. S. Wyatt Assoc., Inc. (R), TX, *225*
The Yaiser Group (C), NJ, *625*
Yankee Hospitality Search (C), CT, *626*

07.0 Finance & accounting

The 500 Granary Inc. (C), ON, *231*
A la Carte Int'l., Inc. (R), VA, *1*
A Permanent Success Employment Services (C), CA, *231*
A-L Assoc., Inc. (R), NY, *1*
A. D. & Assoc. Executive Search, Inc. (C), GA, *231*
A.K.S. Assoc., Ltd. (R), MA, *1*
A.L.S. Group (C), NJ, *232*
Abacus Group LLC (C), NY, *232*
Abbott Associates (R), CA, *1*
The Abbott Group, Inc. (R), MD, *1*
Abécassis Conseil (R), QE, *1*
Abeln, Magy & Assoc., Inc. (R), MN, *1*
Cathy Abelson Legal Search (C), PA, *232*
B. J. Abrams & Assoc. Inc. (C), IL, *233*
Accelerated Data Decision, Inc. (C), NJ, *233*
Accent On Achievement, Inc. (C), MI, *233*
Access/Resources, Inc. (C), MA, *234*
Account Ability Now (C), MI, *234*
Accountancies (C), CA, *234*
Accountants Executive Search (C), CT, *234*
Accountants Executive Search (C), PA, *234*
Accountants On Call (C), NJ, *234*
Accountants On Call (C), FL, *237*
Accountants Executive Search (C), CA, *237*
Accountants On Call (C), TN, *237*
Accounting & Bookkeeping Personnel, Inc. (C), AZ, *237*
Accounting & Computer Personnel (C), NY, *238*
Accounting Additions (C), CA, *238*
Accounting Personnel & Engineering Personnel Consultants (C), LA, *238*
Active Search & Placement Inc. (C), CA, *239*
Adept Tech Recruiting, Inc. (C), NY, *240*
Adirect Recruiting Corp. (C), ON, *240*
ADR Accounting Management Recruiters (C), ON, *240*
Advanced Executive Resources (R), MI, *2*
Advantage Partners, Inc. (R), OH, *2*
Advice Personnel Inc. (C), NY, *241*
Advisors' Search Group, Inc. (C), NY, *241*
The Advisory Group, Inc. (R), CA, *2*
AES Search (C), NJ, *241*
Affordable Executive Recruiters (C), CA, *241*
Aggressive Corporation (C), IL, *242*
AGRI-associates (C), MO, *242*
Agri-Personnel (C), GA, *242*
Agri-Tech Personnel, Inc. (C), MO, *242*
Ahrensdorf & Assoc. (R), PA, *2*
J. R. Akin & Co. (R), MA, *2*
Alexander Associates (R), NJ, *2*
The Alexander Group (R), TX, *3*
The Alfus Group (R), NY, *3*
Allard Associates (C), CA, *244*
Allen & Assoc. (C), NV, *244*
David Allen Assoc. (R), NJ, *3*
Allen Austin Lowe & Powers (R), TX, *3*
Allen, Wayne & Co. LLC (C), WI, *245*
Allen/Associates (R), OH, *4*
Allerton Heneghan & O'Neill (R), IL, *4*
Alliance Executive Search, Inc. (R), MA, *4*
Allied Search, Inc. (C), CA, *245*
Allman & Co., Inc. (C), NC, *245*
Alpha Resource Group, Inc. (C), TX, *246*
Alpha Search (C), FL, *246*
ALW Research Int'l. (R), NJ, *4*
AM & G Certified Public Accountants & Consultants (R), IL, *4*
Amato & Assoc., Inc. (C), CA, *246*
Amato & Associates Insurance Recruiters (C), PA, *247*
Peter W. Ambler Co. (R), TX, *5*
Ambridge Management Corp. (C), ON, *247*
American Executive Management, Inc. (R), MA, *5*
American Professional Search, Inc. (C), TN, *248*
American Resources Corp. (C), IL, *248*
AmeriPro Search, Inc. (C), NC, *248*
AmeriResource Group Inc. (C), OK, *248*
Ames-O'Neill Assoc., Inc. (C), NY, *249*
Amherst Human Resource Group, Ltd. (C), IL, *249*
Aminex Corp. (C), MA, *249*
AMS Int'l. (R), VA, *5*
Analytic Recruiting, Inc. (C), NY, *249*
Anderson & Schwab, Inc. (R), NY, *5*
Anderson Network Group (C), OH, *250*
Andre David & Assoc., Inc. (R), TX, *6*
Andrews & Assoc. (C), NC, *250*
Andrews & Wald Group (C), FL, *250*
Angel Group Int'l. (C), KY, *250*

Angus Employment Ltd. (C), ON, *250*
The Angus Group, Ltd. (C), OH, *251*
APA Search, Inc. (R), NY, *6*
David Aplin & Assoc. (C), AB, *251*
Charles P. Aquavella & Assoc. (C), TX, *252*
Argonaut Partners, LLC (R), CA, *6*
Argus National, Inc. (R), CT, *6*
Ariail & Assoc. (R), NC, *7*
Ariel Recruitment Assoc. (R), NY, *7*
Armitage Associates Ltd. (R), ON, *7*
Armor Personnel (C), ON, *253*
J. S. Armstrong & Assoc., Inc. (R), CA, *7*
Patrick Arnone & Assoc. Inc. (R), VA, *7*
Aronow Assoc., Inc. (C), FL, *253*
Artgo, Inc. (R), OH, *7*
A. Artze Assoc.-Personnel Consultants (C), PR, *253*
The Ascher Group (R), NJ, *7*
Ashlar-Stone Management Consultants Inc. (R), ON, *8*
E. J. Ashton & Assoc., Ltd. (C), IL, *253*
Ashway Ltd. Agency (C), NY, *253*
Ashworth Consultants, Inc. (R), MA, *8*
The Associates, HR Search Executives, Inc. (C), OK, *254*
W. R. Atchison & Assoc., Inc. (C), NC, *254*
Atlanta Executive Partners, Inc. (R), MA, *8*
Atlantic Pacific Group (C), CA, *255*
Atlantic Search Group, Inc. (C), MA, *255*
Atlantic West Int'l. (C), NC, *255*
ATS Executive Recruitment (C), GA, *255*
Aubin Int'l. Inc. (R), MA, *8*
Auerbach Associates, Inc. (R), MA, *9*
A. M. Auster Associates (R), FL, *9*
Austin, Hill & Assoc. (C), MD, *256*
Austin-McGregor Int'l. (R), TX, *9*
AutoPeople (C), VT, *257*
Avalon Health Group, Inc. (R), NY, *9*
Avery Assoc. (R), CA, *9*
The Ayers Group, Inc. (R), NY, *9*
The Badger Group (R), CA, *10*
Baeder Kalinski Int'l. Group, Inc. (R), NH, *10*
Keith Bagg & Assoc., Inc. (C), ON, *257*
Baker Scott & Co. (C), NJ, *258*
Baldwin Associates, LLC (R), CT, *10*
Allen Ballach Assoc. Inc. (R), ON, *10*
The Bankers Register (C), NY, *259*
Barger & Sargeant, Inc. (R), NH, *11*
J. W. Barleycorn, Renard & Assoc., Inc. (R), OH, *11*
Fred A. Barnette & Assoc. (R), NC, *11*
Barr Associates (C), NY, *260*
The Barrett Group (C), NH, *260*
Barrett Hospitality Search (R), CA, *12*
Barrett Partners (C), IL, *260*
Barrett Rose & Lee, Inc. (C), ON, *260*
Barrington Hart, Inc. (R), IL, *12*
Nathan Barry Assoc., Inc. (R), MA, *12*
Barth Smith Company (R), IL, *12*
Bartholdi & Co., Inc. (R), CO, *12*
Bartl & Evins (C), NY, *260*
Barton Assoc., Inc. (R), TX, *12*
Bason Associates (R), OH, *13*
Battalia Winston Int'l./The Euram Consultants Group (R), NY, *13*
Martin H. Bauman Assoc., Inc. (R), NY, *13*
BayResearch Group, Inc. (R), IL, *14*
BCG Search, Inc. (R), FL, *14*
Beach Executive Search Inc. (R), FL, *14*
Beacon Int'l., Inc. (C), VA, *261*
The Beam Group (R), PA, *14*
Becker, Norton & Co. (R), PA, *14*
Becker Personnel (C), FL, *262*
The Bedford Consulting Group Inc. (R), ON, *14*
Behavioral Science Assoc., Inc. (R), AZ, *15*
Neail Behringer Consultants Inc. (R), NY, *15*
Belanger Partners Ltd. (C), ON, *262*
Edward Bell Assoc. (C), CA, *263*
Gary S. Bell Assoc., Inc. (C), NJ, *263*
Bell Oaks Co., Inc. (C), GA, *263*
Bell Wishingrad Partners Inc. (R), NY, *15*
Joy Reed Belt Search Consultants, Inc. (R), OK, *15*
J. P. Bencik Assoc. (C), MI, *263*
Benford & Assoc., Inc. (C), MI, *264*
N. L. Benke & Assoc., Inc. (C), OH, *264*
Bennett & Associates (C), TX, *264*
Bennett Search & Consulting Co. (R), FL, *16*
Benson Associates (C), NY, *264*
Berger & Leff (C), CA, *264*
Bergeris & Co., Inc. (C), NY, *265*
Berglund Int'l. Resources, Inc. (C), TX, *265*
Bertrand, Ross & Assoc., Inc. (C), IL, *266*
BEST/World Assoc. Inc. (R), TX, *16*
BG & Assoc. (C), MD, *266*
BGB Assoc., Inc. (C), IL, *266*
Bialecki Inc. (R), NY, *17*
Bialla & Assoc. Inc. (R), CA, *17*
Billington & Assoc. (R), CA, *17*
Binder Hospitality Group (C), KY, *266*
BioQuest Inc. (R), CA, *17*
Birch & Associes (C), QE, *267*
The Black Leopard (C), CA, *267*
Blackhawk Advantage, Inc. (C), CA, *267*
The Blackman Kallick Search Division (C), IL, *267*
J: Blakslee Int'l., Ltd. (R), CA, *18*
Blaney Executive Search (R), MA, *18*
David Blevins & Assoc. (C), WA, *268*
D. R. Blood & Assoc. (R), AZ, *18*
Boardroom Consultants/Kenny Kindler Tholke (R), NY, *19*
Bodner Inc. (C), NY, *268*
Boettcher Assoc. (R), WI, *19*
Tom Bogle & Assoc. (C), CA, *269*
Bonell Ryan Inc. (R), NY, *19*
Bonifield Assoc. (C), NJ, *269*
Bonnell Assoc. Ltd. (R), CT, *19*
Boone-Scaturro Assoc., Inc. (C), GA, *269*
Bor-Maq Assoc. (C), TX, *269*
Lynn Borne & Co. (C), CA, *270*
Bosch & Assoc., LLC (R), CT, *19*
Boston Professional Search, Inc. (C), MA, *270*
Boulware & Assoc. Inc. (R), IL, *20*
BowdenGlobal, Ltd. (R), OH, *20*
Bowman & Marshall, Inc. (C), KS, *271*
Boyden (R), NY, *20*
Boyle/Ogata Executive Search (R), CA, *21*
The Bradbury Management Group, Inc. (R), CA, *21*
Bradford Executives Int'l. (C), VA, *271*
The Brand Co., Inc. (R), FL, *22*
Brandt Associates (C), PA, *272*
Branthover Assoc. (C), NY, *272*
Brault & Assoc., Ltd. (R), VA, *22*
Jerold Braun & Assoc. (C), CA, *272*
Bredeson Executive Recruitment, LLC (R), TX, *22*
The Brentwood Group, Inc. (R), NJ, *22*
The Brentwood Group Ltd. (R), OR, *23*
Briant Assoc., Inc. (R), IL, *23*
The Bridge (C), CO, *273*
BridgeGate LLC (C), CA, *273*
Brigade, Inc. (R), CA, *23*
Brissenden, McFarland, Fuccella & Reynolds, Inc. (R), NJ, *23*
Bristol Assoc., Inc. (C), CA, *274*
Broad Waverly & Assoc. (C), NJ, *274*
Brookman Associates (C), NY, *274*
Bernard E. Brooks & Assoc., Inc. (R), SC, *24*
D. Brown & Assoc., Inc. (C), OR, *275*
J. B. Brown & Assoc., Inc. (C), OH, *275*
Brown Venture Assoc. (R), CA, *24*
Brush Creek Partners (R), MO, *24*
BRW Search (C), MN, *275*
Bryan, Jason & Assoc. Inc. (C), ON, *275*
Bullis & Co., Inc. (R), CA, *25*
The Burgess Group-Corporate Recruiters Int'l., Inc. (R), NY, *25*
Burke & Assoc./The Westfield Group (C), CT, *276*
Burkholder & Assoc., Inc. (C), TX, *276*
Joseph R. Burns & Assoc., Inc. (R), NJ, *25*
Busch International (R), CA, *25*
Business Solutions Worldwide, Inc. (C), NJ, *277*
The Butlers Co. Insurance Recruiters (C), FL, *277*
Butterfass, Pepe & MacCallan Inc. (R), NJ, *25*
Buzhardt Assoc. (R), MS, *25*
Byron Leonard Int'l., Inc. (R), CA, *25*
C & H Personnel (C), PA, *277*
C and P Marketing, Ltd. (C), OK, *278*
C. G. & Assoc. (R), PA, *26*
C. M. Management Services, Inc. (R), KY, *26*
C. P. Consulting (R), PA, *26*
C.T.E.W. Executive Personnel Services Inc. (C), BC, *278*
C/R Associates (C), NY, *278*
California Management Search (C), CA, *279*
Callan Assoc., Ltd. (R), IL, *27*
Cambridge Group Ltd. - Exec. Search Div. (C), CT, *279*
The Cambridge Group Ltd. (C), CT, *280*
Cambridge Management Planning (R), ON, *27*
T. M. Campbell Co. (R), WA, *27*
Canadian Career Partners (R), AB, *27*
Canny, Bowen Inc. (R), NY, *27*
Canyon Consulting, Inc. (C), TX, *281*
Capital Consulting Group, Inc. (R), MD, *28*
Capital Markets Resources, Inc. (C), NC, *281*
Caplan Assoc., Inc. (R), NJ, *28*
The Caplan-Taylor Group (R), CA, *28*
Capstone Inc. (R), NY, *29*

Career Advisors, Inc. (C), FL, *281*
Career Consultants (R), IN, *29*
Career Counseling Inc. (CCI) (C), KY, *282*
Career Development Associates (C), NV, *282*
Career Marketing Consultants, Inc. (C), GA, *282*
Career Specialists, Inc. (R), WA, *29*
Career Strategies, Inc. (C), CA, *283*
Careerfit, Inc. (C), TX, *283*
Careers/Inc. (C), PR, *284*
Carion Resource Group Inc. (C), ON, *284*
Carlsen Resources, Inc. (R), CO, *29*
Carlson & Czeswik (R), MN, *30*
Carnegie Partners, Inc. (R), IL, *30*
Carpenter, Shackleton & Company (R), IL, *30*
Carrington & Carrington, Ltd. (R), IL, *30*
Carson-Thomas & Assoc. (C), CA, *284*
Carter-Evdemon & Assoc. (C), FL, *285*
Caruso & Assoc., Inc. (R), FL, *31*
Carver Search Consultants (C), CA, *285*
The CARVIR Group, Inc. (C), GA, *285*
Cary & Assoc. (R), FL, *31*
Rosemary Cass Ltd. (R), CT, *31*
The Cassie Group (R), NJ, *31*
Catalyx Group (R), NY, *31*
Michael J. Cavanagh & Assoc. Inc. (R), ON, *31*
CCI - Career Consultants Int'l. (C), CA, *286*
CEC Associates (R), MA, *32*
Cejka Healthcare Executive Search Services (CHESS) (R), MO, *32*
Cella Assoc. (C), GA, *286*
Cemco, Ltd. (C), IL, *286*
The Center for Career Advancement, LLC (C), NJ, *287*
Century Assoc., Inc. (C), PA, *287*
The Century Group (C), CA, *287*
The Century Group (C), KS, *287*
CFOs 2 Go (C), CA, *288*
cFour Partners (R), CA, *32*
CFR Executive Search, Inc. (C), IL, *288*
Chad Management Group (C), ON, *288*
David Chambers & Assoc., Inc. (R), CT, *32*
Vickers Chambless Managed Search (C), GA, *288*
Chanko-Ward, Ltd. (R), NY, *33*
The Chatham Group, Ltd. (C), CT, *289*
Chelsea Resources, Inc. (C), CT, *290*
The Cherbonnier Group, Inc. (R), TX, *33*
Chesapeake Group (C), CT, *290*
Chicago Legal Search, Ltd. (C), IL, *290*
Christenson Hutchison McDowell, LLC (R), NJ, *34*
Christian & Timbers, Inc. (R), OH, *34*
Christmas, McIvor & Assoc. Inc. (C), ON, *290*
Churchill & Affiliates, Inc. (R), PA, *35*
M. A. Churchill & Assoc., Inc. (R), PA, *35*
The Churchill Group (C), ON, *291*
Cizek Assoc., Inc. (R), AZ, *35*
CJA-The Adler Group, Inc. (R), CA, *35*
Claimsearch (C), CA, *291*
Clarey & Andrews, Inc. (R), IL, *35*
Clarey/Napier Int'l., L.C. (R), TX, *35*
Howard Clark Assoc. (C), NJ, *292*
CMC Search Consultants (C), IL, *293*
CMS, Inc. (C), NH, *293*
CMS Management Services LLC (C), IN, *293*
Coast Personnel Services Ltd. (C), BC, *293*
Coastal Int'l., Inc. (R), MA, *36*
COBA Executive Search (R), CO, *36*
Cochran, Cochran & Yale, Inc. (R), NY, *36*
Coe & Co. Int'l. Inc./EMA Partners Int'l. (R), AB, *37*
The Coelyn Group (R), CA, *37*
Cole, Warren & Long, Inc. (R), PA, *37*
J. Kevin Coleman & Assoc., Inc. (R), CA, *37*
Coleman Lew & Assoc., Inc. (R), NC, *37*
Colt Systems Professional Personnel Services (C), CA, *294*
Colton Bernard Inc. (R), CA, *37*
The Colton Partnership, Inc. (R), NY, *38*
Columbia Consulting Group (R), MD, *38*
Compass Group Ltd. (R), MI, *38*
CompuPro (C), IL, *295*
Conard Associates, Inc. (R), NH, *39*
Conasa de Mexico, S.C. (R), MX, *39*
Concorde Search Assoc. (C), NY, *296*
Conex Inc./InterSearch (R), NY, *39*
Robert Connelly & Assoc., Inc. (R), MN, *39*
M. L. Conner (C), FL, *296*
Connors, Lovell & Assoc. Inc. (C), ON, *296*
Conroy Partners Ltd. (R), AB, *39*
Consolidated Management Services (C), ON, *296*
The Consortium (C), NY, *296*
Conspectus, Inc. (C), NY, *297*
Construct Management Services (C), MN, *297*
Consulpro (R), ON, *39*
Consulting Resource Group, Inc. (C), GA, *297*
Consulting Rhonda (C), ON, *297*
Philip Conway Management (R), IL, *40*
P. G. Cook Assoc. (R), TN, *40*
Cook Assoc.,® Inc. (R), IL, *40*
The Cooke Group (R), WI, *40*
David C. Cooper & Assoc. Financial Search (C), GA, *298*
Cornell Group Int'l. Consulting, Inc. (R), NY, *41*
Cornerstone Search Assoc. Inc. (C), MA, *299*
Corporate Advisors, Inc. (C), FL, *299*
The Corporate Advisory Group (R), NJ, *41*
The Corporate Connection, Ltd. (C), VA, *299*
Corporate Image Group (C), TN, *300*
Corporate Resources (C), OH, *301*
Corporate Search Consultants, Inc. (C), FL, *301*
Corporate Search, Inc. (C), NY, *301*
Corporate Select Int'l., Ltd. (C), IL, *301*
The Corporate Source Group, Inc. (R), MA, *41*
Leonard Corwen Assoc. (C), NY, *302*
J. D. Cotter Search Inc. (C), OH, *302*
CountryHouse Hotels Executive Search (C), VA, *302*
Cowell & Associates, Ltd. (R), IL, *42*
Crane, Reed & Co., Inc. (C), NH, *302*
Creative Financial Staffing Inc. (C), ON, *303*
Creative Input, Inc. (C), RI, *303*
Creative Management Strategies, Ltd. (R), NY, *42*
Creative-Leadership, Inc. (R), CA, *42*
CRI Professional Search (C), CA, *303*
The Cris Group, Inc. (R), NY, *42*
Crispi, Wagner & Co., Inc. (R), NY, *43*
Crist Partners, Ltd. (R), IL, *43*
Marlene Critchfield Co. (C), CA, *303*
Criterion Executive Search, Inc. (C), FL, *303*
Cromwell Partners, Inc. (R), NY, *43*
Crowder & Company (R), MI, *43*
Crowe Chizek & Co. (C), IN, *304*
Timothy D. Crowe, Jr. (R), MA, *43*
CTR (R), CA, *43*
Culver Personnel Services (C), CA, *304*
Curran Partners, Inc. (R), CT, *44*
The Currier-Winn Co., Inc. (C), NJ, *305*
Tony Curtis & Associates (C), ON, *305*
The Curtiss Group International (R), FL, *44*
The Custer Group, Inc. (R), TN, *44*
Custom Resources (C), AL, *305*
Cybernautic Corp. (C), CT, *305*
Cyntal Int'l. Ltd. (R), NY, *44*
Cypress Int'l., Inc. (R), FL, *45*
D.A.I Human Resources Consultants (R), QE, *45*
D.A.L. Associates, Inc. (R), CT, *45*
Dahl-Morrow Int'l. (R), VA, *45*
The Danbrook Group, Inc. (C), TX, *306*
Alfred Daniels & Assoc., Inc. (R), CA, *46*
Dapexs Consultants, Inc. (C), NY, *307*
DARE Personnel Inc. (C), ON, *307*
Datamatics Management Services, Inc. (C), NJ, *307*
Daubenspeck & Associates, Ltd. (R), IL, *46*
Davies, Park (R), AB, *46*
Davis & James, Inc. (C), MO, *308*
Joseph A. Davis Consultants, Inc. (R), NY, *47*
Bert Davis Executive Search, Inc. (R), NY, *47*
Bert Davis Publishing Placement Consultants (C), NY, *309*
The Dayton Group, Ltd. (C), NY, *309*
DBL Associates (C), CA, *309*
Dean-MacDonald (R), OH, *47*
DeCaster Assoc. (C), WI, *310*
Defrain Mayer (R), KS, *48*
Thorndike Deland Assoc. LLC (R), NY, *48*
S. W. Delano & Co. (R), CT, *48*
Delta Services (R), TX, *48*
Derhak Ireland & Partners Ltd. (R), ON, *48*
Rob Dey Executive Search (R), FL, *49*
Diamond Tax Recruiting (C), NY, *312*
Dieckmann & Assoc., Ltd. (R), IL, *51*
DieckMueller Group (R), WI, *51*
The Diestel Group (R), UT, *51*
DiMarchi Partners (R), CO, *51*
J. Dinerstein & Co., Inc. (R), NY, *51*
Robert W. Dingman Co., Inc. (R), CA, *52*
Dinte Resources, Inc. (R), VA, *52*
Discovery, The Staffing Specialists, Inc. (C), IL, *312*
Dise & Co. (R), OH, *52*
Diversified Health Search (R), PA, *52*

Diversified Management Resources (C), IL, *313*
Diversified Search, Inc. (R), PA, *52*
Dixie Search Assoc. (C), GA, *313*
DLG Assoc., Inc. (R), NC, *53*
DNA Search, Inc. (C), CA, *313*
Doering & Assoc. (C), CA, *313*
Dominguez-Metz & Assoc. (R), CA, *53*
Domres Professional Search (R), WI, *53*
Donahue/Bales Assoc. (R), IL, *54*
Donini Assoc. (R), VA, *54*
J P Donnelly Assoc., Inc. (C), NY, *314*
The Doty Group (C), TX, *314*
Douglas-Allen, Inc. (R), MA, *54*
Dow Consultants Int'l. (C), NY, *314*
Downing & Downing, Inc. (C), OH, *314*
Drake & Assoc. (C), CA, *315*
Drew Assoc. Int'l. (R), NJ, *54*
Drinkwater & Assoc. (R), MA, *54*
Drummond Assoc., Inc. (C), NY, *315*
DS&A (Doug Sears & Assoc.) (C), FL, *315*
J. H. Dugan & Assoc., Inc. (R), CA, *55*
M. Dunbar & Assoc. (C), TX, *316*
Dunhill Staffing Systems, Inc. (C), NY, *316*
Dunhill Professional Search of Miami (C), FL, *319*
Dunhill of San Francisco, Inc. (C), CA, *319*
Dunhill of Ft. Collins, Inc. (C), CO, *319*
Dunhill Professional Search of Hawaii (C), HI, *320*
Dunhill of Manchester Inc. (C), NH, *321*
Dunhill Search of Medford (C), NJ, *321*
Dunhill Professional Search of Omaha, Inc. (C), NE, *321*
Dunhill Personnel Service of Fargo (C), ND, *322*
Dunhill Personnel of Northeast Tulsa, Inc. (C), OK, *322*
Dunhill Search of Arlington (C), TX, *322*
Dunhill Professional Search of Bucks-Mont., Inc. (C), PA, *322*
Dunhill Professional Search of Wilkes-Barre/Scranton, Inc. (C), PA, *322*
Dunhill Professional Search of Richmond (C), VA, *323*
Dunhill Search of Vermont (C), VT, *323*
Dunlap & Sullivan Assoc. (R), MI, *55*
Dunn Associates (R), PA, *55*
C. A. Durakis Assoc., Inc. (R), MD, *55*
Donald F. Dvorak & Co. (R), IL, *55*
Dwyer Consulting Group, Inc. (R), WV, *56*
Gwen Dycus & Assoc. (C), FL, *323*
Dynamic Staffing Network (C), IL, *324*
The E & K Group (C), NJ, *324*
E T Search Inc. (C), CA, *324*
E/Search Int'l. (C), CT, *325*
EA Plus, Inc. (C), TX, *325*
EagleView, Inc. (C), MA, *325*
Earley Kielty & Assoc., Inc. (R), NY, *56*
Eastman & Beaudine, Inc. (R), TX, *56*
ECG Resources, Inc. (C), NY, *326*
Eden & Assoc., Inc. (C), PA, *326*
The Edge Resource Group (C), PA, *326*
Bruce Edwards & Associates, Inc. (R), NC, *56*
Effective Search, Inc. (R), IL, *57*
D. C. Egan & Assoc. (C), GA, *327*
Richard A. Eisner & Co., LLP (R), NY, *57*
William J. Elam & Assoc. (R), NE, *58*
Elinvar (C), NC, *328*
Yves Elkas Inc. (R), QE, *58*
Gene Ellefson & Assoc. Inc. (C), MI, *328*
Elliot Assoc. Inc. (R), NY, *58*
H. J. Elliot, Inc. (R), IL, *58*
The Elliott Company (R), MA, *58*
Ellis & Associates (C), HI, *328*
Ellis Career Consultants (C), NJ, *328*
Elwell & Assoc., Inc. (R), MI, *59*
Mark Elzweig Co., Ltd. (C), NY, *329*
EMN/Witt/Kieffer (R), MA, *59*
Empire International (R), PA, *59*
Employ® (C), PA, *330*
Epsen, Fuller & Assoc., LLC (R), NJ, *60*
Erikson Consulting Assoc., Inc. (R), NY, *60*
Erlanger Assoc. (R), CT, *60*
Erwin Assoc. (R), IL, *60*
Essential Solutions, Inc. (C), CA, *331*
Ethos Consulting, Inc. (R), CA, *61*
ETI Search Int'l. (R), GA, *61*
The Evans Search Group (R), CT, *61*
Evans Transportation Search (C), ON, *331*
Excalibur Human Resources, Inc. (R), NJ, *61*
The Execu/Search Group (C), NY, *332*
ExecuGroup, Inc. (R), MS, *61*
ExecuQuest, Inc. (R), MI, *61*
ExecuSource Assoc., Inc. (C), GA, *332*
Executive Access Inc. (R), NY, *62*
Executive Careers (R), CA, *62*
Executive Dimensions (R), NY, *62*
Executive Direction, Inc. (C), CA, *333*
The Executive Group, Inc. (R), CA, *62*
Executive Placement Consultants (C), IL, *333*
Executive Recruitment Specialists, Inc. (R), NC, *63*
Executive Referral Services, Inc. (C), IL, *334*
Executive Registry (C), QE, *334*
Executive Resource Inc. (C), WI, *334*
Executive Resource Systems (C), CA, *335*
Executive Search Consultants International, Inc. (R), NY, *63*
Executive Search Consultants, Inc. (C), FL, *335*
Executive Search Consultants Corp. (C), IL, *335*
Executive Search, Ltd. (C), OH, *336*
Executive Search of New England, Inc. (C), ME, *336*
Executive Search Partners (R), NY, *63*
Executive Search Plus, Inc. (C), IN, *336*
Executive Search Team (C), MI, *336*
Executive Solutions (R), MN, *64*
The Executive Source (C), SA, *337*
The Executive Tree (R), FL, *64*
Raymond L. Extract & Assoc. (R), CA, *64*
Eyler Assoc., Inc. (R), IA, *64*
Fabian Assoc. Inc. (C), NY, *338*
Fagan & Company (R), PA, *64*
FAI (C), CO, *338*
Fairfaxx Corp. (R), CT, *64*
Fallstaff Search (C), MD, *338*
Leon A. Farley Assoc. (R), CA, *65*
Faro Consultants Int'l. (C), VA, *338*
Federal Placement Services (C), NY, *339*
Fell & Nicholson Technology Resources (R), CA, *65*
Fenwick Partners (R), MA, *66*
Fenzel Milar Assoc. (C), OH, *339*
Ferneborg & Assoc., Inc. (R), CA, *66*
Ferrari Search Group (C), OH, *340*
Fidelity Search Group, Inc. (R), PA, *66*
Financial Connections Company (C), VA, *340*
Financial Plus Management Solutions Inc. (R), ON, *66*
Financial Resource Assoc., Inc. (C), FL, *340*
Financial Search Corp. (C), IL, *340*
Financial Search Group, Inc. (R), MA, *66*
Financialjobs.com (C), CA, *340*
Finnegan & Assoc. (R), CA, *67*
Finney-Taylor Personnel & Management Consultants Ltd. (C), AB, *341*
First Union Executive Search (R), NC, *67*
Howard Fischer Assoc. Int'l., Inc. (R), PA, *67*
Fishel HR Assoc., Inc. (C), AZ, *341*
The Fisher Group (R), AB, *67*
The Flagship Group (R), MA, *68*
Robert M. Flanagan & Assoc., Ltd. (R), NY, *68*
Flexible Resources, Inc. (C), CT, *342*
Focus Consulting Services, Inc. (C), FL, *342*
Fogec Consultants, Inc. (R), WI, *69*
Foley Proctor Yoskowitz (R), NJ, *69*
Ford & Assoc., Inc. (C), SC, *343*
The Ford Group, Inc. (R), PA, *69*
Forray Assoc., Inc. (R), NY, *70*
Fortune Personnel Consultants of Huntsville, Inc. (C), AL, *343*
F-O-R-T-U-N-E Personnel Consultants of San Diego (C), CA, *344*
F-O-R-T-U-N-E Personnel Consultants (C), MI, *346*
Fortune Personnel Consultants of Hinsdale, IL (C), IL, *346*
F-O-R-T-U-N-E Personnel Consultants of Southwest Indiana (C), IN, *346*
F-O-R-T-U-N-E Search Consultants (C), MO, *347*
Fortune Personnel Consultants of Allentown, Inc. (C), PA, *348*
F-O-R-T-U-N-E Personnel Consultants of Charlotte (C), NC, *348*
Fortune Personnel Consultants of Raleigh, Inc. (C), NC, *348*
F-O-R-T-U-N-E Personnel Consultants of Knoxville (C), TN, *350*
Forum Personnel Inc. (C), NY, *351*
Foster Associates (C), NJ, *351*
Foster Partners (R), NY, *70*
The Fourbes Group, Inc. (C), NJ, *351*
Franklin Allen Consultants, Ltd. (R), NY, *71*
Franstaff Inc. (C), FL, *352*
KS Frary & Assoc. (R), MA, *71*
P. N. French Assoc., Inc. (R), MA, *72*
Friedman Eisenstein Raemer & Schwartz, LLP (R), IL, *72*
C. F. Furr & Co. (R), NC, *72*
The Furst Group, Inc. (R), IL, *72*
Furst Group/MPI (R), IL, *72*

Future Employment Service, Inc. (C), IA, *353*
Futures Int'l. (R), CT, *73*
GAAP Inc. (R), QE, *73*
The Gabriel Group (C), PA, *354*
Gaffney Management Consultants (R), IL, *73*
Gahan Assoc. (R), NY, *73*
Jay Gaines & Company, Inc. (R), NY, *73*
Gaming Consultants, Inc. (R), LA, *74*
The Gammill Group, Inc. (C), OH, *354*
Gans, Gans & Assoc., Inc. (R), FL, *74*
W. N. Garbarini & Assoc. (R), NJ, *74*
Gardiner, Townsend & Assoc. (R), NY, *74*
Dick Garland Consultants (R), NY, *74*
Garrett Assoc. Inc. (R), GA, *75*
Garrison-Randall, Inc. (R), CA, *75*
The Garvis Group, Inc. (C), LA, *355*
GateSource Partners (C), VA, *355*
Gateway Group Personnel, LLC (C), TN, *355*
Gaudry, Shink, Levasseur (R), QE, *75*
Gavin Forbes & Price (R), CA, *75*
Geddes & Rubin Management Inc. (R), ON, *76*
Genel Associates (C), CA, *356*
Genesis Consulting Partners (R), PA, *76*
Genesis Personnel Service, Inc. (C), OH, *356*
Gent & Assoc. (C), CA, *356*
C. R. Gerald & Assoc. (C), ON, *356*
J. Gernetzke & Assoc., Inc. (C), OH, *357*
GES Services, Inc. (R), NY, *76*
GFI Professional Staffing Services (C), NH, *357*
Gielow Assoc., Inc. (R), WI, *76*
John Gilbert Co. (C), TX, *357*
Gilbert Scott Assoc., LLC (C), MA, *357*
Gilbert Tweed Assoc. Inc. (R), NY, *76*
Gilmore & Assoc. (C), CA, *357*
Gilreath Weatherby Inc. (R), MA, *77*
Gimbel & Assoc. (C), FL, *357*
The Glazin Group (R), BC, *77*
J. P. Gleason Assoc., Inc. (R), IL, *77*
Glines Assoc., Inc. (R), IL, *77*
Global 1000 Int'l. Services (C), CA, *358*
Global Career Services, Inc. (C), NY, *358*
Global Consulting Group Inc. (C), ON, *358*
Global Employer's Network, Inc. (R), TX, *77*
Global Executive Search Group (C), MA, *358*
Global HealthCare Partners (R), IL, *78*
Global Technologies Group Inc. (C), NC, *359*
Glou Int'l., Inc. (R), MA, *78*
The Tracy Glover Co. (R), TX, *78*
Gnodde Assoc. (C), IL, *359*
The Gobbell Co. (R), CA, *78*
Godfrey Personnel, Inc. (C), IL, *359*
H. L. Goehring & Assoc., Inc. (C), OH, *359*
The Gogates Group, Inc. (R), NY, *79*
Barry M. Gold & Co. (C), CA, *359*
Joseph Goldring & Assoc. Inc. (C), MI, *360*
Fred J. Goldsmith Assoc. (R), CA, *79*
David Gomez & Assoc., Inc. (R), IL, *79*
Gomez Fregoso y Asociados (C), JAL, *360*
Goodkind Assoc. Inc. (C), NY, *360*
Goodrich & Sherwood Assoc., Inc. (R), NY, *79*
Goodwin & Co. (R), DC, *80*
Gould, McCoy & Chadick, Inc. (R), NY, *80*
The Governance Group, Inc. (R), NJ, *80*
Government Contract Solutions, Inc. (C), VA, *360*
Robert Graham Assoc. (R), RI, *81*
Granger, Counts & Assoc. (R), OH, *81*
Grant Cooper & Assoc., Inc. (R), MO, *81*
Grant-Franks & Assoc. (C), NJ, *361*
Grant/Morgan Assoc., Inc. (C), MD, *361*
Grantham & Co., Inc. (R), NC, *81*
Graphic Search Assoc. Inc. (C), PA, *362*
Grauss & Co. (C), CA, *362*
Annie Gray Assoc., Inc. (R), MO, *81*
Ben Greco Assoc., Inc. (C), CA, *362*
Sheila Greco Assoc. (C), NY, *362*
R. Green & Assoc., Inc. (C), OH, *362*
Greger/Peterson Assoc., Inc. (R), CA, *81*
Gregory, Kyle & Assoc. (C), NC, *363*
Griffith & Werner, Inc. (R), FL, *82*
J. B. Groner Executive Search, Inc. (C), DE, *363*
Grossberg & Assoc. (R), IL, *82*
Groussman & Assoc., Inc. (R), TX, *82*
Growth Strategies, Inc. (R), FL, *83*
David E. Grumney Co. Inc. (R), WA, *83*
GSP International (C), NJ, *364*
GSW Consulting Group, Inc. (R), CA, *83*
The Gullgroup (C), TX, *364*
Gustin Partners, Ltd. (R), MA, *83*
William Guy & Assoc., Inc. (R), CA, *84*
GWS Partners (R), IL, *84*
H R Solutions, Inc. (C), MO, *365*
The H. S. Group, Inc. (C), WI, *365*
H.Q. Search, Inc. (C), IL, *365*
Habelmann & Assoc. (R), MI, *84*
Russ Hadick & Assoc. Inc. (C), OH, *365*
Hahn & Assoc., Inc. (C), OH, *365*
Hale Assoc. (R), IL, *84*
K. C. Hale, Inc. (R), CT, *85*
Robert Half Canada Inc. (C), ON, *366*
Don Hall & Assoc. (C), TX, *366*
Michael J. Hall & Co. (R), WA, *85*
Hall Management Group, Inc. (C), GA, *367*
Hallman Group, Inc. (C), MI, *367*
The Hamilton Group (R), MD, *85*
R. C. Handel Assoc. Inc. (R), CT, *85*
W. L. Handler & Assoc. (R), GA, *85*
Handy HRM (R), NY, *86*
Hanley & Assoc. (R), FL, *86*
The Hanna Group (C), OH, *368*
The Hanover Consulting Group (C), MD, *368*
Hanzel & Co., Inc. (R), NY, *86*
Harbrowe, Inc. (C), NY, *368*
Harcourt & Assoc. (C), AB, *368*
Harcourt Group Ltd. (R), OH, *86*
Hardison & Company (R), TX, *86*
Robert Harkins Assoc., Inc. (C), PA, *369*
Harper Associates (C), MI, *369*
The Harris Consulting Corp. (R), MB, *87*
Harris McCully Assoc., Inc. (C), NY, *369*
Harrison Consulting Group, Inc. (C), CA, *369*
Hartsfield Group, Inc. (R), GA, *87*
Harvard Aimes Group (R), CT, *87*
Harvard Group Int'l. (R), GA, *87*
Harvey Hohauser & Assoc., LLC (R), MI, *87*
The Hawkins Co. (R), CA, *88*
William E. Hay & Co. (R), IL, *88*
Hayden & Assoc., Inc. (C), MN, *370*
Hayden Group, Inc. (R), MA, *88*
Headden Assoc. (R), WA, *88*
Healey Executive Search, Inc. (R), MN, *88*
Health Care Dimensions (C), CO, *371*
Health Search (C), CA, *371*
Healthcare Executive Recruiters, Inc. (C), CA, *372*
Healthcare Management Resources, Inc. (R), GA, *89*
Healthcare Recruiters of the Rockies, Inc. (C), CO, *372*
Healthcare Recruiters Int'l. Bay Area (C), CA, *372*
Healthcare Recruiters of Indiana (C), IN, *372*
Healthcare Recruiters Int'l - Minnesota, Inc. (C), MN, *373*
Healthcare Recruiters Int'l. Philadelphia (C), NJ, *373*
Healthcare Search Associates (C), CA, *374*
The Healthsearch Group, Inc. (C), NY, *374*
F. P. Healy & Co., Inc. (R), NY, *89*
R. W. Hebel Assoc. (R), TX, *89*
HEC Group (C), ON, *375*
Thomas E. Hedefine Assoc. (C), ON, *375*
Hedlund Corp. (C), IL, *375*
Heffelfinger Assoc., Inc. (R), MA, *89*
The Heidrick Partners, Inc. (R), IL, *90*
Jay Heino Company, LLC (C), NY, *375*
Heinze & Assoc. Inc. (R), MN, *91*
Helbling & Assoc., Inc. (R), PA, *91*
Helfer Executive Consultants (R), TN, *91*
Heller Assoc., Ltd. (R), IL, *91*
Hemingway Personnel, Inc. (C), CA, *375*
G. W. Henn & Co. (R), OH, *91*
Bruce Henry Assoc. Inc. (R), CA, *91*
The Hensge Co. (R), IL, *91*
Henson Partners (C), AZ, *376*
Herbeck Kline & Assoc. (R), IL, *92*
Hergenrather & Co. (R), WA, *92*
Hermann & Westmore (R), CA, *92*
A. Herndon & Assoc., Inc. (R), TX, *92*
Herrerias & Assoc. (R), CA, *92*
Herring & Assoc. (C), AR, *376*
The Herrmann Group Ltd. (R), ON, *92*
Hersher Assoc., Ltd. (R), IL, *92*
Stanley Herz & Co. (R), NY, *92*
Robert Hess & Assoc., Inc. (C), CO, *377*
Hessel Assoc., Inc. (C), NY, *377*
The Hetzel Group, Inc. (R), IL, *92*
Higbee Assoc., Inc. (C), CT, *377*
Higdon Prince Inc. (R), NY, *93*
Higgins Assoc., Inc. (R), IL, *93*
B. W. Higgins, Inc. (C), IN, *377*
High-Tech Recruiters (C), CT, *378*
Highland Search Group, L.L.C. (R), NY, *93*
Highlander Search (C), NC, *378*
Higley, Hall & Co., Inc. (R), MA, *93*
Hill Allyn Assoc. (C), CA, *378*
Frank P. Hill (R), MX, *93*
The Hindman Co. (R), KY, *94*
Hobson Assoc. (C), CT, *379*

Hockett Associates, Inc. (R), CA, *94*
Hoffman Recruiters (C), MA, *380*
Hoglund & Assoc., Inc. (R), IL, *94*
Holden & Harlan Assoc., Inc. (C), IL, *380*
Holland Rusk & Assoc. (R), IL, *95*
The Hollins Group, Inc. (R), IL, *95*
Holloway Schulz & Partners (C), BC, *380*
Home Health & Hospital Recruiters, Inc. (C), GA, *380*
Fred Hood & Assoc. (C), CA, *380*
Hook-Up! (C), CA, *380*
David C. Horn Executive Search (C), TX, *381*
Hornberger Management Company (R), DE, *95*
Horton Int'l. Inc. (R), NY, *96*
Hospitality Executive Search, Inc. (R), MA, *96*
Hospitality Int'l. (C), NY, *381*
Houser, Martin, Morris (C), WA, *381*
Houtz•Strawn & Arnold, Inc. (R), TX, *96*
William C. Houze & Co. (R), CA, *96*
Randall Howard & Assoc., Inc. (R), TN, *96*
The Howard-Sloan-Koller Group (R), NY, *97*
Howe & Assoc. (R), PA, *97*
HR Advantage, Inc. (C), VA, *382*
HRCS (R), CA, *97*
Hreshko Consulting Group (C), NJ, *382*
HRI Services, Inc. (C), MA, *382*
The HRM Group, Inc. (C), AL, *382*
HRNI (C), MI, *383*
HRS, Inc. (R), PA, *97*
Human Resource Bureau (C), CA, *384*
Human Resource Dimensions, Inc. (C), TX, *384*
Human Resource Technologies, Inc. (R), IL, *99*
Human Resources Management Hawaii, Inc. (C), HI, *384*
Hunegnaw Executive Search (C), OH, *384*
H.I. Hunt & Co., Ltd. (R), MA, *99*
Hunt & Howe Inc. (R), NY, *99*
The Hunt Co. (R), NY, *99*
The Hunter Group, Inc. (C), MI, *385*
The Hunter Group (C), NC, *385*
Hunter Int'l., Inc. (R), CT, *100*
Hunter Int'l. LLC (C), MA, *385*
Hunter, Rowan & Crowe (C), FL, *386*
Huntress Real Estate Executive Search (R), MO, *100*
W. Hutt Management Resources Ltd. (R), ON, *100*
The Hutton Group, Inc. (C), FL, *386*
HVS Executive Search (R), NY, *100*
Hyde Danforth & Co. (R), TX, *100*
IM Independent Management Recruiters (R), TN, *101*
IMA Search, Inc. (R), NY, *101*
The IMC Group of Companies (R), NY, *101*
Ingram & Aydelotte, Inc. (R), NY, *101*
Innovative Healthcare Services, Inc. (C), GA, *389*
Insurance Career Center, Inc. (C), CT, *389*
Insurance Personnel Resources, Inc. (C), GA, *390*
Insurance Search (C), TX, *390*
Intech Summit Group, Inc. (R), CA, *102*
Integrated Management Solutions (C), NY, *390*
InteliSearch, Inc. (R), CT, *102*
IntelliSearch (C), TX, *391*
Inter Regional Executive Search, Inc. (IRES, Inc.) (C), NJ, *391*
Interactive Search Network (R), CA, *102*
Interim Accounting Professionals (C), CA, *391*
Interim Executive Recruiting (C), GA, *392*
Interim Financial Solutions - Mid-Atlantic Region (C), MD, *392*
Interim Management Resources Inc. (C), ON, *392*
International Business Partners (C), ON, *392*
International Executive Recruiters (C), OH, *393*
International Management Services Inc. (R), IL, *102*
International Market Recruiters (C), NY, *393*
Intersource, Ltd. (R), GA, *103*
IR Search (R), CA, *103*
Jeffrey Irving Assoc., Inc. (R), VA, *104*
Isaacson, Miller (R), MA, *104*
ISC of Atlanta, Inc. (C), GA, *394*
ISC of Houston, Inc. (C), TX, *394*
Ives & Associates, Inc. (C), OH, *395*
J. Nicholas Arthur (R), MA, *104*
J. R. Scott & Assoc., Ltd. (C), IL, *395*
J.D.G. y Asociados, S.A. de C.V. (R), SO, *104*
J.J. & H., Ltd. (R), IL, *104*
Ron Jackson & Assoc. (C), GA, *396*
Jackson Group Int'l. (C), CO, *396*
Jacobson Assoc. (C), IL, *396*
Jakobs & Assoc. Int'l. (R), NY, *105*
Pendleton James Assoc., Inc. (R), NY, *105*
David James Search (C), CA, *397*
JCL & Assoc. (C), FL, *397*
JDC Assoc. (C), NY, *397*
JDH & Assoc. (C), CA, *397*
Jefferson-Ross Assoc. Inc. (C), PA, *398*
Jeffrey Allan Co., Inc. (C), CA, *398*
JenKim Int'l. Ltd., Inc. (C), FL, *398*
Jerome & Co. (C), CA, *398*
JNB Assoc., Inc. (C), MA, *399*
Job Link, Inc. (C), CA, *399*
Job-Born Candidate Selection Bureau (C), ON, *399*
John Jay & Co. (C), ME, *399*
John H. Johnson & Assoc., Inc. (R), IL, *106*
L. J. Johnson & Co. (R), MI, *106*
Johnson & Company (R), CT, *107*
Ronald S. Johnson Assoc., Inc. (R), CA, *107*
Johnson Assoc., Inc. (C), IL, *399*
Johnson Brown Assoc., Inc. (C), IN, *400*
The Johnson Group, Unlimited (C), NY, *400*
Johnson Smith & Knisely (R), NY, *107*
Jonas, Walters & Assoc., Inc. (R), WI, *107*
The Jonathan Stevens Group, Inc. (R), NJ, *108*
Jones and Jones (R), OR, *108*
Jones Consulting Executive Search (C), GA, *400*
Jones Management Co. (R), CT, *108*
Joseph Chris & Assoc. (C), TX, *400*
Joseph Consulting, Inc. (C), FL, *401*
Joseph Michaels (C), CA, *401*
JPM International (C), CA, *401*
JSG Group Management Consultants (R), ON, *109*
JT Assoc. (C), CT, *401*
Judd Associates (R), NJ, *109*
K & C Assoc. (C), CA, *402*
KABL Ability Network (C), CA, *402*
Richard Kader & Assoc. (C), OH, *403*
Kane & Assoc. (C), TX, *403*
Kanzer Assoc., Inc. (R), IL, *109*
Gary Kaplan & Assoc. (R), CA, *109*
Kaplan & Assoc., Inc. (R), PA, *109*
Karel & Co. (R), CA, *109*
Howard Karr & Assoc., Inc. (R), CA, *110*
Martin Kartin & Co., Inc. (R), NY, *110*
Katelyn Partners (C), FL, *404*
Melissa Katzman, Executive Search (C), NY, *404*
Kaufman Assoc. (R), CA, *110*
Jim Kay & Assoc. (C), IL, *404*
The Kay Group of 5th Ave. (C), NY, *404*
Kaye/Bassman Int'l. Corp. (R), TX, *110*
Kazan International, Inc. (R), NJ, *110*
Keane Assoc. (R), MA, *110*
A.T. Kearney Executive Search (R), IL, *111*
Keeley Consulting Inc. (C), ON, *404*
Keena Staffing Services (C), NY, *404*
David Warwick Kennedy & Assoc. (R), BC, *112*
Kennedy & Co. (R), IL, *112*
The Kennett Group, Inc. (R), PA, *112*
Kensington Int'l., Inc. (R), IL, *113*
Kent & Assoc. (R), OH, *113*
Kenzer Corp. (R), NY, *113*
Blair Kershaw Assoc., Inc. (C), PA, *405*
Kershner & Co. (R), DC, *113*
Daniel J. Kerstein, Consultant to Management (R), CO, *114*
Michael L. Ketner & Assoc., Inc. (R), PA, *114*
Keystone Consulting Group (C), GA, *406*
Kimmel & Associates, Inc. (C), NC, *406*
Kincaid Group Inc. (KGI) (C), TX, *406*
Kinderis & Loercher Group (C), IL, *407*
Kingsbury • Wax • Bova (R), MA, *114*
The Kinlin Co., Inc. (R), MA, *115*
Richard Kinser & Assoc. (R), NY, *115*
Kip Williams, Inc. (R), NY, *115*
Kiradjieff & Goode, Inc. (R), MA, *115*
Kittleman & Assoc.,LLC (R), IL, *115*
The Kleinstein Group, Inc. (R), NJ, *116*
Knapp Consultants (R), CT, *116*
The Koehler Group (C), PA, *408*
Lee Koehn Assoc., Inc. (R), OR, *116*
Fred Koffler Assoc. (R), NY, *116*
Koll-Fairfield LLC (C), CT, *408*
Koontz, Jeffries & Assoc., Inc. (R), FL, *117*
Kopplin Search, Inc. (R), CA, *117*
Koren, Rogers Assoc. Inc. (R), NY, *117*
Korn/Ferry Int'l. (R), NY, *117*
Kors Montgomery Int'l. (R), TX, *118*
Kossuth & Assoc., Inc. (R), WA, *119*
Kostmayer Assoc., Inc. (R), MD, *119*
The J. Kovach Group (R), PA, *119*

KPA Assoc., Inc. (C), NY, *408*
Katherine R. Kraemer (R), CA, *120*
Krakower Group, Inc. (R), CA, *120*
Kramer Executive Resources, Inc. (C), NY, *409*
Evie Kreisler Assoc. Inc. (C), CA, *409*
Kremple & Meade, Inc. (R), CA, *120*
Kremple Consulting Group (R), CA, *120*
Kressenberg Assoc. (C), TX, *409*
Todd L. Krueger & Assoc. (C), WA, *409*
Krueger Assoc. (R), IL, *121*
Kuhn Med-Tech (C), CA, *409*
Kulper & Co., L.L.C. (R), NJ, *121*
Kunzer Assoc., Ltd. (R), IL, *121*
Kutcher Tax Careers, Inc. (C), NY, *410*
Kyle Assoc. (C), NY, *410*
L O R (R), NJ, *122*
L T M Assoc. (C), IL, *410*
L&L Assoc. Global Search (C), PA, *411*
Marvin Laba & Assoc. (R), CA, *122*
Rene LaFlamme & Associes (R), QE, *122*
Laguzza Assoc., Ltd. (R), NY, *122*
Lamon + Stuart + Michaels Inc. (R), ON, *124*
E. J. Lance Management Assoc., Inc. (C), NY, *412*
The Landstone Group (C), NY, *412*
The Langford Search, Inc. (C), AL, *412*
LanSo Int'l., Inc. (C), NY, *413*
Lawrence L. Lapham, Inc. (R), NY, *124*
Stephen Laramee & Assoc. Inc. (C), ON, *413*
R. H. Larsen & Assoc., Inc. (R), FL, *125*
Larsen & Lee, Inc. (R), MD, *125*
LAS Management Consulting Group, Inc. (R), NJ, *125*
Lasher Assoc. (R), FL, *125*
Michael Latas & Assoc., Inc. (R), MO, *125*
Latham International, Ltd. (R), NJ, *126*
Lauer, Sbarbaro Assoc., EMA Partners Int'l. (R), IL, *126*
Lautz, Grotte, Engler & Swimley (R), CA, *126*
Madeleine Lav & Assoc. (C), CA, *413*
Lawrence James Assoc. of Florida, Inc. (C), FL, *414*
Lawrence-Leiter & Co. (R), KS, *126*
The Lawson Group, Inc. (C), SC, *414*
Layne-Mendez & Co. (R), TX, *127*
Leader Network (C), PA, *414*
Leader Resources Group (C), GA, *415*
Leader Search Inc. (R), AB, *127*
Leaders-Trust Int'l./Carce y Asociados, S.C. (R), MX, *127*
Lear & Assoc., Inc. (C), FL, *415*
Reynolds Lebus Assoc. (C), AZ, *415*
Lechner & Assoc., Inc. (C), FL, *415*
Ledbetter/Davidson Int'l., Inc. (R), NY, *127*
Albert G. Lee Assoc. (C), RI, *415*
Vincent Lee Assoc. (C), NY, *415*
The Conrad Lee Co. Inc. (R), FL, *127*
Leeds and Leeds (C), TN, *416*
V. J. Lehman & Assoc., Inc. (R), CO, *127*
Lehman McLeskey (R), TX, *128*
Lekan & Assoc., Inc. (R), OH, *128*
Lemming/LeVan, Inc. (R), GA, *128*
Lending Personnel Services (C), CA, *416*
AG Lennox & Assoc. (R), AB, *128*
J. E. Lessner Assoc., Inc. (R), MI, *128*
Levin & Company, Inc. (R), MA, *128*
Alan Levine Assoc. (R), MA, *129*
The Levton Group Inc. (R), ON, *129*
Lewis & Blank Int'l. (R), CA, *129*
Lewis Companies Inc. (R), ON, *129*
Lexington Software Inc. (C), NY, *417*
The Libra Group (C), NC, *417*
J. H. Lindell & Co. (C), CA, *418*
Lipsky Group, Inc. (R), CA, *129*
Livingston, Robert & Co. (R), CT, *130*
Lloyd Associates (R), GA, *130*
Lloyd Prescott & Churchill, Inc. (R), FL, *130*
Lloyd Staffing (C), NY, *419*
Locke & Assoc. (R), NC, *131*
Loderman & Costello (C), GA, *419*
The Logan Group, Inc. (R), MO, *131*
Logic Assoc., Inc. (C), NY, *419*
Logue & Rice Inc. (C), VA, *420*
London Executive Consultants Inc. (C), ON, *420*
Longshore + Simmons (R), PA, *131*
J. S. Lord & Company, Inc. (R), MA, *131*
Bruce Lowery & Assoc. (C), MI, *420*
The John Lucht Consultancy Inc. (R), NY, *131*
The Luciani Group (R), CA, *132*
P. J. Lynch Assoc. (R), CT, *132*
Lynch Miller Moore Partners, Inc. (R), IL, *132*
Lynne Palmer Executive Recruitment, Inc. (C), NY, *421*
Lynx, Inc. (C), MA, *421*
Lyons Pruitt Int'l. (R), PA, *132*
M.C. Executive Search (C), CA, *422*
M/J/A Partners (R), IL, *133*
MacNaughton Assoc. (R), CA, *133*
Maczkov-Biosciences, Inc. (R), CA, *133*
The Madison Group (R), NY, *133*
Magellan Int'l., L.P. (C), TX, *422*
Maglio & Co., Inc. (R), WI, *134*
Maiorino & Weston Assoc., Inc. (R), CT, *134*
Managed Care Consultants (C), AZ, *423*
Management & Human Resources (R), MA, *134*
Management Advisors Int'l., Inc. (C), NC, *424*
Management Alliance Group, Inc. (R), NJ, *134*
Management Assoc. (C), MD, *424*
Management Dimensions Ltd. (R), ON, *134*
Management One Consultants (C), ON, *425*
Management Recruiters of Nassau, Inc. (R), NY, *134*
Management Recruiters of Birmingham, Inc. (C), AL, *438*
Management Recruiters of Birmingham-South, Inc. (C), AL, *438*
Management Recruiters of Aptos (C), CA, *439*
Management Recruiters of Berkeley (C), CA, *439*
Management Recruiters of Fresno (C), CA, *440*
Management Recruiters of Laguna Hills (C), CA, *440*
Management Recruiters Dana Point (C), CA, *440*
Management Recruiters, Inland Empire Agency (C), CA, *441*
Management Recruiters of Roseville (C), CA, *441*
Management Recruiters of Pleasanton (C), CA, *441*
Management Recruiters of Sacramento North (C), CA, *441*
Management Recruiters of Ft. Myers, FL. (C), FL, *443*
Management Recruiters of Bonita Springs, Inc. (C), FL, *443*
Management Recruiters of Anna Maria Island (C), FL, *443*
Management Recruiters of Clearwater (C), FL, *443*
Management Recruiters of Miami-North (C), FL, *443*
Management Recruiters, Inc. (C), FL, *443*
Management Recruiters of St. Augustine (C), FL, *444*
Management Recruiters of Duluth (C), GA, *445*
Management Recruiters of North Fulton (C), GA, *445*
Management Recruiters of Atlanta (C), GA, *445*
Management Recruiters of Atlanta NE (C), GA, *446*
Management Recruiters of Marietta, Inc. (C), GA, *446*
Management Recruiters - Towne Lake (C), GA, *446*
Management Recruiters of St. Charles (C), IL, *447*
Management Recruiters of Chicago West (C), IL, *447*
Management Recruiters of Indianapolis (C), IN, *448*
Management Recruiters of Indianapolis-North (C), IN, *448*
Management Recruiters - Indianapolis (C), IN, *448*
Management Recruiters of Des Moines (C), IA, *449*
Management Recruiters of Williamsburg (C), IA, *449*
Management Recruiters of Siouxland (C), IA, *449*
Management Recruiters of Washington, DC Inc. (C), MD, *450*
Management Recruiters of Muskegon (C), MI, *451*
Management Recruiters of Livonia (C), MI, *451*
Management Recruiters of Southeastern Michigan (C), MI, *451*
Management Recruiters of Detroit & Farmington Hills (C), MI, *451*
Management Recruiters of Dearborn, Inc. (C), MI, *451*
Management Recruiters of Winona (C), MN, *452*
Management Recruiters of Woodbury (C), MN, *452*
Management Recruiters of Cass County, NE (C), NE, *452*

Management Recruiters of North Oakland County, Inc. (C), MI, *452*
Management Recruiters of Princeton (C), NJ, *454*
Management Recruiters of New Providence (C), NJ, *454*
Management Recruiters of Great Neck (C), NY, *454*
Management Recruiters of Broome County, Inc. (C), NY, *454*
Management Recruiters of Manhattan on Broadway (C), NY, *455*
Management Recruiters of Winston-Salem (C), NC, *457*
Management Recruiters of Cleveland (C), OH, *457*
Management Recruiters of Oklahoma City (C), OK, *458*
Management Recruiters of Mentor, Inc. (C), OH, *458*
Management Recruiters of Northwest Ohio, Inc. (C), OH, *458*
Management Recruiters of Lionville, Inc. (C), PA, *459*
Management Recruiters of Pittsburgh (C), PA, *459*
Management Recruiters of Puerto Rico (C), PR, *460*
Management Recruiters of North Charleston (C), SC, *460*
Management Recruiters of Florence (C), SC, *460*
Management Recruiters The Delta Group, Inc. (C), TN, *461*
Management Recruiters of Sioux Falls, LLP (C), SD, *461*
Management Recruiters of Georgetown (C), SC, *461*
Management Recruiters of Houston (C), TX, *462*
Management Recruiters of San Antonio (C), TX, *463*
Management Recruiters of Salt Lake City (C), UT, *464*
Management Recruiters of Kanawha Valley, LLC (C), WV, *465*
Management Recruiters of Spokane (C), WA, *465*
Management Recruiters of Milwaukee-North (C), WI, *466*
Management Recruiters of Stevens Point, Inc. (C), WI, *466*
Management Recruiters of Milwaukee - Downtown (C), WI, *466*
Management Recruiters of Janesville, Inc. (C), WI, *466*
Management Resource Assoc., Inc. (C), FL, *467*
Management Resource Group, Ltd. (C), IA, *467*
Management Resource Group (C), MN, *467*
Management Resources (C), TX, *467*
Management Search Int'l. (C), CA, *467*
Management Search, Inc. (C), IL, *467*
Management Search of R.I. Inc. (R), RI, *135*
Management Solutions, Inc. (C), WA, *468*
Management Solutions, Inc. (C), CA, *468*
Mannard & Assoc., Inc. (R), IL, *135*
Manuso, Alexander & Associates, Inc. (R), NY, *135*
MARBL Consultants, Inc. (C), WI, *469*
Marc-Allen Assoc., Inc. (C), FL, *469*
Marcus & Assoc. (C), NY, *469*
Marentz & Co. (C), TX, *469*
J. L. Mark Assoc., Inc. (R), CO, *135*
Mark Stanley & Co./EMA Partners International (R), FL, *136*
Markent Personnel, Inc. (C), WI, *470*
Market Niche Consulting (C), AZ, *470*
Paula Marks Inc. (R), NY, *136*
Brad Marks Int'l. (R), CA, *136*
The Marlow Group (R), MA, *136*
The Maroon Group (R), CT, *136*
Marra Peters & Partners (R), NJ, *136*
Marsar & Co., Inc. (C), FL, *471*
Marshall-Alan Assoc., Inc. (C), NY, *471*
Marsteller Wilcox Assoc. (C), IL, *471*
Donovan Martin & Assoc. (R), CA, *137*
The Martin Group (R), CA, *137*
Martin Partners, L.L.C. (R), IL, *137*
Marvel Consultants, Inc. (C), OH, *472*
Massey-Horton Int'l. (R), ON, *138*
Richard L. Mather & Assoc. (C), CT, *472*
Matté & Company, Inc. (R), CT, *138*
Matte Consulting Group Inc. (R), QE, *138*
Matthews & Stephens Assoc., Inc. (C), CT, *472*
Maxecon Executive Search Consultants (R), FL, *138*
K. Maxin & Assoc. (R), PA, *139*
Mary L. Mayer, Ltd. (R), MN, *139*
Mayhall Search Group, Inc. (C), IN, *473*
The Mazzitelli Group, Ltd. (R), MN, *139*
McBride Assoc., Inc. (R), DC, *139*
McCann, Choi & Associates, LLC (R), NY, *139*
K. E. McCarthy & Assoc. (R), CA, *139*
McCarthy Assoc. National BancSearch, LLC (C), LA, *473*
McCormack & Assoc. (R), CA, *140*
McCormack & Farrow (R), CA, *140*
McCray, Shriver, Eckdahl & Assoc., Inc. (R), CA, *140*
McDonald Assoc. Int'l. (R), IL, *140*
McDonald, Long & Assoc., Inc. (R), NY, *140*
Clarence E. McFeely, Inc. (R), IL, *141*
McGrath & Assoc., Inc. (R), NJ, *141*
McHale & Assoc. (R), WA, *141*
McIntyre Assoc. (R), CT, *141*
McIntyre Management Resources (C), ON, *474*
McKinley•Arend Int'l. (R), TX, *141*
The McKinnon Management Group Inc. (C), ON, *475*
The McLeod Group, Inc. (R), CT, *141*
Jon McRae & Associates, Inc. (R), GA, *142*
MCS Assoc. (R), CA, *142*
Meder & Assoc., Inc. (R), IL, *142*
Media Recruiting Group, Inc. (C), NY, *476*
The Medley Group (C), CA, *477*
MedSearch Resources, Inc. (C), FL, *478*
MedXec USA, Inc. (C), FL, *478*
Mehta Consulting (C), NJ, *478*
Melancon & Co. (R), TX, *143*
Meng, Finseth & Assoc., Inc. (R), CA, *143*
Mercedes & Co., Inc. (R), MA, *143*
Meridian Resources (C), OH, *479*
Merrick & Moore (C), NC, *479*
Messett Assoc., Inc. (R), FL, *143*
META/MAT, Ltd. (R), NJ, *144*
mfg/Search, Inc. (C), IN, *480*
Lou Michaels Assoc., Inc. (C), MI, *481*
Michigan Consulting Group (R), MI, *144*
Millar Walker & Gay (R), ON, *144*
Miller/Davis & Assoc., Inc. (C), NY, *482*
Danette Milne Corporate Search Inc. (C), ON, *482*
Herbert Mines Assoc., Inc. (R), NY, *145*
Mirtz Morice, Inc. (R), CT, *145*
Paul Misarti Inc. (C), NY, *483*
Mitchell/Wolfson, Assoc. (R), IL, *145*
MIXTEC Group (R), CA, *145*
Moffitt Int'l., Inc. (R), NC, *146*
Molloy Partners (R), NY, *146*
Oscar Montaño, Inc. (R), CA, *146*
The Montgomery Group, Inc. (C), TN, *484*
Montgomery Resources, Inc. (C), CA, *484*
Montgomery West (R), CA, *146*
C. A. Moore & Assoc., Inc. (C), MN, *484*
Morgan Hunter Corp. (C), KS, *485*
Morgan Int'l., Inc. (R), IL, *147*
Morgan Samuels Co. (R), CA, *147*
Morgan Stampfl, Inc. (C), NY, *485*
The Morgan/Geoffries Group (C), CA, *485*
The Morley Group (C), IN, *486*
Morris & Berger (R), CA, *147*
Mortgage & Financial Personnel Services (C), CA, *486*
Mortgage Search Network (C), AZ, *486*
MPA Executive Search Inc. (R), QE, *148*
Mruk & E.M.A. Partners (R), NY, *148*
MSI Int'l. (C), GA, *486*
Much & Co. (R), NY, *148*
Pamela L. Mulligan, Inc. (R), NH, *149*
Jennifer Munro & Partners, Inc. (R), SC, *149*
P. J. Murphy & Assoc., Inc. (R), WI, *150*
Kenneth Murphy & Assoc. (C), NS, *487*
Murphy Partners Int'l. (R), IL, *150*
Musick & Assoc. (C), CA, *487*
The MVP Group (C), NY, *487*
Mycoff & Assoc. (R), CO, *150*
DDJ Myers, Ltd. (R), AZ, *150*
Nason & Nason (C), FL, *488*
National Affirmative Action Career Network, Inc. (C), CO, *488*
National Bank & Finance Executive Search (C), CA, *488*
National Career Search (C), AZ, *489*
National Computerized Employment Service, Inc. (C), PA, *489*
National Corporate Consultants, Inc. (C), IN, *489*
National Metal Services Corp. (C), IN, *489*
National Search, Inc.r (C), FL, *490*
NCC Executive Search Consultants (C), CA, *490*
Don Neal & Assoc. (C), OK, *491*
The Neil Michael Group, Inc./Global Partners (R), NY, *151*
J. Fielding Nelson & Assoc., Inc. (R), UT, *151*
New Directions, Inc. (C), IL, *492*

New Venture Development, Inc. (C), CA, *492*
New World Healthcare Solutions, Inc. (R), NY, *151*
Newell Assoc. (R), NY, *151*
Nichols & Company (R), CO, *151*
Marc Nichols Assoc., Inc. (C), NY, *493*
Nichols Brown Int'l. (R), NY, *151*
P. J. Nicholson & Assoc. (C), IL, *493*
The Niemond Corp. (R), CA, *152*
J. L. Nixon Consulting (C), TX, *493*
NMC & Kay Int'l. (R), CO, *152*
The Noebel Search Group, Inc. (C), TX, *494*
The Nolan Group (C), CA, *494*
Noll Human Resource Services (C), NE, *494*
W. D. Nolte & Company (R), CT, *152*
Nordeman Grimm, Inc. (R), NY, *152*
Norman Broadbent Int'l., Inc. (R), NY, *152*
Norrell Financial Staffing (C), GA, *495*
John B. Norris & Assoc., Inc. (C), MD, *495*
Ronald Norris & Assoc. (C), IL, *495*
NPS of Atlanta, Inc. (C), GA, *496*
NRI Staffing Resources (C), DC, *496*
Nuessle, Kurdziel & Weiss, Inc. (R), PA, *153*
O'Brien and Roof (C), OH, *497*
O'Brien Consulting Services (R), MA, *153*
O'Callaghan Honey/Ray & Berndtson Inc. (R), AB, *153*
O'Connor, O'Connor, Lordi, Ltd. (R), PA, *154*
O'Keefe & Assoc., Inc. (R), CT, *154*
O'Neill & Co. (R), CT, *154*
O'Neill Group (C), NJ, *498*
O'Rourke Companies, Inc. (R), TX, *154*
O'Shea, Divine & Co., Inc. (R), CA, *154*
O'Sullivan Search Inc. (C), ON, *498*
Dennis P. O'Toole & Assoc. Inc. (R), NY, *154*
O'Toole & Company, Inc. (R), IL, *154*
Ober & Company (R), CA, *155*
Oberlander & Co., Inc. (R), IL, *155*
Odell & Assoc., Inc. (C), TX, *498*
The Odessa Group (R), CA, *155*
The Ogdon Partnership (R), NY, *155*
Oliver & Rozner Assoc., Inc. (R), NY, *155*
Ollinger Partners (R), MA, *156*
Olsen/Clark (R), WA, *156*
Olympian Recruitment, Ltd. (C), NY, *498*
Omega Search, Inc. (C), NC, *498*
Omnisearch Assoc. (C), CA, *499*
The Onstott Group (R), MA, *156*
Open Concepts (C), CA, *499*
Oppedisano & Co., Inc. (R), NY, *156*
The Options Group, Inc. (C), NY, *499*
Organization Consulting Ltd. (R), ON, *157*
Organization Resources Inc. (R), MA, *157*
Orion Int'l. Consulting Group, Inc. (C), NC, *499*
Ott & Hansen, Inc. (R), CA, *157*
Overton Consulting (R), WI, *157*
The Oxbridge Group, Ltd. (C), PA, *500*
The Oxford Group (C), TX, *500*
P.A.R. Assoc., Inc. (R), MA, *158*
P.R.H. Management, Inc. (R), CT, *158*
Pacific Coast Recruiters (C), OR, *501*
Pacific Finance Search, Inc. (C), CA, *501*
Pacific Search Group, Inc. (C), CA, *501*
The Pailin Group Professional Search Consultants (R), TX, *158*
Pamenter, Pamenter, Brezer & Deganis Ltd. (R), ON, *159*
Arthur Pann Assoc., Inc. (C), NY, *502*
The PAR Group - Paul A. Reaume, Ltd. (R), IL, *159*
Jim Parham & Assoc., Inc. (R), FL, *159*
The Park Group & Assoc., Inc. (C), MD, *502*
Parker & Lynch (C), CA, *503*
Parker Page Group (C), FL, *503*
Largent Parks & Partners (C), TX, *503*
Michael W. Parres & Assoc. (R), MI, *159*
Parsons Assoc. Inc. (R), IL, *159*
Partners In Human Resources Int'l., Inc. (R), NY, *160*
Partners in Recruiting (C), IL, *503*
Partners Resource Group (C), VA, *504*
The Partnership Group (R), NJ, *160*
Partnervision Consulting Group Inc. (R), ON, *160*
Partridge Assoc., Inc. (R), MA, *160*
Pascale & LaMorte, LLC (C), CT, *504*
The Patience Motivation Belief Group, Inc. (C), GA, *505*
Joel H. Paul & Assoc., Inc. (C), NY, *505*
Paul-Tittle Assoc., Inc. (R), VA, *161*
Pawlik/Dorman Partners (R), IL, *161*
Peak Search Assoc. (C), ON, *506*
Pearson, Caldwell & Farnsworth (R), CA, *161*
Peeney Assoc., Inc. (R), NJ, *161*
M. A. Pelle Assoc., Inc. (C), NY, *506*
The Penn Partners, Inc. (R), PA, *162*
The Pennmor Group (C), NJ, *506*
People Management Mid-South, LLC (R), TN, *162*
People Management Northeast, Inc. (R), CT, *162*
PeopleSource Inc. (C), TX, *506*
Performance Resources, Inc. (C), RI, *507*
PERI Corp/Professional Executive Recruiters, Inc. (C), TX, *507*
The Perkins Group (R), NC, *162*
Perry • Newton Assoc. (C), MD, *507*
Perry-D'Amico & Assoc. (R), CA, *162*
Perry-Martel Int'l., Inc. (R), ON, *163*
Barry Persky & Co., Inc. (R), CT, *163*
PersoNet, Inc. (C), FL, *507*
Personnel Alliance Group (C), NJ, *507*
The Personnel Group, Inc. (R), MN, *163*
Personnel Management Group (C), MB, *508*
Personnel Unlimited/Executive Search (C), WA, *509*
Alec Peters Assoc. Inc./DLR (R), GA, *163*
Richard Peterson & Assoc., Inc. (R), GA, *163*
Petro Staff Int'l. (C), AB, *509*
Robert E. Pfaendler & Assoc., Inc. (C), OR, *509*
Pharmaceutical Search Professionals, Inc. (C), PA, *510*
Phase II Management (R), CT, *164*
J. R. Phillip & Assoc., Inc. (R), CA, *164*
Phillips & Assoc. (R), MA, *164*
Phillips Assoc. (C), FL, *510*
Phillips Int'l., Inc. (C), SC, *510*
Phillips Personnel/Search (C), CO, *510*
Phillips Resource Group (C), SC, *510*
Philo & Associates (C), GA, *511*
Phoenix Search (R), MX, *164*
Physicians Search®, Inc. (C), CA, *511*
PIC Executive Search (C), GA, *511*
Picard Int'l., Ltd. (R), NY, *164*
Pierce & Assoc. (C), CA, *512*
Pinnacle Executive Group Inc. (C), MO, *512*
Pinnacle Group Int'l. (C), AZ, *512*
Pinton Forrest & Madden/EMA Partners Int'l. (R), BC, *165*
Pioneer Consulting Group (C), CA, *512*
Pioneer Executive Consultants (C), ON, *512*
DNPitchon Assoc. (R), NJ, *165*
Placement Solutions (C), WI, *513*
Plante & Moran, LLP (R), MI, *165*
R. L. Plimpton Assoc., Inc. (R), CO, *165*
Yves Plouffe & Assoc. (R), QE, *165*
Plummer & Assoc., Inc. (R), CT, *166*
PMJ & Assoc. (C), ON, *513*
Poirier, Hoevel & Co. (R), CA, *166*
Bob Poline Assoc. Inc. (C), CA, *514*
Polson & Co., Inc. (R), MN, *166*
Al Ponaman Company, Inc. (C), CA, *514*
Don V. Poole & Assoc., Inc. (C), CO, *514*
Porter & Assoc., Inc. (C), FL, *514*
David Powell, Inc. (R), CA, *166*
Power Recruiting Group (C), TX, *515*
Robert Powers & Assoc. (C), CA, *515*
P. G. Prager Search Assoc., Ltd. (C), NY, *515*
The Prairie Group (C), IL, *515*
Prairie Resource Group, Inc. (R), IL, *166*
Elan Pratzer & Partners Inc. (R), ON, *167*
PRAXIS Partners (R), VA, *167*
Precision Executive Search (C), AZ, *516*
Preferred Placement, Inc. (C), NY, *516*
Preferred Professional Recruiters (C), OH, *516*
Preferred Professional Recruiters (C), TX, *516*
George Preger & Associates Inc. (R), ON, *167*
Premier Recruiting Group (C), MI, *516*
The Premier Staffing Group (C), OH, *517*
Preng & Assoc., Inc. (R), TX, *167*
Presley Consultants, Inc. (C), CA, *517*
Preston & Co. (R), NJ, *167*
Preston-Hunter, Inc. (R), IL, *167*
PricewaterhouseCoopers Executive Search (R), ON, *168*
PricewaterhouseCoopers Executive Search (R), MX, *168*
The Primary Group, Inc. (R), FL, *168*
Prime Management Group Inc. (C), ON, *518*
Primus Assoc., L.C. (R), TX, *169*
Princeton Executive Search (C), NJ, *518*
Princeton Search Partners, Inc. (R), NJ, *169*
Prior/Martech Assoc., Inc. (R), WA, *169*
Priority Executive Search (C), FL, *518*
PRO, Inc./Professional Recruiting Offices, Inc. (C), CA, *519*
Probus Executive Search (C), CA, *519*

Professional Personnel Consultants, Inc. (C), MI, *521*
Professional Persons Career Services (C), NY, *521*
Professional Research Services, Inc. (R), IL, *169*
Professional Resources (C), OK, *522*
Professional Search (R), MI, *169*
Professional Search Assoc. (C), CA, *522*
Professional Search Consultants (PSC) (C), TX, *523*
Professional Search, Inc. Int'l. (C), TX, *523*
Professional Selection Services (R), GA, *169*
Professional Support Inc. (C), NY, *523*
Professionals in Recruiting Co. (C), TN, *523*
Profit Pros, Inc. (C), CA, *523*
ProNet, Inc. (C), NC, *524*
ProSearch, Inc. (C), ME, *524*
ProSearch, Inc. (C), OH, *524*
Protocol Inc. (C), CA, *525*
Proven Edge (C), CA, *525*
Pryor & Associates (C), CA, *525*
Quality Search Inc. (C), OH, *526*
The Quest Organization (C), NY, *527*
Questor Consultants, Inc. (C), PA, *527*
QuestPro, Inc. (C), TX, *527*
Quetico Corp. (R), TX, *170*
L. J. Quinn & Assoc., Inc. (R), CA, *170*
QVS Int'l. (R), GA, *170*
R & L Assoc., Ltd. (R), NY, *170*
R M Associates (R), OH, *171*
R. J. Associates (C), NY, *528*
R.A.N. Assoc., Inc. (C), OH, *528*
R/K International Inc. (R), CT, *171*
Raines Int'l. Inc. (R), NY, *171*
Ramm Search (C), NY, *528*
Ramming & Assoc., Inc. (C), NJ, *528*
Rand Assoc. (R), ME, *171*
Rand Thompson Executive Search Consultants (C), NY, *528*
Lea Randolph & Assoc., Inc. (C), TX, *529*
The Rankin Group, Ltd. (R), WI, *171*
The Ransford Group (R), TX, *171*
Joanne E. Ratner Search (C), NY, *529*
Ray & Berndtson/Laurendeau Labrecque (R), QE, *172*
Ray & Berndtson/Lovas Stanley (R), ON, *172*
Ray & Berndtson/Tanton Mitchell (R), BC, *173*
Raymond Karsan Assoc. (C), PA, *529*
Razzino-Claymore Assoc. (C), NJ, *530*
RBW Assoc. Inc. (C), OR, *531*
Real Estate Executive Search, Inc. (C), CA, *531*
Recruiting Services Group, Inc. (C), TN, *532*
The Recruitment Group, Inc. (C), NY, *532*
Redden & McGrath Assoc., Inc. (R), NY, *173*
Redden-Shaffer Group (R), CA, *173*
Reece & Mruk Partners/EMA Partners Int'l. (R), MA, *173*
Reeder & Assoc., Ltd. (R), GA, *173*
Cedric L. Reese Inc. (C), CA, *533*
Michael James Reid & Co. (R), CA, *174*
Reid Ellis Assoc. Inc. (C), ON, *533*
Reifel & Assoc. (R), IL, *174*
Reinecke & Assoc. (C), NJ, *533*
The Douglas Reiter Co., Inc. (R), OR, *174*
Renaissance Resources, LLC (R), VA, *174*
Resource Management Group (C), CT, *534*
Resource Networking Inc. (C), IN, *534*
Resource Recruiting (C), NH, *534*
Resources for Management (R), PA, *175*
Response Staffing Services (C), NY, *534*
L. J. Reszotko & Assoc. (C), IL, *535*
The Retail Network (C), MA, *535*
Retail Recruiters/Spectrum Consultants, Inc. (C), PA, *535*
Retained Search Assoc. (R), NC, *176*
S. Reyman & Assoc., Ltd. (R), IL, *176*
Russell Reynolds Assoc., Inc. (R), NY, *176*
Reynolds Consulting Int'l. (R), ON, *177*
RGE (C), VA, *535*
RHS Assoc. (C), AL, *536*
RIC Corp. (R), FL, *177*
Marshall Rice Assoc. (R), RI, *177*
Jeff Rich Assoc. (C), NJ, *536*
Richard, Wayne & Roberts (C), TX, *536*
Richard Wright Co. (C), CT, *536*
The Richards Group (C), PA, *536*
Riddle & McGrath LLC (R), GA, *178*
Rieser & Assoc., Inc. (R), MO, *178*
Right/McKee Consulting Group (C), TX, *537*
Riley Cole (C), CA, *537*
Riotto-Jones Assoc. (R), NY, *178*
Ritt-Ritt & Assoc., Inc. (C), IL, *537*
RJ Associates (C), CA, *538*
RLM Assoc., Ltd. (R), NY, *179*
Robert William James & Assoc. (C), OR, *539*
Norman Roberts & Assoc., Inc. (R), CA, *179*
Roberts Ryan & Bentley, Inc. (R), MD, *179*
Robertson & Assoc. (C), IL, *539*
Bruce Robinson Assoc. (R), NJ, *180*
Robinson, Fraser Group Ltd. (R), ON, *180*
Robinson-Robinson & Assoc., Inc. (C), MN, *539*
Robison & Associates (R), NC, *180*
Robison Humphreys & Assoc., Inc. (R), ON, *180*
Robsham & Assoc., Inc. (R), MA, *180*
Rockwood Assoc. (C), NY, *540*
Rocky Mountain Recruiters, Inc. (C), CO, *540*
R. A. Rodriguez & Assoc., Inc. (C), TX, *540*
Rodzik & Assoc., Inc. (R), NC, *180*
The Rogan Group, Inc. (C), CA, *541*
Rogish Assoc., Inc. (C), OH, *541*
Rolland Ressources Humaines Inc. (R), QE, *181*
Rollo Assoc. (R), CA, *181*
Romac Int'l. - San Francisco (C), CA, *541*
Romac Int'l. (C), GA, *541*
Romac Int'l. (C), IL, *541*
Romac Int'l. (C), PA, *542*
Romac Int'l. Inc. (R), MA, *181*
Romac Int'l., Inc. (C), FL, *542*
Ropes Associates, Inc. (R), FL, *182*
W. R. Rosato & Assoc., Inc. (R), NY, *182*
Rosenfeld & Co., Inc. (C), MI, *545*
Roster Inc. (C), IN, *545*
Patricia Roth Int'l. (C), FL, *545*
Roth Young Executive Search (C), TX, *546*
Roth Young Seattle (C), WA, *546*
Roth Young Personnel Services of Washington, DC (C), MD, *546*
Rovner Gerner & Assoc. (R), CA, *182*
Rowland Assoc. (C), CA, *547*
Royal Assoc. (C), CA, *547*
RSMR, Inc. (R), IL, *182*
The Rubicon Group (C), AZ, *547*
Ruderfer & Co., Inc. (C), NJ, *548*
Rusher, Loscavio & LoPresto (R), CA, *183*
Rushmore • Judge Inc. (R), ON, *183*
Russillo/Gardner/Spolsino (C), MA, *548*
Rust & Assoc., Inc. (R), IL, *183*
The Ryan Charles Group, Inc. (C), FL, *548*
Ryan, Miller & Assoc. (C), CA, *549*
Ryan-Allen & Assoc., Inc. (C), CA, *549*
Rylan Forbes Consulting Group, Inc. (C), NJ, *549*
Ryman, Bell, Green & Michaels, Inc. (C), TX, *549*
S-H-S TechStaff (C), PA, *549*
S. P. Assoc., Inc. (C), NC, *550*
Saber Group, Inc. (C), TX, *550*
R. S. Sadow Assoc. (C), NJ, *550*
Sage Employment Recruiters (C), IN, *550*
Sales & Management Search, Inc. (C), IL, *551*
Sales Consultants of Birmingham (C), AL, *555*
Sales Consultants of Ft. Myers, Inc. (C), FL, *557*
Sales Consultants of Chicago South (C), IL, *558*
Sales Consultants of Western McHenry County (C), IL, *558*
Sales Consultants (C), IL, *558*
Sales Consultants of Indianapolis-North (C), IN, *558*
Sales Consultants of Bangor, Inc. (C), ME, *559*
Sales Consultants of Princeton, Inc. (C), NJ, *561*
Salveson Stetson Group, Inc. (R), PA, *184*
Salzmann Gay Assoc., Inc. (R), PA, *184*
Sanford Rose Assoc. - Lake Forest (R), IL, *184*
Sanford Rose Assoc. - Mobile (C), AL, *565*
Sanford Rose Assoc. - Athens (C), GA, *566*
Sanford Rose Assoc. - Oak Brook (C), IL, *567*
Sanford Rose Assoc. - Philadelphia North (C), PA, *570*
Sanford Rose Assoc. - Nashville (C), TN, *570*
Sanford Rose Assoc. - Pittsburgh North (C), PA, *570*
Sanford Rose Assoc. - Salt Lake City (C), UT, *571*
Santangelo Consultants Inc. (C), NY, *571*
Sathe & Associates, Inc. (R), MN, *184*
Saviar, Inc. (C), AZ, *571*
Savoy Partners, Ltd. (R), DC, *184*
David Saxner & Assoc., Inc. (DSA, Inc.) (R), IL, *185*
Schall Executive Search Partners (R), MN, *185*
Schattle & Duquette (C), RI, *571*

The Schatz Company (C), MO, *571*
Schenck & Assoc. SC (C), WI, *572*
Schlatter & Assoc. (C), CA, *572*
Schneider, Hill & Spangler, Inc. (R), PA, *185*
Schoales & Assoc. Inc. (C), ON, *572*
Schuyler Assoc., Ltd. (R), GA, *185*
Scott-Wayne Assoc., Inc. (C), MA, *573*
Search Advisors Int'l. Corp. (R), FL, *186*
The Search Alliance, Inc. (R), FL, *186*
Search Assoc., Inc. (C), NJ, *574*
Search Bureau Int'l. (C), IL, *574*
The Search Center Inc. (C), TX, *574*
The Search Committee (C), MD, *574*
The Search Company (R), ON, *186*
Search Consultants, LLC (C), MD, *575*
Search Group Inc. (R), AB, *186*
The Search Group (C), MD, *575*
Search Innovations, Inc. (R), PA, *187*
Search Int'l. (R), MA, *187*
Search Masters Int'l. (R), AZ, *187*
Search North America, Inc. (C), OR, *576*
Search Plus Int'l.-Ohio (C), OH, *576*
Search Research Assoc., Inc. (R), MA, *187*
Search South, Inc. (C), AL, *576*
SearchCorp (C), FL, *577*
SearchCorp International (C), AB, *577*
Searchline Services, Inc. (C), OH, *577*
Secura/Burnett Partners (R), CA, *187*
Sedlar & Miners (R), NY, *188*
J. R. Seehusen Assoc., Inc. (R), IA, *188*
Seiden Krieger Assoc., Inc. (R), NY, *188*
Select Services (C), IL, *578*
Selectis Corp. (C), IL, *578*
Selective Management Services, Inc. (C), FL, *578*
Selective Staffing (C), CA, *579*
Sensible Solutions, Inc. (R), IL, *188*
John Shell Assoc., Inc. (C), SC, *579*
Sherwood Lehman Massucco, Inc. (R), CA, *189*
Shey-Harding Assoc. Inc. (C), CA, *580*
Shifrin-Fischer Group, Inc. (C), NJ, *580*
Shinn & Assoc. (R), CA, *189*
Michael Shirley Assoc. Inc. (R), KS, *190*
Shoemaker & Assoc. (R), GA, *190*
E. L. Shore & Assoc. (R), ON, *190*
Shore Asociados Ejecutivos, S. A. de C.V. (R), MX, *190*
The Shorr Group (R), IL, *190*
The Shotland Group (R), CA, *190*
M. Shulman, Inc. (R), CA, *191*
John Sibbald Assoc., Inc. (R), MO, *191*
Larry Siegel & Assoc. (R), WA, *191*
Peter Siegel & Co. (C), MA, *581*
Siger & Assoc., LLC (C), CT, *581*
Marvin L. Silcott & Assoc., Inc. (C), TX, *581*
L. A. Silver Assoc., Inc. (R), MA, *191*
Silver Associates (C), CA, *581*
D. J. Simpson Assoc. Inc. (R), ON, *191*
Simpson Associates (C), NY, *582*
Sinclair & Co., Inc. (R), MA, *192*
Sink, Walker, Boltrus Int'l. (R), MA, *192*
SKB Enterprises (C), NY, *582*
Skipping Stone Inc. (C), VA, *582*
Ruth Sklar Assoc., Inc. (RSA Executive Search) (R), NY, *192*
Skott/Edwards Consultants (R), NY, *192*
Slayton Int'l., Inc. (R), IL, *192*
J. L. Small Assoc. (C), AL, *583*
Christopher Smallhorn Executive Recruiting, Inc. (R), MA, *193*
Smith & Assoc. (C), CA, *583*
Ralph Smith & Assoc. (C), IL, *584*
Smith & Laue Search (R), OR, *193*
Smith & Sawyer, Inc. (R), NY, *193*
Smith & Syberg, Inc. (R), IN, *193*
G. L. Smith Assoc. (C), CA, *584*
Howard W. Smith Assoc. (R), CT, *193*
Herman Smith Executive Initiatives Inc. (R), ON, *193*
Smith Hanley Assoc., Inc. (C), NY, *584*
Smith James Group, Inc. (R), GA, *194*
Smith Search, S.C. (R), MX, *194*
Smith, Brown & Jones (C), KS, *585*
A. William Smyth, Inc. (R), CA, *194*
Snelling Search (C), AL, *585*
Snelling Search - Transportation Division (C), AR, *585*
Snelling Search (C), LA, *586*
Snelling Search (C), IL, *586*
Snelling Search Recruiters (C), NC, *586*
C. Snow & Assoc. (C), ON, *586*
Snyder & Co. (R), CT, *194*
Sockwell & Assoc. (R), NC, *194*
Robert Sollman & Assoc. (C), FL, *587*
Solomon-Page Healthcare Group (R), NY, *195*
Soltis Management Services (R), PA, *195*
Stephen M. Sonis Assoc. (R), MA, *195*
Southwest Selective Search, Inc. (C), TX, *588*
Southwestern Professional Services (C), TN, *588*
SPC Symcox Personnel Consultants (C), TX, *588*
Spear-Izzo Assoc., LLC (C), PA, *588*
Special Markets Group, Inc. (R), GA, *195*
SpencerStuart (R), NY, *196*
The Spiegel Group (R), MA, *197*
Spilman & Assoc. (R), TX, *197*
Splaine & Assoc., Inc. (R), CA, *198*
Spriggs & Co., Inc. (R), IL, *198*
M. H. Springer & Assoc. (R), CA, *198*
Springer Souder & Assoc. L.L.C. (R), IL, *198*
Staff Extension Int'l. (C), TX, *590*
Staff Resources, Inc. (C), SC, *590*
Staffing Edge, Inc. (C), IA, *590*
Stafford Consulting Group (R), CA, *198*
Stanton Chase Int'l. (R), MD, *198*
Star Search Consultants (C), ON, *591*
The Stark Wilton Group (R), MI, *199*
STAT Search (C), NH, *592*
Steeple Resources & Consulting (R), NJ, *199*
Steinfield & Assoc. (C), TX, *592*
Stentiford & Berardi Assoc. Ltd. (R), NY, *199*
Peter Sterling & Co. (C), TX, *592*
Sterling Int'l. (R), NJ, *200*
Sterling Int'l. Management Recruitment, Ltd. Inc. (C), NC, *592*
Michael Stern Assoc., Inc./Euram (R), ON, *200*
Steven Douglas Assoc. (C), FL, *593*
Steven Michaels & Assoc. (C), NY, *593*
The Stevens Group (C), CA, *593*
The Stevenson Group, Inc. (N.J.) (R), NJ, *200*
The Stewart Group (C), FL, *593*
Stewart, Stein & Scott, Ltd. (R), MN, *200*
Stewart/Greene & Co. of The Triad, Inc. (C), NC, *594*
Stewart/Laurence Assoc., Inc. (R), NJ, *201*
STM Assoc. (R), UT, *201*
Stone Assoc. LLC (C), MI, *594*
Stone Enterprises Ltd. (C), IL, *594*
Stone, Murphy & Olson (R), MN, *201*
DM Stone Personnel Services (C), CA, *594*
The Stonebridge Group (C), PA, *594*
Stoopen Asociados, S.C./EMA Partners Int'l. (R), MX, *202*
Straight & Co. (R), GA, *202*
Strategic Advancement Inc. (R), NJ, *202*
Strategic Alliance Network, Ltd. (C), OH, *595*
Strategic Executives, Inc. (R), CT, *202*
Strategic Search, LLC (C), CA, *595*
StratfordGroup (R), OH, *203*
Stratin Assoc. (C), NJ, *596*
Straube Associates (R), MA, *203*
Strauss Personnel Service (C), PA, *596*
Stroman Int'l., Inc. (R), CO, *204*
Sudina Search, Inc. (C), MD, *596*
Sullivan & Assoc. (R), MI, *204*
Joe Sullivan & Assoc., Inc. (R), NY, *204*
Summit Search Specialists (C), TX, *596*
Swartz & Assoc., Inc. (R), AZ, *204*
Swift & Assoc. (C), ME, *597*
Synagent Inc. (C), ON, *597*
Synapse Human Resource Consulting Group (R), TX, *205*
Synergy 2000 (C), DC, *597*
The Synergy Organization (R), PA, *205*
Systems One Ltd. (C), IL, *598*
Systems Research Inc. (SRI) (C), IL, *598*
T. H. Hunter, Inc. (C), MN, *599*
Tabb & Assoc. (R), OH, *205*
The Talley Group (R), VA, *205*
Roy Talman & Assoc. (C), IL, *599*
The Talon Group (R), TX, *205*
Martin Stevens Tamaren & Assoc., Inc. (R), CA, *206*
Tarbex (C), DC, *599*
Tarnow Int'l. (R), NJ, *206*
Tate & Assoc., Inc. (R), NJ, *207*
Tax Network Resources, Inc. (C), NY, *600*
TaxSearch Inc. (R), OK, *207*
Carl J. Taylor & Co. (R), TX, *207*
Taylor Winfield (R), TX, *207*
TBC, Inc. (C), KY, *600*
TCM Enterprises (C), MD, *600*
Team One Partners, Inc. (C), GA, *600*
Tech-Net (C), TX, *601*
Technifind Int'l. (C), TX, *602*
Techsearch Services Inc. (C), CT, *603*
Techstaff Inc. (C), WI, *603*
Telecom Connections, Inc. (C), TX, *604*
Telford, Adams & Alexander (R), CA, *208*
Tennyson Advisors (R), NY, *208*
The TGA Company (C), TX, *606*
Thomas Mangum Co. (R), CA, *208*
Thomas Resource Group (R), CA, *209*
Thomas, Whelan Assoc., Inc. (C), DC, *606*

Judy Thompson & Assoc., Inc. (C), CA, *606*
Richard Thompson Assoc., Inc. (R), MN, *209*
Thor, Inc. (C), CA, *606*
Thorne, Brieger Assoc., Inc. (R), NY, *209*
The Tidewater Group Inc. (C), CT, *607*
Tittemore Cowan Assoc. (C), AB, *607*
TNS Partners, Inc. (R), TX, *209*
TPS Staffing Solutions (C), IN, *608*
Travel Executive Search (C), NY, *608*
Travis & Co., Inc. (R), MA, *210*
Traynor Confidential, Ltd. (C), NY, *609*
TRH Assoc., Inc. (R), NY, *210*
TriStaff Group (C), CA, *609*
Triumph Consulting, Inc. (R), IA, *210*
Trout & Assoc. Inc. (R), UT, *211*
Trowbridge & Co., Inc. (R), MA, *211*
TRS Staffing Solutions Inc. (C), OH, *610*
The Truman Agency (C), CA, *610*
Tryon & Heideman, LLC (R), MO, *211*
Tschudin Inc. (R), NJ, *211*
TSW Assoc., LLC (R), CT, *211*
TTG/Sterling Services (C), CA, *610*
W. G. Tucker & Assoc. (R), PA, *211*
The Thomas Tucker Co. (R), CA, *211*
Tuft & Assoc., Inc. (R), IL, *212*
Tully/Woodmansee Int'l. Inc. (R), FL, *212*
UniQuest Int'l., Inc. (C), FL, *610*
Unisearch Search & Recruiting Inc. (C), CA, *611*
Unlimited Staffing Solutions, Inc. (C), MI, *611*
The Urban Placement Service (C), TX, *611*
Van Dyke Assoc. (R), IL, *212*
Peter Van Leer & Assoc. (R), MN, *213*
Van Leeuwen Assoc. (R), CA, *213*
VanMaldegiam Assoc., Inc. (R), IL, *213*
VanReypen Enterprises, Ltd. (R), NY, *213*
Venture Resources, Inc. (R), CA, *213*
Verkamp-Joyce Assoc., Inc. (R), IL, *213*
The Verriez Group Inc. (R), ON, *213*
Vincenty & Co. (C), OH, *612*
Vlcek & Company, Inc. (R), CA, *214*
VZ Int'l., Inc. (C), AZ, *613*
The Wabash Group (C), IN, *613*
Wakefield Talabisco Int'l. (R), NY, *214*
Walker Group, Inc. (R), MN, *215*
Wallace Management Co. (R), TN, *215*
Gerald Walsh & Co. Inc. (C), NS, *614*
Deborah Snow Walsh, Inc. (R), IL, *215*
Linda Walter & Associes (C), QE, *615*
Lee H. Walton & Assoc. (R), NY, *215*
Warren Int'l. (R), NY, *215*
Warren, Morris & Madison, Ltd. (C), CA, *616*
R. J. Watkins & Co., Ltd. (R), CA, *216*
Scott Watson & Assoc., Inc. (R), FL, *216*
Watson Int'l., Inc. (R), NY, *216*
Waveland Int'l. (R), IL, *216*
Webb, Johnson Assoc., Inc. (R), NY, *216*
Weber Executive Search (R), NY, *216*
S. B. Webster & Associates (R), MA, *217*
Wegner & Assoc. (C), WI, *617*
Weinstein & Co. (R), MA, *217*
S. E. Weinstein Co. (R), IL, *217*
Wellington Management Group (R), PA, *217*
Wells, Bradley & Assoc., Inc. (C), MN, *618*
Werbin Assoc. Executive Search, Inc. (C), NY, *618*
Jude M. Werra & Assoc. (R), WI, *218*
West Coast Recruiting (C), CA, *619*
Western Management Assoc. (R), CA, *218*
Western Management Consultants (R), BC, *218*
The Westfield Group (C), CT, *619*
WestPacific National Search, Inc. (C), CA, *619*
Weterrings & Agnew, Inc. (C), NY, *619*
S. J. Wexler Assoc., Inc. (R), NY, *219*
Wheeler Assoc. (R), CT, *219*
White, Roberts & Stratton, Inc. (C), IL, *619*
K. L. Whitney Company (R), NJ, *219*
The Whitney Group (R), NY, *219*
Whitney Smith Co. (C), TX, *620*
The Whittaker Group (C), MI, *620*
Whittlesey & Assoc., Inc. (R), PA, *220*
Daniel Wier & Assoc. (R), CA, *220*
Wilcox Bertoux & Miller (R), CA, *220*
Wilcoxen, Blackwell, Niven & Assoc. (R), FL, *220*
Wilder & Assoc. (C), VA, *620*
Wilder, Gammel Partners, Ltd. (R), CA, *220*
Joel H. Wilensky Assoc., Inc. (C), MA, *620*
The Wilkie Group Int'l. (R), ON, *220*
John R. Williams & Assoc., Inc. (C), NC, *621*
Williams Executive Search, Inc. (R), MN, *221*
Williams, Roth & Krueger, Inc. (R), IL, *221*
Willis & Assoc. (R), OH, *221*
William Willis Worldwide Inc. (R), CT, *221*
The Winchester Group (R), CA, *222*
The Windham Group (R), OH, *222*
Windsor Consultants, Inc. (C), TX, *622*
Windsor International (R), GA, *222*
Wing Tips & Pumps, Inc. (C), MI, *623*
Winguth, Grant & Donahue (R), CA, *222*
Winston Search, Inc. (R), MD, *222*
Winter, Wyman & Co. (C), MA, *623*
Winthrop Partners, Inc. (R), NY, *222*
Wisnewski & Assoc. (R), CA, *223*
D. S. Wolf Assoc., Inc. (R), NY, *223*
M. Wood Company (R), IL, *224*
Wood, Franchot Inc. (R), MN, *224*
Wood-Glavin, Inc. (R), KS, *224*
Woodmoor Group (C), CO, *624*
Bruce G. Woods Executive Search (R), TX, *224*
Woodworth Int'l. Group (R), OR, *224*
Working Relationships, Inc. (C), MN, *624*
Worldwide Medical Services (C), CA, *625*
Dick Wray & Consultants, Inc. (R), CA, *225*
WTW Assoc., Inc. (R), NY, *225*
Wyndham Mills Int'l., Inc. (R), GA, *225*
Xavier Associates, Inc. (R), MA, *226*
Yankee Hospitality Search (C), CT, *626*
Yelverton Executive Search (R), CA, *226*
The Yorkshire Group, Ltd. (C), MA, *626*
Yormak & Assoc. (C), CA, *626*
Youngblood Assoc. (C), NC, *626*
Yours In Travel Personnel Agency, Inc. (C), NY, *626*
Steven Yungerberg Assoc., Inc. (R), MN, *226*
The Zammataro Company (R), OH, *226*
Zen Zen Int'l. Inc. (C), MB, *627*
Helen Ziegler & Assoc., Inc. (C), ON, *627*
Zingaro & Company (R), TX, *227*
Zona & Assoc., Inc. (C), NY, *628*
Zweig White & Assoc., Inc. (R), MA, *228*
Zwell Int'l. (R), IL, *228*

07.1 CFO's

A.K.S. Assoc., Ltd. (R), MA, *1*
Abacus Group LLC (C), NY, *232*
The Abbott Group, Inc. (R), MD, *1*
Accent On Achievement, Inc. (C), MI, *233*
Access/Resources, Inc. (C), MA, *234*
Accountancies (C), CA, *234*
Accountants Executive Search (C), CT, *234*
Accountants Executive Search (C), PA, *234*
Accountants On Call (C), FL, *237*
Accountants On Call (C), TN, *237*
Accountants Executive Search (C), CA, *237*
Accounting & Bookkeeping Personnel, Inc. (C), AZ, *237*
Accounting Additions (C), CA, *238*
Advantage Partners, Inc. (R), OH, *2*
Advice Personnel Inc. (C), NY, *241*
AGRI-associates (C), MO, *242*
Agri-Tech Personnel, Inc. (C), MO, *242*
Ahrensdorf & Assoc. (R), PA, *2*
J. R. Akin & Co. (R), MA, *2*
Allen & Assoc. (C), NV, *244*
Allen/Associates (R), OH, *4*
Allerton Heneghan & O'Neill (R), IL, *4*
Alpha Resource Group, Inc. (C), TX, *246*
AM & G Certified Public Accountants & Consultants (R), IL, *4*
Amato & Associates Insurance Recruiters (C), PA, *247*
Peter W. Ambler Co. (R), TX, *5*
AMS Int'l. (R), VA, *5*
Anderson & Schwab, Inc. (R), NY, *5*
Anderson Network Group (C), OH, *250*
Andrews & Assoc. (C), NC, *250*
Andrews & Wald Group (C), FL, *250*
Angus Employment Ltd. (C), ON, *250*
Argonaut Partners, LLC (R), CA, *6*
Argus National, Inc. (R), CT, *6*
Ariail & Assoc. (R), NC, *7*
Ariel Recruitment Assoc. (R), NY, *7*
Armitage Associates Ltd. (R), ON, *7*
Armor Personnel (C), ON, *253*
J. S. Armstrong & Assoc., Inc. (R), CA, *7*
Artgo, Inc. (R), OH, *7*
The Ascher Group (R), NJ, *7*
E. J. Ashton & Assoc., Ltd. (C), IL, *253*
Ashworth Consultants, Inc. (R), MA, *8*
Atlantic Search Group, Inc. (C), MA, *255*
Aubin Int'l. Inc. (R), MA, *8*
Auerbach Associates, Inc. (R), MA, *9*
AutoPeople (C), VT, *257*
Avalon Health Group, Inc. (R), NY, *9*
The Badger Group (R), CA, *10*
Baeder Kalinski Int'l. Group, Inc. (R), NH, *10*

Baker Scott & Co. (C), NJ, *258*
Baldwin Associates, LLC (R), CT, *10*
Allen Ballach Assoc. Inc. (R), ON, *10*
Barger & Sargeant, Inc. (R), NH, *11*
J. W. Barleycorn, Renard & Assoc., Inc. (R), OH, *11*
The Barrett Group (C), NH, *260*
Barrett Hospitality Search (R), CA, *12*
Nathan Barry Assoc., Inc. (R), MA, *12*
Barth Smith Company (R), IL, *12*
Bartholdi & Co., Inc. (R), CO, *12*
Bartl & Evins (C), NY, *260*
Battalia Winston Int'l./The Euram Consultants Group (R), NY, *13*
Martin H. Bauman Assoc., Inc. (R), NY, *13*
BCG Search, Inc. (R), FL, *14*
The Beam Group (R), PA, *14*
Becker, Norton & Co. (R), PA, *14*
The Bedford Consulting Group Inc. (R), ON, *14*
Belanger Partners Ltd. (C), ON, *262*
Gary S. Bell Assoc., Inc. (C), NJ, *263*
BEST/World Assoc. Inc. (R), TX, *16*
Bialla & Assoc. Inc. (R), CA, *17*
Billington & Assoc. (R), CA, *17*
Binder Hospitality Group (C), KY, *266*
BioQuest Inc. (R), CA, *17*
J: Blakslee Int'l., Ltd. (R), CA, *18*
Blaney Executive Search (R), MA, *18*
D. R. Blood & Assoc. (R), AZ, *18*
Boardroom Consultants/Kenny Kindler Tholke (R), NY, *19*
Bodner Inc. (C), NY, *268*
Boone-Scaturro Assoc., Inc. (C), GA, *269*
BowdenGlobal, Ltd. (R), OH, *20*
Boyden (R), NY, *20*
Bradford Executives Int'l. (C), VA, *271*
The Brand Co., Inc. (R), FL, *22*
Brault & Assoc., Ltd. (R), VA, *22*
The Brentwood Group, Inc. (R), NJ, *22*
The Brentwood Group Ltd. (R), OR, *23*
Bernard E. Brooks & Assoc., Inc. (R), SC, *24*
J. B. Brown & Assoc., Inc. (C), OH, *275*
Brown Venture Assoc. (R), CA, *24*
Brush Creek Partners (R), MO, *24*
Bullis & Co., Inc. (R), CA, *25*
Joseph R. Burns & Assoc., Inc. (R), NJ, *25*
Busch International (R), CA, *25*
Butterfass, Pepe & MacCallan Inc. (R), NJ, *25*
Byron Leonard Int'l., Inc. (R), CA, *25*
C. P. Consulting (R), PA, *26*
C/R Associates (C), NY, *278*
California Management Search (C), CA, *279*
Cambridge Group Ltd. - Exec. Search Div. (C), CT, *279*
The Cambridge Group Ltd. (C), CT, *280*
Cambridge Management Planning (R), ON, *27*
Canny, Bowen Inc. (R), NY, *27*
Capital Consulting Group, Inc. (R), MD, *28*
Capstone Inc. (R), NY, *29*
Career Advisors, Inc. (C), FL, *281*
Career Consultants (R), IN, *29*
Career Counseling Inc. (CCI) (C), KY, *282*
Career Development Associates (C), NV, *282*
Career Marketing Consultants, Inc. (C), GA, *282*
Career Specialists, Inc. (R), WA, *29*
Career Strategies, Inc. (C), CA, *283*
Carion Resource Group Inc. (C), ON, *284*
Carlsen Resources, Inc. (R), CO, *29*
Carlson & Czeswik (R), MN, *30*
Carson-Thomas & Assoc. (C), CA, *284*
Carter-Evdemon & Assoc. (C), FL, *285*
Caruso & Assoc., Inc. (R), FL, *31*
Carver Search Consultants (C), CA, *285*
Cary & Assoc. (R), FL, *31*
Catalyx Group (R), NY, *31*
Michael J. Cavanagh & Assoc. Inc. (R), ON, *31*
CEC Associates (R), MA, *32*
Cejka Healthcare Executive Search Services (CHESS) (R), MO, *32*
Cemco, Ltd. (C), IL, *286*
Century Assoc., Inc. (C), PA, *287*
The Century Group (C), CA, *287*
CFOs 2 Go (C), CA, *288*
CFR Executive Search, Inc. (C), IL, *288*
David Chambers & Assoc., Inc. (R), CT, *32*
Vickers Chambless Managed Search (C), GA, *288*
The Cherbonnier Group, Inc. (R), TX, *33*
Chesapeake Group (C), CT, *290*
Christian & Timbers, Inc. (R), OH, *34*
Churchill & Affiliates, Inc. (R), PA, *35*
CJA-The Adler Group, Inc. (R), CA, *35*
CMS, Inc. (C), NH, *293*
Coastal Int'l., Inc. (R), MA, *36*
Cochran, Cochran & Yale, Inc. (R), NY, *36*
Coe & Co. Int'l. Inc./EMA Partners Int'l. (R), AB, *37*
The Coelyn Group (R), CA, *37*
Coleman Lew & Assoc., Inc. (R), NC, *37*
Colton Bernard Inc. (R), CA, *37*
The Colton Partnership, Inc. (R), NY, *38*
Compass Group Ltd. (R), MI, *38*
Conard Associates, Inc. (R), NH, *39*
Robert Connelly & Assoc., Inc. (R), MN, *39*
Conroy Partners Ltd. (R), AB, *39*
Construct Management Services (C), MN, *297*
Consulpro (R), ON, *39*
Philip Conway Management (R), IL, *40*
Cook Assoc.,® Inc. (R), IL, *40*
The Cooke Group (R), WI, *40*
David C. Cooper & Assoc. Financial Search (C), GA, *298*
Cornerstone Search Assoc. Inc. (C), MA, *299*
The Corporate Advisory Group (R), NJ, *41*
The Corporate Connection, Ltd. (C), VA, *299*
CountryHouse Hotels Executive Search (C), VA, *302*
Cowell & Associates, Ltd. (R), IL, *42*
Crane, Reed & Co., Inc. (C), NH, *302*
Creative Financial Staffing Inc. (C), ON, *303*
Creative Management Strategies, Ltd. (R), NY, *42*
Creative-Leadership, Inc. (R), CA, *42*
Crist Partners, Ltd. (R), IL, *43*
Marlene Critchfield Co. (C), CA, *303*
Cromwell Partners, Inc. (R), NY, *43*
Timothy D. Crowe, Jr. (R), MA, *43*
CTR (R), CA, *43*
Culver Personnel Services (C), CA, *304*
Curran Partners, Inc. (R), CT, *44*
The Currier-Winn Co., Inc. (C), NJ, *305*
The Curtiss Group International (R), FL, *44*
Cypress Int'l., Inc. (R), FL, *45*
D.A.I Human Resources Consultants (R), QE, *45*
Dahl-Morrow Int'l. (R), VA, *45*
The Danbrook Group, Inc. (C), TX, *306*
Datamatics Management Services, Inc. (C), NJ, *307*
Daubenspeck & Associates, Ltd. (R), IL, *46*
Davies, Park (R), AB, *46*
Bert Davis Executive Search, Inc. (R), NY, *47*
DBL Associates (C), CA, *309*
DeCaster Assoc. (C), WI, *310*
Defrain Mayer (R), KS, *48*
Thorndike Deland Assoc. LLC (R), NY, *48*
S. W. Delano & Co. (R), CT, *48*
Dieckmann & Assoc., Ltd. (R), IL, *51*
DieckMueller Group (R), WI, *51*
The Diestel Group (R), UT, *51*
DiMarchi Partners (R), CO, *51*
J. Dinerstein & Co., Inc. (R), NY, *51*
Robert W. Dingman Co., Inc. (R), CA, *52*
Dinte Resources, Inc. (R), VA, *52*
Discovery, The Staffing Specialists, Inc. (C), IL, *312*
Diversified Search, Inc. (R), PA, *52*
Dixie Search Assoc. (C), GA, *313*
DLG Assoc., Inc. (R), NC, *53*
DNA Search, Inc. (C), CA, *313*
Drew Assoc. Int'l. (R), NJ, *54*
Drummond Assoc., Inc. (C), NY, *315*
M. Dunbar & Assoc. (C), TX, *316*
Dunhill of Manchester Inc. (C), NH, *321*
Dunhill Search of Medford (C), NJ, *321*
Dunhill Professional Search of Omaha, Inc. (C), NE, *321*
Dunhill Search of Arlington (C), TX, *322*
Dunlap & Sullivan Assoc. (R), MI, *55*
C. A. Durakis Assoc., Inc. (R), MD, *55*
Donald F. Dvorak & Co. (R), IL, *55*
Dwyer Consulting Group, Inc. (R), WV, *56*
Gwen Dycus & Assoc. (C), FL, *323*
The E & K Group (C), NJ, *324*
E/Search Int'l. (C), CT, *325*
EagleView, Inc. (C), MA, *325*
Earley Kielty & Assoc., Inc. (R), NY, *56*
Eastman & Beaudine, Inc. (R), TX, *56*
Eden & Assoc., Inc. (C), PA, *326*
Bruce Edwards & Associates, Inc. (R), NC, *56*
William J. Elam & Assoc. (R), NE, *58*
H. J. Elliot, Inc. (R), IL, *58*
EMN/Witt/Kieffer (R), MA, *59*
Empire International (R), PA, *59*
Erikson Consulting Assoc., Inc. (R), NY, *60*
Erlanger Assoc. (R), CT, *60*
Erwin Assoc. (R), IL, *60*
Ethos Consulting, Inc. (R), CA, *61*
ETI Search Int'l. (R), GA, *61*
The Evans Search Group (R), CT, *61*
Evans Transportation Search (C), ON, *331*

The Execu/Search Group (C), NY, *332*
ExecuSource Assoc., Inc. (C), GA, *332*
Executive Access Inc. (R), NY, *62*
Executive Direction, Inc. (C), CA, *333*
Executive Placement Consultants (C), IL, *333*
Executive Recruitment Specialists, Inc. (R), NC, *63*
Executive Referral Services, Inc. (C), IL, *334*
Executive Resource Inc. (C), WI, *334*
Executive Resource Systems (C), CA, *335*
Executive Search Consultants, Inc. (C), FL, *335*
Executive Search Consultants Corp. (C), IL, *335*
Executive Search of New England, Inc. (C), ME, *336*
Executive Search Partners (R), NY, *63*
Executive Solutions (R), MN, *64*
The Executive Source (C), SA, *337*
Raymond L. Extract & Assoc. (R), CA, *64*
Eyler Assoc., Inc. (R), IA, *64*
Fagan & Company (R), PA, *64*
Fairfaxx Corp. (R), CT, *64*
Leon A. Farley Assoc. (R), CA, *65*
Federal Placement Services (C), NY, *339*
Fell & Nicholson Technology Resources (R), CA, *65*
Fenwick Partners (R), MA, *66*
Fidelity Search Group, Inc. (R), PA, *66*
Financial Connections Company (C), VA, *340*
Financial Search Corp. (C), IL, *340*
Financialjobs.com (C), CA, *340*
Finnegan & Assoc. (R), CA, *67*
Howard Fischer Assoc. Int'l., Inc. (R), PA, *67*
Fishel HR Assoc., Inc. (C), AZ, *341*
The Fisher Group (R), AB, *67*
Foley Proctor Yoskowitz (R), NJ, *69*
The Ford Group, Inc. (R), PA, *69*
Forray Assoc., Inc. (R), NY, *70*
Fortune Personnel Consultants of Huntsville, Inc. (C), AL, *343*
F-O-R-T-U-N-E Personnel Consultants of San Diego (C), CA, *344*
F-O-R-T-U-N-E Personnel Consultants (C), MI, *346*
Fortune Personnel Consultants of Hinsdale, IL (C), IL, *346*
F-O-R-T-U-N-E Personnel Consultants of Southwest Indiana (C), IN, *346*
Forum Personnel Inc. (C), NY, *351*
Foster Associates (C), NJ, *351*
Foster Partners (R), NY, *70*
Franklin Allen Consultants, Ltd. (R), NY, *71*
Franstaff Inc. (C), FL, *352*
KS Frary & Assoc. (R), MA, *71*
P. N. French Assoc., Inc. (R), MA, *72*
Friedman Eisenstein Raemer & Schwartz, LLP (R), IL, *72*
The Furst Group, Inc. (R), IL, *72*
Furst Group/MPI (R), IL, *72*
GAAP Inc. (R), QE, *73*
The Gabriel Group (C), PA, *354*
Gaming Consultants, Inc. (R), LA, *74*
The Gammill Group, Inc. (C), OH, *354*
Gans, Gans & Assoc., Inc. (R), FL, *74*
W. N. Garbarini & Assoc. (R), NJ, *74*
Gardiner, Townsend & Assoc. (R), NY, *74*
Garrett Assoc. Inc. (R), GA, *75*
GateSource Partners (C), VA, *355*
Gateway Group Personnel, LLC (C), TN, *355*
Gavin Forbes & Price (R), CA, *75*
Gent & Assoc. (C), CA, *356*
C. R. Gerald & Assoc. (C), ON, *356*
Gielow Assoc., Inc. (R), WI, *76*
John Gilbert Co. (C), TX, *357*
Gilbert Scott Assoc., LLC (C), MA, *357*
Gilbert Tweed Assoc. Inc. (R), NY, *76*
Gilmore & Assoc. (C), CA, *357*
Gilreath Weatherby Inc. (R), MA, *77*
Global 1000 Int'l. Services (C), CA, *358*
Glou Int'l., Inc. (R), MA, *78*
The Tracy Glover Co. (R), TX, *78*
The Gobbell Co. (R), CA, *78*
Godfrey Personnel, Inc. (C), IL, *359*
H. L. Goehring & Assoc., Inc. (C), OH, *359*
Fred J. Goldsmith Assoc. (R), CA, *79*
Gomez Fregoso y Asociados (C), JAL, *360*
Goodrich & Sherwood Assoc., Inc. (R), NY, *79*
Goodwin & Co. (R), DC, *80*
Gould, McCoy & Chadick, Inc. (R), NY, *80*
Robert Graham Assoc. (R), RI, *81*
Granger, Counts & Assoc. (R), OH, *81*
Grantham & Co., Inc. (R), NC, *81*
Graphic Search Assoc. Inc. (C), PA, *362*
Annie Gray Assoc., Inc. (R), MO, *81*
Ben Greco Assoc., Inc. (C), CA, *362*
Sheila Greco Assoc. (C), NY, *362*
R. Green & Assoc., Inc. (C), OH, *362*
Greger/Peterson Assoc., Inc. (R), CA, *81*
Griffith & Werner, Inc. (R), FL, *82*
J. B. Groner Executive Search, Inc. (C), DE, *363*
Groussman & Assoc., Inc. (R), TX, *82*
David E. Grumney Co. Inc. (R), WA, *83*
GSP International (C), NJ, *364*
GSW Consulting Group, Inc. (R), CA, *83*
The Gullgroup (C), TX, *364*
Gustin Partners, Ltd. (R), MA, *83*
William Guy & Assoc., Inc. (R), CA, *84*
GWS Partners (R), IL, *84*
H R Solutions, Inc. (C), MO, *365*
H.Q. Search, Inc. (C), IL, *365*
Hale Assoc. (R), IL, *84*
Robert Half Canada Inc. (C), ON, *366*
The Hamilton Group (R), MD, *85*
Handy HRM (R), NY, *86*
The Hanover Consulting Group (C), MD, *368*
Hardison & Company (R), TX, *86*
Robert Harkins Assoc., Inc. (C), PA, *369*
The Harris Consulting Corp. (R), MB, *87*
The Hawkins Co. (R), CA, *88*
William E. Hay & Co. (R), IL, *88*
Hayden & Assoc., Inc. (C), MN, *370*
Hayden Group, Inc. (R), MA, *88*
Headden Assoc. (R), WA, *88*
Healey Executive Search, Inc. (R), MN, *88*
Health Care Dimensions (C), CO, *371*
Health Search (C), CA, *371*
Healthcare Management Resources, Inc. (R), GA, *89*
Healthcare Recruiters of the Rockies, Inc. (C), CO, *372*
Healthcare Recruiters of Indiana (C), IN, *372*
Healthcare Recruiters Int'l - Minnesota, Inc. (C), MN, *373*
Healthcare Recruiters Int'l. Philadelphia (C), NJ, *373*
Healthcare Search Associates (C), CA, *374*
F. P. Healy & Co., Inc. (R), NY, *89*
R. W. Hebel Assoc. (R), TX, *89*
The Heidrick Partners, Inc. (R), IL, *90*
Heinze & Assoc. Inc. (R), MN, *91*
Helbling & Assoc., Inc. (R), PA, *91*
Heller Assoc., Ltd. (R), IL, *91*
Hemingway Personnel, Inc. (C), CA, *375*
G. W. Henn & Co. (R), OH, *91*
Bruce Henry Assoc. Inc. (R), CA, *91*
Hermann & Westmore (R), CA, *92*
Herring & Assoc. (C), AR, *376*
Hersher Assoc., Ltd. (R), IL, *92*
Stanley Herz & Co. (R), NY, *92*
Robert Hess & Assoc., Inc. (C), CO, *377*
Hessel Assoc., Inc. (C), NY, *377*
The Hetzel Group, Inc. (R), IL, *92*
Higdon Prince Inc. (R), NY, *93*
B. W. Higgins, Inc. (C), IN, *377*
Highland Search Group, L.L.C. (R), NY, *93*
Higley, Hall & Co., Inc. (R), MA, *93*
Frank P. Hill (R), MX, *93*
The Hindman Co. (R), KY, *94*
Hobson Assoc. (C), CT, *379*
Hockett Associates, Inc. (R), CA, *94*
Hoglund & Assoc., Inc. (R), IL, *94*
Holden & Harlan Assoc., Inc. (C), IL, *380*
Home Health & Hospital Recruiters, Inc. (C), GA, *380*
Hook-Up! (C), CA, *380*
David C. Horn Executive Search (C), TX, *381*
Hornberger Management Company (R), DE, *95*
Hospitality Executive Search, Inc. (R), MA, *96*
Houtz•Strawn & Arnold, Inc. (R), TX, *96*
The Howard-Sloan-Koller Group (R), NY, *97*
Howe & Assoc. (R), PA, *97*
HRI Services, Inc. (C), MA, *382*
Human Resource Bureau (C), CA, *384*
Human Resources Management Hawaii, Inc. (C), HI, *384*
Hunt & Howe Inc. (R), NY, *99*
The Hunt Co. (R), NY, *99*
The Hunter Group, Inc. (C), MI, *385*
Hunter Int'l. LLC (C), MA, *385*
Hunter, Rowan & Crowe (C), FL, *386*
Huntress Real Estate Executive Search (R), MO, *100*
The Hutton Group, Inc. (C), FL, *386*
HVS Executive Search (R), NY, *100*
IM Independent Management Recruiters (R), TN, *101*
The IMC Group of Companies (R), NY, *101*
Insurance Search (C), TX, *390*

Intech Summit Group, Inc. (R), CA, *102*
InteliSearch, Inc. (R), CT, *102*
Inter Regional Executive Search, Inc. (IRES, Inc.) (C), NJ, *391*
Interactive Search Network (R), CA, *102*
Interim Accounting Professionals (C), CA, *391*
International Executive Recruiters (C), OH, *393*
Intersource, Ltd. (R), GA, *103*
IR Search (R), CA, *103*
Isaacson, Miller (R), MA, *104*
ISC of Atlanta, Inc. (C), GA, *394*
ISC of Houston, Inc. (C), TX, *394*
Ives & Associates, Inc. (C), OH, *395*
J. Nicholas Arthur (R), MA, *104*
Ron Jackson & Assoc. (C), GA, *396*
Jacobson Assoc. (C), IL, *396*
Pendleton James Assoc., Inc. (R), NY, *105*
JCL & Assoc. (C), FL, *397*
JDH & Assoc. (C), CA, *397*
JenKim Int'l. Ltd., Inc. (C), FL, *398*
Jerome & Co. (C), CA, *398*
JNB Assoc., Inc. (C), MA, *399*
Johnson & Company (R), CT, *107*
Ronald S. Johnson Assoc., Inc. (R), CA, *107*
Johnson Assoc., Inc. (C), IL, *399*
Jones and Jones (R), OR, *108*
Joseph Michaels (C), CA, *401*
JPM International (C), CA, *401*
JSG Group Management Consultants (R), ON, *109*
JT Assoc. (C), CT, *401*
Judd Associates (R), NJ, *109*
KABL Ability Network (C), CA, *402*
Richard Kader & Assoc. (C), OH, *403*
Gary Kaplan & Assoc. (R), CA, *109*
Kaplan & Assoc., Inc. (R), PA, *109*
Howard Karr & Assoc., Inc. (R), CA, *110*
Katelyn Partners (C), FL, *404*
Kaufman Assoc. (R), CA, *110*
Jim Kay & Assoc. (C), IL, *404*
The Kay Group of 5th Ave. (C), NY, *404*
Keane Assoc. (R), MA, *110*
A.T. Kearney Executive Search (R), IL, *111*
Keeley Consulting Inc. (C), ON, *404*
David Warwick Kennedy & Assoc. (R), BC, *112*
Kennedy & Co. (R), IL, *112*
The Kennett Group, Inc. (R), PA, *112*
Kensington Int'l., Inc. (R), IL, *113*
Kent & Assoc. (R), OH, *113*
Kenzer Corp. (R), NY, *113*
Blair Kershaw Assoc., Inc. (C), PA, *405*
Kershner & Co. (R), DC, *113*
Michael L. Ketner & Assoc., Inc. (R), PA, *114*
Keystone Consulting Group (C), GA, *406*
Kimmel & Associates, Inc. (C), NC, *406*
Kincaid Group Inc. (KGI) (C), TX, *406*
Richard Kinser & Assoc. (R), NY, *115*
Kittleman & Assoc.,LLC (R), IL, *115*
The Koehler Group (C), PA, *408*
Kopplin Search, Inc. (R), CA, *117*
Koren, Rogers Assoc. Inc. (R), NY, *117*
Kors Montgomery Int'l. (R), TX, *118*
Kostmayer Assoc., Inc. (R), MD, *119*
The J. Kovach Group (R), PA, *119*
Katherine R. Kraemer (R), CA, *120*
Krakower Group, Inc. (R), CA, *120*
Kramer Executive Resources, Inc. (C), NY, *409*
Evie Kreisler Assoc. Inc. (C), CA, *409*
Kremple & Meade, Inc. (R), CA, *120*
Kremple Consulting Group (R), CA, *120*
Kressenberg Assoc. (C), TX, *409*
Todd L. Krueger & Assoc. (C), WA, *409*
Kuhn Med-Tech (C), CA, *409*
Marvin Laba & Assoc. (R), CA, *122*
Laguzza Assoc., Ltd. (R), NY, *122*
The Landstone Group (C), NY, *412*
The Langford Search, Inc. (C), AL, *412*
LanSo Int'l., Inc. (C), NY, *413*
Lawrence L. Lapham, Inc. (R), NY, *124*
Stephen Laramee & Assoc. Inc. (C), ON, *413*
Michael Latas & Assoc., Inc. (R), MO, *125*
Lautz, Grotte, Engler & Swimley (R), CA, *126*
Madeleine Lav & Assoc. (C), CA, *413*
Lawrence-Leiter & Co. (R), KS, *126*
Leader Network (C), PA, *414*
Lear & Assoc., Inc. (C), FL, *415*
Ledbetter/Davidson Int'l., Inc. (R), NY, *127*
Leeds and Leeds (C), TN, *416*
Lehman McLeskey (R), TX, *128*
Lemming/LeVan, Inc. (R), GA, *128*
Levin & Company, Inc. (R), MA, *128*
Lewis & Blank Int'l. (R), CA, *129*
J. H. Lindell & Co. (C), CA, *418*
Lipsky Group, Inc. (R), CA, *129*
Livingston, Robert & Co. (R), CT, *130*
Lloyd Associates (R), GA, *130*
Locke & Assoc. (R), NC, *131*
Loderman & Costello (C), GA, *419*
The Logan Group, Inc. (R), MO, *131*
Longshore + Simmons (R), PA, *131*
The John Lucht Consultancy Inc. (R), NY, *131*
The Luciani Group (R), CA, *132*
Lyons Pruitt Int'l. (R), PA, *132*
M.C. Executive Search (C), CA, *422*
M/J/A Partners (R), IL, *133*
MacNaughton Assoc. (R), CA, *133*
Maczkov-Biosciences, Inc. (R), CA, *133*
The Madison Group (R), NY, *133*
Magellan Int'l., L.P. (C), TX, *422*
Management Advisors Int'l., Inc. (C), NC, *424*
Management Assoc. (C), MD, *424*
Management Dimensions Ltd. (R), ON, *134*
Management One Consultants (C), ON, *425*
Management Recruiters of Birmingham, Inc. (C), AL, *438*
Management Recruiters of Fresno (C), CA, *440*
Management Recruiters Dana Point (C), CA, *440*
Management Recruiters, Inland Empire Agency (C), CA, *441*
Management Recruiters of Roseville (C), CA, *441*
Management Recruiters of Pleasanton (C), CA, *441*
Management Recruiters of Ft. Myers, FL. (C), FL, *443*
Management Recruiters of Anna Maria Island (C), FL, *443*
Management Recruiters, Inc. (C), FL, *443*
Management Recruiters of St. Augustine (C), FL, *444*
Management Recruiters of North Fulton (C), GA, *445*
Management Recruiters of Des Moines (C), IA, *449*
Management Recruiters of Williamsburg (C), IA, *449*
Management Recruiters of Muskegon (C), MI, *451*
Management Recruiters of Winona (C), MN, *452*
Management Recruiters of Winston-Salem (C), NC, *457*
Management Recruiters of Cleveland (C), OH, *457*
Management Recruiters of Houston (C), TX, *462*
Management Recruiters of Janesville, Inc. (C), WI, *466*
Management Resource Group, Ltd. (C), IA, *467*
Management Resources (C), TX, *467*
Management Solutions, Inc. (C), CA, *468*
Manuso, Alexander & Associates, Inc. (R), NY, *135*
Marentz & Co. (C), TX, *469*
Mark Stanley & Co./EMA Partners International (R), FL, *136*
Paula Marks Inc. (R), NY, *136*
The Marlow Group (R), MA, *136*
Marsar & Co., Inc. (C), FL, *471*
Marshall-Alan Assoc., Inc. (C), NY, *471*
Donovan Martin & Assoc. (R), CA, *137*
Martin Partners, L.L.C. (R), IL, *137*
Massey-Horton Int'l. (R), ON, *138*
Richard L. Mather & Assoc. (C), CT, *472*
Matthews & Stephens Assoc., Inc. (C), CT, *472*
Maxecon Executive Search Consultants (R), FL, *138*
K. Maxin & Assoc. (R), PA, *139*
McCann, Choi & Associates, LLC (R), NY, *139*
K. E. McCarthy & Assoc. (R), CA, *139*
McCormack & Assoc. (R), CA, *140*
McCray, Shriver, Eckdahl & Assoc., Inc. (R), CA, *140*
McDonald Assoc. Int'l. (R), IL, *140*
Clarence E. McFeely, Inc. (R), IL, *141*
McHale & Assoc. (R), WA, *141*
McIntyre Assoc. (R), CT, *141*
McIntyre Management Resources (C), ON, *474*
McKinley•Arend Int'l. (R), TX, *141*
Jon McRae & Associates, Inc. (R), GA, *142*
MCS Assoc. (R), CA, *142*
Meder & Assoc., Inc. (R), IL, *142*
The Medley Group (C), CA, *477*
MedSearch Resources, Inc. (C), FL, *478*
Meng, Finseth & Assoc., Inc. (R), CA, *143*
Mercedes & Co., Inc. (R), MA, *143*
Meridian Resources (C), OH, *479*
Messett Assoc., Inc. (R), FL, *143*

META/MAT, Ltd. (R), NJ, *144*
Michigan Consulting Group (R), MI, *144*
Millar Walker & Gay (R), ON, *144*
Herbert Mines Assoc., Inc. (R), NY, *145*
Mirtz Morice, Inc. (R), CT, *145*
MIXTEC Group (R), CA, *145*
Moffitt Int'l., Inc. (R), NC, *146*
Molloy Partners (R), NY, *146*
Oscar Montaño, Inc. (R), CA, *146*
The Montgomery Group, Inc. (C), TN, *484*
Montgomery Resources, Inc. (C), CA, *484*
Morgan Hunter Corp. (C), KS, *485*
Morgan Int'l., Inc. (R), IL, *147*
Morris & Berger (R), CA, *147*
Mortgage & Financial Personnel Services (C), CA, *486*
Mortgage Search Network (C), AZ, *486*
Mruk & E.M.A. Partners (R), NY, *148*
MSI Int'l. (C), GA, *486*
Much & Co. (R), NY, *148*
Pamela L. Mulligan, Inc. (R), NH, *149*
P. J. Murphy & Assoc., Inc. (R), WI, *150*
The MVP Group (C), NY, *487*
Mycoff & Assoc. (R), CO, *150*
DDJ Myers, Ltd. (R), AZ, *150*
Nason & Nason (C), FL, *488*
National Bank & Finance Executive Search (C), CA, *488*
National Search, Inc.r (C), FL, *490*
The Neil Michael Group, Inc./Global Partners (R), NY, *151*
J. Fielding Nelson & Assoc., Inc. (R), UT, *151*
New World Healthcare Solutions, Inc. (R), NY, *151*
Newell Assoc. (R), NY, *151*
Nichols & Company (R), CO, *151*
P. J. Nicholson & Assoc. (C), IL, *493*
The Noebel Search Group, Inc. (C), TX, *494*
The Nolan Group (C), CA, *494*
Noll Human Resource Services (C), NE, *494*
Nordeman Grimm, Inc. (R), NY, *152*
Norman Broadbent Int'l., Inc. (R), NY, *152*
Norrell Financial Staffing (C), GA, *495*
John B. Norris & Assoc., Inc. (C), MD, *495*
O'Brien Consulting Services (R), MA, *153*
O'Callaghan Honey/Ray & Berndtson Inc. (R), AB, *153*
O'Connor, O'Connor, Lordi, Ltd. (R), PA, *154*
O'Neill & Co. (R), CT, *154*
O'Neill Group (C), NJ, *498*
O'Rourke Companies, Inc. (R), TX, *154*
Dennis P. O'Toole & Assoc. Inc. (R), NY, *154*
Odell & Assoc., Inc. (C), TX, *498*
The Odessa Group (R), CA, *155*
The Ogdon Partnership (R), NY, *155*
Oliver & Rozner Assoc., Inc. (R), NY, *155*
Ollinger Partners (R), MA, *156*
Olsen/Clark (R), WA, *156*
Omnisearch Assoc. (C), CA, *499*
The Onstott Group (R), MA, *156*
Orion Int'l. Consulting Group, Inc. (C), NC, *499*
P.A.R. Assoc., Inc. (R), MA, *158*
P.R.H. Management, Inc. (R), CT, *158*
Pacific Search Group, Inc. (C), CA, *501*
Pamenter, Pamenter, Brezer & Deganis Ltd. (R), ON, *159*
Arthur Pann Assoc., Inc. (C), NY, *502*
The PAR Group - Paul A. Reaume, Ltd. (R), IL, *159*
Jim Parham & Assoc., Inc. (R), FL, *159*
Parker & Lynch (C), CA, *503*
Parker Page Group (C), FL, *503*
Michael W. Parres & Assoc. (R), MI, *159*
Parsons Assoc. Inc. (R), IL, *159*
Partners Resource Group (C), VA, *504*
The Partnership Group (R), NJ, *160*
Partnervision Consulting Group Inc. (R), ON, *160*
Partridge Assoc., Inc. (R), MA, *160*
Pascale & LaMorte, LLC (C), CT, *504*
Joel H. Paul & Assoc., Inc. (C), NY, *505*
Paul-Tittle Assoc., Inc. (R), VA, *161*
Pearson, Caldwell & Farnsworth (R), CA, *161*
People Management Mid-South, LLC (R), TN, *162*
Performance Resources, Inc. (C), RI, *507*
PERI Corp/Professional Executive Recruiters, Inc. (C), TX, *507*
Perry • Newton Assoc. (C), MD, *507*
Perry-Martel Int'l., Inc. (R), ON, *163*
Barry Persky & Co., Inc. (R), CT, *163*
Personnel Management Group (C), MB, *508*
Richard Peterson & Assoc., Inc. (R), GA, *163*
Robert E. Pfaendler & Assoc., Inc. (C), OR, *509*
Pharmaceutical Search Professionals, Inc. (C), PA, *510*
Phase II Management (R), CT, *164*
J. R. Phillip & Assoc., Inc. (R), CA, *164*
Phillips & Assoc. (R), MA, *164*
Philo & Associates (C), GA, *511*
Phoenix Search (R), MX, *164*
Picard Int'l., Ltd. (R), NY, *164*
Pierce & Assoc. (C), CA, *512*
DNPitchon Assoc. (R), NJ, *165*
Placement Solutions (C), WI, *513*
Plummer & Assoc., Inc. (R), CT, *166*
Poirier, Hoevel & Co. (R), CA, *166*
Bob Poline Assoc. Inc. (C), CA, *514*
Al Ponaman Company, Inc. (C), CA, *514*
Don V. Poole & Assoc., Inc. (C), CO, *514*
David Powell, Inc. (R), CA, *166*
Robert Powers & Assoc. (C), CA, *515*
P. G. Prager Search Assoc., Ltd. (C), NY, *515*
Elan Pratzer & Partners Inc. (R), ON, *167*
PRAXIS Partners (R), VA, *167*
Precision Executive Search (C), AZ, *516*
Preferred Professional Recruiters (C), OH, *516*
George Preger & Associates Inc. (R), ON, *167*
The Premier Staffing Group (C), OH, *517*
Preng & Assoc., Inc. (R), TX, *167*
Presley Consultants, Inc. (C), CA, *517*
Prime Management Group Inc. (C), ON, *518*
Primus Assoc., L.C. (R), TX, *169*
Prior/Martech Assoc., Inc. (R), WA, *169*
Probus Executive Search (C), CA, *519*
Professionals in Recruiting Co. (C), TN, *523*
ProNet, Inc. (C), NC, *524*
ProSearch, Inc. (C), OH, *524*
Protocol Inc. (C), CA, *525*
The Quest Organization (C), NY, *527*
R & L Assoc., Ltd. (R), NY, *170*
R M Associates (R), OH, *171*
Rand Assoc. (R), ME, *171*
Rand Thompson Executive Search Consultants (C), NY, *528*
The Rankin Group, Ltd. (R), WI, *171*
The Ransford Group (R), TX, *171*
Joanne E. Ratner Search (C), NY, *529*
Ray & Berndtson/Lovas Stanley (R), ON, *172*
Ray & Berndtson/Tanton Mitchell (R), BC, *173*
Raymond Karsan Assoc. (C), PA, *529*
Razzino-Claymore Assoc. (C), NJ, *530*
Reece & Mruk Partners/EMA Partners Int'l. (R), MA, *173*
Reeder & Assoc., Ltd. (R), GA, *173*
Reifel & Assoc. (R), IL, *174*
Reinecke & Assoc. (C), NJ, *533*
The Douglas Reiter Co., Inc. (R), OR, *174*
Resource Management Group (C), CT, *534*
Resource Networking Inc. (C), IN, *534*
Resources for Management (R), PA, *175*
The Retail Network (C), MA, *535*
S. Reyman & Assoc., Ltd. (R), IL, *176*
Russell Reynolds Assoc., Inc. (R), NY, *176*
Reynolds Consulting Int'l. (R), ON, *177*
RGE (C), VA, *535*
RHS Assoc. (C), AL, *536*
Marshall Rice Assoc. (R), RI, *177*
Jeff Rich Assoc. (C), NJ, *536*
Rieser & Assoc., Inc. (R), MO, *178*
Riley Cole (C), CA, *537*
Ritt-Ritt & Assoc., Inc. (C), IL, *537*
RJ Associates (C), CA, *538*
RLM Assoc., Ltd. (R), NY, *179*
Robinson, Fraser Group Ltd. (R), ON, *180*
Robison Humphreys & Assoc., Inc. (R), ON, *180*
Rocky Mountain Recruiters, Inc. (C), CO, *540*
The Rogan Group, Inc. (C), CA, *541*
Rogish Assoc., Inc. (C), OH, *541*
Rollo Assoc. (R), CA, *181*
Romac Int'l. (C), GA, *541*
Romac Int'l. (C), IL, *541*
Romac Int'l. (C), PA, *542*
Romac Int'l. Inc. (R), MA, *181*
Ropes Associates, Inc. (R), FL, *182*
Rosenfeld & Co., Inc. (C), MI, *545*
Patricia Roth Int'l. (C), FL, *545*
Rusher, Loscavio & LoPresto (R), CA, *183*
Rushmore • Judge Inc. (R), ON, *183*
Rust & Assoc., Inc. (R), IL, *183*
The Ryan Charles Group, Inc. (C), FL, *548*
Ryan, Miller & Assoc. (C), CA, *549*
Ryan-Allen & Assoc., Inc. (C), CA, *549*
Rylan Forbes Consulting Group, Inc. (C), NJ, *549*
S. P. Assoc., Inc. (C), NC, *550*
Saber Group, Inc. (C), TX, *550*

Sales & Management Search, Inc. (C), IL, *551*
Sales Consultants of Ft. Myers, Inc. (C), FL, *557*
Sales Consultants of Western McHenry County (C), IL, *558*
Sales Consultants of Princeton, Inc. (C), NJ, *561*
Salzmann Gay Assoc., Inc. (R), PA, *184*
Sanford Rose Assoc. - Nashville (C), TN, *570*
Sanford Rose Assoc. - Pittsburgh North (C), PA, *570*
Saviar, Inc. (C), AZ, *571*
David Saxner & Assoc., Inc. (DSA, Inc.) (R), IL, *185*
Schall Executive Search Partners (R), MN, *185*
The Schatz Company (C), MO, *571*
Schenck & Assoc. SC (C), WI, *572*
Schlatter & Assoc. (C), CA, *572*
Schneider, Hill & Spangler, Inc. (R), PA, *185*
Schoales & Assoc. Inc. (C), ON, *572*
The Search Committee (C), MD, *574*
Search Consultants, LLC (C), MD, *575*
Search Group Inc. (R), AB, *186*
Search Int'l. (R), MA, *187*
Search Masters Int'l. (R), AZ, *187*
Search Research Assoc., Inc. (R), MA, *187*
Search South, Inc. (C), AL, *576*
SearchCorp International (C), AB, *577*
Secura/Burnett Partners (R), CA, *187*
J. R. Seehusen Assoc., Inc. (R), IA, *188*
Seiden Krieger Assoc., Inc. (R), NY, *188*
Selectis Corp. (C), IL, *578*
Selective Management Services, Inc. (C), FL, *578*
Shey-Harding Assoc. Inc. (C), CA, *580*
Michael Shirley Assoc. Inc. (R), KS, *190*
Shoemaker & Assoc. (R), GA, *190*
The Shotland Group (R), CA, *190*
M. Shulman, Inc. (R), CA, *191*
Siger & Assoc., LLC (C), CT, *581*
D. J. Simpson Assoc. Inc. (R), ON, *191*
Sinclair & Co., Inc. (R), MA, *192*
SKB Enterprises (C), NY, *582*
Skipping Stone Inc. (C), VA, *582*
Ruth Sklar Assoc., Inc. (RSA Executive Search) (R), NY, *192*
Christopher Smallhorn Executive Recruiting, Inc. (R), MA, *193*
Smith & Laue Search (R), OR, *193*
Smith & Sawyer, Inc. (R), NY, *193*
G. L. Smith Assoc. (C), CA, *584*
Howard W. Smith Assoc. (R), CT, *193*
Herman Smith Executive Initiatives Inc. (R), ON, *193*
Smith Search, S.C. (R), MX, *194*
Smith, Brown & Jones (C), KS, *585*
Snelling Search (C), AL, *585*
Snelling Search (C), LA, *586*
Sockwell & Assoc. (R), NC, *194*
Robert Sollman & Assoc. (C), FL, *587*
Solomon-Page Healthcare Group (R), NY, *195*
Soltis Management Services (R), PA, *195*
Southwestern Professional Services (C), TN, *588*
Special Markets Group, Inc. (R), GA, *195*
SpencerStuart (R), NY, *196*
The Spiegel Group (R), MA, *197*
Spriggs & Co., Inc. (R), IL, *198*
M. H. Springer & Assoc. (R), CA, *198*
Springer Souder & Assoc. L.L.C. (R), IL, *198*
Staff Extension Int'l. (C), TX, *590*
Stafford Consulting Group (R), CA, *198*
Stanton Chase Int'l. (R), MD, *198*
STAT Search (C), NH, *592*
Steinfield & Assoc. (C), TX, *592*
Stentiford & Berardi Assoc. Ltd. (R), NY, *199*
Michael Stern Assoc., Inc./Euram (R), ON, *200*
Steven Douglas Assoc. (C), FL, *593*
The Stevenson Group, Inc. (N.J.) (R), NJ, *200*
Stewart, Stein & Scott, Ltd. (R), MN, *200*
Stewart/Laurence Assoc., Inc. (R), NJ, *201*
Stone Assoc. LLC (C), MI, *594*
Stoopen Asociados, S.C./EMA Partners Int'l. (R), MX, *202*
Straight & Co. (R), GA, *202*
Strategic Alliance Network, Ltd. (C), OH, *595*
StratfordGroup (R), OH, *203*
Straube Associates (R), MA, *203*
Stroman Int'l., Inc. (R), CO, *204*
Sullivan & Assoc. (R), MI, *204*
Joe Sullivan & Assoc., Inc. (R), NY, *204*
Summit Search Specialists (C), TX, *596*
Swartz & Assoc., Inc. (R), AZ, *204*
Swift & Assoc. (C), ME, *597*
The Synergy Organization (R), PA, *205*
Taylor Winfield (R), TX, *207*
Telford, Adams & Alexander (R), CA, *208*
Tennyson Advisors (R), NY, *208*
The TGA Company (C), TX, *606*
Thomas Resource Group (R), CA, *209*
Thomas, Whelan Assoc., Inc. (C), DC, *606*
Judy Thompson & Assoc., Inc. (C), CA, *606*
Richard Thompson Assoc., Inc. (R), MN, *209*
The Tidewater Group Inc. (C), CT, *607*
Tittemore Cowan Assoc. (C), AB, *607*
Travis & Co., Inc. (R), MA, *210*
TriStaff Group (C), CA, *609*
Triumph Consulting, Inc. (R), IA, *210*
The Truman Agency (C), CA, *610*
Tschudin Inc. (R), NJ, *211*
TSW Assoc., LLC (R), CT, *211*
The Thomas Tucker Co. (R), CA, *211*
Tuft & Assoc., Inc. (R), IL, *212*
Van Dyke Assoc. (R), IL, *212*
Van Leeuwen Assoc. (R), CA, *213*
VanMaldegiam Assoc., Inc. (R), IL, *213*
VanReypen Enterprises, Ltd. (R), NY, *213*
Venture Resources, Inc. (R), CA, *213*
The Verriez Group Inc. (R), ON, *213*
Vlcek & Company, Inc. (R), CA, *214*
VZ Int'l., Inc. (C), AZ, *613*
Wakefield Talabisco Int'l. (R), NY, *214*
Walker Group, Inc. (R), MN, *215*
Warren Int'l. (R), NY, *215*
Warren, Morris & Madison, Ltd. (C), CA, *616*
R. J. Watkins & Co., Ltd. (R), CA, *216*
Scott Watson & Assoc., Inc. (R), FL, *216*
Waveland Int'l. (R), IL, *216*
S. B. Webster & Associates (R), MA, *217*
S. E. Weinstein Co. (R), IL, *217*
Wellington Management Group (R), PA, *217*
Jude M. Werra & Assoc. (R), WI, *218*
Western Management Assoc. (R), CA, *218*
Western Management Consultants (R), BC, *218*
Weterrings & Agnew, Inc. (C), NY, *619*
Wheeler Assoc. (R), CT, *219*
Whitney Smith Co. (C), TX, *620*
The Whittaker Group (C), MI, *620*
Wilcox Bertoux & Miller (R), CA, *220*
Wilcoxen, Blackwell, Niven & Assoc. (R), FL, *220*
Joel H. Wilensky Assoc., Inc. (C), MA, *620*
The Wilkie Group Int'l. (R), ON, *220*
Williams Executive Search, Inc. (R), MN, *221*
Williams, Roth & Krueger, Inc. (R), IL, *221*
William Willis Worldwide Inc. (R), CT, *221*
Windsor Consultants, Inc. (C), TX, *622*
Winguth, Grant & Donahue (R), CA, *222*
Winter, Wyman & Co. (C), MA, *623*
M. Wood Company (R), IL, *224*
Wood-Glavin, Inc. (R), KS, *224*
Worldwide Medical Services (C), CA, *625*
Dick Wray & Consultants, Inc. (R), CA, *225*
Xavier Associates, Inc. (R), MA, *226*
Yelverton Executive Search (R), CA, *226*
Yormak & Assoc. (C), CA, *626*
Yours In Travel Personnel Agency, Inc. (C), NY, *626*
Steven Yungerberg Assoc., Inc. (R), MN, *226*
Helen Ziegler & Assoc., Inc. (C), ON, *627*
Zwell Int'l. (R), IL, *228*

07.2 Budgeting, cost controls

Abacus Group LLC (C), NY, *232*
Accent On Achievement, Inc. (C), MI, *233*
Access/Resources, Inc. (C), MA, *234*
Accountancies (C), CA, *234*
Accountants Executive Search (C), CT, *234*
Accountants Executive Search (C), PA, *234*
Accountants On Call (C), FL, *237*
Accountants On Call (C), TN, *237*
Accountants Executive Search (C), CA, *237*
Accounting & Bookkeeping Personnel, Inc. (C), AZ, *237*
Accounting Additions (C), CA, *238*
ADR Accounting Management Recruiters (C), ON, *240*
Advice Personnel Inc. (C), NY, *241*
The Alexander Group (R), TX, *3*
American Professional Search, Inc. (C), TN, *248*
Anderson Network Group (C), OH, *250*
Andre David & Assoc., Inc. (R), TX, *6*
Andrews & Assoc. (C), NC, *250*
The Ascher Group (R), NJ, *7*

E. J. Ashton & Assoc., Ltd. (C), IL, *253*
Atlantic Search Group, Inc. (C), MA, *255*
Bartl & Evins (C), NY, *260*
Battalia Winston Int'l./The Euram Consultants Group (R), NY, *13*
BCG Search, Inc. (R), FL, *14*
Benford & Assoc., Inc. (C), MI, *264*
Berglund Int'l. Resources, Inc. (C), TX, *265*
Binder Hospitality Group (C), KY, *266*
Blackhawk Advantage, Inc. (C), CA, *267*
Bodner Inc. (C), NY, *268*
Boston Professional Search, Inc. (C), MA, *270*
D. Brown & Assoc., Inc. (C), OR, *275*
The Burgess Group-Corporate Recruiters Int'l., Inc. (R), NY, *25*
C.T.E.W. Executive Personnel Services Inc. (C), BC, *278*
C/R Associates (C), NY, *278*
Canyon Consulting, Inc. (C), TX, *281*
Capital Markets Resources, Inc. (C), NC, *281*
Cemco, Ltd. (C), IL, *286*
The Century Group (C), CA, *287*
CFOs 2 Go (C), CA, *288*
CFR Executive Search, Inc. (C), IL, *288*
Howard Clark Assoc. (C), NJ, *292*
P. G. Cook Assoc. (R), TN, *40*
David C. Cooper & Assoc. Financial Search (C), GA, *298*
Creative Financial Staffing Inc. (C), ON, *303*
The Danbrook Group, Inc. (C), TX, *306*
Dapexs Consultants, Inc. (C), NY, *307*
DBL Associates (C), CA, *309*
Diversified Search, Inc. (R), PA, *52*
Domres Professional Search (R), WI, *53*
Dunhill Search of Medford (C), NJ, *321*
Dunhill Professional Search of Omaha, Inc. (C), NE, *321*
Dunhill Professional Search of Bucks-Mont., Inc. (C), PA, *322*
Dunhill Search of Vermont (C), VT, *323*
The Execu/Search Group (C), NY, *332*
Executive Placement Consultants (C), IL, *333*
Executive Search, Ltd. (C), OH, *336*
Executive Search Team (C), MI, *336*
Fabian Assoc. Inc. (C), NY, *338*
Fenzel Milar Assoc. (C), OH, *339*
Financial Search Corp. (C), IL, *340*
Financialjobs.com (C), CA, *340*
Focus Consulting Services, Inc. (C), FL, *342*
Fogec Consultants, Inc. (R), WI, *69*
Ford & Assoc., Inc. (C), SC, *343*
Forray Assoc., Inc. (R), NY, *70*
F-O-R-T-U-N-E Personnel Consultants (C), MI, *346*
Fortune Personnel Consultants of Hinsdale, IL (C), IL, *346*
F-O-R-T-U-N-E Personnel Consultants of Southwest Indiana (C), IN, *346*
Foster Partners (R), NY, *70*
Friedman Eisenstein Raemer & Schwartz, LLP (R), IL, *72*
Dick Garland Consultants (R), NY, *74*
Gateway Group Personnel, LLC (C), TN, *355*
Gavin Forbes & Price (R), CA, *75*
Godfrey Personnel, Inc. (C), IL, *359*
Government Contract Solutions, Inc. (C), VA, *360*
Ben Greco Assoc., Inc. (C), CA, *362*
GSP International (C), NJ, *364*
GWS Partners (R), IL, *84*
Robert Half Canada Inc. (C), ON, *366*
Harper Associates (C), MI, *369*
Hessel Assoc., Inc. (C), NY, *377*
High-Tech Recruiters (C), CT, *378*
Holden & Harlan Assoc., Inc. (C), IL, *380*
The Hutton Group, Inc. (C), FL, *386*
IMA Search, Inc. (R), NY, *101*
InteliSearch, Inc. (R), CT, *102*
Interim Accounting Professionals (C), CA, *391*
Jones Management Co. (R), CT, *108*
Joseph Michaels (C), CA, *401*
Howard Karr & Assoc., Inc. (R), CA, *110*
Katelyn Partners (C), FL, *404*
Melissa Katzman, Executive Search (C), NY, *404*
The Kay Group of 5th Ave. (C), NY, *404*
A.T. Kearney Executive Search (R), IL, *111*
Keeley Consulting Inc. (C), ON, *404*
Kenzer Corp. (R), NY, *113*
Keystone Consulting Group (C), GA, *406*
Kramer Executive Resources, Inc. (C), NY, *409*
Todd L. Krueger & Assoc. (C), WA, *409*
The Langford Search, Inc. (C), AL, *412*
LanSo Int'l., Inc. (C), NY, *413*
Albert G. Lee Assoc. (C), RI, *415*
Logic Assoc., Inc. (C), NY, *419*
The Luciani Group (R), CA, *132*
M.C. Executive Search (C), CA, *422*
Management Recruiters of Birmingham, Inc. (C), AL, *438*
Management Recruiters of Pleasanton (C), CA, *441*
Management Recruiters of Broome County, Inc. (C), NY, *454*
Management Recruiters of Puerto Rico (C), PR, *460*
Management Recruiters of Florence (C), SC, *460*
Management Solutions, Inc. (C), CA, *468*
Meridian Resources (C), OH, *479*
Millar Walker & Gay (R), ON, *144*
Danette Milne Corporate Search Inc. (C), ON, *482*
Oscar Montaño, Inc. (R), CA, *146*
Montgomery Resources, Inc. (C), CA, *484*
The Morley Group (C), IN, *486*
National Computerized Employment Service, Inc. (C), PA, *489*
National Metal Services Corp. (C), IN, *489*
The Niemond Corp. (R), CA, *152*
The Noebel Search Group, Inc. (C), TX, *494*
The Nolan Group (C), CA, *494*
Norman Broadbent Int'l., Inc. (R), NY, *152*
Norrell Financial Staffing (C), GA, *495*
O'Neill & Co. (R), CT, *154*
O'Sullivan Search Inc. (C), ON, *498*
Olympian Recruitment, Ltd. (C), NY, *498*
Pacific Finance Search, Inc. (C), CA, *501*
Arthur Pann Assoc., Inc. (C), NY, *502*
The PAR Group - Paul A. Reaume, Ltd. (R), IL, *159*
Parker & Lynch (C), CA, *503*
Partners Resource Group (C), VA, *504*
Pascale & LaMorte, LLC (C), CT, *504*
Perry • Newton Assoc. (C), MD, *507*
Placement Solutions (C), WI, *513*
PMJ & Assoc. (C), ON, *513*
The Prairie Group (C), IL, *515*
Preston & Co. (R), NJ, *167*
Probus Executive Search (C), CA, *519*
Professional Persons Career Services (C), NY, *521*
Professional Support Inc. (C), NY, *523*
Quality Search Inc. (C), OH, *526*
R.A.N. Assoc., Inc. (C), OH, *528*
Razzino-Claymore Assoc. (C), NJ, *530*
Recruiting Services Group, Inc. (C), TN, *532*
Resource Management Group (C), CT, *534*
Response Staffing Services (C), NY, *534*
Russell Reynolds Assoc., Inc. (R), NY, *176*
Jeff Rich Assoc. (C), NJ, *536*
RJ Associates (C), CA, *538*
Rocky Mountain Recruiters, Inc. (C), CO, *540*
Romac Int'l. - San Francisco (C), CA, *541*
Romac Int'l. (C), GA, *541*
Romac Int'l. (C), IL, *541*
Romac Int'l. (C), PA, *542*
Romac Int'l. Inc. (R), MA, *181*
Rowland Assoc. (C), CA, *547*
Ryan, Miller & Assoc. (C), CA, *549*
Rylan Forbes Consulting Group, Inc. (C), NJ, *549*
S-H-S TechStaff (C), PA, *549*
Sanford Rose Assoc. - Athens (C), GA, *566*
Schenck & Assoc. SC (C), WI, *572*
Schlatter & Assoc. (C), CA, *572*
Search Consultants, LLC (C), MD, *575*
Shoemaker & Assoc. (R), GA, *190*
Southwestern Professional Services (C), TN, *588*
SpencerStuart (R), NY, *196*
The Stark Wilton Group (R), MI, *199*
Steinfield & Assoc. (C), TX, *592*
Steven Douglas Assoc. (C), FL, *593*
Stone Assoc. LLC (C), MI, *594*
DM Stone Personnel Services (C), CA, *594*
Strategic Alliance Network, Ltd. (C), OH, *595*
The TGA Company (C), TX, *606*
Thomas, Whelan Assoc., Inc. (C), DC, *606*
Judy Thompson & Assoc., Inc. (C), CA, *606*
TRS Staffing Solutions Inc. (C), OH, *610*
Wells, Bradley & Assoc., Inc. (C), MN, *618*
The Westfield Group (C), CT, *619*
The Whittaker Group (C), MI, *620*
Wilcox Bertoux & Miller (R), CA, *220*
Winter, Wyman & Co. (C), MA, *623*
Yormak & Assoc. (C), CA, *626*

07.3 Cash management, financing & management of funds, portfolios

A.L.S. Group (C), NJ, *232*
Abacus Group LLC (C), NY, *232*
Accelerated Data Decision, Inc. (C), NJ, *233*
Accent On Achievement, Inc. (C), MI, *233*
Access/Resources, Inc. (C), MA, *234*
Accountancies (C), CA, *234*
Accountants Executive Search (C), CT, *234*
Accountants Executive Search (C), PA, *234*
Accountants On Call (C), FL, *237*
Accountants Executive Search (C), CA, *237*
Accountants On Call (C), TN, *237*
Accounting & Bookkeeping Personnel, Inc. (C), AZ, *237*
Accounting Additions (C), CA, *238*
Active Search & Placement Inc. (C), CA, *239*
Adept Tech Recruiting, Inc. (C), NY, *240*
ADR Accounting Management Recruiters (C), ON, *240*
Advisors' Search Group, Inc. (C), NY, *241*
Allen & Assoc. (C), NV, *244*
Allman & Co., Inc. (C), NC, *245*
Ambridge Management Corp. (C), ON, *247*
American Professional Search, Inc. (C), TN, *248*
Analytic Recruiting, Inc. (C), NY, *249*
Andrews & Assoc. (C), NC, *250*
Angel Group Int'l. (C), KY, *250*
Argonaut Partners, LLC (R), CA, *6*
E. J. Ashton & Assoc., Ltd. (C), IL, *253*
Atlantic Pacific Group (C), CA, *255*
Atlantic Search Group, Inc. (C), MA, *255*
ATS Executive Recruitment (C), GA, *255*
The Ayers Group, Inc. (R), NY, *9*
The Bankers Register (C), NY, *259*
Bartl & Evins (C), NY, *260*
Battalia Winston Int'l./The Euram Consultants Group (R), NY, *13*
BCG Search, Inc. (R), FL, *14*
The Beam Group (R), PA, *14*
Bell Wishingrad Partners Inc. (R), NY, *15*
J. P. Bencik Assoc. (C), MI, *263*
Bergeris & Co., Inc. (C), NY, *265*
Boyden (R), NY, *20*
Bryan, Jason & Assoc. Inc. (C), ON, *275*
Butterfass, Pepe & MacCallan Inc. (R), NJ, *25*
C and P Marketing, Ltd. (C), OK, *278*
C/R Associates (C), NY, *278*
Canny, Bowen Inc. (R), NY, *27*
Capital Markets Resources, Inc. (C), NC, *281*
The Center for Career Advancement, LLC (C), NJ, *287*
The Century Group (C), CA, *287*
CFOs 2 Go (C), CA, *288*
CFR Executive Search, Inc. (C), IL, *288*
The Colton Partnership, Inc. (R), NY, *38*
Conspectus, Inc. (C), NY, *297*
Consulting Rhonda (C), ON, *297*
David C. Cooper & Assoc. Financial Search (C), GA, *298*
Cornell Group Int'l. Consulting, Inc. (R), NY, *41*
Leonard Corwen Assoc. (C), NY, *302*
Creative Financial Staffing Inc. (C), ON, *303*
Crispi, Wagner & Co., Inc. (R), NY, *43*
Cromwell Partners, Inc. (R), NY, *43*
Custom Resources (C), AL, *305*
Alfred Daniels & Assoc., Inc. (R), CA, *46*
Davis & James, Inc. (C), MO, *308*
The Dayton Group, Ltd. (C), NY, *309*
Defrain Mayer (R), KS, *48*
S. W. Delano & Co. (R), CT, *48*
Dise & Co. (R), OH, *52*
Diversified Search, Inc. (R), PA, *52*
DLG Assoc., Inc. (R), NC, *53*
DNA Search, Inc. (C), CA, *313*
J P Donnelly Assoc., Inc. (C), NY, *314*
Douglas-Allen, Inc. (R), MA, *54*
Drummond Assoc., Inc. (C), NY, *315*
Dunhill Search of Medford (C), NJ, *321*
Dunhill Search of Arlington (C), TX, *322*
Mark Elzweig Co., Ltd. (C), NY, *329*
The Execu/Search Group (C), NY, *332*
Executive Access Inc. (R), NY, *62*
Executive Search Consultants Corp. (C), IL, *335*
Fabian Assoc. Inc. (C), NY, *338*
Federal Placement Services (C), NY, *339*
Fidelity Search Group, Inc. (R), PA, *66*
Financial Connections Company (C), VA, *340*
Financial Resource Assoc., Inc. (C), FL, *340*
Financial Search Corp. (C), IL, *340*
Financial Search Group, Inc. (R), MA, *66*
Financialjobs.com (C), CA, *340*
The Flagship Group (R), MA, *68*
Fogec Consultants, Inc. (R), WI, *69*
Forum Personnel Inc. (C), NY, *351*
Foster Partners (R), NY, *70*
C. F. Furr & Co. (R), NC, *72*
Gateway Group Personnel, LLC (C), TN, *355*
Gavin Forbes & Price (R), CA, *75*
GES Services, Inc. (R), NY, *76*
Global Technologies Group Inc. (C), NC, *359*
The Tracy Glover Co. (R), TX, *78*
Gnodde Assoc. (C), IL, *359*
Godfrey Personnel, Inc. (C), IL, *359*
The Gogates Group, Inc. (R), NY, *79*
Grauss & Co. (C), CA, *362*
Ben Greco Assoc., Inc. (C), CA, *362*
GSP International (C), NJ, *364*
H.Q. Search, Inc. (C), IL, *365*
Hale Assoc. (R), IL, *84*
K. C. Hale, Inc. (R), CT, *85*
Robert Half Canada Inc. (C), ON, *366*
Handy HRM (R), NY, *86*
The Hanover Consulting Group (C), MD, *368*
Hanzel & Co., Inc. (R), NY, *86*
The Herrmann Group Ltd. (R), ON, *92*
Hessel Assoc., Inc. (C), NY, *377*
High-Tech Recruiters (C), CT, *378*
Fred Hood & Assoc. (C), CA, *380*
David C. Horn Executive Search (C), TX, *381*
Interim Accounting Professionals (C), CA, *391*
Interim Management Resources Inc. (C), ON, *392*
International Market Recruiters (C), NY, *393*
J. Nicholas Arthur (R), MA, *104*
J. R. Scott & Assoc., Ltd. (C), IL, *395*
Pendleton James Assoc., Inc. (R), NY, *105*
JNB Assoc., Inc. (C), MA, *399*
Johnson Brown Assoc., Inc. (C), IN, *400*
The Jonathan Stevens Group, Inc. (R), NJ, *108*
Joseph Michaels (C), CA, *401*
Kaplan & Assoc., Inc. (R), PA, *109*
Howard Karr & Assoc., Inc. (R), CA, *110*
Katelyn Partners (C), FL, *404*
A.T. Kearney Executive Search (R), IL, *111*
Keeley Consulting Inc. (C), ON, *404*
Kennedy & Co. (R), IL, *112*
Kensington Int'l., Inc. (R), IL, *113*
Kenzer Corp. (R), NY, *113*
Kershner & Co. (R), DC, *113*
Keystone Consulting Group (C), GA, *406*
The Kinlin Co., Inc. (R), MA, *115*
The Koehler Group (C), PA, *408*
Koren, Rogers Assoc. Inc. (R), NY, *117*
Todd L. Krueger & Assoc. (C), WA, *409*
L T M Assoc. (C), IL, *410*
L&L Assoc. Global Search (C), PA, *411*
E. J. Lance Management Assoc., Inc. (C), NY, *412*
LanSo Int'l., Inc. (C), NY, *413*
Larsen & Lee, Inc. (R), MD, *125*
Lawrence James Assoc. of Florida, Inc. (C), FL, *414*
Reynolds Lebus Assoc. (C), AZ, *415*
Leeds and Leeds (C), TN, *416*
The Luciani Group (R), CA, *132*
Lyons Pruitt Int'l. (R), PA, *132*
Management Advisors Int'l., Inc. (C), NC, *424*
Management Alliance Group, Inc. (R), NJ, *134*
Management Recruiters of Nassau, Inc. (R), NY, *134*
Management Recruiters of Berkeley (C), CA, *439*
Management Recruiters of St. Augustine (C), FL, *444*
Management Recruiters of Indianapolis-North (C), IN, *448*
Management Recruiters of Williamsburg (C), IA, *449*
Management Recruiters of Great Neck (C), NY, *454*
Management Recruiters of Manhattan on Broadway (C), NY, *455*
Management Recruiters of Oklahoma City (C), OK, *458*
Management Recruiters of Mentor, Inc. (C), OH, *458*
Management Recruiters of Pittsburgh (C), PA, *459*
Management Recruiters The Delta Group, Inc. (C), TN, *461*
Management Resource Group, Ltd. (C), IA, *467*

Marentz & Co. (C), TX, *469*
Marsar & Co., Inc. (C), FL, *471*
K. E. McCarthy & Assoc. (R), CA, *139*
The McKinnon Management Group Inc. (C), ON, *475*
MCS Assoc. (R), CA, *142*
Meridian Resources (C), OH, *479*
Millar Walker & Gay (R), ON, *144*
Paul Misarti Inc. (C), NY, *483*
Montgomery Resources, Inc. (C), CA, *484*
Morgan Hunter Corp. (C), KS, *485*
Morgan Stampfl, Inc. (C), NY, *485*
The Morgan/Geoffries Group (C), CA, *485*
Much & Co. (R), NY, *148*
Jennifer Munro & Partners, Inc. (R), SC, *149*
Mycoff & Assoc. (R), CO, *150*
DDJ Myers, Ltd. (R), AZ, *150*
Nason & Nason (C), FL, *488*
Marc Nichols Assoc., Inc. (C), NY, *493*
The Nolan Group (C), CA, *494*
Norman Broadbent Int'l., Inc. (R), NY, *152*
Norrell Financial Staffing (C), GA, *495*
NPS of Atlanta, Inc. (C), GA, *496*
O'Neill & Co. (R), CT, *154*
O'Toole & Company, Inc. (R), IL, *154*
Omnisearch Assoc. (C), CA, *499*
Oppedisano & Co., Inc. (R), NY, *156*
The Options Group, Inc. (C), NY, *499*
The Pailin Group Professional Search Consultants (R), TX, *158*
Arthur Pann Assoc., Inc. (C), NY, *502*
Partners Resource Group (C), VA, *504*
Pascale & LaMorte, LLC (C), CT, *504*
Picard Int'l., Ltd. (R), NY, *164*
Pierce & Assoc. (C), CA, *512*
Pinnacle Executive Group Inc. (C), MO, *512*
Placement Solutions (C), WI, *513*
R. L. Plimpton Assoc., Inc. (R), CO, *165*
PMJ & Assoc. (C), ON, *513*
Preston & Co. (R), NJ, *167*
The Primary Group, Inc. (R), FL, *168*
Probus Executive Search (C), CA, *519*
Proven Edge (C), CA, *525*
The Quest Organization (C), NY, *527*
Real Estate Executive Search, Inc. (C), CA, *531*
Resource Management Group (C), CT, *534*
Response Staffing Services (C), NY, *534*
Russell Reynolds Assoc., Inc. (R), NY, *176*
RIC Corp. (R), FL, *177*
Jeff Rich Assoc. (C), NJ, *536*
Riotto-Jones Assoc. (R), NY, *178*
RJ Associates (C), CA, *538*
Rocky Mountain Recruiters, Inc. (C), CO, *540*
Romac Int'l. - San Francisco (C), CA, *541*
Romac Int'l. (C), IL, *541*
Romac Int'l. Inc. (R), MA, *181*
RSMR, Inc. (R), IL, *182*
The Rubicon Group (C), AZ, *547*
Russillo/Gardner/Spolsino (C), MA, *548*
Ryan, Miller & Assoc. (C), CA, *549*
Rylan Forbes Consulting Group, Inc. (C), NJ, *549*
Sales & Management Search, Inc. (C), IL, *551*
Sales Consultants (C), IL, *558*
Sales Consultants of Princeton, Inc. (C), NJ, *561*
Sanford Rose Assoc. - Oak Brook (C), IL, *567*
Sanford Rose Assoc. - Philadelphia North (C), PA, *570*
Schall Executive Search Partners (R), MN, *185*
Schlatter & Assoc. (C), CA, *572*
The Search Center Inc. (C), TX, *574*
Search Consultants, LLC (C), MD, *575*
Search Innovations, Inc. (R), PA, *187*
Shifrin-Fischer Group, Inc. (C), NJ, *580*
Peter Siegel & Co. (C), MA, *581*
Ralph Smith & Assoc. (C), IL, *584*
Smith Hanley Assoc., Inc. (C), NY, *584*
SpencerStuart (R), NY, *196*
Stanton Chase Int'l. (R), MD, *198*
The Stark Wilton Group (R), MI, *199*
Steinfield & Assoc. (C), TX, *592*
Steven Michaels & Assoc. (C), NY, *593*
Stone Assoc. LLC (C), MI, *594*
DM Stone Personnel Services (C), CA, *594*
Strategic Search, LLC (C), CA, *595*
Martin Stevens Tamaren & Assoc., Inc. (R), CA, *206*
Tech-Net (C), TX, *601*
Tennyson Advisors (R), NY, *208*
Thomas, Whelan Assoc., Inc. (C), DC, *606*
Judy Thompson & Assoc., Inc. (C), CA, *606*
TPS Staffing Solutions (C), IN, *608*
TSW Assoc., LLC (R), CT, *211*
Vincenty & Co. (C), OH, *612*
Warren Int'l. (R), NY, *215*
Scott Watson & Assoc., Inc. (R), FL, *216*
The Westfield Group (C), CT, *619*
K. L. Whitney Company (R), NJ, *219*
The Whitney Group (R), NY, *219*
The Whittaker Group (C), MI, *620*
Wing Tips & Pumps, Inc. (C), MI, *623*
Yormak & Assoc. (C), CA, *626*
Youngblood Assoc. (C), NC, *626*
Steven Yungerberg Assoc., Inc. (R), MN, *226*

07.4 Credit & collection

A.L.S. Group (C), NJ, *232*
Abacus Group LLC (C), NY, *232*
Accountancies (C), CA, *234*
Accountants Executive Search (C), CT, *234*
Accountants Executive Search (C), PA, *234*
Accountants On Call (C), FL, *237*
Accountants On Call (C), TN, *237*
Accountants Executive Search (C), CA, *237*
Accounting & Bookkeeping Personnel, Inc. (C), AZ, *237*
Accounting Additions (C), CA, *238*
ADR Accounting Management Recruiters (C), ON, *240*
Affordable Executive Recruiters (C), CA, *241*
Allard Associates (C), CA, *244*
Ambridge Management Corp. (C), ON, *247*
Charles P. Aquavella & Assoc. (C), TX, *252*
Atlantic Pacific Group (C), CA, *255*
Atlantic Search Group, Inc. (C), MA, *255*
ATS Executive Recruitment (C), GA, *255*
The Bankers Register (C), NY, *259*
Bartl & Evins (C), NY, *260*
Bergeris & Co., Inc. (C), NY, *265*
Billington & Assoc. (R), CA, *17*
Bonell Ryan Inc. (R), NY, *19*
Boston Professional Search, Inc. (C), MA, *270*
Bryan, Jason & Assoc. Inc. (C), ON, *275*
C and P Marketing, Ltd. (C), OK, *278*
C/R Associates (C), NY, *278*
The Century Group (C), KS, *287*
CFOs 2 Go (C), CA, *288*
CFR Executive Search, Inc. (C), IL, *288*
Colt Systems Professional Personnel Services (C), CA, *294*
David C. Cooper & Assoc. Financial Search (C), GA, *298*
Creative Financial Staffing Inc. (C), ON, *303*
Custom Resources (C), AL, *305*
DARE Personnel Inc. (C), ON, *307*
Discovery, The Staffing Specialists, Inc. (C), IL, *312*
Diversified Search, Inc. (R), PA, *52*
Dunhill of Ft. Collins, Inc. (C), CO, *319*
Dunhill Professional Search of Omaha, Inc. (C), NE, *321*
Dunhill Personnel of Northeast Tulsa, Inc. (C), OK, *322*
D. C. Egan & Assoc. (C), GA, *327*
The Execu/Search Group (C), NY, *332*
Financialjobs.com (C), CA, *340*
Fogec Consultants, Inc. (R), WI, *69*
Fortune Personnel Consultants of Hinsdale, IL (C), IL, *346*
Foster Partners (R), NY, *70*
The Fourbes Group, Inc. (C), NJ, *351*
Gateway Group Personnel, LLC (C), TN, *355*
Gavin Forbes & Price (R), CA, *75*
GES Services, Inc. (R), NY, *76*
GSP International (C), NJ, *364*
H.Q. Search, Inc. (C), IL, *365*
Robert Half Canada Inc. (C), ON, *366*
Hallman Group, Inc. (C), MI, *367*
The Hanover Consulting Group (C), MD, *368*
Harbrowe, Inc. (C), NY, *368*
Thomas E. Hedefine Assoc. (C), ON, *375*
Hemingway Personnel, Inc. (C), CA, *375*
Human Resource Dimensions, Inc. (C), TX, *384*
Hunegnaw Executive Search (C), OH, *384*
Interim Accounting Professionals (C), CA, *391*
Intersource, Ltd. (R), GA, *103*
JDC Assoc. (C), NY, *397*
Jones Management Co. (R), CT, *108*
Joseph Michaels (C), CA, *401*
JT Assoc. (C), CT, *401*
Kanzer Assoc., Inc. (R), IL, *109*
A.T. Kearney Executive Search (R), IL, *111*
Leaders-Trust Int'l./Carce y Asociados, S.C. (R), MX, *127*
The Levton Group Inc. (R), ON, *129*

Management Recruiters of Duluth (C), GA, *445*
Management Recruiters of Atlanta (C), GA, *445*
Management Recruiters - Towne Lake (C), GA, *446*
Management Recruiters of New Providence (C), NJ, *454*
Management Recruiters of Manhattan on Broadway (C), NY, *455*
Management Resource Group (C), MN, *467*
Management Solutions, Inc. (C), CA, *468*
Market Niche Consulting (C), AZ, *470*
Mayhall Search Group, Inc. (C), IN, *473*
MCS Assoc. (R), CA, *142*
Mehta Consulting (C), NJ, *478*
Millar Walker & Gay (R), ON, *144*
Oscar Montaño, Inc. (R), CA, *146*
Montgomery Resources, Inc. (C), CA, *484*
Mortgage & Financial Personnel Services (C), CA, *486*
The MVP Group (C), NY, *487*
National Bank & Finance Executive Search (C), CA, *488*
Don Neal & Assoc. (C), OK, *491*
Norman Broadbent Int'l., Inc. (R), NY, *152*
Norrell Financial Staffing (C), GA, *495*
Ronald Norris & Assoc. (C), IL, *495*
NPS of Atlanta, Inc. (C), GA, *496*
O'Sullivan Search Inc. (C), ON, *498*
Parker & Lynch (C), CA, *503*
Largent Parks & Partners (C), TX, *503*
Partners Resource Group (C), VA, *504*
Phillips Assoc. (C), FL, *510*
Pinton Forrest & Madden/EMA Partners Int'l. (R), BC, *165*
Placement Solutions (C), WI, *513*
PMJ & Assoc. (C), ON, *513*
Probus Executive Search (C), CA, *519*
Reinecke & Assoc. (C), NJ, *533*
Resource Management Group (C), CT, *534*
Russell Reynolds Assoc., Inc. (R), NY, *176*
Jeff Rich Assoc. (C), NJ, *536*
Rocky Mountain Recruiters, Inc. (C), CO, *540*
Romac Int'l. (C), IL, *541*
Ryan-Allen & Assoc., Inc. (C), CA, *549*
Rylan Forbes Consulting Group, Inc. (C), NJ, *549*
Sales Consultants of Chicago South (C), IL, *558*
Sanford Rose Assoc. - Oak Brook (C), IL, *567*
SpencerStuart (R), NY, *196*
Peter Sterling & Co. (C), TX, *592*
Stone Assoc. LLC (C), MI, *594*
Straight & Co. (R), GA, *202*
Synagent Inc. (C), ON, *597*
T. H. Hunter, Inc. (C), MN, *599*
Judy Thompson & Assoc., Inc. (C), CA, *606*
Thor, Inc. (C), CA, *606*
Wells, Bradley & Assoc., Inc. (C), MN, *618*
Yormak & Assoc. (C), CA, *626*

07.5 Taxes

Abacus Group LLC (C), NY, *232*
Cathy Abelson Legal Search (C), PA, *232*
Accent On Achievement, Inc. (C), MI, *233*
Accountancies (C), CA, *234*
Accountants Executive Search (C), PA, *234*
Accountants On Call (C), FL, *237*
Accountants Executive Search (C), CA, *237*
Accountants On Call (C), TN, *237*
Accounting & Bookkeeping Personnel, Inc. (C), AZ, *237*
Accounting Additions (C), CA, *238*
Advice Personnel Inc. (C), NY, *241*
Andrews & Assoc. (C), NC, *250*
E. J. Ashton & Assoc., Ltd. (C), IL, *253*
Atlantic Search Group, Inc. (C), MA, *255*
Bartl & Evins (C), NY, *260*
Battalia Winston Int'l./The Euram Consultants Group (R), NY, *13*
BayResearch Group, Inc. (R), IL, *14*
Becker, Norton & Co. (R), PA, *14*
Berger & Leff (C), CA, *264*
Blackhawk Advantage, Inc. (C), CA, *267*
Boston Professional Search, Inc. (C), MA, *270*
C/R Associates (C), NY, *278*
Cemco, Ltd. (C), IL, *286*
The Century Group (C), CA, *287*
CFOs 2 Go (C), CA, *288*
CFR Executive Search, Inc. (C), IL, *288*
Vickers Chambless Managed Search (C), GA, *288*
The Consortium (C), NY, *296*
David C. Cooper & Assoc. Financial Search (C), GA, *298*
The Corporate Connection, Ltd. (C), VA, *299*
Creative Financial Staffing Inc. (C), ON, *303*
The Danbrook Group, Inc. (C), TX, *306*
Diamond Tax Recruiting (C), NY, *312*
Diversified Search, Inc. (R), PA, *52*
Dunhill of San Francisco, Inc. (C), CA, *319*
Dunhill Search of Arlington (C), TX, *322*
Dunhill Professional Search of Wilkes-Barre/Scranton, Inc. (C), PA, *322*
Dunhill Search of Vermont (C), VT, *323*
Donald F. Dvorak & Co. (R), IL, *55*
E T Search Inc. (C), CA, *324*
ECG Resources, Inc. (C), NY, *326*
The Execu/Search Group (C), NY, *332*
Executive Resource Systems (C), CA, *335*
Faro Consultants Int'l. (C), VA, *338*
Financial Search Corp. (C), IL, *340*
Financialjobs.com (C), CA, *340*
Finney-Taylor Personnel & Management Consultants Ltd. (C), AB, *341*
Fortune Personnel Consultants of Hinsdale, IL (C), IL, *346*
Fortune Personnel Consultants of Allentown, Inc. (C), PA, *348*
Foster Associates (C), NJ, *351*
Foster Partners (R), NY, *70*
Gateway Group Personnel, LLC (C), TN, *355*
Gavin Forbes & Price (R), CA, *75*
GES Services, Inc. (R), NY, *76*
Ben Greco Assoc., Inc. (C), CA, *362*
GSP International (C), NJ, *364*
Robert Half Canada Inc. (C), ON, *366*
Handy HRM (R), NY, *86*
Harrison Consulting Group, Inc. (C), CA, *369*
Jay Heino Company, LLC (C), NY, *375*
Hemingway Personnel, Inc. (C), CA, *375*
Interim Accounting Professionals (C), CA, *391*
Jackson Group Int'l. (C), CO, *396*
Joseph Michaels (C), CA, *401*
A.T. Kearney Executive Search (R), IL, *111*
Keeley Consulting Inc. (C), ON, *404*
David Warwick Kennedy & Assoc. (R), BC, *112*
Keystone Consulting Group (C), GA, *406*
Koren, Rogers Assoc. Inc. (R), NY, *117*
Kramer Executive Resources, Inc. (C), NY, *409*
Todd L. Krueger & Assoc. (C), WA, *409*
Kulper & Co., L.L.C. (R), NJ, *121*
Kutcher Tax Careers, Inc. (C), NY, *410*
Larsen & Lee, Inc. (R), MD, *125*
The Luciani Group (R), CA, *132*
Management Recruiters of Washington, DC Inc. (C), MD, *450*
Management Solutions, Inc. (C), CA, *468*
Marentz & Co. (C), TX, *469*
Millar Walker & Gay (R), ON, *144*
Montgomery Resources, Inc. (C), CA, *484*
MPA Executive Search Inc. (R), QE, *148*
Murphy Partners Int'l. (R), IL, *150*
The Noebel Search Group, Inc. (C), TX, *494*
Norman Broadbent Int'l., Inc. (R), NY, *152*
Norrell Financial Staffing (C), GA, *495*
Omega Search, Inc. (C), NC, *498*
Pacific Finance Search, Inc. (C), CA, *501*
Pacific Search Group, Inc. (C), CA, *501*
Parker & Lynch (C), CA, *503*
Partners Resource Group (C), VA, *504*
Pascale & LaMorte, LLC (C), CT, *504*
Pierce & Assoc. (C), CA, *512*
Placement Solutions (C), WI, *513*
PMJ & Assoc. (C), ON, *513*
Poirier, Hoevel & Co. (R), CA, *166*
P. G. Prager Search Assoc., Ltd. (C), NY, *515*
Professional Resources (C), OK, *522*
ProSearch, Inc. (C), OH, *524*
The Quest Organization (C), NY, *527*
Lea Randolph & Assoc., Inc. (C), TX, *529*
Resource Management Group (C), CT, *534*
Russell Reynolds Assoc., Inc. (R), NY, *176*
RGE (C), VA, *535*
Jeff Rich Assoc. (C), NJ, *536*
Roberts Ryan & Bentley, Inc. (R), MD, *179*
Rocky Mountain Recruiters, Inc. (C), CO, *540*
Romac Int'l. - San Francisco (C), CA, *541*
Romac Int'l. (C), IL, *541*
Romac Int'l. (C), PA, *542*
Romac Int'l. Inc. (R), MA, *181*
Ryan, Miller & Assoc. (C), CA, *549*
Rylan Forbes Consulting Group, Inc. (C), NJ, *549*
Robert Sollman & Assoc. (C), FL, *587*

SpencerStuart (R), NY, *196*
Steinfield & Assoc. (C), TX, *592*
Sterling Int'l. Management Recruitment, Ltd. Inc. (C), NC, *592*
Steven Douglas Assoc. (C), FL, *593*
Stone Assoc. LLC (C), MI, *594*
Strategic Alliance Network, Ltd. (C), OH, *595*
Tax Network Resources, Inc. (C), NY, *600*
TaxSearch Inc. (R), OK, *207*
The TGA Company (C), TX, *606*
Thomas, Whelan Assoc., Inc. (C), DC, *606*
Judy Thompson & Assoc., Inc. (C), CA, *606*
Tittemore Cowan Assoc. (C), AB, *607*
The Verriez Group Inc. (R), ON, *213*
The Wilkie Group Int'l. (R), ON, *220*
Winthrop Partners, Inc. (R), NY, *222*
D. S. Wolf Assoc., Inc. (R), NY, *223*
Yormak & Assoc. (C), CA, *626*

07.6 Mergers & acquisitions

A.L.S. Group (C), NJ, *232*
Cathy Abelson Legal Search (C), PA, *232*
Accent On Achievement, Inc. (C), MI, *233*
Access/Resources, Inc. (C), MA, *234*
Accountancies (C), CA, *234*
Accountants On Call (C), FL, *237*
Accountants On Call (C), TN, *237*
Accountants Executive Search (C), CA, *237*
Accounting & Bookkeeping Personnel, Inc. (C), AZ, *237*
Advice Personnel Inc. (C), NY, *241*
Affordable Executive Recruiters (C), CA, *241*
Ambridge Management Corp. (C), ON, *247*
Analytic Recruiting, Inc. (C), NY, *249*
Andrews & Assoc. (C), NC, *250*
Armitage Associates Ltd. (R), ON, *7*
E. J. Ashton & Assoc., Ltd. (C), IL, *253*
Ashway Ltd. Agency (C), NY, *253*
ATS Executive Recruitment (C), GA, *255*
The Ayers Group, Inc. (R), NY, *9*
Fred A. Barnette & Assoc. (R), NC, *11*
Barr Associates (C), NY, *260*
Bartl & Evins (C), NY, *260*
Battalia Winston Int'l./The Euram Consultants Group (R), NY, *13*
Behavioral Science Assoc., Inc. (R), AZ, *15*
Bell Wishingrad Partners Inc. (R), NY, *15*
Joy Reed Belt Search Consultants, Inc. (R), OK, *15*
Bergeris & Co., Inc. (C), NY, *265*
Bialecki Inc. (R), NY, *17*
Tom Bogle & Assoc. (C), CA, *269*
Boyden (R), NY, *20*
Butterfass, Pepe & MacCallan Inc. (R), NJ, *25*
Canny, Bowen Inc. (R), NY, *27*
Capital Markets Resources, Inc. (C), NC, *281*
Caplan Assoc., Inc. (R), NJ, *28*
The Center for Career Advancement, LLC (C), NJ, *287*
The Century Group (C), CA, *287*
CFOs 2 Go (C), CA, *288*
CFR Executive Search, Inc. (C), IL, *288*
Vickers Chambless Managed Search (C), GA, *288*
Chicago Legal Search, Ltd. (C), IL, *290*
The Colton Partnership, Inc. (R), NY, *38*
M. L. Conner (C), FL, *296*
Consulting Resource Group, Inc. (C), GA, *297*
David C. Cooper & Assoc. Financial Search (C), GA, *298*
Cornell Group Int'l. Consulting, Inc. (R), NY, *41*
Crispi, Wagner & Co., Inc. (R), NY, *43*
Cromwell Partners, Inc. (R), NY, *43*
Cypress Int'l., Inc. (R), FL, *45*
Davis & James, Inc. (C), MO, *308*
DBL Associates (C), CA, *309*
Dieckmann & Assoc., Ltd. (R), IL, *51*
Dise & Co. (R), OH, *52*
Diversified Search, Inc. (R), PA, *52*
Dow Consultants Int'l. (C), NY, *314*
DS&A (Doug Sears & Assoc.) (C), FL, *315*
J. H. Dugan & Assoc., Inc. (R), CA, *55*
Dunhill Search of Medford (C), NJ, *321*
Dunhill Search of Arlington (C), TX, *322*
Dunhill Search of Vermont (C), VT, *323*
The Evans Search Group (R), CT, *61*
The Executive Group, Inc. (R), CA, *62*
Executive Placement Consultants (C), IL, *333*
FAI (C), CO, *338*
Fenwick Partners (R), MA, *66*
Fidelity Search Group, Inc. (R), PA, *66*
Financialjobs.com (C), CA, *340*
Fortune Personnel Consultants of Hinsdale, IL (C), IL, *346*
Foster Partners (R), NY, *70*
Franklin Allen Consultants, Ltd. (R), NY, *71*
Gardiner, Townsend & Assoc. (R), NY, *74*
Gateway Group Personnel, LLC (C), TN, *355*
Gavin Forbes & Price (R), CA, *75*
Glines Assoc., Inc. (R), IL, *77*
Global Executive Search Group (C), MA, *358*
The Tracy Glover Co. (R), TX, *78*
Goodrich & Sherwood Assoc., Inc. (R), NY, *79*
Grauss & Co. (C), CA, *362*
Ben Greco Assoc., Inc. (C), CA, *362*
Growth Strategies, Inc. (R), FL, *83*
GSP International (C), NJ, *364*
H.Q. Search, Inc. (C), IL, *365*
Robert Half Canada Inc. (C), ON, *366*
Michael J. Hall & Co. (R), WA, *85*
Handy HRM (R), NY, *86*
The Hanover Consulting Group (C), MD, *368*
Hanzel & Co., Inc. (R), NY, *86*
Hardison & Company (R), TX, *86*
Thomas E. Hedefine Assoc. (C), ON, *375*
Jay Heino Company, LLC (C), NY, *375*
Hessel Assoc., Inc. (C), NY, *377*
Holden & Harlan Assoc., Inc. (C), IL, *380*
Home Health & Hospital Recruiters, Inc. (C), GA, *380*
HRI Services, Inc. (C), MA, *382*
Huntress Real Estate Executive Search (R), MO, *100*
The Hutton Group, Inc. (C), FL, *386*
HVS Executive Search (R), NY, *100*
Interim Accounting Professionals (C), CA, *391*
IR Search (R), CA, *103*
J. Nicholas Arthur (R), MA, *104*
J. R. Scott & Assoc., Ltd. (C), IL, *395*
JDH & Assoc. (C), CA, *397*
Jones Management Co. (R), CT, *108*
Joseph Michaels (C), CA, *401*
Karel & Co. (R), CA, *109*
Howard Karr & Assoc., Inc. (R), CA, *110*
Melissa Katzman, Executive Search (C), NY, *404*
A.T. Kearney Executive Search (R), IL, *111*
Keeley Consulting Inc. (C), ON, *404*
Kennedy & Co. (R), IL, *112*
Kenzer Corp. (R), NY, *113*
Kershner & Co. (R), DC, *113*
The Kinlin Co., Inc. (R), MA, *115*
Kip Williams, Inc. (R), NY, *115*
Koren, Rogers Assoc. Inc. (R), NY, *117*
Kramer Executive Resources, Inc. (C), NY, *409*
E. J. Lance Management Assoc., Inc. (C), NY, *412*
Lechner & Assoc., Inc. (C), FL, *415*
The Luciani Group (R), CA, *132*
Management Recruiters of Birmingham, Inc. (C), AL, *438*
Management Recruiters of Aptos (C), CA, *439*
Management Recruiters of Bonita Springs, Inc. (C), FL, *443*
Management Recruiters of Oklahoma City (C), OK, *458*
Management Search, Inc. (C), IL, *467*
The Marlow Group (R), MA, *136*
Marsar & Co., Inc. (C), FL, *471*
McCann, Choi & Associates, LLC (R), NY, *139*
The McLeod Group, Inc. (R), CT, *141*
Millar Walker & Gay (R), ON, *144*
Miller/Davis & Assoc., Inc. (C), NY, *482*
Oscar Montaño, Inc. (R), CA, *146*
Montgomery Resources, Inc. (C), CA, *484*
Morgan Stampfl, Inc. (C), NY, *485*
Much & Co. (R), NY, *148*
Don Neal & Assoc. (C), OK, *491*
New Venture Development, Inc. (C), CA, *492*
Nichols & Company (R), CO, *151*
Nichols Brown Int'l. (R), NY, *151*
P. J. Nicholson & Assoc. (C), IL, *493*
The Nolan Group (C), CA, *494*
Norman Broadbent Int'l., Inc. (R), NY, *152*
Norrell Financial Staffing (C), GA, *495*
The Oxbridge Group, Ltd. (C), PA, *500*
The Oxford Group (C), TX, *500*
Pacific Search Group, Inc. (C), CA, *501*
Parker & Lynch (C), CA, *503*
Partners Resource Group (C), VA, *504*
Pascale & LaMorte, LLC (C), CT, *504*
Physicians Search®, Inc. (C), CA, *511*
Pierce & Assoc. (C), CA, *512*
Pinnacle Executive Group Inc. (C), MO, *512*
Pinnacle Group Int'l. (C), AZ, *512*

Pinton Forrest & Madden/EMA Partners Int'l. (R), BC, *165*
Placement Solutions (C), WI, *513*
Plante & Moran, LLP (R), MI, *165*
PMJ & Assoc. (C), ON, *513*
The Prairie Group (C), IL, *515*
Elan Pratzer & Partners Inc. (R), ON, *167*
Preferred Placement, Inc. (C), NY, *516*
Probus Executive Search (C), CA, *519*
Professional Support Inc. (C), NY, *523*
The Quest Organization (C), NY, *527*
L. J. Quinn & Assoc., Inc. (R), CA, *170*
Joanne E. Ratner Search (C), NY, *529*
Razzino-Claymore Assoc. (C), NJ, *530*
The Recruitment Group, Inc. (C), NY, *532*
Reinecke & Assoc. (C), NJ, *533*
Resource Management Group (C), CT, *534*
Russell Reynolds Assoc., Inc. (R), NY, *176*
Jeff Rich Assoc. (C), NJ, *536*
RJ Associates (C), CA, *538*
RLM Assoc., Ltd. (R), NY, *179*
Rocky Mountain Recruiters, Inc. (C), CO, *540*
The Rogan Group, Inc. (C), CA, *541*
Romac Int'l. (C), IL, *541*
Romac Int'l. Inc. (R), MA, *181*
Ryan, Miller & Assoc. (C), CA, *549*
Rylan Forbes Consulting Group, Inc. (C), NJ, *549*
Ryman, Bell, Green & Michaels, Inc. (C), TX, *549*
Sanford Rose Assoc. - Oak Brook (C), IL, *567*
Schlatter & Assoc. (C), CA, *572*
Schoales & Assoc. Inc. (C), ON, *572*
Search Research Assoc., Inc. (R), MA, *187*
Smith Hanley Assoc., Inc. (C), NY, *584*
SpencerStuart (R), NY, *196*
Spriggs & Co., Inc. (R), IL, *198*
Steinfield & Assoc. (C), TX, *592*
Peter Sterling & Co. (C), TX, *592*
Sterling Int'l. (R), NJ, *200*
Steven Douglas Assoc. (C), FL, *593*
Steven Michaels & Assoc. (C), NY, *593*
Stone Assoc. LLC (C), MI, *594*
Strategic Search, LLC (C), CA, *595*
Synagent Inc. (C), ON, *597*
TBC, Inc. (C), KY, *600*
Thomas, Whelan Assoc., Inc. (C), DC, *606*
Judy Thompson & Assoc., Inc. (C), CA, *606*
Scott Watson & Assoc., Inc. (R), FL, *216*
The Whitney Group (R), NY, *219*
Winston Search, Inc. (R), MD, *222*
Worldwide Medical Services (C), CA, *625*
WTW Assoc., Inc. (R), NY, *225*
Steven Yungerberg Assoc., Inc. (R), MN, *226*
Zweig White & Assoc., Inc. (R), MA, *228*

07.7 Risk management

A la Carte Int'l., Inc. (R), VA, *1*
A.L.S. Group (C), NJ, *232*
Abacus Group LLC (C), NY, *232*
Accountants On Call (C), TN, *237*
Accounting & Bookkeeping Personnel, Inc. (C), AZ, *237*
Allard Associates (C), CA, *244*
Alpha Search (C), FL, *246*
Amato & Assoc., Inc. (C), CA, *246*
Amato & Associates Insurance Recruiters (C), PA, *247*
Ambridge Management Corp. (C), ON, *247*
Aminex Corp. (C), MA, *249*
Analytic Recruiting, Inc. (C), NY, *249*
E. J. Ashton & Assoc., Ltd. (C), IL, *253*
ATS Executive Recruitment (C), GA, *255*
A. M. Auster Associates (R), FL, *9*
The Ayers Group, Inc. (R), NY, *9*
Barr Associates (C), NY, *260*
Battalia Winston Int'l./The Euram Consultants Group (R), NY, *13*
BayResearch Group, Inc. (R), IL, *14*
Bergeris & Co., Inc. (C), NY, *265*
Berglund Int'l. Resources, Inc. (C), TX, *265*
Bonell Ryan Inc. (R), NY, *19*
Boyden (R), NY, *20*
Broad Waverly & Assoc. (C), NJ, *274*
Burkholder & Assoc., Inc. (C), TX, *276*
The Butlers Co. Insurance Recruiters (C), FL, *277*
Butterfass, Pepe & MacCallan Inc. (R), NJ, *25*
California Management Search (C), CA, *279*
Capital Markets Resources, Inc. (C), NC, *281*
Carter-Evdemon & Assoc. (C), FL, *285*
CFOs 2 Go (C), CA, *288*
CFR Executive Search, Inc. (C), IL, *288*
Vickers Chambless Managed Search (C), GA, *288*
Claimsearch (C), CA, *291*
The Colton Partnership, Inc. (R), NY, *38*
Cornell Group Int'l. Consulting, Inc. (R), NY, *41*
CRI Professional Search (C), CA, *303*
Crispi, Wagner & Co., Inc. (R), NY, *43*
Cromwell Partners, Inc. (R), NY, *43*
Cypress Int'l., Inc. (R), FL, *45*
Alfred Daniels & Assoc., Inc. (R), CA, *46*
S. W. Delano & Co. (R), CT, *48*
Dieckmann & Assoc., Ltd. (R), IL, *51*
Discovery, The Staffing Specialists, Inc. (C), IL, *312*
Diversified Search, Inc. (R), PA, *52*
Dow Consultants Int'l. (C), NY, *314*
Downing & Downing, Inc. (C), OH, *314*
Dunhill Search of Medford (C), NJ, *321*
Dunhill Professional Search of Omaha, Inc. (C), NE, *321*
Dunhill Personnel of Northeast Tulsa, Inc. (C), OK, *322*
Dunhill Search of Arlington (C), TX, *322*
D. C. Egan & Assoc. (C), GA, *327*
The Execu/Search Group (C), NY, *332*
Executive Search Consultants, Inc. (C), FL, *335*
Executive Search Consultants Corp. (C), IL, *335*
Federal Placement Services (C), NY, *339*
Financial Resource Assoc., Inc. (C), FL, *340*
The Flagship Group (R), MA, *68*
Foster Partners (R), NY, *70*
Futures Int'l. (R), CT, *73*
Gahan Assoc. (R), NY, *73*
Gateway Group Personnel, LLC (C), TN, *355*
Gavin Forbes & Price (R), CA, *75*
GES Services, Inc. (R), NY, *76*
Gilbert Scott Assoc., LLC (C), MA, *357*
Global Executive Search Group (C), MA, *358*
The Tracy Glover Co. (R), TX, *78*
Gnodde Assoc. (C), IL, *359*
Godfrey Personnel, Inc. (C), IL, *359*
The Gogates Group, Inc. (R), NY, *79*
Barry M. Gold & Co. (C), CA, *359*
Government Contract Solutions, Inc. (C), VA, *360*
GSP International (C), NJ, *364*
H.Q. Search, Inc. (C), IL, *365*
K. C. Hale, Inc. (R), CT, *85*
Robert Half Canada Inc. (C), ON, *366*
Michael J. Hall & Co. (R), WA, *85*
Hallman Group, Inc. (C), MI, *367*
The Hanover Consulting Group (C), MD, *368*
Harvard Aimes Group (R), CT, *87*
Thomas E. Hedefine Assoc. (C), ON, *375*
Hessel Assoc., Inc. (C), NY, *377*
Higbee Assoc., Inc. (C), CT, *377*
B. W. Higgins, Inc. (C), IN, *377*
Holden & Harlan Assoc., Inc. (C), IL, *380*
Human Resource Dimensions, Inc. (C), TX, *384*
Hunter Int'l. LLC (C), MA, *385*
The Hutton Group, Inc. (C), FL, *386*
Insurance Career Center, Inc. (C), CT, *389*
Insurance Search (C), TX, *390*
IntelliSearch (C), TX, *391*
Interim Accounting Professionals (C), CA, *391*
International Business Partners (C), ON, *392*
International Market Recruiters (C), NY, *393*
J. R. Scott & Assoc., Ltd. (C), IL, *395*
J.J. & H., Ltd. (R), IL, *104*
Jacobson Assoc. (C), IL, *396*
Jones Consulting Executive Search (C), GA, *400*
Joseph Michaels (C), CA, *401*
A.T. Kearney Executive Search (R), IL, *111*
Keeley Consulting Inc. (C), ON, *404*
Kenzer Corp. (R), NY, *113*
Kinderis & Loercher Group (C), IL, *407*
L T M Assoc. (C), IL, *410*
LanSo Int'l., Inc. (C), NY, *413*
LAS Management Consulting Group, Inc. (R), NJ, *125*
Leader Resources Group (C), GA, *415*
Lear & Assoc., Inc. (C), FL, *415*
Leeds and Leeds (C), TN, *416*
Lexington Software Inc. (C), NY, *417*
Logic Assoc., Inc. (C), NY, *419*
The Luciani Group (R), CA, *132*
Lyons Pruitt Int'l. (R), PA, *132*
Magellan Int'l., L.P. (C), TX, *422*
Management Recruiters of Berkeley (C), CA, *439*
Management Recruiters of Duluth (C), GA, *445*

Management Recruiters of Atlanta NE (C), GA, *446*
Management Recruiters of Chicago West (C), IL, *447*
Management Recruiters of Cass County, NE (C), NE, *452*
Management Recruiters of New Providence (C), NJ, *454*
Management Recruiters of Great Neck (C), NY, *454*
Management Recruiters of Manhattan on Broadway (C), NY, *455*
Management Recruiters of Lionville, Inc. (C), PA, *459*
Management Recruiters of Kanawha Valley, LLC (C), WV, *465*
Management Recruiters of Stevens Point, Inc. (C), WI, *466*
Mary L. Mayer, Ltd. (R), MN, *139*
McCann, Choi & Associates, LLC (R), NY, *139*
The McKinnon Management Group Inc. (C), ON, *475*
Mehta Consulting (C), NJ, *478*
Meridian Resources (C), OH, *479*
Millar Walker & Gay (R), ON, *144*
Paul Misarti Inc. (C), NY, *483*
Mitchell/Wolfson, Assoc. (R), IL, *145*
Oscar Montaño, Inc. (R), CA, *146*
C. A. Moore & Assoc., Inc. (C), MN, *484*
Morgan Hunter Corp. (C), KS, *485*
Morgan Stampfl, Inc. (C), NY, *485*
Much & Co. (R), NY, *148*
DDJ Myers, Ltd. (R), AZ, *150*
Nason & Nason (C), FL, *488*
National Bank & Finance Executive Search (C), CA, *488*
National Search, Inc.r (C), FL, *490*
Don Neal & Assoc. (C), OK, *491*
Marc Nichols Assoc., Inc. (C), NY, *493*
J. L. Nixon Consulting (C), TX, *493*
Norman Broadbent Int'l., Inc. (R), NY, *152*
O'Neill & Co. (R), CT, *154*
Olympian Recruitment, Ltd. (C), NY, *498*
Pacific Coast Recruiters (C), OR, *501*
Pearson, Caldwell & Farnsworth (R), CA, *161*
PERI Corp/Professional Executive Recruiters, Inc. (C), TX, *507*
Phillips & Assoc. (R), MA, *164*
Picard Int'l., Ltd. (R), NY, *164*
Pierce & Assoc. (C), CA, *512*
Pinnacle Executive Group Inc. (C), MO, *512*
Plante & Moran, LLP (R), MI, *165*
Robert Powers & Assoc. (C), CA, *515*
Preferred Placement, Inc. (C), NY, *516*
The Primary Group, Inc. (R), FL, *168*
Priority Executive Search (C), FL, *518*
PRO, Inc./Professional Recruiting Offices, Inc. (C), CA, *519*
Probus Executive Search (C), CA, *519*
Pryor & Associates (C), CA, *525*
Questor Consultants, Inc. (C), PA, *527*
QuestPro, Inc. (C), TX, *527*
Lea Randolph & Assoc., Inc. (C), TX, *529*
Joanne E. Ratner Search (C), NY, *529*
Razzino-Claymore Assoc. (C), NJ, *530*
Resource Management Group (C), CT, *534*
Russell Reynolds Assoc., Inc. (R), NY, *176*
Jeff Rich Assoc. (C), NJ, *536*
Richard Wright Co. (C), CT, *536*
Riotto-Jones Assoc. (R), NY, *178*
Rockwood Assoc. (C), NY, *540*
W. R. Rosato & Assoc., Inc. (R), NY, *182*
RSMR, Inc. (R), IL, *182*
Russillo/Gardner/Spolsino (C), MA, *548*
Sales Consultants of Chicago South (C), IL, *558*
The Search Center Inc. (C), TX, *574*
The Search Company (R), ON, *186*
The Search Group (C), MD, *575*
Siger & Assoc., LLC (C), CT, *581*
Skipping Stone Inc. (C), VA, *582*
Smith Hanley Assoc., Inc. (C), NY, *584*
Snelling Search - Transportation Division (C), AR, *585*
Southwest Selective Search, Inc. (C), TX, *588*
SpencerStuart (R), NY, *196*
M. H. Springer & Assoc. (R), CA, *198*
The Stark Wilton Group (R), MI, *199*
Peter Sterling & Co. (C), TX, *592*
Stone Assoc. LLC (C), MI, *594*
Straight & Co. (R), GA, *202*
Summit Search Specialists (C), TX, *596*
Synagent Inc. (C), ON, *597*
Roy Talman & Assoc. (C), IL, *599*
Techsearch Services Inc. (C), CT, *603*
Tennyson Advisors (R), NY, *208*
The TGA Company (C), TX, *606*
TSW Assoc., LLC (R), CT, *211*
Peter Van Leer & Assoc. (R), MN, *213*
West Coast Recruiting (C), CA, *619*
The Whitney Group (R), NY, *219*
Helen Ziegler & Assoc., Inc. (C), ON, *627*

08.0 Information technology

The 500 Granary Inc. (C), ON, *231*
A C Personnel Services, Inc. (C), OK, *231*
A First Resource (C), NC, *231*
A Permanent Success Employment Services (C), CA, *231*
A-L Assoc., Inc. (R), NY, *1*
A. D. & Assoc. Executive Search, Inc. (C), GA, *231*
A.K.S. Assoc., Ltd. (R), MA, *1*
A.M.C.R., Inc. (C), OH, *232*
Abbott Associates (R), CA, *1*
The Abbott Group, Inc. (R), MD, *1*
Abraham & London Ltd. (C), CT, *232*
Abraxas Technologies, Inc. (C), FL, *233*
ACC Technical Services (C), OH, *233*
Access Assoc. Inc. (C), MD, *233*
Access Data Personnel, Inc. (C), NH, *233*
ACCESS Technology (C), CA, *234*
Acclaim Services, Inc. (C), TX, *234*
Account Ability Now (C), MI, *234*
Accountants On Call (C), NJ, *234*
Accounting & Computer Personnel (C), NY, *238*
Accounting Personnel & Engineering Personnel Consultants (C), LA, *238*
ACSYS Resources, Inc. (C), DE, *238*
Action Executive Personnel Consulting Inc. (C), ON, *239*
Action Management Corp. (C), MI, *239*
Adam-Bryce Inc. (C), NY, *239*
Adams & Assoc. Int'l. (R), IL, *1*
Adel-Lawrence Assoc., Inc. (C), NJ, *240*
Adept Tech Recruiting, Inc. (C), NY, *240*
Adler Management, Inc. (R), NJ, *2*
Advanced Corporate Search (C), CA, *240*
Advanced Recruiting, Inc. (C), OK, *240*
Advanced Resources, Inc. (C), MO, *241*
Advancement Recruiting Services (C), OH, *241*
Advantage Partners, Inc. (R), OH, *2*
Advisors' Search Group, Inc. (C), NY, *241*
AES Search (C), NJ, *241*
Affinity Executive Search (C), FL, *241*
AJM Professional Services (C), MI, *243*
J. R. Akin & Co. (R), MA, *2*
Alexander Associates (R), NJ, *2*
Alexander Enterprises, Inc. (C), PA, *243*
The Alexander Group (R), TX, *3*
The Alexander Group (R), NJ, *3*
The Alfus Group (R), NY, *3*
Allard Associates (C), CA, *244*
Allen & Assoc. (C), NV, *244*
D. S. Allen Assoc. (C), NJ, *244*
David Allen Assoc. (R), NJ, *3*
Allen Austin Lowe & Powers (R), TX, *3*
Allen Consulting Group, Inc. (C), MO, *244*
Allen Evans Assoc. (R), NY, *4*
Allen-Jeffers Assoc. (C), CA, *245*
Allerton Heneghan & O'Neill (R), IL, *4*
Alliance Executive Search, Inc. (R), MA, *4*
Allied Search, Inc. (C), CA, *245*
Allstaff, Inc. (C), IL, *245*
Alpha Resource Group, Inc. (C), TX, *246*
The Alternatives Group, Inc. (C), TX, *246*
Amato & Assoc., Inc. (C), CA, *246*
Peter W. Ambler Co. (R), TX, *5*
AMD & Associates (C), GA, *247*
American Executive Management, Inc. (R), MA, *5*
American Executive Search (C), FL, *247*
American Heritage Group, Inc. (C), MI, *247*
American Medical Recruiters (C), CO, *248*
American Resources Corp. (C), IL, *248*
American Services Group (C), IL, *248*
AmeriPro Search, Inc. (C), NC, *248*
AmeriResource Group Inc. (C), OK, *248*
Ames-O'Neill Assoc., Inc. (C), NY, *249*
AMS Int'l. (R), VA, *5*
Analytic Recruiting, Inc. (C), NY, *249*
Anderson Network Group (C), OH, *250*
Andex Executive Search (C), CT, *250*
Andrews & Wald Group (C), FL, *250*
Angel Group Int'l. (C), KY, *250*
Angus Employment Ltd. (C), ON, *250*
The Angus Group, Ltd. (C), OH, *251*
David Aplin & Assoc. (C), AB, *251*
Applied Resources, Inc. (C), MN, *252*
Applied Technology Solutions Inc. (C), ON, *252*
Charles P. Aquavella & Assoc. (C), TX, *252*
Argonaut Partners, LLC (R), CA, *6*
The Argus Group Corp. (C), ON, *252*
Armitage Associates Ltd. (R), ON, *7*
J. S. Armstrong & Assoc., Inc. (R), CA, *7*
R & J Arnold & Assoc., Inc. (C), CO, *253*
Patrick Arnone & Assoc. Inc. (R), VA, *7*

Artgo, Inc. (R), OH, *7*
A. Artze Assoc.-Personnel Consultants (C), PR, *253*
Ashford Management Group, Inc. (R), GA, *7*
Ashlar-Stone Management Consultants Inc. (R), ON, *8*
Ashton Computer Professionals, Inc. (C), BC, *253*
Ashworth Consultants, Inc. (R), MA, *8*
ASI (C), CA, *254*
Asset Resource, Inc. (C), CA, *254*
Astro Executive Search Firm (C), LA, *254*
Atkinson Search & Placement, Inc. (C), IA, *255*
Atlanta Executive Partners, Inc. (R), MA, *8*
Aubin Int'l. Inc. (R), MA, *8*
Auerbach Associates, Inc. (R), MA, *9*
Aurora Tech Search (C), ON, *256*
Cami Austin & Assoc. (C), IL, *256*
Austin Park Management Group Inc. (C), ON, *256*
Austin, Hill & Assoc. (C), MD, *256*
Austin-McGregor Int'l. (R), TX, *9*
Automation Technology Search (C), CA, *256*
Avalon Health Group, Inc. (R), NY, *9*
Avion International Technology Inc. (C), ON, *257*
Avondale Search Int'l., Inc. (R), FL, *9*
The Ayers Group, Inc. (R), NY, *9*
The Badger Group (R), CA, *10*
Baeder Kalinski Int'l. Group, Inc. (R), NH, *10*
Keith Bagg & Assoc., Inc. (C), ON, *257*
Baker Scott & Co. (C), NJ, *258*
Baker, Nelms & Montgomery (C), IL, *258*
Baldwin & Assoc. (C), OH, *258*
Baldwin Associates, LLC (R), CT, *10*
Allen Ballach Assoc. Inc. (R), ON, *10*
Barclay Consultants, Inc. (C), NJ, *259*
Barnes & Assoc. Executive Search (C), CA, *259*
Barnes Development Group, LLC (R), WI, *11*
Barrett Hospitality Search (R), CA, *12*
Barrett Partners (C), IL, *260*
Barrett Rose & Lee, Inc. (C), ON, *260*
Bartholdi & Co., Inc. (R), CO, *12*
Barton Assoc., Inc. (R), TX, *12*
Bartz Rogers & Partners (C), MN, *260*
Bason Associates (R), OH, *13*
Bassett Laudi Partners (C), ON, *261*
Battalia Winston Int'l./The Euram Consultants Group (R), NY, *13*
R. Gaines Baty Assoc., Inc. (R), TX, *13*
Bayland Assoc. (C), CA, *261*
BCG Search, Inc. (R), FL, *14*
Beach Executive Search Inc. (R), FL, *14*
Beacon Int'l., Inc. (C), VA, *261*
The Beam Group (R), PA, *14*
The Beardsley Group Inc. (C), CT, *261*
Becker Personnel (C), FL, *262*
Becker Project Resources, Inc. (C), OR, *262*
The Bedford Consulting Group Inc. (R), ON, *14*
Robert Beech West Inc. (C), CA, *262*
Behavioral Science Assoc., Inc. (R), AZ, *15*
Belanger Partners Ltd. (C), ON, *262*
Edward Bell Assoc. (C), CA, *263*
Bell Oaks Co., Inc. (C), GA, *263*
Bellamy & Assoc. (C), GA, *263*
Joy Reed Belt Search Consultants, Inc. (R), OK, *15*
J. P. Bencik Assoc. (C), MI, *263*
N. L. Benke & Assoc., Inc. (C), OH, *264*
Bennett & Associates (C), TX, *264*
Bennett & Co. Consulting Group (C), CA, *264*
The Bennett Group, Inc. (R), IN, *16*
Bennett Search & Consulting Co. (R), FL, *16*
Dick Berg & Assoc. (C), CA, *264*
C. Berger And Company (R), IL, *16*
Berglund Int'l. Resources, Inc. (C), TX, *265*
Berkana Int'l., Inc. (C), WA, *265*
Berman & Larson (C), NJ, *265*
Bernhart Assoc. (C), MN, *265*
Bertrand, Ross & Assoc., Inc. (C), IL, *266*
Besen Assoc. Inc. (C), NJ, *266*
BEST/World Assoc. Inc. (R), TX, *16*
BG & Assoc. (C), MD, *266*
Paul J. Biestek Assoc., Inc. (R), IL, *17*
Bio-Venture Group (C), RI, *266*
BioPharmMed (C), FL, *267*
BioTech Research Recruiters Inc. (C), CA, *267*
Birch & Associes (C), QE, *267*
Bishop Partners (R), NY, *17*
Blackhawk Advantage, Inc. (C), CA, *267*
Blaney Executive Search (R), MA, *18*
Blanton & Co. (C), AL, *268*
Blau Mancino Schroeder (R), NJ, *18*
Block & Assoc. (R), CA, *18*
D. R. Blood & Assoc. (R), AZ, *18*
The BMW Group, Inc. (C), NY, *268*
Boardroom Consultants/Kenny Kindler Tholke (R), NY, *19*
Bolton Group (C), CA, *269*
Boone-Scaturro Assoc., Inc. (C), GA, *269*
Bor-Maq Assoc. (C), TX, *269*
Lynn Borne & Co. (C), CA, *270*
Bornholdt Shivas & Friends Executive Recruiters (C), NY, *270*
The Borton Wallace Co. (R), NC, *19*
Bos Business Consultants (C), NY, *270*
Bosland Gray Assoc. (R), NJ, *20*
Bowden & Co., Inc. (R), OH, *20*
Howard Bowen Consulting (C), FL, *270*
Bower & Associates (C), TX, *271*
Boyden (R), NY, *20*
BR & Assoc. (C), NJ, *271*
The Bradbury Management Group, Inc. (R), CA, *21*
Bradford & Galt, Inc. (C), MO, *271*
M. F. Branch Assoc., Inc. (C), NC, *272*
Brandt Associates (C), PA, *272*
Brandywine Retained Ventures, Inc. (R), CT, *22*
Branthover Assoc. (C), NY, *272*
Bratland & Assoc. (C), IL, *272*
Brault & Assoc., Ltd. (R), VA, *22*
Bredeson Executive Recruitment, LLC (R), TX, *22*
Brei & Assoc., Inc. (C), IA, *272*
The Brentwood Group, Inc. (R), NJ, *22*
Brentwood Int'l. (R), CA, *23*
Brian Assoc., Inc. (C), NY, *273*
The Bridge (C), CO, *273*
Bridgecreek Personnel Agency (C), CA, *273*
BridgeGate LLC (C), CA, *273*
Brigade, Inc. (R), CA, *23*
Bristol Assoc., Inc. (C), CA, *274*
Britt Assoc., Inc. (C), IL, *274*
Broadband Resource Group (C), CA, *274*
Brookman Associates (C), NY, *274*
Bernard E. Brooks & Assoc., Inc. (R), SC, *24*
D. Brown & Assoc., Inc. (C), OR, *275*
Brownstone Sales & Marketing Group, Inc. (C), NY, *275*
Brush Creek Partners (R), MO, *24*
BT&A, LLC (R), CT, *24*
Bullis & Co., Inc. (R), CA, *25*
The Burgess Group-Corporate Recruiters Int'l., Inc. (R), NY, *25*
Joseph R. Burns & Assoc., Inc. (R), NJ, *25*
Business Partners, Inc. (C), FL, *277*
Business Systems of America, Inc. (C), IL, *277*
Butterfield & Co. Int'l., Inc. (C), HI, *277*
Button Group (C), TX, *277*
Buzhardt Assoc. (R), MS, *25*
Byron Leonard Int'l., Inc. (R), CA, *25*
C & H Personnel (C), PA, *277*
C. M. Management Services, Inc. (R), KY, *26*
C.P.S., Inc. (C), IL, *278*
C.T.E.W. Executive Personnel Services Inc. (C), BC, *278*
Cadillac Assoc. (C), CA, *278*
California Management Search (C), CA, *279*
California Search Agency, Inc. (C), CA, *279*
Callan Assoc., Ltd. (R), IL, *27*
Cambridge Group Ltd. - Exec. Search Div. (C), CT, *279*
The Cambridge Group Ltd. (C), CT, *280*
Cambridge Management Planning (R), ON, *27*
T. M. Campbell Co. (R), WA, *27*
Canadian Career Partners (R), AB, *27*
Canny, Bowen Inc. (R), NY, *27*
J. P. Canon Assoc. (C), NY, *280*
Cantrell & Assoc. (C), FL, *280*
Capital Consulting & Research, Inc. (R), CT, *28*
Capital Consulting Group, Inc. (R), MD, *28*
Capital Markets Resources, Inc. (C), NC, *281*
Sally Caplan & Assoc. (C), WA, *281*
Capstone Inc. (R), NY, *29*
Career Advisors, Inc. (C), FL, *281*
Career Consultants (R), IN, *29*
Career Counseling Inc. (CCI) (C), KY, *282*
Career Counseling Ltd. (C.C.L.) (C), NY, *282*
Career Development Associates (C), NV, *282*
Career Enterprises (C), OH, *282*
Career Marketing Assoc., Inc. (C), CO, *282*
Career Marketing Consultants, Inc. (C), GA, *282*
Career Specialists, Inc. (R), WA, *29*

Careerfit, Inc. (C), TX, *283*
Careers First, Inc. (C), NJ, *283*
The Carey Company (C), NC, *284*
Carion Resource Group Inc. (C), ON, *284*
Carlsen Resources, Inc. (R), CO, *29*
Carlson & Czeswik (R), MN, *30*
Carpenter & Assoc. (C), TX, *284*
Carpenter, Shackleton & Company (R), IL, *30*
Carrington & Carrington, Ltd. (R), IL, *30*
K. Carroll & Assoc. (C), IL, *284*
Carter, Lavoie Associates (C), RI, *285*
Carter McKenzie, Inc. (C), NJ, *285*
Carter-Evdemon & Assoc. (C), FL, *285*
Carter/MacKay (C), NJ, *285*
Caruso & Assoc., Inc. (R), FL, *31*
The CARVIR Group, Inc. (C), GA, *285*
Cary & Assoc. (R), FL, *31*
CAS Comsearch Inc. (C), NY, *285*
Casey & Assoc., Inc. (C), TX, *286*
Rosemary Cass Ltd. (R), CT, *31*
Catalyx Group (R), NY, *31*
Michael J. Cavanagh & Assoc. Inc. (R), ON, *31*
CBA Companies (C), CA, *286*
CCI - Career Consultants Int'l. (C), CA, *286*
CEC Associates (R), MA, *32*
Cella Assoc. (C), GA, *286*
Cemco, Ltd. (C), IL, *286*
Cendea Connection Int'l. (R), TX, *32*
The Center for Career Advancement, LLC (C), NJ, *287*
Century Assoc., Inc. (C), PA, *287*
The Century Group (C), KS, *287*
CEO Consulting (C), FL, *287*
cFour Partners (R), CA, *32*
Chacra, Belliveau & Assoc. Inc. (C), QE, *288*
Chad Management Group (C), ON, *288*
Chamberlain Assoc. (C), GA, *288*
Vickers Chambless Managed Search (C), GA, *288*
Elsie Chan & Assoc. (C), CA, *289*
Chanko-Ward, Ltd. (R), NY, *33*
Chapman & Assoc. (C), BC, *289*
The Chapman Group, Inc. (C), AZ, *289*
The Chatham Group, Ltd. (C), CT, *289*
Chatham Search Assoc., Inc. (C), NJ, *290*
Cheney Associates (C), CT, *290*
The Cherbonnier Group, Inc. (R), TX, *33*
Chesapeake Group (C), CT, *290*
Christenson Hutchison McDowell, LLC (R), NJ, *34*
Christian & Timbers, Inc. (R), OH, *34*
R. Christine Assoc. (C), PA, *290*
Christmas, McIvor & Assoc. Inc. (C), ON, *290*
Christopher-Westmont & Assoc., Inc. (R), OH, *34*
M. A. Churchill & Assoc., Inc. (R), PA, *35*
Clarey/Napier Int'l., L.C. (R), TX, *35*
Howard Clark Assoc. (C), NJ, *292*
Ken Clark Int'l. (R), NJ, *36*
The Clayton Edward Group (C), MI, *292*
Clinton, Charles, Wise & Co. (C), FL, *293*
CMS Management Services LLC (C), IN, *293*
CMW & Associates, Inc. (C), IL, *293*
CN Associates (C), CA, *293*
Coast Personnel Services Ltd. (C), BC, *293*
Cochran, Cochran & Yale, Inc. (R), NY, *36*
Ann Coe & Assoc. (C), IL, *294*
Coe & Co. Int'l. Inc./EMA Partners Int'l. (R), AB, *37*
Cole, Warren & Long, Inc. (R), PA, *37*
J. Kevin Coleman & Assoc., Inc. (R), CA, *37*
Collins & Associates (C), MI, *294*
Colt Systems Professional Personnel Services (C), CA, *294*
Colton Bernard Inc. (R), CA, *37*
The Colton Partnership, Inc. (R), NY, *38*
Columbia Consulting Group (R), MD, *38*
Combined Resources Inc. (R), OH, *38*
Commercial Programming Systems, Inc. (C), CA, *294*
Comprehensive Search (C), GA, *294*
CompuPro (C), IL, *295*
Computer Int'l. Consultants, Inc. (C), FL, *295*
Computer Network Resources, Inc. (C), CA, *295*
Computer Personnel, Inc. (C), WA, *295*
Computer Placements Unlimited Inc. (C), NY, *295*
Computer Professionals Unlimited (C), TX, *295*
Computer Recruiters, Inc. (C), CA, *295*
Computer Search Group, Ltd. (R), IL, *39*
Computer Security Placement Service (C), MA, *296*
Conard Associates, Inc. (R), NH, *39*
Conasa de Mexico, S.C. (R), MX, *39*
Concorde Staff Source Inc. (C), WI, *296*
Conex Inc./InterSearch (R), NY, *39*
Connors, Lovell & Assoc. Inc. (C), ON, *296*
Conroy Partners Ltd. (R), AB, *39*
The Consortium (C), NY, *296*
Consulpro (R), ON, *39*
Consultant Recruiters (C), WI, *297*
The Consulting Group of North America, Inc. (C), VA, *297*
Consulting Resource Group, Inc. (C), GA, *297*
ContactBridge, Inc. (R), IL, *40*
Continental Search & Outplacement, Inc. (C), MD, *298*
Conway & Assoc. (R), IL, *40*
Cook Assoc. Int'l., Inc. (C), TN, *298*
P. G. Cook Assoc. (R), TN, *40*
COR Management Services, Ltd. (C), NY, *298*
Cornerstone Resources, Inc. (C), OK, *299*
Corporate Advisors, Inc. (C), FL, *299*
The Corporate Advisory Group (R), NJ, *41*
Corporate Careers, Inc. (C), CA, *299*
Corporate Image Group (C), TN, *300*
Corporate Plus, Ltd. (C), GA, *300*
Corporate Recruiters Ltd. (C), BC, *300*
Corporate Resources Professional Placement (C), MN, *300*
Corporate Resources (C), OH, *301*
Corporate Search Consultants, Inc. (C), FL, *301*
Corporate Select Int'l., Ltd. (C), IL, *301*
The Corporate Source Group, Inc. (R), MA, *41*
Corporate Staffing Group, Inc. (C), PA, *301*
Cosier & Assoc. (C), AB, *302*
J. D. Cotter Search Inc. (C), OH, *302*
Cowell & Associates, Ltd. (R), IL, *42*
Cowin Assoc. (R), NY, *42*
Trudi Cowlan (C), NY, *302*
Creative Financial Staffing (C), MA, *303*
Creative HR Solutions (C), GA, *303*
Creative Input, Inc. (C), RI, *303*
Creative Management Strategies, Ltd. (R), NY, *42*
The Cris Group, Inc. (R), NY, *42*
Criterion Executive Search, Inc. (C), FL, *303*
Cromwell Partners, Inc. (R), NY, *43*
Cross Country Consultants, Inc. (C), MD, *304*
Crowe Chizek & Co. (C), IN, *304*
Timothy D. Crowe, Jr. (R), MA, *43*
CTR (R), CA, *43*
Culver Personnel Services (C), CA, *304*
Curran Partners, Inc. (R), CT, *44*
Current Resource Group, Inc. (C), GA, *305*
Curry, Telleri Group, Inc. (R), NJ, *44*
Tony Curtis & Associates (C), ON, *305*
The Curtiss Group International (R), FL, *44*
The Custer Group, Inc. (R), TN, *44*
Custom Resources (C), AL, *305*
Cybernautic Corp. (C), CT, *305*
Cypress Int'l., Inc. (R), FL, *45*
D.A.L. Associates, Inc. (R), CT, *45*
D.P. Specialists, Inc. (C), CA, *306*
Charles Dahl Group, Inc. (C), MN, *306*
Dahl-Morrow Int'l. (R), VA, *45*
The Dalley Hewitt Co. (R), GA, *45*
Damon & Assoc., Inc. (C), TX, *306*
Alfred Daniels & Assoc., Inc. (R), CA, *46*
Dapexs Consultants, Inc. (C), NY, *307*
DARE Personnel Inc. (C), ON, *307*
Alan Darling Consulting (R), VT, *46*
Data Bank Executive Search (R), OH, *46*
Data Search Network, Inc. (C), FL, *307*
Data-AxIS Corp. (C), FL, *307*
The DataFinders Group, Inc. (C), NJ, *307*
Datamatics Management Services, Inc. (C), NJ, *307*
DataPro Personnel Consultants (C), TX, *308*
Daubenspeck & Associates, Ltd. (R), IL, *46*
Alan N. Daum & Assoc., Inc. (C), OH, *308*
David Anthony Personnel Assoc., Inc. (C), NJ, *308*
Allen Davis & Assoc. (C), MA, *308*
John J. Davis & Assoc., Inc. (R), NY, *47*
Alan Davis & Assoc. Inc. (R), QE, *47*
Joseph A. Davis Consultants, Inc. (R), NY, *47*
Bert Davis Executive Search, Inc. (R), NY, *47*
Bert Davis Publishing Placement Consultants (C), NY, *309*
The Dayton Group, Ltd. (C), NY, *309*
DBC Recruiting Network (C), GA, *309*
DBL Associates (C), CA, *309*
De Funiak & Edwards (R), IN, *47*
Dean-Dzierzawiec Assoc. (C), NJ, *309*

DeCaster Assoc. (C), WI, *310*
DEL Technical Services, Inc. (C), IL, *310*
Thorndike Deland Assoc. LLC (R), NY, *48*
Delta Management Group Ltd. (C), ON, *310*
Delta Resource Group, Ltd. (C), GA, *311*
DeMatteo Associates (C), NY, *311*
Descheneaux Recruitment Services Ltd. (C), BC, *311*
Desktop Staffing, Inc. (C), IL, *311*
Despres & Associates (C), IL, *311*
The Devlin Search Group, Inc. (C), MA, *311*
Rob Dey Executive Search (R), FL, *49*
Dieckmann & Assoc., Ltd. (R), IL, *51*
DieckMueller Group (R), WI, *51*
The Diestel Group (R), UT, *51*
DiMarchi Partners (R), CO, *51*
Dinte Resources, Inc. (R), VA, *52*
Direct Marketing Resources (C), NC, *312*
R. J. Dishaw & Assoc. (R), TX, *52*
DiTech Resources (C), CT, *313*
Diversified Consulting Services, Inc. (C), CO, *313*
Diversified Health Search (R), PA, *52*
Diversified Search, Inc. (R), PA, *52*
DLG Assoc., Inc. (R), NC, *53*
Doering & Assoc. (C), CA, *313*
L. J. Doherty & Assoc. (R), MA, *53*
Doherty Int'l., Inc. (R), IL, *53*
Doleman Enterprises (R), VA, *53*
Dominguez-Metz & Assoc. (R), CA, *53*
Domres Professional Search (R), WI, *53*
Don Allan Assoc., Inc. (C), CA, *313*
Donini Assoc. (R), VA, *54*
J P Donnelly Assoc., Inc. (C), NY, *314*
The Dorfman Group (C), AZ, *314*
Dorst Information Services, Inc. (C), NY, *314*
The Doty Group (C), TX, *314*
Drake & Assoc. (C), CA, *315*
Dreier Consulting (C), NJ, *315*
Robert Drexler Assoc., Inc. (R), NJ, *54*
Drinkwater & Assoc. (R), MA, *54*
Dromeshauser Assoc. (R), MA, *55*
Drummond Assoc., Inc. (C), NY, *315*
DRZ Medical Recruiters (C), CO, *315*
DS&A (Doug Sears & Assoc.) (C), FL, *315*
DuBrul Management Co. (C), NY, *315*
Dunhill Staffing Systems, Inc. (C), NY, *316*
Dunhill Professional Search of Miami (C), FL, *319*
Dunhill Professional Search of San Jose (C), CA, *319*
Dunhill Professional Search of Oakland (C), CA, *319*
Dunhill Professional Search of Tampa (C), FL, *320*
Dunhill Technical Staffing (C), IN, *320*
Dunhill Professional Search of Rolling Meadows (C), IL, *320*
Dunhill Professional Search of Hawaii (C), HI, *320*
Dunhill of Manchester Inc. (C), NH, *321*
Dunhill Professional Search of Greater New Orleans (C), LA, *321*
Dunhill Staffing Systems (C), NC, *321*
Dunhill Professional Search of Byram (C), MS, *321*
Dunhill Professional Search of Winston-Salem (C), NC, *322*
Dunhill Personnel Service of Fargo (C), ND, *322*
Dunhill Search of Arlington (C), TX, *322*
Dunhill Professional Search of Wilkes-Barre/Scranton, Inc. (C), PA, *322*
Dunhill Professional Search of Bucks-Mont., Inc. (C), PA, *322*
Dunlap & Sullivan Assoc. (R), MI, *55*
Dunn Associates (R), PA, *55*
C. A. Durakis Assoc., Inc. (R), MD, *55*
Donald F. Dvorak & Co. (R), IL, *55*
Dynamic Choices Inc. (C), MO, *323*
Dynamic Computer Consultants, Inc. (C), AZ, *324*
Dynamic Search Systems, Inc. (C), IL, *324*
Dynamic Staffing Network (C), IL, *324*
Dynamic Synergy Corp. (R), CA, *56*
E O Technical (C), CT, *324*
EA Plus, Inc. (C), TX, *325*
J. M. Eagle Partners Ltd. (C), WI, *325*
Eagle Search Assoc. (C), CA, *325*
EagleView, Inc. (C), MA, *325*
Earley Kielty & Assoc., Inc. (R), NY, *56*
Eastbourne Assoc. Inc. (R), NY, *56*
Eastman & Beaudine, Inc. (R), TX, *56*
Eastridge Infotech (C), CA, *326*
EBA Group (R), NJ, *56*
Eckler Personnel Network (C), VT, *326*
Eden & Assoc., Inc. (C), PA, *326*
The Edge Resource Group (C), PA, *326*
EDI, Inc. (C), MD, *326*
EDMS Solutions (C), TX, *326*
EDP Staffing Solutions, Inc. (C), AR, *327*
Bruce Edwards & Associates, Inc. (R), NC, *56*
EFCO Consultants, Inc. (C), NY, *327*
Eggers Consulting Co., Inc. (C), NE, *327*
Richard A. Eisner & Co., LLP (R), NY, *57*
Electronic Search, Inc. (C), IL, *327*
Elite Consultants, Inc. (C), FL, *328*
Elite Medical Search (C), GA, *328*
H. J. Elliot, Inc. (R), IL, *58*
Ellis & Associates (C), HI, *328*
David M. Ellner Assoc. (R), NY, *59*
The Elmhurst Group (C), CA, *329*
Emerging Technology Search (C), GA, *329*
EMN/Witt/Kieffer (R), MA, *59*
Empire International (R), PA, *59*
Employ® (C), PA, *330*
Empowered Solutions Corp. (C), GA, *330*
Engineering Futures, LLC (C), CT, *330*
ENI (R), CT, *59*
Epsen, Fuller & Assoc., LLC (R), NJ, *60*
Erikson Consulting Assoc., Inc. (R), NY, *60*
Erlanger Assoc. (R), CT, *60*
ESA (R), CT, *60*
ESS (Executive Search Services) (R), CA, *61*
Essential Solutions, Inc. (C), CA, *331*
ETI Search Int'l. (R), GA, *61*
The Evans Search Group (R), CT, *61*
Evergreen & Co. (C), MA, *331*
Excalibur Human Resources, Inc. (R), NJ, *61*
Exclusive Search Consultants (C), OH, *331*
ExeConnex, LLC (R), GA, *61*
Execu-Tech Search Inc. (C), MN, *332*
ExecuGroup, Inc. (R), MS, *61*
ExecuQuest, Inc. (R), MI, *61*
ExecuSource Assoc., Inc. (C), GA, *332*
Executive Access Inc. (R), NY, *62*
Executive Business Solutions, Inc. (C), WA, *332*
Executive Career Search (C), VA, *332*
Executive Dimensions (R), NY, *62*
Executive Direction, Inc. (C), CA, *333*
Executive Exchange Corp. (C), NJ, *333*
The Executive Group, Inc. (R), CA, *62*
Executive Manning Corp. (R), FL, *63*
Executive Partners Inc. (C), CT, *333*
Executive Recruiters Int'l. (C), MI, *333*
Executive Recruiters Agency, Inc. (C), AR, *333*
Executive Recruiters, Inc. (C), WI, *334*
Executive Recruiters (C), WA, *334*
Executive Recruitment Specialists, Inc. (R), NC, *63*
Executive Recruitment Services, Inc. (ERS, Inc.) (C), GA, *334*
Executive Registry (C), QE, *334*
Executive Resource Group, Inc. (R), ME, *63*
Executive Resource Systems (C), CA, *335*
Executive Search Consultants International, Inc. (R), NY, *63*
Executive Search Group LLC (C), CA, *335*
Executive Search of America, Inc. (C), OH, *336*
Executive Search Partners (R), NY, *63*
Executive Search Plus, Inc. (C), IN, *336*
Executive Search Team (C), MI, *336*
Executive Solutions (R), MN, *64*
Executive Strategies, Inc. (C), GA, *337*
The Executive Tree (R), FL, *64*
ExecutiveFit (C), NY, *337*
Executives Worldwide, Inc. (C), OR, *337*
EXETER 2100 (C), NH, *337*
eXsource Inc. (C), SC, *337*
Raymond L. Extract & Assoc. (R), CA, *64*
Eyler Assoc., Inc. (R), IA, *64*
Fabian Assoc. Inc. (C), NY, *338*
FAI (C), CO, *338*
Fairfaxx Corp. (R), CT, *64*
Dorothy W. Farnath & Assoc., Inc. (C), NJ, *338*
Fast Switch, Ltd. (C), OH, *338*
The Fawcett Group (R), MA, *65*
A. E. Feldman Assoc., Inc. (C), NY, *339*
Fenwick Partners (R), MA, *66*
Fenzel Milar Assoc. (C), OH, *339*
Ferneborg & Assoc., Inc. (R), CA, *66*
Fernow Assoc. (C), PA, *339*
Financial Connections Company (C), VA, *340*
Financial Plus Management Solutions Inc. (R), ON, *66*
Financialjobs.com (C), CA, *340*
Finnegan & Assoc. (R), CA, *67*
Finney-Taylor Personnel & Management Consultants Ltd. (C), AB, *341*
First Advisory Services Int'l., Inc. (R), MD, *67*
First Search Inc. (C), IL, *341*

(R) = Retainer; (C) = Contingency

First Union Executive Search (R), NC, *67*
Howard Fischer Assoc. Int'l., Inc. (R), PA, *67*
Fishel HR Assoc., Inc. (C), AZ, *341*
The Fisher Group (R), AB, *67*
Fisher Personnel Management Services (R), CA, *68*
A. G. Fishkin & Assoc., Inc. (R), MD, *68*
James L. Fisk & Assoc. (C), MO, *342*
Fitzgerald Associates (R), MA, *68*
FitzGibbon & Assoc. (R), PA, *68*
The Flagship Group (R), MA, *68*
Robert M. Flanagan & Assoc., Ltd. (R), NY, *68*
Flexible Resources, Inc. (C), CT, *342*
Flowers & Assoc. (C), OH, *342*
Focus Consulting Services, Inc. (C), FL, *342*
Fogec Consultants, Inc. (R), WI, *69*
Foley Proctor Yoskowitz (R), NJ, *69*
Ford & Assoc., Inc. (C), SC, *343*
Ford & Ford (C), MA, *343*
The Ford Group, Inc. (R), PA, *69*
Fortuna Technologies Inc. (C), CA, *343*
F-O-R-T-U-N-E Personnel Consultants of Boise (R), ID, *70*
Fortune Group Int'l., Inc. (R), PA, *70*
Fortune Personnel Consultants of Huntsville, Inc. (C), AL, *343*
F-O-R-T-U-N-E Personnel Consultants of Denver, Inc. (C), CO, *344*
Fortune Personnel Consultants of Colorado Springs (C), CO, *344*
F-O-R-T-U-N-E Personnel Consultants of Wilmington (C), DE, *344*
Fortune Personnel Consultants of Jacksonville (C), FL, *345*
F-O-R-T-U-N-E Personnel Consultants (C), MI, *346*
F-O-R-T-U-N-E Personnel Consultants of Southwest Indiana (C), IN, *346*
F-O-R-T-U-N-E Search Consultants (C), MO, *347*
Fortune Personnel Consultants of Allentown, Inc. (C), PA, *348*
Fortune Personnel Consultants of Greensboro, NC, Inc. (C), NC, *348*
F-O-R-T-U-N-E Personnel Consultants of Knoxville (C), TN, *350*
Fortune Personnel Consultants of San Antonio, Inc. (C), TX, *350*
FORTUNE Personnel Consultants of North Dallas (C), TX, *350*
F-O-R-T-U-N-E Personnel of Nashville (C), TN, *350*
F-O-R-T-U-N-E Personnel Consultants of the Tri-Cities, Inc. (C), TN, *350*
F-O-R-T-U-N-E Personnel Consultants of East Seattle (C), WA, *351*
Forum Personnel Inc. (C), NY, *351*
Foster Associates (C), NJ, *351*
Foster Partners (R), NY, *70*
Fought, Jameson Assoc. (C), IL, *351*
Fox-Morris Assoc., Inc. (C), PA, *351*
Foy, Schneid & Daniel, Inc. (R), NY, *71*
Franchise Recruiters Ltd. (R), IL, *71*
Franklin Int'l. Search, Inc. (C), MA, *352*
Franstaff Inc. (C), FL, *352*
KS Frary & Assoc. (R), MA, *71*
Mel Frazer Consultant (C), CA, *352*
P. N. French Assoc., Inc. (R), MA, *72*
Friedman Eisenstein Raemer & Schwartz, LLP (R), IL, *72*
Bernard Frigon & Assoc. Inc. (C), QE, *353*
Gerald Frisch Assoc., Inc. (R), NY, *72*
C. F. Furr & Co. (R), NC, *72*
Furst Group/MPI (R), IL, *72*
Future Employment Service, Inc. (C), IA, *353*
G. H. Enterprises (C), AZ, *354*
GAAP Inc. (R), QE, *73*
The Gabriel Group (C), PA, *354*
Gahan Assoc. (R), NY, *73*
Jay Gaines & Company, Inc. (R), NY, *73*
Gallin Associates, Inc. (C), FL, *354*
Gaming Consultants, Inc. (R), LA, *74*
Gans, Gans & Assoc., Inc. (R), FL, *74*
W. N. Garbarini & Assoc. (R), NJ, *74*
Gardiner, Townsend & Assoc. (R), NY, *74*
Gardner-Ross Assoc., Inc. (R), NY, *74*
Garland Assoc. Int'l. (C), CA, *355*
The Garms Group (R), IL, *74*
Garrett Assoc. Inc. (R), GA, *75*
The Garvis Group, Inc. (C), LA, *355*
GateSource Partners (C), VA, *355*
GCO (C), CA, *355*
Geddes & Rubin Management Inc. (R), ON, *76*
Genel Associates (C), CA, *356*
General Engineering Tectonics (C), CA, *356*
Genesis Consulting Partners (R), PA, *76*
Gent & Assoc. (C), CA, *356*
Delores F. George, C.P.C. (C), MA, *356*
C. R. Gerald & Assoc. (C), ON, *356*
GES Services, Inc. (R), NY, *76*
GFI Professional Staffing Services (C), NH, *357*
John Gilbert Co. (C), TX, *357*
Gilbert Scott Assoc., LLC (C), MA, *357*
Gilbert Tweed Assoc. Inc. (R), NY, *76*
Joe L. Giles & Assoc. (C), MI, *357*
Gilmore & Assoc. (C), CA, *357*
Gimbel & Assoc. (C), FL, *357*
The Glazin Group (R), BC, *77*
Global 1000 Int'l. Services (C), CA, *358*
Global Career Services, Inc. (C), NY, *358*
Global Consulting Group Inc. (C), ON, *358*
Global Data Services, Inc. (R), NY, *77*
Global Employer's Network, Inc. (R), TX, *77*
Global HealthCare Partners (R), IL, *78*
Global Technologies Group Inc. (C), NC, *359*
F. Gloss Int'l. (R), VA, *78*
Glou Int'l., Inc. (R), MA, *78*
Robert G. Godfrey Assoc. Ltd. (R), IL, *78*
Joseph Goldring & Assoc. Inc. (C), MI, *360*
Goldstein & Co. (C), CA, *360*
David Gomez & Assoc., Inc. (R), IL, *79*
L. J. Gonzer Assoc. (C), NJ, *360*
The Goodman Group (R), CA, *79*
Goodrich & Sherwood Assoc., Inc. (R), NY, *79*
Gould, McCoy & Chadick, Inc. (R), NY, *80*
The Governance Group, Inc. (R), NJ, *80*
Government Contract Solutions, Inc. (C), VA, *360*
Gowdy Consultants (C), TX, *361*
A. Davis Grant & Co. (R), NJ, *81*
Grant Cooper & Assoc., Inc. (R), MO, *81*
The Grant Search Group, Inc. (C), ON, *361*
Grant-Franks & Assoc. (C), NJ, *361*
Grant/Morgan Assoc., Inc. (C), MD, *361*
Grauss & Co. (C), CA, *362*
Sheila Greco Assoc. (C), NY, *362*
Greenwich Internet (C), CT, *363*
Greenwich Search Partners, LLC (C), CT, *363*
J. B. Groner Executive Search, Inc. (C), DE, *363*
Groton Planning Group (R), ME, *82*
Groupe PCA Inc. (C), QE, *363*
Groupe Ranger Inc. (C), QE, *364*
Growth Strategies, Inc. (R), FL, *83*
GSW Consulting Group, Inc. (R), CA, *83*
Guidry & East Healthcare Search Consultants (R), TX, *83*
The Guild Corp. (C), VA, *364*
The Gullgroup (C), TX, *364*
Gustin Partners, Ltd. (R), MA, *83*
William Guy & Assoc., Inc. (R), CA, *84*
GWS Partners (R), IL, *84*
H R Solutions, Inc. (C), MO, *365*
The H. S. Group, Inc. (C), WI, *365*
Habelmann & Assoc. (R), MI, *84*
Haddad Assoc. (R), FL, *84*
Russ Hadick & Assoc. Inc. (C), OH, *365*
Halbrecht & Co. (C), VA, *365*
Halbrecht Lieberman Assoc., Inc. (R), CT, *84*
Don Hall & Assoc. (C), TX, *366*
Hall Kinion (C), CA, *366*
Hall Management Group, Inc. (C), GA, *367*
Hallman Group, Inc. (C), MI, *367*
The Hamilton Group (R), MD, *85*
W. L. Handler & Assoc. (R), GA, *85*
Handy HRM (R), NY, *86*
Hanley & Assoc. (R), FL, *86*
Harbor Consultants Int'l., Inc. (C), VA, *368*
Harbrowe, Inc. (C), NY, *368*
Harcor Quest & Assoc. (R), OH, *86*
Harcourt & Assoc. (C), AB, *368*
Harcourt Group Ltd. (R), OH, *86*
Hardison & Company (R), TX, *86*
Robert Harkins Assoc., Inc. (C), PA, *369*
Harper Associates (C), MI, *369*
Harper Hewes, Inc. (C), NY, *369*
Harris McCully Assoc., Inc. (C), NY, *369*
Hartsfield Group, Inc. (R), GA, *87*
Harvard Group Int'l. (R), GA, *87*
Harvey Hohauser & Assoc., LLC (R), MI, *87*
William E. Hay & Co. (R), IL, *88*
Hayden & Assoc., Inc. (C), MN, *370*
Hayden Group, Inc. (R), MA, *88*
Hayman Daugherty Assoc., Inc. (C), GA, *370*
Hazlett Associates (R), IL, *88*
HDB Incorporated (C), MO, *371*
Health Search (C), CA, *371*
Healthcare Executive Recruiters, Inc. (C), CA, *372*
Healthcare Management Resources, Inc. (R), GA, *89*

Healthcare Recruiters Int'l. Bay Area (C), CA, *372*
Healthcare Recruiters Int'l. - Alabama (C), AL, *372*
Healthcare Recruiters of Indiana (C), IN, *372*
Healthcare Recruiters International-NY/NJ (C), NJ, *373*
Healthcare Recruiters of New Orleans (C), LA, *373*
Healthcare Recruiters of New York, Inc. (C), NY, *373*
Healthcare Recruiters Int'l. Philadelphia (C), NJ, *373*
F. P. Healy & Co., Inc. (R), NY, *89*
HEC Group (C), ON, *375*
Hechkoff/Work Executive Search Inc. (R), NY, *89*
Hedlund Corp. (C), IL, *375*
Heffelfinger Assoc., Inc. (R), MA, *89*
The Heidrick Partners, Inc. (R), IL, *90*
Heinze & Assoc. Inc. (R), MN, *91*
Helfer Executive Consultants (R), TN, *91*
The Helms Int'l. Group (R), VA, *91*
Hemingway Personnel, Inc. (C), CA, *375*
G. W. Henn & Co. (R), OH, *91*
Bruce Henry Assoc. Inc. (R), CA, *91*
Henson Partners (C), AZ, *376*
Herbeck Kline & Assoc. (R), IL, *92*
J. J. Herlihy & Assoc., Inc. (C), CA, *376*
Hermann & Westmore (R), CA, *92*
A. Herndon & Assoc., Inc. (R), TX, *92*
The Herrmann Group Ltd. (R), ON, *92*
J. D. Hersey & Assoc. (C), OH, *376*
Hersher Assoc., Ltd. (R), IL, *92*
Stanley Herz & Co. (R), NY, *92*
The Hetzel Group, Inc. (R), IL, *92*
Higbee Assoc., Inc. (C), CT, *377*
Higgins Assoc., Inc. (R), IL, *93*
B. W. Higgins, Inc. (C), IN, *377*
High Tech Staffing Group (C), OR, *377*
High-Tech Recruiters (C), CT, *378*
Higley, Hall & Co., Inc. (R), MA, *93*
Hintz Associates (C), NY, *378*
The Hiring Authority, Inc. (C), FL, *379*
Hite Executive Search (R), OH, *94*
HLR Consulting (C), NY, *379*
Hobson Assoc. (C), CT, *379*
Hochman & Assoc. (C), CA, *379*
Hoffman Recruiters (C), MA, *380*
Holden & Harlan Assoc., Inc. (C), IL, *380*
Holland & Assoc., Inc. (R), MI, *94*
Holloway Schulz & Partners (C), BC, *380*
Holohan Group, Ltd. (R), MO, *95*
J. B. Homer Assoc. Inc. (R), NY, *95*
Fred Hood & Assoc. (C), CA, *380*
J. G. Hood Assoc. (C), CT, *380*
Hook-Up! (C), CA, *380*
Horizon Medical Search of NH (C), NH, *381*
David C. Horn Executive Search (C), TX, *381*
Horton Int'l. Inc. (R), NY, *96*
Hospitality Executive Search, Inc. (R), MA, *96*
Hospitality Int'l. (C), NY, *381*
Houser, Martin, Morris (C), WA, *381*
Howe & Assoc. (R), PA, *97*
Robert Howe & Assoc. (R), GA, *97*
HR Advantage, Inc. (C), VA, *382*
HR Consultants (C), GA, *382*
HRCS (R), CA, *97*
Hreshko Consulting Group (C), NJ, *382*
The HRM Group, Inc. (C), AL, *382*
HRS, Inc. (R), PA, *97*
The Hudson Group (C), CT, *383*
Huff Assoc. (R), NJ, *98*
Hughes & Company (R), VA, *98*
Human Resource Bureau (C), CA, *384*
The Human Resource Group, Inc. (R), OH, *98*
Human Resource Technologies, Inc. (R), IL, *99*
Human Resources Management Hawaii, Inc. (C), HI, *384*
Human Resources Personnel Agency (R), AR, *99*
Hunegnaw Executive Search (C), OH, *384*
Leigh Hunt & Assoc., Inc. (C), ME, *384*
Hunt & Howe Inc. (R), NY, *99*
The Hunt Co. (R), NY, *99*
Hunter Adams (C), NC, *385*
Huntington Group (R), CT, *100*
Huntington Personnel Consultants, Inc. (C), NY, *386*
Huntley Associates (Dallas), Inc. (C), TX, *386*
The Hutton Group, Inc. (C), FL, *386*
HVS Executive Search (R), NY, *100*
i.j. & assoc., inc. (C), CO, *386*
IM Independent Management Recruiters (R), TN, *101*
IMA Search, Inc. (R), NY, *101*
The IMC Group of Companies (R), NY, *101*
Impact Search & Strategies (C), PA, *387*
Impact Technical Staffing (C), OR, *387*
Independent Resource Systems (C), CA, *388*
Industry Consultants, Inc. (C), GA, *388*
Information Systems Professionals (C), NC, *388*
Information Technology Search (C), PA, *388*
InfoTech Search (C), TX, *388*
Infovia (C), CA, *388*
Ingram & Aydelotte, Inc. (R), NY, *101*
Innovative Healthcare Services, Inc. (C), GA, *389*
Innovative Resource Group, LLC (C), NC, *389*
The Inside Track (C), TX, *389*
Insight Personnel Group, Inc. (C), TX, *389*
Insurance Personnel Resources, Inc. (C), GA, *390*
InTech Services, Inc. (C), GA, *390*
Intech Summit Group, Inc. (R), CA, *102*
Integrated Management Solutions (C), NY, *390*
Integrated Search Solutions Group, LLC (ISSG) (R), NY, *102*
Integrity Search, Inc. (R), PA, *102*
Intelegra, Inc. (C), NJ, *390*
IntelliSource, inc. (C), PA, *391*
Interactive Search Assoc. (C), PA, *391*
Interactive Search Network (R), CA, *102*
Interim Financial Solutions - Mid-Atlantic Region (C), MD, *392*
International Business Partners (C), ON, *392*
International Consulting Services, Inc. (C), IL, *392*
International Executive Recruiters (C), OH, *393*
International Management Services Inc. (R), IL, *102*
International Management Advisors, Inc. (R), NY, *103*
International Market Recruiters (C), NY, *393*
International Pro Sourcing, Inc. (C), PA, *393*
International Staffing Consultants, Inc. (C), CA, *393*
International Technical Resources (C), FL, *393*
Intersource, Ltd. (R), GA, *103*
Iona Partners (C), CA, *394*
Jeffrey Irving Assoc., Inc. (R), VA, *104*
Isaacson, Miller (R), MA, *104*
ISG Informatics Search Group (C), ON, *395*
Ives & Associates, Inc. (C), OH, *395*
J & D Resources Inc. (C), TN, *395*
J. Joseph & Assoc. (C), OH, *395*
Jackson Group Int'l. (C), CO, *396*
Jaeger Int'l., Inc. (C), OH, *396*
Pendleton James Assoc., Inc. (R), NY, *105*
James Moore & Assoc. (C), CA, *397*
David James Search (C), CA, *397*
JDC Assoc. (C), NY, *397*
JDG Assoc., Ltd. (C), MD, *397*
JDH & Assoc. (C), CA, *397*
Jefferson-Ross Assoc. Inc. (C), PA, *398*
Jeffrey Allan Co., Inc. (C), CA, *398*
Jeffrey Meryl Assoc., Inc. (C), NJ, *398*
Jender & Company (R), IL, *105*
Jenex Technology Placement Inc. (C), BC, *398*
JenKim Int'l. Ltd., Inc. (C), FL, *398*
JFW Associates, LLC (C), CT, *398*
JG Consultants, Inc. (R), TX, *106*
Job Link, Inc. (C), CA, *399*
Job-Born Candidate Selection Bureau (C), ON, *399*
John Ryan Assoc., LLC. (C), NY, *399*
Johnson & Assoc., Inc. (R), CA, *106*
Ronald S. Johnson Assoc., Inc. (R), CA, *107*
Johnson Assoc., Inc. (C), IL, *399*
K. E. Johnson Assoc. (C), WA, *399*
The Johnson Group, Unlimited (C), NY, *400*
Johnson Smith & Knisely (R), NY, *107*
Jonathan Lawrence Assoc. (C), NJ, *400*
The Jonathan Stevens Group, Inc. (R), NJ, *108*
Jones and Jones (R), OR, *108*
Jones Management Co. (R), CT, *108*
Jordon & Jordon, Inc. (R), PA, *108*
J. M. Joseph Assoc. (R), NJ, *109*
Joseph Consulting, Inc. (C), FL, *401*
The Jotorok Group (C), RI, *401*
JRL Executive Recruiters (C), MO, *401*
JSG Group Management Consultants (R), ON, *109*
JT Assoc. (C), CT, *401*

Judd Associates (R), NJ, *109*
Juno Systems, Inc. (C), NY, *402*
A H Justice Search Consultants (C), TX, *402*
K2 Resources, L.P. (C), CT, *402*
Kaas Employment Services (C), IA, *402*
KABL Ability Network (C), CA, *402*
Richard Kader & Assoc. (C), OH, *403*
Kames & Assoc. (C), MD, *403*
Kane & Assoc. (C), TX, *403*
Kanzer Assoc., Inc. (R), IL, *109*
Gary Kaplan & Assoc. (R), CA, *109*
Kaplan & Assoc., Inc. (R), PA, *109*
Allan Karson Assoc., Inc. (R), NJ, *110*
Katelyn Partners (C), FL, *404*
Melissa Katzman, Executive Search (C), NY, *404*
Kaufman Assoc. (R), CA, *110*
Jim Kay & Assoc. (C), IL, *404*
Kay Concepts, Inc. (C), FL, *404*
Kaye/Bassman Int'l. Corp. (R), TX, *110*
Keane Assoc. (R), MA, *110*
A.T. Kearney Executive Search (R), IL, *111*
Keena Staffing Services (C), NY, *404*
Kehn & Gabor, Inc. (C), OH, *405*
The Keith-Murray Partnership (R), ON, *112*
Kenmore Executives Inc. (C), FL, *405*
David Warwick Kennedy & Assoc. (R), BC, *112*
Kennedy & Co. (R), IL, *112*
The Kennett Group, Inc. (R), PA, *112*
Kennison & Assoc. Inc. (C), MO, *405*
Kensington International (R), CA, *113*
Kenzer Corp. (R), NY, *113*
Key Resources Int'l. (C), CA, *405*
Ki Technologies, Inc. (C), UT, *406*
Kiley, Owen & McGovern, Inc. (R), NJ, *114*
Kimmel & Associates, Inc. (C), NC, *406*
Kincaid Group Inc. (KGI) (C), TX, *406*
Kinderis & Loercher Group (C), IL, *407*
King ComputerSearch, Inc. (C), TX, *407*
Kingsley Quinn/USA (R), NJ, *115*
Kiradjieff & Goode, Inc. (R), MA, *115*
Kleber & Assoc. (C), WA, *407*
Raymond J. Klemmer & Assoc. (R), NY, *116*
The Kleven Group, Inc. - Executive Search Division (R), MA, *116*
The Kleven Group, Inc. (C), MA, *407*
KM Associates (C), MA, *407*
Knapp Consultants (R), CT, *116*
Joyce C. Knauff & Assoc. (C), IL, *408*
Lee Koehn Assoc., Inc. (R), OR, *116*
T. J. Koellhoffer & Assoc. (R), NJ, *116*
Koll-Fairfield LLC (C), CT, *408*
Korban Associates (R), PA, *117*
Koren, Rogers Assoc. Inc. (R), NY, *117*
Korn/Ferry Int'l. (R), NY, *117*
Kors Montgomery Int'l. (R), TX, *118*
Kostmayer Assoc., Inc. (R), MD, *119*
KPA Assoc., Inc. (C), NY, *408*
Krakower Group, Inc. (R), CA, *120*
Kramer Executive Resources, Inc. (C), NY, *409*
Krautler Personnel Recruitment (C), FL, *409*
Krecklo Executive Search Inc. (R), ON, *120*
Kremple Consulting Group (R), CA, *120*
Kreutz Consulting Group, Inc. (R), IL, *121*
Krueger Assoc. (R), IL, *121*
John Kuhn & Assoc., Inc. (R), WI, *121*
Kukoy Associates (R), CO, *121*
Kulper & Co., L.L.C. (R), NJ, *121*
Kunzer Assoc., Ltd. (R), IL, *121*
John Kurosky & Assoc. (R), CA, *122*
Kurtz Pro-Search, Inc. (C), NJ, *410*
L & K Assoc. (C), NJ, *410*
L O R (R), NJ, *122*
L T M Assoc. (C), IL, *410*
L. Patrick Group (R), NJ, *122*
Marvin Laba & Assoc. (R), CA, *122*
Laguzza Assoc., Ltd. (R), NY, *122*
Gregory Laka & Co. (C), IL, *411*
Lamay Assoc., Inc. (R), CT, *124*
Lamon + Stuart + Michaels Inc. (R), ON, *124*
Lancaster Assoc., Inc. (C), NJ, *411*
Landon Morgan (C), ON, *412*
The Langford Search, Inc. (C), AL, *412*
Lanken-Kimball-Therrell & Assoc. (C), GA, *412*
Lawrence L. Lapham, Inc. (R), NY, *124*
Robert Larned Assoc., Inc. (C), VA, *413*
R. H. Larsen & Assoc., Inc. (R), FL, *125*
Jack B. Larsen & Assoc., Inc. (C), PA, *413*
Larsen, Whitney, Blecksmith & Zilliacus, Inc. (R), CA, *125*
Larson Assoc. (R), CA, *125*
Larson, Katz & Young, Inc. (C), VA, *413*
LAS Management Consulting Group, Inc. (R), NJ, *125*
Lascelle & Assoc. Inc. (C), ON, *413*
Lasher Assoc. (R), FL, *125*
Lauer, Sbarbaro Assoc., EMA Partners Int'l. (R), IL, *126*
Lautz, Grotte, Engler & Swimley (R), CA, *126*
Madeleine Lav & Assoc. (C), CA, *413*
LaVallee & Associates (C), NC, *413*
Lawrence James Assoc. of Florida, Inc. (C), FL, *414*
The Lawson Group, Inc. (C), SC, *414*
Layne-Mendez & Co. (R), TX, *127*
LCC Companies (C), AZ, *414*
LCS, Inc. (C), TX, *414*
Leader Institute, Inc. (C), GA, *414*
Leader Resources Group (C), GA, *415*
Leaders-Trust Int'l./Carce y Asociados, S.C. (R), MX, *127*
Lear & Assoc., Inc. (C), FL, *415*
Reynolds Lebus Assoc. (C), AZ, *415*
Ledbetter/Davidson Int'l., Inc. (R), NY, *127*
Albert G. Lee Assoc. (C), RI, *415*
Vincent Lee Assoc. (C), NY, *415*
The Conrad Lee Co. Inc. (R), FL, *127*
Legal Network Inc. (C), CA, *416*
Lehman McLeskey (R), TX, *128*
Lekan & Assoc., Inc. (R), OH, *128*
Lemming/LeVan, Inc. (R), GA, *128*
Lending Personnel Services (C), CA, *416*
F. P. Lennon Assoc. (C), PA, *416*
AG Lennox & Assoc. (R), AB, *128*
Leslie Kavanagh Assoc., Inc. (C), NY, *416*
Levin & Company, Inc. (R), MA, *128*
Alan Levine Assoc. (R), MA, *129*
The Levton Group Inc. (R), ON, *129*
Lewis Consulting Service (C), IL, *417*
Lexington Software Inc. (C), NY, *417*
LG Brand, Inc. (C), MD, *417*
The Libra Group (C), NC, *417*
LifeWork, Inc. (C), TX, *418*
Lifter & Assoc. (C), CA, *418*
Livingston, Robert & Co. (R), CT, *130*
Lloyd Associates (R), GA, *130*
Lloyd Prescott & Churchill, Inc. (R), FL, *130*
Lloyd Prescott Assoc., Inc. (C), FL, *418*
Lloyd Staffing (C), NY, *419*
LMB Assoc. (C), IL, *419*
Loderman & Costello (C), GA, *419*
Loewenstein & Assoc., Inc. (R), TX, *131*
The Logan Group, Inc. (R), MO, *131*
Logix, Inc. (C), MA, *420*
Logue & Rice Inc. (C), VA, *420*
London Executive Consultants Inc. (C), ON, *420*
Longo Associates (C), CA, *420*
Longshore + Simmons (R), PA, *131*
Lord & Albus Co. (C), TX, *420*
J. S. Lord & Company, Inc. (R), MA, *131*
The John Lucht Consultancy Inc. (R), NY, *131*
Charles Luntz & Assoc., Inc. (R), MO, *132*
Lutz Associates (C), CT, *421*
P. J. Lynch Assoc. (R), CT, *132*
Lynch Miller Moore Partners, Inc. (R), IL, *132*
Lynne Palmer Executive Recruitment, Inc. (C), NY, *421*
Lynx, Inc. (C), MA, *421*
Lyons Pruitt Int'l. (R), PA, *132*
M/J/A Partners (R), IL, *133*
MacNaughton Assoc. (R), CA, *133*
Carol Maden Group (C), VA, *422*
Madison Executive Search, Inc. (C), NJ, *422*
Magellan Int'l., L.P. (C), TX, *422*
Managed Care Consultants (C), AZ, *423*
Management Alliance Group, Inc. (R), NJ, *134*
Management Assoc. (C), MD, *424*
Management Assoc. (C), CA, *424*
Management Association Network (C), WI, *424*
Management Decision Systems, Inc. (MDSI) (C), NJ, *424*
Management Dimensions Ltd. (R), ON, *134*
Management Recruiters of Nassau, Inc. (R), NY, *134*
Management Recruiters of Birmingham, Inc. (C), AL, *438*
Management Recruiters of Birmingham-South, Inc. (C), AL, *438*
Management Recruiters of Mobile Co., Inc. (C), AL, *438*
Management Recruiters of Birmingham (C), AL, *438*
Management Recruiters of Tucson (C), AZ, *439*
Management Recruiters of Little Rock (C), AR, *439*

Management Recruiters Tucson-Foothills, Inc. (C), AZ, *439*
Management Recruiters Peninsula (C), CA, *439*
Management Recruiters of Fresno (C), CA, *440*
Management Recruiters of Clovis (C), CA, *440*
Management Recruiters Dana Point (C), CA, *440*
Management Recruiters of Colorado Springs (C), CO, *441*
Management Recruiters of Roseville (C), CA, *441*
Management Recruiters of Pleasanton (C), CA, *441*
Management Recruiters of Sacramento North (C), CA, *441*
Management Recruiters Inc. of Silicon Valley (C), CA, *441*
Management Recruiters of Winsted, Inc. (C), CT, *442*
Management Recruiters of Franktown (C), CO, *442*
Management Recruiters of Altamonte (C), FL, *442*
Management Recruiters of Clearwater (C), FL, *443*
Management Recruiters of Melbourne, Inc. (C), FL, *443*
Management Recruiters of St. Lucie County, Inc. (C), FL, *444*
Management Recruiters of Tampa North (C), FL, *444*
Management Recruiters of St. Augustine (C), FL, *444*
Management Recruiters of Forsyth County (C), GA, *445*
Management Recruiters of Columbus, Inc. (C), GA, *445*
Management Recruiters of Venice, Inc. (C), FL, *445*
Management Recruiters of Atlanta (C), GA, *445*
Management Recruiters of Savannah (C), GA, *446*
Management Recruiters of Atlanta North, Inc. (C), GA, *446*
Management Recruiters of Marietta, Inc. (C), GA, *446*
Management Recruiters of Batavia (C), IL, *447*
Management Recruiters of Chicago West (C), IL, *447*
Management Recruiters of Chicago-North Shore (C), IL, *447*
Management Recruiters of Noblesville, Inc. (C), IN, *448*
Management Recruiters of Spencer (C), IA, *448*
Management Recruiters of Indianapolis (C), IN, *448*
Management Recruiters of South Bend (C), IN, *448*
Management Recruiters of Indianapolis-North (C), IN, *448*
Management Recruiters-Cedar Rapids, Inc. (C), IA, *448*
Management Recruiters - Indianapolis (C), IN, *448*
Management Recruiters of Fairfield (C), IA, *449*
Management Recruiters of Des Moines (C), IA, *449*
Management Recruiters of Rockville (C), MD, *450*
Management Recruiters of Frederick, Inc. (C), MD, *450*
Management Recruiters of Washington, DC Inc. (C), MD, *450*
Management Recruiters of the Baltimore Washington Corridor (C), MD, *450*
Management Recruiters of Birmingham (C), MI, *451*
Management Recruiters of Baltimore (C), MD, *451*
Management Recruiters of Dearborn, Inc. (C), MI, *451*
Management Recruiters of Rochester (C), MN, *452*
Management Recruiters of Woodbury (C), MN, *452*
Management Recruiters of Chanhassen (C), MN, *452*
Management Recruiters of North Oakland County, Inc. (C), MI, *452*
Management Recruiters of Bloomington (C), MN, *452*
Management Recruiters of Lake Tahoe, NV (C), NV, *453*
Management Recruiters of Bay Head (C), NJ, *453*
Management Recruiters of Morris County, NJ (C), NJ, *453*
Management Recruiters of Orange County, N.Y., Inc. (C), NJ, *453*
Management Recruiters of Reno (C), NV, *453*
Management Recruiters of Princeton (C), NJ, *454*
Management Recruiters of The Sandias (C), NM, *454*
Management Recruiters of New Providence (C), NJ, *454*
Management Recruiters of Broome County, Inc. (C), NY, *454*
Management Recruiters of Cedar Mountain (C), NC, *455*
Management Recruiters of Woodbury Inc. (C), NY, *455*
Management Recruiters - Kannapolis (C), NC, *456*
Management Recruiters of Charlotte - North, Inc. (C), NC, *456*
Management Recruiters of Boone (C), NC, *456*
Management Recruiters of Dayton, Inc. (C), OH, *457*
Management Recruiters of Columbus (C), OH, *457*
Management Recruiters of Cleveland (C), OH, *457*
Management Recruiters of Oklahoma City (C), OK, *458*
Management Recruiters of Easton, PA (C), PA, *458*
Management Recruiters - North Canton, Inc. (C), OH, *458*
Management Recruiters of Northwest Ohio, Inc. (C), OH, *458*
Management Recruiters of Youngstown (C), OH, *458*
Management Recruiters of Cherry Hill (C), PA, *459*
Management Recruiters of Valley Forge (C), PA, *459*
Management Recruiters of Pittsburgh (C), PA, *459*
Management Recruiters of Pittsburgh-North, Inc. (C), PA, *460*
Management Recruiters of Puerto Rico (C), PR, *460*
Management Recruiters of North Charleston (C), SC, *460*
Management Recruiters of Florence (C), SC, *460*
Management Recruiters of Chattanooga-Brainerd, Inc. (C), TN, *461*
Management Recruiters of Sioux Falls, LLP (C), SD, *461*
Management Recruiters of Georgetown (C), SC, *461*
Management Recruiters of Travelers Rest, Inc. (C), SC, *461*
Management Recruiters of Houston (C), TX, *462*
Management Recruiters Dallas North (MRDN) (C), TX, *462*
Management Recruiters of Austin (C), TX, *462*
Management Recruiters of LBJ Park/Dallas (C), TX, *462*
Management Recruiters of San Marcos (C), TX, *463*
Management Recruiters of Salt Lake City (C), UT, *464*
Management Recruiters of Fairfax, VA (C), VA, *464*
Management Recruiters of Arlington (C), VA, *464*
Management Recruiters of Sugar Land Inc. (C), TX, *464*
Management Recruiters Int'l.-The Woodlands (C), TX, *464*
Management Recruiters of Milwaukee-West (C), WI, *465*
Management Recruiters of Loudoun County South (C), VA, *465*
Management Recruiters of Spokane (C), WA, *465*
Management Recruiters of Appleton (C), WI, *465*
Management Recruiters of Wausau, LLC (C), WI, *466*
Management Recruiters of Stevens Point, Inc. (C), WI, *466*
Management Recruiters of Milwaukee - Downtown (C), WI, *466*
Management Recruiters of Cheyenne (C), WY, *466*
Management Resource Assoc., Inc. (C), FL, *467*
Management Resource Group, Inc. (C), NY, *467*
Management Search Int'l. (C), CA, *467*

Management Search, Inc. (C), IL, *467*
Management Search of R.I. Inc. (R), RI, *135*
Management Solutions, Inc. (C), WA, *468*
Management Solutions, Inc. (C), CA, *468*
Mancini Technical Recruiting (C), VA, *468*
Mangieri/Solutions LLC (C), CT, *468*
Mankuta Gallagher & Assoc., Inc. (C), FL, *468*
F. L. Mannix & Co. (R), MA, *135*
ManTech Consulting (C), NY, *468*
MARBL Consultants, Inc. (C), WI, *469*
Marentz & Co. (C), TX, *469*
Mark Adam Assoc. (R), NJ, *135*
J. L. Mark Assoc., Inc. (R), CO, *135*
Mark Christian & Assoc., Inc. (C), AZ, *469*
Markent Personnel, Inc. (C), WI, *470*
Market Niche Consulting (C), AZ, *470*
Marks & Co., Inc. (R), CT, *136*
Paula Marks Inc. (R), NY, *136*
Brad Marks Int'l. (R), CA, *136*
The Marlow Group (R), MA, *136*
The Maroon Group (R), CT, *136*
Marra Peters & Partners (R), NJ, *136*
Marsar & Co., Inc. (C), FL, *471*
Karen Marshall Assoc. (C), KY, *471*
Marshall-Alan Assoc., Inc. (C), NY, *471*
Donovan Martin & Assoc. (R), CA, *137*
J. Martin & Assoc. (R), CA, *137*
The Martin Group (R), CA, *137*
Martin Partners, L.L.C. (R), IL, *137*
The Martwick Group, Inc. (C), OR, *472*
Marvel Consultants, Inc. (C), OH, *472*
Masserman & Assoc., Inc. (R), NY, *138*
Massey-Horton Int'l. (R), ON, *138*
Richard L. Mather & Assoc. (C), CT, *472*
Matté & Company, Inc. (R), CT, *138*
Matte Consulting Group Inc. (R), QE, *138*
Matthews & Stephens Assoc., Inc. (C), CT, *472*
The Matthews Group, Inc. (C), NJ, *472*
Paul May & Assoc. (C), IL, *473*
The Mayes Group, Ltd. (R), PA, *139*
Mayhall Search Group, Inc. (C), IN, *473*
The Mazzitelli Group, Ltd. (R), MN, *139*
McBride Assoc., Inc. (R), DC, *139*
K. E. McCarthy & Assoc. (R), CA, *139*
McCormack & Farrow (R), CA, *140*
The McCormick Group (C), VA, *473*
McCormick Search Inc. (C), IL, *474*
McCoy Ltd. (C), CA, *474*
McDonald Assoc. Int'l. (R), IL, *140*
McDonald, Long & Assoc., Inc. (R), NY, *140*
McDowell & Co., Recruiters (C), TX, *474*
Clarence E. McFeely, Inc. (R), IL, *141*
McGrath & Assoc., Inc. (R), NJ, *141*
McHale & Assoc. (R), WA, *141*
McIntyre Management Resources (C), ON, *474*
McKee Cyber Search (C), MS, *475*
The McKinnon Management Group Inc. (C), ON, *475*
Dan P. McLean Assoc., Inc. (C), ON, *475*
MDR & Associates (C), AR, *476*
Med Exec Int'l. (C), CA, *476*
MediaCOM Talent Group (C), MA, *476*
MedSearch Resources, Inc. (C), FL, *478*
MedXec USA, Inc. (C), FL, *478*
Mehta Consulting (C), NJ, *478*
Meng, Finseth & Assoc., Inc. (R), CA, *143*
Mercedes & Co., Inc. (R), MA, *143*
J. M. Meredith & Assoc. Inc. (C), CA, *479*
MESA, Inc. (R), CO, *143*
MESA International (C), CA, *480*
Messett Assoc., Inc. (R), FL, *143*
META/MAT, Ltd. (R), NJ, *144*
MGA Executive Search (C), FL, *480*
Michael James & Co. (C), IL, *480*
Michael Thomas, Inc. (C), OH, *480*
Michael/Merrill (C), KS, *481*
E. J. Michaels, Ltd. (C), NY, *481*
Micro Staff Solutions, Inc. (C), TX, *481*
Midas Management (C), CT, *481*
Midland Consultants (C), OH, *481*
Millennium Search Group, Inc. (R), CA, *144*
Miller Denver (C), CO, *482*
Miller-Hall HRISearch (C), NY, *482*
Danette Milne Corporate Search Inc. (C), ON, *482*
Milo Research (R), NY, *145*
Herbert Mines Assoc., Inc. (R), NY, *145*
Mirtz Morice, Inc. (R), CT, *145*
MIS Computer Professionals, Inc. (C), KS, *482*
Paul Misarti Inc. (C), NY, *483*
Mitchell Martin Inc. (C), NY, *483*
MJF Assoc. (C), CT, *483*
MLA Resources, Inc. (C), OK, *483*
Modis (C), MD, *483*
Moffitt Int'l., Inc. (R), NC, *146*
Mogul Consultants, Inc. (C), NY, *483*
Molecular Solutions, Inc. (C), SC, *483*
Molloy Partners (R), NY, *146*
Monarch Technology Management LLC (C), CO, *484*
Montenido Assoc. (R), CA, *146*
Montgomery West (R), CA, *146*
Larry Moore & Assoc. (C), CA, *484*
Mordue, Allen, Roberts, Bonney Ltd. (C), WA, *485*
Morency Assoc. (C), MA, *485*
Morgan & Assoc. (C), MA, *485*
Morgan Hunter Corp. (C), KS, *485*
Morgan/Webber, Inc. (R), NY, *147*
The Morley Group (C), IN, *486*
Robert T. Morton Assoc., Inc. (C), MA, *486*
MRF Enterprises, Inc. (C), TX, *486*
MRI, The Sequel Group, LLC (C), CO, *486*
Mruk & E.M.A. Partners (R), NY, *148*
MSI Int'l. (C), GA, *486*
Mulcahy Co. (C), WI, *487*
Pamela L. Mulligan, Inc. (R), NH, *149*
The Mulshine Co., Inc. (R), NJ, *149*
Multi Processing, Inc. (R), NH, *149*
Jennifer Munro & Partners, Inc. (R), SC, *149*
Kenneth Murphy & Assoc. (C), NS, *487*
Murphy Partners Int'l. (R), IL, *150*
The MVP Group (C), NY, *487*
Mycoff & Assoc. (R), CO, *150*
Myers Career Assoc., Inc. (C), CA, *488*
DDJ Myers, Ltd. (R), AZ, *150*
Nadzam, Lusk, Horgan & Assoc., Inc. (R), CA, *150*
Nason & Nason (C), FL, *488*
National Computerized Employment Service, Inc. (C), PA, *489*
National Corporate Consultants, Inc. (C), IN, *489*
National Executive (C), ON, *489*
National Field Service Corp. (C), NY, *489*
National Metal Services Corp. (C), IN, *489*
National Recruiters (C), OK, *489*
National Search Assoc. (C), CA, *490*
Nationwide Personnel Placement, Inc. (C), OH, *490*
NCC Executive Search Consultants (C), CA, *490*
The NEIS Corp., Inc. (C), FL, *491*
J. Fielding Nelson & Assoc., Inc. (R), UT, *151*
Len Nelson & Assoc., Inc. (C), TX, *491*
The Network Corporate Search Personnel Inc. (C), AB, *491*
Networking Unlimited of NH, Inc. (C), NH, *491*
New Dimensions in Technology, Inc. (C), MA, *492*
New Directions, Inc. (C), IL, *492*
New World Healthcare Solutions, Inc. (R), NY, *151*
Newcomb-Desmond & Assoc., Inc. (C), OH, *492*
Newman-Johnson-King, Inc. (C), TX, *492*
Newport Management (C), NY, *492*
Newport Strategic Search LLC (C), CA, *492*
Next Step Recruiting (C), CA, *493*
NHA Plastics Recruiters (C), FL, *493*
Nichols & Company (R), CO, *151*
Marc Nichols Assoc., Inc. (C), NY, *493*
The Niemond Corp. (R), CA, *152*
Ira Z. Nitzberg (C), NY, *493*
Noll Human Resource Services (C), NE, *494*
W. D. Nolte & Company (R), CT, *152*
Nordeman Grimm, Inc. (R), NY, *152*
Norgate Technology, Inc. (C), NY, *494*
The Norland Group (C), CA, *494*
Paul Winston Norman & Assoc. (R), IL, *152*
Norman Broadbent Int'l., Inc. (R), NY, *152*
The North Peak Group (C), OH, *496*
Northland Employment Services Inc. (C), MN, *496*
NorthStar Technologies, Inc. (C), NY, *496*
Norton & Assoc. (C), IL, *496*
NPS of Atlanta, Inc. (C), GA, *496*
Nuessle, Kurdziel & Weiss, Inc. (R), PA, *153*
NYCOR Search, Inc. (C), MN, *497*
O'Brien Consulting Services (R), MA, *153*
O'Callaghan Honey/Ray & Berndtson Inc. (R), AB, *153*
O'Connor, O'Connor, Lordi, Ltd. (R), PA, *154*
O'Connor Resources (C), TX, *497*
O'Keefe & Assoc. (C), TX, *497*
O'Keefe & Assoc., Inc. (R), CT, *154*
O'Neill Group (C), NJ, *498*
O'Shea, Divine & Co., Inc. (R), CA, *154*
O'Toole & Company, Inc. (R), IL, *154*
Ober & Company (R), CA, *155*
Object Resources Int'l., Inc. (C), CT, *498*

Odell & Assoc., Inc. (C), TX, *498*
The Oldani Group (R), WA, *155*
Ollinger Partners (R), MA, *156*
Omnisearch Assoc. (C), CA, *499*
The Onstott Group (R), MA, *156*
Open Concepts (C), CA, *499*
The Options Group, Inc. (C), NY, *499*
Opus Marketing (R), CA, *156*
Organization Consulting Ltd. (R), ON, *157*
Orion Int'l. Consulting Group, Inc. (C), NC, *499*
Ott & Hansen, Inc. (R), CA, *157*
Robert Ottke Assoc. (R), CA, *157*
LaMonte Owens, Inc. (R), PA, *157*
The Oxford Group (C), TX, *500*
The P & L Group (C), NY, *500*
P.R.H. Management, Inc. (R), CT, *158*
Pacific Crossing (C), CA, *501*
Pacific Search Group, Inc. (C), CA, *501*
T. Page & Assoc. (C), TX, *502*
Page-Wheatcroft & Co., Ltd. (R), TX, *158*
The Pailin Group Professional Search Consultants (R), TX, *158*
Paladin Group, Inc. (C), CO, *502*
Arthur Pann Assoc., Inc. (C), NY, *502*
Paragon Recruiting Officials Inc. (C), OH, *502*
Parenica & Co. (R), NC, *159*
Jim Parham & Assoc., Inc. (R), FL, *159*
The Park Group & Assoc., Inc. (C), MD, *502*
Parker Page Group (C), FL, *503*
Largent Parks & Partners (C), TX, *503*
Parsons Assoc. Inc. (R), IL, *159*
Partners In Human Resources Int'l., Inc. (R), NY, *160*
Partners in Recruiting (C), IL, *503*
The Partners, LLC (C), CA, *504*
Partnervision Consulting Group Inc. (R), ON, *160*
Partridge Assoc., Inc. (R), MA, *160*
Pascale & LaMorte, LLC (C), CT, *504*
Carolyn Smith Paschal Int'l. (R), CA, *160*
Pasona Canada, Inc. (C), ON, *504*
Pathway Executive Search, Inc. (C), NY, *505*
The Patience Motivation Belief Group, Inc. (C), GA, *505*
Patriot Assoc. (C), PA, *505*
Paul-Tittle Assoc., Inc. (R), VA, *161*
PC Assoc. (C), CO, *505*
Peachtree Executive Search (R), GA, *161*
Peak Search Assoc. (C), ON, *506*
Peck & Assoc., Ltd. (R), WI, *161*
Peden & Assoc. (C), CA, *506*
M. A. Pelle Assoc., Inc. (C), NY, *506*
People Management Mid-South, LLC (R), TN, *162*
People Management Northeast, Inc. (R), CT, *162*
PeopleSource Inc. (C), TX, *506*
PERI Corp/Professional Executive Recruiters, Inc. (C), TX, *507*
Perry • Newton Assoc. (C), MD, *507*
Perry Search Assoc. (C), CA, *507*
Perry-Martel Int'l., Inc. (R), ON, *163*
Personnel Alliance Group (C), NJ, *507*
Personnel Assoc. (C), NC, *508*
Personnel, Inc. (C), AL, *508*
Personnel Incorporated (C), IA, *508*
Personnel Management Group (C), MB, *508*
Personnel Unlimited/Executive Search (C), WA, *509*
J. R. Peterman Assoc., Inc. (C), VT, *509*
Alec Peters Assoc. Inc./DLR (R), GA, *163*
Richard Peterson & Assoc., Inc. (R), GA, *163*
Petro Staff Int'l. (C), AB, *509*
Peyser Assoc., Inc. (R), FL, *163*
Robert E. Pfaendler & Assoc., Inc. (C), OR, *509*
PHD Conseil en Ressources Humaines Inc. (C), QE, *510*
Phillips & Assoc. (R), MA, *164*
Phillips Assoc. (C), FL, *510*
Phillips Int'l., Inc. (C), SC, *510*
Phillips Personnel/Search (C), CO, *510*
Phillips Resource Group (C), SC, *510*
Phoenix Search (R), MX, *164*
Physician Associates (C), HI, *511*
Picard Int'l., Ltd. (R), NY, *164*
Pinnacle Executive Group Inc. (C), MO, *512*
The Pinnacle Source, Inc. (C), CO, *512*
Pinton Forrest & Madden/EMA Partners Int'l. (R), BC, *165*
Pioneer Consulting Group (C), CA, *512*
PKS Assoc., Inc. (C), RI, *513*
Place Mart Personnel Service (C), NJ, *513*
Placement Testart Inc. (C), QE, *513*
Plante & Moran, LLP (R), MI, *165*
R. L. Plimpton Assoc., Inc. (R), CO, *165*
Plummer & Assoc., Inc. (R), CT, *166*
Poirier, Hoevel & Co. (R), CA, *166*
The Polen Group (C), PA, *514*
The Pollack Group (C), ON, *514*
Polson & Co., Inc. (R), MN, *166*
Al Ponaman Company, Inc. (C), CA, *514*
Porter & Assoc., Inc. (C), FL, *514*
Jack Porter Assoc., Inc. (C), WA, *514*
David Powell, Inc. (R), CA, *166*
Norman Powers Assoc., Inc. (C), MA, *515*
Powers Consultants, Inc. (R), MO, *166*
PPS Information Systems Staffing (C), MD, *515*
Prairie Resource Group, Inc. (R), IL, *166*
Elan Pratzer & Partners Inc. (R), ON, *167*
PRAXIS Partners (R), VA, *167*
Predictor Systems Corp. (R), CA, *167*
Preferred Professional Recruiters (C), OH, *516*
Preferred Professional Recruiters (C), TX, *516*
George Preger & Associates Inc. (R), ON, *167*
Premier Search Group (C), IN, *517*
Preng & Assoc., Inc. (R), TX, *167*
Presley Consultants, Inc. (C), CA, *517*
Preston-Hunter, Inc. (R), IL, *167*
Prestonwood Assoc. (R), MA, *168*
Price & Assoc., Inc. (C), VA, *518*
Alan J. Price Assoc., Inc. (C), RI, *518*
PricewaterhouseCoopers Executive Search (R), ON, *168*
PricewaterhouseCoopers Executive Search (R), MX, *168*
Prime Management Group Inc. (C), ON, *518*
Primus Assoc., L.C. (R), TX, *169*
Princeton Executive Search (C), NJ, *518*
Princeton Search Partners, Inc. (R), NJ, *169*
Prior/Martech Assoc., Inc. (R), WA, *169*
PRO, Inc./Professional Recruiting Offices, Inc. (C), CA, *519*
Pro Tec Technical Services (C), ON, *519*
Pro-Tech Search, Inc. (C), IL, *519*
Procom (C), ON, *519*
Professional Careers, Inc. (C), NC, *520*
Professional Consulting Network, Inc. (C), CA, *520*
Professional Employment Group (C), MD, *520*
Professional Engineering Technical Personnel Consultants (C), NC, *520*
Professional Personnel Consultants, Inc. (C), MI, *521*
Professional Persons Career Services (C), NY, *521*
Professional Placement Assoc., Inc. (C), NY, *521*
Professional Recruiters (C), UT, *521*
Professional Recruiting Consultants, Inc. (C), DE, *521*
Professional Search (R), MI, *169*
Professional Search Assoc. (C), CA, *522*
Professional Search Centre, Ltd. (C), IL, *522*
Professional Search Consultants (PSC) (C), TX, *523*
Professional Search, Inc. Int'l. (C), TX, *523*
Professional Selection Services (R), GA, *169*
Professional Support Inc. (C), NY, *523*
Professional Team Search, Inc. (R), AZ, *169*
Professionals in Recruiting Co. (C), TN, *523*
Profit Pros, Inc. (C), CA, *523*
ProLink (C), NC, *524*
ProNet, Inc. (C), NC, *524*
ProSearch Recruiting (C), CA, *524*
ProSearch, Inc. (C), PA, *524*
ProSearch, Inc. (C), ME, *524*
ProStar Systems, Inc. (C), MD, *525*
Protocol Inc. (C), CA, *525*
PSD Group, Inc. (C), CA, *525*
PSP Agency (C), NY, *525*
Quality Consulting Group, Inc. (C), WI, *526*
Quality Search Inc. (C), OH, *526*
Quantum EDP Recruiting Services (C), QE, *526*
Quest Enterprises, Ltd. (C), IL, *527*
The Quest Organization (C), NY, *527*
Quest Worldwide Executive Search Corp. (C), CA, *527*
L. J. Quinn & Assoc., Inc. (R), CA, *170*
Quiring Assoc., Inc. (C), IN, *527*
QVS Int'l. (R), GA, *170*
R & L Assoc., Ltd. (R), NY, *170*
R. J. Associates (C), NY, *528*
R2 Services, LLC (C), IL, *528*
Raines Int'l. Inc. (R), NY, *171*
Ramm Search (C), NY, *528*

Rand Thompson Executive Search Consultants (C), NY, *528*
J. E. Ranta Assoc. (C), MA, *529*
Joanne E. Ratner Search (C), NY, *529*
Ray & Berndtson/Laurendeau Labrecque (R), QE, *172*
Ray & Berndtson/Lovas Stanley (R), ON, *172*
Ray & Berndtson/Tanton Mitchell (R), BC, *173*
Raymond Karsan Assoc. (C), PA, *529*
Razzino-Claymore Assoc. (C), NJ, *530*
RBW Assoc. Inc. (C), OR, *531*
Re-Mark Assoc. Inc. (C), NJ, *531*
Recruit Xpress (C), TX, *531*
Recruiting Assoc. of Amarillo (C), TX, *531*
Recruiting Services Group, Inc. (C), TN, *532*
The Recruitment Group, Inc. (C), NY, *532*
Recruitment Specialists, Inc. (C), MD, *532*
Redden-Shaffer Group (R), CA, *173*
Redell Search, Inc. (C), IL, *533*
Redwood Partners Ltd. (R), NY, *173*
Reece & Mruk Partners/EMA Partners Int'l. (R), MA, *173*
Reeder & Assoc., Ltd. (R), GA, *173*
Cedric L. Reese Inc. (C), CA, *533*
The Regency Group, Ltd. (C), NE, *533*
Michael James Reid & Co. (R), CA, *174*
Reid Ellis Assoc. Inc. (C), ON, *533*
The Douglas Reiter Co., Inc. (R), OR, *174*
RemTech Business Solutions, Inc. (C), MI, *534*
The Renaissance Network (C), MA, *534*
Renaissance Resources, LLC (R), VA, *174*
Resource Networking Inc. (C), IN, *534*
Resource Recruiting (C), NH, *534*
Resource Services, Inc. (C), NY, *534*
Response Staffing Services (C), NY, *534*
L. J. Reszotko & Assoc. (C), IL, *535*
Retained Search Assoc. (R), NC, *176*
Retis Assoc., Inc. (C), IL, *535*
S. Reyman & Assoc., Ltd. (R), IL, *176*
Russell Reynolds Assoc., Inc. (R), NY, *176*
Reynolds Consulting Int'l. (R), ON, *177*
RGE (C), VA, *535*
RHAssoc. Inc. (C), KS, *535*
RHI Consulting (C), VA, *536*
RHS Assoc. (C), AL, *536*
RIC Corp. (R), FL, *177*
Rice Cohen Int'l. (R), PA, *178*
Richard, Wayne & Roberts (C), TX, *536*
The Richards Group (C), PA, *536*
W. F. Richer Assoc., Inc. (C), NY, *536*
Jack Richman & Assoc. (C), FL, *537*
Richmond Assoc. (C), NY, *537*
Riddle & McGrath LLC (R), GA, *178*
Ridenour & Assoc. (R), IL, *178*
Right/McKee Consulting Group (C), TX, *537*
Ritech Management Inc. (C), NY, *537*
Ritta Professional Search Inc. (C), NY, *538*
The Riverbend Group (C), MO, *538*
RJ Associates (C), CA, *538*
RLM Assoc., Ltd. (R), NY, *179*
Roberson & Co. (C), AZ, *538*
Robert Shields & Assoc. (C), TX, *538*
Robert William James & Assoc. (C), OR, *539*
Norman Roberts & Assoc., Inc. (R), CA, *179*
Roberts Ryan & Bentley, Inc. (R), MD, *179*
V. Robinson & Co., Inc. (C), MO, *539*
Bruce Robinson Assoc. (R), NJ, *180*
Robinson, Fraser Group Ltd. (R), ON, *180*
Robison & Associates (R), NC, *180*
Roevin Technical People (C), ON, *540*
The Rogan Group, Inc. (C), CA, *541*
Rogers - McManamon Executive Search (R), CA, *180*
ROI International, Inc. (R), WA, *181*
Roll International (C), TX, *541*
Romac Int'l. - San Francisco (C), CA, *541*
Romac Int'l. (C), GA, *541*
Romac Int'l. (C), PA, *542*
Romac Int'l. Inc. (R), MA, *181*
Romac Int'l., Inc. (C), FL, *542*
Romano McAvoy Assoc., Inc. (C), NY, *544*
Romeo-Hudgins & Assoc., Ltd. (C), NJ, *544*
W. R. Rosato & Assoc., Inc. (R), NY, *182*
Emery A. Rose & Assoc. (C), WA, *545*
Rosenfeld & Co., Inc. (C), MI, *545*
Ross Personnel Consultants, Inc. (C), CT, *545*
The Rossi Search Group (C), PA, *545*
Roth Young Executive Search (C), TX, *546*
Roth Young of Tampa (C), FL, *546*
Roth Young Personnel Services of Washington, DC (C), MD, *546*
Rovner & Assoc., Inc. (R), IL, *182*
Rovner Gerner & Assoc. (R), CA, *182*
Rowland Assoc. (C), CA, *547*
The Rubinic Consulting Group (C), OH, *548*
Ruderfer & Co., Inc. (C), NJ, *548*
Louis Rudzinsky Assoc., Inc. (C), MA, *548*
Rusher, Loscavio & LoPresto (R), CA, *183*
Russillo/Gardner/Spolsino (C), MA, *548*
The Ryan Charles Group, Inc. (C), FL, *548*
S-H-S TechStaff (C), PA, *549*
S. P. Assoc., Inc. (C), NC, *550*
S.C.S. & Assoc. (C), NC, *550*
R. S. Sadow Assoc. (C), NJ, *550*
Sage Employment Recruiters (C), IN, *550*
Sales Consultants of Birmingham (C), AL, *555*
Sales Consultants Int'l. of Oakland (C), CA, *556*
Sales Consultants Peninsula, Inc. (C), CA, *556*
Sales Consultants of Scottsdale, Inc. (C), AZ, *556*
Sales Consultants of Silicon Valley (C), CA, *556*
Sales Consultants of Ft. Myers, Inc. (C), FL, *557*
Sales Consultants of Danbury (C), CT, *557*
Sales Consultants of Denver (C), CO, *557*
Sales Consultants (C), IL, *558*
Sales Consultants of Western McHenry County (C), IL, *558*
Sales Consultants of Honolulu (C), HI, *558*
Sales Consultants of Barrington (C), IL, *558*
Sales Consultants of Indianapolis-North (C), IN, *558*
Sales Consultants of Rockville, MD (C), MD, *559*
Sales Consultants of Baltimore (C), MD, *559*
Sales Consultants of Birmingham (C), MI, *559*
Sales Consultants of Farmington Hills (C), MI, *560*
Sales Consultants Bridgewater, Inc. (C), NJ, *560*
Sales Consultants of Cherry Hill (C), NJ, *560*
Sales Consultants of Raleigh-Durham-RTP (C), NC, *561*
Sales Consultants of Harrisburg (C), PA, *561*
Sales Consultants of Westchester-South, Inc. (C), NY, *561*
Sales Consultants of Austin, Inc. (C), TX, *562*
Sales Consultants of Pittsburgh (C), PA, *562*
Sales Consultants King of Prussia (C), PA, *562*
Sales Consultants of Houston (C), TX, *563*
Sampson Medical Search (C), CA, *564*
George D. Sandel Assoc. (C), MA, *565*
Norm Sanders Assoc., Inc. (R), NJ, *184*
Sanders Management Assoc., Inc. (C), NJ, *565*
Sanford Rose Assoc. - Santa Ana (C), CA, *565*
Sanford Rose Assoc. - Laguna Beach (C), CA, *565*
Sanford Rose Assoc. - Mobile (C), AL, *565*
Sanford Rose Assoc. - Santa Barbara (C), CA, *565*
Sanford Rose Assoc. - Anaheim (C), CA, *566*
Sanford Rose Assoc. - Norcross (C), GA, *566*
Sanford Rose Assoc. - Chicago (C), IL, *566*
Sanford Rose Assoc. - Rockford (C), IL, *567*
Sanford Rose Assoc. - Orland Park (C), IL, *567*
Sanford Rose Assoc. - Carmel, IN (C), IN, *567*
Sanford Rose Assoc. - Louisville (C), KY, *567*
Sanford Rose Assoc. - Springfield (C), MO, *568*
Sanford Rose Assoc. - Charlotte (C), NC, *568*
Sanford Rose Assoc. - Amherst, NY (C), NY, *568*
Sanford Rose Assoc. - Rochester (C), MI, *568*
Sanford Rose Assoc. - Burlington, NC (C), NC, *569*
Sanford Rose Assoc. - Columbus North (C), OH, *569*
Sanford Rose Assoc. - Euclid (C), OH, *569*
Sanford Rose Assoc. - Akron (C), OH, *569*
Sanford Rose Assoc. - Youngstown (C), OH, *569*
Sanford Rose Assoc. - Philadelphia North (C), PA, *570*

Sanford Rose Assoc. - Columbia (C), SC, *570*
Sanford Rose Assoc. - Pittsburgh North (C), PA, *570*
Sanford Rose Assoc. - Salt Lake City (C), UT, *571*
Santangelo Consultants Inc. (C), NY, *571*
Sarver & Carruth Assoc. (C), OK, *571*
Sathe & Associates, Inc. (R), MN, *184*
Saviar, Inc. (C), AZ, *571*
Savoy Partners, Ltd. (R), DC, *184*
Schattle & Duquette (C), RI, *571*
Schlatter & Assoc. (C), CA, *572*
Schulenburg & Assoc. (C), GA, *572*
Schuyler Assoc., Ltd. (R), GA, *185*
Robert Scott Assoc. (C), NJ, *573*
Search & Recruit Int'l. (C), VA, *573*
The Search Alliance, Inc. (R), FL, *186*
Search America, Inc. (C), MA, *574*
Search Assoc., Inc. (C), NJ, *574*
Search Assoc., Inc. (C), CA, *574*
Search Bureau Int'l. (C), IL, *574*
Search By Design (C), AZ, *574*
The Search Committee (C), MD, *574*
Search Consultants, LLC (C), MD, *575*
Search Group (C), CA, *575*
Search Int'l. (R), MA, *187*
Search Research Assoc., Inc. (R), MA, *187*
Search Solutions Inc. (C), CA, *576*
SearchCorp (C), FL, *577*
SearchCorp International (C), AB, *577*
Searchline Services, Inc. (C), OH, *577*
SearchOne, Inc. (C), AR, *577*
Searchworks, Inc. (C), FL, *577*
Seco & Zetto Assoc., Inc. (C), NJ, *577*
Secura/Burnett Partners (R), CA, *187*
Sedlar & Miners (R), NY, *188*
J. R. Seehusen Assoc., Inc. (R), IA, *188*
Segal & Assoc. (C), GA, *578*
Selectis Corp. (C), IL, *578*
Selective Management Services, Inc. (C), FL, *578*
Selective Search Associates (C), OH, *578*
Sensible Solutions, Inc. (R), IL, *188*
Setford-Shaw-Najarian Assoc. (C), NY, *579*
Sevcor Int'l., Inc. (R), IL, *188*
Sharp Placement Professionals, Inc. (C), NY, *579*
Sharrow & Assoc., Inc. (C), MI, *579*
M. B. Shattuck & Assoc., Inc. (R), CA, *189*
Shell Technology Group (C), CA, *580*
Shepherd Bueschel & Provus, Inc. (R), IL, *189*
Sherwood Lehman Massucco, Inc. (R), CA, *189*
Shinn & Assoc. (R), CA, *189*
Michael Shirley Assoc. Inc. (R), KS, *190*
E. L. Shore & Assoc. (R), ON, *190*
Shore Asociados Ejecutivos, S. A. de C.V. (R), MX, *190*
M. Shulman, Inc. (R), CA, *191*
Peter Siegel & Co. (C), MA, *581*
Siger & Assoc., LLC (C), CT, *581*
The Silicon Network (C), ON, *581*
L. A. Silver Assoc., Inc. (R), MA, *191*
Silver Associates (C), CA, *581*
SilverSands Int'l. (C), FL, *582*
Daniel A. Silverstein Assoc. Inc. (R), FL, *191*
D. J. Simpson Assoc. Inc. (R), ON, *191*
Simpson Associates (C), NY, *582*
Sinclair & Co., Inc. (R), MA, *192*
Sink, Walker, Boltrus Int'l. (R), MA, *192*
SKB Enterprises (C), NY, *582*
Skipping Stone Inc. (C), VA, *582*
Ruth Sklar Assoc., Inc. (RSA Executive Search) (R), NY, *192*
Skott/Edwards Consultants (R), NY, *192*
Slayton Int'l., Inc. (R), IL, *192*
J. L. Small Assoc. (C), AL, *583*
Smartsource Inc. (C), CA, *583*
Smith & Assoc. (C), CA, *583*
Smith & Assoc. (C), FL, *583*
Smith & Sawyer, Inc. (R), NY, *193*
Smith Assoc. (C), IA, *584*
G. L. Smith Assoc. (C), CA, *584*
Herman Smith Executive Initiatives Inc. (R), ON, *193*
Smith James Group, Inc. (R), GA, *194*
Smith, Roth & Squires (R), NY, *194*
Smith Search, S.C. (R), MX, *194*
A. William Smyth, Inc. (R), CA, *194*
Snelling Search (C), IL, *585*
Snelling Search (C), AL, *585*
Snelling Search - Transportation Division (C), AR, *585*
Snelling Search (C), LA, *586*
Snelling Search Recruiters (C), NC, *586*
Andrea Sobel & Assoc., Inc. (C), CA, *586*
Sockwell & Assoc. (R), NC, *194*
Sofco (C), NY, *586*
Softrix, Inc. (C), NJ, *586*
SoftSearch Inc. (C), NJ, *586*
Software Engineering Solutions, Inc. (C), CA, *586*
Software Resource Consultants (C), TN, *587*
Robert Sollman & Assoc. (C), FL, *587*
Soltis Management Services (R), PA, *195*
Solutions Group (R), AL, *195*
Southern Recruiters & Consultants, Inc. (C), SC, *587*
Southport Int'l. Assoc. Inc. (C), FL, *588*
Southwest Search & Consulting, Inc. (C), AZ, *588*
Southwestern Professional Services (C), TN, *588*
Sparks, McDonough & Assoc., Inc. (C), MO, *588*
SPC Symcox Personnel Consultants (C), TX, *588*
Spear-Izzo Assoc., LLC (C), PA, *588*
Special Markets Group, Inc. (R), GA, *195*
Spectra International LLC (C), AZ, *589*
SpectraWest (C), CA, *589*
SpencerStuart (R), NY, *196*
The Spiegel Group (R), MA, *197*
Spilman & Assoc. (R), TX, *197*
Kenn Spinrad Inc. (C), PA, *589*
Splaine & Assoc., Inc. (R), CA, *198*
Spriggs & Co., Inc. (R), IL, *198*
Springer Souder & Assoc. L.L.C. (R), IL, *198*
Squires Resources Inc. (C), ON, *590*
Staff Resources, Inc. (C), SC, *590*
Staffing Edge, Inc. (C), IA, *590*
C. J. Stafford & Assoc. (C), ON, *591*
StaffWriters Plus (C), NY, *591*
Stanewick, Hart & Assoc., Inc. (C), FL, *591*
The Stanton Group, Inc. (C), IL, *591*
Starbridge Group Inc. (C), VA, *591*
STAT Search (C), NH, *592*
Steinbach & Co. (C), MA, *592*
The Stelton Group, Inc. (C), NJ, *592*
Sterling Int'l. (R), NJ, *200*
Sterling Int'l. Management Recruitment, Ltd. Inc. (C), NC, *592*
Michael Stern Assoc., Inc./Euram (R), ON, *200*
Steven Douglas Assoc. (C), FL, *593*
Stevens Assoc. (C), MA, *593*
The Stevens Group (C), CA, *593*
The Stevenson Group, Inc. (N.J.) (R), NJ, *200*
The Stewart Group (C), FL, *593*
Stewart, Stein & Scott, Ltd. (R), MN, *200*
Linford E. Stiles & Assoc., L.L.C. (R), NH, *201*
Stillinger & Assoc. (R), CA, *201*
Stone Enterprises Ltd. (C), IL, *594*
Stoneburner Assoc., Inc. (C), KS, *594*
Stoopen Asociados, S.C./EMA Partners Int'l. (R), MX, *202*
Storfer & Assoc. (C), NY, *595*
Strategic Alliance Network, Ltd. (C), OH, *595*
Strategic Alternatives (R), CA, *202*
Strategic Assoc., Inc. (C), TX, *595*
StratfordGroup (R), OH, *203*
Stratin Assoc. (C), NJ, *596*
Stroman Int'l., Inc. (R), CO, *204*
Success Seekers Connection (C), FL, *596*
Sudina Search, Inc. (C), MD, *596*
Sullivan & Assoc. (R), MI, *204*
Sullivan & Company (R), NY, *204*
Summerfield Assoc., Inc. (C), TN, *596*
The Summit Group (C), CA, *596*
Summit Search Specialists (C), TX, *596*
Survival Systems Staffing, Inc. (C), CA, *597*
Synapse Human Resource Consulting Group (R), TX, *205*
Synergistech Communications (C), CA, *597*
Synergistics Assoc. Ltd. (R), IL, *205*
Synergy 2000 (C), DC, *597*
The Synergy Organization (R), PA, *205*
Synergy Solutions, Ltd. (C), WA, *597*
Synergy Systems (C), ON, *598*
Systems Careers (C), CA, *598*
Systems One Ltd. (C), IL, *598*
Systems Personnel, Inc. (C), NY, *598*
Systems Research Group (C), CA, *598*
Systems Research Inc. (SRI) (C), IL, *598*
Systems Search (C), IL, *599*
Systems Search Group, Inc. (C), NC, *599*
T. H. Hunter, Inc. (C), MN, *599*
Tactical Alternatives (R), CA, *205*
The Talley Group (R), VA, *205*
Roy Talman & Assoc. (C), IL, *599*
Martin Stevens Tamaren & Assoc., Inc. (R), CA, *206*
Tannura & Assoc., Inc. (R), IL, *206*
Tarbex (C), DC, *599*

Tarnow Int'l. (R), NJ, *206*
Tate & Assoc., Inc. (R), NJ, *207*
Tate Consulting, Inc. (R), FL, *207*
M. L. Tawney & Assoc. (C), TX, *600*
Tax Network Resources, Inc. (C), NY, *600*
Carl J. Taylor & Co. (R), TX, *207*
Taylor Winfield (R), TX, *207*
TBC, Inc. (C), KY, *600*
TCM Enterprises (C), MD, *600*
TE, Inc. (C), IL, *600*
Team One Partners, Inc. (C), GA, *600*
TeamBuilders (C), GA, *600*
Tech 2000 (C), FL, *601*
Tech Connector Group (C), CA, *601*
Tech Consulting (C), FL, *601*
Tech Search (C), CA, *601*
Tech-Net (C), TX, *601*
Techaid Inc. (C), QE, *601*
Technical Connections, Inc. (C), CA, *601*
Technical Employment Consultants (C), PA, *602*
Technical Recruiting Consultants (C), IL, *602*
Technical Skills Consulting Inc. (R), ON, *207*
Technical Staffing Solutions (C), TX, *602*
TechNix Inc. (C), ON, *602*
Techno-Trac Systems, Inc. (C), NY, *603*
Technology Consultants Int'l. (C), CA, *603*
The Technology Group (R), IL, *208*
Technology Management Partners (R), CA, *208*
Technology Search Int'l. (C), CA, *603*
Techsearch Services Inc. (C), CT, *603*
Techstaff Inc. (C), WI, *603*
Tecmark Associates Inc. (C), NY, *604*
Tele-Media Int'l. Inc. (C), PA, *604*
Tele-Solutions of Arizona, Inc. (C), AZ, *604*
Telecom Connections, Inc. (C), TX, *604*
Telecom Recruiters, Inc. (C), VA, *605*
Telequest Communications, Inc. (C), NJ, *605*
Telford, Adams & Alexander (R), CA, *208*
Templeton & Assoc. (C), MN, *605*
The TGA Company (C), TX, *606*
Thomas & Assoc. of Michigan (C), MI, *606*
Thomas Mangum Co. (R), CA, *208*
Thomas, Whelan Assoc., Inc. (C), DC, *606*
Thor, Inc. (C), CA, *606*
Tirocchi, Wright, Inc. (R), CA, *209*
TNS Partners, Inc. (R), TX, *209*
Skip Tolette Executive Search Consulting (R), NJ, *209*
TPG & Assoc. (C), TX, *608*
Trac One (R), NJ, *210*
Trainor/Frank & Assoc. Inc. (C), WI, *608*
Trans-United Consultants Ltd. (C), ON, *608*
Travel Executive Search (C), NY, *608*
Traynor Confidential, Ltd. (C), NY, *609*
Van Treadaway Assoc., Inc. (R), GA, *210*
Triad Technology Group (C), OR, *609*
TriStaff Group (C), CA, *609*
Triumph Consulting, Inc. (R), IA, *210*
Trout & Assoc. Inc. (R), UT, *211*
Trowbridge & Co., Inc. (R), MA, *211*
The Truman Agency (C), CA, *610*
TSI Group/TSI Staffing Services (C), ON, *610*
TSS Consulting, Ltd. (C), AZ, *610*
TSW Assoc., LLC (R), CT, *211*
TTG/Sterling Services (C), CA, *610*
W. G. Tucker & Assoc. (R), PA, *211*
Tucker Assoc. (R), NJ, *211*
The Thomas Tucker Co. (R), CA, *211*
Tully/Woodmansee Int'l. Inc. (R), FL, *212*
UniQuest Int'l., Inc. (C), FL, *610*
Unisearch Search & Recruiting Inc. (C), CA, *611*
United Personnel Services (C), MA, *611*
Unlimited Staffing Solutions, Inc. (C), MI, *611*
Valentine & Assoc. (C), IL, *611*
Vento Assoc. (C), TN, *612*
Victor White Int'l. (C), CA, *612*
Vincenty & Co. (C), OH, *612*
Vlcek & Company, Inc. (R), CA, *214*
The Wabash Group (C), IN, *613*
B. D. Wallace & Assoc. (C), MD, *614*
Wallace Assoc. (C), CT, *614*
Wallace Management Co. (R), TN, *215*
J. D. Walsh & Co. (R), CT, *215*
Deborah Snow Walsh, Inc. (R), IL, *215*
Linda Walter & Associes (C), QE, *615*
Lee H. Walton & Assoc. (R), NY, *215*
Ward Assoc. (C), ON, *615*
Ward-Hoffman & Assoc. (C), ID, *615*
C. D. Warner & Assoc. (C), PA, *615*
Warren Executive Services (C), GA, *616*
Warren, Morris & Madison, Ltd. (C), CA, *616*
The Washington Firm, Ltd. (R), WA, *216*
R. J. Watkins & Co., Ltd. (R), CA, *216*
Watson Int'l., Inc. (R), NY, *216*
Waveland Int'l. (R), IL, *216*
The Wayne Group, Ltd. (C), NY, *616*
Webb, Johnson Assoc., Inc. (R), NY, *216*
S. B. Webster & Associates (R), MA, *217*
Wegner & Assoc. (C), WI, *617*
David Weinfeld Group (C), NC, *617*
Weinman & Assoc. (C), AZ, *617*
Weinpel Search, Inc. (C), NJ, *617*
Weinstein & Co. (R), MA, *217*
S. E. Weinstein Co. (R), IL, *217*
C. Weiss Assoc., Inc. (C), NY, *618*
Weliver & Assoc. (C), MI, *618*
Henry Welker & Assoc. (C), MI, *618*
Wellington Management Group (R), PA, *217*
Wells, Bradley & Assoc., Inc. (C), MN, *618*
Welzig, Lowe & Assoc. (C), CO, *618*
Werbin Assoc. Executive Search, Inc. (C), NY, *618*
Jude M. Werra & Assoc. (R), WI, *218*
Wesley Brown & Bartle Co., Inc. (R), NY, *218*
Western Technical Resources (C), CA, *619*
The Westfield Group (C), CT, *619*
Westfields Int'l., Inc. (C), NY, *619*
WestPacific National Search, Inc. (C), CA, *619*
Weterrings & Agnew, Inc. (C), NY, *619*
Wheeler Assoc. (R), CT, *219*
The Whitaker Companies (C), TX, *619*
Whitehead & Assoc., Inc. (C), MO, *620*
Arch S. Whitehead Assoc. Inc. (ASWA) (R), NY, *219*
The Whitney Group (R), NY, *219*
Whittlesey & Assoc., Inc. (R), PA, *220*
The Whyte Group, Inc. (R), MD, *220*
Wilcox Bertoux & Miller (R), CA, *220*
Wilcoxen, Blackwell, Niven & Assoc. (R), FL, *220*
Wilder & Assoc. (C), VA, *620*
Joel H. Wilensky Assoc., Inc. (C), MA, *620*
Wilkinson & Ives (R), CA, *221*
Wilkinson SoftSearch, Inc. (C), VA, *620*
Dick Williams & Assoc. (C), CA, *621*
Williams & Delmore, Inc. (C), NC, *621*
Willis & Assoc. (R), OH, *221*
The Wilmington Group (C), NC, *622*
Wilson & Assoc. Int'l. Inc. (C), FL, *622*
Wilson McLeran, Inc. (C), CT, *622*
Wilson-Douglas-Jordan (C), IL, *622*
The Windham Group (R), OH, *222*
Wing Tips & Pumps, Inc. (C), MI, *623*
Winguth, Grant & Donahue (R), CA, *222*
Winston Search, Inc. (R), MD, *222*
Winter, Wyman & Co. (C), MA, *623*
Winthrop Partners, Inc. (R), NY, *222*
Wisnewski & Assoc. (R), CA, *223*
Witt/Kieffer, Ford, Hadelman & Lloyd (R), IL, *223*
Wojdula & Assoc., Ltd. (R), WI, *223*
Woltz & Assoc., Inc. (R), IL, *224*
M. Wood Company (R), IL, *224*
Wood West & Partners Inc. (C), BC, *624*
Wood-Glavin, Inc. (R), KS, *224*
Bruce G. Woods Executive Search (R), TX, *224*
Woodworth Int'l. Group (R), OR, *224*
Worlco Computer Resources, Inc. (C), PA, *624*
World Search (C), OH, *625*
Worldwide Medical Services (C), CA, *625*
WTW Assoc., Inc. (R), NY, *225*
John Wylie Assoc., Inc. (C), OK, *625*
Dennis Wynn Assoc., Inc. (C), FL, *625*
Xavier Associates, Inc. (R), MA, *226*
The Yorkshire Group, Ltd. (C), MA, *626*
Bill Young & Assoc. (C), VA, *626*
Yours In Travel Personnel Agency, Inc. (C), NY, *626*
Yungner & Bormann (R), MN, *226*
Zaccaria Int'l. (C), NJ, *627*
The Zammataro Company (R), OH, *226*
ZanExec L.L.C. (R), VA, *226*
The Zarkin Group, Inc. (R), NY, *226*
Zeiger Assoc. L.L.C. (C), CA, *627*
Zen Zen Int'l. Inc. (C), MB, *627*
Helen Ziegler & Assoc., Inc. (C), ON, *627*
P. D. Zier Assoc. (C), CT, *627*
Zingaro & Company (R), TX, *227*
Michael D. Zinn & Assoc., Inc. (R), NJ, *227*
Zona & Assoc., Inc. (C), NY, *628*
Zwell Int'l. (R), IL, *228*

08.1 MIS management (e.g. CIO,VP-MIS)

A C Personnel Services, Inc. (C), OK, *231*
A First Resource (C), NC, *231*

A.K.S. Assoc., Ltd. (R), MA, *1*
The Abbott Group, Inc. (R), MD, *1*
Abraxas Technologies, Inc. (C), FL, *233*
Access Data Personnel, Inc. (C), NH, *233*
Acclaim Services, Inc. (C), TX, *234*
Account Ability Now (C), MI, *234*
Action Management Corp. (C), MI, *239*
Adam-Bryce Inc. (C), NY, *239*
Advanced Recruiting, Inc. (C), OK, *240*
Advanced Resources, Inc. (C), MO, *241*
Advantage Partners, Inc. (R), OH, *2*
AJM Professional Services (C), MI, *243*
J. R. Akin & Co. (R), MA, *2*
Alexander Associates (R), NJ, *2*
Alexander Enterprises, Inc. (C), PA, *243*
The Alexander Group (R), TX, *3*
The Alfus Group (R), NY, *3*
Allen & Assoc. (C), NV, *244*
David Allen Assoc. (R), NJ, *3*
Allen Consulting Group, Inc. (C), MO, *244*
Allen Evans Assoc. (R), NY, *4*
Allerton Heneghan & O'Neill (R), IL, *4*
Alpha Resource Group, Inc. (C), TX, *246*
The Alternatives Group, Inc. (C), TX, *246*
Peter W. Ambler Co. (R), TX, *5*
American Medical Recruiters (C), CO, *248*
AMS Int'l. (R), VA, *5*
Anderson Network Group (C), OH, *250*
Andex Executive Search (C), CT, *250*
Andrews & Wald Group (C), FL, *250*
Angus Employment Ltd. (C), ON, *250*
Applied Technology Solutions Inc. (C), ON, *252*
Charles P. Aquavella & Assoc. (C), TX, *252*
Argonaut Partners, LLC (R), CA, *6*
Armitage Associates Ltd. (R), ON, *7*
J. S. Armstrong & Assoc., Inc. (R), CA, *7*
R & J Arnold & Assoc., Inc. (C), CO, *253*
Artgo, Inc. (R), OH, *7*
Ashford Management Group, Inc. (R), GA, *7*
Ashlar-Stone Management Consultants Inc. (R), ON, *8*
Ashton Computer Professionals, Inc. (C), BC, *253*
Ashworth Consultants, Inc. (R), MA, *8*
ASI (C), CA, *254*
Aubin Int'l. Inc. (R), MA, *8*
Auerbach Associates, Inc. (R), MA, *9*
Avalon Health Group, Inc. (R), NY, *9*
Avion International Technology Inc. (C), ON, *257*
Avondale Search Int'l., Inc. (R), FL, *9*
The Ayers Group, Inc. (R), NY, *9*
The Badger Group (R), CA, *10*
Baker Scott & Co. (C), NJ, *258*
Baker, Nelms & Montgomery (C), IL, *258*
Allen Ballach Assoc. Inc. (R), ON, *10*
Barnes Development Group, LLC (R), WI, *11*
Barrett Hospitality Search (R), CA, *12*
Barrett Partners (C), IL, *260*
Barrett Rose & Lee, Inc. (C), ON, *260*
Bartz Rogers & Partners (C), MN, *260*
Bassett Laudi Partners (C), ON, *261*
Battalia Winston Int'l./The Euram Consultants Group (R), NY, *13*
R. Gaines Baty Assoc., Inc. (R), TX, *13*
BCG Search, Inc. (R), FL, *14*
The Beam Group (R), PA, *14*
The Bedford Consulting Group Inc. (R), ON, *14*
Joy Reed Belt Search Consultants, Inc. (R), OK, *15*
Berkana Int'l., Inc. (C), WA, *265*
Berman & Larson (C), NJ, *265*
Besen Assoc. Inc. (C), NJ, *266*
BEST/World Assoc. Inc. (R), TX, *16*
Bishop Partners (R), NY, *17*
Blackhawk Advantage, Inc. (C), CA, *267*
Blaney Executive Search (R), MA, *18*
Blau Mancino Schroeder (R), NJ, *18*
D. R. Blood & Assoc. (R), AZ, *18*
The BMW Group, Inc. (C), NY, *268*
Boardroom Consultants/Kenny Kindler Tholke (R), NY, *19*
Boone-Scaturro Assoc., Inc. (C), GA, *269*
Bosland Gray Assoc. (R), NJ, *20*
Bowden & Co., Inc. (R), OH, *20*
Boyden (R), NY, *20*
BR & Assoc. (C), NJ, *271*
Bradford & Galt, Inc. (C), MO, *271*
Brandt Associates (C), PA, *272*
Bratland & Assoc. (C), IL, *272*
Brault & Assoc., Ltd. (R), VA, *22*
The Brentwood Group, Inc. (R), NJ, *22*
Bernard E. Brooks & Assoc., Inc. (R), SC, *24*
D. Brown & Assoc., Inc. (C), OR, *275*
Brush Creek Partners (R), MO, *24*
BT&A, LLC (R), CT, *24*
Bullis & Co., Inc. (R), CA, *25*
Joseph R. Burns & Assoc., Inc. (R), NJ, *25*
Business Partners, Inc. (C), FL, *277*
Business Systems of America, Inc. (C), IL, *277*
Butterfield & Co. Int'l., Inc. (C), HI, *277*
Button Group (C), TX, *277*
Byron Leonard Int'l., Inc. (R), CA, *25*
Cambridge Group Ltd. - Exec. Search Div. (C), CT, *279*
The Cambridge Group Ltd. (C), CT, *280*
Cambridge Management Planning (R), ON, *27*
T. M. Campbell Co. (R), WA, *27*
Canny, Bowen Inc. (R), NY, *27*
Cantrell & Assoc. (C), FL, *280*
Capital Consulting Group, Inc. (R), MD, *28*
Career Consultants (R), IN, *29*
Career Counseling Inc. (CCI) (C), KY, *282*
Career Development Associates (C), NV, *282*
Career Enterprises (C), OH, *282*
Career Marketing Consultants, Inc. (C), GA, *282*
Careers First, Inc. (C), NJ, *283*
The Carey Company (C), NC, *284*
Carlsen Resources, Inc. (R), CO, *29*
Carlson & Czeswik (R), MN, *30*
Carpenter & Assoc. (C), TX, *284*
K. Carroll & Assoc. (C), IL, *284*
Carter McKenzie, Inc. (C), NJ, *285*
Carter-Evdemon & Assoc. (C), FL, *285*
Caruso & Assoc., Inc. (R), FL, *31*
Cary & Assoc. (R), FL, *31*
Casey & Assoc., Inc. (C), TX, *286*
Catalyx Group (R), NY, *31*
Michael J. Cavanagh & Assoc. Inc. (R), ON, *31*
CEC Associates (R), MA, *32*
Cemco, Ltd. (C), IL, *286*
Chacra, Belliveau & Assoc. Inc. (C), QE, *288*
Vickers Chambless Managed Search (C), GA, *288*
Chanko-Ward, Ltd. (R), NY, *33*
Chatham Search Assoc., Inc. (C), NJ, *290*
Cheney Associates (C), CT, *290*
The Cherbonnier Group, Inc. (R), TX, *33*
Chesapeake Group (C), CT, *290*
Christian & Timbers, Inc. (R), OH, *34*
Christopher-Westmont & Assoc., Inc. (R), OH, *34*
The Clayton Edward Group (C), MI, *292*
CN Associates (C), CA, *293*
Cochran, Cochran & Yale, Inc. (R), NY, *36*
Ann Coe & Assoc. (C), IL, *294*
Coe & Co. Int'l. Inc./EMA Partners Int'l. (R), AB, *37*
J. Kevin Coleman & Assoc., Inc. (R), CA, *37*
Collins & Associates (C), MI, *294*
Colt Systems Professional Personnel Services (C), CA, *294*
Colton Bernard Inc. (R), CA, *37*
Combined Resources Inc. (R), OH, *38*
Commercial Programming Systems, Inc. (C), CA, *294*
Comprehensive Search (C), GA, *294*
CompuPro (C), IL, *295*
Computer Int'l. Consultants, Inc. (C), FL, *295*
Computer Network Resources, Inc. (C), CA, *295*
Computer Personnel, Inc. (C), WA, *295*
Computer Placements Unlimited Inc. (C), NY, *295*
Computer Professionals Unlimited (C), TX, *295*
Computer Recruiters, Inc. (C), CA, *295*
Computer Search Group, Ltd. (R), IL, *39*
Conard Associates, Inc. (R), NH, *39*
Conroy Partners Ltd. (R), AB, *39*
Consulpro (R), ON, *39*
Consultant Recruiters (C), WI, *297*
The Consulting Group of North America, Inc. (C), VA, *297*
Continental Search & Outplacement, Inc. (C), MD, *298*
P. G. Cook Assoc. (R), TN, *40*
Cornerstone Resources, Inc. (C), OK, *299*
The Corporate Advisory Group (R), NJ, *41*
Corporate Recruiters Ltd. (C), BC, *300*
Cowell & Associates, Ltd. (R), IL, *42*
Creative Financial Staffing (C), MA, *303*
Creative Input, Inc. (C), RI, *303*
Creative Management Strategies, Ltd. (R), NY, *42*
CTR (R), CA, *43*
Culver Personnel Services (C), CA, *304*
Curran Partners, Inc. (R), CT, *44*
The Curtiss Group International (R), FL, *44*
Cypress Int'l., Inc. (R), FL, *45*
D.P. Specialists, Inc. (C), CA, *306*
Dahl-Morrow Int'l. (R), VA, *45*
The Dalley Hewitt Co. (R), GA, *45*

Dapexs Consultants, Inc. (C), NY, *307*
Alan Darling Consulting (R), VT, *46*
Data Bank Executive Search (R), OH, *46*
Data Search Network, Inc. (C), FL, *307*
The DataFinders Group, Inc. (C), NJ, *307*
DataPro Personnel Consultants (C), TX, *308*
David Anthony Personnel Assoc., Inc. (C), NJ, *308*
Allen Davis & Assoc. (C), MA, *308*
John J. Davis & Assoc., Inc. (R), NY, *47*
DBL Associates (C), CA, *309*
De Funiak & Edwards (R), IN, *47*
DeCaster Assoc. (C), WI, *310*
Delta Management Group Ltd. (C), ON, *310*
Delta Resource Group, Ltd. (C), GA, *311*
Descheneaux Recruitment Services Ltd. (C), BC, *311*
Dieckmann & Assoc., Ltd. (R), IL, *51*
DieckMueller Group (R), WI, *51*
The Diestel Group (R), UT, *51*
DiMarchi Partners (R), CO, *51*
Dinte Resources, Inc. (R), VA, *52*
Diversified Consulting Services, Inc. (C), CO, *313*
Diversified Search, Inc. (R), PA, *52*
DLG Assoc., Inc. (R), NC, *53*
Dominguez-Metz & Assoc. (R), CA, *53*
Domres Professional Search (R), WI, *53*
Don Allan Assoc., Inc. (C), CA, *313*
J P Donnelly Assoc., Inc. (C), NY, *314*
Dorst Information Services, Inc. (C), NY, *314*
Robert Drexler Assoc., Inc. (R), NJ, *54*
Dromeshauser Assoc. (R), MA, *55*
Drummond Assoc., Inc. (C), NY, *315*
DRZ Medical Recruiters (C), CO, *315*
DS&A (Doug Sears & Assoc.) (C), FL, *315*
DuBrul Management Co. (C), NY, *315*
Dunhill Technical Staffing (C), IN, *320*
Dunhill Professional Search of Rolling Meadows (C), IL, *320*
Dunhill of Manchester Inc. (C), NH, *321*
Dunhill Professional Search of Greater New Orleans (C), LA, *321*
Dunhill Staffing Systems (C), NC, *321*
Dunhill Professional Search of Byram (C), MS, *321*
Dunhill Professional Search of Winston-Salem (C), NC, *322*
Dunhill Professional Search of Bucks-Mont., Inc. (C), PA, *322*
C. A. Durakis Assoc., Inc. (R), MD, *55*
Donald F. Dvorak & Co. (R), IL, *55*
Dynamic Choices Inc. (C), MO, *323*
Dynamic Computer Consultants, Inc. (C), AZ, *324*
Dynamic Search Systems, Inc. (C), IL, *324*
E O Technical (C), CT, *324*
Eagle Search Assoc. (C), CA, *325*
EagleView, Inc. (C), MA, *325*
Eastbourne Assoc. Inc. (R), NY, *56*
Eastman & Beaudine, Inc. (R), TX, *56*
Eastridge Infotech (C), CA, *326*
Eckler Personnel Network (C), VT, *326*
Eden & Assoc., Inc. (C), PA, *326*
EDI, Inc. (C), MD, *326*
EDP Staffing Solutions, Inc. (C), AR, *327*
Eggers Consulting Co., Inc. (C), NE, *327*
Electronic Search, Inc. (C), IL, *327*
H. J. Elliot, Inc. (R), IL, *58*
Ellis & Associates (C), HI, *328*
David M. Ellner Assoc. (R), NY, *59*
The Elmhurst Group (C), CA, *329*
Emerging Technology Search (C), GA, *329*
EMN/Witt/Kieffer (R), MA, *59*
Empire International (R), PA, *59*
Erikson Consulting Assoc., Inc. (R), NY, *60*
Erlanger Assoc. (R), CT, *60*
ESA (R), CT, *60*
ESS (Executive Search Services) (R), CA, *61*
ETI Search Int'l. (R), GA, *61*
The Evans Search Group (R), CT, *61*
Evergreen & Co. (C), MA, *331*
Exclusive Search Consultants (C), OH, *331*
ExecuGroup, Inc. (R), MS, *61*
ExecuQuest, Inc. (R), MI, *61*
ExecuSource Assoc., Inc. (C), GA, *332*
Executive Dimensions (R), NY, *62*
Executive Manning Corp. (R), FL, *63*
Executive Recruiters Agency, Inc. (C), AR, *333*
Executive Search Group LLC (C), CA, *335*
Executive Search Partners (R), NY, *63*
Executive Solutions (R), MN, *64*
Executives Worldwide, Inc. (C), OR, *337*
EXETER 2100 (C), NH, *337*
eXsource Inc. (C), SC, *337*
Raymond L. Extract & Assoc. (R), CA, *64*
Eyler Assoc., Inc. (R), IA, *64*
Fairfaxx Corp. (R), CT, *64*
Fast Switch, Ltd. (C), OH, *338*
The Fawcett Group (R), MA, *65*
A. E. Feldman Assoc., Inc. (C), NY, *339*
Fenwick Partners (R), MA, *66*
Financial Connections Company (C), VA, *340*
Financialjobs.com (C), CA, *340*
First Advisory Services Int'l., Inc. (R), MD, *67*
First Union Executive Search (R), NC, *67*
Howard Fischer Assoc. Int'l., Inc. (R), PA, *67*
Fishel HR Assoc., Inc. (C), AZ, *341*
The Fisher Group (R), AB, *67*
FitzGibbon & Assoc. (R), PA, *68*
Foley Proctor Yoskowitz (R), NJ, *69*
Ford & Ford (C), MA, *343*
The Ford Group, Inc. (R), PA, *69*
Fortuna Technologies Inc. (C), CA, *343*
F-O-R-T-U-N-E Personnel Consultants of Boise (R), ID, *70*
Fortune Personnel Consultants of Huntsville, Inc. (C), AL, *343*
Forum Personnel Inc. (C), NY, *351*
Foster Partners (R), NY, *70*
Fought, Jameson Assoc. (C), IL, *351*
Fox-Morris Assoc., Inc. (C), PA, *351*
Foy, Schneid & Daniel, Inc. (R), NY, *71*
Franstaff Inc. (C), FL, *352*
KS Frary & Assoc. (R), MA, *71*
Mel Frazer Consultant (C), CA, *352*
P. N. French Assoc., Inc. (R), MA, *72*
Friedman Eisenstein Raemer & Schwartz, LLP (R), IL, *72*
Bernard Frigon & Assoc. Inc. (C), QE, *353*
Gerald Frisch Assoc., Inc. (R), NY, *72*
C. F. Furr & Co. (R), NC, *72*
Furst Group/MPI (R), IL, *72*
GAAP Inc. (R), QE, *73*
Gahan Assoc. (R), NY, *73*
Gaming Consultants, Inc. (R), LA, *74*
Gans, Gans & Assoc., Inc. (R), FL, *74*
W. N. Garbarini & Assoc. (R), NJ, *74*
Gardiner, Townsend & Assoc. (R), NY, *74*
Gardner-Ross Assoc., Inc. (R), NY, *74*
Garland Assoc. Int'l. (C), CA, *355*
Garrett Assoc. Inc. (R), GA, *75*
GateSource Partners (C), VA, *355*
GCO (C), CA, *355*
General Engineering Tectonics (C), CA, *356*
Gent & Assoc. (C), CA, *356*
Delores F. George, C.P.C. (C), MA, *356*
C. R. Gerald & Assoc. (C), ON, *356*
John Gilbert Co. (C), TX, *357*
Gilbert Scott Assoc., LLC (C), MA, *357*
Gilbert Tweed Assoc. Inc. (R), NY, *76*
Global Technologies Group Inc. (C), NC, *359*
Glou Int'l., Inc. (R), MA, *78*
The Goodman Group (R), CA, *79*
Goodrich & Sherwood Assoc., Inc. (R), NY, *79*
Gould, McCoy & Chadick, Inc. (R), NY, *80*
The Governance Group, Inc. (R), NJ, *80*
Gowdy Consultants (C), TX, *361*
A. Davis Grant & Co. (R), NJ, *81*
Grant Cooper & Assoc., Inc. (R), MO, *81*
The Grant Search Group, Inc. (C), ON, *361*
Grant/Morgan Assoc., Inc. (C), MD, *361*
Grauss & Co. (C), CA, *362*
Greenwich Internet (C), CT, *363*
Greenwich Search Partners, LLC (C), CT, *363*
J. B. Groner Executive Search, Inc. (C), DE, *363*
Groton Planning Group (R), ME, *82*
Groupe PCA Inc. (C), QE, *363*
Groupe Ranger Inc. (C), QE, *364*
Growth Strategies, Inc. (R), FL, *83*
GSW Consulting Group, Inc. (R), CA, *83*
Guidry & East Healthcare Search Consultants (R), TX, *83*
The Guild Corp. (C), VA, *364*
The Gullgroup (C), TX, *364*
Gustin Partners, Ltd. (R), MA, *83*
William Guy & Assoc., Inc. (R), CA, *84*
GWS Partners (R), IL, *84*
Halbrecht & Co. (C), VA, *365*
Halbrecht Lieberman Assoc., Inc. (R), CT, *84*
The Hamilton Group (R), MD, *85*
Handy HRM (R), NY, *86*
Hardison & Company (R), TX, *86*
Robert Harkins Assoc., Inc. (C), PA, *369*
Hartsfield Group, Inc. (R), GA, *87*
William E. Hay & Co. (R), IL, *88*
Hayden Group, Inc. (R), MA, *88*
Hayman Daugherty Assoc., Inc. (C), GA, *370*
HDB Incorporated (C), MO, *371*
Health Search (C), CA, *371*

Healthcare Management Resources, Inc. (R), GA, *89*
Healthcare Recruiters of Indiana (C), IN, *372*
Healthcare Recruiters International-NY/NJ (C), NJ, *373*
Healthcare Recruiters of New Orleans (C), LA, *373*
Healthcare Recruiters Int'l. Philadelphia (C), NJ, *373*
F. P. Healy & Co., Inc. (R), NY, *89*
Hechkoff/Work Executive Search Inc. (R), NY, *89*
The Heidrick Partners, Inc. (R), IL, *90*
Heinze & Assoc. Inc. (R), MN, *91*
Hemingway Personnel, Inc. (C), CA, *375*
G. W. Henn & Co. (R), OH, *91*
Bruce Henry Assoc. Inc. (R), CA, *91*
J. J. Herlihy & Assoc., Inc. (C), CA, *376*
Hermann & Westmore (R), CA, *92*
Hersher Assoc., Ltd. (R), IL, *92*
Stanley Herz & Co. (R), NY, *92*
The Hetzel Group, Inc. (R), IL, *92*
Higbee Assoc., Inc. (C), CT, *377*
Higgins Assoc., Inc. (R), IL, *93*
B. W. Higgins, Inc. (C), IN, *377*
High Tech Staffing Group (C), OR, *377*
Higley, Hall & Co., Inc. (R), MA, *93*
The Hiring Authority, Inc. (C), FL, *379*
Hite Executive Search (R), OH, *94*
Hobson Assoc. (C), CT, *379*
Hochman & Assoc. (C), CA, *379*
Holden & Harlan Assoc., Inc. (C), IL, *380*
Holland & Assoc., Inc. (R), MI, *94*
J. B. Homer Assoc. Inc. (R), NY, *95*
Fred Hood & Assoc. (C), CA, *380*
Hook-Up! (C), CA, *380*
David C. Horn Executive Search (C), TX, *381*
Hospitality Executive Search, Inc. (R), MA, *96*
Howe & Assoc. (R), PA, *97*
Hughes & Company (R), VA, *98*
Human Resource Bureau (C), CA, *384*
Leigh Hunt & Assoc., Inc. (C), ME, *384*
Hunt & Howe Inc. (R), NY, *99*
The Hunt Co. (R), NY, *99*
Huntington Group (R), CT, *100*
Huntington Personnel Consultants, Inc. (C), NY, *386*
HVS Executive Search (R), NY, *100*
i.j. & assoc., inc. (C), CO, *386*
IM Independent Management Recruiters (R), TN, *101*
The IMC Group of Companies (R), NY, *101*
Impact Search & Strategies (C), PA, *387*
Impact Technical Staffing (C), OR, *387*
Information Systems Professionals (C), NC, *388*
Information Technology Search (C), PA, *388*
InfoTech Search (C), TX, *388*
Infovia (C), CA, *388*
Insight Personnel Group, Inc. (C), TX, *389*
InTech Services, Inc. (C), GA, *390*
Intech Summit Group, Inc. (R), CA, *102*
Integrated Search Solutions Group, LLC (ISSG) (R), NY, *102*
Integrity Search, Inc. (R), PA, *102*
Intelegra, Inc. (C), NJ, *390*
IntelliSource, inc. (C), PA, *391*
Interactive Search Assoc. (C), PA, *391*
Interactive Search Network (R), CA, *102*
International Executive Recruiters (C), OH, *393*
Intersource, Ltd. (R), GA, *103*
Isaacson, Miller (R), MA, *104*
ISG Informatics Search Group (C), ON, *395*
Ives & Associates, Inc. (C), OH, *395*
J & D Resources Inc. (C), TN, *395*
J. Joseph & Assoc. (C), OH, *395*
Pendleton James Assoc., Inc. (R), NY, *105*
James Moore & Assoc. (C), CA, *397*
David James Search (C), CA, *397*
JDG Assoc., Ltd. (C), MD, *397*
JDH & Assoc. (C), CA, *397*
JFW Associates, LLC (C), CT, *398*
John Ryan Assoc., LLC. (C), NY, *399*
Ronald S. Johnson Assoc., Inc. (R), CA, *107*
Johnson Assoc., Inc. (C), IL, *399*
The Johnson Group, Unlimited (C), NY, *400*
Jonathan Lawrence Assoc. (C), NJ, *400*
The Jonathan Stevens Group, Inc. (R), NJ, *108*
Jones and Jones (R), OR, *108*
J. M. Joseph Assoc. (R), NJ, *109*
Joseph Consulting, Inc. (C), FL, *401*
The Jotorok Group (C), RI, *401*
Judd Associates (R), NJ, *109*
Juno Systems, Inc. (C), NY, *402*
K2 Resources, L.P. (C), CT, *402*
Kaas Employment Services (C), IA, *402*
KABL Ability Network (C), CA, *402*
Richard Kader & Assoc. (C), OH, *403*
Kanzer Assoc., Inc. (R), IL, *109*
Gary Kaplan & Assoc. (R), CA, *109*
Kaplan & Assoc., Inc. (R), PA, *109*
Katelyn Partners (C), FL, *404*
Keane Assoc. (R), MA, *110*
A.T. Kearney Executive Search (R), IL, *111*
Kenmore Executives Inc. (C), FL, *405*
David Warwick Kennedy & Assoc. (R), BC, *112*
Kennedy & Co. (R), IL, *112*
The Kennett Group, Inc. (R), PA, *112*
Kennison & Assoc. Inc. (C), MO, *405*
Kenzer Corp. (R), NY, *113*
Key Resources Int'l. (C), CA, *405*
Kimmel & Associates, Inc. (C), NC, *406*
Kincaid Group Inc. (KGI) (C), TX, *406*
King ComputerSearch, Inc. (C), TX, *407*
The Kleven Group, Inc. - Executive Search Division (R), MA, *116*
The Kleven Group, Inc. (C), MA, *407*
Joyce C. Knauff & Assoc. (C), IL, *408*
Lee Koehn Assoc., Inc. (R), OR, *116*
T. J. Koellhoffer & Assoc. (R), NJ, *116*
Koren, Rogers Assoc. Inc. (R), NY, *117*
Kors Montgomery Int'l. (R), TX, *118*
Kostmayer Assoc., Inc. (R), MD, *119*
Kramer Executive Resources, Inc. (C), NY, *409*
Krecklo Executive Search Inc. (R), ON, *120*
Kremple Consulting Group (R), CA, *120*
John Kuhn & Assoc., Inc. (R), WI, *121*
Kukoy Associates (R), CO, *121*
L & K Assoc. (C), NJ, *410*
L. Patrick Group (R), NJ, *122*
Marvin Laba & Assoc. (R), CA, *122*
Laguzza Assoc., Ltd. (R), NY, *122*
Gregory Laka & Co. (C), IL, *411*
Lamay Assoc., Inc. (R), CT, *124*
Lancaster Assoc., Inc. (C), NJ, *411*
Landon Morgan (C), ON, *412*
The Langford Search, Inc. (C), AL, *412*
Lawrence L. Lapham, Inc. (R), NY, *124*
Robert Larned Assoc., Inc. (C), VA, *413*
Larsen, Whitney, Blecksmith & Zilliacus, Inc. (R), CA, *125*
Larson Assoc. (R), CA, *125*
Lascelle & Assoc. Inc. (C), ON, *413*
Madeleine Lav & Assoc. (C), CA, *413*
LaVallee & Associates (C), NC, *413*
Lawrence James Assoc. of Florida, Inc. (C), FL, *414*
LCC Companies (C), AZ, *414*
LCS, Inc. (C), TX, *414*
Leader Institute, Inc. (C), GA, *414*
Leaders-Trust Int'l./Carce y Asociados, S.C. (R), MX, *127*
Lear & Assoc., Inc. (C), FL, *415*
Ledbetter/Davidson Int'l., Inc. (R), NY, *127*
Albert G. Lee Assoc. (C), RI, *415*
Lehman McLeskey (R), TX, *128*
Lemming/LeVan, Inc. (R), GA, *128*
F. P. Lennon Assoc. (C), PA, *416*
Leslie Kavanagh Assoc., Inc. (C), NY, *416*
Levin & Company, Inc. (R), MA, *128*
Lexington Software Inc. (C), NY, *417*
LG Brand, Inc. (C), MD, *417*
Lifter & Assoc. (C), CA, *418*
Livingston, Robert & Co. (R), CT, *130*
Lloyd Associates (R), GA, *130*
Lloyd Prescott Assoc., Inc. (C), FL, *418*
LMB Assoc. (C), IL, *419*
Loderman & Costello (C), GA, *419*
Loewenstein & Assoc., Inc. (R), TX, *131*
The Logan Group, Inc. (R), MO, *131*
Logix, Inc. (C), MA, *420*
Longshore + Simmons (R), PA, *131*
J. S. Lord & Company, Inc. (R), MA, *131*
The John Lucht Consultancy Inc. (R), NY, *131*
Lyons Pruitt Int'l. (R), PA, *132*
M/J/A Partners (R), IL, *133*
MacNaughton Assoc. (R), CA, *133*
Management Assoc. (C), MD, *424*
Management Dimensions Ltd. (R), ON, *134*
Management Recruiters of Birmingham, Inc. (C), AL, *438*
Management Recruiters of Tucson (C), AZ, *439*
Management Recruiters Tucson-Foothills, Inc. (C), AZ, *439*
Management Recruiters of Little Rock (C), AR, *439*
Management Recruiters of Fresno (C), CA, *440*

(R) = Retainer; (C) = Contingency

Management Recruiters Dana Point (C), CA, *440*
Management Recruiters of St. Lucie County, Inc. (C), FL, *444*
Management Recruiters of Forsyth County (C), GA, *445*
Management Recruiters of Venice, Inc. (C), FL, *445*
Management Recruiters of Columbus, Inc. (C), GA, *445*
Management Recruiters of Batavia (C), IL, *447*
Management Recruiters of Chicago West (C), IL, *447*
Management Recruiters of Chicago-North Shore (C), IL, *447*
Management Recruiters of Des Moines (C), IA, *449*
Management Recruiters of Fairfield (C), IA, *449*
Management Recruiters of Frederick, Inc. (C), MD, *450*
Management Recruiters of Birmingham (C), MI, *451*
Management Recruiters of Rochester (C), MN, *452*
Management Recruiters of Chanhassen (C), MN, *452*
Management Recruiters of Lake Tahoe, NV (C), NV, *453*
Management Recruiters of Reno (C), NV, *453*
Management Recruiters of The Sandias (C), NM, *454*
Management Recruiters of Cedar Mountain (C), NC, *455*
Management Recruiters - Kannapolis (C), NC, *456*
Management Recruiters of Charlotte - North, Inc. (C), NC, *456*
Management Recruiters of Boone (C), NC, *456*
Management Recruiters - North Canton, Inc. (C), OH, *458*
Management Recruiters of Northwest Ohio, Inc. (C), OH, *458*
Management Recruiters of Youngstown (C), OH, *458*
Management Recruiters of Pittsburgh (C), PA, *459*
Management Recruiters of Pittsburgh-North, Inc. (C), PA, *460*
Management Recruiters of Travelers Rest, Inc. (C), SC, *461*
Management Recruiters of Houston (C), TX, *462*
Management Recruiters Int'l.-The Woodlands (C), TX, *464*
Management Recruiters of Wausau, LLC (C), WI, *466*
Management Recruiters of Stevens Point, Inc. (C), WI, *466*
Management Search, Inc. (C), IL, *467*
Management Solutions, Inc. (C), CA, *468*
Mangieri/Solutions LLC (C), CT, *468*
ManTech Consulting (C), NY, *468*
Mark Adam Assoc. (R), NJ, *135*
Market Niche Consulting (C), AZ, *470*
Marks & Co., Inc. (R), CT, *136*
Paula Marks Inc. (R), NY, *136*
The Marlow Group (R), MA, *136*
Marsar & Co., Inc. (C), FL, *471*
Karen Marshall Assoc. (C), KY, *471*
Marshall-Alan Assoc., Inc. (C), NY, *471*
Donovan Martin & Assoc. (R), CA, *137*
Masserman & Assoc., Inc. (R), NY, *138*
Massey-Horton Int'l. (R), ON, *138*
Richard L. Mather & Assoc. (C), CT, *472*
Paul May & Assoc. (C), IL, *473*
The Mayes Group, Ltd. (R), PA, *139*
K. E. McCarthy & Assoc. (R), CA, *139*
McCormick Search Inc. (C), IL, *474*
McDonald Assoc. Int'l. (R), IL, *140*
McDowell & Co., Recruiters (C), TX, *474*
McIntyre Management Resources (C), ON, *474*
Med Exec Int'l. (C), CA, *476*
MedSearch Resources, Inc. (C), FL, *478*
Meng, Finseth & Assoc., Inc. (R), CA, *143*
MESA, Inc. (R), CO, *143*
Messett Assoc., Inc. (R), FL, *143*
META/MAT, Ltd. (R), NJ, *144*
MGA Executive Search (C), FL, *480*
Michael Thomas, Inc. (C), OH, *480*
Michael/Merrill (C), KS, *481*
Micro Staff Solutions, Inc. (C), TX, *481*
Midas Management (C), CT, *481*
Milo Research (R), NY, *145*
Herbert Mines Assoc., Inc. (R), NY, *145*
Mirtz Morice, Inc. (R), CT, *145*
MIS Computer Professionals, Inc. (C), KS, *482*
Paul Misarti Inc. (C), NY, *483*
Modis (C), MD, *483*
Mogul Consultants, Inc. (C), NY, *483*
Molecular Solutions, Inc. (C), SC, *483*
Molloy Partners (R), NY, *146*
Monarch Technology Management LLC (C), CO, *484*
Montenido Assoc. (R), CA, *146*
Mordue, Allen, Roberts, Bonney Ltd. (C), WA, *485*
MRF Enterprises, Inc. (C), TX, *486*
MRI, The Sequel Group, LLC (C), CO, *486*
MSI Int'l. (C), GA, *486*
Pamela L. Mulligan, Inc. (R), NH, *149*
Multi Processing, Inc. (R), NH, *149*
Jennifer Munro & Partners, Inc. (R), SC, *149*
Murphy Partners Int'l. (R), IL, *150*
Mycoff & Assoc. (R), CO, *150*
National Executive (C), ON, *489*
National Field Service Corp. (C), NY, *489*
National Search Assoc. (C), CA, *490*
Networking Unlimited of NH, Inc. (C), NH, *491*
New Dimensions in Technology, Inc. (C), MA, *492*
New World Healthcare Solutions, Inc. (R), NY, *151*
Nichols & Company (R), CO, *151*
The Niemond Corp. (R), CA, *152*
Ira Z. Nitzberg (C), NY, *493*
Noll Human Resource Services (C), NE, *494*
Nordeman Grimm, Inc. (R), NY, *152*
Norgate Technology, Inc. (C), NY, *494*
The Norland Group (C), CA, *494*
Paul Winston Norman & Assoc. (R), IL, *152*
Norman Broadbent Int'l., Inc. (R), NY, *152*
The North Peak Group (C), OH, *496*
NorthStar Technologies, Inc. (C), NY, *496*
Nuessle, Kurdziel & Weiss, Inc. (R), PA, *153*
O'Brien Consulting Services (R), MA, *153*
O'Callaghan Honey/Ray & Berndtson Inc. (R), AB, *153*
O'Connor, O'Connor, Lordi, Ltd. (R), PA, *154*
O'Connor Resources (C), TX, *497*
O'Keefe & Assoc. (C), TX, *497*
Odell & Assoc., Inc. (C), TX, *498*
The Oldani Group (R), WA, *155*
Ollinger Partners (R), MA, *156*
The Onstott Group (R), MA, *156*
The Options Group, Inc. (C), NY, *499*
Orion Int'l. Consulting Group, Inc. (C), NC, *499*
Robert Ottke Assoc. (R), CA, *157*
The Oxford Group (C), TX, *500*
The P & L Group (C), NY, *500*
P.R.H. Management, Inc. (R), CT, *158*
Pacific Crossing (C), CA, *501*
Pacific Search Group, Inc. (C), CA, *501*
Page-Wheatcroft & Co., Ltd. (R), TX, *158*
Paragon Recruiting Officials Inc. (C), OH, *502*
Parenica & Co. (R), NC, *159*
Jim Parham & Assoc., Inc. (R), FL, *159*
Parker Page Group (C), FL, *503*
Largent Parks & Partners (C), TX, *503*
Parsons Assoc. Inc. (R), IL, *159*
The Partners, LLC (C), CA, *504*
Partridge Assoc., Inc. (R), MA, *160*
Pascale & LaMorte, LLC (C), CT, *504*
Pathway Executive Search, Inc. (C), NY, *505*
Paul-Tittle Assoc., Inc. (R), VA, *161*
Peachtree Executive Search (R), GA, *161*
Peck & Assoc., Ltd. (R), WI, *161*
PeopleSource Inc. (C), TX, *506*
PERI Corp/Professional Executive Recruiters, Inc. (C), TX, *507*
Perry • Newton Assoc. (C), MD, *507*
Perry-Martel Int'l., Inc. (R), ON, *163*
Personnel Alliance Group (C), NJ, *507*
Richard Peterson & Assoc., Inc. (R), GA, *163*
Robert E. Pfaendler & Assoc., Inc. (C), OR, *509*
PHD Conseil en Ressources Humaines Inc. (C), QE, *510*
Phillips & Assoc. (R), MA, *164*
Phoenix Search (R), MX, *164*
Picard Int'l., Ltd. (R), NY, *164*
The Pinnacle Source, Inc. (C), CO, *512*
Pinton Forrest & Madden/EMA Partners Int'l. (R), BC, *165*
PKS Assoc., Inc. (C), RI, *513*
Plummer & Assoc., Inc. (R), CT, *166*
Poirier, Hoevel & Co. (R), CA, *166*
Al Ponaman Company, Inc. (C), CA, *514*
Porter & Assoc., Inc. (C), FL, *514*
Jack Porter Assoc., Inc. (C), WA, *514*
David Powell, Inc. (R), CA, *166*
Powers Consultants, Inc. (R), MO, *166*

PPS Information Systems Staffing (C), MD, *515*
Elan Pratzer & Partners Inc. (R), ON, *167*
Predictor Systems Corp. (R), CA, *167*
Preferred Professional Recruiters (C), OH, *516*
George Preger & Associates Inc. (R), ON, *167*
Preng & Assoc., Inc. (R), TX, *167*
Presley Consultants, Inc. (C), CA, *517*
Prestonwood Assoc. (R), MA, *168*
Alan J. Price Assoc., Inc. (C), RI, *518*
PricewaterhouseCoopers Executive Search (R), ON, *168*
Prime Management Group Inc. (C), ON, *518*
Primus Assoc., L.C. (R), TX, *169*
Prior/Martech Assoc., Inc. (R), WA, *169*
Pro-Tech Search, Inc. (C), IL, *519*
Procom (C), ON, *519*
Professional Careers, Inc. (C), NC, *520*
Professional Consulting Network, Inc. (C), CA, *520*
Professional Employment Group (C), MD, *520*
Professional Placement Assoc., Inc. (C), NY, *521*
Professional Recruiters (C), UT, *521*
Professional Search Assoc. (C), CA, *522*
Professional Search Centre, Ltd. (C), IL, *522*
Professional Search Consultants (PSC) (C), TX, *523*
Professional Team Search, Inc. (R), AZ, *169*
Professionals in Recruiting Co. (C), TN, *523*
ProNet, Inc. (C), NC, *524*
ProSearch, Inc. (C), PA, *524*
ProStar Systems, Inc. (C), MD, *525*
Quality Consulting Group, Inc. (C), WI, *526*
Quantum EDP Recruiting Services (C), QE, *526*
Quest Enterprises, Ltd. (C), IL, *527*
The Quest Organization (C), NY, *527*
L. J. Quinn & Assoc., Inc. (R), CA, *170*
R & L Assoc., Ltd. (R), NY, *170*
J. E. Ranta Assoc. (C), MA, *529*
Joanne E. Ratner Search (C), NY, *529*
Ray & Berndtson/Lovas Stanley (R), ON, *172*
Ray & Berndtson/Tanton Mitchell (R), BC, *173*
Raymond Karsan Assoc. (C), PA, *529*
Razzino-Claymore Assoc. (C), NJ, *530*
Recruit Xpress (C), TX, *531*
Recruiting Services Group, Inc. (C), TN, *532*
Recruitment Specialists, Inc. (C), MD, *532*
Redell Search, Inc. (C), IL, *533*
Reece & Mruk Partners/EMA Partners Int'l. (R), MA, *173*
Reeder & Assoc., Ltd. (R), GA, *173*
The Regency Group, Ltd. (C), NE, *533*
The Douglas Reiter Co., Inc. (R), OR, *174*
RemTech Business Solutions, Inc. (C), MI, *534*
The Renaissance Network (C), MA, *534*
Resource Services, Inc. (C), NY, *534*
L. J. Reszotko & Assoc. (C), IL, *535*
Retained Search Assoc. (R), NC, *176*
Retis Assoc., Inc. (C), IL, *535*
S. Reyman & Assoc., Ltd. (R), IL, *176*
Russell Reynolds Assoc., Inc. (R), NY, *176*
Reynolds Consulting Int'l. (R), ON, *177*
RGE (C), VA, *535*
RHAssoc. Inc. (C), KS, *535*
RHI Consulting (C), VA, *536*
RHS Assoc. (C), AL, *536*
RIC Corp. (R), FL, *177*
W. F. Richer Assoc., Inc. (C), NY, *536*
Jack Richman & Assoc. (C), FL, *537*
Riddle & McGrath LLC (R), GA, *178*
Ridenour & Assoc. (R), IL, *178*
The Riverbend Group (C), MO, *538*
RJ Associates (C), CA, *538*
Robert Shields & Assoc. (C), TX, *538*
Robinson, Fraser Group Ltd. (R), ON, *180*
The Rogan Group, Inc. (C), CA, *541*
Rogers - McManamon Executive Search (R), CA, *180*
ROI International, Inc. (R), WA, *181*
Roll International (C), TX, *541*
Romac Int'l. - San Francisco (C), CA, *541*
Romac Int'l. (C), PA, *542*
Romac Int'l. Inc. (R), MA, *181*
W. R. Rosato & Assoc., Inc. (R), NY, *182*
Emery A. Rose & Assoc. (C), WA, *545*
Rosenfeld & Co., Inc. (C), MI, *545*
Roth Young of Tampa (C), FL, *546*
Roth Young Personnel Services of Washington, DC (C), MD, *546*
Rovner & Assoc., Inc. (R), IL, *182*
Rowland Assoc. (C), CA, *547*
The Rubinic Consulting Group (C), OH, *548*
Ruderfer & Co., Inc. (C), NJ, *548*
Rusher, Loscavio & LoPresto (R), CA, *183*
The Ryan Charles Group, Inc. (C), FL, *548*
Sales Consultants of Scottsdale, Inc. (C), AZ, *556*
Sales Consultants Peninsula, Inc. (C), CA, *556*
Sales Consultants of Ft. Myers, Inc. (C), FL, *557*
Sales Consultants of Denver (C), CO, *557*
Sales Consultants (C), IL, *558*
Sales Consultants of Western McHenry County (C), IL, *558*
Sales Consultants of Baltimore (C), MD, *559*
Sales Consultants of Rockville, MD (C), MD, *559*
Sales Consultants of Birmingham (C), MI, *559*
Sales Consultants of Raleigh-Durham-RTP (C), NC, *561*
Sales Consultants of Austin, Inc. (C), TX, *562*
Sampson Medical Search (C), CA, *564*
George D. Sandel Assoc. (C), MA, *565*
Norm Sanders Assoc., Inc. (R), NJ, *184*
Sanders Management Assoc., Inc. (C), NJ, *565*
Sanford Rose Assoc. - Santa Ana (C), CA, *565*
Sanford Rose Assoc. - Laguna Beach (C), CA, *565*
Sanford Rose Assoc. - Santa Barbara (C), CA, *565*
Sanford Rose Assoc. - Anaheim (C), CA, *566*
Sanford Rose Assoc. - Carmel, IN (C), IN, *567*
Sanford Rose Assoc. - Springfield (C), MO, *568*
Sanford Rose Assoc. - Charlotte (C), NC, *568*
Sanford Rose Assoc. - Rochester (C), MI, *568*
Sanford Rose Assoc. - Burlington, NC (C), NC, *569*
Sanford Rose Assoc. - Columbus North (C), OH, *569*
Sanford Rose Assoc. - Youngstown (C), OH, *569*
Sanford Rose Assoc. - Pittsburgh North (C), PA, *570*
Schlatter & Assoc. (C), CA, *572*
Schulenburg & Assoc. (C), GA, *572*
Search America, Inc. (C), MA, *574*
The Search Committee (C), MD, *574*
Search Consultants, LLC (C), MD, *575*
Search Int'l. (R), MA, *187*
Search Research Assoc., Inc. (R), MA, *187*
Search Solutions Inc. (C), CA, *576*
SearchCorp International (C), AB, *577*
Seco & Zetto Assoc., Inc. (C), NJ, *577*
Secura/Burnett Partners (R), CA, *187*
J. R. Seehusen Assoc., Inc. (R), IA, *188*
Selective Management Services, Inc. (C), FL, *578*
Setford-Shaw-Najarian Assoc. (C), NY, *579*
Shell Technology Group (C), CA, *580*
Shepherd Bueschel & Provus, Inc. (R), IL, *189*
Michael Shirley Assoc. Inc. (R), KS, *190*
E. L. Shore & Assoc. (R), ON, *190*
M. Shulman, Inc. (R), CA, *191*
Peter Siegel & Co. (C), MA, *581*
D. J. Simpson Assoc. Inc. (R), ON, *191*
Sinclair & Co., Inc. (R), MA, *192*
Ruth Sklar Assoc., Inc. (RSA Executive Search) (R), NY, *192*
Slayton Int'l., Inc. (R), IL, *192*
Smartsource Inc. (C), CA, *583*
Smith & Sawyer, Inc. (R), NY, *193*
Smith Assoc. (C), IA, *584*
G. L. Smith Assoc. (C), CA, *584*
Herman Smith Executive Initiatives Inc. (R), ON, *193*
Smith Search, S.C. (R), MX, *194*
Snelling Search (C), AL, *585*
Sockwell & Assoc. (R), NC, *194*
Sofco (C), NY, *586*
Softrix, Inc. (C), NJ, *586*
SoftSearch Inc. (C), NJ, *586*
Software Engineering Solutions, Inc. (C), CA, *586*
Robert Sollman & Assoc. (C), FL, *587*
Soltis Management Services (R), PA, *195*
Solutions Group (R), AL, *195*
Southport Int'l. Assoc. Inc. (C), FL, *588*

Southwest Search & Consulting, Inc. (C), AZ, *588*
Special Markets Group, Inc. (R), GA, *195*
Spectra International LLC (C), AZ, *589*
SpencerStuart (R), NY, *196*
The Spiegel Group (R), MA, *197*
Kenn Spinrad Inc. (C), PA, *589*
Spriggs & Co., Inc. (R), IL, *198*
Springer Souder & Assoc. L.L.C. (R), IL, *198*
The Stanton Group, Inc. (C), IL, *591*
STAT Search (C), NH, *592*
Steinbach & Co. (C), MA, *592*
Sterling Int'l. (R), NJ, *200*
Sterling Int'l. Management Recruitment, Ltd. Inc. (C), NC, *592*
Michael Stern Assoc., Inc./Euram (R), ON, *200*
Steven Douglas Assoc. (C), FL, *593*
The Stevenson Group, Inc. (N.J.) (R), NJ, *200*
Stewart, Stein & Scott, Ltd. (R), MN, *200*
Storfer & Assoc. (C), NY, *595*
Strategic Alliance Network, Ltd. (C), OH, *595*
StratfordGroup (R), OH, *203*
Stroman Int'l., Inc. (R), CO, *204*
Sullivan & Assoc. (R), MI, *204*
Sullivan & Company (R), NY, *204*
Summerfield Assoc., Inc. (C), TN, *596*
The Summit Group (C), CA, *596*
Summit Search Specialists (C), TX, *596*
Synapse Human Resource Consulting Group (R), TX, *205*
Synergy 2000 (C), DC, *597*
The Synergy Organization (R), PA, *205*
Synergy Systems (C), ON, *598*
Systems One Ltd. (C), IL, *598*
Systems Personnel, Inc. (C), NY, *598*
Systems Search (C), IL, *599*
Systems Search Group, Inc. (C), NC, *599*
Tactical Alternatives (R), CA, *205*
Roy Talman & Assoc. (C), IL, *599*
Tate Consulting, Inc. (R), FL, *207*
Taylor Winfield (R), TX, *207*
TE, Inc. (C), IL, *600*
TeamBuilders (C), GA, *600*
Tech Connector Group (C), CA, *601*
Tech Search (C), CA, *601*
Technical Connections, Inc. (C), CA, *601*
Technical Recruiting Consultants (C), IL, *602*
Technical Skills Consulting Inc. (R), ON, *207*
TechNix Inc. (C), ON, *602*
Techno-Trac Systems, Inc. (C), NY, *603*
The Technology Group (R), IL, *208*
Techsearch Services Inc. (C), CT, *603*
Telequest Communications, Inc. (C), NJ, *605*
Telford, Adams & Alexander (R), CA, *208*
Thor, Inc. (C), CA, *606*
Skip Tolette Executive Search Consulting (R), NJ, *209*
Trac One (R), NJ, *210*
Trans-United Consultants Ltd. (C), ON, *608*
Van Treadaway Assoc., Inc. (R), GA, *210*
Triad Technology Group (C), OR, *609*
Triumph Consulting, Inc. (R), IA, *210*
TSI Group/TSI Staffing Services (C), ON, *610*
The Thomas Tucker Co. (R), CA, *211*
UniQuest Int'l., Inc. (C), FL, *610*
Vincenty & Co. (C), OH, *612*
Vlcek & Company, Inc. (R), CA, *214*
J. D. Walsh & Co. (R), CT, *215*
Lee H. Walton & Assoc. (R), NY, *215*
Ward-Hoffman & Assoc. (C), ID, *615*
C. D. Warner & Assoc. (C), PA, *615*
Warren Executive Services (C), GA, *616*
Warren, Morris & Madison, Ltd. (C), CA, *616*
R. J. Watkins & Co., Ltd. (R), CA, *216*
Waveland Int'l. (R), IL, *216*
The Wayne Group, Ltd. (C), NY, *616*
Weinman & Assoc. (C), AZ, *617*
S. E. Weinstein Co. (R), IL, *217*
C. Weiss Assoc., Inc. (C), NY, *618*
Weliver & Assoc. (C), MI, *618*
Wellington Management Group (R), PA, *217*
Welzig, Lowe & Assoc. (C), CO, *618*
Jude M. Werra & Assoc. (R), WI, *218*
Wesley Brown & Bartle Co., Inc. (R), NY, *218*
Weterrings & Agnew, Inc. (C), NY, *619*
Wheeler Assoc. (R), CT, *219*
Arch S. Whitehead Assoc. Inc. (ASWA) (R), NY, *219*
The Whitney Group (R), NY, *219*
Joel H. Wilensky Assoc., Inc. (C), MA, *620*
Wilkinson SoftSearch, Inc. (C), VA, *620*
Dick Williams & Assoc. (C), CA, *621*
The Wilmington Group (C), NC, *622*
Wilson & Assoc. Int'l. Inc. (C), FL, *622*
Wilson-Douglas-Jordan (C), IL, *622*
The Windham Group (R), OH, *222*
Winston Search, Inc. (R), MD, *222*
Winter, Wyman & Co. (C), MA, *623*
Witt/Kieffer, Ford, Hadelman & Lloyd (R), IL, *223*
Woltz & Assoc., Inc. (R), IL, *224*
M. Wood Company (R), IL, *224*
Wood-Glavin, Inc. (R), KS, *224*
Bruce G. Woods Executive Search (R), TX, *224*
Worlco Computer Resources, Inc. (C), PA, *624*
Worldwide Medical Services (C), CA, *625*
WTW Assoc., Inc. (R), NY, *225*
Dennis Wynn Assoc., Inc. (C), FL, *625*
Xavier Associates, Inc. (R), MA, *226*
The Yorkshire Group, Ltd. (C), MA, *626*
Bill Young & Assoc. (C), VA, *626*
Yours In Travel Personnel Agency, Inc. (C), NY, *626*
Yungner & Bormann (R), MN, *226*
Zaccaria Int'l. (C), NJ, *627*
The Zammataro Company (R), OH, *226*
ZanExec L.L.C. (R), VA, *226*
Zeiger Assoc. L.L.C. (C), CA, *627*
P. D. Zier Assoc. (C), CT, *627*
Zwell Int'l. (R), IL, *228*

08.2 Systems analysis & design

A C Personnel Services, Inc. (C), OK, *231*
Abraxas Technologies, Inc. (C), FL, *233*
Access Assoc. Inc. (C), MD, *233*
Access Data Personnel, Inc. (C), NH, *233*
Acclaim Services, Inc. (C), TX, *234*
Account Ability Now (C), MI, *234*
ACSYS Resources, Inc. (C), DE, *238*
Adam-Bryce Inc. (C), NY, *239*
Adel-Lawrence Assoc., Inc. (C), NJ, *240*
Adept Tech Recruiting, Inc. (C), NY, *240*
Advanced Recruiting, Inc. (C), OK, *240*
Advanced Resources, Inc. (C), MO, *241*
AJM Professional Services (C), MI, *243*
Allen & Assoc. (C), NV, *244*
Allen Consulting Group, Inc. (C), MO, *244*
Allen Evans Assoc. (R), NY, *4*
Allstaff, Inc. (C), IL, *245*
The Alternatives Group, Inc. (C), TX, *246*
American Medical Recruiters (C), CO, *248*
Andex Executive Search (C), CT, *250*
Applied Technology Solutions Inc. (C), ON, *252*
Artgo, Inc. (R), OH, *7*
Ashton Computer Professionals, Inc. (C), BC, *253*
ASI (C), CA, *254*
Atkinson Search & Placement, Inc. (C), IA, *255*
Cami Austin & Assoc. (C), IL, *256*
Avion International Technology Inc. (C), ON, *257*
Avondale Search Int'l., Inc. (R), FL, *9*
Baker, Nelms & Montgomery (C), IL, *258*
Baldwin & Assoc. (C), OH, *258*
Bartz Rogers & Partners (C), MN, *260*
Bassett Laudi Partners (C), ON, *261*
Battalia Winston Int'l./The Euram Consultants Group (R), NY, *13*
The Beardsley Group Inc. (C), CT, *261*
Becker Project Resources, Inc. (C), OR, *262*
J. P. Bencik Assoc. (C), MI, *263*
Dick Berg & Assoc. (C), CA, *264*
Berman & Larson (C), NJ, *265*
Besen Assoc. Inc. (C), NJ, *266*
The BMW Group, Inc. (C), NY, *268*
Bolton Group (C), CA, *269*
BR & Assoc. (C), NJ, *271*
Bradford & Galt, Inc. (C), MO, *271*
Brandt Associates (C), PA, *272*
Brei & Assoc., Inc. (C), IA, *272*
D. Brown & Assoc., Inc. (C), OR, *275*
The Burgess Group-Corporate Recruiters Int'l., Inc. (R), NY, *25*
Business Partners, Inc. (C), FL, *277*
Business Systems of America, Inc. (C), IL, *277*
C.T.E.W. Executive Personnel Services Inc. (C), BC, *278*
Cantrell & Assoc. (C), FL, *280*
Capital Markets Resources, Inc. (C), NC, *281*
Career Counseling Ltd. (C.C.L.) (C), NY, *282*
Career Enterprises (C), OH, *282*
Career Marketing Assoc., Inc. (C), CO, *282*

Careers First, Inc. (C), NJ, *283*
The Carey Company (C), NC, *284*
Carion Resource Group Inc. (C), ON, *284*
K. Carroll & Assoc. (C), IL, *284*
Carter McKenzie, Inc. (C), NJ, *285*
Casey & Assoc., Inc. (C), TX, *286*
The Century Group (C), KS, *287*
Chacra, Belliveau & Assoc. Inc. (C), QE, *288*
Cheney Associates (C), CT, *290*
R. Christine Assoc. (C), PA, *290*
Ann Coe & Assoc. (C), IL, *294*
Collins & Associates (C), MI, *294*
Colt Systems Professional Personnel Services (C), CA, *294*
Combined Resources Inc. (R), OH, *38*
Commercial Programming Systems, Inc. (C), CA, *294*
CompuPro (C), IL, *295*
Computer Int'l. Consultants, Inc. (C), FL, *295*
Computer Network Resources, Inc. (C), CA, *295*
Computer Personnel, Inc. (C), WA, *295*
Computer Placements Unlimited Inc. (C), NY, *295*
Computer Professionals Unlimited (C), TX, *295*
Computer Recruiters, Inc. (C), CA, *295*
Computer Search Group, Ltd. (R), IL, *39*
The Consortium (C), NY, *296*
Consultant Recruiters (C), WI, *297*
The Consulting Group of North America, Inc. (C), VA, *297*
Consulting Resource Group, Inc. (C), GA, *297*
ContactBridge, Inc. (R), IL, *40*
Continental Search & Outplacement, Inc. (C), MD, *298*
Cook Assoc. Int'l., Inc. (C), TN, *298*
COR Management Services, Ltd. (C), NY, *298*
Cornerstone Resources, Inc. (C), OK, *299*
Corporate Image Group (C), TN, *300*
Corporate Recruiters Ltd. (C), BC, *300*
Cowin Assoc. (R), NY, *42*
Creative Financial Staffing (C), MA, *303*
Creative HR Solutions (C), GA, *303*
Cromwell Partners, Inc. (R), NY, *43*
Current Resource Group, Inc. (C), GA, *305*
Cypress Int'l., Inc. (R), FL, *45*
D.P. Specialists, Inc. (C), CA, *306*
Dapexs Consultants, Inc. (C), NY, *307*
DARE Personnel Inc. (C), ON, *307*
Data Search Network, Inc. (C), FL, *307*
Data-AxIS Corp. (C), FL, *307*
The DataFinders Group, Inc. (C), NJ, *307*
DataPro Personnel Consultants (C), TX, *308*
David Anthony Personnel Assoc., Inc. (C), NJ, *308*
Allen Davis & Assoc. (C), MA, *308*
DBC Recruiting Network (C), GA, *309*
Delta Resource Group, Ltd. (C), GA, *311*
Descheneaux Recruitment Services Ltd. (C), BC, *311*
Diversified Search, Inc. (R), PA, *52*
Domres Professional Search (R), WI, *53*
J P Donnelly Assoc., Inc. (C), NY, *314*
Dorst Information Services, Inc. (C), NY, *314*
Drinkwater & Assoc. (R), MA, *54*
Drummond Assoc., Inc. (C), NY, *315*
DuBrul Management Co. (C), NY, *315*
Dunhill Professional Search of Tampa (C), FL, *320*
Dunhill Technical Staffing (C), IN, *320*
Dunhill Professional Search of Rolling Meadows (C), IL, *320*
Dunhill Staffing Systems (C), NC, *321*
Dunhill Professional Search of Byram (C), MS, *321*
Dunhill Professional Search of Winston-Salem (C), NC, *322*
Dunhill Search of Arlington (C), TX, *322*
Dynamic Choices Inc. (C), MO, *323*
Dynamic Computer Consultants, Inc. (C), AZ, *324*
Dynamic Search Systems, Inc. (C), IL, *324*
Dynamic Staffing Network (C), IL, *324*
Eastridge Infotech (C), CA, *326*
Eckler Personnel Network (C), VT, *326*
EDI, Inc. (C), MD, *326*
EDP Staffing Solutions, Inc. (C), AR, *327*
Electronic Search, Inc. (C), IL, *327*
H. J. Elliot, Inc. (R), IL, *58*
Ellis & Associates (C), HI, *328*
David M. Ellner Assoc. (R), NY, *59*
The Elmhurst Group (C), CA, *329*
Emerging Technology Search (C), GA, *329*
ESA (R), CT, *60*
Evergreen & Co. (C), MA, *331*
Exclusive Search Consultants (C), OH, *331*
ExeConnex, LLC (R), GA, *61*
Executive Access Inc. (R), NY, *62*
Executive Career Search (C), VA, *332*
Executive Direction, Inc. (C), CA, *333*
The Executive Group, Inc. (R), CA, *62*
Executive Partners Inc. (C), CT, *333*
Executive Recruiters Agency, Inc. (C), AR, *333*
Executive Search Team (C), MI, *336*
ExecutiveFit (C), NY, *337*
EXETER 2100 (C), NH, *337*
eXsource Inc. (C), SC, *337*
Fast Switch, Ltd. (C), OH, *338*
First Search Inc. (C), IL, *341*
Flowers & Assoc. (C), OH, *342*
Focus Consulting Services, Inc. (C), FL, *342*
Fortuna Technologies Inc. (C), CA, *343*
F-O-R-T-U-N-E Personnel Consultants of Wilmington (C), DE, *344*
Fortune Personnel Consultants of Allentown, Inc. (C), PA, *348*
Foster Associates (C), NJ, *351*
Foster Partners (R), NY, *70*
Fought, Jameson Assoc. (C), IL, *351*
Bernard Frigon & Assoc. Inc. (C), QE, *353*
Garland Assoc. Int'l. (C), CA, *355*
GateSource Partners (C), VA, *355*
GCO (C), CA, *355*
General Engineering Tectonics (C), CA, *356*
Gent & Assoc. (C), CA, *356*
Delores F. George, C.P.C. (C), MA, *356*
C. R. Gerald & Assoc. (C), ON, *356*
GES Services, Inc. (R), NY, *76*
Groupe PCA Inc. (C), QE, *363*
Groupe Ranger Inc. (C), QE, *364*
The Guild Corp. (C), VA, *364*
The Gullgroup (C), TX, *364*
Halbrecht & Co. (C), VA, *365*
Halbrecht Lieberman Assoc., Inc. (R), CT, *84*
Hall Kinion (C), CA, *366*
Hallman Group, Inc. (C), MI, *367*
Robert Harkins Assoc., Inc. (C), PA, *369*
Hayden & Assoc., Inc. (C), MN, *370*
Hayman Daugherty Assoc., Inc. (C), GA, *370*
HDB Incorporated (C), MO, *371*
J. J. Herlihy & Assoc., Inc. (C), CA, *376*
The Herrmann Group Ltd. (R), ON, *92*
J. D. Hersey & Assoc. (C), OH, *376*
High Tech Staffing Group (C), OR, *377*
Hintz Associates (C), NY, *378*
The Hiring Authority, Inc. (C), FL, *379*
Hochman & Assoc. (C), CA, *379*
The Hudson Group (C), CT, *383*
Hunegnaw Executive Search (C), OH, *384*
Leigh Hunt & Assoc., Inc. (C), ME, *384*
Huntington Group (R), CT, *100*
Huntington Personnel Consultants, Inc. (C), NY, *386*
i.j. & assoc., inc. (C), CO, *386*
IMA Search, Inc. (R), NY, *101*
Impact Technical Staffing (C), OR, *387*
Industry Consultants, Inc. (C), GA, *388*
Information Systems Professionals (C), NC, *388*
Information Technology Search (C), PA, *388*
InfoTech Search (C), TX, *388*
Infovia (C), CA, *388*
Insight Personnel Group, Inc. (C), TX, *389*
InTech Services, Inc. (C), GA, *390*
Intelegra, Inc. (C), NJ, *390*
IntelliSource, inc. (C), PA, *391*
International Pro Sourcing, Inc. (C), PA, *393*
International Technical Resources (C), FL, *393*
Iona Partners (C), CA, *394*
Isaacson, Miller (R), MA, *104*
ISG Informatics Search Group (C), ON, *395*
Ives & Associates, Inc. (C), OH, *395*
J & D Resources Inc. (C), TN, *395*
J. Joseph & Assoc. (C), OH, *395*
Jaeger Int'l., Inc. (C), OH, *396*
James Moore & Assoc. (C), CA, *397*
JDG Assoc., Ltd. (C), MD, *397*
Jeffrey Meryl Assoc., Inc. (C), NJ, *398*
Jenex Technology Placement Inc. (C), BC, *398*
JenKim Int'l. Ltd., Inc. (C), FL, *398*
JFW Associates, LLC (C), CT, *398*
John Ryan Assoc., LLC. (C), NY, *399*
Joseph Consulting, Inc. (C), FL, *401*
The Jotorok Group (C), RI, *401*
Judd Associates (R), NJ, *109*
Juno Systems, Inc. (C), NY, *402*
K2 Resources, L.P. (C), CT, *402*
Kames & Assoc. (C), MD, *403*
Katelyn Partners (C), FL, *404*

Melissa Katzman, Executive Search (C), NY, *404*
A.T. Kearney Executive Search (R), IL, *111*
Kennison & Assoc. Inc. (C), MO, *405*
Kensington International (R), CA, *113*
Joyce C. Knauff & Assoc. (C), IL, *408*
Kukoy Associates (R), CO, *121*
Kurtz Pro-Search, Inc. (C), NJ, *410*
Gregory Laka & Co. (C), IL, *411*
Lancaster Assoc., Inc. (C), NJ, *411*
Jack B. Larsen & Assoc., Inc. (C), PA, *413*
Larson, Katz & Young, Inc. (C), VA, *413*
LAS Management Consulting Group, Inc. (R), NJ, *125*
Lascelle & Assoc. Inc. (C), ON, *413*
LaVallee & Associates (C), NC, *413*
LCC Companies (C), AZ, *414*
LCS, Inc. (C), TX, *414*
Leader Institute, Inc. (C), GA, *414*
Leader Resources Group (C), GA, *415*
F. P. Lennon Assoc. (C), PA, *416*
Lewis Consulting Service (C), IL, *417*
Lexington Software Inc. (C), NY, *417*
LG Brand, Inc. (C), MD, *417*
Lifter & Assoc. (C), CA, *418*
LMB Assoc. (C), IL, *419*
Logix, Inc. (C), MA, *420*
Management Decision Systems, Inc. (MDSI) (C), NJ, *424*
Management Recruiters of Tucson (C), AZ, *439*
Management Recruiters of Pleasanton (C), CA, *441*
Management Recruiters of Melbourne, Inc. (C), FL, *443*
Management Recruiters of Columbus, Inc. (C), GA, *445*
Management Recruiters of Venice, Inc. (C), FL, *445*
Management Recruiters of Chicago West (C), IL, *447*
Management Recruiters of Spencer (C), IA, *448*
Management Recruiters of Indianapolis-North (C), IN, *448*
Management Recruiters of Fairfield (C), IA, *449*
Management Recruiters of Des Moines (C), IA, *449*
Management Recruiters of Baltimore (C), MD, *451*
Management Recruiters of Rochester (C), MN, *452*
Management Recruiters of Chanhassen (C), MN, *452*
Management Recruiters of The Sandias (C), NM, *454*
Management Recruiters of Cedar Mountain (C), NC, *455*
Management Recruiters of Woodbury Inc. (C), NY, *455*
Management Recruiters - Kannapolis (C), NC, *456*
Management Recruiters of Boone (C), NC, *456*
Management Recruiters - North Canton, Inc. (C), OH, *458*
Management Recruiters of Youngstown (C), OH, *458*
Management Recruiters of Pittsburgh (C), PA, *459*
Management Recruiters of Pittsburgh-North, Inc. (C), PA, *460*
Management Recruiters of Travelers Rest, Inc. (C), SC, *461*
Management Recruiters of Arlington (C), VA, *464*
Management Recruiters of Wausau, LLC (C), WI, *466*
Mancini Technical Recruiting (C), VA, *468*
Mankuta Gallagher & Assoc., Inc. (C), FL, *468*
F. L. Mannix & Co. (R), MA, *135*
ManTech Consulting (C), NY, *468*
Marentz & Co. (C), TX, *469*
Mark Adam Assoc. (R), NJ, *135*
Market Niche Consulting (C), AZ, *470*
Karen Marshall Assoc. (C), KY, *471*
Masserman & Assoc., Inc. (R), NY, *138*
Paul May & Assoc. (C), IL, *473*
The McCormick Group (C), VA, *473*
McKee Cyber Search (C), MS, *475*
Mercedes & Co., Inc. (R), MA, *143*
MGA Executive Search (C), FL, *480*
Michael Thomas, Inc. (C), OH, *480*
E. J. Michaels, Ltd. (C), NY, *481*
Micro Staff Solutions, Inc. (C), TX, *481*
Midas Management (C), CT, *481*
Millennium Search Group, Inc. (R), CA, *144*
Miller-Hall HRISearch (C), NY, *482*
Danette Milne Corporate Search Inc. (C), ON, *482*
MIS Computer Professionals, Inc. (C), KS, *482*
Paul Misarti Inc. (C), NY, *483*
Mitchell Martin Inc. (C), NY, *483*
Modis (C), MD, *483*
Monarch Technology Management LLC (C), CO, *484*
Montenido Assoc. (R), CA, *146*
Larry Moore & Assoc. (C), CA, *484*
Mordue, Allen, Roberts, Bonney Ltd. (C), WA, *485*
Morgan & Assoc. (C), MA, *485*
Morgan Hunter Corp. (C), KS, *485*
The Morley Group (C), IN, *486*
Robert T. Morton Assoc., Inc. (C), MA, *486*
MRF Enterprises, Inc. (C), TX, *486*
Multi Processing, Inc. (R), NH, *149*
The MVP Group (C), NY, *487*
National Executive (C), ON, *489*
National Field Service Corp. (C), NY, *489*
National Search Assoc. (C), CA, *490*
Len Nelson & Assoc., Inc. (C), TX, *491*
The Network Corporate Search Personnel Inc. (C), AB, *491*
Networking Unlimited of NH, Inc. (C), NH, *491*
NHA Plastics Recruiters (C), FL, *493*
Ira Z. Nitzberg (C), NY, *493*
Noll Human Resource Services (C), NE, *494*
Norgate Technology, Inc. (C), NY, *494*
The Norland Group (C), CA, *494*
Norman Broadbent Int'l., Inc. (R), NY, *152*
The North Peak Group (C), OH, *496*
NorthStar Technologies, Inc. (C), NY, *496*
NPS of Atlanta, Inc. (C), GA, *496*
NYCOR Search, Inc. (C), MN, *497*
O'Keefe & Assoc. (C), TX, *497*
O'Neill Group (C), NJ, *498*
Odell & Assoc., Inc. (C), TX, *498*
The Options Group, Inc. (C), NY, *499*
Opus Marketing (R), CA, *156*
Pacific Crossing (C), CA, *501*
Pacific Search Group, Inc. (C), CA, *501*
The Pailin Group Professional Search Consultants (R), TX, *158*
Paragon Recruiting Officials Inc. (C), OH, *502*
The Partners, LLC (C), CA, *504*
Pascale & LaMorte, LLC (C), CT, *504*
Pathway Executive Search, Inc. (C), NY, *505*
Paul-Tittle Assoc., Inc. (R), VA, *161*
PeopleSource Inc. (C), TX, *506*
Perry Search Assoc. (C), CA, *507*
Perry-Martel Int'l., Inc. (R), ON, *163*
Personnel Alliance Group (C), NJ, *507*
Personnel Incorporated (C), IA, *508*
PHD Conseil en Ressources Humaines Inc. (C), QE, *510*
Pinnacle Executive Group Inc. (C), MO, *512*
PKS Assoc., Inc. (C), RI, *513*
Place Mart Personnel Service (C), NJ, *513*
Placement Testart Inc. (C), QE, *513*
R. L. Plimpton Assoc., Inc. (R), CO, *165*
The Pollack Group (C), ON, *514*
PPS Information Systems Staffing (C), MD, *515*
Pro-Tech Search, Inc. (C), IL, *519*
Procom (C), ON, *519*
Professional Careers, Inc. (C), NC, *520*
Professional Consulting Network, Inc. (C), CA, *520*
Professional Employment Group (C), MD, *520*
Professional Recruiters (C), UT, *521*
Professional Search Centre, Ltd. (C), IL, *522*
Professional Search Consultants (PSC) (C), TX, *523*
Professional Search, Inc. Int'l. (C), TX, *523*
Professional Team Search, Inc. (R), AZ, *169*
ProNet, Inc. (C), NC, *524*
ProStar Systems, Inc. (C), MD, *525*
PSP Agency (C), NY, *525*
Quality Consulting Group, Inc. (C), WI, *526*
Quality Search Inc. (C), OH, *526*
Quantum EDP Recruiting Services (C), QE, *526*
Quest Enterprises, Ltd. (C), IL, *527*
Quest Worldwide Executive Search Corp. (C), CA, *527*
R2 Services, LLC (C), IL, *528*
J. E. Ranta Assoc. (C), MA, *529*
Recruiting Assoc. of Amarillo (C), TX, *531*
Redell Search, Inc. (C), IL, *533*
The Regency Group, Ltd. (C), NE, *533*

RemTech Business Solutions, Inc. (C), MI, *534*
The Renaissance Network (C), MA, *534*
Retained Search Assoc. (R), NC, *176*
Russell Reynolds Assoc., Inc. (R), NY, *176*
RGE (C), VA, *535*
RHAssoc. Inc. (C), KS, *535*
RHI Consulting (C), VA, *536*
RHS Assoc. (C), AL, *536*
W. F. Richer Assoc., Inc. (C), NY, *536*
Jack Richman & Assoc. (C), FL, *537*
Ritech Management Inc. (C), NY, *537*
The Riverbend Group (C), MO, *538*
RLM Assoc., Ltd. (R), NY, *179*
Robert Shields & Assoc. (C), TX, *538*
ROI International, Inc. (R), WA, *181*
Roll International (C), TX, *541*
Romac Int'l. - San Francisco (C), CA, *541*
W. R. Rosato & Assoc., Inc. (R), NY, *182*
Ross Personnel Consultants, Inc. (C), CT, *545*
Rowland Assoc. (C), CA, *547*
The Rubinic Consulting Group (C), OH, *548*
Louis Rudzinsky Assoc., Inc. (C), MA, *548*
S-H-S TechStaff (C), PA, *549*
Sales Consultants of Denver (C), CO, *557*
Sales Consultants of Baltimore (C), MD, *559*
Sales Consultants of Farmington Hills (C), MI, *560*
Sanders Management Assoc., Inc. (C), NJ, *565*
Sanford Rose Assoc. - Santa Ana (C), CA, *565*
Sanford Rose Assoc. - Laguna Beach (C), CA, *565*
Sanford Rose Assoc. - Norcross (C), GA, *566*
Sanford Rose Assoc. - Charlotte (C), NC, *568*
Sanford Rose Assoc. - Columbus North (C), OH, *569*
Sanford Rose Assoc. - Euclid (C), OH, *569*
Sanford Rose Assoc. - Akron (C), OH, *569*
Sanford Rose Assoc. - Youngstown (C), OH, *569*
Saviar, Inc. (C), AZ, *571*
Schulenburg & Assoc. (C), GA, *572*
Search America, Inc. (C), MA, *574*
Search Assoc., Inc. (C), CA, *574*
Search Consultants, LLC (C), MD, *575*
Search Group (C), CA, *575*
Search Solutions Inc. (C), CA, *576*
Searchworks, Inc. (C), FL, *577*
Seco & Zetto Assoc., Inc. (C), NJ, *577*
Segal & Assoc. (C), GA, *578*
Selectis Corp. (C), IL, *578*
Selective Search Associates (C), OH, *578*
Setford-Shaw-Najarian Assoc. (C), NY, *579*
Sevcor Int'l., Inc. (R), IL, *188*
Shell Technology Group (C), CA, *580*
The Silicon Network (C), ON, *581*
Sinclair & Co., Inc. (R), MA, *192*
Smartsource Inc. (C), CA, *583*
Smith Assoc. (C), IA, *584*
Snelling Search - Transportation Division (C), AR, *585*
Snelling Search (C), LA, *586*
Andrea Sobel & Assoc., Inc. (C), CA, *586*
Sofco (C), NY, *586*
Softrix, Inc. (C), NJ, *586*
SoftSearch Inc. (C), NJ, *586*
Software Engineering Solutions, Inc. (C), CA, *586*
Southern Recruiters & Consultants, Inc. (C), SC, *587*
Southport Int'l. Assoc. Inc. (C), FL, *588*
Southwest Search & Consulting, Inc. (C), AZ, *588*
SpencerStuart (R), NY, *196*
Squires Resources Inc. (C), ON, *590*
Stanewick, Hart & Assoc., Inc. (C), FL, *591*
Starbridge Group Inc. (C), VA, *591*
Steinbach & Co. (C), MA, *592*
Strategic Alliance Network, Ltd. (C), OH, *595*
Sullivan & Company (R), NY, *204*
Summerfield Assoc., Inc. (C), TN, *596*
Survival Systems Staffing, Inc. (C), CA, *597*
Synergistech Communications (C), CA, *597*
Synergy 2000 (C), DC, *597*
Synergy Solutions, Ltd. (C), WA, *597*
Systems One Ltd. (C), IL, *598*
Systems Personnel, Inc. (C), NY, *598*
Systems Search (C), IL, *599*
Systems Search Group, Inc. (C), NC, *599*
Roy Talman & Assoc. (C), IL, *599*
Martin Stevens Tamaren & Assoc., Inc. (R), CA, *206*
Tate Consulting, Inc. (R), FL, *207*
TE, Inc. (C), IL, *600*
TeamBuilders (C), GA, *600*
Tech 2000 (C), FL, *601*
Tech Connector Group (C), CA, *601*
Tech Consulting (C), FL, *601*
Technical Connections, Inc. (C), CA, *601*
Technical Recruiting Consultants (C), IL, *602*
Technical Staffing Solutions (C), TX, *602*
Techno-Trac Systems, Inc. (C), NY, *603*
Technology Search Int'l. (C), CA, *603*
Techsearch Services Inc. (C), CT, *603*
Tele-Solutions of Arizona, Inc. (C), AZ, *604*
Telecom Recruiters, Inc. (C), VA, *605*
Telequest Communications, Inc. (C), NJ, *605*
Skip Tolette Executive Search Consulting (R), NJ, *209*
Trac One (R), NJ, *210*
Trans-United Consultants Ltd. (C), ON, *608*
Van Treadaway Assoc., Inc. (R), GA, *210*
Triad Technology Group (C), OR, *609*
TriStaff Group (C), CA, *609*
TSW Assoc., LLC (R), CT, *211*
Ward Assoc. (C), ON, *615*
The Wayne Group, Ltd. (C), NY, *616*
Weinpel Search, Inc. (C), NJ, *617*
Weliver & Assoc. (C), MI, *618*
Wells, Bradley & Assoc., Inc. (C), MN, *618*
The Westfield Group (C), CT, *619*
Arch S. Whitehead Assoc. Inc. (ASWA) (R), NY, *219*
Wilcox Bertoux & Miller (R), CA, *220*
Wilkinson SoftSearch, Inc. (C), VA, *620*
Dick Williams & Assoc. (C), CA, *621*
Williams & Delmore, Inc. (C), NC, *621*
Wilson McLeran, Inc. (C), CT, *622*
Wilson-Douglas-Jordan (C), IL, *622*
Winter, Wyman & Co. (C), MA, *623*
Winthrop Partners, Inc. (R), NY, *222*
Woltz & Assoc., Inc. (R), IL, *224*
Worlco Computer Resources, Inc. (C), PA, *624*
World Search (C), OH, *625*
Dennis Wynn Assoc., Inc. (C), FL, *625*
Bill Young & Assoc. (C), VA, *626*
ZanExec L.L.C. (R), VA, *226*
P. D. Zier Assoc. (C), CT, *627*

08.3 Software development

A C Personnel Services, Inc. (C), OK, *231*
A First Resource (C), NC, *231*
Abraxas Technologies, Inc. (C), FL, *233*
Access Assoc. Inc. (C), MD, *233*
Access Data Personnel, Inc. (C), NH, *233*
Acclaim Services, Inc. (C), TX, *234*
Account Ability Now (C), MI, *234*
ACSYS Resources, Inc. (C), DE, *238*
Action Executive Personnel Consulting Inc. (C), ON, *239*
Adam-Bryce Inc. (C), NY, *239*
Adel-Lawrence Assoc., Inc. (C), NJ, *240*
Adept Tech Recruiting, Inc. (C), NY, *240*
Advanced Recruiting, Inc. (C), OK, *240*
Advanced Resources, Inc. (C), MO, *241*
Advancement Recruiting Services (C), OH, *241*
Advisors' Search Group, Inc. (C), NY, *241*
Affinity Executive Search (C), FL, *241*
AJM Professional Services (C), MI, *243*
Allen & Assoc. (C), NV, *244*
Allen Consulting Group, Inc. (C), MO, *244*
Allen Evans Assoc. (R), NY, *4*
Allen-Jeffers Assoc. (C), CA, *245*
Allstaff, Inc. (C), IL, *245*
The Alternatives Group, Inc. (C), TX, *246*
Andex Executive Search (C), CT, *250*
Angel Group Int'l. (C), KY, *250*
Applied Technology Solutions Inc. (C), ON, *252*
Ashton Computer Professionals, Inc. (C), BC, *253*
ASI (C), CA, *254*
Asset Resource, Inc. (C), CA, *254*
Atkinson Search & Placement, Inc. (C), IA, *255*
Austin Park Management Group Inc. (C), ON, *256*
Avion International Technology Inc. (C), ON, *257*
Avondale Search Int'l., Inc. (R), FL, *9*
Barclay Consultants, Inc. (C), NJ, *259*
Barrett Partners (C), IL, *260*
Bartholdi & Co., Inc. (R), CO, *12*
Bartz Rogers & Partners (C), MN, *260*
Bassett Laudi Partners (C), ON, *261*
Battalia Winston Int'l./The Euram Consultants Group (R), NY, *13*

Becker Project Resources, Inc. (C), OR, *262*
Behavioral Science Assoc., Inc. (R), AZ, *15*
The Bennett Group, Inc. (R), IN, *16*
Dick Berg & Assoc. (C), CA, *264*
Berglund Int'l. Resources, Inc. (C), TX, *265*
Berkana Int'l., Inc. (C), WA, *265*
Berman & Larson (C), NJ, *265*
Bio-Venture Group (C), RI, *266*
BioTech Research Recruiters Inc. (C), CA, *267*
The BMW Group, Inc. (C), NY, *268*
Bolton Group (C), CA, *269*
Bornholdt Shivas & Friends Executive Recruiters (C), NY, *270*
Bos Business Consultants (C), NY, *270*
BR & Assoc. (C), NJ, *271*
Bradford & Galt, Inc. (C), MO, *271*
M. F. Branch Assoc., Inc. (C), NC, *272*
Brei & Assoc., Inc. (C), IA, *272*
Brentwood Int'l. (R), CA, *23*
Brian Assoc., Inc. (C), NY, *273*
Bridgecreek Personnel Agency (C), CA, *273*
D. Brown & Assoc., Inc. (C), OR, *275*
Business Partners, Inc. (C), FL, *277*
Business Systems of America, Inc. (C), IL, *277*
Cadillac Assoc. (C), CA, *278*
Cantrell & Assoc. (C), FL, *280*
Capital Markets Resources, Inc. (C), NC, *281*
Capstone Inc. (R), NY, *29*
Career Counseling Ltd. (C.C.L.) (C), NY, *282*
Career Enterprises (C), OH, *282*
Career Marketing Assoc., Inc. (C), CO, *282*
Careers First, Inc. (C), NJ, *283*
The Carey Company (C), NC, *284*
K. Carroll & Assoc. (C), IL, *284*
Carter McKenzie, Inc. (C), NJ, *285*
Casey & Assoc., Inc. (C), TX, *286*
CBA Companies (C), CA, *286*
Cemco, Ltd. (C), IL, *286*
The Century Group (C), KS, *287*
CEO Consulting (C), FL, *287*
Chacra, Belliveau & Assoc. Inc. (C), QE, *288*
Chatham Search Assoc., Inc. (C), NJ, *290*
Cheney Associates (C), CT, *290*
Howard Clark Assoc. (C), NJ, *292*
CN Associates (C), CA, *293*
Ann Coe & Assoc. (C), IL, *294*
Collins & Associates (C), MI, *294*
Colt Systems Professional Personnel Services (C), CA, *294*
Combined Resources Inc. (R), OH, *38*
Commercial Programming Systems, Inc. (C), CA, *294*
Comprehensive Search (C), GA, *294*
CompuPro (C), IL, *295*
Computer Int'l. Consultants, Inc. (C), FL, *295*
Computer Network Resources, Inc. (C), CA, *295*
Computer Personnel, Inc. (C), WA, *295*
Computer Placements Unlimited Inc. (C), NY, *295*
Computer Professionals Unlimited (C), TX, *295*
Computer Recruiters, Inc. (C), CA, *295*
Computer Search Group, Ltd. (R), IL, *39*
Concorde Staff Source Inc. (C), WI, *296*
Consultant Recruiters (C), WI, *297*
The Consulting Group of North America, Inc. (C), VA, *297*
Consulting Resource Group, Inc. (C), GA, *297*
ContactBridge, Inc. (R), IL, *40*
Continental Search & Outplacement, Inc. (C), MD, *298*
Cook Assoc. Int'l., Inc. (C), TN, *298*
COR Management Services, Ltd. (C), NY, *298*
Cornerstone Resources, Inc. (C), OK, *299*
Corporate Plus, Ltd. (C), GA, *300*
Corporate Recruiters Ltd. (C), BC, *300*
Corporate Resources Professional Placement (C), MN, *300*
Corporate Staffing Group, Inc. (C), PA, *301*
Cosier & Assoc. (C), AB, *302*
Creative Financial Staffing (C), MA, *303*
Cromwell Partners, Inc. (R), NY, *43*
Timothy D. Crowe, Jr. (R), MA, *43*
Current Resource Group, Inc. (C), GA, *305*
Custom Resources (C), AL, *305*
Cypress Int'l., Inc. (R), FL, *45*
D.P. Specialists, Inc. (C), CA, *306*
Alfred Daniels & Assoc., Inc. (R), CA, *46*
Dapexs Consultants, Inc. (C), NY, *307*
DARE Personnel Inc. (C), ON, *307*
Data Search Network, Inc. (C), FL, *307*
Data-AxIS Corp. (C), FL, *307*
The DataFinders Group, Inc. (C), NJ, *307*
DataPro Personnel Consultants (C), TX, *308*
Alan N. Daum & Assoc., Inc. (C), OH, *308*
David Anthony Personnel Assoc., Inc. (C), NJ, *308*
Allen Davis & Assoc. (C), MA, *308*
DBC Recruiting Network (C), GA, *309*
DEL Technical Services, Inc. (C), IL, *310*
Delta Resource Group, Ltd. (C), GA, *311*
Descheneaux Recruitment Services Ltd. (C), BC, *311*
DiTech Resources (C), CT, *313*
J P Donnelly Assoc., Inc. (C), NY, *314*
Dreier Consulting (C), NJ, *315*
DuBrul Management Co. (C), NY, *315*
Dunhill Professional Search of San Jose (C), CA, *319*
Dunhill Professional Search of Tampa (C), FL, *320*
Dunhill Technical Staffing (C), IN, *320*
Dunhill Professional Search of Rolling Meadows (C), IL, *320*
Dunhill of Manchester Inc. (C), NH, *321*
Dunhill Professional Search of Greater New Orleans (C), LA, *321*
Dunhill Staffing Systems (C), NC, *321*
Dunhill Professional Search of Byram (C), MS, *321*
Dunhill Professional Search of Winston-Salem (C), NC, *322*
Dunhill Search of Arlington (C), TX, *322*
Dynamic Choices Inc. (C), MO, *323*
Dynamic Computer Consultants, Inc. (C), AZ, *324*
Dynamic Search Systems, Inc. (C), IL, *324*
Dynamic Synergy Corp. (R), CA, *56*
EagleView, Inc. (C), MA, *325*
Eastridge Infotech (C), CA, *326*
EBA Group (R), NJ, *56*
Eckler Personnel Network (C), VT, *326*
EDI, Inc. (C), MD, *326*
EDP Staffing Solutions, Inc. (C), AR, *327*
Electronic Search, Inc. (C), IL, *327*
Elite Consultants, Inc. (C), FL, *328*
Elite Medical Search (C), GA, *328*
David M. Ellner Assoc. (R), NY, *59*
The Elmhurst Group (C), CA, *329*
Emerging Technology Search (C), GA, *329*
ESA (R), CT, *60*
Evergreen & Co. (C), MA, *331*
Exclusive Search Consultants (C), OH, *331*
Execu-Tech Search Inc. (C), MN, *332*
Executive Career Search (C), VA, *332*
Executive Direction, Inc. (C), CA, *333*
Executive Recruiters, Inc. (C), WI, *334*
Executive Recruitment Services, Inc. (ERS, Inc.) (C), GA, *334*
Executive Search Group LLC (C), CA, *335*
Executive Search of America, Inc. (C), OH, *336*
Executive Search Team (C), MI, *336*
Executives Worldwide, Inc. (C), OR, *337*
EXETER 2100 (C), NH, *337*
eXsource Inc. (C), SC, *337*
Fabian Assoc. Inc. (C), NY, *338*
Dorothy W. Farnath & Assoc., Inc. (C), NJ, *338*
Fast Switch, Ltd. (C), OH, *338*
A. E. Feldman Assoc., Inc. (C), NY, *339*
First Search Inc. (C), IL, *341*
Focus Consulting Services, Inc. (C), FL, *342*
Fogec Consultants, Inc. (R), WI, *69*
Fortuna Technologies Inc. (C), CA, *343*
F-O-R-T-U-N-E Personnel Consultants of Denver, Inc. (C), CO, *344*
Fortune Personnel Consultants of Colorado Springs (C), CO, *344*
F-O-R-T-U-N-E Personnel Consultants (C), MI, *346*
Foster Partners (R), NY, *70*
Fought, Jameson Assoc. (C), IL, *351*
Bernard Frigon & Assoc. Inc. (C), QE, *353*
G. H. Enterprises (C), AZ, *354*
Garland Assoc. Int'l. (C), CA, *355*
GateSource Partners (C), VA, *355*
GCO (C), CA, *355*
General Engineering Tectonics (C), CA, *356*
Gent & Assoc. (C), CA, *356*
Delores F. George, C.P.C. (C), MA, *356*
GFI Professional Staffing Services (C), NH, *357*
John Gilbert Co. (C), TX, *357*
L. J. Gonzer Assoc. (C), NJ, *360*
Greenwich Internet (C), CT, *363*
Groupe PCA Inc. (C), QE, *363*
Groupe Ranger Inc. (C), QE, *364*
The Guild Corp. (C), VA, *364*
The Gullgroup (C), TX, *364*
Halbrecht & Co. (C), VA, *365*

Hall Kinion (C), CA, *366*
Hallman Group, Inc. (C), MI, *367*
Robert Harkins Assoc., Inc. (C), PA, *369*
Harper Associates (C), MI, *369*
Harper Hewes, Inc. (C), NY, *369*
Hayden & Assoc., Inc. (C), MN, *370*
Hayman Daugherty Assoc., Inc. (C), GA, *370*
HDB Incorporated (C), MO, *371*
Hemingway Personnel, Inc. (C), CA, *375*
High Tech Staffing Group (C), OR, *377*
High-Tech Recruiters (C), CT, *378*
The Hiring Authority, Inc. (C), FL, *379*
Hochman & Assoc. (C), CA, *379*
Hoffman Recruiters (C), MA, *380*
J. G. Hood Assoc. (C), CT, *380*
Hook-Up! (C), CA, *380*
Human Resources Personnel Agency (R), AR, *99*
Hunegnaw Executive Search (C), OH, *384*
Leigh Hunt & Assoc., Inc. (C), ME, *384*
Huntington Group (R), CT, *100*
Huntington Personnel Consultants, Inc. (C), NY, *386*
i.j. & assoc., inc. (C), CO, *386*
Impact Search & Strategies (C), PA, *387*
Impact Technical Staffing (C), OR, *387*
Information Systems Professionals (C), NC, *388*
Information Technology Search (C), PA, *388*
InfoTech Search (C), TX, *388*
Infovia (C), CA, *388*
Insight Personnel Group, Inc. (C), TX, *389*
InTech Services, Inc. (C), GA, *390*
Intelegra, Inc. (C), NJ, *390*
IntelliSource, inc. (C), PA, *391*
International Consulting Services, Inc. (C), IL, *392*
International Pro Sourcing, Inc. (C), PA, *393*
International Technical Resources (C), FL, *393*
Isaacson, Miller (R), MA, *104*
ISG Informatics Search Group (C), ON, *395*
J & D Resources Inc. (C), TN, *395*
Jackson Group Int'l. (C), CO, *396*
Jaeger Int'l., Inc. (C), OH, *396*
James Moore & Assoc. (C), CA, *397*
Jeffrey Meryl Assoc., Inc. (C), NJ, *398*
Jenex Technology Placement Inc. (C), BC, *398*
JenKim Int'l. Ltd., Inc. (C), FL, *398*
JFW Associates, LLC (C), CT, *398*
John Ryan Assoc., LLC. (C), NY, *399*
Johnson & Assoc., Inc. (R), CA, *106*
K. E. Johnson Assoc. (C), WA, *399*
Jonathan Lawrence Assoc. (C), NJ, *400*
Joseph Consulting, Inc. (C), FL, *401*
The Jotorok Group (C), RI, *401*
Juno Systems, Inc. (C), NY, *402*
K2 Resources, L.P. (C), CT, *402*
KABL Ability Network (C), CA, *402*
Kames & Assoc. (C), MD, *403*
Allan Karson Assoc., Inc. (R), NJ, *110*
Katelyn Partners (C), FL, *404*
Kaufman Assoc. (R), CA, *110*
Jim Kay & Assoc. (C), IL, *404*
Kay Concepts, Inc. (C), FL, *404*
Keane Assoc. (R), MA, *110*
A.T. Kearney Executive Search (R), IL, *111*
Kehn & Gabor, Inc. (C), OH, *405*
Kennison & Assoc. Inc. (C), MO, *405*
Kensington International (R), CA, *113*
Key Resources Int'l. (C), CA, *405*
Ki Technologies, Inc. (C), UT, *406*
King ComputerSearch, Inc. (C), TX, *407*
The Kleven Group, Inc. - Executive Search Division (R), MA, *116*
The Kleven Group, Inc. (C), MA, *407*
Joyce C. Knauff & Assoc. (C), IL, *408*
Kors Montgomery Int'l. (R), TX, *118*
Kukoy Associates (R), CO, *121*
Kurtz Pro-Search, Inc. (C), NJ, *410*
L & K Assoc. (C), NJ, *410*
L T M Assoc. (C), IL, *410*
Gregory Laka & Co. (C), IL, *411*
Lancaster Assoc., Inc. (C), NJ, *411*
The Langford Search, Inc. (C), AL, *412*
Larson, Katz & Young, Inc. (C), VA, *413*
LAS Management Consulting Group, Inc. (R), NJ, *125*
Lascelle & Assoc. Inc. (C), ON, *413*
LaVallee & Associates (C), NC, *413*
LCC Companies (C), AZ, *414*
LCS, Inc. (C), TX, *414*
Leader Institute, Inc. (C), GA, *414*
Leader Resources Group (C), GA, *415*
Reynolds Lebus Assoc. (C), AZ, *415*
F. P. Lennon Assoc. (C), PA, *416*
Lewis Consulting Service (C), IL, *417*
Lexington Software Inc. (C), NY, *417*
LG Brand, Inc. (C), MD, *417*
Lifter & Assoc. (C), CA, *418*
LMB Assoc. (C), IL, *419*
Logix, Inc. (C), MA, *420*
Lynx, Inc. (C), MA, *421*
Management Recruiters of Nassau, Inc. (R), NY, *134*
Management Recruiters of Birmingham, Inc. (C), AL, *438*
Management Recruiters of Mobile Co., Inc. (C), AL, *438*
Management Recruiters of Birmingham (C), AL, *438*
Management Recruiters of Tucson (C), AZ, *439*
Management Recruiters of Little Rock (C), AR, *439*
Management Recruiters of Clovis (C), CA, *440*
Management Recruiters Dana Point (C), CA, *440*
Management Recruiters of Colorado Springs (C), CO, *441*
Management Recruiters of Clearwater (C), FL, *443*
Management Recruiters of Melbourne, Inc. (C), FL, *443*
Management Recruiters of Columbus, Inc. (C), GA, *445*
Management Recruiters of Atlanta (C), GA, *445*
Management Recruiters of Atlanta North, Inc. (C), GA, *446*
Management Recruiters of Chicago West (C), IL, *447*
Management Recruiters of Noblesville, Inc. (C), IN, *448*
Management Recruiters of Spencer (C), IA, *448*
Management Recruiters of Indianapolis-North (C), IN, *448*
Management Recruiters-Cedar Rapids, Inc. (C), IA, *448*
Management Recruiters of Fairfield (C), IA, *449*
Management Recruiters of Baltimore (C), MD, *451*
Management Recruiters of Rochester (C), MN, *452*
Management Recruiters of Chanhassen (C), MN, *452*
Management Recruiters of Lake Tahoe, NV (C), NV, *453*
Management Recruiters of Bay Head (C), NJ, *453*
Management Recruiters of The Sandias (C), NM, *454*
Management Recruiters of Woodbury Inc. (C), NY, *455*
Management Recruiters - Kannapolis (C), NC, *456*
Management Recruiters of Boone (C), NC, *456*
Management Recruiters of Charlotte - North, Inc. (C), NC, *456*
Management Recruiters - North Canton, Inc. (C), OH, *458*
Management Recruiters of Easton, PA (C), PA, *458*
Management Recruiters of Northwest Ohio, Inc. (C), OH, *458*
Management Recruiters of Youngstown (C), OH, *458*
Management Recruiters of Pittsburgh (C), PA, *459*
Management Recruiters of Pittsburgh-North, Inc. (C), PA, *460*
Management Recruiters of Puerto Rico (C), PR, *460*
Management Recruiters of Chattanooga-Brainerd, Inc. (C), TN, *461*
Management Recruiters Dallas North (MRDN) (C), TX, *462*
Management Recruiters of LBJ Park/Dallas (C), TX, *462*
Management Recruiters of San Marcos (C), TX, *463*
Management Recruiters of Arlington (C), VA, *464*
Management Recruiters of Wausau, LLC (C), WI, *466*
Management Recruiters of Stevens Point, Inc. (C), WI, *466*
Mancini Technical Recruiting (C), VA, *468*
Mankuta Gallagher & Assoc., Inc. (C), FL, *468*
ManTech Consulting (C), NY, *468*
Marentz & Co. (C), TX, *469*
Mark Adam Assoc. (R), NJ, *135*
Mark Christian & Assoc., Inc. (C), AZ, *469*
Market Niche Consulting (C), AZ, *470*
Marks & Co., Inc. (R), CT, *136*

Marsar & Co., Inc. (C), FL, *471*
Karen Marshall Assoc. (C), KY, *471*
Masserman & Assoc., Inc. (R), NY, *138*
Paul May & Assoc. (C), IL, *473*
Mayhall Search Group, Inc. (C), IN, *473*
The McCormick Group (C), VA, *473*
McCoy Ltd. (C), CA, *474*
McHale & Assoc. (R), WA, *141*
McKee Cyber Search (C), MS, *475*
The McKinnon Management Group Inc. (C), ON, *475*
J. M. Meredith & Assoc. Inc. (C), CA, *479*
MGA Executive Search (C), FL, *480*
Michael Thomas, Inc. (C), OH, *480*
Micro Staff Solutions, Inc. (C), TX, *481*
Midas Management (C), CT, *481*
Millennium Search Group, Inc. (R), CA, *144*
MIS Computer Professionals, Inc. (C), KS, *482*
Paul Misarti Inc. (C), NY, *483*
Mitchell Martin Inc. (C), NY, *483*
MLA Resources, Inc. (C), OK, *483*
Modis (C), MD, *483*
Mogul Consultants, Inc. (C), NY, *483*
Molecular Solutions, Inc. (C), SC, *483*
Monarch Technology Management LLC (C), CO, *484*
Larry Moore & Assoc. (C), CA, *484*
Mordue, Allen, Roberts, Bonney Ltd. (C), WA, *485*
Morency Assoc. (C), MA, *485*
The Morley Group (C), IN, *486*
Robert T. Morton Assoc., Inc. (C), MA, *486*
MRF Enterprises, Inc. (C), TX, *486*
Mruk & E.M.A. Partners (R), NY, *148*
MSI Int'l. (C), GA, *486*
Mulcahy Co. (C), WI, *487*
Myers Career Assoc., Inc. (C), CA, *488*
National Computerized Employment Service, Inc. (C), PA, *489*
National Executive (C), ON, *489*
National Field Service Corp. (C), NY, *489*
National Search Assoc. (C), CA, *490*
The NEIS Corp., Inc. (C), FL, *491*
J. Fielding Nelson & Assoc., Inc. (R), UT, *151*
Len Nelson & Assoc., Inc. (C), TX, *491*
The Network Corporate Search Personnel Inc. (C), AB, *491*
Next Step Recruiting (C), CA, *493*
Ira Z. Nitzberg (C), NY, *493*
Norgate Technology, Inc. (C), NY, *494*
The Norland Group (C), CA, *494*
Paul Winston Norman & Assoc. (R), IL, *152*
Norman Broadbent Int'l., Inc. (R), NY, *152*
The North Peak Group (C), OH, *496*
NorthStar Technologies, Inc. (C), NY, *496*
Norton & Assoc. (C), IL, *496*
NPS of Atlanta, Inc. (C), GA, *496*
NYCOR Search, Inc. (C), MN, *497*
O'Keefe & Assoc. (C), TX, *497*
Opus Marketing (R), CA, *156*
LaMonte Owens, Inc. (R), PA, *157*
Pacific Crossing (C), CA, *501*
Paragon Recruiting Officials Inc. (C), OH, *502*
The Partners, LLC (C), CA, *504*
Pathway Executive Search, Inc. (C), NY, *505*
Patriot Assoc. (C), PA, *505*
PC Assoc. (C), CO, *505*
Peden & Assoc. (C), CA, *506*
PeopleSource Inc. (C), TX, *506*
Perry Search Assoc. (C), CA, *507*
Perry-Martel Int'l., Inc. (R), ON, *163*
Personnel Alliance Group (C), NJ, *507*
Personnel Incorporated (C), IA, *508*
J. R. Peterman Assoc., Inc. (C), VT, *509*
Physician Associates (C), HI, *511*
Pinnacle Executive Group Inc. (C), MO, *512*
PKS Assoc., Inc. (C), RI, *513*
Place Mart Personnel Service (C), NJ, *513*
Placement Testart Inc. (C), QE, *513*
The Pollack Group (C), ON, *514*
Norman Powers Assoc., Inc. (C), MA, *515*
PPS Information Systems Staffing (C), MD, *515*
Price & Assoc., Inc. (C), VA, *518*
PRO, Inc./Professional Recruiting Offices, Inc. (C), CA, *519*
Pro-Tech Search, Inc. (C), IL, *519*
Procom (C), ON, *519*
Professional Careers, Inc. (C), NC, *520*
Professional Consulting Network, Inc. (C), CA, *520*
Professional Engineering Technical Personnel Consultants (C), NC, *520*
Professional Recruiters (C), UT, *521*
Professional Search Centre, Ltd. (C), IL, *522*
Professional Search, Inc. Int'l. (C), TX, *523*
Professional Support Inc. (C), NY, *523*
Professional Team Search, Inc. (R), AZ, *169*
ProNet, Inc. (C), NC, *524*
ProSearch, Inc. (C), PA, *524*
ProStar Systems, Inc. (C), MD, *525*
PSP Agency (C), NY, *525*
Quality Consulting Group, Inc. (C), WI, *526*
Quantum EDP Recruiting Services (C), QE, *526*
Quest Enterprises, Ltd. (C), IL, *527*
Quest Worldwide Executive Search Corp. (C), CA, *527*
R2 Services, LLC (C), IL, *528*
Rand Thompson Executive Search Consultants (C), NY, *528*
J. E. Ranta Assoc. (C), MA, *529*
Recruiting Assoc. of Amarillo (C), TX, *531*
The Recruitment Group, Inc. (C), NY, *532*
Redell Search, Inc. (C), IL, *533*
The Regency Group, Ltd. (C), NE, *533*
RemTech Business Solutions, Inc. (C), MI, *534*
The Renaissance Network (C), MA, *534*
Resource Services, Inc. (C), NY, *534*
Russell Reynolds Assoc., Inc. (R), NY, *176*
RGE (C), VA, *535*
RHAssoc. Inc. (C), KS, *535*
RHI Consulting (C), VA, *536*
RHS Assoc. (C), AL, *536*
W. F. Richer Assoc., Inc. (C), NY, *536*
Jack Richman & Assoc. (C), FL, *537*
Richmond Assoc. (C), NY, *537*
Ritech Management Inc. (C), NY, *537*
Ritta Professional Search Inc. (C), NY, *538*
The Riverbend Group (C), MO, *538*
Robert Shields & Assoc. (C), TX, *538*
Roberts Ryan & Bentley, Inc. (R), MD, *179*
Romac Int'l. - San Francisco (C), CA, *541*
Romano McAvoy Assoc., Inc. (C), NY, *544*
Romeo-Hudgins & Assoc., Ltd. (C), NJ, *544*
W. R. Rosato & Assoc., Inc. (R), NY, *182*
Emery A. Rose & Assoc. (C), WA, *545*
Ross Personnel Consultants, Inc. (C), CT, *545*
The Rubinic Consulting Group (C), OH, *548*
Louis Rudzinsky Assoc., Inc. (C), MA, *548*
S. P. Assoc., Inc. (C), NC, *550*
Sales Consultants of Baltimore (C), MD, *559*
Sales Consultants Bridgewater, Inc. (C), NJ, *560*
Sales Consultants of Austin, Inc. (C), TX, *562*
Sampson Medical Search (C), CA, *564*
George D. Sandel Assoc. (C), MA, *565*
Sanders Management Assoc., Inc. (C), NJ, *565*
Sanford Rose Assoc. - Laguna Beach (C), CA, *565*
Sanford Rose Assoc. - Anaheim (C), CA, *566*
Sanford Rose Assoc. - Norcross (C), GA, *566*
Sanford Rose Assoc. - Charlotte (C), NC, *568*
Sanford Rose Assoc. - Columbus North (C), OH, *569*
Sanford Rose Assoc. - Euclid (C), OH, *569*
Sanford Rose Assoc. - Youngstown (C), OH, *569*
Sanford Rose Assoc. - Columbia (C), SC, *570*
Saviar, Inc. (C), AZ, *571*
Schulenburg & Assoc. (C), GA, *572*
Search America, Inc. (C), MA, *574*
Search Assoc., Inc. (C), CA, *574*
Search Consultants, LLC (C), MD, *575*
Search Group (C), CA, *575*
Search Int'l. (R), MA, *187*
SearchCorp International (C), AB, *577*
Searchworks, Inc. (C), FL, *577*
Seco & Zetto Assoc., Inc. (C), NJ, *577*
Selectis Corp. (C), IL, *578*
Selective Search Associates (C), OH, *578*
Setford-Shaw-Najarian Assoc. (C), NY, *579*
Sevcor Int'l., Inc. (R), IL, *188*
Sharrow & Assoc., Inc. (C), MI, *579*
Shell Technology Group (C), CA, *580*
The Silicon Network (C), ON, *581*
SKB Enterprises (C), NY, *582*
Smartsource Inc. (C), CA, *583*
Smith Assoc. (C), IA, *584*
Snelling Search (C), LA, *586*
Andrea Sobel & Assoc., Inc. (C), CA, *586*
Sofco (C), NY, *586*
Softrix, Inc. (C), NJ, *586*

SoftSearch Inc. (C), NJ, *586*
Software Engineering Solutions, Inc. (C), CA, *586*
Southport Int'l. Assoc. Inc. (C), FL, *588*
Southwest Search & Consulting, Inc. (C), AZ, *588*
Southwestern Professional Services (C), TN, *588*
SpectraWest (C), CA, *589*
SpencerStuart (R), NY, *196*
Squires Resources Inc. (C), ON, *590*
The Stanton Group, Inc. (C), IL, *591*
Steinbach & Co. (C), MA, *592*
The Stelton Group, Inc. (C), NJ, *592*
Sterling Int'l. Management Recruitment, Ltd. Inc. (C), NC, *592*
Stoneburner Assoc., Inc. (C), KS, *594*
Strategic Alliance Network, Ltd. (C), OH, *595*
Summerfield Assoc., Inc. (C), TN, *596*
The Summit Group (C), CA, *596*
Synergistech Communications (C), CA, *597*
Synergy Solutions, Ltd. (C), WA, *597*
Synergy Systems (C), ON, *598*
Systems Careers (C), CA, *598*
Systems One Ltd. (C), IL, *598*
Systems Personnel, Inc. (C), NY, *598*
Systems Search (C), IL, *599*
Systems Search Group, Inc. (C), NC, *599*
Tactical Alternatives (R), CA, *205*
Roy Talman & Assoc. (C), IL, *599*
Martin Stevens Tamaren & Assoc., Inc. (R), CA, *206*
Tate Consulting, Inc. (R), FL, *207*
TE, Inc. (C), IL, *600*
TeamBuilders (C), GA, *600*
Tech 2000 (C), FL, *601*
Tech Connector Group (C), CA, *601*
Tech Consulting (C), FL, *601*
Tech Search (C), CA, *601*
Technical Connections, Inc. (C), CA, *601*
Technical Recruiting Consultants (C), IL, *602*
Technical Staffing Solutions (C), TX, *602*
Techno-Trac Systems, Inc. (C), NY, *603*
Technology Management Partners (R), CA, *208*
Techsearch Services Inc. (C), CT, *603*
Tele-Solutions of Arizona, Inc. (C), AZ, *604*
Thor, Inc. (C), CA, *606*
Skip Tolette Executive Search Consulting (R), NJ, *209*
Trac One (R), NJ, *210*
Van Treadaway Assoc., Inc. (R), GA, *210*
Triad Technology Group (C), OR, *609*
TriStaff Group (C), CA, *609*
TSS Consulting, Ltd. (C), AZ, *610*
B. D. Wallace & Assoc. (C), MD, *614*
Wallace Assoc. (C), CT, *614*
S. B. Webster & Associates (R), MA, *217*
David Weinfeld Group (C), NC, *617*
Weliver & Assoc. (C), MI, *618*
The Whitaker Companies (C), TX, *619*
Whitehead & Assoc., Inc. (C), MO, *620*
Arch S. Whitehead Assoc. Inc. (ASWA) (R), NY, *219*
Joel H. Wilensky Assoc., Inc. (C), MA, *620*
Wilkinson SoftSearch, Inc. (C), VA, *620*
Dick Williams & Assoc. (C), CA, *621*
Williams & Delmore, Inc. (C), NC, *621*
Wilson-Douglas-Jordan (C), IL, *622*
Wing Tips & Pumps, Inc. (C), MI, *623*
Woltz & Assoc., Inc. (R), IL, *224*
Dennis Wynn Assoc., Inc. (C), FL, *625*
Bill Young & Assoc. (C), VA, *626*
ZanExec L.L.C. (R), VA, *226*
P. D. Zier Assoc. (C), CT, *627*

08.4 Systems integration/implementation

A C Personnel Services, Inc. (C), OK, *231*
Abraham & London Ltd. (C), CT, *232*
Abraxas Technologies, Inc. (C), FL, *233*
Access Data Personnel, Inc. (C), NH, *233*
ACCESS Technology (C), CA, *234*
Acclaim Services, Inc. (C), TX, *234*
Account Ability Now (C), MI, *234*
ACSYS Resources, Inc. (C), DE, *238*
Adam-Bryce Inc. (C), NY, *239*
Adel-Lawrence Assoc., Inc. (C), NJ, *240*
Adept Tech Recruiting, Inc. (C), NY, *240*
Advanced Recruiting, Inc. (C), OK, *240*
Advanced Resources, Inc. (C), MO, *241*
AJM Professional Services (C), MI, *243*
Allen Consulting Group, Inc. (C), MO, *244*
Allen Evans Assoc. (R), NY, *4*
Allstaff, Inc. (C), IL, *245*
The Alternatives Group, Inc. (C), TX, *246*
Amato & Assoc., Inc. (C), CA, *246*
American Heritage Group, Inc. (C), MI, *247*
Andex Executive Search (C), CT, *250*
Applied Resources, Inc. (C), MN, *252*
Applied Technology Solutions Inc. (C), ON, *252*
ASI (C), CA, *254*
Atkinson Search & Placement, Inc. (C), IA, *255*
Automation Technology Search (C), CA, *256*
Avion International Technology Inc. (C), ON, *257*
The Ayers Group, Inc. (R), NY, *9*
Baeder Kalinski Int'l. Group, Inc. (R), NH, *10*
Baker, Nelms & Montgomery (C), IL, *258*
Barclay Consultants, Inc. (C), NJ, *259*
Barnes & Assoc. Executive Search (C), CA, *259*
Bartz Rogers & Partners (C), MN, *260*
Bassett Laudi Partners (C), ON, *261*
Battalia Winston Int'l./The Euram Consultants Group (R), NY, *13*
R. Gaines Baty Assoc., Inc. (R), TX, *13*
The Beardsley Group Inc. (C), CT, *261*
Becker Project Resources, Inc. (C), OR, *262*
Belanger Partners Ltd. (C), ON, *262*
Bennett & Co. Consulting Group (C), CA, *264*
Dick Berg & Assoc. (C), CA, *264*
Berglund Int'l. Resources, Inc. (C), TX, *265*
Berman & Larson (C), NJ, *265*
BEST/World Assoc. Inc. (R), TX, *16*
BioTech Research Recruiters Inc. (C), CA, *267*
The BMW Group, Inc. (C), NY, *268*
Howard Bowen Consulting (C), FL, *270*
BR & Assoc. (C), NJ, *271*
Bradford & Galt, Inc. (C), MO, *271*
Brei & Assoc., Inc. (C), IA, *272*
Britt Assoc., Inc. (C), IL, *274*
D. Brown & Assoc., Inc. (C), OR, *275*
Business Partners, Inc. (C), FL, *277*
Business Systems of America, Inc. (C), IL, *277*
Button Group (C), TX, *277*
The Cambridge Group Ltd. (C), CT, *280*
T. M. Campbell Co. (R), WA, *27*
J. P. Canon Assoc. (C), NY, *280*
Capital Consulting & Research, Inc. (R), CT, *28*
Sally Caplan & Assoc. (C), WA, *281*
Career Enterprises (C), OH, *282*
The Carey Company (C), NC, *284*
K. Carroll & Assoc. (C), IL, *284*
Carter McKenzie, Inc. (C), NJ, *285*
Carter/MacKay (C), NJ, *285*
Casey & Assoc., Inc. (C), TX, *286*
CBA Companies (C), CA, *286*
Chacra, Belliveau & Assoc. Inc. (C), QE, *288*
The Chapman Group, Inc. (C), AZ, *289*
Cheney Associates (C), CT, *290*
Clinton, Charles, Wise & Co. (C), FL, *293*
Ann Coe & Assoc. (C), IL, *294*
Collins & Associates (C), MI, *294*
Combined Resources Inc. (R), OH, *38*
Commercial Programming Systems, Inc. (C), CA, *294*
CompuPro (C), IL, *295*
Computer Int'l. Consultants, Inc. (C), FL, *295*
Computer Network Resources, Inc. (C), CA, *295*
Computer Personnel, Inc. (C), WA, *295*
Computer Placements Unlimited Inc. (C), NY, *295*
Computer Professionals Unlimited (C), TX, *295*
Computer Recruiters, Inc. (C), CA, *295*
Computer Search Group, Ltd. (R), IL, *39*
Computer Security Placement Service (C), MA, *296*
Concorde Staff Source Inc. (C), WI, *296*
The Consortium (C), NY, *296*
Consultant Recruiters (C), WI, *297*
The Consulting Group of North America, Inc. (C), VA, *297*
Consulting Resource Group, Inc. (C), GA, *297*
ContactBridge, Inc. (R), IL, *40*
Continental Search & Outplacement, Inc. (C), MD, *298*
Conway & Assoc. (R), IL, *40*
COR Management Services, Ltd. (C), NY, *298*
Corporate Resources Professional Placement (C), MN, *300*
Corporate Staffing Group, Inc. (C), PA, *301*
Creative Financial Staffing (C), MA, *303*
Current Resource Group, Inc. (C), GA, *305*

Cypress Int'l., Inc. (R), FL, *45*
D.P. Specialists, Inc. (C), CA, *306*
Charles Dahl Group, Inc. (C), MN, *306*
Dapexs Consultants, Inc. (C), NY, *307*
Data Search Network, Inc. (C), FL, *307*
Data-AxIS Corp. (C), FL, *307*
The DataFinders Group, Inc. (C), NJ, *307*
DataPro Personnel Consultants (C), TX, *308*
Alan N. Daum & Assoc., Inc. (C), OH, *308*
Allen Davis & Assoc. (C), MA, *308*
Bert Davis Executive Search, Inc. (R), NY, *47*
The Dayton Group, Ltd. (C), NY, *309*
DBC Recruiting Network (C), GA, *309*
DEL Technical Services, Inc. (C), IL, *310*
Delta Management Group Ltd. (C), ON, *310*
Delta Resource Group, Ltd. (C), GA, *311*
Descheneaux Recruitment Services Ltd. (C), BC, *311*
Despres & Associates (C), IL, *311*
Diversified Search, Inc. (R), PA, *52*
Don Allan Assoc., Inc. (C), CA, *313*
J P Donnelly Assoc., Inc. (C), NY, *314*
The Dorfman Group (C), AZ, *314*
DuBrul Management Co. (C), NY, *315*
Dunhill Professional Search of Tampa (C), FL, *320*
Dunhill Technical Staffing (C), IN, *320*
Dunhill Professional Search of Rolling Meadows (C), IL, *320*
Dunhill Staffing Systems (C), NC, *321*
Dunhill Professional Search of Byram (C), MS, *321*
Dunhill Professional Search of Winston-Salem (C), NC, *322*
Dynamic Choices Inc. (C), MO, *323*
Dynamic Computer Consultants, Inc. (C), AZ, *324*
Dynamic Search Systems, Inc. (C), IL, *324*
Eastbourne Assoc. Inc. (R), NY, *56*
Eastridge Infotech (C), CA, *326*
Eckler Personnel Network (C), VT, *326*
EDI, Inc. (C), MD, *326*
EDP Staffing Solutions, Inc. (C), AR, *327*
EFCO Consultants, Inc. (C), NY, *327*
Electronic Search, Inc. (C), IL, *327*
Elite Consultants, Inc. (C), FL, *328*
H. J. Elliot, Inc. (R), IL, *58*
Ellis & Associates (C), HI, *328*
The Elmhurst Group (C), CA, *329*
Emerging Technology Search (C), GA, *329*
Evergreen & Co. (C), MA, *331*
ExeConnex, LLC (R), GA, *61*
Executive Direction, Inc. (C), CA, *333*
Executive Exchange Corp. (C), NJ, *333*
Executive Partners Inc. (C), CT, *333*
Executive Recruitment Services, Inc. (ERS, Inc.) (C), GA, *334*
Executive Search Group LLC (C), CA, *335*
EXETER 2100 (C), NH, *337*
eXsource Inc. (C), SC, *337*
Fast Switch, Ltd. (C), OH, *338*
Fenzel Milar Assoc. (C), OH, *339*
First Search Inc. (C), IL, *341*
A. G. Fishkin & Assoc., Inc. (R), MD, *68*
James L. Fisk & Assoc. (C), MO, *342*
The Ford Group, Inc. (R), PA, *69*
Fortune Personnel Consultants of Greensboro, NC, Inc. (C), NC, *348*
FORTUNE Personnel Consultants of North Dallas (C), TX, *350*
Foster Associates (C), NJ, *351*
Foster Partners (R), NY, *70*
Fought, Jameson Assoc. (C), IL, *351*
Fox-Morris Assoc., Inc. (C), PA, *351*
Garland Assoc. Int'l. (C), CA, *355*
GCO (C), CA, *355*
General Engineering Tectonics (C), CA, *356*
Gent & Assoc. (C), CA, *356*
Delores F. George, C.P.C. (C), MA, *356*
Global Technologies Group Inc. (C), NC, *359*
The Goodman Group (R), CA, *79*
Government Contract Solutions, Inc. (C), VA, *360*
Grauss & Co. (C), CA, *362*
Greenwich Search Partners, LLC (C), CT, *363*
Groupe PCA Inc. (C), QE, *363*
Groupe Ranger Inc. (C), QE, *364*
The Guild Corp. (C), VA, *364*
The Gullgroup (C), TX, *364*
Gustin Partners, Ltd. (R), MA, *83*
Halbrecht & Co. (C), VA, *365*
Halbrecht Lieberman Assoc., Inc. (R), CT, *84*
Hallman Group, Inc. (C), MI, *367*
Harper Hewes, Inc. (C), NY, *369*
Hayman Daugherty Assoc., Inc. (C), GA, *370*
HDB Incorporated (C), MO, *371*
Hechkoff/Work Executive Search Inc. (R), NY, *89*
J. J. Herlihy & Assoc., Inc. (C), CA, *376*
J. D. Hersey & Assoc. (C), OH, *376*
Higbee Assoc., Inc. (C), CT, *377*
High Tech Staffing Group (C), OR, *377*
The Hiring Authority, Inc. (C), FL, *379*
Hochman & Assoc. (C), CA, *379*
Hoffman Recruiters (C), MA, *380*
J. B. Homer Assoc. Inc. (R), NY, *95*
David C. Horn Executive Search (C), TX, *381*
HR Consultants (C), GA, *382*
Hreshko Consulting Group (C), NJ, *382*
The Hudson Group (C), CT, *383*
Leigh Hunt & Assoc., Inc. (C), ME, *384*
Hunter Adams (C), NC, *385*
Huntington Group (R), CT, *100*
Huntington Personnel Consultants, Inc. (C), NY, *386*
The Hutton Group, Inc. (C), FL, *386*
i.j. & assoc., inc. (C), CO, *386*
Impact Technical Staffing (C), OR, *387*
Information Systems Professionals (C), NC, *388*
Information Technology Search (C), PA, *388*
InfoTech Search (C), TX, *388*
Infovia (C), CA, *388*
Insight Personnel Group, Inc. (C), TX, *389*
InTech Services, Inc. (C), GA, *390*
Intech Summit Group, Inc. (R), CA, *102*
Intelegra, Inc. (C), NJ, *390*
IntelliSource, inc. (C), PA, *391*
International Pro Sourcing, Inc. (C), PA, *393*
International Technical Resources (C), FL, *393*
Isaacson, Miller (R), MA, *104*
ISG Informatics Search Group (C), ON, *395*
J & D Resources Inc. (C), TN, *395*
James Moore & Assoc. (C), CA, *397*
JDG Assoc., Ltd. (C), MD, *397*
Jeffrey Meryl Assoc., Inc. (C), NJ, *398*
JFW Associates, LLC (C), CT, *398*
John Ryan Assoc., LLC. (C), NY, *399*
Jonathan Lawrence Assoc. (C), NJ, *400*
The Jotorok Group (C), RI, *401*
JSG Group Management Consultants (R), ON, *109*
Juno Systems, Inc. (C), NY, *402*
K2 Resources, L.P. (C), CT, *402*
Allan Karson Assoc., Inc. (R), NJ, *110*
Melissa Katzman, Executive Search (C), NY, *404*
Keane Assoc. (R), MA, *110*
A.T. Kearney Executive Search (R), IL, *111*
The Kennett Group, Inc. (R), PA, *112*
Kennison & Assoc. Inc. (C), MO, *405*
Kensington International (R), CA, *113*
Kincaid Group Inc. (KGI) (C), TX, *406*
King ComputerSearch, Inc. (C), TX, *407*
Kleber & Assoc. (C), WA, *407*
KM Associates (C), MA, *407*
Joyce C. Knauff & Assoc. (C), IL, *408*
Kukoy Associates (R), CO, *121*
Kurtz Pro-Search, Inc. (C), NJ, *410*
Gregory Laka & Co. (C), IL, *411*
Lamay Assoc., Inc. (R), CT, *124*
Lancaster Assoc., Inc. (C), NJ, *411*
Larson, Katz & Young, Inc. (C), VA, *413*
LAS Management Consulting Group, Inc. (R), NJ, *125*
Lascelle & Assoc. Inc. (C), ON, *413*
LaVallee & Associates (C), NC, *413*
LCC Companies (C), AZ, *414*
LCS, Inc. (C), TX, *414*
Leader Institute, Inc. (C), GA, *414*
Reynolds Lebus Assoc. (C), AZ, *415*
F. P. Lennon Assoc. (C), PA, *416*
Leslie Kavanagh Assoc., Inc. (C), NY, *416*
Lewis Consulting Service (C), IL, *417*
Lexington Software Inc. (C), NY, *417*
LG Brand, Inc. (C), MD, *417*
Lifter & Assoc. (C), CA, *418*
LMB Assoc. (C), IL, *419*
Loewenstein & Assoc., Inc. (R), TX, *131*
Logix, Inc. (C), MA, *420*
Longo Associates (C), CA, *420*
Lynx, Inc. (C), MA, *421*
Carol Maden Group (C), VA, *422*
Magellan Int'l., L.P. (C), TX, *422*
Management Recruiters of Birmingham, Inc. (C), AL, *438*
Management Recruiters of Colorado Springs (C), CO, *441*
Management Recruiters of St. Lucie County, Inc. (C), FL, *444*
Management Recruiters of St. Augustine (C), FL, *444*

Management Recruiters of Columbus, Inc. (C), GA, *445*
Management Recruiters of Savannah (C), GA, *446*
Management Recruiters of Atlanta North, Inc. (C), GA, *446*
Management Recruiters of Batavia (C), IL, *447*
Management Recruiters of Fairfield (C), IA, *449*
Management Recruiters of Rochester (C), MN, *452*
Management Recruiters of Bay Head (C), NJ, *453*
Management Recruiters of The Sandias (C), NM, *454*
Management Recruiters - Kannapolis (C), NC, *456*
Management Recruiters of Boone (C), NC, *456*
Management Recruiters - North Canton, Inc. (C), OH, *458*
Management Recruiters of Youngstown (C), OH, *458*
Management Recruiters of Pittsburgh-North, Inc. (C), PA, *460*
Management Recruiters of Travelers Rest, Inc. (C), SC, *461*
Management Recruiters of Fairfax, VA (C), VA, *464*
Management Recruiters of Arlington (C), VA, *464*
Management Recruiters of Loudoun County South (C), VA, *465*
Management Recruiters of Wausau, LLC (C), WI, *466*
Management Recruiters of Stevens Point, Inc. (C), WI, *466*
Management Search Int'l. (C), CA, *467*
Management Solutions, Inc. (C), CA, *468*
Mancini Technical Recruiting (C), VA, *468*
Mankuta Gallagher & Assoc., Inc. (C), FL, *468*
F. L. Mannix & Co. (R), MA, *135*
ManTech Consulting (C), NY, *468*
Mark Adam Assoc. (R), NJ, *135*
Market Niche Consulting (C), AZ, *470*
Karen Marshall Assoc. (C), KY, *471*
Masserman & Assoc., Inc. (R), NY, *138*
The Matthews Group, Inc. (C), NJ, *472*
Paul May & Assoc. (C), IL, *473*
McDowell & Co., Recruiters (C), TX, *474*
McHale & Assoc. (R), WA, *141*
McKee Cyber Search (C), MS, *475*
MGA Executive Search (C), FL, *480*
Michael Thomas, Inc. (C), OH, *480*
Michael/Merrill (C), KS, *481*
Midas Management (C), CT, *481*
Millennium Search Group, Inc. (R), CA, *144*
MIS Computer Professionals, Inc. (C), KS, *482*
Paul Misarti Inc. (C), NY, *483*
Mitchell Martin Inc. (C), NY, *483*
Modis (C), MD, *483*
Mogul Consultants, Inc. (C), NY, *483*
Monarch Technology Management LLC (C), CO, *484*
Montenido Assoc. (R), CA, *146*
Larry Moore & Assoc. (C), CA, *484*
Mordue, Allen, Roberts, Bonney Ltd. (C), WA, *485*
Morency Assoc. (C), MA, *485*
Morgan & Assoc. (C), MA, *485*
MRF Enterprises, Inc. (C), TX, *486*
Pamela L. Mulligan, Inc. (R), NH, *149*
The MVP Group (C), NY, *487*
National Executive (C), ON, *489*
National Field Service Corp. (C), NY, *489*
Len Nelson & Assoc., Inc. (C), TX, *491*
The Network Corporate Search Personnel Inc. (C), AB, *491*
Networking Unlimited of NH, Inc. (C), NH, *491*
New Dimensions in Technology, Inc. (C), MA, *492*
Newport Strategic Search LLC (C), CA, *492*
Next Step Recruiting (C), CA, *493*
Norgate Technology, Inc. (C), NY, *494*
The Norland Group (C), CA, *494*
Norman Broadbent Int'l., Inc. (R), NY, *152*
Northland Employment Services Inc. (C), MN, *496*
NorthStar Technologies, Inc. (C), NY, *496*
O'Connor Resources (C), TX, *497*
O'Keefe & Assoc. (C), TX, *497*
The Options Group, Inc. (C), NY, *499*
Opus Marketing (R), CA, *156*
T. Page & Assoc. (C), TX, *502*
Paragon Recruiting Officials Inc. (C), OH, *502*
The Partners, LLC (C), CA, *504*
Pathway Executive Search, Inc. (C), NY, *505*
Paul-Tittle Assoc., Inc. (R), VA, *161*
Perry Search Assoc. (C), CA, *507*
Personnel Alliance Group (C), NJ, *507*
Peyser Assoc., Inc. (R), FL, *163*
PHD Conseil en Ressources Humaines Inc. (C), QE, *510*
Phillips Assoc. (C), FL, *510*
The Pinnacle Source, Inc. (C), CO, *512*
PKS Assoc., Inc. (C), RI, *513*
Placement Testart Inc. (C), QE, *513*
The Pollack Group (C), ON, *514*
Powers Consultants, Inc. (R), MO, *166*
PPS Information Systems Staffing (C), MD, *515*
Pro-Tech Search, Inc. (C), IL, *519*
Procom (C), ON, *519*
Professional Careers, Inc. (C), NC, *520*
Professional Consulting Network, Inc. (C), CA, *520*
Professional Placement Assoc., Inc. (C), NY, *521*
Professional Recruiters (C), UT, *521*
Professional Search Centre, Ltd. (C), IL, *522*
Professional Search Consultants (PSC) (C), TX, *523*
Professional Support Inc. (C), NY, *523*
Professional Team Search, Inc. (R), AZ, *169*
ProSearch, Inc. (C), PA, *524*
ProStar Systems, Inc. (C), MD, *525*
Quality Consulting Group, Inc. (C), WI, *526*
Quantum EDP Recruiting Services (C), QE, *526*
Quest Enterprises, Ltd. (C), IL, *527*
Quest Worldwide Executive Search Corp. (C), CA, *527*
J. E. Ranta Assoc. (C), MA, *529*
Razzino-Claymore Assoc. (C), NJ, *530*
Recruiting Assoc. of Amarillo (C), TX, *531*
Redell Search, Inc. (C), IL, *533*
The Regency Group, Ltd. (C), NE, *533*
RemTech Business Solutions, Inc. (C), MI, *534*
The Renaissance Network (C), MA, *534*
Resource Services, Inc. (C), NY, *534*
Response Staffing Services (C), NY, *534*
Russell Reynolds Assoc., Inc. (R), NY, *176*
RGE (C), VA, *535*
RHAssoc. Inc. (C), KS, *535*
RHI Consulting (C), VA, *536*
RHS Assoc. (C), AL, *536*
W. F. Richer Assoc., Inc. (C), NY, *536*
Jack Richman & Assoc. (C), FL, *537*
Richmond Assoc. (C), NY, *537*
Ridenour & Assoc. (R), IL, *178*
Ritech Management Inc. (C), NY, *537*
The Riverbend Group (C), MO, *538*
RLM Assoc., Ltd. (R), NY, *179*
Robert Shields & Assoc. (C), TX, *538*
Roll International (C), TX, *541*
Romac Int'l. - San Francisco (C), CA, *541*
W. R. Rosato & Assoc., Inc. (R), NY, *182*
Ross Personnel Consultants, Inc. (C), CT, *545*
Rovner & Assoc., Inc. (R), IL, *182*
The Rubinic Consulting Group (C), OH, *548*
Louis Rudzinsky Assoc., Inc. (C), MA, *548*
S-H-S TechStaff (C), PA, *549*
Sales Consultants of Silicon Valley (C), CA, *556*
Sales Consultants of Danbury (C), CT, *557*
Sales Consultants of Denver (C), CO, *557*
Sales Consultants of Western McHenry County (C), IL, *558*
Sales Consultants of Rockville, MD (C), MD, *559*
Sales Consultants of Cherry Hill (C), NJ, *560*
Sales Consultants of Raleigh-Durham-RTP (C), NC, *561*
Sanders Management Assoc., Inc. (C), NJ, *565*
Sanford Rose Assoc. - Laguna Beach (C), CA, *565*
Sanford Rose Assoc. - Norcross (C), GA, *566*
Sanford Rose Assoc. - Rockford (C), IL, *567*
Sanford Rose Assoc. - Charlotte (C), NC, *568*
Sanford Rose Assoc. - Columbus North (C), OH, *569*
Sanford Rose Assoc. - Euclid (C), OH, *569*
Sanford Rose Assoc. - Youngstown (C), OH, *569*
Santangelo Consultants Inc. (C), NY, *571*
Sarver & Carruth Assoc. (C), OK, *571*
Saviar, Inc. (C), AZ, *571*
Schulenburg & Assoc. (C), GA, *572*

Search America, Inc. (C), MA, *574*
Search Group (C), CA, *575*
SearchCorp International (C), AB, *577*
Searchworks, Inc. (C), FL, *577*
Seco & Zetto Assoc., Inc. (C), NJ, *577*
Selective Search Associates (C), OH, *578*
Setford-Shaw-Najarian Assoc. (C), NY, *579*
Sevcor Int'l., Inc. (R), IL, *188*
Shell Technology Group (C), CA, *580*
The Silicon Network (C), ON, *581*
SilverSands Int'l. (C), FL, *582*
SKB Enterprises (C), NY, *582*
Smartsource Inc. (C), CA, *583*
Smith Assoc. (C), IA, *584*
Andrea Sobel & Assoc., Inc. (C), CA, *586*
Softrix, Inc. (C), NJ, *586*
Southport Int'l. Assoc. Inc. (C), FL, *588*
Southwest Search & Consulting, Inc. (C), AZ, *588*
SpencerStuart (R), NY, *196*
Squires Resources Inc. (C), ON, *590*
Stanewick, Hart & Assoc., Inc. (C), FL, *591*
The Stanton Group, Inc. (C), IL, *591*
Starbridge Group Inc. (C), VA, *591*
Steinbach & Co. (C), MA, *592*
Sterling Int'l. (R), NJ, *200*
Linford E. Stiles & Assoc., L.L.C. (R), NH, *201*
Strategic Alliance Network, Ltd. (C), OH, *595*
Strategic Assoc., Inc. (C), TX, *595*
Sullivan & Company (R), NY, *204*
The Summit Group (C), CA, *596*
Synergistech Communications (C), CA, *597*
Synergy 2000 (C), DC, *597*
Synergy Solutions, Ltd. (C), WA, *597*
Systems Careers (C), CA, *598*
Systems One Ltd. (C), IL, *598*
Systems Personnel, Inc. (C), NY, *598*
Systems Research Group (C), CA, *598*
Systems Search Group, Inc. (C), NC, *599*
Roy Talman & Assoc. (C), IL, *599*
Tarbex (C), DC, *599*
Tate Consulting, Inc. (R), FL, *207*
TBC, Inc. (C), KY, *600*
TE, Inc. (C), IL, *600*
TeamBuilders (C), GA, *600*
Tech 2000 (C), FL, *601*
Tech Connector Group (C), CA, *601*
Tech Search (C), CA, *601*
Technical Connections, Inc. (C), CA, *601*
Technical Recruiting Consultants (C), IL, *602*
Techno-Trac Systems, Inc. (C), NY, *603*
Technology Consultants Int'l. (C), CA, *603*
Techsearch Services Inc. (C), CT, *603*
Tele-Solutions of Arizona, Inc. (C), AZ, *604*
Telequest Communications, Inc. (C), NJ, *605*
The TGA Company (C), TX, *606*
Thomas, Whelan Assoc., Inc. (C), DC, *606*
Skip Tolette Executive Search Consulting (R), NJ, *209*
Trac One (R), NJ, *210*
Van Treadaway Assoc., Inc. (R), GA, *210*
Triad Technology Group (C), OR, *609*
TSS Consulting, Ltd. (C), AZ, *610*
Valentine & Assoc. (C), IL, *611*
Vento Assoc. (C), TN, *612*
B. D. Wallace & Assoc. (C), MD, *614*
Ward Assoc. (C), ON, *615*
The Wayne Group, Ltd. (C), NY, *616*
David Weinfeld Group (C), NC, *617*
Weliver & Assoc. (C), MI, *618*
Arch S. Whitehead Assoc. Inc. (ASWA) (R), NY, *219*
Wilcoxen, Blackwell, Niven & Assoc. (R), FL, *220*
Wilkinson SoftSearch, Inc. (C), VA, *620*
Williams & Delmore, Inc. (C), NC, *621*
Wilson McLeran, Inc. (C), CT, *622*
Winston Search, Inc. (R), MD, *222*
Woltz & Assoc., Inc. (R), IL, *224*
M. Wood Company (R), IL, *224*
Bruce G. Woods Executive Search (R), TX, *224*
Worlco Computer Resources, Inc. (C), PA, *624*
World Search (C), OH, *625*
Dennis Wynn Assoc., Inc. (C), FL, *625*
Bill Young & Assoc. (C), VA, *626*
P. D. Zier Assoc. (C), CT, *627*

08.5 Support

A C Personnel Services, Inc. (C), OK, *231*
Abraham & London Ltd. (C), CT, *232*
Abraxas Technologies, Inc. (C), FL, *233*
Access Data Personnel, Inc. (C), NH, *233*
Acclaim Services, Inc. (C), TX, *234*
Account Ability Now (C), MI, *234*
Action Executive Personnel Consulting Inc. (C), ON, *239*
Adam-Bryce Inc. (C), NY, *239*
Adel-Lawrence Assoc., Inc. (C), NJ, *240*
Adept Tech Recruiting, Inc. (C), NY, *240*
Advanced Recruiting, Inc. (C), OK, *240*
Advanced Resources, Inc. (C), MO, *241*
Advisors' Search Group, Inc. (C), NY, *241*
AJM Professional Services (C), MI, *243*
Allen Consulting Group, Inc. (C), MO, *244*
Allstaff, Inc. (C), IL, *245*
The Alternatives Group, Inc. (C), TX, *246*
Amato & Assoc., Inc. (C), CA, *246*
Andex Executive Search (C), CT, *250*
Applied Technology Solutions Inc. (C), ON, *252*
Ashton Computer Professionals, Inc. (C), BC, *253*
ASI (C), CA, *254*
Atkinson Search & Placement, Inc. (C), IA, *255*
Austin Park Management Group Inc. (C), ON, *256*
Avion International Technology Inc. (C), ON, *257*
Barclay Consultants, Inc. (C), NJ, *259*
Barrett Partners (C), IL, *260*
Bartz Rogers & Partners (C), MN, *260*
Bassett Laudi Partners (C), ON, *261*
The Beardsley Group Inc. (C), CT, *261*
Becker Project Resources, Inc. (C), OR, *262*
Robert Beech West Inc. (C), CA, *262*
Belanger Partners Ltd. (C), ON, *262*
Bellamy & Assoc. (C), GA, *263*
Berman & Larson (C), NJ, *265*
The BMW Group, Inc. (C), NY, *268*
BR & Assoc. (C), NJ, *271*
Bradford & Galt, Inc. (C), MO, *271*
Business Partners, Inc. (C), FL, *277*
Business Systems of America, Inc. (C), IL, *277*
Career Enterprises (C), OH, *282*
Career Marketing Assoc., Inc. (C), CO, *282*
The Carey Company (C), NC, *284*
K. Carroll & Assoc. (C), IL, *284*
Carter McKenzie, Inc. (C), NJ, *285*
Carter/MacKay (C), NJ, *285*
Casey & Assoc., Inc. (C), TX, *286*
CBA Companies (C), CA, *286*
The Center for Career Advancement, LLC (C), NJ, *287*
Century Assoc., Inc. (C), PA, *287*
Chacra, Belliveau & Assoc. Inc. (C), QE, *288*
Chatham Search Assoc., Inc. (C), NJ, *290*
Clinton, Charles, Wise & Co. (C), FL, *293*
CN Associates (C), CA, *293*
Ann Coe & Assoc. (C), IL, *294*
Collins & Associates (C), MI, *294*
Combined Resources Inc. (R), OH, *38*
Commercial Programming Systems, Inc. (C), CA, *294*
CompuPro (C), IL, *295*
Computer Network Resources, Inc. (C), CA, *295*
Computer Personnel, Inc. (C), WA, *295*
Computer Placements Unlimited Inc. (C), NY, *295*
Computer Recruiters, Inc. (C), CA, *295*
Computer Search Group, Ltd. (R), IL, *39*
Computer Security Placement Service (C), MA, *296*
Concorde Staff Source Inc. (C), WI, *296*
The Consulting Group of North America, Inc. (C), VA, *297*
ContactBridge, Inc. (R), IL, *40*
Continental Search & Outplacement, Inc. (C), MD, *298*
COR Management Services, Ltd. (C), NY, *298*
Trudi Cowlan (C), NY, *302*
Creative Financial Staffing (C), MA, *303*
Creative HR Solutions (C), GA, *303*
Current Resource Group, Inc. (C), GA, *305*
Cypress Int'l., Inc. (R), FL, *45*
D.P. Specialists, Inc. (C), CA, *306*
Dapexs Consultants, Inc. (C), NY, *307*
Data Search Network, Inc. (C), FL, *307*
The DataFinders Group, Inc. (C), NJ, *307*
DataPro Personnel Consultants (C), TX, *308*
Allen Davis & Assoc. (C), MA, *308*
DEL Technical Services, Inc. (C), IL, *310*
Delta Management Group Ltd. (C), ON, *310*
Despres & Associates (C), IL, *311*
Diversified Search, Inc. (R), PA, *52*
J P Donnelly Assoc., Inc. (C), NY, *314*
DuBrul Management Co. (C), NY, *315*
Dunhill Professional Search of Tampa (C), FL, *320*

Dunhill Technical Staffing (C), IN, *320*
Dunhill Professional Search of Rolling Meadows (C), IL, *320*
Dunhill of Manchester Inc. (C), NH, *321*
Dunhill Professional Search of Winston-Salem (C), NC, *322*
Dynamic Computer Consultants, Inc. (C), AZ, *324*
Dynamic Search Systems, Inc. (C), IL, *324*
Dynamic Staffing Network (C), IL, *324*
Eagle Search Assoc. (C), CA, *325*
Eastridge Infotech (C), CA, *326*
Eckler Personnel Network (C), VT, *326*
EDI, Inc. (C), MD, *326*
EDP Staffing Solutions, Inc. (C), AR, *327*
EFCO Consultants, Inc. (C), NY, *327*
Elite Consultants, Inc. (C), FL, *328*
David M. Ellner Assoc. (R), NY, *59*
Emerging Technology Search (C), GA, *329*
Evergreen & Co. (C), MA, *331*
Execu-Tech Search Inc. (C), MN, *332*
Executive Direction, Inc. (C), CA, *333*
Executive Recruiters Agency, Inc. (C), AR, *333*
EXETER 2100 (C), NH, *337*
eXsource Inc. (C), SC, *337*
Fortuna Technologies Inc. (C), CA, *343*
Fortune Personnel Consultants of Colorado Springs (C), CO, *344*
Foster Partners (R), NY, *70*
Fought, Jameson Assoc. (C), IL, *351*
Franklin Int'l. Search, Inc. (C), MA, *352*
Bernard Frigon & Assoc. Inc. (C), QE, *353*
GCO (C), CA, *355*
General Engineering Tectonics (C), CA, *356*
Gent & Assoc. (C), CA, *356*
L. J. Gonzer Assoc. (C), NJ, *360*
Gowdy Consultants (C), TX, *361*
Greenwich Search Partners, LLC (C), CT, *363*
Groupe Ranger Inc. (C), QE, *364*
Halbrecht Lieberman Assoc., Inc. (R), CT, *84*
Hall Kinion (C), CA, *366*
Harbrowe, Inc. (C), NY, *368*
HDB Incorporated (C), MO, *371*
High Tech Staffing Group (C), OR, *377*
Hochman & Assoc. (C), CA, *379*
J. B. Homer Assoc. Inc. (R), NY, *95*
Leigh Hunt & Assoc., Inc. (C), ME, *384*
Hunter Adams (C), NC, *385*
Huntington Group (R), CT, *100*
Huntington Personnel Consultants, Inc. (C), NY, *386*
i.j. & assoc., inc. (C), CO, *386*
Impact Technical Staffing (C), OR, *387*
Information Systems Professionals (C), NC, *388*
InfoTech Search (C), TX, *388*
Infovia (C), CA, *388*
Insight Personnel Group, Inc. (C), TX, *389*
InTech Services, Inc. (C), GA, *390*
Intelegra, Inc. (C), NJ, *390*
IntelliSource, inc. (C), PA, *391*
International Market Recruiters (C), NY, *393*
International Pro Sourcing, Inc. (C), PA, *393*
ISG Informatics Search Group (C), ON, *395*
J & D Resources Inc. (C), TN, *395*
James Moore & Assoc. (C), CA, *397*
JDC Assoc. (C), NY, *397*
Jeffrey Meryl Assoc., Inc. (C), NJ, *398*
Jenex Technology Placement Inc. (C), BC, *398*
JFW Associates, LLC (C), CT, *398*
JG Consultants, Inc. (R), TX, *106*
John Ryan Assoc., LLC. (C), NY, *399*
Jonathan Lawrence Assoc. (C), NJ, *400*
The Jotorok Group (C), RI, *401*
Juno Systems, Inc. (C), NY, *402*
Kaas Employment Services (C), IA, *402*
A.T. Kearney Executive Search (R), IL, *111*
Kennison & Assoc. Inc. (C), MO, *405*
Kensington International (R), CA, *113*
Kiley, Owen & McGovern, Inc. (R), NJ, *114*
King ComputerSearch, Inc. (C), TX, *407*
Kleber & Assoc. (C), WA, *407*
The Kleven Group, Inc. - Executive Search Division (R), MA, *116*
KM Associates (C), MA, *407*
Joyce C. Knauff & Assoc. (C), IL, *408*
Kurtz Pro-Search, Inc. (C), NJ, *410*
L & K Assoc. (C), NJ, *410*
Gregory Laka & Co. (C), IL, *411*
Lancaster Assoc., Inc. (C), NJ, *411*
Larson, Katz & Young, Inc. (C), VA, *413*
Lascelle & Assoc. Inc. (C), ON, *413*
LaVallee & Associates (C), NC, *413*
LCC Companies (C), AZ, *414*
LCS, Inc. (C), TX, *414*
Leader Institute, Inc. (C), GA, *414*
Vincent Lee Assoc. (C), NY, *415*
Legal Network Inc. (C), CA, *416*
The Levton Group Inc. (R), ON, *129*
Lewis Consulting Service (C), IL, *417*
Lexington Software Inc. (C), NY, *417*
LG Brand, Inc. (C), MD, *417*
Lifter & Assoc. (C), CA, *418*
LMB Assoc. (C), IL, *419*
Logix, Inc. (C), MA, *420*
Lynx, Inc. (C), MA, *421*
Carol Maden Group (C), VA, *422*
Management Recruiters of Mobile Co., Inc. (C), AL, *438*
Management Recruiters of Batavia (C), IL, *447*
Management Recruiters of Chicago West (C), IL, *447*
Management Recruiters-Cedar Rapids, Inc. (C), IA, *448*
Management Recruiters of Fairfield (C), IA, *449*
Management Recruiters of Frederick, Inc. (C), MD, *450*
Management Recruiters of Rochester (C), MN, *452*
Management Recruiters of Chanhassen (C), MN, *452*
Management Recruiters of The Sandias (C), NM, *454*
Management Recruiters - Kannapolis (C), NC, *456*
Management Recruiters of Charlotte - North, Inc. (C), NC, *456*
Management Recruiters - North Canton, Inc. (C), OH, *458*
Management Recruiters of Youngstown (C), OH, *458*
Management Recruiters of Pittsburgh (C), PA, *459*
Management Recruiters of Pittsburgh-North, Inc. (C), PA, *460*
Management Recruiters of Wausau, LLC (C), WI, *466*
Management Recruiters of Stevens Point, Inc. (C), WI, *466*
Management Resource Group, Inc. (C), NY, *467*
Management Search Int'l. (C), CA, *467*
Mancini Technical Recruiting (C), VA, *468*
F. L. Mannix & Co. (R), MA, *135*
ManTech Consulting (C), NY, *468*
Mark Adam Assoc. (R), NJ, *135*
Mark Christian & Assoc., Inc. (C), AZ, *469*
Marks & Co., Inc. (R), CT, *136*
Karen Marshall Assoc. (C), KY, *471*
Masserman & Assoc., Inc. (R), NY, *138*
McDowell & Co., Recruiters (C), TX, *474*
The McKinnon Management Group Inc. (C), ON, *475*
Mehta Consulting (C), NJ, *478*
MGA Executive Search (C), FL, *480*
Michael Thomas, Inc. (C), OH, *480*
Michael/Merrill (C), KS, *481*
Midas Management (C), CT, *481*
MIS Computer Professionals, Inc. (C), KS, *482*
Paul Misarti Inc. (C), NY, *483*
Mitchell Martin Inc. (C), NY, *483*
Modis (C), MD, *483*
Mogul Consultants, Inc. (C), NY, *483*
Monarch Technology Management LLC (C), CO, *484*
Larry Moore & Assoc. (C), CA, *484*
Mordue, Allen, Roberts, Bonney Ltd. (C), WA, *485*
MRF Enterprises, Inc. (C), TX, *486*
National Executive (C), ON, *489*
National Field Service Corp. (C), NY, *489*
Newport Management (C), NY, *492*
Norgate Technology, Inc. (C), NY, *494*
The Norland Group (C), CA, *494*
Norman Broadbent Int'l., Inc. (R), NY, *152*
Northland Employment Services Inc. (C), MN, *496*
O'Keefe & Assoc. (C), TX, *497*
Omnisearch Assoc. (C), CA, *499*
The Options Group, Inc. (C), NY, *499*
Opus Marketing (R), CA, *156*
Pacific Crossing (C), CA, *501*
Paragon Recruiting Officials Inc. (C), OH, *502*
The Partners, LLC (C), CA, *504*
Pathway Executive Search, Inc. (C), NY, *505*
Perry Search Assoc. (C), CA, *507*
Personnel Alliance Group (C), NJ, *507*
PHD Conseil en Ressources Humaines Inc. (C), QE, *510*
The Pinnacle Source, Inc. (C), CO, *512*
Placement Testart Inc. (C), QE, *513*

Plante & Moran, LLP (R), MI, *165*
The Pollack Group (C), ON, *514*
PPS Information Systems Staffing (C), MD, *515*
Procom (C), ON, *519*
Professional Consulting Network, Inc. (C), CA, *520*
Professional Search Centre, Ltd. (C), IL, *522*
Professional Search Consultants (PSC) (C), TX, *523*
Professional Team Search, Inc. (R), AZ, *169*
ProStar Systems, Inc. (C), MD, *525*
PSP Agency (C), NY, *525*
Quality Consulting Group, Inc. (C), WI, *526*
Quantum EDP Recruiting Services (C), QE, *526*
Quest Enterprises, Ltd. (C), IL, *527*
Redell Search, Inc. (C), IL, *533*
The Regency Group, Ltd. (C), NE, *533*
RemTech Business Solutions, Inc. (C), MI, *534*
The Renaissance Network (C), MA, *534*
Resource Services, Inc. (C), NY, *534*
Response Staffing Services (C), NY, *534*
RGE (C), VA, *535*
RHAssoc. Inc. (C), KS, *535*
RHI Consulting (C), VA, *536*
RHS Assoc. (C), AL, *536*
W. F. Richer Assoc., Inc. (C), NY, *536*
Jack Richman & Assoc. (C), FL, *537*
Richmond Assoc. (C), NY, *537*
Ritech Management Inc. (C), NY, *537*
The Riverbend Group (C), MO, *538*
Robert Shields & Assoc. (C), TX, *538*
Ross Personnel Consultants, Inc. (C), CT, *545*
The Rubinic Consulting Group (C), OH, *548*
S-H-S TechStaff (C), PA, *549*
Sales Consultants of Honolulu (C), HI, *558*
Sales Consultants of Raleigh-Durham-RTP (C), NC, *561*
Sanders Management Assoc., Inc. (C), NJ, *565*
Sanford Rose Assoc. - Laguna Beach (C), CA, *565*
Sanford Rose Assoc. - Charlotte (C), NC, *568*
Sanford Rose Assoc. - Columbus North (C), OH, *569*
Sanford Rose Assoc. - Euclid (C), OH, *569*
Sanford Rose Assoc. - Youngstown (C), OH, *569*
Schulenburg & Assoc. (C), GA, *572*
Search Group (C), CA, *575*
Search Int'l. (R), MA, *187*
Search Solutions Inc. (C), CA, *576*
Segal & Assoc. (C), GA, *578*
Setford-Shaw-Najarian Assoc. (C), NY, *579*
Sevcor Int'l., Inc. (R), IL, *188*
Shell Technology Group (C), CA, *580*
The Silicon Network (C), ON, *581*
SilverSands Int'l. (C), FL, *582*
Smartsource Inc. (C), CA, *583*
Smith Assoc. (C), IA, *584*
Andrea Sobel & Assoc., Inc. (C), CA, *586*
Sofco (C), NY, *586*
SoftSearch Inc. (C), NJ, *586*
Software Engineering Solutions, Inc. (C), CA, *586*
Southport Int'l. Assoc. Inc. (C), FL, *588*
Southwest Search & Consulting, Inc. (C), AZ, *588*
Southwestern Professional Services (C), TN, *588*
Spectra International LLC (C), AZ, *589*
SpencerStuart (R), NY, *196*
Squires Resources Inc. (C), ON, *590*
StaffWriters Plus (C), NY, *591*
The Stanton Group, Inc. (C), IL, *591*
Steinbach & Co. (C), MA, *592*
Stevens Assoc. (C), MA, *593*
Linford E. Stiles & Assoc., L.L.C. (R), NH, *201*
Synergy Systems (C), ON, *598*
Systems One Ltd. (C), IL, *598*
Systems Personnel, Inc. (C), NY, *598*
Systems Search (C), IL, *599*
Systems Search Group, Inc. (C), NC, *599*
Roy Talman & Assoc. (C), IL, *599*
Tate Consulting, Inc. (R), FL, *207*
TE, Inc. (C), IL, *600*
TeamBuilders (C), GA, *600*
Tech Connector Group (C), CA, *601*
Technical Connections, Inc. (C), CA, *601*
Technical Recruiting Consultants (C), IL, *602*
Techno-Trac Systems, Inc. (C), NY, *603*
Technology Search Int'l. (C), CA, *603*
Tele-Solutions of Arizona, Inc. (C), AZ, *604*
Telequest Communications, Inc. (C), NJ, *605*
Templeton & Assoc. (C), MN, *605*
The TGA Company (C), TX, *606*
Thor, Inc. (C), CA, *606*
Skip Tolette Executive Search Consulting (R), NJ, *209*
Trac One (R), NJ, *210*
Van Treadaway Assoc., Inc. (R), GA, *210*
Triad Technology Group (C), OR, *609*
B. D. Wallace & Assoc. (C), MD, *614*
The Wayne Group, Ltd. (C), NY, *616*
Weliver & Assoc. (C), MI, *618*
Arch S. Whitehead Assoc. Inc. (ASWA) (R), NY, *219*
Dick Williams & Assoc. (C), CA, *621*
Woltz & Assoc., Inc. (R), IL, *224*
Worlco Computer Resources, Inc. (C), PA, *624*
Dennis Wynn Assoc., Inc. (C), FL, *625*
Bill Young & Assoc. (C), VA, *626*
P. D. Zier Assoc. (C), CT, *627*

08.6 Network administration

Access Data Personnel, Inc. (C), NH, *233*
Account Ability Now (C), MI, *234*
Action Executive Personnel Consulting Inc. (C), ON, *239*
Adel-Lawrence Assoc., Inc. (C), NJ, *240*
Advanced Recruiting, Inc. (C), OK, *240*
AJM Professional Services (C), MI, *243*
Allen Consulting Group, Inc. (C), MO, *244*
Allstaff, Inc. (C), IL, *245*
Andex Executive Search (C), CT, *250*
Applied Technology Solutions Inc. (C), ON, *252*
Ashton Computer Professionals, Inc. (C), BC, *253*
Avion International Technology Inc. (C), ON, *257*
Battalia Winston Int'l./The Euram Consultants Group (R), NY, *13*
Broadband Resource Group (C), CA, *274*
D. Brown & Assoc., Inc. (C), OR, *275*
California Management Search (C), CA, *279*
The Cambridge Group Ltd. (C), CT, *280*
Career Enterprises (C), OH, *282*
Careers First, Inc. (C), NJ, *283*
CAS Comsearch Inc. (C), NY, *285*
Casey & Assoc., Inc. (C), TX, *286*
CBA Companies (C), CA, *286*
Chacra, Belliveau & Assoc. Inc. (C), QE, *288*
Chatham Search Assoc., Inc. (C), NJ, *290*
Cheney Associates (C), CT, *290*
Ann Coe & Assoc. (C), IL, *294*
Combined Resources Inc. (R), OH, *38*
Commercial Programming Systems, Inc. (C), CA, *294*
Computer Personnel, Inc. (C), WA, *295*
Computer Placements Unlimited Inc. (C), NY, *295*
Computer Professionals Unlimited (C), TX, *295*
Computer Recruiters, Inc. (C), CA, *295*
The Consulting Group of North America, Inc. (C), VA, *297*
ContactBridge, Inc. (R), IL, *40*
COR Management Services, Ltd. (C), NY, *298*
Cornerstone Resources, Inc. (C), OK, *299*
Corporate Search Consultants, Inc. (C), FL, *301*
Creative Financial Staffing (C), MA, *303*
Current Resource Group, Inc. (C), GA, *305*
Data Search Network, Inc. (C), FL, *307*
Data-AxIS Corp. (C), FL, *307*
DataPro Personnel Consultants (C), TX, *308*
DBC Recruiting Network (C), GA, *309*
Desktop Staffing, Inc. (C), IL, *311*
Dreier Consulting (C), NJ, *315*
Dunhill Technical Staffing (C), IN, *320*
Dunhill Professional Search of Rolling Meadows (C), IL, *320*
Dunhill Professional Search of Greater New Orleans (C), LA, *321*
Dunhill Professional Search of Wilkes-Barre/Scranton, Inc. (C), PA, *322*
Dynamic Choices Inc. (C), MO, *323*
Dynamic Computer Consultants, Inc. (C), AZ, *324*
Dynamic Staffing Network (C), IL, *324*
Eastridge Infotech (C), CA, *326*
Eckler Personnel Network (C), VT, *326*
Eggers Consulting Co., Inc. (C), NE, *327*
Elite Consultants, Inc. (C), FL, *328*
Evergreen & Co. (C), MA, *331*
Executive Direction, Inc. (C), CA, *333*
Executive Partners Inc. (C), CT, *333*

Executive Recruiters, Inc. (C), WI, *334*
Executive Resource Group, Inc. (R), ME, *63*
Executive Search Group LLC (C), CA, *335*
Executive Search of America, Inc. (C), OH, *336*
Fenzel Milar Assoc. (C), OH, *339*
The Fisher Group (R), AB, *67*
A. G. Fishkin & Assoc., Inc. (R), MD, *68*
Fortuna Technologies Inc. (C), CA, *343*
Friedman Eisenstein Raemer & Schwartz, LLP (R), IL, *72*
GCO (C), CA, *355*
Gilmore & Assoc. (C), CA, *357*
Global Technologies Group Inc. (C), NC, *359*
Grant/Morgan Assoc., Inc. (C), MD, *361*
The Gullgroup (C), TX, *364*
Hall Kinion (C), CA, *366*
Hayman Daugherty Assoc., Inc. (C), GA, *370*
High-Tech Recruiters (C), CT, *378*
The Hiring Authority, Inc. (C), FL, *379*
Holden & Harlan Assoc., Inc. (C), IL, *380*
HR Consultants (C), GA, *382*
Leigh Hunt & Assoc., Inc. (C), ME, *384*
Huntington Personnel Consultants, Inc. (C), NY, *386*
i.j. & assoc., inc. (C), CO, *386*
Independent Resource Systems (C), CA, *388*
Information Systems Professionals (C), NC, *388*
Information Technology Search (C), PA, *388*
Infovia (C), CA, *388*
International Pro Sourcing, Inc. (C), PA, *393*
International Technical Resources (C), FL, *393*
ISG Informatics Search Group (C), ON, *395*
J & D Resources Inc. (C), TN, *395*
James Moore & Assoc. (C), CA, *397*
JDC Assoc. (C), NY, *397*
Jeffrey Meryl Assoc., Inc. (C), NJ, *398*
Jenex Technology Placement Inc. (C), BC, *398*
The Jotorok Group (C), RI, *401*
Kames & Assoc. (C), MD, *403*
Melissa Katzman, Executive Search (C), NY, *404*
A.T. Kearney Executive Search (R), IL, *111*
The Kennett Group, Inc. (R), PA, *112*
Kennison & Assoc. Inc. (C), MO, *405*
Kenzer Corp. (R), NY, *113*
Kleber & Assoc. (C), WA, *407*
Kukoy Associates (R), CO, *121*
Kulper & Co., L.L.C. (R), NJ, *121*
LAS Management Consulting Group, Inc. (R), NJ, *125*
Legal Network Inc. (C), CA, *416*
The Levton Group Inc. (R), ON, *129*
Lewis Consulting Service (C), IL, *417*
Lifter & Assoc. (C), CA, *418*
Lynx, Inc. (C), MA, *421*
Carol Maden Group (C), VA, *422*
Management Recruiters of Fresno (C), CA, *440*
Management Recruiters of Melbourne, Inc. (C), FL, *443*
Management Recruiters of Batavia (C), IL, *447*
Management Recruiters-Cedar Rapids, Inc. (C), IA, *448*
Management Recruiters of Rochester (C), MN, *452*
Management Recruiters of The Sandias (C), NM, *454*
Management Recruiters of Boone (C), NC, *456*
Management Recruiters - North Canton, Inc. (C), OH, *458*
Management Recruiters of Youngstown (C), OH, *458*
Management Recruiters of Travelers Rest, Inc. (C), SC, *461*
Management Search, Inc. (C), IL, *467*
Mancini Technical Recruiting (C), VA, *468*
Marks & Co., Inc. (R), CT, *136*
Karen Marshall Assoc. (C), KY, *471*
Masserman & Assoc., Inc. (R), NY, *138*
Paul May & Assoc. (C), IL, *473*
McDowell & Co., Recruiters (C), TX, *474*
McKee Cyber Search (C), MS, *475*
Michael Thomas, Inc. (C), OH, *480*
MIS Computer Professionals, Inc. (C), KS, *482*
Mitchell Martin Inc. (C), NY, *483*
Mogul Consultants, Inc. (C), NY, *483*
Larry Moore & Assoc. (C), CA, *484*
Mulcahy Co. (C), WI, *487*
The Network Corporate Search Personnel Inc. (C), AB, *491*
The North Peak Group (C), OH, *496*
O'Keefe & Assoc. (C), TX, *497*
Opus Marketing (R), CA, *156*
The Oxford Group (C), TX, *500*
Arthur Pann Assoc., Inc. (C), NY, *502*
Paragon Recruiting Officials Inc. (C), OH, *502*
Phillips Assoc. (C), FL, *510*
Norman Powers Assoc., Inc. (C), MA, *515*
Pro-Tech Search, Inc. (C), IL, *519*
Procom (C), ON, *519*
Professional Careers, Inc. (C), NC, *520*
Professional Placement Assoc., Inc. (C), NY, *521*
Professional Search, Inc. Int'l. (C), TX, *523*
ProSearch, Inc. (C), PA, *524*
Protocol Inc. (C), CA, *525*
PSP Agency (C), NY, *525*
Quality Consulting Group, Inc. (C), WI, *526*
Quantum EDP Recruiting Services (C), QE, *526*
Quest Enterprises, Ltd. (C), IL, *527*
J. E. Ranta Assoc. (C), MA, *529*
RemTech Business Solutions, Inc. (C), MI, *534*
Resource Services, Inc. (C), NY, *534*
Russell Reynolds Assoc., Inc. (R), NY, *176*
RHAssoc. Inc. (C), KS, *535*
Jack Richman & Assoc. (C), FL, *537*
Richmond Assoc. (C), NY, *537*
Ritech Management Inc. (C), NY, *537*
Ritta Professional Search Inc. (C), NY, *538*
Robert Shields & Assoc. (C), TX, *538*
Roll International (C), TX, *541*
S-H-S TechStaff (C), PA, *549*
Sales Consultants of Danbury (C), CT, *557*
Sales Consultants of Birmingham (C), MI, *559*
Sanford Rose Assoc. - Columbus North (C), OH, *569*
Sanford Rose Assoc. - Euclid (C), OH, *569*
Sanford Rose Assoc. - Youngstown (C), OH, *569*
Schulenburg & Assoc. (C), GA, *572*
Search & Recruit Int'l. (C), VA, *573*
Selective Search Associates (C), OH, *578*
Shell Technology Group (C), CA, *580*
The Silicon Network (C), ON, *581*
Smartsource Inc. (C), CA, *583*
Smith & Assoc. (C), CA, *583*
Smith Assoc. (C), IA, *584*
Softrix, Inc. (C), NJ, *586*
SoftSearch Inc. (C), NJ, *586*
Software Engineering Solutions, Inc. (C), CA, *586*
Southwest Search & Consulting, Inc. (C), AZ, *588*
Spectra International LLC (C), AZ, *589*
Squires Resources Inc. (C), ON, *590*
Stanewick, Hart & Assoc., Inc. (C), FL, *591*
The Summit Group (C), CA, *596*
Synergistech Communications (C), CA, *597*
Synergy Solutions, Ltd. (C), WA, *597*
Systems Personnel, Inc. (C), NY, *598*
Systems Search (C), IL, *599*
TBC, Inc. (C), KY, *600*
Tech Search (C), CA, *601*
Technical Connections, Inc. (C), CA, *601*
Techno-Trac Systems, Inc. (C), NY, *603*
Tele-Solutions of Arizona, Inc. (C), AZ, *604*
Telequest Communications, Inc. (C), NJ, *605*
Skip Tolette Executive Search Consulting (R), NJ, *209*
B. D. Wallace & Assoc. (C), MD, *614*
Weliver & Assoc. (C), MI, *618*
Bruce G. Woods Executive Search (R), TX, *224*
Bill Young & Assoc. (C), VA, *626*

08.7 Database administration

Access Data Personnel, Inc. (C), NH, *233*
Action Executive Personnel Consulting Inc. (C), ON, *239*
Advanced Recruiting, Inc. (C), OK, *240*
Advisors' Search Group, Inc. (C), NY, *241*
Allard Associates (C), CA, *244*
Allen Consulting Group, Inc. (C), MO, *244*
Allstaff, Inc. (C), IL, *245*
Applied Technology Solutions Inc. (C), ON, *252*
Ashton Computer Professionals, Inc. (C), BC, *253*
Avion International Technology Inc. (C), ON, *257*
Baker, Nelms & Montgomery (C), IL, *258*

Bassett Laudi Partners (C), ON, *261*
Battalia Winston Int'l./The Euram Consultants Group (R), NY, *13*
Bennett & Associates (C), TX, *264*
D. Brown & Assoc., Inc. (C), OR, *275*
Business Partners, Inc. (C), FL, *277*
California Management Search (C), CA, *279*
The Cambridge Group Ltd. (C), CT, *280*
Career Enterprises (C), OH, *282*
Careers First, Inc. (C), NJ, *283*
CAS Comsearch Inc. (C), NY, *285*
CBA Companies (C), CA, *286*
The Center for Career Advancement, LLC (C), NJ, *287*
Chacra, Belliveau & Assoc. Inc. (C), QE, *288*
Chatham Search Assoc., Inc. (C), NJ, *290*
Cheney Associates (C), CT, *290*
Ann Coe & Assoc. (C), IL, *294*
Combined Resources Inc. (R), OH, *38*
Commercial Programming Systems, Inc. (C), CA, *294*
Computer Network Resources, Inc. (C), CA, *295*
Computer Personnel, Inc. (C), WA, *295*
Computer Placements Unlimited Inc. (C), NY, *295*
Computer Professionals Unlimited (C), TX, *295*
Computer Recruiters, Inc. (C), CA, *295*
The Consulting Group of North America, Inc. (C), VA, *297*
ContactBridge, Inc. (R), IL, *40*
Continental Search & Outplacement, Inc. (C), MD, *298*
COR Management Services, Ltd. (C), NY, *298*
Cornerstone Resources, Inc. (C), OK, *299*
Corporate Search Consultants, Inc. (C), FL, *301*
Creative Financial Staffing (C), MA, *303*
Current Resource Group, Inc. (C), GA, *305*
Data Search Network, Inc. (C), FL, *307*
Data-AxIS Corp. (C), FL, *307*
DataPro Personnel Consultants (C), TX, *308*
Allen Davis & Assoc. (C), MA, *308*
Bert Davis Executive Search, Inc. (R), NY, *47*
Desktop Staffing, Inc. (C), IL, *311*
Direct Marketing Resources (C), NC, *312*
Drummond Assoc., Inc. (C), NY, *315*
Dunhill Professional Search of Rolling Meadows (C), IL, *320*
Dunhill Professional Search of Wilkes-Barre/Scranton, Inc. (C), PA, *322*
Dynamic Computer Consultants, Inc. (C), AZ, *324*
Eastridge Infotech (C), CA, *326*
Eckler Personnel Network (C), VT, *326*
Eggers Consulting Co., Inc. (C), NE, *327*
Elite Consultants, Inc. (C), FL, *328*
The Elmhurst Group (C), CA, *329*
Evergreen & Co. (C), MA, *331*
Executive Direction, Inc. (C), CA, *333*
Executive Resource Group, Inc. (R), ME, *63*
Fortuna Technologies Inc. (C), CA, *343*
GCO (C), CA, *355*
Gilmore & Assoc. (C), CA, *357*
The Grant Search Group, Inc. (C), ON, *361*
Hall Kinion (C), CA, *366*
Hallman Group, Inc. (C), MI, *367*
Hazlett Associates (R), IL, *88*
HDB Incorporated (C), MO, *371*
High-Tech Recruiters (C), CT, *378*
The Hiring Authority, Inc. (C), FL, *379*
Holden & Harlan Assoc., Inc. (C), IL, *380*
Huntington Personnel Consultants, Inc. (C), NY, *386*
i.j. & assoc., inc. (C), CO, *386*
Independent Resource Systems (C), CA, *388*
Industry Consultants, Inc. (C), GA, *388*
Information Systems Professionals (C), NC, *388*
Information Technology Search (C), PA, *388*
Infovia (C), CA, *388*
International Business Partners (C), ON, *392*
ISG Informatics Search Group (C), ON, *395*
J & D Resources Inc. (C), TN, *395*
James Moore & Assoc. (C), CA, *397*
Jeffrey Meryl Assoc., Inc. (C), NJ, *398*
Jenex Technology Placement Inc. (C), BC, *398*
The Jotorok Group (C), RI, *401*
Kames & Assoc. (C), MD, *403*
Melissa Katzman, Executive Search (C), NY, *404*
A.T. Kearney Executive Search (R), IL, *111*
The Kennett Group, Inc. (R), PA, *112*
Kennison & Assoc. Inc. (C), MO, *405*
Kenzer Corp. (R), NY, *113*
Kleber & Assoc. (C), WA, *407*
The Kleven Group, Inc. - Executive Search Division (R), MA, *116*
LAS Management Consulting Group, Inc. (R), NJ, *125*
Lascelle & Assoc. Inc. (C), ON, *413*
Reynolds Lebus Assoc. (C), AZ, *415*
Lewis Consulting Service (C), IL, *417*
Lynx, Inc. (C), MA, *421*
Carol Maden Group (C), VA, *422*
Management Recruiters of Melbourne, Inc. (C), FL, *443*
Management Recruiters of Batavia (C), IL, *447*
Management Recruiters of Chicago West (C), IL, *447*
Management Recruiters of Rochester (C), MN, *452*
Management Recruiters of Lake Tahoe, NV (C), NV, *453*
Management Recruiters of The Sandias (C), NM, *454*
Management Recruiters of Boone (C), NC, *456*
Management Recruiters - North Canton, Inc. (C), OH, *458*
Management Recruiters of Youngstown (C), OH, *458*
Management Recruiters of Travelers Rest, Inc. (C), SC, *461*
Management Search, Inc. (C), IL, *467*
Mancini Technical Recruiting (C), VA, *468*
Karen Marshall Assoc. (C), KY, *471*
Masserman & Assoc., Inc. (R), NY, *138*
Paul May & Assoc. (C), IL, *473*
McDowell & Co., Recruiters (C), TX, *474*
Michael Thomas, Inc. (C), OH, *480*
MIS Computer Professionals, Inc. (C), KS, *482*
Mitchell Martin Inc. (C), NY, *483*
Molecular Solutions, Inc. (C), SC, *483*
Monarch Technology Management LLC (C), CO, *484*
Larry Moore & Assoc. (C), CA, *484*
Mulcahy Co. (C), WI, *487*
The Network Corporate Search Personnel Inc. (C), AB, *491*
The North Peak Group (C), OH, *496*
NorthStar Technologies, Inc. (C), NY, *496*
NYCOR Search, Inc. (C), MN, *497*
O'Keefe & Assoc. (C), TX, *497*
Omnisearch Assoc. (C), CA, *499*
Opus Marketing (R), CA, *156*
Arthur Pann Assoc., Inc. (C), NY, *502*
Paragon Recruiting Officials Inc. (C), OH, *502*
Phillips Assoc. (C), FL, *510*
PPS Information Systems Staffing (C), MD, *515*
Pro-Tech Search, Inc. (C), IL, *519*
Procom (C), ON, *519*
Professional Careers, Inc. (C), NC, *520*
Professional Placement Assoc., Inc. (C), NY, *521*
Professional Search, Inc. Int'l. (C), TX, *523*
ProSearch, Inc. (C), PA, *524*
Protocol Inc. (C), CA, *525*
Quality Consulting Group, Inc. (C), WI, *526*
Quantum EDP Recruiting Services (C), QE, *526*
Quest Enterprises, Ltd. (C), IL, *527*
J. E. Ranta Assoc. (C), MA, *529*
RemTech Business Solutions, Inc. (C), MI, *534*
The Renaissance Network (C), MA, *534*
Resource Services, Inc. (C), NY, *534*
Russell Reynolds Assoc., Inc. (R), NY, *176*
RHAssoc. Inc. (C), KS, *535*
Richmond Assoc. (C), NY, *537*
Ritech Management Inc. (C), NY, *537*
The Riverbend Group (C), MO, *538*
Robert Shields & Assoc. (C), TX, *538*
Roll International (C), TX, *541*
S-H-S TechStaff (C), PA, *549*
Sampson Medical Search (C), CA, *564*
Sanford Rose Assoc. - Columbus North (C), OH, *569*
Sanford Rose Assoc. - Euclid (C), OH, *569*
Sanford Rose Assoc. - Youngstown (C), OH, *569*
Schulenburg & Assoc. (C), GA, *572*
Search America, Inc. (C), MA, *574*
Search Solutions Inc. (C), CA, *576*
Selective Search Associates (C), OH, *578*
Sharrow & Assoc., Inc. (C), MI, *579*
Shell Technology Group (C), CA, *580*
Smith & Assoc. (C), FL, *583*
Smith Assoc. (C), IA, *584*

Softrix, Inc. (C), NJ, *586*
SoftSearch Inc. (C), NJ, *586*
Software Engineering Solutions, Inc. (C), CA, *586*
Southwest Search & Consulting, Inc. (C), AZ, *588*
Squires Resources Inc. (C), ON, *590*
Stanewick, Hart & Assoc., Inc. (C), FL, *591*
The Summit Group (C), CA, *596*
Synergistech Communications (C), CA, *597*
Synergy Solutions, Ltd. (C), WA, *597*
Systems Personnel, Inc. (C), NY, *598*
Systems Search (C), IL, *599*
Technical Connections, Inc. (C), CA, *601*
Techno-Trac Systems, Inc. (C), NY, *603*
Tele-Solutions of Arizona, Inc. (C), AZ, *604*
Skip Tolette Executive Search Consulting (R), NJ, *209*
Triad Technology Group (C), OR, *609*
Ward-Hoffman & Assoc. (C), ID, *615*
C. Weiss Assoc., Inc. (C), NY, *618*
Wilkinson SoftSearch, Inc. (C), VA, *620*
The Wilmington Group (C), NC, *622*
Wilson-Douglas-Jordan (C), IL, *622*
Woltz & Assoc., Inc. (R), IL, *224*
Bill Young & Assoc. (C), VA, *626*

09.0 Research & development/scientists

A.M.C.R., Inc. (C), OH, *232*
Adirect Recruiting Corp. (C), ON, *240*
Advanced Corporate Search (C), CA, *240*
Advancement, Inc. (C), IL, *241*
The Advisory Group, Inc. (R), CA, *2*
AES Search (C), NJ, *241*
Agri-Tech Personnel, Inc. (C), MO, *242*
Albrecht & Assoc., Executive Search Consultants (C), TX, *243*
Alexander Enterprises, Inc. (C), PA, *243*
David Allen Assoc. (R), NJ, *3*
Allen-Jeffers Assoc. (C), CA, *245*
The Altco Group (C), NJ, *246*
ALW Research Int'l. (R), NJ, *4*
American Executive Search (C), FL, *247*
American Services Group (C), IL, *248*
Ames-O'Neill Assoc., Inc. (C), NY, *249*
AMS Int'l. (R), VA, *5*
Analog Solutions (C), NY, *249*
Fred Anthony Assoc. (C), WI, *251*
Applied Resources, Inc. (C), MN, *252*
ARJay & Assoc. (C), NC, *252*
J. S. Armstrong & Assoc., Inc. (R), CA, *7*
Asheville Search & Consulting (C), NC, *253*
Ashway Ltd. Agency (C), NY, *253*
W. R. Atchison & Assoc., Inc. (C), NC, *254*
Atlanta Executive Partners, Inc. (R), MA, *8*
Atlantic West Int'l. (C), NC, *255*
Atomic Personnel, Inc. (C), PA, *255*
Austin-McGregor Int'l. (R), TX, *9*
D. W. Baird & Associates (C), MD, *257*
Allen Ballach Assoc. Inc. (R), ON, *10*
Ballos & Co., Inc. (R), NJ, *10*
James Bangert & Assoc., Inc. (R), MN, *11*
Fred A. Barnette & Assoc. (R), NC, *11*
Barr Assoc. (C), PA, *259*
Nathan Barry Assoc., Inc. (R), MA, *12*
Bayland Assoc. (C), CA, *261*
Beach Executive Search Inc. (R), FL, *14*
The Bedford Group (R), RI, *15*
Gary S. Bell Assoc., Inc. (C), NJ, *263*
Bench Int'l. Search, Inc. (R), CA, *15*
The Bennett Group, Inc. (R), IN, *16*
Bernhart Assoc. (C), MN, *265*
Ed Bertolas Assoc., Inc. (C), CA, *265*
Paul J. Biestek Assoc., Inc. (R), IL, *17*
Bio-Venture Group (C), RI, *266*
Biomedical Search Consultants (R), CT, *17*
BioPharmMed (C), FL, *267*
BioQuest Inc. (R), CA, *17*
BioTech Research Recruiters Inc. (C), CA, *267*
BJB Assoc. (C), VA, *267*
The Black Leopard (C), CA, *267*
Blair/Tech Recruiters, Inc. (C), NJ, *268*
J: Blakslee Int'l., Ltd. (R), CA, *18*
Blaney Executive Search (R), MA, *18*
Blanton & Co. (C), AL, *268*
Blau Mancino Schroeder (R), NJ, *18*
The Borton Wallace Co. (R), NC, *19*
Bos Business Consultants (C), NY, *270*
Bosland Gray Assoc. (R), NJ, *20*
Bower & Associates (C), TX, *271*
M. F. Branch Assoc., Inc. (C), NC, *272*
Brei & Assoc., Inc. (C), IA, *272*
Brentwood Int'l. (R), CA, *23*
Brett Personnel Specialists (C), NJ, *273*
Brian Assoc., Inc. (C), NY, *273*
Briant Assoc., Inc. (R), IL, *23*
Bridgecreek Personnel Agency (C), CA, *273*
Brissenden, McFarland, Fuccella & Reynolds, Inc. (R), NJ, *23*
Brookman Associates (C), NY, *274*
Bernard E. Brooks & Assoc., Inc. (R), SC, *24*
Brush Creek Partners (R), MO, *24*
Bryan & Louis Research (C), OH, *275*
Bryant Research (C), NJ, *275*
BT&A, LLC (R), CT, *24*
J. Burkey Assoc. (R), NJ, *25*
Butterfield & Co. Int'l., Inc. (C), HI, *277*
C. P. Consulting (R), PA, *26*
C.P.S., Inc. (C), IL, *278*
Juliette Lang Cahn Executive Search (C), NY, *279*
Caliber Associates (R), PA, *27*
California Search Agency, Inc. (C), CA, *279*
CanMed Consultants Inc. (C), ON, *280*
Canny, Bowen Inc. (R), NY, *27*
Caplan Assoc., Inc. (R), NJ, *28*
The Caplan-Taylor Group (R), CA, *28*
Career +Plus (C), NY, *281*
Career Counseling Inc. (CCI) (C), KY, *282*
Carr Management Services, Inc. (C), PA, *284*
Carver Search Consultants (C), CA, *285*
Rosemary Cass Ltd. (R), CT, *31*
The Cassie Group (R), NJ, *31*
Catalyx Group (R), NY, *31*
Caywood Partners, Ltd. (R), CA, *32*
Cendea Connection Int'l. (R), TX, *32*
Central Executive Search, Inc. (C), OH, *287*
The Century Group (C), KS, *287*
Charles & Associates, Inc. (C), NE, *289*
Chelsea Resources, Inc. (C), CT, *290*
Ken Clark Int'l. (R), NJ, *36*
Coe & Co. Int'l. Inc./EMA Partners Int'l. (R), AB, *37*
The Coelyn Group (R), CA, *37*
Continental Search Assoc. (C), OH, *298*
Conway & Assoc. (R), IL, *40*
Corporate Environment Ltd. (R), IL, *41*
Corporate Recruiters Inc. (C), PA, *300*
Corporate Resources Professional Placement (C), MN, *300*
Corporate Staffing Group, Inc. (C), PA, *301*
Cosier & Assoc. (C), AB, *302*
Cowin Assoc. (R), NY, *42*
Cross Country Consultants, Inc. (C), MD, *304*
Jim Crumpley & Assoc. (C), MO, *304*
CSA/Clinical Staffing Assoc., LLC (C), NJ, *304*
Curry, Telleri Group, Inc. (R), NJ, *44*
Cusack Consulting (R), NY, *44*
CV Associates (C), NY, *305*
D.A.L. Associates, Inc. (R), CT, *45*
Charles Dahl Group, Inc. (C), MN, *306*
Data-AxIS Corp. (C), FL, *307*
Alan Davis & Assoc. Inc. (R), QE, *47*
Debbon Recruiting Group, Inc. (C), MO, *310*
Deeco Int'l. (C), UT, *310*
Delta Services (R), TX, *48*
R. J. Dishaw & Assoc. (R), TX, *52*
DiTech Resources (C), CT, *313*
Diversified Search, Inc. (R), PA, *52*
Dixie Search Assoc. (C), GA, *313*
Doering & Assoc. (C), CA, *313*
Doleman Enterprises (R), VA, *53*
The Domann Organization (R), CA, *53*
Donahue/Bales Assoc. (R), IL, *54*
DSR-Search & Recruitment (C), TX, *315*
J. H. Dugan & Assoc., Inc. (R), CA, *55*
Dukas Assoc. (C), MA, *315*
Dunhill Professional Search of Englewood, Inc. (C), CO, *319*
Dunhill of Corpus Christi, Inc. (C), TX, *323*
Dynamic Synergy Corp. (R), CA, *56*
The E & K Group (C), NJ, *324*
E O Technical (C), CT, *324*
Eagle Consulting Group Inc. (C), TX, *325*
J. M. Eagle Partners Ltd. (C), WI, *325*
Eagle Research, Inc. (C), NJ, *325*
Eastbourne Assoc. Inc. (R), NY, *56*
EGM Consulting, Inc. (R), FL, *57*
William J. Elam & Assoc. (R), NE, *58*
Elite Medical Search (C), GA, *328*
Elite Resources Group (R), OH, *58*
The Elsworth Group (C), TX, *329*
Emerging Medical Technologies, Inc. (C), CO, *329*
Emerson & Co. (C), GA, *329*
Emmett Executive Search, Inc. (C), NY, *330*
Empire International (R), PA, *59*

Employ® (C), PA, *330*
The Energists (R), TX, *59*
Engineering & Scientific Search Assoc. (ESSA) (C), NJ, *330*
Engineering Futures, LLC (C), CT, *330*
Engineering Profiles (C), FL, *330*
Essential Solutions, Inc. (C), CA, *331*
Excalibur Human Resources, Inc. (R), NJ, *61*
Exec Tech, Inc. (C), IL, *332*
ExecuTech (C), IN, *332*
Executive Business Solutions, Inc. (C), WA, *332*
Executive Connection (C), OH, *333*
Executive Manning Corp. (R), FL, *63*
Executive Recruitment Services, Inc. (ERS, Inc.) (C), GA, *334*
Executive Resource Assoc. (C), VA, *334*
Executive Search Consultants (C), CA, *335*
Executive Search Plus, Inc. (C), IN, *336*
Executives Worldwide, Inc. (C), OR, *337*
EXETER 2100 (C), NH, *337*
F.L.A.G. (C), OH, *338*
Fallstaff Search (C), MD, *338*
James Feerst & Assoc., Inc. (C), AZ, *339*
Fenwick Partners (R), MA, *66*
Fernow Assoc. (C), PA, *339*
Guild Fetridge Acoustical Search, Inc. (C), NY, *340*
First Advisory Services Int'l., Inc. (R), MD, *67*
First Choice Search (R), WA, *67*
First Search America, Inc. (C), TN, *341*
Jack Stuart Fisher Assoc. (C), NJ, *341*
Fisher Personnel Management Services (R), CA, *68*
J. G. Flynn & Assoc. Inc. (R), BC, *69*
Forest People Int'l. Search Ltd. (C), BC, *343*
F-O-R-T-U-N-E Personnel Consultants of Denver, Inc. (C), CO, *344*
Fortune Personnel Consultants of Colorado Springs (C), CO, *344*
F-O-R-T-U-N-E Personnel Consultants of Wilmington (C), DE, *344*
Fortune Personnel Consultants (C), CA, *344*
F-O-R-T-U-N-E Personnel Consultants of Atlanta, Inc. (C), GA, *345*
Fortune Personnel Consultants of Topsfield (C), MA, *346*
F-O-R-T-U-N-E Personnel Consultants of Southwest Indiana (C), IN, *346*
Fortune Personnel Consultants (C), MT, *347*
F-O-R-T-U-N-E Personnel Consultants of Menlo Park, Inc. (C), NJ, *347*
F-O-R-T-U-N-E Personnel Consultants of Bergen County Inc. (C), NJ, *347*
Fortune Personnel Consultants of Allentown, Inc. (C), PA, *348*
Fortune Personnel Consultants of Anderson, Inc. (C), SC, *349*
F-O-R-T-U-N-E Personnel Consultants of Houston, Inc. (C), TX, *350*
Fortune Personnel Consultants of San Antonio, Inc. (C), TX, *350*
FORTUNE Personnel Consultants of North Dallas (C), TX, *350*
Fortune Personnel Consultants of Plano (C), TX, *350*
Foster Partners (R), NY, *70*
Franklin Allen Consultants, Ltd. (R), NY, *71*
The Franklin Search Group, Inc./Medzilla (R), WA, *71*
Gallin Associates, Inc. (C), FL, *354*
W. N. Garbarini & Assoc. (R), NJ, *74*
Garland Assoc. Int'l. (C), CA, *355*
The Garms Group (R), IL, *74*
The Garret Group (R), NJ, *75*
Genesis Consulting Partners (R), PA, *76*
Genesis Recruiting (C), CA, *356*
Gilbert & Van Campen Int'l. (R), NY, *76*
Gilbert Tweed Assoc. Inc. (R), NY, *76*
Joe L. Giles & Assoc. (C), MI, *357*
The Glenwood Group (C), IL, *358*
Glines Assoc., Inc. (R), IL, *77*
Global Consulting Group Inc. (C), ON, *358*
Global Data Services, Inc. (R), NY, *77*
Global Engineers Inc. (C), ME, *358*
Global Research Partnership Inc. (R), NY, *78*
F. Gloss Int'l. (R), VA, *78*
The Gobbell Co. (R), CA, *78*
The Gogates Group, Inc. (R), NY, *79*
Gordon/Tyler (R), PA, *80*
Gould, McCoy & Chadick, Inc. (R), NY, *80*
Grantham & Co., Inc. (R), NC, *81*
Grover & Assoc. (R), OH, *82*
The Guild Corp. (C), VA, *364*
Hadley Associates, Inc. (C), NJ, *365*
Halbrecht & Co. (C), VA, *365*
The Hampton Group (C), NY, *367*
Harcor Quest & Assoc. (R), OH, *86*
Hartman & Barnette (R), VA, *87*
Bruce W. Haupt Assoc. (R), DC, *88*
The Haystack Group, Inc. (R), ME, *88*
Health Industry Consultants, Inc. (R), CO, *89*
Healthcare Management Resources, Inc. (R), GA, *89*
Healthcare Recruiters Int'l. Bay Area (C), CA, *372*
Healthcare Recruiters Int'l. - Pittsburgh (C), PA, *373*
HeartBeat Medical, Inc. (C), OR, *374*
R. W. Hebel Assoc. (R), TX, *89*
Heffelfinger Assoc., Inc. (R), MA, *89*
Henson Partners (C), AZ, *376*
Herbeck Kline & Assoc. (R), IL, *92*
The Hetzel Group, Inc. (R), IL, *92*
Hockett Associates, Inc. (R), CA, *94*
The Hogan Group (C), OH, *380*
Hollander Horizon Int'l. (R), CA, *95*
Holohan Group, Ltd. (R), MO, *95*
Horizons Unlimited (C), CA, *381*
Houtz•Strawn & Arnold, Inc. (R), TX, *96*
HR Inc. (C), NC, *382*
The Hudson Group (C), CT, *383*
Huff Assoc. (R), NJ, *98*
The Hunt Group, Inc. (R), NC, *99*
Impact Search & Strategies (C), PA, *387*
Independent Resource Systems (C), CA, *388*
Inter Regional Executive Search, Inc. (IRES, Inc.) (C), NJ, *391*
International Consulting Services, Inc. (C), IL, *392*
International Recruiting Services (C), FL, *393*
International Research Group (R), CA, *103*
Iona Partners (C), CA, *394*
Isaacson, Miller (R), MA, *104*
ISC of Atlanta, Inc. (C), GA, *394*
Jackley Search Consultants (C), MN, *396*
JAG Group (R), MO, *105*
JDG Assoc., Ltd. (C), MD, *397*
JLI-Boston (R), MA, *106*
John Jay & Co. (C), ME, *399*
Johnson & Assoc., Inc. (R), CA, *106*
K. E. Johnson Assoc. (C), WA, *399*
Joslin & Assoc., Ltd. (C), IL, *401*
JPM International (C), CA, *401*
Just Management Services Inc. (C), FL, *402*
A H Justice Search Consultants (C), TX, *402*
KABL Ability Network (C), CA, *402*
Allan Karson Assoc., Inc. (R), NJ, *110*
Martin Kartin & Co., Inc. (R), NY, *110*
Kaufman Assoc. (R), CA, *110*
Jim Kay & Assoc. (C), IL, *404*
Kaye/Bassman Int'l. Corp. (R), TX, *110*
Kazan International, Inc. (R), NJ, *110*
A.T. Kearney Executive Search (R), IL, *111*
Daniel J. Kerstein, Consultant to Management (R), CO, *114*
Kingsley Quinn/USA (R), NJ, *115*
The Kleinstein Group, Inc. (R), NJ, *116*
The Kleven Group, Inc. (C), MA, *407*
T. J. Koellhoffer & Assoc. (R), NJ, *116*
Korban Associates (R), PA, *117*
Korn/Ferry Int'l. (R), NY, *117*
Kremple Consulting Group (R), CA, *120*
Kuhn Med-Tech (C), CA, *409*
Paul Kull & Co. (R), NJ, *121*
D. Kunkle & Assoc. (C), IL, *410*
Laboratory Resource Group (C), MA, *411*
Larkin & Co. (R), CA, *124*
Lasher Assoc. (R), FL, *125*
W. R. Lawry, Inc. (R), CT, *126*
Ledbetter/Davidson Int'l., Inc. (R), NY, *127*
Albert G. Lee Assoc. (C), RI, *415*
Lewis & Blank Int'l. (R), CA, *129*
Lexington Software Inc. (C), NY, *417*
Logix, Inc. (C), MA, *420*
Longo Associates (C), CA, *420*
Lord & Albus Co. (C), TX, *420*
J. S. Lord & Company, Inc. (R), MA, *131*
Lucas Group (C), NY, *421*
Lutz Associates (C), CT, *421*
Lybrook Assoc., Inc. (C), RI, *421*
M H Executive Search Group (C), TX, *422*
M. K. & Assoc. (C), PA, *422*
Maczkov-Biosciences, Inc. (R), CA, *133*
The Madison Group (R), NY, *133*
Management Assoc. (C), CA, *424*
Management Catalysts (R), NJ, *134*
Management Recruiters of San Luis Obispo (C), CA, *439*
Management Recruiters Peninsula (C), CA, *439*
Management Recruiters of Altamonte (C), FL, *442*

Management Recruiters of Milford Inc. (C), CT, *442*
Management Recruiters of Boca Raton (C), FL, *443*
Management Recruiters of Pensacola (C), FL, *444*
Management Recruiters of Plant City, Inc. (C), FL, *444*
Management Recruiters of Duluth (C), GA, *445*
Management Recruiters of Venice, Inc. (C), FL, *445*
Management Recruiters of Savannah (C), GA, *446*
Management Recruiters of Lake Forest, IL (C), IL, *447*
Management Recruiters of Springfield, Inc. (C), IL, *447*
Management Recruiters of South Bend (C), IN, *448*
Management Recruiters of the Baltimore Washington Corridor (C), MD, *450*
Management Recruiters of New Providence (C), NJ, *454*
Management Recruiters of Burlington (C), NC, *455*
Management Recruiters of Woodbury Inc. (C), NY, *455*
Management Recruiters of Rocky Mount - Southwest (C), NC, *456*
Management Recruiters of Raleigh (C), NC, *456*
Management Recruiters of Winston-Salem (C), NC, *457*
Management Recruiters of McMurray, Inc. (C), PA, *459*
Management Recruiters of Westmoreland County, Inc. (C), PA, *459*
Management Recruiters of Florence (C), SC, *460*
Management Recruiters of West Chester, Inc. (C), PA, *460*
Management Recruiters of Aiken (C), SC, *460*
Management Recruiters of Sioux Falls, LLP (C), SD, *461*
Management Recruiters of North West Austin (C), TX, *462*
Management Recruiters of Austin (C), TX, *462*
Management Recruiters Int'l.-The Woodlands (C), TX, *464*
Management Recruiters of Seattle (C), WA, *465*
Management Recruiters of Spokane (C), WA, *465*
Management Recruiters of Roanoke (C), VA, *465*
Management Search, Inc. (C), OK, *468*
Management Solutions, Inc. (C), WA, *468*
Mankuta Gallagher & Assoc., Inc. (C), FL, *468*
Manuso, Alexander & Associates, Inc. (R), NY, *135*
Marcus & Assoc. (C), NY, *469*
Mark III Personnel, Inc. (C), NC, *470*
Marketing Resources (C), MA, *470*
Marsteller Wilcox Assoc. (C), IL, *471*
George R. Martin (R), PA, *137*
Mathey Services (C), IL, *472*
Tom McCall Executive Search (C), IL, *473*
McCooe & Assoc., Inc. (R), NJ, *140*
McCormack & Farrow (R), CA, *140*
McKinley•Arend Int'l. (R), TX, *141*
McManners Assoc., Inc. (R), CA, *142*
MediaCOM Talent Group (C), MA, *476*
Medical Executive Search Assoc., Inc. (C), AZ, *477*
MedQuest Assoc. (C), CO, *478*
J. M. Meredith & Assoc. Inc. (C), CA, *479*
Merlin Int'l. Inc. (C), NJ, *479*
Merrick & Moore (C), NC, *479*
MES Search Co. (C), GA, *479*
MESA International (C), CA, *480*
Midland Consultants (C), OH, *481*
Miller + Miller (C), WA, *482*
Miller Denver (C), CO, *482*
Diedre Moire Corp., Inc. (C), NJ, *483*
Molecular Solutions, Inc. (C), SC, *483*
The Montgomery Group, Inc. (C), TN, *484*
Montgomery West (R), CA, *146*
Montgomery, Thomason & Assoc. (C), ON, *484*
Moore Research Assoc. (R), NJ, *147*
Mordue, Allen, Roberts, Bonney Ltd. (C), WA, *485*
Morton, McCorkle & Assoc. Inc. (R), MO, *147*
Mullen Assoc., Inc. (R), NC, *148*
The Mulshine Company, Ltd. (R), NY, *149*
Munroe, Curry & Bond Assoc. (R), NJ, *149*
The Murray Group (C), IL, *487*
Nachman Biomedical (C), MA, *488*
National Executive (C), ON, *489*
National Recruiters (C), OK, *489*
National Search Assoc. (C), CA, *490*
National Search, Inc. (R), NC, *150*
NaviSearch (C), GA, *490*
NCC Executive Search Consultants (C), CA, *490*
The Neil Michael Group, Inc./Global Partners (R), NY, *151*
The NEIS Corp., Inc. (C), FL, *491*
New Dimensions in Technology, Inc. (C), MA, *492*
Newman-Johnson-King, Inc. (C), TX, *492*
NJ Solutions (C), CA, *493*
NMC & Kay Int'l. (R), CO, *152*
The Noebel Search Group, Inc. (C), TX, *494*
Norris Agency (C), TX, *495*
NorTech Resources (C), NY, *496*
Northland Employment Services Inc. (C), MN, *496*
O'Brien & Bell (R), OH, *153*
Oberlander & Co., Inc. (R), IL, *155*
Oliver & Rozner Assoc., Inc. (R), NY, *155*
Organization Resources Inc. (R), MA, *157*
Robert Ottke Assoc. (R), CA, *157*
P R Management Consultants, Inc. (C), NJ, *500*
Frank Parillo & Assoc. (R), CA, *159*
D. P. Parker & Assoc., Inc. (R), MA, *159*
Patriot Assoc. (C), PA, *505*
Paules Associates (C), CA, *505*
PC Assoc. (C), CO, *505*
Peachtree Executive Search (R), GA, *161*
Pearson & Assoc., Inc. (C), AZ, *506*
Peden & Assoc. (C), CA, *506*
M. A. Pelle Assoc., Inc. (C), NY, *506*
Perry-D'Amico & Assoc. (R), CA, *162*
Petruzzi Assoc. (C), NJ, *509*
Phillips Resource Group (C), SC, *510*
Phoenix BioSearch, Inc. (C), NJ, *511*
Pioneer Consulting Group (C), CA, *512*
Pioneer Executive Consultants (C), ON, *512*
Place Mart Personnel Service (C), NJ, *513*
Placement Testart Inc. (C), QE, *513*
The Polen Group (C), PA, *514*
Jack Porter Assoc., Inc. (C), WA, *514*
Norman Powers Assoc., Inc. (C), MA, *515*
Prairie Resource Group, Inc. (R), IL, *166*
Preferred Professional Recruiters (C), TX, *516*
Premier Business Advisors (C), PA, *516*
Pro Tec Technical Services (C), ON, *519*
Proquest Inc. (C), SC, *524*
Proven Edge (C), CA, *525*
Quantum Int'l., Ltd. (R), FL, *170*
R & K Associates, Inc. (C), AZ, *527*
R2 Services, LLC (C), IL, *528*
Ramming & Assoc., Inc. (C), NJ, *528*
Ray & Berndtson/Laurendeau Labrecque (R), QE, *172*
Re-Mark Assoc. Inc. (C), NJ, *531*
Reifel & Assoc. (R), IL, *174*
Resource Networking Inc. (C), IN, *534*
Resource Perspectives, Inc. (R), CA, *175*
The Revere Assoc., Inc. (R), OH, *176*
Russell Reynolds Assoc., Inc. (R), NY, *176*
Reynolds Partners (R), NY, *177*
Rieser & Assoc., Inc. (R), MO, *178*
Riley Cole (C), CA, *537*
Ritta Professional Search Inc. (C), NY, *538*
Robinson-Robinson & Assoc., Inc. (C), MN, *539*
J. P. Roddy Consultants (C), PA, *540*
Rodzik & Assoc., Inc. (R), NC, *180*
Roevin Technical People (C), ON, *540*
Ropella & Assoc. (R), FL, *181*
Emery A. Rose & Assoc. (C), WA, *545*
The Rossi Search Group (C), PA, *545*
Roth Young of Chicago (C), IL, *546*
Roth Young Personnel Service of Detroit, Inc. (C), MI, *546*
Roth Young Executive Recruiters (C), MN, *546*
Roth Young Executive Search of Milwaukee (C), WI, *547*
RTE Search (C), NJ, *547*
Ruderfer & Co., Inc. (C), NJ, *548*
Louis Rudzinsky Assoc., Inc. (C), MA, *548*
J. D. Ruhmann & Assoc. (C), MO, *548*
S. P. Assoc., Inc. (C), NC, *550*
R. S. Sadow Assoc. (C), NJ, *550*
Sales Consultants of Indianapolis-North (C), IN, *558*
George D. Sandel Assoc. (C), MA, *565*
Sanford Rose Assoc. - Lake Forest (R), IL, *184*
Sanford Rose Assoc. - Chicago (C), IL, *566*
Sanford Rose Assoc. - Columbia, MD (C), MD, *567*
Sanford Rose Assoc. - Louisville (C), KY, *567*

Sanford Rose Assoc. - Amherst, NY (C), NY, *568*
Sanford Rose Assoc. - Fairlawn (C), OH, *569*
Sanford Rose Assoc. - Columbia (C), SC, *570*
Sanford Rose Assoc. - Port Washington (C), WI, *571*
Sarver & Carruth Assoc. (C), OK, *571*
Savalli & Assoc., Inc. (C), MI, *571*
Schuyler Assoc., Ltd. (R), GA, *185*
Schweichler Assoc., Inc. (R), CA, *186*
Scientific Solutions, Inc. (C), MI, *572*
Robert Scott Assoc. (C), NJ, *573*
The Search Alliance, Inc. (R), FL, *186*
Search By Design (C), AZ, *574*
Search Consultants, LLC (C), MD, *575*
Search Group (C), CA, *575*
Search Group Inc. (R), AB, *186*
Search Masters Int'l. (R), AZ, *187*
Search North America, Inc. (C), OR, *576*
Searchforce, Inc. (R), FL, *187*
Searchworks, Inc. (C), FL, *577*
Segal & Assoc. (C), GA, *578*
Sharp Placement Professionals, Inc. (C), NY, *579*
John Sibbald Assoc., Inc. (R), MO, *191*
Marvin L. Silcott & Assoc., Inc. (C), TX, *581*
L. A. Silver Assoc., Inc. (R), MA, *191*
Daniel A. Silverstein Assoc. Inc. (R), FL, *191*
Skott/Edwards Consultants (R), NY, *192*
Tom Sloan & Assoc., Inc. (C), WI, *583*
The Smith Group, Inc. (C), NC, *584*
Smith, Brown & Jones (C), KS, *585*
Snyder & Co. (R), CT, *194*
Soderlund Assoc. Inc. (R), OH, *194*
Software Resource Consultants (C), TN, *587*
Souder & Assoc. (R), VA, *195*
Southern Recruiters & Consultants, Inc. (C), SC, *587*
Southern Research Services (R), FL, *195*
Specialty Employment Services, Inc. (C), GA, *589*
Spectrum Consultants (R), CA, *196*
SpencerStuart (R), NY, *196*
The Spiegel Group (R), MA, *197*
Stanton Chase Int'l. (R), MD, *198*
The Stanton Group, Inc. (C), IL, *591*
Star Search Consultants (C), ON, *591*
Steinbach & Co. (C), MA, *592*
The Stelton Group, Inc. (C), NJ, *592*
Ron Stevens & Assoc., Inc. (C), FL, *593*
The Stevenson Group, Inc. (N.J.) (R), NJ, *200*
The Stewart Group (C), FL, *593*
Allan Stolee Inc. (R), FL, *201*
Stoneburner Assoc., Inc. (C), KS, *594*
Strategic Alternatives (R), CA, *202*
Strategic Resources (C), WA, *595*
Strategic Search Corp. (R), IL, *202*
Strategic Technologies, Inc. (C), TX, *596*
System 1 Search (C), CA, *598*
Tate & Assoc., Inc. (R), NJ, *207*
Tate Consulting, Inc. (R), FL, *207*
Carl J. Taylor & Co. (R), TX, *207*
TCM Enterprises (C), MD, *600*
Tech Consulting (C), FL, *601*
Tech-Net (C), TX, *601*
TechFind, Inc. (R), MA, *207*
Technology Management Partners (R), CA, *208*
Technology Search Int'l. (C), CA, *603*
Tecmark Associates Inc. (C), NY, *604*
Telem Adhesive Search Corp. (C), MD, *605*
Thomson, Sponar & Adams, Inc. (C), WA, *606*
The Tidewater Group Inc. (C), CT, *607*
Fred C. Tippel & Assoc. (C), OH, *607*
TPG & Assoc. (C), TX, *608*
Trambley the Recruiter (C), NM, *608*
Travis & Co., Inc. (R), MA, *210*
Triangle Assoc. (C), PA, *609*
Trowbridge & Co., Inc. (R), MA, *211*
TSC Management Services Group, Inc. (C), IL, *610*
TSS Consulting, Ltd. (C), AZ, *610*
The Thomas Tucker Co. (R), CA, *211*
Tuft & Assoc., Inc. (R), IL, *212*
U.S. Search (C), VA, *610*
Victor White Int'l. (C), CA, *612*
Voigt Assoc. (R), IL, *214*
Ward Assoc. (C), ON, *615*
R. J. Watkins & Co., Ltd. (R), CA, *216*
David Weinfeld Group (C), NC, *617*
Weinpel Search, Inc. (C), NJ, *617*
The Wellesley Group, Inc. (R), IL, *217*
Wellington Management Group (R), PA, *217*
Welzig, Lowe & Assoc. (C), CO, *618*
West & West (R), CA, *218*
Western Technical Resources (C), CA, *619*
Westfields Int'l., Inc. (C), NY, *619*
WestPacific National Search, Inc. (C), CA, *619*
Weterrings & Agnew, Inc. (C), NY, *619*
Whittaker & Assoc., Inc. (C), GA, *620*
Walter K. Wilkins & Co. (R), NJ, *221*
Williams Recruiting, Inc. (C), WA, *621*
Williams, Roth & Krueger, Inc. (R), IL, *221*
William Willis Worldwide Inc. (R), CT, *221*
Winfield Assoc., Inc. (C), MA, *623*
The Witt Group (C), FL, *623*
Wood West & Partners Inc. (C), BC, *624*
Woodmoor Group (C), CO, *624*
The Woodstone Consulting Company, Inc. (R), CO, *224*
The Yaiser Group (C), NJ, *625*
Yelverton Executive Search (R), CA, *226*
Yungner & Bormann (R), MN, *226*
Zackrison Assoc., Inc. (C), FL, *627*
Zeiger Assoc. L.L.C. (C), CA, *627*
Helen Ziegler & Assoc., Inc. (C), ON, *627*
Zingaro & Company (R), TX, *227*
Michael D. Zinn & Assoc., Inc. (R), NJ, *227*

10.0 Engineering

The 500 Granary Inc. (C), ON, *231*
A First Resource (C), NC, *231*
A.M.C.R., Inc. (C), OH, *232*
Abécassis Conseil (R), QE, *1*
Abraham & London Ltd. (C), CT, *232*
ACC Technical Services (C), OH, *233*
Accelerated Data Decision, Inc. (C), NJ, *233*
Access Assoc. Inc. (C), MD, *233*
ACCESS Technology (C), CA, *234*
Accounting Personnel & Engineering Personnel Consultants (C), LA, *238*
Action Management Corp. (C), MI, *239*
Adams & Assoc. Int'l. (R), IL, *1*
G. Adams Partners (R), IL, *2*
The Addison Consulting Group (C), NJ, *239*
Adel-Lawrence Assoc., Inc. (C), NJ, *240*
Advanced Corporate Search (C), CA, *240*
Advanced Executive Resources (R), MI, *2*
Advanced Recruitment, Inc. (C), TN, *240*
Advancement, Inc. (C), IL, *241*
The Advisory Group, Inc. (R), CA, *2*
AES Search (C), NJ, *241*
Affinity Executive Search (C), FL, *241*
Aggressive Corporation (C), IL, *242*
Agra Placements, Ltd. (C), IA, *242*
Agri-Personnel (C), GA, *242*
Agri-Tech Personnel, Inc. (C), MO, *242*
Albrecht & Assoc., Executive Search Consultants (C), TX, *243*
The Alfus Group (R), NY, *3*
Allen, Wayne & Co. LLC (C), WI, *245*
Allen-Jeffers Assoc. (C), CA, *245*
Alpha Executive Search (C), AL, *245*
The Altco Group (C), NJ, *246*
Altec/HRC (C), MI, *246*
ALW Research Int'l. (R), NJ, *4*
American Executive Management, Inc. (R), MA, *5*
American Executive Search (C), FL, *247*
American Professional Search, Inc. (C), TN, *248*
American Services Group (C), IL, *248*
AmeriPro Search, Inc. (C), NC, *248*
AmeriResource Group Inc. (C), OK, *248*
Ames-O'Neill Assoc., Inc. (C), NY, *249*
Analog Solutions (C), NY, *249*
Anderson & Schwab, Inc. (R), NY, *5*
Anderson Bradshaw Assoc., Inc. (R), TX, *6*
Anderson Industrial Assoc., Inc. (C), GA, *250*
Tryg R. Angell, Ltd. (C), CT, *250*
Angus Employment Ltd. (C), ON, *250*
The Angus Group, Ltd. (C), OH, *251*
Ansara, Bickford & Fiske (C), MA, *251*
APA Search, Inc. (R), NY, *6*
David Aplin & Assoc. (C), AB, *251*
Applied Resources (C), MA, *252*
Applied Resources, Inc. (C), MN, *252*
Applied Search Assoc., Inc. (C), GA, *252*
Argus National, Inc. (R), CT, *6*
ARJay & Assoc. (C), NC, *252*
J. S. Armstrong & Assoc., Inc. (R), CA, *7*
R & J Arnold & Assoc., Inc. (C), CO, *253*
Artgo, Inc. (R), OH, *7*
A. Artze Assoc.-Personnel Consultants (C), PR, *253*
Asheville Search & Consulting (C), NC, *253*
Ashton Computer Professionals, Inc. (C), BC, *253*
Ashway Ltd. Agency (C), NY, *253*

Asset Resource, Inc. (C), CA, *254*
The Associates, HR Search Executives, Inc. (C), OK, *254*
Astro Executive Search Firm (C), LA, *254*
W. R. Atchison & Assoc., Inc. (C), NC, *254*
Atkinson Search & Placement, Inc. (C), IA, *255*
Atlantic West Int'l. (C), NC, *255*
Atomic Personnel, Inc. (C), PA, *255*
Aurora Tech Search (C), ON, *256*
Cami Austin & Assoc. (C), IL, *256*
Austin - Allen Co. (C), TN, *256*
Austin Michaels, Ltd., Inc. (C), AZ, *256*
Automation Technology Search (C), CA, *256*
Availability Personnel Consultants (C), NH, *257*
Baeder Kalinski Int'l. Group, Inc. (R), NH, *10*
D. W. Baird & Associates (C), MD, *257*
Baldwin & Assoc. (C), OH, *258*
Allen Ballach Assoc. Inc. (R), ON, *10*
Ballos & Co., Inc. (R), NJ, *10*
James Bangert & Assoc., Inc. (R), MN, *11*
Barber & Assoc. (C), KY, *259*
J. W. Barleycorn, Renard & Assoc., Inc. (R), OH, *11*
Barone Assoc. (C), NJ, *259*
Barr Assoc. (C), PA, *259*
Barrett Partners (C), IL, *260*
Nathan Barry Assoc., Inc. (R), MA, *12*
Bartholdi & Co., Inc. (R), CO, *12*
Bason Associates (R), OH, *13*
Bayland Assoc. (C), CA, *261*
Beach Executive Search Inc. (R), FL, *14*
Becker, Norton & Co. (R), PA, *14*
Behrens and Company (C), WA, *262*
Gary S. Bell Assoc., Inc. (C), NJ, *263*
Bell Oaks Co., Inc. (C), GA, *263*
Benamati & Assoc. (C), CO, *263*
Benford & Assoc., Inc. (C), MI, *264*
The Bennett Group, Inc. (R), IN, *16*
Dick Berg & Assoc. (C), CA, *264*
Berkana Int'l., Inc. (C), WA, *265*
Berkshire Search Assoc. (C), MA, *265*
Ed Bertolas Assoc., Inc. (C), CA, *265*
Bertrand, Ross & Assoc., Inc. (C), IL, *266*
BGB Assoc., Inc. (C), IL, *266*
Paul J. Biestek Assoc., Inc. (R), IL, *17*
Bio-Venture Group (C), RI, *266*
Biomedical Search Consultants (R), CT, *17*
BioPharmMed (C), FL, *267*
BioTech Research Recruiters Inc. (C), CA, *267*
Birch & Associes (C), QE, *267*
Deborah Bishop & Assoc. (R), CA, *17*
BJB Assoc. (C), VA, *267*
The Black Leopard (C), CA, *267*
Blair/Tech Recruiters, Inc. (C), NJ, *268*
J: Blakslee Int'l., Ltd. (R), CA, *18*
Blaney Executive Search (R), MA, *18*
Blanton & Co. (C), AL, *268*
Block & Assoc. (R), CA, *18*
Blum & Co. (R), WI, *19*
Boardroom Consultants/Kenny Kindler Tholke (R), NY, *19*
Bolton Group (C), CA, *269*
Borchert Assoc. (C), TX, *269*
The Borton Wallace Co. (R), NC, *19*
Bos Business Consultants (C), NY, *270*
Bosco-Hubert & Assoc. (C), KS, *270*
Bower & Associates (C), TX, *271*
Boyle/Ogata Executive Search (R), CA, *21*
The Bradbury Management Group, Inc. (R), CA, *21*
Bradley & Assoc. (C), MN, *272*
Brei & Assoc., Inc. (C), IA, *272*
Brentwood Int'l. (R), CA, *23*
Brett Personnel Specialists (C), NJ, *273*
Brian Assoc., Inc. (C), NY, *273*
Briant Assoc., Inc. (R), IL, *23*
The Bridge (C), CO, *273*
Bridgecreek Personnel Agency (C), CA, *273*
Brierwood Group, Inc. (C), IN, *273*
Brigade, Inc. (R), CA, *23*
Brissenden, McFarland, Fuccella & Reynolds, Inc. (R), NJ, *23*
Broadband Resource Group (C), CA, *274*
J. B. Brown & Assoc., Inc. (C), OH, *275*
Bryan & Louis Research (C), OH, *275*
BT&A, LLC (R), CT, *24*
The Burke Group (C), ON, *276*
David S. Burt Assoc. (C), MT, *276*
Butterfield & Co. Int'l., Inc. (C), HI, *277*
Button Group (C), TX, *277*
The C.P.R. Group (C), NJ, *278*
C.P.S., Inc. (C), IL, *278*
CadTech Staffing Services (C), GA, *279*
Cahill Assoc. (C), CT, *279*
Juliette Lang Cahn Executive Search (C), NY, *279*
California Search Agency, Inc. (C), CA, *279*
Callan Assoc., Ltd. (R), IL, *27*
Callos Personnel Services (C), OH, *279*
Cambridge Management Planning (R), ON, *27*
Campa & Assoc. (R), ON, *27*
Cantrell & Assoc. (C), FL, *280*
Capital Consulting Group, Inc. (R), MD, *28*
The Caplan-Taylor Group (R), CA, *28*
Capstone Consulting, Inc. (R), IL, *29*
Capstone Inc. (R), NY, *29*
Career +Plus (C), NY, *281*
Career Consultants (R), IN, *29*
Career Counseling Inc. (CCI) (C), KY, *282*
Career Images (C), FL, *282*
Careerfit, Inc. (C), TX, *283*
Careers Plus (R), CA, *29*
Carnegie Partners, Inc. (R), IL, *30*
Carr Management Services, Inc. (C), PA, *284*
Carter, Lavoie Associates (C), RI, *285*
Case Executive Search (C), MI, *286*
The Cassie Group (R), NJ, *31*
Caywood Partners, Ltd. (R), CA, *32*
CCI - Career Consultants Int'l. (C), CA, *286*
The Center for Career Advancement, LLC (C), NJ, *287*
CEO Consulting (C), FL, *287*
cFour Partners (R), CA, *32*
Chadwell & Assoc., Inc. (C), MI, *288*
Chapman & Assoc. (C), BC, *289*
The Chapman Group, Inc. (C), AZ, *289*
Charles & Associates, Inc. (C), NE, *289*
Robert L. Charon (C), TX, *289*
Chase-Gardner Executive Search Associates, Inc. (C), FL, *289*
The Chatham Group, Ltd. (C), CT, *289*
Chatham Search Assoc., Inc. (C), NJ, *290*
Chelsea Resources, Inc. (C), CT, *290*
Cheney Associates (C), CT, *290*
The Cherbonnier Group, Inc. (R), TX, *33*
R. Christine Assoc. (C), PA, *290*
Christopher and Long (C), MO, *291*
The Churchill Group (C), ON, *291*
CJSI-Cindy Jackson Search Int'l. (C), CA, *291*
Claremont-Branan, Inc. (C), GA, *292*
Clarey/Napier Int'l., L.C. (R), TX, *35*
Howard Clark Assoc. (C), NJ, *292*
Ken Clark Int'l. (R), NJ, *36*
Clark Personnel Service, Inc. (C), AL, *292*
The Clayton Edward Group (C), MI, *292*
CMC Search Consultants (C), IL, *293*
CMS Management Services LLC (C), IN, *293*
CMW & Associates, Inc. (C), IL, *293*
Coast Personnel Services Ltd. (C), BC, *293*
Cochran, Cochran & Yale, Inc. (R), NY, *36*
J. Kevin Coleman & Assoc., Inc. (R), CA, *37*
Computer Professionals Unlimited (C), TX, *295*
Robert Connelly & Assoc., Inc. (R), MN, *39*
Connors, Lovell & Assoc. Inc. (C), ON, *296*
The Consortium (C), NY, *296*
Construct Management Services (C), MN, *297*
Construction Search Specialists, Inc. (C), WI, *297*
Continental Research Search, Inc. (C), WI, *298*
Continental Search Assoc. (C), OH, *298*
P. G. Cook Assoc. (R), TN, *40*
Cook Assoc.,® Inc. (R), IL, *40*
Corbin Packaging Professionals (C), MO, *299*
Cornwall Stockton & Co., Inc. (C), TX, *299*
Corporate Builders, Inc. (C), OR, *299*
The Corporate Connection, Ltd. (C), VA, *299*
Corporate Environment Ltd. (R), IL, *41*
Corporate Management Services (C), PA, *300*
Corporate Recruiters Ltd. (C), BC, *300*
Corporate Resources Professional Placement (C), MN, *300*
Corporate Resources (C), OH, *301*
Corporate Search Consultants, Inc. (C), FL, *301*
Corporate Select Int'l., Ltd. (C), IL, *301*
The Corporate Source Group, Inc. (R), MA, *41*
Corporate Staffing Group, Inc. (C), PA, *301*
Cosier & Assoc. (C), AB, *302*
J. D. Cotter Search Inc. (C), OH, *302*
Cowin Assoc. (R), NY, *42*
Creative-Leadership, Inc. (R), CA, *42*

Criterion Executive Search, Inc. (C), FL, *303*
Cross Country Consultants, Inc. (C), MD, *304*
Crowder & Company (R), MI, *43*
Crowe Chizek & Co. (C), IN, *304*
Timothy D. Crowe, Jr. (R), MA, *43*
Jim Crumpley & Assoc. (C), MO, *304*
CS Associates, LLC (C), AZ, *304*
CTR (R), CA, *43*
Cumberland Group Inc. (C), IL, *304*
Cumberland Professional Search Inc. (C), TN, *304*
Frank Cuomo & Assoc., Inc. (C), NY, *305*
The Currier-Winn Co., Inc. (C), NJ, *305*
Curry, Telleri Group, Inc. (R), NJ, *44*
Cusack Consulting (R), NY, *44*
Custom Resources (C), AL, *305*
CV Associates (C), NY, *305*
D.R. Assoc. (R), CA, *45*
Daggett & Kvistad (R), CA, *45*
Charles Dahl Group, Inc. (C), MN, *306*
Dahl-Morrow Int'l. (R), VA, *45*
Daniel Marks Company (C), OH, *306*
The Danielson Group, Inc. (C), TX, *306*
Data-AxIS Corp. (C), FL, *307*
Alan N. Daum & Assoc., Inc. (C), OH, *308*
Davidson, Laird & Assoc. (C), MI, *308*
Davies, Park (R), AB, *46*
Alan Davis & Assoc. Inc. (R), QE, *47*
Debbon Recruiting Group, Inc. (C), MO, *310*
Defrain Mayer (R), KS, *48*
DEL Technical Services, Inc. (C), IL, *310*
Delta Services (R), TX, *48*
DeMatteo Associates (C), NY, *311*
Derek Associates, Inc. (C), MA, *311*
Derhak Ireland & Partners Ltd. (R), ON, *48*
DieckMueller Group (R), WI, *51*
DiMarchi Partners (R), CO, *51*
R. J. Dishaw & Assoc. (R), TX, *52*
DiTech Resources (C), CT, *313*
Diversified Consulting Services, Inc. (C), CO, *313*
Diversified Search, Inc. (R), PA, *52*
Dixie Search Assoc. (C), GA, *313*
L. J. Doherty & Assoc. (R), MA, *53*
Doleman Enterprises (R), VA, *53*
The Dorfman Group (C), AZ, *314*
Dougherty & Assoc. (C), TN, *314*
CS Dowling Executive Services (R), NJ, *54*
Dreier Consulting (C), NJ, *315*
Robert Drexler Assoc., Inc. (R), NJ, *54*
DSR-Search & Recruitment (C), TX, *315*
J. H. Dugan & Assoc., Inc. (R), CA, *55*
Dukas Assoc. (C), MA, *315*
Dunhill Staffing Systems, Inc. (C), NY, *316*
Dunhill of San Francisco, Inc. (C), CA, *319*
Dunhill Professional Search of Englewood, Inc. (C), CO, *319*
Dunhill of Ft. Collins, Inc. (C), CO, *319*
Dunhill Professional Search of Oakland (C), CA, *319*
Dunhill Professional Search of San Jose (C), CA, *319*
Dunhill of Ft. Wayne, Inc. (C), IN, *320*
Dunhill Search of West Atlanta (C), GA, *320*
Dunhill Professional Search of Augusta (C), GA, *320*
Dunhill Professional Search of Hawaii (C), HI, *320*
Dunhill Executive Search of Brown County (C), IN, *321*
Dunhill Professional Search (C), MO, *321*
Dunhill Professional Search of Byram (C), MS, *321*
Dunhill Personnel Service of Fargo (C), ND, *322*
Dunhill Personnel of St. Andrews (C), SC, *322*
Dunhill Professional Search of Wilkes-Barre/Scranton, Inc. (C), PA, *322*
Dunhill Professional Search, Inc. of McAllen (C), TX, *323*
Dunhill of Corpus Christi, Inc. (C), TX, *323*
Dunhill Professional Search of Richmond (C), VA, *323*
Dunlap & Sullivan Assoc. (R), MI, *55*
Dunn Associates (R), PA, *55*
Dynamic Synergy Corp. (R), CA, *56*
Eagle Consulting Group Inc. (C), TX, *325*
J. M. Eagle Partners Ltd. (C), WI, *325*
EagleView, Inc. (C), MA, *325*
Eastern Executive Assoc. (C), NJ, *325*
EBA Group (R), NJ, *56*
EDP Staffing Solutions, Inc. (C), AR, *327*
Effective Search, Inc. (R), IL, *57*
EGM Consulting, Inc. (R), FL, *57*
W. Robert Eissler & Assoc., Inc. (C), TX, *327*
Electronic Search, Inc. (C), IL, *327*
Elite Consultants, Inc. (C), FL, *328*
Elite Medical Search (C), GA, *328*
Elite Resources Group (R), OH, *58*
Yves Elkas Inc. (R), QE, *58*
Gene Ellefson & Assoc. Inc. (C), MI, *328*
David M. Ellner Assoc. (R), NY, *59*
The Elsworth Group (C), TX, *329*
Elwell & Assoc., Inc. (R), MI, *59*
Emerging Medical Technologies, Inc. (C), CO, *329*
Emmett Executive Search, Inc. (C), NY, *330*
Empire International (R), PA, *59*
Employment Solutions, Inc. (C), TX, *330*
The Energists (R), TX, *59*
Engineering & Scientific Search Assoc. (ESSA) (C), NJ, *330*
Engineering Futures, LLC (C), CT, *330*
Engineering Profiles (C), FL, *330*
Engineering Resource Group, Inc. (C), NJ, *331*
Environmental, Health & Safety Search Assoc. (C), FL, *331*
Erlanger Assoc. (R), CT, *60*
Erwin Assoc. (R), IL, *60*
ESA (R), CT, *60*
ESS (Executive Search Services) (R), CA, *61*
Essential Solutions, Inc. (C), CA, *331*
Ethos Consulting, Inc. (R), CA, *61*
Exclusive Search Consultants (C), OH, *331*
Exec Tech, Inc. (C), IL, *332*
Execu-Tech Search Inc. (C), MN, *332*
ExecuSource Consultants, Inc. (C), TX, *332*
Executech (R), OH, *62*
ExecuTech (C), IN, *332*
Executive Alliance (R), MA, *62*
Executive Business Solutions, Inc. (C), WA, *332*
Executive Career Search (C), VA, *332*
Executive Partners Inc. (C), CT, *333*
Executive Recruiters Int'l. (C), MI, *333*
Executive Recruiters Agency, Inc. (C), AR, *333*
Executive Recruiters, Inc. (C), WI, *334*
Executive Recruiters (C), WA, *334*
Executive Recruitment Specialists, Inc. (R), NC, *63*
Executive Recruitment Services, Inc. (ERS, Inc.) (C), GA, *334*
Executive Registry (C), QE, *334*
Executive Resource Assoc. (C), VA, *334*
Executive Resource Inc. (C), WI, *334*
Executive Resource Systems (C), CA, *335*
Executive Search Consultants (C), CA, *335*
Executive Search, Ltd. (C), OH, *336*
Executive Search of America, Inc. (C), OH, *336*
Executive Search Plus, Inc. (C), IN, *336*
The Executive Source (C), SA, *337*
The Executive Tree (R), FL, *64*
EXETER 2100 (C), NH, *337*
Eyler Assoc., Inc. (R), IA, *64*
F.L.A.G. (C), OH, *338*
Fairfaxx Corp. (R), CT, *64*
James Feerst & Assoc., Inc. (C), AZ, *339*
Fell & Nicholson Technology Resources (R), CA, *65*
Fenwick Partners (R), MA, *66*
Fenzel Milar Assoc. (C), OH, *339*
Fernow Assoc. (C), PA, *339*
Guild Fetridge Acoustical Search, Inc. (C), NY, *340*
Neil Fink Assoc. (R), CA, *66*
Finney-Taylor Personnel & Management Consultants Ltd. (C), AB, *341*
First Advisory Services Int'l., Inc. (R), MD, *67*
First Choice Search (R), WA, *67*
First Search Inc. (C), IL, *341*
Fisher & Assoc. (R), CA, *67*
Jack Stuart Fisher Assoc. (C), NJ, *341*
Fisher Personnel Management Services (R), CA, *68*
Flowers & Assoc. (C), OH, *342*
J. G. Flynn & Assoc. Inc. (R), BC, *69*
Ford & Assoc., Inc. (C), SC, *343*
Forest People Int'l. Search Ltd. (C), BC, *343*
F-O-R-T-U-N-E Personnel Consultants of Boise (R), ID, *70*
Fortune Group Int'l., Inc. (R), PA, *70*
Fortune Personnel Consultants of Huntsville, Inc. (C), AL, *343*
F-O-R-T-U-N-E Personnel Consultants of Denver, Inc. (C), CO, *344*
Fortune Personnel Consultants of Colorado Springs (C), CO, *344*
Fortune Personnel Consultants (C), CA, *344*

F-O-R-T-U-N-E Personnel Consultants of Greenwood Village (C), CO, *344*
F-O-R-T-U-N-E Personnel Consultants of Manatee County (C), FL, *345*
F-O-R-T-U-N-E Personnel Consultants of Palm Beach (C), FL, *345*
Fortune Personnel Consultants of Jacksonville (C), FL, *345*
F-O-R-T-U-N-E Personnel Consultants of Atlanta, Inc. (C), GA, *345*
Fortune of Arlington Heights (C), IL, *345*
F-O-R-T-U-N-E Personnel Consultants of South Bend (C), IN, *346*
Fortune Personnel Consultants of Topsfield (C), MA, *346*
F-O-R-T-U-N-E Personnel Consultants of Southwest Indiana (C), IN, *346*
F-O-R-T-U-N-E Personnel Consultants of St. Louis-West County (C), MO, *347*
F-O-R-T-U-N-E Personnel Consultants of Troy, Inc. (C), MI, *347*
F-O-R-T-U-N-E Personnel Consultants of Menlo Park, Inc. (C), NJ, *347*
Fortune Personnel Consultants (C), MT, *347*
F-O-R-T-U-N-E Search Consultants (C), MO, *347*
F-O-R-T-U-N-E Personnel Consultants of Bergen County Inc. (C), NJ, *347*
F-O-R-T-U-N-E of West Portland (C), OR, *348*
F-O-R-T-U-N-E Personnel Consultants of Rockland County, Inc. (C), NY, *348*
F-O-R-T-U-N-E Personnel Consultants of Charlotte (C), NC, *348*
Fortune Personnel Consultants of Raleigh, Inc. (C), NC, *348*
Fortune Personnel Consultants of Greensboro, NC, Inc. (C), NC, *348*
F-O-R-T-U-N-E Consultants of Memphis (C), TN, *349*
Fortune Personnel Consultants of Chattanooga Inc. (C), TN, *349*
Fortune Personnel Consultants of Anderson, Inc. (C), SC, *349*
F-O-R-T-U-N-E Personnel Consultants of Houston, Inc. (C), TX, *350*
F-O-R-T-U-N-E Personnel Consultants of Knoxville (C), TN, *350*
Fortune Personnel Consultants of San Antonio, Inc. (C), TX, *350*
FORTUNE Personnel Consultants of North Dallas (C), TX, *350*
F-O-R-T-U-N-E Personnel of Nashville (C), TN, *350*
Fortune Personnel Consultants of Plano (C), TX, *350*
F-O-R-T-U-N-E Personnel Consultants of the Tri-Cities, Inc. (C), TN, *350*
F-O-R-T-U-N-E Personnel Consultants of East Seattle (C), WA, *351*
Foster Partners (R), NY, *70*
Fox-Morris Assoc., Inc. (C), PA, *351*
Franklin Int'l. Search, Inc. (C), MA, *352*
KS Frary & Assoc. (R), MA, *71*
P. N. French Assoc., Inc. (R), MA, *72*
Fresquez & Assoc. (C), CA, *352*
Peter Froehlich & Co. (C), TX, *353*
Frye/Joure & Assoc., Inc. (C), TN, *353*
The Furst Group, Inc. (R), IL, *72*
Future Employment Service, Inc. (C), IA, *353*
G. H. Enterprises (C), AZ, *354*
Gaffney Management Consultants (R), IL, *73*
Gaines & Assoc. Int'l., Inc. (R), IL, *73*
Gallin Associates, Inc. (C), FL, *354*
Garland Assoc. Int'l. (C), CA, *355*
The Garms Group (R), IL, *74*
The Garret Group (R), NJ, *75*
Gaudry, Shink, Levasseur (R), QE, *75*
Dianne Gauger & Assoc. (C), CA, *355*
Genel Associates (C), CA, *356*
Genesis Personnel Service, Inc. (C), OH, *356*
Genesis Recruiting (C), CA, *356*
Genesis Research (C), MO, *356*
Delores F. George, C.P.C. (C), MA, *356*
J. Gernetzke & Assoc., Inc. (C), OH, *357*
Joe L. Giles & Assoc. (C), MI, *357*
Glines Assoc., Inc. (R), IL, *77*
Global 1000 Int'l. Services (C), CA, *358*
Global Career Services, Inc. (C), NY, *358*
Global Consulting Group Inc. (C), ON, *358*
Global Employer's Network, Inc. (R), TX, *77*
Global Engineers Inc. (C), ME, *358*
The Gobbell Co. (R), CA, *78*
Goldbeck Recruiting Inc. (C), BC, *359*
Joseph Goldring & Assoc. Inc. (C), MI, *360*
L. J. Gonzer Assoc. (C), NJ, *360*
Gordon/Tyler (R), PA, *80*
Granger, Counts & Assoc. (R), OH, *81*
R. Green & Assoc., Inc. (C), OH, *362*
Greenfields Engineering Search (C), MO, *363*
Greenwich Internet (C), CT, *363*
Gregory, Kyle & Assoc. (C), NC, *363*
J. B. Groner Executive Search, Inc. (C), DE, *363*
Grossberg & Assoc. (R), IL, *82*
Grover & Assoc. (R), OH, *82*
GSW Consulting Group, Inc. (R), CA, *83*
Michael R. Guerin Co. (C), CA, *364*
The Guild Corp. (C), VA, *364*
Haddad Assoc. (R), FL, *84*
Hadley Associates, Inc. (C), NJ, *365*
Hahn & Assoc., Inc. (C), OH, *365*
Haley Associates (R), CA, *85*
Michael J. Hall & Co. (R), WA, *85*
Hall Kinion (C), CA, *366*
Hall Management Group, Inc. (C), GA, *367*
The Hanna Group (C), OH, *368*
Harcor Quest & Assoc. (R), OH, *86*
Harcourt & Assoc. (C), AB, *368*
Hardage Group (C), TN, *369*
Robert Harkins Assoc., Inc. (C), PA, *369*
Harrison Moore Inc. (C), NE, *370*
Harvey Hohauser & Assoc., LLC (R), MI, *87*
The Hawkins Co. (R), CA, *88*
Michael J. Hawkins, Inc. (C), IL, *370*
Hayden & Assoc., Inc. (C), MN, *370*
The Haystack Group, Inc. (R), ME, *88*
HCI Corp. (C), IL, *371*
Health Industry Consultants, Inc. (R), CO, *89*
Healthcare Recruiters Int'l. Bay Area (C), CA, *372*
Healthcare Recruiters of Indiana (C), IN, *372*
Healthcare Recruiters Int'l. Philadelphia (C), NJ, *373*
Healthcare Recruiters Int'l. - Pittsburgh (C), PA, *373*
F. P. Healy & Co., Inc. (R), NY, *89*
HeartBeat Medical, Inc. (C), OR, *374*
Heath/Norton Assoc., Inc. (R), NY, *89*
HEC Group (C), ON, *375*
Helffrich Int'l. (C), FL, *375*
Heller Kil Assoc., Inc. (C), FL, *375*
Henrietta's Personnel & Executive Search, Inc. (C), FL, *376*
Henson Partners (C), AZ, *376*
Hergenrather & Co. (R), WA, *92*
Heritage Pacific Corp. (C), CA, *376*
The Hetzel Group, Inc. (R), IL, *92*
High Tech Opportunities, Inc. (C), NH, *377*
High-Tech Recruiters (C), CT, *378*
Highlander Search (C), NC, *378*
The Hindman Co. (R), KY, *94*
Hite Executive Search (R), OH, *94*
Hobson Assoc. (C), CT, *379*
Hoffman Recruiters (C), MA, *380*
Hoglund & Assoc., Inc. (R), IL, *94*
Holland & Assoc., Inc. (R), MI, *94*
Hollander Horizon Int'l. (R), CA, *95*
Holohan Group, Ltd. (R), MO, *95*
J. G. Hood Assoc. (C), CT, *380*
Horizons Unlimited (C), CA, *381*
Horton Int'l. Inc. (R), NY, *96*
Houser, Martin, Morris (C), WA, *381*
William C. Houze & Co. (R), CA, *96*
Randall Howard & Assoc., Inc. (R), TN, *96*
Robert Howe & Assoc. (R), GA, *97*
HR Advantage, Inc. (C), VA, *382*
HR Inc. (C), NC, *382*
HRNI (C), MI, *383*
The Hudson Group (C), CT, *383*
Huff Assoc. (R), NJ, *98*
Hughes & Assoc. Int'l. Inc. (C), AL, *383*
The Human Resource Group, Inc. (R), OH, *98*
Human Resources Management Hawaii, Inc. (C), HI, *384*
Human Resources Personnel Agency (R), AR, *99*
E. F. Humay Assoc. (C), PA, *384*
Hunt & Howe Inc. (R), NY, *99*
The Hunt Group, Inc. (R), NC, *99*
Hunt Patton & Brazeal, Inc. (C), OK, *385*
Hunter Adams (C), NC, *385*
Hunter Assoc. (C), MA, *385*
The Hunter Group, Inc. (C), MI, *385*
The Hunter Group (C), NC, *385*
Hunter, Rowan & Crowe (C), FL, *386*
Huntley Associates (Dallas), Inc. (C), TX, *386*
W. Hutt Management Resources Ltd. (R), ON, *100*
Hutton Merrill & Assoc. (R), CA, *100*
IDC Executive Search Inc. (C), FL, *387*
Impact Source, Inc. (C), FL, *387*
Impact Technical Staffing (C), OR, *387*
Independent Power Consultants (C), TX, *387*

Independent Resource Systems (C), CA, *388*
Innovative Resource Group, LLC (C), NC, *389*
InSearch (C), CO, *389*
The Inside Track (C), TX, *389*
Inter Regional Executive Search, Inc. (IRES, Inc.) (C), NJ, *391*
Interactive Search Assoc. (C), PA, *391*
Intercontinental Executive Group (C), PA, *391*
Interim Executive Recruiting (C), GA, *392*
Interim Management Resources Inc. (C), ON, *392*
International Consulting Services, Inc. (C), IL, *392*
International Management Services Inc. (R), IL, *102*
International Management Advisors, Inc. (R), NY, *103*
International Management Development Corp. (C), NY, *393*
International Research Group (R), CA, *103*
International Staffing Consultants, Inc. (C), CA, *393*
Isaacson, Miller (R), MA, *104*
ISC of Atlanta, Inc. (C), GA, *394*
J. Joseph & Assoc. (C), OH, *395*
Jackley Search Consultants (C), MN, *396*
Jackson Group Int'l. (C), CO, *396*
Jaeger Int'l., Inc. (C), OH, *396*
JAG Group (R), MO, *105*
R. I. James, Inc. (C), NY, *397*
JDG Assoc., Ltd. (C), MD, *397*
JDH & Assoc. (C), CA, *397*
Jender & Company (R), IL, *105*
Jerome & Co. (C), CA, *398*
JLI-Boston (R), MA, *106*
Job Link, Inc. (C), CA, *399*
Job-Born Candidate Selection Bureau (C), ON, *399*
John H. Johnson & Assoc., Inc. (R), IL, *106*
Johnson & Assoc., Inc. (R), CA, *106*
L. J. Johnson & Co. (R), MI, *106*
Ronald S. Johnson Assoc., Inc. (R), CA, *107*
K. E. Johnson Assoc. (C), WA, *399*
Johnson Brown Assoc., Inc. (C), IN, *400*
The Jonathan Stevens Group, Inc. (R), NJ, *108*
Jones and Jones (R), OR, *108*
Jones Management Co. (R), CT, *108*
Jordan-Sitter Assoc. (R), TX, *108*
JPM International (C), CA, *401*
JRL Executive Recruiters (C), MO, *401*
JSG Group Management Consultants (R), ON, *109*
Just Management Services Inc. (C), FL, *402*
A H Justice Search Consultants (C), TX, *402*
K & C Assoc. (C), CA, *402*
Kaas Employment Services (C), IA, *402*
Kabana Corp. (C), MI, *402*
KABL Ability Network (C), CA, *402*
Kacevich, Lewis & Brown, Inc. (R), MA, *109*
Lisa Kalus & Assoc., Inc. (C), NY, *403*
Kane & Assoc. (C), TX, *403*
Karel & Co. (R), CA, *109*
Jim Kay & Assoc. (C), IL, *404*
Kay Concepts, Inc. (C), FL, *404*
Kaye/Bassman Int'l. Corp. (R), TX, *110*
A.T. Kearney Executive Search (R), IL, *111*
Keena Staffing Services (C), NY, *404*
Kehn & Gabor, Inc. (C), OH, *405*
S. D. Kelly & Assoc., Inc. (R), MA, *112*
Kelly Associates (R), PA, *112*
Kensington International (R), CA, *113*
Blair Kershaw Assoc., Inc. (C), PA, *405*
Daniel J. Kerstein, Consultant to Management (R), CO, *114*
Key Employment (C), NJ, *405*
Ki Technologies, Inc. (C), UT, *406*
Kiley, Owen & McGovern, Inc. (R), NJ, *114*
King ComputerSearch, Inc. (C), TX, *407*
Kingsley Quinn/USA (R), NJ, *115*
Kirkbride Assoc., Inc. (C), WA, *407*
The Kleven Group, Inc. - Executive Search Division (R), MA, *116*
The Kleven Group, Inc. (C), MA, *407*
Knapp Consultants (R), CT, *116*
Lee Koehn Assoc., Inc. (R), OR, *116*
T. J. Koellhoffer & Assoc. (R), NJ, *116*
Fred Koffler Assoc. (R), NY, *116*
Koontz, Jeffries & Assoc., Inc. (R), FL, *117*
Korban Associates (R), PA, *117*
Korn/Ferry Int'l. (R), NY, *117*
Kossuth & Assoc., Inc. (R), WA, *119*
Kozlin Assoc., Inc. (C), NY, *408*
Katherine R. Kraemer (R), CA, *120*
Krakower Group, Inc. (R), CA, *120*
Krautler Personnel Recruitment (C), FL, *409*
Kressenberg Assoc. (C), TX, *409*
Kreutz Consulting Group, Inc. (R), IL, *121*
Krueger Assoc. (R), IL, *121*
John Kuhn & Assoc., Inc. (R), WI, *121*
Kuhn Med-Tech (C), CA, *409*
Paul Kull & Co. (R), NJ, *121*
D. Kunkle & Assoc. (C), IL, *410*
Kunzer Assoc., Ltd. (R), IL, *121*
John Kurosky & Assoc. (R), CA, *122*
L & L Assoc. (C), CA, *410*
L O R (R), NJ, *122*
L. Patrick Group (R), NJ, *122*
The LaBorde Group (C), CA, *411*
LaCosta & Assoc. Int'l. Inc. (C), CA, *411*
Lam Assoc. (C), HI, *411*
Landon Morgan (C), ON, *412*
Lange & Assoc., Inc. (C), IN, *412*
The Langford Search, Inc. (C), AL, *412*
Langley & Associates, Inc. (Executive Search Consultants) (R), CO, *124*
Lanken-Kimball-Therrell & Assoc. (C), GA, *412*
Larkin & Co. (R), CA, *124*
Robert Larned Assoc., Inc. (C), VA, *413*
Jack B. Larsen & Assoc., Inc. (C), PA, *413*
Larsen Int'l., Inc. (R), TX, *125*
Lasher Assoc. (R), FL, *125*
Michael Latas & Assoc., Inc. (R), MO, *125*
Lautz, Grotte, Engler & Swimley (R), CA, *126*
Lawrence-Leiter & Co. (R), KS, *126*
W. R. Lawry, Inc. (R), CT, *126*
LCC Companies (C), AZ, *414*
LCS, Inc. (C), TX, *414*
Leader Network (C), PA, *414*
Leader Search Inc. (R), AB, *127*
The Lear Group, Inc. (R), OH, *127*
Reynolds Lebus Assoc. (C), AZ, *415*
Albert G. Lee Assoc. (C), RI, *415*
Lee Management Group Inc. (C), NJ, *416*
V. J. Lehman & Assoc., Inc. (R), CO, *127*
AG Lennox & Assoc. (R), AB, *128*
Jacques LePage Executive Search Inc. (R), QE, *128*
J. E. Lessner Assoc., Inc. (R), MI, *128*
The Libra Group (C), NC, *417*
LifeWork, Inc. (C), TX, *418*
J. H. Lindell & Co. (C), CA, *418*
Lineal Recruiting Services (C), CT, *418*
Lloyd Prescott Assoc., Inc. (C), FL, *418*
Locke & Assoc. (R), NC, *131*
Locus Inc. (C), WV, *419*
Logix, Inc. (C), MA, *420*
London Executive Consultants Inc. (C), ON, *420*
Longo Associates (C), CA, *420*
Lord & Albus Co. (C), TX, *420*
Lucas Assoc. (C), GA, *421*
Lucas Group (C), NY, *421*
Lutz Associates (C), CT, *421*
Lybrook Assoc., Inc. (C), RI, *421*
M H Executive Search Group (C), TX, *422*
M. K. & Assoc. (C), PA, *422*
M.C. Executive Search (C), CA, *422*
Magellan Int'l., L.P. (C), TX, *422*
Maglio & Co., Inc. (R), WI, *134*
Major Search (C), NJ, *423*
Management Alliance Group, Inc. (R), NJ, *134*
Management Association Network (C), WI, *424*
Management Catalysts (R), NJ, *134*
Management Recruiters of Nassau, Inc. (R), NY, *134*
Management Recruiters of Birmingham, Inc. (C), AL, *438*
Management Recruiters of Birmingham-South, Inc. (C), AL, *438*
Management Recruiters of Mobile Co., Inc. (C), AL, *438*
Management Recruiters of Birmingham (C), AL, *438*
Management Recruiters of Decatur, LLC (C), AL, *438*
Management Recruiters Tucson-Foothills, Inc. (C), AZ, *439*
Management Recruiters of Aptos (C), CA, *439*
Management Recruiters Peninsula (C), CA, *439*
Management Recruiters of Berkeley (C), CA, *439*
Management Recruiters of Clovis (C), CA, *440*
Management Recruiters of Northern California (C), CA, *440*
Management Recruiters of Laguna Hills (C), CA, *440*
Management Recruiters of Colorado Springs (C), CO, *441*

Management Recruiters of Sonoma (C), CA, *441*
Management Recruiters of Sacramento North (C), CA, *441*
Management Recruiters of Winsted, Inc. (C), CT, *442*
Management Recruiters of Franktown (C), CO, *442*
Management Recruiters of Altamonte (C), FL, *442*
Management Recruiters of Milford Inc. (C), CT, *442*
Management Recruiters of Bonita Springs, Inc. (C), FL, *443*
Management Recruiters of Boca Raton (C), FL, *443*
Management Recruiters of Miami-North (C), FL, *443*
Management Recruiters, Inc. (C), FL, *443*
Management Recruiters of Melbourne, Inc. (C), FL, *443*
Management Recruiters of Lake Co., Inc. (C), FL, *444*
Management Recruiters of North Fulton (C), GA, *445*
Management Recruiters of Forsyth County (C), GA, *445*
Management Recruiters of Venice, Inc. (C), FL, *445*
Management Recruiters of Columbus, Inc. (C), GA, *445*
Management Recruiters of Vero Beach (C), FL, *445*
Management Recruiters of Atlanta North, Inc. (C), GA, *446*
Management Recruiters of Savannah (C), GA, *446*
Management Recruiters of Sandy Springs (C), GA, *446*
Management Recruiters of Atlanta NE (C), GA, *446*
Management Recruiters of Boise (C), ID, *446*
Management Recruiters of Springfield, Inc. (C), IL, *447*
Management Recruiters of Barrington (C), IL, *447*
Management Recruiters of Noblesville, Inc. (C), IN, *448*
Management Recruiters of Spencer (C), IA, *448*
Management Recruiters of South Bend (C), IN, *448*
Management Recruiters of Des Moines (C), IA, *449*
Management Recruiters of Danville (C), KY, *449*
Management Recruiters of Siouxland (C), IA, *449*
Management Recruiters of Columbia (C), MD, *450*
Management Recruiters of Rockville (C), MD, *450*
Management Recruiters of Washington, DC Inc. (C), MD, *450*
Management Recruiters of the Baltimore Washington Corridor (C), MD, *450*
Management Recruiters of Monroe, Inc. (C), LA, *450*
Management Recruiters of Muskegon (C), MI, *451*
Management Recruiters of Livonia (C), MI, *451*
Management Recruiters of Birmingham (C), MI, *451*
Management Recruiters of Baltimore (C), MD, *451*
Management Recruiters of Southeastern Michigan (C), MI, *451*
Management Recruiters of Dearborn, Inc. (C), MI, *451*
Management Recruiters of Cass County, NE (C), NE, *452*
Management Recruiters of Chanhassen (C), MN, *452*
Management Recruiters of Bloomington (C), MN, *452*
Management Recruiters of North Oakland County, Inc. (C), MI, *452*
Management Recruiters of Bay Head (C), NJ, *453*
Management Recruiters of Medford, N.J. (C), NJ, *453*
Management Recruiters of North Warren Inc. (C), NJ, *453*
Management Recruiters of Orange County, N.Y., Inc. (C), NJ, *453*
Management Recruiters of Reno (C), NV, *453*
Management Recruiters of Princeton (C), NJ, *454*
Management Recruiters of New Providence (C), NJ, *454*
Management Recruiters of Broome County, Inc. (C), NY, *454*
Management Recruiters of Burlington (C), NC, *455*
Management Recruiters of Fayetteville (C), NC, *455*
Management Recruiters of Asheville, Inc. (C), NC, *455*
Management Recruiters of Rocky Mount - Southwest (C), NC, *456*
Management Recruiters of Kinston (C), NC, *456*
Management Recruiters of Mt. Airy (C), NC, *456*
Management Recruiters of Raleigh (C), NC, *456*
Management Recruiters of Gastonia (C), NC, *456*
Management Recruiters of Winston-Salem (C), NC, *457*
Management Recruiters of Dayton, Inc. (C), OH, *457*
Management Recruiters of Columbus (C), OH, *457*
Management Recruiters of Cincinnati/ Sharonville, Inc. (C), OH, *457*
Management Recruiters of Cleveland (C), OH, *457*
Management Recruiters of Easton, PA (C), PA, *458*
Management Recruiters of Northwest Ohio, Inc. (C), OH, *458*
Management Recruiters of Cherry Hill (C), PA, *459*
Management Recruiters of Valley Forge (C), PA, *459*
Management Recruiters of Puerto Rico (C), PR, *460*
Management Recruiters of Myrtle Beach, Inc. (C), SC, *460*
Management Recruiters of North Charleston (C), SC, *460*
Management Recruiters of Florence (C), SC, *460*
Management Recruiters of West Chester, Inc. (C), PA, *460*
Management Recruiters of Aiken (C), SC, *460*
Management Recruiters The Delta Group, Inc. (C), TN, *461*
Management Recruiters of Sioux Falls, LLP (C), SD, *461*
Management Recruiters of North West Austin (C), TX, *462*
Management Recruiters of Houston (C), TX, *462*
Management Recruiters Dallas North (MRDN) (C), TX, *462*
Management Recruiters of Arlington (C), TX, *462*
Management Recruiters of LBJ Park/Dallas (C), TX, *462*
Management Recruiters - Friendswood (C), TX, *462*
Management Recruiters of Round Rock (C), TX, *463*
Management Recruiters of Ogden (C), UT, *464*
Management Recruiters of Sugar Land Inc. (C), TX, *464*
Management Recruiters of Milwaukee-West (C), WI, *465*
Management Recruiters of Loudoun County South (C), VA, *465*
Management Recruiters of Kanawha Valley, LLC (C), WV, *465*
Management Recruiters of Seattle (C), WA, *465*
Management Recruiters of Lynnwood (C), WA, *465*
Management Recruiters of Milwaukee-North (C), WI, *466*
Management Recruiters of Madison, Inc. (C), WI, *466*
Management Search of R.I. Inc. (R), RI, *135*
Management Solutions, Inc. (C), WA, *468*
Mankuta Gallagher & Assoc., Inc. (C), FL, *468*
Mannard & Assoc., Inc. (R), IL, *135*
F. L. Mannix & Co. (R), MA, *135*
MARBL Consultants, Inc. (C), WI, *469*
Marentz & Co. (C), TX, *469*
Margolin Consultants, Inc. (C), NY, *469*
Mark III Personnel, Inc. (C), NC, *470*
Markent Personnel, Inc. (C), WI, *470*
Marketing Resources (C), MA, *470*
Marsteller Wilcox Assoc. (C), IL, *471*
J. Martin & Assoc. (R), CA, *137*
George R. Martin (R), PA, *137*
The Martwick Group, Inc. (C), OR, *472*
Marvel Consultants, Inc. (C), OH, *472*
Richard L. Mather & Assoc. (C), CT, *472*

Mathey Services (C), IL, *472*
Matthews & Stephens Assoc., Inc. (C), CT, *472*
G. P. Mattocks & Associates (C), NC, *473*
K. Maxin & Assoc. (R), PA, *139*
Tom McCall Executive Search (C), IL, *473*
McCooe & Assoc., Inc. (R), NJ, *140*
McCoy Ltd. (C), CA, *474*
McDowell & Co., Recruiters (C), TX, *474*
McKeen & Company (R), TX, *141*
McKinley•Arend Int'l. (R), TX, *141*
Dan P. McLean Assoc., Inc. (C), ON, *475*
McManners Assoc., Inc. (R), CA, *142*
McNichol Assoc. (R), PA, *142*
Joseph J. McTaggart (C), CA, *476*
MDR & Associates (C), AR, *476*
Media Management Resources, Inc. (R), CO, *142*
MediaCOM Talent Group (C), MA, *476*
Medical Executive Search Assoc., Inc. (C), AZ, *477*
MedQuest Assoc. (C), CO, *478*
Melancon & Co. (R), TX, *143*
Juan Menefee & Assoc. (C), IL, *478*
Mercedes & Co., Inc. (R), MA, *143*
J. M. Meredith & Assoc. Inc. (C), CA, *479*
Merrick & Moore (C), NC, *479*
MES Search Co. (C), GA, *479*
MESA International (C), CA, *480*
META/MAT, Ltd. (R), NJ, *144*
mfg/Search, Inc. (C), IN, *480*
Michael Assoc. (R), IL, *144*
Michael James & Co. (C), IL, *480*
Michaels & Moere (C), WI, *481*
Lou Michaels Assoc., Inc. (C), MI, *481*
Michigan Consulting Group (R), MI, *144*
Midland Consultants (C), OH, *481*
Miller Denver (C), CO, *482*
MJF Assoc. (C), CT, *483*
MLA Resources, Inc. (C), OK, *483*
Modis (C), MD, *483*
Moffitt Int'l., Inc. (R), NC, *146*
Diedre Moire Corp., Inc. (C), NJ, *483*
Montgomery, Thomason & Assoc. (C), ON, *484*
Moore Research Assoc. (R), NJ, *147*
Mordue, Allen, Roberts, Bonney Ltd. (C), WA, *485*
Morgan Samuels Co. (R), CA, *147*
The Morley Group (C), IN, *486*
Robert T. Morton Assoc., Inc. (C), MA, *486*
Morton, McCorkle & Assoc. Inc. (R), MO, *147*
Moss & Co. (R), WA, *148*
MPA Executive Search Inc. (R), QE, *148*
MSI Int'l. (C), GA, *486*
Mulcahy Co. (C), WI, *487*
The Mulshine Co., Inc. (R), NJ, *149*
The Mulshine Company, Ltd. (R), NY, *149*
Multi Processing, Inc. (R), NH, *149*
Multisearch Recruiters (C), CA, *487*
Munroe, Curry & Bond Assoc. (R), NJ, *149*
Mycoff & Assoc. (R), CO, *150*
Nachman Biomedical (C), MA, *488*
Nadzam, Lusk, Horgan & Assoc., Inc. (R), CA, *150*
NaTek Corp. (C), NY, *488*
National Computerized Employment Service, Inc. (C), PA, *489*
National Corporate Consultants, Inc. (C), IN, *489*
National Executive (C), ON, *489*
National Field Service Corp. (C), NY, *489*
National Metal Services Corp. (C), IN, *489*
National Recruiters (C), OK, *489*
National Recruiting Service (C), IN, *489*
National Search Assoc. (C), CA, *490*
National Search, Inc. (R), NC, *150*
Nationwide Personnel Recruiting & Consulting, Inc. (C), OR, *490*
Nationwide Personnel Placement, Inc. (C), OH, *490*
NaviSearch (C), GA, *490*
NCC Executive Search Consultants (C), CA, *490*
The NEIS Corp., Inc. (C), FL, *491*
J. Fielding Nelson & Assoc., Inc. (R), UT, *151*
New Dimensions in Technology, Inc. (C), MA, *492*
Newcomb-Desmond & Assoc., Inc. (C), OH, *492*
Newman-Johnson-King, Inc. (C), TX, *492*
Newport Strategic Search LLC (C), CA, *492*
NHA Plastics Recruiters (C), FL, *493*
Nicholaou & Co. (R), IL, *151*
NJ Solutions (C), CA, *493*
NMC & Kay Int'l. (R), CO, *152*
Norris Agency (C), TX, *495*
NorTech Resources (C), NY, *496*
North Coast Meridian (C), NY, *496*
The North Peak Group (C), OH, *496*
Northern Consultants Inc. (R), ME, *153*
Northland Employment Services Inc. (C), MN, *496*
Norton & Assoc. (C), IL, *496*
NYCOR Search, Inc. (C), MN, *497*
O'Brien & Bell (R), OH, *153*
John R. O'Connor & Assoc. (C), IL, *497*
O'Rourke Companies, Inc. (R), TX, *154*
O'Shea, Divine & Co., Inc. (R), CA, *154*
O'Sullivan Search Inc. (C), ON, *498*
The Odessa Group (R), CA, *155*
OEI, Inc. (C), NJ, *498*
Omega Search, Inc. (C), NC, *498*
Omega Systems, LLC (C), VA, *498*
Open Concepts (C), CA, *499*
Ortman Recruiting Int'l. (C), CA, *500*
P R Management Consultants, Inc. (C), NJ, *500*
P.R.H. Management, Inc. (R), CT, *158*
Packaging Personnel Co., Ltd. (C), WI, *501*
T. Page & Assoc. (C), TX, *502*
Paper Industry Recruitment (P.I.R.) (C), ME, *502*
D. P. Parker & Assoc., Inc. (R), MA, *159*
Parker, McFadden & Assoc. (C), GA, *503*
Parker Page Group (C), FL, *503*
Largent Parks & Partners (C), TX, *503*
Michael W. Parres & Assoc. (R), MI, *159*
Partners in Recruiting (C), IL, *503*
Pasona Canada, Inc. (C), ON, *504*
The Patience Motivation Belief Group, Inc. (C), GA, *505*
Paules Associates (C), CA, *505*
PC Assoc. (C), CO, *505*
Pearson & Assoc., Inc. (C), AZ, *506*
Peden & Assoc. (C), CA, *506*
Paul S. Pelland, P.C. (R), SC, *161*
M. A. Pelle Assoc., Inc. (C), NY, *506*
PeopleSource Inc. (C), TX, *506*
PERI Corp/Professional Executive Recruiters, Inc. (C), TX, *507*
The Perkins Group (R), NC, *162*
Fred Perry Assoc. (C), TX, *507*
Perry Search Assoc. (C), CA, *507*
Perry-D'Amico & Assoc. (R), CA, *162*
Barry Persky & Co., Inc. (R), CT, *163*
Personnel Assoc. (C), NC, *508*
The Personnel Group, Inc. (R), MN, *163*
Personnel, Inc. (C), AL, *508*
Personnel Incorporated (C), IA, *508*
Personnel Management Group (C), MB, *508*
The Personnel Network, Inc. (C), SC, *508*
Personnel Tangent Inc. (C), QE, *509*
Petro Staff Int'l. (C), AB, *509*
Petruzzi Assoc. (C), NJ, *509*
Peyser Assoc., Inc. (R), FL, *163*
Phase II Management (R), CT, *164*
Phelps Personnel Assoc., Inc. (C), SC, *510*
Phillips Resource Group (C), SC, *510*
Philo & Associates (C), GA, *511*
Phoenix BioSearch, Inc. (C), NJ, *511*
PIC Executive Search (C), GA, *511*
Gregory D. Pickens (C), TX, *511*
Pierce & Crow (R), CA, *164*
Pioneer Executive Consultants (C), ON, *512*
PKS Assoc., Inc. (C), RI, *513*
Placement Testart Inc. (C), QE, *513*
R. L. Plimpton Assoc., Inc. (R), CO, *165*
Yves Plouffe & Assoc. (R), QE, *165*
Poirier, Hoevel & Co. (R), CA, *166*
The Polen Group (C), PA, *514*
The Pollack Group (C), ON, *514*
Polytechnical Consultants, Inc. (C), IL, *514*
Jack Porter Assoc., Inc. (C), WA, *514*
David Powell, Inc. (R), CA, *166*
Norman Powers Assoc., Inc. (C), MA, *515*
Powers Consultants, Inc. (R), MO, *166*
Prairie Resource Group, Inc. (R), IL, *166*
George Preger & Associates Inc. (R), ON, *167*
Premier Recruiting Group (C), MI, *516*
The Premier Staffing Group (C), OH, *517*
Preng & Assoc., Inc. (R), TX, *167*
Price & Assoc., Inc. (C), VA, *518*
Alan J. Price Assoc., Inc. (C), RI, *518*
Prichard Kymen Inc. (R), AB, *168*
Prime Resource Assoc. (C), WI, *518*
Primus Assoc., L.C. (R), TX, *169*
Princeton Executive Search (C), NJ, *518*
Pro Tec Technical Services (C), ON, *519*
Probe Technology (C), PA, *519*
Professional Employment Group (C), MD, *520*
Professional Engineering Technical Personnel Consultants (C), NC, *520*
Professional Personnel Services (C), IA, *520*
Professional Personnel Consultants, Inc. (C), MI, *521*

Professional Persons Career Services (C), NY, *521*
Professional Search (R), MI, *169*
Professional Search, Inc. (C), CO, *522*
Professional Search Consultants (PSC) (C), TX, *523*
Professional Team Search, Inc. (R), AZ, *169*
Professions, Inc. (C), OH, *523*
Proquest Inc. (C), SC, *524*
ProTech Nationwide Staffing, Inc. (C), NY, *525*
PSD Group, Inc. (C), CA, *525*
PSP Agency (C), NY, *525*
Quality Control Recruiters (C), CT, *526*
Quality Search (C), IN, *526*
Quality Search Inc. (C), OH, *526*
Quantum Int'l., Ltd. (R), FL, *170*
Quiring Assoc., Inc. (C), IN, *527*
QVS Int'l. (R), GA, *170*
R & K Associates, Inc. (C), AZ, *527*
R M Associates (R), OH, *171*
R. C. Services (C), TX, *528*
R.A.N. Assoc., Inc. (C), OH, *528*
R/K International Inc. (R), CT, *171*
R2 Services, LLC (C), IL, *528*
Ramming & Assoc., Inc. (C), NJ, *528*
Ray & Berndtson/Laurendeau Labrecque (R), QE, *172*
Raymond Karsan Assoc. (C), PA, *529*
Raymond Thomas & Assoc. (C), FL, *530*
RBW Assoc. Inc. (C), OR, *531*
Re-Mark Assoc. Inc. (C), NJ, *531*
Reality Group (C), OK, *531*
Recruit Xpress (C), TX, *531*
Recruiting Assoc. of Amarillo (C), TX, *531*
Recruiting Services Group, Inc. (C), TN, *532*
The Recruitment Group, Inc. (C), NY, *532*
Redden-Shaffer Group (R), CA, *173*
Cedric L. Reese Inc. (C), CA, *533*
The Regis Group, Ltd. (R), GA, *174*
Reid Ellis Assoc. Inc. (C), ON, *533*
The Renaissance Network (C), MA, *534*
Renaissance Resources, LLC (R), VA, *174*
Reserve Technology Institute (R), TX, *175*
The Resource Group (R), NJ, *175*
Resource Inc. (R), MA, *175*
Resource Networking Inc. (C), IN, *534*
Resource Perspectives, Inc. (R), CA, *175*
Resource Recruiting (C), NH, *534*
Resources for Management (R), PA, *175*
L. J. Reszotko & Assoc. (C), IL, *535*
Russell Reynolds Assoc., Inc. (R), NY, *176*
Richard, Wayne & Roberts (C), TX, *536*
Rieser & Assoc., Inc. (R), MO, *178*
Right/McKee Consulting Group (C), TX, *537*
Riley Cole (C), CA, *537*
Ritta Professional Search Inc. (C), NY, *538*
River Region Personnel, Inc. (C), LA, *538*
RML Assoc. (C), PA, *538*
Roberson & Co. (C), AZ, *538*
Norman Roberts & Assoc., Inc. (R), CA, *179*
V. Robinson & Co., Inc. (C), MO, *539*
Robinson-Robinson & Assoc., Inc. (C), MN, *539*
Robison & Associates (R), NC, *180*
J. P. Roddy Consultants (C), PA, *540*
R. A. Rodriguez & Assoc., Inc. (C), TX, *540*
Rodzik & Assoc., Inc. (R), NC, *180*
Roevin Technical People (C), ON, *540*
Rogers - McManamon Executive Search (R), CA, *180*
ROI International, Inc. (R), WA, *181*
Romac Int'l., Inc. (C), FL, *542*
Romeo-Hudgins & Assoc., Ltd. (C), NJ, *544*
Emery A. Rose & Assoc. (C), WA, *545*
The Rossi Search Group (C), PA, *545*
Patricia Roth Int'l. (C), FL, *545*
Roth Young Executive Recruiters (C), MN, *546*
Roth Young Personnel Service of Detroit, Inc. (C), MI, *546*
Roth Young Executive Search of Milwaukee (C), WI, *547*
Rothrock Associates, Inc. (C), NC, *547*
Rowland Assoc. (C), CA, *547*
RSMR, Inc. (R), IL, *182*
Louis Rudzinsky Assoc., Inc. (C), MA, *548*
Ruppert Comann Assoc., Inc. (R), CO, *182*
The Ryan Charles Group, Inc. (C), FL, *548*
S-H-S Int'l. of Cherry Hill (C), NJ, *549*
S.D.P. Contract Recruiters (C), NJ, *550*
R. S. Sadow Assoc. (C), NJ, *550*
Sales Consultants Int'l. of Oakland (C), CA, *556*
Sales Consultants of Daphne (C), AL, *556*
Sales Consultants of Ft. Myers, Inc. (C), FL, *557*
Sales Consultants of Danbury (C), CT, *557*
Sales Consultants of Denver (C), CO, *557*
Sales Consultants of Barrington (C), IL, *558*
Sales Consultants of Baltimore (C), MD, *559*
Sales Consultants of Auburn Hills (C), MI, *559*
Sales Consultants of Farmington Hills (C), MI, *560*
Sales Consultants of Laurel Park, Inc. (C), MI, *560*
Sales Consultants of Cincinnati (C), OH, *561*
Sales Consultants of Pittsburgh (C), PA, *562*
Sales Consultants King of Prussia (C), PA, *562*
Sales Consultants of Orangeburg (C), SC, *562*
Sales Consultants of Appleton (C), WI, *563*
George D. Sandel Assoc. (C), MA, *565*
Sanford Rose Assoc. - Lake Forest (R), IL, *184*
Sanford Rose Assoc. (C), OH, *565*
Sanford Rose Assoc. - Santa Barbara (C), CA, *565*
Sanford Rose Assoc. - Anaheim (C), CA, *566*
Sanford Rose Assoc. - Athens (C), GA, *566*
Sanford Rose Assoc. - Chicago (C), IL, *566*
Sanford Rose Assoc. - Columbia, MD (C), MD, *567*
Sanford Rose Assoc. - Cedar Rapids (C), IA, *567*
Sanford Rose Assoc. - Rockville (C), MD, *567*
Sanford Rose Assoc. - Louisville (C), KY, *567*
Sanford Rose Assoc. - Amherst, NY (C), NY, *568*
Sanford Rose Assoc. - Flemington (C), NJ, *568*
Sanford Rose Assoc. - Canton (C), OH, *569*
Sanford Rose Assoc. - Burlington, NC (C), NC, *569*
Sanford Rose Assoc. - Akron (C), OH, *569*
Sanford Rose Assoc. - Columbia (C), SC, *570*
Sanford Rose Assoc. - Doylestown (C), PA, *570*
Sanford Rose Assoc. - Port Washington (C), WI, *571*
Sarver & Carruth Assoc. (C), OK, *571*
Sathe & Associates, Inc. (R), MN, *184*
David Saxner & Assoc., Inc. (DSA, Inc.) (R), IL, *185*
Schattle & Duquette (C), RI, *571*
Schenck & Assoc. SC (C), WI, *572*
Schick Professional Search, Inc. (C), OH, *572*
Schweichler Assoc., Inc. (R), CA, *186*
Scientific Solutions, Inc. (C), MI, *572*
Robert Scott Assoc. (C), NJ, *573*
Scott Sibley Assoc. (C), NY, *573*
Search Advisors Int'l. Corp. (R), FL, *186*
The Search Alliance, Inc. (R), FL, *186*
Search Assoc. (C), KY, *574*
Search Assoc., Inc. (C), CA, *574*
Search By Design (C), AZ, *574*
Search Consultants Int'l., Inc. (C), TX, *575*
Search Enterprises, Inc. (C), FL, *575*
Search Group Inc. (R), AB, *186*
The Search Network (C), CA, *576*
Search North America, Inc. (C), OR, *576*
Search Plus Int'l.-Ohio (C), OH, *576*
Search South, Inc. (C), AL, *576*
SearchOne, Inc. (C), AR, *577*
Searchworks, Inc. (C), FL, *577*
Segal & Assoc. (C), GA, *578*
Seiden Krieger Assoc., Inc. (R), NY, *188*
Select Services (C), IL, *578*
Selectis Corp. (C), IL, *578*
Selective Recruiting Assoc., Inc. (C), MI, *578*
Sevcor Int'l., Inc. (R), IL, *188*
Sharp Placement Professionals, Inc. (C), NY, *579*
Sharrow & Assoc., Inc. (C), MI, *579*
M. B. Shattuck & Assoc., Inc. (R), CA, *189*
Shinn & Assoc. (R), CA, *189*
The Shorr Group (R), IL, *190*
The Shotland Group (R), CA, *190*
Shupack & Michaels Inc. (C), NY, *580*
Larry Siegel & Assoc. (R), WA, *191*
RitaSue Siegel Resources, Inc. (R), NY, *191*
SignatureSoft Inc. (C), CA, *581*
Marvin L. Silcott & Assoc., Inc. (C), TX, *581*
The Silicon Network (C), ON, *581*
Sill Technical Assoc., Inc. (C), PA, *581*
Skipping Stone Inc. (C), VA, *582*

Ruth Sklar Assoc., Inc. (RSA Executive Search) (R), NY, *192*
Tom Sloan & Assoc., Inc. (C), WI, *583*
Smith & Assoc. (C), FL, *583*
J. Harrington Smith Assoc. (C), IN, *584*
The Smith Group, Inc. (C), NC, *584*
Smith, Roth & Squires (R), NY, *194*
Snelling & Snelling, Inc. (C), FL, *585*
Snelling Search (C), AL, *585*
Snelling Search Recruiters (C), NC, *586*
Soderlund Assoc. Inc. (R), OH, *194*
Softrix, Inc. (C), NJ, *586*
Software Engineering Solutions, Inc. (C), CA, *586*
Software Resource Consultants (C), TN, *587*
Robert Sollman & Assoc. (C), FL, *587*
Solutions Group (R), AL, *195*
Souder & Assoc. (R), VA, *195*
Southern Recruiters & Consultants, Inc. (C), SC, *587*
Southern Research Services (R), FL, *195*
Southwestern Professional Services (C), TN, *588*
Specialized Search Assoc. (C), FL, *589*
Specialty Employment Services, Inc. (C), GA, *589*
Spectra International LLC (C), AZ, *589*
SpectraWest (C), CA, *589*
Spectrum Consultants (R), CA, *196*
SpencerSearch, Inc. (C), CO, *589*
SpencerStuart (R), NY, *196*
Splaine & Assoc., Inc. (R), CA, *198*
SR Wilson, Inc. (C), CA, *590*
Staff Resources, Inc. (C), SC, *590*
Staffing Edge, Inc. (C), IA, *590*
C. J. Stafford & Assoc. (C), ON, *591*
Stanton Chase Int'l. (R), MD, *198*
The Stanton Group, Inc. (C), IL, *591*
Star Search Consultants (C), ON, *591*
Steinbach & Co. (C), MA, *592*
The Stelton Group, Inc. (C), NJ, *592*
Sterling Int'l. Management Recruitment, Ltd. Inc. (C), NC, *592*
Ron Stevens & Assoc., Inc. (C), FL, *593*
Stewart/Greene & Co. of The Triad, Inc. (C), NC, *594*
Charles Stickler Assoc. (R), PA, *201*
STM Assoc. (R), UT, *201*
Allan Stolee Inc. (R), FL, *201*
Stone Enterprises Ltd. (C), IL, *594*
Stone, Murphy & Olson (R), MN, *201*
Stoneburner Assoc., Inc. (C), KS, *594*
Strategic Alternatives (R), CA, *202*
Strategic Assoc., Inc. (C), TX, *595*
Strategic Search Corp. (R), IL, *202*
Strategic Technologies, Inc. (C), TX, *596*
Success Seekers Connection (C), FL, *596*
Joe Sullivan & Assoc., Inc. (R), NY, *204*
Summit Executive Search Consultants, Inc. (R), FL, *204*
Summit Group Int'l., Inc. (R), GA, *204*
Survival Systems Staffing, Inc. (C), CA, *597*
Synergistech Communications (C), CA, *597*
Synergy Solutions, Ltd. (C), WA, *597*
System 1 Search (C), CA, *598*
Systems Careers (C), CA, *598*
Systems Research Group (C), OH, *598*
Systems Research Inc. (SRI) (C), IL, *598*
T E M Assoc. (C), WI, *599*
Tabb & Assoc. (R), OH, *205*
Tactical Alternatives (R), CA, *205*
The Talley Group (R), VA, *205*
Martin Stevens Tamaren & Assoc., Inc. (R), CA, *206*
S. Tanner & Assoc. Inc. (C), ON, *599*
Tanner & Assoc., Inc. (R), TX, *206*
Target Search, Inc. (C), PA, *600*
Tate & Assoc., Inc. (R), NJ, *207*
Tate Consulting, Inc. (R), FL, *207*
M. L. Tawney & Assoc. (C), TX, *600*
TCM Enterprises (C), MD, *600*
Teamsearch, Inc. (C), MI, *601*
Tech Connector Group (C), CA, *601*
Tech Consulting (C), FL, *601*
Tech-Net (C), TX, *601*
Techaid Inc. (C), QE, *601*
Technical Employment Consultants (C), PA, *602*
Technical Resource Assoc. (C), TN, *602*
Technical Search Assoc. (C), OH, *602*
Technical Skills Consulting Inc. (R), ON, *207*
Technical Staffing Solutions (C), TX, *602*
Technifind Int'l. (C), TX, *602*
Technology Consultants Int'l. (C), CA, *603*
Technology Management Partners (R), CA, *208*
Technology Search Int'l. (C), CA, *603*
Techstaff Inc. (C), WI, *603*
Tecmark Associates Inc. (C), NY, *604*
Teknon Employment Resources, Inc. (C), OH, *604*
Tekworx, Inc. (C), OK, *604*
Tele-Solutions of Arizona, Inc. (C), AZ, *604*
Telecom Connections, Inc. (C), TX, *604*
Telecom Recruiters, Inc. (C), VA, *605*
Thomas & Assoc. of Michigan (C), MI, *606*
Thomson, Sponar & Adams, Inc. (C), WA, *606*
Thorne, Brieger Assoc., Inc. (R), NY, *209*
The Tidewater Group Inc. (C), CT, *607*
Tierney Assoc., Inc. (R), PA, *209*
Fred C. Tippel & Assoc. (C), OH, *607*
Tirocchi, Wright, Inc. (R), CA, *209*
Tittemore Cowan Assoc. (C), AB, *607*
TPG & Assoc. (C), TX, *608*
Trac One (R), NJ, *210*
Jay Tracey Assoc. Inc. (C), VT, *608*
Trainor/Frank & Assoc. Inc. (C), WI, *608*
Trambley the Recruiter (C), NM, *608*
Trans-United Consultants Ltd. (C), ON, *608*
Transportation Recruiting Services, Inc. (C), MS, *608*
Travis & Co., Inc. (R), MA, *210*
Traynor Confidential, Ltd. (C), NY, *609*
Triangle Assoc. (C), PA, *609*
TriStaff Group (C), CA, *609*
Trout & Assoc. Inc. (R), UT, *211*
Trowbridge & Co., Inc. (R), MA, *211*
TRS Staffing Solutions Inc. (C), OH, *610*
The Truman Agency (C), CA, *610*
Tryon & Heideman, LLC (R), MO, *211*
TSC Management Services Group, Inc. (C), IL, *610*
TSS Consulting, Ltd. (C), AZ, *610*
The Thomas Tucker Co. (R), CA, *211*
U.S. Search (C), VA, *610*
The Ultimate Source (R), CA, *212*
UniQuest Int'l., Inc. (C), FL, *610*
Unisearch Search & Recruiting Inc. (C), CA, *611*
Unlimited Staffing Solutions, Inc. (C), MI, *611*
The Urban Placement Service (C), TX, *611*
Verkamp-Joyce Assoc., Inc. (R), IL, *213*
Victor White Int'l. (C), CA, *612*
Voigt Assoc. (R), IL, *214*
The Wabash Group (C), IN, *613*
Wachendorfer & Assoc. (C), TX, *613*
Wallace Assoc. (C), CT, *614*
Gerald Walsh & Co. Inc. (C), NS, *614*
Linda Walter & Associes (C), QE, *615*
Ward-Hoffman & Assoc. (C), ID, *615*
Warner & Assoc., Inc. (C), OH, *615*
Warren Executive Services (C), GA, *616*
Warren, Morris & Madison, Ltd. (C), CA, *616*
Wayne Assoc., Inc. (C), VA, *616*
Weber Executive Search (R), NY, *216*
David Weinfeld Group (C), NC, *617*
Weinpel Search, Inc. (C), NJ, *617*
S. E. Weinstein Co. (R), IL, *217*
Henry Welker & Assoc. (C), MI, *618*
The Wellesley Group, Inc. (R), IL, *217*
Welzig, Lowe & Assoc. (C), CO, *618*
Werbin Assoc. Executive Search, Inc. (C), NY, *618*
West & Assoc. (C), IL, *618*
West & West (R), CA, *218*
Western Management Consultants (R), BC, *218*
Western Technical Resources (C), CA, *619*
WestPacific National Search, Inc. (C), CA, *619*
Weterrings & Agnew, Inc. (C), NY, *619*
The Whitaker Companies (C), TX, *619*
White, Roberts & Stratton, Inc. (C), IL, *619*
Whitehead & Assoc., Inc. (C), MO, *620*
Whittaker & Assoc., Inc. (C), GA, *620*
Wilkinson & Ives (R), CA, *221*
Dick Williams & Assoc. (C), CA, *621*
John Williams & Assoc. (C), TX, *621*
Williams & Delmore, Inc. (C), NC, *621*
Williams Recruiting, Inc. (C), WA, *621*
Williams, Roth & Krueger, Inc. (R), IL, *221*
Willis & Assoc. (R), OH, *221*
Wilson & Assoc. Int'l. Inc. (C), FL, *622*
Wilson Personnel, Inc. (C), NC, *622*
The Winchester Group (R), CA, *222*
Windsor International (R), GA, *222*
Winfield Assoc., Inc. (C), MA, *623*
Wing Tips & Pumps, Inc. (C), MI, *623*
Winston Search, Inc. (R), MD, *222*
Wisnewski & Assoc. (R), CA, *223*
The Witt Group (C), FL, *623*
WMD inc. (C), NJ, *623*
Susan L. Wonderling Recruiting (C), PA, *623*
Wood & Assoc./Executive Search Consultants (C), CA, *624*

Wood West & Partners Inc. (C), BC, *624*
Woodmoor Group (C), CO, *624*
Jim Woodson & Assoc., Inc. (C), MS, *624*
Woodworth Int'l. Group (R), OR, *224*
World Search (C), OH, *625*
John Wylie Assoc., Inc. (C), OK, *625*
Wyndham Mills Int'l., Inc. (R), GA, *225*
Xagas & Assoc. (R), IL, *226*
Yelverton Executive Search (R), CA, *226*
Yungner & Bormann (R), MN, *226*
Zeiger Assoc. L.L.C. (C), CA, *627*

11.0 Specialized services

Accountants Executive Search (C), PA, *234*
AST/BRYANT (R), CT, *8*
Austin Park Management Group Inc. (C), ON, *256*
The Baer Group (R), OH, *10*
Battalia Winston Int'l./The Euram Consultants Group (R), NY, *13*
C. Berger And Company (R), IL, *16*
C. G. & Assoc. (R), PA, *26*
The CARVIR Group, Inc. (C), GA, *285*
Arlene Clapp, Ltd. (R), MN, *35*
Conroy Partners Ltd. (R), AB, *39*
Damon & Assoc., Inc. (C), TX, *306*
Joseph A. Davis Consultants, Inc. (R), NY, *47*
EA Plus, Inc. (C), TX, *325*
Elinvar (C), NC, *328*
The Elliott Company (R), MA, *58*
Executive Search Int'l./Transearch (R), MA, *63*
F-O-R-T-U-N-E Personnel Consultants of Troy, Inc. (C), MI, *347*
Foster Partners (R), NY, *70*
Gans, Gans & Assoc., Inc. (R), FL, *74*
Genel Associates (C), CA, *356*
Gilbert & Van Campen Int'l. (R), NY, *76*
The Glazin Group (R), BC, *77*
Global HealthCare Partners (R), IL, *78*
Hill Allyn Assoc. (C), CA, *378*
Hite Executive Search (R), OH, *94*
Holland Rusk & Assoc. (R), IL, *95*
Innovative Healthcare Services, Inc. (C), GA, *389*
International Management Development Corp. (C), NY, *393*
Johnson Smith & Knisely (R), NY, *107*
Joseph Chris & Assoc. (C), TX, *400*
JRL Executive Recruiters (C), MO, *401*
Kass/Abell & Assoc., Inc. (C), CA, *404*
A.T. Kearney Executive Search (R), IL, *111*
Joyce C. Knauff & Assoc. (C), IL, *408*
KPA Assoc., Inc. (C), NY, *408*
Leader Search Inc. (R), AB, *127*
Alan Levine Assoc. (R), MA, *129*
Management Association Network (C), WI, *424*
Management Recruiters of Orange County, N.Y., Inc. (C), NJ, *453*
Management Recruiters of Cherry Hill (C), PA, *459*
Management Recruiters of Madison, Inc. (C), WI, *466*
Marra Peters & Partners (R), NJ, *136*
McDonald Assoc. Int'l. (R), IL, *140*
Clarence E. McFeely, Inc. (R), IL, *141*
Morgan/Webber, Inc. (R), NY, *147*
The Mulshine Co., Inc. (R), NJ, *149*
Nicholaou & Co. (R), IL, *151*
The Park Group & Assoc., Inc. (C), MD, *502*
Bob Poline Assoc. Inc. (C), CA, *514*
The Regis Group, Ltd. (R), GA, *174*
Robsham & Assoc., Inc. (R), MA, *180*
Savoy Partners, Ltd. (R), DC, *184*
Search Assoc., Inc. (C), NJ, *574*
Search Bureau Int'l. (C), IL, *574*
The Shorr Group (R), IL, *190*
Sink, Walker, Boltrus Int'l. (R), MA, *192*
SpencerStuart (R), NY, *196*
Stillinger & Assoc. (R), CA, *201*
Stone, Murphy & Olson (R), MN, *201*
The Talon Group (R), TX, *205*
Tax Network Resources, Inc. (C), NY, *600*
Techstaff Inc. (C), WI, *603*
Webb, Johnson Assoc., Inc. (R), NY, *216*
Weinman & Assoc. (C), AZ, *617*
Wilder & Assoc. (C), VA, *620*
Working Relationships, Inc. (C), MN, *624*
Zona & Assoc., Inc. (C), NY, *628*

11.1 Management consultants

A-L Assoc., Inc. (R), NY, *1*
A.K.S. Assoc., Ltd. (R), MA, *1*
Accounting & Computer Personnel (C), NY, *238*
Ackerman Johnson Inc. (C), TX, *238*
Action Executive Personnel Consulting Inc. (C), ON, *239*
Alexander Associates (R), NJ, *2*
The Alexander Group (R), NJ, *3*
Alexander Ross & Co. (R), NY, *3*
Allard Associates (C), CA, *244*
Allied Search, Inc. (C), CA, *245*
The Alternatives Group, Inc. (C), TX, *246*
ALW Research Int'l. (R), NJ, *4*
American Heritage Group, Inc. (C), MI, *247*
Andre David & Assoc., Inc. (R), TX, *6*
Ashway Ltd. Agency (C), NY, *253*
Ashworth Consultants, Inc. (R), MA, *8*
A. M. Auster Associates (R), FL, *9*
Baeder Kalinski Int'l. Group, Inc. (R), NH, *10*
The Baer Group (R), OH, *10*
Baker, Nelms & Montgomery (C), IL, *258*
Baldwin Associates, LLC (R), CT, *10*
Barclay Consultants, Inc. (C), NJ, *259*
Barton Assoc., Inc. (R), TX, *12*
Battalia Winston Int'l./The Euram Consultants Group (R), NY, *13*
R. Gaines Baty Assoc., Inc. (R), TX, *13*
BayResearch Group, Inc. (R), IL, *14*
Becker Project Resources, Inc. (C), OR, *262*
Behavioral Science Assoc., Inc. (R), AZ, *15*
N. L. Benke & Assoc., Inc. (C), OH, *264*
Robert Bennett Assoc. (C), NY, *264*
BEST/World Assoc. Inc. (R), TX, *16*
BG & Assoc. (C), MD, *266*
Birch & Associes (C), QE, *267*
Bishop Partners (R), NY, *17*
Blackhawk Advantage, Inc. (C), CA, *267*
David Blevins & Assoc. (C), WA, *268*
Boardroom Consultants/Kenny Kindler Tholke (R), NY, *19*
Tom Bogle & Assoc. (C), CA, *269*
Bonnell Assoc. Ltd. (R), CT, *19*
Bornholdt Shivas & Friends Executive Recruiters (C), NY, *270*
Bosland Gray Assoc. (R), NJ, *20*
Howard Bowen Consulting (C), FL, *270*
Brault & Assoc., Ltd. (R), VA, *22*
Bredeson Executive Recruitment, LLC (R), TX, *22*
The Brentwood Group, Inc. (R), NJ, *22*
BridgeGate LLC (C), CA, *273*
Brindisi Search (R), MD, *23*
Charles Buck & Assoc., Inc. (R), NY, *24*
The Buckley Group (C), FL, *276*
Bullis & Co., Inc. (R), CA, *25*
Burke & Assoc./The Westfield Group (C), CT, *276*
The Burke Group (C), ON, *276*
C.T.E.W. Executive Personnel Services Inc. (C), BC, *278*
Campa & Assoc. (R), ON, *27*
T. M. Campbell Co. (R), WA, *27*
Canny, Bowen Inc. (R), NY, *27*
J. P. Canon Assoc. (C), NY, *280*
The Canon Group (C), CA, *280*
Capital Consulting & Research, Inc. (R), CT, *28*
Career Development Associates (C), NV, *282*
The Carlyle Group, Ltd. (R), IL, *30*
Carter McKenzie, Inc. (C), NJ, *285*
Carver Search Consultants (C), CA, *285*
Cejka Healthcare Executive Search Services (CHESS) (R), MO, *32*
Churchill & Affiliates, Inc. (R), PA, *35*
Clarey/Napier Int'l., L.C. (R), TX, *35*
Clayman & Co. (R), MA, *36*
CN Associates (C), CA, *293*
Coleman Lew & Assoc., Inc. (R), NC, *37*
Colton Bernard Inc. (R), CA, *37*
Conard Associates, Inc. (R), NH, *39*
Consultant Recruiters (C), WI, *297*
Consulting Resource Group, Inc. (C), GA, *297*
ContactBridge, Inc. (R), IL, *40*
COR Management Services, Ltd. (C), NY, *298*
Cornell Group Int'l. Consulting, Inc. (R), NY, *41*
Corporate Builders, Inc. (C), OR, *299*
CountryHouse Hotels Executive Search (C), VA, *302*
Cowell & Associates, Ltd. (R), IL, *42*
Creative Management Strategies, Ltd. (R), NY, *42*
Crispi, Wagner & Co., Inc. (R), NY, *43*
Cybernautic Corp. (C), CT, *305*
Cypress Int'l., Inc. (R), FL, *45*
DARE Personnel Inc. (C), ON, *307*
The DataFinders Group, Inc. (C), NJ, *307*
Daubenspeck & Associates, Ltd. (R), IL, *46*
The Dayton Group, Ltd. (C), NY, *309*
DBL Associates (C), CA, *309*
De Funiak & Edwards (R), IN, *47*

Delta Management Group Ltd. (C), ON, *310*
Delta Resource Group, Ltd. (C), GA, *311*
The Devlin Search Group, Inc. (C), MA, *311*
Dieckmann & Assoc., Ltd. (R), IL, *51*
Roger Dietsch & Assoc. (C), MN, *312*
Dinte Resources, Inc. (R), VA, *52*
Diversified Search, Inc. (R), PA, *52*
DLB Assoc. (R), NY, *53*
Don Allan Assoc., Inc. (C), CA, *313*
Donahue/Bales Assoc. (R), IL, *54*
Donini Assoc. (R), VA, *54*
J P Donnelly Assoc., Inc. (C), NY, *314*
Dorst Information Services, Inc. (C), NY, *314*
Drew Assoc. Int'l. (R), NJ, *54*
Drinkwater & Assoc. (R), MA, *54*
Drummond Assoc., Inc. (C), NY, *315*
DS&A (Doug Sears & Assoc.) (C), FL, *315*
DuBrul Management Co. (C), NY, *315*
Dynamic Choices Inc. (C), MO, *323*
Earley Kielty & Assoc., Inc. (R), NY, *56*
EBA Group (R), NJ, *56*
EDI, Inc. (C), MD, *326*
EFCO Consultants, Inc. (C), NY, *327*
Richard A. Eisner & Co., LLP (R), NY, *57*
Elinvar (C), NC, *328*
Empowered Solutions Corp. (C), GA, *330*
The Enfield Company (C), TX, *330*
ENI (R), CT, *59*
Ethos Consulting, Inc. (R), CA, *61*
ExeConnex, LLC (R), GA, *61*
Executive Dimensions (R), NY, *62*
Executive Exchange Corp. (C), NJ, *333*
Executive Partners Inc. (C), CT, *333*
Executive Recruitment Specialists, Inc. (R), NC, *63*
Executive Resource Systems (C), CA, *335*
Executive Search Consultants International, Inc. (R), NY, *63*
Executive Search Consultants Corp. (C), IL, *335*
Executive Search Team (C), MI, *336*
Executive Solutions (R), MN, *64*
Executive Strategies, Inc. (C), GA, *337*
ExecutiveFit (C), NY, *337*
Fabian Assoc. Inc. (C), NY, *338*
Leon A. Farley Assoc. (R), CA, *65*
Faro Consultants Int'l. (C), VA, *338*
A. E. Feldman Assoc., Inc. (C), NY, *339*
Fenwick Partners (R), MA, *66*
Finnegan & Assoc. (R), CA, *67*
Howard Fischer Assoc. Int'l., Inc. (R), PA, *67*
A. G. Fishkin & Assoc., Inc. (R), MD, *68*
James L. Fisk & Assoc. (C), MO, *342*
Flexible Resources, Inc. (C), CT, *342*
Focus Consulting Services, Inc. (C), FL, *342*
The Ford Group, Inc. (R), PA, *69*
Foster Associates (C), NJ, *351*
Foster Partners (R), NY, *70*
Frey & Sher Assoc., Inc. (C), VA, *353*
Bernard Frigon & Assoc. Inc. (C), QE, *353*
Gerald Frisch Assoc., Inc. (R), NY, *72*
Frye/Joure & Assoc., Inc. (C), TN, *353*
Jay Gaines & Company, Inc. (R), NY, *73*
Gans, Gans & Assoc., Inc. (R), FL, *74*
Gardiner, Townsend & Assoc. (R), NY, *74*
Gardner-Ross Assoc., Inc. (R), NY, *74*
The Garms Group (R), IL, *74*
Garrett Assoc. Inc. (R), GA, *75*
Genesis Consulting Partners (R), PA, *76*
Gent & Assoc. (C), CA, *356*
John Gilbert Co. (C), TX, *357*
Gilbert Tweed Assoc. Inc. (R), NY, *76*
Howard Gilmore & Assoc. (R), OH, *77*
Gimbel & Assoc. (C), FL, *357*
Global 1000 Int'l. Services (C), CA, *358*
Global Career Services, Inc. (C), NY, *358*
Global Data Services, Inc. (R), NY, *77*
Global Engineers Inc. (C), ME, *358*
Global Resources Group (R), CA, *78*
Global Technologies Group Inc. (C), NC, *359*
Global Telecommunications, Inc. (C), TX, *359*
F. Gloss Int'l. (R), VA, *78*
H. L. Goehring & Assoc., Inc. (C), OH, *359*
Fred J. Goldsmith Assoc. (R), CA, *79*
L. J. Gonzer Assoc. (C), NJ, *360*
The Goodman Group (R), CA, *79*
Goodrich & Sherwood Assoc., Inc. (R), NY, *79*
Robert Graham Assoc. (R), RI, *81*
Robert Grant Assoc., Inc. (C), CA, *361*
Grant/Morgan Assoc., Inc. (C), MD, *361*
Sheila Greco Assoc. (C), NY, *362*
Greenhaven & Assoc., Inc. (R), NY, *81*
Growth Strategies, Inc. (R), FL, *83*
The Guild Corp. (C), VA, *364*
The Gullgroup (C), TX, *364*
H.Q. Search, Inc. (C), IL, *365*
Haddad Assoc. (R), FL, *84*
Halbrecht & Co. (C), VA, *365*
Halbrecht Lieberman Assoc., Inc. (R), CT, *84*
Hale Assoc. (R), IL, *84*
The Hamilton Group (R), MD, *85*
Harbor Consultants Int'l., Inc. (C), VA, *368*
Harper Hewes, Inc. (C), NY, *369*
Hartsfield Group, Inc. (R), GA, *87*
HDB Incorporated (C), MO, *371*
Hechkoff/Work Executive Search Inc. (R), NY, *89*
Hedlund Corp. (C), IL, *375*
Helbling & Assoc., Inc. (R), PA, *91*
The Helms Int'l. Group (R), VA, *91*
The Hensge Co. (R), IL, *91*
Hermann & Westmore (R), CA, *92*
Herrerias & Assoc. (R), CA, *92*
The Herrmann Group Ltd. (R), ON, *92*
Hersher Assoc., Ltd. (R), IL, *92*
Hessel Assoc., Inc. (C), NY, *377*
Higbee Assoc., Inc. (C), CT, *377*
High Tech Staffing Group (C), OR, *377*
Highland Search Group, L.L.C. (R), NY, *93*
Hintz Associates (C), NY, *378*
David C. Horn Executive Search (C), TX, *381*
Houtz•Strawn & Arnold, Inc. (R), TX, *96*
HR Consultants (C), GA, *382*
HRD Consultants, Inc. (R), NJ, *97*
Hreshko Consulting Group (C), NJ, *382*
HRNI (C), MI, *383*
Human Capital Resources, Inc. (C), FL, *384*
The Human Resource Department Ltd. (R), OH, *98*
Human Resources Management Hawaii, Inc. (C), HI, *384*
Hunt & Howe Inc. (R), NY, *99*
Hunter Douglas Group, Inc. (R), IL, *99*
Huntress Real Estate Executive Search (R), MO, *100*
The Hutton Group, Inc. (C), FL, *386*
Hyland Executive Search (C), AZ, *386*
Hyman & Assoc. (C), TX, *386*
The IMC Group of Companies (R), NY, *101*
InfoTech Search (C), TX, *388*
Innovative Resource Group, LLC (C), NC, *389*
Intech Summit Group, Inc. (R), CA, *102*
Integrated Management Solutions (C), NY, *390*
Integrated Search Solutions Group, LLC (ISSG) (R), NY, *102*
Integrity Search, Inc. (R), PA, *102*
Interquest, Inc. (R), NY, *103*
IPR, Inc. (R), VA, *103*
Isaacson, Miller (R), MA, *104*
Jakobs & Assoc. Int'l. (R), NY, *105*
JDG Assoc., Ltd. (C), MD, *397*
JLI-Boston (R), MA, *106*
John Jay & Co. (C), ME, *399*
John Ryan Assoc., LLC. (C), NY, *399*
L. J. Johnson & Co. (R), MI, *106*
Johnson & Company (R), CT, *107*
The Johnson Group, Unlimited (C), NY, *400*
The Jonathan Stevens Group, Inc. (R), NJ, *108*
Jones Management Co. (R), CT, *108*
Jones-Parker/Starr (R), NC, *108*
JSG Group Management Consultants (R), ON, *109*
Juno Systems, Inc. (C), NY, *402*
Keane Assoc. (R), MA, *110*
A.T. Kearney Executive Search (R), IL, *111*
Kelly Assoc. (R), WI, *112*
Kelly Associates (R), PA, *112*
Kenmore Executives Inc. (C), FL, *405*
David Warwick Kennedy & Assoc. (R), BC, *112*
Barbara Kerner Consultants (C), NY, *405*
Kincaid Group Inc. (KGI) (C), TX, *406*
The Kingsley Group (R), CA, *114*
Kip Williams, Inc. (R), NY, *115*
KL Consultants (C), NJ, *407*
Kleber & Assoc. (C), WA, *407*
Raymond J. Klemmer & Assoc. (R), NY, *116*
T. J. Koellhoffer & Assoc. (R), NJ, *116*
Koll-Fairfield LLC (C), CT, *408*
Kopplin Search, Inc. (R), CA, *117*
Korn/Ferry Int'l. (R), NY, *117*
Katherine R. Kraemer (R), CA, *120*
Kramer Executive Resources, Inc. (C), NY, *409*
Todd L. Krueger & Assoc. (C), WA, *409*
Kurtz Pro-Search, Inc. (C), NJ, *410*

Lamon + Stuart + Michaels Inc. (R), ON, *124*
Robert Larned Assoc., Inc. (C), VA, *413*
Larson Assoc. (R), CA, *125*
LAS Management Consulting Group, Inc. (R), NJ, *125*
Latham International, Ltd. (R), NJ, *126*
Layne-Mendez & Co. (R), TX, *127*
Leaders-Trust Int'l./Carce y Asociados, S.C. (R), MX, *127*
Alan Levine Assoc. (R), MA, *129*
Lifter & Assoc. (C), CA, *418*
Lloyd Associates (R), GA, *130*
Loewenstein & Assoc., Inc. (R), TX, *131*
Logistics Management Resources, Inc. (R), NY, *131*
Logue & Rice Inc. (C), VA, *420*
The Luciani Group (R), CA, *132*
Fran Luisi Assoc. (R), NJ, *132*
M/J/A Partners (R), IL, *133*
The Mackenzie Group (R), MD, *133*
Magellan Int'l., L.P. (C), TX, *422*
Magnum Search (C), IL, *422*
Major Legal Services, Inc. (C), OH, *423*
Management & Human Resources (R), MA, *134*
Management Dimensions Ltd. (R), ON, *134*
Management One Consultants (C), ON, *425*
Management Recruiters of Middlesex (C), CT, *442*
Management Recruiters of Bonita Springs, Inc. (C), FL, *443*
Management Recruiters of Anna Maria Island (C), FL, *443*
Management Recruiters of St. Augustine (C), FL, *444*
Management Recruiters of Marietta, Inc. (C), GA, *446*
Management Recruiters of Detroit & Farmington Hills (C), MI, *451*
Management Recruiters of Princeton (C), NJ, *454*
Management Recruiters of Bordentown (C), NJ, *454*
Management Recruiters of Great Neck (C), NY, *454*
Management Recruiters of Cedar Mountain (C), NC, *455*
Management Recruiters - Kannapolis (C), NC, *456*
Management Recruiters of Charlotte - North, Inc. (C), NC, *456*
Management Recruiters of Oklahoma City (C), OK, *458*
Management Recruiters of Wausau, LLC (C), WI, *466*
Management Recruiters of Milwaukee - Downtown (C), WI, *466*
Management Search Int'l. (C), CA, *467*
Manning Lloyd Assoc. Ltd. (C), NY, *468*
The Martin Group (R), CA, *137*
Martin Partners, L.L.C. (R), IL, *137*
Massey-Horton Int'l. (R), ON, *138*
K. E. McCarthy & Assoc. (R), CA, *139*
The McCormick Group (C), VA, *473*
McCormick Search Inc. (C), IL, *474*
McGrath & Assoc., Inc. (R), NJ, *141*
Meder & Assoc., Inc. (R), IL, *142*
Media Management Resources, Inc. (R), CO, *142*
Medical Recruiters Exchange (C), AZ, *477*
Mengel & McDonald Ltd. (C), IL, *479*
The Mercer Group, Inc. (R), NM, *143*
Meyer Assoc., Inc. (R), GA, *144*
E. J. Michaels, Ltd. (C), NY, *481*
Micro Staff Solutions, Inc. (C), TX, *481*
Midas Management (C), CT, *481*
Millennium Search Group, Inc. (R), CA, *144*
Miller-Hall HRISearch (C), NY, *482*
Herbert Mines Assoc., Inc. (R), NY, *145*
Mirtz Morice, Inc. (R), CT, *145*
Montenido Assoc. (R), CA, *146*
Morgan Samuels Co. (R), CA, *147*
MRI, The Sequel Group, LLC (C), CO, *486*
MSA Executive Search (R), MO, *148*
Murphy Partners Int'l. (R), IL, *150*
Musick & Assoc. (C), CA, *487*
National Field Service Corp. (C), NY, *489*
National Recruiters (C), OK, *489*
National Search, Inc.r (C), FL, *490*
New Venture Development, Inc. (C), CA, *492*
Newport Strategic Search LLC (C), CA, *492*
Next Step Recruiting (C), CA, *493*
Marc Nichols Assoc., Inc. (C), NY, *493*
Ira Z. Nitzberg (C), NY, *493*
J. L. Nixon Consulting (C), TX, *493*
W. D. Nolte & Company (R), CT, *152*
Nordeman Grimm, Inc. (R), NY, *152*
The Norland Group (C), CA, *494*
Norman Broadbent Int'l., Inc. (R), NY, *152*
John B. Norris & Assoc., Inc. (C), MD, *495*
NorthStar Technologies, Inc. (C), NY, *496*
Nursing Technomics (R), PA, *153*
O'Neill & Co. (R), CT, *154*
O'Neill Group (C), NJ, *498*
O'Toole & Company, Inc. (R), IL, *154*
Object Resources Int'l., Inc. (C), CT, *498*
The Onstott Group (R), MA, *156*
The Oxford Group (C), TX, *500*
Page-Wheatcroft & Co., Ltd. (R), TX, *158*
Parenica & Co. (R), NC, *159*
Largent Parks & Partners (C), TX, *503*
Partners In Human Resources Int'l., Inc. (R), NY, *160*
The Partnership Group (R), NJ, *160*
Partnervision Consulting Group Inc. (R), ON, *160*
Paul-Tittle Assoc., Inc. (R), VA, *161*
Pawlik/Dorman Partners (R), IL, *161*
Pearson, Caldwell & Farnsworth (R), CA, *161*
Peck & Assoc., Ltd. (R), WI, *161*
Penn Associates (R), PA, *161*
PHD Conseil en Ressources Humaines Inc. (C), QE, *510*
Phillips Assoc. (C), FL, *510*
Picard Int'l., Ltd. (R), NY, *164*
Plummer & Assoc., Inc. (R), CT, *166*
The Prairie Group (C), IL, *515*
Preferred Placement, Inc. (C), NY, *516*
Preng & Assoc., Inc. (R), TX, *167*
Preston & Co. (R), NJ, *167*
Preston-Hunter, Inc. (R), IL, *167*
Prestonwood Assoc. (R), MA, *168*
PRO, Inc./Professional Recruiting Offices, Inc. (C), CA, *519*
The Professional Sales Search Co., Inc. (C), WA, *522*
Professional Selection Services (R), GA, *169*
Professional Support Inc. (C), NY, *523*
ProLinks Inc. (R), VA, *170*
ProStar Systems, Inc. (C), MD, *525*
Quality Control Recruiters (C), CT, *526*
Quantum Int'l., Ltd. (R), FL, *170*
The Quest Organization (C), NY, *527*
R & L Assoc., Ltd. (R), NY, *170*
Raines Int'l. Inc. (R), NY, *171*
The Ransford Group (R), TX, *171*
Joanne E. Ratner Search (C), NY, *529*
Ray & Assoc., Inc. (C), IA, *529*
Razzino-Claymore Assoc. (C), NJ, *530*
Reifel & Assoc. (R), IL, *174*
The Repovich-Reynolds Group (TRRG, Inc.) (R), CA, *175*
Research Personnel Consultants (C), ON, *534*
Reynolds Consulting Int'l. (R), ON, *177*
Reynolds Partners (R), NY, *177*
Rice Cohen Int'l. (R), PA, *178*
W. F. Richer Assoc., Inc. (C), NY, *536*
Jack Richman & Assoc. (C), FL, *537*
Roberts Ryan & Bentley, Inc. (R), MD, *179*
Robinson, Fraser Group Ltd. (R), ON, *180*
Rockwood Assoc. (C), NY, *540*
Craig Roe & Assoc., LLC (C), MD, *540*
ROI Assoc. (R), NY, *180*
Romac Int'l. Inc. (R), MA, *181*
Rowland Mountain & Assoc. (C), GA, *547*
The Rubicon Group (C), AZ, *547*
The Rubinic Consulting Group (C), OH, *548*
Rust & Assoc., Inc. (R), IL, *183*
Sage Employment Recruiters (C), IN, *550*
Sales Consultants Peninsula, Inc. (C), CA, *556*
Sales Consultants of Stamford-Darien (C), CT, *557*
Sales Consultants (C), IL, *558*
Sales Consultants of Cherokee (C), GA, *558*
Sales Consultants of Omaha, Inc. (C), NE, *560*
Sales Consultants of Cincinnati (C), OH, *561*
Sales Consultants of Princeton, Inc. (C), NJ, *561*
Sales Consultants of Austin, Inc. (C), TX, *562*
Sales Consultants of Pittsburgh (C), PA, *562*
Salveson Stetson Group, Inc. (R), PA, *184*
Salzmann Gay Assoc., Inc. (R), PA, *184*
Sanders Management Assoc., Inc. (C), NJ, *565*
Sanford Rose Assoc. - Pittsburgh North (C), PA, *570*
Santangelo Consultants Inc. (C), NY, *571*
Satterfield & Assoc., Inc. (R), OH, *184*
Robert Scott Assoc. (C), NJ, *573*
Search America, Inc. (C), PA, *573*
Search America, Inc. (C), MA, *574*
Search Group (C), CA, *575*

Search Solutions Inc. (C), CA, *576*
Searchforce, Inc. (R), FL, *187*
Sedlar & Miners (R), NY, *188*
Sensible Solutions, Inc. (R), IL, *188*
Sevcor Int'l., Inc. (R), IL, *188*
Shepherd Bueschel & Provus, Inc. (R), IL, *189*
RitaSue Siegel Resources, Inc. (R), NY, *191*
Siger & Assoc., LLC (C), CT, *581*
Silver Associates (C), CA, *581*
Daniel A. Silverstein Assoc. Inc. (R), FL, *191*
Sinclair & Co., Inc. (R), MA, *192*
Skipping Stone Inc. (C), VA, *582*
Skupsky & Assoc. (C), CO, *582*
James F. Smith & Assoc. (C), GA, *583*
Smith & Sawyer, Inc. (R), NY, *193*
J. Harrington Smith Assoc. (C), IN, *584*
Smith Hanley Assoc., Inc. (C), NY, *584*
Smith, Roth & Squires (R), NY, *194*
Software Resource Consultants (C), TN, *587*
Robert Sollman & Assoc. (C), FL, *587*
Southwestern Professional Services (C), TN, *588*
Sparks, McDonough & Assoc., Inc. (C), MO, *588*
Spear-Izzo Assoc., LLC (C), PA, *588*
SpencerStuart (R), NY, *196*
Spilman & Assoc. (R), TX, *197*
Stanewick, Hart & Assoc., Inc. (C), FL, *591*
Starbridge Group Inc. (C), VA, *591*
The Stark Wilton Group (R), MI, *199*
Steeple Resources & Consulting (R), NJ, *199*
Steinfield & Assoc. (C), TX, *592*
Sterling Int'l. (R), NJ, *200*
The Stevens Group (C), CA, *593*
Stewart/Laurence Assoc., Inc. (R), NJ, *201*
Linford E. Stiles & Assoc., L.L.C. (R), NH, *201*
Stillinger & Assoc. (R), CA, *201*
Strategic Assoc., Inc. (C), TX, *595*
Strategic Executives, Inc. (R), CT, *202*
Strategic Search, LLC (C), CA, *595*
Strauss Personnel Service (C), PA, *596*
Synapse Human Resource Consulting Group (R), TX, *205*
Synergistics Assoc. Ltd. (R), IL, *205*
Systems Careers (C), CA, *598*
Roy Talman & Assoc. (C), IL, *599*
Tarbex (C), DC, *599*
M. L. Tawney & Assoc. (C), TX, *600*
Tax Network Resources, Inc. (C), NY, *600*
Carl J. Taylor & Co. (R), TX, *207*
Taylor Winfield (R), TX, *207*
TechNix Inc. (C), ON, *602*
Techsearch Services Inc. (C), CT, *603*
The TGA Company (C), TX, *606*
Thomas, Whelan Assoc., Inc. (C), DC, *606*
Richard Thompson Assoc., Inc. (R), MN, *209*
Tower Consultants, Ltd. (R), PA, *209*
Van Treadaway Assoc., Inc. (R), GA, *210*
Trebor Weldon Lawrence, Inc. (R), NY, *210*
TRH Assoc., Inc. (R), NY, *210*
Triad Consultants, Inc. (C), NJ, *609*
Tucker Assoc. (R), NJ, *211*
Beverly von Winckler & Assoc. (C), IL, *613*
Wallace Assoc. (C), MA, *614*
J. D. Walsh & Co. (R), CT, *215*
Ward Assoc. (C), ON, *615*
Ward Liebelt Assoc. Inc. (R), CT, *215*
C. D. Warner & Assoc. (C), PA, *615*
Warring & Assoc. (R), CA, *215*
Waterford Executive Group Ltd. (C), IL, *616*
Watson Int'l., Inc. (R), NY, *216*
S. B. Webster & Associates (R), MA, *217*
Weinstein & Co. (R), MA, *217*
Henry Welker & Assoc. (C), MI, *618*
Wellington Thomas Ltd. (C), FL, *618*
The Westfield Group (C), CT, *619*
Wheeler Assoc. (R), CT, *219*
Whittlesey & Assoc., Inc. (R), PA, *220*
Daniel Wier & Assoc. (R), CA, *220*
The Wilkie Group Int'l. (R), ON, *220*
Wilkinson SoftSearch, Inc. (C), VA, *620*
John Williams & Assoc. (C), TX, *621*
Wilson-Douglas-Jordan (C), IL, *622*
Woltz & Assoc., Inc. (R), IL, *224*
M. Wood Company (R), IL, *224*
Bruce G. Woods Executive Search (R), TX, *224*
The Woodstone Consulting Company, Inc. (R), CO, *224*
R. S. Wyatt Assoc., Inc. (R), TX, *225*
Zaccaria Int'l. (C), NJ, *627*
ZanExec L.L.C. (R), VA, *226*
Zweig White & Assoc., Inc. (R), MA, *228*

11.2 Minorities

A-Linko & Assoc. (C), TX, *231*
A. D. & Assoc. Executive Search, Inc. (C), GA, *231*
A.J. & Assoc. (C), FL, *232*
Accent On Achievement, Inc. (C), MI, *233*
Acuity Medical Recruitment (C), MS, *239*
The Alexander Group (R), TX, *3*
The Alexander Group (R), NJ, *3*
Allerton Heneghan & O'Neill (R), IL, *4*
The Altco Group (C), NJ, *246*
Amherst Human Resource Group, Ltd. (C), IL, *249*
Andre David & Assoc., Inc. (R), TX, *6*
Argonaut Partners, LLC (R), CA, *6*
Ariel Recruitment Assoc. (R), NY, *7*
Auerbach Associates, Inc. (R), MA, *9*
Ballantyne & Assoc. (R), CA, *10*
The Bankers Group (C), IL, *258*
L. Battalin & Co. (C), FL, *261*
Bench Int'l. Search, Inc. (R), CA, *15*
Benford & Assoc., Inc. (C), MI, *264*
N. L. Benke & Assoc., Inc. (C), OH, *264*
Bennett Search & Consulting Co. (R), FL, *16*
Berkhemer/Clayton, Inc. (R), CA, *16*
BEST/World Assoc. Inc. (R), TX, *16*
BG & Assoc. (C), MD, *266*
Bonnell Assoc. Ltd. (R), CT, *19*
Bornholdt Shivas & Friends Executive Recruiters (C), NY, *270*
Boulware & Assoc. Inc. (R), IL, *20*
Boyden (R), NY, *20*
The Brentwood Group, Inc. (R), NJ, *22*
Bernard E. Brooks & Assoc., Inc. (R), SC, *24*
J. B. Brown & Assoc., Inc. (C), OH, *275*
The Burgess Group-Corporate Recruiters Int'l., Inc. (R), NY, *25*
Butterfass, Pepe & MacCallan Inc. (R), NJ, *25*
The Cantor Concern, Inc. (R), NY, *28*
Cardwell Enterprises Inc. (R), IL, *29*
Career Profiles (C), NH, *283*
Carlsen Resources, Inc. (R), CO, *29*
Carrington & Carrington, Ltd. (R), IL, *30*
The Center for Career Advancement, LLC (C), NJ, *287*
CEO Consulting (C), FL, *287*
Chicago Legal Search, Ltd. (C), IL, *290*
Christian & Timbers, Inc. (R), OH, *34*
Christopher-Westmont & Assoc., Inc. (R), OH, *34*
Cizek Assoc., Inc. (R), AZ, *35*
Howard Clark Assoc. (C), NJ, *292*
Clinton, Charles, Wise & Co. (C), FL, *293*
CMW & Associates, Inc. (C), IL, *293*
Corporate Plus, Ltd. (C), GA, *300*
Corporate Search Consultants (C), IN, *301*
Creative HR Solutions (C), GA, *303*
Criterion Executive Search, Inc. (C), FL, *303*
Judith Cushman & Assoc. (R), WA, *44*
D & M Associates (C), PA, *306*
Charles Dahl Group, Inc. (C), MN, *306*
Daubenspeck & Associates, Ltd. (R), IL, *46*
DeLalla - Fried Assoc. (C), NY, *310*
Delta Services (R), TX, *48*
Dise & Co. (R), OH, *52*
Diversified Search, Inc. (R), PA, *52*
DLB Assoc. (R), NY, *53*
Doleman Enterprises (R), VA, *53*
Dotson & Assoc. (R), NY, *54*
Dunhill Professional Search, Inc. of McAllen (C), TX, *323*
Employ® (C), PA, *330*
ExecuSource Assoc., Inc. (C), GA, *332*
ExecutiveFit (C), NY, *337*
First Union Executive Search (R), NC, *67*
Howard Fischer Assoc. Int'l., Inc. (R), PA, *67*
Susan Fletcher Attorney Employment Services (C), PA, *342*
Foley Proctor Yoskowitz (R), NJ, *69*
Foster Partners (R), NY, *70*
Fresquez & Assoc. (C), CA, *352*
Garrett Assoc. Inc. (R), GA, *75*
Genesis Personnel Service, Inc. (C), OH, *356*
Gilbert Tweed Assoc. Inc. (R), NY, *76*
Joe L. Giles & Assoc. (C), MI, *357*
Global Research Partnership Inc. (R), NY, *78*
The Tracy Glover Co. (R), TX, *78*
David Gomez & Assoc., Inc. (R), IL, *79*
Goodwin & Co. (R), DC, *80*
Gordon/Tyler (R), PA, *80*
The Governance Group, Inc. (R), NJ, *80*
Gowdy Consultants (C), TX, *361*
Groussman & Assoc., Inc. (R), TX, *82*
William Guy & Assoc., Inc. (R), CA, *84*

Hardison & Company (R), TX, *86*
The Hawkins Co. (R), CA, *88*
Healthcare Recruiters of New England (C), MA, *373*
Healthcare Recruiters of New York, Inc. (C), NY, *373*
Healthcare Recruiters Int'l. - Pittsburgh (C), PA, *373*
Heritage Search Group, Inc. (C), FL, *376*
High-Tech Recruiters (C), CT, *378*
Hoffman Partnership Group Inc. (C), NY, *379*
The Hogan Group (C), OH, *380*
The Hollins Group, Inc. (R), IL, *95*
Hospitality Int'l. (C), NY, *381*
HRD Consultants, Inc. (R), NJ, *97*
Human Resource Technologies, Inc. (R), IL, *99*
The Hunter Group (C), NC, *385*
Hyman & Assoc. (C), TX, *386*
Industry Consultants, Inc. (C), GA, *388*
Innovative Partnerships (R), CA, *101*
International Management Advisors, Inc. (R), NY, *103*
Intersource, Ltd. (R), GA, *103*
Isaacson, Miller (R), MA, *104*
The J. B. Search Group (C), CA, *395*
Ron Jackson & Assoc. (C), GA, *396*
David James Search (C), CA, *397*
Jonathan Lawrence Assoc. (C), NJ, *400*
Jordon & Jordon, Inc. (R), PA, *108*
J. M. Joseph Assoc. (R), NJ, *109*
Kabana Corp. (C), MI, *402*
A.T. Kearney Executive Search (R), IL, *111*
Kelly Associates (R), PA, *112*
Kip Williams, Inc. (R), NY, *115*
KL Consultants (C), NJ, *407*
The Koehler Group (C), PA, *408*
Koll-Fairfield LLC (C), CT, *408*
Koren, Rogers Assoc. Inc. (R), NY, *117*
L&L Assoc. Global Search (C), PA, *411*
LanSo Int'l., Inc. (C), NY, *413*
Latham International, Ltd. (R), NJ, *126*
The Libra Group (C), NC, *417*
Pat Licata & Assoc. (C), NC, *417*
LifeWork, Inc. (C), TX, *418*
LJ Networking, Inc. (C), MD, *418*
Lloyd Associates (R), GA, *130*
Fran Luisi Assoc. (R), NJ, *132*
Charles Luntz & Assoc., Inc. (R), MO, *132*
The Madison Group (R), NY, *133*
Maiorino & Weston Assoc., Inc. (R), CT, *134*
Management Alliance Group, Inc. (R), NJ, *134*
Management Association Network (C), WI, *424*
Management Recruiters of Rockville (C), MD, *450*
Management Recruiters of Round Rock (C), TX, *463*
Management Recruiters of Loudoun County South (C), VA, *465*
Manning Lloyd Assoc. Ltd. (C), NY, *468*
F. L. Mannix & Co. (R), MA, *135*
J. L. Mark Assoc., Inc. (R), CO, *135*
Mark Stanley & Co./EMA Partners International (R), FL, *136*
Marketing Consultants (C), WI, *470*
McCormack & Assoc. (R), CA, *140*
Medical Recruiters Inc. (C), MO, *477*
Juan Menefee & Assoc. (C), IL, *478*
Mercedes & Co., Inc. (R), MA, *143*
Michigan Consulting Group (R), MI, *144*
Milo Research (R), NY, *145*
Montgomery West (R), CA, *146*
The MVP Group (C), NY, *487*
National Affirmative Action Career Network, Inc. (C), CO, *488*
New Venture Development, Inc. (C), CA, *492*
Newell Assoc. (R), NY, *151*
P. J. Nicholson & Assoc. (C), IL, *493*
O'Neill Group (C), NJ, *498*
The Oldani Group (R), WA, *155*
LaMonte Owens, Inc. (R), PA, *157*
P.A.R. Assoc., Inc. (R), MA, *158*
P.R.H. Management, Inc. (R), CT, *158*
The PAR Group - Paul A. Reaume, Ltd. (R), IL, *159*
Partnervision Consulting Group Inc. (R), ON, *160*
Carolyn Smith Paschal Int'l. (R), CA, *160*
Pathways Int'l. (C), CT, *505*
The Patience Motivation Belief Group, Inc. (C), GA, *505*
Penn Associates (R), PA, *161*
Perez-Arton Consultants, Inc. (R), NY, *162*
Personnel Assoc. (C), CA, *508*
Pharmaceutical Search Professionals, Inc. (C), PA, *510*
Placement Solutions (C), WI, *513*
Professional Research Services, Inc. (R), IL, *169*
ProSearch, Inc. (C), PA, *524*
Questor Consultants, Inc. (C), PA, *527*
R.A.N. Assoc., Inc. (C), OH, *528*
R2 Services, LLC (C), IL, *528*
Joanne E. Ratner Search (C), NY, *529*
Ray & Assoc., Inc. (C), IA, *529*
Reifel & Assoc. (R), IL, *174*
The Remington Group (R), IL, *174*
Russell Reynolds Assoc., Inc. (R), NY, *176*
Reynolds Partners (R), NY, *177*
Roberts Ryan & Bentley, Inc. (R), MD, *179*
Robinson-Robinson & Assoc., Inc. (C), MN, *539*
Rolland Ressources Humaines Inc. (R), QE, *181*
Rollo Assoc. (R), CA, *181*
Salzmann Gay Assoc., Inc. (R), PA, *184*
Search Plus Int'l.-Ohio (C), OH, *576*
Robert Sellery Assoc., Ltd. (R), DC, *188*
Shiell Personnel (C), LA, *580*
Shifrin-Fischer Group, Inc. (C), NJ, *580*
SKB Enterprises (C), NY, *582*
Smith & Assoc. (C), CA, *583*
Smith & Sawyer, Inc. (R), NY, *193*
Howard W. Smith Assoc. (R), CT, *193*
Southern Recruiters & Consultants, Inc. (C), SC, *587*
Special Markets Group, Inc. (R), GA, *195*
SpencerSearch, Inc. (C), CO, *589*
SpencerStuart (R), NY, *196*
Spilman & Assoc. (R), TX, *197*
Springer Souder & Assoc. L.L.C. (R), IL, *198*
Summit Executive Search Consultants, Inc. (R), FL, *204*
Synergy 2000 (C), DC, *597*
Target Search, Inc. (C), PA, *600*
Topaz Int'l., Inc., Attorney Search (C), NJ, *607*
Tower Consultants, Ltd. (R), PA, *209*
Traynor Confidential, Ltd. (C), NY, *609*
Tucker Assoc. (R), NJ, *211*
Tyler & Company (R), GA, *212*
The Urban Placement Service (C), TX, *611*
Wakefield Talabisco Int'l. (R), NY, *214*
Wesley Brown & Bartle Co., Inc. (R), NY, *218*
White, Roberts & Stratton, Inc. (C), IL, *619*
Arch S. Whitehead Assoc. Inc. (ASWA) (R), NY, *219*
John Williams & Assoc. (C), TX, *621*
Winston & Green (C), IL, *623*
Dick Wray & Consultants, Inc. (R), CA, *225*
Xagas & Assoc. (R), IL, *226*
Xavier Associates, Inc. (R), MA, *226*

11.3 Fund-raisers & other non-profit services

AST/BRYANT (R), CT, *8*
Auerbach Associates, Inc. (R), MA, *9*
Ballantyne & Assoc. (R), CA, *10*
Battalia Winston Int'l./The Euram Consultants Group (R), NY, *13*
Billington & Assoc. (R), CA, *17*
Bonell Ryan Inc. (R), NY, *19*
Boulware & Assoc. Inc. (R), IL, *20*
Boyden (R), NY, *20*
Bradford Executives Int'l. (C), VA, *271*
The Burgess Group-Corporate Recruiters Int'l., Inc. (R), NY, *25*
Canny, Bowen Inc. (R), NY, *27*
Chaloner Assoc. (R), MA, *32*
Christenson Hutchison McDowell, LLC (R), NJ, *34*
Arlene Clapp, Ltd. (R), MN, *35*
Compass Group Ltd. (R), MI, *38*
Conroy Partners Ltd. (R), AB, *39*
Corporate Search, Inc. (C), NY, *301*
Leonard Corwen Assoc. (C), NY, *302*
D & M Associates (C), PA, *306*
Alan Darling Consulting (R), VT, *46*
DeCorrevont & Assoc. (C), IL, *310*
Development Resource Group (R), NY, *48*
Development Search Specialists (R), MN, *49*
Rob Dey Executive Search (R), FL, *49*
Robert W. Dingman Co., Inc. (R), CA, *52*
Diversified Search, Inc. (R), PA, *52*
Cal Douglas Executive Search, Inc. (R), PA, *54*
C. A. Durakis Assoc., Inc. (R), MD, *55*
Donald F. Dvorak & Co. (R), IL, *55*
Bruce Edwards & Associates, Inc. (R), NC, *56*
EMN/Witt/Kieffer (R), MA, *59*
Executive Careers (R), CA, *62*
The Executive Group, Inc. (R), CA, *62*
Executive Search Consultants Corp. (C), IL, *335*

Fagan & Company (R), PA, *64*
Foster Partners (R), NY, *70*
P. N. French Assoc., Inc. (R), MA, *72*
Gahan Assoc. (R), NY, *73*
Gateway Management Resources (C), IL, *355*
GES Services, Inc. (R), NY, *76*
Goodwin & Co. (R), DC, *80*
Annie Gray Assoc., Inc. (R), MO, *81*
Healey Executive Search, Inc. (R), MN, *88*
The Helms Int'l. Group (R), VA, *91*
The Hyde Group, Inc. (R), CT, *101*
IMA Search, Inc. (R), NY, *101*
Ingram & Aydelotte, Inc. (R), NY, *101*
Innovative Partnerships (R), CA, *101*
Intelligent Marketing Solutions, Inc. (C), NY, *390*
Isaacson, Miller (R), MA, *104*
Gary Kaplan & Assoc. (R), CA, *109*
A.T. Kearney Executive Search (R), IL, *111*
The Keith-Murray Partnership (R), ON, *112*
Kennedy & Co. (R), IL, *112*
Kittleman & Assoc.,LLC (R), IL, *115*
Korn/Ferry Int'l. (R), NY, *117*
Kramer Executive Resources, Inc. (C), NY, *409*
Kulper & Co., L.L.C. (R), NJ, *121*
Layne-Mendez & Co. (R), TX, *127*
Lois L. Lindauer Searches (C), MA, *418*
The Logan Group, Inc. (R), MO, *131*
J. S. Lord & Company, Inc. (R), MA, *131*
MacNaughton Assoc. (R), CA, *133*
Management Resource Group, Ltd. (C), IA, *467*
McCormack & Assoc. (R), CA, *140*
Meng, Finseth & Assoc., Inc. (R), CA, *143*
E. J. Michaels, Ltd. (C), NY, *481*
Molloy Partners (R), NY, *146*
Thomas R. Moore Executive Search (R), TX, *146*
Morris & Berger (R), CA, *147*
MTA Partners (R), TX, *148*
Nordeman Grimm, Inc. (R), NY, *152*
O'Callaghan Honey/Ray & Berndtson Inc. (R), AB, *153*
Opportunity Resources, Inc. (R), NY, *156*
Overton Consulting (R), WI, *157*
The PAR Group - Paul A. Reaume, Ltd. (R), IL, *159*
Carolyn Smith Paschal Int'l. (R), CA, *160*
Joel H. Paul & Assoc., Inc. (C), NY, *505*
People Management Mid-South, LLC (R), TN, *162*
Perez-Arton Consultants, Inc. (R), NY, *162*
Plante & Moran, LLP (R), MI, *165*
The Rankin Group, Ltd. (R), WI, *171*
Ray & Berndtson/Tanton Mitchell (R), BC, *173*
Russell Reynolds Assoc., Inc. (R), NY, *176*
Reynolds Consulting Int'l. (R), ON, *177*
Reynolds Partners (R), NY, *177*
Marshall Rice Assoc. (R), RI, *177*
Norman Roberts & Assoc., Inc. (R), CA, *179*
Rusher, Loscavio & LoPresto (R), CA, *183*
Rushmore • Judge Inc. (R), ON, *183*
The Search Company (R), ON, *186*
Robert Sellery Assoc., Ltd. (R), DC, *188*
Howard W. Smith Assoc. (R), CT, *193*
Sockwell & Assoc. (R), NC, *194*
Soltis Management Services (R), PA, *195*
SpencerStuart (R), NY, *196*
Richard Thompson Assoc., Inc. (R), MN, *209*
Triad Consultants, Inc. (C), NJ, *609*
Tuft & Assoc., Inc. (R), IL, *212*
Van Dyke Assoc. (R), IL, *212*
Van Leeuwen Assoc. (R), CA, *213*
Wallace Management Co. (R), TN, *215*
Warring & Assoc. (R), CA, *215*

11.4 Environmentalists

Anderson & Schwab, Inc. (R), NY, *5*
Anderson Bradshaw Assoc., Inc. (R), TX, *6*
R. W. Apple & Assoc. (C), NJ, *251*
AST/BRYANT (R), CT, *8*
Ballantyne & Assoc. (R), CA, *10*
BayResearch Group, Inc. (R), IL, *14*
Blum & Co. (R), WI, *19*
Borchert Assoc. (C), TX, *269*
Boyden (R), NY, *20*
Dan B. Brockman (C), IL, *274*
Broward-Dobbs, Inc. (C), GA, *274*
David S. Burt Assoc. (C), MT, *276*
Career Images (C), FL, *282*
The Cherbonnier Group, Inc. (R), TX, *33*
Robert Connelly & Assoc., Inc. (R), MN, *39*
Construction Search Specialists, Inc. (C), WI, *297*
Cornwall Stockton & Co., Inc. (C), TX, *299*
Corporate Environment Ltd. (R), IL, *41*
CS Associates, LLC (C), AZ, *304*
Frank Cuomo & Assoc., Inc. (C), NY, *305*
Derek Associates, Inc. (C), MA, *311*
Diversified Search, Inc. (R), PA, *52*
Robert Drexler Assoc., Inc. (R), NJ, *54*
Dunhill of San Francisco, Inc. (C), CA, *319*
Dunhill Professional Search of Augusta (C), GA, *320*
Environmental, Health & Safety Search Assoc. (C), FL, *331*
Foster Partners (R), NY, *70*
Goodwin & Co. (R), DC, *80*
Michael J. Hall & Co. (R), WA, *85*
Helffrich Int'l. (C), FL, *375*
International Recruiting Services (C), FL, *393*
Isaacson, Miller (R), MA, *104*
JAG Group (R), MO, *105*
A.T. Kearney Executive Search (R), IL, *111*
Larkin & Co. (R), CA, *124*
Larsen Int'l., Inc. (R), TX, *125*
Michael Latas & Assoc., Inc. (R), MO, *125*
Management Recruiters of Berkeley (C), CA, *439*
Management Recruiters Dana Point (C), CA, *440*
Management Recruiters of Gastonia (C), NC, *456*
Management Recruiters of Loudoun County South (C), VA, *465*
Management Recruiters of Lynnwood (C), WA, *465*
McCormack & Assoc. (R), CA, *140*
Robert E. McGrath & Assoc. (R), CT, *141*
McNichol Assoc. (R), PA, *142*
National Affirmative Action Career Network, Inc. (C), CO, *488*
The NEIS Corp., Inc. (C), FL, *491*
John R. O'Connor & Assoc. (C), IL, *497*
OEI, Inc. (C), NJ, *498*
The PAR Group - Paul A. Reaume, Ltd. (R), IL, *159*
PC Assoc. (C), CO, *505*
Fred Perry Assoc. (C), TX, *507*
The Personnel Network, Inc. (C), SC, *508*
Reality Group (C), OK, *531*
Russell Reynolds Assoc., Inc. (R), NY, *176*
Ritta Professional Search Inc. (C), NY, *538*
Sales Consultants of Birmingham (C), AL, *555*
Sales Consultants of Omaha, Inc. (C), NE, *560*
Search Consultants Int'l., Inc. (C), TX, *575*
Robert Sellery Assoc., Ltd. (R), DC, *188*
Smith & Assoc. (C), FL, *583*
J. Harrington Smith Assoc. (C), IN, *584*
Southern Research Services (R), FL, *195*
SpencerStuart (R), NY, *196*
Splaine & Assoc., Inc. (R), CA, *198*
C. J. Stafford & Assoc. (C), ON, *591*
Straube Associates (R), MA, *203*
Technical Skills Consulting Inc. (R), ON, *207*
Trout & Assoc. Inc. (R), UT, *211*
Ward-Hoffman & Assoc. (C), ID, *615*
Walter K. Wilkins & Co. (R), NJ, *221*

11.5 Architects

G. Adams Partners (R), IL, *2*
Benamati & Assoc. (C), CO, *263*
Paul J. Biestek Assoc., Inc. (R), IL, *17*
Broward-Dobbs, Inc. (C), GA, *274*
Button Group (C), TX, *277*
C. G. & Assoc. (R), PA, *26*
CadTech Staffing Services (C), GA, *279*
Caruso & Assoc., Inc. (R), FL, *31*
Claremont-Branan, Inc. (C), GA, *292*
CMW & Associates, Inc. (C), IL, *293*
CN Associates (C), CA, *293*
Comprehensive Search (C), GA, *294*
Robert Connelly & Assoc., Inc. (R), MN, *39*
Construct Management Services (C), MN, *297*
Construction Search Specialists, Inc. (C), WI, *297*
CS Associates, LLC (C), AZ, *304*
Custom Resources (C), AL, *305*
Robert Drexler Assoc., Inc. (R), NJ, *54*
The Evans McDonnell Co. (C), TX, *331*
Foster Partners (R), NY, *70*
Gaines & Assoc. Int'l., Inc. (R), IL, *73*
Michael J. Hall & Co. (R), WA, *85*
Robert Hess & Assoc., Inc. (C), CO, *377*
Ruth Hirsch Assoc., Inc. (C), NY, *379*
International Recruiting Services (C), FL, *393*

International Staffing Consultants, Inc. (C), CA, *393*
Joseph Chris & Assoc. (C), TX, *400*
Karel & Co. (R), CA, *109*
A.T. Kearney Executive Search (R), IL, *111*
Kresin Wingard (C), IL, *409*
The LaBorde Group (C), CA, *411*
Larsen Int'l., Inc. (R), TX, *125*
Michael Latas & Assoc., Inc. (R), MO, *125*
Louis Search Group, Inc. (C), NJ, *420*
Management Recruiters, Inland Empire Agency (C), CA, *441*
Management Recruiters of Sonoma (C), CA, *441*
K. Maxin & Assoc. (R), PA, *139*
McNichol Assoc. (R), PA, *142*
Michael Assoc. (R), IL, *144*
Moss & Co. (R), WA, *148*
John R. O'Connor & Assoc. (C), IL, *497*
OEI, Inc. (C), NJ, *498*
Janou Pakter, Inc. (C), NY, *502*
Peak Search Assoc. (C), ON, *506*
Bob Poline Assoc. Inc. (C), CA, *514*
Powers Consultants, Inc. (R), MO, *166*
David Saxner & Assoc., Inc. (DSA, Inc.) (R), IL, *185*
Shupack & Michaels Inc. (C), NY, *580*
RitaSue Siegel Resources, Inc. (R), NY, *191*
Specialized Search Assoc. (C), FL, *589*
SpencerStuart (R), NY, *196*
Systems Research Group (C), OH, *598*
Systems Research Inc. (SRI) (C), IL, *598*
Technical Skills Consulting Inc. (R), ON, *207*
Technology Search Int'l. (C), CA, *603*
TRS Staffing Solutions Inc. (C), OH, *610*
Wilder, Gammel Partners, Ltd. (R), CA, *220*

11.6 Technicians

Adel-Lawrence Assoc., Inc. (C), NJ, *240*
Dick Berg & Assoc. (C), CA, *264*
Broadband Resource Group (C), CA, *274*
CAS Comsearch Inc. (C), NY, *285*
Chatham Search Assoc., Inc. (C), NJ, *290*
CMW & Associates, Inc. (C), IL, *293*
CN Associates (C), CA, *293*
Collins & Associates (C), MI, *294*
Cornwall Stockton & Co., Inc. (C), TX, *299*
DEL Technical Services, Inc. (C), IL, *310*
The Devlin Search Group, Inc. (C), MA, *311*
Dreier Consulting (C), NJ, *315*
Executive Business Solutions, Inc. (C), WA, *332*
Guild Fetridge Acoustical Search, Inc. (C), NY, *340*
Foster Partners (R), NY, *70*
Goldstein & Co. (C), CA, *360*
L. J. Gonzer Assoc. (C), NJ, *360*
Greenwich Internet (C), CT, *363*
Michael J. Hall & Co. (R), WA, *85*
Healthcare Recruiters Int'l. - Pittsburgh (C), PA, *373*
Hunter Adams (C), NC, *385*
Impact Technical Staffing (C), OR, *387*
A.T. Kearney Executive Search (R), IL, *111*
Kirkbride Assoc., Inc. (C), WA, *407*
Kurtz Pro-Search, Inc. (C), NJ, *410*
LCC Companies (C), AZ, *414*
The Levton Group Inc. (R), ON, *129*
Lineal Recruiting Services (C), CT, *418*
Management Recruiters of Sedona (C), AZ, *438*
Management Recruiters of Sonoma (C), CA, *441*
Management Recruiters of Altamonte (C), FL, *442*
Management Recruiters of Lake Co., Inc. (C), FL, *444*
Management Recruiters - Flint (C), MI, *451*
Management Recruiters of Wausau, LLC (C), WI, *466*
Media Management Resources, Inc. (R), CO, *142*
Newport Strategic Search LLC (C), CA, *492*
NHA Plastics Recruiters (C), FL, *493*
North Coast Meridian (C), NY, *496*
Omnisearch Assoc. (C), CA, *499*
Peachtree Executive Search (R), GA, *161*
Personnel Tangent Inc. (C), QE, *509*
The Quantum Group (C), NJ, *526*
Russell Reynolds Assoc., Inc. (R), NY, *176*
J. Rodgers & Associates (C), IL, *540*
Sales Consultants of Daphne (C), AL, *556*
Sales Consultants of Omaha, Inc. (C), NE, *560*
Search & Recruit Int'l. (C), VA, *573*
Shupack & Michaels Inc. (C), NY, *580*
The Silicon Network (C), ON, *581*
Smartsource Inc. (C), CA, *583*
SpencerStuart (R), NY, *196*
Systems Research Inc. (SRI) (C), IL, *598*
Techaid Inc. (C), QE, *601*
Tecmark Associates Inc. (C), NY, *604*
Tele-Media Int'l. Inc. (C), PA, *604*
Jay Tracey Assoc. Inc. (C), VT, *608*
Kelly Walker Assoc. (C), TX, *614*
West & Assoc. (C), IL, *618*

11.7 Attorneys

A-K-A (Anita Kaufmann Assoc.) (C), NY, *231*
A-L Assoc., Inc. (R), NY, *1*
Aaron Consulting, Inc. (C), MO, *232*
Cathy Abelson Legal Search (C), PA, *232*
Accounting & Computer Personnel (C), NY, *238*
Affordable Executive Recruiters (C), CA, *241*
Alexander & Collins (C), CA, *243*
Allen Austin Lowe & Powers (R), TX, *3*
Allied Search, Inc. (C), CA, *245*
Allman & Co., Inc. (C), NC, *245*
Anthony Michael & Co. (C), MA, *251*
Attorneys at Work (C), GA, *255*
Bader Research Corp. (C), NY, *257*
Battalia Winston Int'l./The Euram Consultants Group (R), NY, *13*
Marcia Beilin, Inc. (C), NY, *262*
Joy Reed Belt Search Consultants, Inc. (R), OK, *15*
Robert Bennett Assoc. (C), NY, *264*
Bennett Search & Consulting Co. (R), FL, *16*
Bickerton & Gordon LLC (C), MA, *266*
The Blackman Kallick Search Division (C), IL, *267*
Blane, Stevens & Kellogg (C), FL, *268*
The Howard C. Bloom Co. (C), TX, *268*
Blue Chip Law Consulting, Inc. (C), CA, *268*
Boston Professional Search, Inc. (C), MA, *270*
BowdenGlobal, Ltd. (R), OH, *20*
BowersThomas (C), CA, *271*
Bredeson Executive Recruitment, LLC (R), TX, *22*
Caldwell Legal Recruiting Consultants (C), ME, *279*
Canny, Bowen Inc. (R), NY, *27*
Career Strategies, Inc. (C), CA, *283*
Carpenter Legal Search (C), PA, *284*
Carter-Evdemon & Assoc. (C), FL, *285*
Malin Cederquist, Esq. (C), NY, *286*
The Center for Career Advancement, LLC (C), NJ, *287*
Chicago Legal Search, Ltd. (C), IL, *290*
Claimsearch (C), CA, *291*
Coleman Legal Search Consultants (C), PA, *294*
The Consortium (C), NY, *296*
Corrao, Miller, Rush & Wiesenthal (C), NY, *301*
DeCaster Assoc. (C), WI, *310*
Rob Dey Executive Search (R), FL, *49*
Diversified Search, Inc. (R), PA, *52*
Drake & Assoc. (C), CA, *315*
DS&A (Doug Sears & Assoc.) (C), FL, *315*
Dunhill of Manchester Inc. (C), NH, *321*
Gwen Dycus & Assoc. (C), FL, *323*
Early Cochran & Olson (R), IL, *56*
ECG Resources, Inc. (C), NY, *326*
Elinvar (C), NC, *328*
Emerald Legal Search (C), NH, *329*
Executives Worldwide, Inc. (C), OR, *337*
Faro Consultants Int'l. (C), VA, *338*
Fergus Legal Search & Consulting, Inc. (C), NY, *339*
Financial Connections Company (C), VA, *340*
Finn & Schneider Assoc., Inc. (C), DC, *341*
Susan Fletcher Attorney Employment Services (C), PA, *342*
F-o-r-t-u-n-e Personnel Consultants of Detroit, Inc. (C), MI, *346*
Fortune Consultants of Ft. Washington (C), PA, *349*
Foster Associates (C), NJ, *351*
Foster Partners (R), NY, *70*
Frey & Sher Assoc., Inc. (C), VA, *353*
Garb & Assoc., Legal Placement (C), CA, *354*
Gillard Assoc. Legal Search (C), MA, *357*
Gimbel & Assoc. (C), FL, *357*
Barry Goldberg & Assoc., Inc. (C), CA, *360*
Greene-Levin-Snyder LLC (C), NY, *362*

Stephen Haas Legal Placement (C), NY, *365*
Harbor Consultants Int'l., Inc. (C), VA, *368*
Hartman Greene & Wells (C), DC, *370*
Bruce W. Haupt Assoc. (R), DC, *88*
Phyllis Hawkins & Assoc., Inc. (C), AZ, *370*
Haydon Legal Search (C), IL, *370*
Jay Heino Company, LLC (C), NY, *375*
A. Herndon & Assoc., Inc. (R), TX, *92*
H. Hertner Assoc., Inc. (C), FL, *377*
Houser, Martin, Morris (C), WA, *381*
Howard-Sloan Legal Search, Inc. (C), NY, *382*
Howard/Williams Assoc. (C), FL, *382*
Hughes & Sloan, Inc. (C), GA, *383*
Human Resource Bureau (C), CA, *384*
Hunt & Howe Inc. (R), NY, *99*
Hyde Danforth & Co. (R), TX, *100*
IM Independent Management Recruiters (R), TN, *101*
Impact Search & Strategies (C), PA, *387*
Interquest, Inc. (R), NY, *103*
Isaacson, Miller (R), MA, *104*
Ann Israel & Assoc., Inc. (C), NY, *395*
The Jameson Group (C), CA, *397*
John Michael Assoc. (R), DC, *106*
Karel & Co. (R), CA, *109*
Kass/Abell & Assoc., Inc. (C), CA, *404*
A.T. Kearney Executive Search (R), IL, *111*
Keena Staffing Services (C), NY, *404*
Barbara Kerner Consultants (C), NY, *405*
The Kilman Advisory Group (R), CT, *114*
Klein, Landau & Romm (C), DC, *407*
The Kleinstein Group, Inc. (R), NJ, *116*
Koerner & Assoc., Inc. (C), TN, *408*
Kulper & Co., L.L.C. (R), NJ, *121*
John Kurosky & Assoc. (R), CA, *122*
L & K Assoc. (C), NJ, *410*
Larsen, Whitney, Blecksmith & Zilliacus, Inc. (R), CA, *125*
Leader Resources Group (C), GA, *415*
Legal Network Inc. (C), CA, *416*
Legal Search Assoc. (C), KS, *416*
Lehman McLeskey (R), TX, *128*
Howard Lieberman & Assoc., Inc. (C), MN, *417*
Lipton Assoc., Inc. (R), NY, *130*
Lloyd Prescott & Churchill, Inc. (R), FL, *130*
London & Company (C), NY, *420*
Magellan Int'l., L.P. (C), TX, *422*
Major, Hagen & Africa (C), CA, *423*
Major Legal Services, Inc. (C), OH, *423*
Management Recruiters of Warren County, KY (C), KY, *449*
Management Recruiters of Great Neck (C), NY, *454*
Mark Stanley & Co./EMA Partners International (R), FL, *136*
Brad Marks Int'l. (R), CA, *136*
Marley Group Ltd. (C), NY, *471*
The McCormick Group (C), VA, *473*
McDonald, Long & Assoc., Inc. (R), NY, *140*
William K. McLaughlin Assoc., Inc. (C), NY, *475*
McPherson Square Assoc., Inc. (C), DC, *475*
Meridian Legal Search/Legal Temps (C), NY, *479*
Susan C. Miller Assoc., Inc. (C), DC, *482*
Mims & Associates (R), TX, *145*
Morgenstern Int'l., Inc. (C), FL, *485*
Mruk & E.M.A. Partners (R), NY, *148*
NRI Staffing Resources (C), DC, *496*
O'Callaghan Honey/Ray & Berndtson Inc. (R), AB, *153*
Odell & Assoc., Inc. (C), TX, *498*
The Ogdon Partnership (R), NY, *155*
Omega Search, Inc. (C), NC, *498*
The Options Group, Inc. (C), NY, *499*
Overton Consulting (R), WI, *157*
Page-Wheatcroft & Co., Ltd. (R), TX, *158*
The Pailin Group Professional Search Consultants (R), TX, *158*
Florence Pape Legal Search, Inc. (C), NJ, *502*
Personnel Resources Organization (C), PA, *509*
Pittleman & Assoc. (C), NY, *512*
P. G. Prager Search Assoc., Ltd. (C), NY, *515*
Preferred Placement, Inc. (C), NY, *516*
Prescott Legal Search, Inc. (C), TX, *517*
The Primary Group, Inc. (R), FL, *168*
ProSearch, Inc. (C), OH, *524*
Pursuant Legal Consultants (R), WA, *170*
QD Legal (C), ON, *525*
Questor Consultants, Inc. (C), PA, *527*
L. J. Quinn & Assoc., Inc. (R), CA, *170*
Railey & Assoc. (C), TX, *528*
Vera L. Rast Partners Inc. (C), IL, *529*
Russell Reynolds Assoc., Inc. (R), NY, *176*
Richard, Wayne & Roberts (C), TX, *536*
Rosenfeld & Co., Inc. (C), MI, *545*
The Rubicon Group (C), AZ, *547*
Ryman, Bell, Green & Michaels, Inc. (C), TX, *549*
Sales Consultants of Omaha, Inc. (C), NE, *560*
Sears & Associates (C), CA, *577*
Selective Staffing (C), CA, *579*
Seltzer Fontaine Beckwith (C), CA, *579*
SFB Legal Search (C), NY, *579*
Sharrow & Assoc., Inc. (C), MI, *579*
Shelton, Wiseman & Leon (R), CA, *189*
Marvin L. Silcott & Assoc., Inc. (C), TX, *581*
Howard W. Smith Assoc. (R), CT, *193*
Smythe Masterson & Judd, Inc. (C), NY, *585*
SpencerStuart (R), NY, *196*
SR Wilson, Inc. (C), CA, *590*
Stafford Consulting Group (R), CA, *198*
Summerfield Assoc., Inc. (C), TN, *596*
Templeton & Assoc. (C), MN, *605*
Topaz Int'l., Inc., Attorney Search (C), NJ, *607*
Tucker Assoc. (R), NJ, *211*
UniQuest Int'l., Inc. (C), FL, *610*
Unisearch Search & Recruiting Inc. (C), CA, *611*
Villasenor & Assoc. (C), CA, *612*
Waldorf Associates, Inc. (C), CA, *614*
The Wallace Law Registry (C), CT, *614*
Scott Watson & Assoc., Inc. (R), FL, *216*
Weinman & Assoc. (C), AZ, *617*
The Whitaker Companies (C), TX, *619*
Whitbeck & Assoc. (R), MN, *219*
Windsor Consultants, Inc. (C), TX, *622*
Winston & Green (C), IL, *623*
D. S. Wolf Assoc., Inc. (R), NY, *223*
Zenner Consulting Group (C), IL, *627*

11.8 Graphic artists, designers

Associated Recruiters (C), WI, *254*
Barrington Hart, Inc. (R), IL, *12*
Berkana Int'l., Inc. (C), WA, *265*
Brown, Bernardy, Van Remmen, Inc. (C), CA, *275*
Bryan & Louis Research (C), OH, *275*
Charles Buck & Assoc., Inc. (R), NY, *24*
The C.P.R. Group (C), NJ, *278*
CadTech Staffing Services (C), GA, *279*
Career Strategies, Inc. (C), CA, *283*
Carpenter & Assoc. (C), TX, *284*
Chad Management Group (C), ON, *288*
Chaloner Assoc. (R), MA, *32*
Christmas, McIvor & Assoc. Inc. (C), ON, *290*
Cyr Associates, Inc. (C), MA, *306*
D & M Associates (C), PA, *306*
Desktop Staffing, Inc. (C), IL, *311*
Neil Fink Assoc. (R), CA, *66*
Foster Partners (R), NY, *70*
Gaines & Assoc. Int'l., Inc. (R), IL, *73*
Global Career Services, Inc. (C), NY, *358*
L. J. Gonzer Assoc. (C), NJ, *360*
Graphic Arts Marketing Assoc., Inc. (C), MI, *361*
Greenwich Internet (C), CT, *363*
Gundersen Partners, L.L.C. (R), NY, *83*
Hands-on Broadcast (R), NY, *86*
Kay Henry, Inc. (C), PA, *376*
Hook-Up! (C), CA, *380*
InterNeed (C), TX, *394*
Jaral Consultants, Inc. (C), NJ, *397*
JM & Company (R), PA, *106*
Robert Kaestner & Assoc. (C), FL, *403*
Kanzer Assoc., Inc. (R), IL, *109*
A.T. Kearney Executive Search (R), IL, *111*
Kresin Wingard (C), IL, *409*
Hal Levy & Assoc. (C), NY, *417*
Lloyd Staffing (C), NY, *419*
Louis Search Group, Inc. (C), NJ, *420*
Lutz Associates (C), CT, *421*
Management Recruiters of Northern Palm Beaches (C), FL, *444*
Management Recruiters of Atlanta (C), GA, *445*
Management Recruiters of Cincinnati/Sharonville, Inc. (C), OH, *457*
Management Resource Group, Inc. (C), NY, *467*
MediaCOM Talent Group (C), MA, *476*
Mengel & McDonald Ltd. (C), IL, *479*
Herbert Mines Assoc., Inc. (R), NY, *145*
Myers Career Assoc., Inc. (C), CA, *488*
N.A.P. Executive Services (Canada) Inc. (C), ON, *488*

NDB Assoc., Inc. (C), PA, *491*
Next Step Recruiting (C), CA, *493*
NorthStar Technologies, Inc. (C), NY, *496*
Janou Pakter, Inc. (C), NY, *502*
Kirk Palmer & Assoc., Inc. (R), NY, *158*
Partners Executive Search Consultants Inc. (R), ON, *160*
Porter & Assoc., Inc. (C), FL, *514*
Precision Executive Search (C), AZ, *516*
Recruiting Options, Inc. (C), GA, *531*
Susan Rudich (C), NY, *548*
Sales Consultants of Savannah, GA (C), GA, *557*
Sales Consultants of Bangor, Inc. (C), ME, *559*
Sales Consultants of Omaha, Inc. (C), NE, *560*
Sales Consultants of Middlesex County, Inc. (C), NJ, *561*
Saviar, Inc. (C), AZ, *571*
Search Assoc., Inc. (C), CA, *574*
SearchCom, Inc. (R), TX, *187*
RitaSue Siegel Resources, Inc. (R), NY, *191*
SpencerStuart (R), NY, *196*
StaffWriters Plus (C), NY, *591*
Synergistech Communications (C), CA, *597*
Travaille Executive Search (R), DC, *210*
TSC Management Services Group, Inc. (C), IL, *610*
Beverly von Winckler & Assoc. (C), IL, *613*
Gordon Wahls Executive Search (C), PA, *613*
Williamsburg Group (C), NJ, *621*
The York Group (C), CA, *626*

11.9 Paralegals

Affordable Executive Recruiters (C), CA, *241*
Joy Reed Belt Search Consultants, Inc. (R), OK, *15*
Bennett Search & Consulting Co. (R), FL, *16*
Bickerton & Gordon LLC (C), MA, *266*
Blue Chip Law Consulting, Inc. (C), CA, *268*
Corporate Search, Inc. (C), NY, *301*
Dunhill of Manchester Inc. (C), NH, *321*
Emerald Legal Search (C), NH, *329*
Gillard Assoc. Legal Search (C), MA, *357*
Howard/Williams Assoc. (C), FL, *382*
A.T. Kearney Executive Search (R), IL, *111*
Legal Network Inc. (C), CA, *416*
Major Legal Services, Inc. (C), OH, *423*
NRI Staffing Resources (C), DC, *496*
P. G. Prager Search Assoc., Ltd. (C), NY, *515*
Prescott Legal Search, Inc. (C), TX, *517*
DM Stone Personnel Services (C), CA, *594*
Topaz Int'l., Inc., Attorney Search (C), NJ, *607*
Weinman & Assoc. (C), AZ, *617*
The Whitaker Companies (C), TX, *619*

12.0 International

A.J. & Assoc. (C), FL, *232*
Accelerated Data Decision, Inc. (C), NJ, *233*
Accountants Executive Search (C), CT, *234*
Ackerman Johnson Inc. (C), TX, *238*
Adam-Bryce Inc. (C), NY, *239*
Adams & Assoc. Int'l. (R), IL, *1*
G. Adams Partners (R), IL, *2*
Agri-Personnel (C), GA, *242*
The Alexander Group (R), TX, *3*
D. S. Allen Assoc. (C), NJ, *244*
Allied Search, Inc. (C), CA, *245*
Alpha Resources (C), IL, *246*
AMS Int'l. (R), VA, *5*
Anderson & Schwab, Inc. (R), NY, *5*
Anderson Bradshaw Assoc., Inc. (R), TX, *6*
Angel Group Int'l. (C), KY, *250*
Fred Anthony Assoc. (C), WI, *251*
Anthony Michael & Co. (C), MA, *251*
APA Search, Inc. (R), NY, *6*
Applied Search Assoc., Inc. (C), GA, *252*
ARI Int'l. (R), CA, *6*
The Associates, HR Search Executives, Inc. (C), OK, *254*
Aubin Int'l. Inc. (R), MA, *8*
Austin Group Int'l./Marlar Int'l. (R), TX, *9*
Baker Scott & Co. (C), NJ, *258*
Barone-O'Hara Assoc., Inc. (R), NJ, *11*
Aldonna Barry Personnel & Management (C), ON, *260*
Battalia Winston Int'l./The Euram Consultants Group (R), NY, *13*
Beacon Int'l., Inc. (C), VA, *261*
Behrens and Company (C), WA, *262*
Belanger Partners Ltd. (C), ON, *262*
Benamati & Assoc. (C), CO, *263*
Robert Bennett Assoc. (C), NY, *264*
Berglund Int'l. Resources, Inc. (C), TX, *265*
Bialla & Assoc. Inc. (R), CA, *17*
Bonnell Assoc. Ltd. (R), CT, *19*
Bor-Maq Assoc. (C), TX, *269*
Bornholdt Shivas & Friends Executive Recruiters (C), NY, *270*
Bowden & Co., Inc. (R), OH, *20*
Boyden (R), NY, *20*
Brierwood Group, Inc. (C), IN, *273*
The Buckley Group (C), FL, *276*
Bullis & Co., Inc. (R), CA, *25*
David S. Burt Assoc. (C), MT, *276*
Business Partners, Inc. (C), FL, *277*
Butterfield & Co. Int'l., Inc. (C), HI, *277*
Canny, Bowen Inc. (R), NY, *27*
Carlsen Resources, Inc. (R), CO, *29*
Carpenter Assoc., Inc. (R), IL, *30*
Carpenter, Shackleton & Company (R), IL, *30*
Catalyx Group (R), NY, *31*
Cendea Connection Int'l. (R), TX, *32*
David Chambers & Assoc., Inc. (R), CT, *32*
A. D. Check Assoc., Inc. (R), PA, *33*
The Cherbonnier Group, Inc. (R), TX, *33*
Christian & Timbers, Inc. (R), OH, *34*
Christopher-Westmont & Assoc., Inc. (R), OH, *34*
M. A. Churchill & Assoc., Inc. (R), PA, *35*
Clarey/Napier Int'l., L.C. (R), TX, *35*
COBA Executive Search (R), CO, *36*
Colton Bernard Inc. (R), CA, *37*
Compass Group Ltd. (R), MI, *38*
Conex Inc./InterSearch (R), NY, *39*
Cook Assoc.,® Inc. (R), IL, *40*
Corporate Advisors, Inc. (C), FL, *299*
Corporate Select Int'l., Ltd. (C), IL, *301*
The Corporate Source Group, Inc. (R), MA, *41*
Crane, Reed & Co., Inc. (C), NH, *302*
Cromwell Partners, Inc. (R), NY, *43*
Frank Cuomo & Assoc., Inc. (C), NY, *305*
Curran Partners, Inc. (R), CT, *44*
The Curtiss Group International (R), FL, *44*
Cybernautic Corp. (C), CT, *305*
Cypress Int'l., Inc. (R), FL, *45*
Daggett & Kvistad (R), CA, *45*
Dahl-Morrow Int'l. (R), VA, *45*
Alan Davis & Assoc. Inc. (R), QE, *47*
Delta Services (R), TX, *48*
DieckMueller Group (R), WI, *51*
Roger Dietsch & Assoc. (C), MN, *312*
Diversified Search, Inc. (R), PA, *52*
Doering & Assoc. (C), CA, *313*
L. J. Doherty & Assoc. (R), MA, *53*
Dow Consultants Int'l. (C), NY, *314*
Drew Assoc. Int'l. (R), NJ, *54*
DS&A (Doug Sears & Assoc.) (C), FL, *315*
Dukas Assoc. (C), MA, *315*
Dunhill Professional Search of Miami (C), FL, *319*
Dunhill Professional Search of Hawaii (C), HI, *320*
Dunhill Professional Search of Byram (C), MS, *321*
Dunhill Professional Search of Richmond (C), VA, *323*
Dussick Management Assoc. (C), CT, *323*
Gwen Dycus & Assoc. (C), FL, *323*
E/Search Int'l. (C), CT, *325*
Eagle Research, Inc. (C), NJ, *325*
Electronic Search, Inc. (C), IL, *327*
Gene Ellefson & Assoc. Inc. (C), MI, *328*
Elliot Assoc. Inc. (R), NY, *58*
The Elliott Company (R), MA, *58*
The Energists (R), TX, *59*
ENI (R), CT, *59*
ESS (Executive Search Services) (R), CA, *61*
Exec Tech, Inc. (C), IL, *332*
Executech (R), OH, *62*
Executive Access Inc. (R), NY, *62*
Executive Alliance (R), MA, *62*
Executive Recruiters Int'l. (C), MI, *333*
Executive Referral Services, Inc. (C), IL, *334*
Executive Search Consultants International, Inc. (R), NY, *63*
Executive Search Int'l./Transearch (R), MA, *63*
Executives Worldwide, Inc. (C), OR, *337*
Fairfield Int'l. Resources (R), NY, *65*
Fament, Inc. (C), OH, *338*
Leon A. Farley Assoc. (R), CA, *65*
Faro Consultants Int'l. (C), VA, *338*
Fenwick Partners (R), MA, *66*
Fergus Legal Search & Consulting, Inc. (C), NY, *339*
Fernow Assoc. (C), PA, *339*
Neil Fink Assoc. (R), CA, *66*

Eileen Finn & Assoc., Inc. (C), NY, *341*
First Advisory Services Int'l., Inc. (R), MD, *67*
Howard Fischer Assoc. Int'l., Inc. (R), PA, *67*
Fisher-Todd Assoc. (C), NY, *341*
J. G. Flynn & Assoc. Inc. (R), BC, *69*
Forest People Int'l. Search Ltd. (C), BC, *343*
Fortune Group Int'l., Inc. (R), PA, *70*
Fortune Personnel Consultants of Colorado Springs (C), CO, *344*
F-O-R-T-U-N-E Personnel Consultants of Savannah, Inc. (C), GA, *345*
Fortune Personnel Consultants of Hinsdale, IL (C), IL, *346*
Foster Partners (R), NY, *70*
Franchise Recruiters Ltd. (R), IL, *71*
Franchise Search, Inc. (C), NY, *352*
Franstaff Inc. (C), FL, *352*
Fresquez & Assoc. (C), CA, *352*
Gardiner, Townsend & Assoc. (R), NY, *74*
Gilbert & Van Campen Int'l. (R), NY, *76*
Gilbert Tweed Assoc. Inc. (R), NY, *76*
Global 1000 Int'l. Services (C), CA, *358*
Global Career Services, Inc. (C), NY, *358*
Global Consulting Group Inc. (C), ON, *358*
Global Employer's Network, Inc. (R), TX, *77*
Global Research Partnership Inc. (R), NY, *78*
The GlobalSearch Group (C), TX, *359*
F. Gloss Int'l. (R), VA, *78*
Glou Int'l., Inc. (R), MA, *78*
Gowdy Consultants (C), TX, *361*
Ben Greco Assoc., Inc. (C), CA, *362*
Griffith & Werner, Inc. (R), FL, *82*
Groussman & Assoc., Inc. (R), TX, *82*
Growth Strategies, Inc. (R), FL, *83*
Gundersen Partners, L.L.C. (R), NY, *83*
Gustin Partners, Ltd. (R), MA, *83*
William Guy & Assoc., Inc. (R), CA, *84*
Hadley Associates, Inc. (C), NJ, *365*
Hands-on Broadcast (R), NY, *86*
Harbor Consultants Int'l., Inc. (C), VA, *368*
Harris Heery & Assoc., Inc. (R), CT, *87*
Harris McCully Assoc., Inc. (C), NY, *369*
Hartman & Barnette (R), VA, *87*
HCI Corp. (C), IL, *371*
Healthcare Management Resources, Inc. (R), GA, *89*
Healthcare Recruiters Int'l. - Pittsburgh (C), PA, *373*
Hedman & Assoc. (R), TX, *89*
Heffelfinger Assoc., Inc. (R), MA, *89*
Jay Heino Company, LLC (C), NY, *375*
Helffrich Int'l. (C), FL, *375*
Henrietta's Personnel & Executive Search, Inc. (C), FL, *376*
Higbee Assoc., Inc. (C), CT, *377*
Higdon Prince Inc. (R), NY, *93*
Hill & Assoc. (C), CA, *378*
Hill Allyn Assoc. (C), CA, *378*
David C. Horn Executive Search (C), TX, *381*
Hornberger Management Company (R), DE, *95*
Horton Int'l. Inc. (R), NY, *96*
Hospitality Int'l. (C), NY, *381*
The HRM Group, Inc. (C), AL, *382*
HRS, Inc. (R), PA, *97*
Hughes & Company (R), VA, *98*
E. F. Humay Assoc. (C), PA, *384*
Hunter Int'l. LLC (C), MA, *385*
Huntley Associates (Dallas), Inc. (C), TX, *386*
Huntress Real Estate Executive Search (R), MO, *100*
IM Independent Management Recruiters (R), TN, *101*
Intercontinental Executive Group (C), PA, *391*
Interim Management Resources Inc. (C), ON, *392*
International Business Partners (C), ON, *392*
International Management Development Corp. (C), NY, *393*
International Research Group (R), CA, *103*
International Staffing Consultants, Inc. (C), CA, *393*
J.D.G. y Asociados, S.A. de C.V. (R), SO, *104*
Jackson Group Int'l. (C), CO, *396*
Jeffrey Allan Co., Inc. (C), CA, *398*
JG Consultants, Inc. (R), TX, *106*
Jordan-Sitter Assoc. (R), TX, *108*
Joseph Chris & Assoc. (C), TX, *400*
Juno Systems, Inc. (C), NY, *402*
K & C Assoc. (C), CA, *402*
Kabana Corp. (C), MI, *402*
Kane & Assoc. (C), TX, *403*
Karel & Co. (R), CA, *109*
Allan Karson Assoc., Inc. (R), NJ, *110*
Kazan International, Inc. (R), NJ, *110*
A.T. Kearney Executive Search (R), IL, *111*
S. D. Kelly & Assoc., Inc. (R), MA, *112*
Kent & Assoc. (R), OH, *113*
Ki Technologies, Inc. (C), UT, *406*
Kiley, Owen & McGovern, Inc. (R), NJ, *114*
The Kilman Advisory Group (R), CT, *114*
The Kingsley Group (R), CA, *114*
Kip Williams, Inc. (R), NY, *115*
The Kleinstein Group, Inc. (R), NJ, *116*
Raymond J. Klemmer & Assoc. (R), NY, *116*
Korn/Ferry Int'l. (R), NY, *117*
Kors Montgomery Int'l. (R), TX, *118*
KPA Assoc., Inc. (C), NY, *408*
Krautler Personnel Recruitment (C), FL, *409*
Kreutz Consulting Group, Inc. (R), IL, *121*
Paul Kull & Co. (R), NJ, *121*
L O R (R), NJ, *122*
The LaBorde Group (C), CA, *411*
LaCosta & Assoc. Int'l. Inc. (C), CA, *411*
The Landstone Group (C), NY, *412*
Lawrence L. Lapham, Inc. (R), NY, *124*
Larsen, Whitney, Blecksmith & Zilliacus, Inc. (R), CA, *125*
Latham International, Ltd. (R), NJ, *126*
The Lear Group, Inc. (R), OH, *127*
Lechner & Assoc., Inc. (C), FL, *415*
The Conrad Lee Co. Inc. (R), FL, *127*
Lee Management Group Inc. (C), NJ, *416*
Jacques LePage Executive Search Inc. (R), QE, *128*
J. E. Lessner Assoc., Inc. (R), MI, *128*
Michael Levine Search Consultants (R), NY, *129*
Lipsky Group, Inc. (R), CA, *129*
Lipson & Co. (R), CA, *130*
Livingston, Robert & Co. (R), CT, *130*
Locke & Assoc. (R), NC, *131*
Fran Luisi Assoc. (R), NJ, *132*
Maiorino & Weston Assoc., Inc. (R), CT, *134*
Management Advisors Int'l., Inc. (C), NC, *424*
Management Assoc. (C), MD, *424*
Management Recruiters of Sacramento North (C), CA, *441*
Management Recruiters of Altamonte (C), FL, *442*
Management Recruiters of Bonita Springs, Inc. (C), FL, *443*
Management Recruiters of Miami-North (C), FL, *443*
Management Recruiters of St. Lucie County, Inc. (C), FL, *444*
Management Recruiters of North Fulton (C), GA, *445*
Management Recruiters of Atlanta NE (C), GA, *446*
Management Recruiters - Towne Lake (C), GA, *446*
Management Recruiters of Chicago-North Shore (C), IL, *447*
Management Recruiters of Morris County, NJ (C), NJ, *453*
Management Recruiters of North Warren Inc. (C), NJ, *453*
Management Recruiters of Asheville, Inc. (C), NC, *455*
Management Recruiters of Bethlehem, PA (C), PA, *458*
Management Recruiters of Delaware County (C), PA, *459*
Management Recruiters of Milwaukee-North (C), WI, *466*
Management Resource Assoc., Inc. (C), FL, *467*
Manning Lloyd Assoc. Ltd. (C), NY, *468*
Mark Stanley & Co./EMA Partners International (R), FL, *136*
Marketing & Sales Resources, Inc. (C), FL, *470*
Marketing Consultants (C), WI, *470*
Brad Marks Int'l. (R), CA, *136*
Martin Partners, L.L.C. (R), IL, *137*
Matté & Company, Inc. (R), CT, *138*
Maxecon Executive Search Consultants (R), FL, *138*
McCooe & Assoc., Inc. (R), NJ, *140*
McCray, Shriver, Eckdahl & Assoc., Inc. (R), CA, *140*
McDonald, Long & Assoc., Inc. (R), NY, *140*
G. E. McFarland & Co. (R), GA, *140*
McHale & Assoc. (R), WA, *141*
McIntyre Assoc. (R), CT, *141*
McKinley•Arend Int'l. (R), TX, *141*
McManners Assoc., Inc. (R), CA, *142*
MESA, Inc. (R), CO, *143*

MESA International (C), CA, *480*
Messett Assoc., Inc. (R), FL, *143*
Herbert Mines Assoc., Inc. (R), NY, *145*
MJF Assoc. (C), CT, *483*
MLA Resources, Inc. (C), OK, *483*
Morgan/Webber, Inc. (R), NY, *147*
Mortgage Search Network (C), AZ, *486*
Morton, McCorkle & Assoc. Inc. (R), MO, *147*
Nadzam, Lusk, Horgan & Assoc., Inc. (R), CA, *150*
National Bank & Finance Executive Search (C), CA, *488*
New World Healthcare Solutions, Inc. (R), NY, *151*
Nichols & Company (R), CO, *151*
Marc Nichols Assoc., Inc. (C), NY, *493*
Nichols Brown Int'l. (R), NY, *151*
NMC & Kay Int'l. (R), CO, *152*
Noble & Assoc., Inc. (C), NY, *494*
Norman Broadbent Int'l., Inc. (R), NY, *152*
O'Callaghan Honey/Ray & Berndtson Inc. (R), AB, *153*
O'Neill Group (C), NJ, *498*
Ollinger Partners (R), MA, *156*
The Options Group, Inc. (C), NY, *499*
Ortman Recruiting Int'l. (C), CA, *500*
Robert Ottke Assoc. (R), CA, *157*
P R Management Consultants, Inc. (C), NJ, *500*
Janou Pakter, Inc. (C), NY, *502*
Partners In Human Resources Int'l., Inc. (R), NY, *160*
Pasona Canada, Inc. (C), ON, *504*
PERI Corp/Professional Executive Recruiters, Inc. (C), TX, *507*
Fred Perry Assoc. (C), TX, *507*
Barry Persky & Co., Inc. (R), CT, *163*
J. R. Peterman Assoc., Inc. (C), VT, *509*
Petro Staff Int'l. (C), AB, *509*
Peyser Assoc., Inc. (R), FL, *163*
Phoenix Search (R), MX, *164*
PIC Executive Search (C), GA, *511*
Pierce & Crow (R), CA, *164*
Pioneer Consulting Group (C), CA, *512*
Yves Plouffe & Assoc. (R), QE, *165*
Ray Polhill & Assoc. (R), NC, *166*
Don V. Poole & Assoc., Inc. (C), CO, *514*
Power Recruiting Group (C), TX, *515*
Preferred Placement, Inc. (C), NY, *516*
ProLinks Inc. (R), VA, *170*
PSD Group, Inc. (C), CA, *525*
QuestPro, Inc. (C), TX, *527*
R. C. Services (C), TX, *528*
Rand Thompson Executive Search Consultants (C), NY, *528*
Reinecke & Assoc. (C), NJ, *533*
The Remington Group (R), IL, *174*
Research Personnel Consultants (C), ON, *534*
Reserve Technology Institute (R), TX, *175*
Resolve Assoc. Int'l. (R), FL, *175*
The Resource Group (R), NJ, *175*
Russell Reynolds Assoc., Inc. (R), NY, *176*
Ridenour & Assoc. (R), IL, *178*
Ridgefield Search Int'l. (C), CT, *537*
Ritt-Ritt & Assoc., Inc. (C), IL, *537*
Robison & Associates (R), NC, *180*
R. A. Rodriguez & Assoc., Inc. (C), TX, *540*
Roevin Technical People (C), ON, *540*
Roll International (C), TX, *541*
Patricia Roth Int'l. (C), FL, *545*
Roth Young Personnel Service of Detroit, Inc. (C), MI, *546*
Ruppert Comann Assoc., Inc. (R), CO, *182*
Russillo/Gardner/Spolsino (C), MA, *548*
The Ryan Charles Group, Inc. (C), FL, *548*
Sales Builders, Inc. (R), VA, *183*
Sales Consultants of Honolulu (C), HI, *558*
Sales Consultants of Wellesley, Inc. (C), MA, *559*
Sales Consultants of Princeton, Inc. (C), NJ, *561*
Sales Consultants of Westchester-South, Inc. (C), NY, *561*
Sales Consultants King of Prussia (C), PA, *562*
Sales Consultants of Houston (C), TX, *563*
Sales Search Specialist (C), IL, *564*
Sales Solutions (C), CA, *564*
Sanford Rose Assoc. (C), OH, *565*
Savalli & Assoc., Inc. (C), MI, *571*
Savoy Partners, Ltd. (R), DC, *184*
F. B. Schmidt Int'l. (R), CA, *185*
Schuyler Assoc., Ltd. (R), GA, *185*
Search Advisors Int'l. Corp. (R), FL, *186*
The Search America Group Inc. (C), OH, *573*
Search Assoc., Inc. (C), NJ, *574*
The Search Center Inc. (C), TX, *574*
Search Consultants Int'l., Inc. (C), TX, *575*
Search Group Inc. (R), AB, *186*
Search Int'l. (R), MA, *187*
Search North America, Inc. (C), OR, *576*
SearchCorp (C), FL, *577*
Secura/Burnett Partners (R), CA, *187*
Robert Sellery Assoc., Ltd. (R), DC, *188*
Senior Careers (R), NY, *188*
Shiell Personnel (C), LA, *580*
L. A. Silver Assoc., Inc. (R), MA, *191*
Silver Associates (C), CA, *581*
Sink, Walker, Boltrus Int'l. (R), MA, *192*
Ruth Sklar Assoc., Inc. (RSA Executive Search) (R), NY, *192*
Slayton Int'l., Inc. (R), IL, *192*
James F. Smith & Assoc. (C), GA, *583*
Abbott Smith Assoc., Inc. (R), NY, *193*
Smith, Brown & Jones (C), KS, *585*
A. William Smyth, Inc. (R), CA, *194*
Soderlund Assoc. Inc. (R), OH, *194*
Specialized Search Assoc. (C), FL, *589*
SpencerStuart (R), NY, *196*
The Spiegel Group (R), MA, *197*
SSA Executive Search Int'l. (R), AZ, *198*
C. J. Stafford & Assoc. (C), ON, *591*
The Stevens Group (C), CA, *593*
The Stevenson Group, Inc. (N.J.) (R), NJ, *200*
Stewart/Laurence Assoc., Inc. (R), NJ, *201*
STM Assoc. (R), UT, *201*
Allan Stolee Inc. (R), FL, *201*
Stone Enterprises Ltd. (C), IL, *594*
Strategic Alternatives (R), CA, *202*
Strategic Resources (C), WA, *595*
Strategic Technologies, Inc. (C), TX, *596*
W. R. Strathmann Assoc. (R), NY, *203*
Stroman Int'l., Inc. (R), CO, *204*
Swartz & Assoc., Inc. (R), AZ, *204*
Tanner & Assoc., Inc. (R), TX, *206*
TASA International (R), NY, *206*
Tech Search (C), CA, *601*
Techaid Inc. (C), QE, *601*
Technifind Int'l. (C), TX, *602*
Thomas Lyle & Co. (C), IL, *606*
Topaz Int'l., Inc., Attorney Search (C), NJ, *607*
Tower Consultants, Ltd. (R), PA, *209*
TPG & Assoc. (C), TX, *608*
Travel Executive Search (C), NY, *608*
Trillium Human Resources Inc. (C), ON, *609*
Tryon & Heideman, LLC (R), MO, *211*
The Ultimate Source (R), CA, *212*
The Verriez Group Inc. (R), ON, *213*
Claude Vezina, Conseil en recherche de cadres inc. (R), QE, *213*
Warren, Morris & Madison, Ltd. (C), CA, *616*
Warring & Assoc. (R), CA, *215*
Watring & Assoc., Inc. (C), IL, *616*
Weber Executive Search (R), NY, *216*
S. E. Weinstein Co. (R), IL, *217*
Wells, Bradley & Assoc., Inc. (C), MN, *618*
Welzig, Lowe & Assoc. (C), CO, *618*
West & West (R), CA, *218*
The Whitney Group (R), NY, *219*
The Wilkie Group Int'l. (R), ON, *220*
Walter K. Wilkins & Co. (R), NJ, *221*
William Willis Worldwide Inc. (R), CT, *221*
Wilson & Assoc. Int'l. Inc. (C), FL, *622*
Windsor International (R), GA, *222*
WMD inc. (C), NJ, *623*
S. R. Wolman Assoc., Inc. (R), NY, *224*
WTW Assoc., Inc. (R), NY, *225*
Wyndham Mills Int'l., Inc. (R), GA, *225*
Yelverton Executive Search (R), CA, *226*
Youngblood Assoc. (C), NC, *626*
Steven Yungerberg Assoc., Inc. (R), MN, *226*
Helen Ziegler & Assoc., Inc. (C), ON, *627*
Zona & Assoc., Inc. (C), NY, *628*
Zwell Int'l. (R), IL, *228*

Index by Industries

Firms with (R) are from the Retainer Section, which begins on page 1.
Firms with (C) are from the Contingency Section, which begins on page 231.

Basis of Industries Classification

This classification system is based on the U.S. Government's SIC codes, but has been customized and updated by Kennedy Information to suit our users' needs.

0.00 **GENERALIST**

A.00 **AGRICULTURE, FORESTRY, FISHING, MINING**

B.00 **ENERGY/UTILITIES**

C.00 **CONSTRUCTION**

D.00 **MANUFACTURING INDUSTRIES**
D.10 Food, beverage, tobacco & kindred products
D.11 Textile, apparel, related products
D.12 Lumber, wood, furniture & fixtures
D.13 Paper & allied products
D.14 Printing & allied industry
D.15 Chemicals & allied products
D.16 Soap, perfume, cosmetics
D.17 Drugs, pharmaceuticals
D.18 Medical devices & instruments
D.19 Plastics, rubber products
D.20 Paints, allied products, petroleum products
D.21 Leather, stone, glass, concrete, clay products
D.22 Primary & fabricated metal products
D.23 Industrial machinery & consumer appliances
D.24 Transportation equipment (*e.g. automobiles*)
D.25 Computer equipment & components
D.26 Consumer electronics
D.27 Test & measurement equipment
D.28 Miscellaneous manufacturing industries

E.00 **TRANSPORTATION**

F.00 **WHOLESALE TRADE**

G.00 **RETAIL TRADE**

H.00 **FINANCE**
H.10 Commercial banking
H.11 Investment banking
H.12 Securities & commodities brokers
H.13 Venture capital
H.14 Other financial services

I.00 **SERVICE INDUSTRIES**
I.10 Hospitality; including hotels, resorts, clubs, restaurants, food & beverage services
I.11 Entertainment, leisure, amusement, recreation, sports, travel
I.12 Museums, galleries, music/arts, libraries & information services, membership & other non-profits
I.13 Higher education
I.14 Pharmaceutical (other than manufacturing)
I.15 Legal
I.16 Computer services
I.17 Accounting & miscellaneous business services
I.18 Equipment services, including leasing
I.19 Management consulting
I.20 Human resource services
I.21 Law enforcement, security

J.00 **COMMUNICATIONS/MEDIA**
J.10 Advertising, public relations
J.11 Publishing, print media
J.12 New media (*e.g. Internet, multimedia*)
J.13 TV, cable, motion pictures, video, radio
J.14 Telephone, telecommunications

K.00 **PUBLIC ADMINISTRATION/GOVERNMENT**
K.10 Defense

L.00 **ENVIRONMENTAL SERVICES**
L.10 Hazardous waste, study, clean up

M.00 **AEROSPACE**

N.00 **PACKAGING**

P.00 **INSURANCE**

Q.00 **REAL ESTATE**

R.00 **HIGH TECH**

S.00 **SOFTWARE**

T.00 **BIOTECH/GENETIC ENGINEERING**

U.00 **HEALTHCARE**

V.00 **NON-CLASSIFIABLE INDUSTRIES**

0.00 Generalist

A First Resource (C), NC, *231*
A. D. & Assoc. Executive Search, Inc. (C), GA, *231*
Aaron Consulting, Inc. (C), MO, *232*
Abacus Group LLC (C), NY, *232*
Abbott Associates (R), CA, *1*
The Abbott Group, Inc. (R), MD, *1*
Abeln, Magy & Assoc., Inc. (R), MN, *1*
B. J. Abrams & Assoc. Inc. (C), IL, *233*
Accelerated Data Decision, Inc. (C), NJ, *233*
Accent On Achievement, Inc. (C), MI, *233*
Access Assoc. Inc. (C), MD, *233*
Access Data Personnel, Inc. (C), NH, *233*
Accountancies (C), CA, *234*
Accountants Executive Search (C), CT, *234*
Accountants Executive Search (C), PA, *234*
Accountants On Call (C), NJ, *234*
Accountants Executive Search (C), CA, *237*
Accountants On Call (C), TN, *237*
Accounting & Bookkeeping Personnel, Inc. (C), AZ, *237*
Accounting & Computer Personnel (C), NY, *238*
Accounting Additions (C), CA, *238*
Accounting Personnel & Engineering Personnel Consultants (C), LA, *238*
Action Management Corp. (C), MI, *239*
ADR Accounting Management Recruiters (C), ON, *240*
Advancement Recruiting Services (C), OH, *241*
Advantage Partners, Inc. (R), OH, *2*
Advice Personnel Inc. (C), NY, *241*
AJM Professional Services (C), MI, *243*
Alexander Ross & Co. (R), NY, *3*
Allen Austin Lowe & Powers (R), TX, *3*
Allen Consulting Group, Inc. (C), MO, *244*
Allen Evans Assoc. (R), NY, *4*
Allen, Wayne & Co. LLC (C), WI, *245*
Allen/Associates (R), OH, *4*
Alliance Executive Search, Inc. (R), MA, *4*
Allied Search, Inc. (C), CA, *245*
Tom Allison Assoc. (C), NM, *245*
Altec/HRC (C), MI, *246*
AM & G Certified Public Accountants & Consultants (R), IL, *4*
Peter W. Ambler Co. (R), TX, *5*
American Resources Corp. (C), IL, *248*
AmeriPro Search, Inc. (C), NC, *248*
Amherst Human Resource Group, Ltd. (C), IL, *249*
Amrop International (R), MX, *5*
AMS Int'l. (R), VA, *5*
Anderson & Associates (R), NC, *5*
The Angus Group, Ltd. (C), OH, *251*
APA Employment Agency Inc. (C), OR, *251*
Applied Technology Solutions Inc. (C), ON, *252*
The Argus Group Corp. (C), ON, *252*
Argus National, Inc. (R), CT, *6*
ARI Int'l. (R), CA, *6*
Armor Personnel (C), ON, *253*
R & J Arnold & Assoc., Inc. (C), CO, *253*
William B. Arnold Assoc., Inc. (R), CO, *7*
Patrick Arnone & Assoc. Inc. (R), VA, *7*
Artgo, Inc. (R), OH, *7*
The Ascher Group (R), NJ, *7*
The Associates, HR Search Executives, Inc. (C), OK, *254*
Atlantic Search Group, Inc. (C), MA, *255*
Attorney Search Global, Inc. (C), IL, *255*
Austin, Hill & Assoc. (C), MD, *256*
The Badger Group (R), CA, *10*
Baeder Kalinski Int'l. Group, Inc. (R), NH, *10*
The Baer Group (R), OH, *10*
Baldwin & Assoc. (C), OH, *258*
Carol Ball & Co. (C), CT, *258*
Ballos & Co., Inc. (R), NJ, *10*
Paul C. Banks Assoc. (C), GA, *259*
Barger & Sargeant, Inc. (R), NH, *11*
J. W. Barleycorn, Renard & Assoc., Inc. (R), OH, *11*
Barnes Development Group, LLC (R), WI, *11*
Barrington Hart, Inc. (R), IL, *12*
Aldonna Barry Personnel & Management (C), ON, *260*
Barth Smith Company (R), IL, *12*
Barton Assoc., Inc. (R), TX, *12*
Bartz Rogers & Partners (C), MN, *260*
Bason Associates (R), OH, *13*
Martin H. Bauman Assoc., Inc. (R), NY, *13*
Beach Executive Search Inc. (R), FL, *14*
Becker Personnel (C), FL, *262*
Neail Behringer Consultants Inc. (R), NY, *15*
Joy Reed Belt Search Consultants, Inc. (R), OK, *15*
J. P. Bencik Assoc. (C), MI, *263*
Richard L. Bencin & Assoc. (C), OH, *264*
Bennett Search & Consulting Co. (R), FL, *16*
Bertrand, Ross & Assoc., Inc. (C), IL, *266*
BEST/World Assoc. Inc. (R), TX, *16*
Bickerton & Gordon LLC (C), MA, *266*
Billington & Assoc. (R), CA, *17*
Bio-Venture Group (C), RI, *266*
The Blackman Kallick Search Division (C), IL, *267*
Blackshaw, Olmstead, Lynch & Koenig (R), GA, *18*
BLB Consulting (C), NY, *268*
Blum & Co. (R), WI, *19*
Boardroom Consultants/Kenny Kindler Tholke (R), NY, *19*
Bodner Inc. (C), NY, *268*
Boettcher Assoc. (R), WI, *19*
Bonnell Assoc. Ltd. (R), CT, *19*
John C. Boone & Co. (R), IL, *19*
Boone-Scaturro Assoc., Inc. (C), GA, *269*
Lynn Borne & Co. (C), CA, *270*
Bosland Gray Assoc. (R), NJ, *20*
Boston Professional Search, Inc. (C), MA, *270*
Boulware & Assoc. Inc. (R), IL, *20*
Bowden & Co., Inc. (R), OH, *20*
BowdenGlobal, Ltd. (R), OH, *20*
Boyden (R), NY, *20*
Boyle/Ogata Executive Search (R), CA, *21*
BR & Assoc. (C), NJ, *271*
Bradford & Galt, Inc. (C), MO, *271*
The Brand Co., Inc. (R), FL, *22*
Brandt Associates (C), PA, *272*
Brandywine Management Group (R), MD, *22*
Brandywine Retained Ventures, Inc. (R), CT, *22*
Branthover Assoc. (C), NY, *272*
Brault & Assoc., Ltd. (R), VA, *22*
BridgeGate LLC (C), CA, *273*
Brindisi Search (R), MD, *23*
Britt Assoc., Inc. (C), IL, *274*
Brush Creek Partners (R), MO, *24*
BRW Search (C), MN, *275*
Brystol Cove Assoc. (R), CA, *24*
Charles Buck & Assoc., Inc. (R), NY, *24*
Bullis & Co., Inc. (R), CA, *25*
The Burgess Group-Corporate Recruiters Int'l., Inc. (R), NY, *25*
The Burke Group (C), ON, *276*
Burke, O'Brien & Bishop Assoc., Inc. (R), NJ, *25*
Joseph R. Burns & Assoc., Inc. (R), NJ, *25*
Business Partners, Inc. (C), FL, *277*
Business Solutions Worldwide, Inc. (C), NJ, *277*
Byron Leonard Int'l., Inc. (R), CA, *25*
C & H Personnel (C), PA, *277*
C. M. Management Services, Inc. (R), KY, *26*
C. P. Consulting (R), PA, *26*
C.T.E.W. Executive Personnel Services Inc. (C), BC, *278*
Robert Caldwell & Assoc. (R), CA, *26*
The Caldwell Partners Amrop International (R), ON, *26*
California Search Agency, Inc. (C), CA, *279*
Callan Assoc., Ltd. (R), IL, *27*
Cambridge Group Ltd. - Exec. Search Div. (C), CT, *279*
Cambridge Management Planning (R), ON, *27*
Cameron Consulting Group (R), CA, *27*
Canadian Career Partners (R), AB, *27*
Canny, Bowen Inc. (R), NY, *27*
J. P. Canon Assoc. (C), NY, *280*
The Cantor Concern, Inc. (R), NY, *28*
Capital Consulting Group, Inc. (R), MD, *28*
Capstone Consulting, Inc. (R), IL, *29*
Capstone Inc. (R), NY, *29*
Cardwell Enterprises Inc. (R), IL, *29*
Career Advisors, Inc. (C), FL, *281*
Career Consultants (R), IN, *29*
Career Counseling Inc. (CCI) (C), KY, *282*
Career Enterprises (C), OH, *282*
Career Images (C), FL, *282*
The Carey Company (C), NC, *284*
Carlson & Czeswik (R), MN, *30*
Carnegie Partners, Inc. (R), IL, *30*
Carpenter, Shackleton & Company (R), IL, *30*
Carrington & Carrington, Ltd. (R), IL, *30*
Carris, Jackowitz Assoc. (R), NY, *30*
K. Carroll & Assoc. (C), IL, *284*
Carson-Thomas & Assoc. (C), CA, *284*
Carter, Lavoie Associates (C), RI, *285*
Caruthers & Co., L.L.C. (R), CT, *31*
Cary & Assoc. (R), FL, *31*
Casey & Assoc., Inc. (C), TX, *286*

Michael J. Cavanagh & Assoc. Inc. (R), ON, *31*
CCI - Career Consultants Int'l. (C), CA, *286*
Cella Assoc. (C), GA, *286*
CFOs 2 Go (C), CA, *288*
Chacra, Belliveau & Assoc. Inc. (C), QE, *288*
Chaloner Assoc. (R), MA, *32*
David Chambers & Assoc., Inc. (R), CT, *32*
Joseph Chandler & Assoc., Inc. (R), IL, *33*
Chanko-Ward, Ltd. (R), NY, *33*
Charet & Assoc. (C), NJ, *289*
The Chatham Group, Ltd. (C), CT, *289*
A. D. Check Assoc., Inc. (R), PA, *33*
The Cherbonnier Group, Inc. (R), TX, *33*
Chicago Research Group, Inc. (R), NC, *33*
Chrisman & Co. Inc. (R), CA, *33*
Christenson Hutchison McDowell, LLC (R), NJ, *34*
Christian & Timbers, Inc. (R), OH, *34*
Christopher-Westmont & Assoc., Inc. (R), OH, *34*
Cizek Assoc., Inc. (R), AZ, *35*
Arlene Clapp, Ltd. (R), MN, *35*
Clarey & Andrews, Inc. (R), IL, *35*
Clarey/Napier Int'l., L.C. (R), TX, *35*
Clark Personnel Service, Inc. (C), AL, *292*
Richard Clarke Assoc., Inc. (R), NY, *36*
CMC Search Consultants (C), IL, *293*
CMS Management Services LLC (C), IN, *293*
Coast Personnel Services Ltd. (C), BC, *293*
Dean M. Coe Assoc. (R), MA, *37*
Cole, Warren & Long, Inc. (R), PA, *37*
J. Kevin Coleman & Assoc., Inc. (R), CA, *37*
Coleman Lew & Assoc., Inc. (R), NC, *37*
Collins & Associates (C), MI, *294*
Columbia Consulting Group (R), MD, *38*
Compass Group Ltd. (R), MI, *38*
Computer Personnel, Inc. (C), WA, *295*
Computer Placements Unlimited Inc. (C), NY, *295*
Computer Recruiters, Inc. (C), CA, *295*
Computer Search Group, Ltd. (R), IL, *39*
The Comwell Company, Inc. (C), NJ, *296*
Conard Associates, Inc. (R), NH, *39*
Concorde Staff Source Inc. (C), WI, *296*
Conex Inc./InterSearch (R), NY, *39*
Connors, Lovell & Assoc. Inc. (C), ON, *296*
Consolidated Management Services (C), ON, *296*
Consulpro (R), ON, *39*
Consulting Rhonda (C), ON, *297*
ContactBridge, Inc. (R), IL, *40*
Continental Research Search, Inc. (C), WI, *298*
Philip Conway Management (R), IL, *40*
Cook Assoc.,® Inc. (R), IL, *40*
The Cooke Group (R), WI, *40*
Cooper Assoc., Inc. (C), NY, *298*
The Cooper Executive Search Group Inc. (R), WI, *41*
Corporate Advisors, Inc. (C), FL, *299*
The Corporate Advisory Group (R), NJ, *41*
The Corporate Connection, Ltd. (C), VA, *299*
Corporate Leadership Strategies, Inc. (R), NH, *41*
Corporate Management Services (C), PA, *300*
Corporate Plus, Ltd. (C), GA, *300*
The Corrigan Group (R), CA, *42*
J. D. Cotter Search Inc. (C), OH, *302*
Creative Financial Staffing (C), MA, *303*
Creative Financial Staffing Inc. (C), ON, *303*
Creative HR Solutions (C), GA, *303*
Creative Input, Inc. (C), RI, *303*
The Cris Group, Inc. (R), NY, *42*
Crowder & Company (R), MI, *43*
Curran Partners, Inc. (R), CT, *44*
The Curtiss Group International (R), FL, *44*
Cusack Consulting (R), NY, *44*
Judith Cushman & Assoc. (R), WA, *44*
The Custer Group, Inc. (R), TN, *44*
Cyberna Assoc. Ltd. (C), QE, *305*
Cyntal Int'l. Ltd. (R), NY, *44*
Cypress Int'l., Inc. (R), FL, *45*
Dalton Management Consultants, Ltd. (C), NJ, *306*
Damon & Assoc., Inc. (C), TX, *306*
The Danbrook Group, Inc. (C), TX, *306*
Daniel Marks Company (C), OH, *306*
Dankowski & Assoc., Inc. (C), OH, *307*
Dapexs Consultants, Inc. (C), NY, *307*
Alan Darling Consulting (R), VT, *46*
The Dartmouth Group (R), NY, *46*
Data Bank Executive Search (R), OH, *46*
Data Search Network, Inc. (C), FL, *307*
Datamatics Management Services, Inc. (C), NJ, *307*
DataPro Personnel Consultants (C), TX, *308*
Davidson, Laird & Assoc. (C), MI, *308*
Davies, Park (R), AB, *46*
Allen Davis & Assoc. (C), MA, *308*
John J. Davis & Assoc., Inc. (R), NY, *47*
Davis & Company (R), CA, *47*
Donna Davis Assoc. (C), NJ, *309*
Joseph A. Davis Consultants, Inc. (R), NY, *47*
DBL Associates (C), CA, *309*
DCA Professional Search (C), TX, *309*
Dean-Dzierzawiec Assoc. (C), NJ, *309*
Dean-MacDonald (R), OH, *47*
DeCaster Assoc. (C), WI, *310*
Defrain Mayer (R), KS, *48*
Delphi Systems, Ltd. (R), MO, *48*
DeMatteo Associates (C), NY, *311*
Derhak Ireland & Partners Ltd. (R), ON, *48*
DHR Int'l., Inc. (R), IL, *49*
Diamond Tax Recruiting (C), NY, *312*
The Diestel Group (R), UT, *51*
DiMarchi Partners (R), CO, *51*
J. Dinerstein & Co., Inc. (R), NY, *51*
Robert W. Dingman Co., Inc. (R), CA, *52*
Dinte Resources, Inc. (R), VA, *52*
R. J. Dishaw & Assoc. (R), TX, *52*
DiTech Resources (C), CT, *313*
Diversified Management Resources (C), IL, *313*
Diversified Search, Inc. (R), PA, *52*
Doering & Assoc. (C), CA, *313*
Doherty Int'l., Inc. (R), IL, *53*
Doleman Enterprises (R), VA, *53*
Donahue/Bales Assoc. (R), IL, *54*
Drinkwater & Assoc. (R), MA, *54*
DuBrul Management Co. (C), NY, *315*
Dunhill Professional Search of Miami (C), FL, *319*
Dunhill of San Francisco, Inc. (C), CA, *319*
Dunhill Professional Search of Rolling Meadows (C), IL, *320*
Dunhill Professional Search of Hawaii (C), HI, *320*
Dunhill Professional Search of Tampa (C), FL, *320*
Dunhill Technical Staffing (C), IN, *320*
Dunhill Search of Medford (C), NJ, *321*
Dunhill Search of Vermont (C), VT, *323*
Dunn Associates (R), PA, *55*
Dussick Management Assoc. (C), CT, *323*
Donald F. Dvorak & Co. (R), IL, *55*
Dwyer Consulting Group, Inc. (R), WV, *56*
G. L. Dykstra Assoc., Inc. (C), MI, *323*
Dynamic Computer Consultants, Inc. (C), AZ, *324*
Dynamic Search Systems, Inc. (C), IL, *324*
Dynamic Staffing Network (C), IL, *324*
The E & K Group (C), NJ, *324*
E O Technical (C), CT, *324*
Early Cochran & Olson (R), IL, *56*
Eastman & Beaudine, Inc. (R), TX, *56*
EBA Group (R), NJ, *56*
ECG Resources, Inc. (C), NY, *326*
The Edge Resource Group (C), PA, *326*
Bruce Edwards & Associates, Inc. (R), NC, *56*
EFL Assoc. (R), KS, *57*
EFL Int'l. (R), AZ, *57*
Richard A. Eisner & Co., LLP (R), NY, *57*
Elinvar (C), NC, *328*
Elite Resources Group (R), OH, *58*
H. J. Elliot, Inc. (R), IL, *58*
The Elliott Company (R), MA, *58*
Ellis & Associates (C), HI, *328*
The Ellsworth Group (C), NY, *329*
Elwell & Assoc., Inc. (R), MI, *59*
Emerson & Co. (C), GA, *329*
Emmett Executive Search, Inc. (C), NY, *330*
Empire International (R), PA, *59*
Employ® (C), PA, *330*
The Enfield Company (C), TX, *330*
ENI (R), CT, *59*
The Enns Partners Inc. (R), ON, *59*
The Enterprise Group (R), MA, *60*
Environmental, Health & Safety Search Assoc. (C), FL, *331*
Mary R. Erickson & Assoc. (R), MN, *60*
Erlanger Assoc. (R), CT, *60*
Ethos Consulting, Inc. (R), CA, *61*
Evergreen & Co. (C), MA, *331*
Exclusive Search Consultants (C), OH, *331*
ExecuGroup, Inc. (R), MS, *61*
ExecuQuest, Inc. (R), MI, *61*
ExecuSource Assoc., Inc. (C), GA, *332*
Executech (R), OH, *62*
Executive Alliance (R), MA, *62*
Executive Careers (R), CA, *62*
Executive Connection (C), OH, *333*
The Executive Group, Inc. (R), CA, *62*
Executive Manning Corp. (R), FL, *63*

Executive Placement Consultants (C), IL, *333*
Executive Registry (C), QE, *334*
Executive Resource Assoc. (C), VA, *334*
Executive Search Consultants International, Inc. (R), NY, *63*
Executive Search Inc. (R), MN, *63*
Executive Search Int'l./Transearch (R), MA, *63*
Executive Search of New England, Inc. (C), ME, *336*
Executive Search Plus, Inc. (C), IN, *336*
Executive Strategies, Inc. (C), GA, *337*
The Executive Tree (R), FL, *64*
Raymond L. Extract & Assoc. (R), CA, *64*
FAI (C), CO, *338*
Family-Business Roundtable, Inc. (R), AZ, *65*
Leon A. Farley Assoc. (R), CA, *65*
James Farris Assoc. (R), OK, *65*
Fast Switch, Ltd. (C), OH, *338*
FCI, Inc. (R), NJ, *65*
Feldman Gray & Assoc. Inc. (C), ON, *339*
Fenzel Milar Assoc. (C), OH, *339*
Fergason Assoc., Inc. (C), IL, *339*
Ferneborg & Assoc., Inc. (R), CA, *66*
Guild Fetridge Acoustical Search, Inc. (C), NY, *340*
Financial Search Corp. (C), IL, *340*
First Advisory Services Int'l., Inc. (R), MD, *67*
Howard Fischer Assoc. Int'l., Inc. (R), PA, *67*
The Fisher Group (R), AB, *67*
James L. Fisk & Assoc. (C), MO, *342*
Robert M. Flanagan & Assoc., Ltd. (R), NY, *68*
Flowers & Assoc. (C), OH, *342*
J. G. Flynn & Assoc. Inc. (R), BC, *69*
Flynn, Hannock, Inc. (R), CT, *69*
Forray Assoc., Inc. (R), NY, *70*
Fortune Personnel Consultants of Sarasota Inc. (C), FL, *345*
Fortune Personnel Consultants of Hinsdale, IL (C), IL, *346*
Fortune Personnel Consultants of the Virginia Highlands (C), VA, *351*
Forum Personnel Inc. (C), NY, *351*
Foster Associates (C), NJ, *351*
Foster Partners (R), NY, *70*
Fox-Morris Assoc., Inc. (C), PA, *351*
Franchise Search, Inc. (C), NY, *352*
Francis & Assoc. (R), IA, *71*
Bernard Frigon & Assoc. Inc. (C), QE, *353*
Frye/Joure & Assoc., Inc. (C), TN, *353*
C. F. Furr & Co. (R), NC, *72*
G. H. Enterprises (C), AZ, *354*
GAAP Inc. (R), QE, *73*
The Gabriel Group (C), PA, *354*
Gaffney Management Consultants (R), IL, *73*
Gaines & Assoc. Int'l., Inc. (R), IL, *73*
Jay Gaines & Company, Inc. (R), NY, *73*
Garb & Assoc., Legal Placement (C), CA, *354*
W. N. Garbarini & Assoc. (R), NJ, *74*
The Garvis Group, Inc. (C), LA, *355*
Gateway Group Personnel, LLC (C), TN, *355*
Gatti & Assoc. (C), MA, *355*
Gaudry, Shink, Levasseur (R), QE, *75*
Genesis Personnel Service, Inc. (C), OH, *356*
Gibson & Co., Inc. (R), WI, *76*
Gilbert & Van Campen Int'l. (R), NY, *76*
Gilbert Tweed Assoc. Inc. (R), NY, *76*
Gilreath Weatherby Inc. (R), MA, *77*
Glass & Assoc., Inc. (C), OH, *358*
The Glazin Group (R), BC, *77*
Global Employer's Network, Inc. (R), TX, *77*
Global Research Partnership Inc. (R), NY, *78*
The GlobalSearch Group (C), TX, *359*
Robert G. Godfrey Assoc. Ltd. (R), IL, *78*
H. L. Goehring & Assoc., Inc. (C), OH, *359*
Goldbeck Recruiting Inc. (C), BC, *359*
Joseph Goldring & Assoc. Inc. (C), MI, *360*
David Gomez & Assoc., Inc. (R), IL, *79*
Gomez Fregoso y Asociados (C), JAL, *360*
Goodwin & Co. (R), DC, *80*
Gossage Regan Assoc. (R), NY, *80*
Gould, McCoy & Chadick, Inc. (R), NY, *80*
Robert Graham Assoc. (R), RI, *81*
Granger, Counts & Assoc. (R), OH, *81*
A. Davis Grant & Co. (R), NJ, *81*
Grant Cooper & Assoc., Inc. (R), MO, *81*
Grant-Franks & Assoc. (C), NJ, *361*
Grantham & Co., Inc. (R), NC, *81*
Annie Gray Assoc., Inc. (R), MO, *81*
Ben Greco Assoc., Inc. (C), CA, *362*
Sheila Greco Assoc. (C), NY, *362*
Gregory Michaels & Assoc., Inc. (R), IL, *82*
Groenekamp & Assoc. (C), CA, *363*
Grossberg & Assoc. (R), IL, *82*
Groussman & Assoc., Inc. (R), TX, *82*
Nadine Guber & Assoc., Inc. (C), NY, *364*
The Guild Corp. (C), VA, *364*
William Guy & Assoc., Inc. (R), CA, *84*
Habelmann & Assoc. (R), MI, *84*
Haddad Assoc. (R), FL, *84*
M. A. Haggith Consultants Ltd. (R), ON, *84*
Hale Assoc. (R), IL, *84*
Robert Half Canada Inc. (C), ON, *366*
The Halyburton Co., Inc. (R), NC, *85*
Hamilton-Chase & Assoc., Inc. (R), MA, *85*
R. C. Handel Assoc. Inc. (R), CT, *85*
W. L. Handler & Assoc. (R), GA, *85*
Handy HRM (R), NY, *86*
Harcor Quest & Assoc. (R), OH, *86*
Harcourt Group Ltd. (R), OH, *86*
Robert Harkins Assoc., Inc. (C), PA, *369*
Harrington & O'Brien, Inc. (C), NH, *369*
The Harris Consulting Corp. (R), MB, *87*
Harrison Consulting Group, Inc. (C), CA, *369*
Harvard Aimes Group (R), CT, *87*
Harvey Hohauser & Assoc., LLC (R), MI, *87*
Bruce W. Haupt Assoc. (R), DC, *88*
William E. Hay & Co. (R), IL, *88*
Hayden & Assoc., Inc. (C), MN, *370*
Hayman & Co. (R), TX, *88*
Headden Assoc. (R), WA, *88*
Healey Executive Search, Inc. (R), MN, *88*
Hedman & Assoc. (R), TX, *89*
Heidrick & Struggles, Inc. (R), IL, *90*
The Heidrick Partners, Inc. (R), IL, *90*
Heinze & Assoc. Inc. (R), MN, *91*
Helfer Executive Consultants (R), TN, *91*
Heller Assoc., Ltd. (R), IL, *91*
The Helms Int'l. Group (R), VA, *91*
Hemingway Personnel, Inc. (C), CA, *375*
Hergenrather & Co. (R), WA, *92*
A. Herndon & Assoc., Inc. (R), TX, *92*
Stanley Herz & Co. (R), NY, *92*
The Hetzel Group, Inc. (R), IL, *92*
Heyman Assoc., Inc. (R), NY, *93*
HG & Assoc. (R), IL, *93*
Higdon Prince Inc. (R), NY, *93*
Higgins Assoc., Inc. (R), IL, *93*
Hill Allyn Assoc. (C), CA, *378*
The Hindman Co. (R), KY, *94*
The Hindman Group, Inc. (C), CA, *378*
Hire Authority, Inc. (C), MI, *378*
The Hiring Authority, Inc. (C), FL, *379*
Hite Executive Search (R), OH, *94*
Hodge-Cronin & Assoc., Inc. (R), IL, *94*
Hoglund & Assoc., Inc. (R), IL, *94*
Holland Rusk & Assoc. (R), IL, *95*
The Hollins Group, Inc. (R), IL, *95*
Holohan Group, Ltd. (R), MO, *95*
J. B. Homer Assoc. Inc. (R), NY, *95*
J. G. Hood Assoc. (C), CT, *380*
Horton Int'l. Inc. (R), NY, *96*
Houser, Martin, Morris (C), WA, *381*
Randall Howard & Assoc., Inc. (R), TN, *96*
Howard/Williams Assoc. (C), FL, *382*
Howe & Assoc. (R), PA, *97*
HR Inc. (C), NC, *382*
HRD Consultants, Inc. (R), NJ, *97*
HRNI (C), MI, *383*
HRS, Inc. (R), PA, *97*
Huddleston Assoc. (C), OK, *383*
Huff Assoc. (R), NJ, *98*
Human Resource Bureau (C), CA, *384*
The Human Resource Consulting Group, Inc. (R), CO, *98*
Human Resource Dimensions, Inc. (C), TX, *384*
Human Resource Solutions (R), TX, *98*
Human Resource Technologies, Inc. (R), IL, *99*
Human Resources Management Hawaii, Inc. (C), HI, *384*
Human Resources Personnel Agency (R), AR, *99*
Hunegnaw Executive Search (C), OH, *384*
Hunt & Howe Inc. (R), NY, *99*
The Hunt Co. (R), NY, *99*
Hunt Patton & Brazeal, Inc. (C), OK, *385*
The Hunter Group, Inc. (C), MI, *385*
The Hunter Group (C), NC, *385*
Hunter Int'l., Inc. (R), CT, *100*
Hunter, Rowan & Crowe (C), FL, *386*
Huntington Personnel Consultants, Inc. (C), NY, *386*
W. Hutt Management Resources Ltd. (R), ON, *100*
Hyde Danforth & Co. (R), TX, *100*
Hyman & Assoc. (C), TX, *386*
IMA Search, Inc. (R), NY, *101*
John Imber Assoc., Ltd. (R), IL, *101*

Impact Source, Inc. (C), FL, *387*
Information Systems Professionals (C), NC, *388*
Infovia (C), CA, *388*
Innovative Healthcare Services, Inc. (C), GA, *389*
Innovative Resource Group, LLC (C), NC, *389*
Innovative Search Group, Inc. (R), GA, *102*
InTech Services, Inc. (C), GA, *390*
Intercontinental Executive Group (C), PA, *391*
Interim Accounting Professionals (C), CA, *391*
International Management Services Inc. (R), IL, *102*
International Management Advisors, Inc. (R), NY, *103*
International Management Development Corp. (C), NY, *393*
International Staffing Consultants, Inc. (C), CA, *393*
Interquest, Inc. (R), NY, *103*
Intersource, Ltd. (R), GA, *103*
IprGroup, Inc. (C), GA, *394*
Jeffrey Irving Assoc., Inc. (R), VA, *104*
ISC of Atlanta, Inc. (C), GA, *394*
J & D Resources Inc. (C), TN, *395*
J. Joseph & Assoc. (C), OH, *395*
J. Robert Scott (R), MA, *104*
Ron Jackson & Assoc. (C), GA, *396*
Jacobs & Co. (R), CT, *105*
Jakobs & Assoc. Int'l. (R), NY, *105*
January Management Group (R), OH, *105*
JDavid Assoc., Inc. (R), CT, *105*
JDC Assoc. (C), NY, *397*
Jefferson-Ross Assoc. Inc. (C), PA, *398*
Jender & Company (R), IL, *105*
JFW Associates, LLC (C), CT, *398*
Job-Born Candidate Selection Bureau (C), ON, *399*
John & Powers, Inc. (R), MO, *106*
John Jay & Co. (C), ME, *399*
John H. Johnson & Assoc., Inc. (R), IL, *106*
L. J. Johnson & Co. (R), MI, *106*
Johnson & Company (R), CT, *107*
Ronald S. Johnson Assoc., Inc. (R), CA, *107*
K. E. Johnson Assoc. (C), WA, *399*
Johnson Brown Assoc., Inc. (C), IN, *400*
Jonas, Walters & Assoc., Inc. (R), WI, *107*
Jordon & Jordon, Inc. (R), PA, *108*
J. M. Joseph Assoc. (R), NJ, *109*
Judd Associates (R), NJ, *109*
Juno Systems, Inc. (C), NY, *402*
Just Management Services Inc. (C), FL, *402*
Richard Kader & Assoc. (C), OH, *403*
Kane & Assoc. (C), TX, *403*
Kanzer Assoc., Inc. (R), IL, *109*
Gary Kaplan & Assoc. (R), CA, *109*
Howard Karr & Assoc., Inc. (R), CA, *110*
Karras Personnel, Inc. (C), NJ, *403*
Martin Kartin & Co., Inc. (R), NY, *110*
Melissa Katzman, Executive Search (C), NY, *404*
Jim Kay & Assoc. (C), IL, *404*
A.T. Kearney Executive Search (R), IL, *111*
Kehn & Gabor, Inc. (C), OH, *405*
The Keith-Murray Partnership (R), ON, *112*
Kenmore Executives Inc. (C), FL, *405*
David Warwick Kennedy & Assoc. (R), BC, *112*
Kennison & Assoc. Inc. (C), MO, *405*
Kent & Assoc. (R), OH, *113*
KGA Inc. (C), WI, *406*
The Kilman Advisory Group (R), CT, *114*
The Kingsley Group (R), CA, *114*
Richard Kinser & Assoc. (R), NY, *115*
Kip Williams, Inc. (R), NY, *115*
Kiradjieff & Goode, Inc. (R), MA, *115*
Kirby Assoc. (R), PA, *115*
KL Consultants (C), NJ, *407*
The Kleinstein Group, Inc. (R), NJ, *116*
The Koehler Group (C), PA, *408*
Fred Koffler Assoc. (R), NY, *116*
Koll-Fairfield LLC (C), CT, *408*
Koontz, Jeffries & Assoc., Inc. (R), FL, *117*
Korn/Ferry Int'l. (R), NY, *117*
KPMG Executive Search (R), ON, *119*
Krauthamer & Assoc. (R), MD, *120*
Krecklo Executive Search Inc. (R), ON, *120*
Kremple & Meade, Inc. (R), CA, *120*
Kremple Consulting Group (R), CA, *120*
Kressenberg Assoc. (C), TX, *409*
Kreutz Consulting Group, Inc. (R), IL, *121*
Krueger Assoc. (R), IL, *121*
John Kuhn & Assoc., Inc. (R), WI, *121*
Kukoy Associates (R), CO, *121*
Kunzer Assoc., Ltd. (R), IL, *121*
Kutcher Tax Careers, Inc. (C), NY, *410*
L & K Assoc. (C), NJ, *410*
L&L Assoc. Global Search (C), PA, *411*
L. Patrick Group (R), NJ, *122*
LAI Ward Howell (R), NY, *122*
Lamay Assoc., Inc. (R), CT, *124*
Lamon + Stuart + Michaels Inc. (R), ON, *124*
Landon Morgan (C), ON, *412*
The Langford Search, Inc. (C), AL, *412*
Lawrence L. Lapham, Inc. (R), NY, *124*
Larkin & Co. (R), CA, *124*
R. H. Larsen & Assoc., Inc. (R), FL, *125*
Larsen & Lee, Inc. (R), MD, *125*
Larsen, Whitney, Blecksmith & Zilliacus, Inc. (R), CA, *125*
Larson Assoc. (R), CA, *125*
Lasher Assoc. (R), FL, *125*
Michael Latas & Assoc., Inc. (R), MO, *125*
Latham International, Ltd. (R), NJ, *126*
Lauer, Sbarbaro Assoc., EMA Partners Int'l. (R), IL, *126*
Lautz, Grotte, Engler & Swimley (R), CA, *126*
Lawrence-Leiter & Co. (R), KS, *126*
W. R. Lawry, Inc. (R), CT, *126*
Leader Institute, Inc. (C), GA, *414*
Leader Resources Group (C), GA, *415*
Leader Search Inc. (R), AB, *127*
The Lear Group, Inc. (R), OH, *127*
Albert G. Lee Assoc. (C), RI, *415*
Vincent Lee Assoc. (C), NY, *415*
V. J. Lehman & Assoc., Inc. (R), CO, *127*
Lekan & Assoc., Inc. (R), OH, *128*
Lending Personnel Services (C), CA, *416*
Leslie Kavanagh Assoc., Inc. (C), NY, *416*
Lewis Companies Inc. (R), ON, *129*
The Libra Group (C), NC, *417*
Lifter & Assoc. (C), CA, *418*
Lindsey & Co., Inc. (R), CT, *129*
Litchfield & Willis, Inc. (R), TX, *130*
Livingston, Robert & Co. (R), CT, *130*
Lloyd Associates (R), GA, *130*
Lloyd Prescott & Churchill, Inc. (R), FL, *130*
Lloyd Prescott Assoc., Inc. (C), FL, *418*
LMB Assoc. (C), IL, *419*
Locke & Assoc. (R), NC, *131*
J. P. Logan & Co., Inc. (R), NY, *131*
The Logan Group, Inc. (R), MO, *131*
Logic Assoc., Inc. (C), NY, *419*
Logistics Management Resources, Inc. (R), NY, *131*
Logue & Rice Inc. (C), VA, *420*
Lord & Albus Co. (C), TX, *420*
J. S. Lord & Company, Inc. (R), MA, *131*
The John Lucht Consultancy Inc. (R), NY, *131*
Fran Luisi Assoc. (R), NJ, *132*
Charles Luntz & Assoc., Inc. (R), MO, *132*
Lynch Miller Moore Partners, Inc. (R), IL, *132*
The Macdonald Group, Inc. (R), NJ, *133*
MacNaughton Assoc. (R), CA, *133*
Maglio & Co., Inc. (R), WI, *134*
Magnum Search (C), IL, *422*
Major Search (C), NJ, *423*
Management Assoc. (C), MD, *424*
Management Association Network (C), WI, *424*
Management Recruiters of Nassau, Inc. (R), NY, *134*
Management Recruiters International, Inc. (MRI) (C), OH, *425*
Management Recruiters of Birmingham-South, Inc. (C), AL, *438*
Management Recruiters of Colorado, Inc. (C), CO, *442*
Management Recruiters of Miami-North (C), FL, *443*
Management Recruiters of North Fulton (C), GA, *445*
Management Recruiters of Marietta, Inc. (C), GA, *446*
Management Recruiters of Atlanta North, Inc. (C), GA, *446*
Management Recruiters of Lake Forest, IL (C), IL, *447*
Management Recruiters of Springfield, Inc. (C), IL, *447*
Management Recruiters of Batavia (C), IL, *447*
Management Recruiters of Chicago West (C), IL, *447*
Management Recruiters of Fairfield (C), IA, *449*
Management Recruiters of Danville (C), KY, *449*
Management Recruiters of Rockville (C), MD, *450*
Management Recruiters of Detroit & Farmington Hills (C), MI, *451*

Management Recruiters - Flint (C), MI, *451*
Management Recruiters of Woodbury (C), MN, *452*
Management Recruiters of North Oakland County, Inc. (C), MI, *452*
Management Recruiters of Rochester (C), MN, *452*
Management Recruiters of Chanhassen (C), MN, *452*
Management Recruiters of North Warren Inc. (C), NJ, *453*
Management Recruiters of Orange County, N.Y., Inc. (C), NJ, *453*
Management Recruiters of Fayetteville (C), NC, *455*
Management Recruiters of Manhattan on Broadway (C), NY, *455*
Management Recruiters of Charlotte - North, Inc. (C), NC, *456*
Management Recruiters - Kannapolis (C), NC, *456*
Management Recruiters of Cleveland (C), OH, *457*
Management Recruiters of Youngstown (C), OH, *458*
Management Recruiters of Sidney (C), OH, *458*
Management Recruiters of Northwest Ohio, Inc. (C), OH, *458*
Management Recruiters of Georgetown (C), SC, *461*
Management Recruiters of Memphis, TN (C), TN, *462*
Management Recruiters of Sugar Land Inc. (C), TX, *464*
Management Recruiters of Milwaukee-West (C), WI, *465*
Management Recruiters of Wausau, LLC (C), WI, *466*
Management Recruiters of Milwaukee-North (C), WI, *466*
Management Resource Group, Ltd. (C), IA, *467*
Management Resource Assoc., Inc. (C), FL, *467*
Management Resources Int'l. (R), NY, *135*
Management Search Int'l. (C), CA, *467*
Management Search of R.I. Inc. (R), RI, *135*
Mannard & Assoc., Inc. (R), IL, *135*
Manning Lloyd Assoc. Ltd. (C), NY, *468*
ManTech Consulting (C), NY, *468*
MARBL Consultants, Inc. (C), WI, *469*
Marc-Allen Assoc., Inc. (C), FL, *469*
Marcus & Assoc. (C), NY, *469*
Mark Adam Assoc. (R), NJ, *135*
Mark Stanley & Co./EMA Partners International (R), FL, *136*
MarketPro, Inc. (C), GA, *471*
Marks & Co., Inc. (R), CT, *136*
Paula Marks Inc. (R), NY, *136*
Marley Group Ltd. (C), NY, *471*
The Maroon Group (R), CT, *136*
Marra Peters & Partners (R), NJ, *136*
Marsar & Co., Inc. (C), FL, *471*
Karen Marshall Assoc. (C), KY, *471*
Marshall Consultants, Inc. (R), NY, *137*
The Marshall Group (R), IL, *137*
The Martin Group (R), CA, *137*
Marvel Consultants, Inc. (C), OH, *472*
Maschal/Connors Inc. (R), NJ, *137*
Louis Thomas Masterson & Co. (R), OH, *138*
Matte Consulting Group Inc. (R), QE, *138*
Maxecon Executive Search Consultants (R), FL, *138*
Maximum Management Corp. (C), NY, *473*
The Mazzitelli Group, Ltd. (R), MN, *139*
MB Inc. Executive Search (C), NY, *473*
The McAulay Firm (R), NC, *139*
McCartan Assoc. (R), NJ, *139*
McCooe & Assoc., Inc. (R), NJ, *140*
McCormack & Assoc. (R), CA, *140*
McCormack & Farrow (R), CA, *140*
McDonald, Long & Assoc., Inc. (R), NY, *140*
G. E. McFarland & Co. (R), GA, *140*
Clarence E. McFeely, Inc. (R), IL, *141*
McKinley•Arend Int'l. (R), TX, *141*
McManners Assoc., Inc. (R), CA, *142*
McRoberts & Assoc. (C), OH, *475*
Joseph J. McTaggart (C), CA, *476*
Meder & Assoc., Inc. (R), IL, *142*
MedSearch Resources, Inc. (C), FL, *478*
Melancon & Co. (R), TX, *143*
Mengel & McDonald Ltd. (C), IL, *479*
MES Search Co. (C), GA, *479*
Messett Assoc., Inc. (R), FL, *143*
Meyer Assoc., Inc. (R), GA, *144*
Michigan Consulting Group (R), MI, *144*
Millar Walker & Gay (R), ON, *144*
Miller-Hall HRISearch (C), NY, *482*
Million & Assoc., Inc. (R), OH, *144*
Danette Milne Corporate Search Inc. (C), ON, *482*
Milo Research (R), NY, *145*
Mirtz Morice, Inc. (R), CT, *145*
Laurie Mitchell & Co., Inc. (R), OH, *145*
MIXTEC Group (R), CA, *145*
MJF Assoc. (C), CT, *483*
Moffitt Int'l., Inc. (R), NC, *146*
Monarch Technology Management LLC (C), CO, *484*
Montgomery West (R), CA, *146*
C. A. Moore & Assoc., Inc. (C), MN, *484*
Larry Moore & Assoc. (C), CA, *484*
Moore Research Assoc. (R), NJ, *147*
Morgan Hunter Corp. (C), KS, *485*
Morgan/Webber, Inc. (R), NY, *147*
Moriarty/Fox, Inc. (R), IL, *147*
Morris & Berger (R), CA, *147*
The Morris Group (C), PA, *486*
Morton, McCorkle & Assoc. Inc. (R), MO, *147*
Moyer, Sherwood Assoc., Inc. (R), NY, *148*
MPA Executive Search Inc. (R), QE, *148*
Mruk & E.M.A. Partners (R), NY, *148*
Mullen Assoc., Inc. (R), NC, *148*
The Mulshine Co., Inc. (R), NJ, *149*
Jennifer Munro & Partners, Inc. (R), SC, *149*
P. J. Murphy & Assoc., Inc. (R), WI, *150*
Kenneth Murphy & Assoc. (C), NS, *487*
Murphy Partners Int'l. (R), IL, *150*
Musick & Assoc. (C), CA, *487*
Nagler, Robins & Poe, Inc. (R), MA, *150*
National Register Columbus Inc. (C), OH, *490*
Nationwide Personnel Recruiting & Consulting, Inc. (C), OR, *490*
NaviSearch (C), GA, *490*
NCC Executive Search Consultants (C), CA, *490*
NDI Services (R), MI, *151*
New Dawn Employment Search (C), CA, *491*
Newell Assoc. (R), NY, *151*
Nicholaou & Co. (R), IL, *151*
Nichols & Company (R), CO, *151*
P. J. Nicholson & Assoc. (C), IL, *493*
NMC & Kay Int'l. (R), CO, *152*
Noble & Assoc., Inc. (C), NY, *494*
The Noebel Search Group, Inc. (C), TX, *494*
Noll Human Resource Services (C), NE, *494*
Nordeman Grimm, Inc. (R), NY, *152*
Norman Broadbent Int'l., Inc. (R), NY, *152*
North American Recruiters, Inc. (R), MN, *153*
NPF Assoc. Ltd. Inc. (R), FL, *153*
Nuessle, Kurdziel & Weiss, Inc. (R), PA, *153*
O'Brien and Roof (C), OH, *497*
O'Brien Consulting Services (R), MA, *153*
O'Neill Group (C), NJ, *498*
O'Rourke Companies, Inc. (R), TX, *154*
O'Sullivan Search Inc. (C), ON, *498*
Dennis P. O'Toole & Assoc. Inc. (R), NY, *154*
O'Toole & Company, Inc. (R), IL, *154*
Oberlander & Co., Inc. (R), IL, *155*
Object Resources Int'l., Inc. (C), CT, *498*
The Odessa Group (R), CA, *155*
The Ogdon Partnership (R), NY, *155*
Organization Consulting Ltd. (R), ON, *157*
Organization Resources Inc. (R), MA, *157*
Orion Consulting, Inc. (R), NJ, *157*
OSAGUI S.A. de C.V. (C), MX, *500*
Ott & Hansen, Inc. (R), CA, *157*
Ovca Assoc. Inc. (R), KY, *157*
LaMonte Owens, Inc. (R), PA, *157*
The P & L Group (C), NY, *500*
P.A.R. Assoc., Inc. (R), MA, *158*
Pacific Search Group, Inc. (C), CA, *501*
Page-Wheatcroft & Co., Ltd. (R), TX, *158*
J. Palacios & Assoc., Inc. (R), PR, *158*
The Park Group & Assoc., Inc. (C), MD, *502*
R. Parker & Assoc., Inc. (R), NY, *159*
Largent Parks & Partners (C), TX, *503*
Parsons, Anderson & Gee, Inc. (C), NY, *503*
Parsons Assoc. Inc. (R), IL, *159*
Partners Resource Group (C), VA, *504*
The Partnership Group (R), NJ, *160*
Carolyn Smith Paschal Int'l. (R), CA, *160*
Pasona Canada, Inc. (C), ON, *504*
Pathway Executive Search, Inc. (C), NY, *505*
Pawlik/Dorman Partners (R), IL, *161*
PC Assoc. (C), CO, *505*
Pearce & Assoc. (C), FL, *506*
Peeney Assoc., Inc. (R), NJ, *161*
Penn Associates (R), PA, *161*

INDUSTRIES

People Management Mid-South, LLC (R), TN, *162*
People Management Northeast, Inc. (R), CT, *162*
Performance Resources, Inc. (C), RI, *507*
The Perkins Group (R), NC, *162*
R. H. Perry & Assoc., Inc. (R), DC, *162*
Barry Persky & Co., Inc. (R), CT, *163*
PersoNet, Inc. (C), FL, *507*
Personnel Assoc. (C), NC, *508*
Personnel Incorporated (C), IA, *508*
The Personnel Network, Inc. (C), SC, *508*
Personnel Unlimited/Executive Search (C), WA, *509*
Petrie Partners, Inc. (R), FL, *163*
Peyser Assoc., Inc. (R), FL, *163*
Phase II Management (R), CT, *164*
Phoenix Search (R), MX, *164*
PIC Executive Search (C), GA, *511*
Gregory D. Pickens (C), TX, *511*
Pierce & Assoc. (C), CA, *512*
Pinnacle Executive Group Inc. (C), MO, *512*
Pinsker and Company, Inc. (R), CA, *164*
Pioneer Consulting Group (C), CA, *512*
DNPitchon Assoc. (R), NJ, *165*
PMJ & Assoc. (C), ON, *513*
Poirier, Hoevel & Co. (R), CA, *166*
Ray Polhill & Assoc. (R), NC, *166*
Polson & Co., Inc. (R), MN, *166*
Jack Porter Assoc., Inc. (C), WA, *514*
P. G. Prager Search Assoc., Ltd. (C), NY, *515*
Prairie Resource Group, Inc. (R), IL, *166*
Elan Pratzer & Partners Inc. (R), ON, *167*
PRAXIS Partners (R), VA, *167*
Precision Executive Search (C), AZ, *516*
Preferred Placement, Inc. (C), NY, *516*
Premier Recruiting Group (C), MI, *516*
The Premier Staffing Group (C), OH, *517*
Preston-Hunter, Inc. (R), IL, *167*
PricewaterhouseCoopers Executive Search (R), ON, *168*
PricewaterhouseCoopers Executive Search (R), MX, *168*
Prichard Kymen Inc. (R), AB, *168*
Princeton Executive Search (C), NJ, *518*
Princeton Search Partners, Inc. (R), NJ, *169*
Priority Executive Search (C), FL, *518*
Professional Research Services, Inc. (R), IL, *169*
Professional Resources (C), OK, *522*
Professional Search (R), MI, *169*
Professional Search Consultants (C), KY, *522*
Professional Search Assoc. (C), CA, *522*
Professional Search, Inc. (C), CO, *522*
Professional Search Consultants (PSC) (C), TX, *523*
Professional Search, Inc. Int'l. (C), TX, *523*
Professional Support Inc. (C), NY, *523*
Professions, Inc. (C), OH, *523*
ProFinders, Inc. (C), FL, *523*
ProLink (C), NC, *524*
ProStar Systems, Inc. (C), MD, *525*
Protocol Inc. (C), CA, *525*
QD Legal (C), ON, *525*
Quetico Corp. (R), TX, *170*
QVS Int'l. (R), GA, *170*
R & L Assoc., Ltd. (R), NY, *170*
R M Associates (R), OH, *171*
R. J. Associates (C), NY, *528*
Raines Int'l. Inc. (R), NY, *171*
Ramming & Assoc., Inc. (C), NJ, *528*
Rand Assoc. (R), ME, *171*
Rand Thompson Executive Search Consultants (C), NY, *528*
Lea Randolph & Assoc., Inc. (C), TX, *529*
J. E. Ranta Assoc. (C), MA, *529*
Ray & Berndtson (R), TX, *171*
Ray & Berndtson/Lovas Stanley (R), ON, *172*
Ray & Berndtson/Tanton Mitchell (R), BC, *173*
Redell Search, Inc. (C), IL, *533*
Reece & Mruk Partners/EMA Partners Int'l. (R), MA, *173*
The Regis Group, Ltd. (R), GA, *174*
Michael James Reid & Co. (R), CA, *174*
Reifel & Assoc. (R), IL, *174*
Rein & Co., Inc. (R), NJ, *174*
Renaissance Resources, LLC (R), VA, *174*
RepFinders USA (C), PA, *534*
The Repovich-Reynolds Group (TRRG, Inc.) (R), CA, *175*
Resolve Assoc. Int'l. (R), FL, *175*
Resource Management Group (C), CT, *534*
Resource Recruiting (C), NH, *534*
Resource Services, Inc. (C), NY, *534*
L. J. Reszotko & Assoc. (C), IL, *535*
Retained Search Assoc. (R), NC, *176*
The Revere Assoc., Inc. (R), OH, *176*
S. Reyman & Assoc., Ltd. (R), IL, *176*
Russell Reynolds Assoc., Inc. (R), NY, *176*
RIC Corp. (R), FL, *177*
Jeff Rich Assoc. (C), NJ, *536*
Riddle & McGrath LLC (R), GA, *178*
Rieser & Assoc., Inc. (R), MO, *178*
Riley Cole (C), CA, *537*
The Riverbend Group (C), MO, *538*
RJ Associates (C), CA, *538*
RMA Search (R), TN, *179*
RML Assoc. (C), PA, *538*
Roberson & Co. (C), AZ, *538*
Robert Lowell Int'l. (R), TX, *179*
Robert Shields & Assoc. (C), TX, *538*
Robertson-Surrette Ltd. (R), NS, *179*
Bruce Robinson Assoc. (R), NJ, *180*
Robinson, Fraser Group Ltd. (R), ON, *180*
Robinson-Robinson & Assoc., Inc. (C), MN, *539*
Robison & Associates (R), NC, *180*
Robsham & Assoc., Inc. (R), MA, *180*
Rocky Mountain Recruiters, Inc. (C), CO, *540*
R. A. Rodriguez & Assoc., Inc. (C), TX, *540*
Roevin Technical People (C), ON, *540*
Roll International (C), TX, *541*
Rollo Assoc. (R), CA, *181*
Romac Int'l. - San Francisco (C), CA, *541*
Romac Int'l. (C), GA, *541*
Romac Int'l. (C), IL, *541*
Emery A. Rose & Assoc. (C), WA, *545*
Roster Inc. (C), IN, *545*
Roth Young Executive Search (C), TX, *546*
Rovner Gerner & Assoc. (R), CA, *182*
Rurak & Assoc., Inc (R), DC, *182*
Rushmore • Judge Inc. (R), ON, *183*
W. A. Rutledge & Assoc. (R), CT, *183*
The Ryan Charles Group, Inc. (C), FL, *548*
Ryan, Miller & Assoc. (C), CA, *549*
The S C Group LLC (R), NY, *183*
S.D.P. Contract Recruiters (C), NJ, *550*
The Sager Co. (R), OH, *183*
Sales & Management Search, Inc. (C), IL, *551*
Sales Advantage (C), FL, *551*
Sales Consultants (C), OH, *551*
Sales Consultants (C), IL, *558*
Sales Consultants of Auburn Hills (C), MI, *559*
Sales Consultants of Grand Rapids (C), MI, *560*
Sales Consultants of Northern Jersey, Inc. (C), NJ, *560*
Sales Consultants of Westchester-South, Inc. (C), NY, *561*
Sales Consultants of Chester County, PA (C), PA, *562*
Sales Consultants of Rhode Island, Inc. (C), RI, *562*
Sales Professionals Personnel Services (C), CA, *564*
Salveson Stetson Group, Inc. (R), PA, *184*
Salzmann Gay Assoc., Inc. (R), PA, *184*
Norm Sanders Assoc., Inc. (R), NJ, *184*
Sanford Rose Assoc. - Laguna Beach (C), CA, *565*
Sanford Rose Assoc. - Santa Barbara (C), CA, *565*
Sanford Rose Assoc. - Cedar Rapids (C), IA, *567*
Sanford Rose Assoc. - Evansville (C), IN, *567*
Sanford Rose Assoc. - Columbus North (C), OH, *569*
Sanford Rose Assoc. - Euclid (C), OH, *569*
Sanford Rose Assoc. - Youngstown (C), OH, *569*
Allan Sarn Assoc., Inc. (R), NY, *184*
Sathe & Associates, Inc. (R), MN, *184*
Savoy Partners, Ltd. (R), DC, *184*
Schall Executive Search Partners (R), MN, *185*
Schattle & Duquette (C), RI, *571*
Schenck & Assoc. SC (C), WI, *572*
Schoales & Assoc. Inc. (C), ON, *572*
Schwab-Carrese Assoc., Inc. Executive Search (R), NC, *185*
Scott-Wayne Assoc., Inc. (C), MA, *573*
Search Consultants, Inc. (C), NJ, *575*
Search Excellence (R), CA, *186*
Search Group Inc. (R), AB, *186*
Search Plus Int'l.-Ohio (C), OH, *576*
Search Research Assoc., Inc. (R), MA, *187*
Search South, Inc. (C), AL, *576*
Search West, Inc. (C), CA, *576*
SearchCorp International (C), AB, *577*
Sears & Associates (C), CA, *577*
Seco & Zetto Assoc., Inc. (C), NJ, *577*
Seiden Krieger Assoc., Inc. (R), NY, *188*
Selected Executives, Inc. (C), MA, *578*
Selective Management Services, Inc. (C), FL, *578*
Senior Careers (R), NY, *188*
Sensible Solutions, Inc. (R), IL, *188*

M. B. Shattuck & Assoc., Inc. (R), CA, *189*
John Shell Assoc., Inc. (C), SC, *579*
Shepherd Bueschel & Provus, Inc. (R), IL, *189*
Sherbrooke Assoc., Inc. (C), NJ, *580*
Sheridan Search (R), IL, *189*
Sherwood Lehman Massucco, Inc. (R), CA, *189*
Michael Shirley Assoc. Inc. (R), KS, *190*
Shoemaker & Assoc. (R), GA, *190*
E. L. Shore & Assoc. (R), ON, *190*
Shore Asociados Ejecutivos, S. A. de C.V. (R), MX, *190*
The Shorr Group (R), IL, *190*
M. Shulman, Inc. (R), CA, *191*
John Sibbald Assoc., Inc. (R), MO, *191*
Marvin L. Silcott & Assoc., Inc. (C), TX, *581*
L. A. Silver Assoc., Inc. (R), MA, *191*
Silver Associates (C), CA, *581*
D. J. Simpson Assoc. Inc. (R), ON, *191*
Skott/Edwards Consultants (R), NY, *192*
J. L. Small Assoc. (C), AL, *583*
Christopher Smallhorn Executive Recruiting, Inc. (R), MA, *193*
Smartsource Inc. (C), CA, *583*
Smith & Assoc. (C), CA, *583*
Smith & Assoc. (C), FL, *583*
James F. Smith & Assoc. (C), GA, *583*
Ralph Smith & Assoc. (C), IL, *584*
Smith & Sawyer, Inc. (R), NY, *193*
G. L. Smith Assoc. (C), CA, *584*
Howard W. Smith Assoc. (R), CT, *193*
Abbott Smith Assoc., Inc. (R), NY, *193*
Herman Smith Executive Initiatives Inc. (R), ON, *193*
Smith James Group, Inc. (R), GA, *194*
H. C. Smith Ltd. (R), OH, *194*
Smith Professional Search (C), MI, *584*
Smith, Roth & Squires (R), NY, *194*
Smith, Brown & Jones (C), KS, *585*
Smythe Masterson & Judd, Inc. (C), NY, *585*
Snelling & Snelling, Inc. (C), FL, *585*
Snelling Search (C), IL, *585*
Snelling Search Recruiters (C), NC, *586*
Snelling Search (C), IL, *586*
Andrea Sobel & Assoc., Inc. (C), CA, *586*
Sockwell & Assoc. (R), NC, *194*
Robert Sollman & Assoc. (C), FL, *587*
Soltis Management Services (R), PA, *195*
Solutions Group (R), AL, *195*
Stephen M. Sonis Assoc. (R), MA, *195*
Spear-Izzo Assoc., LLC (C), PA, *588*
Special Markets Group, Inc. (R), GA, *195*
SpencerStuart (R), NY, *196*
Springer Souder & Assoc. L.L.C. (R), IL, *198*
SSA Executive Search Int'l. (R), AZ, *198*
Staff Extension Int'l. (C), TX, *590*
Staff Resources, Inc. (C), SC, *590*
Star Search Consultants (C), ON, *591*
Staub, Warmbold & Assoc., Inc. (R), NY, *199*
Steeple Resources & Consulting (R), NJ, *199*
The Stevens Group (R), TX, *200*
The Stevens Group (C), CA, *593*
Stewart, Stein & Scott, Ltd. (R), MN, *200*
Stillinger & Assoc. (R), CA, *201*
Allan Stolee Inc. (R), FL, *201*
Stone Enterprises Ltd. (C), IL, *594*
Stone, Murphy & Olson (R), MN, *201*
Strategic Advancement Inc. (R), NJ, *202*
Strategic Executives, Inc. (R), CT, *202*
StratfordGroup (R), OH, *203*
W. R. Strathmann Assoc. (R), NY, *203*
Stratin Assoc. (C), NJ, *596*
Straube Associates (R), MA, *203*
Stroman Int'l., Inc. (R), CO, *204*
Joe Sullivan & Assoc., Inc. (R), NY, *204*
Summerfield Assoc., Inc. (C), TN, *596*
Summit Group Int'l., Inc. (R), GA, *204*
Sweeney Harbert & Mummert, Inc. (R), FL, *205*
Synergistics Assoc. Ltd. (R), IL, *205*
Systems One Ltd. (C), IL, *598*
T. H. Hunter, Inc. (C), MN, *599*
S. Tanner & Assoc. Inc. (C), ON, *599*
Tannura & Assoc., Inc. (R), IL, *206*
Tarnow Int'l. (R), NJ, *206*
TASA International (R), NY, *206*
Tate & Assoc., Inc. (R), NJ, *207*
M. L. Tawney & Assoc. (C), TX, *600*
Tax Network Resources, Inc. (C), NY, *600*
TaxSearch Inc. (R), OK, *207*
The TBI Group (R), PA, *207*
TE, Inc. (C), IL, *600*
Tech 2000 (C), FL, *601*
Technical Recruiting Services (C), OH, *602*
The Technology Group (R), IL, *208*
Tekworx, Inc. (C), OK, *604*
Telequest Communications, Inc. (C), NJ, *605*
TEMCO-The Executive Management Consulting Organization (R), WI, *208*
Tesar-Reynes, Inc. (R), IL, *208*
Thomas & Assoc. of Michigan (C), MI, *606*
Thomas Lyle & Co. (C), IL, *606*
Thomas Mangum Co. (R), CA, *208*
Judy Thompson & Assoc., Inc. (C), CA, *606*
Richard Thompson Assoc., Inc. (R), MN, *209*
Thor, Inc. (C), CA, *606*
Thorne, Brieger Assoc., Inc. (R), NY, *209*
The Tidewater Group Inc. (C), CT, *607*
Tittemore Cowan Assoc. (C), AB, *607*
TNS Partners, Inc. (R), TX, *209*
Skip Tolette Executive Search Consulting (R), NJ, *209*
Top Gun Group, Inc. (C), NV, *607*
Topaz Int'l., Inc., Attorney Search (C), NJ, *607*
TPS Staffing Solutions (C), IN, *608*
Trac One (R), NJ, *210*
Trebor Weldon Lawrence, Inc. (R), NY, *210*
Triad Technology Group (C), OR, *609*
Trout & Assoc. Inc. (R), UT, *211*
Tryon & Heideman, LLC (R), MO, *211*
Tschudin Inc. (R), NJ, *211*
Tucker Assoc. (R), NJ, *211*
The Thomas Tucker Co. (R), CA, *211*
Tully/Woodmansee Int'l. Inc. (R), FL, *212*
UniQuest Int'l., Inc. (C), FL, *610*
United Personnel Services (C), MA, *611*
Unlimited Staffing Solutions, Inc. (C), MI, *611*
The Urban Placement Service (C), TX, *611*
Van Dyke Assoc. (R), IL, *212*
Van Leeuwen Assoc. (R), CA, *213*
VanMaldegiam Assoc., Inc. (R), IL, *213*
VanReypen Enterprises, Ltd. (R), NY, *213*
Verkamp-Joyce Assoc., Inc. (R), IL, *213*
The Verriez Group Inc. (R), ON, *213*
Claude Vezina, Conseil en recherche de cadres inc. (R), QE, *213*
Villareal & Assoc., Inc. (R), OK, *214*
Vincenty & Co. (C), OH, *612*
Vlcek & Company, Inc. (R), CA, *214*
Vogel Assoc. (C), PA, *613*
Fred Wackerle, Inc. (R), IL, *214*
Wallace Assoc. (C), CT, *614*
Wallace Management Co. (R), TN, *215*
Gerald Walsh & Co. Inc. (C), NS, *614*
Deborah Snow Walsh, Inc. (R), IL, *215*
Linda Walter & Associes (C), QE, *615*
Karen Wanger & Assoc., Inc. (C), IL, *615*
Martha Ward Executive Search, Inc. (C), NY, *615*
Warring & Assoc. (R), CA, *215*
R. J. Watkins & Co., Ltd. (R), CA, *216*
Scott Watson & Assoc., Inc. (R), FL, *216*
Watson Int'l., Inc. (R), NY, *216*
Webb, Johnson Assoc., Inc. (R), NY, *216*
Wegner & Assoc. (C), WI, *617*
S. E. Weinstein Co. (R), IL, *217*
Weliver & Assoc. (C), MI, *618*
Henry Welker & Assoc. (C), MI, *618*
Welzig, Lowe & Assoc. (C), CO, *618*
The Wentworth Co., Inc. (R), CA, *217*
Jude M. Werra & Assoc. (R), WI, *218*
West & West (R), CA, *218*
The Westfield Group (C), CT, *619*
The Westminster Group, Inc. (R), RI, *218*
Weston Consultants, Inc. (R), MA, *219*
Weterrings & Agnew, Inc. (C), NY, *619*
S. J. Wexler Assoc., Inc. (R), NY, *219*
Wheeler, Moore & Elam Co. (R), TX, *219*
Whitbeck & Assoc. (R), MN, *219*
White, Roberts & Stratton, Inc. (C), IL, *619*
Whittlesey & Assoc., Inc. (R), PA, *220*
Wilder & Assoc. (C), VA, *620*
Walter K. Wilkins & Co. (R), NJ, *221*
Wilkinson & Ives (R), CA, *221*
Williams Executive Search, Inc. (R), MN, *221*
Williams, Roth & Krueger, Inc. (R), IL, *221*
Willmott & Assoc. (C), MA, *622*
Wilson Assoc. Inc. (R), NS, *222*
The Winchester Group (R), CA, *222*
The Windham Group (R), OH, *222*
Windsor International (R), GA, *222*
Wing Tips & Pumps, Inc. (C), MI, *623*
Winguth, Grant & Donahue (R), CA, *222*
Winthrop Partners, Inc. (R), NY, *222*
Wisnewski & Assoc. (R), CA, *223*
Wojdula & Assoc., Ltd. (R), WI, *223*
Susan L. Wonderling Recruiting (C), PA, *623*
M. Wood Company (R), IL, *224*
Wood, Franchot Inc. (R), MN, *224*
Wood-Glavin, Inc. (R), KS, *224*
Woodmoor Group (C), CO, *624*

(R) = Retainer; (C) = Contingency

INDUSTRIES

Woodworth Int'l. Group (R), OR, *224*
Bob Wright Recruiting, Inc. (C), CT, *625*
WTW Assoc., Inc. (R), NY, *225*
Wyndham Mills Int'l., Inc. (R), GA, *225*
Xavier Associates, Inc. (R), MA, *226*
The Zammataro Company (R), OH, *226*
The Zarkin Group, Inc. (R), NY, *226*
Egon Zehnder Int'l. Inc. (R), NY, *227*
Zeiger Assoc. L.L.C. (C), CA, *627*
P. D. Zier Assoc. (C), CT, *627*

A.00 Agriculture, forestry, fishing, mining

Agra Placements, Ltd. (C), IA, *242*
AGRI-associates (C), MO, *242*
Agri-Personnel (C), GA, *242*
Agri-Tech Personnel, Inc. (C), MO, *242*
Tom Allison Assoc. (C), NM, *245*
American Professional Search, Inc. (C), TN, *248*
Anderson & Schwab, Inc. (R), NY, *5*
Barrington Hart, Inc. (R), IL, *12*
The Bedford Consulting Group Inc. (R), ON, *14*
Bosco-Hubert & Assoc. (C), KS, *270*
Bradley & Assoc. (C), MN, *272*
The Bridge (C), CO, *273*
Dan B. Brockman (C), IL, *274*
Bullis & Co., Inc. (R), CA, *25*
C and P Marketing, Ltd. (C), OK, *278*
Carver Search Consultants (C), CA, *285*
Chapman & Assoc. (C), BC, *289*
Coast Personnel Services Ltd. (C), BC, *293*
Robert Connelly & Assoc., Inc. (R), MN, *39*
Construction Search Specialists, Inc. (C), WI, *297*
Marlene Critchfield Co. (C), CA, *303*
CS Associates, LLC (C), AZ, *304*
The Custer Group, Inc. (R), TN, *44*
Davies, Park (R), AB, *46*
Alan Davis & Assoc. Inc. (R), QE, *47*
Dixie Search Assoc. (C), GA, *313*
Doering & Assoc. (C), CA, *313*
Dunhill Professional Search of Omaha, Inc. (C), NE, *321*
Dunhill Search of Arlington (C), TX, *322*
Executive Career Search (C), VA, *332*
Executive Resource Assoc. (C), VA, *334*
First Choice Search (R), WA, *67*
First Search America, Inc. (C), TN, *341*
Florapersonnel, Inc. (R), FL, *68*
J. G. Flynn & Assoc. Inc. (R), BC, *69*
Forest People Int'l. Search Ltd. (C), BC, *343*
F-O-R-T-U-N-E Personnel of Nashville (C), TN, *350*
Foster Partners (R), NY, *70*
GAAP Inc. (R), QE, *73*
Gaudry, Shink, Levasseur (R), QE, *75*
Global Career Services, Inc. (C), NY, *358*
Goldbeck Recruiting Inc. (C), BC, *359*
Harcourt & Assoc. (C), AB, *368*
The Harris Consulting Corp. (R), MB, *87*
The Hensge Co. (R), IL, *91*
Herring & Assoc. (C), AR, *376*
Holohan Group, Ltd. (R), MO, *95*
E. F. Humay Assoc. (C), PA, *384*
W. Hutt Management Resources Ltd. (R), ON, *100*
Interim Management Resources Inc. (C), ON, *392*
International Recruiting Services (C), FL, *393*
Jackson Group Int'l. (C), CO, *396*
Johnson & Assoc., Inc. (R), CA, *106*
Jordan-Sitter Assoc. (R), TX, *108*
Gary Kaplan & Assoc. (R), CA, *109*
A.T. Kearney Executive Search (R), IL, *111*
David Warwick Kennedy & Assoc. (R), BC, *112*
Kincannon & Reed (R), VA, *114*
Korn/Ferry Int'l. (R), NY, *117*
L O R (R), NJ, *122*
AG Lennox & Assoc. (R), AB, *128*
Jacques LePage Executive Search Inc. (R), QE, *128*
Lewis Companies Inc. (R), ON, *129*
Management Recruiters of Tucson (C), AZ, *439*
Management Recruiters of Sacramento North (C), CA, *441*
Management Recruiters of Colorado, Inc. (C), CO, *442*
Management Recruiters of Boise (C), ID, *446*
Management Recruiters of Indianapolis-North (C), IN, *448*
Management Recruiters of Spencer (C), IA, *448*
Management Recruiters of Williamsburg (C), IA, *449*
Management Recruiters of Siouxland (C), IA, *449*
Management Recruiters of Topeka, Inc. (C), KS, *449*
Management Recruiters of Reno (C), NV, *453*
Management Recruiters of Rocky Mount - Southwest (C), NC, *456*
Management Recruiters of Sioux Falls, LLP (C), SD, *461*
Management Recruiters of Houston-Northeast (C), TX, *463*
Management Recruiters of San Marcos (C), TX, *463*
Management Search, Inc. (C), OK, *468*
Mark Stanley & Co./EMA Partners International (R), FL, *136*
Millar Walker & Gay (R), ON, *144*
The Montgomery Group, Inc. (C), TN, *484*
Morton, McCorkle & Assoc. Inc. (R), MO, *147*
PC Assoc. (C), CO, *505*
Pearson & Assoc., Inc. (C), AZ, *506*
PERC, Ltd. (C), AZ, *506*
Yves Plouffe & Assoc. (R), QE, *165*
Ray Polhill & Assoc. (R), NC, *166*
Polson & Co., Inc. (R), MN, *166*
Jack Porter Assoc., Inc. (C), WA, *514*
Prichard Kymen Inc. (R), AB, *168*
Prior/Martech Assoc., Inc. (R), WA, *169*
Pro Tec Technical Services (C), ON, *519*
Ray & Berndtson/Laurendeau Labrecque (R), QE, *172*
Cedric L. Reese Inc. (C), CA, *533*
The Douglas Reiter Co., Inc. (R), OR, *174*
Russell Reynolds Assoc., Inc. (R), NY, *176*
Rieser & Assoc., Inc. (R), MO, *178*
Rocky Mountain Recruiters, Inc. (C), CO, *540*
Ruppert Comann Assoc., Inc. (R), CO, *182*
Sales Consultants of Sacramento (C), CA, *556*
Sales Consultants of Indianapolis-North (C), IN, *558*
Sales Consultants of Omaha, Inc. (C), NE, *560*
The Search America Group Inc. (C), OH, *573*
Search North America, Inc. (C), OR, *576*
Sherwood Lehman Massucco, Inc. (R), CA, *189*
Smith & Laue Search (R), OR, *193*
J. Harrington Smith Assoc. (C), IN, *584*
SpencerStuart (R), NY, *196*
C. J. Stafford & Assoc. (C), ON, *591*
Stewart/Greene & Co. of The Triad, Inc. (C), NC, *594*
STM Assoc. (R), UT, *201*
Strategic Resources (C), WA, *595*
Team One Partners, Inc. (C), GA, *600*
Technical Skills Consulting Inc. (R), ON, *207*
Tittemore Cowan Assoc. (C), AB, *607*
Kelly Walker Assoc. (C), TX, *614*
Ward-Hoffman & Assoc. (C), ID, *615*
Wood West & Partners Inc. (C), BC, *624*

B.00 Energy/utilities

A.K.S. Assoc., Ltd. (R), MA, *1*
Accent On Achievement, Inc. (C), MI, *233*
Accounting Personnel & Engineering Personnel Consultants (C), LA, *238*
J. R. Akin & Co. (R), MA, *2*
Albrecht & Assoc., Executive Search Consultants (C), TX, *243*
The Alexander Group (R), TX, *3*
Frank E. Allen & Assoc. (C), NJ, *244*
David Allen Assoc. (R), NJ, *3*
Allen Austin Lowe & Powers (R), TX, *3*
ALW Research Int'l. (R), NJ, *4*
American Executive Management, Inc. (R), MA, *5*
American Services Group (C), IL, *248*
Anderson & Schwab, Inc. (R), NY, *5*
Anderson Bradshaw Assoc., Inc. (R), TX, *6*
Andex Executive Search (C), CT, *250*
Tryg R. Angell, Ltd. (C), CT, *250*
Applied Resources (C), MA, *252*
ARJay & Assoc. (C), NC, *252*
Ashway Ltd. Agency (C), NY, *253*
Ashworth Consultants, Inc. (R), MA, *8*
Atomic Personnel, Inc. (C), PA, *255*
Attorney Search Global, Inc. (C), IL, *255*
Allen Ballach Assoc. Inc. (R), ON, *10*
Barton Assoc., Inc. (R), TX, *12*
Battalia Winston Int'l./The Euram Consultants Group (R), NY, *13*
Joy Reed Belt Search Consultants, Inc. (R), OK, *15*
Benamati & Assoc. (C), CO, *263*
Bennett & Associates (C), TX, *264*

Berglund Int'l. Resources, Inc. (C), TX, *265*
Berkshire Search Assoc. (C), MA, *265*
Paul J. Biestek Assoc., Inc. (R), IL, *17*
Bowden & Co., Inc. (R), OH, *20*
Bowman & Marshall, Inc. (C), KS, *271*
Boyden (R), NY, *20*
BR & Assoc. (C), NJ, *271*
Bradford Executives Int'l. (C), VA, *271*
The Brand Co., Inc. (R), FL, *22*
Bredeson Executive Recruitment, LLC (R), TX, *22*
The Bridge (C), CO, *273*
Brissenden, McFarland, Fuccella & Reynolds, Inc. (R), NJ, *23*
The Broadmoor Group, L.L.C. (R), TX, *23*
Dan B. Brockman (C), IL, *274*
Broward-Dobbs, Inc. (C), GA, *274*
The Burgess Group-Corporate Recruiters Int'l., Inc. (R), NY, *25*
David S. Burt Assoc. (C), MT, *276*
C. G. & Assoc. (R), PA, *26*
California Search Agency, Inc. (C), CA, *279*
Canadian Career Partners (R), AB, *27*
Canny, Bowen Inc. (R), NY, *27*
Cardwell Enterprises Inc. (R), IL, *29*
Careerfit, Inc. (C), TX, *283*
David Chambers & Assoc., Inc. (R), CT, *32*
The Cherbonnier Group, Inc. (R), TX, *33*
Christian & Timbers, Inc. (R), OH, *34*
Clarey/Napier Int'l., L.C. (R), TX, *35*
Howard Clark Assoc. (C), NJ, *292*
CMW & Associates, Inc. (C), IL, *293*
Coastal Int'l., Inc. (R), MA, *36*
Cochran, Cochran & Yale, Inc. (R), NY, *36*
Coe & Co. Int'l. Inc./EMA Partners Int'l. (R), AB, *37*
Collins & Associates (C), MI, *294*
Computer Int'l. Consultants, Inc. (C), FL, *295*
Conroy Partners Ltd. (R), AB, *39*
Consulting Resource Group, Inc. (C), GA, *297*
Corporate Environment Ltd. (R), IL, *41*
Cosier & Assoc. (C), AB, *302*
Frank Cuomo & Assoc., Inc. (C), NY, *305*
D.P. Specialists, Inc. (C), CA, *306*
Davies, Park (R), AB, *46*
Joseph A. Davis Consultants, Inc. (R), NY, *47*
Defrain Mayer (R), KS, *48*
DEL Technical Services, Inc. (C), IL, *310*
Delta Services (R), TX, *48*
Dinte Resources, Inc. (R), VA, *52*
Diversified Search, Inc. (R), PA, *52*
Dougherty & Assoc. (C), TN, *314*
Robert Drexler Assoc., Inc. (R), NJ, *54*
Dunhill Staffing Systems, Inc. (C), NY, *316*
Dunhill Professional Search of Greater New Orleans (C), LA, *321*
Dunlap & Sullivan Assoc. (R), MI, *55*
Dwyer Consulting Group, Inc. (R), WV, *56*
Eastern Executive Assoc. (C), NJ, *325*
EDI, Inc. (C), MD, *326*
The Energists (R), TX, *59*
ENI (R), CT, *59*
Environmental, Health & Safety Search Assoc. (C), FL, *331*
ESS (Executive Search Services) (R), CA, *61*
ExeConnex, LLC (R), GA, *61*
Executive Business Solutions, Inc. (C), WA, *332*
Executive Search Consultants Corp. (C), IL, *335*
The Executive Source (C), SA, *337*
Executive Strategies, Inc. (C), GA, *337*
EXETER 2100 (C), NH, *337*
Eyler Assoc., Inc. (R), IA, *64*
F.L.A.G. (C), OH, *338*
Guild Fetridge Acoustical Search, Inc. (C), NY, *340*
Finney-Taylor Personnel & Management Consultants Ltd. (C), AB, *341*
The Fisher Group (R), AB, *67*
Susan Fletcher Attorney Employment Services (C), PA, *342*
J. G. Flynn & Assoc. Inc. (R), BC, *69*
Flynn, Hannock, Inc. (R), CT, *69*
Foster Partners (R), NY, *70*
Fought, Jameson Assoc. (C), IL, *351*
P. N. French Assoc., Inc. (R), MA, *72*
The Furst Group, Inc. (R), IL, *72*
GAAP Inc. (R), QE, *73*
Gardiner, Townsend & Assoc. (R), NY, *74*
Genesis Research (C), MO, *356*
Gilbert Scott Assoc., LLC (C), MA, *357*
Gilbert Tweed Assoc. Inc. (R), NY, *76*
Global Data Services, Inc. (R), NY, *77*
Goldbeck Recruiting Inc. (C), BC, *359*
L. J. Gonzer Assoc. (C), NJ, *360*
The Governance Group, Inc. (R), NJ, *80*
Grantham & Co., Inc. (R), NC, *81*
J. B. Groner Executive Search, Inc. (C), DE, *363*
GSP International (C), NJ, *364*
The Gullgroup (C), TX, *364*
Habelmann & Assoc. (R), MI, *84*
Russ Hadick & Assoc. Inc. (C), OH, *365*
Halbrecht Lieberman Assoc., Inc. (R), CT, *84*
Harcourt & Assoc. (C), AB, *368*
Hardison & Company (R), TX, *86*
The Hawkins Co. (R), CA, *88*
The Heidrick Partners, Inc. (R), IL, *90*
Helffrich Int'l. (C), FL, *375*
G. W. Henn & Co. (R), OH, *91*
Hill Allyn Assoc. (C), CA, *378*
Holland Rusk & Assoc. (R), IL, *95*
HRCS (R), CA, *97*
The HRM Group, Inc. (C), AL, *382*
The Human Resource Department Ltd. (R), OH, *98*
Hunt Patton & Brazeal, Inc. (C), OK, *385*
IDC Executive Search Inc. (C), FL, *387*
Independent Power Consultants (C), TX, *387*
Information Systems Professionals (C), NC, *388*
Innovative Resource Group, LLC (C), NC, *389*
Insight Personnel Group, Inc. (C), TX, *389*
Intercontinental Executive Group (C), PA, *391*
Interim Financial Solutions - Mid-Atlantic Region (C), MD, *392*
International Executive Recruiters (C), OH, *393*
International Management Advisors, Inc. (R), NY, *103*
International Management Development Corp. (C), NY, *393*
International Staffing Consultants, Inc. (C), CA, *393*
ISC of Atlanta, Inc. (C), GA, *394*
Jackson Group Int'l. (C), CO, *396*
Jakobs & Assoc. Int'l. (R), NY, *105*
JRL Executive Recruiters (C), MO, *401*
JT Assoc. (C), CT, *401*
A H Justice Search Consultants (C), TX, *402*
Kane & Assoc. (C), TX, *403*
Kanzer Assoc., Inc. (R), IL, *109*
Gary Kaplan & Assoc. (R), CA, *109*
Karel & Co. (R), CA, *109*
A.T. Kearney Executive Search (R), IL, *111*
Kelly Associates (R), PA, *112*
Key Employment (C), NJ, *405*
Kirkbride Assoc., Inc. (C), WA, *407*
Lee Koehn Assoc., Inc. (R), OR, *116*
Korn/Ferry Int'l. (R), NY, *117*
Kors Montgomery Int'l. (R), TX, *118*
Lam Assoc. (C), HI, *411*
Langley & Associates, Inc. (Executive Search Consultants) (R), CO, *124*
Larkin & Co. (R), CA, *124*
W. R. Lawry, Inc. (R), CT, *126*
Layne-Mendez & Co. (R), TX, *127*
Leader Search Inc. (R), AB, *127*
Lectra Search (C), GA, *415*
Lehman McLeskey (R), TX, *128*
AG Lennox & Assoc. (R), AB, *128*
Jacques LePage Executive Search Inc. (R), QE, *128*
LifeWork, Inc. (C), TX, *418*
Lineal Recruiting Services (C), CT, *418*
Locke & Assoc. (R), NC, *131*
Loewenstein & Assoc., Inc. (R), TX, *131*
Magellan Int'l., L.P. (C), TX, *422*
Management Recruiters of Nassau, Inc. (R), NY, *134*
Management Recruiters of Sacramento North (C), CA, *441*
Management Recruiters of Colorado Springs (C), CO, *441*
Management Recruiters of Bonita Springs, Inc. (C), FL, *443*
Management Recruiters of Miami-North (C), FL, *443*
Management Recruiters of Boise (C), ID, *446*
Management Recruiters of Atlanta NE (C), GA, *446*
Management Recruiters of Barrington (C), IL, *447*
Management Recruiters of Des Moines (C), IA, *449*
Management Recruiters of Cass County, NE (C), NE, *452*
Management Recruiters of Great Neck (C), NY, *454*
Management Recruiters of Princeton (C), NJ, *454*

Management Recruiters of Bordentown (C), NJ, *454*
Management Recruiters of Cedar Mountain (C), NC, *455*
Management Recruiters of Cleveland (C), OH, *457*
Management Recruiters - North Canton, Inc. (C), OH, *458*
Management Recruiters of Aiken (C), SC, *460*
Management Recruiters of Arlington (C), TX, *462*
Management Recruiters of Houston (C), TX, *462*
Management Recruiters Int'l.-The Woodlands (C), TX, *464*
Management Recruiters of Kanawha Valley, LLC (C), WV, *465*
Management Recruiters of Appleton (C), WI, *465*
Management Search Int'l. (C), CA, *467*
Marentz & Co. (C), TX, *469*
Richard L. Mather & Assoc. (C), CT, *472*
Matte Consulting Group Inc. (R), QE, *138*
The McAulay Firm (R), NC, *139*
McKee Cyber Search (C), MS, *475*
McKinley•Arend Int'l. (R), TX, *141*
Meder & Assoc., Inc. (R), IL, *142*
The Medley Group (C), CA, *477*
Melancon & Co. (R), TX, *143*
Juan Menefee & Assoc. (C), IL, *478*
Meng, Finseth & Assoc., Inc. (R), CA, *143*
Meridian Legal Search/Legal Temps (C), NY, *479*
Messett Assoc., Inc. (R), FL, *143*
MGA Executive Search (C), FL, *480*
Michael Thomas, Inc. (C), OH, *480*
MLA Resources, Inc. (C), OK, *483*
Moore Research Assoc. (R), NJ, *147*
Morgan Samuels Co. (R), CA, *147*
The Morgan/Geoffries Group (C), CA, *485*
Mortgage Search Network (C), AZ, *486*
Mycoff & Assoc. (R), CO, *150*
NaTek Corp. (C), NY, *488*
Nationwide Personnel Recruiting & Consulting, Inc. (C), OR, *490*
The Network Corporate Search Personnel Inc. (C), AB, *491*
Newman-Johnson-King, Inc. (C), TX, *492*
The Nolan Group (C), CA, *494*
O'Callaghan Honey/Ray & Berndtson Inc. (R), AB, *153*
O'Connor, O'Connor, Lordi, Ltd. (R), PA, *154*
O'Rourke Companies, Inc. (R), TX, *154*
OEI, Inc. (C), NJ, *498*
LaMonte Owens, Inc. (R), PA, *157*
P.A.R. Assoc., Inc. (R), MA, *158*
The Pailin Group Professional Search Consultants (R), TX, *158*
Parenica & Co. (R), NC, *159*
Partnervision Consulting Group Inc. (R), ON, *160*
Pathways Int'l. (C), CT, *505*
Paules Associates (C), CA, *505*
PeopleSource Inc. (C), TX, *506*
PERC, Ltd. (C), AZ, *506*
Personnel Tangent Inc. (C), QE, *509*
Petro Staff Int'l. (C), AB, *509*
Phoenix Search (R), MX, *164*
PIC Executive Search (C), GA, *511*
Pinnacle Executive Group Inc. (C), MO, *512*
Pinton Forrest & Madden/EMA Partners Int'l. (R), BC, *165*
R. L. Plimpton Assoc., Inc. (R), CO, *165*
Yves Plouffe & Assoc. (R), QE, *165*
Jack Porter Assoc., Inc. (C), WA, *514*
Power Recruiting Group (C), TX, *515*
Preng & Assoc., Inc. (R), TX, *167*
Prescott Legal Search, Inc. (C), TX, *517*
PricewaterhouseCoopers Executive Search (R), ON, *168*
Pro Tec Technical Services (C), ON, *519*
Pro-Tech Search, Inc. (C), IL, *519*
Procurement Resources (C), MD, *520*
Professional Persons Career Services (C), NY, *521*
Professional Recruiting Consultants, Inc. (C), DE, *521*
Professional Resources (C), OK, *522*
Professional Search Consultants (PSC) (C), TX, *523*
Quantum EDP Recruiting Services (C), QE, *526*
Quiring Assoc., Inc. (C), IN, *527*
R. C. Services (C), TX, *528*
R.A.N. Assoc., Inc. (C), OH, *528*
Railey & Assoc. (C), TX, *528*
Ray & Berndtson (R), TX, *171*
Ray & Berndtson/Laurendeau Labrecque (R), QE, *172*
Renaissance Resources, LLC (R), VA, *174*
Reserve Technology Institute (R), TX, *175*
The Resource Group (R), NJ, *175*
Russell Reynolds Assoc., Inc. (R), NY, *176*
Rice Cohen Int'l. (R), PA, *178*
Richard, Wayne & Roberts (C), TX, *536*
Right/McKee Consulting Group (C), TX, *537*
Robert Lowell Int'l. (R), TX, *179*
Norman Roberts & Assoc., Inc. (R), CA, *179*
Roberts Ryan & Bentley, Inc. (R), MD, *179*
V. Robinson & Co., Inc. (C), MO, *539*
Robison & Associates (R), NC, *180*
Rockwood Assoc. (C), NY, *540*
Rodzik & Assoc., Inc. (R), NC, *180*
Roll International (C), TX, *541*
Rollo Assoc. (R), CA, *181*
RSMR, Inc. (R), IL, *182*
The Rubicon Group (C), AZ, *547*
Sales Builders, Inc. (R), VA, *183*
Sales Consultants of Princeton, Inc. (C), NJ, *561*
Sanford Rose Assoc. - Amherst, NY (C), NY, *568*
Sanford Rose Assoc. - Doylestown (C), PA, *570*
Schuyler Assoc., Ltd. (R), GA, *185*
Search & Recruit Int'l. (C), VA, *573*
Search Advisors Int'l. Corp. (R), FL, *186*
The Search Center Inc. (C), TX, *574*
The Search Company (R), ON, *186*
Search Consultants Int'l., Inc. (C), TX, *575*
Search North America, Inc. (C), OR, *576*
Search Research Assoc., Inc. (R), MA, *187*
Michael Shirley Assoc. Inc. (R), KS, *190*
Shupack & Michaels Inc. (C), NY, *580*
Marvin L. Silcott & Assoc., Inc. (C), TX, *581*
Skipping Stone Inc. (C), VA, *582*
G. L. Smith Assoc. (C), CA, *584*
Herman Smith Executive Initiatives Inc. (R), ON, *193*
The Smith Group, Inc. (C), NC, *584*
Smith James Group, Inc. (R), GA, *194*
Southern Research Services (R), FL, *195*
SpencerStuart (R), NY, *196*
SR Wilson, Inc. (C), CA, *590*
C. J. Stafford & Assoc. (C), ON, *591*
Stephens Assoc. Ltd., Inc. (R), OH, *200*
Peter Sterling & Co. (C), TX, *592*
Ron Stevens & Assoc., Inc. (C), FL, *593*
STM Assoc. (R), UT, *201*
Stone, Murphy & Olson (R), MN, *201*
Strauss Personnel Service (C), PA, *596*
Survival Systems Staffing, Inc. (C), CA, *597*
M. L. Tawney & Assoc. (C), TX, *600*
TaxSearch Inc. (R), OK, *207*
Carl J. Taylor & Co. (R), TX, *207*
TBC, Inc. (C), KY, *600*
Team One Partners, Inc. (C), GA, *600*
Techaid Inc. (C), QE, *601*
Technifind Int'l. (C), TX, *602*
TeleManagement Search (C), NY, *605*
Thomson, Sponar & Adams, Inc. (C), WA, *606*
Tittemore Cowan Assoc. (C), AB, *607*
TNS Partners, Inc. (R), TX, *209*
TPG & Assoc. (C), TX, *608*
Trowbridge & Co., Inc. (R), MA, *211*
Tryon & Heideman, LLC (R), MO, *211*
W. G. Tucker & Assoc. (R), PA, *211*
United Personnel Services (C), MA, *611*
Kelly Walker Assoc. (C), TX, *614*
Ward-Hoffman & Assoc. (C), ID, *615*
Watson Int'l., Inc. (R), NY, *216*
Henry Welker & Assoc. (C), MI, *618*
West & West (R), CA, *218*
Western Management Consultants (R), BC, *218*
Daniel Wier & Assoc. (R), CA, *220*
Winston Search, Inc. (R), MD, *222*
WMD inc. (C), NJ, *623*
Wood & Assoc./Executive Search Consultants (C), CA, *624*
Bruce G. Woods Executive Search (R), TX, *224*
John Wylie Assoc., Inc. (C), OK, *625*
Wyndham Mills Int'l., Inc. (R), GA, *225*

C.00 Construction

G. Adams Partners (R), IL, *2*
Alaska Executive Search, Inc. (C), AK, *243*
AM & G Certified Public Accountants & Consultants (R), IL, *4*
American Executive Management, Inc. (R), MA, *5*
American Services Group (C), IL, *248*
AmeriResource Group Inc. (C), OK, *248*
Anderson Bradshaw Assoc., Inc. (R), TX, *6*
Tryg R. Angell, Ltd. (C), CT, *250*
Atomic Personnel, Inc. (C), PA, *255*
BCG Search, Inc. (R), FL, *14*

Becker, Norton & Co. (R), PA, *14*
Benamati & Assoc. (C), CO, *263*
Bennett & Associates (C), TX, *264*
Berkshire Search Assoc. (C), MA, *265*
Bosco-Hubert & Assoc. (C), KS, *270*
Bowman & Marshall, Inc. (C), KS, *271*
The Bridge (C), CO, *273*
Broadband Resource Group (C), CA, *274*
Dan B. Brockman (C), IL, *274*
Button Group (C), TX, *277*
C. G. & Assoc. (R), PA, *26*
CadTech Staffing Services (C), GA, *279*
Canny, Bowen Inc. (R), NY, *27*
Careers/Inc. (C), PR, *284*
Caruso & Assoc., Inc. (R), FL, *31*
David Chambers & Assoc., Inc. (R), CT, *32*
Chapman & Assoc. (C), BC, *289*
The Cherbonnier Group, Inc. (R), TX, *33*
Arlene Clapp, Ltd. (R), MN, *35*
Claremont-Branan, Inc. (C), GA, *292*
Compass Group Ltd. (R), MI, *38*
Robert Connelly & Assoc., Inc. (R), MN, *39*
Consolidated Management Services (C), ON, *296*
Construct Management Services (C), MN, *297*
Construction Search Specialists, Inc. (C), WI, *297*
ContactBridge, Inc. (R), IL, *40*
Cook Assoc.,® Inc. (R), IL, *40*
Corporate Builders, Inc. (C), OR, *299*
Corporate Environment Ltd. (R), IL, *41*
Corporate Search, Inc. (C), NY, *301*
Courtright & Assoc., Inc. (R), PA, *42*
Creative-Leadership, Inc. (R), CA, *42*
Crown Advisors, Inc. (R), PA, *43*
CS Associates, LLC (C), AZ, *304*
Frank Cuomo & Assoc., Inc. (C), NY, *305*
Custom Resources (C), AL, *305*
D & M Associates (C), PA, *306*
DEL Technical Services, Inc. (C), IL, *310*
Robert Drexler Assoc., Inc. (R), NJ, *54*
Gwen Dycus & Assoc. (C), FL, *323*
ESS (Executive Search Services) (R), CA, *61*
The Evans McDonnell Co. (C), TX, *331*
Executive Recruiters Int'l. (C), MI, *333*
Executive Referral Services, Inc. (C), IL, *334*
Executive Search Plus, Inc. (C), IN, *336*
FAI (C), CO, *338*
Leon A. Farley Assoc. (R), CA, *65*
Guild Fetridge Acoustical Search, Inc. (C), NY, *340*
J. G. Flynn & Assoc. Inc. (R), BC, *69*
Foster Partners (R), NY, *70*
Friedman Eisenstein Raemer & Schwartz, LLP (R), IL, *72*
Gaffney Management Consultants (R), IL, *73*
Gaines & Assoc. Int'l., Inc. (R), IL, *73*
Gilbert Scott Assoc., LLC (C), MA, *357*
Gilreath Weatherby Inc. (R), MA, *77*
The Glazin Group (R), BC, *77*
Goldbeck Recruiting Inc. (C), BC, *359*
Grant-Franks & Assoc. (C), NJ, *361*
Grant/Morgan Assoc., Inc. (C), MD, *361*
Michael J. Hall & Co. (R), WA, *85*
The Hanna Group (C), OH, *368*
Harcourt & Assoc. (C), AB, *368*
William E. Hay & Co. (R), IL, *88*
Helbling & Assoc., Inc. (R), PA, *91*
Helffrich Int'l. (C), FL, *375*
J. D. Hersey & Assoc. (C), OH, *376*
Robert Hess & Assoc., Inc. (C), CO, *377*
Highland & Assoc. (C), CA, *378*
Holland Rusk & Assoc. (R), IL, *95*
Holloway Schulz & Partners (C), BC, *380*
Hornberger Management Company (R), DE, *95*
E. F. Humay Assoc. (C), PA, *384*
Huntress Real Estate Executive Search (R), MO, *100*
Hyland Executive Search (C), AZ, *386*
Impact Source, Inc. (C), FL, *387*
Intercontinental Executive Group (C), PA, *391*
International Management Development Corp. (C), NY, *393*
International Recruiting Services (C), FL, *393*
International Staffing Consultants, Inc. (C), CA, *393*
ISC of Houston, Inc. (C), TX, *394*
Jackson Group Int'l. (C), CO, *396*
Jordan-Sitter Assoc. (R), TX, *108*
Joseph Chris & Assoc. (C), TX, *400*
JRL Executive Recruiters (C), MO, *401*
K & C Assoc. (C), CA, *402*
Lisa Kalus & Assoc., Inc. (C), NY, *403*
Karel & Co. (R), CA, *109*
Kaye/Bassman Int'l. Corp. (R), TX, *110*
A.T. Kearney Executive Search (R), IL, *111*
Michael L. Ketner & Assoc., Inc. (R), PA, *114*
Key Employment (C), NJ, *405*
Kimmel & Associates, Inc. (C), NC, *406*
Kirkbride Assoc., Inc. (C), WA, *407*
Korn/Ferry Int'l. (R), NY, *117*
The J. Kovach Group (R), PA, *119*
Krueger Assoc. (R), IL, *121*
The LaBorde Group (C), CA, *411*
Larkin & Co. (R), CA, *124*
Larsen Int'l., Inc. (R), TX, *125*
Michael Latas & Assoc., Inc. (R), MO, *125*
J. H. Lindell & Co. (C), CA, *418*
Locke & Assoc. (R), NC, *131*
Scott Love Assoc., Inc. (C), AZ, *420*
Maglio & Co., Inc. (R), WI, *134*
Management Advisors Int'l., Inc. (C), NC, *424*
Management Recruiters Peninsula (C), CA, *439*
Management Recruiters of Aptos (C), CA, *439*
Management Recruiters of Laguna Hills (C), CA, *440*
Management Recruiters of Sacramento North (C), CA, *441*
Management Recruiters of Sonoma (C), CA, *441*
Management Recruiters, Inland Empire Agency (C), CA, *441*
Management Recruiters of Winsted, Inc. (C), CT, *442*
Management Recruiters of Ft. Myers, FL. (C), FL, *443*
Management Recruiters of Bonita Springs, Inc. (C), FL, *443*
Management Recruiters of Miami-North (C), FL, *443*
Management Recruiters of Forsyth County (C), GA, *445*
Management Recruiters of Vero Beach (C), FL, *445*
Management Recruiters of Barrington (C), IL, *447*
Management Recruiters of Siouxland (C), IA, *449*
Management Recruiters of Birmingham (C), MI, *451*
Management Recruiters of Lake Tahoe, NV (C), NV, *453*
Management Recruiters of Medford, N.J. (C), NJ, *453*
Management Recruiters of Orange County, N.Y., Inc. (C), NJ, *453*
Management Recruiters of Gastonia (C), NC, *456*
Management Recruiters of Columbus (C), OH, *457*
Management Recruiters of Cleveland (C), OH, *457*
Management Recruiters of Cincinnati/ Sharonville, Inc. (C), OH, *457*
Management Recruiters of Sioux Falls, LLP (C), SD, *461*
Management Recruiters of Appleton (C), WI, *465*
Management Recruiters of Lynnwood (C), WA, *465*
Management Recruiters of Milwaukee-North (C), WI, *466*
Marketing & Sales Resources, Inc. (C), FL, *470*
Marra Peters & Partners (R), NJ, *136*
K. Maxin & Assoc. (R), PA, *139*
McCooe & Assoc., Inc. (R), NJ, *140*
McIntyre Management Resources (C), ON, *474*
McNichol Assoc. (R), PA, *142*
Meridian Legal Search/Legal Temps (C), NY, *479*
Michael Assoc. (R), IL, *144*
Moffitt Int'l., Inc. (R), NC, *146*
Morgan Int'l., Inc. (R), IL, *147*
Morgan Samuels Co. (R), CA, *147*
Moss & Co. (R), WA, *148*
MSI Int'l. (C), GA, *486*
Jennifer Munro & Partners, Inc. (R), SC, *149*
NaTek Corp. (C), NY, *488*
National Metal Services Corp. (C), IN, *489*
O'Brien and Roof (C), OH, *497*
John R. O'Connor & Assoc. (C), IL, *497*
The Oldani Group (R), WA, *155*
Orion Int'l. Consulting Group, Inc. (C), NC, *499*
Ott & Hansen, Inc. (R), CA, *157*
P.A.R. Assoc., Inc. (R), MA, *158*
Pacific Finance Search, Inc. (C), CA, *501*
Peak Search Assoc. (C), ON, *506*
Pearce & Assoc. (C), FL, *506*

PERI Corp/Professional Executive Recruiters, Inc. (C), TX, *507*
Fred Perry Assoc. (C), TX, *507*
Personnel Alliance Group (C), NJ, *507*
PIC Executive Search (C), GA, *511*
Ray Polhill & Assoc. (R), NC, *166*
Bob Poline Assoc. Inc. (C), CA, *514*
Powers Consultants, Inc. (R), MO, *166*
Preng & Assoc., Inc. (R), TX, *167*
Prescott Legal Search, Inc. (C), TX, *517*
Prichard Kymen Inc. (R), AB, *168*
Prior/Martech Assoc., Inc. (R), WA, *169*
Pro Tec Technical Services (C), ON, *519*
Procurement Resources (C), MD, *520*
Professional Persons Career Services (C), NY, *521*
Professional Search Consultants (PSC) (C), TX, *523*
Profit Pros, Inc. (C), CA, *523*
Quantum Int'l., Ltd. (R), FL, *170*
R. C. Services (C), TX, *528*
Railey & Assoc. (C), TX, *528*
The Recruitment Group, Inc. (C), NY, *532*
Cedric L. Reese Inc. (C), CA, *533*
Reserve Technology Institute (R), TX, *175*
The Revere Assoc., Inc. (R), OH, *176*
Rice Cohen Int'l. (R), PA, *178*
Richard, Wayne & Roberts (C), TX, *536*
Robison & Associates (R), NC, *180*
Robison Humphreys & Assoc., Inc. (R), ON, *180*
Roevin Technical People (C), ON, *540*
Ropes Associates, Inc. (R), FL, *182*
Rowland Assoc. (C), CA, *547*
Royal Assoc. (C), CA, *547*
RSMR, Inc. (R), IL, *182*
Ruppert Comann Assoc., Inc. (R), CO, *182*
Saber Group, Inc. (C), TX, *550*
Sales Consultants of Denver (C), CO, *557*
Sales Consultants of Birmingham (C), MI, *559*
Sales Consultants of Westchester-South, Inc. (C), NY, *561*
Sales Recruiters of Oklahoma City (C), OK, *564*
Sanford Rose Assoc. - Cedar Rapids (C), IA, *567*
Sanford Rose Assoc. - Port Washington (C), WI, *571*
Sathe & Associates, Inc. (R), MN, *184*
SearchCorp International (C), AB, *577*
Sharrow & Assoc., Inc. (C), MI, *579*
Sherwood Lehman Massucco, Inc. (R), CA, *189*
Shore Asociados Ejecutivos, S. A. de C.V. (R), MX, *190*
SHS of Allentown (C), PA, *580*
Shupack & Michaels Inc. (C), NY, *580*
Marvin L. Silcott & Assoc., Inc. (C), TX, *581*
Snelling & Snelling, Inc. (C), FL, *585*
Specialized Search Assoc. (C), FL, *589*
Specialty Consultants Inc. (R), PA, *195*
SpencerStuart (R), NY, *196*
C. J. Stafford & Assoc. (C), ON, *591*
Allan Stolee Inc. (R), FL, *201*
Stoopen Asociados, S.C./EMA Partners Int'l. (R), MX, *202*
StratfordGroup (R), OH, *203*
W. R. Strathmann Assoc. (R), NY, *203*
Stroman Int'l., Inc. (R), CO, *204*
Summit Group Int'l., Inc. (R), GA, *204*
Systems Research Group (C), OH, *598*
The Talon Group (R), TX, *205*
Techaid Inc. (C), QE, *601*
Tekworx, Inc. (C), OK, *604*
Traynor Confidential, Ltd. (C), NY, *609*
TRS Staffing Solutions Inc. (C), OH, *610*
Unisearch Search & Recruiting Inc. (C), CA, *611*
Van Leeuwen Assoc. (R), CA, *213*
Kelly Walker Assoc. (C), TX, *614*
Ward-Hoffman & Assoc. (C), ID, *615*
Weinman & Assoc. (C), AZ, *617*
Wilder, Gammel Partners, Ltd. (R), CA, *220*
Winguth, Grant & Donahue (R), CA, *222*
Wojdula & Assoc., Ltd. (R), WI, *223*
Wood & Assoc./Executive Search Consultants (C), CA, *624*
Wood West & Partners Inc. (C), BC, *624*
Working Relationships, Inc. (C), MN, *624*
Wyndham Mills Int'l., Inc. (R), GA, *225*
The Zarkin Group, Inc. (R), NY, *226*

D.00 Manufacturing

The 500 Granary Inc. (C), ON, *231*
A C Personnel Services, Inc. (C), OK, *231*
A First Resource (C), NC, *231*
A la Carte Int'l., Inc. (R), VA, *1*
A Permanent Success Employment Services (C), CA, *231*
A-Linko & Assoc. (C), TX, *231*
A.J. & Assoc. (C), FL, *232*
A.M.C.R., Inc. (C), OH, *232*
The Abbott Group, Inc. (R), MD, *1*
Abraham & London Ltd. (C), CT, *232*
B. J. Abrams & Assoc. Inc. (C), IL, *233*
Abraxas Technologies, Inc. (C), FL, *233*
ACC Technical Services (C), OH, *233*
Accelerated Data Decision, Inc. (C), NJ, *233*
Access Assoc. Inc. (C), MD, *233*
ACCESS Technology (C), CA, *234*
Access/Resources, Inc. (C), MA, *234*
Accountants Executive Search (C), CA, *237*
Accounting Additions (C), CA, *238*
Ackerman Johnson Inc. (C), TX, *238*
ACSYS Resources, Inc. (C), DE, *238*
Action Management Corp. (C), MI, *239*
Arthur Adams & Assoc. (C), OH, *239*
Adams & Assoc. Int'l. (R), IL, *1*
The Addison Consulting Group (C), NJ, *239*
Adel-Lawrence Assoc., Inc. (C), NJ, *240*
Adirect Recruiting Corp. (C), ON, *240*
ADR Accounting Management Recruiters (C), ON, *240*
Advanced Corporate Search (C), CA, *240*
Advanced Executive Resources (R), MI, *2*
Advanced Recruitment, Inc. (C), TN, *240*
Advancement Recruiting Services (C), OH, *241*
Advancement, Inc. (C), IL, *241*
Advantage Partners, Inc. (R), OH, *2*
The Advisory Group, Inc. (R), CA, *2*
AES Search (C), NJ, *241*
Affinity Executive Search (C), FL, *241*
Affordable Executive Recruiters (C), CA, *241*
Aggressive Corporation (C), IL, *242*
Agra Placements, Ltd. (C), IA, *242*
Agri-Personnel (C), GA, *242*
Agri-Tech Personnel, Inc. (C), MO, *242*
Ahrensdorf & Assoc. (R), PA, *2*
J. R. Akin & Co. (R), MA, *2*
Albrecht & Assoc., Executive Search Consultants (C), TX, *243*
Alexander & Co. (C), CA, *243*
Alexander Associates (R), NJ, *2*
Alexander Enterprises, Inc. (C), PA, *243*
The Alexander Group (R), NJ, *3*
Allen & Assoc. (C), NV, *244*
Frank E. Allen & Assoc. (C), NJ, *244*
David Allen Assoc. (R), NJ, *3*
Allen Austin Lowe & Powers (R), TX, *3*
Allen, Wayne & Co. LLC (C), WI, *245*
Allen-Jeffers Assoc. (C), CA, *245*
Allen/Associates (R), OH, *4*
Allerton Heneghan & O'Neill (R), IL, *4*
Alliance Executive Search, Inc. (R), MA, *4*
Tom Allison Assoc. (C), NM, *245*
Allstaff, Inc. (C), IL, *245*
Alpha Executive Search (C), AL, *245*
Alpha Resources (C), IL, *246*
Alpha Search (C), FL, *246*
The Altco Group (C), NJ, *246*
Altec/HRC (C), MI, *246*
The Alternatives Group, Inc. (C), TX, *246*
ALW Research Int'l. (R), NJ, *4*
AM & G Certified Public Accountants & Consultants (R), IL, *4*
Peter W. Ambler Co. (R), TX, *5*
AMD & Associates (C), GA, *247*
American Executive Search (C), FL, *247*
American Heritage Group, Inc. (C), MI, *247*
American Logistics Consultants, Inc. (C), IL, *247*
American Professional Search, Inc. (C), TN, *248*
American Services Group (C), IL, *248*
AmeriPro Search, Inc. (C), NC, *248*
Ames & Ames (R), CA, *5*
Ames-O'Neill Assoc., Inc. (C), NY, *249*
Amherst Human Resource Group, Ltd. (C), IL, *249*
Amherst Personnel Group Inc. (C), NY, *249*
AMS Int'l. (R), VA, *5*
Analog Solutions (C), NY, *249*
Analytic Recruiting, Inc. (C), NY, *249*
Anderson & Associates (R), NC, *5*
Anderson & Schwab, Inc. (R), NY, *5*
Anderson Bradshaw Assoc., Inc. (R), TX, *6*
Anderson Industrial Assoc., Inc. (C), GA, *250*
Anderson Network Group (C), OH, *250*
Andex Executive Search (C), CT, *250*
Andre David & Assoc., Inc. (R), TX, *6*
The Andre Group, Inc. (R), PA, *6*
Andrews & Assoc. (C), NC, *250*
Andrews & Wald Group (C), FL, *250*
Angel Group Int'l. (C), KY, *250*
Tryg R. Angell, Ltd. (C), CT, *250*

Angus Employment Ltd. (C), ON, *250*
The Angus Group, Ltd. (C), OH, *251*
Ansara, Bickford & Fiske (C), MA, *251*
Fred Anthony Assoc. (C), WI, *251*
APA Employment Agency Inc. (C), OR, *251*
APA Search, Inc. (R), NY, *6*
David Aplin & Assoc. (C), AB, *251*
Applied Resources, Inc. (C), MN, *252*
Applied Search Assoc., Inc. (C), GA, *252*
Charles P. Aquavella & Assoc. (C), TX, *252*
Argus National, Inc. (R), CT, *6*
Ariail & Assoc. (R), NC, *7*
Aries Search Group (C), GA, *252*
ARJay & Assoc. (C), NC, *252*
Patrick Arnone & Assoc. Inc. (R), VA, *7*
Artgo, Inc. (R), OH, *7*
A. Artze Assoc.-Personnel Consultants (C), PR, *253*
Asheville Search & Consulting (C), NC, *253*
Ashlar-Stone Management Consultants Inc. (R), ON, *8*
Ashton Computer Professionals, Inc. (C), BC, *253*
Ashway Ltd. Agency (C), NY, *253*
Ashworth Consultants, Inc. (R), MA, *8*
Asset Resource, Inc. (C), CA, *254*
The Associates, HR Search Executives, Inc. (C), OK, *254*
Association for Sales Force Management (C), WA, *254*
Astro Executive Search Firm (C), LA, *254*
W. R. Atchison & Assoc., Inc. (C), NC, *254*
Atlanta Executive Partners, Inc. (R), MA, *8*
Atlantic Pacific Group (C), CA, *255*
Atlantic West Int'l. (C), NC, *255*
Atomic Personnel, Inc. (C), PA, *255*
Attorney Search Global, Inc. (C), IL, *255*
Aurora Tech Search (C), ON, *256*
A. M. Auster Associates (R), FL, *9*
Cami Austin & Assoc. (C), IL, *256*
Austin - Allen Co. (C), TN, *256*
Austin Group Int'l./Marlar Int'l. (R), TX, *9*
Austin Michaels, Ltd., Inc. (C), AZ, *256*
Austin Park Management Group Inc. (C), ON, *256*
Austin, Hill & Assoc. (C), MD, *256*
Austin-McGregor Int'l. (R), TX, *9*
Automation Technology Search (C), CA, *256*
Availability Personnel Consultants (C), NH, *257*
Avestruz & Assoc. (C), CA, *257*
Avion International Technology Inc. (C), ON, *257*
The Badger Group (R), CA, *10*
Baeder Kalinski Int'l. Group, Inc. (R), NH, *10*
The Baer Group (R), OH, *10*
Keith Bagg & Assoc., Inc. (C), ON, *257*
D. W. Baird & Associates (C), MD, *257*
Baldwin & Assoc. (C), OH, *258*
Baldwin Associates, LLC (R), CT, *10*
The Baldwin Group (R), IL, *10*
The Bales-Waugh Group (C), FL, *258*
Allen Ballach Assoc. Inc. (R), ON, *10*
Ballantyne & Assoc. (R), CA, *10*
Ballos & Co., Inc. (R), NJ, *10*
BallResources (C), MO, *258*
James Bangert & Assoc., Inc. (R), MN, *11*
The Barack Group, Inc. (R), NY, *11*
Barber & Assoc. (C), KY, *259*
Barclay Consultants, Inc. (C), NJ, *259*
J. W. Barleycorn, Renard & Assoc., Inc. (R), OH, *11*
Barnes & Assoc. Executive Search (C), CA, *259*
Barnes Development Group, LLC (R), WI, *11*
Fred A. Barnette & Assoc. (R), NC, *11*
Barone Assoc. (C), NJ, *259*
Barone-O'Hara Assoc., Inc. (R), NJ, *11*
Barr Assoc. (C), PA, *259*
The Barrett Group (C), NH, *260*
Barrett Partners (C), IL, *260*
Barrett Rose & Lee, Inc. (C), ON, *260*
Barrington Hart, Inc. (R), IL, *12*
Nathan Barry Assoc., Inc. (R), MA, *12*
Aldonna Barry Personnel & Management (C), ON, *260*
Barth Smith Company (R), IL, *12*
Bartholdi & Co., Inc. (R), CO, *12*
Barton Assoc., Inc. (R), TX, *12*
The Barton Group, Inc. (C), MI, *260*
Bason Associates (R), OH, *13*
Bast & Assoc., Inc. (C), CA, *261*
Battalia Winston Int'l./The Euram Consultants Group (R), NY, *13*
L. Battalin & Co. (C), FL, *261*
R. Gaines Baty Assoc., Inc. (R), TX, *13*
Martin H. Bauman Assoc., Inc. (R), NY, *13*
The Bauman Group (R), CA, *14*
Bayland Assoc. (C), CA, *261*
BayResearch Group, Inc. (R), IL, *14*
Beacon Int'l., Inc. (C), VA, *261*
The Beam Group (R), PA, *14*
The Beardsley Group Inc. (C), CT, *261*
Beck/Eastwood Recruitment Solutions (C), CA, *261*
Becker, Norton & Co. (R), PA, *14*
Becker Project Resources, Inc. (C), OR, *262*
The Bedford Consulting Group Inc. (R), ON, *14*
The Bedford Group (R), RI, *15*
Robert Beech West Inc. (C), CA, *262*
Behrens and Company (C), WA, *262*
Neail Behringer Consultants Inc. (R), NY, *15*
Belanger Partners Ltd. (C), ON, *262*
Gary S. Bell Assoc., Inc. (C), NJ, *263*
William Bell Assoc., Inc. (C), NJ, *263*
Bell Oaks Co., Inc. (C), GA, *263*
Joy Reed Belt Search Consultants, Inc. (R), OK, *15*
Benamati & Assoc. (C), CO, *263*
Bench Int'l. Search, Inc. (R), CA, *15*
J. P. Bencik Assoc. (C), MI, *263*
Bender Executive Search Management Consulting (R), NY, *16*
Benford & Assoc., Inc. (C), MI, *264*
The Bennett Group, Inc. (R), IN, *16*
Benson Associates (C), NY, *264*
Dick Berg & Assoc. (C), CA, *264*
Berger & Leff (C), CA, *264*
Berkana Int'l., Inc. (C), WA, *265*
Berkhemer/Clayton, Inc. (R), CA, *16*
Berkshire Search Assoc. (C), MA, *265*
Bernhart Assoc. (C), MN, *265*
Ed Bertolas Assoc., Inc. (C), CA, *265*
Jack Bertram, Executive Recruiter (C), PA, *265*
Bertrand, Ross & Assoc., Inc. (C), IL, *266*
Besen Assoc. Inc. (C), NJ, *266*
BEST/World Assoc. Inc. (R), TX, *16*
BG & Assoc. (C), MD, *266*
BGB Assoc., Inc. (C), IL, *266*
Bialla & Assoc. Inc. (R), CA, *17*
Paul J. Biestek Assoc., Inc. (R), IL, *17*
Bio-Venture Group (C), RI, *266*
Biomedical Search Consultants (R), CT, *17*
BioPharmMed (C), FL, *267*
BioQuest Inc. (R), CA, *17*
BioTech Research Recruiters Inc. (C), CA, *267*
Birch & Associes (C), QE, *267*
Deborah Bishop & Assoc. (R), CA, *17*
BJB Assoc. (C), VA, *267*
The Black Leopard (C), CA, *267*
The Blackman Kallick Search Division (C), IL, *267*
Blair/Tech Recruiters, Inc. (C), NJ, *268*
Blake/Hansen Ltd. (R), FL, *18*
J: Blakslee Int'l., Ltd. (R), CA, *18*
Blaney Executive Search (R), MA, *18*
Blanton & Co. (C), AL, *268*
Blau Mancino Schroeder (R), NJ, *18*
David Blevins & Assoc. (C), WA, *268*
Block & Assoc. (R), CA, *18*
D. R. Blood & Assoc. (R), AZ, *18*
Boardroom Consultants/Kenny Kindler Tholke (R), NY, *19*
Boettcher Assoc. (R), WI, *19*
Tom Bogle & Assoc. (C), CA, *269*
Mark Bolno & Assoc. (C), FL, *269*
Ann Bond Assoc. Inc. (C), MD, *269*
John C. Boone & Co. (R), IL, *19*
Boone-Scaturro Assoc., Inc. (C), GA, *269*
Bor-Maq Assoc. (C), TX, *269*
Borchert Assoc. (C), TX, *269*
Bornholdt Shivas & Friends Executive Recruiters (C), NY, *270*
The Borton Wallace Co. (R), NC, *19*
Bos Business Consultants (C), NY, *270*
Bosch & Assoc., LLC (R), CT, *19*
Bosco-Hubert & Assoc. (C), KS, *270*
Bosland Gray Assoc. (R), NJ, *20*
Boulware & Assoc. Inc. (R), IL, *20*
Bowden & Co., Inc. (R), OH, *20*
BowdenGlobal, Ltd. (R), OH, *20*
Howard Bowen Consulting (C), FL, *270*
Bower & Associates (C), TX, *271*
BowersThomas (C), CA, *271*
Bowman & Marshall, Inc. (C), KS, *271*
Boyden (R), NY, *20*
Boyle/Ogata Executive Search (R), CA, *21*
The Bradbury Management Group, Inc. (R), CA, *21*
Bradford Executives Int'l. (C), VA, *271*
Bradley & Assoc. (C), MN, *272*
The Brand Co., Inc. (R), FL, *22*
Brandywine Consulting Group (R), PA, *22*
Brandywine Management Group (R), MD, *22*

INDUSTRIES

Brandywine Retained Ventures, Inc. (R), CT, *22*
Branthover Assoc. (C), NY, *272*
Bratland & Assoc. (C), IL, *272*
Jerold Braun & Assoc. (C), CA, *272*
Bredeson Executive Recruitment, LLC (R), TX, *22*
Brei & Assoc., Inc. (C), IA, *272*
The Brentwood Group, Inc. (R), NJ, *22*
The Brentwood Group Ltd. (R), OR, *23*
Brentwood Int'l. (R), CA, *23*
Brethet, Barnum & Assoc., Inc. (C), ON, *273*
Brett Personnel Specialists (C), NJ, *273*
Brian Assoc., Inc. (C), NY, *273*
Briant Assoc., Inc. (R), IL, *23*
The Bridge (C), CO, *273*
Bridgecreek Personnel Agency (C), CA, *273*
Brierwood Group, Inc. (C), IN, *273*
Brigade, Inc. (R), CA, *23*
Bright Search/Professional Staffing (C), MN, *274*
Brissenden, McFarland, Fuccella & Reynolds, Inc. (R), NJ, *23*
Bristol Assoc., Inc. (C), CA, *274*
Broadband Resource Group (C), CA, *274*
The Broadmoor Group, L.L.C. (R), TX, *23*
Brooke Chase Assoc., Inc. (R), IL, *24*
Brookman Associates (C), NY, *274*
Bernard E. Brooks & Assoc., Inc. (R), SC, *24*
Broward-Dobbs, Inc. (C), GA, *274*
J. B. Brown & Assoc., Inc. (C), OH, *275*
Brown, Bernardy, Van Remmen, Inc. (C), CA, *275*
Brown Venture Assoc. (R), CA, *24*
Brownstone Sales & Marketing Group, Inc. (C), NY, *275*
Brush Creek Partners (R), MO, *24*
Bryan & Louis Research (C), OH, *275*
Bryant Research (C), NJ, *275*
The Buckley Group (C), FL, *276*
Buckman/Enochs & Assoc., Inc. (C), OH, *276*
Bullis & Co., Inc. (R), CA, *25*
The Burgess Group-Corporate Recruiters Int'l., Inc. (R), NY, *25*
J. Burke & Assoc., Inc. (C), TX, *276*
Burke & Assoc./The Westfield Group (C), CT, *276*
The Burke Group (C), ON, *276*
J. Burkey Assoc. (R), NJ, *25*
Joseph R. Burns & Assoc., Inc. (R), NJ, *25*
David S. Burt Assoc. (C), MT, *276*
Busch International (R), CA, *25*
Business Solutions Worldwide, Inc. (C), NJ, *277*
Butterfield & Co. Int'l., Inc. (C), HI, *277*
Button Group (C), TX, *277*
Buzhardt Assoc. (R), MS, *25*
Byron Leonard Int'l., Inc. (R), CA, *25*
C. M. Management Services, Inc. (R), KY, *26*
C.T.E.W. Executive Personnel Services Inc. (C), BC, *278*
C/R Associates (C), NY, *278*
Cadillac Assoc. (C), CA, *278*
Cahill Assoc. (C), CT, *279*
Juliette Lang Cahn Executive Search (C), NY, *279*
Caliber Associates (R), PA, *27*
California Search Agency, Inc. (C), CA, *279*
Callan Assoc., Ltd. (R), IL, *27*
Callos Personnel Services (C), OH, *279*
Cambridge Group Ltd. - Exec. Search Div. (C), CT, *279*
The Cambridge Group Ltd. (C), CT, *280*
Cambridge Management Planning (R), ON, *27*
Campa & Assoc. (R), ON, *27*
T. M. Campbell Co. (R), WA, *27*
Canadian Career Partners (R), AB, *27*
CanMed Consultants Inc. (C), ON, *280*
Canny, Bowen Inc. (R), NY, *27*
J. P. Canon Assoc. (C), NY, *280*
The Cantor Concern, Inc. (R), NY, *28*
Cantrell & Assoc. (C), FL, *280*
Canyon Consulting, Inc. (C), TX, *281*
Capital Consulting Group, Inc. (R), MD, *28*
Capitol Management Consulting, Inc. (C), NJ, *281*
Caplan Assoc., Inc. (R), NJ, *28*
The Caplan-Taylor Group (R), CA, *28*
Caprio & Assoc. Inc. (R), IL, *29*
Capstone Consulting, Inc. (R), IL, *29*
Capstone Inc. (R), NY, *29*
Career +Plus (C), NY, *281*
Career Advisors, Inc. (C), FL, *281*
Career Alternatives Executive Search (C), MI, *281*
Career Consultants (R), IN, *29*
Career Consulting Group, Inc. (C), CT, *281*
Career Counseling Inc. (CCI) (C), KY, *282*
Career Development Associates (C), NV, *282*
Career Images (C), FL, *282*
Career Marketing Assoc., Inc. (C), CO, *282*
Career Marketing Consultants, Inc. (C), GA, *282*
Career Profiles (C), NH, *283*
Career Search Group (C), FL, *283*
Career Specialists, Inc. (R), WA, *29*
Career Strategies, Inc. (C), CA, *283*
Careerfit, Inc. (C), TX, *283*
Careers First, Inc. (C), NJ, *283*
Careers On Track (C), NJ, *283*
Careers Plus (R), CA, *29*
Careers/Inc. (C), PR, *284*
Carion Resource Group Inc. (C), ON, *284*
Carlson & Czeswik (R), MN, *30*
Carnegie Partners, Inc. (R), IL, *30*
Carnegie Resources, Inc. (C), NC, *284*
Carpenter, Shackleton & Company (R), IL, *30*
Carr Management Services, Inc. (C), PA, *284*
Carrington & Carrington, Ltd. (R), IL, *30*
Carter, Lavoie Associates (C), RI, *285*
Carter McKenzie, Inc. (C), NJ, *285*
Carter/MacKay (C), NJ, *285*
Carver Search Consultants (C), CA, *285*
Cary & Assoc. (R), FL, *31*
Case Executive Search (C), MI, *286*
Casey & Assoc., Inc. (C), TX, *286*
Rosemary Cass Ltd. (R), CT, *31*
The Cassie Group (R), NJ, *31*
Catalyx Group (R), NY, *31*
Michael J. Cavanagh & Assoc. Inc. (R), ON, *31*
Caywood Partners, Ltd. (R), CA, *32*
Cella Assoc. (C), GA, *286*
Cemco, Ltd. (C), IL, *286*
Cendea Connection Int'l. (R), TX, *32*
Central Executive Search, Inc. (C), OH, *287*
The Century Group (C), CA, *287*
CEO Consulting (C), FL, *287*
cFour Partners (R), CA, *32*
CFR Executive Search, Inc. (C), IL, *288*
Chad Management Group (C), ON, *288*
Chadwell & Assoc., Inc. (C), MI, *288*
Wayne S. Chamberlain & Assoc. (C), CA, *288*
David Chambers & Assoc., Inc. (R), CT, *32*
Joseph Chandler & Assoc., Inc. (R), IL, *33*
Chapman & Assoc. (C), BC, *289*
The Chapman Group, Inc. (C), AZ, *289*
Robert L. Charon (C), TX, *289*
Chase Partners (R), ON, *33*
Chase-Gardner Executive Search Associates, Inc. (C), FL, *289*
The Chatham Group, Ltd. (C), CT, *289*
A. D. Check Assoc., Inc. (R), PA, *33*
Chelsea Resources, Inc. (C), CT, *290*
Cheney Associates (C), CT, *290*
The Cherbonnier Group, Inc. (R), TX, *33*
Chesapeake Group (C), CT, *290*
Christenson Hutchison McDowell, LLC (R), NJ, *34*
Christian & Timbers, Inc. (R), OH, *34*
R. Christine Assoc. (C), PA, *290*
Christmas, McIvor & Assoc. Inc. (C), ON, *290*
Christopher and Long (C), MO, *291*
William J. Christopher Assoc., Inc. (R), PA, *34*
Christopher-Westmont & Assoc., Inc. (R), OH, *34*
J. F. Church Associates (C), WA, *291*
Churchill & Affiliates, Inc. (R), PA, *35*
M. A. Churchill & Assoc., Inc. (R), PA, *35*
The Churchill Group (C), ON, *291*
Cizek Assoc., Inc. (R), AZ, *35*
CJA-The Adler Group, Inc. (R), CA, *35*
Clanton & Co. (C), CA, *292*
Clarey & Andrews, Inc. (R), IL, *35*
Clarey/Napier Int'l., L.C. (R), TX, *35*
Howard Clark Assoc. (C), NJ, *292*
Toby Clark Assoc. Inc. (C), NY, *292*
Clark Executive Search (C), NY, *292*
Ken Clark Int'l. (R), NJ, *36*
Clark Personnel Service, Inc. (C), AL, *292*
The Clayton Edward Group (C), MI, *292*
CMC Search Consultants (C), IL, *293*
CMS, Inc. (C), NH, *293*
CMS Management Services LLC (C), IN, *293*
CMW & Associates, Inc. (C), IL, *293*
CN Associates (C), CA, *293*
Coast Personnel Services Ltd. (C), BC, *293*
COBA Executive Search (R), CO, *36*
Cochran, Cochran & Yale, Inc. (R), NY, *36*
Coe & Co. Int'l. Inc./EMA Partners Int'l. (R), AB, *37*
The Coelyn Group (R), CA, *37*

Cole, Warren & Long, Inc. (R), PA, *37*
J. Kevin Coleman & Assoc., Inc. (R), CA, *37*
Coleman Lew & Assoc., Inc. (R), NC, *37*
Collins & Associates (C), MI, *294*
S L Collins Assoc. (C), NC, *294*
Colt Systems Professional Personnel Services (C), CA, *294*
Colton Bernard Inc. (R), CA, *37*
Colucci, Blendow & Johnson (R), CA, *38*
Commercial Programming Systems, Inc. (C), CA, *294*
Compass Group Ltd. (R), MI, *38*
Comprehensive Search (C), GA, *294*
CompuPro (C), IL, *295*
Computer Professionals Unlimited (C), TX, *295*
Computer Security Placement Service (C), MA, *296*
The Comwell Company, Inc. (C), NJ, *296*
Conard Associates, Inc. (R), NH, *39*
Conasa de Mexico, S.C. (R), MX, *39*
Robert Connelly & Assoc., Inc. (R), MN, *39*
Connors, Lovell & Assoc. Inc. (C), ON, *296*
Conroy Partners Ltd. (R), AB, *39*
Consolidated Management Services (C), ON, *296*
Construct Management Services (C), MN, *297*
Construction Search Specialists, Inc. (C), WI, *297*
Consulting Rhonda (C), ON, *297*
ContactBridge, Inc. (R), IL, *40*
Continental Research Search, Inc. (C), WI, *298*
Continental Search & Outplacement, Inc. (C), MD, *298*
Continental Search Assoc. (C), OH, *298*
Conway & Assoc. (R), IL, *40*
Cook Assoc. Int'l., Inc. (C), TN, *298*
P. G. Cook Assoc. (R), TN, *40*
Cook Assoc.,® Inc. (R), IL, *40*
The Cooke Group (R), WI, *40*
Corbin Packaging Professionals (C), MO, *299*
Cornwall Stockton & Co., Inc. (C), TX, *299*
The Corporate Advisory Group (R), NJ, *41*
The Corporate Connection, Ltd. (C), VA, *299*
Corporate Environment Ltd. (R), IL, *41*
Corporate Image Group (C), TN, *300*
Corporate Management Services (C), PA, *300*
Corporate Plus, Ltd. (C), GA, *300*
Corporate Recruiters Ltd. (C), BC, *300*
Corporate Recruiters Inc. (C), PA, *300*
Corporate Search Consultants (C), IN, *301*
Corporate Search Consultants, Inc. (C), FL, *301*
Corporate Search, Inc. (C), NY, *301*
Corporate Select Int'l., Ltd. (C), IL, *301*
Corporate Staffing Group, Inc. (C), PA, *301*
Corso, Mizgala + French (R), ON, *42*
Leonard Corwen Assoc. (C), NY, *302*
Cosier & Assoc. (C), AB, *302*
J. D. Cotter Search Inc. (C), OH, *302*
Courtright & Assoc., Inc. (R), PA, *42*
Cowell & Associates, Ltd. (R), IL, *42*
Cowin Assoc. (R), NY, *42*
Crane, Reed & Co., Inc. (C), NH, *302*
Creative HR Solutions (C), GA, *303*
Creative Input, Inc. (C), RI, *303*
Creative-Leadership, Inc. (R), CA, *42*
The Cris Group, Inc. (R), NY, *42*
Crist Partners, Ltd. (R), IL, *43*
Marlene Critchfield Co. (C), CA, *303*
Criterion Executive Search, Inc. (C), FL, *303*
Cross Country Consultants, Inc. (C), MD, *304*
Crowder & Company (R), MI, *43*
Timothy D. Crowe, Jr. (R), MA, *43*
Jim Crumpley & Assoc. (C), MO, *304*
CSA/Clinical Staffing Assoc., LLC (C), NJ, *304*
Culver Personnel Services (C), CA, *304*
Cumberland Group Inc. (C), IL, *304*
Cumberland Professional Search Inc. (C), TN, *304*
Frank Cuomo & Assoc., Inc. (C), NY, *305*
Curran Partners, Inc. (R), CT, *44*
Current Resource Group, Inc. (C), GA, *305*
The Currier-Winn Co., Inc. (C), NJ, *305*
Curry, Telleri Group, Inc. (R), NJ, *44*
Tony Curtis & Associates (C), ON, *305*
Cusack Consulting (R), NY, *44*
The Custer Group, Inc. (R), TN, *44*
CV Associates (C), NY, *305*
Cyntal Int'l. Ltd. (R), NY, *44*
Cypress Int'l., Inc. (R), FL, *45*
Cyr Associates, Inc. (C), MA, *306*
D.A.I Human Resources Consultants (R), QE, *45*
D.A.L. Associates, Inc. (R), CT, *45*
D.R. Assoc. (R), CA, *45*
Daggett & Kvistad (R), CA, *45*
Charles Dahl Group, Inc. (C), MN, *306*
Dahl-Morrow Int'l. (R), VA, *45*
The Dalley Hewitt Co. (R), GA, *45*
Daniel Marks Company (C), OH, *306*
The Danielson Group, Inc. (C), TX, *306*
Alan Darling Consulting (R), VT, *46*
The Dartmouth Group (R), NY, *46*
Data Search Network, Inc. (C), FL, *307*
Data-AxIS Corp. (C), FL, *307*
The DataFinders Group, Inc. (C), NJ, *307*
Alan N. Daum & Assoc., Inc. (C), OH, *308*
David Perry Assoc. (C), NJ, *308*
Davidson, Laird & Assoc. (C), MI, *308*
Alan Davis & Assoc. Inc. (R), QE, *47*
Davis & Company (R), CA, *47*
DBC Recruiting Network (C), GA, *309*
DBL Associates (C), CA, *309*
Dean-MacDonald (R), OH, *47*
Debbon Recruiting Group, Inc. (C), MO, *310*
Deeco Int'l. (C), UT, *310*
DEL Technical Services, Inc. (C), IL, *310*
DeLalla - Fried Assoc. (C), NY, *310*
Thorndike Deland Assoc. LLC (R), NY, *48*
Delta Management Group Ltd. (C), ON, *310*
Delta Resource Group, Ltd. (C), GA, *311*
Delta Services (R), TX, *48*
DeMatteo Associates (C), NY, *311*
Derhak Ireland & Partners Ltd. (R), ON, *48*
Desktop Staffing, Inc. (C), IL, *311*
Despres & Associates (C), IL, *311*
The Devlin Search Group, Inc. (C), MA, *311*
Diamond Tax Recruiting (C), NY, *312*
Dieckmann & Assoc., Ltd. (R), IL, *51*
DieckMueller Group (R), WI, *51*
The Diestel Group (R), UT, *51*
Roger Dietsch & Assoc. (C), MN, *312*
DiMarchi Partners (R), CO, *51*
J. Dinerstein & Co., Inc. (R), NY, *51*
Robert W. Dingman Co., Inc. (R), CA, *52*
Direct Recruiters, Inc. (C), OH, *312*
Dise & Co. (R), OH, *52*
DiTech Resources (C), CT, *313*
Diversified Consulting Services, Inc. (C), CO, *313*
Diversified Search, Inc. (R), PA, *52*
Dixie Search Assoc. (C), GA, *313*
DLB Assoc. (R), NY, *53*
DNA Search, Inc. (C), CA, *313*
Doering & Assoc. (C), CA, *313*
L. J. Doherty & Assoc. (R), MA, *53*
Doherty Int'l., Inc. (R), IL, *53*
Doleman Enterprises (R), VA, *53*
The Domann Organization (R), CA, *53*
Dominguez-Metz & Assoc. (R), CA, *53*
Domres Professional Search (R), WI, *53*
Don Allan Assoc., Inc. (C), CA, *313*
The Donnelly Group-Sales Recruiters, Inc. (C), MO, *314*
The Dorfman Group (C), AZ, *314*
Dougherty & Assoc. (C), TN, *314*
Dreier Consulting (C), NJ, *315*
Robert Drexler Assoc., Inc. (R), NJ, *54*
Dromeshauser Assoc. (R), MA, *55*
DRZ Medical Recruiters (C), CO, *315*
DuBrul Management Co. (C), NY, *315*
J. H. Dugan & Assoc., Inc. (R), CA, *55*
Dukas Assoc. (C), MA, *315*
The Duncan-O'Dell Group Inc. (C), TX, *316*
Dunhill Staffing Systems, Inc. (C), NY, *316*
Dunhill Professional Search of Miami (C), FL, *319*
Dunhill Personnel of Boulder (C), CO, *319*
Dunhill Professional Search of Englewood, Inc. (C), CO, *319*
Dunhill of Ft. Collins, Inc. (C), CO, *319*
Dunhill Professional Search of Oakland (C), CA, *319*
Dunhill Professional Search of San Jose (C), CA, *319*
Dunhill Executive Search of Los Angeles, Inc. (C), CA, *319*
Dunhill of San Francisco, Inc. (C), CA, *319*
Dunhill Professional Search of Augusta (C), GA, *320*
Dunhill Search of West Atlanta (C), GA, *320*
Dunhill Technical Staffing (C), IN, *320*
Dunhill of Ft. Wayne, Inc. (C), IN, *320*
Dunhill Staffing Systems (C), NC, *321*
Dunhill Professional Search of Ramsey (C), NJ, *321*

INDUSTRIES

Dunhill Professional Search of Byram (C), MS, *321*
Dunhill Executive Search of Brown County (C), IN, *321*
Dunhill Professional Search (C), MO, *321*
Dunhill Search of Arlington (C), TX, *322*
Dunhill Professional Search of Winston-Salem (C), NC, *322*
Dunhill Personnel Service of Fargo (C), ND, *322*
Dunhill Personnel of St. Andrews (C), SC, *322*
Dunhill Professional Search of Wilkes-Barre/Scranton, Inc. (C), PA, *322*
Dunhill Professional Search of Bucks-Mont., Inc. (C), PA, *322*
Dunhill of Corpus Christi, Inc. (C), TX, *323*
Dunhill Professional Search, Inc. of McAllen (C), TX, *323*
Dunhill Professional Search of Richmond (C), VA, *323*
Dunlap & Sullivan Assoc. (R), MI, *55*
Dunn Associates (R), PA, *55*
C. A. Durakis Assoc., Inc. (R), MD, *55*
Dussick Management Assoc. (C), CT, *323*
G. L. Dykstra Assoc., Inc. (C), MI, *323*
Dynamic Choices Inc. (C), MO, *323*
Dynamic Search Systems, Inc. (C), IL, *324*
Dynamic Synergy Corp. (R), CA, *56*
E O Technical (C), CT, *324*
E T Search Inc. (C), CA, *324*
E.P. Int'l. (C), NY, *324*
E/Search Int'l. (C), CT, *325*
EA Plus, Inc. (C), TX, *325*
Eagle Consulting Group Inc. (C), TX, *325*
J. M. Eagle Partners Ltd. (C), WI, *325*
Eagle Search Assoc. (C), CA, *325*
EagleView, Inc. (C), MA, *325*
Earley Kielty & Assoc., Inc. (R), NY, *56*
Eastbourne Assoc. Inc. (R), NY, *56*
Eastman & Beaudine, Inc. (R), TX, *56*
EBA Group (R), NJ, *56*
Eden & Assoc., Inc. (C), PA, *326*
The Edge Resource Group (C), PA, *326*
EDI, Inc. (C), MD, *326*
EDI/Executive Dynamics Inc. (C), NJ, *326*
EDP Staffing Solutions, Inc. (C), AR, *327*
Edwards & Assoc. (C), GA, *327*
Bruce Edwards & Associates, Inc. (R), NC, *56*
EFCO Consultants, Inc. (C), NY, *327*
Effective Search, Inc. (R), IL, *57*
EFL Int'l. (R), AZ, *57*
Egan & Assoc. (R), WI, *57*
D. C. Egan & Assoc. (C), GA, *327*
EGM Consulting, Inc. (R), FL, *57*
Richard A. Eisner & Co., LLP (R), NY, *57*
W. Robert Eissler & Assoc., Inc. (C), TX, *327*
William J. Elam & Assoc. (R), NE, *58*
The Eldridge Group, Ltd. (C), IL, *327*
Electronic Search, Inc. (C), IL, *327*
Elinvar (C), NC, *328*
Elite Medical Search (C), GA, *328*
Elite Resources Group (R), OH, *58*
Yves Elkas Inc. (R), QE, *58*
Gene Ellefson & Assoc. Inc. (C), MI, *328*
The Elliott Company (R), MA, *58*
David M. Ellner Assoc. (R), NY, *59*
The Ellsworth Group (C), NY, *329*
The Elmhurst Group (C), CA, *329*
The Elsworth Group (C), TX, *329*
Emerald Legal Search (C), NH, *329*
Emerging Medical Technologies, Inc. (C), CO, *329*
Emerging Technology Search (C), GA, *329*
Emerson & Co. (C), GA, *329*
Emmett Executive Search, Inc. (C), NY, *330*
Empire International (R), PA, *59*
Employ® (C), PA, *330*
Employment Solutions, Inc. (C), TX, *330*
Empowered Solutions Corp. (C), GA, *330*
Engineering & Scientific Search Assoc. (ESSA) (C), NJ, *330*
Engineering Futures, LLC (C), CT, *330*
Engineering Placement Specialists (C), WI, *330*
Engineering Profiles (C), FL, *330*
Engineering Resource Group, Inc. (C), NJ, *331*
ENI (R), CT, *59*
Environmental, Health & Safety Search Assoc. (C), FL, *331*
Epsen, Fuller & Assoc., LLC (R), NJ, *60*
Erlanger Assoc. (R), CT, *60*
Erwin Assoc. (R), IL, *60*
ESA (R), CT, *60*
ESS (Executive Search Services) (R), CA, *61*
Essential Solutions, Inc. (C), CA, *331*
Ethos Consulting, Inc. (R), CA, *61*
Evergreen & Co. (C), MA, *331*
Excalibur Human Resources, Inc. (R), NJ, *61*
Exclusive Search Consultants (C), OH, *331*
Exec Tech, Inc. (C), IL, *332*
ExeConnex, LLC (R), GA, *61*
Execu-Tech Search Inc. (C), MN, *332*
ExecuQuest, Inc. (R), MI, *61*
ExecuSource Assoc., Inc. (C), GA, *332*
ExecuSource Consultants, Inc. (C), TX, *332*
Executech (R), OH, *62*
ExecuTech (C), IN, *332*
Executive Business Solutions, Inc. (C), WA, *332*
Executive Career Search (C), VA, *332*
Executive Connection (C), OH, *333*
Executive Dimensions (R), NY, *62*
Executive Directions (R), OH, *62*
Executive Manning Corp. (R), FL, *63*
Executive Partners Inc. (C), CT, *333*
Executive Placement Consultants (C), IL, *333*
Executive Recruiters Int'l. (C), MI, *333*
Executive Recruiters Agency, Inc. (C), AR, *333*
Executive Recruiters (C), WA, *334*
Executive Recruiters, Inc. (C), WI, *334*
Executive Recruitment Specialists, Inc. (R), NC, *63*
Executive Recruitment Services, Inc. (ERS, Inc.) (C), GA, *334*
Executive Registry (C), QE, *334*
Executive Resource Assoc. (C), VA, *334*
Executive Resource Group, Inc. (R), ME, *63*
Executive Resource Inc. (C), WI, *334*
Executive Resource Systems (C), CA, *335*
Executive Sales Search (C), CO, *335*
Executive Search Int'l./Transearch (R), MA, *63*
Executive Search Int'l. (C), TX, *335*
Executive Search, Ltd. (C), OH, *336*
Executive Search of America, Inc. (C), OH, *336*
Executive Search Partners (R), NY, *63*
Executive Search Plus, Inc. (C), IN, *336*
Executive Search Team (C), MI, *336*
Executive Solutions (R), MN, *64*
The Executive Source (C), SA, *337*
The Executive Tree (R), FL, *64*
ExecutiveFit (C), NY, *337*
EXETER 2100 (C), NH, *337*
Raymond L. Extract & Assoc. (R), CA, *64*
Eyler Assoc., Inc. (R), IA, *64*
F.L.A.G. (C), OH, *338*
Fabian Assoc. Inc. (C), NY, *338*
Fagan & Company (R), PA, *64*
Fairfaxx Corp. (R), CT, *64*
Fairfield Int'l. Resources (R), NY, *65*
Paul Falcone Assoc. (R), NJ, *65*
Leon A. Farley Assoc. (R), CA, *65*
Dorothy W. Farnath & Assoc., Inc. (C), NJ, *338*
James Feerst & Assoc., Inc. (C), AZ, *339*
Fenwick Partners (R), MA, *66*
Fenzel Milar Assoc. (C), OH, *339*
Fergason Assoc., Inc. (C), IL, *339*
Ferneborg & Assoc., Inc. (R), CA, *66*
Fernow Assoc. (C), PA, *339*
Guild Fetridge Acoustical Search, Inc. (C), NY, *340*
Fidelity Search Group, Inc. (R), PA, *66*
Financialjobs.com (C), CA, *340*
Neil Fink Assoc. (R), CA, *66*
Finnegan & Assoc. (R), CA, *67*
Finney-Taylor Personnel & Management Consultants Ltd. (C), AB, *341*
First Choice Search (R), WA, *67*
First Search America, Inc. (C), TN, *341*
First Search Inc. (C), IL, *341*
Howard Fischer Assoc. Int'l., Inc. (R), PA, *67*
Fishel HR Assoc., Inc. (C), AZ, *341*
Fisher & Assoc. (R), CA, *67*
Jack Stuart Fisher Assoc. (C), NJ, *341*
The Fisher Group (R), AB, *67*
Fisher Personnel Management Services (R), CA, *68*
Fisher-Todd Assoc. (C), NY, *341*
James L. Fisk & Assoc. (C), MO, *342*
Robert M. Flanagan & Assoc., Ltd. (R), NY, *68*
Susan Fletcher Attorney Employment Services (C), PA, *342*
Flexible Resources, Inc. (C), CT, *342*
Florapersonnel, Inc. (R), FL, *68*
Flowers & Assoc. (C), OH, *342*
J. G. Flynn & Assoc. Inc. (R), BC, *69*
Flynn, Hannock, Inc. (R), CT, *69*
David Fockler & Assoc., Inc. (C), CA, *342*
Focus Executive Search (C), MN, *343*
L. W. Foote Co. (R), WA, *69*

Ford & Assoc., Inc. (C), SC, *343*
The Ford Group, Inc. (R), PA, *69*
Forest People Int'l. Search Ltd. (C), BC, *343*
Fortuna Technologies Inc. (C), CA, *343*
F-O-R-T-U-N-E Personnel Consultants of Boise (R), ID, *70*
Fortune Group Int'l., Inc. (R), PA, *70*
Fortune Personnel Consultants of Huntsville, Inc. (C), AL, *343*
F-O-R-T-U-N-E Personnel Consultants of Tampa (C), FL, *344*
Fortune Personnel Consultants of Colorado Springs (C), CO, *344*
F-O-R-T-U-N-E Personnel Consultants of Wilmington (C), DE, *344*
F-O-R-T-U-N-E Personnel Consultants of Denver, Inc. (C), CO, *344*
F-O-R-T-U-N-E Personnel Consultants of Greenwood Village (C), CO, *344*
F-O-R-T-U-N-E Personnel Consultants of San Diego (C), CA, *344*
Fortune Personnel Consultants (C), CA, *344*
F-O-R-T-U-N-E Personnel Consultants of Savannah, Inc. (C), GA, *345*
Fortune Personnel Consultants of Jacksonville (C), FL, *345*
F-O-R-T-U-N-E Personnel Consultants of Palm Beach (C), FL, *345*
F-O-R-T-U-N-E Personnel Consultants of Manatee County (C), FL, *345*
Fortune of Arlington Heights (C), IL, *345*
F-O-R-T-U-N-E Personnel Consultants of Atlanta, Inc. (C), GA, *345*
F-O-R-T-U-N-E Personnel Consultants (C), MI, *346*
Fortune Personnel Consultants of Hinsdale, IL (C), IL, *346*
Fortune Personnel Consultants of Bloomfield, Inc. (C), MI, *346*
F-O-R-T-U-N-E Personnel Consultants of South Bend (C), IN, *346*
F-o-r-t-u-n-e of Owensboro, Inc. (C), KY, *346*
F-O-R-T-U-N-E Personnel Consultants of Southwest Indiana (C), IN, *346*
Fortune Personnel Consultants of Topsfield (C), MA, *346*
F-O-R-T-U-N-E Personnel Consultants of Troy, Inc. (C), MI, *347*
F-O-R-T-U-N-E Personnel Consultants of St. Louis-West County (C), MO, *347*
F-O-R-T-U-N-E Personnel Consultants of Menlo Park, Inc. (C), NJ, *347*
Fortune Personnel Consultants (C), MT, *347*
Fortune Personnel Consultants (C), NH, *347*
F-O-R-T-U-N-E Personnel Consultants of Bergen County Inc. (C), NJ, *347*
F-O-R-T-U-N-E Search Consultants (C), MO, *347*
F-O-R-T-U-N-E of West Portland (C), OR, *348*
F-O-R-T-U-N-E Personnel Consultants of Rockland County, Inc. (C), NY, *348*
Fortune Personnel Consultants of Raleigh, Inc. (C), NC, *348*
Fortune Personnel Consultants of Greensboro, NC, Inc. (C), NC, *348*
F-O-R-T-U-N-E Personnel Consultants of Charlotte (C), NC, *348*
F-O-R-T-U-N-E Personnel Consultants of Cincinnati (C), OH, *348*
Fortune Personnel Consultants of Allentown, Inc. (C), PA, *348*
Fortune Personnel Consultants of Hilton Head (C), SC, *349*
F-O-R-T-U-N-E Consultants of Memphis (C), TN, *349*
Fortune Personnel Consultants of Chattanooga Inc. (C), TN, *349*
FORTUNE Personnel Consultants of Charleston, Inc. (C), SC, *349*
Fortune Personnel Consultants of Anderson, Inc. (C), SC, *349*
FORTUNE Personnel Consultants of North Dallas (C), TX, *350*
F-O-R-T-U-N-E Personnel of Nashville (C), TN, *350*
Fortune Personnel Consultants of Plano (C), TX, *350*
F-O-R-T-U-N-E Personnel Consultants of Knoxville (C), TN, *350*
Fortune Personnel Consultants of San Antonio, Inc. (C), TX, *350*
F-O-R-T-U-N-E Personnel Consultants of Houston, Inc. (C), TX, *350*
F-O-R-T-U-N-E Personnel Consultants of the Tri-Cities, Inc. (C), TN, *350*
F-O-R-T-U-N-E Personnel Consultants of East Seattle (C), WA, *351*
Fortune Personnel Consultants of the Virginia Highlands (C), VA, *351*
Forum Personnel Inc. (C), NY, *351*
Foster Partners (R), NY, *70*
Fought, Jameson Assoc. (C), IL, *351*
The Fourbes Group, Inc. (C), NJ, *351*
Fox, White & Assoc. (C), FL, *351*
Foy, Schneid & Daniel, Inc. (R), NY, *71*
Franklin Allen Consultants, Ltd. (R), NY, *71*
Franklin Int'l. Search, Inc. (C), MA, *352*
The Franklin Search Group, Inc./Medzilla (R), WA, *71*
KS Frary & Assoc. (R), MA, *71*
Mel Frazer Consultant (C), CA, *352*
Fresquez & Assoc. (C), CA, *352*
Friedman Eisenstein Raemer & Schwartz, LLP (R), IL, *72*
Gerald Frisch Assoc., Inc. (R), NY, *72*
Frye/Joure & Assoc., Inc. (C), TN, *353*
Furlong Search, Inc. (R), CA, *72*
The Furst Group, Inc. (R), IL, *72*
Future Employment Service, Inc. (C), IA, *353*
Futures, Inc. (C), NH, *354*
G. H. Enterprises (C), AZ, *354*
GAAP Inc. (R), QE, *73*
The Gabriel Group (C), PA, *354*
Gabriele & Company (C), MA, *354*
Gaffney Management Consultants (R), IL, *73*
Jay Gaines & Company, Inc. (R), NY, *73*
Gallin Associates, Inc. (C), FL, *354*
W. N. Garbarini & Assoc. (R), NJ, *74*
Gardner-Ross Assoc., Inc. (R), NY, *74*
Garland Assoc. Int'l. (C), CA, *355*
The Garms Group (R), IL, *74*
The Garret Group (R), NJ, *75*
Gateway Group Personnel, LLC (C), TN, *355*
Gaudry, Shink, Levasseur (R), QE, *75*
Dianne Gauger & Assoc. (C), CA, *355*
Geddes & Rubin Management Inc. (R), ON, *76*
Genel Associates (C), CA, *356*
General Engineering Tectonics (C), CA, *356*
Genesis Consulting Partners (R), PA, *76*
Genesis Personnel Service, Inc. (C), OH, *356*
Genesis Recruiting (C), CA, *356*
Genesis Research (C), MO, *356*
C. R. Gerald & Assoc. (C), ON, *356*
GFI Professional Staffing Services (C), NH, *357*
Gilbert & Van Campen Int'l. (R), NY, *76*
Gilbert Tweed Assoc. Inc. (R), NY, *76*
Joe L. Giles & Assoc. (C), MI, *357*
Howard Gilmore & Assoc. (R), OH, *77*
Gilreath Weatherby Inc. (R), MA, *77*
Lawrence Glaser Assoc., Inc. (C), NJ, *357*
J. P. Gleason Assoc., Inc. (R), IL, *77*
The Glenwood Group (C), IL, *358*
Glines Assoc., Inc. (R), IL, *77*
Global Career Services, Inc. (C), NY, *358*
Global Consulting Group Inc. (C), ON, *358*
Global Data Services, Inc. (R), NY, *77*
Global Employer's Network, Inc. (R), TX, *77*
Global Engineers Inc. (C), ME, *358*
Global Research Partnership Inc. (R), NY, *78*
Global Telecommunications, Inc. (C), TX, *359*
The GlobalSearch Group (C), TX, *359*
Glou Int'l., Inc. (R), MA, *78*
The Gobbell Co. (R), CA, *78*
Robert G. Godfrey Assoc. Ltd. (R), IL, *78*
H. L. Goehring & Assoc., Inc. (C), OH, *359*
Goldbeck Recruiting Inc. (C), BC, *359*
Goldman+Bell, LLC (C), NY, *360*
Joseph Goldring & Assoc. Inc. (C), MI, *360*
Fred J. Goldsmith Assoc. (R), CA, *79*
Goldstein & Co. (C), CA, *360*
Gomez Fregoso y Asociados (C), JAL, *360*
L. J. Gonzer Assoc. (C), NJ, *360*
The Goodman Group (R), CA, *79*
Goodrich & Sherwood Assoc., Inc. (R), NY, *79*
Gordon/Tyler (R), PA, *80*
Gould, McCoy & Chadick, Inc. (R), NY, *80*
The Governance Group, Inc. (R), NJ, *80*
Gowdy Consultants (C), TX, *361*
Graham & Co. (R), NJ, *80*
Alexander Graham Assoc. (C), NJ, *361*
Robert Graham Assoc. (R), RI, *81*
Granger, Counts & Assoc. (R), OH, *81*
Robert Grant Assoc., Inc. (C), CA, *361*
Grant Cooper & Assoc., Inc. (R), MO, *81*
The Grant Search Group, Inc. (C), ON, *361*
Grantham & Co., Inc. (R), NC, *81*
Graphic Arts Marketing Assoc., Inc. (C), MI, *361*

INDUSTRIES

Graphic Search Assoc. Inc. (C), PA, *362*
Sheila Greco Assoc. (C), NY, *362*
R. Green & Assoc., Inc. (C), OH, *362*
Greene Personnel Consultants (C), RI, *362*
Greene-Levin-Snyder LLC (C), NY, *362*
Greenfields Engineering Search (C), MO, *363*
Greenwich Internet (C), CT, *363*
Greenwich Search Partners, LLC (C), CT, *363*
Gregory, Kyle & Assoc. (C), NC, *363*
Griffith & Werner, Inc. (R), FL, *82*
Gros Executive Search, Inc. (C), TN, *363*
Grossberg & Assoc. (R), IL, *82*
Groton Planning Group (R), ME, *82*
Grover & Assoc. (R), OH, *82*
Growth Strategies, Inc. (R), FL, *83*
David E. Grumney Co. Inc. (R), WA, *83*
GSP International (C), NJ, *364*
GSW Consulting Group, Inc. (R), CA, *83*
Michael R. Guerin Co. (C), CA, *364*
Wolf Gugler & Assoc. Ltd. (R), ON, *83*
Guidarelli Assoc., Inc. (R), MI, *83*
The Guild Corp. (C), VA, *364*
The Gullgroup (C), TX, *364*
Gundersen Partners, L.L.C. (R), NY, *83*
Gustin Partners, Ltd. (R), MA, *83*
William Guy & Assoc., Inc. (R), CA, *84*
GWS Partners (R), IL, *84*
The H. S. Group, Inc. (C), WI, *365*
Habelmann & Assoc. (R), MI, *84*
Haddad Assoc. (R), FL, *84*
Russ Hadick & Assoc. Inc. (C), OH, *365*
Hadley Associates, Inc. (C), NJ, *365*
Hahn & Assoc., Inc. (C), OH, *365*
Halbrecht & Co. (C), VA, *365*
Halbrecht Lieberman Assoc., Inc. (R), CT, *84*
Hale Assoc. (R), IL, *84*
Haley Associates (R), CA, *85*
Don Hall & Assoc. (C), TX, *366*
Hall Kinion (C), CA, *366*
Hall Management Group, Inc. (C), GA, *367*
Hallman Group, Inc. (C), MI, *367*
The Hamilton Group (R), MD, *85*
The Hampton Group (C), NY, *367*
R. C. Handel Assoc. Inc. (R), CT, *85*
W. L. Handler & Assoc. (R), GA, *85*
Handy HRM (R), NY, *86*
Hanley & Assoc. (R), FL, *86*
The Hanna Group (C), OH, *368*
Hansen Executive Search, Inc. (C), NE, *368*
Harbrowe, Inc. (C), NY, *368*
Harcor Quest & Assoc. (R), OH, *86*
Harcourt & Assoc. (C), AB, *368*
Harcourt Group Ltd. (R), OH, *86*
Hardage Group (C), TN, *369*
Hardison & Company (R), TX, *86*
Robert Harkins Assoc., Inc. (C), PA, *369*
Harper Hewes, Inc. (C), NY, *369*
Harrington & O'Brien, Inc. (C), NH, *369*
The Harris Consulting Corp. (R), MB, *87*
Harris Heery & Assoc., Inc. (R), CT, *87*
Harris McCully Assoc., Inc. (C), NY, *369*
Harrison Moore Inc. (C), NE, *370*
Hartman & Barnette (R), VA, *87*
Harvey Hohauser & Assoc., LLC (R), MI, *87*
The Hawkins Co. (R), CA, *88*
Michael J. Hawkins, Inc. (C), IL, *370*
Hayden & Assoc., Inc. (C), MN, *370*
Hayman Daugherty Assoc., Inc. (C), GA, *370*
The Haystack Group, Inc. (R), ME, *88*
Hazlett Associates (R), IL, *88*
HCI Corp. (C), IL, *371*
Healey Executive Search, Inc. (R), MN, *88*
Health Industry Consultants, Inc. (R), CO, *89*
Healthcare Management Resources, Inc. (R), GA, *89*
Healthcare Recruiters Int'l. Orange County (C), CA, *372*
Healthcare Recruiters of the Rockies, Inc. (C), CO, *372*
Healthcare Recruiters Int'l. Phoenix (C), AZ, *372*
Healthcare Recruiters of Indiana (C), IN, *372*
Healthcare Recruiters Int'l. - Los Angeles (C), CA, *372*
Healthcare Recruiters Int'l. - Alabama (C), AL, *372*
Healthcare Recruiters Int'l. Philadelphia (C), NJ, *373*
Healthcare Recruiters International-NY/NJ (C), NJ, *373*
Healthcare Recruiters of New England (C), MA, *373*
Healthcare Recruiters of New Orleans (C), LA, *373*
Healthcare Recruiters Int'l - Minnesota, Inc. (C), MN, *373*
Healthcare Recruiters of New York, Inc. (C), NY, *373*
Healthcare Recruiters Int'l. - Pittsburgh (C), PA, *373*
Healthcare Recruiters of Dallas (C), TX, *374*
Healthcare Resources Group (C), OK, *374*
F. P. Healy & Co., Inc. (R), NY, *89*
HeartBeat Medical, Inc. (C), OR, *374*
Heath/Norton Assoc., Inc. (R), NY, *89*
R. W. Hebel Assoc. (R), TX, *89*
HEC Group (C), ON, *375*
Hechkoff/Work Executive Search Inc. (R), NY, *89*
Heffelfinger Assoc., Inc. (R), MA, *89*
The Heidrick Partners, Inc. (R), IL, *90*
Jay Heino Company, LLC (C), NY, *375*
Heinze & Assoc. Inc. (R), MN, *91*
Helfer Executive Consultants (R), TN, *91*
Helffrich Int'l. (C), FL, *375*
Heller Assoc., Ltd. (R), IL, *91*
Heller Kil Assoc., Inc. (C), FL, *375*
G. W. Henn & Co. (R), OH, *91*
The Hensge Co. (R), IL, *91*
Henson Partners (C), AZ, *376*
Herbeck Kline & Assoc. (R), IL, *92*
Hergenrather & Co. (R), WA, *92*
Heritage Pacific Corp. (C), CA, *376*
Heritage Search Group, Inc. (C), FL, *376*
J. J. Herlihy & Assoc., Inc. (C), CA, *376*
Herring & Assoc. (C), AR, *376*
J. D. Hersey & Assoc. (C), OH, *376*
Hessel Assoc., Inc. (C), NY, *377*
The Hetzel Group, Inc. (R), IL, *92*
Higbee Assoc., Inc. (C), CT, *377*
High Tech Staffing Group (C), OR, *377*
High-Tech Recruiters (C), CT, *378*
Highlander Search (C), NC, *378*
Hill & Assoc. (C), CA, *378*
Hill Allyn Assoc. (C), CA, *378*
Frank P. Hill (R), MX, *93*
The Hindman Co. (R), KY, *94*
The Hindman Group, Inc. (C), CA, *378*
Hintz Associates (C), NY, *378*
Hire Authority, Inc. (C), MI, *378*
The Hiring Authority, Inc. (C), FL, *379*
Hite Executive Search (R), OH, *94*
Hobson Assoc. (C), CT, *379*
Hockett Associates, Inc. (R), CA, *94*
Hodge-Cronin & Assoc., Inc. (R), IL, *94*
Hoffman Partnership Group Inc. (C), NY, *379*
Hoffman Recruiters (C), MA, *380*
The Hogan Group (C), OH, *380*
Holland & Assoc., Inc. (R), MI, *94*
Holland Rusk & Assoc. (R), IL, *95*
Hollander Horizon Int'l. (R), CA, *95*
The Hollins Group, Inc. (R), IL, *95*
Holloway Schulz & Partners (C), BC, *380*
Holohan Group, Ltd. (R), MO, *95*
J. G. Hood Assoc. (C), CT, *380*
Horizons Unlimited (C), CA, *381*
Horton Int'l. Inc. (R), NY, *96*
Hospitality Executive Search, Inc. (R), MA, *96*
Houser, Martin, Morris (C), WA, *381*
Houtz•Strawn & Arnold, Inc. (R), TX, *96*
William C. Houze & Co. (R), CA, *96*
Howe & Assoc. (R), PA, *97*
Robert Howe & Assoc. (R), GA, *97*
HR Inc. (C), NC, *382*
HRCS (R), CA, *97*
Hreshko Consulting Group (C), NJ, *382*
The HRM Group, Inc. (C), AL, *382*
HRNI (C), MI, *383*
HRS, Inc. (R), PA, *97*
The Hudson Group (C), CT, *383*
Huff Assoc. (R), NJ, *98*
Hughes & Assoc. Int'l. Inc. (C), AL, *383*
E. A. Hughes & Co., Inc. (R), NY, *98*
Hughes & Company (R), VA, *98*
Human Resource Bureau (C), CA, *384*
The Human Resource Department Ltd. (R), OH, *98*
The Human Resource Group, Inc. (R), OH, *98*
Human Resource Solutions (R), TX, *98*
Human Resource Technologies, Inc. (R), IL, *99*
Human Resources Personnel Agency (R), AR, *99*
Leigh Hunt & Assoc., Inc. (C), ME, *384*
Hunt & Howe Inc. (R), NY, *99*
The Hunt Group, Inc. (R), NC, *99*
Hunt Ltd. (C), NJ, *385*
Hunt Patton & Brazeal, Inc. (C), OK, *385*
Hunter Adams (C), NC, *385*
Hunter Douglas Group, Inc. (R), IL, *99*
The Hunter Group, Inc. (C), MI, *385*
The Hunter Group (C), NC, *385*
Hunter Int'l., Inc. (R), CT, *100*
Hunter Int'l. LLC (C), MA, *385*
Hunter, Rowan & Crowe (C), FL, *386*

Huntington Personnel Consultants, Inc. (C), NY, *386*
Huntley Associates (Dallas), Inc. (C), TX, *386*
W. Hutt Management Resources Ltd. (R), ON, *100*
Hutton Merrill & Assoc. (R), CA, *100*
Hyman & Assoc. (C), TX, *386*
The Icard Group, Inc. (C), MI, *387*
Icon Recruiters, LLC (C), CA, *387*
IMA Search, Inc. (R), NY, *101*
Impact Source, Inc. (C), FL, *387*
Impact Technical Staffing (C), OR, *387*
Independent Resource Systems (C), CA, *388*
Industry Consultants, Inc. (C), GA, *388*
Information Technology Search (C), PA, *388*
Infovia (C), CA, *388*
Ingram & Aydelotte, Inc. (R), NY, *101*
Innovative Healthcare Services, Inc. (C), GA, *389*
Innovative Resource Group, LLC (C), NC, *389*
InSearch (C), CO, *389*
The Inside Track (C), TX, *389*
Insight Consulting Co. (C), NY, *389*
Integrated Search Solutions Group, LLC (ISSG) (R), NY, *102*
Intelegra, Inc. (C), NJ, *390*
IntelliSource, inc. (C), PA, *391*
Inter Regional Executive Search, Inc. (IRES, Inc.) (C), NJ, *391*
Interactive Search Assoc. (C), PA, *391*
Interactive Search Network (R), CA, *102*
Intercontinental Executive Group (C), PA, *391*
Interim Accounting Professionals (C), CA, *391*
Interim Executive Recruiting (C), GA, *392*
Interim Financial Solutions - Mid-Atlantic Region (C), MD, *392*
Interim Management Resources Inc. (C), ON, *392*
International Business Partners (C), ON, *392*
International Consulting Services, Inc. (C), IL, *392*
International Executive Recruiters (C), OH, *393*
International Management Services Inc. (R), IL, *102*
International Management Development Corp. (C), NY, *393*
International Research Group (R), CA, *103*
International Staffing Consultants, Inc. (C), CA, *393*
Interquest, Inc. (R), NY, *103*
Intersource, Ltd. (R), GA, *103*
Interspace Interactive, Inc. (C), NY, *394*
Iona Partners (C), CA, *394*
Isaacson, Miller (R), MA, *104*
Joan Isbister Consultants (C), NY, *394*
ISC of Atlanta, Inc. (C), GA, *394*
ISC of Cincinnati Inc. (C), OH, *394*
ISG Informatics Search Group (C), ON, *395*
J. B. Linde & Assoc. (C), MO, *395*
The J. B. Search Group (C), CA, *395*
J. Joseph & Assoc. (C), OH, *395*
J. Robert Scott (R), MA, *104*
J.D.G. y Asociados, S.A. de C.V. (R), SO, *104*
J.N. Adams & Assoc., Inc. (C), PA, *396*
Jackley Search Consultants (C), MN, *396*
Ron Jackson & Assoc. (C), GA, *396*
Jackson Resources (R), TX, *105*
K. Jaeger & Assoc. (C), MA, *396*
Jaeger Int'l., Inc. (C), OH, *396*
JAG Group (R), MO, *105*
Jakobs & Assoc. Int'l. (R), NY, *105*
R. I. James, Inc. (C), NY, *397*
James Moore & Assoc. (C), CA, *397*
January Management Group (R), OH, *105*
Jaral Consultants, Inc. (C), NJ, *397*
JCL & Assoc. (C), FL, *397*
JDC Assoc. (C), NY, *397*
Jeffrey Allan Co., Inc. (C), CA, *398*
Jeffrey Meryl Assoc., Inc. (C), NJ, *398*
Jender & Company (R), IL, *105*
Jerome & Co. (C), CA, *398*
JLI-Boston (R), MA, *106*
JM & Company (R), PA, *106*
Job Link, Inc. (C), CA, *399*
Job-Born Candidate Selection Bureau (C), ON, *399*
John Jay & Co. (C), ME, *399*
Johnson & Assoc., Inc. (R), CA, *106*
John H. Johnson & Assoc., Inc. (R), IL, *106*
L. J. Johnson & Co. (R), MI, *106*
Johnson & Company (R), CT, *107*
Ronald S. Johnson Assoc., Inc. (R), CA, *107*
Johnson Assoc., Inc. (C), IL, *399*
K. E. Johnson Assoc. (C), WA, *399*
Johnson Brown Assoc., Inc. (C), IN, *400*
The Johnson Group, Unlimited (C), NY, *400*
Johnson, Kemper & Assoc. (C), TX, *400*
Johnson Smith & Knisely (R), NY, *107*
Jonas, Walters & Assoc., Inc. (R), WI, *107*
The Jonathan Stevens Group, Inc. (R), NJ, *108*
Jordan-Sitter Assoc. (R), TX, *108*
J. M. Joseph Assoc. (R), NJ, *109*
Joseph Consulting, Inc. (C), FL, *401*
Joseph Michaels (C), CA, *401*
Joslin & Assoc., Ltd. (C), IL, *401*
JPM International (C), CA, *401*
JRL Executive Recruiters (C), MO, *401*
JSG Group Management Consultants (R), ON, *109*
JT Assoc. (C), CT, *401*
Judd Associates (R), NJ, *109*
Just Management Services Inc. (C), FL, *402*
A H Justice Search Consultants (C), TX, *402*
K & C Assoc. (C), CA, *402*
Kaas Employment Services (C), IA, *402*
Kabana Corp. (C), MI, *402*
KABL Ability Network (C), CA, *402*
Kacevich, Lewis & Brown, Inc. (R), MA, *109*
Robert Kaestner & Assoc. (C), FL, *403*
Kames & Assoc. (C), MD, *403*
Kane & Assoc. (C), TX, *403*
Kanzer Assoc., Inc. (R), IL, *109*
Gary Kaplan & Assoc. (R), CA, *109*
Karp & Assoc. (C), FL, *403*
Howard Karr & Assoc., Inc. (R), CA, *110*
Allan Karson Assoc., Inc. (R), NJ, *110*
Martin Kartin & Co., Inc. (R), NY, *110*
Jim Kay & Assoc. (C), IL, *404*
Kay Concepts, Inc. (C), FL, *404*
The Kay Group of 5th Ave. (C), NY, *404*
Kaye/Bassman Int'l. Corp. (R), TX, *110*
Kazan International, Inc. (R), NJ, *110*
Keane Assoc. (R), MA, *110*
A.T. Kearney Executive Search (R), IL, *111*
Keena Staffing Services (C), NY, *404*
Kelley & Keller, Inc. (C), FL, *405*
S. D. Kelly & Assoc., Inc. (R), MA, *112*
Kelly Associates (R), PA, *112*
David Warwick Kennedy & Assoc. (R), BC, *112*
Kensington Int'l., Inc. (R), IL, *113*
Kent & Assoc. (R), OH, *113*
Kenzer Corp. (R), NY, *113*
Blair Kershaw Assoc., Inc. (C), PA, *405*
Daniel J. Kerstein, Consultant to Management (R), CO, *114*
Key Employment (C), NJ, *405*
Key Resources Int'l. (C), CA, *405*
Ki Technologies, Inc. (C), UT, *406*
Kiley, Owen & McGovern, Inc. (R), NJ, *114*
Kincannon & Reed (R), VA, *114*
Kingsbury • Wax • Bova (R), MA, *114*
Kingsley Quinn/USA (R), NJ, *115*
Richard Kinser & Assoc. (R), NY, *115*
Kip Williams, Inc. (R), NY, *115*
Kiradjieff & Goode, Inc. (R), MA, *115*
Kirby Assoc. (R), PA, *115*
The Kleinstein Group, Inc. (R), NJ, *116*
Raymond J. Klemmer & Assoc. (R), NY, *116*
The Kleven Group, Inc. - Executive Search Division (R), MA, *116*
The Kleven Group, Inc. (C), MA, *407*
Knapp Consultants (R), CT, *116*
Koehler & Co. (R), WI, *116*
The Koehler Group (C), PA, *408*
Lee Koehn Assoc., Inc. (R), OR, *116*
Koltnow & Company (R), NY, *117*
Koontz, Jeffries & Assoc., Inc. (R), FL, *117*
Korban Associates (R), PA, *117*
Kordus Consulting Group (C), WI, *408*
Koren, Rogers Assoc. Inc. (R), NY, *117*
Korn/Ferry Int'l. (R), NY, *117*
Kors Montgomery Int'l. (R), TX, *118*
Kossuth & Assoc., Inc. (R), WA, *119*
Kozlin Assoc., Inc. (C), NY, *408*
Katherine R. Kraemer (R), CA, *120*
Krakower Group, Inc. (R), CA, *120*
Kramer Executive Resources, Inc. (C), NY, *409*
Krautler Personnel Recruitment (C), FL, *409*
Evie Kreisler Assoc. Inc. (C), CA, *409*
Kremple & Meade, Inc. (R), CA, *120*
Kremple Consulting Group (R), CA, *120*
Kressenberg Assoc. (C), TX, *409*
Kreutz Consulting Group, Inc. (R), IL, *121*
Krueger Assoc. (R), IL, *121*

INDUSTRIES

John Kuhn & Assoc., Inc. (R), WI, *121*
Kuhn Med-Tech (C), CA, *409*
Paul Kull & Co. (R), NJ, *121*
Kulper & Co., L.L.C. (R), NJ, *121*
D. Kunkle & Assoc. (C), IL, *410*
John Kurosky & Assoc. (R), CA, *122*
Kurtz Pro-Search, Inc. (C), NJ, *410*
Kutt, Inc. (C), CO, *410*
L & L Assoc. (C), CA, *410*
L O R (R), NJ, *122*
L&L Assoc. Global Search (C), PA, *411*
Marvin Laba & Assoc. (R), CA, *122*
Laboratory Resource Group (C), MA, *411*
Rene LaFlamme & Associes (R), QE, *122*
Laguzza Assoc., Ltd. (R), NY, *122*
Lamay Assoc., Inc. (R), CT, *124*
Lamon + Stuart + Michaels Inc. (R), ON, *124*
Lancaster Assoc., Inc. (C), NJ, *411*
Landon Morgan (C), ON, *412*
The Landstone Group (C), NY, *412*
Lange & Assoc., Inc. (C), IN, *412*
The Langford Search, Inc. (C), AL, *412*
Lanken-Kimball-Therrell & Assoc. (C), GA, *412*
Stephen Laramee & Assoc. Inc. (C), ON, *413*
Robert Larned Assoc., Inc. (C), VA, *413*
Jack B. Larsen & Assoc., Inc. (C), PA, *413*
Larsen Int'l., Inc. (R), TX, *125*
Larson Assoc. (R), CA, *125*
Lascelle & Assoc. Inc. (C), ON, *413*
Lasher Assoc. (R), FL, *125*
Latham International, Ltd. (R), NJ, *126*
Lauer, Sbarbaro Assoc., EMA Partners Int'l. (R), IL, *126*
Lautz, Grotte, Engler & Swimley (R), CA, *126*
LaVallee & Associates (C), NC, *413*
Lawrence-Balakonis & Assoc., Inc. (C), GA, *414*
W. R. Lawry, Inc. (R), CT, *126*
The Lawson Group, Inc. (C), SC, *414*
LCS, Inc. (C), TX, *414*
Leader Institute, Inc. (C), GA, *414*
Leader Network (C), PA, *414*
Leader Search Inc. (R), AB, *127*
Leaders-Trust Int'l./Carce y Asociados, S.C. (R), MX, *127*
The Lear Group, Inc. (R), OH, *127*
Reynolds Lebus Assoc. (C), AZ, *415*
Lechner & Assoc., Inc. (C), FL, *415*
Ledbetter/Davidson Int'l., Inc. (R), NY, *127*
Albert G. Lee Assoc. (C), RI, *415*
Ricci Lee Assoc., Inc. (C), CA, *415*
The Conrad Lee Co. Inc. (R), FL, *127*
Lee Management Group Inc. (C), NJ, *416*
V. J. Lehman & Assoc., Inc. (R), CO, *127*
Lehman McLeskey (R), TX, *128*
Leith & Assoc., Inc. (C), OH, *416*
Lekan & Assoc., Inc. (R), OH, *128*
Lemming/LeVan, Inc. (R), GA, *128*
Jacques LePage Executive Search Inc. (R), QE, *128*
Leslie Kavanagh Assoc., Inc. (C), NY, *416*
J. E. Lessner Assoc., Inc. (R), MI, *128*
Levin & Company, Inc. (R), MA, *128*
Alan Levine Assoc. (R), MA, *129*
Michael Levine Search Consultants (R), NY, *129*
The Levton Group Inc. (R), ON, *129*
Lewis & Blank Int'l. (R), CA, *129*
Lewis Companies Inc. (R), ON, *129*
Lewis Consulting Service (C), IL, *417*
The Libra Group (C), NC, *417*
Pat Licata & Assoc. (C), NC, *417*
LifeWork, Inc. (C), TX, *418*
Lifter & Assoc. (C), CA, *418*
Linden Group, Inc. (C), NC, *418*
Ginger Lindsey & Assoc., Inc. (C), TX, *418*
Lineal Recruiting Services (C), CT, *418*
Lipsky Group, Inc. (R), CA, *129*
Livingston, Robert & Co. (R), CT, *130*
Lloyd Associates (R), GA, *130*
Lloyd Prescott & Churchill, Inc. (R), FL, *130*
Lloyd Prescott Assoc., Inc. (C), FL, *418*
Locke & Assoc. (R), NC, *131*
Locus Inc. (C), WV, *419*
Loewenstein & Assoc., Inc. (R), TX, *131*
Logic Assoc., Inc. (C), NY, *419*
Logistics Management Resources, Inc. (R), NY, *131*
London Executive Consultants Inc. (C), ON, *420*
Longo Associates (C), CA, *420*
Longshore + Simmons (R), PA, *131*
Lord & Albus Co. (C), TX, *420*
J. S. Lord & Company, Inc. (R), MA, *131*
Bruce Lowery & Assoc. (C), MI, *420*
Lucas Assoc. (C), GA, *421*
Lucas Group (C), NY, *421*
The John Lucht Consultancy Inc. (R), NY, *131*
The Luciani Group (R), CA, *132*
Ludwig & Assoc., Inc. (C), VA, *421*
Fran Luisi Assoc. (R), NJ, *132*
Charles Luntz & Assoc., Inc. (R), MO, *132*
Lutz Associates (C), CT, *421*
Lybrook Assoc., Inc. (C), RI, *421*
P. J. Lynch Assoc. (R), CT, *132*
Lynx, Inc. (C), MA, *421*
Lyons & Assoc., Inc. (C), IL, *422*
Lyons Pruitt Int'l. (R), PA, *132*
M H Executive Search Group (C), TX, *422*
M. K. & Assoc. (C), PA, *422*
M.C. Executive Search (C), CA, *422*
M/J/A Partners (R), IL, *133*
The Macdonald Group, Inc. (R), NJ, *133*
The Mackenzie Group (R), MD, *133*
Carol Maden Group (C), VA, *422*
The Madison Group (R), NY, *133*
Madison MacArthur Inc. (R), ON, *133*
Magellan Int'l., L.P. (C), TX, *422*
Magnum Search (C), IL, *422*
Maiola & Co. (C), OH, *423*
Maiorino & Weston Assoc., Inc. (R), CT, *134*
The Mallard Group (C), IN, *423*
Management Alliance Group, Inc. (R), NJ, *134*
Management Assoc. (C), CA, *424*
Management Association Network (C), WI, *424*
Management Catalysts (R), NJ, *134*
Management Consultants Corporate Recruiters (C), AZ, *424*
Management Dimensions Ltd. (R), ON, *134*
Management One Consultants (C), ON, *425*
Management Recruiters of Nassau, Inc. (R), NY, *134*
Management Recruiters of Decatur, LLC (C), AL, *438*
Management Recruiters of Birmingham-South, Inc. (C), AL, *438*
Management Recruiters of Birmingham, Inc. (C), AL, *438*
Management Recruiters of Birmingham (C), AL, *438*
Management Recruiters of Mobile Co., Inc. (C), AL, *438*
Management Recruiters of Tucson (C), AZ, *439*
Management Recruiters of Little Rock (C), AR, *439*
Management Recruiters of San Luis Obispo (C), CA, *439*
Management Recruiters Tucson-Foothills, Inc. (C), AZ, *439*
Management Recruiters Peninsula (C), CA, *439*
Management Recruiters of Clovis (C), CA, *440*
Management Recruiters of Laguna Hills (C), CA, *440*
Management Recruiters of Emeryville (C), CA, *440*
Management Recruiters of Northern California (C), CA, *440*
Management Recruiters of Sacramento North (C), CA, *441*
Management Recruiters Inc. of Silicon Valley (C), CA, *441*
Management Recruiters of Pleasanton (C), CA, *441*
Management Recruiters of Roseville (C), CA, *441*
Management Recruiters of Colorado Springs (C), CO, *441*
Management Recruiters of Milford Inc. (C), CT, *442*
Management Recruiters of Winsted, Inc. (C), CT, *442*
Management Recruiters of Colchester (C), CT, *442*
Management Recruiters of Middlesex (C), CT, *442*
Management Recruiters of Colorado, Inc. (C), CO, *442*
Management Recruiters of Franktown (C), CO, *442*
Management Recruiters of Melbourne, Inc. (C), FL, *443*
Management Recruiters of Ft. Myers, FL. (C), FL, *443*
Management Recruiters of Bonita Springs, Inc. (C), FL, *443*
Management Recruiters of Anna Maria Island (C), FL, *443*
Management Recruiters of Boca Raton (C), FL, *443*
Management Recruiters of Clearwater (C), FL, *443*

Management Recruiters of Miami-North (C), FL, *443*
Management Recruiters, Inc. (C), FL, *443*
Management Recruiters of Tampa North (C), FL, *444*
Management Recruiters of Plant City, Inc. (C), FL, *444*
Management Recruiters of Pensacola (C), FL, *444*
Management Recruiters of Lake Co., Inc. (C), FL, *444*
Management Recruiters of Atlanta West, Inc. (C), GA, *445*
Management Recruiters of Columbus, Inc. (C), GA, *445*
Management Recruiters of Venice, Inc. (C), FL, *445*
Management Recruiters of Duluth (C), GA, *445*
Management Recruiters of North Fulton (C), GA, *445*
Management Recruiters of Vero Beach (C), FL, *445*
Management Recruiters of Boise (C), ID, *446*
Management Recruiters of Sandy Springs (C), GA, *446*
Management Recruiters of Marietta, Inc. (C), GA, *446*
Management Recruiters of Atlanta NE (C), GA, *446*
Management Recruiters of Savannah (C), GA, *446*
Management Recruiters of Atlanta North, Inc. (C), GA, *446*
Management Recruiters of Lake Forest, IL (C), IL, *447*
Management Recruiters of Springfield, Inc. (C), IL, *447*
Management Recruiters of Sun Valley (C), ID, *447*
Management Recruiters of St. Charles (C), IL, *447*
Management Recruiters of Chicago West (C), IL, *447*
Management Recruiters of Chicago-North Shore (C), IL, *447*
Management Recruiters of Barrington (C), IL, *447*
Management Recruiters of Indianapolis (C), IN, *448*
Management Recruiters of South Bend (C), IN, *448*
Management Recruiters of Indianapolis-North (C), IN, *448*
Management Recruiters of Noblesville, Inc. (C), IN, *448*
Management Recruiters of Spencer (C), IA, *448*
Management Recruiters-Cedar Rapids, Inc. (C), IA, *448*
Management Recruiters of Fairfield (C), IA, *449*
Management Recruiters of Des Moines (C), IA, *449*
Management Recruiters of Richmond (C), KY, *449*
Management Recruiters of Siouxland (C), IA, *449*
Management Recruiters of Danville (C), KY, *449*
Management Recruiters of Topeka, Inc. (C), KS, *449*
Management Recruiters of Columbia (C), MD, *450*
Management Recruiters of Rockville (C), MD, *450*
Management Recruiters of the Baltimore Washington Corridor (C), MD, *450*
Management Recruiters of Frederick, Inc. (C), MD, *450*
Management Recruiters of Monroe, Inc. (C), LA, *450*
Management Recruiters of Livonia (C), MI, *451*
Management Recruiters of Birmingham (C), MI, *451*
Management Recruiters of Southeastern Michigan (C), MI, *451*
Management Recruiters of Dearborn, Inc. (C), MI, *451*
Management Recruiters of Muskegon (C), MI, *451*
Management Recruiters - Flint (C), MI, *451*
Management Recruiters of Baltimore (C), MD, *451*
Management Recruiters of Woodbury (C), MN, *452*
Management Recruiters of North Oakland County, Inc. (C), MI, *452*
Management Recruiters of Bloomington (C), MN, *452*
Management Recruiters of Rankin Co. (C), MS, *452*
Management Recruiters of Chanhassen (C), MN, *452*
Management Recruiters of Bay Head (C), NJ, *453*
Management Recruiters of Morris County, NJ (C), NJ, *453*
Management Recruiters of Medford, N.J. (C), NJ, *453*
Management Recruiters of Orange County, N.Y., Inc. (C), NJ, *453*
Management Recruiters of North Warren Inc. (C), NJ, *453*
Management Recruiters of Reno (C), NV, *453*
Management Recruiters of Middlesex County NJ (C), NJ, *454*
Management Recruiters of The Sandias (C), NM, *454*
Management Recruiters of New Providence (C), NJ, *454*
Management Recruiters of Broome County, Inc. (C), NY, *454*
Management Recruiters of Asheville, Inc. (C), NC, *455*
Management Recruiters of Fayetteville (C), NC, *455*
Management Recruiters of Burlington (C), NC, *455*
Management Recruiters of Woodbury Inc. (C), NY, *455*
Management Recruiters of Raleigh (C), NC, *456*
Management Recruiters of Kinston (C), NC, *456*
Management Recruiters of Mt. Airy (C), NC, *456*
Management Recruiters of Rocky Mount - Southwest (C), NC, *456*
Management Recruiters of Akron (C), OH, *457*
Management Recruiters of Winston-Salem (C), NC, *457*
Management Recruiters of Columbus (C), OH, *457*
Management Recruiters of Wilmington (C), NC, *457*
Management Recruiters of Cincinnati/ Sharonville, Inc. (C), OH, *457*
Management Recruiters of Cleveland (C), OH, *457*
Management Recruiters of Cleveland (C), OH, *457*
Management Recruiters of Dayton, Inc. (C), OH, *457*
Management Recruiters of Easton, PA (C), PA, *458*
Management Recruiters - North Canton, Inc. (C), OH, *458*
Management Recruiters of Sidney (C), OH, *458*
Management Recruiters of Bethlehem, PA (C), PA, *458*
Management Recruiters of Northwest Ohio, Inc. (C), OH, *458*
Management Recruiters of Valley Forge (C), PA, *459*
Management Recruiters of Delaware County (C), PA, *459*
Management Recruiters of Westmoreland County, Inc. (C), PA, *459*
Management Recruiters of Cherry Hill (C), PA, *459*
Management Recruiters of Lionville, Inc. (C), PA, *459*
Management Recruiters of McMurray, Inc. (C), PA, *459*
Management Recruiters of Pittsburgh-North, Inc. (C), PA, *460*
Management Recruiters of Puerto Rico (C), PR, *460*
Management Recruiters of North Charleston (C), SC, *460*
Management Recruiters of Myrtle Beach, Inc. (C), SC, *460*
Management Recruiters of Greenville (C), SC, *460*
Management Recruiters of Aiken (C), SC, *460*
Management Recruiters of West Chester, Inc. (C), PA, *460*
Management Recruiters of Florence (C), SC, *460*
Management Recruiters of Columbia, Tennessee (C), TN, *461*
Management Recruiters The Delta Group, Inc. (C), TN, *461*
Management Recruiters of Chattanooga-Brainerd, Inc. (C), TN, *461*
Management Recruiters of Sioux Falls, LLP (C), SD, *461*
Management Recruiters of Travelers Rest, Inc. (C), SC, *461*

INDUSTRIES

Management Recruiters of Franklin, Inc. (C), TN, *461*
Management Recruiters of Georgetown (C), SC, *461*
Management Recruiters of Champions (C), TX, *462*
Management Recruiters of Austin (C), TX, *462*
Management Recruiters of Arlington (C), TX, *462*
Management Recruiters of LBJ Park/Dallas (C), TX, *462*
Management Recruiters - Friendswood (C), TX, *462*
Management Recruiters of North West Austin (C), TX, *462*
Management Recruiters Dallas North (MRDN) (C), TX, *462*
Management Recruiters of Houston (C), TX, *462*
Management Recruiters of Round Rock (C), TX, *463*
Management Recruiters of Houston-Northeast (C), TX, *463*
Management Recruiters of San Antonio (C), TX, *463*
Management Recruiters of Lubbock (C), TX, *463*
Management Recruiters of Ogden (C), UT, *464*
Management Recruiters of Arlington (C), VA, *464*
Management Recruiters of Sugar Land Inc. (C), TX, *464*
Management Recruiters - Piedmont (C), VA, *464*
Management Recruiters of Salt Lake City (C), UT, *464*
Management Recruiters of Fairfax, VA (C), VA, *464*
Management Recruiters of Spokane (C), WA, *465*
Management Recruiters of Milwaukee-West (C), WI, *465*
Management Recruiters of Seattle (C), WA, *465*
Management Recruiters of Loudoun County South (C), VA, *465*
Management Recruiters of Appleton (C), WI, *465*
Management Recruiters of Roanoke (C), VA, *465*
Management Recruiters of Madison, Inc. (C), WI, *466*
Management Recruiters of Janesville, Inc. (C), WI, *466*
Management Recruiters of Stevens Point, Inc. (C), WI, *466*
Management Recruiters of Milwaukee-North (C), WI, *466*
Management Recruiters of Cheyenne (C), WY, *466*
Management Resource Group (C), MN, *467*
Management Resource Assoc., Inc. (C), FL, *467*
Management Search Int'l. (C), CA, *467*
Management Search of R.I. Inc. (R), RI, *135*
Management Solutions, Inc. (C), WA, *468*
Management Solutions, Inc. (C), CA, *468*
Mankuta Gallagher & Assoc., Inc. (C), FL, *468*
Mannard & Assoc., Inc. (R), IL, *135*
F. L. Mannix & Co. (R), MA, *135*
Manuso, Alexander & Associates, Inc. (R), NY, *135*
The Marathon Group (C), FL, *469*
MARBL Consultants, Inc. (C), WI, *469*
Marcus & Assoc. (C), NY, *469*
Margolin Consultants, Inc. (C), NY, *469*
Mark Adam Assoc. (R), NJ, *135*
J. L. Mark Assoc., Inc. (R), CO, *135*
Mark Christian & Assoc., Inc. (C), AZ, *469*
Mark III Personnel, Inc. (C), NC, *470*
Mark Stanley & Co./EMA Partners International (R), FL, *136*
Markent Personnel, Inc. (C), WI, *470*
Market Niche Consulting (C), AZ, *470*
Marketing & Sales Resources, Inc. (C), FL, *470*
Marketing Consultants (C), WI, *470*
Marketing Recruiters, Inc. (C), NC, *470*
Marketing Resources (C), MA, *470*
Marketing Search Inc. (C), OH, *471*
Paula Marks Inc. (R), NY, *136*
The Marlow Group (R), MA, *136*
The Maroon Group (R), CT, *136*
Marsar & Co., Inc. (C), FL, *471*
Karen Marshall Assoc. (C), KY, *471*
Marsteller Wilcox Assoc. (C), IL, *471*
Donovan Martin & Assoc. (R), CA, *137*
J. Martin & Assoc. (R), CA, *137*
George R. Martin (R), PA, *137*
The Martin Group (R), CA, *137*
Martin Partners, L.L.C. (R), IL, *137*
The Martwick Group, Inc. (C), OR, *472*
Marvel Consultants, Inc. (C), OH, *472*
Maschal/Connors Inc. (R), NJ, *137*
Mason & Nicastri Ltd. (R), CA, *138*
Massey-Horton Int'l. (R), ON, *138*
Louis Thomas Masterson & Co. (R), OH, *138*
Richard L. Mather & Assoc. (C), CT, *472*
Mathey Services (C), IL, *472*
Matrix Consultants, Inc. (C), NC, *472*
Matté & Company, Inc. (R), CT, *138*
Matte Consulting Group Inc. (R), QE, *138*
The Matthews Group, Inc. (C), NJ, *472*
G. P. Mattocks & Associates (C), NC, *473*
Maxecon Executive Search Consultants (R), FL, *138*
Mayhall Search Group, Inc. (C), IN, *473*
The Mazzitelli Group, Ltd. (R), MN, *139*
MB Inc. Executive Search (C), NY, *473*
The McAulay Firm (R), NC, *139*
McBride Assoc., Inc. (R), DC, *139*
Tom McCall Executive Search (C), IL, *473*
McCooe & Assoc., Inc. (R), NJ, *140*
McCormack & Farrow (R), CA, *140*
McCoy Ltd. (C), CA, *474*
McCray, Shriver, Eckdahl & Assoc., Inc. (R), CA, *140*
Earl L. McDermid & Assoc. (C), IL, *474*
McDonald Assoc. Int'l. (R), IL, *140*
Robert E. McGrath & Assoc. (R), CT, *141*
McGrath & Assoc., Inc. (R), NJ, *141*
McInturff & Assoc., Inc. (C), MA, *474*
McIntyre Management Resources (C), ON, *474*
McKee Cyber Search (C), MS, *475*
McKinley•Arend Int'l. (R), TX, *141*
The McKinnon Management Group Inc. (C), ON, *475*
Dan P. McLean Assoc., Inc. (C), ON, *475*
McManners Assoc., Inc. (R), CA, *142*
Joseph J. McTaggart (C), CA, *476*
James Mead & Co. (R), CT, *142*
Med Exec Int'l. (C), CA, *476*
Meder & Assoc., Inc. (R), IL, *142*
Medical Executive Recruiters (C), CA, *477*
Medical Executive Search Assoc., Inc. (C), AZ, *477*
Medical Innovations (C), NY, *477*
Medical Recruiters Inc. (C), MO, *477*
MedQuest Assoc. (C), CO, *478*
MedSearch Resources, Inc. (C), FL, *478*
Melancon & Co. (R), TX, *143*
Juan Menefee & Assoc. (C), IL, *478*
Mercedes & Co., Inc. (R), MA, *143*
J. M. Meredith & Assoc. Inc. (C), CA, *479*
Meridian Legal Search/Legal Temps (C), NY, *479*
Merit Professional Search, Inc. (C), TN, *479*
Merlin Int'l. Inc. (C), NJ, *479*
Merrick & Moore (C), NC, *479*
MES Search Co. (C), GA, *479*
MESA, Inc. (R), CO, *143*
MESA International (C), CA, *480*
Messett Assoc., Inc. (R), FL, *143*
META/MAT, Ltd. (R), NJ, *144*
Walter Meyer & Assoc. (R), NY, *144*
mfg/Search, Inc. (C), IN, *480*
MGA Executive Search (C), FL, *480*
Michael Assoc. (R), IL, *144*
Michael James & Co. (C), IL, *480*
Michael Wayne Recruiters (C), IL, *480*
Michael/Merrill (C), KS, *481*
Michaels & Moere (C), WI, *481*
Lou Michaels Assoc., Inc. (C), MI, *481*
Michigan Consulting Group (R), MI, *144*
Midland Consultants (C), OH, *481*
Millennium Search Group, Inc. (R), CA, *144*
Miller + Miller (C), WA, *482*
Miller Denver (C), CO, *482*
Milo Research (R), NY, *145*
Herbert Mines Assoc., Inc. (R), NY, *145*
Mirtz Morice, Inc. (R), CT, *145*
Paul Misarti Inc. (C), NY, *483*
Mitchell Martin Inc. (C), NY, *483*
MIXTEC Group (R), CA, *145*
MJF Assoc. (C), CT, *483*
Moffitt Int'l., Inc. (R), NC, *146*
Mogul Consultants, Inc. (C), NY, *483*
Diedre Moire Corp., Inc. (C), NJ, *483*
Montenido Assoc. (R), CA, *146*
The Montgomery Group, Inc. (C), TN, *484*
Montgomery Resources, Inc. (C), CA, *484*
Montgomery West (R), CA, *146*
Montgomery, Thomason & Assoc. (C), ON, *484*
Larry Moore & Assoc. (C), CA, *484*
Moore Research Assoc. (R), NJ, *147*
The Moran Group (C), IL, *484*

Mordue, Allen, Roberts, Bonney Ltd. (C), WA, *485*
Morency Assoc. (C), MA, *485*
Morgan & Assoc. (C), MA, *485*
Morgan Hunter Corp. (C), KS, *485*
Morgan Int'l., Inc. (R), IL, *147*
Morgan Samuels Co. (R), CA, *147*
The Morgan/Geoffries Group (C), CA, *485*
The Morley Group (C), IN, *486*
Morris & Berger (R), CA, *147*
Robert T. Morton Assoc., Inc. (C), MA, *486*
Morton, McCorkle & Assoc. Inc. (R), MO, *147*
MPA Executive Search Inc. (R), QE, *148*
MTA Partners (R), TX, *148*
Mulcahy Co. (C), WI, *487*
Mullen Assoc., Inc. (R), NC, *148*
The Mulshine Co., Inc. (R), NJ, *149*
The Mulshine Company, Ltd. (R), NY, *149*
Multisearch Recruiters (C), CA, *487*
R. F. Mulvaney & Assoc., Inc. (R), MO, *149*
Munroe, Curry & Bond Assoc. (R), NJ, *149*
The Murray Group (C), IL, *487*
Musick & Assoc. (C), CA, *487*
N.A.P. Executive Services (Canada) Inc. (C), ON, *488*
Nachman Biomedical (C), MA, *488*
Nadzam, Lusk, Horgan & Assoc., Inc. (R), CA, *150*
Nagler, Robins & Poe, Inc. (R), MA, *150*
NaTek Corp. (C), NY, *488*
National Computerized Employment Service, Inc. (C), PA, *489*
National Corporate Consultants, Inc. (C), IN, *489*
National Executive (C), ON, *489*
National Field Service Corp. (C), NY, *489*
National Metal Services Corp. (C), IN, *489*
National Recruiting Service (C), IN, *489*
National Search Assoc. (C), CA, *490*
National Search, Inc. (R), NC, *150*
Nationwide Personnel Recruiting & Consulting, Inc. (C), OR, *490*
Nationwide Personnel Placement, Inc. (C), OH, *490*
NaviSearch (C), GA, *490*
NCC Executive Search Consultants (C), CA, *490*
The Neil Michael Group, Inc./Global Partners (R), NY, *151*
The NEIS Corp., Inc. (C), FL, *491*
J. Fielding Nelson & Assoc., Inc. (R), UT, *151*
Len Nelson & Assoc., Inc. (C), TX, *491*
New Directions, Inc. (C), IL, *492*
New Venture Development, Inc. (C), CA, *492*
Newcomb-Desmond & Assoc., Inc. (C), OH, *492*
Newell Assoc. (R), NY, *151*
Newman-Johnson-King, Inc. (C), TX, *492*
Newport Management (C), NY, *492*
NHA Plastics Recruiters (C), FL, *493*
Nicholaou & Co. (R), IL, *151*
Nichols & Company (R), CO, *151*
P. J. Nicholson & Assoc. (C), IL, *493*
The Niemond Corp. (R), CA, *152*
Ira Z. Nitzberg (C), NY, *493*
NJ Solutions (C), CA, *493*
NMC & Kay Int'l. (R), CO, *152*
Noble & Assoc., Inc. (C), NY, *494*
The Noebel Search Group, Inc. (C), TX, *494*
The Nolan Group (C), CA, *494*
Noll Human Resource Services (C), NE, *494*
W. D. Nolte & Company (R), CT, *152*
Nordeman Grimm, Inc. (R), NY, *152*
The Norland Group (C), CA, *494*
Paul Winston Norman & Assoc. (R), IL, *152*
Norman Broadbent Int'l., Inc. (R), NY, *152*
The Normyle/Erstling Health Search Group (C), NJ, *494*
Norrell Financial Staffing (C), GA, *495*
John B. Norris & Assoc., Inc. (C), MD, *495*
Norris Agency (C), TX, *495*
NorTech Resources (C), NY, *496*
North Coast Meridian (C), NY, *496*
The North Peak Group (C), OH, *496*
Northern Consultants Inc. (R), ME, *153*
Norton & Assoc. (C), IL, *496*
NPF Assoc. Ltd. Inc. (R), FL, *153*
Nuessle, Kurdziel & Weiss, Inc. (R), PA, *153*
NYCOR Search, Inc. (C), MN, *497*
O'Brien & Bell (R), OH, *153*
O'Brien and Roof (C), OH, *497*
O'Brien Consulting Services (R), MA, *153*
O'Callaghan Honey/Ray & Berndtson Inc. (R), AB, *153*
O'Connell Group Inc. (C), CT, *497*
John R. O'Connor & Assoc. (C), IL, *497*
O'Connor, O'Connor, Lordi, Ltd. (R), PA, *154*
O'Connor Resources (C), TX, *497*
O'Keefe & Assoc., Inc. (R), CT, *154*
O'Neill & Co. (R), CT, *154*
O'Neill Group (C), NJ, *498*
O'Rourke Companies, Inc. (R), TX, *154*
O'Shea, Divine & Co., Inc. (R), CA, *154*
Ober & Company (R), CA, *155*
Oberlander & Co., Inc. (R), IL, *155*
Odell & Assoc., Inc. (C), TX, *498*
The Odessa Group (R), CA, *155*
Oliver & Rozner Assoc., Inc. (R), NY, *155*
Olsen/Clark (R), WA, *156*
Omega Search, Inc. (C), NC, *498*
Omega Systems, LLC (C), VA, *498*
OmniSearch, Inc. (C), FL, *499*
The Onstott Group (R), MA, *156*
Open Concepts (C), CA, *499*
Opus Marketing (R), CA, *156*
Organization Consulting Ltd. (R), ON, *157*
Organization Resources Inc. (R), MA, *157*
Orion Int'l. Consulting Group, Inc. (C), NC, *499*
Ortman Recruiting Int'l. (C), CA, *500*
K. Ossow & Co. (C), NY, *500*
Ott & Hansen, Inc. (R), CA, *157*
Robert Ottke Assoc. (R), CA, *157*
Overton Consulting (R), WI, *157*
LaMonte Owens, Inc. (R), PA, *157*
The Oxford Group (C), TX, *500*
P R Management Consultants, Inc. (C), NJ, *500*
Pacific Advisory Service, Inc. (C), IL, *501*
Pacific Coast Recruiting (C), CA, *501*
Pacific Crossing (C), CA, *501*
Pacific Finance Search, Inc. (C), CA, *501*
Packaging Personnel Co., Ltd. (C), WI, *501*
T. Page & Assoc. (C), TX, *502*
The Pailin Group Professional Search Consultants (R), TX, *158*
Pamenter, Pamenter, Brezer & Deganis Ltd. (R), ON, *159*
Arthur Pann Assoc., Inc. (C), NY, *502*
Paper Industry Recruitment (P.I.R.) (C), ME, *502*
Parenica & Co. (R), NC, *159*
Frank Parillo & Assoc. (R), CA, *159*
R. Parker & Assoc., Inc. (R), NY, *159*
D. P. Parker & Assoc., Inc. (R), MA, *159*
Parker, McFadden & Assoc. (C), GA, *503*
Michael W. Parres & Assoc. (R), MI, *159*
Parsons, Anderson & Gee, Inc. (C), NY, *503*
Partners In Human Resources Int'l., Inc. (R), NY, *160*
Partners in Recruiting (C), IL, *503*
The Partnership Group (R), NJ, *160*
Partnervision Consulting Group Inc. (R), ON, *160*
Rick Pascal & Assoc., Inc. (C), NJ, *504*
Carolyn Smith Paschal Int'l. (R), CA, *160*
Pasona Canada, Inc. (C), ON, *504*
Pathway Executive Search, Inc. (C), NY, *505*
Pathways Int'l. (C), CT, *505*
Patriot Assoc. (C), PA, *505*
Paules Associates (C), CA, *505*
Pawlik/Dorman Partners (R), IL, *161*
PC Assoc. (C), CO, *505*
Peachtree Executive Search (R), GA, *161*
Pearson & Assoc., Inc. (C), AZ, *506*
Peck & Assoc., Ltd. (R), WI, *161*
Peeney Assoc., Inc. (R), NJ, *161*
Paul S. Pelland, P.C. (R), SC, *161*
M. A. Pelle Assoc., Inc. (C), NY, *506*
The Penn Partners, Inc. (R), PA, *162*
People Management Mid-South, LLC (R), TN, *162*
People Management Northeast, Inc. (R), CT, *162*
PeopleSource Inc. (C), TX, *506*
PERC, Ltd. (C), AZ, *506*
Performance Resources, Inc. (C), RI, *507*
The Perkins Group (R), NC, *162*
Perry Search Assoc. (C), CA, *507*
Perry-D'Amico & Assoc. (R), CA, *162*
Perry-Martel Int'l., Inc. (R), ON, *163*
Barry Persky & Co., Inc. (R), CT, *163*
PersoNet, Inc. (C), FL, *507*
Personnel Alliance Group (C), NJ, *507*
Personnel Assoc. (C), NC, *508*
The Personnel Group, Inc. (R), MN, *163*
Personnel, Inc. (C), AL, *508*
Personnel Incorporated (C), IA, *508*
Personnel Management Group (C), MB, *508*
The Personnel Network, Inc. (C), SC, *508*
Personnel Solutions (C), AZ, *509*
Personnel Tangent Inc. (C), QE, *509*
Personnel Unlimited/Executive Search (C), WA, *509*

Petrie Partners, Inc. (R), FL, *163*
Petro Staff Int'l. (C), AB, *509*
Petruzzi Assoc. (C), NJ, *509*
Peyser Assoc., Inc. (R), FL, *163*
Pharmaceutical Recruiters, Inc. (R), NY, *163*
Phase II Management (R), CT, *164*
Phelps Personnel Assoc., Inc. (C), SC, *510*
J. R. Phillip & Assoc., Inc. (R), CA, *164*
Phillips Assoc. (C), FL, *510*
Phillips Int'l., Inc. (C), SC, *510*
Phillips Resource Group (C), SC, *510*
Philo & Associates (C), GA, *511*
Phoenix BioSearch, Inc. (C), NJ, *511*
Phoenix Partners, Inc. (C), GA, *511*
Phoenix Search (R), MX, *164*
PIC Executive Search (C), GA, *511*
Gregory D. Pickens (C), TX, *511*
Pierce & Assoc. (C), CA, *512*
Pinnacle Executive Group Inc. (C), MO, *512*
The Pinnacle Source, Inc. (C), CO, *512*
Pinsker and Company, Inc. (R), CA, *164*
Pinton Forrest & Madden/EMA Partners Int'l. (R), BC, *165*
Pioneer Consulting Group (C), CA, *512*
DNPitchon Assoc. (R), NJ, *165*
PKS Assoc., Inc. (C), RI, *513*
PLA, Inc. (C), NJ, *513*
Place Mart Personnel Service (C), NJ, *513*
Placement Solutions (C), WI, *513*
Placement Testart Inc. (C), QE, *513*
Plante & Moran, LLP (R), MI, *165*
Rene Plessner Assoc., Inc. (R), NY, *165*
R. L. Plimpton Assoc., Inc. (R), CO, *165*
Yves Plouffe & Assoc. (R), QE, *165*
Plummer & Assoc., Inc. (R), CT, *166*
PMJ & Assoc. (C), ON, *513*
The Polen Group (C), PA, *514*
Ray Polhill & Assoc. (R), NC, *166*
The Pollack Group (C), ON, *514*
Polson & Co., Inc. (R), MN, *166*
Polytechnical Consultants, Inc. (C), IL, *514*
Don V. Poole & Assoc., Inc. (C), CO, *514*
Jack Porter Assoc., Inc. (C), WA, *514*
David Powell, Inc. (R), CA, *166*
Robert Powers & Assoc. (C), CA, *515*
Norman Powers Assoc., Inc. (C), MA, *515*
Powers Consultants, Inc. (R), MO, *166*
P. G. Prager Search Assoc., Ltd. (C), NY, *515*
The Prairie Group (C), IL, *515*
Prairie Resource Group, Inc. (R), IL, *166*
PRAXIS Partners (R), VA, *167*
Precision Executive Search (C), AZ, *516*
Predictor Systems Corp. (R), CA, *167*
Preferred Placement, Inc. (C), NY, *516*
Preferred Professional Recruiters (C), OH, *516*
Preferred Professional Recruiters (C), TX, *516*
George Preger & Associates Inc. (R), ON, *167*
Premier Business Advisors (C), PA, *516*
Premier Recruiting Group (C), MI, *516*
Premier Search Group (C), IN, *517*
The Premier Staffing Group (C), OH, *517*
Preng & Assoc., Inc. (R), TX, *167*
Prescott Legal Search, Inc. (C), TX, *517*
Prestige Inc. (C), WI, *517*
Preston-Hunter, Inc. (R), IL, *167*
Prestonwood Assoc. (R), MA, *168*
Price & Assoc., Inc. (C), VA, *518*
Alan J. Price Assoc., Inc. (C), RI, *518*
PricewaterhouseCoopers Executive Search (R), ON, *168*
Prichard Kymen Inc. (R), AB, *168*
Prime Management Group Inc. (C), ON, *518*
Prime Resource Assoc. (C), WI, *518*
Prime Search (C), NC, *518*
Princeton Executive Search (C), NJ, *518*
Prior/Martech Assoc., Inc. (R), WA, *169*
Pro Tec Technical Services (C), ON, *519*
Pro-Tech Search, Inc. (C), IL, *519*
Probe Technology (C), PA, *519*
Procurement Resources (C), MD, *520*
Professional Employment Group (C), MD, *520*
Professional Engineering Technical Personnel Consultants (C), NC, *520*
Professional Personnel Services (C), IA, *520*
Professional Personnel Consultants, Inc. (C), MI, *521*
Professional Persons Career Services (C), NY, *521*
Professional Recruiters Inc. (C), MN, *521*
Professional Recruiting Consultants (C), FL, *521*
Professional Recruiting Network (C), CA, *521*
Professional Recruiters (C), UT, *521*
Professional Recruiting Consultants, Inc. (C), DE, *521*
Professional Research Services, Inc. (R), IL, *169*
Professional Resources (C), NY, *522*
Professional Resources (C), OK, *522*
The Professional Sales Search Co., Inc. (C), WA, *522*
Professional Search (R), MI, *169*
Professional Search Assoc. (C), CA, *522*
Professional Search Consultants (PSC) (C), TX, *523*
Professional Support Inc. (C), NY, *523*
Professional Team Search, Inc. (R), AZ, *169*
Professions, Inc. (C), OH, *523*
ProNet, Inc. (C), NC, *524*
Proquest Inc. (C), SC, *524*
ProSearch, Inc. (C), PA, *524*
ProSearch, Inc. (C), OH, *524*
ProTech Nationwide Staffing, Inc. (C), NY, *525*
Protocol Inc. (C), CA, *525*
Proven Edge (C), CA, *525*
PSD Group, Inc. (C), CA, *525*
PSP Agency (C), NY, *525*
Quality Consulting Group, Inc. (C), WI, *526*
Quality Control Recruiters (C), CT, *526*
Quality Search (C), IN, *526*
Quality Search Inc. (C), OH, *526*
Quantum EDP Recruiting Services (C), QE, *526*
Quantum Int'l., Ltd. (R), FL, *170*
L. J. Quinn & Assoc., Inc. (R), CA, *170*
Quiring Assoc., Inc. (C), IN, *527*
QVS Int'l. (R), GA, *170*
R & K Associates, Inc. (C), AZ, *527*
R. J. Associates (C), NY, *528*
R.A.N. Assoc., Inc. (C), OH, *528*
R/K International Inc. (R), CT, *171*
R2 Services, LLC (C), IL, *528*
Radosevic Assoc. (R), CA, *171*
Railey & Assoc. (C), TX, *528*
Raines Int'l. Inc. (R), NY, *171*
Ramming & Assoc., Inc. (C), NJ, *528*
Rand Assoc. (R), ME, *171*
Joanne E. Ratner Search (C), NY, *529*
Ray & Berndtson (R), TX, *171*
Ray & Berndtson/Laurendeau Labrecque (R), QE, *172*
Ray & Berndtson/Lovas Stanley (R), ON, *172*
Raymond Karsan Assoc. (C), PA, *529*
Raymond Thomas & Assoc. (C), FL, *530*
Razzino-Claymore Assoc. (C), NJ, *530*
RBW Assoc. Inc. (C), OR, *531*
RCI Employment Solutions (C), FL, *531*
Re-Mark Assoc. Inc. (C), NJ, *531*
Reality Group (C), OK, *531*
Recruit Xpress (C), TX, *531*
Recruiting Assoc. of Amarillo (C), TX, *531*
Recruiting Services Group, Inc. (C), TN, *532*
Recruiting/Solutions (C), CA, *532*
The Recruitment Group, Inc. (C), NY, *532*
Recruitment Resources (C), CA, *532*
Mary Rector & Assoc., Inc. (C), IL, *533*
Redden & McGrath Assoc., Inc. (R), NY, *173*
Redden-Shaffer Group (R), CA, *173*
Reece & Mruk Partners/EMA Partners Int'l. (R), MA, *173*
Reese Assoc. (R), PA, *174*
Cedric L. Reese Inc. (C), CA, *533*
Reeve & Assoc. (C), CT, *533*
The Regis Group, Ltd. (R), GA, *174*
Reid Ellis Assoc. Inc. (C), ON, *533*
Reifel & Assoc. (R), IL, *174*
The Douglas Reiter Co., Inc. (R), OR, *174*
The Remington Group (R), IL, *174*
Renaissance Resources, LLC (R), VA, *174*
Research Personnel Consultants (C), ON, *534*
The Resource Group (R), NJ, *175*
Resource Inc. (R), MA, *175*
Resource Management Group (C), CT, *534*
Resource Networking Inc. (C), IN, *534*
Resource Perspectives, Inc. (R), CA, *175*
Resource Services, Inc. (C), NY, *534*
Resources for Management (R), PA, *175*
Retail Recruiters/Spectrum Consultants, Inc. (C), PA, *535*
Retained Search Assoc. (R), NC, *176*
The Revere Assoc., Inc. (R), OH, *176*
S. Reyman & Assoc., Ltd. (R), IL, *176*
Russell Reynolds Assoc., Inc. (R), NY, *176*
Reynolds Consulting Int'l. (R), ON, *177*
RIC Corp. (R), FL, *177*
Rice Cohen Int'l. (R), PA, *178*
Richard, Wayne & Roberts (C), TX, *536*
Richards Assoc., Inc. (R), NY, *178*
The Richards Group (C), PA, *536*
Terry Richards (C), OH, *536*

Riddle & McGrath LLC (R), GA, *178*
Rieser & Assoc., Inc. (R), MO, *178*
Right/McKee Consulting Group (C), TX, *537*
Riley Cole (C), CA, *537*
Ritta Professional Search Inc. (C), NY, *538*
River Region Personnel, Inc. (C), LA, *538*
RJN Consulting (R), NY, *179*
RML Assoc. (C), PA, *538*
Roberson & Co. (C), AZ, *538*
Robert Lowell Int'l. (R), TX, *179*
Robert William James & Assoc. (C), OR, *539*
Bruce Robinson Assoc. (R), NJ, *180*
Robinson-Robinson & Assoc., Inc. (C), MN, *539*
Robison & Associates (R), NC, *180*
Robison Humphreys & Assoc., Inc. (R), ON, *180*
Rocky Mountain Recruiters, Inc. (C), CO, *540*
J. P. Roddy Consultants (C), PA, *540*
J. Rodgers & Associates (C), IL, *540*
R. A. Rodriguez & Assoc., Inc. (C), TX, *540*
Rodzik & Assoc., Inc. (R), NC, *180*
Craig Roe & Assoc., LLC (C), MD, *540*
Roevin Technical People (C), ON, *540*
Rogers - McManamon Executive Search (R), CA, *180*
ROI Assoc. (R), NY, *180*
Rojek Marketing Group, Inc. (R), OH, *181*
Roll International (C), TX, *541*
Rolland Ressources Humaines Inc. (R), QE, *181*
Rollins & Assoc. (C), CA, *541*
Rollo Assoc. (R), CA, *181*
Romac Int'l. (C), GA, *541*
Romac Int'l. (C), IL, *541*
Romac Int'l., Inc. (C), FL, *542*
Romano McAvoy Assoc., Inc. (C), NY, *544*
Romeo-Hudgins & Assoc., Ltd. (C), NJ, *544*
Rooney Assoc., Inc. (R), IL, *181*
Ropella & Assoc. (R), FL, *181*
Ross Personnel Consultants, Inc. (C), CT, *545*
Rossi & Assoc. Inc. (C), BC, *545*
The Rossi Search Group (C), PA, *545*
Roster Inc. (C), IN, *545*
Roth Young Personnel Services of Washington, DC (C), MD, *546*
Roth Young Personnel Service of Detroit, Inc. (C), MI, *546*
Roth Young of Chicago (C), IL, *546*
Roth Young of Pittsburgh (C), PA, *546*
Roth Young Executive Search (C), TX, *546*
Roth Young Executive Recruiters (C), MN, *546*
Roth Young of Tampa (C), FL, *546*
Roth Young Seattle (C), WA, *546*
Roth Young Executive Search of Milwaukee (C), WI, *547*
Rothrock Associates, Inc. (C), NC, *547*
Rovner & Assoc., Inc. (R), IL, *182*
Rovner Gerner & Assoc. (R), CA, *182*
Rowland Assoc. (C), CA, *547*
Rowland Mountain & Assoc. (C), GA, *547*
RSMR, Inc. (R), IL, *182*
RTE Search (C), NJ, *547*
The Rubinic Consulting Group (C), OH, *548*
Ruderfer & Co., Inc. (C), NJ, *548*
Susan Rudich (C), NY, *548*
Louis Rudzinsky Assoc., Inc. (C), MA, *548*
J. D. Ruhmann & Assoc. (C), MO, *548*
Rusher, Loscavio & LoPresto (R), CA, *183*
K. Russo Assoc. Inc. (C), CT, *548*
Rust & Assoc., Inc. (R), IL, *183*
W. A. Rutledge & Assoc. (R), CT, *183*
The Ryan Charles Group, Inc. (C), FL, *548*
Ryan, Miller & Assoc. (C), CA, *549*
Ryan-Allen & Assoc., Inc. (C), CA, *549*
Rylan Forbes Consulting Group, Inc. (C), NJ, *549*
R. L. Rystrom & Assoc., Inc. (C), MN, *549*
S-H-S Int'l. of Cherry Hill (C), NJ, *549*
S-H-S TechStaff (C), PA, *549*
S. P. Assoc., Inc. (C), NC, *550*
S.C.S. & Assoc. (C), NC, *550*
S.D.P. Contract Recruiters (C), NJ, *550*
Saber Group, Inc. (C), TX, *550*
R. S. Sadow Assoc. (C), NJ, *550*
Sage Employment Recruiters (C), IN, *550*
The Sager Co. (R), OH, *183*
Sales & Marketing Search, Inc. (C), MA, *551*
Sales Builders, Inc. (R), VA, *183*
Sales Consultants of Birmingham (C), AL, *555*
Sales Consultants of Silicon Valley (C), CA, *556*
Sales Consultants of Chico (C), CA, *556*
Sales Consultants of Scottsdale, Inc. (C), AZ, *556*
Sales Consultants Peninsula, Inc. (C), CA, *556*
Sales Consultants of Sacramento (C), CA, *556*
Sales Consultants of Daphne (C), AL, *556*
Sales Consultants of Boca Raton, Inc. (C), FL, *557*
Sales Consultants of Savannah, GA (C), GA, *557*
Sales Consultants of Ft. Lauderdale, Inc. (C), FL, *557*
Sales Consultants of Honolulu (C), HI, *558*
Sales Consultants of Cherokee (C), GA, *558*
Sales Consultants of Barrington (C), IL, *558*
Sales Consultants of Indianapolis-North (C), IN, *558*
Sales Consultants of Indianapolis (C), IN, *558*
Sales Consultants of Auburn Hills (C), MI, *559*
Sales Consultants - Bristol County (C), MA, *559*
Sales Consultants of Wellesley, Inc. (C), MA, *559*
Sales Consultants of Brockton, Inc. (C), MA, *559*
Sales Consultants of Rockville, MD (C), MD, *559*
Sales Consultants of Baltimore (C), MD, *559*
Sales Consultants of Birmingham (C), MI, *559*
Sales Consultants of Bangor, Inc. (C), ME, *559*
Sales Consultants of Laurel Park, Inc. (C), MI, *560*
Sales Consultants of Nashua-Manchester (C), NH, *560*
Sales Consultants of Farmington Hills (C), MI, *560*
Sales Consultants of Grand Rapids (C), MI, *560*
Sales Consultants of Cherry Hill (C), NJ, *560*
Sales Consultants of Omaha, Inc. (C), NE, *560*
Sales Consultants of Raleigh-Durham-RTP (C), NC, *561*
Sales Consultants of Cincinnati (C), OH, *561*
Sales Consultants of Princeton, Inc. (C), NJ, *561*
Sales Consultants of Morris County, Inc. (C), NJ, *561*
Sales Consultants of Westchester-South, Inc. (C), NY, *561*
Sales Consultants of Middlesex County, Inc. (C), NJ, *561*
Sales Consultants of Austin, Inc. (C), TX, *562*
Sales Consultants King of Prussia (C), PA, *562*
Sales Consultants of Orangeburg (C), SC, *562*
Sales Consultants of Pittsburgh (C), PA, *562*
Sales Consultants of Greenville, Inc. (C), SC, *562*
Sales Consultants of Madison (C), WI, *563*
Sales Consultants of Milwaukee (C), WI, *563*
Sales Consultants of Appleton (C), WI, *563*
Sales Consultants of Dallas (C), TX, *563*
Sales Consultants of Houston (C), TX, *563*
Sales Executives, Inc. (C), MI, *563*
Sales Management Resources (C), CA, *563*
Sales Recruiters of Oklahoma City (C), OK, *564*
Sales Recruiting Network (C), PA, *564*
Sales Search (C), ON, *564*
Sales Search Specialist (C), IL, *564*
Sales Solutions (C), CA, *564*
Sampson Medical Search (C), CA, *564*
George D. Sandel Assoc. (C), MA, *565*
Sanders Management Assoc., Inc. (C), NJ, *565*
Sanford Rose Assoc. - Lake Forest (R), IL, *184*
Sanford Rose Assoc. (C), OH, *565*
Sanford Rose Assoc. - Laguna Beach (C), CA, *565*
Sanford Rose Assoc. - Santa Ana (C), CA, *565*
Sanford Rose Assoc. - Mobile (C), AL, *565*
Sanford Rose Assoc. - Santa Barbara (C), CA, *565*
Sanford Rose Assoc. - Fairhope (C), AL, *565*
Sanford Rose Assoc. - Chicago (C), IL, *566*

INDUSTRIES

Sanford Rose Assoc. - Clearwater (C), FL, *566*
Sanford Rose Assoc. - Athens (C), GA, *566*
Sanford Rose Assoc. - Effingham (C), IL, *566*
Sanford Rose Assoc. - Orland Park (C), IL, *567*
Sanford Rose Assoc. - Columbia, MD (C), MD, *567*
Sanford Rose Assoc. - Rockford (C), IL, *567*
Sanford Rose Assoc. - Louisville (C), KY, *567*
Sanford Rose Assoc. - Cedar Rapids (C), IA, *567*
Sanford Rose Assoc. - Evansville (C), IN, *567*
Sanford Rose Assoc. - Rockville (C), MD, *567*
Sanford Rose Assoc. - Charlotte (C), NC, *568*
Sanford Rose Assoc. - Gastonia (C), NC, *568*
Sanford Rose Assoc. - Amherst, NY (C), NY, *568*
Sanford Rose Assoc. - Rochester (C), MI, *568*
Sanford Rose Assoc. - Fairlawn (C), OH, *569*
Sanford Rose Assoc. - Canton (C), OH, *569*
Sanford Rose Assoc. - Burlington, NC (C), NC, *569*
Sanford Rose Assoc. - Greensboro (C), NC, *569*
Sanford Rose Assoc. - Euclid (C), OH, *569*
Sanford Rose Assoc. - Akron (C), OH, *569*
Sanford Rose Assoc. - Nashville (C), TN, *570*
Sanford Rose Assoc. - Columbia (C), SC, *570*
Sanford Rose Assoc. - Philadelphia North (C), PA, *570*
Sanford Rose Assoc. - Austin (C), TX, *570*
Sanford Rose Assoc. - Portland (C), OR, *570*
Sanford Rose Assoc. - Doylestown (C), PA, *570*
Sanford Rose Assoc. - Salt Lake City (C), UT, *571*
Sanford Rose Assoc. - Port Washington (C), WI, *571*
Sarver & Carruth Assoc. (C), OK, *571*
Sathe & Associates, Inc. (R), MN, *184*
Satterfield & Assoc., Inc. (R), OH, *184*
Savalli & Assoc., Inc. (C), MI, *571*
Schall Executive Search Partners (R), MN, *185*
Schattle & Duquette (C), RI, *571*
The Schatz Company (C), MO, *571*
Schenck & Assoc. SC (C), WI, *572*
Schick Professional Search, Inc. (C), OH, *572*
A.D. Schiff & Assoc., Ltd. (C), IL, *572*
Schlatter & Assoc. (C), CA, *572*
F. B. Schmidt Int'l. (R), CA, *185*
Schneider, Hill & Spangler, Inc. (R), PA, *185*
Schuyler, Baker & Parker, Inc. (R), GA, *185*
Schweichler Assoc., Inc. (R), CA, *186*
Scientific Solutions, Inc. (C), MI, *572*
Robert Scott Assoc. (C), NJ, *573*
Scott Executive Search, Inc. (R), NY, *186*
Scott Sibley Assoc. (C), NY, *573*
Scott-Thaler Assoc. Agency, Inc. (C), CA, *573*
Scott-Wayne Assoc., Inc. (C), MA, *573*
Search & Recruit Int'l. (C), VA, *573*
Search Advisors Int'l. Corp. (R), FL, *186*
The Search Alliance, Inc. (R), FL, *186*
The Search America Group Inc. (C), OH, *573*
Search Assoc. (C), KY, *574*
Search Assoc., Inc. (C), CA, *574*
Search Assoc., Inc. (C), NJ, *574*
Search By Design (C), AZ, *574*
The Search Committee (C), MD, *574*
Search Consultants Int'l., Inc. (C), TX, *575*
Search Consultants, LLC (C), MD, *575*
Search Enterprises, Inc. (C), FL, *575*
Search Group (C), CA, *575*
Search Group Inc. (R), AB, *186*
Search Int'l. (R), MA, *187*
Search Masters Int'l. (R), AZ, *187*
Search Masters, USA (C), FL, *576*
The Search Network (C), CA, *576*
Search North America, Inc. (C), OR, *576*
Search Northwest Assoc. (C), OR, *576*
Search Plus Int'l.-Ohio (C), OH, *576*
Search South, Inc. (C), AL, *576*
SearchCom, Inc. (R), TX, *187*
SearchCorp (C), FL, *577*
Searchforce, Inc. (R), FL, *187*
Searchline Services, Inc. (C), OH, *577*
SearchOne, Inc. (C), AR, *577*
Searchworks, Inc. (C), FL, *577*
Sedlar & Miners (R), NY, *188*
J. R. Seehusen Assoc., Inc. (R), IA, *188*
Segal & Assoc. (C), GA, *578*
Seiden Krieger Assoc., Inc. (R), NY, *188*
Seitchik Corwin & Seitchik Inc. (R), CA, *188*
Select Services (C), IL, *578*
Selectis Corp. (C), IL, *578*
Selective Management Services, Inc. (C), FL, *578*
Selective Recruiting Assoc., Inc. (C), MI, *578*
Selective Search Associates (C), OH, *578*
Selig Executive Search (C), NH, *579*
SFB Legal Search (C), NY, *579*
Sharp Placement Professionals, Inc. (C), NY, *579*
Sharrow & Assoc., Inc. (C), MI, *579*
M. B. Shattuck & Assoc., Inc. (R), CA, *189*
Shepherd Bueschel & Provus, Inc. (R), IL, *189*
Sherwood Lehman Massucco, Inc. (R), CA, *189*
Shinn & Assoc. (R), CA, *189*
Michael Shirley Assoc. Inc. (R), KS, *190*
Shoemaker & Assoc. (R), GA, *190*
E. L. Shore & Assoc. (R), ON, *190*
Shore Asociados Ejecutivos, S. A. de C.V. (R), MX, *190*
The Shorr Group (R), IL, *190*
The Shotland Group (R), CA, *190*
SHS of Allentown (C), PA, *580*
John Sibbald Assoc., Inc. (R), MO, *191*
Larry Siegel & Assoc. (R), WA, *191*
Peter Siegel & Co. (C), MA, *581*
RitaSue Siegel Resources, Inc. (R), NY, *191*
Marvin L. Silcott & Assoc., Inc. (C), TX, *581*
The Silicon Network (C), ON, *581*
Sill Technical Assoc., Inc. (C), PA, *581*
L. A. Silver Assoc., Inc. (R), MA, *191*
Daniel A. Silverstein Assoc. Inc. (R), FL, *191*
The Simmons Group (C), CA, *582*
D. J. Simpson Assoc. Inc. (R), ON, *191*
Simpson Associates (C), NY, *582*
Sinclair & Co., Inc. (R), MA, *192*
Singleton & Assoc. (C), VA, *582*
Sink, Walker, Boltrus Int'l. (R), MA, *192*
Ruth Sklar Assoc., Inc. (RSA Executive Search) (R), NY, *192*
Skott/Edwards Consultants (R), NY, *192*
Slayton Int'l., Inc. (R), IL, *192*
Tom Sloan & Assoc., Inc. (C), WI, *583*
Sloan & Assoc., Inc. (C), VA, *583*
J. L. Small Assoc. (C), AL, *583*
Christopher Smallhorn Executive Recruiting, Inc. (R), MA, *193*
Smith & Assoc. (C), CA, *583*
Smith & Assoc. (C), FL, *583*
James F. Smith & Assoc. (C), GA, *583*
Ralph Smith & Assoc. (C), IL, *584*
Smith & Laue Search (R), OR, *193*
Smith & Syberg, Inc. (R), IN, *193*
G. L. Smith Assoc. (C), CA, *584*
J. Harrington Smith Assoc. (C), IN, *584*
Herman Smith Executive Initiatives Inc. (R), ON, *193*
The Smith Group, Inc. (C), NC, *584*
Smith Hanley Assoc., Inc. (C), NY, *584*
Smith James Group, Inc. (R), GA, *194*
Smith, Roth & Squires (R), NY, *194*
Smith Search, S.C. (R), MX, *194*
Smith's Fifth Avenue (C), NY, *585*
Smith, Brown & Jones (C), KS, *585*
A. William Smyth, Inc. (R), CA, *194*
Snelling & Snelling, Inc. (C), FL, *585*
Snelling Search (C), AL, *585*
Snelling Search (C), LA, *586*
Snelling Search Recruiters (C), NC, *586*
C. Snow & Assoc. (C), ON, *586*
Snyder & Co. (R), CT, *194*
Sockwell & Assoc. (R), NC, *194*
Softrix, Inc. (C), NJ, *586*
Software Engineering Solutions, Inc. (C), CA, *586*
Software Resource Consultants (C), TN, *587*
Robert Sollman & Assoc. (C), FL, *587*
Solutions Group (R), AL, *195*
Somerset Group, Inc. (C), CT, *587*
Souder & Assoc. (R), VA, *195*
Southern Chemical & Plastics Search (C), GA, *587*
Southern Recruiters & Consultants, Inc. (C), SC, *587*
Southern Research Services (R), FL, *195*
Southport Int'l. Assoc. Inc. (C), FL, *588*
Sparks, McDonough & Assoc., Inc. (C), MO, *588*

Spear-Izzo Assoc., LLC (C), PA, *588*
Special Markets Group, Inc. (R), GA, *195*
Specialty Consultants Inc. (R), PA, *195*
Specialty Employment Services, Inc. (C), GA, *589*
SpectraWest (C), CA, *589*
Spectrum Consultants (R), CA, *196*
SpencerSearch, Inc. (C), CO, *589*
SpencerStuart (R), NY, *196*
The Spiegel Group (R), MA, *197*
Spilman & Assoc. (R), TX, *197*
Kenn Spinrad Inc. (C), PA, *589*
Splaine & Assoc., Inc. (R), CA, *198*
Sports Group Int'l. (R), NC, *198*
Spriggs & Co., Inc. (R), IL, *198*
Springer Souder & Assoc. L.L.C. (R), IL, *198*
Sprout/Standish, Inc. (C), NH, *589*
SR Wilson, Inc. (C), CA, *590*
Staff Resources, Inc. (C), SC, *590*
Staffing Edge, Inc. (C), IA, *590*
StaffWriters Plus (C), NY, *591*
Stanton Chase Int'l. (R), MD, *198*
The Stanton Group, Inc. (C), IL, *591*
Star Search Consultants (C), ON, *591*
The Stark Wilton Group (R), MI, *199*
Steinfield & Assoc. (C), TX, *592*
The Stelton Group, Inc. (C), NJ, *592*
Stephens Assoc. Ltd., Inc. (R), OH, *200*
Sterling Int'l. (R), NJ, *200*
Sterling Int'l. Management Recruitment, Ltd. Inc. (C), NC, *592*
Michael Stern Assoc., Inc./Euram (R), ON, *200*
Ron Stevens & Assoc., Inc. (C), FL, *593*
Stevens Assoc. (C), MA, *593*
The Stevens Group (R), TX, *200*
The Stevenson Group, Inc. (N.J.) (R), NJ, *200*
Stewart Assoc. (C), PA, *593*
Stewart, Stein & Scott, Ltd. (R), MN, *200*
Stewart/Greene & Co. of The Triad, Inc. (C), NC, *594*
Stewart/Laurence Assoc., Inc. (R), NJ, *201*
Charles Stickler Assoc. (R), PA, *201*
Linford E. Stiles & Assoc., L.L.C. (R), NH, *201*
STM Assoc. (R), UT, *201*
Allan Stolee Inc. (R), FL, *201*
Stone Assoc. LLC (C), MI, *594*
Stone Enterprises Ltd. (C), IL, *594*
Stone, Murphy & Olson (R), MN, *201*
The Stonebridge Group (C), PA, *594*
Stoneburner Assoc., Inc. (C), KS, *594*
Stoopen Asociados, S.C./EMA Partners Int'l. (R), MX, *202*
Storfer & Assoc. (C), NY, *595*
Strategic Advancement Inc. (R), NJ, *202*
Strategic Alliance Network, Ltd. (C), OH, *595*
Strategic Alternatives (R), CA, *202*
Strategic Assoc., Inc. (C), TX, *595*
Strategic Executives, Inc. (R), CT, *202*
Strategic Resources Biotechnology & Medical Group (C), WA, *595*
Strategic Resources (C), WA, *595*
Strategic Search Corp. (R), IL, *202*
Strategic Search, LLC (C), CA, *595*
Strategic Technologies, Inc. (C), TX, *596*
StratfordGroup (R), OH, *203*
Stratin Assoc. (C), NJ, *596*
Straube Associates (R), MA, *203*
Strauss Personnel Service (C), PA, *596*
J. Stroll Assoc., Inc. (R), CT, *203*
Stroman Int'l., Inc. (R), CO, *204*
Success Seekers Connection (C), FL, *596*
Sullivan & Assoc. (R), MI, *204*
Summerfield Assoc., Inc. (C), TN, *596*
Summit Executive Search Consultants, Inc. (R), FL, *204*
Summit Group Int'l., Inc. (R), GA, *204*
Ron Sunshine & Assoc. (C), IL, *597*
Survival Systems Staffing, Inc. (C), CA, *597*
Swartz & Assoc., Inc. (R), AZ, *204*
Swift & Assoc. (C), ME, *597*
Synapse Human Resource Consulting Group (R), TX, *205*
Synergy Solutions, Ltd. (C), WA, *597*
System 1 Search (C), CA, *598*
Systems Personnel, Inc. (C), NY, *598*
Systems Research Group (C), CA, *598*
Systems Research Inc. (SRI) (C), IL, *598*
Systems Search (C), IL, *599*
T E M Assoc. (C), WI, *599*
Tabb & Assoc. (R), OH, *205*
Tactical Alternatives (R), CA, *205*
The Talley Group (R), VA, *205*
Martin Stevens Tamaren & Assoc., Inc. (R), CA, *206*
S. Tanner & Assoc. Inc. (C), ON, *599*
Tate & Assoc., Inc. (R), NJ, *207*
Tate Consulting, Inc. (R), FL, *207*
M. L. Tawney & Assoc. (C), TX, *600*
TaxSearch Inc. (R), OK, *207*
Carl J. Taylor & Co. (R), TX, *207*
Taylor Winfield (R), TX, *207*
TBC, Inc. (C), KY, *600*
The TBI Group (R), PA, *207*
TCM Enterprises (C), MD, *600*
Team One Partners, Inc. (C), GA, *600*
Teamsearch, Inc. (C), MI, *601*
Tech Connector Group (C), CA, *601*
Tech Consulting (C), FL, *601*
Tech Search (C), CA, *601*
Tech-Net (C), TX, *601*
Techaid Inc. (C), QE, *601*
TechFind, Inc. (R), MA, *207*
Technical Employment Consultants (C), PA, *602*
Technical Recruiting Services (C), OH, *602*
Technical Resource Assoc. (C), TN, *602*
Technical Search Assoc. (C), OH, *602*
Technical Skills Consulting Inc. (R), ON, *207*
Technical Staffing Solutions (C), TX, *602*
Technifind Int'l. (C), TX, *602*
TechNix Inc. (C), ON, *602*
The Technology Group (R), IL, *208*
Technology Management Partners (R), CA, *208*
Technology Search Int'l. (C), CA, *603*
Techstaff Inc. (C), WI, *603*
Tecmark Associates Inc. (C), NY, *604*
Teknon Employment Resources, Inc. (C), OH, *604*
Tekworx, Inc. (C), OK, *604*
Telem Adhesive Search Corp. (C), MD, *605*
Telford, Adams & Alexander (R), CA, *208*
The TGA Company (C), TX, *606*
Thomas & Assoc. of Michigan (C), MI, *606*
Thomas Mangum Co. (R), CA, *208*
Thomas Resource Group (R), CA, *209*
Richard Thompson Assoc., Inc. (R), MN, *209*
Thomson, Sponar & Adams, Inc. (C), WA, *606*
Thorne, Brieger Assoc., Inc. (R), NY, *209*
The Tidewater Group Inc. (C), CT, *607*
Tierney Assoc., Inc. (R), PA, *209*
Fred C. Tippel & Assoc. (C), OH, *607*
Tirocchi, Wright, Inc. (R), CA, *209*
Tittemore Cowan Assoc. (C), AB, *607*
TNS Partners, Inc. (R), TX, *209*
Tondorf & Assoc. Inc. (C), MA, *607*
Top Gun Group, Inc. (C), NV, *607*
The Touchstone Group (C), MA, *607*
Tower Consultants, Ltd. (R), PA, *209*
TPS Staffing Solutions (C), IN, *608*
Jay Tracey Assoc. Inc. (C), VT, *608*
Trainor/Frank & Assoc. Inc. (C), WI, *608*
Trambley the Recruiter (C), NM, *608*
Trans-United Consultants Ltd. (C), ON, *608*
Transportation Recruiting Services, Inc. (C), MS, *608*
Travis & Co., Inc. (R), MA, *210*
Traynor Confidential, Ltd. (C), NY, *609*
Trebor Weldon Lawrence, Inc. (R), NY, *210*
Triangle Assoc. (C), PA, *609*
TriStaff Group (C), CA, *609*
Triumph Consulting, Inc. (R), IA, *210*
Trowbridge & Co., Inc. (R), MA, *211*
TRS Staffing Solutions Inc. (C), OH, *610*
The Truman Agency (C), CA, *610*
Tryon & Heideman, LLC (R), MO, *211*
TSC Management Services Group, Inc. (C), IL, *610*
Tschudin Inc. (R), NJ, *211*
TSI Group/TSI Staffing Services (C), ON, *610*
TSS Consulting, Ltd. (C), AZ, *610*
TTG/Sterling Services (C), CA, *610*
W. G. Tucker & Assoc. (R), PA, *211*
The Thomas Tucker Co. (R), CA, *211*
Tully/Woodmansee Int'l. Inc. (R), FL, *212*
Tuttle Venture Group, Inc. (R), TX, *212*
U.S. Search (C), VA, *610*
The Ultimate Source (R), CA, *212*
UniQuest Int'l., Inc. (C), FL, *610*
Unisearch Search & Recruiting Inc. (C), CA, *611*
United Personnel Services (C), MA, *611*
Unlimited Staffing Solutions, Inc. (C), MI, *611*
The Urban Placement Service (C), TX, *611*
Valentine & Assoc. (C), IL, *611*
Van Dyke Assoc. (R), IL, *212*
VanMaldegiam Assoc., Inc. (R), IL, *213*
Vaughan & Co. (C), CA, *612*
Vento Assoc. (C), TN, *612*
Venture Resources, Inc. (R), CA, *213*
Verkamp-Joyce Assoc., Inc. (R), IL, *213*

INDUSTRIES

The Verriez Group Inc. (R), ON, *213*
Victor White Int'l. (C), CA, *612*
C. J. Vincent Assoc., LLC (C), MD, *612*
Vincenty & Co. (C), OH, *612*
The Viscusi Group, Inc. (R), NY, *214*
Vlcek & Company, Inc. (R), CA, *214*
Voigt Assoc. (R), IL, *214*
W. P. Assoc. (C), CA, *613*
The Wabash Group (C), IN, *613*
Wachendorfer & Assoc. (C), TX, *613*
Gordon Wahls Executive Search (C), PA, *613*
Wakefield Talabisco Int'l. (R), NY, *214*
Kelly Walker Assoc. (C), TX, *614*
B. D. Wallace & Assoc. (C), MD, *614*
Wallace Assoc. (C), CT, *614*
Linda Walter & Associes (C), QE, *615*
Lee H. Walton & Assoc. (R), NY, *215*
Martha Ward Executive Search, Inc. (C), NY, *615*
The Ward Group (R), MA, *215*
Ward Liebelt Assoc. Inc. (R), CT, *215*
Ward-Hoffman & Assoc. (C), ID, *615*
Warner & Assoc., Inc. (C), OH, *615*
Warren Executive Services (C), GA, *616*
Wasserman Assoc. Inc. (C), MD, *616*
R. J. Watkins & Co., Ltd. (R), CA, *216*
Watring & Assoc., Inc. (C), IL, *616*
Waveland Int'l. (R), IL, *216*
Wayne Assoc., Inc. (C), VA, *616*
Webb, Johnson Assoc., Inc. (R), NY, *216*
Weber Executive Search (R), NY, *216*
S. B. Webster & Associates (R), MA, *217*
Wegner & Assoc. (C), WI, *617*
Lee Weil Assoc., Inc. (C), IL, *617*
David Weinfeld Group (C), NC, *617*
Weinpel Search, Inc. (C), NJ, *617*
Weinstein & Co. (R), MA, *217*
S. E. Weinstein Co. (R), IL, *217*
D. L. Weiss & Assoc. (R), CA, *217*
Henry Welker & Assoc. (C), MI, *618*
The Wellesley Group, Inc. (R), IL, *217*
Wellington Management Group (R), PA, *217*
R. A. Wells Co. (C), GA, *618*
Werbin Assoc. Executive Search, Inc. (C), NY, *618*
Jude M. Werra & Assoc. (R), WI, *218*
Wesley Brown & Bartle Co., Inc. (R), NY, *218*
West & Assoc. (C), IL, *618*
West & West (R), CA, *218*
West Coast Recruiting (C), CA, *619*
Western Management Assoc. (R), CA, *218*
Westfields Int'l., Inc. (C), NY, *619*
WestPacific National Search, Inc. (C), CA, *619*
S. J. Wexler Assoc., Inc. (R), NY, *219*
The Whitaker Companies (C), TX, *619*
White, Roberts & Stratton, Inc. (C), IL, *619*
Whitehead & Assoc., Inc. (C), MO, *620*
Arch S. Whitehead Assoc. Inc. (ASWA) (R), NY, *219*
The Whitney Group (C), GA, *620*
Whitney Smith Co. (C), TX, *620*
Whittaker & Assoc., Inc. (C), GA, *620*
Whittlesey & Assoc., Inc. (R), PA, *220*
Daniel Wier & Assoc. (R), CA, *220*
Walter K. Wilkins & Co. (R), NJ, *221*
Wilkinson & Ives (R), CA, *221*
William-Johns Co., Inc. (C), CA, *621*
John R. Williams & Assoc., Inc. (C), NC, *621*
John Williams & Assoc. (C), TX, *621*
Williams Recruiting, Inc. (C), WA, *621*
Williamsburg Group (C), NJ, *621*
Willis & Assoc. (R), OH, *221*
William Willis Worldwide Inc. (R), CT, *221*
N. Willner & Co., Inc. (R), NJ, *221*
Wills Consulting Assoc. Inc. (R), CT, *221*
The Wilmington Group (C), NC, *622*
Wilson & Assoc. Int'l. Inc. (C), FL, *622*
Wilson Personnel, Inc. (C), NC, *622*
The Winchester Group (R), CA, *222*
The Windham Group (R), OH, *222*
Windsor International (R), GA, *222*
Winfield Assoc., Inc. (C), MA, *623*
Wing Tips & Pumps, Inc. (C), MI, *623*
Winguth, Grant & Donahue (R), CA, *222*
Winston Search, Inc. (R), MD, *222*
Winter, Wyman & Co. (C), MA, *623*
Winthrop Partners, Inc. (R), NY, *222*
The Witt Group (C), FL, *623*
WMD inc. (C), NJ, *623*
Wojdula & Assoc., Ltd. (R), WI, *223*
S. R. Wolman Assoc., Inc. (R), NY, *224*
Woltz & Assoc., Inc. (R), IL, *224*
Susan L. Wonderling Recruiting (C), PA, *623*
Wood West & Partners Inc. (C), BC, *624*
Jim Woodson & Assoc., Inc. (C), MS, *624*
Woodworth Int'l. Group (R), OR, *224*
World Search (C), OH, *625*
Jay Wren & Assoc. (C), CA, *625*
Bob Wright Recruiting, Inc. (C), CT, *625*
WTW Assoc., Inc. (R), NY, *225*
John Wylie Assoc., Inc. (C), OK, *625*
Xagas & Assoc. (R), IL, *226*
The Yaiser Group (C), NJ, *625*
Yelverton Executive Search (R), CA, *226*
The York Group (C), CA, *626*
Yungner & Bormann (R), MN, *226*
Zackrison Assoc., Inc. (C), FL, *627*
The Zammataro Company (R), OH, *226*
The Zarkin Group, Inc. (R), NY, *226*
Zeiger Assoc. L.L.C. (C), CA, *627*
Zen Zen Int'l. Inc. (C), MB, *627*
Zingaro & Company (R), TX, *227*
Michael D. Zinn & Assoc., Inc. (R), NJ, *227*
Zwell Int'l. (R), IL, *228*

D.10 Food, beverage, tobacco & kindred products

A C Personnel Services, Inc. (C), OK, *231*
A la Carte Int'l., Inc. (R), VA, *1*
A-Linko & Assoc. (C), TX, *231*
A.J. & Assoc. (C), FL, *232*
Accelerated Data Decision, Inc. (C), NJ, *233*
Accounting Additions (C), CA, *238*
Advanced Executive Resources (R), MI, *2*
Affordable Executive Recruiters (C), CA, *241*
Aggressive Corporation (C), IL, *242*
Agra Placements, Ltd. (C), IA, *242*
Agri-Personnel (C), GA, *242*
Agri-Tech Personnel, Inc. (C), MO, *242*
Allen & Assoc. (C), NV, *244*
David Allen Assoc. (R), NJ, *3*
Tom Allison Assoc. (C), NM, *245*
Alpha Search (C), FL, *246*
The Altco Group (C), NJ, *246*
AMD & Associates (C), GA, *247*
American Executive Search (C), FL, *247*
Amherst Human Resource Group, Ltd. (C), IL, *249*
Amherst Personnel Group Inc. (C), NY, *249*
Analytic Recruiting, Inc. (C), NY, *249*
Anderson & Associates (R), NC, *5*
Andre David & Assoc., Inc. (R), TX, *6*
Charles P. Aquavella & Assoc. (C), TX, *252*
The Associates, HR Search Executives, Inc. (C), OK, *254*
W. R. Atchison & Assoc., Inc. (C), NC, *254*
Austin, Hill & Assoc. (C), MD, *256*
Automation Technology Search (C), CA, *256*
Keith Bagg & Assoc., Inc. (C), ON, *257*
The Baldwin Group (R), IL, *10*
Ballantyne & Assoc. (R), CA, *10*
The Barack Group, Inc. (R), NY, *11*
Barton Assoc., Inc. (R), TX, *12*
Bast & Assoc., Inc. (C), CA, *261*
Battalia Winston Int'l./The Euram Consultants Group (R), NY, *13*
L. Battalin & Co. (C), FL, *261*
Martin H. Bauman Assoc., Inc. (R), NY, *13*
The Beam Group (R), PA, *14*
The Bedford Consulting Group Inc. (R), ON, *14*
Behrens and Company (C), WA, *262*
Joy Reed Belt Search Consultants, Inc. (R), OK, *15*
Benford & Assoc., Inc. (C), MI, *264*
Benson Associates (C), NY, *264*
Berkhemer/Clayton, Inc. (R), CA, *16*
BEST/World Assoc. Inc. (R), TX, *16*
BGB Assoc., Inc. (C), IL, *266*
Bialla & Assoc. Inc. (R), CA, *17*
Paul J. Biestek Assoc., Inc. (R), IL, *17*
Blair/Tech Recruiters, Inc. (C), NJ, *268*
David Blevins & Assoc. (C), WA, *268*
Mark Bolno & Assoc. (C), FL, *269*
Ann Bond Assoc. Inc. (C), MD, *269*
John C. Boone & Co. (R), IL, *19*
Bornholdt Shivas & Friends Executive Recruiters (C), NY, *270*
Bosch & Assoc., LLC (R), CT, *19*
Boyden (R), NY, *20*
Bradley & Assoc. (C), MN, *272*
Briant Assoc., Inc. (R), IL, *23*
Bridgecreek Personnel Agency (C), CA, *273*
Bright Search/Professional Staffing (C), MN, *274*
Bristol Assoc., Inc. (C), CA, *274*
Brookman Associates (C), NY, *274*
J. B. Brown & Assoc., Inc. (C), OH, *275*
Brown, Bernardy, Van Remmen, Inc. (C), CA, *275*

J. Burke & Assoc., Inc. (C), TX, *276*
Burke & Assoc./The Westfield Group (C), CT, *276*
Canny, Bowen Inc. (R), NY, *27*
J. P. Canon Assoc. (C), NY, *280*
The Cantor Concern, Inc. (R), NY, *28*
Capitol Management Consulting, Inc. (C), NJ, *281*
Career Alternatives Executive Search (C), MI, *281*
Career Consulting Group, Inc. (C), CT, *281*
Career Images (C), FL, *282*
Career Profiles (C), NH, *283*
Career Search Group (C), FL, *283*
Careers On Track (C), NJ, *283*
Carion Resource Group Inc. (C), ON, *284*
Carlson & Czeswik (R), MN, *30*
Carrington & Carrington, Ltd. (R), IL, *30*
Carver Search Consultants (C), CA, *285*
Cary & Assoc. (R), FL, *31*
Cella Assoc. (C), GA, *286*
Chadwell & Assoc., Inc. (C), MI, *288*
The Chatham Group, Ltd. (C), CT, *289*
The Churchill Group (C), ON, *291*
Clanton & Co. (C), CA, *292*
Howard Clark Assoc. (C), NJ, *292*
Clark Personnel Service, Inc. (C), AL, *292*
COBA Executive Search (R), CO, *36*
Cochran, Cochran & Yale, Inc. (R), NY, *36*
Robert Connelly & Assoc., Inc. (R), MN, *39*
Consulting Rhonda (C), ON, *297*
Corbin Packaging Professionals (C), MO, *299*
The Corporate Advisory Group (R), NJ, *41*
Corporate Plus, Ltd. (C), GA, *300*
Corporate Search Consultants (C), IN, *301*
Corso, Mizgala + French (R), ON, *42*
The Cris Group, Inc. (R), NY, *42*
Crist Partners, Ltd. (R), IL, *43*
Marlene Critchfield Co. (C), CA, *303*
Culver Personnel Services (C), CA, *304*
Curran Partners, Inc. (R), CT, *44*
The Currier-Winn Co., Inc. (C), NJ, *305*
Cypress Int'l., Inc. (R), FL, *45*
Cyr Associates, Inc. (C), MA, *306*
Daniel Marks Company (C), OH, *306*
The Dartmouth Group (R), NY, *46*
Alan N. Daum & Assoc., Inc. (C), OH, *308*
David Perry Assoc. (C), NJ, *308*
DBL Associates (C), CA, *309*
Debbon Recruiting Group, Inc. (C), MO, *310*
DeLalla - Fried Assoc. (C), NY, *310*
Thorndike Deland Assoc. LLC (R), NY, *48*
Diamond Tax Recruiting (C), NY, *312*
DieckMueller Group (R), WI, *51*
J. Dinerstein & Co., Inc. (R), NY, *51*
Dise & Co. (R), OH, *52*
Diversified Search, Inc. (R), PA, *52*
Dixie Search Assoc. (C), GA, *313*
The Dorfman Group (C), AZ, *314*
Dougherty & Assoc. (C), TN, *314*
DuBrul Management Co. (C), NY, *315*
Dunhill Personnel of Boulder (C), CO, *319*
Dunhill Professional Search of Englewood, Inc. (C), CO, *319*
Dunhill Professional Search of Oakland (C), CA, *319*
Dunhill Search of West Atlanta (C), GA, *320*
Dunhill of Ft. Wayne, Inc. (C), IN, *320*
Dunhill Professional Search of Winston-Salem (C), NC, *322*
Dunhill Professional Search of Bucks-Mont., Inc. (C), PA, *322*
Dunhill Professional Search, Inc. of McAllen (C), TX, *323*
Dunhill of Corpus Christi, Inc. (C), TX, *323*
Dunhill Professional Search of Richmond (C), VA, *323*
Dussick Management Assoc. (C), CT, *323*
Eastman & Beaudine, Inc. (R), TX, *56*
Eden & Assoc., Inc. (C), PA, *326*
EDI/Executive Dynamics Inc. (C), NJ, *326*
EFL Int'l. (R), AZ, *57*
D. C. Egan & Assoc. (C), GA, *327*
The Eldridge Group, Ltd. (C), IL, *327*
Yves Elkas Inc. (R), QE, *58*
Emerging Medical Technologies, Inc. (C), CO, *329*
Engineering Resource Group, Inc. (C), NJ, *331*
Execu-Tech Search Inc. (C), MN, *332*
Executive Connection (C), OH, *333*
Executive Dimensions (R), NY, *62*
Executive Placement Consultants (C), IL, *333*
ExecutiveFit (C), NY, *337*
Paul Falcone Assoc. (R), NJ, *65*
Leon A. Farley Assoc. (R), CA, *65*
Ferneborg & Assoc., Inc. (R), CA, *66*
Financialjobs.com (C), CA, *340*
First Search America, Inc. (C), TN, *341*
Fisher-Todd Assoc. (C), NY, *341*
David Fockler & Assoc., Inc. (C), CA, *342*
Focus Executive Search (C), MN, *343*
L. W. Foote Co. (R), WA, *69*
F-O-R-T-U-N-E Personnel Consultants of Boise (R), ID, *70*
F-O-R-T-U-N-E Personnel Consultants of Greenwood Village (C), CO, *344*
F-O-R-T-U-N-E Personnel Consultants of Atlanta, Inc. (C), GA, *345*
F-O-R-T-U-N-E Personnel Consultants of Menlo Park, Inc. (C), NJ, *347*
F-O-R-T-U-N-E Personnel Consultants of Cincinnati (C), OH, *348*
F-O-R-T-U-N-E Consultants of Memphis (C), TN, *349*
Foster Partners (R), NY, *70*
Fox, White & Assoc. (C), FL, *351*
Foy, Schneid & Daniel, Inc. (R), NY, *71*
KS Frary & Assoc. (R), MA, *71*
Fresquez & Assoc. (C), CA, *352*
Gerald Frisch Assoc., Inc. (R), NY, *72*
The Furst Group, Inc. (R), IL, *72*
Futures, Inc. (C), NH, *354*
W. N. Garbarini & Assoc. (R), NJ, *74*
The Garret Group (R), NJ, *75*
Gilbert Tweed Assoc. Inc. (R), NY, *76*
Lawrence Glaser Assoc., Inc. (C), NJ, *357*
J. P. Gleason Assoc., Inc. (R), IL, *77*
The Glenwood Group (C), IL, *358*
Goldbeck Recruiting Inc. (C), BC, *359*
Gomez Fregoso y Asociados (C), JAL, *360*
Goodrich & Sherwood Assoc., Inc. (R), NY, *79*
Gordon/Tyler (R), PA, *80*
Gould, McCoy & Chadick, Inc. (R), NY, *80*
Gowdy Consultants (C), TX, *361*
Alexander Graham Assoc. (C), NJ, *361*
Granger, Counts & Assoc. (R), OH, *81*
Robert Grant Assoc., Inc. (C), CA, *361*
The Grant Search Group, Inc. (C), ON, *361*
Greene Personnel Consultants (C), RI, *362*
Griffith & Werner, Inc. (R), FL, *82*
Guidarelli Assoc., Inc. (R), MI, *83*
GWS Partners (R), IL, *84*
The H. S. Group, Inc. (C), WI, *365*
Hall Management Group, Inc. (C), GA, *367*
Handy HRM (R), NY, *86*
Hansen Executive Search, Inc. (C), NE, *368*
Harris Heery & Assoc., Inc. (R), CT, *87*
The Hawkins Co. (R), CA, *88*
Michael J. Hawkins, Inc. (C), IL, *370*
Hazlett Associates (R), IL, *88*
Heath/Norton Assoc., Inc. (R), NY, *89*
The Heidrick Partners, Inc. (R), IL, *90*
Heller Assoc., Ltd. (R), IL, *91*
Henson Partners (C), AZ, *376*
Heritage Search Group, Inc. (C), FL, *376*
Herring & Assoc. (C), AR, *376*
Hill & Assoc. (C), CA, *378*
The Hindman Group, Inc. (C), CA, *378*
Hoffman Partnership Group Inc. (C), NY, *379*
Hollander Horizon Int'l. (R), CA, *95*
The Hollins Group, Inc. (R), IL, *95*
Horton Int'l. Inc. (R), NY, *96*
Hospitality Executive Search, Inc. (R), MA, *96*
Howe & Assoc. (R), PA, *97*
Robert Howe & Assoc. (R), GA, *97*
HRNI (C), MI, *383*
Hughes & Company (R), VA, *98*
The Hunt Group, Inc. (R), NC, *99*
Hunt Ltd. (C), NJ, *385*
Hunter Int'l., Inc. (R), CT, *100*
Industry Consultants, Inc. (C), GA, *388*
Interim Accounting Professionals (C), CA, *391*
ISC of Atlanta, Inc. (C), GA, *394*
The J. B. Search Group (C), CA, *395*
Ron Jackson & Assoc. (C), GA, *396*
Jeffrey Allan Co., Inc. (C), CA, *398*
L. J. Johnson & Co. (R), MI, *106*
Johnson & Company (R), CT, *107*
Johnson Assoc., Inc. (C), IL, *399*
The Jonathan Stevens Group, Inc. (R), NJ, *108*
J. M. Joseph Assoc. (R), NJ, *109*
Judd Associates (R), NJ, *109*
Kaas Employment Services (C), IA, *402*
Karp & Assoc. (C), FL, *403*
Martin Kartin & Co., Inc. (R), NY, *110*
A.T. Kearney Executive Search (R), IL, *111*
Kelley & Keller, Inc. (C), FL, *405*
Kelly Associates (R), PA, *112*
David Warwick Kennedy & Assoc. (R), BC, *112*
Kensington Int'l., Inc. (R), IL, *113*

(R) = Retainer; (C) = Contingency

Blair Kershaw Assoc., Inc. (C), PA, *405*
Key Employment (C), NJ, *405*
Kincannon & Reed (R), VA, *114*
Kingsley Quinn/USA (R), NJ, *115*
Raymond J. Klemmer & Assoc. (R), NY, *116*
The Koehler Group (C), PA, *408*
Kordus Consulting Group (C), WI, *408*
Koren, Rogers Assoc. Inc. (R), NY, *117*
Korn/Ferry Int'l. (R), NY, *117*
Kozlin Assoc., Inc. (C), NY, *408*
Kremple & Meade, Inc. (R), CA, *120*
D. Kunkle & Assoc. (C), IL, *410*
L&L Assoc. Global Search (C), PA, *411*
Laboratory Resource Group (C), MA, *411*
Lancaster Assoc., Inc. (C), NJ, *411*
Stephen Laramee & Assoc. Inc. (C), ON, *413*
Robert Larned Assoc., Inc. (C), VA, *413*
Lawrence-Balakonis & Assoc., Inc. (C), GA, *414*
Leaders-Trust Int'l./Carce y Asociados, S.C. (R), MX, *127*
Lechner & Assoc., Inc. (C), FL, *415*
Leslie Kavanagh Assoc., Inc. (C), NY, *416*
Linden Group, Inc. (C), NC, *418*
Ginger Lindsey & Assoc., Inc. (C), TX, *418*
Lloyd Prescott Assoc., Inc. (C), FL, *418*
Logic Assoc., Inc. (C), NY, *419*
J. S. Lord & Company, Inc. (R), MA, *131*
Lucas Assoc. (C), GA, *421*
Ludwig & Assoc., Inc. (C), VA, *421*
P. J. Lynch Assoc. (R), CT, *132*
M. K. & Assoc. (C), PA, *422*
M.C. Executive Search (C), CA, *422*
Madison MacArthur Inc. (R), ON, *133*
Maiorino & Weston Assoc., Inc. (R), CT, *134*
Management Alliance Group, Inc. (R), NJ, *134*
Management Catalysts (R), NJ, *134*
Management One Consultants (C), ON, *425*
Management Recruiters of Birmingham (C), AL, *438*
Management Recruiters Peninsula (C), CA, *439*
Management Recruiters of Little Rock (C), AR, *439*
Management Recruiters of Clovis (C), CA, *440*
Management Recruiters of Colorado Springs (C), CO, *441*
Management Recruiters of Milford Inc. (C), CT, *442*
Management Recruiters of Colorado, Inc. (C), CO, *442*
Management Recruiters of Anna Maria Island (C), FL, *443*
Management Recruiters of Lake Co., Inc. (C), FL, *444*
Management Recruiters of Atlanta West, Inc. (C), GA, *445*
Management Recruiters of North Fulton (C), GA, *445*
Management Recruiters of Boise (C), ID, *446*
Management Recruiters of Atlanta North, Inc. (C), GA, *446*
Management Recruiters of St. Charles (C), IL, *447*
Management Recruiters of Chicago-North Shore (C), IL, *447*
Management Recruiters of Spencer (C), IA, *448*
Management Recruiters-Cedar Rapids, Inc. (C), IA, *448*
Management Recruiters of Fairfield (C), IA, *449*
Management Recruiters of the Baltimore Washington Corridor (C), MD, *450*
Management Recruiters of Baltimore (C), MD, *451*
Management Recruiters of Rankin Co. (C), MS, *452*
Management Recruiters of Reno (C), NV, *453*
Management Recruiters of New Providence (C), NJ, *454*
Management Recruiters of Rocky Mount - Southwest (C), NC, *456*
Management Recruiters of Winston-Salem (C), NC, *457*
Management Recruiters of Cleveland (C), OH, *457*
Management Recruiters of Sidney (C), OH, *458*
Management Recruiters of Bethlehem, PA (C), PA, *458*
Management Recruiters of Valley Forge (C), PA, *459*
Management Recruiters of Puerto Rico (C), PR, *460*
Management Recruiters of Myrtle Beach, Inc. (C), SC, *460*
Management Recruiters of West Chester, Inc. (C), PA, *460*
Management Recruiters The Delta Group, Inc. (C), TN, *461*
Management Recruiters of Champions (C), TX, *462*
Management Recruiters - Friendswood (C), TX, *462*
Management Recruiters of Round Rock (C), TX, *463*
Management Recruiters of San Antonio (C), TX, *463*
Management Recruiters of Spokane (C), WA, *465*
Management Recruiters of Seattle (C), WA, *465*
Management Resource Group (C), MN, *467*
Mannard & Assoc., Inc. (R), IL, *135*
Mark Adam Assoc. (R), NJ, *135*
Mark Stanley & Co./EMA Partners International (R), FL, *136*
Markent Personnel, Inc. (C), WI, *470*
Marketing Consultants (C), WI, *470*
Marketing Search Inc. (C), OH, *471*
The Martin Group (R), CA, *137*
Martin Partners, L.L.C. (R), IL, *137*
Mason & Nicastri Ltd. (R), CA, *138*
Massey-Horton Int'l. (R), ON, *138*
Matrix Consultants, Inc. (C), NC, *472*
Matté & Company, Inc. (R), CT, *138*
The Matthews Group, Inc. (C), NJ, *472*
Maxecon Executive Search Consultants (R), FL, *138*
MB Inc. Executive Search (C), NY, *473*
Earl L. McDermid & Assoc. (C), IL, *474*
McInturff & Assoc., Inc. (C), MA, *474*
McIntyre Management Resources (C), ON, *474*
James Mead & Co. (R), CT, *142*
Meder & Assoc., Inc. (R), IL, *142*
Medical Recruiters Inc. (C), MO, *477*
Juan Menefee & Assoc. (C), IL, *478*
Meridian Legal Search/Legal Temps (C), NY, *479*
Merit Professional Search, Inc. (C), TN, *479*
Merrick & Moore (C), NC, *479*
MESA International (C), CA, *480*
Messett Assoc., Inc. (R), FL, *143*
Michael Wayne Recruiters (C), IL, *480*
Michael/Merrill (C), KS, *481*
Herbert Mines Assoc., Inc. (R), NY, *145*
Mirtz Morice, Inc. (R), CT, *145*
MIXTEC Group (R), CA, *145*
The Montgomery Group, Inc. (C), TN, *484*
Montgomery Resources, Inc. (C), CA, *484*
Morgan Int'l., Inc. (R), IL, *147*
Morton, McCorkle & Assoc. Inc. (R), MO, *147*
The Mulshine Company, Ltd. (R), NY, *149*
The Murray Group (C), IL, *487*
Nichols & Company (R), CO, *151*
Noble & Assoc., Inc. (C), NY, *494*
Nordeman Grimm, Inc. (R), NY, *152*
Norman Broadbent Int'l., Inc. (R), NY, *152*
John B. Norris & Assoc., Inc. (C), MD, *495*
Norris Agency (C), TX, *495*
NPF Assoc. Ltd. Inc. (R), FL, *153*
O'Callaghan Honey/Ray & Berndtson Inc. (R), AB, *153*
O'Connell Group Inc. (C), CT, *497*
O'Connor, O'Connor, Lordi, Ltd. (R), PA, *154*
O'Keefe & Assoc., Inc. (R), CT, *154*
Oliver & Rozner Assoc., Inc. (R), NY, *155*
Olsen/Clark (R), WA, *156*
Omega Search, Inc. (C), NC, *498*
OmniSearch, Inc. (C), FL, *499*
K. Ossow & Co. (C), NY, *500*
Pacific Coast Recruiting (C), CA, *501*
T. Page & Assoc. (C), TX, *502*
Pamenter, Pamenter, Brezer & Deganis Ltd. (R), ON, *159*
Arthur Pann Assoc., Inc. (C), NY, *502*
R. Parker & Assoc., Inc. (R), NY, *159*
Partners in Recruiting (C), IL, *503*
Partnervision Consulting Group Inc. (R), ON, *160*
Rick Pascal & Assoc., Inc. (C), NJ, *504*
Carolyn Smith Paschal Int'l. (R), CA, *160*
Pathway Executive Search, Inc. (C), NY, *505*
The Penn Partners, Inc. (R), PA, *162*
PERC, Ltd. (C), AZ, *506*
Performance Resources, Inc. (C), RI, *507*
Personnel Incorporated (C), IA, *508*
Peyser Assoc., Inc. (R), FL, *163*
Philo & Associates (C), GA, *511*
DNPitchon Assoc. (R), NJ, *165*
PLA, Inc. (C), NJ, *513*

PMJ & Assoc. (C), ON, *513*
Jack Porter Assoc., Inc. (C), WA, *514*
Robert Powers & Assoc. (C), CA, *515*
Powers Consultants, Inc. (R), MO, *166*
The Prairie Group (C), IL, *515*
Premier Search Group (C), IN, *517*
Prestige Inc. (C), WI, *517*
Procurement Resources (C), MD, *520*
Professional Search Assoc. (C), CA, *522*
ProTech Nationwide Staffing, Inc. (C), NY, *525*
Quality Control Recruiters (C), CT, *526*
Quality Search (C), IN, *526*
R. J. Associates (C), NY, *528*
Raines Int'l. Inc. (R), NY, *171*
Rand Assoc. (R), ME, *171*
Joanne E. Ratner Search (C), NY, *529*
Ray & Berndtson (R), TX, *171*
Ray & Berndtson/Lovas Stanley (R), ON, *172*
Razzino-Claymore Assoc. (C), NJ, *530*
Recruiting/Solutions (C), CA, *532*
Mary Rector & Assoc., Inc. (C), IL, *533*
Redden & McGrath Assoc., Inc. (R), NY, *173*
The Remington Group (R), IL, *174*
Research Personnel Consultants (C), ON, *534*
Resource Inc. (R), MA, *175*
Resource Perspectives, Inc. (R), CA, *175*
Resource Services, Inc. (C), NY, *534*
Retained Search Assoc. (R), NC, *176*
S. Reyman & Assoc., Ltd. (R), IL, *176*
Russell Reynolds Assoc., Inc. (R), NY, *176*
Richards Assoc., Inc. (R), NY, *178*
Rieser & Assoc., Inc. (R), MO, *178*
Riley Cole (C), CA, *537*
RJN Consulting (R), NY, *179*
Robison Humphreys & Assoc., Inc. (R), ON, *180*
Craig Roe & Assoc., LLC (C), MD, *540*
ROI Assoc. (R), NY, *180*
Rollins & Assoc. (C), CA, *541*
Roth Young Personnel Services of Washington, DC (C), MD, *546*
Roth Young of Chicago (C), IL, *546*
Roth Young Personnel Service of Detroit, Inc. (C), MI, *546*
Roth Young Executive Recruiters (C), MN, *546*
Roth Young of Pittsburgh (C), PA, *546*
Roth Young of Tampa (C), FL, *546*
Roth Young Seattle (C), WA, *546*
Roth Young Executive Search of Milwaukee (C), WI, *547*
Rowland Assoc. (C), CA, *547*
RTE Search (C), NJ, *547*
K. Russo Assoc. Inc. (C), CT, *548*
S-H-S Int'l. of Cherry Hill (C), NJ, *549*
S-H-S TechStaff (C), PA, *549*
Sales Consultants of Birmingham (C), AL, *555*
Sales Consultants of Scottsdale, Inc. (C), AZ, *556*
Sales Consultants Peninsula, Inc. (C), CA, *556*
Sales Consultants of Ft. Lauderdale, Inc. (C), FL, *557*
Sales Consultants of Brockton, Inc. (C), MA, *559*
Sales Consultants of Baltimore (C), MD, *559*
Sales Consultants of Laurel Park, Inc. (C), MI, *560*
Sales Consultants of Farmington Hills (C), MI, *560*
Sales Consultants of Cincinnati (C), OH, *561*
Sales Consultants of Morris County, Inc. (C), NJ, *561*
Sales Consultants of Westchester-South, Inc. (C), NY, *561*
Sales Consultants of Dallas (C), TX, *563*
Sales Consultants of Appleton (C), WI, *563*
Sales Executives, Inc. (C), MI, *563*
Sales Management Resources (C), CA, *563*
Sales Recruiting Network (C), PA, *564*
Sales Search Specialist (C), IL, *564*
Sanford Rose Assoc. - Mobile (C), AL, *565*
Sanford Rose Assoc. - Rockville (C), MD, *567*
Sanford Rose Assoc. - Columbia (C), SC, *570*
Sanford Rose Assoc. - Portland (C), OR, *570*
Sanford Rose Assoc. - Salt Lake City (C), UT, *571*
Satterfield & Assoc., Inc. (R), OH, *184*
Savalli & Assoc., Inc. (C), MI, *571*
Schall Executive Search Partners (R), MN, *185*
F. B. Schmidt Int'l. (R), CA, *185*
Schneider, Hill & Spangler, Inc. (R), PA, *185*
Scott Executive Search, Inc. (R), NY, *186*
Scott-Thaler Assoc. Agency, Inc. (C), CA, *573*
Search Enterprises, Inc. (C), FL, *575*
Search Int'l. (R), MA, *187*
SearchCom, Inc. (R), TX, *187*
SearchCorp (C), FL, *577*
J. R. Seehusen Assoc., Inc. (R), IA, *188*
Selective Search Associates (C), OH, *578*
Michael Shirley Assoc. Inc. (R), KS, *190*
Shoemaker & Assoc. (R), GA, *190*
Shore Asociados Ejecutivos, S. A. de C.V. (R), MX, *190*
John Sibbald Assoc., Inc. (R), MO, *191*
RitaSue Siegel Resources, Inc. (R), NY, *191*
D. J. Simpson Assoc. Inc. (R), ON, *191*
Skott/Edwards Consultants (R), NY, *192*
Tom Sloan & Assoc., Inc. (C), WI, *583*
Sloan & Assoc., Inc. (C), VA, *583*
Christopher Smallhorn Executive Recruiting, Inc. (R), MA, *193*
Smith & Assoc. (C), CA, *583*
Ralph Smith & Assoc. (C), IL, *584*
Smith & Laue Search (R), OR, *193*
Smith & Syberg, Inc. (R), IN, *193*
Smith, Roth & Squires (R), NY, *194*
Smith Search, S.C. (R), MX, *194*
Smith's Fifth Avenue (C), NY, *585*
A. William Smyth, Inc. (R), CA, *194*
Snelling Search (C), AL, *585*
C. Snow & Assoc. (C), ON, *586*
Snyder & Co. (R), CT, *194*
Somerset Group, Inc. (C), CT, *587*
Special Markets Group, Inc. (R), GA, *195*
SpencerStuart (R), NY, *196*
Spilman & Assoc. (R), TX, *197*
Spriggs & Co., Inc. (R), IL, *198*
Staff Resources, Inc. (C), SC, *590*
Stanton Chase Int'l. (R), MD, *198*
The Stark Wilton Group (R), MI, *199*
The Stelton Group, Inc. (C), NJ, *592*
Storfer & Assoc. (C), NY, *595*
Strategic Assoc., Inc. (C), TX, *595*
Strategic Executives, Inc. (R), CT, *202*
Strategic Search, LLC (C), CA, *595*
StratfordGroup (R), OH, *203*
The Talley Group (R), VA, *205*
S. Tanner & Assoc. Inc. (C), ON, *599*
Tate & Assoc., Inc. (R), NJ, *207*
The TBI Group (R), PA, *207*
Team One Partners, Inc. (C), GA, *600*
Thomas Resource Group (R), CA, *209*
The Tidewater Group Inc. (C), CT, *607*
Tondorf & Assoc. Inc. (C), MA, *607*
Top Gun Group, Inc. (C), NV, *607*
Trebor Weldon Lawrence, Inc. (R), NY, *210*
TRS Staffing Solutions Inc. (C), OH, *610*
The Truman Agency (C), CA, *610*
Tschudin Inc. (R), NJ, *211*
TTG/Sterling Services (C), CA, *610*
Tully/Woodmansee Int'l. Inc. (R), FL, *212*
Van Dyke Assoc. (R), IL, *212*
Verkamp-Joyce Assoc., Inc. (R), IL, *213*
Wachendorfer & Assoc. (C), TX, *613*
Martha Ward Executive Search, Inc. (C), NY, *615*
The Ward Group (R), MA, *215*
Ward Liebelt Assoc. Inc. (R), CT, *215*
Ward-Hoffman & Assoc. (C), ID, *615*
Wasserman Assoc. Inc. (C), MD, *616*
Waveland Int'l. (R), IL, *216*
Weber Executive Search (R), NY, *216*
Lee Weil Assoc., Inc. (C), IL, *617*
Weinstein & Co. (R), MA, *217*
S. E. Weinstein Co. (R), IL, *217*
White, Roberts & Stratton, Inc. (C), IL, *619*
Whittaker & Assoc., Inc. (C), GA, *620*
Daniel Wier & Assoc. (R), CA, *220*
John Williams & Assoc. (C), TX, *621*
William Willis Worldwide Inc. (R), CT, *221*
N. Willner & Co., Inc. (R), NJ, *221*
Winthrop Partners, Inc. (R), NY, *222*
S. R. Wolman Assoc., Inc. (R), NY, *224*
Xagas & Assoc. (R), IL, *226*

D.11 Textile, apparel, related products

A First Resource (C), NC, *231*
Aggressive Corporation (C), IL, *242*
Allen/Associates (R), OH, *4*
A. Artze Assoc.-Personnel Consultants (C), PR, *253*
Ashworth Consultants, Inc. (R), MA, *8*
W. R. Atchison & Assoc., Inc. (C), NC, *254*
L. Battalin & Co. (C), FL, *261*

INDUSTRIES

Neail Behringer Consultants Inc. (R), NY, *15*
BJB Assoc. (C), VA, *267*
Boyden (R), NY, *20*
Jerold Braun & Assoc. (C), CA, *272*
Briant Assoc., Inc. (R), IL, *23*
Cambridge Group Ltd. - Exec. Search Div. (C), CT, *279*
The Cambridge Group Ltd. (C), CT, *280*
Canny, Bowen Inc. (R), NY, *27*
Career Specialists, Inc. (R), WA, *29*
Carion Resource Group Inc. (C), ON, *284*
Christopher and Long (C), MO, *291*
Clark Personnel Service, Inc. (C), AL, *292*
Colton Bernard Inc. (R), CA, *37*
Comprehensive Search (C), GA, *294*
Consulting Rhonda (C), ON, *297*
The Corporate Advisory Group (R), NJ, *41*
Creative Input, Inc. (C), RI, *303*
Curran Partners, Inc. (R), CT, *44*
Tony Curtis & Associates (C), ON, *305*
Cyr Associates, Inc. (C), MA, *306*
David Perry Assoc. (C), NJ, *308*
Thorndike Deland Assoc. LLC (R), NY, *48*
J. Dinerstein & Co., Inc. (R), NY, *51*
Diversified Search, Inc. (R), PA, *52*
Dominguez-Metz & Assoc. (R), CA, *53*
Dougherty & Assoc. (C), TN, *314*
Dunhill Search of West Atlanta (C), GA, *320*
Dunhill Professional Search of Winston-Salem (C), NC, *322*
Dussick Management Assoc. (C), CT, *323*
ExecuTech (C), IN, *332*
Fairfaxx Corp. (R), CT, *64*
Fairfield Int'l. Resources (R), NY, *65*
L. W. Foote Co. (R), WA, *69*
Ford & Assoc., Inc. (C), SC, *343*
F-O-R-T-U-N-E Personnel Consultants of Savannah, Inc. (C), GA, *345*
Fortune Personnel Consultants of Greensboro, NC, Inc. (C), NC, *348*
Fortune Personnel Consultants of Chattanooga Inc. (C), TN, *349*
FORTUNE Personnel Consultants of Charleston, Inc. (C), SC, *349*
Foster Partners (R), NY, *70*
Goldman+Bell, LLC (C), NY, *360*
Goodrich & Sherwood Assoc., Inc. (R), NY, *79*
Alexander Graham Assoc. (C), NJ, *361*
Greene Personnel Consultants (C), RI, *362*
Harris McCully Assoc., Inc. (C), NY, *369*
Hodge-Cronin & Assoc., Inc. (R), IL, *94*
Robert Howe & Assoc. (R), GA, *97*
E. A. Hughes & Co., Inc. (R), NY, *98*
Human Resources Personnel Agency (R), AR, *99*
The Hunter Group (C), NC, *385*
Interactive Search Network (R), CA, *102*
The J. B. Search Group (C), CA, *395*
Ron Jackson & Assoc. (C), GA, *396*
Jaral Consultants, Inc. (C), NJ, *397*
JCL & Assoc. (C), FL, *397*
Johnson & Company (R), CT, *107*
The Jonathan Stevens Group, Inc. (R), NJ, *108*
Just Management Services Inc. (C), FL, *402*
Martin Kartin & Co., Inc. (R), NY, *110*
A.T. Kearney Executive Search (R), IL, *111*
Kenzer Corp. (R), NY, *113*
Koltnow & Company (R), NY, *117*
Korn/Ferry Int'l. (R), NY, *117*
Kramer Executive Resources, Inc. (C), NY, *409*
Evie Kreisler Assoc. Inc. (C), CA, *409*
Marvin Laba & Assoc. (R), CA, *122*
Stephen Laramee & Assoc. Inc. (C), ON, *413*
LaVallee & Associates (C), NC, *413*
Lee Management Group Inc. (C), NJ, *416*
Leith & Assoc., Inc. (C), OH, *416*
Lemming/LeVan, Inc. (R), GA, *128*
Locke & Assoc. (R), NC, *131*
J. S. Lord & Company, Inc. (R), MA, *131*
Management Recruiters of Birmingham, Inc. (C), AL, *438*
Management Recruiters of Columbus, Inc. (C), GA, *445*
Management Recruiters of Rockville (C), MD, *450*
Management Recruiters of Raleigh (C), NC, *456*
Management Recruiters of Aiken (C), SC, *460*
Management Recruiters of Travelers Rest, Inc. (C), SC, *461*
Mark III Personnel, Inc. (C), NC, *470*
MB Inc. Executive Search (C), NY, *473*
The McAulay Firm (R), NC, *139*
McIntyre Management Resources (C), ON, *474*
Meridian Legal Search/Legal Temps (C), NY, *479*
MESA International (C), CA, *480*
Herbert Mines Assoc., Inc. (R), NY, *145*
The Moran Group (C), IL, *484*
MPA Executive Search Inc. (R), QE, *148*
Multisearch Recruiters (C), CA, *487*
N.A.P. Executive Services (Canada) Inc. (C), ON, *488*
Norman Broadbent Int'l., Inc. (R), NY, *152*
Omega Search, Inc. (C), NC, *498*
P R Management Consultants, Inc. (C), NJ, *500*
Packaging Personnel Co., Ltd. (C), WI, *501*
Parenica & Co. (R), NC, *159*
R. Parker & Assoc., Inc. (R), NY, *159*
Personnel Alliance Group (C), NJ, *507*
The Personnel Network, Inc. (C), SC, *508*
Phillips Int'l., Inc. (C), SC, *510*
Phillips Resource Group (C), SC, *510*
Rene Plessner Assoc., Inc. (R), NY, *165*
Plummer & Assoc., Inc. (R), CT, *166*
George Preger & Associates Inc. (R), ON, *167*
Professional Resources (C), NY, *522*
Quantum Int'l., Ltd. (R), FL, *170*
Mary Rector & Assoc., Inc. (C), IL, *533*
The Remington Group (R), IL, *174*
Retail Recruiters/Spectrum Consultants, Inc. (C), PA, *535*
Russell Reynolds Assoc., Inc. (R), NY, *176*
Rollins & Assoc. (C), CA, *541*
Susan Rudich (C), NY, *548*
S. P. Assoc., Inc. (C), NC, *550*
Sales Management Resources (C), CA, *563*
Scott-Thaler Assoc. Agency, Inc. (C), CA, *573*
Seitchik Corwin & Seitchik Inc. (R), CA, *188*
Selig Executive Search (C), NH, *579*
Peter Siegel & Co. (C), MA, *581*
Simpson Associates (C), NY, *582*
SpencerStuart (R), NY, *196*
Kenn Spinrad Inc. (C), PA, *589*
Sports Group Int'l. (R), NC, *198*
Sterling Int'l. Management Recruitment, Ltd. Inc. (C), NC, *592*
The Stevenson Group, Inc. (N.J.) (R), NJ, *200*
Stewart/Greene & Co. of The Triad, Inc. (C), NC, *594*
Strategic Resources (C), WA, *595*
Technical Skills Consulting Inc. (R), ON, *207*
Thorne, Brieger Assoc., Inc. (R), NY, *209*
Fred C. Tippel & Assoc. (C), OH, *607*
Tower Consultants, Ltd. (R), PA, *209*
The Viscusi Group, Inc. (R), NY, *214*
Martha Ward Executive Search, Inc. (C), NY, *615*
John R. Williams & Assoc., Inc. (C), NC, *621*
N. Willner & Co., Inc. (R), NJ, *221*
Wilson & Assoc. Int'l. Inc. (C), FL, *622*
S. R. Wolman Assoc., Inc. (R), NY, *224*

D.12 Lumber, wood, furniture & fixtures

A First Resource (C), NC, *231*
Advanced Executive Resources (R), MI, *2*
Aggressive Corporation (C), IL, *242*
Charles P. Aquavella & Assoc. (C), TX, *252*
Ariail & Assoc. (R), NC, *7*
The Barton Group, Inc. (C), MI, *260*
Boyden (R), NY, *20*
Brandywine Management Group (R), MD, *22*
Brooke Chase Assoc., Inc. (R), IL, *24*
Bryan & Louis Research (C), OH, *275*
Career Counseling Inc. (CCI) (C), KY, *282*
Career Specialists, Inc. (R), WA, *29*
Clark Personnel Service, Inc. (C), AL, *292*
The Clayton Edward Group (C), MI, *292*
Coast Personnel Services Ltd. (C), BC, *293*
Comprehensive Search (C), GA, *294*
Dunhill Professional Search of Augusta (C), GA, *320*
Dunlap & Sullivan Assoc. (R), MI, *55*
Dunn Associates (R), PA, *55*
E T Search Inc. (C), CA, *324*
Emerging Technology Search (C), GA, *329*
Erwin Assoc. (R), IL, *60*
ExecuQuest, Inc. (R), MI, *61*
Executive Resource Inc. (C), WI, *334*
Eyler Assoc., Inc. (R), IA, *64*
Forest People Int'l. Search Ltd. (C), BC, *343*
Foster Partners (R), NY, *70*
J. P. Gleason Assoc., Inc. (R), IL, *77*
Goldbeck Recruiting Inc. (C), BC, *359*

Goodrich & Sherwood Assoc., Inc. (R), NY, *79*
Alexander Graham Assoc. (C), NJ, *361*
Wolf Gugler & Assoc. Ltd. (R), ON, *83*
Don Hall & Assoc. (C), TX, *366*
Highlander Search (C), NC, *378*
Hodge-Cronin & Assoc., Inc. (R), IL, *94*
Impact Source, Inc. (C), FL, *387*
JAG Group (R), MO, *105*
Jakobs & Assoc. Int'l. (R), NY, *105*
Robert Kaestner & Assoc. (C), FL, *403*
A.T. Kearney Executive Search (R), IL, *111*
Korn/Ferry Int'l. (R), NY, *117*
John Kuhn & Assoc., Inc. (R), WI, *121*
Stephen Laramee & Assoc. Inc. (C), ON, *413*
Lloyd Associates (R), GA, *130*
Management Recruiters of Ft. Myers, FL. (C), FL, *443*
Management Recruiters of North Fulton (C), GA, *445*
Management Recruiters of Sandy Springs (C), GA, *446*
Management Recruiters of Chicago-North Shore (C), IL, *447*
Management Recruiters of Indianapolis (C), IN, *448*
Management Recruiters of Fairfield (C), IA, *449*
Management Recruiters of Monroe, Inc. (C), LA, *450*
Management Recruiters of Muskegon (C), MI, *451*
Management Recruiters of Cincinnati/Sharonville, Inc. (C), OH, *457*
Management Recruiters of Cleveland (C), OH, *457*
Management Recruiters of Travelers Rest, Inc. (C), SC, *461*
Management Recruiters of Houston-Northeast (C), TX, *463*
Management Recruiters of Sugar Land Inc. (C), TX, *464*
Margolin Consultants, Inc. (C), NY, *469*
McIntyre Management Resources (C), ON, *474*
Meridian Legal Search/Legal Temps (C), NY, *479*
Michael Assoc. (R), IL, *144*
Michaels & Moere (C), WI, *481*
Multisearch Recruiters (C), CA, *487*
Newell Assoc. (R), NY, *151*
Norman Broadbent Int'l., Inc. (R), NY, *152*
Premier Recruiting Group (C), MI, *516*
The Premier Staffing Group (C), OH, *517*
Prestige Inc. (C), WI, *517*
Prichard Kymen Inc. (R), AB, *168*
Recruiting/Solutions (C), CA, *532*
The Douglas Reiter Co., Inc. (R), OR, *174*
The Remington Group (R), IL, *174*
RML Assoc. (C), PA, *538*
Robison Humphreys & Assoc., Inc. (R), ON, *180*
Rowland Assoc. (C), CA, *547*
Sales Consultants of Birmingham (C), AL, *555*
Sales Consultants of Baltimore (C), MD, *559*
Sales Consultants of Westchester-South, Inc. (C), NY, *561*
Sanford Rose Assoc. - Greensboro (C), NC, *569*
Search By Design (C), AZ, *574*
Search North America, Inc. (C), OR, *576*
Simpson Associates (C), NY, *582*
SpencerStuart (R), NY, *196*
Springer Souder & Assoc. L.L.C. (R), IL, *198*
Stanton Chase Int'l. (R), MD, *198*
Stewart/Greene & Co. of The Triad, Inc. (C), NC, *594*
Summerfield Assoc., Inc. (C), TN, *596*
The TBI Group (R), PA, *207*
The Viscusi Group, Inc. (R), NY, *214*
John R. Williams & Assoc., Inc. (C), NC, *621*
The Zarkin Group, Inc. (R), NY, *226*

D.13 Paper & allied products

A.J. & Assoc. (C), FL, *232*
Advanced Recruitment, Inc. (C), TN, *240*
Anderson Industrial Assoc., Inc. (C), GA, *250*
Tryg R. Angell, Ltd. (C), CT, *250*
Applied Search Assoc., Inc. (C), GA, *252*
A. Artze Assoc.-Personnel Consultants (C), PR, *253*
Ashworth Consultants, Inc. (R), MA, *8*
W. R. Atchison & Assoc., Inc. (C), NC, *254*
D. W. Baird & Associates (C), MD, *257*
Ballos & Co., Inc. (R), NJ, *10*
Battalia Winston Int'l./The Euram Consultants Group (R), NY, *13*
The Bedford Consulting Group Inc. (R), ON, *14*
Behrens and Company (C), WA, *262*
Berkshire Search Assoc. (C), MA, *265*
BJB Assoc. (C), VA, *267*
John C. Boone & Co. (R), IL, *19*
The Borton Wallace Co. (R), NC, *19*
Boyden (R), NY, *20*
Brandywine Consulting Group (R), PA, *22*
Brooke Chase Assoc., Inc. (R), IL, *24*
Broward-Dobbs, Inc. (C), GA, *274*
J. Burke & Assoc., Inc. (C), TX, *276*
The Burke Group (C), ON, *276*
David S. Burt Assoc. (C), MT, *276*
Canny, Bowen Inc. (R), NY, *27*
J. P. Canon Assoc. (C), NY, *280*
Cantrell & Assoc. (C), FL, *280*
Capitol Management Consulting, Inc. (C), NJ, *281*
Caprio & Assoc. Inc. (R), IL, *29*
Capstone Inc. (R), NY, *29*
Career Alternatives Executive Search (C), MI, *281*
Career Counseling Inc. (CCI) (C), KY, *282*
Career Images (C), FL, *282*
Central Executive Search, Inc. (C), OH, *287*
William J. Christopher Assoc., Inc. (R), PA, *34*
The Churchill Group (C), ON, *291*
Clark Personnel Service, Inc. (C), AL, *292*
Coast Personnel Services Ltd. (C), BC, *293*
Conard Associates, Inc. (R), NH, *39*
Construct Management Services (C), MN, *297*
Continental Research Search, Inc. (C), WI, *298*
Corbin Packaging Professionals (C), MO, *299*
The Corporate Connection, Ltd. (C), VA, *299*
Corporate Image Group (C), TN, *300*
Creative Input, Inc. (C), RI, *303*
Alan N. Daum & Assoc., Inc. (C), OH, *308*
DieckMueller Group (R), WI, *51*
Domres Professional Search (R), WI, *53*
Dougherty & Assoc. (C), TN, *314*
Dunhill Search of West Atlanta (C), GA, *320*
Dunhill Professional Search of Augusta (C), GA, *320*
Dunhill Professional Search of Bucks-Mont., Inc. (C), PA, *322*
Dunhill Professional Search of Richmond (C), VA, *323*
Engineering Placement Specialists (C), WI, *330*
Engineering Profiles (C), FL, *330*
Environmental, Health & Safety Search Assoc. (C), FL, *331*
Executive Connection (C), OH, *333*
Executive Directions (R), OH, *62*
Executive Manning Corp. (R), FL, *63*
Executive Resource Inc. (C), WI, *334*
Executive Search, Ltd. (C), OH, *336*
First Choice Search (R), WA, *67*
Forest People Int'l. Search Ltd. (C), BC, *343*
F-O-R-T-U-N-E Personnel Consultants of Boise (R), ID, *70*
F-O-R-T-U-N-E Personnel Consultants of Savannah, Inc. (C), GA, *345*
F-O-R-T-U-N-E of West Portland (C), OR, *348*
Fortune Personnel Consultants of Greensboro, NC, Inc. (C), NC, *348*
F-O-R-T-U-N-E Personnel Consultants of Cincinnati (C), OH, *348*
F-O-R-T-U-N-E Consultants of Memphis (C), TN, *349*
Foster Partners (R), NY, *70*
Gateway Group Personnel, LLC (C), TN, *355*
Genesis Research (C), MO, *356*
Gilbert Tweed Assoc. Inc. (R), NY, *76*
The Glenwood Group (C), IL, *358*
Goldbeck Recruiting Inc. (C), BC, *359*
Goodrich & Sherwood Assoc., Inc. (R), NY, *79*
Gould, McCoy & Chadick, Inc. (R), NY, *80*
Gowdy Consultants (C), TX, *361*
GWS Partners (R), IL, *84*
The H. S. Group, Inc. (C), WI, *365*
Hahn & Assoc., Inc. (C), OH, *365*
Hansen Executive Search, Inc. (C), NE, *368*
Harbrowe, Inc. (C), NY, *368*
Michael J. Hawkins, Inc. (C), IL, *370*
G. W. Henn & Co. (R), OH, *91*
Heritage Pacific Corp. (C), CA, *376*

Heritage Search Group, Inc. (C), FL, *376*
Hoffman Partnership Group Inc. (C), NY, *379*
Hughes & Assoc. Int'l. Inc. (C), AL, *383*
Hughes & Company (R), VA, *98*
Hunt Ltd. (C), NJ, *385*
Hunter Int'l. LLC (C), MA, *385*
ISC of Cincinnati Inc. (C), OH, *394*
J. Joseph & Assoc. (C), OH, *395*
JM & Company (R), PA, *106*
John H. Johnson & Assoc., Inc. (R), IL, *106*
Kaas Employment Services (C), IA, *402*
A.T. Kearney Executive Search (R), IL, *111*
Kingsbury • Wax • Bova (R), MA, *114*
Kirby Assoc. (R), PA, *115*
Korn/Ferry Int'l. (R), NY, *117*
Lange & Assoc., Inc. (C), IN, *412*
Stephen Laramee & Assoc. Inc. (C), ON, *413*
Lawrence-Balakonis & Assoc., Inc. (C), GA, *414*
The Lawson Group, Inc. (C), SC, *414*
Lybrook Assoc., Inc. (C), RI, *421*
M H Executive Search Group (C), TX, *422*
Magnum Search (C), IL, *422*
Management Recruiters of Decatur, LLC (C), AL, *438*
Management Recruiters of Birmingham (C), AL, *438*
Management Recruiters of Ft. Myers, FL. (C), FL, *443*
Management Recruiters of Bonita Springs, Inc. (C), FL, *443*
Management Recruiters of Clearwater (C), FL, *443*
Management Recruiters of Pensacola (C), FL, *444*
Management Recruiters of North Fulton (C), GA, *445*
Management Recruiters of Monroe, Inc. (C), LA, *450*
Management Recruiters of Burlington (C), NC, *455*
Management Recruiters of Kinston (C), NC, *456*
Management Recruiters of Cincinnati/ Sharonville, Inc. (C), OH, *457*
Management Recruiters of Westmoreland County, Inc. (C), PA, *459*
Management Recruiters of West Chester, Inc. (C), PA, *460*
Management Recruiters of Travelers Rest, Inc. (C), SC, *461*
Management Recruiters of Arlington (C), TX, *462*
Management Recruiters of Houston-Northeast (C), TX, *463*
Management Recruiters of Sugar Land Inc. (C), TX, *464*
Management Recruiters of Appleton (C), WI, *465*
Management Recruiters of Roanoke (C), VA, *465*
Mannard & Assoc., Inc. (R), IL, *135*
The Marathon Group (C), FL, *469*
Mark III Personnel, Inc. (C), NC, *470*
Markent Personnel, Inc. (C), WI, *470*
Marketing Consultants (C), WI, *470*
Marsteller Wilcox Assoc. (C), IL, *471*
Robert E. McGrath & Assoc. (R), CT, *141*
McInturff & Assoc., Inc. (C), MA, *474*
McKinley•Arend Int'l. (R), TX, *141*
James Mead & Co. (R), CT, *142*
Medical Recruiters Inc. (C), MO, *477*
Meridian Legal Search/Legal Temps (C), NY, *479*
Merrick & Moore (C), NC, *479*
Mulcahy Co. (C), WI, *487*
NaTek Corp. (C), NY, *488*
Norman Broadbent Int'l., Inc. (R), NY, *152*
Northern Consultants Inc. (R), ME, *153*
O'Connell Group Inc. (C), CT, *497*
O'Rourke Companies, Inc. (R), TX, *154*
T. Page & Assoc. (C), TX, *502*
Paper Industry Recruitment (P.I.R.) (C), ME, *502*
Pearson & Assoc., Inc. (C), AZ, *506*
Performance Resources, Inc. (C), RI, *507*
Phillips Resource Group (C), SC, *510*
DNPitchon Assoc. (R), NJ, *165*
Placement Solutions (C), WI, *513*
PRAXIS Partners (R), VA, *167*
Procurement Resources (C), MD, *520*
Professions, Inc. (C), OH, *523*
Quality Control Recruiters (C), CT, *526*
QVS Int'l. (R), GA, *170*
Rand Assoc. (R), ME, *171*
RBW Assoc. Inc. (C), OR, *531*
Reality Group (C), OK, *531*
Recruiting/Solutions (C), CA, *532*
Reid Ellis Assoc. Inc. (C), ON, *533*
Resource Inc. (R), MA, *175*
Resource Perspectives, Inc. (R), CA, *175*
Resources for Management (R), PA, *175*
The Revere Assoc., Inc. (R), OH, *176*
Russell Reynolds Assoc., Inc. (R), NY, *176*
Riddle & McGrath LLC (R), GA, *178*
River Region Personnel, Inc. (C), LA, *538*
Rolland Ressources Humaines Inc. (R), QE, *181*
Rossi & Assoc. Inc. (C), BC, *545*
The Rossi Search Group (C), PA, *545*
S-H-S Int'l. of Cherry Hill (C), NJ, *549*
S. P. Assoc., Inc. (C), NC, *550*
S.D.P. Contract Recruiters (C), NJ, *550*
Saber Group, Inc. (C), TX, *550*
Sales Consultants of Savannah, GA (C), GA, *557*
Sales Consultants of Bangor, Inc. (C), ME, *559*
Sales Consultants of Laurel Park, Inc. (C), MI, *560*
Sales Consultants of Princeton, Inc. (C), NJ, *561*
Sales Consultants of Middlesex County, Inc. (C), NJ, *561*
Sales Consultants of Appleton (C), WI, *563*
Sales Management Resources (C), CA, *563*
Sales Recruiting Network (C), PA, *564*
Sales Search Specialist (C), IL, *564*
Sanford Rose Assoc. - Rockville (C), MD, *567*
Sanford Rose Assoc. - Greensboro (C), NC, *569*
Sanford Rose Assoc. - Nashville (C), TN, *570*
Sanford Rose Assoc. - Philadelphia North (C), PA, *570*
Savalli & Assoc., Inc. (C), MI, *571*
Schenck & Assoc. SC (C), WI, *572*
Search By Design (C), AZ, *574*
Search North America, Inc. (C), OR, *576*
Selective Management Services, Inc. (C), FL, *578*
Sill Technical Assoc., Inc. (C), PA, *581*
J. L. Small Assoc. (C), AL, *583*
J. Harrington Smith Assoc. (C), IN, *584*
Southern Chemical & Plastics Search (C), GA, *587*
Specialty Employment Services, Inc. (C), GA, *589*
SpencerStuart (R), NY, *196*
Ron Stevens & Assoc., Inc. (C), FL, *593*
STM Assoc. (R), UT, *201*
Strategic Advancement Inc. (R), NJ, *202*
Stratin Assoc. (C), NJ, *596*
Summerfield Assoc., Inc. (C), TN, *596*
T E M Assoc. (C), WI, *599*
The Talley Group (R), VA, *205*
Team One Partners, Inc. (C), GA, *600*
Technical Skills Consulting Inc. (R), ON, *207*
Telem Adhesive Search Corp. (C), MD, *605*
Fred C. Tippel & Assoc. (C), OH, *607*
Jay Tracey Assoc. Inc. (C), VT, *608*
TRS Staffing Solutions Inc. (C), OH, *610*
U.S. Search (C), VA, *610*
Gordon Wahls Executive Search (C), PA, *613*
Wasserman Assoc. Inc. (C), MD, *616*
Wayne Assoc., Inc. (C), VA, *616*
Wesley Brown & Bartle Co., Inc. (R), NY, *218*
N. Willner & Co., Inc. (R), NJ, *221*
The Wilmington Group (C), NC, *622*
Jay Wren & Assoc. (C), CA, *625*

D.14 Printing & allied industry

The Abbott Group, Inc. (R), MD, *1*
Peter W. Ambler Co. (R), TX, *5*
Tryg R. Angell, Ltd. (C), CT, *250*
Association for Sales Force Management (C), WA, *254*
Behrens and Company (C), WA, *262*
Neail Behringer Consultants Inc. (R), NY, *15*
BJB Assoc. (C), VA, *267*
Boyden (R), NY, *20*
Bright Search/Professional Staffing (C), MN, *274*
Bryan & Louis Research (C), OH, *275*
Capitol Management Consulting, Inc. (C), NJ, *281*
Caprio & Assoc. Inc. (R), IL, *29*
Central Executive Search, Inc. (C), OH, *287*
William J. Christopher Assoc., Inc. (R), PA, *34*
Leonard Corwen Assoc. (C), NY, *302*
The Dalley Hewitt Co. (R), GA, *45*
DieckMueller Group (R), WI, *51*

DiTech Resources (C), CT, *313*
Diversified Search, Inc. (R), PA, *52*
Domres Professional Search (R), WI, *53*
Dunlap & Sullivan Assoc. (R), MI, *55*
The Elmhurst Group (C), CA, *329*
Emerson & Co. (C), GA, *329*
Employment Solutions, Inc. (C), TX, *330*
Executech (R), OH, *62*
Executive Directions (R), OH, *62*
Executive Resource Group, Inc. (R), ME, *63*
Executive Search Partners (R), NY, *63*
The Fisher Group (R), AB, *67*
F-O-R-T-U-N-E Personnel Consultants of Rockland County, Inc. (C), NY, *348*
F-O-R-T-U-N-E of West Portland (C), OR, *348*
F-O-R-T-U-N-E Personnel Consultants of Cincinnati (C), OH, *348*
Fortune Personnel Consultants of Allentown, Inc. (C), PA, *348*
Foster Partners (R), NY, *70*
Genesis Recruiting (C), CA, *356*
GFI Professional Staffing Services (C), NH, *357*
Gilbert Tweed Assoc. Inc. (R), NY, *76*
H. L. Goehring & Assoc., Inc. (C), OH, *359*
Goldstein & Co. (C), CA, *360*
Graphic Arts Marketing Assoc., Inc. (C), MI, *361*
Graphic Search Assoc. Inc. (C), PA, *362*
David E. Grumney Co. Inc. (R), WA, *83*
Hardage Group (C), TN, *369*
Hazlett Associates (R), IL, *88*
Heath/Norton Assoc., Inc. (R), NY, *89*
The Heidrick Partners, Inc. (R), IL, *90*
Helfer Executive Consultants (R), TN, *91*
Hodge-Cronin & Assoc., Inc. (R), IL, *94*
Human Resources Personnel Agency (R), AR, *99*
Industry Consultants, Inc. (C), GA, *388*
Interim Management Resources Inc. (C), ON, *392*
Joan Isbister Consultants (C), NY, *394*
ISC of Cincinnati Inc. (C), OH, *394*
J. Joseph & Assoc. (C), OH, *395*
JM & Company (R), PA, *106*
John H. Johnson & Assoc., Inc. (R), IL, *106*
A.T. Kearney Executive Search (R), IL, *111*
Kingsbury • Wax • Bova (R), MA, *114*
Korn/Ferry Int'l. (R), NY, *117*
Kutt, Inc. (C), CO, *410*
The Lawson Group, Inc. (C), SC, *414*
Leaders-Trust Int'l./Carce y Asociados, S.C. (R), MX, *127*
Lewis Consulting Service (C), IL, *417*
Lyons & Assoc., Inc. (C), IL, *422*
Maiola & Co. (C), OH, *423*
Management Consultants Corporate Recruiters (C), AZ, *424*
Management Recruiters of Decatur, LLC (C), AL, *438*
Management Recruiters of Anna Maria Island (C), FL, *443*
Management Recruiters of Clearwater (C), FL, *443*
Management Recruiters of Pensacola (C), FL, *444*
Management Recruiters of Indianapolis (C), IN, *448*
Management Recruiters of Burlington (C), NC, *455*
Management Recruiters of Cincinnati/Sharonville, Inc. (C), OH, *457*
Management Recruiters of Cleveland (C), OH, *457*
Management Recruiters of Franklin, Inc. (C), TN, *461*
Management Recruiters of Arlington (C), TX, *462*
The McKinnon Management Group Inc. (C), ON, *475*
Midland Consultants (C), OH, *481*
Morency Assoc. (C), MA, *485*
Mullen Assoc., Inc. (R), NC, *148*
Norman Broadbent Int'l., Inc. (R), NY, *152*
Omega Search, Inc. (C), NC, *498*
Organization Resources Inc. (R), MA, *157*
Pamenter, Pamenter, Brezer & Deganis Ltd. (R), ON, *159*
Performance Resources, Inc. (C), RI, *507*
Professions, Inc. (C), OH, *523*
ProSearch, Inc. (C), OH, *524*
Proven Edge (C), CA, *525*
RCI Employment Solutions (C), FL, *531*
Reid Ellis Assoc. Inc. (C), ON, *533*
The Revere Assoc., Inc. (R), OH, *176*
Riddle & McGrath LLC (R), GA, *178*
Robison Humphreys & Assoc., Inc. (R), ON, *180*
Rossi & Assoc. Inc. (C), BC, *545*
Louis Rudzinsky Assoc., Inc. (C), MA, *548*
S. P. Assoc., Inc. (C), NC, *550*
S.C.S. & Assoc. (C), NC, *550*
Sales Consultants of Savannah, GA (C), GA, *557*
Sales Consultants of Honolulu (C), HI, *558*
Sales Consultants of Omaha, Inc. (C), NE, *560*
Sales Consultants of Westchester-South, Inc. (C), NY, *561*
Sales Consultants of Middlesex County, Inc. (C), NJ, *561*
Sales Consultants of Milwaukee (C), WI, *563*
Sanford Rose Assoc. (C), OH, *565*
Sanford Rose Assoc. - Fairhope (C), AL, *565*
Sanford Rose Assoc. - Effingham (C), IL, *566*
Sanford Rose Assoc. - Evansville (C), IN, *567*
Sanford Rose Assoc. - Rockville (C), MD, *567*
Sanford Rose Assoc. - Rochester (C), MI, *568*
Sanford Rose Assoc. - Greensboro (C), NC, *569*
Sanford Rose Assoc. - Nashville (C), TN, *570*
Sanford Rose Assoc. - Philadelphia North (C), PA, *570*
Selective Management Services, Inc. (C), FL, *578*
Sockwell & Assoc. (R), NC, *194*
SpencerStuart (R), NY, *196*
Sprout/Standish, Inc. (C), NH, *589*
Stewart Assoc. (C), PA, *593*
Stewart/Laurence Assoc., Inc. (R), NJ, *201*
Summerfield Assoc., Inc. (C), TN, *596*
The Talley Group (R), VA, *205*
S. Tanner & Assoc. Inc. (C), ON, *599*
Fred C. Tippel & Assoc. (C), OH, *607*
Jay Tracey Assoc. Inc. (C), VT, *608*
The Truman Agency (C), CA, *610*
Gordon Wahls Executive Search (C), PA, *613*
Whitehead & Assoc., Inc. (C), MO, *620*
The Wilmington Group (C), NC, *622*
Bob Wright Recruiting, Inc. (C), CT, *625*

D.15 Chemicals & allied products

A-Linko & Assoc. (C), TX, *231*
A.M.C.R., Inc. (C), OH, *232*
Accelerated Data Decision, Inc. (C), NJ, *233*
Advancement Recruiting Services (C), OH, *241*
AES Search (C), NJ, *241*
Agri-Tech Personnel, Inc. (C), MO, *242*
The Altco Group (C), NJ, *246*
Anderson & Schwab, Inc. (R), NY, *5*
Anderson Bradshaw Assoc., Inc. (R), TX, *6*
Anderson Industrial Assoc., Inc. (C), GA, *250*
Tryg R. Angell, Ltd. (C), CT, *250*
Fred Anthony Assoc. (C), WI, *251*
A. Artze Assoc.-Personnel Consultants (C), PR, *253*
Astro Executive Search Firm (C), LA, *254*
W. R. Atchison & Assoc., Inc. (C), NC, *254*
Austin - Allen Co. (C), TN, *256*
Keith Bagg & Assoc., Inc. (C), ON, *257*
D. W. Baird & Associates (C), MD, *257*
Ballos & Co., Inc. (R), NJ, *10*
BallResources (C), MO, *258*
Barnes Development Group, LLC (R), WI, *11*
Barone Assoc. (C), NJ, *259*
Barton Assoc., Inc. (R), TX, *12*
Battalia Winston Int'l./The Euram Consultants Group (R), NY, *13*
Gary S. Bell Assoc., Inc. (C), NJ, *263*
William Bell Assoc., Inc. (C), NJ, *263*
Bench Int'l. Search, Inc. (R), CA, *15*
Berkshire Search Assoc. (C), MA, *265*
Biomedical Search Consultants (R), CT, *17*
BJB Assoc. (C), VA, *267*
Blair/Tech Recruiters, Inc. (C), NJ, *268*
Blanton & Co. (C), AL, *268*
The Borton Wallace Co. (R), NC, *19*
Bosland Gray Assoc. (R), NJ, *20*
BowdenGlobal, Ltd. (R), OH, *20*
Boyden (R), NY, *20*
Bradley & Assoc. (C), MN, *272*
Brandywine Management Group (R), MD, *22*
The Brentwood Group, Inc. (R), NJ, *22*
Brett Personnel Specialists (C), NJ, *273*
The Bridge (C), CO, *273*

INDUSTRIES

Brierwood Group, Inc. (C), IN, *273*
Brissenden, McFarland, Fuccella & Reynolds, Inc. (R), NJ, *23*
Broward-Dobbs, Inc. (C), GA, *274*
Brush Creek Partners (R), MO, *24*
Bryan & Louis Research (C), OH, *275*
J. Burke & Assoc., Inc. (C), TX, *276*
David S. Burt Assoc. (C), MT, *276*
Cahill Assoc. (C), CT, *279*
Juliette Lang Cahn Executive Search (C), NY, *279*
Caliber Associates (R), PA, *27*
Callan Assoc., Ltd. (R), IL, *27*
Canny, Bowen Inc. (R), NY, *27*
Cantrell & Assoc. (C), FL, *280*
Capitol Management Consulting, Inc. (C), NJ, *281*
Caprio & Assoc. Inc. (R), IL, *29*
Capstone Inc. (R), NY, *29*
Career Images (C), FL, *282*
Careers First, Inc. (C), NJ, *283*
Carlson & Czeswik (R), MN, *30*
Carnegie Resources, Inc. (C), NC, *284*
Carter, Lavoie Associates (C), RI, *285*
Central Executive Search, Inc. (C), OH, *287*
Christian & Timbers, Inc. (R), OH, *34*
Clarey/Napier Int'l., L.C. (R), TX, *35*
Clark Executive Search (C), NY, *292*
Clark Personnel Service, Inc. (C), AL, *292*
Cochran, Cochran & Yale, Inc. (R), NY, *36*
The Comwell Company, Inc. (C), NJ, *296*
Conway & Assoc. (R), IL, *40*
Cornwall Stockton & Co., Inc. (C), TX, *299*
The Corporate Connection, Ltd. (C), VA, *299*
Corporate Image Group (C), TN, *300*
Corporate Search Consultants (C), IN, *301*
Corporate Select Int'l., Ltd. (C), IL, *301*
Creative Input, Inc. (C), RI, *303*
Crist Partners, Ltd. (R), IL, *43*
Cross Country Consultants, Inc. (C), MD, *304*
The Currier-Winn Co., Inc. (C), NJ, *305*
Curry, Telleri Group, Inc. (R), NJ, *44*
Cypress Int'l., Inc. (R), FL, *45*
Daggett & Kvistad (R), CA, *45*
Alan N. Daum & Assoc., Inc. (C), OH, *308*
Delta Services (R), TX, *48*
DieckMueller Group (R), WI, *51*
Diversified Search, Inc. (R), PA, *52*
Dougherty & Assoc. (C), TN, *314*
Robert Drexler Assoc., Inc. (R), NJ, *54*
J. H. Dugan & Assoc., Inc. (R), CA, *55*
Dukas Assoc. (C), MA, *315*
Dunhill Personnel of Boulder (C), CO, *319*
Dunhill Professional Search of San Jose (C), CA, *319*
Dunhill Executive Search of Los Angeles, Inc. (C), CA, *319*
Dunhill of San Francisco, Inc. (C), CA, *319*
Dunhill Professional Search of Augusta (C), GA, *320*
Dunhill of Ft. Wayne, Inc. (C), IN, *320*
Dunhill Professional Search of Richmond (C), VA, *323*
Dunn Associates (R), PA, *55*
E T Search Inc. (C), CA, *324*
E.P. Int'l. (C), NY, *324*
D. C. Egan & Assoc. (C), GA, *327*
W. Robert Eissler & Assoc., Inc. (C), TX, *327*
Elite Resources Group (R), OH, *58*
The Elsworth Group (C), TX, *329*
Emerald Legal Search (C), NH, *329*
Emerging Medical Technologies, Inc. (C), CO, *329*
Emmett Executive Search, Inc. (C), NY, *330*
Empire International (R), PA, *59*
Employment Solutions, Inc. (C), TX, *330*
Engineering & Scientific Search Assoc. (ESSA) (C), NJ, *330*
Engineering Profiles (C), FL, *330*
Environmental, Health & Safety Search Assoc. (C), FL, *331*
Execu-Tech Search Inc. (C), MN, *332*
Executech (R), OH, *62*
ExecuTech (C), IN, *332*
Executive Career Search (C), VA, *332*
Executive Recruiters Agency, Inc. (C), AR, *333*
Executive Resource Assoc. (C), VA, *334*
F.L.A.G. (C), OH, *338*
Fabian Assoc. Inc. (C), NY, *338*
Fenzel Milar Assoc. (C), OH, *339*
First Choice Search (R), WA, *67*
Howard Fischer Assoc. Int'l., Inc. (R), PA, *67*
Jack Stuart Fisher Assoc. (C), NJ, *341*
Florapersonnel, Inc. (R), FL, *68*
Focus Executive Search (C), MN, *343*
Ford & Assoc., Inc. (C), SC, *343*
Fortune Group Int'l., Inc. (R), PA, *70*
F-O-R-T-U-N-E Personnel Consultants of Atlanta, Inc. (C), GA, *345*
Fortune Personnel Consultants of Hinsdale, IL (C), IL, *346*
F-O-R-T-U-N-E Personnel Consultants of Southwest Indiana (C), IN, *346*
F-O-R-T-U-N-E Personnel Consultants of Menlo Park, Inc. (C), NJ, *347*
Fortune Personnel Consultants of Greensboro, NC, Inc. (C), NC, *348*
Fortune Personnel Consultants of Chattanooga Inc. (C), TN, *349*
Fortune Personnel Consultants of Anderson, Inc. (C), SC, *349*
F-O-R-T-U-N-E Personnel Consultants of Houston, Inc. (C), TX, *350*
Foster Partners (R), NY, *70*
Foy, Schneid & Daniel, Inc. (R), NY, *71*
G. H. Enterprises (C), AZ, *354*
Gaffney Management Consultants (R), IL, *73*
Gallin Associates, Inc. (C), FL, *354*
Genesis Recruiting (C), CA, *356*
Genesis Research (C), MO, *356*
Gilbert Tweed Assoc. Inc. (R), NY, *76*
Global Engineers Inc. (C), ME, *358*
Fred J. Goldsmith Assoc. (R), CA, *79*
Gomez Fregoso y Asociados (C), JAL, *360*
Gould, McCoy & Chadick, Inc. (R), NY, *80*
The Grant Search Group, Inc. (C), ON, *361*
Grover & Assoc. (R), OH, *82*
Harcourt & Assoc. (C), AB, *368*
Hardage Group (C), TN, *369*
Hardison & Company (R), TX, *86*
Harvey Hohauser & Assoc., LLC (R), MI, *87*
Michael J. Hawkins, Inc. (C), IL, *370*
Healthcare Recruiters of Indiana (C), IN, *372*
Healthcare Recruiters International-NY/NJ (C), NJ, *373*
Jay Heino Company, LLC (C), NY, *375*
Helffrich Int'l. (C), FL, *375*
Heritage Search Group, Inc. (C), FL, *376*
Frank P. Hill (R), MX, *93*
The Hindman Co. (R), KY, *94*
Holohan Group, Ltd. (R), MO, *95*
Horizons Unlimited (C), CA, *381*
Horton Int'l. Inc. (R), NY, *96*
Robert Howe & Assoc. (R), GA, *97*
Hughes & Assoc. Int'l. Inc. (C), AL, *383*
The Hunt Group, Inc. (R), NC, *99*
Hunt Ltd. (C), NJ, *385*
Hunt Patton & Brazeal, Inc. (C), OK, *385*
Hunter Int'l. LLC (C), MA, *385*
Industry Consultants, Inc. (C), GA, *388*
Information Technology Search (C), PA, *388*
Inter Regional Executive Search, Inc. (IRES, Inc.) (C), NJ, *391*
Interactive Search Assoc. (C), PA, *391*
ISC of Atlanta, Inc. (C), GA, *394*
K. Jaeger & Assoc. (C), MA, *396*
JLI-Boston (R), MA, *106*
JM & Company (R), PA, *106*
K. E. Johnson Assoc. (C), WA, *399*
JT Assoc. (C), CT, *401*
Kaas Employment Services (C), IA, *402*
Kaye/Bassman Int'l. Corp. (R), TX, *110*
A.T. Kearney Executive Search (R), IL, *111*
Kelly Associates (R), PA, *112*
Kensington Int'l., Inc. (R), IL, *113*
Key Employment (C), NJ, *405*
Kincannon & Reed (R), VA, *114*
The Kleinstein Group, Inc. (R), NJ, *116*
Koontz, Jeffries & Assoc., Inc. (R), FL, *117*
Korn/Ferry Int'l. (R), NY, *117*
Kors Montgomery Int'l. (R), TX, *118*
Kozlin Assoc., Inc. (C), NY, *408*
Laboratory Resource Group (C), MA, *411*
Lancaster Assoc., Inc. (C), NJ, *411*
Stephen Laramee & Assoc. Inc. (C), ON, *413*
Larson Assoc. (R), CA, *125*
LaVallee & Associates (C), NC, *413*
W. R. Lawry, Inc. (R), CT, *126*
Leith & Assoc., Inc. (C), OH, *416*
Livingston, Robert & Co. (R), CT, *130*
Loewenstein & Assoc., Inc. (R), TX, *131*
Lucas Assoc. (C), GA, *421*
Charles Luntz & Assoc., Inc. (R), MO, *132*
Lybrook Assoc., Inc. (C), RI, *421*
Lyons Pruitt Int'l. (R), PA, *132*
The Madison Group (R), NY, *133*
Magellan Int'l., L.P. (C), TX, *422*
Management Recruiters of Birmingham (C), AL, *438*
Management Recruiters of Mobile Co., Inc. (C), AL, *438*

Management Recruiters of Laguna Hills (C), CA, *440*
Management Recruiters of Milford Inc. (C), CT, *442*
Management Recruiters of Middlesex (C), CT, *442*
Management Recruiters of Bonita Springs, Inc. (C), FL, *443*
Management Recruiters of Boca Raton (C), FL, *443*
Management Recruiters of Plant City, Inc. (C), FL, *444*
Management Recruiters of Lake Co., Inc. (C), FL, *444*
Management Recruiters of Vero Beach (C), FL, *445*
Management Recruiters of Boise (C), ID, *446*
Management Recruiters of Savannah (C), GA, *446*
Management Recruiters of Atlanta North, Inc. (C), GA, *446*
Management Recruiters of Springfield, Inc. (C), IL, *447*
Management Recruiters of St. Charles (C), IL, *447*
Management Recruiters of Indianapolis-North (C), IN, *448*
Management Recruiters of Fairfield (C), IA, *449*
Management Recruiters of the Baltimore Washington Corridor (C), MD, *450*
Management Recruiters of Dearborn, Inc. (C), MI, *451*
Management Recruiters of Baltimore (C), MD, *451*
Management Recruiters of Medford, N.J. (C), NJ, *453*
Management Recruiters of Reno (C), NV, *453*
Management Recruiters of Burlington (C), NC, *455*
Management Recruiters of Raleigh (C), NC, *456*
Management Recruiters of Winston-Salem (C), NC, *457*
Management Recruiters of Cincinnati/ Sharonville, Inc. (C), OH, *457*
Management Recruiters of Bethlehem, PA (C), PA, *458*
Management Recruiters of Westmoreland County, Inc. (C), PA, *459*
Management Recruiters of McMurray, Inc. (C), PA, *459*
Management Recruiters of Puerto Rico (C), PR, *460*
Management Recruiters of West Chester, Inc. (C), PA, *460*
Management Recruiters of Chattanooga-Brainerd, Inc. (C), TN, *461*
Management Recruiters of Travelers Rest, Inc. (C), SC, *461*
Management Recruiters - Friendswood (C), TX, *462*
Management Recruiters of North West Austin (C), TX, *462*
Management Recruiters of Houston (C), TX, *462*
Management Recruiters of Ogden (C), UT, *464*
Management Recruiters of Loudoun County South (C), VA, *465*
Management Recruiters of Roanoke (C), VA, *465*
Mark III Personnel, Inc. (C), NC, *470*
Marketing & Sales Resources, Inc. (C), FL, *470*
Marsteller Wilcox Assoc. (C), IL, *471*
George R. Martin (R), PA, *137*
Louis Thomas Masterson & Co. (R), OH, *138*
Mathey Services (C), IL, *472*
Matrix Consultants, Inc. (C), NC, *472*
McCooe & Assoc., Inc. (R), NJ, *140*
Robert E. McGrath & Assoc. (R), CT, *141*
McInturff & Assoc., Inc. (C), MA, *474*
McKinley•Arend Int'l. (R), TX, *141*
J. M. Meredith & Assoc. Inc. (C), CA, *479*
Merrick & Moore (C), NC, *479*
Midland Consultants (C), OH, *481*
Montgomery, Thomason & Assoc. (C), ON, *484*
Morgan Int'l., Inc. (R), IL, *147*
Morton, McCorkle & Assoc. Inc. (R), MO, *147*
Mulcahy Co. (C), WI, *487*
Mullen Assoc., Inc. (R), NC, *148*
The Mulshine Co., Inc. (R), NJ, *149*
The Mulshine Company, Ltd. (R), NY, *149*
R. F. Mulvaney & Assoc., Inc. (R), MO, *149*
National Search, Inc. (R), NC, *150*
Nationwide Personnel Recruiting & Consulting, Inc. (C), OR, *490*
NaviSearch (C), GA, *490*
The NEIS Corp., Inc. (C), FL, *491*
J. Fielding Nelson & Assoc., Inc. (R), UT, *151*
P. J. Nicholson & Assoc. (C), IL, *493*
NJ Solutions (C), CA, *493*
Norman Broadbent Int'l., Inc. (R), NY, *152*
NorTech Resources (C), NY, *496*
North Coast Meridian (C), NY, *496*
Norton & Assoc. (C), IL, *496*
O'Connor, O'Connor, Lordi, Ltd. (R), PA, *154*
Omega Systems, LLC (C), VA, *498*
Ortman Recruiting Int'l. (C), CA, *500*
Pacific Coast Recruiting (C), CA, *501*
Frank Parillo & Assoc. (R), CA, *159*
D. P. Parker & Assoc., Inc. (R), MA, *159*
Partners in Recruiting (C), IL, *503*
Rick Pascal & Assoc., Inc. (C), NJ, *504*
PC Assoc. (C), CO, *505*
Peachtree Executive Search (R), GA, *161*
Petruzzi Assoc. (C), NJ, *509*
Phelps Personnel Assoc., Inc. (C), SC, *510*
Phillips Resource Group (C), SC, *510*
PIC Executive Search (C), GA, *511*
DNPitchon Assoc. (R), NJ, *165*
Placement Solutions (C), WI, *513*
The Polen Group (C), PA, *514*
The Prairie Group (C), IL, *515*
Preferred Professional Recruiters (C), OH, *516*
Preng & Assoc., Inc. (R), TX, *167*
Princeton Executive Search (C), NJ, *518*
Probe Technology (C), PA, *519*
Professional Recruiting Consultants, Inc. (C), DE, *521*
ProTech Nationwide Staffing, Inc. (C), NY, *525*
Proven Edge (C), CA, *525*
Quality Search (C), IN, *526*
Quantum Int'l., Ltd. (R), FL, *170*
QVS Int'l. (R), GA, *170*
R.A.N. Assoc., Inc. (C), OH, *528*
Ray & Berndtson (R), TX, *171*
Raymond Karsan Assoc. (C), PA, *529*
RBW Assoc. Inc. (C), OR, *531*
Reality Group (C), OK, *531*
Recruiting Assoc. of Amarillo (C), TX, *531*
Reifel & Assoc. (R), IL, *174*
Resources for Management (R), PA, *175*
The Revere Assoc., Inc. (R), OH, *176*
Russell Reynolds Assoc., Inc. (R), NY, *176*
Richard, Wayne & Roberts (C), TX, *536*
River Region Personnel, Inc. (C), LA, *538*
J. P. Roddy Consultants (C), PA, *540*
ROI Assoc. (R), NY, *180*
Rolland Ressources Humaines Inc. (R), QE, *181*
Ropella & Assoc. (R), FL, *181*
The Rossi Search Group (C), PA, *545*
Roth Young Personnel Service of Detroit, Inc. (C), MI, *546*
Rowland Assoc. (C), CA, *547*
Rowland Mountain & Assoc. (C), GA, *547*
Ruderfer & Co., Inc. (C), NJ, *548*
W. A. Rutledge & Assoc. (R), CT, *183*
Rylan Forbes Consulting Group, Inc. (C), NJ, *549*
Sales Consultants of Birmingham (C), AL, *555*
Sales Consultants Peninsula, Inc. (C), CA, *556*
Sales Consultants of Indianapolis-North (C), IN, *558*
Sales Consultants of Wellesley, Inc. (C), MA, *559*
Sales Consultants - Bristol County (C), MA, *559*
Sales Consultants of Laurel Park, Inc. (C), MI, *560*
Sales Consultants of Cincinnati (C), OH, *561*
Sales Consultants of Morris County, Inc. (C), NJ, *561*
Sales Consultants of Greenville, Inc. (C), SC, *562*
Sales Consultants of Pittsburgh (C), PA, *562*
Sales Consultants of Appleton (C), WI, *563*
Sales Consultants of Houston (C), TX, *563*
Sales Recruiting Network (C), PA, *564*
Sales Solutions (C), CA, *564*
Sanford Rose Assoc. - Mobile (C), AL, *565*
Sanford Rose Assoc. - Columbia, MD (C), MD, *567*
Sanford Rose Assoc. - Rockville (C), MD, *567*
Sanford Rose Assoc. - Amherst, NY (C), NY, *568*
Sanford Rose Assoc. - Fairlawn (C), OH, *569*

Sanford Rose Assoc. - Greensboro (C), NC, *569*
Sanford Rose Assoc. - Doylestown (C), PA, *570*
Sanford Rose Assoc. - Port Washington (C), WI, *571*
Schattle & Duquette (C), RI, *571*
The Schatz Company (C), MO, *571*
Scientific Solutions, Inc. (C), MI, *572*
Robert Scott Assoc. (C), NJ, *573*
Search Consultants Int'l., Inc. (C), TX, *575*
Search Enterprises, Inc. (C), FL, *575*
Search Masters Int'l. (R), AZ, *187*
Search Northwest Assoc. (C), OR, *576*
Search South, Inc. (C), AL, *576*
Searchforce, Inc. (R), FL, *187*
SHS of Allentown (C), PA, *580*
J. L. Small Assoc. (C), AL, *583*
Smith Search, S.C. (R), MX, *194*
Snelling Search (C), LA, *586*
Southern Chemical & Plastics Search (C), GA, *587*
Specialty Employment Services, Inc. (C), GA, *589*
SpencerStuart (R), NY, *196*
Spriggs & Co., Inc. (R), IL, *198*
Springer Souder & Assoc. L.L.C. (R), IL, *198*
Stanton Chase Int'l. (R), MD, *198*
Ron Stevens & Assoc., Inc. (C), FL, *593*
The Stevenson Group, Inc. (N.J.) (R), NJ, *200*
STM Assoc. (R), UT, *201*
Allan Stolee Inc. (R), FL, *201*
Stoneburner Assoc., Inc. (C), KS, *594*
Strategic Search Corp. (R), IL, *202*
System 1 Search (C), CA, *598*
T E M Assoc. (C), WI, *599*
Tabb & Assoc. (R), OH, *205*
M. L. Tawney & Assoc. (C), TX, *600*
Team One Partners, Inc. (C), GA, *600*
Technical Resource Assoc. (C), TN, *602*
Technical Staffing Solutions (C), TX, *602*
Tekworx, Inc. (C), OK, *604*
Telem Adhesive Search Corp. (C), MD, *605*
The TGA Company (C), TX, *606*
Thomson, Sponar & Adams, Inc. (C), WA, *606*
Thorne, Brieger Assoc., Inc. (R), NY, *209*
The Tidewater Group Inc. (C), CT, *607*
Fred C. Tippel & Assoc. (C), OH, *607*
Tower Consultants, Ltd. (R), PA, *209*
Triangle Assoc. (C), PA, *609*
Triumph Consulting, Inc. (R), IA, *210*
TRS Staffing Solutions Inc. (C), OH, *610*
The Truman Agency (C), CA, *610*
W. G. Tucker & Assoc. (R), PA, *211*
U.S. Search (C), VA, *610*
Waveland Int'l. (R), IL, *216*
Wayne Assoc., Inc. (C), VA, *616*
R. A. Wells Co. (C), GA, *618*
Jude M. Werra & Assoc. (R), WI, *218*
The Whitaker Companies (C), TX, *619*
Whitney Smith Co. (C), TX, *620*
John R. Williams & Assoc., Inc. (C), NC, *621*
Williamsburg Group (C), NJ, *621*
William Willis Worldwide Inc. (R), CT, *221*
Wills Consulting Assoc. Inc. (R), CT, *221*
Windsor International (R), GA, *222*
The Witt Group (C), FL, *623*
Yelverton Executive Search (R), CA, *226*
The Zammataro Company (R), OH, *226*

D.16 Soap, perfume, cosmetics

A-Linko & Assoc. (C), TX, *231*
A.J. & Assoc. (C), FL, *232*
Accelerated Data Decision, Inc. (C), NJ, *233*
The Altco Group (C), NJ, *246*
Amherst Personnel Group Inc. (C), NY, *249*
Austin, Hill & Assoc. (C), MD, *256*
Ballantyne & Assoc. (R), CA, *10*
Bast & Assoc., Inc. (C), CA, *261*
Battalia Winston Int'l./The Euram Consultants Group (R), NY, *13*
L. Battalin & Co. (C), FL, *261*
Martin H. Bauman Assoc., Inc. (R), NY, *13*
Gary S. Bell Assoc., Inc. (C), NJ, *263*
William Bell Assoc., Inc. (C), NJ, *263*
Besen Assoc. Inc. (C), NJ, *266*
BEST/World Assoc. Inc. (R), TX, *16*
BGB Assoc., Inc. (C), IL, *266*
Biomedical Search Consultants (R), CT, *17*
Brett Personnel Specialists (C), NJ, *273*
J. Burke & Assoc., Inc. (C), TX, *276*
Caliber Associates (R), PA, *27*
Canny, Bowen Inc. (R), NY, *27*
J. P. Canon Assoc. (C), NY, *280*
Capitol Management Consulting, Inc. (C), NJ, *281*
Career Alternatives Executive Search (C), MI, *281*
Career Profiles (C), NH, *283*
Careers On Track (C), NJ, *283*
Cochran, Cochran & Yale, Inc. (R), NY, *36*
Corbin Packaging Professionals (C), MO, *299*
Corporate Search Consultants (C), IN, *301*
Curran Partners, Inc. (R), CT, *44*
Cyr Associates, Inc. (C), MA, *306*
The Dartmouth Group (R), NY, *46*
David Perry Assoc. (C), NJ, *308*
Debbon Recruiting Group, Inc. (C), MO, *310*
DeLalla - Fried Assoc. (C), NY, *310*
Dunhill Professional Search of Englewood, Inc. (C), CO, *319*
Dunhill of Ft. Wayne, Inc. (C), IN, *320*
Dussick Management Assoc. (C), CT, *323*
EDI/Executive Dynamics Inc. (C), NJ, *326*
The Eldridge Group, Ltd. (C), IL, *327*
Executive Search Int'l. (C), TX, *335*
Fairfield Int'l. Resources (R), NY, *65*
Paul Falcone Assoc. (R), NJ, *65*
First Choice Search (R), WA, *67*
Fisher-Todd Assoc. (C), NY, *341*
David Fockler & Assoc., Inc. (C), CA, *342*
F-O-R-T-U-N-E Personnel Consultants of Greenwood Village (C), CO, *344*
F-O-R-T-U-N-E Personnel Consultants of Atlanta, Inc. (C), GA, *345*
F-O-R-T-U-N-E Personnel Consultants of Menlo Park, Inc. (C), NJ, *347*
F-O-R-T-U-N-E Consultants of Memphis (C), TN, *349*
Fortune Personnel Consultants of Anderson, Inc. (C), SC, *349*
Foster Partners (R), NY, *70*
The Fourbes Group, Inc. (C), NJ, *351*
Fox, White & Assoc. (C), FL, *351*
Franklin Allen Consultants, Ltd. (R), NY, *71*
The Garret Group (R), NJ, *75*
Gilbert Tweed Assoc. Inc. (R), NY, *76*
Lawrence Glaser Assoc., Inc. (C), NJ, *357*
The Glenwood Group (C), IL, *358*
Goodrich & Sherwood Assoc., Inc. (R), NY, *79*
Gordon/Tyler (R), PA, *80*
Gould, McCoy & Chadick, Inc. (R), NY, *80*
The Grant Search Group, Inc. (C), ON, *361*
Greene Personnel Consultants (C), RI, *362*
Guidarelli Assoc., Inc. (R), MI, *83*
Hansen Executive Search, Inc. (C), NE, *368*
Harris Heery & Assoc., Inc. (R), CT, *87*
Heritage Search Group, Inc. (C), FL, *376*
Herring & Assoc. (C), AR, *376*
Frank P. Hill (R), MX, *93*
Hoffman Partnership Group Inc. (C), NY, *379*
Hollander Horizon Int'l. (R), CA, *95*
Hughes & Company (R), VA, *98*
The Hunt Group, Inc. (R), NC, *99*
Hunt Ltd. (C), NJ, *385*
Hunter Int'l. LLC (C), MA, *385*
Industry Consultants, Inc. (C), GA, *388*
Ingram & Aydelotte, Inc. (R), NY, *101*
Inter Regional Executive Search, Inc. (IRES, Inc.) (C), NJ, *391*
International Executive Recruiters (C), OH, *393*
The J. B. Search Group (C), CA, *395*
Judd Associates (R), NJ, *109*
Martin Kartin & Co., Inc. (R), NY, *110*
A.T. Kearney Executive Search (R), IL, *111*
Kelley & Keller, Inc. (C), FL, *405*
Kordus Consulting Group (C), WI, *408*
Korn/Ferry Int'l. (R), NY, *117*
D. Kunkle & Assoc. (C), IL, *410*
L&L Assoc. Global Search (C), PA, *411*
Marvin Laba & Assoc. (R), CA, *122*
Laboratory Resource Group (C), MA, *411*
Lawrence-Balakonis & Assoc., Inc. (C), GA, *414*
Michael Levine Search Consultants (R), NY, *129*
J. S. Lord & Company, Inc. (R), MA, *131*
Ludwig & Assoc., Inc. (C), VA, *421*
M.C. Executive Search (C), CA, *422*
Maiorino & Weston Assoc., Inc. (R), CT, *134*
Management Catalysts (R), NJ, *134*
Management One Consultants (C), ON, *425*
Management Recruiters of Middlesex (C), CT, *442*

Management Recruiters of Lake Co., Inc. (C), FL, *444*
Management Recruiters of Atlanta West, Inc. (C), GA, *445*
Management Recruiters of Atlanta North, Inc. (C), GA, *446*
Management Recruiters of St. Charles (C), IL, *447*
Management Recruiters of Columbia (C), MD, *450*
Management Recruiters of New Providence (C), NJ, *454*
Management Recruiters of Winston-Salem (C), NC, *457*
Management Recruiters of Westmoreland County, Inc. (C), PA, *459*
Management Recruiters of McMurray, Inc. (C), PA, *459*
Management Recruiters of West Chester, Inc. (C), PA, *460*
Management Recruiters The Delta Group, Inc. (C), TN, *461*
Management Recruiters - Friendswood (C), TX, *462*
Marcus & Assoc. (C), NY, *469*
Marketing & Sales Resources, Inc. (C), FL, *470*
Marketing Consultants (C), WI, *470*
Marketing Search Inc. (C), OH, *471*
Maxecon Executive Search Consultants (R), FL, *138*
James Mead & Co. (R), CT, *142*
META/MAT, Ltd. (R), NJ, *144*
Herbert Mines Assoc., Inc. (R), NY, *145*
Mirtz Morice, Inc. (R), CT, *145*
The Mulshine Company, Ltd. (R), NY, *149*
The Neil Michael Group, Inc./Global Partners (R), NY, *151*
Norman Broadbent Int'l., Inc. (R), NY, *152*
NPF Assoc. Ltd. Inc. (R), FL, *153*
O'Connell Group Inc. (C), CT, *497*
OmniSearch, Inc. (C), FL, *499*
Pacific Coast Recruiting (C), CA, *501*
Packaging Personnel Co., Ltd. (C), WI, *501*
Arthur Pann Assoc., Inc. (C), NY, *502*
R. Parker & Assoc., Inc. (R), NY, *159*
Partners In Human Resources Int'l., Inc. (R), NY, *160*
Rick Pascal & Assoc., Inc. (C), NJ, *504*
Performance Resources, Inc. (C), RI, *507*
Petruzzi Assoc. (C), NJ, *509*
PLA, Inc. (C), NJ, *513*
Rene Plessner Assoc., Inc. (R), NY, *165*
ProTech Nationwide Staffing, Inc. (C), NY, *525*
Quality Search (C), IN, *526*
R. J. Associates (C), NY, *528*
Ray & Berndtson (R), TX, *171*
Recruiting/Solutions (C), CA, *532*
Mary Rector & Assoc., Inc. (C), IL, *533*
Redden & McGrath Assoc., Inc. (R), NY, *173*
The Remington Group (R), IL, *174*
Resource Inc. (R), MA, *175*
Resource Perspectives, Inc. (R), CA, *175*
Russell Reynolds Assoc., Inc. (R), NY, *176*
Riley Cole (C), CA, *537*
RJN Consulting (R), NY, *179*
ROI Assoc. (R), NY, *180*
Rojek Marketing Group, Inc. (R), OH, *181*
Rollins & Assoc. (C), CA, *541*
Roth Young of Chicago (C), IL, *546*
Sales Consultants of Middlesex County, Inc. (C), NJ, *561*
Sales Management Resources (C), CA, *563*
Sales Recruiting Network (C), PA, *564*
Sales Search Specialist (C), IL, *564*
Sanford Rose Assoc. - Clearwater (C), FL, *566*
Sanford Rose Assoc. - Rockford (C), IL, *567*
Sanford Rose Assoc. - Fairlawn (C), OH, *569*
Sanford Rose Assoc. - Salt Lake City (C), UT, *571*
Satterfield & Assoc., Inc. (R), OH, *184*
Savalli & Assoc., Inc. (C), MI, *571*
F. B. Schmidt Int'l. (R), CA, *185*
Scott Executive Search, Inc. (R), NY, *186*
Search Enterprises, Inc. (C), FL, *575*
Searchforce, Inc. (R), FL, *187*
Shoemaker & Assoc. (R), GA, *190*
The Shotland Group (R), CA, *190*
John Sibbald Assoc., Inc. (R), MO, *191*
Ruth Sklar Assoc., Inc. (RSA Executive Search) (R), NY, *192*
Christopher Smallhorn Executive Recruiting, Inc. (R), MA, *193*
Smith & Assoc. (C), CA, *583*
Ralph Smith & Assoc. (C), IL, *584*
Smith, Roth & Squires (R), NY, *194*
A. William Smyth, Inc. (R), CA, *194*
Somerset Group, Inc. (C), CT, *587*
Southern Recruiters & Consultants, Inc. (C), SC, *587*
SpencerStuart (R), NY, *196*
Spriggs & Co., Inc. (R), IL, *198*
The Stelton Group, Inc. (C), NJ, *592*
Storfer & Assoc. (C), NY, *595*
Stratin Assoc. (C), NJ, *596*
T E M Assoc. (C), WI, *599*
The TBI Group (R), PA, *207*
Telford, Adams & Alexander (R), CA, *208*
The Tidewater Group Inc. (C), CT, *607*
Tondorf & Assoc. Inc. (C), MA, *607*
Top Gun Group, Inc. (C), NV, *607*
Trebor Weldon Lawrence, Inc. (R), NY, *210*
Triangle Assoc. (C), PA, *609*
TRS Staffing Solutions Inc. (C), OH, *610*
Verkamp-Joyce Assoc., Inc. (R), IL, *213*
W. P. Assoc. (C), CA, *613*
Wakefield Talabisco Int'l. (R), NY, *214*
Martha Ward Executive Search, Inc. (C), NY, *615*
Ward Liebelt Assoc. Inc. (R), CT, *215*
Wasserman Assoc. Inc. (C), MD, *616*
Weber Executive Search (R), NY, *216*
White, Roberts & Stratton, Inc. (C), IL, *619*
John Williams & Assoc. (C), TX, *621*
Williamsburg Group (C), NJ, *621*
William Willis Worldwide Inc. (R), CT, *221*
N. Willner & Co., Inc. (R), NJ, *221*
Wilson Personnel, Inc. (C), NC, *622*
The Witt Group (C), FL, *623*
S. R. Wolman Assoc., Inc. (R), NY, *224*
Jay Wren & Assoc. (C), CA, *625*

D.17 Drugs, pharmaceuticals

A-Linko & Assoc. (C), TX, *231*
ACSYS Resources, Inc. (C), DE, *238*
ADR Accounting Management Recruiters (C), ON, *240*
AES Search (C), NJ, *241*
Agri-Tech Personnel, Inc. (C), MO, *242*
Ahrensdorf & Assoc. (R), PA, *2*
Albrecht & Assoc., Executive Search Consultants (C), TX, *243*
Alexander Associates (R), NJ, *2*
Alexander Enterprises, Inc. (C), PA, *243*
Allerton Heneghan & O'Neill (R), IL, *4*
Alpha Search (C), FL, *246*
The Altco Group (C), NJ, *246*
AMD & Associates (C), GA, *247*
Ames & Ames (R), CA, *5*
Amherst Personnel Group Inc. (C), NY, *249*
Analytic Recruiting, Inc. (C), NY, *249*
A. Artze Assoc.-Personnel Consultants (C), PR, *253*
Ashway Ltd. Agency (C), NY, *253*
Ashworth Consultants, Inc. (R), MA, *8*
Astro Executive Search Firm (C), LA, *254*
W. R. Atchison & Assoc., Inc. (C), NC, *254*
Atlantic Pacific Group (C), CA, *255*
Atlantic West Int'l. (C), NC, *255*
The Bales-Waugh Group (C), FL, *258*
Ballos & Co., Inc. (R), NJ, *10*
Fred A. Barnette & Assoc. (R), NC, *11*
Barone Assoc. (C), NJ, *259*
Nathan Barry Assoc., Inc. (R), MA, *12*
Aldonna Barry Personnel & Management (C), ON, *260*
Battalia Winston Int'l./The Euram Consultants Group (R), NY, *13*
The Bauman Group (R), CA, *14*
Beck/Eastwood Recruitment Solutions (C), CA, *261*
The Bedford Consulting Group Inc. (R), ON, *14*
Gary S. Bell Assoc., Inc. (C), NJ, *263*
Bench Int'l. Search, Inc. (R), CA, *15*
Berger & Leff (C), CA, *264*
Biomedical Search Consultants (R), CT, *17*
BioPharmMed (C), FL, *267*
BioQuest Inc. (R), CA, *17*
BioTech Research Recruiters Inc. (C), CA, *267*
Birch & Associes (C), QE, *267*
Blair/Tech Recruiters, Inc. (C), NJ, *268*
J: Blakslee Int'l., Ltd. (R), CA, *18*
Blanton & Co. (C), AL, *268*
Blau Mancino Schroeder (R), NJ, *18*
D. R. Blood & Assoc. (R), AZ, *18*
Tom Bogle & Assoc. (C), CA, *269*
John C. Boone & Co. (R), IL, *19*
Bornholdt Shivas & Friends Executive Recruiters (C), NY, *270*
Bosch & Assoc., LLC (R), CT, *19*
Bosland Gray Assoc. (R), NJ, *20*
Boyden (R), NY, *20*
Bradford Executives Int'l. (C), VA, *271*
Brandywine Consulting Group (R), PA, *22*
Brandywine Management Group (R), MD, *22*

INDUSTRIES

The Brentwood Group, Inc. (R), NJ, *22*
Brethet, Barnum & Assoc., Inc. (C), ON, *273*
Brett Personnel Specialists (C), NJ, *273*
Brissenden, McFarland, Fuccella & Reynolds, Inc. (R), NJ, *23*
Brookman Associates (C), NY, *274*
Bryant Research (C), NJ, *275*
Buckman/Enochs & Assoc., Inc. (C), OH, *276*
Burke & Assoc./The Westfield Group (C), CT, *276*
J. Burkey Assoc. (R), NJ, *25*
Button Group (C), TX, *277*
Cadillac Assoc. (C), CA, *278*
Caliber Associates (R), PA, *27*
Cambridge Group Ltd. - Exec. Search Div. (C), CT, *279*
The Cambridge Group Ltd. (C), CT, *280*
CanMed Consultants Inc. (C), ON, *280*
Canny, Bowen Inc. (R), NY, *27*
J. P. Canon Assoc. (C), NY, *280*
Capital Consulting Group, Inc. (R), MD, *28*
Capitol Management Consulting, Inc. (C), NJ, *281*
Caplan Assoc., Inc. (R), NJ, *28*
The Caplan-Taylor Group (R), CA, *28*
Career Advisors, Inc. (C), FL, *281*
Career Alternatives Executive Search (C), MI, *281*
Career Consulting Group, Inc. (C), CT, *281*
Career Profiles (C), NH, *283*
Career Search Group (C), FL, *283*
Careers On Track (C), NJ, *283*
Carr Management Services, Inc. (C), PA, *284*
Carrington & Carrington, Ltd. (R), IL, *30*
Carter, Lavoie Associates (C), RI, *285*
Carter McKenzie, Inc. (C), NJ, *285*
Carter/MacKay (C), NJ, *285*
Carver Search Consultants (C), CA, *285*
Rosemary Cass Ltd. (R), CT, *31*
Catalyx Group (R), NY, *31*
Michael J. Cavanagh & Assoc. Inc. (R), ON, *31*
Chadwell & Assoc., Inc. (C), MI, *288*
Christopher-Westmont & Assoc., Inc. (R), OH, *34*
The Churchill Group (C), ON, *291*
Howard Clark Assoc. (C), NJ, *292*
Clark Executive Search (C), NY, *292*
The Coelyn Group (R), CA, *37*
S L Collins Assoc. (C), NC, *294*
Colucci, Blendow & Johnson (R), CA, *38*
Conway & Assoc. (R), IL, *40*
Corbin Packaging Professionals (C), MO, *299*
The Corporate Advisory Group (R), NJ, *41*
Corporate Recruiters Inc. (C), PA, *300*
Corporate Search Consultants (C), IN, *301*
Corso, Mizgala + French (R), ON, *42*
Courtright & Assoc., Inc. (R), PA, *42*
Jim Crumpley & Assoc. (C), MO, *304*
CSA/Clinical Staffing Assoc., LLC (C), NJ, *304*
Culver Personnel Services (C), CA, *304*
Curran Partners, Inc. (R), CT, *44*
The Currier-Winn Co., Inc. (C), NJ, *305*
Curry, Telleri Group, Inc. (R), NJ, *44*
Cypress Int'l., Inc. (R), FL, *45*
D.A.I Human Resources Consultants (R), QE, *45*
The Danielson Group, Inc. (C), TX, *306*
The Dartmouth Group (R), NY, *46*
Alan N. Daum & Assoc., Inc. (C), OH, *308*
David Perry Assoc. (C), NJ, *308*
Debbon Recruiting Group, Inc. (C), MO, *310*
Deeco Int'l. (C), UT, *310*
Dieckmann & Assoc., Ltd. (R), IL, *51*
Diversified Search, Inc. (R), PA, *52*
Doleman Enterprises (R), VA, *53*
The Domann Organization (R), CA, *53*
The Donnelly Group-Sales Recruiters, Inc. (C), MO, *314*
DRZ Medical Recruiters (C), CO, *315*
DuBrul Management Co. (C), NY, *315*
Dukas Assoc. (C), MA, *315*
Dunhill Personnel of Boulder (C), CO, *319*
Dunhill Professional Search of Englewood, Inc. (C), CO, *319*
Dunhill Search of West Atlanta (C), GA, *320*
Dunhill of Ft. Wayne, Inc. (C), IN, *320*
Dunhill Professional Search of Ramsey (C), NJ, *321*
Dunhill Professional Search of Winston-Salem (C), NC, *322*
C. A. Durakis Assoc., Inc. (R), MD, *55*
Dussick Management Assoc. (C), CT, *323*
Eagle Consulting Group Inc. (C), TX, *325*
J. M. Eagle Partners Ltd. (C), WI, *325*
Eastbourne Assoc. Inc. (R), NY, *56*
EDI/Executive Dynamics Inc. (C), NJ, *326*
Effective Search, Inc. (R), IL, *57*
D. C. Egan & Assoc. (C), GA, *327*
EGM Consulting, Inc. (R), FL, *57*
W. Robert Eissler & Assoc., Inc. (C), TX, *327*
William J. Elam & Assoc. (R), NE, *58*
The Eldridge Group, Ltd. (C), IL, *327*
Emerging Medical Technologies, Inc. (C), CO, *329*
Emmett Executive Search, Inc. (C), NY, *330*
Engineering & Scientific Search Assoc. (ESSA) (C), NJ, *330*
Engineering Futures, LLC (C), CT, *330*
Engineering Resource Group, Inc. (C), NJ, *331*
Excalibur Human Resources, Inc. (R), NJ, *61*
Exec Tech, Inc. (C), IL, *332*
Execu-Tech Search Inc. (C), MN, *332*
ExecuTech (C), IN, *332*
Executive Dimensions (R), NY, *62*
Executive Partners Inc. (C), CT, *333*
Executive Search Int'l. (C), TX, *335*
James Feerst & Assoc., Inc. (C), AZ, *339*
Fidelity Search Group, Inc. (R), PA, *66*
First Search America, Inc. (C), TN, *341*
Howard Fischer Assoc. Int'l., Inc. (R), PA, *67*
Jack Stuart Fisher Assoc. (C), NJ, *341*
Fisher-Todd Assoc. (C), NY, *341*
Ford & Assoc., Inc. (C), SC, *343*
The Ford Group, Inc. (R), PA, *69*
Fortune Group Int'l., Inc. (R), PA, *70*
F-O-R-T-U-N-E Personnel Consultants of Wilmington (C), DE, *344*
F-O-R-T-U-N-E Personnel Consultants of Denver, Inc. (C), CO, *344*
F-O-R-T-U-N-E Personnel Consultants of Greenwood Village (C), CO, *344*
Fortune Personnel Consultants (C), CA, *344*
F-O-R-T-U-N-E Personnel Consultants of San Diego (C), CA, *344*
F-O-R-T-U-N-E Personnel Consultants of Atlanta, Inc. (C), GA, *345*
F-O-R-T-U-N-E Personnel Consultants of Menlo Park, Inc. (C), NJ, *347*
Fortune Personnel Consultants (C), MT, *347*
Fortune Personnel Consultants (C), NH, *347*
F-O-R-T-U-N-E Personnel Consultants of Bergen County Inc. (C), NJ, *347*
Fortune Personnel Consultants of Greensboro, NC, Inc. (C), NC, *348*
Fortune Personnel Consultants of Hilton Head (C), SC, *349*
Fortune Personnel Consultants of Anderson, Inc. (C), SC, *349*
FORTUNE Personnel Consultants of North Dallas (C), TX, *350*
Fortune Personnel Consultants of Plano (C), TX, *350*
F-O-R-T-U-N-E Personnel Consultants of Houston, Inc. (C), TX, *350*
Fortune Personnel Consultants of the Virginia Highlands (C), VA, *351*
Foster Partners (R), NY, *70*
Fox, White & Assoc. (C), FL, *351*
Franklin Allen Consultants, Ltd. (R), NY, *71*
The Franklin Search Group, Inc./Medzilla (R), WA, *71*
Gerald Frisch Assoc., Inc. (R), NY, *72*
Gardner-Ross Assoc., Inc. (R), NY, *74*
The Garret Group (R), NJ, *75*
Genesis Consulting Partners (R), PA, *76*
Gilbert Tweed Assoc. Inc. (R), NY, *76*
The Glenwood Group (C), IL, *358*
Glines Assoc., Inc. (R), IL, *77*
Global Engineers Inc. (C), ME, *358*
Global Research Partnership Inc. (R), NY, *78*
Gomez Fregoso y Asociados (C), JAL, *360*
Goodrich & Sherwood Assoc., Inc. (R), NY, *79*
Gordon/Tyler (R), PA, *80*
Gould, McCoy & Chadick, Inc. (R), NY, *80*
Gowdy Consultants (C), TX, *361*
Robert Grant Assoc., Inc. (C), CA, *361*
The Grant Search Group, Inc. (C), ON, *361*
Greene Personnel Consultants (C), RI, *362*
Griffith & Werner, Inc. (R), FL, *82*
Groton Planning Group (R), ME, *82*
Grover & Assoc. (R), OH, *82*
Guidarelli Assoc., Inc. (R), MI, *83*
GWS Partners (R), IL, *84*
Hadley Associates, Inc. (C), NJ, *365*
Halbrecht Lieberman Assoc., Inc. (R), CT, *84*
Hall Management Group, Inc. (C), GA, *367*

The Hampton Group (C), NY, *367*
Hansen Executive Search, Inc. (C), NE, *368*
Harbrowe, Inc. (C), NY, *368*
Harrington & O'Brien, Inc. (C), NH, *369*
Hartman & Barnette (R), VA, *87*
The Haystack Group, Inc. (R), ME, *88*
Healthcare Management Resources, Inc. (R), GA, *89*
Healthcare Recruiters Int'l. Orange County (C), CA, *372*
Healthcare Recruiters of the Rockies, Inc. (C), CO, *372*
Healthcare Recruiters Int'l. - Alabama (C), AL, *372*
Healthcare Recruiters Int'l. - Los Angeles (C), CA, *372*
Healthcare Recruiters Int'l. Philadelphia (C), NJ, *373*
Healthcare Recruiters International-NY/NJ (C), NJ, *373*
Healthcare Recruiters of New England (C), MA, *373*
Healthcare Recruiters Int'l - Minnesota, Inc. (C), MN, *373*
Healthcare Recruiters of New York, Inc. (C), NY, *373*
Healthcare Recruiters Int'l. - Pittsburgh (C), PA, *373*
Healthcare Resources Group (C), OK, *374*
F. P. Healy & Co., Inc. (R), NY, *89*
R. W. Hebel Assoc. (R), TX, *89*
Jay Heino Company, LLC (C), NY, *375*
Heritage Search Group, Inc. (C), FL, *376*
The Hetzel Group, Inc. (R), IL, *92*
Higbee Assoc., Inc. (C), CT, *377*
Hill & Assoc. (C), CA, *378*
Frank P. Hill (R), MX, *93*
Hockett Associates, Inc. (R), CA, *94*
Hoffman Partnership Group Inc. (C), NY, *379*
The Hogan Group (C), OH, *380*
Hollander Horizon Int'l. (R), CA, *95*
Holohan Group, Ltd. (R), MO, *95*
Horton Int'l. Inc. (R), NY, *96*
Houtz•Strawn & Arnold, Inc. (R), TX, *96*
HRCS (R), CA, *97*
Huff Assoc. (R), NJ, *98*
Hughes & Company (R), VA, *98*
The Hunt Group, Inc. (R), NC, *99*
Hunt Ltd. (C), NJ, *385*
Hunter Douglas Group, Inc. (R), IL, *99*
Hunter Int'l. LLC (C), MA, *385*
Icon Recruiters, LLC (C), CA, *387*
Industry Consultants, Inc. (C), GA, *388*
Information Technology Search (C), PA, *388*
Insight Consulting Co. (C), NY, *389*
Inter Regional Executive Search, Inc. (IRES, Inc.) (C), NJ, *391*
International Research Group (R), CA, *103*
Interspace Interactive, Inc. (C), NY, *394*
ISC of Atlanta, Inc. (C), GA, *394*
JDC Assoc. (C), NY, *397*
Jeffrey Meryl Assoc., Inc. (C), NJ, *398*
Joslin & Assoc., Ltd. (C), IL, *401*
JPM International (C), CA, *401*
JT Assoc. (C), CT, *401*
Karp & Assoc. (C), FL, *403*
Martin Kartin & Co., Inc. (R), NY, *110*
Kazan International, Inc. (R), NJ, *110*
A.T. Kearney Executive Search (R), IL, *111*
Kincannon & Reed (R), VA, *114*
Kingsley Quinn/USA (R), NJ, *115*
The Kleinstein Group, Inc. (R), NJ, *116*
Koontz, Jeffries & Assoc., Inc. (R), FL, *117*
Koren, Rogers Assoc. Inc. (R), NY, *117*
Korn/Ferry Int'l. (R), NY, *117*
Kozlin Assoc., Inc. (C), NY, *408*
Kuhn Med-Tech (C), CA, *409*
D. Kunkle & Assoc. (C), IL, *410*
L & L Assoc. (C), CA, *410*
L O R (R), NJ, *122*
L&L Assoc. Global Search (C), PA, *411*
Laboratory Resource Group (C), MA, *411*
Laguzza Assoc., Ltd. (R), NY, *122*
Stephen Laramee & Assoc. Inc. (C), ON, *413*
Robert Larned Assoc., Inc. (C), VA, *413*
Lasher Assoc. (R), FL, *125*
Lawrence-Balakonis & Assoc., Inc. (C), GA, *414*
W. R. Lawry, Inc. (R), CT, *126*
Ledbetter/Davidson Int'l., Inc. (R), NY, *127*
Albert G. Lee Assoc. (C), RI, *415*
Leslie Kavanagh Assoc., Inc. (C), NY, *416*
Levin & Company, Inc. (R), MA, *128*
Lewis & Blank Int'l. (R), CA, *129*
Pat Licata & Assoc. (C), NC, *417*
Lloyd Prescott Assoc., Inc. (C), FL, *418*
Logic Assoc., Inc. (C), NY, *419*
Longshore + Simmons (R), PA, *131*
J. S. Lord & Company, Inc. (R), MA, *131*
The John Lucht Consultancy Inc. (R), NY, *131*
Lybrook Assoc., Inc. (C), RI, *421*
P. J. Lynch Assoc. (R), CT, *132*
The Macdonald Group, Inc. (R), NJ, *133*
The Mackenzie Group (R), MD, *133*
Madison MacArthur Inc. (R), ON, *133*
Management Alliance Group, Inc. (R), NJ, *134*
Management Catalysts (R), NJ, *134*
Management Recruiters of San Luis Obispo (C), CA, *439*
Management Recruiters of Emeryville (C), CA, *440*
Management Recruiters of Middlesex (C), CT, *442*
Management Recruiters of Anna Maria Island (C), FL, *443*
Management Recruiters of Plant City, Inc. (C), FL, *444*
Management Recruiters of Lake Co., Inc. (C), FL, *444*
Management Recruiters of Atlanta West, Inc. (C), GA, *445*
Management Recruiters of Duluth (C), GA, *445*
Management Recruiters of Atlanta North, Inc. (C), GA, *446*
Management Recruiters of Savannah (C), GA, *446*
Management Recruiters of Springfield, Inc. (C), IL, *447*
Management Recruiters of Columbia (C), MD, *450*
Management Recruiters of Frederick, Inc. (C), MD, *450*
Management Recruiters of Medford, N.J. (C), NJ, *453*
Management Recruiters of Middlesex County NJ (C), NJ, *454*
Management Recruiters of New Providence (C), NJ, *454*
Management Recruiters of Asheville, Inc. (C), NC, *455*
Management Recruiters of Woodbury Inc. (C), NY, *455*
Management Recruiters of Bethlehem, PA (C), PA, *458*
Management Recruiters of Lionville, Inc. (C), PA, *459*
Management Recruiters of McMurray, Inc. (C), PA, *459*
Management Recruiters of Puerto Rico (C), PR, *460*
Management Recruiters of West Chester, Inc. (C), PA, *460*
Management Recruiters The Delta Group, Inc. (C), TN, *461*
Management Recruiters of Chattanooga-Brainerd, Inc. (C), TN, *461*
Management Recruiters of Travelers Rest, Inc. (C), SC, *461*
Management Recruiters of Georgetown (C), SC, *461*
Management Recruiters of Champions (C), TX, *462*
Management Recruiters - Friendswood (C), TX, *462*
Management Recruiters of North West Austin (C), TX, *462*
Management Recruiters - Piedmont (C), VA, *464*
Management Recruiters of Fairfax, VA (C), VA, *464*
Management Recruiters of Milwaukee-West (C), WI, *465*
Management Recruiters of Loudoun County South (C), VA, *465*
Mankuta Gallagher & Assoc., Inc. (C), FL, *468*
Manuso, Alexander & Associates, Inc. (R), NY, *135*
Marcus & Assoc. (C), NY, *469*
Mark Adam Assoc. (R), NJ, *135*
Marketing Resources (C), MA, *470*
Marketing Search Inc. (C), OH, *471*
George R. Martin (R), PA, *137*
Massey-Horton Int'l. (R), ON, *138*
Matté & Company, Inc. (R), CT, *138*
Maxecon Executive Search Consultants (R), FL, *138*
McBride Assoc., Inc. (R), DC, *139*
Robert E. McGrath & Assoc. (R), CT, *141*
McKinley•Arend Int'l. (R), TX, *141*
James Mead & Co. (R), CT, *142*
Medical Executive Search Assoc., Inc. (C), AZ, *477*
Medical Innovations (C), NY, *477*
Medical Recruiters Inc. (C), MO, *477*
MedQuest Assoc. (C), CO, *478*
MedSearch Resources, Inc. (C), FL, *478*
Mercedes & Co., Inc. (R), MA, *143*
Merlin Int'l. Inc. (C), NJ, *479*

INDUSTRIES

Messett Assoc., Inc. (R), FL, *143*
Michael James & Co. (C), IL, *480*
Miller + Miller (C), WA, *482*
Mitchell Martin Inc. (C), NY, *483*
Moffitt Int'l., Inc. (R), NC, *146*
Diedre Moire Corp., Inc. (C), NJ, *483*
MTA Partners (R), TX, *148*
The Mulshine Company, Ltd. (R), NY, *149*
Munroe, Curry & Bond Assoc. (R), NJ, *149*
Nachman Biomedical (C), MA, *488*
National Search Assoc. (C), CA, *490*
National Search, Inc. (R), NC, *150*
NCC Executive Search Consultants (C), CA, *490*
The Neil Michael Group, Inc./Global Partners (R), NY, *151*
Ira Z. Nitzberg (C), NY, *493*
The Noebel Search Group, Inc. (C), TX, *494*
Norman Broadbent Int'l., Inc. (R), NY, *152*
The Normyle/Erstling Health Search Group (C), NJ, *494*
John B. Norris & Assoc., Inc. (C), MD, *495*
O'Connell Group Inc. (C), CT, *497*
O'Connor Resources (C), TX, *497*
O'Keefe & Assoc., Inc. (R), CT, *154*
O'Neill Group (C), NJ, *498*
Oliver & Rozner Assoc., Inc. (R), NY, *155*
OmniSearch, Inc. (C), FL, *499*
Orion Int'l. Consulting Group, Inc. (C), NC, *499*
K. Ossow & Co. (C), NY, *500*
Robert Ottke Assoc. (R), CA, *157*
LaMonte Owens, Inc. (R), PA, *157*
P R Management Consultants, Inc. (C), NJ, *500*
Pacific Coast Recruiting (C), CA, *501*
T. Page & Assoc. (C), TX, *502*
Frank Parillo & Assoc. (R), CA, *159*
R. Parker & Assoc., Inc. (R), NY, *159*
D. P. Parker & Assoc., Inc. (R), MA, *159*
Partners In Human Resources Int'l., Inc. (R), NY, *160*
Rick Pascal & Assoc., Inc. (C), NJ, *504*
Pathway Executive Search, Inc. (C), NY, *505*
Patriot Assoc. (C), PA, *505*
PC Assoc. (C), CO, *505*
Peachtree Executive Search (R), GA, *161*
PERC, Ltd. (C), AZ, *506*
Performance Resources, Inc. (C), RI, *507*
Perry-D'Amico & Assoc. (R), CA, *162*
Personnel Solutions (C), AZ, *509*
Petrie Partners, Inc. (R), FL, *163*
Petruzzi Assoc. (C), NJ, *509*
Pharmaceutical Recruiters, Inc. (R), NY, *163*
J. R. Phillip & Assoc., Inc. (R), CA, *164*
Phoenix BioSearch, Inc. (C), NJ, *511*
PIC Executive Search (C), GA, *511*
PLA, Inc. (C), NJ, *513*
Place Mart Personnel Service (C), NJ, *513*
Placement Testart Inc. (C), QE, *513*
Powers Consultants, Inc. (R), MO, *166*
Preferred Professional Recruiters (C), TX, *516*
Premier Business Advisors (C), PA, *516*
Prichard Kymen Inc. (R), AB, *168*
Prime Search (C), NC, *518*
Professional Recruiting Consultants, Inc. (C), DE, *521*
Proquest Inc. (C), SC, *524*
ProSearch, Inc. (C), PA, *524*
ProTech Nationwide Staffing, Inc. (C), NY, *525*
Proven Edge (C), CA, *525*
Quality Search (C), IN, *526*
Raines Int'l. Inc. (R), NY, *171*
Ray & Berndtson (R), TX, *171*
Raymond Karsan Assoc. (C), PA, *529*
Razzino-Claymore Assoc. (C), NJ, *530*
Recruitment Resources (C), CA, *532*
Mary Rector & Assoc., Inc. (C), IL, *533*
Resource Perspectives, Inc. (R), CA, *175*
Russell Reynolds Assoc., Inc. (R), NY, *176*
Riley Cole (C), CA, *537*
Craig Roe & Assoc., LLC (C), MD, *540*
ROI Assoc. (R), NY, *180*
Rolland Ressources Humaines Inc. (R), QE, *181*
Rollins & Assoc. (C), CA, *541*
Romeo-Hudgins & Assoc., Ltd. (C), NJ, *544*
Roth Young of Chicago (C), IL, *546*
Roth Young Personnel Service of Detroit, Inc. (C), MI, *546*
Ruderfer & Co., Inc. (C), NJ, *548*
J. D. Ruhmann & Assoc. (C), MO, *548*
W. A. Rutledge & Assoc. (R), CT, *183*
Ryan-Allen & Assoc., Inc. (C), CA, *549*
Rylan Forbes Consulting Group, Inc. (C), NJ, *549*
S. P. Assoc., Inc. (C), NC, *550*
S.D.P. Contract Recruiters (C), NJ, *550*
Sales Consultants of Birmingham (C), AL, *555*
Sales Consultants of Chico (C), CA, *556*
Sales Consultants of Scottsdale, Inc. (C), AZ, *556*
Sales Consultants of Boca Raton, Inc. (C), FL, *557*
Sales Consultants of Wellesley, Inc. (C), MA, *559*
Sales Consultants of Brockton, Inc. (C), MA, *559*
Sales Consultants of Bangor, Inc. (C), ME, *559*
Sales Consultants of Morris County, Inc. (C), NJ, *561*
Sales Consultants of Pittsburgh (C), PA, *562*
Sales Management Resources (C), CA, *563*
Sales Recruiting Network (C), PA, *564*
Sales Search Specialist (C), IL, *564*
Sampson Medical Search (C), CA, *564*
Sanford Rose Assoc. - Lake Forest (R), IL, *184*
Sanford Rose Assoc. (C), OH, *565*
Sanford Rose Assoc. - Mobile (C), AL, *565*
Sanford Rose Assoc. - Chicago (C), IL, *566*
Sanford Rose Assoc. - Clearwater (C), FL, *566*
Sanford Rose Assoc. - Columbia, MD (C), MD, *567*
Sanford Rose Assoc. - Louisville (C), KY, *567*
Sanford Rose Assoc. - Rochester (C), MI, *568*
Sanford Rose Assoc. - Fairlawn (C), OH, *569*
Sanford Rose Assoc. - Columbia (C), SC, *570*
Sanford Rose Assoc. - Salt Lake City (C), UT, *571*
Savalli & Assoc., Inc. (C), MI, *571*
A.D. Schiff & Assoc., Ltd. (C), IL, *572*
F. B. Schmidt Int'l. (R), CA, *185*
Schneider, Hill & Spangler, Inc. (R), PA, *185*
Robert Scott Assoc. (C), NJ, *573*
Scott-Thaler Assoc. Agency, Inc. (C), CA, *573*
The Search Committee (C), MD, *574*
Search Enterprises, Inc. (C), FL, *575*
Search Masters Int'l. (R), AZ, *187*
Search Masters, USA (C), FL, *576*
Searchforce, Inc. (R), FL, *187*
Searchworks, Inc. (C), FL, *577*
Sedlar & Miners (R), NY, *188*
Selective Management Services, Inc. (C), FL, *578*
Shoemaker & Assoc. (R), GA, *190*
The Shotland Group (R), CA, *190*
John Sibbald Assoc., Inc. (R), MO, *191*
Daniel A. Silverstein Assoc. Inc. (R), FL, *191*
Ruth Sklar Assoc., Inc. (RSA Executive Search) (R), NY, *192*
Skott/Edwards Consultants (R), NY, *192*
Christopher Smallhorn Executive Recruiting, Inc. (R), MA, *193*
Smith & Laue Search (R), OR, *193*
Smith Hanley Assoc., Inc. (C), NY, *584*
Snyder & Co. (R), CT, *194*
Somerset Group, Inc. (C), CT, *587*
Spear-Izzo Assoc., LLC (C), PA, *588*
Specialty Consultants Inc. (R), PA, *195*
SpencerStuart (R), NY, *196*
Spilman & Assoc. (R), TX, *197*
Stanton Chase Int'l. (R), MD, *198*
The Stark Wilton Group (R), MI, *199*
The Stevenson Group, Inc. (N.J.) (R), NJ, *200*
Stewart Assoc. (C), PA, *593*
Allan Stolee Inc. (R), FL, *201*
Storfer & Assoc. (C), NY, *595*
Strategic Advancement Inc. (R), NJ, *202*
Strategic Resources Biotechnology & Medical Group (C), WA, *595*
Strategic Search Corp. (R), IL, *202*
J. Stroll Assoc., Inc. (R), CT, *203*
Success Seekers Connection (C), FL, *596*
System 1 Search (C), CA, *598*
S. Tanner & Assoc. Inc. (C), ON, *599*
Tate & Assoc., Inc. (R), NJ, *207*
Carl J. Taylor & Co. (R), TX, *207*
TechFind, Inc. (R), MA, *207*
Telem Adhesive Search Corp. (C), MD, *605*
The TGA Company (C), TX, *606*
Thomas Resource Group (R), CA, *209*
The Tidewater Group Inc. (C), CT, *607*
Tondorf & Assoc. Inc. (C), MA, *607*
Travis & Co., Inc. (R), MA, *210*
Trebor Weldon Lawrence, Inc. (R), NY, *210*
Triangle Assoc. (C), PA, *609*

TRS Staffing Solutions Inc. (C), OH, *610*
Tschudin Inc. (R), NJ, *211*
W. G. Tucker & Assoc. (R), PA, *211*
Victor White Int'l. (C), CA, *612*
Voigt Assoc. (R), IL, *214*
W. P. Assoc. (C), CA, *613*
Wakefield Talabisco Int'l. (R), NY, *214*
Martha Ward Executive Search, Inc. (C), NY, *615*
Ward Liebelt Assoc. Inc. (R), CT, *215*
Wasserman Assoc. Inc. (C), MD, *616*
Watring & Assoc., Inc. (C), IL, *616*
The Wellesley Group, Inc. (R), IL, *217*
Wellington Management Group (R), PA, *217*
Wesley Brown & Bartle Co., Inc. (R), NY, *218*
Westfields Int'l., Inc. (C), NY, *619*
WestPacific National Search, Inc. (C), CA, *619*
William-Johns Co., Inc. (C), CA, *621*
John R. Williams & Assoc., Inc. (C), NC, *621*
John Williams & Assoc. (C), TX, *621*
Williams Recruiting, Inc. (C), WA, *621*
Williamsburg Group (C), NJ, *621*
William Willis Worldwide Inc. (R), CT, *221*
N. Willner & Co., Inc. (R), NJ, *221*
Wills Consulting Assoc. Inc. (R), CT, *221*
The Winchester Group (R), CA, *222*
Winfield Assoc., Inc. (C), MA, *623*
The Witt Group (C), FL, *623*
S. R. Wolman Assoc., Inc. (R), NY, *224*
Jay Wren & Assoc. (C), CA, *625*
The Yaiser Group (C), NJ, *625*
The York Group (C), CA, *626*
Yungner & Bormann (R), MN, *226*
Zackrison Assoc., Inc. (C), FL, *627*
Zingaro & Company (R), TX, *227*
Michael D. Zinn & Assoc., Inc. (R), NJ, *227*

D.18 Medical devices & instruments

A-Linko & Assoc. (C), TX, *231*
Abraham & London Ltd. (C), CT, *232*
Access Assoc. Inc. (C), MD, *233*
Access/Resources, Inc. (C), MA, *234*
Ackerman Johnson Inc. (C), TX, *238*
The Addison Consulting Group (C), NJ, *239*
Adel-Lawrence Assoc., Inc. (C), NJ, *240*
Alexander Enterprises, Inc. (C), PA, *243*
Allen-Jeffers Assoc. (C), CA, *245*
The Altco Group (C), NJ, *246*
AMD & Associates (C), GA, *247*
AmeriPro Search, Inc. (C), NC, *248*
Ames & Ames (R), CA, *5*
Ames-O'Neill Assoc., Inc. (C), NY, *249*
Amherst Personnel Group Inc. (C), NY, *249*
Anderson Industrial Assoc., Inc. (C), GA, *250*
Andrews & Wald Group (C), FL, *250*
Applied Resources, Inc. (C), MN, *252*
Aries Search Group (C), GA, *252*
Atlantic Pacific Group (C), CA, *255*
Atlantic West Int'l. (C), NC, *255*
Austin - Allen Co. (C), TN, *256*
Availability Personnel Consultants (C), NH, *257*
Avestruz & Assoc. (C), CA, *257*
The Badger Group (R), CA, *10*
The Bales-Waugh Group (C), FL, *258*
James Bangert & Assoc., Inc. (R), MN, *11*
Fred A. Barnette & Assoc. (R), NC, *11*
Barone Assoc. (C), NJ, *259*
Barone-O'Hara Assoc., Inc. (R), NJ, *11*
The Barrett Group (C), NH, *260*
Nathan Barry Assoc., Inc. (R), MA, *12*
Battalia Winston Int'l./The Euram Consultants Group (R), NY, *13*
The Bauman Group (R), CA, *14*
Bayland Assoc. (C), CA, *261*
Beck/Eastwood Recruitment Solutions (C), CA, *261*
The Bedford Group (R), RI, *15*
Gary S. Bell Assoc., Inc. (C), NJ, *263*
Bench Int'l. Search, Inc. (R), CA, *15*
Dick Berg & Assoc. (C), CA, *264*
Berger & Leff (C), CA, *264*
Ed Bertolas Assoc., Inc. (C), CA, *265*
Paul J. Biestek Assoc., Inc. (R), IL, *17*
Biomedical Search Consultants (R), CT, *17*
BioPharmMed (C), FL, *267*
BioQuest Inc. (R), CA, *17*
BioTech Research Recruiters Inc. (C), CA, *267*
J: Blakslee Int'l., Ltd. (R), CA, *18*
Blaney Executive Search (R), MA, *18*
Blanton & Co. (C), AL, *268*
Tom Bogle & Assoc. (C), CA, *269*
John C. Boone & Co. (R), IL, *19*
Boone-Scaturro Assoc., Inc. (C), GA, *269*
Boyden (R), NY, *20*
Boyle/Ogata Executive Search (R), CA, *21*
The Bradbury Management Group, Inc. (R), CA, *21*
Bradford Executives Int'l. (C), VA, *271*
Brandywine Consulting Group (R), PA, *22*
Bratland & Assoc. (C), IL, *272*
The Brentwood Group, Inc. (R), NJ, *22*
Brethet, Barnum & Assoc., Inc. (C), ON, *273*
Brett Personnel Specialists (C), NJ, *273*
Brian Assoc., Inc. (C), NY, *273*
Brierwood Group, Inc. (C), IN, *273*
Bright Search/Professional Staffing (C), MN, *274*
Brissenden, McFarland, Fuccella & Reynolds, Inc. (R), NJ, *23*
The Broadmoor Group, L.L.C. (R), TX, *23*
Brookman Associates (C), NY, *274*
J. B. Brown & Assoc., Inc. (C), OH, *275*
Buckman/Enochs & Assoc., Inc. (C), OH, *276*
J. Burkey Assoc. (R), NJ, *25*
Butterfield & Co. Int'l., Inc. (C), HI, *277*
Button Group (C), TX, *277*
Cadillac Assoc. (C), CA, *278*
Cahill Assoc. (C), CT, *279*
Caliber Associates (R), PA, *27*
Canny, Bowen Inc. (R), NY, *27*
Canyon Consulting, Inc. (C), TX, *281*
The Caplan-Taylor Group (R), CA, *28*
Career +Plus (C), NY, *281*
Career Images (C), FL, *282*
Career Profiles (C), NH, *283*
Career Search Group (C), FL, *283*
Carr Management Services, Inc. (C), PA, *284*
Carter/MacKay (C), NJ, *285*
Carver Search Consultants (C), CA, *285*
Rosemary Cass Ltd. (R), CT, *31*
The Cassie Group (R), NJ, *31*
Catalyx Group (R), NY, *31*
Chase-Gardner Executive Search Associates, Inc. (C), FL, *289*
A. D. Check Assoc., Inc. (R), PA, *33*
Chelsea Resources, Inc. (C), CT, *290*
Christian & Timbers, Inc. (R), OH, *34*
R. Christine Assoc. (C), PA, *290*
Clark Executive Search (C), NY, *292*
Ken Clark Int'l. (R), NJ, *36*
The Coelyn Group (R), CA, *37*
S L Collins Assoc. (C), NC, *294*
Colucci, Blendow & Johnson (R), CA, *38*
Construct Management Services (C), MN, *297*
Continental Research Search, Inc. (C), WI, *298*
Cook Assoc. Int'l., Inc. (C), TN, *298*
P. G. Cook Assoc. (R), TN, *40*
Corporate Recruiters Inc. (C), PA, *300*
Corporate Select Int'l., Ltd. (C), IL, *301*
Criterion Executive Search, Inc. (C), FL, *303*
Timothy D. Crowe, Jr. (R), MA, *43*
Jim Crumpley & Assoc. (C), MO, *304*
CSA/Clinical Staffing Assoc., LLC (C), NJ, *304*
Cypress Int'l., Inc. (R), FL, *45*
D.A.I Human Resources Consultants (R), QE, *45*
D.A.L. Associates, Inc. (R), CT, *45*
Charles Dahl Group, Inc. (C), MN, *306*
Deeco Int'l. (C), UT, *310*
Roger Dietsch & Assoc. (C), MN, *312*
Diversified Consulting Services, Inc. (C), CO, *313*
Diversified Search, Inc. (R), PA, *52*
DNA Search, Inc. (C), CA, *313*
The Domann Organization (R), CA, *53*
The Donnelly Group-Sales Recruiters, Inc. (C), MO, *314*
Dreier Consulting (C), NJ, *315*
DRZ Medical Recruiters (C), CO, *315*
Dukas Assoc. (C), MA, *315*
Dunhill Professional Search of Englewood, Inc. (C), CO, *319*
Dunhill Professional Search, Inc. of McAllen (C), TX, *323*
E/Search Int'l. (C), CT, *325*
J. M. Eagle Partners Ltd. (C), WI, *325*
Edwards & Assoc. (C), GA, *327*
EGM Consulting, Inc. (R), FL, *57*
W. Robert Eissler & Assoc., Inc. (C), TX, *327*
The Eldridge Group, Ltd. (C), IL, *327*
Elite Medical Search (C), GA, *328*
The Elmhurst Group (C), CA, *329*
Emerging Medical Technologies, Inc. (C), CO, *329*
Emerson & Co. (C), GA, *329*

Emmett Executive Search, Inc. (C), NY, *330*
Engineering & Scientific Search Assoc. (ESSA) (C), NJ, *330*
Exec Tech, Inc. (C), IL, *332*
Executive Business Solutions, Inc. (C), WA, *332*
Executive Recruitment Services, Inc. (ERS, Inc.) (C), GA, *334*
Executive Resource Inc. (C), WI, *334*
Executive Search Int'l. (C), TX, *335*
Executive Search, Ltd. (C), OH, *336*
Dorothy W. Farnath & Assoc., Inc. (C), NJ, *338*
James Feerst & Assoc., Inc. (C), AZ, *339*
James L. Fisk & Assoc. (C), MO, *342*
Fortune Group Int'l., Inc. (R), PA, *70*
F-O-R-T-U-N-E Personnel Consultants of Tampa (C), FL, *344*
F-O-R-T-U-N-E Personnel Consultants of Denver, Inc. (C), CO, *344*
F-O-R-T-U-N-E Personnel Consultants of San Diego (C), CA, *344*
Fortune Personnel Consultants (C), CA, *344*
F-O-R-T-U-N-E Personnel Consultants of Manatee County (C), FL, *345*
F-O-R-T-U-N-E Personnel Consultants of Palm Beach (C), FL, *345*
F-O-R-T-U-N-E Personnel Consultants of Atlanta, Inc. (C), GA, *345*
Fortune Personnel Consultants of Hinsdale, IL (C), IL, *346*
F-o-r-t-u-n-e of Owensboro, Inc. (C), KY, *346*
F-O-R-T-U-N-E Personnel Consultants of Troy, Inc. (C), MI, *347*
Fortune Personnel Consultants (C), MT, *347*
Fortune Personnel Consultants (C), NH, *347*
F-O-R-T-U-N-E Personnel Consultants of Bergen County Inc. (C), NJ, *347*
F-O-R-T-U-N-E Search Consultants (C), MO, *347*
F-O-R-T-U-N-E Personnel Consultants of Charlotte (C), NC, *348*
Fortune Personnel Consultants of Hilton Head (C), SC, *349*
F-O-R-T-U-N-E Consultants of Memphis (C), TN, *349*
Fortune Personnel Consultants of Anderson, Inc. (C), SC, *349*
FORTUNE Personnel Consultants of North Dallas (C), TX, *350*
Fortune Personnel Consultants of Plano (C), TX, *350*
F-O-R-T-U-N-E Personnel Consultants of Knoxville (C), TN, *350*
Fortune Personnel Consultants of San Antonio, Inc. (C), TX, *350*
F-O-R-T-U-N-E Personnel Consultants of Houston, Inc. (C), TX, *350*
Fortune Personnel Consultants of the Virginia Highlands (C), VA, *351*
Foster Partners (R), NY, *70*
The Franklin Search Group, Inc./Medzilla (R), WA, *71*
KS Frary & Assoc. (R), MA, *71*
Gabriele & Company (C), MA, *354*
Gallin Associates, Inc. (C), FL, *354*
W. N. Garbarini & Assoc. (R), NJ, *74*
The Garret Group (R), NJ, *75*
Gateway Group Personnel, LLC (C), TN, *355*
Genesis Consulting Partners (R), PA, *76*
GFI Professional Staffing Services (C), NH, *357*
Gilbert Tweed Assoc. Inc. (R), NY, *76*
The Glenwood Group (C), IL, *358*
Glines Assoc., Inc. (R), IL, *77*
Global Engineers Inc. (C), ME, *358*
Glou Int'l., Inc. (R), MA, *78*
The Goodman Group (R), CA, *79*
Goodrich & Sherwood Assoc., Inc. (R), NY, *79*
Gould, McCoy & Chadick, Inc. (R), NY, *80*
Griffith & Werner, Inc. (R), FL, *82*
Hadley Associates, Inc. (C), NJ, *365*
Hall Management Group, Inc. (C), GA, *367*
The Hampton Group (C), NY, *367*
Harbrowe, Inc. (C), NY, *368*
Harrington & O'Brien, Inc. (C), NH, *369*
Hartman & Barnette (R), VA, *87*
The Haystack Group, Inc. (R), ME, *88*
HCI Corp. (C), IL, *371*
Health Industry Consultants, Inc. (R), CO, *89*
Healthcare Management Resources, Inc. (R), GA, *89*
Healthcare Recruiters Int'l. Orange County (C), CA, *372*
Healthcare Recruiters of the Rockies, Inc. (C), CO, *372*
Healthcare Recruiters Int'l. Phoenix (C), AZ, *372*
Healthcare Recruiters of Indiana (C), IN, *372*
Healthcare Recruiters Int'l. - Los Angeles (C), CA, *372*
Healthcare Recruiters Int'l. - Alabama (C), AL, *372*
Healthcare Recruiters International-NY/NJ (C), NJ, *373*
Healthcare Recruiters of New England (C), MA, *373*
Healthcare Recruiters of New Orleans (C), LA, *373*
Healthcare Recruiters Int'l - Minnesota, Inc. (C), MN, *373*
Healthcare Recruiters of New York, Inc. (C), NY, *373*
Healthcare Recruiters Int'l. - Pittsburgh (C), PA, *373*
Healthcare Recruiters of Dallas (C), TX, *374*
Healthcare Resources Group (C), OK, *374*
HeartBeat Medical, Inc. (C), OR, *374*
Heath/Norton Assoc., Inc. (R), NY, *89*
R. W. Hebel Assoc. (R), TX, *89*
Heinze & Assoc. Inc. (R), MN, *91*
G. W. Henn & Co. (R), OH, *91*
High Tech Staffing Group (C), OR, *377*
High-Tech Recruiters (C), CT, *378*
Hill & Assoc. (C), CA, *378*
Hintz Associates (C), NY, *378*
Hockett Associates, Inc. (R), CA, *94*
Horton Int'l. Inc. (R), NY, *96*
Houtz•Strawn & Arnold, Inc. (R), TX, *96*
Robert Howe & Assoc. (R), GA, *97*
HRCS (R), CA, *97*
Leigh Hunt & Assoc., Inc. (C), ME, *384*
Hunt Ltd. (C), NJ, *385*
Hunter Int'l., Inc. (R), CT, *100*
Hunter Int'l. LLC (C), MA, *385*
IMA Search, Inc. (R), NY, *101*
Information Technology Search (C), PA, *388*
Innovative Healthcare Services, Inc. (C), GA, *389*
InSearch (C), CO, *389*
The Inside Track (C), TX, *389*
Insight Consulting Co. (C), NY, *389*
Inter Regional Executive Search, Inc. (IRES, Inc.) (C), NJ, *391*
International Consulting Services, Inc. (C), IL, *392*
International Research Group (R), CA, *103*
Interquest, Inc. (R), NY, *103*
Iona Partners (C), CA, *394*
J. B. Linde & Assoc. (C), MO, *395*
J. Joseph & Assoc. (C), OH, *395*
J.N. Adams & Assoc., Inc. (C), PA, *396*
Jackley Search Consultants (C), MN, *396*
JDC Assoc. (C), NY, *397*
JLI-Boston (R), MA, *106*
Job Link, Inc. (C), CA, *399*
Johnson & Assoc., Inc. (R), CA, *106*
Jonas, Walters & Assoc., Inc. (R), WI, *107*
J. M. Joseph Assoc. (R), NJ, *109*
JPM International (C), CA, *401*
Just Management Services Inc. (C), FL, *402*
Kanzer Assoc., Inc. (R), IL, *109*
Karp & Assoc. (C), FL, *403*
Howard Karr & Assoc., Inc. (R), CA, *110*
Kay Concepts, Inc. (C), FL, *404*
Kazan International, Inc. (R), NJ, *110*
A.T. Kearney Executive Search (R), IL, *111*
Daniel J. Kerstein, Consultant to Management (R), CO, *114*
Ki Technologies, Inc. (C), UT, *406*
Kingsley Quinn/USA (R), NJ, *115*
Knapp Consultants (R), CT, *116*
Koontz, Jeffries & Assoc., Inc. (R), FL, *117*
Korn/Ferry Int'l. (R), NY, *117*
Kozlin Assoc., Inc. (C), NY, *408*
Kuhn Med-Tech (C), CA, *409*
Paul Kull & Co. (R), NJ, *121*
D. Kunkle & Assoc. (C), IL, *410*
L O R (R), NJ, *122*
Laboratory Resource Group (C), MA, *411*
Lasher Assoc. (R), FL, *125*
W. R. Lawry, Inc. (R), CT, *126*
The Lear Group, Inc. (R), OH, *127*
Reynolds Lebus Assoc. (C), AZ, *415*
Lechner & Assoc., Inc. (C), FL, *415*
Ledbetter/Davidson Int'l., Inc. (R), NY, *127*
Levin & Company, Inc. (R), MA, *128*
Lewis & Blank Int'l. (R), CA, *129*
Pat Licata & Assoc. (C), NC, *417*
Lucas Assoc. (C), GA, *421*
Lucas Group (C), NY, *421*
Lutz Associates (C), CT, *421*
The Mackenzie Group (R), MD, *133*

Management Catalysts (R), NJ, *134*
Management Recruiters of San Luis Obispo (C), CA, *439*
Management Recruiters of Northern California (C), CA, *440*
Management Recruiters of Emeryville (C), CA, *440*
Management Recruiters of Pleasanton (C), CA, *441*
Management Recruiters of Milford Inc. (C), CT, *442*
Management Recruiters of Tampa North (C), FL, *444*
Management Recruiters of Plant City, Inc. (C), FL, *444*
Management Recruiters of Lake Forest, IL (C), IL, *447*
Management Recruiters of Springfield, Inc. (C), IL, *447*
Management Recruiters of Des Moines (C), IA, *449*
Management Recruiters of Columbia (C), MD, *450*
Management Recruiters of the Baltimore Washington Corridor (C), MD, *450*
Management Recruiters of Frederick, Inc. (C), MD, *450*
Management Recruiters of Medford, N.J. (C), NJ, *453*
Management Recruiters of North Warren Inc. (C), NJ, *453*
Management Recruiters of Asheville, Inc. (C), NC, *455*
Management Recruiters of Woodbury Inc. (C), NY, *455*
Management Recruiters of McMurray, Inc. (C), PA, *459*
Management Recruiters of Pittsburgh-North, Inc. (C), PA, *460*
Management Recruiters The Delta Group, Inc. (C), TN, *461*
Management Recruiters of Georgetown (C), SC, *461*
Management Recruiters - Piedmont (C), VA, *464*
Management Recruiters of Seattle (C), WA, *465*
Manuso, Alexander & Associates, Inc. (R), NY, *135*
Marketing Recruiters, Inc. (C), NC, *470*
Marketing Resources (C), MA, *470*
The Marlow Group (R), MA, *136*
The Martwick Group, Inc. (C), OR, *472*
McCooe & Assoc., Inc. (R), NJ, *140*
McCormack & Farrow (R), CA, *140*
Robert E. McGrath & Assoc. (R), CT, *141*
McInturff & Assoc., Inc. (C), MA, *474*
McManners Assoc., Inc. (R), CA, *142*
Med Exec Int'l. (C), CA, *476*
Medical Executive Recruiters (C), CA, *477*
Medical Executive Search Assoc., Inc. (C), AZ, *477*
Medical Innovations (C), NY, *477*
Medical Recruiters Inc. (C), MO, *477*
MedQuest Assoc. (C), CO, *478*
MedSearch Resources, Inc. (C), FL, *478*
J. M. Meredith & Assoc. Inc. (C), CA, *479*
META/MAT, Ltd. (R), NJ, *144*
Walter Meyer & Assoc. (R), NY, *144*
Michael James & Co. (C), IL, *480*
Lou Michaels Assoc., Inc. (C), MI, *481*
Miller + Miller (C), WA, *482*
Miller Denver (C), CO, *482*
Diedre Moire Corp., Inc. (C), NJ, *483*
Mordue, Allen, Roberts, Bonney Ltd. (C), WA, *485*
Morgan Int'l., Inc. (R), IL, *147*
Robert T. Morton Assoc., Inc. (C), MA, *486*
MTA Partners (R), TX, *148*
Munroe, Curry & Bond Assoc. (R), NJ, *149*
Nachman Biomedical (C), MA, *488*
National Computerized Employment Service, Inc. (C), PA, *489*
National Search Assoc. (C), CA, *490*
National Search, Inc. (R), NC, *150*
Nationwide Personnel Placement, Inc. (C), OH, *490*
NaviSearch (C), GA, *490*
NCC Executive Search Consultants (C), CA, *490*
The Neil Michael Group, Inc./Global Partners (R), NY, *151*
Len Nelson & Assoc., Inc. (C), TX, *491*
New Venture Development, Inc. (C), CA, *492*
P. J. Nicholson & Assoc. (C), IL, *493*
The Niemond Corp. (R), CA, *152*
Paul Winston Norman & Assoc. (R), IL, *152*
Norman Broadbent Int'l., Inc. (R), NY, *152*
The Normyle/Erstling Health Search Group (C), NJ, *494*
O'Shea, Divine & Co., Inc. (R), CA, *154*
Oliver & Rozner Assoc., Inc. (R), NY, *155*
Olsen/Clark (R), WA, *156*
Omega Search, Inc. (C), NC, *498*
OmniSearch, Inc. (C), FL, *499*
Organization Resources Inc. (R), MA, *157*
Ortman Recruiting Int'l. (C), CA, *500*
Robert Ottke Assoc. (R), CA, *157*
P R Management Consultants, Inc. (C), NJ, *500*
Pacific Advisory Service, Inc. (C), IL, *501*
Pacific Coast Recruiting (C), CA, *501*
Frank Parillo & Assoc. (R), CA, *159*
Partners In Human Resources Int'l., Inc. (R), NY, *160*
Partners in Recruiting (C), IL, *503*
Rick Pascal & Assoc., Inc. (C), NJ, *504*
Patriot Assoc. (C), PA, *505*
Paules Associates (C), CA, *505*
PC Assoc. (C), CO, *505*
Performance Resources, Inc. (C), RI, *507*
Perry-D'Amico & Assoc. (R), CA, *162*
Personnel Solutions (C), AZ, *509*
Petrie Partners, Inc. (R), FL, *163*
Petruzzi Assoc. (C), NJ, *509*
J. R. Phillip & Assoc., Inc. (R), CA, *164*
Pierce & Assoc. (C), CA, *512*
Place Mart Personnel Service (C), NJ, *513*
Placement Testart Inc. (C), QE, *513*
Polytechnical Consultants, Inc. (C), IL, *514*
Norman Powers Assoc., Inc. (C), MA, *515*
Preferred Professional Recruiters (C), TX, *516*
George Preger & Associates Inc. (R), ON, *167*
Prestonwood Assoc. (R), MA, *168*
Prime Search (C), NC, *518*
Probe Technology (C), PA, *519*
Professional Recruiting Network (C), CA, *521*
Professional Recruiting Consultants, Inc. (C), DE, *521*
The Professional Sales Search Co., Inc. (C), WA, *522*
Proquest Inc. (C), SC, *524*
Quality Control Recruiters (C), CT, *526*
Quality Search (C), IN, *526*
Quality Search Inc. (C), OH, *526*
Quiring Assoc., Inc. (C), IN, *527*
R. J. Associates (C), NY, *528*
R2 Services, LLC (C), IL, *528*
Radosevic Assoc. (R), CA, *171*
Ray & Berndtson (R), TX, *171*
Razzino-Claymore Assoc. (C), NJ, *530*
Recruitment Resources (C), CA, *532*
Resource Inc. (R), MA, *175*
S. Reyman & Assoc., Ltd. (R), IL, *176*
Russell Reynolds Assoc., Inc. (R), NY, *176*
Robert Lowell Int'l. (R), TX, *179*
R. A. Rodriguez & Assoc., Inc. (C), TX, *540*
Craig Roe & Assoc., LLC (C), MD, *540*
ROI Assoc. (R), NY, *180*
Romeo-Hudgins & Assoc., Ltd. (C), NJ, *544*
Rowland Assoc. (C), CA, *547*
Ruderfer & Co., Inc. (C), NJ, *548*
Louis Rudzinsky Assoc., Inc. (C), MA, *548*
J. D. Ruhmann & Assoc. (C), MO, *548*
The Ryan Charles Group, Inc. (C), FL, *548*
Ryan-Allen & Assoc., Inc. (C), CA, *549*
S-H-S Int'l. of Cherry Hill (C), NJ, *549*
Sales Consultants of Chico (C), CA, *556*
Sales Consultants of Scottsdale, Inc. (C), AZ, *556*
Sales Consultants Peninsula, Inc. (C), CA, *556*
Sales Consultants of Boca Raton, Inc. (C), FL, *557*
Sales Consultants of Ft. Lauderdale, Inc. (C), FL, *557*
Sales Consultants of Honolulu (C), HI, *558*
Sales Consultants of Brockton, Inc. (C), MA, *559*
Sales Consultants of Baltimore (C), MD, *559*
Sales Consultants of Omaha, Inc. (C), NE, *560*
Sales Consultants of Raleigh-Durham-RTP (C), NC, *561*
Sales Consultants of Austin, Inc. (C), TX, *562*
Sales Consultants of Pittsburgh (C), PA, *562*
Sales Consultants of Dallas (C), TX, *563*
Sales Consultants of Appleton (C), WI, *563*
Sales Executives, Inc. (C), MI, *563*
Sales Recruiters of Oklahoma City (C), OK, *564*
Sampson Medical Search (C), CA, *564*
George D. Sandel Assoc. (C), MA, *565*
Sanford Rose Assoc. - Lake Forest (R), IL, *184*
Sanford Rose Assoc. (C), OH, *565*

Sanford Rose Assoc. - Santa Barbara (C), CA, *565*
Sanford Rose Assoc. - Chicago (C), IL, *566*
Sanford Rose Assoc. - Clearwater (C), FL, *566*
Sanford Rose Assoc. - Athens (C), GA, *566*
Sanford Rose Assoc. - Columbia, MD (C), MD, *567*
Sanford Rose Assoc. - Louisville (C), KY, *567*
Sanford Rose Assoc. - Rochester (C), MI, *568*
Sanford Rose Assoc. - Columbia (C), SC, *570*
Savalli & Assoc., Inc. (C), MI, *571*
Schall Executive Search Partners (R), MN, *185*
A.D. Schiff & Assoc., Ltd. (C), IL, *572*
Schneider, Hill & Spangler, Inc. (R), PA, *185*
Robert Scott Assoc. (C), NJ, *573*
Search Masters Int'l. (R), AZ, *187*
Search Masters, USA (C), FL, *576*
The Search Network (C), CA, *576*
Searchforce, Inc. (R), FL, *187*
Segal & Assoc. (C), GA, *578*
Selective Search Associates (C), OH, *578*
SFB Legal Search (C), NY, *579*
Sharp Placement Professionals, Inc. (C), NY, *579*
M. B. Shattuck & Assoc., Inc. (R), CA, *189*
The Shotland Group (R), CA, *190*
RitaSue Siegel Resources, Inc. (R), NY, *191*
Daniel A. Silverstein Assoc. Inc. (R), FL, *191*
Skott/Edwards Consultants (R), NY, *192*
Christopher Smallhorn Executive Recruiting, Inc. (R), MA, *193*
Smith & Syberg, Inc. (R), IN, *193*
Smith, Roth & Squires (R), NY, *194*
Snyder & Co. (R), CT, *194*
Southern Research Services (R), FL, *195*
Spectrum Consultants (R), CA, *196*
SpencerStuart (R), NY, *196*
The Stark Wilton Group (R), MI, *199*
Stewart Assoc. (C), PA, *593*
Allan Stolee Inc. (R), FL, *201*
Stoneburner Assoc., Inc. (C), KS, *594*
Strategic Resources Biotechnology & Medical Group (C), WA, *595*
Strategic Search Corp. (R), IL, *202*
Straube Associates (R), MA, *203*
Ron Sunshine & Assoc. (C), IL, *597*
Tate & Assoc., Inc. (R), NJ, *207*
TechFind, Inc. (R), MA, *207*
Technical Resource Assoc. (C), TN, *602*
Techstaff Inc. (C), WI, *603*
Tecmark Associates Inc. (C), NY, *604*
Telem Adhesive Search Corp. (C), MD, *605*
The TGA Company (C), TX, *606*
Thomas Resource Group (R), CA, *209*
Richard Thompson Assoc., Inc. (R), MN, *209*
Thomson, Sponar & Adams, Inc. (C), WA, *606*
Thorne, Brieger Assoc., Inc. (R), NY, *209*
Tierney Assoc., Inc. (R), PA, *209*
Fred C. Tippel & Assoc. (C), OH, *607*
Tondorf & Assoc. Inc. (C), MA, *607*
Trainor/Frank & Assoc. Inc. (C), WI, *608*
Travis & Co., Inc. (R), MA, *210*
Triangle Assoc. (C), PA, *609*
Tschudin Inc. (R), NJ, *211*
Tuttle Venture Group, Inc. (R), TX, *212*
Vento Assoc. (C), TN, *612*
Venture Resources, Inc. (R), CA, *213*
Verkamp-Joyce Assoc., Inc. (R), IL, *213*
Victor White Int'l. (C), CA, *612*
W. P. Assoc. (C), CA, *613*
Wallace Assoc. (C), CT, *614*
Warren Executive Services (C), GA, *616*
Watring & Assoc., Inc. (C), IL, *616*
WestPacific National Search, Inc. (C), CA, *619*
White, Roberts & Stratton, Inc. (C), IL, *619*
William-Johns Co., Inc. (C), CA, *621*
Williams Recruiting, Inc. (C), WA, *621*
Williamsburg Group (C), NJ, *621*
Wilson Personnel, Inc. (C), NC, *622*
Winfield Assoc., Inc. (C), MA, *623*
Winthrop Partners, Inc. (R), NY, *222*
Jim Woodson & Assoc., Inc. (C), MS, *624*
Xagas & Assoc. (R), IL, *226*
The York Group (C), CA, *626*
Yungner & Bormann (R), MN, *226*
The Zammataro Company (R), OH, *226*
Zingaro & Company (R), TX, *227*
Michael D. Zinn & Assoc., Inc. (R), NJ, *227*

D.19 Plastics, rubber products

A.M.C.R., Inc. (C), OH, *232*
Abraxas Technologies, Inc. (C), FL, *233*
ACC Technical Services (C), OH, *233*
Access/Resources, Inc. (C), MA, *234*
Advanced Executive Resources (R), MI, *2*
Advanced Recruitment, Inc. (C), TN, *240*
Advancement Recruiting Services (C), OH, *241*
Ahrensdorf & Assoc. (R), PA, *2*
Allen, Wayne & Co. LLC (C), WI, *245*
Allen-Jeffers Assoc. (C), CA, *245*
The Altco Group (C), NJ, *246*
Altec/HRC (C), MI, *246*
Peter W. Ambler Co. (R), TX, *5*
American Professional Search, Inc. (C), TN, *248*
AmeriPro Search, Inc. (C), NC, *248*
Anderson Industrial Assoc., Inc. (C), GA, *250*
Applied Resources, Inc. (C), MN, *252*
Applied Search Assoc., Inc. (C), GA, *252*
ARJay & Assoc. (C), NC, *252*
A. Artze Assoc.-Personnel Consultants (C), PR, *253*
The Associates, HR Search Executives, Inc. (C), OK, *254*
Astro Executive Search Firm (C), LA, *254*
Austin - Allen Co. (C), TN, *256*
Availability Personnel Consultants (C), NH, *257*
D. W. Baird & Associates (C), MD, *257*
Ballos & Co., Inc. (R), NJ, *10*
BallResources (C), MO, *258*
Barber & Assoc. (C), KY, *259*
Barnes Development Group, LLC (R), WI, *11*
Barone Assoc. (C), NJ, *259*
Barrington Hart, Inc. (R), IL, *12*
Aldonna Barry Personnel & Management (C), ON, *260*
Battalia Winston Int'l./The Euram Consultants Group (R), NY, *13*
J. P. Bencik Assoc. (C), MI, *263*
Berkshire Search Assoc. (C), MA, *265*
BGB Assoc., Inc. (C), IL, *266*
BioPharmMed (C), FL, *267*
BJB Assoc. (C), VA, *267*
Blanton & Co. (C), AL, *268*
Bor-Maq Assoc. (C), TX, *269*
BowdenGlobal, Ltd. (R), OH, *20*
Brett Personnel Specialists (C), NJ, *273*
Bridgecreek Personnel Agency (C), CA, *273*
Brierwood Group, Inc. (C), IN, *273*
Bright Search/Professional Staffing (C), MN, *274*
Brooke Chase Assoc., Inc. (R), IL, *24*
Broward-Dobbs, Inc. (C), GA, *274*
J. Burke & Assoc., Inc. (C), TX, *276*
David S. Burt Assoc. (C), MT, *276*
Cahill Assoc. (C), CT, *279*
Juliette Lang Cahn Executive Search (C), NY, *279*
Campa & Assoc. (R), ON, *27*
Capstone Inc. (R), NY, *29*
Career Alternatives Executive Search (C), MI, *281*
Career Consultants (R), IN, *29*
Career Counseling Inc. (CCI) (C), KY, *282*
Career Images (C), FL, *282*
Carion Resource Group Inc. (C), ON, *284*
Carnegie Resources, Inc. (C), NC, *284*
Carter, Lavoie Associates (C), RI, *285*
Carver Search Consultants (C), CA, *285*
Case Executive Search (C), MI, *286*
Central Executive Search, Inc. (C), OH, *287*
Wayne S. Chamberlain & Assoc. (C), CA, *288*
Joseph Chandler & Assoc., Inc. (R), IL, *33*
Chase-Gardner Executive Search Associates, Inc. (C), FL, *289*
Chelsea Resources, Inc. (C), CT, *290*
Christopher and Long (C), MO, *291*
CJA-The Adler Group, Inc. (R), CA, *35*
The Clayton Edward Group (C), MI, *292*
CMS, Inc. (C), NH, *293*
Cochran, Cochran & Yale, Inc. (R), NY, *36*
Continental Search Assoc. (C), OH, *298*
Cook Assoc. Int'l., Inc. (C), TN, *298*
P. G. Cook Assoc. (R), TN, *40*
Corbin Packaging Professionals (C), MO, *299*
Corporate Image Group (C), TN, *300*
Corporate Management Services (C), PA, *300*
Corporate Select Int'l., Ltd. (C), IL, *301*
Creative Input, Inc. (C), RI, *303*
Cross Country Consultants, Inc. (C), MD, *304*
Crowder & Company (R), MI, *43*

Cumberland Professional Search Inc. (C), TN, *304*
The Currier-Winn Co., Inc. (C), NJ, *305*
Curry, Telleri Group, Inc. (R), NJ, *44*
Cyr Associates, Inc. (C), MA, *306*
Daniel Marks Company (C), OH, *306*
The Danielson Group, Inc. (C), TX, *306*
The Dartmouth Group (R), NY, *46*
Alan N. Daum & Assoc., Inc. (C), OH, *308*
Davidson, Laird & Assoc. (C), MI, *308*
Delta Services (R), TX, *48*
DieckMueller Group (R), WI, *51*
Dise & Co. (R), OH, *52*
Diversified Search, Inc. (R), PA, *52*
The Donnelly Group-Sales Recruiters, Inc. (C), MO, *314*
Robert Drexler Assoc., Inc. (R), NJ, *54*
J. H. Dugan & Assoc., Inc. (R), CA, *55*
Dunhill of Ft. Collins, Inc. (C), CO, *319*
Dunhill Professional Search of Augusta (C), GA, *320*
Dunhill Professional Search of Richmond (C), VA, *323*
Dunn Associates (R), PA, *55*
G. L. Dykstra Assoc., Inc. (C), MI, *323*
E O Technical (C), CT, *324*
Effective Search, Inc. (R), IL, *57*
W. Robert Eissler & Assoc., Inc. (C), TX, *327*
The Eldridge Group, Ltd. (C), IL, *327*
Elite Resources Group (R), OH, *58*
Gene Ellefson & Assoc. Inc. (C), MI, *328*
The Elsworth Group (C), TX, *329*
Emerald Legal Search (C), NH, *329*
Engineering & Scientific Search Assoc. (ESSA) (C), NJ, *330*
Engineering Futures, LLC (C), CT, *330*
Engineering Resource Group, Inc. (C), NJ, *331*
Erwin Assoc. (R), IL, *60*
Executech (R), OH, *62*
ExecuTech (C), IN, *332*
Executive Connection (C), OH, *333*
Executive Directions (R), OH, *62*
Executive Recruiters Agency, Inc. (C), AR, *333*
Executive Recruiters, Inc. (C), WI, *334*
Executive Resource Assoc. (C), VA, *334*
Executive Resource Inc. (C), WI, *334*
Executive Search, Ltd. (C), OH, *336*
Executive Search Plus, Inc. (C), IN, *336*
Fergason Assoc., Inc. (C), IL, *339*
Flowers & Assoc. (C), OH, *342*
Ford & Assoc., Inc. (C), SC, *343*
Fortune Personnel Consultants of Huntsville, Inc. (C), AL, *343*
F-O-R-T-U-N-E Personnel Consultants of Palm Beach (C), FL, *345*
F-O-R-T-U-N-E Personnel Consultants of Atlanta, Inc. (C), GA, *345*
F-O-R-T-U-N-E Personnel Consultants (C), MI, *346*
Fortune Personnel Consultants of Hinsdale, IL (C), IL, *346*
F-o-r-t-u-n-e of Owensboro, Inc. (C), KY, *346*
F-O-R-T-U-N-E Personnel Consultants of Southwest Indiana (C), IN, *346*
Fortune Personnel Consultants of Topsfield (C), MA, *346*
F-O-R-T-U-N-E Personnel Consultants of St. Louis-West County (C), MO, *347*
F-O-R-T-U-N-E Personnel Consultants of Troy, Inc. (C), MI, *347*
F-O-R-T-U-N-E Search Consultants (C), MO, *347*
F-O-R-T-U-N-E of West Portland (C), OR, *348*
F-O-R-T-U-N-E Personnel Consultants of Cincinnati (C), OH, *348*
F-O-R-T-U-N-E Consultants of Memphis (C), TN, *349*
Fortune Personnel Consultants of Chattanooga Inc. (C), TN, *349*
FORTUNE Personnel Consultants of Charleston, Inc. (C), SC, *349*
F-O-R-T-U-N-E Personnel of Nashville (C), TN, *350*
FORTUNE Personnel Consultants of North Dallas (C), TX, *350*
F-O-R-T-U-N-E Personnel Consultants of Knoxville (C), TN, *350*
F-O-R-T-U-N-E Personnel Consultants of Houston, Inc. (C), TX, *350*
F-O-R-T-U-N-E Personnel Consultants of the Tri-Cities, Inc. (C), TN, *350*
Fortune Personnel Consultants of the Virginia Highlands (C), VA, *351*
Foster Partners (R), NY, *70*
Friedman Eisenstein Raemer & Schwartz, LLP (R), IL, *72*
The Furst Group, Inc. (R), IL, *72*
Gallin Associates, Inc. (C), FL, *354*
Genesis Research (C), MO, *356*
Gilbert Tweed Assoc. Inc. (R), NY, *76*
Gilreath Weatherby Inc. (R), MA, *77*
The Glenwood Group (C), IL, *358*
Gowdy Consultants (C), TX, *361*
Graham & Co. (R), NJ, *80*
Alexander Graham Assoc. (C), NJ, *361*
The Grant Search Group, Inc. (C), ON, *361*
R. Green & Assoc., Inc. (C), OH, *362*
Gregory, Kyle & Assoc. (C), NC, *363*
Gros Executive Search, Inc. (C), TN, *363*
Grossberg & Assoc. (R), IL, *82*
Grover & Assoc. (R), OH, *82*
Hahn & Assoc., Inc. (C), OH, *365*
Hall Management Group, Inc. (C), GA, *367*
The Hanna Group (C), OH, *368*
Hardage Group (C), TN, *369*
Robert Harkins Assoc., Inc. (C), PA, *369*
Harvey Hohauser & Assoc., LLC (R), MI, *87*
Michael J. Hawkins, Inc. (C), IL, *370*
HEC Group (C), ON, *375*
Helfer Executive Consultants (R), TN, *91*
The Hetzel Group, Inc. (R), IL, *92*
The Hindman Co. (R), KY, *94*
Hite Executive Search (R), OH, *94*
Hobson Assoc. (C), CT, *379*
Hodge-Cronin & Assoc., Inc. (R), IL, *94*
J. G. Hood Assoc. (C), CT, *380*
HRNI (C), MI, *383*
Hughes & Assoc. Int'l. Inc. (C), AL, *383*
Human Resources Personnel Agency (R), AR, *99*
Leigh Hunt & Assoc., Inc. (C), ME, *384*
The Hunter Group, Inc. (C), MI, *385*
The Icard Group, Inc. (C), MI, *387*
Information Technology Search (C), PA, *388*
International Executive Recruiters (C), OH, *393*
The J. B. Search Group (C), CA, *395*
J.N. Adams & Assoc., Inc. (C), PA, *396*
Jackley Search Consultants (C), MN, *396*
K. Jaeger & Assoc. (C), MA, *396*
Jaeger Int'l., Inc. (C), OH, *396*
JLI-Boston (R), MA, *106*
JM & Company (R), PA, *106*
Job Link, Inc. (C), CA, *399*
L. J. Johnson & Co. (R), MI, *106*
Jonas, Walters & Assoc., Inc. (R), WI, *107*
Just Management Services Inc. (C), FL, *402*
Kaas Employment Services (C), IA, *402*
Kabana Corp. (C), MI, *402*
Kay Concepts, Inc. (C), FL, *404*
A.T. Kearney Executive Search (R), IL, *111*
Kelly Associates (R), PA, *112*
Kensington Int'l., Inc. (R), IL, *113*
Blair Kershaw Assoc., Inc. (C), PA, *405*
Raymond J. Klemmer & Assoc. (R), NY, *116*
Korn/Ferry Int'l. (R), NY, *117*
Kozlin Assoc., Inc. (C), NY, *408*
John Kuhn & Assoc., Inc. (R), WI, *121*
Kuhn Med-Tech (C), CA, *409*
D. Kunkle & Assoc. (C), IL, *410*
L & L Assoc. (C), CA, *410*
Landon Morgan (C), ON, *412*
Lange & Assoc., Inc. (C), IN, *412*
Jack B. Larsen & Assoc., Inc. (C), PA, *413*
Larson Assoc. (R), CA, *125*
Leaders-Trust Int'l./Carce y Asociados, S.C. (R), MX, *127*
The Lear Group, Inc. (R), OH, *127*
J. E. Lessner Assoc., Inc. (R), MI, *128*
Lybrook Assoc., Inc. (C), RI, *421*
Lyons Pruitt Int'l. (R), PA, *132*
M H Executive Search Group (C), TX, *422*
M.C. Executive Search (C), CA, *422*
Magnum Search (C), IL, *422*
Management Recruiters of Decatur, LLC (C), AL, *438*
Management Recruiters of Little Rock (C), AR, *439*
Management Recruiters of Pleasanton (C), CA, *441*
Management Recruiters of Colorado Springs (C), CO, *441*
Management Recruiters of Ft. Myers, FL. (C), FL, *443*
Management Recruiters of Boca Raton (C), FL, *443*
Management Recruiters of Clearwater (C), FL, *443*
Management Recruiters of Plant City, Inc. (C), FL, *444*
Management Recruiters of Pensacola (C), FL, *444*
Management Recruiters of Atlanta West, Inc. (C), GA, *445*
Management Recruiters of Savannah (C), GA, *446*

INDUSTRIES

Management Recruiters of St. Charles (C), IL, *447*
Management Recruiters of Noblesville, Inc. (C), IN, *448*
Management Recruiters of Richmond (C), KY, *449*
Management Recruiters of Danville (C), KY, *449*
Management Recruiters of Columbia (C), MD, *450*
Management Recruiters of Monroe, Inc. (C), LA, *450*
Management Recruiters of Livonia (C), MI, *451*
Management Recruiters of Dearborn, Inc. (C), MI, *451*
Management Recruiters of Southeastern Michigan (C), MI, *451*
Management Recruiters of Muskegon (C), MI, *451*
Management Recruiters - Flint (C), MI, *451*
Management Recruiters of Baltimore (C), MD, *451*
Management Recruiters of Reno (C), NV, *453*
Management Recruiters of Asheville, Inc. (C), NC, *455*
Management Recruiters of Burlington (C), NC, *455*
Management Recruiters of Mt. Airy (C), NC, *456*
Management Recruiters of Raleigh (C), NC, *456*
Management Recruiters of Akron (C), OH, *457*
Management Recruiters of Winston-Salem (C), NC, *457*
Management Recruiters of Columbus (C), OH, *457*
Management Recruiters of Cincinnati/ Sharonville, Inc. (C), OH, *457*
Management Recruiters of Dayton, Inc. (C), OH, *457*
Management Recruiters of Westmoreland County, Inc. (C), PA, *459*
Management Recruiters of McMurray, Inc. (C), PA, *459*
Management Recruiters of Myrtle Beach, Inc. (C), SC, *460*
Management Recruiters of Aiken (C), SC, *460*
Management Recruiters of West Chester, Inc. (C), PA, *460*
Management Recruiters of Columbia, Tennessee (C), TN, *461*
Management Recruiters of Travelers Rest, Inc. (C), SC, *461*
Management Recruiters of North West Austin (C), TX, *462*
Management Recruiters of Round Rock (C), TX, *463*
Management Recruiters of Loudoun County South (C), VA, *465*
Management Recruiters of Appleton (C), WI, *465*
Management Recruiters of Janesville, Inc. (C), WI, *466*
Management Search of R.I. Inc. (R), RI, *135*
Mannard & Assoc., Inc. (R), IL, *135*
F. L. Mannix & Co. (R), MA, *135*
The Marathon Group (C), FL, *469*
MARBL Consultants, Inc. (C), WI, *469*
Margolin Consultants, Inc. (C), NY, *469*
Mark III Personnel, Inc. (C), NC, *470*
Markent Personnel, Inc. (C), WI, *470*
Marketing & Sales Resources, Inc. (C), FL, *470*
George R. Martin (R), PA, *137*
Marvel Consultants, Inc. (C), OH, *472*
Richard L. Mather & Assoc. (C), CT, *472*
Mathey Services (C), IL, *472*
G. P. Mattocks & Associates (C), NC, *473*
Mayhall Search Group, Inc. (C), IN, *473*
Tom McCall Executive Search (C), IL, *473*
McCooe & Assoc., Inc. (R), NJ, *140*
McDonald Assoc. Int'l. (R), IL, *140*
Robert E. McGrath & Assoc. (R), CT, *141*
Medical Executive Search Assoc., Inc. (C), AZ, *477*
Michael Assoc. (R), IL, *144*
Michaels & Moere (C), WI, *481*
Lou Michaels Assoc., Inc. (C), MI, *481*
Michigan Consulting Group (R), MI, *144*
Midland Consultants (C), OH, *481*
Montgomery, Thomason & Assoc. (C), ON, *484*
Mulcahy Co. (C), WI, *487*
Mullen Assoc., Inc. (R), NC, *148*
The Mulshine Company, Ltd. (R), NY, *149*
Multisearch Recruiters (C), CA, *487*
R. F. Mulvaney & Assoc., Inc. (R), MO, *149*
The Murray Group (C), IL, *487*
NaTek Corp. (C), NY, *488*
National Computerized Employment Service, Inc. (C), PA, *489*
National Recruiting Service (C), IN, *489*
Len Nelson & Assoc., Inc. (C), TX, *491*
New Directions, Inc. (C), IL, *492*
NHA Plastics Recruiters (C), FL, *493*
Nichols & Company (R), CO, *151*
NorTech Resources (C), NY, *496*
North Coast Meridian (C), NY, *496*
Northern Consultants Inc. (R), ME, *153*
O'Brien & Bell (R), OH, *153*
O'Shea, Divine & Co., Inc. (R), CA, *154*
Orion Int'l. Consulting Group, Inc. (C), NC, *499*
P R Management Consultants, Inc. (C), NJ, *500*
Pacific Advisory Service, Inc. (C), IL, *501*
Pacific Coast Recruiting (C), CA, *501*
D. P. Parker & Assoc., Inc. (R), MA, *159*
Partners in Recruiting (C), IL, *503*
Rick Pascal & Assoc., Inc. (C), NJ, *504*
Peck & Assoc., Ltd. (R), WI, *161*
Petruzzi Assoc. (C), NJ, *509*
Phelps Personnel Assoc., Inc. (C), SC, *510*
Phillips Resource Group (C), SC, *510*
Gregory D. Pickens (C), TX, *511*
Placement Solutions (C), WI, *513*
The Polen Group (C), PA, *514*
Polytechnical Consultants, Inc. (C), IL, *514*
Preferred Professional Recruiters (C), OH, *516*
Premier Recruiting Group (C), MI, *516*
Premier Search Group (C), IN, *517*
The Premier Staffing Group (C), OH, *517*
Prime Management Group Inc. (C), ON, *518*
ProSearch, Inc. (C), OH, *524*
Proven Edge (C), CA, *525*
Quality Control Recruiters (C), CT, *526*
Quality Search Inc. (C), OH, *526*
Quantum Int'l., Ltd. (R), FL, *170*
R/K International Inc. (R), CT, *171*
Rand Assoc. (R), ME, *171*
Reality Group (C), OK, *531*
Recruiting Assoc. of Amarillo (C), TX, *531*
Recruiting Services Group, Inc. (C), TN, *532*
Reid Ellis Assoc. Inc. (C), ON, *533*
The Douglas Reiter Co., Inc. (R), OR, *174*
The Remington Group (R), IL, *174*
Resource Networking Inc. (C), IN, *534*
The Revere Assoc., Inc. (R), OH, *176*
S. Reyman & Assoc., Ltd. (R), IL, *176*
Russell Reynolds Assoc., Inc. (R), NY, *176*
River Region Personnel, Inc. (C), LA, *538*
RML Assoc. (C), PA, *538*
J. P. Roddy Consultants (C), PA, *540*
R. A. Rodriguez & Assoc., Inc. (C), TX, *540*
The Rossi Search Group (C), PA, *545*
Rowland Mountain & Assoc. (C), GA, *547*
The Ryan Charles Group, Inc. (C), FL, *548*
S-H-S TechStaff (C), PA, *549*
S. P. Assoc., Inc. (C), NC, *550*
Saber Group, Inc. (C), TX, *550*
Sales Consultants of Birmingham (C), AL, *555*
Sales Consultants of Daphne (C), AL, *556*
Sales Consultants of Boca Raton, Inc. (C), FL, *557*
Sales Consultants - Bristol County (C), MA, *559*
Sales Consultants of Baltimore (C), MD, *559*
Sales Consultants of Laurel Park, Inc. (C), MI, *560*
Sales Consultants of Omaha, Inc. (C), NE, *560*
Sales Consultants of Middlesex County, Inc. (C), NJ, *561*
Sales Consultants of Pittsburgh (C), PA, *562*
Sales Consultants of Milwaukee (C), WI, *563*
Sales Management Resources (C), CA, *563*
Sales Solutions (C), CA, *564*
Sanford Rose Assoc. - Athens (C), GA, *566*
Sanford Rose Assoc. - Rockford (C), IL, *567*
Sanford Rose Assoc. - Amherst, NY (C), NY, *568*
Sanford Rose Assoc. - Fairlawn (C), OH, *569*
Sanford Rose Assoc. - Canton (C), OH, *569*
Sanford Rose Assoc. - Burlington, NC (C), NC, *569*
Sanford Rose Assoc. - Akron (C), OH, *569*
Sanford Rose Assoc. - Salt Lake City (C), UT, *571*
Sanford Rose Assoc. - Port Washington (C), WI, *571*
Scientific Solutions, Inc. (C), MI, *572*

Robert Scott Assoc. (C), NJ, *573*
Search Plus Int'l.-Ohio (C), OH, *576*
Search South, Inc. (C), AL, *576*
Segal & Assoc. (C), GA, *578*
Select Services (C), IL, *578*
Selectis Corp. (C), IL, *578*
Selective Recruiting Assoc., Inc. (C), MI, *578*
Selective Search Associates (C), OH, *578*
Selig Executive Search (C), NH, *579*
Sharrow & Assoc., Inc. (C), MI, *579*
The Shotland Group (R), CA, *190*
Sill Technical Assoc., Inc. (C), PA, *581*
Smith & Assoc. (C), FL, *583*
Southern Chemical & Plastics Search (C), GA, *587*
Southern Recruiters & Consultants, Inc. (C), SC, *587*
Southern Research Services (R), FL, *195*
Specialty Employment Services, Inc. (C), GA, *589*
SpencerStuart (R), NY, *196*
Stanton Chase Int'l. (R), MD, *198*
The Stark Wilton Group (R), MI, *199*
Ron Stevens & Assoc., Inc. (C), FL, *593*
Stewart Assoc. (C), PA, *593*
Allan Stolee Inc. (R), FL, *201*
Stoneburner Assoc., Inc. (C), KS, *594*
Storfer & Assoc. (C), NY, *595*
Strategic Technologies, Inc. (C), TX, *596*
Sullivan & Assoc. (R), MI, *204*
Summit Executive Search Consultants, Inc. (R), FL, *204*
Ron Sunshine & Assoc. (C), IL, *597*
Systems Research Group (C), CA, *598*
Tabb & Assoc. (R), OH, *205*
S. Tanner & Assoc. Inc. (C), ON, *599*
Technical Employment Consultants (C), PA, *602*
Technical Resource Assoc. (C), TN, *602*
Techstaff Inc. (C), WI, *603*
Teknon Employment Resources, Inc. (C), OH, *604*
Telem Adhesive Search Corp. (C), MD, *605*
Tierney Assoc., Inc. (R), PA, *209*
Fred C. Tippel & Assoc. (C), OH, *607*
Jay Tracey Assoc. Inc. (C), VT, *608*
Trainor/Frank & Assoc. Inc. (C), WI, *608*
Triangle Assoc. (C), PA, *609*
Triumph Consulting, Inc. (R), IA, *210*
U.S. Search (C), VA, *610*
Unisearch Search & Recruiting Inc. (C), CA, *611*
Vaughan & Co. (C), CA, *612*
W. P. Assoc. (C), CA, *613*
The Wabash Group (C), IN, *613*
Wallace Assoc. (C), CT, *614*
Warner & Assoc., Inc. (C), OH, *615*
Warren Executive Services (C), GA, *616*
Wasserman Assoc. Inc. (C), MD, *616*
Wayne Assoc., Inc. (C), VA, *616*
R. A. Wells Co. (C), GA, *618*
The Whitaker Companies (C), TX, *619*
The Whitney Group (C), GA, *620*
John R. Williams & Assoc., Inc. (C), NC, *621*
Williamsburg Group (C), NJ, *621*
The Wilmington Group (C), NC, *622*
Wilson Personnel, Inc. (C), NC, *622*
The Windham Group (R), OH, *222*
Wing Tips & Pumps, Inc. (C), MI, *623*
The Witt Group (C), FL, *623*
Susan L. Wonderling Recruiting (C), PA, *623*
Jim Woodson & Assoc., Inc. (C), MS, *624*
World Search (C), OH, *625*
Xagas & Assoc. (R), IL, *226*
The Zammataro Company (R), OH, *226*

D.20 Paints, allied products, petroleum products

American Heritage Group, Inc. (C), MI, *247*
Tryg R. Angell, Ltd. (C), CT, *250*
Fred Anthony Assoc. (C), WI, *251*
APA Search, Inc. (R), NY, *6*
Argus National, Inc. (R), CT, *6*
Astro Executive Search Firm (C), LA, *254*
D. W. Baird & Associates (C), MD, *257*
The Baldwin Group (R), IL, *10*
Ballos & Co., Inc. (R), NJ, *10*
Aldonna Barry Personnel & Management (C), ON, *260*
Blair/Tech Recruiters, Inc. (C), NJ, *268*
Boyden (R), NY, *20*
The Brentwood Group, Inc. (R), NJ, *22*
Brett Personnel Specialists (C), NJ, *273*
Brooke Chase Assoc., Inc. (R), IL, *24*
David S. Burt Assoc. (C), MT, *276*
Caprio & Assoc. Inc. (R), IL, *29*
Career Consultants (R), IN, *29*
Central Executive Search, Inc. (C), OH, *287*
Comprehensive Search (C), GA, *294*
Cornwall Stockton & Co., Inc. (C), TX, *299*
Cosier & Assoc. (C), AB, *302*
Cross Country Consultants, Inc. (C), MD, *304*
Curry, Telleri Group, Inc. (R), NJ, *44*
Alan N. Daum & Assoc., Inc. (C), OH, *308*
Delta Services (R), TX, *48*
Dougherty & Assoc. (C), TN, *314*
J. H. Dugan & Assoc., Inc. (R), CA, *55*
Dunhill Professional Search of Augusta (C), GA, *320*
G. L. Dykstra Assoc., Inc. (C), MI, *323*
E.P. Int'l. (C), NY, *324*
The Elsworth Group (C), TX, *329*
Emerald Legal Search (C), NH, *329*
Employment Solutions, Inc. (C), TX, *330*
Engineering & Scientific Search Assoc. (ESSA) (C), NJ, *330*
Engineering Profiles (C), FL, *330*
Executive Resource Assoc. (C), VA, *334*
Fergason Assoc., Inc. (C), IL, *339*
First Choice Search (R), WA, *67*
F-O-R-T-U-N-E Personnel Consultants of Southwest Indiana (C), IN, *346*
F-O-R-T-U-N-E Personnel Consultants of Menlo Park, Inc. (C), NJ, *347*
F-O-R-T-U-N-E Personnel Consultants of Houston, Inc. (C), TX, *350*
Foster Partners (R), NY, *70*
Gallin Associates, Inc. (C), FL, *354*
Genesis Recruiting (C), CA, *356*
Genesis Research (C), MO, *356*
Gilbert Tweed Assoc. Inc. (R), NY, *76*
Goodrich & Sherwood Assoc., Inc. (R), NY, *79*
Wolf Gugler & Assoc. Ltd. (R), ON, *83*
Horizons Unlimited (C), CA, *381*
Hughes & Assoc. Int'l. Inc. (C), AL, *383*
Leigh Hunt & Assoc., Inc. (C), ME, *384*
Hunter Int'l. LLC (C), MA, *385*
Information Technology Search (C), PA, *388*
Interactive Search Assoc. (C), PA, *391*
ISC of Cincinnati Inc. (C), OH, *394*
The J. B. Search Group (C), CA, *395*
JLI-Boston (R), MA, *106*
A.T. Kearney Executive Search (R), IL, *111*
Key Employment (C), NJ, *405*
Korn/Ferry Int'l. (R), NY, *117*
Lewis Consulting Service (C), IL, *417*
Charles Luntz & Assoc., Inc. (R), MO, *132*
Lybrook Assoc., Inc. (C), RI, *421*
M.C. Executive Search (C), CA, *422*
Management Recruiters of Middlesex (C), CT, *442*
Management Recruiters of Vero Beach (C), FL, *445*
Management Recruiters of Boise (C), ID, *446*
Management Recruiters of Westmoreland County, Inc. (C), PA, *459*
Management Recruiters of McMurray, Inc. (C), PA, *459*
Management Recruiters of West Chester, Inc. (C), PA, *460*
Management Recruiters of Loudoun County South (C), VA, *465*
Management Recruiters of Roanoke (C), VA, *465*
The Marathon Group (C), FL, *469*
Marsteller Wilcox Assoc. (C), IL, *471*
Louis Thomas Masterson & Co. (R), OH, *138*
META/MAT, Ltd. (R), NJ, *144*
Midland Consultants (C), OH, *481*
Montgomery, Thomason & Assoc. (C), ON, *484*
Mullen Assoc., Inc. (R), NC, *148*
NJ Solutions (C), CA, *493*
NorTech Resources (C), NY, *496*
O'Connor, O'Connor, Lordi, Ltd. (R), PA, *154*
Packaging Personnel Co., Ltd. (C), WI, *501*
Petruzzi Assoc. (C), NJ, *509*
Proven Edge (C), CA, *525*
PSP Agency (C), NY, *525*
Quality Control Recruiters (C), CT, *526*
Quality Search (C), IN, *526*
Reifel & Assoc. (R), IL, *174*
The Remington Group (R), IL, *174*
Russell Reynolds Assoc., Inc. (R), NY, *176*
S-H-S Int'l. of Cherry Hill (C), NJ, *549*
Sales Consultants - Bristol County (C), MA, *559*
Sales Search Specialist (C), IL, *564*
Sales Solutions (C), CA, *564*
Sanford Rose Assoc. - Mobile (C), AL, *565*

Sanford Rose Assoc. - Rockville (C), MD, *567*
Sanford Rose Assoc. - Fairlawn (C), OH, *569*
Sanford Rose Assoc. - Greensboro (C), NC, *569*
Scientific Solutions, Inc. (C), MI, *572*
Search Consultants Int'l., Inc. (C), TX, *575*
Search Enterprises, Inc. (C), FL, *575*
Southern Chemical & Plastics Search (C), GA, *587*
Specialty Employment Services, Inc. (C), GA, *589*
SpencerStuart (R), NY, *196*
Stanton Chase Int'l. (R), MD, *198*
Ron Stevens & Assoc., Inc. (C), FL, *593*
The Stevenson Group, Inc. (N.J.) (R), NJ, *200*
Stewart/Greene & Co. of The Triad, Inc. (C), NC, *594*
Stoneburner Assoc., Inc. (C), KS, *594*
Telem Adhesive Search Corp. (C), MD, *605*
Tower Consultants, Ltd. (R), PA, *209*
Triangle Assoc. (C), PA, *609*
U.S. Search (C), VA, *610*
Wayne Assoc., Inc. (C), VA, *616*
The Witt Group (C), FL, *623*

D.21 Leather, stone, glass, concrete, clay products

David Aplin & Assoc. (C), AB, *251*
Brett Personnel Specialists (C), NJ, *273*
CMS, Inc. (C), NH, *293*
The Currier-Winn Co., Inc. (C), NJ, *305*
Tony Curtis & Associates (C), ON, *305*
Executive Career Search (C), VA, *332*
First Choice Search (R), WA, *67*
Foster Partners (R), NY, *70*
R. Green & Assoc., Inc. (C), OH, *362*
Gregory, Kyle & Assoc. (C), NC, *363*
Grover & Assoc. (R), OH, *82*
Impact Source, Inc. (C), FL, *387*
Jonas, Walters & Assoc., Inc. (R), WI, *107*
K & C Assoc. (C), CA, *402*
A.T. Kearney Executive Search (R), IL, *111*
Korn/Ferry Int'l. (R), NY, *117*
Management Recruiters of Vero Beach (C), FL, *445*
Management Recruiters of Atlanta North, Inc. (C), GA, *446*
Management Recruiters of Richmond (C), KY, *449*
Management Recruiters of Raleigh (C), NC, *456*
Management Recruiters of Northwest Ohio, Inc. (C), OH, *458*
Management Recruiters of Myrtle Beach, Inc. (C), SC, *460*
Management Recruiters of Aiken (C), SC, *460*
The Partnership Group (R), NJ, *160*
Reese Assoc. (R), PA, *174*
Russell Reynolds Assoc., Inc. (R), NY, *176*
Rowland Assoc. (C), CA, *547*
Sales Consultants of Dallas (C), TX, *563*
Sanford Rose Assoc. - Cedar Rapids (C), IA, *567*
Sanford Rose Assoc. - Canton (C), OH, *569*
Search Consultants Int'l., Inc. (C), TX, *575*
Selig Executive Search (C), NH, *579*
SHS of Allentown (C), PA, *580*
Specialty Employment Services, Inc. (C), GA, *589*
SpencerStuart (R), NY, *196*
Summit Group Int'l., Inc. (R), GA, *204*
Swift & Assoc. (C), ME, *597*
U.S. Search (C), VA, *610*
Windsor International (R), GA, *222*

D.22 Primary & fabricated metal products

A.M.C.R., Inc. (C), OH, *232*
ACC Technical Services (C), OH, *233*
Accelerated Data Decision, Inc. (C), NJ, *233*
Advanced Recruitment, Inc. (C), TN, *240*
Advancement Recruiting Services (C), OH, *241*
Aggressive Corporation (C), IL, *242*
Alpha Executive Search (C), AL, *245*
Altec/HRC (C), MI, *246*
American Executive Search (C), FL, *247*
American Professional Search, Inc. (C), TN, *248*
Anderson & Schwab, Inc. (R), NY, *5*
Anderson Industrial Assoc., Inc. (C), GA, *250*
Andrews & Wald Group (C), FL, *250*
Tryg R. Angell, Ltd. (C), CT, *250*
APA Search, Inc. (R), NY, *6*
David Aplin & Assoc. (C), AB, *251*
Applied Search Assoc., Inc. (C), GA, *252*
Argus National, Inc. (R), CT, *6*
Artgo, Inc. (R), OH, *7*
Asheville Search & Consulting (C), NC, *253*
The Associates, HR Search Executives, Inc. (C), OK, *254*
W. R. Atchison & Assoc., Inc. (C), NC, *254*
Automation Technology Search (C), CA, *256*
Availability Personnel Consultants (C), NH, *257*
D. W. Baird & Associates (C), MD, *257*
BallResources (C), MO, *258*
Barber & Assoc. (C), KY, *259*
J. W. Barleycorn, Renard & Assoc., Inc. (R), OH, *11*
Barnes Development Group, LLC (R), WI, *11*
Barone Assoc. (C), NJ, *259*
Barth Smith Company (R), IL, *12*
Battalia Winston Int'l./The Euram Consultants Group (R), NY, *13*
Becker, Norton & Co. (R), PA, *14*
Behrens and Company (C), WA, *262*
Berkshire Search Assoc. (C), MA, *265*
Jack Bertram, Executive Recruiter (C), PA, *265*
Boettcher Assoc. (R), WI, *19*
Borchert Assoc. (C), TX, *269*
Howard Bowen Consulting (C), FL, *270*
The Brand Co., Inc. (R), FL, *22*
Brandywine Management Group (R), MD, *22*
Briant Assoc., Inc. (R), IL, *23*
Bright Search/Professional Staffing (C), MN, *274*
Brissenden, McFarland, Fuccella & Reynolds, Inc. (R), NJ, *23*
Brooke Chase Assoc., Inc. (R), IL, *24*
Bryan & Louis Research (C), OH, *275*
Cahill Assoc. (C), CT, *279*
Callan Assoc., Ltd. (R), IL, *27*
Campa & Assoc. (R), ON, *27*
Canny, Bowen Inc. (R), NY, *27*
Canyon Consulting, Inc. (C), TX, *281*
Capstone Consulting, Inc. (R), IL, *29*
Career Consultants (R), IN, *29*
Career Counseling Inc. (CCI) (C), KY, *282*
Career Images (C), FL, *282*
Career Specialists, Inc. (R), WA, *29*
Carnegie Partners, Inc. (R), IL, *30*
Case Executive Search (C), MI, *286*
Joseph Chandler & Assoc., Inc. (R), IL, *33*
Robert L. Charon (C), TX, *289*
Chase-Gardner Executive Search Associates, Inc. (C), FL, *289*
A. D. Check Assoc., Inc. (R), PA, *33*
Cheney Associates (C), CT, *290*
R. Christine Assoc. (C), PA, *290*
Christopher and Long (C), MO, *291*
The Churchill Group (C), ON, *291*
Clark Personnel Service, Inc. (C), AL, *292*
The Clayton Edward Group (C), MI, *292*
Coast Personnel Services Ltd. (C), BC, *293*
Construct Management Services (C), MN, *297*
Continental Search Assoc. (C), OH, *298*
The Cooke Group (R), WI, *40*
Corporate Image Group (C), TN, *300*
Corporate Management Services (C), PA, *300*
Cowin Assoc. (R), NY, *42*
Crowder & Company (R), MI, *43*
Cumberland Group Inc. (C), IL, *304*
Frank Cuomo & Assoc., Inc. (C), NY, *305*
The Currier-Winn Co., Inc. (C), NJ, *305*
Daniel Marks Company (C), OH, *306*
Davis & Company (R), CA, *47*
Dieckmann & Assoc., Ltd. (R), IL, *51*
The Donnelly Group-Sales Recruiters, Inc. (C), MO, *314*
The Dorfman Group (C), AZ, *314*
The Duncan-O'Dell Group Inc. (C), TX, *316*
Dunhill of Ft. Collins, Inc. (C), CO, *319*
Dunhill of San Francisco, Inc. (C), CA, *319*
Dunhill Search of West Atlanta (C), GA, *320*
Dunhill Executive Search of Brown County (C), IN, *321*
Dunhill Professional Search (C), MO, *321*
Dunhill Personnel of St. Andrews (C), SC, *322*
Dunhill Professional Search, Inc. of McAllen (C), TX, *323*
Dunhill of Corpus Christi, Inc. (C), TX, *323*
Dunn Associates (R), PA, *55*

Effective Search, Inc. (R), IL, *57*
W. Robert Eissler & Assoc., Inc. (C), TX, *327*
Gene Ellefson & Assoc. Inc. (C), MI, *328*
Empire International (R), PA, *59*
Erwin Assoc. (R), IL, *60*
Execu-Tech Search Inc. (C), MN, *332*
ExecuQuest, Inc. (R), MI, *61*
Executive Connection (C), OH, *333*
Executive Directions (R), OH, *62*
Executive Recruiters, Inc. (C), WI, *334*
Executive Search, Ltd. (C), OH, *336*
Executive Search Plus, Inc. (C), IN, *336*
The Executive Source (C), SA, *337*
Eyler Assoc., Inc. (R), IA, *64*
Fagan & Company (R), PA, *64*
Fenzel Milar Assoc. (C), OH, *339*
Fisher Personnel Management Services (R), CA, *68*
Flowers & Assoc. (C), OH, *342*
Ford & Assoc., Inc. (C), SC, *343*
F-O-R-T-U-N-E Personnel Consultants of Savannah, Inc. (C), GA, *345*
Fortune Personnel Consultants of Bloomfield, Inc. (C), MI, *346*
F-o-r-t-u-n-e of Owensboro, Inc. (C), KY, *346*
F-O-R-T-U-N-E Personnel Consultants of Troy, Inc. (C), MI, *347*
F-O-R-T-U-N-E Personnel Consultants of St. Louis-West County (C), MO, *347*
F-O-R-T-U-N-E Personnel Consultants of Bergen County Inc. (C), NJ, *347*
F-O-R-T-U-N-E Search Consultants (C), MO, *347*
F-O-R-T-U-N-E Personnel Consultants of Rockland County, Inc. (C), NY, *348*
F-O-R-T-U-N-E Personnel Consultants of Charlotte (C), NC, *348*
F-O-R-T-U-N-E Personnel Consultants of Cincinnati (C), OH, *348*
F-O-R-T-U-N-E Consultants of Memphis (C), TN, *349*
FORTUNE Personnel Consultants of Charleston, Inc. (C), SC, *349*
F-O-R-T-U-N-E Personnel of Nashville (C), TN, *350*
F-O-R-T-U-N-E Personnel Consultants of Knoxville (C), TN, *350*
F-O-R-T-U-N-E Personnel Consultants of Houston, Inc. (C), TX, *350*
F-O-R-T-U-N-E Personnel Consultants of the Tri-Cities, Inc. (C), TN, *350*
Foster Partners (R), NY, *70*
Friedman Eisenstein Raemer & Schwartz, LLP (R), IL, *72*
The Furst Group, Inc. (R), IL, *72*
Gabriele & Company (C), MA, *354*
Gaffney Management Consultants (R), IL, *73*
Genesis Research (C), MO, *356*
Howard Gilmore & Assoc. (R), OH, *77*
Gilreath Weatherby Inc. (R), MA, *77*
J. P. Gleason Assoc., Inc. (R), IL, *77*
H. L. Goehring & Assoc., Inc. (C), OH, *359*
Gomez Fregoso y Asociados (C), JAL, *360*
Graham & Co. (R), NJ, *80*
Alexander Graham Assoc. (C), NJ, *361*
Greenfields Engineering Search (C), MO, *363*
Gregory, Kyle & Assoc. (C), NC, *363*
Grover & Assoc. (R), OH, *82*
Wolf Gugler & Assoc. Ltd. (R), ON, *83*
Hahn & Assoc., Inc. (C), OH, *365*
Hale Assoc. (R), IL, *84*
The Hanna Group (C), OH, *368*
Harcourt & Assoc. (C), AB, *368*
Hardage Group (C), TN, *369*
Robert Harkins Assoc., Inc. (C), PA, *369*
Harrison Moore Inc. (C), NE, *370*
Harvey Hohauser & Assoc., LLC (R), MI, *87*
Healey Executive Search, Inc. (R), MN, *88*
The Heidrick Partners, Inc. (R), IL, *90*
Helfer Executive Consultants (R), TN, *91*
Helffrich Int'l. (C), FL, *375*
Highlander Search (C), NC, *378*
The Hindman Co. (R), KY, *94*
Hite Executive Search (R), OH, *94*
Horton Int'l. Inc. (R), NY, *96*
Robert Howe & Assoc. (R), GA, *97*
HRS, Inc. (R), PA, *97*
Human Resources Personnel Agency (R), AR, *99*
The Hunter Group, Inc. (C), MI, *385*
The Icard Group, Inc. (C), MI, *387*
Impact Source, Inc. (C), FL, *387*
Information Technology Search (C), PA, *388*
Interim Management Resources Inc. (C), ON, *392*
J. B. Linde & Assoc. (C), MO, *395*
J.N. Adams & Assoc., Inc. (C), PA, *396*
K. Jaeger & Assoc. (C), MA, *396*
John H. Johnson & Assoc., Inc. (R), IL, *106*
Johnson & Company (R), CT, *107*
Jonas, Walters & Assoc., Inc. (R), WI, *107*
Jordan-Sitter Assoc. (R), TX, *108*
Just Management Services Inc. (C), FL, *402*
K & C Assoc. (C), CA, *402*
Kay Concepts, Inc. (C), FL, *404*
The Kay Group of 5th Ave. (C), NY, *404*
A.T. Kearney Executive Search (R), IL, *111*
Kensington Int'l., Inc. (R), IL, *113*
Blair Kershaw Assoc., Inc. (C), PA, *405*
Daniel J. Kerstein, Consultant to Management (R), CO, *114*
Knapp Consultants (R), CT, *116*
Lee Koehn Assoc., Inc. (R), OR, *116*
Koontz, Jeffries & Assoc., Inc. (R), FL, *117*
Korn/Ferry Int'l. (R), NY, *117*
Kozlin Assoc., Inc. (C), NY, *408*
John Kuhn & Assoc., Inc. (R), WI, *121*
L O R (R), NJ, *122*
Lange & Assoc., Inc. (C), IN, *412*
Stephen Laramee & Assoc. Inc. (C), ON, *413*
Jack B. Larsen & Assoc., Inc. (C), PA, *413*
Larson Assoc. (R), CA, *125*
Leader Network (C), PA, *414*
J. E. Lessner Assoc., Inc. (R), MI, *128*
The Levton Group Inc. (R), ON, *129*
Linden Group, Inc. (C), NC, *418*
Locke & Assoc. (R), NC, *131*
Locus Inc. (C), WV, *419*
Charles Luntz & Assoc., Inc. (R), MO, *132*
Lutz Associates (C), CT, *421*
M.C. Executive Search (C), CA, *422*
Magnum Search (C), IL, *422*
The Mallard Group (C), IN, *423*
Management Association Network (C), WI, *424*
Management Recruiters of Nassau, Inc. (R), NY, *134*
Management Recruiters of Birmingham, Inc. (C), AL, *438*
Management Recruiters of Birmingham (C), AL, *438*
Management Recruiters of Mobile Co., Inc. (C), AL, *438*
Management Recruiters of Little Rock (C), AR, *439*
Management Recruiters of Winsted, Inc. (C), CT, *442*
Management Recruiters of Melbourne, Inc. (C), FL, *443*
Management Recruiters of Anna Maria Island (C), FL, *443*
Management Recruiters of Lake Co., Inc. (C), FL, *444*
Management Recruiters of Venice, Inc. (C), FL, *445*
Management Recruiters of Columbus, Inc. (C), GA, *445*
Management Recruiters of Vero Beach (C), FL, *445*
Management Recruiters of St. Charles (C), IL, *447*
Management Recruiters of Barrington (C), IL, *447*
Management Recruiters of Indianapolis (C), IN, *448*
Management Recruiters of Noblesville, Inc. (C), IN, *448*
Management Recruiters of Spencer (C), IA, *448*
Management Recruiters of Siouxland (C), IA, *449*
Management Recruiters of Danville (C), KY, *449*
Management Recruiters of Topeka, Inc. (C), KS, *449*
Management Recruiters of Monroe, Inc. (C), LA, *450*
Management Recruiters of Livonia (C), MI, *451*
Management Recruiters of Dearborn, Inc. (C), MI, *451*
Management Recruiters of Southeastern Michigan (C), MI, *451*
Management Recruiters of Muskegon (C), MI, *451*
Management Recruiters - Flint (C), MI, *451*
Management Recruiters of North Oakland County, Inc. (C), MI, *452*
Management Recruiters of Rankin Co. (C), MS, *452*
Management Recruiters of North Warren Inc. (C), NJ, *453*
Management Recruiters of Asheville, Inc. (C), NC, *455*
Management Recruiters of Fayetteville (C), NC, *455*

INDUSTRIES

Management Recruiters of Winston-Salem (C), NC, *457*
Management Recruiters of Dayton, Inc. (C), OH, *457*
Management Recruiters of Northwest Ohio, Inc. (C), OH, *458*
Management Recruiters of Valley Forge (C), PA, *459*
Management Recruiters of Puerto Rico (C), PR, *460*
Management Recruiters of Aiken (C), SC, *460*
Management Recruiters of Columbia, Tennessee (C), TN, *461*
Management Recruiters of Chattanooga-Brainerd, Inc. (C), TN, *461*
Management Recruiters of Arlington (C), TX, *462*
Management Recruiters of Round Rock (C), TX, *463*
Management Recruiters of San Antonio (C), TX, *463*
Management Recruiters of Ogden (C), UT, *464*
Management Recruiters of Milwaukee-West (C), WI, *465*
Management Recruiters of Janesville, Inc. (C), WI, *466*
Management Recruiters of Milwaukee-North (C), WI, *466*
Management Recruiters of Cheyenne (C), WY, *466*
Mannard & Assoc., Inc. (R), IL, *135*
The Marathon Group (C), FL, *469*
Margolin Consultants, Inc. (C), NY, *469*
Markent Personnel, Inc. (C), WI, *470*
George R. Martin (R), PA, *137*
Maschal/Connors Inc. (R), NJ, *137*
G. P. Mattocks & Associates (C), NC, *473*
Mayhall Search Group, Inc. (C), IN, *473*
McKinley•Arend Int'l. (R), TX, *141*
MESA, Inc. (R), CO, *143*
MESA International (C), CA, *480*
Walter Meyer & Assoc. (R), NY, *144*
Michael Assoc. (R), IL, *144*
Michaels & Moere (C), WI, *481*
Lou Michaels Assoc., Inc. (C), MI, *481*
Michigan Consulting Group (R), MI, *144*
Midland Consultants (C), OH, *481*
Miller Denver (C), CO, *482*
Morgan & Assoc. (C), MA, *485*
The Morgan/Geoffries Group (C), CA, *485*
Mulcahy Co. (C), WI, *487*
Multisearch Recruiters (C), CA, *487*
R. F. Mulvaney & Assoc., Inc. (R), MO, *149*
National Computerized Employment Service, Inc. (C), PA, *489*
National Metal Services Corp. (C), IN, *489*
National Recruiting Service (C), IN, *489*
J. Fielding Nelson & Assoc., Inc. (R), UT, *151*
New Directions, Inc. (C), IL, *492*
Newell Assoc. (R), NY, *151*
Nichols & Company (R), CO, *151*
P. J. Nicholson & Assoc. (C), IL, *493*
North Coast Meridian (C), NY, *496*
Nuessle, Kurdziel & Weiss, Inc. (R), PA, *153*
O'Brien & Bell (R), OH, *153*
O'Connor, O'Connor, Lordi, Ltd. (R), PA, *154*
Oliver & Rozner Assoc., Inc. (R), NY, *155*
Omega Systems, LLC (C), VA, *498*
D. P. Parker & Assoc., Inc. (R), MA, *159*
Parker, McFadden & Assoc. (C), GA, *503*
Michael W. Parres & Assoc. (R), MI, *159*
Partners in Recruiting (C), IL, *503*
Peeney Assoc., Inc. (R), NJ, *161*
Paul S. Pelland, P.C. (R), SC, *161*
Barry Persky & Co., Inc. (R), CT, *163*
Phelps Personnel Assoc., Inc. (C), SC, *510*
Gregory D. Pickens (C), TX, *511*
Placement Solutions (C), WI, *513*
Polytechnical Consultants, Inc. (C), IL, *514*
The Prairie Group (C), IL, *515*
PRAXIS Partners (R), VA, *167*
Preferred Professional Recruiters (C), OH, *516*
Premier Recruiting Group (C), MI, *516*
Premier Search Group (C), IN, *517*
The Premier Staffing Group (C), OH, *517*
Alan J. Price Assoc., Inc. (C), RI, *518*
Prime Resource Assoc. (C), WI, *518*
Probe Technology (C), PA, *519*
Procurement Resources (C), MD, *520*
Professional Employment Group (C), MD, *520*
Professional Personnel Services (C), IA, *520*
Professional Personnel Consultants, Inc. (C), MI, *521*
Professional Support Inc. (C), NY, *523*
Quality Control Recruiters (C), CT, *526*
R/K International Inc. (R), CT, *171*
Rand Assoc. (R), ME, *171*
Ray & Berndtson (R), TX, *171*
Raymond Thomas & Assoc. (C), FL, *530*
Recruiting Assoc. of Amarillo (C), TX, *531*
Reese Assoc. (R), PA, *174*
S. Reyman & Assoc., Ltd. (R), IL, *176*
Russell Reynolds Assoc., Inc. (R), NY, *176*
Terry Richards (C), OH, *536*
RML Assoc. (C), PA, *538*
Robert Lowell Int'l. (R), TX, *179*
Robison Humphreys & Assoc., Inc. (R), ON, *180*
Rothrock Associates, Inc. (C), NC, *547*
Rowland Assoc. (C), CA, *547*
Rusher, Loscavio & LoPresto (R), CA, *183*
The Ryan Charles Group, Inc. (C), FL, *548*
S-H-S Int'l. of Cherry Hill (C), NJ, *549*
S. P. Assoc., Inc. (C), NC, *550*
Sage Employment Recruiters (C), IN, *550*
Sales Consultants of Daphne (C), AL, *556*
Sales Consultants of Orangeburg (C), SC, *562*
Sales Consultants of Pittsburgh (C), PA, *562*
Sales Consultants of Milwaukee (C), WI, *563*
Sanford Rose Assoc. - Santa Ana (C), CA, *565*
Sanford Rose Assoc. - Athens (C), GA, *566*
Sanford Rose Assoc. - Rockford (C), IL, *567*
Sanford Rose Assoc. - Gastonia (C), NC, *568*
Sanford Rose Assoc. - Canton (C), OH, *569*
Sanford Rose Assoc. - Burlington, NC (C), NC, *569*
Sanford Rose Assoc. - Akron (C), OH, *569*
Sanford Rose Assoc. - Doylestown (C), PA, *570*
Sanford Rose Assoc. - Port Washington (C), WI, *571*
The Schatz Company (C), MO, *571*
Schenck & Assoc. SC (C), WI, *572*
Schick Professional Search, Inc. (C), OH, *572*
Search Assoc. (C), KY, *574*
Search Northwest Assoc. (C), OR, *576*
Search South, Inc. (C), AL, *576*
Seiden Krieger Assoc., Inc. (R), NY, *188*
Select Services (C), IL, *578*
Selective Recruiting Assoc., Inc. (C), MI, *578*
Selective Search Associates (C), OH, *578*
M. B. Shattuck & Assoc., Inc. (R), CA, *189*
The Shotland Group (R), CA, *190*
Larry Siegel & Assoc. (R), WA, *191*
Sill Technical Assoc., Inc. (C), PA, *581*
Singleton & Assoc. (C), VA, *582*
Slayton Int'l., Inc. (R), IL, *192*
Smith & Assoc. (C), FL, *583*
James F. Smith & Assoc. (C), GA, *583*
Smith & Syberg, Inc. (R), IN, *193*
Snelling Search (C), LA, *586*
Southern Recruiters & Consultants, Inc. (C), SC, *587*
Southern Research Services (R), FL, *195*
SpencerStuart (R), NY, *196*
Kenn Spinrad Inc. (C), PA, *589*
Stanton Chase Int'l. (R), MD, *198*
The Stelton Group, Inc. (C), NJ, *592*
Sterling Int'l. Management Recruitment, Ltd. Inc. (C), NC, *592*
Ron Stevens & Assoc., Inc. (C), FL, *593*
Stewart Assoc. (C), PA, *593*
Charles Stickler Assoc. (R), PA, *201*
Summit Executive Search Consultants, Inc. (R), FL, *204*
Ron Sunshine & Assoc. (C), IL, *597*
Tabb & Assoc. (R), OH, *205*
Teamsearch, Inc. (C), MI, *601*
Technical Recruiting Services (C), OH, *602*
Technical Resource Assoc. (C), TN, *602*
Techstaff Inc. (C), WI, *603*
The TGA Company (C), TX, *606*
Tierney Assoc., Inc. (R), PA, *209*
Jay Tracey Assoc. Inc. (C), VT, *608*
Trainor/Frank & Assoc. Inc. (C), WI, *608*
Trambley the Recruiter (C), NM, *608*
The Truman Agency (C), CA, *610*
Tschudin Inc. (R), NJ, *211*
Vaughan & Co. (C), CA, *612*
Verkamp-Joyce Assoc., Inc. (R), IL, *213*
The Wabash Group (C), IN, *613*
Wallace Assoc. (C), CT, *614*
Warner & Assoc., Inc. (C), OH, *615*
Jude M. Werra & Assoc. (R), WI, *218*
West & Assoc. (C), IL, *618*
Whitehead & Assoc., Inc. (C), MO, *620*
The Whitney Group (C), GA, *620*
Williamsburg Group (C), NJ, *621*
The Wilmington Group (C), NC, *622*
Wilson Personnel, Inc. (C), NC, *622*

Susan L. Wonderling Recruiting (C), PA, 623
Jim Woodson & Assoc., Inc. (C), MS, 624
World Search (C), OH, 625
Xagas & Assoc. (R), IL, 226
The Zammataro Company (R), OH, 226

D.23 Industrial machinery & consumer appliances

The Abbott Group, Inc. (R), MD, 1
ACC Technical Services (C), OH, 233
Access/Resources, Inc. (C), MA, 234
Action Management Corp. (C), MI, 239
Advanced Recruitment, Inc. (C), TN, 240
Aggressive Corporation (C), IL, 242
Tom Allison Assoc. (C), NM, 245
Alpha Executive Search (C), AL, 245
Altec/HRC (C), MI, 246
Peter W. Ambler Co. (R), TX, 5
American Executive Search (C), FL, 247
American Heritage Group, Inc. (C), MI, 247
American Professional Search, Inc. (C), TN, 248
AmeriPro Search, Inc. (C), NC, 248
Anderson & Schwab, Inc. (R), NY, 5
Anderson Industrial Assoc., Inc. (C), GA, 250
Andrews & Wald Group (C), FL, 250
Ansara, Bickford & Fiske (C), MA, 251
Applied Search Assoc., Inc. (C), GA, 252
Argus National, Inc. (R), CT, 6
ARJay & Assoc. (C), NC, 252
Asheville Search & Consulting (C), NC, 253
W. R. Atchison & Assoc., Inc. (C), NC, 254
Austin - Allen Co. (C), TN, 256
Automation Technology Search (C), CA, 256
D. W. Baird & Associates (C), MD, 257
The Baldwin Group (R), IL, 10
BallResources (C), MO, 258
Barber & Assoc. (C), KY, 259
J. W. Barleycorn, Renard & Assoc., Inc. (R), OH, 11
Barnes Development Group, LLC (R), WI, 11
Barth Smith Company (R), IL, 12
Battalia Winston Int'l./The Euram Consultants Group (R), NY, 13
Behrens and Company (C), WA, 262
J. P. Bencik Assoc. (C), MI, 263
The Bennett Group, Inc. (R), IN, 16
Jack Bertram, Executive Recruiter (C), PA, 265
BGB Assoc., Inc. (C), IL, 266
Paul J. Biestek Assoc., Inc. (R), IL, 17
Blair/Tech Recruiters, Inc. (C), NJ, 268
Blanton & Co. (C), AL, 268
Boettcher Assoc. (R), WI, 19
John C. Boone & Co. (R), IL, 19
Borchert Assoc. (C), TX, 269
Boyden (R), NY, 20
The Brand Co., Inc. (R), FL, 22
Brian Assoc., Inc. (C), NY, 273
Briant Assoc., Inc. (R), IL, 23
Bridgecreek Personnel Agency (C), CA, 273
Brierwood Group, Inc. (C), IN, 273
Bryan & Louis Research (C), OH, 275
J. Burke & Assoc., Inc. (C), TX, 276
Byron Leonard Int'l., Inc. (R), CA, 25
Campa & Assoc. (R), ON, 27
Canyon Consulting, Inc. (C), TX, 281
Carnegie Resources, Inc. (C), NC, 284
Case Executive Search (C), MI, 286
Chadwell & Assoc., Inc. (C), MI, 288
Joseph Chandler & Assoc., Inc. (R), IL, 33
The Chapman Group, Inc. (C), AZ, 289
Robert L. Charon (C), TX, 289
Chase-Gardner Executive Search Associates, Inc. (C), FL, 289
A. D. Check Assoc., Inc. (R), PA, 33
Cheney Associates (C), CT, 290
R. Christine Assoc. (C), PA, 290
Christopher and Long (C), MO, 291
The Clayton Edward Group (C), MI, 292
Cochran, Cochran & Yale, Inc. (R), NY, 36
Continental Search Assoc. (C), OH, 298
The Cooke Group (R), WI, 40
Corbin Packaging Professionals (C), MO, 299
The Corporate Connection, Ltd. (C), VA, 299
Corporate Image Group (C), TN, 300
Corporate Management Services (C), PA, 300
Corporate Select Int'l., Ltd. (C), IL, 301
Crist Partners, Ltd. (R), IL, 43
Cross Country Consultants, Inc. (C), MD, 304
Crowder & Company (R), MI, 43
Timothy D. Crowe, Jr. (R), MA, 43
Cumberland Group Inc. (C), IL, 304
Daniel Marks Company (C), OH, 306
DieckMueller Group (R), WI, 51
Roger Dietsch & Assoc. (C), MN, 312
Domres Professional Search (R), WI, 53
The Donnelly Group-Sales Recruiters, Inc. (C), MO, 314
The Dorfman Group (C), AZ, 314
The Duncan-O'Dell Group Inc. (C), TX, 316
Dunhill Professional Search of Miami (C), FL, 319
Dunhill of San Francisco, Inc. (C), CA, 319
Dunhill Personnel Service of Fargo (C), ND, 322
Dunhill Personnel of St. Andrews (C), SC, 322
Dunhill Professional Search of Wilkes-Barre/Scranton, Inc. (C), PA, 322
Dunhill of Corpus Christi, Inc. (C), TX, 323
Dunhill Professional Search, Inc. of McAllen (C), TX, 323
Dunhill Professional Search of Richmond (C), VA, 323
Dunlap & Sullivan Assoc. (R), MI, 55
Dunn Associates (R), PA, 55
Effective Search, Inc. (R), IL, 57
Elite Resources Group (R), OH, 58
Erwin Assoc. (R), IL, 60
Executech (R), OH, 62
Executive Recruiters Agency, Inc. (C), AR, 333
Executive Recruiters, Inc. (C), WI, 334
Executive Recruitment Services, Inc. (ERS, Inc.) (C), GA, 334
Executive Resource Inc. (C), WI, 334
Executive Search, Ltd. (C), OH, 336
Executive Search Plus, Inc. (C), IN, 336
Eyler Assoc., Inc. (R), IA, 64
Fagan & Company (R), PA, 64
Fenzel Milar Assoc. (C), OH, 339
Financialjobs.com (C), CA, 340
Fisher Personnel Management Services (R), CA, 68
Flowers & Assoc. (C), OH, 342
Focus Executive Search (C), MN, 343
Ford & Assoc., Inc. (C), SC, 343
F-O-R-T-U-N-E Personnel Consultants of Savannah, Inc. (C), GA, 345
Fortune Personnel Consultants of Bloomfield, Inc. (C), MI, 346
F-o-r-t-u-n-e of Owensboro, Inc. (C), KY, 346
F-O-R-T-U-N-E Personnel Consultants of St. Louis-West County (C), MO, 347
F-O-R-T-U-N-E Search Consultants (C), MO, 347
F-O-R-T-U-N-E of West Portland (C), OR, 348
F-O-R-T-U-N-E Personnel Consultants of Rockland County, Inc. (C), NY, 348
F-O-R-T-U-N-E Personnel Consultants of Charlotte (C), NC, 348
F-O-R-T-U-N-E Personnel Consultants of Cincinnati (C), OH, 348
F-O-R-T-U-N-E Consultants of Memphis (C), TN, 349
FORTUNE Personnel Consultants of Charleston, Inc. (C), SC, 349
F-O-R-T-U-N-E Personnel Consultants of Knoxville (C), TN, 350
Fortune Personnel Consultants of San Antonio, Inc. (C), TX, 350
F-O-R-T-U-N-E Personnel Consultants of the Tri-Cities, Inc. (C), TN, 350
F-O-R-T-U-N-E Personnel Consultants of East Seattle (C), WA, 351
Fortune Personnel Consultants of the Virginia Highlands (C), VA, 351
Foster Partners (R), NY, 70
Frye/Joure & Assoc., Inc. (C), TN, 353
The Furst Group, Inc. (R), IL, 72
G. H. Enterprises (C), AZ, 354
Gabriele & Company (C), MA, 354
Gaffney Management Consultants (R), IL, 73
Dianne Gauger & Assoc. (C), CA, 355
Gilbert Tweed Assoc. Inc. (R), NY, 76
Global Engineers Inc. (C), ME, 358
H. L. Goehring & Assoc., Inc. (C), OH, 359
Gomez Fregoso y Asociados (C), JAL, 360
L. J. Gonzer Assoc. (C), NJ, 360
Granger, Counts & Assoc. (R), OH, 81
Grossberg & Assoc. (R), IL, 82
Hahn & Assoc., Inc. (C), OH, 365
Hall Management Group, Inc. (C), GA, 367
The Hanna Group (C), OH, 368
Hardage Group (C), TN, 369
Robert Harkins Assoc., Inc. (C), PA, 369

INDUSTRIES

Heath/Norton Assoc., Inc. (R), NY, *89*
The Heidrick Partners, Inc. (R), IL, *90*
Heinze & Assoc. Inc. (R), MN, *91*
Heller Assoc., Ltd. (R), IL, *91*
G. W. Henn & Co. (R), OH, *91*
The Hetzel Group, Inc. (R), IL, *92*
J. G. Hood Assoc. (C), CT, *380*
Horton Int'l. Inc. (R), NY, *96*
William C. Houze & Co. (R), CA, *96*
Human Resources Personnel Agency (R), AR, *99*
The Hunter Group, Inc. (C), MI, *385*
The Hunter Group (C), NC, *385*
Hunter Int'l. LLC (C), MA, *385*
Impact Source, Inc. (C), FL, *387*
Interactive Search Assoc. (C), PA, *391*
Intercontinental Executive Group (C), PA, *391*
Interim Executive Recruiting (C), GA, *392*
J. B. Linde & Assoc. (C), MO, *395*
Jackley Search Consultants (C), MN, *396*
Jaeger Int'l., Inc. (C), OH, *396*
John H. Johnson & Assoc., Inc. (R), IL, *106*
Jonas, Walters & Assoc., Inc. (R), WI, *107*
Jordan-Sitter Assoc. (R), TX, *108*
K & C Assoc. (C), CA, *402*
Kaas Employment Services (C), IA, *402*
A.T. Kearney Executive Search (R), IL, *111*
Blair Kershaw Assoc., Inc. (C), PA, *405*
Daniel J. Kerstein, Consultant to Management (R), CO, *114*
Knapp Consultants (R), CT, *116*
Korn/Ferry Int'l. (R), NY, *117*
Kozlin Assoc., Inc. (C), NY, *408*
Kremple & Meade, Inc. (R), CA, *120*
John Kuhn & Assoc., Inc. (R), WI, *121*
Paul Kull & Co. (R), NJ, *121*
L & L Assoc. (C), CA, *410*
Laguzza Assoc., Ltd. (R), NY, *122*
Jack B. Larsen & Assoc., Inc. (C), PA, *413*
Latham International, Ltd. (R), NJ, *126*
The Lear Group, Inc. (R), OH, *127*
Reynolds Lebus Assoc. (C), AZ, *415*
Lineal Recruiting Services (C), CT, *418*
Locus Inc. (C), WV, *419*
Lutz Associates (C), CT, *421*
M.C. Executive Search (C), CA, *422*
The Macdonald Group, Inc. (R), NJ, *133*
Magnum Search (C), IL, *422*
The Mallard Group (C), IN, *423*
Management Recruiters of Birmingham, Inc. (C), AL, *438*
Management Recruiters of Mobile Co., Inc. (C), AL, *438*
Management Recruiters of Colorado Springs (C), CO, *441*
Management Recruiters of Melbourne, Inc. (C), FL, *443*
Management Recruiters, Inc. (C), FL, *443*
Management Recruiters of Columbus, Inc. (C), GA, *445*
Management Recruiters of Sun Valley (C), ID, *447*
Management Recruiters of Chicago-North Shore (C), IL, *447*
Management Recruiters of Barrington (C), IL, *447*
Management Recruiters of Indianapolis-North (C), IN, *448*
Management Recruiters of Spencer (C), IA, *448*
Management Recruiters of Noblesville, Inc. (C), IN, *448*
Management Recruiters of Siouxland (C), IA, *449*
Management Recruiters of Danville (C), KY, *449*
Management Recruiters of Columbia (C), MD, *450*
Management Recruiters of the Baltimore Washington Corridor (C), MD, *450*
Management Recruiters of Monroe, Inc. (C), LA, *450*
Management Recruiters of Livonia (C), MI, *451*
Management Recruiters of Dearborn, Inc. (C), MI, *451*
Management Recruiters - Flint (C), MI, *451*
Management Recruiters of Bay Head (C), NJ, *453*
Management Recruiters of North Warren Inc. (C), NJ, *453*
Management Recruiters of Asheville, Inc. (C), NC, *455*
Management Recruiters of Fayetteville (C), NC, *455*
Management Recruiters of Mt. Airy (C), NC, *456*
Management Recruiters of Raleigh (C), NC, *456*
Management Recruiters of Kinston (C), NC, *456*
Management Recruiters of Winston-Salem (C), NC, *457*
Management Recruiters of Cleveland (C), OH, *457*
Management Recruiters of Dayton, Inc. (C), OH, *457*
Management Recruiters of Easton, PA (C), PA, *458*
Management Recruiters of Bethlehem, PA (C), PA, *458*
Management Recruiters of Valley Forge (C), PA, *459*
Management Recruiters of Columbia, Tennessee (C), TN, *461*
Management Recruiters of Champions (C), TX, *462*
Management Recruiters of LBJ Park/Dallas (C), TX, *462*
Management Recruiters of Round Rock (C), TX, *463*
Management Recruiters of San Antonio (C), TX, *463*
Management Recruiters of Ogden (C), UT, *464*
Management Recruiters of Milwaukee-West (C), WI, *465*
Management Recruiters of Appleton (C), WI, *465*
Management Recruiters of Madison, Inc. (C), WI, *466*
Management Recruiters of Janesville, Inc. (C), WI, *466*
Management Recruiters of Milwaukee-North (C), WI, *466*
Management Recruiters of Cheyenne (C), WY, *466*
Mannard & Assoc., Inc. (R), IL, *135*
MARBL Consultants, Inc. (C), WI, *469*
Margolin Consultants, Inc. (C), NY, *469*
Markent Personnel, Inc. (C), WI, *470*
Marketing & Sales Resources, Inc. (C), FL, *470*
Marvel Consultants, Inc. (C), OH, *472*
Maschal/Connors Inc. (R), NJ, *137*
Tom McCall Executive Search (C), IL, *473*
McInturff & Assoc., Inc. (C), MA, *474*
MESA, Inc. (R), CO, *143*
Michael Assoc. (R), IL, *144*
Michaels & Moere (C), WI, *481*
Michigan Consulting Group (R), MI, *144*
Miller Denver (C), CO, *482*
MJF Assoc. (C), CT, *483*
Morgan & Assoc. (C), MA, *485*
The Morgan/Geoffries Group (C), CA, *485*
Morton, McCorkle & Assoc. Inc. (R), MO, *147*
Mulcahy Co. (C), WI, *487*
R. F. Mulvaney & Assoc., Inc. (R), MO, *149*
NaTek Corp. (C), NY, *488*
National Metal Services Corp. (C), IN, *489*
New Directions, Inc. (C), IL, *492*
North Coast Meridian (C), NY, *496*
Northern Consultants Inc. (R), ME, *153*
O'Brien & Bell (R), OH, *153*
O'Brien Consulting Services (R), MA, *153*
O'Connor, O'Connor, Lordi, Ltd. (R), PA, *154*
Omega Search, Inc. (C), NC, *498*
Ortman Recruiting Int'l. (C), CA, *500*
Pacific Advisory Service, Inc. (C), IL, *501*
Pacific Coast Recruiting (C), CA, *501*
Parker, McFadden & Assoc. (C), GA, *503*
Partners in Recruiting (C), IL, *503*
Peeney Assoc., Inc. (R), NJ, *161*
The Penn Partners, Inc. (R), PA, *162*
Barry Persky & Co., Inc. (R), CT, *163*
Phelps Personnel Assoc., Inc. (C), SC, *510*
Phillips Int'l., Inc. (C), SC, *510*
Phillips Resource Group (C), SC, *510*
PKS Assoc., Inc. (C), RI, *513*
Ray Polhill & Assoc. (R), NC, *166*
Polytechnical Consultants, Inc. (C), IL, *514*
Premier Recruiting Group (C), MI, *516*
Premier Search Group (C), IN, *517*
The Premier Staffing Group (C), OH, *517*
Prichard Kymen Inc. (R), AB, *168*
Prime Resource Assoc. (C), WI, *518*
Probe Technology (C), PA, *519*
Professional Employment Group (C), MD, *520*
Professional Engineering Technical Personnel Consultants (C), NC, *520*
Professional Personnel Services (C), IA, *520*
Professional Recruiters Inc. (C), MN, *521*
ProSearch, Inc. (C), OH, *524*
Rand Assoc. (R), ME, *171*
Ray & Berndtson (R), TX, *171*
Raymond Thomas & Assoc. (C), FL, *530*
Recruiting Assoc. of Amarillo (C), TX, *531*
Recruiting Services Group, Inc. (C), TN, *532*

Reese Assoc. (R), PA, *174*
The Remington Group (R), IL, *174*
The Resource Group (R), NJ, *175*
Resource Networking Inc. (C), IN, *534*
Russell Reynolds Assoc., Inc. (R), NY, *176*
Terry Richards (C), OH, *536*
Riley Cole (C), CA, *537*
Ritta Professional Search Inc. (C), NY, *538*
RML Assoc. (C), PA, *538*
R. A. Rodriguez & Assoc., Inc. (C), TX, *540*
The Rossi Search Group (C), PA, *545*
RSMR, Inc. (R), IL, *182*
The Ryan Charles Group, Inc. (C), FL, *548*
S-H-S Int'l. of Cherry Hill (C), NJ, *549*
The Sager Co. (R), OH, *183*
Sales Consultants of Birmingham (C), AL, *555*
Sales Consultants of Sacramento (C), CA, *556*
Sales Consultants of Daphne (C), AL, *556*
Sales Consultants of Farmington Hills (C), MI, *560*
Sales Consultants of Raleigh-Durham-RTP (C), NC, *561*
Sales Consultants of Morris County, Inc. (C), NJ, *561*
Sales Consultants of Orangeburg (C), SC, *562*
Sales Consultants of Greenville, Inc. (C), SC, *562*
Sales Consultants of Milwaukee (C), WI, *563*
Sales Consultants of Dallas (C), TX, *563*
Sales Solutions (C), CA, *564*
Sanford Rose Assoc. - Santa Ana (C), CA, *565*
Sanford Rose Assoc. - Athens (C), GA, *566*
Sanford Rose Assoc. - Rockford (C), IL, *567*
Sanford Rose Assoc. - Canton (C), OH, *569*
Sanford Rose Assoc. - Burlington, NC (C), NC, *569*
Sanford Rose Assoc. - Austin (C), TX, *570*
Sanford Rose Assoc. - Doylestown (C), PA, *570*
The Schatz Company (C), MO, *571*
Schick Professional Search, Inc. (C), OH, *572*
Search Northwest Assoc. (C), OR, *576*
Search South, Inc. (C), AL, *576*
Segal & Assoc. (C), GA, *578*
Seiden Krieger Assoc., Inc. (R), NY, *188*
Select Services (C), IL, *578*
Selective Recruiting Assoc., Inc. (C), MI, *578*
Selective Search Associates (C), OH, *578*
M. B. Shattuck & Assoc., Inc. (R), CA, *189*
SHS of Allentown (C), PA, *580*
John Sibbald Assoc., Inc. (R), MO, *191*
Larry Siegel & Assoc. (R), WA, *191*
Sill Technical Assoc., Inc. (C), PA, *581*
Slayton Int'l., Inc. (R), IL, *192*
Ralph Smith & Assoc. (C), IL, *584*
The Smith Group, Inc. (C), NC, *584*
SpencerStuart (R), NY, *196*
Kenn Spinrad Inc. (C), PA, *589*
Staff Resources, Inc. (C), SC, *590*
Stanton Chase Int'l. (R), MD, *198*
The Stelton Group, Inc. (C), NJ, *592*
Sterling Int'l. Management Recruitment, Ltd. Inc. (C), NC, *592*
Stewart Assoc. (C), PA, *593*
Linford E. Stiles & Assoc., L.L.C. (R), NH, *201*
Summit Executive Search Consultants, Inc. (R), FL, *204*
Ron Sunshine & Assoc. (C), IL, *597*
T E M Assoc. (C), WI, *599*
Tabb & Assoc. (R), OH, *205*
Teamsearch, Inc. (C), MI, *601*
Technical Resource Assoc. (C), TN, *602*
Techstaff Inc. (C), WI, *603*
Tecmark Associates Inc. (C), NY, *604*
Teknon Employment Resources, Inc. (C), OH, *604*
The TGA Company (C), TX, *606*
Richard Thompson Assoc., Inc. (R), MN, *209*
Thorne, Brieger Assoc., Inc. (R), NY, *209*
Jay Tracey Assoc. Inc. (C), VT, *608*
Trainor/Frank & Assoc. Inc. (C), WI, *608*
Trambley the Recruiter (C), NM, *608*
Triumph Consulting, Inc. (R), IA, *210*
The Truman Agency (C), CA, *610*
Tschudin Inc. (R), NJ, *211*
U.S. Search (C), VA, *610*
Vaughan & Co. (C), CA, *612*
Kelly Walker Assoc. (C), TX, *614*
Wallace Assoc. (C), CT, *614*
Warner & Assoc., Inc. (C), OH, *615*
Wegner & Assoc. (C), WI, *617*
Jude M. Werra & Assoc. (R), WI, *218*
West & Assoc. (C), IL, *618*
Whitehead & Assoc., Inc. (C), MO, *620*
The Whitney Group (C), GA, *620*
The Wilmington Group (C), NC, *622*
Wilson Personnel, Inc. (C), NC, *622*
WMD inc. (C), NJ, *623*
Susan L. Wonderling Recruiting (C), PA, *623*
Jim Woodson & Assoc., Inc. (C), MS, *624*
Yelverton Executive Search (R), CA, *226*

D.24 Transportation equipment (e.g. automobiles)

The 500 Granary Inc. (C), ON, *231*
ACC Technical Services (C), OH, *233*
Access Assoc. Inc. (C), MD, *233*
Access/Resources, Inc. (C), MA, *234*
Action Management Corp. (C), MI, *239*
Aggressive Corporation (C), IL, *242*
Allen, Wayne & Co. LLC (C), WI, *245*
Allerton Heneghan & O'Neill (R), IL, *4*
Altec/HRC (C), MI, *246*
American Professional Search, Inc. (C), TN, *248*
AmeriPro Search, Inc. (C), NC, *248*
Anderson Network Group (C), OH, *250*
Angus Employment Ltd. (C), ON, *250*
APA Search, Inc. (R), NY, *6*
Argus National, Inc. (R), CT, *6*
ARJay & Assoc. (C), NC, *252*
Artgo, Inc. (R), OH, *7*
Asheville Search & Consulting (C), NC, *253*
Austin - Allen Co. (C), TN, *256*
Austin, Hill & Assoc. (C), MD, *256*
The Baldwin Group (R), IL, *10*
Allen Ballach Assoc. Inc. (R), ON, *10*
Barber & Assoc. (C), KY, *259*
The Barton Group, Inc. (C), MI, *260*
Battalia Winston Int'l./The Euram Consultants Group (R), NY, *13*
Benford & Assoc., Inc. (C), MI, *264*
The Bennett Group, Inc. (R), IN, *16*
Jack Bertram, Executive Recruiter (C), PA, *265*
BGB Assoc., Inc. (C), IL, *266*
Blake/Hansen Ltd. (R), FL, *18*
D. R. Blood & Assoc. (R), AZ, *18*
Boardroom Consultants/Kenny Kindler Tholke (R), NY, *19*
John C. Boone & Co. (R), IL, *19*
Borchert Assoc. (C), TX, *269*
BowdenGlobal, Ltd. (R), OH, *20*
Howard Bowen Consulting (C), FL, *270*
Boyden (R), NY, *20*
Brian Assoc., Inc. (C), NY, *273*
Brierwood Group, Inc. (C), IN, *273*
Bullis & Co., Inc. (R), CA, *25*
The Burke Group (C), ON, *276*
C. M. Management Services, Inc. (R), KY, *26*
Cambridge Management Planning (R), ON, *27*
Campa & Assoc. (R), ON, *27*
Canny, Bowen Inc. (R), NY, *27*
Career Counseling Inc. (CCI) (C), KY, *282*
Carion Resource Group Inc. (C), ON, *284*
Case Executive Search (C), MI, *286*
Michael J. Cavanagh & Assoc. Inc. (R), ON, *31*
Robert L. Charon (C), TX, *289*
Chase-Gardner Executive Search Associates, Inc. (C), FL, *289*
A. D. Check Assoc., Inc. (R), PA, *33*
R. Christine Assoc. (C), PA, *290*
Christopher and Long (C), MO, *291*
Christopher-Westmont & Assoc., Inc. (R), OH, *34*
The Clayton Edward Group (C), MI, *292*
Commercial Programming Systems, Inc. (C), CA, *294*
P. G. Cook Assoc. (R), TN, *40*
Corporate Select Int'l., Ltd. (C), IL, *301*
Corso, Mizgala + French (R), ON, *42*
Creative Input, Inc. (C), RI, *303*
Creative-Leadership, Inc. (R), CA, *42*
Criterion Executive Search, Inc. (C), FL, *303*
Crowder & Company (R), MI, *43*
Daniel Marks Company (C), OH, *306*
Davidson, Laird & Assoc. (C), MI, *308*
Davis & Company (R), CA, *47*
Diversified Search, Inc. (R), PA, *52*
Dunhill Search of West Atlanta (C), GA, *320*
Dunhill Executive Search of Brown County (C), IN, *321*
Dunhill Professional Search of Winston-Salem (C), NC, *322*
Dunhill Personnel of St. Andrews (C), SC, *322*

INDUSTRIES

Dunhill Professional Search of Wilkes-Barre/Scranton, Inc. (C), PA, *322*
Dunhill Professional Search, Inc. of McAllen (C), TX, *323*
Dunlap & Sullivan Assoc. (R), MI, *55*
Dunn Associates (R), PA, *55*
G. L. Dykstra Assoc., Inc. (C), MI, *323*
E/Search Int'l. (C), CT, *325*
William J. Elam & Assoc. (R), NE, *58*
Gene Ellefson & Assoc. Inc. (C), MI, *328*
Environmental, Health & Safety Search Assoc. (C), FL, *331*
Erwin Assoc. (R), IL, *60*
Executive Connection (C), OH, *333*
Executive Recruiters Int'l. (C), MI, *333*
Executive Recruiters Agency, Inc. (C), AR, *333*
Executive Search Plus, Inc. (C), IN, *336*
Fenzel Milar Assoc. (C), OH, *339*
Fisher Personnel Management Services (R), CA, *68*
Flowers & Assoc. (C), OH, *342*
Ford & Assoc., Inc. (C), SC, *343*
F-O-R-T-U-N-E Personnel Consultants of Boise (R), ID, *70*
Fortune Personnel Consultants of Huntsville, Inc. (C), AL, *343*
F-O-R-T-U-N-E Personnel Consultants of Savannah, Inc. (C), GA, *345*
F-O-R-T-U-N-E Personnel Consultants of Palm Beach (C), FL, *345*
Fortune of Arlington Heights (C), IL, *345*
F-O-R-T-U-N-E Personnel Consultants (C), MI, *346*
Fortune Personnel Consultants of Hinsdale, IL (C), IL, *346*
Fortune Personnel Consultants of Bloomfield, Inc. (C), MI, *346*
F-O-R-T-U-N-E Personnel Consultants of South Bend (C), IN, *346*
F-o-r-t-u-n-e of Owensboro, Inc. (C), KY, *346*
F-O-R-T-U-N-E Personnel Consultants of Southwest Indiana (C), IN, *346*
F-O-R-T-U-N-E Personnel Consultants of St. Louis-West County (C), MO, *347*
F-O-R-T-U-N-E Personnel Consultants of Troy, Inc. (C), MI, *347*
F-O-R-T-U-N-E Search Consultants (C), MO, *347*
F-O-R-T-U-N-E of West Portland (C), OR, *348*
F-O-R-T-U-N-E Personnel Consultants of Rockland County, Inc. (C), NY, *348*
F-O-R-T-U-N-E Personnel Consultants of Charlotte (C), NC, *348*
Fortune Personnel Consultants of Hilton Head (C), SC, *349*
FORTUNE Personnel Consultants of Charleston, Inc. (C), SC, *349*
F-O-R-T-U-N-E Personnel of Nashville (C), TN, *350*
F-O-R-T-U-N-E Personnel Consultants of Knoxville (C), TN, *350*
Fortune Personnel Consultants of San Antonio, Inc. (C), TX, *350*
F-O-R-T-U-N-E Personnel Consultants of the Tri-Cities, Inc. (C), TN, *350*
F-O-R-T-U-N-E Personnel Consultants of East Seattle (C), WA, *351*
Fortune Personnel Consultants of the Virginia Highlands (C), VA, *351*
Foster Partners (R), NY, *70*
Gaffney Management Consultants (R), IL, *73*
Gilbert Tweed Assoc. Inc. (R), NY, *76*
Graham & Co. (R), NJ, *80*
Granger, Counts & Assoc. (R), OH, *81*
R. Green & Assoc., Inc. (C), OH, *362*
Gregory, Kyle & Assoc. (C), NC, *363*
GWS Partners (R), IL, *84*
Hahn & Assoc., Inc. (C), OH, *365*
Hall Management Group, Inc. (C), GA, *367*
The Hanna Group (C), OH, *368*
Hardage Group (C), TN, *369*
Harvey Hohauser & Assoc., LLC (R), MI, *87*
The Hawkins Co. (R), CA, *88*
F. P. Healy & Co., Inc. (R), NY, *89*
Heller Kil Assoc., Inc. (C), FL, *375*
Highlander Search (C), NC, *378*
The Hindman Co. (R), KY, *94*
Hintz Associates (C), NY, *378*
Horton Int'l. Inc. (R), NY, *96*
William C. Houze & Co. (R), CA, *96*
HRNI (C), MI, *383*
Hunt & Howe Inc. (R), NY, *99*
The Hunter Group, Inc. (C), MI, *385*
The Hunter Group (C), NC, *385*
The Icard Group, Inc. (C), MI, *387*
Interim Executive Recruiting (C), GA, *392*
Interim Management Resources Inc. (C), ON, *392*
J. B. Linde & Assoc. (C), MO, *395*
J.N. Adams & Assoc., Inc. (C), PA, *396*
Jaeger Int'l., Inc. (C), OH, *396*
L. J. Johnson & Co. (R), MI, *106*
K & C Assoc. (C), CA, *402*
Kaas Employment Services (C), IA, *402*
Kabana Corp. (C), MI, *402*
A.T. Kearney Executive Search (R), IL, *111*
Korn/Ferry Int'l. (R), NY, *117*
Kressenberg Assoc. (C), TX, *409*
Lange & Assoc., Inc. (C), IN, *412*
Leaders-Trust Int'l./Carce y Asociados, S.C. (R), MX, *127*
J. E. Lessner Assoc., Inc. (R), MI, *128*
Linden Group, Inc. (C), NC, *418*
Lineal Recruiting Services (C), CT, *418*
Locus Inc. (C), WV, *419*
Fran Luisi Assoc. (R), NJ, *132*
Management Recruiters of Little Rock (C), AR, *439*
Management Recruiters of Melbourne, Inc. (C), FL, *443*
Management Recruiters, Inc. (C), FL, *443*
Management Recruiters of Lake Co., Inc. (C), FL, *444*
Management Recruiters of Spencer (C), IA, *448*
Management Recruiters of Noblesville, Inc. (C), IN, *448*
Management Recruiters of Richmond (C), KY, *449*
Management Recruiters of Danville (C), KY, *449*
Management Recruiters of Monroe, Inc. (C), LA, *450*
Management Recruiters of Livonia (C), MI, *451*
Management Recruiters of Birmingham (C), MI, *451*
Management Recruiters of Dearborn, Inc. (C), MI, *451*
Management Recruiters of Southeastern Michigan (C), MI, *451*
Management Recruiters of Muskegon (C), MI, *451*
Management Recruiters - Flint (C), MI, *451*
Management Recruiters of North Oakland County, Inc. (C), MI, *452*
Management Recruiters of Rankin Co. (C), MS, *452*
Management Recruiters of North Warren Inc. (C), NJ, *453*
Management Recruiters of Asheville, Inc. (C), NC, *455*
Management Recruiters of Fayetteville (C), NC, *455*
Management Recruiters of Kinston (C), NC, *456*
Management Recruiters of Raleigh (C), NC, *456*
Management Recruiters of Mt. Airy (C), NC, *456*
Management Recruiters of Dayton, Inc. (C), OH, *457*
Management Recruiters of Northwest Ohio, Inc. (C), OH, *458*
Management Recruiters of Myrtle Beach, Inc. (C), SC, *460*
Management Recruiters of Aiken (C), SC, *460*
Management Recruiters of Columbia, Tennessee (C), TN, *461*
Management Recruiters of Houston-Northeast (C), TX, *463*
Management Recruiters of San Antonio (C), TX, *463*
Management Recruiters of Milwaukee-West (C), WI, *465*
Management Recruiters of Madison, Inc. (C), WI, *466*
Management Recruiters of Janesville, Inc. (C), WI, *466*
Management Recruiters of Milwaukee-North (C), WI, *466*
Management Recruiters of Cheyenne (C), WY, *466*
MARBL Consultants, Inc. (C), WI, *469*
Markent Personnel, Inc. (C), WI, *470*
Marsteller Wilcox Assoc. (C), IL, *471*
Maschal/Connors Inc. (R), NJ, *137*
Meder & Assoc., Inc. (R), IL, *142*
MESA, Inc. (R), CO, *143*
Michael Wayne Recruiters (C), IL, *480*
Lou Michaels Assoc., Inc. (C), MI, *481*
Michigan Consulting Group (R), MI, *144*
The Morgan/Geoffries Group (C), CA, *485*
The Morley Group (C), IN, *486*
Mulcahy Co. (C), WI, *487*
Multisearch Recruiters (C), CA, *487*
National Computerized Employment Service, Inc. (C), PA, *489*

Nationwide Personnel Placement, Inc. (C), OH, *490*
Len Nelson & Assoc., Inc. (C), TX, *491*
New Directions, Inc. (C), IL, *492*
Nichols & Company (R), CO, *151*
Norman Broadbent Int'l., Inc. (R), NY, *152*
North Coast Meridian (C), NY, *496*
O'Brien & Bell (R), OH, *153*
John R. O'Connor & Assoc. (C), IL, *497*
Oliver & Rozner Assoc., Inc. (R), NY, *155*
Pacific Advisory Service, Inc. (C), IL, *501*
Parker, McFadden & Assoc. (C), GA, *503*
Michael W. Parres & Assoc. (R), MI, *159*
Pasona Canada, Inc. (C), ON, *504*
Peeney Assoc., Inc. (R), NJ, *161*
PERC, Ltd. (C), AZ, *506*
Phelps Personnel Assoc., Inc. (C), SC, *510*
DNPitchon Assoc. (R), NJ, *165*
PLA, Inc. (C), NJ, *513*
The Prairie Group (C), IL, *515*
George Preger & Associates Inc. (R), ON, *167*
Premier Recruiting Group (C), MI, *516*
Premier Search Group (C), IN, *517*
The Premier Staffing Group (C), OH, *517*
Prime Management Group Inc. (C), ON, *518*
Prime Resource Assoc. (C), WI, *518*
Professional Personnel Services (C), IA, *520*
Professional Personnel Consultants, Inc. (C), MI, *521*
Quality Control Recruiters (C), CT, *526*
Ray & Berndtson (R), TX, *171*
Recruiting Services Group, Inc. (C), TN, *532*
Reid Ellis Assoc. Inc. (C), ON, *533*
Resource Networking Inc. (C), IN, *534*
Russell Reynolds Assoc., Inc. (R), NY, *176*
Reynolds Consulting Int'l. (R), ON, *177*
RIC Corp. (R), FL, *177*
Terry Richards (C), OH, *536*
RML Assoc. (C), PA, *538*
Robison Humphreys & Assoc., Inc. (R), ON, *180*
J. P. Roddy Consultants (C), PA, *540*
Romac Int'l., Inc. (C), FL, *542*
Sage Employment Recruiters (C), IN, *550*
The Sager Co. (R), OH, *183*
Sales Consultants of Birmingham (C), MI, *559*
Sanford Rose Assoc. - Santa Ana (C), CA, *565*
Sanford Rose Assoc. - Athens (C), GA, *566*
Sanford Rose Assoc. - Rockford (C), IL, *567*
Sanford Rose Assoc. - Cedar Rapids (C), IA, *567*
Sanford Rose Assoc. - Gastonia (C), NC, *568*
Sanford Rose Assoc. - Amherst, NY (C), NY, *568*
Sanford Rose Assoc. - Rochester (C), MI, *568*
Sanford Rose Assoc. - Canton (C), OH, *569*
Sanford Rose Assoc. - Burlington, NC (C), NC, *569*
Sanford Rose Assoc. - Austin (C), TX, *570*
Sanford Rose Assoc. - Port Washington (C), WI, *571*
The Schatz Company (C), MO, *571*
Schick Professional Search, Inc. (C), OH, *572*
Scientific Solutions, Inc. (C), MI, *572*
Search Plus Int'l.-Ohio (C), OH, *576*
Select Services (C), IL, *578*
Selectis Corp. (C), IL, *578*
Selective Recruiting Assoc., Inc. (C), MI, *578*
Sharrow & Assoc., Inc. (C), MI, *579*
SHS of Allentown (C), PA, *580*
Sill Technical Assoc., Inc. (C), PA, *581*
Singleton & Assoc. (C), VA, *582*
Slayton Int'l., Inc. (R), IL, *192*
Smith & Assoc. (C), FL, *583*
Smith & Syberg, Inc. (R), IN, *193*
Snelling Search (C), LA, *586*
Spear-Izzo Assoc., LLC (C), PA, *588*
SpencerStuart (R), NY, *196*
Springer Souder & Assoc. L.L.C. (R), IL, *198*
The Stanton Group, Inc. (C), IL, *591*
Sullivan & Assoc. (R), MI, *204*
Summit Executive Search Consultants, Inc. (R), FL, *204*
Ron Sunshine & Assoc. (C), IL, *597*
Synergy Solutions, Ltd. (C), WA, *597*
The Talley Group (R), VA, *205*
Teamsearch, Inc. (C), MI, *601*
Technical Resource Assoc. (C), TN, *602*
Technical Search Assoc. (C), OH, *602*
Teknon Employment Resources, Inc. (C), OH, *604*
Tittemore Cowan Assoc. (C), AB, *607*
Trainor/Frank & Assoc. Inc. (C), WI, *608*
Trambley the Recruiter (C), NM, *608*
Transportation Recruiting Services, Inc. (C), MS, *608*
The Wabash Group (C), IN, *613*
Warner & Assoc., Inc. (C), OH, *615*
Warren Executive Services (C), GA, *616*
Lee Weil Assoc., Inc. (C), IL, *617*
D. L. Weiss & Assoc. (R), CA, *217*
Jude M. Werra & Assoc. (R), WI, *218*
West & Assoc. (C), IL, *618*
Whitehead & Assoc., Inc. (C), MO, *620*
The Wilmington Group (C), NC, *622*
Wing Tips & Pumps, Inc. (C), MI, *623*
Susan L. Wonderling Recruiting (C), PA, *623*
Jim Woodson & Assoc., Inc. (C), MS, *624*
Xagas & Assoc. (R), IL, *226*
Zen Zen Int'l. Inc. (C), MB, *627*
Zwell Int'l. (R), IL, *228*

D.25 Computer equipment & components

A C Personnel Services, Inc. (C), OK, *231*
A la Carte Int'l., Inc. (R), VA, *1*
Abraham & London Ltd. (C), CT, *232*
ACCESS Technology (C), CA, *234*
Access/Resources, Inc. (C), MA, *234*
Accounting Additions (C), CA, *238*
Ackerman Johnson Inc. (C), TX, *238*
Arthur Adams & Assoc. (C), OH, *239*
Adel-Lawrence Assoc., Inc. (C), NJ, *240*
Advanced Corporate Search (C), CA, *240*
Advanced Recruitment, Inc. (C), TN, *240*
Advancement, Inc. (C), IL, *241*
The Advisory Group, Inc. (R), CA, *2*
J. R. Akin & Co. (R), MA, *2*
Alexander & Co. (C), CA, *243*
Allen & Assoc. (C), NV, *244*
Allen-Jeffers Assoc. (C), CA, *245*
Allstaff, Inc. (C), IL, *245*
The Alternatives Group, Inc. (C), TX, *246*
American Executive Search (C), FL, *247*
American Heritage Group, Inc. (C), MI, *247*
Ames-O'Neill Assoc., Inc. (C), NY, *249*
Analog Solutions (C), NY, *249*
Andrews & Wald Group (C), FL, *250*
Ansara, Bickford & Fiske (C), MA, *251*
Argus National, Inc. (R), CT, *6*
ARJay & Assoc. (C), NC, *252*
Patrick Arnone & Assoc. Inc. (R), VA, *7*
A. Artze Assoc.-Personnel Consultants (C), PR, *253*
Asheville Search & Consulting (C), NC, *253*
Ashton Computer Professionals, Inc. (C), BC, *253*
Ashworth Consultants, Inc. (R), MA, *8*
Asset Resource, Inc. (C), CA, *254*
Atlanta Executive Partners, Inc. (R), MA, *8*
Aurora Tech Search (C), ON, *256*
Austin - Allen Co. (C), TN, *256*
Austin Group Int'l./Marlar Int'l. (R), TX, *9*
Austin Michaels, Ltd., Inc. (C), AZ, *256*
Austin Park Management Group Inc. (C), ON, *256*
Automation Technology Search (C), CA, *256*
The Badger Group (R), CA, *10*
Keith Bagg & Assoc., Inc. (C), ON, *257*
Baldwin Associates, LLC (R), CT, *10*
James Bangert & Assoc., Inc. (R), MN, *11*
Barclay Consultants, Inc. (C), NJ, *259*
Barnes & Assoc. Executive Search (C), CA, *259*
Barone Assoc. (C), NJ, *259*
Barr Assoc. (C), PA, *259*
Barrett Rose & Lee, Inc. (C), ON, *260*
Barrington Hart, Inc. (R), IL, *12*
Bartholdi & Co., Inc. (R), CO, *12*
Barton Assoc., Inc. (R), TX, *12*
Battalia Winston Int'l./The Euram Consultants Group (R), NY, *13*
BayResearch Group, Inc. (R), IL, *14*
The Beardsley Group Inc. (C), CT, *261*
Beck/Eastwood Recruitment Solutions (C), CA, *261*
The Bedford Group (R), RI, *15*
Robert Beech West Inc. (C), CA, *262*
Belanger Partners Ltd. (C), ON, *262*
The Bennett Group, Inc. (R), IN, *16*
Berger & Leff (C), CA, *264*
Berkana Int'l., Inc. (C), WA, *265*
Besen Assoc. Inc. (C), NJ, *266*
BGB Assoc., Inc. (C), IL, *266*
Bialla & Assoc. Inc. (R), CA, *17*
BioPharmMed (C), FL, *267*
Deborah Bishop & Assoc. (R), CA, *17*
Blaney Executive Search (R), MA, *18*

Blanton & Co. (C), AL, *268*
Block & Assoc. (R), CA, *18*
Bower & Associates (C), TX, *271*
Boyden (R), NY, *20*
The Bradbury Management Group, Inc. (R), CA, *21*
Bratland & Assoc. (C), IL, *272*
Brei & Assoc., Inc. (C), IA, *272*
The Brentwood Group Ltd. (R), OR, *23*
Brentwood Int'l. (R), CA, *23*
Brian Assoc., Inc. (C), NY, *273*
The Bridge (C), CO, *273*
Brierwood Group, Inc. (C), IN, *273*
Brigade, Inc. (R), CA, *23*
Bernard E. Brooks & Assoc., Inc. (R), SC, *24*
Brown Venture Assoc. (R), CA, *24*
Brush Creek Partners (R), MO, *24*
The Buckley Group (C), FL, *276*
Buckman/Enochs & Assoc., Inc. (C), OH, *276*
Bullis & Co., Inc. (R), CA, *25*
Joseph R. Burns & Assoc., Inc. (R), NJ, *25*
Busch International (R), CA, *25*
Butterfield & Co. Int'l., Inc. (C), HI, *277*
Byron Leonard Int'l., Inc. (R), CA, *25*
Cadillac Assoc. (C), CA, *278*
Canny, Bowen Inc. (R), NY, *27*
Career Advisors, Inc. (C), FL, *281*
Career Counseling Inc. (CCI) (C), KY, *282*
Career Marketing Assoc., Inc. (C), CO, *282*
Careers First, Inc. (C), NJ, *283*
Careers Plus (R), CA, *29*
Carnegie Resources, Inc. (C), NC, *284*
Carter/MacKay (C), NJ, *285*
Caywood Partners, Ltd. (R), CA, *32*
Cendea Connection Int'l. (R), TX, *32*
CEO Consulting (C), FL, *287*
Wayne S. Chamberlain & Assoc. (C), CA, *288*
The Cherbonnier Group, Inc. (R), TX, *33*
Chesapeake Group (C), CT, *290*
Christian & Timbers, Inc. (R), OH, *34*
J. F. Church Associates (C), WA, *291*
M. A. Churchill & Assoc., Inc. (R), PA, *35*
The Churchill Group (C), ON, *291*
CJA-The Adler Group, Inc. (R), CA, *35*
Howard Clark Assoc. (C), NJ, *292*
CN Associates (C), CA, *293*
Comprehensive Search (C), GA, *294*
CompuPro (C), IL, *295*
Computer Professionals Unlimited (C), TX, *295*
Computer Security Placement Service (C), MA, *296*
Corporate Recruiters Ltd. (C), BC, *300*
Corporate Select Int'l., Ltd. (C), IL, *301*
Corporate Staffing Group, Inc. (C), PA, *301*
Cowell & Associates, Ltd. (R), IL, *42*
Cowin Assoc. (R), NY, *42*
Crane, Reed & Co., Inc. (C), NH, *302*
Creative-Leadership, Inc. (R), CA, *42*
Timothy D. Crowe, Jr. (R), MA, *43*
Current Resource Group, Inc. (C), GA, *305*
Curry, Telleri Group, Inc. (R), NJ, *44*
CV Associates (C), NY, *305*
Cypress Int'l., Inc. (R), FL, *45*
D.A.L. Associates, Inc. (R), CT, *45*
Charles Dahl Group, Inc. (C), MN, *306*
Dahl-Morrow Int'l. (R), VA, *45*
Data-AxIS Corp. (C), FL, *307*
The DataFinders Group, Inc. (C), NJ, *307*
DBC Recruiting Network (C), GA, *309*
Deeco Int'l. (C), UT, *310*
Delta Management Group Ltd. (C), ON, *310*
Delta Resource Group, Ltd. (C), GA, *311*
Despres & Associates (C), IL, *311*
The Devlin Search Group, Inc. (C), MA, *311*
Dise & Co. (R), OH, *52*
Diversified Consulting Services, Inc. (C), CO, *313*
Diversified Search, Inc. (R), PA, *52*
L. J. Doherty & Assoc. (R), MA, *53*
Don Allan Assoc., Inc. (C), CA, *313*
Dreier Consulting (C), NJ, *315*
Dromeshauser Assoc. (R), MA, *55*
Dunhill Professional Search of Miami (C), FL, *319*
Dunhill of Ft. Collins, Inc. (C), CO, *319*
Dunhill Professional Search of San Jose (C), CA, *319*
Dunhill Professional Search of Ramsey (C), NJ, *321*
Dunhill Executive Search of Brown County (C), IN, *321*
Dunhill Professional Search of Bucks-Mont., Inc. (C), PA, *322*
C. A. Durakis Assoc., Inc. (R), MD, *55*
Dynamic Choices Inc. (C), MO, *323*
Dynamic Search Systems, Inc. (C), IL, *324*
Dynamic Synergy Corp. (R), CA, *56*
E/Search Int'l. (C), CT, *325*
J. M. Eagle Partners Ltd. (C), WI, *325*
Eagle Search Assoc. (C), CA, *325*
EagleView, Inc. (C), MA, *325*
EBA Group (R), NJ, *56*
Bruce Edwards & Associates, Inc. (R), NC, *56*
EFCO Consultants, Inc. (C), NY, *327*
Effective Search, Inc. (R), IL, *57*
EFL Int'l. (R), AZ, *57*
The Eldridge Group, Ltd. (C), IL, *327*
Electronic Search, Inc. (C), IL, *327*
David M. Ellner Assoc. (R), NY, *59*
The Elmhurst Group (C), CA, *329*
Emerald Legal Search (C), NH, *329*
Empire International (R), PA, *59*
Empowered Solutions Corp. (C), GA, *330*
Engineering Resource Group, Inc. (C), NJ, *331*
ENI (R), CT, *59*
Environmental, Health & Safety Search Assoc. (C), FL, *331*
Epsen, Fuller & Assoc., LLC (R), NJ, *60*
Essential Solutions, Inc. (C), CA, *331*
ExecuSource Assoc., Inc. (C), GA, *332*
ExecuSource Consultants, Inc. (C), TX, *332*
Executive Business Solutions, Inc. (C), WA, *332*
Executive Directions (R), OH, *62*
Executive Manning Corp. (R), FL, *63*
Executive Recruiters Agency, Inc. (C), AR, *333*
Executive Recruiters (C), WA, *334*
Executive Recruiters, Inc. (C), WI, *334*
Executive Recruitment Services, Inc. (ERS, Inc.) (C), GA, *334*
Executive Sales Search (C), CO, *335*
Executive Search Plus, Inc. (C), IN, *336*
Raymond L. Extract & Assoc. (R), CA, *64*
Fenwick Partners (R), MA, *66*
Financialjobs.com (C), CA, *340*
Neil Fink Assoc. (R), CA, *66*
Finnegan & Assoc. (R), CA, *67*
First Search Inc. (C), IL, *341*
Fishel HR Assoc., Inc. (C), AZ, *341*
Fisher & Assoc. (R), CA, *67*
Fisher Personnel Management Services (R), CA, *68*
Flowers & Assoc. (C), OH, *342*
L. W. Foote Co. (R), WA, *69*
Fortune Personnel Consultants of Huntsville, Inc. (C), AL, *343*
F-O-R-T-U-N-E Personnel Consultants of Tampa (C), FL, *344*
Fortune Personnel Consultants of Colorado Springs (C), CO, *344*
F-O-R-T-U-N-E Personnel Consultants of Savannah, Inc. (C), GA, *345*
F-O-R-T-U-N-E Personnel Consultants of Manatee County (C), FL, *345*
Fortune Personnel Consultants of Bloomfield, Inc. (C), MI, *346*
F-o-r-t-u-n-e of Owensboro, Inc. (C), KY, *346*
F-O-R-T-U-N-E Personnel Consultants of St. Louis-West County (C), MO, *347*
F-O-R-T-U-N-E Personnel Consultants of Bergen County Inc. (C), NJ, *347*
F-O-R-T-U-N-E Search Consultants (C), MO, *347*
Fortune Personnel Consultants of Allentown, Inc. (C), PA, *348*
Fortune Personnel Consultants of Hilton Head (C), SC, *349*
FORTUNE Personnel Consultants of North Dallas (C), TX, *350*
Fortune Personnel Consultants of Plano (C), TX, *350*
Fortune Personnel Consultants of San Antonio, Inc. (C), TX, *350*
Foster Partners (R), NY, *70*
Franklin Int'l. Search, Inc. (C), MA, *352*
KS Frary & Assoc. (R), MA, *71*
Mel Frazer Consultant (C), CA, *352*
Furlong Search, Inc. (R), CA, *72*
The Furst Group, Inc. (R), IL, *72*
GAAP Inc. (R), QE, *73*
Gabriele & Company (C), MA, *354*
Gallin Associates, Inc. (C), FL, *354*
Garland Assoc. Int'l. (C), CA, *355*
The Garms Group (R), IL, *74*
Dianne Gauger & Assoc. (C), CA, *355*
General Engineering Tectonics (C), CA, *356*
C. R. Gerald & Assoc. (C), ON, *356*
Gilbert Tweed Assoc. Inc. (R), NY, *76*
Lawrence Glaser Assoc., Inc. (C), NJ, *357*
J. P. Gleason Assoc., Inc. (R), IL, *77*
Global Engineers Inc. (C), ME, *358*
Global Telecommunications, Inc. (C), TX, *359*
Glou Int'l., Inc. (R), MA, *78*

The Gobbell Co. (R), CA, *78*
Fred J. Goldsmith Assoc. (R), CA, *79*
Goldstein & Co. (C), CA, *360*
Goodrich & Sherwood Assoc., Inc. (R), NY, *79*
The Governance Group, Inc. (R), NJ, *80*
Gowdy Consultants (C), TX, *361*
Greenwich Internet (C), CT, *363*
Greenwich Search Partners, LLC (C), CT, *363*
Groton Planning Group (R), ME, *82*
Growth Strategies, Inc. (R), FL, *83*
GSW Consulting Group, Inc. (R), CA, *83*
Michael R. Guerin Co. (C), CA, *364*
The Guild Corp. (C), VA, *364*
Gustin Partners, Ltd. (R), MA, *83*
Haddad Assoc. (R), FL, *84*
Haley Associates (R), CA, *85*
Hall Kinion (C), CA, *366*
The Hamilton Group (R), MD, *85*
Handy HRM (R), NY, *86*
Hanley & Assoc. (R), FL, *86*
Harcourt & Assoc. (C), AB, *368*
Hardison & Company (R), TX, *86*
Robert Harkins Assoc., Inc. (C), PA, *369*
Harper Hewes, Inc. (C), NY, *369*
Harris Heery & Assoc., Inc. (R), CT, *87*
Hayden & Assoc., Inc. (C), MN, *370*
Healey Executive Search, Inc. (R), MN, *88*
Healthcare Recruiters Int'l. Philadelphia (C), NJ, *373*
F. P. Healy & Co., Inc. (R), NY, *89*
HEC Group (C), ON, *375*
Hechkoff/Work Executive Search Inc. (R), NY, *89*
Heffelfinger Assoc., Inc. (R), MA, *89*
Heller Assoc., Ltd. (R), IL, *91*
Henson Partners (C), AZ, *376*
J. J. Herlihy & Assoc., Inc. (C), CA, *376*
J. D. Hersey & Assoc. (C), OH, *376*
The Hetzel Group, Inc. (R), IL, *92*
The Hindman Group, Inc. (C), CA, *378*
Hite Executive Search (R), OH, *94*
Hobson Assoc. (C), CT, *379*
Hoffman Recruiters (C), MA, *380*
Holland & Assoc., Inc. (R), MI, *94*
J. G. Hood Assoc. (C), CT, *380*
Horton Int'l. Inc. (R), NY, *96*
The Hudson Group (C), CT, *383*
Leigh Hunt & Assoc., Inc. (C), ME, *384*
Hunter Adams (C), NC, *385*
Hutton Merrill & Assoc. (R), CA, *100*
IMA Search, Inc. (R), NY, *101*
Impact Technical Staffing (C), OR, *387*
Independent Resource Systems (C), CA, *388*
InSearch (C), CO, *389*
Integrated Search Solutions Group, LLC (ISSG) (R), NY, *102*
Intelegra, Inc. (C), NJ, *390*
Interim Accounting Professionals (C), CA, *391*
International Consulting Services, Inc. (C), IL, *392*
Interspace Interactive, Inc. (C), NY, *394*
Isaacson, Miller (R), MA, *104*
J. B. Linde & Assoc. (C), MO, *395*
J. Joseph & Assoc. (C), OH, *395*
Jackley Search Consultants (C), MN, *396*
Jackson Resources (R), TX, *105*
K. Jaeger & Assoc. (C), MA, *396*
Jaeger Int'l., Inc. (C), OH, *396*
Jakobs & Assoc. Int'l. (R), NY, *105*
James Moore & Assoc. (C), CA, *397*
Jeffrey Meryl Assoc., Inc. (C), NJ, *398*
Job Link, Inc. (C), CA, *399*
Johnson & Assoc., Inc. (R), CA, *106*
Ronald S. Johnson Assoc., Inc. (R), CA, *107*
K. E. Johnson Assoc. (C), WA, *399*
Johnson, Kemper & Assoc. (C), TX, *400*
JSG Group Management Consultants (R), ON, *109*
Judd Associates (R), NJ, *109*
Kabana Corp. (C), MI, *402*
KABL Ability Network (C), CA, *402*
Kacevich, Lewis & Brown, Inc. (R), MA, *109*
Kames & Assoc. (C), MD, *403*
Karp & Assoc. (C), FL, *403*
Allan Karson Assoc., Inc. (R), NJ, *110*
Jim Kay & Assoc. (C), IL, *404*
Kay Concepts, Inc. (C), FL, *404*
Keane Assoc. (R), MA, *110*
A.T. Kearney Executive Search (R), IL, *111*
S. D. Kelly & Assoc., Inc. (R), MA, *112*
Key Resources Int'l. (C), CA, *405*
Ki Technologies, Inc. (C), UT, *406*
Kiley, Owen & McGovern, Inc. (R), NJ, *114*
Kingsley Quinn/USA (R), NJ, *115*
Richard Kinser & Assoc. (R), NY, *115*
Raymond J. Klemmer & Assoc. (R), NY, *116*
The Kleven Group, Inc. - Executive Search Division (R), MA, *116*
Knapp Consultants (R), CT, *116*
Koren, Rogers Assoc. Inc. (R), NY, *117*
Korn/Ferry Int'l. (R), NY, *117*
Kossuth & Assoc., Inc. (R), WA, *119*
Katherine R. Kraemer (R), CA, *120*
Krakower Group, Inc. (R), CA, *120*
Kremple & Meade, Inc. (R), CA, *120*
Kremple Consulting Group (R), CA, *120*
Paul Kull & Co. (R), NJ, *121*
Kulper & Co., L.L.C. (R), NJ, *121*
Kurtz Pro-Search, Inc. (C), NJ, *410*
L & L Assoc. (C), CA, *410*
The Landstone Group (C), NY, *412*
Larson Assoc. (R), CA, *125*
Lasher Assoc. (R), FL, *125*
LCS, Inc. (C), TX, *414*
Albert G. Lee Assoc. (C), RI, *415*
Ricci Lee Assoc., Inc. (C), CA, *415*
The Conrad Lee Co. Inc. (R), FL, *127*
Leith & Assoc., Inc. (C), OH, *416*
Leslie Kavanagh Assoc., Inc. (C), NY, *416*
The Levton Group Inc. (R), ON, *129*
Ginger Lindsey & Assoc., Inc. (C), TX, *418*
Lipsky Group, Inc. (R), CA, *129*
Lloyd Prescott Assoc., Inc. (C), FL, *418*
Loewenstein & Assoc., Inc. (R), TX, *131*
Longo Associates (C), CA, *420*
Lucas Group (C), NY, *421*
The Luciani Group (R), CA, *132*
Management Assoc. (C), CA, *424*
Management Association Network (C), WI, *424*
Management Dimensions Ltd. (R), ON, *134*
Management Recruiters Tucson-Foothills, Inc. (C), AZ, *439*
Management Recruiters of Northern California (C), CA, *440*
Management Recruiters Inc. of Silicon Valley (C), CA, *441*
Management Recruiters of Roseville (C), CA, *441*
Management Recruiters of Colorado Springs (C), CO, *441*
Management Recruiters of Milford Inc. (C), CT, *442*
Management Recruiters of Winsted, Inc. (C), CT, *442*
Management Recruiters of Colchester (C), CT, *442*
Management Recruiters of Franktown (C), CO, *442*
Management Recruiters, Inc. (C), FL, *443*
Management Recruiters of Venice, Inc. (C), FL, *445*
Management Recruiters of Boise (C), ID, *446*
Management Recruiters of Atlanta NE (C), GA, *446*
Management Recruiters of Savannah (C), GA, *446*
Management Recruiters of Des Moines (C), IA, *449*
Management Recruiters of Fairfield (C), IA, *449*
Management Recruiters of Birmingham (C), MI, *451*
Management Recruiters of Bay Head (C), NJ, *453*
Management Recruiters of Morris County, NJ (C), NJ, *453*
Management Recruiters of Mt. Airy (C), NC, *456*
Management Recruiters of Kinston (C), NC, *456*
Management Recruiters of Easton, PA (C), PA, *458*
Management Recruiters The Delta Group, Inc. (C), TN, *461*
Management Recruiters of Travelers Rest, Inc. (C), SC, *461*
Management Recruiters of LBJ Park/Dallas (C), TX, *462*
Management Recruiters of Arlington (C), VA, *464*
Management Recruiters of Stevens Point, Inc. (C), WI, *466*
Management Recruiters of Cheyenne (C), WY, *466*
Management Solutions, Inc. (C), CA, *468*
F. L. Mannix & Co. (R), MA, *135*
J. L. Mark Assoc., Inc. (R), CO, *135*
Mark Christian & Assoc., Inc. (C), AZ, *469*
Market Niche Consulting (C), AZ, *470*
The Marlow Group (R), MA, *136*
Donovan Martin & Assoc. (R), CA, *137*
J. Martin & Assoc. (R), CA, *137*
The Martwick Group, Inc. (C), OR, *472*
Maschal/Connors Inc. (R), NJ, *137*

INDUSTRIES

Richard L. Mather & Assoc. (C), CT, *472*
Matté & Company, Inc. (R), CT, *138*
Maxecon Executive Search Consultants (R), FL, *138*
McCoy Ltd. (C), CA, *474*
McCray, Shriver, Eckdahl & Assoc., Inc. (R), CA, *140*
Dan P. McLean Assoc., Inc. (C), ON, *475*
McManners Assoc., Inc. (R), CA, *142*
Joseph J. McTaggart (C), CA, *476*
Medical Innovations (C), NY, *477*
Medical Recruiters Inc. (C), MO, *477*
J. M. Meredith & Assoc. Inc. (C), CA, *479*
Michaels & Moere (C), WI, *481*
Miller Denver (C), CO, *482*
Paul Misarti Inc. (C), NY, *483*
MJF Assoc. (C), CT, *483*
Mogul Consultants, Inc. (C), NY, *483*
Montenido Assoc. (R), CA, *146*
Mordue, Allen, Roberts, Bonney Ltd. (C), WA, *485*
Morency Assoc. (C), MA, *485*
Morgan & Assoc. (C), MA, *485*
The Morgan/Geoffries Group (C), CA, *485*
Robert T. Morton Assoc., Inc. (C), MA, *486*
Mulcahy Co. (C), WI, *487*
The Mulshine Co., Inc. (R), NJ, *149*
National Computerized Employment Service, Inc. (C), PA, *489*
National Executive (C), ON, *489*
National Field Service Corp. (C), NY, *489*
National Search Assoc. (C), CA, *490*
Nationwide Personnel Placement, Inc. (C), OH, *490*
NCC Executive Search Consultants (C), CA, *490*
J. Fielding Nelson & Assoc., Inc. (R), UT, *151*
Len Nelson & Assoc., Inc. (C), TX, *491*
New Directions, Inc. (C), IL, *492*
Newport Management (C), NY, *492*
The Niemond Corp. (R), CA, *152*
Ira Z. Nitzberg (C), NY, *493*
The Nolan Group (C), CA, *494*
Nordeman Grimm, Inc. (R), NY, *152*
Paul Winston Norman & Assoc. (R), IL, *152*
Norman Broadbent Int'l., Inc. (R), NY, *152*
North Coast Meridian (C), NY, *496*
Norton & Assoc. (C), IL, *496*
NYCOR Search, Inc. (C), MN, *497*
O'Connell Group Inc. (C), CT, *497*
The Odessa Group (R), CA, *155*
Olsen/Clark (R), WA, *156*
Omega Search, Inc. (C), NC, *498*
Omega Systems, LLC (C), VA, *498*
Opus Marketing (R), CA, *156*
Pacific Crossing (C), CA, *501*
Packaging Personnel Co., Ltd. (C), WI, *501*
T. Page & Assoc. (C), TX, *502*
Partners in Recruiting (C), IL, *503*
Pawlik/Dorman Partners (R), IL, *161*
M. A. Pelle Assoc., Inc. (C), NY, *506*
Perry Search Assoc. (C), CA, *507*
Perry-Martel Int'l., Inc. (R), ON, *163*
Personnel, Inc. (C), AL, *508*
Phelps Personnel Assoc., Inc. (C), SC, *510*
Phillips Assoc. (C), FL, *510*
Phoenix Partners, Inc. (C), GA, *511*
Pinnacle Executive Group Inc. (C), MO, *512*
The Pinnacle Source, Inc. (C), CO, *512*
Pinsker and Company, Inc. (R), CA, *164*
PKS Assoc., Inc. (C), RI, *513*
PLA, Inc. (C), NJ, *513*
Rene Plessner Assoc., Inc. (R), NY, *165*
R. L. Plimpton Assoc., Inc. (R), CO, *165*
The Pollack Group (C), ON, *514*
Don V. Poole & Assoc., Inc. (C), CO, *514*
Norman Powers Assoc., Inc. (C), MA, *515*
Predictor Systems Corp. (R), CA, *167*
Prestonwood Assoc. (R), MA, *168*
Price & Assoc., Inc. (C), VA, *518*
Alan J. Price Assoc., Inc. (C), RI, *518*
Princeton Executive Search (C), NJ, *518*
Probe Technology (C), PA, *519*
Professional Engineering Technical Personnel Consultants (C), NC, *520*
Professional Personnel Services (C), IA, *520*
Professional Recruiting Consultants (C), FL, *521*
Professional Recruiters Inc. (C), MN, *521*
Professional Recruiters (C), UT, *521*
The Professional Sales Search Co., Inc. (C), WA, *522*
Professional Search Consultants (PSC) (C), TX, *523*
Professional Team Search, Inc. (R), AZ, *169*
ProNet, Inc. (C), NC, *524*
PSD Group, Inc. (C), CA, *525*
Quality Search Inc. (C), OH, *526*
L. J. Quinn & Assoc., Inc. (R), CA, *170*
R & K Associates, Inc. (C), AZ, *527*
R/K International Inc. (R), CT, *171*
R2 Services, LLC (C), IL, *528*
Radosevic Assoc. (R), CA, *171*
Ray & Berndtson (R), TX, *171*
RCI Employment Solutions (C), FL, *531*
Recruit Xpress (C), TX, *531*
Recruiting Services Group, Inc. (C), TN, *532*
Redden-Shaffer Group (R), CA, *173*
Reeve & Assoc. (C), CT, *533*
Resource Networking Inc. (C), IN, *534*
Russell Reynolds Assoc., Inc. (R), NY, *176*
RIC Corp. (R), FL, *177*
Terry Richards (C), OH, *536*
Robert Lowell Int'l. (R), TX, *179*
J. Rodgers & Associates (C), IL, *540*
Rogers - McManamon Executive Search (R), CA, *180*
ROI Assoc. (R), NY, *180*
Rollins & Assoc. (C), CA, *541*
Romano McAvoy Assoc., Inc. (C), NY, *544*
Rooney Assoc., Inc. (R), IL, *181*
Ross Personnel Consultants, Inc. (C), CT, *545*
The Rossi Search Group (C), PA, *545*
Rothrock Associates, Inc. (C), NC, *547*
Louis Rudzinsky Assoc., Inc. (C), MA, *548*
Rusher, Loscavio & LoPresto (R), CA, *183*
Rylan Forbes Consulting Group, Inc. (C), NJ, *549*
R. L. Rystrom & Assoc., Inc. (C), MN, *549*
Sales & Marketing Search, Inc. (C), MA, *551*
Sales Consultants of Silicon Valley (C), CA, *556*
Sales Consultants of Scottsdale, Inc. (C), AZ, *556*
Sales Consultants Peninsula, Inc. (C), CA, *556*
Sales Consultants of Honolulu (C), HI, *558*
Sales Consultants of Barrington (C), IL, *558*
Sales Consultants of Rockville, MD (C), MD, *559*
Sales Consultants of Farmington Hills (C), MI, *560*
Sales Consultants of Nashua-Manchester (C), NH, *560*
Sales Consultants of Omaha, Inc. (C), NE, *560*
Sales Consultants of Raleigh-Durham-RTP (C), NC, *561*
Sales Consultants King of Prussia (C), PA, *562*
Sales Consultants of Orangeburg (C), SC, *562*
Sales Consultants of Madison (C), WI, *563*
Sales Executives, Inc. (C), MI, *563*
George D. Sandel Assoc. (C), MA, *565*
Sanford Rose Assoc. - Santa Barbara (C), CA, *565*
Sanford Rose Assoc. - Charlotte (C), NC, *568*
Sanford Rose Assoc. - Greensboro (C), NC, *569*
Sanford Rose Assoc. - Akron (C), OH, *569*
Sanford Rose Assoc. - Philadelphia North (C), PA, *570*
Sanford Rose Assoc. - Austin (C), TX, *570*
Sanford Rose Assoc. - Salt Lake City (C), UT, *571*
Sarver & Carruth Assoc. (C), OK, *571*
Satterfield & Assoc., Inc. (R), OH, *184*
Schweichler Assoc., Inc. (R), CA, *186*
The Search Alliance, Inc. (R), FL, *186*
Search Assoc., Inc. (C), CA, *574*
Search Group (C), CA, *575*
Search Int'l. (R), MA, *187*
The Search Network (C), CA, *576*
Search Northwest Assoc. (C), OR, *576*
SearchCom, Inc. (R), TX, *187*
Segal & Assoc. (C), GA, *578*
Seiden Krieger Assoc., Inc. (R), NY, *188*
Selectis Corp. (C), IL, *578*
Selective Search Associates (C), OH, *578*
SFB Legal Search (C), NY, *579*
Sharp Placement Professionals, Inc. (C), NY, *579*
M. B. Shattuck & Assoc., Inc. (R), CA, *189*
Shinn & Assoc. (R), CA, *189*
The Silicon Network (C), ON, *581*
L. A. Silver Assoc., Inc. (R), MA, *191*
The Simmons Group (C), CA, *582*
Sinclair & Co., Inc. (R), MA, *192*
Sink, Walker, Boltrus Int'l. (R), MA, *192*
Smith & Assoc. (C), CA, *583*
Smith, Roth & Squires (R), NY, *194*
A. William Smyth, Inc. (R), CA, *194*
C. Snow & Assoc. (C), ON, *586*
Softrix, Inc. (C), NJ, *586*

Software Engineering Solutions, Inc. (C), CA, *586*
Software Resource Consultants (C), TN, *587*
Somerset Group, Inc. (C), CT, *587*
Southern Recruiters & Consultants, Inc. (C), SC, *587*
Southport Int'l. Assoc. Inc. (C), FL, *588*
Sparks, McDonough & Assoc., Inc. (C), MO, *588*
Special Markets Group, Inc. (R), GA, *195*
SpectraWest (C), CA, *589*
Spectrum Consultants (R), CA, *196*
SpencerSearch, Inc. (C), CO, *589*
SpencerStuart (R), NY, *196*
The Spiegel Group (R), MA, *197*
Splaine & Assoc., Inc. (R), CA, *198*
StaffWriters Plus (C), NY, *591*
Stanton Chase Int'l. (R), MD, *198*
The Stanton Group, Inc. (C), IL, *591*
Sterling Int'l. Management Recruitment, Ltd. Inc. (C), NC, *592*
Stevens Assoc. (C), MA, *593*
Stewart/Laurence Assoc., Inc. (R), NJ, *201*
The Stonebridge Group (C), PA, *594*
Strategic Alliance Network, Ltd. (C), OH, *595*
Strategic Alternatives (R), CA, *202*
Strategic Assoc., Inc. (C), TX, *595*
Strategic Executives, Inc. (R), CT, *202*
Strategic Search Corp. (R), IL, *202*
Straube Associates (R), MA, *203*
Success Seekers Connection (C), FL, *596*
Survival Systems Staffing, Inc. (C), CA, *597*
Swartz & Assoc., Inc. (R), AZ, *204*
System 1 Search (C), CA, *598*
Systems Personnel, Inc. (C), NY, *598*
Tactical Alternatives (R), CA, *205*
Martin Stevens Tamaren & Assoc., Inc. (R), CA, *206*
Tate Consulting, Inc. (R), FL, *207*
M. L. Tawney & Assoc. (C), TX, *600*
Taylor Winfield (R), TX, *207*
Tech Connector Group (C), CA, *601*
Tech Consulting (C), FL, *601*
Tech Search (C), CA, *601*
Tech-Net (C), TX, *601*
Technical Employment Consultants (C), PA, *602*
Technical Search Assoc. (C), OH, *602*
TechNix Inc. (C), ON, *602*
The Technology Group (R), IL, *208*
Technology Management Partners (R), CA, *208*
Technology Search Int'l. (C), CA, *603*
Tecmark Associates Inc. (C), NY, *604*
Telford, Adams & Alexander (R), CA, *208*
Thomson, Sponar & Adams, Inc. (C), WA, *606*
Tierney Assoc., Inc. (R), PA, *209*
Tirocchi, Wright, Inc. (R), CA, *209*
The Touchstone Group (C), MA, *607*
Tower Consultants, Ltd. (R), PA, *209*
Jay Tracey Assoc. Inc. (C), VT, *608*
Trainor/Frank & Assoc. Inc. (C), WI, *608*
Travis & Co., Inc. (R), MA, *210*
TriStaff Group (C), CA, *609*
TSS Consulting, Ltd. (C), AZ, *610*
The Thomas Tucker Co. (R), CA, *211*
UniQuest Int'l., Inc. (C), FL, *610*
Unisearch Search & Recruiting Inc. (C), CA, *611*
Vaughan & Co. (C), CA, *612*
Vento Assoc. (C), TN, *612*
Venture Resources, Inc. (R), CA, *213*
C. J. Vincent Assoc., LLC (C), MD, *612*
B. D. Wallace & Assoc. (C), MD, *614*
Warner & Assoc., Inc. (C), OH, *615*
R. J. Watkins & Co., Ltd. (R), CA, *216*
David Weinfeld Group (C), NC, *617*
Werbin Assoc. Executive Search, Inc. (C), NY, *618*
Whitehead & Assoc., Inc. (C), MO, *620*
Arch S. Whitehead Assoc. Inc. (ASWA) (R), NY, *219*
Wilkinson & Ives (R), CA, *221*
Wilson Personnel, Inc. (C), NC, *622*
Windsor International (R), GA, *222*
Winter, Wyman & Co. (C), MA, *623*
Jim Woodson & Assoc., Inc. (C), MS, *624*
World Search (C), OH, *625*
WTW Assoc., Inc. (R), NY, *225*
Yelverton Executive Search (R), CA, *226*
The Zammataro Company (R), OH, *226*
Zeiger Assoc. L.L.C. (C), CA, *627*

D.26 Consumer electronics

ACC Technical Services (C), OH, *233*
Adel-Lawrence Assoc., Inc. (C), NJ, *240*
Advancement, Inc. (C), IL, *241*
Affinity Executive Search (C), FL, *241*
Alexander & Co. (C), CA, *243*
Allstaff, Inc. (C), IL, *245*
Peter W. Ambler Co. (R), TX, *5*
American Heritage Group, Inc. (C), MI, *247*
Ames-O'Neill Assoc., Inc. (C), NY, *249*
Analog Solutions (C), NY, *249*
Anderson Industrial Assoc., Inc. (C), GA, *250*
ARJay & Assoc. (C), NC, *252*
Association for Sales Force Management (C), WA, *254*
Cami Austin & Assoc. (C), IL, *256*
Austin Group Int'l./Marlar Int'l. (R), TX, *9*
Austin Michaels, Ltd., Inc. (C), AZ, *256*
Allen Ballach Assoc. Inc. (R), ON, *10*
Ballantyne & Assoc. (R), CA, *10*
Barclay Consultants, Inc. (C), NJ, *259*
Bartholdi & Co., Inc. (R), CO, *12*
The Barton Group, Inc. (C), MI, *260*
Bast & Assoc., Inc. (C), CA, *261*
Battalia Winston Int'l./The Euram Consultants Group (R), NY, *13*
BayResearch Group, Inc. (R), IL, *14*
The Bennett Group, Inc. (R), IN, *16*
BGB Assoc., Inc. (C), IL, *266*
Bialla & Assoc. Inc. (R), CA, *17*
Bor-Maq Assoc. (C), TX, *269*
Bornholdt Shivas & Friends Executive Recruiters (C), NY, *270*
Bosland Gray Assoc. (R), NJ, *20*
Brei & Assoc., Inc. (C), IA, *272*
The Brentwood Group Ltd. (R), OR, *23*
Brentwood Int'l. (R), CA, *23*
Briant Assoc., Inc. (R), IL, *23*
Brierwood Group, Inc. (C), IN, *273*
Brooke Chase Assoc., Inc. (R), IL, *24*
The Buckley Group (C), FL, *276*
Canny, Bowen Inc. (R), NY, *27*
Canyon Consulting, Inc. (C), TX, *281*
Capstone Consulting, Inc. (R), IL, *29*
Career Alternatives Executive Search (C), MI, *281*
Carnegie Resources, Inc. (C), NC, *284*
Wayne S. Chamberlain & Assoc. (C), CA, *288*
Christian & Timbers, Inc. (R), OH, *34*
R. Christine Assoc. (C), PA, *290*
Christmas, McIvor & Assoc. Inc. (C), ON, *290*
P. G. Cook Assoc. (R), TN, *40*
Corporate Image Group (C), TN, *300*
Corporate Recruiters Ltd. (C), BC, *300*
Corporate Staffing Group, Inc. (C), PA, *301*
Crist Partners, Ltd. (R), IL, *43*
Cross Country Consultants, Inc. (C), MD, *304*
CV Associates (C), NY, *305*
Cyr Associates, Inc. (C), MA, *306*
Data-AxIS Corp. (C), FL, *307*
Robert W. Dingman Co., Inc. (R), CA, *52*
DiTech Resources (C), CT, *313*
Diversified Search, Inc. (R), PA, *52*
Dreier Consulting (C), NJ, *315*
Dunhill Professional Search of Miami (C), FL, *319*
Dunhill Executive Search of Los Angeles, Inc. (C), CA, *319*
C. A. Durakis Assoc., Inc. (R), MD, *55*
Dussick Management Assoc. (C), CT, *323*
Dynamic Synergy Corp. (R), CA, *56*
E.P. Int'l. (C), NY, *324*
E/Search Int'l. (C), CT, *325*
Effective Search, Inc. (R), IL, *57*
Epsen, Fuller & Assoc., LLC (R), NJ, *60*
Essential Solutions, Inc. (C), CA, *331*
Executive Business Solutions, Inc. (C), WA, *332*
Executive Career Search (C), VA, *332*
Executive Recruitment Services, Inc. (ERS, Inc.) (C), GA, *334*
Executive Search, Ltd. (C), OH, *336*
Executive Search of America, Inc. (C), OH, *336*
ExecutiveFit (C), NY, *337*
Fenwick Partners (R), MA, *66*
Fergason Assoc., Inc. (C), IL, *339*
Financialjobs.com (C), CA, *340*
Neil Fink Assoc. (R), CA, *66*
Finnegan & Assoc. (R), CA, *67*
First Search Inc. (C), IL, *341*
Fishel HR Assoc., Inc. (C), AZ, *341*
Fortune Personnel Consultants of Huntsville, Inc. (C), AL, *343*
Fortune Personnel Consultants of Colorado Springs (C), CO, *344*
F-O-R-T-U-N-E Personnel Consultants of Savannah, Inc. (C), GA, *345*
F-O-R-T-U-N-E Personnel Consultants of Manatee County (C), FL, *345*
F-O-R-T-U-N-E Personnel Consultants of Atlanta, Inc. (C), GA, *345*

INDUSTRIES

Fortune Personnel Consultants of Bloomfield, Inc. (C), MI, *346*
F-o-r-t-u-n-e of Owensboro, Inc. (C), KY, *346*
F-O-R-T-U-N-E Personnel Consultants of St. Louis-West County (C), MO, *347*
F-O-R-T-U-N-E Personnel Consultants of Rockland County, Inc. (C), NY, *348*
Fortune Personnel Consultants of Allentown, Inc. (C), PA, *348*
Fortune Personnel Consultants of Hilton Head (C), SC, *349*
Fortune Personnel Consultants of Chattanooga Inc. (C), TN, *349*
Fortune Personnel Consultants of Plano (C), TX, *350*
Fortune Personnel Consultants of San Antonio, Inc. (C), TX, *350*
F-O-R-T-U-N-E Personnel Consultants of the Tri-Cities, Inc. (C), TN, *350*
F-O-R-T-U-N-E Personnel Consultants of East Seattle (C), WA, *351*
Fortune Personnel Consultants of the Virginia Highlands (C), VA, *351*
Foster Partners (R), NY, *70*
Mel Frazer Consultant (C), CA, *352*
Furlong Search, Inc. (R), CA, *72*
Gabriele & Company (C), MA, *354*
Gaffney Management Consultants (R), IL, *73*
Gallin Associates, Inc. (C), FL, *354*
The Garms Group (R), IL, *74*
The Garret Group (R), NJ, *75*
Gilbert Tweed Assoc. Inc. (R), NY, *76*
Lawrence Glaser Assoc., Inc. (C), NJ, *357*
The Gobbell Co. (R), CA, *78*
Goodrich & Sherwood Assoc., Inc. (R), NY, *79*
Alexander Graham Assoc. (C), NJ, *361*
Growth Strategies, Inc. (R), FL, *83*
Hahn & Assoc., Inc. (C), OH, *365*
Handy HRM (R), NY, *86*
Heath/Norton Assoc., Inc. (R), NY, *89*
Heinze & Assoc. Inc. (R), MN, *91*
Heller Assoc., Ltd. (R), IL, *91*
Henson Partners (C), AZ, *376*
High Tech Staffing Group (C), OR, *377*
The Hindman Co. (R), KY, *94*
Hodge-Cronin & Assoc., Inc. (R), IL, *94*
Holland & Assoc., Inc. (R), MI, *94*
Horton Int'l. Inc. (R), NY, *96*
William C. Houze & Co. (R), CA, *96*
The Hudson Group (C), CT, *383*
Human Resources Personnel Agency (R), AR, *99*
InSearch (C), CO, *389*
The Inside Track (C), TX, *389*
Inter Regional Executive Search, Inc. (IRES, Inc.) (C), NJ, *391*
Jeffrey Allan Co., Inc. (C), CA, *398*
Allan Karson Assoc., Inc. (R), NJ, *110*
Jim Kay & Assoc. (C), IL, *404*
Kay Concepts, Inc. (C), FL, *404*
A.T. Kearney Executive Search (R), IL, *111*
Kelley & Keller, Inc. (C), FL, *405*
Key Employment (C), NJ, *405*
The Kleven Group, Inc. - Executive Search Division (R), MA, *116*
Korn/Ferry Int'l. (R), NY, *117*
Katherine R. Kraemer (R), CA, *120*
Kramer Executive Resources, Inc. (C), NY, *409*
Kremple Consulting Group (R), CA, *120*
John Kuhn & Assoc., Inc. (R), WI, *121*
Paul Kull & Co. (R), NJ, *121*
D. Kunkle & Assoc. (C), IL, *410*
The Landstone Group (C), NY, *412*
Lautz, Grotte, Engler & Swimley (R), CA, *126*
LCS, Inc. (C), TX, *414*
Ricci Lee Assoc., Inc. (C), CA, *415*
The Conrad Lee Co. Inc. (R), FL, *127*
The Levton Group Inc. (R), ON, *129*
Ginger Lindsey & Assoc., Inc. (C), TX, *418*
Lucas Group (C), NY, *421*
Lutz Associates (C), CT, *421*
Magnum Search (C), IL, *422*
Maiorino & Weston Assoc., Inc. (R), CT, *134*
The Mallard Group (C), IN, *423*
Management One Consultants (C), ON, *425*
Management Recruiters Tucson-Foothills, Inc. (C), AZ, *439*
Management Recruiters of Northern California (C), CA, *440*
Management Recruiters Inc. of Silicon Valley (C), CA, *441*
Management Recruiters of Winsted, Inc. (C), CT, *442*
Management Recruiters of Franktown (C), CO, *442*
Management Recruiters of Des Moines (C), IA, *449*
Management Recruiters of Medford, N.J. (C), NJ, *453*
Management Recruiters of Broome County, Inc. (C), NY, *454*
Management Recruiters of Woodbury Inc. (C), NY, *455*
Management Recruiters of Mt. Airy (C), NC, *456*
Management Recruiters of Kinston (C), NC, *456*
Management Recruiters of Easton, PA (C), PA, *458*
Management Recruiters of Puerto Rico (C), PR, *460*
Management Recruiters of Myrtle Beach, Inc. (C), SC, *460*
Management Recruiters of LBJ Park/Dallas (C), TX, *462*
Management Recruiters of Round Rock (C), TX, *463*
Management Recruiters of Lubbock (C), TX, *463*
Management Recruiters of Cheyenne (C), WY, *466*
Management Search of R.I. Inc. (R), RI, *135*
Markent Personnel, Inc. (C), WI, *470*
Maxecon Executive Search Consultants (R), FL, *138*
Mayhall Search Group, Inc. (C), IN, *473*
McCray, Shriver, Eckdahl & Assoc., Inc. (R), CA, *140*
McInturff & Assoc., Inc. (C), MA, *474*
Joseph J. McTaggart (C), CA, *476*
James Mead & Co. (R), CT, *142*
Mercedes & Co., Inc. (R), MA, *143*
Michaels & Moere (C), WI, *481*
Miller Denver (C), CO, *482*
Len Nelson & Assoc., Inc. (C), TX, *491*
New Directions, Inc. (C), IL, *492*
Nordeman Grimm, Inc. (R), NY, *152*
Norman Broadbent Int'l., Inc. (R), NY, *152*
North Coast Meridian (C), NY, *496*
Norton & Assoc. (C), IL, *496*
T. Page & Assoc. (C), TX, *502*
Pawlik/Dorman Partners (R), IL, *161*
Pearson & Assoc., Inc. (C), AZ, *506*
The Penn Partners, Inc. (R), PA, *162*
Phelps Personnel Assoc., Inc. (C), SC, *510*
Polytechnical Consultants, Inc. (C), IL, *514*
Norman Powers Assoc., Inc. (C), MA, *515*
George Preger & Associates Inc. (R), ON, *167*
Alan J. Price Assoc., Inc. (C), RI, *518*
Professional Engineering Technical Personnel Consultants (C), NC, *520*
Professional Personnel Services (C), IA, *520*
Professional Recruiting Consultants (C), FL, *521*
Professional Team Search, Inc. (R), AZ, *169*
PSD Group, Inc. (C), CA, *525*
PSP Agency (C), NY, *525*
Quality Search (C), IN, *526*
R2 Services, LLC (C), IL, *528*
Radosevic Assoc. (R), CA, *171*
Ray & Berndtson (R), TX, *171*
RCI Employment Solutions (C), FL, *531*
Recruit Xpress (C), TX, *531*
Recruiting Services Group, Inc. (C), TN, *532*
Redden-Shaffer Group (R), CA, *173*
Russell Reynolds Assoc., Inc. (R), NY, *176*
Rice Cohen Int'l. (R), PA, *178*
Terry Richards (C), OH, *536*
ROI Assoc. (R), NY, *180*
Romano McAvoy Assoc., Inc. (C), NY, *544*
Rooney Assoc., Inc. (R), IL, *181*
Ross Personnel Consultants, Inc. (C), CT, *545*
Rothrock Associates, Inc. (C), NC, *547*
W. A. Rutledge & Assoc. (R), CT, *183*
Sales Consultants of Silicon Valley (C), CA, *556*
Sanford Rose Assoc. - Santa Barbara (C), CA, *565*
Sanford Rose Assoc. - Akron (C), OH, *569*
Sanford Rose Assoc. - Salt Lake City (C), UT, *571*
Schick Professional Search, Inc. (C), OH, *572*
F. B. Schmidt Int'l. (R), CA, *185*
Schweichler Assoc., Inc. (R), CA, *186*
Search Assoc., Inc. (C), CA, *574*
The Search Network (C), CA, *576*
SearchCom, Inc. (R), TX, *187*
Select Services (C), IL, *578*
Shinn & Assoc. (R), CA, *189*
The Shotland Group (R), CA, *190*
Larry Siegel & Assoc. (R), WA, *191*

RitaSue Siegel Resources, Inc. (R), NY, *191*
Sill Technical Assoc., Inc. (C), PA, *581*
Smith & Assoc. (C), FL, *583*
Smith & Syberg, Inc. (R), IN, *193*
Southern Recruiters & Consultants, Inc. (C), SC, *587*
Southport Int'l. Assoc. Inc. (C), FL, *588*
SpencerStuart (R), NY, *196*
Spilman & Assoc. (R), TX, *197*
Stanton Chase Int'l. (R), MD, *198*
The Stanton Group, Inc. (C), IL, *591*
Sterling Int'l. Management Recruitment, Ltd. Inc. (C), NC, *592*
Strategic Alternatives (R), CA, *202*
Strategic Assoc., Inc. (C), TX, *595*
Tech Search (C), CA, *601*
Technical Search Assoc. (C), OH, *602*
Technology Management Partners (R), CA, *208*
Techstaff Inc. (C), WI, *603*
Tecmark Associates Inc. (C), NY, *604*
Teknon Employment Resources, Inc. (C), OH, *604*
Tierney Assoc., Inc. (R), PA, *209*
Tirocchi, Wright, Inc. (R), CA, *209*
The Touchstone Group (C), MA, *607*
Triumph Consulting, Inc. (R), IA, *210*
TSC Management Services Group, Inc. (C), IL, *610*
The Thomas Tucker Co. (R), CA, *211*
Warner & Assoc., Inc. (C), OH, *615*
Warren Executive Services (C), GA, *616*
Wasserman Assoc. Inc. (C), MD, *616*
Weinpel Search, Inc. (C), NJ, *617*
Wesley Brown & Bartle Co., Inc. (R), NY, *218*
Whitehead & Assoc., Inc. (C), MO, *620*
Arch S. Whitehead Assoc. Inc. (ASWA) (R), NY, *219*
Wilkinson & Ives (R), CA, *221*
N. Willner & Co., Inc. (R), NJ, *221*
Wills Consulting Assoc. Inc. (R), CT, *221*
The Windham Group (R), OH, *222*
Jim Woodson & Assoc., Inc. (C), MS, *624*
Zeiger Assoc. L.L.C. (C), CA, *627*

D.27 Test & measurement equipment

ACCESS Technology (C), CA, *234*
Adel-Lawrence Assoc., Inc. (C), NJ, *240*
The Advisory Group, Inc. (R), CA, *2*
Affinity Executive Search (C), FL, *241*
Alpha Executive Search (C), AL, *245*
Alpha Resources (C), IL, *246*
Ames-O'Neill Assoc., Inc. (C), NY, *249*
Andrews & Wald Group (C), FL, *250*
Angus Employment Ltd. (C), ON, *250*
Ansara, Bickford & Fiske (C), MA, *251*
Applied Search Assoc., Inc. (C), GA, *252*
Argus National, Inc. (R), CT, *6*
Aries Search Group (C), GA, *252*
Asheville Search & Consulting (C), NC, *253*
Ashton Computer Professionals, Inc. (C), BC, *253*
Association for Sales Force Management (C), WA, *254*
Atlanta Executive Partners, Inc. (R), MA, *8*
Cami Austin & Assoc. (C), IL, *256*
Austin Michaels, Ltd., Inc. (C), AZ, *256*
BallResources (C), MO, *258*
James Bangert & Assoc., Inc. (R), MN, *11*
Bartholdi & Co., Inc. (R), CO, *12*
Battalia Winston Int'l./The Euram Consultants Group (R), NY, *13*
Blair/Tech Recruiters, Inc. (C), NJ, *268*
J: Blakslee Int'l., Ltd. (R), CA, *18*
Blaney Executive Search (R), MA, *18*
Blanton & Co. (C), AL, *268*
Bower & Associates (C), TX, *271*
The Bradbury Management Group, Inc. (R), CA, *21*
Broadband Resource Group (C), CA, *274*
David S. Burt Assoc. (C), MT, *276*
Button Group (C), TX, *277*
Canyon Consulting, Inc. (C), TX, *281*
Career +Plus (C), NY, *281*
Career Marketing Assoc., Inc. (C), CO, *282*
Careers Plus (R), CA, *29*
Carnegie Resources, Inc. (C), NC, *284*
Case Executive Search (C), MI, *286*
The Chapman Group, Inc. (C), AZ, *289*
A. D. Check Assoc., Inc. (R), PA, *33*
R. Christine Assoc. (C), PA, *290*
Churchill & Affiliates, Inc. (R), PA, *35*
Ken Clark Int'l. (R), NJ, *36*
Corporate Staffing Group, Inc. (C), PA, *301*
Creative HR Solutions (C), GA, *303*
Timothy D. Crowe, Jr. (R), MA, *43*
Cumberland Group Inc. (C), IL, *304*
Frank Cuomo & Assoc., Inc. (C), NY, *305*
CV Associates (C), NY, *305*
D.A.L. Associates, Inc. (R), CT, *45*
Daggett & Kvistad (R), CA, *45*
Davis & Company (R), CA, *47*
DiTech Resources (C), CT, *313*
Diversified Search, Inc. (R), PA, *52*
Dreier Consulting (C), NJ, *315*
Dukas Assoc. (C), MA, *315*
The Duncan-O'Dell Group Inc. (C), TX, *316*
Dunhill Professional Search of San Jose (C), CA, *319*
Dunhill Personnel of St. Andrews (C), SC, *322*
E/Search Int'l. (C), CT, *325*
W. Robert Eissler & Assoc., Inc. (C), TX, *327*
Erwin Assoc. (R), IL, *60*
Essential Solutions, Inc. (C), CA, *331*
ExecuSource Consultants, Inc. (C), TX, *332*
Executive Business Solutions, Inc. (C), WA, *332*
Executive Career Search (C), VA, *332*
Executive Recruiters, Inc. (C), WI, *334*
Executive Search of America, Inc. (C), OH, *336*
Raymond L. Extract & Assoc. (R), CA, *64*
F.L.A.G. (C), OH, *338*
Fairfaxx Corp. (R), CT, *64*
Fenwick Partners (R), MA, *66*
Fergason Assoc., Inc. (C), IL, *339*
Fortune Personnel Consultants of Huntsville, Inc. (C), AL, *343*
F-O-R-T-U-N-E Personnel Consultants of Manatee County (C), FL, *345*
F-O-R-T-U-N-E Personnel Consultants of Troy, Inc. (C), MI, *347*
F-O-R-T-U-N-E Search Consultants (C), MO, *347*
Fortune Personnel Consultants of Allentown, Inc. (C), PA, *348*
Fortune Personnel Consultants of San Antonio, Inc. (C), TX, *350*
F-O-R-T-U-N-E Personnel Consultants of the Tri-Cities, Inc. (C), TN, *350*
Foster Partners (R), NY, *70*
Franklin Int'l. Search, Inc. (C), MA, *352*
KS Frary & Assoc. (R), MA, *71*
Mel Frazer Consultant (C), CA, *352*
Furlong Search, Inc. (R), CA, *72*
Gabriele & Company (C), MA, *354*
Dianne Gauger & Assoc. (C), CA, *355*
Gilbert Tweed Assoc. Inc. (R), NY, *76*
Michael R. Guerin Co. (C), CA, *364*
The Guild Corp. (C), VA, *364*
Hall Kinion (C), CA, *366*
High Tech Staffing Group (C), OR, *377*
Hobson Assoc. (C), CT, *379*
Hodge-Cronin & Assoc., Inc. (R), IL, *94*
Horton Int'l. Inc. (R), NY, *96*
Hutton Merrill & Assoc. (R), CA, *100*
The Icard Group, Inc. (C), MI, *387*
Impact Technical Staffing (C), OR, *387*
Independent Resource Systems (C), CA, *388*
Interactive Search Assoc. (C), PA, *391*
International Consulting Services, Inc. (C), IL, *392*
International Research Group (R), CA, *103*
J. B. Linde & Assoc. (C), MO, *395*
Jackley Search Consultants (C), MN, *396*
K. Jaeger & Assoc. (C), MA, *396*
JPM International (C), CA, *401*
Kanzer Assoc., Inc. (R), IL, *109*
A.T. Kearney Executive Search (R), IL, *111*
S. D. Kelly & Assoc., Inc. (R), MA, *112*
Raymond J. Klemmer & Assoc. (R), NY, *116*
The Kleven Group, Inc. - Executive Search Division (R), MA, *116*
Korn/Ferry Int'l. (R), NY, *117*
Kossuth & Assoc., Inc. (R), WA, *119*
Kressenberg Assoc. (C), TX, *409*
Paul Kull & Co. (R), NJ, *121*
L & L Assoc. (C), CA, *410*
Larsen Int'l., Inc. (R), TX, *125*
Larson Assoc. (R), CA, *125*
Leith & Assoc., Inc. (C), OH, *416*
Lineal Recruiting Services (C), CT, *418*
Lucas Group (C), NY, *421*
Management Recruiters Tucson-Foothills, Inc. (C), AZ, *439*
Management Recruiters Inc. of Silicon Valley (C), CA, *441*
Management Recruiters of Colchester (C), CT, *442*
Management Recruiters of Chicago-North Shore (C), IL, *447*

Management Recruiters of Danville (C), KY, *449*
Management Recruiters of Livonia (C), MI, *451*
Management Recruiters - Flint (C), MI, *451*
Management Recruiters of Bay Head (C), NJ, *453*
Management Recruiters of Morris County, NJ (C), NJ, *453*
Management Recruiters of Kinston (C), NC, *456*
Management Recruiters of Valley Forge (C), PA, *459*
Management Recruiters of LBJ Park/Dallas (C), TX, *462*
Management Solutions, Inc. (C), CA, *468*
The Marathon Group (C), FL, *469*
Marketing & Sales Resources, Inc. (C), FL, *470*
Marketing Resources (C), MA, *470*
George R. Martin (R), PA, *137*
The Martwick Group, Inc. (C), OR, *472*
Marvel Consultants, Inc. (C), OH, *472*
Dan P. McLean Assoc., Inc. (C), ON, *475*
Medical Executive Search Assoc., Inc. (C), AZ, *477*
J. M. Meredith & Assoc. Inc. (C), CA, *479*
Miller Denver (C), CO, *482*
Mordue, Allen, Roberts, Bonney Ltd. (C), WA, *485*
Morgan & Assoc. (C), MA, *485*
The Morgan/Geoffries Group (C), CA, *485*
National Metal Services Corp. (C), IN, *489*
Nationwide Personnel Recruiting & Consulting, Inc. (C), OR, *490*
New Directions, Inc. (C), IL, *492*
New Venture Development, Inc. (C), CA, *492*
The Niemond Corp. (R), CA, *152*
The Normyle/Erstling Health Search Group (C), NJ, *494*
Norton & Assoc. (C), IL, *496*
O'Shea, Divine & Co., Inc. (R), CA, *154*
Omega Systems, LLC (C), VA, *498*
The Oxford Group (C), TX, *500*
The Partnership Group (R), NJ, *160*
Paules Associates (C), CA, *505*
J. R. Phillip & Assoc., Inc. (R), CA, *164*
Gregory D. Pickens (C), TX, *511*
Pierce & Assoc. (C), CA, *512*
Pinsker and Company, Inc. (R), CA, *164*
Polytechnical Consultants, Inc. (C), IL, *514*
Don V. Poole & Assoc., Inc. (C), CO, *514*
Norman Powers Assoc., Inc. (C), MA, *515*
George Preger & Associates Inc. (R), ON, *167*
Price & Assoc., Inc. (C), VA, *518*
Probe Technology (C), PA, *519*
Professional Engineering Technical Personnel Consultants (C), NC, *520*
Professional Recruiting Consultants (C), FL, *521*
Professional Recruiters Inc. (C), MN, *521*
PSD Group, Inc. (C), CA, *525*
PSP Agency (C), NY, *525*
R & K Associates, Inc. (C), AZ, *527*
R/K International Inc. (R), CT, *171*
Radosevic Assoc. (R), CA, *171*
Reese Assoc. (R), PA, *174*
Resources for Management (R), PA, *175*
The Revere Assoc., Inc. (R), OH, *176*
Russell Reynolds Assoc., Inc. (R), NY, *176*
Ritta Professional Search Inc. (C), NY, *538*
Louis Rudzinsky Assoc., Inc. (C), MA, *548*
R. L. Rystrom & Assoc., Inc. (C), MN, *549*
The Sager Co. (R), OH, *183*
Sales & Marketing Search, Inc. (C), MA, *551*
Sales Consultants of Silicon Valley (C), CA, *556*
Sales Consultants of Sacramento (C), CA, *556*
Sales Consultants of Baltimore (C), MD, *559*
Sales Consultants of Raleigh-Durham-RTP (C), NC, *561*
Sales Consultants of Morris County, Inc. (C), NJ, *561*
Sales Consultants of Orangeburg (C), SC, *562*
Sanford Rose Assoc. - Santa Ana (C), CA, *565*
Sanford Rose Assoc. - Santa Barbara (C), CA, *565*
Sanford Rose Assoc. - Canton (C), OH, *569*
Sanford Rose Assoc. - Austin (C), TX, *570*
Sanford Rose Assoc. - Doylestown (C), PA, *570*
Sarver & Carruth Assoc. (C), OK, *571*
Search Group (C), CA, *575*
Search Masters, USA (C), FL, *576*
Sharp Placement Professionals, Inc. (C), NY, *579*
Shinn & Assoc. (R), CA, *189*
Sill Technical Assoc., Inc. (C), PA, *581*
The Simmons Group (C), CA, *582*
Sink, Walker, Boltrus Int'l. (R), MA, *192*
The Smith Group, Inc. (C), NC, *584*
SpencerStuart (R), NY, *196*
Stevens Assoc. (C), MA, *593*
The Stevens Group (R), TX, *200*
Linford E. Stiles & Assoc., L.L.C. (R), NH, *201*
The Stonebridge Group (C), PA, *594*
Survival Systems Staffing, Inc. (C), CA, *597*
Synergy Solutions, Ltd. (C), WA, *597*
TBC, Inc. (C), KY, *600*
Teamsearch, Inc. (C), MI, *601*
Tech-Net (C), TX, *601*
Tecmark Associates Inc. (C), NY, *604*
Thomson, Sponar & Adams, Inc. (C), WA, *606*
Tierney Assoc., Inc. (R), PA, *209*
Tirocchi, Wright, Inc. (R), CA, *209*
The Touchstone Group (C), MA, *607*
Trainor/Frank & Assoc. Inc. (C), WI, *608*
Trambley the Recruiter (C), NM, *608*
Tschudin Inc. (R), NJ, *211*
TSS Consulting, Ltd. (C), AZ, *610*
Vento Assoc. (C), TN, *612*
Venture Resources, Inc. (R), CA, *213*
C. J. Vincent Assoc., LLC (C), MD, *612*
David Weinfeld Group (C), NC, *617*
West & Assoc. (C), IL, *618*
Whitehead & Assoc., Inc. (C), MO, *620*
The Whitney Group (C), GA, *620*
Susan L. Wonderling Recruiting (C), PA, *623*
Yelverton Executive Search (R), CA, *226*

D.28 Miscellaneous manufacturing industries

ACC Technical Services (C), OH, *233*
ADR Accounting Management Recruiters (C), ON, *240*
Advanced Recruitment, Inc. (C), TN, *240*
Affinity Executive Search (C), FL, *241*
Aggressive Corporation (C), IL, *242*
Allen/Associates (R), OH, *4*
Alliance Executive Search, Inc. (R), MA, *4*
Alpha Executive Search (C), AL, *245*
Alpha Search (C), FL, *246*
Altec/HRC (C), MI, *246*
AMD & Associates (C), GA, *247*
American Professional Search, Inc. (C), TN, *248*
Amherst Human Resource Group, Ltd. (C), IL, *249*
Anderson Network Group (C), OH, *250*
APA Employment Agency Inc. (C), OR, *251*
Charles P. Aquavella & Assoc. (C), TX, *252*
ARJay & Assoc. (C), NC, *252*
A. Artze Assoc.-Personnel Consultants (C), PR, *253*
Asheville Search & Consulting (C), NC, *253*
The Associates, HR Search Executives, Inc. (C), OK, *254*
Austin - Allen Co. (C), TN, *256*
Automation Technology Search (C), CA, *256*
BallResources (C), MO, *258*
Barber & Assoc. (C), KY, *259*
Barone Assoc. (C), NJ, *259*
Aldonna Barry Personnel & Management (C), ON, *260*
Battalia Winston Int'l./The Euram Consultants Group (R), NY, *13*
Behrens and Company (C), WA, *262*
J. P. Bencik Assoc. (C), MI, *263*
Jack Bertram, Executive Recruiter (C), PA, *265*
D. R. Blood & Assoc. (R), AZ, *18*
Bor-Maq Assoc. (C), TX, *269*
Borchert Assoc. (C), TX, *269*
Bosland Gray Assoc. (R), NJ, *20*
Boyden (R), NY, *20*
The Brand Co., Inc. (R), FL, *22*
Brandywine Management Group (R), MD, *22*
Bright Search/Professional Staffing (C), MN, *274*
Broadband Resource Group (C), CA, *274*
Broward-Dobbs, Inc. (C), GA, *274*
Brownstone Sales & Marketing Group, Inc. (C), NY, *275*
Brush Creek Partners (R), MO, *24*
C/R Associates (C), NY, *278*
Cahill Assoc. (C), CT, *279*
The Cambridge Group Ltd. (C), CT, *280*
Campa & Assoc. (R), ON, *27*

Canyon Consulting, Inc. (C), TX, *281*
Capstone Consulting, Inc. (R), IL, *29*
Career Alternatives Executive Search (C), MI, *281*
Career Specialists, Inc. (R), WA, *29*
Carion Resource Group Inc. (C), ON, *284*
Case Executive Search (C), MI, *286*
Cemco, Ltd. (C), IL, *286*
Joseph Chandler & Assoc., Inc. (R), IL, *33*
A. D. Check Assoc., Inc. (R), PA, *33*
R. Christine Assoc. (C), PA, *290*
Toby Clark Assoc. Inc. (C), NY, *292*
The Clayton Edward Group (C), MI, *292*
CMC Search Consultants (C), IL, *293*
CMS, Inc. (C), NH, *293*
Coleman Lew & Assoc., Inc. (R), NC, *37*
Colt Systems Professional Personnel Services (C), CA, *294*
Comprehensive Search (C), GA, *294*
The Comwell Company, Inc. (C), NJ, *296*
Cook Assoc.,® Inc. (R), IL, *40*
The Cooke Group (R), WI, *40*
Corporate Management Services (C), PA, *300*
Crowder & Company (R), MI, *43*
Timothy D. Crowe, Jr. (R), MA, *43*
Cumberland Group Inc. (C), IL, *304*
Daniel Marks Company (C), OH, *306*
Data Search Network, Inc. (C), FL, *307*
DBL Associates (C), CA, *309*
Desktop Staffing, Inc. (C), IL, *311*
DiMarchi Partners (R), CO, *51*
DiTech Resources (C), CT, *313*
Diversified Search, Inc. (R), PA, *52*
The Dorfman Group (C), AZ, *314*
J. H. Dugan & Assoc., Inc. (R), CA, *55*
The Duncan-O'Dell Group Inc. (C), TX, *316*
Dunhill of San Francisco, Inc. (C), CA, *319*
Dunhill Executive Search of Brown County (C), IN, *321*
Dunhill Personnel of St. Andrews (C), SC, *322*
Dunhill Professional Search, Inc. of McAllen (C), TX, *323*
Dunlap & Sullivan Assoc. (R), MI, *55*
E.P. Int'l. (C), NY, *324*
Earley Kielty & Assoc., Inc. (R), NY, *56*
EDI, Inc. (C), MD, *326*
EDP Staffing Solutions, Inc. (C), AR, *327*
EFL Int'l. (R), AZ, *57*
The Eldridge Group, Ltd. (C), IL, *327*
Elite Resources Group (R), OH, *58*
Yves Elkas Inc. (R), QE, *58*
The Elsworth Group (C), TX, *329*
Emerson & Co. (C), GA, *329*
Employ® (C), PA, *330*
Execu-Tech Search Inc. (C), MN, *332*
ExecuQuest, Inc. (R), MI, *61*
Executech (R), OH, *62*
Executive Connection (C), OH, *333*
Executive Resource Assoc. (C), VA, *334*
Raymond L. Extract & Assoc. (R), CA, *64*
Fabian Assoc. Inc. (C), NY, *338*
Financialjobs.com (C), CA, *340*
Howard Fischer Assoc. Int'l., Inc. (R), PA, *67*
James L. Fisk & Assoc. (C), MO, *342*
Flynn, Hannock, Inc. (R), CT, *69*
F-O-R-T-U-N-E Personnel Consultants of Palm Beach (C), FL, *345*
F-O-R-T-U-N-E Personnel Consultants (C), MI, *346*
Fortune Personnel Consultants of Bloomfield, Inc. (C), MI, *346*
F-O-R-T-U-N-E Personnel Consultants of St. Louis-West County (C), MO, *347*
F-O-R-T-U-N-E Personnel Consultants of Rockland County, Inc. (C), NY, *348*
F-O-R-T-U-N-E of West Portland (C), OR, *348*
F-O-R-T-U-N-E Personnel of Nashville (C), TN, *350*
F-O-R-T-U-N-E Personnel Consultants of Knoxville (C), TN, *350*
F-O-R-T-U-N-E Personnel Consultants of the Tri-Cities, Inc. (C), TN, *350*
Forum Personnel Inc. (C), NY, *351*
Foster Partners (R), NY, *70*
The Fourbes Group, Inc. (C), NJ, *351*
Foy, Schneid & Daniel, Inc. (R), NY, *71*
KS Frary & Assoc. (R), MA, *71*
Frye/Joure & Assoc., Inc. (C), TN, *353*
G. H. Enterprises (C), AZ, *354*
Gabriele & Company (C), MA, *354*
Gardner-Ross Assoc., Inc. (R), NY, *74*
Genesis Research (C), MO, *356*
GFI Professional Staffing Services (C), NH, *357*
Howard Gilmore & Assoc. (R), OH, *77*
Goodrich & Sherwood Assoc., Inc. (R), NY, *79*
Alexander Graham Assoc. (C), NJ, *361*
Robert Graham Assoc. (R), RI, *81*
Granger, Counts & Assoc. (R), OH, *81*
R. Green & Assoc., Inc. (C), OH, *362*
Greenfields Engineering Search (C), MO, *363*
Gregory, Kyle & Assoc. (C), NC, *363*
Grossberg & Assoc. (R), IL, *82*
Hahn & Assoc., Inc. (C), OH, *365*
Harbrowe, Inc. (C), NY, *368*
Harrison Moore Inc. (C), NE, *370*
Heath/Norton Assoc., Inc. (R), NY, *89*
The Heidrick Partners, Inc. (R), IL, *90*
Heinze & Assoc. Inc. (R), MN, *91*
Helfer Executive Consultants (R), TN, *91*
Hintz Associates (C), NY, *378*
J. G. Hood Assoc. (C), CT, *380*
Horizons Unlimited (C), CA, *381*
Howe & Assoc. (R), PA, *97*
The Hunter Group, Inc. (C), MI, *385*
Intercontinental Executive Group (C), PA, *391*
Interim Executive Recruiting (C), GA, *392*
Interim Management Resources Inc. (C), ON, *392*
International Executive Recruiters (C), OH, *393*
ISC of Atlanta, Inc. (C), GA, *394*
J. B. Linde & Assoc. (C), MO, *395*
The J. B. Search Group (C), CA, *395*
Ron Jackson & Assoc. (C), GA, *396*
Jaeger Int'l., Inc. (C), OH, *396*
John Jay & Co. (C), ME, *399*
Jonas, Walters & Assoc., Inc. (R), WI, *107*
Joseph Michaels (C), CA, *401*
Just Management Services Inc. (C), FL, *402*
Jim Kay & Assoc. (C), IL, *404*
A.T. Kearney Executive Search (R), IL, *111*
Kelley & Keller, Inc. (C), FL, *405*
Kelly Associates (R), PA, *112*
Kent & Assoc. (R), OH, *113*
Blair Kershaw Assoc., Inc. (C), PA, *405*
Daniel J. Kerstein, Consultant to Management (R), CO, *114*
Kip Williams, Inc. (R), NY, *115*
Korn/Ferry Int'l. (R), NY, *117*
Kressenberg Assoc. (C), TX, *409*
Lancaster Assoc., Inc. (C), NJ, *411*
Landon Morgan (C), ON, *412*
Lange & Assoc., Inc. (C), IN, *412*
Robert Larned Assoc., Inc. (C), VA, *413*
Jack B. Larsen & Assoc., Inc. (C), PA, *413*
Larson Assoc. (R), CA, *125*
Lascelle & Assoc. Inc. (C), ON, *413*
Lawrence-Balakonis & Assoc., Inc. (C), GA, *414*
The Lear Group, Inc. (R), OH, *127*
Leslie Kavanagh Assoc., Inc. (C), NY, *416*
Lineal Recruiting Services (C), CT, *418*
Locus Inc. (C), WV, *419*
M/J/A Partners (R), IL, *133*
The Macdonald Group, Inc. (R), NJ, *133*
The Madison Group (R), NY, *133*
Management Recruiters of Decatur, LLC (C), AL, *438*
Management Recruiters of Birmingham-South, Inc. (C), AL, *438*
Management Recruiters of Mobile Co., Inc. (C), AL, *438*
Management Recruiters of Tucson (C), AZ, *439*
Management Recruiters of Clovis (C), CA, *440*
Management Recruiters of Pleasanton (C), CA, *441*
Management Recruiters of Middlesex (C), CT, *442*
Management Recruiters of Vero Beach (C), FL, *445*
Management Recruiters of Springfield, Inc. (C), IL, *447*
Management Recruiters of Indianapolis (C), IN, *448*
Management Recruiters of Spencer (C), IA, *448*
Management Recruiters of Noblesville, Inc. (C), IN, *448*
Management Recruiters of Fairfield (C), IA, *449*
Management Recruiters of Siouxland (C), IA, *449*
Management Recruiters of Monroe, Inc. (C), LA, *450*
Management Recruiters of Livonia (C), MI, *451*
Management Recruiters of Dearborn, Inc. (C), MI, *451*
Management Recruiters of Muskegon (C), MI, *451*
Management Recruiters - Flint (C), MI, *451*
Management Recruiters of Chanhassen (C), MN, *452*

INDUSTRIES

Management Recruiters of North Warren Inc. (C), NJ, *453*
Management Recruiters of Reno (C), NV, *453*
Management Recruiters of Broome County, Inc. (C), NY, *454*
Management Recruiters of Mt. Airy (C), NC, *456*
Management Recruiters of Raleigh (C), NC, *456*
Management Recruiters of Wilmington (C), NC, *457*
Management Recruiters of Dayton, Inc. (C), OH, *457*
Management Recruiters of Easton, PA (C), PA, *458*
Management Recruiters of Northwest Ohio, Inc. (C), OH, *458*
Management Recruiters of Valley Forge (C), PA, *459*
Management Recruiters of Myrtle Beach, Inc. (C), SC, *460*
Management Recruiters of Chattanooga-Brainerd, Inc. (C), TN, *461*
Management Recruiters of Arlington (C), TX, *462*
Management Recruiters Dallas North (MRDN) (C), TX, *462*
Management Recruiters of Round Rock (C), TX, *463*
Management Recruiters of Ogden (C), UT, *464*
Management Recruiters of Loudoun County South (C), VA, *465*
Management Recruiters of Appleton (C), WI, *465*
Management Recruiters of Madison, Inc. (C), WI, *466*
Management Recruiters of Janesville, Inc. (C), WI, *466*
Management Recruiters of Milwaukee-North (C), WI, *466*
MARBL Consultants, Inc. (C), WI, *469*
Marketing & Sales Resources, Inc. (C), FL, *470*
The Maroon Group (R), CT, *136*
Marsar & Co., Inc. (C), FL, *471*
George R. Martin (R), PA, *137*
Maschal/Connors Inc. (R), NJ, *137*
McInturff & Assoc., Inc. (C), MA, *474*
McManners Assoc., Inc. (R), CA, *142*
Walter Meyer & Assoc. (R), NY, *144*
MGA Executive Search (C), FL, *480*
Michael Assoc. (R), IL, *144*
Michaels & Moere (C), WI, *481*
Lou Michaels Assoc., Inc. (C), MI, *481*
MJF Assoc. (C), CT, *483*
Montgomery, Thomason & Assoc. (C), ON, *484*
Morgan & Assoc. (C), MA, *485*
The Morgan/Geoffries Group (C), CA, *485*
Morris & Berger (R), CA, *147*
Multisearch Recruiters (C), CA, *487*
R. F. Mulvaney & Assoc., Inc. (R), MO, *149*
Nagler, Robins & Poe, Inc. (R), MA, *150*
NaTek Corp. (C), NY, *488*
Nationwide Personnel Recruiting & Consulting, Inc. (C), OR, *490*
Nichols & Company (R), CO, *151*
P. J. Nicholson & Assoc. (C), IL, *493*
Noll Human Resource Services (C), NE, *494*
Nordeman Grimm, Inc. (R), NY, *152*
Norrell Financial Staffing (C), GA, *495*
NPF Assoc. Ltd. Inc. (R), FL, *153*
NYCOR Search, Inc. (C), MN, *497*
O'Brien & Bell (R), OH, *153*
O'Brien Consulting Services (R), MA, *153*
O'Keefe & Assoc., Inc. (R), CT, *154*
O'Rourke Companies, Inc. (R), TX, *154*
Odell & Assoc., Inc. (C), TX, *498*
The Odessa Group (R), CA, *155*
Omega Systems, LLC (C), VA, *498*
Orion Int'l. Consulting Group, Inc. (C), NC, *499*
Pacific Advisory Service, Inc. (C), IL, *501*
Packaging Personnel Co., Ltd. (C), WI, *501*
T. Page & Assoc. (C), TX, *502*
Pamenter, Pamenter, Brezer & Deganis Ltd. (R), ON, *159*
Parker, McFadden & Assoc. (C), GA, *503*
Michael W. Parres & Assoc. (R), MI, *159*
Paul S. Pelland, P.C. (R), SC, *161*
M. A. Pelle Assoc., Inc. (C), NY, *506*
PERC, Ltd. (C), AZ, *506*
Personnel, Inc. (C), AL, *508*
Personnel Incorporated (C), IA, *508*
Petro Staff Int'l. (C), AB, *509*
Phillips Resource Group (C), SC, *510*
Gregory D. Pickens (C), TX, *511*
Pinsker and Company, Inc. (R), CA, *164*
PKS Assoc., Inc. (C), RI, *513*
Plante & Moran, LLP (R), MI, *165*
Polytechnical Consultants, Inc. (C), IL, *514*
Don V. Poole & Assoc., Inc. (C), CO, *514*
Jack Porter Assoc., Inc. (C), WA, *514*
P. G. Prager Search Assoc., Ltd. (C), NY, *515*
Premier Recruiting Group (C), MI, *516*
Professional Engineering Technical Personnel Consultants (C), NC, *520*
Professional Personnel Services (C), IA, *520*
Professional Recruiters (C), UT, *521*
Professional Search Assoc. (C), CA, *522*
Quality Consulting Group, Inc. (C), WI, *526*
L. J. Quinn & Assoc., Inc. (R), CA, *170*
Railey & Assoc. (C), TX, *528*
Raymond Thomas & Assoc. (C), FL, *530*
RBW Assoc. Inc. (C), OR, *531*
Recruiting Assoc. of Amarillo (C), TX, *531*
Reese Assoc. (R), PA, *174*
Reid Ellis Assoc. Inc. (C), ON, *533*
Resources for Management (R), PA, *175*
Russell Reynolds Assoc., Inc. (R), NY, *176*
Terry Richards (C), OH, *536*
Riddle & McGrath LLC (R), GA, *178*
RML Assoc. (C), PA, *538*
R. A. Rodriguez & Assoc., Inc. (C), TX, *540*
The Rossi Search Group (C), PA, *545*
Roth Young Executive Recruiters (C), MN, *546*
Roth Young Seattle (C), WA, *546*
Rowland Mountain & Assoc. (C), GA, *547*
The Ryan Charles Group, Inc. (C), FL, *548*
Ryan, Miller & Assoc. (C), CA, *549*
S-H-S Int'l. of Cherry Hill (C), NJ, *549*
The Sager Co. (R), OH, *183*
Sales Consultants of Cherokee (C), GA, *558*
Sales Consultants of Farmington Hills (C), MI, *560*
Sales Consultants of Orangeburg (C), SC, *562*
Sales Consultants of Milwaukee (C), WI, *563*
Sales Consultants of Dallas (C), TX, *563*
Sales Management Resources (C), CA, *563*
Sanford Rose Assoc. - Santa Ana (C), CA, *565*
Sanford Rose Assoc. - Rockford (C), IL, *567*
Sanford Rose Assoc. - Doylestown (C), PA, *570*
Schall Executive Search Partners (R), MN, *185*
The Schatz Company (C), MO, *571*
Schick Professional Search, Inc. (C), OH, *572*
Scott Sibley Assoc. (C), NY, *573*
Scott-Thaler Assoc. Agency, Inc. (C), CA, *573*
Search Group Inc. (R), AB, *186*
Search Northwest Assoc. (C), OR, *576*
Search Plus Int'l.-Ohio (C), OH, *576*
Search South, Inc. (C), AL, *576*
Seiden Krieger Assoc., Inc. (R), NY, *188*
Select Services (C), IL, *578*
Selective Management Services, Inc. (C), FL, *578*
Selective Recruiting Assoc., Inc. (C), MI, *578*
Selective Search Associates (C), OH, *578*
Selig Executive Search (C), NH, *579*
The Shotland Group (R), CA, *190*
Larry Siegel & Assoc. (R), WA, *191*
D. J. Simpson Assoc. Inc. (R), ON, *191*
Sink, Walker, Boltrus Int'l. (R), MA, *192*
J. L. Small Assoc. (C), AL, *583*
James F. Smith & Assoc. (C), GA, *583*
The Smith Group, Inc. (C), NC, *584*
Robert Sollman & Assoc. (C), FL, *587*
Southern Research Services (R), FL, *195*
SpencerStuart (R), NY, *196*
Stanton Chase Int'l. (R), MD, *198*
The Stelton Group, Inc. (C), NJ, *592*
Stewart Assoc. (C), PA, *593*
Linford E. Stiles & Assoc., L.L.C. (R), NH, *201*
Strategic Assoc., Inc. (C), TX, *595*
Stratin Assoc. (C), NJ, *596*
Straube Associates (R), MA, *203*
Summit Executive Search Consultants, Inc. (R), FL, *204*
Systems Search (C), IL, *599*
Tabb & Assoc. (R), OH, *205*
S. Tanner & Assoc. Inc. (C), ON, *599*
The TBI Group (R), PA, *207*
Teamsearch, Inc. (C), MI, *601*
Techstaff Inc. (C), WI, *603*
The TGA Company (C), TX, *606*
Tittemore Cowan Assoc. (C), AB, *607*
Top Gun Group, Inc. (C), NV, *607*
Tower Consultants, Ltd. (R), PA, *209*

Trambley the Recruiter (C), NM, *608*
The Truman Agency (C), CA, *610*
TSC Management Services Group, Inc. (C), IL, *610*
Vaughan & Co. (C), CA, *612*
Verkamp-Joyce Assoc., Inc. (R), IL, *213*
The Viscusi Group, Inc. (R), NY, *214*
The Wabash Group (C), IN, *613*
S. B. Webster & Associates (R), MA, *217*
West & Assoc. (C), IL, *618*
West Coast Recruiting (C), CA, *619*
White, Roberts & Stratton, Inc. (C), IL, *619*
The Whitney Group (C), GA, *620*
Daniel Wier & Assoc. (R), CA, *220*
Walter K. Wilkins & Co. (R), NJ, *221*
John R. Williams & Assoc., Inc. (C), NC, *621*
Williamsburg Group (C), NJ, *621*
N. Willner & Co., Inc. (R), NJ, *221*
Wilson Personnel, Inc. (C), NC, *622*
The Winchester Group (R), CA, *222*
Winthrop Partners, Inc. (R), NY, *222*
Susan L. Wonderling Recruiting (C), PA, *623*
Xagas & Assoc. (R), IL, *226*
The Zammataro Company (R), OH, *226*

E.00 Transportation

Agri-Tech Personnel, Inc. (C), MO, *242*
Ahrensdorf & Assoc. (R), PA, *2*
ALW Research Int'l. (R), NJ, *4*
American Logistics Consultants, Inc. (C), IL, *247*
American Services Group (C), IL, *248*
Anderson Network Group (C), OH, *250*
Angel Group Int'l. (C), KY, *250*
Angus Employment Ltd. (C), ON, *250*
APA Employment Agency Inc. (C), OR, *251*
A. M. Auster Associates (R), FL, *9*
Austin-McGregor Int'l. (R), TX, *9*
Avondale Search Int'l., Inc. (R), FL, *9*
The Barton Group, Inc. (C), MI, *260*
Bason Associates (R), OH, *13*
Martin H. Bauman Assoc., Inc. (R), NY, *13*
Blake/Hansen Ltd. (R), FL, *18*
Boettcher Assoc. (R), WI, *19*
Bowie & Associates, Inc. (C), MD, *271*
Boyden (R), NY, *20*
The Bren Group (C), AZ, *273*
Bernard E. Brooks & Assoc., Inc. (R), SC, *24*
Business Partners, Inc. (C), FL, *277*
C.P.S., Inc. (C), IL, *278*
Canadian Career Partners (R), AB, *27*
Canny, Bowen Inc. (R), NY, *27*
Career Advisors, Inc. (C), FL, *281*
Carpenter, Shackleton & Company (R), IL, *30*
Cary & Assoc. (R), FL, *31*
CFR Executive Search, Inc. (C), IL, *288*
Christmas, McIvor & Assoc. Inc. (C), ON, *290*
The Clayton Edward Group (C), MI, *292*
Coe & Co. Int'l. Inc./EMA Partners Int'l. (R), AB, *37*
Coleman Lew & Assoc., Inc. (R), NC, *37*
Computer Int'l. Consultants, Inc. (C), FL, *295*
Consolidated Management Services (C), ON, *296*
Construction Search Specialists, Inc. (C), WI, *297*
Consulting Rhonda (C), ON, *297*
Continental Search & Outplacement, Inc. (C), MD, *298*
Corporate Plus, Ltd. (C), GA, *300*
Corporate Search, Inc. (C), NY, *301*
Craig Affiliates, Inc. (C), TX, *302*
Davis & Company (R), CA, *47*
Dinte Resources, Inc. (R), VA, *52*
Diversified Search, Inc. (R), PA, *52*
Dixie Search Assoc. (C), GA, *313*
Doherty Int'l., Inc. (R), IL, *53*
The Doty Group (C), TX, *314*
Dunhill Staffing Systems, Inc. (C), NY, *316*
Dunhill Personnel of Boulder (C), CO, *319*
Dunhill Search of Arlington (C), TX, *322*
G. L. Dykstra Assoc., Inc. (C), MI, *323*
Eden & Assoc., Inc. (C), PA, *326*
Elite Resources Group (R), OH, *58*
Yves Elkas Inc. (R), QE, *58*
Gene Ellefson & Assoc. Inc. (C), MI, *328*
Ellis Career Consultants (C), NJ, *328*
Emerson & Co. (C), GA, *329*
ESS (Executive Search Services) (R), CA, *61*
Evans Transportation Search (C), ON, *331*
ExecuSource Assoc., Inc. (C), GA, *332*
Executive Placement Consultants (C), IL, *333*
The Executive Tree (R), FL, *64*
EXETER 2100 (C), NH, *337*
Finney-Taylor Personnel & Management Consultants Ltd. (C), AB, *341*
Focus Executive Search (C), MN, *343*
Ford & Ford (C), MA, *343*
F-O-R-T-U-N-E Personnel Consultants of Tampa (C), FL, *344*
Fortune Personnel Consultants of Greensboro, NC, Inc. (C), NC, *348*
Fortune Personnel Consultants of Chattanooga Inc. (C), TN, *349*
Foster Partners (R), NY, *70*
Genesis Personnel Service, Inc. (C), OH, *356*
Gilbert & Van Campen Int'l. (R), NY, *76*
Gilbert Tweed Assoc. Inc. (R), NY, *76*
Global 1000 Int'l. Services (C), CA, *358*
The GlobalSearch Group (C), TX, *359*
F. Gloss Int'l. (R), VA, *78*
The Gobbell Co. (R), CA, *78*
Fred J. Goldsmith Assoc. (R), CA, *79*
Grant-Franks & Assoc. (C), NJ, *361*
Griffith & Werner, Inc. (R), FL, *82*
Halbrecht & Co. (C), VA, *365*
Michael J. Hall & Co. (R), WA, *85*
The Hanna Group (C), OH, *368*
Harbrowe, Inc. (C), NY, *368*
Hardage Group (C), TN, *369*
William E. Hay & Co. (R), IL, *88*
Heller Kil Assoc., Inc. (C), FL, *375*
The Hensge Co. (R), IL, *91*
Herbeck Kline & Assoc. (R), IL, *92*
Hergenrather & Co. (R), WA, *92*
Herring & Assoc. (C), AR, *376*
The Hindman Group, Inc. (C), CA, *378*
Hire Authority, Inc. (C), MI, *378*
Holland Rusk & Assoc. (R), IL, *95*
Holloway Schulz & Partners (C), BC, *380*
Houser, Martin, Morris (C), WA, *381*
HRNI (C), MI, *383*
Hughes & Wilden Assoc. (C), PA, *383*
The Human Resource Department Ltd. (R), OH, *98*
Human Resource Technologies, Inc. (R), IL, *99*
The Hunt Group, Inc. (R), NC, *99*
The Hunter Group (C), NC, *385*
W. Hutt Management Resources Ltd. (R), ON, *100*
Hyman & Assoc. (C), TX, *386*
Infovia (C), CA, *388*
Ingram & Aydelotte, Inc. (R), NY, *101*
International Management Development Corp. (C), NY, *393*
Isaacson, Miller (R), MA, *104*
R. I. James, Inc. (C), NY, *397*
L. J. Johnson & Co. (R), MI, *106*
Johnson Assoc., Inc. (C), IL, *399*
JRL Executive Recruiters (C), MO, *401*
Kabana Corp. (C), MI, *402*
A.T. Kearney Executive Search (R), IL, *111*
Kelly Associates (R), PA, *112*
Kenzer Corp. (R), NY, *113*
The Kingsley Group (R), CA, *114*
Korn/Ferry Int'l. (R), NY, *117*
Kreutz Consulting Group, Inc. (R), IL, *121*
The LaBorde Group (C), CA, *411*
Lange & Assoc., Inc. (C), IN, *412*
Lanken-Kimball-Therrell & Assoc. (C), GA, *412*
Lascelle & Assoc. Inc. (C), ON, *413*
Lawrence James Assoc. of Florida, Inc. (C), FL, *414*
The Conrad Lee Co. Inc. (R), FL, *127*
V. J. Lehman & Assoc., Inc. (R), CO, *127*
Leith & Assoc., Inc. (C), OH, *416*
AG Lennox & Assoc. (R), AB, *128*
J. E. Lessner Assoc., Inc. (R), MI, *128*
Alan Levine Assoc. (R), MA, *129*
Lewis Companies Inc. (R), ON, *129*
LifeWork, Inc. (C), TX, *418*
Logistics Management Resources, Inc. (R), NY, *131*
London Executive Consultants Inc. (C), ON, *420*
Management Recruiters of Sedona (C), AZ, *438*
Management Recruiters of Berkeley (C), CA, *439*
Management Recruiters Dana Point (C), CA, *440*
Management Recruiters, Inland Empire Agency (C), CA, *441*
Management Recruiters, Inc. (C), FL, *443*
Management Recruiters of Atlanta (C), GA, *445*
Management Recruiters of Marietta, Inc. (C), GA, *446*
Management Recruiters of South Bend (C), IN, *448*

INDUSTRIES

Management Recruiters of Danville (C), KY, *449*
Management Recruiters of Lake Tahoe, NV (C), NV, *453*
Management Recruiters of Orange County, N.Y., Inc. (C), NJ, *453*
Management Recruiters of Winston-Salem (C), NC, *457*
Management Recruiters of Columbus (C), OH, *457*
Management Recruiters - North Canton, Inc. (C), OH, *458*
Management Recruiters of Cherry Hill (C), PA, *459*
Management Recruiters Dallas North (MRDN) (C), TX, *462*
Marsteller Wilcox Assoc. (C), IL, *471*
The Paul McDaniel Co. (C), TN, *474*
MESA, Inc. (R), CO, *143*
Oscar Montaño, Inc. (R), CA, *146*
Larry Moore & Assoc. (C), CA, *484*
Morgan Samuels Co. (R), CA, *147*
MPA Executive Search Inc. (R), QE, *148*
DDJ Myers, Ltd. (R), AZ, *150*
NMC & Kay Int'l. (R), CO, *152*
Norrell Financial Staffing (C), GA, *495*
NPF Assoc. Ltd. Inc. (R), FL, *153*
O'Callaghan Honey/Ray & Berndtson Inc. (R), AB, *153*
John R. O'Connor & Assoc. (C), IL, *497*
Oberlander & Co., Inc. (R), IL, *155*
OEI, Inc. (C), NJ, *498*
Olsen/Clark (R), WA, *156*
Jim Parham & Assoc., Inc. (R), FL, *159*
Largent Parks & Partners (C), TX, *503*
Michael W. Parres & Assoc. (R), MI, *159*
Pearson & Assoc., Inc. (C), AZ, *506*
PERC, Ltd. (C), AZ, *506*
The Perkins Group (R), NC, *162*
Barry Persky & Co., Inc. (R), CT, *163*
Personnel Management Group (C), MB, *508*
Personnel Tangent Inc. (C), QE, *509*
Phoenix Search (R), MX, *164*
DNPitchon Assoc. (R), NJ, *165*
Preferred Professional Recruiters (C), OH, *516*
Prestige Inc. (C), WI, *517*
PricewaterhouseCoopers Executive Search (R), MX, *168*
Prichard Kymen Inc. (R), AB, *168*
Procom (C), ON, *519*
Procurement Resources (C), MD, *520*
The Professional Sales Search Co., Inc. (C), WA, *522*
Railey & Assoc. (C), TX, *528*
Raines Int'l. Inc. (R), NY, *171*
Recruiting Services Group, Inc. (C), TN, *532*
Reinecke & Assoc. (C), NJ, *533*
Resource Inc. (R), MA, *175*
Russell Reynolds Assoc., Inc. (R), NY, *176*
Reynolds Consulting Int'l. (R), ON, *177*
RIC Corp. (R), FL, *177*
Riddle & McGrath LLC (R), GA, *178*
Robert Lowell Int'l. (R), TX, *179*
Norman Roberts & Assoc., Inc. (R), CA, *179*
Rollins & Assoc. (C), CA, *541*
Roth Young Executive Search (C), TX, *546*
Sales Consultants of Cherokee (C), GA, *558*
Sales Consultants of Cherry Hill (C), NJ, *560*
Sales Consultants Bridgewater, Inc. (C), NJ, *560*
Norm Sanders Assoc., Inc. (R), NJ, *184*
Sanford Rose Assoc. - Orland Park (C), IL, *567*
Sanford Rose Assoc. - Cedar Rapids (C), IA, *567*
Sanford Rose Assoc. - Rockville (C), MD, *567*
Schick Professional Search, Inc. (C), OH, *572*
Scott-Thaler Assoc. Agency, Inc. (C), CA, *573*
Search North America, Inc. (C), OR, *576*
SearchOne, Inc. (C), AR, *577*
Selective Recruiting Assoc., Inc. (C), MI, *578*
Sherwood Lehman Massucco, Inc. (R), CA, *189*
Shey-Harding Assoc. Inc. (C), CA, *580*
Shore Asociados Ejecutivos, S. A. de C.V. (R), MX, *190*
Shupack & Michaels Inc. (C), NY, *580*
RitaSue Siegel Resources, Inc. (R), NY, *191*
Smith & Syberg, Inc. (R), IN, *193*
Herman Smith Executive Initiatives Inc. (R), ON, *193*
Snelling Search - Transportation Division (C), AR, *585*
Souder & Assoc. (R), VA, *195*
SpencerStuart (R), NY, *196*
Springer Souder & Assoc. L.L.C. (R), IL, *198*
SR Wilson, Inc. (C), CA, *590*
Stanewick, Hart & Assoc., Inc. (C), FL, *591*
Star Search Consultants (C), ON, *591*
Stone Enterprises Ltd. (C), IL, *594*
Summit Group Int'l., Inc. (R), GA, *204*
TCM Enterprises (C), MD, *600*
Telford, Adams & Alexander (R), CA, *208*
Travel Executive Search (C), NY, *608*
Travel Personnel (C), OH, *609*
TSI Group/TSI Staffing Services (C), ON, *610*
Unlimited Staffing Solutions, Inc. (C), MI, *611*
Valentine & Assoc. (C), IL, *611*
Wallace Management Co. (R), TN, *215*
Linda Walter & Associes (C), QE, *615*
Wegner & Assoc. (C), WI, *617*
Henry Welker & Assoc. (C), MI, *618*
Western Management Consultants (R), BC, *218*
Wilcoxen, Blackwell, Niven & Assoc. (R), FL, *220*
The Wilkie Group Int'l. (R), ON, *220*
Winguth, Grant & Donahue (R), CA, *222*
Winston Search, Inc. (R), MD, *222*
World Search (C), OH, *625*
Your Advantage Staffing Consultants Inc. (C), ON, *626*

F.00 Wholesale trade

The 500 Granary Inc. (C), ON, *231*
Abécassis Conseil (R), QE, *1*
Accounting Personnel & Engineering Personnel Consultants (C), LA, *238*
Advice Personnel Inc. (C), NY, *241*
Allen Austin Lowe & Powers (R), TX, *3*
Allen/Associates (R), OH, *4*
Tom Allison Assoc. (C), NM, *245*
Alpha Search (C), FL, *246*
AM & G Certified Public Accountants & Consultants (R), IL, *4*
American Logistics Consultants, Inc. (C), IL, *247*
Andrews & Assoc. (C), NC, *250*
APA Search, Inc. (R), NY, *6*
David Aplin & Assoc. (C), AB, *251*
Attorney Search Global, Inc. (C), IL, *255*
Austin-McGregor Int'l. (R), TX, *9*
Barth Smith Company (R), IL, *12*
Bartl & Evins (C), NY, *260*
R. Gaines Baty Assoc., Inc. (R), TX, *13*
Martin H. Bauman Assoc., Inc. (R), NY, *13*
Best, Coleman & Co., Inc. (R), MA, *16*
David Blevins & Assoc. (C), WA, *268*
Bowman & Marshall, Inc. (C), KS, *271*
Boyden (R), NY, *20*
Jerold Braun & Assoc. (C), CA, *272*
BRW Search (C), MN, *275*
Business Solutions Worldwide, Inc. (C), NJ, *277*
Buzhardt Assoc. (R), MS, *25*
Canny, Bowen Inc. (R), NY, *27*
Cary & Assoc. (R), FL, *31*
Cella Assoc. (C), GA, *286*
CFR Executive Search, Inc. (C), IL, *288*
CMS, Inc. (C), NH, *293*
Coleman Lew & Assoc., Inc. (R), NC, *37*
Conasa de Mexico, S.C. (R), MX, *39*
Consultant Recruiters (C), WI, *297*
ContactBridge, Inc. (R), IL, *40*
The Cooke Group (R), WI, *40*
The Corporate Advisory Group (R), NJ, *41*
Craig Affiliates, Inc. (C), TX, *302*
Tony Curtis & Associates (C), ON, *305*
Cyr Associates, Inc. (C), MA, *306*
Thorndike Deland Assoc. LLC (R), NY, *48*
Direct Recruiters, Inc. (C), OH, *312*
Dixie Search Assoc. (C), GA, *313*
Dunhill Staffing Systems, Inc. (C), NY, *316*
Dunhill Search of Arlington (C), TX, *322*
Dunhill Professional Search of Winston-Salem (C), NC, *322*
Eden & Assoc., Inc. (C), PA, *326*
William J. Elam & Assoc. (R), NE, *58*
Ellis Career Consultants (C), NJ, *328*
Epsen, Fuller & Assoc., LLC (R), NJ, *60*
Erlanger Assoc. (R), CT, *60*
ExecuQuest, Inc. (R), MI, *61*
ExecuSource Consultants, Inc. (C), TX, *332*
Fairfield Int'l. Resources (R), NY, *65*
Robert M. Flanagan & Assoc., Ltd. (R), NY, *68*
Ford & Ford (C), MA, *343*
Fortuna Technologies Inc. (C), CA, *343*

Fortune Personnel Consultants of Greensboro, NC, Inc. (C), NC, *348*
Foster Partners (R), NY, *70*
GFI Professional Staffing Services (C), NH, *357*
Grant Cooper & Assoc., Inc. (R), MO, *81*
Groussman & Assoc., Inc. (R), TX, *82*
Growth Consultants of America (R), MI, *82*
GWS Partners (R), IL, *84*
Don Hall & Assoc. (C), TX, *366*
The Hensge Co. (R), IL, *91*
Highlander Search (C), NC, *378*
The Hindman Group, Inc. (C), CA, *378*
E. F. Humay Assoc. (C), PA, *384*
The Hunt Group, Inc. (R), NC, *99*
Impact Source, Inc. (C), FL, *387*
International Recruiting Services (C), FL, *393*
J.D.G. y Asociados, S.A. de C.V. (R), SO, *104*
R. I. James, Inc. (C), NY, *397*
Jaral Consultants, Inc. (C), NJ, *397*
Johnson Assoc., Inc. (C), IL, *399*
Johnson Brown Assoc., Inc. (C), IN, *400*
Robert Kaestner & Assoc. (C), FL, *403*
A.T. Kearney Executive Search (R), IL, *111*
David Warwick Kennedy & Assoc. (R), BC, *112*
Kenzer Corp. (R), NY, *113*
Kirby Assoc. (R), PA, *115*
Koltnow & Company (R), NY, *117*
Korn/Ferry Int'l. (R), NY, *117*
Lawrence James Assoc. of Florida, Inc. (C), FL, *414*
Alan Levine Assoc. (R), MA, *129*
The Levton Group Inc. (R), ON, *129*
Louis Search Group, Inc. (C), NJ, *420*
Management Recruiters of Little Rock (C), AR, *439*
Management Recruiters Peninsula (C), CA, *439*
Management Recruiters of South Bend (C), IN, *448*
Management Recruiters of Bay Head (C), NJ, *453*
Management Recruiters of Puerto Rico (C), PR, *460*
Management Recruiters of North Charleston (C), SC, *460*
Management Recruiters Dallas North (MRDN) (C), TX, *462*
Marsteller Wilcox Assoc. (C), IL, *471*
The Martin Group (R), CA, *137*
The Mazzitelli Group, Ltd. (R), MN, *139*
The Paul McDaniel Co. (C), TN, *474*
McIntyre Management Resources (C), ON, *474*
Michael Wayne Recruiters (C), IL, *480*
Herbert Mines Assoc., Inc. (R), NY, *145*
John B. Norris & Assoc., Inc. (C), MD, *495*
Open Concepts (C), CA, *499*
Pacific Search Group, Inc. (C), CA, *501*
Kirk Palmer & Assoc., Inc. (R), NY, *158*
Pasona Canada, Inc. (C), ON, *504*
Plummer & Assoc., Inc. (R), CT, *166*
Poirier, Hoevel & Co. (R), CA, *166*
P. G. Prager Search Assoc., Ltd. (C), NY, *515*
Prestige Inc. (C), WI, *517*
Professional Resources (C), OK, *522*
Terry Richards (C), OH, *536*
Riley Cole (C), CA, *537*
Robert William James & Assoc. (C), OR, *539*
Rollins & Assoc. (C), CA, *541*
Roth Young Personnel Services of Washington, DC (C), MD, *546*
Roth Young of Chicago (C), IL, *546*
Roth Young of Pittsburgh (C), PA, *546*
Roth Young Executive Recruiters (C), MN, *546*
Roth Young Executive Search (C), TX, *546*
R. S. Sadow Assoc. (C), NJ, *550*
Sales Builders, Inc. (R), VA, *183*
Sales Consultants of Indianapolis (C), IN, *558*
Sales Consultants of Farmington Hills (C), MI, *560*
Sales Search (C), ON, *564*
Sanford Rose Assoc. - Orland Park (C), IL, *567*
The Search America Group Inc. (C), OH, *573*
Search Consultants Int'l., Inc. (C), TX, *575*
Searchline Services, Inc. (C), OH, *577*
Peter Siegel & Co. (C), MA, *581*
Simpson Associates (C), NY, *582*
Snelling & Snelling, Inc. (C), FL, *585*
Snelling Search (C), AL, *585*
Stephen M. Sonis Assoc. (R), MA, *195*
SPC Symcox Personnel Consultants (C), TX, *588*
SpencerStuart (R), NY, *196*
Stewart/Greene & Co. of The Triad, Inc. (C), NC, *594*
Strategic Resources (C), WA, *595*
TNS Partners, Inc. (R), TX, *209*
Kelly Walker Assoc. (C), TX, *614*
Wallace Management Co. (R), TN, *215*
Linda Walter & Associes (C), QE, *615*
Weber Executive Search (R), NY, *216*
Western Management Assoc. (R), CA, *218*
Winguth, Grant & Donahue (R), CA, *222*
Woltz & Assoc., Inc. (R), IL, *224*
R. S. Wyatt Assoc., Inc. (R), TX, *225*
The Zarkin Group, Inc. (R), NY, *226*

G.00 Retail trade

Adirect Recruiting Corp. (C), ON, *240*
The Alice Groves Co., Inc. (C), CT, *244*
Allen Evans Assoc. (R), NY, *4*
Allen/Associates (R), OH, *4*
Tom Allison Assoc. (C), NM, *245*
Alpha Search (C), FL, *246*
AM & G Certified Public Accountants & Consultants (R), IL, *4*
Peter W. Ambler Co. (R), TX, *5*
American Logistics Consultants, Inc. (C), IL, *247*
Amherst Personnel Group Inc. (C), NY, *249*
Andrews & Assoc. (C), NC, *250*
Angel Group Int'l. (C), KY, *250*
The Angus Group, Ltd. (C), OH, *251*
APA Employment Agency Inc. (C), OR, *251*
APA Search, Inc. (R), NY, *6*
Charles P. Aquavella & Assoc. (C), TX, *252*
Ashford Management Group, Inc. (R), GA, *7*
Ashlar-Stone Management Consultants Inc. (R), ON, *8*
Austin, Hill & Assoc. (C), MD, *256*
Austin-McGregor Int'l. (R), TX, *9*
AutoPeople (C), VT, *257*
Barger & Sargeant, Inc. (R), NH, *11*
Barth Smith Company (R), IL, *12*
Bartl & Evins (C), NY, *260*
R. Gaines Baty Assoc., Inc. (R), TX, *13*
Beacon Int'l., Inc. (C), VA, *261*
The Beam Group (R), PA, *14*
Becker, Norton & Co. (R), PA, *14*
Neail Behringer Consultants Inc. (R), NY, *15*
Bender Executive Search Management Consulting (R), NY, *16*
Best, Coleman & Co., Inc. (R), MA, *16*
Birch & Associes (C), QE, *267*
David Blevins & Assoc. (C), WA, *268*
Bosland Gray Assoc. (R), NJ, *20*
Bowman & Marshall, Inc. (C), KS, *271*
Boyden (R), NY, *20*
BR & Assoc. (C), NJ, *271*
Jerold Braun & Assoc. (C), CA, *272*
BRW Search (C), MN, *275*
Business Solutions Worldwide, Inc. (C), NJ, *277*
Buzhardt Assoc. (R), MS, *25*
Campbell, Edgar Inc. (C), BC, *280*
Canny, Bowen Inc. (R), NY, *27*
Carlson & Czeswik (R), MN, *30*
Carpenter & Assoc. (C), TX, *284*
Cary & Assoc. (R), FL, *31*
Casey & Assoc., Inc. (C), TX, *286*
Cella Assoc. (C), GA, *286*
CFR Executive Search, Inc. (C), IL, *288*
Christopher and Long (C), MO, *291*
CMS, Inc. (C), NH, *293*
Coleman Lew & Assoc., Inc. (R), NC, *37*
Collins & Associates (C), MI, *294*
Colton Bernard Inc. (R), CA, *37*
Conasa de Mexico, S.C. (R), MX, *39*
ContactBridge, Inc. (R), IL, *40*
Continental Search & Outplacement, Inc. (C), MD, *298*
Cook Assoc.,® Inc. (R), IL, *40*
Cooper Management Assoc., Inc. (C), NJ, *298*
The Corporate Advisory Group (R), NJ, *41*
Cowell & Associates, Ltd. (R), IL, *42*
Craig Affiliates, Inc. (C), TX, *302*
Creative-Leadership, Inc. (R), CA, *42*
Culver Personnel Services (C), CA, *304*
Tony Curtis & Associates (C), ON, *305*
Alan Darling Consulting (R), VT, *46*
Data Bank Executive Search (R), OH, *46*
Data Search Network, Inc. (C), FL, *307*
Davies, Park (R), AB, *46*
Thorndike Deland Assoc. LLC (R), NY, *48*
J. Dinerstein & Co., Inc. (R), NY, *51*
Diversified Search, Inc. (R), PA, *52*
Dixie Search Assoc. (C), GA, *313*
Dominguez-Metz & Assoc. (R), CA, *53*
Donini Assoc. (R), VA, *54*

Downing & Downing, Inc. (C), OH, *314*
Drinkwater & Assoc. (R), MA, *54*
Dumont & Co. (C), BC, *316*
Dunhill Executive Search of Los Angeles, Inc. (C), CA, *319*
Dunhill Search of Arlington (C), TX, *322*
E T Search Inc. (C), CA, *324*
Eden & Assoc., Inc. (C), PA, *326*
Bruce Edwards & Associates, Inc. (R), NC, *56*
Eggers Consulting Co., Inc. (C), NE, *327*
Yves Elkas Inc. (R), QE, *58*
Ellis & Associates (C), HI, *328*
Ellis Career Consultants (C), NJ, *328*
Epsen, Fuller & Assoc., LLC (R), NJ, *60*
Executive Careers (R), CA, *62*
Executive Placement Services (C), GA, *333*
Executive Recruitment Specialists, Inc. (R), NC, *63*
Executive Referral Services, Inc. (C), IL, *334*
Executive Registry (C), QE, *334*
Executive Search Consultants International, Inc. (R), NY, *63*
Executive Search Int'l./Transearch (R), MA, *63*
Executive/Retail Placement Assoc. (C), MD, *337*
Fairfaxx Corp. (R), CT, *64*
Fairfield Int'l. Resources (R), NY, *65*
A. E. Feldman Assoc., Inc. (C), NY, *339*
Ferneborg & Assoc., Inc. (R), CA, *66*
Fisher-Todd Assoc. (C), NY, *341*
FitzGibbon & Assoc. (R), PA, *68*
Ford & Ford (C), MA, *343*
Fortune Personnel Consultants of Greensboro, NC, Inc. (C), NC, *348*
Foster Partners (R), NY, *70*
Foy, Schneid & Daniel, Inc. (R), NY, *71*
Franstaff Inc. (C), FL, *352*
Fresquez & Assoc. (C), CA, *352*
Gaines & Assoc. Int'l., Inc. (R), IL, *73*
J. Gernetzke & Assoc., Inc. (C), OH, *357*
The Glazin Group (R), BC, *77*
Global Research Partnership Inc. (R), NY, *78*
Grantham & Co., Inc. (R), NC, *81*
Ben Greco Assoc., Inc. (C), CA, *362*
Groussman & Assoc., Inc. (R), TX, *82*
Growth Consultants of America (R), MI, *82*
Wolf Gugler & Assoc. Ltd. (R), ON, *83*
Gundersen Partners, L.L.C. (R), NY, *83*
William Guy & Assoc., Inc. (R), CA, *84*
Habelmann & Assoc. (R), MI, *84*
Halbrecht Lieberman Assoc., Inc. (R), CT, *84*
Don Hall & Assoc. (C), TX, *366*
Harmeling & Associates (C), CA, *369*
Harper Associates (C), MI, *369*
Herbeck Kline & Assoc. (R), IL, *92*
Herring & Assoc. (C), AR, *376*
J. D. Hersey & Assoc. (C), OH, *376*
Highlander Search (C), NC, *378*
Hill & Assoc. (C), CA, *378*
Hill Allyn Assoc. (C), CA, *378*
Frank P. Hill (R), MX, *93*
E. A. Hughes & Co., Inc. (R), NY, *98*
Human Resource Solutions (R), TX, *98*
Hunt Ltd. (C), NJ, *385*
Huntress Real Estate Executive Search (R), MO, *100*
Hyman & Assoc. (C), TX, *386*
Infovia (C), CA, *388*
Interactive Search Network (R), CA, *102*
Interim Executive Recruiting (C), GA, *392*
International Recruiting Services (C), FL, *393*
Ives & Associates, Inc. (C), OH, *395*
J.B.A. Assoc. (R), WA, *104*
J.D.G. y Asociados, S.A. de C.V. (R), SO, *104*
Pendleton James Assoc., Inc. (R), NY, *105*
R. I. James, Inc. (C), NY, *397*
January Management Group (R), OH, *105*
Jaral Consultants, Inc. (C), NJ, *397*
Jeffrey Allan Co., Inc. (C), CA, *398*
Johnson & Company (R), CT, *107*
Johnson Assoc., Inc. (C), IL, *399*
Johnson Smith & Knisely (R), NY, *107*
Jordon & Jordon, Inc. (R), PA, *108*
Karel & Co. (R), CA, *109*
Martin Kartin & Co., Inc. (R), NY, *110*
A.T. Kearney Executive Search (R), IL, *111*
Kenzer Corp. (R), NY, *113*
Koltnow & Company (R), NY, *117*
Korn/Ferry Int'l. (R), NY, *117*
Michael Kosmetos & Assoc., Inc. (C), OH, *408*
Kramer Executive Resources, Inc. (C), NY, *409*
Evie Kreisler Assoc. Inc. (C), CA, *409*
Marvin Laba & Assoc. (R), CA, *122*
Lauer, Sbarbaro Assoc., EMA Partners Int'l. (R), IL, *126*
Madeleine Lav & Assoc. (C), CA, *413*
Lawrence James Assoc. of Florida, Inc. (C), FL, *414*
Leader Institute, Inc. (C), GA, *414*
Albert G. Lee Assoc. (C), RI, *415*
The Conrad Lee Co. Inc. (R), FL, *127*
Lemming/LeVan, Inc. (R), GA, *128*
Alan Levine Assoc. (R), MA, *129*
Michael Levine Search Consultants (R), NY, *129*
The Levton Group Inc. (R), ON, *129*
Logic Assoc., Inc. (C), NY, *419*
Management Recruiters of Grass Valley (C), CA, *440*
Management Recruiters of Laguna Hills (C), CA, *440*
Management Recruiters of St. Lucie County, Inc. (C), FL, *444*
Management Recruiters of Forsyth County (C), GA, *445*
Management Recruiters of Chicago West (C), IL, *447*
Management Recruiters of Chicago-North Shore (C), IL, *447*
Management Recruiters of Rockville (C), MD, *450*
Management Recruiters of Lake Tahoe, NV (C), NV, *453*
Management Recruiters of Cherry Hill (C), PA, *459*
Management Recruiters of Houston (C), TX, *462*
Management Recruiters Dallas North (MRDN) (C), TX, *462*
Marc-Allen Assoc., Inc. (C), FL, *469*
Paula Marks Inc. (R), NY, *136*
Marra Peters & Partners (R), NJ, *136*
Marsar & Co., Inc. (C), FL, *471*
The Martin Group (R), CA, *137*
The Mazzitelli Group, Ltd. (R), MN, *139*
McCormack & Farrow (R), CA, *140*
The Paul McDaniel Co. (C), TN, *474*
MESA International (C), CA, *480*
Millennium Search Group, Inc. (R), CA, *144*
Herbert Mines Assoc., Inc. (R), NY, *145*
The Moran Group (C), IL, *484*
Murphy Partners Int'l. (R), IL, *150*
N.A.P. Executive Services (Canada) Inc. (C), ON, *488*
National Executive (C), ON, *489*
Next Step Recruiting (C), CA, *493*
NMC & Kay Int'l. (R), CO, *152*
Noll Human Resource Services (C), NE, *494*
Nordeman Grimm, Inc. (R), NY, *152*
Norman Broadbent Int'l., Inc. (R), NY, *152*
John B. Norris & Assoc., Inc. (C), MD, *495*
NPF Assoc. Ltd. Inc. (R), FL, *153*
Nuessle, Kurdziel & Weiss, Inc. (R), PA, *153*
O'Brien and Roof (C), OH, *497*
O'Toole & Company, Inc. (R), IL, *154*
Ollinger Partners (R), MA, *156*
Organization Consulting Ltd. (R), ON, *157*
Pacific Search Group, Inc. (C), CA, *501*
T. Page & Assoc. (C), TX, *502*
Kirk Palmer & Assoc., Inc. (R), NY, *158*
Perry • Newton Assoc. (C), MD, *507*
Phoenix Search (R), MX, *164*
Plummer & Assoc., Inc. (R), CT, *166*
Poirier, Hoevel & Co. (R), CA, *166*
Bob Poline Assoc. Inc. (C), CA, *514*
Porter & Assoc., Inc. (C), FL, *514*
Robert Powers & Assoc. (C), CA, *515*
PRAXIS Partners (R), VA, *167*
Prestige Inc. (C), WI, *517*
Professional Resources (C), NY, *522*
Professional Resources (C), OK, *522*
Quantum EDP Recruiting Services (C), QE, *526*
Quetico Corp. (R), TX, *170*
R & L Assoc., Ltd. (R), NY, *170*
Rand-Curtis Resources (C), AZ, *529*
Recruiting Specialists (C), MA, *532*
Mary Rector & Assoc., Inc. (C), IL, *533*
Retail Connection, Inc. (C), NJ, *535*
Retail Executive Search (C), FL, *535*
The Retail Network (C), MA, *535*
Retail Recruiters (C), CT, *535*
Retail Recruiters/Spectrum Consultants, Inc. (C), PA, *535*
Russell Reynolds Assoc., Inc. (R), NY, *176*
RHI Consulting (C), VA, *536*
RIC Corp. (R), FL, *177*
The Richards Group (C), PA, *536*
Riley Cole (C), CA, *537*
Rojek Marketing Group, Inc. (R), OH, *181*
Roth Young of Chicago (C), IL, *546*
Roth Young Personnel Service of Detroit, Inc. (C), MI, *546*

Roth Young Executive Recruiters (C), MN, 546
Roth Young of Pittsburgh (C), PA, 546
Roth Young Executive Search (C), TX, 546
Rovner Gerner & Assoc. (R), CA, 182
Sales Consultants of Cincinnati (C), OH, 561
Salzmann Gay Assoc., Inc. (R), PA, 184
Norm Sanders Assoc., Inc. (R), NJ, 184
Sanford Rose Assoc. - Orland Park (C), IL, 567
Sanford Rose Assoc. - Louisville (C), KY, 567
Savalli & Assoc., Inc. (C), MI, 571
Schall Executive Search Partners (R), MN, 185
Scott-Thaler Assoc. Agency, Inc. (C), CA, 573
Search Advisors Int'l. Corp. (R), FL, 186
The Search America Group Inc. (C), OH, 573
Search America, Inc. (C), MA, 574
SearchCorp (C), FL, 577
Searchline Services, Inc. (C), OH, 577
Seitchik Corwin & Seitchik Inc. (R), CA, 188
Shepherd Bueschel & Provus, Inc. (R), IL, 189
E. L. Shore & Assoc. (R), ON, 190
John Sibbald Assoc., Inc. (R), MO, 191
Peter Siegel & Co. (C), MA, 581
D. J. Simpson Assoc. Inc. (R), ON, 191
Simpson Associates (C), NY, 582
Skott/Edwards Consultants (R), NY, 192
Sloan & Assoc., Inc. (C), VA, 583
Smith & Assoc. (C), CA, 583
James F. Smith & Assoc. (C), GA, 583
Smith & Sawyer, Inc. (R), NY, 193
Snelling Search (C), AL, 585
Stephen M. Sonis Assoc. (R), MA, 195
SPC Symcox Personnel Consultants (C), TX, 588
Spectra International LLC (C), AZ, 589
SpencerStuart (R), NY, 196
Squires Resources Inc. (C), ON, 590
Stanton Chase Int'l. (R), MD, 198
Steinfield & Assoc. (C), TX, 592
Sterling Int'l. (R), NJ, 200
Michael Stern Assoc., Inc./Euram (R), ON, 200
Strategic Resources (C), WA, 595
Swift & Assoc. (C), ME, 597
Target Search, Inc. (C), PA, 600
The TBI Group (R), PA, 207
Thorne, Brieger Assoc., Inc. (R), NY, 209
TPS Staffing Solutions (C), IN, 608
TTG/Sterling Services (C), CA, 610
Tully/Woodmansee Int'l. Inc. (R), FL, 212
Van Leeuwen Assoc. (R), CA, 213
Vlcek & Company, Inc. (R), CA, 214
Walker Group, Inc. (R), MN, 215
Linda Walter & Associes (C), QE, 615
West Coast Recruiting (C), CA, 619
Joel H. Wilensky Assoc., Inc. (C), MA, 620
The Wilkie Group Int'l. (R), ON, 220
Wilson & Assoc. Int'l. Inc. (C), FL, 622
The Windham Group (R), OH, 222
Winguth, Grant & Donahue (R), CA, 222
The Woodstone Consulting Company, Inc. (R), CO, 224
Working Relationships, Inc. (C), MN, 624
R. S. Wyatt Assoc., Inc. (R), TX, 225
Wyndham Mills Int'l., Inc. (R), GA, 225
Xavier Associates, Inc. (R), MA, 226
Zaccaria Int'l. (C), NJ, 627
The Zarkin Group, Inc. (R), NY, 226
Zwell Int'l. (R), IL, 228

H.00 Finance

A Permanent Success Employment Services (C), CA, 231
A-L Assoc., Inc. (R), NY, 1
A. D. & Assoc. Executive Search, Inc. (C), GA, 231
A.K.S. Assoc., Ltd. (R), MA, 1
A.L.S. Group (C), NJ, 232
Abacus Group LLC (C), NY, 232
Abbott Associates (R), CA, 1
Abécassis Conseil (R), QE, 1
Accent On Achievement, Inc. (C), MI, 233
Account Ability Now (C), MI, 234
Accountants Executive Search (C), CT, 234
Accountants On Call (C), FL, 237
Accounting Additions (C), CA, 238
Accounting Personnel & Engineering Personnel Consultants (C), LA, 238
ACSYS Resources, Inc. (C), DE, 238
Active Search & Placement Inc. (C), CA, 239
Adept Tech Recruiting, Inc. (C), NY, 240
Adler Management, Inc. (R), NJ, 2
Advantage Partners, Inc. (R), OH, 2
Advice Personnel Inc. (C), NY, 241
Advisors' Search Group, Inc. (C), NY, 241
The Advisory Group, Inc. (R), CA, 2
Affordable Executive Recruiters (C), CA, 241
Ahrensdorf & Assoc. (R), PA, 2
Alaska Executive Search, Inc. (C), AK, 243
Alexander Associates (R), NJ, 2
The Alexander Group (R), NJ, 3
The Alexander Group (R), TX, 3
Allard Associates (C), CA, 244
Allen & Assoc. (C), NV, 244
Frank E. Allen & Assoc. (C), NJ, 244
David Allen Assoc. (R), NJ, 3
Allen Evans Assoc. (R), NY, 4
Allen, Wayne & Co. LLC (C), WI, 245
Allen-Jeffers Assoc. (C), CA, 245
Allerton Heneghan & O'Neill (R), IL, 4
Alliance Executive Search, Inc. (R), MA, 4
Allman & Co., Inc. (C), NC, 245
Alpha Search (C), FL, 246
ALW Research Int'l. (R), NJ, 4
Ambridge Management Corp. (C), ON, 247
AmeriResource Group Inc. (C), OK, 248
Ames Assoc. Inc. (C), MD, 249
Amherst Human Resource Group, Ltd. (C), IL, 249
AMS Int'l. (R), VA, 5
Analytic Recruiting, Inc. (C), NY, 249
Anderson & Associates (R), NC, 5
Anderson & Schwab, Inc. (R), NY, 5
Andex Executive Search (C), CT, 250
The Andre Group, Inc. (R), PA, 6
Andrews & Assoc. (C), NC, 250
Angel Group Int'l. (C), KY, 250
The Angus Group, Ltd. (C), OH, 251
Anthony Michael & Co. (C), MA, 251
Argonaut Partners, LLC (R), CA, 6
Armitage Associates Ltd. (R), ON, 7
Aronow Assoc., Inc. (C), FL, 253
The Associates, HR Search Executives, Inc. (C), OK, 254
Atlantic Pacific Group (C), CA, 255
ATS Executive Recruitment (C), GA, 255
Attorney Search Global, Inc. (C), IL, 255
Aurora Tech Search (C), ON, 256
Austin Park Management Group Inc. (C), ON, 256
Avion International Technology Inc. (C), ON, 257
The Ayers Group, Inc. (R), NY, 9
Keith Bagg & Assoc., Inc. (C), ON, 257
Baker, Nelms & Montgomery (C), IL, 258
Baldwin & Assoc. (C), OH, 258
James Bangert & Assoc., Inc. (R), MN, 11
The Bankers Group (C), IL, 258
The Bankers Register (C), NY, 259
Bankers Search, L.L.C. (C), CT, 259
Barger & Sargeant, Inc. (R), NH, 11
J. W. Barleycorn, Renard & Assoc., Inc. (R), OH, 11
Barr Associates (C), NY, 260
Barrett Partners (C), IL, 260
Barrington Hart, Inc. (R), IL, 12
Nathan Barry Assoc., Inc. (R), MA, 12
Barth Smith Company (R), IL, 12
Bartholdi & Co., Inc. (R), CO, 12
Bartl & Evins (C), NY, 260
Barton Assoc., Inc. (R), TX, 12
Bason Associates (R), OH, 13
Battalia Winston Int'l./The Euram Consultants Group (R), NY, 13
Martin H. Bauman Assoc., Inc. (R), NY, 13
Beacon Int'l., Inc. (C), VA, 261
The Beam Group (R), PA, 14
Becker, Norton & Co. (R), PA, 14
Becker Project Resources, Inc. (C), OR, 262
Behavioral Science Assoc., Inc. (R), AZ, 15
Edward Bell Assoc. (C), CA, 263
Bell Oaks Co., Inc. (C), GA, 263
Bell Wishingrad Partners Inc. (R), NY, 15
Bender Executive Search Management Consulting (R), NY, 16
N. L. Benke & Assoc., Inc. (C), OH, 264
Bennett Search & Consulting Co. (R), FL, 16
Benson Associates (C), NY, 264
C. Berger And Company (R), IL, 16
Bergeris & Co., Inc. (C), NY, 265
Berkana Int'l., Inc. (C), WA, 265
Berkhemer/Clayton, Inc. (R), CA, 16
Bernhart Assoc. (C), MN, 265
BEST/World Assoc. Inc. (R), TX, 16
BFW, Inc. (C), GA, 266
BG & Assoc. (C), MD, 266
Bialecki Inc. (R), NY, 17
Birch & Associes (C), QE, 267
Blackhawk Advantage, Inc. (C), CA, 267
The Blackman Kallick Search Division (C), IL, 267
J: Blakslee Int'l., Ltd. (R), CA, 18
Blaney Executive Search (R), MA, 18

INDUSTRIES

Blau Mancino Schroeder (R), NJ, *18*
BLB Consulting (C), NY, *268*
The BMW Group, Inc. (C), NY, *268*
Boardroom Consultants/Kenny Kindler Tholke (R), NY, *19*
Bonell Ryan Inc. (R), NY, *19*
Bonifield Assoc. (C), NJ, *269*
Bonnell Assoc. Ltd. (R), CT, *19*
Bor-Maq Assoc. (C), TX, *269*
Bosch & Assoc., LLC (R), CT, *19*
Boulware & Assoc. Inc. (R), IL, *20*
Bowden & Co., Inc. (R), OH, *20*
BowdenGlobal, Ltd. (R), OH, *20*
BowersThomas (C), CA, *271*
Boyden (R), NY, *20*
Brandjes Assoc. (C), MD, *272*
Brandt Associates (C), PA, *272*
Branthover Assoc. (C), NY, *272*
Brault & Assoc., Ltd. (R), VA, *22*
Bredeson Executive Recruitment, LLC (R), TX, *22*
The Brentwood Group, Inc. (R), NJ, *22*
Brigade, Inc. (R), CA, *23*
Brindisi Search (R), MD, *23*
The Broadmoor Group, L.L.C. (R), TX, *23*
Brookman Associates (C), NY, *274*
J. B. Brown & Assoc., Inc. (C), OH, *275*
Brown Venture Assoc. (R), CA, *24*
Brush Creek Partners (R), MO, *24*
The Burgess Group-Corporate Recruiters Int'l., Inc. (R), NY, *25*
Joseph R. Burns & Assoc., Inc. (R), NJ, *25*
Business Solutions Worldwide, Inc. (C), NJ, *277*
Butterfass, Pepe & MacCallan Inc. (R), NJ, *25*
C and P Marketing, Ltd. (C), OK, *278*
C. M. Management Services, Inc. (R), KY, *26*
C. P. Consulting (R), PA, *26*
C. R. Assoc. (C), CA, *278*
C.P.S., Inc. (C), IL, *278*
C.T.E.W. Executive Personnel Services Inc. (C), BC, *278*
C/R Associates (C), NY, *278*
Cambridge Management Planning (R), ON, *27*
Canadian Career Partners (R), AB, *27*
Canny, Bowen Inc. (R), NY, *27*
The Cantor Concern, Inc. (R), NY, *28*
Capital Consulting & Research, Inc. (R), CT, *28*
Capital Consulting Group, Inc. (R), MD, *28*
Capital Markets Resources, Inc. (C), NC, *281*
Cardwell Enterprises Inc. (R), IL, *29*
Career Advisors, Inc. (C), FL, *281*
Career Consultants (R), IN, *29*
Career Consulting Group, Inc. (C), CT, *281*
Career Specialists, Inc. (R), WA, *29*
Career Strategies, Inc. (C), CA, *283*
Careerfit, Inc. (C), TX, *283*
Careers/Inc. (C), PR, *284*
Carlson & Czeswik (R), MN, *30*
Carnegie Partners, Inc. (R), IL, *30*
Carpenter, Shackleton & Company (R), IL, *30*
Carrington & Carrington, Ltd. (R), IL, *30*
Carson-Thomas & Assoc. (C), CA, *284*
Carter McKenzie, Inc. (C), NJ, *285*
Caruso & Assoc., Inc. (R), FL, *31*
The CARVIR Group, Inc. (C), GA, *285*
Rosemary Cass Ltd. (R), CT, *31*
Catalyx Group (R), NY, *31*
Caywood Partners, Ltd. (R), CA, *32*
CEC Associates (R), MA, *32*
The Center for Career Advancement, LLC (C), NJ, *287*
The Century Group (C), CA, *287*
cFour Partners (R), CA, *32*
CFR Executive Search, Inc. (C), IL, *288*
Chad Management Group (C), ON, *288*
Chase Partners (R), ON, *33*
Chesapeake Group (C), CT, *290*
Chicago Legal Search, Ltd. (C), IL, *290*
Christenson Hutchison McDowell, LLC (R), NJ, *34*
Christian & Timbers, Inc. (R), OH, *34*
Christmas, McIvor & Assoc. Inc. (C), ON, *290*
The Christopher Group (C), NC, *291*
M. A. Churchill & Assoc., Inc. (R), PA, *35*
Cizek Assoc., Inc. (R), AZ, *35*
Arlene Clapp, Ltd. (R), MN, *35*
Howard Clark Assoc. (C), NJ, *292*
Toby Clark Assoc. Inc. (C), NY, *292*
Clinton, Charles, Wise & Co. (C), FL, *293*
CMC Search Consultants (C), IL, *293*
CMW & Associates, Inc. (C), IL, *293*
Cochran, Cochran & Yale, Inc. (R), NY, *36*
Cole, Warren & Long, Inc. (R), PA, *37*
Collins & Associates (C), MI, *294*
Colt Systems Professional Personnel Services (C), CA, *294*
The Colton Partnership, Inc. (R), NY, *38*
Columbia Consulting Group (R), MD, *38*
Combined Resources Inc. (R), OH, *38*
Commercial Programming Systems, Inc. (C), CA, *294*
Compass Group Ltd. (R), MI, *38*
CompuPro (C), IL, *295*
Computer Int'l. Consultants, Inc. (C), FL, *295*
Computer Security Placement Service (C), MA, *296*
The Comwell Company, Inc. (C), NJ, *296*
Conard Associates, Inc. (R), NH, *39*
Conasa de Mexico, S.C. (R), MX, *39*
Concorde Search Assoc. (C), NY, *296*
Connors, Lovell & Assoc. Inc. (C), ON, *296*
Conroy Partners Ltd. (R), AB, *39*
Consolidated Management Services (C), ON, *296*
The Consortium (C), NY, *296*
Conspectus, Inc. (C), NY, *297*
Consultant Recruiters (C), WI, *297*
The Consulting Group Ltd. (R), NY, *40*
Consulting Resource Group, Inc. (C), GA, *297*
Continental Search & Outplacement, Inc. (C), MD, *298*
Cook Assoc. Int'l., Inc. (C), TN, *298*
Cook Assoc.,® Inc. (R), IL, *40*
COR Management Services, Ltd. (C), NY, *298*
Cornell Group Int'l. Consulting, Inc. (R), NY, *41*
Corporate Search Consultants, Inc. (C), FL, *301*
Corporate Search, Inc. (C), NY, *301*
Corporate Select Int'l., Ltd. (C), IL, *301*
The Corporate Source Group, Inc. (R), MA, *41*
Corso, Mizgala + French (R), ON, *42*
Leonard Corwen Assoc. (C), NY, *302*
J. D. Cotter Search Inc. (C), OH, *302*
Creative Financial Staffing (C), MA, *303*
Creative Financial Staffing Inc. (C), ON, *303*
The Cris Group, Inc. (R), NY, *42*
Crispi, Wagner & Co., Inc. (R), NY, *43*
Crist Partners, Ltd. (R), IL, *43*
Cromwell Partners, Inc. (R), NY, *43*
Crown Advisors, Inc. (R), PA, *43*
Tony Curtis & Associates (C), ON, *305*
The Custer Group, Inc. (R), TN, *44*
Custom Resources (C), AL, *305*
Cybernautic Corp. (C), CT, *305*
Cypress Int'l., Inc. (R), FL, *45*
D & M Associates (C), PA, *306*
D.A.L. Associates, Inc. (R), CT, *45*
D.P. Specialists, Inc. (C), CA, *306*
Dahl-Morrow Int'l. (R), VA, *45*
The Dalley Hewitt Co. (R), GA, *45*
The Danbrook Group, Inc. (C), TX, *306*
Alfred Daniels & Assoc., Inc. (R), CA, *46*
DARE Personnel Inc. (C), ON, *307*
Alan Darling Consulting (R), VT, *46*
Data Bank Executive Search (R), OH, *46*
Data Search Network, Inc. (C), FL, *307*
Daubenspeck & Associates, Ltd. (R), IL, *46*
David Anthony Personnel Assoc., Inc. (C), NJ, *308*
Davis & James, Inc. (C), MO, *308*
Joseph A. Davis Consultants, Inc. (R), NY, *47*
The Dayton Group, Ltd. (C), NY, *309*
Dean-MacDonald (R), OH, *47*
Defrain Mayer (R), KS, *48*
Thorndike Deland Assoc. LLC (R), NY, *48*
S. W. Delano & Co. (R), CT, *48*
Delta Management Group Ltd. (C), ON, *310*
Delta Services (R), TX, *48*
Derhak Ireland & Partners Ltd. (R), ON, *48*
Descheneaux Recruitment Services Ltd. (C), BC, *311*
Rob Dey Executive Search (R), FL, *49*
Diamond Tax Recruiting (C), NY, *312*
Dieckmann & Assoc., Ltd. (R), IL, *51*
The Diestel Group (R), UT, *51*
Roger Dietsch & Assoc. (C), MN, *312*
DiMarchi Partners (R), CO, *51*
J. Dinerstein & Co., Inc. (R), NY, *51*
Dinte Resources, Inc. (R), VA, *52*
Discovery, The Staffing Specialists, Inc. (C), IL, *312*
Dise & Co. (R), OH, *52*
Diversified Search, Inc. (R), PA, *52*
DLB Assoc. (R), NY, *53*
DLG Assoc., Inc. (R), NC, *53*
Doering & Assoc. (C), CA, *313*
J P Donnelly Assoc., Inc. (C), NY, *314*
Dotson & Assoc. (R), NY, *54*
The Doty Group (C), TX, *314*
Douglas-Allen, Inc. (R), MA, *54*

Dow Consultants Int'l. (C), NY, *314*
Drake & Assoc. (C), CA, *315*
Drinkwater & Assoc. (R), MA, *54*
Drummond Assoc., Inc. (C), NY, *315*
DS&A (Doug Sears & Assoc.) (C), FL, *315*
DuBrul Management Co. (C), NY, *315*
Dunhill Staffing Systems, Inc. (C), NY, *316*
Dunhill Professional Search of Miami (C), FL, *319*
Dunhill of Ft. Collins, Inc. (C), CO, *319*
Dunhill Professional Search of Hawaii (C), HI, *320*
Dunhill Technical Staffing (C), IN, *320*
Dunhill Staffing Systems (C), NC, *321*
Dunhill Professional Search of Byram (C), MS, *321*
Dunhill of Manchester Inc. (C), NH, *321*
Dunhill Professional Search of Omaha, Inc. (C), NE, *321*
Dunhill Professional Search of Winston-Salem (C), NC, *322*
Dunhill Personnel of Northeast Tulsa, Inc. (C), OK, *322*
Dunhill Personnel Service of Fargo (C), ND, *322*
Dunhill Professional Search of Wilkes-Barre/Scranton, Inc. (C), PA, *322*
Dunhill Professional Search of Bucks-Mont., Inc. (C), PA, *322*
Dunhill Professional Search of Richmond (C), VA, *323*
Dynamic Choices Inc. (C), MO, *323*
E O Technical (C), CT, *324*
EA Plus, Inc. (C), TX, *325*
EagleView, Inc. (C), MA, *325*
Earley Kielty & Assoc., Inc. (R), NY, *56*
Eastman & Beaudine, Inc. (R), TX, *56*
Eastridge Infotech (C), CA, *326*
The Edge Resource Group (C), PA, *326*
EDI, Inc. (C), MD, *326*
Bruce Edwards & Associates, Inc. (R), NC, *56*
D. C. Egan & Assoc. (C), GA, *327*
Egan Search Group (R), NY, *57*
Eggers Consulting Co., Inc. (C), NE, *327*
Richard A. Eisner & Co., LLP (R), NY, *57*
William J. Elam & Assoc. (R), NE, *58*
Electronic Search, Inc. (C), IL, *327*
Elinvar (C), NC, *328*
Yves Elkas Inc. (R), QE, *58*
H. J. Elliot, Inc. (R), IL, *58*
The Elliott Company (R), MA, *58*
Ellis & Associates (C), HI, *328*
Steve Ellis (C), CA, *328*
David M. Ellner Assoc. (R), NY, *59*
The Ellsworth Group (C), NY, *329*
Mark Elzweig Co., Ltd. (C), NY, *329*
Emerging Technology Search (C), GA, *329*
Empire International (R), PA, *59*
Employ® (C), PA, *330*
Erikson Consulting Assoc., Inc. (R), NY, *60*
Erlanger Assoc. (R), CT, *60*
Essential Solutions, Inc. (C), CA, *331*
Ethos Consulting, Inc. (R), CA, *61*
The Evans Search Group (R), CT, *61*
ExeConnex, LLC (R), GA, *61*
The Execu/Search Group (C), NY, *332*
ExecuGroup, Inc. (R), MS, *61*
ExecuQuest, Inc. (R), MI, *61*
Executive Access Inc. (R), NY, *62*
Executive Careers (R), CA, *62*
Executive Dimensions (R), NY, *62*
Executive Manning Corp. (R), FL, *63*
Executive Partners Inc. (C), CT, *333*
Executive Placement Consultants (C), IL, *333*
Executive Referral Services, Inc. (C), IL, *334*
Executive Resource Inc. (C), WI, *334*
Executive Resource Systems (C), CA, *335*
Executive Search Consultants International, Inc. (R), NY, *63*
Executive Search Consultants, Inc. (C), FL, *335*
Executive Search Partners (R), NY, *63*
Executive Search Placements, Inc. (C), CO, *336*
Executive Search Team (C), MI, *336*
Executive Solutions (R), MN, *64*
The Executive Source Inc. (R), NY, *64*
The Executive Source (C), SA, *337*
The Executive Tree (R), FL, *64*
EXETER 2100 (C), NH, *337*
eXsource Inc. (C), SC, *337*
Eyler Assoc., Inc. (R), IA, *64*
Fabian Assoc. Inc. (C), NY, *338*
Fagan & Company (R), PA, *64*
Leon A. Farley Assoc. (R), CA, *65*
Federal Placement Services (C), NY, *339*
Fenwick Partners (R), MA, *66*
Ferrari Search Group (C), OH, *340*
Fidelity Search Group, Inc. (R), PA, *66*
Financial Connections Company (C), VA, *340*
Financial Plus Management Solutions Inc. (R), ON, *66*
Financial Resource Assoc., Inc. (C), FL, *340*
Financial Search Group, Inc. (R), MA, *66*
Eileen Finn & Assoc., Inc. (C), NY, *341*
Finnegan & Assoc. (R), CA, *67*
First Advisory Services Int'l., Inc. (R), MD, *67*
First Union Executive Search (R), NC, *67*
Fishel HR Assoc., Inc. (C), AZ, *341*
Jack Stuart Fisher Assoc. (C), NJ, *341*
Fisher-Todd Assoc. (C), NY, *341*
The Flagship Group (R), MA, *68*
Robert M. Flanagan & Assoc., Ltd. (R), NY, *68*
Susan Fletcher Attorney Employment Services (C), PA, *342*
Flexible Resources, Inc. (C), CT, *342*
Flynn, Hannock, Inc. (R), CT, *69*
Focus Consulting Services, Inc. (C), FL, *342*
Fogec Consultants, Inc. (R), WI, *69*
Ford & Ford (C), MA, *343*
The Ford Group, Inc. (R), PA, *69*
Fortuna Technologies Inc. (C), CA, *343*
F-O-R-T-U-N-E Personnel Consultants of Boise (R), ID, *70*
F-O-R-T-U-N-E Personnel Consultants (C), MI, *346*
Fortune Personnel Consultants of Raleigh, Inc. (C), NC, *348*
F-O-R-T-U-N-E Personnel Consultants of Charlotte (C), NC, *348*
Fortune Consultants of Ft. Washington (C), PA, *349*
Forum Personnel Inc. (C), NY, *351*
Foster Associates (C), NJ, *351*
Foster Partners (R), NY, *70*
Fought, Jameson Assoc. (C), IL, *351*
Franklin Allen Consultants, Ltd. (R), NY, *71*
The Franklin Search Group, Inc./Medzilla (R), WA, *71*
Friedman Eisenstein Raemer & Schwartz, LLP (R), IL, *72*
Gerald Frisch Assoc., Inc. (R), NY, *72*
C. F. Furr & Co. (R), NC, *72*
The Furst Group, Inc. (R), IL, *72*
Futures Int'l. (R), CT, *73*
The Gabriel Group (C), PA, *354*
Gahan Assoc. (R), NY, *73*
Jay Gaines & Company, Inc. (R), NY, *73*
Gardiner, Townsend & Assoc. (R), NY, *74*
Gardner-Ross Assoc., Inc. (R), NY, *74*
Dick Garland Consultants (R), NY, *74*
The Garvis Group, Inc. (C), LA, *355*
Peter Gasperini & Assoc., Inc. (R), NY, *75*
Gateway Group Personnel, LLC (C), TN, *355*
Gaudry, Shink, Levasseur (R), QE, *75*
Gavin Forbes & Price (R), CA, *75*
Geddes & Rubin Management Inc. (R), ON, *76*
Genel Associates (C), CA, *356*
Genesis Consulting Partners (R), PA, *76*
Geneva Group Int'l. (R), CA, *76*
C. R. Gerald & Assoc. (C), ON, *356*
GES Services, Inc. (R), NY, *76*
Gielow Assoc., Inc. (R), WI, *76*
Gilbert & Van Campen Int'l. (R), NY, *76*
Gilbert Scott Assoc., LLC (C), MA, *357*
Gilbert Tweed Assoc. Inc. (R), NY, *76*
Gilreath Weatherby Inc. (R), MA, *77*
Gimbel & Assoc. (C), FL, *357*
J. P. Gleason Assoc., Inc. (R), IL, *77*
Global Career Services, Inc. (C), NY, *358*
Global Consulting Group Inc. (C), ON, *358*
Global Data Services, Inc. (R), NY, *77*
Global Employer's Network, Inc. (R), TX, *77*
Global Executive Search Group (C), MA, *358*
Global HealthCare Partners (R), IL, *78*
Global Technologies Group Inc. (C), NC, *359*
F. Gloss Int'l. (R), VA, *78*
The Tracy Glover Co. (R), TX, *78*
Gnodde Assoc. (C), IL, *359*
The Gobbell Co. (R), CA, *78*
The Gogates Group, Inc. (R), NY, *79*
The Goldman Group Inc. (R), NY, *79*
Joseph Goldring & Assoc. Inc. (C), MI, *360*
Goodkind Assoc. Inc. (C), NY, *360*
Goodrich & Sherwood Assoc., Inc. (R), NY, *79*
Gould, McCoy & Chadick, Inc. (R), NY, *80*
The Governance Group, Inc. (R), NJ, *80*
Government Contract Solutions, Inc. (C), VA, *360*

INDUSTRIES

Robert Graham Assoc. (R), RI, *81*
Granger, Counts & Assoc. (R), OH, *81*
Grant Cooper & Assoc., Inc. (R), MO, *81*
Grant-Franks & Assoc. (C), NJ, *361*
Grant/Morgan Assoc., Inc. (C), MD, *361*
Grantham & Co., Inc. (R), NC, *81*
Grauss & Co. (C), CA, *362*
Greene & Co. (C), MA, *362*
Greene Personnel Consultants (C), RI, *362*
Greene-Levin-Snyder LLC (C), NY, *362*
Greenwich Internet (C), CT, *363*
Griffith & Werner, Inc. (R), FL, *82*
J. B. Groner Executive Search, Inc. (C), DE, *363*
Groussman & Assoc., Inc. (R), TX, *82*
GSP International (C), NJ, *364*
GSW Consulting Group, Inc. (R), CA, *83*
The Gullgroup (C), TX, *364*
Gundersen Partners, L.L.C. (R), NY, *83*
Gustin Partners, Ltd. (R), MA, *83*
William Guy & Assoc., Inc. (R), CA, *84*
The H. S. Group, Inc. (C), WI, *365*
H.Q. Search, Inc. (C), IL, *365*
Habelmann & Assoc. (R), MI, *84*
Russ Hadick & Assoc. Inc. (C), OH, *365*
Hadley Lockwood, Inc. (R), NY, *84*
Halbrecht Lieberman Assoc., Inc. (R), CT, *84*
Hale Assoc. (R), IL, *84*
K. C. Hale, Inc. (R), CT, *85*
Haley Associates (R), CA, *85*
Hall Kinion (C), CA, *366*
R. C. Handel Assoc. Inc. (R), CT, *85*
W. L. Handler & Assoc. (R), GA, *85*
Hands-on Broadcast (R), NY, *86*
Handy HRM (R), NY, *86*
Hanley & Assoc. (R), FL, *86*
The Hanover Consulting Group (C), MD, *368*
Hansen Executive Search, Inc. (C), NE, *368*
Hanzel & Co., Inc. (R), NY, *86*
Harcourt Group Ltd. (R), OH, *86*
Hardison & Company (R), TX, *86*
Harper Associates (C), MI, *369*
The Harris Consulting Corp. (R), MB, *87*
Harris McCully Assoc., Inc. (C), NY, *369*
Hartman & Barnette (R), VA, *87*
Harvey Hohauser & Assoc., LLC (R), MI, *87*
Hayden & Assoc., Inc. (C), MN, *370*
Hayden Group, Inc. (R), MA, *88*
Hayman Daugherty Assoc., Inc. (C), GA, *370*
Healey Executive Search, Inc. (R), MN, *88*
Healthcare Management Resources, Inc. (R), GA, *89*
F. P. Healy & Co., Inc. (R), NY, *89*
R. W. Hebel Assoc. (R), TX, *89*
Thomas E. Hedefine Assoc. (C), ON, *375*
Hedlund Corp. (C), IL, *375*
Jay Heino Company, LLC (C), NY, *375*
Helfer Executive Consultants (R), TN, *91*
G. W. Henn & Co. (R), OH, *91*
Henrietta's Personnel & Executive Search, Inc. (C), FL, *376*
Hergenrather & Co. (R), WA, *92*
Hessel Assoc., Inc. (C), NY, *377*
Higbee Assoc., Inc. (C), CT, *377*
Higdon Prince Inc. (R), NY, *93*
High-Tech Recruiters (C), CT, *378*
Highland Search Group, L.L.C. (R), NY, *93*
Higley, Hall & Co., Inc. (R), MA, *93*
Hill Allyn Assoc. (C), CA, *378*
The Hindman Co. (R), KY, *94*
Hintz Associates (C), NY, *378*
Hite Executive Search (R), OH, *94*
HLR Consulting (C), NY, *379*
Hochman & Assoc. (C), CA, *379*
Hockett Associates, Inc. (R), CA, *94*
Hoffman Recruiters (C), MA, *380*
The Hollins Group, Inc. (R), IL, *95*
Holloway Schulz & Partners (C), BC, *380*
David C. Horn Executive Search (C), TX, *381*
Horton Int'l. Inc. (R), NY, *96*
Houser, Martin, Morris (C), WA, *381*
Howe & Assoc. (R), PA, *97*
Hreshko Consulting Group (C), NJ, *382*
The HRM Group, Inc. (C), AL, *382*
HRS, Inc. (R), PA, *97*
Human Capital Resources, Inc. (C), FL, *384*
Human Resource Bureau (C), CA, *384*
The Human Resource Department Ltd. (R), OH, *98*
Human Resource Solutions (R), TX, *98*
Human Resource Technologies, Inc. (R), IL, *99*
Human Resources Management Hawaii, Inc. (C), HI, *384*
Hunegnaw Executive Search (C), OH, *384*
H.I. Hunt & Co., Ltd. (R), MA, *99*
Hunt & Howe Inc. (R), NY, *99*
Hunter Int'l., Inc. (R), CT, *100*
Hunter, Rowan & Crowe (C), FL, *386*
Huntington Personnel Consultants, Inc. (C), NY, *386*
Huntress Real Estate Executive Search (R), MO, *100*
W. Hutt Management Resources Ltd. (R), ON, *100*
Hyde Danforth & Co. (R), TX, *100*
IM Independent Management Recruiters (R), TN, *101*
IMA Search, Inc. (R), NY, *101*
Information Systems Professionals (C), NC, *388*
Infovia (C), CA, *388*
Ingram & Aydelotte, Inc. (R), NY, *101*
Innovative Healthcare Services, Inc. (C), GA, *389*
Innovative Partnerships (R), CA, *101*
Innovative Resource Group, LLC (C), NC, *389*
Intech Summit Group, Inc. (R), CA, *102*
Integrated Management Solutions (C), NY, *390*
Integrity Search, Inc. (R), PA, *102*
InteliSearch, Inc. (R), CT, *102*
IntelliSearch (C), TX, *391*
IntelliSource, inc. (C), PA, *391*
Interim Accounting Professionals (C), CA, *391*
Interim Executive Recruiting (C), GA, *392*
Interim Financial Solutions - Mid-Atlantic Region (C), MD, *392*
International Business Partners (C), ON, *392*
International Executive Recruiters (C), OH, *393*
International Market Recruiters (C), NY, *393*
Interquest, Inc. (R), NY, *103*
Interspace Interactive, Inc. (C), NY, *394*
Iona Partners (C), CA, *394*
Jeffrey Irving Assoc., Inc. (R), VA, *104*
Isaacson, Miller (R), MA, *104*
ISC of Houston, Inc. (C), TX, *394*
ISG Informatics Search Group (C), ON, *395*
Ives & Associates, Inc. (C), OH, *395*
J. Nicholas Arthur (R), MA, *104*
J. R. Scott & Assoc., Ltd. (C), IL, *395*
J.D.G. y Asociados, S.A. de C.V. (R), SO, *104*
Jacobs & Co. (R), CT, *105*
Pendleton James Assoc., Inc. (R), NY, *105*
James Moore & Assoc. (C), CA, *397*
Jefferson-Ross Assoc. Inc. (C), PA, *398*
Jeffrey Meryl Assoc., Inc. (C), NJ, *398*
JG Consultants, Inc. (R), TX, *106*
JNB Assoc., Inc. (C), MA, *399*
John Jay & Co. (C), ME, *399*
John Ryan Assoc., LLC. (C), NY, *399*
Johnson Brown Assoc., Inc. (C), IN, *400*
The Johnson Group, Unlimited (C), NY, *400*
Johnson Smith & Knisely (R), NY, *107*
Jonathan Lawrence Assoc. (C), NJ, *400*
The Jonathan Stevens Group, Inc. (R), NJ, *108*
Jones Management Co. (R), CT, *108*
Joseph Consulting, Inc. (C), FL, *401*
Joseph Michaels (C), CA, *401*
JSG Group Management Consultants (R), ON, *109*
JT Assoc. (C), CT, *401*
Juno Systems, Inc. (C), NY, *402*
Kane & Assoc. (C), TX, *403*
Gary Kaplan & Assoc. (R), CA, *109*
Kaplan & Assoc., Inc. (R), PA, *109*
Howard Karr & Assoc., Inc. (R), CA, *110*
Kaufman Assoc. (R), CA, *110*
Kazan International, Inc. (R), NJ, *110*
A.T. Kearney Executive Search (R), IL, *111*
Keeley Consulting Inc. (C), ON, *404*
Kennedy & Co. (R), IL, *112*
The Kennett Group, Inc. (R), PA, *112*
Kensington Int'l., Inc. (R), IL, *113*
Kenzer Corp. (R), NY, *113*
Kershner & Co. (R), DC, *113*
Keystone Consulting Group (C), GA, *406*
Kingsbury • Wax • Bova (R), MA, *114*
The Kinlin Co., Inc. (R), MA, *115*
Richard Kinser & Assoc. (R), NY, *115*
Kip Williams, Inc. (R), NY, *115*
Kiradjieff & Goode, Inc. (R), MA, *115*
The Kleinstein Group, Inc. (R), NJ, *116*
The Koehler Group (C), PA, *408*
Lee Koehn Assoc., Inc. (R), OR, *116*
Korn/Ferry Int'l. (R), NY, *117*
Kossuth & Assoc., Inc. (R), WA, *119*
KPA Assoc., Inc. (C), NY, *408*
Katherine R. Kraemer (R), CA, *120*

Kramer Executive Resources, Inc. (C), NY, *409*
Kremple & Meade, Inc. (R), CA, *120*
D. A. Kreuter Assoc., Inc. (R), PA, *121*
Kulper & Co., L.L.C. (R), NJ, *121*
John Kurosky & Assoc. (R), CA, *122*
Kyle Assoc. (C), NY, *410*
L O R (R), NJ, *122*
L T M Assoc. (C), IL, *410*
L&L Assoc. Global Search (C), PA, *411*
Marvin Laba & Assoc. (R), CA, *122*
Rene LaFlamme & Associes (R), QE, *122*
Lamay Assoc., Inc. (R), CT, *124*
Lamon + Stuart + Michaels Inc. (R), ON, *124*
E. J. Lance Management Assoc., Inc. (C), NY, *412*
The Langford Search, Inc. (C), AL, *412*
LanSo Int'l., Inc. (C), NY, *413*
Lawrence L. Lapham, Inc. (R), NY, *124*
Larsen & Lee, Inc. (R), MD, *125*
Larsen, Whitney, Blecksmith & Zilliacus, Inc. (R), CA, *125*
LAS Management Consulting Group, Inc. (R), NJ, *125*
Lascelle & Assoc. Inc. (C), ON, *413*
Latham International, Ltd. (R), NJ, *126*
Lauer, Sbarbaro Assoc., EMA Partners Int'l. (R), IL, *126*
Lautz, Grotte, Engler & Swimley (R), CA, *126*
Layne-Mendez & Co. (R), TX, *127*
Leader Institute, Inc. (C), GA, *414*
Leader Resources Group (C), GA, *415*
Leader Search Inc. (R), AB, *127*
Leaders-Trust Int'l./Carce y Asociados, S.C. (R), MX, *127*
Lechner & Assoc., Inc. (C), FL, *415*
Ledbetter/Davidson Int'l., Inc. (R), NY, *127*
Vincent Lee Assoc. (C), NY, *415*
Leeds and Leeds (C), TN, *416*
V. J. Lehman & Assoc., Inc. (R), CO, *127*
Lekan & Assoc., Inc. (R), OH, *128*
Lending Personnel Services (C), CA, *416*
AG Lennox & Assoc. (R), AB, *128*
Leslie Kavanagh Assoc., Inc. (C), NY, *416*
Lewis & Blank Int'l. (R), CA, *129*
Lewis Companies Inc. (R), ON, *129*
Lewis Consulting Service (C), IL, *417*
Lexington Software Inc. (C), NY, *417*
The Libra Group (C), NC, *417*
Lifter & Assoc. (C), CA, *418*
Lipsky Group, Inc. (R), CA, *129*
Livingston, Robert & Co. (R), CT, *130*
Lloyd Associates (R), GA, *130*
Lloyd Staffing (C), NY, *419*
Locke & Assoc. (R), NC, *131*
Logix, Inc. (C), MA, *420*
Logue & Rice Inc. (C), VA, *420*
Louis Search Group, Inc. (C), NJ, *420*
Lucas Assoc. (C), GA, *421*
Charles Luntz & Assoc., Inc. (R), MO, *132*
Lynx, Inc. (C), MA, *421*
Lyons Pruitt Int'l. (R), PA, *132*
M/J/A Partners (R), IL, *133*
MacNaughton Assoc. (R), CA, *133*
The Madison Group (R), NY, *133*
Madison MacArthur Inc. (R), ON, *133*
Magellan Int'l., L.P. (C), TX, *422*
Management Advisors Int'l., Inc. (C), NC, *424*
Management Alliance Group, Inc. (R), NJ, *134*
Management Assoc. (C), MD, *424*
Management One Consultants (C), ON, *425*
Management Recruiters of Nassau, Inc. (R), NY, *134*
Management Recruiters of Birmingham-South, Inc. (C), AL, *438*
Management Recruiters of Berkeley (C), CA, *439*
Management Recruiters of Laguna Hills (C), CA, *440*
Management Recruiters of Sacramento North (C), CA, *441*
Management Recruiters of Pleasanton (C), CA, *441*
Management Recruiters of Middlesex (C), CT, *442*
Management Recruiters of Melbourne, Inc. (C), FL, *443*
Management Recruiters of Ft. Myers, FL. (C), FL, *443*
Management Recruiters of Miami-North (C), FL, *443*
Management Recruiters of St. Augustine (C), FL, *444*
Management Recruiters of Columbus, Inc. (C), GA, *445*
Management Recruiters of Duluth (C), GA, *445*
Management Recruiters of Atlanta (C), GA, *445*
Management Recruiters - Towne Lake (C), GA, *446*
Management Recruiters of Chicago-North Shore (C), IL, *447*
Management Recruiters of Chicago West (C), IL, *447*
Management Recruiters of Indianapolis (C), IN, *448*
Management Recruiters of Indianapolis-North (C), IN, *448*
Management Recruiters - Indianapolis (C), IN, *448*
Management Recruiters of Williamsburg (C), IA, *449*
Management Recruiters of Siouxland (C), IA, *449*
Management Recruiters of Woodbury (C), MN, *452*
Management Recruiters of Cass County, NE (C), NE, *452*
Management Recruiters of Bloomington (C), MN, *452*
Management Recruiters of North Oakland County, Inc. (C), MI, *452*
Management Recruiters of Chanhassen (C), MN, *452*
Management Recruiters of Great Neck (C), NY, *454*
Management Recruiters of Princeton (C), NJ, *454*
Management Recruiters of The Sandias (C), NM, *454*
Management Recruiters of Cedar Mountain (C), NC, *455*
Management Recruiters of Manhattan on Broadway (C), NY, *455*
Management Recruiters of Cleveland (C), OH, *457*
Management Recruiters of Youngstown (C), OH, *458*
Management Recruiters of Oklahoma City (C), OK, *458*
Management Recruiters - North Canton, Inc. (C), OH, *458*
Management Recruiters of Mentor, Inc. (C), OH, *458*
Management Recruiters of Pittsburgh (C), PA, *459*
Management Recruiters of Cherry Hill (C), PA, *459*
Management Recruiters of Lionville, Inc. (C), PA, *459*
Management Recruiters of Puerto Rico (C), PR, *460*
Management Recruiters of North Charleston (C), SC, *460*
Management Recruiters The Delta Group, Inc. (C), TN, *461*
Management Recruiters of Sioux Falls, LLP (C), SD, *461*
Management Recruiters of Champions (C), TX, *462*
Management Recruiters of Houston (C), TX, *462*
Management Recruiters of San Marcos (C), TX, *463*
Management Recruiters of San Antonio - North (C), TX, *463*
Management Recruiters of Spokane (C), WA, *465*
Management Recruiters of Milwaukee - Downtown (C), WI, *466*
Management Resource Group, Ltd. (C), IA, *467*
Management Resource Group (C), MN, *467*
Management Resource Assoc., Inc. (C), FL, *467*
Management Search Int'l. (C), CA, *467*
Management Search, Inc. (C), IL, *467*
Management Search of R.I. Inc. (R), RI, *135*
Management Solutions, Inc. (C), WA, *468*
ManTech Consulting (C), NY, *468*
Marentz & Co. (C), TX, *469*
J. L. Mark Assoc., Inc. (R), CO, *135*
Market Niche Consulting (C), AZ, *470*
Marketing Search Inc. (C), OH, *471*
Marketing/Public Relations Research Recruiting (C), CT, *471*
The Martin Group (R), CA, *137*
Martin Partners, L.L.C. (R), IL, *137*
Marvel Consultants, Inc. (C), OH, *472*
Masserman & Assoc., Inc. (R), NY, *138*
Massey-Horton Int'l. (R), ON, *138*
Louis Thomas Masterson & Co. (R), OH, *138*
Matté & Company, Inc. (R), CT, *138*
Matte Consulting Group Inc. (R), QE, *138*
Mayhall Search Group, Inc. (C), IN, *473*
The McAulay Firm (R), NC, *139*
McBride Assoc., Inc. (R), DC, *139*

INDUSTRIES

McCann, Choi & Associates, LLC (R), NY, *139*
K. E. McCarthy & Assoc. (R), CA, *139*
McCarthy Assoc. National BancSearch, LLC (C), LA, *473*
McDonald Assoc. Int'l. (R), IL, *140*
McDonald, Long & Assoc., Inc. (R), NY, *140*
McGrath & Assoc., Inc. (R), NJ, *141*
McHale & Assoc. (R), WA, *141*
The McKinnon Management Group Inc. (C), ON, *475*
Dan P. McLean Assoc., Inc. (C), ON, *475*
The McLeod Group, Inc. (R), CT, *141*
MCS Assoc. (R), CA, *142*
Meder & Assoc., Inc. (R), IL, *142*
The Medley Group (C), CA, *477*
Mehta Consulting (C), NJ, *478*
Melancon & Co. (R), TX, *143*
Juan Menefee & Assoc. (C), IL, *478*
Merrick & Moore (C), NC, *479*
Messett Assoc., Inc. (R), FL, *143*
META/MAT, Ltd. (R), NJ, *144*
Walter Meyer & Assoc. (R), NY, *144*
MGA Executive Search (C), FL, *480*
Michael Thomas, Inc. (C), OH, *480*
Millar Walker & Gay (R), ON, *144*
Millennium Search Group, Inc. (R), CA, *144*
Miller/Davis & Assoc., Inc. (C), NY, *482*
Milo Research (R), NY, *145*
MIS Computer Professionals, Inc. (C), KS, *482*
Paul Misarti Inc. (C), NY, *483*
Mitchell Martin Inc. (C), NY, *483*
Moffitt Int'l., Inc. (R), NC, *146*
Mogul Consultants, Inc. (C), NY, *483*
Oscar Montaño, Inc. (R), CA, *146*
Montgomery Resources, Inc. (C), CA, *484*
Montgomery West (R), CA, *146*
C. A. Moore & Assoc., Inc. (C), MN, *484*
Larry Moore & Assoc. (C), CA, *484*
Moore Research Assoc. (R), NJ, *147*
Morgan Hunter Corp. (C), KS, *485*
Morgan Stampfl, Inc. (C), NY, *485*
Morris & Berger (R), CA, *147*
Mortgage & Financial Personnel Services (C), CA, *486*
Mortgage Search Network (C), AZ, *486*
MSI Int'l. (C), GA, *486*
Much & Co. (R), NY, *148*
The Mulshine Co., Inc. (R), NJ, *149*
Jennifer Munro & Partners, Inc. (R), SC, *149*
The MVP Group (C), NY, *487*
DDJ Myers, Ltd. (R), AZ, *150*
Nagler, Robins & Poe, Inc. (R), MA, *150*
Nason & Nason (C), FL, *488*
National Affirmative Action Career Network, Inc. (C), CO, *488*
National Bank & Finance Executive Search (C), CA, *488*
National Field Service Corp. (C), NY, *489*
National Register Columbus Inc. (C), OH, *490*
National Search, Inc.r (C), FL, *490*
Don Neal & Assoc. (C), OK, *491*
The Neil Michael Group, Inc./Global Partners (R), NY, *151*
New Venture Development, Inc. (C), CA, *492*
Marc Nichols Assoc., Inc. (C), NY, *493*
Nichols Brown Int'l. (R), NY, *151*
W. D. Nolte & Company (R), CT, *152*
Nordeman Grimm, Inc. (R), NY, *152*
Norgate Technology, Inc. (C), NY, *494*
The Norland Group (C), CA, *494*
Norman Broadbent Int'l., Inc. (R), NY, *152*
Norrell Financial Staffing (C), GA, *495*
Ronald Norris & Assoc. (C), IL, *495*
The North Peak Group (C), OH, *496*
NorthStar Technologies, Inc. (C), NY, *496*
Nuessle, Kurdziel & Weiss, Inc. (R), PA, *153*
O'Brien & Bell (R), OH, *153*
O'Brien Consulting Services (R), MA, *153*
O'Callaghan Honey/Ray & Berndtson Inc. (R), AB, *153*
O'Connor Resources (C), TX, *497*
O'Keefe & Assoc., Inc. (R), CT, *154*
O'Neill & Co. (R), CT, *154*
O'Shea, Divine & Co., Inc. (R), CA, *154*
O'Sullivan Search Inc. (C), ON, *498*
O'Toole & Company, Inc. (R), IL, *154*
Ober & Company (R), CA, *155*
The Odessa Group (R), CA, *155*
The Ogdon Partnership (R), NY, *155*
Ollinger Partners (R), MA, *156*
Olympian Recruitment, Ltd. (C), NY, *498*
The Onstott Group (R), MA, *156*
Oppedisano & Co., Inc. (R), NY, *156*
The Options Group, Inc. (C), NY, *499*
Organization Resources Inc. (R), MA, *157*
Orion Int'l. Consulting Group, Inc. (C), NC, *499*
Overton Consulting (R), WI, *157*
LaMonte Owens, Inc. (R), PA, *157*
The Oxbridge Group, Ltd. (C), PA, *500*
P.R.H. Management, Inc. (R), CT, *158*
Page-Wheatcroft & Co., Ltd. (R), TX, *158*
The Pailin Group Professional Search Consultants (R), TX, *158*
Arthur Pann Assoc., Inc. (C), NY, *502*
Parenica & Co. (R), NC, *159*
Carol Park (C), MO, *502*
The Park Group & Assoc., Inc. (C), MD, *502*
Parker Page Group (C), FL, *503*
Largent Parks & Partners (C), TX, *503*
Partners In Human Resources Int'l., Inc. (R), NY, *160*
The Partnership Group (R), NJ, *160*
Partnervision Consulting Group Inc. (R), ON, *160*
Pasona Canada, Inc. (C), ON, *504*
Pathway Executive Search, Inc. (C), NY, *505*
Pathways Int'l. (C), CT, *505*
The Patience Motivation Belief Group, Inc. (C), GA, *505*
Peak Search Assoc. (C), ON, *506*
Pearson, Caldwell & Farnsworth (R), CA, *161*
Peck & Assoc., Ltd. (R), WI, *161*
Penn Associates (R), PA, *161*
The Penn Partners, Inc. (R), PA, *162*
The Pennmor Group (C), NJ, *506*
People Management Mid-South, LLC (R), TN, *162*
People Management Northeast, Inc. (R), CT, *162*
PeopleSource Inc. (C), TX, *506*
The Perkins Group (R), NC, *162*
PersoNet, Inc. (C), FL, *507*
Personnel Assoc. (C), NC, *508*
The Personnel Group, Inc. (R), MN, *163*
Richard Peterson & Assoc., Inc. (R), GA, *163*
Peyser Assoc., Inc. (R), FL, *163*
Robert E. Pfaendler & Assoc., Inc. (C), OR, *509*
Phillips Personnel/Search (C), CO, *510*
Phillips Resource Group (C), SC, *510*
PIC Executive Search (C), GA, *511*
Picard Int'l., Ltd. (R), NY, *164*
Pinnacle Executive Group Inc. (C), MO, *512*
Pinnacle Group Int'l. (C), AZ, *512*
Pinton Forrest & Madden/EMA Partners Int'l. (R), BC, *165*
Pioneer Consulting Group (C), CA, *512*
Pittleman & Assoc. (C), NY, *512*
Placement Solutions (C), WI, *513*
Plante & Moran, LLP (R), MI, *165*
R. L. Plimpton Assoc., Inc. (R), CO, *165*
Yves Plouffe & Assoc. (R), QE, *165*
Plummer & Assoc., Inc. (R), CT, *166*
PMJ & Assoc. (C), ON, *513*
Poirier, Hoevel & Co. (R), CA, *166*
Al Ponaman Company, Inc. (C), CA, *514*
Robert Powers & Assoc. (C), CA, *515*
P. G. Prager Search Assoc., Ltd. (C), NY, *515*
The Prairie Group (C), IL, *515*
Prairie Resource Group, Inc. (R), IL, *166*
Elan Pratzer & Partners Inc. (R), ON, *167*
PRAXIS Partners (R), VA, *167*
Preferred Placement, Inc. (C), NY, *516*
The Premier Staffing Group (C), OH, *517*
Prescott Legal Search, Inc. (C), TX, *517*
Preston & Co. (R), NJ, *167*
PricewaterhouseCoopers Executive Search (R), ON, *168*
The Primary Group, Inc. (R), FL, *168*
Prime Management Group Inc. (C), ON, *518*
Princeton Search Partners, Inc. (R), NJ, *169*
Pro-Tech Search, Inc. (C), IL, *519*
Procom (C), ON, *519*
Professional Personnel Consultants, Inc. (C), MI, *521*
Professional Persons Career Services (C), NY, *521*
Professional Research Services, Inc. (R), IL, *169*
Professional Resources (C), NY, *522*
Professional Resources (C), OK, *522*
Professional Search (R), MI, *169*
Professional Search Assoc. (C), CA, *522*
Professional Search, Inc. (C), CO, *522*
Professional Selection Services (R), GA, *169*
Profit Pros, Inc. (C), CA, *523*
Prospective Personnel Service, Inc. (C), OK, *524*
Protocol Inc. (C), CA, *525*

Quantum EDP Recruiting Services (C), QE, *526*
The Quest Organization (C), NY, *527*
Quetico Corp. (R), TX, *170*
L. J. Quinn & Assoc., Inc. (R), CA, *170*
Quiring Assoc., Inc. (C), IN, *527*
Quirk-Corporon & Assoc., Inc. (C), WI, *527*
R & L Assoc., Ltd. (R), NY, *170*
R.A.N. Assoc., Inc. (C), OH, *528*
Raines Int'l. Inc. (R), NY, *171*
Ramming & Assoc., Inc. (C), NJ, *528*
Rand Thompson Executive Search Consultants (C), NY, *528*
Lea Randolph & Assoc., Inc. (C), TX, *529*
The Rankin Group, Ltd. (R), WI, *171*
Joanne E. Ratner Search (C), NY, *529*
Ray & Berndtson (R), TX, *171*
Ray & Berndtson/Laurendeau Labrecque (R), QE, *172*
Ray & Berndtson/Lovas Stanley (R), ON, *172*
Razzino-Claymore Assoc. (C), NJ, *530*
Real Estate Executive Search, Inc. (C), CA, *531*
Redden & McGrath Assoc., Inc. (R), NY, *173*
Redden-Shaffer Group (R), CA, *173*
Reece & Mruk Partners/EMA Partners Int'l. (R), MA, *173*
Reeve & Assoc. (C), CT, *533*
The Regis Group, Ltd. (R), GA, *174*
Reifel & Assoc. (R), IL, *174*
Renaissance Resources, LLC (R), VA, *174*
Research Personnel Consultants (C), ON, *534*
Resource Management Group (C), CT, *534*
Resource Services, Inc. (C), NY, *534*
Response Staffing Services (C), NY, *534*
Retained Search Assoc. (R), NC, *176*
Russell Reynolds Assoc., Inc. (R), NY, *176*
Reynolds Consulting Int'l. (R), ON, *177*
RHI Consulting (C), VA, *536*
Rhodes Associates (R), NY, *177*
Rice Cohen Int'l. (R), PA, *178*
Richard, Wayne & Roberts (C), TX, *536*
The Richards Group (C), PA, *536*
Ridenour & Assoc. (R), IL, *178*
Rieser & Assoc., Inc. (R), MO, *178*
Right/McKee Consulting Group (C), TX, *537*
Riotto-Jones Assoc. (R), NY, *178*
RLM Assoc., Ltd. (R), NY, *179*
Robert William James & Assoc. (C), OR, *539*
Roberts Ryan & Bentley, Inc. (R), MD, *179*
Robertson & Assoc. (C), IL, *539*
Robinson-Robinson & Assoc., Inc. (C), MN, *539*
Robison & Associates (R), NC, *180*
Robsham & Assoc., Inc. (R), MA, *180*
Rockwood Assoc. (C), NY, *540*
Rocky Mountain Recruiters, Inc. (C), CO, *540*
Rodgers, Ramsey, Inc. (C), TX, *540*
Rodzik & Assoc., Inc. (R), NC, *180*
The Rogan Group, Inc. (C), CA, *541*
ROI International, Inc. (R), WA, *181*
Rojek Marketing Group, Inc. (R), OH, *181*
Roll International (C), TX, *541*
Rolland Ressources Humaines Inc. (R), QE, *181*
Rollo Assoc. (R), CA, *181*
Romac Int'l. (C), IL, *541*
Romac Int'l. (C), PA, *542*
Romac Int'l. Inc. (R), MA, *181*
W. R. Rosato & Assoc., Inc. (R), NY, *182*
Roster Inc. (C), IN, *545*
Rovner & Assoc., Inc. (R), IL, *182*
Rovner Gerner & Assoc. (R), CA, *182*
Royal Assoc. (C), CA, *547*
RSMR, Inc. (R), IL, *182*
The Rubicon Group (C), AZ, *547*
The Rubinic Consulting Group (C), OH, *548*
Rusher, Loscavio & LoPresto (R), CA, *183*
Russillo/Gardner/Spolsino (C), MA, *548*
K. Russo Assoc. Inc. (C), CT, *548*
Rust & Assoc., Inc. (R), IL, *183*
W. A. Rutledge & Assoc. (R), CT, *183*
Ryan, Miller & Assoc. (C), CA, *549*
Ryan-Allen & Assoc., Inc. (C), CA, *549*
Rylan Forbes Consulting Group, Inc. (C), NJ, *549*
Ryman, Bell, Green & Michaels, Inc. (C), TX, *549*
Sales & Management Search, Inc. (C), IL, *551*
Sales Consultants of Northwest Arkansas, Inc. (C), AR, *556*
Sales Consultants of Ft. Lauderdale, Inc. (C), FL, *557*
Sales Consultants of Indianapolis-North (C), IN, *558*
Sales Consultants of Indianapolis (C), IN, *558*
Sales Consultants of Chicago South (C), IL, *558*
Sales Consultants (C), IL, *558*
Sales Consultants of Wellesley, Inc. (C), MA, *559*
Sales Consultants of Bangor, Inc. (C), ME, *559*
Sales Consultants of Laurel Park, Inc. (C), MI, *560*
Sales Consultants of Nashua-Manchester (C), NH, *560*
Sales Consultants of Grand Rapids (C), MI, *560*
Sales Consultants Bridgewater, Inc. (C), NJ, *560*
Sales Consultants of Cherry Hill (C), NJ, *560*
Sales Consultants of Princeton, Inc. (C), NJ, *561*
A. N. Salloway Executive Search & Consulting, L.L.C. (C), MA, *564*
Salzmann Gay Assoc., Inc. (R), PA, *184*
Norm Sanders Assoc., Inc. (R), NJ, *184*
Sanders Management Assoc., Inc. (C), NJ, *565*
Sanford Rose Assoc. - Chicago (C), IL, *566*
Sanford Rose Assoc. - Clearwater (C), FL, *566*
Sanford Rose Assoc. - Atlanta North (C), GA, *566*
Sanford Rose Assoc. - Oak Brook (C), IL, *567*
Sanford Rose Assoc. - Philadelphia North (C), PA, *570*
Sanford Rose Assoc. - Pittsburgh North (C), PA, *570*
Santangelo Consultants Inc. (C), NY, *571*
Sathe & Associates, Inc. (R), MN, *184*
Savoy Partners, Ltd. (R), DC, *184*
Schall Executive Search Partners (R), MN, *185*
Schattle & Duquette (C), RI, *571*
The Schatz Company (C), MO, *571*
Schenck & Assoc. SC (C), WI, *572*
Schlatter & Assoc. (C), CA, *572*
F. B. Schmidt Int'l. (R), CA, *185*
Schoales & Assoc. Inc. (C), ON, *572*
Schulenburg & Assoc. (C), GA, *572*
Schuyler Assoc., Ltd. (R), GA, *185*
Schuyler, Baker & Parker, Inc. (R), GA, *185*
Scott Sibley Assoc. (C), NY, *573*
Scott-Wayne Assoc., Inc. (C), MA, *573*
Search Advisors Int'l. Corp. (R), FL, *186*
The Search Alliance, Inc. (R), FL, *186*
Search America, Inc. (C), PA, *573*
Search Assoc., Inc. (C), NJ, *574*
Search Bureau Int'l. (C), IL, *574*
The Search Center Inc. (C), TX, *574*
The Search Company (R), ON, *186*
Search Consultants, LLC (C), MD, *575*
Search Group Inc. (R), AB, *186*
Search Innovations, Inc. (R), PA, *187*
Search Int'l. (R), MA, *187*
Search Research Assoc., Inc. (R), MA, *187*
SearchCorp (C), FL, *577*
SearchCorp International (C), AB, *577*
Searchline Services, Inc. (C), OH, *577*
SearchOne, Inc. (C), AR, *577*
Secura/Burnett Partners (R), CA, *187*
Sedlar & Miners (R), NY, *188*
J. R. Seehusen Assoc., Inc. (R), IA, *188*
Setford-Shaw-Najarian Assoc. (C), NY, *579*
Sevcor Int'l., Inc. (R), IL, *188*
SFB Legal Search (C), NY, *579*
Shannahan & Co., Inc. (R), CA, *189*
Sherwood Lehman Massucco, Inc. (R), CA, *189*
Michael Shirley Assoc. Inc. (R), KS, *190*
E. L. Shore & Assoc. (R), ON, *190*
Shore Asociados Ejecutivos, S. A. de C.V. (R), MX, *190*
The Shorr Group (R), IL, *190*
Siger & Assoc., LLC (C), CT, *581*
Marvin L. Silcott & Assoc., Inc. (C), TX, *581*
Daniel A. Silverstein Assoc. Inc. (R), FL, *191*
D. J. Simpson Assoc. Inc. (R), ON, *191*
Sink, Walker, Boltrus Int'l. (R), MA, *192*
Skipping Stone Inc. (C), VA, *582*
Ruth Sklar Assoc., Inc. (RSA Executive Search) (R), NY, *192*
Skott/Edwards Consultants (R), NY, *192*
Slayton Int'l., Inc. (R), IL, *192*
Christopher Smallhorn Executive Recruiting, Inc. (R), MA, *193*
Smith & Assoc. (C), CA, *583*
Smith & Laue Search (R), OR, *193*
Howard W. Smith Assoc. (R), CT, *193*

INDUSTRIES

(R) = Retainer; (C) = Contingency

Herman Smith Executive Initiatives Inc. (R), ON, *193*
Smith Hanley Assoc., Inc. (C), NY, *584*
Smith Search, S.C. (R), MX, *194*
Smith, Brown & Jones (C), KS, *585*
A. William Smyth, Inc. (R), CA, *194*
Smythe Masterson & Judd, Inc. (C), NY, *585*
Snelling Search (C), LA, *586*
C. Snow & Assoc. (C), ON, *586*
Snyder & Co. (R), CT, *194*
Andrea Sobel & Assoc., Inc. (C), CA, *586*
Sockwell & Assoc. (R), NC, *194*
Software Engineering Solutions, Inc. (C), CA, *586*
Solutions Group (R), AL, *195*
Souder & Assoc. (R), VA, *195*
Special Markets Group, Inc. (R), GA, *195*
Specialty Consultants Inc. (R), PA, *195*
Spectra International LLC (C), AZ, *589*
SpencerStuart (R), NY, *196*
The Spiegel Group (R), MA, *197*
Spilman & Assoc. (R), TX, *197*
Spriggs & Co., Inc. (R), IL, *198*
M. H. Springer & Assoc. (R), CA, *198*
Squires Resources Inc. (C), ON, *590*
Staff Resources, Inc. (C), SC, *590*
Staffing Edge, Inc. (C), IA, *590*
C. J. Stafford & Assoc. (C), ON, *591*
Stafford Consulting Group (R), CA, *198*
StaffWriters Plus (C), NY, *591*
Stanton Chase Int'l. (R), MD, *198*
The Stark Wilton Group (R), MI, *199*
Steinfield & Assoc. (C), TX, *592*
Stephens Assoc. Ltd., Inc. (R), OH, *200*
Peter Sterling & Co. (C), TX, *592*
Sterling Int'l. (R), NJ, *200*
Steven Douglas Assoc. (C), FL, *593*
Steven Michaels & Assoc. (C), NY, *593*
The Stevens Group (R), TX, *200*
Stevens, Valentine & McKeever (C), NJ, *593*
The Stewart Group (C), FL, *593*
Stewart, Stein & Scott, Ltd. (R), MN, *200*
Stone Assoc. LLC (C), MI, *594*
Stone Enterprises Ltd. (C), IL, *594*
Stone, Murphy & Olson (R), MN, *201*
DM Stone Personnel Services (C), CA, *594*
Stoopen Asociados, S.C./EMA Partners Int'l. (R), MX, *202*
Straight & Co. (R), GA, *202*
Mark Stranberg & Assoc. Inc. (R), MA, *202*
Strategic Advancement Inc. (R), NJ, *202*
Strategic Alliance Network, Ltd. (C), OH, *595*
Strategic Alternatives (R), CA, *202*
Strategic Executives, Inc. (R), CT, *202*
W. R. Strathmann Assoc. (R), NY, *203*
Stratin Assoc. (C), NJ, *596*
Strauss Personnel Service (C), PA, *596*
Stroman Int'l., Inc. (R), CO, *204*
Success Seekers Connection (C), FL, *596*
Sudina Search, Inc. (C), MD, *596*
Sullivan & Company (R), NY, *204*
Synagent Inc. (C), ON, *597*
Synapse Human Resource Consulting Group (R), TX, *205*
Synergy 2000 (C), DC, *597*
Systems One Ltd. (C), IL, *598*
Systems Personnel, Inc. (C), NY, *598*
Systems Research Inc. (SRI) (C), IL, *598*
Systems Search (C), IL, *599*
T. H. Hunter, Inc. (C), MN, *599*
The Talley Group (R), VA, *205*
Roy Talman & Assoc. (C), IL, *599*
Martin Stevens Tamaren & Assoc., Inc. (R), CA, *206*
Tarbex (C), DC, *599*
Tate & Assoc., Inc. (R), NJ, *207*
Tax Network Resources, Inc. (C), NY, *600*
TaxSearch Inc. (R), OK, *207*
Taylor Winfield (R), TX, *207*
Techno-Trac Systems, Inc. (C), NY, *603*
Techsearch Services Inc. (C), CT, *603*
TeleManagement Search (C), NY, *605*
Telford, Adams & Alexander (R), CA, *208*
Tennyson Advisors (R), NY, *208*
Thomas Lyle & Co. (C), IL, *606*
Thomas Mangum Co. (R), CA, *208*
Thomas, Whelan Assoc., Inc. (C), DC, *606*
Richard Thompson Assoc., Inc. (R), MN, *209*
Thor, Inc. (C), CA, *606*
Tittemore Cowan Assoc. (C), AB, *607*
TPS Staffing Solutions (C), IN, *608*
Traynor Confidential, Ltd. (C), NY, *609*
TRH Assoc., Inc. (R), NY, *210*
Triad Consultants, Inc. (C), NJ, *609*
Triumph Consulting, Inc. (R), IA, *210*
Trout & Assoc. Inc. (R), UT, *211*
Trowbridge & Co., Inc. (R), MA, *211*
Tryon & Heideman, LLC (R), MO, *211*
TSW Assoc., LLC (R), CT, *211*
Tucker Assoc. (R), NJ, *211*
The Thomas Tucker Co. (R), CA, *211*
Tully/Woodmansee Int'l. Inc. (R), FL, *212*
Tuttle Venture Group, Inc. (R), TX, *212*
Unisearch Search & Recruiting Inc. (C), CA, *611*
United Personnel Services (C), MA, *611*
Unlimited Staffing Solutions, Inc. (C), MI, *611*
The Urban Placement Service (C), TX, *611*
Verkamp-Joyce Assoc., Inc. (R), IL, *213*
The Verriez Group Inc. (R), ON, *213*
Victor White Int'l. (C), CA, *612*
Vincenty & Co. (C), OH, *612*
Vlcek & Company, Inc. (R), CA, *214*
Beverly von Winckler & Assoc. (C), IL, *613*
Robert H. Wadsworth & Assoc., Inc. (R), AZ, *214*
Wallace Management Co. (R), TN, *215*
Linda Walter & Associes (C), QE, *615*
Lee H. Walton & Assoc. (R), NY, *215*
The Ward Group (R), MA, *215*
R. J. Watkins & Co., Ltd. (R), CA, *216*
Scott Watson & Assoc., Inc. (R), FL, *216*
The Wayne Group, Ltd. (C), NY, *616*
Webb, Johnson Assoc., Inc. (R), NY, *216*
S. B. Webster & Associates (R), MA, *217*
Wegner & Assoc. (C), WI, *617*
Weinstein & Co. (R), MA, *217*
S. E. Weinstein Co. (R), IL, *217*
D. L. Weiss & Assoc. (R), CA, *217*
C. Weiss Assoc., Inc. (C), NY, *618*
The Wellesley Group, Inc. (R), IL, *217*
Wellington Management Group (R), PA, *217*
Wells, Bradley & Assoc., Inc. (C), MN, *618*
Werbin Assoc. Executive Search, Inc. (C), NY, *618*
Western Management Consultants (R), BC, *218*
WestPacific National Search, Inc. (C), CA, *619*
S. J. Wexler Assoc., Inc. (R), NY, *219*
K. L. Whitney Company (R), NJ, *219*
The Whitney Group (R), NY, *219*
Whitney Smith Co. (C), TX, *620*
Whittlesey & Assoc., Inc. (R), PA, *220*
Daniel Wier & Assoc. (R), CA, *220*
Wilcox Bertoux & Miller (R), CA, *220*
Wilder & Assoc. (C), VA, *620*
Wilder, Gammel Partners, Ltd. (R), CA, *220*
The Wilkie Group Int'l. (R), ON, *220*
Williams Executive Search, Inc. (R), MN, *221*
Willis & Assoc. (R), OH, *221*
William Willis Worldwide Inc. (R), CT, *221*
Wills Consulting Assoc. Inc. (R), CT, *221*
The Windham Group (R), OH, *222*
Windsor International (R), GA, *222*
Wing Tips & Pumps, Inc. (C), MI, *623*
Winter, Wyman & Co. (C), MA, *623*
Wisnewski & Assoc. (R), CA, *223*
D. S. Wolf Assoc., Inc. (R), NY, *223*
Louise Wood & Assoc. (C), NY, *624*
Wood, Franchot Inc. (R), MN, *224*
Woodworth Int'l. Group (R), OR, *224*
Working Relationships, Inc. (C), MN, *624*
Worldwide Medical Services (C), CA, *625*
WTW Assoc., Inc. (R), NY, *225*
R. S. Wyatt Assoc., Inc. (R), TX, *225*
Wyndham Mills Int'l., Inc. (R), GA, *225*
Xavier Associates, Inc. (R), MA, *226*
Yormak & Assoc. (C), CA, *626*
Youngblood Assoc. (C), NC, *626*
Steven Yungerberg Assoc., Inc. (R), MN, *226*
Yungner & Bormann (R), MN, *226*
Zen Zen Int'l. Inc. (C), MB, *627*
Zingaro & Company (R), TX, *227*
Michael D. Zinn & Assoc., Inc. (R), NJ, *227*
Zona & Assoc., Inc. (C), NY, *628*
Zwell Int'l. (R), IL, *228*

H.10 Commercial banking

A.L.S. Group (C), NJ, *232*
Abacus Group LLC (C), NY, *232*
The Alexander Group (R), TX, *3*
Allman & Co., Inc. (C), NC, *245*
Ambridge Management Corp. (C), ON, *247*
Ames Assoc. Inc. (C), MD, *249*
Analytic Recruiting, Inc. (C), NY, *249*
Angel Group Int'l. (C), KY, *250*
Argonaut Partners, LLC (R), CA, *6*
ATS Executive Recruitment (C), GA, *255*
Aurora Tech Search (C), ON, *256*
The Ayers Group, Inc. (R), NY, *9*
Baker, Nelms & Montgomery (C), IL, *258*

The Bankers Group (C), IL, *258*
The Bankers Register (C), NY, *259*
Bankers Search, L.L.C. (C), CT, *259*
Barger & Sargeant, Inc. (R), NH, *11*
Barr Associates (C), NY, *260*
Barton Assoc., Inc. (R), TX, *12*
Battalia Winston Int'l./The Euram Consultants Group (R), NY, *13*
Becker, Norton & Co. (R), PA, *14*
Becker Project Resources, Inc. (C), OR, *262*
Bell Wishingrad Partners Inc. (R), NY, *15*
Bennett Search & Consulting Co. (R), FL, *16*
Bergeris & Co., Inc. (C), NY, *265*
Berkhemer/Clayton, Inc. (R), CA, *16*
Birch & Associes (C), QE, *267*
Blackhawk Advantage, Inc. (C), CA, *267*
The Blackman Kallick Search Division (C), IL, *267*
The BMW Group, Inc. (C), NY, *268*
Boardroom Consultants/Kenny Kindler Tholke (R), NY, *19*
Bonifield Assoc. (C), NJ, *269*
Brandjes Assoc. (C), MD, *272*
J. B. Brown & Assoc., Inc. (C), OH, *275*
Butterfass, Pepe & MacCallan Inc. (R), NJ, *25*
C and P Marketing, Ltd. (C), OK, *278*
C. P. Consulting (R), PA, *26*
C. R. Assoc. (C), CA, *278*
C/R Associates (C), NY, *278*
Cambridge Management Planning (R), ON, *27*
Canny, Bowen Inc. (R), NY, *27*
Capital Markets Resources, Inc. (C), NC, *281*
Career Consultants (R), IN, *29*
Christian & Timbers, Inc. (R), OH, *34*
The Christopher Group (C), NC, *291*
Howard Clark Assoc. (C), NJ, *292*
Clinton, Charles, Wise & Co. (C), FL, *293*
Cochran, Cochran & Yale, Inc. (R), NY, *36*
Computer Security Placement Service (C), MA, *296*
The Consortium (C), NY, *296*
Consulting Resource Group, Inc. (C), GA, *297*
COR Management Services, Ltd. (C), NY, *298*
Cornell Group Int'l. Consulting, Inc. (R), NY, *41*
Corporate Search, Inc. (C), NY, *301*
Corso, Mizgala + French (R), ON, *42*
Creative Financial Staffing (C), MA, *303*
Crist Partners, Ltd. (R), IL, *43*
Cromwell Partners, Inc. (R), NY, *43*
Crown Advisors, Inc. (R), PA, *43*
Tony Curtis & Associates (C), ON, *305*
Custom Resources (C), AL, *305*
Cypress Int'l., Inc. (R), FL, *45*
D & M Associates (C), PA, *306*
Alfred Daniels & Assoc., Inc. (R), CA, *46*
DARE Personnel Inc. (C), ON, *307*
Alan Darling Consulting (R), VT, *46*
David Anthony Personnel Assoc., Inc. (C), NJ, *308*
Davis & James, Inc. (C), MO, *308*
Delta Management Group Ltd. (C), ON, *310*
Delta Services (R), TX, *48*
Diamond Tax Recruiting (C), NY, *312*
Dieckmann & Assoc., Ltd. (R), IL, *51*
Discovery, The Staffing Specialists, Inc. (C), IL, *312*
Dise & Co. (R), OH, *52*
Diversified Search, Inc. (R), PA, *52*
DLG Assoc., Inc. (R), NC, *53*
J P Donnelly Assoc., Inc. (C), NY, *314*
Dotson & Assoc. (R), NY, *54*
Dow Consultants Int'l. (C), NY, *314*
Drummond Assoc., Inc. (C), NY, *315*
DuBrul Management Co. (C), NY, *315*
Dunhill of Ft. Collins, Inc. (C), CO, *319*
Dunhill Professional Search of Omaha, Inc. (C), NE, *321*
Dunhill Professional Search of Winston-Salem (C), NC, *322*
Dunhill Personnel Service of Fargo (C), ND, *322*
Dunhill Professional Search of Bucks-Mont., Inc. (C), PA, *322*
Dunhill Professional Search of Richmond (C), VA, *323*
E O Technical (C), CT, *324*
EDI, Inc. (C), MD, *326*
D. C. Egan & Assoc. (C), GA, *327*
Egan Search Group (R), NY, *57*
Eggers Consulting Co., Inc. (C), NE, *327*
William J. Elam & Assoc. (R), NE, *58*
Steve Ellis (C), CA, *328*
The Executive Source Inc. (R), NY, *64*
eXsource Inc. (C), SC, *337*
Eyler Assoc., Inc. (R), IA, *64*
Federal Placement Services (C), NY, *339*
Fidelity Search Group, Inc. (R), PA, *66*
Financial Resource Assoc., Inc. (C), FL, *340*
Eileen Finn & Assoc., Inc. (C), NY, *341*
Finnegan & Assoc. (R), CA, *67*
First Union Executive Search (R), NC, *67*
Flynn, Hannock, Inc. (R), CT, *69*
Fogec Consultants, Inc. (R), WI, *69*
F-O-R-T-U-N-E Personnel Consultants of Boise (R), ID, *70*
Foster Partners (R), NY, *70*
Gerald Frisch Assoc., Inc. (R), NY, *72*
C. F. Furr & Co. (R), NC, *72*
The Furst Group, Inc. (R), IL, *72*
Gardiner, Townsend & Assoc. (R), NY, *74*
Peter Gasperini & Assoc., Inc. (R), NY, *75*
Gateway Group Personnel, LLC (C), TN, *355*
Gavin Forbes & Price (R), CA, *75*
GES Services, Inc. (R), NY, *76*
Gielow Assoc., Inc. (R), WI, *76*
Gilbert Scott Assoc., LLC (C), MA, *357*
Gimbel & Assoc. (C), FL, *357*
J. P. Gleason Assoc., Inc. (R), IL, *77*
Global Technologies Group Inc. (C), NC, *359*
The Tracy Glover Co. (R), TX, *78*
Gnodde Assoc. (C), IL, *359*
The Gogates Group, Inc. (R), NY, *79*
Gould, McCoy & Chadick, Inc. (R), NY, *80*
Robert Graham Assoc. (R), RI, *81*
Grauss & Co. (C), CA, *362*
Greene & Co. (C), MA, *362*
Greene-Levin-Snyder LLC (C), NY, *362*
H.Q. Search, Inc. (C), IL, *365*
Russ Hadick & Assoc. Inc. (C), OH, *365*
Hale Assoc. (R), IL, *84*
Handy HRM (R), NY, *86*
Hanley & Assoc. (R), FL, *86*
The Hanover Consulting Group (C), MD, *368*
Harris McCully Assoc., Inc. (C), NY, *369*
Hayden Group, Inc. (R), MA, *88*
Thomas E. Hedefine Assoc. (C), ON, *375*
G. W. Henn & Co. (R), OH, *91*
Henrietta's Personnel & Executive Search, Inc. (C), FL, *376*
Hessel Assoc., Inc. (C), NY, *377*
Higdon Prince Inc. (R), NY, *93*
Highland Search Group, L.L.C. (R), NY, *93*
Higley, Hall & Co., Inc. (R), MA, *93*
Hintz Associates (C), NY, *378*
Hochman & Assoc. (C), CA, *379*
The Hollins Group, Inc. (R), IL, *95*
David C. Horn Executive Search (C), TX, *381*
Howe & Assoc. (R), PA, *97*
Human Capital Resources, Inc. (C), FL, *384*
Human Resources Management Hawaii, Inc. (C), HI, *384*
Hunegnaw Executive Search (C), OH, *384*
Hunt & Howe Inc. (R), NY, *99*
Hyde Danforth & Co. (R), TX, *100*
IM Independent Management Recruiters (R), TN, *101*
InteliSearch, Inc. (R), CT, *102*
International Executive Recruiters (C), OH, *393*
International Market Recruiters (C), NY, *393*
Interspace Interactive, Inc. (C), NY, *394*
Iona Partners (C), CA, *394*
Isaacson, Miller (R), MA, *104*
Ives & Associates, Inc. (C), OH, *395*
J. Nicholas Arthur (R), MA, *104*
J. R. Scott & Assoc., Ltd. (C), IL, *395*
Jeffrey Meryl Assoc., Inc. (C), NJ, *398*
JNB Assoc., Inc. (C), MA, *399*
John Ryan Assoc., LLC. (C), NY, *399*
The Jonathan Stevens Group, Inc. (R), NJ, *108*
Kaplan & Assoc., Inc. (R), PA, *109*
A.T. Kearney Executive Search (R), IL, *111*
Keeley Consulting Inc. (C), ON, *404*
Kennedy & Co. (R), IL, *112*
Kensington Int'l., Inc. (R), IL, *113*
Kershner & Co. (R), DC, *113*
Keystone Consulting Group (C), GA, *406*
Lee Koehn Assoc., Inc. (R), OR, *116*
KPA Assoc., Inc. (C), NY, *408*
Kyle Assoc. (C), NY, *410*
L T M Assoc. (C), IL, *410*
Lamay Assoc., Inc. (R), CT, *124*
LanSo Int'l., Inc. (C), NY, *413*
Lawrence L. Lapham, Inc. (R), NY, *124*
Larsen & Lee, Inc. (R), MD, *125*

INDUSTRIES

Larsen, Whitney, Blecksmith & Zilliacus, Inc. (R), CA, *125*
Lascelle & Assoc. Inc. (C), ON, *413*
Leaders-Trust Int'l./Carce y Asociados, S.C. (R), MX, *127*
Vincent Lee Assoc. (C), NY, *415*
Lifter & Assoc. (C), CA, *418*
Lloyd Associates (R), GA, *130*
Locke & Assoc. (R), NC, *131*
Charles Luntz & Assoc., Inc. (R), MO, *132*
Lyons Pruitt Int'l. (R), PA, *132*
M/J/A Partners (R), IL, *133*
Madison MacArthur Inc. (R), ON, *133*
Management Advisors Int'l., Inc. (C), NC, *424*
Management One Consultants (C), ON, *425*
Management Recruiters of Nassau, Inc. (R), NY, *134*
Management Recruiters of Birmingham-South, Inc. (C), AL, *438*
Management Recruiters of Berkeley (C), CA, *439*
Management Recruiters of Ft. Myers, FL. (C), FL, *443*
Management Recruiters of St. Augustine (C), FL, *444*
Management Recruiters of Columbus, Inc. (C), GA, *445*
Management Recruiters of Duluth (C), GA, *445*
Management Recruiters - Towne Lake (C), GA, *446*
Management Recruiters of Chicago-North Shore (C), IL, *447*
Management Recruiters of North Oakland County, Inc. (C), MI, *452*
Management Recruiters of Princeton (C), NJ, *454*
Management Recruiters of Manhattan on Broadway (C), NY, *455*
Management Recruiters of Youngstown (C), OH, *458*
Management Recruiters of Mentor, Inc. (C), OH, *458*
Management Recruiters of Pittsburgh (C), PA, *459*
Management Recruiters of Puerto Rico (C), PR, *460*
Management Recruiters The Delta Group, Inc. (C), TN, *461*
Management Recruiters of San Marcos (C), TX, *463*
Management Recruiters of Spokane (C), WA, *465*
Management Recruiters of Milwaukee - Downtown (C), WI, *466*
Management Resource Group, Ltd. (C), IA, *467*
Management Resource Group (C), MN, *467*
Masserman & Assoc., Inc. (R), NY, *138*
K. E. McCarthy & Assoc. (R), CA, *139*
McCarthy Assoc. National BancSearch, LLC (C), LA, *473*
MCS Assoc. (R), CA, *142*
Mehta Consulting (C), NJ, *478*
Walter Meyer & Assoc. (R), NY, *144*
Michael Thomas, Inc. (C), OH, *480*
Millar Walker & Gay (R), ON, *144*
Miller/Davis & Assoc., Inc. (C), NY, *482*
Paul Misarti Inc. (C), NY, *483*
Mitchell Martin Inc. (C), NY, *483*
Mogul Consultants, Inc. (C), NY, *483*
Oscar Montaño, Inc. (R), CA, *146*
Morgan Stampfl, Inc. (C), NY, *485*
Mortgage & Financial Personnel Services (C), CA, *486*
MSI Int'l. (C), GA, *486*
The MVP Group (C), NY, *487*
DDJ Myers, Ltd. (R), AZ, *150*
Nason & Nason (C), FL, *488*
National Bank & Finance Executive Search (C), CA, *488*
National Register Columbus Inc. (C), OH, *490*
Don Neal & Assoc. (C), OK, *491*
Marc Nichols Assoc., Inc. (C), NY, *493*
Norman Broadbent Int'l., Inc. (R), NY, *152*
Ronald Norris & Assoc. (C), IL, *495*
NorthStar Technologies, Inc. (C), NY, *496*
O'Brien & Bell (R), OH, *153*
O'Toole & Company, Inc. (R), IL, *154*
Olympian Recruitment, Ltd. (C), NY, *498*
The Options Group, Inc. (C), NY, *499*
Arthur Pann Assoc., Inc. (C), NY, *502*
Carol Park (C), MO, *502*
Parker Page Group (C), FL, *503*
Pearson, Caldwell & Farnsworth (R), CA, *161*
Richard Peterson & Assoc., Inc. (R), GA, *163*
Robert E. Pfaendler & Assoc., Inc. (C), OR, *509*
Phillips Resource Group (C), SC, *510*
Picard Int'l., Ltd. (R), NY, *164*
Plante & Moran, LLP (R), MI, *165*
Al Ponaman Company, Inc. (C), CA, *514*
Elan Pratzer & Partners Inc. (R), ON, *167*
Preston & Co. (R), NJ, *167*
The Primary Group, Inc. (R), FL, *168*
Prime Management Group Inc. (C), ON, *518*
Procom (C), ON, *519*
Professional Personnel Consultants, Inc. (C), MI, *521*
Prospective Personnel Service, Inc. (C), OK, *524*
Quirk-Corporon & Assoc., Inc. (C), WI, *527*
R.A.N. Assoc., Inc. (C), OH, *528*
Joanne E. Ratner Search (C), NY, *529*
Ray & Berndtson (R), TX, *171*
Razzino-Claymore Assoc. (C), NJ, *530*
Real Estate Executive Search, Inc. (C), CA, *531*
Redden & McGrath Assoc., Inc. (R), NY, *173*
Redden-Shaffer Group (R), CA, *173*
Research Personnel Consultants (C), ON, *534*
Resource Services, Inc. (C), NY, *534*
Response Staffing Services (C), NY, *534*
Russell Reynolds Assoc., Inc. (R), NY, *176*
Reynolds Consulting Int'l. (R), ON, *177*
Rhodes Associates (R), NY, *177*
Riotto-Jones Assoc. (R), NY, *178*
Roberts Ryan & Bentley, Inc. (R), MD, *179*
Rockwood Assoc. (C), NY, *540*
The Rogan Group, Inc. (C), CA, *541*
Ryan-Allen & Assoc., Inc. (C), CA, *549*
Ryman, Bell, Green & Michaels, Inc. (C), TX, *549*
Sales & Management Search, Inc. (C), IL, *551*
Sales Consultants of Nashua-Manchester (C), NH, *560*
Salzmann Gay Assoc., Inc. (R), PA, *184*
Sanford Rose Assoc. - Atlanta North (C), GA, *566*
Sanford Rose Assoc. - Oak Brook (C), IL, *567*
Sanford Rose Assoc. - Philadelphia North (C), PA, *570*
Sanford Rose Assoc. - Pittsburgh North (C), PA, *570*
Santangelo Consultants Inc. (C), NY, *571*
Schattle & Duquette (C), RI, *571*
Schenck & Assoc. SC (C), WI, *572*
Schulenburg & Assoc. (C), GA, *572*
Scott Sibley Assoc. (C), NY, *573*
Search America, Inc. (C), PA, *573*
The Search Company (R), ON, *186*
Search Innovations, Inc. (R), PA, *187*
Secura/Burnett Partners (R), CA, *187*
J. R. Seehusen Assoc., Inc. (R), IA, *188*
SFB Legal Search (C), NY, *579*
Shannahan & Co., Inc. (R), CA, *189*
Siger & Assoc., LLC (C), CT, *581*
Smith Search, S.C. (R), MX, *194*
Snelling Search (C), LA, *586*
Andrea Sobel & Assoc., Inc. (C), CA, *586*
Specialty Consultants Inc. (R), PA, *195*
SpencerStuart (R), NY, *196*
Stafford Consulting Group (R), CA, *198*
Peter Sterling & Co. (C), TX, *592*
Steven Michaels & Assoc. (C), NY, *593*
The Stevens Group (R), TX, *200*
Stone Assoc. LLC (C), MI, *594*
DM Stone Personnel Services (C), CA, *594*
Stoopen Asociados, S.C./EMA Partners Int'l. (R), MX, *202*
Mark Stranberg & Assoc. Inc. (R), MA, *202*
W. R. Strathmann Assoc. (R), NY, *203*
Stratin Assoc. (C), NJ, *596*
Success Seekers Connection (C), FL, *596*
Sullivan & Company (R), NY, *204*
Synagent Inc. (C), ON, *597*
Systems Personnel, Inc. (C), NY, *598*
The Talley Group (R), VA, *205*
Tax Network Resources, Inc. (C), NY, *600*
Techno-Trac Systems, Inc. (C), NY, *603*
Techsearch Services Inc. (C), CT, *603*
TeleManagement Search (C), NY, *605*
Thomas, Whelan Assoc., Inc. (C), DC, *606*
TRH Assoc., Inc. (R), NY, *210*
Triad Consultants, Inc. (C), NJ, *609*
Triumph Consulting, Inc. (R), IA, *210*
Tully/Woodmansee Int'l. Inc. (R), FL, *212*
Unisearch Search & Recruiting Inc. (C), CA, *611*
The Ward Group (R), MA, *215*
Scott Watson & Assoc., Inc. (R), FL, *216*
S. E. Weinstein Co. (R), IL, *217*
C. Weiss Assoc., Inc. (C), NY, *618*
Wells, Bradley & Assoc., Inc. (C), MN, *618*

The Whitney Group (R), NY, *219*
Whitney Smith Co. (C), TX, *620*
Daniel Wier & Assoc. (R), CA, *220*
Wilcox Bertoux & Miller (R), CA, *220*
Wilder & Assoc. (C), VA, *620*
The Wilkie Group Int'l. (R), ON, *220*
Wills Consulting Assoc. Inc. (R), CT, *221*
Wing Tips & Pumps, Inc. (C), MI, *623*
D. S. Wolf Assoc., Inc. (R), NY, *223*
Youngblood Assoc. (C), NC, *626*

H.11 Investment banking

A.L.S. Group (C), NJ, *232*
Abacus Group LLC (C), NY, *232*
Accent On Achievement, Inc. (C), MI, *233*
ACSYS Resources, Inc. (C), DE, *238*
Active Search & Placement Inc. (C), CA, *239*
Advisors' Search Group, Inc. (C), NY, *241*
Allman & Co., Inc. (C), NC, *245*
Ames Assoc. Inc. (C), MD, *249*
Analytic Recruiting, Inc. (C), NY, *249*
Anthony Michael & Co. (C), MA, *251*
Argonaut Partners, LLC (R), CA, *6*
Atlantic Pacific Group (C), CA, *255*
ATS Executive Recruitment (C), GA, *255*
The Ayers Group, Inc. (R), NY, *9*
Baker, Nelms & Montgomery (C), IL, *258*
The Bankers Group (C), IL, *258*
Barr Associates (C), NY, *260*
Bartholdi & Co., Inc. (R), CO, *12*
Battalia Winston Int'l./The Euram Consultants Group (R), NY, *13*
Bell Wishingrad Partners Inc. (R), NY, *15*
Benson Associates (C), NY, *264*
Bergeris & Co., Inc. (C), NY, *265*
BFW, Inc. (C), GA, *266*
Bialecki Inc. (R), NY, *17*
Birch & Associes (C), QE, *267*
The Blackman Kallick Search Division (C), IL, *267*
BLB Consulting (C), NY, *268*
The BMW Group, Inc. (C), NY, *268*
Bonifield Assoc. (C), NJ, *269*
Brandjes Assoc. (C), MD, *272*
The Brentwood Group, Inc. (R), NJ, *22*
Butterfass, Pepe & MacCallan Inc. (R), NJ, *25*
Canny, Bowen Inc. (R), NY, *27*
Capital Consulting & Research, Inc. (R), CT, *28*
Capital Consulting Group, Inc. (R), MD, *28*
Capital Markets Resources, Inc. (C), NC, *281*
Career Consultants (R), IN, *29*
Rosemary Cass Ltd. (R), CT, *31*
CEC Associates (R), MA, *32*
Computer Security Placement Service (C), MA, *296*
The Consortium (C), NY, *296*
Conspectus, Inc. (C), NY, *297*
The Consulting Group Ltd. (R), NY, *40*
COR Management Services, Ltd. (C), NY, *298*
Cornell Group Int'l. Consulting, Inc. (R), NY, *41*
Creative Financial Staffing (C), MA, *303*
Crispi, Wagner & Co., Inc. (R), NY, *43*
Crist Partners, Ltd. (R), IL, *43*
Cromwell Partners, Inc. (R), NY, *43*
Crown Advisors, Inc. (R), PA, *43*
Cypress Int'l., Inc. (R), FL, *45*
Alfred Daniels & Assoc., Inc. (R), CA, *46*
Davis & James, Inc. (C), MO, *308*
The Dayton Group, Ltd. (C), NY, *309*
Defrain Mayer (R), KS, *48*
S. W. Delano & Co. (R), CT, *48*
Diamond Tax Recruiting (C), NY, *312*
Discovery, The Staffing Specialists, Inc. (C), IL, *312*
Diversified Search, Inc. (R), PA, *52*
DLG Assoc., Inc. (R), NC, *53*
J P Donnelly Assoc., Inc. (C), NY, *314*
Douglas-Allen, Inc. (R), MA, *54*
Dow Consultants Int'l. (C), NY, *314*
Drinkwater & Assoc. (R), MA, *54*
Drummond Assoc., Inc. (C), NY, *315*
Dunhill Professional Search of Bucks-Mont., Inc. (C), PA, *322*
Egan Search Group (R), NY, *57*
Mark Elzweig Co., Ltd. (C), NY, *329*
Empire International (R), PA, *59*
Erikson Consulting Assoc., Inc. (R), NY, *60*
The Evans Search Group (R), CT, *61*
The Execu/Search Group (C), NY, *332*
Executive Access Inc. (R), NY, *62*
Executive Partners Inc. (C), CT, *333*
Executive Search Partners (R), NY, *63*
Executive Search Placements, Inc. (C), CO, *336*
The Executive Source Inc. (R), NY, *64*
Fabian Assoc. Inc. (C), NY, *338*
Fagan & Company (R), PA, *64*
Financial Connections Company (C), VA, *340*
Financial Resource Assoc., Inc. (C), FL, *340*
Financial Search Group, Inc. (R), MA, *66*
Eileen Finn & Assoc., Inc. (C), NY, *341*
First Union Executive Search (R), NC, *67*
Focus Consulting Services, Inc. (C), FL, *342*
Fogec Consultants, Inc. (R), WI, *69*
F-O-R-T-U-N-E Personnel Consultants of Boise (R), ID, *70*
Foster Associates (C), NJ, *351*
Foster Partners (R), NY, *70*
Franklin Allen Consultants, Ltd. (R), NY, *71*
Gerald Frisch Assoc., Inc. (R), NY, *72*
Futures Int'l. (R), CT, *73*
Gardiner, Townsend & Assoc. (R), NY, *74*
Peter Gasperini & Assoc., Inc. (R), NY, *75*
Gateway Group Personnel, LLC (C), TN, *355*
GES Services, Inc. (R), NY, *76*
Gilbert Scott Assoc., LLC (C), MA, *357*
Gilbert Tweed Assoc. Inc. (R), NY, *76*
Global Executive Search Group (C), MA, *358*
Global Technologies Group Inc. (C), NC, *359*
The Tracy Glover Co. (R), TX, *78*
Gnodde Assoc. (C), IL, *359*
The Gogates Group, Inc. (R), NY, *79*
Goodkind Assoc. Inc. (C), NY, *360*
Goodrich & Sherwood Assoc., Inc. (R), NY, *79*
Grant Cooper & Assoc., Inc. (R), MO, *81*
Grauss & Co. (C), CA, *362*
Greene & Co. (C), MA, *362*
Greene-Levin-Snyder LLC (C), NY, *362*
H.Q. Search, Inc. (C), IL, *365*
Hadley Lockwood, Inc. (R), NY, *84*
Hale Assoc. (R), IL, *84*
K. C. Hale, Inc. (R), CT, *85*
Handy HRM (R), NY, *86*
The Hanover Consulting Group (C), MD, *368*
Hanzel & Co., Inc. (R), NY, *86*
Harris McCully Assoc., Inc. (C), NY, *369*
Thomas E. Hedefine Assoc. (C), ON, *375*
Jay Heino Company, LLC (C), NY, *375*
Hessel Assoc., Inc. (C), NY, *377*
Higbee Assoc., Inc. (C), CT, *377*
Higdon Prince Inc. (R), NY, *93*
Highland Search Group, L.L.C. (R), NY, *93*
Hochman & Assoc. (C), CA, *379*
Howe & Assoc. (R), PA, *97*
Hreshko Consulting Group (C), NJ, *382*
Hunt & Howe Inc. (R), NY, *99*
Integrated Management Solutions (C), NY, *390*
International Market Recruiters (C), NY, *393*
Iona Partners (C), CA, *394*
Isaacson, Miller (R), MA, *104*
Ives & Associates, Inc. (C), OH, *395*
J. Nicholas Arthur (R), MA, *104*
J. R. Scott & Assoc., Ltd. (C), IL, *395*
Pendleton James Assoc., Inc. (R), NY, *105*
Jeffrey Meryl Assoc., Inc. (C), NJ, *398*
JNB Assoc., Inc. (C), MA, *399*
John Ryan Assoc., LLC. (C), NY, *399*
The Jonathan Stevens Group, Inc. (R), NJ, *108*
JT Assoc. (C), CT, *401*
A.T. Kearney Executive Search (R), IL, *111*
Keeley Consulting Inc. (C), ON, *404*
Kennedy & Co. (R), IL, *112*
Kershner & Co. (R), DC, *113*
Keystone Consulting Group (C), GA, *406*
The Kinlin Co., Inc. (R), MA, *115*
KPA Assoc., Inc. (C), NY, *408*
John Kurosky & Assoc. (R), CA, *122*
Kyle Assoc. (C), NY, *410*
L T M Assoc. (C), IL, *410*
L&L Assoc. Global Search (C), PA, *411*
E. J. Lance Management Assoc., Inc. (C), NY, *412*
LanSo Int'l., Inc. (C), NY, *413*
Larsen, Whitney, Blecksmith & Zilliacus, Inc. (R), CA, *125*
LAS Management Consulting Group, Inc. (R), NJ, *125*
Lascelle & Assoc. Inc. (C), ON, *413*
Layne-Mendez & Co. (R), TX, *127*
Leslie Kavanagh Assoc., Inc. (C), NY, *416*
Lewis & Blank Int'l. (R), CA, *129*
Livingston, Robert & Co. (R), CT, *130*
Lloyd Associates (R), GA, *130*
Lyons Pruitt Int'l. (R), PA, *132*
Magellan Int'l., L.P. (C), TX, *422*

Management Alliance Group, Inc. (R), NJ, *134*
Management Recruiters of Nassau, Inc. (R), NY, *134*
Management Recruiters of Ft. Myers, FL. (C), FL, *443*
Management Recruiters of St. Augustine (C), FL, *444*
Management Recruiters of Duluth (C), GA, *445*
Management Recruiters of Siouxland (C), IA, *449*
Management Recruiters of Great Neck (C), NY, *454*
Management Recruiters of Princeton (C), NJ, *454*
Management Recruiters of Manhattan on Broadway (C), NY, *455*
Management Recruiters of Pittsburgh (C), PA, *459*
Management Recruiters The Delta Group, Inc. (C), TN, *461*
Management Recruiters of Houston (C), TX, *462*
ManTech Consulting (C), NY, *468*
Martin Partners, L.L.C. (R), IL, *137*
Masserman & Assoc., Inc. (R), NY, *138*
McCann, Choi & Associates, LLC (R), NY, *139*
McCarthy Assoc. National BancSearch, LLC (C), LA, *473*
The McLeod Group, Inc. (R), CT, *141*
The Medley Group (C), CA, *477*
Mehta Consulting (C), NJ, *478*
META/MAT, Ltd. (R), NJ, *144*
Millar Walker & Gay (R), ON, *144*
Miller/Davis & Assoc., Inc. (C), NY, *482*
Paul Misarti Inc. (C), NY, *483*
Mitchell Martin Inc. (C), NY, *483*
Mogul Consultants, Inc. (C), NY, *483*
Morgan Stampfl, Inc. (C), NY, *485*
MSI Int'l. (C), GA, *486*
Much & Co. (R), NY, *148*
Jennifer Munro & Partners, Inc. (R), SC, *149*
The MVP Group (C), NY, *487*
DDJ Myers, Ltd. (R), AZ, *150*
Nason & Nason (C), FL, *488*
National Affirmative Action Career Network, Inc. (C), CO, *488*
National Bank & Finance Executive Search (C), CA, *488*
National Search, Inc.r (C), FL, *490*
Marc Nichols Assoc., Inc. (C), NY, *493*
Nichols Brown Int'l. (R), NY, *151*
Nordeman Grimm, Inc. (R), NY, *152*
Norman Broadbent Int'l., Inc. (R), NY, *152*
NorthStar Technologies, Inc. (C), NY, *496*
O'Sullivan Search Inc. (C), ON, *498*
O'Toole & Company, Inc. (R), IL, *154*
Olympian Recruitment, Ltd. (C), NY, *498*
The Options Group, Inc. (C), NY, *499*
The Oxbridge Group, Ltd. (C), PA, *500*
Pearson, Caldwell & Farnsworth (R), CA, *161*
Robert E. Pfaendler & Assoc., Inc. (C), OR, *509*
Picard Int'l., Ltd. (R), NY, *164*
Pinnacle Executive Group Inc. (C), MO, *512*
Pinnacle Group Int'l. (C), AZ, *512*
Pittleman & Assoc. (C), NY, *512*
The Prairie Group (C), IL, *515*
Preston & Co. (R), NJ, *167*
The Primary Group, Inc. (R), FL, *168*
The Quest Organization (C), NY, *527*
Rand Thompson Executive Search Consultants (C), NY, *528*
The Rankin Group, Ltd. (R), WI, *171*
Joanne E. Ratner Search (C), NY, *529*
Ray & Berndtson (R), TX, *171*
Reeve & Assoc. (C), CT, *533*
Response Staffing Services (C), NY, *534*
Russell Reynolds Assoc., Inc. (R), NY, *176*
Rhodes Associates (R), NY, *177*
Riotto-Jones Assoc. (R), NY, *178*
Rockwood Assoc. (C), NY, *540*
Rolland Ressources Humaines Inc. (R), QE, *181*
W. R. Rosato & Assoc., Inc. (R), NY, *182*
Royal Assoc. (C), CA, *547*
Russillo/Gardner/Spolsino (C), MA, *548*
Rylan Forbes Consulting Group, Inc. (C), NJ, *549*
Ryman, Bell, Green & Michaels, Inc. (C), TX, *549*
Sales & Management Search, Inc. (C), IL, *551*
Sales Consultants of Laurel Park, Inc. (C), MI, *560*
Sanford Rose Assoc. - Chicago (C), IL, *566*
Sanford Rose Assoc. - Oak Brook (C), IL, *567*
Sanford Rose Assoc. - Pittsburgh North (C), PA, *570*
Schoales & Assoc. Inc. (C), ON, *572*
Schulenburg & Assoc. (C), GA, *572*
Search America, Inc. (C), PA, *573*
The Search Center Inc. (C), TX, *574*
The Search Company (R), ON, *186*
Search Innovations, Inc. (R), PA, *187*
Search Int'l. (R), MA, *187*
Secura/Burnett Partners (R), CA, *187*
Shannahan & Co., Inc. (R), CA, *189*
Siger & Assoc., LLC (C), CT, *581*
Skipping Stone Inc. (C), VA, *582*
Smith Search, S.C. (R), MX, *194*
Sockwell & Assoc. (R), NC, *194*
Specialty Consultants Inc. (R), PA, *195*
SpencerStuart (R), NY, *196*
Spriggs & Co., Inc. (R), IL, *198*
M. H. Springer & Assoc. (R), CA, *198*
The Stark Wilton Group (R), MI, *199*
Peter Sterling & Co. (C), TX, *592*
Steven Douglas Assoc. (C), FL, *593*
Steven Michaels & Assoc. (C), NY, *593*
Stone Assoc. LLC (C), MI, *594*
DM Stone Personnel Services (C), CA, *594*
Mark Stranberg & Assoc. Inc. (R), MA, *202*
W. R. Strathmann Assoc. (R), NY, *203*
Sullivan & Company (R), NY, *204*
Techno-Trac Systems, Inc. (C), NY, *603*
Techsearch Services Inc. (C), CT, *603*
Tennyson Advisors (R), NY, *208*
Thomas, Whelan Assoc., Inc. (C), DC, *606*
Tittemore Cowan Assoc. (C), AB, *607*
TRH Assoc., Inc. (R), NY, *210*
TSW Assoc., LLC (R), CT, *211*
The Thomas Tucker Co. (R), CA, *211*
Vincenty & Co. (C), OH, *612*
The Wayne Group, Ltd. (C), NY, *616*
The Whitney Group (R), NY, *219*
Daniel Wier & Assoc. (R), CA, *220*
The Wilkie Group Int'l. (R), ON, *220*
William Willis Worldwide Inc. (R), CT, *221*
Wills Consulting Assoc. Inc. (R), CT, *221*
D. S. Wolf Assoc., Inc. (R), NY, *223*
Youngblood Assoc. (C), NC, *626*

H.12 Securities & commodities brokers

Abécassis Conseil (R), QE, *1*
ACSYS Resources, Inc. (C), DE, *238*
Active Search & Placement Inc. (C), CA, *239*
Allman & Co., Inc. (C), NC, *245*
Anthony Michael & Co. (C), MA, *251*
Argonaut Partners, LLC (R), CA, *6*
ATS Executive Recruitment (C), GA, *255*
The Ayers Group, Inc. (R), NY, *9*
Baker, Nelms & Montgomery (C), IL, *258*
The Bankers Group (C), IL, *258*
Behavioral Science Assoc., Inc. (R), AZ, *15*
Bell Wishingrad Partners Inc. (R), NY, *15*
Bergeris & Co., Inc. (C), NY, *265*
BFW, Inc. (C), GA, *266*
The BMW Group, Inc. (C), NY, *268*
Brandjes Assoc. (C), MD, *272*
Butterfass, Pepe & MacCallan Inc. (R), NJ, *25*
Capital Markets Resources, Inc. (C), NC, *281*
CEC Associates (R), MA, *32*
The Center for Career Advancement, LLC (C), NJ, *287*
Computer Security Placement Service (C), MA, *296*
Conspectus, Inc. (C), NY, *297*
The Consulting Group Ltd. (R), NY, *40*
COR Management Services, Ltd. (C), NY, *298*
Creative Financial Staffing (C), MA, *303*
Crispi, Wagner & Co., Inc. (R), NY, *43*
Crist Partners, Ltd. (R), IL, *43*
Cypress Int'l., Inc. (R), FL, *45*
Alfred Daniels & Assoc., Inc. (R), CA, *46*
DARE Personnel Inc. (C), ON, *307*
Davis & James, Inc. (C), MO, *308*
The Dayton Group, Ltd. (C), NY, *309*
S. W. Delano & Co. (R), CT, *48*
Descheneaux Recruitment Services Ltd. (C), BC, *311*
Discovery, The Staffing Specialists, Inc. (C), IL, *312*
Diversified Search, Inc. (R), PA, *52*
Drummond Assoc., Inc. (C), NY, *315*
Mark Elzweig Co., Ltd. (C), NY, *329*
The Execu/Search Group (C), NY, *332*
Financial Connections Company (C), VA, *340*
Financial Resource Assoc., Inc. (C), FL, *340*

Eileen Finn & Assoc., Inc. (C), NY, *341*
First Union Executive Search (R), NC, *67*
Fogec Consultants, Inc. (R), WI, *69*
Fortune Consultants of Ft. Washington (C), PA, *349*
Foster Partners (R), NY, *70*
C. F. Furr & Co. (R), NC, *72*
Futures Int'l. (R), CT, *73*
Peter Gasperini & Assoc., Inc. (R), NY, *75*
GES Services, Inc. (R), NY, *76*
Global Executive Search Group (C), MA, *358*
The Tracy Glover Co. (R), TX, *78*
The Gogates Group, Inc. (R), NY, *79*
Gould, McCoy & Chadick, Inc. (R), NY, *80*
Grauss & Co. (C), CA, *362*
Greene-Levin-Snyder LLC (C), NY, *362*
H.Q. Search, Inc. (C), IL, *365*
Hadley Lockwood, Inc. (R), NY, *84*
Hale Assoc. (R), IL, *84*
K. C. Hale, Inc. (R), CT, *85*
Handy HRM (R), NY, *86*
The Hanover Consulting Group (C), MD, *368*
Hanzel & Co., Inc. (R), NY, *86*
Harris McCully Assoc., Inc. (C), NY, *369*
Jay Heino Company, LLC (C), NY, *375*
Hessel Assoc., Inc. (C), NY, *377*
Higdon Prince Inc. (R), NY, *93*
Highland Search Group, L.L.C. (R), NY, *93*
Hochman & Assoc. (C), CA, *379*
Human Capital Resources, Inc. (C), FL, *384*
Integrated Management Solutions (C), NY, *390*
InteliSearch, Inc. (R), CT, *102*
International Market Recruiters (C), NY, *393*
J. Nicholas Arthur (R), MA, *104*
J. R. Scott & Assoc., Ltd. (C), IL, *395*
Jacobs & Co. (R), CT, *105*
Pendleton James Assoc., Inc. (R), NY, *105*
Jeffrey Meryl Assoc., Inc. (C), NJ, *398*
JNB Assoc., Inc. (C), MA, *399*
John Ryan Assoc., LLC. (C), NY, *399*
A.T. Kearney Executive Search (R), IL, *111*
Keeley Consulting Inc. (C), ON, *404*
Kennedy & Co. (R), IL, *112*
Kershner & Co. (R), DC, *113*
The Kinlin Co., Inc. (R), MA, *115*
Kramer Executive Resources, Inc. (C), NY, *409*
Kyle Assoc. (C), NY, *410*
LanSo Int'l., Inc. (C), NY, *413*
Lascelle & Assoc. Inc. (C), ON, *413*
Leaders-Trust Int'l./Carce y Asociados, S.C. (R), MX, *127*
Vincent Lee Assoc. (C), NY, *415*
Management Advisors Int'l., Inc. (C), NC, *424*
Management Recruiters of Birmingham-South, Inc. (C), AL, *438*
Management Recruiters of St. Augustine (C), FL, *444*
Management Recruiters of Siouxland (C), IA, *449*
Management Recruiters of Manhattan on Broadway (C), NY, *455*
Management Resource Group, Ltd. (C), IA, *467*
Masserman & Assoc., Inc. (R), NY, *138*
Mehta Consulting (C), NJ, *478*
Millar Walker & Gay (R), ON, *144*
Paul Misarti Inc. (C), NY, *483*
Mitchell Martin Inc. (C), NY, *483*
Mogul Consultants, Inc. (C), NY, *483*
Mortgage Search Network (C), AZ, *486*
MSI Int'l. (C), GA, *486*
Much & Co. (R), NY, *148*
Jennifer Munro & Partners, Inc. (R), SC, *149*
The MVP Group (C), NY, *487*
DDJ Myers, Ltd. (R), AZ, *150*
Nason & Nason (C), FL, *488*
National Field Service Corp. (C), NY, *489*
Nordeman Grimm, Inc. (R), NY, *152*
Norman Broadbent Int'l., Inc. (R), NY, *152*
NorthStar Technologies, Inc. (C), NY, *496*
Olympian Recruitment, Ltd. (C), NY, *498*
The Options Group, Inc. (C), NY, *499*
Pathway Executive Search, Inc. (C), NY, *505*
The Pennmor Group (C), NJ, *506*
PIC Executive Search (C), GA, *511*
Pinnacle Executive Group Inc. (C), MO, *512*
Preston & Co. (R), NJ, *167*
The Primary Group, Inc. (R), FL, *168*
Professional Resources (C), NY, *522*
The Quest Organization (C), NY, *527*
Rand Thompson Executive Search Consultants (C), NY, *528*
Ray & Berndtson (R), TX, *171*
Russell Reynolds Assoc., Inc. (R), NY, *176*
Riotto-Jones Assoc. (R), NY, *178*
Rockwood Assoc. (C), NY, *540*
Russillo/Gardner/Spolsino (C), MA, *548*
Ryman, Bell, Green & Michaels, Inc. (C), TX, *549*
Schoales & Assoc. Inc. (C), ON, *572*
Schulenburg & Assoc. (C), GA, *572*
Search America, Inc. (C), PA, *573*
The Search Center Inc. (C), TX, *574*
SearchCorp International (C), AB, *577*
Secura/Burnett Partners (R), CA, *187*
SFB Legal Search (C), NY, *579*
Shannahan & Co., Inc. (R), CA, *189*
Skipping Stone Inc. (C), VA, *582*
SpencerStuart (R), NY, *196*
C. J. Stafford & Assoc. (C), ON, *591*
Steven Michaels & Assoc. (C), NY, *593*
DM Stone Personnel Services (C), CA, *594*
Mark Stranberg & Assoc. Inc. (R), MA, *202*
Sullivan & Company (R), NY, *204*
Roy Talman & Assoc. (C), IL, *599*
Techno-Trac Systems, Inc. (C), NY, *603*
Techsearch Services Inc. (C), CT, *603*
Tennyson Advisors (R), NY, *208*
TSW Assoc., LLC (R), CT, *211*
Vincenty & Co. (C), OH, *612*
The Ward Group (R), MA, *215*
S. B. Webster & Associates (R), MA, *217*
The Whitney Group (R), NY, *219*
D. S. Wolf Assoc., Inc. (R), NY, *223*
Wyndham Mills Int'l., Inc. (R), GA, *225*

H.13 Venture capital

A.L.S. Group (C), NJ, *232*
Adler Management, Inc. (R), NJ, *2*
Advisors' Search Group, Inc. (C), NY, *241*
The Advisory Group, Inc. (R), CA, *2*
Allen-Jeffers Assoc. (C), CA, *245*
Argonaut Partners, LLC (R), CA, *6*
Atlantic Pacific Group (C), CA, *255*
Nathan Barry Assoc., Inc. (R), MA, *12*
Barth Smith Company (R), IL, *12*
Bartholdi & Co., Inc. (R), CO, *12*
Battalia Winston Int'l./The Euram Consultants Group (R), NY, *13*
Bell Wishingrad Partners Inc. (R), NY, *15*
Bergeris & Co., Inc. (C), NY, *265*
Berkana Int'l., Inc. (C), WA, *265*
BFW, Inc. (C), GA, *266*
J: Blakslee Int'l., Ltd. (R), CA, *18*
Blaney Executive Search (R), MA, *18*
Blau Mancino Schroeder (R), NJ, *18*
The BMW Group, Inc. (C), NY, *268*
Brandjes Assoc. (C), MD, *272*
The Broadmoor Group, L.L.C. (R), TX, *23*
Brown Venture Assoc. (R), CA, *24*
Butterfass, Pepe & MacCallan Inc. (R), NJ, *25*
Canny, Bowen Inc. (R), NY, *27*
Capital Consulting & Research, Inc. (R), CT, *28*
Capital Markets Resources, Inc. (C), NC, *281*
Rosemary Cass Ltd. (R), CT, *31*
Catalyx Group (R), NY, *31*
Caywood Partners, Ltd. (R), CA, *32*
The Center for Career Advancement, LLC (C), NJ, *287*
Christian & Timbers, Inc. (R), OH, *34*
Conspectus, Inc. (C), NY, *297*
The Consulting Group Ltd. (R), NY, *40*
Cornell Group Int'l. Consulting, Inc. (R), NY, *41*
Creative Financial Staffing (C), MA, *303*
Crispi, Wagner & Co., Inc. (R), NY, *43*
Cypress Int'l., Inc. (R), FL, *45*
Dahl-Morrow Int'l. (R), VA, *45*
Alfred Daniels & Assoc., Inc. (R), CA, *46*
S. W. Delano & Co. (R), CT, *48*
DiMarchi Partners (R), CO, *51*
J. Dinerstein & Co., Inc. (R), NY, *51*
Dise & Co. (R), OH, *52*
Diversified Search, Inc. (R), PA, *52*
DLG Assoc., Inc. (R), NC, *53*
Eastman & Beaudine, Inc. (R), TX, *56*
Bruce Edwards & Associates, Inc. (R), NC, *56*
Yves Elkas Inc. (R), QE, *58*
Erikson Consulting Assoc., Inc. (R), NY, *60*
Executive Access Inc. (R), NY, *62*
Fenwick Partners (R), MA, *66*
Jack Stuart Fisher Assoc. (C), NJ, *341*
Foster Partners (R), NY, *70*
The Franklin Search Group, Inc./Medzilla (R), WA, *71*
Genesis Consulting Partners (R), PA, *76*
Geneva Group Int'l. (R), CA, *76*

(R) = Retainer; (C) = Contingency

INDUSTRIES

Gilbert Tweed Assoc. Inc. (R), NY, *76*
Gilreath Weatherby Inc. (R), MA, *77*
Global HealthCare Partners (R), IL, *78*
Gould, McCoy & Chadick, Inc. (R), NY, *80*
Grauss & Co. (C), CA, *362*
GSW Consulting Group, Inc. (R), CA, *83*
Gustin Partners, Ltd. (R), MA, *83*
H.Q. Search, Inc. (C), IL, *365*
Hadley Lockwood, Inc. (R), NY, *84*
Haley Associates (R), CA, *85*
Handy HRM (R), NY, *86*
The Hanover Consulting Group (C), MD, *368*
Hanzel & Co., Inc. (R), NY, *86*
Hardison & Company (R), TX, *86*
Harris McCully Assoc., Inc. (C), NY, *369*
Hartman & Barnette (R), VA, *87*
Healthcare Management Resources, Inc. (R), GA, *89*
R. W. Hebel Assoc. (R), TX, *89*
Thomas E. Hedefine Assoc. (C), ON, *375*
Jay Heino Company, LLC (C), NY, *375*
Higdon Prince Inc. (R), NY, *93*
Highland Search Group, L.L.C. (R), NY, *93*
Hockett Associates, Inc. (R), CA, *94*
Integrated Management Solutions (C), NY, *390*
Isaacson, Miller (R), MA, *104*
J. Nicholas Arthur (R), MA, *104*
J. R. Scott & Assoc., Ltd. (C), IL, *395*
Pendleton James Assoc., Inc. (R), NY, *105*
JG Consultants, Inc. (R), TX, *106*
Kaplan & Assoc., Inc. (R), PA, *109*
Howard Karr & Assoc., Inc. (R), CA, *110*
Kazan International, Inc. (R), NJ, *110*
A.T. Kearney Executive Search (R), IL, *111*
Keeley Consulting Inc. (C), ON, *404*
Kershner & Co. (R), DC, *113*
Kip Williams, Inc. (R), NY, *115*
Kossuth & Assoc., Inc. (R), WA, *119*
Katherine R. Kraemer (R), CA, *120*
John Kurosky & Assoc. (R), CA, *122*
Lautz, Grotte, Engler & Swimley (R), CA, *126*
Layne-Mendez & Co. (R), TX, *127*
Lechner & Assoc., Inc. (C), FL, *415*
Lewis & Blank Int'l. (R), CA, *129*
Lipsky Group, Inc. (R), CA, *129*
Lyons Pruitt Int'l. (R), PA, *132*
The Madison Group (R), NY, *133*
Management Recruiters of Manhattan on Broadway (C), NY, *455*
Management Search, Inc. (C), IL, *467*
Martin Partners, L.L.C. (R), IL, *137*
Millar Walker & Gay (R), ON, *144*
Much & Co. (R), NY, *148*
National Bank & Finance Executive Search (C), CA, *488*
The Neil Michael Group, Inc./Global Partners (R), NY, *151*
New Venture Development, Inc. (C), CA, *492*
Nordeman Grimm, Inc. (R), NY, *152*
Norman Broadbent Int'l., Inc. (R), NY, *152*
O'Connor Resources (C), TX, *497*
The Ogdon Partnership (R), NY, *155*
The Oxbridge Group, Ltd. (C), PA, *500*
Pinnacle Executive Group Inc. (C), MO, *512*
Pinnacle Group Int'l. (C), AZ, *512*
Plummer & Assoc., Inc. (R), CT, *166*
Elan Pratzer & Partners Inc. (R), ON, *167*
PRAXIS Partners (R), VA, *167*
L. J. Quinn & Assoc., Inc. (R), CA, *170*
Ray & Berndtson (R), TX, *171*
Russell Reynolds Assoc., Inc. (R), NY, *176*
Rhodes Associates (R), NY, *177*
Riotto-Jones Assoc. (R), NY, *178*
ROI International, Inc. (R), WA, *181*
Rolland Ressources Humaines Inc. (R), QE, *181*
Romac Int'l. Inc. (R), MA, *181*
Sanford Rose Assoc. - Clearwater (C), FL, *566*
Sanford Rose Assoc. - Oak Brook (C), IL, *567*
Schattle & Duquette (C), RI, *571*
Secura/Burnett Partners (R), CA, *187*
Shannahan & Co., Inc. (R), CA, *189*
Daniel A. Silverstein Assoc. Inc. (R), FL, *191*
D. J. Simpson Assoc. Inc. (R), ON, *191*
Christopher Smallhorn Executive Recruiting, Inc. (R), MA, *193*
SpencerStuart (R), NY, *196*
The Spiegel Group (R), MA, *197*
Stafford Consulting Group (R), CA, *198*
Steven Michaels & Assoc. (C), NY, *593*
DM Stone Personnel Services (C), CA, *594*
Strategic Alternatives (R), CA, *202*
Stroman Int'l., Inc. (R), CO, *204*
Sullivan & Company (R), NY, *204*
Martin Stevens Tamaren & Assoc., Inc. (R), CA, *206*
Taylor Winfield (R), TX, *207*
Tennyson Advisors (R), NY, *208*
TSW Assoc., LLC (R), CT, *211*
Tuttle Venture Group, Inc. (R), TX, *212*
Victor White Int'l. (C), CA, *612*
The Wayne Group, Ltd. (C), NY, *616*
Wellington Management Group (R), PA, *217*
The Whitney Group (R), NY, *219*
Williams Executive Search, Inc. (R), MN, *221*
R. S. Wyatt Assoc., Inc. (R), TX, *225*
Yungner & Bormann (R), MN, *226*
Zingaro & Company (R), TX, *227*

H.14 Other financial services

A.L.S. Group (C), NJ, *232*
Accountants On Call (C), FL, *237*
Active Search & Placement Inc. (C), CA, *239*
Advisors' Search Group, Inc. (C), NY, *241*
Affordable Executive Recruiters (C), CA, *241*
Alexander Associates (R), NJ, *2*
Allard Associates (C), CA, *244*
Allen & Assoc. (C), NV, *244*
Allen Evans Assoc. (R), NY, *4*
Ames Assoc. Inc. (C), MD, *249*
Amherst Human Resource Group, Ltd. (C), IL, *249*
Andrews & Assoc. (C), NC, *250*
Anthony Michael & Co. (C), MA, *251*
Argonaut Partners, LLC (R), CA, *6*
The Associates, HR Search Executives, Inc. (C), OK, *254*
ATS Executive Recruitment (C), GA, *255*
Keith Bagg & Assoc., Inc. (C), ON, *257*
The Bankers Group (C), IL, *258*
Behavioral Science Assoc., Inc. (R), AZ, *15*
Bell Wishingrad Partners Inc. (R), NY, *15*
Bergeris & Co., Inc. (C), NY, *265*
BFW, Inc. (C), GA, *266*
The BMW Group, Inc. (C), NY, *268*
Bonell Ryan Inc. (R), NY, *19*
Bonifield Assoc. (C), NJ, *269*
Bor-Maq Assoc. (C), TX, *269*
C. P. Consulting (R), PA, *26*
C. R. Assoc. (C), CA, *278*
C.P.S., Inc. (C), IL, *278*
C.T.E.W. Executive Personnel Services Inc. (C), BC, *278*
Career Consulting Group, Inc. (C), CT, *281*
CFR Executive Search, Inc. (C), IL, *288*
The Christopher Group (C), NC, *291*
Arlene Clapp, Ltd. (R), MN, *35*
Toby Clark Assoc. Inc. (C), NY, *292*
Computer Int'l. Consultants, Inc. (C), FL, *295*
Conspectus, Inc. (C), NY, *297*
The Consulting Group Ltd. (R), NY, *40*
Cornell Group Int'l. Consulting, Inc. (R), NY, *41*
Corporate Select Int'l., Ltd. (C), IL, *301*
Leonard Corwen Assoc. (C), NY, *302*
Creative Financial Staffing (C), MA, *303*
Crispi, Wagner & Co., Inc. (R), NY, *43*
Cromwell Partners, Inc. (R), NY, *43*
Cypress Int'l., Inc. (R), FL, *45*
D.P. Specialists, Inc. (C), CA, *306*
David Anthony Personnel Assoc., Inc. (C), NJ, *308*
The Dayton Group, Ltd. (C), NY, *309*
S. W. Delano & Co. (R), CT, *48*
Descheneaux Recruitment Services Ltd. (C), BC, *311*
Roger Dietsch & Assoc. (C), MN, *312*
Discovery, The Staffing Specialists, Inc. (C), IL, *312*
DLG Assoc., Inc. (R), NC, *53*
J P Donnelly Assoc., Inc. (C), NY, *314*
Douglas-Allen, Inc. (R), MA, *54*
Drummond Assoc., Inc. (C), NY, *315*
DS&A (Doug Sears & Assoc.) (C), FL, *315*
DuBrul Management Co. (C), NY, *315*
Dunhill Professional Search of Omaha, Inc. (C), NE, *321*
Dunhill Personnel of Northeast Tulsa, Inc. (C), OK, *322*
Dunhill Professional Search of Wilkes-Barre/Scranton, Inc. (C), PA, *322*
EagleView, Inc. (C), MA, *325*
D. C. Egan & Assoc. (C), GA, *327*
Electronic Search, Inc. (C), IL, *327*
Steve Ellis (C), CA, *328*
David M. Ellner Assoc. (R), NY, *59*
Mark Elzweig Co., Ltd. (C), NY, *329*
Emerging Technology Search (C), GA, *329*
Executive Search Consultants, Inc. (C), FL, *335*

eXsource Inc. (C), SC, *337*
Fabian Assoc. Inc. (C), NY, *338*
Fagan & Company (R), PA, *64*
Federal Placement Services (C), NY, *339*
Financial Connections Company (C), VA, *340*
Financial Resource Assoc., Inc. (C), FL, *340*
Financial Search Group, Inc. (R), MA, *66*
First Union Executive Search (R), NC, *67*
F-O-R-T-U-N-E Personnel Consultants (C), MI, *346*
Foster Partners (R), NY, *70*
Friedman Eisenstein Raemer & Schwartz, LLP (R), IL, *72*
C. F. Furr & Co. (R), NC, *72*
Futures Int'l. (R), CT, *73*
Dick Garland Consultants (R), NY, *74*
Peter Gasperini & Assoc., Inc. (R), NY, *75*
GES Services, Inc. (R), NY, *76*
Gilbert Tweed Assoc. Inc. (R), NY, *76*
Global Executive Search Group (C), MA, *358*
F. Gloss Int'l. (R), VA, *78*
Gnodde Assoc. (C), IL, *359*
The Gogates Group, Inc. (R), NY, *79*
The Goldman Group Inc. (R), NY, *79*
Gould, McCoy & Chadick, Inc. (R), NY, *80*
Government Contract Solutions, Inc. (C), VA, *360*
Granger, Counts & Assoc. (R), OH, *81*
Greene & Co. (C), MA, *362*
Greene Personnel Consultants (C), RI, *362*
H.Q. Search, Inc. (C), IL, *365*
Hadley Lockwood, Inc. (R), NY, *84*
K. C. Hale, Inc. (R), CT, *85*
Handy HRM (R), NY, *86*
Harper Associates (C), MI, *369*
Harris McCully Assoc., Inc. (C), NY, *369*
Hayden Group, Inc. (R), MA, *88*
Thomas E. Hedefine Assoc. (C), ON, *375*
Hessel Assoc., Inc. (C), NY, *377*
Higdon Prince Inc. (R), NY, *93*
Highland Search Group, L.L.C. (R), NY, *93*
Higley, Hall & Co., Inc. (R), MA, *93*
Hochman & Assoc. (C), CA, *379*
Human Capital Resources, Inc. (C), FL, *384*
Innovative Healthcare Services, Inc. (C), GA, *389*
Integrated Management Solutions (C), NY, *390*
InteliSearch, Inc. (R), CT, *102*
IntelliSearch (C), TX, *391*
International Market Recruiters (C), NY, *393*
ISC of Houston, Inc. (C), TX, *394*
J. Nicholas Arthur (R), MA, *104*
J. R. Scott & Assoc., Ltd. (C), IL, *395*
JNB Assoc., Inc. (C), MA, *399*
Jonathan Lawrence Assoc. (C), NJ, *400*
Joseph Michaels (C), CA, *401*
JSG Group Management Consultants (R), ON, *109*
JT Assoc. (C), CT, *401*
A.T. Kearney Executive Search (R), IL, *111*
Keeley Consulting Inc. (C), ON, *404*
Kennedy & Co. (R), IL, *112*
The Kennett Group, Inc. (R), PA, *112*
Kershner & Co. (R), DC, *113*
Keystone Consulting Group (C), GA, *406*
The Kinlin Co., Inc. (R), MA, *115*
L T M Assoc. (C), IL, *410*
Marvin Laba & Assoc. (R), CA, *122*
Lamay Assoc., Inc. (R), CT, *124*
LanSo Int'l., Inc. (C), NY, *413*
Lawrence L. Lapham, Inc. (R), NY, *124*
Leeds and Leeds (C), TN, *416*
AG Lennox & Assoc. (R), AB, *128*
Lewis Consulting Service (C), IL, *417*
M/J/A Partners (R), IL, *133*
Management Alliance Group, Inc. (R), NJ, *134*
Management Recruiters of Berkeley (C), CA, *439*
Management Recruiters of Pleasanton (C), CA, *441*
Management Recruiters of Middlesex (C), CT, *442*
Management Recruiters of Melbourne, Inc. (C), FL, *443*
Management Recruiters of Ft. Myers, FL. (C), FL, *443*
Management Recruiters of Columbus, Inc. (C), GA, *445*
Management Recruiters of Duluth (C), GA, *445*
Management Recruiters - Towne Lake (C), GA, *446*
Management Recruiters of Cass County, NE (C), NE, *452*
Management Recruiters of Manhattan on Broadway (C), NY, *455*
Management Recruiters of Oklahoma City (C), OK, *458*
Management Recruiters of Lionville, Inc. (C), PA, *459*
Management Recruiters of Champions (C), TX, *462*
Management Resource Group, Ltd. (C), IA, *467*
Management Resource Group (C), MN, *467*
Market Niche Consulting (C), AZ, *470*
Marketing Search Inc. (C), OH, *471*
Masserman & Assoc., Inc. (R), NY, *138*
McCann, Choi & Associates, LLC (R), NY, *139*
McHale & Assoc. (R), WA, *141*
MCS Assoc. (R), CA, *142*
Michael Thomas, Inc. (C), OH, *480*
Miller/Davis & Assoc., Inc. (C), NY, *482*
MIS Computer Professionals, Inc. (C), KS, *482*
Oscar Montaño, Inc. (R), CA, *146*
C. A. Moore & Assoc., Inc. (C), MN, *484*
Morris & Berger (R), CA, *147*
Mortgage Search Network (C), AZ, *486*
National Affirmative Action Career Network, Inc. (C), CO, *488*
National Bank & Finance Executive Search (C), CA, *488*
Marc Nichols Assoc., Inc. (C), NY, *493*
Nichols Brown Int'l. (R), NY, *151*
Nordeman Grimm, Inc. (R), NY, *152*
Norman Broadbent Int'l., Inc. (R), NY, *152*
Norrell Financial Staffing (C), GA, *495*
O'Sullivan Search Inc. (C), ON, *498*
Ollinger Partners (R), MA, *156*
Oppedisano & Co., Inc. (R), NY, *156*
The Options Group, Inc. (C), NY, *499*
Orion Int'l. Consulting Group, Inc. (C), NC, *499*
The Oxbridge Group, Ltd. (C), PA, *500*
P.R.H. Management, Inc. (R), CT, *158*
Arthur Pann Assoc., Inc. (C), NY, *502*
Pearson, Caldwell & Farnsworth (R), CA, *161*
PeopleSource Inc. (C), TX, *506*
Robert E. Pfaendler & Assoc., Inc. (C), OR, *509*
Phillips Personnel/Search (C), CO, *510*
Al Ponaman Company, Inc. (C), CA, *514*
Preston & Co. (R), NJ, *167*
The Primary Group, Inc. (R), FL, *168*
L. J. Quinn & Assoc., Inc. (R), CA, *170*
The Rankin Group, Ltd. (R), WI, *171*
Joanne E. Ratner Search (C), NY, *529*
Real Estate Executive Search, Inc. (C), CA, *531*
Redden & McGrath Assoc., Inc. (R), NY, *173*
Reifel & Assoc. (R), IL, *174*
Russell Reynolds Assoc., Inc. (R), NY, *176*
Rice Cohen Int'l. (R), PA, *178*
Ridenour & Assoc. (R), IL, *178*
Riotto-Jones Assoc. (R), NY, *178*
Rodgers, Ramsey, Inc. (C), TX, *540*
The Rogan Group, Inc. (C), CA, *541*
W. R. Rosato & Assoc., Inc. (R), NY, *182*
The Rubicon Group (C), AZ, *547*
Rusher, Loscavio & LoPresto (R), CA, *183*
Russillo/Gardner/Spolsino (C), MA, *548*
W. A. Rutledge & Assoc. (R), CT, *183*
Sales & Management Search, Inc. (C), IL, *551*
Sales Consultants of Northwest Arkansas, Inc. (C), AR, *556*
Sales Consultants of Chicago South (C), IL, *558*
Sales Consultants of Nashua-Manchester (C), NH, *560*
Sales Consultants Bridgewater, Inc. (C), NJ, *560*
Sales Consultants of Cherry Hill (C), NJ, *560*
A. N. Salloway Executive Search & Consulting, L.L.C. (C), MA, *564*
Salzmann Gay Assoc., Inc. (R), PA, *184*
Sanford Rose Assoc. - Atlanta North (C), GA, *566*
Sanford Rose Assoc. - Oak Brook (C), IL, *567*
Sanford Rose Assoc. - Pittsburgh North (C), PA, *570*
Santangelo Consultants Inc. (C), NY, *571*
The Schatz Company (C), MO, *571*
Search America, Inc. (C), PA, *573*
Search Innovations, Inc. (R), PA, *187*
Search Research Assoc., Inc. (R), MA, *187*
Sedlar & Miners (R), NY, *188*
J. R. Seehusen Assoc., Inc. (R), IA, *188*
Sevcor Int'l., Inc. (R), IL, *188*
Shannahan & Co., Inc. (R), CA, *189*

INDUSTRIES

Skipping Stone Inc. (C), VA, *582*
Ruth Sklar Assoc., Inc. (RSA Executive Search) (R), NY, *192*
Smith & Laue Search (R), OR, *193*
C. Snow & Assoc. (C), ON, *586*
Software Engineering Solutions, Inc. (C), CA, *586*
SpencerStuart (R), NY, *196*
M. H. Springer & Assoc. (R), CA, *198*
Stafford Consulting Group (R), CA, *198*
StaffWriters Plus (C), NY, *591*
DM Stone Personnel Services (C), CA, *594*
Straight & Co. (R), GA, *202*
Mark Stranberg & Assoc. Inc. (R), MA, *202*
Strategic Alliance Network, Ltd. (C), OH, *595*
Stratin Assoc. (C), NJ, *596*
Sullivan & Company (R), NY, *204*
Synagent Inc. (C), ON, *597*
Roy Talman & Assoc. (C), IL, *599*
Techsearch Services Inc. (C), CT, *603*
Tennyson Advisors (R), NY, *208*
Thomas Lyle & Co. (C), IL, *606*
TSW Assoc., LLC (R), CT, *211*
Vincenty & Co. (C), OH, *612*
Robert H. Wadsworth & Assoc., Inc. (R), AZ, *214*
C. Weiss Assoc., Inc. (C), NY, *618*
WestPacific National Search, Inc. (C), CA, *619*
K. L. Whitney Company (R), NJ, *219*
The Whitney Group (R), NY, *219*
Whitney Smith Co. (C), TX, *620*
Wilcox Bertoux & Miller (R), CA, *220*
D. S. Wolf Assoc., Inc. (R), NY, *223*
Louise Wood & Assoc. (C), NY, *624*
Worldwide Medical Services (C), CA, *625*
Youngblood Assoc. (C), NC, *626*
Zen Zen Int'l. Inc. (C), MB, *627*
Zona & Assoc., Inc. (C), NY, *628*

I.00 Services

The 500 Granary Inc. (C), ON, *231*
A C Personnel Services, Inc. (C), OK, *231*
A First Resource (C), NC, *231*
A la Carte Int'l., Inc. (R), VA, *1*
A Permanent Success Employment Services (C), CA, *231*
A-K-A (Anita Kaufmann Assoc.) (C), NY, *231*
A-L Assoc., Inc. (R), NY, *1*
A-Linko & Assoc. (C), TX, *231*
A. D. & Assoc. Executive Search, Inc. (C), GA, *231*
A.J. & Assoc. (C), FL, *232*
A.K.S. Assoc., Ltd. (R), MA, *1*
A.L.S. Group (C), NJ, *232*
A.M.C.R., Inc. (C), OH, *232*
Aaron Consulting, Inc. (C), MO, *232*
Abbott Associates (R), CA, *1*
Abécassis Conseil (R), QE, *1*
Cathy Abelson Legal Search (C), PA, *232*
Abraxas Technologies, Inc. (C), FL, *233*
Accent On Achievement, Inc. (C), MI, *233*
Access Assoc. Inc. (C), MD, *233*
Access Data Personnel, Inc. (C), NH, *233*
ACCESS Technology (C), CA, *234*
Access/Resources, Inc. (C), MA, *234*
Acclaim Services, Inc. (C), TX, *234*
Accountants On Call (C), FL, *237*
Accountants Executive Search (C), CA, *237*
Accounting Personnel & Engineering Personnel Consultants (C), LA, *238*
Ackerman Johnson Inc. (C), TX, *238*
Action Management Corp. (C), MI, *239*
Adam-Bryce Inc. (C), NY, *239*
Arthur Adams & Assoc. (C), OH, *239*
Adams & Assoc. Int'l. (R), IL, *1*
Adel-Lawrence Assoc., Inc. (C), NJ, *240*
Adept Tech Recruiting, Inc. (C), NY, *240*
Adirect Recruiting Corp. (C), ON, *240*
ADR Accounting Management Recruiters (C), ON, *240*
Advice Personnel Inc. (C), NY, *241*
Affordable Executive Recruiters (C), CA, *241*
Agri-Tech Personnel, Inc. (C), MO, *242*
Ahrensdorf & Assoc. (R), PA, *2*
J. R. Akin & Co. (R), MA, *2*
Alaska Executive Search, Inc. (C), AK, *243*
Albrecht & Assoc., Executive Search Consultants (C), TX, *243*
Alexander & Collins (C), CA, *243*
Alexander Associates (R), NJ, *2*
Alexander Enterprises, Inc. (C), PA, *243*
The Alexander Group (R), NJ, *3*
The Alexander Group (R), TX, *3*
The Alfus Group (R), NY, *3*
Allen & Assoc. (C), NV, *244*
D. S. Allen Assoc. (C), NJ, *244*
David Allen Assoc. (R), NJ, *3*
Allen Austin Lowe & Powers (R), TX, *3*
Allen Evans Assoc. (R), NY, *4*
Allen, Wayne & Co. LLC (C), WI, *245*
Allerton Heneghan & O'Neill (R), IL, *4*
Alliance Executive Search, Inc. (R), MA, *4*
Alliance Search Management Inc. (R), TX, *4*
Tom Allison Assoc. (C), NM, *245*
Allman & Co., Inc. (C), NC, *245*
Alpha Resource Group, Inc. (C), TX, *246*
Alpha Search (C), FL, *246*
The Alternatives Group, Inc. (C), TX, *246*
ALW Research Int'l. (R), NJ, *4*
AM & G Certified Public Accountants & Consultants (R), IL, *4*
AMD & Associates (C), GA, *247*
American Executive Management, Inc. (R), MA, *5*
American Logistics Consultants, Inc. (C), IL, *247*
AmeriResource Group Inc. (C), OK, *248*
Amherst Human Resource Group, Ltd. (C), IL, *249*
AMS Int'l. (R), VA, *5*
Analytic Recruiting, Inc. (C), NY, *249*
Anderson & Associates (R), NC, *5*
Anderson Bradshaw Assoc., Inc. (R), TX, *6*
Anderson Network Group (C), OH, *250*
Andex Executive Search (C), CT, *250*
Andre David & Assoc., Inc. (R), TX, *6*
The Andre Group, Inc. (R), PA, *6*
Andrews & Assoc. (C), NC, *250*
Andrews & Wald Group (C), FL, *250*
Angel Group Int'l. (C), KY, *250*
Angus Employment Ltd. (C), ON, *250*
The Angus Group, Ltd. (C), OH, *251*
Ansara, Bickford & Fiske (C), MA, *251*
APA Employment Agency Inc. (C), OR, *251*
David Aplin & Assoc. (C), AB, *251*
Applied Resources, Inc. (C), MN, *252*
Charles P. Aquavella & Assoc. (C), TX, *252*
Ariel Recruitment Assoc. (R), NY, *7*
Armitage Associates Ltd. (R), ON, *7*
Patrick Arnone & Assoc. Inc. (R), VA, *7*
Artgo, Inc. (R), OH, *7*
The Ascher Group (R), NJ, *7*
Ashton Computer Professionals, Inc. (C), BC, *253*
Ashway Ltd. Agency (C), NY, *253*
Ashworth Consultants, Inc. (R), MA, *8*
ASI (C), CA, *254*
Association Executive Resources Group (R), MD, *8*
Association for Sales Force Management (C), WA, *254*
AST/BRYANT (R), CT, *8*
Astro Executive Search Firm (C), LA, *254*
Atkinson Search & Placement, Inc. (C), IA, *255*
Atlanta Executive Partners, Inc. (R), MA, *8*
Atlantic Pacific Group (C), CA, *255*
Atlantic West Int'l. (C), NC, *255*
Attorney Search Global, Inc. (C), IL, *255*
Attorneys at Work (C), GA, *255*
Aubin Int'l. Inc. (R), MA, *8*
Auerbach Associates, Inc. (R), MA, *9*
Aurora Tech Search (C), ON, *256*
A. M. Auster Associates (R), FL, *9*
Austin Group Int'l./Marlar Int'l. (R), TX, *9*
Austin Park Management Group Inc. (C), ON, *256*
Austin, Hill & Assoc. (C), MD, *256*
Austin-McGregor Int'l. (R), TX, *9*
Avion International Technology Inc. (C), ON, *257*
Avondale Search Int'l., Inc. (R), FL, *9*
The Ayers Group, Inc. (R), NY, *9*
Bader Research Corp. (C), NY, *257*
The Badger Group (R), CA, *10*
Baeder Kalinski Int'l. Group, Inc. (R), NH, *10*
The Baer Group (R), OH, *10*
Baker, Nelms & Montgomery (C), IL, *258*
Baldwin & Assoc. (C), OH, *258*
Baldwin Associates, LLC (R), CT, *10*
The Baldwin Group (R), IL, *10*
Carol Ball & Co. (C), CT, *258*
Allen Ballach Assoc. Inc. (R), ON, *10*
Ballantyne & Assoc. (R), CA, *10*
James Bangert & Assoc., Inc. (R), MN, *11*
The Bankers Group (C), IL, *258*
The Barack Group, Inc. (R), NY, *11*
Barclay Consultants, Inc. (C), NJ, *259*
J. W. Barleycorn, Renard & Assoc., Inc. (R), OH, *11*
Barnes & Assoc. Executive Search (C), CA, *259*
Barnes Development Group, LLC (R), WI, *11*
Fred A. Barnette & Assoc. (R), NC, *11*
Barrett Hospitality Search (R), CA, *12*

Barrett Partners (C), IL, *260*
Barrett Rose & Lee, Inc. (C), ON, *260*
Barrington Hart, Inc. (R), IL, *12*
Bartl & Evins (C), NY, *260*
Barton Assoc., Inc. (R), TX, *12*
Bast & Assoc., Inc. (C), CA, *261*
Battalia Winston Int'l./The Euram Consultants Group (R), NY, *13*
R. Gaines Baty Assoc., Inc. (R), TX, *13*
The Bauman Group (R), CA, *14*
BayResearch Group, Inc. (R), IL, *14*
BCG Search, Inc. (R), FL, *14*
Beach Executive Search Inc. (R), FL, *14*
Beacon Int'l., Inc. (C), VA, *261*
Beck/Eastwood Recruitment Solutions (C), CA, *261*
Beckman & Assoc. Legal Search (C), OH, *262*
The Bedford Consulting Group Inc. (R), ON, *14*
The Bedford Group (R), RI, *15*
Robert Beech West Inc. (C), CA, *262*
Behavioral Science Assoc., Inc. (R), AZ, *15*
Neail Behringer Consultants Inc. (R), NY, *15*
Marcia Beilin, Inc. (C), NY, *262*
Belanger Partners Ltd. (C), ON, *262*
Edward Bell Assoc. (C), CA, *263*
Gary S. Bell Assoc., Inc. (C), NJ, *263*
Bellamy & Assoc. (C), GA, *263*
Joy Reed Belt Search Consultants, Inc. (R), OK, *15*
Bench Int'l. Search, Inc. (R), CA, *15*
J. P. Bencik Assoc. (C), MI, *263*
Bender Executive Search Management Consulting (R), NY, *16*
N. L. Benke & Assoc., Inc. (C), OH, *264*
Bennett & Associates (C), TX, *264*
Bennett & Co. Consulting Group (C), CA, *264*
Robert Bennett Assoc. (C), NY, *264*
Bennett Search & Consulting Co. (R), FL, *16*
Benson Associates (C), NY, *264*
Dick Berg & Assoc. (C), CA, *264*
Berger & Leff (C), CA, *264*
C. Berger And Company (R), IL, *16*
Berglund Int'l. Resources, Inc. (C), TX, *265*
Berkhemer/Clayton, Inc. (R), CA, *16*
Bernhart Assoc. (C), MN, *265*
Bertrand, Ross & Assoc., Inc. (C), IL, *266*
Besen Assoc. Inc. (C), NJ, *266*
BEST/World Assoc. Inc. (R), TX, *16*
BG & Assoc. (C), MD, *266*
Bialla & Assoc. Inc. (R), CA, *17*
Binder Hospitality Group (C), KY, *266*
BioPharmMed (C), FL, *267*
BioQuest Inc. (R), CA, *17*
Birch & Associes (C), QE, *267*
Bishop Partners (R), NY, *17*
The Black Leopard (C), CA, *267*
The Blackman Kallick Search Division (C), IL, *267*
Blane, Stevens & Kellogg (C), FL, *268*
Blau Mancino Schroeder (R), NJ, *18*
BLB Consulting (C), NY, *268*
David Blevins & Assoc. (C), WA, *268*
Block & Assoc. (R), CA, *18*
D. R. Blood & Assoc. (R), AZ, *18*
The Howard C. Bloom Co. (C), TX, *268*
Blue Chip Law Consulting, Inc. (C), CA, *268*
Boardroom Consultants/Kenny Kindler Tholke (R), NY, *19*
Boettcher Assoc. (R), WI, *19*
Tom Bogle & Assoc. (C), CA, *269*
Mark Bolno & Assoc. (C), FL, *269*
Bonell Ryan Inc. (R), NY, *19*
Bonifield Assoc. (C), NJ, *269*
Bonnell Assoc. Ltd. (R), CT, *19*
Boone-Scaturro Assoc., Inc. (C), GA, *269*
Bornholdt Shivas & Friends Executive Recruiters (C), NY, *270*
Bosland Gray Assoc. (R), NJ, *20*
Boston Professional Search, Inc. (C), MA, *270*
Boulware & Assoc. Inc. (R), IL, *20*
Bowden & Co., Inc. (R), OH, *20*
Howard Bowen Consulting (C), FL, *270*
BowersThomas (C), CA, *271*
Bowman & Assoc. (C), CA, *271*
Boyden (R), NY, *20*
Bradford Executives Int'l. (C), VA, *271*
Brandt Associates (C), PA, *272*
Brandywine Consulting Group (R), PA, *22*
Brandywine Retained Ventures, Inc. (R), CT, *22*
Branthover Assoc. (C), NY, *272*
Brault & Assoc., Ltd. (R), VA, *22*
Bredeson Executive Recruitment, LLC (R), TX, *22*
The Bren Group (C), AZ, *273*
The Brentwood Group, Inc. (R), NJ, *22*
The Brentwood Group Ltd. (R), OR, *23*
Brentwood Int'l. (R), CA, *23*
Brethet, Barnum & Assoc., Inc. (C), ON, *273*
Briant Assoc., Inc. (R), IL, *23*
The Bridge (C), CO, *273*
Brigade, Inc. (R), CA, *23*
Brindisi Search (R), MD, *23*
Bristol Assoc., Inc. (C), CA, *274*
The Broadmoor Group, L.L.C. (R), TX, *23*
Bernard E. Brooks & Assoc., Inc. (R), SC, *24*
J. B. Brown & Assoc., Inc. (C), OH, *275*
Brown, Bernardy, Van Remmen, Inc. (C), CA, *275*
Brownstone Sales & Marketing Group, Inc. (C), NY, *275*
Bryant Research (C), NJ, *275*
BT&A, LLC (R), CT, *24*
Charles Buck & Assoc., Inc. (R), NY, *24*
Bullis & Co., Inc. (R), CA, *25*
The Burgess Group-Corporate Recruiters Int'l., Inc. (R), NY, *25*
Burke & Assoc./The Westfield Group (C), CT, *276*
The Burke Group (C), ON, *276*
Business Partners, Inc. (C), FL, *277*
Business Systems of America, Inc. (C), IL, *277*
Butterfass, Pepe & MacCallan Inc. (R), NJ, *25*
Byron Leonard Int'l., Inc. (R), CA, *25*
C Assoc. (C), DC, *278*
C. M. Management Services, Inc. (R), KY, *26*
C. P. Consulting (R), PA, *26*
The C.P.R. Group (C), NJ, *278*
C.P.S., Inc. (C), IL, *278*
C.T.E.W. Executive Personnel Services Inc. (C), BC, *278*
C/R Associates (C), NY, *278*
Caldwell Legal Recruiting Consultants (C), ME, *279*
Caliber Associates (R), PA, *27*
Callan Assoc., Ltd. (R), IL, *27*
Cambridge Group Ltd. - Exec. Search Div. (C), CT, *279*
The Cambridge Group Ltd. (C), CT, *280*
Cambridge Management Planning (R), ON, *27*
T. M. Campbell Co. (R), WA, *27*
CanMed Consultants Inc. (C), ON, *280*
Canny, Bowen Inc. (R), NY, *27*
J. P. Canon Assoc. (C), NY, *280*
The Canon Group (C), CA, *280*
The Cantor Concern, Inc. (R), NY, *28*
Cantrell & Assoc. (C), FL, *280*
Capital Consulting & Research, Inc. (R), CT, *28*
Capital Consulting Group, Inc. (R), MD, *28*
Caplan Assoc., Inc. (R), NJ, *28*
Capstone Inc. (R), NY, *29*
Cardwell Enterprises Inc. (R), IL, *29*
Career Consultants (R), IN, *29*
Career Consulting Group, Inc. (C), CT, *281*
Career Counseling Ltd. (C.C.L.) (C), NY, *282*
Career Development Associates (C), NV, *282*
Career Marketing Consultants, Inc. (C), GA, *282*
Career Profiles (C), NH, *283*
Career Strategies, Inc. (C), CA, *283*
Careerfit, Inc. (C), TX, *283*
Careers First, Inc. (C), NJ, *283*
Careers On Track (C), NJ, *283*
Careers/Inc. (C), PR, *284*
Carion Resource Group Inc. (C), ON, *284*
The Carlyle Group, Ltd. (R), IL, *30*
Carnegie Partners, Inc. (R), IL, *30*
Carpenter Legal Search (C), PA, *284*
Carpenter, Shackleton & Company (R), IL, *30*
Carson-Thomas & Assoc. (C), CA, *284*
Carter/MacKay (C), NJ, *285*
Caruso & Assoc., Inc. (R), FL, *31*
The CARVIR Group, Inc. (C), GA, *285*
Cary & Assoc. (R), FL, *31*
CAS Comsearch Inc. (C), NY, *285*
Casey & Assoc., Inc. (C), TX, *286*
The Cassie Group (R), NJ, *31*
Michael J. Cavanagh & Assoc. Inc. (R), ON, *31*
CBA Companies (C), CA, *286*
Malin Cederquist, Esq. (C), NY, *286*
Cella Assoc. (C), GA, *286*
Cemco, Ltd. (C), IL, *286*
Cendea Connection Int'l. (R), TX, *32*
The Center for Career Advancement, LLC (C), NJ, *287*
Century Assoc., Inc. (C), PA, *287*
The Century Group (C), CA, *287*
The Century Group (C), KS, *287*
CEO Consulting (C), FL, *287*

INDUSTRIES

cFour Partners (R), CA, *32*
CFR Executive Search, Inc. (C), IL, *288*
Chad Management Group (C), ON, *288*
David Chambers & Assoc., Inc. (R), CT, *32*
Elsie Chan & Assoc. (C), CA, *289*
Chapman & Assoc. (C), BC, *289*
The Chapman Group, Inc. (C), AZ, *289*
ChaseAmerica, Inc. (R), FL, *33*
The Chatham Group, Ltd. (C), CT, *289*
Chatham Search Assoc., Inc. (C), NJ, *290*
Cheney Associates (C), CT, *290*
The Cherbonnier Group, Inc. (R), TX, *33*
Chesapeake Group (C), CT, *290*
Christenson Hutchison McDowell, LLC (R), NJ, *34*
Christian & Timbers, Inc. (R), OH, *34*
Christmas, McIvor & Assoc. Inc. (C), ON, *290*
The Christopher Group (C), NC, *291*
Christopher-Westmont & Assoc., Inc. (R), OH, *34*
J. F. Church Associates (C), WA, *291*
M. A. Churchill & Assoc., Inc. (R), PA, *35*
Cizek Assoc., Inc. (R), AZ, *35*
CJA-The Adler Group, Inc. (R), CA, *35*
Claimsearch (C), CA, *291*
Clarey/Napier Int'l., L.C. (R), TX, *35*
Howard Clark Assoc. (C), NJ, *292*
Toby Clark Assoc. Inc. (C), NY, *292*
Clark Executive Search (C), NY, *292*
Ken Clark Int'l. (R), NJ, *36*
Clayman & Co. (R), MA, *36*
Clinton, Charles, Wise & Co. (C), FL, *293*
CMC Search Consultants (C), IL, *293*
CMS Management Services LLC (C), IN, *293*
CMW & Associates, Inc. (C), IL, *293*
CN Associates (C), CA, *293*
Coastal Int'l., Inc. (R), MA, *36*
Cole, Warren & Long, Inc. (R), PA, *37*
Coleman Legal Search Consultants (C), PA, *294*
Coleman Lew & Assoc., Inc. (R), NC, *37*
S L Collins Assoc. (C), NC, *294*
Colt Systems Professional Personnel Services (C), CA, *294*
Colucci, Blendow & Johnson (R), CA, *38*
Columbia Consulting Group (R), MD, *38*
Combined Resources Inc. (R), OH, *38*
Commercial Programming Systems, Inc. (C), CA, *294*
Compass Group Ltd. (R), MI, *38*
Comprehensive Search (C), GA, *294*
CompuPro (C), IL, *295*
Computer Int'l. Consultants, Inc. (C), FL, *295*
Computer Network Resources, Inc. (C), CA, *295*
Computer Personnel, Inc. (C), WA, *295*
Computer Professionals Unlimited (C), TX, *295*
Computer Security Placement Service (C), MA, *296*
The Comwell Company, Inc. (C), NJ, *296*
Conard Associates, Inc. (R), NH, *39*
Conasa de Mexico, S.C. (R), MX, *39*
Connors, Lovell & Assoc. Inc. (C), ON, *296*
Conroy Partners Ltd. (R), AB, *39*
Consolidated Management Services (C), ON, *296*
The Consortium (C), NY, *296*
Construct Management Services (C), MN, *297*
Construction Search Specialists, Inc. (C), WI, *297*
Consulpro (R), ON, *39*
Consultant Recruiters (C), WI, *297*
The Consulting Group of North America, Inc. (C), VA, *297*
Consulting Resource Group, Inc. (C), GA, *297*
Consumer Search Inc. (C), MA, *298*
ContactBridge, Inc. (R), IL, *40*
Continental Research Search, Inc. (C), WI, *298*
Conway & Assoc. (R), IL, *40*
Cook Assoc. Int'l., Inc. (C), TN, *298*
P. G. Cook Assoc. (R), TN, *40*
Cooper Assoc., Inc. (C), NY, *298*
Cornell Group Int'l. Consulting, Inc. (R), NY, *41*
Cornerstone Resources, Inc. (C), OK, *299*
The Corporate Connection, Ltd. (C), VA, *299*
Corporate Environment Ltd. (R), IL, *41*
Corporate Image Group (C), TN, *300*
Corporate Plus, Ltd. (C), GA, *300*
Corporate Recruiters Inc. (C), PA, *300*
Corporate Search Consultants, Inc. (C), FL, *301*
Corporate Search, Inc. (C), NY, *301*
Corrao, Miller, Rush & Wiesenthal (C), NY, *301*
Corso, Mizgala + French (R), ON, *42*
Leonard Corwen Assoc. (C), NY, *302*
J. D. Cotter Search Inc. (C), OH, *302*
CountryHouse Hotels Executive Search (C), VA, *302*
Cowell & Associates, Ltd. (R), IL, *42*
Trudi Cowlan (C), NY, *302*
Creative Financial Staffing (C), MA, *303*
Creative HR Solutions (C), GA, *303*
Creative-Leadership, Inc. (R), CA, *42*
The Cris Group, Inc. (R), NY, *42*
Crispi, Wagner & Co., Inc. (R), NY, *43*
Criterion Executive Search, Inc. (C), FL, *303*
CSA/Clinical Staffing Assoc., LLC (C), NJ, *304*
Culver Personnel Services (C), CA, *304*
Curran Partners, Inc. (R), CT, *44*
Current Resource Group, Inc. (C), GA, *305*
The Custer Group, Inc. (R), TN, *44*
Custom Resources (C), AL, *305*
Cyntal Int'l. Ltd. (R), NY, *44*
Cypress Int'l., Inc. (R), FL, *45*
Cyr Associates, Inc. (C), MA, *306*
D.A.I Human Resources Consultants (R), QE, *45*
Daggett & Kvistad (R), CA, *45*
Charles Dahl Group, Inc. (C), MN, *306*
The Dalley Hewitt Co. (R), GA, *45*
The Danbrook Group, Inc. (C), TX, *306*
Alfred Daniels & Assoc., Inc. (R), CA, *46*
DARE Personnel Inc. (C), ON, *307*
The Dartmouth Group (R), NY, *46*
Data Bank Executive Search (R), OH, *46*
Data Search Network, Inc. (C), FL, *307*
Data-AxIS Corp. (C), FL, *307*
The DataFinders Group, Inc. (C), NJ, *307*
Daubenspeck & Associates, Ltd. (R), IL, *46*
Alan N. Daum & Assoc., Inc. (C), OH, *308*
David Perry Assoc. (C), NJ, *308*
Davies, Park (R), AB, *46*
Allen Davis & Assoc. (C), MA, *308*
Joseph A. Davis Consultants, Inc. (R), NY, *47*
The Dayton Group, Ltd. (C), NY, *309*
DBC Recruiting Network (C), GA, *309*
DBL Associates (C), CA, *309*
De Funiak & Edwards (R), IN, *47*
DeCorrevont & Assoc. (C), IL, *310*
Deeco Int'l. (C), UT, *310*
Defrain Mayer (R), KS, *48*
DEL Technical Services, Inc. (C), IL, *310*
DeLalla - Fried Assoc. (C), NY, *310*
Delta Management Group Ltd. (C), ON, *310*
Delta Resource Group, Ltd. (C), GA, *311*
Delta Services (R), TX, *48*
DeMatteo Associates (C), NY, *311*
Despres & Associates (C), IL, *311*
Development Resource Group (R), NY, *48*
Development Search Specialists (R), MN, *49*
The Devlin Search Group, Inc. (C), MA, *311*
Rob Dey Executive Search (R), FL, *49*
Diamond Tax Recruiting (C), NY, *312*
Dieckmann & Assoc., Ltd. (R), IL, *51*
The Diestel Group (R), UT, *51*
Robert W. Dingman Co., Inc. (R), CA, *52*
Dinte Resources, Inc. (R), VA, *52*
Discovery, The Staffing Specialists, Inc. (C), IL, *312*
Diversified Consulting Services, Inc. (C), CO, *313*
Diversified Search, Inc. (R), PA, *52*
Dixie Search Assoc. (C), GA, *313*
DLB Assoc. (R), NY, *53*
DLG Assoc., Inc. (R), NC, *53*
DNA Search, Inc. (C), CA, *313*
L. J. Doherty & Assoc. (R), MA, *53*
Doherty Int'l., Inc. (R), IL, *53*
Doleman Enterprises (R), VA, *53*
The Domann Organization (R), CA, *53*
Dominguez-Metz & Assoc. (R), CA, *53*
Don Allan Assoc., Inc. (C), CA, *313*
Donini Assoc. (R), VA, *54*
J P Donnelly Assoc., Inc. (C), NY, *314*
Dotson & Assoc. (R), NY, *54*
Cal Douglas Executive Search, Inc. (R), PA, *54*
Downing & Downing, Inc. (C), OH, *314*
Drake & Assoc. (C), CA, *315*
Drew Assoc. Int'l. (R), NJ, *54*
Robert Drexler Assoc., Inc. (R), NJ, *54*
Drinkwater & Assoc. (R), MA, *54*
Drummond Assoc., Inc. (C), NY, *315*
DS&A (Doug Sears & Assoc.) (C), FL, *315*
The Duncan-O'Dell Group Inc. (C), TX, *316*
Dunhill Staffing Systems, Inc. (C), NY, *316*
Dunhill Executive Search of Los Angeles, Inc. (C), CA, *319*

Dunhill Professional Search of Hawaii (C), HI, *320*
Dunhill Technical Staffing (C), IN, *320*
Dunhill Professional Search of Tampa (C), FL, *320*
Dunhill Professional Search of Greater New Orleans (C), LA, *321*
Dunhill Professional Search of Byram (C), MS, *321*
Dunhill of Manchester Inc. (C), NH, *321*
Dunhill Search of Arlington (C), TX, *322*
Dunhill Personnel Service of Fargo (C), ND, *322*
Dunhill Professional Search of Bucks-Mont., Inc. (C), PA, *322*
Dunhill Professional Search of Wilkes-Barre/Scranton, Inc. (C), PA, *322*
Dunhill of Corpus Christi, Inc. (C), TX, *323*
C. A. Durakis Assoc., Inc. (R), MD, *55*
Dussick Management Assoc. (C), CT, *323*
Dwyer Consulting Group, Inc. (R), WV, *56*
Dynamic Choices Inc. (C), MO, *323*
Dynamic Search Systems, Inc. (C), IL, *324*
Dynamic Synergy Corp. (R), CA, *56*
E O Technical (C), CT, *324*
E T Search Inc. (C), CA, *324*
EA Plus, Inc. (C), TX, *325*
Eagle Consulting Group Inc. (C), TX, *325*
Eagle Research, Inc. (C), NJ, *325*
Eagle Search Assoc. (C), CA, *325*
EagleView, Inc. (C), MA, *325*
Earley Kielty & Assoc., Inc. (R), NY, *56*
Eastbourne Assoc. Inc. (R), NY, *56*
Eastman & Beaudine, Inc. (R), TX, *56*
EBA Group (R), NJ, *56*
The Edge Resource Group (C), PA, *326*
EDI, Inc. (C), MD, *326*
EDP Staffing Solutions, Inc. (C), AR, *327*
Edwards & Assoc. (C), GA, *327*
EFCO Consultants, Inc. (C), NY, *327*
EFL Int'l. (R), AZ, *57*
Eggers Consulting Co., Inc. (C), NE, *327*
EGM Consulting, Inc. (R), FL, *57*
Richard A. Eisner & Co., LLP (R), NY, *57*
Electronic Search, Inc. (C), IL, *327*
Elinvar (C), NC, *328*
Elite Medical Search (C), GA, *328*
Elliot Assoc. Inc. (R), NY, *58*
H. J. Elliot, Inc. (R), IL, *58*
The Elliott Company (R), MA, *58*
Ellis & Associates (C), HI, *328*
Ellis Career Consultants (C), NJ, *328*
Steve Ellis (C), CA, *328*
David M. Ellner Assoc. (R), NY, *59*
The Ellsworth Group (C), NY, *329*
Emerald Legal Search (C), NH, *329*
Emerging Medical Technologies, Inc. (C), CO, *329*
Emmett Executive Search, Inc. (C), NY, *330*
EMN/Witt/Kieffer (R), MA, *59*
Empowered Solutions Corp. (C), GA, *330*
The Enfield Company (C), TX, *330*
Engineering & Scientific Search Assoc. (ESSA) (C), NJ, *330*
ENI (R), CT, *59*
Erlanger Assoc. (R), CT, *60*
Ethos Consulting, Inc. (R), CA, *61*
ETI Search Int'l. (R), GA, *61*
The Evans McDonnell Co. (C), TX, *331*
The Evans Search Group (R), CT, *61*
Evergreen & Co. (C), MA, *331*
Excalibur Human Resources, Inc. (R), NJ, *61*
ExeConnex, LLC (R), GA, *61*
The Execu/Search Group (C), NY, *332*
ExecuGroup, Inc. (R), MS, *61*
ExecuQuest, Inc. (R), MI, *61*
ExecuSource Assoc., Inc. (C), GA, *332*
Executive Careers (R), CA, *62*
Executive Dimensions (R), NY, *62*
Executive Exchange Corp. (C), NJ, *333*
Executive Manning Corp. (R), FL, *63*
Executive Partners Inc. (C), CT, *333*
Executive Placement Consultants (C), IL, *333*
Executive Placement Services (C), GA, *333*
Executive Recruiters Int'l. (C), MI, *333*
Executive Recruiters Agency, Inc. (C), AR, *333*
Executive Recruiters (C), WA, *334*
Executive Recruitment Specialists, Inc. (R), NC, *63*
Executive Referral Services, Inc. (C), IL, *334*
Executive Registry (C), QE, *334*
Executive Resource Group, Inc. (R), ME, *63*
Executive Resource Systems (C), CA, *335*
Executive Sales Search (C), CO, *335*
Executive Search Consultants International, Inc. (R), NY, *63*
Executive Search Consultants, Inc. (C), FL, *335*
Executive Search Group, Inc. (C), CT, *335*
Executive Search Int'l./Transearch (R), MA, *63*
Executive Search Partners (R), NY, *63*
Executive Search Team (C), MI, *336*
Executive Solutions (R), MN, *64*
The Executive Source Inc. (R), NY, *64*
The Executive Source (C), SA, *337*
Executive Strategies, Inc. (C), GA, *337*
The Executive Tree (R), FL, *64*
ExecutiveFit (C), NY, *337*
Executives Worldwide, Inc. (C), OR, *337*
EXETER 2100 (C), NH, *337*
eXsource Inc. (C), SC, *337*
Fabian Assoc. Inc. (C), NY, *338*
Fagan & Company (R), PA, *64*
Fairfaxx Corp. (R), CT, *64*
Fairfield Int'l. Resources (R), NY, *65*
Paul Falcone Assoc. (R), NJ, *65*
Fallstaff Search (C), MD, *338*
Leon A. Farley Assoc. (R), CA, *65*
Faro Consultants Int'l. (C), VA, *338*
Fast Switch, Ltd. (C), OH, *338*
The Fawcett Group (R), MA, *65*
James Feerst & Assoc., Inc. (C), AZ, *339*
A. E. Feldman Assoc., Inc. (C), NY, *339*
Fell & Nicholson Technology Resources (R), CA, *65*
Fenwick Partners (R), MA, *66*
Fergus Legal Search & Consulting, Inc. (C), NY, *339*
Ferneborg & Assoc., Inc. (R), CA, *66*
Fernow Assoc. (C), PA, *339*
Financial Connections Company (C), VA, *340*
Financial Plus Management Solutions Inc. (R), ON, *66*
Financial Search Group, Inc. (R), MA, *66*
Financialjobs.com (C), CA, *340*
Eileen Finn & Assoc., Inc. (C), NY, *341*
Finn & Schneider Assoc., Inc. (C), DC, *341*
Finnegan & Assoc. (R), CA, *67*
First Advisory Services Int'l., Inc. (R), MD, *67*
First Union Executive Search (R), NC, *67*
Howard Fischer Assoc. Int'l., Inc. (R), PA, *67*
Fishel HR Assoc., Inc. (C), AZ, *341*
Jack Stuart Fisher Assoc. (C), NJ, *341*
A. G. Fishkin & Assoc., Inc. (R), MD, *68*
James L. Fisk & Assoc. (C), MO, *342*
Fitzgerald Associates (R), MA, *68*
FitzGibbon & Assoc. (R), PA, *68*
Robert M. Flanagan & Assoc., Ltd. (R), NY, *68*
Susan Fletcher Attorney Employment Services (C), PA, *342*
Flexible Resources, Inc. (C), CT, *342*
Focus Consulting Services, Inc. (C), FL, *342*
Fogec Consultants, Inc. (R), WI, *69*
Foley Proctor Yoskowitz (R), NJ, *69*
L. W. Foote Co. (R), WA, *69*
The Ford Group, Inc. (R), PA, *69*
Fortuna Technologies Inc. (C), CA, *343*
Fortune Group Int'l., Inc. (R), PA, *70*
F-O-R-T-U-N-E Personnel Consultants of Boise (R), ID, *70*
Fortune Personnel Consultants of Huntsville, Inc. (C), AL, *343*
Fortune Personnel Consultants of Colorado Springs (C), CO, *344*
F-O-R-T-U-N-E Personnel Consultants of Wilmington (C), DE, *344*
F-O-R-T-U-N-E Personnel Consultants of San Diego (C), CA, *344*
F-O-R-T-U-N-E Personnel Consultants of Manatee County (C), FL, *345*
F-O-R-T-U-N-E Personnel Consultants (C), MI, *346*
F-O-R-T-U-N-E Personnel Consultants of Southwest Indiana (C), IN, *346*
F-o-r-t-u-n-e Personnel Consultants of Detroit, Inc. (C), MI, *346*
Fortune Personnel Consultants (C), MT, *347*
F-O-R-T-U-N-E Personnel Consultants of Bergen County Inc. (C), NJ, *347*
Fortune Personnel Consultants of Raleigh, Inc. (C), NC, *348*
Fortune Personnel Consultants of Allentown, Inc. (C), PA, *348*
Fortune Personnel Consultants of Chattanooga Inc. (C), TN, *349*
Fortune Personnel Consultants of Anderson, Inc. (C), SC, *349*
Forum Personnel Inc. (C), NY, *351*
Foster Associates (C), NJ, *351*
Foster Partners (R), NY, *70*
Fought, Jameson Assoc. (C), IL, *351*
The Fourbes Group, Inc. (C), NJ, *351*
Foy, Schneid & Daniel, Inc. (R), NY, *71*

Franchise Search, Inc. (C), NY, *352*
Franklin Allen Consultants, Ltd. (R), NY, *71*
The Franklin Search Group, Inc./Medzilla (R), WA, *71*
Franstaff Inc. (C), FL, *352*
P. N. French Assoc., Inc. (R), MA, *72*
Fresquez & Assoc. (C), CA, *352*
Frey & Sher Assoc., Inc. (C), VA, *353*
Friedman Eisenstein Raemer & Schwartz, LLP (R), IL, *72*
Gerald Frisch Assoc., Inc. (R), NY, *72*
Frye/Joure & Assoc., Inc. (C), TN, *353*
C. F. Furr & Co. (R), NC, *72*
Furst Group/MPI (R), IL, *72*
Further Management Group (C), MD, *353*
Future Employment Service, Inc. (C), IA, *353*
Futures, Inc. (C), NH, *354*
G. H. Enterprises (C), AZ, *354*
The Gabriel Group (C), PA, *354*
Gahan Assoc. (R), NY, *73*
Gaming Consultants, Inc. (R), LA, *74*
Gans, Gans & Assoc., Inc. (R), FL, *74*
Garb & Assoc., Legal Placement (C), CA, *354*
W. N. Garbarini & Assoc. (R), NJ, *74*
Gardiner, Townsend & Assoc. (R), NY, *74*
The Garms Group (R), IL, *74*
The Garvis Group, Inc. (C), LA, *355*
GateSource Partners (C), VA, *355*
Gateway Group Personnel, LLC (C), TN, *355*
Gateway Management Resources (C), IL, *355*
Geddes & Rubin Management Inc. (R), ON, *76*
Genel Associates (C), CA, *356*
General Engineering Tectonics (C), CA, *356*
Genesis Personnel Service, Inc. (C), OH, *356*
C. R. Gerald & Assoc. (C), ON, *356*
J. Gernetzke & Assoc., Inc. (C), OH, *357*
GFI Professional Staffing Services (C), NH, *357*
Gielow Assoc., Inc. (R), WI, *76*
Gilbert & Van Campen Int'l. (R), NY, *76*
Gilbert Scott Assoc., LLC (C), MA, *357*
Gilbert Tweed Assoc. Inc. (R), NY, *76*
Gillard Assoc. Legal Search (C), MA, *357*
Lawrence Glaser Assoc., Inc. (C), NJ, *357*
The Glazin Group (R), BC, *77*
J. P. Gleason Assoc., Inc. (R), IL, *77*
Global 1000 Int'l. Services (C), CA, *358*
Global Data Services, Inc. (R), NY, *77*
Global HealthCare Partners (R), IL, *78*
Global Research Partnership Inc. (R), NY, *78*
Global Resources Group (R), CA, *78*
Global Technologies Group Inc. (C), NC, *359*
Global Telecommunications, Inc. (C), TX, *359*
The GlobalSearch Group (C), TX, *359*
F. Gloss Int'l. (R), VA, *78*
Glou Int'l., Inc. (R), MA, *78*
The Gobbell Co. (R), CA, *78*
Robert G. Godfrey Assoc. Ltd. (R), IL, *78*
H. L. Goehring & Assoc., Inc. (C), OH, *359*
Barry M. Gold & Co. (C), CA, *359*
Barry Goldberg & Assoc., Inc. (C), CA, *360*
The Goldman Group Inc. (R), NY, *79*
Goldman+Bell, LLC (C), NY, *360*
Fred J. Goldsmith Assoc. (R), CA, *79*
David Gomez & Assoc., Inc. (R), IL, *79*
L. J. Gonzer Assoc. (C), NJ, *360*
The Goodman Group (R), CA, *79*
Goodrich & Sherwood Assoc., Inc. (R), NY, *79*
Gossage Regan Assoc. (R), NY, *80*
Gould, McCoy & Chadick, Inc. (R), NY, *80*
The Governance Group, Inc. (R), NJ, *80*
Gowdy Consultants (C), TX, *361*
Robert Graham Assoc. (R), RI, *81*
Granger, Counts & Assoc. (R), OH, *81*
Grant Cooper & Assoc., Inc. (R), MO, *81*
Grant/Morgan Assoc., Inc. (C), MD, *361*
Grauss & Co. (C), CA, *362*
Ben Greco Assoc., Inc. (C), CA, *362*
Sheila Greco Assoc. (C), NY, *362*
Greene & Co. (C), MA, *362*
Greenhaven & Assoc., Inc. (R), NY, *81*
Greenwich Internet (C), CT, *363*
Greenwich Search Partners, LLC (C), CT, *363*
Greger/Peterson Assoc., Inc. (R), CA, *81*
Gregory, Kyle & Assoc. (C), NC, *363*
J. B. Groner Executive Search, Inc. (C), DE, *363*
Grossberg & Assoc. (R), IL, *82*
Groton Planning Group (R), ME, *82*
Groupe PCA Inc. (C), QE, *363*
Grover & Assoc. (R), OH, *82*
Growth Strategies, Inc. (R), FL, *83*
GSP International (C), NJ, *364*
Michael R. Guerin Co. (C), CA, *364*
Wolf Gugler & Assoc. Ltd. (R), ON, *83*
The Guild Corp. (C), VA, *364*
Gundersen Partners, L.L.C. (R), NY, *83*
William Guy & Assoc., Inc. (R), CA, *84*
H R Solutions, Inc. (C), MO, *365*
The H. S. Group, Inc. (C), WI, *365*
Stephen Haas Legal Placement (C), NY, *365*
Haddad Assoc. (R), FL, *84*
Hadley Associates, Inc. (C), NJ, *365*
Halbrecht & Co. (C), VA, *365*
Halbrecht Lieberman Assoc., Inc. (R), CT, *84*
Hale Assoc. (R), IL, *84*
K. C. Hale, Inc. (R), CT, *85*
Hall Kinion (C), CA, *366*
The Hamilton Group (R), MD, *85*
W. L. Handler & Assoc. (R), GA, *85*
Hands-on Broadcast (R), NY, *86*
Hanley & Assoc. (R), FL, *86*
Harbor Consultants Int'l., Inc. (C), VA, *368*
Harbrowe, Inc. (C), NY, *368*
Harcor Quest & Assoc. (R), OH, *86*
Harcourt Group Ltd. (R), OH, *86*
Hardison & Company (R), TX, *86*
Robert Harkins Assoc., Inc. (C), PA, *369*
Harper Associates (C), MI, *369*
Harper Hewes, Inc. (C), NY, *369*
Harris Heery & Assoc., Inc. (R), CT, *87*
Harris McCully Assoc., Inc. (C), NY, *369*
Hart & Co. (C), NY, *370*
Hartman & Barnette (R), VA, *87*
Harvey Hohauser & Assoc., LLC (R), MI, *87*
Bruce W. Haupt Assoc. (R), DC, *88*
Phyllis Hawkins & Assoc., Inc. (C), AZ, *370*
The Hawkins Co. (R), CA, *88*
William E. Hay & Co. (R), IL, *88*
Hayden & Assoc., Inc. (C), MN, *370*
Haydon Legal Search (C), IL, *370*
Hayman Daugherty Assoc., Inc. (C), GA, *370*
The Haystack Group, Inc. (R), ME, *88*
Hazard, Young, Attea & Assoc., Ltd. (C), IL, *371*
Hazlett Associates (R), IL, *88*
HDB Incorporated (C), MO, *371*
Healey Executive Search, Inc. (R), MN, *88*
Healthcare Recruiters Int'l. Orange County (C), CA, *372*
Healthcare Recruiters of the Rockies, Inc. (C), CO, *372*
Healthcare Recruiters Int'l. Phoenix (C), AZ, *372*
Healthcare Recruiters Int'l. - Alabama (C), AL, *372*
Healthcare Recruiters Int'l. - Los Angeles (C), CA, *372*
Healthcare Recruiters International-NY/NJ (C), NJ, *373*
Healthcare Recruiters of New Orleans (C), LA, *373*
Healthcare Recruiters Int'l - Minnesota, Inc. (C), MN, *373*
Healthcare Recruiters of New York, Inc. (C), NY, *373*
Healthcare Recruiters Int'l. - Pittsburgh (C), PA, *373*
Healthcare Recruiters - Northwest (C), WA, *374*
Healthcare Recruiters of Dallas (C), TX, *374*
Heartland National Medical Search (C), IL, *374*
R. W. Hebel Assoc. (R), TX, *89*
Hechkoff/Work Executive Search Inc. (R), NY, *89*
Thomas E. Hedefine Assoc. (C), ON, *375*
Heffelfinger Assoc., Inc. (R), MA, *89*
Jay Heino Company, LLC (C), NY, *375*
The Helms Int'l. Group (R), VA, *91*
G. W. Henn & Co. (R), OH, *91*
Kay Henry, Inc. (C), PA, *376*
The Hensge Co. (R), IL, *91*
Hergenrather & Co. (R), WA, *92*
Heritage Search Group, Inc. (C), FL, *376*
J. J. Herlihy & Assoc., Inc. (C), CA, *376*
Hermann & Westmore (R), CA, *92*
Herrerias & Assoc. (R), CA, *92*
H. Hertner Assoc., Inc. (C), FL, *377*
Higbee Assoc., Inc. (C), CT, *377*
High Tech Staffing Group (C), OR, *377*
High-Tech Recruiters (C), CT, *378*
Hill & Assoc. (C), CA, *378*
Hill Allyn Assoc. (C), CA, *378*
The Hindman Group, Inc. (C), CA, *378*
Hire Authority, Inc. (C), MI, *378*

The Hiring Authority, Inc. (C), FL, *379*
HLR Consulting (C), NY, *379*
Hobson Assoc. (C), CT, *379*
Hochman & Assoc. (C), CA, *379*
Hockett Associates, Inc. (R), CA, *94*
Hoffman Recruiters (C), MA, *380*
The Hogan Group (C), OH, *380*
The Hollins Group, Inc. (R), IL, *95*
Holloway Schulz & Partners (C), BC, *380*
Holohan Group, Ltd. (R), MO, *95*
Fred Hood & Assoc. (C), CA, *380*
David C. Horn Executive Search (C), TX, *381*
Hospitality Executive Search, Inc. (R), MA, *96*
Hospitality Int'l. (C), NY, *381*
Houser, Martin, Morris (C), WA, *381*
Houtz•Strawn & Arnold, Inc. (R), TX, *96*
Howard-Sloan Legal Search, Inc. (C), NY, *382*
Howard/Williams Assoc. (C), FL, *382*
Robert Howe & Assoc. (R), GA, *97*
HR Consultants (C), GA, *382*
HR Inc. (C), NC, *382*
HRCS (R), CA, *97*
Hreshko Consulting Group (C), NJ, *382*
HRI Services, Inc. (C), MA, *382*
HRNI (C), MI, *383*
Huff Assoc. (R), NJ, *98*
Hughes & Company (R), VA, *98*
Hughes & Sloan, Inc. (C), GA, *383*
Human Resource Bureau (C), CA, *384*
The Human Resource Department Ltd. (R), OH, *98*
Human Resource Dimensions, Inc. (C), TX, *384*
The Human Resource Group, Inc. (R), OH, *98*
Human Resource Solutions (R), TX, *98*
Human Resources Management Hawaii, Inc. (C), HI, *384*
Hunegnaw Executive Search (C), OH, *384*
Leigh Hunt & Assoc., Inc. (C), ME, *384*
H.I. Hunt & Co., Ltd. (R), MA, *99*
Hunt & Howe Inc. (R), NY, *99*
Hunter Douglas Group, Inc. (R), IL, *99*
Hunter Int'l., Inc. (R), CT, *100*
Hunter, Rowan & Crowe (C), FL, *386*
Huntington Group (R), CT, *100*
Huntington Personnel Consultants, Inc. (C), NY, *386*
Huntley Associates (Dallas), Inc. (C), TX, *386*
Huntress Real Estate Executive Search (R), MO, *100*
HVS Executive Search (R), NY, *100*
Hyde Danforth & Co. (R), TX, *100*
The Hyde Group, Inc. (R), CT, *101*
Hyman & Assoc. (C), TX, *386*
i.j. & assoc., inc. (C), CO, *386*
IM Independent Management Recruiters (R), TN, *101*
The IMC Group of Companies (R), NY, *101*
Impact Search & Strategies (C), PA, *387*
Impact Technical Staffing (C), OR, *387*
Independent Power Consultants (C), TX, *387*
Independent Resource Systems (C), CA, *388*
Information Systems Professionals (C), NC, *388*
InfoTech Search (C), TX, *388*
Ingram & Aydelotte, Inc. (R), NY, *101*
Innovative Healthcare Services, Inc. (C), GA, *389*
Innovative Partnerships (R), CA, *101*
Innovative Resource Group, LLC (C), NC, *389*
InSearch (C), CO, *389*
Insight Personnel Group, Inc. (C), TX, *389*
Intech Summit Group, Inc. (R), CA, *102*
Integrated Management Solutions (C), NY, *390*
Integrated Search Solutions Group, LLC (ISSG) (R), NY, *102*
Integrity Search, Inc. (R), PA, *102*
Intelegra, Inc. (C), NJ, *390*
Intelligent Marketing Solutions, Inc. (C), NY, *390*
IntelliSource, inc. (C), PA, *391*
Inter Regional Executive Search, Inc. (IRES, Inc.) (C), NJ, *391*
Interactive Search Assoc. (C), PA, *391*
Interactive Search Network (R), CA, *102*
Intercontinental Executive Group (C), PA, *391*
Interim Financial Solutions - Mid-Atlantic Region (C), MD, *392*
International Management Services Inc. (R), IL, *102*
International Management Advisors, Inc. (R), NY, *103*
International Management Development Corp. (C), NY, *393*
International Pro Sourcing, Inc. (C), PA, *393*
International Recruiting Services (C), FL, *393*
International Staffing Consultants, Inc. (C), CA, *393*
Interquest, Inc. (R), NY, *103*
Intersource, Ltd. (R), GA, *103*
Iona Partners (C), CA, *394*
IPR, Inc. (R), VA, *103*
IR Search (R), CA, *103*
Isaacson, Miller (R), MA, *104*
ISC of Houston, Inc. (C), TX, *394*
ISG Informatics Search Group (C), ON, *395*
Ann Israel & Assoc., Inc. (C), NY, *395*
Ives & Associates, Inc. (C), OH, *395*
J. Robert Scott (R), MA, *104*
J.B.A. Assoc. (R), WA, *104*
J.D.G. y Asociados, S.A. de C.V. (R), SO, *104*
Ron Jackson & Assoc. (C), GA, *396*
Jackson Resources (R), TX, *105*
JAG Group (R), MO, *105*
Jakobs & Assoc. Int'l. (R), NY, *105*
R. I. James, Inc. (C), NY, *397*
James Moore & Assoc. (C), CA, *397*
The Jameson Group (C), CA, *397*
JDC Assoc. (C), NY, *397*
JDG Assoc., Ltd. (C), MD, *397*
JDH & Assoc. (C), CA, *397*
Jefferson-Ross Assoc. Inc. (C), PA, *398*
Jeffrey Allan Co., Inc. (C), CA, *398*
Jeffrey Meryl Assoc., Inc. (C), NJ, *398*
Jender & Company (R), IL, *105*
JenKim Int'l. Ltd., Inc. (C), FL, *398*
JFW Associates, LLC (C), CT, *398*
JG Consultants, Inc. (R), TX, *106*
JLI-Boston (R), MA, *106*
Job-Born Candidate Selection Bureau (C), ON, *399*
John Jay & Co. (C), ME, *399*
John Michael Assoc. (R), DC, *106*
John Ryan Assoc., LLC. (C), NY, *399*
Johnson & Assoc., Inc. (R), CA, *106*
L. J. Johnson & Co. (R), MI, *106*
Johnson & Company (R), CT, *107*
Ronald S. Johnson Assoc., Inc. (R), CA, *107*
Johnson Assoc., Inc. (C), IL, *399*
Johnson Brown Assoc., Inc. (C), IN, *400*
Johnson, Kemper & Assoc. (C), TX, *400*
Johnson Smith & Knisely (R), NY, *107*
Jonathan Lawrence Assoc. (C), NJ, *400*
The Jonathan Stevens Group, Inc. (R), NJ, *108*
Jones-Parker/Starr (R), NC, *108*
Jordon & Jordon, Inc. (R), PA, *108*
J. M. Joseph Assoc. (R), NJ, *109*
Joseph Chris & Assoc. (C), TX, *400*
Joseph Consulting, Inc. (C), FL, *401*
Joseph Michaels (C), CA, *401*
JSG Group Management Consultants (R), ON, *109*
JT Assoc. (C), CT, *401*
A H Justice Search Consultants (C), TX, *402*
K & C Assoc. (C), CA, *402*
K2 Resources, L.P. (C), CT, *402*
KABL Ability Network (C), CA, *402*
Kames & Assoc. (C), MD, *403*
Kanzer Assoc., Inc. (R), IL, *109*
Gary Kaplan & Assoc. (R), CA, *109*
Kaplan & Assoc., Inc. (R), PA, *109*
Karel & Co. (R), CA, *109*
Allan Karson Assoc., Inc. (R), NJ, *110*
Kass/Abell & Assoc., Inc. (C), CA, *404*
Chris Kauffman & Company (R), GA, *110*
Kaye/Bassman Int'l. Corp. (R), TX, *110*
Kazan International, Inc. (R), NJ, *110*
Keane Assoc. (R), MA, *110*
A.T. Kearney Executive Search (R), IL, *111*
Keena Staffing Services (C), NY, *404*
Kelley & Keller, Inc. (C), FL, *405*
Kelly Assoc. (R), WI, *112*
Kenmore Executives Inc. (C), FL, *405*
David Warwick Kennedy & Assoc. (R), BC, *112*
The Kennett Group, Inc. (R), PA, *112*
Kenzer Corp. (R), NY, *113*
Barbara Kerner Consultants (C), NY, *405*
Daniel J. Kerstein, Consultant to Management (R), CO, *114*
Key Resources Int'l. (C), CA, *405*
Keystone Consulting Group (C), GA, *406*
Kiley, Owen & McGovern, Inc. (R), NJ, *114*
Kincaid Group Inc. (KGI) (C), TX, *406*
Kincannon & Reed (R), VA, *114*
Kingsley Quinn/USA (R), NJ, *115*

INDUSTRIES

Richard Kinser & Assoc. (R), NY, *115*
Kip Williams, Inc. (R), NY, *115*
Kiradjieff & Goode, Inc. (R), MA, *115*
Kittleman & Assoc.,LLC (R), IL, *115*
KL Consultants (C), NJ, *407*
Kleber & Assoc. (C), WA, *407*
Klein, Landau & Romm (C), DC, *407*
Raymond J. Klemmer & Assoc. (R), NY, *116*
KM Associates (C), MA, *407*
The Koehler Group (C), PA, *408*
Koerner & Assoc., Inc. (C), TN, *408*
Kopplin Search, Inc. (R), CA, *117*
Koren, Rogers Assoc. Inc. (R), NY, *117*
Korn/Ferry Int'l. (R), NY, *117*
Kors Montgomery Int'l. (R), TX, *118*
The J. Kovach Group (R), PA, *119*
KPA Assoc., Inc. (C), NY, *408*
Krakower Group, Inc. (R), CA, *120*
Kramer Executive Resources, Inc. (C), NY, *409*
Kremple & Meade, Inc. (R), CA, *120*
Kremple Consulting Group (R), CA, *120*
Kreutz Consulting Group, Inc. (R), IL, *121*
Todd L. Krueger & Assoc. (C), WA, *409*
John Kuhn & Assoc., Inc. (R), WI, *121*
Kukoy Associates (R), CO, *121*
Kulper & Co., L.L.C. (R), NJ, *121*
John Kurosky & Assoc. (R), CA, *122*
Kurtz Pro-Search, Inc. (C), NJ, *410*
Kyle Assoc. (C), NY, *410*
L O R (R), NJ, *122*
L T M Assoc. (C), IL, *410*
Marvin Laba & Assoc. (R), CA, *122*
Rene LaFlamme & Associes (R), QE, *122*
Laguzza Assoc., Ltd. (R), NY, *122*
Gregory Laka & Co. (C), IL, *411*
Lamay Assoc., Inc. (R), CT, *124*
Lamon + Stuart + Michaels Inc. (R), ON, *124*
Lancaster Assoc., Inc. (C), NJ, *411*
The Landstone Group (C), NY, *412*
Lanken-Kimball-Therrell & Assoc. (C), GA, *412*
Lawrence L. Lapham, Inc. (R), NY, *124*
Robert Larned Assoc., Inc. (C), VA, *413*
Larsen & Lee, Inc. (R), MD, *125*
Larsen, Whitney, Blecksmith & Zilliacus, Inc. (R), CA, *125*
LAS Management Consulting Group, Inc. (R), NJ, *125*
Latham International, Ltd. (R), NJ, *126*
Lauer, Sbarbaro Assoc., EMA Partners Int'l. (R), IL, *126*
Madeleine Lav & Assoc. (C), CA, *413*
LaVallee & Associates (C), NC, *413*
Layne-Mendez & Co. (R), TX, *127*
LCS, Inc. (C), TX, *414*
Leader Institute, Inc. (C), GA, *414*
Leader Resources Group (C), GA, *415*
Leader Search Inc. (R), AB, *127*
Lear & Assoc., Inc. (C), FL, *415*
Ledbetter/Davidson Int'l., Inc. (R), NY, *127*
Albert G. Lee Assoc. (C), RI, *415*
Vincent Lee Assoc. (C), NY, *415*
The Conrad Lee Co. Inc. (R), FL, *127*
Legal Network Inc. (C), CA, *416*
Legal Search Assoc. (C), KS, *416*
V. J. Lehman & Assoc., Inc. (R), CO, *127*
Lekan & Assoc., Inc. (R), OH, *128*
Lending Personnel Services (C), CA, *416*
F. P. Lennon Assoc. (C), PA, *416*
AG Lennox & Assoc. (R), AB, *128*
Alan Levine Assoc. (R), MA, *129*
Michael Levine Search Consultants (R), NY, *129*
Lewis Companies Inc. (R), ON, *129*
Lewis Consulting Service (C), IL, *417*
Lexington Software Inc. (C), NY, *417*
LG Brand, Inc. (C), MD, *417*
The Libra Group (C), NC, *417*
Pat Licata & Assoc. (C), NC, *417*
Howard Lieberman & Assoc., Inc. (C), MN, *417*
Lifter & Assoc. (C), CA, *418*
Lineal Recruiting Services (C), CT, *418*
Lipsky Group, Inc. (R), CA, *129*
Lipton Assoc., Inc. (R), NY, *130*
Livingston, Robert & Co. (R), CT, *130*
Lloyd Associates (R), GA, *130*
Lloyd Prescott & Churchill, Inc. (R), FL, *130*
Lloyd Prescott Assoc., Inc. (C), FL, *418*
Locke & Assoc. (R), NC, *131*
Loewenstein & Assoc., Inc. (R), TX, *131*
The Logan Group, Inc. (R), MO, *131*
Logistics Management Resources, Inc. (R), NY, *131*
Logix, Inc. (C), MA, *420*
Logue & Rice Inc. (C), VA, *420*
Longshore + Simmons (R), PA, *131*
Louis Search Group, Inc. (C), NJ, *420*
Bruce Lowery & Assoc. (C), MI, *420*
Lucas Group (C), NY, *421*
Ludwig & Assoc., Inc. (C), VA, *421*
Fran Luisi Assoc. (R), NJ, *132*
Lynne Palmer Executive Recruitment, Inc. (C), NY, *421*
Lynx, Inc. (C), MA, *421*
Lyons Assoc. (R), NY, *132*
M/J/A Partners (R), IL, *133*
The Macdonald Group, Inc. (R), NJ, *133*
The Mackenzie Group (R), MD, *133*
MacNaughton Assoc. (R), CA, *133*
Carol Maden Group (C), VA, *422*
The Madison Group (R), NY, *133*
Magellan Int'l., L.P. (C), TX, *422*
Maglio & Co., Inc. (R), WI, *134*
Magnum Search (C), IL, *422*
Maiorino & Weston Assoc., Inc. (R), CT, *134*
Major, Hagen & Africa (C), CA, *423*
Major Legal Services, Inc. (C), OH, *423*
Management & Human Resources (R), MA, *134*
Management Alliance Group, Inc. (R), NJ, *134*
Management Assoc. (C), MD, *424*
Management Decision Systems, Inc. (MDSI) (C), NJ, *424*
Management Dimensions Ltd. (R), ON, *134*
Management Recruiters of Birmingham, Inc. (C), AL, *438*
Management Recruiters of Tucson (C), AZ, *439*
Management Recruiters Peninsula (C), CA, *439*
Management Recruiters of Little Rock (C), AR, *439*
Management Recruiters of Laguna Hills (C), CA, *440*
Management Recruiters of Emeryville (C), CA, *440*
Management Recruiters of Sacramento North (C), CA, *441*
Management Recruiters, Inland Empire Agency (C), CA, *441*
Management Recruiters Inc. of Silicon Valley (C), CA, *441*
Management Recruiters of Pleasanton (C), CA, *441*
Management Recruiters of Colorado Springs (C), CO, *441*
Management Recruiters of Milford Inc. (C), CT, *442*
Management Recruiters of Colchester (C), CT, *442*
Management Recruiters of Middlesex (C), CT, *442*
Management Recruiters of Franktown (C), CO, *442*
Management Recruiters of Melbourne, Inc. (C), FL, *443*
Management Recruiters of Bonita Springs, Inc. (C), FL, *443*
Management Recruiters of Anna Maria Island (C), FL, *443*
Management Recruiters of Boca Raton (C), FL, *443*
Management Recruiters of Clearwater (C), FL, *443*
Management Recruiters of St. Augustine (C), FL, *444*
Management Recruiters of Tampa North (C), FL, *444*
Management Recruiters of St. Lucie County, Inc. (C), FL, *444*
Management Recruiters of Northern Palm Beaches (C), FL, *444*
Management Recruiters of Plant City, Inc. (C), FL, *444*
Management Recruiters of Forsyth County (C), GA, *445*
Management Recruiters of Venice, Inc. (C), FL, *445*
Management Recruiters of Duluth (C), GA, *445*
Management Recruiters of Atlanta (C), GA, *445*
Management Recruiters of Marietta, Inc. (C), GA, *446*
Management Recruiters of Springfield, Inc. (C), IL, *447*
Management Recruiters of Chicago-North Shore (C), IL, *447*
Management Recruiters of Chicago West (C), IL, *447*
Management Recruiters of Indianapolis-North (C), IN, *448*
Management Recruiters - Indianapolis (C), IN, *448*
Management Recruiters-Cedar Rapids, Inc. (C), IA, *448*
Management Recruiters of Warren County, KY (C), KY, *449*

Management Recruiters of Topeka, Inc. (C), KS, *449*
Management Recruiters of Rockville (C), MD, *450*
Management Recruiters of Frederick, Inc. (C), MD, *450*
Management Recruiters of Washington, DC Inc. (C), MD, *450*
Management Recruiters of Dearborn, Inc. (C), MI, *451*
Management Recruiters of Muskegon (C), MI, *451*
Management Recruiters of Cass County, NE (C), NE, *452*
Management Recruiters of North Oakland County, Inc. (C), MI, *452*
Management Recruiters of Bloomington (C), MN, *452*
Management Recruiters of Chanhassen (C), MN, *452*
Management Recruiters of Lake Tahoe, NV (C), NV, *453*
Management Recruiters of Morris County, NJ (C), NJ, *453*
Management Recruiters of North Warren Inc. (C), NJ, *453*
Management Recruiters of Middlesex County NJ (C), NJ, *454*
Management Recruiters of Great Neck (C), NY, *454*
Management Recruiters of Princeton (C), NJ, *454*
Management Recruiters of The Sandias (C), NM, *454*
Management Recruiters of Broome County, Inc. (C), NY, *454*
Management Recruiters of New Providence (C), NJ, *454*
Management Recruiters of Asheville, Inc. (C), NC, *455*
Management Recruiters of Cedar Mountain (C), NC, *455*
Management Recruiters of Woodbury Inc. (C), NY, *455*
Management Recruiters of Mt. Airy (C), NC, *456*
Management Recruiters of Rocky Mount - Southwest (C), NC, *456*
Management Recruiters of Wilmington (C), NC, *457*
Management Recruiters of Cleveland (C), OH, *457*
Management Recruiters of Cleveland (C), OH, *457*
Management Recruiters of Oklahoma City (C), OK, *458*
Management Recruiters - North Canton, Inc. (C), OH, *458*
Management Recruiters of Bethlehem, PA (C), PA, *458*
Management Recruiters of Northwest Ohio, Inc. (C), OH, *458*
Management Recruiters of Pittsburgh (C), PA, *459*
Management Recruiters of Valley Forge (C), PA, *459*
Management Recruiters of Cherry Hill (C), PA, *459*
Management Recruiters of Lionville, Inc. (C), PA, *459*
Management Recruiters of Aiken (C), SC, *460*
Management Recruiters of Chattanooga-Brainerd, Inc. (C), TN, *461*
Management Recruiters of Georgetown (C), SC, *461*
Management Recruiters of Champions (C), TX, *462*
Management Recruiters of Austin (C), TX, *462*
Management Recruiters - Friendswood (C), TX, *462*
Management Recruiters of Houston (C), TX, *462*
Management Recruiters of San Antonio - North (C), TX, *463*
Management Recruiters of Arlington (C), VA, *464*
Management Recruiters - Piedmont (C), VA, *464*
Management Recruiters of Fairfax, VA (C), VA, *464*
Management Recruiters of Milwaukee-West (C), WI, *465*
Management Recruiters of Loudoun County South (C), VA, *465*
Management Recruiters of Appleton (C), WI, *465*
Management Recruiters of Milwaukee - Downtown (C), WI, *466*
Management Recruiters of Stevens Point, Inc. (C), WI, *466*
Management Resource Group, Ltd. (C), IA, *467*
Management Resource Group, Inc. (C), NY, *467*
Management Search Int'l. (C), CA, *467*
Management Search, Inc. (C), IL, *467*
Management Solutions, Inc. (C), WA, *468*
Management Solutions, Inc. (C), CA, *468*
Mancini Technical Recruiting (C), VA, *468*
Mankuta Gallagher & Assoc., Inc. (C), FL, *468*
Manning Lloyd Assoc. Ltd. (C), NY, *468*
F. L. Mannix & Co. (R), MA, *135*
Manuso, Alexander & Associates, Inc. (R), NY, *135*
MARBL Consultants, Inc. (C), WI, *469*
Marcus & Assoc. (C), NY, *469*
Marentz & Co. (C), TX, *469*
Mark Adam Assoc. (R), NJ, *135*
J. L. Mark Assoc., Inc. (R), CO, *135*
Mark Christian & Assoc., Inc. (C), AZ, *469*
Mark III Personnel, Inc. (C), NC, *470*
Market Niche Consulting (C), AZ, *470*
Marketing Resources (C), MA, *470*
Marketing/Public Relations Research Recruiting (C), CT, *471*
Paula Marks Inc. (R), NY, *136*
Brad Marks Int'l. (R), CA, *136*
The Maroon Group (R), CT, *136*
Marra Peters & Partners (R), NJ, *136*
Marsar & Co., Inc. (C), FL, *471*
Marshall-Alan Assoc., Inc. (C), NY, *471*
Marsteller Wilcox Assoc. (C), IL, *471*
The Martin Group (R), CA, *137*
Maschal/Connors Inc. (R), NJ, *137*
Mason & Nicastri Ltd. (R), CA, *138*
Masserman & Assoc., Inc. (R), NY, *138*
Massey-Horton Int'l. (R), ON, *138*
Louis Thomas Masterson & Co. (R), OH, *138*
Matté & Company, Inc. (R), CT, *138*
The Matthews Group, Inc. (C), NJ, *472*
The Mazzitelli Group, Ltd. (R), MN, *139*
MB Inc. Executive Search (C), NY, *473*
McBride Assoc., Inc. (R), DC, *139*
K. E. McCarthy & Assoc. (R), CA, *139*
McCooe & Assoc., Inc. (R), NJ, *140*
McCormack & Assoc. (R), CA, *140*
The McCormick Group (C), VA, *473*
McCoy Ltd. (C), CA, *474*
McCray, Shriver, Eckdahl & Assoc., Inc. (R), CA, *140*
Earl L. McDermid & Assoc. (C), IL, *474*
McDonald Assoc. Int'l. (R), IL, *140*
McDonald, Long & Assoc., Inc. (R), NY, *140*
McDowell & Co., Recruiters (C), TX, *474*
McGrath & Assoc., Inc. (R), NJ, *141*
McHale & Assoc. (R), WA, *141*
McIntyre Management Resources (C), ON, *474*
McKinley•Arend Int'l. (R), TX, *141*
William K. McLaughlin Assoc., Inc. (C), NY, *475*
Dan P. McLean Assoc., Inc. (C), ON, *475*
McPherson Square Assoc., Inc. (C), DC, *475*
Jon McRae & Associates, Inc. (R), GA, *142*
MCS Assoc. (R), CA, *142*
MDR & Associates (C), AR, *476*
James Mead & Co. (R), CT, *142*
Med Exec Int'l. (C), CA, *476*
Meder & Assoc., Inc. (R), IL, *142*
Media Recruiting Group, Inc. (C), NY, *476*
Medical Innovations (C), NY, *477*
Medical Recruiters Exchange (C), AZ, *477*
Medical Recruiters Inc. (C), MO, *477*
Medicorp, Inc. (C), MO, *477*
The Medley Group (C), CA, *477*
MedQuest Assoc. (C), CO, *478*
MedSearch Resources, Inc. (C), FL, *478*
Medserve & Assoc. Inc. (C), MD, *478*
Mee Derby & Co. (C), DC, *478*
Melancon & Co. (R), TX, *143*
Meng, Finseth & Assoc., Inc. (R), CA, *143*
Mercedes & Co., Inc. (R), MA, *143*
The Mercer Group, Inc. (R), NM, *143*
Merlin Int'l. Inc. (C), NJ, *479*
MESA International (C), CA, *480*
META/MAT, Ltd. (R), NJ, *144*
Meyer Assoc., Inc. (R), GA, *144*
Michael Thomas, Inc. (C), OH, *480*
Michael Wayne Recruiters (C), IL, *480*
Michael/Merrill (C), KS, *481*
E. J. Michaels, Ltd. (C), NY, *481*
Midas Management (C), CT, *481*
Midland Consultants (C), OH, *481*
Millennium Search Group, Inc. (R), CA, *144*
Miller & Assoc. (C), FL, *481*
Susan C. Miller Assoc., Inc. (C), DC, *482*
Milo Research (R), NY, *145*
Mims & Associates (R), TX, *145*
Herbert Mines Assoc., Inc. (R), NY, *145*

INDUSTRIES

Mirtz Morice, Inc. (R), CT, *145*
MIS Computer Professionals, Inc. (C), KS, *482*
Paul Misarti Inc. (C), NY, *483*
MJF Assoc. (C), CT, *483*
Mogul Consultants, Inc. (C), NY, *483*
Molecular Solutions, Inc. (C), SC, *483*
Molloy Partners (R), NY, *146*
Oscar Montaño, Inc. (R), CA, *146*
Montenido Assoc. (R), CA, *146*
Montgomery Resources, Inc. (C), CA, *484*
C. A. Moore & Assoc., Inc. (C), MN, *484*
Larry Moore & Assoc. (C), CA, *484*
Thomas R. Moore Executive Search (R), TX, *146*
The Moran Group (C), IL, *484*
Morency Assoc. (C), MA, *485*
Morgan Hunter Corp. (C), KS, *485*
Morgan Int'l., Inc. (R), IL, *147*
Morgan/Webber, Inc. (R), NY, *147*
Morgenstern Int'l., Inc. (C), FL, *485*
The Morley Group (C), IN, *486*
Morris & Berger (R), CA, *147*
The Morris Group (C), PA, *486*
Mortgage & Financial Personnel Services (C), CA, *486*
Robert T. Morton Assoc., Inc. (C), MA, *486*
MPA Executive Search Inc. (R), QE, *148*
MSA Executive Search (R), MO, *148*
MTA Partners (R), TX, *148*
Multi Processing, Inc. (R), NH, *149*
Jennifer Munro & Partners, Inc. (R), SC, *149*
Musick & Assoc. (C), CA, *487*
DDJ Myers, Ltd. (R), AZ, *150*
Nagler, Robins & Poe, Inc. (R), MA, *150*
Nason & Nason (C), FL, *488*
National Affirmative Action Career Network, Inc. (C), CO, *488*
National Computerized Employment Service, Inc. (C), PA, *489*
National Corporate Consultants, Inc. (C), IN, *489*
National Executive (C), ON, *489*
National Field Service Corp. (C), NY, *489*
National Recruiters (C), OK, *489*
National Register Columbus Inc. (C), OH, *490*
National Restaurant Search, Inc. (R), GA, *150*
National Search, Inc.r (C), FL, *490*
NaviSearch (C), GA, *490*
The Neil Michael Group, Inc./Global Partners (R), NY, *151*
J. Fielding Nelson & Assoc., Inc. (R), UT, *151*
Networking Unlimited of NH, Inc. (C), NH, *491*
New Dawn Employment Search (C), CA, *491*
New Dimensions in Technology, Inc. (C), MA, *492*
Newcomb-Desmond & Assoc., Inc. (C), OH, *492*
Newell Assoc. (R), NY, *151*
Newman-Johnson-King, Inc. (C), TX, *492*
Newport Management (C), NY, *492*
Newport Strategic Search LLC (C), CA, *492*
Next Step Recruiting (C), CA, *493*
Nichols & Company (R), CO, *151*
Marc Nichols Assoc., Inc. (C), NY, *493*
Nichols Brown Int'l. (R), NY, *151*
Ira Z. Nitzberg (C), NY, *493*
Noble & Assoc., Inc. (C), NY, *494*
The Nolan Group (C), CA, *494*
W. D. Nolte & Company (R), CT, *152*
Nordeman Grimm, Inc. (R), NY, *152*
Paul Winston Norman & Assoc. (R), IL, *152*
Norman Broadbent Int'l., Inc. (R), NY, *152*
The Normyle/Erstling Health Search Group (C), NJ, *494*
Norrell Financial Staffing (C), GA, *495*
John B. Norris & Assoc., Inc. (C), MD, *495*
Ronald Norris & Assoc. (C), IL, *495*
The North Peak Group (C), OH, *496*
Northern Consultants Inc. (R), ME, *153*
Northland Employment Services Inc. (C), MN, *496*
NorthStar Technologies, Inc. (C), NY, *496*
NPF Assoc. Ltd. Inc. (R), FL, *153*
NRI Staffing Resources (C), DC, *496*
Nuessle, Kurdziel & Weiss, Inc. (R), PA, *153*
NYCOR Search, Inc. (C), MN, *497*
O'Brien & Bell (R), OH, *153*
O'Brien and Roof (C), OH, *497*
O'Callaghan Honey/Ray & Berndtson Inc. (R), AB, *153*
O'Connell Group Inc. (C), CT, *497*
O'Connor Resources (C), TX, *497*
O'Keefe & Assoc. (C), TX, *497*
O'Keefe & Assoc., Inc. (R), CT, *154*
O'Neill & Co. (R), CT, *154*
O'Rourke Companies, Inc. (R), TX, *154*
O'Sullivan Search Inc. (C), ON, *498*
Dennis P. O'Toole & Assoc. Inc. (R), NY, *154*
O'Toole & Company, Inc. (R), IL, *154*
Ober & Company (R), CA, *155*
Oberlander & Co., Inc. (R), IL, *155*
Odell & Assoc., Inc. (C), TX, *498*
The Ogdon Partnership (R), NY, *155*
The Oldani Group (R), WA, *155*
Ollinger Partners (R), MA, *156*
Olsen/Clark (R), WA, *156*
Olympian Recruitment, Ltd. (C), NY, *498*
Omnisearch Assoc. (C), CA, *499*
The Onstott Group (R), MA, *156*
Opportunity Resources, Inc. (R), NY, *156*
The Options Group, Inc. (C), NY, *499*
Opus Marketing (R), CA, *156*
Organization Consulting Ltd. (R), ON, *157*
Organization Resources Inc. (R), MA, *157*
Ott & Hansen, Inc. (R), CA, *157*
Robert Ottke Assoc. (R), CA, *157*
Overton Consulting (R), WI, *157*
LaMonte Owens, Inc. (R), PA, *157*
The Oxford Group (C), TX, *500*
P.A.R. Assoc., Inc. (R), MA, *158*
P.R.H. Management, Inc. (R), CT, *158*
Pacific Advisory Service, Inc. (C), IL, *501*
Pacific Crossing (C), CA, *501*
Pacific Finance Search, Inc. (C), CA, *501*
Pacific Search Group, Inc. (C), CA, *501*
Page-Wheatcroft & Co., Ltd. (R), TX, *158*
Paladin Group, Inc. (C), CO, *502*
Pamenter, Pamenter, Brezer & Deganis Ltd. (R), ON, *159*
Arthur Pann Assoc., Inc. (C), NY, *502*
Florence Pape Legal Search, Inc. (C), NJ, *502*
The PAR Group - Paul A. Reaume, Ltd. (R), IL, *159*
Parenica & Co. (R), NC, *159*
The Park Group & Assoc., Inc. (C), MD, *502*
Parker Page Group (C), FL, *503*
Largent Parks & Partners (C), TX, *503*
Partners Executive Search Consultants Inc. (R), ON, *160*
Partners In Human Resources Int'l., Inc. (R), NY, *160*
The Partners, LLC (C), CA, *504*
Partners Resource Group (C), VA, *504*
The Partnership Group (R), NJ, *160*
Partnervision Consulting Group Inc. (R), ON, *160*
Partridge Assoc., Inc. (R), MA, *160*
Carolyn Smith Paschal Int'l. (R), CA, *160*
Pasona Canada, Inc. (C), ON, *504*
Pathway Executive Search, Inc. (C), NY, *505*
The Patience Motivation Belief Group, Inc. (C), GA, *505*
Patrice & Assoc. (C), MD, *505*
Patriot Assoc. (C), PA, *505*
Paul-Tittle Assoc., Inc. (R), VA, *161*
Pawlik/Dorman Partners (R), IL, *161*
Peak Search Assoc. (C), ON, *506*
Pearce & Assoc. (C), FL, *506*
Pearson, Caldwell & Farnsworth (R), CA, *161*
Peeney Assoc., Inc. (R), NJ, *161*
M. A. Pelle Assoc., Inc. (C), NY, *506*
Penn Associates (R), PA, *161*
The Penn Partners, Inc. (R), PA, *162*
Pennington Consulting Group (C), NJ, *506*
The Pennmor Group (C), NJ, *506*
People Management Mid-South, LLC (R), TN, *162*
People Management Northeast, Inc. (R), CT, *162*
PeopleSource Inc. (C), TX, *506*
Perez-Arton Consultants, Inc. (R), NY, *162*
R. H. Perry & Assoc., Inc. (R), DC, *162*
Perry Search Assoc. (C), CA, *507*
Perry-D'Amico & Assoc. (R), CA, *162*
Perry-Martel Int'l., Inc. (R), ON, *163*
PersoNet, Inc. (C), FL, *507*
Personnel Alliance Group (C), NJ, *507*
Personnel Assoc. (C), CA, *508*
The Personnel Group, Inc. (R), MN, *163*
Personnel Incorporated (C), IA, *508*
Personnel Management Group (C), MB, *508*
The Personnel Network, Inc. (C), SC, *508*
Personnel Resources Organization (C), PA, *509*
Personnel Unlimited/Executive Search (C), WA, *509*
Petrie Partners, Inc. (R), FL, *163*
Robert E. Pfaendler & Assoc., Inc. (C), OR, *509*

Pharmaceutical Recruiters, Inc. (R), NY, *163*
Pharmaceutical Search Professionals, Inc. (C), PA, *510*
PHD Conseil en Ressources Humaines Inc. (C), QE, *510*
J. R. Phillip & Assoc., Inc. (R), CA, *164*
Phillips & Assoc. (R), MA, *164*
Phillips Assoc. (C), FL, *510*
Phillips Personnel/Search (C), CO, *510*
Phoenix Partners, Inc. (C), GA, *511*
Physicians Search®, Inc. (C), CA, *511*
Picard Int'l., Ltd. (R), NY, *164*
The Pinnacle Source, Inc. (C), CO, *512*
Pinton Forrest & Madden/EMA Partners Int'l. (R), BC, *165*
DNPitchon Assoc. (R), NJ, *165*
Pittleman & Assoc. (C), NY, *512*
PKS Assoc., Inc. (C), RI, *513*
Place Mart Personnel Service (C), NJ, *513*
Placement Solutions (C), WI, *513*
Plante & Moran, LLP (R), MI, *165*
R. L. Plimpton Assoc., Inc. (R), CO, *165*
Yves Plouffe & Assoc. (R), QE, *165*
Plummer & Assoc., Inc. (R), CT, *166*
Bob Poline Assoc. Inc. (C), CA, *514*
The Pollack Group (C), ON, *514*
Robert Powers & Assoc. (C), CA, *515*
Powers Consultants, Inc. (R), MO, *166*
PPS Information Systems Staffing (C), MD, *515*
P. G. Prager Search Assoc., Ltd. (C), NY, *515*
The Prairie Group (C), IL, *515*
Prairie Resource Group, Inc. (R), IL, *166*
Elan Pratzer & Partners Inc. (R), ON, *167*
Precision Executive Search (C), AZ, *516*
Preferred Placement, Inc. (C), NY, *516*
Preferred Professional Recruiters (C), TX, *516*
Premier Business Advisors (C), PA, *516*
Preng & Assoc., Inc. (R), TX, *167*
Prescott Legal Search, Inc. (C), TX, *517*
Presley Consultants, Inc. (C), CA, *517*
Prestige Inc. (C), WI, *517*
Preston & Co. (R), NJ, *167*
Preston-Hunter, Inc. (R), IL, *167*
Prestonwood Assoc. (R), MA, *168*
Price & Assoc., Inc. (C), VA, *518*
PricewaterhouseCoopers Executive Search (R), MX, *168*
The Primary Group, Inc. (R), FL, *168*
Prime Management Group Inc. (C), ON, *518*
Princeton Executive Search (C), NJ, *518*
Princeton Search Partners, Inc. (R), NJ, *169*
Priority Executive Search (C), FL, *518*
PRO, Inc./Professional Recruiting Offices, Inc. (C), CA, *519*
Pro-Tech Search, Inc. (C), IL, *519*
Procom (C), ON, *519*
Professional Employment Group (C), MD, *520*
Professional Personnel Consultants, Inc. (C), MI, *521*
Professional Recruiters (C), UT, *521*
Professional Research Services, Inc. (R), IL, *169*
Professional Resources (C), NY, *522*
Professional Resources (C), OK, *522*
The Professional Sales Search Co., Inc. (C), WA, *522*
Professional Search (R), MI, *169*
Professional Search Centre, Ltd. (C), IL, *522*
Professional Search Assoc. (C), CA, *522*
Professional Search, Inc. (C), CO, *522*
Professional Selection Services (R), GA, *169*
Professional Support Inc. (C), NY, *523*
ProFinders, Inc. (C), FL, *523*
Profit Pros, Inc. (C), CA, *523*
ProLinks Inc. (R), VA, *170*
ProSearch, Inc. (C), OH, *524*
Protocol Inc. (C), CA, *525*
Pursuant Legal Consultants (R), WA, *170*
Quality Consulting Group, Inc. (C), WI, *526*
Quantum Int'l., Ltd. (R), FL, *170*
The Quest Organization (C), NY, *527*
Quetico Corp. (R), TX, *170*
Quigley Assoc. (R), MD, *170*
Quiring Assoc., Inc. (C), IN, *527*
Quirk-Corporon & Assoc., Inc. (C), WI, *527*
QVS Int'l. (R), GA, *170*
R. J. Associates (C), NY, *528*
R.A.N. Assoc., Inc. (C), OH, *528*
Railey & Assoc. (C), TX, *528*
Rand Thompson Executive Search Consultants (C), NY, *528*
Rand-Curtis Resources (C), AZ, *529*
Lea Randolph & Assoc., Inc. (C), TX, *529*
The Rankin Group, Ltd. (R), WI, *171*
The Ransford Group (R), TX, *171*
J. E. Ranta Assoc. (C), MA, *529*
Harold L. Rapp Assoc. (C), NY, *529*
Vera L. Rast Partners Inc. (C), IL, *529*
Ray & Berndtson (R), TX, *171*
Raymond Karsan Assoc. (C), PA, *529*
Razzino-Claymore Assoc. (C), NJ, *530*
RCI Employment Solutions (C), FL, *531*
Recruit Xpress (C), TX, *531*
Recruiting Resources Int'l. (C), CA, *532*
Recruiting Specialists (C), MA, *532*
Recruiting/Solutions (C), CA, *532*
The Recruitment Group, Inc. (C), NY, *532*
Recruitment Resources (C), CA, *532*
P. J. Reda & Assoc., Inc. (C), GA, *533*
Redden & McGrath Assoc., Inc. (R), NY, *173*
Redden-Shaffer Group (R), CA, *173*
Redwood Partners Ltd. (R), NY, *173*
Reece & Mruk Partners/EMA Partners Int'l. (R), MA, *173*
Cedric L. Reese Inc. (C), CA, *533*
The Regency Group, Ltd. (C), NE, *533*
The Regis Group, Ltd. (R), GA, *174*
Reifel & Assoc. (R), IL, *174*
Reinecke & Assoc. (C), NJ, *533*
RemTech Business Solutions, Inc. (C), MI, *534*
The Renaissance Network (C), MA, *534*
Renaissance Resources, LLC (R), VA, *174*
Research Personnel Consultants (C), ON, *534*
Resource Management Group (C), CT, *534*
Resource Perspectives, Inc. (R), CA, *175*
Resource Services, Inc. (C), NY, *534*
Resources for Management (R), PA, *175*
Response Staffing Services (C), NY, *534*
Retail Recruiters/Spectrum Consultants, Inc. (C), PA, *535*
Retained Search Assoc. (R), NC, *176*
S. Reyman & Assoc., Ltd. (R), IL, *176*
Russell Reynolds Assoc., Inc. (R), NY, *176*
Reynolds Consulting Int'l. (R), ON, *177*
Reynolds Partners (R), NY, *177*
RHI Consulting (C), VA, *536*
RHS Assoc. (C), AL, *536*
Marshall Rice Assoc. (R), RI, *177*
Rice Cohen Int'l. (R), PA, *178*
Richards Assoc., Inc. (R), NY, *178*
The Richards Group (C), PA, *536*
Ridenour & Assoc. (R), IL, *178*
Rieser & Assoc., Inc. (R), MO, *178*
Right/McKee Consulting Group (C), TX, *537*
Wilson Riles & Assoc., Inc. (R), CA, *178*
Ritt-Ritt & Assoc., Inc. (C), IL, *537*
Ritta Professional Search Inc. (C), NY, *538*
Rivera Legal Search, Inc. (C), CA, *538*
Roberson & Co. (C), AZ, *538*
Robert William James & Assoc. (C), OR, *539*
Norman Roberts & Assoc., Inc. (R), CA, *179*
Roberts Ryan & Bentley, Inc. (R), MD, *179*
Robertson & Assoc. (C), IL, *539*
Bruce Robinson Assoc. (R), NJ, *180*
The Robinson Group, D.A., Ltd. (C), IL, *539*
Robison & Associates (R), NC, *180*
Rocky Mountain Recruiters, Inc. (C), CO, *540*
R. A. Rodriguez & Assoc., Inc. (C), TX, *540*
Rodzik & Assoc., Inc. (R), NC, *180*
Craig Roe & Assoc., LLC (C), MD, *540*
Rogish Assoc., Inc. (C), OH, *541*
Rojek Marketing Group, Inc. (R), OH, *181*
Roll International (C), TX, *541*
Rollo Assoc. (R), CA, *181*
Romac Int'l. (C), GA, *541*
Romac Int'l. (C), IL, *541*
Romac Int'l. (C), PA, *542*
Romac Int'l. Inc. (R), MA, *181*
Romac Int'l., Inc. (C), FL, *542*
Ropes Associates, Inc. (R), FL, *182*
Emery A. Rose & Assoc. (C), WA, *545*
Rosenfeld & Co., Inc. (C), MI, *545*
Ross Personnel Consultants, Inc. (C), CT, *545*
Rossi & Assoc. Inc. (C), BC, *545*
Roster Inc. (C), IN, *545*
Roth Young Personnel Services of Washington, DC (C), MD, *546*
Roth Young of Chicago (C), IL, *546*
Roth Young Personnel Service of Detroit, Inc. (C), MI, *546*
Roth Young of Pittsburgh (C), PA, *546*
Roth Young Executive Recruiters (C), MN, *546*
Roth Young Executive Search (C), TX, *546*
Roth Young Seattle (C), WA, *546*
Roth Young of Tampa (C), FL, *546*
Rovner & Assoc., Inc. (R), IL, *182*

Rovner Gerner & Assoc. (R), CA, *182*
Rowland Mountain & Assoc. (C), GA, *547*
Royal Assoc. (C), CA, *547*
The Rubicon Group (C), AZ, *547*
The Rubinic Consulting Group (C), OH, *548*
Ruderfer & Co., Inc. (C), NJ, *548*
K. Russo Assoc. Inc. (C), CT, *548*
Rust & Assoc., Inc. (R), IL, *183*
Ryan, Miller & Assoc. (C), CA, *549*
Rylan Forbes Consulting Group, Inc. (C), NJ, *549*
Ryman, Bell, Green & Michaels, Inc. (C), TX, *549*
R. L. Rystrom & Assoc., Inc. (C), MN, *549*
S-H-S TechStaff (C), PA, *549*
S. C. Int'l., Ltd. (C), IL, *550*
S. P. Assoc., Inc. (C), NC, *550*
S.C.S. & Assoc. (C), NC, *550*
R. S. Sadow Assoc. (C), NJ, *550*
Sales & Management Search, Inc. (C), IL, *551*
Sales & Marketing Search, Inc. (C), MA, *551*
Sales Consultants of Birmingham (C), AL, *555*
Sales Consultants of Silicon Valley (C), CA, *556*
Sales Consultants of Chico (C), CA, *556*
Sales Consultants Peninsula, Inc. (C), CA, *556*
Sales Consultants of Sacramento (C), CA, *556*
Sales Consultants of Northwest Arkansas, Inc. (C), AR, *556*
Sales Consultants of Ft. Lauderdale, Inc. (C), FL, *557*
Sales Consultants of Stamford-Darien (C), CT, *557*
Sales Consultants of Honolulu (C), HI, *558*
Sales Consultants of Barrington (C), IL, *558*
Sales Consultants of Indianapolis-North (C), IN, *558*
Sales Consultants (C), IL, *558*
Sales Consultants of Western McHenry County (C), IL, *558*
Sales Consultants of Indianapolis (C), IN, *558*
Sales Consultants of Chicago South (C), IL, *558*
Sales Consultants of Wellesley, Inc. (C), MA, *559*
Sales Consultants of Auburn Hills (C), MI, *559*
Sales Consultants of Rockville, MD (C), MD, *559*
Sales Consultants of Bangor, Inc. (C), ME, *559*
Sales Consultants of Laurel Park, Inc. (C), MI, *560*
Sales Consultants of Grand Rapids (C), MI, *560*
Sales Consultants Bridgewater, Inc. (C), NJ, *560*
Sales Consultants of Cherry Hill (C), NJ, *560*
Sales Consultants of Omaha, Inc. (C), NE, *560*
Sales Consultants of Princeton, Inc. (C), NJ, *561*
Sales Consultants of Austin, Inc. (C), TX, *562*
Sales Consultants King of Prussia (C), PA, *562*
Sales Consultants of Pittsburgh (C), PA, *562*
Sales Consultants of Madison (C), WI, *563*
Sales Consultants of Milwaukee (C), WI, *563*
Sales Consultants of Dallas (C), TX, *563*
Sales Consultants of Houston (C), TX, *563*
Sales Executives, Inc. (C), MI, *563*
Sales Recruiters of Oklahoma City (C), OK, *564*
Sales Search (C), ON, *564*
Sales Search Specialist (C), IL, *564*
A. N. Salloway Executive Search & Consulting, L.L.C. (C), MA, *564*
Salzmann Gay Assoc., Inc. (R), PA, *184*
Sampson Medical Search (C), CA, *564*
Norm Sanders Assoc., Inc. (R), NJ, *184*
Sanders Management Assoc., Inc. (C), NJ, *565*
Sanford Rose Assoc. - Lake Forest (R), IL, *184*
Sanford Rose Assoc. (C), OH, *565*
Sanford Rose Assoc. - Laguna Beach (C), CA, *565*
Sanford Rose Assoc. - Mobile (C), AL, *565*
Sanford Rose Assoc. - Clearwater (C), FL, *566*
Sanford Rose Assoc. - Norcross (C), GA, *566*
Sanford Rose Assoc. - Orland Park (C), IL, *567*
Sanford Rose Assoc. - Louisville (C), KY, *567*
Sanford Rose Assoc. - Charlotte (C), NC, *568*
Sanford Rose Assoc. - Springfield (C), MO, *568*
Sanford Rose Assoc. - Gastonia (C), NC, *568*
Sanford Rose Assoc. - Amherst, NY (C), NY, *568*
Sanford Rose Assoc. - Rochester (C), MI, *568*
Sanford Rose Assoc. - Euclid (C), OH, *569*
Sanford Rose Assoc. - Akron (C), OH, *569*
Sanford Rose Assoc. - Columbia (C), SC, *570*
Sanford Rose Assoc. - Philadelphia North (C), PA, *570*
Sanford Rose Assoc. - Pittsburgh North (C), PA, *570*
Sanford Rose Assoc. - Salt Lake City (C), UT, *571*
Santangelo Consultants Inc. (C), NY, *571*
Sathe & Associates, Inc. (R), MN, *184*
Satterfield & Assoc., Inc. (R), OH, *184*
Saviar, Inc. (C), AZ, *571*
Savoy Partners, Ltd. (R), DC, *184*
The Schatz Company (C), MO, *571*
Schenck & Assoc. SC (C), WI, *572*
A.D. Schiff & Assoc., Ltd. (C), IL, *572*
Schlatter & Assoc. (C), CA, *572*
F. B. Schmidt Int'l. (R), CA, *185*
Schneider, Hill & Spangler, Inc. (R), PA, *185*
Schuyler Assoc., Ltd. (R), GA, *185*
Schuyler, Baker & Parker, Inc. (R), GA, *185*
G. L. Schwartz & Assoc., Inc. (C), GA, *572*
Devin Scott Assoc. (C), NJ, *572*
Scott Sibley Assoc. (C), NY, *573*
Scott-Thaler Assoc. Agency, Inc. (C), CA, *573*
Scott-Wayne Assoc., Inc. (C), MA, *573*
Search & Recruit Int'l. (C), VA, *573*
Search Advisors Int'l. Corp. (R), FL, *186*
The Search Alliance, Inc. (R), FL, *186*
The Search America Group Inc. (C), OH, *573*
Search America, Inc. (C), PA, *573*
Search America, Inc. (C), MA, *574*
Search Assoc., Inc. (C), NJ, *574*
Search Consultants, LLC (C), MD, *575*
Search Group (C), CA, *575*
Search Group Inc. (R), AB, *186*
Search Innovations, Inc. (R), PA, *187*
Search Int'l. (R), MA, *187*
Search Masters Int'l. (R), AZ, *187*
Search Masters, USA (C), FL, *576*
Search Plus Int'l.-Ohio (C), OH, *576*
Search Research Assoc., Inc. (R), MA, *187*
Search Solutions Inc. (C), CA, *576*
SearchCorp (C), FL, *577*
SearchCorp International (C), AB, *577*
Searchforce, Inc. (R), FL, *187*
Searchworks, Inc. (C), FL, *577*
Seco & Zetto Assoc., Inc. (C), NJ, *577*
Sedlar & Miners (R), NY, *188*
Select Services (C), IL, *578*
Robert Sellery Assoc., Ltd. (R), DC, *188*
Seltzer Fontaine Beckwith (C), CA, *579*
Sensible Solutions, Inc. (R), IL, *188*
Setford-Shaw-Najarian Assoc. (C), NY, *579*
Sevcor Int'l., Inc. (R), IL, *188*
SFB Legal Search (C), NY, *579*
Sharrow & Assoc., Inc. (C), MI, *579*
Shell Technology Group (C), CA, *580*
Shepherd Bueschel & Provus, Inc. (R), IL, *189*
Shey-Harding Assoc. Inc. (C), CA, *580*
Shiell Personnel (C), LA, *580*
Michael Shirley Assoc. Inc. (R), KS, *190*
Shoemaker & Assoc. (R), GA, *190*
E. L. Shore & Assoc. (R), ON, *190*
Shore Asociados Ejecutivos, S. A. de C.V. (R), MX, *190*
The Shorr Group (R), IL, *190*
Shupack & Michaels Inc. (C), NY, *580*
John Sibbald Assoc., Inc. (R), MO, *191*
RitaSue Siegel Resources, Inc. (R), NY, *191*
Siger & Assoc., LLC (C), CT, *581*
Marvin L. Silcott & Assoc., Inc. (C), TX, *581*
The Silicon Network (C), ON, *581*
Silver Associates (C), CA, *581*
Daniel A. Silverstein Assoc. Inc. (R), FL, *191*
The Simmons Group (C), CA, *582*
Sinclair & Co., Inc. (R), MA, *192*

Ruth Sklar Assoc., Inc. (RSA Executive Search) (R), NY, *192*
Sloan & Assoc., Inc. (C), VA, *583*
J. L. Small Assoc. (C), AL, *583*
Smartsource Inc. (C), CA, *583*
Smith & Assoc. (C), FL, *583*
James F. Smith & Assoc. (C), GA, *583*
Peter A. Smith & Assoc. (C), OR, *584*
Smith & Sawyer, Inc. (R), NY, *193*
G. L. Smith Assoc. (C), CA, *584*
Howard W. Smith Assoc. (R), CT, *193*
Abbott Smith Assoc., Inc. (R), NY, *193*
J. Harrington Smith Assoc. (C), IN, *584*
Smith Hanley Assoc., Inc. (C), NY, *584*
Smith James Group, Inc. (R), GA, *194*
Smith Search, S.C. (R), MX, *194*
Smith, Brown & Jones (C), KS, *585*
A. William Smyth, Inc. (R), CA, *194*
Smythe Masterson & Judd, Inc. (C), NY, *585*
Snelling & Snelling, Inc. (C), FL, *585*
Snelling Search (C), LA, *586*
Snelling Search Recruiters (C), NC, *586*
Andrea Sobel & Assoc., Inc. (C), CA, *586*
Sockwell & Assoc. (R), NC, *194*
Softrix, Inc. (C), NJ, *586*
Software Engineering Solutions, Inc. (C), CA, *586*
Software Resource Consultants (C), TN, *587*
Robert Sollman & Assoc. (C), FL, *587*
Solomon-Page Healthcare Group (R), NY, *195*
Solutions Group (R), AL, *195*
Stephen M. Sonis Assoc. (R), MA, *195*
Souder & Assoc. (R), VA, *195*
Southport Int'l. Assoc. Inc. (C), FL, *588*
Southwestern Professional Services (C), TN, *588*
Sparks, McDonough & Assoc., Inc. (C), MO, *588*
SPC Symcox Personnel Consultants (C), TX, *588*
Spear-Izzo Assoc., LLC (C), PA, *588*
Special Markets Group, Inc. (R), GA, *195*
Specialty Consultants Inc. (R), PA, *195*
Spectra International LLC (C), AZ, *589*
SpencerStuart (R), NY, *196*
The Spiegel Group (R), MA, *197*
Kenn Spinrad Inc. (C), PA, *589*
Splaine & Assoc., Inc. (R), CA, *198*
Sports Group Int'l. (R), NC, *198*
Spriggs & Co., Inc. (R), IL, *198*
Squires Resources Inc. (C), ON, *590*
SR Wilson, Inc. (C), CA, *590*
Staff Resources, Inc. (C), SC, *590*
Staffing Edge, Inc. (C), IA, *590*
C. J. Stafford & Assoc. (C), ON, *591*
Stafford Consulting Group (R), CA, *198*
StaffWriters Plus (C), NY, *591*
Stanewick, Hart & Assoc., Inc. (C), FL, *591*
Stanton Chase Int'l. (R), MD, *198*
Starbridge Group Inc. (C), VA, *591*
The Stark Wilton Group (R), MI, *199*
STAT Search (C), NH, *592*
Steinfield & Assoc. (C), TX, *592*
Stentiford & Berardi Assoc. Ltd. (R), NY, *199*
Sterling Int'l. (R), NJ, *200*
Daniel Stern & Assoc. (C), PA, *592*
Michael Stern Assoc., Inc./Euram (R), ON, *200*
Steven Douglas Assoc. (C), FL, *593*
Stevens Assoc. (C), MA, *593*
The Stevens Group (R), TX, *200*
Stevens, Valentine & McKeever (C), NJ, *593*
The Stevenson Group, Inc. (N.J.) (R), NJ, *200*
The Stewart Group (C), FL, *593*
Stewart, Stein & Scott, Ltd. (R), MN, *200*
Stewart/Greene & Co. of The Triad, Inc. (C), NC, *594*
Stewart/Laurence Assoc., Inc. (R), NJ, *201*
Linford E. Stiles & Assoc., L.L.C. (R), NH, *201*
Stillinger & Assoc. (R), CA, *201*
Stone & Youngblood (C), MA, *594*
Stone Assoc. LLC (C), MI, *594*
Stone Enterprises Ltd. (C), IL, *594*
Stone, Murphy & Olson (R), MN, *201*
DM Stone Personnel Services (C), CA, *594*
Stoopen Asociados, S.C./EMA Partners Int'l. (R), MX, *202*
Strategic Alliance Network, Ltd. (C), OH, *595*
Strategic Assoc., Inc. (C), TX, *595*
Strategic Executives, Inc. (R), CT, *202*
Strategic Resources Biotechnology & Medical Group (C), WA, *595*
Strategic Resources (C), WA, *595*
Strategic Search, LLC (C), CA, *595*
StratfordGroup (R), OH, *203*
Straube Associates (R), MA, *203*
Strauss Personnel Service (C), PA, *596*
J. Stroll Assoc., Inc. (R), CT, *203*
Stroman Int'l., Inc. (R), CO, *204*
Sudina Search, Inc. (C), MD, *596*
Sullivan & Assoc. (R), MI, *204*
Joe Sullivan & Assoc., Inc. (R), NY, *204*
Summerfield Assoc., Inc. (C), TN, *596*
Summit Executive Search Consultants, Inc. (R), FL, *204*
Summit Group Int'l., Inc. (R), GA, *204*
The Summit Group (C), CA, *596*
Ron Sunshine & Assoc. (C), IL, *597*
Swartz & Assoc., Inc. (R), AZ, *204*
Synapse Human Resource Consulting Group (R), TX, *205*
Synergistech Communications (C), CA, *597*
Synergy 2000 (C), DC, *597*
The Synergy Organization (R), PA, *205*
Synergy Solutions, Ltd. (C), WA, *597*
Systems Careers (C), CA, *598*
Systems One Ltd. (C), IL, *598*
Systems Personnel, Inc. (C), NY, *598*
Systems Research Inc. (SRI) (C), IL, *598*
Systems Search (C), IL, *599*
Systems Search Group, Inc. (C), NC, *599*
T. H. Hunter, Inc. (C), MN, *599*
Tabb & Assoc. (R), OH, *205*
Tactical Alternatives (R), CA, *205*
The Talley Group (R), VA, *205*
Roy Talman & Assoc. (C), IL, *599*
The Talon Group (R), TX, *205*
Tarbex (C), DC, *599*
Target Search, Inc. (C), PA, *600*
M. L. Tawney & Assoc. (C), TX, *600*
Tax Network Resources, Inc. (C), NY, *600*
TaxSearch Inc. (R), OK, *207*
Carl J. Taylor & Co. (R), TX, *207*
Taylor Winfield (R), TX, *207*
TBC, Inc. (C), KY, *600*
Team One Partners, Inc. (C), GA, *600*
TeamBuilders (C), GA, *600*
Tech 2000 (C), FL, *601*
Tech Consulting (C), FL, *601*
Tech Search (C), CA, *601*
Tech-Net (C), TX, *601*
TechFind, Inc. (R), MA, *207*
TechNix Inc. (C), ON, *602*
Techno-Trac Systems, Inc. (C), NY, *603*
The Technology Group (R), IL, *208*
Technology Search Int'l. (C), CA, *603*
TeleManagement Search (C), NY, *605*
Templeton & Assoc. (C), MN, *605*
The TGA Company (C), TX, *606*
Thomas Lyle & Co. (C), IL, *606*
Thomas Mangum Co. (R), CA, *208*
Thomas, Whelan Assoc., Inc. (C), DC, *606*
Judy Thompson & Assoc., Inc. (C), CA, *606*
Richard Thompson Assoc., Inc. (R), MN, *209*
Thor, Inc. (C), CA, *606*
Tirocchi, Wright, Inc. (R), CA, *209*
Tittemore Cowan Assoc. (C), AB, *607*
TNS Partners, Inc. (R), TX, *209*
Tomlinson Assoc. Inc. (C), IL, *607*
Tondorf & Assoc. Inc. (C), MA, *607*
Top Gun Group, Inc. (C), NV, *607*
Topaz Int'l., Inc., Attorney Search (C), NJ, *607*
The Touchstone Group (C), MA, *607*
TPS Staffing Solutions (C), IN, *608*
Trac One (R), NJ, *210*
Travel Executive Search (C), NY, *608*
Travel Personnel (C), OH, *609*
Traynor Confidential, Ltd. (C), NY, *609*
Van Treadaway Assoc., Inc. (R), GA, *210*
Trebor Weldon Lawrence, Inc. (R), NY, *210*
TRH Assoc., Inc. (R), NY, *210*
Triad Consultants, Inc. (C), NJ, *609*
TriStaff Group (C), CA, *609*
Tryon & Heideman, LLC (R), MO, *211*
TSC Management Services Group, Inc. (C), IL, *610*
TSW Assoc., LLC (R), CT, *211*
TTG/Sterling Services (C), CA, *610*
W. G. Tucker & Assoc. (R), PA, *211*
The Thomas Tucker Co. (R), CA, *211*
Tuft & Assoc., Inc. (R), IL, *212*
Tully/Woodmansee Int'l. Inc. (R), FL, *212*
Tuttle Venture Group, Inc. (R), TX, *212*
UniQuest Int'l., Inc. (C), FL, *610*
Unlimited Staffing Solutions, Inc. (C), MI, *611*
The Urban Placement Service (C), TX, *611*
V.I.P. Resources, Inc. (C), NY, *611*
Van Leeuwen Assoc. (R), CA, *213*
VanMaldegiam Assoc., Inc. (R), IL, *213*
Venture Resources, Inc. (R), CA, *213*
The Verriez Group Inc. (R), ON, *213*
Vezan Assoc. (C), CT, *612*

INDUSTRIES

Victor White Int'l. (C), CA, *612*
Villasenor & Assoc. (C), CA, *612*
C. J. Vincent Assoc., LLC (C), MD, *612*
Vlcek & Company, Inc. (R), CA, *214*
Voigt Assoc. (R), IL, *214*
Beverly von Winckler & Assoc. (C), IL, *613*
W. P. Assoc. (C), CA, *613*
The Wabash Group (C), IN, *613*
Wakefield Talabisco Int'l. (R), NY, *214*
Waldorf Associates, Inc. (C), CA, *614*
Kelly Walker Assoc. (C), TX, *614*
B. D. Wallace & Assoc. (C), MD, *614*
The Wallace Law Registry (C), CT, *614*
Wallace Management Co. (R), TN, *215*
J. D. Walsh & Co. (R), CT, *215*
Lee H. Walton & Assoc. (R), NY, *215*
Ward Liebelt Assoc. Inc. (R), CT, *215*
C. D. Warner & Assoc. (C), PA, *615*
Waterford Executive Group Ltd. (C), IL, *616*
R. J. Watkins & Co., Ltd. (R), CA, *216*
Watring & Assoc., Inc. (C), IL, *616*
Scott Watson & Assoc., Inc. (R), FL, *216*
Watson Int'l., Inc. (R), NY, *216*
Waveland Int'l. (R), IL, *216*
The Wayne Group, Ltd. (C), NY, *616*
Webb, Johnson Assoc., Inc. (R), NY, *216*
Weber Executive Search (R), NY, *216*
S. B. Webster & Associates (R), MA, *217*
Wegner & Assoc. (C), WI, *617*
Lee Weil Assoc., Inc. (C), IL, *617*
David Weinfeld Group (C), NC, *617*
Weinman & Assoc. (C), AZ, *617*
Weinstein & Co. (R), MA, *217*
S. E. Weinstein Co. (R), IL, *217*
D. L. Weiss & Assoc. (R), CA, *217*
Henry Welker & Assoc. (C), MI, *618*
The Wellesley Group, Inc. (R), IL, *217*
Werbin Assoc. Executive Search, Inc. (C), NY, *618*
West Coast Recruiting (C), CA, *619*
Western Management Assoc. (R), CA, *218*
Western Management Consultants (R), BC, *218*
Westfields Int'l., Inc. (C), NY, *619*
S. J. Wexler Assoc., Inc. (R), NY, *219*
Wheeler Assoc. (R), CT, *219*
The Whitaker Companies (C), TX, *619*
Whitbeck & Assoc. (R), MN, *219*
White, Roberts & Stratton, Inc. (C), IL, *619*
Arch S. Whitehead Assoc. Inc. (ASWA) (R), NY, *219*
The Whitney Group (C), GA, *620*
Whitney Smith Co. (C), TX, *620*
The Whittaker Group (C), MI, *620*
Whittlesey & Assoc., Inc. (R), PA, *220*
The Whyte Group, Inc. (R), MD, *220*
Daniel Wier & Assoc. (R), CA, *220*
Wilcox Bertoux & Miller (R), CA, *220*
Wilcoxen, Blackwell, Niven & Assoc. (R), FL, *220*
Wilder & Assoc. (C), VA, *620*
Walter K. Wilkins & Co. (R), NJ, *221*
Wilkinson & Ives (R), CA, *221*
Wilkinson SoftSearch, Inc. (C), VA, *620*
William-Johns Co., Inc. (C), CA, *621*
Williams Recruiting, Inc. (C), WA, *621*
Willis & Assoc. (R), OH, *221*
Wills Consulting Assoc. Inc. (R), CT, *221*
Wilson McLeran, Inc. (C), CT, *622*
Wilson-Douglas-Jordan (C), IL, *622*
The Winchester Group (R), CA, *222*
Windsor Consultants, Inc. (C), TX, *622*
Windsor International (R), GA, *222*
Winter, Wyman & Co. (C), MA, *623*
Winthrop Partners, Inc. (R), NY, *222*
Witt/Kieffer, Ford, Hadelman & Lloyd (R), IL, *223*
Wojdula & Assoc., Ltd. (R), WI, *223*
D. S. Wolf Assoc., Inc. (R), NY, *223*
S. R. Wolman Assoc., Inc. (R), NY, *224*
Woltz & Assoc., Inc. (R), IL, *224*
Louise Wood & Assoc. (C), NY, *624*
M. Wood Company (R), IL, *224*
Bruce G. Woods Executive Search (R), TX, *224*
The Woodstone Consulting Company, Inc. (R), CO, *224*
Working Relationships, Inc. (C), MN, *624*
Worlco Computer Resources, Inc. (C), PA, *624*
Worldwide Medical Services (C), CA, *625*
Dick Wray & Consultants, Inc. (R), CA, *225*
Bob Wright Recruiting, Inc. (C), CT, *625*
WTW Assoc., Inc. (R), NY, *225*
R. S. Wyatt Assoc., Inc. (R), TX, *225*
Dennis Wynn Assoc., Inc. (C), FL, *625*
Yankee Hospitality Search (C), CT, *626*
The York Group (C), CA, *626*
Yormak & Assoc. (C), CA, *626*
Bill Young & Assoc. (C), VA, *626*
Yours In Travel Personnel Agency, Inc. (C), NY, *626*
Yungner & Bormann (R), MN, *226*
Zackrison Assoc., Inc. (C), FL, *627*
ZanExec L.L.C. (R), VA, *226*
Zeiger Assoc. L.L.C. (C), CA, *627*
Zen Zen Int'l. Inc. (C), MB, *627*
Zenner Consulting Group (C), IL, *627*
P. D. Zier Assoc. (C), CT, *627*
Zingaro & Company (R), TX, *227*
Zona & Assoc., Inc. (C), NY, *628*
Zurick, Davis & Co., Inc. (R), MA, *227*
Zwell Int'l. (R), IL, *228*

I.10 Hospitality; including hotels, resorts, clubs, restaurants, food & beverage services

A C Personnel Services, Inc. (C), OK, *231*
A la Carte Int'l., Inc. (R), VA, *1*
A-Linko & Assoc. (C), TX, *231*
A.J. & Assoc. (C), FL, *232*
Abbott Associates (R), CA, *1*
Ackerman Johnson Inc. (C), TX, *238*
The Alfus Group (R), NY, *3*
Allen & Assoc. (C), NV, *244*
Alliance Executive Search, Inc. (R), MA, *4*
Alliance Search Management Inc. (R), TX, *4*
Tom Allison Assoc. (C), NM, *245*
Alpha Resource Group, Inc. (C), TX, *246*
Alpha Search (C), FL, *246*
Anderson & Associates (R), NC, *5*
Charles P. Aquavella & Assoc. (C), TX, *252*
Armitage Associates Ltd. (R), ON, *7*
Artgo, Inc. (R), OH, *7*
ASI (C), CA, *254*
Association Executive Resources Group (R), MD, *8*
Atlantic Pacific Group (C), CA, *255*
A. M. Auster Associates (R), FL, *9*
Austin, Hill & Assoc. (C), MD, *256*
Barrett Hospitality Search (R), CA, *12*
BCG Search, Inc. (R), FL, *14*
The Bedford Consulting Group Inc. (R), ON, *14*
Bennett Search & Consulting Co. (R), FL, *16*
Berkhemer/Clayton, Inc. (R), CA, *16*
Besen Assoc. Inc. (C), NJ, *266*
Binder Hospitality Group (C), KY, *266*
David Blevins & Assoc. (C), WA, *268*
Mark Bolno & Assoc. (C), FL, *269*
Bonnell Assoc. Ltd. (R), CT, *19*
Bowman & Assoc. (C), CA, *271*
The Bren Group (C), AZ, *273*
Brentwood Int'l. (R), CA, *23*
Brindisi Search (R), MD, *23*
Bristol Assoc., Inc. (C), CA, *274*
Brown, Bernardy, Van Remmen, Inc. (C), CA, *275*
The Burke Group (C), ON, *276*
Canny, Bowen Inc. (R), NY, *27*
The Cantor Concern, Inc. (R), NY, *28*
Career Development Associates (C), NV, *282*
Caruso & Assoc., Inc. (R), FL, *31*
Cary & Assoc. (R), FL, *31*
Michael J. Cavanagh & Assoc. Inc. (R), ON, *31*
Cella Assoc. (C), GA, *286*
Chapman & Assoc. (C), BC, *289*
The Christopher Group (C), NC, *291*
Comprehensive Search (C), GA, *294*
Continental Research Search, Inc. (C), WI, *298*
Cornerstone Resources, Inc. (C), OK, *299*
Corporate Plus, Ltd. (C), GA, *300*
Corso, Mizgala + French (R), ON, *42*
CountryHouse Hotels Executive Search (C), VA, *302*
Creative Financial Staffing (C), MA, *303*
Creative HR Solutions (C), GA, *303*
Creative-Leadership, Inc. (R), CA, *42*
Cyr Associates, Inc. (C), MA, *306*
Daubenspeck & Associates, Ltd. (R), IL, *46*
Davies, Park (R), AB, *46*
Rob Dey Executive Search (R), FL, *49*
Robert W. Dingman Co., Inc. (R), CA, *52*
Diversified Search, Inc. (R), PA, *52*
Dixie Search Assoc. (C), GA, *313*
DNA Search, Inc. (C), CA, *313*
Doleman Enterprises (R), VA, *53*
Donini Assoc. (R), VA, *54*
Dunhill Professional Search of Hawaii (C), HI, *320*
Dunhill Personnel Service of Fargo (C), ND, *322*
EFL Int'l. (R), AZ, *57*
Elliot Assoc. Inc. (R), NY, *58*
Ellis & Associates (C), HI, *328*

Ellis Career Consultants (C), NJ, *328*
Steve Ellis (C), CA, *328*
The Evans McDonnell Co. (C), TX, *331*
Executive Careers (R), CA, *62*
Executive Placement Services (C), GA, *333*
Executive Referral Services, Inc. (C), IL, *334*
Paul Falcone Assoc. (R), NJ, *65*
The Fawcett Group (R), MA, *65*
First Advisory Services Int'l., Inc. (R), MD, *67*
Foster Partners (R), NY, *70*
Franchise Search, Inc. (C), NY, *352*
Franklin Allen Consultants, Ltd. (R), NY, *71*
Franstaff Inc. (C), FL, *352*
Fresquez & Assoc. (C), CA, *352*
Further Management Group (C), MD, *353*
Futures, Inc. (C), NH, *354*
Gaming Consultants, Inc. (R), LA, *74*
The Garvis Group, Inc. (C), LA, *355*
J. Gernetzke & Assoc., Inc. (C), OH, *357*
Goodrich & Sherwood Assoc., Inc. (R), NY, *79*
Gould, McCoy & Chadick, Inc. (R), NY, *80*
Sheila Greco Assoc. (C), NY, *362*
Greger/Peterson Assoc., Inc. (R), CA, *81*
H R Solutions, Inc. (C), MO, *365*
Harper Associates (C), MI, *369*
The Hawkins Co. (R), CA, *88*
William E. Hay & Co. (R), IL, *88*
Hill & Assoc. (C), CA, *378*
The Hindman Group, Inc. (C), CA, *378*
Fred Hood & Assoc. (C), CA, *380*
Hospitality Executive Search, Inc. (R), MA, *96*
Hospitality Int'l. (C), NY, *381*
Robert Howe & Assoc. (R), GA, *97*
HRI Services, Inc. (C), MA, *382*
Huff Assoc. (R), NJ, *98*
Hughes & Company (R), VA, *98*
Human Resource Dimensions, Inc. (C), TX, *384*
Hunter Int'l., Inc. (R), CT, *100*
HVS Executive Search (R), NY, *100*
Hyde Danforth & Co. (R), TX, *100*
Hyman & Assoc. (C), TX, *386*
The IMC Group of Companies (R), NY, *101*
International Recruiting Services (C), FL, *393*
IR Search (R), CA, *103*
J.B.A. Assoc. (R), WA, *104*
Jakobs & Assoc. Int'l. (R), NY, *105*
Jeffrey Allan Co., Inc. (C), CA, *398*
John Jay & Co. (C), ME, *399*
Johnson Assoc., Inc. (C), IL, *399*
Chris Kauffman & Company (R), GA, *110*
A.T. Kearney Executive Search (R), IL, *111*
Kelley & Keller, Inc. (C), FL, *405*
Kelly Assoc. (R), WI, *112*
Kenzer Corp. (R), NY, *113*
Kopplin Search, Inc. (R), CA, *117*
Korn/Ferry Int'l. (R), NY, *117*
The J. Kovach Group (R), PA, *119*
John Kurosky & Assoc. (R), CA, *122*
Larsen, Whitney, Blecksmith & Zilliacus, Inc. (R), CA, *125*
Madeleine Lav & Assoc. (C), CA, *413*
Leader Search Inc. (R), AB, *127*
Lear & Assoc., Inc. (C), FL, *415*
The Conrad Lee Co. Inc. (R), FL, *127*
Alan Levine Assoc. (R), MA, *129*
The Logan Group, Inc. (R), MO, *131*
Lyons Assoc. (R), NY, *132*
The Madison Group (R), NY, *133*
Maglio & Co., Inc. (R), WI, *134*
Maiorino & Weston Assoc., Inc. (R), CT, *134*
Management Recruiters of Laguna Hills (C), CA, *440*
Management Recruiters of St. Lucie County, Inc. (C), FL, *444*
Management Recruiters of Atlanta (C), GA, *445*
Management Recruiters - Indianapolis (C), IN, *448*
Management Recruiters of Frederick, Inc. (C), MD, *450*
Management Recruiters of Lake Tahoe, NV (C), NV, *453*
Management Recruiters of Asheville, Inc. (C), NC, *455*
Management Recruiters of Rocky Mount - Southwest (C), NC, *456*
Management Recruiters of Oklahoma City (C), OK, *458*
Management Recruiters of Valley Forge (C), PA, *459*
Marentz & Co. (C), TX, *469*
Marshall-Alan Assoc., Inc. (C), NY, *471*
Mason & Nicastri Ltd. (R), CA, *138*
The Matthews Group, Inc. (C), NJ, *472*
Earl L. McDermid & Assoc. (C), IL, *474*
McDowell & Co., Recruiters (C), TX, *474*
McIntyre Management Resources (C), ON, *474*
MDR & Associates (C), AR, *476*
Meng, Finseth & Assoc., Inc. (R), CA, *143*
Michael Wayne Recruiters (C), IL, *480*
Herbert Mines Assoc., Inc. (R), NY, *145*
Mirtz Morice, Inc. (R), CT, *145*
Montgomery Resources, Inc. (C), CA, *484*
Jennifer Munro & Partners, Inc. (R), SC, *149*
National Restaurant Search, Inc. (R), GA, *150*
New Dawn Employment Search (C), CA, *491*
Nordeman Grimm, Inc. (R), NY, *152*
Norman Broadbent Int'l., Inc. (R), NY, *152*
NPF Assoc. Ltd. Inc. (R), FL, *153*
O'Brien and Roof (C), OH, *497*
Dennis P. O'Toole & Assoc. Inc. (R), NY, *154*
The Ogdon Partnership (R), NY, *155*
Ollinger Partners (R), MA, *156*
Olsen/Clark (R), WA, *156*
Ott & Hansen, Inc. (R), CA, *157*
P.A.R. Assoc., Inc. (R), MA, *158*
Parker Page Group (C), FL, *503*
Partridge Assoc., Inc. (R), MA, *160*
The Patience Motivation Belief Group, Inc. (C), GA, *505*
Patrice & Assoc. (C), MD, *505*
Penn Associates (R), PA, *161*
The Personnel Network, Inc. (C), SC, *508*
Robert E. Pfaendler & Assoc., Inc. (C), OR, *509*
Pinton Forrest & Madden/EMA Partners Int'l. (R), BC, *165*
DNPitchon Assoc. (R), NJ, *165*
Plummer & Assoc., Inc. (R), CT, *166*
Robert Powers & Assoc. (C), CA, *515*
Powers Consultants, Inc. (R), MO, *166*
Presley Consultants, Inc. (C), CA, *517*
Prestige Inc. (C), WI, *517*
Professional Search Assoc. (C), CA, *522*
Professional Search, Inc. (C), CO, *522*
ProFinders, Inc. (C), FL, *523*
Profit Pros, Inc. (C), CA, *523*
ProLinks Inc. (R), VA, *170*
Quetico Corp. (R), TX, *170*
R.A.N. Assoc., Inc. (C), OH, *528*
Rand-Curtis Resources (C), AZ, *529*
RCI Employment Solutions (C), FL, *531*
Recruiting Specialists (C), MA, *532*
The Recruitment Group, Inc. (C), NY, *532*
P. J. Reda & Assoc., Inc. (C), GA, *533*
Redden & McGrath Assoc., Inc. (R), NY, *173*
Resource Perspectives, Inc. (R), CA, *175*
Russell Reynolds Assoc., Inc. (R), NY, *176*
Ridenour & Assoc. (R), IL, *178*
Ritt-Ritt & Assoc., Inc. (C), IL, *537*
Rollo Assoc. (R), CA, *181*
Ropes Associates, Inc. (R), FL, *182*
Roth Young Personnel Services of Washington, DC (C), MD, *546*
Roth Young of Chicago (C), IL, *546*
Roth Young Personnel Service of Detroit, Inc. (C), MI, *546*
Roth Young Executive Recruiters (C), MN, *546*
Roth Young of Tampa (C), FL, *546*
Roth Young Seattle (C), WA, *546*
Sales Consultants of Honolulu (C), HI, *558*
Sales Consultants of Laurel Park, Inc. (C), MI, *560*
Sales Consultants of Dallas (C), TX, *563*
Sales Search Specialist (C), IL, *564*
Norm Sanders Assoc., Inc. (R), NJ, *184*
Sanford Rose Assoc. - Mobile (C), AL, *565*
Sanford Rose Assoc. - Louisville (C), KY, *567*
Saviar, Inc. (C), AZ, *571*
F. B. Schmidt Int'l. (R), CA, *185*
Devin Scott Assoc. (C), NJ, *572*
Search Int'l. (R), MA, *187*
Michael Shirley Assoc. Inc. (R), KS, *190*
Shore Asociados Ejecutivos, S. A. de C.V. (R), MX, *190*
John Sibbald Assoc., Inc. (R), MO, *191*
James F. Smith & Assoc. (C), GA, *583*
Peter A. Smith & Assoc. (C), OR, *584*
Smythe Masterson & Judd, Inc. (C), NY, *585*
Stephen M. Sonis Assoc. (R), MA, *195*
Special Markets Group, Inc. (R), GA, *195*
SpencerStuart (R), NY, *196*
The Stewart Group (C), FL, *593*
Strategic Search, LLC (C), CA, *595*
Straube Associates (R), MA, *203*
Summerfield Assoc., Inc. (C), TN, *596*

INDUSTRIES

Target Search, Inc. (C), PA, *600*
Team One Partners, Inc. (C), GA, *600*
Thomas Lyle & Co. (C), IL, *606*
Thor, Inc. (C), CA, *606*
Top Gun Group, Inc. (C), NV, *607*
Travel Executive Search (C), NY, *608*
Travel Personnel (C), OH, *609*
TTG/Sterling Services (C), CA, *610*
Van Leeuwen Assoc. (R), CA, *213*
Wakefield Talabisco Int'l. (R), NY, *214*
Ward Liebelt Assoc. Inc. (R), CT, *215*
Weber Executive Search (R), NY, *216*
Weinman & Assoc. (C), AZ, *617*
Whitney Smith Co. (C), TX, *620*
The Whyte Group, Inc. (R), MD, *220*
Wilcoxen, Blackwell, Niven & Assoc. (R), FL, *220*
William-Johns Co., Inc. (C), CA, *621*
The Winchester Group (R), CA, *222*
Windsor Consultants, Inc. (C), TX, *622*
M. Wood Company (R), IL, *224*
The Woodstone Consulting Company, Inc. (R), CO, *224*
Dick Wray & Consultants, Inc. (R), CA, *225*
Yankee Hospitality Search (C), CT, *626*
Yormak & Assoc. (C), CA, *626*
Yours In Travel Personnel Agency, Inc. (C), NY, *626*

I.11 Entertainment, leisure, amusement, recreation, sports, travel

A la Carte Int'l., Inc. (R), VA, *1*
Affordable Executive Recruiters (C), CA, *241*
The Alfus Group (R), NY, *3*
David Allen Assoc. (R), NJ, *3*
Allen Evans Assoc. (R), NY, *4*
Alliance Executive Search, Inc. (R), MA, *4*
Alpha Resource Group, Inc. (C), TX, *246*
American Executive Management, Inc. (R), MA, *5*
Andre David & Assoc., Inc. (R), TX, *6*
Andrews & Wald Group (C), FL, *250*
Ariel Recruitment Assoc. (R), NY, *7*
ASI (C), CA, *254*
Ballantyne & Assoc. (R), CA, *10*
The Barack Group, Inc. (R), NY, *11*
Bartl & Evins (C), NY, *260*
Bast & Assoc., Inc. (C), CA, *261*
Battalia Winston Int'l./The Euram Consultants Group (R), NY, *13*
Robert Bennett Assoc. (C), NY, *264*
Bialla & Assoc. Inc. (R), CA, *17*
Bishop Partners (R), NY, *17*
D. R. Blood & Assoc. (R), AZ, *18*
Bowman & Assoc. (C), CA, *271*
The Bren Group (C), AZ, *273*
The Brentwood Group, Inc. (R), NJ, *22*
Brentwood Int'l. (R), CA, *23*
Bristol Assoc., Inc. (C), CA, *274*
Brown, Bernardy, Van Remmen, Inc. (C), CA, *275*
Brownstone Sales & Marketing Group, Inc. (C), NY, *275*
Charles Buck & Assoc., Inc. (R), NY, *24*
The C.P.R. Group (C), NJ, *278*
Cary & Assoc. (R), FL, *31*
CAS Comsearch Inc. (C), NY, *285*
Cella Assoc. (C), GA, *286*
Chad Management Group (C), ON, *288*
David Chambers & Assoc., Inc. (R), CT, *32*
ChaseAmerica, Inc. (R), FL, *33*
CJA-The Adler Group, Inc. (R), CA, *35*
Colt Systems Professional Personnel Services (C), CA, *294*
Commercial Programming Systems, Inc. (C), CA, *294*
Corporate Image Group (C), TN, *300*
CountryHouse Hotels Executive Search (C), VA, *302*
Trudi Cowlan (C), NY, *302*
Cyntal Int'l. Ltd. (R), NY, *44*
Cypress Int'l., Inc. (R), FL, *45*
David Perry Assoc. (C), NJ, *308*
DBL Associates (C), CA, *309*
DeLalla - Fried Assoc. (C), NY, *310*
Diamond Tax Recruiting (C), NY, *312*
Robert W. Dingman Co., Inc. (R), CA, *52*
Diversified Search, Inc. (R), PA, *52*
DLB Assoc. (R), NY, *53*
Dotson & Assoc. (R), NY, *54*
E T Search Inc. (C), CA, *324*
Earley Kielty & Assoc., Inc. (R), NY, *56*
Eastman & Beaudine, Inc. (R), TX, *56*
Elliot Assoc. Inc. (R), NY, *58*
Ellis Career Consultants (C), NJ, *328*
David M. Ellner Assoc. (R), NY, *59*
The Enfield Company (C), TX, *330*
Executive Careers (R), CA, *62*
Executive Placement Services (C), GA, *333*
Executive Referral Services, Inc. (C), IL, *334*
Fabian Assoc. Inc. (C), NY, *338*
Fairfaxx Corp. (R), CT, *64*
Fairfield Int'l. Resources (R), NY, *65*
The Fawcett Group (R), MA, *65*
Ferneborg & Assoc., Inc. (R), CA, *66*
Financialjobs.com (C), CA, *340*
Eileen Finn & Assoc., Inc. (C), NY, *341*
Foster Partners (R), NY, *70*
Franstaff Inc. (C), FL, *352*
P. N. French Assoc., Inc. (R), MA, *72*
Gaming Consultants, Inc. (R), LA, *74*
Garb & Assoc., Legal Placement (C), CA, *354*
The Garvis Group, Inc. (C), LA, *355*
Gateway Group Personnel, LLC (C), TN, *355*
J. P. Gleason Assoc., Inc. (R), IL, *77*
The Gobbell Co. (R), CA, *78*
Goodrich & Sherwood Assoc., Inc. (R), NY, *79*
Gould, McCoy & Chadick, Inc. (R), NY, *80*
Ben Greco Assoc., Inc. (C), CA, *362*
Greger/Peterson Assoc., Inc. (R), CA, *81*
Wolf Gugler & Assoc. Ltd. (R), ON, *83*
Hands-on Broadcast (R), NY, *86*
Hardison & Company (R), TX, *86*
Harris Heery & Assoc., Inc. (R), CT, *87*
Harris McCully Assoc., Inc. (C), NY, *369*
Heritage Search Group, Inc. (C), FL, *376*
The Hindman Group, Inc. (C), CA, *378*
Hockett Associates, Inc. (R), CA, *94*
Holohan Group, Ltd. (R), MO, *95*
Hospitality Executive Search, Inc. (R), MA, *96*
Hospitality Int'l. (C), NY, *381*
HRCS (R), CA, *97*
HRI Services, Inc. (C), MA, *382*
Huff Assoc. (R), NJ, *98*
The IMC Group of Companies (R), NY, *101*
InSearch (C), CO, *389*
Interquest, Inc. (R), NY, *103*
Ron Jackson & Assoc. (C), GA, *396*
Jakobs & Assoc. Int'l. (R), NY, *105*
JDH & Assoc. (C), CA, *397*
Jeffrey Allan Co., Inc. (C), CA, *398*
A.T. Kearney Executive Search (R), IL, *111*
Kelley & Keller, Inc. (C), FL, *405*
Kelly Assoc. (R), WI, *112*
Kenzer Corp. (R), NY, *113*
Kopplin Search, Inc. (R), CA, *117*
Koren, Rogers Assoc. Inc. (R), NY, *117*
Kramer Executive Resources, Inc. (C), NY, *409*
Kremple Consulting Group (R), CA, *120*
Todd L. Krueger & Assoc. (C), WA, *409*
Marvin Laba & Assoc. (R), CA, *122*
Larsen, Whitney, Blecksmith & Zilliacus, Inc. (R), CA, *125*
Leader Search Inc. (R), AB, *127*
The Conrad Lee Co. Inc. (R), FL, *127*
Michael Levine Search Consultants (R), NY, *129*
Livingston, Robert & Co. (R), CT, *130*
Ludwig & Assoc., Inc. (C), VA, *421*
Maiorino & Weston Assoc., Inc. (R), CT, *134*
Management Recruiters of Pleasanton (C), CA, *441*
Management Recruiters of St. Lucie County, Inc. (C), FL, *444*
Management Recruiters of Northern Palm Beaches (C), FL, *444*
Management Recruiters of New Providence (C), NJ, *454*
Management Recruiters of Cherry Hill (C), PA, *459*
Management Resource Group, Inc. (C), NY, *467*
Mark Adam Assoc. (R), NJ, *135*
Brad Marks Int'l. (R), CA, *136*
Marshall-Alan Assoc., Inc. (C), NY, *471*
Earl L. McDermid & Assoc. (C), IL, *474*
McIntyre Management Resources (C), ON, *474*
James Mead & Co. (R), CT, *142*
Media Recruiting Group, Inc. (C), NY, *476*
The Medley Group (C), CA, *477*
MESA International (C), CA, *480*
Herbert Mines Assoc., Inc. (R), NY, *145*
Montenido Assoc. (R), CA, *146*
Morgan/Webber, Inc. (R), NY, *147*
National Restaurant Search, Inc. (R), GA, *150*
Marc Nichols Assoc., Inc. (C), NY, *493*
Noble & Assoc., Inc. (C), NY, *494*
Nordeman Grimm, Inc. (R), NY, *152*
Norman Broadbent Int'l., Inc. (R), NY, *152*
O'Connell Group Inc. (C), CT, *497*

O'Keefe & Assoc., Inc. (R), CT, *154*
O'Neill & Co. (R), CT, *154*
Dennis P. O'Toole & Assoc. Inc. (R), NY, *154*
Olympian Recruitment, Ltd. (C), NY, *498*
Ott & Hansen, Inc. (R), CA, *157*
Pacific Search Group, Inc. (C), CA, *501*
Arthur Pann Assoc., Inc. (C), NY, *502*
The PAR Group - Paul A. Reaume, Ltd. (R), IL, *159*
Parker Page Group (C), FL, *503*
Partners Executive Search Consultants Inc. (R), ON, *160*
Patrice & Assoc. (C), MD, *505*
Petrie Partners, Inc. (R), FL, *163*
Robert E. Pfaendler & Assoc., Inc. (C), OR, *509*
Pinton Forrest & Madden/EMA Partners Int'l. (R), BC, *165*
Pittleman & Assoc. (C), NY, *512*
Plummer & Assoc., Inc. (R), CT, *166*
ProFinders, Inc. (C), FL, *523*
Profit Pros, Inc. (C), CA, *523*
ProLinks Inc. (R), VA, *170*
The Quest Organization (C), NY, *527*
R. J. Associates (C), NY, *528*
Razzino-Claymore Assoc. (C), NJ, *530*
Russell Reynolds Assoc., Inc. (R), NY, *176*
Richards Assoc., Inc. (R), NY, *178*
Ridenour & Assoc. (R), IL, *178*
Ritt-Ritt & Assoc., Inc. (C), IL, *537*
Ropes Associates, Inc. (R), FL, *182*
K. Russo Assoc. Inc. (C), CT, *548*
Ryan, Miller & Assoc. (C), CA, *549*
Saviar, Inc. (C), AZ, *571*
Search Int'l. (R), MA, *187*
Setford-Shaw-Najarian Assoc. (C), NY, *579*
RitaSue Siegel Resources, Inc. (R), NY, *191*
Silver Associates (C), CA, *581*
Ruth Sklar Assoc., Inc. (RSA Executive Search) (R), NY, *192*
A. William Smyth, Inc. (R), CA, *194*
Andrea Sobel & Assoc., Inc. (C), CA, *586*
Stephen M. Sonis Assoc. (R), MA, *195*
SpencerStuart (R), NY, *196*
Sports Group Int'l. (R), NC, *198*
C. J. Stafford & Assoc. (C), ON, *591*
Stoopen Asociados, S.C./EMA Partners Int'l. (R), MX, *202*
Joe Sullivan & Assoc., Inc. (R), NY, *204*
Ron Sunshine & Assoc. (C), IL, *597*
Target Search, Inc. (C), PA, *600*
TeleManagement Search (C), NY, *605*
Thor, Inc. (C), CA, *606*
Top Gun Group, Inc. (C), NV, *607*
Travel Executive Search (C), NY, *608*
Travel Personnel (C), OH, *609*
TSC Management Services Group, Inc. (C), IL, *610*
Van Leeuwen Assoc. (R), CA, *213*
Wakefield Talabisco Int'l. (R), NY, *214*
Ward Liebelt Assoc. Inc. (R), CT, *215*
Weber Executive Search (R), NY, *216*
Lee Weil Assoc., Inc. (C), IL, *617*
Weinstein & Co. (R), MA, *217*
White, Roberts & Stratton, Inc. (C), IL, *619*
The Whyte Group, Inc. (R), MD, *220*
Wilcoxen, Blackwell, Niven & Assoc. (R), FL, *220*
S. R. Wolman Assoc., Inc. (R), NY, *224*
The Woodstone Consulting Company, Inc. (R), CO, *224*
WTW Assoc., Inc. (R), NY, *225*
R. S. Wyatt Assoc., Inc. (R), TX, *225*
Yankee Hospitality Search (C), CT, *626*
Yormak & Assoc. (C), CA, *626*
Yours In Travel Personnel Agency, Inc. (C), NY, *626*
Zwell Int'l. (R), IL, *228*

I.12 Museums, galleries, music/arts, libraries & information services, membership / non-profits

Abécassis Conseil (R), QE, *1*
Andrews & Wald Group (C), FL, *250*
Association Executive Resources Group (R), MD, *8*
AST/BRYANT (R), CT, *8*
Auerbach Associates, Inc. (R), MA, *9*
Baker, Nelms & Montgomery (C), IL, *258*
Barnes Development Group, LLC (R), WI, *11*
Battalia Winston Int'l./The Euram Consultants Group (R), NY, *13*
BCG Search, Inc. (R), FL, *14*
C. Berger And Company (R), IL, *16*
Boulware & Assoc. Inc. (R), IL, *20*
Boyden (R), NY, *20*
Bradford Executives Int'l. (C), VA, *271*
Charles Buck & Assoc., Inc. (R), NY, *24*
Carpenter, Shackleton & Company (R), IL, *30*
The Corporate Connection, Ltd. (C), VA, *299*
DeCorrevont & Assoc. (C), IL, *310*
Defrain Mayer (R), KS, *48*
Development Resource Group (R), NY, *48*
Development Search Specialists (R), MN, *49*
Rob Dey Executive Search (R), FL, *49*
Diversified Search, Inc. (R), PA, *52*
Doherty Int'l., Inc. (R), IL, *53*
Cal Douglas Executive Search, Inc. (R), PA, *54*
EMN/Witt/Kieffer (R), MA, *59*
Executive Careers (R), CA, *62*
Fagan & Company (R), PA, *64*
FitzGibbon & Assoc. (R), PA, *68*
Foster Partners (R), NY, *70*
Foy, Schneid & Daniel, Inc. (R), NY, *71*
The Franklin Search Group, Inc./Medzilla (R), WA, *71*
P. N. French Assoc., Inc. (R), MA, *72*
Gateway Management Resources (C), IL, *355*
Gielow Assoc., Inc. (R), WI, *76*
Gossage Regan Assoc. (R), NY, *80*
J. B. Groner Executive Search, Inc. (C), DE, *363*
Harvey Hohauser & Assoc., LLC (R), MI, *87*
William E. Hay & Co. (R), IL, *88*
Healey Executive Search, Inc. (R), MN, *88*
The Helms Int'l. Group (R), VA, *91*
The Hollins Group, Inc. (R), IL, *95*
HRCS (R), CA, *97*
The Hyde Group, Inc. (R), CT, *101*
Innovative Partnerships (R), CA, *101*
Intelligent Marketing Solutions, Inc. (C), NY, *390*
Interactive Search Network (R), CA, *102*
International Management Advisors, Inc. (R), NY, *103*
Isaacson, Miller (R), MA, *104*
JDG Assoc., Ltd. (C), MD, *397*
A.T. Kearney Executive Search (R), IL, *111*
Kenzer Corp. (R), NY, *113*
Kittleman & Assoc.,LLC (R), IL, *115*
Raymond J. Klemmer & Assoc. (R), NY, *116*
Layne-Mendez & Co. (R), TX, *127*
Lekan & Assoc., Inc. (R), OH, *128*
AG Lennox & Assoc. (R), AB, *128*
Alan Levine Assoc. (R), MA, *129*
Lloyd Associates (R), GA, *130*
Management & Human Resources (R), MA, *134*
Management Resource Group, Ltd. (C), IA, *467*
F. L. Mannix & Co. (R), MA, *135*
McCormack & Assoc. (R), CA, *140*
McDonald, Long & Assoc., Inc. (R), NY, *140*
Jon McRae & Associates, Inc. (R), GA, *142*
Herbert Mines Assoc., Inc. (R), NY, *145*
Thomas R. Moore Executive Search (R), TX, *146*
Morris & Berger (R), CA, *147*
Nordeman Grimm, Inc. (R), NY, *152*
O'Callaghan Honey/Ray & Berndtson Inc. (R), AB, *153*
O'Rourke Companies, Inc. (R), TX, *154*
The Oldani Group (R), WA, *155*
Opportunity Resources, Inc. (R), NY, *156*
Organization Resources Inc. (R), MA, *157*
P.A.R. Assoc., Inc. (R), MA, *158*
The PAR Group - Paul A. Reaume, Ltd. (R), IL, *159*
Carolyn Smith Paschal Int'l. (R), CA, *160*
Perez-Arton Consultants, Inc. (R), NY, *162*
RCI Employment Solutions (C), FL, *531*
Russell Reynolds Assoc., Inc. (R), NY, *176*
Marshall Rice Assoc. (R), RI, *177*
Ridenour & Assoc. (R), IL, *178*
Norman Roberts & Assoc., Inc. (R), CA, *179*
Search Research Assoc., Inc. (R), MA, *187*
Robert Sellery Assoc., Ltd. (R), DC, *188*
SpencerStuart (R), NY, *196*
Stanton Chase Int'l. (R), MD, *198*
Sullivan & Assoc. (R), MI, *204*
Richard Thompson Assoc., Inc. (R), MN, *209*
Travel Executive Search (C), NY, *608*
Travel Personnel (C), OH, *609*
Tryon & Heideman, LLC (R), MO, *211*
W. G. Tucker & Assoc. (R), PA, *211*
Tuft & Assoc., Inc. (R), IL, *212*
Wakefield Talabisco Int'l. (R), NY, *214*
Wilson McLeran, Inc. (C), CT, *622*
Bob Wright Recruiting, Inc. (C), CT, *625*

I.13 Higher education

A.K.S. Assoc., Ltd. (R), MA, *1*
Alliance Search Management Inc. (R), TX, *4*
AST/BRYANT (R), CT, *8*
Auerbach Associates, Inc. (R), MA, *9*
Bernard E. Brooks & Assoc., Inc. (R), SC, *24*
C.T.E.W. Executive Personnel Services Inc. (C), BC, *278*
CanMed Consultants Inc. (C), ON, *280*
Carpenter, Shackleton & Company (R), IL, *30*
The Chatham Group, Ltd. (C), CT, *289*
Conard Associates, Inc. (R), NH, *39*
The Dalley Hewitt Co. (R), GA, *45*
Development Resource Group (R), NY, *48*
Development Search Specialists (R), MN, *49*
Rob Dey Executive Search (R), FL, *49*
Diversified Search, Inc. (R), PA, *52*
Doherty Int'l., Inc. (R), IL, *53*
Cal Douglas Executive Search, Inc. (R), PA, *54*
Eagle Search Assoc. (C), CA, *325*
EMN/Witt/Kieffer (R), MA, *59*
The Enfield Company (C), TX, *330*
The Executive Source (C), SA, *337*
Foster Partners (R), NY, *70*
P. N. French Assoc., Inc. (R), MA, *72*
Gateway Management Resources (C), IL, *355*
Robert G. Godfrey Assoc. Ltd. (R), IL, *78*
Hazard, Young, Attea & Assoc., Ltd. (C), IL, *371*
The Hollins Group, Inc. (R), IL, *95*
IM Independent Management Recruiters (R), TN, *101*
Innovative Partnerships (R), CA, *101*
Isaacson, Miller (R), MA, *104*
Gary Kaplan & Assoc. (R), CA, *109*
A.T. Kearney Executive Search (R), IL, *111*
Kittleman & Assoc.,LLC (R), IL, *115*
Layne-Mendez & Co. (R), TX, *127*
M/J/A Partners (R), IL, *133*
MacNaughton Assoc. (R), CA, *133*
Management Recruiters of Broome County, Inc. (C), NY, *454*
K. E. McCarthy & Assoc. (R), CA, *139*
McCooe & Assoc., Inc. (R), NJ, *140*
Jon McRae & Associates, Inc. (R), GA, *142*
Meng, Finseth & Assoc., Inc. (R), CA, *143*
The Mercer Group, Inc. (R), NM, *143*
Molloy Partners (R), NY, *146*
Thomas R. Moore Executive Search (R), TX, *146*
Morris & Berger (R), CA, *147*
Opportunity Resources, Inc. (R), NY, *156*
Overton Consulting (R), WI, *157*
Pamenter, Pamenter, Brezer & Deganis Ltd. (R), ON, *159*
Carolyn Smith Paschal Int'l. (R), CA, *160*
Perez-Arton Consultants, Inc. (R), NY, *162*
R. H. Perry & Assoc., Inc. (R), DC, *162*
Personnel Assoc. (C), CA, *508*
Phillips & Assoc. (R), MA, *164*
Recruiting Resources Int'l. (C), CA, *532*
Redden-Shaffer Group (R), CA, *173*
Russell Reynolds Assoc., Inc. (R), NY, *176*
Marshall Rice Assoc. (R), RI, *177*
Wilson Riles & Assoc., Inc. (R), CA, *178*
Norman Roberts & Assoc., Inc. (R), CA, *179*
Scott Sibley Assoc. (C), NY, *573*
Robert Sellery Assoc., Ltd. (R), DC, *188*
Sockwell & Assoc. (R), NC, *194*
Solutions Group (R), AL, *195*
SpencerStuart (R), NY, *196*
Stanton Chase Int'l. (R), MD, *198*
Starbridge Group Inc. (C), VA, *591*
Stentiford & Berardi Assoc. Ltd. (R), NY, *199*
Daniel Stern & Assoc. (C), PA, *592*
Stroman Int'l., Inc. (R), CO, *204*
Sullivan & Assoc. (R), MI, *204*
Tuft & Assoc., Inc. (R), IL, *212*
Witt/Kieffer, Ford, Hadelman & Lloyd (R), IL, *223*

I.14 Pharmaceutical (other than manufacturing)

The 500 Granary Inc. (C), ON, *231*
Ackerman Johnson Inc. (C), TX, *238*
ADR Accounting Management Recruiters (C), ON, *240*
Albrecht & Assoc., Executive Search Consultants (C), TX, *243*
Alexander Enterprises, Inc. (C), PA, *243*
ALW Research Int'l. (R), NJ, *4*
AMD & Associates (C), GA, *247*
Ansara, Bickford & Fiske (C), MA, *251*
Ashworth Consultants, Inc. (R), MA, *8*
Atlantic West Int'l. (C), NC, *255*
Carol Ball & Co. (C), CT, *258*
Fred A. Barnette & Assoc. (R), NC, *11*
Battalia Winston Int'l./The Euram Consultants Group (R), NY, *13*
The Bauman Group (R), CA, *14*
Gary S. Bell Assoc., Inc. (C), NJ, *263*
Bench Int'l. Search, Inc. (R), CA, *15*
Besen Assoc. Inc. (C), NJ, *266*
BioPharmMed (C), FL, *267*
BioQuest Inc. (R), CA, *17*
Blau Mancino Schroeder (R), NJ, *18*
Bonifield Assoc. (C), NJ, *269*
Boone-Scaturro Assoc., Inc. (C), GA, *269*
Boston Professional Search, Inc. (C), MA, *270*
Boyden (R), NY, *20*
Bradford Executives Int'l. (C), VA, *271*
Brandywine Consulting Group (R), PA, *22*
Brethet, Barnum & Assoc., Inc. (C), ON, *273*
Brown, Bernardy, Van Remmen, Inc. (C), CA, *275*
Bryant Research (C), NJ, *275*
C. P. Consulting (R), PA, *26*
Caliber Associates (R), PA, *27*
Cambridge Management Planning (R), ON, *27*
CanMed Consultants Inc. (C), ON, *280*
Canny, Bowen Inc. (R), NY, *27*
Caplan Assoc., Inc. (R), NJ, *28*
Cardwell Enterprises Inc. (R), IL, *29*
Career Counseling Ltd. (C.C.L.) (C), NY, *282*
The Cassie Group (R), NJ, *31*
Century Assoc., Inc. (C), PA, *287*
The Century Group (C), KS, *287*
Christian & Timbers, Inc. (R), OH, *34*
Toby Clark Assoc. Inc. (C), NY, *292*
Clark Executive Search (C), NY, *292*
Ken Clark Int'l. (R), NJ, *36*
S L Collins Assoc. (C), NC, *294*
Colucci, Blendow & Johnson (R), CA, *38*
Consumer Search Inc. (C), MA, *298*
Continental Research Search, Inc. (C), WI, *298*
P. G. Cook Assoc. (R), TN, *40*
Corporate Recruiters Inc. (C), PA, *300*
CSA/Clinical Staffing Assoc., LLC (C), NJ, *304*
Culver Personnel Services (C), CA, *304*
Curran Partners, Inc. (R), CT, *44*
Cypress Int'l., Inc. (R), FL, *45*
D.A.I Human Resources Consultants (R), QE, *45*
The Dartmouth Group (R), NY, *46*
Deeco Int'l. (C), UT, *310*
Diversified Search, Inc. (R), PA, *52*
DNA Search, Inc. (C), CA, *313*
Doleman Enterprises (R), VA, *53*
The Domann Organization (R), CA, *53*
Robert Drexler Assoc., Inc. (R), NJ, *54*
Dunhill Personnel Service of Fargo (C), ND, *322*
Dunhill Professional Search of Bucks-Mont., Inc. (C), PA, *322*
C. A. Durakis Assoc., Inc. (R), MD, *55*
Dussick Management Assoc. (C), CT, *323*
Dwyer Consulting Group, Inc. (R), WV, *56*
Eagle Consulting Group Inc. (C), TX, *325*
Eagle Research, Inc. (C), NJ, *325*
Edwards & Assoc. (C), GA, *327*
EGM Consulting, Inc. (R), FL, *57*
Elite Medical Search (C), GA, *328*
Emerging Medical Technologies, Inc. (C), CO, *329*
Emmett Executive Search, Inc. (C), NY, *330*
Engineering & Scientific Search Assoc. (ESSA) (C), NJ, *330*
Excalibur Human Resources, Inc. (R), NJ, *61*
Executive Dimensions (R), NY, *62*
Executive Manning Corp. (R), FL, *63*
Executive Placement Consultants (C), IL, *333*
Executives Worldwide, Inc. (C), OR, *337*
Fallstaff Search (C), MD, *338*
James Feerst & Assoc., Inc. (C), AZ, *339*
Jack Stuart Fisher Assoc. (C), NJ, *341*
Fitzgerald Associates (R), MA, *68*
Fortune Group Int'l., Inc. (R), PA, *70*
F-O-R-T-U-N-E Personnel Consultants of Wilmington (C), DE, *344*
F-O-R-T-U-N-E Personnel Consultants of San Diego (C), CA, *344*
Fortune Personnel Consultants (C), MT, *347*
F-O-R-T-U-N-E Personnel Consultants of Bergen County Inc. (C), NJ, *347*

Fortune Personnel Consultants of Anderson, Inc. (C), SC, *349*
Foster Partners (R), NY, *70*
Franklin Allen Consultants, Ltd. (R), NY, *71*
Gerald Frisch Assoc., Inc. (R), NY, *72*
C. F. Furr & Co. (R), NC, *72*
Furst Group/MPI (R), IL, *72*
Gahan Assoc. (R), NY, *73*
W. N. Garbarini & Assoc. (R), NJ, *74*
Gielow Assoc., Inc. (R), WI, *76*
Gilbert Tweed Assoc. Inc. (R), NY, *76*
Global HealthCare Partners (R), IL, *78*
Global Resources Group (R), CA, *78*
The Goldman Group Inc. (R), NY, *79*
Goldman+Bell, LLC (C), NY, *360*
Goodrich & Sherwood Assoc., Inc. (R), NY, *79*
Gould, McCoy & Chadick, Inc. (R), NY, *80*
Gowdy Consultants (C), TX, *361*
Sheila Greco Assoc. (C), NY, *362*
Groton Planning Group (R), ME, *82*
Hadley Associates, Inc. (C), NJ, *365*
Hartman & Barnette (R), VA, *87*
The Haystack Group, Inc. (R), ME, *88*
Healthcare Recruiters Int'l. Orange County (C), CA, *372*
Healthcare Recruiters of the Rockies, Inc. (C), CO, *372*
Healthcare Recruiters Int'l. Phoenix (C), AZ, *372*
Healthcare Recruiters Int'l. - Alabama (C), AL, *372*
Healthcare Recruiters Int'l. - Los Angeles (C), CA, *372*
Healthcare Recruiters International-NY/NJ (C), NJ, *373*
Healthcare Recruiters of New Orleans (C), LA, *373*
Healthcare Recruiters Int'l - Minnesota, Inc. (C), MN, *373*
Healthcare Recruiters of New York, Inc. (C), NY, *373*
Healthcare Recruiters Int'l. - Pittsburgh (C), PA, *373*
Healthcare Recruiters - Northwest (C), WA, *374*
Healthcare Recruiters of Dallas (C), TX, *374*
Heartland National Medical Search (C), IL, *374*
R. W. Hebel Assoc. (R), TX, *89*
G. W. Henn & Co. (R), OH, *91*
Kay Henry, Inc. (C), PA, *376*
Hockett Associates, Inc. (R), CA, *94*
The Hogan Group (C), OH, *380*
Houtz•Strawn & Arnold, Inc. (R), TX, *96*
Hughes & Company (R), VA, *98*
Human Resource Dimensions, Inc. (C), TX, *384*
Impact Search & Strategies (C), PA, *387*
Innovative Healthcare Services, Inc. (C), GA, *389*
IntelliSource, inc. (C), PA, *391*
Inter Regional Executive Search, Inc. (IRES, Inc.) (C), NJ, *391*
International Pro Sourcing, Inc. (C), PA, *393*
Iona Partners (C), CA, *394*
Kazan International, Inc. (R), NJ, *110*
A.T. Kearney Executive Search (R), IL, *111*
Kenzer Corp. (R), NY, *113*
Kincannon & Reed (R), VA, *114*
Kingsley Quinn/USA (R), NJ, *115*
Koren, Rogers Assoc. Inc. (R), NY, *117*
Kulper & Co., L.L.C. (R), NJ, *121*
L O R (R), NJ, *122*
Laguzza Assoc., Ltd. (R), NY, *122*
Lancaster Assoc., Inc. (C), NJ, *411*
LAS Management Consulting Group, Inc. (R), NJ, *125*
Ledbetter/Davidson Int'l., Inc. (R), NY, *127*
Albert G. Lee Assoc. (C), RI, *415*
LG Brand, Inc. (C), MD, *417*
Pat Licata & Assoc. (C), NC, *417*
The Macdonald Group, Inc. (R), NJ, *133*
The Mackenzie Group (R), MD, *133*
Carol Maden Group (C), VA, *422*
Magellan Int'l., L.P. (C), TX, *422*
Management Recruiters of Emeryville (C), CA, *440*
Management Recruiters of Milford Inc. (C), CT, *442*
Management Recruiters of Anna Maria Island (C), FL, *443*
Management Recruiters of Plant City, Inc. (C), FL, *444*
Management Recruiters of Atlanta (C), GA, *445*
Management Recruiters of Springfield, Inc. (C), IL, *447*
Management Recruiters of Frederick, Inc. (C), MD, *450*
Management Recruiters of Washington, DC Inc. (C), MD, *450*
Management Recruiters of Middlesex County NJ (C), NJ, *454*
Management Recruiters of Woodbury Inc. (C), NY, *455*
Management Recruiters of Lionville, Inc. (C), PA, *459*
Management Recruiters of Georgetown (C), SC, *461*
Management Recruiters of Houston (C), TX, *462*
Management Recruiters - Piedmont (C), VA, *464*
Management Recruiters of Fairfax, VA (C), VA, *464*
Mankuta Gallagher & Assoc., Inc. (C), FL, *468*
Manuso, Alexander & Associates, Inc. (R), NY, *135*
Marcus & Assoc. (C), NY, *469*
Marketing Resources (C), MA, *470*
MB Inc. Executive Search (C), NY, *473*
McCormack & Assoc. (R), CA, *140*
McGrath & Assoc., Inc. (R), NJ, *141*
Med Exec Int'l. (C), CA, *476*
Medical Innovations (C), NY, *477*
Medical Recruiters Inc. (C), MO, *477*
MedQuest Assoc. (C), CO, *478*
MedSearch Resources, Inc. (C), FL, *478*
Mercedes & Co., Inc. (R), MA, *143*
Merlin Int'l. Inc. (C), NJ, *479*
META/MAT, Ltd. (R), NJ, *144*
E. J. Michaels, Ltd. (C), NY, *481*
Molecular Solutions, Inc. (C), SC, *483*
MTA Partners (R), TX, *148*
National Search, Inc.r (C), FL, *490*
NaviSearch (C), GA, *490*
The Neil Michael Group, Inc./Global Partners (R), NY, *151*
Networking Unlimited of NH, Inc. (C), NH, *491*
The Normyle/Erstling Health Search Group (C), NJ, *494*
John B. Norris & Assoc., Inc. (C), MD, *495*
Robert Ottke Assoc. (R), CA, *157*
Largent Parks & Partners (C), TX, *503*
The Patience Motivation Belief Group, Inc. (C), GA, *505*
Patriot Assoc. (C), PA, *505*
Pharmaceutical Recruiters, Inc. (R), NY, *163*
Pharmaceutical Search Professionals, Inc. (C), PA, *510*
J. R. Phillip & Assoc., Inc. (R), CA, *164*
Place Mart Personnel Service (C), NJ, *513*
Preferred Professional Recruiters (C), TX, *516*
Premier Business Advisors (C), PA, *516*
Priority Executive Search (C), FL, *518*
ProFinders, Inc. (C), FL, *523*
Ray & Berndtson (R), TX, *171*
Raymond Karsan Assoc. (C), PA, *529*
RCI Employment Solutions (C), FL, *531*
Recruiting Resources Int'l. (C), CA, *532*
Recruitment Resources (C), CA, *532*
Research Personnel Consultants (C), ON, *534*
Resources for Management (R), PA, *175*
Russell Reynolds Assoc., Inc. (R), NY, *176*
Reynolds Partners (R), NY, *177*
Rogish Assoc., Inc. (C), OH, *541*
Romac Int'l., Inc. (C), FL, *542*
Roth Young Personnel Service of Detroit, Inc. (C), MI, *546*
Rowland Mountain & Assoc. (C), GA, *547*
Rylan Forbes Consulting Group, Inc. (C), NJ, *549*
Sales Consultants of Chico (C), CA, *556*
Sales Consultants of Indianapolis (C), IN, *558*
Sales Consultants of Pittsburgh (C), PA, *562*
Sales Consultants of Houston (C), TX, *563*
Sales Recruiters of Oklahoma City (C), OK, *564*
Sampson Medical Search (C), CA, *564*
Sanford Rose Assoc. - Lake Forest (R), IL, *184*
Sanford Rose Assoc. - Clearwater (C), FL, *566*
Sanford Rose Assoc. - Louisville (C), KY, *567*
Sanford Rose Assoc. - Rochester (C), MI, *568*
Sanford Rose Assoc. - Columbia (C), SC, *570*
Santangelo Consultants Inc. (C), NY, *571*
A.D. Schiff & Assoc., Ltd. (C), IL, *572*
Schneider, Hill & Spangler, Inc. (R), PA, *185*
Search America, Inc. (C), PA, *573*

Search Innovations, Inc. (R), PA, *187*
Search Masters Int'l. (R), AZ, *187*
Search Masters, USA (C), FL, *576*
Searchforce, Inc. (R), FL, *187*
Searchworks, Inc. (C), FL, *577*
SFB Legal Search (C), NY, *579*
Shiell Personnel (C), LA, *580*
Shoemaker & Assoc. (R), GA, *190*
Shupack & Michaels Inc. (C), NY, *580*
Daniel A. Silverstein Assoc. Inc. (R), FL, *191*
Smith Hanley Assoc., Inc. (C), NY, *584*
Solomon-Page Healthcare Group (R), NY, *195*
Specialty Consultants Inc. (R), PA, *195*
SpencerStuart (R), NY, *196*
StaffWriters Plus (C), NY, *591*
STAT Search (C), NH, *592*
The Stewart Group (C), FL, *593*
Strategic Resources Biotechnology & Medical Group (C), WA, *595*
J. Stroll Assoc., Inc. (R), CT, *203*
TechFind, Inc. (R), MA, *207*
Tondorf & Assoc. Inc. (C), MA, *607*
Vezan Assoc. (C), CT, *612*
Victor White Int'l. (C), CA, *612*
Voigt Assoc. (R), IL, *214*
W. P. Assoc. (C), CA, *613*
R. J. Watkins & Co., Ltd. (R), CA, *216*
Watring & Assoc., Inc. (C), IL, *616*
Western Management Consultants (R), BC, *218*
Westfields Int'l., Inc. (C), NY, *619*
The Whittaker Group (C), MI, *620*
Walter K. Wilkins & Co. (R), NJ, *221*
William-Johns Co., Inc. (C), CA, *621*
Williams Recruiting, Inc. (C), WA, *621*
The Winchester Group (R), CA, *222*
Windsor Consultants, Inc. (C), TX, *622*
Winthrop Partners, Inc. (R), NY, *222*
Louise Wood & Assoc. (C), NY, *624*
M. Wood Company (R), IL, *224*
The York Group (C), CA, *626*
Yungner & Bormann (R), MN, *226*
Zackrison Assoc., Inc. (C), FL, *627*
Zingaro & Company (R), TX, *227*
Zurick, Davis & Co., Inc. (R), MA, *227*

I.15 Legal

A-K-A (Anita Kaufmann Assoc.) (C), NY, *231*
A-L Assoc., Inc. (R), NY, *1*
A.K.S. Assoc., Ltd. (R), MA, *1*
Aaron Consulting, Inc. (C), MO, *232*
Cathy Abelson Legal Search (C), PA, *232*
Alexander & Collins (C), CA, *243*
The Alexander Group (R), TX, *3*
AM & G Certified Public Accountants & Consultants (R), IL, *4*
Attorney Search Global, Inc. (C), IL, *255*
Attorneys at Work (C), GA, *255*
Bader Research Corp. (C), NY, *257*
Battalia Winston Int'l./The Euram Consultants Group (R), NY, *13*
Beckman & Assoc. Legal Search (C), OH, *262*
Marcia Beilin, Inc. (C), NY, *262*
The Blackman Kallick Search Division (C), IL, *267*
Blane, Stevens & Kellogg (C), FL, *268*
The Howard C. Bloom Co. (C), TX, *268*
Blue Chip Law Consulting, Inc. (C), CA, *268*
Boston Professional Search, Inc. (C), MA, *270*
BowersThomas (C), CA, *271*
J. B. Brown & Assoc., Inc. (C), OH, *275*
Charles Buck & Assoc., Inc. (R), NY, *24*
C. P. Consulting (R), PA, *26*
Caldwell Legal Recruiting Consultants (C), ME, *279*
Canny, Bowen Inc. (R), NY, *27*
Careerfit, Inc. (C), TX, *283*
Carpenter Legal Search (C), PA, *284*
Malin Cederquist, Esq. (C), NY, *286*
The Center for Career Advancement, LLC (C), NJ, *287*
Claimsearch (C), CA, *291*
Coleman Legal Search Consultants (C), PA, *294*
Coleman Lew & Assoc., Inc. (R), NC, *37*
Combined Resources Inc. (R), OH, *38*
Consulpro (R), ON, *39*
Corrao, Miller, Rush & Wiesenthal (C), NY, *301*
Criterion Executive Search, Inc. (C), FL, *303*
Charles Dahl Group, Inc. (C), MN, *306*
Diversified Search, Inc. (R), PA, *52*
Drake & Assoc. (C), CA, *315*
Dunhill of Manchester Inc. (C), NH, *321*
E O Technical (C), CT, *324*
E T Search Inc. (C), CA, *324*
Eagle Search Assoc. (C), CA, *325*
David M. Ellner Assoc. (R), NY, *59*
Emerald Legal Search (C), NH, *329*
Executives Worldwide, Inc. (C), OR, *337*
Leon A. Farley Assoc. (R), CA, *65*
Faro Consultants Int'l. (C), VA, *338*
Fergus Legal Search & Consulting, Inc. (C), NY, *339*
Financial Connections Company (C), VA, *340*
Finn & Schneider Assoc., Inc. (C), DC, *341*
Susan Fletcher Attorney Employment Services (C), PA, *342*
F-o-r-t-u-n-e Personnel Consultants of Detroit, Inc. (C), MI, *346*
Fortune Personnel Consultants of Raleigh, Inc. (C), NC, *348*
Foster Associates (C), NJ, *351*
Foster Partners (R), NY, *70*
Frey & Sher Assoc., Inc. (C), VA, *353*
Genel Associates (C), CA, *356*
Gillard Assoc. Legal Search (C), MA, *357*
Barry Goldberg & Assoc., Inc. (C), CA, *360*
Stephen Haas Legal Placement (C), NY, *365*
Harbor Consultants Int'l., Inc. (C), VA, *368*
Bruce W. Haupt Assoc. (R), DC, *88*
Phyllis Hawkins & Assoc., Inc. (C), AZ, *370*
Haydon Legal Search (C), IL, *370*
Jay Heino Company, LLC (C), NY, *375*
H. Hertner Assoc., Inc. (C), FL, *377*
Houser, Martin, Morris (C), WA, *381*
Howard-Sloan Legal Search, Inc. (C), NY, *382*
Howard/Williams Assoc. (C), FL, *382*
Hughes & Sloan, Inc. (C), GA, *383*
Human Resource Bureau (C), CA, *384*
Hunt & Howe Inc. (R), NY, *99*
Hyde Danforth & Co. (R), TX, *100*
Impact Search & Strategies (C), PA, *387*
Ingram & Aydelotte, Inc. (R), NY, *101*
Intelligent Marketing Solutions, Inc. (C), NY, *390*
Interquest, Inc. (R), NY, *103*
Isaacson, Miller (R), MA, *104*
Ann Israel & Assoc., Inc. (C), NY, *395*
JAG Group (R), MO, *105*
The Jameson Group (C), CA, *397*
John Michael Assoc. (R), DC, *106*
Kass/Abell & Assoc., Inc. (C), CA, *404*
A.T. Kearney Executive Search (R), IL, *111*
Keena Staffing Services (C), NY, *404*
Barbara Kerner Consultants (C), NY, *405*
Klein, Landau & Romm (C), DC, *407*
Koerner & Assoc., Inc. (C), TN, *408*
John Kurosky & Assoc. (R), CA, *122*
Leader Resources Group (C), GA, *415*
Legal Network Inc. (C), CA, *416*
Legal Search Assoc. (C), KS, *416*
Lekan & Assoc., Inc. (R), OH, *128*
LG Brand, Inc. (C), MD, *417*
Howard Lieberman & Assoc., Inc. (C), MN, *417*
Lipton Assoc., Inc. (R), NY, *130*
Lloyd Prescott & Churchill, Inc. (R), FL, *130*
Lloyd Prescott Assoc., Inc. (C), FL, *418*
Major, Hagen & Africa (C), CA, *423*
Major Legal Services, Inc. (C), OH, *423*
Management Recruiters of Warren County, KY (C), KY, *449*
Management Recruiters of Cass County, NE (C), NE, *452*
Management Recruiters of Great Neck (C), NY, *454*
Brad Marks Int'l. (R), CA, *136*
The McCormick Group (C), VA, *473*
McDonald, Long & Assoc., Inc. (R), NY, *140*
William K. McLaughlin Assoc., Inc. (C), NY, *475*
McPherson Square Assoc., Inc. (C), DC, *475*
MCS Assoc. (R), CA, *142*
Miller & Assoc. (C), FL, *481*
Susan C. Miller Assoc., Inc. (C), DC, *482*
Mims & Associates (R), TX, *145*
Morgenstern Int'l., Inc. (C), FL, *485*
Nason & Nason (C), FL, *488*
The Nolan Group (C), CA, *494*
Nordeman Grimm, Inc. (R), NY, *152*
NRI Staffing Resources (C), DC, *496*
O'Callaghan Honey/Ray & Berndtson Inc. (R), AB, *153*
Odell & Assoc., Inc. (C), TX, *498*
The Ogdon Partnership (R), NY, *155*
The Options Group, Inc. (C), NY, *499*
Page-Wheatcroft & Co., Ltd. (R), TX, *158*

Florence Pape Legal Search, Inc. (C), NJ, *502*
Personnel Resources Organization (C), PA, *509*
Pittleman & Assoc. (C), NY, *512*
Bob Poline Assoc. Inc. (C), CA, *514*
P. G. Prager Search Assoc., Ltd. (C), NY, *515*
Preferred Placement, Inc. (C), NY, *516*
The Primary Group, Inc. (R), FL, *168*
ProSearch, Inc. (C), OH, *524*
Pursuant Legal Consultants (R), WA, *170*
Vera L. Rast Partners Inc. (C), IL, *529*
Russell Reynolds Assoc., Inc. (R), NY, *176*
Rivera Legal Search, Inc. (C), CA, *538*
Rosenfeld & Co., Inc. (C), MI, *545*
The Rubicon Group (C), AZ, *547*
Ryman, Bell, Green & Michaels, Inc. (C), TX, *549*
Sales Consultants (C), IL, *558*
Sales Consultants of Omaha, Inc. (C), NE, *560*
Sanford Rose Assoc. (C), OH, *565*
Seltzer Fontaine Beckwith (C), CA, *579*
Sharrow & Assoc., Inc. (C), MI, *579*
Howard W. Smith Assoc. (R), CT, *193*
Smith, Brown & Jones (C), KS, *585*
Smythe Masterson & Judd, Inc. (C), NY, *585*
SpencerStuart (R), NY, *196*
Splaine & Assoc., Inc. (R), CA, *198*
SR Wilson, Inc. (C), CA, *590*
Stafford Consulting Group (R), CA, *198*
The Stevens Group (R), TX, *200*
DM Stone Personnel Services (C), CA, *594*
J. Stroll Assoc., Inc. (R), CT, *203*
TeamBuilders (C), GA, *600*
Templeton & Assoc. (C), MN, *605*
Topaz Int'l., Inc., Attorney Search (C), NJ, *607*
Tully/Woodmansee Int'l. Inc. (R), FL, *212*
UniQuest Int'l., Inc. (C), FL, *610*
Villasenor & Assoc. (C), CA, *612*
Waldorf Associates, Inc. (C), CA, *614*
The Wallace Law Registry (C), CT, *614*
Scott Watson & Assoc., Inc. (R), FL, *216*
The Whitaker Companies (C), TX, *619*
Whitbeck & Assoc. (R), MN, *219*
Windsor Consultants, Inc. (C), TX, *622*
D. S. Wolf Assoc., Inc. (R), NY, *223*
WTW Assoc., Inc. (R), NY, *225*
Zenner Consulting Group (C), IL, *627*

I.16 Computer services

A C Personnel Services, Inc. (C), OK, *231*
A First Resource (C), NC, *231*
A-L Assoc., Inc. (R), NY, *1*
A. D. & Assoc. Executive Search, Inc. (C), GA, *231*
Abraxas Technologies, Inc. (C), FL, *233*
Access Data Personnel, Inc. (C), NH, *233*
Acclaim Services, Inc. (C), TX, *234*
Adam-Bryce Inc. (C), NY, *239*
Arthur Adams & Assoc. (C), OH, *239*
Adel-Lawrence Assoc., Inc. (C), NJ, *240*
Adept Tech Recruiting, Inc. (C), NY, *240*
Alexander Associates (R), NJ, *2*
The Alexander Group (R), TX, *3*
Allen & Assoc. (C), NV, *244*
The Alternatives Group, Inc. (C), TX, *246*
AMD & Associates (C), GA, *247*
AmeriResource Group Inc. (C), OK, *248*
Patrick Arnone & Assoc. Inc. (R), VA, *7*
Ashton Computer Professionals, Inc. (C), BC, *253*
Association for Sales Force Management (C), WA, *254*
Astro Executive Search Firm (C), LA, *254*
Atkinson Search & Placement, Inc. (C), IA, *255*
Aubin Int'l. Inc. (R), MA, *8*
Aurora Tech Search (C), ON, *256*
Austin Group Int'l./Marlar Int'l. (R), TX, *9*
Avondale Search Int'l., Inc. (R), FL, *9*
The Ayers Group, Inc. (R), NY, *9*
The Badger Group (R), CA, *10*
Baldwin Associates, LLC (R), CT, *10*
The Baldwin Group (R), IL, *10*
Allen Ballach Assoc. Inc. (R), ON, *10*
James Bangert & Assoc., Inc. (R), MN, *11*
Barclay Consultants, Inc. (C), NJ, *259*
J. W. Barleycorn, Renard & Assoc., Inc. (R), OH, *11*
Barnes & Assoc. Executive Search (C), CA, *259*
Barrett Rose & Lee, Inc. (C), ON, *260*
Bartl & Evins (C), NY, *260*
Barton Assoc., Inc. (R), TX, *12*
Battalia Winston Int'l./The Euram Consultants Group (R), NY, *13*
R. Gaines Baty Assoc., Inc. (R), TX, *13*
Beck/Eastwood Recruitment Solutions (C), CA, *261*
The Bedford Group (R), RI, *15*
Robert Beech West Inc. (C), CA, *262*
Belanger Partners Ltd. (C), ON, *262*
Edward Bell Assoc. (C), CA, *263*
Bellamy & Assoc. (C), GA, *263*
N. L. Benke & Assoc., Inc. (C), OH, *264*
Dick Berg & Assoc. (C), CA, *264*
Berglund Int'l. Resources, Inc. (C), TX, *265*
BG & Assoc. (C), MD, *266*
Bishop Partners (R), NY, *17*
Boardroom Consultants/Kenny Kindler Tholke (R), NY, *19*
Boettcher Assoc. (R), WI, *19*
Bornholdt Shivas & Friends Executive Recruiters (C), NY, *270*
Brandt Associates (C), PA, *272*
Brault & Assoc., Ltd. (R), VA, *22*
The Brentwood Group Ltd. (R), OR, *23*
The Broadmoor Group, L.L.C. (R), TX, *23*
Brownstone Sales & Marketing Group, Inc. (C), NY, *275*
BT&A, LLC (R), CT, *24*
Bullis & Co., Inc. (R), CA, *25*
Business Partners, Inc. (C), FL, *277*
Business Systems of America, Inc. (C), IL, *277*
Byron Leonard Int'l., Inc. (R), CA, *25*
C Assoc. (C), DC, *278*
C.P.S., Inc. (C), IL, *278*
Callan Assoc., Ltd. (R), IL, *27*
T. M. Campbell Co. (R), WA, *27*
Cantrell & Assoc. (C), FL, *280*
Capital Consulting & Research, Inc. (R), CT, *28*
Capstone Inc. (R), NY, *29*
Career Counseling Ltd. (C.C.L.) (C), NY, *282*
Career Marketing Consultants, Inc. (C), GA, *282*
Careers First, Inc. (C), NJ, *283*
Carion Resource Group Inc. (C), ON, *284*
Carter/MacKay (C), NJ, *285*
CAS Comsearch Inc. (C), NY, *285*
CBA Companies (C), CA, *286*
Cemco, Ltd. (C), IL, *286*
Cendea Connection Int'l. (R), TX, *32*
The Century Group (C), KS, *287*
CEO Consulting (C), FL, *287*
Elsie Chan & Assoc. (C), CA, *289*
The Chapman Group, Inc. (C), AZ, *289*
Chatham Search Assoc., Inc. (C), NJ, *290*
Cheney Associates (C), CT, *290*
The Cherbonnier Group, Inc. (R), TX, *33*
Chesapeake Group (C), CT, *290*
Christenson Hutchison McDowell, LLC (R), NJ, *34*
J. F. Church Associates (C), WA, *291*
M. A. Churchill & Assoc., Inc. (R), PA, *35*
Clarey/Napier Int'l., L.C. (R), TX, *35*
Clayman & Co. (R), MA, *36*
Clinton, Charles, Wise & Co. (C), FL, *293*
CMW & Associates, Inc. (C), IL, *293*
CN Associates (C), CA, *293*
Cole, Warren & Long, Inc. (R), PA, *37*
Colt Systems Professional Personnel Services (C), CA, *294*
Combined Resources Inc. (R), OH, *38*
Comprehensive Search (C), GA, *294*
CompuPro (C), IL, *295*
Computer Int'l. Consultants, Inc. (C), FL, *295*
Computer Network Resources, Inc. (C), CA, *295*
Computer Personnel, Inc. (C), WA, *295*
Computer Professionals Unlimited (C), TX, *295*
The Consortium (C), NY, *296*
Construct Management Services (C), MN, *297*
The Consulting Group of North America, Inc. (C), VA, *297*
Cook Assoc. Int'l., Inc. (C), TN, *298*
Cooper Assoc., Inc. (C), NY, *298*
Cornerstone Resources, Inc. (C), OK, *299*
Corporate Search Consultants, Inc. (C), FL, *301*
Current Resource Group, Inc. (C), GA, *305*
Cypress Int'l., Inc. (R), FL, *45*
Data Bank Executive Search (R), OH, *46*
Data Search Network, Inc. (C), FL, *307*
Data-AxIS Corp. (C), FL, *307*
The DataFinders Group, Inc. (C), NJ, *307*
Allen Davis & Assoc. (C), MA, *308*
Joseph A. Davis Consultants, Inc. (R), NY, *47*
DBC Recruiting Network (C), GA, *309*
De Funiak & Edwards (R), IN, *47*
DeCorrevont & Assoc. (C), IL, *310*
DEL Technical Services, Inc. (C), IL, *310*
Delta Management Group Ltd. (C), ON, *310*
Delta Resource Group, Ltd. (C), GA, *311*
Despres & Associates (C), IL, *311*

Diversified Consulting Services, Inc. (C), CO, *313*
Diversified Search, Inc. (R), PA, *52*
DLG Assoc., Inc. (R), NC, *53*
Don Allan Assoc., Inc. (C), CA, *313*
J P Donnelly Assoc., Inc. (C), NY, *314*
DS&A (Doug Sears & Assoc.) (C), FL, *315*
Dunhill Executive Search of Los Angeles, Inc. (C), CA, *319*
Dunhill Professional Search of Greater New Orleans (C), LA, *321*
Dunhill Professional Search of Byram (C), MS, *321*
Dunhill Personnel Service of Fargo (C), ND, *322*
Dunhill Professional Search of Wilkes-Barre/Scranton, Inc. (C), PA, *322*
Dunhill of Corpus Christi, Inc. (C), TX, *323*
Dynamic Choices Inc. (C), MO, *323*
Dynamic Search Systems, Inc. (C), IL, *324*
Dynamic Synergy Corp. (R), CA, *56*
Eagle Search Assoc. (C), CA, *325*
EagleView, Inc. (C), MA, *325*
EDP Staffing Solutions, Inc. (C), AR, *327*
Edwards & Assoc. (C), GA, *327*
EFCO Consultants, Inc. (C), NY, *327*
Eggers Consulting Co., Inc. (C), NE, *327*
Electronic Search, Inc. (C), IL, *327*
H. J. Elliot, Inc. (R), IL, *58*
Empowered Solutions Corp. (C), GA, *330*
Engineering & Scientific Search Assoc. (ESSA) (C), NJ, *330*
ExecuSource Assoc., Inc. (C), GA, *332*
Executive Exchange Corp. (C), NJ, *333*
Executive Manning Corp. (R), FL, *63*
Executive Recruiters (C), WA, *334*
Executive Sales Search (C), CO, *335*
Executive Solutions (R), MN, *64*
Executive Strategies, Inc. (C), GA, *337*
eXsource Inc. (C), SC, *337*
Fast Switch, Ltd. (C), OH, *338*
A. E. Feldman Assoc., Inc. (C), NY, *339*
Fell & Nicholson Technology Resources (R), CA, *65*
Fenwick Partners (R), MA, *66*
Financial Connections Company (C), VA, *340*
A. G. Fishkin & Assoc., Inc. (R), MD, *68*
James L. Fisk & Assoc. (C), MO, *342*
Focus Consulting Services, Inc. (C), FL, *342*
Fogec Consultants, Inc. (R), WI, *69*
L. W. Foote Co. (R), WA, *69*
Fortune Personnel Consultants of Colorado Springs (C), CO, *344*
F-O-R-T-U-N-E Personnel Consultants of Manatee County (C), FL, *345*
F-O-R-T-U-N-E Personnel Consultants (C), MI, *346*
Foster Partners (R), NY, *70*
P. N. French Assoc., Inc. (R), MA, *72*
Frye/Joure & Assoc., Inc. (C), TN, *353*
The Garms Group (R), IL, *74*
GateSource Partners (C), VA, *355*
C. R. Gerald & Assoc. (C), ON, *356*
Gilbert Tweed Assoc. Inc. (R), NY, *76*
Lawrence Glaser Assoc., Inc. (C), NJ, *357*
Global Technologies Group Inc. (C), NC, *359*
F. Gloss Int'l. (R), VA, *78*
Glou Int'l., Inc. (R), MA, *78*
The Goodman Group (R), CA, *79*
Goodrich & Sherwood Assoc., Inc. (R), NY, *79*
Greenhaven & Assoc., Inc. (R), NY, *81*
Greenwich Internet (C), CT, *363*
Greenwich Search Partners, LLC (C), CT, *363*
Groupe PCA Inc. (C), QE, *363*
Michael R. Guerin Co. (C), CA, *364*
The Guild Corp. (C), VA, *364*
Halbrecht & Co. (C), VA, *365*
Hall Kinion (C), CA, *366*
The Hamilton Group (R), MD, *85*
Hanley & Assoc. (R), FL, *86*
Harcor Quest & Assoc. (R), OH, *86*
Robert Harkins Assoc., Inc. (C), PA, *369*
Harper Associates (C), MI, *369*
Harper Hewes, Inc. (C), NY, *369*
Hayden & Assoc., Inc. (C), MN, *370*
Hazlett Associates (R), IL, *88*
HDB Incorporated (C), MO, *371*
Healthcare Recruiters Int'l. - Alabama (C), AL, *372*
Hechkoff/Work Executive Search Inc. (R), NY, *89*
Heffelfinger Assoc., Inc. (R), MA, *89*
J. J. Herlihy & Assoc., Inc. (C), CA, *376*
Higbee Assoc., Inc. (C), CT, *377*
High Tech Staffing Group (C), OR, *377*
High-Tech Recruiters (C), CT, *378*
Hobson Assoc. (C), CT, *379*
Hochman & Assoc. (C), CA, *379*
Hoffman Recruiters (C), MA, *380*
David C. Horn Executive Search (C), TX, *381*
Hreshko Consulting Group (C), NJ, *382*
The Human Resource Group, Inc. (R), OH, *98*
Human Resources Management Hawaii, Inc. (C), HI, *384*
Hunegnaw Executive Search (C), OH, *384*
Leigh Hunt & Assoc., Inc. (C), ME, *384*
Hunt & Howe Inc. (R), NY, *99*
Huntington Group (R), CT, *100*
Huntington Personnel Consultants, Inc. (C), NY, *386*
Huntley Associates (Dallas), Inc. (C), TX, *386*
i.j. & assoc., inc. (C), CO, *386*
Impact Search & Strategies (C), PA, *387*
Impact Technical Staffing (C), OR, *387*
Independent Resource Systems (C), CA, *388*
Information Systems Professionals (C), NC, *388*
InfoTech Search (C), TX, *388*
Insight Personnel Group, Inc. (C), TX, *389*
Integrated Search Solutions Group, LLC (ISSG) (R), NY, *102*
Intelegra, Inc. (C), NJ, *390*
Interactive Search Assoc. (C), PA, *391*
Isaacson, Miller (R), MA, *104*
Jackson Resources (R), TX, *105*
James Moore & Assoc. (C), CA, *397*
JDG Assoc., Ltd. (C), MD, *397*
Jefferson-Ross Assoc. Inc. (C), PA, *398*
Jeffrey Meryl Assoc., Inc. (C), NJ, *398*
Jender & Company (R), IL, *105*
JenKim Int'l. Ltd., Inc. (C), FL, *398*
JFW Associates, LLC (C), CT, *398*
JG Consultants, Inc. (R), TX, *106*
John Ryan Assoc., LLC. (C), NY, *399*
Johnson & Assoc., Inc. (R), CA, *106*
Ronald S. Johnson Assoc., Inc. (R), CA, *107*
Johnson, Kemper & Assoc. (C), TX, *400*
Jonathan Lawrence Assoc. (C), NJ, *400*
J. M. Joseph Assoc. (R), NJ, *109*
JT Assoc. (C), CT, *401*
A H Justice Search Consultants (C), TX, *402*
K2 Resources, L.P. (C), CT, *402*
KABL Ability Network (C), CA, *402*
Kames & Assoc. (C), MD, *403*
Kanzer Assoc., Inc. (R), IL, *109*
Kaplan & Assoc., Inc. (R), PA, *109*
Allan Karson Assoc., Inc. (R), NJ, *110*
Kaye/Bassman Int'l. Corp. (R), TX, *110*
A.T. Kearney Executive Search (R), IL, *111*
The Kennett Group, Inc. (R), PA, *112*
Key Resources Int'l. (C), CA, *405*
Kiley, Owen & McGovern, Inc. (R), NJ, *114*
Kleber & Assoc. (C), WA, *407*
KM Associates (C), MA, *407*
Kors Montgomery Int'l. (R), TX, *118*
KPA Assoc., Inc. (C), NY, *408*
Krakower Group, Inc. (R), CA, *120*
Kukoy Associates (R), CO, *121*
Kurtz Pro-Search, Inc. (C), NJ, *410*
L T M Assoc. (C), IL, *410*
Gregory Laka & Co. (C), IL, *411*
Lancaster Assoc., Inc. (C), NJ, *411*
The Landstone Group (C), NY, *412*
LAS Management Consulting Group, Inc. (R), NJ, *125*
LaVallee & Associates (C), NC, *413*
Layne-Mendez & Co. (R), TX, *127*
LCS, Inc. (C), TX, *414*
Leader Resources Group (C), GA, *415*
Vincent Lee Assoc. (C), NY, *415*
Lending Personnel Services (C), CA, *416*
F. P. Lennon Assoc. (C), PA, *416*
Lewis Consulting Service (C), IL, *417*
Lexington Software Inc. (C), NY, *417*
LG Brand, Inc. (C), MD, *417*
Lifter & Assoc. (C), CA, *418*
Lloyd Associates (R), GA, *130*
Loewenstein & Assoc., Inc. (R), TX, *131*
The Logan Group, Inc. (R), MO, *131*
Logix, Inc. (C), MA, *420*
Lynx, Inc. (C), MA, *421*
MacNaughton Assoc. (R), CA, *133*
Major Legal Services, Inc. (C), OH, *423*
Management Decision Systems, Inc. (MDSI) (C), NJ, *424*
Management Dimensions Ltd. (R), ON, *134*
Management Recruiters of Birmingham, Inc. (C), AL, *438*
Management Recruiters of Tucson (C), AZ, *439*

Management Recruiters of Little Rock (C), AR, *439*
Management Recruiters Inc. of Silicon Valley (C), CA, *441*
Management Recruiters of Colorado Springs (C), CO, *441*
Management Recruiters of Colchester (C), CT, *442*
Management Recruiters of Franktown (C), CO, *442*
Management Recruiters of Clearwater (C), FL, *443*
Management Recruiters of Tampa North (C), FL, *444*
Management Recruiters of St. Lucie County, Inc. (C), FL, *444*
Management Recruiters of Forsyth County (C), GA, *445*
Management Recruiters of Venice, Inc. (C), FL, *445*
Management Recruiters of Chicago-North Shore (C), IL, *447*
Management Recruiters of Indianapolis-North (C), IN, *448*
Management Recruiters-Cedar Rapids, Inc. (C), IA, *448*
Management Recruiters of Dearborn, Inc. (C), MI, *451*
Management Recruiters of North Oakland County, Inc. (C), MI, *452*
Management Recruiters of Chanhassen (C), MN, *452*
Management Recruiters of Morris County, NJ (C), NJ, *453*
Management Recruiters of Woodbury Inc. (C), NY, *455*
Management Recruiters of Bethlehem, PA (C), PA, *458*
Management Recruiters of Pittsburgh (C), PA, *459*
Management Recruiters of Aiken (C), SC, *460*
Management Recruiters of Chattanooga-Brainerd, Inc. (C), TN, *461*
Management Recruiters of Georgetown (C), SC, *461*
Management Recruiters of Austin (C), TX, *462*
Management Recruiters of Loudoun County South (C), VA, *465*
Management Recruiters of Appleton (C), WI, *465*
Management Recruiters of Stevens Point, Inc. (C), WI, *466*
Management Search, Inc. (C), IL, *467*
Management Solutions, Inc. (C), CA, *468*
Mancini Technical Recruiting (C), VA, *468*
F. L. Mannix & Co. (R), MA, *135*
MARBL Consultants, Inc. (C), WI, *469*
J. L. Mark Assoc., Inc. (R), CO, *135*
Mark Christian & Assoc., Inc. (C), AZ, *469*
Market Niche Consulting (C), AZ, *470*
The Maroon Group (R), CT, *136*
Masserman & Assoc., Inc. (R), NY, *138*
Matté & Company, Inc. (R), CT, *138*
K. E. McCarthy & Assoc. (R), CA, *139*
The McCormick Group (C), VA, *473*
McCoy Ltd. (C), CA, *474*
McCray, Shriver, Eckdahl & Assoc., Inc. (R), CA, *140*
McDowell & Co., Recruiters (C), TX, *474*
McHale & Assoc. (R), WA, *141*
Dan P. McLean Assoc., Inc. (C), ON, *475*
Medical Innovations (C), NY, *477*
Mee Derby & Co. (C), DC, *478*
Michael Thomas, Inc. (C), OH, *480*
Midas Management (C), CT, *481*
Midland Consultants (C), OH, *481*
MIS Computer Professionals, Inc. (C), KS, *482*
Mogul Consultants, Inc. (C), NY, *483*
Montenido Assoc. (R), CA, *146*
Larry Moore & Assoc. (C), CA, *484*
Morency Assoc. (C), MA, *485*
The Morley Group (C), IN, *486*
Multi Processing, Inc. (R), NH, *149*
Nason & Nason (C), FL, *488*
National Computerized Employment Service, Inc. (C), PA, *489*
National Executive (C), ON, *489*
National Field Service Corp. (C), NY, *489*
National Register Columbus Inc. (C), OH, *490*
J. Fielding Nelson & Assoc., Inc. (R), UT, *151*
Networking Unlimited of NH, Inc. (C), NH, *491*
Newcomb-Desmond & Assoc., Inc. (C), OH, *492*
Newell Assoc. (R), NY, *151*
Newman-Johnson-King, Inc. (C), TX, *492*
Newport Management (C), NY, *492*
Next Step Recruiting (C), CA, *493*
Marc Nichols Assoc., Inc. (C), NY, *493*
Ira Z. Nitzberg (C), NY, *493*
W. D. Nolte & Company (R), CT, *152*
Nordeman Grimm, Inc. (R), NY, *152*
Paul Winston Norman & Assoc. (R), IL, *152*
Norman Broadbent Int'l., Inc. (R), NY, *152*
The North Peak Group (C), OH, *496*
Northland Employment Services Inc. (C), MN, *496*
NYCOR Search, Inc. (C), MN, *497*
O'Keefe & Assoc. (C), TX, *497*
Odell & Assoc., Inc. (C), TX, *498*
Omnisearch Assoc. (C), CA, *499*
Opus Marketing (R), CA, *156*
Robert Ottke Assoc. (R), CA, *157*
P.R.H. Management, Inc. (R), CT, *158*
Pacific Crossing (C), CA, *501*
Page-Wheatcroft & Co., Ltd. (R), TX, *158*
Paladin Group, Inc. (C), CO, *502*
Parenica & Co. (R), NC, *159*
The Partners, LLC (C), CA, *504*
Paul-Tittle Assoc., Inc. (R), VA, *161*
Pearce & Assoc. (C), FL, *506*
M. A. Pelle Assoc., Inc. (C), NY, *506*
People Management Northeast, Inc. (R), CT, *162*
Perry Search Assoc. (C), CA, *507*
Perry-Martel Int'l., Inc. (R), ON, *163*
Personnel Alliance Group (C), NJ, *507*
Personnel Incorporated (C), IA, *508*
Personnel Management Group (C), MB, *508*
PHD Conseil en Ressources Humaines Inc. (C), QE, *510*
Phillips Assoc. (C), FL, *510*
Phillips Personnel/Search (C), CO, *510*
Phoenix Partners, Inc. (C), GA, *511*
The Pinnacle Source, Inc. (C), CO, *512*
PKS Assoc., Inc. (C), RI, *513*
Place Mart Personnel Service (C), NJ, *513*
R. L. Plimpton Assoc., Inc. (R), CO, *165*
The Pollack Group (C), ON, *514*
PPS Information Systems Staffing (C), MD, *515*
Elan Pratzer & Partners Inc. (R), ON, *167*
Preston & Co. (R), NJ, *167*
Price & Assoc., Inc. (C), VA, *518*
Princeton Executive Search (C), NJ, *518*
Princeton Search Partners, Inc. (R), NJ, *169*
PRO, Inc./Professional Recruiting Offices, Inc. (C), CA, *519*
Procom (C), ON, *519*
Professional Employment Group (C), MD, *520*
Professional Personnel Consultants, Inc. (C), MI, *521*
Professional Recruiters (C), UT, *521*
Professional Search Centre, Ltd. (C), IL, *522*
Professional Support Inc. (C), NY, *523*
ProFinders, Inc. (C), FL, *523*
Quality Consulting Group, Inc. (C), WI, *526*
Quiring Assoc., Inc. (C), IN, *527*
R.A.N. Assoc., Inc. (C), OH, *528*
Rand Thompson Executive Search Consultants (C), NY, *528*
J. E. Ranta Assoc. (C), MA, *529*
Ray & Berndtson (R), TX, *171*
Recruit Xpress (C), TX, *531*
Recruiting/Solutions (C), CA, *532*
Redwood Partners Ltd. (R), NY, *173*
The Regency Group, Ltd. (C), NE, *533*
RemTech Business Solutions, Inc. (C), MI, *534*
The Renaissance Network (C), MA, *534*
Retained Search Assoc. (R), NC, *176*
Russell Reynolds Assoc., Inc. (R), NY, *176*
RHI Consulting (C), VA, *536*
RHS Assoc. (C), AL, *536*
Ritta Professional Search Inc. (C), NY, *538*
Roberts Ryan & Bentley, Inc. (R), MD, *179*
R. A. Rodriguez & Assoc., Inc. (C), TX, *540*
Ross Personnel Consultants, Inc. (C), CT, *545*
The Rubinic Consulting Group (C), OH, *548*
S-H-S TechStaff (C), PA, *549*
S. P. Assoc., Inc. (C), NC, *550*
S.C.S. & Assoc. (C), NC, *550*
Sales & Marketing Search, Inc. (C), MA, *551*
Sales Consultants of Silicon Valley (C), CA, *556*
Sales Consultants of Sacramento (C), CA, *556*
Sales Consultants of Northwest Arkansas, Inc. (C), AR, *556*
Sales Consultants of Indianapolis-North (C), IN, *558*

INDUSTRIES

Sales Consultants (C), IL, *558*
Sales Consultants of Western McHenry County (C), IL, *558*
Sales Consultants of Wellesley, Inc. (C), MA, *559*
Sales Consultants of Rockville, MD (C), MD, *559*
Sales Consultants of Austin, Inc. (C), TX, *562*
Sales Consultants King of Prussia (C), PA, *562*
Sales Consultants of Madison (C), WI, *563*
Sales Consultants of Milwaukee (C), WI, *563*
Sales Executives, Inc. (C), MI, *563*
Sales Search (C), ON, *564*
Sampson Medical Search (C), CA, *564*
Sanford Rose Assoc. - Charlotte (C), NC, *568*
Sanford Rose Assoc. - Springfield (C), MO, *568*
Sanford Rose Assoc. - Amherst, NY (C), NY, *568*
Sanford Rose Assoc. - Euclid (C), OH, *569*
Sanford Rose Assoc. - Akron (C), OH, *569*
Sanford Rose Assoc. - Columbia (C), SC, *570*
Sanford Rose Assoc. - Philadelphia North (C), PA, *570*
Sanford Rose Assoc. - Salt Lake City (C), UT, *571*
Saviar, Inc. (C), AZ, *571*
Search & Recruit Int'l. (C), VA, *573*
The Search Alliance, Inc. (R), FL, *186*
Search America, Inc. (C), MA, *574*
Search Group (C), CA, *575*
Search Plus Int'l.-Ohio (C), OH, *576*
Search Solutions Inc. (C), CA, *576*
Seco & Zetto Assoc., Inc. (C), NJ, *577*
Sensible Solutions, Inc. (R), IL, *188*
Sevcor Int'l., Inc. (R), IL, *188*
Sharrow & Assoc., Inc. (C), MI, *579*
Shell Technology Group (C), CA, *580*
The Silicon Network (C), ON, *581*
Sinclair & Co., Inc. (R), MA, *192*
Smartsource Inc. (C), CA, *583*
Smith Search, S.C. (R), MX, *194*
Snelling Search (C), LA, *586*
Softrix, Inc. (C), NJ, *586*
Software Engineering Solutions, Inc. (C), CA, *586*
Software Resource Consultants (C), TN, *587*
Southport Int'l. Assoc. Inc. (C), FL, *588*
Sparks, McDonough & Assoc., Inc. (C), MO, *588*
SPC Symcox Personnel Consultants (C), TX, *588*
SpencerStuart (R), NY, *196*
Kenn Spinrad Inc. (C), PA, *589*
Spriggs & Co., Inc. (R), IL, *198*
Squires Resources Inc. (C), ON, *590*
Staff Resources, Inc. (C), SC, *590*
C. J. Stafford & Assoc. (C), ON, *591*
Stanewick, Hart & Assoc., Inc. (C), FL, *591*
Starbridge Group Inc. (C), VA, *591*
Sterling Int'l. (R), NJ, *200*
Steven Douglas Assoc. (C), FL, *593*
Stevens Assoc. (C), MA, *593*
The Stevenson Group, Inc. (N.J.) (R), NJ, *200*
Stewart/Laurence Assoc., Inc. (R), NJ, *201*
Linford E. Stiles & Assoc., L.L.C. (R), NH, *201*
Stillinger & Assoc. (R), CA, *201*
Stone Enterprises Ltd. (C), IL, *594*
Stoopen Asociados, S.C./EMA Partners Int'l. (R), MX, *202*
Strategic Alliance Network, Ltd. (C), OH, *595*
Sudina Search, Inc. (C), MD, *596*
The Summit Group (C), CA, *596*
Swartz & Assoc., Inc. (R), AZ, *204*
Synergistech Communications (C), CA, *597*
Synergy Solutions, Ltd. (C), WA, *597*
Systems Careers (C), CA, *598*
Systems One Ltd. (C), IL, *598*
Systems Personnel, Inc. (C), NY, *598*
Systems Research Inc. (SRI) (C), IL, *598*
Systems Search (C), IL, *599*
T. H. Hunter, Inc. (C), MN, *599*
Tactical Alternatives (R), CA, *205*
Roy Talman & Assoc. (C), IL, *599*
M. L. Tawney & Assoc. (C), TX, *600*
Taylor Winfield (R), TX, *207*
TBC, Inc. (C), KY, *600*
TeamBuilders (C), GA, *600*
Tech 2000 (C), FL, *601*
Tech Consulting (C), FL, *601*
Tech Search (C), CA, *601*
Tech-Net (C), TX, *601*
TechNix Inc. (C), ON, *602*
Techno-Trac Systems, Inc. (C), NY, *603*
The Technology Group (R), IL, *208*
Technology Search Int'l. (C), CA, *603*
Thor, Inc. (C), CA, *606*
Tirocchi, Wright, Inc. (R), CA, *209*
The Touchstone Group (C), MA, *607*
Trac One (R), NJ, *210*
Van Treadaway Assoc., Inc. (R), GA, *210*
TriStaff Group (C), CA, *609*
TSW Assoc., LLC (R), CT, *211*
TTG/Sterling Services (C), CA, *610*
W. G. Tucker & Assoc. (R), PA, *211*
The Thomas Tucker Co. (R), CA, *211*
Tuttle Venture Group, Inc. (R), TX, *212*
C. J. Vincent Assoc., LLC (C), MD, *612*
The Wabash Group (C), IN, *613*
B. D. Wallace & Assoc. (C), MD, *614*
J. D. Walsh & Co. (R), CT, *215*
C. D. Warner & Assoc. (C), PA, *615*
S. B. Webster & Associates (R), MA, *217*
David Weinfeld Group (C), NC, *617*
Henry Welker & Assoc. (C), MI, *618*
Werbin Assoc. Executive Search, Inc. (C), NY, *618*
Wheeler Assoc. (R), CT, *219*
The Whitaker Companies (C), TX, *619*
Arch S. Whitehead Assoc. Inc. (ASWA) (R), NY, *219*
Wilder & Assoc. (C), VA, *620*
Wilkinson & Ives (R), CA, *221*
Wilkinson SoftSearch, Inc. (C), VA, *620*
Willis & Assoc. (R), OH, *221*
Wilson-Douglas-Jordan (C), IL, *622*
Windsor Consultants, Inc. (C), TX, *622*
Winter, Wyman & Co. (C), MA, *623*
M. Wood Company (R), IL, *224*
Bruce G. Woods Executive Search (R), TX, *224*
Worlco Computer Resources, Inc. (C), PA, *624*
Worldwide Medical Services (C), CA, *625*
Dennis Wynn Assoc., Inc. (C), FL, *625*
Bill Young & Assoc. (C), VA, *626*
ZanExec L.L.C. (R), VA, *226*
Zeiger Assoc. L.L.C. (C), CA, *627*
P. D. Zier Assoc. (C), CT, *627*

I.17 Accounting & miscellaneous business services

A-L Assoc., Inc. (R), NY, *1*
A. D. & Assoc. Executive Search, Inc. (C), GA, *231*
A.L.S. Group (C), NJ, *232*
Accent On Achievement, Inc. (C), MI, *233*
Access/Resources, Inc. (C), MA, *234*
Accountants On Call (C), FL, *237*
ADR Accounting Management Recruiters (C), ON, *240*
Advice Personnel Inc. (C), NY, *241*
Affordable Executive Recruiters (C), CA, *241*
Allman & Co., Inc. (C), NC, *245*
AM & G Certified Public Accountants & Consultants (R), IL, *4*
AmeriResource Group Inc. (C), OK, *248*
Andrews & Assoc. (C), NC, *250*
Angel Group Int'l. (C), KY, *250*
The Angus Group, Ltd. (C), OH, *251*
The Ascher Group (R), NJ, *7*
Atlantic Pacific Group (C), CA, *255*
The Ayers Group, Inc. (R), NY, *9*
The Bankers Group (C), IL, *258*
Bartl & Evins (C), NY, *260*
Barton Assoc., Inc. (R), TX, *12*
Edward Bell Assoc. (C), CA, *263*
N. L. Benke & Assoc., Inc. (C), OH, *264*
Berger & Leff (C), CA, *264*
Birch & Associes (C), QE, *267*
The Blackman Kallick Search Division (C), IL, *267*
Boone-Scaturro Assoc., Inc. (C), GA, *269*
Boston Professional Search, Inc. (C), MA, *270*
Boyden (R), NY, *20*
Brandt Associates (C), PA, *272*
Bristol Assoc., Inc. (C), CA, *274*
Burke & Assoc./The Westfield Group (C), CT, *276*
C. M. Management Services, Inc. (R), KY, *26*
C/R Associates (C), NY, *278*
Callan Assoc., Ltd. (R), IL, *27*
The Cambridge Group Ltd. (C), CT, *280*
T. M. Campbell Co. (R), WA, *27*
Canny, Bowen Inc. (R), NY, *27*
Capital Consulting & Research, Inc. (R), CT, *28*
Cemco, Ltd. (C), IL, *286*
M. A. Churchill & Assoc., Inc. (R), PA, *35*
Clarey/Napier Int'l., L.C. (R), TX, *35*
CMC Search Consultants (C), IL, *293*

Coleman Lew & Assoc., Inc. (R), NC, *37*
Combined Resources Inc. (R), OH, *38*
Construct Management Services (C), MN, *297*
Consulting Resource Group, Inc. (C), GA, *297*
The Corporate Connection, Ltd. (C), VA, *299*
Corporate Search Consultants, Inc. (C), FL, *301*
Leonard Corwen Assoc. (C), NY, *302*
CountryHouse Hotels Executive Search (C), VA, *302*
The Cris Group, Inc. (R), NY, *42*
Custom Resources (C), AL, *305*
Daggett & Kvistad (R), CA, *45*
The Danbrook Group, Inc. (C), TX, *306*
Alfred Daniels & Assoc., Inc. (R), CA, *46*
Diversified Search, Inc. (R), PA, *52*
DLG Assoc., Inc. (R), NC, *53*
Dunhill Professional Search of Hawaii (C), HI, *320*
Dunhill Professional Search of Tampa (C), FL, *320*
Dunhill of Manchester Inc. (C), NH, *321*
Dunhill Personnel Service of Fargo (C), ND, *322*
Dynamic Choices Inc. (C), MO, *323*
Eagle Search Assoc. (C), CA, *325*
EagleView, Inc. (C), MA, *325*
Edwards & Assoc. (C), GA, *327*
The Evans Search Group (R), CT, *61*
The Execu/Search Group (C), NY, *332*
Executive Recruiters Agency, Inc. (C), AR, *333*
Executive Referral Services, Inc. (C), IL, *334*
Executive Resource Systems (C), CA, *335*
Executive Search Consultants, Inc. (C), FL, *335*
Executive Search Team (C), MI, *336*
Executive Solutions (R), MN, *64*
ExecutiveFit (C), NY, *337*
Financial Connections Company (C), VA, *340*
Financial Plus Management Solutions Inc. (R), ON, *66*
Susan Fletcher Attorney Employment Services (C), PA, *342*
Fogec Consultants, Inc. (R), WI, *69*
Foley Proctor Yoskowitz (R), NJ, *69*
Fortune Personnel Consultants of Huntsville, Inc. (C), AL, *343*
F-O-R-T-U-N-E Personnel Consultants (C), MI, *346*
F-O-R-T-U-N-E Personnel Consultants of Southwest Indiana (C), IN, *346*
Fortune Personnel Consultants of Raleigh, Inc. (C), NC, *348*
Forum Personnel Inc. (C), NY, *351*
Foster Associates (C), NJ, *351*
Foster Partners (R), NY, *70*
The Fourbes Group, Inc. (C), NJ, *351*
Friedman Eisenstein Raemer & Schwartz, LLP (R), IL, *72*
G. H. Enterprises (C), AZ, *354*
Gateway Group Personnel, LLC (C), TN, *355*
GFI Professional Staffing Services (C), NH, *357*
Gilbert Scott Assoc., LLC (C), MA, *357*
The Goldman Group Inc. (R), NY, *79*
David Gomez & Assoc., Inc. (R), IL, *79*
Gowdy Consultants (C), TX, *361*
Granger, Counts & Assoc. (R), OH, *81*
Grauss & Co. (C), CA, *362*
Ben Greco Assoc., Inc. (C), CA, *362*
Greenwich Search Partners, LLC (C), CT, *363*
Grossberg & Assoc. (R), IL, *82*
Groupe PCA Inc. (C), QE, *363*
The H. S. Group, Inc. (C), WI, *365*
Hale Assoc. (R), IL, *84*
K. C. Hale, Inc. (R), CT, *85*
Harbrowe, Inc. (C), NY, *368*
Robert Harkins Assoc., Inc. (C), PA, *369*
Harper Associates (C), MI, *369*
Jay Heino Company, LLC (C), NY, *375*
Hermann & Westmore (R), CA, *92*
Herrerias & Assoc. (R), CA, *92*
Howard/Williams Assoc. (C), FL, *382*
Human Resource Bureau (C), CA, *384*
Hyde Danforth & Co. (R), TX, *100*
Impact Search & Strategies (C), PA, *387*
Integrated Management Solutions (C), NY, *390*
Intelligent Marketing Solutions, Inc. (C), NY, *390*
ISC of Houston, Inc. (C), TX, *394*
Ron Jackson & Assoc. (C), GA, *396*
JDC Assoc. (C), NY, *397*
Joseph Chris & Assoc. (C), TX, *400*
Joseph Michaels (C), CA, *401*
A.T. Kearney Executive Search (R), IL, *111*
David Warwick Kennedy & Assoc. (R), BC, *112*
Daniel J. Kerstein, Consultant to Management (R), CO, *114*
Keystone Consulting Group (C), GA, *406*
KPA Assoc., Inc. (C), NY, *408*
Todd L. Krueger & Assoc. (C), WA, *409*
John Kuhn & Assoc., Inc. (R), WI, *121*
Larsen & Lee, Inc. (R), MD, *125*
LAS Management Consulting Group, Inc. (R), NJ, *125*
Leader Resources Group (C), GA, *415*
Vincent Lee Assoc. (C), NY, *415*
Lekan & Assoc., Inc. (R), OH, *128*
LG Brand, Inc. (C), MD, *417*
Locke & Assoc. (R), NC, *131*
M/J/A Partners (R), IL, *133*
MacNaughton Assoc. (R), CA, *133*
Carol Maden Group (C), VA, *422*
Management Recruiters of Birmingham, Inc. (C), AL, *438*
Management Recruiters, Inland Empire Agency (C), CA, *441*
Management Recruiters of Clearwater (C), FL, *443*
Management Recruiters of St. Augustine (C), FL, *444*
Management Recruiters-Cedar Rapids, Inc. (C), IA, *448*
Management Recruiters of Topeka, Inc. (C), KS, *449*
Management Recruiters of Frederick, Inc. (C), MD, *450*
Management Recruiters of Washington, DC Inc. (C), MD, *450*
Management Recruiters of Muskegon (C), MI, *451*
Management Recruiters of Great Neck (C), NY, *454*
Management Recruiters of Northwest Ohio, Inc. (C), OH, *458*
Management Recruiters of Houston (C), TX, *462*
Management Recruiters of Milwaukee-West (C), WI, *465*
Management Recruiters of Milwaukee - Downtown (C), WI, *466*
Management Solutions, Inc. (C), CA, *468*
Marentz & Co. (C), TX, *469*
Marsar & Co., Inc. (C), FL, *471*
McHale & Assoc. (R), WA, *141*
The Medley Group (C), CA, *477*
Meng, Finseth & Assoc., Inc. (R), CA, *143*
Michael Wayne Recruiters (C), IL, *480*
Oscar Montaño, Inc. (R), CA, *146*
C. A. Moore & Assoc., Inc. (C), MN, *484*
The Morley Group (C), IN, *486*
Nason & Nason (C), FL, *488*
National Affirmative Action Career Network, Inc. (C), CO, *488*
Next Step Recruiting (C), CA, *493*
Marc Nichols Assoc., Inc. (C), NY, *493*
The Nolan Group (C), CA, *494*
W. D. Nolte & Company (R), CT, *152*
Norman Broadbent Int'l., Inc. (R), NY, *152*
Norrell Financial Staffing (C), GA, *495*
NRI Staffing Resources (C), DC, *496*
Nuessle, Kurdziel & Weiss, Inc. (R), PA, *153*
O'Sullivan Search Inc. (C), ON, *498*
Omnisearch Assoc. (C), CA, *499*
Pacific Advisory Service, Inc. (C), IL, *501*
Arthur Pann Assoc., Inc. (C), NY, *502*
Partners Resource Group (C), VA, *504*
Pasona Canada, Inc. (C), ON, *504*
Pearson, Caldwell & Farnsworth (R), CA, *161*
The Pennmor Group (C), NJ, *506*
PeopleSource Inc. (C), TX, *506*
Personnel Alliance Group (C), NJ, *507*
Personnel Management Group (C), MB, *508*
Phillips Personnel/Search (C), CO, *510*
Placement Solutions (C), WI, *513*
Plante & Moran, LLP (R), MI, *165*
Bob Poline Assoc. Inc. (C), CA, *514*
Robert Powers & Assoc. (C), CA, *515*
Precision Executive Search (C), AZ, *516*
Preston & Co. (R), NJ, *167*
Prime Management Group Inc. (C), ON, *518*
Princeton Executive Search (C), NJ, *518*
Princeton Search Partners, Inc. (R), NJ, *169*
Professional Search Assoc. (C), CA, *522*
Profit Pros, Inc. (C), CA, *523*
ProSearch, Inc. (C), OH, *524*
Protocol Inc. (C), CA, *525*
Quantum Int'l., Ltd. (R), FL, *170*
The Quest Organization (C), NY, *527*

Quirk-Corporon & Assoc., Inc. (C), WI, 527
Lea Randolph & Assoc., Inc. (C), TX, 529
Ray & Berndtson (R), TX, 171
Razzino-Claymore Assoc. (C), NJ, 530
Reinecke & Assoc. (C), NJ, 533
Response Staffing Services (C), NY, 534
Russell Reynolds Assoc., Inc. (R), NY, 176
RHS Assoc. (C), AL, 536
Ritt-Ritt & Assoc., Inc. (C), IL, 537
Robertson & Assoc. (C), IL, 539
The Robinson Group, D.A., Ltd. (C), IL, 539
Romac Int'l. (C), PA, 542
Romac Int'l., Inc. (C), FL, 542
Ruderfer & Co., Inc. (C), NJ, 548
S-H-S TechStaff (C), PA, 549
R. S. Sadow Assoc. (C), NJ, 550
Sales & Management Search, Inc. (C), IL, 551
Sales Consultants Peninsula, Inc. (C), CA, 556
Sales Consultants of Chicago South (C), IL, 558
Schenck & Assoc. SC (C), WI, 572
Searchworks, Inc. (C), FL, 577
Sensible Solutions, Inc. (R), IL, 188
Shey-Harding Assoc. Inc. (C), CA, 580
Silver Associates (C), CA, 581
J. L. Small Assoc. (C), AL, 583
Smith Hanley Assoc., Inc. (C), NY, 584
Robert Sollman & Assoc. (C), FL, 587
SPC Symcox Personnel Consultants (C), TX, 588
SpencerStuart (R), NY, 196
Squires Resources Inc. (C), ON, 590
Stafford Consulting Group (R), CA, 198
Starbridge Group Inc. (C), VA, 591
Steinfield & Assoc. (C), TX, 592
Steven Douglas Assoc. (C), FL, 593
The Stevens Group (R), TX, 200
DM Stone Personnel Services (C), CA, 594
Strategic Alliance Network, Ltd. (C), OH, 595
Strauss Personnel Service (C), PA, 596
Sudina Search, Inc. (C), MD, 596
Sullivan & Assoc. (R), MI, 204
Systems One Ltd. (C), IL, 598
T. H. Hunter, Inc. (C), MN, 599
The Talley Group (R), VA, 205
Tax Network Resources, Inc. (C), NY, 600
TeamBuilders (C), GA, 600
Tech 2000 (C), FL, 601
The TGA Company (C), TX, 606
Thomas, Whelan Assoc., Inc. (C), DC, 606
Judy Thompson & Assoc., Inc. (C), CA, 606
TRH Assoc., Inc. (R), NY, 210
TSW Assoc., LLC (R), CT, 211
TTG/Sterling Services (C), CA, 610
W. G. Tucker & Assoc. (R), PA, 211
Tully/Woodmansee Int'l. Inc. (R), FL, 212
UniQuest Int'l., Inc. (C), FL, 610
Scott Watson & Assoc., Inc. (R), FL, 216
Wegner & Assoc. (C), WI, 617
S. E. Weinstein Co. (R), IL, 217
White, Roberts & Stratton, Inc. (C), IL, 619
The Whitney Group (C), GA, 620
Whitney Smith Co. (C), TX, 620
Wilcox Bertoux & Miller (R), CA, 220
Wilder & Assoc. (C), VA, 620
D. S. Wolf Assoc., Inc. (R), NY, 223
M. Wood Company (R), IL, 224
Worldwide Medical Services (C), CA, 625
Zen Zen Int'l. Inc. (C), MB, 627
Zwell Int'l. (R), IL, 228

I.18 Equipment services, including leasing

American Executive Management, Inc. (R), MA, 5
Angus Employment Ltd. (C), ON, 250
Barrington Hart, Inc. (R), IL, 12
Dick Berg & Assoc. (C), CA, 264
Careers On Track (C), NJ, 283
Cendea Connection Int'l. (R), TX, 32
Christmas, McIvor & Assoc. Inc. (C), ON, 290
Howard Clark Assoc. (C), NJ, 292
Construction Search Specialists, Inc. (C), WI, 297
Cypress Int'l., Inc. (R), FL, 45
Diversified Search, Inc. (R), PA, 52
Dunhill Professional Search of Wilkes-Barre/Scranton, Inc. (C), PA, 322
Dunhill Professional Search of Bucks-Mont., Inc. (C), PA, 322
Edwards & Assoc. (C), GA, 327
EFCO Consultants, Inc. (C), NY, 327
Empowered Solutions Corp. (C), GA, 330
Financial Plus Management Solutions Inc. (R), ON, 66
Financial Search Group, Inc. (R), MA, 66
Foster Partners (R), NY, 70
Global Telecommunications, Inc. (C), TX, 359
Greene & Co. (C), MA, 362
Michael R. Guerin Co. (C), CA, 364
Thomas E. Hedefine Assoc. (C), ON, 375
Intercontinental Executive Group (C), PA, 391
Iona Partners (C), CA, 394
K & C Assoc. (C), CA, 402
A.T. Kearney Executive Search (R), IL, 111
Kremple & Meade, Inc. (R), CA, 120
Todd L. Krueger & Assoc. (C), WA, 409
L T M Assoc. (C), IL, 410
Lanken-Kimball-Therrell & Assoc. (C), GA, 412
Lineal Recruiting Services (C), CT, 418
Management Recruiters Peninsula (C), CA, 439
Management Recruiters of Melbourne, Inc. (C), FL, 443
Management Recruiters of Forsyth County (C), GA, 445
Management Recruiters of Duluth (C), GA, 445
Management Recruiters of Cleveland (C), OH, 457
MJF Assoc. (C), CT, 483
The Moran Group (C), IL, 484
DDJ Myers, Ltd. (R), AZ, 150
Newell Assoc. (R), NY, 151
Ronald Norris & Assoc. (C), IL, 495
P.R.H. Management, Inc. (R), CT, 158
The Professional Sales Search Co., Inc. (C), WA, 522
Ray & Berndtson (R), TX, 171
S. Reyman & Assoc., Ltd. (R), IL, 176
Robertson & Assoc. (C), IL, 539
Ross Personnel Consultants, Inc. (C), CT, 545
Rossi & Assoc. Inc. (C), BC, 545
Sales Consultants of Northwest Arkansas, Inc. (C), AR, 556
Sales Consultants Bridgewater, Inc. (C), NJ, 560
Sales Search (C), ON, 564
Southwestern Professional Services (C), TN, 588
SpencerStuart (R), NY, 196
Summit Group Int'l., Inc. (R), GA, 204
The Talley Group (R), VA, 205
Kelly Walker Assoc. (C), TX, 614

I.19 Management consulting

A-L Assoc., Inc. (R), NY, 1
A.J. & Assoc. (C), FL, 232
A.K.S. Assoc., Ltd. (R), MA, 1
Abécassis Conseil (R), QE, 1
Ackerman Johnson Inc. (C), TX, 238
Albrecht & Assoc., Executive Search Consultants (C), TX, 243
Alexander Associates (R), NJ, 2
The Alfus Group (R), NY, 3
D. S. Allen Assoc. (C), NJ, 244
Allerton Heneghan & O'Neill (R), IL, 4
ALW Research Int'l. (R), NJ, 4
Analytic Recruiting, Inc. (C), NY, 249
Andre David & Assoc., Inc. (R), TX, 6
Patrick Arnone & Assoc. Inc. (R), VA, 7
The Ascher Group (R), NJ, 7
Ashway Ltd. Agency (C), NY, 253
Ashworth Consultants, Inc. (R), MA, 8
Atlanta Executive Partners, Inc. (R), MA, 8
A. M. Auster Associates (R), FL, 9
Baeder Kalinski Int'l. Group, Inc. (R), NH, 10
Baker, Nelms & Montgomery (C), IL, 258
Baldwin Associates, LLC (R), CT, 10
The Baldwin Group (R), IL, 10
Carol Ball & Co. (C), CT, 258
Barclay Consultants, Inc. (C), NJ, 259
Barton Assoc., Inc. (R), TX, 12
Battalia Winston Int'l./The Euram Consultants Group (R), NY, 13
R. Gaines Baty Assoc., Inc. (R), TX, 13
BayResearch Group, Inc. (R), IL, 14
Behavioral Science Assoc., Inc. (R), AZ, 15
Neail Behringer Consultants Inc. (R), NY, 15
N. L. Benke & Assoc., Inc. (C), OH, 264
BEST/World Assoc. Inc. (R), TX, 16
BG & Assoc. (C), MD, 266
Blau Mancino Schroeder (R), NJ, 18
BLB Consulting (C), NY, 268
Boardroom Consultants/Kenny Kindler Tholke (R), NY, 19
Tom Bogle & Assoc. (C), CA, 269
Bonell Ryan Inc. (R), NY, 19
Bosland Gray Assoc. (R), NJ, 20
Howard Bowen Consulting (C), FL, 270

Bradford Executives Int'l. (C), VA, *271*
Brault & Assoc., Ltd. (R), VA, *22*
Briant Assoc., Inc. (R), IL, *23*
Brigade, Inc. (R), CA, *23*
Bernard E. Brooks & Assoc., Inc. (R), SC, *24*
Charles Buck & Assoc., Inc. (R), NY, *24*
Bullis & Co., Inc. (R), CA, *25*
Cambridge Group Ltd. - Exec. Search Div. (C), CT, *279*
T. M. Campbell Co. (R), WA, *27*
J. P. Canon Assoc. (C), NY, *280*
The Canon Group (C), CA, *280*
Capital Consulting & Research, Inc. (R), CT, *28*
Capital Consulting Group, Inc. (R), MD, *28*
Career Consulting Group, Inc. (C), CT, *281*
Career Development Associates (C), NV, *282*
Careers On Track (C), NJ, *283*
The Carlyle Group, Ltd. (R), IL, *30*
CBA Companies (C), CA, *286*
The Center for Career Advancement, LLC (C), NJ, *287*
Century Assoc., Inc. (C), PA, *287*
The Chapman Group, Inc. (C), AZ, *289*
Chesapeake Group (C), CT, *290*
Clarey/Napier Int'l., L.C. (R), TX, *35*
Coastal Int'l., Inc. (R), MA, *36*
Combined Resources Inc. (R), OH, *38*
CompuPro (C), IL, *295*
Computer Network Resources, Inc. (C), CA, *295*
Computer Security Placement Service (C), MA, *296*
Consultant Recruiters (C), WI, *297*
The Consulting Group of North America, Inc. (C), VA, *297*
Consulting Resource Group, Inc. (C), GA, *297*
Cornell Group Int'l. Consulting, Inc. (R), NY, *41*
Cowell & Associates, Ltd. (R), IL, *42*
The Cris Group, Inc. (R), NY, *42*
Crispi, Wagner & Co., Inc. (R), NY, *43*
Cypress Int'l., Inc. (R), FL, *45*
Data-AxIS Corp. (C), FL, *307*
The DataFinders Group, Inc. (C), NJ, *307*
Alan N. Daum & Assoc., Inc. (C), OH, *308*
Allen Davis & Assoc. (C), MA, *308*
The Dayton Group, Ltd. (C), NY, *309*
De Funiak & Edwards (R), IN, *47*
Delta Services (R), TX, *48*
The Devlin Search Group, Inc. (C), MA, *311*
Dieckmann & Assoc., Ltd. (R), IL, *51*
Dinte Resources, Inc. (R), VA, *52*
Discovery, The Staffing Specialists, Inc. (C), IL, *312*
Diversified Search, Inc. (R), PA, *52*
DLB Assoc. (R), NY, *53*
DNA Search, Inc. (C), CA, *313*
L. J. Doherty & Assoc. (R), MA, *53*
Don Allan Assoc., Inc. (C), CA, *313*
Donini Assoc. (R), VA, *54*
Drew Assoc. Int'l. (R), NJ, *54*
Drinkwater & Assoc. (R), MA, *54*
Drummond Assoc., Inc. (C), NY, *315*
Earley Kielty & Assoc., Inc. (R), NY, *56*
EBA Group (R), NJ, *56*
EDI, Inc. (C), MD, *326*
EFCO Consultants, Inc. (C), NY, *327*
Electronic Search, Inc. (C), IL, *327*
H. J. Elliot, Inc. (R), IL, *58*
David M. Ellner Assoc. (R), NY, *59*
Empowered Solutions Corp. (C), GA, *330*
The Enfield Company (C), TX, *330*
ENI (R), CT, *59*
ETI Search Int'l. (R), GA, *61*
Executive Dimensions (R), NY, *62*
Executive Exchange Corp. (C), NJ, *333*
Executive Partners Inc. (C), CT, *333*
Executive Recruitment Specialists, Inc. (R), NC, *63*
Executive Search Team (C), MI, *336*
The Executive Source Inc. (R), NY, *64*
Executive Strategies, Inc. (C), GA, *337*
Faro Consultants Int'l. (C), VA, *338*
Fast Switch, Ltd. (C), OH, *338*
A. E. Feldman Assoc., Inc. (C), NY, *339*
Fenwick Partners (R), MA, *66*
Eileen Finn & Assoc., Inc. (C), NY, *341*
Finnegan & Assoc. (R), CA, *67*
First Advisory Services Int'l., Inc. (R), MD, *67*
First Union Executive Search (R), NC, *67*
Howard Fischer Assoc. Int'l., Inc. (R), PA, *67*
A. G. Fishkin & Assoc., Inc. (R), MD, *68*
James L. Fisk & Assoc. (C), MO, *342*
The Ford Group, Inc. (R), PA, *69*
Foster Associates (C), NJ, *351*
Foster Partners (R), NY, *70*
Foy, Schneid & Daniel, Inc. (R), NY, *71*
Frey & Sher Assoc., Inc. (C), VA, *353*
Gerald Frisch Assoc., Inc. (R), NY, *72*
Furst Group/MPI (R), IL, *72*
Gahan Assoc. (R), NY, *73*
Gans, Gans & Assoc., Inc. (R), FL, *74*
Gardiner, Townsend & Assoc. (R), NY, *74*
C. R. Gerald & Assoc. (C), ON, *356*
Gielow Assoc., Inc. (R), WI, *76*
Gilbert Tweed Assoc. Inc. (R), NY, *76*
Global Data Services, Inc. (R), NY, *77*
Global Resources Group (R), CA, *78*
Barry M. Gold & Co. (C), CA, *359*
The Goldman Group Inc. (R), NY, *79*
Fred J. Goldsmith Assoc. (R), CA, *79*
David Gomez & Assoc., Inc. (R), IL, *79*
L. J. Gonzer Assoc. (C), NJ, *360*
The Goodman Group (R), CA, *79*
Goodrich & Sherwood Assoc., Inc. (R), NY, *79*
Gould, McCoy & Chadick, Inc. (R), NY, *80*
The Governance Group, Inc. (R), NJ, *80*
Robert Graham Assoc. (R), RI, *81*
Grant/Morgan Assoc., Inc. (C), MD, *361*
Greenhaven & Assoc., Inc. (R), NY, *81*
Greenwich Search Partners, LLC (C), CT, *363*
Growth Strategies, Inc. (R), FL, *83*
Haddad Assoc. (R), FL, *84*
Halbrecht & Co. (C), VA, *365*
Hale Assoc. (R), IL, *84*
Harbor Consultants Int'l., Inc. (C), VA, *368*
Harper Hewes, Inc. (C), NY, *369*
Hart & Co. (C), NY, *370*
William E. Hay & Co. (R), IL, *88*
Hazard, Young, Attea & Assoc., Ltd. (C), IL, *371*
HDB Incorporated (C), MO, *371*
Hechkoff/Work Executive Search Inc. (R), NY, *89*
The Hensge Co. (R), IL, *91*
Heritage Search Group, Inc. (C), FL, *376*
J. J. Herlihy & Assoc., Inc. (C), CA, *376*
Hermann & Westmore (R), CA, *92*
Higbee Assoc., Inc. (C), CT, *377*
Hoffman Recruiters (C), MA, *380*
David C. Horn Executive Search (C), TX, *381*
HR Consultants (C), GA, *382*
HRNI (C), MI, *383*
Human Resources Management Hawaii, Inc. (C), HI, *384*
Hunt & Howe Inc. (R), NY, *99*
Hunter Douglas Group, Inc. (R), IL, *99*
Huntington Group (R), CT, *100*
Huntress Real Estate Executive Search (R), MO, *100*
The Hyde Group, Inc. (R), CT, *101*
Hyman & Assoc. (C), TX, *386*
The IMC Group of Companies (R), NY, *101*
Independent Power Consultants (C), TX, *387*
InfoTech Search (C), TX, *388*
Ingram & Aydelotte, Inc. (R), NY, *101*
Intech Summit Group, Inc. (R), CA, *102*
Integrated Management Solutions (C), NY, *390*
Integrated Search Solutions Group, LLC (ISSG) (R), NY, *102*
Integrity Search, Inc. (R), PA, *102*
Intelligent Marketing Solutions, Inc. (C), NY, *390*
IntelliSource, inc. (C), PA, *391*
International Management Advisors, Inc. (R), NY, *103*
IPR, Inc. (R), VA, *103*
Isaacson, Miller (R), MA, *104*
R. I. James, Inc. (C), NY, *397*
JDG Assoc., Ltd. (C), MD, *397*
JLI-Boston (R), MA, *106*
John Ryan Assoc., LLC. (C), NY, *399*
L. J. Johnson & Co. (R), MI, *106*
Johnson & Company (R), CT, *107*
The Jonathan Stevens Group, Inc. (R), NJ, *108*
Jones-Parker/Starr (R), NC, *108*
JSG Group Management Consultants (R), ON, *109*
Keane Assoc. (R), MA, *110*
A.T. Kearney Executive Search (R), IL, *111*
Kelly Assoc. (R), WI, *112*
Kenmore Executives Inc. (C), FL, *405*
David Warwick Kennedy & Assoc. (R), BC, *112*
The Kennett Group, Inc. (R), PA, *112*
Kincaid Group Inc. (KGI) (C), TX, *406*
Richard Kinser & Assoc. (R), NY, *115*
Kip Williams, Inc. (R), NY, *115*
KL Consultants (C), NJ, *407*
Kopplin Search, Inc. (R), CA, *117*
KPA Assoc., Inc. (C), NY, *408*

Todd L. Krueger & Assoc. (C), WA, *409*
Kurtz Pro-Search, Inc. (C), NJ, *410*
Lancaster Assoc., Inc. (C), NJ, *411*
The Landstone Group (C), NY, *412*
Robert Larned Assoc., Inc. (C), VA, *413*
LAS Management Consulting Group, Inc. (R), NJ, *125*
Latham International, Ltd. (R), NJ, *126*
LaVallee & Associates (C), NC, *413*
Layne-Mendez & Co. (R), TX, *127*
Lifter & Assoc. (C), CA, *418*
Lipsky Group, Inc. (R), CA, *129*
Lloyd Associates (R), GA, *130*
Loewenstein & Assoc., Inc. (R), TX, *131*
Logue & Rice Inc. (C), VA, *420*
M/J/A Partners (R), IL, *133*
Magellan Int'l., L.P. (C), TX, *422*
Major Legal Services, Inc. (C), OH, *423*
Management & Human Resources (R), MA, *134*
Management Alliance Group, Inc. (R), NJ, *134*
Management Recruiters Inc. of Silicon Valley (C), CA, *441*
Management Recruiters of Middlesex (C), CT, *442*
Management Recruiters of Bonita Springs, Inc. (C), FL, *443*
Management Recruiters of St. Augustine (C), FL, *444*
Management Recruiters of St. Lucie County, Inc. (C), FL, *444*
Management Recruiters of Forsyth County (C), GA, *445*
Management Recruiters of Marietta, Inc. (C), GA, *446*
Management Recruiters of Great Neck (C), NY, *454*
Management Recruiters of Princeton (C), NJ, *454*
Management Recruiters of Wilmington (C), NC, *457*
Management Recruiters of Cherry Hill (C), PA, *459*
Management Recruiters of Champions (C), TX, *462*
Management Recruiters of Milwaukee - Downtown (C), WI, *466*
Mankuta Gallagher & Assoc., Inc. (C), FL, *468*
Marra Peters & Partners (R), NJ, *136*
The Martin Group (R), CA, *137*
Masserman & Assoc., Inc. (R), NY, *138*
Massey-Horton Int'l. (R), ON, *138*
MB Inc. Executive Search (C), NY, *473*
K. E. McCarthy & Assoc. (R), CA, *139*
The McCormick Group (C), VA, *473*
Dan P. McLean Assoc., Inc. (C), ON, *475*
James Mead & Co. (R), CT, *142*
Meder & Assoc., Inc. (R), IL, *142*
Medical Recruiters Exchange (C), AZ, *477*
The Mercer Group, Inc. (R), NM, *143*
Meyer Assoc., Inc. (R), GA, *144*
E. J. Michaels, Ltd. (C), NY, *481*
Midas Management (C), CT, *481*
Millennium Search Group, Inc. (R), CA, *144*
Herbert Mines Assoc., Inc. (R), NY, *145*
Mirtz Morice, Inc. (R), CT, *145*
MIS Computer Professionals, Inc. (C), KS, *482*
Paul Misarti Inc. (C), NY, *483*
Oscar Montaño, Inc. (R), CA, *146*
Montenido Assoc. (R), CA, *146*
Morgan Int'l., Inc. (R), IL, *147*
Robert T. Morton Assoc., Inc. (C), MA, *486*
DDJ Myers, Ltd. (R), AZ, *150*
Nagler, Robins & Poe, Inc. (R), MA, *150*
National Field Service Corp. (C), NY, *489*
National Recruiters (C), OK, *489*
New Dimensions in Technology, Inc. (C), MA, *492*
Newport Strategic Search LLC (C), CA, *492*
Next Step Recruiting (C), CA, *493*
Nichols & Company (R), CO, *151*
Marc Nichols Assoc., Inc. (C), NY, *493*
Ira Z. Nitzberg (C), NY, *493*
W. D. Nolte & Company (R), CT, *152*
Nordeman Grimm, Inc. (R), NY, *152*
Norman Broadbent Int'l., Inc. (R), NY, *152*
Norrell Financial Staffing (C), GA, *495*
John B. Norris & Assoc., Inc. (C), MD, *495*
Northern Consultants Inc. (R), ME, *153*
NorthStar Technologies, Inc. (C), NY, *496*
O'Brien & Bell (R), OH, *153*
O'Connor Resources (C), TX, *497*
O'Neill & Co. (R), CT, *154*
O'Toole & Company, Inc. (R), IL, *154*
The Onstott Group (R), MA, *156*
Robert Ottke Assoc. (R), CA, *157*
Page-Wheatcroft & Co., Ltd. (R), TX, *158*
Parker Page Group (C), FL, *503*
Largent Parks & Partners (C), TX, *503*
Partners In Human Resources Int'l., Inc. (R), NY, *160*
Partnervision Consulting Group Inc. (R), ON, *160*
Pathway Executive Search, Inc. (C), NY, *505*
Paul-Tittle Assoc., Inc. (R), VA, *161*
Pearson, Caldwell & Farnsworth (R), CA, *161*
The Penn Partners, Inc. (R), PA, *162*
Pennington Consulting Group (C), NJ, *506*
PHD Conseil en Ressources Humaines Inc. (C), QE, *510*
Phillips & Assoc. (R), MA, *164*
Picard Int'l., Ltd. (R), NY, *164*
The Pinnacle Source, Inc. (C), CO, *512*
Pittleman & Assoc. (C), NY, *512*
Plummer & Assoc., Inc. (R), CT, *166*
The Prairie Group (C), IL, *515*
Prairie Resource Group, Inc. (R), IL, *166*
Preng & Assoc., Inc. (R), TX, *167*
Preston & Co. (R), NJ, *167*
Prestonwood Assoc. (R), MA, *168*
Princeton Search Partners, Inc. (R), NJ, *169*
PRO, Inc./Professional Recruiting Offices, Inc. (C), CA, *519*
Procom (C), ON, *519*
Professional Selection Services (R), GA, *169*
Professional Support Inc. (C), NY, *523*
ProFinders, Inc. (C), FL, *523*
ProLinks Inc. (R), VA, *170*
Quantum Int'l., Ltd. (R), FL, *170*
The Rankin Group, Ltd. (R), WI, *171*
The Ransford Group (R), TX, *171*
Harold L. Rapp Assoc. (C), NY, *529*
Ray & Berndtson (R), TX, *171*
Reifel & Assoc. (R), IL, *174*
Reinecke & Assoc. (C), NJ, *533*
Reynolds Consulting Int'l. (R), ON, *177*
Reynolds Partners (R), NY, *177*
RHS Assoc. (C), AL, *536*
Rice Cohen Int'l. (R), PA, *178*
Ridenour & Assoc. (R), IL, *178*
Roberts Ryan & Bentley, Inc. (R), MD, *179*
Craig Roe & Assoc., LLC (C), MD, *540*
Rogish Assoc., Inc. (C), OH, *541*
Romac Int'l. Inc. (R), MA, *181*
Emery A. Rose & Assoc. (C), WA, *545*
Roth Young of Pittsburgh (C), PA, *546*
The Rubinic Consulting Group (C), OH, *548*
R. L. Rystrom & Assoc., Inc. (C), MN, *549*
Sales Consultants of Silicon Valley (C), CA, *556*
Sales Consultants Peninsula, Inc. (C), CA, *556*
Sales Consultants of Stamford-Darien (C), CT, *557*
Sales Consultants of Barrington (C), IL, *558*
Sales Consultants of Rockville, MD (C), MD, *559*
Sales Consultants of Princeton, Inc. (C), NJ, *561*
Sales Consultants of Austin, Inc. (C), TX, *562*
A. N. Salloway Executive Search & Consulting, L.L.C. (C), MA, *564*
Salzmann Gay Assoc., Inc. (R), PA, *184*
Sanford Rose Assoc. - Norcross (C), GA, *566*
Sanford Rose Assoc. - Charlotte (C), NC, *568*
Sanford Rose Assoc. - Gastonia (C), NC, *568*
Santangelo Consultants Inc. (C), NY, *571*
Satterfield & Assoc., Inc. (R), OH, *184*
Scott-Thaler Assoc. Agency, Inc. (C), CA, *573*
The Search America Group Inc. (C), OH, *573*
Search America, Inc. (C), PA, *573*
Search America, Inc. (C), MA, *574*
Search Group (C), CA, *575*
Search Solutions Inc. (C), CA, *576*
SearchCorp International (C), AB, *577*
Seco & Zetto Assoc., Inc. (C), NJ, *577*
Sedlar & Miners (R), NY, *188*
Sensible Solutions, Inc. (R), IL, *188*
Sevcor Int'l., Inc. (R), IL, *188*
Shepherd Bueschel & Provus, Inc. (R), IL, *189*
Shey-Harding Assoc. Inc. (C), CA, *580*
Siger & Assoc., LLC (C), CT, *581*
Silver Associates (C), CA, *581*
Daniel A. Silverstein Assoc. Inc. (R), FL, *191*
The Simmons Group (C), CA, *582*
Sinclair & Co., Inc. (R), MA, *192*
James F. Smith & Assoc. (C), GA, *583*
Smith & Sawyer, Inc. (R), NY, *193*

Smith Hanley Assoc., Inc. (C), NY, *584*
Software Resource Consultants (C), TN, *587*
Robert Sollman & Assoc. (C), FL, *587*
Spear-Izzo Assoc., LLC (C), PA, *588*
SpencerStuart (R), NY, *196*
The Spiegel Group (R), MA, *197*
Stanewick, Hart & Assoc., Inc. (C), FL, *591*
Starbridge Group Inc. (C), VA, *591*
The Stark Wilton Group (R), MI, *199*
Steinfield & Assoc. (C), TX, *592*
Sterling Int'l. (R), NJ, *200*
Daniel Stern & Assoc. (C), PA, *592*
Stevens, Valentine & McKeever (C), NJ, *593*
Stewart/Greene & Co. of The Triad, Inc. (C), NC, *594*
Stewart/Laurence Assoc., Inc. (R), NJ, *201*
Stillinger & Assoc. (R), CA, *201*
Stoopen Asociados, S.C./EMA Partners Int'l. (R), MX, *202*
Strategic Assoc., Inc. (C), TX, *595*
Strategic Executives, Inc. (R), CT, *202*
StratfordGroup (R), OH, *203*
Strauss Personnel Service (C), PA, *596*
The Summit Group (C), CA, *596*
Synapse Human Resource Consulting Group (R), TX, *205*
Synergy 2000 (C), DC, *597*
Synergy Solutions, Ltd. (C), WA, *597*
Systems Careers (C), CA, *598*
Systems Search Group, Inc. (C), NC, *599*
Roy Talman & Assoc. (C), IL, *599*
The Talon Group (R), TX, *205*
Tarbex (C), DC, *599*
M. L. Tawney & Assoc. (C), TX, *600*
Carl J. Taylor & Co. (R), TX, *207*
Taylor Winfield (R), TX, *207*
TBC, Inc. (C), KY, *600*
TechNix Inc. (C), ON, *602*
Thomas, Whelan Assoc., Inc. (C), DC, *606*
Trac One (R), NJ, *210*
Van Treadaway Assoc., Inc. (R), GA, *210*
Trebor Weldon Lawrence, Inc. (R), NY, *210*
TRH Assoc., Inc. (R), NY, *210*
TriStaff Group (C), CA, *609*
Victor White Int'l. (C), CA, *612*
Beverly von Winckler & Assoc. (C), IL, *613*
J. D. Walsh & Co. (R), CT, *215*
Ward Liebelt Assoc. Inc. (R), CT, *215*
C. D. Warner & Assoc. (C), PA, *615*
Waterford Executive Group Ltd. (C), IL, *616*
R. J. Watkins & Co., Ltd. (R), CA, *216*
Watson Int'l., Inc. (R), NY, *216*
The Wayne Group, Ltd. (C), NY, *616*
S. B. Webster & Associates (R), MA, *217*
Lee Weil Assoc., Inc. (C), IL, *617*
Weinstein & Co. (R), MA, *217*
Werbin Assoc. Executive Search, Inc. (C), NY, *618*
Wheeler Assoc. (R), CT, *219*
Daniel Wier & Assoc. (R), CA, *220*
Wilcox Bertoux & Miller (R), CA, *220*
Wilkinson SoftSearch, Inc. (C), VA, *620*
Wills Consulting Assoc. Inc. (R), CT, *221*
Wilson-Douglas-Jordan (C), IL, *622*
Windsor Consultants, Inc. (C), TX, *622*
Winter, Wyman & Co. (C), MA, *623*
M. Wood Company (R), IL, *224*
Bruce G. Woods Executive Search (R), TX, *224*
The Woodstone Consulting Company, Inc. (R), CO, *224*
Bob Wright Recruiting, Inc. (C), CT, *625*
R. S. Wyatt Assoc., Inc. (R), TX, *225*
Zona & Assoc., Inc. (C), NY, *628*

I.20 Human resource services

A. D. & Assoc. Executive Search, Inc. (C), GA, *231*
A.M.C.R., Inc. (C), OH, *232*
Access Assoc. Inc. (C), MD, *233*
ACCESS Technology (C), CA, *234*
Action Management Corp. (C), MI, *239*
Agri-Tech Personnel, Inc. (C), MO, *242*
J. R. Akin & Co. (R), MA, *2*
Alexander Enterprises, Inc. (C), PA, *243*
The Alexander Group (R), TX, *3*
The Alfus Group (R), NY, *3*
Allen, Wayne & Co. LLC (C), WI, *245*
Alliance Search Management Inc. (R), TX, *4*
Alpha Resource Group, Inc. (C), TX, *246*
ALW Research Int'l. (R), NJ, *4*
Amherst Human Resource Group, Ltd. (C), IL, *249*
Anderson Bradshaw Assoc., Inc. (R), TX, *6*
Anderson Network Group (C), OH, *250*
Angus Employment Ltd. (C), ON, *250*
The Angus Group, Ltd. (C), OH, *251*
David Aplin & Assoc. (C), AB, *251*
Applied Resources, Inc. (C), MN, *252*
Charles P. Aquavella & Assoc. (C), TX, *252*
The Ascher Group (R), NJ, *7*
Austin, Hill & Assoc. (C), MD, *256*
The Bankers Group (C), IL, *258*
J. W. Barleycorn, Renard & Assoc., Inc. (R), OH, *11*
Barton Assoc., Inc. (R), TX, *12*
Battalia Winston Int'l./The Euram Consultants Group (R), NY, *13*
Behavioral Science Assoc., Inc. (R), AZ, *15*
Joy Reed Belt Search Consultants, Inc. (R), OK, *15*
J. P. Bencik Assoc. (C), MI, *263*
Bennett & Co. Consulting Group (C), CA, *264*
Benson Associates (C), NY, *264*
The Black Leopard (C), CA, *267*
Block & Assoc. (R), CA, *18*
Boettcher Assoc. (R), WI, *19*
Bonnell Assoc. Ltd. (R), CT, *19*
Boulware & Assoc. Inc. (R), IL, *20*
Boyden (R), NY, *20*
Brandt Associates (C), PA, *272*
The Bridge (C), CO, *273*
J. B. Brown & Assoc., Inc. (C), OH, *275*
Burke & Assoc./The Westfield Group (C), CT, *276*
Business Systems of America, Inc. (C), IL, *277*
Butterfass, Pepe & MacCallan Inc. (R), NJ, *25*
C. M. Management Services, Inc. (R), KY, *26*
Canny, Bowen Inc. (R), NY, *27*
The Canon Group (C), CA, *280*
Career Consultants (R), IN, *29*
Career Marketing Consultants, Inc. (C), GA, *282*
The Carlyle Group, Ltd. (R), IL, *30*
The Cherbonnier Group, Inc. (R), TX, *33*
Christenson Hutchison McDowell, LLC (R), NJ, *34*
Christmas, McIvor & Assoc. Inc. (C), ON, *290*
Christopher-Westmont & Assoc., Inc. (R), OH, *34*
Clarey/Napier Int'l., L.C. (R), TX, *35*
Ken Clark Int'l. (R), NJ, *36*
CMC Search Consultants (C), IL, *293*
The Comwell Company, Inc. (C), NJ, *296*
Conroy Partners Ltd. (R), AB, *39*
The Consulting Group of North America, Inc. (C), VA, *297*
Conway & Assoc. (R), IL, *40*
Cornerstone Resources, Inc. (C), OK, *299*
The Corporate Connection, Ltd. (C), VA, *299*
Corporate Plus, Ltd. (C), GA, *300*
Leonard Corwen Assoc. (C), NY, *302*
CountryHouse Hotels Executive Search (C), VA, *302*
Creative-Leadership, Inc. (R), CA, *42*
Current Resource Group, Inc. (C), GA, *305*
Custom Resources (C), AL, *305*
Cypress Int'l., Inc. (R), FL, *45*
DARE Personnel Inc. (C), ON, *307*
Joseph A. Davis Consultants, Inc. (R), NY, *47*
The Dayton Group, Ltd. (C), NY, *309*
Dinte Resources, Inc. (R), VA, *52*
Diversified Search, Inc. (R), PA, *52*
DLG Assoc., Inc. (R), NC, *53*
DNA Search, Inc. (C), CA, *313*
Dominguez-Metz & Assoc. (R), CA, *53*
Donini Assoc. (R), VA, *54*
DS&A (Doug Sears & Assoc.) (C), FL, *315*
The Duncan-O'Dell Group Inc. (C), TX, *316*
Dunhill of Manchester Inc. (C), NH, *321*
E O Technical (C), CT, *324*
Eagle Search Assoc. (C), CA, *325*
Eastman & Beaudine, Inc. (R), TX, *56*
H. J. Elliot, Inc. (R), IL, *58*
Ellis Career Consultants (C), NJ, *328*
ExecuGroup, Inc. (R), MS, *61*
Executive Dimensions (R), NY, *62*
Executive Exchange Corp. (C), NJ, *333*
Executive Resource Group, Inc. (R), ME, *63*
Executive Search Partners (R), NY, *63*
Executive Search Team (C), MI, *336*
The Executive Source Inc. (R), NY, *64*
Executive Strategies, Inc. (C), GA, *337*
ExecutiveFit (C), NY, *337*
Faro Consultants Int'l. (C), VA, *338*
The Fawcett Group (R), MA, *65*
Financial Plus Management Solutions Inc. (R), ON, *66*

Eileen Finn & Assoc., Inc. (C), NY, *341*
Fishel HR Assoc., Inc. (C), AZ, *341*
Focus Consulting Services, Inc. (C), FL, *342*
Fogec Consultants, Inc. (R), WI, *69*
Foley Proctor Yoskowitz (R), NJ, *69*
The Ford Group, Inc. (R), PA, *69*
F-O-R-T-U-N-E Personnel Consultants of Boise (R), ID, *70*
Fortune Personnel Consultants of Raleigh, Inc. (C), NC, *348*
Fortune Personnel Consultants of Allentown, Inc. (C), PA, *348*
Fortune Personnel Consultants of Chattanooga Inc. (C), TN, *349*
Foster Partners (R), NY, *70*
Franstaff Inc. (C), FL, *352*
Fresquez & Assoc. (C), CA, *352*
Friedman Eisenstein Raemer & Schwartz, LLP (R), IL, *72*
Frye/Joure & Assoc., Inc. (C), TN, *353*
Future Employment Service, Inc. (C), IA, *353*
General Engineering Tectonics (C), CA, *356*
Gielow Assoc., Inc. (R), WI, *76*
Gilbert Tweed Assoc. Inc. (R), NY, *76*
Global 1000 Int'l. Services (C), CA, *358*
Global Resources Group (R), CA, *78*
H. L. Goehring & Assoc., Inc. (C), OH, *359*
Fred J. Goldsmith Assoc. (R), CA, *79*
Gould, McCoy & Chadick, Inc. (R), NY, *80*
Robert Graham Assoc. (R), RI, *81*
Grant/Morgan Assoc., Inc. (C), MD, *361*
Gregory, Kyle & Assoc. (C), NC, *363*
Groupe PCA Inc. (C), QE, *363*
Grover & Assoc. (R), OH, *82*
The H. S. Group, Inc. (C), WI, *365*
K. C. Hale, Inc. (R), CT, *85*
Harbor Consultants Int'l., Inc. (C), VA, *368*
Harbrowe, Inc. (C), NY, *368*
The Helms Int'l. Group (R), VA, *91*
J. J. Herlihy & Assoc., Inc. (C), CA, *376*
Hire Authority, Inc. (C), MI, *378*
David C. Horn Executive Search (C), TX, *381*
Hreshko Consulting Group (C), NJ, *382*
HRNI (C), MI, *383*
Human Resource Dimensions, Inc. (C), TX, *384*
The Human Resource Group, Inc. (R), OH, *98*
Human Resources Management Hawaii, Inc. (C), HI, *384*
H.I. Hunt & Co., Ltd. (R), MA, *99*
Hunter Douglas Group, Inc. (R), IL, *99*
The Hyde Group, Inc. (R), CT, *101*
Hyman & Assoc. (C), TX, *386*
The IMC Group of Companies (R), NY, *101*
Impact Search & Strategies (C), PA, *387*
Independent Power Consultants (C), TX, *387*
InfoTech Search (C), TX, *388*
Intech Summit Group, Inc. (R), CA, *102*
Integrity Search, Inc. (R), PA, *102*
International Management Advisors, Inc. (R), NY, *103*
International Staffing Consultants, Inc. (C), CA, *393*
IPR, Inc. (R), VA, *103*
Ives & Associates, Inc. (C), OH, *395*
JenKim Int'l. Ltd., Inc. (C), FL, *398*
John Jay & Co. (C), ME, *399*
John Ryan Assoc., LLC. (C), NY, *399*
L. J. Johnson & Co. (R), MI, *106*
Karel & Co. (R), CA, *109*
A.T. Kearney Executive Search (R), IL, *111*
Kenzer Corp. (R), NY, *113*
Kincaid Group Inc. (KGI) (C), TX, *406*
Kip Williams, Inc. (R), NY, *115*
KL Consultants (C), NJ, *407*
Raymond J. Klemmer & Assoc. (R), NY, *116*
Kulper & Co., L.L.C. (R), NJ, *121*
Kyle Assoc. (C), NY, *410*
Marvin Laba & Assoc. (R), CA, *122*
Lamon + Stuart + Michaels Inc. (R), ON, *124*
Lawrence L. Lapham, Inc. (R), NY, *124*
Madeleine Lav & Assoc. (C), CA, *413*
Legal Network Inc. (C), CA, *416*
Lending Personnel Services (C), CA, *416*
AG Lennox & Assoc. (R), AB, *128*
Lewis Consulting Service (C), IL, *417*
Longshore + Simmons (R), PA, *131*
Lucas Group (C), NY, *421*
Fran Luisi Assoc. (R), NJ, *132*
Lynne Palmer Executive Recruitment, Inc. (C), NY, *421*
MacNaughton Assoc. (R), CA, *133*
Maiorino & Weston Assoc., Inc. (R), CT, *134*
Major Legal Services, Inc. (C), OH, *423*
Management & Human Resources (R), MA, *134*
Management Assoc. (C), MD, *424*
Management Recruiters of Birmingham, Inc. (C), AL, *438*
Management Recruiters, Inland Empire Agency (C), CA, *441*
Management Recruiters of Boca Raton (C), FL, *443*
Management Recruiters of St. Augustine (C), FL, *444*
Management Recruiters of Rockville (C), MD, *450*
Management Recruiters of Muskegon (C), MI, *451*
Management Recruiters of North Oakland County, Inc. (C), MI, *452*
Management Recruiters of North Warren Inc. (C), NJ, *453*
Management Recruiters of Mt. Airy (C), NC, *456*
Management Recruiters of Wilmington (C), NC, *457*
Management Recruiters of Cherry Hill (C), PA, *459*
Management Recruiters - Friendswood (C), TX, *462*
Management Recruiters of Arlington (C), VA, *464*
Management Resource Group, Inc. (C), NY, *467*
Manning Lloyd Assoc. Ltd. (C), NY, *468*
Mark III Personnel, Inc. (C), NC, *470*
Marsteller Wilcox Assoc. (C), IL, *471*
Matté & Company, Inc. (R), CT, *138*
McKinley•Arend Int'l. (R), TX, *141*
Medicorp, Inc. (C), MO, *477*
Medserve & Assoc. Inc. (C), MD, *478*
Mee Derby & Co. (C), DC, *478*
The Mercer Group, Inc. (R), NM, *143*
META/MAT, Ltd. (R), NJ, *144*
Michael Wayne Recruiters (C), IL, *480*
Michael/Merrill (C), KS, *481*
Herbert Mines Assoc., Inc. (R), NY, *145*
Mirtz Morice, Inc. (R), CT, *145*
Paul Misarti Inc. (C), NY, *483*
Molloy Partners (R), NY, *146*
The Morris Group (C), PA, *486*
Mortgage & Financial Personnel Services (C), CA, *486*
MPA Executive Search Inc. (R), QE, *148*
MSA Executive Search (R), MO, *148*
DDJ Myers, Ltd. (R), AZ, *150*
National Affirmative Action Career Network, Inc. (C), CO, *488*
National Search, Inc.r (C), FL, *490*
Newcomb-Desmond & Assoc., Inc. (C), OH, *492*
Next Step Recruiting (C), CA, *493*
Nichols Brown Int'l. (R), NY, *151*
Nordeman Grimm, Inc. (R), NY, *152*
Norman Broadbent Int'l., Inc. (R), NY, *152*
Northern Consultants Inc. (R), ME, *153*
NRI Staffing Resources (C), DC, *496*
Nuessle, Kurdziel & Weiss, Inc. (R), PA, *153*
O'Keefe & Assoc., Inc. (R), CT, *154*
Ollinger Partners (R), MA, *156*
LaMonte Owens, Inc. (R), PA, *157*
The Oxford Group (C), TX, *500*
Parker Page Group (C), FL, *503*
Partners In Human Resources Int'l., Inc. (R), NY, *160*
The Partnership Group (R), NJ, *160*
Partnervision Consulting Group Inc. (R), ON, *160*
The Patience Motivation Belief Group, Inc. (C), GA, *505*
Peeney Assoc., Inc. (R), NJ, *161*
Pennington Consulting Group (C), NJ, *506*
The Pennmor Group (C), NJ, *506*
PeopleSource Inc. (C), TX, *506*
Perry-D'Amico & Assoc. (R), CA, *162*
The Personnel Network, Inc. (C), SC, *508*
Petrie Partners, Inc. (R), FL, *163*
Physicians Search®, Inc. (C), CA, *511*
Picard Int'l., Ltd. (R), NY, *164*
Pittleman & Assoc. (C), NY, *512*
Plante & Moran, LLP (R), MI, *165*
Bob Poline Assoc. Inc. (C), CA, *514*
The Pollack Group (C), ON, *514*
Robert Powers & Assoc. (C), CA, *515*
P. G. Prager Search Assoc., Ltd. (C), NY, *515*
Prestonwood Assoc. (R), MA, *168*
Price & Assoc., Inc. (C), VA, *518*
Prime Management Group Inc. (C), ON, *518*
Princeton Executive Search (C), NJ, *518*
PRO, Inc./Professional Recruiting Offices, Inc. (C), CA, *519*

Professional Resources (C), NY, *522*
Professional Search Centre, Ltd. (C), IL, *522*
Professional Search Assoc. (C), CA, *522*
ProFinders, Inc. (C), FL, *523*
Quetico Corp. (R), TX, *170*
Quigley Assoc. (R), MD, *170*
Quiring Assoc., Inc. (C), IN, *527*
Rand Thompson Executive Search Consultants (C), NY, *528*
Ray & Berndtson (R), TX, *171*
P. J. Reda & Assoc., Inc. (C), GA, *533*
Reifel & Assoc. (R), IL, *174*
Retail Recruiters/Spectrum Consultants, Inc. (C), PA, *535*
Retained Search Assoc. (R), NC, *176*
Russell Reynolds Assoc., Inc. (R), NY, *176*
Reynolds Partners (R), NY, *177*
Rieser & Assoc., Inc. (R), MO, *178*
Ritt-Ritt & Assoc., Inc. (C), IL, *537*
Rogish Assoc., Inc. (C), OH, *541*
Roth Young of Pittsburgh (C), PA, *546*
Royal Assoc. (C), CA, *547*
Ruderfer & Co., Inc. (C), NJ, *548*
K. Russo Assoc. Inc. (C), CT, *548*
S. C. Int'l., Ltd. (C), IL, *550*
Sales & Management Search, Inc. (C), IL, *551*
Sales Consultants of Birmingham (C), AL, *555*
Sales Consultants of Stamford-Darien (C), CT, *557*
Sampson Medical Search (C), CA, *564*
Sanford Rose Assoc. - Charlotte (C), NC, *568*
Sanford Rose Assoc. - Gastonia (C), NC, *568*
Sanford Rose Assoc. - Rochester (C), MI, *568*
The Schatz Company (C), MO, *571*
Scott Sibley Assoc. (C), NY, *573*
The Search America Group Inc. (C), OH, *573*
Search Innovations, Inc. (R), PA, *187*
Search Research Assoc., Inc. (R), MA, *187*
Search Solutions Inc. (C), CA, *576*
Select Services (C), IL, *578*
Robert Sellery Assoc., Ltd. (R), DC, *188*
Sensible Solutions, Inc. (R), IL, *188*
Sevcor Int'l., Inc. (R), IL, *188*
Shey-Harding Assoc. Inc. (C), CA, *580*
The Shorr Group (R), IL, *190*
The Simmons Group (C), CA, *582*
Sloan & Assoc., Inc. (C), VA, *583*
J. L. Small Assoc. (C), AL, *583*
Smith & Assoc. (C), FL, *583*
Abbott Smith Assoc., Inc. (R), NY, *193*
J. Harrington Smith Assoc. (C), IN, *584*
Stephen M. Sonis Assoc. (R), MA, *195*
Spectra International LLC (C), AZ, *589*
SpencerStuart (R), NY, *196*
Kenn Spinrad Inc. (C), PA, *589*
Splaine & Assoc., Inc. (R), CA, *198*
Staff Resources, Inc. (C), SC, *590*
Starbridge Group Inc. (C), VA, *591*
Steinfield & Assoc. (C), TX, *592*
Daniel Stern & Assoc. (C), PA, *592*
Steven Douglas Assoc. (C), FL, *593*
Stevens, Valentine & McKeever (C), NJ, *593*
Stewart/Greene & Co. of The Triad, Inc. (C), NC, *594*
Stillinger & Assoc. (R), CA, *201*
Strategic Resources Biotechnology & Medical Group (C), WA, *595*
Summit Executive Search Consultants, Inc. (R), FL, *204*
The Synergy Organization (R), PA, *205*
Systems One Ltd. (C), IL, *598*
Systems Search Group, Inc. (C), NC, *599*
Tabb & Assoc. (R), OH, *205*
Tactical Alternatives (R), CA, *205*
The Talon Group (R), TX, *205*
Tech-Net (C), TX, *601*
Tittemore Cowan Assoc. (C), AB, *607*
Trac One (R), NJ, *210*
Van Treadaway Assoc., Inc. (R), GA, *210*
TRH Assoc., Inc. (R), NY, *210*
Triad Consultants, Inc. (C), NJ, *609*
W. G. Tucker & Assoc. (R), PA, *211*
Tuft & Assoc., Inc. (R), IL, *212*
Tully/Woodmansee Int'l. Inc. (R), FL, *212*
V.I.P. Resources, Inc. (C), NY, *611*
Venture Resources, Inc. (R), CA, *213*
Vezan Assoc. (C), CT, *612*
Vlcek & Company, Inc. (R), CA, *214*
Beverly von Winckler & Assoc. (C), IL, *613*
Wakefield Talabisco Int'l. (R), NY, *214*
Waterford Executive Group Ltd. (C), IL, *616*
The Wayne Group, Ltd. (C), NY, *616*
The Wellesley Group, Inc. (R), IL, *217*
Whitney Smith Co. (C), TX, *620*
The Whyte Group, Inc. (R), MD, *220*
Daniel Wier & Assoc. (R), CA, *220*
The Woodstone Consulting Company, Inc. (R), CO, *224*
Worldwide Medical Services (C), CA, *625*
Zen Zen Int'l. Inc. (C), MB, *627*
Zona & Assoc., Inc. (C), NY, *628*

I.21 Law enforcement, security

Bennett Search & Consulting Co. (R), FL, *16*
Brandywine Retained Ventures, Inc. (R), CT, *22*
Career Development Associates (C), NV, *282*
Diversified Search, Inc. (R), PA, *52*
Downing & Downing, Inc. (C), OH, *314*
Foster Partners (R), NY, *70*
A.T. Kearney Executive Search (R), IL, *111*
Magnum Search (C), IL, *422*
Maschal/Connors Inc. (R), NJ, *137*
The Oldani Group (R), WA, *155*
The PAR Group - Paul A. Reaume, Ltd. (R), IL, *159*
Russell Reynolds Assoc., Inc. (R), NY, *176*
Sales Consultants of Houston (C), TX, *563*
SpencerStuart (R), NY, *196*
Strategic Resources (C), WA, *595*
West Coast Recruiting (C), CA, *619*

J.00 Communications/media

A C Personnel Services, Inc. (C), OK, *231*
A la Carte Int'l., Inc. (R), VA, *1*
A. D. & Assoc. Executive Search, Inc. (C), GA, *231*
Abacus Group LLC (C), NY, *232*
Abbott Associates (R), CA, *1*
Abécassis Conseil (R), QE, *1*
Abraham & London Ltd. (C), CT, *232*
B. J. Abrams & Assoc. Inc. (C), IL, *233*
Abraxas Technologies, Inc. (C), FL, *233*
Access Data Personnel, Inc. (C), NH, *233*
ACCESS Technology (C), CA, *234*
Accountants Executive Search (C), CA, *237*
Accounting Personnel & Engineering Personnel Consultants (C), LA, *238*
Ackerman Johnson Inc. (C), TX, *238*
ACSYS Resources, Inc. (C), DE, *238*
Action Management Corp. (C), MI, *239*
Adam-Bryce Inc. (C), NY, *239*
Adept Tech Recruiting, Inc. (C), NY, *240*
Adirect Recruiting Corp. (C), ON, *240*
Adler Management, Inc. (R), NJ, *2*
ADR Accounting Management Recruiters (C), ON, *240*
Advanced Corporate Search (C), CA, *240*
Advanced Recruiting, Inc. (C), OK, *240*
Advancement, Inc. (C), IL, *241*
Advice Personnel Inc. (C), NY, *241*
The Advisory Group, Inc. (R), CA, *2*
AES Search (C), NJ, *241*
Affordable Executive Recruiters (C), CA, *241*
AKH Executive Search (C), OR, *243*
J. R. Akin & Co. (R), MA, *2*
Alaska Executive Search, Inc. (C), AK, *243*
Alexander & Co. (C), CA, *243*
Alexander Associates (R), NJ, *2*
The Alexander Group (R), NJ, *3*
The Alfus Group (R), NY, *3*
Frank E. Allen & Assoc. (C), NJ, *244*
D. S. Allen Assoc. (C), NJ, *244*
David Allen Assoc. (R), NJ, *3*
Allen Austin Lowe & Powers (R), TX, *3*
Allerton Heneghan & O'Neill (R), IL, *4*
Alliance Executive Search, Inc. (R), MA, *4*
Allstaff, Inc. (C), IL, *245*
The Alternatives Group, Inc. (C), TX, *246*
American Executive Management, Inc. (R), MA, *5*
AmeriResource Group Inc. (C), OK, *248*
Analytic Recruiting, Inc. (C), NY, *249*
Angel Group Int'l. (C), KY, *250*
Angus Employment Ltd. (C), ON, *250*
The Angus Group, Ltd. (C), OH, *251*
Ansara, Bickford & Fiske (C), MA, *251*
APA Search, Inc. (R), NY, *6*
David Aplin & Assoc. (C), AB, *251*
Ariel Recruitment Assoc. (R), NY, *7*
Patrick Arnone & Assoc. Inc. (R), VA, *7*
Ashlar-Stone Management Consultants Inc. (R), ON, *8*
Ashton Computer Professionals, Inc. (C), BC, *253*
ASI (C), CA, *254*
Ask Guy Tucker (C), GA, *254*
Asset Resource, Inc. (C), CA, *254*

INDUSTRIES

Association for Sales Force Management (C), WA, *254*
Atlantic Pacific Group (C), CA, *255*
Aubin Int'l. Inc. (R), MA, *8*
Aurora Tech Search (C), ON, *256*
Cami Austin & Assoc. (C), IL, *256*
Austin Park Management Group Inc. (C), ON, *256*
Austin-McGregor Int'l. (R), TX, *9*
Avery Assoc. (R), CA, *9*
Avion International Technology Inc. (C), ON, *257*
The Badger Group (R), CA, *10*
Keith Bagg & Assoc., Inc. (C), ON, *257*
Baker Scott & Co. (C), NJ, *258*
Baker, Nelms & Montgomery (C), IL, *258*
Baldwin & Assoc. (C), OH, *258*
Baldwin Associates, LLC (R), CT, *10*
Carol Ball & Co. (C), CT, *258*
Allen Ballach Assoc. Inc. (R), ON, *10*
Ballantyne & Assoc. (R), CA, *10*
James Bangert & Assoc., Inc. (R), MN, *11*
The Barack Group, Inc. (R), NY, *11*
Barnes & Assoc. Executive Search (C), CA, *259*
Barr Assoc. (C), PA, *259*
Barrett Partners (C), IL, *260*
Barrett Rose & Lee, Inc. (C), ON, *260*
Barrington Hart, Inc. (R), IL, *12*
Barton Assoc., Inc. (R), TX, *12*
Bason Associates (R), OH, *13*
Bast & Assoc., Inc. (C), CA, *261*
Battalia Winston Int'l./The Euram Consultants Group (R), NY, *13*
Beacon Int'l., Inc. (C), VA, *261*
The Beam Group (R), PA, *14*
The Beardsley Group Inc. (C), CT, *261*
Beck/Eastwood Recruitment Solutions (C), CA, *261*
The Bedford Group (R), RI, *15*
Robert Beech West Inc. (C), CA, *262*
Belanger Partners Ltd. (C), ON, *262*
Bell Oaks Co., Inc. (C), GA, *263*
Joy Reed Belt Search Consultants, Inc. (R), OK, *15*
Bender Executive Search Management Consulting (R), NY, *16*
Bennett & Associates (C), TX, *264*
Benson Associates (C), NY, *264*
C. Berger And Company (R), IL, *16*
Berkana Int'l., Inc. (C), WA, *265*
Berkhemer/Clayton, Inc. (R), CA, *16*
Bernhart Assoc. (C), MN, *265*
Bertrand, Ross & Assoc., Inc. (C), IL, *266*
Besen Assoc. Inc. (C), NJ, *266*
BG & Assoc. (C), MD, *266*
Bialla & Assoc. Inc. (R), CA, *17*
Bio-Venture Group (C), RI, *266*
Birch & Associes (C), QE, *267*
Deborah Bishop & Assoc. (R), CA, *17*
Bishop Partners (R), NY, *17*
The Black Leopard (C), CA, *267*
Blaney Executive Search (R), MA, *18*
BLB Consulting (C), NY, *268*
Block & Assoc. (R), CA, *18*
D. R. Blood & Assoc. (R), AZ, *18*
Bolton Group (C), CA, *269*
Bonell Ryan Inc. (R), NY, *19*
Bonnell Assoc. Ltd. (R), CT, *19*
Bornholdt Shivas & Friends Executive Recruiters (C), NY, *270*
Bosch & Assoc., LLC (R), CT, *19*
Howard Bowen Consulting (C), FL, *270*
Bower & Associates (C), TX, *271*
BowersThomas (C), CA, *271*
Boyden (R), NY, *20*
BR & Assoc. (C), NJ, *271*
M. F. Branch Assoc., Inc. (C), NC, *272*
Brandt Associates (C), PA, *272*
Brandywine Retained Ventures, Inc. (R), CT, *22*
Branthover Assoc. (C), NY, *272*
Bratland & Assoc. (C), IL, *272*
Bredeson Executive Recruitment, LLC (R), TX, *22*
Brei & Assoc., Inc. (C), IA, *272*
The Brentwood Group Ltd. (R), OR, *23*
Bridgecreek Personnel Agency (C), CA, *273*
Brigade, Inc. (R), CA, *23*
Brindisi Search (R), MD, *23*
Bristol Assoc., Inc. (C), CA, *274*
Broadband Resource Group (C), CA, *274*
The Broadmoor Group, L.L.C. (R), TX, *23*
Brookman Associates (C), NY, *274*
Bernard E. Brooks & Assoc., Inc. (R), SC, *24*
Broward-Dobbs, Inc. (C), GA, *274*
J. B. Brown & Assoc., Inc. (C), OH, *275*
Brown, Bernardy, Van Remmen, Inc. (C), CA, *275*
Brown Venture Assoc. (R), CA, *24*
Brownstone Sales & Marketing Group, Inc. (C), NY, *275*
Brush Creek Partners (R), MO, *24*
BRW Search (C), MN, *275*
Bryan & Louis Research (C), OH, *275*
BT&A, LLC (R), CT, *24*
Charles Buck & Assoc., Inc. (R), NY, *24*
The Buckley Group (C), FL, *276*
The Burgess Group-Corporate Recruiters Int'l., Inc. (R), NY, *25*
Burke & Assoc./The Westfield Group (C), CT, *276*
Joseph R. Burns & Assoc., Inc. (R), NJ, *25*
Business Partners, Inc. (C), FL, *277*
Button Group (C), TX, *277*
Byron Leonard Int'l., Inc. (R), CA, *25*
C. M. Management Services, Inc. (R), KY, *26*
C/R Associates (C), NY, *278*
Cambridge Group Ltd. - Exec. Search Div. (C), CT, *279*
T. M. Campbell Co. (R), WA, *27*
Canny, Bowen Inc. (R), NY, *27*
The Cantor Concern, Inc. (R), NY, *28*
Cantrell & Assoc. (C), FL, *280*
Capital Consulting Group, Inc. (R), MD, *28*
Caplan Assoc., Inc. (R), NJ, *28*
Caprio & Assoc. Inc. (R), IL, *29*
Cardwell Enterprises Inc. (R), IL, *29*
Career Advisors, Inc. (C), FL, *281*
Career Consulting Group, Inc. (C), CT, *281*
Career Marketing Assoc., Inc. (C), CO, *282*
Career Profiles (C), NH, *283*
Career Strategies, Inc. (C), CA, *283*
Careers First, Inc. (C), NJ, *283*
Careers On Track (C), NJ, *283*
Careers Plus (R), CA, *29*
Carion Resource Group Inc. (C), ON, *284*
Carlsen Resources, Inc. (R), CO, *29*
Carnegie Partners, Inc. (R), IL, *30*
Carpenter Assoc., Inc. (R), IL, *30*
Carpenter, Shackleton & Company (R), IL, *30*
Carrington & Carrington, Ltd. (R), IL, *30*
Carson-Thomas & Assoc. (C), CA, *284*
Carter McKenzie, Inc. (C), NJ, *285*
The CARVIR Group, Inc. (C), GA, *285*
CAS Comsearch Inc. (C), NY, *285*
Cassell & Kaye (C), NY, *286*
Catalyx Group (R), NY, *31*
Caywood Partners, Ltd. (R), CA, *32*
Cella Assoc. (C), GA, *286*
Cendea Connection Int'l. (R), TX, *32*
Central Executive Search, Inc. (C), OH, *287*
The Century Group (C), CA, *287*
CEO Consulting (C), FL, *287*
cFour Partners (R), CA, *32*
Chad Management Group (C), ON, *288*
Chapman & Assoc. (C), BC, *289*
The Chatham Group, Ltd. (C), CT, *289*
Chatham Search Assoc., Inc. (C), NJ, *290*
Chicago Legal Search, Ltd. (C), IL, *290*
Christian & Timbers, Inc. (R), OH, *34*
Christmas, McIvor & Assoc. Inc. (C), ON, *290*
Churchill & Affiliates, Inc. (R), PA, *35*
M. A. Churchill & Assoc., Inc. (R), PA, *35*
CJA-The Adler Group, Inc. (R), CA, *35*
Howard Clark Assoc. (C), NJ, *292*
Toby Clark Assoc. Inc. (C), NY, *292*
Clayman & Co. (R), MA, *36*
CN Associates (C), CA, *293*
COBA Executive Search (R), CO, *36*
Coe & Co. Int'l. Inc./EMA Partners Int'l. (R), AB, *37*
Colt Systems Professional Personnel Services (C), CA, *294*
The Colton Partnership, Inc. (R), NY, *38*
Columbia Consulting Group (R), MD, *38*
Commercial Programming Systems, Inc. (C), CA, *294*
Compass Group Ltd. (R), MI, *38*
CompuPro (C), IL, *295*
Computer Int'l. Consultants, Inc. (C), FL, *295*
Computer Professionals Unlimited (C), TX, *295*
Computer Security Placement Service (C), MA, *296*
The Comwell Company, Inc. (C), NJ, *296*
Consolidated Management Services (C), ON, *296*
Consulpro (R), ON, *39*
Consulting Resource Group, Inc. (C), GA, *297*
Consulting Rhonda (C), ON, *297*
Continental Search & Outplacement, Inc. (C), MD, *298*
Conway & Assoc. (R), IL, *40*
Cooper Assoc., Inc. (C), NY, *298*
Cornell Group Int'l. Consulting, Inc. (R), NY, *41*
The Corporate Advisory Group (R), NJ, *41*
Corporate Plus, Ltd. (C), GA, *300*

The Corporate Source Group, Inc. (R), MA, *41*
Corporate Staffing Group, Inc. (C), PA, *301*
Corso, Mizgala + French (R), ON, *42*
Leonard Corwen Assoc. (C), NY, *302*
CountryHouse Hotels Executive Search (C), VA, *302*
Cowell & Associates, Ltd. (R), IL, *42*
Trudi Cowlan (C), NY, *302*
Crane, Reed & Co., Inc. (C), NH, *302*
Creative HR Solutions (C), GA, *303*
Criterion Executive Search, Inc. (C), FL, *303*
Cross Country Consultants, Inc. (C), MD, *304*
Current Resource Group, Inc. (C), GA, *305*
Cusack Consulting (R), NY, *44*
Judith Cushman & Assoc. (R), WA, *44*
Custom Resources (C), AL, *305*
CV Associates (C), NY, *305*
Cyntal Int'l. Ltd. (R), NY, *44*
Cypress Int'l., Inc. (R), FL, *45*
D & M Associates (C), PA, *306*
D.A.I Human Resources Consultants (R), QE, *45*
D.A.L. Associates, Inc. (R), CT, *45*
D.P. Specialists, Inc. (C), CA, *306*
Dahl-Morrow Int'l. (R), VA, *45*
The Dalley Hewitt Co. (R), GA, *45*
DARE Personnel Inc. (C), ON, *307*
Data-AxIS Corp. (C), FL, *307*
The DataFinders Group, Inc. (C), NJ, *307*
Daubenspeck & Associates, Ltd. (R), IL, *46*
David Perry Assoc. (C), NJ, *308*
Alan Davis & Assoc. Inc. (R), QE, *47*
Joseph A. Davis Consultants, Inc. (R), NY, *47*
Bert Davis Executive Search, Inc. (R), NY, *47*
Bert Davis Publishing Placement Consultants (C), NY, *309*
DBC Recruiting Network (C), GA, *309*
DCA Professional Search (C), TX, *309*
Dean-MacDonald (R), OH, *47*
Defrain Mayer (R), KS, *48*
DeLalla - Fried Assoc. (C), NY, *310*
Thorndike Deland Assoc. LLC (R), NY, *48*
Delta Management Group Ltd. (C), ON, *310*
Delta Resource Group, Ltd. (C), GA, *311*
DeMatteo Associates (C), NY, *311*
Desktop Staffing, Inc. (C), IL, *311*
Despres & Associates (C), IL, *311*
Development Resource Group (R), NY, *48*
The Devlin Search Group, Inc. (C), MA, *311*
Rob Dey Executive Search (R), FL, *49*
Diamond Tax Recruiting (C), NY, *312*
The Diestel Group (R), UT, *51*
Roger Dietsch & Assoc. (C), MN, *312*
DiMarchi Partners (R), CO, *51*
J. Dinerstein & Co., Inc. (R), NY, *51*
Diversified Consulting Services, Inc. (C), CO, *313*
Diversified Search, Inc. (R), PA, *52*
DLB Assoc. (R), NY, *53*
Doering & Assoc. (C), CA, *313*
L. J. Doherty & Assoc. (R), MA, *53*
Don Allan Assoc., Inc. (C), CA, *313*
The Donnelly Group-Sales Recruiters, Inc. (C), MO, *314*
Dorst Information Services, Inc. (C), NY, *314*
Dotson & Assoc. (R), NY, *54*
The Doty Group (C), TX, *314*
Dreier Consulting (C), NJ, *315*
Drinkwater & Assoc. (R), MA, *54*
Dromeshauser Assoc. (R), MA, *55*
DSR-Search & Recruitment (C), TX, *315*
Dunhill Staffing Systems, Inc. (C), NY, *316*
Dunhill Professional Search of Miami (C), FL, *319*
Dunhill Professional Search of Augusta (C), GA, *320*
Dunhill Professional Search of Hawaii (C), HI, *320*
Dunhill Professional Search of Greater New Orleans (C), LA, *321*
Dunhill Professional Search of Ramsey (C), NJ, *321*
Dunhill Search of Arlington (C), TX, *322*
Dunhill Professional Search of Winston-Salem (C), NC, *322*
Dunhill Professional Search of Wilkes-Barre/Scranton, Inc. (C), PA, *322*
Gwen Dycus & Assoc. (C), FL, *323*
Dynamic Choices Inc. (C), MO, *323*
Dynamic Search Systems, Inc. (C), IL, *324*
E T Search Inc. (C), CA, *324*
E.P. Int'l. (C), NY, *324*
E/Search Int'l. (C), CT, *325*
EA Plus, Inc. (C), TX, *325*
EagleView, Inc. (C), MA, *325*
Earley Kielty & Assoc., Inc. (R), NY, *56*
Eastbourne Assoc. Inc. (R), NY, *56*
EBA Group (R), NJ, *56*
Eden & Assoc., Inc. (C), PA, *326*
EDI/Executive Dynamics Inc. (C), NJ, *326*
EDP Staffing Solutions, Inc. (C), AR, *327*
Edwards & Assoc. (C), GA, *327*
EFCO Consultants, Inc. (C), NY, *327*
Richard A. Eisner & Co., LLP (R), NY, *57*
W. Robert Eissler & Assoc., Inc. (C), TX, *327*
Electronic Search, Inc. (C), IL, *327*
Elite Consultants, Inc. (C), FL, *328*
Yves Elkas Inc. (R), QE, *58*
The Elliott Company (R), MA, *58*
Ellis & Associates (C), HI, *328*
David M. Ellner Assoc. (R), NY, *59*
The Ellsworth Group (C), NY, *329*
The Elmhurst Group (C), CA, *329*
Emerging Technology Search (C), GA, *329*
Emmett Executive Search, Inc. (C), NY, *330*
Empire International (R), PA, *59*
Employ® (C), PA, *330*
The Enfield Company (C), TX, *330*
Engineering Resource Group, Inc. (C), NJ, *331*
Entelechy Group Ltd. (R), MD, *59*
Epsen, Fuller & Assoc., LLC (R), NJ, *60*
ESS (Executive Search Services) (R), CA, *61*
Essential Solutions, Inc. (C), CA, *331*
Ethos Consulting, Inc. (R), CA, *61*
ETI Search Int'l. (R), GA, *61*
The Evans Search Group (R), CT, *61*
Evergreen & Co. (C), MA, *331*
ExeConnex, LLC (R), GA, *61*
The Execu/Search Group (C), NY, *332*
ExecuSource Assoc., Inc. (C), GA, *332*
ExecuSource Consultants, Inc. (C), TX, *332*
Executive Careers (R), CA, *62*
Executive Partners Inc. (C), CT, *333*
Executive Placement Consultants (C), IL, *333*
Executive Recruiters (C), WA, *334*
Executive Resource Group, Inc. (R), ME, *63*
Executive Resource Systems (C), CA, *335*
Executive Sales Search (C), CO, *335*
Executive Search Consultants International, Inc. (R), NY, *63*
Executive Search Consultants Corp. (C), IL, *335*
Executive Search Int'l./Transearch (R), MA, *63*
Executive Search of America, Inc. (C), OH, *336*
Executive Search Partners (R), NY, *63*
Executive Solutions (R), MN, *64*
The Executive Tree (R), FL, *64*
Executive/Retail Placement Assoc. (C), MD, *337*
ExecutiveFit (C), NY, *337*
Executives Worldwide, Inc. (C), OR, *337*
Fagan & Company (R), PA, *64*
Fairfield Int'l. Resources (R), NY, *65*
Paul Falcone Assoc. (R), NJ, *65*
Fast Switch, Ltd. (C), OH, *338*
The Fawcett Group (R), MA, *65*
A. E. Feldman Assoc., Inc. (C), NY, *339*
Fenwick Partners (R), MA, *66*
Ferneborg & Assoc., Inc. (R), CA, *66*
Fernow Assoc. (C), PA, *339*
Jerry Fields Assoc. (C), NY, *340*
Financialjobs.com (C), CA, *340*
Neil Fink Assoc. (R), CA, *66*
Finnegan & Assoc. (R), CA, *67*
Finney-Taylor Personnel & Management Consultants Ltd. (C), AB, *341*
First Search Inc. (C), IL, *341*
Howard Fischer Assoc. Int'l., Inc. (R), PA, *67*
The Fisher Group (R), AB, *67*
Fisher Personnel Management Services (R), CA, *68*
Fisher-Todd Assoc. (C), NY, *341*
A. G. Fishkin & Assoc., Inc. (R), MD, *68*
Robert M. Flanagan & Assoc., Ltd. (R), NY, *68*
Flexible Resources, Inc. (C), CT, *342*
Florapersonnel, Inc. (R), FL, *68*
J. G. Flynn & Assoc. Inc. (R), BC, *69*
Focus Consulting Services, Inc. (C), FL, *342*
Foley Proctor Yoskowitz (R), NJ, *69*
L. W. Foote Co. (R), WA, *69*
Ford & Ford (C), MA, *343*
The Ford Group, Inc. (R), PA, *69*
Fortuna Technologies Inc. (C), CA, *343*
Fortune Group Int'l., Inc. (R), PA, *70*

INDUSTRIES

Fortune Personnel Consultants of Colorado Springs (C), CO, *344*
F-O-R-T-U-N-E Personnel Consultants of Tampa (C), FL, *344*
Fortune Personnel Consultants of Jacksonville (C), FL, *345*
F-O-R-T-U-N-E Personnel Consultants of Manatee County (C), FL, *345*
Fortune of Arlington Heights (C), IL, *345*
Forum Personnel Inc. (C), NY, *351*
Foster Partners (R), NY, *70*
Foy, Schneid & Daniel, Inc. (R), NY, *71*
Neil Frank & Co. (R), CA, *71*
Franklin Int'l. Search, Inc. (C), MA, *352*
Franstaff Inc. (C), FL, *352*
P. N. French Assoc., Inc. (R), MA, *72*
Friedman Eisenstein Raemer & Schwartz, LLP (R), IL, *72*
Gerald Frisch Assoc., Inc. (R), NY, *72*
Peter Froehlich & Co. (C), TX, *353*
The Fry Group, Inc. (C), NY, *353*
Frye/Joure & Assoc., Inc. (C), TN, *353*
Future Employment Service, Inc. (C), IA, *353*
GAAP Inc. (R), QE, *73*
The Gabriel Group (C), PA, *354*
Jay Gaines & Company, Inc. (R), NY, *73*
Gans, Gans & Assoc., Inc. (R), FL, *74*
Gardiner, Townsend & Assoc. (R), NY, *74*
Gardner-Ross Assoc., Inc. (R), NY, *74*
Garland Assoc. Int'l. (C), CA, *355*
The Garms Group (R), IL, *74*
The Garvis Group, Inc. (C), LA, *355*
GateSource Partners (C), VA, *355*
Gaudry, Shink, Levasseur (R), QE, *75*
Geddes & Rubin Management Inc. (R), ON, *76*
Genel Associates (C), CA, *356*
General Engineering Tectonics (C), CA, *356*
Genesis Personnel Service, Inc. (C), OH, *356*
Geneva Group Int'l. (R), CA, *76*
C. R. Gerald & Assoc. (C), ON, *356*
Gilbert & Van Campen Int'l. (R), NY, *76*
Gilbert Tweed Assoc. Inc. (R), NY, *76*
Gimbel & Assoc. (C), FL, *357*
Lawrence Glaser Assoc., Inc. (C), NJ, *357*
Global 1000 Int'l. Services (C), CA, *358*
Global Career Services, Inc. (C), NY, *358*
Global Consulting Group Inc. (C), ON, *358*
Global Employer's Network, Inc. (R), TX, *77*
Global Research Partnership Inc. (R), NY, *78*
Global Technologies Group Inc. (C), NC, *359*
Global Telecommunications, Inc. (C), TX, *359*
The GlobalSearch Group (C), TX, *359*
Glou Int'l., Inc. (R), MA, *78*
H. L. Goehring & Assoc., Inc. (C), OH, *359*
The Goldman Group Inc. (R), NY, *79*
Goldman+Bell, LLC (C), NY, *360*
Goldstein & Co. (C), CA, *360*
David Gomez & Assoc., Inc. (R), IL, *79*
L. J. Gonzer Assoc. (C), NJ, *360*
Goodkind Assoc. Inc. (C), NY, *360*
Goodrich & Sherwood Assoc., Inc. (R), NY, *79*
Gould, McCoy & Chadick, Inc. (R), NY, *80*
The Governance Group, Inc. (R), NJ, *80*
Robert Grant Assoc., Inc. (C), CA, *361*
The Grant Search Group, Inc. (C), ON, *361*
Graphic Arts Marketing Assoc., Inc. (C), MI, *361*
Ben Greco Assoc., Inc. (C), CA, *362*
Sheila Greco Assoc. (C), NY, *362*
Greene Personnel Consultants (C), RI, *362*
Greene-Levin-Snyder LLC (C), NY, *362*
Greenhaven & Assoc., Inc. (R), NY, *81*
Greenwich Internet (C), CT, *363*
Greger/Peterson Assoc., Inc. (R), CA, *81*
Griffith & Werner, Inc. (R), FL, *82*
J. B. Groner Executive Search, Inc. (C), DE, *363*
Growth Consultants of America (R), MI, *82*
Growth Strategies, Inc. (R), FL, *83*
David E. Grumney Co. Inc. (R), WA, *83*
GSP International (C), NJ, *364*
GSW Consulting Group, Inc. (R), CA, *83*
Nadine Guber & Assoc., Inc. (C), NY, *364*
Michael R. Guerin Co. (C), CA, *364*
Wolf Gugler & Assoc. Ltd. (R), ON, *83*
The Gullgroup (C), TX, *364*
Gumbinner/Haubenstock, Inc. (C), NY, *364*
Gundersen Partners, L.L.C. (R), NY, *83*
Gustin Partners, Ltd. (R), MA, *83*
GWS Partners (R), IL, *84*
Haddad Assoc. (R), FL, *84*
Halbrecht Lieberman Assoc., Inc. (R), CT, *84*
Haley Associates (R), CA, *85*
Don Hall & Assoc. (C), TX, *366*
Susan Hall Executive Search (C), TX, *366*
Hamilton & Co. (C), OH, *367*
The Hamilton Group (R), MD, *85*
W. L. Handler & Assoc. (R), GA, *85*
Hands-on Broadcast (R), NY, *86*
Handy HRM (R), NY, *86*
The Hanna Group (C), OH, *368*
Hansen Executive Search, Inc. (C), NE, *368*
Janet Harberth & Assoc., Inc. (C), GA, *368*
Harbor Consultants Int'l., Inc. (C), VA, *368*
Hardison & Company (R), TX, *86*
Harper Hewes, Inc. (C), NY, *369*
Harris Heery & Assoc., Inc. (R), CT, *87*
Hart & Co. (C), NY, *370*
Hartsfield Group, Inc. (R), GA, *87*
Harvard Group Int'l. (R), GA, *87*
The Hawkins Co. (R), CA, *88*
Hayden & Assoc., Inc. (C), MN, *370*
Hayman Daugherty Assoc., Inc. (C), GA, *370*
Hazlett Associates (R), IL, *88*
Headden Assoc. (R), WA, *88*
Healey Executive Search, Inc. (R), MN, *88*
Hechkoff/Work Executive Search Inc. (R), NY, *89*
Hedlund Corp. (C), IL, *375*
Heffelfinger Assoc., Inc. (R), MA, *89*
Heller Assoc., Ltd. (R), IL, *91*
The Helms Int'l. Group (R), VA, *91*
Kay Henry, Inc. (C), PA, *376*
The Hensge Co. (R), IL, *91*
Herbeck Kline & Assoc. (R), IL, *92*
J. J. Herlihy & Assoc., Inc. (C), CA, *376*
Herrerias & Assoc. (R), CA, *92*
J. D. Hersey & Assoc. (C), OH, *376*
Heyman Assoc., Inc. (R), NY, *93*
Higbee Assoc., Inc. (C), CT, *377*
High Tech Opportunities, Inc. (C), NH, *377*
High Tech Staffing Group (C), OR, *377*
High-Tech Recruiters (C), CT, *378*
Hill & Assoc. (C), CA, *378*
Hill Allyn Assoc. (C), CA, *378*
The Hiring Authority, Inc. (C), FL, *379*
HLR Consulting (C), NY, *379*
Hodge-Cronin & Assoc., Inc. (R), IL, *94*
Hoffman Recruiters (C), MA, *380*
Holland & Assoc., Inc. (R), MI, *94*
The Hollins Group, Inc. (R), IL, *95*
Hook-Up! (C), CA, *380*
Horton Int'l. Inc. (R), NY, *96*
Howard-Sloan Assoc. (C), NY, *381*
The Howard-Sloan-Koller Group (R), NY, *97*
Howe & Assoc. (R), PA, *97*
HR Advantage, Inc. (C), VA, *382*
HRCS (R), CA, *97*
The HRM Group, Inc. (C), AL, *382*
HRS, Inc. (R), PA, *97*
Arnold Huberman Assoc., Inc. (R), NY, *97*
The Hudson Group (C), CT, *383*
Hughes & Company (R), VA, *98*
Human Resource Bureau (C), CA, *384*
Human Resource Dimensions, Inc. (C), TX, *384*
Human Resources Management Hawaii, Inc. (C), HI, *384*
Hunter Adams (C), NC, *385*
Hunter, Rowan & Crowe (C), FL, *386*
Huntington Personnel Consultants, Inc. (C), NY, *386*
Huntley Associates (Dallas), Inc. (C), TX, *386*
The Hyde Group, Inc. (R), CT, *101*
i.j. & assoc., inc. (C), CO, *386*
IM Independent Management Recruiters (R), TN, *101*
IMA Search, Inc. (R), NY, *101*
Independent Resource Systems (C), CA, *388*
Ingram & Aydelotte, Inc. (R), NY, *101*
Innovative Partnerships (R), CA, *101*
Innovative Resource Group, LLC (C), NC, *389*
InSearch (C), CO, *389*
The Inside Track (C), TX, *389*
Intech Summit Group, Inc. (R), CA, *102*
Integrity Search, Inc. (R), PA, *102*
Intelegra, Inc. (C), NJ, *390*
InteliSearch, Inc. (R), CT, *102*
Intelligent Marketing Solutions, Inc. (C), NY, *390*
Interactive Search Network (R), CA, *102*
Interim Executive Recruiting (C), GA, *392*
International Business Partners (C), ON, *392*
International Consulting Services, Inc. (C), IL, *392*
International Management Services Inc. (R), IL, *102*

International Staffing Consultants, Inc. (C), CA, *393*
Interquest, Inc. (R), NY, *103*
Intersource, Ltd. (R), GA, *103*
Interspace Interactive, Inc. (C), NY, *394*
Jeffrey Irving Assoc., Inc. (R), VA, *104*
Isaacson, Miller (R), MA, *104*
ISG Informatics Search Group (C), ON, *395*
Ives & Associates, Inc. (C), OH, *395*
J. Robert Scott (R), MA, *104*
J.D.G. y Asociados, S.A. de C.V. (R), SO, *104*
Ron Jackson & Assoc. (C), GA, *396*
Jackson Group Int'l. (C), CO, *396*
Jaeger Int'l., Inc. (C), OH, *396*
JAG Group (R), MO, *105*
JDH & Assoc. (C), CA, *397*
Jeffrey Allan Co., Inc. (C), CA, *398*
Jeffrey Meryl Assoc., Inc. (C), NJ, *398*
Jender & Company (R), IL, *105*
JenKim Int'l. Ltd., Inc. (C), FL, *398*
JG Consultants, Inc. (R), TX, *106*
JL & Co. (C), CA, *399*
Johnson & Assoc., Inc. (R), CA, *106*
Johnson & Company (R), CT, *107*
Ronald S. Johnson Assoc., Inc. (R), CA, *107*
K. E. Johnson Assoc. (C), WA, *399*
Johnson Brown Assoc., Inc. (C), IN, *400*
The Johnson Group, Unlimited (C), NY, *400*
Johnson, Kemper & Assoc. (C), TX, *400*
Johnson Smith & Knisely (R), NY, *107*
Jones Management Co. (R), CT, *108*
Jordon & Jordon, Inc. (R), PA, *108*
Joseph Consulting, Inc. (C), FL, *401*
JPM International (C), CA, *401*
JSG Group Management Consultants (R), ON, *109*
Julian Assoc., Inc. (C), CT, *401*
Juno Systems, Inc. (C), NY, *402*
A H Justice Search Consultants (C), TX, *402*
K2 Resources, L.P. (C), CT, *402*
KABL Ability Network (C), CA, *402*
Kacevich, Lewis & Brown, Inc. (R), MA, *109*
Kames & Assoc. (C), MD, *403*
Kanzer Assoc., Inc. (R), IL, *109*
Gary Kaplan & Assoc. (R), CA, *109*
Kaplan & Assoc., Inc. (R), PA, *109*
Karp & Assoc. (C), FL, *403*
Howard Karr & Assoc., Inc. (R), CA, *110*
Allan Karson Assoc., Inc. (R), NJ, *110*
Martin Kartin & Co., Inc. (R), NY, *110*
Jim Kay & Assoc. (C), IL, *404*
The Kay Group of 5th Ave. (C), NY, *404*
Keane Assoc. (R), MA, *110*
A.T. Kearney Executive Search (R), IL, *111*
Kelley & Keller, Inc. (C), FL, *405*
Kelly Associates (R), PA, *112*
Kensington International (R), CA, *113*
Kenzer Corp. (R), NY, *113*
Key Employment (C), NJ, *405*
Key Resources Int'l. (C), CA, *405*
Ki Technologies, Inc. (C), UT, *406*
Kiley, Owen & McGovern, Inc. (R), NJ, *114*
Richard Kinser & Assoc. (R), NY, *115*
Kip Williams, Inc. (R), NY, *115*
Kittleman & Assoc.,LLC (R), IL, *115*
Kleber & Assoc. (C), WA, *407*
The Kleven Group, Inc. (C), MA, *407*
The Koehler Group (C), PA, *408*
Lee Koehn Assoc., Inc. (R), OR, *116*
T. J. Koellhoffer & Assoc. (R), NJ, *116*
Korban Associates (R), PA, *117*
Kordus Consulting Group (C), WI, *408*
Koren, Rogers Assoc. Inc. (R), NY, *117*
Korn/Ferry Int'l. (R), NY, *117*
Kors Montgomery Int'l. (R), TX, *118*
Kossuth & Assoc., Inc. (R), WA, *119*
Katherine R. Kraemer (R), CA, *120*
Krakower Group, Inc. (R), CA, *120*
Kramer Executive Resources, Inc. (C), NY, *409*
Krautler Personnel Recruitment (C), FL, *409*
Kremple Consulting Group (R), CA, *120*
Kresin Wingard (C), IL, *409*
Kreutz Consulting Group, Inc. (R), IL, *121*
Kukoy Associates (R), CO, *121*
Kulper & Co., L.L.C. (R), NJ, *121*
John Kurosky & Assoc. (R), CA, *122*
Kurtz Pro-Search, Inc. (C), NJ, *410*
L&L Assoc. Global Search (C), PA, *411*
Marvin Laba & Assoc. (R), CA, *122*
LaCosta & Assoc. Int'l. Inc. (C), CA, *411*
Rene LaFlamme & Associes (R), QE, *122*
Lamay Assoc., Inc. (R), CT, *124*
The Landstone Group (C), NY, *412*
Langley & Associates, Inc. (Executive Search Consultants) (R), CO, *124*
Larkin & Co. (R), CA, *124*
Robert Larned Assoc., Inc. (C), VA, *413*
Jack B. Larsen & Assoc., Inc. (C), PA, *413*
Lasher Assoc. (R), FL, *125*
Lauer, Sbarbaro Assoc., EMA Partners Int'l. (R), IL, *126*
Lautz, Grotte, Engler & Swimley (R), CA, *126*
W. R. Lawry, Inc. (R), CT, *126*
LCC Companies (C), AZ, *414*
LCS, Inc. (C), TX, *414*
Leader Institute, Inc. (C), GA, *414*
Ricci Lee Assoc., Inc. (C), CA, *415*
V. J. Lehman & Assoc., Inc. (R), CO, *127*
Lehman McLeskey (R), TX, *128*
Jacques LePage Executive Search Inc. (R), QE, *128*
Michael Levine Search Consultants (R), NY, *129*
Hal Levy & Assoc. (C), NY, *417*
Lewis Companies Inc. (R), ON, *129*
LG Brand, Inc. (C), MD, *417*
The Libra Group Inc. (C), CT, *417*
Ginger Lindsey & Assoc., Inc. (C), TX, *418*
Lipsky Group, Inc. (R), CA, *129*
Lipson & Co. (R), CA, *130*
Livingston, Robert & Co. (R), CT, *130*
Lloyd Prescott Assoc., Inc. (C), FL, *418*
Lloyd Staffing (C), NY, *419*
The Logan Group, Inc. (R), MO, *131*
Logic Assoc., Inc. (C), NY, *419*
Logix, Inc. (C), MA, *420*
Logue & Rice Inc. (C), VA, *420*
Louis Search Group, Inc. (C), NJ, *420*
Lucas Assoc. (C), GA, *421*
The John Lucht Consultancy Inc. (R), NY, *131*
The Luciani Group (R), CA, *132*
Fran Luisi Assoc. (R), NJ, *132*
Charles Luntz & Assoc., Inc. (R), MO, *132*
Lutz Associates (C), CT, *421*
P. J. Lynch Assoc. (R), CT, *132*
Lynne Palmer Executive Recruitment, Inc. (C), NY, *421*
Lyons & Assoc., Inc. (C), IL, *422*
Madison Executive Search, Inc. (C), NJ, *422*
Madison MacArthur Inc. (R), ON, *133*
Maiorino & Weston Assoc., Inc. (R), CT, *134*
Management Assoc. (C), MD, *424*
Management One Consultants (C), ON, *425*
Management Recruiters of Tucson (C), AZ, *439*
Management Recruiters Peninsula (C), CA, *439*
Management Recruiters Dana Point (C), CA, *440*
Management Recruiters of Laguna Hills (C), CA, *440*
Management Recruiters of Northern California (C), CA, *440*
Management Recruiters of Roseville (C), CA, *441*
Management Recruiters of Winsted, Inc. (C), CT, *442*
Management Recruiters of Colchester (C), CT, *442*
Management Recruiters of Altamonte (C), FL, *442*
Management Recruiters of Franktown (C), CO, *442*
Management Recruiters of Melbourne, Inc. (C), FL, *443*
Management Recruiters of Bonita Springs, Inc. (C), FL, *443*
Management Recruiters, Inc. (C), FL, *443*
Management Recruiters of St. Augustine (C), FL, *444*
Management Recruiters of Tampa North (C), FL, *444*
Management Recruiters of St. Lucie County, Inc. (C), FL, *444*
Management Recruiters of Northern Palm Beaches (C), FL, *444*
Management Recruiters of Venice, Inc. (C), FL, *445*
Management Recruiters of Atlanta (C), GA, *445*
Management Recruiters of Atlanta NE (C), GA, *446*
Management Recruiters of Savannah (C), GA, *446*
Management Recruiters of Indianapolis (C), IN, *448*
Management Recruiters of South Bend (C), IN, *448*
Management Recruiters - Indianapolis (C), IN, *448*

INDUSTRIES

Management Recruiters-Cedar Rapids, Inc. (C), IA, *448*
Management Recruiters of Fairfield (C), IA, *449*
Management Recruiters of the Baltimore Washington Corridor (C), MD, *450*
Management Recruiters of Birmingham (C), MI, *451*
Management Recruiters of Baltimore (C), MD, *451*
Management Recruiters of Winona (C), MN, *452*
Management Recruiters of Bloomington (C), MN, *452*
Management Recruiters of Chanhassen (C), MN, *452*
Management Recruiters of Rankin Co. (C), MS, *452*
Management Recruiters of Morris County, NJ (C), NJ, *453*
Management Recruiters of Middlesex County NJ (C), NJ, *454*
Management Recruiters of The Sandias (C), NM, *454*
Management Recruiters of Cedar Mountain (C), NC, *455*
Management Recruiters of Fayetteville (C), NC, *455*
Management Recruiters of Gramercy, Inc. (C), NY, *455*
Management Recruiters of Columbus (C), OH, *457*
Management Recruiters of Youngstown (C), OH, *458*
Management Recruiters of Oklahoma City (C), OK, *458*
Management Recruiters of Pittsburgh (C), PA, *459*
Management Recruiters of Lionville, Inc. (C), PA, *459*
Management Recruiters of North Charleston (C), SC, *460*
Management Recruiters of Austin (C), TX, *462*
Management Recruiters of LBJ Park/Dallas (C), TX, *462*
Management Recruiters Dallas North (MRDN) (C), TX, *462*
Management Recruiters of San Marcos (C), TX, *463*
Management Recruiters of Lubbock (C), TX, *463*
Management Recruiters of Arlington (C), VA, *464*
Management Recruiters of Ogden (C), UT, *464*
Management Recruiters Int'l.-The Woodlands (C), TX, *464*
Management Recruiters of Fairfax, VA (C), VA, *464*
Management Recruiters of Spokane (C), WA, *465*
Management Recruiters of Madison, Inc. (C), WI, *466*
Management Recruiters of Milwaukee - Downtown (C), WI, *466*
Management Recruiters of Stevens Point, Inc. (C), WI, *466*
Management Recruiters of Milwaukee-North (C), WI, *466*
Management Resource Group (C), MN, *467*
Management Resource Group, Inc. (C), NY, *467*
Management Search Int'l. (C), CA, *467*
Management Search, Inc. (C), IL, *467*
F. L. Mannix & Co. (R), MA, *135*
Margolin Consultants, Inc. (C), NY, *469*
Mark Adam Assoc. (R), NJ, *135*
J. L. Mark Assoc., Inc. (R), CO, *135*
Mark Christian & Assoc., Inc. (C), AZ, *469*
Marketing Search Inc. (C), OH, *471*
Marketing/Public Relations Research Recruiting (C), CT, *471*
Paula Marks Inc. (R), NY, *136*
Brad Marks Int'l. (R), CA, *136*
The Marlow Group (R), MA, *136*
The Maroon Group (R), CT, *136*
Marra Peters & Partners (R), NJ, *136*
Marsar & Co., Inc. (C), FL, *471*
Karen Marshall Assoc. (C), KY, *471*
J. Martin & Assoc. (R), CA, *137*
Martin Partners, L.L.C. (R), IL, *137*
The Martwick Group, Inc. (C), OR, *472*
Massey-Horton Int'l. (R), ON, *138*
Richard L. Mather & Assoc. (C), CT, *472*
Matte Consulting Group Inc. (R), QE, *138*
Maxecon Executive Search Consultants (R), FL, *138*
K. Maxin & Assoc. (R), PA, *139*
The Mazzitelli Group, Ltd. (R), MN, *139*
MB Inc. Executive Search (C), NY, *473*
McBride Assoc., Inc. (R), DC, *139*
McCarthy Assoc. National BancSearch, LLC (C), LA, *473*
The McCormick Group (C), VA, *473*
McCray, Shriver, Eckdahl & Assoc., Inc. (R), CA, *140*
McDonald Assoc. Int'l. (R), IL, *140*
McDonald, Long & Assoc., Inc. (R), NY, *140*
McDowell & Co., Recruiters (C), TX, *474*
McGrath & Assoc., Inc. (R), NJ, *141*
McKee Cyber Search (C), MS, *475*
The McKinnon Management Group Inc. (C), ON, *475*
McManners Assoc., Inc. (R), CA, *142*
Joseph J. McTaggart (C), CA, *476*
Meads & Assoc. (R), FL, *142*
Media Management Resources, Inc. (R), CO, *142*
Media Recruiting Group, Inc. (C), NY, *476*
MediaCOM Talent Group (C), MA, *476*
The Medley Group (C), CA, *477*
Mehta Consulting (C), NJ, *478*
Juan Menefee & Assoc. (C), IL, *478*
Meng, Finseth & Assoc., Inc. (R), CA, *143*
Mengel & McDonald Ltd. (C), IL, *479*
Merlin Int'l. Inc. (C), NJ, *479*
MES Search Co. (C), GA, *479*
META/MAT, Ltd. (R), NJ, *144*
Meyer Assoc., Inc. (R), GA, *144*
Millennium Search Group, Inc. (R), CA, *144*
Milo Research (R), NY, *145*
Milrod Assoc. (C), NJ, *482*
Herbert Mines Assoc., Inc. (R), NY, *145*
MIS Computer Professionals, Inc. (C), KS, *482*
Laurie Mitchell & Co., Inc. (R), OH, *145*
Mitchell Martin Inc. (C), NY, *483*
MJF Assoc. (C), CT, *483*
Modis (C), MD, *483*
Mogul Consultants, Inc. (C), NY, *483*
Montenido Assoc. (R), CA, *146*
Montgomery Resources, Inc. (C), CA, *484*
Montgomery West (R), CA, *146*
Moore Research Assoc. (R), NJ, *147*
Morency Assoc. (C), MA, *485*
Morgan Hunter Corp. (C), KS, *485*
Morgan/Webber, Inc. (R), NY, *147*
The Morley Group (C), IN, *486*
Robert T. Morton Assoc., Inc. (C), MA, *486*
Moyer, Sherwood Assoc., Inc. (R), NY, *148*
Much & Co. (R), NY, *148*
Multi Processing, Inc. (R), NH, *149*
Jennifer Munro & Partners, Inc. (R), SC, *149*
Musick & Assoc. (C), CA, *487*
Mycoff & Assoc. (R), CO, *150*
Myers Career Assoc., Inc. (C), CA, *488*
Nadzam, Lusk, Horgan & Assoc., Inc. (R), CA, *150*
Nagler, Robins & Poe, Inc. (R), MA, *150*
National Affirmative Action Career Network, Inc. (C), CO, *488*
National Executive (C), ON, *489*
National Field Service Corp. (C), NY, *489*
National Recruiters (C), OK, *489*
National Register Columbus Inc. (C), OH, *490*
Nationwide Personnel Placement, Inc. (C), OH, *490*
NDB Assoc., Inc. (C), PA, *491*
The NEIS Corp., Inc. (C), FL, *491*
New Dimensions in Technology, Inc. (C), MA, *492*
New Venture Development, Inc. (C), CA, *492*
Newman-Johnson-King, Inc. (C), TX, *492*
Newport Strategic Search LLC (C), CA, *492*
NMC & Kay Int'l. (R), CO, *152*
Noble & Assoc., Inc. (C), NY, *494*
Nordeman Grimm, Inc. (R), NY, *152*
Paul Winston Norman & Assoc. (R), IL, *152*
Norman Broadbent Int'l., Inc. (R), NY, *152*
NorTech Resources (C), NY, *496*
The North Peak Group (C), OH, *496*
NorthStar Technologies, Inc. (C), NY, *496*
Nuessle, Kurdziel & Weiss, Inc. (R), PA, *153*
NYCOR Search, Inc. (C), MN, *497*
O'Brien and Roof (C), OH, *497*
O'Connell Group Inc. (C), CT, *497*
O'Connor Resources (C), TX, *497*
O'Keefe & Assoc. (C), TX, *497*
O'Keefe & Assoc., Inc. (R), CT, *154*
O'Neill & Co. (R), CT, *154*
O'Neill Group (C), NJ, *498*
O'Shea, Divine & Co., Inc. (R), CA, *154*
Odell & Assoc., Inc. (C), TX, *498*
The Ogdon Partnership (R), NY, *155*

The Onstott Group (R), MA, *156*
Open Concepts (C), CA, *499*
Opus Marketing (R), CA, *156*
K. Ossow & Co. (C), NY, *500*
The Oxford Group (C), TX, *500*
P.R.H. Management, Inc. (R), CT, *158*
Pacific Crossing (C), CA, *501*
Pacific Search Group, Inc. (C), CA, *501*
The Pailin Group Professional Search Consultants (R), TX, *158*
Janou Pakter, Inc. (C), NY, *502*
Paladin Group, Inc. (C), CO, *502*
Arthur Pann Assoc., Inc. (C), NY, *502*
Parker-Worthington, Inc. (C), TX, *503*
Largent Parks & Partners (C), TX, *503*
Parsons, Anderson & Gee, Inc. (C), NY, *503*
Partners Executive Search Consultants Inc. (R), ON, *160*
Partners In Human Resources Int'l., Inc. (R), NY, *160*
Partners Resource Group (C), VA, *504*
Partnervision Consulting Group Inc. (R), ON, *160*
Carolyn Smith Paschal Int'l. (R), CA, *160*
Pathway Executive Search, Inc. (C), NY, *505*
Pathways Int'l. (C), CT, *505*
The Patience Motivation Belief Group, Inc. (C), GA, *505*
Paul-Tittle Assoc., Inc. (R), VA, *161*
Pawlik/Dorman Partners (R), IL, *161*
Peachtree Executive Search (R), GA, *161*
Pearce & Assoc. (C), FL, *506*
Pearson & Assoc., Inc. (C), AZ, *506*
Penn Associates (R), PA, *161*
Pennington Consulting Group (C), NJ, *506*
The Pennmor Group (C), NJ, *506*
Perez & Assoc. (C), MI, *507*
Fred Perry Assoc. (C), TX, *507*
Perry Search Assoc. (C), CA, *507*
Perry-Martel Int'l., Inc. (R), ON, *163*
Barry Persky & Co., Inc. (R), CT, *163*
PersoNet, Inc. (C), FL, *507*
Personnel Assoc. (C), NC, *508*
Personnel Assoc. (C), CA, *508*
The Personnel Group, Inc. (R), MN, *163*
Personnel, Inc. (C), AL, *508*
Personnel Unlimited/Executive Search (C), WA, *509*
PHD Conseil en Ressources Humaines Inc. (C), QE, *510*
Phillips Assoc. (C), FL, *510*
Phillips Int'l., Inc. (C), SC, *510*
Phillips Personnel/Search (C), CO, *510*
PIC Executive Search (C), GA, *511*
The Pinnacle Source, Inc. (C), CO, *512*
Pinton Forrest & Madden/EMA Partners Int'l. (R), BC, *165*
Pittleman & Assoc. (C), NY, *512*
Placement Solutions (C), WI, *513*
Placement Testart Inc. (C), QE, *513*
Placements by Jesse Reid Assoc., Inc. (C), NY, *513*
Plante & Moran, LLP (R), MI, *165*
Rene Plessner Assoc., Inc. (R), NY, *165*
Yves Plouffe & Assoc. (R), QE, *165*
Poirier, Hoevel & Co. (R), CA, *166*
Polson & Co., Inc. (R), MN, *166*
Don V. Poole & Assoc., Inc. (C), CO, *514*
David Powell, Inc. (R), CA, *166*
Robert Powers & Assoc. (C), CA, *515*
PPS Information Systems Staffing (C), MD, *515*
Prairie Resource Group, Inc. (R), IL, *166*
Precision Executive Search (C), AZ, *516*
Preferred Placement, Inc. (C), NY, *516*
Preston-Hunter, Inc. (R), IL, *167*
Prestonwood Assoc. (R), MA, *168*
Price & Assoc., Inc. (C), VA, *518*
Alan J. Price Assoc., Inc. (C), RI, *518*
PricewaterhouseCoopers Executive Search (R), ON, *168*
PricewaterhouseCoopers Executive Search (R), MX, *168*
Prime Management Group Inc. (C), ON, *518*
Professional Persons Career Services (C), NY, *521*
Professional Recruiting Consultants, Inc. (C), DE, *521*
Professional Search (R), MI, *169*
Professional Search, Inc. (C), CO, *522*
Professional Selection Services (R), GA, *169*
Professional Team Search, Inc. (R), AZ, *169*
Profit Pros, Inc. (C), CA, *523*
ProNet, Inc. (C), NC, *524*
ProSearch Recruiting (C), CA, *524*
Proven Edge (C), CA, *525*
PSD Group, Inc. (C), CA, *525*
PSP Agency (C), NY, *525*
Quality Search Inc. (C), OH, *526*
Quantum EDP Recruiting Services (C), QE, *526*
The Quantum Group (C), NJ, *526*
The Quest Organization (C), NY, *527*
L. J. Quinn & Assoc., Inc. (R), CA, *170*
R & L Assoc., Ltd. (R), NY, *170*
R. J. Associates (C), NY, *528*
R/K International Inc. (R), CT, *171*
R2 Services, LLC (C), IL, *528*
Raines Int'l. Inc. (R), NY, *171*
The Ransford Group (R), TX, *171*
J. E. Ranta Assoc. (C), MA, *529*
Joanne E. Ratner Search (C), NY, *529*
Ray & Berndtson (R), TX, *171*
Ray & Berndtson/Lovas Stanley (R), ON, *172*
Razzino-Claymore Assoc. (C), NJ, *530*
Re-Mark Assoc. Inc. (C), NJ, *531*
Recruit Xpress (C), TX, *531*
Recruiting Options, Inc. (C), GA, *531*
Recruiting Resources Int'l. (C), CA, *532*
Recruiting/Solutions (C), CA, *532*
Mary Rector & Assoc., Inc. (C), IL, *533*
Redden & McGrath Assoc., Inc. (R), NY, *173*
Redden-Shaffer Group (R), CA, *173*
Redwood Partners Ltd. (R), NY, *173*
Reece & Mruk Partners/EMA Partners Int'l. (R), MA, *173*
Reeve & Assoc. (C), CT, *533*
The Regency Group, Ltd. (C), NE, *533*
The Renaissance Network (C), MA, *534*
Research Personnel Consultants (C), ON, *534*
Resource Management Group (C), CT, *534*
Resource Services, Inc. (C), NY, *534*
Retail Recruiters/Spectrum Consultants, Inc. (C), PA, *535*
Russell Reynolds Assoc., Inc. (R), NY, *176*
Reynolds Consulting Int'l. (R), ON, *177*
Reynolds Partners (R), NY, *177*
RHI Consulting (C), VA, *536*
RIC Corp. (R), FL, *177*
Rice Cohen Int'l. (R), PA, *178*
Richard, Wayne & Roberts (C), TX, *536*
Richards Assoc., Inc. (R), NY, *178*
The Richards Group (C), PA, *536*
W. F. Richer Assoc., Inc. (C), NY, *536*
Ridenour & Assoc. (R), IL, *178*
Ritt-Ritt & Assoc., Inc. (C), IL, *537*
Ritta Professional Search Inc. (C), NY, *538*
RJN Consulting (R), NY, *179*
Roberson & Co. (C), AZ, *538*
Robert William James & Assoc. (C), OR, *539*
Norman Roberts & Assoc., Inc. (R), CA, *179*
Bruce Robinson Assoc. (R), NJ, *180*
Robison Humphreys & Assoc., Inc. (R), ON, *180*
Robsham & Assoc., Inc. (R), MA, *180*
Rocky Mountain Recruiters, Inc. (C), CO, *540*
R. A. Rodriguez & Assoc., Inc. (C), TX, *540*
Rodzik & Assoc., Inc. (R), NC, *180*
Rogers - McManamon Executive Search (R), CA, *180*
ROI International, Inc. (R), WA, *181*
Rojek Marketing Group, Inc. (R), OH, *181*
Rolland Ressources Humaines Inc. (R), QE, *181*
Romac Int'l. (C), GA, *541*
Romac Int'l. (C), IL, *541*
Romac Int'l. Inc. (R), MA, *181*
Rooney Assoc., Inc. (R), IL, *181*
Emery A. Rose & Assoc. (C), WA, *545*
Ross Personnel Consultants, Inc. (C), CT, *545*
Rossi & Assoc. Inc. (C), BC, *545*
Roth Young Executive Search (C), TX, *546*
Rovner & Assoc., Inc. (R), IL, *182*
Rovner Gerner & Assoc. (R), CA, *182*
Rowland Mountain & Assoc. (C), GA, *547*
Royal Assoc. (C), CA, *547*
The Rubicon Group (C), AZ, *547*
Ruderfer & Co., Inc. (C), NJ, *548*
K. Russo Assoc. Inc. (C), CT, *548*
Rust & Assoc., Inc. (R), IL, *183*
Ryan, Miller & Assoc. (C), CA, *549*
Rylan Forbes Consulting Group, Inc. (C), NJ, *549*
Ryman, Bell, Green & Michaels, Inc. (C), TX, *549*
R. S. Sadow Assoc. (C), NJ, *550*
Sales & Marketing Search, Inc. (C), MA, *551*
Sales Consultants of Scottsdale, Inc. (C), AZ, *556*
Sales Consultants Int'l. of Oakland (C), CA, *556*
Sales Consultants of Sacramento (C), CA, *556*

INDUSTRIES

Sales Consultants of Boca Raton, Inc. (C), FL, *557*
Sales Consultants of Savannah, GA (C), GA, *557*
Sales Consultants of Ft. Lauderdale, Inc. (C), FL, *557*
Sales Consultants of Stamford-Darien (C), CT, *557*
Sales Consultants of Tampa North, Inc. (C), FL, *557*
Sales Consultants of Denver (C), CO, *557*
Sales Consultants of Danbury (C), CT, *557*
Sales Consultants of Ft. Myers, Inc. (C), FL, *557*
Sales Consultants of Honolulu (C), HI, *558*
Sales Consultants of Barrington (C), IL, *558*
Sales Consultants of Chicago South (C), IL, *558*
Sales Consultants (C), IL, *558*
Sales Consultants of Wellesley, Inc. (C), MA, *559*
Sales Consultants of Rockville, MD (C), MD, *559*
Sales Consultants of Birmingham (C), MI, *559*
Sales Consultants of Bangor, Inc. (C), ME, *559*
Sales Consultants of Farmington Hills (C), MI, *560*
Sales Consultants of Grand Rapids (C), MI, *560*
Sales Consultants of Cherry Hill (C), NJ, *560*
Sales Consultants of Omaha, Inc. (C), NE, *560*
Sales Consultants of Butler County (C), PA, *561*
Sales Consultants of Raleigh-Durham-RTP (C), NC, *561*
Sales Consultants of Westchester-South, Inc. (C), NY, *561*
Sales Consultants of Newtown, Inc. (C), PA, *562*
Sales Consultants of Austin, Inc. (C), TX, *562*
Sales Consultants King of Prussia (C), PA, *562*
Sales Consultants of Madison (C), WI, *563*
Sales Consultants of Milwaukee (C), WI, *563*
Sales Consultants of Houston (C), TX, *563*
Sales Executives, Inc. (C), MI, *563*
Sales Search (C), ON, *564*
A. N. Salloway Executive Search & Consulting, L.L.C. (C), MA, *564*
Norm Sanders Assoc., Inc. (R), NJ, *184*
Sanders Management Assoc., Inc. (C), NJ, *565*
Sanford Rose Assoc. - Fairhope (C), AL, *565*
Sanford Rose Assoc. - Santa Barbara (C), CA, *565*
Sanford Rose Assoc. - Norcross (C), GA, *566*
Sanford Rose Assoc. - Evansville (C), IN, *567*
Sanford Rose Assoc. - Charlotte (C), NC, *568*
Sanford Rose Assoc. - Springfield (C), MO, *568*
Sanford Rose Assoc. - Lake St. Louis (C), MO, *568*
Sanford Rose Assoc. - Euclid (C), OH, *569*
Sanford Rose Assoc. - Nashville (C), TN, *570*
Sanford Rose Assoc. - Philadelphia North (C), PA, *570*
Sanford Rose Assoc. - Port Washington (C), WI, *571*
Santangelo Consultants Inc. (C), NY, *571*
Sarver & Carruth Assoc. (C), OK, *571*
Sathe & Associates, Inc. (R), MN, *184*
Satterfield & Assoc., Inc. (R), OH, *184*
Savalli & Assoc., Inc. (C), MI, *571*
Saviar, Inc. (C), AZ, *571*
Savoy Partners, Ltd. (R), DC, *184*
F. B. Schmidt Int'l. (R), CA, *185*
Schuyler, Baker & Parker, Inc. (R), GA, *185*
Schweichler Assoc., Inc. (R), CA, *186*
Scott Executive Search, Inc. (R), NY, *186*
Search & Recruit Int'l. (C), VA, *573*
The Search America Group Inc. (C), OH, *573*
Search Assoc., Inc. (C), CA, *574*
Search Assoc., Inc. (C), NJ, *574*
Search Bureau Int'l. (C), IL, *574*
The Search Company (R), ON, *186*
Search Consultants, LLC (C), MD, *575*
Search Group (C), CA, *575*
Search Group Inc. (R), AB, *186*
Search Innovations, Inc. (R), PA, *187*
The Search Network (C), CA, *576*
Search Northwest Assoc. (C), OR, *576*
Search South, Inc. (C), AL, *576*
SearchCom, Inc. (R), TX, *187*
SearchCorp (C), FL, *577*
Seco & Zetto Assoc., Inc. (C), NJ, *577*
Sedlar & Miners (R), NY, *188*
Segal & Assoc. (C), GA, *578*
Seiden Krieger Assoc., Inc. (R), NY, *188*
Selectis Corp. (C), IL, *578*
Sensible Solutions, Inc. (R), IL, *188*
Setford-Shaw-Najarian Assoc. (C), NY, *579*
SFB Legal Search (C), NY, *579*
Sharp Placement Professionals, Inc. (C), NY, *579*
Shell Technology Group (C), CA, *580*
Shepherd Bueschel & Provus, Inc. (R), IL, *189*
Shinn & Assoc. (R), CA, *189*
Shoemaker & Assoc. (R), GA, *190*
Shore Asociados Ejecutivos, S. A. de C.V. (R), MX, *190*
The Shorr Group (R), IL, *190*
Larry Siegel & Assoc. (R), WA, *191*
RitaSue Siegel Resources, Inc. (R), NY, *191*
Siger & Assoc., LLC (C), CT, *581*
SignatureSoft Inc. (C), CA, *581*
L. A. Silver Assoc., Inc. (R), MA, *191*
Silver Associates (C), CA, *581*
Sink, Walker, Boltrus Int'l. (R), MA, *192*
Skipping Stone Inc. (C), VA, *582*
Ruth Sklar Assoc., Inc. (RSA Executive Search) (R), NY, *192*
Slayton Int'l., Inc. (R), IL, *192*
Ralph Smith & Assoc. (C), IL, *584*
Smith & Sawyer, Inc. (R), NY, *193*
The Smith Group, Inc. (C), NC, *584*
Smith Hanley Assoc., Inc. (C), NY, *584*
Smith James Group, Inc. (R), GA, *194*
Smith, Roth & Squires (R), NY, *194*
Smith Search, S.C. (R), MX, *194*
Smith's Fifth Avenue (C), NY, *585*
Smythe Masterson & Judd, Inc. (C), NY, *585*
Snelling & Snelling, Inc. (C), FL, *585*
Snelling Search Recruiters (C), NC, *586*
C. Snow & Assoc. (C), ON, *586*
Softrix, Inc. (C), NJ, *586*
Software Resource Consultants (C), TN, *587*
Phyllis Solomon Executive Search, Inc. (C), NJ, *587*
Solutions Group (R), AL, *195*
Stephen M. Sonis Assoc. (R), MA, *195*
Souder & Assoc. (R), VA, *195*
Southport Int'l. Assoc. Inc. (C), FL, *588*
Southwestern Professional Services (C), TN, *588*
Sparks, McDonough & Assoc., Inc. (C), MO, *588*
SPC Symcox Personnel Consultants (C), TX, *588*
Special Markets Group, Inc. (R), GA, *195*
Specialty Employment Services, Inc. (C), GA, *589*
SpectraWest (C), CA, *589*
Spectrum Consultants (R), CA, *196*
SpencerStuart (R), NY, *196*
The Spiegel Group (R), MA, *197*
Splaine & Assoc., Inc. (R), CA, *198*
Spriggs & Co., Inc. (R), IL, *198*
Springer Souder & Assoc. L.L.C. (R), IL, *198*
Sprout/Standish, Inc. (C), NH, *589*
Squires Resources Inc. (C), ON, *590*
SR Wilson, Inc. (C), CA, *590*
Staffing Edge, Inc. (C), IA, *590*
StaffWriters Plus (C), NY, *591*
Stanton Chase Int'l. (R), MD, *198*
The Stanton Group, Inc. (C), IL, *591*
Starbridge Group Inc. (C), VA, *591*
Steinbach & Co. (C), MA, *592*
Stentiford & Berardi Assoc. Ltd. (R), NY, *199*
Stephens Assoc. Ltd., Inc. (R), OH, *200*
Sterling Int'l. (R), NJ, *200*
Michael Stern Assoc., Inc./Euram (R), ON, *200*
Stevens Assoc. (C), MA, *593*
The Stewart Group (C), FL, *593*
Stewart, Stein & Scott, Ltd. (R), MN, *200*
Stewart/Laurence Assoc., Inc. (R), NJ, *201*
Stillinger & Assoc. (R), CA, *201*
Stone & Youngblood (C), MA, *594*
Stoopen Asociados, S.C./EMA Partners Int'l. (R), MX, *202*
Strategic Alternatives (R), CA, *202*
Strategic Executives, Inc. (R), CT, *202*
Strategic Resources (C), WA, *595*
Strategic Search, LLC (C), CA, *595*
StratfordGroup (R), OH, *203*
W. R. Strathmann Assoc. (R), NY, *203*

Success Seekers Connection (C), FL, *596*
Joe Sullivan & Assoc., Inc. (R), NY, *204*
Summerfield Assoc., Inc. (C), TN, *596*
The Summit Group (C), CA, *596*
Ron Sunshine & Assoc. (C), IL, *597*
Survival Systems Staffing, Inc. (C), CA, *597*
Swartz & Assoc., Inc. (R), AZ, *204*
Swift & Assoc. (C), ME, *597*
Synapse Human Resource Consulting Group (R), TX, *205*
Synergistech Communications (C), CA, *597*
Systems Careers (C), CA, *598*
Systems Personnel, Inc. (C), NY, *598*
T. H. Hunter, Inc. (C), MN, *599*
Tactical Alternatives (R), CA, *205*
The Talon Group (R), TX, *205*
Martin Stevens Tamaren & Assoc., Inc. (R), CA, *206*
Tanner & Assoc., Inc. (R), TX, *206*
Tarbex (C), DC, *599*
Tate & Assoc., Inc. (R), NJ, *207*
TaxSearch Inc. (R), OK, *207*
Carl J. Taylor & Co. (R), TX, *207*
Taylor Winfield (R), TX, *207*
TBC, Inc. (C), KY, *600*
TeamBuilders (C), GA, *600*
Tech 2000 (C), FL, *601*
Tech Connector Group (C), CA, *601*
Tech Consulting (C), FL, *601*
Tech Search (C), CA, *601*
Techaid Inc. (C), QE, *601*
TechNix Inc. (C), ON, *602*
The Technology Group (R), IL, *208*
Technology Management Partners (R), CA, *208*
Technology Search Int'l. (C), CA, *603*
Tele-Solutions of Arizona, Inc. (C), AZ, *604*
Telecom Connections, Inc. (C), TX, *604*
Telecom Executive Group (C), NJ, *605*
Telecom Recruiters, Inc. (C), VA, *605*
TeleManagement Search (C), NY, *605*
Telequest Communications, Inc. (C), NJ, *605*
Tell/Com Recruiters (C), PA, *605*
Thomas Lyle & Co. (C), IL, *606*
Thomas Resource Group (R), CA, *209*
Thomas, Whelan Assoc., Inc. (C), DC, *606*
Thor, Inc. (C), CA, *606*
The Touchstone Group (C), MA, *607*
TPS Staffing Solutions (C), IN, *608*
Trac One (R), NJ, *210*
Travaille Executive Search (R), DC, *210*
Travel Executive Search (C), NY, *608*
Travel Personnel (C), OH, *609*
Travis & Co., Inc. (R), MA, *210*
Traynor Confidential, Ltd. (C), NY, *609*
Van Treadaway Assoc., Inc. (R), GA, *210*
Trebor Weldon Lawrence, Inc. (R), NY, *210*
TriStaff Group (C), CA, *609*
Triumph Consulting, Inc. (R), IA, *210*
Trowbridge & Co., Inc. (R), MA, *211*
Tryon & Heideman, LLC (R), MO, *211*
TSC Management Services Group, Inc. (C), IL, *610*
TTG/Sterling Services (C), CA, *610*
Tucker Assoc. (R), NJ, *211*
Tuft & Assoc., Inc. (R), IL, *212*
Tuttle Venture Group, Inc. (R), TX, *212*
The Ultimate Source (R), CA, *212*
Venture Resources, Inc. (R), CA, *213*
The Verriez Group Inc. (R), ON, *213*
Vintage Resources, Inc. (C), NY, *613*
Beverly von Winckler & Assoc. (C), IL, *613*
Gordon Wahls Executive Search (C), PA, *613*
B. D. Wallace & Assoc. (C), MD, *614*
Wallace Assoc. (C), MA, *614*
Wallace Management Co. (R), TN, *215*
J. D. Walsh & Co. (R), CT, *215*
Martha Ward Executive Search, Inc. (C), NY, *615*
The Ward Group (R), MA, *215*
C. D. Warner & Assoc. (C), PA, *615*
Warren, Morris & Madison, Ltd. (C), CA, *616*
The Washington Firm, Ltd. (R), WA, *216*
Waveland Int'l. (R), IL, *216*
Webb, Johnson Assoc., Inc. (R), NY, *216*
Lee Weil Assoc., Inc. (C), IL, *617*
David Weinfeld Group (C), NC, *617*
Weinstein & Co. (R), MA, *217*
S. E. Weinstein Co. (R), IL, *217*
D. L. Weiss & Assoc. (R), CA, *217*
Weliver & Assoc. (C), MI, *618*
The Wellesley Group, Inc. (R), IL, *217*
Wellington Management Group (R), PA, *217*
Werbin Assoc. Executive Search, Inc. (C), NY, *618*
Wesley Brown & Bartle Co., Inc. (R), NY, *218*
West & West (R), CA, *218*
Western Technical Resources (C), CA, *619*
S. J. Wexler Assoc., Inc. (R), NY, *219*
Wheelless Group (R), IL, *219*
Whittlesey & Assoc., Inc. (R), PA, *220*
The Whyte Group, Inc. (R), MD, *220*
Wilder & Assoc. (C), VA, *620*
The Wilkie Group Int'l. (R), ON, *220*
Wilkinson & Ives (R), CA, *221*
Dick Williams & Assoc. (C), CA, *621*
Williams & Delmore, Inc. (C), NC, *621*
Willis & Assoc. (R), OH, *221*
William Willis Worldwide Inc. (R), CT, *221*
Wills Consulting Assoc. Inc. (R), CT, *221*
The Wilmington Group (C), NC, *622*
Wilson McLeran, Inc. (C), CT, *622*
Wilson-Douglas-Jordan (C), IL, *622*
The Winchester Group (R), CA, *222*
Winston Search, Inc. (R), MD, *222*
Winthrop Partners, Inc. (R), NY, *222*
Wisnewski & Assoc. (R), CA, *223*
S. R. Wolman Assoc., Inc. (R), NY, *224*
Woltz & Assoc., Inc. (R), IL, *224*
Louise Wood & Assoc. (C), NY, *624*
Wood, Franchot Inc. (R), MN, *224*
Wood West & Partners Inc. (C), BC, *624*
Bruce G. Woods Executive Search (R), TX, *224*
Woodworth Int'l. Group (R), OR, *224*
Working Relationships, Inc. (C), MN, *624*
The Worth Group (C), GA, *625*
Bob Wright Recruiting, Inc. (C), CT, *625*
WTW Assoc., Inc. (R), NY, *225*
Wyndham Mills Int'l., Inc. (R), GA, *225*
Xavier Associates, Inc. (R), MA, *226*
The York Group (C), CA, *626*
Yormak & Assoc. (C), CA, *626*
Bill Young & Assoc. (C), VA, *626*
ZanExec L.L.C. (R), VA, *226*
Zeiger Assoc. L.L.C. (C), CA, *627*
Zen Zen Int'l. Inc. (C), MB, *627*
P. D. Zier Assoc. (C), CT, *627*
Chuck Zimering Advertising Recruitment (CZAR) (C), NY, *627*

J.10 Advertising, public relations

A la Carte Int'l., Inc. (R), VA, *1*
ADR Accounting Management Recruiters (C), ON, *240*
AKH Executive Search (C), OR, *243*
Alexander & Co. (C), CA, *243*
The Alfus Group (R), NY, *3*
Analytic Recruiting, Inc. (C), NY, *249*
The Angus Group, Ltd. (C), OH, *251*
Ask Guy Tucker (C), GA, *254*
Carol Ball & Co. (C), CT, *258*
Ballantyne & Assoc. (R), CA, *10*
The Barack Group, Inc. (R), NY, *11*
Barnes & Assoc. Executive Search (C), CA, *259*
Barton Assoc., Inc. (R), TX, *12*
Joy Reed Belt Search Consultants, Inc. (R), OK, *15*
Benson Associates (C), NY, *264*
Berkhemer/Clayton, Inc. (R), CA, *16*
Bornholdt Shivas & Friends Executive Recruiters (C), NY, *270*
Brigade, Inc. (R), CA, *23*
Bristol Assoc., Inc. (C), CA, *274*
Brown, Bernardy, Van Remmen, Inc. (C), CA, *275*
Brownstone Sales & Marketing Group, Inc. (C), NY, *275*
Charles Buck & Assoc., Inc. (R), NY, *24*
Caplan Assoc., Inc. (R), NJ, *28*
Caprio & Assoc. Inc. (R), IL, *29*
Careers On Track (C), NJ, *283*
Carlsen Resources, Inc. (R), CO, *29*
Carpenter Assoc., Inc. (R), IL, *30*
Cassell & Kaye (C), NY, *286*
Cella Assoc. (C), GA, *286*
Churchill & Affiliates, Inc. (R), PA, *35*
Toby Clark Assoc. Inc. (C), NY, *292*
Clayman & Co. (R), MA, *36*
Consulpro (R), ON, *39*
Consulting Rhonda (C), ON, *297*
Conway & Assoc. (R), IL, *40*
Leonard Corwen Assoc. (C), NY, *302*
CountryHouse Hotels Executive Search (C), VA, *302*
Trudi Cowlan (C), NY, *302*
Judith Cushman & Assoc. (R), WA, *44*
Custom Resources (C), AL, *305*
Cypress Int'l., Inc. (R), FL, *45*
D & M Associates (C), PA, *306*
D.A.I Human Resources Consultants (R), QE, *45*

INDUSTRIES

Bert Davis Executive Search, Inc. (R), NY, *47*
Bert Davis Publishing Placement Consultants (C), NY, *309*
DCA Professional Search (C), TX, *309*
DeLalla - Fried Assoc. (C), NY, *310*
Desktop Staffing, Inc. (C), IL, *311*
Development Resource Group (R), NY, *48*
The Devlin Search Group, Inc. (C), MA, *311*
Roger Dietsch & Assoc. (C), MN, *312*
J. Dinerstein & Co., Inc. (R), NY, *51*
Diversified Search, Inc. (R), PA, *52*
Gwen Dycus & Assoc. (C), FL, *323*
Eden & Assoc., Inc. (C), PA, *326*
EDI/Executive Dynamics Inc. (C), NJ, *326*
The Evans Search Group (R), CT, *61*
Executive Search Partners (R), NY, *63*
Executive Solutions (R), MN, *64*
Executive/Retail Placement Assoc. (C), MD, *337*
ExecutiveFit (C), NY, *337*
Fairfield Int'l. Resources (R), NY, *65*
Jerry Fields Assoc. (C), NY, *340*
J. G. Flynn & Assoc. Inc. (R), BC, *69*
Foley Proctor Yoskowitz (R), NJ, *69*
Fortune of Arlington Heights (C), IL, *345*
Forum Personnel Inc. (C), NY, *351*
Foster Partners (R), NY, *70*
Neil Frank & Co. (R), CA, *71*
Franstaff Inc. (C), FL, *352*
The Fry Group, Inc. (C), NY, *353*
Frye/Joure & Assoc., Inc. (C), TN, *353*
The Garvis Group, Inc. (C), LA, *355*
The Goldman Group Inc. (R), NY, *79*
Goldman+Bell, LLC (C), NY, *360*
David Gomez & Assoc., Inc. (R), IL, *79*
Goodrich & Sherwood Assoc., Inc. (R), NY, *79*
The Governance Group, Inc. (R), NJ, *80*
Graphic Arts Marketing Assoc., Inc. (C), MI, *361*
Sheila Greco Assoc. (C), NY, *362*
Greene Personnel Consultants (C), RI, *362*
David E. Grumney Co. Inc. (R), WA, *83*
Nadine Guber & Assoc., Inc. (C), NY, *364*
Gumbinner/Haubenstock, Inc. (C), NY, *364*
Don Hall & Assoc. (C), TX, *366*
Susan Hall Executive Search (C), TX, *366*
Hamilton & Co. (C), OH, *367*
Hands-on Broadcast (R), NY, *86*
Handy HRM (R), NY, *86*
Janet Harberth & Assoc., Inc. (C), GA, *368*
Hart & Co. (C), NY, *370*
Hazlett Associates (R), IL, *88*
Kay Henry, Inc. (C), PA, *376*
Heyman Assoc., Inc. (R), NY, *93*
Hill & Assoc. (C), CA, *378*
Howard-Sloan Assoc. (C), NY, *381*
The Howard-Sloan-Koller Group (R), NY, *97*
Arnold Huberman Assoc., Inc. (R), NY, *97*
Human Resource Bureau (C), CA, *384*
The Hyde Group, Inc. (R), CT, *101*
Innovative Partnerships (R), CA, *101*
Intelligent Marketing Solutions, Inc. (C), NY, *390*
Interspace Interactive, Inc. (C), NY, *394*
Ives & Associates, Inc. (C), OH, *395*
JAG Group (R), MO, *105*
JDH & Assoc. (C), CA, *397*
Jeffrey Meryl Assoc., Inc. (C), NJ, *398*
Julian Assoc., Inc. (C), CT, *401*
The Kay Group of 5th Ave. (C), NY, *404*
A.T. Kearney Executive Search (R), IL, *111*
Kenzer Corp. (R), NY, *113*
Key Employment (C), NJ, *405*
Kittleman & Assoc.,LLC (R), IL, *115*
Kordus Consulting Group (C), WI, *408*
Kramer Executive Resources, Inc. (C), NY, *409*
Kresin Wingard (C), IL, *409*
Marvin Laba & Assoc. (R), CA, *122*
Ricci Lee Assoc., Inc. (C), CA, *415*
Hal Levy & Assoc. (C), NY, *417*
The Libra Group Inc. (C), CT, *417*
Ginger Lindsey & Assoc., Inc. (C), TX, *418*
Lipsky Group, Inc. (R), CA, *129*
Lloyd Prescott Assoc., Inc. (C), FL, *418*
Charles Luntz & Assoc., Inc. (R), MO, *132*
Lynne Palmer Executive Recruitment, Inc. (C), NY, *421*
Madison MacArthur Inc. (R), ON, *133*
Management One Consultants (C), ON, *425*
Management Recruiters of Northern Palm Beaches (C), FL, *444*
Management Recruiters of Atlanta (C), GA, *445*
Management Recruiters of Middlesex County NJ (C), NJ, *454*
Management Recruiters of Gramercy, Inc. (C), NY, *455*
Management Recruiters of Austin (C), TX, *462*
Mark Adam Assoc. (R), NJ, *135*
Marketing Search Inc. (C), OH, *471*
Marketing/Public Relations Research Recruiting (C), CT, *471*
The Marlow Group (R), MA, *136*
Maxecon Executive Search Consultants (R), FL, *138*
MB Inc. Executive Search (C), NY, *473*
Joseph J. McTaggart (C), CA, *476*
Meads & Assoc. (R), FL, *142*
Media Recruiting Group, Inc. (C), NY, *476*
Mengel & McDonald Ltd. (C), IL, *479*
Merlin Int'l. Inc. (C), NJ, *479*
Milrod Assoc. (C), NJ, *482*
Herbert Mines Assoc., Inc. (R), NY, *145*
Laurie Mitchell & Co., Inc. (R), OH, *145*
Mitchell Martin Inc. (C), NY, *483*
Morgan/Webber, Inc. (R), NY, *147*
Moyer, Sherwood Assoc., Inc. (R), NY, *148*
NDB Assoc., Inc. (C), PA, *491*
Noble & Assoc., Inc. (C), NY, *494*
Nordeman Grimm, Inc. (R), NY, *152*
Norman Broadbent Int'l., Inc. (R), NY, *152*
O'Brien and Roof (C), OH, *497*
O'Keefe & Assoc., Inc. (R), CT, *154*
The Ogdon Partnership (R), NY, *155*
K. Ossow & Co. (C), NY, *500*
Janou Pakter, Inc. (C), NY, *502*
Partners Executive Search Consultants Inc. (R), ON, *160*
Carolyn Smith Paschal Int'l. (R), CA, *160*
Peachtree Executive Search (R), GA, *161*
Perez & Assoc. (C), MI, *507*
Phillips Assoc. (C), FL, *510*
Rene Plessner Assoc., Inc. (R), NY, *165*
Robert Powers & Assoc. (C), CA, *515*
Precision Executive Search (C), AZ, *516*
ProSearch Recruiting (C), CA, *524*
Proven Edge (C), CA, *525*
Joanne E. Ratner Search (C), NY, *529*
Recruiting Options, Inc. (C), GA, *531*
Mary Rector & Assoc., Inc. (C), IL, *533*
Reeve & Assoc. (C), CT, *533*
Russell Reynolds Assoc., Inc. (R), NY, *176*
Richards Assoc., Inc. (R), NY, *178*
Ridenour & Assoc. (R), IL, *178*
Ritt-Ritt & Assoc., Inc. (C), IL, *537*
RJN Consulting (R), NY, *179*
Ruderfer & Co., Inc. (C), NJ, *548*
K. Russo Assoc. Inc. (C), CT, *548*
Ryman, Bell, Green & Michaels, Inc. (C), TX, *549*
Sanford Rose Assoc. - Norcross (C), GA, *566*
Sanford Rose Assoc. - Evansville (C), IN, *567*
Savalli & Assoc., Inc. (C), MI, *571*
The Search Company (R), ON, *186*
Search Innovations, Inc. (R), PA, *187*
SearchCom, Inc. (R), TX, *187*
Shoemaker & Assoc. (R), GA, *190*
Ralph Smith & Assoc. (C), IL, *584*
Smith Hanley Assoc., Inc. (C), NY, *584*
Smith's Fifth Avenue (C), NY, *585*
Phyllis Solomon Executive Search, Inc. (C), NJ, *587*
SpencerStuart (R), NY, *196*
StaffWriters Plus (C), NY, *591*
Stone & Youngblood (C), MA, *594*
Success Seekers Connection (C), FL, *596*
TechNix Inc. (C), ON, *602*
Travaille Executive Search (R), DC, *210*
Travel Executive Search (C), NY, *608*
Travel Personnel (C), OH, *609*
Trebor Weldon Lawrence, Inc. (R), NY, *210*
Vintage Resources, Inc. (C), NY, *613*
B. D. Wallace & Assoc. (C), MD, *614*
Martha Ward Executive Search, Inc. (C), NY, *615*
The Ward Group (R), MA, *215*
Warren, Morris & Madison, Ltd. (C), CA, *616*
Lee Weil Assoc., Inc. (C), IL, *617*
S. E. Weinstein Co. (R), IL, *217*
Wesley Brown & Bartle Co., Inc. (R), NY, *218*
Wheelless Group (R), IL, *219*
The Whyte Group, Inc. (R), MD, *220*
Wills Consulting Assoc. Inc. (R), CT, *221*
S. R. Wolman Assoc., Inc. (R), NY, *224*
Louise Wood & Assoc. (C), NY, *624*
Bob Wright Recruiting, Inc. (C), CT, *625*
The York Group (C), CA, *626*
Zen Zen Int'l. Inc. (C), MB, *627*
Chuck Zimering Advertising Recruitment (CZAR) (C), NY, *627*

J.11 Publishing, print media

Adler Management, Inc. (R), NJ, *2*
Alexander & Co. (C), CA, *243*
Ariel Recruitment Assoc. (R), NY, *7*
Ask Guy Tucker (C), GA, *254*
Ballantyne & Assoc. (R), CA, *10*
Battalia Winston Int'l./The Euram Consultants Group (R), NY, *13*
Bishop Partners (R), NY, *17*
The Black Leopard (C), CA, *267*
Bonnell Assoc. Ltd. (R), CT, *19*
Brown, Bernardy, Van Remmen, Inc. (C), CA, *275*
Brownstone Sales & Marketing Group, Inc. (C), NY, *275*
Charles Buck & Assoc., Inc. (R), NY, *24*
The Buckley Group (C), FL, *276*
Burke & Assoc./The Westfield Group (C), CT, *276*
Capital Consulting Group, Inc. (R), MD, *28*
Caplan Assoc., Inc. (R), NJ, *28*
Caprio & Assoc. Inc. (R), IL, *29*
Career Advisors, Inc. (C), FL, *281*
Career Consulting Group, Inc. (C), CT, *281*
Carpenter Assoc., Inc. (R), IL, *30*
Central Executive Search, Inc. (C), OH, *287*
Christian & Timbers, Inc. (R), OH, *34*
Leonard Corwen Assoc. (C), NY, *302*
Trudi Cowlan (C), NY, *302*
Cypress Int'l., Inc. (R), FL, *45*
D & M Associates (C), PA, *306*
DARE Personnel Inc. (C), ON, *307*
Bert Davis Executive Search, Inc. (R), NY, *47*
Bert Davis Publishing Placement Consultants (C), NY, *309*
Desktop Staffing, Inc. (C), IL, *311*
Diversified Search, Inc. (R), PA, *52*
EDI/Executive Dynamics Inc. (C), NJ, *326*
David M. Ellner Assoc. (R), NY, *59*
Employ® (C), PA, *330*
The Enfield Company (C), TX, *330*
Executive Resource Group, Inc. (R), ME, *63*
Executive Sales Search (C), CO, *335*
Executive Search Partners (R), NY, *63*
Neil Fink Assoc. (R), CA, *66*
Fisher Personnel Management Services (R), CA, *68*
Florapersonnel, Inc. (R), FL, *68*
Foster Partners (R), NY, *70*
Gerald Frisch Assoc., Inc. (R), NY, *72*
Gardiner, Townsend & Assoc. (R), NY, *74*
Gardner-Ross Assoc., Inc. (R), NY, *74*
H. L. Goehring & Assoc., Inc. (C), OH, *359*
Goldstein & Co. (C), CA, *360*
Gould, McCoy & Chadick, Inc. (R), NY, *80*
The Grant Search Group, Inc. (C), ON, *361*
Graphic Arts Marketing Assoc., Inc. (C), MI, *361*
Greenhaven & Assoc., Inc. (R), NY, *81*
David E. Grumney Co. Inc. (R), WA, *83*
GWS Partners (R), IL, *84*
Hands-on Broadcast (R), NY, *86*
Handy HRM (R), NY, *86*
Kay Henry, Inc. (C), PA, *376*
Hodge-Cronin & Assoc., Inc. (R), IL, *94*
Howard-Sloan Assoc. (C), NY, *381*
The Howard-Sloan-Koller Group (R), NY, *97*
InteliSearch, Inc. (R), CT, *102*
Interspace Interactive, Inc. (C), NY, *394*
Jeffrey Irving Assoc., Inc. (R), VA, *104*
Isaacson, Miller (R), MA, *104*
JDH & Assoc. (C), CA, *397*
Johnson & Company (R), CT, *107*
The Kay Group of 5th Ave. (C), NY, *404*
A.T. Kearney Executive Search (R), IL, *111*
The Koehler Group (C), PA, *408*
Kresin Wingard (C), IL, *409*
Ricci Lee Assoc., Inc. (C), CA, *415*
Hal Levy & Assoc. (C), NY, *417*
Lipson & Co. (R), CA, *130*
Livingston, Robert & Co. (R), CT, *130*
The John Lucht Consultancy Inc. (R), NY, *131*
P. J. Lynch Assoc. (R), CT, *132*
Lynne Palmer Executive Recruitment, Inc. (C), NY, *421*
Management Recruiters of Northern Palm Beaches (C), FL, *444*
Management Recruiters of Gramercy, Inc. (C), NY, *455*
Management Resource Group, Inc. (C), NY, *467*
Mark Adam Assoc. (R), NJ, *135*
McDonald, Long & Assoc., Inc. (R), NY, *140*
The McKinnon Management Group Inc. (C), ON, *475*
McManners Assoc., Inc. (R), CA, *142*
Media Recruiting Group, Inc. (C), NY, *476*
Milrod Assoc. (C), NJ, *482*
Laurie Mitchell & Co., Inc. (R), OH, *145*
Morgan/Webber, Inc. (R), NY, *147*
NDB Assoc., Inc. (C), PA, *491*
Nordeman Grimm, Inc. (R), NY, *152*
Norman Broadbent Int'l., Inc. (R), NY, *152*
The Ogdon Partnership (R), NY, *155*
Janou Pakter, Inc. (C), NY, *502*
Partners Executive Search Consultants Inc. (R), ON, *160*
Pathway Executive Search, Inc. (C), NY, *505*
Barry Persky & Co., Inc. (R), CT, *163*
Personnel Assoc. (C), CA, *508*
Placements by Jesse Reid Assoc., Inc. (C), NY, *513*
Precision Executive Search (C), AZ, *516*
ProSearch Recruiting (C), CA, *524*
Proven Edge (C), CA, *525*
R. J. Associates (C), NY, *528*
Recruiting Resources Int'l. (C), CA, *532*
Redden & McGrath Assoc., Inc. (R), NY, *173*
Russell Reynolds Assoc., Inc. (R), NY, *176*
Robison Humphreys & Assoc., Inc. (R), ON, *180*
R. S. Sadow Assoc. (C), NJ, *550*
Sales Consultants of Sacramento (C), CA, *556*
Sales Consultants of Savannah, GA (C), GA, *557*
Sales Consultants of Houston (C), TX, *563*
Norm Sanders Assoc., Inc. (R), NJ, *184*
Sanford Rose Assoc. - Fairhope (C), AL, *565*
Sanford Rose Assoc. - Nashville (C), TN, *570*
SearchCom, Inc. (R), TX, *187*
SFB Legal Search (C), NY, *579*
Shepherd Bueschel & Provus, Inc. (R), IL, *189*
Smith's Fifth Avenue (C), NY, *585*
Southwestern Professional Services (C), TN, *588*
SpencerStuart (R), NY, *196*
Sprout/Standish, Inc. (C), NH, *589*
Stentiford & Berardi Assoc. Ltd. (R), NY, *199*
Stone & Youngblood (C), MA, *594*
The Summit Group (C), CA, *596*
Synergistech Communications (C), CA, *597*
The Talon Group (R), TX, *205*
Thomas, Whelan Assoc., Inc. (C), DC, *606*
Travaille Executive Search (R), DC, *210*
TriStaff Group (C), CA, *609*
Triumph Consulting, Inc. (R), IA, *210*
Tuft & Assoc., Inc. (R), IL, *212*
Vintage Resources, Inc. (C), NY, *613*
Gordon Wahls Executive Search (C), PA, *613*
The Wilkie Group Int'l. (R), ON, *220*
Wilson McLeran, Inc. (C), CT, *622*
Winthrop Partners, Inc. (R), NY, *222*
Louise Wood & Assoc. (C), NY, *624*
Bob Wright Recruiting, Inc. (C), CT, *625*

J.12 New media (e.g. Internet, multimedia)

Abraham & London Ltd. (C), CT, *232*
Adept Tech Recruiting, Inc. (C), NY, *240*
Adler Management, Inc. (R), NJ, *2*
Advanced Corporate Search (C), CA, *240*
Advanced Recruiting, Inc. (C), OK, *240*
Advancement, Inc. (C), IL, *241*
The Advisory Group, Inc. (R), CA, *2*
Alexander & Co. (C), CA, *243*
D. S. Allen Assoc. (C), NJ, *244*
Angus Employment Ltd. (C), ON, *250*
David Aplin & Assoc. (C), AB, *251*
Ariel Recruitment Assoc. (R), NY, *7*
Ashton Computer Professionals, Inc. (C), BC, *253*
ASI (C), CA, *254*
Ask Guy Tucker (C), GA, *254*
Aubin Int'l. Inc. (R), MA, *8*
The Badger Group (R), CA, *10*
Baker Scott & Co. (C), NJ, *258*
Ballantyne & Assoc. (R), CA, *10*
The Barack Group, Inc. (R), NY, *11*
Barnes & Assoc. Executive Search (C), CA, *259*
Bast & Assoc., Inc. (C), CA, *261*
Berkana Int'l., Inc. (C), WA, *265*
Berkhemer/Clayton, Inc. (R), CA, *16*
Bishop Partners (R), NY, *17*
Blaney Executive Search (R), MA, *18*
Block & Assoc. (R), CA, *18*
Bolton Group (C), CA, *269*

Bonell Ryan Inc. (R), NY, *19*
Bornholdt Shivas & Friends Executive Recruiters (C), NY, *270*
Bower & Associates (C), TX, *271*
Boyden (R), NY, *20*
Bredeson Executive Recruitment, LLC (R), TX, *22*
Bridgecreek Personnel Agency (C), CA, *273*
Brown, Bernardy, Van Remmen, Inc. (C), CA, *275*
Brown Venture Assoc. (R), CA, *24*
BT&A, LLC (R), CT, *24*
The Buckley Group (C), FL, *276*
Joseph R. Burns & Assoc., Inc. (R), NJ, *25*
Business Partners, Inc. (C), FL, *277*
Byron Leonard Int'l., Inc. (R), CA, *25*
Canny, Bowen Inc. (R), NY, *27*
Caplan Assoc., Inc. (R), NJ, *28*
Career Consulting Group, Inc. (C), CT, *281*
Careers First, Inc. (C), NJ, *283*
Carlsen Resources, Inc. (R), CO, *29*
Carpenter Assoc., Inc. (R), IL, *30*
CAS Comsearch Inc. (C), NY, *285*
Catalyx Group (R), NY, *31*
Caywood Partners, Ltd. (R), CA, *32*
CEO Consulting (C), FL, *287*
Christian & Timbers, Inc. (R), OH, *34*
Toby Clark Assoc. Inc. (C), NY, *292*
Clayman & Co. (R), MA, *36*
CN Associates (C), CA, *293*
The Colton Partnership, Inc. (R), NY, *38*
CompuPro (C), IL, *295*
Computer Int'l. Consultants, Inc. (C), FL, *295*
Computer Security Placement Service (C), MA, *296*
Trudi Cowlan (C), NY, *302*
Judith Cushman & Assoc. (R), WA, *44*
Cypress Int'l., Inc. (R), FL, *45*
Dahl-Morrow Int'l. (R), VA, *45*
The Dalley Hewitt Co. (R), GA, *45*
DARE Personnel Inc. (C), ON, *307*
Data-AxIS Corp. (C), FL, *307*
Bert Davis Executive Search, Inc. (R), NY, *47*
Bert Davis Publishing Placement Consultants (C), NY, *309*
Despres & Associates (C), IL, *311*
The Diestel Group (R), UT, *51*
J. Dinerstein & Co., Inc. (R), NY, *51*
L. J. Doherty & Assoc. (R), MA, *53*
Dorst Information Services, Inc. (C), NY, *314*
Dotson & Assoc. (R), NY, *54*
EDI/Executive Dynamics Inc. (C), NJ, *326*
EFCO Consultants, Inc. (C), NY, *327*
Ellis & Associates (C), HI, *328*
Emerging Technology Search (C), GA, *329*
Empire International (R), PA, *59*
The Enfield Company (C), TX, *330*
Epsen, Fuller & Assoc., LLC (R), NJ, *60*
Executive Partners Inc. (C), CT, *333*
Executive Recruiters (C), WA, *334*
Executive Resource Group, Inc. (R), ME, *63*
Executive Search of America, Inc. (C), OH, *336*
Executive Search Partners (R), NY, *63*
Fast Switch, Ltd. (C), OH, *338*
The Fawcett Group (R), MA, *65*
A. E. Feldman Assoc., Inc. (C), NY, *339*
Fenwick Partners (R), MA, *66*
Jerry Fields Assoc. (C), NY, *340*
Neil Fink Assoc. (R), CA, *66*
First Search Inc. (C), IL, *341*
A. G. Fishkin & Assoc., Inc. (R), MD, *68*
Fortune Personnel Consultants of Colorado Springs (C), CO, *344*
Foster Partners (R), NY, *70*
Foy, Schneid & Daniel, Inc. (R), NY, *71*
Frye/Joure & Assoc., Inc. (C), TN, *353*
Garland Assoc. Int'l. (C), CA, *355*
The Garms Group (R), IL, *74*
Geneva Group Int'l. (R), CA, *76*
Global 1000 Int'l. Services (C), CA, *358*
Global Employer's Network, Inc. (R), TX, *77*
Global Technologies Group Inc. (C), NC, *359*
Global Telecommunications, Inc. (C), TX, *359*
Glou Int'l., Inc. (R), MA, *78*
The Goldman Group Inc. (R), NY, *79*
Goldman+Bell, LLC (C), NY, *360*
Goldstein & Co. (C), CA, *360*
Graphic Arts Marketing Assoc., Inc. (C), MI, *361*
Greene Personnel Consultants (C), RI, *362*
Greenwich Internet (C), CT, *363*
Greger/Peterson Assoc., Inc. (R), CA, *81*
J. B. Groner Executive Search, Inc. (C), DE, *363*
Growth Strategies, Inc. (R), FL, *83*
GSW Consulting Group, Inc. (R), CA, *83*
Nadine Guber & Assoc., Inc. (C), NY, *364*
Wolf Gugler & Assoc. Ltd. (R), ON, *83*
Gustin Partners, Ltd. (R), MA, *83*
Haley Associates (R), CA, *85*
Hamilton & Co. (C), OH, *367*
The Hamilton Group (R), MD, *85*
Hands-on Broadcast (R), NY, *86*
Janet Harberth & Assoc., Inc. (C), GA, *368*
Hartsfield Group, Inc. (R), GA, *87*
Hazlett Associates (R), IL, *88*
Headden Assoc. (R), WA, *88*
Hechkoff/Work Executive Search Inc. (R), NY, *89*
Kay Henry, Inc. (C), PA, *376*
J. J. Herlihy & Assoc., Inc. (C), CA, *376*
Herrerias & Assoc. (R), CA, *92*
J. D. Hersey & Assoc. (C), OH, *376*
Higbee Assoc., Inc. (C), CT, *377*
Hook-Up! (C), CA, *380*
Howard-Sloan Assoc. (C), NY, *381*
The Howard-Sloan-Koller Group (R), NY, *97*
HRCS (R), CA, *97*
Hughes & Company (R), VA, *98*
Huntington Personnel Consultants, Inc. (C), NY, *386*
i.j. & assoc., inc. (C), CO, *386*
The Inside Track (C), TX, *389*
Integrity Search, Inc. (R), PA, *102*
Intelligent Marketing Solutions, Inc. (C), NY, *390*
Interactive Search Network (R), CA, *102*
Isaacson, Miller (R), MA, *104*
JDH & Assoc. (C), CA, *397*
JL & Co. (C), CA, *399*
Johnson & Assoc., Inc. (R), CA, *106*
Ronald S. Johnson Assoc., Inc. (R), CA, *107*
K2 Resources, L.P. (C), CT, *402*
Kaplan & Assoc., Inc. (R), PA, *109*
Allan Karson Assoc., Inc. (R), NJ, *110*
The Kay Group of 5th Ave. (C), NY, *404*
Keane Assoc. (R), MA, *110*
A.T. Kearney Executive Search (R), IL, *111*
Ki Technologies, Inc. (C), UT, *406*
Kleber & Assoc. (C), WA, *407*
The Kleven Group, Inc. (C), MA, *407*
T. J. Koellhoffer & Assoc. (R), NJ, *116*
Katherine R. Kraemer (R), CA, *120*
Krakower Group, Inc. (R), CA, *120*
Kresin Wingard (C), IL, *409*
Kurtz Pro-Search, Inc. (C), NJ, *410*
The Landstone Group (C), NY, *412*
Lasher Assoc. (R), FL, *125*
LCS, Inc. (C), TX, *414*
Ricci Lee Assoc., Inc. (C), CA, *415*
Hal Levy & Assoc. (C), NY, *417*
Lipson & Co. (R), CA, *130*
Logix, Inc. (C), MA, *420*
The John Lucht Consultancy Inc. (R), NY, *131*
The Luciani Group (R), CA, *132*
Fran Luisi Assoc. (R), NJ, *132*
P. J. Lynch Assoc. (R), CT, *132*
Lynne Palmer Executive Recruitment, Inc. (C), NY, *421*
Lyons & Assoc., Inc. (C), IL, *422*
Madison MacArthur Inc. (R), ON, *133*
Management Recruiters of Northern California (C), CA, *440*
Management Recruiters of Roseville (C), CA, *441*
Management Recruiters of St. Lucie County, Inc. (C), FL, *444*
Management Recruiters of Northern Palm Beaches (C), FL, *444*
Management Recruiters of Birmingham (C), MI, *451*
Management Recruiters of Gramercy, Inc. (C), NY, *455*
Management Recruiters of Arlington (C), VA, *464*
Management Recruiters Int'l.-The Woodlands (C), TX, *464*
Management Recruiters of Milwaukee - Downtown (C), WI, *466*
Management Resource Group, Inc. (C), NY, *467*
Management Search, Inc. (C), IL, *467*
The Marlow Group (R), MA, *136*
Karen Marshall Assoc. (C), KY, *471*
Joseph J. McTaggart (C), CA, *476*
Media Recruiting Group, Inc. (C), NY, *476*
MediaCOM Talent Group (C), MA, *476*
Mengel & McDonald Ltd. (C), IL, *479*
Milrod Assoc. (C), NJ, *482*
Laurie Mitchell & Co., Inc. (R), OH, *145*
Montenido Assoc. (R), CA, *146*
Moyer, Sherwood Assoc., Inc. (R), NY, *148*
Much & Co. (R), NY, *148*

Multi Processing, Inc. (R), NH, *149*
Myers Career Assoc., Inc. (C), CA, *488*
Nagler, Robins & Poe, Inc. (R), MA, *150*
National Recruiters (C), OK, *489*
NDB Assoc., Inc. (C), PA, *491*
New Dimensions in Technology, Inc. (C), MA, *492*
Noble & Assoc., Inc. (C), NY, *494*
Nordeman Grimm, Inc. (R), NY, *152*
Norman Broadbent Int'l., Inc. (R), NY, *152*
NorthStar Technologies, Inc. (C), NY, *496*
O'Connor Resources (C), TX, *497*
The Ogdon Partnership (R), NY, *155*
P.R.H. Management, Inc. (R), CT, *158*
Pacific Crossing (C), CA, *501*
Janou Pakter, Inc. (C), NY, *502*
Paladin Group, Inc. (C), CO, *502*
Parker-Worthington, Inc. (C), TX, *503*
Partners Executive Search Consultants Inc. (R), ON, *160*
Partners Resource Group (C), VA, *504*
Pathway Executive Search, Inc. (C), NY, *505*
Paul-Tittle Assoc., Inc. (R), VA, *161*
Pearson & Assoc., Inc. (C), AZ, *506*
Perry Search Assoc. (C), CA, *507*
Perry-Martel Int'l., Inc. (R), ON, *163*
Personnel Assoc. (C), CA, *508*
PHD Conseil en Ressources Humaines Inc. (C), QE, *510*
Phillips Assoc. (C), FL, *510*
Phillips Personnel/Search (C), CO, *510*
The Pinnacle Source, Inc. (C), CO, *512*
Placements by Jesse Reid Assoc., Inc. (C), NY, *513*
Precision Executive Search (C), AZ, *516*
Prime Management Group Inc. (C), ON, *518*
ProSearch Recruiting (C), CA, *524*
J. E. Ranta Assoc. (C), MA, *529*
Ray & Berndtson (R), TX, *171*
Recruit Xpress (C), TX, *531*
Recruiting Options, Inc. (C), GA, *531*
Recruiting Resources Int'l. (C), CA, *532*
Recruiting/Solutions (C), CA, *532*
Redwood Partners Ltd. (R), NY, *173*
Reeve & Assoc. (C), CT, *533*
Resource Services, Inc. (C), NY, *534*
Russell Reynolds Assoc., Inc. (R), NY, *176*
Rice Cohen Int'l. (R), PA, *178*
Richards Assoc., Inc. (R), NY, *178*
W. F. Richer Assoc., Inc. (C), NY, *536*
Ridenour & Assoc. (R), IL, *178*
Rooney Assoc., Inc. (R), IL, *181*
Royal Assoc. (C), CA, *547*
Sales Consultants of Boca Raton, Inc. (C), FL, *557*
Sales Consultants of Stamford-Darien (C), CT, *557*
Sales Consultants of Barrington (C), IL, *558*
Sales Consultants of Chicago South (C), IL, *558*
Sales Consultants of Birmingham (C), MI, *559*
Sales Consultants King of Prussia (C), PA, *562*
Sales Consultants of Madison (C), WI, *563*
Sanford Rose Assoc. - Norcross (C), GA, *566*
Sanford Rose Assoc. - Euclid (C), OH, *569*
Sanford Rose Assoc. - Philadelphia North (C), PA, *570*
Saviar, Inc. (C), AZ, *571*
Schweichler Assoc., Inc. (R), CA, *186*
Scott Executive Search, Inc. (R), NY, *186*
The Search Company (R), ON, *186*
Search Group (C), CA, *575*
The Search Network (C), CA, *576*
Search South, Inc. (C), AL, *576*
Seco & Zetto Assoc., Inc. (C), NJ, *577*
Sedlar & Miners (R), NY, *188*
Setford-Shaw-Najarian Assoc. (C), NY, *579*
Sharp Placement Professionals, Inc. (C), NY, *579*
Shell Technology Group (C), CA, *580*
RitaSue Siegel Resources, Inc. (R), NY, *191*
Smith & Sawyer, Inc. (R), NY, *193*
Smith's Fifth Avenue (C), NY, *585*
Sparks, McDonough & Assoc., Inc. (C), MO, *588*
SpencerStuart (R), NY, *196*
Splaine & Assoc., Inc. (R), CA, *198*
Sprout/Standish, Inc. (C), NH, *589*
Squires Resources Inc. (C), ON, *590*
StaffWriters Plus (C), NY, *591*
Starbridge Group Inc. (C), VA, *591*
Steinbach & Co. (C), MA, *592*
Stentiford & Berardi Assoc. Ltd. (R), NY, *199*
Stevens Assoc. (C), MA, *593*
Stone & Youngblood (C), MA, *594*
Strategic Alternatives (R), CA, *202*
Swartz & Assoc., Inc. (R), AZ, *204*
Swift & Assoc. (C), ME, *597*
Synergistech Communications (C), CA, *597*
Systems Careers (C), CA, *598*
Tactical Alternatives (R), CA, *205*
Martin Stevens Tamaren & Assoc., Inc. (R), CA, *206*
TBC, Inc. (C), KY, *600*
Tech 2000 (C), FL, *601*
Techaid Inc. (C), QE, *601*
Technology Management Partners (R), CA, *208*
Technology Search Int'l. (C), CA, *603*
Telecom Executive Group (C), NJ, *605*
Thomas Resource Group (R), CA, *209*
Thomas, Whelan Assoc., Inc. (C), DC, *606*
Travaille Executive Search (R), DC, *210*
Travel Executive Search (C), NY, *608*
Travis & Co., Inc. (R), MA, *210*
TSC Management Services Group, Inc. (C), IL, *610*
Vintage Resources, Inc. (C), NY, *613*
B. D. Wallace & Assoc. (C), MD, *614*
Wallace Assoc. (C), MA, *614*
The Ward Group (R), MA, *215*
Warren, Morris & Madison, Ltd. (C), CA, *616*
Waveland Int'l. (R), IL, *216*
Weliver & Assoc. (C), MI, *618*
Wellington Management Group (R), PA, *217*
Western Technical Resources (C), CA, *619*
Wheelless Group (R), IL, *219*
Dick Williams & Assoc. (C), CA, *621*
Wilson McLeran, Inc. (C), CT, *622*
Wilson-Douglas-Jordan (C), IL, *622*
Louise Wood & Assoc. (C), NY, *624*
ZanExec L.L.C. (R), VA, *226*

J.13 TV, cable, motion pictures, video, radio

Abraxas Technologies, Inc. (C), FL, *233*
ACSYS Resources, Inc. (C), DE, *238*
Adam-Bryce Inc. (C), NY, *239*
Advancement, Inc. (C), IL, *241*
Ariel Recruitment Assoc. (R), NY, *7*
Ask Guy Tucker (C), GA, *254*
Association for Sales Force Management (C), WA, *254*
Baker Scott & Co. (C), NJ, *258*
Allen Ballach Assoc. Inc. (R), ON, *10*
The Barack Group, Inc. (R), NY, *11*
Bast & Assoc., Inc. (C), CA, *261*
Benson Associates (C), NY, *264*
Bishop Partners (R), NY, *17*
Block & Assoc. (R), CA, *18*
D. R. Blood & Assoc. (R), AZ, *18*
Bolton Group (C), CA, *269*
Broadband Resource Group (C), CA, *274*
C/R Associates (C), NY, *278*
Canny, Bowen Inc. (R), NY, *27*
Cantrell & Assoc. (C), FL, *280*
Career Consulting Group, Inc. (C), CT, *281*
Carlsen Resources, Inc. (R), CO, *29*
Carpenter Assoc., Inc. (R), IL, *30*
Christian & Timbers, Inc. (R), OH, *34*
Howard Clark Assoc. (C), NJ, *292*
CN Associates (C), CA, *293*
Commercial Programming Systems, Inc. (C), CA, *294*
Trudi Cowlan (C), NY, *302*
Cypress Int'l., Inc. (R), FL, *45*
D.P. Specialists, Inc. (C), CA, *306*
Delta Management Group Ltd. (C), ON, *310*
Diamond Tax Recruiting (C), NY, *312*
Don Allan Assoc., Inc. (C), CA, *313*
Dotson & Assoc. (R), NY, *54*
EBA Group (R), NJ, *56*
Executive Resource Group, Inc. (R), ME, *63*
Executive Search Consultants Corp. (C), IL, *335*
Fairfield Int'l. Resources (R), NY, *65*
Financialjobs.com (C), CA, *340*
Neil Fink Assoc. (R), CA, *66*
Howard Fischer Assoc. Int'l., Inc. (R), PA, *67*
Foster Partners (R), NY, *70*
P. N. French Assoc., Inc. (R), MA, *72*
Gardiner, Townsend & Assoc. (R), NY, *74*
Gilbert Tweed Assoc. Inc. (R), NY, *76*
Global Telecommunications, Inc. (C), TX, *359*
Graphic Arts Marketing Assoc., Inc. (C), MI, *361*
Ben Greco Assoc., Inc. (C), CA, *362*
Griffith & Werner, Inc. (R), FL, *82*

INDUSTRIES

Growth Consultants of America (R), MI, *82*
Gustin Partners, Ltd. (R), MA, *83*
Hands-on Broadcast (R), NY, *86*
Hart & Co. (C), NY, *370*
Holland & Assoc., Inc. (R), MI, *94*
Howard-Sloan Assoc. (C), NY, *381*
The Howard-Sloan-Koller Group (R), NY, *97*
HRCS (R), CA, *97*
Innovative Partnerships (R), CA, *101*
InteliSearch, Inc. (R), CT, *102*
Isaacson, Miller (R), MA, *104*
JDH & Assoc. (C), CA, *397*
Jeffrey Allan Co., Inc. (C), CA, *398*
Jender & Company (R), IL, *105*
JenKim Int'l. Ltd., Inc. (C), FL, *398*
A.T. Kearney Executive Search (R), IL, *111*
T. J. Koellhoffer & Assoc. (R), NJ, *116*
Kors Montgomery Int'l. (R), TX, *118*
Kossuth & Assoc., Inc. (R), WA, *119*
Katherine R. Kraemer (R), CA, *120*
Michael Levine Search Consultants (R), NY, *129*
The Libra Group Inc. (C), CT, *417*
Lipson & Co. (R), CA, *130*
Logic Assoc., Inc. (C), NY, *419*
Logix, Inc. (C), MA, *420*
The John Lucht Consultancy Inc. (R), NY, *131*
The Luciani Group (R), CA, *132*
Fran Luisi Assoc. (R), NJ, *132*
Madison Executive Search, Inc. (C), NJ, *422*
Madison MacArthur Inc. (R), ON, *133*
Management Recruiters Dana Point (C), CA, *440*
Management Recruiters of Roseville (C), CA, *441*
Management Recruiters of Melbourne, Inc. (C), FL, *443*
Management Recruiters of Northern Palm Beaches (C), FL, *444*
Management Recruiters of Gramercy, Inc. (C), NY, *455*
Management Recruiters of Columbus (C), OH, *457*
Management Recruiters Int'l.-The Woodlands (C), TX, *464*
F. L. Mannix & Co. (R), MA, *135*
Mark Adam Assoc. (R), NJ, *135*
Karen Marshall Assoc. (C), KY, *471*
Richard L. Mather & Assoc. (C), CT, *472*
McCray, Shriver, Eckdahl & Assoc., Inc. (R), CA, *140*
Media Management Resources, Inc. (R), CO, *142*
Media Recruiting Group, Inc. (C), NY, *476*
The Medley Group (C), CA, *477*
Mengel & McDonald Ltd. (C), IL, *479*
Milrod Assoc. (C), NJ, *482*
Morgan/Webber, Inc. (R), NY, *147*
Multi Processing, Inc. (R), NH, *149*
Jennifer Munro & Partners, Inc. (R), SC, *149*
National Executive (C), ON, *489*
National Field Service Corp. (C), NY, *489*
National Recruiters (C), OK, *489*
The NEIS Corp., Inc. (C), FL, *491*
Nordeman Grimm, Inc. (R), NY, *152*
Norman Broadbent Int'l., Inc. (R), NY, *152*
Janou Pakter, Inc. (C), NY, *502*
Partners Executive Search Consultants Inc. (R), ON, *160*
Partners In Human Resources Int'l., Inc. (R), NY, *160*
Partners Resource Group (C), VA, *504*
Pathways Int'l. (C), CT, *505*
Phillips Assoc. (C), FL, *510*
The Pinnacle Source, Inc. (C), CO, *512*
Placement Solutions (C), WI, *513*
Price & Assoc., Inc. (C), VA, *518*
PSD Group, Inc. (C), CA, *525*
The Quest Organization (C), NY, *527*
Joanne E. Ratner Search (C), NY, *529*
Redden & McGrath Assoc., Inc. (R), NY, *173*
Russell Reynolds Assoc., Inc. (R), NY, *176*
Richards Assoc., Inc. (R), NY, *178*
ROI International, Inc. (R), WA, *181*
Royal Assoc. (C), CA, *547*
Sales Consultants of Wellesley, Inc. (C), MA, *559*
Sales Consultants King of Prussia (C), PA, *562*
Sales Consultants of Madison (C), WI, *563*
Search Assoc., Inc. (C), CA, *574*
Search Group (C), CA, *575*
The Smith Group, Inc. (C), NC, *584*
Smith's Fifth Avenue (C), NY, *585*
Spectrum Consultants (R), CA, *196*
SpencerStuart (R), NY, *196*
Spriggs & Co., Inc. (R), IL, *198*
Steinbach & Co. (C), MA, *592*
Stone & Youngblood (C), MA, *594*
StratfordGroup (R), OH, *203*
Joe Sullivan & Assoc., Inc. (R), NY, *204*
Ron Sunshine & Assoc. (C), IL, *597*
Survival Systems Staffing, Inc. (C), CA, *597*
Systems Personnel, Inc. (C), NY, *598*
Martin Stevens Tamaren & Assoc., Inc. (R), CA, *206*
The Technology Group (R), IL, *208*
Telecom Executive Group (C), NJ, *605*
Travel Executive Search (C), NY, *608*
TriStaff Group (C), CA, *609*
TSC Management Services Group, Inc. (C), IL, *610*
TTG/Sterling Services (C), CA, *610*
Venture Resources, Inc. (R), CA, *213*
Vintage Resources, Inc. (C), NY, *613*
Warren, Morris & Madison, Ltd. (C), CA, *616*
David Weinfeld Group (C), NC, *617*
William Willis Worldwide Inc. (R), CT, *221*
The Winchester Group (R), CA, *222*
Yormak & Assoc. (C), CA, *626*

J.14 Telephone, telecommunications

A C Personnel Services, Inc. (C), OK, *231*
A. D. & Assoc. Executive Search, Inc. (C), GA, *231*
Abécassis Conseil (R), QE, *1*
Abraham & London Ltd. (C), CT, *232*
Abraxas Technologies, Inc. (C), FL, *233*
Access Data Personnel, Inc. (C), NH, *233*
ACCESS Technology (C), CA, *234*
Ackerman Johnson Inc. (C), TX, *238*
ACSYS Resources, Inc. (C), DE, *238*
Action Management Corp. (C), MI, *239*
Adam-Bryce Inc. (C), NY, *239*
Adept Tech Recruiting, Inc. (C), NY, *240*
Adler Management, Inc. (R), NJ, *2*
Advanced Corporate Search (C), CA, *240*
Advanced Recruiting, Inc. (C), OK, *240*
Advancement, Inc. (C), IL, *241*
The Advisory Group, Inc. (R), CA, *2*
AES Search (C), NJ, *241*
J. R. Akin & Co. (R), MA, *2*
Alexander Associates (R), NJ, *2*
The Alexander Group (R), NJ, *3*
D. S. Allen Assoc. (C), NJ, *244*
Allerton Heneghan & O'Neill (R), IL, *4*
Allstaff, Inc. (C), IL, *245*
The Alternatives Group, Inc. (C), TX, *246*
American Executive Management, Inc. (R), MA, *5*
Ansara, Bickford & Fiske (C), MA, *251*
Ashton Computer Professionals, Inc. (C), BC, *253*
ASI (C), CA, *254*
Asset Resource, Inc. (C), CA, *254*
Association for Sales Force Management (C), WA, *254*
Atlantic Pacific Group (C), CA, *255*
Aubin Int'l. Inc. (R), MA, *8*
Aurora Tech Search (C), ON, *256*
Cami Austin & Assoc. (C), IL, *256*
Baker Scott & Co. (C), NJ, *258*
Baker, Nelms & Montgomery (C), IL, *258*
James Bangert & Assoc., Inc. (R), MN, *11*
Barnes & Assoc. Executive Search (C), CA, *259*
Barr Assoc. (C), PA, *259*
Barrett Rose & Lee, Inc. (C), ON, *260*
Barton Assoc., Inc. (R), TX, *12*
Bast & Assoc., Inc. (C), CA, *261*
The Beardsley Group Inc. (C), CT, *261*
Beck/Eastwood Recruitment Solutions (C), CA, *261*
The Bedford Group (R), RI, *15*
Robert Beech West Inc. (C), CA, *262*
Belanger Partners Ltd. (C), ON, *262*
Bennett & Associates (C), TX, *264*
Berkana Int'l., Inc. (C), WA, *265*
Bertrand, Ross & Assoc., Inc. (C), IL, *266*
Besen Assoc. Inc. (C), NJ, *266*
Birch & Associes (C), QE, *267*
Deborah Bishop & Assoc. (R), CA, *17*
Bishop Partners (R), NY, *17*
Blaney Executive Search (R), MA, *18*
Block & Assoc. (R), CA, *18*
Bolton Group (C), CA, *269*
Bornholdt Shivas & Friends Executive Recruiters (C), NY, *270*
Bosch & Assoc., LLC (R), CT, *19*
Howard Bowen Consulting (C), FL, *270*
Bower & Associates (C), TX, *271*
Boyden (R), NY, *20*
BR & Assoc. (C), NJ, *271*
M. F. Branch Assoc., Inc. (C), NC, *272*
Brandt Associates (C), PA, *272*

Brandywine Retained Ventures, Inc. (R), CT, *22*
Bratland & Assoc. (C), IL, *272*
Brei & Assoc., Inc. (C), IA, *272*
The Brentwood Group Ltd. (R), OR, *23*
Bridgecreek Personnel Agency (C), CA, *273*
Bristol Assoc., Inc. (C), CA, *274*
Broadband Resource Group (C), CA, *274*
Bernard E. Brooks & Assoc., Inc. (R), SC, *24*
Broward-Dobbs, Inc. (C), GA, *274*
J. B. Brown & Assoc., Inc. (C), OH, *275*
Brown Venture Assoc. (R), CA, *24*
Brush Creek Partners (R), MO, *24*
The Buckley Group (C), FL, *276*
Burke & Assoc./The Westfield Group (C), CT, *276*
Business Partners, Inc. (C), FL, *277*
Button Group (C), TX, *277*
Cambridge Group Ltd. - Exec. Search Div. (C), CT, *279*
T. M. Campbell Co. (R), WA, *27*
Canny, Bowen Inc. (R), NY, *27*
Cantrell & Assoc. (C), FL, *280*
Cardwell Enterprises Inc. (R), IL, *29*
Career Marketing Assoc., Inc. (C), CO, *282*
Careers First, Inc. (C), NJ, *283*
Careers On Track (C), NJ, *283*
Careers Plus (R), CA, *29*
Carion Resource Group Inc. (C), ON, *284*
Carlsen Resources, Inc. (R), CO, *29*
Carpenter Assoc., Inc. (R), IL, *30*
Carrington & Carrington, Ltd. (R), IL, *30*
CAS Comsearch Inc. (C), NY, *285*
Caywood Partners, Ltd. (R), CA, *32*
Cendea Connection Int'l. (R), TX, *32*
CEO Consulting (C), FL, *287*
Chatham Search Assoc., Inc. (C), NJ, *290*
Chicago Legal Search, Ltd. (C), IL, *290*
Christian & Timbers, Inc. (R), OH, *34*
Christmas, McIvor & Assoc. Inc. (C), ON, *290*
Churchill & Affiliates, Inc. (R), PA, *35*
CJA-The Adler Group, Inc. (R), CA, *35*
Clayman & Co. (R), MA, *36*
CN Associates (C), CA, *293*
COBA Executive Search (R), CO, *36*
Colt Systems Professional Personnel Services (C), CA, *294*
Commercial Programming Systems, Inc. (C), CA, *294*
Computer Int'l. Consultants, Inc. (C), FL, *295*
Computer Professionals Unlimited (C), TX, *295*
Computer Security Placement Service (C), MA, *296*
Consulpro (R), ON, *39*
Continental Search & Outplacement, Inc. (C), MD, *298*
Conway & Assoc. (R), IL, *40*
Cooper Assoc., Inc., Inc. (C), NY, *298*
Cornell Group Int'l. Consulting, Inc. (R), NY, *41*
The Corporate Advisory Group (R), NJ, *41*
Corporate Plus, Ltd. (C), GA, *300*
Corporate Staffing Group, Inc. (C), PA, *301*
Corso, Mizgala + French (R), ON, *42*
Cowell & Associates, Ltd. (R), IL, *42*
Crane, Reed & Co., Inc. (C), NH, *302*
Creative HR Solutions (C), GA, *303*
Criterion Executive Search, Inc. (C), FL, *303*
Cross Country Consultants, Inc. (C), MD, *304*
Current Resource Group, Inc. (C), GA, *305*
Custom Resources (C), AL, *305*
CV Associates (C), NY, *305*
Cypress Int'l., Inc. (R), FL, *45*
Dahl-Morrow Int'l. (R), VA, *45*
The DataFinders Group, Inc. (C), NJ, *307*
David Perry Assoc. (C), NJ, *308*
DBC Recruiting Network (C), GA, *309*
Defrain Mayer (R), KS, *48*
Delta Management Group Ltd. (C), ON, *310*
Delta Resource Group, Ltd. (C), GA, *311*
Despres & Associates (C), IL, *311*
The Devlin Search Group, Inc. (C), MA, *311*
DiMarchi Partners (R), CO, *51*
Diversified Consulting Services, Inc. (C), CO, *313*
Diversified Search, Inc. (R), PA, *52*
L. J. Doherty & Assoc. (R), MA, *53*
Don Allan Assoc., Inc. (C), CA, *313*
The Donnelly Group-Sales Recruiters, Inc. (C), MO, *314*
Dorst Information Services, Inc. (C), NY, *314*
Dotson & Assoc. (R), NY, *54*
Dreier Consulting (C), NJ, *315*
Drinkwater & Assoc. (R), MA, *54*
Dromeshauser Assoc. (R), MA, *55*
DSR-Search & Recruitment (C), TX, *315*
Dunhill Professional Search of Augusta (C), GA, *320*
Dunhill Professional Search of Hawaii (C), HI, *320*
Dunhill Professional Search of Greater New Orleans (C), LA, *321*
Dunhill Professional Search of Ramsey (C), NJ, *321*
Dunhill Professional Search of Winston-Salem (C), NC, *322*
Dunhill Professional Search of Wilkes-Barre/Scranton, Inc. (C), PA, *322*
Dynamic Choices Inc. (C), MO, *323*
Dynamic Search Systems, Inc. (C), IL, *324*
E.P. Int'l. (C), NY, *324*
E/Search Int'l. (C), CT, *325*
EagleView, Inc. (C), MA, *325*
Eastbourne Assoc. Inc. (R), NY, *56*
EBA Group (R), NJ, *56*
EDP Staffing Solutions, Inc. (C), AR, *327*
Edwards & Assoc. (C), GA, *327*
W. Robert Eissler & Assoc., Inc. (C), TX, *327*
Electronic Search, Inc. (C), IL, *327*
Elite Consultants, Inc. (C), FL, *328*
Ellis & Associates (C), HI, *328*
The Elmhurst Group (C), CA, *329*
Emerging Technology Search (C), GA, *329*
Engineering Resource Group, Inc. (C), NJ, *331*
ESS (Executive Search Services) (R), CA, *61*
ETI Search Int'l. (R), GA, *61*
ExecuSource Assoc., Inc. (C), GA, *332*
ExecuSource Consultants, Inc. (C), TX, *332*
Executive Partners Inc. (C), CT, *333*
Executive Resource Group, Inc. (R), ME, *63*
Executive Sales Search (C), CO, *335*
Executive Search Consultants Corp. (C), IL, *335*
Executive Search of America, Inc. (C), OH, *336*
ExecutiveFit (C), NY, *337*
Fagan & Company (R), PA, *64*
Fast Switch, Ltd. (C), OH, *338*
The Fawcett Group (R), MA, *65*
A. E. Feldman Assoc., Inc. (C), NY, *339*
Fenwick Partners (R), MA, *66*
Jerry Fields Assoc. (C), NY, *340*
Finnegan & Assoc. (R), CA, *67*
First Search Inc. (C), IL, *341*
Howard Fischer Assoc. Int'l., Inc. (R), PA, *67*
The Fisher Group (R), AB, *67*
Fisher-Todd Assoc. (C), NY, *341*
A. G. Fishkin & Assoc., Inc. (R), MD, *68*
Focus Consulting Services, Inc. (C), FL, *342*
L. W. Foote Co. (R), WA, *69*
Ford & Ford (C), MA, *343*
The Ford Group, Inc. (R), PA, *69*
Fortune Group Int'l., Inc. (R), PA, *70*
F-O-R-T-U-N-E Personnel Consultants of Tampa (C), FL, *344*
Fortune Personnel Consultants of Colorado Springs (C), CO, *344*
Fortune Personnel Consultants of Jacksonville (C), FL, *345*
F-O-R-T-U-N-E Personnel Consultants of Manatee County (C), FL, *345*
Foster Partners (R), NY, *70*
Franklin Int'l. Search, Inc. (C), MA, *352*
Friedman Eisenstein Raemer & Schwartz, LLP (R), IL, *72*
Peter Froehlich & Co. (C), TX, *353*
GAAP Inc. (R), QE, *73*
Gardiner, Townsend & Assoc. (R), NY, *74*
Garland Assoc. Int'l. (C), CA, *355*
The Garms Group (R), IL, *74*
GateSource Partners (C), VA, *355*
General Engineering Tectonics (C), CA, *356*
C. R. Gerald & Assoc. (C), ON, *356*
Gilbert Tweed Assoc. Inc. (R), NY, *76*
Gimbel & Assoc. (C), FL, *357*
Lawrence Glaser Assoc., Inc. (C), NJ, *357*
Global Employer's Network, Inc. (R), TX, *77*
Global Technologies Group Inc. (C), NC, *359*
Global Telecommunications, Inc. (C), TX, *359*
Glou Int'l., Inc. (R), MA, *78*
Gould, McCoy & Chadick, Inc. (R), NY, *80*
The Grant Search Group, Inc. (C), ON, *361*
Greenhaven & Assoc., Inc. (R), NY, *81*

INDUSTRIES

Growth Strategies, Inc. (R), FL, *83*
GSW Consulting Group, Inc. (R), CA, *83*
Nadine Guber & Assoc., Inc. (C), NY, *364*
Michael R. Guerin Co. (C), CA, *364*
Gustin Partners, Ltd. (R), MA, *83*
Haley Associates (R), CA, *85*
The Hamilton Group (R), MD, *85*
Hardison & Company (R), TX, *86*
Harper Hewes, Inc. (C), NY, *369*
Harris Heery & Assoc., Inc. (R), CT, *87*
Hartsfield Group, Inc. (R), GA, *87*
Harvard Group Int'l. (R), GA, *87*
Hayden & Assoc., Inc. (C), MN, *370*
Headden Assoc. (R), WA, *88*
Healey Executive Search, Inc. (R), MN, *88*
Hechkoff/Work Executive Search Inc. (R), NY, *89*
Heffelfinger Assoc., Inc. (R), MA, *89*
Higbee Assoc., Inc. (C), CT, *377*
High Tech Opportunities, Inc. (C), NH, *377*
High Tech Staffing Group (C), OR, *377*
High-Tech Recruiters (C), CT, *378*
Holland & Assoc., Inc. (R), MI, *94*
The Hollins Group, Inc. (R), IL, *95*
Howard-Sloan Assoc. (C), NY, *381*
The Howard-Sloan-Koller Group (R), NY, *97*
Howe & Assoc. (R), PA, *97*
HR Advantage, Inc. (C), VA, *382*
HRS, Inc. (R), PA, *97*
The Hudson Group (C), CT, *383*
Human Resource Dimensions, Inc. (C), TX, *384*
Human Resources Management Hawaii, Inc. (C), HI, *384*
Hunter Adams (C), NC, *385*
The Hyde Group, Inc. (R), CT, *101*
i.j. & assoc., inc. (C), CO, *386*
IM Independent Management Recruiters (R), TN, *101*
Independent Resource Systems (C), CA, *388*
InSearch (C), CO, *389*
The Inside Track (C), TX, *389*
Intech Summit Group, Inc. (R), CA, *102*
Integrity Search, Inc. (R), PA, *102*
Intelegra, Inc. (C), NJ, *390*
InteliSearch, Inc. (R), CT, *102*
Interim Executive Recruiting (C), GA, *392*
International Consulting Services, Inc. (C), IL, *392*
International Management Services Inc. (R), IL, *102*
International Staffing Consultants, Inc. (C), CA, *393*
Interspace Interactive, Inc. (C), NY, *394*
Ives & Associates, Inc. (C), OH, *395*
Ron Jackson & Assoc. (C), GA, *396*
Jackson Group Int'l. (C), CO, *396*
Jaeger Int'l., Inc. (C), OH, *396*
JDH & Assoc. (C), CA, *397*
Jender & Company (R), IL, *105*
JenKim Int'l. Ltd., Inc. (C), FL, *398*
JG Consultants, Inc. (R), TX, *106*
Johnson & Assoc., Inc. (R), CA, *106*
Ronald S. Johnson Assoc., Inc. (R), CA, *107*
K. E. Johnson Assoc. (C), WA, *399*
Johnson, Kemper & Assoc. (C), TX, *400*
JPM International (C), CA, *401*
JSG Group Management Consultants (R), ON, *109*
A H Justice Search Consultants (C), TX, *402*
KABL Ability Network (C), CA, *402*
Kacevich, Lewis & Brown, Inc. (R), MA, *109*
Kames & Assoc. (C), MD, *403*
Kaplan & Assoc., Inc. (R), PA, *109*
Karp & Assoc. (C), FL, *403*
Allan Karson Assoc., Inc. (R), NJ, *110*
Jim Kay & Assoc. (C), IL, *404*
Keane Assoc. (R), MA, *110*
A.T. Kearney Executive Search (R), IL, *111*
Kelly Associates (R), PA, *112*
Kensington International (R), CA, *113*
Key Resources Int'l. (C), CA, *405*
Ki Technologies, Inc. (C), UT, *406*
Kiley, Owen & McGovern, Inc. (R), NJ, *114*
The Kleven Group, Inc. (C), MA, *407*
Lee Koehn Assoc., Inc. (R), OR, *116*
T. J. Koellhoffer & Assoc. (R), NJ, *116*
Koren, Rogers Assoc. Inc. (R), NY, *117*
Kors Montgomery Int'l. (R), TX, *118*
Kossuth & Assoc., Inc. (R), WA, *119*
Katherine R. Kraemer (R), CA, *120*
Krakower Group, Inc. (R), CA, *120*
Krautler Personnel Recruitment (C), FL, *409*
Kremple Consulting Group (R), CA, *120*
Kukoy Associates (R), CO, *121*
Kulper & Co., L.L.C. (R), NJ, *121*
Kurtz Pro-Search, Inc. (C), NJ, *410*
L&L Assoc. Global Search (C), PA, *411*
LaCosta & Assoc. Int'l. Inc. (C), CA, *411*
Langley & Associates, Inc. (Executive Search Consultants) (R), CO, *124*
Larkin & Co. (R), CA, *124*
Robert Larned Assoc., Inc. (C), VA, *413*
Jack B. Larsen & Assoc., Inc. (C), PA, *413*
W. R. Lawry, Inc. (R), CT, *126*
LCC Companies (C), AZ, *414*
LCS, Inc. (C), TX, *414*
Ricci Lee Assoc., Inc. (C), CA, *415*
Lehman McLeskey (R), TX, *128*
LG Brand, Inc. (C), MD, *417*
The Logan Group, Inc. (R), MO, *131*
Logix, Inc. (C), MA, *420*
Logue & Rice Inc. (C), VA, *420*
The Luciani Group (R), CA, *132*
Lutz Associates (C), CT, *421*
Madison Executive Search, Inc. (C), NJ, *422*
Madison MacArthur Inc. (R), ON, *133*
Management One Consultants (C), ON, *425*
Management Recruiters of Tucson (C), AZ, *439*
Management Recruiters Peninsula (C), CA, *439*
Management Recruiters Dana Point (C), CA, *440*
Management Recruiters of Laguna Hills (C), CA, *440*
Management Recruiters of Northern California (C), CA, *440*
Management Recruiters of Roseville (C), CA, *441*
Management Recruiters of Winsted, Inc. (C), CT, *442*
Management Recruiters of Colchester (C), CT, *442*
Management Recruiters of Altamonte (C), FL, *442*
Management Recruiters of Melbourne, Inc. (C), FL, *443*
Management Recruiters of Bonita Springs, Inc. (C), FL, *443*
Management Recruiters, Inc. (C), FL, *443*
Management Recruiters of Tampa North (C), FL, *444*
Management Recruiters of St. Augustine (C), FL, *444*
Management Recruiters of Venice, Inc. (C), FL, *445*
Management Recruiters of Atlanta NE (C), GA, *446*
Management Recruiters of Savannah (C), GA, *446*
Management Recruiters of Indianapolis (C), IN, *448*
Management Recruiters-Cedar Rapids, Inc. (C), IA, *448*
Management Recruiters - Indianapolis (C), IN, *448*
Management Recruiters of Fairfield (C), IA, *449*
Management Recruiters of the Baltimore Washington Corridor (C), MD, *450*
Management Recruiters of Birmingham (C), MI, *451*
Management Recruiters of Baltimore (C), MD, *451*
Management Recruiters of Winona (C), MN, *452*
Management Recruiters of Bloomington (C), MN, *452*
Management Recruiters of Rankin Co. (C), MS, *452*
Management Recruiters of Morris County, NJ (C), NJ, *453*
Management Recruiters of Fayetteville (C), NC, *455*
Management Recruiters of Cedar Mountain (C), NC, *455*
Management Recruiters of Gramercy, Inc. (C), NY, *455*
Management Recruiters of Youngstown (C), OH, *458*
Management Recruiters of Oklahoma City (C), OK, *458*
Management Recruiters of Pittsburgh (C), PA, *459*
Management Recruiters of Lionville, Inc. (C), PA, *459*
Management Recruiters of LBJ Park/Dallas (C), TX, *462*
Management Recruiters Dallas North (MRDN) (C), TX, *462*
Management Recruiters of San Marcos (C), TX, *463*
Management Recruiters of Lubbock (C), TX, *463*
Management Recruiters of Ogden (C), UT, *464*

Management Recruiters of Arlington (C), VA, *464*
Management Recruiters Int'l.-The Woodlands (C), TX, *464*
Management Recruiters of Fairfax, VA (C), VA, *464*
Management Recruiters of Spokane (C), WA, *465*
Management Recruiters of Madison, Inc. (C), WI, *466*
Management Recruiters of Milwaukee - Downtown (C), WI, *466*
Management Recruiters of Stevens Point, Inc. (C), WI, *466*
Management Recruiters of Milwaukee-North (C), WI, *466*
Management Resource Group (C), MN, *467*
Management Search, Inc. (C), IL, *467*
Margolin Consultants, Inc. (C), NY, *469*
Mark Christian & Assoc., Inc. (C), AZ, *469*
Marketing Search Inc. (C), OH, *471*
The Maroon Group (R), CT, *136*
Marsar & Co., Inc. (C), FL, *471*
Karen Marshall Assoc. (C), KY, *471*
J. Martin & Assoc. (R), CA, *137*
The Martwick Group, Inc. (C), OR, *472*
Richard L. Mather & Assoc. (C), CT, *472*
K. Maxin & Assoc. (R), PA, *139*
McCray, Shriver, Eckdahl & Assoc., Inc. (R), CA, *140*
McDonald Assoc. Int'l. (R), IL, *140*
McDowell & Co., Recruiters (C), TX, *474*
McGrath & Assoc., Inc. (R), NJ, *141*
The McKinnon Management Group Inc. (C), ON, *475*
Media Management Resources, Inc. (R), CO, *142*
MediaCOM Talent Group (C), MA, *476*
Mehta Consulting (C), NJ, *478*
MES Search Co. (C), GA, *479*
META/MAT, Ltd. (R), NJ, *144*
Meyer Assoc., Inc. (R), GA, *144*
Milo Research (R), NY, *145*
Milrod Assoc. (C), NJ, *482*
MIS Computer Professionals, Inc. (C), KS, *482*
MJF Assoc. (C), CT, *483*
Modis (C), MD, *483*
Mogul Consultants, Inc. (C), NY, *483*
Morency Assoc. (C), MA, *485*
The Morley Group (C), IN, *486*
Robert T. Morton Assoc., Inc. (C), MA, *486*
Much & Co. (R), NY, *148*
Multi Processing, Inc. (R), NH, *149*
Mycoff & Assoc. (R), CO, *150*
National Affirmative Action Career Network, Inc. (C), CO, *488*
National Executive (C), ON, *489*
National Field Service Corp. (C), NY, *489*
National Recruiters (C), OK, *489*
National Register Columbus Inc. (C), OH, *490*
Nationwide Personnel Placement, Inc. (C), OH, *490*
The NEIS Corp., Inc. (C), FL, *491*
New Dimensions in Technology, Inc. (C), MA, *492*
New Venture Development, Inc. (C), CA, *492*
Newman-Johnson-King, Inc. (C), TX, *492*
Newport Strategic Search LLC (C), CA, *492*
Nordeman Grimm, Inc. (R), NY, *152*
Paul Winston Norman & Assoc. (R), IL, *152*
Norman Broadbent Int'l., Inc. (R), NY, *152*
NYCOR Search, Inc. (C), MN, *497*
O'Connell Group Inc. (C), CT, *497*
O'Connor Resources (C), TX, *497*
O'Keefe & Assoc. (C), TX, *497*
O'Shea, Divine & Co., Inc. (R), CA, *154*
Odell & Assoc., Inc. (C), TX, *498*
Opus Marketing (R), CA, *156*
The Oxford Group (C), TX, *500*
P.R.H. Management, Inc. (R), CT, *158*
Pacific Crossing (C), CA, *501*
Paladin Group, Inc. (C), CO, *502*
Arthur Pann Assoc., Inc. (C), NY, *502*
Largent Parks & Partners (C), TX, *503*
Partners Executive Search Consultants Inc. (R), ON, *160*
Partners Resource Group (C), VA, *504*
Partnervision Consulting Group Inc. (R), ON, *160*
The Patience Motivation Belief Group, Inc. (C), GA, *505*
Paul-Tittle Assoc., Inc. (R), VA, *161*
Pawlik/Dorman Partners (R), IL, *161*
Pearce & Assoc. (C), FL, *506*
Pennington Consulting Group (C), NJ, *506*
Fred Perry Assoc. (C), TX, *507*
Perry Search Assoc. (C), CA, *507*
Personnel, Inc. (C), AL, *508*
PHD Conseil en Ressources Humaines Inc. (C), QE, *510*
Phillips Assoc. (C), FL, *510*
Phillips Int'l., Inc. (C), SC, *510*
Phillips Personnel/Search (C), CO, *510*
PIC Executive Search (C), GA, *511*
Pittleman & Assoc. (C), NY, *512*
Placement Testart Inc. (C), QE, *513*
Plante & Moran, LLP (R), MI, *165*
Poirier, Hoevel & Co. (R), CA, *166*
Don V. Poole & Assoc., Inc. (C), CO, *514*
PPS Information Systems Staffing (C), MD, *515*
Prairie Resource Group, Inc. (R), IL, *166*
Prestonwood Assoc. (R), MA, *168*
Price & Assoc., Inc. (C), VA, *518*
Alan J. Price Assoc., Inc. (C), RI, *518*
Professional Recruiting Consultants, Inc. (C), DE, *521*
Professional Selection Services (R), GA, *169*
Professional Team Search, Inc. (R), AZ, *169*
ProNet, Inc. (C), NC, *524*
PSD Group, Inc. (C), CA, *525*
PSP Agency (C), NY, *525*
Quality Search Inc. (C), OH, *526*
The Quantum Group (C), NJ, *526*
L. J. Quinn & Assoc., Inc. (R), CA, *170*
R. J. Associates (C), NY, *528*
R/K International Inc. (R), CT, *171*
R2 Services, LLC (C), IL, *528*
The Ransford Group (R), TX, *171*
J. E. Ranta Assoc. (C), MA, *529*
Ray & Berndtson (R), TX, *171*
Razzino-Claymore Assoc. (C), NJ, *530*
Recruit Xpress (C), TX, *531*
Redden-Shaffer Group (R), CA, *173*
The Regency Group, Ltd. (C), NE, *533*
The Renaissance Network (C), MA, *534*
Research Personnel Consultants (C), ON, *534*
Russell Reynolds Assoc., Inc. (R), NY, *176*
Reynolds Consulting Int'l. (R), ON, *177*
RIC Corp. (R), FL, *177*
Richard, Wayne & Roberts (C), TX, *536*
Ritta Professional Search Inc. (C), NY, *538*
Norman Roberts & Assoc., Inc. (R), CA, *179*
R. A. Rodriguez & Assoc., Inc. (C), TX, *540*
Rogers - McManamon Executive Search (R), CA, *180*
ROI International, Inc. (R), WA, *181*
Rolland Ressources Humaines Inc. (R), QE, *181*
Romac Int'l. Inc. (R), MA, *181*
Rooney Assoc., Inc. (R), IL, *181*
Emery A. Rose & Assoc. (C), WA, *545*
Ross Personnel Consultants, Inc. (C), CT, *545*
Rossi & Assoc. Inc. (C), BC, *545*
Rowland Mountain & Assoc. (C), GA, *547*
The Rubicon Group (C), AZ, *547*
Rylan Forbes Consulting Group, Inc. (C), NJ, *549*
Sales & Marketing Search, Inc. (C), MA, *551*
Sales Consultants of Scottsdale, Inc. (C), AZ, *556*
Sales Consultants of Boca Raton, Inc. (C), FL, *557*
Sales Consultants of Tampa North, Inc. (C), FL, *557*
Sales Consultants of Ft. Myers, Inc. (C), FL, *557*
Sales Consultants of Danbury (C), CT, *557*
Sales Consultants of Honolulu (C), HI, *558*
Sales Consultants of Barrington (C), IL, *558*
Sales Consultants of Rockville, MD (C), MD, *559*
Sales Consultants of Farmington Hills (C), MI, *560*
Sales Consultants of Cherry Hill (C), NJ, *560*
Sales Consultants of Omaha, Inc. (C), NE, *560*
Sales Consultants of Butler County (C), PA, *561*
Sales Consultants of Raleigh-Durham-RTP (C), NC, *561*
Sales Consultants of Newtown, Inc. (C), PA, *562*
Sales Consultants of Austin, Inc. (C), TX, *562*
Sales Consultants King of Prussia (C), PA, *562*
Sales Consultants of Milwaukee (C), WI, *563*
Sales Consultants of Houston (C), TX, *563*
Sales Executives, Inc. (C), MI, *563*

INDUSTRIES

Sales Search (C), ON, *564*
A. N. Salloway Executive Search & Consulting, L.L.C. (C), MA, *564*
Sanford Rose Assoc. - Santa Barbara (C), CA, *565*
Sanford Rose Assoc. - Norcross (C), GA, *566*
Sanford Rose Assoc. - Charlotte (C), NC, *568*
Sanford Rose Assoc. - Springfield (C), MO, *568*
Sanford Rose Assoc. - Lake St. Louis (C), MO, *568*
Sanford Rose Assoc. - Euclid (C), OH, *569*
Sanford Rose Assoc. - Port Washington (C), WI, *571*
Sarver & Carruth Assoc. (C), OK, *571*
Satterfield & Assoc., Inc. (R), OH, *184*
Saviar, Inc. (C), AZ, *571*
Schweichler Assoc., Inc. (R), CA, *186*
Scott Executive Search, Inc. (R), NY, *186*
Search & Recruit Int'l. (C), VA, *573*
Search Assoc., Inc. (C), CA, *574*
Search Group (C), CA, *575*
The Search Network (C), CA, *576*
Search Northwest Assoc. (C), OR, *576*
Segal & Assoc. (C), GA, *578*
Seiden Krieger Assoc., Inc. (R), NY, *188*
Selectis Corp. (C), IL, *578*
Sensible Solutions, Inc. (R), IL, *188*
SFB Legal Search (C), NY, *579*
Sharp Placement Professionals, Inc. (C), NY, *579*
Shell Technology Group (C), CA, *580*
Shinn & Assoc. (R), CA, *189*
Siger & Assoc., LLC (C), CT, *581*
Sink, Walker, Boltrus Int'l. (R), MA, *192*
Skipping Stone Inc. (C), VA, *582*
Ruth Sklar Assoc., Inc. (RSA Executive Search) (R), NY, *192*
Slayton Int'l., Inc. (R), IL, *192*
Smith & Sawyer, Inc. (R), NY, *193*
The Smith Group, Inc. (C), NC, *584*
Smith, Roth & Squires (R), NY, *194*
Smith Search, S.C. (R), MX, *194*
Smith's Fifth Avenue (C), NY, *585*
Snelling Search Recruiters (C), NC, *586*
C. Snow & Assoc. (C), ON, *586*
Softrix, Inc. (C), NJ, *586*
Software Resource Consultants (C), TN, *587*
Solutions Group (R), AL, *195*
Southport Int'l. Assoc. Inc. (C), FL, *588*
Southwestern Professional Services (C), TN, *588*
Sparks, McDonough & Assoc., Inc. (C), MO, *588*
SPC Symcox Personnel Consultants (C), TX, *588*
Specialty Employment Services, Inc. (C), GA, *589*
SpectraWest (C), CA, *589*
Spectrum Consultants (R), CA, *196*
SpencerStuart (R), NY, *196*
The Spiegel Group (R), MA, *197*
Spriggs & Co., Inc. (R), IL, *198*
Springer Souder & Assoc. L.L.C. (R), IL, *198*
Stanton Chase Int'l. (R), MD, *198*
The Stanton Group, Inc. (C), IL, *591*
Steinbach & Co. (C), MA, *592*
Stevens Assoc. (C), MA, *593*
Stewart/Laurence Assoc., Inc. (R), NJ, *201*
Stone & Youngblood (C), MA, *594*
Stoopen Asociados, S.C./EMA Partners Int'l. (R), MX, *202*
Strategic Alternatives (R), CA, *202*
Summerfield Assoc., Inc. (C), TN, *596*
The Summit Group (C), CA, *596*
Survival Systems Staffing, Inc. (C), CA, *597*
Synergistech Communications (C), CA, *597*
Systems Personnel, Inc. (C), NY, *598*
T. H. Hunter, Inc. (C), MN, *599*
Tactical Alternatives (R), CA, *205*
Martin Stevens Tamaren & Assoc., Inc. (R), CA, *206*
Tanner & Assoc., Inc. (R), TX, *206*
Tarbex (C), DC, *599*
Taylor Winfield (R), TX, *207*
TBC, Inc. (C), KY, *600*
TeamBuilders (C), GA, *600*
Tech 2000 (C), FL, *601*
Tech Connector Group (C), CA, *601*
Tech Consulting (C), FL, *601*
Tech Search (C), CA, *601*
Techaid Inc. (C), QE, *601*
The Technology Group (R), IL, *208*
Technology Management Partners (R), CA, *208*
Telecom Connections, Inc. (C), TX, *604*
Telecom Executive Group (C), NJ, *605*
Telecom Recruiters, Inc. (C), VA, *605*
TeleManagement Search (C), NY, *605*
Telequest Communications, Inc. (C), NJ, *605*
Tell/Com Recruiters (C), PA, *605*
Thomas Lyle & Co. (C), IL, *606*
Thomas Resource Group (R), CA, *209*
Thomas, Whelan Assoc., Inc. (C), DC, *606*
The Touchstone Group (C), MA, *607*
Trac One (R), NJ, *210*
Van Treadaway Assoc., Inc. (R), GA, *210*
Vintage Resources, Inc. (C), NY, *613*
B. D. Wallace & Assoc. (C), MD, *614*
J. D. Walsh & Co. (R), CT, *215*
Martha Ward Executive Search, Inc. (C), NY, *615*
C. D. Warner & Assoc. (C), PA, *615*
Warren, Morris & Madison, Ltd. (C), CA, *616*
The Washington Firm, Ltd. (R), WA, *216*
Waveland Int'l. (R), IL, *216*
Lee Weil Assoc., Inc. (C), IL, *617*
David Weinfeld Group (C), NC, *617*
The Wellesley Group, Inc. (R), IL, *217*
Wellington Management Group (R), PA, *217*
Wesley Brown & Bartle Co., Inc. (R), NY, *218*
Western Technical Resources (C), CA, *619*
Wheelless Group (R), IL, *219*
Wilder & Assoc. (C), VA, *620*
Wilkinson & Ives (R), CA, *221*
Williams & Delmore, Inc. (C), NC, *621*
The Wilmington Group (C), NC, *622*
Wilson-Douglas-Jordan (C), IL, *622*
The Winchester Group (R), CA, *222*
Louise Wood & Assoc. (C), NY, *624*
Bruce G. Woods Executive Search (R), TX, *224*
The Worth Group (C), GA, *625*
WTW Assoc., Inc. (R), NY, *225*
Wyndham Mills Int'l., Inc. (R), GA, *225*
Bill Young & Assoc. (C), VA, *626*
ZanExec L.L.C. (R), VA, *226*
Zeiger Assoc. L.L.C. (C), CA, *627*
P. D. Zier Assoc. (C), CT, *627*

K.00 Public administration/ government

The Abbott Group, Inc. (R), MD, *1*
Advanced Corporate Search (C), CA, *240*
American Executive Management, Inc. (R), MA, *5*
Anderson Bradshaw Assoc., Inc. (R), TX, *6*
Atlanta Executive Partners, Inc. (R), MA, *8*
Auerbach Associates, Inc. (R), MA, *9*
Avery Assoc. (R), CA, *9*
Avion International Technology Inc. (C), ON, *257*
The Baldwin Group (R), IL, *10*
Battalia Winston Int'l./The Euram Consultants Group (R), NY, *13*
Bell Oaks Co., Inc. (C), GA, *263*
C. Berger And Company (R), IL, *16*
Paul J. Biestek Assoc., Inc. (R), IL, *17*
Blake/Hansen Ltd. (R), FL, *18*
Boulware & Assoc. Inc. (R), IL, *20*
The Burke Group (C), ON, *276*
Business Solutions Worldwide, Inc. (C), NJ, *277*
T. M. Campbell Co. (R), WA, *27*
Canadian Career Partners (R), AB, *27*
Capital Consulting Group, Inc. (R), MD, *28*
Carter McKenzie, Inc. (C), NJ, *285*
The Center for Career Advancement, LLC (C), NJ, *287*
Christenson Hutchison McDowell, LLC (R), NJ, *34*
Commercial Programming Systems, Inc. (C), CA, *294*
Conroy Partners Ltd. (R), AB, *39*
Creative HR Solutions (C), GA, *303*
Creative-Leadership, Inc. (R), CA, *42*
D & M Associates (C), PA, *306*
DARE Personnel Inc. (C), ON, *307*
Davies, Park (R), AB, *46*
Alan Davis & Assoc. Inc. (R), QE, *47*
Dean-MacDonald (R), OH, *47*
The Devlin Search Group, Inc. (C), MA, *311*
Diversified Search, Inc. (R), PA, *52*
Doleman Enterprises (R), VA, *53*
Executive Recruiters Int'l. (C), MI, *333*
Executive Recruitment Specialists, Inc. (R), NC, *63*
The Executive Source (C), SA, *337*
Fernow Assoc. (C), PA, *339*
Finney-Taylor Personnel & Management Consultants Ltd. (C), AB, *341*
Foster Partners (R), NY, *70*
F. Gloss Int'l. (R), VA, *78*

Government Contract Solutions, Inc. (C), VA, *360*
David M. Griffith & Assoc., Ltd. (R), CA, *82*
J. B. Groner Executive Search, Inc. (C), DE, *363*
Habelmann & Assoc. (R), MI, *84*
Michael J. Hall & Co. (R), WA, *85*
The Hawkins Co. (R), CA, *88*
William E. Hay & Co. (R), IL, *88*
William C. Houze & Co. (R), CA, *96*
The Hudson Group (C), CT, *383*
The Human Resource Group, Inc. (R), OH, *98*
i.j. & assoc., inc. (C), CO, *386*
IM Independent Management Recruiters (R), TN, *101*
Innovative Partnerships (R), CA, *101*
Intech Summit Group, Inc. (R), CA, *102*
International Consulting Services, Inc. (C), IL, *392*
International Management Development Corp. (C), NY, *393*
Isaacson, Miller (R), MA, *104*
JDG Assoc., Ltd. (C), MD, *397*
Jerome & Co. (C), CA, *398*
Kames & Assoc. (C), MD, *403*
A.T. Kearney Executive Search (R), IL, *111*
The Kleven Group, Inc. (C), MA, *407*
Knapp Consultants (R), CT, *116*
Korn/Ferry Int'l. (R), NY, *117*
Krautler Personnel Recruitment (C), FL, *409*
Laguzza Assoc., Ltd. (R), NY, *122*
Larkin & Co. (R), CA, *124*
The Libra Group (C), NC, *417*
Bruce Lowery & Assoc. (C), MI, *420*
Management Recruiters of Altamonte (C), FL, *442*
Mark Stanley & Co./EMA Partners International (R), FL, *136*
Marra Peters & Partners (R), NJ, *136*
The Mercer Group, Inc. (R), NM, *143*
Montgomery West (R), CA, *146*
Morris & Berger (R), CA, *147*
Robert T. Morton Assoc., Inc. (C), MA, *486*
National Field Service Corp. (C), NY, *489*
New Venture Development, Inc. (C), CA, *492*
The Norland Group (C), CA, *494*
NYCOR Search, Inc. (C), MN, *497*
The Oldani Group (R), WA, *155*
The PAR Group - Paul A. Reaume, Ltd. (R), IL, *159*
M. A. Pelle Assoc., Inc. (C), NY, *506*
People Management Mid-South, LLC (R), TN, *162*
Barry Persky & Co., Inc. (R), CT, *163*
The Personnel Network, Inc. (C), SC, *508*
Pinton Forrest & Madden/EMA Partners Int'l. (R), BC, *165*
Ray & Berndtson/Lovas Stanley (R), ON, *172*
Russell Reynolds Assoc., Inc. (R), NY, *176*
Wilson Riles & Assoc., Inc. (R), CA, *178*
Norman Roberts & Assoc., Inc. (R), CA, *179*
Emery A. Rose & Assoc. (C), WA, *545*
Schoales & Assoc. Inc. (C), ON, *572*
Search & Recruit Int'l. (C), VA, *573*
Robert Sellery Assoc., Ltd. (R), DC, *188*
James F. Smith & Assoc. (C), GA, *583*
Herman Smith Executive Initiatives Inc. (R), ON, *193*
SpencerStuart (R), NY, *196*
Synergy 2000 (C), DC, *597*
TCM Enterprises (C), MD, *600*
Telford, Adams & Alexander (R), CA, *208*
TPG & Assoc. (C), TX, *608*
Trout & Assoc. Inc. (R), UT, *211*
Van Leeuwen Assoc. (R), CA, *213*
Kelly Walker Assoc. (C), TX, *614*
Weinpel Search, Inc. (C), NJ, *617*
ZanExec L.L.C. (R), VA, *226*

K.10 Defense

The Abbott Group, Inc. (R), MD, *1*
Advanced Corporate Search (C), CA, *240*
American Executive Management, Inc. (R), MA, *5*
Anderson Bradshaw Assoc., Inc. (R), TX, *6*
The Baldwin Group (R), IL, *10*
Battalia Winston Int'l./The Euram Consultants Group (R), NY, *13*
Paul J. Biestek Assoc., Inc. (R), IL, *17*
Blake/Hansen Ltd. (R), FL, *18*
Capital Consulting Group, Inc. (R), MD, *28*
Creative HR Solutions (C), GA, *303*
Dean-MacDonald (R), OH, *47*
Doleman Enterprises (R), VA, *53*
Fernow Assoc. (C), PA, *339*
Foster Partners (R), NY, *70*
F. Gloss Int'l. (R), VA, *78*
Government Contract Solutions, Inc. (C), VA, *360*
William C. Houze & Co. (R), CA, *96*
The Hudson Group (C), CT, *383*
The Human Resource Group, Inc. (R), OH, *98*
i.j. & assoc., inc. (C), CO, *386*
International Consulting Services, Inc. (C), IL, *392*
JDG Assoc., Ltd. (C), MD, *397*
Jerome & Co. (C), CA, *398*
Kames & Assoc. (C), MD, *403*
A.T. Kearney Executive Search (R), IL, *111*
The Kleven Group, Inc. (C), MA, *407*
Knapp Consultants (R), CT, *116*
Laguzza Assoc., Ltd. (R), NY, *122*
Larkin & Co. (R), CA, *124*
Management Recruiters of Altamonte (C), FL, *442*
Robert T. Morton Assoc., Inc. (C), MA, *486*
New Venture Development, Inc. (C), CA, *492*
NYCOR Search, Inc. (C), MN, *497*
M. A. Pelle Assoc., Inc. (C), NY, *506*
Emery A. Rose & Assoc. (C), WA, *545*
Search & Recruit Int'l. (C), VA, *573*
James F. Smith & Assoc. (C), GA, *583*
SpencerStuart (R), NY, *196*
Synergy 2000 (C), DC, *597*
TCM Enterprises (C), MD, *600*
TPG & Assoc. (C), TX, *608*
Trout & Assoc. Inc. (R), UT, *211*
Weinpel Search, Inc. (C), NJ, *617*
ZanExec L.L.C. (R), VA, *226*

L.00 Environmental services

A C Personnel Services, Inc. (C), OK, *231*
A.M.C.R., Inc. (C), OH, *232*
Accelerated Data Decision, Inc. (C), NJ, *233*
Alaska Executive Search, Inc. (C), AK, *243*
Alliance Executive Search, Inc. (R), MA, *4*
Anderson & Schwab, Inc. (R), NY, *5*
Anderson Bradshaw Assoc., Inc. (R), TX, *6*
R. W. Apple & Assoc. (C), NJ, *251*
Applied Search Assoc., Inc. (C), GA, *252*
Ashway Ltd. Agency (C), NY, *253*
Atomic Personnel, Inc. (C), PA, *255*
Attorney Search Global, Inc. (C), IL, *255*
Baeder Kalinski Int'l. Group, Inc. (R), NH, *10*
D. W. Baird & Associates (C), MD, *257*
Ballos & Co., Inc. (R), NJ, *10*
Berkshire Search Assoc. (C), MA, *265*
Boyden (R), NY, *20*
The Bradbury Management Group, Inc. (R), CA, *21*
Brandt Associates (C), PA, *272*
Bridgecreek Personnel Agency (C), CA, *273*
Dan B. Brockman (C), IL, *274*
Broward-Dobbs, Inc. (C), GA, *274*
David S. Burt Assoc. (C), MT, *276*
C.T.E.W. Executive Personnel Services Inc. (C), BC, *278*
Canadian Career Partners (R), AB, *27*
Canny, Bowen Inc. (R), NY, *27*
Caruso & Assoc., Inc. (R), FL, *31*
Chase-Gardner Executive Search Associates, Inc. (C), FL, *289*
Christian & Timbers, Inc. (R), OH, *34*
Coastal Int'l., Inc. (R), MA, *36*
Robert Connelly & Assoc., Inc. (R), MN, *39*
Construction Search Specialists, Inc. (C), WI, *297*
Conway & Assoc. (R), IL, *40*
Cornwall Stockton & Co., Inc. (C), TX, *299*
Corporate Environment Ltd. (R), IL, *41*
J. D. Cotter Search Inc. (C), OH, *302*
Frank Cuomo & Assoc., Inc. (C), NY, *305*
Dahl-Morrow Int'l. (R), VA, *45*
DEL Technical Services, Inc. (C), IL, *310*
Delta Services (R), TX, *48*
Derek Associates, Inc. (C), MA, *311*
Diversified Search, Inc. (R), PA, *52*
Robert Drexler Assoc., Inc. (R), NJ, *54*
Dunhill Professional Search of Englewood, Inc. (C), CO, *319*
Dunhill Executive Search of Los Angeles, Inc. (C), CA, *319*
Dunhill of San Francisco, Inc. (C), CA, *319*
ESS (Executive Search Services) (R), CA, *61*
Executive Recruiters Int'l. (C), MI, *333*
Executives Worldwide, Inc. (C), OR, *337*

Guild Fetridge Acoustical Search, Inc. (C), NY, *340*
Florapersonnel, Inc. (R), FL, *68*
Fortune Personnel Consultants of Jacksonville (C), FL, *345*
Foster Partners (R), NY, *70*
Gilbert Tweed Assoc. Inc. (R), NY, *76*
Global 1000 Int'l. Services (C), CA, *358*
Global Consulting Group Inc. (C), ON, *358*
Goodrich & Sherwood Assoc., Inc. (R), NY, *79*
Government Contract Solutions, Inc. (C), VA, *360*
Grover & Assoc. (R), OH, *82*
Haddad Assoc. (R), FL, *84*
Don Hall & Assoc. (C), TX, *366*
Michael J. Hall & Co. (R), WA, *85*
Harbor Consultants Int'l., Inc. (C), VA, *368*
Helffrich Int'l. (C), FL, *375*
Herring & Assoc. (C), AR, *376*
Holland Rusk & Assoc. (R), IL, *95*
William C. Houze & Co. (R), CA, *96*
Hunt Patton & Brazeal, Inc. (C), OK, *385*
Interim Accounting Professionals (C), CA, *391*
International Business Partners (C), ON, *392*
International Recruiting Services (C), FL, *393*
Isaacson, Miller (R), MA, *104*
Jackson Group Int'l. (C), CO, *396*
Jakobs & Assoc. Int'l. (R), NY, *105*
Jones Management Co. (R), CT, *108*
JRL Executive Recruiters (C), MO, *401*
KABL Ability Network (C), CA, *402*
Karel & Co. (R), CA, *109*
A.T. Kearney Executive Search (R), IL, *111*
Korn/Ferry Int'l. (R), NY, *117*
The LaBorde Group (C), CA, *411*
Lam Assoc. (C), HI, *411*
Larkin & Co. (R), CA, *124*
Larsen Int'l., Inc. (R), TX, *125*
Michael Latas & Assoc., Inc. (R), MO, *125*
Lechner & Assoc., Inc. (C), FL, *415*
London Executive Consultants Inc. (C), ON, *420*
Bruce Lowery & Assoc. (C), MI, *420*
Management & Human Resources (R), MA, *134*
Management Alliance Group, Inc. (R), NJ, *134*
Management Recruiters Peninsula (C), CA, *439*
Management Recruiters of Berkeley (C), CA, *439*
Management Recruiters Dana Point (C), CA, *440*
Management Recruiters of Savannah (C), GA, *446*
Management Recruiters of Orange County, N.Y., Inc. (C), NJ, *453*
Management Recruiters of Great Neck (C), NY, *454*
Management Recruiters of Gastonia (C), NC, *456*
Management Recruiters of Cleveland (C), OH, *457*
Management Recruiters of Lynnwood (C), WA, *465*
Management Recruiters of Stevens Point, Inc. (C), WI, *466*
The Marathon Group (C), FL, *469*
Mark III Personnel, Inc. (C), NC, *470*
Mark Stanley & Co./EMA Partners International (R), FL, *136*
McCormack & Assoc. (R), CA, *140*
McKee Cyber Search (C), MS, *475*
McNichol Assoc. (R), PA, *142*
Montgomery, Thomason & Assoc. (C), ON, *484*
Morgan Samuels Co. (R), CA, *147*
MPA Executive Search Inc. (R), QE, *148*
National Affirmative Action Career Network, Inc. (C), CO, *488*
National Metal Services Corp. (C), IN, *489*
The NEIS Corp., Inc. (C), FL, *491*
The Niemond Corp. (R), CA, *152*
NorTech Resources (C), NY, *496*
The North Peak Group (C), OH, *496*
John R. O'Connor & Assoc. (C), IL, *497*
OEI, Inc. (C), NJ, *498*
Ortman Recruiting Int'l. (C), CA, *500*
Parsons, Anderson & Gee, Inc. (C), NY, *503*
PC Assoc. (C), CO, *505*
Penn Associates (R), PA, *161*
PERI Corp/Professional Executive Recruiters, Inc. (C), TX, *507*
Fred Perry Assoc. (C), TX, *507*
Personnel Alliance Group (C), NJ, *507*
Personnel Assoc. (C), NC, *508*
The Personnel Network, Inc. (C), SC, *508*
Personnel Tangent Inc. (C), QE, *509*
Yves Plouffe & Assoc. (R), QE, *165*
David Powell, Inc. (R), CA, *166*
Powers Consultants, Inc. (R), MO, *166*
Preferred Professional Recruiters (C), OH, *516*
Preng & Assoc., Inc. (R), TX, *167*
Pro Tec Technical Services (C), ON, *519*
Professional Personnel Consultants, Inc. (C), MI, *521*
Professional Persons Career Services (C), NY, *521*
Professional Search, Inc. (C), CO, *522*
Protocol Inc. (C), CA, *525*
QVS Int'l. (R), GA, *170*
R. C. Services (C), TX, *528*
R.A.N. Assoc., Inc. (C), OH, *528*
The Recruitment Group, Inc. (C), NY, *532*
Reserve Technology Institute (R), TX, *175*
Russell Reynolds Assoc., Inc. (R), NY, *176*
Rice Cohen Int'l. (R), PA, *178*
Ritta Professional Search Inc. (C), NY, *538*
River Region Personnel, Inc. (C), LA, *538*
Rossi & Assoc. Inc. (C), BC, *545*
RSMR, Inc. (R), IL, *182*
S-H-S TechStaff (C), PA, *549*
Sales Builders, Inc. (R), VA, *183*
Sales Consultants Peninsula, Inc. (C), CA, *556*
Sales Consultants of Honolulu (C), HI, *558*
Sales Consultants of Auburn Hills (C), MI, *559*
Sales Consultants of Princeton, Inc. (C), NJ, *561*
Search Consultants Int'l., Inc. (C), TX, *575*
Search Group Inc. (R), AB, *186*
Search Plus Int'l.-Ohio (C), OH, *576*
Shey-Harding Assoc. Inc. (C), CA, *580*
Smith & Assoc. (C), FL, *583*
G. L. Smith Assoc. (C), CA, *584*
Smith, Brown & Jones (C), KS, *585*
Southern Recruiters & Consultants, Inc. (C), SC, *587*
Southern Research Services (R), FL, *195*
Specialized Search Assoc. (C), FL, *589*
SpencerStuart (R), NY, *196*
Splaine & Assoc., Inc. (R), CA, *198*
SR Wilson, Inc. (C), CA, *590*
Stanton Chase Int'l. (R), MD, *198*
Stephens Assoc. Ltd., Inc. (R), OH, *200*
Ron Stevens & Assoc., Inc. (C), FL, *593*
J. Stroll Assoc., Inc. (R), CT, *203*
Target Search, Inc. (C), PA, *600*
TCM Enterprises (C), MD, *600*
Technical Skills Consulting Inc. (R), ON, *207*
Technifind Int'l. (C), TX, *602*
Tekworx, Inc. (C), OK, *604*
Thomas & Assoc. of Michigan (C), MI, *606*
TPG & Assoc. (C), TX, *608*
Trans-United Consultants Ltd. (C), ON, *608*
Trout & Assoc. Inc. (R), UT, *211*
Ward-Hoffman & Assoc. (C), ID, *615*
Jude M. Werra & Assoc. (R), WI, *218*
Western Management Assoc. (R), CA, *218*
The Whitaker Companies (C), TX, *619*
Walter K. Wilkins & Co. (R), NJ, *221*
John R. Williams & Assoc., Inc. (C), NC, *621*
Wing Tips & Pumps, Inc. (C), MI, *623*
Wood & Assoc./Executive Search Consultants (C), CA, *624*
Wood West & Partners Inc. (C), BC, *624*
Working Relationships, Inc. (C), MN, *624*
John Wylie Assoc., Inc. (C), OK, *625*
Zweig White & Assoc., Inc. (R), MA, *228*

L.10 Hazardous waste, study, cleanup

Anderson Bradshaw Assoc., Inc. (R), TX, *6*
R. W. Apple & Assoc. (C), NJ, *251*
Atomic Personnel, Inc. (C), PA, *255*
Baeder Kalinski Int'l. Group, Inc. (R), NH, *10*
Christian & Timbers, Inc. (R), OH, *34*
Conway & Assoc. (R), IL, *40*
Cornwall Stockton & Co., Inc. (C), TX, *299*
Corporate Environment Ltd. (R), IL, *41*
Frank Cuomo & Assoc., Inc. (C), NY, *305*
DEL Technical Services, Inc. (C), IL, *310*
Derek Associates, Inc. (C), MA, *311*
Foster Partners (R), NY, *70*
Gilbert Tweed Assoc. Inc. (R), NY, *76*
Government Contract Solutions, Inc. (C), VA, *360*
Don Hall & Assoc. (C), TX, *366*
William C. Houze & Co. (R), CA, *96*
Hunt Patton & Brazeal, Inc. (C), OK, *385*

International Recruiting Services (C), FL, 393
Karel & Co. (R), CA, 109
A.T. Kearney Executive Search (R), IL, 111
Larkin & Co. (R), CA, 124
Lechner & Assoc., Inc. (C), FL, 415
Management Alliance Group, Inc. (R), NJ, 134
Management Recruiters of Great Neck (C), NY, 454
Management Recruiters of Lynnwood (C), WA, 465
The Marathon Group (C), FL, 469
McCormack & Assoc. (R), CA, 140
McNichol Assoc. (R), PA, 142
MPA Executive Search Inc. (R), QE, 148
National Affirmative Action Career Network, Inc. (C), CO, 488
National Metal Services Corp. (C), IN, 489
The NEIS Corp., Inc. (C), FL, 491
The Niemond Corp. (R), CA, 152
NorTech Resources (C), NY, 496
OEI, Inc. (C), NJ, 498
Fred Perry Assoc. (C), TX, 507
Protocol Inc. (C), CA, 525
R. C. Services (C), TX, 528
R.A.N. Assoc., Inc. (C), OH, 528
S-H-S TechStaff (C), PA, 549
Sales Consultants Peninsula, Inc. (C), CA, 556
Search Consultants Int'l., Inc. (C), TX, 575
Search Plus Int'l.-Ohio (C), OH, 576
Shey-Harding Assoc. Inc. (C), CA, 580
Specialized Search Assoc. (C), FL, 589
SpencerStuart (R), NY, 196
Tekworx, Inc. (C), OK, 604
TPG & Assoc. (C), TX, 608

M.00 Aerospace

The 500 Granary Inc. (C), ON, 231
The Abbott Group, Inc. (R), MD, 1
Access Assoc. Inc. (C), MD, 233
ACCESS Technology (C), CA, 234
Adirect Recruiting Corp. (C), ON, 240
Advanced Executive Resources (R), MI, 2
The Alexander Group (R), NJ, 3
Frank E. Allen & Assoc. (C), NJ, 244
American Services Group (C), IL, 248
AmeriResource Group Inc. (C), OK, 248
Ames-O'Neill Assoc., Inc. (C), NY, 249
Anderson Bradshaw Assoc., Inc. (R), TX, 6
Andex Executive Search (C), CT, 250
Artgo, Inc. (R), OH, 7
Asheville Search & Consulting (C), NC, 253
The Associates, HR Search Executives, Inc. (C), OK, 254
Atlanta Executive Partners, Inc. (R), MA, 8
Aurora Tech Search (C), ON, 256
A. M. Auster Associates (R), FL, 9
Cami Austin & Assoc. (C), IL, 256
The Badger Group (R), CA, 10
Allen Ballach Assoc. Inc. (R), ON, 10
Barton Assoc., Inc. (R), TX, 12
Battalia Winston Int'l./The Euram Consultants Group (R), NY, 13
Beach Executive Search Inc. (R), FL, 14
Becker Project Resources, Inc. (C), OR, 262
The Bedford Group (R), RI, 15
J. P. Bencik Assoc. (C), MI, 263
Berkana Int'l., Inc. (C), WA, 265
Paul J. Biestek Assoc., Inc. (R), IL, 17
Bio-Venture Group (C), RI, 266
Blake/Hansen Ltd. (R), FL, 18
Bos Business Consultants (C), NY, 270
Bowden & Co., Inc. (R), OH, 20
BowdenGlobal, Ltd. (R), OH, 20
Howard Bowen Consulting (C), FL, 270
Bowman & Marshall, Inc. (C), KS, 271
Boyle/Ogata Executive Search (R), CA, 21
Brei & Assoc., Inc. (C), IA, 272
Brentwood Int'l. (R), CA, 23
Cahill Assoc. (C), CT, 279
California Search Agency, Inc. (C), CA, 279
Cambridge Management Planning (R), ON, 27
Campa & Assoc. (R), ON, 27
Career +Plus (C), NY, 281
Michael J. Cavanagh & Assoc. Inc. (R), ON, 31
cFour Partners (R), CA, 32
David Chambers & Assoc., Inc. (R), CT, 32
Cizek Assoc., Inc. (R), AZ, 35
CMW & Associates, Inc. (C), IL, 293
J. Kevin Coleman & Assoc., Inc. (R), CA, 37
Connors, Lovell & Assoc. Inc. (C), ON, 296
Cowin Assoc. (R), NY, 42
CV Associates (C), NY, 305
Alan Davis & Assoc. Inc. (R), QE, 47
Davis & Company (R), CA, 47
Dean-MacDonald (R), OH, 47
Derhak Ireland & Partners Ltd. (R), ON, 48
The Devlin Search Group, Inc. (C), MA, 311
The Diestel Group (R), UT, 51
Dise & Co. (R), OH, 52
Diversified Search, Inc. (R), PA, 52
Dunhill Personnel of St. Andrews (C), SC, 322
Dynamic Synergy Corp. (R), CA, 56
E T Search Inc. (C), CA, 324
Eastern Executive Assoc. (C), NJ, 325
The Elsworth Group (C), TX, 329
Engineering Futures, LLC (C), CT, 330
Engineering Resource Group, Inc. (C), NJ, 331
ESA (R), CT, 60
Executive Search Consultants Corp. (C), IL, 335
Executive Search Group, Inc. (C), CT, 335
Executive Search of America, Inc. (C), OH, 336
Leon A. Farley Assoc. (R), CA, 65
Fernow Assoc. (C), PA, 339
Guild Fetridge Acoustical Search, Inc. (C), NY, 340
Fishel HR Assoc., Inc. (C), AZ, 341
Fisher Personnel Management Services (R), CA, 68
J. G. Flynn & Assoc. Inc. (R), BC, 69
F-O-R-T-U-N-E Personnel Consultants of Tampa (C), FL, 344
Fortune Personnel Consultants of Allentown, Inc. (C), PA, 348
Foster Partners (R), NY, 70
Gaudry, Shink, Levasseur (R), QE, 75
Gilreath Weatherby Inc. (R), MA, 77
F. Gloss Int'l. (R), VA, 78
The Gobbell Co. (R), CA, 78
L. J. Gonzer Assoc. (C), NJ, 360
Grant/Morgan Assoc., Inc. (C), MD, 361
Grantham & Co., Inc. (R), NC, 81
The Hamilton Group (R), MD, 85
Harcourt Group Ltd. (R), OH, 86
The Harris Consulting Corp. (R), MB, 87
Hartsfield Group, Inc. (R), GA, 87
Harvard Group Int'l. (R), GA, 87
Heath/Norton Assoc., Inc. (R), NY, 89
HEC Group (C), ON, 375
Herbeck Kline & Assoc. (R), IL, 92
Hergenrather & Co. (R), WA, 92
The Hetzel Group, Inc. (R), IL, 92
Hobson Assoc. (C), CT, 379
Horton Int'l. Inc. (R), NY, 96
William C. Houze & Co. (R), CA, 96
The Hudson Group (C), CT, 383
The Human Resource Group, Inc. (R), OH, 98
Hunter Assoc. (C), MA, 385
The Hunter Group (C), NC, 385
Huntley Associates (Dallas), Inc. (C), TX, 386
W. Hutt Management Resources Ltd. (R), ON, 100
i.j. & assoc., inc. (C), CO, 386
IM Independent Management Recruiters (R), TN, 101
IMA Search, Inc. (R), NY, 101
Independent Resource Systems (C), CA, 388
Interim Management Resources Inc. (C), ON, 392
K. Jaeger & Assoc. (C), MA, 396
JAG Group (R), MO, 105
Jerome & Co. (C), CA, 398
Job-Born Candidate Selection Bureau (C), ON, 399
John H. Johnson & Assoc., Inc. (R), IL, 106
KABL Ability Network (C), CA, 402
Kames & Assoc. (C), MD, 403
A.T. Kearney Executive Search (R), IL, 111
The Kleven Group, Inc. - Executive Search Division (R), MA, 116
Knapp Consultants (R), CT, 116
T. J. Koellhoffer & Assoc. (R), NJ, 116
Korn/Ferry Int'l. (R), NY, 117
Krautler Personnel Recruitment (C), FL, 409
L & L Assoc. (C), CA, 410
Lam Assoc. (C), HI, 411
Lange & Assoc., Inc. (C), IN, 412
Lanken-Kimball-Therrell & Assoc. (C), GA, 412
LCC Companies (C), AZ, 414
Jacques LePage Executive Search Inc. (R), QE, 128
J. E. Lessner Assoc., Inc. (R), MI, 128
LifeWork, Inc. (C), TX, 418
Locus Inc. (C), WV, 419

INDUSTRIES

London Executive Consultants Inc. (C), ON, *420*
Lucas Group (C), NY, *421*
Charles Luntz & Assoc., Inc. (R), MO, *132*
Maglio & Co., Inc. (R), WI, *134*
Management Association Network (C), WI, *424*
Management Recruiters of Sedona (C), AZ, *438*
Management Recruiters of Altamonte (C), FL, *442*
Management Recruiters of Marietta, Inc. (C), GA, *446*
Management Recruiters of The Sandias (C), NM, *454*
Management Recruiters of Broome County, Inc. (C), NY, *454*
Management Recruiters of Rocky Mount - Southwest (C), NC, *456*
Management Recruiters of North Charleston (C), SC, *460*
Management Recruiters of Seattle (C), WA, *465*
Management Search Int'l. (C), CA, *467*
Management Solutions, Inc. (C), WA, *468*
Massey-Horton Int'l. (R), ON, *138*
Tom McCall Executive Search (C), IL, *473*
McCormack & Farrow (R), CA, *140*
McCray, Shriver, Eckdahl & Assoc., Inc. (R), CA, *140*
McKee Cyber Search (C), MS, *475*
McManners Assoc., Inc. (R), CA, *142*
Meng, Finseth & Assoc., Inc. (R), CA, *143*
J. M. Meredith & Assoc. Inc. (C), CA, *479*
MESA, Inc. (R), CO, *143*
MGA Executive Search (C), FL, *480*
Michigan Consulting Group (R), MI, *144*
Morgan Samuels Co. (R), CA, *147*
The Mulshine Co., Inc. (R), NJ, *149*
Nadzam, Lusk, Horgan & Assoc., Inc. (R), CA, *150*
National Corporate Consultants, Inc. (C), IN, *489*
New Venture Development, Inc. (C), CA, *492*
P. J. Nicholson & Assoc. (C), IL, *493*
The Niemond Corp. (R), CA, *152*
NMC & Kay Int'l. (R), CO, *152*
Norton & Assoc. (C), IL, *496*
O'Neill Group (C), NJ, *498*
The Odessa Group (R), CA, *155*
Open Concepts (C), CA, *499*
Orion Int'l. Consulting Group, Inc. (C), NC, *499*
Ott & Hansen, Inc. (R), CA, *157*
The Oxford Group (C), TX, *500*
D. P. Parker & Assoc., Inc. (R), MA, *159*
Parker, McFadden & Assoc. (C), GA, *503*
M. A. Pelle Assoc., Inc. (C), NY, *506*
The Perkins Group (R), NC, *162*
Perry-Martel Int'l., Inc. (R), ON, *163*
The Personnel Group, Inc. (R), MN, *163*
Personnel, Inc. (C), AL, *508*
Personnel Management Group (C), MB, *508*
Personnel Tangent Inc. (C), QE, *509*
Petro Staff Int'l. (C), AB, *509*
PHD Conseil en Ressources Humaines Inc. (C), QE, *510*
Pioneer Consulting Group (C), CA, *512*
Placement Testart Inc. (C), QE, *513*
Rene Plessner Assoc., Inc. (R), NY, *165*
Poirier, Hoevel & Co. (R), CA, *166*
The Polen Group (C), PA, *514*
The Pollack Group (C), ON, *514*
Jack Porter Assoc., Inc. (C), WA, *514*
George Preger & Associates Inc. (R), ON, *167*
Alan J. Price Assoc., Inc. (C), RI, *518*
Professional Employment Group (C), MD, *520*
Professional Team Search, Inc. (R), AZ, *169*
ProSearch, Inc. (C), PA, *524*
Quality Search Inc. (C), OH, *526*
R2 Services, LLC (C), IL, *528*
Radosevic Assoc. (R), CA, *171*
Re-Mark Assoc. Inc. (C), NJ, *531*
The Recruitment Group, Inc. (C), NY, *532*
Russell Reynolds Assoc., Inc. (R), NY, *176*
Reynolds Consulting Int'l. (R), ON, *177*
Reynolds Partners (R), NY, *177*
Robert Lowell Int'l. (R), TX, *179*
Robinson-Robinson & Assoc., Inc. (C), MN, *539*
Roevin Technical People (C), ON, *540*
Romano McAvoy Assoc., Inc. (C), NY, *544*
Emery A. Rose & Assoc. (C), WA, *545*
Louis Rudzinsky Assoc., Inc. (C), MA, *548*
W. A. Rutledge & Assoc. (R), CT, *183*
R. S. Sadow Assoc. (C), NJ, *550*
George D. Sandel Assoc. (C), MA, *565*
Sanford Rose Assoc. - Athens (C), GA, *566*
Sanford Rose Assoc. - Cedar Rapids (C), IA, *567*
Sanford Rose Assoc. - Flemington (C), NJ, *568*
Sanford Rose Assoc. - Burlington, NC (C), NC, *569*
Sanford Rose Assoc. - Akron (C), OH, *569*
Sanford Rose Assoc. - Austin (C), TX, *570*
Sanford Rose Assoc. - Doylestown (C), PA, *570*
Savoy Partners, Ltd. (R), DC, *184*
Search & Recruit Int'l. (C), VA, *573*
Search Advisors Int'l. Corp. (R), FL, *186*
Search Plus Int'l.-Ohio (C), OH, *576*
SearchOne, Inc. (C), AR, *577*
Seiden Krieger Assoc., Inc. (R), NY, *188*
E. L. Shore & Assoc. (R), ON, *190*
Larry Siegel & Assoc. (R), WA, *191*
Singleton & Assoc. (C), VA, *582*
Slayton Int'l., Inc. (R), IL, *192*
Smith & Syberg, Inc. (R), IN, *193*
Software Resource Consultants (C), TN, *587*
Robert Sollman & Assoc. (C), FL, *587*
Spectrum Consultants (R), CA, *196*
SpencerStuart (R), NY, *196*
Star Search Consultants (C), ON, *591*
Linford E. Stiles & Assoc., L.L.C. (R), NH, *201*
Success Seekers Connection (C), FL, *596*
Survival Systems Staffing, Inc. (C), CA, *597*
Synergy Solutions, Ltd. (C), WA, *597*
Systems Research Inc. (SRI) (C), IL, *598*
TCM Enterprises (C), MD, *600*
Tech-Net (C), TX, *601*
Technical Employment Consultants (C), PA, *602*
Technical Recruiting Services (C), OH, *602*
Technical Resource Assoc. (C), TN, *602*
Technical Search Assoc. (C), OH, *602*
Technical Skills Consulting Inc. (R), ON, *207*
Thomas Mangum Co. (R), CA, *208*
Thomson, Sponar & Adams, Inc. (C), WA, *606*
The Tidewater Group Inc. (C), CT, *607*
TNS Partners, Inc. (R), TX, *209*
Tower Consultants, Ltd. (R), PA, *209*
TPG & Assoc. (C), TX, *608*
Trans-United Consultants Ltd. (C), ON, *608*
Trout & Assoc. Inc. (R), UT, *211*
TSS Consulting, Ltd. (C), AZ, *610*
Tuttle Venture Group, Inc. (R), TX, *212*
The Urban Placement Service (C), TX, *611*
Vaughan & Co. (C), CA, *612*
Linda Walter & Associes (C), QE, *615*
Warren Executive Services (C), GA, *616*
Weinpel Search, Inc. (C), NJ, *617*
D. L. Weiss & Assoc. (R), CA, *217*
West & West (R), CA, *218*
Western Management Consultants (R), BC, *218*
Western Technical Resources (C), CA, *619*
Winston Search, Inc. (R), MD, *222*
World Search (C), OH, *625*
ZanExec L.L.C. (R), VA, *226*
Zen Zen Int'l. Inc. (C), MB, *627*

N.00 Packaging

ACC Technical Services (C), OH, *233*
AES Search (C), NJ, *241*
Agri-Tech Personnel, Inc. (C), MO, *242*
J. R. Akin & Co. (R), MA, *2*
The Altco Group (C), NJ, *246*
Anderson & Associates (R), NC, *5*
Ansara, Bickford & Fiske (C), MA, *251*
APA Search, Inc. (R), NY, *6*
Applied Resources, Inc. (C), MN, *252*
Ashlar-Stone Management Consultants Inc. (R), ON, *8*
Associated Recruiters (C), WI, *254*
Atomic Personnel, Inc. (C), PA, *255*
BallResources (C), MO, *258*
Aldonna Barry Personnel & Management (C), ON, *260*
Behrens and Company (C), WA, *262*
Gary S. Bell Assoc., Inc. (C), NJ, *263*
Besen Assoc. Inc. (C), NJ, *266*
BJB Assoc. (C), VA, *267*
Blair/Tech Recruiters, Inc. (C), NJ, *268*
The Borton Wallace Co. (R), NC, *19*
Bos Business Consultants (C), NY, *270*
Bosco-Hubert & Assoc. (C), KS, *270*
Bowman & Marshall, Inc. (C), KS, *271*
The Brand Co., Inc. (R), FL, *22*
Brooke Chase Assoc., Inc. (R), IL, *24*
Bryan & Louis Research (C), OH, *275*
Business Solutions Worldwide, Inc. (C), NJ, *277*
C.P.S., Inc. (C), IL, *278*

California Search Agency, Inc. (C), CA, *279*
Callan Assoc., Ltd. (R), IL, *27*
Canny, Bowen Inc. (R), NY, *27*
J. P. Canon Assoc. (C), NY, *280*
Caprio & Assoc. Inc. (R), IL, *29*
Central Executive Search, Inc. (C), OH, *287*
Chadwell & Assoc., Inc. (C), MI, *288*
William J. Christopher Assoc., Inc. (R), PA, *34*
Christopher-Westmont & Assoc., Inc. (R), OH, *34*
The Churchill Group (C), ON, *291*
Coe & Co. Int'l. Inc./EMA Partners Int'l. (R), AB, *37*
S L Collins Assoc. (C), NC, *294*
Conard Associates, Inc. (R), NH, *39*
Connors, Lovell & Assoc. Inc. (C), ON, *296*
ContactBridge, Inc. (R), IL, *40*
Cook Assoc.,® Inc. (R), IL, *40*
The Cooke Group (R), WI, *40*
Corbin Packaging Professionals (C), MO, *299*
Creative Input, Inc. (C), RI, *303*
Crowder & Company (R), MI, *43*
Charles Dahl Group, Inc. (C), MN, *306*
The Dartmouth Group (R), NY, *46*
Dean-MacDonald (R), OH, *47*
Derhak Ireland & Partners Ltd. (R), ON, *48*
Desktop Staffing, Inc. (C), IL, *311*
DieckMueller Group (R), WI, *51*
Direct Recruiters, Inc. (C), OH, *312*
Dixie Search Assoc. (C), GA, *313*
Doherty Int'l., Inc. (R), IL, *53*
The Dorfman Group (C), AZ, *314*
J. H. Dugan & Assoc., Inc. (R), CA, *55*
Dunhill Professional Search of Englewood, Inc. (C), CO, *319*
Dunhill Professional Search, Inc. of McAllen (C), TX, *323*
Elite Resources Group (R), OH, *58*
Yves Elkas Inc. (R), QE, *58*
Erlanger Assoc. (R), CT, *60*
Execu-Tech Search Inc. (C), MN, *332*
Executive Directions (R), OH, *62*
Executive Registry (C), QE, *334*
Executive Search Group, Inc. (C), CT, *335*
Executive Search, Ltd. (C), OH, *336*
Executive Solutions (R), MN, *64*
Fergason Assoc., Inc. (C), IL, *339*
Fidelity Search Group, Inc. (R), PA, *66*
Robert M. Flanagan & Assoc., Ltd. (R), NY, *68*
F-O-R-T-U-N-E Personnel Consultants of Tampa (C), FL, *344*
Fortune Personnel Consultants of Jacksonville (C), FL, *345*
Fortune Personnel Consultants of Hinsdale, IL (C), IL, *346*
F-O-R-T-U-N-E Personnel Consultants of Troy, Inc. (C), MI, *347*
F-O-R-T-U-N-E Personnel Consultants of Menlo Park, Inc. (C), NJ, *347*
Fortune Personnel Consultants (C), MT, *347*
F-O-R-T-U-N-E of West Portland (C), OR, *348*
Fortune Personnel Consultants of Chattanooga Inc. (C), TN, *349*
F-O-R-T-U-N-E Personnel Consultants of Houston, Inc. (C), TX, *350*
Foster Partners (R), NY, *70*
Gardner-Ross Assoc., Inc. (R), NY, *74*
The Garret Group (R), NJ, *75*
Gaudry, Shink, Levasseur (R), QE, *75*
Gilbert Tweed Assoc. Inc. (R), NY, *76*
Gilreath Weatherby Inc. (R), MA, *77*
The Glenwood Group (C), IL, *358*
Global 1000 Int'l. Services (C), CA, *358*
Global Career Services, Inc. (C), NY, *358*
Goldstein & Co. (C), CA, *360*
Goodrich & Sherwood Assoc., Inc. (R), NY, *79*
Gould, McCoy & Chadick, Inc. (R), NY, *80*
Grant-Franks & Assoc. (C), NJ, *361*
Grantham & Co., Inc. (R), NC, *81*
David E. Grumney Co. Inc. (R), WA, *83*
GWS Partners (R), IL, *84*
Helfer Executive Consultants (R), TN, *91*
G. W. Henn & Co. (R), OH, *91*
The Hensge Co. (R), IL, *91*
Howe & Assoc. (R), PA, *97*
The Human Resource Department Ltd. (R), OH, *98*
Hunter, Rowan & Crowe (C), FL, *386*
W. Hutt Management Resources Ltd. (R), ON, *100*
Innovative Resource Group, LLC (C), NC, *389*
The Inside Track (C), TX, *389*
International Business Partners (C), ON, *392*
ISC of Cincinnati Inc. (C), OH, *394*
The J. B. Search Group (C), CA, *395*
JLI-Boston (R), MA, *106*
JM & Company (R), PA, *106*
Job-Born Candidate Selection Bureau (C), ON, *399*
John H. Johnson & Assoc., Inc. (R), IL, *106*
Johnson Brown Assoc., Inc. (C), IN, *400*
Jones Management Co. (R), CT, *108*
J. M. Joseph Assoc. (R), NJ, *109*
Kane & Assoc. (C), TX, *403*
A.T. Kearney Executive Search (R), IL, *111*
The Kleinstein Group, Inc. (R), NJ, *116*
Lee Koehn Assoc., Inc. (R), OR, *116*
Korn/Ferry Int'l. (R), NY, *117*
Kresin Wingard (C), IL, *409*
Krueger Assoc. (R), IL, *121*
Paul Kull & Co. (R), NJ, *121*
D. Kunkle & Assoc. (C), IL, *410*
Laboratory Resource Group (C), MA, *411*
Rene LaFlamme & Associes (R), QE, *122*
The Lawson Group, Inc. (C), SC, *414*
Leaders-Trust Int'l./Carce y Asociados, S.C. (R), MX, *127*
Lekan & Assoc., Inc. (R), OH, *128*
The Libra Group (C), NC, *417*
LifeWork, Inc. (C), TX, *418*
Logistics Management Resources, Inc. (R), NY, *131*
London Executive Consultants Inc. (C), ON, *420*
Lord & Albus Co. (C), TX, *420*
Louis Search Group, Inc. (C), NJ, *420*
Lucas Assoc. (C), GA, *421*
Lyons & Assoc., Inc. (C), IL, *422*
M H Executive Search Group (C), TX, *422*
M.C. Executive Search (C), CA, *422*
Maglio & Co., Inc. (R), WI, *134*
Management Association Network (C), WI, *424*
Management Recruiters of Decatur, LLC (C), AL, *438*
Management Recruiters of Birmingham-South, Inc. (C), AL, *438*
Management Recruiters of Clearwater (C), FL, *443*
Management Recruiters, Inc. (C), FL, *443*
Management Recruiters of Atlanta West, Inc. (C), GA, *445*
Management Recruiters of Duluth (C), GA, *445*
Management Recruiters of North Fulton (C), GA, *445*
Management Recruiters of Boise (C), ID, *446*
Management Recruiters of Indianapolis (C), IN, *448*
Management Recruiters of South Bend (C), IN, *448*
Management Recruiters of Noblesville, Inc. (C), IN, *448*
Management Recruiters of Columbia (C), MD, *450*
Management Recruiters of Southeastern Michigan (C), MI, *451*
Management Recruiters of Baltimore (C), MD, *451*
Management Recruiters of Woodbury (C), MN, *452*
Management Recruiters of Broome County, Inc. (C), NY, *454*
Management Recruiters of Cincinnati/Sharonville, Inc. (C), OH, *457*
Management Recruiters of Florence (C), SC, *460*
Management Recruiters of Champions (C), TX, *462*
Management Recruiters of Arlington (C), TX, *462*
Management Recruiters - Friendswood (C), TX, *462*
Management Recruiters of North West Austin (C), TX, *462*
Mannard & Assoc., Inc. (R), IL, *135*
The Marathon Group (C), FL, *469*
Margolin Consultants, Inc. (C), NY, *469*
Matte Consulting Group Inc. (R), QE, *138*
The McKinnon Management Group Inc. (C), ON, *475*
Meder & Assoc., Inc. (R), IL, *142*
Merrick & Moore (C), NC, *479*
MESA International (C), CA, *480*
Midland Consultants (C), OH, *481*
MIXTEC Group (R), CA, *145*
Morton, McCorkle & Assoc. Inc. (R), MO, *147*
Mullen Assoc., Inc. (R), NC, *148*
The Mulshine Company, Ltd. (R), NY, *149*
The Murray Group (C), IL, *487*

National Computerized Employment Service, Inc. (C), PA, *489*
NaviSearch (C), GA, *490*
Newman-Johnson-King, Inc. (C), TX, *492*
John B. Norris & Assoc., Inc. (C), MD, *495*
Northern Consultants Inc. (R), ME, *153*
Oberlander & Co., Inc. (R), IL, *155*
Omega Search, Inc. (C), NC, *498*
P R Management Consultants, Inc. (C), NJ, *500*
Packaging Personnel Co., Ltd. (C), WI, *501*
Pamenter, Pamenter, Brezer & Deganis Ltd. (R), ON, *159*
Parsons, Anderson & Gee, Inc. (C), NY, *503*
Rick Pascal & Assoc., Inc. (C), NJ, *504*
Peachtree Executive Search (R), GA, *161*
The Perkins Group (R), NC, *162*
PersoNet, Inc. (C), FL, *507*
Personnel Assoc. (C), NC, *508*
Personnel Tangent Inc. (C), QE, *509*
Petruzzi Assoc. (C), NJ, *509*
Phase II Management (R), CT, *164*
Phillips Int'l., Inc. (C), SC, *510*
PMJ & Assoc. (C), ON, *513*
The Polen Group (C), PA, *514*
Premier Search Group (C), IN, *517*
PricewaterhouseCoopers Executive Search (R), MX, *168*
Prime Resource Assoc. (C), WI, *518*
Professions, Inc. (C), OH, *523*
ProSearch, Inc. (C), OH, *524*
ProTech Nationwide Staffing, Inc. (C), NY, *525*
PSD Group, Inc. (C), CA, *525*
QVS Int'l. (R), GA, *170*
Ramming & Assoc., Inc. (C), NJ, *528*
RBW Assoc. Inc. (C), OR, *531*
The Recruitment Group, Inc. (C), NY, *532*
The Regis Group, Ltd. (R), GA, *174*
Reid Ellis Assoc. Inc. (C), ON, *533*
Resource Perspectives, Inc. (R), CA, *175*
Riddle & McGrath LLC (R), GA, *178*
River Region Personnel, Inc. (C), LA, *538*
The Rossi Search Group (C), PA, *545*
Roth Young Executive Recruiters (C), MN, *546*
S.C.S. & Assoc. (C), NC, *550*
S.D.P. Contract Recruiters (C), NJ, *550*
Sales Builders, Inc. (R), VA, *183*
Sales Consultants Int'l. of Oakland (C), CA, *556*
Sales Consultants of Sacramento (C), CA, *556*
Sales Consultants of Savannah, GA (C), GA, *557*
Sales Consultants of Ft. Lauderdale, Inc. (C), FL, *557*
Sales Consultants of Indianapolis (C), IN, *558*
Sales Consultants of Baltimore (C), MD, *559*
Sales Consultants of Laurel Park, Inc. (C), MI, *560*
Sales Consultants of Grand Rapids (C), MI, *560*
Sales Consultants of Princeton, Inc. (C), NJ, *561*
Sales Consultants of Westchester-South, Inc. (C), NY, *561*
Sales Consultants of Appleton (C), WI, *563*
Sales Consultants of Houston (C), TX, *563*
Sales Search (C), ON, *564*
Sanford Rose Assoc. - Chicago (C), IL, *566*
Sanford Rose Assoc. - Athens (C), GA, *566*
Sanford Rose Assoc. - Orland Park (C), IL, *567*
Sanford Rose Assoc. - Rockford (C), IL, *567*
Sanford Rose Assoc. - Cedar Rapids (C), IA, *567*
Sanford Rose Assoc. - Rockville (C), MD, *567*
Sanford Rose Assoc. - Greensboro (C), NC, *569*
Sathe & Associates, Inc. (R), MN, *184*
Schenck & Assoc. SC (C), WI, *572*
Scott Executive Search, Inc. (R), NY, *186*
Search Northwest Assoc. (C), OR, *576*
SearchOne, Inc. (C), AR, *577*
Selective Management Services, Inc. (C), FL, *578*
Shoemaker & Assoc. (R), GA, *190*
Ralph Smith & Assoc. (C), IL, *584*
Smith & Laue Search (R), OR, *193*
Smith, Brown & Jones (C), KS, *585*
Southern Chemical & Plastics Search (C), GA, *587*
Southern Recruiters & Consultants, Inc. (C), SC, *587*
Spectra International LLC (C), AZ, *589*
SpencerStuart (R), NY, *196*
Spilman & Assoc. (R), TX, *197*
Sprout/Standish, Inc. (C), NH, *589*
Star Search Consultants (C), ON, *591*
The Stelton Group, Inc. (C), NJ, *592*
Storfer & Assoc. (C), NY, *595*
Strategic Search Corp. (R), IL, *202*
T E M Assoc. (C), WI, *599*
S. Tanner & Assoc. Inc. (C), ON, *599*
Tate & Assoc., Inc. (R), NJ, *207*
Technifind Int'l. (C), TX, *602*
Thomas & Assoc. of Michigan (C), MI, *606*
Thomas Lyle & Co. (C), IL, *606*
Fred C. Tippel & Assoc. (C), OH, *607*
Tirocchi, Wright, Inc. (R), CA, *209*
Trans-United Consultants Ltd. (C), ON, *608*
TRS Staffing Solutions Inc. (C), OH, *610*
The Truman Agency (C), CA, *610*
U.S. Search (C), VA, *610*
Gordon Wahls Executive Search (C), PA, *613*
Weber Executive Search (R), NY, *216*
R. A. Wells Co. (C), GA, *618*
Jude M. Werra & Assoc. (R), WI, *218*
Western Management Assoc. (R), CA, *218*
S. J. Wexler Assoc., Inc. (R), NY, *219*
The Whitney Group (C), GA, *620*
Willis & Assoc. (R), OH, *221*
Wing Tips & Pumps, Inc. (C), MI, *623*
S. R. Wolman Assoc., Inc. (R), NY, *224*

P.00 Insurance

A.K.S. Assoc., Ltd. (R), MA, *1*
Abacus Group LLC (C), NY, *232*
Abécassis Conseil (R), QE, *1*
Abraxas Technologies, Inc. (C), FL, *233*
Accountants On Call (C), FL, *237*
ADR Accounting Management Recruiters (C), ON, *240*
Advantage Partners, Inc. (R), OH, *2*
AES Search (C), NJ, *241*
Affordable Executive Recruiters (C), CA, *241*
Alaska Executive Search, Inc. (C), AK, *243*
Albrecht & Assoc., Executive Search Consultants (C), TX, *243*
Frank E. Allen & Assoc. (C), NJ, *244*
Allen, Wayne & Co. LLC (C), WI, *245*
Alliance Search Management Inc. (R), TX, *4*
Amato & Assoc., Inc. (C), CA, *246*
Amato & Associates Insurance Recruiters (C), PA, *247*
Aminex Corp. (C), MA, *249*
Andex Executive Search (C), CT, *250*
Armitage Associates Ltd. (R), ON, *7*
E. J. Ashton & Assoc., Ltd. (C), IL, *253*
Ashway Ltd. Agency (C), NY, *253*
A. M. Auster Associates (R), FL, *9*
The Ayers Group, Inc. (R), NY, *9*
Baeder Kalinski Int'l. Group, Inc. (R), NH, *10*
The Bankers Group (C), IL, *258*
Barger & Sargeant, Inc. (R), NH, *11*
Barrett Partners (C), IL, *260*
Battalia Winston Int'l./The Euram Consultants Group (R), NY, *13*
Martin H. Bauman Assoc., Inc. (R), NY, *13*
Beacon Int'l., Inc. (C), VA, *261*
The Beam Group (R), PA, *14*
Behavioral Science Assoc., Inc. (R), AZ, *15*
Bender Executive Search Management Consulting (R), NY, *16*
Robert Bennett Assoc. (C), NY, *264*
C. Berger And Company (R), IL, *16*
Bernhart Assoc. (C), MN, *265*
BLB Consulting (C), NY, *268*
Bonifield Assoc. (C), NJ, *269*
Bonnell Assoc. Ltd. (R), CT, *19*
Bowden & Co., Inc. (R), OH, *20*
BowdenGlobal, Ltd. (R), OH, *20*
Bradford Executives Int'l. (C), VA, *271*
The Brentwood Group, Inc. (R), NJ, *22*
Broad Waverly & Assoc. (C), NJ, *274*
Dan B. Brockman (C), IL, *274*
J. B. Brown & Assoc., Inc. (C), OH, *275*
The Burgess Group-Corporate Recruiters Int'l., Inc. (R), NY, *25*
Burkholder & Assoc., Inc. (C), TX, *276*
The Butlers Co. Insurance Recruiters (C), FL, *277*
Butterfass, Pepe & MacCallan Inc. (R), NJ, *25*
C. M. Management Services, Inc. (R), KY, *26*
C. P. Consulting (R), PA, *26*
C.P.S., Inc. (C), IL, *278*
California Management Search (C), CA, *279*
Canny, Bowen Inc. (R), NY, *27*
The Canon Group (C), CA, *280*
Career Advisors, Inc. (C), FL, *281*

Carlson & Czeswik (R), MN, *30*
Carson-Thomas & Assoc. (C), CA, *284*
Carter McKenzie, Inc. (C), NJ, *285*
Carter-Evdemon & Assoc. (C), FL, *285*
The Center for Career Advancement, LLC (C), NJ, *287*
CFR Executive Search, Inc. (C), IL, *288*
Chicago Legal Search, Ltd. (C), IL, *290*
Christenson Hutchison McDowell, LLC (R), NJ, *34*
Christian & Timbers, Inc. (R), OH, *34*
Claimsearch (C), CA, *291*
CMC Search Consultants (C), IL, *293*
CMS, Inc. (C), NH, *293*
CMW & Associates, Inc. (C), IL, *293*
Dean M. Coe Assoc. (R), MA, *37*
Cole, Warren & Long, Inc. (R), PA, *37*
Colt Systems Professional Personnel Services (C), CA, *294*
Computer Network Resources, Inc. (C), CA, *295*
M. L. Conner (C), FL, *296*
The Consortium (C), NY, *296*
Construct Management Services (C), MN, *297*
The Consulting Group Ltd. (R), NY, *40*
Consulting Resource Group, Inc. (C), GA, *297*
Cook Assoc.,® Inc. (R), IL, *40*
Cornell Group Int'l. Consulting, Inc. (R), NY, *41*
Corporate Leadership Strategies, Inc. (R), NH, *41*
Corporate Plus, Ltd. (C), GA, *300*
Corporate Suite, Ltd. (C), IA, *301*
Cowell & Associates, Ltd. (R), IL, *42*
Creative Financial Staffing Inc. (C), ON, *303*
Creative Management Strategies, Ltd. (R), NY, *42*
CRI Professional Search (C), CA, *303*
Criterion Executive Search, Inc. (C), FL, *303*
Custom Resources (C), AL, *305*
Cypress Int'l., Inc. (R), FL, *45*
D.P. Specialists, Inc. (C), CA, *306*
The Danbrook Group, Inc. (C), TX, *306*
Data Bank Executive Search (R), OH, *46*
Daubenspeck & Associates, Ltd. (R), IL, *46*
Carolyn Davis Assoc., Inc. (C), NY, *309*
The Dayton Group, Ltd. (C), NY, *309*
De Funiak & Edwards (R), IN, *47*
DeCorrevont & Assoc. (C), IL, *310*
Thorndike Deland Assoc. LLC (R), NY, *48*
S. W. Delano & Co. (R), CT, *48*
DeMatteo Associates (C), NY, *311*
Descheneaux Recruitment Services Ltd. (C), BC, *311*
Diamond Tax Recruiting (C), NY, *312*
Dieckmann & Assoc., Ltd. (R), IL, *51*
Roger Dietsch & Assoc. (C), MN, *312*
Diversified Search, Inc. (R), PA, *52*
Douglas-Allen, Inc. (R), MA, *54*
DS&A (Doug Sears & Assoc.) (C), FL, *315*
Dunhill Professional Search of Hawaii (C), HI, *320*
Dunhill Technical Staffing (C), IN, *320*
Dunhill of Manchester Inc. (C), NH, *321*
C. A. Durakis Assoc., Inc. (R), MD, *55*
E O Technical (C), CT, *324*
Eastman & Beaudine, Inc. (R), TX, *56*
EDI, Inc. (C), MD, *326*
EDP Staffing Solutions, Inc. (C), AR, *327*
Eggers Consulting Co., Inc. (C), NE, *327*
Elinvar (C), NC, *328*
Evergreen & Co. (C), MA, *331*
Executive Search Consultants, Inc. (C), FL, *335*
Executive Search Consultants Corp. (C), IL, *335*
Executive Search Group LLC (C), CA, *335*
Executive Search Team (C), MI, *336*
Eyler Assoc., Inc. (R), IA, *64*
Fabian Assoc. Inc. (C), NY, *338*
Fament, Inc. (C), OH, *338*
Ferrari Search Group (C), OH, *340*
Financial Connections Company (C), VA, *340*
Howard Fischer Assoc. Int'l., Inc. (R), PA, *67*
Fitzgerald Associates (R), MA, *68*
Flynn, Hannock, Inc. (R), CT, *69*
Focus Consulting Services, Inc. (C), FL, *342*
Foley Proctor Yoskowitz (R), NJ, *69*
Ford & Ford (C), MA, *343*
F-O-R-T-U-N-E Personnel Consultants of Palm Beach (C), FL, *345*
Fortune Consultants of Ft. Washington (C), PA, *349*
Foster Partners (R), NY, *70*
The Fourbes Group, Inc. (C), NJ, *351*
Furst Group/MPI (R), IL, *72*
The Gabriel Group (C), PA, *354*
Gahan Assoc. (R), NY, *73*
Jay Gaines & Company, Inc. (R), NY, *73*
The Gammill Group, Inc. (C), OH, *354*
Gans, Gans & Assoc., Inc. (R), FL, *74*
The Garrison Organization (R), IA, *75*
Gelpi & Assoc. (C), LA, *355*
GFI Professional Staffing Services (C), NH, *357*
Gielow Assoc., Inc. (R), WI, *76*
Gilbert Scott Assoc., LLC (C), MA, *357*
Global Consulting Group Inc. (C), ON, *358*
Global HealthCare Partners (R), IL, *78*
Global Resources Group (R), CA, *78*
The Tracy Glover Co. (R), TX, *78*
Godfrey Personnel, Inc. (C), IL, *359*
Barry M. Gold & Co. (C), CA, *359*
Gould, McCoy & Chadick, Inc. (R), NY, *80*
The Governance Group, Inc. (R), NJ, *80*
Grant-Franks & Assoc. (C), NJ, *361*
Greene-Levin-Snyder LLC (C), NY, *362*
GSP International (C), NJ, *364*
Gundersen Partners, L.L.C. (R), NY, *83*
The H. S. Group, Inc. (C), WI, *365*
K. C. Hale, Inc. (R), CT, *85*
Halo Insurance Service (C), AL, *367*
R. C. Handel Assoc. Inc. (R), CT, *85*
Hanley & Assoc. (R), FL, *86*
The Harris Consulting Corp. (R), MB, *87*
Harris Heery & Assoc., Inc. (R), CT, *87*
Healthcare Recruiters of New York, Inc. (C), NY, *373*
Healthcare Recruiters Int'l. - Pittsburgh (C), PA, *373*
Heartland National Medical Search (C), IL, *374*
Hedlund Corp. (C), IL, *375*
Heinze & Assoc. Inc. (R), MN, *91*
Hessel Assoc., Inc. (C), NY, *377*
B. W. Higgins, Inc. (C), IN, *377*
High-Tech Recruiters (C), CT, *378*
Hintz Associates (C), NY, *378*
HLR Consulting (C), NY, *379*
Holden & Harlan Assoc., Inc. (C), IL, *380*
Horton Int'l. Inc. (R), NY, *96*
Hreshko Consulting Group (C), NJ, *382*
The HRM Group, Inc. (C), AL, *382*
Hudson Assoc. Inc. (C), IN, *383*
Hughes & Assoc. (C), TX, *383*
Human Capital Resources, Inc. (C), FL, *384*
Hunter Douglas Group, Inc. (R), IL, *99*
Hunter Int'l., Inc. (R), CT, *100*
Hyde Danforth & Co. (R), TX, *100*
Innovative Healthcare Services, Inc. (C), GA, *389*
Insurance Career Center, Inc. (C), CT, *389*
Insurance People (C), IN, *390*
Insurance Personnel Resources, Inc. (C), GA, *390*
Insurance Recruiting Specialists (C), OH, *390*
Insurance Search (C), TX, *390*
InteliSearch, Inc. (R), CT, *102*
Inter Regional Executive Search, Inc. (IRES, Inc.) (C), NJ, *391*
Interactive Search Assoc. (C), PA, *391*
IR Search (R), CA, *103*
J.J. & H., Ltd. (R), IL, *104*
Jacobson Assoc. (C), IL, *396*
Jefferson-Ross Assoc. Inc. (C), PA, *398*
Job-Born Candidate Selection Bureau (C), ON, *399*
The Johnson Group, Unlimited (C), NY, *400*
Jones Consulting Executive Search (C), GA, *400*
JSG Group Management Consultants (R), ON, *109*
Kanzer Assoc., Inc. (R), IL, *109*
Kaye/Bassman Int'l. Corp. (R), TX, *110*
A.T. Kearney Executive Search (R), IL, *111*
William W. Kenney (C), CT, *405*
Kensington Int'l., Inc. (R), IL, *113*
Kershner & Co. (R), DC, *113*
Kinderis & Loercher Group (C), IL, *407*
The Koehler Group (C), PA, *408*
Koontz, Jeffries & Assoc., Inc. (R), FL, *117*
Korn/Ferry Int'l. (R), NY, *117*
C. R. Krafski & Assoc., Inc. (R), IL, *120*
Kulper & Co., L.L.C. (R), NJ, *121*
Kyle Assoc. (C), NY, *410*
Laguzza Assoc., Ltd. (R), NY, *122*
Lamon + Stuart + Michaels Inc. (R), ON, *124*
Lawrence L. Lapham, Inc. (R), NY, *124*
LaVallee & Associates (C), NC, *413*
Leader Resources Group (C), GA, *415*
Lear & Assoc., Inc. (C), FL, *415*
Reynolds Lebus Assoc. (C), AZ, *415*
Lechner & Assoc., Inc. (C), FL, *415*
Vincent Lee Assoc. (C), NY, *415*

Leeds and Leeds (C), TN, *416*
Lending Personnel Services (C), CA, *416*
Lifter & Assoc. (C), CA, *418*
Lloyd Prescott & Churchill, Inc. (R), FL, *130*
Logic Assoc., Inc. (C), NY, *419*
Longshore + Simmons (R), PA, *131*
The John Lucht Consultancy Inc. (R), NY, *131*
Lynx, Inc. (C), MA, *421*
Managed Care Resources (C), TX, *424*
Management One Consultants (C), ON, *425*
Management Recruiters of Birmingham, Inc. (C), AL, *438*
Management Recruiters of Colorado, Inc. (C), CO, *442*
Management Recruiters of Tampa North (C), FL, *444*
Management Recruiters of Columbus, Inc. (C), GA, *445*
Management Recruiters of Atlanta NE (C), GA, *446*
Management Recruiters-Cedar Rapids, Inc. (C), IA, *448*
Management Recruiters - Indianapolis (C), IN, *448*
Management Recruiters of Des Moines (C), IA, *449*
Management Recruiters of Livonia (C), MI, *451*
Management Recruiters of Birmingham (C), MI, *451*
Management Recruiters of Woodbury (C), MN, *452*
Management Recruiters of Bloomington (C), MN, *452*
Management Recruiters of Reno (C), NV, *453*
Management Recruiters of Bordentown (C), NJ, *454*
Management Recruiters of Cedar Mountain (C), NC, *455*
Management Recruiters of Woodbury Inc. (C), NY, *455*
Management Recruiters of Cleveland (C), OH, *457*
Management Recruiters of Lionville, Inc. (C), PA, *459*
Management Recruiters of Sioux Falls, LLP (C), SD, *461*
Management Recruiters of Georgetown (C), SC, *461*
Management Recruiters of Houston-Northeast (C), TX, *463*
Management Recruiters of San Antonio - North (C), TX, *463*
Management Recruiters of Fairfax, VA (C), VA, *464*
Management Recruiters of Janesville, Inc. (C), WI, *466*
Management Recruiters of Stevens Point, Inc. (C), WI, *466*
Management Search, Inc. (C), IL, *467*
J. L. Mark Assoc., Inc. (R), CO, *135*
The Maroon Group (R), CT, *136*
Martin Grant Assoc. Inc., Insurance Personnel (C), MA, *472*
Massey-Horton Int'l. (R), ON, *138*
Matthews & Stephens Assoc., Inc. (C), CT, *472*
Mary L. Mayer, Ltd. (R), MN, *139*
The McAulay Firm (R), NC, *139*
The McCormick Group (C), VA, *473*
McDonald, Long & Assoc., Inc. (R), NY, *140*
MCS Assoc. (R), CA, *142*
Messett Assoc., Inc. (R), FL, *143*
MGA Executive Search (C), FL, *480*
Michael Thomas, Inc. (C), OH, *480*
Mirtz Morice, Inc. (R), CT, *145*
Mitchell Martin Inc. (C), NY, *483*
Mitchell/Wolfson, Assoc. (R), IL, *145*
C. A. Moore & Assoc., Inc. (C), MN, *484*
Morgan Hunter Corp. (C), KS, *485*
MSA Executive Search (R), MO, *148*
Much & Co. (R), NY, *148*
Pamela L. Mulligan, Inc. (R), NH, *149*
Musick & Assoc. (C), CA, *487*
National Affirmative Action Career Network, Inc. (C), CO, *488*
National Search, Inc.r (C), FL, *490*
Beverly Nelson & Assoc. Inc. (C), CA, *491*
The Network Corporate Search Personnel Inc. (C), AB, *491*
New Dimensions in Technology, Inc. (C), MA, *492*
Newcomb-Desmond & Assoc., Inc. (C), OH, *492*
J. L. Nixon Consulting (C), TX, *493*
Noll Human Resource Services (C), NE, *494*
W. D. Nolte & Company (R), CT, *152*
Nordeman Grimm, Inc. (R), NY, *152*
The Norland Group (C), CA, *494*
Norman Broadbent Int'l., Inc. (R), NY, *152*
The Normyle/Erstling Health Search Group (C), NJ, *494*
Nuance Personnel Search, Inc. (C), NC, *497*
O'Connor Resources (C), TX, *497*
O'Sullivan Search Inc. (C), ON, *498*
Ollinger Partners (R), MA, *156*
P.A.R. Assoc., Inc. (R), MA, *158*
Pacific Coast Recruiters (C), OR, *501*
The Park Group & Assoc., Inc. (C), MD, *502*
Largent Parks & Partners (C), TX, *503*
Pathways Int'l. (C), CT, *505*
Peachtree Executive Search (R), GA, *161*
Peak Search Assoc. (C), ON, *506*
The Pennmor Group (C), NJ, *506*
People Management Northeast, Inc. (R), CT, *162*
Personnel Assoc. Inc. (C), NY, *508*
Personnel Consultants (C), WA, *508*
J. R. Peterman Assoc., Inc. (C), VT, *509*
Peyser Assoc., Inc. (R), FL, *163*
Pioneer Placement, Inc. (C), MA, *512*
Pittleman & Assoc. (C), NY, *512*
R. L. Plimpton Assoc., Inc. (R), CO, *165*
PMJ & Assoc. (C), ON, *513*
P. G. Prager Search Assoc., Ltd. (C), NY, *515*
Primary Care Service Corp. (C), GA, *518*
The Primary Group, Inc. (R), FL, *168*
Princeton Search Partners, Inc. (R), NJ, *169*
Priority Executive Search (C), FL, *518*
PRO, Inc./Professional Recruiting Offices, Inc. (C), CA, *519*
Pro-Tech Search, Inc. (C), IL, *519*
Procom (C), ON, *519*
Professionals in Recruiting Co. (C), TN, *523*
ProSearch, Inc. (C), ME, *524*
Pryor & Associates (C), CA, *525*
Questor Consultants, Inc. (C), PA, *527*
QuestPro, Inc. (C), TX, *527*
Quigley Assoc. (R), MD, *170*
Quirk-Corporon & Assoc., Inc. (C), WI, *527*
R & L Assoc., Ltd. (R), NY, *170*
Rand Thompson Executive Search Consultants (C), NY, *528*
Ray & Berndtson (R), TX, *171*
Ray & Berndtson/Laurendeau Labrecque (R), QE, *172*
Raymond Karsan Assoc. (C), PA, *529*
Real Estate Executive Search, Inc. (C), CA, *531*
Research Personnel Consultants (C), ON, *534*
Response Staffing Services (C), NY, *534*
Russell Reynolds Assoc., Inc. (R), NY, *176*
RHI Consulting (C), VA, *536*
RHS Assoc. (C), AL, *536*
Richard Wright Co. (C), CT, *536*
The Richards Group (C), PA, *536*
Roberts Ryan & Bentley, Inc. (R), MD, *179*
Robertson & Assoc. (C), IL, *539*
Bruce Robinson Assoc. (R), NJ, *180*
Robison & Associates (R), NC, *180*
Rodgers, Ramsey, Inc. (C), TX, *540*
The Rogan Group, Inc. (C), CA, *541*
Rogish Assoc., Inc. (C), OH, *541*
Rollins Search Group, Inc. (C), GA, *541*
Rollo Assoc. (R), CA, *181*
Rovner Gerner & Assoc. (R), CA, *182*
The Rubicon Group (C), AZ, *547*
The Rubinic Consulting Group (C), OH, *548*
Rusher, Loscavio & LoPresto (R), CA, *183*
Russillo/Gardner/Spolsino (C), MA, *548*
S. C. Int'l., Ltd. (C), IL, *550*
Sales & Management Search, Inc. (C), IL, *551*
Sales Consultants of Denver (C), CO, *557*
Sales Consultants of Wellesley, Inc. (C), MA, *559*
Sales Consultants of Birmingham (C), MI, *559*
Sales Consultants of Nashua-Manchester (C), NH, *560*
Sales Consultants Bridgewater, Inc. (C), NJ, *560*
Sales Consultants of Cherry Hill (C), NJ, *560*
Sales Consultants of Morris County, Inc. (C), NJ, *561*
Sales Consultants of Newtown, Inc. (C), PA, *562*
Sales Consultants of Madison (C), WI, *563*
A. N. Salloway Executive Search & Consulting, L.L.C. (C), MA, *564*
Salzmann Gay Assoc., Inc. (R), PA, *184*
Sanders Management Assoc., Inc. (C), NJ, *565*

Sanford Rose Assoc. (C), OH, *565*
Sanford Rose Assoc. - Carmel, IN (C), IN, *567*
Sanford Rose Assoc. - Euclid (C), OH, *569*
Schall Executive Search Partners (R), MN, *185*
Schulenburg & Assoc. (C), GA, *572*
Schuyler Assoc., Ltd. (R), GA, *185*
Scott Douglas Inc. (C), CA, *573*
The Search Alliance, Inc. (R), FL, *186*
Search Assoc., Inc. (C), NJ, *574*
The Search Committee (C), MD, *574*
The Search Group (C), MD, *575*
Search Innovations, Inc. (R), PA, *187*
Search Research Assoc., Inc. (R), MA, *187*
Searchline Services, Inc. (C), OH, *577*
Searchworks, Inc. (C), FL, *577*
Secura/Burnett Partners (R), CA, *187*
Selectis Corp. (C), IL, *578*
Selective Staffing (C), CA, *579*
Setford-Shaw-Najarian Assoc. (C), NY, *579*
Sevcor Int'l., Inc. (R), IL, *188*
Shiloh Careers Int'l., Inc. (C), TN, *580*
Michael Shirley Assoc. Inc. (R), KS, *190*
The Shorr Group (R), IL, *190*
D. W. Simpson & Co. (C), IL, *582*
Howard W. Smith Assoc. (R), CT, *193*
Smith Hanley Assoc., Inc. (C), NY, *584*
Snyder & Co. (R), CT, *194*
Solomon-Page Healthcare Group (R), NY, *195*
Solutions Group (R), AL, *195*
Southwest Selective Search, Inc. (C), TX, *588*
Southwestern Professional Services (C), TN, *588*
Spear-Izzo Assoc., LLC (C), PA, *588*
Special Markets Group, Inc. (R), GA, *195*
SpencerStuart (R), NY, *196*
Squires Resources Inc. (C), ON, *590*
Staffing Edge, Inc. (C), IA, *590*
Stafford Consulting Group (R), CA, *198*
Star Search Consultants (C), ON, *591*
STAT Search (C), NH, *592*
Stevens, Valentine & McKeever (C), NJ, *593*
Stone Assoc. LLC (C), MI, *594*
Stone, Murphy & Olson (R), MN, *201*
The Stonebridge Group (C), PA, *594*
Mark Stranberg & Assoc. Inc. (R), MA, *202*
Strategic Advancement Inc. (R), NJ, *202*
Stratin Assoc. (C), NJ, *596*
Success Seekers Connection (C), FL, *596*
Sullivan & Company (R), NY, *204*
Summit Group Int'l., Inc. (R), GA, *204*
Summit Search Specialists (C), TX, *596*
Systems Search (C), IL, *599*
Tax Network Resources, Inc. (C), NY, *600*
TeleManagement Search (C), NY, *605*
Thorne, Brieger Assoc., Inc. (R), NY, *209*
TPS Staffing Solutions (C), IN, *608*
Triad Consultants, Inc. (C), NJ, *609*
Tucker Assoc. (R), NJ, *211*
UniQuest Int'l., Inc. (C), FL, *610*
United Personnel Services (C), MA, *611*
Peter Van Leer & Assoc. (R), MN, *213*
The Verriez Group Inc. (R), ON, *213*
Vincenty & Co. (C), OH, *612*
Walker Personnel, Inc. (C), LA, *614*
Lee H. Walton & Assoc. (R), NY, *215*
Karen Wanger & Assoc., Inc. (C), IL, *615*
Warring & Assoc. (R), CA, *215*
The Wayne Group, Ltd. (C), NY, *616*
WestPacific National Search, Inc. (C), CA, *619*
Wilder, Gammel Partners, Ltd. (R), CA, *220*
The Wilkie Group Int'l. (R), ON, *220*
Walter K. Wilkins & Co. (R), NJ, *221*
Willis & Assoc. (R), OH, *221*
The Windham Group (R), OH, *222*
The Winn Group, Inc. (C), KS, *623*
Witt/Kieffer, Ford, Hadelman & Lloyd (R), IL, *223*
Xavier Associates, Inc. (R), MA, *226*
The Yorkshire Group, Ltd. (C), MA, *626*
Zona & Assoc., Inc. (C), NY, *628*

Q.00 Real estate

A Permanent Success Employment Services (C), CA, *231*
A.L.S. Group (C), NJ, *232*
Abacus Group LLC (C), NY, *232*
Accountants On Call (C), FL, *237*
Accounting Additions (C), CA, *238*
ACSYS Resources, Inc. (C), DE, *238*
G. Adams Partners (R), IL, *2*
Advice Personnel Inc. (C), NY, *241*
The Alfus Group (R), NY, *3*
Alpha Executive Search (C), AL, *245*
Ames Assoc. Inc. (C), MD, *249*
Anderson & Associates (R), NC, *5*
Argonaut Partners, LLC (R), CA, *6*
Armitage Associates Ltd. (R), ON, *7*
Bartl & Evins (C), NY, *260*
BCG Search, Inc. (R), FL, *14*
Beach Executive Search Inc. (R), FL, *14*
Becker, Norton & Co. (R), PA, *14*
Edward Bell Assoc. (C), CA, *263*
Joy Reed Belt Search Consultants, Inc. (R), OK, *15*
N. L. Benke & Assoc., Inc. (C), OH, *264*
Robert Bennett Assoc. (C), NY, *264*
Bennett Search & Consulting Co. (R), FL, *16*
The Blackman Kallick Search Division (C), IL, *267*
Boulware & Assoc. Inc. (R), IL, *20*
BowersThomas (C), CA, *271*
Bryan, Jason & Assoc. Inc. (C), ON, *275*
C. G. & Assoc. (R), PA, *26*
Canny, Bowen Inc. (R), NY, *27*
Capital Markets Resources, Inc. (C), NC, *281*
The Carlyle Group, Ltd. (R), IL, *30*
Carson-Thomas & Assoc. (C), CA, *284*
Caruso & Assoc., Inc. (R), FL, *31*
Cemco, Ltd. (C), IL, *286*
Chicago Legal Search, Ltd. (C), IL, *290*
The Christopher Group (C), NC, *291*
Arlene Clapp, Ltd. (R), MN, *35*
CMC Search Consultants (C), IL, *293*
Dean M. Coe Assoc. (R), MA, *37*
Robert Connelly & Assoc., Inc. (R), MN, *39*
Construction Search Specialists, Inc. (C), WI, *297*
The Consulting Group Ltd. (R), NY, *40*
Corporate Search, Inc. (C), NY, *301*
Crown Advisors, Inc. (R), PA, *43*
D & M Associates (C), PA, *306*
Dieckmann & Assoc., Ltd. (R), IL, *51*
Discovery, The Staffing Specialists, Inc. (C), IL, *312*
Diversified Search, Inc. (R), PA, *52*
Drake & Assoc. (C), CA, *315*
Drummond Assoc., Inc. (C), NY, *315*
Dunhill Executive Search of Los Angeles, Inc. (C), CA, *319*
Gwen Dycus & Assoc. (C), FL, *323*
Eastman & Beaudine, Inc. (R), TX, *56*
Eden & Assoc., Inc. (C), PA, *326*
Elinvar (C), NC, *328*
ENI (R), CT, *59*
The Evans McDonnell Co. (C), TX, *331*
The Execu/Search Group (C), NY, *332*
Executive Referral Services, Inc. (C), IL, *334*
Executive Registry (C), QE, *334*
Executive Search Team (C), MI, *336*
Fallstaff Search (C), MD, *338*
Financial Resource Assoc., Inc. (C), FL, *340*
Foster Associates (C), NJ, *351*
Foster Partners (R), NY, *70*
Franstaff Inc. (C), FL, *352*
Gaines & Assoc. Int'l., Inc. (R), IL, *73*
Garb & Assoc., Legal Placement (C), CA, *354*
Gilbert Scott Assoc., LLC (C), MA, *357*
The Glazin Group (R), BC, *77*
Global Career Services, Inc. (C), NY, *358*
The Tracy Glover Co. (R), TX, *78*
Gnodde Assoc. (C), IL, *359*
David Gomez & Assoc., Inc. (R), IL, *79*
Gould, McCoy & Chadick, Inc. (R), NY, *80*
Ben Greco Assoc., Inc. (C), CA, *362*
Greene & Co. (C), MA, *362*
GSP International (C), NJ, *364*
Habelmann & Assoc. (R), MI, *84*
The Heidrick Partners, Inc. (R), IL, *90*
Helbling & Assoc., Inc. (R), PA, *91*
J. D. Hersey & Assoc. (C), OH, *376*
Robert Hess & Assoc., Inc. (C), CO, *377*
Higbee Assoc., Inc. (C), CT, *377*
Highland & Assoc. (C), CA, *378*
Highland Search Group, L.L.C. (R), NY, *93*
Huntress Real Estate Executive Search (R), MO, *100*
Hyde Danforth & Co. (R), TX, *100*
Hyland Executive Search (C), AZ, *386*
IM Independent Management Recruiters (R), TN, *101*
Interim Financial Solutions - Mid-Atlantic Region (C), MD, *392*
ISC of Houston, Inc. (C), TX, *394*
Jones Management Co. (R), CT, *108*
Joseph Chris & Assoc. (C), TX, *400*
Joseph Michaels (C), CA, *401*
Lisa Kalus & Assoc., Inc. (C), NY, *403*
Karel & Co. (R), CA, *109*
Kaye/Bassman Int'l. Corp. (R), TX, *110*

INDUSTRIES

A.T. Kearney Executive Search (R), IL, *111*
Kenzer Corp. (R), NY, *113*
Kershner & Co. (R), DC, *113*
Kimmel & Associates, Inc. (C), NC, *406*
Kiradjieff & Goode, Inc. (R), MA, *115*
Korn/Ferry Int'l. (R), NY, *117*
The J. Kovach Group (R), PA, *119*
Kramer Executive Resources, Inc. (C), NY, *409*
Michael Latas & Assoc., Inc. (R), MO, *125*
The Conrad Lee Co. Inc. (R), FL, *127*
Lending Personnel Services (C), CA, *416*
Alan Levine Assoc. (R), MA, *129*
J. H. Lindell & Co. (C), CA, *418*
Lloyd Staffing (C), NY, *419*
Management Advisors Int'l., Inc. (C), NC, *424*
Management Recruiters of Aptos (C), CA, *439*
Management Recruiters of Laguna Hills (C), CA, *440*
Management Recruiters of Altamonte (C), FL, *442*
Management Recruiters of Bethlehem, PA (C), PA, *458*
Marentz & Co. (C), TX, *469*
Marra Peters & Partners (R), NJ, *136*
K. Maxin & Assoc. (R), PA, *139*
The McAulay Firm (R), NC, *139*
McDonald, Long & Assoc., Inc. (R), NY, *140*
MCS Assoc. (R), CA, *142*
Millar Walker & Gay (R), ON, *144*
Miller/Davis & Assoc., Inc. (C), NY, *482*
Herbert Mines Assoc., Inc. (R), NY, *145*
Moffitt Int'l., Inc. (R), NC, *146*
Tina Morbitzer & Assoc. (C), FL, *485*
Morgan Samuels Co. (R), CA, *147*
Mortgage & Financial Personnel Services (C), CA, *486*
Moss & Co. (R), WA, *148*
Murphy Partners Int'l. (R), IL, *150*
Musick & Assoc. (C), CA, *487*
New Dawn Employment Search (C), CA, *491*
The Nolan Group (C), CA, *494*
Nordeman Grimm, Inc. (R), NY, *152*
O'Brien and Roof (C), OH, *497*
Pacific Finance Search, Inc. (C), CA, *501*
Peak Search Assoc. (C), ON, *506*
Personnel Alliance Group (C), NJ, *507*
Physicians Search®, Inc. (C), CA, *511*
Plante & Moran, LLP (R), MI, *165*
Bob Poline Assoc. Inc. (C), CA, *514*
Powers Consultants, Inc. (R), MO, *166*
Elan Pratzer & Partners Inc. (R), ON, *167*
Preferred Placement, Inc. (C), NY, *516*
Prescott Legal Search, Inc. (C), TX, *517*
The Primary Group, Inc. (R), FL, *168*
Profit Pros, Inc. (C), CA, *523*
Protocol Inc. (C), CA, *525*
The Quest Organization (C), NY, *527*
Quetico Corp. (R), TX, *170*
L. J. Quinn & Assoc., Inc. (R), CA, *170*
Real Estate Executive Search, Inc. (C), CA, *531*
Resource Management Group (C), CT, *534*
Response Staffing Services (C), NY, *534*
Russell Reynolds Assoc., Inc. (R), NY, *176*
Rhodes Associates (R), NY, *177*
Romac Int'l. (C), IL, *541*
Romac Int'l. Inc. (R), MA, *181*
Ropes Associates, Inc. (R), FL, *182*
Royal Assoc. (C), CA, *547*
RSMR, Inc. (R), IL, *182*
David Saxner & Assoc., Inc. (DSA, Inc.) (R), IL, *185*
Schlatter & Assoc. (C), CA, *572*
Search Bureau Int'l. (C), IL, *574*
Secura/Burnett Partners (R), CA, *187*
Sharrow & Assoc., Inc. (C), MI, *579*
Howard W. Smith Assoc. (R), CT, *193*
Sockwell & Assoc. (R), NC, *194*
Southwestern Professional Services (C), TN, *588*
Specialty Consultants Inc. (R), PA, *195*
SpencerStuart (R), NY, *196*
Michael Stern Assoc., Inc./Euram (R), ON, *200*
Steven Douglas Assoc. (C), FL, *593*
The Stevens Group (R), TX, *200*
Stone Assoc. LLC (C), MI, *594*
W. R. Strathmann Assoc. (R), NY, *203*
Summit Group Int'l., Inc. (R), GA, *204*
The Talon Group (R), TX, *205*
Peter R. Taylor Assoc., Inc. (C), NY, *600*
Traynor Confidential, Ltd. (C), NY, *609*
Van Leeuwen Assoc. (R), CA, *213*
Wegner & Assoc. (C), WI, *617*
Western Management Consultants (R), BC, *218*
The Whitney Group (R), NY, *219*
The Whyte Group, Inc. (R), MD, *220*
Wilder, Gammel Partners, Ltd. (R), CA, *220*
Working Relationships, Inc. (C), MN, *624*
Yormak & Assoc. (C), CA, *626*
The Zarkin Group, Inc. (R), NY, *226*

R.00 High tech

The 500 Granary Inc. (C), ON, *231*
A First Resource (C), NC, *231*
A Permanent Success Employment Services (C), CA, *231*
A-L Assoc., Inc. (R), NY, *1*
A. D. & Assoc. Executive Search, Inc. (C), GA, *231*
A.M.C.R., Inc. (C), OH, *232*
Abbott Associates (R), CA, *1*
The Abbott Group, Inc. (R), MD, *1*
Abécassis Conseil (R), QE, *1*
Abraham & London Ltd. (C), CT, *232*
Abraxas Technologies, Inc. (C), FL, *233*
Accelerated Data Decision, Inc. (C), NJ, *233*
Accent On Achievement, Inc. (C), MI, *233*
Access Assoc. Inc. (C), MD, *233*
Access Data Personnel, Inc. (C), NH, *233*
ACCESS Technology (C), CA, *234*
Accountants On Call (C), FL, *237*
Accountants Executive Search (C), CA, *237*
Accounting Additions (C), CA, *238*
Adam-Bryce Inc. (C), NY, *239*
Adams & Assoc. Int'l. (R), IL, *1*
Adel-Lawrence Assoc., Inc. (C), NJ, *240*
Adept Tech Recruiting, Inc. (C), NY, *240*
Adler Management, Inc. (R), NJ, *2*
Advanced Corporate Search (C), CA, *240*
Advanced Executive Resources (R), MI, *2*
Advanced Recruiting, Inc. (C), OK, *240*
Advanced Resources, Inc. (C), MO, *241*
Advancement Recruiting Services (C), OH, *241*
Advancement, Inc. (C), IL, *241*
Advice Personnel Inc. (C), NY, *241*
The Advisory Group, Inc. (R), CA, *2*
Affinity Executive Search (C), FL, *241*
Alexander & Co. (C), CA, *243*
The Alexander Group (R), NJ, *3*
The Alexander Group (R), TX, *3*
Frank E. Allen & Assoc. (C), NJ, *244*
D. S. Allen Assoc. (C), NJ, *244*
Allen Austin Lowe & Powers (R), TX, *3*
Allen Evans Assoc. (R), NY, *4*
Allen, Wayne & Co. LLC (C), WI, *245*
Allerton Heneghan & O'Neill (R), IL, *4*
Alpha Resources (C), IL, *246*
The Alternatives Group, Inc. (C), TX, *246*
Peter W. Ambler Co. (R), TX, *5*
American Executive Search (C), FL, *247*
American Heritage Group, Inc. (C), MI, *247*
American Services Group (C), IL, *248*
Ames-O'Neill Assoc., Inc. (C), NY, *249*
AMS Int'l. (R), VA, *5*
Andex Executive Search (C), CT, *250*
The Andre Group, Inc. (R), PA, *6*
Ansara, Bickford & Fiske (C), MA, *251*
David Aplin & Assoc. (C), AB, *251*
Applied Resources, Inc. (C), MN, *252*
Applied Search Assoc., Inc. (C), GA, *252*
Applied Technology Solutions Inc. (C), ON, *252*
Armitage Associates Ltd. (R), ON, *7*
J. S. Armstrong & Assoc., Inc. (R), CA, *7*
Patrick Arnone & Assoc. Inc. (R), VA, *7*
The Ascher Group (R), NJ, *7*
Ashton Computer Professionals, Inc. (C), BC, *253*
Ashway Ltd. Agency (C), NY, *253*
ASI (C), CA, *254*
Asset Resource, Inc. (C), CA, *254*
Association for Sales Force Management (C), WA, *254*
Atlanta Executive Partners, Inc. (R), MA, *8*
Atomic Personnel, Inc. (C), PA, *255*
Aubin Int'l. Inc. (R), MA, *8*
Aurora Tech Search (C), ON, *256*
Cami Austin & Assoc. (C), IL, *256*
Austin Michaels, Ltd., Inc. (C), AZ, *256*
Austin Park Management Group Inc. (C), ON, *256*
Austin-McGregor Int'l. (R), TX, *9*
Avery Assoc. (R), CA, *9*
Avestruz & Assoc. (C), CA, *257*
Avion International Technology Inc. (C), ON, *257*
Avondale Search Int'l., Inc. (R), FL, *9*
Keith Bagg & Assoc., Inc. (C), ON, *257*
Baker, Nelms & Montgomery (C), IL, *258*
Baldwin & Assoc. (C), OH, *258*
Baldwin Associates, LLC (R), CT, *10*
James Bangert & Assoc., Inc. (R), MN, *11*
Barclay Consultants, Inc. (C), NJ, *259*

Barger & Sargeant, Inc. (R), NH, *11*
Barnes & Assoc. Executive Search (C), CA, *259*
Barr Assoc. (C), PA, *259*
Barrett Partners (C), IL, *260*
Barrett Rose & Lee, Inc. (C), ON, *260*
Barton Assoc., Inc. (R), TX, *12*
Bason Associates (R), OH, *13*
Battalia Winston Int'l./The Euram Consultants Group (R), NY, *13*
R. Gaines Baty Assoc., Inc. (R), TX, *13*
Bayland Assoc. (C), CA, *261*
BayResearch Group, Inc. (R), IL, *14*
Beach Executive Search Inc. (R), FL, *14*
Beacon Int'l., Inc. (C), VA, *261*
The Beardsley Group Inc. (C), CT, *261*
Beck/Eastwood Recruitment Solutions (C), CA, *261*
Becker Project Resources, Inc. (C), OR, *262*
The Bedford Group (R), RI, *15*
Behavioral Science Assoc., Inc. (R), AZ, *15*
Belanger Partners Ltd. (C), ON, *262*
Bell Oaks Co., Inc. (C), GA, *263*
Bellamy & Assoc. (C), GA, *263*
Bender Executive Search Management Consulting (R), NY, *16*
N. L. Benke & Assoc., Inc. (C), OH, *264*
Bennett & Associates (C), TX, *264*
The Bennett Group, Inc. (R), IN, *16*
Dick Berg & Assoc. (C), CA, *264*
Berger & Leff (C), CA, *264*
C. Berger And Company (R), IL, *16*
Berkana Int'l., Inc. (C), WA, *265*
Berkhemer/Clayton, Inc. (R), CA, *16*
Bernhart Assoc. (C), MN, *265*
Bertrand, Ross & Assoc., Inc. (C), IL, *266*
BEST/World Assoc. Inc. (R), TX, *16*
Bialla & Assoc. Inc. (R), CA, *17*
Bio-Venture Group (C), RI, *266*
BioPharmMed (C), FL, *267*
Birch & Associes (C), QE, *267*
Deborah Bishop & Assoc. (R), CA, *17*
Blake/Hansen Ltd. (R), FL, *18*
BLB Consulting (C), NY, *268*
Block & Assoc. (R), CA, *18*
The BMW Group, Inc. (C), NY, *268*
Bonell Ryan Inc. (R), NY, *19*
Bos Business Consultants (C), NY, *270*
Bosch & Assoc., LLC (R), CT, *19*
Boston Professional Search, Inc. (C), MA, *270*
Howard Bowen Consulting (C), FL, *270*
Bower & Associates (C), TX, *271*
BowersThomas (C), CA, *271*
Boyden (R), NY, *20*
Boyle/Ogata Executive Search (R), CA, *21*
The Bradbury Management Group, Inc. (R), CA, *21*
M. F. Branch Assoc., Inc. (C), NC, *272*
The Brand Co., Inc. (R), FL, *22*
Brandywine Retained Ventures, Inc. (R), CT, *22*
Branthover Assoc. (C), NY, *272*
Bratland & Assoc. (C), IL, *272*
Brault & Assoc., Ltd. (R), VA, *22*
Bredeson Executive Recruitment, LLC (R), TX, *22*
Brei & Assoc., Inc. (C), IA, *272*
The Brentwood Group Ltd. (R), OR, *23*
Brentwood Int'l. (R), CA, *23*
Brian Assoc., Inc. (C), NY, *273*
The Bridge (C), CO, *273*
Bridgecreek Personnel Agency (C), CA, *273*
Brigade, Inc. (R), CA, *23*
Brissenden, McFarland, Fuccella & Reynolds, Inc. (R), NJ, *23*
Broadband Resource Group (C), CA, *274*
The Broadmoor Group, L.L.C. (R), TX, *23*
D. Brown & Assoc., Inc. (C), OR, *275*
Brown Venture Assoc. (R), CA, *24*
BRW Search (C), MN, *275*
BT&A, LLC (R), CT, *24*
The Buckley Group (C), FL, *276*
Buckman/Enochs & Assoc., Inc. (C), OH, *276*
Bullis & Co., Inc. (R), CA, *25*
Busch International (R), CA, *25*
Business Partners, Inc. (C), FL, *277*
Business Systems of America, Inc. (C), IL, *277*
Butterfield & Co. Int'l., Inc. (C), HI, *277*
Button Group (C), TX, *277*
Byron Leonard Int'l., Inc. (R), CA, *25*
C Assoc. (C), DC, *278*
C.T.E.W. Executive Personnel Services Inc. (C), BC, *278*
Cadillac Assoc. (C), CA, *278*
Cahill Assoc. (C), CT, *279*
California Management Search (C), CA, *279*
California Search Agency, Inc. (C), CA, *279*
The Cambridge Group Ltd. (C), CT, *280*
Cambridge Management Planning (R), ON, *27*
Campa & Assoc. (R), ON, *27*
Canny, Bowen Inc. (R), NY, *27*
Capital Consulting Group, Inc. (R), MD, *28*
Capital Markets Resources, Inc. (C), NC, *281*
Sally Caplan & Assoc. (C), WA, *281*
Capstone Inc. (R), NY, *29*
Cardwell Enterprises Inc. (R), IL, *29*
Career Marketing Assoc., Inc. (C), CO, *282*
Career Marketing Consultants, Inc. (C), GA, *282*
Career Specialists, Inc. (R), WA, *29*
Career Strategies, Inc. (C), CA, *283*
Careerfit, Inc. (C), TX, *283*
Careers First, Inc. (C), NJ, *283*
Careers Plus (R), CA, *29*
Carter, Lavoie Associates (C), RI, *285*
Caruso & Assoc., Inc. (R), FL, *31*
The CARVIR Group, Inc. (C), GA, *285*
CAS Comsearch Inc. (C), NY, *285*
Casey & Assoc., Inc. (C), TX, *286*
Catalyx Group (R), NY, *31*
Michael J. Cavanagh & Assoc. Inc. (R), ON, *31*
Caywood Partners, Ltd. (R), CA, *32*
CBA Companies (C), CA, *286*
Cendea Connection Int'l. (R), TX, *32*
Century Assoc., Inc. (C), PA, *287*
The Century Group (C), CA, *287*
CEO Consulting (C), FL, *287*
cFour Partners (R), CA, *32*
Chad Management Group (C), ON, *288*
Wayne S. Chamberlain & Assoc. (C), CA, *288*
Elsie Chan & Assoc. (C), CA, *289*
Chapman & Assoc. (C), BC, *289*
Chase-Gardner Executive Search Associates, Inc. (C), FL, *289*
The Chatham Group, Ltd. (C), CT, *289*
Chatham Search Assoc., Inc. (C), NJ, *290*
Chelsea Resources, Inc. (C), CT, *290*
Cheney Associates (C), CT, *290*
The Cherbonnier Group, Inc. (R), TX, *33*
Chesapeake Group (C), CT, *290*
Chicago Legal Search, Ltd. (C), IL, *290*
Christian & Timbers, Inc. (R), OH, *34*
Christmas, McIvor & Assoc. Inc. (C), ON, *290*
Christopher-Westmont & Assoc., Inc. (R), OH, *34*
Churchill & Affiliates, Inc. (R), PA, *35*
M. A. Churchill & Assoc., Inc. (R), PA, *35*
Cizek Assoc., Inc. (R), AZ, *35*
CJA-The Adler Group, Inc. (R), CA, *35*
CJSI-Cindy Jackson Search Int'l. (C), CA, *291*
Clayman & Co. (R), MA, *36*
Clinton, Charles, Wise & Co. (C), FL, *293*
CMW & Associates, Inc. (C), IL, *293*
CN Associates (C), CA, *293*
Coast Personnel Services Ltd. (C), BC, *293*
Coastal Int'l., Inc. (R), MA, *36*
COBA Executive Search (R), CO, *36*
Ann Coe & Assoc. (C), IL, *294*
Coe & Co. Int'l. Inc./EMA Partners Int'l. (R), AB, *37*
J. Kevin Coleman & Assoc., Inc. (R), CA, *37*
Collins & Associates (C), MI, *294*
Colt Systems Professional Personnel Services (C), CA, *294*
The Colton Partnership, Inc. (R), NY, *38*
Columbia Consulting Group (R), MD, *38*
Combined Resources Inc. (R), OH, *38*
Commonwealth Consultants (C), GA, *294*
Compass Group Ltd. (R), MI, *38*
CompuPro (C), IL, *295*
Computer Network Resources, Inc. (C), CA, *295*
Computer Personnel, Inc. (C), WA, *295*
Computer Professionals (R), IL, *38*
Computer Professionals Unlimited (C), TX, *295*
Computer Recruiters, Inc. (C), CA, *295*
Conard Associates, Inc. (R), NH, *39*
Conasa de Mexico, S.C. (R), MX, *39*
Connors, Lovell & Assoc. Inc. (C), ON, *296*
Conroy Partners Ltd. (R), AB, *39*
The Consortium (C), NY, *296*
Consulpro (R), ON, *39*
The Consulting Group of North America, Inc. (C), VA, *297*
Consulting Rhonda (C), ON, *297*
Continental Search & Outplacement, Inc. (C), MD, *298*
Cooper Assoc., Inc., Inc. (C), NY, *298*
COR Management Services, Ltd. (C), NY, *298*
Cornerstone Resources, Inc. (C), OK, *299*

INDUSTRIES

Corporate Careers, Inc. (C), CA, *299*
Corporate Dynamix (C), AZ, *300*
Corporate Environment Ltd. (R), IL, *41*
Corporate Recruiters Ltd. (C), BC, *300*
Corporate Resources Professional Placement (C), MN, *300*
The Corporate Source Group, Inc. (R), MA, *41*
Corporate Staffing Group, Inc. (C), PA, *301*
Cowell & Associates, Ltd. (R), IL, *42*
Cowin Assoc. (R), NY, *42*
Crane, Reed & Co., Inc. (C), NH, *302*
Creative HR Solutions (C), GA, *303*
The Cris Group, Inc. (R), NY, *42*
Criterion Executive Search, Inc. (C), FL, *303*
Cross Country Consultants, Inc. (C), MD, *304*
Timothy D. Crowe, Jr. (R), MA, *43*
Crown Advisors, Inc. (R), PA, *43*
CTR (R), CA, *43*
Cumberland Group Inc. (C), IL, *304*
Current Resource Group, Inc. (C), GA, *305*
The Currier-Winn Co., Inc. (C), NJ, *305*
Judith Cushman & Assoc. (R), WA, *44*
The Custer Group, Inc. (R), TN, *44*
CV Associates (C), NY, *305*
Cybernautic Corp. (C), CT, *305*
Cyntal Int'l. Ltd. (R), NY, *44*
Cypress Int'l., Inc. (R), FL, *45*
Daggett & Kvistad (R), CA, *45*
Charles Dahl Group, Inc. (C), MN, *306*
Dahl-Morrow Int'l. (R), VA, *45*
The Dalley Hewitt Co. (R), GA, *45*
DARE Personnel Inc. (C), ON, *307*
Alan Darling Consulting (R), VT, *46*
Data Bank Executive Search (R), OH, *46*
Data-AxIS Corp. (C), FL, *307*
The DataFinders Group, Inc. (C), NJ, *307*
Daubenspeck & Associates, Ltd. (R), IL, *46*
David Anthony Personnel Assoc., Inc. (C), NJ, *308*
Allen Davis & Assoc. (C), MA, *308*
Alan Davis & Assoc. Inc. (R), QE, *47*
Davis & Company (R), CA, *47*
Joseph A. Davis Consultants, Inc. (R), NY, *47*
DBC Recruiting Network (C), GA, *309*
DBL Associates (C), CA, *309*
Deeco Int'l. (C), UT, *310*
DEL Technical Services, Inc. (C), IL, *310*
Delta Management Group Ltd. (C), ON, *310*
Delta Resource Group, Ltd. (C), GA, *311*
Derhak Ireland & Partners Ltd. (R), ON, *48*
Desktop Staffing, Inc. (C), IL, *311*
Despres & Associates (C), IL, *311*
Rob Dey Executive Search (R), FL, *49*
Dieckmann & Assoc., Ltd. (R), IL, *51*
The Diestel Group (R), UT, *51*
DiMarchi Partners (R), CO, *51*
Robert W. Dingman Co., Inc. (R), CA, *52*
Dinte Resources, Inc. (R), VA, *52*
Direct Recruiters, Inc. (C), OH, *312*
Discovery, The Staffing Specialists, Inc. (C), IL, *312*
DiTech Resources (C), CT, *313*
Diversified Consulting Services, Inc. (C), CO, *313*
Diversified Search, Inc. (R), PA, *52*
DLB Assoc. (R), NY, *53*
Doering & Assoc. (C), CA, *313*
L. J. Doherty & Assoc. (R), MA, *53*
Doleman Enterprises (R), VA, *53*
Don Allan Assoc., Inc. (C), CA, *313*
Donini Assoc. (R), VA, *54*
J P Donnelly Assoc., Inc. (C), NY, *314*
Dorst Information Services, Inc. (C), NY, *314*
Dotson & Assoc. (R), NY, *54*
Drake & Assoc. (C), CA, *315*
Dreier Consulting (C), NJ, *315*
Drinkwater & Assoc. (R), MA, *54*
Dromeshauser Assoc. (R), MA, *55*
Drummond Assoc., Inc. (C), NY, *315*
DSR-Search & Recruitment (C), TX, *315*
J. H. Dugan & Assoc., Inc. (R), CA, *55*
Dunhill Professional Search of Miami (C), FL, *319*
Dunhill of Ft. Collins, Inc. (C), CO, *319*
Dunhill Professional Search of San Jose (C), CA, *319*
Dunhill Professional Search of Oakland (C), CA, *319*
Dunhill of San Francisco, Inc. (C), CA, *319*
Dunhill Professional Search of Hawaii (C), HI, *320*
Dunhill Technical Staffing (C), IN, *320*
Dunhill Professional Search of Greater New Orleans (C), LA, *321*
Dunhill Professional Search of Byram (C), MS, *321*
Dunhill of Manchester Inc. (C), NH, *321*
C. A. Durakis Assoc., Inc. (R), MD, *55*
Dwyer Consulting Group, Inc. (R), WV, *56*
Dynamic Choices Inc. (C), MO, *323*
Dynamic Search Systems, Inc. (C), IL, *324*
Dynamic Synergy Corp. (R), CA, *56*
E.P. Int'l. (C), NY, *324*
E/Search Int'l. (C), CT, *325*
EA Plus, Inc. (C), TX, *325*
J. M. Eagle Partners Ltd. (C), WI, *325*
Eagle Search Assoc. (C), CA, *325*
EagleView, Inc. (C), MA, *325*
Earley Kielty & Assoc., Inc. (R), NY, *56*
Eastbourne Assoc. Inc. (R), NY, *56*
Eastern Executive Assoc. (C), NJ, *325*
Eastridge Infotech (C), CA, *326*
EBA Group (R), NJ, *56*
Eckler Personnel Network (C), VT, *326*
The Edge Resource Group (C), PA, *326*
EDP Staffing Solutions, Inc. (C), AR, *327*
Bruce Edwards & Associates, Inc. (R), NC, *56*
EFCO Consultants, Inc. (C), NY, *327*
Effective Search, Inc. (R), IL, *57*
EFL Int'l. (R), AZ, *57*
Electronic Search, Inc. (C), IL, *327*
Elinvar (C), NC, *328*
Elite Consultants, Inc. (C), FL, *328*
The Ellsworth Group (C), NY, *329*
The Elmhurst Group (C), CA, *329*
The Elsworth Group (C), TX, *329*
Emerald Legal Search (C), NH, *329*
Emerging Technology Search (C), GA, *329*
Empire International (R), PA, *59*
Empowered Solutions Corp. (C), GA, *330*
Engineering Futures, LLC (C), CT, *330*
Environmental, Health & Safety Search Assoc. (C), FL, *331*
Epsen, Fuller & Assoc., LLC (R), NJ, *60*
Erikson Consulting Assoc., Inc. (R), NY, *60*
ESA (R), CT, *60*
ESS (Executive Search Services) (R), CA, *61*
Essential Solutions, Inc. (C), CA, *331*
Ethos Consulting, Inc. (R), CA, *61*
ETI Search Int'l. (R), GA, *61*
The Evans Search Group (R), CT, *61*
Evergreen & Co. (C), MA, *331*
ExeConnex, LLC (R), GA, *61*
ExecuSource Assoc., Inc. (C), GA, *332*
ExecuSource Consultants, Inc. (C), TX, *332*
Executive Alliance (R), MA, *62*
Executive Business Solutions, Inc. (C), WA, *332*
Executive Partners Inc. (C), CT, *333*
Executive Recruiters Int'l. (C), MI, *333*
Executive Recruiters Agency, Inc. (C), AR, *333*
Executive Recruiters (C), WA, *334*
Executive Recruiters, Inc. (C), WI, *334*
Executive Recruitment Specialists, Inc. (R), NC, *63*
Executive Recruitment Services, Inc. (ERS, Inc.) (C), GA, *334*
Executive Registry (C), QE, *334*
Executive Resource Systems (C), CA, *335*
Executive Sales Search (C), CO, *335*
Executive Search Consultants International, Inc. (R), NY, *63*
Executive Search Consultants (C), CA, *335*
Executive Search Int'l./Transearch (R), MA, *63*
Executive Search of America, Inc. (C), OH, *336*
Executive Strategies, Inc. (C), GA, *337*
Executives Worldwide, Inc. (C), OR, *337*
EXETER 2100 (C), NH, *337*
eXsource Inc. (C), SC, *337*
Raymond L. Extract & Assoc. (R), CA, *64*
FAI (C), CO, *338*
Leon A. Farley Assoc. (R), CA, *65*
Fast Switch, Ltd. (C), OH, *338*
The Fawcett Group (R), MA, *65*
A. E. Feldman Assoc., Inc. (C), NY, *339*
Fell & Nicholson Technology Resources (R), CA, *65*
Fenwick Partners (R), MA, *66*
Ferneborg & Assoc., Inc. (R), CA, *66*
Fernow Assoc. (C), PA, *339*
Guild Fetridge Acoustical Search, Inc. (C), NY, *340*
Fidelity Search Group, Inc. (R), PA, *66*
Financial Plus Management Solutions Inc. (R), ON, *66*
Finnegan & Assoc. (R), CA, *67*
First Advisory Services Int'l., Inc. (R), MD, *67*
First Search Inc. (C), IL, *341*
Howard Fischer Assoc. Int'l., Inc. (R), PA, *67*
Fishel HR Assoc., Inc. (C), AZ, *341*

Fisher & Assoc. (R), CA, *67*
The Fisher Group (R), AB, *67*
Fisher Personnel Management Services (R), CA, *68*
A. G. Fishkin & Assoc., Inc. (R), MD, *68*
James L. Fisk & Assoc. (C), MO, *342*
Susan Fletcher Attorney Employment Services (C), PA, *342*
Flexible Resources, Inc. (C), CT, *342*
Flowers & Assoc. (C), OH, *342*
Focus Consulting Services, Inc. (C), FL, *342*
L. W. Foote Co. (R), WA, *69*
The Forbes Group (R), GA, *69*
The Ford Group, Inc. (R), PA, *69*
Fortune Group Int'l., Inc. (R), PA, *70*
F-O-R-T-U-N-E Personnel Consultants of Boise (R), ID, *70*
F-O-R-T-U-N-E Personnel Consultants of Tampa (C), FL, *344*
Fortune Personnel Consultants of Colorado Springs (C), CO, *344*
Fortune Personnel Consultants of Jacksonville (C), FL, *345*
F-O-R-T-U-N-E Personnel Consultants of Manatee County (C), FL, *345*
Fortune Personnel Consultants of Bloomfield, Inc. (C), MI, *346*
F-O-R-T-U-N-E Personnel Consultants of Bergen County Inc. (C), NJ, *347*
Fortune Personnel Consultants of Raleigh, Inc. (C), NC, *348*
FORTUNE Personnel Consultants of North Dallas (C), TX, *350*
Fortune Personnel Consultants of Plano (C), TX, *350*
F-O-R-T-U-N-E Personnel Consultants of Knoxville (C), TN, *350*
F-O-R-T-U-N-E Personnel Consultants of East Seattle (C), WA, *351*
Foster Partners (R), NY, *70*
Fought, Jameson Assoc. (C), IL, *351*
Franklin Int'l. Search, Inc. (C), MA, *352*
KS Frary & Assoc. (R), MA, *71*
Mel Frazer Consultant (C), CA, *352*
Fresquez & Assoc. (C), CA, *352*
Furlong Search, Inc. (R), CA, *72*
G. H. Enterprises (C), AZ, *354*
GAAP Inc. (R), QE, *73*
The Gabriel Group (C), PA, *354*
Gahan Assoc. (R), NY, *73*
Jay Gaines & Company, Inc. (R), NY, *73*
Gardner-Ross Assoc., Inc. (R), NY, *74*
Garland Assoc. Int'l. (C), CA, *355*
The Garms Group (R), IL, *74*
The Garvis Group, Inc. (C), LA, *355*
GateSource Partners (C), VA, *355*
Dianne Gauger & Assoc. (C), CA, *355*
Geddes & Rubin Management Inc. (R), ON, *76*
Genel Associates (C), CA, *356*
General Engineering Tectonics (C), CA, *356*
Geneva Group Int'l. (R), CA, *76*
Delores F. George, C.P.C. (C), MA, *356*
C. R. Gerald & Assoc. (C), ON, *356*
Gilbert Tweed Assoc. Inc. (R), NY, *76*
Joe L. Giles & Assoc. (C), MI, *357*
The Glazin Group (R), BC, *77*
J. P. Gleason Assoc., Inc. (R), IL, *77*
Global 1000 Int'l. Services (C), CA, *358*
Global Consulting Group Inc. (C), ON, *358*
Global Data Services, Inc. (R), NY, *77*
Global Employer's Network, Inc. (R), TX, *77*
Global Engineers Inc. (C), ME, *358*
Global HealthCare Partners (R), IL, *78*
Global Research Partnership Inc. (R), NY, *78*
Global Technologies Group Inc. (C), NC, *359*
Global Telecommunications, Inc. (C), TX, *359*
The GlobalSearch Group (C), TX, *359*
F. Gloss Int'l. (R), VA, *78*
Glou Int'l., Inc. (R), MA, *78*
The Tracy Glover Co. (R), TX, *78*
The Gobbell Co. (R), CA, *78*
Goldman+Bell, LLC (C), NY, *360*
Fred J. Goldsmith Assoc. (R), CA, *79*
Goldstein & Co. (C), CA, *360*
David Gomez & Assoc., Inc. (R), IL, *79*
L. J. Gonzer Assoc. (C), NJ, *360*
The Goodman Group (R), CA, *79*
Goodrich & Sherwood Assoc., Inc. (R), NY, *79*
Gould, McCoy & Chadick, Inc. (R), NY, *80*
The Governance Group, Inc. (R), NJ, *80*
Government Contract Solutions, Inc. (C), VA, *360*
Robert Grant Assoc., Inc. (C), CA, *361*
Grant/Morgan Assoc., Inc. (C), MD, *361*
Grauss & Co. (C), CA, *362*
Ben Greco Assoc., Inc. (C), CA, *362*
Sheila Greco Assoc. (C), NY, *362*
Greenhaven & Assoc., Inc. (R), NY, *81*
Greenwich Internet (C), CT, *363*
J. B. Groner Executive Search, Inc. (C), DE, *363*
Grossberg & Assoc. (R), IL, *82*
Groton Planning Group (R), ME, *82*
Growth Strategies, Inc. (R), FL, *83*
GSW Consulting Group, Inc. (R), CA, *83*
Michael R. Guerin Co. (C), CA, *364*
The Guild Corp. (C), VA, *364*
The Gullgroup (C), TX, *364*
Gundersen Partners, L.L.C. (R), NY, *83*
Gustin Partners, Ltd. (R), MA, *83*
William Guy & Assoc., Inc. (R), CA, *84*
Haddad Assoc. (R), FL, *84*
Russ Hadick & Assoc. Inc. (C), OH, *365*
Halbrecht & Co. (C), VA, *365*
Haley Associates (R), CA, *85*
Michael J. Hall & Co. (R), WA, *85*
Hall Kinion (C), CA, *366*
The Hamilton Group (R), MD, *85*
W. L. Handler & Assoc. (R), GA, *85*
Handy HRM (R), NY, *86*
Hanley & Assoc. (R), FL, *86*
Harbor Consultants Int'l., Inc. (C), VA, *368*
Harcor Quest & Assoc. (R), OH, *86*
Harcourt & Assoc. (C), AB, *368*
Harcourt Group Ltd. (R), OH, *86*
Hardison & Company (R), TX, *86*
Harper Hewes, Inc. (C), NY, *369*
The Harris Consulting Corp. (R), MB, *87*
Harris Heery & Assoc., Inc. (R), CT, *87*
Hartsfield Group, Inc. (R), GA, *87*
Harvard Group Int'l. (R), GA, *87*
Hayden & Assoc., Inc. (C), MN, *370*
Hayman Daugherty Assoc., Inc. (C), GA, *370*
HDB Incorporated (C), MO, *371*
Headden Assoc. (R), WA, *88*
Healthcare Recruiters of Indiana (C), IN, *372*
Healthcare Recruiters Int'l. - Los Angeles (C), CA, *372*
F. P. Healy & Co., Inc. (R), NY, *89*
Heath/Norton Assoc., Inc. (R), NY, *89*
HEC Group (C), ON, *375*
Hechkoff/Work Executive Search Inc. (R), NY, *89*
Heffelfinger Assoc., Inc. (R), MA, *89*
Heinze & Assoc. Inc. (R), MN, *91*
The Helms Int'l. Group (R), VA, *91*
Henson Partners (C), AZ, *376*
Herbeck Kline & Assoc. (R), IL, *92*
Hergenrather & Co. (R), WA, *92*
J. J. Herlihy & Assoc., Inc. (C), CA, *376*
J. D. Hersey & Assoc. (C), OH, *376*
The Hetzel Group, Inc. (R), IL, *92*
High Tech Opportunities, Inc. (C), NH, *377*
High Tech Staffing Group (C), OR, *377*
High-Tech Recruiters (C), CT, *378*
The Hiring Authority, Inc. (C), FL, *379*
Hite Executive Search (R), OH, *94*
HLR Consulting (C), NY, *379*
Hobson Assoc. (C), CT, *379*
Hoffman Recruiters (C), MA, *380*
Holland & Assoc., Inc. (R), MI, *94*
Holloway Schulz & Partners (C), BC, *380*
Holohan Group, Ltd. (R), MO, *95*
J. G. Hood Assoc. (C), CT, *380*
Houser, Martin, Morris (C), WA, *381*
William C. Houze & Co. (R), CA, *96*
Robert Howe & Assoc. (R), GA, *97*
HR Advantage, Inc. (C), VA, *382*
The HRM Group, Inc. (C), AL, *382*
HRS, Inc. (R), PA, *97*
The Hudson Group (C), CT, *383*
Human Resource Bureau (C), CA, *384*
The Human Resource Group, Inc. (R), OH, *98*
Human Resource Solutions (R), TX, *98*
Human Resource Technologies, Inc. (R), IL, *99*
Hunt Patton & Brazeal, Inc. (C), OK, *385*
Hunter Adams (C), NC, *385*
Hunter Assoc. (C), MA, *385*
The Hunter Group, Inc. (C), MI, *385*
Hunter, Rowan & Crowe (C), FL, *386*
Huntington Group (R), CT, *100*
Huntington Personnel Consultants, Inc. (C), NY, *386*
Huntley Associates (Dallas), Inc. (C), TX, *386*
Hutton Merrill & Assoc. (R), CA, *100*
i.j. & assoc., inc. (C), CO, *386*
Impact Search & Strategies (C), PA, *387*
Impact Technical Staffing (C), OR, *387*
Independent Resource Systems (C), CA, *388*
InfoTech Search (C), TX, *388*
Infovia (C), CA, *388*

INDUSTRIES

Innovative Healthcare Services, Inc. (C), GA, *389*
InSearch (C), CO, *389*
The Inside Track (C), TX, *389*
Insight Personnel Group, Inc. (C), TX, *389*
Intech Summit Group, Inc. (R), CA, *102*
Integrated Search Solutions Group, LLC (ISSG) (R), NY, *102*
Intelegra, Inc. (C), NJ, *390*
IntelliSource, inc. (C), PA, *391*
Interim Accounting Professionals (C), CA, *391*
Interim Financial Solutions - Mid-Atlantic Region (C), MD, *392*
International Consulting Services, Inc. (C), IL, *392*
International Executive Recruiters (C), OH, *393*
International Management Services Inc. (R), IL, *102*
International Management Advisors, Inc. (R), NY, *103*
International Pro Sourcing, Inc. (C), PA, *393*
International Staffing Consultants, Inc. (C), CA, *393*
International Technical Resources (C), FL, *393*
Intersource, Ltd. (R), GA, *103*
Iona Partners (C), CA, *394*
Jeffrey Irving Assoc., Inc. (R), VA, *104*
Isaacson, Miller (R), MA, *104*
ISG Informatics Search Group (C), ON, *395*
Jackson Group Int'l. (C), CO, *396*
Jackson Resources (R), TX, *105*
K. Jaeger & Assoc. (C), MA, *396*
Jaeger Int'l., Inc. (C), OH, *396*
James Moore & Assoc. (C), CA, *397*
JDG Assoc., Ltd. (C), MD, *397*
Jender & Company (R), IL, *105*
Jenex Technology Placement Inc. (C), BC, *398*
JG Consultants, Inc. (R), TX, *106*
JL & Co. (C), CA, *399*
Job Link, Inc. (C), CA, *399*
Ronald S. Johnson Assoc., Inc. (R), CA, *107*
K. E. Johnson Assoc. (C), WA, *399*
Johnson Smith & Knisely (R), NY, *107*
Jonathan Lawrence Assoc. (C), NJ, *400*
The Jonathan Stevens Group, Inc. (R), NJ, *108*
Jones and Jones (R), OR, *108*
Jordon & Jordon, Inc. (R), PA, *108*
Joseph Consulting, Inc. (C), FL, *401*
Joseph Michaels (C), CA, *401*
JPM International (C), CA, *401*
JRL Executive Recruiters (C), MO, *401*
JSG Group Management Consultants (R), ON, *109*
Judd Associates (R), NJ, *109*
A H Justice Search Consultants (C), TX, *402*
K2 Resources, L.P. (C), CT, *402*
Kabana Corp. (C), MI, *402*
KABL Ability Network (C), CA, *402*
Kacevich, Lewis & Brown, Inc. (R), MA, *109*
Kaczmar & Assoc. (C), PA, *403*
Kames & Assoc. (C), MD, *403*
Kane & Assoc. (C), TX, *403*
Kaplan & Assoc., Inc. (R), PA, *109*
Howard Karr & Assoc., Inc. (R), CA, *110*
Allan Karson Assoc., Inc. (R), NJ, *110*
Melissa Katzman, Executive Search (C), NY, *404*
Kaufman Assoc. (R), CA, *110*
Jim Kay & Assoc. (C), IL, *404*
Kay Concepts, Inc. (C), FL, *404*
Keane Assoc. (R), MA, *110*
A.T. Kearney Executive Search (R), IL, *111*
Thomas A. Kelley & Assoc. (R), CA, *112*
S. D. Kelly & Assoc., Inc. (R), MA, *112*
The Kennett Group, Inc. (R), PA, *112*
Kensington International (R), CA, *113*
Kent & Assoc. (R), OH, *113*
Kenzer Corp. (R), NY, *113*
Key Resources Int'l. (C), CA, *405*
Ki Technologies, Inc. (C), UT, *406*
Kincaid Group Inc. (KGI) (C), TX, *406*
King ComputerSearch, Inc. (C), TX, *407*
Kingsley Quinn/USA (R), NJ, *115*
Richard Kinser & Assoc. (R), NY, *115*
Kirkbride Assoc., Inc. (C), WA, *407*
Kleber & Assoc. (C), WA, *407*
Raymond J. Klemmer & Assoc. (R), NY, *116*
The Kleven Group, Inc. - Executive Search Division (R), MA, *116*
The Kleven Group, Inc. (C), MA, *407*
KM Associates (C), MA, *407*
Knapp Consultants (R), CT, *116*
Lee Koehn Assoc., Inc. (R), OR, *116*
T. J. Koellhoffer & Assoc. (R), NJ, *116*
Korban Associates (R), PA, *117*
Korn/Ferry Int'l. (R), NY, *117*
Kors Montgomery Int'l. (R), TX, *118*
Kossuth & Assoc., Inc. (R), WA, *119*
Katherine R. Kraemer (R), CA, *120*
J. Krauss Assoc. (R), FL, *120*
Krautler Personnel Recruitment (C), FL, *409*
Kremple & Meade, Inc. (R), CA, *120*
Kremple Consulting Group (R), CA, *120*
Kressenberg Assoc. (C), TX, *409*
Kreutz Consulting Group, Inc. (R), IL, *121*
Todd L. Krueger & Assoc. (C), WA, *409*
Kuhn Med-Tech (C), CA, *409*
Kukoy Associates (R), CO, *121*
John Kurosky & Assoc. (R), CA, *122*
Kurtz Pro-Search, Inc. (C), NJ, *410*
L T M Assoc. (C), IL, *410*
L&L Assoc. Global Search (C), PA, *411*
Rene LaFlamme & Associes (R), QE, *122*
Lamon + Stuart + Michaels Inc. (R), ON, *124*
The Landstone Group (C), NY, *412*
Lanken-Kimball-Therrell & Assoc. (C), GA, *412*
Lawrence L. Lapham, Inc. (R), NY, *124*
Larkin & Co. (R), CA, *124*
Jack B. Larsen & Assoc., Inc. (C), PA, *413*
Larsen, Whitney, Blecksmith & Zilliacus, Inc. (R), CA, *125*
Larson, Katz & Young, Inc. (C), VA, *413*
LAS Management Consulting Group, Inc. (R), NJ, *125*
Lascelle & Assoc. Inc. (C), ON, *413*
Lasher Assoc. (R), FL, *125*
Latham International, Ltd. (R), NJ, *126*
Lautz, Grotte, Engler & Swimley (R), CA, *126*
W. R. Lawry, Inc. (R), CT, *126*
LCC Companies (C), AZ, *414*
LCS, Inc. (C), TX, *414*
The Lear Group, Inc. (R), OH, *127*
Ledbetter/Davidson Int'l., Inc. (R), NY, *127*
Albert G. Lee Assoc. (C), RI, *415*
V. J. Lehman & Assoc., Inc. (R), CO, *127*
Lending Personnel Services (C), CA, *416*
Jacques LePage Executive Search Inc. (R), QE, *128*
J. E. Lessner Assoc., Inc. (R), MI, *128*
Michael Levine Search Consultants (R), NY, *129*
The Levton Group Inc. (R), ON, *129*
Lexington Software Inc. (C), NY, *417*
LG Brand, Inc. (C), MD, *417*
LifeWork, Inc. (C), TX, *418*
Ginger Lindsey & Assoc., Inc. (C), TX, *418*
Lipsky Group, Inc. (R), CA, *129*
Livingston, Robert & Co. (R), CT, *130*
Lloyd Prescott & Churchill, Inc. (R), FL, *130*
Lloyd Staffing (C), NY, *419*
Loewenstein & Assoc., Inc. (R), TX, *131*
The Logan Group, Inc. (R), MO, *131*
Logix, Inc. (C), MA, *420*
Logue & Rice Inc. (C), VA, *420*
Longo Associates (C), CA, *420*
Lord & Albus Co. (C), TX, *420*
J. S. Lord & Company, Inc. (R), MA, *131*
Lucas Assoc. (C), GA, *421*
Lucas Group (C), NY, *421*
The John Lucht Consultancy Inc. (R), NY, *131*
The Luciani Group (R), CA, *132*
Lutz Associates (C), CT, *421*
P. J. Lynch Assoc. (R), CT, *132*
Lynx, Inc. (C), MA, *421*
Lyons Pruitt Int'l. (R), PA, *132*
M/J/A Partners (R), IL, *133*
The Macdonald Group, Inc. (R), NJ, *133*
Madison Executive Search, Inc. (C), NJ, *422*
The Madison Group (R), NY, *133*
Magellan Int'l., L.P. (C), TX, *422*
Maglio & Co., Inc. (R), WI, *134*
Management & Human Resources (R), MA, *134*
Management Assoc. (C), MD, *424*
Management Assoc. (C), CA, *424*
Management Decision Systems, Inc. (MDSI) (C), NJ, *424*
Management Dimensions Ltd. (R), ON, *134*
Management Recruiters of Nassau, Inc. (R), NY, *134*
Management Recruiters of Birmingham-South, Inc. (C), AL, *438*
Management Recruiters Tucson-Foothills, Inc. (C), AZ, *439*

Management Recruiters Peninsula (C), CA, *439*
Management Recruiters of Northern California (C), CA, *440*
Management Recruiters Inc. of Silicon Valley (C), CA, *441*
Management Recruiters of Pleasanton (C), CA, *441*
Management Recruiters of Roseville (C), CA, *441*
Management Recruiters of Colorado Springs (C), CO, *441*
Management Recruiters of Milford Inc. (C), CT, *442*
Management Recruiters of Altamonte (C), FL, *442*
Management Recruiters of Franktown (C), CO, *442*
Management Recruiters of Miami-North (C), FL, *443*
Management Recruiters, Inc. (C), FL, *443*
Management Recruiters of Tampa North (C), FL, *444*
Management Recruiters of Plant City, Inc. (C), FL, *444*
Management Recruiters of Forsyth County (C), GA, *445*
Management Recruiters of Venice, Inc. (C), FL, *445*
Management Recruiters of North Fulton (C), GA, *445*
Management Recruiters of Marietta, Inc. (C), GA, *446*
Management Recruiters of Atlanta NE (C), GA, *446*
Management Recruiters of Chicago West (C), IL, *447*
Management Recruiters of Des Moines (C), IA, *449*
Management Recruiters of the Baltimore Washington Corridor (C), MD, *450*
Management Recruiters of Washington, DC Inc. (C), MD, *450*
Management Recruiters of Baltimore (C), MD, *451*
Management Recruiters of Bloomington (C), MN, *452*
Management Recruiters of Chanhassen (C), MN, *452*
Management Recruiters of Lake Tahoe, NV (C), NV, *453*
Management Recruiters of Bay Head (C), NJ, *453*
Management Recruiters of Morris County, NJ (C), NJ, *453*
Management Recruiters of Medford, N.J. (C), NJ, *453*
Management Recruiters of Orange County, N.Y., Inc. (C), NJ, *453*
Management Recruiters of Princeton (C), NJ, *454*
Management Recruiters of The Sandias (C), NM, *454*
Management Recruiters of New Providence (C), NJ, *454*
Management Recruiters of Broome County, Inc. (C), NY, *454*
Management Recruiters of Easton, PA (C), PA, *458*
Management Recruiters of Youngstown (C), OH, *458*
Management Recruiters of Pittsburgh (C), PA, *459*
Management Recruiters of Delaware County (C), PA, *459*
Management Recruiters of Sioux Falls, LLP (C), SD, *461*
Management Recruiters of Austin (C), TX, *462*
Management Recruiters of Arlington (C), TX, *462*
Management Recruiters of LBJ Park/Dallas (C), TX, *462*
Management Recruiters Int'l.-The Woodlands (C), TX, *464*
Management Recruiters of Salt Lake City (C), UT, *464*
Management Recruiters of Fairfax, VA (C), VA, *464*
Management Recruiters of Spokane (C), WA, *465*
Management Recruiters of Seattle (C), WA, *465*
Management Recruiters of Loudoun County South (C), VA, *465*
Management Recruiters of Milwaukee-West (C), WI, *465*
Management Recruiters of Milwaukee - Downtown (C), WI, *466*
Management Recruiters of Cheyenne (C), WY, *466*
Management Resource Assoc., Inc. (C), FL, *467*
Management Search, Inc. (C), IL, *467*
Management Search of R.I. Inc. (R), RI, *135*
Management Solutions, Inc. (C), WA, *468*
Management Solutions, Inc. (C), CA, *468*
Mancini Technical Recruiting (C), VA, *468*
Mangieri/Solutions LLC (C), CT, *468*
Mankuta Gallagher & Assoc., Inc. (C), FL, *468*
F. L. Mannix & Co. (R), MA, *135*
ManTech Consulting (C), NY, *468*
Margolin Consultants, Inc. (C), NY, *469*
J. L. Mark Assoc., Inc. (R), CO, *135*
Market Niche Consulting (C), AZ, *470*
The Marlow Group (R), MA, *136*
The Maroon Group (R), CT, *136*
Karen Marshall Assoc. (C), KY, *471*
Donovan Martin & Assoc. (R), CA, *137*
J. Martin & Assoc. (R), CA, *137*
The Martwick Group, Inc. (C), OR, *472*
Masserman & Assoc., Inc. (R), NY, *138*
Richard L. Mather & Assoc. (C), CT, *472*
Matté & Company, Inc. (R), CT, *138*
Mayhall Search Group, Inc. (C), IN, *473*
The Mazzitelli Group, Ltd. (R), MN, *139*
McBride Assoc., Inc. (R), DC, *139*
K. E. McCarthy & Assoc. (R), CA, *139*
McCormack & Farrow (R), CA, *140*
The McCormick Group (C), VA, *473*
McCoy Ltd. (C), CA, *474*
McDonald Assoc. Int'l. (R), IL, *140*
McDowell & Co., Recruiters (C), TX, *474*
McGrath & Assoc., Inc. (R), NJ, *141*
McHale & Assoc. (R), WA, *141*
McIntyre Assoc. (R), CT, *141*
McKee Cyber Search (C), MS, *475*
The McKinnon Management Group Inc. (C), ON, *475*
Dan P. McLean Assoc., Inc. (C), ON, *475*
McManners Assoc., Inc. (R), CA, *142*
MediaCOM Talent Group (C), MA, *476*
Medical Executive Search Assoc., Inc. (C), AZ, *477*
Melancon & Co. (R), TX, *143*
Juan Menefee & Assoc. (C), IL, *478*
Mercedes & Co., Inc. (R), MA, *143*
J. M. Meredith & Assoc. Inc. (C), CA, *479*
MES Search Co. (C), GA, *479*
MESA, Inc. (R), CO, *143*
MESA International (C), CA, *480*
MetroVantage Personnel Systems (C), CA, *480*
MGA Executive Search (C), FL, *480*
Michael Thomas, Inc. (C), OH, *480*
Millennium Search Group, Inc. (R), CA, *144*
Milo Research (R), NY, *145*
MIS Computer Professionals, Inc. (C), KS, *482*
MJF Assoc. (C), CT, *483*
MK & Assoc. (R), CA, *146*
Modis (C), MD, *483*
Molloy Partners (R), NY, *146*
Monarch Technology Management LLC (C), CO, *484*
Montenido Assoc. (R), CA, *146*
Montgomery Resources, Inc. (C), CA, *484*
Montgomery West (R), CA, *146*
Larry Moore & Assoc. (C), CA, *484*
Mordue, Allen, Roberts, Bonney Ltd. (C), WA, *485*
Morency Assoc. (C), MA, *485*
Morgan & Assoc. (C), MA, *485*
Morgan Hunter Corp. (C), KS, *485*
Morgan/Webber, Inc. (R), NY, *147*
Robert T. Morton Assoc., Inc. (C), MA, *486*
MPA Executive Search Inc. (R), QE, *148*
MRF Enterprises, Inc. (C), TX, *486*
MRI, The Sequel Group, LLC (C), CO, *486*
MSI Int'l. (C), GA, *486*
Pamela L. Mulligan, Inc. (R), NH, *149*
The Mulshine Co., Inc. (R), NJ, *149*
Multi Processing, Inc. (R), NH, *149*
Jennifer Munro & Partners, Inc. (R), SC, *149*
Kenneth Murphy & Assoc. (C), NS, *487*
Murphy Partners Int'l. (R), IL, *150*
Musick & Assoc. (C), CA, *487*
Myers Career Assoc., Inc. (C), CA, *488*
Nadzam, Lusk, Horgan & Assoc., Inc. (R), CA, *150*
Nagler, Robins & Poe, Inc. (R), MA, *150*
National Bank & Finance Executive Search (C), CA, *488*
National Corporate Consultants, Inc. (C), IN, *489*
National Executive (C), ON, *489*
National Recruiters (C), OK, *489*
National Register Columbus Inc. (C), OH, *490*
National Search Assoc. (C), CA, *490*
Nationwide Personnel Recruiting & Consulting, Inc. (C), OR, *490*

INDUSTRIES

Nationwide Personnel Placement, Inc. (C), OH, *490*
NCC Executive Search Consultants (C), CA, *490*
The NEIS Corp., Inc. (C), FL, *491*
J. Fielding Nelson & Assoc., Inc. (R), UT, *151*
Len Nelson & Assoc., Inc. (C), TX, *491*
The Network Corporate Search Personnel Inc. (C), AB, *491*
Networking Unlimited of NH, Inc. (C), NH, *491*
New Dimensions in Technology, Inc. (C), MA, *492*
New Venture Development, Inc. (C), CA, *492*
Newcomb-Desmond & Assoc., Inc. (C), OH, *492*
Next Step Recruiting (C), CA, *493*
P. J. Nicholson & Assoc. (C), IL, *493*
NMC & Kay Int'l. (R), CO, *152*
The Nolan Group (C), CA, *494*
Noll Human Resource Services (C), NE, *494*
Nordeman Grimm, Inc. (R), NY, *152*
Norgate Technology, Inc. (C), NY, *494*
The Norland Group (C), CA, *494*
Paul Winston Norman & Assoc. (R), IL, *152*
Norrell Financial Staffing (C), GA, *495*
The North Peak Group (C), OH, *496*
Northland Employment Services Inc. (C), MN, *496*
NorthStar Technologies, Inc. (C), NY, *496*
Norton & Assoc. (C), IL, *496*
Nyborg•Dow Assoc., Inc. (C), CA, *497*
NYCOR Search, Inc. (C), MN, *497*
O'Brien Consulting Services (R), MA, *153*
O'Callaghan Honey/Ray & Berndtson Inc. (R), AB, *153*
O'Connor, O'Connor, Lordi, Ltd. (R), PA, *154*
O'Keefe & Assoc. (C), TX, *497*
O'Neill Group (C), NJ, *498*
O'Shea, Divine & Co., Inc. (R), CA, *154*
Oak Assoc. (R), CA, *155*
Ober & Company (R), CA, *155*
Oberlander & Co., Inc. (R), IL, *155*
Odell & Assoc., Inc. (C), TX, *498*
The Odessa Group (R), CA, *155*
Oliver & Rozner Assoc., Inc. (R), NY, *155*
Olsen/Clark (R), WA, *156*
Omega Systems, LLC (C), VA, *498*
Omnisearch Assoc. (C), CA, *499*
The Onstott Group (R), MA, *156*
Open Concepts (C), CA, *499*
Opus Marketing (R), CA, *156*
Organization Consulting Ltd. (R), ON, *157*
Organization Resources Inc. (R), MA, *157*
Ortman Recruiting Int'l. (C), CA, *500*
Ott & Hansen, Inc. (R), CA, *157*
The Oxford Group (C), TX, *500*
The P & L Group (C), NY, *500*
P.R.H. Management, Inc. (R), CT, *158*
Pacific Crossing (C), CA, *501*
Pacific Finance Search, Inc. (C), CA, *501*
Page-Wheatcroft & Co., Ltd. (R), TX, *158*
The Pailin Group Professional Search Consultants (R), TX, *158*
Paladin Group, Inc. (C), CO, *502*
Parenica & Co. (R), NC, *159*
The Park Group & Assoc., Inc. (C), MD, *502*
D. P. Parker & Assoc., Inc. (R), MA, *159*
Parker Page Group (C), FL, *503*
The Partners, LLC (C), CA, *504*
Partners Resource Group (C), VA, *504*
The Partnership Group (R), NJ, *160*
Partnervision Consulting Group Inc. (R), ON, *160*
Paul-Tittle Assoc., Inc. (R), VA, *161*
Paules Associates (C), CA, *505*
Pawlik/Dorman Partners (R), IL, *161*
PC Assoc. (C), CO, *505*
Peachtree Executive Search (R), GA, *161*
Peak Search Assoc. (C), ON, *506*
Peck & Assoc., Ltd. (R), WI, *161*
Peden & Assoc. (C), CA, *506*
M. A. Pelle Assoc., Inc. (C), NY, *506*
Penn Associates (R), PA, *161*
People Management Mid-South, LLC (R), TN, *162*
PeopleSource Inc. (C), TX, *506*
The Perkins Group (R), NC, *162*
Perry Search Assoc. (C), CA, *507*
Perry-Martel Int'l., Inc. (R), ON, *163*
Barry Persky & Co., Inc. (R), CT, *163*
PersoNet, Inc. (C), FL, *507*
Personnel Assoc. (C), NC, *508*
Personnel, Inc. (C), AL, *508*
Personnel Incorporated (C), IA, *508*
Personnel Management Group (C), MB, *508*
Personnel Unlimited/Executive Search (C), WA, *509*
Petro Staff Int'l. (C), AB, *509*
Peyser Assoc., Inc. (R), FL, *163*
PHD Conseil en Ressources Humaines Inc. (C), QE, *510*
Phillips Assoc. (C), FL, *510*
Phillips Personnel/Search (C), CO, *510*
Phoenix Partners, Inc. (C), GA, *511*
Phoenix Search (R), MX, *164*
Picard Int'l., Ltd. (R), NY, *164*
Pierce & Assoc. (C), CA, *512*
Pierce & Crow (R), CA, *164*
Pinnacle Executive Group Inc. (C), MO, *512*
The Pinnacle Source, Inc. (C), CO, *512*
Pinsker and Company, Inc. (R), CA, *164*
Pioneer Consulting Group (C), CA, *512*
PKS Assoc., Inc. (C), RI, *513*
Placement Testart Inc. (C), QE, *513*
Rene Plessner Assoc., Inc. (R), NY, *165*
PMJ & Assoc. (C), ON, *513*
Poirier, Hoevel & Co. (R), CA, *166*
The Polen Group (C), PA, *514*
The Pollack Group (C), ON, *514*
Polson & Co., Inc. (R), MN, *166*
Don V. Poole & Assoc., Inc. (C), CO, *514*
David Powell, Inc. (R), CA, *166*
Power Search (C), TX, *515*
Norman Powers Assoc., Inc. (C), MA, *515*
PPS Information Systems Staffing (C), MD, *515*
Prairie Resource Group, Inc. (R), IL, *166*
Elan Pratzer & Partners Inc. (R), ON, *167*
PRAXIS Partners (R), VA, *167*
Predictor Systems Corp. (R), CA, *167*
Prescott Legal Search, Inc. (C), TX, *517*
Preston-Hunter, Inc. (R), IL, *167*
Prestonwood Assoc. (R), MA, *168*
Alan J. Price Assoc., Inc. (C), RI, *518*
PricewaterhouseCoopers Executive Search (R), ON, *168*
PricewaterhouseCoopers Executive Search (R), MX, *168*
Prime Resource Assoc. (C), WI, *518*
Primus Assoc., L.C. (R), TX, *169*
Princeton Executive Search (C), NJ, *518*
Pro Tec Technical Services (C), ON, *519*
Pro-Tech Search, Inc. (C), IL, *519*
Probe Technology (C), PA, *519*
Probus Executive Search (C), CA, *519*
Procom (C), ON, *519*
Professional Consulting Network, Inc. (C), CA, *520*
Professional Employment Group (C), MD, *520*
Professional Engineering Technical Personnel Consultants (C), NC, *520*
Professional Personnel Consultants, Inc. (C), MI, *521*
Professional Persons Career Services (C), NY, *521*
Professional Recruiting Consultants (C), FL, *521*
Professional Recruiters Inc. (C), MN, *521*
Professional Recruiters (C), UT, *521*
The Professional Sales Search Co., Inc. (C), WA, *522*
Professional Search (R), MI, *169*
Professional Search, Inc. (C), CO, *522*
Professional Search Consultants (PSC) (C), TX, *523*
Professional Selection Services (R), GA, *169*
Professional Support Inc. (C), NY, *523*
Professional Team Search, Inc. (R), AZ, *169*
ProSearch Recruiting (C), CA, *524*
ProSearch, Inc. (C), PA, *524*
ProSearch, Inc. (C), OH, *524*
PSD Group, Inc. (C), CA, *525*
PSP Agency (C), NY, *525*
Quality Consulting Group, Inc. (C), WI, *526*
Quality Search Inc. (C), OH, *526*
Quantum EDP Recruiting Services (C), QE, *526*
Quest Enterprises, Ltd. (C), IL, *527*
Quest Worldwide Executive Search Corp. (C), CA, *527*
R & K Associates, Inc. (C), AZ, *527*
R & L Assoc., Ltd. (R), NY, *170*
R/K International Inc. (R), CT, *171*
R2 Services, LLC (C), IL, *528*
Radosevic Assoc. (R), CA, *171*
Railey & Assoc. (C), TX, *528*
Raines Int'l. Inc. (R), NY, *171*
Ramming & Assoc., Inc. (C), NJ, *528*
Rand Assoc. (R), ME, *171*
The Ransford Group (R), TX, *171*
J. E. Ranta Assoc. (C), MA, *529*
Ray & Berndtson (R), TX, *171*
Ray & Berndtson/Laurendeau Labrecque (R), QE, *172*

Ray & Berndtson/Lovas Stanley (R), ON, *172*
Raymond Karsan Assoc. (C), PA, *529*
RBW Assoc. Inc. (C), OR, *531*
RCI Employment Solutions (C), FL, *531*
Re-Mark Assoc. Inc. (C), NJ, *531*
Recruit Xpress (C), TX, *531*
Recruiting Resources Int'l. (C), CA, *532*
Redden-Shaffer Group (R), CA, *173*
Redell Search, Inc. (C), IL, *533*
Redwood Partners Ltd. (R), NY, *173*
Reeve & Assoc. (C), CT, *533*
The Regency Group, Ltd. (C), NE, *533*
The Regis Group, Ltd. (R), GA, *174*
Reid Ellis Assoc. Inc. (C), ON, *533*
The Douglas Reiter Co., Inc. (R), OR, *174*
RemTech Business Solutions, Inc. (C), MI, *534*
The Renaissance Network (C), MA, *534*
Renaissance Resources, LLC (R), VA, *174*
Resource Management Group (C), CT, *534*
Resource Networking Inc. (C), IN, *534*
Russell Reynolds Assoc., Inc. (R), NY, *176*
Reynolds Consulting Int'l. (R), ON, *177*
RHS Assoc. (C), AL, *536*
RIC Corp. (R), FL, *177*
Rice Cohen Int'l. (R), PA, *178*
Richard, Wayne & Roberts (C), TX, *536*
W. F. Richer Assoc., Inc. (C), NY, *536*
Jack Richman & Assoc. (C), FL, *537*
Richmond Assoc. (C), NY, *537*
Right/McKee Consulting Group (C), TX, *537*
Ritech Management Inc. (C), NY, *537*
Ritta Professional Search Inc. (C), NY, *538*
RLM Assoc., Ltd. (R), NY, *179*
Roberson & Co. (C), AZ, *538*
Robert William James & Assoc. (C), OR, *539*
Robinson-Robinson & Assoc., Inc. (C), MN, *539*
Rodzik & Assoc., Inc. (R), NC, *180*
Roevin Technical People (C), ON, *540*
Rogers - McManamon Executive Search (R), CA, *180*
ROI International, Inc. (R), WA, *181*
Roll International (C), TX, *541*
Romac Int'l. (C), GA, *541*
Romac Int'l. (C), IL, *541*
Romac Int'l. Inc. (R), MA, *181*
Romano McAvoy Assoc., Inc. (C), NY, *544*
Rooney Assoc., Inc. (R), IL, *181*
Emery A. Rose & Assoc. (C), WA, *545*
Ross Personnel Consultants, Inc. (C), CT, *545*
Rossi & Assoc. Inc. (C), BC, *545*
Rothrock Associates, Inc. (C), NC, *547*
Rovner & Assoc., Inc. (R), IL, *182*
Rowland Mountain & Assoc. (C), GA, *547*
The Rubicon Group (C), AZ, *547*
Louis Rudzinsky Assoc., Inc. (C), MA, *548*
Rusher, Loscavio & LoPresto (R), CA, *183*
Rust & Assoc., Inc. (R), IL, *183*
The Ryan Charles Group, Inc. (C), FL, *548*
Ryan-Allen & Assoc., Inc. (C), CA, *549*
Rylan Forbes Consulting Group, Inc. (C), NJ, *549*
R. L. Rystrom & Assoc., Inc. (C), MN, *549*
S-H-S TechStaff (C), PA, *549*
S.C.S. & Assoc. (C), NC, *550*
R. S. Sadow Assoc. (C), NJ, *550*
Sales & Marketing Search, Inc. (C), MA, *551*
Sales Builders, Inc. (R), VA, *183*
Sales Consultants of Silicon Valley (C), CA, *556*
Sales Consultants Int'l. of Oakland (C), CA, *556*
Sales Consultants of Northwest Arkansas, Inc. (C), AR, *556*
Sales Consultants of Ft. Lauderdale, Inc. (C), FL, *557*
Sales Consultants of Tampa North, Inc. (C), FL, *557*
Sales Consultants of Denver (C), CO, *557*
Sales Consultants of Ft. Myers, Inc. (C), FL, *557*
Sales Consultants of Danbury (C), CT, *557*
Sales Consultants of Barrington (C), IL, *558*
Sales Consultants of Indianapolis-North (C), IN, *558*
Sales Consultants of Indianapolis (C), IN, *558*
Sales Consultants of Wellesley, Inc. (C), MA, *559*
Sales Consultants of Baltimore (C), MD, *559*
Sales Consultants of Rockville, MD (C), MD, *559*
Sales Consultants of Farmington Hills (C), MI, *560*
Sales Consultants of Nashua-Manchester (C), NH, *560*
Sales Consultants Bridgewater, Inc. (C), NJ, *560*
Sales Consultants of Raleigh-Durham-RTP (C), NC, *561*
Sales Consultants of Harrisburg (C), PA, *561*
Sales Consultants of Newtown, Inc. (C), PA, *562*
Sales Consultants of Austin, Inc. (C), TX, *562*
Sales Consultants King of Prussia (C), PA, *562*
Sales Consultants of Orangeburg (C), SC, *562*
Sales Consultants of Greenville, Inc. (C), SC, *562*
Sales Consultants of Madison (C), WI, *563*
Sales Consultants of Houston (C), TX, *563*
Sales Executives, Inc. (C), MI, *563*
Sales Recruiters of Oklahoma City (C), OK, *564*
Sales Solutions (C), CA, *564*
George D. Sandel Assoc. (C), MA, *565*
Norm Sanders Assoc., Inc. (R), NJ, *184*
Sanders Management Assoc., Inc. (C), NJ, *565*
Sanford Rose Assoc. (C), OH, *565*
Sanford Rose Assoc. - Laguna Beach (C), CA, *565*
Sanford Rose Assoc. - Mobile (C), AL, *565*
Sanford Rose Assoc. - Santa Barbara (C), CA, *565*
Sanford Rose Assoc. - Anaheim (C), CA, *566*
Sanford Rose Assoc. - Norcross (C), GA, *566*
Sanford Rose Assoc. - Charlotte (C), NC, *568*
Sanford Rose Assoc. - Springfield (C), MO, *568*
Sanford Rose Assoc. - Amherst, NY (C), NY, *568*
Sanford Rose Assoc. - Burlington, NC (C), NC, *569*
Sanford Rose Assoc. - Austin (C), TX, *570*
Sanford Rose Assoc. - Portland (C), OR, *570*
Sanford Rose Assoc. - Port Washington (C), WI, *571*
Sarver & Carruth Assoc. (C), OK, *571*
Satterfield & Assoc., Inc. (R), OH, *184*
Saviar, Inc. (C), AZ, *571*
Savoy Partners, Ltd. (R), DC, *184*
Schattle & Duquette (C), RI, *571*
Schlatter & Assoc. (C), CA, *572*
Schneider, Hill & Spangler, Inc. (R), PA, *185*
Schuyler Assoc., Ltd. (R), GA, *185*
Schuyler, Baker & Parker, Inc. (R), GA, *185*
Schweichler Assoc., Inc. (R), CA, *186*
Robert Scott Assoc. (C), NJ, *573*
Scott Sibley Assoc. (C), NY, *573*
Scott-Wayne Assoc., Inc. (C), MA, *573*
Search & Recruit Int'l. (C), VA, *573*
Search Advisors Int'l. Corp. (R), FL, *186*
The Search Alliance, Inc. (R), FL, *186*
Search America, Inc. (C), MA, *574*
Search Assoc., Inc. (C), CA, *574*
Search Assoc., Inc. (C), NJ, *574*
Search Consultants, LLC (C), MD, *575*
Search Group Inc. (R), AB, *186*
The Search Network (C), CA, *576*
Search Solutions Inc. (C), CA, *576*
SearchCom, Inc. (R), TX, *187*
SearchCorp (C), FL, *577*
SearchCorp International (C), AB, *577*
Searchline Services, Inc. (C), OH, *577*
SearchOne, Inc. (C), AR, *577*
Seco & Zetto Assoc., Inc. (C), NJ, *577*
Sedlar & Miners (R), NY, *188*
Segal & Assoc. (C), GA, *578*
Selectis Corp. (C), IL, *578*
Sevcor Int'l., Inc. (R), IL, *188*
Sharp Placement Professionals, Inc. (C), NY, *579*
M. B. Shattuck & Assoc., Inc. (R), CA, *189*
Shell Technology Group (C), CA, *580*
Shepherd Bueschel & Provus, Inc. (R), IL, *189*
Sherwood Lehman Massucco, Inc. (R), CA, *189*
Shey-Harding Assoc. Inc. (C), CA, *580*
Shinn & Assoc. (R), CA, *189*
E. L. Shore & Assoc. (R), ON, *190*
Shupack & Michaels Inc. (C), NY, *580*
RitaSue Siegel Resources, Inc. (R), NY, *191*
Siger & Assoc., LLC (C), CT, *581*
SignatureSoft Inc. (C), CA, *581*

INDUSTRIES

Marvin L. Silcott & Assoc., Inc. (C), TX, *581*
The Silicon Network (C), ON, *581*
L. A. Silver Assoc., Inc. (R), MA, *191*
Silver Associates (C), CA, *581*
The Simmons Group (C), CA, *582*
D. J. Simpson Assoc. Inc. (R), ON, *191*
Sinclair & Co., Inc. (R), MA, *192*
Sink, Walker, Boltrus Int'l. (R), MA, *192*
SKB Enterprises (C), NY, *582*
Ruth Sklar Assoc., Inc. (RSA Executive Search) (R), NY, *192*
Slayton Int'l., Inc. (R), IL, *192*
Smith & Sawyer, Inc. (R), NY, *193*
G. L. Smith Assoc. (C), CA, *584*
Herman Smith Executive Initiatives Inc. (R), ON, *193*
The Smith Group, Inc. (C), NC, *584*
Smith James Group, Inc. (R), GA, *194*
Smith, Roth & Squires (R), NY, *194*
Smith Search, S.C. (R), MX, *194*
A. William Smyth, Inc. (R), CA, *194*
Snelling Search (C), AL, *585*
Snelling Search Recruiters (C), NC, *586*
C. Snow & Assoc. (C), ON, *586*
Soderlund Assoc. Inc. (R), OH, *194*
Sofco (C), NY, *586*
Softrix, Inc. (C), NJ, *586*
SoftSearch Inc. (C), NJ, *586*
Software Engineering Solutions, Inc. (C), CA, *586*
Software Resource Consultants (C), TN, *587*
Robert Sollman & Assoc. (C), FL, *587*
Somerset Group, Inc. (C), CT, *587*
Souder & Assoc. (R), VA, *195*
Southern Chemical & Plastics Search (C), GA, *587*
Southern Research Services (R), FL, *195*
Southport Int'l. Assoc. Inc. (C), FL, *588*
Southwestern Professional Services (C), TN, *588*
Sparks, McDonough & Assoc., Inc. (C), MO, *588*
SPC Symcox Personnel Consultants (C), TX, *588*
Specialty Employment Services, Inc. (C), GA, *589*
Spectra International LLC (C), AZ, *589*
SpectraWest (C), CA, *589*
Spectrum Consultants (R), CA, *196*
SpencerSearch, Inc. (C), CO, *589*
SpencerStuart (R), NY, *196*
The Spiegel Group (R), MA, *197*
Spilman & Assoc. (R), TX, *197*
Kenn Spinrad Inc. (C), PA, *589*
Splaine & Assoc., Inc. (R), CA, *198*
Springer Souder & Assoc. L.L.C. (R), IL, *198*
SR Wilson, Inc. (C), CA, *590*
Staffing Edge, Inc. (C), IA, *590*
StaffWriters Plus (C), NY, *591*
Stanewick, Hart & Assoc., Inc. (C), FL, *591*
Stanton Chase Int'l. (R), MD, *198*
The Stanton Group, Inc. (C), IL, *591*
Star Search Consultants (C), ON, *591*
The Stark Wilton Group (R), MI, *199*
Steinbach & Co. (C), MA, *592*
Steinfield & Assoc. (C), TX, *592*
Stephens Assoc. Ltd., Inc. (R), OH, *200*
Michael Stern Assoc., Inc./Euram (R), ON, *200*
Stevens Assoc. (C), MA, *593*
The Stewart Group (C), FL, *593*
Stewart, Stein & Scott, Ltd. (R), MN, *200*
Linford E. Stiles & Assoc., L.L.C. (R), NH, *201*
Stillinger & Assoc. (R), CA, *201*
Stone Assoc. LLC (C), MI, *594*
Stone Enterprises Ltd. (C), IL, *594*
Stone, Murphy & Olson (R), MN, *201*
Stoneburner Assoc., Inc. (C), KS, *594*
Strategic Alternatives (R), CA, *202*
Strategic Assoc., Inc. (C), TX, *595*
Strategic Search Corp. (R), IL, *202*
Strategic Search, LLC (C), CA, *595*
StratfordGroup (R), OH, *203*
Straube Associates (R), MA, *203*
Strauss Personnel Service (C), PA, *596*
Stroman Int'l., Inc. (R), CO, *204*
Sudina Search, Inc. (C), MD, *596*
The Summit Group (C), CA, *596*
Survival Systems Staffing, Inc. (C), CA, *597*
Swartz & Assoc., Inc. (R), AZ, *204*
Synapse Human Resource Consulting Group (R), TX, *205*
Synergistech Communications (C), CA, *597*
Synergy 2000 (C), DC, *597*
Synergy Solutions, Ltd. (C), WA, *597*
Synergy Systems (C), ON, *598*
System 1 Search (C), CA, *598*
Systems Careers (C), CA, *598*
Systems Personnel, Inc. (C), NY, *598*
Systems Research Group (C), CA, *598*
Systems Research Inc. (SRI) (C), IL, *598*
Systems Search (C), IL, *599*
Systems Search Group, Inc. (C), NC, *599*
Tactical Alternatives (R), CA, *205*
Roy Talman & Assoc. (C), IL, *599*
Martin Stevens Tamaren & Assoc., Inc. (R), CA, *206*
Tarbex (C), DC, *599*
Tate Consulting, Inc. (R), FL, *207*
TaxSearch Inc. (R), OK, *207*
Taylor Winfield (R), TX, *207*
The TBI Group (R), PA, *207*
TCM Enterprises (C), MD, *600*
TeamBuilders (C), GA, *600*
Tech 2000 (C), FL, *601*
Tech Connector Group (C), CA, *601*
Tech Consulting (C), FL, *601*
Tech Search (C), CA, *601*
Tech-Net (C), TX, *601*
Techaid Inc. (C), QE, *601*
Technical Employment Consultants (C), PA, *602*
Technical Search Assoc. (C), OH, *602*
Technical Skills Consulting Inc. (R), ON, *207*
Technical Staffing Solutions (C), TX, *602*
Technifind Int'l. (C), TX, *602*
TechNix Inc. (C), ON, *602*
Techno-Trac Systems, Inc. (C), NY, *603*
Technology Consultants Int'l. (C), CA, *603*
The Technology Group (R), IL, *208*
Technology Management Partners (R), CA, *208*
Technology Search Int'l. (C), CA, *603*
Tecmark Associates Inc. (C), NY, *604*
Teknon Employment Resources, Inc. (C), OH, *604*
Tekworx, Inc. (C), OK, *604*
Tele-Solutions of Arizona, Inc. (C), AZ, *604*
TeleManagement Search (C), NY, *605*
Tell/Com Recruiters (C), PA, *605*
Thomas & Assoc. of Michigan (C), MI, *606*
Thomas Mangum Co. (R), CA, *208*
Richard Thompson Assoc., Inc. (R), MN, *209*
Thomson, Sponar & Adams, Inc. (C), WA, *606*
Tirocchi, Wright, Inc. (R), CA, *209*
TNS Partners, Inc. (R), TX, *209*
Tomlinson Assoc. Inc. (C), IL, *607*
The Touchstone Group (C), MA, *607*
Tower Consultants, Ltd. (R), PA, *209*
TPG & Assoc. (C), TX, *608*
Trac One (R), NJ, *210*
Jay Tracey Assoc. Inc. (C), VT, *608*
Trans-United Consultants Ltd. (C), ON, *608*
Traynor Confidential, Ltd. (C), NY, *609*
Van Treadaway Assoc., Inc. (R), GA, *210*
Triad Technology Group (C), OR, *609*
Trowbridge & Co., Inc. (R), MA, *211*
TSC Management Services Group, Inc. (C), IL, *610*
TSS Consulting, Ltd. (C), AZ, *610*
The Thomas Tucker Co. (R), CA, *211*
Tuttle Venture Group, Inc. (R), TX, *212*
The Ultimate Source (R), CA, *212*
Unisearch Search & Recruiting Inc. (C), CA, *611*
United Personnel Services (C), MA, *611*
Unlimited Staffing Solutions, Inc. (C), MI, *611*
Vaughan & Co. (C), CA, *612*
Venpro Consulting Inc. (C), ON, *612*
Vento Assoc. (C), TN, *612*
Venture Resources, Inc. (R), CA, *213*
The Verriez Group Inc. (R), ON, *213*
C. J. Vincent Assoc., LLC (C), MD, *612*
Beverly von Winckler & Assoc. (C), IL, *613*
VZ Int'l., Inc. (C), AZ, *613*
B. D. Wallace & Assoc. (C), MD, *614*
Wallace Assoc. (C), CT, *614*
Wallace Assoc. (C), MA, *614*
The Ward Group (R), MA, *215*
C. D. Warner & Assoc. (C), PA, *615*
Warren Executive Services (C), GA, *616*
Warren, Morris & Madison, Ltd. (C), CA, *616*
The Washington Firm, Ltd. (R), WA, *216*
Waveland Int'l. (R), IL, *216*
Webb, Johnson Assoc., Inc. (R), NY, *216*
Lee Weil Assoc., Inc. (C), IL, *617*
Weinpel Search, Inc. (C), NJ, *617*
Weinstein & Co. (R), MA, *217*
D. L. Weiss & Assoc. (R), CA, *217*
Henry Welker & Assoc. (C), MI, *618*
The Wellesley Group, Inc. (R), IL, *217*

R. A. Wells Co. (C), GA, *618*
Werbin Assoc. Executive Search, Inc. (C), NY, *618*
West Coast Recruiting (C), CA, *619*
Western Management Assoc. (R), CA, *218*
Western Management Consultants (R), BC, *218*
Western Technical Resources (C), CA, *619*
WestPacific National Search, Inc. (C), CA, *619*
S. J. Wexler Assoc., Inc. (R), NY, *219*
Wheeler Assoc. (R), CT, *219*
Arch S. Whitehead Assoc. Inc. (ASWA) (R), NY, *219*
Whittlesey & Assoc., Inc. (R), PA, *220*
Wilder & Assoc. (C), VA, *620*
The Wilkie Group Int'l. (R), ON, *220*
Wilkinson & Ives (R), CA, *221*
Wilkinson SoftSearch, Inc. (C), VA, *620*
Dick Williams & Assoc. (C), CA, *621*
Williams & Delmore, Inc. (C), NC, *621*
Wilson-Douglas-Jordan (C), IL, *622*
Winguth, Grant & Donahue (R), CA, *222*
Winston Search, Inc. (R), MD, *222*
Winter, Wyman & Co. (C), MA, *623*
Wisnewski & Assoc. (R), CA, *223*
Woltz & Assoc., Inc. (R), IL, *224*
Wood & Assoc./Executive Search Consultants (C), CA, *624*
Wood West & Partners Inc. (C), BC, *624*
Bruce G. Woods Executive Search (R), TX, *224*
Woodworth Int'l. Group (R), OR, *224*
WTW Assoc., Inc. (R), NY, *225*
Wyatt & Jaffe (R), MN, *225*
John Wylie Assoc., Inc. (C), OK, *625*
Xagas & Assoc. (R), IL, *226*
Xavier Associates, Inc. (R), MA, *226*
Yelverton Executive Search (R), CA, *226*
Bill Young & Assoc. (C), VA, *626*
ZanExec L.L.C. (R), VA, *226*
Zeiger Assoc. L.L.C. (C), CA, *627*
Helen Ziegler & Assoc., Inc. (C), ON, *627*
P. D. Zier Assoc. (C), CT, *627*
Michael D. Zinn & Assoc., Inc. (R), NJ, *227*
Zwell Int'l. (R), IL, *228*

S.00 Software

The 500 Granary Inc. (C), ON, *231*
A Permanent Success Employment Services (C), CA, *231*
A-L Assoc., Inc. (R), NY, *1*
A.M.C.R., Inc. (C), OH, *232*
Abbott Associates (R), CA, *1*
The Abbott Group, Inc. (R), MD, *1*
Abraham & London Ltd. (C), CT, *232*
Abraxas Technologies, Inc. (C), FL, *233*
Accent On Achievement, Inc. (C), MI, *233*
Access Assoc. Inc. (C), MD, *233*
Access Data Personnel, Inc. (C), NH, *233*
ACCESS Technology (C), CA, *234*
Acclaim Services, Inc. (C), TX, *234*
Accountants Executive Search (C), CA, *237*
Accounting Additions (C), CA, *238*
Ackerman Johnson Inc. (C), TX, *238*
ACSYS Resources, Inc. (C), DE, *238*
Action Management Corp. (C), MI, *239*
Arthur Adams & Assoc. (C), OH, *239*
Adams & Assoc. Int'l. (R), IL, *1*
Adel-Lawrence Assoc., Inc. (C), NJ, *240*
Adept Tech Recruiting, Inc. (C), NY, *240*
Adler Management, Inc. (R), NJ, *2*
Advanced Corporate Search (C), CA, *240*
Advanced Executive Resources (R), MI, *2*
Advanced Recruiting, Inc. (C), OK, *240*
Advanced Resources, Inc. (C), MO, *241*
Advancement Recruiting Services (C), OH, *241*
Advancement, Inc. (C), IL, *241*
The Advisory Group, Inc. (R), CA, *2*
AES Search (C), NJ, *241*
Affinity Executive Search (C), FL, *241*
Alexander & Co. (C), CA, *243*
Allen & Assoc. (C), NV, *244*
D. S. Allen Assoc. (C), NJ, *244*
David Allen Assoc. (R), NJ, *3*
Allen Evans Assoc. (R), NY, *4*
Allerton Heneghan & O'Neill (R), IL, *4*
Allstaff, Inc. (C), IL, *245*
The Alternatives Group, Inc. (C), TX, *246*
American Executive Search (C), FL, *247*
American Heritage Group, Inc. (C), MI, *247*
American Services Group (C), IL, *248*
AmeriPro Search, Inc. (C), NC, *248*
AmeriResource Group Inc. (C), OK, *248*
Ames-O'Neill Assoc., Inc. (C), NY, *249*
AMS Int'l. (R), VA, *5*
Analog Solutions (C), NY, *249*
Angus Employment Ltd. (C), ON, *250*
Applied Resources, Inc. (C), MN, *252*
Applied Technology Solutions Inc. (C), ON, *252*
Ariel Recruitment Assoc. (R), NY, *7*
Aries Search Group (C), GA, *252*
Armitage Associates Ltd. (R), ON, *7*
Patrick Arnone & Assoc. Inc. (R), VA, *7*
Ashton Computer Professionals, Inc. (C), BC, *253*
ASI (C), CA, *254*
Asset Resource, Inc. (C), CA, *254*
Astro Executive Search Firm (C), LA, *254*
Atkinson Search & Placement, Inc. (C), IA, *255*
Atlanta Executive Partners, Inc. (R), MA, *8*
Aubin Int'l. Inc. (R), MA, *8*
Aurora Tech Search (C), ON, *256*
Austin Group Int'l./Marlar Int'l. (R), TX, *9*
Austin Michaels, Ltd., Inc. (C), AZ, *256*
Austin Park Management Group Inc. (C), ON, *256*
Automation Technology Search (C), CA, *256*
Avery Assoc. (R), CA, *9*
Avestruz & Assoc. (C), CA, *257*
Avion International Technology Inc. (C), ON, *257*
Avondale Search Int'l., Inc. (R), FL, *9*
The Badger Group (R), CA, *10*
Keith Bagg & Assoc., Inc. (C), ON, *257*
Baker Scott & Co. (C), NJ, *258*
Baldwin & Assoc. (C), OH, *258*
Baldwin Associates, LLC (R), CT, *10*
Allen Ballach Assoc. Inc. (R), ON, *10*
Barclay Consultants, Inc. (C), NJ, *259*
Barnes & Assoc. Executive Search (C), CA, *259*
Barrett Rose & Lee, Inc. (C), ON, *260*
Barton Assoc., Inc. (R), TX, *12*
Bassett Laudi Partners (C), ON, *261*
Battalia Winston Int'l./The Euram Consultants Group (R), NY, *13*
R. Gaines Baty Assoc., Inc. (R), TX, *13*
Bayland Assoc. (C), CA, *261*
BayResearch Group, Inc. (R), IL, *14*
Beach Executive Search Inc. (R), FL, *14*
Beck/Eastwood Recruitment Solutions (C), CA, *261*
Becker Project Resources, Inc. (C), OR, *262*
The Bedford Consulting Group Inc. (R), ON, *14*
The Bedford Group (R), RI, *15*
Robert Beech West Inc. (C), CA, *262*
Behavioral Science Assoc., Inc. (R), AZ, *15*
Belanger Partners Ltd. (C), ON, *262*
Edward Bell Assoc. (C), CA, *263*
Bell Oaks Co., Inc. (C), GA, *263*
Bellamy & Assoc. (C), GA, *263*
J. P. Bencik Assoc. (C), MI, *263*
N. L. Benke & Assoc., Inc. (C), OH, *264*
Bennett & Associates (C), TX, *264*
Bennett & Co. Consulting Group (C), CA, *264*
The Bennett Group, Inc. (R), IN, *16*
Dick Berg & Assoc. (C), CA, *264*
Berger & Leff (C), CA, *264*
Berkana Int'l., Inc. (C), WA, *265*
Bernhart Assoc. (C), MN, *265*
Bertrand, Ross & Assoc., Inc. (C), IL, *266*
BEST/World Assoc. Inc. (R), TX, *16*
BG & Assoc. (C), MD, *266*
Bialla & Assoc. Inc. (R), CA, *17*
Bio-Venture Group (C), RI, *266*
Deborah Bishop & Assoc. (R), CA, *17*
Blaney Executive Search (R), MA, *18*
Block & Assoc. (R), CA, *18*
D. R. Blood & Assoc. (R), AZ, *18*
The BMW Group, Inc. (C), NY, *268*
Boettcher Assoc. (R), WI, *19*
Boone-Scaturro Assoc., Inc. (C), GA, *269*
Bos Business Consultants (C), NY, *270*
Bosch & Assoc., LLC (R), CT, *19*
Boston Professional Search, Inc. (C), MA, *270*
Howard Bowen Consulting (C), FL, *270*
Bower & Associates (C), TX, *271*
Boyden (R), NY, *20*
Boyle/Ogata Executive Search (R), CA, *21*
The Bradbury Management Group, Inc. (R), CA, *21*
M. F. Branch Assoc., Inc. (C), NC, *272*
Brault & Assoc., Ltd. (R), VA, *22*
Bredeson Executive Recruitment, LLC (R), TX, *22*
Brei & Assoc., Inc. (C), IA, *272*
The Brentwood Group Ltd. (R), OR, *23*
Brentwood Int'l. (R), CA, *23*
Brian Assoc., Inc. (C), NY, *273*
Brigade, Inc. (R), CA, *23*
The Broadmoor Group, L.L.C. (R), TX, *23*
D. Brown & Assoc., Inc. (C), OR, *275*
Brown Venture Assoc. (R), CA, *24*
BRW Search (C), MN, *275*

BT&A, LLC (R), CT, *24*
The Buckley Group (C), FL, *276*
Burke & Assoc./The Westfield Group (C), CT, *276*
Joseph R. Burns & Assoc., Inc. (R), NJ, *25*
Busch International (R), CA, *25*
Business Partners, Inc. (C), FL, *277*
Butterfield & Co. Int'l., Inc. (C), HI, *277*
Button Group (C), TX, *277*
Byron Leonard Int'l., Inc. (R), CA, *25*
C Assoc. (C), DC, *278*
C.P.S., Inc. (C), IL, *278*
C.T.E.W. Executive Personnel Services Inc. (C), BC, *278*
Cadillac Assoc. (C), CA, *278*
California Search Agency, Inc. (C), CA, *279*
Callan Assoc., Ltd. (R), IL, *27*
Cambridge Group Ltd. - Exec. Search Div. (C), CT, *279*
The Cambridge Group Ltd. (C), CT, *280*
T. M. Campbell Co. (R), WA, *27*
Canny, Bowen Inc. (R), NY, *27*
The Cantor Concern, Inc. (R), NY, *28*
Cantrell & Assoc. (C), FL, *280*
Capital Markets Resources, Inc. (C), NC, *281*
Sally Caplan & Assoc. (C), WA, *281*
Capstone Inc. (R), NY, *29*
Career Marketing Assoc., Inc. (C), CO, *282*
Career Marketing Consultants, Inc. (C), GA, *282*
Career Specialists, Inc. (R), WA, *29*
Career Strategies, Inc. (C), CA, *283*
Careerfit, Inc. (C), TX, *283*
Careers First, Inc. (C), NJ, *283*
Careers/Inc. (C), PR, *284*
Carson-Thomas & Assoc. (C), CA, *284*
Carter, Lavoie Associates (C), RI, *285*
Carter McKenzie, Inc. (C), NJ, *285*
Carter/MacKay (C), NJ, *285*
CAS Comsearch Inc. (C), NY, *285*
Casey & Assoc., Inc. (C), TX, *286*
Catalyx Group (R), NY, *31*
Caywood Partners, Ltd. (R), CA, *32*
CBA Companies (C), CA, *286*
Cendea Connection Int'l. (R), TX, *32*
The Center for Career Advancement, LLC (C), NJ, *287*
Century Assoc., Inc. (C), PA, *287*
The Century Group (C), CA, *287*
CEO Consulting (C), FL, *287*
cFour Partners (R), CA, *32*
Elsie Chan & Assoc. (C), CA, *289*
Chapman & Assoc. (C), BC, *289*
The Chapman Group, Inc. (C), AZ, *289*
The Chatham Group, Ltd. (C), CT, *289*
Chatham Search Assoc., Inc. (C), NJ, *290*
Chelsea Resources, Inc. (C), CT, *290*
Cheney Associates (C), CT, *290*
Chesapeake Group (C), CT, *290*
Christian & Timbers, Inc. (R), OH, *34*
J. F. Church Associates (C), WA, *291*
Churchill & Affiliates, Inc. (R), PA, *35*
M. A. Churchill & Assoc., Inc. (R), PA, *35*
CJA-The Adler Group, Inc. (R), CA, *35*
CJSI-Cindy Jackson Search Int'l. (C), CA, *291*
Clayman & Co. (R), MA, *36*
Clinton, Charles, Wise & Co. (C), FL, *293*
CMS Management Services LLC (C), IN, *293*
CN Associates (C), CA, *293*
Coast Personnel Services Ltd. (C), BC, *293*
Coastal Int'l., Inc. (R), MA, *36*
Ann Coe & Assoc. (C), IL, *294*
Collins & Associates (C), MI, *294*
The Colton Partnership, Inc. (R), NY, *38*
Combined Resources Inc. (R), OH, *38*
Commonwealth Consultants (C), GA, *294*
CompuPro (C), IL, *295*
Computer Int'l. Consultants, Inc. (C), FL, *295*
Computer Network Resources, Inc. (C), CA, *295*
Computer Personnel, Inc. (C), WA, *295*
Computer Professionals (R), IL, *38*
Computer Professionals Unlimited (C), TX, *295*
Computer Recruiters, Inc. (C), CA, *295*
Conasa de Mexico, S.C. (R), MX, *39*
Conroy Partners Ltd. (R), AB, *39*
The Consortium (C), NY, *296*
Consulpro (R), ON, *39*
Consultant Recruiters (C), WI, *297*
The Consulting Group of North America, Inc. (C), VA, *297*
Continental Search & Outplacement, Inc. (C), MD, *298*
Cook Assoc. Int'l., Inc. (C), TN, *298*
COR Management Services, Ltd. (C), NY, *298*
Cornerstone Resources, Inc. (C), OK, *299*
Corporate Dynamix (C), AZ, *300*
Corporate Recruiters Ltd. (C), BC, *300*
Corporate Resources Professional Placement (C), MN, *300*
The Corporate Source Group, Inc. (R), MA, *41*
Corporate Staffing Group, Inc. (C), PA, *301*
J. D. Cotter Search Inc. (C), OH, *302*
Cowell & Associates, Ltd. (R), IL, *42*
Crane, Reed & Co., Inc. (C), NH, *302*
Creative HR Solutions (C), GA, *303*
Culver Personnel Services (C), CA, *304*
Current Resource Group, Inc. (C), GA, *305*
Curry, Telleri Group, Inc. (R), NJ, *44*
Judith Cushman & Assoc. (R), WA, *44*
CV Associates (C), NY, *305*
Cybernautic Corp. (C), CT, *305*
Cypress Int'l., Inc. (R), FL, *45*
Charles Dahl Group, Inc. (C), MN, *306*
Data Bank Executive Search (R), OH, *46*
Data Search Network, Inc. (C), FL, *307*
Data-AxIS Corp. (C), FL, *307*
The DataFinders Group, Inc. (C), NJ, *307*
Daubenspeck & Associates, Ltd. (R), IL, *46*
David Anthony Personnel Assoc., Inc. (C), NJ, *308*
Allen Davis & Assoc. (C), MA, *308*
Alan Davis & Assoc. Inc. (R), QE, *47*
Bert Davis Publishing Placement Consultants (C), NY, *309*
DBC Recruiting Network (C), GA, *309*
DBL Associates (C), CA, *309*
DeCorrevont & Assoc. (C), IL, *310*
DEL Technical Services, Inc. (C), IL, *310*
Delta Management Group Ltd. (C), ON, *310*
Delta Resource Group, Ltd. (C), GA, *311*
DeMatteo Associates (C), NY, *311*
Desktop Staffing, Inc. (C), IL, *311*
Despres & Associates (C), IL, *311*
The Devlin Search Group, Inc. (C), MA, *311*
Devoto & Assoc. (C), CA, *312*
DiMarchi Partners (R), CO, *51*
Robert W. Dingman Co., Inc. (R), CA, *52*
Direct Recruiters, Inc. (C), OH, *312*
DiTech Resources (C), CT, *313*
DLB Assoc. (R), NY, *53*
Doering & Assoc. (C), CA, *313*
L. J. Doherty & Assoc. (R), MA, *53*
Doleman Enterprises (R), VA, *53*
Don Allan Assoc., Inc. (C), CA, *313*
The Donnelly Group-Sales Recruiters, Inc. (C), MO, *314*
Dorst Information Services, Inc. (C), NY, *314*
The Doty Group (C), TX, *314*
Drake & Assoc. (C), CA, *315*
Dreier Consulting (C), NJ, *315*
Drinkwater & Assoc. (R), MA, *54*
Dromeshauser Assoc. (R), MA, *55*
DS&A (Doug Sears & Assoc.) (C), FL, *315*
DSR-Search & Recruitment (C), TX, *315*
Dunhill of Ft. Collins, Inc. (C), CO, *319*
Dunhill Professional Search of San Jose (C), CA, *319*
Dunhill Executive Search of Los Angeles, Inc. (C), CA, *319*
Dunhill Technical Staffing (C), IN, *320*
Dunhill Professional Search of Greater New Orleans (C), LA, *321*
Dunhill Professional Search of Byram (C), MS, *321*
Dunhill of Manchester Inc. (C), NH, *321*
Dunhill Personnel Service of Fargo (C), ND, *322*
Dynamic Choices Inc. (C), MO, *323*
Dynamic Search Systems, Inc. (C), IL, *324*
Dynamic Synergy Corp. (R), CA, *56*
J. M. Eagle Partners Ltd. (C), WI, *325*
EagleView, Inc. (C), MA, *325*
Earley Kielty & Assoc., Inc. (R), NY, *56*
Eastbourne Assoc. Inc. (R), NY, *56*
Eastridge Infotech (C), CA, *326*
EBA Group (R), NJ, *56*
Eckler Personnel Network (C), VT, *326*
The Edge Resource Group (C), PA, *326*
EDMS Solutions (C), TX, *326*
EDP Staffing Solutions, Inc. (C), AR, *327*
Edwards & Assoc. (C), GA, *327*
Bruce Edwards & Associates, Inc. (R), NC, *56*
EFCO Consultants, Inc. (C), NY, *327*
EFL Int'l. (R), AZ, *57*
Richard A. Eisner & Co., LLP (R), NY, *57*
Electronic Search, Inc. (C), IL, *327*
Elite Consultants, Inc. (C), FL, *328*
H. J. Elliot, Inc. (R), IL, *58*
The Elliott Company (R), MA, *58*
David M. Ellner Assoc. (R), NY, *59*
The Elmhurst Group (C), CA, *329*
The Elsworth Group (C), TX, *329*
Emerald Legal Search (C), NH, *329*

Emerging Technology Search (C), GA, *329*
Empowered Solutions Corp. (C), GA, *330*
The Enfield Company (C), TX, *330*
Engineering Futures, LLC (C), CT, *330*
Engineering Resource Group, Inc. (C), NJ, *331*
Epsen, Fuller & Assoc., LLC (R), NJ, *60*
ESA (R), CT, *60*
Essential Solutions, Inc. (C), CA, *331*
The Evans Search Group (R), CT, *61*
Evergreen & Co. (C), MA, *331*
Exclusive Search Consultants (C), OH, *331*
ExeConnex, LLC (R), GA, *61*
Execu-Tech Search Inc. (C), MN, *332*
ExecuSource Assoc., Inc. (C), GA, *332*
ExecuSource Consultants, Inc. (C), TX, *332*
Executive Alliance (R), MA, *62*
Executive Business Solutions, Inc. (C), WA, *332*
Executive Direction, Inc. (C), CA, *333*
Executive Recruiters (C), WA, *334*
Executive Recruiters, Inc. (C), WI, *334*
Executive Recruitment Specialists, Inc. (R), NC, *63*
Executive Recruitment Services, Inc. (ERS, Inc.) (C), GA, *334*
Executive Resource Assoc. (C), VA, *334*
Executive Search Consultants (C), CA, *335*
Executive Search of America, Inc. (C), OH, *336*
Executive Strategies, Inc. (C), GA, *337*
ExecutiveFit (C), NY, *337*
Executives Worldwide, Inc. (C), OR, *337*
EXETER 2100 (C), NH, *337*
eXsource Inc. (C), SC, *337*
FAI (C), CO, *338*
Fast Switch, Ltd. (C), OH, *338*
The Fawcett Group (R), MA, *65*
A. E. Feldman Assoc., Inc. (C), NY, *339*
Fell & Nicholson Technology Resources (R), CA, *65*
Fenwick Partners (R), MA, *66*
Ferneborg & Assoc., Inc. (R), CA, *66*
Fernow Assoc. (C), PA, *339*
Financial Plus Management Solutions Inc. (R), ON, *66*
Neil Fink Assoc. (R), CA, *66*
Finnegan & Assoc. (R), CA, *67*
Finney-Taylor Personnel & Management Consultants Ltd. (C), AB, *341*
First Search Inc. (C), IL, *341*
Fishel HR Assoc., Inc. (C), AZ, *341*
Fisher & Assoc. (R), CA, *67*
A. G. Fishkin & Assoc., Inc. (R), MD, *68*
Fitzgerald Associates (R), MA, *68*
Susan Fletcher Attorney Employment Services (C), PA, *342*
Flexible Resources, Inc. (C), CT, *342*
Focus Consulting Services, Inc. (C), FL, *342*
L. W. Foote Co. (R), WA, *69*
The Forbes Group (R), GA, *69*
Ford & Ford (C), MA, *343*
Fortuna Technologies Inc. (C), CA, *343*
Fortune Personnel Consultants of Huntsville, Inc. (C), AL, *343*
Fortune Personnel Consultants of Colorado Springs (C), CO, *344*
Fortune Personnel Consultants of Jacksonville (C), FL, *345*
F-O-R-T-U-N-E Personnel Consultants of Southwest Indiana (C), IN, *346*
Fortune Personnel Consultants of Allentown, Inc. (C), PA, *348*
FORTUNE Personnel Consultants of North Dallas (C), TX, *350*
Fortune Personnel Consultants of Plano (C), TX, *350*
Fortune Personnel Consultants of San Antonio, Inc. (C), TX, *350*
F-O-R-T-U-N-E Personnel Consultants of East Seattle (C), WA, *351*
Foster Partners (R), NY, *70*
Fought, Jameson Assoc. (C), IL, *351*
Franklin Int'l. Search, Inc. (C), MA, *352*
KS Frary & Assoc. (R), MA, *71*
Fresquez & Assoc. (C), CA, *352*
Furlong Search, Inc. (R), CA, *72*
G. H. Enterprises (C), AZ, *354*
Jay Gaines & Company, Inc. (R), NY, *73*
Gallin Associates, Inc. (C), FL, *354*
Gardner-Ross Assoc., Inc. (R), NY, *74*
Garland Assoc. Int'l. (C), CA, *355*
The Garms Group (R), IL, *74*
GateSource Partners (C), VA, *355*
Dianne Gauger & Assoc. (C), CA, *355*
Geddes & Rubin Management Inc. (R), ON, *76*
Genel Associates (C), CA, *356*
Geneva Group Int'l. (R), CA, *76*
Delores F. George, C.P.C. (C), MA, *356*
C. R. Gerald & Assoc. (C), ON, *356*
Gilbert Tweed Assoc. Inc. (R), NY, *76*
Joe L. Giles & Assoc. (C), MI, *357*
Gilmore & Assoc. (C), CA, *357*
Lawrence Glaser Assoc., Inc. (C), NJ, *357*
Global Career Services, Inc. (C), NY, *358*
Global Consulting Group Inc. (C), ON, *358*
Global Data Services, Inc. (R), NY, *77*
Global Employer's Network, Inc. (R), TX, *77*
Global HealthCare Partners (R), IL, *78*
Global Technologies Group Inc. (C), NC, *359*
F. Gloss Int'l. (R), VA, *78*
Glou Int'l., Inc. (R), MA, *78*
Fred J. Goldsmith Assoc. (R), CA, *79*
Goldstein & Co. (C), CA, *360*
David Gomez & Assoc., Inc. (R), IL, *79*
L. J. Gonzer Assoc. (C), NJ, *360*
The Goodman Group (R), CA, *79*
Goodrich & Sherwood Assoc., Inc. (R), NY, *79*
Government Contract Solutions, Inc. (C), VA, *360*
Robert Grant Assoc., Inc. (C), CA, *361*
Grant/Morgan Assoc., Inc. (C), MD, *361*
Greenwich Internet (C), CT, *363*
Greenwich Search Partners, LLC (C), CT, *363*
Groton Planning Group (R), ME, *82*
GSW Consulting Group, Inc. (R), CA, *83*
Michael R. Guerin Co. (C), CA, *364*
The Guild Corp. (C), VA, *364*
The Gullgroup (C), TX, *364*
Gustin Partners, Ltd. (R), MA, *83*
Russ Hadick & Assoc. Inc. (C), OH, *365*
Halbrecht & Co. (C), VA, *365*
Haley Associates (R), CA, *85*
Hall Kinion (C), CA, *366*
The Hamilton Group (R), MD, *85*
Handy HRM (R), NY, *86*
Hanley & Assoc. (R), FL, *86*
Harcor Quest & Assoc. (R), OH, *86*
Harcourt Group Ltd. (R), OH, *86*
Harper Hewes, Inc. (C), NY, *369*
Hayden & Assoc., Inc. (C), MN, *370*
Hayman Daugherty Assoc., Inc. (C), GA, *370*
HDB Incorporated (C), MO, *371*
Healthcare Recruiters of Indiana (C), IN, *372*
Healthcare Recruiters Int'l. - Alabama (C), AL, *372*
Healthcare Recruiters International-NY/NJ (C), NJ, *373*
Healthcare Recruiters of New England (C), MA, *373*
Healthcare Recruiters of New York, Inc. (C), NY, *373*
Healthcare Recruiters - Northwest (C), WA, *374*
F. P. Healy & Co., Inc. (R), NY, *89*
HEC Group (C), ON, *375*
Hechkoff/Work Executive Search Inc. (R), NY, *89*
Hedlund Corp. (C), IL, *375*
Heffelfinger Assoc., Inc. (R), MA, *89*
Heller Assoc., Ltd. (R), IL, *91*
The Helms Int'l. Group (R), VA, *91*
Henson Partners (C), AZ, *376*
J. J. Herlihy & Assoc., Inc. (C), CA, *376*
Herrerias & Assoc. (R), CA, *92*
J. D. Hersey & Assoc. (C), OH, *376*
High Tech Opportunities, Inc. (C), NH, *377*
High Tech Staffing Group (C), OR, *377*
High-Tech Recruiters (C), CT, *378*
The Hiring Authority, Inc. (C), FL, *379*
HLR Consulting (C), NY, *379*
Hobson Assoc. (C), CT, *379*
Hochman & Assoc. (C), CA, *379*
Hoffman Recruiters (C), MA, *380*
Holland & Assoc., Inc. (R), MI, *94*
Holloway Schulz & Partners (C), BC, *380*
J. G. Hood Assoc. (C), CT, *380*
David C. Horn Executive Search (C), TX, *381*
Horton Int'l. Inc. (R), NY, *96*
Houser, Martin, Morris (C), WA, *381*
HR Consultants (C), GA, *382*
Hreshko Consulting Group (C), NJ, *382*
HRS, Inc. (R), PA, *97*
The Hudson Group (C), CT, *383*
Huff Assoc. (R), NJ, *98*
The Human Resource Group, Inc. (R), OH, *98*
Human Resource Technologies, Inc. (R), IL, *99*
Human Resources Management Hawaii, Inc. (C), HI, *384*
Leigh Hunt & Assoc., Inc. (C), ME, *384*
Hunt Patton & Brazeal, Inc. (C), OK, *385*
Hunter Adams (C), NC, *385*
Hunter Assoc. (C), MA, *385*
Huntington Group (R), CT, *100*

INDUSTRIES

Huntington Personnel Consultants, Inc. (C), NY, *386*
Huntley Associates (Dallas), Inc. (C), TX, *386*
Hutton Merrill & Assoc. (R), CA, *100*
i.j. & assoc., inc. (C), CO, *386*
Impact Technical Staffing (C), OR, *387*
Independent Resource Systems (C), CA, *388*
Information Systems Professionals (C), NC, *388*
InfoTech Search (C), TX, *388*
Infovia (C), CA, *388*
Innovative Partnerships (R), CA, *101*
InSearch (C), CO, *389*
The Inside Track (C), TX, *389*
Insight Personnel Group, Inc. (C), TX, *389*
Integrated Search Solutions Group, LLC (ISSG) (R), NY, *102*
Intelegra, Inc. (C), NJ, *390*
IntelliSource, inc. (C), PA, *391*
International Business Partners (C), ON, *392*
International Consulting Services, Inc. (C), IL, *392*
International Executive Recruiters (C), OH, *393*
International Management Services Inc. (R), IL, *102*
International Pro Sourcing, Inc. (C), PA, *393*
International Technical Resources (C), FL, *393*
Intersource, Ltd. (R), GA, *103*
Jeffrey Irving Assoc., Inc. (R), VA, *104*
Isaacson, Miller (R), MA, *104*
ISG Informatics Search Group (C), ON, *395*
J. Robert Scott (R), MA, *104*
Jackson Group Int'l. (C), CO, *396*
Jackson Resources (R), TX, *105*
James Moore & Assoc. (C), CA, *397*
JDG Assoc., Ltd. (C), MD, *397*
Jefferson-Ross Assoc. Inc. (C), PA, *398*
Jender & Company (R), IL, *105*
Jenex Technology Placement Inc. (C), BC, *398*
JFW Associates, LLC (C), CT, *398*
JG Consultants, Inc. (R), TX, *106*
JL & Co. (C), CA, *399*
Johnson & Assoc., Inc. (R), CA, *106*
Ronald S. Johnson Assoc., Inc. (R), CA, *107*
K. E. Johnson Assoc. (C), WA, *399*
Johnson, Kemper & Assoc. (C), TX, *400*
Jonathan Lawrence Assoc. (C), NJ, *400*
Jones Management Co. (R), CT, *108*
Jordon & Jordon, Inc. (R), PA, *108*
J. M. Joseph Assoc. (R), NJ, *109*
Joseph Consulting, Inc. (C), FL, *401*
Joseph Michaels (C), CA, *401*
JRL Executive Recruiters (C), MO, *401*
JSG Group Management Consultants (R), ON, *109*
Judd Associates (R), NJ, *109*
Juno Systems, Inc. (C), NY, *402*
A H Justice Search Consultants (C), TX, *402*
K2 Resources, L.P. (C), CT, *402*
Kaas Employment Services (C), IA, *402*
Kabana Corp. (C), MI, *402*
KABL Ability Network (C), CA, *402*
Kaczmar & Assoc. (C), PA, *403*
Kames & Assoc. (C), MD, *403*
Kane & Assoc. (C), TX, *403*
Howard Karr & Assoc., Inc. (R), CA, *110*
Allan Karson Assoc., Inc. (R), NJ, *110*
Kaufman Assoc. (R), CA, *110*
Jim Kay & Assoc. (C), IL, *404*
Kay Concepts, Inc. (C), FL, *404*
Keane Assoc. (R), MA, *110*
A.T. Kearney Executive Search (R), IL, *111*
Thomas A. Kelley & Assoc. (R), CA, *112*
S. D. Kelly & Assoc., Inc. (R), MA, *112*
The Kennett Group, Inc. (R), PA, *112*
Kensington International (R), CA, *113*
Kent & Assoc. (R), OH, *113*
Blair Kershaw Assoc., Inc. (C), PA, *405*
Key Resources Int'l. (C), CA, *405*
Ki Technologies, Inc. (C), UT, *406*
Kiley, Owen & McGovern, Inc. (R), NJ, *114*
King ComputerSearch, Inc. (C), TX, *407*
Kleber & Assoc. (C), WA, *407*
The Kleven Group, Inc. - Executive Search Division (R), MA, *116*
The Kleven Group, Inc. (C), MA, *407*
KM Associates (C), MA, *407*
T. J. Koellhoffer & Assoc. (R), NJ, *116*
Korban Associates (R), PA, *117*
Koren, Rogers Assoc. Inc. (R), NY, *117*
Korn/Ferry Int'l. (R), NY, *117*
Kors Montgomery Int'l. (R), TX, *118*
Kossuth & Assoc., Inc. (R), WA, *119*
KPA Assoc., Inc. (C), NY, *408*
Krakower Group, Inc. (R), CA, *120*
J. Krauss Assoc. (R), FL, *120*
Krautler Personnel Recruitment (C), FL, *409*
Kremple Consulting Group (R), CA, *120*
Kreutz Consulting Group, Inc. (R), IL, *121*
Kuhn Med-Tech (C), CA, *409*
Kukoy Associates (R), CO, *121*
Paul Kull & Co. (R), NJ, *121*
Kulper & Co., L.L.C. (R), NJ, *121*
Kurtz Pro-Search, Inc. (C), NJ, *410*
L & L Assoc. (C), CA, *410*
L O R (R), NJ, *122*
L T M Assoc. (C), IL, *410*
Gregory Laka & Co. (C), IL, *411*
Lam Assoc. (C), HI, *411*
Lamon + Stuart + Michaels Inc. (R), ON, *124*
The Landstone Group (C), NY, *412*
The Langford Search, Inc. (C), AL, *412*
Robert Larned Assoc., Inc. (C), VA, *413*
Larson, Katz & Young, Inc. (C), VA, *413*
LAS Management Consulting Group, Inc. (R), NJ, *125*
Lascelle & Assoc. Inc. (C), ON, *413*
Lautz, Grotte, Engler & Swimley (R), CA, *126*
LaVallee & Associates (C), NC, *413*
LCC Companies (C), AZ, *414*
LCS, Inc. (C), TX, *414*
Leader Institute, Inc. (C), GA, *414*
Reynolds Lebus Assoc. (C), AZ, *415*
Lehman McLeskey (R), TX, *128*
Leith & Assoc., Inc. (C), OH, *416*
F. P. Lennon Assoc. (C), PA, *416*
Jacques LePage Executive Search Inc. (R), QE, *128*
Leslie Kavanagh Assoc., Inc. (C), NY, *416*
Michael Levine Search Consultants (R), NY, *129*
Lexington Software Inc. (C), NY, *417*
LG Brand, Inc. (C), MD, *417*
The Libra Group (C), NC, *417*
LifeWork, Inc. (C), TX, *418*
Lifter & Assoc. (C), CA, *418*
Lipsky Group, Inc. (R), CA, *129*
Lipson & Co. (R), CA, *130*
Livingston, Robert & Co. (R), CT, *130*
Lloyd Staffing (C), NY, *419*
Loewenstein & Assoc., Inc. (R), TX, *131*
Logistics Management Resources, Inc. (R), NY, *131*
Logix, Inc. (C), MA, *420*
Logue & Rice Inc. (C), VA, *420*
Longo Associates (C), CA, *420*
Lord & Albus Co. (C), TX, *420*
Louis Search Group, Inc. (C), NJ, *420*
The Luciani Group (R), CA, *132*
Fran Luisi Assoc. (R), NJ, *132*
Lutz Associates (C), CT, *421*
P. J. Lynch Assoc. (R), CT, *132*
Lynx, Inc. (C), MA, *421*
Lyons Pruitt Int'l. (R), PA, *132*
Madison Executive Search, Inc. (C), NJ, *422*
Management & Human Resources (R), MA, *134*
Management Association Network (C), WI, *424*
Management Decision Systems, Inc. (MDSI) (C), NJ, *424*
Management Dimensions Ltd. (R), ON, *134*
Management Recruiters of Birmingham-South, Inc. (C), AL, *438*
Management Recruiters of Tucson (C), AZ, *439*
Management Recruiters Dana Point (C), CA, *440*
Management Recruiters of Northern California (C), CA, *440*
Management Recruiters of Sacramento North (C), CA, *441*
Management Recruiters Inc. of Silicon Valley (C), CA, *441*
Management Recruiters of Pleasanton (C), CA, *441*
Management Recruiters of Roseville (C), CA, *441*
Management Recruiters of Winsted, Inc. (C), CT, *442*
Management Recruiters of Colchester (C), CT, *442*
Management Recruiters of Altamonte (C), FL, *442*
Management Recruiters of Franktown (C), CO, *442*
Management Recruiters of Miami-North (C), FL, *443*
Management Recruiters of Tampa North (C), FL, *444*

INDUSTRIES

Management Recruiters of St. Lucie County, Inc. (C), FL, *444*
Management Recruiters of Forsyth County (C), GA, *445*
Management Recruiters of Venice, Inc. (C), FL, *445*
Management Recruiters of North Fulton (C), GA, *445*
Management Recruiters of Marietta, Inc. (C), GA, *446*
Management Recruiters of Atlanta NE (C), GA, *446*
Management Recruiters of Chicago West (C), IL, *447*
Management Recruiters of Indianapolis-North (C), IN, *448*
Management Recruiters of Spencer (C), IA, *448*
Management Recruiters - Indianapolis (C), IN, *448*
Management Recruiters-Cedar Rapids, Inc. (C), IA, *448*
Management Recruiters of Des Moines (C), IA, *449*
Management Recruiters of the Baltimore Washington Corridor (C), MD, *450*
Management Recruiters of Frederick, Inc. (C), MD, *450*
Management Recruiters of Birmingham (C), MI, *451*
Management Recruiters of Woodbury (C), MN, *452*
Management Recruiters of Bloomington (C), MN, *452*
Management Recruiters of Chanhassen (C), MN, *452*
Management Recruiters of Lake Tahoe, NV (C), NV, *453*
Management Recruiters of Bay Head (C), NJ, *453*
Management Recruiters of Orange County, N.Y., Inc. (C), NJ, *453*
Management Recruiters of Reno (C), NV, *453*
Management Recruiters of The Sandias (C), NM, *454*
Management Recruiters of Broome County, Inc. (C), NY, *454*
Management Recruiters of New Providence (C), NJ, *454*
Management Recruiters of Woodbury Inc. (C), NY, *455*
Management Recruiters of Boone (C), NC, *456*
Management Recruiters of Columbus (C), OH, *457*
Management Recruiters of Oklahoma City (C), OK, *458*
Management Recruiters of Youngstown (C), OH, *458*
Management Recruiters of Easton, PA (C), PA, *458*
Management Recruiters of Northwest Ohio, Inc. (C), OH, *458*
Management Recruiters of Pittsburgh (C), PA, *459*
Management Recruiters of Delaware County (C), PA, *459*
Management Recruiters of North Charleston (C), SC, *460*
Management Recruiters of Chattanooga-Brainerd, Inc. (C), TN, *461*
Management Recruiters of Sioux Falls, LLP (C), SD, *461*
Management Recruiters of Austin (C), TX, *462*
Management Recruiters of LBJ Park/Dallas (C), TX, *462*
Management Recruiters of Arlington (C), VA, *464*
Management Recruiters of Salt Lake City (C), UT, *464*
Management Recruiters of Spokane (C), WA, *465*
Management Recruiters of Seattle (C), WA, *465*
Management Recruiters of Milwaukee - Downtown (C), WI, *466*
Management Recruiters of Stevens Point, Inc. (C), WI, *466*
Management Recruiters of Cheyenne (C), WY, *466*
Management Resource Group (C), MN, *467*
Management Resource Assoc., Inc. (C), FL, *467*
Management Search, Inc. (C), IL, *467*
Management Search of R.I. Inc. (R), RI, *135*
Management Solutions, Inc. (C), WA, *468*
Management Solutions, Inc. (C), CA, *468*
Mancini Technical Recruiting (C), VA, *468*
Mangieri/Solutions LLC (C), CT, *468*
Mankuta Gallagher & Assoc., Inc. (C), FL, *468*
F. L. Mannix & Co. (R), MA, *135*
ManTech Consulting (C), NY, *468*
MARBL Consultants, Inc. (C), WI, *469*
Marentz & Co. (C), TX, *469*
Mark Christian & Assoc., Inc. (C), AZ, *469*
Market Niche Consulting (C), AZ, *470*
Marketing Resources (C), MA, *470*
The Marlow Group (R), MA, *136*
The Maroon Group (R), CT, *136*
Marsar & Co., Inc. (C), FL, *471*
Donovan Martin & Assoc. (R), CA, *137*
J. Martin & Assoc. (R), CA, *137*
The Martin Group (R), CA, *137*
Martin Partners, L.L.C. (R), IL, *137*
The Martwick Group, Inc. (C), OR, *472*
Marvel Consultants, Inc. (C), OH, *472*
Mayhall Search Group, Inc. (C), IN, *473*
McBride Assoc., Inc. (R), DC, *139*
K. E. McCarthy & Assoc. (R), CA, *139*
The McCormick Group (C), VA, *473*
McCormick Search Inc. (C), IL, *474*
McCoy Ltd. (C), CA, *474*
McCray, Shriver, Eckdahl & Assoc., Inc. (R), CA, *140*
McDowell & Co., Recruiters (C), TX, *474*
McGrath & Assoc., Inc. (R), NJ, *141*
McHale & Assoc. (R), WA, *141*
McIntyre Assoc. (R), CT, *141*
McKee Cyber Search (C), MS, *475*
Dan P. McLean Assoc., Inc. (C), ON, *475*
MediaCOM Talent Group (C), MA, *476*
Medical Executive Recruiters (C), CA, *477*
Mercedes & Co., Inc. (R), MA, *143*
J. M. Meredith & Assoc. Inc. (C), CA, *479*
Messett Assoc., Inc. (R), FL, *143*
MetroVantage Personnel Systems (C), CA, *480*
Michael Thomas, Inc. (C), OH, *480*
Michigan Consulting Group (R), MI, *144*
Midas Management (C), CT, *481*
Miller Denver (C), CO, *482*
MIS Computer Professionals, Inc. (C), KS, *482*
Paul Misarti Inc. (C), NY, *483*
MK & Assoc. (R), CA, *146*
Modis (C), MD, *483*
Moffitt Int'l., Inc. (R), NC, *146*
Mogul Consultants, Inc. (C), NY, *483*
Molloy Partners (R), NY, *146*
Monarch Technology Management LLC (C), CO, *484*
Montenido Assoc. (R), CA, *146*
Montgomery Resources, Inc. (C), CA, *484*
Larry Moore & Assoc. (C), CA, *484*
Mordue, Allen, Roberts, Bonney Ltd. (C), WA, *485*
Morgan & Assoc. (C), MA, *485*
Morgan Int'l., Inc. (R), IL, *147*
Robert T. Morton Assoc., Inc. (C), MA, *486*
MRF Enterprises, Inc. (C), TX, *486*
MRI, The Sequel Group, LLC (C), CO, *486*
The Mulshine Co., Inc. (R), NJ, *149*
Multi Processing, Inc. (R), NH, *149*
Murphy Partners Int'l. (R), IL, *150*
Myers Career Assoc., Inc. (C), CA, *488*
Nadzam, Lusk, Horgan & Assoc., Inc. (R), CA, *150*
Nagler, Robins & Poe, Inc. (R), MA, *150*
National Executive (C), ON, *489*
National Recruiters (C), OK, *489*
National Register Columbus Inc. (C), OH, *490*
National Search Assoc. (C), CA, *490*
Nationwide Personnel Recruiting & Consulting, Inc. (C), OR, *490*
Nationwide Personnel Placement, Inc. (C), OH, *490*
NCC Executive Search Consultants (C), CA, *490*
J. Fielding Nelson & Assoc., Inc. (R), UT, *151*
Len Nelson & Assoc., Inc. (C), TX, *491*
The Network Corporate Search Personnel Inc. (C), AB, *491*
Networking Unlimited of NH, Inc. (C), NH, *491*
New Dimensions in Technology, Inc. (C), MA, *492*
Newcomb-Desmond & Assoc., Inc. (C), OH, *492*
Newell Assoc. (R), NY, *151*
Newman-Johnson-King, Inc. (C), TX, *492*
Newport Management (C), NY, *492*
Next Step Recruiting (C), CA, *493*
Ira Z. Nitzberg (C), NY, *493*
Noll Human Resource Services (C), NE, *494*
W. D. Nolte & Company (R), CT, *152*
Nordeman Grimm, Inc. (R), NY, *152*
Norgate Technology, Inc. (C), NY, *494*

The Norland Group (C), CA, *494*
Norman Broadbent Int'l., Inc. (R), NY, *152*
The North Peak Group (C), OH, *496*
Northland Employment Services Inc. (C), MN, *496*
NorthStar Technologies, Inc. (C), NY, *496*
Norton & Assoc. (C), IL, *496*
Nyborg•Dow Assoc., Inc. (C), CA, *497*
NYCOR Search, Inc. (C), MN, *497*
O'Brien Consulting Services (R), MA, *153*
O'Keefe & Assoc. (C), TX, *497*
O'Neill & Co. (R), CT, *154*
Oak Assoc. (R), CA, *155*
Ober & Company (R), CA, *155*
Odell & Assoc., Inc. (C), TX, *498*
Omega Systems, LLC (C), VA, *498*
Omnisearch Assoc. (C), CA, *499*
The Onstott Group (R), MA, *156*
Open Concepts (C), CA, *499*
Opus Marketing (R), CA, *156*
Organization Consulting Ltd. (R), ON, *157*
Organization Resources Inc. (R), MA, *157*
LaMonte Owens, Inc. (R), PA, *157*
The Oxford Group (C), TX, *500*
P.R.H. Management, Inc. (R), CT, *158*
Pacific Crossing (C), CA, *501*
Pacific Finance Search, Inc. (C), CA, *501*
Page-Wheatcroft & Co., Ltd. (R), TX, *158*
The Pailin Group Professional Search Consultants (R), TX, *158*
Paladin Group, Inc. (C), CO, *502*
The Park Group & Assoc., Inc. (C), MD, *502*
Parker-Worthington, Inc. (C), TX, *503*
Partners Executive Search Consultants Inc. (R), ON, *160*
The Partners, LLC (C), CA, *504*
Pasona Canada, Inc. (C), ON, *504*
Patriot Assoc. (C), PA, *505*
Paul-Tittle Assoc., Inc. (R), VA, *161*
Peachtree Executive Search (R), GA, *161*
Peak Search Assoc. (C), ON, *506*
Peden & Assoc. (C), CA, *506*
M. A. Pelle Assoc., Inc. (C), NY, *506*
People Management Northeast, Inc. (R), CT, *162*
PeopleSource Inc. (C), TX, *506*
Perry Search Assoc. (C), CA, *507*
Perry-Martel Int'l., Inc. (R), ON, *163*
Personnel Alliance Group (C), NJ, *507*
Personnel Assoc. (C), CA, *508*
Personnel, Inc. (C), AL, *508*
Personnel Incorporated (C), IA, *508*
Personnel Management Group (C), MB, *508*
Personnel Unlimited/Executive Search (C), WA, *509*
Petro Staff Int'l. (C), AB, *509*
Peyser Assoc., Inc. (R), FL, *163*
PHD Conseil en Ressources Humaines Inc. (C), QE, *510*
J. R. Phillip & Assoc., Inc. (R), CA, *164*
Phillips & Assoc. (R), MA, *164*
Phillips Personnel/Search (C), CO, *510*
Phoenix Partners, Inc. (C), GA, *511*
Phoenix Search (R), MX, *164*
Picard Int'l., Ltd. (R), NY, *164*
Pierce & Assoc. (C), CA, *512*
Pierce & Crow (R), CA, *164*
The Pinnacle Source, Inc. (C), CO, *512*
Pioneer Consulting Group (C), CA, *512*
PKS Assoc., Inc. (C), RI, *513*
Placement Testart Inc. (C), QE, *513*
R. L. Plimpton Assoc., Inc. (R), CO, *165*
The Polen Group (C), PA, *514*
The Pollack Group (C), ON, *514*
Jack Porter Assoc., Inc. (C), WA, *514*
David Powell, Inc. (R), CA, *166*
Power Search (C), TX, *515*
Norman Powers Assoc., Inc. (C), MA, *515*
PPS Information Systems Staffing (C), MD, *515*
Prairie Resource Group, Inc. (R), IL, *166*
Elan Pratzer & Partners Inc. (R), ON, *167*
Precision Executive Search (C), AZ, *516*
Predictor Systems Corp. (R), CA, *167*
Preferred Professional Recruiters (C), OH, *516*
Premier Search Group (C), IN, *517*
Preston-Hunter, Inc. (R), IL, *167*
Prestonwood Assoc. (R), MA, *168*
Price & Assoc., Inc. (C), VA, *518*
Alan J. Price Assoc., Inc. (C), RI, *518*
PricewaterhouseCoopers Executive Search (R), MX, *168*
Prime Resource Assoc. (C), WI, *518*
Primus Assoc., L.C. (R), TX, *169*
Pro Tec Technical Services (C), ON, *519*
Pro-Tech Search, Inc. (C), IL, *519*
Probus Executive Search (C), CA, *519*
Procom (C), ON, *519*
Professional Employment Group (C), MD, *520*
Professional Engineering Technical Personnel Consultants (C), NC, *520*
Professional Recruiting Consultants (C), FL, *521*
Professional Recruiters (C), UT, *521*
Professional Recruiting Consultants, Inc. (C), DE, *521*
Professional Research Services, Inc. (R), IL, *169*
The Professional Sales Search Co., Inc. (C), WA, *522*
Professional Search (R), MI, *169*
Professional Search Centre, Ltd. (C), IL, *522*
Professional Search, Inc. (C), CO, *522*
Professional Search Consultants (PSC) (C), TX, *523*
Professional Support Inc. (C), NY, *523*
Professional Team Search, Inc. (R), AZ, *169*
ProNet, Inc. (C), NC, *524*
PSP Agency (C), NY, *525*
Quality Consulting Group, Inc. (C), WI, *526*
Quality Search Inc. (C), OH, *526*
Quantum EDP Recruiting Services (C), QE, *526*
Quest Enterprises, Ltd. (C), IL, *527*
Quest Worldwide Executive Search Corp. (C), CA, *527*
L. J. Quinn & Assoc., Inc. (R), CA, *170*
Quiring Assoc., Inc. (C), IN, *527*
R & K Associates, Inc. (C), AZ, *527*
R.A.N. Assoc., Inc. (C), OH, *528*
R/K International Inc. (R), CT, *171*
R2 Services, LLC (C), IL, *528*
The Ransford Group (R), TX, *171*
J. E. Ranta Assoc. (C), MA, *529*
Ray & Berndtson (R), TX, *171*
Recruit Xpress (C), TX, *531*
Recruiting Assoc. of Amarillo (C), TX, *531*
Recruiting Resources Int'l. (C), CA, *532*
Recruiting/Solutions (C), CA, *532*
The Recruitment Group, Inc. (C), NY, *532*
Redell Search, Inc. (C), IL, *533*
Redwood Partners Ltd. (R), NY, *173*
Cedric L. Reese Inc. (C), CA, *533*
The Regency Group, Ltd. (C), NE, *533*
The Renaissance Network (C), MA, *534*
Renaissance Resources, LLC (R), VA, *174*
Resource Networking Inc. (C), IN, *534*
Resource Services, Inc. (C), NY, *534*
Russell Reynolds Assoc., Inc. (R), NY, *176*
RHS Assoc. (C), AL, *536*
Rice Cohen Int'l. (R), PA, *178*
W. F. Richer Assoc., Inc. (C), NY, *536*
Richmond Assoc. (C), NY, *537*
Right/McKee Consulting Group (C), TX, *537*
Ritech Management Inc. (C), NY, *537*
Ritta Professional Search Inc. (C), NY, *538*
RLM Assoc., Ltd. (R), NY, *179*
Roberson & Co. (C), AZ, *538*
Robert William James & Assoc. (C), OR, *539*
Roberts Ryan & Bentley, Inc. (R), MD, *179*
Robsham & Assoc., Inc. (R), MA, *180*
Rodzik & Assoc., Inc. (R), NC, *180*
ROI International, Inc. (R), WA, *181*
Rollins Search Group, Inc. (C), GA, *541*
Romac Int'l. (C), GA, *541*
Romac Int'l. Inc. (R), MA, *181*
Romano McAvoy Assoc., Inc. (C), NY, *544*
Rooney Assoc., Inc. (R), IL, *181*
Emery A. Rose & Assoc. (C), WA, *545*
Ross Personnel Consultants, Inc. (C), CT, *545*
Rovner & Assoc., Inc. (R), IL, *182*
Rowland Mountain & Assoc. (C), GA, *547*
The Rubinic Consulting Group (C), OH, *548*
Louis Rudzinsky Assoc., Inc. (C), MA, *548*
Rusher, Loscavio & LoPresto (R), CA, *183*
Russillo/Gardner/Spolsino (C), MA, *548*
Ryan, Miller & Assoc. (C), CA, *549*
Ryan-Allen & Assoc., Inc. (C), CA, *549*
R. L. Rystrom & Assoc., Inc. (C), MN, *549*
S.C.S. & Assoc. (C), NC, *550*
R. S. Sadow Assoc. (C), NJ, *550*
Sales & Marketing Search, Inc. (C), MA, *551*
Sales Consultants of Silicon Valley (C), CA, *556*
Sales Consultants Int'l. of Oakland (C), CA, *556*
Sales Consultants of Northwest Arkansas, Inc. (C), AR, *556*
Sales Consultants of Tampa North, Inc. (C), FL, *557*
Sales Consultants of Denver (C), CO, *557*
Sales Consultants of Danbury (C), CT, *557*
Sales Consultants of Cherokee (C), GA, *558*

Sales Consultants of Honolulu (C), HI, *558*
Sales Consultants of Barrington (C), IL, *558*
Sales Consultants of Indianapolis-North (C), IN, *558*
Sales Consultants (C), IL, *558*
Sales Consultants of Western McHenry County (C), IL, *558*
Sales Consultants of Rockville, MD (C), MD, *559*
Sales Consultants of Birmingham (C), MI, *559*
Sales Consultants of Nashua-Manchester (C), NH, *560*
Sales Consultants of Grand Rapids (C), MI, *560*
Sales Consultants Bridgewater, Inc. (C), NJ, *560*
Sales Consultants of Raleigh-Durham-RTP (C), NC, *561*
Sales Consultants of Cincinnati (C), OH, *561*
Sales Consultants of Morris County, Inc. (C), NJ, *561*
Sales Consultants King of Prussia (C), PA, *562*
Sales Consultants of Greenville, Inc. (C), SC, *562*
Sales Consultants of Madison (C), WI, *563*
Sales Consultants of Dallas (C), TX, *563*
Sales Executives, Inc. (C), MI, *563*
Sales Search (C), ON, *564*
George D. Sandel Assoc. (C), MA, *565*
Sanford Rose Assoc. (C), OH, *565*
Sanford Rose Assoc. - Laguna Beach (C), CA, *565*
Sanford Rose Assoc. - Mobile (C), AL, *565*
Sanford Rose Assoc. - Anaheim (C), CA, *566*
Sanford Rose Assoc. - Norcross (C), GA, *566*
Sanford Rose Assoc. - Charlotte (C), NC, *568*
Sanford Rose Assoc. - Springfield (C), MO, *568*
Sanford Rose Assoc. - Euclid (C), OH, *569*
Sanford Rose Assoc. - Philadelphia North (C), PA, *570*
Sanford Rose Assoc. - Portland (C), OR, *570*
Santangelo Consultants Inc. (C), NY, *571*
Satterfield & Assoc., Inc. (R), OH, *184*
Saviar, Inc. (C), AZ, *571*
Schlatter & Assoc. (C), CA, *572*
Schulenburg & Assoc. (C), GA, *572*
Schuyler Assoc., Ltd. (R), GA, *185*
Schuyler, Baker & Parker, Inc. (R), GA, *185*
Robert Scott Assoc. (C), NJ, *573*
Scott Sibley Assoc. (C), NY, *573*
Scott-Wayne Assoc., Inc. (C), MA, *573*
The Search Alliance, Inc. (R), FL, *186*
Search America, Inc. (C), MA, *574*
Search Assoc., Inc. (C), CA, *574*
Search Assoc., Inc. (C), NJ, *574*
The Search Network (C), CA, *576*
Search Solutions Inc. (C), CA, *576*
SearchCorp (C), FL, *577*
SearchCorp International (C), AB, *577*
Searchline Services, Inc. (C), OH, *577*
SearchOne, Inc. (C), AR, *577*
Searchworks, Inc. (C), FL, *577*
Seco & Zetto Assoc., Inc. (C), NJ, *577*
Sedlar & Miners (R), NY, *188*
Segal & Assoc. (C), GA, *578*
Selectis Corp. (C), IL, *578*
Selective Staffing (C), CA, *579*
Sevcor Int'l., Inc. (R), IL, *188*
Sharp Placement Professionals, Inc. (C), NY, *579*
M. B. Shattuck & Assoc., Inc. (R), CA, *189*
Shell Technology Group (C), CA, *580*
Shepherd Bueschel & Provus, Inc. (R), IL, *189*
Shinn & Assoc. (R), CA, *189*
SignatureSoft Inc. (C), CA, *581*
The Silicon Network (C), ON, *581*
L. A. Silver Assoc., Inc. (R), MA, *191*
SilverSands Int'l. (C), FL, *582*
The Simmons Group (C), CA, *582*
Sinclair & Co., Inc. (R), MA, *192*
Sink, Walker, Boltrus Int'l. (R), MA, *192*
SKB Enterprises (C), NY, *582*
Skipping Stone Inc. (C), VA, *582*
Smith & Sawyer, Inc. (R), NY, *193*
Smith James Group, Inc. (R), GA, *194*
A. William Smyth, Inc. (R), CA, *194*
Snelling & Snelling, Inc. (C), FL, *585*
Snelling Search (C), AL, *585*
Snelling Search Recruiters (C), NC, *586*
C. Snow & Assoc. (C), ON, *586*
Softrix, Inc. (C), NJ, *586*
Software Engineering Solutions, Inc. (C), CA, *586*
Software Resource Consultants (C), TN, *587*
Robert Sollman & Assoc. (C), FL, *587*
Southport Int'l. Assoc. Inc. (C), FL, *588*
Sparks, McDonough & Assoc., Inc. (C), MO, *588*
SPC Symcox Personnel Consultants (C), TX, *588*
Spectra International LLC (C), AZ, *589*
SpectraWest (C), CA, *589*
Spectrum Consultants (R), CA, *196*
SpencerStuart (R), NY, *196*
The Spiegel Group (R), MA, *197*
Spilman & Assoc. (R), TX, *197*
Kenn Spinrad Inc. (C), PA, *589*
Splaine & Assoc., Inc. (R), CA, *198*
Squires Resources Inc. (C), ON, *590*
StaffWriters Plus (C), NY, *591*
Stanewick, Hart & Assoc., Inc. (C), FL, *591*
Stanton Chase Int'l. (R), MD, *198*
The Stanton Group, Inc. (C), IL, *591*
Steinbach & Co. (C), MA, *592*
Sterling Int'l. Management Recruitment, Ltd. Inc. (C), NC, *592*
Stevens Assoc. (C), MA, *593*
The Stevenson Group, Inc. (N.J.) (R), NJ, *200*
Stewart/Laurence Assoc., Inc. (R), NJ, *201*
Linford E. Stiles & Assoc., L.L.C. (R), NH, *201*
Stone & Youngblood (C), MA, *594*
Stone Enterprises Ltd. (C), IL, *594*
Stoneburner Assoc., Inc. (C), KS, *594*
Mark Stranberg & Assoc. Inc. (R), MA, *202*
Strategic Alliance Network, Ltd. (C), OH, *595*
Strategic Alternatives (R), CA, *202*
Straube Associates (R), MA, *203*
Sudina Search, Inc. (C), MD, *596*
Sullivan & Assoc. (R), MI, *204*
The Summit Group (C), CA, *596*
Swartz & Assoc., Inc. (R), AZ, *204*
Synergistech Communications (C), CA, *597*
Synergy 2000 (C), DC, *597*
Synergy Solutions, Ltd. (C), WA, *597*
Synergy Systems (C), ON, *598*
System 1 Search (C), CA, *598*
Systems Careers (C), CA, *598*
Systems One Ltd. (C), IL, *598*
Systems Personnel, Inc. (C), NY, *598*
Systems Research Group (C), CA, *598*
Systems Research Inc. (SRI) (C), IL, *598*
Systems Search (C), IL, *599*
T. H. Hunter, Inc. (C), MN, *599*
Tactical Alternatives (R), CA, *205*
Roy Talman & Assoc. (C), IL, *599*
Martin Stevens Tamaren & Assoc., Inc. (R), CA, *206*
Tarbex (C), DC, *599*
Tate Consulting, Inc. (R), FL, *207*
M. L. Tawney & Assoc. (C), TX, *600*
Taylor Winfield (R), TX, *207*
TBC, Inc. (C), KY, *600*
TCM Enterprises (C), MD, *600*
TeamBuilders (C), GA, *600*
Tech 2000 (C), FL, *601*
Tech Connector Group (C), CA, *601*
Tech Consulting (C), FL, *601*
Tech Search (C), CA, *601*
Tech-Net (C), TX, *601*
Techaid Inc. (C), QE, *601*
Technical Employment Consultants (C), PA, *602*
Technical Search Assoc. (C), OH, *602*
Technifind Int'l. (C), TX, *602*
TechNix Inc. (C), ON, *602*
Techno-Trac Systems, Inc. (C), NY, *603*
Technology Consultants Int'l. (C), CA, *603*
The Technology Group (R), IL, *208*
Technology Management Partners (R), CA, *208*
Technology Search Int'l. (C), CA, *603*
Techstaff Inc. (C), WI, *603*
Teknon Employment Resources, Inc. (C), OH, *604*
Tekworx, Inc. (C), OK, *604*
Tele-Solutions of Arizona, Inc. (C), AZ, *604*
Tell/Com Recruiters (C), PA, *605*
Thomas & Assoc. of Michigan (C), MI, *606*
Thompson Assoc. (C), CA, *606*
Tirocchi, Wright, Inc. (R), CA, *209*
The Touchstone Group (C), MA, *607*
TPG & Assoc. (C), TX, *608*
Trac One (R), NJ, *210*
Jay Tracey Assoc. Inc. (C), VT, *608*
Trans-United Consultants Ltd. (C), ON, *608*
Travis & Co., Inc. (R), MA, *210*

INDUSTRIES

Van Treadaway Assoc., Inc. (R), GA, *210*
Triad Technology Group (C), OR, *609*
Trout & Assoc. Inc. (R), UT, *211*
Trowbridge & Co., Inc. (R), MA, *211*
TSC Management Services Group, Inc. (C), IL, *610*
The Thomas Tucker Co. (R), CA, *211*
Tuttle Venture Group, Inc. (R), TX, *212*
The Ultimate Source (R), CA, *212*
UniQuest Int'l., Inc. (C), FL, *610*
United Personnel Services (C), MA, *611*
Valentine & Assoc. (C), IL, *611*
Venpro Consulting Inc. (C), ON, *612*
Vento Assoc. (C), TN, *612*
Vick & Assoc. (R), TX, *214*
C. J. Vincent Assoc., LLC (C), MD, *612*
Beverly von Winckler & Assoc. (C), IL, *613*
The Wabash Group (C), IN, *613*
B. D. Wallace & Assoc. (C), MD, *614*
Wallace Assoc. (C), CT, *614*
J. D. Walsh & Co. (R), CT, *215*
Ward-Hoffman & Assoc. (C), ID, *615*
C. D. Warner & Assoc. (C), PA, *615*
Warren Executive Services (C), GA, *616*
The Washington Firm, Ltd. (R), WA, *216*
The Wayne Group, Ltd. (C), NY, *616*
David Weinfeld Group (C), NC, *617*
Weinpel Search, Inc. (C), NJ, *617*
Weinstein & Co. (R), MA, *217*
Henry Welker & Assoc. (C), MI, *618*
Wellington Management Group (R), PA, *217*
Welzig, Lowe & Assoc. (C), CO, *618*
Werbin Assoc. Executive Search, Inc. (C), NY, *618*
West & West (R), CA, *218*
Western Management Assoc. (R), CA, *218*
Western Technical Resources (C), CA, *619*
Wheeler Assoc. (R), CT, *219*
The Whitaker Companies (C), TX, *619*
Arch S. Whitehead Assoc. Inc. (ASWA) (R), NY, *219*
The Whyte Group, Inc. (R), MD, *220*
Wilcox Bertoux & Miller (R), CA, *220*
Wilcoxen, Blackwell, Niven & Assoc. (R), FL, *220*
Wilder & Assoc. (C), VA, *620*
Wilkinson & Ives (R), CA, *221*
Wilkinson SoftSearch, Inc. (C), VA, *620*
Dick Williams & Assoc. (C), CA, *621*
Williams & Delmore, Inc. (C), NC, *621*
Willis & Assoc. (R), OH, *221*
Wilson-Douglas-Jordan (C), IL, *622*
The Windham Group (R), OH, *222*
Wing Tips & Pumps, Inc. (C), MI, *623*
Winston Search, Inc. (R), MD, *222*
Winter, Wyman & Co. (C), MA, *623*
Wisnewski & Assoc. (R), CA, *223*
Woltz & Assoc., Inc. (R), IL, *224*
Wood West & Partners Inc. (C), BC, *624*
Bruce G. Woods Executive Search (R), TX, *224*
Woodworth Int'l. Group (R), OR, *224*
Worlco Computer Resources, Inc. (C), PA, *624*
John Wylie Assoc., Inc. (C), OK, *625*
Dennis Wynn Assoc., Inc. (C), FL, *625*
Yelverton Executive Search (R), CA, *226*
Yormak & Assoc. (C), CA, *626*
Bill Young & Assoc. (C), VA, *626*
ZanExec L.L.C. (R), VA, *226*
Zeiger Assoc. L.L.C. (C), CA, *627*
Zen Zen Int'l. Inc. (C), MB, *627*
P. D. Zier Assoc. (C), CT, *627*
Michael D. Zinn & Assoc., Inc. (R), NJ, *227*

T.00 Biotech/genetic engineering

Accountants Executive Search (C), CA, *237*
Adirect Recruiting Corp. (C), ON, *240*
Ahrensdorf & Assoc. (R), PA, *2*
Albrecht & Assoc., Executive Search Consultants (C), TX, *243*
Alexander Enterprises, Inc. (C), PA, *243*
The Alexander Group (R), TX, *3*
Allen-Jeffers Assoc. (C), CA, *245*
AMS Int'l. (R), VA, *5*
The Andre Group, Inc. (R), PA, *6*
Aries Search Group (C), GA, *252*
Ashway Ltd. Agency (C), NY, *253*
Astro Executive Search Firm (C), LA, *254*
Atlantic West Int'l. (C), NC, *255*
Avery Assoc. (R), CA, *9*
Avestruz & Assoc. (C), CA, *257*
Fred A. Barnette & Assoc. (R), NC, *11*
Barrett Partners (C), IL, *260*
Nathan Barry Assoc., Inc. (R), MA, *12*
The Bauman Group (R), CA, *14*
BayResearch Group, Inc. (R), IL, *14*
Gary S. Bell Assoc., Inc. (C), NJ, *263*
Bell Oaks Co., Inc. (C), GA, *263*
Bench Int'l. Search, Inc. (R), CA, *15*
Dick Berg & Assoc. (C), CA, *264*
Berger & Leff (C), CA, *264*
Ed Bertolas Assoc., Inc. (C), CA, *265*
Besen Assoc. Inc. (C), NJ, *266*
Bio-Venture Group (C), RI, *266*
Biomedical Search Consultants (R), CT, *17*
BioPharmMed (C), FL, *267*
BioQuest Inc. (R), CA, *17*
BioTech Research Recruiters Inc. (C), CA, *267*
J: Blakslee Int'l., Ltd. (R), CA, *18*
Blau Mancino Schroeder (R), NJ, *18*
BowersThomas (C), CA, *271*
Boyle/Ogata Executive Search (R), CA, *21*
The Bradbury Management Group, Inc. (R), CA, *21*
Brandywine Retained Ventures, Inc. (R), CT, *22*
The Brentwood Group Ltd. (R), OR, *23*
Brethet, Barnum & Assoc., Inc. (C), ON, *273*
Brissenden, McFarland, Fuccella & Reynolds, Inc. (R), NJ, *23*
Dan B. Brockman (C), IL, *274*
Brush Creek Partners (R), MO, *24*
Bryant Research (C), NJ, *275*
Buckman/Enochs & Assoc., Inc. (C), OH, *276*
Cadillac Assoc. (C), CA, *278*
Caliber Associates (R), PA, *27*
Canny, Bowen Inc. (R), NY, *27*
Capitol Management Consulting, Inc. (C), NJ, *281*
Caplan Assoc., Inc. (R), NJ, *28*
The Caplan-Taylor Group (R), CA, *28*
Career Marketing Assoc., Inc. (C), CO, *282*
Carr Management Services, Inc. (C), PA, *284*
Carter/MacKay (C), NJ, *285*
Carver Search Consultants (C), CA, *285*
Rosemary Cass Ltd. (R), CT, *31*
The Cassie Group (R), NJ, *31*
Catalyx Group (R), NY, *31*
CEC Associates (R), MA, *32*
Century Assoc., Inc. (C), PA, *287*
The Century Group (C), KS, *287*
Chelsea Resources, Inc. (C), CT, *290*
Christian & Timbers, Inc. (R), OH, *34*
Clark Executive Search (C), NY, *292*
Ken Clark Int'l. (R), NJ, *36*
COBA Executive Search (R), CO, *36*
Coe & Co. Int'l. Inc./EMA Partners Int'l. (R), AB, *37*
The Coelyn Group (R), CA, *37*
S L Collins Assoc. (C), NC, *294*
Colucci, Blendow & Johnson (R), CA, *38*
Columbia Consulting Group (R), MD, *38*
Continental Search Assoc. (C), OH, *298*
Corporate Environment Ltd. (R), IL, *41*
Corporate Leadership Strategies, Inc. (R), NH, *41*
Corporate Recruiters Inc. (C), PA, *300*
Corporate Resources Professional Placement (C), MN, *300*
Courtright & Assoc., Inc. (R), PA, *42*
CSA/Clinical Staffing Assoc., LLC (C), NJ, *304*
Culver Personnel Services (C), CA, *304*
Curran Partners, Inc. (R), CT, *44*
Curry, Telleri Group, Inc. (R), NJ, *44*
Cypress Int'l., Inc. (R), FL, *45*
D.A.L. Associates, Inc. (R), CT, *45*
Charles Dahl Group, Inc. (C), MN, *306*
Dahl-Morrow Int'l. (R), VA, *45*
The Dalley Hewitt Co. (R), GA, *45*
Alfred Daniels & Assoc., Inc. (R), CA, *46*
Deeco Int'l. (C), UT, *310*
Diversified Consulting Services, Inc. (C), CO, *313*
Diversified Search, Inc. (R), PA, *52*
Doherty Int'l., Inc. (R), IL, *53*
The Domann Organization (R), CA, *53*
Robert Drexler Assoc., Inc. (R), NJ, *54*
Dukas Assoc. (C), MA, *315*
Dwyer Consulting Group, Inc. (R), WV, *56*
J. M. Eagle Partners Ltd. (C), WI, *325*
Eastbourne Assoc. Inc. (R), NY, *56*
Bruce Edwards & Associates, Inc. (R), NC, *56*
EGM Consulting, Inc. (R), FL, *57*
William J. Elam & Assoc. (R), NE, *58*
The Elliott Company (R), MA, *58*
The Elmhurst Group (C), CA, *329*
Emerging Medical Technologies, Inc. (C), CO, *329*
Engineering Futures, LLC (C), CT, *330*
Erikson Consulting Assoc., Inc. (R), NY, *60*
Excalibur Human Resources, Inc. (R), NJ, *61*

Exec Tech, Inc. (C), IL, *332*
Executive Resource Systems (C), CA, *335*
Executives Worldwide, Inc. (C), OR, *337*
Raymond L. Extract & Assoc. (R), CA, *64*
Fallstaff Search (C), MD, *338*
Dorothy W. Farnath & Assoc., Inc. (C), NJ, *338*
James Feerst & Assoc., Inc. (C), AZ, *339*
First Advisory Services Int'l., Inc. (R), MD, *67*
Howard Fischer Assoc. Int'l., Inc. (R), PA, *67*
Jack Stuart Fisher Assoc. (C), NJ, *341*
Florapersonnel, Inc. (R), FL, *68*
Focus Executive Search (C), MN, *343*
Fortuna Technologies Inc. (C), CA, *343*
Fortune Group Int'l., Inc. (R), PA, *70*
F-O-R-T-U-N-E Personnel Consultants of Wilmington (C), DE, *344*
F-O-R-T-U-N-E Personnel Consultants of Denver, Inc. (C), CO, *344*
Fortune Personnel Consultants (C), CA, *344*
F-O-R-T-U-N-E Personnel Consultants of San Diego (C), CA, *344*
Fortune Personnel Consultants (C), NH, *347*
F-O-R-T-U-N-E Personnel Consultants of Bergen County Inc. (C), NJ, *347*
Fortune Personnel Consultants of Anderson, Inc. (C), SC, *349*
FORTUNE Personnel Consultants of North Dallas (C), TX, *350*
Fortune Personnel Consultants of Plano (C), TX, *350*
Foster Partners (R), NY, *70*
Franklin Allen Consultants, Ltd. (R), NY, *71*
The Franklin Search Group, Inc./Medzilla (R), WA, *71*
Future Employment Service, Inc. (C), IA, *353*
The Garret Group (R), NJ, *75*
Geddes & Rubin Management Inc. (R), ON, *76*
Genel Associates (C), CA, *356*
Gilbert Tweed Assoc. Inc. (R), NY, *76*
Joe L. Giles & Assoc. (C), MI, *357*
Glines Assoc., Inc. (R), IL, *77*
Global Engineers Inc. (C), ME, *358*
The GlobalSearch Group (C), TX, *359*
Joseph Goldring & Assoc. Inc. (C), MI, *360*
Gould, McCoy & Chadick, Inc. (R), NY, *80*
Robert Grant Assoc., Inc. (C), CA, *361*
Groton Planning Group (R), ME, *82*
Growth Strategies, Inc. (R), FL, *83*
GSW Consulting Group, Inc. (R), CA, *83*
Haddad Assoc. (R), FL, *84*
Hadley Associates, Inc. (C), NJ, *365*
The Hampton Group (C), NY, *367*
Harcor Quest & Assoc. (R), OH, *86*
Hartman & Barnette (R), VA, *87*
The Haystack Group, Inc. (R), ME, *88*
HCI Corp. (C), IL, *371*
Healthcare Management Resources, Inc. (R), GA, *89*
Healthcare Recruiters Int'l. Orange County (C), CA, *372*
Healthcare Recruiters Int'l. Phoenix (C), AZ, *372*
Healthcare Recruiters of Indiana (C), IN, *372*
Healthcare Recruiters Int'l. Bay Area (C), CA, *372*
Healthcare Recruiters Int'l. - Alabama (C), AL, *372*
Healthcare Recruiters Int'l. - Los Angeles (C), CA, *372*
Healthcare Recruiters Int'l. Philadelphia (C), NJ, *373*
Healthcare Recruiters International-NY/NJ (C), NJ, *373*
Healthcare Recruiters of New England (C), MA, *373*
Healthcare Recruiters Int'l - Minnesota, Inc. (C), MN, *373*
Healthcare Recruiters of New York, Inc. (C), NY, *373*
Healthcare Recruiters Int'l. - Pittsburgh (C), PA, *373*
Healthcare Recruiters of Midsouth (C), TN, *373*
Healthcare Recruiters - Northwest (C), WA, *374*
Healthcare Recruiters of Dallas (C), TX, *374*
R. W. Hebel Assoc. (R), TX, *89*
Herbeck Kline & Assoc. (R), IL, *92*
Herrerias & Assoc. (R), CA, *92*
Hockett Associates, Inc. (R), CA, *94*
The Hogan Group (C), OH, *380*
Holohan Group, Ltd. (R), MO, *95*
Horton Int'l. Inc. (R), NY, *96*
Houtz•Strawn & Arnold, Inc. (R), TX, *96*
Huff Assoc. (R), NJ, *98*
Interim Accounting Professionals (C), CA, *391*
International Management Advisors, Inc. (R), NY, *103*
International Pro Sourcing, Inc. (C), PA, *393*
International Research Group (R), CA, *103*
Iona Partners (C), CA, *394*
ISC of Atlanta, Inc. (C), GA, *394*
ISG Informatics Search Group (C), ON, *395*
J. Robert Scott (R), MA, *104*
James Moore & Assoc. (C), CA, *397*
JDG Assoc., Ltd. (C), MD, *397*
Job Link, Inc. (C), CA, *399*
John Jay & Co. (C), ME, *399*
K. E. Johnson Assoc. (C), WA, *399*
Joseph Michaels (C), CA, *401*
JPM International (C), CA, *401*
A H Justice Search Consultants (C), TX, *402*
Karp & Assoc. (C), FL, *403*
Howard Karr & Assoc., Inc. (R), CA, *110*
Kaye/Bassman Int'l. Corp. (R), TX, *110*
Kazan International, Inc. (R), NJ, *110*
Keane Assoc. (R), MA, *110*
A.T. Kearney Executive Search (R), IL, *111*
Kensington International (R), CA, *113*
Kincannon & Reed (R), VA, *114*
Kingsley Quinn/USA (R), NJ, *115*
Kiradjieff & Goode, Inc. (R), MA, *115*
The Kleven Group, Inc. - Executive Search Division (R), MA, *116*
T. J. Koellhoffer & Assoc. (R), NJ, *116*
Korban Associates (R), PA, *117*
Korn/Ferry Int'l. (R), NY, *117*
Kuhn Med-Tech (C), CA, *409*
John Kurosky & Assoc. (R), CA, *122*
Laboratory Resource Group (C), MA, *411*
Rene LaFlamme & Associes (R), QE, *122*
Laguzza Assoc., Ltd. (R), NY, *122*
Lam Assoc. (C), HI, *411*
Lasher Assoc. (R), FL, *125*
Ledbetter/Davidson Int'l., Inc. (R), NY, *127*
Albert G. Lee Assoc. (C), RI, *415*
Levin & Company, Inc. (R), MA, *128*
Lewis & Blank Int'l. (R), CA, *129*
Lloyd Staffing (C), NY, *419*
Logue & Rice Inc. (C), VA, *420*
Lord & Albus Co. (C), TX, *420*
J. S. Lord & Company, Inc. (R), MA, *131*
The Luciani Group (R), CA, *132*
Lybrook Assoc., Inc. (C), RI, *421*
The Mackenzie Group (R), MD, *133*
Maczkov-Biosciences, Inc. (R), CA, *133*
The Madison Group (R), NY, *133*
Management Advisors Int'l., Inc. (C), NC, *424*
Management Assoc. (C), MD, *424*
Management Catalysts (R), NJ, *134*
Management Recruiters of Emeryville (C), CA, *440*
Management Recruiters of Milford Inc. (C), CT, *442*
Management Recruiters of Plant City, Inc. (C), FL, *444*
Management Recruiters of Duluth (C), GA, *445*
Management Recruiters of Springfield, Inc. (C), IL, *447*
Management Recruiters of South Bend (C), IN, *448*
Management Recruiters of Washington, DC Inc. (C), MD, *450*
Management Recruiters of Medford, N.J. (C), NJ, *453*
Management Recruiters of Princeton (C), NJ, *454*
Management Recruiters of New Providence (C), NJ, *454*
Management Recruiters of Bethlehem, PA (C), PA, *458*
Management Recruiters of Lionville, Inc. (C), PA, *459*
Management Recruiters of Austin (C), TX, *462*
Management Recruiters of San Marcos (C), TX, *463*
Management Recruiters of Spokane (C), WA, *465*
Management Recruiters of Seattle (C), WA, *465*
Management Solutions, Inc. (C), WA, *468*
Management Solutions, Inc. (C), CA, *468*
Mankuta Gallagher & Assoc., Inc. (C), FL, *468*
Manuso, Alexander & Associates, Inc. (R), NY, *135*
Marcus & Assoc. (C), NY, *469*

Mark Stanley & Co./EMA Partners International (R), FL, *136*
Marketing Resources (C), MA, *470*
The Marlow Group (R), MA, *136*
Karen Marshall Assoc. (C), KY, *471*
George R. Martin (R), PA, *137*
Richard L. Mather & Assoc. (C), CT, *472*
Matrix Consultants, Inc. (C), NC, *472*
McBride Assoc., Inc. (R), DC, *139*
McDonald Assoc. Int'l. (R), IL, *140*
Med Exec Int'l. (C), CA, *476*
MediaCOM Talent Group (C), MA, *476*
Medical Executive Recruiters (C), CA, *477*
Medical Executive Search Assoc., Inc. (C), AZ, *477*
MedQuest Assoc. (C), CO, *478*
MedSearch Resources, Inc. (C), FL, *478*
Mercedes & Co., Inc. (R), MA, *143*
MES Search Co. (C), GA, *479*
Miller + Miller (C), WA, *482*
MIXTEC Group (R), CA, *145*
Diedre Moire Corp., Inc. (C), NJ, *483*
Molecular Solutions, Inc. (C), SC, *483*
Moore Research Assoc. (R), NJ, *147*
Morgan Int'l., Inc. (R), IL, *147*
Morgan/Webber, Inc. (R), NY, *147*
Morton, McCorkle & Assoc. Inc. (R), MO, *147*
MTA Partners (R), TX, *148*
Much & Co. (R), NY, *148*
The Mulshine Company, Ltd. (R), NY, *149*
Munroe, Curry & Bond Assoc. (R), NJ, *149*
Murphy Partners Int'l. (R), IL, *150*
Nachman Biomedical (C), MA, *488*
Nadzam, Lusk, Horgan & Assoc., Inc. (R), CA, *150*
National Search Assoc. (C), CA, *490*
NaviSearch (C), GA, *490*
NCC Executive Search Consultants (C), CA, *490*
The Neil Michael Group, Inc./Global Partners (R), NY, *151*
Newman-Johnson-King, Inc. (C), TX, *492*
The Noebel Search Group, Inc. (C), TX, *494*
Paul Winston Norman & Assoc. (R), IL, *152*
The Normyle/Erstling Health Search Group (C), NJ, *494*
Northland Employment Services Inc. (C), MN, *496*
O'Brien Consulting Services (R), MA, *153*
O'Neill & Co. (R), CT, *154*
O'Shea, Divine & Co., Inc. (R), CA, *154*
Ober & Company (R), CA, *155*
Oberlander & Co., Inc. (R), IL, *155*
Opus Marketing (R), CA, *156*
Organization Consulting Ltd. (R), ON, *157*
Ortman Recruiting Int'l. (C), CA, *500*
Robert Ottke Assoc. (R), CA, *157*
P R Management Consultants, Inc. (C), NJ, *500*
Frank Parillo & Assoc. (R), CA, *159*
D. P. Parker & Assoc., Inc. (R), MA, *159*
Patriot Assoc. (C), PA, *505*
Paules Associates (C), CA, *505*
Perfect Search, Inc. (C), FL, *507*
Perry-D'Amico & Assoc. (R), CA, *162*
Pharmaceutical Search Professionals, Inc. (C), PA, *510*
J. R. Phillip & Assoc., Inc. (R), CA, *164*
Phoenix BioSearch, Inc. (C), NJ, *511*
Physician Associates (C), HI, *511*
Pierce & Assoc. (C), CA, *512*
Pioneer Consulting Group (C), CA, *512*
Place Mart Personnel Service (C), NJ, *513*
David Powell, Inc. (R), CA, *166*
Powers Consultants, Inc. (R), MO, *166*
Preferred Professional Recruiters (C), TX, *516*
Premier Business Advisors (C), PA, *516*
Prime Management Group Inc. (C), ON, *518*
Probus Executive Search (C), CA, *519*
Professional Research Services, Inc. (R), IL, *169*
Professional Team Search, Inc. (R), AZ, *169*
Proquest Inc. (C), SC, *524*
ProTech Nationwide Staffing, Inc. (C), NY, *525*
PSP Agency (C), NY, *525*
Radosevic Assoc. (R), CA, *171*
Ray & Berndtson/Laurendeau Labrecque (R), QE, *172*
Raymond Karsan Assoc. (C), PA, *529*
Re-Mark Assoc. Inc. (C), NJ, *531*
Redden-Shaffer Group (R), CA, *173*
Reece & Mruk Partners/EMA Partners Int'l. (R), MA, *173*
Resource Networking Inc. (C), IN, *534*
Russell Reynolds Assoc., Inc. (R), NY, *176*
Reynolds Partners (R), NY, *177*
Rocky Mountain Recruiters, Inc. (C), CO, *540*
Craig Roe & Assoc., LLC (C), MD, *540*
Romac Int'l. Inc. (R), MA, *181*
Romeo-Hudgins & Assoc., Ltd. (C), NJ, *544*
Ruderfer & Co., Inc. (C), NJ, *548*
J. D. Ruhmann & Assoc. (C), MO, *548*
Rust & Assoc., Inc. (R), IL, *183*
W. A. Rutledge & Assoc. (R), CT, *183*
Sales Consultants of Chico (C), CA, *556*
Sales Consultants Int'l. of Oakland (C), CA, *556*
Sales Consultants of Boca Raton, Inc. (C), FL, *557*
Sales Consultants of Bangor, Inc. (C), ME, *559*
Sales Consultants of Princeton, Inc. (C), NJ, *561*
Sales Consultants of Austin, Inc. (C), TX, *562*
George D. Sandel Assoc. (C), MA, *565*
Sanford Rose Assoc. - Lake Forest (R), IL, *184*
Sanford Rose Assoc. - Chicago (C), IL, *566*
Sanford Rose Assoc. - Clearwater (C), FL, *566*
Sanford Rose Assoc. - Columbia, MD (C), MD, *567*
Sanford Rose Assoc. - Louisville (C), KY, *567*
Sanford Rose Assoc. - Rochester (C), MI, *568*
Sanford Rose Assoc. - Fairlawn (C), OH, *569*
Sanford Rose Assoc. - Columbia (C), SC, *570*
A.D. Schiff & Assoc., Ltd. (C), IL, *572*
Schlatter & Assoc. (C), CA, *572*
Schneider, Hill & Spangler, Inc. (R), PA, *185*
Schweichler Assoc., Inc. (R), CA, *186*
Scott-Wayne Assoc., Inc. (C), MA, *573*
Search Consultants, LLC (C), MD, *575*
Search Enterprises, Inc. (C), FL, *575*
Search Masters Int'l. (R), AZ, *187*
Search Masters, USA (C), FL, *576*
Searchforce, Inc. (R), FL, *187*
Searchworks, Inc. (C), FL, *577*
Daniel A. Silverstein Assoc. Inc. (R), FL, *191*
Skott/Edwards Consultants (R), NY, *192*
Smith & Laue Search (R), OR, *193*
Smith, Brown & Jones (C), KS, *585*
Snyder & Co. (R), CT, *194*
Sockwell & Assoc. (R), NC, *194*
Specialty Consultants Inc. (R), PA, *195*
SpencerStuart (R), NY, *196*
The Spiegel Group (R), MA, *197*
The Stelton Group, Inc. (C), NJ, *592*
Stephens Assoc. Ltd., Inc. (R), OH, *200*
Sterling Int'l. Management Recruitment, Ltd. Inc. (C), NC, *592*
The Stevens Group (R), TX, *200*
The Stewart Group (C), FL, *593*
Stewart/Laurence Assoc., Inc. (R), NJ, *201*
Allan Stolee Inc. (R), FL, *201*
Stoneburner Assoc., Inc. (C), KS, *594*
Strategic Resources Biotechnology & Medical Group (C), WA, *595*
J. Stroll Assoc., Inc. (R), CT, *203*
Synergistech Communications (C), CA, *597*
System 1 Search (C), CA, *598*
TechFind, Inc. (R), MA, *207*
Technical Employment Consultants (C), PA, *602*
Telford, Adams & Alexander (R), CA, *208*
Thomas Resource Group (R), CA, *209*
Richard Thompson Assoc., Inc. (R), MN, *209*
TPG & Assoc. (C), TX, *608*
Travis & Co., Inc. (R), MA, *210*
Trowbridge & Co., Inc. (R), MA, *211*
The Ultimate Source (R), CA, *212*
Venture Resources, Inc. (R), CA, *213*
Vezan Assoc. (C), CT, *612*
Victor White Int'l. (C), CA, *612*
Vlcek & Company, Inc. (R), CA, *214*
Voigt Assoc. (R), IL, *214*
W. P. Assoc. (C), CA, *613*
R. J. Watkins & Co., Ltd. (R), CA, *216*
Watring & Assoc., Inc. (C), IL, *616*
The Wellesley Group, Inc. (R), IL, *217*
Wellington Management Group (R), PA, *217*
West & West (R), CA, *218*
Western Technical Resources (C), CA, *619*
Westfields Int'l., Inc. (C), NY, *619*
WestPacific National Search, Inc. (C), CA, *619*
Walter K. Wilkins & Co. (R), NJ, *221*

Williams Recruiting, Inc. (C), WA, *621*
William Willis Worldwide Inc. (R), CT, *221*
Winfield Assoc., Inc. (C), MA, *623*
Wisnewski & Assoc. (R), CA, *223*
The Witt Group (C), FL, *623*
Yelverton Executive Search (R), CA, *226*
Yungner & Bormann (R), MN, *226*
Zackrison Assoc., Inc. (C), FL, *627*
Zingaro & Company (R), TX, *227*
Michael D. Zinn & Assoc., Inc. (R), NJ, *227*
Zurick, Davis & Co., Inc. (R), MA, *227*

U.00 Healthcare

A.K.S. Assoc., Ltd. (R), MA, *1*
B. J. Abrams & Assoc. Inc. (C), IL, *233*
ACC Consultants, Inc. (C), NM, *233*
Accountants On Call (C), FL, *237*
Adept Tech Recruiting, Inc. (C), NY, *240*
Adirect Recruiting Corp. (C), ON, *240*
Advancement Recruiting Services (C), OH, *241*
AES Search (C), NJ, *241*
Agriesti & Assoc. (C), CA, *243*
Ahrensdorf & Assoc. (R), PA, *2*
J. R. Akin & Co. (R), MA, *2*
Alaska Executive Search, Inc. (C), AK, *243*
Albrecht & Assoc., Executive Search Consultants (C), TX, *243*
The Alexander Group (R), NJ, *3*
The Alfus Group (R), NY, *3*
Jay Allen & Assoc. (C), FL, *244*
David Allen Assoc. (R), NJ, *3*
Allen-Jeffers Assoc. (C), CA, *245*
Allhands Placement Consultants (C), IN, *245*
Alliance Search Management Inc. (R), TX, *4*
AMD & Associates (C), GA, *247*
American Executive Search (C), FL, *247*
American Group Practice, Inc. (R), NY, *5*
American Medical Consultants, Inc. (C), FL, *247*
American Medical Recruiting Co. Inc. (C), MS, *248*
American Medical Recruiters (C), CO, *248*
Amherst Human Resource Group, Ltd. (C), IL, *249*
Amherst Personnel Group Inc. (C), NY, *249*
Anderson & Associates (R), NC, *5*
The Andre Group, Inc. (R), PA, *6*
David Aplin & Assoc. (C), AB, *251*
R & J Arnold & Assoc., Inc. (C), CO, *253*
Aster Search Group (R), NY, *8*
Auerbach Associates, Inc. (R), MA, *9*
A. M. Auster Associates (R), FL, *9*
Avalon Health Group, Inc. (R), NY, *9*
Avestruz & Assoc. (C), CA, *257*
The Ayers Group, Inc. (R), NY, *9*
Baeder Kalinski Int'l. Group, Inc. (R), NH, *10*
The Baer Group (R), OH, *10*
Bailey Employment System Inc. (C), CT, *257*
The Bales-Waugh Group (C), FL, *258*
Barger & Sargeant, Inc. (R), NH, *11*
J. W. Barleycorn, Renard & Assoc., Inc. (R), OH, *11*
Barnes Development Group, LLC (R), WI, *11*
Fred A. Barnette & Assoc. (R), NC, *11*
Nathan Barry Assoc., Inc. (R), MA, *12*
Bason Associates (R), OH, *13*
Battalia Winston Int'l./The Euram Consultants Group (R), NY, *13*
The Bauman Group (R), CA, *14*
BayResearch Group, Inc. (R), IL, *14*
BCG Search, Inc. (R), FL, *14*
The Beam Group (R), PA, *14*
The Bedford Consulting Group Inc. (R), ON, *14*
Neail Behringer Consultants Inc. (R), NY, *15*
Joy Reed Belt Search Consultants, Inc. (R), OK, *15*
Bench Int'l. Search, Inc. (R), CA, *15*
Bennett & Associates (C), TX, *264*
Dick Berg & Assoc. (C), CA, *264*
Berkhemer/Clayton, Inc. (R), CA, *16*
Bertrand, Ross & Assoc., Inc. (C), IL, *266*
J: Blakslee Int'l., Ltd. (R), CA, *18*
Blau Mancino Schroeder (R), NJ, *18*
Boardroom Consultants/Kenny Kindler Tholke (R), NY, *19*
Bonnell Assoc. Ltd. (R), CT, *19*
Boone-Scaturro Assoc., Inc. (C), GA, *269*
Born & Bicknell, Inc. (C), FL, *270*
Boston Professional Search, Inc. (C), MA, *270*
Boyden (R), NY, *20*
Brandywine Consulting Group (R), PA, *22*
Brandywine Management Group (R), MD, *22*
Brethet, Barnum & Assoc., Inc. (C), ON, *273*
Bristol Assoc., Inc. (C), CA, *274*
Brookman Associates (C), NY, *274*
Bernard E. Brooks & Assoc., Inc. (R), SC, *24*
D. Brown & Assoc., Inc. (C), OR, *275*
Brownstone Sales & Marketing Group, Inc. (C), NY, *275*
BRW Search (C), MN, *275*
Buckman/Enochs & Assoc., Inc. (C), OH, *276*
Joseph R. Burns & Assoc., Inc. (R), NJ, *25*
Butterfield & Co. Int'l., Inc. (C), HI, *277*
C/R Associates (C), NY, *278*
Cadillac Assoc. (C), CA, *278*
Lee Calhoon & Co., Inc. (R), PA, *26*
Caliber Associates (R), PA, *27*
California Management Search (C), CA, *279*
Cambridge Group Ltd. - Exec. Search Div. (C), CT, *279*
The Cambridge Group Ltd. (C), CT, *280*
Cambridge Management Planning (R), ON, *27*
Canny, Bowen Inc. (R), NY, *27*
The Cantor Concern, Inc. (R), NY, *28*
Cantrell & Assoc. (C), FL, *280*
Caplan Assoc., Inc. (R), NJ, *28*
The Caplan-Taylor Group (R), CA, *28*
Career Counseling Ltd. (C.C.L.) (C), NY, *282*
Career Profiles (C), NH, *283*
Career Search Group (C), FL, *283*
Career Strategies, Inc. (C), CA, *283*
Carlson & Czeswik (R), MN, *30*
The Carlyle Group, Ltd. (R), IL, *30*
Carter, Lavoie Associates (C), RI, *285*
Carter McKenzie, Inc. (C), NJ, *285*
Carter/MacKay (C), NJ, *285*
Caruso & Assoc., Inc. (R), FL, *31*
Casey & Assoc., Inc. (C), TX, *286*
The Cassie Group (R), NJ, *31*
Michael J. Cavanagh & Assoc. Inc. (R), ON, *31*
CEC Associates (R), MA, *32*
Cejka Healthcare Executive Search Services (CHESS) (R), MO, *32*
Cemco, Ltd. (C), IL, *286*
The Century Group (C), CA, *287*
The Century Group (C), KS, *287*
Chamberlain Assoc. (C), GA, *288*
David Chambers & Assoc., Inc. (R), CT, *32*
Vickers Chambless Managed Search (C), GA, *288*
Cheney Associates (C), CT, *290*
Chicago Legal Search, Ltd. (C), IL, *290*
Christian & Timbers, Inc. (R), OH, *34*
Christopher and Long (C), MO, *291*
Circlewood Search Group, Inc. (C), MI, *291*
Cizek Assoc., Inc. (R), AZ, *35*
Ken Clark Int'l. (R), NJ, *36*
CMS, Inc. (C), NH, *293*
COBA Executive Search (R), CO, *36*
Dean M. Coe Assoc. (R), MA, *37*
The Coelyn Group (R), CA, *37*
Cole, Warren & Long, Inc. (R), PA, *37*
Computer Network Resources, Inc. (C), CA, *295*
The Comwell Company, Inc. (C), NJ, *296*
Conard Associates, Inc. (R), NH, *39*
Concorde Staff Source Inc. (C), WI, *296*
The Consortium (C), NY, *296*
Consulting Resource Group, Inc. (C), GA, *297*
Continental Research Search, Inc. (C), WI, *298*
Cook Assoc. Int'l., Inc. (C), TN, *298*
P. G. Cook Assoc. (R), TN, *40*
Cornerstone Resources, Inc. (C), OK, *299*
Cornerstone Search Assoc. Inc. (C), MA, *299*
Corporate Leadership Strategies, Inc. (R), NH, *41*
Corporate Recruiters Inc. (C), PA, *300*
Corporate Search, Inc. (C), NY, *301*
Corso, Mizgala + French (R), ON, *42*
J. D. Cotter Search Inc. (C), OH, *302*
Creative Management Strategies, Ltd. (R), NY, *42*
CRI Professional Search (C), CA, *303*
The Cris Group, Inc. (R), NY, *42*
Criterion Executive Search, Inc. (C), FL, *303*
Judith Cushman & Assoc. (R), WA, *44*
The Custer Group, Inc. (R), TN, *44*
Cypress Int'l., Inc. (R), FL, *45*
D.A.L. Associates, Inc. (R), CT, *45*
The Danielson Group, Inc. (C), TX, *306*
Alan Darling Consulting (R), VT, *46*

Daudlin, De Beaupre & Co., Inc. (R), MI, *46*
Davies, Park (R), AB, *46*
Davis-Smith, Inc. (C), MI, *309*
The Dayton Group, Ltd. (C), NY, *309*
DBL Associates (C), CA, *309*
DeCorrevont & Assoc. (C), IL, *310*
Deeco Int'l. (C), UT, *310*
Delacore Resources (C), MN, *310*
Delta Medical Search Assoc. (C), OH, *310*
Delta ProSearch (C), PA, *311*
Derhak Ireland & Partners Ltd. (R), ON, *48*
Desktop Staffing, Inc. (C), IL, *311*
Despres & Associates (C), IL, *311*
Development Resource Group (R), NY, *48*
Development Search Specialists (R), MN, *49*
Rob Dey Executive Search (R), FL, *49*
Roger Dietsch & Assoc. (C), MN, *312*
Diversified Health Search (R), PA, *52*
Diversified Search, Inc. (R), PA, *52*
DNA Search, Inc. (C), CA, *313*
Donini Assoc. (R), VA, *54*
Dotson & Assoc. (R), NY, *54*
Cal Douglas Executive Search, Inc. (R), PA, *54*
Drew Assoc. Int'l. (R), NJ, *54*
DRZ Medical Recruiters (C), CO, *315*
DS&A (Doug Sears & Assoc.) (C), FL, *315*
M. Dunbar & Assoc. (C), TX, *316*
Dunhill Professional Search of Tampa (C), FL, *320*
Dunhill Staffing Systems (C), NC, *321*
Dunhill Executive Search of Brown County (C), IN, *321*
Dunhill Professional Search of Wilkes-Barre/Scranton, Inc. (C), PA, *322*
C. A. Durakis Assoc., Inc. (R), MD, *55*
E O Technical (C), CT, *324*
EA Plus, Inc. (C), TX, *325*
Eagle Consulting Group Inc. (C), TX, *325*
J. M. Eagle Partners Ltd. (C), WI, *325*
Eagle Research, Inc. (C), NJ, *325*
EDI, Inc. (C), MD, *326*
EDP Staffing Solutions, Inc. (C), AR, *327*
Richard A. Eisner & Co., LLP (R), NY, *57*
William J. Elam & Assoc. (R), NE, *58*
Elite Medical Search (C), GA, *328*
Ellis & Associates (C), HI, *328*
The Ellsworth Group (C), NY, *329*
Emerging Medical Technologies, Inc. (C), CO, *329*
Emerging Technology Search (C), GA, *329*
Emmett Executive Search, Inc. (C), NY, *330*
EMN/Witt/Kieffer (R), MA, *59*
ENI (R), CT, *59*
Ensearch Management Consultants (C), CA, *331*
Entelechy Group Ltd. (R), MD, *59*
Erlanger Assoc. (R), CT, *60*
Ethos Consulting, Inc. (R), CA, *61*
ETI Search Int'l. (R), GA, *61*
Excalibur Human Resources, Inc. (R), NJ, *61*
Executive Dimensions (R), NY, *62*
Executive Manning Corp. (R), FL, *63*
Executive Recruitment Specialists, Inc. (R), NC, *63*
Executive Resource Systems (C), CA, *335*
Executive Solutions (R), MN, *64*
The Executive Source (C), SA, *337*
eXsource Inc. (C), SC, *337*
Raymond L. Extract & Assoc. (R), CA, *64*
Eyler Assoc., Inc. (R), IA, *64*
Fallstaff Search (C), MD, *338*
Dorothy W. Farnath & Assoc., Inc. (C), NJ, *338*
Faro Consultants Int'l. (C), VA, *338*
James Feerst & Assoc., Inc. (C), AZ, *339*
Fidelity Search Group, Inc. (R), PA, *66*
First Advisory Services Int'l., Inc. (R), MD, *67*
Howard Fischer Assoc. Int'l., Inc. (R), PA, *67*
Fisher-Todd Assoc. (C), NY, *341*
James L. Fisk & Assoc. (C), MO, *342*
Fitzgerald Associates (R), MA, *68*
Flexible Resources, Inc. (C), CT, *342*
Flynn, Hannock, Inc. (R), CT, *69*
Foley Proctor Yoskowitz (R), NJ, *69*
The Ford Group, Inc. (R), PA, *69*
F-O-R-T-U-N-E Personnel Consultants of Troy, Inc. (C), MI, *347*
Fortune Personnel Consultants of Raleigh, Inc. (C), NC, *348*
Foster Partners (R), NY, *70*
Fought, Jameson Assoc. (C), IL, *351*
Franklin Allen Consultants, Ltd. (R), NY, *71*
The Franklin Search Group, Inc./Medzilla (R), WA, *71*
C. F. Furr & Co. (R), NC, *72*
Furst Group/MPI (R), IL, *72*
Gable Healthcare Group, Inc. (R), FL, *73*
Gahan Assoc. (R), NY, *73*
The Gammill Group, Inc. (C), OH, *354*
Gans, Gans & Assoc., Inc. (R), FL, *74*
Garb & Assoc., Legal Placement (C), CA, *354*
W. N. Garbarini & Assoc. (R), NJ, *74*
Garrett Assoc. Inc. (R), GA, *75*
Garrison-Randall, Inc. (R), CA, *75*
Genesis Consulting Partners (R), PA, *76*
Genesis Personnel Service, Inc. (C), OH, *356*
Gielow Assoc., Inc. (R), WI, *76*
Gilbert & Van Campen Int'l. (R), NY, *76*
John Gilbert Co. (C), TX, *357*
Gilbert Tweed Assoc. Inc. (R), NY, *76*
Gilmore & Assoc. (C), CA, *357*
The Glazin Group (R), BC, *77*
Global 1000 Int'l. Services (C), CA, *358*
Global HealthCare Partners (R), IL, *78*
Global Resources Group (R), CA, *78*
Barry M. Gold & Co. (C), CA, *359*
Goldman+Bell, LLC (C), NY, *360*
Joseph Goldring & Assoc. Inc. (C), MI, *360*
The Goodman Group (R), CA, *79*
Goodrich & Sherwood Assoc., Inc. (R), NY, *79*
Gould, McCoy & Chadick, Inc. (R), NY, *80*
Robert Graham Assoc. (R), RI, *81*
Robert Grant Assoc., Inc. (C), CA, *361*
Grant Cooper & Assoc., Inc. (R), MO, *81*
J. B. Groner Executive Search, Inc. (C), DE, *363*
Groton Planning Group (R), ME, *82*
Growth Consultants of America (R), MI, *82*
Guidry & East Healthcare Search Consultants (R), TX, *83*
William Guy & Assoc., Inc. (R), CA, *84*
H R Solutions, Inc. (C), MO, *365*
Hadley Associates, Inc. (C), NJ, *365*
Halbrecht Lieberman Assoc., Inc. (R), CT, *84*
K. C. Hale, Inc. (R), CT, *85*
R. C. Handel Assoc. Inc. (R), CT, *85*
Hanley & Assoc. (R), FL, *86*
Harbor Consultants Int'l., Inc. (C), VA, *368*
Harper Associates (C), MI, *369*
Harrington & O'Brien Inc. (C), NH, *369*
Hartman & Barnette (R), VA, *87*
Bruce W. Haupt Assoc. (R), DC, *88*
Hayman Daugherty Assoc., Inc. (C), GA, *370*
The Haystack Group, Inc. (R), ME, *88*
HCI Corp. (C), IL, *371*
Health Care Dimensions (C), CO, *371*
Health Care Plus, Inc. (C), MD, *371*
Health Network USA (C), TX, *371*
Health Search (C), CA, *371*
Health Search, Inc. (C), KS, *371*
Healthcare Executive Recruiters, Inc. (C), CA, *372*
Healthcare Management Resources, Inc. (R), GA, *89*
Healthcare Recruiters Int'l. Orange County (C), CA, *372*
Healthcare Recruiters of the Rockies, Inc. (C), CO, *372*
Healthcare Recruiters of Indiana (C), IN, *372*
Healthcare Recruiters Int'l. Bay Area (C), CA, *372*
Healthcare Recruiters Int'l. - Alabama (C), AL, *372*
Healthcare Recruiters Int'l. - Los Angeles (C), CA, *372*
Healthcare Recruiters Int'l. Philadelphia (C), NJ, *373*
Healthcare Recruiters International-NY/NJ (C), NJ, *373*
Healthcare Recruiters of New England (C), MA, *373*
Healthcare Recruiters of New Orleans (C), LA, *373*
Healthcare Recruiters Int'l - Minnesota, Inc. (C), MN, *373*
Healthcare Recruiters of New York, Inc. (C), NY, *373*
Healthcare Recruiters Int'l. - Pittsburgh (C), PA, *373*
Healthcare Recruiters of Midsouth (C), TN, *373*
Healthcare Recruiters - Northwest (C), WA, *374*
Healthcare Recruiters of Dallas (C), TX, *374*
Healthcare Resources Group (C), OK, *374*
Healthcare Search Associates (C), CA, *374*
HealthSearch Assoc. (C), MD, *374*
F. P. Healy & Co., Inc. (R), NY, *89*
Heartland National Medical Search (C), IL, *374*
Heath/Norton Assoc., Inc. (R), NY, *89*

Hedlund Corp. (C), IL, *375*
Bruce Henry Assoc. Inc. (R), CA, *91*
Hersher Assoc., Ltd. (R), IL, *92*
Hintz Associates (C), NY, *378*
Hitchens & Foster, Inc. (C), MO, *379*
HLR Consulting (C), NY, *379*
Hockett Associates, Inc. (R), CA, *94*
Holland & Assoc., Inc. (R), MI, *94*
Home Health & Hospital Recruiters, Inc. (C), GA, *380*
Horizon Medical Search of NH (C), NH, *381*
Hospitality Int'l. (C), NY, *381*
HR Consultants (C), GA, *382*
The HRM Group, Inc. (C), AL, *382*
Huff Assoc. (R), NJ, *98*
Hughes & Assoc. (C), TX, *383*
The Human Resource Department Ltd. (R), OH, *98*
Human Resource Solutions (R), TX, *98*
Human Resource Technologies, Inc. (R), IL, *99*
Hunter Douglas Group, Inc. (R), IL, *99*
Hunter Int'l., Inc. (R), CT, *100*
The Hutton Group, Inc. (C), FL, *386*
IMA Search, Inc. (R), NY, *101*
Impact Search & Strategies (C), PA, *387*
Information Systems Professionals (C), NC, *388*
Ingram & Aydelotte, Inc. (R), NY, *101*
Innovative Healthcare Services, Inc. (C), GA, *389*
innovativestaffsearch (C), TX, *389*
Insurance Personnel Resources, Inc. (C), GA, *390*
Insurance Search (C), TX, *390*
Intech Summit Group, Inc. (R), CA, *102*
Integrity Search, Inc. (R), PA, *102*
IntelliSource, inc. (C), PA, *391*
Interactive Search Assoc. (C), PA, *391*
Interim Financial Solutions - Mid-Atlantic Region (C), MD, *392*
International Business Partners (C), ON, *392*
International Management Services Inc. (R), IL, *102*
International Pro Sourcing, Inc. (C), PA, *393*
Interquest, Inc. (R), NY, *103*
Isaacson, Miller (R), MA, *104*
ISC of Cincinnati Inc. (C), OH, *394*
ISC of Houston, Inc. (C), TX, *394*
J. Robert Scott (R), MA, *104*
J.D.G. y Asociados, S.A. de C.V. (R), SO, *104*
J.J. & H., Ltd. (R), IL, *104*
Jackson & Coker (C), GA, *396*
Jacobson Assoc. (C), IL, *396*
JAG Group (R), MO, *105*
James Moore & Assoc. (C), CA, *397*
JDC Assoc. (C), NY, *397*
Jefferson-Ross Assoc. Inc. (C), PA, *398*
John Jay & Co. (C), ME, *399*
J. M. Johnson & Assoc. (C), MN, *399*
Johnson Smith & Knisely (R), NY, *107*
Roye Johnston Assoc., Inc. (C), CA, *400*
Jones Management Co. (R), CT, *108*
Jordon & Jordon, Inc. (R), PA, *108*
J. M. Joseph Assoc. (R), NJ, *109*
Joseph Consulting, Inc. (C), FL, *401*
JPM International (C), CA, *401*
Judd Associates (R), NJ, *109*
Karp & Assoc. (C), FL, *403*
Katelyn Partners (C), FL, *404*
Kaye/Bassman Int'l. Corp. (R), TX, *110*
A.T. Kearney Executive Search (R), IL, *111*
Kendall & Davis Co., Inc. (C), MO, *405*
Kensington Int'l., Inc. (R), IL, *113*
Kensington International (R), CA, *113*
Kent & Assoc. (R), OH, *113*
Kincaid Group Inc. (KGI) (C), TX, *406*
Kincannon & Reed (R), VA, *114*
Kip Williams, Inc. (R), NY, *115*
Kiradjieff & Goode, Inc. (R), MA, *115*
The Kleinstein Group, Inc. (R), NJ, *116*
Lee Koehn Assoc., Inc. (R), OR, *116*
Koontz, Jeffries & Assoc., Inc. (R), FL, *117*
Korban Associates (R), PA, *117*
Korn/Ferry Int'l. (R), NY, *117*
The J. Kovach Group (R), PA, *119*
Kressenberg Assoc. (C), TX, *409*
Kuhn Med-Tech (C), CA, *409*
Laguzza Assoc., Ltd. (R), NY, *122*
Lake Medical Associates (C), ME, *411*
Lam Assoc. (C), HI, *411*
The Langford Search, Inc. (C), AL, *412*
Lawrence L. Lapham, Inc. (R), NY, *124*
Larsen, Whitney, Blecksmith & Zilliacus, Inc. (R), CA, *125*
Larson & Trent Assoc. (C), TN, *413*
Larson, Katz & Young, Inc. (C), VA, *413*
Lauer, Sbarbaro Assoc., EMA Partners Int'l. (R), IL, *126*
LaVallee & Associates (C), NC, *413*
Lear & Assoc., Inc. (C), FL, *415*
Reynolds Lebus Assoc. (C), AZ, *415*
Ledbetter/Davidson Int'l., Inc. (R), NY, *127*
Lehman McLeskey (R), TX, *128*
AG Lennox & Assoc. (R), AB, *128*
Levison Search Assoc. (R), CA, *129*
The Levton Group Inc. (R), ON, *129*
Lewis & Blank Int'l. (R), CA, *129*
Lewis Consulting Service (C), IL, *417*
Pat Licata & Assoc. (C), NC, *417*
LJ Networking, Inc. (C), MD, *418*
Lloyd Prescott & Churchill, Inc. (R), FL, *130*
Lloyd Prescott Assoc., Inc. (C), FL, *418*
Loderman & Costello (C), GA, *419*
The Logan Group, Inc. (R), MO, *131*
Logic Assoc., Inc. (C), NY, *419*
Longshore + Simmons (R), PA, *131*
Louis Search Group, Inc. (C), NJ, *420*
The Macdonald Group, Inc. (R), NJ, *133*
The Mackenzie Group (R), MD, *133*
MacNaughton Assoc. (R), CA, *133*
Maczkov-Biosciences, Inc. (R), CA, *133*
The Madeira Group (R), PA, *133*
Managed Care Consultants (C), AZ, *423*
Managed Care Resources (C), TX, *424*
Management & Human Resources (R), MA, *134*
Management Advisors Int'l., Inc. (C), NC, *424*
Management Assoc. (C), MD, *424*
Management Recruiters of Mobile Co., Inc. (C), AL, *438*
Management Recruiters of Little Rock (C), AR, *439*
Management Recruiters of Berkeley (C), CA, *439*
Management Recruiters of Roseville (C), CA, *441*
Management Recruiters of Monterey (C), CA, *441*
Management Recruiters of Colorado, Inc. (C), CO, *442*
Management Recruiters of Anna Maria Island (C), FL, *443*
Management Recruiters of Clearwater (C), FL, *443*
Management Recruiters of Tampa North (C), FL, *444*
Management Recruiters of Columbus, Inc. (C), GA, *445*
Management Recruiters of Atlanta North, Inc. (C), GA, *446*
Management Recruiters of Indianapolis-North (C), IN, *448*
Management Recruiters of Topeka, Inc. (C), KS, *449*
Management Recruiters of Washington, DC Inc. (C), MD, *450*
Management Recruiters of Frederick, Inc. (C), MD, *450*
Management Recruiters of North Oakland County, Inc. (C), MI, *452*
Management Recruiters of Gramercy, Inc. (C), NY, *455*
Management Recruiters of Kinston (C), NC, *456*
Management Recruiters of Boone (C), NC, *456*
Management Recruiters of Cleveland (C), OH, *457*
Management Recruiters of Dayton, Inc. (C), OH, *457*
Management Recruiters of Youngstown (C), OH, *458*
Management Recruiters of Oklahoma City (C), OK, *458*
Management Recruiters of Pittsburgh (C), PA, *459*
Management Recruiters of Westmoreland County, Inc. (C), PA, *459*
Management Recruiters of Pittsburgh-North, Inc. (C), PA, *460*
Management Recruiters of North Charleston (C), SC, *460*
Management Recruiters of Myrtle Beach, Inc. (C), SC, *460*
Management Recruiters of Chattanooga-Brainerd, Inc. (C), TN, *461*
Management Recruiters of Georgetown (C), SC, *461*
Management Recruiters of Austin (C), TX, *462*
Management Recruiters - Friendswood (C), TX, *462*
Management Recruiters of Houston (C), TX, *462*
Management Recruiters of San Antonio - North (C), TX, *463*
Management Recruiters of Lubbock (C), TX, *463*

INDUSTRIES

Management Recruiters - Piedmont (C), VA, *464*
Management Recruiters of Salt Lake City (C), UT, *464*
Management Recruiters of Spokane (C), WA, *465*
Management Recruiters of Seattle (C), WA, *465*
Management Recruiters of Janesville, Inc. (C), WI, *466*
Management Resources (C), TX, *467*
Management Search Assoc., Inc. (C), GA, *467*
Mangieri/Solutions LLC (C), CT, *468*
Mankuta Gallagher & Assoc., Inc. (C), FL, *468*
Manuso, Alexander & Associates, Inc. (R), NY, *135*
Marcus & Assoc. (C), NY, *469*
Marentz & Co. (C), TX, *469*
J. L. Mark Assoc., Inc. (R), CO, *135*
Mark Stanley & Co./EMA Partners International (R), FL, *136*
Marketing Resources (C), MA, *470*
Marsar & Co., Inc. (C), FL, *471*
J. Martin & Assoc. (R), CA, *137*
Martin Partners, L.L.C. (R), IL, *137*
Marvel Consultants, Inc. (C), OH, *472*
Louis Thomas Masterson & Co. (R), OH, *138*
Matte Consulting Group Inc. (R), QE, *138*
Matthews & Stephens Assoc., Inc. (C), CT, *472*
The Mayes Group, Ltd. (R), PA, *139*
McCooe & Assoc., Inc. (R), NJ, *140*
McCormack & Assoc. (R), CA, *140*
McCormack & Farrow (R), CA, *140*
McGrath & Assoc., Inc. (R), NJ, *141*
McHale & Assoc. (R), WA, *141*
McKavis Assoc. (C), CA, *475*
The McKinnon Management Group Inc. (C), ON, *475*
MDR Associates, Inc. (C), FL, *476*
Med-Ex Services (C), OH, *476*
Medfall Inc. (C), ON, *476*
Medical Executive Recruiters (C), CA, *477*
Medical Executive Search Assoc., Inc. (C), AZ, *477*
Medical Recruiters Exchange (C), AZ, *477*
Medical Recruiters Inc. (C), MO, *477*
Medical Search of America, Inc. (C), GA, *477*
Medicorp, Inc. (C), MO, *477*
MedPro Personnel, Inc. (C), GA, *478*
MedSearch Resources, Inc. (C), FL, *478*
Medserve & Assoc. Inc. (C), MD, *478*
MedXec USA, Inc. (C), FL, *478*
Martin H. Meisel Assoc., Inc. (R), NY, *143*
Juan Menefee & Assoc. (C), IL, *478*
Meng, Finseth & Assoc., Inc. (R), CA, *143*
Mercedes & Co., Inc. (R), MA, *143*
Merlin Int'l. Inc. (C), NJ, *479*
Meyer Assoc., Inc. (R), GA, *144*
MGA Executive Search (C), FL, *480*
E. J. Michaels, Ltd. (C), NY, *481*
Millennium Search Group, Inc. (R), CA, *144*
Mitchell Martin Inc. (C), NY, *483*
MIXTEC Group (R), CA, *145*
Moffitt Int'l., Inc. (R), NC, *146*
Molloy Partners (R), NY, *146*
Montgomery West (R), CA, *146*
Thomas R. Moore Executive Search (R), TX, *146*
Moore Research Assoc. (R), NJ, *147*
The Morley Group (C), IN, *486*
MPA Executive Search Inc. (R), QE, *148*
MSA Executive Search (R), MO, *148*
MSI Int'l. (C), GA, *486*
MTA Partners (R), TX, *148*
Pamela L. Mulligan, Inc. (R), NH, *149*
R. F. Mulvaney & Assoc., Inc. (R), MO, *149*
Murphy Partners Int'l. (R), IL, *150*
Nadzam, Lusk, Horgan & Assoc., Inc. (R), CA, *150*
National Career Search (C), AZ, *489*
National Register Columbus Inc. (C), OH, *490*
National Search, Inc.r (C), FL, *490*
NDI Services (R), MI, *151*
The Neil Michael Group, Inc./Global Partners (R), NY, *151*
The NEIS Corp., Inc. (C), FL, *491*
Networking Unlimited of NH, Inc. (C), NH, *491*
New Dawn Employment Search (C), CA, *491*
New Dimensions in Technology, Inc. (C), MA, *492*
New World Healthcare Solutions, Inc. (R), NY, *151*
Nino Recruiting & Staffing, Inc. (C), TX, *493*
Ira Z. Nitzberg (C), NY, *493*
J. L. Nixon Consulting (C), TX, *493*
The Nolan Group (C), CA, *494*
Noll Human Resource Services (C), NE, *494*
Paul Winston Norman & Assoc. (R), IL, *152*
Norman Broadbent Int'l., Inc. (R), NY, *152*
The Normyle/Erstling Health Search Group (C), NJ, *494*
NRI Staffing Resources (C), DC, *496*
O'Connor Resources (C), TX, *497*
O'Neill Group (C), NJ, *498*
Ober & Company (R), CA, *155*
Odell & Assoc., Inc. (C), TX, *498*
The Odessa Group (R), CA, *155*
Oliver & Rozner Assoc., Inc. (R), NY, *155*
Olsen/Clark (R), WA, *156*
Omni Search, Inc. (C), CA, *499*
Orion Int'l. Consulting Group, Inc. (C), NC, *499*
The Oxford Group (C), TX, *500*
P R Management Consultants, Inc. (C), NJ, *500*
P.A.R. Assoc., Inc. (R), MA, *158*
Pacific Advisory Service, Inc. (C), IL, *501*
Pacific Finance Search, Inc. (C), CA, *501*
Pacific Search Group, Inc. (C), CA, *501*
The Pailin Group Professional Search Consultants (R), TX, *158*
The Park Group & Assoc., Inc. (C), MD, *502*
Parker Page Group (C), FL, *503*
Partners Resource Group (C), VA, *504*
The Partnership Group (R), NJ, *160*
Carolyn Smith Paschal Int'l. (R), CA, *160*
Pathfinders (C), CA, *504*
Patriot Assoc. (C), PA, *505*
Paul-Tittle Assoc., Inc. (R), VA, *161*
PCD Partners (R), PA, *161*
Pearson & Assoc., Inc. (C), AZ, *506*
Penn Associates (R), PA, *161*
People Management Mid-South, LLC (R), TN, *162*
People Management Northeast, Inc. (R), CT, *162*
Perfect Search, Inc. (C), FL, *507*
The Personnel Group, Inc. (R), MN, *163*
Personnel Incorporated (C), IA, *508*
The Personnel Network, Inc. (C), SC, *508*
Personnel Unlimited/Executive Search (C), WA, *509*
Petro Staff Int'l. (C), AB, *509*
J. R. Phillip & Assoc., Inc. (R), CA, *164*
Phillips & Assoc. (R), MA, *164*
Physician Associates (C), HI, *511*
Physician Executive Management Center (R), FL, *164*
Physician Recruiting Services, Inc. (C), MO, *511*
Physicians Search®, Inc. (C), CA, *511*
Picard Int'l., Ltd. (R), NY, *164*
Pierce & Assoc. (C), CA, *512*
Plante & Moran, LLP (R), MI, *165*
Plemmons Assoc., Inc. (R), GA, *165*
The Pollack Group (C), ON, *514*
Polson & Co., Inc. (R), MN, *166*
David Powell, Inc. (R), CA, *166*
Practice Dynamics, Inc. (C), TX, *515*
Preferred Professional Recruiters (C), TX, *516*
Premier Business Advisors (C), PA, *516*
Premier Healthcare Recruiters, Inc. (C), MI, *516*
Presley Consultants, Inc. (C), CA, *517*
Prestige Inc. (C), WI, *517*
Preston-Hunter, Inc. (R), IL, *167*
PricewaterhouseCoopers Executive Search (R), ON, *168*
Primary Care Service Corp. (C), GA, *518*
Princeton Search Partners, Inc. (R), NJ, *169*
Prior/Martech Assoc., Inc. (R), WA, *169*
Priority Executive Search (C), FL, *518*
PRO, Inc./Professional Recruiting Offices, Inc. (C), CA, *519*
Professional Healthcare Search & Consultants, Inc. (C), CA, *520*
Professional Personnel Consultants, Inc. (C), MI, *521*
Professional Placement Assoc., Inc. (C), NY, *521*
Professional Recruiters, Inc. (C), PA, *521*
Professional Research Services, Inc. (R), IL, *169*
The Professional Sales Search Co., Inc. (C), WA, *522*
Professional Selection Services (R), GA, *169*
Professionals in Recruiting Co. (C), TN, *523*
ProSearch, Inc. (C), PA, *524*
Protocol Inc. (C), CA, *525*
Questor Consultants, Inc. (C), PA, *527*

Quetico Corp. (R), TX, *170*
Quigley Assoc. (R), MD, *170*
Quiring Assoc., Inc. (C), IN, *527*
Quirk-Corporon & Assoc., Inc. (C), WI, *527*
R & L Assoc., Ltd. (R), NY, *170*
Ramming & Assoc., Inc. (C), NJ, *528*
Lea Randolph & Assoc., Inc. (C), TX, *529*
Ray & Berndtson (R), TX, *171*
Ray & Berndtson/Lovas Stanley (R), ON, *172*
Raymond Karsan Assoc. (C), PA, *529*
Recruiters Professional Network - Fairview (C), MO, *531*
Recruitment Specialists, Inc. (C), MD, *532*
Reece & Mruk Partners/EMA Partners Int'l. (R), MA, *173*
Reeder & Assoc., Ltd. (R), GA, *173*
Reeve & Assoc. (C), CT, *533*
The Regis Group, Ltd. (R), GA, *174*
Retail Recruiters/Spectrum Consultants, Inc. (C), PA, *535*
Retis Assoc., Inc. (C), IL, *535*
S. Reyman & Assoc., Ltd. (R), IL, *176*
Russell Reynolds Assoc., Inc. (R), NY, *176*
Reynolds Partners (R), NY, *177*
RHI Consulting (C), VA, *536*
RHS Assoc. (C), AL, *536*
Rice Cohen Int'l. (R), PA, *178*
Richard, Wayne & Roberts (C), TX, *536*
The Richards Group (C), PA, *536*
Right/McKee Consulting Group (C), TX, *537*
Ritt-Ritt & Assoc., Inc. (C), IL, *537*
Roberson & Co. (C), AZ, *538*
Norman Roberts & Assoc., Inc. (R), CA, *179*
Roberts Ryan & Bentley, Inc. (R), MD, *179*
Bruce Robinson Assoc. (R), NJ, *180*
Robinson-Robinson & Assoc., Inc. (C), MN, *539*
Rodgers, Ramsey, Inc. (C), TX, *540*
Craig Roe & Assoc., LLC (C), MD, *540*
Roevin Technical People (C), ON, *540*
The Rogan Group, Inc. (C), CA, *541*
Rogish Assoc., Inc. (C), OH, *541*
Rojek Marketing Group, Inc. (R), OH, *181*
Roll International (C), TX, *541*
Rollo Assoc. (R), CA, *181*
Romac Int'l., Inc. (C), FL, *542*
The Rose Search Group, Inc. (C), NC, *545*
Roth Young Personnel Service of Detroit, Inc. (C), MI, *546*
Roth Young of Chicago (C), IL, *546*
Roth Young of Pittsburgh (C), PA, *546*
Roth Young Executive Recruiters (C), MN, *546*
David Rowe & Assoc., Inc. (R), IL, *182*
Royal Assoc. (C), CA, *547*
The Rubicon Group (C), AZ, *547*
The Rubinic Consulting Group (C), OH, *548*
Rust & Assoc., Inc. (R), IL, *183*
S. C. Int'l., Ltd. (C), IL, *550*
Sales Builders, Inc. (R), VA, *183*
Sales Consultants of Scottsdale, Inc. (C), AZ, *556*
Sales Consultants Int'l. of Oakland (C), CA, *556*
Sales Consultants of Sacramento (C), CA, *556*
Sales Consultants of Denver (C), CO, *557*
Sales Consultants of Western McHenry County (C), IL, *558*
Sales Consultants of Indianapolis (C), IN, *558*
Sales Consultants of Auburn Hills (C), MI, *559*
Sales Consultants of Bangor, Inc. (C), ME, *559*
Sales Consultants of Cincinnati (C), OH, *561*
Sales Consultants of Austin, Inc. (C), TX, *562*
Sales Consultants of Pittsburgh (C), PA, *562*
Salzmann Gay Assoc., Inc. (R), PA, *184*
Sampson Medical Search (C), CA, *564*
George D. Sandel Assoc. (C), MA, *565*
Sanders Management Assoc., Inc. (C), NJ, *565*
Sanford Rose Assoc. - Lake Forest (R), IL, *184*
Sanford Rose Assoc. - Laguna Beach (C), CA, *565*
Sanford Rose Assoc. - Clearwater (C), FL, *566*
Sanford Rose Assoc. - Louisville (C), KY, *567*
Sanford Rose Assoc. - Carmel, IN (C), IN, *567*
Sanford Rose Assoc. - Columbia (C), SC, *570*
Santangelo Consultants Inc. (C), NY, *571*
Savoy Partners, Ltd. (R), DC, *184*
Schenck & Assoc. SC (C), WI, *572*
A.D. Schiff & Assoc., Ltd. (C), IL, *572*
Schneider, Hill & Spangler, Inc. (R), PA, *185*
Schulenburg & Assoc. (C), GA, *572*
Schuyler Assoc., Ltd. (R), GA, *185*
Schuyler, Baker & Parker, Inc. (R), GA, *185*
G. L. Schwartz & Assoc., Inc. (C), GA, *572*
Scott Douglas Inc. (C), CA, *573*
Scott Sibley Assoc. (C), NY, *573*
The Search Alliance, Inc. (R), FL, *186*
Search America, Inc. (C), PA, *573*
Search Assoc., Inc. (C), CA, *574*
The Search Committee (C), MD, *574*
Search Consultants, LLC (C), MD, *575*
Search Masters Int'l. (R), AZ, *187*
Search Masters, USA (C), FL, *576*
Search Research Assoc., Inc. (R), MA, *187*
SearchCom, Inc. (R), TX, *187*
Searchforce, Inc. (R), FL, *187*
Searchworks, Inc. (C), FL, *577*
J. R. Seehusen Assoc., Inc. (R), IA, *188*
Selective Staffing (C), CA, *579*
Robert Sellery Assoc., Ltd. (R), DC, *188*
Sensible Solutions, Inc. (R), IL, *188*
Sherriff & Assoc. (C), KS, *580*
Shiell Personnel (C), LA, *580*
Michael Shirley Assoc. Inc. (R), KS, *190*
The Shorr Group (R), IL, *190*
Siger & Assoc., LLC (C), CT, *581*
Daniel A. Silverstein Assoc. Inc. (R), FL, *191*
D. J. Simpson Assoc. Inc. (R), ON, *191*
Ruth Sklar Assoc., Inc. (RSA Executive Search) (R), NY, *192*
Skupsky & Assoc. (C), CO, *582*
Christopher Smallhorn Executive Recruiting, Inc. (R), MA, *193*
Howard W. Smith Assoc. (R), CT, *193*
Snelling Search (C), AL, *585*
Snelling Search (C), LA, *586*
Snelling Search Recruiters (C), NC, *586*
Snyder & Co. (R), CT, *194*
Andrea Sobel & Assoc., Inc. (C), CA, *586*
Sockwell & Assoc. (R), NC, *194*
Solomon-Page Healthcare Group (R), NY, *195*
Solutions Group (R), AL, *195*
Souder & Assoc. (R), VA, *195*
Southwestern Professional Services (C), TN, *588*
Spear-Izzo Assoc., LLC (C), PA, *588*
SpencerStuart (R), NY, *196*
Stanton Chase Int'l. (R), MD, *198*
STAT Search (C), NH, *592*
Sterling Int'l. (R), NJ, *200*
Daniel Stern & Assoc. (C), PA, *592*
Michael Stern Assoc., Inc./Euram (R), ON, *200*
Steven Douglas Assoc. (C), FL, *593*
The Stevenson Group, Inc. (N.J.) (R), NJ, *200*
The Stewart Group (C), FL, *593*
Stewart, Stein & Scott, Ltd. (R), MN, *200*
The Stonebridge Group (C), PA, *594*
Strategic Executives, Inc. (R), CT, *202*
Strategic Resources Biotechnology & Medical Group (C), WA, *595*
StratfordGroup (R), OH, *203*
J. Stroll Assoc., Inc. (R), CT, *203*
Stroman Int'l., Inc. (R), CO, *204*
Sudina Search, Inc. (C), MD, *596*
Sullivan & Assoc. (R), MI, *204*
Synapse Human Resource Consulting Group (R), TX, *205*
Synergy 2000 (C), DC, *597*
The Synergy Organization (R), PA, *205*
Systems Search (C), IL, *599*
T. H. Hunter, Inc. (C), MN, *599*
Tarbex (C), DC, *599*
Tax Network Resources, Inc. (C), NY, *600*
Carl J. Taylor & Co. (R), TX, *207*
Team One Partners, Inc. (C), GA, *600*
TeleManagement Search (C), NY, *605*
Telford, Adams & Alexander (R), CA, *208*
Thomas Lyle & Co. (C), IL, *606*
Thomas Mangum Co. (R), CA, *208*
Thomas Resource Group (R), CA, *209*
The Tidewater Group Inc. (C), CT, *607*
Travis & Co., Inc. (R), MA, *210*
Trillium Human Resources Inc. (C), ON, *609*
TriStaff Group (C), CA, *609*
Triumph Consulting, Inc. (R), IA, *210*
Trout & Assoc. Inc. (R), UT, *211*
Trowbridge & Co., Inc. (R), MA, *211*
TTG/Sterling Services (C), CA, *610*
Tuft & Assoc., Inc. (R), IL, *212*
Tyler & Company (R), GA, *212*
The Ultimate Source (R), CA, *212*
UniQuest Int'l., Inc. (C), FL, *610*

Unisearch Search & Recruiting Inc. (C), CA, *611*
The Urban Placement Service (C), TX, *611*
V.I.P. Resources, Inc. (C), NY, *611*
Van Dyke Assoc. (R), IL, *212*
Vezan Assoc. (C), CT, *612*
Victor White Int'l. (C), CA, *612*
Beverly von Winckler & Assoc. (C), IL, *613*
Walker Group, Inc. (R), MN, *215*
K. K. Walker Professional Recruitment (C), CA, *614*
Wallace Management Co. (R), TN, *215*
Lee H. Walton & Assoc. (R), NY, *215*
Warring & Assoc. (R), CA, *215*
Waterford Executive Group Ltd. (C), IL, *616*
Weatherby Healthcare (C), CT, *617*
Webb, Johnson Assoc., Inc. (R), NY, *216*
Wegner & Assoc. (C), WI, *617*
The Wellesley Group, Inc. (R), IL, *217*
Wellington Management Group (R), PA, *217*
Wellington Thomas Ltd. (C), FL, *618*
WestPacific National Search, Inc. (C), CA, *619*
The Whitaker Companies (C), TX, *619*
Whitney Smith Co. (C), TX, *620*
The Whittaker Group (C), MI, *620*
Whittlesey & Assoc., Inc. (R), PA, *220*
The Whyte Group, Inc. (R), MD, *220*
Wilcox Bertoux & Miller (R), CA, *220*
Walter K. Wilkins & Co. (R), NJ, *221*
William-Johns Co., Inc. (C), CA, *621*
Windsor Consultants, Inc. (C), TX, *622*
Winthrop Partners, Inc. (R), NY, *222*
Witt/Kieffer, Ford, Hadelman & Lloyd (R), IL, *223*
Woltz & Assoc., Inc. (R), IL, *224*
Louise Wood & Assoc. (C), NY, *624*
Wood & Assoc./Executive Search Consultants (C), CA, *624*
M. Wood Company (R), IL, *224*
Wood, Franchot Inc. (R), MN, *224*
Bruce G. Woods Executive Search (R), TX, *224*
Woodworth Int'l. Group (R), OR, *224*
Worldwide Medical Services (C), CA, *625*
Wyndham Mills Int'l., Inc. (R), GA, *225*
Xavier Associates, Inc. (R), MA, *226*
Yormak & Assoc. (C), CA, *626*
Yungner & Bormann (R), MN, *226*
Helen Ziegler & Assoc., Inc. (C), ON, *627*
Zingaro & Company (R), TX, *227*
Zona & Assoc., Inc. (C), NY, *628*
Zurick, Davis & Co., Inc. (R), MA, *227*

V.00 Non-classifiable industries

A First Resource (C), NC, *231*
Alpha Executive Search (C), AL, *245*
Anderson Network Group (C), OH, *250*
APA Employment Agency Inc. (C), OR, *251*
Barth Smith Company (R), IL, *12*
C. Berger And Company (R), IL, *16*
Carnegie Partners, Inc. (R), IL, *30*
Corporate Careers, Inc. (C), CA, *299*
Cyntal Int'l. Ltd. (R), NY, *44*
J. H. Dugan & Assoc., Inc. (R), CA, *55*
Gwen Dycus & Assoc. (C), FL, *323*
Executive Search Group, Inc. (C), CT, *335*
The Executive Source (C), SA, *337*
The Executive Tree (R), FL, *64*
Fabian Assoc. Inc. (C), NY, *338*
Foster Partners (R), NY, *70*
Franstaff Inc. (C), FL, *352*
GAAP Inc. (R), QE, *73*
Gaines & Assoc. Int'l., Inc. (R), IL, *73*
Dick Garland Consultants (R), NY, *74*
Genesis Consulting Partners (R), PA, *76*
Genesis Personnel Service, Inc. (C), OH, *356*
The Gullgroup (C), TX, *364*
Michael J. Hall & Co. (R), WA, *85*
Hazard, Young, Attea & Assoc., Ltd. (C), IL, *371*
Healthcare Recruiters of New England (C), MA, *373*
Healthcare Resources Group (C), OK, *374*
Helffrich Int'l. (C), FL, *375*
The Hiring Authority, Inc. (C), FL, *379*
Intercontinental Executive Group (C), PA, *391*
Jacobs & Co. (R), CT, *105*
Job-Born Candidate Selection Bureau (C), ON, *399*
Johnson Assoc., Inc. (C), IL, *399*
A.T. Kearney Executive Search (R), IL, *111*
The Kennett Group, Inc. (R), PA, *112*
Kiley, Owen & McGovern, Inc. (R), NJ, *114*
Korn/Ferry Int'l. (R), NY, *117*
J. Krauss Assoc. (R), FL, *120*
Lanken-Kimball-Therrell & Assoc. (C), GA, *412*
Leader Resources Group (C), GA, *415*
Leader Search Inc. (R), AB, *127*
Management Recruiters of Mobile Co., Inc. (C), AL, *438*
Management Recruiters of Woodbury (C), MN, *452*
Management Recruiters of Lionville, Inc. (C), PA, *459*
The Norland Group (C), CA, *494*
Opalka Dixon Consultants to Management (R), VA, *156*
Ortman Recruiting Int'l. (C), CA, *500*
The PAR Group - Paul A. Reaume, Ltd. (R), IL, *159*
The Patience Motivation Belief Group, Inc. (C), GA, *505*
Alec Peters Assoc. Inc./DLR (R), GA, *163*
ProLinks Inc. (R), VA, *170*
Harold L. Rapp Assoc. (C), NY, *529*
Joanne E. Ratner Search (C), NY, *529*
Research Personnel Consultants (C), ON, *534*
The Resource Group (R), CT, *175*
Russell Reynolds Assoc., Inc. (R), NY, *176*
Rice Cohen Int'l. (R), PA, *178*
Ritt-Ritt & Assoc., Inc. (C), IL, *537*
Bruce Robinson Assoc. (R), NJ, *180*
Rusher, Loscavio & LoPresto (R), CA, *183*
D. W. Simpson & Co. (C), IL, *582*
SpencerStuart (R), NY, *196*
Stanewick, Hart & Assoc., Inc. (C), FL, *591*
Technical Connections, Inc. (C), CA, *601*
TSI Group/TSI Staffing Services (C), ON, *610*
Zweig White & Assoc., Inc. (R), MA, *228*

Recruiter Specialties Index

Firms with (R) are from the Retainer Section, which begins on page 1.

Firms with (C) are from the Contingency Section, which begins on page 231.

This is a relatively new index allowing individuals to pinpoint their particular area of specialization in addition to or in conjunction with, what their firms have selected. It is a particularly helpful tool both for identifying individuals within the larger firms and when your need is very specific.

Consisting of 429 majors and 23 minors, the categories were created by the recruiters themselves, without the constraints of established (but limited) indexes such as the Standard Industrial Classification. While this enabled us to collect deep and detailed data, it proved an ambitious task to corral into a logical index. We present it largely as it was collected; hence broad headings with several hundred entries appearing next to unique, detailed ones with but a single entry.

To maximize the usefulness of this indexing approach, we encourage you to scan the master list with as many key words as you can associate with your need. For example, Hospitality would produce a long list, but searches on bakery, food, beverage, casinos, clubs, food service, hotels, restaurants and tourism might get you closer to a specific breakout of hospitality.

In the index, you will find the recruiter's name, his/her firm, whether firm operates on R (retainer) or C (contingency) basis, state office is in and page number. Please note minor categories are listed alphabetically under their major headings (for example: computer hardware is listed under hardware within computers).

Accounting
- Big 6
- Public

Accounting & finance
Acoustics
Actuarials
Adhesives
Administration
Advertising
Aerospace
Agribusiness/agriculture
Aluminum
Amusement parks
Analysts
Animation
Annuities
Apparel
Appliances
Applied research
Arcade games
Architects/architecture
Art
Artificial intelligence
AS/400
ASIC
Assessment
Asset management
Assets & liabilities
Associations
ATM
Audio
Audits
Automation
Automotive
Aviation
BAAN
Bakery
Banking
- Corporate

Benefits
Beverages
Bilingual
Biology
Biomedical
Biometrics
Biotechnology
Blow molding
Board search
Bond underwriting
Brand management
Bridges
Broadcasting
Brokerage
BSME
Building products
Business development
Cable
CAD/CAM
Call centers
Capital Markets
Capital goods
Casinos
Catalogs
CATV
Cellular
Cement/concrete
CEOs
Ceramics
CFOs
Change management
Chemical
CIOs
Citrus
Civil
Clerical
Client/server
Clinical
Closely-held business
Club
Coatings
COBOL
Communications
Compensation
Compliance
Components
Composites
Compounds
Computers
- Engineering
- Hardware
- Marketing
- Support

Confectionary
Conference centers
Construction
Consulting
Consumer
- General
- Marketing
- Packaged goods

Controllers
Convention centers
Convergence
Converting
COOs
Copiers
Corporate communication
Cosmetics
Crafts & hobbies
Creative
Credit
Credit cards
Cruise management
Culinary

Customer services
Dairy
Data communication
Databases
Defense
Dental
Derivatives
Design
Diagnostics
Diecast
Digital
Direct marketing
Dirt
Disaster recovery
Distribution
Diversity
Domestic
E-Mail
Economic development
Editorial
EDP
Education
Electrical
Electromechanical
Electronic commerce
Electronics
Embroidery
Energy
Engineering
Entertainment
Environmental
Equipment
Escrow
Estates
Executives
Exploration
Exports
Extrusion
Fabrication
Facilities engineering
Facility
Family business
Fashion
Film converting
Filtration
Finance
Finance & accounting
Financial
Management
Financial services
Fire protection
Floriculture
Food
Food service
Footwear
Forest industry
Forest products
Fortune Plus
Foundries
Franchising
Freight
Fundraising
Furniture
Galleries
Gaming
Gas
Gay/lesbian
General management
Generalists
Genetics
Geology
Gifts
Giftware
Golf
Government
GPS
Graphics
Groceries
Hardware
Health
Healthcare
Heavy industry
High purity water
High technology
Hispanic
Home
Home health
Horticulture
Hospitality
Hospitals
Hotels
Human resources
HVAC
Imaging
Industrial
Information
Information service
Injection molding
Ink
Instrumentation
Insurance
Casualty
Claims
Intellectual property
Interactive
Interim
Interior design
International
Internet
Internetworking
Intranet
Investment
Investment management
Investor relations
Iron
IS
ISO 9000
IT
Jewelry
Juvenile products
Labor
Laboratory
Landscaping
Leasing
Legal
Attorneys
Law
Lawyers
Leisure
Lending
Libraries
Licensing
Loans
Long term care
Loss
Lotus notes
Lubricants
Lumber
Machine tools
Machinery
Machining
Magazine
Maintenance
Managed care
Management
Management consulting
Manufacturing
Manufacturing management
Marine
Market research
Marketing
Consumer
Materials
Management
Mathematics
MBAs
Meat
Mechanical
Media
Medical
Medical devices
Medicine
Merchandising
Mergers & acquisitions
Metals
Micro brew
Microwave
Middle management
Military
Millwork
Mineral processing
Mining
Minorities
MIS
Mission critical
Mobile equipment
Multimedia
Music
Mutual funds
Natural resources
Networking
New media
Noise control
Non-profit
Nuclear power
Nursing
OB/GYN
Occupational therapy
Off shore

Office
Products
Services
Support
Oil
On-line
Operations
Management
Oracle
Organizational development
Orthopedics
OTC
Owner reps
Packaging
Paint
Paper
PeopleSoft
Pesticides
Pet food
Petrochemical
Pharmaceutical
PHDs
Physical therapy
Physicians
Pipe & tube
Pipeline
Plant
Plastics
Plywood
Polymers
Polyurethane
Portfolio management
Poultry
Power
Presidents
Pricing
Printing
Process control
Procurement
Produce
Product development
Product management
Production
Professional services
Programming
Property management
Public relations
Public sector
Publishing
Pulp
Pumps
Purchasing
Quality
Radio frequency
Railroad
Re-engineering
Real estate
Recreational vehicles
Recruiters
Recycling
Refining
Refrigeration
Regulatory
Rehabilitation
Research
Research & development
Resins
Resorts
Restaurants
Retail
Retirement housing
Risk management
Rubber
Safety
Sales
Management
Sales & marketing
Sanitation
SAP
Satellites
Sawmill
Science
Seafood
Security
Semiconductors
Senior management
Service industry
Shopping centers
Social services
Software
Speech
Sports
Staffing
Start-up companies
Steel
Strategic planning
Subacute healthcare
Superconductivity
Supermarkets
Suppliers
Surgery
Surgical
Systems
Tax
Technical
Technicians
Technology
Telecommunications
Telemarketing
Telephony
Television
Temporary
Test
Textiles
Thermoforming
Tooling
Tourism
Toxicology
Toys
Trading
Traffic
Training
Transportation
Travel
Treasury
Trust
Underwriting
Unix
Utilities
Valves
Van conversion
Venture capital
Veterinary
Vice president
Virtual reality
Vision
VSAT
Wall Street
WANs
Waste water
Watches
Welding
Wholesale
Wireless
Women
Wood
World Wide Web
Worldwide
Year 2000

Accounting

Adams, Amy, Richard, Wayne & Roberts (C), TX, *536*
Allen, Barbara A., Allen & Assoc. (C), NV, *244*
Andersen, Phil, Blackhawk Advantage, Inc. (C), CA, *267*
Anderson, Wayne F., Anderson Network Group (C), OH, *250*
Andrews, Dwight L., Andrews & Assoc. (C), NC, *250*
Angel, Steve, Angel Group Int'l. (C), KY, *250*
Arnold, Jay, Staffing Edge, Inc. (C), KS, *590*
Aylward, John, Hemingway Personnel, Inc. (C), CA, *375*
Baert, Yvonne, Personnel Management Group (C), MB, *508*
Bandzerewicz, Deborah, Management Recruiters of Washington, DC Inc. (C), MD, *450*
Barkocy, Andrew B., Princeton Executive Search (C), NJ, *518*
Baron, Robert, Peak Search Assoc. (C), ON, *506*
Becker, Matthew, Becker Personnel (C), FL, *262*
Behrens, Mark, Interim Accounting Professionals (C), CA, *391*
Belaiche, Marc, Creative Financial Staffing Inc. (C), ON, *303*
Bell, Andy, Norrell Financial Staffing (C), TN, *495*
Bell, Edward, Edward Bell Assoc. (C), CA, *263*
Benke, Norman L., N. L. Benke & Assoc., Inc. (C), OH, *264*
Bereck, Brian, Abacus Group LLC (C), NY, *232*
Berglund, Sharon, Berglund Int'l. Resources, Inc. (C), TX, *265*
Beste, Kevin M., Andrews & Assoc. (C), NC, *250*
Billingsley, Dennis, Joseph Michaels (C), CA, *401*
Bloodworth, Traci, Cook Assoc. Int'l., Inc. (C), TN, *298*
Bodner, Marilyn S., Bodner Inc. (C), NY, *269*
Bolt, Kathryn, Robert Half Canada Inc. (C), ON, *366*
Booker, Calvin, National Affirmative Action Career Network, Inc. (C), CO, *488*
Boyle, Lori, JDC Assoc. (C), NY, *397*
Brauninger, John C., AmeriPro Search, Inc. (C), NC, *248*
Breen, Susan V., GFI Professional Staffing Services (C), NH, *357*
Brody, Steve, Executive Resource Systems (C), CA, *335*
Brown, Charlene N., Accent On Achievement, Inc. (C), MI, *233*
Burns, Donita, Norrell Financial Staffing (C), PA, *495*
Burton, Rob, Interim Accounting Professionals (C), CA, *391*
Campbell, Vicki, Management Solutions, Inc. (C), WA, *468*
Cannon, Alexis, Richard, Wayne & Roberts (C), TX, *536*
Carlson, LuAnn, Houser, Martin, Morris (C), WA, *381*
Carson, Sandra, Carson-Thomas & Assoc. (C), CA, *284*
Casanova, Laura, Hemingway Personnel, Inc. (C), CA, *376*
Casey, Darren M., Management Solutions, Inc. (C), WA, *468*
Christie, Stephen G., Marsar & Co., Inc. (C), FL, *471*
Cochran, Ginny, Romac Int'l., Inc. (C), TX, *544*
Colman, Michael, Executive Placement Consultants (C), IL, *333*
Conner, Chuck, Strauss Personnel Service (C), PA, *596*
Cooper, David C., David C. Cooper & Assoc. Financial Search (C), GA, *298*
Cramer, Paul J., C/R Associates (C), NY, *278*
Creech, Bud, McCarthy Assoc. National BancSearch, LLC (C), LA, *473*
Cullen, Andrew, The Pennmor Group (C), NJ, *506*
Custer, George, Dynamic Staffing Network (C), IL, *324*
Cutshaw, Robert, F-O-R-T-U-N-E Personnel Consultants of Knoxville (C), TN, *350*
Davenport, Charles, S-H-S TechStaff (C), PA, *550*
Denn, Paula, Norrell Financial Staffing (C), TX, *495*
Desgrosellier, Shawn, Personnel Unlimited/Executive Search (C), WA, *509*
Diefenbach, John C., Hreshko Consulting Group (C), NJ, *382*
Dinse, Elizabeth, Management Recruiters of Sacramento North (C), CA, *441*
Dixon, Anita, Cook Assoc. Int'l., Inc. (C), TN, *298*
Doty, Eleanor C., The Doty Group (C), TX, *314*
Douglas, Courtney, Norrell Financial Staffing (C), CA, *495*
Dowell, Mary K., Professional Search Assoc. (C), CA, *522*
Dressen, Ronald, Romac Int'l., Inc. (C), MN, *543*
Dyer, John, Pacific Finance Search, Inc. (C), CA, *501*
Dykes, Mimi, Staffing Edge, Inc. (C), TX, *591*
Eastmer, Paul H., Professional Support Inc. (C), NY, *523*
Eden, Dianne, Steeple Resources & Consulting (R), NJ, *199*
Ellis, Milton H., Accountants On Call (C), TN, *237*
Engel, Walter E., F-O-R-T-U-N-E Personnel Consultants of the Tri-Cities, Inc. (C), TN, *350*
Ergas, Patricia, Unisearch Search & Recruiting Inc. (C), CA, *611*
Etlinger, Alan C., Resource Recruiting (C), NH, *534*
Faller, Laura McGrath, Redden & McGrath Assoc., Inc. (R), NY, *173*
Fenton, Steve, Interim Accounting Professionals (C), TX, *392*
Ferrara, David K., David Anthony Personnel Assoc., Inc. (C), NJ, *308*
Fiala, Joanne C., The Westfield Group (C), CT, *619*
Fink, Allen, PMJ & Assoc. (C), ON, *513*
Finley, Kerry, Recruiting Services Group, Inc. (C), TN, *532*
Fischer, Judith, RJ Associates (C), CA, *538*
Fischer, Ronald, RJ Associates (C), CA, *538*
Fishel, Richard A., Fishel HR Assoc., Inc. (C), AZ, *341*
Frankel, Len, Abacus Group LLC (C), NY, *232*
Froelich, Kris, Norrell Financial Staffing (C), PA, *495*
Fruchtman, Gary, Management Recruiters of Northwest Ohio, Inc. (C), OH, *458*
Gerarde, Paul S., Keena Staffing Services (C), NY, *404*
Gimbel, Mike, Gimbel & Assoc. (C), FL, *357*
Gleckman, Mark, Winter, Wyman & Co. (C), MA, *623*
Gmutza, Al, F-O-R-T-U-N-E Personnel Consultants of Southwest Indiana (C), IN, *346*
Goldstein, Barry, Interim Financial Solutions (C), VA, *392*
Griffin, Deana A., Souder & Assoc. (R), VA, *195*
Gross, Dean, Becker Personnel (C), FL, *262*
Habelmann, Gerald B., Habelmann & Assoc. (R), MI, *84*
Haddad, Charles G., Gateway Group Personnel, LLC (C), TN, *355*
Hale, Dillon, Cemco, Ltd. (C), IL, *286*
Halladay, Patti, Intersource, Ltd. (R), TX, *103*
Halstead, Richard, CMS Management Services LLC (C), IN, *293*
Hanson, Richard, Dunhill Staffing Systems, Inc. (C), NJ, *317*
Harrington, Cherie, Human Resources Personnel Agency (R), AR, *99*
Harrington, Robert C., Resource Recruiting (C), NH, *534*
Hawke, Marjorie, Becker Personnel (C), FL, *262*
Hellebusch, Jerry, Morgan Hunter Corp. (C), KS, *485*
Heller, Jason, Norrell Financial Staffing (C), NC, *495*
Hemmings, Jackie, S-H-S TechStaff (C), PA, *550*
Henderson, John, Staffing Edge, Inc. (C), AZ, *590*
Herbert, Kevin, Pacific Finance Search, Inc. (C), CA, *501*
Hester, Teresa, Romac Int'l., Inc. (C), CA, *542*

Hewitt, Diane, AmeriResource Group Inc. (C), OK, *249*
Hills, Glen, G. H. Enterprises (C), AZ, *354*
Hirsch, Neal, Richard, Wayne & Roberts (C), TX, *536*
Holmes, Dave, Hreshko Consulting Group (C), NJ, *382*
Holt, Elaine, Norrell Financial Staffing (C), CO, *495*
Homrich, Patricia J., David C. Cooper & Assoc. Financial Search (C), GA, *298*
Hreshko, Frank M., Hreshko Consulting Group (C), NJ, *382*
Infanti, Diana, Robert Half Canada Inc. (C), BC, *366*
Johnson, John Kimbrough, Johnson Brown Assoc., Inc. (C), IN, *400*
Justiss, Ted, David C. Cooper & Assoc. Financial Search (C), GA, *298*
Justus, Janet, Dunhill Executive Search of Los Angeles, Inc. (C), CA, *319*
Kelly, John, Rand Thompson Executive Search Consultants (C), NY, *528*
Kern, Tina, R. Green & Assoc., Inc. (C), OH, *362*
King, Jim, Career Strategies, Inc. (C), CA, *283*
Knose, II, Joseph M., Corporate Image Group (C), TN, *300*
Kolacia, V., Murphy Partners Int'l. (R), IL, *150*
Koppes, Jenny, Future Employment Service, Inc. (C), IA, *354*
Kramer, Alan L., Kramer Executive Resources, Inc. (C), NY, *409*
Kramer, Mitchel, Interim Accounting Professionals (C), FL, *392*
Kuntz, William A., Management Recruiters of Indianapolis (C), IN, *448*
Laderman, David, ACSYS Resources, Inc. (C), PA, *239*
LaMorte, Brian A., Pascale & LaMorte, LLC (C), CT, *504*
Lange, Jim, Lange & Assoc., Inc. (C), IN, *412*
Lasee, Jeff, The H. S. Group, Inc. (C), WI, *365*
Lasse, Daniel C., Management Recruiters of St. Charles (C), IL, *447*
Lawson, Debra, Management Recruiters of Detroit & Farmington Hills (C), MI, *451*
Layhee, Pat, Norrell Financial Staffing (C), GA, *495*
LeBoeuf, Michel, Robert Half Canada Inc. (C), QE, *366*
Lee, Barbara A., Management Recruiters, Inc. (C), FL, *443*
Lee, Jess J., Management Search Int'l. (C), CA, *467*
Leininger, Dennis, Staffing Edge, Inc. (C), IA, *590*
Lennon, Bill, Hall Management Group, Inc. (C), GA, *367*
Lieff, Shelley, Advice Personnel Inc. (C), NY, *241*
Lomax, J. Alan, ADR Accounting Management Recruiters (C), ON, *240*
Long, David B., DBL Associates (C), CA, *309*
Loria, Frank, Accounting Personnel & Engineering Personnel Consultants (C), LA, *238*
Lucas, Kelly J., Protocol Inc. (C), CA, *525*
Lucifero, Lisa, ACSYS Resources, Inc. (C), NJ, *238*
Lucy, Christine, Robert Half Canada Inc. (C), ON, *366*
Lyon, Jenny K., Marra Peters & Partners (R), NC, *136*
MacDougall, Audrey, Robert Half Canada Inc. (C), AB, *366*
Malek, L., Professional Search Consultants (PSC) (C), TX, *523*
Mand, Tammy, Norrell Financial Staffing (C), IL, *495*
Manning, Roger, Executive Search Team (C), MI, *336*
Marino, Chet, Cochran, Cochran & Yale, Inc. (R), CO, *37*
Marino, Mike, Tax Network Resources, Inc. (C), NY, *600*
Marra, Jr., John, Marra Peters & Partners (R), NJ, *136*
Marsar, Kevin P., Marsar & Co., Inc. (C), FL, *471*
Marshall, P. William, Dise & Co. (R), OH, *52*
Martin, Susan, Howard/Williams Assoc. (C), FL, *382*
Mayes, Kay H., John Shell Assoc., Inc. (C), SC, *580*
McCarthy, Debra, Becker Personnel (C), FL, *262*
McCartt, IV, E. J., Professional Search, Inc. Int'l. (C), TX, *523*
McGowan, Malcolm, Holloway Schulz & Partners (C), BC, *380*
McKersie, Edward S., ProSearch, Inc. (C), ME, *524*
Merrick, George, Pacific Finance Search, Inc. (C), CA, *501*
Miletti, Carol, Interim Accounting Professionals (C), MN, *392*
Miller, Marlene, Management Recruiters-Cedar Rapids, Inc. (C), IA, *448*
Mincy, Jim, Corporate Image Group (C), GA, *300*
Mitzmacher, Michael, Edward Bell Assoc. (C), CA, *263*
Molitor, John L., Barrett Partners (C), IL, *260*
Molkentine, Jon, Dunhill Search of Arlington (C), TX, *322*
Montijo, Alicia, NCC Executive Search Consultants (C), CA, *491*
Muller, Michael, Financialjobs.com (C), CA, *340*
Murphy, Darlene R., Gateway Group Personnel, LLC (C), TN, *355*
Musick, Diana, Musick & Assoc. (C), CA, *487*
Musick, Stephen, Musick & Assoc. (C), CA, *487*
Nadherny, Pete, The Angus Group, Ltd. (C), OH, *251*
Nanney, Jerry, Lou Michaels Assoc., Inc. (C), MI, *481*
Nimmo, Richard, AmeriResource Group Inc. (C), OK, *248*
Norris, Kris, Interim Accounting Professionals (C), CA, *391*
Noto, Joseph A., CMS Management Services LLC (C), IN, *293*
O'Connell, Michael, Ryan, Miller & Assoc. (C), CA, *549*
O'Rourke, Bart, Abacus Group LLC (C), NY, *232*
Park, Cleve A., Management Recruiters of Birmingham, Inc. (C), AL, *438*
Pascale, Ron, Pascale & LaMorte, LLC (C), CT, *504*
Pelayo, Joe, Joseph Michaels (C), CA, *401*
Phillips, David, Matthews & Stephens Assoc., Inc. (C), CT, *472*
Phillips, Mimi, Snelling Search Recruiters (C), NC, *586*
Pinedo, Mario, Bor-Maq Assoc. (C), TX, *269*
Pober, Andrew, Interim Accounting Professionals (C), FL, *391*
Polyzos, Ginia M., Management Advisors Int'l., Inc. (C), NC, *424*
Postlethwaite, John, Edward Bell Assoc. (C), CA, *263*
Powell, Mike, Marc-Allen Assoc., Inc. (C), FL, *469*
Pradarelli, Dennis J., MARBL Consultants, Inc. (C), WI, *469*
Prehogan, Avalee, Robert Half Canada Inc. (C), ON, *366*
Randolph, Troy, Lea Randolph & Assoc., Inc. (C), TX, *529*
Raniere, Rich, Romac Int'l., Inc. (C), FL, *542*
Ratner, Joanne E., Joanne E. Ratner Search (C), NY, *529*
Razzino, Janelle, Razzino-Claymore Assoc. (C), NJ, *530*
Reiter, Steve, Romac Int'l. - San Francisco (C), CA, *541*
Remillard, Brad M., CJA-The Adler Group, Inc. (R), CA, *35*
Rexroad, Nancy, Strauss Personnel Service (C), PA, *596*
Risalvato, Frank G., Inter Regional Executive Search, Inc. (IRES, Inc.) (C), NJ, *391*
Roberts, Nick, Pacific Search Group, Inc. (C), CA, *501*
Rosenblatt, Michael F., The Quest Organization (C), NY, *527*
Ross, Cheryl Molliver, Thomas, Whelan Assoc., Inc. (C), DC, *606*
Ross, Craig, Norrell Financial Staffing (C), GA, *495*
Rothman, Judith L., Royal Assoc. (C), CA, *547*
Ruthrauff, Debbie, Kelly Associates (R), PA, *112*
Rutkovsky, Laurence, Benson Associates (C), NY, *264*
Ryan, Lee, Ryan, Miller & Assoc. (C), CA, *549*
Sadow, Raymond, R. S. Sadow Assoc. (C), NJ, *550*

Sall, Ron, Interim Financial Solutions (C), VA, *392*
Samuels, Jonathan, Boston Professional Search, Inc. (C), MA, *270*
Sanchez, Jorge, Interim Accounting Professionals (C), FL, *392*
Sauer, Harry, ACSYS Resources, Inc. (C), PA, *239*
Sawyer, Scott J., Management Search Int'l. (C), CA, *467*
Schalk, Julie, Account Ability Now (C), MI, *234*
Schichtle, Nick, Accountants Executive Search (C), CA, *237*
Schlatter, Craig, Schlatter & Assoc. (C), CA, *572*
Seal, Jock, The H. S. Group, Inc. (C), WI, *365*
Sears, Keith, Edward Bell Assoc. (C), CA, *263*
Shedroff, Michael, ACSYS Resources, Inc. (C), NJ, *238*
Shell, III, John C., John Shell Assoc., Inc. (C), SC, *580*
Shor, Hillary, Interim Accounting Professionals (C), CA, *391*
Short, Mary Sue, Placement Solutions (C), WI, *513*
Singer, Lloyd R., Romac Int'l. (C), IL, *542*
Small, Jim, J. L. Small Assoc. (C), AL, *583*
Smith, Aaron, Staffing Edge, Inc. (C), CO, *590*
Smith, Jill, ACSYS Resources, Inc. (C), PA, *239*
Smith, Marvin E., Management Solutions, Inc. (C), WA, *468*
Snow, Christine, C. Snow & Assoc. (C), ON, *586*
Souder, Jr., E. G., Souder & Assoc. (R), VA, *195*
Sponseller, Vern, Richard Kader & Assoc. (C), OH, *403*
Squires, Frank, Squires Resources Inc. (C), ON, *590*
Steele, Kevin, Winter, Wyman & Co. (C), MA, *623*
Steinfield, David, Steinfield & Assoc. (C), TX, *592*
Stollenmaier, Nadine, Dunhill Professional Search of Hawaii (C), HI, *320*
Stone, Richard, Stone Assoc. LLC (C), MI, *594*
Stone, Susan L., Stone Enterprises Ltd. (C), IL, *594*
Stubblefield, Janine, Angel Group Int'l. (C), KY, *250*
Sudina, Chuck, Sudina Search, Inc. (C), MD, *596*
Sussman, Patti, Weinman & Assoc. (C), AZ, *617*
Sutherland, Grant, C.T.E.W. Executive Personnel Services Inc. (C), BC, *278*
Szabad, C., The Talley Group (R), VA, *205*
Taylor, Staci, Interim Accounting Professionals (C), CA, *391*
Teter, Sandra, The Danbrook Group, Inc. (C), TX, *306*
Thunberg, Richard A., Jeff Rich Assoc. (C), NJ, *536*
Tobin, Kathryn, Norrell Financial Staffing (C), AZ, *495*
Trasatti, Anthony, The Pennmor Group (C), NJ, *506*
Treney, Sue, Norrell Financial Staffing (C), FL, *495*
Turner, Tami, Robert Half Canada Inc. (C), ON, *366*
Vacca, Domenic L., ACSYS Resources, Inc. (C), DE, *238*
Van Gyseghem, Marc, Stone Assoc. LLC (C), MI, *594*
Voigt, Jeff, APA Employment Agency Inc. (C), OR, *251*
Wade, Bridgette, Norrell Financial Staffing (C), CA, *495*
Waldon, Jeffrey, Accountants On Call (C), FL, *237*
Waldon, Maita, Accountants On Call (C), FL, *237*
Walker, Warren T., Millar Walker & Gay (R), ON, *144*
Watkins, Jeff, Norrell Financial Staffing (C), GA, *495*
Wayne, Cary S., ProSearch, Inc. (C), OH, *524*
Weiner, Arlene, Sanford Rose Assoc. - Athens (C), GA, *566*
Wilkinson, Charla, Norrell Financial Staffing (C), FL, *495*
Williams, Trish, Interim Accounting Professionals (C), CA, *391*
Winnewisser, William E., Accounting & Computer Personnel (C), NY, *238*
Wlodawsky, Wayne, Romac Int'l., Inc. (C), TX, *544*
Yakimishyn, Michael, Zen Zen Int'l. Inc. (C), MB, *627*
Young, Arthur L., Search South, Inc. (C), AL, *576*
Zalman, Andrew, Interim Accounting Professionals (C), FL, *392*

Big 6

Robinson, Donald Alan, The Robinson Group, D.A., Ltd. (C), IL, *539*

Public

Zukerman, Claire, Corporate Search, Inc. (C), NY, *301*

Accounting & finance

Barefield, Ernest, Gans, Gans & Assoc., Inc. (R), PA, *74*
Barry, James, CFR Executive Search, Inc. (C), IL, *288*
Besso, Sandy, Intersource, Ltd. (R), TX, *103*
Besso, Thom, Intersource, Ltd. (R), TX, *103*
Bethmann, Chris, Southern Recruiters & Consultants, Inc. (C), SC, *587*
Boxer, Harry, The Century Group (C), CA, *287*
Brown, Gina R., Strategic Alliance Network, Ltd. (C), OH, *595*
Bui, Allison, Accountancies (C), CA, *234*
Casey, Daniel J., Creative Financial Staffing (C), PA, *303*
Champagne, Richard, Koll-Fairfield LLC (C), CT, *408*
Clements, Paulette, Probus Executive Search (C), CA, *519*
Cohen, Barry, Response Staffing Services (C), NY, *535*
Collins, Robert J., Financial Search Corp. (C), IL, *340*
Cox, Joan, The Pailin Group Professional Search Consultants (R), TX, *158*
Davis, Theresa, Management Recruiters of Milwaukee - Downtown (C), WI, *466*
de La Hoz Ramirez, Armando, OSAGUI S.A. de C.V. (C), MX, *500*
Dow, R. Steven, Scott-Wayne Assoc., Inc. (C), MA, *573*
Epstein, Robert G., RGE (C), VA, *535*
Etter, Duane, Accounting & Bookkeeping Personnel, Inc. (C), AZ, *238*
Fischer, Karl W., Dunhill Search of Medford (C), NJ, *321*
Gillenwater, Patti, Elinvar (C), NC, *328*
Glennon, Tony, GSP International (C), NJ, *364*
Gobdel, Bruce, Creative Financial Staffing (C), MA, *303*
Gray, Betty, Accent On Achievement, Inc. (C), MI, *233*
Gray, Kent, Romac Int'l. - San Francisco (C), CA, *541*
Gurney, Darrell W., A Permanent Success Employment Services (C), CA, *231*
Hauser, Herb, Dunhill Search of Vermont (C), VT, *323*
Howard, Marybeth, Accounting & Bookkeeping Personnel, Inc. (C), AZ, *238*
Hudson, Reginald M., Search Bureau Int'l. (C), IL, *574*
Hurd, Philip J., Lynx, Inc. (C), MA, *421*
Kaye, Edward, GSP International (C), NJ, *364*
Kenny, Megan, Partners Resource Group (C), MD, *504*
Konrad, William, ISC of Atlanta, Inc. (C), GA, *394*
Krueger, Todd L., Todd L. Krueger & Assoc. (C), WA, *409*
Langford, Matt, Fortune Personnel Consultants of Huntsville, Inc. (C), AL, *344*
Libes, Mark S., Accountants Executive Search (C), PA, *234*
McNeal, Jack, Probus Executive Search (C), CA, *519*
McNear, Jeffrey, Barrett Partners (C), IL, *260*
Mitton, William H., Executive Resource Inc. (C), WI, *334*
Negus, Suzie, Norrell Financial Staffing (C), GA, *495*
Nolan, Michael, Accounting & Bookkeeping Personnel, Inc. (C), AZ, *238*
Olenick, John G., Partners Resource Group (C), VA, *504*
Pailin, Sr., David L., The Pailin Group Professional Search Consultants (R), TX, *158*
Parker, Rael, Accountancies (C), CA, *234*

RECRUITER SPECIALTIES

Pirre, Ray, GSP International (C), NJ, *364*
Proul, Ron, The Century Group (C), CA, *287*
Puckett, William E., Searchline Services, Inc. (C), OH, *577*
Rand, Chris, Accounting Additions (C), CA, *238*
Sexton, Joseph, CFR Executive Search, Inc. (C), IL, *288*
Sicilia, John, GSP International (C), NJ, *364*
Simon, Bernard, Accountants Executive Search (C), CT, *234*
Smith, Joseph E., Smith & Syberg, Inc. (R), IN, *193*
Stalowicz, Bruce, Koll-Fairfield LLC (C), CT, *408*
Stauffer, Joseph K., Rylan Forbes Consulting Group, Inc. (C), NJ, *549*
Sternlicht, Marvin, Accountants Executive Search (C), CT, *234*
Stone, Dave M., DM Stone Personnel Services (C), CA, *594*
Sveinbjornson, Lynn, The Verriez Group Inc. (R), ON, *213*
Thompson, Judy, Judy Thompson & Assoc., Inc. (C), CA, *606*
Tomack, Arthur, Koll-Fairfield LLC (C), CT, *408*
Tomko, Jeffrey M., Searchline Services, Inc. (C), OH, *577*
Traynor, Thomas H., Traynor Confidential, Ltd. (C), NY, *609*
Turner, Michael, Rocky Mountain Recruiters, Inc. (C), CO, *540*
Vasu, George, CCI - Career Consultants Int'l. (C), CA, *286*
Verriez, Paul M., The Verriez Group Inc. (R), ON, *213*
Von Recklinghausen, Renate, Dunhill Search of Vermont (C), VT, *323*
Wasmuth, Doug, Accountancies (C), CA, *234*
Wenzel, Tim, DM Stone Personnel Services (C), CA, *594*
Wolowicz, Frank, Diversified Management Resources (C), IL, *313*
Worton, Craig, Rylan Forbes Consulting Group, Inc. (C), PA, *549*
Yaeger, Don, The Century Group (C), CA, *287*
Yormak, Stuart I., Yormak & Assoc. (C), CA, *626*

Acoustics

Fetridge, Guild, Guild Fetridge Acoustical Search, Inc. (C), NY, *340*

Actuarials

Amato, George, Faro Consultants Int'l. (C), VA, *338*
Dixon, Anita, Cook Assoc. Int'l., Inc. (C), TN, *298*
Genel, George, Genel Associates (C), CA, *356*
Hayes, Jerry, Holden & Harlan Assoc., Inc. (C), IL, *380*
Jacobsen, Patricia, D. W. Simpson & Co. (C), IL, *582*
Kenny, Peter J., Rob Dey Executive Search (R), FL, *49*
Lear, Roger R., Lear & Assoc., Inc. (C), FL, *415*
O'Neill, Sean, Waterford Executive Group Ltd. (C), IL, *616*
Puestow, Michael, The Beam Group (R), IL, *14*
Rollins, Scott, S. C. Int'l., Ltd. (C), IL, *550*
Simpson, David, D. W. Simpson & Co. (C), IL, *582*
Smith, Richard, HCI Corp. (C), IL, *371*
Steffke, Sandra, D. W. Simpson & Co. (C), IL, *582*
Wolfson, Robert H., Mitchell/Wolfson, Assoc. (R), IL, *145*

Adhesives

Fisher, Lawrence C., Mullen Assoc., Inc. (R), NC, *149*
Gres, Ed, Pioneer Executive Consultants (C), ON, *512*
McDowell, Jane, Cook Assoc.,® Inc. (R), IL, *40*
Mullen, James J., Mullen Assoc., Inc. (R), NC, *149*
Sgro, David J., Midland Consultants (C), OH, *481*
Sinclair, Paul, Pioneer Executive Consultants (C), ON, *512*
Telem, Peter B., Telem Adhesive Search Corp. (C), MD, *605*

Administration

Atchison, Ann G., W. R. Atchison & Assoc., Inc. (C), NC, *255*
Attea, William, Hazard, Young, Attea & Assoc., Ltd. (C), IL, *371*
Avazian, Mary Ann, National Field Service Corp. (C), NY, *489*
Bagg, Mary, Keith Bagg & Assoc., Inc. (C), ON, *257*
Belvedere, Tina, Wesley Brown & Bartle Co., Inc. (R), NY, *218*
Billington, Brian J., Billington & Assoc. (R), CA, *17*
Bloodworth, Traci, Cook Assoc. Int'l., Inc. (C), TN, *298*
Boone, Charles C., Boone-Scaturro Assoc., Inc. (C), GA, *269*
Bourque, Jack, Management Recruiters of Winsted, Inc. (C), CT, *442*
Breen, Susan V., GFI Professional Staffing Services (C), NH, *357*
Clark, Michael, Cornerstone Search Assoc. Inc. (C), MA, *299*
Clarke, Karen, HEC Group (C), ON, *375*
Cobb, Kimberly, Interim Financial Solutions - Mid-Atlantic Region (C), MD, *392*
Cook, P. Gene, P. G. Cook Assoc. (R), TN, *40*
Cooper, Michael, Chad Management Group (C), ON, *288*
Cuthbert, Bruce, McKavis Assoc. (C), CA, *475*
Dettra, Arthur C., Dunhill Professional Search of Bucks-Mont., Inc. (C), PA, *322*
Dunbar, Meg, M. Dunbar & Assoc. (C), TX, *316*
Eden, Don, Management Recruiters of Livonia (C), MI, *451*
Eden, Earl M., Eden & Assoc., Inc. (C), PA, *326*
Fagan, III, Charles A., Fagan & Company (R), PA, *64*
Feingold, Robin, Cornerstone Search Assoc. Inc. (C), MA, *299*
Forman, Margaret M., National Field Service Corp. (C), NY, *489*
Fruchtman, Gary, Management Recruiters of Northwest Ohio, Inc. (C), OH, *458*
Fumano, Gary W., Chapman & Assoc. (C), BC, *289*
Gasga, Pedro Salinas, Michigan Consulting Group (R), MI, *144*
Gillenwater, Patti, Elinvar (C), NC, *328*
Gilliam, Dale, Management Recruiters of Spokane (C), WA, *465*
Gowdy, Olga M., Gowdy Consultants (C), TX, *361*
Guidry, Jim, Guidry & East Healthcare Search Consultants (R), TX, *83*
Harrell, Stephen G., The Personnel Network, Inc. (C), SC, *508*
Haugen, Audrey D., Roger Dietsch & Assoc. (C), MN, *312*
Hemmings, Jackie, S-H-S TechStaff (C), PA, *550*
Hugsman, Rob, Russ Hadick & Assoc. Inc. (C), OH, *365*
Hutt, Gayle, W. Hutt Management Resources Ltd. (R), ON, *100*
Hyman, Jean W., Management Search Assoc., Inc. (C), GA, *467*
Jacobs, Martin, The Rubicon Group (C), AZ, *547*
Jones, Bonita, Global Career Services, Inc. (C), NY, *358*
Jones, Bonnie, Jones Management Co. (R), NY, *108*
Kaye, Francine C., MedSearch Resources, Inc. (C), FL, *478*
Koenig, Barbara, Royal Assoc. (C), CA, *547*
Larsen, Charles L., The Personnel Network, Inc. (C), SC, *508*
Lawson, Debra, Management Recruiters of Detroit & Farmington Hills (C), MI, *451*
Lawson, Trina R., Search Assoc., Inc. (C), NJ, *574*
Lee, Barbara A., Management Recruiters, Inc. (C), FL, *443*
Leggett, Amy, APA Employment Agency Inc. (C), WA, *251*
Lubaroff, Beth, Impact Search & Strategies (C), PA, *387*
Lyness, Cindy, Management Recruiters-Cedar Rapids, Inc. (C), IA, *448*
Mangum, Maria, Thomas Mangum Co. (R), CA, *208*
Martin, Susan, Howard/Williams Assoc. (C), FL, *382*

McKenna, Elaine, Weterrings & Agnew, Inc. (C), NY, *619*
McNamara, Timothy C., Horton Int'l. Inc. (R), MD, *96*
Merjos, Susan, The Beam Group (R), NY, *14*
Milne, Carole, Danette Milne Corporate Search Inc. (C), ON, *482*
Monset, Rachel, NCC Executive Search Consultants (C), CA, *490*
Montijo, Alicia, NCC Executive Search Consultants (C), CA, *491*
Oglesby, Peggy, F-O-R-T-U-N-E Personnel of Nashville (C), TN, *350*
Olson, Judy A., Management Recruiters of Woodbury (C), MN, *430*
Olson, Judy A., Management Recruiters of Woodbury (C), MN, *452*
Pailin, Cheryl, The Pailin Group Professional Search Consultants (R), TX, *158*
Phillips, Mimi, Snelling Search Recruiters (C), NC, *586*
Polak, Traci, Landon Morgan (C), ON, *412*
Presley, Linda C., Presley Consultants, Inc. (C), CA, *517*
Rosen, Richard, Cornerstone Search Assoc. Inc. (C), MA, *299*
Scaturro, Mary Ellen, Boone-Scaturro Assoc., Inc. (C), GA, *269*
Schoenfeld, Marian, Dunhill of Manchester Inc. (C), NH, *321*
Sherwood, Rose-Marie, DARE Personnel Inc. (C), ON, *307*
Shooshan, Daniel M., Hunter Assoc. (C), MA, *385*
Sikes, Charles R., Medical Search of America, Inc. (C), GA, *477*
Soltwedel, Michelle, TPS Staffing Solutions (C), IN, *608*
Stackhouse, Cathy, Strauss Personnel Service (C), PA, *596*
Stoa, Jackie, PERC, Ltd. (C), AZ, *506*
Voigt, Jeff, APA Employment Agency Inc. (C), OR, *251*
Weiss, John P., Star Search Consultants (C), ON, *591*
Wilder, Diane, Wilder & Assoc. (C), VA, *620*
Woods, Eleanor, National Metal Services Corp. (C), IN, *489*
Ziegler, Helen, Helen Ziegler & Assoc., Inc. (C), ON, *627*
Zukerman, Claire, Corporate Search, Inc. (C), NY, *301*

Advertising

Abrahamson, Susan, SearchCom, Inc. (R), TX, *187*
Aguirre, Doris, DCA Professional Search (C), TX, *309*
Andrews, Robert L., Allen Austin Lowe & Powers (R), TX, *3*
Bornholdt, John, Bornholdt Shivas & Friends Executive Recruiters (C), NY, *270*
Brolin, Lawrence E., DLB Assoc. (R), NY, *53*
Brown, Buzz, Brown, Bernardy, Van Remmen, Inc. (C), CA, *275*
Brownstein, Joan, Julian Assoc., Inc. (C), CT, *401*
Brownstein, Julian, Julian Assoc., Inc. (C), CT, *401*
Bucci, Michael T., The Partnership Group (R), NJ, *160*
Burke, Sally, Chaloner Assoc. (R), MA, *32*
Capra, Jamie V., Warren, Morris & Madison, Ltd. (C), NH, *616*
Cardwell, Jean, Cardwell Enterprises Inc. (R), IL, *29*
Carpenter, Elsie, Carpenter & Assoc. (C), TX, *284*
Cecilio, Cesca, Montgomery West (R), CA, *146*
Conlin, Edward T., Allen Austin Lowe & Powers (R), TX, *3*
Cowlan, Trudi, Trudi Cowlan (C), NY, *302*
Crawford, Jacqueline, Graphic Arts Marketing Assoc., Inc. (C), MI, *361*
Crawford, Roger, Graphic Arts Marketing Assoc., Inc. (C), MI, *361*
Crawford, Tom, The Crawford Group (C), GA, *303*
Dell'Aquilla, Joseph, Allen Austin Lowe & Powers (R), TX, *3*
Deutschman, Michele, Placements by Jesse Reid Assoc., Inc. (C), NY, *513*
Dolan-Brady, Nancy, NDB Assoc., Inc. (C), PA, *491*
Eskew, Martha, Recruiting Options, Inc. (C), GA, *532*
Feinberg, Bernard A., The Kay Group of 5th Ave. (C), NY, *404*
Fippinger, Stephanie, PLA, Inc. (C), NJ, *513*
Fippinger, Steve, PLA, Inc. (C), NJ, *513*
Fitzpatrick, Alan, Merlin Int'l. Inc. (C), NJ, *479*
Forbes, Kay Koob, Sanford Rose Assoc. - Evansville (C), IN, *567*
Forbes, Kenneth P., Sanford Rose Assoc. - Evansville (C), IN, *567*
Fristoe, Jack, Fristoe & Carleton, Inc. (C), OH, *353*
Garcia, Abel, Allen Austin Lowe & Powers (R), TX, *3*
Geiser, Diane, The York Group (C), CA, *626*
Goheen, Joyce, Meads & Assoc. (R), FL, *142*
Goldberg, Risa, Media Recruiting Group, Inc. (C), NY, *476*
Goodman-Brolin, Dorothy, DLB Assoc. (R), NY, *53*
Gregory, Rose, Kay Henry, Inc. (C), PA, *376*
Guber, Nadine B., Nadine Guber & Assoc., Inc. (C), NY, *364*
Gumbinner, Paul S., Gumbinner/Haubenstock, Inc. (C), NY, *364*
Gundersen, Steven G., Gundersen Partners, L.L.C. (R), NY, *83*
Hall, Susan, Susan Hall Executive Search (C), TX, *366*
Hamilton, Lisa J., Hamilton & Co. (C), OH, *367*
Harberth, Janet, Janet Harberth & Assoc., Inc. (C), GA, *368*
Hart, Gerry, Hart & Co. (C), NY, *370*
Haubenstock, Eileen, Gumbinner/Haubenstock, Inc. (C), NY, *364*
Henry, Kay, Kay Henry, Inc. (C), PA, *376*
Herman, Joyce Ralph, Management Assoc. (C), MD, *424*
Humphreys, William M., Robison Humphreys & Assoc., Inc. (R), ON, *180*
Jones, Geoffrey J., Precision Executive Search (C), AZ, *516*
Kay, Joseph H., The Kay Group of 5th Ave. (C), NY, *404*
Kaye, Shelley, Cassell & Kaye (C), NY, *286*
Kissel, James R., Management Recruiters of Northern Palm Beaches (C), FL, *444*
Klein, Ariel, AKH Executive Search (C), OR, *243*
Lee, Carol Ricci, Ricci Lee Assoc., Inc. (C), CA, *415*
Leety, Murray, Fox-Morris Assoc., Inc. (C), PA, *352*
Lipton, Pat, PLA, Inc. (C), FL, *513*
MacArthur, Sylvia, Madison MacArthur Inc. (R), ON, *133*
Marini, Larry, Management Recruiters of Northern Palm Beaches (C), FL, *444*
Marshall, Larry, Marshall Consultants, Inc. (R), NY, *137*
McCandless, Hugh, Marshall Consultants, Inc. (R), NY, *137*
McDonald, Thomas W., Mengel & McDonald Ltd. (C), IL, *479*
Meads, Walter F., Meads & Assoc. (R), FL, *142*
Miller, Shelley, Kay Henry, Inc. (C), PA, *376*
Mitchell, Laurie, Laurie Mitchell & Co., Inc. (R), OH, *145*
Mittenthal, Robert H., David Gomez & Assoc., Inc. (R), IL, *79*
Montgomery, Scott, Rojek Marketing Group, Inc. (R), OH, *181*
Ossow, Kitty, K. Ossow & Co. (C), NY, *500*
Owens, Robyn, Sanford Rose Assoc. - Norcross (C), GA, *566*
Petry, Georgia M., Placements by Jesse Reid Assoc., Inc. (C), NY, *513*
Poutouves, Paul, Martha Ward Executive Search, Inc. (C), NY, *615*
Quinn, Gail, Marshall Consultants, Inc. (R), NY, *137*
Robison, Margaret H., Robison Humphreys & Assoc., Inc. (R), ON, *180*
Rojek, Lorraine, Rojek Marketing Group, Inc. (R), OH, *181*
Sabbio, Kathy, The Brentwood Group, Inc. (R), NJ, *22*
Schechter, Phil, Management Recruiters of Atlanta (C), GA, *445*
Schwartz, Stephen D., Management Recruiters of Gramercy, Inc. (C), NY, *455*
Scott, Corwyn J., Warren, Morris & Madison, Ltd. (C), NH, *616*
Silverman, Marjorie, Marshall Consultants, Inc. (R), NY, *137*

RECRUITER SPECIALTIES

Solomon, Phyllis, Phyllis Solomon Executive Search, Inc. (C), NJ, *587*
Spielman, Sharon, Jerry Fields Assoc. (C), NY, *340*
Swift, Catherine, Swift & Assoc. (C), ME, *597*
Tucker, Guy, Ask Guy Tucker (C), GA, *254*
Van Remmen, Roger, Brown, Bernardy, Van Remmen, Inc. (C), CA, *275*
Vendetti, Lisa, The Alfus Group (R), NY, *3*
Walmsley, Scott, Association for Sales Force Management (C), WA, *254*
Warren, Ted, Strategic Resources (C), WA, *595*
Weil, Lee, Lee Weil Assoc., Inc. (C), IL, *617*
Welti, Rene, Direct Marketing Resources (C), NC, *312*
White, Richard B., SpencerStuart (R), CT, *196*
York, Karen, The York Group (C), CA, *626*
Zimering, Chuck, Chuck Zimering Advertising Recruitment (CZAR) (C), NY, *627*

Aerospace

Cantus, Jane-Scott, Christian & Timbers, Inc. (R), VA, *34*
Cowin, David M., Cowin Assoc. (R), NY, *42*
Crosbie, D. C., Interim Management Resources Inc. (C), ON, *392*
Denis, Liz, Brentwood Int'l. (R), CA, *23*
Du Ket, David R., New Venture Development, Inc. (C), CA, *492*
Fisher, Neal, Fisher Personnel Management Services (R), CA, *68*
Goodman, Goody, Harvard Group Int'l. (R), CO, *87*
Gordy, Thomas, Harvard Group Int'l. (R), GA, *87*
Hamilton, Marilyn, Fisher Personnel Management Services (R), CA, *68*
Hansen, Ty E., Blake/Hansen Ltd. (R), FL, *18*
Howe, Phillip T., Management Recruiters of Sedona (C), AZ, *438*
Kay, Peter, NMC & Kay Int'l. (R), CO, *152*
Lightner Jr., Ralph H., Stanton Chase Int'l. (R), MD, *199*
O'Daniel, Beverly W., The Elsworth Group (C), TX, *329*
Poore, Larry D., LAI Ward Howell (R), IL, *123*
Sherwood, Rose-Marie, DARE Personnel Inc. (C), ON, *307*
Sweet, Robert J., Atlanta Executive Partners, Inc. (R), MA, *8*
Whittaker, Cynthia, Brentwood Int'l. (R), CA, *23*

Agribusiness/agriculture

Allison, Tom, Tom Allison Assoc. (C), NM, *245*
Berry, Charles D., Management Recruiters of San Marcos (C), TX, *463*
Cavolina, Michael, Carver Search Consultants (C), CA, *285*
Critchfield, Marlene, Marlene Critchfield Co. (C), CA, *303*
Dach, Brad, Management Recruiters of Spencer (C), IA, *448*
David, Dave, Executive Resource Assoc. (C), VA, *334*
Davidson, Mary Anne, KPMG Executive Search (R), SA, *120*
DeJong, Jack, Management Recruiters of Tucson (C), AZ, *439*
Dostal, Kris, Sales Consultants of Omaha, Inc. (C), NE, *560*
Fowler, Jim, First Search America, Inc. (C), TN, *341*
Garman, Herb, Management Recruiters of Tucson (C), AZ, *439*
Good, David J., Management Recruiters of Sioux Falls, LLP (C), SD, *461*
Kagan, Philip, Strategic Resources (C), WA, *595*
Lehnst, John J., Management Recruiters of Williamsburg (C), IA, *449*
Leonard, Mell D., International Recruiting Services (C), FL, *393*
Olsen, Robert F., Robert Connelly & Assoc., Inc. (R), MN, *39*
Orwig, David L., Management Search, Inc. (C), OK, *468*
Person, Glenn J., AGRI-associates (C), MO, *242*
Pickering, Dale, Agri-Tech Personnel, Inc. (C), MO, *242*
Priseler, Michael, IR Search (R), CA, *103*
Sitter, William P., Jordan-Sitter Assoc. (R), TX, *108*
Smith, Charles D., Smith & Laue Search (R), OR, *193*
Smith, Donald L., Smith, Brown & Jones (C), KS, *585*
Stoa, Gordon, PERC, Ltd. (C), AZ, *506*
Suchomski, Larry, The Montgomery Group, Inc. (C), TN, *484*
Thomas, Sharon, Management Recruiters of Williamsburg (C), IA, *449*
Weller, Paul S., Mark Stanley & Co. (R), DC, *136*
Whitney, Ron, Sales Consultants of Sacramento (C), CA, *556*
Young, Mark E., Foster Partners (R), FL, *70*

Aluminum

Leader, D. June, Leader Network (C), PA, *414*
Vogel, Don, Dunhill Professional Search (C), MO, *321*

Amusement parks

Casey, David, The Alfus Group (R), NY, *3*

Analysts

Babicky, Kay, Management Recruiters of Wausau, LLC (C), WI, *466*
Campbell, Sandra, Management Recruiters of Milford Inc. (C), CT, *442*
Cohen, Richard, Management Recruiters of Manhattan on Broadway (C), NY, *455*
Curry, Donna, Don Neal & Assoc. (C), OK, *491*
Fabian, Jeanne, Fabian Assoc. Inc. (C), NY, *338*
Fry, Don, Dunhill of Corpus Christi, Inc. (C), TX, *323*
Gogates, Andrew, The Gogates Group, Inc. (R), NY, *79*
Hall, Shannon Kelly, Sampson Medical Search (C), CA, *564*
Heacock, Barbara, B. D. Wallace & Assoc. (C), MD, *614*
Kubiak, Thomas J., Halbrecht & Co. (C), CT, *365*
Maltby, Thomas J., Halbrecht & Co. (C), VA, *365*
McKee, Edward F., McKee Cyber Search (C), MS, *475*
Neal, Don, Don Neal & Assoc. (C), OK, *491*
Pickens, Gregory D., Gregory D. Pickens (C), TX, *512*
Press, Fredrick R., Adept Tech Recruiting, Inc. (C), NY, *240*
Rountree, III, John B., Lexington Software Inc. (C), NY, *417*
Samet, Saul, Fisher-Todd Assoc. (C), NY, *342*
Van Gyseghem, Marc, Stone Assoc. LLC (C), MI, *594*
Wachuku, Bobbiette, Management Recruiters-Cedar Rapids, Inc. (C), IA, *448*
Whitehead, Elizabeth S., Whitehead & Assoc., Inc. (C), MO, *620*

Animation

Bege, Lorraine, Hands-on Broadcast (R), NY, *86*

Annuities

Simmons, Sandra, IR Search (R), CA, *103*

Apparel

Carideo, Joseph J., Thorndike Deland Assoc. LLC (R), NY, *48*
Clayman, Stan, CMS, Inc. (C), NH, *293*
Corwin, J. Blade, Seitchik Corwin & Seitchik Inc. (R), CA, *188*
Curtis, Howard, Tony Curtis & Associates (C), ON, *305*
Curtis, Tony, Tony Curtis & Associates (C), ON, *305*
Daniel, David S., SpencerStuart (R), NY, *196*
Fuller, Thomas, Epsen, Fuller & Assoc., LLC (R), NJ, *60*
Glynn, Mary Anne, E. A. Hughes & Co., Inc. (R), NY, *98*
Harshman, Donald, The Stevenson Group, Inc. (N.J.) (R), NJ, *200*
Hart, Susan S., SpencerStuart (R), CT, *196*

Hays, Brenda, Fortune Personnel Consultants of Chattanooga Inc. (C), TN, *349*
Hughes, Elaine A., E. A. Hughes & Co., Inc. (R), NY, *98*
Just, Debra, Just Management Services Inc. (C), TN, *402*
Just, Susan, Just Management Services Inc. (C), FL, *402*
Koltnow, Emily, Koltnow & Company (R), NY, *117*
Lee, Barbara, Lee Management Group Inc. (C), NJ, *416*
LeVan, Salli, Lemming/LeVan, Inc. (R), GA, *128*
Lord, Marvin, E. A. Hughes & Co., Inc. (R), NY, *98*
Naulty, Sharon, Koltnow & Company (R), NY, *117*
Phillips, Walter, Phillips Int'l., Inc. (C), SC, *510*
Presser, Janet, N.A.P. Executive Services (Canada) Inc. (C), QE, *488*
Rothstein, Steve, N.A.P. Executive Services (Canada) Inc. (C), ON, *488*
Seitchik, Jack, Seitchik Corwin & Seitchik Inc. (R), CA, *188*
Seitchik, William, Seitchik Corwin & Seitchik Inc. (R), NY, *188*
Selig, Robert J., Selig Executive Search (C), NH, *579*
Spinrad, Sharon, Kenn Spinrad Inc. (C), PA, *589*
Stefan, David E., ChaseAmerica, Inc. (R), FL, *33*
Thaler, Brian D., Scott-Thaler Assoc. Agency, Inc. (C), CA, *573*
Thiemann, Brian, Christopher and Long (C), MO, *291*
Thomas, Jeffrey, Fairfaxx Corp. (R), CT, *64*
Vennetti, Carie, Strategic Resources (C), WA, *595*
White, Joseph A., Sports Group Int'l. (R), NC, *198*
Whiting, Frank, Cook Assoc.,® Inc. (R), IL, *40*

Appliances

Carieri, Carl R., American Executive Search (C), FL, *247*

Applied research

Koellhoffer, Thomas J., T. J. Koellhoffer & Assoc. (R), NJ, *116*

Arcade games

Stanton, Grant, TSC Management Services Group, Inc. (C), IL, *610*

Architects/architecture

Adams, Gerald, G. Adams Partners (R), IL, *2*
Brown-Alcala, Sheila, Michael J. Hall & Co. (R), WA, *85*
Catton, Chris Lea, Zweig White & Assoc., Inc. (R), CA, *228*
Chamberland, Roland, Management Recruiters of Sonoma (C), CA, *441*
Cole, James, Systems Research Group (C), OH, *598*
Collins, Phil, Claremont-Branan, Inc. (C), GA, *292*
Connelly, III, Joseph H., CS Associates, LLC (C), AZ, *304*
Connelly, Susan D., CS Associates, LLC (C), AZ, *304*
Dupilka, John M., Michael Latas & Assoc., Inc. (R), MO, *126*
Fairlie, Suzanne F., ProSearch, Inc. (C), PA, *524*
Gaines, Donna, Gaines & Assoc. Int'l., Inc. (R), IL, *73*
Gavura, Nicholas J., Michael Latas & Assoc., Inc. (R), MO, *126*
Glymph, Tina, Michael J. Hall & Co. (R), WA, *85*
Hall, Michael J., Michael J. Hall & Co. (R), WA, *85*
Hirsch, Ruth, Ruth Hirsch Assoc., Inc. (C), NY, *379*
Karel, Stephen A., Karel & Co. (R), CA, *109*
Kohn, Adam, Christian & Timbers, Inc. (R), OH, *34*
Kreiss, John P., Zweig White & Assoc., Inc. (R), MA, *228*
LaBorde, Michael, The LaBorde Group (C), CA, *411*
Lawrence, Kent L., Michael Latas & Assoc., Inc. (R), MO, *126*
Lewis, Bryn, Systems Research Group (C), OH, *598*
Love, Cindi M., Michael Latas & Assoc., Inc. (R), MO, *126*
Lyngen, Robert, Construct Management Services (C), MN, *297*
Lyngen, Trish, Construct Management Services (C), MN, *297*
Martin, Bob, The LaBorde Group (C), CA, *411*
Michaels, Ellen, Shupack & Michaels Inc. (C), NY, *581*
O'Connor, John R., John R. O'Connor & Assoc. (C), IL, *497*
Olsen, Robert F., Robert Connelly & Assoc., Inc. (R), MN, *39*
Peart, Carolyn, Cook Assoc.,® Inc. (R), IL, *40*
Powers, William D., Powers Consultants, Inc. (R), MO, *166*
Shupack, Joseph, Shupack & Michaels Inc. (C), NY, *581*
Siegel, RitaSue, RitaSue Siegel Resources, Inc. (R), NY, *191*
Sloane, Ron, Management Recruiters of Milwaukee-North (C), WI, *466*
Sprankle, Kathryn, Zweig White & Assoc., Inc. (R), DC, *228*
Sprankle, Kathryn, Zweig White & Assoc., Inc. (R), MA, *228*
Stoll, Steve, Sharrow & Assoc., Inc. (C), KY, *579*
Telford, Daniel W., CadTech Staffing Services (C), GA, *279*

Art

Growick, Philip, Jerry Fields Assoc. (C), NY, *340*

Artificial intelligence

Rountree, III, John B., Lexington Software Inc. (C), NY, *417*

AS/400

Aitken, Carol, Information Technology Search (C), PA, *388*
Ciaramitaro, Paul, Corporate Search Consultants, Inc. (C), FL, *301*
Hawkins, Max, Management Recruiters of Wausau, LLC (C), WI, *466*
Wachuku, Bobbiette, Management Recruiters-Cedar Rapids, Inc. (C), IA, *448*

ASIC

Zeiger, David Barkin, Zeiger Assoc. L.L.C. (C), CA, *627*
Zeiger, Stephen A., Zeiger Assoc. L.L.C. (C), CA, *627*

Assessment

Rice, Gene, Rice Cohen Int'l. (R), PA, *178*
Vardaris, Richard, Lekan & Assoc., Inc. (R), OH, *128*

Asset management

Bell, Jeff, SpencerStuart (R), PA, *197*
Brown, Franklin Key, Handy HRM (R), NY, *86*
Esposito, Mark, Christian & Timbers, Inc. (R), OH, *34*
Hoffman, Glenn, Huntress Real Estate Executive Search (R), MO, *100*
Humes, James, Management Recruiters of Nassau, Inc. (R), NY, *134*
Jacobson, Rick, The Windham Group (R), OH, *222*
Sprehe, J. Christopher, The Christopher Group (C), NC, *291*

Assets & liabilities

Myers, Deedee, DDJ Myers, Ltd. (R), AZ, *150*
Myers, John, DDJ Myers, Ltd. (R), MA, *150*

Associations

Emerick, Sylvia E., Amherst Human Resource Group, Ltd. (C), IL, *249*
Harcourt, Judy, Harcourt & Assoc. (C), AB, *368*

Hurley, Gerard F., Association Executive Resources Group (R), MD, *8*
McMillin, Robert, Price Waterhouse Executive Search (R), BC, *168*
Metzger, Pete, Foster Partners (R), DC, *70*
Rumbarger, Charles D., Association Executive Resources Group (R), MD, *8*
Tuft, Mary Ann, Tuft & Assoc., Inc. (R), IL, *212*
Vautour, Eric L., Russell Reynolds Assoc., Inc. (R), DC, *176*

ATM

Ashok, T. C., Fortuna Technologies Inc. (C), CA, *343*

Audio

Fetridge, Guild, Guild Fetridge Acoustical Search, Inc. (C), NY, *340*
Foster, Barton T., The Barton Group, Inc. (C), MI, *260*
Mirsky, Al, The Barton Group, Inc. (C), MI, *260*

Audits

Andersen, Phil, Blackhawk Advantage, Inc. (C), CA, *267*
Bontempo, David M., Dunhill Professional Search of Bucks-Mont., Inc. (C), PA, *322*
Brown, Charlene N., Accent On Achievement, Inc. (C), MI, *233*
Ciaramitaro, Joseph, Corporate Search Consultants, Inc. (C), FL, *301*
Davidson, Julie, Drinkwater & Assoc. (R), MA, *55*
Downing, Gus, Downing & Downing, Inc. (C), OH, *314*
Downing, Jacqueline, Downing & Downing, Inc. (C), OH, *314*
Edington, Patti D., Drinkwater & Assoc. (R), MA, *55*
Fox, Candy, D. R. Blood & Assoc. (R), AZ, *18*
Haddad, Charles G., Gateway Group Personnel, LLC (C), TN, *355*
Hauser, Herb, Dunhill Search of Vermont (C), VT, *323*
Hermann, George A., Hermann & Westmore (R), NY, *92*
James, David, David James Search (C), CA, *397*
Knose, II, Joseph M., Corporate Image Group (C), TN, *300*
Kramer, Donald J., Dunhill Professional Search of Tampa (C), FL, *320*
Kramer, Peter, Dunhill Professional Search of Tampa (C), FL, *320*
Marino, Mike, Tax Network Resources, Inc. (C), NY, *600*
McElroy, Brian, Drinkwater & Assoc. (R), MA, *55*
Mincy, Jim, Corporate Image Group (C), GA, *300*
Molkentine, Jon, Dunhill Search of Arlington (C), TX, *322*
Murphy, Darlene R., Gateway Group Personnel, LLC (C), TN, *355*
Musick, Diana, Musick & Assoc. (C), CA, *487*
Musick, Stephen, Musick & Assoc. (C), CA, *487*
Razzino, Janelle, Razzino-Claymore Assoc. (C), NJ, *530*
Salzman, John W., Dunhill Staffing Systems, Inc. (C), OH, *318*
Steinfield, David, Steinfield & Assoc. (C), TX, *592*
Tatar, Steven M., Magellan Int'l., L.P. (C), TX, *422*
Thunberg, Richard A., Jeff Rich Assoc. (C), NJ, *536*
Von Recklinghausen, Renate, Dunhill Search of Vermont (C), VT, *323*
Westmore, Robert J., Hermann & Westmore (R), CA, *92*

Automation

Ansara, Peter, Ansara, Bickford & Fiske (C), MA, *251*
Auriema, Mark H., Jay Tracey Assoc. Inc. (C), VT, *608*
Barz, James M., International Management Services Inc. (R), IL, *102*
Bishop, Sandy, Management Recruiters of Delaware County (C), PA, *459*
Bruder, Dan, CS Dowling Executive Services (R), NJ, *54*
Chapman, Jeff H., The Chapman Group, Inc. (C), AZ, *289*
Difatta, Jon, Management Recruiters of Barrington (C), IL, *447*
Egan, David C., D. C. Egan & Assoc. (C), GA, *327*
Garland, Mike, Raymond Thomas & Assoc. (C), FL, *530*
Gilbert, Mark, Sales Consultants of Farmington Hills (C), MI, *560*
Hertz, Al, Carter/MacKay (C), NC, *285*
Hohlstein, Jodi, Management Recruiters of Round Rock (C), TX, *463*
Huegel, Ray, Raymond Thomas & Assoc. (C), FL, *530*
Kelly, Susan D., S. D. Kelly & Assoc., Inc. (R), MA, *112*
Klebba, Arthur, Morgan & Assoc. (C), MA, *485*
Morgan, Diane R., Morgan & Assoc. (C), MA, *485*
Passon, Steven A., Teamsearch, Inc. (C), MI, *601*
Pepin, J. Lawrence, The Morgan/Geoffries Group (C), CA, *485*
Phillips, Walter, Phillips Int'l., Inc. (C), SC, *510*
Polvere, Gary T., Management Recruiters of Barrington (C), IL, *447*
Rowell, Mike, Carter/MacKay (C), MA, *285*
Searboro, M.D., Management Recruiters of Greenville (C), SC, *460*
Tracey, Jay E., Jay Tracey Assoc. Inc. (C), VT, *608*
Witt, Stan, Fortune Personnel Consultants of San Antonio, Inc. (C), TX, *350*
Xagas, Steve, Xagas & Assoc. (R), IL, *226*

Automotive

Antonio, Marshall, Fortune of Arlington Heights (C), IL, *346*
Barber, Bill C., Barber & Assoc. (C), KY, *259*
Barranco, Leticia, Leaders-Trust Int'l./ Carce y Asociados, S.C. (R), MX, *127*
Bennett, M.D., The Bennett Group, Inc. (R), IN, *16*
Birarda, Richard W., JSG Group Management Consultants (R), ON, *109*
Blaushild, Eric, AutoPeople (C), TX, *257*
Blaushild, Eric, AutoPeople (C), VT, *257*
Borchert, Gregory L., Borchert Assoc. (C), TX, *269*
Bramblett, Richard V., Dunhill Personnel of St. Andrews (C), SC, *322*
Colbourn, Ken, F-O-R-T-U-N-E Personnel Consultants of Knoxville (C), TN, *350*
Cunningham, Douglas, Staff Resources, Inc. (C), SC, *590*
Davidson, Arthur J., LAI Ward Howell (R), IL, *123*
Dietrich, Sandra, Fortune Personnel Consultants of Hilton Head (C), SC, *349*
Ellefson, Gene, Gene Ellefson & Assoc. Inc. (C), MI, *328*
Falcon, Elizabeth, Leaders-Trust Int'l./ Carce y Asociados, S.C. (R), MX, *127*
Fisher, Neal, Fisher Personnel Management Services (R), CA, *68*
Freeman, Evelyn, Brierwood Group, Inc. (C), IN, *274*
Fruchtman, Gary, Management Recruiters of Northwest Ohio, Inc. (C), OH, *458*
Gelatka, Charles T., The Bennett Group, Inc. (R), IN, *16*
Hackett, Donald F., Management Recruiters of Mt. Airy (C), NC, *456*
Hamilton, Marilyn, Fisher Personnel Management Services (R), CA, *68*
Henry, Jeremy, A First Resource (C), NC, *231*
Holliday, John, American Heritage Group, Inc. (C), MI, *247*
Icard, Sr., Bob, The Icard Group, Inc. (C), MI, *387*
Icard, Jr., Robert, The Icard Group, Inc. (C), MI, *387*
Johnson, John F., LAI Ward Howell (R), OH, *123*
Kabanuk, James Allen, Kabana Corp. (C), MI, *402*
Kabanuk, Steven E., Kabana Corp. (C), MI, *402*
Kay, Peter, NMC & Kay Int'l. (R), CO, *152*
Laird, Meri, Davidson, Laird & Assoc. (C), MI, *308*
Langley, Ted, Jaeger Int'l., Inc. (C), OH, *396*
Lindal, Bruce G., Linden Group, Inc. (C), NC, *418*
Montaño, Oscar W., Oscar Montaño, Inc. (R), CA, *146*

Mooney, Penny, Christian & Timbers, Inc. (R), OH, *34*
Morin, Paul, F-O-R-T-U-N-E Personnel Consultants of Knoxville (C), TN, *350*
Muir, Sherry, The Hunter Group, Inc. (C), MI, *385*
Olsen, Elizabeth Clark, Olsen/Clark (R), WA, *156*
Olszewski, Larry D., PRAXIS Partners (R), VA, *167*
Parekh, Dinesh V., Sanford Rose Assoc. - Amherst, NY (C), NY, *568*
Peeney, James D., Peeney Assoc., Inc. (R), NJ, *161*
Richards, Paul E., Executive Directions (R), OH, *62*
Robinson, Steve, Marsteller Wilcox Assoc. (C), IL, *471*
Roddy, Jack P., J. P. Roddy Consultants (C), PA, *540*
Schultz, Craig, F-O-R-T-U-N-E Personnel Consultants of St. Louis-West County (C), MO, *347*
Scott, Harold, Graham & Co. (R), NJ, *80*
Sears, Richard G., The Wilmington Group (C), NC, *622*
Smith, Douglas M., LAI Ward Howell (R), IL, *123*
Souder, Elizabeth W., Springer Souder & Assoc. L.L.C. (R), IL, *198*
Springer, Neil A., Springer Souder & Assoc. L.L.C. (R), IL, *198*
Storer, Steve, Executive Search, Ltd. (C), OH, *336*
Sturtz, James W., Compass Group Ltd. (R), MI, *38*
Toole, Thomas J., Management Recruiters of Laguna Hills (C), CA, *440*
Vague, Mark, F-O-R-T-U-N-E of West Portland (C), OR, *348*
Valencia-Icard, Cheryl, The Icard Group, Inc. (C), MI, *387*
Westphal, Birgit, Reynolds Consulting Int'l. (R), ON, *177*
Wilson, Donald, Allerton Heneghan & O'Neill (R), IL, *4*
Wolohan, Sarah, Cook Assoc.,® Inc. (R), IL, *40*
Woods, Jacques, Ray & Berndtson/Laurendeau Labrecque (R), QE, *172*

Aviation

Bell, Michael, SpencerStuart (R), FL, *197*
Fisher, Neal, Fisher Personnel Management Services (R), CA, *68*
Hamilton, Marilyn, Fisher Personnel Management Services (R), CA, *68*
Hansen, Ty E., Blake/Hansen Ltd. (R), FL, *18*
Howe, Phillip T., Management Recruiters of Sedona (C), AZ, *438*
Kendrick, M. Steven, LAI Ward Howell (R), TX, *124*
Smith, Joseph E., Smith & Syberg, Inc. (R), IN, *193*
Vaughan, David B., Vaughan & Co. (C), CA, *612*

BAAN

Capps, Norm, MIS Computer Professionals, Inc. (C), KS, *482*
Davis Wolfe, Kathryn, HDB Incorporated (C), MO, *371*
Huntley, David E., Huntley Associates (Dallas), Inc. (C), TX, *386*
Mesina, Roman, The Consulting Group of North America, Inc. (C), VA, *297*
Swami, Pad N., Fortuna Technologies Inc. (C), CA, *343*

Bakery

Joy, Kevin, HCI Corp. (C), IL, *371*
Winkler, Brad, Whittaker & Assoc., Inc. (C), GA, *620*

Banking

Adler, Rita, Discovery, The Staffing Specialists, Inc. (C), CA, *312*
Allman, Steven L., Allman & Co., Inc. (C), NC, *245*
Ames, Mildred S., Ames Assoc. Inc. (C), MD, *249*
Angott, Mark, Management Recruiters of North Oakland County, Inc. (C), MI, *452*
Arceri, John Mark, John Ryan Assoc., LLC. (C), NY, *399*
Ashton, Neil K., Sales Consultants of Bangor, Inc. (C), ME, *559*
Back, Bobbie, National Bank & Finance Executive Search (C), CA, *488*
Baker, Jr., Joseph N., JNB Assoc., Inc. (C), MA, *399*
Bard, Ann, Management Recruiters of St. Augustine (C), FL, *444*
Bard, Cliff, Management Recruiters of St. Augustine (C), FL, *444*
Baron, Sheldon S., Sales Consultants of Nashua-Manchester (C), NH, *560*
Bauer, Noelle, Youngblood Assoc. (C), NC, *626*
Beals, Calvin, Management Recruiters of Ft. Myers, FL. (C), FL, *443*
Bell, Jeff, SpencerStuart (R), PA, *197*
Benke, Norman L., N. L. Benke & Assoc., Inc. (C), OH, *264*
Bennett, Jr., Robert C., Bennett Search & Consulting Co. (R), FL, *16*
Berry, Harold B., The Hindman Co. (R), KY, *94*
Bertoux, Michael P., Wilcox Bertoux & Miller (R), CA, *220*
Bialkin, Joan, Federal Placement Services (C), NY, *339*
Bishop, Sandra K., F-O-R-T-U-N-E Personnel Consultants of Boise (R), ID, *70*
Bloch, Carla, Lending Personnel Services (C), CA, *416*
Bogart, James, The Bankers Register (C), NY, *259*
Bradshaw, Patrick M., The Patience Motivation Belief Group, Inc. (C), GA, *505*
Brady, Marty, The Oxbridge Group, Ltd. (C), PA, *500*
Brandjes, Michael, Brandjes Assoc. (C), MD, *272*
Breen, Susan V., GFI Professional Staffing Services (C), NH, *357*
Brennan, Patrick, Handy HRM (R), NY, *86*
Brown, Jeffrey B., J. B. Brown & Assoc., Inc. (C), OH, *275*
Bruno, Deborah F., The Hindman Co. (R), KY, *94*
Bryant, Robert L., Renaissance Resources, LLC (R), VA, *174*
Busser-Andersen, Phyllis, Blackhawk Advantage, Inc. (C), CA, *267*
Cannavino, John, Financial Resource Assoc., Inc. (C), FL, *340*
Castell, Jr., William J., Management Advisors Int'l., Inc. (C), NC, *424*
Chappell, Peter, The Bankers Group (C), IL, *258*
Ciaramitaro, Anthony, Corporate Search Consultants, Inc. (C), FL, *301*
Ciaramitaro, Joseph, Corporate Search Consultants, Inc. (C), FL, *301*
Cohen, Richard, Management Recruiters of Manhattan on Broadway (C), NY, *455*
Courtney, Brendan, Interim Financial Solutions - Mid-Atlantic Region (C), MD, *392*
Cramer, Paul J., C/R Associates (C), NY, *278*
Creech, Bud, McCarthy Assoc. National BancSearch, LLC (C), LA, *473*
Crumbaker, Robert H., LAI Ward Howell (R), OH, *123*
Dabich, Thomas M., Robert Harkins Assoc., Inc. (C), PA, *369*
de Cholnoky, Andrea, SpencerStuart (R), NY, *196*
Dow, Ian James, Dow Consultants Int'l. (C), NY, *314*
Edman, Silas E. G., The Partnership Group (R), NJ, *160*
Ellis, Steve, Steve Ellis (C), CA, *328*
Esposito, Mark, Christian & Timbers, Inc. (R), OH, *34*
Farmer, David W., Whitney Smith Co. (C), TX, *620*
Fee, J. Curtis, SpencerStuart (R), IL, *197*
Ferrara, David K., David Anthony Personnel Assoc., Inc. (C), NJ, *308*
Fogec, Thomas G., Fogec Consultants, Inc. (R), WI, *69*
Frock, Suzanne, Brandjes Assoc. (C), MD, *272*
Frost, Edward W., Mortgage Search Network (C), AZ, *486*
Frumess, Gregory, Foster Partners (R), NY, *70*
Gilliam, Dale, Management Recruiters of Spokane (C), WA, *465*
Gnodde, R. Dirk, Gnodde Assoc. (C), IL, *359*
Goldsmith, Jerry, The Primary Group, Inc. (R), FL, *168*
Good, Robert B., Management Recruiters of Sioux Falls, LLP (C), SD, *461*
Goodson, Jr., W. Kenneth, DLG Assoc., Inc. (R), NC, *53*

RECRUITER SPECIALTIES

Graff, Thomas D. B., The Hanover Consulting Group (C), MD, *368*
Greene, Timothy G., Greene & Co. (C), MA, *362*
Greenwald, Anita, Concorde Search Assoc. (C), NY, *296*
Guidroz, Ken, Management Recruiters of San Marcos (C), TX, *463*
Guilford, David J., DLG Assoc., Inc. (R), NC, *53*
Gutterman, Allen, Response Staffing Services (C), NY, *535*
Haddad, Charles G., Gateway Group Personnel, LLC (C), TN, *355*
Hall, Donald L., Higley, Hall & Co., Inc. (R), MA, *93*
Hall, Peter V., Argonaut Partners, LLC (R), CA, *6*
Hannock, III, Elwin W., Flynn, Hannock, Inc. (R), CT, *69*
Harfenist, Harry, Parker Page Group (C), FL, *503*
Haupert, Thomas J., MCS Assoc. (R), CA, *142*
Hayden, Dale, Sanford Rose Assoc. - Pittsburgh North (C), PA, *570*
Helnore, Douglas, Partners in Recruiting (C), IL, *504*
Hester, Teresa, Romac Int'l., Inc. (C), CA, *542*
Hindman, Neil C., The Hindman Co. (R), KY, *94*
Hinkle, Alfred, Renaissance Resources, LLC (R), VA, *174*
Hochman, Judi, Hochman & Assoc. (C), CA, *379*
Hoffman, Tala R., TRH Assoc., Inc. (R), NY, *210*
Holzberger, Georges L., Highland Search Group, L.L.C. (R), NY, *93*
Hopard, Stuart M., Olympian Recruitment, Ltd. (C), NY, *498*
Hopson, Bradford J., IntelliSearch (C), TX, *391*
Horton, Scott, Capital Markets Resources, Inc. (C), NC, *281*
Howard, Richard H., Management Recruiters of Berkeley (C), CA, *439*
Hughes, R. Kevin, Handy HRM (R), NY, *86*
Hurd, J. Nicholas, Russell Reynolds Assoc., Inc. (R), MA, *177*
Jablo, Steven A., Dieckmann & Assoc., Ltd. (R), IL, *51*
James, Cindy, Discovery, The Staffing Specialists, Inc. (C), DE, *312*
Jaspersen, Kenneth A., Dunhill Professional Search of Omaha, Inc. (C), NE, *321*
Johnson, Suzanne M., Miller/Davis & Assoc., Inc. (C), NY, *482*
Jones, Michael A., The Century Group (C), KS, *287*
Kapral, Shannon M., Sanford Rose Assoc. - Philadelphia North (C), PA, *570*
Katz, Norman, MCS Assoc. (R), CA, *142*
Keogh, James, Sanford Rose Assoc. - Oak Brook (C), IL, *567*
Kinney, Linda, Prospective Personnel Service, Inc. (C), OK, *524*
Klos, Larry, MSI Int'l. (C), TX, *487*
Kraftson, Ann, The Oxbridge Group, Ltd. (C), NY, *500*
Krauser, H. James, SpencerStuart (R), CT, *196*
Krick, Terry L., Financial Resource Assoc., Inc. (C), FL, *340*
Krienke, Paul G., C and P Marketing, Ltd. (C), OK, *278*
Laderman, David, ACSYS Resources, Inc. (C), PA, *239*
Lamb, Peter, Executive Resource Inc. (C), WI, *334*
Larsen, Richard F., Larsen, Whitney, Blecksmith & Zilliacus, Inc. (R), CA, *125*
Leininger, Dennis, Staffing Edge, Inc. (C), IA, *590*
Lindberg, Gillis, Wells, Bradley & Assoc., Inc. (C), MN, *618*
Lloyd, Carolyn T., Lloyd Associates (R), GA, *130*
Loughlin, Timothy M., Bankers Search, L.L.C. (C), CT, *259*
Lysenko, Lisa, A.L.S. Group (C), NJ, *232*
Lysenko, Scott, A.L.S. Group (C), NJ, *232*
Mahoney, Molly, McCarthy Assoc. National BancSearch, LLC (C), LA, *473*
Mangiafico, Jane, Largent Parks & Partners (C), TX, *503*
Marentez, Frank, Marentz & Co. (C), TX, *469*
Marshall, P. William, Dise & Co. (R), OH, *52*
Martin, Charles E., Management Recruiters of Birmingham-South, Inc. (C), AL, *438*
Massucco, Harry A., Sherwood Lehman Massucco, Inc. (R), CA, *189*
McCann, Connie B., SpencerStuart (R), PA, *197*
McCarthy, Richard, McCarthy Assoc. National BancSearch, LLC (C), LA, *473*
McCormick, Gregg J., Retained Search Assoc. (R), NC, *176*
McFarlan, Cydney, Discovery, The Staffing Specialists, Inc. (C), CA, *312*
McKenna, Elaine, Weterrings & Agnew, Inc. (C), NY, *619*
McPherson, Ron, National Bank & Finance Executive Search (C), CA, *488*
Miller, Roger, Ryan, Miller & Assoc. (C), CA, *549*
Miller, Roxxanne, The Pailin Group Professional Search Consultants (R), TX, *158*
Misarti, Paul R., Paul Misarti Inc. (C), NY, *483*
Munro, Jennifer, Jennifer Munro & Partners, Inc. (R), SC, *149*
Murphy, Clarke, Russell Reynolds Assoc., Inc. (R), NY, *177*
Murphy, Darlene R., Gateway Group Personnel, LLC (C), TN, *355*
Nadherny, Pete, The Angus Group, Ltd. (C), OH, *251*
Nason, Dennis H., Nason & Nason (C), FL, *488*
Nason-Robson, Nayda, Nason & Nason (C), FL, *488*
Paddock, Jeff, Management Recruiters The Delta Group, Inc. (C), TN, *461*
Paetzhold, Jerry, Davis & James, Inc. (C), MO, *308*
Palmer, James H., The Hindman Co. (R), KY, *94*
Park, Carol, Carol Park (C), MO, *502*
Pfaendler, Robert E., Robert E. Pfaendler & Assoc., Inc. (C), OR, *510*
Phillips, Richard K., Handy HRM (R), NY, *86*
Pittleman, Linda, Pittleman & Assoc. (C), NY, *513*
Polyzos, Ginia M., Management Advisors Int'l., Inc. (C), NC, *424*
Ponaman, Albert L., Al Ponaman Company, Inc. (C), CA, *514*
Porges, John M., Nason & Nason (C), FL, *488*
Posselt, Jeffrey, Cook Assoc.,® Inc. (R), IL, *40*
Potter, Steven B., Highland Search Group, L.L.C. (R), NY, *93*
Powers, Janet, Powers Consultants, Inc. (R), MO, *166*
Price, Daniel, Gavin Forbes & Price (R), CA, *75*
Ramirez, Richard, Marentz & Co. (C), TX, *469*
Range, Mary Jane, Bishop Partners (R), NY, *17*
Rank, Christy L., Mortgage Search Network (C), AZ, *486*
Ray, Marianne C., Callan Assoc., Ltd. (R), IL, *27*
Regush, Catherine, Ambridge Management Corp. (C), ON, *247*
Richards, Vivian, The Bankers Register (C), NY, *259*
Richter, Ryan, John Ryan Assoc., LLC. (C), NY, *399*
Rupert, James A., Management Recruiters of Siouxland (C), IA, *449*
Sanders, Gail, Discovery, The Staffing Specialists, Inc. (C), IL, *312*
Sauer, Harry, ACSYS Resources, Inc. (C), PA, *239*
Selbach, Barbara, SpencerStuart (R), NY, *196*
Shea, Kathleen P., Thomas E. Hedefine Assoc. (C), ON, *375*
Shedroff, Michael, ACSYS Resources, Inc. (C), NJ, *238*
Sherman, Robert, Mortgage & Financial Personnel Services (C), CA, *486*
Sherman, Susan, Mortgage & Financial Personnel Services (C), CA, *486*
Sherwin, Gordon K., Ambridge Management Corp. (C), ON, *247*
Singer, Lloyd R., Romac Int'l. (C), IL, *542*
Sklar, Ruth, Ruth Sklar Assoc., Inc. (RSA Executive Search) (R), NY, *192*
Smith, Aaron, Staffing Edge, Inc. (C), CO, *590*
Smith, Barry, Sales Consultants Bridgewater, Inc. (C), NJ, *560*
Smith, Jill, ACSYS Resources, Inc. (C), PA, *239*
Smith, Patti, Discovery, The Staffing Specialists, Inc. (C), TX, *313*

Smith, Stacy, Smith James Group, Inc. (R), GA, *194*
Snowden, Debra, Mortgage & Financial Personnel Services (C), CA, *486*
Sprehe, J. Christopher, The Christopher Group (C), NC, *291*
Stafford, Chris, Stafford Consulting Group (R), CA, *198*
Stafford, Norma, Stafford Consulting Group (R), CA, *198*
Stephenson, Harold, C. R. Assoc. (C), CA, *278*
Sterling, Cheryl, Management Recruiters of Mentor, Inc. (C), OH, *458*
Sterling, Ronald, Management Recruiters of Mentor, Inc. (C), OH, *458*
Stone, Richard, Stone Assoc. LLC (C), MI, *594*
Stranberg, Mark, Mark Stranberg & Assoc. Inc. (R), MA, *202*
Strom, Justin V., Overton Consulting (R), WI, *157*
Swift, Nina E., The Oxbridge Group, Ltd. (C), PA, *500*
Totah, Tamara, The Oxbridge Group, Ltd. (C), NY, *500*
Tucci, Joseph, Fairfaxx Corp. (R), CT, *64*
Vacca, Domenic L., ACSYS Resources, Inc. (C), DE, *238*
Watson, Jim, MSI Int'l. (C), GA, *487*
Watson, Lynn, Joy Reed Belt Search Consultants, Inc. (R), OK, *15*
Watson, Scott, Scott Watson & Assoc., Inc. (R), FL, *216*
Wedderien, Wayne, National Bank & Finance Executive Search (C), CA, *488*
Weiss, Cathy, C. Weiss Assoc., Inc. (C), NY, *618*
Westerfield, Dick, Russ Hadick & Assoc. Inc. (C), OH, *365*
Wieder, Thomas, Management Recruiters of Nassau, Inc. (R), NY, *134*
Winnewisser, William E., Accounting & Computer Personnel (C), NY, *238*
Wolfson, Gary M., The Blackman Kallick Search Division (C), IL, *267*
Womak, Joseph, The Bankers Group (C), IL, *258*
Youngblood, Robert S., Youngblood Assoc. (C), NC, *626*
Zaher, Richard, Fox-Morris Assoc., Inc. (C), NY, *352*
Zinn, Michael D., Michael D. Zinn & Assoc., Inc. (R), NJ, *227*

Corporate

Aral, Stephanie, Henrietta's Personnel & Executive Search, Inc. (C), FL, *376*

Benefits

Amato, George, Faro Consultants Int'l. (C), VA, *338*
Barkley, James, Management Recruiters of Champions (C), TX, *462*
Baron, Sheldon S., Sales Consultants of Nashua-Manchester (C), NH, *560*
Bleau, Donn E., Global Resources Group (R), CA, *78*
Brown, Charlene N., Accent On Achievement, Inc. (C), MI, *233*
Cunningham, Douglas, Staff Resources, Inc. (C), SC, *590*
Daudt, Jack, Triad Consultants, Inc. (C), NJ, *609*
Dixon, Anita, Cook Assoc. Int'l., Inc. (C), TN, *298*
Faubert, Denis, DARE Personnel Inc. (C), ON, *307*
Gold, Barry M., Barry M. Gold & Co. (C), CA, *359*
Gross, Joe, V.I.P. Resources, Inc. (C), NY, *611*
O'Neill, Sean, Waterford Executive Group Ltd. (C), IL, *616*
Peterman, James R., J. R. Peterman Assoc., Inc. (C), VT, *509*
Rodgers, Gayle, Rodgers, Ramsey, Inc. (C), TX, *540*
Stevens, Mal, The Dayton Group, Ltd. (C), NY, *309*
Tomaras, David, Willmott & Assoc. (C), MA, *622*
Vujeec, John, Executive Search, Ltd. (C), OH, *336*

Beverages

Alvarez, E. Linda, RJN Consulting (R), NY, *179*
Bailey, Edward L., The Patience Motivation Belief Group, Inc. (C), GA, *505*
Blevins, David C., David Blevins & Assoc. (C), WA, *268*
Boruff, Doug, Dunhill Personnel of Boulder (C), CO, *319*
Boruff, Fran, Dunhill Personnel of Boulder (C), CO, *319*
Glaser, Larry, Lawrence Glaser Assoc., Inc. (C), NJ, *358*
Hall, Earl R., Management Recruiters of Little Rock (C), AR, *439*
Harvey, E. Graeme, Sales Consultants of Appleton (C), WI, *563*
Hendrickson, Gary, Management Recruiters of Clovis (C), CA, *440*
Herbert, Paul, David Blevins & Assoc. (C), WA, *268*
Humphreys, Scott W., Robison Humphreys & Assoc., Inc. (R), ON, *180*
Kensington, Holland, Kensington International (R), CA, *113*
Kiken, Mark E., COBA Executive Search (R), CO, *36*
Laux, Frank J., StratfordGroup (R), TX, *203*
Mason, Morgan, Mason & Nicastri Ltd. (R), CA, *138*
Milius, Kent, Management Recruiters of Colorado, Inc. (C), CO, *442*
Nepple, Rosemarie, Management Recruiters of Upper Westchester (C), NY, *454*
Nepple, Vern D., Management Recruiters of Upper Westchester (C), NY, *454*
Newman, Richard J., RJN Consulting (R), NY, *179*
Nicastri, Diane, Mason & Nicrasti Ltd. (R), CA, *138*
Norris, Cathy A., Norris Agency (C), TX, *496*
Olsen, Rex, Olsen/Clark (R), WA, *156*
Peterson, Greg, Sales Consultants of Ft. Lauderdale, Inc. (C), FL, *557*
Pike, Geoff, F-O-R-T-U-N-E Personnel Consultants of Greenwood Village (C), CO, *344*
Presley, Jason T., Presley Consultants, Inc. (C), CA, *517*
Presley, Jason T., Presley Consultants, Inc. (C), MT, *517*
Rach, Walter, Cook Assoc.,® Inc. (R), IL, *40*
Roe, Craig T., Craig Roe & Assoc., LLC (C), MD, *540*
Shaffer, Michael, Management Recruiters Peninsula (C), CA, *439*
Shalinsky, John, Rice Cohen Int'l. (R), PA, *178*
Stanley, Harry, Whittaker & Assoc., Inc. (C), GA, *620*
Stockton, J. R., Management Catalysts (R), NJ, *134*
Wonderfund, Vicky, Management Recruiters of Columbia (C), MD, *450*

Bilingual

Dickens, Marcia, R. Gaines Baty Assoc., Inc. (R), GA, *13*
Frankel, Miriam, PMJ & Assoc. (C), ON, *513*
Fresquez, Ernesto, Fresquez & Assoc. (C), CA, *353*
Gutierrez, Mary Rose, Job Link, Inc. (C), CA, *399*
Haywood, Joy, Pasona Canada, Inc. (C), ON, *504*
Onizuka, Sayoko, Pasona Canada, Inc. (C), ON, *504*
Wada, Fumie, Pasona Canada, Inc. (C), ON, *504*

Biology

Jolly, Janine, The Hampton Group (C), NY, *368*

Biomedical

Bawza, Leo F., Chelsea Resources, Inc. (C), CT, *290*
Blank, Paula, Lewis & Blank Int'l. (R), CA, *129*
Koellhoffer, Thomas J., T. J. Koellhoffer & Assoc. (R), NJ, *116*
Levin, Becky, Levin & Company, Inc. (R), MA, *128*
Lewis, Daphne V., Lewis & Blank Int'l. (R), CA, *129*
Ottke, Robert C., Robert Ottke Assoc. (R), CA, *157*
Regan, Ray, Fortune Personnel Consultants (C), MT, *347*
Soo Hoo, Patrick J., Chelsea Resources, Inc. (C), CT, *290*

RECRUITER SPECIALTIES

Stevenson, Alex, Search Masters, USA (C), FL, *576*
Watkins, Robert J., R. J. Watkins & Co., Ltd. (R), CA, *216*

Biometrics

Jolly, Janine, The Hampton Group (C), NY, *368*

Biotechnology

Archie, Otis, Kuhn Med-Tech (C), CA, *409*
Arnold, Jerome M., Houtz•Strawn & Arnold, Inc. (R), TX, *96*
Arons, Richard, Korn/Ferry Int'l. (R), NJ, *118*
Barkley, Keith, The Mackenzie Group (R), MD, *133*
Bauer, Robert, Sampson Medical Search (C), AZ, *564*
Bauman, Ina, The Bauman Group (R), CA, *14*
Berry, Charles D., Management Recruiters of San Marcos (C), TX, *463*
Blakslee, Jan H., J: Blakslee Int'l., Ltd. (R), CA, *18*
Boccuzi, Joseph H., SpencerStuart (R), NY, *196*
Boje, Bruce A., Westfields Int'l., Inc. (C), NY, *619*
Bormann, David C., Yungner & Bormann (R), MN, *226*
Bouchard, Rena Roberts, Strategic Resources Biotechnology & Medical Group (C), WA, *595*
Bowman, Mary, Healthcare Management Resources, Inc. (R), GA, *89*
Bunker, Ralph, Management Recruiters of San Luis Obispo (C), CA, *439*
Caplan, John, The Caplan-Taylor Group (R), CA, *28*
Caplan, Shellie, Caplan Assoc., Inc. (R), NJ, *28*
Cavolina, Michael, Carver Search Consultants (C), CA, *285*
Cimicata, Richard, National Search Assoc. (C), CA, *490*
Clark, Ellen H., Clark Executive Search (C), NY, *292*
Cobb, Lynn A., Management Recruiters of Springfield, Inc. (C), IL, *447*
Collins, Steve L., S L Collins Assoc. (C), NC, *294*
Connolly, Claire E., CEC Associates (R), MA, *32*
Courtright, Robert J., Courtright & Assoc., Inc. (R), PA, *42*
Cunneff, Harry J., Management Recruiters of Lake Forest, IL (C), IL, *447*
Curry, Joseph, MediaCOM Talent Group (C), MA, *477*
Curry, Michael J., Curry, Telleri Group, Inc. (R), NJ, *44*
Daniels, Donna, Jonas, Walters & Assoc., Inc. (R), WI, *108*
DeMan, Denise, Bench Int'l. Search, Inc. (R), CA, *15*
Diblasi, Joseph J., First Advisory Services Int'l., Inc. (R), MD, *67*
Dimke, Tom, Raymond Karsan Assoc. (C), PA, *530*
Dukas, Theodore, Dukas Assoc. (C), MA, *315*
Duncan, James W., Sanford Rose Assoc. - Lake Forest (R), IL, *184*
Elsom, Jr., Kendall A., Genesis Consulting Partners (R), PA, *76*
Emory, Vaughn, BayResearch Group, Inc. (R), IL, *14*
Estrada, Barbara, Montgomery West (R), CA, *146*
Fisher, Jack Stuart, Jack Stuart Fisher Assoc. (C), NJ, *341*
Fleishman, William M., First Advisory Services Int'l., Inc. (R), MD, *67*
Gallagher, Michael, Mankuta Gallagher & Assoc., Inc. (C), FL, *468*
Gasbarre, John, The Haystack Group, Inc. (R), ME, *88*
Genel, George, Genel Associates (C), CA, *356*
Gostin, Howard I., Sanford Rose Assoc. - Columbia, MD (C), MD, *567*
Greenblatt, Stephanie, The Bauman Group (R), CA, *14*
Hamburg, Jennifer P., Ledbetter/Davidson Int'l., Inc. (R), NY, *127*
Hansen, Bente K., DHR Int'l., Inc. (R), CA, *49*
Harris, Bea, Exec Tech, Inc. (C), IL, *332*
Haverty, Carol, Iona Partners (C), CA, *394*
Hebel, Robert W., R. W. Hebel Assoc. (R), TX, *89*
Hoffman, Mark, Management Recruiters of Emeryville (C), CA, *440*
Hogan, Ann B., The Hogan Group (C), OH, *380*
Holodnak, William A., J. Robert Scott (R), MA, *104*
Jackowitz, Todd, J. Robert Scott (R), MA, *104*
Jensen, David G., Search Masters Int'l. (R), AZ, *187*
Johnson, Mark, Sampson Medical Search (C), CA, *564*
Jolly, Janine, The Hampton Group (C), NY, *368*
Joseph, Craig, Management Assoc. (C), MD, *424*
Kasten, Marc, Fortune Personnel Consultants (C), CA, *344*
Kazan, J. Neil, Kazan International, Inc. (R), NJ, *110*
Klein, Howard G., F-O-R-T-U-N-E Personnel Consultants of Bergen County Inc. (C), NJ, *347*
Kleinman, Victor, The Stevenson Group, Inc. (R), FL, *200*
Korytko, Lesia, COBA Executive Search (R), CO, *36*
Kuhn, Larry A., Kuhn Med-Tech (C), CA, *409*
Lareau, Belle, The Hampton Group (C), NY, *368*
Lareau, Gerard A., The Hampton Group (C), NY, *368*
Layton, Bernard, Morgan Int'l., Inc. (R), IL, *147*
Lerner, Joel S., Sanford Rose Assoc. - Louisville (C), KY, *567*
Levin, Becky, Levin & Company, Inc. (R), MA, *128*
Lord, J. Scott, J. S. Lord & Company, Inc. (R), MA, *131*
Lurier, Amy B., TechFind, Inc. (R), MA, *207*
Lybrook, David, Lybrook Assoc., Inc. (C), RI, *421*
Mankuta, Eric G., EGM Consulting, Inc. (R), FL, *57*
Mazziota, Daniel R., Ruth Sklar Assoc., Inc. (RSA Executive Search) (R), NY, *192*
McDermott, Tom, Corporate Environment Ltd. (R), IL, *41*
Miller, Shirley, Miller + Miller (C), WA, *482*
Montgomery, Rita, Healthcare Recruiters Int'l. - Los Angeles (C), CA, *372*
Morse, Mary K., Travis & Co., Inc. (R), MA, *210*
Mustin, Joyce, J: Blakslee Int'l., Ltd. (R), CA, *18*
Norindr, Bev, The Hampton Group (C), NY, *368*
Nowakowski, Mark R., Global Engineers Inc. (C), ME, *358*
Ortman, Jim, Ortman Recruiting Int'l. (C), CA, *500*
Pacini, Joseph, Premier Business Advisors (C), PA, *516*
Paine, Donne G., Fortune Personnel Consultants of Hilton Head (C), SC, *349*
Peluso, Philip, National Search Assoc. (C), CA, *490*
Pencarski, Robert, Bio-Venture Group (C), RI, *266*
Perry, Len, The Caplan-Taylor Group (R), CA, *28*
Piatkiewicz, Mary Lou, Medical Executive Search Assoc., Inc. (C), AZ, *477*
Piatkiewicz, William L., Medical Executive Search Assoc., Inc. (C), AZ, *477*
Roe, Sylvia A., Craig Roe & Assoc., LLC (C), MD, *540*
Romanchek, Walter R., Wellington Management Group (R), PA, *217*
Romeo, Paul C., Romeo-Hudgins & Assoc., Ltd. (C), NJ, *545*
Rutkauskas, Patsy A., Sales Consultants of Bangor, Inc. (C), ME, *559*
Sampson, Judie, Sampson Medical Search (C), CA, *564*
Sampson, Kellie, Sampson Medical Search (C), CA, *564*
Sawhill, Louise, Healthcare Management Resources, Inc. (R), GA, *89*
Schall, William, The Stevenson Group, Inc. (R), FL, *200*
Scott, George, Raymond Karsan Assoc. (C), PA, *530*
Shiley, Bob, Brethet, Barnum & Assoc., Inc. (C), ON, *273*
Stevenson, Jani, Howard Fischer Assoc. Int'l., Inc. (R), TX, *67*

Stewart, Tina Hunter, BioPharmMed (C), FL, *267*
Strand, Michael G., Fortune Group Int'l., Inc. (R), PA, *70*
Stratman, Sandra, Management Recruiters of Milford Inc. (C), CT, *442*
Strawn, William M., Houtz•Strawn & Arnold, Inc. (R), TX, *96*
Sullivan, Donald S., Executives Worldwide, Inc. (C), OR, *337*
Taylor, John, The Caplan-Taylor Group (R), AZ, *28*
Travis, John A., Travis & Co., Inc. (R), MA, *210*
VanDolah, A. F., Management Recruiters of Lionville, Inc. (C), PA, *459*
Westmore, Diane, Healthcare Management Resources, Inc. (R), GA, *89*
Wilkins, A. M., International Research Group (R), CA, *103*
Wilkins, Sherrie, International Research Group (R), CA, *103*
Williams, Kandi, Medical Executive Recruiters (C), CA, *477*
Wimberly, Jim, Healthcare Recruiters of Dallas (C), TX, *374*
Yungner, Steven J., Yungner & Bormann (R), MN, *226*
Zackrison, Walter, Zackrison Assoc., Inc. (C), FL, *627*
Zaring, David, Management Recruiters of Plant City, Inc. (C), FL, *444*

Blow molding

Murray, Patrick, The Murray Group (C), IL, *487*
Villee, Mark, Management Recruiters of Columbia (C), MD, *450*

Board search

Albertini, Nancy L., Taylor Winfield (R), TX, *207*
Allen, David, Century Assoc., Inc. (C), PA, *287*
Almour, Chloe, Kramer Executive Resources, Inc. (C), NY, *409*
Ambra, Glenn P., J. R. Phillip & Assoc., Inc. (R), CA, *164*
Bacher, Judith, SpencerStuart (R), NY, *196*
Barger, H. Carter, Barger & Sargeant, Inc. (R), NH, *11*
Bell, Michael, SpencerStuart (R), FL, *197*
Boren, Susan, SpencerStuart (R), MN, *197*
Boutin, Jean, Pharmaceutical Search Professionals, Inc. (C), PA, *510*
Brown, Jr., Hobson, Russell Reynolds Assoc., Inc. (R), NY, *176*
Callan, Robert M., Callan Assoc., Ltd. (R), IL, *27*
Carey, Dennis C., SpencerStuart (R), PA, *197*
Chambers, David E., David Chambers & Assoc., Inc. (R), CT, *32*
Christian, Jeffrey E., Christian & Timbers, Inc. (R), OH, *34*
Clark, Kenneth, Ken Clark Int'l. (R), NJ, *36*
Crist, Peter D., Crist Partners, Ltd. (R), IL, *43*
Czamanske, Paul, Compass Group Ltd. (R), MI, *38*
Daum, Julie H., SpencerStuart (R), NY, *196*
DeClouet, J. Michael, The J. B. Search Group (C), CA, *395*
Dise, Jr., Ralph A., Dise & Co. (R), OH, *52*
Donnelly, George J., SpencerStuart (R), TX, *197*
Earle, Paul W., SpencerStuart (R), IL, *197*
Edman, Silas E. G., The Partnership Group (R), NJ, *160*
Fairlie, Suzanne F., ProSearch, Inc. (C), PA, *524*
Farah, James C., The S C Group LLC (R), NY, *183*
Fee, J. Curtis, SpencerStuart (R), IL, *197*
Fischer, Howard, Howard Fischer Assoc. Int'l., Inc. (R), PA, *67*
Fischer, Howard, Howard Fischer Assoc. Int'l., Inc. (R), TX, *67*
Fitzgerald, Diane, Fitzgerald Associates (R), MA, *68*
Fitzgerald, Jon K., Health Industry Consultants, Inc. (R), CO, *89*
Frank, Jr., William E., The Curtiss Group International (R), FL, *44*
Fuller, Craig, Korn/Ferry Int'l. (R), DC, *118*
Gabel, Greg, Canny, Bowen Inc. (R), NY, *28*
Gaffney, Keith, Gaffney Management Consultants (R), IL, *73*
Glou, Alan, Glou Int'l., Inc. (R), MA, *78*
Goodwin, Joe D., LAI Ward Howell (R), GA, *123*
Grady, Richard F., Drew Assoc. Int'l. (R), NJ, *54*
Graham, David, Pharmaceutical Search Professionals, Inc. (C), PA, *510*
Griesedieck, Jr., Joseph E., SpencerStuart (R), CA, *196*
Guidry, Jim, Guidry & East Healthcare Search Consultants (R), TX, *83*
Hardison, Richard L., Hardison & Company (R), TX, *86*
Jacobs, James W., Callan Assoc., Ltd. (R), IL, *27*
Jakobs, Frederick H., Jakobs & Assoc. Int'l. (R), NY, *105*
Johnson, John F., LAI Ward Howell (R), OH, *123*
Kenny, Roger M., Boardroom Consultants/ Kenny Kindler Tholke (R), NY, *19*
Kierstead, Robert, High Tech Opportunities, Inc. (C), NH, *377*
Kindler, Peter A., Boardroom Consultants/ Kenny Kindler Tholke (R), NY, *19*
Kukoy, Stephen J., Kukoy Associates (R), CO, *121*
MacDougall, Andrew J., SpencerStuart (R), ON, *197*
Mangum, Maria, Thomas Mangum Co. (R), CA, *208*
Martin, Nancy A., EMN/Witt/Kieffer (R), MA, *59*
Middleton, Alfred, The Neil Michael Group, Inc./Global Partners (R), NY, *151*
Mruk, Edwin S., Mruk & E.M.A. Partners (R), NY, *148*
Murphy, Bob, Murphy Partners Int'l. (R), IL, *150*
Murrell, Maxine W., Professionals in Recruiting Co. (C), TN, *523*
Neff, Thomas J., SpencerStuart (R), NY, *196*
Ogden, Dayton, SpencerStuart (R), CT, *196*
Ott, George W., Ott & Hansen, Inc. (R), CA, *157*
Pearson, Robert L., LAI Ward Howell (R), TX, *124*
Phillip, John R., J. R. Phillip & Assoc., Inc. (R), CA, *164*
Pinsker, Richard J., Pinsker and Company, Inc. (R), CA, *164*
Posner, Gary J., EMN/Witt/Kieffer (R), TN, *59*
Poster, Lawrence D., Catalyx Group (R), NY, *31*
Redmond, Andrea, Russell Reynolds Assoc., Inc. (R), IL, *176*
Rieger, Louis J., SpencerStuart (R), TX, *197*
Roher, Howard F., Franklin Allen Consultants, Ltd. (R), NY, *71*
Rossi, Alfred F., The Rossi Search Group (C), PA, *545*
Seiden, Steven A., Seiden Krieger Assoc., Inc. (R), NY, *188*
Shoemaker, Richard, IR Search (R), CA, *103*
Shultz, Susan F., SSA Executive Search Int'l. (R), AZ, *198*
Silverman, Gary, GWS Partners (R), CA, *84*
Silverman, Gary, GWS Partners (R), IL, *84*
Simmons, J. Gerald, Handy HRM (R), NY, *86*
Smith, Herman M., Herman Smith Executive Initiatives Inc. (R), ON, *193*
Soderlund, Eric, Soderlund Assoc. Inc. (R), OH, *195*
Spatt, Jonathan M., Hospitality Executive Search, Inc. (R), MA, *96*
Sur, William K., Canny, Bowen Inc. (R), NY, *28*
Tholke, William E., Boardroom Consultants/Kenny Kindler Tholke (R), NY, *19*
Tribbett, III, Charles A., Russell Reynolds Assoc., Inc. (R), IL, *176*
Vennat, Manon, SpencerStuart (R), QE, *197*
Wilkie, Glenn A., The Wilkie Group Int'l. (R), ON, *220*
Winitz, Joel M., GSW Consulting Group, Inc. (R), CA, *83*
Wuko, John D., Pharmaceutical Search Professionals, Inc. (C), PA, *510*
Zeiger, Stephen A., Zeiger Assoc. L.L.C. (C), CA, *627*
Zilliacus, Patrick W., Larsen, Whitney, Blecksmith & Zilliacus, Inc. (R), CA, *125*

RECRUITER SPECIALTIES

Bond underwriting

Bevivino, Sal, Questor Consultants, Inc. (C), PA, *527*

Brand management

Aronin, Michael, Fisher-Todd Assoc. (C), NY, *342*
Balakonis, Charles L., Lawrence-Balakonis & Assoc., Inc. (C), GA, *414*
Franz, Ronald, Fisher-Todd Assoc. (C), NY, *342*
Nalley, Ginger, Executive Search Int'l. (C), TX, *336*
Rogers, Linda, Executive Search Int'l. (C), TX, *336*
Samet, Saul, Fisher-Todd Assoc. (C), NY, *342*
Savalli, Frank, Savalli & Assoc., Inc. (C), MI, *571*
Smith, Martin, Hughes & Company (R), VA, *98*
Wascovich, Tina, Rojek Marketing Group, Inc. (R), OH, *181*
Wasserman, Stan, Wasserman Assoc. Inc. (C), MD, *616*

Bridges

Haentzler, Robert A, Michael Latas & Assoc., Inc. (R), MO, *126*
Palumbo, Michael J., Michael Latas & Assoc., Inc. (R), MO, *126*
Robinson, Rodney L., Michael Latas & Assoc., Inc. (R), MO, *126*
Waller, Jody W., Michael Latas & Assoc., Inc. (R), MO, *126*

Broadcasting

Bege, Lorraine, Hands-on Broadcast (R), NY, *86*
Burz, Christina, Bishop Partners (R), NY, *17*
Frazier, Scott, Ron Sunshine & Assoc. (C), IL, *597*
Haggard, Jr., John H., Growth Consultants of America (R), MI, *82*
Mannix, Francis L., F. L. Mannix & Co. (R), MA, *135*
Miggins, Bob, Brad Marks Int'l. (R), CA, *136*
Timoney, Laura, Bishop Partners (R), NY, *17*

Brokerage

Arceri, John Mark, John Ryan Assoc., LLC. (C), NY, *399*
Boscacci, Gene, IR Search (R), CA, *104*
Fischer, Sherwin J., J. R. Scott & Assoc., Ltd. (C), IL, *395*
Higgins, Susan, The Rogan Group, Inc. (C), CA, *541*
Koenig, Barbara, Royal Assoc. (C), CA, *547*
Priseler, Michael, IR Search (R), CA, *103*
Richter, Ryan, John Ryan Assoc., LLC. (C), NY, *399*
Rogan, Daniel, The Rogan Group, Inc. (C), CA, *541*

BSME

Walt, Lee, M H Executive Search Group (C), TX, *422*

Building products

Brauninger, Elaine, AmeriPro Search, Inc. (C), NC, *248*
Brown, Bob, Management Recruiters of Sandy Springs (C), GA, *446*
Caracciolo, Peter, Management Recruiters of Nassau, Inc. (R), NY, *134*
Dinse, Karl, Management Recruiters of Sacramento North (C), CA, *441*
Hamel, Ed, Sales Consultants of Dallas (C), TX, *563*
Harvey, John K., Management Recruiters of North Fulton (C), GA, *445*
Lynge, R. J., Management Recruiters of Ft. Myers, FL. (C), FL, *443*
O'Reilly, William E., Management Recruiters of Cincinnati/Sharonville, Inc. (C), OH, *457*
Peterson, David A., Management Recruiters of Vero Beach (C), FL, *445*
Peterson, Diana K., Management Recruiters of Vero Beach (C), FL, *445*
Porada, Stephen D., S.D.P. Contract Recruiters (C), NJ, *550*
Schrandt, Fred, Rice Cohen Int'l. (R), PA, *178*
Sinclair, Rachel, Management Recruiters of Fresno (C), CA, *440*
VanSlyke, Dayton, Search By Design (C), AZ, *574*
Whitney, Ron, Sales Consultants of Sacramento (C), CA, *556*
Wolohan, Sarah, Cook Assoc.,® Inc. (R), IL, *40*

Business development

Adams, Chris, Fortune Group Int'l., Inc. (R), PA, *70*
Brentari, Michael, Search Consultants Int'l., Inc. (C), TX, *575*
Brindisi, Thomas J., Brindisi Search (R), MD, *23*
Caplan, Shellie, Caplan Assoc., Inc. (R), NJ, *28*
Crossman, Chuck, The Stewart Group (C), FL, *593*
Edmond, Bruce, Corporate Recruiters Ltd. (C), BC, *300*
Fitzpatrick, Alan, Merlin Int'l. Inc. (C), NJ, *479*
Howe, Timothy L., The Resource Group (R), NJ, *175*
Larkin, Dick, Larkin & Co. (R), CA, *125*
Lins, Peter T., McGrath & Assoc., Inc. (R), NJ, *141*
Martin, Vicki, Janou Pakter, Inc. (C), NY, *502*
Norindr, Bev, The Hampton Group (C), NY, *368*
Otsuka, Fyllis L., Holohan Group, Ltd. (R), MO, *95*
Simmons, Anneta, Fortune Personnel Consultants of Huntsville, Inc. (C), AL, *344*
Young, Susan M., Management Recruiters of Morris County, NJ (C), NJ, *453*

Cable

Bege, Lorraine, Hands-on Broadcast (R), NY, *86*
Burz, Christina, Bishop Partners (R), NY, *17*
Christidis, Aurora, Brad Marks Int'l. (R), CA, *136*
Forbes, Catherine M., StratfordGroup (R), CO, *203*
Frazier, Scott, Ron Sunshine & Assoc. (C), IL, *597*
Garman, Herb, Management Recruiters of Tucson (C), AZ, *439*
Haggard, Jr., John H., Growth Consultants of America (R), MI, *82*
Levitt, Peter, Sales Consultants King of Prussia (C), PA, *562*
Machi, Michael T., Management Recruiters of Pleasanton (C), CA, *441*
Ott, Robert S., Global Telecommunications, Inc. (C), TX, *359*
Pennella, Neil, Brad Marks Int'l. (R), CA, *136*
Stover, Bruce, StratfordGroup (R), CO, *203*
Timoney, Laura, Bishop Partners (R), NY, *17*

CAD/CAM

Barbosa, Franklin J., Skott/Edwards Consultants (R), NJ, *192*
Cooper, Ron, High Tech Opportunities, Inc. (C), NH, *377*
Gilson, Dirk S., Key Resources Int'l. (C), CA, *406*
Pinger, Earl, Systems Research Group (C), CA, *598*
Reyes, Randolph, Management Recruiters of Columbia (C), MD, *450*

Call centers

Bencin, Richard L., Richard L. Bencin & Assoc. (C), OH, *264*
Brown, Jeffrey B., J. B. Brown & Assoc., Inc. (C), OH, *275*
Burgess, Rick, Human Resource Dimensions, Inc. (C), TX, *384*
Caroli, Connie, TeleManagement Search (C), NY, *605*
Farrar, Carolyn, Sanford Rose Assoc. - Springfield (C), MO, *568*
Farrar, Gary, Sanford Rose Assoc. - Springfield (C), MO, *568*
Mulliken, Ken, Human Resource Dimensions, Inc. (C), MO, *384*

O'Neill, Kevin, J. B. Brown & Assoc., Inc. (C), OH, *275*
Ott, Robert S., Global Telecommunications, Inc. (C), TX, *359*
Ranta, Ed, J. E. Ranta Assoc. (C), MA, *529*
Speciale, Pamela, Austin Group Int'l./Marlar Int'l. (R), TX, *9*
York, Felecia, Human Resource Dimensions, Inc. (C), TX, *384*

Capital goods

Pilcher, James P., F-O-R-T-U-N-E Personnel Consultants of Cincinnati (C), OH, *348*
Schroeder, John W., SpencerStuart (R), TX, *197*

Capital markets

Anwar, Tarin, Jay Gaines & Company, Inc. (R), NY, *74*
Ayers, Jr., William L., The Ayers Group, Inc. (R), NY, *10*
Brookes, Michael T., Executive Access Inc. (R), NY, *62*
Ciaramitaro, Joseph, Corporate Search Consultants, Inc. (C), FL, *301*
Goodson, Jr., W. Kenneth, DLG Assoc., Inc. (R), NC, *53*
Guilford, David J., DLG Assoc., Inc. (R), NC, *53*
Hopard, Stuart M., Olympian Recruitment, Ltd. (C), NY, *498*
Miller, David, Global Executive Search Group (C), MA, *358*
Mochwart, Donald, Drummond Assoc., Inc. (C), NY, *315*
Morgan, David G., Morgan Stampfl, Inc. (C), NY, *485*
Olman, Robert, COR Management Services, Ltd. (C), NY, *298*
Orchant, Edward, A-L Assoc., Inc. (R), NY, *1*

Casinos

Casey, David, The Alfus Group (R), NY, *3*
Stafford, Susan P., Hospitality Int'l. (C), NY, *381*

Catalogs

Chapas, Kristyn, Cook Assoc.,® Inc. (R), IL, *40*
Glynn, Mary Anne, E. A. Hughes & Co., Inc. (R), NY, *98*
Hughes, Elaine A., E. A. Hughes & Co., Inc. (R), NY, *98*
Jackowitz, Todd, J. Robert Scott (R), MA, *104*
Levine, Alan C., Alan Levine Assoc. (R), MA, *129*
Lord, Marvin, E. A. Hughes & Co., Inc. (R), NY, *98*
Mayers, Lawrence S., Lamay Assoc., Inc. (R), CT, *124*
Simpson, Terre, Simpson Associates (C), NY, *582*

CATV

Capra, Jamie V., Warren, Morris & Madison, Ltd. (C), NH, *616*
Gorberg, Richard D., Fortune Personnel Consultants of Raleigh, Inc. (C), NC, *348*
Karkow, Drew, David Weinfeld Group (C), NC, *617*
Morris, Charles C., Warren, Morris & Madison, Ltd. (C), CA, *616*
Schmidt, Susan, David Weinfeld Group (C), NC, *617*
Scott, Corwyn J., Warren, Morris & Madison, Ltd. (C), NH, *616*
Warren, Scott C., Warren, Morris & Madison, Ltd. (C), NH, *616*
Weinfeld, David C., David Weinfeld Group (C), NC, *617*

Cellular

McCain, Barbara, Tele-Solutions of Arizona, Inc. (C), AZ, *604*
Moore, Michael H., The Inside Track (C), TX, *389*
Ott, Robert S., Global Telecommunications, Inc. (C), TX, *359*

Cement/concrete

Baker, S. Joseph, Search Consultants Int'l., Inc. (C), TX, *575*
Haentzler, Robert A, Michael Latas & Assoc., Inc. (R), MO, *126*
Palumbo, Michael J., Michael Latas & Assoc., Inc. (R), MO, *126*
Robinson, Rodney L., Michael Latas & Assoc., Inc. (R), MO, *126*
Waller, Jody W., Michael Latas & Assoc., Inc. (R), MO, *126*

CEO's

Ast, Steven T., AST/BRYANT (R), CT, *8*
Baldwin, W. Keith, Baldwin & Assoc. (C), OH, *258*
Belt, Joy Reed, Joy Reed Belt Search Consultants, Inc. (R), OK, *15*
Blaney, John A., Blaney Executive Search (R), MA, *18*
Boutin, Jean, Pharmaceutical Search Professionals, Inc. (C), PA, *510*
Bryant, Christopher P., AST/BRYANT (R), CA, *8*
Christian, Jeffrey E., Christian & Timbers, Inc. (R), OH, *34*
Cimino, James J., Executive Search, Ltd. (C), OH, *336*
Clark, Kenneth, Ken Clark Int'l. (R), NJ, *36*
Crist, Peter D., Crist Partners, Ltd. (R), IL, *43*
Czamanske, Paul, Compass Group Ltd. (R), MI, *38*
Dahl, Charles, Charles Dahl Group, Inc. (C), MN, *306*
Deckelbaum, Rick, Fortune Personnel Consultants of Raleigh, Inc. (C), NC, *348*
Dee, Vincent W., Hartsfield Group, Inc. (R), GA, *87*
Desley, Carolyn M., Erlanger Assoc. (R), CT, *60*
Dey, Robert L., Rob Dey Executive Search (R), FL, *49*
Edmond, Bruce, Corporate Recruiters Ltd. (C), BC, *300*
Edwards, S. Bruce, Bruce Edwards & Associates, Inc. (R), NC, *56*
Erlanger, Richard A., Erlanger Assoc. (R), CT, *60*
Fischer, Howard, Howard Fischer Assoc. Int'l., Inc. (R), PA, *67*
Fischer, Howard, Howard Fischer Assoc. Int'l., Inc. (R), TX, *67*
Fisher, Gary E., Fisher & Assoc. (R), CA, *67*
Gaffney, William, Gaffney Management Consultants (R), IL, *73*
Gibson, Bruce, Gibson & Co., Inc. (R), WI, *76*
Glick, Douglas I., MedSearch Resources, Inc. (C), FL, *478*
Goldring, Joe, Joseph Goldring & Assoc. Inc. (C), MI, *360*
Graham, David, Pharmaceutical Search Professionals, Inc. (C), PA, *510*
Guarino, Alan, Cornell Group Int'l. Consulting, Inc. (R), NY, *41*
Guarino, Kathleen, Cornell Group Int'l. Consulting, Inc. (R), NY, *41*
Heffelfinger, Thomas V., Heffelfinger Assoc., Inc. (R), MA, *89*
Heinschel, Phil, Phillips Personnel/Search (C), CO, *510*
Hewett, Martin J., McCray, Shriver, Eckdahl & Assoc., Inc. (R), CA, *140*
Humphreys, William M., Robison Humphreys & Assoc., Inc. (R), ON, *180*
Johnston, J. Reid, Hughes & Company (R), VA, *98*
King, Margaret, Christian & Timbers, Inc. (R), OH, *34*
Kohn, Steven, Affinity Executive Search (C), FL, *241*
Levin, Phillip, Executive Search Team (C), MI, *336*
Lindberg, Eric J., MSI Int'l. (C), GA, *486*
Lowery, Bruce N., Bruce Lowery & Assoc. (C), MI, *420*
Martin, Donovan, Donovan Martin & Assoc. (R), CA, *137*
McClain, Duane, Construction Search Specialists, Inc. (C), WI, *297*
McCray, Harold C., McCray, Shriver, Eckdahl & Assoc., Inc. (R), CA, *140*
McFeely, Clarence E., Clarence E. McFeely, Inc. (R), IL, *141*
Newell, Donald Pierce, Newell Assoc. (R), NY, *151*
Poster, Lawrence D., Catalyx Group (R), NY, *31*
Potter, Steven B., Highland Search Group, L.L.C. (R), NY, *93*
Roberts, Nick, Pacific Search Group, Inc. (C), CA, *501*

RECRUITER SPECIALTIES

Rolfe, Pamela, Career Specialists, Inc. (R), WA, *29*
Shoemaker, Richard, IR Search (R), CA, *103*
Smith, George D., Bruce Edwards & Associates, Inc. (R), NC, *57*
Smith, Herman M., Herman Smith Executive Initiatives Inc. (R), ON, *193*
Stack, Kevin M., Circuit Search (C), NY, *291*
Tyler, J. Larry, Tyler & Company (R), GA, *212*
Wackerle, Frederick W., Fred Wackerle, Inc. (R), IL, *214*
Walker, Douglas G., Sink, Walker, Boltrus Int'l. (R), MA, *192*
Wilkie, Glenn A., The Wilkie Group Int'l. (R), ON, *220*
Willis, Jr., William H., William Willis Worldwide Inc. (R), CT, *221*
Wuko, John D., Pharmaceutical Search Professionals, Inc. (C), PA, *510*
Zilliacus, Patrick W., Larsen, Whitney, Blecksmith & Zilliacus, Inc. (R), CA, *125*

Ceramics

Bethmann, Chris, Southern Recruiters & Consultants, Inc. (C), SC, *587*
Hiller, Arnie, U.S. Search (C), VA, *610*

CFO's

Alexander, Susan M., Manuso, Alexander & Associates, Inc. (R), NY, *135*
Aruza, Al, Cornell Group Int'l. Consulting, Inc. (R), NY, *41*
Boxer, Harry, The Century Group (C), CA, *287*
Castine, Michael P., Highland Search Group, L.L.C. (R), NY, *93*
Crist, Peter D., Crist Partners, Ltd. (R), IL, *43*
Cuddy, Brian C., Romac Int'l. Inc. (R), MA, *181*
Dey, Robert L., Rob Dey Executive Search (R), FL, *49*
Dieckmann, Ralph E., Dieckmann & Assoc., Ltd. (R), IL, *51*
Erder, Debra, Canny, Bowen Inc. (R), NY, *28*
Evins, Susan, Bartl & Evins (C), NY, *260*
Fineman, David M., Manuso, Alexander & Associates, Inc. (R), NY, *135*
Fisher, Richard, Richard A. Eisner & Co., LLP (R), NY, *57*
Gibson, Bruce, Gibson & Co., Inc. (R), WI, *76*
Glick, Douglas I., MedSearch Resources, Inc. (C), FL, *478*
Graham, Robert W., Robert Graham Assoc. (R), RI, *81*
Grantham, John D., Grantham & Co., Inc. (R), NC, *81*
Griffiths, William J., Romac Int'l. Inc. (R), MA, *181*
Hayden, Lynn, Erlanger Assoc. (R), FL, *60*
Hiesiger, Emile M., Manuso, Alexander & Associates, Inc. (R), NY, *135*
Humphreys, William M., Robison Humphreys & Assoc., Inc. (R), ON, *180*
Johnston, J. Reid, Hughes & Company (R), VA, *98*
Karr, Cynthia, Howard Karr & Assoc., Inc. (R), CA, *110*
Karr, Howard L., Howard Karr & Assoc., Inc. (R), CA, *110*
Karr, Liz, Howard Karr & Assoc., Inc. (R), CA, *110*
Kramer, Alan L., Kramer Executive Resources, Inc. (C), NY, *409*
Leff, Ilene J., Richard A. Eisner & Co., LLP (R), NY, *57*
Levin, Phillip, Executive Search Team (C), MI, *336*
Lieff, Shelley, Advice Personnel Inc. (C), NY, *241*
Lowery, Bruce N., Bruce Lowery & Assoc. (C), MI, *420*
Manuso, James S. J., Manuso, Alexander & Associates, Inc. (R), NY, *135*
Martin, Donovan, Donovan Martin & Assoc. (R), CA, *137*
McFeely, Clarence E., Clarence E. McFeely, Inc. (R), IL, *141*
Murphy, Bob, Murphy Partners Int'l. (R), IL, *150*
Pierce, Matthew J., Pierce & Assoc. (C), CA, *512*
Proul, Ron, The Century Group (C), CA, *287*
Prouty, Alden F., Manuso, Alexander & Associates, Inc. (R), NY, *135*
Schiavone, Mary Rose, Canny, Bowen Inc. (R), NY, *28*
Seehusen, Joseph R., J. R. Seehusen Assoc., Inc. (R), IA, *188*
Shoemaker, Richard, IR Search (R), CA, *103*
Siciliano, Gene, Western Management Assoc. (R), CA, *218*
Sur, William K., Canny, Bowen Inc. (R), NY, *28*
Turnblacer, John, The Gabriel Group (C), PA, *354*
Whitlow, M. Blanton, Manuso, Alexander & Associates, Inc. (R), NY, *135*
Wilkie, Glenn A., The Wilkie Group Int'l. (R), ON, *220*
Yaeger, Don, The Century Group (C), CA, *287*

Change management

Atkinson, Patrick J., Waterford Executive Group Ltd. (C), IL, *616*
Brindisi, Thomas J., Brindisi Search (R), MD, *23*
Stillinger, Scott R., Stillinger & Assoc. (R), CA, *201*
Tomei, Ted, Waterford Executive Group Ltd. (C), IL, *616*
Whittier, Richard, The Ransford Group (R), TX, *171*

Chemical

Allen, Jr., Lindsay, Mark III Personnel, Inc. (C), NC, *470*
Andrews, Charles, The Borton Wallace Co. (R), TN, *19*
Arnold, Robert W., R & J Arnold & Assoc., Inc. (C), CO, *253*
Aslaksen, James S., LAI Ward Howell (R), IL, *123*
Bellview, Louis, Management Recruiters - Friendswood (C), TX, *462*
Bremer, Michael, Woodmoor Group (C), CO, *624*
Burnaugh, Reg, Management Recruiters of Ogden (C), UT, *464*
Burt, David S., David S. Burt Assoc. (C), MT, *276*
Campbell, Sandra, Management Recruiters of Milford Inc. (C), CT, *442*
Collins, Victoria, Sales Consultants of Dallas (C), TX, *563*
Cooper, Bill, Management Recruiters of Chattanooga-Brainerd, Inc. (C), TN, *461*
Creeger, David, Sanford Rose Assoc. - Fairlawn (C), OH, *569*
Daniel, Beverly R., Foy, Schneid & Daniel, Inc. (R), NY, *71*
David, Dave, Executive Resource Assoc. (C), VA, *334*
deMartino, Cathy, Lucas Assoc. (C), GA, *421*
Dougherty, Robert E., Dougherty & Assoc. (C), TN, *314*
Duke, Ann, Sanford Rose Assoc. - Fairlawn (C), OH, *569*
Fahey, Michael T., NorTech Resources (C), NY, *496*
Fidelle, Thomas P., ExecuTech (C), IN, *332*
Fink, Don J., Technical Staffing Solutions (C), TX, *602*
Fisher, Lawrence C., Mullen Assoc., Inc. (R), NC, *149*
Ford, Travis, Ford & Assoc., Inc. (C), SC, *343*
Fosnot, Michael, Management Recruiters of McMurray, Inc. (C), PA, *459*
Fox, Gary, F-O-R-T-U-N-E Personnel Consultants of Southwest Indiana (C), IN, *346*
Fremon, Michael W., The Revere Assoc., Inc. (R), OH, *176*
Froelich, K., Murphy Partners Int'l. (R), IL, *150*
Gagola, J., American Executive Management, Inc. (R), MA, *5*
Gehle, Frederick P., Dunhill Professional Search of Augusta (C), GA, *320*
Gilmore, Jerry, Management Recruiters of Loudoun County South (C), VA, *465*
Gres, Ed, Pioneer Executive Consultants (C), ON, *512*
Hageman, Jr., Leo, HR Inc. (C), NC, *382*
Harbaugh, Jr., Paul J., International Management Advisors, Inc. (R), NY, *103*
Heybroek, Eric J., Sanford Rose Assoc. - Rockville (C), MD, *568*

Hughes, Tim, Hughes & Assoc. Int'l. Inc. (C), AL, *383*
Hytowitz, Allan, Southern Chemical & Plastics Search (C), GA, *587*
Irwin, Bill, Southern Recruiters & Consultants, Inc. (C), SC, *587*
Johnson, Randall, Inter Regional Executive Search, Inc. (IRES, Inc.) (C), NJ, *391*
Johnston, Gail, NJ Solutions (C), CA, *493*
Jordan, Bill, Matrix Consultants, Inc. (C), NC, *472*
Kawahara, Wade, HCI Corp. (C), IL, *371*
Kleames, Jerry, Genesis Recruiting (C), CA, *356*
Labadie, Ernie, Management Recruiters of Boca Raton (C), FL, *443*
Lambre, Glenn C., McCooe & Assoc., Inc. (R), NJ, *140*
Lane, Andrew J., Overton Consulting (R), WI, *157*
Lybrook, Karen, Lybrook Assoc., Inc. (C), RI, *421*
Maphet, Harriet, The Stevenson Group, Inc. (N.J.) (R), NJ, *200*
Marion, Joe, Matrix Consultants, Inc. (C), NC, *472*
McDowell, Jane, Cook Assoc.,® Inc. (R), IL, *40*
McElhaney, Ron, Management Recruiters of Savannah (C), GA, *446*
McElhaney, Jr., Ron, Management Recruiters of Savannah (C), GA, *446*
McGee, Tom, Lucas Assoc. (C), GA, *421*
McGeehan, Gayle A., Management Recruiters of Bethlehem, PA (C), PA, *458*
McGrath, Robert E., Robert E. McGrath & Assoc. (R), CT, *141*
Meitz, Robert, Management Recruiters of West Chester, Inc. (C), PA, *460*
Meyer, Fred R., Management Recruiters of Bethlehem, PA (C), PA, *458*
Molliver, Marshall E., National Search, Inc. (R), NC, *151*
Mullen, James J., Mullen Assoc., Inc. (R), NC, *149*
Mullen, Maryrose H., Emmett Executive Search, Inc. (C), NY, *330*
Neidenberg, Steven, William Bell Assoc., Inc. (C), NJ, *263*
Nix Gilmore, Pamela, Management Recruiters of Loudoun County South (C), VA, *465*
Nowakowski, Mark R., Global Engineers Inc. (C), ME, *358*
Noyes, Jim, Sales Consultants - Bristol County (C), MA, *559*
O'Daniel, James E., The Elsworth Group (C), TX, *329*
O'Keefe, Frank, The Marathon Group (C), FL, *469*
O'Reilly, William E., Management Recruiters of Cincinnati/Sharonville, Inc. (C), OH, *457*
Pike, Dick, Management Recruiters of Burlington (C), NC, *455*
Pirro, Anthony S., Cornwall Stockton & Co., Inc. (C), TX, *299*
Poeppelmeier, David J., ISC of Cincinnati Inc. (C), OH, *394*
Preng, David E., Preng & Assoc., Inc. (R), TX, *167*
Price, William G., Engineering Profiles (C), FL, *330*
Ralley, P. Neil, E.P. Int'l. (C), NJ, *325*
Ralley, P. Neil, E.P. Int'l. (C), NY, *324*
Rathborne, Kenneth J., Blair/Tech Recruiters, Inc. (C), NJ, *268*
Romanchek, Walter R., Wellington Management Group (R), PA, *217*
Ropella, Patrick B., Ropella & Assoc. (R), FL, *181*
Rossi, Alfred F., The Rossi Search Group (C), PA, *545*
Scott, Harold, Graham & Co. (R), NJ, *80*
Scrivines, Hank, Search Northwest Assoc. (C), OR, *576*
Sharp, Paul S., Management Recruiters of Roanoke (C), VA, *465*
Sinclair, Paul, Pioneer Executive Consultants (C), ON, *512*
Sinisi, Vinny, W. Robert Eissler & Assoc., Inc. (C), TX, *327*
Smith, Gayle, J. Burke & Assoc., Inc. (C), TX, *276*
Snider, Jr., Les, Bryan & Louis Research (C), OH, *275*
Souder, Elizabeth W., Springer Souder & Assoc. L.L.C. (R), IL, *198*
Steinman, Stephen M., The Stevenson Group, Inc. (N.J.) (R), NJ, *200*
Telleri, Frank C., Curry, Telleri Group, Inc. (R), NJ, *44*
Van Buskirk, Bruce, Horizons Unlimited (C), CA, *381*
Vosika, Duane, Sales Consultants of Omaha, Inc. (C), NE, *560*
White, Ken, Management Recruiters of Winston-Salem (C), NC, *457*
Wilcox, Alex B., The Bridge (C), CO, *273*
Williamson, Frank, Management Recruiters of Westmoreland County, Inc. (C), PA, *459*
Witt, Gerald E., The Witt Group (C), FL, *623*
Worthing, Ellen, Management Recruiters of the Baltimore Washington Corridor (C), MD, *450*
Wylie, John L., John Wylie Assoc., Inc. (C), OK, *625*
Young, Steven J., Career Counseling Inc. (CCI) (C), KY, *282*
Zamjahn, Charles J., River Region Personnel, Inc. (C), LA, *538*
Zaring, David, Management Recruiters of Plant City, Inc. (C), FL, *444*
Zillifro, Keith, Management Recruiters of Roanoke (C), VA, *465*

CIO's

Borenstine, Alvin J., Synergistics Assoc. Ltd. (R), IL, *205*
Critchley, Walter Y., Cochran, Cochran & Yale, Inc. (R), NY, *36*
Dahl, Charles, Charles Dahl Group, Inc. (C), MN, *306*
Daily, John, Christian & Timbers, Inc. (R), OH, *34*
Daily, John C., Handy HRM (R), NY, *86*
Detling, John, Executive Search, Ltd. (C), OH, *336*
Diersing, Joe, Executive Search, Ltd. (C), OH, *336*
Dong, Steven, Executive Search, Ltd. (C), OH, *336*
Fafard, Lina, Montgomery West (R), CA, *146*
Gibson, Bruce, Gibson & Co., Inc. (R), WI, *76*
Grossman, Allan D., A. Davis Grant & Co. (R), NJ, *81*
Heffelfinger, Thomas V., Heffelfinger Assoc., Inc. (R), MA, *89*
Kukoy, Stephen J., Kukoy Associates (R), CO, *121*
Levin, Phillip, Executive Search Team (C), MI, *336*
McFeely, Clarence E., Clarence E. McFeely, Inc. (R), IL, *141*
McManamon, Tim, Rogers - McManamon Executive Search (R), CA, *180*
Olsen, David G., Handy HRM (R), NY, *86*
Rogers, Gay, Rogers - McManamon Executive Search (R), CA, *180*
Sabrin, Joe, ManTech Consulting (C), NY, *468*
Seehusen, Joseph R., J. R. Seehusen Assoc., Inc. (R), IA, *188*

Citrus

Holford, Jay, MIXTEC Group (R), CA, *145*

Civil

Munger, Donald, Berkshire Search Assoc. (C), MA, *265*

Clerical

Arnold, Jay, Staffing Edge, Inc. (C), KS, *590*
Avazian, Mary Ann, National Field Service Corp. (C), NY, *489*
Dykes, Mimi, Staffing Edge, Inc. (C), TX, *591*
Folletta, Wallamena, Action Executive Personnel Consulting Inc. (C), ON, *239*
Henderson, John, Staffing Edge, Inc. (C), AZ, *590*
Kindig, Becky, Management Recruiters-Cedar Rapids, Inc. (C), IA, *448*
Martin, Susan, Howard/Williams Assoc. (C), FL, *382*
Postlethwaite, John, Edward Bell Assoc. (C), CA, *263*
Sears, Keith, Edward Bell Assoc. (C), CA, *263*
Sherwood, Rose-Marie, DARE Personnel Inc. (C), ON, *307*
Smith, Aaron, Staffing Edge, Inc. (C), CO, *590*

Client/server

Allen, Mark, Computer Professionals Unlimited (C), TX, *295*
Arceri, John Mark, John Ryan Assoc., LLC. (C), NY, *399*
Bell, Dixie Lee, MIS Computer Professionals, Inc. (C), KS, *482*
Bouchard, Rodney, Management Recruiters of Winsted, Inc. (C), CT, *442*
Capozzi, John, C Assoc. (C), DC, *278*
Capps, Norm, MIS Computer Professionals, Inc. (C), KS, *482*
Ciaramitaro, Paul, Corporate Search Consultants, Inc. (C), FL, *301*
Cohen, Lawrence J., Norgate Technology, Inc. (C), NY, *494*
Dangerfield, Chris, Technology Search Int'l. (C), CA, *603*
Dyson, Steve, Technology Search Int'l. (C), CA, *603*
Fairlie, Suzanne F., ProSearch, Inc. (C), PA, *524*
Galka, John, Huntley Associates (Dallas), Inc. (C), TX, *386*
Gordon, Dave, Cemco, Ltd. (C), IL, *287*
Gross, Jerry, Creative HR Solutions (C), GA, *303*
Lingle, Bruce, ContactBridge, Inc. (R), IL, *40*
Newman, Gloria, Jack Richman & Assoc. (C), FL, *537*
Plavin, Avery, The Consulting Group of North America, Inc. (C), VA, *297*
Richman, Jack, Jack Richman & Assoc. (C), FL, *537*
Richter, Ryan, John Ryan Assoc., LLC. (C), NY, *399*
Sieler, Susan, C Assoc. (C), DC, *278*
Steuer, Ira, Cemco, Ltd. (C), MO, *287*

Clinical

Boutin, Jean, Pharmaceutical Search Professionals, Inc. (C), PA, *510*
Bryant, Tom, Bryant Research (C), NJ, *276*
Clark, Michael, Cornerstone Search Assoc. Inc. (C), MA, *299*
Clements, Denise, Marcus & Assoc. (C), NY, *469*
Cracknell, Jo Anne, NCC Executive Search Consultants (C), CA, *490*
Crossman, Chuck, The Stewart Group (C), FL, *593*
Cunneff, Harry J., Management Recruiters of Lake Forest, IL (C), IL, *447*
DeRario, Donna, F-O-R-T-U-N-E Personnel Consultants of San Diego (C), CA, *344*
Domann, Jr., William A., The Domann Organization (R), CA, *53*
Dunbar, Meg, M. Dunbar & Assoc. (C), TX, *316*
Feingold, Robin, Cornerstone Search Assoc. Inc. (C), MA, *299*
Fitzgerald, Diane, Fitzgerald Associates (R), MA, *68*
Furioso, Carmine A., F-O-R-T-U-N-E Personnel Consultants of San Diego (C), CA, *344*
Graham, David, Pharmaceutical Search Professionals, Inc. (C), PA, *510*
Handler, Marilyn, MedXec USA, Inc. (C), FL, *478*
Lihan, Dana L., MedXec USA, Inc. (C), FL, *478*
Oberman, Heidi, Medical Recruiters Inc. (C), MO, *477*
Osborne, Julie, Rogish Assoc., Inc. (C), OH, *541*
Paine, Donne G., Fortune Personnel Consultants of Hilton Head (C), SC, *349*
Rosen, Richard, Cornerstone Search Assoc. Inc. (C), MA, *299*
Stewart, James H., The Stewart Group (C), FL, *593*
Watring, Bernie, Watring & Assoc., Inc. (C), IL, *616*
Wottowa, Denise, Medical Recruiters Inc. (C), MO, *477*

Closely-held business

Schwartz, Alan, Advice Personnel Inc. (C), NY, *241*

Club

Bennett, Jr., Robert C., Bennett Search & Consulting Co. (R), FL, *16*
Francis, Joseph, Hospitality Int'l. (C), NY, *381*
Kopplin, Richard M., Kopplin Search, Inc. (R), CA, *117*
Reda, Pat, P. J. Reda & Assoc., Inc. (C), GA, *533*
Reich, Joshua, The Alfus Group (R), NY, *3*
Smith, Grant, Price Waterhouse Executive Search (R), BC, *168*

Coatings

Hunt, Leigh, Leigh Hunt & Assoc., Inc. (C), ME, *384*
Kleames, Jerry, Genesis Recruiting (C), CA, *356*
Lybrook, David, Lybrook Assoc., Inc. (C), RI, *421*
McDowell, Jane, Cook Assoc.,® Inc. (R), IL, *40*
Paterson, David, Scientific Solutions, Inc. (C), MI, *572*
Paterson, Sharon, Scientific Solutions, Inc. (C), MI, *572*
Poeppelmeier, David J., ISC of Cincinnati Inc. (C), OH, *394*
Sharrow, Beth S., Sharrow & Assoc., Inc. (C), MI, *579*
Telem, Peter B., Telem Adhesive Search Corp. (C), MD, *605*
Telleri, Frank C., Curry, Telleri Group, Inc. (R), NJ, *44*
Tippel, Fred C., Fred C. Tippel & Assoc. (C), OH, *607*

COBOL

Lynch, William E., Fortuna Technologies Inc. (C), CA, *343*

Communications

Alexander, Penelope, Alexander & Co. (C), CA, *243*
Allen, Jean E., LAI Ward Howell (R), NY, *122*
Ardi, Dana B., LAI Ward Howell (R), CA, *123*
Arnone, Patrick J., Patrick Arnone & Assoc. Inc. (R), VA, *7*
Aronin, Michael, Fisher-Todd Assoc. (C), NY, *342*
Austin, Larry, Lucas Assoc. (C), TX, *421*
Avazian, Richard W., National Field Service Corp. (C), NY, *489*
Bailin, Fred, Asset Resource, Inc. (C), CA, *254*
Bakehorn, Thomas, Martin Stevens Tamaren & Assoc., Inc. (R), CA, *206*
Barbosa, Franklin J., Skott/Edwards Consultants (R), NJ, *192*
Bard, Justin, Management Recruiters of St. Augustine (C), FL, *444*
Beaudine, Jr., Frank R., Eastman & Beaudine, Inc. (R), GA, *56*
Belanger, Richard, Kingsley Allen Partners Inc. (R), ON, *114*
Belanger, Rick, Belanger Partners Ltd. (C), ON, *262*
Bodin, Thomas H., The Personnel Group, Inc. (R), MN, *163*
Booker, Calvin, National Affirmative Action Career Network, Inc. (C), CO, *488*
Branch, Minnie, M. F. Branch Assoc., Inc. (C), NC, *272*
Butler, Vandy, Management Recruiters of Ogden (C), UT, *464*
Cardwell, Jean, Cardwell Enterprises Inc. (R), IL, *29*
Carey, Dennis C., SpencerStuart (R), PA, *197*
Carmena, Jane, SpencerStuart (R), CA, *196*
Cebak, William, Entelechy Group Ltd. (R), MD, *60*
Chambers, Cindy, Entelechy Group Ltd. (R), MD, *60*
Chisum, Jeanne, Executive Sales Search (C), CO, *335*
Christoff, Matt, SpencerStuart (R), MN, *197*
Clark, David A., Sprout/Standish, Inc. (C), NH, *590*
Cohen, Robert C., Intech Summit Group, Inc. (R), CA, *102*
Colling, Douglas, KPMG Executive Search (R), ON, *119*
Conlin, Edward T., Allen Austin Lowe & Powers (R), TX, *3*
Corey, Patrick M., LAI Ward Howell (R), WI, *124*
Cornehlsen, James H., Skott/Edwards Consultants (R), NY, *192*
Corwen, Leonard, Leonard Corwen Assoc. (C), NY, *302*

Costello, Lynda, Coe & Co. Int'l. Inc./EMA Partners Int'l. (R), AB, *37*
DeGrasse, Bob, SignatureSoft Inc. (C), CA, *581*
Dell'Aquilla, Joseph, Allen Austin Lowe & Powers (R), TX, *3*
Denison, Susan, Johnson Smith & Knisely (R), NY, *107*
Devlin, Jack, The Devlin Search Group, Inc. (C), MA, *312*
Doherty, Leonard J., L. J. Doherty & Assoc. (R), MA, *53*
Edwards, Charles R., LAI Ward Howell (R), GA, *123*
Eldredge, Peter, Johnson Smith & Knisely (R), NY, *107*
Emerzian, Jennifer, Johnson Smith & Knisely (R), NY, *107*
Eskew, Martha, Recruiting Options, Inc. (C), GA, *532*
Flesher, Susan, Flesher & Assoc., Inc. (R), CA, *68*
Forman, Margaret M., National Field Service Corp. (C), NY, *489*
Frank, Neil, Neil Frank & Co. (R), CA, *71*
Franz, Ronald, Fisher-Todd Assoc. (C), NY, *342*
Gallagher, Alice, Synergistech Communications (C), CA, *597*
Gardiner, E. Nicholas P., Gardiner, Townsend & Assoc. (R), NY, *74*
Gibson, Jan, Advanced Corporate Search (C), CA, *240*
Goodman, Goody, Harvard Group Int'l. (R), CO, *87*
Gordy, Thomas, Harvard Group Int'l. (R), GA, *87*
Grady, Jerry, The Ward Group (R), MA, *215*
Graham-Bryce, Robert, PSD Group, Inc. (C), CA, *525*
Greene, Dorcas P., Greene Personnel Consultants (C), RI, *362*
Hall, Susan, Susan Hall Executive Search (C), TX, *366*
Hammond, Karla, People Management Northeast, Inc. (R), CT, *162*
Hayward, Robert M., National Field Service Corp. (C), NY, *489*
Hazan, Lynn, Beverly von Winckler & Assoc. (C), IL, *613*
Heath, Jeffrey A., The Landstone Group (C), NY, *412*
Holton, David, PSD Group, Inc. (C), CA, *525*
Hudson, Betty, SpencerStuart (R), NY, *196*
Hughes, Cathy N., The Ogdon Partnership (R), NY, *155*
Humphreys, Scott W., Robison Humphreys & Assoc., Inc. (R), ON, *180*
Johnson, Kathleen N., The Repovich-Reynolds Group (TRRG, Inc.) (R), CA, *175*
Jones, Dale E., LAI Ward Howell (R), GA, *123*
Kelly, Rory, The Ellsworth Group (C), NY, *329*
Kiken, Mark E., COBA Executive Search (R), CO, *36*
Kneen, Linda, General Engineering Tectonics (C), CA, *356*
Landon, Susan J., LAI Ward Howell (R), NY, *122*
Lee, Carol Ricci, Ricci Lee Assoc., Inc. (C), CA, *415*
Leighton, Nina, The Ogdon Partnership (R), NY, *155*
LeMon, Monet M., The Repovich-Reynolds Group (TRRG, Inc.) (R), CA, *175*
Lombardi, Nancy, WTW Assoc., Inc. (R), NY, *225*
Long, Benjamin H., Travaille Executive Search (R), DC, *210*
Long, Janet R., Integrity Search, Inc. (R), PA, *102*
MacArthur, Sylvia, Madison MacArthur Inc. (R), ON, *133*
MacEachern, David, SpencerStuart (R), ON, *197*
Malcom, John W., Johnson Smith & Knisely (R), NY, *107*
Marshall, Larry, Marshall Consultants, Inc. (R), NY, *137*
Mastandrea, Pat, Johnson Smith & Knisely (R), NY, *107*
McCandless, Hugh, Marshall Consultants, Inc. (R), NY, *137*
McCormick-Kelch, Anna, Johnson Smith & Knisely (R), IL, *107*
McLean, E. Peter, SpencerStuart (R), NY, *196*
McManamon, Tim, Rogers - McManamon Executive Search (R), CA, *180*
Morris, Charles C., Warren, Morris & Madison, Ltd. (C), CA, *616*
Nagy, Lou, The Ward Group (R), MA, *215*
Nicklas, Kirk, The Ellsworth Group (C), NY, *329*
Nosky, Richard E., LAI Ward Howell (R), AZ, *123*
Offutt, Brian, SpencerStuart (R), NY, *196*
Ogdon, Thomas H., The Ogdon Partnership (R), NY, *155*
Orton, Linda Sedloff, Intelligent Marketing Solutions, Inc. (C), NY, *390*
Ott, Robert S., Global Telecommunications, Inc. (C), TX, *359*
Palmer, Connie, The Touchstone Group (C), MA, *607*
Parisi, Frank, Worlco Computer Resources, Inc. (C), PA, *624*
Paschal, Carolyn Smith, Carolyn Smith Paschal Int'l. (R), CA, *160*
Phillips, Veronica, Phillips Assoc. (C), FL, *510*
Pickering, Dorothy C., Livingston, Robert & Co. (R), CT, *130*
Pryor, Carrie Looms, LAI Ward Howell (R), NY, *123*
Quinn, Gail, Marshall Consultants, Inc. (R), NY, *137*
Reynolds, Smooch S., The Repovich-Reynolds Group (TRRG, Inc.) (R), CA, *175*
Rogers, Gay, Rogers - McManamon Executive Search (R), CA, *180*
Sabbio, Kathy, The Brentwood Group, Inc. (R), NJ, *22*
Salloway, Andrew N., A. N. Salloway Executive Search & Consulting, L.L.C. (C), MA, *564*
Sheth, Pinakini, Software Resource Consultants (C), TN, *587*
Sheweloff, William J., McCray, Shriver, Eckdahl & Assoc., Inc. (R), CA, *140*
Shindler, Stanley L., Franklin Int'l. Search, Inc. (C), MA, *352*
Shulman, Fran, Asset Resource, Inc. (C), CA, *254*
Silverman, Marjorie, Marshall Consultants, Inc. (R), NY, *137*
Spring, Dennis, Spring Assoc., Inc. (R), NY, *198*
Starling, Dick, ProNet, Inc. (C), NC, *524*
Stevens, Martin, Martin Stevens Tamaren & Assoc., Inc. (R), CA, *206*
Suchesk, Lisa, PSD Group, Inc. (C), CA, *525*
Sweet, Robert J., Atlanta Executive Partners, Inc. (R), MA, *8*
Therizien, Greg, The Devlin Search Group, Inc. (C), MA, *312*
Thompson, Carlton W., SpencerStuart (R), CT, *196*
Uhrig, Scott, LAI Ward Howell (R), TX, *124*
VanDolah, A. F., Management Recruiters of Lionville, Inc. (C), PA, *459*
Vennat, Manon, SpencerStuart (R), QE, *197*
Virgili, Franca, Johnson Smith & Knisely (R), CA, *107*
von Baillou, Astrid, Richard Kinser & Assoc. (R), NY, *115*
Waite, Thomas M., Sales Consultants of Harrisburg (C), PA, *561*
Ward, James M., The Ward Group (R), MA, *215*
Wasp, Jr., Warren T., WTW Assoc., Inc. (R), NY, *225*
Watkins, Jean T., The Repovich-Reynolds Group (TRRG, Inc.) (R), CA, *175*
Webster, Larry, Technology Management Partners (R), CA, *208*
Whelan, David, Ethos Consulting, Inc. (R), CA, *61*
Wills, James C., Wills Consulting Assoc. Inc. (R), CT, *222*
Woods, Jacques, Ray & Berndtson/Laurendeau Labrecque (R), QE, *172*
Yarwood, Samantha, Madison MacArthur Inc. (R), ON, *133*
Zivic, Janis M., SpencerStuart (R), CA, *196*

Compensation

Atkinson, Patrick J., Waterford Executive Group Ltd. (C), IL, *616*
Boscacci, Gene, IR Search (R), CA, *104*
Daudt, Jack, Triad Consultants, Inc. (C), NJ, *609*
Doele, Don, Goodrich & Sherwood Assoc., Inc. (R), NJ, *80*
Manning, Dianne, Manning Lloyd Assoc. Ltd. (C), NY, *468*
Perry, Lisa Lepore, Aminex Corp. (C), MA, *249*

(R) = Retainer; (C) = Contingency

RECRUITER SPECIALTIES

Tomaras, David, Willmott & Assoc. (C), MA, *622*
Tomei, Ted, Waterford Executive Group Ltd. (C), IL, *616*
Vujeec, John, Executive Search, Ltd. (C), OH, *336*

Compliance

Bunker, Ralph, Management Recruiters of San Luis Obispo (C), CA, *439*
Curry, Donna, Don Neal & Assoc. (C), OK, *491*
Jacobs, David M., Jacobs & Co. (R), CT, *105*
Kaufmann, Anita D., A-K-A (Anita Kaufmann Assoc.) (C), NY, *231*
Neal, Don, Don Neal & Assoc. (C), OK, *491*

Components

Kraemer, Katherine R., Katherine R. Kraemer (R), CA, *120*
Saso, Maria, Dunhill Professional Search of San Jose (C), CA, *319*

Composites

Hiller, Arnie, U.S. Search (C), VA, *610*
Taylor, Sandi M., Strategic Technologies, Inc. (C), TX, *596*

Compounds

Richards, R. Glenn, Executive Directions (R), OH, *62*
Tippel, Fred C., Fred C. Tippel & Assoc. (C), OH, *607*

Computers

Alexander, Gary, Mark Christian & Assoc., Inc. (C), AZ, *470*
Alexander, Myra, Mark Christian & Assoc., Inc. (C), AZ, *470*
Alexander, Penelope, Alexander & Co. (C), CA, *243*
Bakehorn, Thomas, Martin Stevens Tamaren & Assoc., Inc. (R), CA, *206*
Barker, Thomas E., EBA Group (R), NJ, *56*
Bechard, Lori, Lascelle & Assoc. Inc. (C), ON, *413*
Belanger, Rick, Belanger Partners Ltd. (C), ON, *262*
Belsjoe, Robert, Robert Belsjoe (C), TX, *528*
Bouchard, Rodney, Management Recruiters of Winsted, Inc. (C), CT, *442*
Boyle, Angelique, Management Recruiters - Indianapolis (C), IN, *448*
Bradley, Mark, The Landstone Group (C), NY, *412*
Campbell, Robert Scott, Wellington Management Group (R), PA, *217*
Cipriani, Jr., Jim, Systems Personnel, Inc. (C), NY, *598*
Cipriani, Sr., Jim, Systems Personnel, Inc. (C), NY, *598*
Clinton, Omari, Clinton, Charles, Wise & Co. (C), FL, *293*
Collins, Philip M., Collins & Associates (C), MI, *294*
Connor, Jean, Management Recruiters - Indianapolis (C), IN, *448*
Coughlin, Linda, Partners in Recruiting (C), IL, *504*
Cowan, Bruce, Synergy Systems (C), ON, *598*
Credidio, Thomas J., The DataFinders Group, Inc. (C), NJ, *307*
de Lottinville, Brian L., Trans-United Consultants Ltd. (C), ON, *608*
deMartino, Cathy, Lucas Assoc. (C), GA, *421*
Doherty, Leonard J., L. J. Doherty & Assoc. (R), MA, *53*
Donnelly, John P., J P Donnelly Assoc., Inc. (C), NY, *314*
Drohan, Robert, American Heritage Group, Inc. (C), MI, *247*
Dromeshauser, Peter, Dromeshauser Assoc. (R), MA, *55*
Ehrenreich, Lisa C., Greenhaven & Assoc., Inc. (R), NY, *81*
Fafard, Lina, The Partners, LLC (C), CA, *504*
Fair, Carolyn, Dunhill Executive Search of Los Angeles, Inc. (C), CA, *319*
Fare, Sarah, Management Recruiters-Cedar Rapids, Inc. (C), IA, *448*
Fernow, Charles S., Fernow Assoc. (C), PA, *340*
Franklin, Gary, FAI (C), CO, *338*
Fraser, William, Windsor Consultants, Inc. (C), TX, *622*
Frazer, Mel, Mel Frazer Consultant (C), CA, *352*
Frishman, Robert, Greenwich Search Partners, LLC (C), CT, *363*
Galka, John, Huntley Associates (Dallas), Inc. (C), TX, *386*
Gilson, Dirk S., Key Resources Int'l. (C), CA, *406*
Gilson, Linda L., Key Resources Int'l. (C), CA, *406*
Gionta, Michael, Management Recruiters of Colchester (C), CT, *442*
Graham, Tony, Executives Worldwide, Inc. (C), OR, *337*
Greenwood, Harry, The Partners, LLC (C), CA, *504*
Griffith, Doug, Caywood Partners, Ltd. (R), CA, *32*
Gurney, Darrell W., A Permanent Success Employment Services (C), CA, *231*
Hall, John, Synergy Systems (C), ON, *598*
Hall, Scott, Advancement, Inc. (C), IL, *241*
Handy, Linda, Management Recruiters - Indianapolis (C), IN, *448*
Harper, Deborah, Harper Hewes, Inc. (C), NY, *369*
Henson, Jeff, Henson Partners (C), AZ, *376*
Hills, Glen, G. H. Enterprises (C), AZ, *354*
Holliday, John, American Heritage Group, Inc. (C), MI, *247*
Howlett, Tracy A., Ross Personnel Consultants, Inc. (C), CT, *545*
Jackson, Jennifer, Jackson Resources (R), TX, *105*
Johnson, Paul, Johnson, Kemper & Assoc. (C), TX, *400*
Jones, M. Susan, Greenwich Search Partners, LLC (C), CT, *363*
Kaiser, Greg, Execu-Tech Search Inc. (C), MN, *332*
Karkow, Drew, David Weinfeld Group (C), NC, *617*
Kelly, Elizabeth Ann, Wellington Management Group (R), PA, *217*
Koppes, Jenny, Future Employment Service, Inc. (C), IA, *354*
Lawrence, James B., The Hamilton Group (R), VA, *85*
Leofsky, Peter J., Dapexs Consultants, Inc. (C), NY, *307*
LePatner, Steve, Dunhill Executive Search of Los Angeles, Inc. (C), CA, *319*
Lynch, William E., Fortuna Technologies Inc. (C), CA, *343*
Mader, Stephen P., Christian & Timbers, Inc. (R), MA, *34*
Mader, Steve, Christian & Timbers, Inc. (R), OH, *34*
Martin, Judy R., J. Martin & Assoc. (R), CA, *137*
McDowell, John, McDowell & Co., Recruiters (C), TX, *474*
McGee, Tom, Lucas Assoc. (C), GA, *421*
Miller, Marlene, Management Recruiters-Cedar Rapids, Inc. (C), IA, *448*
Nair, Sanjay, Fortuna Technologies Inc. (C), NJ, *343*
Norton, Robert W., JenKim Int'l. Ltd., Inc. (C), FL, *398*
Panchella, Joseph J., Wellington Management Group (R), PA, *217*
Parisi, Frank, Worlco Computer Resources, Inc. (C), PA, *624*
Park, Tammy, Robert Larned Assoc., Inc. (C), VA, *413*
Prochnow, Laurie, Management Recruiters of Wausau, LLC (C), WI, *466*
Ranta, Ed, J. E. Ranta Assoc. (C), MA, *529*
Reichardt, Karl J., R & K Associates, Inc. (C), AZ, *528*
Richards, David P., Insight Personnel Group, Inc. (C), TX, *389*
Rystrom, R. L., R. L. Rystrom & Assoc., Inc. (C), MN, *549*
Sajankila, Raj, Softrix, Inc. (C), NJ, *586*
Salottolo, Al, Tactical Alternatives (R), CA, *205*
Sanders, David, Management Recruiters of Roseville (C), CA, *441*
Schlarmann, Erika, The Partners, LLC (C), CA, *504*
Schmidt, Susan, David Weinfeld Group (C), NC, *617*
Schultz, William A., Sales Consultants of Madison (C), WI, *563*
Sikora, Keda, Management Recruiters - Indianapolis (C), IN, *448*
Skillern, Steve, Management Recruiters - Indianapolis (C), IN, *448*

Stanton, Grant, TSC Management Services Group, Inc. (C), IL, *610*
Stephens, Teresa, Leader Resources Group (C), GA, *415*
Stepler, Paul, Gallin Associates of Naples, FL (C), FL, *354*
Stevens, Martin, Martin Stevens Tamaren & Assoc., Inc. (R), CA, *206*
Suri, Prem, Fortuna Technologies Inc. (C), GA, *343*
Tabor, Gary, Careers On Track (C), NJ, *283*
Testart, Marion, Placement Testart Inc. (C), QE, *513*
Tommarello, Tony, Lucas Assoc. (C), CA, *421*
Train, John L., Trans-United Consultants Ltd. (C), ON, *608*
Venditti, Paul, The Stewart Group (C), FL, *593*
Warns, Peter, The DataFinders Group, Inc. (C), NJ, *307*
Weinfeld, David C., David Weinfeld Group (C), NC, *617*
Whitney, Ron, Sales Consultants of Sacramento (C), CA, *556*
Wilbur, John, JFW Associates, LLC (C), CT, *398*
Winnewisser, William E., Accounting & Computer Personnel (C), NY, *238*
Wise, Craig D., Clinton, Charles, Wise & Co. (C), FL, *293*
Young, Philip M., Ross Personnel Consultants, Inc. (C), CT, *545*
Zell, David M., Logix West (C), CA, *420*
Zell, David M., Logix, Inc. (C), MA, *420*

Engineering

Curtis, Ron, Fortune Personnel Consultants of Colorado Springs (C), CO, *344*

Hardware

Lewis, Marc, Christian & Timbers, Inc. (R), OH, *34*
Mason, Marlene, Richard Kader & Assoc. (C), OH, *403*

Marketing

Church, Jim, J. F. Church Associates (C), WA, *291*
Villano, George, Carter/MacKay (C), NJ, *285*

Support

Deakmann, Richard, Management Decision Systems, Inc. (MDSI) (C), NJ, *425*
Delray, Victor, Management Decision Systems, Inc. (MDSI) (C), NJ, *425*
Mahoney, Brian, Management Decision Systems, Inc. (MDSI) (C), NJ, *425*
Messina, Angelo, Management Decision Systems, Inc. (MDSI) (C), NJ, *425*
Michaels, Ben, Ritech Management Inc. (C), NY, *537*

Confectionary

Glaser, Larry, Lawrence Glaser Assoc., Inc. (C), NJ, *358*

Conference centers

Wilner, Susan, The Alfus Group (R), NY, *3*

Construction

Adams, Gerald, G. Adams Partners (R), IL, *2*
Anderson, Robert W., Anderson Bradshaw Assoc., Inc. (R), TX, *6*
Arnold, Lindy, The Glazin Group (R), BC, *77*
Austin, Larry, Lucas Assoc. (C), TX, *421*
Baert, Robert A., Personnel Management Group (C), MB, *508*
Baron, Robert, Peak Search Assoc. (C), ON, *506*
Barrett, Dan, Management Recruiters of Forsyth County (C), GA, *445*
Buckland, G. Russell, The Bedford Consulting Group Inc. (R), ON, *15*
Button, David R., Button Group (C), TX, *277*
Callahan, Tom, Crown Advisors, Inc. (R), PA, *43*
Cargill, Jim, Management Recruiters of Lake Tahoe, NV (C), NV, *453*
Cavoto, Bob, Cook Assoc.,® Inc. (R), IL, *40*
Chamberland, Roland, Management Recruiters of Sonoma (C), CA, *441*
Clapp, Arlene, Arlene Clapp, Ltd. (R), MN, *35*
Cole, James, Systems Research Group (C), OH, *598*
Collier, Gordon L., R. C. Services (C), TX, *528*
Connelly, III, Joseph H., CS Associates, LLC (C), AZ, *304*
Connelly, Susan D., CS Associates, LLC (C), AZ, *304*
Courtright, Robert J., Courtright & Assoc., Inc. (R), PA, *42*
Dremely, Mark, Richard, Wayne & Roberts (C), TX, *536*
Dupilka, John M., Michael Latas & Assoc., Inc. (R), MO, *126*
Dycus, Gwen, Gwen Dycus & Assoc. (C), FL, *323*
Evans, Patrick, The Evans McDonnell Co. (C), TX, *331*
Gaines, Donna, Gaines & Assoc. Int'l., Inc. (R), IL, *73*
Gavura, Nicholas J., Michael Latas & Assoc., Inc. (R), MO, *126*
Glazin, Lynne, The Glazin Group (R), BC, *77*
Hamilton, Frank, Gwen Dycus & Assoc. (C), FL, *323*
Helbling, Thomas J., Helbling & Assoc., Inc. (R), PA, *91*
Henderson, Cathy, Management Recruiters of Aptos (C), CA, *439*
Hirsch, Ruth, Ruth Hirsch Assoc., Inc. (C), NY, *379*
Hornberger, Jr., Frederick C., Hornberger Management Company (R), DE, *96*
Howard, Michael, Allen Austin Lowe & Powers (R), TX, *3*
Ingalise, James, Sales Consultants of Omaha, Inc. (C), NE, *560*
Jones, Kevin, Crown Advisors, Inc. (R), PA, *43*
Kalinski, Jr., Felix, Baeder Kalinski Int'l. Group, Inc. (R), NH, *10*
Kalus, Lisa, Lisa Kalus & Assoc., Inc. (C), NY, *403*
Karel, Stephen A., Karel & Co. (R), CA, *109*
Kelly, Jim, The LaBorde Group (C), CA, *411*
Ketner, Michael L., Michael L. Ketner & Assoc., Inc. (R), PA, *114*
Kimmel, Joe W., Kimmel & Associates, Inc. (C), NC, *406*
Kovach, Jerry, The J. Kovach Group (R), PA, *119*
Krier, Michael S., Overton Consulting (R), WI, *157*
Kriesel, David W., Management Recruiters of Woodbury (C), MN, *430*
Kriesel, David W., Management Recruiters of Woodbury (C), MN, *452*
Kuhnmuench, R. G., K & C Assoc. (C), CA, *402*
LaBorde, John, The LaBorde Group (C), CA, *411*
LaBorde, Michael, The LaBorde Group (C), CA, *411*
Lawrence, Kent L., Michael Latas & Assoc., Inc. (R), MO, *126*
Layton, Bernard, Morgan Int'l., Inc. (R), IL, *147*
Love, Cindi M., Michael Latas & Assoc., Inc. (R), MO, *126*
Love, Scott T., Scott Love Assoc., Inc. (C), AZ, *420*
Lyngen, Robert, Construct Management Services (C), MN, *297*
Lyngen, Trish, Construct Management Services (C), MN, *297*
MacTadyen, David, Sharrow & Assoc., Inc. (C), IN, *579*
Maxin, Keith A., K. Maxin & Assoc. (R), PA, *139*
Maxin, Keith A., Michael L. Ketner & Assoc., Inc. (R), PA, *114*
McNichol, Jr., John, McNichol Assoc. (R), PA, *142*
Mears, Jack, Kelly Walker Assoc. (C), TX, *614*
Meyers, Maurice R., Management Recruiters, Inland Empire Agency (C), CA, *441*
Morgan, Richard, Morgan Samuels Co. (R), CA, *147*
Moss, Barbara, Moss & Co. (R), WA, *148*
Naff, Bud, Management Recruiters of Lynnwood (C), WA, *465*
Neuweiler, Mark, Saber Group, Inc. (C), TX, *550*
O'Reilly, William E., Management Recruiters of Cincinnati/Sharonville, Inc. (C), OH, *457*
Olsen, Robert F., Robert Connelly & Assoc., Inc. (R), MN, *39*
Palumbo, Robert F., The Recruitment Group, Inc. (C), NY, *532*

RECRUITER SPECIALTIES

Powers, William D., Powers Consultants, Inc. (R), MO, *166*
Pruitt, Glen O., Locke & Assoc. (R), AL, *131*
Roth, Patricia, Patricia Roth Int'l. (C), FL, *545*
Samuels, Lew, Morgan Samuels Co. (R), CA, *147*
Schlect, Nancy, Morgan Samuels Co. (R), CA, *147*
Sharpe, Charles, C. J. Stafford & Assoc. (C), ON, *591*
Sitter, William P., Jordan-Sitter Assoc. (R), TX, *108*
Sloane, Ron, Management Recruiters of Milwaukee-North (C), WI, *466*
Smith, Robert, Sales Consultants of Omaha, Inc. (C), NE, *560*
Stoll, Steve, Sharrow & Assoc., Inc. (C), KY, *579*
Stynetski, Bill, Largent Parks & Partners (C), TX, *503*
Sussman, Patti, Weinman & Assoc. (C), AZ, *617*
Traynor, Thomas H., Traynor Confidential, Ltd. (C), NY, *609*
Upham, Suzanne, Snelling & Snelling, Inc. (C), FL, *585*
Walker, Kelly, Kelly Walker Assoc. (C), TX, *614*
Ward, Al L., Ward-Hoffman & Assoc. (C), ID, *615*
West, Fred, Wood West & Partners Inc. (C), BC, *624*
Wilcox, Alex B., The Bridge (C), CO, *273*
Wisdom, T. J., Management Recruiters of Fresno (C), CA, *440*

Consulting

Albergato, Vincent, Raymond Karsan Assoc. (C), MA, *530*
Apple, Richard W., R. W. Apple & Assoc. (C), NJ, *251*
Ash, Robert I., Ashworth Consultants, Inc. (R), MA, *8*
Atkinson, Arthur, Atkinson Search & Placement, Inc. (C), IA, *255*
Auster, A. Marc, A. M. Auster Associates (R), FL, *9*
Bard, Cliff, Management Recruiters of St. Augustine (C), FL, *444*
Baty, R. Gaines, R. Gaines Baty Assoc., Inc. (R), TX, *13*
Benkwitt, Barbara, The Brentwood Group, Inc. (R), NJ, *22*
Bhandari, Parul, Tarbex (C), DC, *599*
Brest, Dan, Capital Consulting Group, Inc. (R), MD, *28*
Buehler, Brad, The Goodman Group (R), CA, *79*
Cabugos, Ted, NCC Executive Search Consultants (C), CA, *490*
Campbell, Brian H., Venpro Consulting Inc. (C), ON, *612*
Castanet, Emile, Don Hall & Assoc. (C), GA, *366*
Cohen, Michael R., Intech Summit Group, Inc. (R), CA, *102*
Cole, Christopher, Tech-Net (C), TX, *601*
Cyphers, Ralph, Strategic Assoc., Inc. (C), TX, *595*
Dangerfield, Chris, Technology Search Int'l. (C), CA, *603*
Daubenspeck, Kenneth, Daubenspeck & Associates, Ltd. (R), IL, *46*
Davis, Glenn S., Next Step Recruiting (C), CA, *493*
Davis, Jeff, DataPro Personnel Consultants (C), TX, *308*
Dermady, Timothy J., ExecutiveFit (C), NY, *337*
Dorst, Martin, Dorst Information Services, Inc. (C), NY, *314*
Drinkwater, Wendy A., Drinkwater & Assoc. (R), MA, *54*
Edington, Patti D., Drinkwater & Assoc. (R), MA, *55*
Elinski, Mike, Human Resources Management Hawaii, Inc. (C), HI, *384*
Erickson, Mary R., Mary R. Erickson & Assoc. (R), MN, *60*
Fienberg, Chester A., Drummond Assoc., Inc. (C), NY, *315*
Fisk, James L., James L. Fisk & Assoc. (C), MO, *342*
Fitzpatrick, Susan, Management Recruiters of Milwaukee - Downtown (C), WI, *466*
Fox, Glenn M., Strategic Search, LLC (C), CA, *595*
Frishman, Robert, Greenwich Search Partners, LLC (C), CT, *363*
Gilbert, John, John Gilbert Co. (C), TX, *357*
Gimbel, Mike, Gimbel & Assoc. (C), FL, *357*
Goldman, Jeff, Global 1000 Int'l. Services (C), CA, *358*
Goldman, Michael L., Strategic Assoc., Inc. (C), TX, *595*
Goldstein, Steven G., The Jonathan Stevens Group, Inc. (R), NJ, *108*
Gordon, Donald E., Interim Management Resources Inc. (C), ON, *392*
Graham, Robert W., Robert Graham Assoc. (R), RI, *81*
Guevara, Charles, The Colton Partnership, Inc. (R), NY, *38*
Harris, Maria, Barton Assoc., Inc. (R), TX, *12*
Hazan, Lynn, Beverly von Winckler & Assoc. (C), IL, *613*
Hintz, George, Hintz Associates (C), NY, *378*
Hoffman, Tala R., TRH Assoc., Inc. (R), NY, *210*
Holsopple, Ben V., ACSYS Resources, Inc. (C), NJ, *238*
Hunter, David, Stanewick, Hart & Assoc., Inc. (C), FL, *591*
Hutton, M. Joan, The Hutton Group, Inc. (C), FL, *386*
Jefferies, George, Hintz Associates (C), NY, *378*
Jeffers, Richard B., Dieckmann & Assoc., Ltd. (R), IL, *51*
Johnson, John, HRNI (C), MI, *383*
Johnson, Kathleen, Barton Assoc., Inc. (R), TX, *12*
Kaczmar, Michael A., Kaczmar & Assoc. (C), PA, *403*
Kahn, Beverly A., New Dimensions in Technology, Inc. (C), MA, *492*
Kaufman, Stuart, Management Recruiters of Great Neck (C), NY, *454*
Kick, James, The Prairie Group (C), IL, *515*
King, Karl, Capital Consulting Group, Inc. (R), MD, *28*
Kohn, Adam, Christian & Timbers, Inc. (R), OH, *34*
Kool, Joan, Professional Recruiters, Inc. (C), PA, *521*
Kreiss, John P., Zweig White & Assoc., Inc. (R), MA, *228*
Kurke, David S., Starbridge Group Inc. (C), VA, *591*
Lennon, Frank P., F. P. Lennon Assoc. (C), PA, *416*
Lennox, Charles, PricewaterhouseCoopers Executive Search (R), ON, *168*
Lenobel, Stephen, Professional Recruiters, Inc. (C), PA, *521*
Levine, Alan C., Alan Levine Assoc. (R), MA, *129*
Lieff, Shelley, Advice Personnel Inc. (C), NY, *241*
Lombardo, Steve, Search America, Inc. (C), MA, *574*
Mason, Kimball L., KM Associates (C), MA, *407*
McElroy, Brian, Drinkwater & Assoc. (R), MA, *55*
McGrath, Steven L., McGrath & Assoc., Inc. (R), NJ, *141*
McKeown, Morgan, Christian & Timbers, Inc. (R), NY, *34*
McNamara, Robert, Global Career Services, Inc. (C), NY, *358*
Michaels, Ellen, Shupack & Michaels Inc. (C), NY, *581*
Michaels, Stewart, Topaz Int'l., Inc., Attorney Search (C), NJ, *607*
Moe, Susan Lee, Faro Consultants Int'l. (C), VA, *338*
Moyse, Richard G., Thorndike Deland Assoc. LLC (R), NY, *48*
Nagler, Leon G., Nagler, Robins & Poe, Inc. (R), MA, *150*
Neves, Trever, TriStaff Group (C), CA, *609*
O'Neill, Sean, Waterford Executive Group Ltd. (C), IL, *616*
Osborn, Ted, Paladin Group, Inc. (C), CO, *502*
Pagana, Pat, The Brentwood Group, Inc. (R), NJ, *22*
Page, Theresa, T. Page & Assoc. (C), TX, *502*
Perkins, Barbara, Harcourt & Assoc. (C), AB, *368*
Perry, Fred, Fred Perry Assoc. (C), TX, *507*
Prusak, Julie J., Ethos Consulting, Inc. (R), CA, *61*
Rehner, Leonard, R & L Assoc., Ltd. (R), NY, *170*

Reiser, Ellen, Thorndike Deland Assoc. LLC (R), NY, *48*
Rice, Gene, Rice Cohen Int'l. (R), PA, *178*
Robins, Jeri N., Nagler, Robins & Poe, Inc. (R), MA, *150*
Robinson, P. Andrew, Consulting Resource Group, Inc. (C), GA, *297*
Sarchett, A. Wayne, Systems Careers (C), CA, *598*
Schmidt, Susan, David Weinfeld Group (C), NC, *617*
Scott, Evan, Howard Fischer Assoc. Int'l., Inc. (R), PA, *67*
Sheedy, III, Edward J., Dieckmann & Assoc., Ltd. (R), IL, *51*
Shupack, Joseph, Shupack & Michaels Inc. (C), NY, *581*
Siegel, RitaSue, RitaSue Siegel Resources, Inc. (R), NY, *191*
Sprankle, Kathryn, Zweig White & Assoc., Inc. (R), MA, *228*
Stevens, Brett M., Sales Consultants of Cherokee (C), GA, *558*
Stiles, Jake, Linford E. Stiles & Assoc., L.L.C. (R), NH, *201*
Stow, Ralph P., Page-Wheatcroft & Co., Ltd. (R), TX, *158*
Tabor, Gary, Careers On Track (C), NJ, *283*
Taylor, M. Kent, Prairie Resource Group, Inc. (R), IL, *166*
Tello, Fernando, Korn/Ferry, Int'l., S.A. de C.V. (R), MX, *118*
Tomlinson, Betsy, Tomlinson Assoc. Inc. (C), IL, *607*
Turner, Kim, Barton Assoc., Inc. (R), TX, *12*
Wade, Elliott, Search Int'l. (R), MA, *187*
Webster, William L., S. B. Webster & Associates (R), MA, *217*
Weinfeld, David C., David Weinfeld Group (C), NC, *617*
Weinstein, Lewis R., Weinstein & Co. (R), MA, *217*
Williams, Steve, Barton Assoc., Inc. (R), TX, *13*
Wyatt, Robert S., R. S. Wyatt Assoc., Inc. (R), TX, *225*

Consumer

Agriesti, Kay, Agriesti & Assoc. (C), CA, *243*
Allison, Tom, Tom Allison Assoc. (C), NM, *245*
Archibald, David E., The Eldridge Group, Ltd. (C), IL, *327*
Argenio, Paul J., Tierney Assoc., Inc. (R), PA, *209*
Aswell, Judy, Management Recruiters of San Marcos (C), TX, *463*
Ayers, Joseph, Hollander Horizon Int'l. (R), MN, *95*
Bailey, III, Joseph A., Russell Reynolds Assoc., Inc. (R), TX, *177*
Bailey, Paul, Preston-Hunter, Inc. (R), IL, *167*
Baker, Walter U., LAI Ward Howell (R), FL, *123*
Barnes, David, Johnson Smith & Knisely (R), NY, *107*
Barranco, Leticia, Leaders-Trust Int'l./ Carce y Asociados, S.C. (R), MX, *127*
Barton, Gary, Barton Assoc., Inc. (R), TX, *12*
Bauman, Bobbi, BJB Assoc. (C), VA, *267*
Berke, Michael J., LAI Ward Howell (R), IL, *123*
Besso, Sandy, Intersource, Ltd. (R), TX, *103*
Besso, Thom, Intersource, Ltd. (R), TX, *103*
Boren, Susan, SpencerStuart (R), MN, *197*
Borkenhagen, Christine, Morgan Samuels Co. (R), CA, *147*
Boruff, Doug, Dunhill Personnel of Boulder (C), CO, *319*
Boruff, Fran, Dunhill Personnel of Boulder (C), CO, *319*
Bratches, Howard, Thorndike Deland Assoc. LLC (R), NY, *48*
Brown, Gene, Management Recruiters of Atlanta West, Inc. (C), GA, *445*
Buller, Juergen E., Sales Consultants of Boca Raton, Inc. (C), FL, *557*
Cain, Douglas, Sales Recruiting Network (C), PA, *564*
Campbell, Robert Scott, Wellington Management Group (R), PA, *217*
Chambers, Jere, Sales Consultants of Cherry Hill (C), NJ, *560*
Cherney, Steven D., Resource Perspectives, Inc. (R), CA, *175*
Christoff, Matt, SpencerStuart (R), MN, *197*
Citrin, James M., SpencerStuart (R), CT, *196*
Clark, Larry A., The Clark Group (C), MI, *292*
Clarkson, Roger, SpencerStuart (R), ON, *197*
Coe, Karen, Coe & Co. Int'l. Inc./EMA Partners Int'l. (R), AB, *37*
Cole-Hill, Susan, Brentwood Int'l. (R), CA, *23*
Collins, Judy, Sales Consultants of Chicago South (C), IL, *558*
Concannon, Bob, StratfordGroup (R), CA, *203*
Cornelison, Mike, M.C. Executive Search (C), CA, *422*
Crabtree, G. A., Roger Dietsch & Assoc. (C), MN, *312*
Cyr, Maury N., Cyr Associates, Inc. (C), MA, *306*
Damon, Robert A., SpencerStuart (R), NY, *196*
Daniel, David S., SpencerStuart (R), NY, *196*
Daum, Julie H., SpencerStuart (R), NY, *196*
deMartino, Cathy, Lucas Assoc. (C), GA, *421*
Dickson, David W., Fortune Personnel Consultants of Chattanooga Inc. (C), TN, *349*
Dorfman, Kim, Rice Cohen Int'l. (R), PA, *178*
Douglass, Suzanne, Harris Heery & Assoc., Inc. (R), CT, *87*
Drury, III, James J., SpencerStuart (R), IL, *197*
Duffy, Kevin, Kensington Int'l., Inc. (R), IL, *113*
Ellis-Kirk, Matrice, SpencerStuart (R), TX, *197*
Enochs, Steve, Buckman/Enochs & Assoc., Inc. (C), OH, *276*
Falcon, Elizabeth, Leaders-Trust Int'l./ Carce y Asociados, S.C. (R), MX, *127*
Filippelli, Frank J., The Glenwood Group (C), IL, *358*
Fockler, David B., David Fockler & Assoc., Inc. (C), CA, *342*
Fuller, Thomas, Epsen, Fuller & Assoc., LLC (R), NJ, *60*
Gallagher, David W., LAI Ward Howell (R), GA, *123*
Gates, Will, Morgan Samuels Co. (R), CA, *147*
George, Bethany W., Rollo Assoc. (R), CA, *181*
Gilreath, James M., Gilreath Weatherby Inc. (R), MA, *77*
Giries, Juliet, Barton Assoc., Inc. (R), TX, *12*
Glaser, Larry, Lawrence Glaser Assoc., Inc. (C), NJ, *358*
Goldberg, Steve, Media Recruiting Group, Inc. (C), NY, *476*
Goldstein, Steven G., The Jonathan Stevens Group, Inc. (R), NJ, *108*
Goodwin, Joe D., LAI Ward Howell (R), GA, *123*
Gore, Les, Executive Search Int'l./ Transearch (R), MA, *63*
Gragg, Robert, Montgomery West (R), CA, *146*
Griesedieck, Jr., Joseph E., SpencerStuart (R), CA, *196*
Guidarelli, Shelley, Guidarelli Assoc., Inc. (R), MI, *83*
Hall, Sharon, SpencerStuart (R), GA, *197*
Hardy, Thomas G., SpencerStuart (R), NY, *196*
Harragan, James K., Management Recruiters of Gramercy, Inc. (C), NY, *455*
Harris, Andrew S., Harris Heery & Assoc., Inc. (R), CT, *87*
Hart, Susan S., SpencerStuart (R), CT, *196*
Hauswirth, Jeffrey M., SpencerStuart (R), ON, *197*
Heath, Jeffrey A., The Landstone Group (C), NY, *412*
Heery, William J., Harris Heery & Assoc., Inc. (R), CT, *87*
Heissan, Arlene, P. J. Lynch Assoc. (R), CT, *132*
Henard, John B., LAI Ward Howell (R), FL, *123*
Hennessy, Robert, Ken Clark Int'l. (R), NJ, *36*
Henson, Jeff, Henson Partners (C), AZ, *376*
Higbee, Joan, Thorndike Deland Assoc. LLC (R), NY, *48*
Hill, Tom, Hill & Assoc. (C), CA, *378*

RECRUITER SPECIALTIES

Hollander, Michael, Hollander Horizon Int'l. (R), NJ, *95*
Howe, Vance A., LAI Ward Howell (R), AZ, *123*
Hughes, Donald J., Hughes & Company (R), VA, *98*
Hughes, Jr., John E., LAI Ward Howell (R), PA, *123*
Jones, Dale E., LAI Ward Howell (R), GA, *123*
Keller, Barbara, Barton Assoc., Inc. (R), TX, *12*
Kelley, Randall D., SpencerStuart (R), TX, *197*
Kelly, Claudia L., SpencerStuart (R), CT, *196*
Kenny, Roger M., Boardroom Consultants/ Kenny Kindler Tholke (R), NY, *19*
Kier, Mary, Cook Assoc.,® Inc. (R), IL, *40*
Klavins, Larissa R., Briant Assoc., Inc. (R), IL, *23*
Kopsick, Joseph M., SpencerStuart (R), IL, *197*
Kreutz, Gary L., Kreutz Consulting Group, Inc. (R), IL, *121*
Krier, Michael S., Overton Consulting (R), WI, *157*
Lapham, Lawrence L., Lawrence L. Lapham, Inc. (R), NY, *124*
Laux, Frank J., StratfordGroup (R), TX, *203*
Lee, Amy T., Sanford Rose Assoc. - Salt Lake City (C), UT, *571*
Lee, Rodger A., Sanford Rose Assoc. - Salt Lake City (C), UT, *571*
Lemming, Jeff, Lemming/LeVan, Inc. (R), GA, *128*
Leonard, Linda, Harris Heery & Assoc., Inc. (R), CT, *87*
Lipson, Harriet L., Lipson & Co. (R), CA, *130*
Lipson, Howard R., Lipson & Co. (R), CA, *130*
Long, Helga, Horton Int'l. Inc. (R), NY, *96*
Lord, J. Scott, J. S. Lord & Company, Inc. (R), MA, *131*
Ludwig, Bob, Ludwig & Assoc., Inc. (C), VA, *421*
Lussier, Grant, SpencerStuart (R), MX, *197*
Lyman, David M., Schall Executive Search Partners (R), MN, *185*
MacEachern, David, SpencerStuart (R), ON, *197*
Martin, Suzanne, The Beam Group (R), PA, *14*
Matthews, Alyce, The Matthews Group, Inc. (C), NJ, *472*
McCormick, Gregg J., Retained Search Assoc. (R), NC, *176*
McCracken, Terri, T E M Assoc. (C), WI, *599*
McCreary, Charles, Austin-McGregor Int'l. (R), TX, *9*
McGee, Tom, Lucas Assoc. (C), GA, *421*
McKeown, Morgan, Christian & Timbers, Inc. (R), NY, *34*
McKeown, Morgan, Christian & Timbers, Inc. (R), OH, *34*
Meagher-Clare, Patricia, SpencerStuart (R), IL, *197*
Miller, Andrew S., Management Recruiters of New Providence (C), NJ, *454*
Miller, Darryl, Management Alliance Group, Inc. (R), NJ, *134*
Miners, Richard A., Sedlar & Miners (R), NY, *188*
Mitchell, Laurie, Laurie Mitchell & Co., Inc. (R), OH, *145*
Montaño, Oscar W., Oscar Montaño, Inc. (R), CA, *146*
Mooney, Penny, Christian & Timbers, Inc. (R), CT, *34*
Mooney, Penny, Christian & Timbers, Inc. (R), OH, *34*
Moore, Meredith, StratfordGroup (R), CA, *203*
Nadherny, Christopher C., SpencerStuart (R), IL, *197*
Nalley, Ed, Executive Search Int'l. (C), TX, *336*
Nalley, Jeff, Executive Search Int'l. (C), TX, *336*
Nein, Lawrence F., LAI Ward Howell (R), IL, *123*
Newell, Carlyle, Management Alliance Group, Inc. (R), NJ, *134*
Northrop, Michael S., Management Resource Group (C), MN, *467*
O'Brien, Timothy M., O'Brien & Bell (R), OH, *153*
O'Maley, Kimberlee, SpencerStuart (R), CA, *196*
Oberman, Heidi, Medical Recruiters Inc. (C), MO, *477*
Palmlund, III, David W., LAI Ward Howell (R), TX, *124*
Parsons, Allison, Barton Assoc., Inc. (R), TX, *12*
Pearson, Robert L., LAI Ward Howell (R), TX, *124*
Penney, Robert J., Sales Consultants of Westchester-South, Inc. (C), NY, *561*
Pettersson, Tara L., LAI Ward Howell (R), TX, *124*
Pettway, Samuel H., SpencerStuart (R), GA, *197*
Pezim, Howard J., The Bedford Consulting Group Inc. (R), ON, *15*
Pezim, Steven G., The Bedford Consulting Group Inc. (R), ON, *15*
Pickens, Barbara, Johnson Smith & Knisely (R), NY, *107*
Porter, Lindsay, HCI Corp. (C), IL, *371*
Prusak, Julie J., Ethos Consulting, Inc. (R), CA, *61*
Reddick, David C., Horton Int'l. Inc. (R), GA, *96*
Reiser, Ellen, Thorndike Deland Assoc. LLC (R), NY, *48*
Rice, Joel, Recruiting/Solutions (C), CA, *532*
Roberts, Scott, Jonas, Walters & Assoc., Inc. (R), WI, *108*
Robertson, Bruce J., LAI Ward Howell (R), NY, *122*
Robins, Jeri N., Nagler, Robins & Poe, Inc. (R), MA, *150*
Rodriguez, Andrew, A.J. & Assoc. (C), FL, *232*
Roe, Craig T., Craig Roe & Assoc., LLC (C), MD, *540*
Rosenthal, Abbe L., ALW Research Int'l. (R), NJ, *4*
Ruthrauff, Debbie, Kelly Associates (R), PA, *112*
Salway, Clancy, Sales Management Resources (C), CA, *563*
Sammons, James A., Prestige Inc. (C), WI, *517*
Santamaria, Jay, The Beam Group (R), NY, *14*
Savalli, Frank, Savalli & Assoc., Inc. (C), MI, *571*
Schmidt, Paul W., LAI Ward Howell (R), IL, *123*
Scott, Ronald, Richard Kader & Assoc. (C), OH, *403*
Shaffer, Michael, Management Recruiters Peninsula (C), CA, *439*
Shaffer, Michael T., Sales Consultants Peninsula, Inc. (C), CA, *556*
Shariff, Hassan, The Johnson Group, Unlimited (C), NY, *400*
Sklar, Ruth, Ruth Sklar Assoc., Inc. (RSA Executive Search) (R), NY, *192*
Slusser, Christine M., Lawrence Glaser Assoc., Inc. (C), NJ, *358*
Smith, Martin, Hughes & Company (R), VA, *98*
Snyder, Jr., James F., Snyder & Co. (R), CT, *194*
Snyder, Thomas J., SpencerStuart (R), IL, *197*
Spann, Richard E., Goodrich & Sherwood Assoc., Inc. (R), CT, *80*
Stark, Mary, The Stark Wilton Group (R), MI, *199*
Steinman, Stephen M., The Stevenson Group, Inc. (N.J.) (R), NJ, *200*
Stenholm, Gilbert R., SpencerStuart (R), IL, *197*
Stewart, Wilfred C., KPMG Executive Search (R), ON, *119*
Stockton, J. R., Management Catalysts (R), NJ, *134*
Sullivan, Tami, Culver Personnel Services (C), CA, *304*
Sumurdy, Melinda M., LAI Ward Howell (R), TX, *124*
Swann, Al, The Beam Group (R), NY, *14*
Sweet, Eleanor Anne, The Remington Group (R), IL, *174*
Swiff, Jeffrey G., Thorndike Deland Assoc. LLC (R), NY, *48*
Talabisco, Barbara, Wakefield Talabisco Int'l. (R), NY, *214*
Taylor, Ernest A., LAI Ward Howell (R), GA, *123*
Thiemann, Brian, Christopher and Long (C), MO, *291*
Thomas, Jeffrey, Fairfaxx Corp. (R), CT, *64*
Trueb, Dick, Strategic Resources (C), WA, *595*
Tumbiolo, Lisa, Agriesti & Assoc. (C), CA, *243*

Utroska, Donald R., LAI Ward Howell (R), IL, *123*
Valdes, Maria Elena, Korn/Ferry, Int'l., S.A. de C.V. (R), MX, *118*
Van Nostrand, Mara, Barton Assoc., Inc. (R), TX, *12*
Wakefield, J. Alvin, Wakefield Talabisco Int'l. (R), VT, *214*
Walters, William F., Jonas, Walters & Assoc., Inc. (R), WI, *107*
Wayne, Vici, Christian & Timbers, Inc. (R), OH, *34*
Weber, Ronald R., Weber Executive Search (R), NY, *216*
Weiss, Cathy, C. Weiss Assoc., Inc. (C), NY, *618*
White, Joseph A., Sports Group Int'l. (R), NC, *198*
White, Richard B., SpencerStuart (R), CT, *196*
Williams Badanes, Anne, Marketing Search Inc. (C), OH, *471*
Witt, Stan, Fortune Personnel Consultants of San Antonio, Inc. (C), TX, *350*
Witte, David L., LAI Ward Howell (R), TX, *124*
Wojcik, Raymond F., Management Recruiters The Delta Group, Inc. (C), TN, *461*
Wood, John, SpencerStuart (R), NY, *196*
Wottowa, Denise, Medical Recruiters Inc. (C), MO, *477*
Wyatt, Robert S., R. S. Wyatt Assoc., Inc. (R), TX, *225*
Zimmerman, Arnold, Hollander Horizon Int'l. (R), CA, *95*

General

Ogdon, Thomas H., The Ogdon Partnership (R), NY, *155*

Marketing

Fidlow, Elliott, Sales Search Specialist (C), IL, *564*
Gladstone, Elaine, Roth Young Executive Search (C), TX, *546*
Hansen, James P., Hansen Executive Search, Inc. (C), NE, *368*
Hodde, Fred, Heritage Search Group, Inc. (C), CT, *376*
Tripician, Philip, Heritage Search Group, Inc. (C), FL, *376*

Packaged goods

Trilling, Dean D., LAI Ward Howell (R), OH, *123*

Controllers

Bartl, Frank, Bartl & Evins (C), NY, *260*
Boxer, Harry, The Century Group (C), CA, *287*
Cuddy, Brian C., Romac Int'l. Inc. (R), MA, *181*
Griffiths, William J., Romac Int'l. Inc. (R), MA, *181*
Karr, Cynthia, Howard Karr & Assoc., Inc. (R), CA, *110*
Karr, Liz, Howard Karr & Assoc., Inc. (R), CA, *110*
Kramer, Alan L., Kramer Executive Resources, Inc. (C), NY, *409*
Laguzza, John, Laguzza Assoc., Ltd. (R), NY, *122*
Proul, Ron, The Century Group (C), CA, *287*
Siciliano, Gene, Western Management Assoc. (R), CA, *218*
Van Gyseghem, Marc, Stone Assoc. LLC (C), MI, *594*
Yaeger, Don, The Century Group (C), CA, *287*

Convention centers

Hill, Michelle, The Alfus Group (R), NY, *3*
Stafford, Susan P., Hospitality Int'l. (C), NY, *381*

Convergence

Weinstein, Lewis R., Weinstein & Co. (R), MA, *217*

Converting

Bauman, Bobbi, BJB Assoc. (C), VA, *267*
Brown, C.C. Jay, Fortune Personnel Consultants of Raleigh, Inc. (C), NC, *348*
Caprio, Jerry, Caprio & Assoc. Inc. (R), IL, *29*
Estes, Gregory A., The Lawson Group, Inc. (C), SC, *414*
McCracken, Terri, T E M Assoc. (C), WI, *599*
Richards, R. Glenn, Executive Directions (R), OH, *62*
Young, Paula G., Career Counseling Inc. (CCI) (C), KY, *282*

COO's

Blaney, John A., Blaney Executive Search (R), MA, *18*
Cimino, James J., Executive Search, Ltd. (C), OH, *336*
Crist, Peter D., Crist Partners, Ltd. (R), IL, *43*
Czamanske, Paul, Compass Group Ltd. (R), MI, *38*
Desley, Carolyn M., Erlanger Assoc. (R), CT, *60*
Edwards, S. Bruce, Bruce Edwards & Associates, Inc. (R), NC, *56*
Erlanger, Richard A., Erlanger Assoc. (R), CT, *60*
Gibson, Bruce, Gibson & Co., Inc. (R), WI, *76*
Glick, Douglas I., MedSearch Resources, Inc. (C), FL, *478*
Goldring, Joe, Joseph Goldring & Assoc. Inc. (C), MI, *360*
Graham, Robert W., Robert Graham Assoc. (R), RI, *81*
Grantham, John D., Grantham & Co., Inc. (R), NC, *81*
Guarino, Kathleen, Cornell Group Int'l. Consulting, Inc. (R), NY, *41*
Hughes, Donald J., Hughes & Company (R), VA, *98*
Humphreys, William M., Robison Humphreys & Assoc., Inc. (R), ON, *180*
Leff, Ilene J., Richard A. Eisner & Co., LLP (R), NY, *57*
Levin, Phillip, Executive Search Team (C), MI, *336*
Lowery, Bruce N., Bruce Lowery & Assoc. (C), MI, *420*
Malinski, Mark, The Ransford Group (R), TX, *171*
McFeely, Clarence E., Clarence E. McFeely, Inc. (R), IL, *141*
Roberts, Nick, Pacific Search Group, Inc. (C), CA, *501*
Shoemaker, Richard, IR Search (R), CA, *103*
Smith, George D., Bruce Edwards & Associates, Inc. (R), NC, *57*
Wilkie, Glenn A., The Wilkie Group Int'l. (R), ON, *220*

Copiers

Howlett, Tracy A., Ross Personnel Consultants, Inc. (C), CT, *545*

Corporate communication

Ball, Carol, Carol Ball & Co. (C), CT, *258*
Barnes, Gary B., Brigade, Inc. (R), CA, *23*
Bartle, Tom, Wesley Brown & Bartle Co., Inc. (R), NY, *218*
Brand, Elizabeth, Carol Ball & Co. (C), NJ, *258*
Brolin, Lawrence E., DLB Assoc. (R), NY, *53*
Cardwell, Jean, Cardwell Enterprises Inc. (R), IL, *29*
Chaloner, Edward H., Chaloner Assoc. (R), MA, *32*
Charet, Sandra, Charet & Assoc. (C), NJ, *289*
Corwen, Leonard, Leonard Corwen Assoc. (C), NY, *302*
Flesher, Susan, Flesher & Assoc., Inc. (R), CA, *68*
Frank, Neil, Neil Frank & Co. (R), CA, *71*
Fry, John M., The Fry Group, Inc. (C), NY, *353*
Goodman-Brolin, Dorothy, DLB Assoc. (R), NY, *53*
Grimm, Peter G., Nordeman Grimm, Inc. (R), NY, *152*
Harberth, Janet, Janet Harberth & Assoc., Inc. (C), GA, *368*
Hopkins, Chester A., Handy HRM (R), NY, *86*
Metzger, Pete, Foster Partners (R), DC, *70*
Moyer, David S., Moyer, Sherwood Assoc., Inc. (R), NY, *148*
Spring, Dennis, Spring Assoc., Inc. (R), NY, *198*
Wascovich, Tina, Rojek Marketing Group, Inc. (R), OH, *181*
Wills, James C., Wills Consulting Assoc. Inc. (R), CT, *222*
Young, Rich, Chaloner Assoc. (R), MA, *32*

(R) = Retainer; (C) = Contingency

Cosmetics

Neidenberg, Steven, William Bell Assoc., Inc. (C), NJ, *263*
Provda, Peter, F-O-R-T-U-N-E Personnel Consultants of Menlo Park, Inc. (C), NJ, *347*
Reifersen, Ruth F., The Jonathan Stevens Group, Inc. (R), NJ, *108*
Reyes, Renee, Management Recruiters of Columbia (C), MD, *450*
Storfer, Herbert F., Storfer & Assoc. (C), NY, *595*
Storfer, Herbert F., The Dartmouth Group (R), NY, *46*

Crafts & hobbies

Boyer, Adrienne, Cook Assoc.,® Inc. (R), IL, *40*

Creative

Crawford, Jacqueline, Graphic Arts Marketing Assoc., Inc. (C), MI, *361*
Danziger, Karen, Howard-Sloan Assoc. (C), NY, *381*
Danziger, Karen, The Howard-Sloan-Koller Group (R), NY, *97*
Growick, Philip, Jerry Fields Assoc. (C), NY, *340*
Harrison, C.A., Chad Management Group (C), ON, *288*
Moore, Tina, Gundersen Partners, L.L.C. (R), NY, *83*
Perlmutter, Martin, Hook-Up! (C), CA, *380*
Ragaza, Jessica, RitaSue Siegel Resources, Inc. (R), NY, *191*
Raver, Miki, Hook-Up! (C), CA, *380*
Rudich, Susan, Susan Rudich (C), NY, *548*

Credit

Collins, Judy, Sales Consultants of Chicago South (C), IL, *558*
Frankel, Miriam, PMJ & Assoc. (C), ON, *513*
Hopard, Stuart M., Olympian Recruitment, Ltd. (C), NY, *498*
Jaspersen, Kenneth A., Dunhill Professional Search of Omaha, Inc. (C), NE, *321*
Kasperski, Leon, Rice Cohen Int'l. (R), PA, *178*
LaBarge-Wilson, Cynthia, Largent Parks & Partners (C), TX, *503*
Mangiafico, Jane, Largent Parks & Partners (C), TX, *503*
Meissner, Bob, Management Recruiters of Milwaukee-North (C), WI, *466*
Ponaman, Albert L., Al Ponaman Company, Inc. (C), CA, *514*

Credit cards

Cohen, Richard, Management Recruiters of Manhattan on Broadway (C), NY, *455*
Garland, Dick, Dick Garland Consultants (R), NY, *74*
Kendrick, M. Steven, LAI Ward Howell (R), TX, *124*
Lindberg, Gillis, Wells, Bradley & Assoc., Inc. (C), MN, *618*
Porrello, Joy M., Dunhill Personnel of Northeast Tulsa, Inc. (C), OK, *322*
Pruitt, Jim, Lyons Pruitt Int'l. (R), PA, *132*
Strom, Justin V., Overton Consulting (R), WI, *157*

Cruise management

Stafford, Susan P., Hospitality Int'l. (C), NY, *381*

Culinary

Eagar, Brian, Search Int'l. (R), MA, *187*
McKay, Bob, Further Management Group (C), MD, *353*
Reich, Joshua, The Alfus Group (R), NY, *3*
Stanley, John, Search Int'l. (R), MA, *187*
White, Clyde, Further Management Group (C), MD, *353*

Customer services

Buggy, Linda, Bonnell Assoc. Ltd. (R), CT, *19*
Connelly, Amy Reece, Johnson Brown Assoc., Inc. (C), IN, *400*
Cullen, Andrew, The Pennmor Group (C), NJ, *506*
Kindig, Becky, Management Recruiters-Cedar Rapids, Inc. (C), IA, *448*
Voigt, Jeff, APA Employment Agency Inc. (C), OR, *251*

Dairy

Stanley, Harry, Whittaker & Assoc., Inc. (C), GA, *620*

Data communication

Bryant, Ed, Kiley, Owen & McGovern, Inc. (R), NJ, *114*
Calder, Darryl, The Silicon Network (C), ON, *581*
Chisum, Jeanne, Executive Sales Search (C), CO, *335*
Cooper, Liz, The Beardsley Group Inc. (C), CT, *261*
Cowlishaw, Ronnette, Sales Consultants of Denver (C), CO, *557*
Cropp, Wes, Management Recruiters of Franktown (C), CO, *442*
Dermady, Timothy J., ExecutiveFit (C), NY, *337*
Dreier, John S., Dreier Consulting (C), NJ, *315*
Engler, Christine, CEO Consulting (C), FL, *287*
Faucher, Cornel, Sink, Walker, Boltrus Int'l. (R), MA, *192*
Fernandez, Michael, The Silicon Network (C), ON, *581*
Griffith, Doug, Caywood Partners, Ltd. (R), CA, *32*
Gross, Jerry, Creative HR Solutions (C), GA, *303*
Hall, Scott, Advancement, Inc. (C), IL, *241*
Hertz, Al, Carter/MacKay (C), NC, *285*
Hobbins, Elaine K., Barnes & Assoc. Executive Search (C), CA, *259*
Hoffman, Adele, The Beardsley Group Inc. (C), CT, *261*
Hoffman, Brian, Sales Consultants of Rockville, MD (C), MD, *559*
Jacobson, Priscilla, Tech Connector Group (C), CA, *601*
Joyce, William J., The Guild Corp. (C), VA, *364*
Junker, Sherry, Bolton Group (C), CA, *269*
Karkow, Drew, David Weinfeld Group (C), NC, *617*
Kohonoski, Michael M., The Guild Corp. (C), VA, *364*
Ku, Theresa, Sanford Rose Assoc. - Anaheim (C), CA, *566*
Landwerb, Sandy, Capital Consulting Group, Inc. (R), MD, *28*
Laresen, Rolph, The Silicon Network (C), ON, *581*
Leone, Joan, The Beardsley Group Inc. (C), CT, *261*
Lewis, Marc, Christian & Timbers, Inc. (R), OH, *34*
Mader, Stephen P., Christian & Timbers, Inc. (R), MA, *34*
Mader, Steve, Christian & Timbers, Inc. (R), OH, *34*
Marshall, Dennis, L O R (R), NJ, *122*
McCormack, Kathy, The Beardsley Group Inc. (C), CT, *261*
McDowell, John, McDowell & Co., Recruiters (C), TX, *474*
McGinty, Kevin, The Silicon Network (C), ON, *581*
McGovern, Sheila M., Kiley, Owen & McGovern, Inc. (R), NJ, *114*
Newell, Beverly, The Beardsley Group Inc. (C), CT, *261*
Nicolosi, Charles, CN Associates (C), CA, *293*
Owen, Ralph, Kiley, Owen & McGovern, Inc. (R), NJ, *114*
Roscoe, Harry, The Beardsley Group Inc. (C), CT, *261*
Rowell, Mike, Carter/MacKay (C), MA, *285*
Rystrom, R. L., R. L. Rystrom & Assoc., Inc. (C), MN, *549*
Schmidt, Susan, David Weinfeld Group (C), NC, *617*
Selker, Gregory, Christian & Timbers, Inc. (R), OH, *34*
Shindler, Stanley L., Franklin Int'l. Search, Inc. (C), MA, *352*
Siker, Paul W., The Guild Corp. (C), VA, *364*
Smith, Gregory K., Global Technologies Group Inc. (C), NC, *359*
Stelika, Kit, Southport Int'l. Assoc. Inc. (C), FL, *588*

Stepler, Paul, Gallin Associates of Naples, FL (C), FL, *354*
Upton, Noreen, The Beardsley Group Inc. (C), CT, *261*
Vandegrift, Tom, Kiley, Owen & McGovern, Inc. (R), NJ, *114*
Weinfeld, David C., David Weinfeld Group (C), NC, *617*
Wilson, Patricia, Global Technologies Group Inc. (C), NC, *359*
Wimmer, Walter, The Silicon Network (C), ON, *581*
Young, Susan M., Management Recruiters of Morris County, NJ (C), NJ, *453*
Young, Wayne T., Management Recruiters of Morris County, NJ (C), NJ, *453*

Databases

Ashok, T. C., Fortuna Technologies Inc. (C), CA, *343*
Bliss, Barbara P., Lamay Assoc., Inc. (R), CT, *124*
Capel, Rob, Research Personnel Consultants (C), ON, *534*
Capozzi, John, C Assoc. (C), DC, *278*
Ciaramitaro, Paul, Corporate Search Consultants, Inc. (C), FL, *301*
Cornehlsen, James H., Skott/Edwards Consultants (R), NY, *192*
Coughlin, Linda, Partners in Recruiting (C), IL, *504*
Darcy, Dawn, Direct Marketing Resources (C), NC, *312*
Davis, Jeff, DataPro Personnel Consultants (C), TX, *308*
Dyson, Steve, Technology Search Int'l. (C), CA, *603*
Fairlie, Suzanne F., ProSearch, Inc. (C), PA, *524*
Flowers, Terry, Russ Hadick & Assoc. Inc. (C), OH, *365*
Goldberg, Steve, Media Recruiting Group, Inc. (C), NY, *476*
Graham, Pat, Milrod Assoc. (C), NJ, *482*
Harrison, Harold M., InfoTech Search (C), TX, *388*
Ingala, Thomas A., Direct Marketing Solutions (C), KY, *312*
Lombardo, Steve, Search America, Inc. (C), MA, *574*
Lynch, William E., Fortuna Technologies Inc. (C), CA, *343*
Ornstein, Robert, Trebor Weldon Lawrence, Inc. (R), NY, *210*
Peragine, Ralph, The Resource Group (R), CT, *175*
Peragine, Ralph P., The Resource Group (R), CT, *175*
Pickens, Gregory D., Gregory D. Pickens (C), TX, *512*
Shindler, Stanley L., Franklin Int'l. Search, Inc. (C), MA, *352*
Sieler, Susan, C Assoc. (C), DC, *278*
Sirey, Don, Technology Search Int'l. (C), CA, *603*
Sullivan, Dan, Direct Marketing Resources (C), NC, *312*
Swami, Pad N., Fortuna Technologies Inc. (C), CA, *343*
Weiss, Cathy, C. Weiss Assoc., Inc. (C), NY, *618*

Defense

Fisher, Neal, Fisher Personnel Management Services (R), CA, *68*
Hamilton, Marilyn, Fisher Personnel Management Services (R), CA, *68*
Hansen, Ty E., Blake/Hansen Ltd. (R), FL, *18*
Metzger, Pete, Foster Partners (R), DC, *70*
Poore, Larry D., LAI Ward Howell (R), IL, *123*

Dental

Berger, Jerry, ACC Consultants, Inc. (C), NM, *233*
DuBois, Jr., Joseph W., Horizon Medical Search of NH (C), NH, *381*
Dye, Bill, Bruce Henry Assoc. Inc. (R), TX, *91*
Henry, Bruce, Bruce Henry Assoc. Inc. (R), CA, *91*
Hutchinson, Vicki, Snelling & Snelling, Inc. (C), FL, *585*
Oliveros, Nancy P., New Dawn Employment Search (C), CA, *491*
Seebinger, Larry, ACC Consultants, Inc. (C), NM, *233*
Seebinger, Virginia, ACC Consultants, Inc. (C), NM, *233*

Derivatives

Foltz, T. J., Capital Markets Resources, Inc. (C), NC, *281*
Miller, David, Global Executive Search Group (C), MA, *358*
Rountree, III, John B., Lexington Software Inc. (C), NY, *417*

Design

Aswell, Judy, Management Recruiters of San Marcos (C), TX, *463*
Bono, Jeffrey D., Michael Latas & Assoc., Inc. (R), MO, *126*
Buck, Jr., Charles A., Charles Buck & Assoc., Inc. (R), NY, *24*
Buckley, Michael, High Tech Opportunities, Inc. (C), NH, *377*
Burns, Gale, Snelling Search Recruiters (C), NC, *586*
Conroy, Daniel J., Michael Latas & Assoc., Inc. (R), MO, *126*
Cooper, Ron, High Tech Opportunities, Inc. (C), NH, *377*
Evans, Patrick, The Evans McDonnell Co. (C), TX, *331*
Foster, Kathie, Michael Latas & Assoc., Inc. (R), MO, *126*
Heacock, Barbara, B. D. Wallace & Assoc. (C), MD, *614*
Holland, Lee, Carnegie Resources, Inc. (C), NC, *284*
Hosey, Debra, The Pailin Group Professional Search Consultants (R), TX, *158*
Hudson, Judy K., The Hudson Group (C), CT, *383*
Jesberg, Gary H., Michael Latas & Assoc., Inc. (R), MO, *126*
Leonard, William C., Michael Latas & Assoc., Inc. (R), MO, *126*
Munger, Donald, Berkshire Search Assoc. (C), MA, *265*
Natowitz, Robert, DeMatteo Associates (C), NY, *311*
Putiri, Vincent, Asheville Search & Consulting (C), NC, *253*
Reyes, Randolph, Management Recruiters of Columbia (C), MD, *450*
Siegel, RitaSue, RitaSue Siegel Resources, Inc. (R), NY, *191*
Sloane, Ron, Management Recruiters of Milwaukee-North (C), WI, *466*
Swift, Catherine, Swift & Assoc. (C), ME, *597*
Vucicevic, Andy, General Engineering Tectonics (C), CA, *356*

Diagnostics

Barkley, Keith, The Mackenzie Group (R), MD, *133*
Besen, Douglas, Besen Assoc. Inc. (C), NJ, *266*
Bowman, Mary, Healthcare Management Resources, Inc. (R), GA, *89*
Brissenden, Hoke, Brissenden, McFarland, Fuccella & Reynolds, Inc. (R), NJ, *23*
Clos, Barbara, Carr Management Services, Inc. (C), PA, *284*
Hebel, Robert W., R. W. Hebel Assoc. (R), TX, *89*
Kazan, J. Neil, Kazan International, Inc. (R), NJ, *110*
Lareau, Belle, The Hampton Group (C), NY, *368*
Len, Ronald D., Healthcare Recruiters International-NY/NJ (C), NJ, *373*
Lowry, James, Carr Management Services, Inc. (C), PA, *284*
Moore, Richard, Healthcare Recruiters of the Rockies, Inc. (C), CO, *372*
Pencarski, Robert, Bio-Venture Group (C), RI, *266*
Robbins, Melvyn, Healthcare Recruiters of New England (C), MA, *373*
Sawhill, Louise, Healthcare Management Resources, Inc. (R), GA, *89*
Steinman, Richard, Career Marketing Assoc., Inc. (C), CO, *282*
Stratman, Sandra, Management Recruiters of Milford Inc. (C), CT, *442*
Westmore, Diane, Healthcare Management Resources, Inc. (R), GA, *89*
Wimberly, Jim, Healthcare Recruiters of Dallas (C), TX, *374*

Diecast

Michaels, Lou, Lou Michaels Assoc., Inc. (C), MI, *481*

Digital

Bellano, Robert W., cFour Partners (R), CA, *32*
Happillon, Jennifer, cFour Partners (R), CA, *32*
Hudson, Judy K., The Hudson Group (C), CT, *383*
Hudson, Paul E., The Hudson Group (C), CT, *383*
Romstein, Christina, cFour Partners (R), CA, *32*
Schultz, William A., Sales Consultants of Madison (C), WI, *563*

Direct marketing

Banach-Osenni, Doris, The Brentwood Group, Inc. (R), NJ, *22*
Belanger, Richard, Kingsley Allen Partners Inc. (R), ON, *114*
Bernhart, Jerry, Bernhart Assoc. (C), MN, *265*
Bliss, Barbara P., Lamay Assoc., Inc. (R), CT, *124*
Bratches, Howard, Thorndike Deland Assoc. LLC (R), NY, *48*
Brolin, Lawrence E., DLB Assoc. (R), NY, *53*
Brownstein, Joan, Julian Assoc., Inc. (C), CT, *401*
Brownstein, Julian, Julian Assoc., Inc. (C), CT, *401*
Carpenter, Judi, Carpenter Assoc., Inc. (R), IL, *30*
Chapas, Kristyn, Cook Assoc.,® Inc. (R), IL, *40*
Coughlin, Linda, Partners in Recruiting (C), IL, *504*
Cyr, Maury N., Cyr Associates, Inc. (C), MA, *306*
Dixon, Violet, Opalka Dixon Consultants to Management (R), VA, *156*
Fabian, Jeanne, Fabian Assoc. Inc. (C), NY, *338*
Faller, Laura McGrath, Redden & McGrath Assoc., Inc. (R), NY, *173*
FitzGibbon, Michael T., FitzGibbon & Assoc. (R), PA, *68*
Ford, Eileen F., Ford & Ford (C), MA, *343*
Glynn, Mary Anne, E. A. Hughes & Co., Inc. (R), NY, *98*
Goldberg, Steve, Media Recruiting Group, Inc. (C), NY, *476*
Goodman-Brolin, Dorothy, DLB Assoc. (R), NY, *53*
Gore, Les, Executive Search Int'l./Transearch (R), MA, *63*
Greene, Dorcas P., Greene Personnel Consultants (C), RI, *362*
Hamilton, Lisa J., Hamilton & Co. (C), OH, *367*
Hoyda, Louis A., Thorndike Deland Assoc. LLC (R), NY, *48*
Hughes, Elaine A., E. A. Hughes & Co., Inc. (R), NY, *98*
Ingala, Thomas A., Direct Marketing Solutions (C), KY, *312*
Lapham, Lawrence L., Lawrence L. Lapham, Inc. (R), NY, *124*
Levy, Eve, Hal Levy & Assoc. (C), NY, *417*
Levy, Hal, Hal Levy & Assoc. (C), NY, *417*
Lord, Marvin, E. A. Hughes & Co., Inc. (R), NY, *98*
Mangieri, Chris, Mangieri/Solutions LLC (C), CT, *468*
Marquez, Paul, Sanford Rose Assoc. - Fairhope (C), AL, *565*
Mayers, Lawrence S., Lamay Assoc., Inc. (R), CT, *124*
Milrod, Jane, Milrod Assoc. (C), NJ, *482*
Moore, Connie, C. A. Moore & Assoc., Inc. (C), MN, *484*
Morris, Barbara, Chad Management Group (C), ON, *288*
Nadherny, Christopher C., SpencerStuart (R), IL, *197*
Peragine, Ralph, The Resource Group (R), CT, *175*
Peragine, Ralph P., The Resource Group (R), CT, *175*
Perlstadt, Douglas, Interactive Search Network (R), CA, *102*
Ridenour, Suzanne S., Ridenour & Assoc. (R), IL, *178*
Siegel, Peter A., Peter Siegel & Co. (C), MA, *581*
Talabisco, Barbara, Wakefield Talabisco Int'l. (R), NY, *214*
Troyanos, Dennis, Gundersen Partners, L.L.C. (R), NY, *83*
VanReypen, Robert D., VanReypen Enterprises, Ltd. (R), NY, *213*
VanReypen, Shirley, VanReypen Enterprises, Ltd. (R), NY, *213*
Weiss, Cathy, C. Weiss Assoc., Inc. (C), NY, *618*
Wood, Louise, Louise Wood & Assoc. (C), NY, *624*

Dirt

Haentzler, Robert A, Michael Latas & Assoc., Inc. (R), MO, *126*
Palumbo, Michael J., Michael Latas & Assoc., Inc. (R), MO, *126*
Robinson, Rodney L., Michael Latas & Assoc., Inc. (R), MO, *126*
Waller, Jody W., Michael Latas & Assoc., Inc. (R), MO, *126*

Disaster recovery

Carey, Cameron, Computer Security Placement Service (C), MA, *296*

Distribution

Anderson, Jim, Howard Clark Assoc. (C), NJ, *292*
Anderson, Wayne F., Anderson Network Group (C), OH, *250*
Bailey, David C., Management Recruiters of Lake Tahoe, NV (C), NV, *453*
Bell, Lindy, Fortune Personnel Consultants of Huntsville, Inc. (C), AL, *344*
Berlet, William, KPMG Executive Search (R), ON, *119*
Bright, William, The Perkins Group (R), NC, *162*
Buntrock, George, Management Recruiters Dallas North (MRDN) (C), TX, *462*
Caplan, Deborah, PricewaterhouseCoopers Executive Search (R), ON, *168*
Carey, Harvey, Carion Resource Group Inc. (C), ON, *284*
Coleman, Greg, Strategic Assoc., Inc. (C), TX, *595*
Cousins, John L., Procurement Resources (C), MD, *520*
Cunningham, Douglas, Staff Resources, Inc. (C), SC, *590*
Donahue, Timothy J., Kelly Associates (R), PA, *112*
Faller, Laura McGrath, Redden & McGrath Assoc., Inc. (R), NY, *173*
Ford, Eileen F., Ford & Ford (C), MA, *343*
Foster, William A., Bridgecreek Personnel Agency (C), CA, *273*
Fountain, Ray, Management Recruiters of North Charleston (C), SC, *460*
Gladstone, Robert, Roth Young Executive Search (C), TX, *546*
Goldsmith, Fred J., Fred J. Goldsmith Assoc. (R), CA, *79*
Heinschel, Phil, Phillips Personnel/Search (C), CO, *510*
Herring, Bill, Herring & Assoc. (C), AR, *376*
Hodges, Whitney, Recruiting Services Group, Inc. (C), TN, *532*
Hood, Fred L., Fred Hood & Assoc. (C), CA, *380*
Horne, Tony, Herring & Assoc. (C), AR, *376*
Hurtubise, Jean Pierre, Reynolds Consulting Int'l. (R), QE, *177*
Jacobson, Donald, Hunt Ltd. (C), NJ, *385*
Johnson, Scott, Johnson Assoc., Inc. (C), IL, *399*
Krumel, Richard, The Perkins Group (R), NC, *162*
Landsman, Jeffrey B., Roth Young Personnel Services of Washington, DC (C), MD, *546*
Letson, Susan, KPMG Executive Search (R), NS, *119*
Lichtenauer, William E., Britt Assoc., Inc. (C), IL, *274*
Marunick, Kevin, Fortune Personnel Consultants of Chattanooga Inc. (C), TN, *349*
Metz, Alex, Hunt Ltd. (C), NJ, *385*
Moore, Robert, Management Recruiters of Rockville (C), MD, *450*

Nickels, Edward L., Michael Latas & Assoc., Inc. (R), MO, *126*
Nunziata, Fred A., Eden & Assoc., Inc. (C), PA, *326*
Orlich, Joseph, Hughes & Wilden Assoc. (C), PA, *383*
Page, Theresa, T. Page & Assoc. (C), TX, *502*
Pelisson, Charles J., Marra Peters & Partners (R), NJ, *136*
Perkins, Arthur, Management Alliance Group, Inc. (R), NJ, *134*
Perkins, R. Patrick, The Perkins Group (R), NC, *162*
Provost, Ed L., Management Recruiters Dana Point (C), CA, *440*
Provost, Todd, Management Recruiters Dana Point (C), CA, *440*
Ragan, William E., Michael Latas & Assoc., Inc. (R), MO, *126*
Raulerson, Derek, Search South, Inc. (C), AL, *576*
Remillard, Brad M., CJA-The Adler Group, Inc. (R), CA, *35*
Richards, Terry, Terry Richards (C), OH, *536*
Rodriguez, Janet, T. Page & Assoc. (C), TX, *502*
Selig, Robert J., Selig Executive Search (C), NH, *579*
Spilman, Mary P., Spilman & Assoc. (R), TX, *197*
Stewart, Wilfred C., KPMG Executive Search (R), ON, *119*
Stillings, Eleanor, Alpha Search (C), FL, *246*
Stone, Susan L., Stone Enterprises Ltd. (C), IL, *594*
Sulkowski, Roger, Hughes & Wilden Assoc. (C), PA, *383*
Thaler, Brian D., Scott-Thaler Assoc. Agency, Inc. (C), CA, *573*
Thiras, Ted, MIXTEC Group (R), CA, *145*
Tommarello, Tony, Lucas Assoc. (C), CA, *421*
Young, Arthur L., Search South, Inc. (C), AL, *576*
Zarkin, Norman, The Zarkin Group, Inc. (R), NY, *226*
Zaslav, Debra M., Telford, Adams & Alexander (R), CA, *208*

Diversity

Allerton, Donald, Allerton Heneghan & O'Neill (R), IL, *4*
Bartle, Tom, Wesley Brown & Bartle Co., Inc. (R), NY, *218*
Bright, Develous A., The Urban Placement Service (C), TX, *611*
Bright, Willie S., The Urban Placement Service (C), TX, *611*
Buggy, Linda, Bonnell Assoc. Ltd. (R), CT, *19*
Cecilio, Cesca, Montgomery West (R), CA, *146*
Dahl, Charles, Charles Dahl Group, Inc. (C), MN, *306*
Engler, Christine, CEO Consulting (C), FL, *287*
Fafard, Lina, Montgomery West (R), CA, *146*
Greene, Jeff, Wesley Brown & Bartle Co., Inc. (R), NY, *218*
Hamilton, Denman, Synergy 2000 (C), DC, *597*
Holland, Susan R., Holland Rusk & Assoc. (R), IL, *95*
Howard, Grazell R., The Libra Group (C), NC, *417*
McCarthy, Frank X., Xavier Associates, Inc. (R), MA, *226*
McCormack, Joseph A., McCormack & Assoc. (R), CA, *140*
Medley, Jerry, The Medley Group (C), CA, *477*
Mogg, Dennis, Partnervision Consulting Group Inc. (R), ON, *160*
Owens, LaMonte, LaMonte Owens, Inc. (R), PA, *158*
Tribbett, III, Charles A., Russell Reynolds Assoc., Inc. (R), IL, *176*
Tucker, Weida G., W. G. Tucker & Assoc. (R), PA, *211*
Wilson, Donald, Allerton Heneghan & O'Neill (R), IL, *4*

Domestic

Finch, John Juanito, Resolve Assoc. Int'l. (R), FL, *175*
Flannery, Thomas T., Resources for Management (R), PA, *176*
Isaacs, Rhoda, R. I. James, Inc. (C), NY, *397*
Martinolich, Michael, Tennyson Advisors (R), NY, *208*
Scott, Gordon, Search Advisors Int'l. Corp. (R), FL, *186*
Solomon, Phyllis, Phyllis Solomon Executive Search, Inc. (C), NJ, *587*
Weinstein, Stanley E., S. E. Weinstein Co. (R), IL, *217*

E-Mail

Van Campen, Jerry, Gilbert & Van Campen Int'l. (R), NY, *76*

Economic development

Erickson-Pearson, David, Boulware & Assoc. Inc. (R), IL, *20*
Zweifler, Rhyan, Boulware & Assoc. Inc. (R), IL, *20*

Editorial

Caravello, Cindy, Desktop Staffing, Inc. (C), IL, *311*
Cardwell, Jean, Cardwell Enterprises Inc. (R), IL, *29*
Danziger, Karen, Howard-Sloan Assoc. (C), NY, *381*
Danziger, Karen, The Howard-Sloan-Koller Group (R), NY, *97*
Munson, Brad, ProSearch Recruiting (C), CA, *524*

EDP

Allen, Thomas R., Allen Consulting Group, Inc. (C), MO, *244*
Arceri, John Mark, John Ryan Assoc., LLC. (C), NY, *399*
Bean, Marjean, EDP Staffing Solutions, Inc. (C), AR, *327*
Beldon, Richard, Professional Support Inc. (C), OH, *523*
Branch, Len, Advanced Recruiting, Inc. (C), OK, *240*
Brody, Ilana, Edward Bell Assoc. (C), CA, *263*
Brown, David, Snelling Search (C), AL, *585*
Bryan, Amber, Premier Search Group (C), IN, *517*
Carpenter, Edward, Executive Search of America, Inc. (C), OH, *336*
Clark, Howard L., Howard Clark Assoc. (C), NJ, *292*
Cohen, Robert C., Intech Summit Group, Inc. (R), CA, *102*
Cook, Martin E., Cook Assoc. Int'l., Inc. (C), TN, *298*
Cornett, Kristine, Management Recruiters of Boone (C), NC, *456*
Dabich, Thomas M., Robert Harkins Assoc., Inc. (C), PA, *369*
Daugherty-Hill, Kimberly J., Hayman Daugherty Assoc., Inc. (C), GA, *370*
Dralle, Robert D., Odell & Assoc., Inc. (C), TX, *498*
Driscoll, Donald L., Management Recruiters of Boone (C), NC, *456*
Eason, James M., JRL Executive Recruiters (C), GA, *401*
Edwards, Verba Lee, Wing Tips & Pumps, Inc. (C), MI, *623*
Favero, Luigi, Edward Bell Assoc. (C), CA, *263*
Ferrara, David K., David Anthony Personnel Assoc., Inc. (C), NJ, *308*
Forman, Margaret M., National Field Service Corp. (C), NY, *489*
Fox, Candy, D. R. Blood & Assoc. (R), AZ, *18*
Gavin, David R., Northland Employment Services Inc. (C), MN, *496*
Geiman, Barry, Leader Institute, Inc. (C), GA, *414*
Guardiani, Janet, Edward Bell Assoc. (C), CA, *263*
Harrington, Cherie, Human Resources Personnel Agency (R), AR, *99*
Holzheimer, Robert, Exclusive Search Consultants (C), OH, *331*
Hughes, Tom, Fox-Morris Assoc., Inc. (C), NJ, *352*
Hulme, Doug, Leader Institute, Inc. (C), GA, *414*
Hunter, David, Stanewick, Hart & Assoc., Inc. (C), FL, *591*
Jones, Jeff, Management Recruiters of Atlanta (C), GA, *445*

RECRUITER SPECIALTIES

Lawrence, Gina, Micro Staff Solutions, Inc. (C), TX, *481*
Lucifero, Lisa, ACSYS Resources, Inc. (C), NJ, *238*
Marshall, John L., Fishel HR Assoc., Inc. (C), AZ, *341*
Martineau, Bill, Dunhill Professional Search of Winston-Salem (C), NC, *322*
Martineau, Bob, Dunhill Professional Search of Winston-Salem (C), NC, *322*
Martineau, Dan, Dunhill Professional Search of Winston-Salem (C), NC, *322*
Moore, Bob, Computer Recruiters, Inc. (C), CA, *295*
Murray, Matthew, Management Recruiters of Boone (C), NC, *456*
Nashleanas, Richard P., Monarch Technology Management LLC (C), CO, *484*
Norris, Dan, Management Recruiters of Boone (C), NC, *456*
O'Keefe, John P., O'Keefe & Assoc. (C), TX, *498*
Odia, Frank Michael, High Tech Staffing Group (C), OR, *377*
Owens, Lynn, Advanced Recruiting, Inc. (C), CO, *240*
Peet, John, Management Recruiters of Boone (C), NC, *456*
Perkins, Yvonne, Leader Institute, Inc. (C), GA, *414*
Peterson, Greg, Sales Consultants of Ft. Lauderdale, Inc. (C), FL, *557*
Pradarelli, Dennis J., MARBL Consultants, Inc. (C), WI, *469*
Quiring, Patti L., Quiring Assoc., Inc. (C), IN, *527*
Randell, Candace, Management Recruiters of Boone (C), NC, *456*
Richter, Ryan, John Ryan Assoc., LLC. (C), NY, *399*
Robinson, Michael, Management Recruiters of Atlanta (C), GA, *445*
Sandusky, Edward, Professional Support Inc. (C), NY, *523*
Schoenfeld, Jack, Dunhill of Manchester Inc. (C), NH, *321*
Sharpe, Jocelyn, Dunhill Professional Search of Winston-Salem (C), NC, *322*
Sharrow, Beth S., Sharrow & Assoc., Inc. (C), MI, *579*
Sillery, Charles H., Executive Career Search (C), VA, *332*
Silverstein, Michael L., Management Recruiters of Columbus, Inc. (C), GA, *445*
Simmons, Lynn D., Management Recruiters of Boone (C), NC, *456*
Socha, Rudy, Advancement Recruiting Services (C), OH, *241*
Sparks, Michele Benum, Micro Staff Solutions, Inc. (C), TX, *481*
Sparks, Michele Benum, The Alternatives Group, Inc. (C), TX, *246*
Stanewick, B. David, Stanewick, Hart & Assoc., Inc. (C), FL, *591*
Thorpe, James, Kenn Spinrad Inc. (C), PA, *589*
Townsend, Carol A., Future Employment Service, Inc. (C), IA, *353*
Vacca, Domenic L., ACSYS Resources, Inc. (C), DE, *238*
Vlahos, Ben, Leader Institute, Inc. (C), GA, *414*
Welker, Henry A., Henry Welker & Assoc. (C), MI, *618*
Wood, Thomas C., Trac One (R), NJ, *210*
Young, Arthur, Management Recruiters of Stanhope (C), NJ, *432*
Zabor, Richard, Leader Institute, Inc. (C), GA, *414*
Zidwick, Christiana, WTW Assoc., Inc. (R), NY, *225*

Education

Archer, Helen, Executive Search Consultants (R), CA, *63*
Attea, William, Hazard, Young, Attea & Assoc., Ltd. (C), IL, *371*
Auerbach, Judith A., Auerbach Associates, Inc. (R), MA, *9*
Bachhuber, Thomas, Management Alliance Group, Inc. (R), NJ, *134*
Carabelli, Paula, Witt/Kieffer, Ford, Hadelman & Lloyd (R), CA, *223*
Clayton, Frank, Executive Search Consultants (R), CA, *63*
Corabelli, Paula, EMN/Witt/Kieffer (R), CA, *59*
Costello, Lynda, Coe & Co. Int'l. Inc./EMA Partners Int'l. (R), AB, *37*
Decker, Robert, Ray & Assoc., Inc. (C), IA, *529*
Diaz, Norm, The Canon Group (C), CA, *280*
Funk, Bill, Korn/Ferry Int'l. (R), TX, *118*
Glassick, Charles E., Jon McRae & Associates, Inc. (R), GA, *142*
Hall, Nancy M., The Hollins Group, Inc. (R), GA, *95*
Hockett, Bill, Hockett Associates, Inc. (R), CA, *94*
Howe, Vance A., LAI Ward Howell (R), AZ, *123*
Hurley, Paula B., Auerbach Associates, Inc. (R), MA, *9*
Isaacson, John, Isaacson, Miller (R), MA, *104*
Kaufmann, Robert E., SpencerStuart (R), CT, *197*
Kelly, William W., Jon McRae & Associates, Inc. (R), GA, *142*
Koenig, Allen E., R. H. Perry & Assoc., Inc. (R), OH, *162*
Kolacia, V., Murphy Partners Int'l. (R), IL, *150*
Letson, Susan, KPMG Executive Search (R), NS, *119*
Lyttle, Jordene, KPMG Executive Search (R), ON, *119*
MacNaughton, Sperry, MacNaughton Assoc. (R), CA, *133*
Martin, Nancy A., EMN/Witt/Kieffer (R), MA, *59*
McLean, B. Keith, PricewaterhouseCoopers Executive Search (R), ON, *168*
McRae, O. Jon, Jon McRae & Associates, Inc. (R), GA, *142*
Meehling, Catherine E., First Advisory Services Int'l., Inc. (R), MD, *67*
Meehling, Catherine E., Management Assoc. (C), MD, *424*
Molloy, Thomas, Molloy Partners (R), NY, *146*
Noeske, Nancy R., Overton Consulting (R), WI, *157*
Orr, Kenneth B., Jon McRae & Associates, Inc. (R), GA, *142*
Pamenter, Fred, Pamenter, Pamenter, Brezer & Deganis Ltd. (R), ON, *159*
Park, K. Darwin, Davies, Park (R), AB, *46*
Paul, Joel H., Joel H. Paul & Assoc., Inc. (C), NY, *505*
Perry, R. H., R. H. Perry & Assoc., Inc. (R), DC, *162*
Posner, Gary J., EMN/Witt/Kieffer (R), TN, *59*
Ray, Gary L., Ray & Assoc., Inc. (C), IA, *529*
Riles, Wilson, Wilson Riles & Assoc., Inc. (R), CA, *178*
Sheridan, James J., Executive Search Consultants (R), CA, *63*
Slaughter, Katherine T., Compass Group Ltd. (R), MI, *38*
Solomon, Phyllis, Phyllis Solomon Executive Search, Inc. (C), NJ, *587*
Taylor, Charles E., LAI Ward Howell (R), GA, *123*
Victor, Johnathon, The Executive Tree (R), FL, *64*
Wenzel, Dawn, Partners in Recruiting (C), IL, *504*
Wheel, Eric, Management Recruiters of Northern California (C), CA, *440*
Wyche, Ellen Adair, Jon McRae & Associates, Inc. (R), GA, *142*
Zera, Ronald J., SpencerStuart (R), TX, *197*

Electrical

Akin, J. R., J. R. Akin & Co. (R), MA, *2*
Anderson, Gregory D., Anderson Industrial Assoc., Inc. (C), GA, *250*
Bowers, Bob, Claremont-Branan, Inc. (C), GA, *292*
Brookes, Cindy, Technical Employment Consultants (C), PA, *602*
Catherman, H. O., Lectra Search (C), GA, *415*
Chamberland, Roland, Management Recruiters of Sonoma (C), CA, *441*
Corcoran, Gary, Southern Chemical & Plastics Search (C), GA, *587*
DeForrest, Liz, Rice Cohen Int'l. (R), PA, *178*
Fisher, Earl, Management Recruiters of Cass County, NE (C), NE, *453*
Flannery, Peter, Jonas, Walters & Assoc., Inc. (R), WI, *108*
Gilbert, Mark, Sales Consultants of Farmington Hills (C), MI, *560*
Helnore, Diann, Partners in Recruiting (C), IL, *504*
Hohlstein, Jodi, Management Recruiters of Round Rock (C), TX, *463*

Joyce, Mark, Louis Rudzinsky Assoc., Inc. (C), MA, *548*
McAleavy, Steve, Search Consultants Int'l., Inc. (C), TX, *575*
Mulcahy, Patrick, Mulcahy Co. (C), WI, *487*
Munger, Donald, Berkshire Search Assoc. (C), MA, *265*
Nickels, Edward L., Michael Latas & Assoc., Inc. (R), MO, *126*
O'Brien, Brent, Executive Search Consultants Corp. (C), IL, *335*
Rafferty, Mark, Management Recruiters of Chicago-North Shore (C), IL, *447*
Ragan, William E., Michael Latas & Assoc., Inc. (R), MO, *126*
Reinitz, Robert, Professional Recruiters Inc. (C), MN, *521*
Richards, Carl, Technical Employment Consultants (C), PA, *602*
Schwartz, Lou, Technical Employment Consultants (C), PA, *602*
Searboro, M.D., Management Recruiters of Greenville (C), SC, *460*
Shearer, Gary F., Management Recruiters of Bonita Springs, Inc. (C), FL, *443*
Turner, Linda, Kuhn Med-Tech (C), CA, *409*
Williams, Bill, Executive Search Consultants Corp. (C), IL, *335*

Electromechanical

Bertram, John J., Jack Bertram, Executive Recruiter (C), PA, *265*
Hohlstein, Jodi, Management Recruiters of Round Rock (C), TX, *463*
Langford, Bob, Fortune Personnel Consultants of Huntsville, Inc. (C), AL, *343*
Lineal, Lisa, Lineal Recruiting Services (C), CT, *418*
Reed, Dave, Management Recruiters - Flint (C), MI, *451*
Ryan, David, The Recruitment Group, Inc. (C), NY, *532*
Young, Steven J., Career Counseling Inc. (CCI) (C), KY, *282*

Electronic commerce

Flannery, Michael, Redwood Partners Ltd. (R), NY, *173*
Frankovich, John, BRW Search (C), MN, *275*
Gunning, Phill, TBC, Inc. (C), KY, *600*
Kendrick, M. Steven, LAI Ward Howell (R), TX, *124*
McIntyre, Jeffrey F., McIntyre Assoc. (R), CT, *141*
Poster, Lawrence D., Catalyx Group (R), NY, *31*
Rotter, Stephen, RSMR, Inc. (R), IL, *182*
Salvatore, Philip A., LAS Management Consulting Group, Inc. (R), NJ, *125*
Ziarko, Michael E., Selective Search Associates (C), OH, *578*

Electronics

Adams, Frank S., Thomson, Sponar & Adams, Inc. (C), WA, *606*
Ames, A. P., Ames & Ames (R), CA, *5*
Ames, George C., Ames-O'Neill Assoc., Inc. (C), NY, *249*
Ansara, Peter, Ansara, Bickford & Fiske (C), MA, *251*
Argenio, Paul J., Tierney Assoc., Inc. (R), PA, *209*
Bennett, M.D., The Bennett Group, Inc. (R), IN, *16*
Buckley, Michael, High Tech Opportunities, Inc. (C), NH, *377*
Burneikis, Monica, Dunhill Professional Search of San Jose (C), CA, *319*
Byrne, Jill, Snelling Search (C), AL, *585*
Ceresi, Carole, Management Recruiters of Bay Head (C), NJ, *453*
Ceresi, Robert P., Management Recruiters of Bay Head (C), NJ, *453*
Chamberlain, Wayne, Wayne S. Chamberlain & Assoc. (C), CA, *288*
Cook, Daniel P., Alpha Resources (C), IL, *246*
Cooper, Ron, High Tech Opportunities, Inc. (C), NH, *377*
Corcoran, Gary, Southern Chemical & Plastics Search (C), GA, *587*
Cormier, Don, National Executive (C), ON, *489*
Cunningham, Douglas, Staff Resources, Inc. (C), SC, *590*
D'Andrea, Albert P., EDMS Solutions (C), TX, *326*
Deckelbaum, Stan, Fortune Personnel Consultants of Raleigh, Inc. (C), NC, *348*
DeForrest, Liz, Rice Cohen Int'l. (R), PA, *178*
DeLuca, Matthew J., Management Resource Group, Inc. (C), NY, *467*
Dietrich, Sandra, Fortune Personnel Consultants of Hilton Head (C), SC, *349*
Dreier, John S., Dreier Consulting (C), NJ, *315*
Du Ket, David R., New Venture Development, Inc. (C), CA, *492*
Edwards, John W., The Bedford Group (R), RI, *15*
Edwards, Lillian E., The Bedford Group (R), RI, *15*
Everett, Jim, EA Plus, Inc. (C), TX, *325*
Fernow, Charles S., Fernow Assoc. (C), PA, *340*
Fischer, Sabine, Linford E. Stiles & Assoc., L.L.C. (R), NH, *201*
Fisher, Neal, Fisher Personnel Management Services (R), CA, *68*
Gelatka, Charles T., The Bennett Group, Inc. (R), IN, *16*
Gilson, Dirk S., Key Resources Int'l. (C), CA, *406*
Gregg, Larry, Christopher-Westmont & Assoc., Inc. (R), OH, *35*
Guarniere, John W., RCE Assoc. (R), NJ, *173*
Hall, Dwight, The Landstone Group (C), NY, *412*
Hamilton, Marilyn, Fisher Personnel Management Services (R), CA, *68*
Helnore, Diann, Partners in Recruiting (C), IL, *504*
Henard, John B., LAI Ward Howell (R), FL, *123*
Houchins, Buster, Christian & Timbers, Inc. (R), OH, *34*
Houchins, William C. Buster, Christian & Timbers, Inc. (R), MD, *34*
Hudson, Paul E., The Hudson Group (C), CT, *383*
Jackson, Cindy, CJSI-Cindy Jackson Search Int'l. (C), CA, *291*
Johnson, Carl A., Bertrand, Ross & Assoc., Inc. (C), IL, *266*
Johnson, Carl A., International Management Services Inc. (R), IL, *102*
Kay, Heidi, Kay Concepts, Inc. (C), FL, *404*
Kelly, Susan D., S. D. Kelly & Assoc., Inc. (R), MA, *112*
Kennedy, Bradford M., Tecmark Associates Inc. (C), NY, *604*
Langford, Bob, Fortune Personnel Consultants of Huntsville, Inc. (C), AL, *343*
Lechtenberg, Richard C., Dick Berg & Assoc. (C), CA, *264*
Lightner Jr., Ralph H., Stanton Chase Int'l. (R), MD, *199*
Mader, Stephen P., Christian & Timbers, Inc. (R), MA, *34*
Mader, Steve, Christian & Timbers, Inc. (R), OH, *34*
Marseline, Tracy, CJSI-Cindy Jackson Search Int'l. (C), CA, *291*
Mather, David, Christian & Timbers, Inc. (R), OH, *34*
Mather, David R., Christian & Timbers, Inc. (R), CA, *34*
McDonald, John R., TSS Consulting, Ltd. (C), AZ, *610*
McLean, Robert T., Tecmark Associates Inc. (C), MA, *604*
Middlebrook, C. Jay, Sales Consultants of Austin, Inc. (C), TX, *562*
Morin, Paul, F-O-R-T-U-N-E Personnel Consultants of Knoxville (C), TN, *350*
Myatt, Jr., James S., Sanford Rose Assoc. - Santa Barbara (C), CA, *565*
Nelson, Len, Len Nelson & Assoc., Inc. (C), TX, *491*
Newcomb, Carol A., Tierney Assoc., Inc. (R), PA, *209*
Newman, Keith, W. Robert Eissler & Assoc., Inc. (C), TX, *327*
Norton, Greg, Norton & Assoc. (C), IL, *496*
Noyes, Jim, Sales Consultants - Bristol County (C), MA, *559*
Powers, Norman S., Norman Powers Assoc., Inc. (C), MA, *515*
Quiros, Vince, CV Associates (C), NY, *305*
Rafferty, Mark, Management Recruiters of Chicago-North Shore (C), IL, *447*
Raulerson, Derek, Search South, Inc. (C), AL, *576*
Reinitz, Robert, Professional Recruiters Inc. (C), MN, *521*

RECRUITER SPECIALTIES

Rooney, Joseph J., Rooney Assoc., Inc. (R), IL, *181*
Rose, James L., Unisearch Search & Recruiting Inc. (C), CA, *611*
Rosenthal, Abbe L., ALW Research Int'l. (R), NJ, *4*
Rosner, David, Dunhill Professional Search of San Jose (C), CA, *319*
Ruden, Shauna, Dunhill Professional Search of San Jose (C), CA, *319*
Sajankila, Raj, Softrix, Inc. (C), NJ, *586*
Schlabach, Charles F., Carnegie Partners, Inc. (R), IL, *30*
Schreiber, Sandy, Survival Systems Staffing, Inc. (C), CA, *597*
Stack, Kevin M., Circuit Search (C), NY, *291*
Testart, Marion, Placement Testart Inc. (C), QE, *513*
Tierney, George F., Tierney Assoc., Inc. (R), PA, *209*
Valentine, Donald R., Tecmark Associates Inc. (C), NY, *604*
Wagner, R. J., TSC Management Services Group, Inc. (C), IL, *610*
Walters, William F., Jonas, Walters & Assoc., Inc. (R), WI, *107*
Wilkenson, Charles R., Tecmark Associates Inc. (C), CA, *604*

Embroidery

Just, Susan, Just Management Services Inc. (C), FL, *402*

Energy

Adams, Frank S., Thomson, Sponar & Adams, Inc. (C), WA, *606*
Baker, S. Joseph, Search Consultants Int'l., Inc. (C), TX, *575*
Berry, Skip, PIC Executive Search (C), GA, *511*
Bodnar, Robert J., Management Recruiters of Princeton (C), NJ, *454*
Bodnar, Robert J., Sales Consultants of Princeton, Inc. (C), NJ, *561*
Brentari, Michael, Search Consultants Int'l., Inc. (C), TX, *575*
Brock, John, Korn/Ferry Int'l. (R), TX, *118*
Bruder, Dan, CS Dowling Executive Services (R), NJ, *54*
Collard, Joseph A., SpencerStuart (R), TX, *197*
Cooke, Gerald W., STM Assoc. (R), UT, *201*
Crystal, Jonathan A., SpencerStuart (R), TX, *197*
Daugbjerg, Ray J., LAI Ward Howell (R), TX, *124*
Difatta, Jon, Management Recruiters of Barrington (C), IL, *447*
Dillon, Mark E., NaTek Corp. (C), NY, *488*
Donnelly, George J., SpencerStuart (R), TX, *197*
Epstein, Kathy J., LAI Ward Howell (R), MA, *123*
Escandon, Rafael, SpencerStuart (R), MX, *197*
Fisher, Earl, Management Recruiters of Cass County, NE (C), NE, *453*
Fodge, Robert, Management Recruiters of Washington, DC Inc. (C), MD, *450*
Fodge, Robert C., Skipping Stone Inc. (C), VA, *582*
Frabetti, Alton J., Applied Resources (C), MA, *252*
French, William G., Preng & Assoc., Inc. (R), TX, *167*
Gardiner, E. Nicholas P., Gardiner, Townsend & Assoc. (R), NY, *74*
Glandon, Stephanie, Management Recruiters of Kanawha Valley, LLC (C), WV, *465*
Goodwin, Joe D., LAI Ward Howell (R), GA, *123*
Grayson, E. C., SpencerStuart (R), CA, *196*
Hernandez, Jr., Luis A., Independent Power Consultants (C), TX, *387*
Hofner, Kevin E., LAI Ward Howell (R), TX, *124*
Howe, Vance A., LAI Ward Howell (R), AZ, *123*
Johnson, Kathleen, Barton Assoc., Inc. (R), TX, *12*
Kasbaum, David J., The Ransford Group (R), TX, *171*
Lussier, Grant, SpencerStuart (R), MX, *197*
Magnani, Susan M., The Search Center Inc. (C), TX, *574*
Marentez, Frank, Marentz & Co. (C), TX, *469*
McAleavy, Steve, Search Consultants Int'l., Inc. (C), TX, *575*
Meadows, C. David, Right/McKee Consulting Group (C), TX, *537*
Merriman, Jack, Management Recruiters of Colorado Springs (C), CO, *441*
Merriman, Mark, Management Recruiters of Colorado Springs (C), CO, *441*
Morris, Kevin, PIC Executive Search (C), GA, *511*
Nosky, Richard E., LAI Ward Howell (R), AZ, *123*
Pellitier, Matt, PIC Executive Search (C), GA, *511*
Polvere, Gary T., Management Recruiters of Barrington (C), IL, *447*
Poore, Larry D., LAI Ward Howell (R), IL, *123*
Preng, David E., Preng & Assoc., Inc. (R), TX, *167*
Preng, Richard J., SpencerStuart (R), TX, *197*
Raben, Steven, Ray & Berndtson (R), TX, *172*
Ramirez, Richard, Marentz & Co. (C), TX, *469*
Rasmussen, Traci, Skipping Stone Inc. (C), TX, *582*
Ray, Breck, Ray & Berndtson (R), TX, *172*
Ray, Jr., Harry, Management Recruiters of Kanawha Valley, LLC (C), WV, *465*
Rieger, Louis J., SpencerStuart (R), TX, *197*
Robertson, William R., LAI Ward Howell (R), GA, *123*
Rodriguez, Larry, Marentz & Co. (C), TX, *469*
Roylance, Robert L., STM Assoc. (R), UT, *201*
Ruschak, Randy R., Management Recruiters of Bordentown (C), NJ, *454*
Schlect, Nancy, Morgan Samuels Co. (R), CA, *147*
Shields, Robert G., SpencerStuart (R), IL, *197*
Simmons, Thomas M., SpencerStuart (R), TX, *197*
Sonne, Bill, PeopleSource Inc. (C), TX, *506*
Stevens, Ralph, Preng & Assoc., Inc. (R), TX, *167*
Stewart, Robyn, Independent Power Consultants (C), TX, *387*
Swan, Christopher, RSMR, Inc. (R), IL, *182*
Walker, Jr., J. Ewing, LAI Ward Howell (R), TX, *124*
Williams, Steve, Barton Assoc., Inc. (R), TX, *13*
Wilson, Thomas H., LAI Ward Howell (R), TX, *124*
Witte, David L., LAI Ward Howell (R), TX, *124*
Woods, Deborah T., LAI Ward Howell (R), TX, *124*

Engineering

Abbott, Robert, Pacific Coast Recruiting (C), CA, *501*
Adams, Chris, Fortune Group Int'l., Inc. (R), PA, *70*
Adams, Gerald, G. Adams Partners (R), IL, *2*
Adzima, Allan G., MARBL Consultants, Inc. (C), WI, *469*
Agnello, Frank, Systems Research Inc. (SRI) (C), IL, *598*
Alisbrook, William, Fortune Personnel Consultants of Chattanooga Inc. (C), TN, *349*
Allen, Jr., Lindsay, Mark III Personnel, Inc. (C), NC, *470*
Ambruster, David L., Renaissance Resources, LLC (R), VA, *174*
Ames, George C., Ames-O'Neill Assoc., Inc. (C), NY, *249*
Anderson, Gregory D., Anderson Industrial Assoc., Inc. (C), GA, *250*
Anderson, Jim, Howard Clark Assoc. (C), NJ, *292*
Anderson, Robert W., Anderson Bradshaw Assoc., Inc. (R), TX, *6*
Andrews, David, Engineering Futures, LLC (C), CT, *330*
Anton, Michael, Michael James & Co. (C), IL, *480*
Armstrong, Don, Dunhill Professional Search of Byram (C), MS, *321*
Arnold, Dave, Markent Personnel (C), WI, *470*
Arnold, Jay, Staffing Edge, Inc. (C), KS, *590*

Arnold, Robert W., R & J Arnold & Assoc., Inc. (C), CO, *253*
Arredondo, Fred, SpectraWest (C), CA, *589*
Aspell, Tim, New Venture Development, Inc. (C), CA, *492*
Atchison, W. R., W. R. Atchison & Assoc., Inc. (C), NC, *255*
Babcock, James A., The Premier Staffing Group (C), OH, *517*
Babka, James, Roth Young of Chicago (C), IL, *546*
Baehl, Thomas A., World Search (C), OH, *625*
Baert, Yvonne, Personnel Management Group (C), MB, *508*
Bailin, Fred, Asset Resource, Inc. (C), CA, *254*
Baine, Mike, California Search Agency, Inc. (C), CA, *279*
Ballach, Allen, Allen Ballach Assoc. Inc. (R), ON, *10*
Ballou, Jodie, Management Recruiters of the Baltimore Washington Corridor (C), MD, *450*
Baraniuk, Reg, Pro Tec Technical Services (C), ON, *519*
Barkocy, Andrew B., Princeton Executive Search (C), NJ, *518*
Barr, Charly, Barr Assoc. (C), PA, *259*
Barry, Cheryl, Management Recruiters of Atlanta NE (C), GA, *446*
Bartesch, Heinz, Professional Consulting Network, Inc. (C), CA, *520*
Beaudin, Elizabeth C., Callan Assoc., Ltd. (R), IL, *27*
Becker, Ralph L., Automation Technology Search (C), CA, *256*
Belle Isle, Bill, F-O-R-T-U-N-E Search Consultants (C), MO, *347*
Belle Isle, Patrice, F-O-R-T-U-N-E Search Consultants (C), MO, *347*
Benamati, Nancy, Benamati & Assoc. (C), CO, *263*
Bencik, James P., J. P. Bencik Assoc. (C), MI, *263*
Berg, Charlie, Management Recruiters of Lake Forest, IL (C), IL, *447*
Bernal, Joan M., Barnes & Assoc. Executive Search (C), CA, *259*
Bertsch, Gary D., Sanford Rose Assoc. - Flemington (C), NJ, *568*
Binke, Elle, Sales Consultants of Birmingham (C), MI, *559*
Blaney, John A., Blaney Executive Search (R), MA, *18*
Boje, Bruce A., Westfields Int'l., Inc. (C), NY, *619*
Bone, Gilda, Selective Recruiting Assoc., Inc. (C), MI, *578*
Bos, John, Bos Business Consultants (C), NY, *270*
Bourque, Jack, Management Recruiters of Winsted, Inc. (C), CT, *442*
Bowers, Bob, Claremont-Branan, Inc. (C), GA, *292*
Bradford, Karen, Phillips Resource Group (C), SC, *510*
Bradley, T. John, Bradley & Assoc. (C), MN, *272*
Brakel, H. R., ProTech Nationwide Staffing, Inc. (C), NY, *525*
Brandvold, Steven C., Executive Connection (C), OH, *333*
Brann, Rudy, Executive Search Group, Inc. (C), CT, *335*
Brecciaroli, Diane, DiTech Resources (C), CT, *313*
Breen, Bill, Personnel, Inc. (C), AL, *508*
Brei, Randy, Brei & Assoc., Inc. (C), IA, *272*
Brentari, Michael, Search Consultants Int'l., Inc. (C), TX, *575*
Brockman, Dan B., Dan B. Brockman (C), IL, *274*
Brody, Steve, Executive Resource Systems (C), CA, *335*
Brookes, Cindy, Technical Employment Consultants (C), PA, *602*
Brown-Alcala, Sheila, Michael J. Hall & Co. (R), WA, *85*
Brunschwig, John M., Technical Search Assoc. (C), OH, *602*
Bryant, Ed, Kiley, Owen & McGovern, Inc. (R), NJ, *114*
Buckland, G. Russell, The Bedford Consulting Group Inc. (R), ON, *15*
Bulmer, Robert E., Alaska Executive Search, Inc. (C), AK, *243*
Burchell, Robert A., Fernow Assoc. (C), PA, *340*
Burkhill, J. L., The Talley Group (R), VA, *205*
Button, David R., Button Group (C), TX, *277*
Cagan, Randy A., Fortune Personnel Consultants of Raleigh, Inc. (C), NC, *348*
Cahill, Danny, Hobson Assoc. (C), CT, *379*
Cahill, Peter, Cahill Assoc. (C), CT, *279*
Calder, Darryl, The Silicon Network (C), ON, *581*
Calhoun, Dave, Selective Recruiting Assoc., Inc. (C), MI, *578*
Capanna, Patricia A., Management Recruiters of Madison, Inc. (C), WI, *466*
Carieri, Carl R., American Executive Search (C), FL, *247*
Carpenter, Edward, Executive Search of America, Inc. (C), OH, *336*
Carpenter, Traci, Transportation Recruiting Services, Inc. (C), MS, *608*
Carter, Wayne A., The Personnel Group, Inc. (R), MN, *163*
Case, David R., Case Executive Search (C), MI, *286*
Catton, Chris Lea, Zweig White & Assoc., Inc. (R), CA, *228*
Cavolina, Michael, Carver Search Consultants (C), CA, *285*
Cavoto, Bob, Cook Assoc.,® Inc. (R), IL, *40*
Cegelski, Chris, The H. S. Group, Inc. (C), WI, *365*
Cepull, Janeen, Elite Consultants, Inc. (C), FL, *328*
Chadwell, Rebecca A., Chadwell & Assoc., Inc. (C), MI, *288*
Chaffin, Denise M., Professional Team Search, Inc. (R), AZ, *169*
Chamberland, Roland, Management Recruiters of Sonoma (C), CA, *441*
Chambers, Judy, Global Consulting Group Inc. (C), ON, *358*
Chavons, Crawford, Phillips Resource Group (C), SC, *510*
Cheng, Karen, Specialty Employment Services, Inc. (C), GA, *589*
Chester, Frank G., The Libra Group (C), NC, *417*
Christine, Rich, R. Christine Assoc. (C), PA, *290*
Chrobak, John J., Pro Tec Technical Services (C), ON, *519*
Ciari, Kate Regan, Fortune Personnel Consultants (C), MT, *347*
Clark, Ronda, Management Recruiters of Seattle (C), WA, *465*
Clarke, Debra, NMC & Kay Int'l. (R), CO, *152*
Clingan, Robert H., Management Recruiters of Broome County, Inc. (C), NY, *454*
Cobb, Mark A., Management Recruiters of Springfield, Inc. (C), IL, *447*
Cochlan, Paul T., PC Assoc. (C), CO, *505*
Cohen, Michael R., Intech Summit Group, Inc. (R), CA, *102*
Cole, Don, Riley Cole (C), CA, *537*
Cole, Floyd, National Field Service Corp. (C), NY, *489*
Cole, James, Systems Research Group (C), OH, *598*
Collier, Gordon L., R. C. Services (C), TX, *528*
Collins, Phil, Claremont-Branan, Inc. (C), GA, *292*
Connelly, III, Joseph H., CS Associates, LLC (C), AZ, *304*
Connelly, Susan D., CS Associates, LLC (C), AZ, *304*
Connors, Brian J., S. Tanner & Assoc. Inc. (C), ON, *599*
Cook, Clifford L., CEO Consulting (C), FL, *287*
Cook, Gene, Cook Assoc. Int'l., Inc. (C), TN, *298*
Cook, Martin E., Cook Assoc. Int'l., Inc. (C), TN, *298*
Cook, Stephen G., Cook Assoc. Int'l., Inc. (C), TN, *298*
Cooke, Katherine H., Horton International Inc. (R), CT, *96*
Corey, Joe, Industry Consultants, Inc. (C), AZ, *388*
Corey, Richard F., Weterrings & Agnew, Inc. (C), NY, *619*
Cormier, Don, National Executive (C), ON, *489*
Cosier, Brian, Cosier & Assoc. (C), AB, *302*
Cougle, Nancy, Advanced Recruitment, Inc. (C), TN, *240*
Crane, Don, California Search Agency, Inc. (C), CA, *279*
Crosbie, D. C., Interim Management Resources Inc. (C), ON, *392*

RECRUITER SPECIALTIES

Crossman, Chuck, The Stewart Group (C), FL, *593*
Cruz, Raymond, A-Linko & Assoc. (C), TX, *231*
Culli, Ray, Christopher and Long (C), MO, *291*
Cunneff, Harry J., Management Recruiters of Lake Forest, IL (C), IL, *447*
Cupp, C. A., Austin - Allen Co. (C), TN, *256*
Dagneau, Thierry, Personnel Tangent Inc. (C), QE, *509*
Dailey, Monika, Southern Recruiters & Consultants, Inc. (C), SC, *587*
Danielsen, Annemarie T., Astro Executive Search Firm (C), LA, *254*
Davis, Charlie, Dunhill of Ft. Wayne, Inc. (C), IN, *320*
Davis, Frank, Bertrand, Ross & Assoc., Inc. (C), IL, *266*
Davis, Ronald, International Management Development Corp. (C), NY, *393*
de Lottinville, Brian L., Trans-United Consultants Ltd. (C), ON, *608*
De Riviera, Sandra, Parker Page Group (C), TX, *503*
DeGrasse, Bob, SignatureSoft Inc. (C), CA, *581*
Diaz, Del, Management Recruiters of Miami-North (C), FL, *444*
DiLorenzo, Matthew B., The Inside Track (C), TX, *389*
Diorio, Scott, Management Recruiters of Fresno (C), CA, *440*
Dishaw, Raymond J., R. J. Dishaw & Assoc. (R), TX, *52*
Dixon, Jim L., MESA International (C), CA, *480*
Dmytrow, Eric D., F-O-R-T-U-N-E Personnel Consultants of Palm Beach (C), FL, *345*
Dodson, Ellen, ADECCO Employment Services (C), VA, *240*
Doleman, Robert J., Doleman Enterprises (R), VA, *53*
Dorfman, Jan, F-O-R-T-U-N-E Personnel Consultants of Denver, Inc. (C), CO, *344*
Downs, Greg, Executive Recruiters Agency, Inc. (C), AR, *333*
Doyen, Mike, Greenfields Engineering Search (C), MO, *363*
Doyle, David, System 1 Search (C), CA, *598*
Dubuque, Bill, Christopher and Long (C), MO, *291*
Dunlap, Thomas, Charles Dahl Group, Inc. (C), MN, *306*
Dunn, Sharon M., The Morley Group (C), IN, *486*
Dupilka, John M., Michael Latas & Assoc., Inc. (R), MO, *126*
Dusome, Terry, Holloway Schulz & Partners (C), BC, *380*
Dykes, Mimi, Staffing Edge, Inc. (C), TX, *591*
Eason, James M., JRL Executive Recruiters (C), GA, *401*
Eason, Larry E., JRL Executive Recruiters (C), MO, *401*
Edwards, Verba Lee, Wing Tips & Pumps, Inc. (C), MI, *623*
Egan, David C., D. C. Egan & Assoc. (C), GA, *327*
Elrick, Bill, Mayhall Search Group, Inc. (C), IN, *473*
Emory, Vaughn, BayResearch Group, Inc. (R), IL, *14*
Engel, Walter E., F-O-R-T-U-N-E Personnel Consultants of the Tri-Cities, Inc. (C), TN, *350*
English, Robert, RTE Search (C), NJ, *547*
English, Robert, RTE Search (C), VA, *547*
Estes, Susan, The Associates, HR Search Executives, Inc. (C), OK, *254*
Fehrenbach, Ray, Southern Recruiters & Consultants, Inc. (C), SC, *587*
Feightner, Ted, BioTech Research Recruiters Inc. (C), CA, *267*
Fenyves, Leslie, James Moore & Assoc. (C), CA, *397*
Fernandez, Michael, The Silicon Network (C), ON, *581*
Fernow, Charles S., Fernow Assoc. (C), PA, *340*
Finn, James N., The Garret Group (R), FL, *75*
Fisher, Neal, PPS Information Systems Staffing (C), MD, *515*
Fishkin, Anita, A. G. Fishkin & Assoc., Inc. (R), MD, *68*
Ford, Neil, R. Green & Assoc., Inc. (C), OH, *362*
Foster, Holly, A First Resource (C), NC, *231*
Foster, William A., Bridgecreek Personnel Agency (C), CA, *273*
Fowler, Gary, Analog Solutions (C), NY, *249*
Fox, Gary, F-O-R-T-U-N-E Personnel Consultants of Southwest Indiana (C), IN, *346*
Frankel, Howard, Recruit Xpress (C), TX, *531*
Frankel, Marcia, Recruit Xpress (C), TX, *531*
Frazier, Steven M., Sanford Rose Assoc. - Philadelphia North (C), PA, *570*
Frease, Don, Management Recruiters The Delta Group, Inc. (C), TN, *461*
Fry, Don, Dunhill of Corpus Christi, Inc. (C), TX, *323*
Fumano, Gary W., Chapman & Assoc. (C), BC, *289*
Furioso, Carmine A., F-O-R-T-U-N-E Personnel Consultants of San Diego (C), CA, *344*
Furman, Matt, MJF Assoc. (C), CT, *483*
Gaines, Donna, Gaines & Assoc. Int'l., Inc. (R), IL, *73*
Gale, Rhoda, Management Recruiters of the Baltimore Washington Corridor (C), MD, *450*
Galka, John, Huntley Associates (Dallas), Inc. (C), TX, *386*
Gallin, Lawrence, Gallin Associates, Inc. (C), FL, *354*
Gamache, Valerie, Joe L. Giles & Assoc. (C), MI, *357*
Gardiner, Gary, Management Recruiters of Cleveland (C), OH, *457*
Gardner, Richard E., Russillo/Gardner/Spolsino (C), MA, *548*
Gardner, Sidney, Chase-Gardner Executive Search Associates, Inc. (C), FL, *289*
Garoufalis, Byron T., International Management Services Inc. (R), IL, *102*
Gasga, Pedro Salinas, Michigan Consulting Group (R), MI, *144*
Gavin, David R., Northland Employment Services Inc. (C), MN, *496*
Gavura, Nicholas J., Michael Latas & Assoc., Inc. (R), MO, *126*
Gehle, Frederick P., Dunhill Professional Search of Augusta (C), GA, *320*
Gélinas, Normand, Yves Plouffe & Assoc. (R), QE, *165*
Gilbert, James, Dynamic Staffing Network (C), IL, *324*
Gilchrist, Robert J., Horton International Inc. (R), CT, *96*
Giles, Joe L., Joe L. Giles & Assoc. (C), MI, *357*
Gilliam, Jon, LCS, Inc. (C), TX, *414*
Gilmore, Jerry, Management Recruiters of Loudoun County South (C), VA, *465*
Glandon, Stephanie, Management Recruiters of Kanawha Valley, LLC (C), WV, *465*
Golding, Michael S., Michael Assoc. (R), IL, *144*
Gomez, Margie, Bor-Maq Assoc. (C), TX, *269*
Gomez, Veronica, Engineering Futures, LLC (C), CT, *330*
Gonzer, Lawrence J., L. J. Gonzer Assoc. (C), NJ, *360*
Goodere, Greg, Montgomery West (R), CA, *146*
Gordon, Gregory, Wallace Assoc. (C), CT, *614*
Gottesfeld, Sheldon, Cross Country Consultants, Inc. (C), MD, *304*
Graham, Robert, Michael J. Hall & Co. (R), WA, *85*
Grant, Anthony, Management Recruiters of Columbia (C), MD, *450*
Greene, Jr., W. Luke, Broward-Dobbs, Inc. (C), GA, *274*
Greenwood, Katherine, Fortune Personnel Consultants of Plano (C), TX, *350*
Hadick, Russ, Russ Hadick & Assoc. Inc. (C), OH, *365*
Hageman, Jr., Leo, HR Inc. (C), NC, *382*
Hall, Michael J., Michael J. Hall & Co. (R), WA, *85*
Hanna, Jr., M. A. Jack, The Hanna Group (C), OH, *368*
Hannas, Jeanine K., Executive Business Solutions, Inc. (C), WA, *332*
Hansen, Arthur E., Ritta Professional Search Inc. (C), NY, *538*
Harbin, Steve, Dunhill Personnel of St. Andrews (C), SC, *322*
Hardage, Phillip, Hardage Group (C), TN, *369*
Harfenist, Harry, Parker Page Group (C), FL, *503*

Harkins, Robert E., Robert Harkins Assoc., Inc. (C), PA, *369*
Hartig, Dave, The Angus Group, Ltd. (C), OH, *251*
Hayes, Jim, Orion Int'l. Consulting Group, Inc. (C), OH, *499*
Hebert, Chris, Management Recruiters of Nassau, Inc. (R), NY, *134*
Hebert, Robert R., Austin Michaels, Ltd., Inc. (C), AZ, *256*
Helfer, Frederick W., Helfer Executive Consultants (R), TN, *91*
Helnore, Diann, Partners in Recruiting (C), IL, *504*
Henderson, John, Staffing Edge, Inc. (C), AZ, *590*
Henry, Jeannette A., Huntington Personnel Consultants, Inc. (C), NY, *386*
Henry, Jeremy, A First Resource (C), NC, *231*
Henry, Pat, Fortune Personnel Consultants of Huntsville, Inc. (C), AL, *343*
Henshaw, Andrew, Fortune Personnel Consultants of Huntsville, Inc. (C), AL, *343*
Henshaw, Bob, Fortune Personnel Consultants of Huntsville, Inc. (C), AL, *343*
Henton, Sara, Management Recruiters-Cedar Rapids, Inc. (C), IA, *448*
Hetherington, Don, Landon Morgan (C), ON, *412*
Hewitt, Diane, AmeriResource Group Inc. (C), OK, *249*
Hillner, Jill, Continental Research Search, Inc. (C), WI, *298*
Hills, Glen, G. H. Enterprises (C), AZ, *354*
Hirsch, Tom, InSearch (C), CO, *389*
Hobbins, Elaine K., Barnes & Assoc. Executive Search (C), CA, *259*
Hoglund, Gerald C., Hoglund & Assoc., Inc. (R), IL, *94*
Holland, Daniel O., Holland & Assoc., Inc. (R), WI, *95*
Holtz, Richard D., Technical Resource Assoc. (C), TN, *602*
Holzheimer, Robert, Exclusive Search Consultants (C), OH, *331*
Hucko, Donald, Jonas, Walters & Assoc., Inc. (R), WI, *108*
Hughes, Tim, Hughes & Assoc. Int'l. Inc. (C), AL, *383*
Hummel, D. Linda, Careerfit, Inc. (C), TX, *283*
Hunkins, Deborah J., Career Images (C), FL, *282*
Hunter, Helen, The Wabash Group (C), IN, *613*
Hurley, Art, Systems Research Inc. (SRI) (C), IL, *598*
Icard, Jr., Robert, The Icard Group, Inc. (C), MI, *387*
Irwin, Bill, Southern Recruiters & Consultants, Inc. (C), SC, *587*
Isenberg, H. Peter, Management Recruiters of Noblesville, Inc. (C), IN, *448*
Jackley, Brian D., Jackley Search Consultants (C), MN, *396*
Jackson, Cindy, CJSI-Cindy Jackson Search Int'l. (C), CA, *291*
Jebens, Harry, Markent Personnel (C), MN, *470*
Jilka, Dan, Management Recruiters of Seattle (C), WA, *465*
Johnson, Bill, Global Consulting Group Inc. (C), ON, *358*
Johnson, Robert J., Quality Search Inc. (C), OH, *526*
Johnson, Walt, Pacific Crossing (C), CA, *501*
Jordan, Dick, Staff Resources, Inc. (C), SC, *590*
Jorgensen, T. C., The Talley Group (R), VA, *205*
Joseph, Patti D., CBA Companies (C), CA, *286*
Joseph, Surette, Marsteller Wilcox Assoc. (C), IL, *471*
Kaas, Linda M., Kaas Employment Services (C), IA, *402*
Kaiser, Greg, Execu-Tech Search Inc. (C), MN, *332*
Kaiser, Marv, Execu-Tech Search Inc. (C), MN, *332*
Kalinski, Jr., Felix, Baeder Kalinski Int'l. Group, Inc. (R), NH, *10*
Kalus, Lisa, Lisa Kalus & Assoc., Inc. (C), NY, *403*
Kane, Rich, Systems Research Inc. (SRI) (C), IL, *598*
Kapetan, Nicholas, Barrett Partners (C), IL, *260*
Karel, Stephen A., Karel & Co. (R), CA, *109*
Kay, Heidi, Kay Concepts, Inc. (C), FL, *404*
Keister, John, The Stanton Group, Inc. (C), IL, *591*
Kelly, Jim, The LaBorde Group (C), CA, *411*
Kendle, Vernon S., New Venture Development, Inc. (C), CA, *492*
Keren, Yardena, Search Group (C), CA, *575*
Kershaw, Blair, Blair Kershaw Assoc., Inc. (C), PA, *405*
Kessler, Roy, J. B. Linde & Assoc. (C), MO, *395*
Keyser, James M., Career +Plus (C), NY, *281*
King, J. C., A H Justice Search Consultants (C), TX, *402*
King, Jack, Newman-Johnson-King, Inc. (C), TX, *492*
Kirkbride, Robert, Kirkbride Assoc., Inc. (C), WA, *407*
Klebba, Arthur, Morgan & Assoc. (C), MA, *485*
Koellhoffer, Thomas J., T. J. Koellhoffer & Assoc. (R), NJ, *116*
Kohn, Steven, Affinity Executive Search (C), FL, *241*
Kotler, Gerald R., Management Recruiters of Dayton, Inc. (C), OH, *457*
Kreiss, John P., Zweig White & Assoc., Inc. (R), MA, *228*
Krezo, Rich, Michigan Consulting Group (R), MI, *144*
Krezo, Rich, Premier Recruiting Group (C), MI, *516*
Kriesel, David W., Management Recruiters of Woodbury (C), MN, *430*
Kriesel, David W., Management Recruiters of Woodbury (C), MN, *452*
Kuehnling, William, Sanford Rose Assoc. - Canton (C), OH, *569*
Kuesis, Dan, Systems Research Inc. (SRI) (C), IL, *598*
Kunkle, Denise, D. Kunkle & Assoc. (C), IL, *410*
Kuschnov, Janice, Charles Dahl Group, Inc. (C), MN, *306*
Kwapisz, Arthur, ISC of Atlanta, Inc. (C), GA, *394*
LaBorde, John, The LaBorde Group (C), CA, *411*
Laird, Meri, Davidson, Laird & Assoc. (C), MI, *308*
Lalagos, Dee, DEL Technical Services, Inc. (C), IL, *310*
Lange, Jack, Lange & Assoc., Inc. (C), IN, *412*
Lange, Jim, Lange & Assoc., Inc. (C), IN, *412*
Laresen, Rolph, The Silicon Network (C), ON, *581*
Larned, Robert T., Robert Larned Assoc., Inc. (C), VA, *413*
Larsen, C. Lars, The Personnel Network, Inc. (C), SC, *508*
Larson, Ila, i.j. & assoc., inc. (C), CO, *387*
Latimer, Dick, Technical Recruiting Consultants (C), IL, *602*
Law, Grace, Software Engineering Solutions, Inc. (C), CA, *587*
Lawrence, Ellen B., Holohan Group, Ltd. (R), MO, *95*
Lawrence, Kent L., Michael Latas & Assoc., Inc. (R), MO, *126*
Lawry, William R., W. R. Lawry, Inc. (R), CT, *126*
Lay, Jim, A-Linko & Assoc. (C), TX, *231*
Layton, Bernard, Morgan Int'l., Inc. (R), IL, *147*
Lear, Daniel, Omega Systems, LLC (C), VA, *498*
Leavy, Renee, Affinity Executive Search (C), FL, *241*
Leety, Murray, Fox-Morris Assoc., Inc. (C), PA, *352*
Lehrman, Peter A., Emerging Technology Search (C), GA, *329*
Leininger, Dennis, Staffing Edge, Inc. (C), IA, *590*
Lerner, Joel S., Sanford Rose Assoc. - Louisville (C), KY, *567*
Lessner, Mark, J. E. Lessner Assoc., Inc. (R), MI, *128*
Levine, Donald, Sharp Placement Professionals, Inc. (C), NY, *579*
Levine, Jamie, TRS Staffing Solutions Inc. (C), OH, *610*
Levy, William M., Sherbrooke Assoc., Inc. (C), NJ, *580*
Lewis, Al, The Stelton Group, Inc. (C), NJ, *592*

RECRUITER SPECIALTIES

Lilja, Raymond, American Services Group (C), IL, *248*
Little, John J., Alpha Executive Search (C), AL, *246*
Loewenstein, Ron, Loewenstein & Assoc., Inc. (R), TX, *131*
Loftus, Michael G., Interim Executive Recruiting (C), GA, *392*
Logie, Richard, Kirkbride Assoc., Inc. (C), WA, *407*
Loria, Frank, Accounting Personnel & Engineering Personnel Consultants (C), LA, *238*
Love, Cindi M., Michael Latas & Assoc., Inc. (R), MO, *126*
Lutz, Allen, Lutz Associates (C), CT, *421*
Lybrook, Christian, Lybrook Assoc., Inc. (C), RI, *421*
Lybrook, David, Lybrook Assoc., Inc. (C), RI, *421*
Lynch, Jack, Michigan Consulting Group (R), MI, *144*
Lynch, Jack, Premier Recruiting Group (C), MI, *516*
Lyons, Jerold, Dunhill of Ft. Collins, Inc. (C), CO, *319*
Lyons, M. Don, L O R (R), NJ, *122*
MacBean, Paul, Technical Skills Consulting Inc. (R), ON, *207*
MacKenzie, Bruce J., Chapman & Assoc. (C), BC, *289*
Magnusen, Henry F., Management Recruiters of North Warren Inc. (C), NJ, *453*
Maher, Kevin, TBC, Inc. (C), KY, *600*
Makhani, Thukbir, LCS, Inc. (C), TX, *414*
Malatesta, Roger, Professional Recruiting Consultants, Inc. (C), DE, *521*
Malek, L., Professional Search Consultants (PSC) (C), TX, *523*
Marino, Chet, Cochran, Cochran & Yale, Inc. (R), CO, *37*
Marlow, Bill, Straube Associates (R), MA, *203*
Mars, Roxanne, Technical Skills Consulting Inc. (R), ON, *207*
Marshall, John L., Fishel HR Assoc., Inc. (C), AZ, *341*
Martire, Nick, AmeriResource Group Inc. (C), OK, *248*
Mathews, Barry C., Corporate Image Group (C), TN, *300*
Mathias, William J., Preng & Assoc., Inc. (R), TX, *167*
Mayhall, Dale, Mayhall Search Group, Inc. (C), IN, *473*
McCowan, Elle, Management Recruiters of Birmingham (C), MI, *451*
McFadden, James, PSP Agency (C), NY, *525*
McGinnis, William A., National Metal Services Corp. (C), IN, *489*
McGinty, Kevin, The Silicon Network (C), ON, *581*
McGlawn, Walter, Corporate Plus, Ltd. (C), GA, *300*
McKee, Edward F., McKee Cyber Search (C), MS, *475*
McKinney, Adrienne, Wachendorfer & Assoc. (C), TX, *613*
McManamon, Tim, Rogers - McManamon Executive Search (R), CA, *180*
McNear, Jeffrey, Barrett Partners (C), IL, *260*
McPoyle, Jr., Thomas C., TCM Enterprises (C), MD, *600*
McRoberts, C. F., McRoberts & Assoc. (C), OH, *475*
Meadows, C. David, Right/McKee Consulting Group (C), TX, *537*
Meister, Verle, Management Recruiters of Cheyenne (C), WY, *466*
Meyers, Maurice R., Management Recruiters, Inland Empire Agency (C), CA, *441*
Michaels, Ben, Ritech Management Inc. (C), NY, *537*
Michalisin, Jr., Nicholas J., S-H-S TechStaff (C), PA, *550*
Mihalka, Laura, NCC Executive Search Consultants (C), CA, *490*
Miller, Eric L., Miller Denver (C), CO, *482*
Miller, Thomas C., Emerging Medical Technologies, Inc. (C), CO, *329*
Miller, William, V. Robinson & Co., Inc. (C), MO, *539*
Milne, Carole, Danette Milne Corporate Search Inc. (C), ON, *482*
Milne, Danette, Danette Milne Corporate Search Inc. (C), ON, *482*
Mincy, Jim, Corporate Image Group (C), GA, *300*
Minso, Eugene A., Sanford Rose Assoc. - Burlington, NC (C), NC, *569*
Mojek, Chuck, American Resources Corp. (C), IL, *248*
Mols, Jeff, Aurora Tech Search (C), ON, *256*
Moore, Robert, Management Recruiters of Rockville (C), MD, *450*
Moore, Sandee, Moore Research Assoc. (R), NJ, *147*
Morgan, Richard, Morgan Samuels Co. (R), CA, *147*
Morris, Leonard, Specialized Search Assoc. (C), FL, *589*
Moser, Amy, TriStaff Group (C), CA, *609*
Mueller, William, Noll Human Resource Services (C), MO, *494*
Muhlfelder, Daniel J., L. J. Gonzer Assoc. (C), NJ, *360*
Mulcahy, Patrick, Mulcahy Co. (C), WI, *487*
Murawski, Joseph S., Teknon Employment Resources, Inc. (C), OH, *604*
Mygatt, Marlena, Software Engineering Solutions, Inc. (C), CA, *587*
Naff, Bud, Management Recruiters of Lynnwood (C), WA, *465*
Narita, Art, Essential Solutions, Inc. (C), CA, *331*
Natowitz, Robert, DeMatteo Associates (C), NY, *311*
Needham, Mary, Reserve Technology Institute (R), TX, *175*
Nelson, Paul, London Executive Consultants Inc. (C), ON, *420*
Nelson, Richard, Pacific Crossing (C), CA, *501*
Neuweiler, Mark, Saber Group, Inc. (C), TX, *550*
Newell, Wayne, Management Alliance Group, Inc. (R), NJ, *134*
Nicholls, R. J., Interim Management Resources Inc. (C), ON, *392*
Nickerson, Dennis, Survival Systems Staffing, Inc. (C), CA, *597*
Niedbalski, Michael, Executive Search Plus, Inc. (C), IN, *336*
Nimmo, Richard, AmeriResource Group Inc. (C), OK, *248*
Nix Gilmore, Pamela, Management Recruiters of Loudoun County South (C), VA, *465*
Nyborg, Marilyn, Nyborg•Dow Assoc., Inc. (C), CA, *497*
O'Brien, David, Finney-Taylor Personnel & Management Consultants Ltd. (C), AB, *341*
O'Brien, Frank E., Austin Michaels, Ltd., Inc. (C), AZ, *256*
O'Connor, Fred, F-O-R-T-U-N-E Consultants of Memphis (C), TN, *349*
O'Connor, John R., John R. O'Connor & Assoc. (C), IL, *497*
O'Keefe, Ian, O'Keefe & Assoc. (C), AR, *498*
O'Keefe, John P., O'Keefe & Assoc. (C), TX, *498*
Odia, Frank Michael, High Tech Staffing Group (C), OR, *377*
Oglesby, Tom, F-O-R-T-U-N-E Personnel of Nashville (C), TN, *350*
Olesen, Jeannette, Management Recruiters of the Baltimore Washington Corridor (C), MD, *450*
Ormond, Mark R., Capstone Consulting, Inc. (R), IL, *29*
Ormson, Gilbert E., Executive Recruiters, Inc. (C), WI, *334*
Ostroff, Stephen R., Triangle Assoc. (C), PA, *609*
Otsuka, Fyllis L., Holohan Group, Ltd. (R), MO, *95*
Ozoroski, Tom, Barr Assoc. (C), PA, *259*
Pagana, Pat, The Brentwood Group, Inc. (R), NJ, *22*
Pailin, Cheryl, The Pailin Group Professional Search Consultants (R), TX, *158*
Palazzolo, Kathy, Michigan Consulting Group (R), MI, *144*
Palazzolo, Kathy, Premier Recruiting Group (C), MI, *516*
Parfitt, Bill, Management Solutions, Inc. (C), WA, *468*
Park, Cleve A., Management Recruiters of Birmingham (C), AL, *438*
Park, Cleve A., Sales Consultants of Birmingham (C), AL, *556*
Park, Tammy, Robert Larned Assoc., Inc. (C), VA, *413*
Patchin, Rory J., R2 Services, LLC (C), IL, *528*
Patton, Gary, Career Marketing Assoc., Inc. (C), CO, *282*
Payne, Joe, Van Treadaway Assoc., Inc. (R), GA, *210*

Pepple, Bob, Fortune Personnel Consultants of Jacksonville (C), FL, *345*
Perry, Fred, Fred Perry Assoc. (C), TX, *507*
Peters, Peter Louis, Success Seekers Connection (C), FL, *596*
Petras, Michael, F-O-R-T-U-N-E Personnel Consultants of South Bend (C), IN, *346*
Petruzzi, Vincent J., Petruzzi Assoc. (C), NJ, *509*
Phelps, Ronald A., Phelps Personnel Assoc., Inc. (C), SC, *510*
Pierson, Kevin, ACC Technical Services (C), OH, *233*
Plouffe, Yves J., Yves Plouffe & Assoc. (R), QE, *165*
Polacek, Frank, Search Enterprises, Inc. (C), FL, *575*
Powers, William D., Powers Consultants, Inc. (R), MO, *166*
Presley-Cannon, Judy, Corporate Image Group (C), TN, *300*
Price, Debra J., UniQuest Int'l., Inc. (C), FL, *611*
Price, Velinda Hodge, Price & Assoc., Inc. (C), VA, *518*
Provda, Peter, F-O-R-T-U-N-E Personnel Consultants of Menlo Park, Inc. (C), NJ, *347*
Pruitt, Glen O., Locke & Assoc. (R), AL, *131*
Putman, Joseph, Snelling Search (C), AL, *585*
Putnam, Denise, Elite Consultants, Inc. (C), FL, *328*
Raab, Julie, Vaughan & Co. (C), CA, *612*
Radzely, Larry, Adel-Lawrence Assoc., Inc. (C), NJ, *240*
Ramirez, Richard, Marentz & Co. (C), TX, *469*
Raney, Albert, Dunhill Personnel Service of Fargo (C), ND, *322*
Rathborne, Kenneth J., Blair/Tech Recruiters, Inc. (C), NJ, *268*
Refi, Thomas, Robert Harkins Assoc., Inc. (C), PA, *369*
Regina, Aida, Brigade, Inc. (R), CA, *23*
Reilly, Toni Marie, Fox-Morris Assoc., Inc. (C), NC, *352*
Reitz, Doris, The Rossi Search Group (C), PA, *545*
Reynolds, John H., Brissenden, McFarland, Fuccella & Reynolds, Inc. (R), NJ, *23*
Richards, Carl, Technical Employment Consultants (C), PA, *602*
Richter, Earl, The Wabash Group (C), IN, *613*
Riddle, James E., Riddle & McGrath LLC (R), GA, *178*
Rivera, Monica, NCC Executive Search Consultants (C), CA, *491*
Roberts, Scott, Jonas, Walters & Assoc., Inc. (R), WI, *108*
Robertson, Janice, Tele-Solutions of Arizona, Inc. (C), AZ, *604*
Robinson, Mel, MDR & Associates (C), AR, *476*
Rockwell, Sr., Richard B., Applied Search Assoc., Inc. (C), GA, *252*
Rodriguez, Larry, Marentz & Co. (C), TX, *469*
Rogers, Gay, Rogers - McManamon Executive Search (R), CA, *180*
Rogers, George W., Dunhill Executive Search of Brown County (C), IN, *321*
Rogers, S. L., Dunhill Executive Search of Brown County (C), IN, *321*
Ross, Larry, The Summit Group (C), CA, *596*
Ross, William J., Flowers & Assoc. (C), OH, *342*
Rotella, Marshall W., The Corporate Connection, Ltd. (C), VA, *300*
Routh, Maria, The Kleven Group, Inc. (C), MA, *407*
Rowland, John R., Rowland Assoc. (C), CA, *547*
Rudzinsky, Jeff, Louis Rudzinsky Assoc., Inc. (C), MA, *548*
Rueppel, Melvin L., Holohan Group, Ltd. (R), MO, *95*
Rumson, Barbara A., Management Recruiters of Asheville, Inc. (C), NC, *455*
Rumson, Paul M., Management Recruiters of Asheville, Inc. (C), NC, *455*
Sacchetti, Lisa, The Renaissance Network (C), MA, *534*
Sajankila, Raj, Softrix, Inc. (C), NJ, *586*
Samuels, Lew, Morgan Samuels Co. (R), CA, *147*
Sarantino, Tina, Management Recruiters of Fresno (C), CA, *440*
Sarver, Catherine J., Sarver & Carruth Assoc. (C), OK, *571*
Sather, Jan, Career Marketing Assoc., Inc. (C), CO, *282*
Scanlon, James D., Sherbrooke Assoc., Inc. (C), NJ, *580*
Scaparotti, Jim, Fox-Morris Assoc., Inc. (C), OH, *352*
Schaefer, John, Professional Employment Group (C), MD, *520*
Schapira, Kenneth, Wilson Personnel, Inc. (C), NC, *622*
Schick, Rex, Schick Professional Search, Inc. (C), OH, *572*
Schneider, Paul J., Prime Resource Assoc. (C), WI, *518*
Schriber, Floyd, F-O-R-T-U-N-E Consultants of Memphis (C), TN, *349*
Schroeder, Tim, F-O-R-T-U-N-E Personnel of Nashville (C), TN, *350*
Schwartz, Lou, Technical Employment Consultants (C), PA, *602*
Scott, Bob, Robert Scott Assoc. (C), NJ, *573*
Scott, Sabrina, Professional Search, Inc. Int'l. (C), TX, *523*
Scrivens, Dan, Snelling Search (C), AL, *585*
Sears, Kirk P., The Wilmington Group (C), NC, *622*
Sedak, George, Curry, Telleri Group, Inc. (R), NJ, *44*
Segal, Sheila, Segal & Assoc. (C), GA, *578*
Sendler, Peter A., International Consulting Services, Inc. (C), IL, *392*
Sewell, Jerry, Fox-Morris Assoc., Inc. (C), TX, *352*
Shapiro, Larry, Heller Kil Assoc., Inc. (C), IL, *375*
Sharpe, Charles, C. J. Stafford & Assoc. (C), ON, *591*
Sharrow, Beth S., Sharrow & Assoc., Inc. (C), MI, *579*
Shaw, R. William, Management Recruiters of South Bend (C), IN, *448*
Shearer, Gary F., Management Recruiters of Bonita Springs, Inc. (C), FL, *443*
Shearer, Thomas, Carnegie Resources, Inc. (C), NC, *284*
Shetler, James W., Professional Personnel Services (C), IA, *520*
Shooshan, Daniel M., Hunter Assoc. (C), MA, *385*
Shotland, David R., The Shotland Group (R), CA, *190*
Shulman, Fran, Asset Resource, Inc. (C), CA, *254*
Shute, Randall, Executive Recruitment Services, Inc. (ERS, Inc.) (C), GA, *334*
Siegel, Alec, Halbrecht & Co. (C), VA, *365*
Silberger, Gary, Key Employment (C), NJ, *405*
Sill, Darrell E., Sill Technical Assoc., Inc. (C), PA, *581*
Sillery, Charles H., Executive Career Search (C), VA, *332*
Simmons, Anneta, Fortune Personnel Consultants of Huntsville, Inc. (C), AL, *344*
Skelton, Brenda, Cumberland Professional Search Inc. (C), TN, *304*
Skewes, Gail, Reid Ellis Assoc. Inc. (C), ON, *533*
Sloan, Tom, Tom Sloan & Assoc., Inc. (C), WI, *583*
Small, Jim, J. L. Small Assoc. (C), AL, *583*
Smith, Clark W., F-O-R-T-U-N-E Personnel Consultants of Savannah, Inc. (C), GA, *345*
Smith, Michael R., Michaels & Moere (C), WI, *481*
Smith, Randall E., R2 Services, LLC (C), IL, *528*
Smith, Robert, Fox-Morris Assoc., Inc. (C), GA, *352*
Smith, Sally, Smith, Brown & Jones (C), KS, *585*
Smitter, Janet, Carol Maden Group (C), VA, *422*
Snellbaker, Mary W., Management Recruiters of Southeastern Michigan (C), MI, *451*
Snyder, Gary, F-O-R-T-U-N-E Personnel Consultants (C), MI, *346*
Socha, Rudy, Advancement Recruiting Services (C), OH, *241*
Sondhi, Rick, Raymond Karsan Assoc. (C), IL, *530*
Sotelo, Henry, Dunhill Professional Search of Hawaii (C), HI, *320*
Southworth, David E., Michigan Consulting Group (R), MI, *144*
Southworth, David E., Premier Recruiting Group (C), MI, *516*

RECRUITER SPECIALTIES

Spears, Robert, FORTUNE Personnel Consultants of Charleston, Inc. (C), SC, *349*
Spencer, Glenda, HR Inc. (C), NC, *382*
Spinn, Mark, LCS, Inc. (C), TX, *414*
Sprankle, Kathryn, Zweig White & Assoc., Inc. (R), DC, *228*
Sprankle, Kathryn, Zweig White & Assoc., Inc. (R), MA, *228*
Spremulli, Paul L., PKS Assoc., Inc. (C), RI, *513*
Stacey, Bryce A., Chapman & Assoc. (C), BC, *289*
Stack, Kevin M., Circuit Search (C), NY, *291*
Stanley, Wade, Management Recruiters of Raleigh (C), NC, *456*
Stecker, Bernd, The Garret Group (R), NJ, *75*
Steele, Dolores M., Dunhill Professional Search, Inc. of McAllen (C), TX, *323*
Steele, Kevin, Winter, Wyman & Co. (C), MA, *623*
Steele, Lloyd F., Dunhill Professional Search, Inc. of McAllen (C), TX, *323*
Stepler, Paul, Gallin Associates, Inc. (C), FL, *354*
Stokes, George N., The Inside Track (C), TX, *389*
Stoll, Steve, Sharrow & Assoc., Inc. (C), KY, *579*
Stollenmaier, Nadine, Dunhill Professional Search of Hawaii (C), HI, *320*
Strong, Duane, Executive Resource Inc. (C), WI, *334*
Stroud, Robert, Industry Consultants, Inc. (C), GA, *388*
Stynetski, Bill, Largent Parks & Partners (C), TX, *503*
Suhay, Gary T., Elite Resources Group (R), OH, *58*
Sunshine, Ron, Ron Sunshine & Assoc. (C), IL, *597*
Susleck, Matthew M., ESS (Executive Search Services) (R), CA, *61*
Swan, Christopher, RSMR, Inc. (R), IL, *182*
Tamayo, Roland, Management Recruiters of Fresno (C), CA, *440*
Tanner, Joanne, S. Tanner & Assoc. Inc. (C), ON, *599*
Tanner, Steve, S. Tanner & Assoc. Inc. (C), ON, *599*
Tashima, Spencer S., Essential Solutions, Inc. (C), CA, *331*
Tate, Andrew, Tate Consulting, Inc. (R), FL, *207*
Telford, Daniel W., CadTech Staffing Services (C), GA, *279*
Terry, Jeff, Southern Recruiters & Consultants, Inc. (C), SC, *587*
Thomaschek, Charles F., North Coast Meridian (C), NY, *496*
Thomason, Ronald, Montgomery, Thomason & Assoc. (C), ON, *484*
Thorpe, James, Kenn Spinrad Inc. (C), PA, *589*
Tillman, Allen, Hardage Group (C), TN, *369*
Tinker, J. Jay, Management Recruiters of the Baltimore Washington Corridor (C), MD, *450*
Toke, Ron, Russ Hadick & Assoc. Inc. (C), OH, *365*
Townsend, James C., Future Employment Service, Inc. (C), IA, *353*
Train, John L., Trans-United Consultants Ltd. (C), ON, *608*
Trainor, James F., Trainor/Frank & Assoc. Inc. (C), WI, *608*
Trambley, J. Brian, Trambley the Recruiter (C), NM, *608*
Trapani, Chris, ExecuSource Consultants, Inc. (C), TX, *332*
Traynor, Thomas H., Traynor Confidential, Ltd. (C), NY, *609*
Treadaway, Van, Van Treadaway Assoc., Inc. (R), GA, *210*
Turkal, Terry, Advanced Recruitment, Inc. (C), TN, *240*
Udulutch, Mark, Markent Personnel, Inc. (C), WI, *470*
Udulutch, Thomas L., Markent Personnel, Inc. (C), WI, *470*
Valencia-Icard, Cheryl, The Icard Group, Inc. (C), MI, *387*
Van Eaton, Jim, Management Recruiters of Barrington (C), IL, *447*
Van Wick, Mike, Management Recruiters of Rankin Co. (C), MS, *452*
Vance, Joe, F-o-r-t-u-n-e of Owensboro, Inc. (C), KY, *346*
Vaughan, David B., Vaughan & Co. (C), CA, *612*
Veblan, Jennifer, NCC Executive Search Consultants (C), CA, *490*
Vitanza, Jocelyne, DARE Personnel Inc. (C), ON, *307*
Von Villas, Lynne, Employment Solutions, Inc. (C), TX, *330*
Wachendorfer, Nancy, Wachendorfer & Assoc. (C), TX, *613*
Wainwright, Nancy, Locus Inc. (C), WV, *419*
Walker, Donald G., Executive Search Plus, Inc. (C), IN, *336*
Wallace, Dennis M., Sanford Rose Assoc. - Rockford (C), IL, *567*
Walters, Tom, Bor-Maq Assoc. (C), TX, *269*
Walters, William F., Jonas, Walters & Assoc., Inc. (R), WI, *107*
Ward, Al L., Ward-Hoffman & Assoc. (C), ID, *615*
Warriner, Bob, Job-Born Candidate Selection Bureau (C), ON, *399*
Weil, Richard, LCS, Inc. (C), TX, *414*
Weiner, Art, Sanford Rose Assoc. - Athens (C), GA, *566*
Weiner, Ken, Sanford Rose Assoc. - Athens (C), GA, *566*
Weinpel, Charles J., Weinpel Search, Inc. (C), NJ, *617*
Weinstein, Bruce, Western Technical Resources (C), CA, *619*
Weiss, John P., Star Search Consultants (C), ON, *591*
Weiss, Michael G., Applied Resources, Inc. (C), MN, *252*
Welch, Lauren, Management Recruiters of Lake Forest, IL (C), IL, *447*
Weliver, Edward A., Weliver & Assoc. (C), MI, *618*
Welker, Henry A., Henry Welker & Assoc. (C), MI, *618*
Wenom, Carol Dibb, The Whitaker Companies (C), TX, *619*
West, Fred, Wood West & Partners Inc. (C), BC, *624*
Wharton, John P., The Garret Group (R), NJ, *75*
Whitehead, Robert S., Whitehead & Assoc., Inc. (C), MO, *620*
Wichansky, Carole, Tele-Solutions of Arizona, Inc. (C), AZ, *604*
Wilcox, Mark, Marsteller Wilcox Assoc. (C), IL, *471*
Willden, Vincent G. B., Coast Personnel Services Ltd. (C), BC, *293*
Williams, Dick, Dick Williams & Assoc. (C), CA, *621*
Williams, John G., John Williams & Assoc. (C), TX, *621*
Wimmer, Walter, The Silicon Network (C), ON, *581*
Winter, Peter, Catalyx Group - Canada (R), ON, *31*
Wonderling, Susan, Susan L. Wonderling Recruiting (C), PA, *623*
Woo, Aaron C., Essential Solutions, Inc. (C), CA, *331*
Wood, Bill, Search Plus Int'l.-Ohio (C), OH, *576*
Worthing, Ellen, Management Recruiters of the Baltimore Washington Corridor (C), MD, *450*
Wright, John, Corporate Image Group (C), TN, *300*
Yakimishyn, Michael, Zen Zen Int'l. Inc. (C), MB, *627*
Young, Paula G., Career Counseling Inc. (CCI) (C), KY, *282*
Young, Steven J., Career Counseling Inc. (CCI) (C), KY, *282*
Zapotocky, V. J., Computer Professionals Unlimited (C), TX, *295*
Zeiger, Stephen A., Zeiger Assoc. L.L.C. (C), CA, *627*
Zimmer, Walt, Polytechnical Consultants, Inc. (C), IL, *514*
Zonka, Thomas J., Thomas & Assoc. of Michigan (C), MI, *606*

Entertainment

Ardi, Dana B., LAI Ward Howell (R), CA, *123*
Bailey, III, Joseph A., Russell Reynolds Assoc., Inc. (R), TX, *177*
Beaudine, Frank R., Eastman & Beaudine, Inc. (R), TX, *56*
Bege, Lorraine, Hands-on Broadcast (R), NY, *86*
Bishop, Anne, Johnson Smith & Knisely (R), IL, *107*
Bishop, Susan, Bishop Partners (R), NY, *17*

Blood, Dennis R., D. R. Blood & Assoc. (R), AZ, *18*
Borkenhagen, Christine, Morgan Samuels Co. (R), CA, *147*
Bowman, David, TTG/Sterling Services (C), CA, *610*
Cecilio, Cesca, Montgomery West (R), CA, *146*
Corey, Patrick M., LAI Ward Howell (R), WI, *124*
DeLuca, Matthew J., Management Resource Group, Inc. (C), NY, *467*
Denison, Susan, Johnson Smith & Knisely (R), NY, *107*
Edwards, Charles R., LAI Ward Howell (R), GA, *123*
Eldredge, Peter, Johnson Smith & Knisely (R), NY, *107*
Emerzian, Jennifer, Johnson Smith & Knisely (R), NY, *107*
Ericksen, Bruce, MESA International (C), OR, *480*
Erickson, Cara, Johnson Smith & Knisely (R), NY, *107*
Fell, Robert M., Fell & Nicholson Technology Resources (R), CA, *65*
Fitzpatrick, John, Newport Strategic Search LLC (C), CA, *492*
Gallagher, David W., LAI Ward Howell (R), GA, *123*
Gates, Will, Morgan Samuels Co. (R), CA, *147*
Genel, George, Genel Associates (C), CA, *356*
Glazin, Lynne, The Glazin Group (R), BC, *77*
Gray, Mark, Executive Referral Services, Inc. (C), IL, *334*
Greger, Kenneth R., Greger/Peterson Assoc., Inc. (R), OR, *82*
Hannafin, James D., JDH & Assoc. (C), CA, *398*
Happillon, Jennifer, cFour Partners (R), CA, *32*
Hurley, Gerard F., Association Executive Resources Group (R), MD, *8*
James, Chip, Morgan Samuels Co. (R), CA, *147*
Johnson, Daniel, Morgan Samuels Co. (R), CA, *147*
Kolacia, V., Murphy Partners Int'l. (R), IL, *150*
Kolburne, Barbara, Foster Partners (R), NY, *70*
Landon, Susan J., LAI Ward Howell (R), NY, *122*
Lipson, Harriet L., Lipson & Co. (R), CA, *130*
Lipson, Howard R., Lipson & Co. (R), CA, *130*
MacEachern, David, SpencerStuart (R), ON, *197*
Malcom, John W., Johnson Smith & Knisely (R), NY, *107*
Marks, Brad, Brad Marks Int'l. (R), CA, *136*
Mastandrea, Pat, Johnson Smith & Knisely (R), NY, *107*
McCormick-Kelch, Anna, Johnson Smith & Knisely (R), IL, *107*
McCreary, Charles, Austin-McGregor Int'l. (R), TX, *9*
Myers, Bonnie, Myers Career Assoc., Inc. (C), CA, *488*
Nosky, Richard E., LAI Ward Howell (R), AZ, *123*
O'Toole, Dennis P., Dennis P. O'Toole & Assoc. Inc. (R), NY, *154*
Pepper, Marci, Johnson Smith & Knisely (R), NY, *107*
Pitman, P., American Executive Management, Inc. (R), MA, *5*
Pryor, Carrie Looms, LAI Ward Howell (R), NY, *123*
Richards, Sharon, Richards Assoc., Inc. (R), NY, *178*
Romstein, Christina, cFour Partners (R), CA, *32*
Sachs, Susan, Johnson Smith & Knisely (R), NY, *107*
Sanders, David, Management Recruiters of Roseville (C), CA, *441*
Shulman, Mel, M. Shulman, Inc. (R), CA, *191*
Silver, Susan, Silver Associates (C), CA, *581*
Thompson, Carlton W., SpencerStuart (R), CT, *196*
Truesdell, Michael, Ethos Consulting, Inc. (R), CA, *61*
Tudi, Mark, DHR Int'l., Inc. (R), AZ, *49*
Uhrig, Scott, LAI Ward Howell (R), TX, *124*
Virgili, Franca, Johnson Smith & Knisely (R), CA, *107*
Wasp, Jr., Warren T., WTW Assoc., Inc. (R), NY, *225*
Weinstein, Lewis R., Weinstein & Co. (R), MA, *217*
Whitney, William A., Larsen, Whitney, Blecksmith & Zilliacus, Inc. (R), CA, *125*

Environmental

Allen, Jr., Lindsay, Mark III Personnel, Inc. (C), NC, *470*
Apple, Richard W., R. W. Apple & Assoc. (C), NJ, *251*
Barnhart, David, Lechner & Assoc., Inc. (C), FL, *415*
Brown, Alan V., Personnel Alliance Group (C), NJ, *508*
Brown, Jeffrey W., Comprehensive Search (C), GA, *295*
Bruns, Matthew, The North Peak Group (C), OH, *496*
Catton, Chris Lea, Zweig White & Assoc., Inc. (R), CA, *228*
Cech, Raymond R., Dunhill Executive Search of Los Angeles, Inc. (C), CA, *319*
Collins, Phil, Claremont-Branan, Inc. (C), GA, *292*
Corey, Joe, Industry Consultants, Inc. (C), AZ, *388*
Dahl, Stan, C.T.E.W. Executive Personnel Services Inc. (C), BC, *278*
Donelon, Wayne, WMD inc. (C), NJ, *623*
Fehrenbach, Ray, Southern Recruiters & Consultants, Inc. (C), SC, *587*
Fiore, Richard, Search Consultants Int'l., Inc. (C), TX, *575*
Fishback, Joren, Derek Associates, Inc. (C), MA, *311*
Forest, Adam, McCormack & Assoc. (R), CA, *140*
Henshaw, Bob, Fortune Personnel Consultants of Huntsville, Inc. (C), AL, *343*
Hockett, Bill, Hockett Associates, Inc. (R), CA, *94*
Hunkins, Deborah J., Career Images (C), FL, *282*
Johnson, Mike, The Wabash Group (C), IN, *613*
Johnston, Gail, NJ Solutions (C), CA, *493*
Karel, Stephen A., Karel & Co. (R), CA, *109*
Kaufman, Stuart, Management Recruiters of Great Neck (C), NY, *454*
Kohn, Adam, Christian & Timbers, Inc. (R), OH, *34*
Kratimenos, Peter, Ansara, Bickford & Fiske (C), MA, *251*
Kreiss, John P., Zweig White & Assoc., Inc. (R), MA, *228*
Larkin, Dick, Larkin & Co. (R), CA, *125*
Larsen, Charles L., The Personnel Network, Inc. (C), SC, *508*
Mallinson, Robert, Ritta Professional Search Inc. (C), NY, *538*
McAllister, Lon, Search Consultants Int'l., Inc. (C), TX, *575*
McDermott, Tom, Corporate Environment Ltd. (R), IL, *41*
McNichol, Jr., John, McNichol Assoc. (R), PA, *142*
Morin, Gail, Comprehensive Search (C), GA, *295*
Munger, Donald, Berkshire Search Assoc. (C), MA, *265*
Naff, Bud, Management Recruiters of Lynnwood (C), WA, *465*
Newell, Wayne, Management Alliance Group, Inc. (R), NJ, *134*
O'Connor, John R., John R. O'Connor & Assoc. (C), IL, *497*
Palos, Michael V., Kelly Associates (R), PA, *112*
Pompelli, Jean, JAG Group (R), MO, *105*
Powers, Janet, Powers Consultants, Inc. (R), MO, *166*
Razuri, Patrick, Management Recruiters of Savannah (C), GA, *446*
Schlect, Nancy, Morgan Samuels Co. (R), CA, *147*
Shelton, Merritt S., Comprehensive Search (C), GA, *295*
Simkanin, Christine, Michael J. Hall & Co. (R), WA, *85*
Simpson, Cathy G., Conroy Partners Ltd. (R), AB, *39*
Sims, Larry, Reality Group (C), OK, *531*
Smith, Perry, Noll Human Resource Services (C), TX, *494*
Smith, Robert, Sales Consultants of Omaha, Inc. (C), NE, *560*

RECRUITER SPECIALTIES

Sprankle, Kathryn, Zweig White & Assoc., Inc. (R), DC, *228*
Sprankle, Kathryn, Zweig White & Assoc., Inc. (R), MA, *228*
Standard, Gail W., Comprehensive Search (C), GA, *295*
Tomeo, Pat, S-H-S TechStaff (C), PA, *550*
White, Ken, Management Recruiters of Winston-Salem (C), NC, *457*
Wilcox, Alex B., The Bridge (C), CO, *273*
Wilkins, Walter K., Walter K. Wilkins & Co. (R), NJ, *221*
Williams, Randy L., Environmental, Health & Safety Search Assoc. (C), FL, *331*
Wilson, Stoney, SR Wilson, Inc. (C), CA, *590*

Equipment

Bason, Maurice L., Bason Associates (R), OH, *13*
Bickerstaff, John, Synagent Inc. (C), ON, *597*
Bower, Richard, Bower & Associates (C), TX, *271*
Campbell, Sandra, Management Recruiters of Milford Inc. (C), CT, *442*
Chin, Daniel, F-O-R-T-U-N-E Personnel Consultants of East Seattle (C), WA, *351*
Dummer, Charles F., Charles & Associates, Inc. (C), NE, *289*
Eissler, W. Robert, W. Robert Eissler & Assoc., Inc. (C), TX, *327*
Flannery, Peter, Jonas, Walters & Assoc., Inc. (R), WI, *108*
Froelich, K., Murphy Partners Int'l. (R), IL, *150*
Giles, Kenn, Dick Williams & Assoc. (C), CA, *621*
Grim, Gene, Sales Consultants of Cherry Hill (C), NJ, *560*
Harris, Bea, Exec Tech, Inc. (C), IL, *332*
Hawkins, Michael J., Michael J. Hawkins, Inc. (C), IL, *370*
Hedefine, Thomas E., Thomas E. Hedefine Assoc. (C), ON, *375*
Hiller, Arnie, U.S. Search (C), VA, *610*
Holder, Robin, The Donnelly Group-Sales Recruiters, Inc. (C), MO, *314*
Howe, Timothy L., The Resource Group (R), NJ, *175*
Keifer, Kevin A. P., Dunhill Professional Search of San Jose (C), CA, *319*
Kelly, Susan D., S. D. Kelly & Assoc., Inc. (R), MA, *112*
Kotloski, Dennis, Management Recruiters of Chicago-North Shore (C), IL, *447*
Lampl, Tom, Management Recruiters of Sun Valley (C), ID, *447*
Luther, Paul T., Financial Search Group, Inc. (R), MA, *66*
Marks, Ira Alan, J. M. Meredith & Assoc. Inc. (C), CA, *479*
Monroe, Jr., Kenneth R., Sanford Rose Assoc. - Clearwater (C), FL, *566*
O'Keefe, Frank, The Marathon Group (C), FL, *469*
Olson, John, Cook Assoc.,® Inc. (R), IL, *40*
Roth, Patricia, Patricia Roth Int'l. (C), FL, *545*
Schultz, Craig, F-O-R-T-U-N-E Personnel Consultants of St. Louis-West County (C), MO, *347*
Shiell, Donald M., Shiell Personnel (C), LA, *580*
Sink, Clifton W., Sink, Walker, Boltrus Int'l. (R), TX, *192*
Springer, Neil A., Springer Souder & Assoc. L.L.C. (R), IL, *198*
Vogus, Jerry, Cumberland Group Inc. (C), IL, *304*
Williams, Dick, Dick Williams & Assoc. (C), CA, *621*
Wilson, Denver, Sales Consultants of Northwest Arkansas, Inc. (C), AR, *556*

Escrow

Bloch, Carla, Lending Personnel Services (C), CA, *416*

Estates

Edelman, Diane, Stephen Haas Legal Placement (C), NY, *365*
Glaser, David, ECG Resources, Inc. (C), NY, *326*
Hawthorne, Christine, Search Int'l. (R), MA, *187*

Executives

Aldana, Manny, Bor-Maq Assoc. (C), TX, *269*
Ast, Steven T., AST/BRYANT (R), CT, *8*
Baker, Gary M., Cochran, Cochran & Yale, Inc. (R), NY, *36*
Beck, Larry, Synergy Solutions, Ltd. (C), WA, *597*
Bertsch, Gary D., Sanford Rose Assoc. - Flemington (C), NJ, *568*
Black, Dean A., TPS Staffing Solutions (C), IN, *608*
Blake, Barbara, Ron Sunshine & Assoc. (C), IL, *597*
Blevins, David C., David Blevins & Assoc. (C), WA, *268*
Bolls, Rich, Management Recruiters of Houston (C), TX, *463*
Bolno, Mark, Mark Bolno & Assoc. (C), FL, *269*
Boone, Charles C., Boone-Scaturro Assoc., Inc. (C), GA, *269*
Bouzan, Paul X., The Executive Group, Inc. (R), CA, *62*
Bozell, Jeanna, Professional Resource Group, Inc. (C), IN, *522*
Breen, Bill, Personnel, Inc. (C), AL, *508*
Bryant, Christopher P., AST/BRYANT (R), CA, *8*
Ceryak, George V., Management Recruiters of Indianapolis-North (C), IN, *448*
Ceryak, George V., Sales Consultants of Indianapolis-North (C), IN, *558*
Chambers, Patricia, Global Consulting Group Inc. (C), ON, *358*
Clark, Larry A., The Clark Group (C), MI, *292*
Cobb-West, Rosemary G., West & West (R), CA, *218*
Cole, Leslie C., Management Recruiters of Middlesex (C), CT, *442*
Corbett, Charles C., Davis-Smith, Inc. (C), MI, *309*
Cowan, Gordon, Tittemore Cowan Assoc. (C), AB, *607*
Craig, Randy H., J. Fielding Nelson & Assoc., Inc. (R), UT, *151*
Daugenti, Gary, Gent & Assoc. (C), CA, *356*
DeCaster, Paul, DeCaster Assoc. (C), WI, *310*
Deighen, Roderick P., Dean-MacDonald (R), OH, *47*
Denis, McReginald H., PersoNet, Inc. (C), FL, *507*
Dietsch, Roger A., Roger Dietsch & Assoc. (C), MN, *312*
Dmytrow, Eric D., F-O-R-T-U-N-E Personnel Consultants of Palm Beach (C), FL, *345*
Dumont, Brenda, Dumont & Co. (C), BC, *316*
Edwards, S. Bruce, Bruce Edwards & Associates, Inc. (R), NC, *56*
Ehman, John, Executive Placement Services (C), MD, *333*
Ericson, Pam, Major Search (C), NJ, *423*
Farah, James C., The S C Group LLC (R), NY, *183*
Fawcett, Marcia A., The Fawcett Group (R), MA, *65*
Fisher, Gary E., Fisher & Assoc. (R), CA, *67*
Fleischer, Susan, Healthcare Executive Recruiters, Inc. (C), CA, *372*
Furst, Stephen, Strategic Resources (C), WA, *595*
Gaffney, William, Gaffney Management Consultants (R), IL, *73*
Gahan, Ann M., Gahan Assoc. (R), NY, *73*
Gahan, Thomas M., Gahan Assoc. (R), NY, *73*
Garland, R. Darryl, Garland Assoc. Int'l. (C), CA, *355*
Gates, Becky, Primus Assoc., L.C. (R), TX, *169*
Gebler, Stephen, Systems Research Group (C), CA, *598*
Gilbert, Jerry, Gilbert & Van Campen Int'l. (R), NY, *76*
Glaser, David, ECG Resources, Inc. (C), NY, *326*
Glick, Douglas I., MedSearch Resources, Inc. (C), FL, *478*
Glou, Alan, Glou Int'l., Inc. (R), MA, *78*
Gossage, Wayne, Gossage Regan Assoc. (R), NY, *80*
Gould, Cotter Ray, Executives Worldwide, Inc. (C), OR, *337*
Groner, James B., J. B. Groner Executive Search, Inc. (C), DE, *363*
Guerrier, Alain M., PersoNet, Inc. (C), FL, *507*

Gutierrez, Mary Rose, Job Link, Inc. (C), CA, *399*
Hamilton, Melanie, Strategic Resources (C), WA, *595*
Harrington, Robert J., Sanford Rose Assoc. - Greensboro (C), NC, *569*
Hay, Elaine, Campbell, Edgar Inc. (C), BC, *280*
Hunter, Debra, F-O-R-T-U-N-E Personnel Consultants of Troy, Inc. (C), MI, *347*
Hutton, M. Joan, The Hutton Group, Inc. (C), FL, *386*
Jackson, George E., Jackson Group Int'l. (C), CO, *396*
Jakobs, Frederick H., Jakobs & Assoc. Int'l. (R), NY, *105*
Kaczmar, Michael A., Kaczmar & Assoc. (C), PA, *403*
Kaffke, Cas, Major Search (C), NJ, *423*
Kahng, Alex, C.T.E.W. Executive Personnel Services Inc. (C), BC, *278*
Kaulius-Barry, Aldonna, Aldonna Barry Personnel & Management (C), ON, *260*
Kierstead, Robert, High Tech Opportunities, Inc. (C), NH, *377*
Kincaid, Raymond W., Kincaid Group Inc. (KGI) (C), TX, *406*
Klein, Mel Stewart, Stewart/Laurence Assoc., Inc. (R), NJ, *201*
Kleven, Robert, The Kleven Group, Inc. - Executive Search Division (R), MA, *116*
Kors, R. Paul, Kors Montgomery Int'l. (R), TX, *118*
LaMotta, Steve, Human Resource Solutions (R), TX, *98*
Larsen, Richard F., Larsen, Whitney, Blecksmith & Zilliacus, Inc. (R), CA, *125*
Larsen, Robert H., R. H. Larsen & Assoc., Inc. (R), FL, *125*
Lau, Hayley, C.T.E.W. Executive Personnel Services Inc. (C), ON, *278*
Leader, D. June, Leader Network (C), PA, *414*
Leadford, Charles, Primus Assoc., L.C. (R), TX, *169*
Lebow, Allan J., RHS Assoc. (C), AL, *536*
Lehman, Jan A., Lehman McLeskey (R), TX, *128*
Lennox, Allan, AG Lennox & Assoc. (R), AB, *128*
Levine, Alan M., MB Inc. Executive Search (C), NY, *473*
Lihan, Dana L., MedXec USA, Inc. (C), FL, *478*
Luciani, Thomas G., The Luciani Group (R), CA, *132*
Lybrook, Karen, Lybrook Assoc., Inc. (C), RI, *421*
Magic, Michael F., Scott Douglas Inc. (C), CA, *573*
Manning, Sheila, O'Neill Group (C), NJ, *498*
Marks, Ira M., Strategic Alternatives (R), CA, *202*
Martin, Donovan, Donovan Martin & Assoc. (R), CA, *137*
Martire, Nick, AmeriResource Group Inc. (C), OK, *248*
Matucan, Ariel B., Search Advisors Int'l. Corp. (R), FL, *186*
McAleavy, Steve, Search Consultants Int'l., Inc. (C), TX, *575*
McGurk, Stacey, The Luciani Group (R), CA, *132*
McIntyre, Marlene, McIntyre Management Resources (C), ON, *475*
McKinney, Pat, Prichard Kymen Inc. (R), AB, *168*
McLeskey, Penny, Lehman McLeskey (R), TX, *128*
Meadows, C. David, Right/McKee Consulting Group (C), TX, *537*
Montgomery, Scott, Rojek Marketing Group, Inc. (R), OH, *181*
Naderi, Fred, Executive Direction, Inc. (C), CA, *333*
Naples, Len Di, Roth Young of Pittsburgh (C), PA, *546*
Neumann, Joan, Gossage Regan Assoc. (R), NY, *80*
Nichols, E. Diane, Nichols Brown Int'l. (R), NY, *151*
Nimmo, Richard, AmeriResource Group Inc. (C), OK, *248*
Nitzberg, Ira Z., Ira Z. Nitzberg (C), NY, *493*
Oliveros, Nancy P., New Dawn Employment Search (C), CA, *491*
Ordini, Lou, Major Search (C), NJ, *423*
Oruche, Osita, American Resources Corp. (C), IL, *248*
Pearson, Chuck, Pearson & Assoc., Inc. (C), AZ, *506*
Perry, Cole, Jay Allen & Assoc. (C), FL, *244*
Peterson, Greg, Sales Consultants of Ft. Lauderdale, Inc. (C), FL, *557*
Pinsker, Richard J., Pinsker and Company, Inc. (R), CA, *164*
Pollack, Paul, The Pollack Group (C), ON, *514*
Price, Velinda Hodge, Price & Assoc., Inc. (C), VA, *518*
Ramey, Pamela R., Lear & Assoc., Inc. (C), FL, *415*
Rankin, Ed, Human Resource Solutions (R), TX, *98*
Reynolds, Arlen, Executive Dimensions (R), AL, *62*
Robinson, Stephen, Robinson, Fraser Group Ltd. (R), ON, *180*
Root, Leslie A., The Wright Group (C), TX, *625*
Ross, Andrew, DARE Personnel Inc. (C), ON, *307*
Rossi, Larry, The Executive Group, Inc. (R), CA, *62*
Rossow, Bob, E/Search Int'l. (C), CT, *325*
Scaturro, Mary Ellen, Boone-Scaturro Assoc., Inc. (C), GA, *269*
Schoff, Diane L., The Edge Resource Group (C), PA, *326*
Schumann, Robert, Reinecke & Assoc. (C), NJ, *533*
Scott, Gordon, Search Advisors Int'l. Corp. (R), FL, *186*
Siegel, Peter A., Peter Siegel & Co. (C), MA, *581*
Sinclair, Douglas L., Sinclair & Co., Inc. (R), MA, *192*
Sklut, Eric, Executive Recruitment Specialists, Inc. (R), NC, *63*
Smith, George D., Bruce Edwards & Associates, Inc. (R), NC, *57*
Sondhi, Rick, Human Resource Technologies, Inc. (R), IL, *99*
Sparks, Robert W., Protocol Inc. (C), CA, *525*
Stanton, Robert G., TSC Management Services Group, Inc. (C), IL, *610*
Steffensrud, Dick, Staff Extension Int'l. (C), TX, *590*
Strom, Mark N., Search Advisors Int'l. Corp. (R), FL, *186*
Sutherland, Grant, C.T.E.W. Executive Personnel Services Inc. (C), BC, *278*
Sweet, Eleanor Anne, The Remington Group (R), IL, *174*
Tague, Maureen, The Moran Group (C), IL, *484*
Tann, Robert, Staff Extension, Int'l. (C), TX, *590*
Taylor, Jeffrey A., Sales Consultants of Ft. Lauderdale, Inc. (C), FL, *557*
Thompson, Dennis, Thompson Assoc. (C), CA, *606*
Toole, Thomas J., Management Recruiters of Laguna Hills (C), CA, *440*
Van Campen, Stephen B., Gilbert & Van Campen Int'l. (R), NY, *76*
Vick, Bill, Vick & Assoc. (R), TX, *214*
Vitanza, Jocelyne, DARE Personnel Inc. (C), ON, *307*
Warner, C. Douglas, C. D. Warner & Assoc. (C), PA, *615*
Warner, Susan C., C. D. Warner & Assoc. (C), PA, *615*
Webster, Larry, Technology Management Partners (R), CA, *208*
Weinstein, Stanley E., S. E. Weinstein Co. (R), IL, *217*
Weis, Robert, CFOs 2 Go (C), CA, *288*
West, Paul A., West & West (R), CA, *218*
White, Michele, The Kleven Group, Inc. - Executive Search Division (R), MA, *116*
Wilkerson, Jerry C., Franchise Recruiters Ltd. (R), IL, *71*
Williams, Jack R., Staff Extension Int'l. (C), TX, *590*
Wilson, Edward, Search Advisors Int'l. Corp. (R), FL, *186*
Wilson, Wayne, Wilson & Assoc. Int'l. Inc. (C), FL, *622*
Winitz, Joel M., GSW Consulting Group, Inc. (R), CA, *83*
Winter, Peter, Catalyx Group - Canada (R), ON, *31*
Wood, Bill, Search Plus Int'l.-Ohio (C), OH, *576*
Wright, Jay, The Wright Group (C), TX, *625*
Young, Paula G., Career Counseling Inc. (CCI) (C), KY, *282*
Zeiger, Stephen A., Zeiger Assoc. L.L.C. (C), CA, *627*

RECRUITER SPECIALTIES

Zonka, Thomas J., Thomas & Assoc. of Michigan (C), MI, *606*

Exploration

Buckingham, Ian D., Anderson & Schwab, Inc. (R), NY, *6*
Macurda, Bradford, The Energists (R), TX, *59*
Mathias, William J., Preng & Assoc., Inc. (R), TX, *167*
McAllister, Lon, Search Consultants Int'l., Inc. (C), TX, *575*
Preston, Alex, The Energists (R), TX, *59*

Exports

Meissner, Bob, Management Recruiters of Milwaukee-North (C), WI, *466*

Extrusion

Cahn, Juliette Lang, Juliette Lang Cahn Executive Search (C), NY, *279*
Villee, Mark, Management Recruiters of Columbia (C), MD, *450*

Fabrication

Barber, Bill C., Barber & Assoc. (C), KY, *259*
Ford, Travis, Ford & Assoc., Inc. (C), SC, *343*
Halek, Frederick D., Sanford Rose Assoc. - Gastonia (C), NC, *568*
Royfe, Dan, D.R. Assoc. (R), CA, *45*
Schultz, Craig, F-O-R-T-U-N-E Personnel Consultants of St. Louis-West County (C), MO, *347*

Facilities engineering

Love, Cindi M., Michael Latas & Assoc., Inc. (R), MO, *126*

Facility

Button, David R., Button Group (C), TX, *277*

Family business

Crosby, Georgann, Family-Business Roundtable, Inc. (R), AZ, *65*

Fashion

Barron, Robert, Johnson Smith & Knisely (R), NY, *107*
Carideo, Joseph J., Thorndike Deland Assoc. LLC (R), NY, *48*
Feldman, Abe, A. E. Feldman Assoc., Inc. (C), NY, *339*
Kanal, David S., Johnson Smith & Knisely (R), NY, *107*
Kirk, Ruth, Campbell, Edgar Inc. (C), BC, *280*
Maher, William J., Johnson Smith & Knisely (R), NY, *107*
Morgan, Joseph, Jaral Consultants, Inc. (C), NJ, *397*
Pickering, Dorothy C., Livingston, Robert & Co. (R), CT, *130*
Shufelt, Douglas G., Sink, Walker, Boltrus Int'l. (R), MA, *192*

Film converting

Knapp, Miranda, Cook Assoc.,® Inc. (R), IL, *40*
Pike, Dick, Management Recruiters of Burlington (C), NC, *455*
Telem, Peter B., Telem Adhesive Search Corp. (C), MD, *605*
Wynn, John, Cook Assoc.,® Inc. (R), IL, *40*

Filtration

Ralley, P. Neil, E.P. Int'l. (C), NJ, *325*
Ralley, P. Neil, E.P. Int'l. (C), NY, *324*

Finance

Adler, Rita, Discovery, The Staffing Specialists, Inc. (C), CA, *312*
Allen, Barbara A., Allen & Assoc. (C), NV, *244*
Aller, Joan, L O R (R), NJ, *122*
Alves, Manuel J., M/J/A Partners (R), IL, *133*
Anderson, George Wright, Gans, Gans & Assoc., Inc. (R), IL, *74*
Arnold, David, Management Solutions, Inc. (C), CA, *468*
Aronin, Michael, Fisher-Todd Assoc. (C), NY, *342*
Ashton, Neil K., Sales Consultants of Bangor, Inc. (C), ME, *559*
Aylward, John, Hemingway Personnel, Inc. (C), CA, *375*
Bacher, Judith, SpencerStuart (R), NY, *196*
Back, Bobbie, National Bank & Finance Executive Search (C), CA, *488*
Baggott, Richard, Executive Search Placements, Inc. (C), CO, *336*
Baker, Gary M., Cochran, Cochran & Yale, Inc. (R), NY, *36*
Balian, Christina L., Compass Group Ltd. (R), MI, *38*
Bard, Cliff, Management Recruiters of St. Augustine (C), FL, *444*
Barnes, Gary B., Brigade, Inc. (R), CA, *23*
Barranco, Leticia, Leaders-Trust Int'l./ Carce y Asociados, S.C. (R), MX, *127*
Bauman, Martin H., Martin H. Bauman Assoc., Inc. (R), NY, *13*
Becker, Matthew, Becker Personnel (C), FL, *262*
Behrens, Mark, Interim Accounting Professionals (C), CA, *391*
Bell, Andy, Norrell Financial Staffing (C), TN, *495*
Bell, Edward, Edward Bell Assoc. (C), CA, *263*
Benke, Norman L., N. L. Benke & Assoc., Inc. (C), OH, *264*
Bereck, Brian, Abacus Group LLC (C), NY, *232*
Berry, Harold B., The Hindman Co. (R), KY, *94*
Bickerstaff, John, Synagent Inc. (C), ON, *597*
Billingsley, Dennis, Joseph Michaels (C), CA, *401*
Billington, Brian J., Billington & Assoc. (R), CA, *17*
Birnbaum, Richard, R. J. Associates (C), NY, *528*
Bodner, Marilyn S., Bodner Inc. (C), NY, *269*
Bolt, Kathryn, Robert Half Canada Inc. (C), ON, *366*
Bonnell, William R., Bonnell Assoc. Ltd. (R), CT, *19*
Bosch, Eric E., Bosch & Assoc., LLC (R), CT, *20*
Brennan, Patrick, Handy HRM (R), NY, *86*
Briggs, Farris R., Staff Resources, Inc. (C), SC, *590*
Brody, Steve, Executive Resource Systems (C), CA, *335*
Brown, Charlene N., Accent On Achievement, Inc. (C), MI, *233*
Bruno, Deborah F., The Hindman Co. (R), KY, *94*
Bryant, Robert L., Renaissance Resources, LLC (R), VA, *174*
Burchill, Barbara E., BGB Assoc., Inc. (C), IL, *266*
Burgess, III, William H., The Burgess Group-Corporate Recruiters Int'l., Inc. (R), NY, *25*
Burke, T. Michael, Burke & Assoc./The Westfield Group (C), CT, *276*
Burns, Donita, Norrell Financial Staffing (C), PA, *495*
Burns, Patricia, Flexible Resources, Inc. (C), NY, *342*
Burton, Rob, Interim Accounting Professionals (C), CA, *391*
Byrne, Carolyn M., The TGA Company (C), TX, *606*
Campbell, Vicki, Management Solutions, Inc. (C), WA, *468*
Carlson, LuAnn, Houser, Martin, Morris (C), WA, *381*
Casanova, Laura, Hemingway Personnel, Inc. (C), CA, *376*
Casey, Darren M., Management Solutions, Inc. (C), WA, *468*
Chappell, Peter C., Robertson & Assoc. (C), IL, *539*
Chin, Joe, Cornell Group Int'l. Consulting, Inc. (R), NY, *41*
Christie, Stephen G., Marsar & Co., Inc. (C), FL, *471*
Citrin, James M., SpencerStuart (R), CT, *196*
Clark, Howard L., Howard Clark Assoc. (C), NJ, *292*
Clarke, Brian G., Kensington Int'l., Inc. (R), IL, *113*

Clawson, Kathy, Mayhall Search Group, Inc. (C), IN, *473*
Cochran, Ginny, Romac Int'l., Inc. (C), TX, *544*
Cohen, Irwin, Benson Associates (C), NY, *264*
Colman, Michael, Executive Placement Consultants (C), IL, *333*
Conner, Chuck, Strauss Personnel Service (C), PA, *596*
Cooper, David C., David C. Cooper & Assoc. Financial Search (C), GA, *298*
Cooper, Elizabeth, Creative-Leadership, Inc. (R), CA, *42*
Cordell, Cindy Andrew, Corporate Resources (C), OH, *301*
Cramer, Paul J., C/R Associates (C), NY, *278*
Creech, Bud, McCarthy Assoc. National BancSearch, LLC (C), LA, *473*
Critchley, Walter, Cochran, Cochran & Yale, Inc. (R), NY, *37*
Cullen, Andrew, The Pennmor Group (C), NJ, *506*
Dabich, Thomas M., Robert Harkins Assoc., Inc. (C), PA, *369*
Danforth, Andrea, Ethos Consulting, Inc. (R), CA, *61*
De Riviera, Sandra, Parker Page Group (C), TX, *503*
Denn, Paula, Norrell Financial Staffing (C), TX, *495*
Doty, Eleanor C., The Doty Group (C), TX, *314*
Douglas, Courtney, Norrell Financial Staffing (C), CA, *495*
Doupe, S. Scott, Conroy Partners Ltd. (R), AB, *39*
Dowell, Mary K., Professional Search Assoc. (C), CA, *522*
Dressen, Ronald, Romac Int'l., Inc. (C), MN, *543*
Dycus, Gwen, Gwen Dycus & Assoc. (C), FL, *323*
Dyer, John, Pacific Finance Search, Inc. (C), CA, *501*
Edelberg, Frank, Management One Consultants (C), ON, *425*
Eden, Dianne, Steeple Resources & Consulting (R), NJ, *199*
Edwards, Verba Lee, Wing Tips & Pumps, Inc. (C), MI, *623*
Elizondo, Jennifer, Management Recruiters of Fresno (C), CA, *440*
Elliott, Gene, The Whyte Group, Inc. (R), MD, *220*
Engel, Walter E., F-O-R-T-U-N-E Personnel Consultants of the Tri-Cities, Inc. (C), TN, *350*
Ergas, Patricia, Unisearch Search & Recruiting Inc. (C), CA, *611*
Etlinger, Alan C., Resource Recruiting (C), NH, *534*
Falcon, Elizabeth, Leaders-Trust Int'l./Carce y Asociados, S.C. (R), MX, *127*
Farrell, John A., The Curtiss Group International (R), FL, *44*
Fenton, Steve, Interim Accounting Professionals (C), TX, *392*
Fiala, Joanne C., The Westfield Group (C), CT, *619*
Fink, Allen, PMJ & Assoc. (C), ON, *513*
Fischer, Judith, RJ Associates (C), CA, *538*
Fischer, Ronald, RJ Associates (C), CA, *538*
Fisher, Mel V., The Fisher Group (R), AB, *67*
Fitzpatrick, John, Newport Strategic Search LLC (C), CA, *492*
Fludd, Virgil L., The CARVIR Group, Inc. (C), GA, *285*
Foltz, T. J., Capital Markets Resources, Inc. (C), NC, *281*
Ford, Sandra D., The Ford Group, Inc. (R), PA, *69*
Foster, Nancy, Baldwin & Assoc. (C), OH, *258*
Fox, Glenn M., Strategic Search, LLC (C), CA, *595*
Fox, Michael L., Management Recruiters of Woodbury (C), MN, *430*
Fox, Michael L., Management Recruiters of Woodbury (C), MN, *452*
Foxman, Marty, Pierce & Assoc. (C), CA, *512*
Frankel, Len, Abacus Group LLC (C), NY, *232*
Franz, Ronald, Fisher-Todd Assoc. (C), NY, *342*
Froelich, Kris, Norrell Financial Staffing (C), PA, *495*
Fumano, Gary W., Chapman & Assoc. (C), BC, *289*
Gabel, Greg, Canny, Bowen Inc. (R), NY, *28*
Gay, Martha, Salzmann Gay Assoc., Inc. (R), PA, *184*
Gerard, William, Fox-Morris Assoc., Inc. (C), CA, *352*
Gilbert, John, John Gilbert Co. (C), TX, *357*
Gimbel, Mike, Gimbel & Assoc. (C), FL, *357*
Giorgetti, Richard, Management Solutions, Inc. (C), CA, *468*
Glatzer, Neil, Management Solutions, Inc. (C), CA, *468*
Gleason, James P., J. P. Gleason Assoc., Inc. (R), IL, *77*
Gleckman, Mark, Winter, Wyman & Co. (C), MA, *623*
Gmutza, Al, F-O-R-T-U-N-E Personnel Consultants of Southwest Indiana (C), IN, *346*
Goldbach, Linda J., Beacon Int'l., Inc. (C), VA, *261*
Goldstein, Barry, Interim Financial Solutions (C), VA, *392*
Goldstein, Steven G., The Jonathan Stevens Group, Inc. (R), NJ, *108*
Goodere, Greg, Montgomery West (R), CA, *146*
Gragg, Robert, Montgomery West (R), CA, *146*
Green, Thomas R., The TGA Company (C), TX, *606*
Greenwald, Anita, Concorde Search Assoc. (C), NY, *296*
Grimm, Peter G., Nordeman Grimm, Inc. (R), NY, *152*
Gross, Dean, Becker Personnel (C), FL, *262*
Groussman, Maria, Groussman & Assoc., Inc. (R), TX, *82*
Guest, Denise, Jones Management Co. (R), CT, *108*
Habelmann, Gerald B., Habelmann & Assoc. (R), MI, *84*
Hale, Dillon, Cemco, Ltd. (C), IL, *286*
Halladay, Patti, Intersource, Ltd. (R), TX, *103*
Halstead, Richard, CMS Management Services LLC (C), IN, *293*
Hamilton, Denman, Synergy 2000 (C), DC, *597*
Hamilton, Frank, Gwen Dycus & Assoc. (C), FL, *323*
Hanna, Jr., M. A. Jack, The Hanna Group (C), OH, *368*
Hanrahan, Kevin, Crist Partners, Ltd. (R), IL, *43*
Hardage, Phillip, Hardage Group (C), TN, *369*
Harfenist, Harry, Parker Page Group (C), FL, *503*
Harrington, Robert C., Resource Recruiting (C), NH, *534*
Haupert, Thomas J., MCS Assoc. (R), CA, *142*
Hawke, Marjorie, Becker Personnel (C), FL, *262*
Hellebusch, Jerry, Morgan Hunter Corp. (C), KS, *485*
Heller, Jason, Norrell Financial Staffing (C), NC, *495*
Helnore, Douglas, Partners in Recruiting (C), IL, *504*
Herbert, Kevin, Pacific Finance Search, Inc. (C), CA, *501*
Hernandez, Rafael E., SearchCorp (C), FL, *577*
Herrerias, Paul, Herrerias & Assoc. (R), CA, *92*
Hester, Teresa, Romac Int'l., Inc. (C), CA, *542*
Hindman, Neil C., The Hindman Co. (R), KY, *94*
Hinkle, Alfred, Renaissance Resources, LLC (R), VA, *174*
Hochman, Judi, Hochman & Assoc. (C), CA, *379*
Hoffenberg, Elliot, H. J. Elliot, Inc. (R), IL, *58*
Hoffman, Tala R., TRH Assoc., Inc. (R), NY, *210*
Holt, Elaine, Norrell Financial Staffing (C), CO, *495*
Homrich, Patricia J., David C. Cooper & Assoc. Financial Search (C), GA, *298*
Horn, David C., David C. Horn Executive Search (C), TX, *381*
Horton, Scott, Capital Markets Resources, Inc. (C), NC, *281*
Hucko, Donald, Jonas, Walters & Assoc., Inc. (R), WI, *108*
Hugsman, Rob, Russ Hadick & Assoc. Inc. (C), OH, *365*

RECRUITER SPECIALTIES

Infanti, Diana, Robert Half Canada Inc. (C), BC, *366*
James, Cindy, Discovery, The Staffing Specialists, Inc. (C), DE, *312*
Johnson, John Kimbrough, Johnson Brown Assoc., Inc. (C), IN, *400*
Johnson, Kathleen, Barton Assoc., Inc. (R), TX, *12*
Jones, Gary, BGB Assoc., Inc. (C), IL, *266*
Jordan, Dick, Staff Resources, Inc. (C), SC, *590*
Juska, Frank A., Rusher, Loscavio & LoPresto (R), CA, *183*
Justiss, Ted, David C. Cooper & Assoc. Financial Search (C), GA, *298*
Kahng, Alex, C.T.E.W. Executive Personnel Services Inc. (C), BC, *278*
Kanzer, William F., Kanzer Assoc., Inc. (R), IL, *109*
Katz, Norman, MCS Assoc. (R), CA, *142*
Katzman, Melissa, Melissa Katzman, Executive Search (C), NY, *404*
Kelly, John, Rand Thompson Executive Search Consultants (C), NY, *528*
Kershaw, Blair, Blair Kershaw Assoc., Inc. (C), PA, *405*
Kick, James, The Prairie Group (C), IL, *515*
Kindler, Peter A., Boardroom Consultants/ Kenny Kindler Tholke (R), NY, *19*
Knose, II, Joseph M., Corporate Image Group (C), TN, *300*
Knowles, Scott, Management Recruiters of Georgetown (C), SC, *461*
Koehler, Frank R., The Koehler Group (C), PA, *408*
Koren, Michael, Koren, Rogers Assoc. Inc. (R), NY, *117*
Kramer, Mitchel, Interim Accounting Professionals (C), FL, *392*
Kusnetz, Ellen G., Business Solutions Worldwide, Inc. (C), NJ, *277*
Laderman, David, ACSYS Resources, Inc. (C), PA, *239*
LaMorte, Brian A., Pascale & LaMorte, LLC (C), CT, *504*
Lanken, Joel, Lanken-Kimball-Therrell & Assoc. (C), GA, *412*
LaPolice, Denis, Resource Management Group (C), CT, *534*
Lasee, Jeff, The H. S. Group, Inc. (C), WI, *365*
Layhee, Pat, Norrell Financial Staffing (C), GA, *495*
LeBoeuf, Michel, Robert Half Canada Inc. (C), QE, *366*
Legal, Dale, Capital Consulting Group, Inc. (R), MD, *28*
Leininger, Dennis, Staffing Edge, Inc. (C), IA, *590*
Lewis, Marc D., Handy HRM (R), NY, *86*
Lomax, J. Alan, ADR Accounting Management Recruiters (C), ON, *240*
Lombardi, Nancy, WTW Assoc., Inc. (R), NY, *225*
Loscavio, J. Michael, Rusher, Loscavio & LoPresto (R), CA, *183*
Lucifero, Lisa, ACSYS Resources, Inc. (C), NJ, *238*
Lucy, Christine, Robert Half Canada Inc. (C), ON, *366*
Lyon, Jenny K., Marra Peters & Partners (R), NC, *136*
Lysenko, Lisa, A.L.S. Group (C), NJ, *232*
Lysenko, Scott, A.L.S. Group (C), NJ, *232*
MacDougall, Audrey, Robert Half Canada Inc. (C), AB, *366*
Malek, L., Professional Search Consultants (PSC) (C), TX, *523*
Mand, Tammy, Norrell Financial Staffing (C), IL, *495*
Marino, Chet, Cochran, Cochran & Yale, Inc. (R), CO, *37*
Marra, Jr., John, Marra Peters & Partners (R), NJ, *136*
Marsar, Kevin P., Marsar & Co., Inc. (C), FL, *471*
Marshall, P. William, Dise & Co. (R), OH, *52*
Martin, Charles E., Management Recruiters of Birmingham-South, Inc. (C), AL, *438*
Martire, Nick, AmeriResource Group Inc. (C), OK, *248*
Mayes, Kay H., John Shell Assoc., Inc. (C), SC, *580*
McCarthy, Debra, Becker Personnel (C), FL, *262*
McDermott, Jeffrey T., Vlcek & Company, Inc. (R), CA, *214*
McFarlan, Cydney, Discovery, The Staffing Specialists, Inc. (C), CA, *312*
McGrath, Steven L., McGrath & Assoc., Inc. (R), NJ, *141*
McHale, John P., McHale & Assoc. (R), WA, *141*
McKenna, Catherine, Marcus & Assoc. (C), NY, *469*
McKenna, Elaine, Weterrings & Agnew, Inc. (C), NY, *619*
McKersie, Edward S., ProSearch, Inc. (C), ME, *524*
McLaughlin, Brad, Meridian Resources (C), OH, *479*
McPherson, Ron, National Bank & Finance Executive Search (C), CA, *488*
McShane, Keith, Chesapeake Group (C), CT, *290*
Mendez, Larry W., Layne-Mendez & Co. (R), TX, *127*
Menefee, Shawn, Corporate Plus, Ltd. (C), GA, *300*
Merjos, Susan, The Beam Group (R), NY, *14*
Merrell, Randy, Management Solutions, Inc. (C), CA, *468*
Merrick, George, Pacific Finance Search, Inc. (C), CA, *501*
Miletti, Carol, Interim Accounting Professionals (C), MN, *392*
Millar, James G., Millar Walker & Gay (R), ON, *144*
Miller, Roger, Ryan, Miller & Assoc. (C), CA, *549*
Milne, Danette, Danette Milne Corporate Search Inc. (C), ON, *482*
Mincy, Jim, Corporate Image Group (C), GA, *300*
Mitchell, John, Fred Hood & Assoc. (C), CA, *380*
Mitzmacher, Michael, Edward Bell Assoc. (C), CA, *263*
Morgan, David G., Morgan Stampfl, Inc. (C), NY, *485*
Morris, Barbara, Chad Management Group (C), ON, *288*
Morrison, Susan S., Quetico Corp. (R), TX, *170*
Munro, Jennifer, Jennifer Munro & Partners, Inc. (R), SC, *149*
Murray, David, Ray & Berndtson/Lovas Stanley (R), ON, *172*
Murray, David, Ray & Berndtson/Lovas Stanley (R), ON, *173*
Musick, Diana, Musick & Assoc. (C), CA, *487*
Musick, Stephen, Musick & Assoc. (C), CA, *487*
Myers, Deedee, DDJ Myers, Ltd. (R), AZ, *150*
Myers, John, DDJ Myers, Ltd. (R), MA, *150*
Nadherny, Pete, The Angus Group, Ltd. (C), OH, *251*
Nason, Dennis H., Nason & Nason (C), FL, *488*
Nason-Robson, Nayda, Nason & Nason (C), FL, *488*
Nelson, David G., The Personnel Group, Inc. (R), MN, *163*
Neufeld, Max, Partners In Human Resources Int'l., Inc. (R), NY, *160*
Nicholls, R. J., Interim Management Resources Inc. (C), ON, *392*
Nicholson, Philip J., P. J. Nicholson & Assoc. (C), IL, *493*
Noebel, Todd R., The Noebel Search Group, Inc. (C), TX, *494*
Nordeman, Jacques C., Nordeman Grimm, Inc. (R), NY, *152*
Norris, Kris, Interim Accounting Professionals (C), CA, *391*
Norris, Ronald, Ronald Norris & Assoc. (C), IL, *495*
Noto, Joseph A., CMS Management Services LLC (C), IN, *293*
O'Neill, Stephen A., O'Neill & Co. (R), CT, *154*
O'Rourke, Bart, Abacus Group LLC (C), NY, *232*
Ouellet, Jacques E., Yves Elkas Inc. (R), QE, *58*
Palmer, James H., The Hindman Co. (R), KY, *94*
Pascale, Ron, Pascale & LaMorte, LLC (C), CT, *504*
Patenge, David W., Handy HRM (R), NY, *86*
Peasback, David R., Canny, Bowen Inc. (R), NY, *28*
Pelayo, Joe, Joseph Michaels (C), CA, *401*
Pierce, Sharon S., Pierce & Assoc. (C), CA, *512*
Pinedo, Mario, Bor-Maq Assoc. (C), TX, *269*
Plyley, Jr., C. Ace, The Stelton Group, Inc. (C), NJ, *592*

Pober, Andrew, Interim Accounting Professionals (C), FL, *391*
Polyzos, Ginia M., Management Advisors Int'l., Inc. (C), NC, *424*
Postlethwaite, John, Edward Bell Assoc. (C), CA, *263*
Potter, Aggie, Management Solutions, Inc. (C), CA, *468*
Powell, Mike, Marc-Allen Assoc., Inc. (C), FL, *469*
Pradarelli, Dennis J., MARBL Consultants, Inc. (C), WI, *469*
Prehogan, Avalee, Robert Half Canada Inc. (C), ON, *366*
Randolph, Troy, Lea Randolph & Assoc., Inc. (C), TX, *529*
Raniere, Rich, Romac Int'l., Inc. (C), FL, *542*
Ratner, Joanne E., Joanne E. Ratner Search (C), NY, *529*
Ray, Marianne C., Callan Assoc., Ltd. (R), IL, *27*
Razzino, Janelle, Razzino-Claymore Assoc. (C), NJ, *530*
Regina, Aida, Brigade, Inc. (R), CA, *23*
Reiter, Steve, Romac Int'l. - San Francisco (C), CA, *541*
Remillard, Brad M., CJA-The Adler Group, Inc. (R), CA, *35*
Rexroad, Nancy, Strauss Personnel Service (C), PA, *596*
Ribeiro, Claudia, Ledbetter/Davidson Int'l., Inc. (R), NY, *127*
Richner, George A., Search Assoc., Inc. (C), NJ, *574*
Ritchings, David, David Allen Assoc. (R), NJ, *3*
Roberts, Keith, Boyden (R), NY, *21*
Robsham, Beverly H., Robsham & Assoc., Inc. (R), MA, *180*
Rodriguez, George L., InteliSearch, Inc. (R), CT, *102*
Roll, M. A., Roll International (C), TX, *541*
Romano, Joseph C., Romano McAvoy Assoc., Inc. (C), NY, *544*
Rosemarin, Gloria J., Barrington Hart, Inc. (R), IL, *12*
Rosenblatt, Michael F., The Quest Organization (C), NY, *527*
Ross, Cheryl Molliver, Thomas, Whelan Assoc., Inc. (C), DC, *606*
Ross, Craig, Norrell Financial Staffing (C), GA, *495*
Rotter, Stephen, RSMR, Inc. (R), IL, *182*
Rupert, James A., Management Recruiters of Siouxland (C), IA, *449*
Ryan, Bernard J., Brissenden, McFarland, Fuccella & Reynolds, Inc. (R), NJ, *23*
Ryan, John, RSMR, Inc. (R), IL, *182*
Sall, Ron, Interim Financial Solutions (C), VA, *392*
Salmela, Alexander K., A.K.S. Assoc., Ltd. (R), MA, *1*
Sanchez, Jorge, Interim Accounting Professionals (C), FL, *392*
Sanders, Gail, Discovery, The Staffing Specialists, Inc. (C), IL, *312*
Sauer, Harry, ACSYS Resources, Inc. (C), PA, *239*
Schichtle, Nick, Accountants Executive Search (C), CA, *237*
Schlatter, Craig, Schlatter & Assoc. (C), CA, *572*
Schoenfeld, Jack, Dunhill of Manchester Inc. (C), NH, *321*
Seal, Jock, The H. S. Group, Inc. (C), WI, *365*
Sears, Keith, Edward Bell Assoc. (C), CA, *263*
Selig, Robert J., Selig Executive Search (C), NH, *579*
Shea, Kathleen P., Thomas E. Hedefine Assoc. (C), ON, *375*
Shedroff, Michael, ACSYS Resources, Inc. (C), NJ, *238*
Shell, III, John C., John Shell Assoc., Inc. (C), SC, *580*
Shor, Hillary, Interim Accounting Professionals (C), CA, *391*
Singer, Lloyd R., Romac Int'l. (C), IL, *542*
Sklar, Ruth, Ruth Sklar Assoc., Inc. (RSA Executive Search) (R), NY, *192*
Smith, Jill, ACSYS Resources, Inc. (C), PA, *239*
Smith, Marvin E., Management Solutions, Inc. (C), WA, *468*
Smith, Patti, Discovery, The Staffing Specialists, Inc. (C), TX, *313*
Smith, Robert, Fox-Morris Assoc., Inc. (C), GA, *352*
Smith, Stacy, Smith James Group, Inc. (R), GA, *194*
Snyder, Gary, F-O-R-T-U-N-E Personnel Consultants (C), MI, *346*
Stacey, Bryce A., Chapman & Assoc. (C), BC, *289*
Stecker, Lori, Management Recruiters of Williamsburg (C), IA, *449*
Steele, Kevin, Winter, Wyman & Co. (C), MA, *623*
Steinfield, David, Steinfield & Assoc. (C), TX, *592*
Stephenson, Harold, C. R. Assoc. (C), CA, *278*
Stewart, Harvey, Executive Registry (C), QE, *334*
Stone, Richard, Stone Assoc. LLC (C), MI, *594*
Stork, Jennifer, Goodkind Assoc. Inc. (C), NY, *360*
Sudina, Chuck, Sudina Search, Inc. (C), MD, *596*
Sutherland, Grant, C.T.E.W. Executive Personnel Services Inc. (C), BC, *278*
Swift, Catherine, Swift & Assoc. (C), ME, *597*
Talan, Marv, Executive Search Team (C), MI, *336*
Taylor, Ernest A., LAI Ward Howell (R), GA, *123*
Taylor, Staci, Interim Accounting Professionals (C), CA, *391*
Telford, Jr., John H., Telford, Adams & Alexander (R), CA, *208*
Teter, Sandra, The Danbrook Group, Inc. (C), TX, *306*
Thomas, Frank, Carson-Thomas & Assoc. (C), CA, *284*
Thunberg, Richard A., Jeff Rich Assoc. (C), NJ, *536*
Tillman, Rob, Crist Partners, Ltd. (R), IL, *43*
Tobin, Kathryn, Norrell Financial Staffing (C), AZ, *495*
Townsend, James C., Future Employment Service, Inc. (C), IA, *353*
Trasatti, Anthony, The Pennmor Group (C), NJ, *506*
Treney, Sue, Norrell Financial Staffing (C), FL, *495*
Turner, Tami, Robert Half Canada Inc. (C), ON, *366*
Vacca, Domenic L., ACSYS Resources, Inc. (C), DE, *238*
Valone, Judith, UniQuest Int'l., Inc. (C), FL, *611*
Wade, Bridgette, Norrell Financial Staffing (C), CA, *495*
Wallace, Mark J., Management Recruiters of Broome County, Inc. (C), NY, *454*
Watkins, Jeff, Norrell Financial Staffing (C), GA, *495*
Watson, Scott, Scott Watson & Assoc., Inc. (R), FL, *216*
Wax, Robert M., Kingsbury • Wax • Bova (R), MA, *114*
Wedderien, Wayne, National Bank & Finance Executive Search (C), CA, *488*
Weiss, John P., Star Search Consultants (C), ON, *591*
Werbin, Susan, Werbin Assoc. Executive Search, Inc. (C), NY, *618*
Wilkinson, Charla, Norrell Financial Staffing (C), FL, *495*
Williams, Richard, Management Solutions, Inc. (C), CA, *468*
Williams, Trish, Interim Accounting Professionals (C), CA, *391*
Wlodawsky, Wayne, Romac Int'l., Inc. (C), TX, *544*
Wood, Michael D., Wood, Franchot Inc. (R), MN, *224*
Wooller, Edmund A. M., Windsor International (R), GA, *222*
Zaher, Richard, Fox-Morris Assoc., Inc. (C), NY, *352*
Zalman, Andrew, Interim Accounting Professionals (C), FL, *392*
Zaring, Judy, Management Recruiters of Plant City, Inc. (C), FL, *444*
Zincavage, David, Cybernautic Corp. (C), CT, *305*
Zukerman, Claire, Corporate Search, Inc. (C), NY, *301*

Finance & accounting

Alexander, Richard J., Alexander Associates (R), NJ, *2*
Anderson, Ashlee, Management Solutions, Inc. (C), WA, *468*
Bailey, Jerald W., Dunhill Professional Search of Greater New Orleans (C), LA, *321*
Baskowski, Stephen A., Matthews & Stephens Assoc., Inc. (C), CT, *472*

RECRUITER SPECIALTIES

Belochi, Michael, Parker & Lynch (C), CA, *503*
Binney, David, NMC & Kay Int'l. (R), CO, *152*
Bredeson, Sheri, Bredeson Executive Recruitment, LLC (R), TX, *22*
Brown, Alan V., Personnel Alliance Group (C), NJ, *508*
Brugh, Amy, Management Recruiters - Indianapolis (C), IN, *448*
Coffey, Michael O., The Langford Search, Inc. (C), AL, *412*
Cooper, Linda, BG & Assoc. (C), MD, *266*
Dailey, Linda, Allen Austin Lowe & Powers (R), TX, *3*
Désilets, Georges H., Yves Plouffe & Assoc. (R), QE, *165*
Fogec, Thomas G., Fogec Consultants, Inc. (R), WI, *69*
Gold, Don, Executive Search, Ltd. (C), OH, *336*
Gray, Brian A., BG & Assoc. (C), MD, *266*
Halbrich, Mitch, Interim Financial Solutions (C), MD, *392*
Halbrich, Mitch, Interim Financial Solutions - Mid-Atlantic Region (C), MD, *392*
Hayek, Kim, Norrell Financial Staffing (C), VA, *495*
Heneghan, Donald A., Allerton Heneghan & O'Neill (R), IL, *4*
Jones, Judy, Management Recruiters of Winston-Salem (C), NC, *457*
Jorgensen, T. C., The Talley Group (R), VA, *205*
Kalember, Jr., Robert J., Fortune Personnel Consultants of Hinsdale, IL (C), IL, *346*
Kenny, Peter J., Rob Dey Executive Search (R), FL, *49*
Kiken, Mark E., COBA Executive Search (R), CO, *36*
Lanctot, Dominique, Matte Consulting Group Inc. (R), QE, *138*
Langford, K. R. Dick, The Langford Search, Inc. (C), AL, *412*
Lee, Jess J., Management Search Int'l. (C), CA, *467*
Machi, Michael T., Management Recruiters of Pleasanton (C), CA, *441*
Marenger, Christine, Yves Plouffe & Assoc. (R), QE, *165*
May, Donald C., Allied Search, Inc. (C), CA, *245*
Medley, Jerry, The Medley Group (C), CA, *477*
Miller, Carol, Systems Research Inc. (SRI) (C), IL, *598*
Mittenthal, Robert H., David Gomez & Assoc., Inc. (R), IL, *79*
Nelson, Allan C., Davies, Park (R), AB, *47*
Nolan, Nancy C., The Nolan Group (C), CA, *494*
Nolan, Thomas P., The Nolan Group (C), CA, *494*
Pann, Arthur J., Arthur Pann Assoc., Inc. (C), NY, *502*
Parker, Montie, Parker & Lynch (C), CA, *503*
Rallerty, James, Wilder & Assoc. (C), VA, *620*
Rehmeyer, Kelly, Allen Austin Lowe & Powers (R), TX, *3*
Schneiderman, Gerald, Management Resource Assoc., Inc. (C), FL, *467*
Sonne, Bill, PeopleSource Inc. (C), TX, *506*
Symcox, Jim, SPC Symcox Personnel Consultants (C), TX, *588*
Taylor, Jerry, Executive Recruiters (C), WA, *334*
Thayer, Robert T., Executive Search of New England, Inc. (C), ME, *336*
Tootsey, Mark, Interim Financial Solutions (C), DC, *392*
Tootsey, Mark A., Interim Financial Solutions (C), MD, *392*
Walker, Craig, Interim Financial Solutions - Mid-Atlantic Region (C), MD, *392*
Wallace, William J., Wallace Management Co. (R), TN, *215*
Whetstone-Smith, B. K., Allen Austin Lowe & Powers (R), TX, *3*
Wright, Carl A. J., Interim Financial Solutions - Mid-Atlantic Region (C), MD, *392*

Financial

Andrews, Dwight L., Andrews & Assoc. (C), NC, *250*
Angel, Steve, Angel Group Int'l. (C), KY, *250*
Atchison, W. R., W. R. Atchison & Assoc., Inc. (C), NC, *255*
Baker, Jr., Joseph N., JNB Assoc., Inc. (C), MA, *399*
Baldwin, Stephen, SearchCorp International (C), AB, *577*
Belaiche, Marc, Creative Financial Staffing Inc. (C), ON, *303*
Berglund, Sharon, Berglund Int'l. Resources, Inc. (C), TX, *265*
Beste, Kevin M., Andrews & Assoc. (C), NC, *250*
Bishop, Sandra K., F-O-R-T-U-N-E Personnel Consultants of Boise (R), ID, *70*
Bontempo, David M., Dunhill Professional Search of Bucks-Mont., Inc. (C), PA, *322*
Bova, Barry A., Kingsbury • Wax • Bova (R), NY, *114*
Brook, Marsha, C. M. Management Services, Inc. (R), KY, *26*
Brown, Bob, Smith, Brown & Jones (C), KS, *585*
Brown, Dennis S., D. Brown & Assoc., Inc. (C), OR, *275*
Butler, Carol, Leonard Corwen Assoc. (C), NY, *302*
Casillo, Robert, Razzino-Claymore Assoc. (C), NJ, *530*
Cason, Lyn, Brad Marks Int'l. (R), CA, *136*
Charles, Kamal, Clinton, Charles, Wise & Co. (C), FL, *293*
Conroy, M. J., Conroy Partners Ltd. (R), AB, *39*
Corporon, Charles E., Quirk-Corporon & Assoc., Inc. (C), WI, *527*
Cutshaw, Robert, F-O-R-T-U-N-E Personnel Consultants of Knoxville (C), TN, *350*
Dickens, Marcia, R. Gaines Baty Assoc., Inc. (R), GA, *13*
Donovan, John, Human Capital Resources, Inc. (C), FL, *384*
Dowell, Pat, M.C. Executive Search (C), CA, *422*
Duckett, Tim, Creative HR Solutions (C), GA, *303*
Elinski, Mike, Human Resources Management Hawaii, Inc. (C), HI, *384*
Flood, Michael, Norman Broadbent Int'l., Inc. (R), NY, *152*
Gerson, Fred, Affordable Executive Recruiters (C), CA, *241*
Goldshore, Steven, Winthrop Partners, Inc. (R), NY, *222*
Grauss, Bryan J., Grauss & Co. (C), CA, *362*
Grauss, Debra M., Grauss & Co. (C), CA, *362*
Hall, Donald L., Higley, Hall & Co., Inc. (R), MA, *93*
Hall, Peter V., Argonaut Partners, LLC (R), CA, *6*
Haller, Thomas, International Executive Recruiters (C), OH, *393*
Hare, Beth C., Fidelity Search Group, Inc. (R), PA, *66*
Hawkins, Jr., Jack M., First Advisory Services Int'l., Inc. (R), MD, *67*
Hogan, Sandra M., Larsen, Whitney, Blecksmith & Zilliacus, Inc. (R), CA, *125*
Holsopple, Ben V., ACSYS Resources, Inc. (C), NJ, *238*
Hoover, Catherine B., J. L. Mark Assoc., Inc. (R), CO, *135*
Hughes, Jr., John E., LAI Ward Howell (R), PA, *123*
Hunt, James E., Hunt & Howe Inc. (R), NY, *99*
Hyman, Jean W., Management Search Assoc., Inc. (C), GA, *467*
Joffe, Barry, Bason Associates (R), OH, *13*
Justus, Janet, Dunhill Executive Search of Los Angeles, Inc. (C), CA, *319*
Kane, Bernie, Kane & Assoc. (C), TX, *403*
Kasperski, Leon, Rice Cohen Int'l. (R), PA, *178*
Kaufman, Susan, Kaufman Assoc. (R), CA, *110*
King, Jim, Career Strategies, Inc. (C), CA, *283*
Klingensmith, Steve, The Hunter Group, Inc. (C), MI, *385*
Laguzza, John, Laguzza Assoc., Ltd. (R), NY, *122*
Lee, Jess J., Management Search Int'l. (C), CA, *467*
Lee, Joseph J., Larsen & Lee, Inc. (R), MD, *125*
Lehman, Neal G., Sherwood Lehman Massucco, Inc. (R), CA, *189*
Leighton, Nina, The Ogdon Partnership (R), NY, *155*
Levine, Alan M., MB Inc. Executive Search (C), NY, *473*

Lieff, Shelley, Advice Personnel Inc. (C), NY, *241*
McCutcheon, Pat, Iona Partners (C), CA, *394*
McGregor, Jock, Reynolds Consulting Int'l. (R), ON, *177*
Meissner, Bob, Management Recruiters of Milwaukee-North (C), WI, *466*
Miller, Kenneth, Computer Network Resources, Inc. (C), CA, *295*
Molitor, John L., Barrett Partners (C), IL, *260*
Monset, Rachel, NCC Executive Search Consultants (C), CA, *490*
Muller, Michael, Financialjobs.com (C), CA, *340*
Nunziata, Fred A., Eden & Assoc., Inc. (C), PA, *326*
Paetzhold, Jerry, Davis & James, Inc. (C), MO, *308*
Pauling, John, C. J. Stafford & Assoc. (C), ON, *591*
Plummer, Cyril, The McKinnon Management Group Inc. (C), ON, *475*
Prager, Paul Gershon, P. G. Prager Search Assoc., Ltd. (C), NY, *515*
Purcell, Kathryn, The Executive Tree (R), FL, *64*
Quirk, Therese M., Quirk-Corporon & Assoc., Inc. (C), WI, *527*
Racht, Janet G., Crowe Chizek & Co. (C), IN, *304*
Raemer-Rodriguez, Susan, Friedman Eisenstein Raemer & Schwartz, LLP (R), IL, *72*
Rascher, Linda, Bert Davis Publishing Placement Consultants (C), NY, *309*
Reeder, Kirk, Sales Consultants of Omaha, Inc. (C), NE, *560*
Reid, Michael J., Michael James Reid & Co. (R), CA, *174*
Ross, Andrew, DARE Personnel Inc. (C), ON, *307*
Rotella, Marshall W., The Corporate Connection, Ltd. (C), VA, *300*
Rothman, Judith L., Royal Assoc. (C), CA, *547*
Scaturro, Leonard, Boone-Scaturro Assoc., Inc. (C), GA, *269*
Schenck, Kurt, Management Recruiters of North Charleston (C), SC, *460*
Schwartz, Alan, Advice Personnel Inc. (C), NY, *241*
Scott, Gordon S., Search Research Assoc., Inc. (R), MA, *187*
Spencer, Gene, American Resources Corp. (C), IL, *248*
Sponseller, Vern, Richard Kader & Assoc. (C), OH, *403*
Steffensrud, Dick, Staff Extension Int'l. (C), TX, *590*
Stephens, Ken, Leader Resources Group (C), GA, *415*
Stubblefield, Janine, Angel Group Int'l. (C), KY, *250*
Tedla, Solomon, Creative HR Solutions (C), GA, *303*
Tracy, Susan, Wheeler Assoc. (R), CT, *219*
Trendl, Joseph, J. R. Scott & Assoc., Ltd. (C), IL, *395*
Vangel, Peter V., Access/Resources, Inc. (C), MA, *234*
Vitanza, Jocelyne, DARE Personnel Inc. (C), ON, *307*
Warren, Robert, Warren Int'l. (R), NY, *215*
Wegner, Carl, Wegner & Assoc. (C), WI, *617*
Werlin, Paul A., Human Capital Resources, Inc. (C), FL, *384*
Westphal, Birgit, Reynolds Consulting Int'l. (R), ON, *177*
Wieder, Thomas, Management Recruiters of Nassau, Inc. (R), NY, *134*
Wilcox, Fred T., Wilcox Bertoux & Miller (R), CA, *220*
Wilson, Gordon, Ray & Berndtson/Lovas Stanley (R), ON, *172*
Wong, Douglas, International Market Recruiters (C), PA, *393*

Management

Vincenty, Lorraine, Vincenty & Co. (C), OH, *612*

Financial Services

Abert, Janice, Johnson Smith & Knisely (R), NY, *107*
Adams, Len, KPA Assoc., Inc. (C), NY, *408*
Ahrensdorf, Lee, Ahrensdorf & Assoc. (R), PA, *2*
Allgire, Mary, Kenzer Corp. (R), IL, *113*
Allman, Steven L., Allman & Co., Inc. (C), NC, *245*
Anderson, Jr., Glenn G., LAI Ward Howell (R), OH, *123*
Armitage, John D., Armitage Associates Ltd. (R), ON, *7*
Aronow, Lawrence E., Aronow Assoc., Inc. (C), FL, *253*
Aruza, Al, Cornell Group Int'l. Consulting, Inc. (R), NY, *41*
Bagley, James M., Russell Reynolds Assoc., Inc. (R), NY, *177*
Banach-Osenni, Doris, The Brentwood Group, Inc. (R), NJ, *22*
Barnum, Toni M., Stone, Murphy & Olson (R), MN, *201*
Baron, Robert, Peak Search Assoc. (C), ON, *506*
Bell, Jeff, SpencerStuart (R), PA, *197*
Bell, Nelson C., Bell Wishingrad Partners Inc. (R), NY, *15*
Blair, Juliet, Johnson Smith & Knisely (R), NY, *107*
Bliley, Jerry, SpencerStuart (R), ON, *197*
Bonnell, William R., Bonnell Assoc. Ltd. (R), CT, *19*
Boren, Susan, SpencerStuart (R), MN, *197*
Borkenhagen, Christine, Morgan Samuels Co. (R), CA, *147*
Bothereau, Elizabeth, Kenzer Corp. (R), MN, *113*
Bovich, Maryann C., Higdon Prince Inc. (R), NY, *93*
Brady, Marty, The Oxbridge Group, Ltd. (C), PA, *500*
Bratches, Howard, Thorndike Deland Assoc. LLC (R), NY, *48*
Bray, Robert C., Organization Resources Inc. (R), MA, *157*
Bregman, Barry I., Sullivan & Company (R), NY, *204*
Brenner, Michael, LAI Ward Howell (R), NY, *122*
Brown, Franklin Key, Horton Int'l. Inc. (R), NY, *96*
Brown, Jennifer, Johnson Smith & Knisely (R), NY, *107*
Brown, Timothy A., LAI Ward Howell (R), TX, *124*
Brown, William Thomas, Overton Consulting (R), WI, *157*
Bruccoleri, Theodore A., StratfordGroup (R), OH, *203*
Bruce, Michael C., SpencerStuart (R), CA, *196*
Burnett, Brendan G., Sullivan & Company (R), NY, *204*
Burns, Terry, Foster Partners (R), IL, *70*
Bussey, Sharon, The Center for Career Advancement, LLC (C), NJ, *287*
Butler, Donald W., Management Recruiters of Milwaukee - Downtown (C), WI, *466*
Butler, T. Christopher, SpencerStuart (R), CA, *196*
Cage, Jack H., Sullivan & Company (R), NY, *204*
Cantus, Jane-Scott, Christian & Timbers, Inc. (R), VA, *34*
Cashen, Anthony B., LAI Ward Howell (R), NY, *122*
Castriota, Dominic, Rhodes Associates (R), NY, *177*
Chadick, Susan L., Gould, McCoy & Chadick, Inc. (R), NY, *80*
Chamberlain, Ann H., Keeley Consulting Inc. (C), ON, *404*
Choi, Julie A., McCann, Choi & Associates, LLC (R), NY, *139*
Ciaramitaro, Joseph, Corporate Search Consultants, Inc. (C), FL, *301*
Cicchino, William M., LAI Ward Howell (R), NY, *122*
Clark, Donald B., Ray & Berndtson (R), IL, *172*
Clarke, Terry M., LAI Ward Howell (R), WI, *124*
Clemens, Bill, SpencerStuart (R), CT, *196*
Coff, Scott, Johnson Smith & Knisely (R), NY, *107*
Cohen, Stephanie, Johnson Smith & Knisely (R), NY, *107*
Coleman, John A., Boardroom Consultants/Kenny Kindler Tholke (R), NY, *19*
Collins, Steve, The Johnson Group, Unlimited (C), NY, *400*
Colton, W. Hoyt, The Colton Partnership, Inc. (R), NY, *38*
Conley, Kevin E., LAI Ward Howell (R), MA, *123*
Connelly, Kevin M., SpencerStuart (R), IL, *197*
Constant, Rene, Milrod Assoc. (C), NJ, *482*

RECRUITER SPECIALTIES

Cooke, Katherine H., Horton International Inc. (R), CT, *96*
Coppola, Anna, The Flagship Group (R), MA, *68*
Corey, Michael J., LAI Ward Howell (R), WI, *124*
Corso, Glen S., LAI Ward Howell (R), CA, *123*
Costa, Karen, The Kinlin Co., Inc. (R), MA, *115*
Crane, Howard C., LAI Ward Howell (R), CA, *123*
Crath, Paul F., PricewaterhouseCoopers Executive Search (R), ON, *168*
Crystal, Jonathan A., SpencerStuart (R), TX, *197*
Curtin, Michelle, Brentwood Int'l. (R), CA, *23*
Davidson, Julie, Drinkwater & Assoc. (R), MA, *55*
Davis, Stephanie, Morgan Samuels Co. (R), CA, *147*
Davis, Steven M., Sullivan & Company (R), NY, *204*
de Cholnoky, Andrea, SpencerStuart (R), NY, *196*
de Wilde, David, LAI Ward Howell (R), CA, *123*
deBerry, Marian Alexander, Boulware & Assoc. Inc. (R), IL, *20*
DeMarlie, Gary P., LAI Ward Howell (R), WI, *124*
Dodd Perry, Dena, The Hollins Group, Inc. (R), IL, *95*
Donnelly, Patrick, Christopher-Westmont & Assoc., Inc. (R), OH, *35*
Drinkwater, Wendy A., Drinkwater & Assoc. (R), MA, *54*
Egan, David C., D. C. Egan & Assoc. (C), GA, *327*
Egan, John, Egan Search Group (R), NY, *57*
Einsel, A. Ray, Grant Cooper & Assoc., Inc. (R), MO, *81*
Ellis, Steve, Steve Ellis (C), CA, *328*
Ellis-Kirk, Matrice, SpencerStuart (R), TX, *197*
Epstein, Joel P., StratfordGroup (R), OH, *203*
Erickson, Elaine, Kenzer Corp. (R), NY, *113*
Escandon, Rafael, SpencerStuart (R), MX, *197*
Fagan, III, Charles A., Fagan & Company (R), PA, *64*
Farrell, John A., The Curtiss Group International (R), FL, *44*
Farrell, John A., The Curtiss Group, Int'l (R), FL, *44*
Fee, J. Curtis, SpencerStuart (R), IL, *197*
Fell, III, John R., Howe & Assoc. (R), PA, *97*
Finn, Eileen, Eileen Finn & Assoc., Inc. (C), NY, *341*
Fisher, Richard, Richard A. Eisner & Co., LLP (R), NY, *57*
Flam, Rick M., LAI Ward Howell (R), CA, *123*
Flanagan, Dale M., LAI Ward Howell (R), NY, *122*
Ford, Eileen F., Ford & Ford (C), MA, *343*
Franklin, Michael, Hreshko Consulting Group (C), NJ, *382*
Furr, C. Franklin, C. F. Furr & Co. (R), NC, *72*
Galante, Suzanne, Vlcek & Company, Inc. (R), CA, *214*
Gardiner, E. Nicholas P., Gardiner, Townsend & Assoc. (R), NY, *74*
Gasperini, Peter, Peter Gasperini & Assoc., Inc. (R), NY, *75*
Genel, George, Genel Associates (C), CA, *356*
Gesing, Rand W., Rand Assoc. (R), ME, *171*
Gnodde, R. Dirk, Gnodde Assoc. (C), IL, *359*
Gogates, Andrew, The Gogates Group, Inc. (R), NY, *79*
Gold, Lisa, Stratin Assoc. (C), NJ, *596*
Goldenberg, Susan T., Grant Cooper & Assoc., Inc. (R), MO, *81*
Goldsmith, Joseph B., Higdon Prince Inc. (R), NY, *93*
Gow, Roderick C., LAI Ward Howell (R), NY, *122*
Graham, Don, H.Q. Search, Inc. (C), IL, *365*
Greene, Dorcas P., Greene Personnel Consultants (C), RI, *362*
Guarino, Alan, Cornell Group Int'l. Consulting, Inc. (R), NY, *41*
Guerrero, Daniel, Kenzer Corp. (R), CA, *113*
Guilford, David J., DLG Assoc., Inc. (R), NC, *53*
Gulian, Randolph S., Strategic Executives, Inc. (R), CT, *202*
Gundersen, Jeff, Gundersen Partners, L.L.C. (R), NY, *83*
Gurliacci, Lisa, Johnson Smith & Knisely (R), NY, *107*
Hall, Nancy M., The Hollins Group, Inc. (R), GA, *95*
Hall, Peter V., Argonaut Partners, LLC (R), CA, *6*
Hamlin, Rachel, Johnson Smith & Knisely (R), NY, *107*
Hankins, George, First Advisory Services Int'l., Inc. (R), MD, *67*
Hankins, George, Management Assoc. (C), MD, *424*
Hanson, Paul David, LAI Ward Howell (R), WI, *124*
Hanson, Paul L., LAI Ward Howell (R), WI, *124*
Hawley, Robert E., Hayden Group, Inc. (R), MA, *88*
Hayden, Dale, Sanford Rose Assoc. - Pittsburgh North (C), PA, *570*
Heller, Paul M., Cromwell Partners, Inc. (R), NY, *43*
Hellinger, Audrey, Martin H. Bauman Assoc., Inc. (R), IL, *14*
Hendrickson, Jill, Johnson Smith & Knisely (R), IL, *107*
Herbst, jody, Management Recruiters of Milwaukee - Downtown (C), WI, *466*
Herget, James P., Harcourt Group Ltd. (R), OH, *86*
Herget, Jane K., Harcourt Group Ltd. (R), OH, *86*
Higdon, Henry G., Higdon Prince Inc. (R), NY, *93*
Holmes, Dave, Hreshko Consulting Group (C), NJ, *382*
Holodnak, William A., J. Robert Scott (R), MA, *104*
Horn, David C., David C. Horn Executive Search (C), TX, *381*
Hubbard, Ted L., KS Frary & Assoc. (R), MA, *71*
Hunt, III, Herbert I., H.I. Hunt & Co., Ltd. (R), MA, *99*
Hutchison, Robert, Overton Consulting (R), WI, *157*
Ikle, A. Donald, LAI Ward Howell (R), NY, *123*
Jackowitz, Todd, J. Robert Scott (R), MA, *104*
Jenkins, Virginia L., The Center for Career Advancement (C), MD, *287*
Johnson, Dan, Johnson Smith & Knisely (R), NY, *107*
Johnson, Daniel, Morgan Samuels Co. (R), CA, *147*
Jones, Donald, Kenzer Corp. (R), TX, *113*
Kampmann, Sara, Johnson Smith & Knisely (R), CA, *107*
Kaplan, Alan J., Kaplan & Assoc., Inc. (R), PA, *109*
Kapral, Shannon M., Sanford Rose Assoc. - Philadelphia North (C), PA, *570*
Karp, Michael, The Options Group, Inc. (C), NY, *499*
Keeley, Stephanie Brooks, Keeley Consulting Inc. (C), ON, *404*
Keeley, Timothy J., Keeley Consulting Inc. (C), ON, *404*
Kelly, Claudia L., SpencerStuart (R), CT, *196*
Kelly, Jeanine P., Integrated Management Solutions (C), NY, *390*
Kelly, Peter W., Rollo Assoc. (R), CA, *181*
Kensington, Holland, Kensington International (R), CA, *113*
Kenzer, Robert D., Kenzer Corp. (R), NY, *113*
Keogh, James, Sanford Rose Assoc. - Oak Brook (C), IL, *567*
Kershner, Bruce, Kershner & Co. (R), DC, *113*
Kien-Jersey, Tammy, SpencerStuart (R), CT, *197*
King, James B., The Westminster Group, Inc. (R), RI, *218*
Klebanoff, Elizabeth, Johnson Smith & Knisely (R), NY, *107*
Kohlbry, Cynthia J., Grant Cooper & Assoc., Inc. (R), MO, *81*
Konstans, Gregory C., LAI Ward Howell (R), TX, *124*
Kopelan, Rolfe I., Boyden (R), NY, *21*
Kostmayer, John B., Kostmayer Assoc., Inc. (R), NY, *119*

Kostmayer, Roger C., Kostmayer Assoc., Inc. (R), MD, *119*
Krell, Richard B., Russell Reynolds Assoc., Inc. (R), CA, *176*
Kulper, Keith D., Kulper & Co., L.L.C. (R), NJ, *121*
L'Hote, Jeffrey R., LAI Ward Howell (R), NY, *122*
Laderman, David, ACSYS Resources, Inc. (C), PA, *239*
Landon, Susan J., LAI Ward Howell (R), NY, *122*
Lapham, Lawrence L., Lawrence L. Lapham, Inc. (R), NY, *124*
Latini, Anthony A., Princeton Search Partners, Inc. (R), NJ, *169*
Laurendeau, J. E., Ray & Berndtson/Laurendeau Labrecque (R), QE, *172*
Leslie, C.C., Johnson Smith & Knisely (R), NY, *107*
Lew, Edwin, LanSo Int'l., Inc. (C), NY, *413*
Lewisohn, Dina K. S., LAI Ward Howell (R), NY, *122*
Lightner Jr., Ralph H., Stanton Chase Int'l. (R), MD, *199*
Lockleer, Julia, EA Plus, Inc. (C), TX, *325*
Long, William G., McDonald, Long & Assoc., Inc. (R), NY, *140*
Lord, Anthony W. G., LAI Ward Howell (R), NY, *123*
Lucifero, Lisa, ACSYS Resources, Inc. (C), NJ, *238*
Lussier, Grant, SpencerStuart (R), MX, *197*
Luther, Paul T., Financial Search Group, Inc. (R), MA, *66*
Lyman, David M., Schall Executive Search Partners (R), MN, *185*
Lyons, Denis B. K., SpencerStuart (R), NY, *196*
Lyons, Scott, Lyons Pruitt Int'l. (R), PA, *132*
MacArthur, Ian, Madison MacArthur Inc. (R), ON, *133*
MacDougall, Andrew J., SpencerStuart (R), ON, *197*
Mack, Linda, Johnson Smith & Knisely (R), IL, *107*
Macomber, Keith S., Sullivan & Company (R), NY, *204*
Maher, Peter T., The Partnership Group (R), NJ, *160*
Manheim, Gene S., Sullivan & Company (R), NY, *204*
Marchetti, James, International Market Recruiters (C), NC, *393*
Marino, Jory J., Sullivan & Company (R), NY, *204*
May, Patricia, Johnson Smith & Knisely (R), NY, *107*
McBryde, Marnie, SpencerStuart (R), NY, *196*
McCann, Connie B., SpencerStuart (R), PA, *197*
McCann, III, Joseph H., McCann, Choi & Associates, LLC (R), NY, *139*
McCormick, Harry B., Hayden Group, Inc. (R), MA, *88*
McCoy, Millington F., Gould, McCoy & Chadick, Inc. (R), NY, *80*
McElroy, Brian, Drinkwater & Assoc. (R), MA, *55*
McFadden, Ashton S., Johnson Smith & Knisely (R), NY, *107*
McKenna, Scott, The Beam Group (R), PA, *14*
McLean, E. Peter, SpencerStuart (R), NY, *196*
McMahon, Marguerite A., Sullivan & Company (R), NY, *204*
McPherson, Stephen M., LAI Ward Howell (R), NY, *123*
Merrigan, Eileen M., LAI Ward Howell (R), NY, *122*
Miller, Curt, A-L Assoc., Inc. (R), NY, *1*
Miller, Darryl, Management Alliance Group, Inc. (R), NJ, *134*
Miller, Roxxanne, The Pailin Group Professional Search Consultants (R), TX, *158*
Millonzi, Joel C., Johnson Smith & Knisely (R), NY, *107*
Milo, J. Raymond, Siger & Assoc., LLC (C), CT, *581*
Monahan, Stephen C., Management Recruiters - Towne Lake (C), GA, *446*
Moore, Connie, C. A. Moore & Assoc., Inc. (C), MN, *484*
Moore, Richard C. E., Russell Reynolds Assoc., Inc. (R), ON, *177*
Moran, Thomas F., LAI Ward Howell (R), WI, *124*
Morin, Michelle, SpencerStuart (R), ON, *197*
Morris, David W., WTW Assoc., Inc. (R), NY, *225*
Morse, Mary K., Travis & Co., Inc. (R), MA, *210*
Mowatt, Ginny, SpencerStuart (R), IL, *197*
Moyse, Richard G., Thorndike Deland Assoc. LLC (R), NY, *48*
Nagler, Leon G., Nagler, Robins & Poe, Inc. (R), MA, *150*
Nein, Lawrence F., LAI Ward Howell (R), IL, *123*
Norton, III, James B., LAI Ward Howell (R), GA, *123*
O'Gorman, David J., DHR Int'l., Inc. (R), IL, *49*
O'Maley, Kimberlee, SpencerStuart (R), CA, *196*
Ogden, Dayton, SpencerStuart (R), CT, *196*
Ollinger, Chuck, Ollinger Partners (R), MA, *156*
Orchant, Edward, A-L Assoc., Inc. (R), NY, *1*
Ortega de Diego, Estela, Dunhill Professional Search of Miami (C), FL, *320*
Paddock, Jeff, Management Recruiters The Delta Group, Inc. (C), TN, *461*
Paetzhold, Jerry, Davis & James, Inc. (C), MO, *308*
Perunovich, Lise, The Park Group & Assoc., Inc. (C), MD, *503*
Peterson, Michael T., BayResearch Group, Inc. (R), IL, *14*
Peyser, Robert E., Peyser Assoc., Inc. (R), FL, *163*
Phillips, Catherine, C. P. Consulting (R), PA, *26*
Picard, Daniel A., Picard Int'l., Ltd. (R), NY, *164*
Pierson, Edward J., Johnson Smith & Knisely (R), NY, *107*
Posselt, Jeffrey, Cook Assoc.,® Inc. (R), IL, *40*
Powell, Marie, Kenzer Corp. (R), GA, *113*
Power, Alex G., H.I. Hunt & Co., Ltd. (R), MA, *99*
Pratz, Robert P., The Park Group & Assoc., Inc. (C), MD, *503*
Preston, Joe, Preston & Co. (R), NJ, *167*
Priem, Windle B., Korn/Ferry Int'l. (R), NY, *117*
Prince, Marylin L., Higdon Prince Inc. (R), NY, *93*
Pugrant, Mark A., Grant/Morgan Assoc., Inc. (C), MD, *361*
Putrim, Thomas G., LAI Ward Howell (R), IL, *123*
Redmond, Andrea, Russell Reynolds Assoc., Inc. (R), IL, *176*
Redwood, Derek, Rushmore • Judge Inc. (R), ON, *183*
Reed, Bob, The Options Group, Inc. (C), NY, *499*
Reeves, William B., SpencerStuart (R), GA, *197*
Rehner, Leonard, R & L Assoc., Ltd. (R), NY, *170*
Rich, Kenneth M., Ray & Berndtson (R), NY, *172*
Richard, David A., Financial Connections Company (C), VA, *340*
Richardson, J. Rick, SpencerStuart (R), CT, *196*
Rieger, Louis J., SpencerStuart (R), TX, *197*
Ritchings, David, David Allen Assoc. (R), NJ, *3*
Roberts, Scott, Jonas, Walters & Assoc., Inc. (R), WI, *108*
Rolland, Guy, Rolland Ressources Humaines Inc. (R), QE, *181*
Roth, Jim, Management Recruiters of Des Moines (C), IA, *449*
Rowe, K. Michael, Management Resource Group (C), MN, *467*
Rowe, William, Foster Partners (R), TX, *71*
Rupp, Sandra, Johnson Smith & Knisely (R), NY, *107*
Russell, Robin, Kenzer Corp. (R), NY, *113*
Ryder Stone, Robert, LAI Ward Howell (R), CT, *123*
Satenstein, Sloan, Higdon Prince Inc. (R), NY, *93*
Sauer, Harry, ACSYS Resources, Inc. (C), PA, *239*
Savard, Jr., Robert F., Horton International Inc. (R), CT, *96*
Savoy, Michelle, SpencerStuart (R), ON, *197*
Schall, David R., Schall Executive Search Partners (R), MN, *185*
Schibli, Peter, H.I. Hunt & Co., Ltd. (R), MA, *99*
Schoales, Michael, Schoales & Assoc. Inc. (C), ON, *572*

RECRUITER SPECIALTIES

Schroeder, John W., SpencerStuart (R), TX, *197*
Schwartz, Alan, Advice Personnel Inc. (C), NY, *241*
Schwartz, Deborah, Ollinger Partners (R), MA, *156*
Schwartz, Kenneth, John Kurosky & Assoc. (R), CA, *122*
Segal, Eric B., Kenzer Corp. (R), NY, *113*
Selbach, Barbara, SpencerStuart (R), NY, *196*
Shannahan, Peter, Shannahan & Co., Inc. (R), CA, *189*
Shariff, Hassan, The Johnson Group, Unlimited (C), NY, *400*
Shedroff, Michael, ACSYS Resources, Inc. (C), NJ, *238*
Sherwin, Gordon K., Ambridge Management Corp. (C), ON, *247*
Shufelt, Douglas G., Sink, Walker, Boltrus Int'l. (R), MA, *192*
Simmons, Thomas M., SpencerStuart (R), TX, *197*
Singer, Lloyd R., Romac Int'l. (C), IL, *542*
Skrypuch, Roman M., Financial Plus Management Solutions Inc. (R), ON, *66*
Slepin, Matthew B., Argonaut Partners, LLC (R), CA, *6*
Smith, F. Clawson, LAI Ward Howell (R), CT, *123*
Smith, Howard O., The Johnson Group, Unlimited (C), NY, *400*
Smith, Jill, ACSYS Resources, Inc. (C), PA, *239*
Smith, Scott B., LAI Ward Howell (R), WI, *124*
Snyder, Jr., James F., Snyder & Co. (R), CT, *194*
Soren, Robin, SpencerStuart (R), NY, *196*
Spence, Jr., Joseph T., Russell Reynolds Assoc., Inc. (R), GA, *176*
Spiegel, Deborah, Kenzer Corp. (R), NY, *113*
Spindel, Howard, Integrated Management Solutions (C), NY, *390*
Springer, Mark H., M. H. Springer & Assoc. (R), CA, *198*
Stafford, Peter B., Stafford Consulting Group (R), CA, *198*
Stern, Leslie W., Sullivan & Company (R), NY, *204*
Stevens, III, David S., Johnson Smith & Knisely (R), NY, *107*
Stevens, Leonard W., Stevens, Valentine & McKeever (C), NJ, *593*
Stewart, Wilfred C., KPMG Executive Search (R), ON, *119*
Straight, Gary R., Straight & Co. (R), GA, *202*
Stupay, Michael E., Integrated Management Solutions (C), NY, *390*
Sullivan, Brian M., Sullivan & Company (R), NY, *204*
Sullivan, Joseph M., International Market Recruiters (C), NY, *393*
Swiff, Jeffrey G., Thorndike Deland Assoc. LLC (R), NY, *48*
Swift, Nina E., The Oxbridge Group, Ltd. (C), PA, *500*
Tappan, Michael A., LAI Ward Howell (R), NY, *123*
Townsend, John W., Gardiner, Townsend & Assoc. (R), NY, *74*
Ursin, Kathleen, Johnson Smith & Knisely (R), CA, *107*
Vacca, Domenic L., ACSYS Resources, Inc. (C), DE, *238*
Vande Water, Katie E., J. Robert Scott (R), MA, *104*
Venable, William, Thorndike Deland Assoc. LLC (R), NY, *48*
von Stein, William, Johnson Smith & Knisely (R), CA, *107*
Walker, Douglas G., Sink, Walker, Boltrus Int'l. (R), MA, *192*
Ward, Madeleine, L T M Assoc. (C), IL, *410*
Warring, J. T., Warring & Assoc. (R), CA, *215*
Watkins, III, Thomas M., LAI Ward Howell (R), TX, *124*
Weiler, Wendy C., Rhodes Associates (R), NY, *177*
Werlin, Paul A., Human Capital Resources, Inc. (C), FL, *384*
White, Richard B., SpencerStuart (R), CT, *196*
Whiting, Anthony, Johnson Smith & Knisely (R), NY, *107*
Willbanks, Bret, TTG/Sterling Services (C), CA, *610*
Williams, Walter E., LAI Ward Howell (R), MA, *123*
Willis, Jr., William H., William Willis Worldwide Inc. (R), CT, *221*
Wilson, Harry W., First Union Executive Search (R), NC, *67*
Wilson, Thomas H., LAI Ward Howell (R), TX, *124*
Wishingrad, Vivian, Bell Wishingrad Partners Inc. (R), CT, *15*
Wishingrad, Vivian, Bell Wishingrad Partners Inc. (R), NY, *15*
Wood, Karen, Armitage Associates Ltd. (R), ON, *7*
Woods, Bruce Gilbert, Bruce G. Woods Executive Search (R), TX, *224*
Work, Alan J., Hechkoff/Work Executive Search Inc. (R), NY, *89*
Wysocki, Robert, Cornell Group Int'l. Consulting, Inc. (R), NY, *41*
Young, Nicholas, SpencerStuart (R), NY, *196*
Yungerberg, Steven A., Steven Yungerberg Assoc., Inc. (R), MN, *226*
Zadek, Kate, Johnson Smith & Knisely (R), NY, *107*
Ziccardi, Joseph, Cromwell Partners, Inc. (R), NY, *43*
Zinn, Michael D., Michael D. Zinn & Assoc., Inc. (R), NJ, *227*
Zivic, Janis M., SpencerStuart (R), CA, *196*

Fire protection

Creasy, Nancy, Michael Latas & Assoc., Inc. (R), MO, *126*
Richey, Nancy, The Stonebridge Group (C), PA, *594*

Floriculture

Leonard, Mell D., International Recruiting Services (C), FL, *393*

Food

Alexander, Craig R., Management Recruiters of Boise (C), ID, *446*
Allison, Tom, Tom Allison Assoc. (C), NM, *245*
Alstrin, Robert W., Roth Young Executive Search of Milwaukee (C), WI, *547*
Andrews, Robert L., Allen Austin Lowe & Powers (R), TX, *3*
Arledge, Tom, Allen Austin Lowe & Powers (R), TX, *3*
Ayers, Joseph, Hollander Horizon Int'l. (R), MN, *95*
Bellview, Louis, Management Recruiters - Friendswood (C), TX, *462*
Bilinski, Kalyna, Coe & Co. Int'l. Inc./EMA Partners Int'l. (R), AB, *37*
Bingham, Rick, Briant Assoc., Inc. (R), IL, *23*
Blake, Barbara, Ron Sunshine & Assoc. (C), IL, *597*
Boruff, Doug, Dunhill Personnel of Boulder (C), CO, *319*
Boruff, Fran, Dunhill Personnel of Boulder (C), CO, *319*
Brenneman, Thomas E., Roth Young Executive Search of Milwaukee (C), WI, *547*
Burke, Kaye, J. Burke & Assoc., Inc. (C), TX, *276*
Carrigan, Denise, Management Recruiters of San Antonio (C), TX, *463*
Cegelski, Chris, The H. S. Group, Inc. (C), WI, *365*
Charles, Rebecca, Matrix Consultants, Inc. (C), NC, *472*
Clark, Larry A., The Clark Group (C), MI, *292*
Cornelison, Mike, M.C. Executive Search (C), CA, *422*
Critchfield, Marlene, Marlene Critchfield Co. (C), CA, *303*
Cruz, Raymond, A-Linko & Assoc. (C), TX, *231*
Daffala, Ronald, Merit Professional Search, Inc. (C), TN, *479*
Dework, Frank M., Kingsley Quinn/USA (R), NJ, *115*
Egan, David C., D. C. Egan & Assoc. (C), GA, *327*
Fockler, David B., David Fockler & Assoc., Inc. (C), CA, *342*
Fredericks, Ward A., MIXTEC Group (R), CA, *145*
Froelich, K., Murphy Partners Int'l. (R), IL, *150*
Goldsmith, Fred J., Fred J. Goldsmith Assoc. (R), CA, *79*
Gorry, John E., Cella Assoc. (C), GA, *286*
Hanson, Ralph, Massey-Horton Int'l. (R), ON, *138*

Hawkins, Michael J., Michael J. Hawkins, Inc. (C), IL, *370*
Henson, Jeff, Henson Partners (C), AZ, *376*
Henton, Sara, Management Recruiters-Cedar Rapids, Inc. (C), IA, *448*
Heybroek, Eric J., Sanford Rose Assoc. - Rockville (C), MD, *568*
Hill, Michelle, The Alfus Group (R), NY, *3*
Holford, Jay, MIXTEC Group (R), FL, *146*
Hollander, Michael, Hollander Horizon Int'l. (R), NJ, *95*
Hughes, Donald J., Hughes & Company (R), VA, *98*
Irwin, Bill, Southern Recruiters & Consultants, Inc. (C), SC, *587*
Kirkwood, Vincent, Executive Connection (C), OH, *333*
Knowlson, Maureen, M. K. & Assoc. (C), PA, *422*
Kurbatoff, Jerry, The Black Leopard (C), CA, *267*
Kurbatoff, Lauren, The Black Leopard (C), CA, *267*
Laue, Elizabeth, Smith & Laue Search (R), OR, *193*
Lay, Jim, A-Linko & Assoc. (C), TX, *231*
Lindal, Bruce G., Linden Group, Inc. (C), NC, *418*
Manning, Bob, Management Recruiters of Rocky Mount - Southwest (C), NC, *456*
Mason, Morgan, Mason & Nicastri Ltd. (R), CA, *138*
McGeehan, Gayle A., Management Recruiters of Bethlehem, PA (C), PA, *458*
McKinney, Adrienne, Wachendorfer & Assoc. (C), TX, *613*
McLafferty, Tim, Focus Executive Search (C), MN, *343*
Meyer, Fred R., Management Recruiters of Bethlehem, PA (C), PA, *458*
Milanese, Diane, Management Recruiters of Sidney (C), OH, *458*
Mitchell, Lauren, Wachendorfer & Assoc. (C), TX, *613*
Mossman, John G., M. K. & Assoc. (C), PA, *422*
Murray, Jeanette M., The Murray Group (C), IL, *487*
Nepple, Rosemarie, Management Recruiters of Upper Westchester (C), NY, *454*
Nepple, Vern D., Management Recruiters of Upper Westchester (C), NY, *454*
Newell, Carlyle, Management Alliance Group, Inc. (R), NJ, *134*
Nicastri, Diane, Mason & Nicrasti Ltd. (R), CA, *138*
Norris, Cathy A., Norris Agency (C), TX, *496*
Norris, John B., John B. Norris & Assoc., Inc. (C), MD, *495*
Oster, R. Rush, Management Recruiters of Anna Maria Island (C), FL, *443*
Pickering, Dale, Agri-Tech Personnel, Inc. (C), MO, *242*
Powers, Janet, Powers Consultants, Inc. (R), MO, *166*
Ritt, Arthur, Ritt-Ritt & Assoc., Inc. (C), IL, *537*
Roe, Craig T., Craig Roe & Assoc., LLC (C), MD, *540*
Ruthrauff, Debbie, Kelly Associates (R), PA, *112*
Salzberg, David, Roth Young Seattle (C), WA, *546*
Sarantino, Tina, Management Recruiters of Fresno (C), CA, *440*
Scott, E. Ann, Scott Executive Search, Inc. (R), NY, *186*
Seal, Jock, The H. S. Group, Inc. (C), WI, *365*
Shalinsky, John, Rice Cohen Int'l. (R), PA, *178*
Sherman, Terri, Tom Sloan & Assoc., Inc. (C), WI, *583*
Smith, Charles D., Smith & Laue Search (R), OR, *193*
Smith, Donald L., Smith, Brown & Jones (C), KS, *585*
Smith, Patrick, Smith & Syberg, Inc. (R), IN, *193*
Smitherman, Jim, Merit Professional Search, Inc. (C), TN, *479*
Stiles, Timothy W., Sanford Rose Assoc. - Portland (C), OR, *570*
Stoa, Gordon, PERC, Ltd. (C), AZ, *506*
Stockton, J. R., Management Catalysts (R), NJ, *134*
Suchomski, Larry, The Montgomery Group, Inc. (C), TN, *484*
Uniacke, Keith J., Management Recruiters of Sidney (C), OH, *458*
Wachendorfer, Nancy, Wachendorfer & Assoc. (C), TX, *613*
Wachendorfer, Tom, Wachendorfer & Assoc. (C), TX, *613*
Weddell, Dave, Management Recruiters of Rocky Mount - Southwest (C), NC, *456*
Weitzel, Freda, Management Recruiters of Winston-Salem (C), NC, *457*
White, J.W., Schneider, Hill & Spangler, Inc. (R), PA, *185*
Williams, John G., John Williams & Assoc. (C), TX, *621*
Willis, Jr., William H., William Willis Worldwide Inc. (R), CT, *221*
Wolcott, Tracy, Recruiting Specialists (C), MA, *532*
Wolf, Lisa, Lawrence Glaser Assoc., Inc. (C), NJ, *358*
Womble, O. J., Matrix Consultants, Inc. (C), NC, *472*
Zimmerman, Arnold, Hollander Horizon Int'l. (R), CA, *95*
Zipfel, John, Debbon Recruiting Group, Inc. (C), MO, *310*

Food service

Cain, Douglas, Sales Recruiting Network (C), PA, *564*
Carieri, Carl R., American Executive Search (C), FL, *247*
Charles, Rebecca, Matrix Consultants, Inc. (C), NC, *472*
Clanton, Diane, Clanton & Co. (C), CA, *292*
Colacchio, Thomas P., Futures, Inc. (C), NH, *354*
Garcia, Abel, Allen Austin Lowe & Powers (R), TX, *3*
Gentry, Allen, Hospitality Int'l. (C), AZ, *381*
Gladstone, Robert, Roth Young Executive Search (C), TX, *546*
Helnore, Douglas, Partners in Recruiting (C), IL, *504*
Lav, Madeleine, Madeleine Lav & Assoc. (C), CA, *413*
Marino, Frank, Hospitality Int'l. (C), NY, *381*
McDaniel, Paul, The Paul McDaniel Co. (C), TN, *474*
McDermid, Earl, Earl L. McDermid & Assoc. (C), IL, *474*
McGinnis, W. John, Earl L. McDermid & Assoc. (C), IL, *474*
Nemec, Edward C., Craig Affiliates, Inc. (C), TX, *302*
Palmlund, III, David W., LAI Ward Howell (R), TX, *124*
Radice, Joseph A., Hospitality Int'l. (C), NY, *381*
Reich, Joshua, The Alfus Group (R), NY, *3*
Tommarello, Tony, Lucas Assoc. (C), CA, *421*
Wilkson, James, Allen Austin Lowe & Powers (R), TX, *3*

Footwear

Clayman, Stan, CMS, Inc. (C), NH, *293*
Corwin, J. Blade, Seitchik Corwin & Seitchik Inc. (R), CA, *188*
Seitchik, Jack, Seitchik Corwin & Seitchik Inc. (R), CA, *188*
Seitchik, William, Seitchik Corwin & Seitchik Inc. (R), NY, *188*
Selig, Robert J., Selig Executive Search (C), NH, *579*
White, Joseph A., Sports Group Int'l. (R), NC, *198*
Whiting, Frank, Cook Assoc.,® Inc. (R), IL, *40*

Forest industry

Hogg, Ronald J., Forest People Int'l. Search Ltd. (C), BC, *343*
Lachance, Roger, Ray & Berndtson/Laurendeau Labrecque (R), QE, *172*
Laurence, David, Forest People Int'l. Search Ltd. (C), BC, *343*
McRobbie, Jason, Forest People Int'l. Search Ltd. (C), BC, *343*
Waschuk, Bill, Forest People Int'l. Search Ltd. (C), BC, *343*

Forest products

Copeland, Gates, Management Recruiters of Houston-Northeast (C), TX, *463*
Copeland, Linda, Management Recruiters of Houston-Northeast (C), TX, *463*

Jansen, Carl, Search North America, Inc. (C), OR, *576*
Myers, Jamie, Management Recruiters of Houston-Northeast (C), TX, *463*
Shearer, Gary F., Management Recruiters of Bonita Springs, Inc. (C), FL, *443*

Fortune Plus

Arceri, John Mark, John Ryan Assoc., LLC. (C), NY, *399*
Brown, Richard E., O'Connor, O'Connor, Lordi, Ltd. (R), PA, *154*
Clarke, Brian G., Kensington Int'l., Inc. (R), IL, *113*
George, Richard, Kensington Int'l., Inc. (R), IL, *113*
Hart, Robert T., Foster Partners (R), NY, *70*
O'Connor, Thomas F., O'Connor, O'Connor, Lordi, Ltd. (R), PA, *154*
Richter, Ryan, John Ryan Assoc., LLC. (C), NY, *399*

Foundries

Borchert, Gregory L., Borchert Assoc. (C), TX, *269*
Jansen, Douglas L., Search Northwest Assoc. (C), OR, *576*
Mayberry, Karen Sue, Singleton & Assoc. (C), VA, *582*
McLey, Curt, Harrison Moore Inc. (C), NE, *370*
Michaels, Lou, Lou Michaels Assoc., Inc. (C), MI, *481*
Michaels, Randy, Lou Michaels Assoc., Inc. (C), MI, *481*
Pelland, Paul S., Paul S. Pelland, P.C. (R), SC, *161*
Singleton, Steven L., Singleton & Assoc. (C), VA, *582*
Storer, Steve, Executive Search, Ltd. (C), OH, *336*
Taylor, Jane A., Paul S. Pelland, P.C. (R), SC, *161*

Franchising

Capodice, Peter, Franstaff Inc. (C), FL, *352*
Coffee, Michael, Franstaff Inc. (C), FL, *352*
Dement, James W., Franstaff Inc. (C), FL, *352*
Kinzie, George, Franchise Recruiters Ltd. (R), ON, *71*
Kushell, Douglas T., Franchise Search, Inc. (C), NY, *352*
McCutcheon, Scott, John Kurosky & Assoc. (R), CA, *122*
Wilson, Denver, Sales Consultants of Northwest Arkansas, Inc. (C), AR, *556*

Freight

Wilson, Akira, Largent Parks & Partners (C), TX, *503*

Fundraising

Bronder, Stephanie L., Fagan & Company (R), PA, *64*
Hurley, Gerard F., Association Executive Resources Group (R), MD, *8*
Lindauer, Lois L., Lois L. Lindauer Searches (C), MA, *418*
Paschal, Carolyn Smith, Carolyn Smith Paschal Int'l. (R), CA, *160*
Roy, Ruth, Lois L. Lindauer Searches (C), MA, *418*

Furniture

Ariail, Randolph C., Ariail & Assoc. (R), NC, *7*
Corder, Eutha, RBW Assoc. Inc. (C), AR, *531*
Dussling, Kate, Cook Assoc.,® Inc. (R), IL, *40*
Greene, William, Stewart/Greene & Co. of The Triad, Inc. (C), NC, *594*
Ibsen, John, Stewart/Greene & Co. of The Triad, Inc. (C), NC, *594*
Kaestner, Bob, Robert Kaestner & Assoc. (C), FL, *403*
Pawelczyk, Art, Cook Assoc.,® Inc. (R), IL, *40*
Penley, Jeffrey M., Highlander Search (C), NC, *378*
Souder, Elizabeth W., Springer Souder & Assoc. L.L.C. (R), IL, *198*
Spangler, Jeffrey, Next Step Recruiting (C), CA, *493*
Stewart, Tom, Stewart/Greene & Company of the Triad, Inc. (C), NC, *594*
Underwood, David L., Sales Consultants of Grand Rapids (C), MI, *560*
VanSlyke, Dayton, Search By Design (C), AZ, *574*
Viscusi, Stephen P., The Viscusi Group, Inc. (R), NY, *214*

Galleries

Buchanan, Martha, Wilson McLeran, Inc. (C), CT, *622*

Gaming

Bright, Jr., James J., Bristol Assoc., Inc. (C), CA, *274*
Cargill, Jim, Management Recruiters of Lake Tahoe, NV (C), NV, *453*
Casey, David, The Alfus Group (R), NY, *3*
Fields, Sharon K., Career Development Associates (C), NV, *282*
Rios, Dyann, Career Development Associates (C), NV, *282*
Rutherford, Frank H., Gaming Consultants, Inc. (R), LA, *74*

Gas

Collier, Gordon L., R. C. Services (C), TX, *528*
Fisher, Earl, Management Recruiters of Cass County, NE (C), NE, *453*
Gagola, J., American Executive Management, Inc. (R), MA, *5*
Hayward, Robert M., National Field Service Corp. (C), NY, *489*
O'Brien, Brent, Executive Search Consultants Corp. (C), IL, *335*
Williams, Bill, Executive Search Consultants Corp. (C), IL, *335*

Gay/lesbian

McCormack, Joseph A., McCormack & Assoc. (R), CA, *140*

General management

Akin, J. R., J. R. Akin & Co. (R), MA, *2*
Allerton, Donald, Allerton Heneghan & O'Neill (R), IL, *4*
Alman, Paul D., Holland & Assoc., Inc. (R), MI, *94*
Alves, Manuel J., M/J/A Partners (R), IL, *133*
Angus, Thomas R., The Angus Group, Ltd. (C), OH, *251*
Ascher, Daniel, D.A.I Human Resources Consultants (R), QE, *45*
Babcock, James A., The Premier Staffing Group (C), OH, *517*
Babka, James, Roth Young of Chicago (C), IL, *546*
Bailey, Paul, Preston-Hunter, Inc. (R), IL, *167*
Balian, Christina L., Compass Group Ltd. (R), MI, *38*
Barefield, Ernest, Gans, Gans & Assoc., Inc. (R), PA, *74*
Baron, Harvey J., Management Recruiters of San Diego (C), CA, *426*
Barton, Gary, Barton Assoc., Inc. (R), TX, *12*
Bason, Maurice L., Bason Associates (R), OH, *13*
Baty, R. Gaines, R. Gaines Baty Assoc., Inc. (R), TX, *13*
Beatty, Jr., Robert L., The Curtiss Group International (R), FL, *44*
Beaudine, Frank R., Eastman & Beaudine, Inc. (R), TX, *56*
Bencik, James P., J. P. Bencik Assoc. (C), MI, *263*
Bennett, Joan, Adams & Assoc. Int'l. (R), IL, *1*
Bennett, Mark, Bennett & Associates (C), TX, *264*
Billington, Brian J., Billington & Assoc. (R), CA, *17*
Birnbaum, Richard, R. J. Associates (C), NY, *528*
Blanchard, Sr., Richard E., C. M. Management Services, Inc. (R), KY, *26*
Bodin, Thomas H., The Personnel Group, Inc. (R), MN, *163*
Bogue, Randall L., TBC, Inc. (C), KY, *600*
Bond, James, People Management Northeast, Inc. (R), CT, *162*

Bondi, Nikki C., Advantage Partners, Inc. (R), OH, *2*
Bosch, Diane, Bosch & Assoc., LLC (R), CT, *20*
Bosch, Eric E., Bosch & Assoc., LLC (R), CT, *20*
Boule, James P., F-O-R-T-U-N-E Personnel Consultants of Cincinnati (C), OH, *348*
Bowden, II, Otis H., BowdenGlobal, Ltd. (R), OH, *20*
Bowman, David, TTG/Sterling Services (C), CA, *610*
Bujold, Joseph M., The Curtiss Group International (R), FL, *44*
Burfield, Elaine, Skott/Edwards Consultants (R), NY, *192*
Burkland, Skott B., Skott/Edwards Consultants (R), NY, *192*
Callan, Robert M., Callan Assoc., Ltd. (R), IL, *27*
Caplan, Shellie, Caplan Assoc., Inc. (R), NJ, *28*
Carey, Dennis C., SpencerStuart (R), PA, *197*
Carter, Wayne A., The Personnel Group, Inc. (R), MN, *163*
Casati, Christine, China Human Resources Group (R), NJ, *33*
Cason, Lyn, Brad Marks Int'l. (R), CA, *136*
Chad, Rick A., Chad Management Group (C), ON, *288*
Chambers, David E., David Chambers & Assoc., Inc. (R), CT, *32*
Christensen, Garn, F-O-R-T-U-N-E Personnel Consultants of Boise (R), ID, *70*
Cloutier, E. J., American Executive Management, Inc. (R), MA, *5*
Clovis, Jr., James R., Handy HRM (R), NY, *86*
Cole, Ronald, Cole, Warren & Long, Inc. (R), PA, *37*
Combs, Stephen, StratfordGroup (R), CA, *203*
Conroy, M. J., Conroy Partners Ltd. (R), AB, *39*
Courtright, Robert J., Courtright & Assoc., Inc. (R), PA, *42*
Cowell, Roy A., Cowell & Associates, Ltd. (R), IL, *42*
Crabtree, G. A., Roger Dietsch & Assoc. (C), MN, *312*
Critchley, Walter Y., Cochran, Cochran & Yale, Inc. (R), NY, *36*
Cruse, O. D., SpencerStuart (R), TX, *197*
Cunningham, Sheila, Adams & Assoc. Int'l. (R), IL, *1*
Damon, Robert A., SpencerStuart (R), NY, *196*
Dant, Wendy A., Hire Authority, Inc. (C), MI, *379*
Darter, Steven, People Management Northeast, Inc. (R), CT, *162*
Daubenspeck, Rima, Daubenspeck & Associates, Ltd. (R), IL, *46*
DeBaugh, David H., PRAXIS Partners (R), VA, *167*
Dee, Vincent W., Hartsfield Group, Inc. (R), GA, *87*
Desley, Carolyn M., Erlanger Assoc. (R), CT, *60*
Despres, Raoul, Despres & Associates (C), IL, *311*
Diaz, Del, Management Recruiters of Miami-North (C), FL, *444*
Dieckmann, Ralph E., Dieckmann & Assoc., Ltd. (R), IL, *51*
Doupe, S. Scott, Conroy Partners Ltd. (R), AB, *39*
Doyle, Don, Bosch & Assoc., LLC (R), CT, *20*
Drury, III, James J., SpencerStuart (R), IL, *197*
Duggan, Lou, Armor Personnel (C), ON, *253*
Earle, Holland R., Executive Strategies, Inc. (C), GA, *337*
Edmond, Bruce, Corporate Recruiters Ltd. (C), BC, *300*
Erlanger, Richard A., Erlanger Assoc. (R), CT, *60*
Extract, Raymond L., Raymond L. Extract & Assoc. (R), CA, *64*
Farmer, David W., Whitney Smith Co. (C), TX, *620*
Fishel, Richard A., Fishel HR Assoc., Inc. (C), AZ, *341*
Flanagan, Robert M., Robert M. Flanagan & Assoc., Ltd. (R), NY, *68*
Flynn, Jerry, J. G. Flynn & Assoc. Inc. (R), BC, *69*
Franchot, Douglas W., Wood, Franchot Inc. (R), MN, *224*
Frankovich, John, BRW Search (C), MN, *275*
Frazier, Steven M., Sanford Rose Assoc. - Philadelphia North (C), PA, *570*
Frisch, Gerald, Gerald Frisch Assoc., Inc. (R), NY, *72*
Gabel, Greg, Canny, Bowen Inc. (R), NY, *28*
Gaines, Jay, Jay Gaines & Company, Inc. (R), NY, *74*
Gélinas, Normand, Yves Plouffe & Assoc. (R), QE, *165*
Grantham, John D., Grantham & Co., Inc. (R), NC, *81*
Grebenstein, Charles R., Skott/Edwards Consultants (R), NJ, *192*
Green, John A., JAG Group (R), MO, *105*
Grimm, Peter G., Nordeman Grimm, Inc. (R), NY, *152*
Gundersen, Steven G., Gundersen Partners, L.L.C. (R), NY, *83*
Hale, Maureen D., Hale Assoc. (R), IL, *84*
Hannock, III, Elwin W., Flynn, Hannock, Inc. (R), CT, *69*
Hartig, Dave, The Angus Group, Ltd. (C), OH, *251*
Healey, David, Healey Executive Search, Inc. (R), MN, *88*
Hedman, Kent R., Hedman & Assoc. (R), TX, *89*
Heinschel, Phil, Phillips Personnel/Search (C), CO, *510*
Heinze, David, Heinze & Assoc. Inc. (R), MN, *91*
Heller, Phillip, Heller Kil Assoc., Inc. (C), FL, *375*
Henn, Jr., George W., G. W. Henn & Co. (R), OH, *91*
Hernandez, Rafael E., SearchCorp (C), FL, *577*
Hite, III, William A., Hite Executive Search (R), OH, *94*
Holley, Ray, Austin Group Int'l./Marlar Int'l. (R), TX, *9*
Hopkins, Chester A., Handy HRM (R), NY, *86*
Horton, Robert H., Horton Int'l. Inc. (R), NY, *96*
Howe, William S., Hunt & Howe Inc. (R), NY, *99*
Huebner, Mary C., Hire Authority, Inc. (C), MI, *378*
Hunt, James E., Hunt & Howe Inc. (R), NY, *99*
Hyman, Derry, Hyman & Assoc. (C), TX, *386*
Jacobs, James W., Callan Assoc., Ltd. (R), IL, *27*
Jacobs, Judith, The Rubicon Group (C), AZ, *547*
James, E. Pendleton, Pendleton James Assoc., Inc. (R), NY, *105*
Jeffers, Richard B., Dieckmann & Assoc., Ltd. (R), IL, *51*
Jerome, Gerald E., Jerome & Co. (C), CA, *398*
Johnson, Carl A., International Management Services Inc. (R), IL, *102*
Johnson, Stanley C., Johnson & Company (R), CT, *107*
Kaye, Francine C., MedSearch Resources, Inc. (C), FL, *478*
Keefe, Steve, The Search America Group Inc. (C), OH, *573*
Klemmer, Raymond J., Raymond J. Klemmer & Assoc. (R), NY, *116*
Koller, Jr., Edward R., Howard-Sloan Assoc. (C), NY, *381*
Koller, Jr., Edward R., Jerry Fields Assoc. (C), NY, *340*
Koller, Jr., Edward R., The Howard-Sloan-Koller Group (R), NY, *97*
Koren, Michael, Koren, Rogers Assoc. Inc. (R), NY, *117*
Krauss, Jack, J. Krauss Assoc. (R), FL, *120*
Kuntz, William A., Management Recruiters of Indianapolis (C), IN, *448*
Lanctot, Dominique, Matte Consulting Group Inc. (R), QE, *138*
Lange, Jack, Lange & Assoc., Inc. (C), IN, *412*
Langford, K. R. Dick, The Langford Search, Inc. (C), AL, *412*
Larkin, Dick, Larkin & Co. (R), CA, *125*
Leff, Ilene J., Richard A. Eisner & Co., LLP (R), NY, *57*
Lehman, Neal G., Sherwood Lehman Massucco, Inc. (R), CA, *189*
Levine, Alan M., MB Inc. Executive Search (C), NY, *473*
Lewis, Bill, Adams & Assoc. Int'l. (R), IL, *1*
Lewis, Marc D., Handy HRM (R), NY, *86*

RECRUITER SPECIALTIES

Lipe, Jerold L., Compass Group Ltd. (R), MI, *38*
Livingston, Hyman, The P & L Group (C), NY, *500*
Livingston, Peter R., Livingston, Robert & Co. (R), CT, *130*
Locke, Jr., M. Fred, Locke & Assoc. (R), NC, *131*
Lockton, Kathy, StratfordGroup (R), CA, *203*
Lyon, Jenny K., Marra Peters & Partners (R), NC, *136*
Mangum, William T., Thomas Mangum Co. (R), CA, *208*
Manson, Phyllis, BG & Assoc. (C), MD, *266*
Marra, Jr., John, Marra Peters & Partners (R), NJ, *136*
Massucco, Harry A., Sherwood Lehman Massucco, Inc. (R), CA, *189*
Masterson, Louis T., Louis Thomas Masterson & Co. (R), OH, *138*
Matte, Richard, Matte Consulting Group Inc. (R), QE, *138*
McCarthy, Deborah, The Whyte Group, Inc. (R), MD, *220*
McElmeel, Joseph J., Brooke Chase Assoc., Inc. (R), IL, *24*
McKenna, Elaine, Weterrings & Agnew, Inc. (C), NY, *619*
McPolin, James B., Advantage Partners, Inc. (R), OH, *2*
Migdol, Kenneth, Ramm Search (C), NY, *528*
Miner, David B., The Curtiss Group International (R), FL, *44*
Miners, Richard A., Sedlar & Miners (R), NY, *188*
Morrisey, Jim, Fortune Personnel Consultants of San Antonio, Inc. (C), TX, *350*
Mruk, Edwin S., Mruk & E.M.A. Partners (R), NY, *148*
Murphy, Irene, StratfordGroup (R), CA, *203*
Murphy, Patrick J., P. J. Murphy & Assoc., Inc. (R), WI, *150*
Nadherny, Pete, The Angus Group, Ltd. (C), OH, *251*
Nathasingh, Steve, Growth Strategies, Inc. (R), FL, *83*
Neff, Thomas J., SpencerStuart (R), NY, *196*
Nicholson, Philip J., P. J. Nicholson & Assoc. (C), IL, *493*
Nordeman, Jacques C., Nordeman Grimm, Inc. (R), NY, *152*
Noyes, Jim, Sales Consultants - Bristol County (C), MA, *559*
O'Brien, Timothy M., O'Brien & Bell (R), OH, *153*
Ogden, Dayton, SpencerStuart (R), CT, *196*
Oliveira, Beatriz J., Priority Executive Search (C), FL, *518*
Palma, Frank R., Goodrich & Sherwood Assoc., Inc. (R), NJ, *80*
Palos, Michael V., Kelly Associates (R), PA, *112*
Parenica, Jim, Parenica & Co. (R), NC, *159*
Parry, William H., Horton Int'l. Inc. (R), CA, *96*
Parsons, Allison, Barton Assoc., Inc. (R), TX, *12*
Pezim, Steven G., The Bedford Consulting Group Inc. (R), ON, *15*
Powell, Mike, Marc-Allen Assoc., Inc. (C), FL, *469*
Prusak, Conrad E., Ethos Consulting, Inc. (R), CA, *61*
Reinecke, G., Reinecke & Assoc. (C), NJ, *533*
Richner, George A., Search Assoc., Inc. (C), NJ, *574*
Riddle, James E., Riddle & McGrath LLC (R), GA, *178*
Rodriguez, George L., InteliSearch, Inc. (R), CT, *102*
Romaniw, Michael J., A la Carte Int'l., Inc. (R), VA, *1*
Rooney, Joseph J., Rooney Assoc., Inc. (R), IL, *181*
Rose, John M., The Curtiss Group International (R), FL, *44*
Rosenow, Richard, Heath/Norton Assoc., Inc. (R), NY, *89*
Salmela, Alexander K., A.K.S. Assoc., Ltd. (R), MA, *1*
Satterfield, Jr., Richard W., Satterfield & Assoc., Inc. (R), OH, *184*
Schatz, Jr., William G., The Schatz Company (C), MO, *571*
Schiavone, Mary Rose, Canny, Bowen Inc. (R), NY, *28*
Schneiderman, Sheila, Management Resource Assoc., Inc. (C), FL, *467*
Schulz, Bill, Holloway Schulz & Partners (C), BC, *380*
Sedlar, Jeri L., Sedlar & Miners (R), NY, *188*
Sherwood, Andrew, Goodrich & Sherwood Assoc., Inc. (R), NY, *79*
Sherwood, Robert F., Sherwood Lehman Massucco, Inc. (R), CA, *189*
Shetler, James W., Professional Personnel Services (C), IA, *520*
Shetler, Patricia A., Professional Personnel Services (C), IA, *520*
Sheweloff, William J., McCray, Shriver, Eckdahl & Assoc., Inc. (R), CA, *140*
Sklut, Eric, Executive Recruitment Specialists, Inc. (R), NC, *63*
Snow, Thomas J., The Search America Group Inc. (C), OH, *573*
Southworth, David E., Michigan Consulting Group (R), MI, *144*
Spadaro, Raymond, David Perry Assoc. (C), NJ, *308*
Spann, Richard E., Goodrich & Sherwood Assoc., Inc. (R), CT, *80*
Sted, Eric, The Search America Group Inc. (C), OH, *573*
Stewart, Harvey, Executive Registry (C), QE, *334*
Stewart, Larry, American Resources Corp. (C), IL, *248*
Stoller, Richard S., Heath/Norton Assoc., Inc. (R), NY, *89*
Sur, William K., Canny, Bowen Inc. (R), NY, *28*
Tabb, Roosevelt, Tabb & Assoc. (R), OH, *205*
Taylor, Charles E., LAI Ward Howell (R), GA, *123*
Telford, Jr., John H., Telford, Adams & Alexander (R), CA, *208*
Tholke, William E., Boardroom Consultants/Kenny Kindler Tholke (R), NY, *19*
Thornton, Bill, C. M. Management Services, Inc. (R), KY, *26*
Toole, Thomas J., Management Recruiters of Laguna Hills (C), CA, *440*
Vangel, Peter V., Access/Resources, Inc. (C), MA, *234*
Villareal, Morey J., Villareal & Assoc., Inc. (R), OK, *214*
Visnich, L. Christine, Bason Associates (R), OH, *13*
Vlcek, Thomas J., Vlcek & Company, Inc. (R), CA, *214*
Wallace, William J., Wallace Management Co. (R), TN, *215*
Warren, Richard, Cole, Warren & Long, Inc. (R), PA, *37*
Webster, William L., S. B. Webster & Associates (R), MA, *217*
Wegner, Carl, Wegner & Assoc. (C), WI, *617*
Weiss, Dick, Richard, Wayne & Roberts (C), TX, *536*
Wittlin, Brian D., Brian Assoc., Inc. (C), NY, *273*
Wood, Michael D., Wood, Franchot Inc. (R), MN, *224*
Wooller, Edmund A. M., Windsor International (R), GA, *222*
Wright, J. Robert, Bob Wright Recruiting, Inc. (C), CT, *625*
Zinn, Michael D., Michael D. Zinn & Assoc., Inc. (R), NJ, *227*

Generalists

Abbott, Brenda L., Abbott Associates (R), CA, *1*
Abécassis, Pauline P., Abécassis Conseil (R), QE, *1*
Abrams, Burton J., B. J. Abrams & Assoc. Inc. (C), IL, *233*
Abruzzo, James, A.T. Kearney Executive Search (R), NY, *111*
Adams, Oscar, Shore Asociados Ejecutivos, S. A. de C.V. (R), MX, *190*
Allen, Leslie, Straube Associates (R), MA, *203*
Allen, Rita, Gatti & Assoc. (C), MA, *355*
Alvear, Clemente, Brandywine Retained Ventures, Inc. (R), CT, *22*
Ambler, Peter W., Peter W. Ambler Co. (R), TX, *5*
Anderson, Kristine M., Rollo Assoc. (R), CA, *181*
Anderson, Richard L., Grant Cooper & Assoc., Inc. (R), MO, *81*
Antoniazzi, Marie, Neail Behringer Consultants Inc. (R), NY, *15*

Antonochi, Pat, Cypress Int'l., Inc. (R), FL, *45*
Arend, Lewis, McKinley•Arend Int'l. (R), TX, *141*
Arnold, Sheridan J., William B. Arnold Assoc., Inc. (R), CO, *7*
Arnold, William B., William B. Arnold Assoc., Inc. (R), CO, *7*
Aruza, Al, Cornell Group Int'l. Consulting, Inc. (R), NY, *41*
Ascher, Susan, The Ascher Group (R), NJ, *7*
Atkinson, Faith, Lamon + Stuart + Michaels Inc. (R), ON, *124*
Aydelotte, G. Thomas, Ingram & Aydelotte, Inc. (R), NY, *101*
Baker, Gerry, A.T. Kearney Executive Search (R), ON, *111*
Baker, Howard, The Johnson Group, Unlimited (C), NY, *400*
Baldwin, II, Arthur D., Artgo, Inc. (R), OH, *7*
Balian, Christina L., Compass Group Ltd. (R), MI, *38*
Ballos, Constantine J., Ballos & Co., Inc. (R), NJ, *11*
Ballos, H. P., Ballos & Co., Inc. (R), NJ, *11*
Barbour, Mary Beth, Tully/Woodmansee Int'l., Inc. (R), WA, *212*
Barnette, Fred A., Fred A. Barnette & Assoc. (R), NC, *11*
Barnette, Fred A., Fred A. Barnette & Assoc. (R), NJ, *11*
Barton, Gary, Barton Assoc., Inc. (R), TX, *12*
Basil, Marvin B., Marvel Consultants, Inc. (C), OH, *472*
Bastoky, Bruce M., January Management Group (R), OH, *105*
Baxter, Sheryl, Vincent Lee Assoc. (C), NY, *415*
Beach, William L., Beach Executive Search Inc. (R), FL, *14*
Beaupre, Joe, Price Waterhouse Executive Search (R), QE, *168*
Beechey, Lynn, Connors, Lovell & Assoc. Inc. (C), ON, *296*
Behringer, Neail, Neail Behringer Consultants Inc. (R), NY, *15*
Belen, Linda A., DNPitchon Assoc. (R), NJ, *165*
Bell, Michael, SpencerStuart (R), FL, *197*
Beller, Robert, T. H. Hunter, Inc. (C), MN, *599*
Belletieri, Nancy, Probe Technology (C), PA, *519*
Belletieri, Thomas F., Probe Technology (C), PA, *519*
Bellontine, Joanne, Brandywine Retained Ventures, Inc. (R), CT, *22*
Belt, Joy Reed, Joy Reed Belt Search Consultants, Inc. (R), OK, *15*
Bennett, Jr., Robert C., Bennett Search & Consulting Co. (R), FL, *16*
Berman, Lynn, Goodkind Assoc. Inc. (C), NY, *360*
Bhandari, Parul, Tarbex (C), DC, *599*
Biestek, Paul J., Paul J. Biestek Assoc., Inc. (R), IL, *17*
Blackshaw, Brian, Blackshaw, Olmstead, Lynch & Koenig (R), GA, *18*
Blecksmith, Edward L., Larsen, Whitney, Blecksmith & Zilliacus, Inc. (R), CA, *125*
Blumenthal, Joan H., Lauer, Sbarbaro Assoc., EMA Partners Int'l. (R), IL, *126*
Boettcher, Jack W., Boettcher Assoc. (R), WI, *19*
Bond, James, People Management Northeast, Inc. (R), CT, *162*
Bono, Jeffrey D., Michael Latas & Assoc., Inc. (R), MO, *126*
Boone, John C., John C. Boone & Co. (R), IL, *19*
Booth, III, Otis, A.T. Kearney Executive Search (R), CA, *111*
Boren, Susan, SpencerStuart (R), MN, *197*
Boujemaa, Ben, Hunt Patton & Brazeal, Inc. (C), TX, *385*
Bouzan, Paul X., The Executive Group, Inc. (R), CA, *62*
Bowles, Mary, RMA Search (R), TN, *179*
Bradshaw, Jack W., StratfordGroup (R), TX, *203*
Bray, A. D., Rodzik & Assoc., Inc. (R), NC, *180*
Brest, Dan, Capital Consulting Group, Inc. (R), MD, *28*
Bronson, Daniel B., Lasher Assoc. (R), FL, *125*
Brook, Marsha, C. M. Management Services, Inc. (R), KY, *26*
Brookman, Geoffrey, Brookman Associates (C), NY, *274*
Brooks, Bernard E., Bernard E. Brooks & Assoc., Inc. (R), SC, *24*
Brooks, Jan, The Personnel Network, Inc. (C), NC, *509*
Brudno, Robert J., Savoy Partners, Ltd. (R), DC, *185*
Buckingham, Derrick R., The Hollins Group, Inc. (R), IL, *95*
Buckman, Bob, Hunt Patton & Brazeal, Inc. (C), TX, *385*
Bump, Gerald J., Foster Partners (R), GA, *70*
Burns, Joseph R., Joseph R. Burns & Assoc., Inc. (R), NJ, *25*
Burns, Patrick, Tekworx, Inc. (C), TX, *604*
Butler, Robert J., Smith, Roth & Squires (R), AZ, *194*
Byrd, Chantel, Performance Resources, Inc. (C), RI, *507*
Caldwell, Clarke, Carnegie Partners, Inc. (R), IL, *30*
Campbell, Joanna Williams, Sterling Int'l. Management Recruitment, Ltd. Inc. (C), NC, *592*
Campbell, Margaret, PricewaterhouseCoopers Executive Search (R), ON, *168*
Canavan, Patricia, United Personnel Services (C), MA, *611*
Capello, Christa A., Carnegie Partners, Inc. (R), IL, *30*
Caplan, Deborah, PricewaterhouseCoopers Executive Search (R), ON, *168*
Carlson, Gregory P., Carlson & Czeswik (R), IA, *30*
Carpenter, Eric G., Carpenter, Shackleton & Company (R), IL, *30*
Carris, S. Joseph, Carris, Jackowitz Assoc. (R), NY, *30*
Carter, James D., Bennett Search & Consulting Co. (R), FL, *16*
Carter, Jane, Bennett Search & Consulting Co. (R), FL, *16*
Cary, Con, Cary & Assoc. (R), FL, *31*
Casey, Steve, Orion Int'l. Consulting Group, Inc. (C), TX, *500*
Cassady, Pat, Michael Shirley Assoc. Inc. (R), KS, *190*
Cecilio, Cesca, Montgomery West (R), CA, *146*
Chadick, Susan L., Gould, McCoy & Chadick, Inc. (R), NY, *80*
Chambers, Judy, Global Consulting Group Inc. (C), ON, *358*
Chandler, Joseph J., Joseph Chandler & Assoc., Inc. (R), IL, *33*
Charette, Anne, The Burke Group (C), ON, *276*
Chermak, Carolyn A., Management Recruiters of Orange County, N.Y., Inc. (C), NJ, *453*
Cherney, Lynn K., Martin Partners, L.L.C. (R), IL, *137*
Chrisman, Timothy, Chrisman & Co. Inc. (R), CA, *34*
Christoff, Matt, SpencerStuart (R), MN, *197*
Citarella, Richard A., A.T. Kearney Executive Search (R), GA, *111*
Cizek, John T., Cizek Assoc., Inc. (R), IL, *35*
Cizek, Marti J., Cizek Assoc., Inc. (R), AZ, *35*
Clark, Donna, Clark Personnel Service, Inc. (C), AL, *292*
Clarkson, Dave, Lamon + Stuart + Michaels Inc. (R), ON, *124*
Clauhsen, Elizabeth, Savoy Partners, Ltd. (R), DC, *185*
Clement, Laura K., Stroman Int'l., Inc. (R), CO, *204*
Cohen, Samuel N., Professions, Inc. (C), OH, *523*
Coleman, J. Kevin, J. Kevin Coleman & Assoc., Inc. (R), CA, *37*
Coleman, John A., Boardroom Consultants/ Kenny Kindler Tholke (R), NY, *19*
Coleman, William, Stephens Assoc. Ltd., Inc. (R), OH, *200*
Collins, Kenneth B., Executive Search Partners (R), NY, *63*
Conroy, Daniel J., Michael Latas & Assoc., Inc. (R), MO, *126*
Conroy, Martin, T. H. Hunter, Inc. (C), MN, *599*
Cook, Amanda, Partnervision Consulting Group Inc. (R), ON, *160*
Cook, Dennis F., MESA, Inc. (R), CO, *143*
Cook, Thomas, Cypress Int'l., Inc. (R), FL, *45*
Cooper, B. V., QVS Int'l. (R), GA, *170*
Cooper, Norman, Cooper Assoc., Inc. (C), NY, *298*

RECRUITER SPECIALTIES

Cooper, Robert M., The Cooper Executive Search Group Inc. (R), WI, *41*
Corrigan, Gerald F., The Corrigan Group (R), CA, *42*
Crath, Paul F., PricewaterhouseCoopers Executive Search (R), ON, *168*
Crawford, Arlen, PIC Executive Search (C), GA, *511*
Cronin, Richard J., Hodge-Cronin & Assoc., Inc. (R), IL, *94*
Croteau, Paul, KPMG Executive Search (R), MB, *119*
Crowder, Edward W., Crowder & Company (R), MI, *43*
Crowe, Thomas H., Hunter, Rowan & Crowe (C), FL, *386*
Csorba, Les, A.T. Kearney Executive Search (R), TX, *111*
Cunningham, Jack, Cypress Int'l., Inc. (R), FL, *45*
Curran, Martin, M. J. Curran & Assoc., Inc. (R), MA, *43*
Curry, Robert, KPMG Executive Search (R), ON, *119*
Curtiss, George R., Dunhill of San Francisco, Inc. (C), CA, *319*
Cusack, Peter, Cusack Consulting (R), NY, *44*
Czamanske, Peter M., Compass Group Ltd. (R), MI, *38*
Czeswik, Frederick R., Carlson & Czeswik (R), MN, *30*
Dahl, Stan, C.T.E.W. Executive Personnel Services Inc. (C), BC, *278*
Daigneault, Claude, Price Waterhouse Executive Search (R), QE, *168*
Daily, John, Christian & Timbers, Inc. (R), OH, *34*
Dale, Dick, Tully/Woodmansee Int'l., Inc. (R), MO, *212*
Danford, Dan, Neail Behringer Consultants Inc. (R), NY, *15*
Danforth, W. Michael, Hyde Danforth & Co. (R), TX, *100*
Danoff, Richard, Tschudin Inc. (R), NJ, *211*
Darling, Alan, Alan Darling Consulting (R), VT, *46*
Darter, Steven, People Management Northeast, Inc. (R), CT, *162*
Davidson, Julie, Drinkwater & Assoc. (R), MA, *55*
Davis, G. Gordon, Davis & Company (R), CA, *47*
Davis, Troy M., Davis & Company (R), CA, *47*
Daxon, Corey, Feldman Gray & Assoc. Inc. (C), ON, *339*
De Cordova, Fernando Fernandez, Shore Asociados Ejecutivos, S. A. de C.V. (R), MX, *190*
DeLaney, Patricia, Jude M. Werra & Assoc. (R), WI, *218*
Denker, Robert, Carpenter, Shackleton & Company (R), IL, *30*
Denman, Anna Marie, AMD & Associates (C), GA, *247*
Dickey, Chester W., Bowden & Co., Inc. (R), OH, *20*
Dilworth, Lawrence A., StratfordGroup (R), VA, *203*
Donald, R.J., Feldman Gray & Assoc. Inc. (C), ON, *339*
Donnelly, George J., SpencerStuart (R), TX, *197*
Dreyfus, Rita, Cypress Int'l., Inc. (R), FL, *45*
Drinkwater, Wendy A., Drinkwater & Assoc. (R), MA, *54*
Dryer, Laura, Michael Shirley Assoc. Inc. (R), KS, *190*
Dunn, Margaret A., Dunn Associates (R), PA, *55*
Durakis, Jr., Charles A., C. A. Durakis Assoc., Inc. (R), MD, *55*
Durakis, Sr., Charles A., C. A. Durakis Assoc., Inc. (R), FL, *55*
Eaton, Bob, PricewaterhouseCoopers Executive Search (R), ON, *168*
Eckhart, Kenneth V., SpencerStuart (R), FL, *197*
Edington, Patti D., Drinkwater & Assoc. (R), MA, *55*
Edwards, Edward C. P., Ingram & Aydelotte, Inc. (R), NY, *101*
Egan, Daniel K., Egan & Assoc. (R), WI, *57*
Egan, John, Egan Search Group (R), NY, *57*
Elam, Robert W., Wheeler, Moore & Elam Co. (R), TX, *219*
Elam, Jr., William J., William J. Elam & Assoc. (R), NE, *58*
Elkas, Yves, Yves Elkas Inc. (R), QE, *58*
Ellner, David M., David M. Ellner Assoc. (R), NY, *59*
Engler, Peter G., Lautz, Grotte, Engler & Swimley (R), CA, *126*
Erder, Debra, Canny, Bowen Inc. (R), NY, *28*
Esecson, Diane P., Drinkwater & Assoc. (R), MA, *55*
Esposito, Kathy, Vincent Lee Assoc. (C), NY, *415*
Estes, Susan, The Associates, HR Search Executives, Inc. (C), OK, *254*
Faber, Jill S., A.T. Kearney Executive Search (R), AZ, *111*
Fandel, Arthur J., Parsons, Anderson & Gee, Inc. (C), NY, *503*
Farris, James W., James Farris Assoc. (R), OK, *65*
Feinson, Milton M., Sales Consultants of Brockton, Inc. (C), MA, *559*
Fincher, Richard P., Phase II Management (R), CT, *164*
Finnigan Werra, Nora, Jude M. Werra & Assoc. (R), WI, *218*
Fisher, Neal, Fisher Personnel Management Services (R), CA, *68*
Flannery, Thomas T., Resources for Management (R), PA, *176*
Flores, Laura Chávez, PricewaterhouseCoopers Executive Search (R), MX, *168*
Flynn, Peter, Partnervision Consulting Group Inc. (R), ON, *160*
Fooce, Denise, Stephens Assoc. Ltd., Inc. (R), OH, *200*
Ford, Merlin B., Ford & Assoc., Inc. (C), SC, *343*
Foreman, David C., Koontz, Jeffries & Assoc., Inc. (R), FL, *117*
Foster, Kathie, Michael Latas & Assoc., Inc. (R), MO, *126*
Franco, Virginia, Shore Asociados Ejecutivos, S. A. de C.V. (R), MX, *190*
Franquemont, Jeffrey D., EFL Int'l. (R), AZ, *57*
Franquemont, William R., EFL Int'l. (R), AZ, *57*
Frantz, Sally, Martin Partners, L.L.C. (R), IL, *137*
Fraser, William, Windsor Consultants, Inc. (C), TX, *622*
Fretz, William, The 500 Granary Inc. (C), ON, *231*
Furr, C. Franklin, C. F. Furr & Co. (R), NC, *72*
Gabel, Greg, Canny, Bowen Inc. (R), NY, *28*
Gaffney, Keith, Gaffney Management Consultants (R), IL, *73*
Galbraith, Deborah M., StratfordGroup (R), OH, *203*
Gallagher, David A., Sweeney Harbert & Mummert, Inc. (R), FL, *205*
Garofolo, Frank A., StratfordGroup (R), PA, *203*
Geddes, Murray, Geddes & Rubin Management Inc. (R), ON, *76*
George, Bethany W., Rollo Assoc. (R), CA, *181*
Gerner, Jeri, Rovner Gerner & Assoc. (R), CA, *182*
Gernetzke, James, J. Gernetzke & Assoc., Inc. (C), OH, *357*
Gilbert, Jr., H. Harry, Gilbert Scott Assoc., LLC (C), MA, *357*
Giordano, Louis P., L. Patrick Group (R), NJ, *122*
Gonzalez, Romulo, Korn/Ferry, Int'l., S.A. de C.V. (R), NL, *118*
Goodkind, Peter, Goodkind Assoc. Inc. (C), NY, *360*
Gould, William E., Gould, McCoy & Chadick, Inc. (R), NY, *80*
Grady, April, BEST/World Assoc. Inc. (R), TX, *16*
Gray, Frank, Feldman Gray & Assoc. Inc. (C), ON, *339*
Grayem, Tim, The Canon Group (C), CA, *280*
Greco, Ben, Ben Greco Assoc., Inc. (C), CA, *362*
Greco, Sheila, Sheila Greco Assoc. (C), NY, *362*
Greebe, Neil, Preferred Professional Recruiters (C), OH, *516*
Green, Rita, R. Green & Assoc., Inc. (C), OH, *362*
Greene, William, Stewart/Greene & Co. of The Triad, Inc. (C), NC, *594*
Griffin, Cathy, A.T. Kearney Executive Search (R), OR, *111*
Groban, Jack L., A.T. Kearney Executive Search (R), CA, *111*

Groenekamp, William A., Groenekamp & Assoc. (C), CA, *363*
Grossberg, Robert M., Grossberg & Assoc. (R), IL, *82*
Grotte, Lawrence C., Lautz, Grotte, Engler & Swimley (R), CA, *126*
Guarino, Alan, Cornell Group Int'l. Consulting, Inc. (R), NY, *41*
Gunning, Phill, TBC, Inc. (C), KY, *600*
Habelmann, Gerald B., Habelmann & Assoc. (R), MI, *84*
Haggith, Marvin, M. A. Haggith Consultants Ltd. (R), ON, *84*
Hajek, Kathleen Lehman, Martin Partners, L.L.C. (R), IL, *137*
Hamilton, Marilyn, Fisher Personnel Management Services (R), CA, *68*
Hammond, Karla, People Management Northeast, Inc. (R), CT, *162*
Handler, William L., W. L. Handler & Assoc. (R), GA, *86*
Hanley, Alan P., Williams, Roth & Krueger, Inc. (R), IL, *221*
Hansen, David G., Ott & Hansen, Inc. (R), CA, *157*
Harbert, David O., Sweeney Harbert & Mummert, Inc. (R), FL, *205*
Harris, Joan, The Ryan Charles Group, Inc. (C), FL, *549*
Hayes, Jim, Orion Int'l. Consulting Group, Inc. (C), OH, *499*
Headden, Jr., William P., Headden Assoc. (R), WA, *88*
Healy, William C., Management Recruiters of Milwaukee-West (C), WI, *465*
Helfenbein, Sr., Robert J., Snelling Search Recruiters (C), NC, *586*
Heller, Gary A., Heller Assoc., Ltd. (R), IL, *91*
Heller, Steven A., Martin H. Bauman Assoc., Inc. (R), NY, *13*
Hellinger, Audrey, Martin H. Bauman Assoc., Inc. (R), IL, *14*
Hensley, Bert C., Morgan Samuels Co. (R), CA, *147*
Hergenrather, Edmund R., Hergenrather & Co. (R), WA, *92*
Hergenrather, Richard A., Hergenrather & Co. (R), WA, *92*
Herring, Bill, Herring & Assoc. (C), AR, *376*
Herrmann, Gerlinde, The Herrmann Group Ltd. (R), ON, *92*
Hersey, Jeffrey D., J. D. Hersey & Assoc. (C), OH, *377*
Hertan, Richard L., Executive Manning Corp. (R), FL, *63*
Hetzel, William G., The Hetzel Group, Inc. (R), IL, *93*
Hewitt, Rives D., The Dalley Hewitt Co. (R), GA, *45*
Hill, Emery, MSI Int'l. (C), NC, *487*
Hill, Frank P., Frank P. Hill (R), MX, *93*
Hill, Jennifer, Lamon + Stuart + Michaels Inc. (R), ON, *124*
Hill, Paul, Cypress Int'l., Inc. (R), FL, *45*
Hoevel, Michael J., Poirier, Hoevel & Co. (R), CA, *166*
Hogan, Sandra M., Larsen, Whitney, Blecksmith & Zilliacus, Inc. (R), CA, *125*
Hoglund, Gerald C., Hoglund & Assoc., Inc. (R), IL, *94*
Hohman, Daniel G., Bosco-Hubert & Assoc. (C), KS, *270*
Hokanson, Mark D., Crowder & Company (R), MI, *43*
Holland, Rose Mary, Price Waterhouse Executive Search (R), AB, *168*
Hollins, Lawrence I., The Hollins Group, Inc. (R), IL, *95*
Hollis, Robert W., Carnegie Partners, Inc. (R), IL, *30*
Horne, Tony, Herring & Assoc. (C), AR, *376*
Houze, Geoffry Clayton, William C. Houze & Co. (R), CA, *96*
Houze, William C., William C. Houze & Co. (R), CA, *96*
Howard, Tracy L., Brush Creek Partners (R), MO, *24*
Howe, Jr., Edward R., Howe & Assoc. (R), PA, *97*
Huddleston, Linda, Hunt Patton & Brazeal, Inc. (C), OK, *385*
Huddleston, Linda, Tekworx, Inc. (C), OK, *604*
Hutt, Wayne, W. Hutt Management Resources Ltd. (R), ON, *100*
Hwang, Anthony T., Lindsey & Co., Inc. (R), CT, *129*
Hyde, W. Jerry, Hyde Danforth & Co. (R), TX, *100*
Hykes, Don, A.T. Kearney Executive Search (R), MN, *111*
Ibsen, John, Stewart/Greene & Co. of The Triad, Inc. (C), NC, *594*
Imely, Larry S., StratfordGroup (R), OH, *203*
Ingram, D. John, Ingram & Aydelotte, Inc. (R), NY, *101*
Irving, Jeffrey J., Jeffrey Irving Assoc., Inc. (R), VA, *104*
Israel, Ehud, Search Innovations, Inc. (R), PA, *187*
Izzo, Thomas M., Spear-Izzo Assoc., LLC (C), GA, *589*
Jackowitz, Ronald N., Carris, Jackowitz Assoc. (R), NJ, *31*
Jackson, Ron, Ron Jackson & Assoc. (C), GA, *396*
Jacobs, David M., Jacobs & Co. (R), CT, *105*
Jadewald, James, Tekworx, Inc. (C), CO, *604*
Jagielo, Thomas A., Martin Partners, L.L.C. (R), IL, *137*
Jensen, Don, J. Gernetzke & Assoc., Inc. (C), OH, *357*
Jesberg, Gary H., Michael Latas & Assoc., Inc. (R), MO, *126*
Jochems, Julie A., StratfordGroup (R), OH, *203*
Jock, Lawrence M., Professional Search, Inc. (C), CO, *522*
John, Harold A., John & Powers, Inc. (R), MO, *106*
Johns, Joel, Brandywine Retained Ventures, Inc. (R), CT, *22*
Johnson, Priscilla, The Johnson Group, Unlimited (C), NY, *400*
Johnson, Robert, A.T. Kearney Executive Search (R), TX, *111*
Jones, Bonita, Global Career Services, Inc. (C), NY, *358*
Jones, Courtney A., The Hollins Group, Inc. (R), IL, *95*
Jones, Francis E., Jones Management Co. (R), CT, *108*
Jones, Frank, Global Career Services, Inc. (C), NY, *358*
Jones, Geoffrey J., Precision Executive Search (C), AZ, *516*
Joure, Sylvia A., Frye/Joure & Assoc., Inc. (C), TN, *353*
Juarez, Lyn A., Stoopen Asociados, S.C./ EMA Partners Int'l. (R), MX, *202*
Kalyna, Adrianne, Martin Partners, L.L.C. (R), IL, *137*
Kane, Michael, Kane & Assoc. (C), TX, *403*
Kaplan, Gary, Gary Kaplan & Assoc. (R), CA, *109*
Kaplan, Robert, The Executive Group, Inc. (R), CA, *62*
Katz, Arthur, Management Recruiters of Atlanta North, Inc. (C), GA, *446*
Kay, Jim, Jim Kay & Assoc. (C), IL, *404*
Kay, Phyllis, William Bell Assoc., Inc. (C), NJ, *263*
Keenan, James, Brentwood Int'l. (R), CA, *23*
Kelly, Ron, Hunter Int'l., Inc. (R), CT, *100*
Kelso, Pat, Barton Assoc., Inc. (R), TX, *12*
Kennedy, David, David Warwick Kennedy & Assoc. (R), BC, *112*
Kent, Melvin, Kent & Assoc. (R), OH, *113*
Kessler, Vivian, Search Innovations, Inc. (R), PA, *187*
Kinser, Richard, Richard Kinser & Assoc. (R), NY, *115*
Kirby, William P., Kirby Assoc. (R), PA, *115*
Klages, Constance W., International Management Advisors, Inc. (R), NY, *103*
Knutson, David A., North American Recruiters, Inc. (R), MN, *153*
Koenig, Barbara, Royal Assoc. (C), CA, *547*
Koenig, Joel S., Blackshaw, Olmstead, Lynch & Koenig (R), GA, *18*
Kolh, Barbara, Executive Solutions (R), MN, *64*
Koontz, Donald N., Koontz, Jeffries & Assoc., Inc. (R), FL, *117*
Kopsick, Joseph M., SpencerStuart (R), IL, *197*
Kost, Harold, Rand Thompson Executive Search Consultants (C), NY, *528*
Kozachok, Peter D., Executive Solutions (R), MN, *64*
Krell, Richard B., Russell Reynolds Assoc., Inc. (R), CA, *176*
Krumel, Richard G., The Perkins Group (R), NC, *162*

RECRUITER SPECIALTIES

Kunzer, Diane S., Kunzer Assoc., Ltd. (R), IL, *121*
Kunzer, William J., Kunzer Assoc., Ltd. (R), IL, *121*
Kuric, Mary J., Juno Systems, Inc. (C), NY, *402*
Kurkowski, A. R., Koontz, Jeffries & Assoc., Inc. (R), FL, *117*
Kurosky, John, John Kurosky & Assoc. (R), CA, *122*
Kusnetz, Ellen G., Business Solutions Worldwide, Inc. (C), NJ, *277*
Lamon, Wayne, Lamon + Stuart + Michaels Inc. (R), ON, *124*
Lampert, Bill, Michael Stern Assoc., Inc./Euram (R), ON, *200*
Lardner, Lucy, Tully/Woodmansee Int'l., Inc. (R), NJ, *212*
Larsen, C. Lars, The Personnel Network, Inc. (C), SC, *508*
Lasher, Charles M., Lasher Assoc. (R), FL, *125*
Laskowski, Peter R., Goodrich & Sherwood Assoc., Inc. (R), MX, *80*
Latas, Michael, Michael Latas & Assoc., Inc. (R), MO, *126*
Latas, Richard L., Michael Latas & Assoc., Inc. (R), MO, *126*
Lauderback, David R., A.T. Kearney Executive Search (R), OH, *111*
Lautz, Lindsay A., Lautz, Grotte, Engler & Swimley (R), CA, *126*
Lavender, Steven M., Morgan/Webber, Inc. (R), NY, *147*
Lavoie, Gille, The 500 Granary Inc. (C), QE, *231*
Lavoie, Leo R., Carter, Lavoie Associates (C), RI, *285*
Leduc, Normand, Groupe Ranger Inc. (C), QE, *364*
Lee, Brian, Vincent Lee Assoc. (C), NY, *415*
Lee, Kenneth D., Special Markets Group, Inc. (R), GA, *195*
Lee, Vincent, Vincent Lee Assoc. (C), NY, *415*
Lefebvre, Lynn, Partnervision Consulting Group Inc. (R), ON, *160*
Lehman, Victor J., V. J. Lehman & Assoc., Inc. (R), CO, *127*
Leib, Bruce, The Ryan Charles Group, Inc. (C), FL, *549*
Leinwetter, Theresa, Michael Shirley Assoc. Inc. (R), KS, *190*
Lempicke, Martha, The Hunter Group (C), NC, *385*
Lempicke, Todd, The Hunter Group (C), NC, *385*
Leonard, William C., Michael Latas & Assoc., Inc. (R), MO, *126*
Leone, Nicholas A., Conex Inc./InterSearch (R), NY, *39*
Lewis, Lorraine, Lewis Companies Inc. (R), ON, *129*
Lheureau, J. Randall, Spear-Izzo Assoc., LLC (C), PA, *589*
Liggett, Wilson M., Michael/Merrill (C), KS, *481*
Lilienthal, Russ, Working Relationships, Inc. (C), MN, *624*
Lindsey, Lary L., Lindsey & Co., Inc. (R), CT, *129*
Linton, Leonard M., Byron Leonard Int'l., Inc. (R), CA, *26*
Lipe, Jerold L., Compass Group Ltd. (R), IL, *38*
Lipe, Jerold L., Compass Group Ltd. (R), MI, *38*
Littman, Cheryl L., The Penn Partners, Inc. (R), PA, *162*
Litvin, Bruce, Windsor Consultants, Inc. (C), TX, *622*
Llaguno, Juan F., Korn/Ferry, Int'l., S.A. de C.V. (R), NL, *118*
Loeb, Stephen H., Grant Cooper & Assoc., Inc. (R), MO, *81*
Long, Keith A., Christopher and Long (C), MO, *291*
Lopez, Christina, Conex Inc./InterSearch (R), NY, *39*
Lovas, W. Carl, Ray & Berndtson/Lovas Stanley (R), ON, *172*
Lovell, Andrée, Connors, Lovell & Assoc. Inc. (C), ON, *296*
Lowery, Andrew, Search Int'l. (R), MA, *187*
Lucas, III, Charles C., The McAulay Firm (R), NC, *139*
Lunn, Jerry D., Brush Creek Partners (R), MO, *24*
MacCarthy, Dave, Michael Stern Assoc., Inc./Euram (R), ON, *200*
MacDougall, Andrew J., SpencerStuart (R), ON, *197*
Madrigal, Debbie, William Bell Assoc., Inc. (C), NJ, *263*
Mae, Bonita, TE, Inc. (C), IL, *600*
Magee, Harrison R., Bowden & Co., Inc. (R), OH, *20*
Magennis, Sean, Kingsley Allen Partners Inc. (R), ON, *114*
Marcovich, Carol, CMC Search Consultants (C), IL, *293*
Mark, John L., J. L. Mark Assoc., Inc. (R), CO, *135*
Mark, Lynne B., J. L. Mark Assoc., Inc. (R), CO, *135*
Marling, Richard A., R M Associates (R), OH, *171*
Marshall, Don, The Marshall Group (R), IL, *137*
Martin, Charles E., Management Recruiters of Birmingham-South, Inc. (C), AL, *438*
Martin, Jr., Theodore B., Martin Partners, L.L.C. (R), IL, *137*
Martinez, Stephen A., Stephens Assoc. Ltd., Inc. (R), OH, *200*
Maschal, Chuck, Maschal/Connors Inc. (R), NJ, *137*
Massar, Joy V., Egan & Assoc. (R), WI, *57*
Massey, Bruce, Massey-Horton Int'l. (R), ON, *138*
Massey, III, H. Heath, Robison & Associates (R), NC, *180*
Matthews, James M., Stanton Chase Int'l. (R), MD, *199*
Mattox, Robert D., SpencerStuart (R), GA, *197*
Maude, Elaine, The Burke Group (C), ON, *276*
Maximo, Anita, The Gabriel Group (C), PA, *354*
Mazzitelli, Teresa, The Mazzitelli Group, Ltd. (R), MN, *139*
McAulay, Jr., Albert L., The McAulay Firm (R), NC, *139*
McCormick, Brian D., The McCormick Group (C), VA, *474*
McCormick, William J., The McCormick Group (C), VA, *474*
McCoy, Millington F., Gould, McCoy & Chadick, Inc. (R), NY, *80*
McDonald, Elizabeth A., R. H. Larsen & Assoc., Inc. (R), FL, *125*
McDonald, Stanleigh B., McDonald Assoc. Int'l. (R), IL, *140*
McElroy, Brian, Drinkwater & Assoc. (R), MA, *55*
McFaul, William, Management Assoc. (C), MD, *424*
McGurn, Sharman, B. J. Abrams & Assoc. Inc. (C), IL, *233*
McInerney, Thomas K., Lindsey & Co., Inc. (R), CT, *129*
McIvor, Jim, Christmas, McIvor & Assoc. Inc. (C), ON, *290*
McKinley, James M., McKinley•Arend Int'l. (R), TX, *141*
McLean, B. Keith, PricewaterhouseCoopers Executive Search (R), ON, *168*
McLean, E. Peter, SpencerStuart (R), NY, *196*
McMahon, Mark J., A.T. Kearney Executive Search (R), CT, *111*
McManners, Donald E., McManners Assoc., Inc. (R), CA, *142*
McMillin, Robert, Price Waterhouse Executive Search (R), BC, *168*
McMullan, Don, The Associates, HR Search Executives, Inc. (C), OK, *254*
McNally, Glenna Q., Cusack Consulting (R), NY, *44*
McNichols, Walter B., Gary Kaplan & Assoc. (R), CA, *109*
McSweeney, Arlene, The Chatham Group, Ltd. (C), CT, *289*
Meadows, C. David, Right/McKee Consulting Group (C), TX, *537*
Meagher-Clare, Patricia, SpencerStuart (R), IL, *197*
Meier, J. Dale, Grant Cooper & Assoc., Inc. (R), MO, *81*
Melancon, Robert M., Melancon & Co. (R), TX, *143*
Messett, III, William J., Messett Assoc., Inc. (R), FL, *143*
Mestepey, John T., A.T. Kearney Executive Search (R), FL, *111*
Metzger, Susan, Techstaff Inc. (C), WI, *603*
Meyers, Ron, Feldman Gray & Assoc. Inc. (C), ON, *339*
Michaels, Lynda, Cypress Int'l., Inc. (R), FL, *45*
Milar, John F., Fenzel Milar Assoc. (C), OH, *339*

Miller, Howard, Doleman Enterprises (R), VA, *53*
Mirtz, P. John, Mirtz Morice, Inc. (R), CT, *145*
Mistura, Dan, Professional Personnel Consultants, Inc. (C), MI, *521*
Mitchell, Jr., John R., Management Recruiters of Muskegon (C), MI, *451*
Mitchell, Judith, Stephens Assoc. Ltd., Inc. (R), OH, *200*
Mitchell, Kyle, Ray & Berndtson/Tanton Mitchell (R), BC, *172*
Mitchell, Kyle, Ray & Berndtson/Tanton Mitchell (R), BC, *173*
Moffitt, Timothy D., Moffitt Int'l., Inc. (R), NC, *146*
Monte, Linda, Vincent Lee Assoc. (C), NY, *415*
Montgomery, Thomas, Techstaff Inc. (C), WI, *603*
Moore, Anne, KPMG Executive Search (R), BC, *119*
Moore, Bill, Marc Nichols Assoc., Inc. (C), NY, *493*
Moore, Connie, C. A. Moore & Assoc., Inc. (C), MN, *484*
Moore, Mark H., Wheeler, Moore & Elam Co. (R), TX, *219*
Morgan, Hillary A., Lindsey & Co., Inc. (R), CT, *129*
Morgan, Joyce, People Management Mid-South, LLC (R), TN, *162*
Morgan, Richard, Ray & Berndtson/Lovas Stanley (R), ON, *172*
Morgan, Richard, Ray & Berndtson/Lovas Stanley (R), ON, *173*
Morice, James L., Mirtz Morice, Inc. (R), CT, *145*
Morrison, Stephen, Lewis Companies Inc. (R), ON, *129*
Mrozek, Joe, Moffitt Int'l., Inc. (R), NJ, *146*
Muendel, H. Edward, Stanton Chase Int'l. (R), MD, *199*
Mummert, Dennis D., Sweeney Harbert & Mummert, Inc. (R), FL, *205*
Muñoz, Francisco Noriega, PricewaterhouseCoopers Executive Search (R), MX, *168*
Murphy, Robert, Cypress Int'l., Inc. (R), FL, *45*
Murray, John, Cypress Int'l., Inc. (R), FL, *45*
Muthersbaugh, Jeff, Brandywine Retained Ventures, Inc. (R), CT, *22*
Nadeau, Robert, KPMG Executive Search (R), QE, *120*
Neighbors, Betty, Personnel Assoc. (C), NC, *508*
Neighbors, Cliff, Personnel Assoc. (C), NC, *508*
Nelson, Allan C., Davies, Park (R), AB, *47*
Nelson, Randy, Orion Int'l. Consulting Group, Inc. (C), NC, *499*
Newman, Edgar F., ENI (R), CT, *59*
Nichols, Gary, Koontz, Jeffries & Assoc., Inc. (R), FL, *117*
Nichols, Marc, Marc Nichols Assoc., Inc. (C), NY, *493*
Noll, William T., Noll Human Resource Services (C), NE, *494*
Nolte, Jr., William D., W. D. Nolte & Company (R), CT, *152*
O'Brien, Lindy, O'Brien and Roof (C), OH, *497*
O'Connell, Michael, Ryan, Miller & Assoc. (C), CA, *549*
O'Maley, Kimberlee, SpencerStuart (R), CA, *196*
O'Neill, Kathleen A., RIC Corp. (R), FL, *177*
O'Neill, Kevin R., Performance Resources, Inc. (C), RI, *507*
O'Reilly, John D., StratfordGroup (R), OH, *203*
Ober, Lynn W., Ober & Company (R), CA, *155*
Oda, Lynn, The Hollins Group, Inc. (R), IL, *95*
Oliveros, Nancy P., New Dawn Employment Search (C), CA, *491*
Olmstead, George T., Blackshaw, Olmstead, Lynch & Koenig (R), GA, *18*
Olsen, Carl M., A.T. Kearney Executive Search (R), CA, *111*
Ott, George W., Ott & Hansen, Inc. (R), CA, *157*
Overson, Donna, Michael Shirley Assoc. Inc. (R), KS, *190*
Owens, LaMonte, LaMonte Owens, Inc. (R), PA, *158*
Owens, Reggie, The Gabriel Group (C), PA, *354*
Pappas, Timothy C., Jude M. Werra & Assoc. (R), WI, *218*
Paquet, Marc, MPA Executive Search Inc. (R), QE, *148*
Parker, Thomas, Anderson & Schwab, Inc. (R), NY, *6*
Parsons, Sue N., Parsons Assoc. Inc. (R), IL, *159*
Pasquale, Thomas S. O., Spear-Izzo Assoc., LLC (C), PA, *589*
Patrick, Donald R., Sanford Rose Assoc. - Norcross (C), GA, *566*
Patton, M. Pat, Tekworx, Inc. (C), OK, *604*
Patton, Pat, Hunt Patton & Brazeal, Inc. (C), CO, *385*
Patton, Pat, Tekworx, Inc. (C), CO, *604*
Pawlik, Bernadette, Pawlik/Dorman Partners (R), IL, *161*
Payton, Andrew J., Professional Search Consultants (C), KY, *522*
Peasback, David R., Canny, Bowen Inc. (R), NY, *28*
Perkins, R. Patrick, The Perkins Group (R), NC, *162*
Perras, Paul, KPMG Executive Search (R), ON, *119*
Perry, Philip, Lindsey & Co., Inc. (R), OH, *129*
Peters, Ray, J. Stroll Assoc., Inc. (R), CT, *204*
Peterson, Eric N., StratfordGroup (R), OH, *203*
Pezim, Howard J., The Bedford Consulting Group Inc. (R), ON, *15*
Pfeiffer, Irene, Price Waterhouse Executive Search (R), AB, *168*
Phillips, K. Jerry, Snelling & Snelling, Inc. (C), FL, *585*
Pistentis, Jean, Dunn Associates (R), PA, *55*
Pitchon, Daniel N., DNPitchon Assoc. (R), NJ, *165*
Pizzariello, Ann Marie, Conex Inc./InterSearch (R), NY, *39*
Pliszka, Donald J., PRAXIS Partners (R), VA, *167*
Plock, Gerald R., The PAR Group - Paul A. Reaume, Ltd. (R), IL, *159*
Poirier, Roland L., Poirier, Hoevel & Co. (R), CA, *166*
Polson, Christopher C., Polson & Co., Inc. (R), MN, *166*
Pope, Carla, Straube Associates (R), MA, *203*
Popham, Harold C., Emerson & Co. (C), GA, *329*
Poracky, John W., M. Wood Company (R), IL, *224*
Poriotis, Wesley, Wesley Brown & Bartle Co., Inc. (R), NY, *218*
Porter, Jack, Jack Porter Assoc., Inc. (C), WA, *514*
Powell, Lloyd, KPMG Executive Search (R), NF, *119*
Preng, Richard J., SpencerStuart (R), TX, *197*
Proct, Nina, Martin H. Bauman Assoc., Inc. (R), NY, *13*
Pruitt, Diane, MARBL Consultants, Inc. (C), WI, *469*
Pryde, Marcia P., A.T. Kearney Executive Search (R), CO, *111*
Rabinowitz, Peter A., P.A.R. Assoc., Inc. (R), MA, *158*
Ralles, Vickie, Feldman Gray & Assoc. Inc. (C), ON, *339*
Randolph, Lea, Lea Randolph & Assoc., Inc. (C), TX, *529*
Randolph, Troy, Lea Randolph & Assoc., Inc. (C), TX, *529*
Reaume, Paul A., The PAR Group - Paul A. Reaume, Ltd. (R), IL, *159*
Redwood, Guy W., Massey-Horton Int'l. (R), ON, *138*
Reece, Christopher S., Reece & Mruk Partners/EMA Partners Int'l. (R), MA, *173*
Reeves, William B., SpencerStuart (R), GA, *197*
Reifel, Laurie L., Reifel & Assoc. (R), IL, *174*
Reusser, Mary, Michael Shirley Assoc. Inc. (R), KS, *190*
Reyman, Susan, S. Reyman & Assoc., Ltd. (R), IL, *176*
Rice, Marie, Jay Gaines & Company, Inc. (R), NY, *74*
Richards, Terry, Terry Richards (C), OH, *536*
Rieger, Louis J., SpencerStuart (R), TX, *197*
Rieser, John D., Rieser & Assoc., Inc. (R), MO, *178*

Rios, Lorena Zuñiga, PricewaterhouseCoopers Executive Search (R), MX, *168*
Roberts, Libby, Global Consulting Group Inc. (C), ON, *358*
Robinson, Bruce, Bruce Robinson Assoc. (R), NJ, *180*
Robinson, Bunny, Robinson-Robinson & Assoc., Inc. (C), MN, *539*
Robinson, Eric, Bruce Robinson Assoc. (R), NJ, *180*
Robinson, Joanne, The 500 Granary Inc. (C), ON, *231*
Robinson, John, Bruce Robinson Assoc. (R), NJ, *180*
Robinson, Sam, Robinson-Robinson & Assoc., Inc. (C), MN, *539*
Robison, John H., Robison & Associates (R), NC, *180*
Robyn, Eric W., QVS Int'l. (R), GA, *170*
Rodzik, C. L., Rodzik & Assoc., Inc. (R), NC, *180*
Rodzik, Gerald F., Rodzik & Assoc., Inc. (R), NC, *180*
Rolfe, Pamela, Career Specialists, Inc. (R), WA, *29*
Rollo, Robert S., Rollo Assoc. (R), CA, *181*
Roof, Howard, O'Brien and Roof (C), OH, *497*
Rose, Emery, Emery A. Rose & Assoc. (C), WA, *545*
Ross, Karen M., The Hetzel Group, Inc. (R), IL, *93*
Rossi, Larry, The Executive Group, Inc. (R), CA, *62*
Roth, Robert J., Williams, Roth & Krueger, Inc. (R), IL, *221*
Roth, Ronald P., Smith, Roth & Squires (R), NY, *194*
Rouleau, Gilles, Lamon + Stuart + Michaels Inc. (R), QE, *124*
Rovner, Louis, Rovner Gerner & Assoc. (R), CA, *182*
Rubin, Ron, Geddes & Rubin Management Inc. (R), ON, *76*
Ruf, Ines, Stoopen Asociados, S.C./EMA Partners Int'l. (R), MX, *202*
Russo, Joseph E., Hamilton-Chase & Assoc., Inc. (R), MA, *85*
Rust, John R., Rust & Assoc., Inc. (R), IL, *183*
Ryan, Brian, The Logan Group, Inc. (R), MO, *131*
Ryan, Lee, Ryan, Miller & Assoc. (C), CA, *549*
Sadaka, Steve, Steven Douglas Assoc. (C), FL, *593*
Sadovnick, Mark, Steven Douglas Assoc. (C), FL, *593*
Samet, Saul, Fisher-Todd Assoc. (C), NY, *342*
Sandor, Richard, Flynn, Hannock, Inc. (R), CT, *69*
Sathe, Mark, Sathe & Associates, Inc. (R), MN, *184*
Sauer, Andrea Garcia, Frank P. Hill (R), MX, *93*
Savage, Edward J., Stanton Chase Int'l. (R), CA, *199*
Sbarbaro, Richard D., Lauer, Sbarbaro Assoc., EMA Partners Int'l. (R), IL, *126*
Scanlon, Carol-Anne, The 500 Granary Inc. (C), ON, *231*
Scaparotti, Jim, Fox-Morris Assoc., Inc. (C), OH, *352*
Schaller, Susan, Jay Gaines & Company, Inc. (R), NY, *74*
Schegg, John P., Goodrich & Sherwood Assoc., Inc. (R), CT, *80*
Schoff, Diane L., The Edge Resource Group (C), PA, *326*
Schuller, Eric K., TE, Inc. (C), IL, *600*
Schulz, Chris, Wilson Assoc. Inc. (R), NS, *222*
Scott, Robin, Stanton Chase Int'l. (R), MD, *199*
Segil, Annette R., Executive Careers (R), CA, *62*
Segovia, Barbara, KPMG Executive Search (R), BC, *119*
Seitz, Charles, Neail Behringer Consultants Inc. (R), NY, *15*
Sekera, Roger I., A.T. Kearney Executive Search (R), VA, *111*
Shackleton, George M., Carpenter, Shackleton & Company (R), IL, *30*
Shackleton, Michael, Carpenter, Shackleton & Company (R), IL, *30*
Shalet, Lisa, Blackshaw, Olmstead, Lynch & Koenig (R), GA, *18*
Shea, Kathleen M., The Penn Partners, Inc. (R), PA, *162*
Shirley, Michael R., Michael Shirley Assoc. Inc. (R), KS, *190*
Shore, Linda, Shore Asociados Ejecutivos, S. A. de C.V. (R), MX, *190*
Shore, Susan, Shore Asociados Ejecutivos, S. A. de C.V. (R), MX, *190*
Shotland, David R., The Shotland Group (R), CA, *190*
Shultz, Susan F., SSA Executive Search Int'l. (R), AZ, *198*
Sibbald, John R., John Sibbald Assoc., Inc. (R), MO, *191*
Siegel, Fred, Conex Inc./InterSearch (R), NY, *39*
Silcott, Marvin L., Marvin L. Silcott & Assoc., Inc. (C), TX, *581*
Silvas, Stephen D., Roberson & Co. (C), AZ, *538*
Sinclair, Tom, PricewaterhouseCoopers Executive Search (R), ON, *168*
Singer, Suzanne, GFI Professional Staffing Services (C), VT, *357*
Sistek, Walter J., First Advisory Services Int'l., Inc. (R), MD, *67*
Sistek, Walter J., Management Assoc. (C), MD, *424*
Slaughter, Katherine T., Compass Group Ltd. (R), MI, *38*
Smith, Grant, Price Waterhouse Executive Search (R), BC, *168*
Smith, Jr., John E., Smith Search, S.C. (R), MX, *194*
Smith, John F., The Penn Partners, Inc. (R), PA, *162*
Smith, Michael, Smith James Group, Inc. (R), GA, *194*
Smith, Ralph E., Ralph Smith & Assoc. (C), IL, *584*
Smith, Steven B., The McAulay Firm (R), NC, *139*
Snoddy, Jr., Mark F., Peachtree Executive Search (R), GA, *161*
Sollman, Robert, Robert Sollman & Assoc. (C), FL, *587*
Soltis, Charles W., Soltis Management Services (R), PA, *195*
Soutouras, James, Smith James Group, Inc. (R), GA, *194*
Spear, Kenneth T., Spear-Izzo Assoc., LLC (C), PA, *589*
Squires, R. James, Smith, Roth & Squires (R), NY, *194*
St. Jean, Norman D., The Ryan Charles Group, Inc. (C), FL, *549*
Stanley, Paul R. A., Ray & Berndtson/Lovas Stanley (R), ON, *172*
Stanton, John, StratfordGroup (R), TX, *203*
Stein, Terry W., Stewart, Stein & Scott, Ltd. (R), MN, *200*
Steinberg, Paul D., IMA Search, Inc. (R), NY, *101*
Stenfors, Lyle, Thomas Lyle & Co. (C), IL, *606*
Stern, Michael, Michael Stern Assoc., Inc./Euram (R), ON, *200*
Stevens, Ken G., The Stevens Group (R), TX, *200*
Stewart, Evan, Angus Employment Ltd. (C), ON, *250*
Stewart, Jeffrey O., Stewart, Stein & Scott, Ltd. (R), MN, *200*
Stewart, Tom, Stewart/Greene & Company of the Triad, Inc. (C), NC, *594*
Stolee, Allan J., Allan Stolee Inc. (R), FL, *201*
Stoopen, Josefina, Stoopen Asociados, S.C./EMA Partners Int'l. (R), MX, *202*
Strathmann, Winfried R., W. R. Strathmann Assoc. (R), NY, *203*
Straube, Stan, Straube Associates (R), MA, *203*
Stroman, III, Alfred L., Stroman Int'l., Inc. (R), CO, *204*
Stuart, Bob, Lamon + Stuart + Michaels Inc. (R), ON, *124*
Stubbs, Judy N., LAI Ward Howell (R), TX, *124*
Sturgess, Bob, Michael Stern Assoc., Inc./Euram (R), ON, *200*
Sturtz, James W., Compass Group Ltd. (R), MI, *38*
Sullivan, Tom, Brandywine Retained Ventures, Inc. (R), CT, *22*
Swartz, Karen M., The Penn Partners, Inc. (R), PA, *162*
Sweeney, James W., Sweeney Harbert & Mummert, Inc. (R), FL, *205*
Sweet, Charles W., A.T. Kearney Executive Search (R), IL, *111*
Swystun, Karen, Price Waterhouse Executive Search (R), MB, *168*
Talbott Creed, Pamela, The Hollins Group, Inc. (R), IL, *95*
Tanton, John, Ray & Berndtson/Tanton Mitchell (R), BC, *172*

Tanton, John, Ray & Berndtson/Tanton Mitchell (R), BC, *173*
Tate, Gene M., Tate & Assoc., Inc. (R), NJ, *207*
Tattersfield, Roberto E., Frank P. Hill (R), MX, *93*
Textor, Jack T., Personnel Incorporated (C), IA, *508*
Thibault, Raymond, Career Advisors, Inc. (C), FL, *281*
Thomas, Tommy, People Management Mid-South, LLC (R), TN, *162*
Thompson, Tammy, Connors, Lovell & Assoc. Inc. (C), ON, *296*
Thornton, John M., StratfordGroup (R), OH, *203*
Tindall, Chasity, Personnel Assoc. (C), NC, *508*
Trammell, Kay, Kressenberg Assoc. (C), TX, *409*
Trout, Thomas L., Trout & Assoc. Inc. (R), UT, *211*
Trueba, Lucia, Stoopen Asociados, S.C./ EMA Partners Int'l. (R), MX, *202*
Tschudin, Hugo, Tschudin Inc. (R), NJ, *211*
Tschudin, Ruth, Tschudin Inc. (R), NJ, *211*
Tucker, Weida G., W. G. Tucker & Assoc. (R), PA, *211*
Tufenkjian, Richard, C. A. Durakis Assoc., Inc. (R), MA, *55*
Tully, Jim, Orion Int'l. Consulting Group, Inc. (C), NC, *499*
Tully, Margo L., Tully/Woodmansee Int'l. Inc. (R), FL, *212*
Tunney, Jr., William, Grant Cooper & Assoc., Inc. (R), MO, *81*
Turk, Jeffrey M., Omega Search, Inc. (C), NC, *498*
Ullstein, Ashley B., Drinkwater & Assoc. (R), MA, *55*
Valle, Javier, A.T. Kearney Executive Search (R), MX, *111*
van Biesen, Coby, Search Group Inc. (R), AB, *186*
Van Dyke, Roger, Van Dyke Assoc. (R), IL, *212*
Vanderleeuw, Jim, Connors, Lovell & Assoc. Inc. (C), ON, *296*
VanMaldegiam, Norman E., VanMaldegiam Assoc., Inc. (R), IL, *213*
VanNus, Rob, Price Waterhouse Executive Search (R), BC, *168*
Vant, Randy, Landon Morgan (C), ON, *412*
Verchot, Hinky, Solutions Group (R), AL, *195*
Vialosky, John, Brandywine Retained Ventures, Inc. (R), CT, *22*
Vignet, Gayle Hill, Hill Allyn Assoc. (C), CA, *378*
Vignuolo, Olga, Hreshko Consulting Group (C), NJ, *382*
Vockley, James, Moffitt Int'l., Inc. (R), NC, *146*
Vojta, Marilyn B., Lindsey & Co., Inc. (R), CT, *129*
Voss, Erik, Sheila Greco Assoc. (C), NY, *362*
Waanders, William L., ExecuQuest, Inc. (R), MI, *61*
Walch, Hutch, Working Relationships, Inc. (C), MN, *624*
Wallens, Charles N., Allen, Wayne & Co. LLC (C), WI, *245*
Walton, Lee H., Lee H. Walton & Assoc. (R), NY, *215*
Wanger, Karen, Karen Wanger & Assoc., Inc. (C), IL, *615*
Warriner, Bob, Job-Born Candidate Selection Bureau (C), ON, *399*
Watkins, Melissa, Michael Shirley Assoc. Inc. (R), KS, *190*
Watson, Hanan S., Watson Int'l., Inc. (R), NY, *216*
Welch, R. Thomas, RIC Corp. (R), FL, *177*
Welling, Suzanne, IMA Search, Inc. (R), NY, *101*
Welzig, Frank E., Welzig, Lowe & Assoc. (C), CO, *618*
Werra, Jude M., Jude M. Werra & Assoc. (R), WI, *218*
Wesley, Donald, Spear-Izzo Assoc., LLC (C), PA, *589*
Wheeler, Bruce, Cypress Int'l., Inc. (R), FL, *45*
Wheless, Michael, Solutions Group (R), AL, *195*
Whitbeck, Elizabeth C., Whitbeck & Assoc. (R), MN, *219*
Whitney, William A., Larsen, Whitney, Blecksmith & Zilliacus, Inc. (R), CA, *125*
Wilder, Bruce, Wilder & Assoc. (C), VA, *620*
Willcox, David R., Senior Careers (R), NY, *188*
Williams, April M., The Hollins Group, Inc. (R), IL, *95*
Williams, Roger K., Williams, Roth & Krueger, Inc. (R), IL, *221*
Williams, Steve, Cypress Int'l., Inc. (R), FL, *45*
Wilson, G.H., Wilson Assoc. Inc. (R), NS, *222*
Wilson, Jim, Wilson Assoc. Inc. (R), NS, *222*
Winters, Angela, The Hollins Group, Inc. (R), IL, *95*
Wolf, Stephen M., Byron Leonard Int'l., Inc. (R), CA, *26*
Wood, Milton M., M. Wood Company (R), IL, *224*
Woodmansee, Bruce, Tully/Woodmansee Int'l., Inc. (R), OH, *212*
Woodson, Jim, Jim Woodson & Assoc., Inc. (C), MS, *624*
Wyman, Michael B., Martin Partners, L.L.C. (R), IL, *137*
Yacullo, William J., Lauer, Sbarbaro Assoc., EMA Partners Int'l. (R), IL, *126*
Zaleta, Andy R., A.T. Kearney Executive Search (R), MA, *111*
Zander, Craig, Jefferson-Ross Assoc. Inc. (C), PA, *398*
Zivic, Janis M., SpencerStuart (R), CA, *196*

Genetics

Romeo, Paul C., Romeo-Hudgins & Assoc., Ltd. (C), NJ, *545*
Ruhmann, John D., J. D. Ruhmann & Assoc. (C), MO, *548*

Geology

Brien, Jason, Kane & Assoc. (C), TX, *403*
Buckingham, Ian D., Anderson & Schwab, Inc. (R), NY, *6*
Cosier, Brian, Cosier & Assoc. (C), AB, *302*
Sonne, Bill, PeopleSource Inc. (C), TX, *506*

Gifts

Keoughan, Thomas, The C.P.R. Group (C), NJ, *278*
Moran, Marilyn, RitaSue Siegel Resources, Inc. (R), NY, *191*

Giftware

Boyer, Adrienne, Cook Assoc.,® Inc. (R), IL, *40*

Golf

Hughes, Don, ProLinks Inc. (R), VA, *170*
Hurley, Gerard F., Association Executive Resources Group (R), MD, *8*
Kelly, Mary K., Kelly Assoc. (R), WI, *112*
Kelly, Ronald, Kelly Assoc. (R), WI, *112*
Kopplin, Richard M., Kopplin Search, Inc. (R), CA, *117*
Stefan, David E., ChaseAmerica, Inc. (R), FL, *33*
White, Joseph A., Sports Group Int'l. (R), NC, *198*

Government

Anderson, George Wright, Gans, Gans & Assoc., Inc. (R), IL, *74*
Antoniak, Peggy, The Executive Tree (R), MD, *64*
Bono, Jeffrey D., Michael Latas & Assoc., Inc. (R), MO, *126*
Colling, Douglas, KPMG Executive Search (R), ON, *119*
Davidson, Mary Anne, KPMG Executive Search (R), SA, *120*
Habelmann, Gerald B., Habelmann & Assoc. (R), MI, *84*
Harrell, Stephen G., The Personnel Network, Inc. (C), SC, *508*
Kuhnmuench, R. G., K & C Assoc. (C), CA, *402*
McNamara, Timothy C., Horton Int'l. Inc. (R), MD, *96*
Mercer, James L., The Mercer Group, Inc. (R), NM, *143*
Park, K. Darwin, Davies, Park (R), AB, *46*

RECRUITER SPECIALTIES

Raperto, Marie T., The Cantor Concern, Inc. (R), NY, *28*
Reid, Gary, KPMG Executive Search (R), ON, *119*
Taylor, Charles E., LAI Ward Howell (R), GA, *123*
Uhlich, Jeff, KPMG Executive Search (R), AB, *119*
Vautour, Eric L., Russell Reynolds Assoc., Inc. (R), DC, *176*
Wallace, Clarke, PricewaterhouseCoopers Executive Search (R), ON, *168*

GPS

Gibson, Jan, Advanced Corporate Search (C), CA, *240*

Graphics

Caravello, Cindy, Desktop Staffing, Inc. (C), IL, *311*
Forbes, Kenneth P., Sanford Rose Assoc. - Evansville (C), IN, *567*
Grumney, David E., David E. Grumney Co. Inc. (R), WA, *83*
Lyons, Kent T., Lyons & Assoc., Inc. (C), IL, *422*
Maiola, Diana E., Maiola & Co. (C), OH, *423*
Moran, Marilyn, RitaSue Siegel Resources, Inc. (R), NY, *191*
Pulito, Carol M., Maiola & Co. (C), OH, *423*
Tringle, Terry, Sanford Rose Assoc. - Nashville (C), TN, *570*

Groceries

Chesla, Garry, Executive Referral Services, Inc. (C), IL, *334*
Glaser, Larry, Lawrence Glaser Assoc., Inc. (C), NJ, *358*
Goldberg, Sybil, Spectra International LLC (C), AZ, *589*
Hughes, Donald J., Hughes & Company (R), VA, *98*
Van Leeuwen, Lee, Van Leeuwen Assoc. (R), CA, *213*

Hardware

Arredondo, Fred, SpectraWest (C), CA, *589*
Bailin, Fred, Asset Resource, Inc. (C), CA, *254*
Bakken, Roger, J. Rodgers & Associates (C), IL, *540*
Barnes, Vern, Capital Consulting Group, Inc. (R), MD, *28*
Bauzenberger, III, E. H., The Currier-Winn Co., Inc. (C), NJ, *305*
Brandle, James, McCoy Ltd. (C), CA, *474*
Burns, Gale, Snelling Search Recruiters (C), NC, *586*
Campbell, Brian H., Venpro Consulting Inc. (C), ON, *612*
Cleary, Jeanne, The Rossi Search Group (C), PA, *545*
Deckelbaum, Stan, Fortune Personnel Consultants of Raleigh, Inc. (C), NC, *348*
DiMauro, Paula, Sales Consultants of Omaha, Inc. (C), NE, *560*
Dixon, Jim L., MESA International (C), CA, *480*
Dorst, Martin, Dorst Information Services, Inc. (C), NY, *314*
Endres, Devlin, Allstaff, Inc. (C), IL, *245*
Fair, Carolyn, Dunhill Executive Search of Los Angeles, Inc. (C), CA, *319*
Fowler, Gary, Analog Solutions (C), NY, *249*
Gibson, Jan, Advanced Corporate Search (C), CA, *240*
Hassel, Elizabeth, Cook Assoc.,® Inc. (R), IL, *40*
Heisser, Robert, MRI, The Sequel Group, LLC (C), CO, *486*
Henry, Pat, Fortune Personnel Consultants of Huntsville, Inc. (C), AL, *343*
Jacobs, Bob, StratfordGroup (R), CA, *203*
Johnson, Walt, Pacific Crossing (C), CA, *501*
Joyce, Mark, Louis Rudzinsky Assoc., Inc. (C), MA, *548*
Kier, Mary, Cook Assoc.,® Inc. (R), IL, *40*
Kierstead, Robert, High Tech Opportunities, Inc. (C), NH, *377*
Landwerb, Sandy, Capital Consulting Group, Inc. (R), MD, *28*
Lane, Douglas, Management Recruiters of Milwaukee - Downtown (C), WI, *466*
LePatner, Steve, Dunhill Executive Search of Los Angeles, Inc. (C), CA, *319*
Loftus, Daniel P., McCoy Ltd. (C), CA, *474*
McCabe, William, Allstaff, Inc. (C), IL, *245*
McNally, John R., McCoy Ltd. (C), CA, *474*
Nelson, Len, Len Nelson & Assoc., Inc. (C), TX, *491*
Nelson, Richard, Pacific Crossing (C), CA, *501*
Norman, Marcie, Management Recruiters of Franktown (C), CO, *442*
O'Keefe, Ian, O'Keefe & Assoc. (C), AR, *498*
Powers, Norman S., Norman Powers Assoc., Inc. (C), MA, *515*
Robertson, Janice, Tele-Solutions of Arizona, Inc. (C), AZ, *604*
Rowland, John R., Rowland Assoc. (C), CA, *547*
Rudzinsky, Jeff, Louis Rudzinsky Assoc., Inc. (C), MA, *548*
Russell, Steven, Nyborg•Dow Assoc., Inc. (C), CA, *497*
Rystrom, R. L., R. L. Rystrom & Assoc., Inc. (C), MN, *549*
Sanders, David, Management Recruiters of Roseville (C), CA, *441*
Shinn, Michael, Shinn & Assoc. (R), CA, *189*
Shue, Colleen, Bennett Search & Consulting Co. (R), FL, *16*
Shulman, Fran, Asset Resource, Inc. (C), CA, *254*
Starling, Dick, ProNet, Inc. (C), NC, *524*
Steinbach, David M., Steinbach & Co. (C), MA, *592*
Stepler, Paul, Gallin Associates, Inc. (C), FL, *354*
Stone, Susan L., Stone Enterprises Ltd. (C), IL, *594*
Travis, Michael J., Travis & Co., Inc. (R), MA, *210*
Walker, Bob, McCoy Ltd. (C), CA, *474*
Zeiger, David Barkin, Zeiger Assoc. L.L.C. (C), CA, *627*

Health

Banister, John, Delta ProSearch (C), PA, *311*
Bryant, Tom, Bryant Research (C), NJ, *276*
Cerra, Ken, William Bell Assoc., Inc. (C), NJ, *263*
Conville, RJ (Kip), The Park Group & Assoc., Inc. (C), MD, *503*
Ector, John, Insurance Personnel Resources, Inc. (C), GA, *390*
Fehrenbach, Ray, Southern Recruiters & Consultants, Inc. (C), SC, *587*
Lapham, Lawrence L., Lawrence L. Lapham, Inc. (R), NY, *124*
Mallinson, Robert, Ritta Professional Search Inc. (C), NY, *538*
Noone, Christine, Cook Assoc.,® Inc. (R), IL, *40*
Razuri, Patrick, Management Recruiters of Savannah (C), GA, *446*
Rector-Gable, Mary, Mary Rector & Assoc., Inc. (C), IL, *533*
Sims, Larry, Reality Group (C), OK, *531*
Storfer, Herbert F., The Dartmouth Group (R), NY, *46*
Tomei, Ted, Waterford Executive Group Ltd. (C), IL, *616*
Winterburn, Karen, Heartland National Medical Search (C), IL, *374*

Healthcare

Adamson, C. Lynn, Levison Search Assoc. (R), CA, *129*
Ahrensdorf, Lee, Ahrensdorf & Assoc. (R), PA, *2*
Alexander, David, Elite Medical Search (C), GA, *328*
Altieri, Robert J., StratfordGroup (R), PA, *203*
Arnold, Janet N., R & J Arnold & Assoc., Inc. (C), CO, *253*
Arnold, Lindy, The Glazin Group (R), BC, *77*
Arons, Richard, Korn/Ferry Int'l. (R), NJ, *118*
Arsenault, Alfred J., Insight Consulting Co. (C), NY, *389*
Artze, Angeles, A. Artze Assoc.-Personnel Consultants (C), PR, *253*
Auerbach, Judith A., Auerbach Associates, Inc. (R), MA, *9*

Auman, Patrick A., Executive Solutions (R), MN, *64*
Auster, A. Marc, A. M. Auster Associates (R), FL, *9*
Babson, Lelia, Dunhill Staffing Systems (C), NC, *321*
Balk, Gregorius K., Healthcare Search Associates (C), CA, *374*
Ballein, Kathleen, Witt/Kieffer, Ford, Hadelman & Lloyd (R), IL, *223*
Barch, Sherrie L., Furst Group/MPI (R), IL, *72*
Barefield, Simone Gans, Gans, Gans & Assoc., Inc. (R), FL, *74*
Barkley, Keith, The Mackenzie Group (R), MD, *133*
Barnette, Fred A., Fred A. Barnette & Assoc. (R), NC, *11*
Barnette, Fred A., Fred A. Barnette & Assoc. (R), NJ, *11*
Barnette, Fred A., Hartman & Barnette (R), NC, *87*
Barowsky, Diane M., LAI Ward Howell (R), IL, *123*
Baumann, John, J.J. & H., Ltd. (R), GA, *105*
Baumann, John, Jacobson Assoc. (C), GA, *396*
Beckman, Susan R., Beckman & Assoc. Legal Search (C), OH, *262*
Bellview, Sibyl, Management Recruiters - Friendswood (C), TX, *462*
Benjamin, Judy D., LAI Ward Howell (R), GA, *123*
Berman, Shirlee J., Retail Recruiters/Spectrum Consultants, Inc. (C), PA, *535*
Berquist, Gailmarie, American Medical Recruiters (C), CO, *248*
Blanchard, Jeb, Healthcare Recruiters of Midsouth (C), TN, *373*
Bleau, Donn E., Global Resources Group (R), CA, *78*
Boccuzi, Joseph H., SpencerStuart (R), NY, *196*
Bodin, Thomas H., The Personnel Group, Inc. (R), MN, *163*
Bogdajewicz, John J., Executive Solutions (R), MO, *64*
Bonnell, William R., Bonnell Assoc. Ltd. (R), CT, *19*
Borman, Theodore H., LAI Ward Howell (R), NY, *122*
Bormann, David C., Yungner & Bormann (R), MN, *226*
Bowman, Susan C., Managed Care Resources (C), TX, *424*
Brace, Betsy, Bertrand, Ross & Assoc., Inc. (C), IL, *266*
Brace, Betsy, International Management Services Inc. (R), IL, *102*
Bradley, Sandy, MTA Partners (R), TX, *148*
Brickner, William J., Princeton Search Partners, Inc. (R), NJ, *169*
Brin, Bradley, Concorde Staff Source Inc. (C), WI, *296*
Broadhurst, Jr., Austin, LAI Ward Howell (R), CT, *123*
Brod, Walt, MSI Int'l. (C), VA, *487*
Brown, Dennis S., D. Brown & Assoc., Inc. (C), OR, *275*
Brown, Larry, Horton International Inc. (R), CT, *96*
Brown, Timothy A., LAI Ward Howell (R), TX, *124*
Buggy, Linda, Bonnell Assoc. Ltd. (R), CT, *19*
Burke, Karen, ISC of Houston, Inc. (C), TX, *394*
Burke, Markey, Brandywine Management Group (R), MD, *22*
Burnett, Glenn, WestPacific National Search, Inc. (C), CA, *619*
Bussey, Sharon, The Center for Career Advancement, LLC (C), NJ, *287*
Cabugos, Ted, NCC Executive Search Consultants (C), CA, *490*
Caliguiri, Edward, Response Staffing Services (C), NY, *535*
Callicott, Robin D., Perfect Search, Inc. (C), FL, *507*
Campos, Lily, Marentz & Co. (C), TX, *469*
Canady, Sonja, Cook Assoc. Int'l., Inc. (C), TN, *298*
Caplan, John, The Caplan-Taylor Group (R), CA, *28*
Carol, Barbara, Health Search (C), CA, *371*
Cary, John, Cornerstone Resources, Inc. (C), GA, *299*
Cejka, Susan, Cejka Healthcare Executive Search Services (CHESS) (R), MO, *32*
Cesafsky, Barry R., LAI Ward Howell (R), IL, *123*
Chamberlain, Inga, Chamberlain Assoc. (C), GA, *288*
Chambless, Vickers, Vickers Chambless Managed Search (C), GA, *289*
Chandler, Brad J., Furst Group/MPI (R), MN, *72*
Chandler, Carole A., StratfordGroup (R), OH, *203*
Chandler, Robert C., LAI Ward Howell (R), GA, *123*
Cianchetti, Frank, HCI Corp. (C), IL, *371*
Clark, Jerry, Executive Solutions (R), MN, *64*
Clarke, J. Robert, Furst Group/MPI (R), IL, *72*
Cohen, Eve, Aster Search Group (R), NY, *8*
Cohen, Kenneth R., The Synergy Organization (R), PA, *205*
Cohen, Michael R., Intech Summit Group, Inc. (R), CA, *102*
Cohen, Robert C., Intech Summit Group, Inc. (R), CA, *102*
Conant, Harold B., Healthcare Recruiters International-NY/NJ (C), NJ, *373*
Connolly, Claire E., CEC Associates (R), MA, *32*
Conyngham, Beth, Excalibur Human Resources, Inc. (R), NJ, *61*
Cook, Gene, Cook Assoc. Int'l., Inc. (C), TN, *298*
Corey, Michael J., Witt/Kieffer, Ford, Hadelman & Lloyd (R), IL, *223*
Cripe, Joyce, MIXTEC Group (R), CA, *145*
Crone, Russell, Maczkov-Biosciences, Inc. (R), CA, *133*
Crystal, Jonathan A., SpencerStuart (R), TX, *197*
Culbertson, Beth, Sales Consultants of Milwaukee (C), WI, *563*
Danforth, Andrea, Ethos Consulting, Inc. (R), CA, *61*
Daniels, Donna, Jonas, Walters & Assoc., Inc. (R), WI, *108*
Daudlin, Paul T., Daudlin, De Beaupre & Co., Inc. (R), MI, *46*
Daugherty-Hill, Kimberly J., Hayman Daugherty Assoc., Inc. (C), GA, *370*
Davies, A. Gerry, Davies, Park (R), AB, *46*
Davis, Stephanie, Morgan Samuels Co. (R), CA, *147*
De Beaupre, Mary Anne, Daudlin, De Beaupre & Co., Inc. (R), MI, *46*
De Mange, Jean M., Wellington Thomas Ltd. (C), FL, *618*
DeCorrevont, James, DeCorrevont & Assoc. (C), IL, *310*
DeCristoforo, Ralph B., DHR Int'l., Inc. (R), CT, *49*
Deerwester, Dave, Snelling Search (C), AL, *585*
Delmotte, James, Daudlin, De Beaupre & Co., Inc. (R), MI, *46*
Despres, Suzzett, Despres & Associates (C), IL, *311*
Detore, Robert R., Drew Assoc. Int'l. (R), NJ, *54*
Dickey, Avis D., Innovative Healthcare Services, Inc. (C), GA, *389*
Doherty, Shawn, Doherty Healthcare Consultants (C), ME, *313*
Donnelly, John J., Management & Human Resources (R), MA, *134*
Doody, Michael F., Witt/Kieffer, Ford, Hadelman & Lloyd (R), IL, *223*
Douglas, Bob, Hunter Douglas Group, Inc. (R), IL, *99*
DuBois, Jr., Joseph W., Horizon Medical Search of NH (C), NH, *381*
Dunbar, Meg, M. Dunbar & Assoc. (C), TX, *316*
Dye, Bill, Bruce Henry Assoc. Inc. (R), TX, *91*
Dye, Carson E., LAI Ward Howell (R), OH, *123*
Earle, Paul W., SpencerStuart (R), IL, *197*
Eastham, Marvene, Witt/Kieffer, Ford, Hadelman & Lloyd (R), TX, *223*
Elliott, C. J., Health Network USA (C), TX, *371*
Elliott, David J., Health Network USA (C), TX, *371*
Emery, Jodie A., LAI Ward Howell (R), CT, *123*
Emmott, Carol B., SpencerStuart (R), CA, *196*
Emory, Vaughn, BayResearch Group, Inc. (R), IL, *14*
Eren, Sal, Medserve & Assoc. Inc. (C), MD, *478*
Estrada, Barbara, Montgomery West (R), CA, *146*
Everett, Jim, EA Plus, Inc. (C), TX, *325*
Fagan, III, Charles A., Fagan & Company (R), PA, *64*

RECRUITER SPECIALTIES

Fisk, James L., James L. Fisk & Assoc. (C), MO, *342*
Fitzgerald, Geoffrey, Fitzgerald Associates (R), MA, *68*
Ford, J. Daniel, Witt/Kieffer, Ford, Hadelman & Lloyd (R), IL, *223*
Fornino, Rita M., Garrison-Randall, Inc. (R), CA, *75*
Fossett, Gary J., John Michael Assoc. (R), DC, *106*
Foster, David, Doherty Healthcare Consultants (C), ME, *313*
Fountain, Ray, Management Recruiters of North Charleston (C), SC, *460*
Frischman, Timothy, Furst Group/MPI (R), MN, *72*
Furr, C. Franklin, C. F. Furr & Co. (R), NC, *72*
Gable, Jacqueline S., Gable Healthcare Group, Inc. (R), FL, *73*
Gamboa, Mark, Solomon-Page Healthcare Group (R), CA, *195*
Garfield, Patricia, Healthcare Recruiters Int'l. Bay Area (C), CA, *372*
Garland, David C., Healthcare Recruiters - Northwest (C), WA, *374*
Garrett, Donald L., Garrett Assoc. Inc. (R), GA, *75*
Garrett, Linda M., Garrett Assoc. Inc. (R), GA, *75*
Gates, Will, Morgan Samuels Co. (R), CA, *147*
Gauss, James, Witt/Kieffer, Ford, Hadelman & Lloyd (R), CA, *223*
Geiser, Diane, The York Group (C), CA, *626*
Genel, George, Genel Associates (C), CA, *356*
Genser, Elaina Spitaels, Witt/Kieffer, Ford, Hadelman & Lloyd (R), CA, *223*
Giannerini, Roxanne, Recruitment Specialists, Inc. (C), MD, *532*
Gibney, Patrick, Medfall Inc. (C), ON, *476*
Gielow, Curtis C., Gielow Assoc., Inc. (R), WI, *76*
Gilbert, John, John Gilbert Co. (C), TX, *357*
Gildea, Catherine T., The Whyte Group, Inc. (R), MD, *220*
Gilmore, Roger, Gilmore & Assoc. (C), CA, *357*
Godfrey, Robert G., Robert G. Godfrey Assoc. Ltd. (R), IL, *79*
Goehring, Susan, STAT Search (C), NH, *592*
Goldman, Jeff, Global 1000 Int'l. Services (C), CA, *358*
Goldstein, Don, JAG Group (R), MO, *105*
Goodspeed, Peter, Witt/Kieffer, Ford, Hadelman & Lloyd (R), TX, *223*
Gordon, Alan, The Healthsearch Group, Inc. (C), NY, *374*
Gordon, Jeff, The Healthsearch Group, Inc. (C), NY, *374*
Gould, Nanci, National Search, Inc.® (C), FL, *490*
Gouran, Marc S., Solomon-Page Healthcare Group (R), NY, *195*
Graver, Patricia, Excalibur Human Resources, Inc. (R), NJ, *61*
Grayson, George, Health Search (C), CA, *371*
Green, Bruce, Carter/MacKay (C), NJ, *285*
Green, Heide, JAG Group (R), MO, *105*
Green, John A., JAG Group (R), MO, *105*
Groves, Jane, MSA Executive Search (R), MO, *148*
Guidry, Jim, Guidry & East Healthcare Search Consultants (R), TX, *83*
Hackett, Carrie, Cejka Healthcare Executive Search Services (CHESS) (R), MO, *32*
Hadelman, Jordan M., Witt/Kieffer, Ford, Hadelman & Lloyd (R), IL, *223*
Hadley, Thomas M., Hadley Associates, Inc. (C), NJ, *365*
Haggard, Jr., John H., Growth Consultants of America (R), MI, *82*
Hale, Dillon, Cemco, Ltd. (C), IL, *286*
Halstead, Frederick A., LAI Ward Howell (R), TX, *124*
Hamburg, Jennifer P., Ledbetter/Davidson Int'l., Inc. (R), NY, *127*
Hamm, Gary, Witt/Kieffer, Ford, Hadelman & Lloyd (R), CA, *223*
Hanna, Dwight, Cadillac Assoc. (C), CA, *278*
Hannigan, Melissa, JPM International (C), CA, *401*
Hanson, Darlene, Healthcare Recruiters Int'l. Phoenix (C), AZ, *372*
Harrison, Sally, Brandywine Management Group (R), MD, *22*
Hartman, Beverly, Management Assoc. (C), MD, *424*
Hartman, Robert J., Hartman & Barnette (R), VA, *87*
Harvey, Stephen W., Matthews & Stephens Assoc., Inc. (C), CT, *472*
Hebel, Robert W., R. W. Hebel Assoc. (R), TX, *89*
Hedberg, Cindy, Executive Solutions (R), MN, *64*
Henderson, Etta Ish, Boulware & Assoc. Inc. (R), IL, *20*
Hennessy, Robert, Ken Clark Int'l. (R), NJ, *36*
Henry, Bruce, Bruce Henry Assoc. Inc. (R), CA, *91*
Henry, Jim, MTA Partners (R), TX, *148*
Herbruck, Gretchen S., The Baer Group (R), OH, *10*
Hersher, Betsy S., Hersher Assoc., Ltd. (R), IL, *92*
Hertz, Al, Carter/MacKay (C), NC, *285*
Hewitt, Diane, AmeriResource Group Inc. (C), OK, *249*
Hillner, Jill, Continental Research Search, Inc. (C), WI, *298*
Hodges, Linda B., Hersher Assoc., Ltd. (R), IL, *92*
Hoffman, Theresa E., Wellington Management Group (R), PA, *217*
Hollander, Heidi, Career Counseling Ltd. (C.C.L.) (C), IL, *282*
Holodnak, William A., J. Robert Scott (R), MA, *104*
Howard, Lee Ann, LAI Ward Howell (R), CT, *123*
Hoyda, Louis A., Thorndike Deland Assoc. LLC (R), NY, *48*
Huff, Margaret L., Huff Assoc. (R), NJ, *98*
Huff, William Z., Huff Assoc. (R), NJ, *98*
Hunter, Debra, F-O-R-T-U-N-E Personnel Consultants of Troy, Inc. (C), MI, *347*
Hurd, Jane, Rollo Assoc. (R), CA, *181*
Hurley, Paula B., Auerbach Associates, Inc. (R), MA, *9*
Imler-Diskin, Lydia, David Rowe & Assoc., Inc. (R), IL, *182*
Isaacson, John, Isaacson, Miller (R), MA, *104*
Jacobs, Phillip E., E. J. Michaels, Ltd. (C), NY, *481*
Jenkins, Virginia L., The Center for Career Advancement (C), MD, *287*
Joffe, Jon, Meridian Resources (C), OH, *479*
Johnson, Frank Y., Healthcare Recruiters Int'l. - Alabama (C), AL, *372*
Jones, Michael A., The Century Group (C), KS, *287*
Kashinsky, Richard J., Management Recruiters of Monterey (C), CA, *441*
Katz, Arthur, Management Recruiters of Atlanta North, Inc. (C), GA, *446*
Kausch, Rolf H., Priority Executive Search (C), FL, *518*
Kay, Jerry L., LAI Ward Howell (R), CA, *123*
Kaye, Francine C., MedSearch Resources, Inc. (C), FL, *478*
Kazan, J. Neil, Kazan International, Inc. (R), NJ, *110*
Kenny, Roger M., Boardroom Consultants/ Kenny Kindler Tholke (R), NY, *19*
King, Gary, Management Recruiters of Tampa North (C), FL, *444*
Kirkman, Angie, MTA Partners (R), TX, *148*
Klos, Larry, MSI Int'l. (C), TX, *487*
Knauf, Shirley, Managed Care Resources (C), TX, *424*
Kool, Joan, Professional Recruiters, Inc. (C), PA, *521*
Korban, Richard O., Korban Associates (R), PA, *117*
Korytko, Lesia, COBA Executive Search (R), CO, *36*
Kosteva, David, NDI Services (R), MI, *151*
Kovach, Jerry, The J. Kovach Group (R), PA, *119*
Krawetz, Ben, National Career Search (C), AZ, *489*
Kreps, Charles D., The Normyle/Erstling Health Search Group (C), NJ, *494*
Kupchik, Allen B., Franklin Allen Consultants, Ltd. (R), NY, *71*
Kuypers, Arnold, LAI Ward Howell (R), TX, *124*
Lambre, Glenn C., McCooe & Assoc., Inc. (R), NJ, *140*
Latini, Anthony A., Princeton Search Partners, Inc. (R), NJ, *169*
Lee, Jacquelene, Royal Assoc. (C), CA, *547*

Lee, Jacquelene R., Healthcare Search Associates (C), CA, *374*
Leevy, Daniel, DNA Search, Inc. (C), CA, *313*
Lehn, Mallory, Vickers Chambless Managed Search (C), GA, *289*
Lenobel, Stephen, Professional Recruiters, Inc. (C), PA, *521*
Levison, Michael, Levison Search Assoc. (R), CA, *129*
Levison, Regina, Levison Search Assoc. (R), CA, *129*
Lihan, Dana L., MedXec USA, Inc. (C), FL, *478*
Lloyd, John S., Witt/Kieffer, Ford, Hadelman & Lloyd (R), IL, *223*
Lockleer, Julia, EA Plus, Inc. (C), TX, *325*
Lowderman, William, Loderman & Costello (C), GA, *419*
Lyttle, Jordene, KPMG Executive Search (R), ON, *119*
Maczkov, Nicholas, Maczkov-Biosciences, Inc. (R), CA, *133*
Maphet, Harriet, The Stevenson Group, Inc. (N.J.) (R), NJ, *200*
Martin, Judy R., J. Martin & Assoc. (R), CA, *137*
Martin, Mary Lou, Neail Behringer Consultants Inc. (R), NY, *15*
Martin, Sr., Robert, The Pailin Group Professional Search Consultants (R), TX, *158*
Martin, Roz, STAT Search (C), MA, *592*
Maslan, Neal L., LAI Ward Howell (R), CA, *123*
Mattis, Tim, Ensearch Management Consultants (C), CA, *331*
McCann, Mary Ellen, Wellington Management Group (R), PA, *217*
McCartt, Sandra, Professional Search, Inc. Int'l. (C), TX, *523*
McGurn, Sharman, B. J. Abrams & Assoc. Inc. (C), IL, *233*
McHale, John P., McHale & Assoc. (R), WA, *141*
McKeown, Morgan, Christian & Timbers, Inc. (R), NY, *34*
McKeown, Morgan, Christian & Timbers, Inc. (R), OH, *34*
McLaughlin, Brad, Meridian Resources (C), OH, *479*
McNitt, Dean, Healthcare Recruiters of New York, Inc. (C), NY, *373*
McSpadden, Stephen, First Advisory Services Int'l., Inc. (R), MD, *67*
Meisel, Martin H., Martin H. Meisel Assoc., Inc. (R), NY, *143*
Meltser, Thomas, Patriot Assoc. (C), PA, *505*
Metzger, Norman, Martin H. Meisel Assoc., Inc. (R), NY, *143*
Milius, Kent, Management Recruiters of Colorado, Inc. (C), CO, *442*
Miller, Kenneth, Computer Network Resources, Inc. (C), CA, *295*
Montgomery, Rita, Healthcare Recruiters Int'l. - Los Angeles (C), CA, *372*
Mooney, Jill, STAT Search (C), NH, *592*
Moore, Ann M., Healthcare Recruiters International-NY/NJ (C), NJ, *373*
Moore, Sandee, Moore Research Assoc. (R), NJ, *147*
Moore, Sherrie, The Alfus Group (R), NY, *3*
Morrison, Janis, Garrett Assoc. Inc. (R), GA, *75*
Morrison, Susan S., Quetico Corp. (R), TX, *170*
Morse, Jeffrey A., Brandywine Management Group (R), MD, *22*
Mruk, Edwin S., Mruk & E.M.A. Partners (R), NY, *148*
Mulligan, Pamela L., Pamela L. Mulligan, Inc. (R), NH, *149*
Mulvaney, Ronald F., R. F. Mulvaney & Assoc., Inc. (R), MO, *149*
Murphy, Marsha, MTA Partners (R), TX, *148*
Murrell, James O., Professionals in Recruiting Co. (C), TN, *523*
Myers, Roy, National Career Search (C), AZ, *489*
Naples, Len Di, Roth Young of Pittsburgh (C), PA, *546*
Newpoff, Brad L., Furst Group/MPI (R), IL, *72*
Newpoff, Brad L., Global HealthCare Partners (R), IL, *78*
Nichipor, Michael A., Sanford Rose Assoc. - Carmel, IN (C), IN, *567*
Nickley, Sandy, Executive Search, Ltd. (C), OH, *336*
Nixon, Barbara, PricewaterhouseCoopers Executive Search (R), ON, *168*
Norman, Paul W., Paul Winston Norman & Assoc. (R), IL, *152*
O'Keefe, Michael, Ray & Berndtson/Lovas Stanley (R), ON, *172*
O'Keefe, Michael, Ray & Berndtson/Lovas Stanley (R), ON, *173*
Oliveros, Nancy P., New Dawn Employment Search (C), CA, *491*
Olsen, Elizabeth Clark, Olsen/Clark (R), WA, *156*
Osborne, Julie, Rogish Assoc., Inc. (C), OH, *541*
Ostarticki-Sanchez, Karen, STAT Search (C), FL, *592*
Otto, Karen, Witt/Kieffer, Ford, Hadelman & Lloyd (R), IL, *223*
Pajak, Michael A., The Danielson Group, Inc. (C), TX, *306*
Palazola, Vic, Healthcare Recruiters of New Orleans (C), LA, *373*
Pallman-David, Cynthia, Bonnell Assoc. Ltd. (R), CT, *19*
Pankratz, Dennis L., Furst Group/MPI (R), IL, *72*
Pappas, James, PCD Partners (R), PA, *161*
Patlovich, Michael J., Witt/Kieffer, Ford, Hadelman & Lloyd (R), MA, *223*
Paul, Joel H., Joel H. Paul & Assoc., Inc. (C), NY, *505*
Paxton, James W., Stanton Chase Int'l. (R), MD, *199*
Peck, James, Peggy Shea & Assoc. (R), CA, *189*
Peeney, James D., Peeney Assoc., Inc. (R), NJ, *161*
Pelton, Margaret, PricewaterhouseCoopers Executive Search (R), ON, *168*
Perlman, Dan, Romac Int'l., Inc. (C), FL, *543*
Perry, Len, The Caplan-Taylor Group (R), CA, *28*
Perunovich, Lise, The Park Group & Assoc., Inc. (C), MD, *503*
Pezim, Howard J., The Bedford Consulting Group Inc. (R), ON, *15*
Pfannenstiel, Roseann, Fortune Group Int'l., Inc. (R), PA, *70*
Pfannkuche, Anthony V., SpencerStuart (R), CA, *196*
Pfeiffer, Joseph, Insurance Personnel Resources, Inc. (C), NC, *390*
Phillips, Anna W., Witt/Kieffer, Ford, Hadelman & Lloyd (R), MD, *223*
Phillips, Sharin, Rice Cohen Int'l. (R), PA, *178*
Picard, Daniel A., Picard Int'l., Ltd. (R), NY, *164*
Poklemba, Dale, STAT Search (C), NH, *592*
Polyzos, Ginia M., Management Advisors Int'l., Inc. (C), NC, *424*
Porter, Carlton, Windsor Consultants, Inc. (C), TX, *622*
Powell-Florip, Kathy, Alliance Search Management Inc. (R), TX, *4*
Pratt, Tyler P., Furst Group/MPI (R), IL, *72*
Press, Fredrick R., Adept Tech Recruiting, Inc. (C), NY, *240*
Proctor, Richard W., Foley Proctor Yoskowitz (R), NJ, *69*
Quick, Roger A., Norman Broadbent Int'l., Inc. (R), IL, *153*
Rabinowitz, Peter A., P.A.R. Assoc., Inc. (R), MA, *158*
Rae, Fern, Career Counseling Ltd. (C.C.L.) (C), IL, *282*
Raheja, Marc C., CanMed Consultants Inc. (C), ON, *280*
Randolph, Lea, Lea Randolph & Assoc., Inc. (C), TX, *529*
Raskin, John, Healthcare Search Associates (C), CA, *374*
Reeder, Michael S., Reeder & Assoc., Ltd. (R), GA, *173*
Retis, Lillian, Retis Assoc., Inc. (C), IL, *535*
Richards, Christos, Stanton Chase Int'l. (R), CA, *199*
Richter, Heidi, Career Counseling Ltd. (C.C.L.) (C), IL, *282*
Richter, Michael, Career Counseling Ltd. (C.C.L.) (C), FL, *282*
Richter, Michael, Career Counseling Ltd. (C.C.L.) (C), NY, *282*
Robbins, Jeffrey, Health Search (C), CA, *371*
Robinow, Larry, Health Search (C), CA, *371*
Roe, Sylvia A., Craig Roe & Assoc., LLC (C), MD, *540*
Rogish, Nick, Rogish Assoc., Inc. (C), OH, *541*

RECRUITER SPECIALTIES

Romanchek, Walter R., Wellington Management Group (R), PA, *217*
Rosenberger, Jim, The Rose Search Group, Inc. (C), NC, *545*
Ross, Irene, New World Healthcare Solutions, Inc. (R), NY, *151*
Ross, Marty, LAI Ward Howell (R), CA, *123*
Rowe, David E., David Rowe & Assoc., Inc. (R), IL, *182*
Rowell, Mike, Carter/MacKay (C), MA, *285*
Rozenboom, Carol E., David Rowe & Assoc., Inc. (R), IL, *182*
Rutkauskas, Patsy A., Sales Consultants of Bangor, Inc. (C), ME, *559*
Ryan, Katherine, The Park Group & Assoc., Inc. (C), MD, *503*
Ryan, Nancy, Health Search (C), CA, *371*
Sands, Tony, Healthcare Search Associates (C), CA, *374*
Schachter, Laura J., Professional Placement Assoc., Inc. (C), NY, *521*
Scherck, III, Henry J., LAI Ward Howell (R), NY, *123*
Schindel, Kim, Searchworks, Inc. (C), FL, *577*
Schmidt, James, Cejka Healthcare Executive Search Services (CHESS) (R), MO, *32*
Schneider, Steven A., Schneider, Hill & Spangler, Inc. (R), PA, *185*
Schwartz, Beth O., G. L. Schwartz & Assoc., Inc. (C), GA, *572*
Schwartz, Gary L., G. L. Schwartz & Assoc., Inc. (C), GA, *572*
Secor, David B., The Search Committee (C), MD, *574*
Shabot, David, Korn/Ferry Int'l. (R), PA, *118*
Shapiro, Ira E., New World Healthcare Solutions, Inc. (R), NY, *151*
Shea, Peggy, Peggy Shea & Assoc. (R), CA, *189*
Sheehan, Thomas L., Managed Care Resources (C), TX, *424*
Sherriff, Julie A., Sherriff & Assoc. (C), KS, *580*
Sherriff, William W., Sherriff & Assoc. (C), KS, *580*
Shiley, Bob, Brethet, Barnum & Assoc., Inc. (C), ON, *273*
Sierra, Rafael A., LAI Ward Howell (R), GA, *123*
Sikes, Charles R., Medical Search of America, Inc. (C), GA, *477*
Sikes, Laurie L., Medical Search of America, Inc. (C), GA, *477*
Silberman, Allen, Global HealthCare Partners (R), PA, *78*
Silverstein, Daniel A., Daniel A. Silverstein Assoc. Inc. (R), FL, *191*
Sklar, Ruth, Ruth Sklar Assoc., Inc. (RSA Executive Search) (R), NY, *192*
Smith, Dan, Healthcare Resources Group (C), OK, *374*
Smith, Kyle A., MedXec USA, Inc. (C), OH, *478*
Smith, Mark, Cornerstone Resources, Inc. (C), OK, *299*
Smith, Phyllis E., ISC of Cincinnati Inc. (C), OH, *394*
Smith, Sandra, DNA Search, Inc. (C), CA, *313*
Snyder, C. Edward, Horton International Inc. (R), CT, *96*
Snyder, Jr., James F., Snyder & Co. (R), CT, *194*
Southerland, Keith, Witt/Kieffer, Ford, Hadelman & Lloyd (R), TX, *223*
Spencer, Randall W., Management Recruiters of San Antonio - North (C), TX, *463*
Staggemeier, Debbie, Executive Solutions (R), MO, *64*
Stark, Mary, The Stark Wilton Group (R), MI, *199*
Steadman, Reyn, Vickers Chambless Managed Search (C), GA, *289*
Steinau, Peter B., International Management Services Inc. (R), IL, *102*
Stoll, Joan, Medfall Inc. (C), ON, *476*
Stubberfield, Lee, Management Recruiters of the Baltimore Washington Corridor (C), MD, *450*
Sudina, Chuck, Sudina Search, Inc. (C), MD, *596*
Sullivan, Steve, Jackson & Coker (C), GA, *396*
Swan, Richard A., Witt/Kieffer, Ford, Hadelman & Lloyd (R), CA, *223*
Tabisz, Susanne, Executive Referral Services, Inc. (C), IL, *334*
Talbott Creed, Pamela, The Hollins Group, Inc. (R), IL, *95*
Taylor, John, The Caplan-Taylor Group (R), AZ, *28*
Taylor, Michael, Cejka Healthcare Executive Search Services (CHESS) (R), MO, *32*
Tholke, William E., Boardroom Consultants/Kenny Kindler Tholke (R), NY, *19*
Toney, Roger, MTA Partners (R), TX, *148*
Tracy, Patricia, USA Medical Placement Inc. (C), TX, *611*
Trosin, Walt, Johnson Smith & Knisely (R), NJ, *107*
Tucker, Michael, MTA Partners (R), TX, *148*
Vachon-Vierra, Ronald, The Madeira Group (R), PA, *133*
Valone, Anthony F., UniQuest Int'l., Inc. (C), FL, *611*
Valone, Judith, UniQuest Int'l., Inc. (C), FL, *611*
Valone, Michael, UniQuest Int'l., Inc. (C), FL, *611*
van Eik, Gary, TriStaff Group (C), CA, *609*
Venekotter, Mike, UniQuest Int'l., Inc. (C), FL, *611*
Vergara, Gail H., SpencerStuart (R), IL, *197*
Verros, Jill Hodgins, Daudlin, De Beaupre & Co., Inc. (R), MI, *46*
Vezan, Henry D., Vezan Assoc. (C), CT, *612*
Visnich, L. Christine, Bason Associates (R), OH, *13*
Waldman, Noah W., LAI Ward Howell (R), GA, *123*
Walker, Karen K., K. K. Walker Professional Recruitment (C), CA, *614*
Walker, Walter G., Walker Group, Inc. (R), MN, *215*
Walter, MaryAnn, SpencerStuart (R), CA, *196*
Warden, Shannon, Peggy Shea & Assoc. (R), CA, *189*
Watson, Jim, MSI Int'l. (C), GA, *487*
Watson, Lynn, Joy Reed Belt Search Consultants, Inc. (R), OK, *15*
Webb, Melissa, Circlewood Search Group, Inc. (C), MI, *291*
Wesolich, Elizabeth S., Executive Solutions (R), MO, *64*
White, Edward, Katelyn Partners (C), FL, *404*
Whittaker-Jhaveri, Michelle A., The Whittaker Group (C), MI, *620*
Wilcox, Fred T., Wilcox Bertoux & Miller (R), CA, *220*
Willbanks, Bret, TTG/Sterling Services (C), CA, *610*
Williams, Alexander H., Witt/Kieffer, Ford, Hadelman & Lloyd (R), NY, *223*
Williams, Laurelle, MSI Int'l. (C), LA, *487*
Wilson, Jeffrey M., Sales Consultants of Western McHenry County (C), IL, *558*
Winterburn, Karen, Heartland National Medical Search (C), IL, *374*
Woods, Bruce Gilbert, Bruce G. Woods Executive Search (R), TX, *224*
York, Karen, The York Group (C), CA, *626*
Yoskowitz, Reggie, Foley Proctor Yoskowitz (R), NJ, *69*
Yungner, Steven J., Yungner & Bormann (R), MN, *226*
Zahradka, James F., P. J. Murphy & Assoc., Inc. (R), WI, *150*
Zegas, Jeffrey M., Zurick, Davis & Co., Inc. (R), MA, *227*
Zehner, Donna, Dunhill Professional Search of Wilkes-Barre/Scranton, Inc. (C), PA, *322*
Zenzer, Anne, Witt/Kieffer, Ford, Hadelman & Lloyd (R), IL, *223*
Zera, Ronald J., SpencerStuart (R), TX, *197*
Zivic, Janis M., SpencerStuart (R), CA, *196*

Heavy industry

Pilz, Alfred N., Fagan & Company (R), PA, *64*

High purity water

Ortman, Jim, Ortman Recruiting Int'l. (C), CA, *500*

High technology

Adler, Louis S., CJA-The Adler Group, Inc. (R), CA, *35*
Allen, Paul, Berkana Int'l., Inc. (C), WA, *265*

Allerton, Donald, Allerton Heneghan & O'Neill (R), IL, *4*
Allgire, Mary, Kenzer Corp. (R), IL, *113*
Allred, J. Michael, SpencerStuart (R), GA, *197*
Armitage, John D., Armitage Associates Ltd. (R), ON, *7*
Arnone, Patrick J., Patrick Arnone & Assoc. Inc. (R), VA, *7*
Aubin, Richard E., Aubin Int'l. Inc. (R), MA, *8*
Austin, Peter T., Organization Resources Inc. (R), MA, *157*
Bailey, Paul, Preston-Hunter, Inc. (R), IL, *167*
Baker, Chet, Diversified Consulting Services, Inc. (C), CO, *313*
Bakken, Roger, J. Rodgers & Associates (C), IL, *540*
Barbosa, Franklin J., Skott/Edwards Consultants (R), NJ, *192*
Barr, Linda, Brentwood Int'l. (R), CA, *23*
Bartholdi, Jr., Theodore G., Bartholdi & Co., Inc. (R), NH, *12*
Bartholdi, Sr., Theodore G., Bartholdi & Co., Inc. (R), AZ, *12*
Bass, Mary, SpencerStuart (R), TX, *197*
Bassett, Mark, Hobson Assoc. (C), CT, *379*
Bates, Ron, StratfordGroup (R), CA, *203*
Beatty, Jr., Robert L., The Curtiss Group International (R), FL, *44*
Beck, Larry, Synergy Solutions, Ltd. (C), WA, *597*
Bellamy, William J., Bellamy & Assoc. (C), GA, *263*
Belsjoe, Robert, Robert Belsjoe (C), TX, *528*
Bentley, Lynn H., The Curtiss Group International (R), FL, *44*
Besso, Sandy, Intersource, Ltd. (R), TX, *103*
Besso, Thom, Intersource, Ltd. (R), TX, *103*
Birch, Stanley, Birch & Associes (C), QE, *267*
Bliley, Jerry, SpencerStuart (R), ON, *197*
Bluhm, Claudia Cole, Schweichler Assoc., Inc. (R), CA, *186*
Boltrus, Richard, Sink, Walker, Boltrus Int'l. (R), MA, *192*
Bongiovanni, Vincent, ESA (R), CT, *60*
Bothereau, Elizabeth, Kenzer Corp. (R), MN, *113*
Bradbury, Jr., Paul W., The Bradbury Management Group, Inc. (R), CA, *21*
Bradshaw, Chris, The McKinnon Management Group Inc. (C), ON, *475*
Brault, J. P., Brault & Assoc., Ltd. (R), VA, *22*
Brennan, Vincent, Clayman & Co. (R), MA, *36*
Brennen, Richard J., SpencerStuart (R), IL, *197*
Bruccoleri, Theodore A., StratfordGroup (R), OH, *203*
Bunting, David F., Crane, Reed & Co., Inc. (C), NH, *302*
Buono, Angelo, Raymond Karsan Assoc. (C), MA, *530*
Burns, Gale, Snelling Search Recruiters (C), NC, *586*
Butler, Kevin, SpencerStuart (R), CT, *197*
Campbell, Elizabeth, The Bradbury Management Group, Inc. (R), CA, *21*
Caplan, Sally, Sally Caplan & Assoc. (C), WA, *281*
Carey, Dennis C., SpencerStuart (R), PA, *197*
Carmena, Jane, SpencerStuart (R), CA, *196*
Cecilio, Cesca, Montgomery West (R), CA, *146*
Chambers, Patricia, Global Consulting Group Inc. (C), ON, *358*
Chandler, Carole A., StratfordGroup (R), OH, *203*
Clark, J. Arthur, Barrett Rose & Lee, Inc. (C), ON, *260*
Clarke, Debra, NMC & Kay Int'l. (R), CO, *152*
Clayman, Steven G., Clayman & Co. (R), MA, *36*
Coe, Karen, Coe & Co. Int'l. Inc./EMA Partners Int'l. (R), AB, *37*
Cohen, Robert C., Intech Summit Group, Inc. (R), CA, *102*
Cole-Hill, Susan, Brentwood Int'l. (R), CA, *23*
Combs, Stephen, StratfordGroup (R), CA, *203*
Cook, Dennis F., MESA, Inc. (R), CO, *143*
Cooper, Michael, Chad Management Group (C), ON, *288*
Corder, Eutha, RBW Assoc. Inc. (C), AR, *531*
Courbat, Thomas, Bartholdi & Co., Inc. (R), CA, *12*
Cox, James O., MES Search Co. (C), GA, *479*
Crath, Paul F., PricewaterhouseCoopers Executive Search (R), ON, *168*
Crawford, John H., Clayman & Co. (R), MA, *36*
Crosby, Kimberly A., Fast Switch, Ltd. (C), OH, *338*
Crumbaker, Robert H., LAI Ward Howell (R), OH, *123*
Cruse, O. D., SpencerStuart (R), TX, *197*
Cyphers, Ralph, Strategic Assoc., Inc. (C), TX, *595*
Daugenti, Gary, Gent & Assoc. (C), CA, *356*
Davis, Stephanie, Morgan Samuels Co. (R), CA, *147*
DeCorrevont, James, DeCorrevont & Assoc. (C), IL, *310*
Denis, Liz, Brentwood Int'l. (R), CA, *23*
Dermott, Paula, Dan P. McLean Assoc., Inc. (C), ON, *475*
Diblasi, Joseph J., First Advisory Services Int'l., Inc. (R), MD, *67*
Dicker, Barry L., ESA (R), CT, *60*
Dillon, Larry A., Predictor Systems Corp. (R), CA, *167*
Doyle, William J., Kingsley Quinn/USA (R), NY, *115*
Dressler, Carol F., Haley Associates (R), CA, *85*
England, Marc, Austin-McGregor Int'l. (R), TX, *9*
Erickson, Elaine, Kenzer Corp. (R), NY, *113*
Estrada, Barbara, Montgomery West (R), CA, *146*
Fair, Carolyn, Dunhill Executive Search of Los Angeles, Inc. (C), CA, *319*
Feinberg, Erika, Pearson & Assoc., Inc. (C), AZ, *506*
Felactu, Odessa J., The Odessa Group (R), CA, *155*
Ferrel, James L., Career Marketing Consultants, Inc. (C), GA, *283*
Fitzpatrick, John, Newport Strategic Search LLC (C), CA, *492*
Fleishman, William M., First Advisory Services Int'l., Inc. (R), MD, *67*
Flesher, Susan, Flesher & Assoc., Inc. (R), CA, *68*
Franquemont, Jeffrey D., EFL Int'l. (R), AZ, *57*
Frary, Kevin S., KS Frary & Assoc. (R), MA, *71*
Freeman, Mark, ESA (R), CT, *60*
Gassett, Sam, Primus Assoc., L.C. (R), TX, *169*
Gates, Becky, Primus Assoc., L.C. (R), TX, *169*
Genel, George, Genel Associates (C), CA, *356*
Gideon, Mark, Eagle Search Assoc. (C), CA, *325*
Gilchrist, Carl, SpencerStuart (R), GA, *197*
Gilson, Dirk S., Key Resources Int'l. (C), CA, *406*
Goldberg, Sybil, Spectra International LLC (C), AZ, *589*
Goldstein, Michael, Goldstein & Co. (C), CA, *360*
Goodere, Greg, Montgomery West (R), CA, *146*
Goodman, Goody, Harvard Group Int'l. (R), CO, *87*
Gordy, Thomas, Harvard Group Int'l. (R), GA, *87*
Gostyla, Rick, SpencerStuart (R), CA, *196*
Gottenberg, Norbert, SpencerStuart (R), NY, *196*
Graham, Robert E., Fortune Personnel Consultants of Allentown, Inc. (C), PA, *348*
Graham, Tony, Executives Worldwide, Inc. (C), OR, *337*
Gregg, Larry, Christopher-Westmont & Assoc., Inc. (R), OH, *35*
Griffin, Al, Gardner-Ross Assoc., Inc. (R), NY, *74*
Guerrero, Daniel, Kenzer Corp. (R), CA, *113*
Guld, Allison, Jenex Technology Placement Inc. (C), BC, *398*
Gutierrez, Mary Rose, Job Link, Inc. (C), CA, *399*
Hall, Elizabeth, Bason Associates (R), OH, *13*
Halladay, Patti, Intersource, Ltd. (R), TX, *103*
Hamilton, Denman, Synergy 2000 (C), DC, *597*

RECRUITER SPECIALTIES

Hanna, Dwight, Cadillac Assoc. (C), CA, *278*
Hansen, Ty E., Blake/Hansen Ltd. (R), FL, *18*
Harmon, Jerry, Delta Resource Group, Ltd. (C), GA, *311*
Hauswirth, Jeffrey M., SpencerStuart (R), ON, *197*
Hawksworth, A. Dwight, A. D. & Assoc. Executive Search, Inc. (C), GA, *231*
Heinemann, H. Peter, Barrett Rose & Lee, Inc. (C), ON, *260*
Hendelman, Peter R., P.R.H. Management, Inc. (R), CT, *158*
Henderson, J. Fred, Bartholdi & Co., Inc. (R), CO, *12*
Henderson, Kaaren Liz, The Search Network (C), CA, *576*
Henson, Jeff, Henson Partners (C), AZ, *376*
Herlihy, Jack, J. J. Herlihy & Assoc., Inc. (C), CA, *376*
Holloway, Clive, Holloway Schulz & Partners (C), BC, *380*
Holt, Carol, Bartholdi & Co., Inc. (R), VA, *12*
Horton, Jim, Creative-Leadership, Inc. (R), CA, *42*
Ives, Richard K., Wilkinson & Ives (R), CA, *221*
James, Chip, Morgan Samuels Co. (R), CA, *147*
Johnson, Carl A., Bertrand, Ross & Assoc., Inc. (C), IL, *266*
Johnson, Daniel, Morgan Samuels Co. (R), CA, *147*
Johnson, Karl, K. E. Johnson Assoc. (C), WA, *400*
Johnston, Phil, SpencerStuart (R), CA, *196*
Jones, Donald, Kenzer Corp. (R), TX, *113*
Jones, Pamela K., Jones and Jones (R), OR, *108*
Joseph, Craig, Management Assoc. (C), MD, *424*
Juska, Frank A., Rusher, Loscavio & LoPresto (R), CA, *183*
Karson, Allan, Allan Karson Assoc., Inc. (R), NJ, *110*
Kase, Philip, Re-Mark Assoc. Inc. (C), NJ, *531*
Kelley, Randall D., SpencerStuart (R), TX, *197*
Kenny, Roger M., Boardroom Consultants/ Kenny Kindler Tholke (R), NY, *19*
Kensington, Holland, Kensington International (R), CA, *113*
Kenzer, Robert D., Kenzer Corp. (R), NY, *113*
Kerrigan, Geoffrey M., ESA (R), CT, *60*
King, J. C., A H Justice Search Consultants (C), TX, *402*
Kins, Arnie, Cook Assoc.,® Inc. (R), IL, *40*
Knapp, Ronald A., Knapp Consultants (R), CT, *116*
Kraemer, Katherine R., Katherine R. Kraemer (R), CA, *120*
Krakower, Bernard H., Krakower Group, Inc. (R), CA, *120*
Kreutz, Gary L., Kreutz Consulting Group, Inc. (R), IL, *121*
Kull, Paul, Paul Kull & Co. (R), NJ, *121*
Kulper, Keith D., Kulper & Co., L.L.C. (R), NJ, *121*
Kurosky, John, John Kurosky & Assoc. (R), CA, *122*
L'Archevesque, Lee, Sink, Walker, Boltrus Int'l. (R), MA, *192*
Lai, Karen, C.T.E.W. Executive Personnel Services Inc. (C), BC, *278*
Leadford, Charles, Primus Assoc., L.C. (R), TX, *169*
Lear, Daniel, Omega Systems, LLC (C), VA, *498*
Leffer, Gary, Re-Mark Assoc. Inc. (C), NJ, *531*
Leimpeter, Peter, Goldstein & Co. (C), CA, *360*
Lennox, Charles, PricewaterhouseCoopers Executive Search (R), ON, *168*
LePatner, Steve, Dunhill Executive Search of Los Angeles, Inc. (C), CA, *319*
Linton, Leonard M., Byron Leonard Int'l., Inc. (R), CA, *26*
Lipsky, Marla J., Lipsky Group, Inc. (R), CA, *129*
Lockton, Kathy, StratfordGroup (R), CA, *203*
LoPresto, Robert L., Rusher, Loscavio & LoPresto (R), CA, *183*
Lord, J. Scott, J. S. Lord & Company, Inc. (R), MA, *131*
Lyons, J. David, Aubin Int'l. Inc. (R), MA, *8*
MacKenzie, Bruce J., Chapman & Assoc. (C), BC, *289*
Malouf, Terry, Bartholdi & Co., Inc. (R), CO, *12*
Mancini, Deborah, Mancini Technical Recruiting (C), VA, *468*
Mannix, Francis L., F. L. Mannix & Co. (R), MA, *135*
Marks, Ira Alan, J. M. Meredith & Assoc. Inc. (C), CA, *479*
Marks, Ira M., Strategic Alternatives (R), CA, *202*
Marlow, Bill, Straube Associates (R), MA, *203*
Martin, Judy R., J. Martin & Assoc. (R), CA, *137*
Martinez, Stephen A., Stephens Assoc. Ltd., Inc. (R), OH, *200*
Mason, Maurice, McCray, Shriver, Eckdahl & Assoc., Inc. (R), CA, *140*
Mazziota, Daniel R., Ruth Sklar Assoc., Inc. (RSA Executive Search) (R), NY, *192*
McCreary, Charles, Austin-McGregor Int'l. (R), TX, *9*
McDonald, John R., TSS Consulting, Ltd. (C), AZ, *610*
McHale, John P., McHale & Assoc. (R), WA, *141*
McIvor, Mike, Christmas, McIvor & Assoc. Inc. (C), ON, *290*
McLean, Dan P., Dan P. McLean Assoc., Inc. (C), ON, *475*
McLean, Luella, Dan P. McLean Assoc., Inc. (C), ON, *475*
McMann, Dean E., The Ransford Group (R), TX, *171*
McMillan, Dwight, Management Recruiters of Atlanta NE (C), GA, *446*
Mikula, Linda, Schweichler Assoc., Inc. (R), CA, *186*
Miller, Kenneth, Computer Network Resources, Inc. (C), CA, *295*
Milton, Charles E., Smith James Group, Inc. (R), GA, *194*
Moon, Thomas A., Power Search (C), TX, *515*
Mordue, Michael J., Mordue, Allen, Roberts, Bonney Ltd. (C), WA, *485*
Mortensen, Kenneth A., Kingsley Quinn/ USA (R), NJ, *115*
Morton, Nancy J., Robert T. Morton Assoc., Inc. (C), MA, *486*
Morton, Robert T., Robert T. Morton Assoc., Inc. (C), MA, *486*
Moscow, Frank, The Brentwood Group Ltd. (R), OR, *23*
Murphy, Irene, StratfordGroup (R), CA, *203*
Nadel, R. J., ACCESS Technology (C), CA, *234*
Nathasingh, Steve, Growth Strategies, Inc. (R), FL, *83*
Nixon, Ted, TechNix Inc. (C), ON, *602*
O'Brien, Frank E., Austin Michaels, Ltd., Inc. (C), AZ, *256*
O'Daniel, Beverly W., The Elsworth Group (C), TX, *329*
O'Donnell, M. Theresa, Grant/Morgan Assoc., Inc. (C), MD, *361*
O'Keefe, John P., O'Keefe & Assoc. (C), TX, *498*
O'Leary, James, The Brentwood Group Ltd. (R), OR, *23*
O'Rourke, Kevin, Ward Assoc. (C), ON, *615*
O'Rourke, Kevin, Ward Assoc. (C), QE, *615*
Olsen, Elizabeth Clark, Olsen/Clark (R), WA, *156*
Olsen, Rex, Olsen/Clark (R), WA, *156*
Outman, Timothy J., CTR (R), CA, *43*
Peckenpaugh, Ann, Schweichler Assoc., Inc. (R), CA, *186*
Peden, Ann, Peden & Assoc. (C), CA, *506*
Piché, Jérôme, SpencerStuart (R), QE, *197*
Pigott, A. Daniel, ESA (R), NC, *60*
Pinger, Earl, Systems Research Group (C), CA, *598*
Powell, Marie, Kenzer Corp. (R), GA, *113*
Pukita, Mark, Fast Switch, Ltd. (C), OH, *338*
Quiros, Vince, CV Associates (C), NY, *305*
Raab, Julie, Vaughan & Co. (C), CA, *612*
Radosevic, Frank, Radosevic Assoc. (R), CA, *171*
Radosevic, Tanya C., Radosevic Assoc. (R), CA, *171*
Reichardt, Karl J., R & K Associates, Inc. (C), AZ, *528*
Reid, Gary, KPMG Executive Search (R), ON, *119*
Reinitz, Robert, Professional Recruiters Inc. (C), MN, *521*
Richards, Christos, Stanton Chase Int'l. (R), CA, *199*

Richards, David P., Insight Personnel Group, Inc. (C), TX, *389*
Rigal, Jennifer, Jenex Technology Placement Inc. (C), BC, *398*
Rizk, Nayla, SpencerStuart (R), CA, *196*
Roberts, Libby, Global Consulting Group Inc. (C), ON, *358*
Rodriguez, Steven, SpencerStuart (R), CA, *196*
Romanello, Daniel P., SpencerStuart (R), CT, *196*
Rooney, Joseph J., Rooney Assoc., Inc. (R), IL, *181*
Rosica, John, Management Recruiters Inc. of Silicon Valley (C), CA, *441*
Rosica, John, Sales Consultants of Silicon Valley (C), CA, *556*
Rowe, William, Foster Partners (R), TX, *71*
Russell, Robin, Kenzer Corp. (R), NY, *113*
Samuels, Ivan R., George D. Sandel Assoc. (C), MA, *565*
Scardifield, David, Omnisearch Assoc. (C), CA, *499*
Schultz, Helen, Predictor Systems Corp. (R), CA, *167*
Schultz, Sheila A., Mordue, Allen, Roberts, Bonney Ltd. (C), WA, *485*
Schweichler, Lee, Schweichler Assoc., Inc. (R), CA, *186*
Segal, Eric B., Kenzer Corp. (R), NY, *113*
Segal, Sheila, Segal & Assoc. (C), GA, *578*
Seidel, James, Holloway Schulz & Partners (C), BC, *380*
Shattuck, M. B., M. B. Shattuck & Assoc., Inc. (R), CA, *189*
Sheedy, III, Edward J., Dieckmann & Assoc., Ltd. (R), IL, *51*
Sheehan-Armstrong, Jennifer, J. S. Armstrong & Assoc., Inc. (R), CA, *7*
Shufelt, Douglas G., Sink, Walker, Boltrus Int'l. (R), MA, *192*
Silver, Lee, L. A. Silver Assoc., Inc. (R), MA, *191*
Simmons, Noel A., The Simmons Group (C), CA, *582*
Simpson, Cathy G., Conroy Partners Ltd. (R), AB, *39*
Sink, Clifton W., Sink, Walker, Boltrus Int'l. (R), TX, *192*
Smith, Wilton, The Stark Wilton Group (R), MI, *199*
Snyder, Suzanne, Wilkinson & Ives (R), CA, *221*
Soderlund, Eric, Soderlund Assoc. Inc. (R), OH, *195*
Souder, Elizabeth W., Springer Souder & Assoc. L.L.C. (R), IL, *198*
Sparks, Jr., R. Thomas, Sparks, McDonough & Assoc., Inc. (C), MO, *588*
Speth, Don, Independent Resource Systems (C), CA, *388*
Spiegel, Deborah, Kenzer Corp. (R), NY, *113*
Spiegel, Gayle, The Spiegel Group (R), MA, *197*
Splaine, Charles, Splaine & Assoc., Inc. (R), CA, *198*
Springstein, Bob, Dan P. McLean Assoc., Inc. (C), ON, *475*
Steinberg, Paul D., IMA Search, Inc. (R), NY, *101*
Stephenson, Jay, JG Consultants, Inc. (R), TX, *106*
Stevens, Wayne J., Stevens Assoc. (C), MA, *593*
Stevenson, Terry, Bartholdi & Co., Inc. (R), CO, *12*
Stirn, Bradley A., SpencerStuart (R), CA, *196*
Strain, Stephen R., SpencerStuart (R), CA, *196*
Stringer, Dann P., Foster Partners (R), DC, *70*
Sullivan, G. Kay, Rusher, Loscavio & LoPresto (R), CA, *183*
Taylor, M. Kent, Prairie Resource Group, Inc. (R), IL, *166*
Testart, Marion, Placement Testart Inc. (C), QE, *513*
Tholke, William E., Boardroom Consultants/Kenny Kindler Tholke (R), NY, *19*
Tierney, John F., Dunhill Professional Search of Oakland (C), CA, *319*
Tirocchi, Fred, Tirocchi, Wright, Inc. (R), CA, *209*
Truesdell, Michael, Ethos Consulting, Inc. (R), CA, *61*
Tucci, Joseph, Fairfaxx Corp. (R), CT, *64*
Vaccaro, George, The Advisory Group, Inc. (R), CA, *2*
Vance, D., Ki Technologies, Inc. (C), UT, *406*
VanDolah, A. F., Management Recruiters of Lionville, Inc. (C), PA, *459*
Veblan, Jennifer, NCC Executive Search Consultants (C), CA, *490*
Vento, Joseph P., Vento Assoc. (C), TN, *612*
Vourakis, Zan, ZanExec L.L.C. (R), VA, *226*
Walker, Douglas G., Sink, Walker, Boltrus Int'l. (R), MA, *192*
Ward, Peter, Ward Assoc. (C), ON, *615*
Ware, John, SpencerStuart (R), CA, *196*
Wasson, Thomas W., SpencerStuart (R), CT, *196*
Webster, Doug, The Buckley Group (C), NJ, *276*
Weinstein, Lewis R., Weinstein & Co. (R), MA, *217*
Welzig, Frank E., Welzig, Lowe & Assoc. (C), CO, *618*
Whelan, David, Ethos Consulting, Inc. (R), CA, *61*
Whitaker, Geraldine, Rusher, Loscavio & LoPresto (R), CA, *183*
White, Jonathan O., SpencerStuart (R), CA, *196*
White, Lenny, The Brentwood Group Ltd. (R), OR, *23*
White, William C., Venture Resources, Inc. (R), CA, *213*
Whittaker, Cynthia, Brentwood Int'l. (R), CA, *23*
Willcocks, Roy, Dan P. McLean Assoc., Inc. (C), ON, *475*
Wolf, Stephen M., Byron Leonard Int'l., Inc. (R), CA, *26*
Wolf, Stephen M., Montenido Assoc. (R), CA, *146*
Wood, Karen, Armitage Associates Ltd. (R), ON, *7*
Woods, Bruce Gilbert, Bruce G. Woods Executive Search (R), TX, *224*
Wright, Paula G., Tirocchi, Wright, Inc. (R), CA, *209*
Zak, Adam, Horton Int'l. Inc. (R), IL, *96*
Zier, Patricia D., P. D. Zier Assoc. (C), CT, *627*

Hispanic

Fresquez, Ernesto, Fresquez & Assoc. (C), CA, *353*

Home

Bennett, Bob, ISC of Houston, Inc. (C), TX, *394*
Cleveland, Anthony, The Talon Group (R), TX, *206*
Glynn, Mary Anne, E. A. Hughes & Co., Inc. (R), NY, *98*
Hall, Rodney, The Talon Group (R), TX, *205*
Hughes, Elaine A., E. A. Hughes & Co., Inc. (R), NY, *98*
Lord, Marvin, E. A. Hughes & Co., Inc. (R), NY, *98*
Mason, Jean, The Talon Group (R), TX, *206*
McNeil, Janet, Cook Assoc.,® Inc. (R), IL, *40*
Piper, Robert A., The Talon Group (R), TX, *205*
Sheppard, Jerry, Don Hall & Assoc. (C), CA, *366*
Spinrad, Kenn, Kenn Spinrad Inc. (C), PA, *589*
VanSlyke, Dayton, Search By Design (C), AZ, *574*
Wilson, Wayne, Wilson & Assoc. Int'l. Inc. (C), FL, *622*

Home health

Dankowski, Eden, Professional Healthcare Search & Consultants, Inc. (C), CA, *520*
Gale, Michael, Professional Healthcare Search & Consultants, Inc. (C), CA, *520*
McDaniel, James, H R Solutions, Inc. (C), MO, *365*
Sands, Tony, Healthcare Search Associates (C), CA, *374*
Yorba, Anissa, Professional Healthcare Search & Consultants, Inc. (C), CA, *520*

Horticulture

Dalton, Joseph, Florapersonnel, Inc. (R), FL, *68*
Leonard, Mell D., International Recruiting Services (C), FL, *393*
Zahra, Robert F., Florapersonnel, Inc. (R), FL, *68*

RECRUITER SPECIALTIES

Hospitality

Alfus, Phillip, The Alfus Group (R), NY, *3*
Allgire, Mary, Kenzer Corp. (R), IL, *113*
Barrett, Peter, Barrett Hospitality Search (R), CA, *12*
Bauer, Benjamin, Rob Dey Executive Search (R), FL, *49*
Binder, Kenneth K., Binder Hospitality Group (C), KY, *266*
Blecksmith, Edward L., Larsen, Whitney, Blecksmith & Zilliacus, Inc. (R), CA, *125*
Blevins, David C., David Blevins & Assoc. (C), WA, *268*
Borkenhagen, Christine, Morgan Samuels Co. (R), CA, *147*
Bothereau, Elizabeth, Kenzer Corp. (R), MN, *113*
Citrin, James M., SpencerStuart (R), CT, *196*
Collier, Carmen Anne, William-Johns Co., Inc. (C), CA, *621*
Costick, Kathryn J., John Sibbald Assoc., Inc. (R), MO, *191*
Damon, Robert A., SpencerStuart (R), NY, *196*
De Riviera, Sandra, Parker Page Group (C), TX, *503*
Dey, Irene, Rob Dey Executive Search (R), FL, *49*
Dresner, Rhonda, Recruiting Specialists (C), MA, *532*
Duncan, Robin, Weinman & Assoc. (C), AZ, *617*
Eagar, Brian, Search Int'l. (R), MA, *187*
Elliot, Alice, Elliot Assoc. Inc. (R), NY, *58*
Erickson, Elaine, Kenzer Corp. (R), NY, *113*
Fedele, Rocco M., Devin Scott Assoc. (C), NJ, *572*
Fields, Sharon K., Career Development Associates (C), NV, *282*
Franz, Bill, Cornerstone Resources, Inc. (C), OK, *299*
Freier, Bruce, Executive Referral Services, Inc. (C), IL, *334*
Gallagher, David W., LAI Ward Howell (R), GA, *123*
Gibeault, Joe, Cornerstone Resources, Inc. (C), OK, *299*
Glazin, Lynne, The Glazin Group (R), BC, *77*
Greger, Kenneth R., Greger/Peterson Assoc., Inc. (R), OR, *82*
Guerrero, Daniel, Kenzer Corp. (R), CA, *113*
Hamill, Robert W., Robert Howe & Assoc. (R), GA, *97*
Hanna, Dwight, Cadillac Assoc. (C), CA, *278*
Hansen, David G., Ott & Hansen, Inc. (R), CA, *157*
Harfenist, Harry, Parker Page Group (C), FL, *503*
Hawthorne, Christine, Search Int'l. (R), MA, *187*
Hillner, Jill, Continental Research Search, Inc. (C), WI, *298*
Howlett, Grant, CountryHouse Hotels Executive Search (C), VA, *302*
Huff, Margaret L., Huff Assoc. (R), NJ, *98*
Huff, William Z., Huff Assoc. (R), NJ, *98*
Hughes, J. Reilly, ProLinks Inc. (R), VA, *170*
Hunter, Jr., John B., John Sibbald Assoc., Inc. (R), MO, *191*
Jennings, Allison, The Personnel Network, Inc. (C), SC, *509*
Jones, Donald, Kenzer Corp. (R), TX, *113*
Kelly, Mary K., Kelly Assoc. (R), WI, *112*
Kelly, Ronald, Kelly Assoc. (R), WI, *112*
Kenzer, Robert D., Kenzer Corp. (R), NY, *113*
Keymer, Robert J., H R Solutions, Inc. (C), MO, *365*
Kolacia, V., Murphy Partners Int'l. (R), IL, *150*
Krainen, Cindy, Harper Associates (C), MI, *369*
Kresich, William J., William-Johns Co., Inc. (C), CA, *621*
Kushell, Douglas T., Franchise Search, Inc. (C), NY, *352*
Lamond, Elizabeth, The Whyte Group, Inc. (R), MD, *220*
Lowery, Andrew, Search Int'l. (R), MA, *187*
Lyons, Sean J., Lyons Assoc. (R), NY, *132*
Manassero, Henri J. P., International Management Advisors, Inc. (R), NY, *103*
Martin, Randall, John Sibbald Assoc., Inc. (R), MO, *191*
Massarsky, Alan, Marshall-Alan Assoc., Inc. (C), NY, *471*
McCormick, Pat, Barrett Hospitality Search (R), CA, *12*
Meagher, III, Edward A., The Woodstone Consulting Company, Inc. (R), CO, *224*
Meagher, Linda J., The Woodstone Consulting Company, Inc. (R), CO, *224*
Mettler, Renate, William-Johns Co., Inc. (C), CA, *621*
O'Toole, Dennis P., Dennis P. O'Toole & Assoc. Inc. (R), NY, *154*
Ollinger, Chuck, Ollinger Partners (R), MA, *156*
Page, Susan, John Kurosky & Assoc. (R), CA, *122*
Phillips, Mimi, Snelling Search Recruiters (C), NC, *586*
Pitman, P., American Executive Management, Inc. (R), MA, *5*
Pitzer, Steve, Barrett Hospitality Search (R), CA, *12*
Powell, Marie, Kenzer Corp. (R), GA, *113*
Powers, Robert, Robert Powers & Assoc. (C), CA, *515*
Powers, Susan, Robert Powers & Assoc. (C), CA, *515*
Powers, William D., Powers Consultants, Inc. (R), MO, *166*
Reda, Pat, P. J. Reda & Assoc., Inc. (C), GA, *533*
Rios, Dyann, Career Development Associates (C), NV, *282*
Ritt, Arthur, Ritt-Ritt & Assoc., Inc. (C), IL, *537*
Robinson, Mel, MDR & Associates (C), AR, *476*
Rubin, Karen, Travel Executive Search (C), NY, *608*
Rumson, Paul Michael, Management Recruiters of Asheville, Inc. (C), NC, *455*
Russell, Robin, Kenzer Corp. (R), NY, *113*
Salzberg, David, Roth Young Seattle (C), WA, *546*
Samuels, Steve, CountryHouse Hotels Executive Search (C), VA, *302*
Schwartz, Bennett, Harper Associates (C), MI, *369*
Schwartz, Deborah, Ollinger Partners (R), MA, *156*
Schweiger, Michael, Search Int'l. (R), MA, *187*
Segal, Eric B., Kenzer Corp. (R), NY, *113*
Smith, Peter A., Peter A. Smith & Assoc. (C), OR, *584*
Spatt, Jonathan M., Hospitality Executive Search, Inc. (R), MA, *96*
Spiegel, Deborah, Kenzer Corp. (R), NY, *113*
Stanley, John, Search Int'l. (R), MA, *187*
Steinberg, Joan, Marshall-Alan Assoc., Inc. (C), NY, *471*
Thomas III, William, William-Johns Co., Inc. (C), CA, *621*
Truesdell, Michael, Ethos Consulting, Inc. (R), CA, *61*
Van Leeuwen, Lee, Van Leeuwen Assoc. (R), CA, *213*
Wagenknecht, Jason, H R Solutions, Inc. (C), MO, *365*
Weinman, Mary, Weinman & Assoc. (C), AZ, *617*
Whitney, William A., Larsen, Whitney, Blecksmith & Zilliacus, Inc. (R), CA, *125*
Whyte, Roger J., The Whyte Group, Inc. (R), MD, *220*
Wilkson, James, Allen Austin Lowe & Powers (R), TX, *3*
Wolcott, Tracy, Recruiting Specialists (C), MA, *532*
Woods, Bruce Gilbert, Bruce G. Woods Executive Search (R), TX, *224*

Hospitals

Barkley, Keith, The Mackenzie Group (R), MD, *133*
Hyman, Jean W., Management Search Assoc., Inc. (C), GA, *467*
Kinney, Diane C., The Stewart Group (C), FL, *593*
Lee, Jacquelene R., Healthcare Search Associates (C), CA, *374*
Lowderman, William, Loderman & Costello (C), GA, *419*
Moore, Sherrie, The Alfus Group (R), NY, *3*
Smith, Judy, JPM International (C), CA, *401*
Warren, Lester, Management Recruiters of Lubbock (C), TX, *463*
Wisdom, T. J., Management Recruiters of Fresno (C), CA, *440*

Hotels

Alfus, Phillip, The Alfus Group (R), NY, *3*
Brown, Beirne, Bennett Search & Consulting Co. (R), FL, *16*
Casey, David, The Alfus Group (R), NY, *3*
Claybaugh, Brian, Roth Young Executive Search (C), TX, *546*
Francis, Joseph, Hospitality Int'l. (C), NY, *381*
Gentry, Allen, Hospitality Int'l. (C), AZ, *381*
Lanum, Monica, Executive Referral Services, Inc. (C), IL, *334*
Pappas, Sewell B., Alpha Resource Group, Inc. (C), TX, *246*
Radice, Joseph A., Hospitality Int'l. (C), NY, *381*
Reda, Pat, P. J. Reda & Assoc., Inc. (C), GA, *533*
Stafford, Susan P., Hospitality Int'l. (C), NY, *381*
Thieringer, Stephan, Search Int'l. (R), MA, *187*
Wilner, Susan, The Alfus Group (R), NY, *3*

Human resources

Abrams, Burton J., B. J. Abrams & Assoc. Inc. (C), IL, *233*
Akin, J. R., J. R. Akin & Co. (R), MA, *2*
Allen, Frank, Frank E. Allen & Assoc. (C), NJ, *244*
Allen, Mark, Frank E. Allen & Assoc. (C), NJ, *244*
Allen, Rita, Gatti & Assoc. (C), MA, *355*
Allerton, Donald, Allerton Heneghan & O'Neill (R), IL, *4*
Alves, Manuel J., M/J/A Partners (R), IL, *133*
Amato, George, Faro Consultants Int'l. (C), VA, *338*
Anderson, Wayne F., Anderson Network Group (C), OH, *250*
Angus, Thomas R., The Angus Group, Ltd. (C), OH, *251*
Arnold, David, Management Solutions, Inc. (C), CA, *468*
Arrants, Becky, F-O-R-T-U-N-E Personnel Consultants of Knoxville (C), TN, *350*
Ashton, Neil K., Sales Consultants of Bangor, Inc. (C), ME, *559*
Atchison, W. R., W. R. Atchison & Assoc., Inc. (C), NC, *255*
Atkinson, Patrick J., Waterford Executive Group Ltd. (C), IL, *616*
Attewell, Brad J., Dise & Co. (R), OH, *52*
Bacher, Judith, SpencerStuart (R), NY, *196*
Bachhuber, Thomas, Management Alliance Group, Inc. (R), NJ, *134*
Bagley, James M., Russell Reynolds Assoc., Inc. (R), NY, *177*
Bailey, Jerald W., Dunhill Professional Search of Greater New Orleans (C), LA, *321*
Baker, Gary M., Cochran, Cochran & Yale, Inc. (R), NY, *36*
Banker, Judith, Gatti & Assoc. (C), MA, *355*
Bard, Cliff, Management Recruiters of St. Augustine (C), FL, *444*
Bargholz, Harry L., Management Recruiters of Wilmington (C), NC, *457*
Barkocy, Andrew B., Princeton Executive Search (C), NJ, *518*
Bartell, Barbara L., BLB Consulting (C), NY, *268*
Barton, Gary, Barton Assoc., Inc. (R), TX, *12*
Bauer, Benjamin, Rob Dey Executive Search (R), FL, *49*
Beaudine, Jr., Frank R., Eastman & Beaudine, Inc. (R), GA, *56*
Becker, Matthew, Becker Personnel (C), FL, *262*
Bennett, Linda E., Bennett & Co. Consulting Group (C), CA, *264*
Bennett, Mark, Bennett & Associates (C), TX, *264*
Bentley, Lynn H., The Curtiss Group International (R), FL, *44*
Besso, Sandy, Intersource, Ltd. (R), TX, *103*
Besso, Thom, Intersource, Ltd. (R), TX, *103*
Birnbaum, Richard, R. J. Associates (C), NY, *528*
Black, Dean A., TPS Staffing Solutions (C), IN, *608*
Blakemore, Linda, Atlantic Pacific Group (C), CA, *255*
Bleau, Donn E., Global Resources Group (R), CA, *78*
Bloomfield, Mary, Gatti & Assoc. (C), MA, *355*
Bodin, Thomas H., The Personnel Group, Inc. (R), MN, *163*
Bosch, Diane, Bosch & Assoc., LLC (R), CT, *20*
Bradshaw, Patrick M., The Patience Motivation Belief Group, Inc. (C), GA, *505*
Brandt, William E., Brandt Associates (C), PA, *272*
Breaks, Nick, The Levton Group Inc. (R), ON, *129*
Briggs, Farris R., Staff Resources, Inc. (C), SC, *590*
Brindisi, Thomas J., Brindisi Search (R), MD, *23*
Brinkerhoff, David W., Abbott Smith Assoc., Inc. (R), NY, *193*
Brody, Steve, Executive Resource Systems (C), CA, *335*
Bronder, Stephanie L., Fagan & Company (R), PA, *64*
Brook, Marsha, C. M. Management Services, Inc. (R), KY, *26*
Brooks, Natalie, Raymond Karsan Assoc. (C), NJ, *530*
Brophy, Melissa, Maximum Management Corp. (C), NY, *473*
Brown, Bonny, Career Marketing Consultants, Inc. (C), GA, *283*
Brown, Larry, Horton International Inc. (R), CT, *96*
Bryan, Paula, Angel Group Int'l. (C), KY, *250*
Burchill, Barbara E., BGB Assoc., Inc. (C), IL, *266*
Burgess, Rick, Human Resource Dimensions, Inc. (C), TX, *384*
Burkhill, J. L., The Talley Group (R), VA, *205*
Burkholder, John, Burkholder & Assoc., Inc. (C), TX, *276*
Burt, James M., Sales Consultants of Stamford-Darien (C), CT, *557*
Butler, Carol, Leonard Corwen Assoc. (C), NY, *302*
Calzaretta, Frank, Abbott Smith Assoc., Inc. (R), IL, *193*
Campbell, Vicki, Management Solutions, Inc. (C), WA, *468*
Carson, Sandra, Carson-Thomas & Assoc. (C), CA, *284*
Carter, Wayne A., The Personnel Group, Inc. (R), MN, *163*
Casey, Darren M., Management Solutions, Inc. (C), WA, *468*
Chadick, Susan L., Gould, McCoy & Chadick, Inc. (R), NY, *80*
Chandler, Carole A., StratfordGroup (R), OH, *203*
Chester, Frank G., The Libra Group (C), NC, *417*
Christie, Stephen G., Marsar & Co., Inc. (C), FL, *471*
Clark, Howard L., Howard Clark Assoc. (C), NJ, *292*
Clarke, Karen, HEC Group (C), ON, *375*
Cognac, Michael, Retained Search Assoc. (R), NC, *176*
Cohen, Irwin, Benson Associates (C), NY, *264*
Cohen, Michael R., Intech Summit Group, Inc. (R), CA, *102*
Collins, Lynn, Computer Placements Unlimited Inc. (C), NY, *295*
Colman, Michael, Executive Placement Consultants (C), IL, *333*
Cook, Gene, Cook Assoc. Int'l., Inc. (C), TN, *298*
Cooper, Linda, BG & Assoc. (C), MD, *266*
Cordell, Cindy Andrew, Corporate Resources (C), OH, *301*
Cougle, Nancy, Advanced Recruitment, Inc. (C), TN, *240*
Cox, Larry, Human Resource Solutions (R), TX, *99*
Cozzillio, Larry, The Andre Group, Inc. (R), PA, *6*
Cramer, Paul J., C/R Associates (C), NY, *278*
Critchley, Walter, Cochran, Cochran & Yale, Inc. (R), NY, *37*
Cullen, Andrew, The Pennmor Group (C), NJ, *506*
Cunningham, Douglas, Staff Resources, Inc. (C), SC, *590*
Cupp, C. A., Austin - Allen Co. (C), TN, *256*
Dalenberg, David D., Abbott Smith Assoc., Inc. (R), IL, *193*
Dalton, Evonne, Dalton Management Consultants, Ltd. (C), NJ, *306*

RECRUITER SPECIALTIES

Danforth, Andrea, Ethos Consulting, Inc. (R), CA, *61*
Dankowski, Tom, Dankowski & Assoc., Inc. (C), OH, *307*
Davis, Donna, Donna Davis Assoc. (C), NJ, *309*
Dean, James L., Dean-Dzierzawiec Assoc. (C), NJ, *309*
DeBaugh, David H., PRAXIS Partners (R), VA, *167*
deBerry, Marian Alexander, Boulware & Assoc. Inc. (R), IL, *20*
DeHart, Donna, Tower Consultants, Ltd. (R), PA, *210*
deVry, Kim, Tower Consultants, Ltd. (R), PA, *210*
Dickerson, Joseph A., Penn Associates (R), PA, *162*
Dickson, David W., Fortune Personnel Consultants of Chattanooga Inc. (C), TN, *349*
Dinse, Elizabeth, Management Recruiters of Sacramento North (C), CA, *441*
Doele, Don, Goodrich & Sherwood Assoc., Inc. (R), NJ, *80*
Doherty, John J., Doherty Int'l., Inc. (R), IL, *53*
Donovan, Jerry, Management Recruiters of Arlington (C), VA, *464*
Doty, Eleanor C., The Doty Group (C), TX, *314*
Doupe, S. Scott, Conroy Partners Ltd. (R), AB, *39*
Duff, Michael, West Coast Recruiting (C), CA, *619*
Duke, Lawrence, Management Recruiters of Charlotte - North, Inc. (C), NC, *456*
Dye, Carson E., LAI Ward Howell (R), OH, *123*
Dzierzawiec, Kenneth J., Dean-Dzierzawiec Assoc. (C), NJ, *309*
Elkas, Yves, Yves Elkas Inc. (R), QE, *58*
Engel, Walter E., F-O-R-T-U-N-E Personnel Consultants of the Tri-Cities, Inc. (C), TN, *350*
Extract, Raymond L., Raymond L. Extract & Assoc. (R), CA, *64*
Faller, Laura McGrath, Redden & McGrath Assoc., Inc. (R), NY, *173*
Farmer, David W., Whitney Smith Co. (C), TX, *620*
Faubert, Denis, DARE Personnel Inc. (C), ON, *307*
Fehrenbach, Ray, Southern Recruiters & Consultants, Inc. (C), SC, *587*
Fell, David W., LAI Ward Howell (R), OH, *123*
Ferrel, James L., Career Marketing Consultants, Inc. (C), GA, *283*
Fiala, Joanne C., Burke & Assoc./The Westfield Group (C), CT, *276*
Fiala, Joanne C., The Westfield Group (C), CT, *619*
Finn, Eileen, Eileen Finn & Assoc., Inc. (C), NY, *341*
Fischer, Karl W., Dunhill Search of Medford (C), NJ, *321*
Fischler, Nick P., NPF Assoc. Ltd. Inc. (R), FL, *153*
Fishel, Richard A., Fishel HR Assoc., Inc. (C), AZ, *341*
Fleming, Richard, Gatti & Assoc. (C), MA, *355*
Fludd, Virgil L., The CARVIR Group, Inc. (C), GA, *285*
Fogec, Thomas G., Fogec Consultants, Inc. (R), WI, *69*
Ford, Sandra D., The Ford Group, Inc. (R), PA, *69*
Fox, Allis, Intersource, Ltd. (R), GA, *103*
Foxman, Marty, Pierce & Assoc. (C), CA, *512*
Friedman, Donna L., Tower Consultants, Ltd. (R), FL, *210*
Gahan, Carolyn M., Gahan Assoc. (R), NY, *73*
Gatti, Robert D., Gatti & Assoc. (C), MA, *355*
Gay, Richard C., IprGroup, Inc. (C), GA, *394*
Gélinas, Normand, Yves Plouffe & Assoc. (R), QE, *165*
Gerard, William, Fox-Morris Assoc., Inc. (C), CA, *352*
Gerarde, Paul S., Keena Staffing Services (C), NY, *404*
Glatman, Marcia, HRD Consultants, Inc. (R), NJ, *97*
Gleason, James P., J. P. Gleason Assoc., Inc. (R), IL, *77*
Glynn, Thomas J., Fox-Morris Assoc., Inc. (C), PA, *352*
Goich, S. George, Fernow Assoc. (C), PA, *340*
Goldshore, Steven, Winthrop Partners, Inc. (R), NY, *222*
Gonzalez, Cecelia, Brystol Cove Assoc. (R), CA, *24*
Gonzalez, Joe, Brystol Cove Assoc. (R), CA, *24*
Goodere, Greg, Montgomery West (R), CA, *146*
Gragg, Robert, Montgomery West (R), CA, *146*
Graham, Robert W., Robert Graham Assoc. (R), RI, *81*
Gray, Brian A., BG & Assoc. (C), MD, *266*
Green, Mark, Rice Cohen Int'l. (R), PA, *178*
Greenwood, Katherine, Fortune Personnel Consultants of Plano (C), TX, *350*
Gregg, Larry, Christopher-Westmont & Assoc., Inc. (R), OH, *35*
Griffin, Deana A., Souder & Assoc. (R), VA, *195*
Grimm, Peter G., Nordeman Grimm, Inc. (R), NY, *152*
Gross, Dean, Becker Personnel (C), FL, *262*
Gunkel, Keith J., KGA Inc. (C), WI, *406*
Gurney, Darrell W., A Permanent Success Employment Services (C), CA, *231*
Hageman, Jr., Leo, HR Inc. (C), NC, *382*
Haggerty, Noreen, K. Russo Assoc. Inc. (C), CT, *548*
Haines, Linda, Human Resource Solutions (R), TX, *99*
Halladay, Patti, Intersource, Ltd. (R), TX, *103*
Hammond, Karla, People Management Northeast, Inc. (R), CT, *162*
Hangartner, Robin, Intersource, Ltd. (R), GA, *103*
Hannock, III, Elwin W., Flynn, Hannock, Inc. (R), CT, *69*
Hardage, Phillip, Hardage Group (C), TN, *369*
Hare, Beth C., Fidelity Search Group, Inc. (R), PA, *66*
Harkins, Robert E., Robert Harkins Assoc., Inc. (C), PA, *369*
Hartman, Beverly, Management Assoc. (C), MD, *424*
Hawke, Marjorie, Becker Personnel (C), FL, *262*
Hayden, Dale, Sanford Rose Assoc. - Pittsburgh North (C), PA, *570*
Helms, Mary P., The Helms Int'l. Group (R), VA, *91*
Henshaw, Bob, Fortune Personnel Consultants of Huntsville, Inc. (C), AL, *343*
Herrerias, Paul, Herrerias & Assoc. (R), CA, *92*
Herring, Bill, Herring & Assoc. (C), AR, *376*
Hildy, Edward V., Systems One Ltd. (C), IL, *598*
Hind, Catherine, Frank E. Allen & Assoc. (C), NJ, *244*
Hoglund, Gerald C., Hoglund & Assoc., Inc. (R), IL, *94*
Horne, Tony, Herring & Assoc. (C), AR, *376*
Hosey, Debra, The Pailin Group Professional Search Consultants (R), TX, *158*
Howe, William S., Hunt & Howe Inc. (R), NY, *99*
Hughes, Tom, Fox-Morris Assoc., Inc. (C), NJ, *352*
Hugsman, Rob, Russ Hadick & Assoc. Inc. (C), OH, *365*
Hutchison, Robert, Overton Consulting (R), WI, *157*
Hyman, Derry, Hyman & Assoc. (C), TX, *386*
Ives, Phyllis E., Ives & Associates, Inc. (C), OH, *395*
Joffe, Barry, Bason Associates (R), OH, *13*
Johnson, Harold E., LAI Ward Howell (R), NY, *122*
Johnson, John F., LAI Ward Howell (R), OH, *123*
Johnson, John Kimbrough, Johnson Brown Assoc., Inc. (C), IN, *400*
Johnson, Kathleen, Barton Assoc., Inc. (R), TX, *12*
Jones, Judy, Management Recruiters of Winston-Salem (C), NC, *457*
Jordan, Dick, Staff Resources, Inc. (C), SC, *590*
Kanzer, William F., Kanzer Assoc., Inc. (R), IL, *109*
Karras, Bill, Karras Personnel, Inc. (C), NJ, *403*
Keller, Barbara, Barton Assoc., Inc. (R), TX, *12*

Kelso, Pat, Barton Assoc., Inc. (R), TX, *12*
Kenton, Dianne, Partnervision Consulting Group Inc. (R), ON, *160*
Kern, Tina, R. Green & Assoc., Inc. (C), OH, *362*
Kirby, William P., Kirby Assoc. (R), PA, *115*
Klages, Constance W., International Management Advisors, Inc. (R), NY, *103*
Koehler, Frank R., The Koehler Group (C), PA, *408*
Kraft, M. Katherine, Princeton Search Partners, Inc. (R), NJ, *169*
Krumholz, Jill, KL Consultants (C), NJ, *407*
Kuntz, William A., Management Recruiters of Indianapolis (C), IN, *448*
Kuypers, Marcia L., Hire Authority, Inc. (C), MI, *378*
Kyle, Donald, Kyle Assoc. (C), NY, *410*
LaMotta, Steve, Human Resource Solutions (R), TX, *98*
Lasee, Jeff, The H. S. Group, Inc. (C), WI, *365*
Lasse, Daniel C., Management Recruiters of St. Charles (C), IL, *447*
Lawson, Debra, Management Recruiters of Detroit & Farmington Hills (C), MI, *451*
Leety, Murray, Fox-Morris Assoc., Inc. (C), PA, *352*
Lennon, Bill, Hall Management Group, Inc. (C), GA, *367*
Levy, Warren, The Gabriel Group (C), PA, *354*
Lipe, Jerold L., Compass Group Ltd. (R), MI, *38*
Lippincott, Roger, Dunhill Professional Search of Ramsey (C), NJ, *321*
Lombardi, Nancy, WTW Assoc., Inc. (R), NY, *225*
Luisi, Francis J., Fran Luisi Assoc. (R), NJ, *132*
Macdonald, Craig, Houser, Martin, Morris (C), WA, *381*
Magnusen, Henry F., Management Recruiters of North Warren Inc. (C), NJ, *453*
Mahr, Toni, K. Russo Assoc. Inc. (C), CT, *548*
Malatesta, Roger, Professional Recruiting Consultants, Inc. (C), DE, *521*
Manning, Sheila, O'Neill Group (C), NJ, *498*
Manzo, Romero, The Prairie Group (C), IL, *515*
Marenger, Christine, Yves Plouffe & Assoc. (R), QE, *165*
Marino, Chet, Cochran, Cochran & Yale, Inc. (R), CO, *37*
Marsar, Kevin P., Marsar & Co., Inc. (C), FL, *471*
Martin, Leslie, Donna Davis Assoc. (C), NJ, *309*
Martire, Nick, AmeriResource Group Inc. (C), OK, *248*
Maximo, Anita, The Gabriel Group (C), PA, *354*
McAnney, Michael, S-H-S TechStaff (C), PA, *550*
McCarthy, Debra, Becker Personnel (C), FL, *262*
McDermott, Jeffrey T., Vlcek & Company, Inc. (R), CA, *214*
McGlawn, Walter, Corporate Plus, Ltd. (C), GA, *300*
McKenna, Catherine, Marcus & Assoc. (C), NY, *469*
McKenna, Elaine, Weterrings & Agnew, Inc. (C), NY, *619*
McKenna, Scott, The Beam Group (R), PA, *14*
McNamara, Robert, Global Career Services, Inc. (C), NY, *358*
McWilliams, Sara P., Abbott Smith Assoc., Inc. (R), NY, *193*
Meagher, Daniel J., Willmott & Assoc. (C), MA, *622*
Merjos, Susan, The Beam Group (R), NY, *14*
Merrell, Randy, Management Solutions, Inc. (C), CA, *468*
Milne, Danette, Danette Milne Corporate Search Inc. (C), ON, *482*
Mitton, William H., Executive Resource Inc. (C), WI, *334*
Morgan, Nancy, K. Russo Assoc. Inc. (C), CT, *548*
Morin, Michelle, SpencerStuart (R), ON, *197*
Morrison, C. Robert, Quetico Corp. (R), TX, *170*
Murphy, Gary J., Stone, Murphy & Olson (R), MN, *201*
Neiman, Jennifer, Brentwood Int'l. (R), CA, *23*
Neufeld, Max, Partners In Human Resources Int'l., Inc. (R), NY, *160*
Niles, Charles K., The Human Resource Department Ltd. (R), OH, *98*
Norris, Terry, Creative-Leadership, Inc. (R), CA, *42*
O'Hara, Kelly, Goodkind Assoc. Inc. (C), NY, *360*
Oglesby, Tom, F-O-R-T-U-N-E Personnel of Nashville (C), TN, *350*
Olson, Judy A., Management Recruiters of Woodbury (C), MN, *430*
Olson, Judy A., Management Recruiters of Woodbury (C), MN, *452*
Ormond, Mark R., Capstone Consulting, Inc. (R), IL, *29*
Ouellet, Jacques E., Yves Elkas Inc. (R), QE, *58*
Owens, Reggie, The Gabriel Group (C), PA, *354*
Palos, Michael V., Kelly Associates (R), PA, *112*
Pann, Arthur J., Arthur Pann Assoc., Inc. (C), NY, *502*
Paredes, Patricia, Brystol Cove Assoc. (R), CA, *24*
Parenica, Jim, Parenica & Co. (R), NC, *159*
Park, Cleve A., Management Recruiters of Birmingham, Inc. (C), AL, *438*
Patch, Terry, Andre David & Assoc., Inc. (R), TX, *6*
Peasback, David R., Canny, Bowen Inc. (R), NY, *28*
Pelisson, Charles J., Marra Peters & Partners (R), NJ, *136*
Perog, Walter, Search Consultants, Inc. (C), NJ, *575*
Peterson, Jerry, MARBL Consultants, Inc. (C), WI, *469*
Phelps, Grace, Hardage Group (C), TN, *369*
Plyley, Jr., C. Ace, The Stelton Group, Inc. (C), NJ, *592*
Pollack, Marcy L., Business Solutions Worldwide, Inc. (C), NJ, *277*
Presley-Cannon, Judy, Corporate Image Group (C), TN, *300*
Purcell, Carol, The Executive Tree (R), FL, *64*
Quiring, Patti L., Quiring Assoc., Inc. (C), IN, *527*
Rankin, Ed, Human Resource Solutions (R), TX, *98*
Regan, Thomas J., Tower Consultants, Ltd. (R), FL, *210*
Reid, Michael J., Michael James Reid & Co. (R), CA, *174*
Reilly, Toni Marie, Fox-Morris Assoc., Inc. (C), NC, *352*
Richter, Earl, The Wabash Group (C), IN, *613*
Rodriguez, George L., InteliSearch, Inc. (R), CT, *102*
Romano, Joseph C., Romano McAvoy Assoc., Inc. (C), NY, *544*
Rose, Greta, Access Assoc. Inc. (C), MD, *233*
Rosenblatt, Michael F., The Quest Organization (C), NY, *527*
Ross, Andrew, DARE Personnel Inc. (C), ON, *307*
Ross, Terri, Soderlund Assoc. Inc. (R), OH, *195*
Russo, Antonella, The Zarkin Group, Inc. (R), NY, *226*
Russo, Karen, K. Russo Assoc. Inc. (C), CT, *548*
Sandor, Richard, Flynn, Hannock, Inc. (R), CT, *69*
Sarn, Allan G., Allan Sarn Assoc., Inc. (R), NY, *184*
Saunders, Wayne, Lanken-Kimball-Therrell & Assoc. (C), GA, *412*
Scanlon, James D., Sherbrooke Assoc., Inc. (C), NJ, *580*
Scaparotti, Jim, Fox-Morris Assoc., Inc. (C), OH, *352*
Schall, David R., Schall Executive Search Partners (R), MN, *185*
Schneiderman, Sheila, Management Resource Assoc., Inc. (C), FL, *467*
Schoff, Diane L., The Edge Resource Group (C), PA, *326*
Schrepferman, William W., Baldwin & Assoc. (C), OH, *258*
Schutz, Andrea, Ken Clark Int'l. (R), NJ, *36*
Scott, Mark, The Prairie Group (C), IL, *515*
Seal, Jock, The H. S. Group, Inc. (C), WI, *365*
Sewell, Jerry, Fox-Morris Assoc., Inc. (C), TX, *352*

RECRUITER SPECIALTIES

Shandler, Donald, First Advisory Services Int'l., Inc. (R), MD, *67*
Shield, Nancy, Maximum Management Corp. (C), NY, *473*
Simmons, George, Fox-Morris Assoc., Inc. (C), MD, *352*
Singel, Jo, Jonathan Lawrence Assoc. (C), NJ, *400*
Smith, Clark W., F-O-R-T-U-N-E Personnel Consultants of Savannah, Inc. (C), GA, *345*
Smith, Marvin E., Management Solutions, Inc. (C), WA, *468*
Smith, Robert, Fox-Morris Assoc., Inc. (C), GA, *352*
Smith, Susan P., Smith Professional Search (C), MI, *585*
Snyder, C. Edward, Horton International Inc. (R), CT, *96*
Soth, Mark, Management Recruiters of Fairfield (C), IA, *449*
Souder, Jr., E. G., Souder & Assoc. (R), VA, *195*
Sparks, Francine, Willmott & Assoc. (C), MA, *622*
Spencer, Glenda, HR Inc. (C), NC, *382*
Steffensrud, Dick, Staff Extension Int'l. (C), TX, *590*
Steinfield, David, Steinfield & Assoc. (C), TX, *592*
Stephens, Ken, Leader Resources Group (C), GA, *415*
Stillings, Bob, Alpha Search (C), FL, *246*
Storfer, Paul D., Storfer & Assoc. (C), NY, *595*
Summerfield-Beall, Dotty, Summerfield Assoc., Inc. (C), TN, *596*
Sutkamp, Paige, Soderlund Assoc. Inc. (R), OH, *195*
Sveinbjornson, Lynn, The Verriez Group Inc. (R), ON, *213*
Swaak, Rick A., Frank E. Allen & Assoc. (C), NJ, *244*
Szabad, C., The Talley Group (R), VA, *205*
Szymanski, C., The Hanna Group (C), OH, *368*
Talan, Marv, Executive Search Team (C), MI, *336*
Tann, Robert, Staff Extension, Int'l. (C), TX, *590*
Taylor, H. Gordon, F-O-R-T-U-N-E Consultants of Memphis (C), TN, *349*
Telford, Jr., John H., Telford, Adams & Alexander (R), CA, *208*
Tracy, Susan, Wheeler Assoc. (R), CT, *219*
Trasatti, Anthony, The Pennmor Group (C), NJ, *506*
Trocina, Linda, Intersource, Ltd. (R), GA, *103*
Turkal, Terry, Advanced Recruitment, Inc. (C), TN, *240*
Turnblacer, John, The Gabriel Group (C), PA, *354*
Vacca, Domenic L., ACSYS Resources, Inc. (C), DE, *238*
Vaughn, Emmett, American Resources Corp. (C), IL, *248*
Vitanza, Jocelyne, DARE Personnel Inc. (C), ON, *307*
Vlcek, Thomas J., Vlcek & Company, Inc. (R), CA, *214*
Vogel, Michael S., Vogel Assoc. (C), PA, *613*
Voigt, Jeff, APA Employment Agency Inc. (C), OR, *251*
Vujeec, John, Executive Search, Ltd. (C), OH, *336*
Walker, Donald G., Executive Search Plus, Inc. (C), IN, *336*
Wallace, William J., Wallace Management Co. (R), TN, *215*
Wallis, Ginger, Intersource, Ltd. (R), GA, *103*
Walsh, Richard, The Gabriel Group (C), PA, *354*
Weiss, Linda, Prichard Kymen Inc. (R), AB, *168*
Weliver, Edward A., Weliver & Assoc. (C), MI, *618*
Wenzel, Dawn, Partners in Recruiting (C), IL, *504*
Wexler, Suzanne, S. J. Wexler Assoc., Inc. (R), NY, *219*
Williams, Jack R., Staff Extension Int'l. (C), TX, *590*
Williams, Richard, Management Solutions, Inc. (C), CA, *468*
Willmott, D. Clark, Willmott & Assoc. (C), MA, *622*
Wilson, Dick, Fox-Morris Assoc., Inc. (C), PA, *352*
Wright, John, Corporate Image Group (C), TN, *300*
Yakimishyn, Michael, Zen Zen Int'l. Inc. (C), MB, *627*
York, Felecia, Human Resource Dimensions, Inc. (C), TX, *384*
Zaring, Judy, Management Recruiters of Plant City, Inc. (C), FL, *444*
Zukerman, Claire, Corporate Search, Inc. (C), NY, *301*

HVAC

Baehl, Thomas A., World Search (C), OH, *625*
Baker, Ray, Management Recruiters of Ogden (C), UT, *464*
Bruder, Dan, CS Dowling Executive Services (R), NJ, *54*
Colbourn, Ken, F-O-R-T-U-N-E Personnel Consultants of Knoxville (C), TN, *350*
Creasy, Nancy, Michael Latas & Assoc., Inc. (R), MO, *126*
Difatta, Jon, Management Recruiters of Barrington (C), IL, *447*
Fetridge, Guild, Guild Fetridge Acoustical Search, Inc. (C), NY, *340*
Fry, Don, Dunhill of Corpus Christi, Inc. (C), TX, *323*
Gardiner, Gary, Management Recruiters of Cleveland (C), OH, *457*
Glandon, Stephanie, Management Recruiters of Kanawha Valley, LLC (C), WV, *465*
Kirkbride, Robert, Kirkbride Assoc., Inc. (C), WA, *407*
Kratimenos, Peter, Ansara, Bickford & Fiske (C), MA, *251*
Logie, Richard, Kirkbride Assoc., Inc. (C), WA, *407*
Morin, Paul, F-O-R-T-U-N-E Personnel Consultants of Knoxville (C), TN, *350*
Polvere, Gary T., Management Recruiters of Barrington (C), IL, *447*

Imaging

Bogle, Tom, Tom Bogle & Assoc. (C), CA, *269*
Butterfield, N. Blair, Butterfield & Co. Int'l., Inc. (C), HI, *277*
Chisum, Jeanne, Executive Sales Search (C), CO, *335*
Pollack, Jonathan, Executive Sales Search (C), CO, *335*
Rudzinsky, Howard, Louis Rudzinsky Assoc., Inc. (C), MA, *548*

Industrial

Addison, Mike, Sales Consultants of Dallas (C), TX, *563*
Arndt, Greg, Management Recruiters of Boise (C), ID, *446*
Aslaksen, James S., LAI Ward Howell (R), IL, *123*
Auriema, Mark H., Jay Tracey Assoc. Inc. (C), VT, *608*
Bailey, Dan, Johnson Smith & Knisely (R), GA, *107*
Baker, Walter U., LAI Ward Howell (R), FL, *123*
Ball, Ronald D., BallResources (C), MO, *258*
Barranco, Leticia, Leaders-Trust Int'l./Carce y Asociados, S.C. (R), MX, *127*
Berke, Michael J., LAI Ward Howell (R), IL, *123*
Berry, Harold B., The Hindman Co. (R), KY, *94*
Brady, Colin, Johnson Smith & Knisely (R), GA, *107*
Bruno, Deborah F., The Hindman Co. (R), KY, *94*
Cain, Douglas, Sales Recruiting Network (C), PA, *564*
Chambers, Jere, Sales Consultants of Cherry Hill (C), NJ, *560*
Chin, Daniel, F-O-R-T-U-N-E Personnel Consultants of East Seattle (C), WA, *351*
Cooke, Katherine H., Horton International Inc. (R), CT, *96*
Cox, James O., MES Search Co. (C), GA, *479*
Crumbaker, Robert H., LAI Ward Howell (R), OH, *123*
Culbertson, Beth, Sales Consultants of Milwaukee (C), WI, *563*
Davidson, Arthur J., LAI Ward Howell (R), IL, *123*
Donahue, Timothy J., Kelly Associates (R), PA, *112*
Drury, III, James J., SpencerStuart (R), IL, *197*

Eckhart, Kenneth V., SpencerStuart (R), FL, *197*
Elliott, Mark P., LAI Ward Howell (R), OH, *123*
Fell, David W., LAI Ward Howell (R), OH, *123*
Fleming, Michael, Sanford Rose Assoc. - Cedar Rapids (C), IA, *567*
Fountain, Ray, Management Recruiters of North Charleston (C), SC, *460*
Grayson, E. C., SpencerStuart (R), CA, *196*
Hennessy, Robert, Ken Clark Int'l. (R), NJ, *36*
Herget, James P., Harcourt Group Ltd. (R), OH, *86*
Herget, Jane K., Harcourt Group Ltd. (R), OH, *86*
Hindman, Neil C., The Hindman Co. (R), KY, *94*
Hirsch, Tom, InSearch (C), CO, *389*
Hohlstein, Jeff, Management Recruiters of Round Rock (C), TX, *463*
Huffman, Richard B., Professional Engineering Technical Personnel Consultants (C), NC, *520*
Hughes, Jr., John E., LAI Ward Howell (R), PA, *123*
Johnson, John F., LAI Ward Howell (R), OH, *123*
Johnson, Mike, The Wabash Group (C), IN, *613*
Jurenovich, Gary S., The Stewart Group (C), FL, *593*
Kirkbride, Robert, Kirkbride Assoc., Inc. (C), WA, *407*
Knox, Dave, APA Employment Agency Inc. (C), OR, *251*
Konrad, William, ISC of Atlanta, Inc. (C), GA, *394*
Kopsick, Joseph M., SpencerStuart (R), IL, *197*
Kuhnmuench, R. G., K & C Assoc. (C), CA, *402*
Kull, Paul, Paul Kull & Co. (R), NJ, *121*
Larsen, James K., The Personnel Network, Inc. (C), SC, *508*
Larson, Ray, Larson Assoc. (R), CA, *125*
Leggett, Amy, APA Employment Agency Inc. (C), WA, *251*
Logie, Richard, Kirkbride Assoc., Inc. (C), WA, *407*
Luckey, Horace, Sales Consultants of Daphne (C), AL, *556*
Macdonald, Jr., Robert W., Russell Reynolds Assoc., Inc. (R), MN, *177*
Manly, Jo, Management Recruiters of Round Rock (C), TX, *463*
Marion, Bradford B., LAI Ward Howell (R), IL, *123*
Matras, Debbie, Sales Consultants of Milwaukee (C), WI, *563*
McCreary, Charles, Austin-McGregor Int'l. (R), TX, *9*
McDermott, Tom, Corporate Environment Ltd. (R), IL, *41*
McSherry, Terry, Johnson Smith & Knisely (R), IL, *107*
Miller, Paul McG., LAI Ward Howell (R), IL, *123*
Mooney, Penny, Christian & Timbers, Inc. (R), OH, *34*
Morrow, Michael, RSMR, Inc. (R), IL, *182*
O'Brien, Timothy M., O'Brien & Bell (R), OH, *153*
O'Donnell, Tim, Johnson Smith & Knisely (R), IL, *107*
Palmer, James H., The Hindman Co. (R), KY, *94*
Petrello-Pray, Gina, Direct Recruiters, Inc. (C), OH, *312*
Pezim, Howard J., The Bedford Consulting Group Inc. (R), ON, *15*
Poore, Larry D., LAI Ward Howell (R), IL, *123*
Price, P. Anthony, Russell Reynolds Assoc., Inc. (R), CA, *176*
Raab, Julie, Vaughan & Co. (C), CA, *612*
Raben, Steven, Ray & Berndtson (R), TX, *172*
Ragaza, Jessica, RitaSue Siegel Resources, Inc. (R), NY, *191*
Ray, Breck, Ray & Berndtson (R), TX, *172*
Reese, Jr., Charles D., Reese Assoc. (R), PA, *174*
Reifersen, Ruth F., The Jonathan Stevens Group, Inc. (R), NJ, *108*
Rimele, J. R., Sales Recruiters of Oklahoma City (C), OK, *564*
Roberts, Scott, Jonas, Walters & Assoc., Inc. (R), WI, *108*
Robinson, Mel, MDR & Associates (C), AR, *476*
Rosenthal, Abbe L., ALW Research Int'l. (R), NJ, *4*
Schmidt, Paul W., LAI Ward Howell (R), IL, *123*
Schuhmacher, Daniel, Management Recruiters of Round Rock (C), TX, *463*
Searboro, M.D., Management Recruiters of Greenville (C), SC, *460*
Siegel, RitaSue, RitaSue Siegel Resources, Inc. (R), NY, *191*
Smith, Douglas M., LAI Ward Howell (R), IL, *123*
Snider, Jr., Les, Bryan & Louis Research (C), OH, *275*
Sondhi, Rick, Raymond Karsan Assoc. (C), IL, *530*
Turner, Alvan, SpencerStuart (R), IL, *197*
Utroska, Donald R., LAI Ward Howell (R), IL, *123*
Vaughan, David B., Vaughan & Co. (C), CA, *612*
Vosika, Duane, Sales Consultants of Omaha, Inc. (C), NE, *560*
Wakefield, J. Alvin, Wakefield Talabisco Int'l. (R), VT, *214*
Walker, Kelly, Kelly Walker Assoc. (C), TX, *614*
Walt, Lee, M H Executive Search Group (C), TX, *422*
Warner, Thomas P., Warner & Assoc., Inc. (C), OH, *615*
Whitney, Ron, Sales Consultants of Sacramento (C), CA, *556*
Williams, Randy L., Environmental, Health & Safety Search Assoc. (C), FL, *331*
Wojeik, Christine, Johnson Smith & Knisely (R), IL, *107*
Wood, Bill, Search Plus Int'l.-Ohio (C), OH, *576*
Zera, Ronald J., SpencerStuart (R), TX, *197*

Information

Bartlett, Phil, P. J. Lynch Assoc. (R), CT, *132*
Daniel, Beverly R., Foy, Schneid & Daniel, Inc. (R), NY, *71*
Dean, Bruce A., Recruiting Resources Int'l. (C), CA, *532*
Detling, John, Executive Search, Ltd. (C), OH, *336*
Esposito, Mark, Christian & Timbers, Inc. (R), OH, *34*
Fitzgerald, Geoffrey, Fitzgerald Associates (R), MA, *68*
Hall, Shannon Kelly, Sampson Medical Search (C), CA, *564*
Knowles, Scott, Management Recruiters of Georgetown (C), SC, *461*
Kolburne, Barbara, Foster Partners (R), NY, *70*
Kunkel, Thomas J., Bayland Assoc. (C), CA, *261*
Lynch, Patrick J., P. J. Lynch Assoc. (R), CT, *132*
Morris, Robert J., Dunhill Staffing Systems, Inc. (C), NY, *318*
Straight, Gary R., Straight & Co. (R), GA, *202*
Sullivan, Peggy, Tuft & Assoc., Inc. (R), IL, *212*
Weinstein, Bruce, Western Technical Resources (C), CA, *619*

Information service

Axne, Glen A., Access Data Personnel, Inc. (C), NH, *233*
Brenner, Michael, LAI Ward Howell (R), NY, *122*
Campbell, Robert Scott, Wellington Management Group (R), PA, *217*
Cornehlsen, James H., Skott/Edwards Consultants (R), NY, *192*
Crusit, Francis, Sanford Rose Assoc. - Santa Barbara (C), CA, *565*
Gulian, Randolph S., Strategic Executives, Inc. (R), CT, *202*
Hoffman, Theresa E., Wellington Management Group (R), PA, *217*
Jacobs, James W., Callan Assoc., Ltd. (R), IL, *27*
Kelly, Elizabeth Ann, Wellington Management Group (R), PA, *217*
McCann, Mary Ellen, Wellington Management Group (R), PA, *217*
Panchella, Joseph J., Wellington Management Group (R), PA, *217*
Pappalardo, Chuck, Christian & Timbers, Inc. (R), OH, *34*
Perry, James A., Strategic Executives, Inc. (R), IL, *202*
Skiba, Jeff, Management Recruiters of Lake Tahoe, NV (C), NV, *453*

Smith, Perry, Noll Human Resource Services (C), TX, *494*
Sobel, Andrea, Andrea Sobel & Assoc., Inc. (C), CA, *586*
Wade, Elliott, Search Int'l. (R), MA, *187*

Injection molding

Guarniere, John W., RCE Assoc. (R), NJ, *173*
Murray, Patrick, The Murray Group (C), IL, *487*
Tippel, Fred C., Fred C. Tippel & Assoc. (C), OH, *607*

Ink

Fisher, Lawrence C., Mullen Assoc., Inc. (R), NC, *149*
Mullen, James J., Mullen Assoc., Inc. (R), NC, *149*

Instrumentation

Adams, Frank S., Thomson, Sponar & Adams, Inc. (C), WA, *606*
Bawza, Leo F., Chelsea Resources, Inc. (C), CT, *290*
Daniels, Donna, Jonas, Walters & Assoc., Inc. (R), WI, *108*
Flannery, Peter, Jonas, Walters & Assoc., Inc. (R), WI, *108*
Frazer, Mel, Mel Frazer Consultant (C), CA, *352*
Gersin, Harvey, Sales Consultants of Farmington Hills (C), MI, *560*
Harris, Bea, Exec Tech, Inc. (C), IL, *332*
Kelly, Susan D., S. D. Kelly & Assoc., Inc. (R), MA, *112*
Kerstein, Daniel J., Daniel J. Kerstein, Consultant to Management (R), CO, *114*
Kunkel, Thomas J., Bayland Assoc. (C), CA, *261*
Montgomery, Denis, Healthcare Recruiters of New England (C), MA, *373*
Olson, John, Cook Assoc.,® Inc. (R), IL, *40*
Patronella, Larry, W. Robert Eissler & Assoc., Inc. (C), TX, *327*
Paules, Paul E., Paules Associates (C), CA, *505*
Soo Hoo, Patrick J., Chelsea Resources, Inc. (C), CT, *290*

Insurance

Albergato, Vincent, Raymond Karsan Assoc. (C), MA, *530*
Amato, Bobbi, Amato & Associates Insurance Recruiters (C), PA, *247*
Amato, Joseph D., Amato & Assoc., Inc. (C), CA, *246*
Ashton, Edward J., E. J. Ashton & Assoc., Ltd. (C), IL, *253*
Auster, A. Marc, A. M. Auster Associates (R), FL, *9*
Barick, Bradford L., Management Recruiters of Stevens Point, Inc. (C), WI, *466*
Barker, Steve, Insurance Recruiting Specialists (C), OH, *390*
Baron, Robert, Peak Search Assoc. (C), ON, *506*
Baron, Sheldon S., Sales Consultants of Nashua-Manchester (C), NH, *560*
Baskin, Peter J., Personnel Assoc. Inc. (C), NY, *508*
Bass, Nate, J.J. & H., Ltd. (R), PA, *105*
Bass, Nate, Jacobson Assoc. (C), PA, *396*
Batozech, Jeff, IR Search (R), CA, *103*
Bayard, Thomas E., Claimsearch (C), CA, *291*
Beaudine, Robert E., Eastman & Beaudine, Inc. (R), TX, *56*
Benkwitt, Barbara, The Brentwood Group, Inc. (R), NJ, *22*
Bevivino, Sal, Questor Consultants, Inc. (C), PA, *527*
Blount, K. Michael, The Maroon Group (R), CT, *136*
Blythe, Thomas J., Halo Insurance Service (C), AL, *367*
Bond, James, People Management Northeast, Inc. (R), CT, *162*
Bonham, Apryl, Claimsearch (C), CA, *291*
Brown, Pat, Corporate Suite, Ltd. (C), IA, *301*
Buchanan, Christine, Management Recruiters of Bordentown (C), NJ, *454*
Bunce, David S., Summit Search Specialists (C), TX, *596*
Burkholder, John, Burkholder & Assoc., Inc. (C), TX, *276*
Burnett, Glenn, WestPacific National Search, Inc. (C), CA, *619*
Butler, Jr., Kirby B., The Butlers Co. Insurance Recruiters (C), FL, *277*
Butler, Martha, The Butlers Co. Insurance Recruiters (C), FL, *277*
Carter, Jeffrey M., Carter-Evdemon & Assoc. (C), FL, *285*
Cauallo, Vincent L., Behavioral Science Assoc., Inc. (R), AZ, *15*
Clarke, Terry M., LAI Ward Howell (R), WI, *124*
Cohen, Barry, Response Staffing Services (C), NY, *535*
Conner, Marlene L., M. L. Conner (C), FL, *296*
Copeland, Dawn, Descheneaux Recruitment Services Ltd. (C), BC, *311*
Corey, Michael J., LAI Ward Howell (R), WI, *124*
Corey, Patrick M., LAI Ward Howell (R), WI, *124*
Corporon, Charles E., Quirk-Corporon & Assoc., Inc. (C), WI, *527*
Darter, Steven, People Management Northeast, Inc. (R), CT, *162*
Davis, Andrew, Smith Hanley Assoc., Inc. (C), CT, *584*
Davis, Barry, Martin Grant Assoc. Inc., Insurance Personnel (C), MA, *472*
Davis, Carolyn, Carolyn Davis Assoc., Inc. (C), NY, *309*
de Funiak, William S., De Funiak & Edwards (R), IN, *47*
DeMarlie, Gary P., LAI Ward Howell (R), WI, *124*
Descheneaux, Pat, Descheneaux Recruitment Services Ltd. (C), BC, *311*
Diaz, Norm, The Canon Group (C), CA, *280*
Dieckmann, Ralph E., Dieckmann & Assoc., Ltd. (R), IL, *51*
Dietsch, Roger A., Roger Dietsch & Assoc. (C), MN, *312*
Dionne, Bert, Insurance Search (C), TX, *390*
Doyle, John, Search Research Assoc., Inc. (R), MA, *187*
Dykes, Larry L., Personnel Consultants (C), WA, *508*
Ector, John, Insurance Personnel Resources, Inc. (C), GA, *390*
Edwards, Randolph J., De Funiak & Edwards (R), MD, *47*
Ehrenzeller, Tony, Management Recruiters of Fairfax, VA (C), VA, *464*
Eickhoff, Mike, Management Recruiters - Indianapolis (C), IN, *448*
Elizondo, Jennifer, Management Recruiters of Fresno (C), CA, *440*
Esposito, Mark, Christian & Timbers, Inc. (R), OH, *34*
Evan-Cook, James, Cook Assoc.,® Inc. (R), IL, *40*
Evdemon, II, Michael S., Carter-Evdemon & Assoc. (C), FL, *285*
Ferguson, Cindy, The Canon Group (C), CA, *280*
Florence, Kathy, Pryor & Associates (C), CA, *525*
Flynn, Jack, Executive Search Consultants Corp. (C), IL, *335*
Fox, Michael L., Management Recruiters of Woodbury (C), MN, *430*
Fox, Michael L., Management Recruiters of Woodbury (C), MN, *452*
Frankel, Miriam, PMJ & Assoc. (C), ON, *513*
Friedman, Ken, The Primary Group, Inc. (R), FL, *168*
Garbutt, Mimi, Harcourt & Assoc. (C), AB, *368*
Garrison, Ed, The Garrison Organization (R), IA, *75*
Gazzolo, Diana, Martin Grant Assoc. Inc., Insurance Personnel (C), MA, *472*
Gelpi, Gerry, Gelpi & Assoc. (C), LA, *355*
Genel, George, Genel Associates (C), CA, *356*
Gibbons, Ronald L., Flynn, Hannock, Inc. (R), CT, *69*
Gilchrist, Robert J., Horton International Inc. (R), CT, *96*
Godfrey, James R., Godfrey Personnel, Inc. (C), IL, *359*
Gold, Barry M., Barry M. Gold & Co. (C), CA, *359*
Gold, Lisa, Strategic Advancement Inc. (R), NJ, *202*
Goldbach, Linda J., Beacon Int'l., Inc. (C), VA, *261*
Goldsmith, Jerry, The Primary Group, Inc. (R), FL, *168*

Green, Lynn, Nuance Personnel Search, Inc. (C), NC, *497*
Gustafson, Terry, Matthews & Stephens Assoc., Inc. (C), CT, *472*
Hanson, Paul David, LAI Ward Howell (R), WI, *124*
Hanson, Paul L., LAI Ward Howell (R), WI, *124*
Haugen, Audrey D., Roger Dietsch & Assoc. (C), MN, *312*
Hayes, Jerry, Holden & Harlan Assoc., Inc. (C), IL, *380*
Heath, Pamela A., The Winn Group, Inc. (C), KS, *623*
Heath, Thomas A., The Winn Group, Inc. (C), KS, *623*
Hellebusch, Jerry, Morgan Hunter Corp. (C), KS, *485*
Hesselgrave, Katherine, Insurance People (C), IN, *390*
Higgins, Bruce W., B. W. Higgins, Inc. (C), IN, *377*
Higgins, Susan, The Rogan Group, Inc. (C), CA, *541*
Hodges, Wanda, Insurance Search (C), TX, *390*
Howe, W. Lawrence, C. R. Krafski & Assoc., Inc. (R), IL, *120*
Hudson, George A., Hudson Assoc. Inc. (C), IN, *383*
Hughes, Ken, Hughes & Assoc. (C), TX, *383*
Hugley, Trey, QuestPro, Inc. (C), TX, *527*
Ikle, A. Donald, LAI Ward Howell (R), NY, *123*
Jablo, Steven A., Dieckmann & Assoc., Ltd. (R), IL, *51*
Jacobson, David N., J.J. & H., Ltd. (R), IL, *104*
Jacobson, Gregory, Jacobson Assoc. (C), GA, *396*
Jacobson, Gregory P., J.J. & H., Ltd. (R), GA, *105*
Jacobson, Rick, The Windham Group (R), OH, *222*
Jayroe, Laurie, The Canon Group (C), CA, *280*
Jones, James A., Jones Consulting Executive Search (C), GA, *400*
Keifer, Danna, Dunhill Professional Search of San Jose (C), CA, *319*
Kennedy, Michael, The Danbrook Group, Inc. (C), TX, *306*
Kenney, George T., Search Research Assoc., Inc. (R), MA, *187*
Kenney, William, William W. Kenney (C), CT, *405*
Kinderis, Paul, Kinderis & Loercher Group (C), IL, *407*
Kiner, Linda, Insurance Career Center, Inc. (C), CT, *390*
King, Damon, The Canon Group (C), CA, *280*
King, Gail, Management Recruiters of Tampa North (C), FL, *444*
King, Robert E., Behavioral Science Assoc., Inc. (R), AZ, *15*
King, Steven, Ashway Ltd. Agency (C), NY, *253*
Knowles, Scott, Management Recruiters of Georgetown (C), SC, *461*
Kolacia, V., Murphy Partners Int'l. (R), IL, *150*
Krafski, Charlene, C. R. Krafski & Assoc., Inc. (R), IL, *120*
Kurtz, Leonard A., Executive Search Consultants, Inc. (C), FL, *335*
Lacy-Higgins, Lynda, B. W. Higgins, Inc. (C), IN, *377*
Lamb, Angus, Raymond Karsan Assoc. (C), PA, *530*
Lear, Roger R., Lear & Assoc., Inc. (C), FL, *415*
Leeds, Gerald I., Leeds and Leeds (C), TN, *416*
Leininger, Dennis, Staffing Edge, Inc. (C), IA, *590*
Levinson, Lauren, QuestPro, Inc. (C), TX, *527*
Levy, Stefan, Management Search, Inc. (C), IL, *467*
Lomax, J. Alan, ADR Accounting Management Recruiters (C), ON, *240*
Loscavio, J. Michael, Rusher, Loscavio & LoPresto (R), CA, *183*
Lynch, J. F., Management Recruiters of Lionville, Inc. (C), PA, *459*
Lynch, Sean, Raymond Karsan Assoc. (C), PA, *529*
MacDougall, Andrew J., SpencerStuart (R), ON, *197*
Maggs, Richard, Lechner & Assoc., Inc. (C), FL, *415*
Magic, Michael F., Scott Douglas Inc. (C), CA, *573*
Mann, Douglas G., LAI Ward Howell (R), WI, *124*
Marsh, Norman R., California Management Search (C), CA, *279*
Marsteller, Franklin D., SpencerStuart (R), PA, *197*
Mayer, Mary L., Mary L. Mayer, Ltd. (R), MN, *139*
McCarthy, Maureen, Management Recruiters of Fresno (C), CA, *440*
McGeehan, Gayle A., Management Recruiters of Bethlehem, PA (C), PA, *458*
McKay, Kim, The Network Corporate Search Personnel Inc. (C), AB, *491*
McMath, George R., Insurance People (C), IN, *390*
Meyer, Fred R., Management Recruiters of Bethlehem, PA (C), PA, *458*
Meyer, Michael F., Witt/Kieffer, Ford, Hadelman & Lloyd (R), AZ, *223*
Milkint, Margaret Resce, J.J. & H., Ltd. (R), IL, *104*
Miller, Kenneth, Computer Network Resources, Inc. (C), CA, *295*
Miller, Roxxanne, The Pailin Group Professional Search Consultants (R), TX, *158*
Milo, William P., The Stonebridge Group (C), PA, *594*
Moore, Connie, C. A. Moore & Assoc., Inc. (C), MN, *484*
Moran, Thomas F., LAI Ward Howell (R), WI, *124*
Morin, Michelle, SpencerStuart (R), ON, *197*
Morris, David W., WTW Assoc., Inc. (R), NY, *225*
Moyse, Richard G., Thorndike Deland Assoc. LLC (R), NY, *48*
Mulligan, Pamela L., Pamela L. Mulligan, Inc. (R), NH, *149*
Murrell, James O., Professionals in Recruiting Co. (C), TN, *523*
Neir, Karla, Southwest Selective Search, Inc. (C), TX, *588*
Neir, Paul, Southwest Selective Search, Inc. (C), TX, *588*
Nelson, Beverly M., Beverly Nelson & Assoc. Inc. (C), CA, *491*
Nichipor, Michael A., Sanford Rose Assoc. - Carmel, IN (C), IN, *567*
Nixon, Jeffrey L., J. L. Nixon Consulting (C), TX, *493*
O'Sullivan, Kathleen, O'Sullivan Search Inc. (C), ON, *498*
Oliveira, Beatriz J., Priority Executive Search (C), FL, *518*
Ongirski, Richard P., Raymond Karsan Assoc. (C), PA, *529*
Oppenheimer, A. M., M. L. Conner (C), FL, *296*
Oppenheimer, Toni, M. L. Conner (C), FL, *296*
Pace, Susan A., Horton International Inc. (R), CT, *96*
Pahls, Jud, Management Recruiters of Altamonte (C), FL, *442*
Pallman-David, Cynthia, Bonnell Assoc. Ltd. (R), CT, *19*
Parker, P. Grant, Raymond Karsan Assoc. (C), PA, *529*
Pelusi, Tiziana, Synagent Inc. (C), ON, *597*
Perry, Lisa Lepore, Aminex Corp. (C), MA, *249*
Peterman, James R., J. R. Peterman Assoc., Inc. (C), VT, *509*
Pfeiffer, Joseph, Insurance Personnel Resources, Inc. (C), NC, *390*
Phillips, Sharin, Rice Cohen Int'l. (R), PA, *178*
Pisano, Robert, Rand Thompson Executive Search Consultants (C), NY, *528*
Plappert, James F., Sales Consultants of Newtown, Inc. (C), PA, *562*
Powell, Curtis, Burkholder & Assoc., Inc. (C), TX, *276*
Prager, Paul Gershon, P. G. Prager Search Assoc., Ltd. (C), NY, *515*
Pryor, Jo-Ann, Pryor & Associates (C), CA, *525*
Quinlin, Carolyn, Descheneaux Recruitment Services Ltd. (C), BC, *311*
Quirk, Therese M., Quirk-Corporon & Assoc., Inc. (C), WI, *527*
Rabinowitz, Peter A., P.A.R. Assoc., Inc. (R), MA, *158*
Range, Mary Jane, Bishop Partners (R), NY, *17*
Redmond, Andrea, Russell Reynolds Assoc., Inc. (R), IL, *176*
Reeves, William B., SpencerStuart (R), GA, *197*

RECRUITER SPECIALTIES

Richard, David A., Financial Connections Company (C), VA, *340*
Richards, Suzanne S., Fortune Consultants of Ft. Washington (C), PA, *349*
Risalvato, Frank G., Inter Regional Executive Search, Inc. (IRES, Inc.) (C), NJ, *391*
Rivard, Richard L., Management Recruiters of Atlanta NE (C), GA, *446*
Rivera-Lopez, Elba, Raymond Karsan Assoc. (C), PA, *529*
Rogish, Nick, Rogish Assoc., Inc. (C), OH, *541*
Rosenthal, Nathan, Pioneer Placement, Inc. (C), MA, *512*
Roth, Jim, Management Recruiters of Des Moines (C), IA, *449*
Rowls, Gene, E. J. Ashton & Assoc., Ltd. (C), IL, *253*
Rusher, Jr., William H., Rusher, Loscavio & LoPresto (R), CA, *183*
Russillo, Thomas P., Russillo/Gardner/Spolsino (C), MA, *548*
Rutledge, Andy, Management Recruiters - Indianapolis (C), IN, *448*
Saloukas, Bill I., Broad Waverly & Assoc. (C), NJ, *274*
Schere, Ivan, National Search, Inc.® (C), FL, *490*
Schoenfeld, Marian, Dunhill of Manchester Inc. (C), NH, *321*
Schrenzel, Steven N., The Governance Group, Inc. (R), NJ, *80*
Scott, Gordon S., Search Research Assoc., Inc. (R), MA, *187*
Shuherk, Marty, Fament, Inc. (C), OH, *338*
Sinks, Lucius F., Aminex Corp. (C), MA, *249*
Smith, Scott B., LAI Ward Howell (R), WI, *124*
Spencer, Randall W., Management Recruiters of San Antonio - North (C), TX, *463*
Spolsino, Robert J., Russillo/Gardner/Spolsino (C), MA, *548*
Srolis, Robert B., Raymond Karsan Assoc. (C), PA, *529*
Stafford, Norma, Stafford Consulting Group (R), CA, *198*
Stephenson, Phil, Executive Search Group LLC (C), CA, *335*
Stollenmaier, Nadine, Dunhill Professional Search of Hawaii (C), HI, *320*
Stranberg, Mark, Mark Stranberg & Assoc. Inc. (R), MA, *202*
Svetic, Mark, Lear & Assoc., Inc. (C), FL, *415*
Swiff, Jeffrey G., Thorndike Deland Assoc. LLC (R), NY, *48*
Tholke, William E., Boardroom Consultants/Kenny Kindler Tholke (R), NY, *19*
Tolstrup, Rick, Aminex Corp. (C), MA, *249*
Tyson, Richard L., Bonifield Assoc. (C), NJ, *269*
Valone, Anthony F., UniQuest Int'l., Inc. (C), FL, *611*
Van Leer, Peter, Peter Van Leer & Assoc. (R), MN, *213*
Varney, Rudy, J. L. Nixon Consulting (C), TX, *493*
Volk, Donald, Raymond Karsan Assoc. (C), PA, *529*
Walker, Linda G., Walker Personnel, Inc. (C), LA, *614*
Wanger, Karen, Karen Wanger & Assoc., Inc. (C), IL, *615*
Warriner, Mary Ann, Job-Born Candidate Selection Bureau (C), ON, *399*
Watson, David L. B., Pacific Coast Recruiters (C), OR, *501*
Weatherstone, William, Executive Search Consultants Corp. (C), IL, *335*
Weaver, John T., C. R. Krafski & Assoc., Inc. (R), IL, *120*
Webber, Mary Ann, Shiloh Careers Int'l., Inc. (C), TN, *580*
Werlin, Paul A., Human Capital Resources, Inc. (C), FL, *384*
Wilkin, Terry, Management Recruiters - Indianapolis (C), IN, *448*
Wilson, Mary, Matthews & Stephens Assoc., Inc. (C), CT, *472*
Winn, James G., The Winn Group, Inc. (C), KS, *623*
Wolchansky, Beth, Largent Parks & Partners (C), TX, *503*
Wolfson, Robert H., Mitchell/Wolfson, Assoc. (R), IL, *145*
Wood, William M., Wood-Glavin, Inc. (R), KS, *224*
Woodson, Benjamin N., Warring & Assoc. (R), TX, *216*

Casualty

Hruska, Thomas, The Search Group (C), MD, *575*
Lerch, Brent, Insurance Personnel Resources, Inc. (C), GA, *390*
McGraw, John, The Rogan Group, Inc. (C), CA, *541*
Rogan, Daniel, The Rogan Group, Inc. (C), CA, *541*
Schindel, Kim, Searchworks, Inc. (C), FL, *577*
Watson, David L. B., Pacific Coast Recruiters (C), OR, *501*

Claims

DeMatteo, Robena, DeMatteo Associates (C), NY, *311*
Eickenhorst, Richard, Richard Wright Co. (C), CT, *536*

Intellectual property

Arnautovic, Zora, Consulpro (R), ON, *39*
Caldwell, Kate, Caldwell Legal Recruiting Consultants (C), ME, *279*
Fossett, Gary J., John Michael Assoc. (R), DC, *106*
Markessinis, Barbara, Berkshire Search Assoc. (C), MA, *265*
McLaughlin, John F., William K. McLaughlin Assoc., Inc. (C), NY, *475*
McLaughlin, Patricia A., William K. McLaughlin Assoc., Inc. (C), CO, *475*
McLaughlin, William K., William K. McLaughlin Assoc., Inc. (C), NY, *475*
Narsh, Daniel, Windsor Consultants, Inc. (C), TX, *622*
Sharrow, Beth S., Sharrow & Assoc., Inc. (C), MI, *579*
Weber, Fran, Marley Group Ltd. (C), NY, *471*
Wilson, Pamela J., SR Wilson, Inc. (C), CA, *590*
Wilson, Stoney, SR Wilson, Inc. (C), CA, *590*

Interactive

Flannery, Michael, Redwood Partners Ltd. (R), NY, *173*
Lewis, Marc, Christian & Timbers, Inc. (R), OH, *34*
Mather, David, Christian & Timbers, Inc. (R), OH, *34*
Mather, David R., Christian & Timbers, Inc. (R), CA, *34*
Pappalardo, Chuck, Christian & Timbers, Inc. (R), OH, *34*
Perlstadt, Douglas, Interactive Search Network (R), CA, *102*
Ragaza, Jessica, RitaSue Siegel Resources, Inc. (R), NY, *191*
Richards, Sharon, Richards Assoc., Inc. (R), NY, *178*
Ridenour, Suzanne S., Ridenour & Assoc. (R), IL, *178*
Schoenfeld, Randy, Redwood Partners Ltd. (R), NY, *173*
Selker, Gregory, Christian & Timbers, Inc. (R), OH, *34*

Interim

Gibbons, Ronald L., Flynn, Hannock, Inc. (R), CT, *69*
Greene, Sharon, Stewart/Greene & Co. of The Triad, Inc. (C), NC, *594*

Interior design

Gaines, Donna, Gaines & Assoc. Int'l., Inc. (R), IL, *73*
Hirsch, Ruth, Ruth Hirsch Assoc., Inc. (C), NY, *379*
Moran, Marilyn, RitaSue Siegel Resources, Inc. (R), NY, *191*
Peart, Carolyn, Cook Assoc.,® Inc. (R), IL, *40*
Siegel, RitaSue, RitaSue Siegel Resources, Inc. (R), NY, *191*

International

Aldana, Manny, Bor-Maq Assoc. (C), TX, *269*
Ammann, Elisabeth, The Stevenson Group, Inc. (N.J.) (R), NJ, *200*
Bailey, Ralph, Ridgefield Search Int'l. (C), CT, *537*
Baker, Walter U., LAI Ward Howell (R), FL, *123*

Bales, Sally, The Bales-Waugh Group (C), FL, *258*
Bornholdt, John, Bornholdt Shivas & Friends Executive Recruiters (C), NY, *270*
Chaves-Gregg, Cecilia, Dunhill Professional Search of Miami (C), FL, *320*
Christidis, Aurora, Brad Marks Int'l. (R), CA, *136*
Cohen, Diane, Michael Levine Search Consultants (R), NY, *129*
Crosbie, D. C., Interim Management Resources Inc. (C), ON, *392*
Cygan, H., American Executive Management, Inc. (R), MA, *5*
Dahl, Charles, Charles Dahl Group, Inc. (C), MN, *306*
Désilets, Georges H., Yves Plouffe & Assoc. (R), QE, *165*
Eckhart, Kenneth V., SpencerStuart (R), FL, *197*
Fenwick, J. Brett, Sales Builders, Inc. (R), VA, *184*
Flannery, Thomas T., Resources for Management (R), PA, *176*
Fossett, Gary J., John Michael Assoc. (R), DC, *106*
Foster, Dwight E., Foster Partners (R), NY, *70*
French, William G., Preng & Assoc., Inc. (R), TX, *167*
Galitzine, Gai, Global Research Partnership Inc. (R), NY, *78*
Gould, William E., Gould, McCoy & Chadick, Inc. (R), NY, *80*
Gregg, Paul J., Dunhill Professional Search of Miami (C), FL, *320*
Groussman, Maria, Groussman & Assoc., Inc. (R), TX, *82*
Gurrola, Jose D., J.D.G. y Asociados, S.A. de C.V. (R), SO, *104*
Hernandez, Rafael E., SearchCorp (C), FL, *577*
Horton, Robert H., Horton Int'l. Inc. (R), NY, *96*
Kins, John, Cook Assoc.,® Inc. (R), IL, *40*
Lawler, Tim, Sales Consultants of Milwaukee (C), WI, *563*
Lawler, III, Timothy M., Management Recruiters of Milwaukee-North (C), WI, *466*
Madison, T. Dean, Warren, Morris & Madison, Ltd. (C), VA, *616*
Martinolich, Michael, Tennyson Advisors (R), NY, *208*
McHale, John P., McHale & Assoc. (R), WA, *141*
Morris, Charles C., Warren, Morris & Madison, Ltd. (C), CA, *616*
Murphy, Bob, Murphy Partners Int'l. (R), IL, *150*
Payette, Angela, Greene Personnel Consultants (C), RI, *362*
Pennella, Neil, Brad Marks Int'l. (R), CA, *136*
Plouffe, Yves J., Yves Plouffe & Assoc. (R), QE, *165*
Ralley, P. Neil, E.P. Int'l. (C), NJ, *325*
Ralley, P. Neil, E.P. Int'l. (C), NY, *324*
Rodriguez Smithson, Raquel, R. A. Rodriguez & Assoc., Inc. (C), TX, *540*
Roll, M. A., Roll International (C), TX, *541*
Scott, Gordon, Search Advisors Int'l. Corp. (R), FL, *186*
Smithson, Fred, R. A. Rodriguez & Assoc., Inc. (C), TX, *540*
Spiegel, Gayle, The Spiegel Group (R), MA, *197*
Sur, William K., Canny, Bowen Inc. (R), NY, *28*
Tomita, Betty Wong, Global Research Partnership Inc. (R), NY, *78*
Warren, Scott C., Warren, Morris & Madison, Ltd. (C), NH, *616*
Washburn, Natalie, Smith Hanley Assoc., Inc. (C), GA, *584*
Waugh, Chris, The Bales-Waugh Group (C), FL, *258*
Weinstein, Stanley E., S. E. Weinstein Co. (R), IL, *217*
Weiss, Karen, Foster Partners (R), NY, *70*
Willis, Jr., William H., William Willis Worldwide Inc. (R), CT, *221*
Wilson, Akira, Largent Parks & Partners (C), TX, *503*
Wilson, Wayne, Wilson & Assoc. Int'l. Inc. (C), FL, *622*
Wooller, Edmund A. M., Windsor International (R), GA, *222*
Wright, Leslie, The Stevenson Group, Inc. (N.J.) (R), NJ, *200*
Zak, Adam, Horton Int'l. Inc. (R), IL, *96*

Internet

Arnone, Patrick J., Patrick Arnone & Assoc. Inc. (R), VA, *7*
Baker, Chet, Diversified Consulting Services, Inc. (C), CO, *313*
Bouchard, Rodney, Management Recruiters of Winsted, Inc. (C), CT, *442*
Cavicchio, Dan, Greenwich Internet (C), CT, *363*
Christian, Jeffrey E., Christian & Timbers, Inc. (R), OH, *34*
Curry, Joseph, MediaCOM Talent Group (C), MA, *477*
Curtis, Susan J., ProSearch Recruiting (C), CA, *524*
Ertaud, Wilfrid, MediaCOM Talent Group (C), MA, *477*
Faucher, Cornel, Sink, Walker, Boltrus Int'l. (R), MA, *192*
Gunning, Phill, TBC, Inc. (C), KY, *600*
Haberman, Rebecca Powers, Norman Powers Assoc., Inc. (C), MA, *515*
Kacevich, Jr., Joseph B., Kacevich, Lewis & Brown, Inc. (R), MA, *109*
Kahn, Beverly A., New Dimensions in Technology, Inc. (C), MA, *492*
King, Margaret, Christian & Timbers, Inc. (R), OH, *34*
Kossuth, David, Kossuth & Assoc., Inc. (R), WA, *119*
Kossuth, Jane, Kossuth & Assoc., Inc. (R), WA, *119*
Levy, Stefan, Management Search, Inc. (C), IL, *467*
Lewis, Marc, Christian & Timbers, Inc. (R), OH, *34*
Love, Jon R., JL & Co. (C), CA, *399*
Maher, Kevin, TBC, Inc. (C), KY, *600*
Marks, Ira M., Strategic Alternatives (R), CA, *202*
Mather, David, Christian & Timbers, Inc. (R), OH, *34*
Mather, David R., Christian & Timbers, Inc. (R), CA, *34*
McKeown, Morgan, Christian & Timbers, Inc. (R), NY, *34*
Milton, Charles E., Smith James Group, Inc. (R), GA, *194*
Muller, Michael, Financialjobs.com (C), CA, *340*
Munson, Brad, ProSearch Recruiting (C), CA, *524*
Myers, Bonnie, Myers Career Assoc., Inc. (C), CA, *488*
Peragine, Ralph, The Resource Group (R), CT, *175*
Peragine, Ralph P., The Resource Group (R), CT, *175*
Richer, Joyce Eidenberg, W. F. Richer Assoc., Inc. (C), NY, *537*
Richer, William F., W. F. Richer Assoc., Inc. (C), NY, *536*
Smith, Gregory K., Global Technologies Group Inc. (C), NC, *359*
Wayne, Vici, Christian & Timbers, Inc. (R), OH, *34*
Wilson, Patricia, Global Technologies Group Inc. (C), NC, *359*

Internetworking

Young, Wayne T., Management Recruiters of Morris County, NJ (C), NJ, *453*

Intranet

Cavicchio, Dan, Greenwich Internet (C), CT, *363*
Kahn, Beverly A., New Dimensions in Technology, Inc. (C), MA, *492*
Sheweloff, William J., McCray, Shriver, Eckdahl & Assoc., Inc. (R), CA, *140*

Investment

Anwar, Tarin, Jay Gaines & Company, Inc. (R), NY, *74*
Baggott, Richard, Executive Search Placements, Inc. (C), CO, *336*
Bergeris, Jim, Bergeris & Co., Inc. (C), NY, *265*
Bovich, Maryann C., Higdon Prince Inc. (R), NY, *93*
Brady, Marty, The Oxbridge Group, Ltd. (C), PA, *500*
Brookes, Michael T., Executive Access Inc. (R), NY, *62*
Castine, Michael P., Highland Search Group, L.L.C. (R), NY, *93*
Cohen, Richard, Management Recruiters of Manhattan on Broadway (C), NY, *455*

Coppola, Anna, The Flagship Group (R), MA, *68*
Crispi, Nicholas, Crispi, Wagner & Co., Inc. (R), NY, *43*
Daniels, Alfred, Alfred Daniels & Assoc., Inc. (R), CA, *46*
Dow, Ian James, Dow Consultants Int'l. (C), NY, *314*
Eagar, Brian, Search Int'l. (R), MA, *187*
Erikson, Theodore J., Erikson Consulting Assoc., Inc. (R), NY, *60*
Flanagan, Robert M., Robert M. Flanagan & Assoc., Ltd. (R), NY, *68*
Flynn, Joanne T., Pinnacle Group Int'l. (C), AZ, *512*
Flynn, Stephen F., Pinnacle Group Int'l. (C), AZ, *512*
Foltz, T. J., Capital Markets Resources, Inc. (C), NC, *281*
Frumess, Gregory, Foster Partners (R), NY, *70*
Goldsmith, Joseph B., Higdon Prince Inc. (R), NY, *93*
Goldstein, Steven G., The Jonathan Stevens Group, Inc. (R), NJ, *108*
Greene, Timothy G., Greene & Co. (C), MA, *362*
Harvey, Warren, Management Recruiters of Nassau, Inc. (R), NY, *134*
Hatch, Michael, The Kinlin Co., Inc. (R), MA, *115*
Higdon, Henry G., Higdon Prince Inc. (R), NY, *93*
Hochman, Judi, Hochman & Assoc. (C), CA, *379*
Holt, Carol, Bartholdi & Co., Inc. (R), VA, *12*
Holzberger, Georges L., Highland Search Group, L.L.C. (R), NY, *93*
Hopard, Stuart M., Olympian Recruitment, Ltd. (C), NY, *498*
Humes, James, Management Recruiters of Nassau, Inc. (R), NY, *134*
Hunt, James E., Hunt & Howe Inc. (R), NY, *99*
Kaufman, Susan, Kaufman Assoc. (R), CA, *110*
Kay, Elizabeth, E. J. Lance Management Assoc., Inc. (C), NY, *412*
Kraftson, Ann, The Oxbridge Group, Ltd. (C), NY, *500*
Kulesza, Michael, Anthony Michael & Co. (C), MA, *251*
Liebowitz, Michael, Highland Search Group, L.L.C. (R), NY, *93*
Livingston, Peter R., Livingston, Robert & Co. (R), CT, *130*
Lyons, Denis B. K., SpencerStuart (R), NY, *196*
Marshall, P. William, Dise & Co. (R), OH, *52*
Martinolich, Michael, Tennyson Advisors (R), NY, *208*
Miller, Roger, Ryan, Miller & Assoc. (C), CA, *549*
Much, Isaac, Much & Co. (R), NY, *148*
Nordeman, Jacques C., Nordeman Grimm, Inc. (R), NY, *152*
Oppedisano, Edward, Oppedisano & Co., Inc. (R), NY, *156*
Parker, Michele, Management Alliance Group, Inc. (R), NY, *134*
Patenge, David W., Handy HRM (R), NY, *86*
Phillips, Jr., James L., Highland Search Group, L.L.C. (R), NY, *93*
Phillips, Richard K., Handy HRM (R), NY, *86*
Pittleman, Linda, Pittleman & Assoc. (C), NY, *513*
Potter, Steven B., Highland Search Group, L.L.C. (R), NY, *93*
Prince, Marylin L., Higdon Prince Inc. (R), NY, *93*
Rehner, Leonard, R & L Assoc., Ltd. (R), NY, *170*
Reisfeld, Lynn Scullion, Alfred Daniels & Assoc., Inc. (R), CA, *46*
Riotto, Anthony R., Riotto-Jones Assoc. (R), NY, *179*
Sabbio, Kathy, The Brentwood Group, Inc. (R), NJ, *22*
Satenstein, Sloan, Higdon Prince Inc. (R), NY, *93*
Stevens, Robert D., Douglas-Allen, Inc. (R), MA, *54*
Stork, Jennifer, Goodkind Assoc. Inc. (C), NY, *360*
Stranberg, Mark, Mark Stranberg & Assoc. Inc. (R), MA, *202*
Swift, Nina E., The Oxbridge Group, Ltd. (C), PA, *500*
Totah, Tamara, The Oxbridge Group, Ltd. (C), NY, *500*
Van Weelde, Ron, ATS Executive Recruitment (C), GA, *255*
Venable, William, Thorndike Deland Assoc. LLC (R), NY, *48*
Weinstock, Michael A., Advisors' Search Group, Inc. (C), NY, *241*
Werlin, Paul A., Human Capital Resources, Inc. (C), FL, *384*
Whitney, Jr., Kenneth L., K. L. Whitney Company (R), NJ, *219*
Wilkinson, Frank M., TSW Assoc., LLC (R), CT, *211*
Williston, Nada D., Active Search & Placement Inc. (C), CA, *239*
Wolfson, Gary M., The Blackman Kallick Search Division (C), IL, *267*
Youngblood, Robert S., Youngblood Assoc. (C), NC, *626*
Yungerberg, Steven A., Steven Yungerberg Assoc., Inc. (R), MN, *226*
Zaher, Richard, Fox-Morris Assoc., Inc. (C), NY, *352*

Investment management

Bufkin, E. Ralph, BFW, Inc. (C), GA, *266*
Kinlin, Ellen C., The Kinlin Co., Inc. (R), MA, *115*

Investor relations

Charet, Sandra, Charet & Assoc. (C), NJ, *289*
Johnson, Kathleen N., The Repovich-Reynolds Group (TRRG, Inc.) (R), CA, *175*
LeMon, Monet M., The Repovich-Reynolds Group (TRRG, Inc.) (R), CA, *175*
Marshall, Larry, Marshall Consultants, Inc. (R), NY, *137*
McCandless, Hugh, Marshall Consultants, Inc. (R), NY, *137*
McLean, Chris, Chaloner Assoc. (R), MA, *32*
Paschal, Carolyn Smith, Carolyn Smith Paschal Int'l. (R), CA, *160*
Quinn, Gail, Marshall Consultants, Inc. (R), NY, *137*
Raperto, Marie T., The Cantor Concern, Inc. (R), NY, *28*
Reynolds, Smooch S., The Repovich-Reynolds Group (TRRG, Inc.) (R), CA, *175*
Silverman, Marjorie, Marshall Consultants, Inc. (R), NY, *137*
Watkins, Jean T., The Repovich-Reynolds Group (TRRG, Inc.) (R), CA, *175*
Wills, James C., Wills Consulting Assoc. Inc. (R), CT, *222*

Iron

Mayberry, Karen Sue, Singleton & Assoc. (C), VA, *582*
Singleton, Steven L., Singleton & Assoc. (C), VA, *582*

IS

Allen, Debbie, Hall Kinion (C), CA, *366*
Allen, Thomas R., Allen Consulting Group, Inc. (C), MO, *244*
Atley, David, Joe L. Giles & Assoc. (C), MI, *357*
Barbosa, Franklin J., Skott/Edwards Consultants (R), NJ, *192*
Barkocy, Andrew B., Princeton Executive Search (C), NJ, *518*
Barrow, Dan J., The Regency Group, Ltd. (C), NE, *533*
Bartz, Douglas, Bartz Rogers & Partners (C), MN, *261*
Battipaglia, Vincent, Winthrop Partners, Inc. (R), NY, *222*
Bedard, Felix, Groupe PCA Inc. (C), ON, *364*
Beldon, Richard, Professional Support Inc. (C), OH, *523*
Bell, Thomas D., John J. Davis & Assoc., Inc. (R), NY, *47*
Black, Dennis, Action Executive Personnel Consulting Inc. (C), ON, *239*
Blonsky, Lorena M., LMB Assoc. (C), IL, *419*
Boag, John, Norm Sanders Assoc., Inc. (R), NJ, *184*
Boje, Bruce A., Westfields Int'l., Inc. (C), NY, *619*
Bond, James, People Management Northeast, Inc. (R), CT, *162*
Boone, Jr., Joseph E., Premier Search Group (C), IN, *517*
Bradley, Richard, Dynamic Staffing Network (C), IL, *324*

Brady, Eileen, Systems Search Group, Inc. (C), NC, *599*
Brandt, William E., Brandt Associates (C), PA, *272*
Briggs, Farris R., Staff Resources, Inc. (C), SC, *590*
Brown, Ashley, Premier Search Group (C), IL, *517*
Brown, Dennis S., D. Brown & Assoc., Inc. (C), OR, *275*
Bryant, Robert L., Renaissance Resources, LLC (R), VA, *174*
Buehler, Brad, The Goodman Group (R), CA, *79*
Carroll, Kathy, K. Carroll & Assoc. (C), IL, *284*
Carter, Guy W., Management Recruiters of Travelers Rest, Inc. (C), SC, *461*
Chan, Elsie, Elsie Chan & Assoc. (C), CA, *289*
Chartrand, Pierre, Groupe PCA Inc. (C), QE, *363*
Chelston, Joseph, SoftSearch Inc. (C), NJ, *586*
Christ, Celeste, Quality Consulting Group, Inc. (C), WI, *526*
Cicci, Mary, Squires Resources Inc. (C), ON, *590*
Cohen, Barry, Response Staffing Services (C), NY, *535*
Cokins, Nicholas, The Hiring Authority, Inc. (C), FL, *379*
Cordell, Cindy Andrew, Corporate Resources (C), OH, *301*
Craig, Lynn, The Riverbend Group (C), MO, *538*
Crosby, Kimberly A., Fast Switch, Ltd. (C), OH, *338*
Davis, Jack, John J. Davis & Assoc., Inc. (R), NY, *47*
Davis, John J., John J. Davis & Assoc., Inc. (R), NY, *47*
Davis, Linda, Sanford Rose Assoc. - Youngstown (C), NC, *569*
Diersing, Joe, Executive Search, Ltd. (C), OH, *336*
Domby, Samuel F., eXsource Inc. (C), SC, *337*
Dong, Steven, Executive Search, Ltd. (C), OH, *336*
Dougherty, Carolyn, IntelliSource, inc. (C), PA, *391*
Dubois, Denis R., Networking Unlimited of NH, Inc. (C), NH, *491*
Earhart, Bill, Sanford Rose Assoc. - Columbus North (C), OH, *570*
Eastmer, Gregory, Professional Support Inc. (C), NY, *523*
Eastmer, Paul H., Professional Support Inc. (C), NY, *523*
Eckler, Geoffrey N., Eckler Personnel Network (C), VT, *326*
Elinski, Mike, Human Resources Management Hawaii, Inc. (C), HI, *384*
Emory, Vaughn, BayResearch Group, Inc. (R), IL, *14*
Estes, S., The Talley Group (R), VA, *205*
Faas, Vicki L., Healthcare Recruiters of the Rockies, Inc. (C), CO, *372*
Fells, Norman, EFCO Consultants, Inc. (C), NY, *327*
Fisher, Mel V., The Fisher Group (R), AB, *67*
Folletta, Wallamena, Action Executive Personnel Consulting Inc. (C), ON, *239*
Ford, Sandra D., The Ford Group, Inc. (R), PA, *69*
Foster, William A., Bridgecreek Personnel Agency (C), CA, *273*
Gallagher, Michael, Mankuta Gallagher & Assoc., Inc. (C), FL, *468*
Gamache, Valerie, Joe L. Giles & Assoc. (C), MI, *357*
Gardner, Glen, Sanford Rose Assoc. - Columbus North (C), OH, *570*
Gawitt, Dan, Management Recruiters of the Baltimore Washington Corridor (C), MD, *450*
Gerlach, Mary, Quality Consulting Group, Inc. (C), WI, *526*
Giles, Joe L., Joe L. Giles & Assoc. (C), MI, *357*
Glavin, James E., Wood-Glavin, Inc. (R), KS, *224*
Glomski, Jane, Management Recruiters of Rochester (C), MN, *452*
Goldman, Jeff, Global 1000 Int'l. Services (C), CA, *358*
Goodman, Lion, The Goodman Group (R), CA, *79*
Greathouse, Lesa, Premier Search Group (C), IN, *517*
Greenberg, Jordan A., The Pinnacle Source, Inc. (C), CO, *512*
Gross, Ken, Data Search Network, Inc. (C), FL, *307*
Hall, Larry D., Miller-Hall HRISearch (C), CA, *482*
Hall, Marcia, Larson, Katz & Young, Inc. (C), VA, *413*
Hancock, Jason, Hall Kinion (C), CA, *366*
Hannas, Jeanine K., Executive Business Solutions, Inc. (C), WA, *332*
Harper, Deborah, Harper Hewes, Inc. (C), NY, *369*
Harrington, Cherie, Human Resources Personnel Agency (R), AR, *99*
Harris, John, Management Recruiters of Rochester (C), MN, *452*
Hawkins, Max, Management Recruiters of Wausau, LLC (C), WI, *466*
Hebert, Sylvain, Groupe PCA Inc. (C), QE, *363*
Helgeson, Burton H., Norm Sanders Assoc., Inc. (R), NJ, *184*
Hendershot, Janie, Dunhill Professional Search of Wilkes-Barre/Scranton, Inc. (C), PA, *322*
Hinkle, Alfred, Renaissance Resources, LLC (R), VA, *174*
Ho, John, Management Recruiters of Chanhassen (C), MN, *452*
Hoehne, Rebecca, Advanced Resources, Inc. (C), MO, *241*
Hoffenberg, Elliot, H. J. Elliot, Inc. (R), IL, *58*
Hughes, Louis B., Norm Sanders Assoc., Inc. (R), NJ, *184*
Hulse, Jeanne, Richmond Assoc. (C), NY, *537*
Hutts, Mark, InTech Services, Inc. (C), GA, *390*
Ivey, Wayne, Data Bank Executive Search (R), OH, *46*
Jacobson, Rick, The Windham Group (R), OH, *222*
James, David, David James Search (C), CA, *397*
Johnson, Maria, Search Int'l. (R), MA, *187*
Johnston, J. Reid, Hughes & Company (R), VA, *98*
Johnston, James E., Computer Search Group, Ltd. (R), IL, *39*
Jones, Jeff, Management Recruiters of Atlanta (C), GA, *445*
Just, Susan, Just Management Services Inc. (C), FL, *402*
Katzman, Melissa, Melissa Katzman, Executive Search (C), NY, *404*
Kelley, Carolyn, The CARVIR Group, Inc. (C), GA, *285*
Klages, Constance W., International Management Advisors, Inc. (R), NY, *103*
Koers, Trina, TRS Staffing Solutions Inc. (C), OH, *610*
Koppelman, William, Kingsley Quinn/USA (R), NJ, *115*
Kremer, Erica, Brigade, Inc. (R), CA, *23*
Lara, Dolores, Hemingway Personnel, Inc. (C), CA, *375*
Larson, Ila, i.j. & assoc., inc. (C), CO, *387*
Larson, Robert, Berman & Larson (C), NJ, *265*
LaVallee, Michael J., LaVallee & Associates (C), NC, *413*
Lawrence, Ellen B., Holohan Group, Ltd. (R), MO, *95*
Layton, Bradford, Bradford & Galt, Inc. (C), MO, *271*
Lehman, Neal G., Sherwood Lehman Massucco, Inc. (R), CA, *189*
Lindsey, Mary M., Norm Sanders Assoc., Inc. (R), NJ, *184*
Long, Jack P., John J. Davis & Assoc., Inc. (R), NY, *47*
Loria, Frank, Accounting Personnel & Engineering Personnel Consultants (C), LA, *238*
Maltby, Thomas J., Halbrecht & Co. (C), VA, *365*
Mannix, Francis L., F. L. Mannix & Co. (R), MA, *135*
Marrin, Rick, Finney-Taylor Personnel & Management Consultants Ltd. (C), AB, *341*
Martineau, Bill, Dunhill Professional Search of Winston-Salem (C), NC, *322*
Martineau, Bob, Dunhill Professional Search of Winston-Salem (C), NC, *322*
Martineau, Dan, Dunhill Professional Search of Winston-Salem (C), NC, *322*
Mathias, William J., Preng & Assoc., Inc. (R), TX, *167*
May, Paul, Paul May & Assoc. (C), IL, *473*
Mayo, Buz, TeamBuilders (C), GA, *601*
McCarthy, Maureen, Management Recruiters of Fresno (C), CA, *440*

RECRUITER SPECIALTIES

McGuigan, Walter J., Norm Sanders Assoc., Inc. (R), NJ, *184*
Miller, Marc S., Miller-Hall HRISearch (C), NY, *482*
Miller, William, V. Robinson & Co., Inc. (C), MO, *539*
Molkentine, Jon, Dunhill Search of Arlington (C), TX, *322*
Molloy, Harry, Data Bank Executive Search (R), OH, *46*
Moore, Larry W., Larry Moore & Assoc. (C), CA, *484*
Moore, Richard, Healthcare Recruiters of the Rockies, Inc. (C), CO, *372*
Moses, Brad, Information Systems Professionals (C), NC, *388*
Mueller, William, Noll Human Resource Services (C), MO, *494*
Mullenhoff, James A., Rob Dey Executive Search (R), FL, *49*
Newman, Gloria, Jack Richman & Assoc. (C), FL, *537*
Noll, William T., Noll Human Resource Services (C), NE, *494*
Orkin, Ralph, Sanford Rose Assoc. - Euclid (C), OH, *569*
Orkin, Sheilah, Sanford Rose Assoc. - Euclid (C), OH, *569*
Paul, Mary, Premier Search Group (C), IL, *517*
Payne, Joe, Van Treadaway Assoc., Inc. (R), GA, *210*
Pharr, Thomas, Baldwin & Assoc. (C), OH, *258*
Poitras, Sandy, Squires Resources Inc. (C), ON, *590*
Poracky, John W., M. Wood Company (R), IL, *224*
Powers, Keith, Baldwin & Assoc. (C), OH, *258*
Procopio, Vince, Paragon Recruiting Officials Inc. (C), OH, *502*
Puckett, William E., Searchline Services, Inc. (C), OH, *577*
Pukita, Mark, Fast Switch, Ltd. (C), OH, *338*
Randolph, Bob, Career Counseling Inc. (CCI) (C), KY, *282*
Raney, Albert, Dunhill Personnel Service of Fargo (C), ND, *322*
Redell, John, Redell Search, Inc. (C), IL, *533*
Reep, Walt, Data Bank Executive Search (R), OH, *46*
Rembisz, Laura, RemTech Business Solutions, Inc. (C), MI, *534*
Richman, Jack, Jack Richman & Assoc. (C), FL, *537*
Rien, David, Jeffrey Meryl Assoc., Inc. (C), NJ, *398*
Roberts, Marc, Action Executive Personnel Consulting Inc. (C), ON, *239*
Robinson, Michael, Management Recruiters of Atlanta (C), GA, *445*
Roby, Joan, Management Recruiters of Georgetown (C), SC, *461*
Rogers, Scott, Bartz Rogers & Partners (C), MN, *261*
Roll, M. A., Roll International (C), TX, *541*
Rollins, Jay M., Rollins Search Group, Inc. (C), GA, *541*
Rowe, Mark, Dunhill Technical Staffing (C), IN, *320*
Sabrin, Joe, ManTech Consulting (C), NY, *468*
Sakuru, Anita, Raymond Karsan Assoc. (C), MA, *530*
Salvatore, Philip A., LAS Management Consulting Group, Inc. (R), NJ, *125*
Sampson, Ron, Market Niche Consulting (C), AZ, *470*
Sanders, Karen M., Norm Sanders Assoc., Inc. (R), NJ, *184*
Sanders, Marlaine, Shell Technology Group (C), CA, *580*
Sanders, Norman D., Norm Sanders Assoc., Inc. (R), NJ, *184*
Sanders, Todd A., Norm Sanders Assoc., Inc. (R), NJ, *184*
Sandusky, Edward, Professional Support Inc. (C), NY, *523*
Schalk, Julie, Account Ability Now (C), MI, *234*
Schoff, Diane L., The Edge Resource Group (C), PA, *326*
Schulenburg, Neil P., Schulenburg & Assoc. (C), GA, *572*
Schultz, Bob, Wegner & Assoc. (C), WI, *617*
Schumer, Marvin, R & L Assoc., Ltd. (R), NY, *170*
Searing, James M., Korn/Ferry Int'l. (R), VA, *118*
Sharpe, Jocelyn, Dunhill Professional Search of Winston-Salem (C), NC, *322*
Sheridan, Lynda, The Goodman Group (R), CA, *79*
Siegel, Alec, Halbrecht & Co. (C), VA, *365*
Silverman, Craig, Hall Kinion (C), CA, *366*
Silverstein, Michael L., Management Recruiters of Columbus, Inc. (C), GA, *445*
Simkanin, Christine, Michael J. Hall & Co. (R), WA, *85*
Simon, John D., John J. Davis & Assoc., Inc. (R), NY, *47*
Singel, Don, Jonathan Lawrence Assoc. (C), NJ, *400*
Sirena, Evelyn, Winthrop Partners, Inc. (R), NY, *222*
Skode, David, Finney-Taylor Personnel & Management Consultants Ltd. (C), AB, *341*
Skorupski, JoAnn, Data Search Network, Inc. (C), NJ, *307*
Smirnoff, Olga, Management Recruiters of Fresno (C), CA, *440*
Smith, Eric, Dunhill Technical Staffing (C), IN, *320*
Smith, Ken, Smith Assoc. (C), IA, *584*
Somers, Donald A., Management Recruiters of Youngstown (C), OH, *458*
Spremulli, Paul L., PKS Assoc., Inc. (C), RI, *513*
Squires, Frank, Squires Resources Inc. (C), ON, *590*
Sroka, John, The Riverbend Group (C), MO, *538*
Stephens, Susan, Sales Consultants of Chicago South (C), IL, *558*
Stollenmaier, Nadine, Dunhill Professional Search of Hawaii (C), HI, *320*
Stoltz, Richard, Management Recruiters of Columbus (C), OH, *457*
Stroud, Toni, Management Recruiters of the Baltimore Washington Corridor (C), MD, *450*
Sturgill, Vicki Hayes, Professional Careers, Inc. (C), NC, *520*
Sudina, Chuck, Sudina Search, Inc. (C), MD, *596*
Summerfield-Beall, Dotty, Summerfield Assoc., Inc. (C), TN, *596*
Tannura, Robert P., Tannura & Assoc., Inc. (R), IL, *206*
Tansey, Char, Management Recruiters of Rochester (C), MN, *452*
Taylor, Patricia, Smartsource Inc. (C), CA, *583*
Thieme, Sue, The Riverbend Group (C), MO, *538*
Tomaras, David, Willmott & Assoc. (C), MA, *622*
Tomko, Jeffrey M., Searchline Services, Inc. (C), OH, *577*
Traynor, Thomas H., Traynor Confidential, Ltd. (C), NY, *609*
Treadaway, Van, Van Treadaway Assoc., Inc. (R), GA, *210*
Van Beek, Mel, Dunhill Personnel Service of Fargo (C), ND, *322*
Vierkant, Robert, Management Recruiters of Rochester (C), MN, *452*
Waldrip, Jennifer, Hall Kinion (C), CA, *366*
Webster, Bruce, Sales Consultants of Milwaukee (C), WI, *563*
Webster, William L., S. B. Webster & Associates (R), MA, *217*
Wells, Patricia, Fortune Group Int'l., Inc. (R), PA, *70*
Whitaker, Bryan, Data Bank Executive Search (R), OH, *46*
Whitehurst, James, Katelyn Partners (C), FL, *404*
Whitley, T. H., Management Recruiters - Kannapolis (C), NC, *456*
Wilkinson, Frank M., TSW Assoc., LLC (R), CT, *211*
Williams, Bob, Information Systems Professionals (C), NC, *388*
Wimberly, Jim, Healthcare Recruiters of Dallas (C), TX, *374*
Womack, Chris, MESA International (C), OR, *480*
Wood, Milton M., M. Wood Company (R), IL, *224*
Young, William H., Bill Young & Assoc. (C), VA, *626*
Zier, Patricia D., P. D. Zier Assoc. (C), CT, *627*

ISO 9000

Walt, Lee, M H Executive Search Group (C), TX, *422*

IT

Albertson, Rob, Dick Williams & Assoc. (C), CA, *621*
Alexander, Karen Vacheron, BT&A, LLC (R), CT, *24*
Alexander, Richard J., Alexander Associates (R), NJ, *2*
Amicci, Bruno C., Triad Technology Group (C), OR, *609*
Anderson, George Wright, Gans, Gans & Assoc., Inc. (R), IL, *74*
Anderson, Harry, Andex Executive Search (C), CT, *250*
Andrews, Dan, BR & Assoc. (C), NJ, *271*
Andrews, David, Engineering Futures, LLC (C), CT, *330*
Anton, Michael, Michael James & Co. (C), IL, *480*
Aplin, David, David Aplin & Assoc. (C), AB, *251*
Aplin, Jeff, David Aplin & Assoc. (C), AB, *251*
Armstrong, C.J., Dunhill Professional Search of Byram (C), MS, *321*
Armstrong, Don, Dunhill Professional Search of Byram (C), MS, *321*
Arnold, Jay, Staffing Edge, Inc. (C), KS, *590*
Arnone, Patrick J., Patrick Arnone & Assoc. Inc. (R), VA, *7*
Ashton, Barbara L., Ashton Computer Professionals, Inc. (C), BC, *253*
Atley, David, Joe L. Giles & Assoc. (C), MI, *357*
Avazian, Richard W., National Field Service Corp. (C), NY, *489*
Badger, Fred H., The Badger Group (R), CA, *10*
Baez, Ana Luisa, Sales Consultants of Ft. Myers, Inc. (C), FL, *557*
Bailey, Edward L., The Patience Motivation Belief Group, Inc. (C), GA, *505*
Bailey, Jerald W., Dunhill Professional Search of Greater New Orleans (C), LA, *321*
Baker, Susan F., Diversified Consulting Services, Inc. (C), CO, *313*
Baniqued, Douglas J., CompuPro (C), IL, *295*
Bard, Justin, Management Recruiters of St. Augustine (C), FL, *444*
Barefield, Ernest, Gans, Gans & Assoc., Inc. (R), PA, *74*
Barefield, Simone Gans, Gans, Gans & Assoc., Inc. (R), FL, *74*
Bascom, Janet, Pro-Tech Search, Inc. (C), IL, *519*
Bassett, Martyn, Bassett Laudi Partners (C), ON, *261*
Baty, R. Gaines, R. Gaines Baty Assoc., Inc. (R), TX, *13*
Baumgaertel, Ingrid, Hedlund Corp. (C), IL, *375*
Baxter, Peter, ISG Informatics Search Group (C), ON, *395*
Beck, Steven, Beck/Eastwood Recruitment Solutions (C), CA, *261*
Becker, John, Becker Project Resources, Inc. (C), OR, *262*
Beckerat, Michael, Michael Thomas, Inc. (C), OH, *480*
Bedard, Felix, Applied Technology Solutions Inc. (C), ON, *252*
Beller, Rick, CMS Management Services LLC (C), TN, *293*
Benke, Norman L., N. L. Benke & Assoc., Inc. (C), OH, *264*
Benkwitt, Barbara, The Brentwood Group, Inc. (R), NJ, *22*
Bennett, Mark, Bennett & Associates (C), TX, *264*
Berger, Joel, Midas Management (C), CT, *481*
Berglund, Sharon, Berglund Int'l. Resources, Inc. (C), TX, *265*
Berkowitz, Edwin, Wesley Brown & Bartle Co., Inc. (R), NY, *218*
Bhandari, Parul, Tarbex (C), DC, *599*
Binke, Brian, Management Recruiters of Birmingham (C), MI, *451*
Binke, Brian, Sales Consultants of Birmingham (C), MI, *559*
Birdie, Khurshed F., NorthStar Technologies, Inc. (C), NY, *496*
Black, George, Robert Shields & Assoc. (C), TX, *538*
Blount, K. Michael, The Maroon Group (R), CT, *136*
Boehm, Maureen, Management Recruiters of Fairfield (C), IA, *449*
Booth, David, Kane & Assoc. (C), TX, *403*
Borenstine, Alvin J., Synergistics Assoc. Ltd. (R), IL, *205*
Boyle, Elizabeth, Infovia (C), CA, *388*
Bradley, Virgina, Fell & Nicholson Technology Resources (R), CA, *66*
Bradshaw, Patrick M., The Patience Motivation Belief Group, Inc. (C), GA, *505*
Breen, Susan V., GFI Professional Staffing Services (C), NH, *357*
Brin, Bradley, Concorde Staff Source Inc. (C), WI, *296*
Brod, Walt, MSI Int'l. (C), VA, *487*
Brooks, Peter, Phillips Resource Group (C), SC, *510*
Brown, Dennis S., D. Brown & Assoc., Inc. (C), OR, *275*
Brown, Dudley G., BridgeGate LLC (C), CA, *273*
Brown, Ian, SearchCorp International (C), AB, *577*
Brown, Kevin, Raymond Karsan Assoc. (C), PA, *530*
Bruce, Dick, The Badger Group (R), CA, *10*
Brust, Sharon, Pro-Tech Search, Inc. (C), IL, *519*
Bruton, Bob, Sanford Rose Assoc. - Charlotte (C), NC, *568*
Brzezinski, Ronald T., Callan Assoc., Ltd. (R), IL, *27*
Bunce, David C., Sales Consultants of Raleigh-Durham-RTP (C), NC, *561*
Bunges, Colin, BT&A, LLC (R), CT, *24*
Buonavita, Tina, Adam-Bryce Inc. (C), NY, *239*
Burfield, Elaine, Skott/Edwards Consultants (R), NY, *192*
Burgess, III, William H., The Burgess Group-Corporate Recruiters Int'l., Inc. (R), NY, *25*
Burny, Holly, Hedlund Corp. (C), IL, *375*
Butler, Daniel, Hreshko Consulting Group (C), NJ, *382*
Butler, Donald W., Management Recruiters of Milwaukee - Downtown (C), WI, *466*
Camus, Louis, Quantum EDP Recruiting Services (C), QE, *526*
Carey, Brenda, The Carey Company (C), NC, *284*
Carpenter, Edward, Executive Search of America, Inc. (C), OH, *336*
Carson, Sandra, Carson-Thomas & Assoc. (C), CA, *284*
Casey, Carol M., Casey & Assoc., Inc. (C), TX, *286*
Cason, Lyn, Brad Marks Int'l. (R), CA, *136*
Chacra, Steven, Chacra, Belliveau & Assoc. Inc. (C), QE, *288*
Chambers, Patricia, Global Consulting Group Inc. (C), ON, *358*
Chanski, Vern, Hobson Assoc. (C), CT, *379*
Chazen, Jennifer, Sanford Rose Assoc. - Amherst, NY (C), NY, *568*
Cheney, Timothy W., Cheney Associates (C), CT, *290*
Christie, Stephen G., Marsar & Co., Inc. (C), FL, *471*
Ciaramitaro, Paul, Corporate Search Consultants, Inc. (C), FL, *301*
Cioffoletti, Anthony, Gahan Assoc. (R), NY, *73*
Clegg, James J., Sanford Rose Assoc. - Charlotte (C), NC, *568*
Clingan, Robert H., Management Recruiters of Broome County, Inc. (C), NY, *454*
Cochran, Ginny, Romac Int'l., Inc. (C), TX, *544*
Cohen, Michael R., Intech Summit Group, Inc. (R), CA, *102*
Cokins, Nicholas, The Hiring Authority, Inc. (C), FL, *379*
Colling, Douglas, KPMG Executive Search (R), ON, *119*
Collins, Bart, Computer Placements Unlimited Inc. (C), NY, *295*
Colton, Scott C., The Colton Partnership, Inc. (R), NY, *38*
Cook, Martin E., Cook Assoc. Int'l., Inc. (C), TN, *298*
Cooper, Linda, BG & Assoc. (C), MD, *266*
Cotterell, Dirk A., Management Recruiters of Salt Lake City (C), UT, *464*
Cutshaw, Robert, F-O-R-T-U-N-E Personnel Consultants of Knoxville (C), TN, *350*
Czamanske, Peter M., Compass Group Ltd. (R), MI, *38*
D'Amora, Jim, Eastridge Infotech (C), NV, *326*
Dailey, Monika, Southern Recruiters & Consultants, Inc. (C), SC, *587*
Daily, John, Christian & Timbers, Inc. (R), OH, *34*

RECRUITER SPECIALTIES

Daily, John C., Handy HRM (R), NY, *86*
Danner, David, Combined Resources Inc. (R), OH, *38*
Daubenspeck, Kenneth, Daubenspeck & Associates, Ltd. (R), IL, *46*
Daubenspeck, Rima, Daubenspeck & Associates, Ltd. (R), IL, *46*
Daugherty-Hill, Kimberly J., Hayman Daugherty Assoc., Inc. (C), GA, *370*
Davenport, Charles, S-H-S TechStaff (C), PA, *550*
Davis, Allen, Allen Davis & Assoc. (C), MA, *308*
Davis, III, Samuel, PRAXIS Partners (R), VA, *167*
de Funiak, William S., De Funiak & Edwards (R), IN, *47*
Dean, Bruce, Recruiting/Solutions (C), CA, *532*
Dean, James L., Dean-Dzierzawiec Assoc. (C), NJ, *309*
Degges, Victoria, Impact Search & Strategies (C), PA, *387*
Delisle, Pierre H., PHD Conseil en Ressources Humaines Inc. (C), QE, *510*
Demarest, Gretchen, Sanford Rose Assoc. - Charlotte (C), NC, *568*
DeMatteo, Robena, DeMatteo Associates (C), NY, *311*
DePhillipo, William R., Tele-Media Int'l. Inc. (C), PA, *604*
DerAris, Neal, A. E. Feldman Assoc., Inc. (C), NY, *339*
Detling, John, Executive Search, Ltd. (C), OH, *336*
Dickerson, Ken, Management Recruiters of Des Moines (C), IA, *449*
Dickey, Chester W., Bowden & Co., Inc. (R), OH, *20*
Diersing, Joe, Executive Search, Ltd. (C), OH, *336*
DiMucchio, Joe, The Jotorok Group (C), RI, *401*
Docker, William, Raymond Karsan Assoc. (C), MA, *530*
Dodson, Ellen, ADECCO Employment Services (C), VA, *240*
Dong, Steven, Executive Search, Ltd. (C), OH, *336*
Doroba, Carol, Impact Search & Strategies (C), PA, *387*
Downs, James L., Sanford Rose Assoc. - Charlotte (C), NC, *568*
Dralle, Robert D., Odell & Assoc., Inc. (C), TX, *498*
DuBrul, Donald C., DuBrul Management Co. (C), NY, *315*
Dudley, Robert R., Sanford Rose Assoc. - Laguna Beach (C), CA, *565*
Dunn, John G., Management Dimensions Ltd. (R), ON, *134*
Dykes, Mimi, Staffing Edge, Inc. (C), TX, *591*
Earle, Holland R., Executive Strategies, Inc. (C), GA, *337*
Easterling, Yvonne, A First Resource (C), NC, *231*
Eastwood, Gary, Beck/Eastwood Recruitment Solutions (C), CA, *261*
Eddington, Steve, Electronic Search, Inc. (C), IL, *328*
Edwards, Jim, Cornerstone Resources, Inc. (C), OK, *299*
Edwards, Randolph J., De Funiak & Edwards (R), MD, *47*
Ellis, James P., Ellis & Associates (C), HI, *328*
Ellison, Richard H., Sanford Rose Assoc. - Youngstown (C), OH, *569*
Empey, David, Management Recruiters of Franktown (C), CO, *442*
Epstein, Robert G., RGE (C), VA, *535*
Fafard, Lina, Montgomery West (R), CA, *146*
Faso, Nancy, Management Recruiters of Chicago West (C), IL, *447*
Feldman, Mitchell, A. E. Feldman Assoc., Inc. (C), NY, *339*
Fell, David W., LAI Ward Howell (R), OH, *123*
Fell, Robert M., Fell & Nicholson Technology Resources (R), CA, *65*
Fenyves, Leslie, James Moore & Assoc. (C), CA, *397*
Fernow, Charles S., Fernow Assoc. (C), PA, *340*
Ferrante, Peter, National Executive (C), ON, *489*
Fienberg, Chester A., Drummond Assoc., Inc. (C), NY, *315*
Finkle, Linda, LG Brand, Inc. (C), MD, *417*
Fischer, John C., Horton Int'l. Inc. (R), NY, *96*
Fischer, Judith, RJ Associates (C), CA, *538*
Fischer, Ronald, RJ Associates (C), CA, *538*
Fisher, Mel V., The Fisher Group (R), AB, *67*
Fishkin, Anita, A. G. Fishkin & Assoc., Inc. (R), MD, *68*
Fitzgibbons, David, International Executive Recruiters (C), OH, *393*
Ford, Eileen F., Ford & Ford (C), MA, *343*
Fortin-Menendez, Joanne, Avion International Technology Inc. (C), ON, *257*
Fountain, Ray, Management Recruiters of North Charleston (C), SC, *460*
Frankian, Joseph R., Allstaff, Inc. (C), IL, *245*
Frease, Don, Management Recruiters The Delta Group, Inc. (C), TN, *461*
Fridley, Patricia, Carol Maden Group (C), VA, *422*
Frigon, Bernard, Bernard Frigon & Assoc. Inc. (C), QE, *353*
Fruchtman, Gary, Management Recruiters of Northwest Ohio, Inc. (C), OH, *458*
Funk, Terry L., International Technical Resources (C), FL, *394*
Gaines, Jay, Jay Gaines & Company, Inc. (R), NY, *74*
Galka, John, Huntley Associates (Dallas), Inc. (C), TX, *386*
Gamache, Valerie, Joe L. Giles & Assoc. (C), MI, *357*
Gardella, Richard, The Whyte Group, Inc. (R), MD, *220*
Gardner, Richard E., Russillo/Gardner/Spolsino (C), MA, *548*
Garrote, L. Ignacio, Phoenix Search (R), MX, *164*
Gasbarre, John, The Haystack Group, Inc. (R), ME, *88*
Gates, Will, Morgan Samuels Co. (R), CA, *147*
Gawitt, Dan, Management Recruiters of the Baltimore Washington Corridor (C), MD, *450*
George, Delores F., Delores F. George, C.P.C. (C), MA, *356*
Gerald, C. Richard, C. R. Gerald & Assoc. (C), ON, *356*
Gerarde, Paul S., Keena Staffing Services (C), NY, *404*
Germain, Valerie, Jay Gaines & Company, Inc. (R), NY, *74*
Germaine, Debra, Fenwick Partners (R), MA, *66*
Gibson, Holli, Sales Consultants of Dallas (C), TX, *563*
Giles, Joe L., Joe L. Giles & Assoc. (C), MI, *357*
Gimbel, Mike, Gimbel & Assoc. (C), FL, *357*
Givens, Steve, Chesapeake Group (C), CT, *290*
Gladwell, Don, ProLink (C), NC, *524*
Godfrey, Robert G., Robert G. Godfrey Assoc. Ltd. (R), IL, *79*
Goldstein, Peggy, Goldstein & Co. (C), CA, *360*
Goldstein, Steven G., The Jonathan Stevens Group, Inc. (R), NJ, *108*
Gomez, David P., David Gomez & Assoc., Inc. (R), IL, *79*
Gomez, Veronica, Engineering Futures, LLC (C), CT, *330*
Gonzer, Lawrence J., L. J. Gonzer Assoc. (C), NJ, *360*
Goyette, Marc, ROI International, Inc. (R), WA, *181*
Gracin, Ada, Computer Placements Unlimited Inc. (C), NY, *295*
Grady, William A., Romac Int'l. Inc. (R), MA, *181*
Gray, Brian A., BG & Assoc. (C), MD, *266*
Gray, Kent, Romac Int'l. - San Francisco (C), CA, *541*
Grebenstein, Charles R., Skott/Edwards Consultants (R), NJ, *192*
Green, Jane, Phillips Resource Group (C), SC, *510*
Groban, Jack L., A.T. Kearney Executive Search (R), CA, *111*
Gross, Richard, Robert Shields & Assoc. (C), TX, *538*
Grossman, Allan D., A. Davis Grant & Co. (R), NJ, *81*
Guinn, Andrea, ISG Informatics Search Group (C), ON, *395*
Habelmann, Gerald B., Habelmann & Assoc. (R), MI, *84*
Hacker, Russell, RHAssoc. Inc. (C), KS, *535*
Hager, Eve, Eastridge Infotech (C), CA, *326*

Halding, Jennifer L., Brian Assoc., Inc. (C), NY, *273*
Hall, Nancy L., Hallman Group, Inc. (C), MI, *367*
Hall, Nancy M., The Hollins Group, Inc. (R), GA, *95*
Hamilton, Casey, Crowe Chizek & Co. (C), IN, *304*
Hanssen, Barbara, Executive Search Team (C), MI, *336*
Hardesty, Kelly, Phillips Resource Group (C), SC, *510*
Harris, T. J., Sales Consultants of Ft. Myers, Inc. (C), FL, *557*
Harris, Thomas E., Sales Consultants of Ft. Myers, Inc. (C), FL, *557*
Harrison, Priscilla, Phillips Resource Group (C), SC, *510*
Hartman, Caroline, Avion International Technology Inc. (C), ON, *257*
Hay, Jennifer, The Pollack Group (C), ON, *514*
Heacock, Barbara, B. D. Wallace & Assoc. (C), MD, *614*
Hearne, Shannan, Sanford Rose Assoc. - Charlotte (C), NC, *568*
Hebert, Chris, Management Recruiters of Nassau, Inc. (R), NY, *134*
Hebert, Lise, Groupe Ranger Inc. (C), QE, *364*
Hechkoff, Robert B., Hechkoff/Work Executive Search Inc. (R), NY, *89*
Hedlund, David, Hedlund Corp. (C), IL, *375*
Heller, Shelly, Ira Z. Nitzberg (C), NY, *493*
Hemmings, Jackie, S-H-S TechStaff (C), PA, *550*
Henard, John B., LAI Ward Howell (R), FL, *123*
Henderson, John, Staffing Edge, Inc. (C), AZ, *590*
Heneghan, Donald A., Allerton Heneghan & O'Neill (R), IL, *4*
Henry, Jeannette A., Huntington Personnel Consultants, Inc. (C), NY, *386*
Herrin, Jill T., J & D Resources Inc. (C), TN, *395*
Hildy, Edward V., Systems One Ltd. (C), IL, *598*
Hirschel, Jerry S., Professional Search Centre, Ltd. (C), IL, *522*
Hirshman, Kenneth A., McGrath & Assoc., Inc. (R), NJ, *141*
Holert, Robert, Houser, Martin, Morris (C), WA, *381*
Holmes, Jeff, Hreshko Consulting Group (C), NJ, *382*
Holsopple, Ben V., ACSYS Resources, Inc. (C), NJ, *238*
Holtzman, Gene, Mitchell Martin Inc. (C), NY, *483*
Homer, Judy B., J. B. Homer Assoc. Inc. (R), NY, *95*
Honquest, Richard W., Quest Enterprises, Ltd. (C), IL, *527*
Hope, Elizabeth, Search Consultants, LLC (C), VA, *575*
Horn, David C., David C. Horn Executive Search (C), TX, *381*
Houchins, Buster, Christian & Timbers, Inc. (R), OH, *34*
Houchins, William C. Buster, Christian & Timbers, Inc. (R), MD, *34*
Howard, Linda J., Doleman Enterprises (R), VA, *53*
Hreshko, Frank M., Hreshko Consulting Group (C), NJ, *382*
Hunt, Leigh, Leigh Hunt & Assoc., Inc. (C), ME, *384*
Hussey, Wayne, Krecklo Executive Search Inc. (R), ON, *120*
James, Chip, Morgan Samuels Co. (R), CA, *147*
Janis, Laurence, Integrated Search Solutions Group, LLC (ISSG) (R), NY, *102*
Jarvis, Daniel G., Boyden (R), NY, *21*
Johnson, Bill, Global Consulting Group Inc. (C), ON, *358*
Johnson, Daniel, Morgan Samuels Co. (R), CA, *147*
Johnson, Jerry A., Sanford Rose Assoc. - Charlotte (C), NC, *568*
Johnson, Joe, Business Partners, Inc. (C), FL, *277*
Johnson, Peter, ZanExec L.L.C. (R), VA, *226*
Johnston, Debbie, Harcourt & Associates (C), AB, *369*
Jones, Jeffrey, AJM Professional Services (C), MI, *243*
Jones, Michael A., The Century Group (C), KS, *287*
Jordan, Dick, Phillips Resource Group (C), NC, *511*
Joswick, Thomas, Michael Thomas, Inc. (C), OH, *480*
Kaye, Francine C., MedSearch Resources, Inc. (C), FL, *478*
Kelleher, Patricia C., Fenwick Partners (R), MA, *66*
Keller, Jason, GCO (C), CA, *355*
Kendrick, M. Steven, LAI Ward Howell (R), TX, *124*
Kennedy, IV, Joseph W., Quest Enterprises, Ltd. (C), IL, *527*
Khan, Nick, NorthStar Technologies, Inc. (C), NY, *496*
Kidd, Bobby, Phillips Resource Group (C), NC, *511*
Kilcoyne, Richard, Carter McKenzie, Inc. (C), NJ, *285*
Killman, Kenneth, Hallman Group, Inc. (C), MI, *367*
Kindler, Peter A., Boardroom Consultants/Kenny Kindler Tholke (R), NY, *19*
King, J. C., A H Justice Search Consultants (C), TX, *402*
King, Jack, Newman-Johnson-King, Inc. (C), TX, *492*
King, Karl, Capital Consulting Group, Inc. (R), MD, *28*
King, Liz, Newman-Johnson-King, Inc. (C), TX, *492*
Kinsey, Joanne, Eastridge Infotech (C), CA, *326*
Kling, Constance W., LAI Ward Howell (R), IL, *123*
Ko, Jane, Phillips Resource Group (C), SC, *510*
Koers, Trina, TRS Staffing Solutions Inc. (C), OH, *610*
Kollaritsch, Lynn, DataPro Personnel Consultants (C), TX, *308*
Kornfeld, Warren, Management Recruiters of Woodbury Inc. (C), NY, *455*
Kostadinova, Kosta, The Search Committee, Inc. (C), FL, *575*
Krautler, William, Krautler Personnel Recruitment (C), FL, *409*
Krecklo, Brian D., Krecklo Executive Search Inc. (R), ON, *120*
Krell, Barry, Cosier & Assoc. (C), AB, *302*
Kunke, Russ, Dunhill Professional Search of Rolling Meadows (C), IL, *320*
Kuntz, William A., Management Recruiters of Indianapolis (C), IN, *448*
Kurtz, Sheldon I., Kurtz Pro-Search, Inc. (C), NJ, *410*
Kush, Max S., Management Recruiters of Easton, PA (C), PA, *458*
Laake, Patrick B., CMS Management Services LLC (C), IN, *293*
Labrecque, B. F., Ray & Berndtson/Laurendeau Labrecque (R), QE, *172*
Laderman, David, ACSYS Resources, Inc. (C), PA, *239*
Lai, Karen, C.T.E.W. Executive Personnel Services Inc. (C), BC, *278*
Laks, Naomi, Adam-Bryce Inc. (C), NY, *239*
Lalagos, Dee, DEL Technical Services, Inc. (C), IL, *310*
Lamontagne, Manon, Groupe Ranger Inc. (C), QE, *364*
Lancaster, Jr., Raymond F., Lancaster Assoc., Inc. (C), NJ, *412*
Langford, Ann S., The Langford Search, Inc. (C), AL, *412*
Langford, K. R. Dick, The Langford Search, Inc. (C), AL, *412*
Lasee, Jeff, The H. S. Group, Inc. (C), WI, *365*
Lau, Hayley, C.T.E.W. Executive Personnel Services Inc. (C), ON, *278*
Lauber, Mark, Management Recruiters of Sugar Land Inc. (C), TX, *464*
Laudi, Mario, Bassett Laudi Partners (C), ON, *261*
Lawrence, Gina, Micro Staff Solutions, Inc. (C), TX, *481*
Lee, James, Sanford Rose Assoc. - Charlotte (C), NC, *568*
Legal, Dale, Capital Consulting Group, Inc. (R), MD, *28*
Leimpeter, Peter, Goldstein & Co. (C), CA, *360*
Leininger, Dennis, Staffing Edge, Inc. (C), IA, *590*
Lennon, Bill, Hall Management Group, Inc. (C), GA, *367*
Lennox, Charles, PricewaterhouseCoopers Executive Search (R), ON, *168*
Leonard, Tom, The Jotorok Group (C), RI, *401*
Lewis, Donnie, Lewis Consulting Service (C), IL, *417*

RECRUITER SPECIALTIES

Lewis, Lynn, A. Davis Grant & Co. (R), NJ, *81*
Lieberman, Beverly, Halbrecht Lieberman Assoc., Inc. (R), CT, *84*
Lifter, Barbara, Lifter & Assoc. (C), CA, *418*
Lifter, Jay, Lifter & Assoc. (C), CA, *418*
Lightner Jr., Ralph H., Stanton Chase Int'l. (R), MD, *199*
Lilja, Raymond, American Services Group (C), IL, *248*
Lins, Peter T., McGrath & Assoc., Inc. (R), NJ, *141*
Loewenstein, Ron, Loewenstein & Assoc., Inc. (R), TX, *131*
Lutostanski, Frank, Selectis Corp. (C), IL, *578*
Lyons, Bonnie, The Whitaker Companies (C), TX, *619*
Lyons, M. Don, L O R (R), NJ, *122*
MacKinnon, Helen, Technical Connections, Inc. (C), CA, *602*
MacLean, Veroushka, Becker Personnel (C), FL, *262*
Malatesta, Roger, Professional Recruiting Consultants, Inc. (C), DE, *521*
Malek, L., Professional Search Consultants (PSC) (C), TX, *523*
Malouin, Etienne, The Pollack Group (C), ON, *514*
Manning, Roger, Executive Search Team (C), MI, *336*
Marino, Jory J., Sullivan & Company (R), NY, *204*
Marra, Jr., John, Marra Peters & Partners (R), NJ, *136*
Marsar, Kevin P., Marsar & Co., Inc. (C), FL, *471*
Masserman, Bruce, Masserman & Assoc., Inc. (R), NY, *138*
Masters, Meri, MESA International (C), CA, *480*
Matte, Richard, Matte Consulting Group Inc. (R), QE, *138*
Mauk, Patricia, Evergreen & Co. (C), MA, *331*
May, Donald C., Allied Search, Inc. (C), CA, *245*
Mazzuckelli, Katie, Tyler & Company (R), GA, *212*
McAnney, Michael, S-H-S TechStaff (C), PA, *550*
McCarter, John, Sanford Rose Assoc. - Charlotte (C), NC, *568*
McConnell, Greg, Winter, Wyman & Co. (C), GA, *623*
McCormick, Jim, McCormick Search Inc. (C), IL, *474*
McCoy, Karl, Pro-Tech Search, Inc. (C), IL, *519*
McCrea, Frank, Procom (C), ON, *519*
McCutcheon, Pat, Iona Partners (C), CA, *394*
McDowell, John, McDowell & Co., Recruiters (C), TX, *474*
McGee, Jerry, Joseph Consulting, Inc. (C), FL, *401*
McIntyre, Marlene, McIntyre Management Resources (C), ON, *475*
McKenna, Brian, The Pollack Group (C), ON, *514*
McKeown, Morgan, Christian & Timbers, Inc. (R), OH, *34*
McKersie, Edward S., ProSearch, Inc. (C), ME, *524*
McKinney, Danny L., J & D Resources Inc. (C), TN, *395*
McNamara, Robert, Global Career Services, Inc. (C), NY, *358*
Medtlie, Peder, Management Recruiters of Milwaukee-West (C), WI, *465*
Meints, Ron, Computer Personnel, Inc. (C), WA, *295*
Meller, Peggy, Hedlund Corp. (C), IL, *375*
Melmet, Dee Dee, Smartsource Inc. (C), CA, *583*
Mendez, Larry W., Layne-Mendez & Co. (R), TX, *127*
Meyer, Rick M., Meyer Assoc., Inc. (R), GA, *144*
Meyer, Tom, CCI - Career Consultants Int'l. (C), CA, *286*
Michalisin, Jr., Nicholas J., S-H-S TechStaff (C), PA, *550*
Miller, Andrew S., Management Recruiters of New Providence (C), NJ, *454*
Miller, David, Global Executive Search Group (C), MA, *358*
Miller, Gordon, Comprehensive Search (C), GA, *295*
Miller, L. D., Eggers Consulting Co., Inc. (C), NE, *327*
Miller, Sharon, The Elmhurst Group (C), CA, *329*
Miller, William, V. Robinson & Co., Inc. (C), MO, *539*
Miners, Richard A., Sedlar & Miners (R), NY, *188*
Misarti, Paul R., Paul Misarti Inc. (C), NY, *483*
Mols, Jeff, Aurora Tech Search (C), ON, *256*
Montville, Bruce A., EXETER 2100 (C), NH, *337*
Moore, Allen, PRAXIS Partners (R), VA, *167*
Moran, Paul, Fenwick Partners (R), MA, *66*
Morgan, Vincent, Bishop Partners (R), NY, *17*
Morse, Sy, Sofco (C), NY, *586*
Moser, Amy, TriStaff Group (C), CA, *609*
Moss, Rich, Quest Enterprises, Ltd. (C), IL, *527*
Muhlfelder, Daniel J., L. J. Gonzer Assoc. (C), NJ, *360*
Mulcahy, Patrick, Mulcahy Co. (C), WI, *487*
Muller, Charles A., AJM Professional Services (C), MI, *243*
Munn, Bill, RHS Assoc. (C), AL, *536*
Murphy, Dan, The Pollack Group (C), ON, *514*
Murphy, James, MSI Int'l. (C), GA, *487*
Murphy, Ken, Kenneth Murphy & Assoc. (C), NS, *487*
Mussato, Ray, Dick Williams & Assoc. (C), CA, *621*
Myers, Ed, D.P. Specialists, Inc. (C), CA, *306*
Myers, Hal, Fortune Personnel Consultants of Huntsville, Inc. (C), AL, *344*
Naderi, Fred, Executive Direction, Inc. (C), CA, *333*
Nathan, Edward, Systems Search (C), IL, *599*
Neufeld, Max, Partners In Human Resources Int'l., Inc. (R), NY, *160*
Nicholson, Jack F., Fell & Nicholson Technology Resources (R), CA, *65*
Nitzberg, Ira Z., Ira Z. Nitzberg (C), NY, *493*
Norman, Paul W., Paul Winston Norman & Assoc. (R), IL, *152*
O'Connor, Kerry, Fell & Nicholson Technology Resources (R), CA, *66*
O'Rourke, Kevin, Ward Assoc. (C), ON, *615*
O'Rourke, Kevin, Ward Assoc. (C), QE, *615*
Oldfield, Theresa L., Strategic Alliance Network, Ltd. (C), OH, *595*
Olman, Robert, COR Management Services, Ltd. (C), NY, *298*
Olsen, David G., Handy HRM (R), NY, *86*
Ormson, Gilbert E., Executive Recruiters, Inc. (C), WI, *334*
Oruche, Osita, American Resources Corp. (C), IL, *248*
Osborn, Ted, Paladin Group, Inc. (C), CO, *502*
Pacini, Lauren R., Hite Executive Search (R), OH, *94*
Palmer, John A., Intelegra, Inc. (C), NJ, *390*
Pann, Arthur J., Arthur Pann Assoc., Inc. (C), NY, *502*
Pappalardo, Chuck, Christian & Timbers, Inc. (R), OH, *34*
Parenica, Jim, Parenica & Co. (R), NC, *159*
Parfitt, Bill, Management Solutions, Inc. (C), WA, *468*
Parfitt, Jan, Management Solutions, Inc. (C), WA, *468*
Pascale, Ron, Pascale & LaMorte, LLC (C), CT, *504*
Pearson, Anna Lee, Sales Consultants of Concord (C), NC, *554*
Pearson, Robert L., LAI Ward Howell (R), TX, *124*
Perea, Cheryl, Tele-Solutions of Arizona, Inc. (C), AZ, *604*
Perkins, Barbara, Harcourt & Assoc. (C), AB, *368*
Perry, David, Perry-Martel Int'l., Inc. (R), ON, *163*
Pesco, Michelle, Chatham Search Assoc., Inc. (C), NJ, *290*
Peters, Peter Louis, Success Seekers Connection (C), FL, *596*
Pettersson, Tara L., LAI Ward Howell (R), TX, *124*
Pharr, Thomas, Baldwin & Assoc. (C), OH, *258*
Phillips, Walter, Phillips Int'l., Inc. (C), SC, *510*

Pickens, Gregory D., Gregory D. Pickens (C), TX, *512*
Pierce, Jonathan, Pro-Tech Search, Inc. (C), IL, *519*
Pierson, Kevin, ACC Technical Services (C), OH, *233*
Plimpton, Ralph L., R. L. Plimpton Assoc., Inc. (R), CO, *165*
Polachi, Jr., Charles A., Fenwick Partners (R), MA, *66*
Polachi, Peter V., Fenwick Partners (R), MA, *66*
Polak, Traci, Landon Morgan (C), ON, *412*
Pollack, Jonathan, Executive Sales Search (C), CO, *335*
Porter, Nanci, Eastridge Infotech (C), CA, *326*
Powers, Keith, Baldwin & Assoc. (C), OH, *258*
Press, Fredrick R., Adept Tech Recruiting, Inc. (C), NY, *240*
Purvis, Iain, Pro Tec Technical Services (C), ON, *519*
Ramsey, Donald M., RHI Consulting (C), VA, *536*
Range, Mary Jane, Bishop Partners (R), NY, *17*
Ranger, Jean-Jacques, Groupe Ranger Inc. (C), QE, *364*
Raniere, Rich, Romac Int'l., Inc. (C), FL, *542*
Ratliff, Steve, GateSource Partners (C), VA, *355*
Razzino, Janelle, Razzino-Claymore Assoc. (C), NJ, *530*
Real, Toffee, Eastridge Infotech (C), CA, *326*
Reid, Michael J., Michael James Reid & Co. (R), CA, *174*
Reiss, Phyllis, Adam-Bryce Inc. (C), NY, *239*
Reynolds, Tom, Koll-Fairfield LLC (C), CT, *408*
Richer, Joyce Eidenberg, W. F. Richer Assoc., Inc. (C), NY, *537*
Richer, William F., W. F. Richer Assoc., Inc. (C), NY, *536*
Riddell, Pat, The Network Corporate Search Personnel Inc. (C), AB, *491*
Riehl, Nancy J., Dynamic Choices Inc. (C), MO, *324*
Rizzo, Deborah M., Brian Assoc., Inc. (C), NY, *273*
Roberts, Marc, The Stevenson Group, Inc. (N.J.) (R), NJ, *200*
Robinson, Adrienne, R. L. Plimpton Assoc., Inc. (R), CO, *165*
Robinson, Tom, Sanford Rose Assoc. - Norcross (C), GA, *566*
Rogers, Roc, Dynamic Computer Consultants, Inc. (C), AZ, *324*
Rose, Author, Sofco (C), NY, *586*
Rosenberg, Kevin M., BridgeGate LLC (C), CA, *273*
Ross, Larry, The Summit Group (C), CA, *596*
Rotsky, Bernard, BR & Assoc. (C), NJ, *271*
Rotter, E. Joseph, Search Assoc., Inc. (C), NJ, *574*
Routh, Maria, The Kleven Group, Inc. (C), MA, *407*
Rovner, Bettyann, Rovner & Assoc., Inc. (R), IL, *182*
Rubin, Nadine, Adam-Bryce Inc. (C), NY, *239*
Rubinic, Michael, The Rubinic Consulting Group (C), OH, *548*
Rubinic, Roxanna, The Rubinic Consulting Group (C), OH, *548*
Rupp, Jane M., MRF Enterprises, Inc. (C), TX, *486*
Ryan, James A., The Gullgroup (C), TX, *364*
Ryan-Ulyatt, Theresa, Chatham Search Assoc., Inc. (C), NJ, *290*
Sacchetti, Lisa, The Renaissance Network (C), MA, *534*
Sadow, Raymond, R. S. Sadow Assoc. (C), NJ, *550*
Sakuru, Anita, Raymond Karsan Assoc. (C), MA, *530*
Salzman, John W., Dunhill Staffing Systems, Inc. (C), OH, *318*
Sanders, David, Management Recruiters of Roseville (C), CA, *441*
Sauer, Harry, ACSYS Resources, Inc. (C), PA, *239*
Schiavone, Mary Rose, Canny, Bowen Inc. (R), NY, *28*
Schlender, Lesly, Rovner & Assoc., Inc. (R), IL, *182*
Schmidt, Susan, David Weinfeld Group (C), NC, *617*
Schneider, Thomas P., WTW Assoc., Inc. (R), NY, *225*
Schuback, Donna, DataPro Personnel Consultants (C), TX, *308*
Schumer, Marvin, R & L Assoc., Ltd. (R), NY, *170*
Schwam, Carol, A. E. Feldman Assoc., Inc. (C), NY, *339*
Schwan, John, The Technology Group (R), IL, *208*
Schwarz, Meredith Barnes, Barnes & Assoc. Executive Search (C), CA, *259*
Schwimmer, Samuel, The Wayne Group, Ltd. (C), NY, *617*
Scott, Evan, Howard Fischer Assoc. Int'l., Inc. (R), PA, *67*
Sears, Kirk P., The Wilmington Group (C), NC, *622*
Sedak, George, Curry, Telleri Group, Inc. (R), NJ, *44*
Sedlar, Jeri L., Sedlar & Miners (R), NY, *188*
Sessa, Vincent J., Integrated Search Solutions Group, LLC (ISSG) (R), NY, *102*
Shakes, Joe, Fell & Nicholson Technology Resources (R), CA, *66*
Shapiro, Eve, Hedlund Corp. (C), IL, *375*
Sharp, Lee, DHR Int'l., Inc. (R), CA, *49*
Shaw, R. William, Management Recruiters of South Bend (C), IN, *448*
Shea, Christopher J., Ingram & Aydelotte, Inc. (R), NY, *101*
Shearer, Edie, R. L. Plimpton Assoc., Inc. (R), CO, *165*
Shedroff, Michael, ACSYS Resources, Inc. (C), NJ, *238*
Sherman, Gilbert, Combined Resources Inc. (R), OH, *38*
Siegel, Brigid Oliveri, Fenwick Partners (R), MA, *66*
Simpson, Cathy G., Conroy Partners Ltd. (R), AB, *39*
Skalet, Ira, A. E. Feldman Assoc., Inc. (C), NY, *339*
Skiba, Jeff, Management Recruiters of Lake Tahoe, NV (C), NV, *453*
Sklarski, Kevin, The Jotorok Group (C), RI, *401*
Slepin, Matthew B., Argonaut Partners, LLC (R), CA, *6*
Slusser, Cindy L., The Stelton Group, Inc. (C), NJ, *592*
Smith, Aaron, Staffing Edge, Inc. (C), CO, *590*
Smith, David P., HRS, Inc. (R), PA, *97*
Smith, Jill, ACSYS Resources, Inc. (C), PA, *239*
Smith, Sam, Romac Int'l., Inc. (C), KY, *543*
Sowers, John, Marvel Consultants, Inc. (C), OH, *472*
Sparks, Michele Benum, Micro Staff Solutions, Inc. (C), TX, *481*
Spotswood, Mel, Consulpro (R), ON, *39*
Starner, William S., Fenwick Partners (R), MA, *66*
Steele, Kevin, Winter, Wyman & Co. (C), MA, *623*
Stefunek, Paul C., StratfordGroup (R), OH, *203*
Steinman, Stephen M., The Stevenson Group, Inc. (N.J.) (R), NJ, *200*
Stenhouse, Judy, Phillips Resource Group (C), SC, *510*
Stiles, Jr., Cortland, Fenwick Partners (R), MA, *66*
Stillinger, Scott R., Stillinger & Assoc. (R), CA, *201*
Stillinger, Skip, Stillinger & Assoc. (R), CA, *201*
Strayhorn, Larry, Management Recruiters of Chicago West (C), IL, *447*
Strayhorn, Patricia, Management Recruiters of Chicago West (C), IL, *447*
Stroud, Toni, Management Recruiters of the Baltimore Washington Corridor (C), MD, *450*
Swan, Barbara, Lancaster Assoc., Inc. (C), NJ, *412*
Symcox, Jim, SPC Symcox Personnel Consultants (C), TX, *588*
Szesny, Jim, Lechner & Assoc., Inc. (C), FL, *415*
Talman, Ilya, Roy Talman & Assoc. (C), IL, *599*
Tang, Cliff, Wood West & Partners Inc. (C), BC, *624*
Taylor, Charles E., LAI Ward Howell (R), GA, *123*
Taylor, Walter W., Management Recruiters of Venice, Inc. (C), FL, *445*
Tedla, Solomon, Creative HR Solutions (C), GA, *303*

Tessman, Russ, Management Recruiters of Des Moines (C), IA, *449*
Thibault, Elaine, Adam-Bryce Inc. (C), NY, *239*
Thomas, G. Alan, IPR, Inc. (R), VA, *103*
Thompson, Ken, Allen & Assoc. (C), NV, *244*
Thormodsgaard, Terry, Thor, Inc. (C), CA, *606*
Tittle, David M., Paul-Tittle Assoc., Inc. (R), VA, *161*
Tolette, Skip, Skip Tolette Executive Search Consulting (R), NJ, *209*
Tomasco, Raymond, Boehmer, Tomasco & Alexander (R), CT, *24*
Tomasco, Raymond, BT&A, LLC (R), CT, *24*
Tomasco, Raymond, Huntington Group (R), CT, *100*
Trachtenberg, Mort, Techno-Trac Systems, Inc. (C), NY, *603*
Tracy, Susan, Wheeler Assoc. (R), CT, *219*
Trilling, Dean D., LAI Ward Howell (R), OH, *123*
Turczyn, Charlene, CMW & Associates, Inc. (C), IL, *293*
Uhrig, Scott, LAI Ward Howell (R), TX, *124*
Vacca, Domenic L., ACSYS Resources, Inc. (C), DE, *238*
Vacheron Alexander, Karen, Huntington Group (R), CT, *100*
Valente, Joseph, Management Recruiters of Batavia (C), IL, *447*
Vande Water, Katie E., J. Robert Scott (R), MA, *104*
Vande Woude, John, NorthStar Technologies, Inc. (C), NY, *496*
Verner, Josef, Houser, Martin, Morris (C), WA, *381*
Vitanza, Jocelyne, DARE Personnel Inc. (C), ON, *307*
Vrabel, Frank, ISG Informatics Search Group (C), ON, *395*
Wallace, William J., Wallace Management Co. (R), TN, *215*
Walsh, Richard, The Gabriel Group (C), PA, *354*
Walton, Craig, Management Recruiters of San Marcos (C), TX, *463*
Ward, Jennifer, David Aplin & Assoc. (C), AB, *251*
Ward, Peter, Ward Assoc. (C), ON, *615*
Warner, C. Douglas, C. D. Warner & Assoc. (C), PA, *615*
Watkins, Robert J., R. J. Watkins & Co., Ltd. (R), CA, *216*
Watkinson, Jim, The Badger Group (R), CA, *10*
Weinfeld, David C., David Weinfeld Group (C), NC, *617*
Weinhold, Jean, LCC Companies (C), AZ, *414*
Weinhold, Ray, LCC Companies (C), AZ, *414*
Weliver, Edward A., Weliver & Assoc. (C), MI, *618*
Werbin, Susan, Werbin Assoc. Executive Search, Inc. (C), NY, *618*
West, Fred, Wood West & Partners Inc. (C), BC, *624*
Westhoff, Clifford, RHAssoc. Inc. (C), KS, *535*
Whiteford, Scott, Modis (C), MD, *483*
Whitehead, III, Arch S., Arch S. Whitehead Assoc. Inc. (ASWA) (R), NY, *219*
Wilkinson, Ann Trego, Wilkinson SoftSearch, Inc. (C), VA, *621*
Wilkinson, Kurt A., Wilkinson SoftSearch, Inc. (C), VA, *620*
Willbanks, Bret, TTG/Sterling Services (C), CA, *610*
Williams, Dick, Dick Williams & Assoc. (C), CA, *621*
Wilson, John T., Wilson-Douglas-Jordan (C), IL, *622*
Wilson, Paul, NorthStar Technologies, Inc. (C), NY, *496*
Wink, Cheryl, Sanford Rose Assoc. - Salt Lake City (C), UT, *571*
Wisnewski, Edward J., Wisnewski & Assoc. (R), CA, *223*
Wittner, Jean, Hedlund Corp. (C), IL, *375*
Wlodawsky, Wayne, Romac Int'l., Inc. (C), TX, *544*
Wnek, Ron, The Jotorok Group (C), RI, *401*
Wolf, Stephen M., Montenido Assoc. (R), CA, *146*
Woltz, Kenneth A., Woltz & Assoc., Inc. (R), IL, *224*
Wood, Ron, Wood West & Partners Inc. (C), BC, *624*
Work, Alan J., Hechkoff/Work Executive Search Inc. (R), NY, *89*
Yakimishyn, Michael, Zen Zen Int'l. Inc. (C), MB, *627*
Yossem, Sheila, Bishop Partners (R), NY, *17*
Zaslav, Debra M., Telford, Adams & Alexander (R), CA, *208*
Ziarko, Michael E., Selective Search Associates (C), OH, *578*
Zincavage, David, Cybernautic Corp. (C), CT, *305*
Zulpo, Darcy, Quest Enterprises, Ltd. (C), IL, *527*

Jewelry

Feldman, Abe, A. E. Feldman Assoc., Inc. (C), NY, *339*
Rapp, Harold L., Harold L. Rapp Assoc. (C), NY, *529*

Juvenile products

Keoughan, Thomas, The C.P.R. Group (C), NJ, *278*

Labor

Edelman, Diane, Stephen Haas Legal Placement (C), NY, *365*
Goich, S. George, Fernow Assoc. (C), PA, *340*
Johnson, John Kimbrough, Johnson Brown Assoc., Inc. (C), IN, *400*

Laboratory

Len, Ronald D., Healthcare Recruiters International-NY/NJ (C), NJ, *373*
Mendrala, Karen, Lab Market Specialists (C), UT, *411*

Landscaping

Dummer, Charles F., Charles & Associates, Inc. (C), NE, *289*
Thomason, Penny, F-O-R-T-U-N-E Personnel Consultants of East Seattle (C), WA, *351*

Leasing

Barnett, Dan, J. B. Brown & Assoc., Inc. (C), OH, *275*
Bickerstaff, John, Synagent Inc. (C), ON, *597*
Dycus, Gwen, Gwen Dycus & Assoc. (C), FL, *323*
Hamilton, Frank, Gwen Dycus & Assoc. (C), FL, *323*
Harmeling, Dutch, Harmeling & Associates (C), CA, *369*
Lysaght, Evan J., The Moran Group (C), IL, *484*
Norris, Ronald, Ronald Norris & Assoc. (C), IL, *495*
Regush, Catherine, Ambridge Management Corp. (C), ON, *247*
Ward, Madeleine, L T M Assoc. (C), IL, *410*
Wax, Robert M., Kingsbury • Wax • Bova (R), MA, *114*

Legal

Abelson, Cathy B., Cathy Abelson Legal Search (C), PA, *232*
Africa, Martha Fay, Major, Hagen & Africa (C), CA, *423*
Albergato, Vincent, Raymond Karsan Assoc. (C), MA, *530*
Armstrong, Anna Marie, Major, Hagen & Africa (C), CA, *423*
Arnautovic, Zora, Consulpro (R), ON, *39*
Arnold, Jay, Staffing Edge, Inc. (C), KS, *590*
Arnold, Patrick A., Attorneys at Work (C), GA, *256*
Avazian, Richard W., National Field Service Corp. (C), NY, *489*
Bader, Sam, Bader Research Corp. (C), NY, *257*
Barnes, Sheryl, Blane, Stevens & Kellogg (C), FL, *268*
Bashor, Terry W., Legal Search Assoc. (C), KS, *416*
Bauly, Ted, John Kurosky & Assoc. (R), CA, *122*
Beckman, Susan R., Beckman & Assoc. Legal Search (C), OH, *262*

Beckwith, Randy, Seltzer Fontaine Beckwith (C), CA, *579*
Beilin, Marcia, Marcia Beilin, Inc. (C), NY, *262*
Berger, Joel, Meridian Legal Search/Legal Temps (C), NY, *479*
Berger, Mitchell L., Howard-Sloan Legal Search, Inc. (C), NY, *382*
Bickerton, Brion, Bickerton & Gordon LLC (C), MA, *266*
Block, David J., H. Hertner Assoc., Inc. (C), FL, *377*
Bloom, Howard, The Howard C. Bloom Co. (C), TX, *268*
Bloom, Joyce, The Howard C. Bloom Co. (C), TX, *268*
Bloom, Mary, Robert Bennett Assoc. (C), NY, *264*
Boggus, Francis O., Sales Consultants of Omaha, Inc. (C), NE, *560*
Bonham, Apryl, Claimsearch (C), CA, *291*
Bradford, Philip, Major, Hagen & Africa (C), NY, *423*
Bredeson, D. A., Bredeson Executive Recruitment, LLC (R), TX, *22*
Brest, Dan, Capital Consulting Group, Inc. (R), MD, *28*
Brogan, Pat, Human Resource Bureau (C), CA, *384*
Buckner, Carol, Mruk & E.M.A. Partners (R), NY, *148*
Butts, Catherine P., Major, Hagen & Africa (C), GA, *423*
Byington, S. John, Page-Wheatcroft & Co., Ltd. (R), TX, *158*
Calkins, Quentin D., Major, Hagen & Africa (C), IL, *423*
Carr, III, W. Lyles, The McCormick Group (C), VA, *474*
Cederquist, Malin, Malin Cederquist, Esq. (C), NY, *286*
Christidis, Aurora, Brad Marks Int'l. (R), CA, *136*
Cohen, Pamela S., Topaz Int'l., Inc., Attorney Search (C), NJ, *607*
Collins, Sara E., Alexander & Collins (C), CA, *243*
D'Alessio, Gary A., Chicago Legal Search, Ltd. (C), IL, *290*
DeCaster, Paul, DeCaster Assoc. (C), WI, *310*
DeLena, Robert, Boston Professional Search, Inc. (C), MA, *270*
Dey, Irene, Rob Dey Executive Search (R), FL, *49*
Dickson Parigi, Maria, Prescott Legal Search (C), TX, *517*
Dobbs, Wesley Q., Major, Hagen & Africa (C), GA, *423*
Draper, Michael P., Blane, Stevens & Kellogg (C), FL, *268*
Dubin, Scott M., Major, Hagen & Africa (C), CA, *423*
Dycus, Gwen, Gwen Dycus & Assoc. (C), FL, *323*
Edelman, Diane, Stephen Haas Legal Placement (C), NY, *365*
Eichbaum, June, Major, Hagen & Africa (C), NY, *423*
English Jones, Suzanne, Vera L. Rast Partners Inc. (C), IL, *529*
Erickson, Keith, Executives Worldwide, Inc. (C), OR, *337*
Escher, W. Jon, Major, Hagen & Africa (C), CA, *423*
Fanning, Jr., Charles J., Major, Hagen & Africa (C), CA, *423*
Fergus, Colin, Fergus Legal Search & Consulting, Inc. (C), NY, *339*
Fergus, Jean M. H., Fergus Legal Search & Consulting, Inc. (C), NY, *339*
Finn, Jacquelyn, Finn & Schneider Assoc., Inc. (C), DC, *341*
Flam, Rick M., LAI Ward Howell (R), CA, *123*
Fontaine, Valerie A., Seltzer Fontaine Beckwith (C), CA, *579*
Frank, Miriam J., Major, Hagen & Africa (C), IL, *423*
Frey, Florence, Frey & Sher Assoc., Inc. (C), VA, *353*
Fullerton, Kimberly, Major, Hagen & Africa (C), CA, *423*
Gaines, Ronni L., Topaz Int'l., Inc., Attorney Search (C), NJ, *607*
Garb, Sheila, Garb & Assoc., Legal Placement (C), CA, *354*
Genel, George, Genel Associates (C), CA, *356*
Gillard, Cheryl A., Gillard Assoc. Legal Search (C), MA, *357*
Gillard, Elizabeth A., Gillard Assoc. Legal Search (C), MA, *357*
Gillenwater, Patti, Elinvar (C), NC, *328*
Gold, Leslie, Major, Hagen & Africa (C), NY, *423*
Goldberg, Barry, Barry Goldberg & Assoc., Inc. (C), CA, *360*
Goldman, Elaine, Phyllis Hawkins & Assoc., Inc. (C), AZ, *370*
Gordon, Richards, Bickerton & Gordon LLC (C), MA, *266*
Grandin, Valerie J., H. Hertner Assoc., Inc. (C), FL, *377*
Green, Lucille K., Attorney Search Global, Inc. (C), IL, *255*
Greene, Karin L., Greene-Levin-Snyder LLC (C), NY, *362*
Greene, Zina L., Hartman Greene & Wells (C), DC, *370*
Griffin, Helen, Major, Hagen & Africa (C), NY, *423*
Haberman, Meyer, Interquest, Inc. (R), NY, *103*
Hagen, Laura J., Major, Hagen & Africa (C), IL, *423*
Hamilton, Frank, Gwen Dycus & Assoc. (C), FL, *323*
Hammes-Briggs, Renee, Templeton & Assoc. (C), MN, *605*
Harrell, Stephen G., The Personnel Network, Inc. (C), SC, *508*
Harris, Victoria, Houser, Martin, Morris (C), WA, *381*
Haupt, Bruce W., Bruce W. Haupt Assoc. (R), DC, *88*
Hawkins, Phyllis, Phyllis Hawkins & Assoc., Inc. (C), AZ, *370*
Haydon, Meredith, Haydon Legal Search (C), IL, *370*
Henderson, John, Staffing Edge, Inc. (C), AZ, *590*
Hertner, Herbert H., H. Hertner Assoc., Inc. (C), FL, *377*
Hertner, Pamela R., H. Hertner Assoc., Inc. (C), FL, *377*
Highfill, Steven B., Blane, Stevens & Kellogg (C), FL, *268*
Howard, George, Howard/Williams Assoc. (C), FL, *382*
Hunt, James E., Hunt & Howe Inc. (R), NY, *99*
Hunter, Steven, Diamond Tax Recruiting (C), NY, *312*
Hyde, Tonda, Prescott Legal Search, Inc. (C), TX, *517*
Israel, Ann M., Ann Israel & Assoc., Inc. (C), NY, *395*
Jester, Jillian, Major, Hagen & Africa (C), IL, *423*
Johnson, Daniel, Morgan Samuels Co. (R), CA, *147*
Kam, Connie, Major, Hagen & Africa (C), NY, *423*
Kaplan, Robert, The Executive Group, Inc. (R), CA, *62*
Kass, Roberta, Seltzer Fontaine Beckwith (C), CA, *579*
Katzman, Sheri B., Rosenfeld & Co., Inc. (C), MI, *545*
Kaufman, Stuart, Management Recruiters of Great Neck (C), NY, *454*
Kaufmann, Anita D., A-K-A (Anita Kaufmann Assoc.) (C), NY, *231*
Kellett, Jr., Samuel B., Attorneys at Work (C), GA, *256*
Kerner, Barbara, Barbara Kerner Consultants (C), NY, *405*
Keyser, Amy L., Major, Hagen & Africa (C), CA, *423*
Kilman, Paul H., The Kilman Advisory Group (R), CT, *114*
Koerner, Pam L., Koerner & Assoc., Inc. (C), TN, *408*
Kuschnov, Janice, Charles Dahl Group, Inc. (C), MN, *306*
Leace, Elyse, Impact Search & Strategies (C), PA, *387*
Leighton, Nina, The Ogdon Partnership (R), NY, *155*
Leon-Shelton, Diana, Shelton, Wiseman & Leon (R), CA, *189*
Levin, Alisa F., Greene-Levin-Snyder LLC (C), NY, *362*
Lieberman, Howard, Howard Lieberman & Assoc., Inc. (C), MN, *417*
Lindsey, Jonathan, Major, Hagen & Africa (C), NY, *423*
Lipton, Robert J., Lipton Assoc., Inc. (R), NY, *130*
Litvin, Bruce, Windsor Consultants, Inc. (C), TX, *622*
Lombardi, Nancy, WTW Assoc., Inc. (R), NY, *225*
London, Anne, London & Company (C), NY, *420*

RECRUITER SPECIALTIES

Macdonald, Jr., Robert W., Russell Reynolds Assoc., Inc. (R), MN, *177*
Major, Jr., Robert A., Major, Hagen & Africa (C), CA, *423*
Manning, Jr., Joseph R., Blue Chip Law Consulting, Inc. (C), CA, *268*
Mannix, Sandra G., Cathy Abelson Legal Search (C), PA, *232*
Markessinis, Barbara, Berkshire Search Assoc. (C), MA, *265*
Markoff, Janet, Major, Hagen & Africa (C), NY, *423*
Marti, Lydia S., Major, Hagen & Africa (C), IL, *423*
Martin, Sr., Robert, The Pailin Group Professional Search Consultants (R), TX, *158*
Martin, Susan, Howard/Williams Assoc. (C), FL, *382*
Mattes, Jr., Edward C., The Ogdon Partnership (R), NY, *155*
Maxwell, R. Patrick, Templeton & Assoc. (C), MN, *605*
Mayfield, Barbara L., Prescott Legal Search, Inc. (C), TX, *517*
McClendon, III, Sidney, Allen Austin Lowe & Powers (R), TX, *3*
McSpadden, Stephen, First Advisory Services Int'l., Inc. (R), MD, *67*
Meadows, C. David, Right/McKee Consulting Group (C), TX, *537*
Michaels, Stewart, Topaz Int'l., Inc., Attorney Search (C), NJ, *607*
Miller, Dixie, Miller & Assoc. (C), FL, *481*
Miller, Susan C., Susan C. Miller Assoc., Inc. (C), DC, *482*
Mims, Stephen S., Mims & Associates (R), TX, *145*
Minor, Anne, Susan C. Miller Assoc., Inc. (C), DC, *482*
Mitchell, Susan J., Major, Hagen & Africa (C), IL, *423*
Mizel, Lynn, Weinman & Assoc. (C), AZ, *617*
Morgenstern, Richard L., Morgenstern Int'l., Inc. (C), CA, *485*
Morgenstern, Richard L., Morgenstern Int'l., Inc. (C), FL, *485*
Mullenhoff, James A., Rob Dey Executive Search (R), FL, *49*
Mulligan, Judy, Emerald Legal Search (C), NH, *329*
Narsh, Daniel, Windsor Consultants, Inc. (C), TX, *622*
Nathan, Catherine R., LAI Ward Howell (R), NY, *123*
Nelson, Nancy, Howard Lieberman & Assoc., Inc. (C), MN, *417*
Norman, Allen G., Pursuant Legal Consultants (R), WA, *170*
Oberlander, James, Major, Hagen & Africa (C), IL, *423*
Pape, Florence, Florence Pape Legal Search, Inc. (C), NJ, *502*
Peasback, David R., Canny, Bowen Inc. (R), NY, *28*
Pennella, Neil, Brad Marks Int'l. (R), CA, *136*
Percival, Chris, Chicago Legal Search, Ltd. (C), IL, *290*
Peters, Ray, J. Stroll Assoc., Inc. (R), CT, *204*
Pittleman, Steven, Pittleman & Assoc. (C), NY, *513*
Prager, Paul Gershon, P. G. Prager Search Assoc., Ltd. (C), NY, *515*
Prescott, Larry W., Prescott Legal Search, Inc. (C), TX, *517*
Prescott, Lauren Eaton, Prescott Legal Search, Inc. (C), TX, *517*
Qureshi, Julie, Major, Hagen & Africa (C), CA, *423*
Rahaim, Richard D., Howard/Williams Assoc. (C), FL, *382*
Railey, J. Larry, Railey & Assoc. (C), TX, *528*
Rast, Vera L., Vera L. Rast Partners Inc. (C), IL, *529*
Redgrove, Peter J., Kass/Abell & Assoc., Inc. (C), CA, *404*
Richards, Suzanne S., Fortune Consultants of Ft. Washington (C), PA, *349*
Rivera, Al, Rivera Legal Search, Inc. (C), CA, *538*
Rodzik, T. A., Rodzik & Assoc., Inc. (R), NC, *180*
Rosenfeld, Martin J., Rosenfeld & Co., Inc. (C), MI, *545*
Ross, Allison, Major, Hagen & Africa (C), NY, *423*
Rubenstein, Alan J., Chicago Legal Search, Ltd. (C), IL, *290*
Rubin, Lauren H., Morgenstern Int'l., Inc. (C), NY, *486*
Russell, Ronald G., McPherson Square Assoc., Inc. (C), DC, *475*
Schlanger, Ruth, Richard, Wayne & Roberts (C), TX, *536*
Schneider, Susan, Finn & Schneider Assoc., Inc. (C), DC, *341*
Schoenfeld, Marian, Dunhill of Manchester Inc. (C), NH, *321*
Schwartz, Mark L., F-o-r-t-u-n-e Personnel Consultants of Detroit, Inc. (C), MI, *346*
Sears, J. Douglas, DS&A (Doug Sears & Assoc.) (C), FL, *315*
Sears, Jerry, Sears & Associates (C), CA, *577*
Segal, Laura, Major, Hagen & Africa (C), NY, *423*
Seltzer, Madeleine E., Seltzer Fontaine Beckwith (C), CA, *579*
Shapiro, Liz, Cathy Abelson Legal Search (C), PA, *232*
Shelton, Frederick L., Shelton, Wiseman & Leon (R), CA, *189*
Sher, Eileen, Frey & Sher Assoc., Inc. (C), VA, *353*
Sher, Jared, Susan C. Miller Assoc., Inc. (C), DC, *482*
Sibul, Shelly Remen, Chicago Legal Search, Ltd. (C), IL, *290*
Sinden, Peter, Attorneys at Work (C), GA, *256*
Smith, Aaron, Staffing Edge, Inc. (C), CO, *590*
Snyder, Susan Kurz, Greene-Levin-Snyder LLC (C), NY, *362*
Stephens, Ken, Leader Resources Group (C), GA, *415*
Stroll, Joseph, J. Stroll Assoc., Inc. (R), CT, *204*
Strom, Justin V., Overton Consulting (R), WI, *157*
Tabler, Tracy, Phyllis Hawkins & Assoc., Inc. (C), AZ, *370*
Templeton, Denise, Templeton & Assoc. (C), MN, *605*
Thomas, Frank, Carson-Thomas & Assoc. (C), CA, *284*
Trent, Alex, Vera L. Rast Partners Inc. (C), IL, *529*
Tribbett, III, Charles A., Russell Reynolds Assoc., Inc. (R), IL, *176*
Valone, Anthony F., UniQuest Int'l., Inc. (C), FL, *611*
Valone, Judith, UniQuest Int'l., Inc. (C), FL, *611*
Van Zandt, Eric, Prescott Legal Search, Inc. (C), TX, *517*
Waldorf, Michael, Waldorf Associates, Inc. (C), CA, *614*
Wampole, Carole, Legal Network Inc. (C), CA, *416*
Wampole, Daniel, Legal Network Inc. (C), CA, *416*
Ward, Catherine M., Blue Chip Law Consulting, Inc. (C), CA, *268*
Watson, Scott, Scott Watson & Assoc., Inc. (R), FL, *216*
Whitbeck, Elizabeth C., Whitbeck & Assoc. (R), MN, *219*
Williams, Aaron, Aaron Consulting, Inc. (C), MO, *232*
Williams, John, Howard/Williams Assoc. (C), FL, *382*
Wilson, Stoney, SR Wilson, Inc. (C), CA, *590*
Winnewisser, William E., Accounting & Computer Personnel (C), NY, *238*
Wolfson, Gary M., The Blackman Kallick Search Division (C), IL, *267*
Worth, Anita S., Prescott Legal Search (C), TX, *517*
Young, Monique S., Blane, Stevens & Kellogg (C), FL, *268*
Zaher, Richard, Fox-Morris Assoc., Inc. (C), NY, *352*
Zeefe, Herrick A., Morgenstern Int'l., Inc. (C), FL, *485*
Zenner, Teri E., Zenner Consulting Group (C), IL, *627*

Attorneys

Carpenter, Lori J., Carpenter Legal Search (C), PA, *284*
Foster, Dennis J., Major Legal Services, Inc. (C), OH, *423*
Jameson, John B., The Jameson Group (C), CA, *397*
Kinkopf, Lesley, Major Legal Services, Inc. (C), OH, *423*
Lenz, Kathryn, Major Legal Services, Inc. (C), OH, *423*

Lippens, Susan, Major Legal Services, Inc. (C), OH, *423*
Peters, Deborah L., Major Legal Services, Inc. (C), OH, *423*

Law
Fletcher, Susan, Susan Fletcher Attorney Employment Services (C), PA, *342*
Green, Larry A., Winston & Green (C), IL, *623*
Thomas, Pat Bowers, BowersThomas (C), CA, *271*

Lawyers
Baldwin, Stephen, SearchCorp International (C), AB, *577*

Leisure
Alfus, Phillip, The Alfus Group (R), NY, *3*
Blecksmith, Edward L., Larsen, Whitney, Blecksmith & Zilliacus, Inc. (R), CA, *125*
Moran, Rion J., Bowman & Assoc. (C), CA, *271*
Whitney, William A., Larsen, Whitney, Blecksmith & Zilliacus, Inc. (R), CA, *125*

Lending
Creech, Bud, McCarthy Assoc. National BancSearch, LLC (C), LA, *473*
Graff, Thomas D. B., The Hanover Consulting Group (C), MD, *368*
Guilford, David J., DLG Assoc., Inc. (R), NC, *53*
Haupert, Thomas J., MCS Assoc. (R), CA, *142*
Hedefine, Thomas E., Thomas E. Hedefine Assoc. (C), ON, *375*
Katz, Norman, MCS Assoc. (R), CA, *142*

Libraries
Bartholomew, Catherine, C. Berger And Company (R), IL, *16*
Berger, Carol A., C. Berger And Company (R), IL, *16*
Bodine, Christine, C. Berger And Company (R), IL, *16*
Sullivan, Peggy, Tuft & Assoc., Inc. (R), IL, *212*

Licensing
Aswell, Judy, Management Recruiters of San Marcos (C), TX, *463*
DeLuca, Matthew J., Management Resource Group, Inc. (C), NY, *467*
Richards, Sharon, Richards Assoc., Inc. (R), NY, *178*

Loans
Curry, Donna, Don Neal & Assoc. (C), OK, *491*
Neal, Don, Don Neal & Assoc. (C), OK, *491*
Stafford, Chris, Stafford Consulting Group (R), CA, *198*

Long term care
Barnes, Roanne L., Barnes Development Group, LLC (R), WI, *11*
Carter, Christine, Health Care Dimensions (C), CO, *371*
Clark, Michael, Cornerstone Search Assoc. Inc. (C), MA, *299*
Feingold, Robin, Cornerstone Search Assoc. Inc. (C), MA, *299*
Hazelton, Lisa, Health Care Dimensions (C), CO, *371*
Howard, Jill, Health Care Dimensions (C), CO, *371*
McCammon, Betsy, Rogish Assoc., Inc. (C), OH, *541*
Osborne, Julie, Rogish Assoc., Inc. (C), OH, *541*
Rosen, Richard, Cornerstone Search Assoc. Inc. (C), MA, *299*
Royer, Dade, The Stonebridge Group (C), PA, *594*
Shasteen, Martha F., Primary Care Service Corp. (C), GA, *518*
Waldman, Noah W., LAI Ward Howell (R), GA, *123*
West, Nancy, Health Care Dimensions (C), CO, *371*

Loss
Coleman, Tracy A., West Coast Recruiting (C), CA, *619*
Mayer, Mary L., Mary L. Mayer, Ltd. (R), MN, *139*

Lotus notes
Capps, Norm, MIS Computer Professionals, Inc. (C), KS, *482*

Lubricants
Warren, Tom S., F.L.A.G. (C), OH, *338*

Lumber
Corder, Eutha, RBW Assoc. Inc. (C), AR, *531*
Gandee, Joan C., Management Recruiters of Sugar Land Inc. (C), TX, *464*
Gandee, John R., Management Recruiters of Sugar Land Inc. (C), TX, *464*
Hayes, Don, Management Recruiters of Sugar Land Inc. (C), TX, *464*

Machine tools
Garland, Mike, Raymond Thomas & Assoc. (C), FL, *530*
Huegel, Ray, Raymond Thomas & Assoc. (C), FL, *530*
Passon, Steven A., Teamsearch, Inc. (C), MI, *601*
Royfe, Dan, D.R. Assoc. (R), CA, *45*
West, Al, West & Assoc. (C), IL, *618*

Machinery
Behrens, Rick, Behrens and Company (C), WA, *262*
Bittner, Greg, NHA Plastics Recruiters (C), FL, *493*
Bittner, Susan E., NHA Plastics Recruiters (C), FL, *493*
Bryza, Robert M., Robert Lowell Int'l. (R), TX, *179*
Gersin, Harvey, Sales Consultants of Farmington Hills (C), MI, *560*
Just, Susan, Just Management Services Inc. (C), FL, *402*
Kerstein, Daniel J., Daniel J. Kerstein, Consultant to Management (R), CO, *114*
Kirkpatrick, Robert L., Reese Assoc. (R), PA, *174*
McCollum, Ken, MESA International (C), CA, *480*
Olesen, Jeannette, Management Recruiters of the Baltimore Washington Corridor (C), MD, *450*
Passon, Steven A., Teamsearch, Inc. (C), MI, *601*
Reese, Jr., Charles D., Reese Assoc. (R), PA, *174*
Schultz, Craig, F-O-R-T-U-N-E Personnel Consultants of St. Louis-West County (C), MO, *347*

Machining
Linstead, Rick, Carnegie Resources, Inc. (C), NC, *284*
McLey, Curt, Harrison Moore Inc. (C), NE, *370*
Michaels, Lou, Lou Michaels Assoc., Inc. (C), MI, *481*
Pilcher, James P., F-O-R-T-U-N-E Personnel Consultants of Cincinnati (C), OH, *348*
Reed, Dave, Management Recruiters - Flint (C), MI, *451*

Magazine
Baker, Wendy, Bert Davis Publishing Placement Consultants (C), NY, *309*

Maintenance
Anderson, Robert W., Anderson Bradshaw Assoc., Inc. (R), TX, *6*
Corey, Joe, Industry Consultants, Inc. (C), AZ, *388*
Goodall, Rhys, C. J. Stafford & Assoc. (C), ON, *591*

Managed care
Anderer, Albert M., Managed Care Consultants (C), AZ, *424*

Babson, Lelia, Dunhill Staffing Systems (C), NC, *321*
Banister, John, Delta ProSearch (C), PA, *311*
Barkley, Keith, The Mackenzie Group (R), MD, *133*
Bleau, Donn E., Global Resources Group (R), CA, *78*
Bond, James, People Management Northeast, Inc. (R), CT, *162*
Bonnell, William R., Bonnell Assoc. Ltd. (R), CT, *19*
Breadon, Peggy, Managed Care Consultants (C), AZ, *424*
Buggy, Linda, Bonnell Assoc. Ltd. (R), CT, *19*
Burnett, Glenn, WestPacific National Search, Inc. (C), CA, *619*
Calhoon, Lee, Lee Calhoon & Co., Inc. (R), PA, *26*
Carroll, Richard J., HMO Executive Search (C), IN, *379*
Cuthbert, Bruce, McKavis Assoc. (C), CA, *475*
Darter, Steven, People Management Northeast, Inc. (R), CT, *162*
De Mange, Jean M., Wellington Thomas Ltd. (C), FL, *618*
Dietsch, Roger A., Roger Dietsch & Assoc. (C), MN, *312*
Fitzgerald, Diane, Fitzgerald Associates (R), MA, *68*
Fitzgerald, Geoffrey, Fitzgerald Associates (R), MA, *68*
Gelpi, Gerry, Gelpi & Assoc. (C), LA, *355*
Gibbons, Ronald L., Flynn, Hannock, Inc. (R), CT, *69*
Gold, Barry M., Barry M. Gold & Co. (C), CA, *359*
Greaney, Francis J., Corporate Leadership Strategies, Inc. (R), NH, *41*
Heineman, James W., Management Resources (C), TX, *467*
Henderson, Etta Ish, Boulware & Assoc. Inc. (R), IL, *20*
Hughes, Ken, Hughes & Assoc. (C), TX, *383*
Hutton, M. Joan, The Hutton Group, Inc. (C), FL, *386*
Johnson, Ron L., Management Recruiters of Fresno (C), CA, *440*
Kinney, Diane C., The Stewart Group (C), FL, *593*
Kratz, Stephen J., Tyler & Company (R), GA, *212*
Kressenberg, Sammye Jo, Kressenberg Assoc. (C), TX, *409*
Mayes, Abby, The Mayes Group, Ltd. (R), PA, *139*
McKavis, Adel, McKavis Assoc. (C), CA, *475*
Meyer, Michael F., Witt/Kieffer, Ford, Hadelman & Lloyd (R), AZ, *223*
Meyers, Stuart, Management Recruiters of Washington, DC Inc. (C), MD, *450*
Milius, Kent, Management Recruiters of Colorado, Inc. (C), CO, *442*
Moore, Ann M., Healthcare Recruiters International-NY/NJ (C), NJ, *373*
Mulligan, Pamela L., Pamela L. Mulligan, Inc. (R), NH, *149*
Murray, Megan, The Mayes Group, Ltd. (R), PA, *139*
Nash, James, The Gammill Group, Inc. (C), OH, *354*
Nixon, Jeffrey L., J. L. Nixon Consulting (C), TX, *493*
Pallman-David, Cynthia, Bonnell Assoc. Ltd. (R), CT, *19*
Perry, Lisa Lepore, Aminex Corp. (C), MA, *249*
Pirnack, Margaret, McKavis Assoc. (C), CA, *475*
Puestow, Michael, The Beam Group (R), IL, *14*
Pufahl, John P., Avalon Health Group, Inc. (R), NY, *9*
Raskin, John, Healthcare Search Associates (C), CA, *374*
Reeder, Michael S., Reeder & Assoc., Ltd. (R), GA, *173*
Reinecke, Mark, Tyler & Company (R), GA, *212*
Silver, Barbara, Management Recruiters of Washington, DC Inc. (C), MD, *450*
Spencer, Randall W., Management Recruiters of San Antonio - North (C), TX, *463*
Strieker, Mike, Healthcare Recruiters Int'l. Phoenix (C), AZ, *372*
Varney, Rudy, J. L. Nixon Consulting (C), TX, *493*
Venekotter, Mike, UniQuest Int'l., Inc. (C), FL, *611*
Waldman, Noah W., LAI Ward Howell (R), GA, *123*
Whittaker-Jhaveri, Michelle A., The Whittaker Group (C), MI, *620*
Wilkins, Walter K., Walter K. Wilkins & Co. (R), NJ, *221*

Management

Aguirrezabal, Angelina, OSAGUI S.A. de C.V. (C), MX, *500*
Alexander, Gary, Mark Christian & Assoc., Inc. (C), AZ, *470*
Anderson, Dean, Corporate Resources Professional Placement (C), MN, *301*
Anderson, Jim, Howard Clark Assoc. (C), NJ, *292*
Archibald, David E., The Eldridge Group, Ltd. (C), IL, *327*
Baker, Susan F., Diversified Consulting Services, Inc. (C), CO, *313*
Baldwin, Stephen, SearchCorp International (C), AB, *577*
Baldwin, W. Keith, Baldwin & Assoc. (C), OH, *258*
Ballou, Jodie, Management Recruiters of the Baltimore Washington Corridor (C), MD, *450*
Bard, Ann, Management Recruiters of St. Augustine (C), FL, *444*
Batista, Daniel T., Careerfit, Inc. (C), TX, *283*
Bauer, Noelle, Youngblood Assoc. (C), NC, *626*
Belastock, Gary, The Retail Network (C), MA, *535*
Blumenthal, Paula, J. P. Canon Assoc. (C), NY, *280*
Bouzan, Paul X., The Executive Group, Inc. (R), CA, *62*
Breen, Bill, Personnel, Inc. (C), AL, *508*
Brogan, Pat, Human Resource Bureau (C), CA, *384*
Brown, Gene, Management Recruiters of Atlanta West, Inc. (C), GA, *445*
Bulmer, Robert E., Alaska Executive Search, Inc. (C), AK, *243*
Callicott, Robin D., Perfect Search, Inc. (C), FL, *507*
Carey, Harvey, Carion Resource Group Inc. (C), ON, *284*
Carson, Sandra, Carson-Thomas & Assoc. (C), CA, *284*
Christy, Tim, The Partnership Group (R), NJ, *160*
Cinco, Lawrence K., Management Recruiters of Melbourne, Inc. (C), FL, *443*
Cole, Leslie C., Management Recruiters of Middlesex (C), CT, *442*
Coughlin, Linda, Partners in Recruiting (C), IL, *504*
Curry, Donna, Don Neal & Assoc. (C), OK, *491*
Daniel, Beverly R., Foy, Schneid & Daniel, Inc. (R), NY, *71*
Dankowski, Eden, Professional Healthcare Search & Consultants, Inc. (C), CA, *520*
Davis, Colette, ExeConnex, LLC (R), GA, *61*
Davis, Ronald, International Management Development Corp. (C), NY, *393*
DeRario, Donna, F-O-R-T-U-N-E Personnel Consultants of San Diego (C), CA, *344*
DeRose, Rick, Telecom Executive Group (C), NJ, *605*
Dishaw, Raymond J., R. J. Dishaw & Assoc. (R), TX, *52*
Dixon, Sayre, Employ® (C), PA, *330*
Doutre, Judy, Dumont & Co. (C), BC, *316*
Downs, Greg, Executive Recruiters Agency, Inc. (C), AR, *333*
Empey, David, Management Recruiters of Franktown (C), CO, *442*
Ericksen, Bruce, MESA International (C), OR, *480*
Ericson, Pam, Major Search (C), NJ, *423*
Eskra, Michael D., Sanford Rose Assoc. - Port Washington (C), WI, *571*
Fitzgerald, Geoffrey, Fitzgerald Associates (R), MA, *68*
Gale, Michael, Professional Healthcare Search & Consultants, Inc. (C), CA, *520*
Gale, Rhoda, Management Recruiters of the Baltimore Washington Corridor (C), MD, *450*
Gallin, Lawrence, Gallin Associates, Inc. (C), FL, *354*
Garland, R. Darryl, Garland Assoc. Int'l. (C), CA, *355*
Garrison, Ed, The Garrison Organization (R), IA, *75*

Gauger, Dianne, Dianne Gauger & Assoc. (C), CA, *355*
Gawitt, Dan, Management Recruiters of the Baltimore Washington Corridor (C), MD, *450*
Gentry, Allen, Hospitality Int'l. (C), AZ, *381*
Gideon, Mark, Eagle Search Assoc. (C), CA, *325*
Glosser, Elizabeth B., Executive Exchange Corp. (C), NJ, *333*
Glou, Alan, Glou Int'l., Inc. (R), MA, *78*
Golding, Michael S., Michael Assoc. (R), IL, *144*
Guzzetta, Christy, GES Services, Inc. (R), NY, *76*
Hadick, Russ, Russ Hadick & Assoc. Inc. (C), OH, *365*
Havens, J. A., Real Estate Executive Search, Inc. (C), CA, *531*
Hawthorne, Christine, Search Int'l. (R), MA, *187*
Hendricks, II, Stanley M., National Recruiting Service (C), IN, *489*
Holder, Lee, Gowdy Consultants (C), TX, *361*
Holsopple, Ben V., ACSYS Resources, Inc. (C), NJ, *238*
Holtz, Richard D., Technical Resource Assoc. (C), TN, *602*
Horn, David C., David C. Horn Executive Search (C), TX, *381*
Hughes, Donald J., Hughes & Company (R), VA, *98*
Johnson, Frank Y., Healthcare Recruiters Int'l. - Alabama (C), AL, *372*
Johnson, Robert J., Quality Search Inc. (C), OH, *526*
Johnson, Sean M., Healthcare Recruiters Int'l. - Alabama (C), AL, *372*
Johnston, J. Reid, Hughes & Company (R), VA, *98*
Kaffke, Cas, Major Search (C), NJ, *423*
Karp, Linda S., Karp & Assoc. (C), FL, *403*
Kelly, Sussannah, Herman Smith Executive Initiatives Inc. (R), ON, *193*
Kershaw, Blair, Blair Kershaw Assoc., Inc. (C), PA, *405*
Kierstead, Robert, High Tech Opportunities, Inc. (C), NH, *377*
King, Damon, The Canon Group (C), CA, *280*
Kool, Joan, Professional Recruiters, Inc. (C), PA, *521*
Krieger, Dennis F., Seiden Krieger Assoc., Inc. (R), NY, *188*
Kuehnling, William, Sanford Rose Assoc. - Canton (C), OH, *569*
Kussner, Janice N., Herman Smith Executive Initiatives Inc. (R), ON, *193*
Lanctot, Bill, Corporate Resources Professional Placement (C), MN, *301*
Lane-Dodge, Lori, PersoNet, Inc. (C), FL, *507*
Langford, Bob, Fortune Personnel Consultants of Huntsville, Inc. (C), AL, *343*
Lantz, Delores, A C Personnel Services, Inc. (C), OK, *231*
Larson, Ray, Larson Assoc. (R), CA, *125*
Lee, Jess J., Management Search Int'l. (C), CA, *467*
Leggett, Amy, APA Employment Agency Inc. (C), WA, *251*
Lenobel, Stephen, Professional Recruiters, Inc. (C), PA, *521*
Levine, Donald, Sharp Placement Professionals, Inc. (C), NY, *579*
Lindauer, Lois L., Lois L. Lindauer Searches (C), MA, *418*
Lucas, Kelly J., Protocol Inc. (C), CA, *525*
Luzar, James, Sales Consultants of Milwaukee (C), WI, *563*
Lybrook, Karen, Lybrook Assoc., Inc. (C), RI, *421*
Lyness, Cindy, Management Recruiters-Cedar Rapids, Inc. (C), IA, *448*
Lyons, M. Don, L O R (R), NJ, *122*
Malatesta, Roger, Professional Recruiting Consultants, Inc. (C), DE, *521*
Manatine, Tony, Career Search Group (C), FL, *283*
Margolin, Efraim, Margolin Consultants, Inc. (C), NY, *469*
Marin, Natalie, Campbell, Edgar Inc. (C), BC, *280*
Martin, Carol, Medical Innovations (C), NY, *477*
Martin, Jean M., The Ultimate Source (R), CA, *212*
Mason, Kimball L., KM Associates (C), MA, *407*
Matteson, Larry, The Rubinic Consulting Group (C), OH, *548*
Maul, Lisa M., Professional Persons Career Services (C), NY, *521*
McClain, Duane, Construction Search Specialists, Inc. (C), WI, *297*
McCormick, Jim, McCormick Search Inc. (C), IL, *474*
McCowan, Elle, Management Recruiters of Birmingham (C), MI, *451*
McKay, Bob, Further Management Group (C), MD, *353*
McLean, Robert T., Tecmark Associates Inc. (C), MA, *604*
McRobbie, Jason, Forest People Int'l. Search Ltd. (C), BC, *343*
Meyer, Walter E., Walter Meyer & Assoc. (R), NY, *144*
Miller, Diane, Wilcox Bertoux & Miller (R), CA, *220*
Minso, Eugene A., Sanford Rose Assoc. - Burlington, NC (C), NC, *569*
Munro, Jennifer, Jennifer Munro & Partners, Inc. (R), SC, *149*
Nanney, Jerry, Lou Michaels Assoc., Inc. (C), MI, *481*
Natowitz, Robert, DeMatteo Associates (C), NY, *311*
Neal, Don, Don Neal & Assoc. (C), OK, *491*
Nicolaas, Gina, Dumont & Co. (C), BC, *316*
Nigro, Marci Yacker, Telecom Executive Group (C), NY, *605*
Norman, Marcie, Management Recruiters of Franktown (C), CO, *442*
Olesen, Jeannette, Management Recruiters of the Baltimore Washington Corridor (C), MD, *450*
Ordini, Lou, Major Search (C), NJ, *423*
Osborn, Ted, Paladin Group, Inc. (C), CO, *502*
Ostroff, Stephen R., Triangle Assoc. (C), PA, *609*
Pamenter, Craig, Pamenter, Pamenter, Brezer & Deganis Ltd. (R), ON, *159*
Patchin, Rory J., R2 Services, LLC (C), IL, *528*
Paterson, David, Scientific Solutions, Inc. (C), MI, *572*
Paterson, Sharon, Scientific Solutions, Inc. (C), MI, *572*
Pearce, Frank, Pearce & Assoc. (C), FL, *506*
Perl, Eric, BR & Assoc. (C), NJ, *271*
Perry, Lisa Lepore, Aminex Corp. (C), MA, *249*
Petry, Georgia M., Placements by Jesse Reid Assoc., Inc. (C), NY, *513*
Plouffe, Yves J., Yves Plouffe & Assoc. (R), QE, *165*
Prager, Paul Gershon, P. G. Prager Search Assoc., Ltd. (C), NY, *515*
Pugrant, Mark A., Grant/Morgan Assoc., Inc. (C), MD, *361*
Radice, Joseph A., Hospitality Int'l. (C), NY, *381*
Rank, Christy L., Mortgage Search Network (C), AZ, *486*
Richter, Earl, The Wabash Group (C), IN, *613*
Roberts, Luke, The Retail Network (C), MA, *535*
Robinson, Verneda, V. Robinson & Co., Inc. (C), KS, *539*
Robinson, Verneda, V. Robinson & Co., Inc. (C), MO, *539*
Ross, Cheryl Molliver, Thomas, Whelan Assoc., Inc. (C), DC, *606*
Ross, Heather, Management Recruiters-Cedar Rapids, Inc. (C), IA, *448*
Roy, Ruth, Lois L. Lindauer Searches (C), MA, *418*
Sabbio, Kathy, The Brentwood Group, Inc. (R), NJ, *22*
Sajankila, Raj, Softrix, Inc. (C), NJ, *586*
Saracen, Robert R., The Libra Group Inc. (C), CT, *417*
Schiff, Arlene D., A.D. Schiff & Assoc., Ltd. (C), IL, *572*
Schrepferman, William W., Baldwin & Assoc. (C), OH, *258*
Schuckman, Dalon W., Joy Reed Belt Search Consultants, Inc. (R), OK, *15*
Seco, William M., Seco & Zetto Assoc., Inc. (C), NJ, *577*
Sendler, Peter A., International Consulting Services, Inc. (C), IL, *392*
Shapiro, Alan, Technology Search Int'l. (C), CA, *603*
Sinclair, Rachel, Management Recruiters of Fresno (C), CA, *440*
Sinks, Lucius F., Aminex Corp. (C), MA, *249*

RECRUITER SPECIALTIES

Skewes, Gail, Reid Ellis Assoc. Inc. (C), ON, *533*
Sloane, Ron, Management Recruiters of Milwaukee-North (C), WI, *466*
Smith, Randall E., R2 Services, LLC (C), IL, *528*
Stafford, Chris, Stafford Consulting Group (R), CA, *198*
Stanton, Robert G., TSC Management Services Group, Inc. (C), IL, *610*
Steinbach, David M., Steinbach & Co. (C), MA, *592*
Stroud, Toni, Management Recruiters of the Baltimore Washington Corridor (C), MD, *450*
Susleck, Matthew M., ESS (Executive Search Services) (R), CA, *61*
Sweet, Eleanor Anne, The Remington Group (R), IL, *174*
Thomas, Lori, J. E. Lessner Assoc., Inc. (R), MI, *128*
Tinker, J. Jay, Management Recruiters of the Baltimore Washington Corridor (C), MD, *450*
Tolstrup, Rick, Aminex Corp. (C), MA, *249*
Toms, Dennis M., National Recruiting Service (C), IN, *489*
Voigt, Jeff, APA Employment Agency Inc. (C), OR, *251*
Wainwright, Nancy, Locus Inc. (C), WV, *419*
Wald, E. Steven, Andrews & Wald Group (C), FL, *250*
Waschuk, Bill, Forest People Int'l. Search Ltd. (C), BC, *343*
Watson, Wally, Management Recruiters of Memphis, TN (C), TN, *462*
Watters, Tamara, Construction Search Specialists, Inc. (C), WI, *297*
Weiss, Michael G., Applied Resources, Inc. (C), MN, *252*
Wells, Patricia, Fortune Group Int'l., Inc. (R), PA, *70*
White, Clyde, Further Management Group (C), MD, *353*
Wilkenson, Charles R., Tecmark Associates Inc. (C), CA, *604*
Wilson, Steven, Herman Smith Executive Initiatives Inc. (R), ON, *193*
Wolfson, Gary M., The Blackman Kallick Search Division (C), IL, *267*
Worthing, Ellen, Management Recruiters of the Baltimore Washington Corridor (C), MD, *450*
Yorba, Anissa, Professional Healthcare Search & Consultants, Inc. (C), CA, *520*
Zetto, Kathryn, Seco & Zetto Assoc., Inc. (C), NJ, *577*

Management consulting

Abkin, Stephen J., Millennium Search Group, Inc. (R), CA, *144*
Alexander, Richard J., Alexander Associates (R), NJ, *2*
Banach-Osenni, Doris, The Brentwood Group, Inc. (R), NJ, *22*
Barefield, Simone Gans, Gans, Gans & Assoc., Inc. (R), FL, *74*
Berman, Mitchell, The Carlyle Group, Ltd. (R), IL, *30*
Bodnar, Robert J., Management Recruiters of Princeton (C), NJ, *454*
Bowen, Howard, Howard Bowen Consulting (C), FL, *270*
Bredeson, Sheri, Bredeson Executive Recruitment, LLC (R), TX, *22*
Bussey, Sharon, The Center for Career Advancement, LLC (C), NJ, *287*
Christidis, Aurora, Brad Marks Int'l. (R), CA, *136*
Cole, Leslie C., Management Recruiters of Middlesex (C), CT, *442*
Cooper, Linda, BG & Assoc. (C), MD, *266*
Cornell, Don, Consultant Recruiters (C), WI, *297*
Craig, Michael C., Magellan Int'l., L.P. (C), TX, *422*
DeGioia, Joseph, JDG Assoc., Ltd. (C), MD, *397*
DeZara, Max, The Carlyle Group, Ltd. (R), IL, *30*
Douglas, Bob, Hunter Douglas Group, Inc. (R), IL, *99*
Duke, Lawrence, Management Recruiters of Charlotte - North, Inc. (C), NC, *456*
Evans, Chester P., Greenhaven & Assoc., Inc. (R), NY, *81*
Ferrara, David M., Millennium Search Group, Inc. (R), CA, *144*
Fisk, James L., James L. Fisk & Assoc. (C), MO, *342*
Ford, Sandra D., The Ford Group, Inc. (R), PA, *69*
Fought, Jay D., Fought, Jameson Assoc. (C), IL, *351*
French, William G., Preng & Assoc., Inc. (R), TX, *167*
Gahan, Ann M., Gahan Assoc. (R), NY, *73*
Gamboa, Victor, Quest Worldwide Executive Search Corp. (C), CA, *527*
Giacoponello, Thomas V., Search America, Inc. (C), PA, *573*
Goodman, Lion, The Goodman Group (R), CA, *79*
Gragg, Bryan L., Millennium Search Group, Inc. (R), CA, *144*
Gray, Brian A., BG & Assoc. (C), MD, *266*
Halper, Harlan R., Strategic Executives, Inc. (R), NY, *202*
Harper, Deborah, Harper Hewes, Inc. (C), NY, *369*
Hayes, William, The Ransford Group (R), TX, *171*
Hechkoff, Robert B., Hechkoff/Work Executive Search Inc. (R), NY, *89*
Higbee, R. W., Higbee Assoc., Inc. (C), CT, *377*
Howe, William S., Hunt & Howe Inc. (R), NY, *99*
Hyde, Anne P., The Hyde Group, Inc. (R), CT, *101*
Jameson, Brad M., Fought, Jameson Assoc. (C), IL, *351*
Jenkins, Virginia L., The Center for Career Advancement (C), MD, *287*
Johnson, Timothy W., Magellan Int'l., L.P. (C), TX, *422*
Jones-Parker, Janet, Jones-Parker/Starr (R), NC, *108*
Kalinski, Jr., Felix, Baeder Kalinski Int'l. Group, Inc. (R), NH, *10*
Kasbaum, David J., The Ransford Group (R), TX, *171*
Kirby, James E., Management Recruiters of Marietta, Inc. (C), GA, *446*
Kubiak, Thomas J., Halbrecht & Co. (C), CT, *365*
Lombardo, Steve, Search America, Inc. (C), MA, *574*
Long, Janet R., Integrity Search, Inc. (R), PA, *102*
Loprete, Lawrence D., Kenmore Executives Inc. (C), FL, *405*
LoPrete, Steven, Kenmore Executives Inc. (C), FL, *405*
May, Donald C., Allied Search, Inc. (C), CA, *245*
McMann, Dean E., The Ransford Group (R), TX, *171*
Meyer, Rick M., Meyer Assoc., Inc. (R), GA, *144*
Miners, Richard A., Sedlar & Miners (R), NY, *188*
Orr, Marilyn, Kenmore Executives Inc. (C), FL, *405*
Phillips, Jonathan H., Magellan Int'l., L.P. (C), TX, *422*
Picard, Daniel A., Picard Int'l., Ltd. (R), NY, *164*
Pittleman, Steven, Pittleman & Assoc. (C), NY, *513*
Rice, Gene, Rice Cohen Int'l. (R), PA, *178*
Robinson, P. Andrew, Consulting Resource Group, Inc. (C), GA, *297*
Rubinic, Michael, The Rubinic Consulting Group (C), OH, *548*
Ruschak, Randy R., Management Recruiters of Bordentown (C), NJ, *454*
Santangelo, Richard, Santangelo Consultants Inc. (C), NY, *571*
Schwartz, Michael, Synapse Human Resource Consulting Group (R), TX, *205*
Sedlar, Jeri L., Sedlar & Miners (R), NY, *188*
Seymour, Holly, Executive Partners Inc. (C), CT, *333*
Shearer, Gary F., Management Recruiters of Bonita Springs, Inc. (C), FL, *443*
Starr, Jonathan, Jones-Parker/Starr (R), GA, *108*
Stevens, Ralph, Preng & Assoc., Inc. (R), TX, *167*
Stillinger, Regina V., Stillinger & Assoc. (R), CA, *201*
Stillinger, Scott R., Stillinger & Assoc. (R), CA, *201*
Stillinger, Skip, Stillinger & Assoc. (R), CA, *201*
Tatar, Steven M., Magellan Int'l., L.P. (C), TX, *422*
Thomas, Frank, Carson-Thomas & Assoc. (C), CA, *284*
Truitt, Tom, Southwestern Professional Services (C), TN, *588*

Whittier, Richard, The Ransford Group (R), TX, *171*
Wilson, John T., Wilson-Douglas-Jordan (C), IL, *622*
Work, Alan J., Hechkoff/Work Executive Search Inc. (R), NY, *89*

Manufacturing

Abbott, Robert, Pacific Coast Recruiting (C), CA, *501*
Abrams, Burton J., B. J. Abrams & Assoc. Inc. (C), IL, *233*
Adler, Louis S., CJA-The Adler Group, Inc. (R), CA, *35*
Adzima, Allan G., MARBL Consultants, Inc. (C), WI, *469*
Agnello, Frank, Systems Research Inc. (SRI) (C), IL, *598*
Akin, Gary K., Management Recruiters of Champions (C), TX, *462*
Albus, John P., Lord & Albus Co. (C), TX, *420*
Alexander, Susan M., Manuso, Alexander & Associates, Inc. (R), NY, *135*
Alisbrook, William, Fortune Personnel Consultants of Chattanooga Inc. (C), TN, *349*
Allen, James R., Continental Search Assoc. (C), OH, *298*
Allgire, Mary, Kenzer Corp. (R), IL, *113*
Ambruster, David L., Renaissance Resources, LLC (R), VA, *174*
Anderson, Jr., Glenn G., LAI Ward Howell (R), OH, *123*
Andrews, Robert L., Allen Austin Lowe & Powers (R), TX, *3*
Ansara, Peter, Ansara, Bickford & Fiske (C), MA, *251*
Aquavella, Charles P., Charles P. Aquavella & Assoc. (C), TX, *252*
Arledge, Tom, Allen Austin Lowe & Powers (R), TX, *3*
Attewell, Brad J., Dise & Co. (R), OH, *52*
Atwood, Bob, Canyon Consulting, Inc. (C), TX, *281*
Baert, Yvonne, Personnel Management Group (C), MB, *508*
Bailey, Paul, Preston-Hunter, Inc. (R), IL, *167*
Baine, Mike, California Search Agency, Inc. (C), CA, *279*
Baker, Gary M., Cochran, Cochran & Yale, Inc. (R), NY, *36*
Baker, Jake A., Allen Austin Lowe & Powers (R), TX, *3*
Baker, Ray, Management Recruiters of Ogden (C), UT, *464*
Ballach, Allen, Allen Ballach Assoc. Inc. (R), ON, *10*
Barnes, Richard E., Barnes Development Group, LLC (R), WI, *11*
Bartlett, Phil, P. J. Lynch Assoc. (R), CT, *132*
Bauman, Bobbi, BJB Assoc. (C), VA, *267*
Beaton, Carrie, Strategic Assoc., Inc. (C), TX, *595*
Beaudine, Jr., Frank R., Eastman & Beaudine, Inc. (R), GA, *56*
Becker, Ralph L., Automation Technology Search (C), CA, *256*
Bedingfield, Ray N., Woodmoor Group (C), CO, *624*
Beehler, Lance, Fortune Personnel Consultants of Hilton Head (C), SC, *349*
Bell, Greg, Cook Assoc. Int'l., Inc. (C), TN, *298*
Belle Isle, Bill, F-O-R-T-U-N-E Search Consultants (C), MO, *347*
Belle Isle, Patrice, F-O-R-T-U-N-E Search Consultants (C), MO, *347*
Bender, Alan, Bender Executive Search Management Consulting (R), NY, *16*
Berkowitz, Edwin, Wesley Brown & Bartle Co., Inc. (R), NY, *218*
Berlet, William, KPMG Executive Search (R), ON, *119*
Berry, Harold B., The Hindman Co. (R), KY, *94*
Bertsch, Gary D., Sanford Rose Assoc. - Flemington (C), NJ, *568*
Bliley, Jerry, SpencerStuart (R), ON, *197*
Blood, Dennis R., D. R. Blood & Assoc. (R), AZ, *18*
Bolno, Mark, Mark Bolno & Assoc. (C), FL, *269*
Boruff, Doug, Dunhill Personnel of Boulder (C), CO, *319*
Boruff, Fran, Dunhill Personnel of Boulder (C), CO, *319*
Bos, John, Bos Business Consultants (C), NY, *270*
Bothereau, Elizabeth, Kenzer Corp. (R), MN, *113*
Boxer, Kay S., Roth Young Executive Search of Milwaukee (C), WI, *547*
Bradford, Karen, Phillips Resource Group (C), SC, *510*
Brakel, H. R., ProTech Nationwide Staffing, Inc. (C), NY, *525*
Brauninger, Elaine, AmeriPro Search, Inc. (C), NC, *248*
Breen, Susan V., GFI Professional Staffing Services (C), NH, *357*
Brien, Richard H., Creative Input, Inc. (C), RI, *303*
Bright, William, The Perkins Group (R), NC, *162*
Brill, Ted, F-O-R-T-U-N-E Personnel Consultants of Tampa (C), FL, *345*
Brook, Marsha, C. M. Management Services, Inc. (R), KY, *26*
Brookes, Cindy, Technical Employment Consultants (C), PA, *602*
Brown, Bonny, Career Marketing Consultants, Inc. (C), GA, *283*
Brown, Daniel P., Johnson Brown Assoc., Inc. (C), IN, *400*
Brubaker, Denny, Fortune Personnel Consultants of San Antonio, Inc. (C), TX, *350*
Bruno, Deborah F., The Hindman Co. (R), KY, *94*
Bryant, Robert L., Renaissance Resources, LLC (R), VA, *174*
Buchholtz, Bruce Barton, Fairfield Int'l. Resources (R), NY, *65*
Cahill, Peter, Cahill Assoc. (C), CT, *279*
Caple, Robert, Coe & Co. Int'l. Inc./EMA Partners Int'l. (R), AB, *37*
Cappellini, Gloria, Lemming/LeVan, Inc. (R), NY, *128*
Capra, Jamie V., Warren, Morris & Madison, Ltd. (C), NH, *616*
Carey, Harvey, Carion Resource Group Inc. (C), ON, *284*
Carieri, Carl R., American Executive Search (C), FL, *247*
Carter, Guy W., Management Recruiters of Travelers Rest, Inc. (C), SC, *461*
Cary, Con, Cary & Assoc. (R), FL, *31*
Case, David R., Case Executive Search (C), MI, *286*
Chandler, Joseph J., Joseph Chandler & Assoc., Inc. (R), IL, *33*
Chavons, Crawford, Phillips Resource Group (C), SC, *510*
Check, Andrew D., A. D. Check Assoc., Inc. (R), PA, *33*
Christine, Rich, R. Christine Assoc. (C), PA, *290*
Christy, Tim, The Partnership Group (R), NJ, *160*
Clark, David A., Sprout/Standish, Inc. (C), NH, *590*
Clingan, Robert H., Management Recruiters of Broome County, Inc. (C), NY, *454*
Cole, Don, Riley Cole (C), CA, *537*
Coleman, William, Stephens Assoc. Ltd., Inc. (R), OH, *200*
Collins, Susan, Creative-Leadership, Inc. (R), CA, *42*
Conroy, Daniel J., Michael Latas & Assoc., Inc. (R), MO, *126*
Cook, Dennis F., MESA, Inc. (R), CO, *143*
Cook, Gene, Cook Assoc. Int'l., Inc. (C), TN, *298*
Cook, Stephen G., Cook Assoc. Int'l., Inc. (C), TN, *298*
Cooke, Jeffrey R., The Cooke Group (R), WI, *40*
Cooper, Bill, Management Recruiters of Chattanooga-Brainerd, Inc. (C), TN, *461*
Corey, Richard F., Weterrings & Agnew, Inc. (C), NY, *619*
Cornelison, Mike, M.C. Executive Search (C), CA, *422*
Cornfoot, James L., Management Recruiters of San Antonio (C), TX, *463*
Cougle, Nancy, Advanced Recruitment, Inc. (C), TN, *240*
Cox, James O., MES Search Co. (C), GA, *479*
Crane, Don, California Search Agency, Inc. (C), CA, *279*
Crath, Paul F., PricewaterhouseCoopers Executive Search (R), ON, *168*
Creasy, Nancy, Michael Latas & Assoc., Inc. (R), MO, *126*
Critchfield, Marlene, Marlene Critchfield Co. (C), CA, *303*
Critchley, Walter, Cochran, Cochran & Yale, Inc. (R), NY, *37*
Critchley, Walter Y., Cochran, Cochran & Yale, Inc. (R), NY, *36*
Crosbie, D. C., Interim Management Resources Inc. (C), ON, *392*

RECRUITER SPECIALTIES

Cuenca, Christine, mfg/Search, Inc. (C), IN, *480*
Culli, Ray, Christopher and Long (C), MO, *291*
Cunneff, Harry J., Management Recruiters of Lake Forest, IL (C), IL, *447*
Curran, Nick, Management Recruiters of Milwaukee-North (C), WI, *466*
Custer, George, Dynamic Staffing Network (C), IL, *324*
Dach, Brad, Management Recruiters of Spencer (C), IA, *448*
Daniel, Beverly R., Foy, Schneid & Daniel, Inc. (R), NY, *71*
Dant, Wendy A., Hire Authority, Inc. (C), MI, *379*
Darter, Steven, People Management Northeast, Inc. (R), CT, *162*
David, Dave, Executive Resource Assoc. (C), VA, *334*
Davis, Charlie, Dunhill of Ft. Wayne, Inc. (C), IN, *320*
Davis, Frank, Bertrand, Ross & Assoc., Inc. (C), IL, *266*
DeBaugh, David H., PRAXIS Partners (R), VA, *167*
Deckelbaum, Stan, Fortune Personnel Consultants of Raleigh, Inc. (C), NC, *348*
Dickey, Chester W., Bowden & Co., Inc. (R), OH, *20*
Dickson, David W., Fortune Personnel Consultants of Chattanooga Inc. (C), TN, *349*
Dieck, Daniel W., DieckMueller Group (R), WI, *51*
Dillon, Mark E., NaTek Corp. (C), NY, *488*
Dishaw, Raymond J., R. J. Dishaw & Assoc. (R), TX, *52*
Domann, Jr., William A., The Domann Organization (R), CA, *53*
Dominguez, Connie, Dominguez-Metz & Assoc. (R), CA, *53*
Donnelly, Christopher, Christopher-Westmont & Assoc., Inc. (R), OH, *35*
Donnelly, John R., Christopher-Westmont & Assoc., Inc. (R), OH, *35*
Dow, Lori, Davidson, Laird & Assoc. (C), MI, *308*
Dowell, Pat, M.C. Executive Search (C), CA, *422*
Doyen, Mike, Greenfields Engineering Search (C), MO, *363*
Drury, III, James J., SpencerStuart (R), IL, *197*
Dubeck, Michael, F-O-R-T-U-N-E Personnel Consultants of Troy, Inc. (C), MI, *347*
Dubuque, Bill, Christopher and Long (C), MO, *291*
Dusome, Terry, Holloway Schulz & Partners (C), BC, *380*
Eason, Larry E., JRL Executive Recruiters (C), MO, *401*
Edwards, Verba Lee, Wing Tips & Pumps, Inc. (C), MI, *623*
Egeland, Noel, Peter Froehlich & Co. (C), TX, *353*
Eisert, Robert M., Sanford Rose Assoc. - Doylestown (C), PA, *570*
Engel, Walter E., F-O-R-T-U-N-E Personnel Consultants of the Tri-Cities, Inc. (C), TN, *350*
English, Robert, RTE Search (C), NJ, *547*
English, Robert, RTE Search (C), VA, *547*
Erickson, Elaine, Kenzer Corp. (R), NY, *113*
Everett, Jim, EA Plus, Inc. (C), TX, *325*
Feimster, Alan, Management Recruiters of Florence (C), SC, *460*
Ferrel, James L., Career Marketing Consultants, Inc. (C), GA, *283*
Filippelli, Frank J., The Glenwood Group (C), IL, *358*
Fineman, David M., Manuso, Alexander & Associates, Inc. (R), NY, *135*
Fisk, James L., James L. Fisk & Assoc. (C), MO, *342*
Fockler, David B., David Fockler & Assoc., Inc. (C), CA, *342*
Ford, Travis, Ford & Assoc., Inc. (C), SC, *343*
Foster, Barton T., The Barton Group, Inc. (C), MI, *260*
Foster, Holly, A First Resource (C), NC, *231*
Foster, William A., Bridgecreek Personnel Agency (C), CA, *273*
Fountain, Ray, Management Recruiters of North Charleston (C), SC, *460*
Fox, Gary, F-O-R-T-U-N-E Personnel Consultants of Southwest Indiana (C), IN, *346*
Frary, Kevin S., KS Frary & Assoc. (R), MA, *71*
French, William G., Preng & Assoc., Inc. (R), TX, *167*
Fry, Don, Dunhill of Corpus Christi, Inc. (C), TX, *323*
Fullerton, Murray, The Churchill Group (C), ON, *291*
Gabel, Greg, Canny, Bowen Inc. (R), NY, *28*
Gabriele, Leslie, Gabriele & Company (C), MA, *354*
Gallagher, Dennis, Multisearch Recruiters (C), CA, *487*
Gardner, Sidney, Chase-Gardner Executive Search Associates, Inc. (C), FL, *289*
Gasga, Pedro Salinas, Michigan Consulting Group (R), MI, *144*
Gélinas, Normand, Yves Plouffe & Assoc. (R), QE, *165*
Genel, George, Genel Associates (C), CA, *356*
George, Alan, Ken Clark Int'l. (R), NJ, *36*
George, Richard, Kensington Int'l., Inc. (R), IL, *113*
Gerard, William, Fox-Morris Assoc., Inc. (C), CA, *352*
Gerarde, Paul S., Keena Staffing Services (C), NY, *404*
Gesing, Rand W., Rand Assoc. (R), ME, *171*
Gleason, Helen, Management Recruiters of Clearwater (C), FL, *443*
Gleason, James P., J. P. Gleason Assoc., Inc. (R), IL, *77*
Goldbach, Linda J., Beacon Int'l., Inc. (C), VA, *261*
Golding, Michael S., Michael Assoc. (R), IL, *144*
Goldman, Michael L., Strategic Assoc., Inc. (C), TX, *595*
Goodrich, III, Dana C., First Advisory Services Int'l., Inc. (R), MD, *67*
Goodwin, Joe D., LAI Ward Howell (R), GA, *123*
Graham, Robert E., Fortune Personnel Consultants of Allentown, Inc. (C), PA, *348*
Grant, Anthony, Management Recruiters of Columbia (C), MD, *450*
Greebe, Neil, Preferred Professional Recruiters (C), OH, *516*
Green, John A., JAG Group (R), MO, *105*
Grindlinger, Arthur R., Fortune Personnel Consultants of Sarasota Inc. (C), FL, *345*
Gross, Kathy, Evie Kreisler Assoc. Inc. (C), NY, *409*
Guerrero, Daniel, Kenzer Corp. (R), CA, *113*
Gutierrez, Mary Rose, Job Link, Inc. (C), CA, *399*
Hackett, Donald F., Management Recruiters of Mt. Airy (C), NC, *456*
Hahn, Kenneth R., Hahn & Assoc., Inc. (C), OH, *365*
Hahn, Loel G., Fergason Assoc., Inc. (C), IL, *339*
Hall, James E., The Duncan-O'Dell Group Inc. (C), TX, *316*
Hamill, Robert W., Robert Howe & Assoc. (R), GA, *97*
Harbin, Steve, Dunhill Personnel of St. Andrews (C), SC, *322*
Harcourt, Peter, Harcourt & Assoc. (C), AB, *368*
Hardwick, Michael, Management Recruiters of Aiken (C), SC, *460*
Harkins, Robert E., Robert Harkins Assoc., Inc. (C), PA, *369*
Hartig, Dave, The Angus Group, Ltd. (C), OH, *251*
Harvey, Bob, Mayhall Search Group, Inc. (C), IN, *473*
Harvill, Jon, Dunhill Search of West Atlanta (C), GA, *320*
Hauck, Fred P., The Cassie Group (R), NJ, *31*
Hebert, Robert R., Austin Michaels, Ltd., Inc. (C), AZ, *256*
Helfer, Frederick W., Helfer Executive Consultants (R), TN, *91*
Helnore, Diann, Partners in Recruiting (C), IL, *504*
Henry, Jeremy, A First Resource (C), NC, *231*
Hickel, Stephen, mfg/Search, Inc. (C), MI, *480*
Hiesiger, Emile M., Manuso, Alexander & Associates, Inc. (R), NY, *135*
Hindman, Jeffrey J., The Hindman Group, Inc. (C), CA, *378*
Hindman, Neil C., The Hindman Co. (R), KY, *94*
Hirshman, Kenneth A., McGrath & Assoc., Inc. (R), NJ, *141*

Hodges, Whitney, Recruiting Services Group, Inc. (C), TN, *532*
Holt, Douglas, Management Recruiters of Columbia, Tennessee (C), TN, *461*
Holzheimer, Robert, Exclusive Search Consultants (C), OH, *331*
Houchins, William C. Buster, Christian & Timbers, Inc. (R), MD, *34*
Howell, Tom, Mayhall Search Group, Inc. (C), IN, *473*
Hubbard, Ted L., KS Frary & Assoc. (R), MA, *71*
Hucko, Donald, Jonas, Walters & Assoc., Inc. (R), WI, *108*
Hudson, Bill, Sage Employment Recruiters (C), IN, *550*
Hudson, Kevin, Raymond Karsan Assoc. (C), PA, *530*
Huff, Margaret L., Huff Assoc. (R), NJ, *98*
Huff, William Z., Huff Assoc. (R), NJ, *98*
Humay, Gene, E. F. Humay Assoc. (C), PA, *384*
Humay, Jane, E. F. Humay Assoc. (C), PA, *384*
Hurley, Art, Systems Research Inc. (SRI) (C), IL, *598*
Hursey, Bruce, Management Recruiters of Monroe, Inc. (C), LA, *450*
Hurtubise, Jean Pierre, Reynolds Consulting Int'l. (R), QE, *177*
Jackson, Noel, Sanford Rose Assoc. - Mobile (C), AL, *565*
Jacobs, James W., Callan Assoc., Ltd. (R), IL, *27*
Jacobson, Rick, The Windham Group (R), OH, *222*
Jocke, John, Management Recruiters of Boise (C), ID, *446*
Joffe, Barry, Bason Associates (R), OH, *13*
Johnson, L. J., L. J. Johnson & Co. (R), MI, *106*
Johnson, Mike, The 500 Granary Inc. (C), ON, *231*
Jones, Donald, Kenzer Corp. (R), TX, *113*
Jones, Yvonne, T. Page & Assoc. (C), TX, *502*
Jordan, Dick, Staff Resources, Inc. (C), SC, *590*
Kaas, Linda M., Kaas Employment Services (C), IA, *402*
Kaiser, Marv, Execu-Tech Search Inc. (C), MN, *332*
Kane, Rich, Systems Research Inc. (SRI) (C), IL, *598*
Kanzer, William F., Kanzer Assoc., Inc. (R), IL, *109*
Katz, Arthur, Management Recruiters of Atlanta North, Inc. (C), GA, *446*
Katzman, Melissa, Melissa Katzman, Executive Search (C), NY, *404*
Kay, Heidi, Kay Concepts, Inc. (C), FL, *404*
Keefe, John, Kelly Associates (R), PA, *112*
Kelly, Susan D., S. D. Kelly & Assoc., Inc. (R), MA, *112*
Kenney, George T., Search Research Assoc., Inc. (R), MA, *187*
Kenny, Roger M., Boardroom Consultants/Kenny Kindler Tholke (R), NY, *19*
Kenzer, Robert D., Kenzer Corp. (R), NY, *113*
Kershaw, Blair, Blair Kershaw Assoc., Inc. (C), PA, *405*
Kessler, Roy, J. B. Linde & Assoc. (C), MO, *395*
King, J. C., A H Justice Search Consultants (C), TX, *402*
King, Michael, Fortune Personnel Consultants of San Antonio, Inc. (C), TX, *350*
Knapp, Ronald A., Knapp Consultants (R), CT, *116*
Kohn, Steven, Affinity Executive Search (C), FL, *241*
Koppes, Jenny, Future Employment Service, Inc. (C), IA, *354*
Korban, Richard O., Korban Associates (R), PA, *117*
Korytko, Lesia, COBA Executive Search (R), CO, *36*
Kreisler, Debbi, Evie Kreisler Assoc. Inc. (C), GA, *409*
Kreisler, Evie, Evie Kreisler Assoc. Inc. (C), CA, *409*
Kreutz, Gary L., Kreutz Consulting Group, Inc. (R), IL, *121*
Krezo, Rich, Michigan Consulting Group (R), MI, *144*
Krezo, Rich, Premier Recruiting Group (C), MI, *516*
Kriesel, David W., Management Recruiters of Woodbury (C), MN, *430*
Kriesel, David W., Management Recruiters of Woodbury (C), MN, *452*
Krumel, Richard, The Perkins Group (R), NC, *162*
Kuehnling, William, Sanford Rose Assoc. - Canton (C), OH, *569*
Kuesis, Dan, Systems Research Inc. (SRI) (C), IL, *598*
Kuhn, John J., John Kuhn & Assoc., Inc. (R), WI, *121*
Kuntz, William A., Management Recruiters of Indianapolis (C), IN, *448*
Kwapisz, Arthur, ISC of Atlanta, Inc. (C), GA, *394*
Lachance, Roger, Ray & Berndtson/Laurendeau Labrecque (R), QE, *172*
Lambre, Glenn C., McCooe & Assoc., Inc. (R), NJ, *140*
Lane, Andrew J., Overton Consulting (R), WI, *157*
Lange, Jim, Lange & Assoc., Inc. (C), IN, *412*
Langford, Bob, Fortune Personnel Consultants of Huntsville, Inc. (C), AL, *343*
Langford, Matt, Fortune Personnel Consultants of Huntsville, Inc. (C), AL, *344*
Langley, Ted, Jaeger Int'l., Inc. (C), OH, *396*
Latimer, Dick, Technical Recruiting Consultants (C), IL, *602*
Latona, Catherine, Management Recruiters of Fresno (C), CA, *440*
Laurence, David, Forest People Int'l. Search Ltd. (C), BC, *343*
Laurendeau, J. E., Ray & Berndtson/Laurendeau Labrecque (R), QE, *172*
Lawler, Tim, Sales Consultants of Milwaukee (C), WI, *563*
Lawler, III, Timothy M., Management Recruiters of Milwaukee-North (C), WI, *466*
Leety, Murray, Fox-Morris Assoc., Inc. (C), PA, *352*
Lennon, Bill, Hall Management Group, Inc. (C), GA, *367*
Lessner, Mark, J. E. Lessner Assoc., Inc. (R), MI, *128*
Letson, Susan, KPMG Executive Search (R), NS, *119*
Levine, Eileen, Williamsburg Group (C), NJ, *621*
Lewis, Mark E., Management Recruiters of Myrtle Beach, Inc. (C), SC, *460*
Lewis, Richard, Cole, Warren & Long, Inc. (R), PA, *37*
Lilja, Raymond, American Services Group (C), IL, *248*
Lippe, John L., Dunhill Professional Search of Englewood, Inc. (C), CO, *319*
Little, John J., Alpha Executive Search (C), AL, *246*
Livingston, Hyman, The P & L Group (C), NY, *500*
Loftus, Michael G., Interim Executive Recruiting (C), GA, *392*
Lowery, Bruce N., Bruce Lowery & Assoc. (C), MI, *420*
Lynch, Jack, Michigan Consulting Group (R), MI, *144*
Lynch, Jack, Premier Recruiting Group (C), MI, *516*
Lynge, R. J., Management Recruiters of Ft. Myers, FL. (C), FL, *443*
Lyngen, C. J., Construct Management Services (C), MN, *297*
Lyngen, Trish, Construct Management Services (C), MN, *297*
Lyons, Jerold, Dunhill of Ft. Collins, Inc. (C), CO, *319*
Lyons, M. Don, L O R (R), NJ, *122*
Macdonald, Craig, Houser, Martin, Morris (C), WA, *381*
MacEachern, David, SpencerStuart (R), ON, *197*
MacTadyen, David, Sharrow & Assoc., Inc. (C), IN, *579*
Magee, Charles R., DieckMueller Group (R), WI, *51*
Magee, Harrison R., Bowden & Co., Inc. (R), OH, *20*
Malouf, Terry, Bartholdi & Co., Inc. (R), CO, *12*
Mannard, Thomas B., Mannard & Assoc., Inc. (R), IL, *135*
Manning, Jerry, Management Recruiters of Ogden (C), UT, *464*
Manuso, James S. J., Manuso, Alexander & Associates, Inc. (R), NY, *135*
Marenger, Christine, Yves Plouffe & Assoc. (R), QE, *165*
Marshall, John L., Fishel HR Assoc., Inc. (C), AZ, *341*
Mason, Maurice, McCray, Shriver, Eckdahl & Assoc., Inc. (R), CA, *140*

Matte, Richard, Matte Consulting Group Inc. (R), QE, *138*
Maun, Fran, Roth Young of Tampa (C), FL, *546*
McClosky, Evan, Open Concepts (C), CA, *499*
McClosky, John, John Kurosky & Assoc. (R), CA, *122*
McClosky, John, Open Concepts (C), CA, *499*
McClosky, Linda, Open Concepts (C), CA, *499*
McCollum, Ken, MESA International (C), CA, *480*
McGeehan, Gayle A., Management Recruiters of Bethlehem, PA (C), PA, *458*
McGregor, Jock, Reynolds Consulting Int'l. (R), ON, *177*
McInturff, Robert E., McInturff & Assoc., Inc. (C), MA, *474*
McIntyre, Joel, Phillips Resource Group (C), NC, *511*
McLean, E. Peter, SpencerStuart (R), NY, *196*
McMillin, Robert, Price Waterhouse Executive Search (R), BC, *168*
McQuiddy, Brian, Woodmoor Group (C), CO, *624*
Mears, Jack, Kelly Walker Assoc. (C), TX, *614*
Meister, Verle, Management Recruiters of Cheyenne (C), WY, *466*
Menefee, Shawn, Corporate Plus, Ltd. (C), GA, *300*
Metz, Nancy, Dominguez-Metz & Assoc. (R), CA, *53*
Meyer, Rick M., Meyer Assoc., Inc. (R), GA, *144*
Miller, Eric L., Miller Denver (C), CO, *482*
Mills, Joseph, Select Services (C), IL, *578*
Mincy, Jim, Corporate Image Group (C), GA, *300*
Mirsky, Al, The Barton Group, Inc. (C), MI, *260*
Mojek, Chuck, American Resources Corp. (C), IL, *248*
Molina, Dominique, Winthrop Partners, Inc. (R), NY, *222*
Moore, Sandee, Moore Research Assoc. (R), NJ, *147*
Morrow, Michael, RSMR, Inc. (R), IL, *182*
Mueller, Howard, mfg/Search, Inc. (C), IN, *480*
Mueller, Michael S., DieckMueller Group (R), WI, *51*
Mueller, William, Noll Human Resource Services (C), MO, *494*
Mulvaney, Ronald F., R. F. Mulvaney & Assoc., Inc. (R), MO, *149*
Murphy, Cornelius J., Goodrich & Sherwood Assoc., Inc. (R), NY, *80*
Nagler, Leon G., Nagler, Robins & Poe, Inc. (R), MA, *150*
Natowitz, Robert, DeMatteo Associates (C), NY, *311*
Nelson, David G., The Personnel Group, Inc. (R), MN, *163*
Nelson, Len, Len Nelson & Assoc., Inc. (C), TX, *491*
Nelson, Paul, London Executive Consultants Inc. (C), ON, *420*
Nepovadny, John A., The Langford Search, Inc. (C), AL, *412*
Nicholls, R. J., Interim Management Resources Inc. (C), ON, *392*
Nix Gilmore, Pamela, Management Recruiters of Loudoun County South (C), VA, *465*
Noonan, Michael A., Management Association Network (C), WI, *424*
O'Brien, Frank E., Austin Michaels, Ltd., Inc. (C), AZ, *256*
O'Brien, Timothy M., O'Brien & Bell (R), OH, *153*
O'Daniel, Beverly W., The Elsworth Group (C), TX, *329*
O'Daniel, James E., The Elsworth Group (C), TX, *329*
O'Neill, Ted, Russ Hadick & Assoc. Inc. (C), OH, *365*
O'Steen, Ray, American Professional Search, Inc. (C), TN, *248*
Olszewski, Larry D., PRAXIS Partners (R), VA, *167*
Owens, Reggie, The Gabriel Group (C), PA, *354*
Pailin, Cheryl, The Pailin Group Professional Search Consultants (R), TX, *158*
Palazzolo, Kathy, Michigan Consulting Group (R), MI, *144*
Palazzolo, Kathy, Premier Recruiting Group (C), MI, *516*
Palma, Frank R., Goodrich & Sherwood Assoc., Inc. (R), NJ, *80*
Palmer, James H., The Hindman Co. (R), KY, *94*
Palumbo, Robert F., The Recruitment Group, Inc. (C), NY, *532*
Park, Cleve A., Management Recruiters of Birmingham, Inc. (C), AL, *438*
Parr, Thomas A., Holland & Assoc., Inc. (R), MI, *94*
Parres, Mike, Michael W. Parres & Assoc. (R), MI, *159*
Parry, William H., Horton Int'l. Inc. (R), CA, *96*
Parsons, Crystal, Management Recruiters Peninsula (C), CA, *439*
Patterson, Brenda, Management Recruiters - Indianapolis (C), IN, *448*
Pearson, Brian, Roth Young Executive Search (C), TX, *546*
Pearson, Robert L., LAI Ward Howell (R), TX, *124*
Pedelty, Lori K., Capstone Consulting, Inc. (R), IL, *29*
Penley, Jeffrey M., Highlander Search (C), NC, *378*
Pepple, Bob, Fortune Personnel Consultants of Jacksonville (C), FL, *345*
Perkins, R. Patrick, The Perkins Group (R), NC, *162*
Peters, Peter Louis, Success Seekers Connection (C), FL, *596*
Petrello-Pray, Gina, Direct Recruiters, Inc. (C), OH, *312*
Petruzzi, Vincent J., Petruzzi Assoc. (C), NJ, *509*
Phillips, Mike, FORTUNE Personnel Consultants of Charleston, Inc. (C), SC, *349*
Philo, Dave, Philo & Associates (C), GA, *511*
Picarella, Greg, Gregory, Kyle & Assoc. (C), NC, *363*
Pickens, Gregory D., Gregory D. Pickens (C), TX, *512*
Pike, Geoff, F-O-R-T-U-N-E Personnel Consultants of Greenwood Village (C), CO, *344*
Plunkett, Mike, Phillips Resource Group (C), NC, *511*
Poore, Larry D., LAI Ward Howell (R), IL, *123*
Popham, Harold C., Emerson & Co. (C), GA, *329*
Portanova, Peter M., ROI Assoc. (R), NY, *181*
Powell, Donald L., Proquest Inc. (C), SC, *524*
Powell, Marie, Kenzer Corp. (R), GA, *113*
Powers, Norman S., Norman Powers Assoc., Inc. (C), MA, *515*
Poyck, Walter S., Stewart Assoc. (C), PA, *593*
Presley-Cannon, Judy, Corporate Image Group (C), TN, *300*
Priftis, Tony, Evie Kreisler Assoc. Inc. (C), TX, *409*
Pritchett, Philip H., FORTUNE Personnel Consultants of North Dallas (C), TX, *350*
Prouty, Alden F., Manuso, Alexander & Associates, Inc. (R), NY, *135*
Provda, Peter, F-O-R-T-U-N-E Personnel Consultants of Menlo Park, Inc. (C), NJ, *347*
Putiri, Vincent, Asheville Search & Consulting (C), NC, *253*
Raab, Julie, Vaughan & Co. (C), CA, *612*
Randolph, Bob, Career Counseling Inc. (CCI) (C), KY, *282*
Rardin, Ed, Brentwood Int'l. (R), CA, *23*
Raulerson, Derek, Search South, Inc. (C), AL, *576*
Reilly, Toni Marie, Fox-Morris Assoc., Inc. (C), NC, *352*
Reyes, Randolph, Management Recruiters of Columbia (C), MD, *450*
Richards, Carl, Technical Employment Consultants (C), PA, *602*
Richards, Terry, Terry Richards (C), OH, *536*
Richardson, Karrie, Management Recruiters of Round Rock (C), TX, *463*
Riddle, James E., Riddle & McGrath LLC (R), GA, *178*
Rieger, Louis J., SpencerStuart (R), TX, *197*
Robinson, Mel, MDR & Associates (C), AR, *476*
Robinson, Steve, Marsteller Wilcox Assoc. (C), IL, *471*
Rockwell, Sr., Richard B., Applied Search Assoc., Inc. (C), GA, *252*
Rodriguez Smithson, Raquel, R. A. Rodriguez & Assoc., Inc. (C), TX, *540*
Rogers, George W., Dunhill Executive Search of Brown County (C), IN, *321*

Rogers, S. L., Dunhill Executive Search of Brown County (C), IN, *321*
Rolland, Guy, Rolland Ressources Humaines Inc. (R), QE, *181*
Romaniw, Michael J., A la Carte Int'l., Inc. (R), VA, *1*
Roodvoets, Jan, J. E. Lessner Assoc., Inc. (R), MI, *128*
Rose, John M., The Curtiss Group International (R), FL, *44*
Rosenow, Richard, Heath/Norton Assoc., Inc. (R), NY, *89*
Ross, William J., Flowers & Assoc. (C), OH, *342*
Rossow, Bob, E/Search Int'l. (C), CT, *325*
Rowland, John R., Rowland Assoc. (C), CA, *547*
Rubin, Stephanie, Amherst Human Resource Group, Ltd. (C), IL, *249*
Rueppel, Melvin L., Holohan Group, Ltd. (R), MO, *95*
Rupert, James A., Management Recruiters of Siouxland (C), IA, *449*
Russell, Robin, Kenzer Corp. (R), NY, *113*
Ryan, David, The Recruitment Group, Inc. (C), NY, *532*
Salinas, Pedro, Premier Recruiting Group (C), MI, *516*
Salzberg, David, Roth Young Seattle (C), WA, *546*
Sargis, Scott R., Strategic Search Corp. (R), IL, *202*
Sawyer, Pierce, Phillips Resource Group (C), NC, *511*
Schaefer, Jr., Frederick M., StratfordGroup (R), CO, *203*
Scharringhausen, Michael C., Saber Group, Inc. (C), TX, *550*
Schatz, Jr., William G., The Schatz Company (C), MO, *571*
Schiavone, Mary Rose, Canny, Bowen Inc. (R), NY, *28*
Schneider, Paul J., Prime Resource Assoc. (C), WI, *518*
Schultz, Tim, Focus Executive Search (C), MN, *343*
Schwartz, Lou, Technical Employment Consultants (C), PA, *602*
Scott, Bob, Robert Scott Assoc. (C), NJ, *573*
Scott, Corwyn J., Warren, Morris & Madison, Ltd. (C), NH, *616*
Scott, Harold, Graham & Co. (R), NJ, *80*
Seal, Jock, The H. S. Group, Inc. (C), WI, *365*
Sears, Richard G., The Wilmington Group (C), NC, *622*
Segal, Eric B., Kenzer Corp. (R), NY, *113*
Selig, Robert J., Selig Executive Search (C), NH, *579*
Semmes, John R., Management Recruiters of Fayetteville (C), NC, *455*
Seymour, Janice F., Baldwin & Assoc. (C), OH, *258*
Shapiro, Larry, Heller Kil Assoc., Inc. (C), IL, *375*
Sharrow, Beth S., Sharrow & Assoc., Inc. (C), MI, *579*
Shattuck, M. B., M. B. Shattuck & Assoc., Inc. (R), CA, *189*
Shaw, R. William, Management Recruiters of South Bend (C), IN, *448*
Shearer, Thomas, Carnegie Resources, Inc. (C), NC, *284*
Shotland, David R., The Shotland Group (R), CA, *190*
Shufelt, Douglas G., Sink, Walker, Boltrus Int'l. (R), MA, *192*
Siegel, Carl W., Winfield Assoc., Inc. (C), MA, *623*
Simpson, Terre, Simpson Associates (C), NY, *582*
Sinclair, Kathleen A., Executive Recruiters Int'l. (C), MI, *333*
Skewes, Gail, Reid Ellis Assoc. Inc. (C), ON, *533*
Skirbe, Douglas, The Zarkin Group, Inc. (R), NY, *226*
Sloan, Tom, Tom Sloan & Assoc., Inc. (C), WI, *583*
Small, Jim, J. L. Small Assoc. (C), AL, *583*
Smith, Carroll V., Management Recruiters of Janesville, Inc. (C), WI, *466*
Smith, Clark W., F-O-R-T-U-N-E Personnel Consultants of Savannah, Inc. (C), GA, *345*
Smith, David P., HRS, Inc. (R), PA, *97*
Smith, Douglas M., LAI Ward Howell (R), IL, *123*
Smith, Michael R., Michaels & Moere (C), WI, *481*
Smith, Michael W., Management Recruiters of Danville (C), KY, *449*
Smith, Robert, Fox-Morris Assoc., Inc. (C), GA, *352*
Smith, Sylvia, Smith & Assoc. (C), FL, *583*
Smith, Wilton, The Stark Wilton Group (R), MI, *199*
Smithson, Fred, R. A. Rodriguez & Assoc., Inc. (C), TX, *540*
Snellbaker, Mary W., Management Recruiters of Southeastern Michigan (C), MI, *451*
Socha, Rudy, Advancement Recruiting Services (C), OH, *241*
Sondhi, Rick, Raymond Karsan Assoc. (C), IL, *530*
Southworth, David E., Michigan Consulting Group (R), MI, *144*
Southworth, David E., Premier Recruiting Group (C), MI, *516*
Spears, Robert, FORTUNE Personnel Consultants of Charleston, Inc. (C), SC, *349*
Spencer, Norman, FORTUNE Personnel Consultants of North Dallas (C), TX, *350*
Spiegel, Deborah, Kenzer Corp. (R), NY, *113*
Spremulli, Paul L., PKS Assoc., Inc. (C), RI, *513*
Stanley, Wade, Management Recruiters of Raleigh (C), NC, *456*
Steiner, Judy, Future Employment Service, Inc. (C), IA, *354*
Stevens, Ralph, Preng & Assoc., Inc. (R), TX, *167*
Stevenson, Jani, Howard Fischer Assoc. Int'l., Inc. (R), TX, *67*
Stevenson, Terry, Bartholdi & Co., Inc. (R), CO, *12*
Stevick, Marianne, Management Recruiters of Columbia, Tennessee (C), TN, *461*
Stewart, Wilfred C., KPMG Executive Search (R), ON, *119*
Stiles, Jake, Linford E. Stiles & Assoc., L.L.C. (R), NH, *201*
Stoa, Gordon, PERC, Ltd. (C), AZ, *506*
Stone, Susan L., Stone Enterprises Ltd. (C), IL, *594*
Stranberg, James R., Callan Assoc., Ltd. (R), IL, *27*
Strong, Duane, Executive Resource Inc. (C), WI, *334*
Sunshine, Ron, Ron Sunshine & Assoc. (C), IL, *597*
Sweet, Robert J., Atlanta Executive Partners, Inc. (R), MA, *8*
Syberg, Keith A., Smith & Syberg, Inc. (R), IN, *193*
Szymanski, C., The Hanna Group (C), OH, *368*
Tadda, Wayne, Evie Kreisler Assoc. Inc. (C), IL, *409*
Tambor, Morris, Reynolds Consulting Int'l. (R), ON, *177*
Tanaka, Jun, Premier Recruiting Group (C), MI, *516*
Taylor, Winifred C., Management Recruiters of Venice, Inc. (C), FL, *445*
Tedla, Solomon, Creative HR Solutions (C), GA, *303*
Terry, Jeff, Southern Recruiters & Consultants, Inc. (C), SC, *587*
Thomas, Bruce, Angel Group Int'l. (C), KY, *250*
Thomas, Roger C., Innovative Resource Group, LLC (C), NC, *389*
Thomaschek, Charles F., North Coast Meridian (C), NY, *496*
Townsend, Carol A., Future Employment Service, Inc. (C), IA, *353*
Trambley, J. Brian, Trambley the Recruiter (C), NM, *608*
Traylor, M. Ben, Human Resources Personnel Agency (R), AR, *99*
Truman, Robert P., The Truman Agency (C), CA, *610*
Turkal, Terry, Advanced Recruitment, Inc. (C), TN, *240*
VanEs, Judith, mfg/Search, Inc. (C), IN, *480*
Vann, Dianne, Button Group (C), TX, *277*
Voelker, Larry, mfg/Search, Inc. (C), MI, *480*
Walker, Donald G., Executive Search Plus, Inc. (C), IN, *336*
Walker, Douglas G., Sink, Walker, Boltrus Int'l. (R), MA, *192*
Walsh, Richard, The Gabriel Group (C), PA, *354*
Warner, Thomas P., Warner & Assoc., Inc. (C), OH, *615*
Watson, Lisa, mfg/Search, Inc. (C), IN, *480*
Weiner, Al, Lucas Group (C), NY, *421*
Weiss, Michael G., Applied Resources, Inc. (C), MN, *252*

RECRUITER SPECIALTIES

Wells, Juli C., Cook Assoc. Int'l., Inc. (C), TN, *298*
West, Al, West & Assoc. (C), IL, *618*
West, Fred, Wood West & Partners Inc. (C), BC, *624*
Westphal, Birgit, Reynolds Consulting Int'l. (R), ON, *177*
Whitehead, Robert S., Whitehead & Assoc., Inc. (C), MO, *620*
Whitlow, M. Blanton, Manuso, Alexander & Associates, Inc. (R), NY, *135*
Wilcox, Alex B., The Bridge (C), CO, *273*
Williams, John G., John Williams & Assoc. (C), TX, *621*
Williams, John R., John R. Williams & Assoc., Inc. (C), NC, *621*
Wilson, Deborah, Healthcare Recruiters Int'l. - Los Angeles (C), CA, *372*
Wolfson, Gary M., The Blackman Kallick Search Division (C), IL, *267*
Wonderling, Susan, Susan L. Wonderling Recruiting (C), PA, *623*
Wood, Bill, Search Plus Int'l.-Ohio (C), OH, *576*
Wood, Martin F., LAI Ward Howell (R), TX, *124*
Wright, John, Corporate Image Group (C), TN, *300*
Wylie, John L., John Wylie Assoc., Inc. (C), OK, *625*
Young, Arthur L., Search South, Inc. (C), AL, *576*
Young, Nicholas, SpencerStuart (R), NY, *196*
Zak, Adam, Horton Int'l. Inc. (R), IL, *96*
Zamjahn, Charles J., River Region Personnel, Inc. (C), LA, *538*
Zielazny, William A., mfg/Search, Inc. (C), OH, *480*
Zimmermann, Karl, Fortune Personnel Consultants of Bloomfield, Inc. (C), MI, *346*
Zonka, Thomas J., Thomas & Assoc. of Michigan (C), MI, *606*

Management

Antonio, Marshall, Fortune of Arlington Heights (C), IL, *346*
Berke, Carl E., The Cassie Group (R), PA, *31*
Edgerton, Paul, The Cassie Group (R), PA, *31*
Kuhn, John J., John Kuhn & Assoc., Inc. (R), WI, *121*
Lowe, Daniel M., Daniel Marks Company (C), OH, *306*
Ormson, Gilbert E., Executive Recruiters, Inc. (C), WI, *334*
Sackmary, Stephen M., Sanford Rose Assoc. - Austin (C), TX, *570*
Sangster, Jeffrey A., F-O-R-T-U-N-E Personnel Consultants of Manatee County (C), FL, *345*

Marine

Alvey, Frank, Sage Employment Recruiters (C), IN, *550*
Pollan, Arthur, Snelling & Snelling, Inc. (C), FL, *585*

Market research

Babka, James, Roth Young of Chicago (C), IL, *546*
Bender, Alan, Bender Executive Search Management Consulting (R), NY, *16*
Black, Jr., Frank S., Management Recruiters of Washington, DC Inc. (C), MD, *450*
Brenner, Richard, Somerset Group, Inc. (C), CT, *587*
Capel, Rob, Research Personnel Consultants (C), ON, *534*
Cook, Robin, Impact Search & Strategies (C), PA, *387*
Forbes, Kay Koob, Sanford Rose Assoc. - Evansville (C), IN, *567*
Giacoponello, Thomas V., Search America, Inc. (C), PA, *573*
Godfrey, Robert G., Robert G. Godfrey Assoc. Ltd. (R), IL, *79*
Greene, Dorcas P., Greene Personnel Consultants (C), RI, *362*
King, Gregory, Somerset Group, Inc. (C), CT, *587*
Lindsey, Ginger, Ginger Lindsey & Assoc., Inc. (C), TX, *418*
O'Connell, Brian M., O'Connell Group Inc. (C), CT, *497*
Parker, Gayle W., Trebor Weldon Lawrence, Inc. (R), NY, *210*
Payette, Angela, Greene Personnel Consultants (C), RI, *362*
Redden, Mary, Redden & McGrath Assoc., Inc. (R), NY, *173*
Root, Leslie A., The Wright Group (C), TX, *625*
Samet, Saul, Fisher-Todd Assoc. (C), NY, *342*
Savalli, Frank, Savalli & Assoc., Inc. (C), MI, *571*
Teicher, Arthur, Smith's Fifth Avenue (C), NY, *585*
Tomlinson, Betsy, Tomlinson Assoc. Inc. (C), IL, *607*
Tringle, Terry, Sanford Rose Assoc. - Nashville (C), TN, *570*
Weil, Lee, Lee Weil Assoc., Inc. (C), IL, *617*
Werbin, Susan, Werbin Assoc. Executive Search, Inc. (C), NY, *618*
Werner, Vivian, Smith's Fifth Avenue (C), NY, *585*
Wright, Jay, The Wright Group (C), TX, *625*

Marketing

Abrahamson, Susan, SearchCom, Inc. (R), TX, *187*
Adler, David, Don Allan Assoc., Inc. (C), CA, *313*
Adler, Louis S., CJA-The Adler Group, Inc. (R), CA, *35*
Alexander, Penelope, Alexander & Co. (C), CA, *243*
Alexander, Susan M., Manuso, Alexander & Associates, Inc. (R), NY, *135*
Altschuler, Joseph, Management Recruiters of Gramercy, Inc. (C), NY, *455*
Andrews, Charles, The Borton Wallace Co. (R), TN, *19*
Angell, Tryg R., Tryg R. Angell, Ltd. (C), CT, *250*
Attewell, Brad J., Dise & Co. (R), OH, *52*
Babka, James, Roth Young of Chicago (C), IL, *546*
Baer, Curtis L., Sales Consultants of Barrington (C), IL, *558*
Balakonis, Charles L., Lawrence-Balakonis & Assoc., Inc. (C), GA, *414*
Barnes, Gary B., Brigade, Inc. (R), CA, *23*
Barr, Sharon A., Barr Assoc. (C), PA, *259*
Barrett, Bill, The Barrett Group (C), NH, *260*
Bayer, Richard L., Top Gun Group, Inc. (C), NV, *607*
Beaudin, Elizabeth C., Callan Assoc., Ltd. (R), IL, *27*
Beaudine, Jr., Frank R., Eastman & Beaudine, Inc. (R), GA, *56*
Belanger, Richard, Kingsley Allen Partners Inc. (R), ON, *114*
Bender, Alan, Bender Executive Search Management Consulting (R), NY, *16*
Berg, Charlie, Management Recruiters of Lake Forest, IL (C), IL, *447*
Bissell, John, Gundersen Partners, L.L.C. (R), MI, *83*
Black, Jr., Frank S., Management Recruiters of Washington, DC Inc. (C), MD, *450*
Bodnaryk, David, The Grant Search Group, Inc. (C), ON, *361*
Bonnell, William R., Bonnell Assoc. Ltd. (R), CT, *19*
Booker, Calvin, National Affirmative Action Career Network, Inc. (C), CO, *488*
Bornholdt, John, Bornholdt Shivas & Friends Executive Recruiters (C), NY, *270*
Bos, John, Bos Business Consultants (C), NY, *270*
Bosch, Diane, Bosch & Assoc., LLC (R), CT, *20*
Bosch, Eric E., Bosch & Assoc., LLC (R), CT, *20*
Brauninger, John C., AmeriPro Search, Inc. (C), NC, *248*
Brody, Stuart, R. Green & Assoc., Inc. (C), OH, *362*
Brolin, Lawrence E., DLB Assoc. (R), NY, *53*
Brook, Marsha, C. M. Management Services, Inc. (R), KY, *26*
Brookes, Michael T., Executive Access Inc. (R), NY, *62*
Brown, Buzz, Brown, Bernardy, Van Remmen, Inc. (C), CA, *275*
Brown, Gene, Management Recruiters of Atlanta West, Inc. (C), GA, *445*
Buck, Jr., Charles A., Charles Buck & Assoc., Inc. (R), NY, *24*
Buckley, Daniel, The Buckley Group (C), FL, *276*
Burchill, Gregory J., BGB Assoc., Inc. (C), IL, *266*
Burgess, III, William H., The Burgess Group-Corporate Recruiters Int'l., Inc. (R), NY, *25*

Burke, Sally, Chaloner Assoc. (R), MA, *32*
Burkhill, J. L., The Talley Group (R), VA, *205*
Burtch, Linda, Smith Hanley Assoc., Inc. (C), IL, *584*
Butler, Carol, Leonard Corwen Assoc. (C), NY, *302*
Buxton, Carolyn J., Sinclair & Co. Inc. (R), FL, *192*
Cahill, Peter, Cahill Assoc. (C), CT, *279*
Callicott, Robin D., Perfect Search, Inc. (C), FL, *507*
Capel, Rob, Research Personnel Consultants (C), ON, *534*
Caplan, Shellie, Caplan Assoc., Inc. (R), NJ, *28*
Carrigan, Denise, Management Recruiters of San Antonio (C), TX, *463*
Caruthers, Robert D., Caruthers & Co., L.L.C. (R), CT, *31*
Chad, Rick A., Chad Management Group (C), ON, *288*
Charet, Sandra, Charet & Assoc. (C), NJ, *289*
Cherney, Steven D., Resource Perspectives, Inc. (R), CA, *175*
Ciak, Rosemarie, Ken Clark Int'l. (R), NJ, *36*
Cobb, Mark A., Management Recruiters of Springfield, Inc. (C), IL, *447*
Cohen, Diane, Michael Levine Search Consultants (R), NY, *129*
Cohen, Irwin, Benson Associates (C), NY, *264*
Cohen, Richard, Management Recruiters of Manhattan on Broadway (C), NY, *455*
Cole, Leslie C., Management Recruiters of Middlesex (C), CT, *442*
Cook, Robin, Impact Search & Strategies (C), PA, *387*
Cornehlsen, James H., Skott/Edwards Consultants (R), NY, *192*
Cotton, Peter C., Sales Consultants of Rhode Island, Inc. (C), RI, *562*
Cowan, Bruce, Synergy Systems (C), ON, *598*
Crawford, Roger, Graphic Arts Marketing Assoc., Inc. (C), MI, *361*
Critchley, Walter Y., Cochran, Cochran & Yale, Inc. (R), NY, *36*
Cullen, Andrew, The Pennmor Group (C), NJ, *506*
DeClouet, J. Michael, The J. B. Search Group (C), CA, *395*
Denney, Christopher, Goodkind Assoc. Inc. (C), NY, *360*
Deutschman, Michele, Placements by Jesse Reid Assoc., Inc. (C), NY, *513*
Devlin, Jack, The Devlin Search Group, Inc. (C), MA, *312*
Dowell, Mary K., Professional Search Assoc. (C), CA, *522*
Doyle, Don, Bosch & Assoc., LLC (R), CT, *20*
Doyle, John, Search Research Assoc., Inc. (R), MA, *187*
Dukas, Theodore, Dukas Assoc. (C), MA, *315*
Dussick, Vince, Dussick Management Assoc. (C), CT, *323*
Edelberg, Frank, Management One Consultants (C), ON, *425*
Elzweig, Mark, Mark Elzweig Co., Ltd. (C), NY, *329*
Erder, Debra, Canny, Bowen Inc. (R), NY, *28*
Ferguson, Cindy, The Canon Group (C), CA, *280*
Fineman, David M., Manuso, Alexander & Associates, Inc. (R), NY, *135*
Fippinger, Stephanie, PLA, Inc. (C), NJ, *513*
Fippinger, Steve, PLA, Inc. (C), NJ, *513*
Fisher, Gary E., Fisher & Assoc. (R), CA, *67*
Fisher, Iris L., Healthcare Recruiters International-NY/NJ (C), NJ, *373*
Fitzgibbons, David, International Executive Recruiters (C), OH, *393*
Fitzpatrick, Alan, Merlin Int'l. Inc. (C), NJ, *479*
Fixler, Eugene, Ariel Recruitment Assoc. (R), NY, *7*
Flannery, Michael, Redwood Partners Ltd. (R), NY, *173*
Fludd, Virgil L., The CARVIR Group, Inc. (C), GA, *285*
Franchot, Douglas W., Wood, Franchot Inc. (R), MN, *224*
Frazier, Steven M., Sanford Rose Assoc. - Philadelphia North (C), PA, *570*
Frishman, Robert, Greenwich Search Partners, LLC (C), CT, *363*
Fumano, Gary W., Chapman & Assoc. (C), BC, *289*
Furman, Matt, MJF Assoc. (C), CT, *483*
Gahan, Thomas M., Gahan Assoc. (R), NY, *73*
Gardner, Brian, Bosch & Assoc., LLC (R), CT, *20*
Garrison, Ed, The Garrison Organization (R), IA, *75*
Gay, Martha, Salzmann Gay Assoc., Inc. (R), PA, *184*
Gibbons, Ronald L., Flynn, Hannock, Inc. (R), CT, *69*
Glassberg, Bob, Sales Search (C), ON, *564*
Gleason, James P., J. P. Gleason Assoc., Inc. (R), IL, *77*
Glynn, Thomas J., Fox-Morris Assoc., Inc. (C), PA, *352*
Goldberg, Risa, Media Recruiting Group, Inc. (C), NY, *476*
Goldshore, Steven, Winthrop Partners, Inc. (R), NY, *222*
Goodman-Brolin, Dorothy, DLB Assoc. (R), NY, *53*
Gorberg, Richard D., Fortune Personnel Consultants of Raleigh, Inc. (C), NC, *348*
Grady, Jerry, The Ward Group (R), MA, *215*
Gragg, Robert, Montgomery West (R), CA, *146*
Graham, Robert W., Robert Graham Assoc. (R), RI, *81*
Graham, Tony, Synergy Systems (C), ON, *598*
Grantham, John D., Grantham & Co., Inc. (R), NC, *81*
Green, John A., JAG Group (R), MO, *105*
Greenberg, Jordan A., The Pinnacle Source, Inc. (C), CO, *512*
Gregory, Rose, Kay Henry, Inc. (C), PA, *376*
Grimm, Peter G., Nordeman Grimm, Inc. (R), NY, *152*
Groussman, Maria, Groussman & Assoc., Inc. (R), TX, *82*
Haberman, Rebecca Powers, Norman Powers Assoc., Inc. (C), MA, *515*
Haggard, Melissa M., MarketPro, Inc. (C), GA, *471*
Hakim, Ronald J., The GlobalSearch Group (C), TX, *359*
Hall, John, Synergy Systems (C), ON, *598*
Hannock, III, Elwin W., Flynn, Hannock, Inc. (R), CT, *69*
Harbaugh, Jr., Paul J., International Management Advisors, Inc. (R), NY, *103*
Harmeling, Dutch, Harmeling & Associates (C), CA, *369*
Haugen, Audrey D., Roger Dietsch & Assoc. (C), MN, *312*
Hayden, Lynn, Erlanger Assoc. (R), FL, *60*
Hazan, Lynn, Beverly von Winckler & Assoc. (C), IL, *613*
Heller, Phillip, Heller Kil Assoc., Inc. (C), FL, *375*
Henry, Kay, Kay Henry, Inc. (C), PA, *376*
Herman, Joyce Ralph, Management Assoc. (C), MD, *424*
Herrerias, Paul, Herrerias & Assoc. (R), CA, *92*
Hiesiger, Emile M., Manuso, Alexander & Associates, Inc. (R), NY, *135*
Hoglund, Gerald C., Hoglund & Assoc., Inc. (R), IL, *94*
Hopard, Stuart M., Olympian Recruitment, Ltd. (C), NY, *498*
Hopkins, Chester A., Handy HRM (R), NY, *86*
Humay, Gene, E. F. Humay Assoc. (C), PA, *384*
Humay, Jane, E. F. Humay Assoc. (C), PA, *384*
Humphreys, Scott W., Robison Humphreys & Assoc., Inc. (R), ON, *180*
Humphreys, William M., Robison Humphreys & Assoc., Inc. (R), ON, *180*
Hyde, Anne P., The Hyde Group, Inc. (R), CT, *101*
Israel, Sheldon, Sales Professionals Personnel Services (C), CA, *564*
Ives, Phyllis E., Ives & Associates, Inc. (C), OH, *395*
Jackson, Cindy, CJSI-Cindy Jackson Search Int'l. (C), CA, *291*
Jackson, Eric, ProFinders, Inc. (C), FL, *523*
Johnson, Frank Y., Healthcare Recruiters Int'l. - Alabama (C), AL, *372*
Johnson, K. L., Sales Consultants of Chico (C), CA, *556*
Johnson, Kathleen N., The Repovich-Reynolds Group (TRRG, Inc.) (R), CA, *175*
Jones, Gary, BGB Assoc., Inc. (C), IL, *266*

Joseph, Allen F., CBA Companies (C), CA, *286*
Kallfelz, Paul F., A. G. Fishkin & Assoc., Inc. (R), MD, *68*
Karp, Linda S., Karp & Assoc. (C), FL, *403*
Kay, Heidi, Kay Concepts, Inc. (C), FL, *404*
Keefe, Steve, The Search America Group Inc. (C), OH, *573*
Kelley, Verne, Kelley & Keller, Inc. (C), FL, *405*
Kelly, Rory, The Ellsworth Group (C), NY, *329*
Kick, James, The Prairie Group (C), IL, *515*
Kimball, Dex, Lanken-Kimball-Therrell & Assoc. (C), GA, *412*
Kinney, Carol, Dussick Management Assoc. (C), CT, *323*
Kip, Luanne S., Kip Williams, Inc. (R), NY, *115*
Kirkendorfer, Laura, The Kingsley Group (R), CA, *115*
Koch, Gail Kleinberg, CAS Comsearch Inc. (C), NY, *286*
Koehler, Frank R., The Koehler Group (C), PA, *408*
Koenig, Jerrold, P R Management Consultants, Inc. (C), NJ, *500*
Komorner, Paul, The Whitney Group (C), GA, *620*
Kool, Joan, Professional Recruiters, Inc. (C), PA, *521*
Kubiak, Thomas J., Halbrecht & Co. (C), CT, *365*
Kuhlenbeck, Phillip, Austin Group Int'l./Marlar Int'l. (R), TX, *9*
Kuntz, William A., Sales Consultants of Indianapolis (C), IN, *559*
Lanken, Joel, Lanken-Kimball-Therrell & Assoc. (C), GA, *412*
Larsen, Michael G., Barnes & Assoc. Executive Search (C), CA, *259*
Lear, Daniel, Omega Systems, LLC (C), VA, *498*
Lee, Carol Ricci, Ricci Lee Assoc., Inc. (C), CA, *415*
Lefier, Deborah D., Strategic Search, LLC (C), CA, *595*
LeMon, Monet M., The Repovich-Reynolds Group (TRRG, Inc.) (R), CA, *175*
Lenobel, Stephen, Professional Recruiters, Inc. (C), PA, *521*
Levine, Lawrence, Trebor Weldon Lawrence, Inc. (R), NY, *210*
Liles, Cheryl, Snelling Search Recruiters (C), NC, *586*
Lipton, Pat, PLA, Inc. (C), FL, *513*
Livingston, Hyman, The P & L Group (C), NY, *500*
Lomax, J. Alan, ADR Accounting Management Recruiters (C), ON, *240*
Long, Janet R., Integrity Search, Inc. (R), PA, *102*
Luden, Ben V., Marketing/Public Relations Research Recruiting (C), CT, *471*
MacArthur, Sylvia, Madison MacArthur Inc. (R), ON, *133*
MacKenzie, Bruce J., Chapman & Assoc. (C), BC, *289*
MacNaughton, Sperry, MacNaughton Assoc. (R), CA, *133*
Madden, Heather, Bosch & Assoc., LLC (R), CT, *20*
Maher, Kevin, TBC, Inc. (C), KY, *600*
Manatine, Tony, Career Search Group (C), FL, *283*
Manuso, James S. J., Manuso, Alexander & Associates, Inc. (R), NY, *135*
Marks, Ira M., Strategic Alternatives (R), CA, *202*
Marra, Jr., John, Marra Peters & Partners (R), NJ, *136*
Martin, Carol, Medical Innovations (C), NY, *477*
Martinez, Roberto, Strategic Resources (C), WA, *595*
Mathias, Kathy A., Stone, Murphy & Olson (R), MN, *201*
Matthews, Alyce, The Matthews Group, Inc. (C), NJ, *472*
McAleavy, Steve, Search Consultants Int'l., Inc. (C), TX, *575*
McAndrew, Cindy, Aries Search Group (C), GA, *252*
McDonald, Thomas W., Mengel & McDonald Ltd. (C), IL, *479*
McElmeel, Joseph J., Brooke Chase Assoc., Inc. (R), IL, *24*
McGeehan, Gayle A., Management Recruiters of Bethlehem, PA (C), PA, *458*
McGurn, Sharman, B. J. Abrams & Assoc. Inc. (C), IL, *233*
McKenna, Scott, The Beam Group (R), PA, *14*
McKersie, Edward S., ProSearch, Inc. (C), ME, *524*
McLean, Chris, Chaloner Assoc. (R), MA, *32*
Medley, Jerry, The Medley Group (C), CA, *477*
Mendrala, Karen, Lab Market Specialists (C), UT, *411*
Meyer, Fred R., Management Recruiters of Bethlehem, PA (C), PA, *458*
Miller, Nancy, Mark Elzweig Co., Ltd. (C), NY, *329*
Miller, Shelley, Kay Henry, Inc. (C), PA, *376*
Miller, Thomas C., Emerging Medical Technologies, Inc. (C), CO, *329*
Mitchell, Sheri, ProFinders, Inc. (C), FL, *523*
Moere, Linda A., Michaels & Moere (C), WI, *481*
Molloy, Thomas, Molloy Partners (R), NY, *146*
Moore, Michael H., The Inside Track (C), TX, *389*
Moran, Gayle, Dussick Management Assoc. (C), CT, *323*
Morris, David W., WTW Assoc., Inc. (R), NY, *225*
Nagy, Lou, The Ward Group (R), MA, *215*
Neufeld, Max, Partners In Human Resources Int'l., Inc. (R), NY, *160*
Nicklas, Kirk, The Ellsworth Group (C), NY, *329*
Norindr, Bev, The Hampton Group (C), NY, *368*
Normann, Amy, Robert M. Flanagan & Assoc., Ltd. (R), NY, *68*
Noyes, Jim, Sales Consultants - Bristol County (C), MA, *559*
O'Connell, Brian M., O'Connell Group Inc. (C), CT, *497*
O'Hara, Kelly, Goodkind Assoc. Inc. (C), NY, *360*
O'Neal, Jane, Austin Group Int'l./Marlar Int'l. (R), TX, *9*
O'Neill, Stephen A., O'Neill & Co. (R), CT, *154*
Orton, Linda Sedloff, Intelligent Marketing Solutions, Inc. (C), NY, *390*
Ossow, Kitty, K. Ossow & Co. (C), NY, *500*
Paige, Jacqueline, Smith Hanley Assoc., Inc. (C), CT, *584*
Paine, Donne G., Fortune Personnel Consultants of Hilton Head (C), SC, *349*
Parisien, Simon, Yves Elkas Inc. (R), QE, *58*
Payette, Angela, Greene Personnel Consultants (C), RI, *362*
Pelisson, Charles J., Marra Peters & Partners (R), NJ, *136*
Perry, Lisa Lepore, Aminex Corp. (C), MA, *249*
Peskosky, Mike, Prime Search (C), NC, *518*
Peterson, Michael T., BayResearch Group, Inc. (R), IL, *14*
Petry, Georgia M., Placements by Jesse Reid Assoc., Inc. (C), NY, *513*
Piccione, Mike, Dussick Management Assoc. (C), CT, *323*
Pickering, Dorothy C., Livingston, Robert & Co. (R), CT, *130*
Pierce, Sharon S., Pierce & Assoc. (C), CA, *512*
Poole, Don V., Don V. Poole & Assoc., Inc. (C), CO, *514*
Powers, Norman S., Norman Powers Assoc., Inc. (C), MA, *515*
Prager, Paul Gershon, P. G. Prager Search Assoc., Ltd. (C), NY, *515*
Price, Lynn M., Alan J. Price Assoc., Inc. (C), RI, *518*
Prouty, Alden F., Manuso, Alexander & Associates, Inc. (R), NY, *135*
Prusak, Julie J., Ethos Consulting, Inc. (R), CA, *61*
Quinn, Thomas H., Weterrings & Agnew, Inc. (C), NY, *619*
Rardin, Ed, Brentwood Int'l. (R), CA, *23*
Ratner, Joanne E., Joanne E. Ratner Search (C), NY, *529*
Redden, Mary, Redden & McGrath Assoc., Inc. (R), NY, *173*
Reeve, Philip, Reeve & Assoc. (C), CT, *533*
Reynolds, Smooch S., The Repovich-Reynolds Group (TRRG, Inc.) (R), CA, *175*
Richner, George A., Search Assoc., Inc. (C), NJ, *574*

Riley, Brian, Austin Group Int'l./Marlar Int'l. (R), TX, *9*
Ritchings, David, David Allen Assoc. (R), NJ, *3*
Robins, Jeri N., Nagler, Robins & Poe, Inc. (R), MA, *150*
Robinson, Scott, Kensington Int'l., Inc. (R), IL, *113*
Robsham, Beverly H., Robsham & Assoc., Inc. (R), MA, *180*
Rockwell, Sr., Richard B., Applied Search Assoc., Inc. (C), GA, *252*
Romaniw, Michael J., A la Carte Int'l., Inc. (R), VA, *1*
Ryan, Debra, Bonell Ryan Inc. (R), NY, *19*
Schiavone, Mary Rose, Canny, Bowen Inc. (R), NY, *28*
Schoenfeld, Randy, Redwood Partners Ltd. (R), NY, *173*
Schrenzel, Steven N., The Governance Group, Inc. (R), NJ, *80*
Schwartz, Stephen D., Management Recruiters of Gramercy, Inc. (C), NY, *455*
Schwarz, Meredith Barnes, Barnes & Assoc. Executive Search (C), CA, *259*
Scoggins, Tim, Jackson Resources (R), TX, *105*
Scott, Gordon S., Search Research Assoc., Inc. (R), MA, *187*
Shotland, David R., The Shotland Group (R), CA, *190*
Siegel, Michael, Specialty Employment Services, Inc. (C), GA, *589*
Silberger, Gary, Key Employment (C), NJ, *405*
Sinks, Lucius F., Aminex Corp. (C), MA, *249*
Sirey, Don, Technology Search Int'l. (C), CA, *603*
Small, Carol D., Quantum Int'l., Ltd. (R), FL, *170*
Smolizer, Carole E., Marketing Consultants (C), WI, *470*
Snow, Christine, C. Snow & Assoc. (C), ON, *586*
Snow, Thomas J., The Search America Group Inc. (C), OH, *573*
Solomon, Phyllis, Phyllis Solomon Executive Search, Inc. (C), NJ, *587*
Spadaro, Raymond, David Perry Assoc. (C), NJ, *308*
Speciale, Pamela, Austin Group Int'l./Marlar Int'l. (R), TX, *9*
Spielman, Sharon, Jerry Fields Assoc. (C), NY, *340*
Sted, Eric, The Search America Group Inc. (C), OH, *573*
Stevenson, Alex, Search Masters, USA (C), FL, *576*
Stewart, Dana, Management One Consultants (C), ON, *425*
Stewart, James H., The Stewart Group (C), FL, *593*
Stewart, Larry, American Resources Corp. (C), IL, *248*
Straight, Gary R., Straight & Co. (R), GA, *202*
Susleck, Matthew M., ESS (Executive Search Services) (R), CA, *61*
Swift, Catherine, Swift & Assoc. (C), ME, *597*
Tabor, Gary, Careers On Track (C), NJ, *283*
Talabisco, Barbara, Wakefield Talabisco Int'l. (R), NY, *214*
Talan, Marv, Executive Search Team (C), MI, *336*
Tazzia, Ed, Gundersen Partners, L.L.C. (R), MI, *83*
Telford, Jr., John H., Telford, Adams & Alexander (R), CA, *208*
Therizien, Greg, The Devlin Search Group, Inc. (C), MA, *312*
Thomas, Frank, Carson-Thomas & Assoc. (C), CA, *284*
Tolstrup, Rick, Aminex Corp. (C), MA, *249*
Toole, Mary, Management Recruiters of Laguna Hills (C), CA, *440*
Townsend, James C., Future Employment Service, Inc. (C), IA, *353*
Trapani, Chris, ExecuSource Consultants, Inc. (C), TX, *332*
Trapani, Delores, ExecuSource Consultants, Inc. (C), TX, *332*
Trasatti, Anthony, The Pennmor Group (C), NJ, *506*
Tringle, Terry, Sanford Rose Assoc. - Nashville (C), TN, *570*
Van Remmen, Roger, Brown, Bernardy, Van Remmen, Inc. (C), CA, *275*
Vaughan, David B., Vaughan & Co. (C), CA, *612*
Vendetti, Lisa, The Alfus Group (R), NY, *3*
Volpe, Louis, Fox, White & Assoc. (C), FL, *351*
von Baillou, Astrid, Richard Kinser & Assoc. (R), NY, *115*
Vozekas, James P., The Touchstone Group (C), MA, *607*
Walt, Lee, M H Executive Search Group (C), TX, *422*
Ward, James M., The Ward Group (R), MA, *215*
Ward, Martha, Martha Ward Executive Search, Inc. (C), NY, *615*
Wasserman, Stan, Wasserman Assoc. Inc. (C), MD, *616*
Watkins, Jean T., The Repovich-Reynolds Group (TRRG, Inc.) (R), CA, *175*
Weil, Lee, Lee Weil Assoc., Inc. (C), IL, *617*
Whelan, Fred, StratfordGroup (R), CA, *203*
White, Evelyne F., Fox, White & Assoc. (C), FL, *351*
Whitlow, M. Blanton, Manuso, Alexander & Associates, Inc. (R), NY, *135*
Williamson, Bob, Grossberg & Assoc. (R), IL, *82*
Wood, Michael D., Wood, Franchot Inc. (R), MN, *224*
Wright, J. Robert, Bob Wright Recruiting, Inc. (C), CT, *625*
Young, Susan M., Management Recruiters of Morris County, NJ (C), NJ, *453*

Consumer

Ballantyne, Tom, Ballantyne & Assoc. (R), CA, *10*
Hoffman, Bradley D., Hoffman Partnership Group Inc. (C), NY, *379*
Hoffman, Lisa M., Hoffman Partnership Group Inc. (C), NY, *379*

Materials

Adzima, Allan G., MARBL Consultants, Inc. (C), WI, *469*
Agnello, Frank, Systems Research Inc. (SRI) (C), IL, *598*
Allen, Jr., Lindsay, Mark III Personnel, Inc. (C), NC, *470*
Antonio, Marshall, Fortune of Arlington Heights (C), IL, *346*
Banks, Paul C., Paul C. Banks Assoc. (C), GA, *259*
Beck, Larry, Synergy Solutions, Ltd. (C), WA, *597*
Bethmann, Chris, Southern Recruiters & Consultants, Inc. (C), SC, *587*
Blumenthal, Paula, J. P. Canon Assoc. (C), NY, *280*
Bremer, Rich, Fortune Personnel Consultants of Greensboro, NC, Inc. (C), NC, *348*
Brill, Michael, F-O-R-T-U-N-E Personnel Consultants of Tampa (C), FL, *345*
Chin, Daniel, F-O-R-T-U-N-E Personnel Consultants of East Seattle (C), WA, *351*
Coleman, Greg, Strategic Assoc., Inc. (C), TX, *595*
Cousins, John L., Procurement Resources (C), MD, *520*
Dietrich, Sandra, Fortune Personnel Consultants of Hilton Head (C), SC, *349*
Fenimore, Joseph S., F-O-R-T-U-N-E Personnel Consultants of Cincinnati (C), OH, *348*
Fisk, James L., James L. Fisk & Assoc. (C), MO, *342*
Flamer, Michael, The Dorfman Group (C), AZ, *314*
Gabriele, Leslie, Gabriele & Company (C), MA, *354*
Gilmour, Ian, NMC & Kay Int'l. (R), CO, *152*
Haentzler, Robert A, Michael Latas & Assoc., Inc. (R), MO, *126*
Helnore, Kim, Partners in Recruiting (C), IL, *504*
Holzheimer, Robert, Exclusive Search Consultants (C), OH, *331*
Howell, Jean, Fortune Personnel Consultants of the Virginia Highlands (C), VA, *351*
Huebner, Mary C., Hire Authority, Inc. (C), MI, *378*
Hurley, Art, Systems Research Inc. (SRI) (C), IL, *598*
Jacobson, Donald, Hunt Ltd. (C), NJ, *385*
Jones, Mike, Management Recruiters of Winston-Salem (C), NC, *457*
Jordan, Dick, Staff Resources, Inc. (C), SC, *590*

RECRUITER SPECIALTIES

Kane, J. Michael, Sanford Rose Assoc. - Orland Park (C), IL, *567*
Kane, Rich, Systems Research Inc. (SRI) (C), IL, *598*
Keefe, John, Kelly Associates (R), PA, *112*
Keller, Andrea, F-O-R-T-U-N-E Personnel Consultants of Palm Beach (C), FL, *345*
Kensinger, John P., Sanford Rose Assoc. - Burlington, NC (C), NC, *569*
Klein, Howard G., F-O-R-T-U-N-E Personnel Consultants of Bergen County Inc. (C), NJ, *347*
Kuesis, Dan, Systems Research Inc. (SRI) (C), IL, *598*
Lang, Nick, Technical Recruiting Services (C), OH, *602*
Lichtenauer, William E., Britt Assoc., Inc. (C), IL, *274*
Livingston, Hyman, The P & L Group (C), NY, *500*
Manson, Phyllis, BG & Assoc. (C), MD, *266*
Marunick, Kevin, Fortune Personnel Consultants of Chattanooga Inc. (C), TN, *349*
McDermott, Tom, Corporate Environment Ltd. (R), IL, *41*
McDowell, Ron, Carnegie Resources, Inc. (C), NC, *284*
McInturff, Robert E., McInturff & Assoc., Inc. (C), MA, *474*
Metz, Alex, Hunt Ltd. (C), NJ, *385*
Nepovadny, John A., The Langford Search, Inc. (C), AL, *412*
Oglesby, Tom, F-O-R-T-U-N-E Personnel of Nashville (C), TN, *350*
Palumbo, Michael J., Michael Latas & Assoc., Inc. (R), MO, *126*
Pepple, Bob, Fortune Personnel Consultants of Jacksonville (C), FL, *345*
Perkins, Arthur, Management Alliance Group, Inc. (R), NJ, *134*
Peterson, Jerry, MARBL Consultants, Inc. (C), WI, *469*
Portanova, Peter M., ROI Assoc. (R), NY, *181*
Price, Rita A., Human Resources Personnel Agency (R), AR, *99*
Provda, Peter, F-O-R-T-U-N-E Personnel Consultants of Menlo Park, Inc. (C), NJ, *347*
Robinson, Rodney L., Michael Latas & Assoc., Inc. (R), MO, *126*
Roodvoets, Jan, J. E. Lessner Assoc., Inc. (R), MI, *128*
Rossen, Michael, Direct Recruiters, Inc. (C), OH, *312*
Rusnov, Samuel, Michael Latas & Assoc., Inc. (R), OH, *126*
Slater, Marjorie, Logistics Management Resources, Inc. (R), NY, *131*
Smith, Michael R., Michaels & Moere (C), WI, *481*
Storfer, Herbert F., The Dartmouth Group (R), NY, *46*
Stroud, Robert, Industry Consultants, Inc. (C), GA, *388*
Symcox, Jim, SPC Symcox Personnel Consultants (C), TX, *588*
Valentine, Linda S., Valentine & Assoc. (C), IL, *611*
Walker, Donald G., Executive Search Plus, Inc. (C), IN, *336*
Waller, Jody W., Michael Latas & Assoc., Inc. (R), MO, *126*
Weiner, Al, Lucas Group (C), NY, *421*
Weiner, Arlene, Sanford Rose Assoc. - Athens (C), GA, *566*
Wells, Lee, F-O-R-T-U-N-E Personnel Consultants of East Seattle (C), WA, *351*
Zimmermann, Karl, Fortune Personnel Consultants of Bloomfield, Inc. (C), MI, *346*

Management

Atchison, W. R., W. R. Atchison & Assoc., Inc. (C), NC, *255*

Mathematics

Sendler, Peter A., International Consulting Services, Inc. (C), IL, *392*

MBA's

Long, David B., DBL Associates (C), CA, *309*
Muller, Michael, Financialjobs.com (C), CA, *340*
O'Connell, Michael, Ryan, Miller & Assoc. (C), CA, *549*
Ryan, Lee, Ryan, Miller & Assoc. (C), CA, *549*

Meat

Daffala, Ronald, Merit Professional Search, Inc. (C), TN, *479*
Howell, Jeff, Whittaker & Assoc., Inc. (C), GA, *620*
Smitherman, Jim, Merit Professional Search, Inc. (C), TN, *479*

Mechanical

Bowers, Bob, Claremont-Branan, Inc. (C), GA, *292*
Chamberland, Roland, Management Recruiters of Sonoma (C), CA, *441*
Creasy, Nancy, Michael Latas & Assoc., Inc. (R), MO, *126*
Gardiner, Gary, Management Recruiters of Cleveland (C), OH, *457*
Goodall, Rhys, C. J. Stafford & Assoc. (C), ON, *591*
Helnore, Diann, Partners in Recruiting (C), IL, *504*
Hudson, Judy K., The Hudson Group (C), CT, *383*
Joyce, Mark, Louis Rudzinsky Assoc., Inc. (C), MA, *548*
Munger, Donald, Berkshire Search Assoc. (C), MA, *265*
Snider, Jr., Les, Bryan & Louis Research (C), OH, *275*
Turner, Linda, Kuhn Med-Tech (C), CA, *409*

Media

Bishop, Anne, Johnson Smith & Knisely (R), IL, *107*
Bishop, Susan, Bishop Partners (R), NY, *17*
Cornehlsen, James H., Skott/Edwards Consultants (R), NY, *192*
Cowlan, Trudi, Trudi Cowlan (C), NY, *302*
Dell'Aquilla, Joseph, Allen Austin Lowe & Powers (R), TX, *3*
Denison, Susan, Johnson Smith & Knisely (R), NY, *107*
Eldredge, Peter, Johnson Smith & Knisely (R), NY, *107*
Emerzian, Jennifer, Johnson Smith & Knisely (R), NY, *107*
Erickson, Cara, Johnson Smith & Knisely (R), NY, *107*
Eskew, Martha, Recruiting Options, Inc. (C), GA, *532*
Fixler, Eugene, Ariel Recruitment Assoc. (R), NY, *7*
Forbes, Kay Koob, Sanford Rose Assoc. - Evansville (C), IN, *567*
Gardiner, E. Nicholas P., Gardiner, Townsend & Assoc. (R), NY, *74*
Goldbach, Linda J., Beacon Int'l., Inc. (C), VA, *261*
Jackson, Laurie, McHale & Assoc. (R), WA, *141*
Malcom, John W., Johnson Smith & Knisely (R), NY, *107*
Mastandrea, Pat, Johnson Smith & Knisely (R), NY, *107*
McCormick-Kelch, Anna, Johnson Smith & Knisely (R), IL, *107*
Morgan, Vincent, Bishop Partners (R), NY, *17*
O'Donnell, M. Theresa, Grant/Morgan Assoc., Inc. (C), MD, *361*
Papike, Richard, TriStaff Group (C), CA, *609*
Pepper, Marci, Johnson Smith & Knisely (R), NY, *107*
Piché, Jérôme, SpencerStuart (R), QE, *197*
Sachs, Susan, Johnson Smith & Knisely (R), NY, *107*
Virgili, Franca, Johnson Smith & Knisely (R), CA, *107*
Wayne, Vici, Christian & Timbers, Inc. (R), OH, *34*
Weinstein, Lewis R., Weinstein & Co. (R), MA, *217*
Whelan, David, Ethos Consulting, Inc. (R), CA, *61*
Yossem, Sheila, Bishop Partners (R), NY, *17*
Zidwick, Christiana, WTW Assoc., Inc. (R), NY, *225*
Zimering, Chuck, Chuck Zimering Advertising Recruitment (CZAR) (C), NY, *627*

Medical

Acridge, Charles W., CRI Professional Search (C), CA, *303*
Agriesti, Kay, Agriesti & Assoc. (C), CA, *243*

Albers, Joan, Carver Search Consultants (C), CA, *285*
Altieri, Robert J., StratfordGroup (R), PA, *203*
Bagley, Rass, Marketing Recruiters, Inc. (C), NC, *470*
Barrett, Bill, The Barrett Group (C), NH, *260*
Bauman, Ina, The Bauman Group (R), CA, *14*
Beamer, Thomas G., Thomas Lyle & Co. (C), IL, *606*
Beiter, Sheila M., Pathfinders Int'l. (C), MI, *504*
Berman, Shirlee J., Retail Recruiters/Spectrum Consultants, Inc. (C), PA, *535*
Black, David A., Lake Medical Associates (C), ME, *411*
Blanchard, Jeb, Healthcare Recruiters of Midsouth (C), TN, *373*
Bogle, Tom, Tom Bogle & Assoc. (C), CA, *269*
Cassie, Ronald L., The Cassie Group (R), NJ, *31*
Chapa, Victor, Victor White Int'l. (C), CA, *612*
Charles, Kamal, Clinton, Charles, Wise & Co. (C), FL, *293*
Chertkof, Robert, Fallstaff Search (C), MD, *338*
Cooper, Bill, Management Recruiters of Chattanooga-Brainerd, Inc. (C), TN, *461*
Cooper, Larry, Management Recruiters of Atlanta (C), GA, *445*
Cunningham, John, Medical Executive Recruiters (C), CA, *477*
De Mange, Jean M., Wellington Thomas Ltd. (C), FL, *618*
Deerwester, Dave, Snelling Search (C), AL, *585*
Deffler, Karin E., Med-Ex Services (C), OH, *476*
deMartino, Cathy, Lucas Assoc. (C), GA, *421*
Dent, Vickie, Recruiters Professional Network - Fairview (C), MO, *531*
Dion, Frank, The Barrett Group (C), NH, *260*
Domann, Jr., William A., The Domann Organization (R), CA, *53*
Dreier, John S., Dreier Consulting (C), NJ, *315*
Dubois, Denis R., Networking Unlimited of NH, Inc. (C), NH, *491*
Dukas, Theodore, Dukas Assoc. (C), MA, *315*
Duncan, James W., Sanford Rose Assoc. - Lake Forest (R), IL, *184*
Eastwood, Gary, Beck/Eastwood Recruitment Solutions (C), CA, *261*
Fabian, Kristina, Networking Unlimited of NH, Inc. (C), FL, *491*
Feingold, Marilyn, MedPro Personnel, Inc. (C), GA, *478*
Felactu, Odessa J., The Odessa Group (R), CA, *155*
Fitzgerald, Diane, Fitzgerald Associates (R), MA, *68*
Flash, James, Richard Kader & Assoc. (C), OH, *403*
Freeman, Evelyn, Brierwood Group, Inc. (C), IN, *274*
Galante, Suzanne, Vlcek & Company, Inc. (R), CA, *214*
Glines, Larry, Glines Assoc., Inc. (R), IL, *77*
Hale, Dillon, Cemco, Ltd. (C), IL, *286*
Hannigan, Melissa, JPM International (C), CA, *401*
Harfenist, Harry, Parker Page Group (C), FL, *503*
Haupt, Bruce W., Bruce W. Haupt Assoc. (R), DC, *88*
Heller, Shelly, Ira Z. Nitzberg (C), NY, *493*
Hetzel, Ben W., Sales Consultants of Chester County, PA (C), PA, *562*
Hewitt, Diane, AmeriResource Group Inc. (C), OK, *249*
Hill, Ted, Culver Personnel Services (C), CA, *304*
Hirschbein, Don, Management Recruiters Peninsula (C), CA, *439*
Hirschbein, Donald, Sales Consultants Peninsula, Inc. (C), CA, *556*
Hurley, Michael, Century Assoc., Inc. (C), PA, *287*
Jackson, Randy, Sales Consultants of Omaha, Inc. (C), NE, *560*
Johnson, Carol, Sales Consultants of Chico (C), CA, *556*
Johnson, Glen, Sales Recruiters of Oklahoma City (C), OK, *564*
Johnson, Greg, Sales Recruiters of Oklahoma City (C), OK, *564*
Johnson, K. L., Sales Consultants of Chico (C), CA, *556*
Jurenovich, Gary S., The Stewart Group (C), FL, *593*
Karp, Linda S., Karp & Assoc. (C), FL, *403*
Kase, Philip, Re-Mark Assoc. Inc. (C), NJ, *531*
Kausch, Rolf H., Priority Executive Search (C), FL, *518*
Kins, Arnie, Cook Assoc.,® Inc. (R), IL, *40*
Korban, Richard O., Korban Associates (R), PA, *117*
Kreps, Charles D., The Normyle/Erstling Health Search Group (C), NJ, *494*
Lam, Pat, Physician Associates (C), HI, *511*
Lambrecht, Pat, Lam Assoc. (C), HI, *411*
Larsen, Merlyne T., The Personnel Network, Inc. (C), SC, *508*
LeBow, Joanne, Harbrowe, Inc. (C), NY, *368*
Licata, Pat, Pat Licata & Assoc. (C), NC, *417*
Lynne, Robyn, Search Masters, USA (C), FL, *576*
Manatine, Tony, Career Search Group (C), FL, *283*
Martin, Carol, Medical Innovations (C), NY, *477*
Martin, Patricia, Management Recruiters of Birmingham-South, Inc. (C), AL, *438*
Matras, Debbie, Sales Consultants of Milwaukee (C), WI, *563*
Mattes, Jr., Edward C., The Ogdon Partnership (R), NY, *155*
McAndrew, Cindy, Aries Search Group (C), GA, *252*
McBride, Dee, Deeco Int'l. (C), UT, *310*
McDermott, Jeffrey T., Vlcek & Company, Inc. (R), CA, *214*
McElhearn, Scott S., Scott Sibley Assoc. (C), NY, *573*
McGee, Tom, Lucas Assoc. (C), GA, *421*
Miller, Shirley, Miller + Miller (C), WA, *482*
Morse, Mary K., Travis & Co., Inc. (R), MA, *210*
Mullen, Maryrose H., Emmett Executive Search, Inc. (C), NY, *330*
Nachman, Philip S., Nachman Biomedical (C), MA, *488*
O'Callaghan, William, Ken Clark Int'l. (R), NJ, *36*
Oberman, Heidi, Medical Recruiters Inc. (C), MO, *477*
Oliveros, Nancy P., New Dawn Employment Search (C), CA, *491*
Oster, R. Rush, Management Recruiters of Anna Maria Island (C), FL, *443*
Perry, Len, Perry-D'Amico & Assoc. (R), CA, *163*
Perry, Virginia, Perry-D'Amico & Assoc. (R), CA, *163*
Peskosky, Mike, Prime Search (C), NC, *518*
Phillips, Mimi, Snelling Search Recruiters (C), NC, *586*
Powell, Donald L., Proquest Inc. (C), SC, *524*
Quiring, Patti L., Quiring Assoc., Inc. (C), IN, *527*
Raia, Carol, Healthcare Recruiters Int'l. Orange County (C), CA, *372*
Raia, Tony, Healthcare Recruiters Int'l. Orange County (C), CA, *372*
Raney, Albert, Dunhill Personnel Service of Fargo (C), ND, *322*
Richter, Heidi, Career Counseling Ltd. (C.C.L.) (C), IL, *282*
Richter, Michael, Career Counseling Ltd. (C.C.L.) (C), FL, *282*
Richter, Michael, Career Counseling Ltd. (C.C.L.) (C), NY, *282*
Rimele, J. R., Sales Recruiters of Oklahoma City (C), OK, *564*
Roe, Sylvia A., Craig Roe & Assoc., LLC (C), MD, *540*
Ross, Ruthie M., Recruitment Resources (C), CA, *532*
Savransky, Alan, Home Health & Hospital Recruiters, Inc. (C), GA, *380*
Savransky, Barry P., Home Health & Hospital Recruiters, Inc. (C), GA, *380*
Schachter, Laura J., Professional Placement Assoc., Inc. (C), NY, *521*
Schiff, Arlene D., A.D. Schiff & Assoc., Ltd. (C), IL, *572*
Schraeter, Jack M., Lake Medical Associates (C), ME, *411*
Schwartz, Beth O., G. L. Schwartz & Assoc., Inc. (C), GA, *572*

RECRUITER SPECIALTIES

Schwartz, Gary L., G. L. Schwartz & Assoc., Inc. (C), GA, *572*
Secor, David B., The Search Committee (C), MD, *574*
Sheedy, Joseph D., Marketing Resources (C), MA, *470*
Sheridan, Lynda, The Goodman Group (R), CA, *79*
Shiley, Bob, Brethet, Barnum & Assoc., Inc. (C), ON, *273*
Shulman, Mel, M. Shulman, Inc. (R), CA, *191*
Simpson, Clair, Professional Recruiters (C), UT, *522*
Spargo, Rick, Personnel Solutions (C), AZ, *509*
Statson, Dale E., Sales Executives, Inc. (C), MI, *563*
Stevenson, Alex, Search Masters, USA (C), FL, *576*
Stewart, James H., The Stewart Group (C), FL, *593*
Taylor, Jeffrey A., Sales Consultants of Ft. Lauderdale, Inc. (C), FL, *557*
Thrower, Tom, Sales Consultants Int'l. of Oakland (C), CA, *556*
Tommarello, Tony, Lucas Assoc. (C), CA, *421*
Victor, Johnathon, The Executive Tree (R), FL, *64*
Viescas, Diana, Professional Recruiters (C), UT, *522*
Ward, Gayle E., Ward-Hoffman & Assoc. (C), ID, *615*
Watring, Bernie, Watring & Assoc., Inc. (C), IL, *616*
Waugh, Chris, The Bales-Waugh Group (C), FL, *258*
Webb, Melissa, Circlewood Search Group, Inc. (C), MI, *291*
Wilder, Mark, International Research Group (R), CA, *103*
Wilkins, A. M., International Research Group (R), CA, *103*
Wilkins, Sherrie, International Research Group (R), CA, *103*
Wilkins, Sid, International Research Group (R), CA, *103*
Williams, Kandi, Medical Executive Recruiters (C), CA, *477*
Wottowa, Denise, Medical Recruiters Inc. (C), MO, *477*
Ziarko, Jacqueline R., Selective Search Associates (C), OH, *578*
Zickerman, Donna, DRZ Medical Recruiters (C), CO, *315*

Medical devices

Adams, Lauren, Fortune Group Int'l., Inc. (R), PA, *70*
Ames, A. P., Ames & Ames (R), CA, *5*
Archie, Otis, Kuhn Med-Tech (C), CA, *409*
Avestruz, Alner, Avestruz & Assoc. (C), CA, *257*
Bailey, Scott, HeartBeat Medical, Inc. (C), OR, *374*
Bales, Sally, The Bales-Waugh Group (C), FL, *258*
Ballou, Jodie, Management Recruiters of the Baltimore Washington Corridor (C), MD, *450*
Barone, Marialice, Barone-O'Hara Assoc., Inc. (R), NJ, *11*
Barry, Nathan, Nathan Barry Assoc., Inc. (R), MA, *12*
Bawza, Leo F., Chelsea Resources, Inc. (C), CT, *290*
Beehler, Lance, Fortune Personnel Consultants of Hilton Head (C), SC, *349*
Berg, Charlie, Management Recruiters of Lake Forest, IL (C), IL, *447*
Blakslee, Jan H., J: Blakslee Int'l., Ltd. (R), CA, *18*
Bormann, David C., Yungner & Bormann (R), MN, *226*
Bouchard, Rena Roberts, Strategic Resources Biotechnology & Medical Group (C), WA, *595*
Bowman, Mary, Healthcare Management Resources, Inc. (R), GA, *89*
Brissenden, Hoke, Brissenden, McFarland, Fuccella & Reynolds, Inc. (R), NJ, *23*
Browning, Ed, HeartBeat Medical, Inc. (C), OR, *374*
Burkey, Julie V., J. Burkey Assoc. (R), NJ, *25*
Christopher, Rosemarie, Med Exec Int'l. (C), CA, *476*
Ciari, Kate Regan, Fortune Personnel Consultants (C), MT, *347*
Colbourn, Ken, F-O-R-T-U-N-E Personnel Consultants of Knoxville (C), TN, *350*
Cunneff, Harry J., Management Recruiters of Lake Forest, IL (C), IL, *447*
Daniels, Donna, Jonas, Walters & Assoc., Inc. (R), WI, *108*
Dietrich, Sandra, Fortune Personnel Consultants of Hilton Head (C), SC, *349*
Ducharme, David J., Fortune Personnel Consultants of Hilton Head (C), SC, *349*
Faas, Vicki L., Healthcare Recruiters of the Rockies, Inc. (C), CO, *372*
Fitzgerald, Jon K., Health Industry Consultants, Inc. (R), CO, *89*
Flannery, Peter, Jonas, Walters & Assoc., Inc. (R), WI, *108*
Gasbarre, John, The Haystack Group, Inc. (R), ME, *88*
Gostin, Howard I., Sanford Rose Assoc. - Columbia, MD (C), MD, *567*
Greenblatt, Stephanie, The Bauman Group (R), CA, *14*
Griffith, David B., F-O-R-T-U-N-E Personnel Consultants of Charlotte (C), NC, *348*
Grillo, Scott, Professional Recruiting Network (C), CA, *521*
Harris, Bea, Exec Tech, Inc. (C), IL, *332*
Hoffman, Mark, Management Recruiters of Emeryville (C), CA, *440*
Houchins, Buster, Christian & Timbers, Inc. (R), OH, *34*
Houchins, William C. Buster, Christian & Timbers, Inc. (R), MD, *34*
Hunt, Leigh, Leigh Hunt & Assoc., Inc. (C), ME, *384*
Jeffers, Robert, Allen-Jeffers Assoc. (C), CA, *245*
Kasten, Marc, Fortune Personnel Consultants (C), CA, *344*
Kazan, J. Neil, Kazan International, Inc. (R), NJ, *110*
Klein, Howard G., F-O-R-T-U-N-E Personnel Consultants of Bergen County Inc. (C), NJ, *347*
Korkuch, Sandy, The Addison Consulting Group (C), NJ, *239*
Kress, Daryl, Fortune Personnel Consultants of Anderson, Inc. (C), SC, *349*
Kuhn, Larry A., Kuhn Med-Tech (C), CA, *409*
Kunkel, Thomas J., Bayland Assoc. (C), CA, *261*
Lawry, William R., W. R. Lawry, Inc. (R), CT, *126*
Leech, David M., Houtz•Strawn & Arnold, Inc. (R), TX, *96*
Lennon, Bill, Hall Management Group, Inc. (C), GA, *367*
Lerner, Joel S., Sanford Rose Assoc. - Louisville (C), KY, *567*
Lewis, Al, The Stelton Group, Inc. (C), NJ, *592*
Middlebrook, Linda, Sales Consultants of Austin, Inc. (C), TX, *562*
Miller, Matt, HeartBeat Medical, Inc. (C), OR, *374*
Monroe, Jr., Kenneth R., Sanford Rose Assoc. - Clearwater (C), FL, *566*
Morgan, Paul, Sanford Rose Assoc. - Columbia (C), SC, *570*
Morin, Paul, F-O-R-T-U-N-E Personnel Consultants of Knoxville (C), TN, *350*
Mustin, Joyce, J: Blakslee Int'l., Ltd. (R), CA, *18*
O'Hara, James J., Barone-O'Hara Assoc., Inc. (R), NJ, *11*
Olsen, Rex, Olsen/Clark (R), WA, *156*
Paine, Donne G., Fortune Personnel Consultants of Hilton Head (C), SC, *349*
Pelegrino, John, Kuhn Med-Tech (C), CA, *409*
Piatkiewicz, Mary Lou, Medical Executive Search Assoc., Inc. (C), AZ, *477*
Piatkiewicz, William L., Medical Executive Search Assoc., Inc. (C), AZ, *477*
Piper, William D., W. P. Assoc. (C), CA, *613*
Pritchett, Philip H., FORTUNE Personnel Consultants of North Dallas (C), TX, *350*
Robertson, R. Vic, Sanford Rose Assoc. - Chicago (C), IL, *566*
Romeo, Paul C., Romeo-Hudgins & Assoc., Ltd. (C), NJ, *545*
Rosenthal, Abbe L., ALW Research Int'l. (R), NJ, *4*
Sawhill, Louise, Healthcare Management Resources, Inc. (R), GA, *89*
Shiley, Bob, Brethet, Barnum & Assoc., Inc. (C), ON, *273*
Shipherd, John T., The Cassie Group (R), NC, *31*
Soo Hoo, Patrick J., Chelsea Resources, Inc. (C), CT, *290*

Spencer, Norman, FORTUNE Personnel Consultants of North Dallas (C), TX, *350*
Steinman, Richard, Career Marketing Assoc., Inc. (C), CO, *282*
Stewart, Tina Hunter, BioPharmMed (C), FL, *267*
Stiles, Judy, MedQuest Assoc. (C), CO, *478*
Strand, Michael G., Fortune Group Int'l., Inc. (R), PA, *70*
Stubberfield, Lee, Management Recruiters of the Baltimore Washington Corridor (C), MD, *450*
Telem, Peter B., Telem Adhesive Search Corp. (C), MD, *605*
Travis, John A., Travis & Co., Inc. (R), MA, *210*
Turner, Linda, Kuhn Med-Tech (C), CA, *409*
Vague, Mark, F-O-R-T-U-N-E of West Portland (C), OR, *348*
Visnich, L. Christine, Bason Associates (R), OH, *13*
Washburn, Ron, Elite Medical Search (C), GA, *328*
Westmore, Diane, Healthcare Management Resources, Inc. (R), GA, *89*
Yungner, Steven J., Yungner & Bormann (R), MN, *226*

Medicine

McKavis, Adel, McKavis Assoc. (C), CA, *475*
Pirnack, Margaret, McKavis Assoc. (C), CA, *475*
Rachels, John, Southwestern Professional Services (C), VA, *588*
Sierra, Rafael A., LAI Ward Howell (R), GA, *123*
Waller, Victoria, Health Search, Inc. (C), KS, *371*
Wilkins, Walter K., Walter K. Wilkins & Co. (R), NJ, *221*

Merchandising

Aswell, Judy, Management Recruiters of San Marcos (C), TX, *463*
Cahn, Jeff, Gundersen Partners, L.L.C. (R), NY, *83*
Penwell, Wayne, Recruiting Specialists (C), MA, *532*

Mergers & acquisitions

Beller, Allen, Michael Latas & Assoc., Inc. (R), MO, *126*
Castanet, Emile, Don Hall & Assoc. (C), GA, *366*
Fox, James P., Michael Latas & Assoc., Inc. (R), MO, *126*
Gilreath, James M., Gilreath Weatherby Inc. (R), MA, *77*
Higgins, Susan, The Rogan Group, Inc. (C), CA, *541*
Murphy, Bob, Murphy Partners Int'l. (R), IL, *150*
Patton, Michael, Hunt Patton & Brazeal, Inc. (C), OK, *385*
Rogan, Daniel, The Rogan Group, Inc. (C), CA, *541*
Schiller, Christian, Cook Assoc.,® Inc. (R), IL, *40*
Waldorf, Michael, Waldorf Associates, Inc. (C), CA, *614*

Metals

Bauzenberger, III, E. H., The Currier-Winn Co., Inc. (C), NJ, *305*
Borchert, Gregory L., Borchert Assoc. (C), TX, *269*
Caracciolo, Peter, Management Recruiters of Nassau, Inc. (R), NY, *134*
Dixon, Glenda, Search Assoc. (C), KY, *574*
Goodall, Rhys, C. J. Stafford & Assoc. (C), ON, *591*
Grace, Patty, Management Recruiters of Siouxland (C), IA, *449*
Guarniere, John W., RCE Assoc. (R), NJ, *173*
Hansen, Charles A., Management Recruiters of Jacksonville-South (C), FL, *427*
Hendricks, II, Stanley M., National Recruiting Service (C), IN, *489*
Jansen, Douglas L., Search Northwest Assoc. (C), OR, *576*
Johnstone, Bill, Search Assoc. (C), KY, *574*
Just, Susan, Just Management Services Inc. (C), FL, *402*
Kirkpatrick, Robert L., Reese Assoc. (R), PA, *174*
Krezo, Rich, Michigan Consulting Group (R), MI, *144*
Lang, Nick, Technical Recruiting Services (C), OH, *602*
Latterell, Jeffrey D., HRS, Inc. (R), PA, *97*
Lentz, Ina, Management Recruiters of Valley Forge (C), PA, *459*
Lentz, James, Management Recruiters of Valley Forge (C), PA, *459*
Linstead, Rick, Carnegie Resources, Inc. (C), NC, *284*
Mattocks, Paul, G. P. Mattocks & Associates (C), NC, *473*
Nanney, Brenda, Lou Michaels Assoc., Inc. (C), MI, *481*
Park, Cleve A., Management Recruiters of Birmingham (C), AL, *438*
Pelland, Paul S., Paul S. Pelland, P.C. (R), SC, *161*
Penrod, John V., National Metal Services Corp. (C), IN, *489*
Reed, Dave, Management Recruiters - Flint (C), MI, *451*
Reese, Jr., Charles D., Reese Assoc. (R), PA, *174*
Royfe, Dan, D.R. Assoc. (R), CA, *45*
Rusnov, Samuel, Michael Latas & Assoc., Inc. (R), OH, *126*
Schoeling, Beverly, Tom McCall Executive Search (C), IL, *473*
Snyder, Amy, Southern Recruiters & Consultants, Inc. (C), SC, *587*
Southworth, David E., Premier Recruiting Group (C), MI, *516*
Stafford, Chris, C. J. Stafford & Assoc. (C), ON, *591*
Stein, Jodi, Tom McCall Executive Search (C), IL, *473*
Stickler, III, Charles W., Charles Stickler Assoc. (R), PA, *201*
Stickler, IV, Charles W., Charles Stickler Assoc. (R), PA, *201*
Symanski, Donald G., Tierney Assoc., Inc. (R), PA, *209*
Taylor, Jane A., Paul S. Pelland, P.C. (R), SC, *161*
Tierney, George F., Tierney Assoc., Inc. (R), PA, *209*
Vogus, Jerry, Cumberland Group Inc. (C), IL, *304*
Walters, William F., Jonas, Walters & Assoc., Inc. (R), WI, *107*
Wasiele, Brian D., Carnegie Partners, Inc. (R), IL, *30*

Micro brew

Eagar, Brian, Search Int'l. (R), MA, *187*

Microwave

Austin, Cami, Cami Austin & Assoc. (C), IL, *256*
Hudson, Paul E., The Hudson Group (C), CT, *383*

Middle management

Cooke, Jeffrey R., The Cooke Group (R), WI, *40*
Cooper, B. V., QVS Int'l. (R), GA, *170*
Cowall, Frank A., Altec/HRC (C), MI, *246*
Daugenti, Gary, Gent & Assoc. (C), CA, *356*
Daxon, Corey, Feldman Gray & Assoc. Inc. (C), ON, *339*
DeClouet, J. Michael, The J. B. Search Group (C), CA, *395*
Dix, Bradley, Interim Management Resources Inc. (C), ON, *392*
Dmytrow, Eric D., F-O-R-T-U-N-E Personnel Consultants of Palm Beach (C), FL, *345*
Edwards, Greg, Eden & Assoc., Inc. (C), PA, *326*
Gaffney, Keith, Gaffney Management Consultants (R), IL, *73*
Gahan, Carolyn M., Gahan Assoc. (R), NY, *73*
Gahan, Thomas M., Gahan Assoc. (R), NY, *73*
Gehn, Valerie, Harbrowe, Inc. (C), NY, *368*
Gilbert, Jacqueline, GAAP Inc. (R), QE, *73*
Gold, Walter, Proven Edge (C), CA, *525*
Harrington, Robert J., Sanford Rose Assoc. - Greensboro (C), NC, *569*
Kurosky, John, John Kurosky & Assoc. (R), CA, *122*

RECRUITER SPECIALTIES

McDowell, Sally A., Professional Selection Services (R), GA, *169*
McKinney, Pat, Prichard Kymen Inc. (R), AB, *168*
Nunziata, Fred A., Eden & Assoc., Inc. (C), PA, *326*
Pask, Mike, Peter Froehlich & Co. (C), TX, *353*
Proctor, Richard W., Foley Proctor Yoskowitz (R), NJ, *69*
Ralles, Vickie, Feldman Gray & Assoc. Inc. (C), ON, *339*
Robyn, Eric W., QVS Int'l. (R), GA, *170*
Villareal, Victoria, Conasa de Mexico, S.C. (R), MX, *39*

Military

Casey, Steve, Orion Int'l. Consulting Group, Inc. (C), TX, *500*
Larned, Robert T., Robert Larned Assoc., Inc. (C), VA, *413*
Nelson, Randy, Orion Int'l. Consulting Group, Inc. (C), NC, *499*
Stratton, Scott, LifeWork, Inc. (C), TX, *418*
Tully, Jim, Orion Int'l. Consulting Group, Inc. (C), NC, *499*

Millwork

Castanet, Emile, Don Hall & Assoc. (C), GA, *366*
Gandee, John R., Management Recruiters of Sugar Land Inc. (C), TX, *464*
Hall, Don, Don Hall & Assoc. (C), TX, *366*
Hall, Joann, Don Hall & Assoc. (C), TX, *366*
Sheppard, Jerry, Don Hall & Assoc. (C), CA, *366*

Mineral processing

Goodall, Rhys, C. J. Stafford & Assoc. (C), ON, *591*

Mining

Arndt, Greg, Management Recruiters of Boise (C), ID, *446*
Berlet, William, KPMG Executive Search (R), ON, *119*
Buckland, G. Russell, The Bedford Consulting Group Inc. (R), ON, *15*
Collier, Gordon L., R. C. Services (C), TX, *528*
Cooke, Gerald W., STM Assoc. (R), UT, *201*
Crath, Paul F., PricewaterhouseCoopers Executive Search (R), ON, *168*
Crosbie, D. C., Interim Management Resources Inc. (C), ON, *392*
Kirkpatrick, Robert L., Reese Assoc. (R), PA, *174*
Kuhnmuench, R. G., K & C Assoc. (C), CA, *402*
Mears, Jack, Kelly Walker Assoc. (C), TX, *614*
Milius, Kent, Management Recruiters of Colorado, Inc. (C), CO, *442*
Roylance, Robert L., STM Assoc. (R), UT, *201*
Scott, Nat, C. J. Stafford & Assoc. (C), ON, *591*
Sitter, William P., Jordan-Sitter Assoc. (R), TX, *108*
Smith, Grant, Price Waterhouse Executive Search (R), BC, *168*
Smith, James H., J. Harrington Smith Assoc. (C), IN, *584*
Stafford, Chris, C. J. Stafford & Assoc. (C), ON, *591*
Sturgess, Don, Wood West & Partners Inc. (C), BC, *624*
Ward, Al L., Ward-Hoffman & Assoc. (C), ID, *615*
Wilcox, Alex B., The Bridge (C), CO, *273*

Minorities

Bennett, Delora, Genesis Personnel Service, Inc. (C), OH, *356*
Burnett, Joan Cooper, Pathways Int'l. (C), CT, *505*
Green, Larry A., Winston & Green (C), IL, *623*
High, Claude, Action Managment Corp. (C), VA, *239*
Hyde, Anne P., The Hyde Group, Inc. (R), CT, *101*
June, Valerie L., Action Management Corp. (C), MI, *239*
Lee, Kenneth D., Special Markets Group, Inc. (R), GA, *195*
Manson, Phyllis, BG & Assoc. (C), MD, *266*
McCormack, Joseph A., McCormack & Assoc. (R), CA, *140*
Rodriguez, Louise, Carpenter, Shackleton & Company (R), IL, *30*

MIS

Allen, Mark, Computer Professionals Unlimited (C), TX, *295*
Almour, Chloe, Kramer Executive Resources, Inc. (C), NY, *409*
Arcand, Arthur J., Tech 2000 (C), FL, *601*
Arons, Sheldon, Colt Systems Professional Personnel Services (C), CA, *294*
Barick, Linda R., Management Recruiters of Stevens Point, Inc. (C), WI, *466*
Barrett, Dan, Management Recruiters of Forsyth County (C), GA, *445*
Bartesch, Heinz, Professional Consulting Network, Inc. (C), CA, *520*
Bascom, Shirley R., Management Recruiters - North Canton, Inc. (C), OH, *458*
Beard, Barbara, Angel Group Int'l. (C), KY, *250*
Branch, Len, Advanced Recruiting, Inc. (C), OK, *240*
Brandt, William E., Brandt Associates (C), PA, *272*
Brauninger, John C., AmeriPro Search, Inc. (C), NC, *248*
Brindise, Michael J., Dynamic Search Systems, Inc. (C), IL, *324*
Brooks, Harvey, Fox-Morris Assoc., Inc. (C), PA, *352*
Brown, Alan V., Personnel Alliance Group (C), NJ, *508*
Brown, David, Snelling Search (C), AL, *585*
Bruns, Matthew, The North Peak Group (C), OH, *496*
Byrne, Carolyn M., The TGA Company (C), TX, *606*
Christine, Rich, R. Christine Assoc. (C), PA, *290*
Clark, Howard L., Howard Clark Assoc. (C), NJ, *292*
Cleary, Jeanne, The Rossi Search Group (C), PA, *545*
Coe, Ann, Ann Coe & Assoc. (C), IL, *294*
Cook, Martin E., Cook Assoc. Int'l., Inc. (C), TN, *298*
Corey, Richard F., Weterrings & Agnew, Inc. (C), NY, *619*
Crossman, Chuck, The Stewart Group (C), FL, *593*
Crusit, Francis, Sanford Rose Assoc. - Santa Barbara (C), CA, *565*
Daugherty-Hill, Kimberly J., Hayman Daugherty Assoc., Inc. (C), GA, *370*
Desmond, Mike, Newcomb-Desmond & Assoc., Inc. (C), OH, *492*
Detling, John, Executive Search, Ltd. (C), OH, *336*
Diersing, Joe, Executive Search, Ltd. (C), OH, *336*
Diorio, Scott, Management Recruiters of Fresno (C), CA, *440*
Dong, Steven, Executive Search, Ltd. (C), OH, *336*
Dowell, Mary K., Professional Search Assoc. (C), CA, *522*
DuBrul, Donald C., DuBrul Management Co. (C), NY, *315*
Dunlap, Thomas, Charles Dahl Group, Inc. (C), MN, *306*
Easterling, Yvonne, A First Resource (C), NC, *231*
Emery, Karlan, Emerging Medical Technologies, Inc. (C), CO, *329*
Etlinger, Alan C., Resource Recruiting (C), NH, *534*
Fairlie, Suzanne F., ProSearch, Inc. (C), PA, *524*
Farrar, Carolyn, Sanford Rose Assoc. - Springfield (C), MO, *568*
Farrar, Gary, Sanford Rose Assoc. - Springfield (C), MO, *568*
Fawkes, Gary S., Kennison & Assoc. Inc. (C), MO, *405*
Fiala, Joanne C., The Westfield Group (C), CT, *619*
Finley, Kerry, Recruiting Services Group, Inc. (C), TN, *532*
Frazier, Steven M., Sanford Rose Assoc. - Philadelphia North (C), PA, *570*
Frisch, Gerald, Gerald Frisch Assoc., Inc. (R), NY, *72*
Galka, John, Huntley Associates (Dallas), Inc. (C), TX, *386*

Gideon, Mark, Eagle Search Assoc. (C), CA, *325*
Gilbert, John, John Gilbert Co. (C), TX, *357*
Givens, Steve, Chesapeake Group (C), CT, *290*
Goldberg, Sybil, Spectra International LLC (C), AZ, *589*
Gordon, Dave, Cemco, Ltd. (C), IL, *287*
Gruszecki, Irene, Management Recruiters of Wausau, LLC (C), WI, *466*
Gurney, Darrell W., A Permanent Success Employment Services (C), CA, *231*
Hall, Shannon Kelly, Sampson Medical Search (C), CA, *564*
Hammrick, Jennifer, Mayhall Search Group, Inc. (C), IN, *473*
Harrington, Robert C., Resource Recruiting (C), NH, *534*
Harrison, Harold M., InfoTech Search (C), TX, *388*
Hawkins, Max, Management Recruiters of Wausau, LLC (C), WI, *466*
Hayden, Dale, Sanford Rose Assoc. - Pittsburgh North (C), PA, *570*
Helfenbein, Sr., Robert J., Snelling Search Recruiters (C), NC, *586*
Hellebusch, Jerry, Morgan Hunter Corp. (C), KS, *485*
Holzheimer, Robert, Exclusive Search Consultants (C), OH, *331*
Hunt, James E., Hunt & Howe Inc. (R), NY, *99*
Johnson, Walt, Pacific Crossing (C), CA, *501*
Jones, Roberta, Tech 2000 (C), FL, *601*
Kenney, George T., Search Research Assoc., Inc. (R), MA, *187*
Kennison, Victoria, Kennison & Assoc. Inc. (C), MO, *405*
Kline, Keith, Marcus & Assoc. (C), NY, *469*
Knauff, Joyce C., Joyce C. Knauff & Assoc. (C), IL, *408*
Koppelman, William, Kingsley Quinn/USA (R), NJ, *115*
Kuschnov, Janice, Charles Dahl Group, Inc. (C), MN, *306*
Laguzza, John, Laguzza Assoc., Ltd. (R), NY, *122*
Lampl, Joni, Management Recruiters of Pittsburgh-North, Inc. (C), PA, *460*
Larry, Melvin P., ExecuSource Assoc., Inc. (C), GA, *332*
Latimer, Dick, Technical Recruiting Consultants (C), IL, *602*
Latondresse, Heather G., Holloway Schulz & Partners (C), BC, *380*
Lee, Jess J., Management Search Int'l. (C), CA, *467*
Lingle, Bruce, ContactBridge, Inc. (R), IL, *40*
Marino, Chet, Cochran, Cochran & Yale, Inc. (R), CO, *37*
Marshall, John L., Fishel HR Assoc., Inc. (C), AZ, *341*
Marshall, Karen, Karen Marshall Assoc. (C), KY, *471*
Martire, Nick, AmeriResource Group Inc. (C), OK, *248*
McCartt, Sandra, Professional Search, Inc. Int'l. (C), TX, *523*
McGlawn, Walter, Corporate Plus, Ltd. (C), GA, *300*
McLaughlin, John, Romac Int'l. - San Francisco (C), CA, *541*
Mogul, Gene, Mogul Consultants, Inc. (C), NY, *483*
Nelson, Richard, Pacific Crossing (C), CA, *501*
Nimmo, Richard, AmeriResource Group Inc. (C), OK, *248*
O'Keefe, Ian, O'Keefe & Assoc. (C), AR, *498*
Owens, Lynn, Advanced Recruiting, Inc. (C), CO, *240*
Peters, Peter Louis, Success Seekers Connection (C), FL, *596*
Pharr, Thomas, Baldwin & Assoc. (C), OH, *258*
Phillips, David, Matthews & Stephens Assoc., Inc. (C), CT, *472*
Pinedo, Mario, Bor-Maq Assoc. (C), TX, *269*
Powers, Keith, Baldwin & Assoc. (C), OH, *258*
Pradarelli, Dennis J., MARBL Consultants, Inc. (C), WI, *469*
Prochnow, Laurie, Management Recruiters of Wausau, LLC (C), WI, *466*
Raj, Amritha, Softrix, Inc. (C), NJ, *586*
Rice, Inge, Automation Technology Search (C), CA, *257*
Roberts, Nick, Pacific Search Group, Inc. (C), CA, *501*
Salmela, Alexander K., A.K.S. Assoc., Ltd. (R), MA, *1*
Samet, Saul, Fisher-Todd Assoc. (C), NY, *342*
Sawyer, Scott J., Management Search Int'l. (C), CA, *467*
Schultz, Bob, Wegner & Assoc. (C), WI, *617*
Scrivens, Dan, Snelling Search (C), AL, *585*
Simmons, Daniel C., Continental Search & Outplacement, Inc. (C), MD, *298*
Sonne, Bill, PeopleSource Inc. (C), TX, *506*
Sprouse, Laurie, Tech-Net (C), TX, *601*
Steinbach, David M., Steinbach & Co. (C), MA, *592*
Stephenson, Phil, Executive Search Group LLC (C), CA, *335*
Steuer, Ira, Cemco, Ltd. (C), MO, *287*
Sussman, Patti, Weinman & Assoc. (C), AZ, *617*
Tamayo, Roland, Management Recruiters of Fresno (C), CA, *440*
Van Campen, Jerry, Gilbert & Van Campen Int'l. (R), NY, *76*
Whitehead, Elizabeth S., Whitehead & Assoc., Inc. (C), MO, *620*
Wisnewski, Edward J., Wisnewski & Assoc. (R), CA, *223*
Zidwick, Christiana, WTW Assoc., Inc. (R), NY, *225*
Zonka, Thomas J., Thomas & Assoc. of Michigan (C), MI, *606*

Mission critical

Bialecki, Linda, Bialecki Inc. (R), NY, *17*

Mobile equipment

Cinco, Sue K., Management Recruiters of Melbourne, Inc. (C), FL, *443*
Thomason, Penny, F-O-R-T-U-N-E Personnel Consultants of East Seattle (C), WA, *351*

Multimedia

Bacher, Judith, SpencerStuart (R), NY, *196*
Capecci, Eileen, Rice Cohen Int'l. (R), PA, *178*
Citrin, James M., SpencerStuart (R), CT, *196*
Curry, Joseph, MediaCOM Talent Group (C), MA, *477*
Doroba, Carol, Impact Search & Strategies (C), PA, *387*
Ertaud, Wilfrid, MediaCOM Talent Group (C), MA, *477*
Estrada, Barbara, Montgomery West (R), CA, *146*
Faucher, Cornel, Sink, Walker, Boltrus Int'l. (R), MA, *192*
Hall, Scott, Advancement, Inc. (C), IL, *241*
Higgins, David J., Warren, Morris & Madison, Ltd. (C), NH, *616*
Kahn, Beverly A., New Dimensions in Technology, Inc. (C), MA, *492*
King, Margaret, Christian & Timbers, Inc. (R), OH, *34*
Kurke, David S., Starbridge Group Inc. (C), VA, *591*
Lipson, Harriet L., Lipson & Co. (R), CA, *130*
Lipson, Howard R., Lipson & Co. (R), CA, *130*
Madison, T. Dean, Warren, Morris & Madison, Ltd. (C), VA, *616*
Mather, David, Christian & Timbers, Inc. (R), OH, *34*
Mather, David R., Christian & Timbers, Inc. (R), CA, *34*
Morris, Charles C., Warren, Morris & Madison, Ltd. (C), CA, *616*
Myers, Bonnie, Myers Career Assoc., Inc. (C), CA, *488*
Ritchings, David, David Allen Assoc. (R), NJ, *3*
Sanders, David, Management Recruiters of Roseville (C), CA, *441*
Schneider, Thomas P., WTW Assoc., Inc. (R), NY, *225*
Sharf, Bernard, Search Assoc., Inc. (C), CA, *574*
Travis, Michael J., Travis & Co., Inc. (R), MA, *210*
Warren, Scott C., Warren, Morris & Madison, Ltd. (C), NH, *616*

RECRUITER SPECIALTIES

Wasp, Jr., Warren T., WTW Assoc., Inc. (R), NY, *225*
Young, Arthur L., Search South, Inc. (C), AL, *576*

Music

Buchanan, Martha, Wilson McLeran, Inc. (C), CT, *622*

Mutual funds

Friedman, Ken, The Primary Group, Inc. (R), FL, *168*
Harvey, Warren, Management Recruiters of Nassau, Inc. (R), NY, *134*
Salloway, Andrew N., A. N. Salloway Executive Search & Consulting, L.L.C. (C), MA, *564*
Schrenzel, Steven N., The Governance Group, Inc. (R), NJ, *80*
Stranberg, Mark, Mark Stranberg & Assoc. Inc. (R), MA, *202*
Wadsworth, Robert H., Robert H. Wadsworth & Assoc., Inc. (R), AZ, *214*
Werlin, Paul A., Human Capital Resources, Inc. (C), FL, *384*
Williston, Nada D., Active Search & Placement Inc. (C), CA, *239*

Natural resources

Cooke, Gerald W., STM Assoc. (R), UT, *201*
Dickin, Noranne, Reynolds Consulting Int'l. (R), BC, *177*
Dickin, Noranne, Reynolds Consulting Int'l. (R), AB, *177*
Epstein, Kathy J., LAI Ward Howell (R), MA, *123*
Goldsmith, Fred J., Fred J. Goldsmith Assoc. (R), CA, *79*
Hofner, Kevin E., LAI Ward Howell (R), TX, *124*
Mendez, Larry W., Layne-Mendez & Co. (R), TX, *127*
Preng, David E., Preng & Assoc., Inc. (R), TX, *167*
Robertson, William R., LAI Ward Howell (R), GA, *123*
Roylance, Robert L., STM Assoc. (R), UT, *201*
Wilson, Thomas H., LAI Ward Howell (R), TX, *124*
Witte, David L., LAI Ward Howell (R), TX, *124*
Young, Nicholas, SpencerStuart (R), NY, *196*

Networking

Albertson, Rob, Dick Williams & Assoc. (C), CA, *621*
Bakehorn, Thomas, Martin Stevens Tamaren & Assoc., Inc. (R), CA, *206*
Baker, Chet, Diversified Consulting Services, Inc. (C), CO, *313*
Chalmers, Lynda, Delta Management Group Ltd. (C), ON, *310*
Cooper, Liz, The Beardsley Group Inc. (C), CT, *261*
DeGrasse, Bob, SignatureSoft Inc. (C), CA, *581*
Hebert, Chris, Management Recruiters of Nassau, Inc. (R), NY, *134*
Hoffman, Adele, The Beardsley Group Inc. (C), CT, *261*
Howlett, Tracy A., Ross Personnel Consultants, Inc. (C), CT, *545*
Junker, Sherry, Bolton Group (C), CA, *269*
Kacevich, Jr., Joseph B., Kacevich, Lewis & Brown, Inc. (R), MA, *109*
Kennedy, Mike, MK & Assoc. (R), CA, *146*
Kennedy, Sharon, MK & Assoc. (R), CA, *146*
Kratimenos, Peter, Ansara, Bickford & Fiske (C), MA, *251*
Kurtz, Sheldon I., Kurtz Pro-Search, Inc. (C), NJ, *410*
Lehrman, Peter A., Emerging Technology Search (C), GA, *329*
Leone, Joan, The Beardsley Group Inc. (C), CT, *261*
Lingle, Bruce, ContactBridge, Inc. (R), IL, *40*
McCormack, Kathy, The Beardsley Group Inc. (C), CT, *261*
McDowell, John, McDowell & Co., Recruiters (C), TX, *474*
Mussato, Ray, Dick Williams & Assoc. (C), CA, *621*
Newell, Beverly, The Beardsley Group Inc. (C), CT, *261*
Pitchford, Gavin, Delta Management Group Ltd. (C), ON, *310*
Prencipe, Michael, Raymond Karsan Assoc. (C), VA, *530*
Raj, Amritha, Softrix, Inc. (C), NJ, *586*
Renwick, David, John Kurosky & Assoc. (R), CA, *122*
Roscoe, Harry, The Beardsley Group Inc. (C), CT, *261*
Rudolph, Lee, Management Recruiters of Franktown (C), CO, *442*
Salcido, Chris, Protocol Inc. (C), CA, *525*
Sanders, Marlaine, Shell Technology Group (C), CA, *580*
Schoff, Frank J., Management Recruiters of Cedar Mountain (C), NC, *455*
Selker, Gregory, Christian & Timbers, Inc. (R), OH, *34*
Shindler, Stanley L., Franklin Int'l. Search, Inc. (C), MA, *352*
Stevens, Martin, Martin Stevens Tamaren & Assoc., Inc. (R), CA, *206*
Talarico, Joseph, Hreshko Consulting Group (C), NJ, *382*
Upton, Noreen, The Beardsley Group Inc. (C), CT, *261*
Young, Philip M., Ross Personnel Consultants, Inc. (C), CT, *545*
Zapotocky, V. J., Computer Professionals Unlimited (C), TX, *295*

New media

Campbell, Robert Scott, Wellington Management Group (R), PA, *217*
Cantus, Jane-Scott, Christian & Timbers, Inc. (R), VA, *34*
Collins, Kenneth B., Executive Search Partners (R), NY, *63*
Flannery, Michael, Redwood Partners Ltd. (R), NY, *173*
Gallagher, Kelly, K2 Resources, L.P. (C), CT, *402*
Goldberg, Steve, Media Recruiting Group, Inc. (C), NY, *476*
Greger, Kenneth R., Greger/Peterson Assoc., Inc. (R), OR, *82*
Kelly, Elizabeth Ann, Wellington Management Group (R), PA, *217*
Koch, Gail Kleinberg, CAS Comsearch Inc. (C), NY, *286*
Macaluso, Kelly, K2 Resources, L.P. (C), CT, *402*
Mattes, Jr., Edward C., The Ogdon Partnership (R), NY, *155*
McKeown, Morgan, Christian & Timbers, Inc. (R), NY, *34*
McKeown, Morgan, Christian & Timbers, Inc. (R), OH, *34*
Nicolai, Linda, Brad Marks Int'l. (R), CA, *136*
Panchella, Joseph J., Wellington Management Group (R), PA, *217*
Ridenour, Suzanne S., Ridenour & Assoc. (R), IL, *178*
Ross, Elsa, Gardner-Ross Assoc., Inc. (R), NY, *74*
Schoenfeld, Randy, Redwood Partners Ltd. (R), NY, *173*
Stefunek, Paul C., StratfordGroup (R), OH, *203*
Timoney, Laura, Bishop Partners (R), NY, *17*
Webster, Larry, Technology Management Partners (R), CA, *208*
Wilson, Robert F., Wilson McLeran, Inc. (C), CT, *622*

Noise control

Fetridge, Guild, Guild Fetridge Acoustical Search, Inc. (C), NY, *340*

Non-profit

Ast, Steven T., AST/BRYANT (R), CT, *8*
Auerbach, Judith A., Auerbach Associates, Inc. (R), MA, *9*
Barnes, Roanne L., Barnes Development Group, LLC (R), WI, *11*
Boulware, Christine, Boulware & Assoc. Inc. (R), IL, *20*
Bronder, Stephanie L., Fagan & Company (R), PA, *64*
Bryant, Christopher P., AST/BRYANT (R), CA, *8*
Burgess, III, William H., The Burgess Group-Corporate Recruiters Int'l., Inc. (R), NY, *25*

Dey, Robert L., Rob Dey Executive Search (R), FL, *49*
Doyle, John, Search Research Assoc., Inc. (R), MA, *187*
Erickson-Pearson, David, Boulware & Assoc. Inc. (R), IL, *20*
Fields, Fredric L., C. A. Durakis Assoc., Inc. (R), MD, *55*
French, Peter N., P. N. French Assoc., Inc. (R), MA, *72*
Gahan, Carolyn M., Gahan Assoc. (R), NY, *73*
Gielow, Curtis C., Gielow Assoc., Inc. (R), WI, *76*
Glassick, Charles E., Jon McRae & Associates, Inc. (R), GA, *142*
Hurley, Paula B., Auerbach Associates, Inc. (R), MA, *9*
Hyde, Anne P., The Hyde Group, Inc. (R), CT, *101*
Isaacson, John, Isaacson, Miller (R), MA, *104*
Kaufmann, Robert E., SpencerStuart (R), CT, *197*
Kelly, William W., Jon McRae & Associates, Inc. (R), GA, *142*
Kile, Robert W., Rusher, Loscavio & LoPresto (R), CA, *183*
Krier, Michael S., Overton Consulting (R), WI, *157*
Kulper, Keith D., Kulper & Co., L.L.C. (R), NJ, *121*
Lindauer, Lois L., Lois L. Lindauer Searches (C), MA, *418*
Lyttle, Jordene, KPMG Executive Search (R), ON, *119*
Marcello, Joe, Executive Search Consultants Corp. (C), IL, *335*
McCormack, Joseph A., McCormack & Assoc. (R), CA, *140*
McLean, B. Keith, PricewaterhouseCoopers Executive Search (R), ON, *168*
McRae, O. Jon, Jon McRae & Associates, Inc. (R), GA, *142*
Mindlin, Freda, Opportunity Resources, Inc. (R), NY, *156*
Moore, Thomas R., Thomas R. Moore Executive Search (R), TX, *146*
Nixon, Barbara, PricewaterhouseCoopers Executive Search (R), ON, *168*
Noeske, Nancy R., Overton Consulting (R), WI, *157*
Orr, Kenneth B., Jon McRae & Associates, Inc. (R), GA, *142*
Paul, Joel H., Joel H. Paul & Assoc., Inc. (C), NY, *505*
Pelton, Margaret, PricewaterhouseCoopers Executive Search (R), ON, *168*
Pettway, Samuel H., SpencerStuart (R), GA, *197*
Roy, Ruth, Lois L. Lindauer Searches (C), MA, *418*
Schaefer, Jr., Frederick M., StratfordGroup (R), CO, *203*
Scott, Gordon S., Search Research Assoc., Inc. (R), MA, *187*
Sellery, Jr., Robert A., Robert Sellery Assoc., Ltd. (R), DC, *188*
Slaughter, Katherine T., Compass Group Ltd. (R), MI, *38*
Smith, Toni S., SpencerStuart (R), IL, *197*
Stockwell, Kye, Gateway Management Resources (C), IL, *355*
Taylor, Charles E., LAI Ward Howell (R), GA, *123*
Tittlemore, Jim, Tittemore Cowan Assoc. (C), AB, *607*
Wakefield, J. Alvin, Wakefield Talabisco Int'l. (R), VT, *214*
Whitney, William A., Larsen, Whitney, Blecksmith & Zilliacus, Inc. (R), CA, *125*
Wyche, Ellen Adair, Jon McRae & Associates, Inc. (R), GA, *142*
Zera, Ronald J., SpencerStuart (R), TX, *197*
Zivic, Janis M., SpencerStuart (R), CA, *196*
Zweifler, Rhyan, Boulware & Assoc. Inc. (R), IL, *20*

Nuclear power

Earle, Holland R., Executive Strategies, Inc. (C), GA, *337*

Nursing

Anderson, Trevor, Kincaid Group Inc. (KGI) (C), TX, *406*
Bozell, Jeanna, Professional Resource Group, Inc. (C), IN, *522*
Brown, Billye, Tuft & Assoc., Inc. (R), IL, *212*
Corkum, Jennifer, Doherty Healthcare Consultants (C), ME, *313*
De Mange, Jean M., Wellington Thomas Ltd. (C), FL, *618*
Dinino, Sabina, Trillium Human Resources Inc. (C), ON, *609*
DuBois, Jr., Joseph W., Horizon Medical Search of NH (C), NH, *381*
Estelle, Tracy, Kincaid Group Inc. (KGI) (C), TX, *406*
Estok, Patricia, Tuft & Assoc., Inc. (R), IL, *212*
Fleischer, Susan, Healthcare Executive Recruiters, Inc. (C), CA, *372*
Gallman, LaVerne, Tuft & Assoc., Inc. (R), IL, *212*
Gaudette, Charles L., Medical Recruiters Exchange (C), AZ, *477*
Hollander, Heidi, Career Counseling Ltd. (C.C.L.) (C), NY, *282*
Hyman, Jean W., Management Search Assoc., Inc. (C), GA, *467*
Johnson, Lee, Kincaid Group Inc. (KGI) (C), TX, *406*
McCrea, Joan I., Nursing Technomics (R), PA, *153*
Mero, Kevin J., innovativestaffsearch (C), TX, *389*
Mero, Kevin J., innovativestaffsearch (C), WI, *389*
Meyer, Verne, Delacore Resources (C), MN, *310*
Oberman, Heidi, Medical Recruiters Inc. (C), MO, *477*
Rosenbaum, Bette, Healthcare Executive Recruiters, Inc. (C), CA, *372*
Sands, Tony, Healthcare Search Associates (C), CA, *374*
Schraeter, Jack M., Lake Medical Associates (C), ME, *411*
Smith, Judy, JPM International (C), CA, *401*
Talbot, Lorri, Trillium Human Resources Inc. (C), ON, *609*
Thomas, Betty J., Tuft & Assoc., Inc. (R), IL, *212*
Watring, Bernie, Watring & Assoc., Inc. (C), IL, *616*
Watson, Diana L., Premier Healthcare Recruiters, Inc. (C), MI, *516*
Winterburn, Karen, Heartland National Medical Search (C), IL, *374*
Wottowa, Denise, Medical Recruiters Inc. (C), MO, *477*

OB/GYN

Allhands, Kelly, Allhands Placement Consultants (C), IN, *245*

Occupational therapy

Dinino, Sabina, Trillium Human Resources Inc. (C), ON, *609*
Hollander, Heidi, Career Counseling Ltd. (C.C.L.) (C), NY, *282*
Talbot, Lorri, Trillium Human Resources Inc. (C), ON, *609*
Waller, Victoria, Health Search, Inc. (C), KS, *371*

Off shore

Anderson, Robert W., Anderson Bradshaw Assoc., Inc. (R), TX, *6*

Office

Products

Bakken, Roger, J. Rodgers & Associates (C), IL, *540*
Dussling, Kate, Cook Assoc.,® Inc. (R), IL, *40*
Thurber, Raymond N., Overton Consulting (R), WI, *157*

Services

Bontempo, Mary F., Dunhill Professional Search of Bucks-Mont., Inc. (C), PA, *322*
Phillips, Mimi, Snelling Search Recruiters (C), NC, *586*
Zukerman, Claire, Corporate Search, Inc. (C), NY, *301*

Support

Boyle, Lori, JDC Assoc. (C), NY, *397*
Gehn, Valerie, Harbrowe, Inc. (C), NY, *368*

Oil

Anderson, Robert W., Anderson Bradshaw Assoc., Inc. (R), TX, *6*
Aslaksen, James S., LAI Ward Howell (R), IL, *123*
Ayling, Michael L., MLA Resources, Inc. (C), OK, *483*
Caple, Robert, Coe & Co. Int'l. Inc./EMA Partners Int'l. (R), AB, *37*
Coe, Karen, Coe & Co. Int'l. Inc./EMA Partners Int'l. (R), AB, *37*
Cole, Floyd, National Field Service Corp. (C), NY, *489*
Conroy, M. J., Conroy Partners Ltd. (R), AB, *39*
Cosier, Brian, Cosier & Assoc. (C), AB, *302*
Costello, Lynda, Coe & Co. Int'l. Inc./EMA Partners Int'l. (R), AB, *37*
Dickin, Noranne, Reynolds Consulting Int'l. (R), BC, *177*
Dickin, Noranne, Reynolds Consulting Int'l. (R), AB, *177*
Edwards, Peter G., Conroy Partners Ltd. (R), AB, *39*
Gagola, J., American Executive Management, Inc. (R), MA, *5*
Manthey, Merv, KPMG Executive Search (R), AB, *119*
Morgan, Richard, Morgan Samuels Co. (R), CA, *147*
Nelson, Allan C., Davies, Park (R), AB, *47*
O'Brien, Brent, Executive Search Consultants Corp. (C), IL, *335*
O'Daniel, James E., The Elsworth Group (C), TX, *329*
Pfeiffer, Irene, Price Waterhouse Executive Search (R), AB, *168*
Samuels, Lew, Morgan Samuels Co. (R), CA, *147*
Uhlich, Jeff, KPMG Executive Search (R), AB, *119*
Williams, Bill, Executive Search Consultants Corp. (C), IL, *335*
Williams, Lee, Woodmoor Group (C), CO, *624*

On-line

Selker, Gregory, Christian & Timbers, Inc. (R), OH, *34*

Operations

Abbott, Robert, Pacific Coast Recruiting (C), CA, *501*
Adams, Chris, Fortune Group Int'l., Inc. (R), PA, *70*
Atchison, W. R., W. R. Atchison & Assoc., Inc. (C), NC, *255*
Babcock, James A., The Premier Staffing Group (C), OH, *517*
Barr, Charly, Barr Assoc. (C), PA, *259*
Birnbaum, Richard, R. J. Associates (C), NY, *528*
Boltrus, Richard, Sink, Walker, Boltrus Int'l. (R), MA, *192*
Bottero, Paul, ISG Informatics Search Group (C), ON, *395*
Boule, James P., F-O-R-T-U-N-E Personnel Consultants of Cincinnati (C), OH, *348*
Brandvold, Steven C., Executive Connection (C), OH, *333*
Briggs, Farris R., Staff Resources, Inc. (C), SC, *590*
Brill, Ted, F-O-R-T-U-N-E Personnel Consultants of Tampa (C), FL, *345*
Brooks, Harvey, Fox-Morris Assoc., Inc. (C), PA, *352*
Bruno, David A., DHR Int'l., Inc. (R), AZ, *49*
Burchill, Gregory J., BGB Assoc., Inc. (C), IL, *266*
Burke, T. Michael, Burke & Assoc./The Westfield Group (C), CT, *276*
Carrigan, Denise, Management Recruiters of San Antonio (C), TX, *463*
Cerra, Ken, William Bell Assoc., Inc. (C), NJ, *263*
Christy, Tim, The Partnership Group (R), NJ, *160*
Cimino, Terry, Executive Search, Ltd. (C), OH, *336*
Connors, Brian J., S. Tanner & Assoc. Inc. (C), ON, *599*
Critchley, Walter, Cochran, Cochran & Yale, Inc. (R), NY, *37*
Critchley, Walter Y., Cochran, Cochran & Yale, Inc. (R), NY, *36*
Curran, Nick, Management Recruiters of Milwaukee-North (C), WI, *466*
DeLany, Donald F., Resource Perspectives, Inc. (R), CA, *175*
Domann, Jr., William A., The Domann Organization (R), CA, *53*
Dowell, Mary K., Professional Search Assoc. (C), CA, *522*
Eden, Dianne, Steeple Resources & Consulting (R), NJ, *199*
Etlinger, Alan C., Resource Recruiting (C), NH, *534*
Furst, Stephen, Strategic Resources (C), WA, *595*
Gasga, Pedro Salinas, Michigan Consulting Group (R), MI, *144*
Germain, Valerie, Jay Gaines & Company, Inc. (R), NY, *74*
Griffin, Deana A., Souder & Assoc. (R), VA, *195*
Hahn, Loel G., Fergason Assoc., Inc. (C), IL, *339*
Hanna, Jr., M. A. Jack, The Hanna Group (C), OH, *368*
Hartig, Dave, The Angus Group, Ltd. (C), OH, *251*
Hayden, Lynn, Erlanger Assoc. (R), FL, *60*
Henshaw, Bob, Fortune Personnel Consultants of Huntsville, Inc. (C), AL, *343*
Hirshman, Kenneth A., McGrath & Assoc., Inc. (R), NJ, *141*
Hodges, Whitney, Recruiting Services Group, Inc. (C), TN, *532*
Hoffman, Tala R., TRH Assoc., Inc. (R), NY, *210*
Hyman, Derry, Hyman & Assoc. (C), TX, *386*
Jackson, Eric, ProFinders, Inc. (C), FL, *523*
Jones, Gary, BGB Assoc., Inc. (C), IL, *266*
Joseph, Surette, Marsteller Wilcox Assoc. (C), IL, *471*
Kimball, Dex, Lanken-Kimball-Therrell & Assoc. (C), GA, *412*
Kirk, Ruth, Campbell, Edgar Inc. (C), AB, *280*
Kirk, Ruth, Campbell, Edgar Inc. (C), BC, *280*
Koller, Jr., Edward R., Jerry Fields Assoc. (C), NY, *340*
L'Archevesque, Lee, Sink, Walker, Boltrus Int'l. (R), MA, *192*
Langford, Bob, Fortune Personnel Consultants of Huntsville, Inc. (C), AL, *343*
Leavy, Renee, Affinity Executive Search (C), FL, *241*
Levy, William M., Sherbrooke Assoc., Inc. (C), NJ, *580*
Lewis, Mark E., Management Recruiters of Myrtle Beach, Inc. (C), SC, *460*
Lynch, Jack, Michigan Consulting Group (R), MI, *144*
Lynch, Jack, Premier Recruiting Group (C), MI, *516*
Lyon, Jenny K., Marra Peters & Partners (R), NC, *136*
Mangum, William T., Thomas Mangum Co. (R), CA, *208*
Martin, Bill, Fortune Personnel Consultants of Greensboro, NC, Inc. (C), NC, *348*
Martin, Suzanne, The Beam Group (R), PA, *14*
McIvor, Mike, Christmas, McIvor & Assoc. Inc. (C), ON, *290*
Mehta, Narinder K., Mehta Consulting (C), NJ, *478*
Mitchell, Sheri, ProFinders, Inc. (C), FL, *523*
Mochwart, Donald, Drummond Assoc., Inc. (C), NY, *315*
Mojek, Chuck, American Resources Corp. (C), IL, *248*
Musick, Diana, Musick & Assoc. (C), CA, *487*
Musick, Stephen, Musick & Assoc. (C), CA, *487*
Newell, Wayne, Management Alliance Group, Inc. (R), NJ, *134*
Nicholson, Philip J., P. J. Nicholson & Assoc. (C), IL, *493*
O'Connor, Fred, F-O-R-T-U-N-E Consultants of Memphis (C), TN, *349*
O'Neill, Kevin R., Performance Resources, Inc. (C), RI, *507*
Oglesby, Tom, F-O-R-T-U-N-E Personnel of Nashville (C), TN, *350*
Palazzolo, Kathy, Michigan Consulting Group (R), MI, *144*
Parr, Thomas A., Holland & Assoc., Inc. (R), MI, *94*
Petras, Michael, F-O-R-T-U-N-E Personnel Consultants of South Bend (C), IN, *346*
Pleva, Will, Leslie Kavanagh Assoc., Inc. (C), NY, *416*
Presley, Jason T., Presley Consultants, Inc. (C), CA, *517*

Presley, Jason T., Presley Consultants, Inc. (C), MT, *517*
Presley, Linda C., Presley Consultants, Inc. (C), CA, *517*
Presley, Philip E., Presley Consultants, Inc. (C), CA, *517*
Regan, Ray, Fortune Personnel Consultants (C), MT, *347*
Roach, Ronald R., Sanford Rose Assoc. - Burlington, NC (C), NC, *569*
Rosenblatt, Michael F., The Quest Organization (C), NY, *527*
Ross, Andrew, DARE Personnel Inc. (C), ON, *307*
Ryan, Debra, Bonell Ryan Inc. (R), NY, *19*
Santamaria, Jay, The Beam Group (R), NY, *14*
Scanlon, James D., Sherbrooke Assoc., Inc. (C), NJ, *580*
Schatz, Jr., William G., The Schatz Company (C), MO, *571*
Schriber, Floyd, F-O-R-T-U-N-E Consultants of Memphis (C), TN, *349*
Scott, Bob, Robert Scott Assoc. (C), NJ, *573*
Smith, Clark W., F-O-R-T-U-N-E Personnel Consultants of Savannah, Inc. (C), GA, *345*
Smith, Michael R., Michaels & Moere (C), WI, *481*
Souder, Jr., E. G., Souder & Assoc. (R), VA, *195*
Stecker, Bernd, The Garret Group (R), NJ, *75*
Suchomski, Larry, The Montgomery Group, Inc. (C), TN, *484*
Tann, Robert, Staff Extension, Int'l. (C), TX, *590*
Tanner, Joanne, S. Tanner & Assoc. Inc. (C), ON, *599*
Tanner, Steve, S. Tanner & Assoc. Inc. (C), ON, *599*
Taylor, M. Kent, Prairie Resource Group, Inc. (R), IL, *166*
Taylor, Patricia, Smartsource Inc. (C), CA, *583*
Therrell, Brock, Lanken-Kimball-Therrell & Assoc. (C), GA, *412*
Thomas, Roger C., Innovative Resource Group, LLC (C), NC, *389*
Tierney, Linda, Avalon Health Group, Inc. (R), NY, *9*
Trasatti, Anthony, The Pennmor Group (C), NJ, *506*
Van Wick, Mike, Management Recruiters of Rankin Co. (C), MS, *452*
Vlcek, Thomas J., Vlcek & Company, Inc. (R), CA, *214*
Weiner, Art, Sanford Rose Assoc. - Athens (C), GA, *566*
Welch, Lauren, Management Recruiters of Lake Forest, IL (C), IL, *447*
Wells, Juli C., Cook Assoc. Int'l., Inc. (C), TN, *298*
Wharton, John P., The Garret Group (R), NJ, *75*
Wilcox, Mark, Marsteller Wilcox Assoc. (C), IL, *471*
Wong, Ed, Campbell, Edgar Inc. (C), BC, *280*
Zilliacus, Patrick W., Larsen, Whitney, Blecksmith & Zilliacus, Inc. (R), CA, *125*

Management

Weiner, Ken, Sanford Rose Assoc. - Athens (C), GA, *566*
Wilcox, Fred T., Wilcox Bertoux & Miller (R), CA, *220*

Oracle

Bechard, Lori, Lascelle & Assoc. Inc. (C), ON, *413*
Bell, Dixie Lee, MIS Computer Professionals, Inc. (C), KS, *482*
Davis Wolfe, Kathryn, HDB Incorporated (C), MO, *371*
Geiman, Barry, Leader Institute, Inc. (C), GA, *414*
Harmon, Jerry, Delta Resource Group, Ltd. (C), GA, *311*
Hulme, Doug, Leader Institute, Inc. (C), GA, *414*
Mesina, Roman, The Consulting Group of North America, Inc. (C), VA, *297*
Perkins, Yvonne, Leader Institute, Inc. (C), GA, *414*
Plavin, Avery, The Consulting Group of North America, Inc. (C), VA, *297*
Robbins, Mark, Search Solutions Inc. (C), CA, *576*
Salvatore, Philip A., LAS Management Consulting Group, Inc. (R), NJ, *125*
Swami, Pad N., Fortuna Technologies Inc. (C), CA, *343*
Vlahos, Ben, Leader Institute, Inc. (C), GA, *414*
Zabor, Richard, Leader Institute, Inc. (C), GA, *414*

Organizational development

Atkinson, Patrick J., Waterford Executive Group Ltd. (C), IL, *616*
Giries, Juliet, Barton Assoc., Inc. (R), TX, *12*
Green, Mark, Rice Cohen Int'l. (R), PA, *178*
Heissan, Arlene, P. J. Lynch Assoc. (R), CT, *132*
Hosey, Debra, The Pailin Group Professional Search Consultants (R), TX, *158*
Lessner, Jack, J. E. Lessner Assoc., Inc. (R), MI, *128*
MacNaughton, Sperry, MacNaughton Assoc. (R), CA, *133*
Stillinger, Regina V., Stillinger & Assoc. (R), CA, *201*
Tomei, Ted, Waterford Executive Group Ltd. (C), IL, *616*
Vujeec, John, Executive Search, Ltd. (C), OH, *336*

Orthopedics

Montgomery, Denis, Healthcare Recruiters of New England (C), MA, *373*

OTC

Besen, Douglas, Besen Assoc. Inc. (C), NJ, *266*
Musso, Connie, Consumer Search Inc. (C), MA, *298*

Owner reps

Bono, Jeffrey D., Michael Latas & Assoc., Inc. (R), MO, *126*
Conroy, Daniel J., Michael Latas & Assoc., Inc. (R), MO, *126*
Foster, Kathie, Michael Latas & Assoc., Inc. (R), MO, *126*
Jesberg, Gary H., Michael Latas & Assoc., Inc. (R), MO, *126*
Leonard, William C., Michael Latas & Assoc., Inc. (R), MO, *126*

Packaging

Altreuter, Ken, The Altco Group (C), NJ, *246*
Andrews, Charles, The Borton Wallace Co. (R), TN, *19*
Austin, Larry, Lucas Assoc. (C), TX, *421*
Baker, Craig, JM & Company (R), PA, *106*
Bason, Maurice L., Bason Associates (R), OH, *13*
Battalin, Laurence H., L. Battalin & Co. (C), FL, *261*
Bauman, Bobbi, BJB Assoc. (C), VA, *267*
Bilinski, Kalyna, Coe & Co. Int'l. Inc./EMA Partners Int'l. (R), AB, *37*
Boule, James P., F-O-R-T-U-N-E Personnel Consultants of Cincinnati (C), OH, *348*
Brann, Rudy, Executive Search Group, Inc. (C), CT, *335*
Bridgett, Cal, Sales Consultants of Savannah, GA (C), GA, *557*
Brown, C.C. Jay, Fortune Personnel Consultants of Raleigh, Inc. (C), NC, *348*
Brown, Kenneth, ISC of Cincinnati Inc. (C), OH, *394*
Bucci, Michael T., The Partnership Group (R), NJ, *160*
Burke, Kaye, J. Burke & Assoc., Inc. (C), TX, *276*
Burke, Stoney, J. Burke & Assoc., Inc. (C), TX, *276*
Caprio, Jerry, Caprio & Assoc. Inc. (R), IL, *29*
Champion, Dale, The Marathon Group (C), GA, *469*
Cizynski, Katherine W., James Mead & Co. (R), CT, *142*
Coco, Jr., Carl, Professions, Inc. (C), OH, *523*
Corbin, Earl, Corbin Packaging Professionals (C), MO, *299*
Corrigan, George T., Jr., Howe & Assoc. (R), PA, *97*

RECRUITER SPECIALTIES

DeLalla, Barbara, DeLalla - Fried Assoc. (C), NY, *310*
DeLany, Donald F., Resource Perspectives, Inc. (R), CA, *175*
Dermady, Timothy J., ExecutiveFit (C), NY, *337*
Donnelly, John, MIXTEC Group (R), CA, *145*
Edwards, Tom, Southern Chemical & Plastics Search (C), FL, *587*
Ellis, Walter, Packaging Personnel Co., Ltd. (C), WI, *502*
Filippelli, Frank J., The Glenwood Group (C), IL, *358*
Flamer, Michael, The Dorfman Group (C), AZ, *314*
Fried, Ann, DeLalla - Fried Assoc. (C), NY, *310*
Glancey, Jr., Thomas F., Gordon Wahls Executive Search (C), PA, *613*
Gleason, Helen, Management Recruiters of Clearwater (C), FL, *443*
Goldsmith, Fred J., Fred J. Goldsmith Assoc. (R), CA, *79*
Griffin, Al, Gardner-Ross Assoc., Inc. (R), NY, *74*
Gross, Philip, Professions, Inc. (C), OH, *523*
Hanson, Ralph, Massey-Horton Int'l. (R), ON, *138*
Harvey, John K., Management Recruiters of North Fulton (C), GA, *445*
Heintz, William, MIXTEC Group (R), CA, *145*
Heintz, William, MIXTEC Group (R), CA, *146*
Hochwalt, Mike, M H Executive Search Group (C), TX, *422*
Holland, John H., Sloan & Assoc., Inc. (C), VA, *583*
Huettl, Robin, Packaging Personnel Co., Ltd. (C), WI, *501*
Ingram, Meredith, Meredith Ingram, Ltd. (C), IL, *388*
Kensington, Holland, Kensington International (R), CA, *113*
Knapp, Miranda, Cook Assoc.,® Inc. (R), IL, *40*
Kratimenos, Peter, Ansara, Bickford & Fiske (C), MA, *251*
Krenz, Ron, MESA International (C), CA, *480*
Kunkle, Denise, D. Kunkle & Assoc. (C), IL, *410*
Lee, Robert, Management Recruiters, Inc. (C), FL, *443*
Levine, Alan C., Alan Levine Assoc. (R), MA, *129*
Malloy, James K., Sales Consultants of Middlesex County, Inc. (C), NJ, *561*
Marshall, John C., JM & Company (R), PA, *106*
May, William M., Management Recruiters of Decatur, LLC (C), AL, *438*
McCollum, Ken, MESA International (C), CA, *480*
Mooney, Penny, Christian & Timbers, Inc. (R), CT, *34*
Mooney, Penny, Christian & Timbers, Inc. (R), OH, *34*
Moran, Marilyn, RitaSue Siegel Resources, Inc. (R), NY, *191*
Morton, Sam, Sloan & Assoc., Inc. (C), VA, *583*
Nelson, Christopher, MIXTEC Group (R), CA, *145*
Noone, Christine, Cook Assoc.,® Inc. (R), IL, *40*
O'Reilly, William E., Management Recruiters of Cincinnati/Sharonville, Inc. (C), OH, *457*
Palumbo, Robert F., The Recruitment Group, Inc. (C), NY, *532*
Parker, Roberta, R. Parker & Assoc., Inc. (R), NY, *159*
Pascal, Rick, Rick Pascal & Assoc., Inc. (C), NJ, *504*
Penney, Robert J., Sales Consultants of Westchester-South, Inc. (C), NY, *561*
Pettengill, Maurice A., Associated Recruiters (C), WI, *254*
Phillips, Jim, Executive Search, Ltd. (C), OH, *336*
Phillips, Walter, Phillips Int'l., Inc. (C), SC, *510*
Plattenburg, Ted W., Bason Associates (R), OH, *13*
Putnam, A.E., ISC of Cincinnati Inc. (C), OH, *394*
Reyes, Randolph, Management Recruiters of Columbia (C), MD, *450*
Reyes, Renee, Management Recruiters of Columbia (C), MD, *450*
Richards, R. Glenn, Executive Directions (R), OH, *62*
Richards, Robert A., Jr., Sloan & Assoc., Inc. (C), VA, *583*
Riley, Jim, Riley Cole (C), CA, *537*
Rossen, Michael, Direct Recruiters, Inc. (C), OH, *312*
Rusnov, Samuel, Michael Latas & Assoc., Inc. (R), OH, *126*
Sargent, Robert A., JM & Company (R), PA, *106*
Schinke, Brenda, HCI Corp. (C), IL, *371*
Schmidt, Jeri E., Blake/Hansen & Schmidt, Ltd. (R), NY, *18*
Schroeder, John W., SpencerStuart (R), TX, *197*
Schwartz, Alan M., Selective Management Services, Inc. (C), FL, *578*
Scott, E. Ann, Scott Executive Search, Inc. (R), NY, *186*
Shea, John, The Altco Group (C), NJ, *246*
Shehan, Paul, Sales Consultants of Dallas (C), TX, *563*
Sloan, Michael D., Sloan & Assoc., Inc. (C), VA, *583*
Smith, Gayle, J. Burke & Assoc., Inc. (C), TX, *276*
Steel, Mark D., Selective Management Services, Inc. (C), FL, *578*
Steinberg, Paul D., IMA Search, Inc. (R), NY, *101*
Storfer, Herbert F., Storfer & Assoc. (C), NY, *595*
Storfer, Herbert F., The Dartmouth Group (R), NY, *46*
Sweet, Eleanor Anne, The Remington Group (R), IL, *174*
Tabor, Gary, Careers On Track (C), NJ, *283*
Tawney, Mel, M. L. Tawney & Assoc. (C), TX, *600*
Taylor, Dick, Packaging Personnel Co., Ltd. (C), WI, *501*
Terlizzi, R. Louis, Bryan & Louis Research (C), OH, *275*
Tippel, Fred C., Fred C. Tippel & Assoc. (C), OH, *607*
Vague, Mark, F-O-R-T-U-N-E of West Portland (C), OR, *348*
Valmore, Kim, Professions, Inc. (C), OH, *523*
Volpe, Louis, Fox, White & Assoc. (C), FL, *351*
White, Evelyne F., Fox, White & Assoc. (C), FL, *351*
White, J.W., Schneider, Hill & Spangler, Inc. (R), PA, *185*
Wilfong, Jean, Johnson Brown Assoc., Inc. (C), IN, *400*
Woods, Jacques, Ray & Berndtson/Laurendeau Labrecque (R), QE, *172*
Wren, Jay, Jay Wren & Assoc. (C), CA, *625*
Wren, Shelly, Sloan & Assoc., Inc. (C), VA, *583*
Wynn, John, Cook Assoc.,® Inc. (R), IL, *40*
Zamjahn, Charles J., River Region Personnel, Inc. (C), LA, *538*

Paint

Fisher, Lawrence C., Mullen Assoc., Inc. (R), NC, *149*
Gres, Ed, Pioneer Executive Consultants (C), ON, *512*
Mullen, James J., Mullen Assoc., Inc. (R), NC, *149*
Sinclair, Paul, Pioneer Executive Consultants (C), ON, *512*

Paper

Ambruster, David L., Renaissance Resources, LLC (R), VA, *174*
Andrews, Charles, The Borton Wallace Co. (R), TN, *19*
Angell, Tryg R., Tryg R. Angell, Ltd. (C), CT, *250*
Bjong, Mary, The Lawson Group, Inc. (C), SC, *414*
Brown, C.C. Jay, Fortune Personnel Consultants of Raleigh, Inc. (C), NC, *348*
Buckland, G. Russell, The Bedford Consulting Group Inc. (R), ON, *15*
Cegelski, Chris, The H. S. Group, Inc. (C), WI, *365*
Charron, Maynard G., Paper Industry Recruitment (P.I.R.) (C), ME, *502*
Christensen, Garn, F-O-R-T-U-N-E Personnel Consultants of Boise (R), ID, *70*

Coco, Jr., Carl, Professions, Inc. (C), OH, *523*
Corder, Eutha, RBW Assoc. Inc. (C), AR, *531*
Dillon, Mark E., NaTek Corp. (C), NY, *488*
Domres, Terry A., Domres Professional Search (R), WI, *53*
Draper, Gary, Heritage Pacific Corp. (C), CA, *376*
Fremon, Michael W., The Revere Assoc., Inc. (R), OH, *176*
Froelich, K., Murphy Partners Int'l. (R), IL, *150*
Gandee, Joan C., Management Recruiters of Sugar Land Inc. (C), TX, *464*
Gaw, F. William, Brandywine Management Group (R), MD, *22*
Gehle, Frederick P., Dunhill Professional Search of Augusta (C), GA, *320*
Gross, Philip, Professions, Inc. (C), OH, *523*
Heybroek, Eric J., Sanford Rose Assoc. - Rockville (C), MD, *568*
Hillner, Jill, Continental Research Search, Inc. (C), WI, *298*
Hughes, Tim, Hughes & Assoc. Int'l. Inc. (C), AL, *383*
Jansen, Carl, Search North America, Inc. (C), OR, *576*
Kirchgessner, Ken, Management Recruiters of Pensacola (C), FL, *444*
Knapp, Miranda, Cook Assoc.,® Inc. (R), IL, *40*
Lachance, Roger, Ray & Berndtson/Laurendeau Labrecque (R), QE, *172*
Lasini, Dennis, Genesis Research (C), MO, *356*
Lawson, James W., The Lawson Group, Inc. (C), SC, *414*
Marsteller, Linda, Marsteller Wilcox Assoc. (C), IL, *471*
Martin, Wayne, Human Resources Personnel Agency (R), AR, *99*
May, William M., Management Recruiters of Decatur, LLC (C), AL, *438*
McCracken, Terri, T E M Assoc. (C), WI, *599*
McGrath, Robert E., Robert E. McGrath & Assoc. (R), CT, *141*
McRobbie, Jason, Forest People Int'l. Search Ltd. (C), BC, *343*
Morse, Jeffrey A., Brandywine Management Group (R), MD, *22*
Newcomb, Carol A., Tierney Assoc., Inc. (R), PA, *209*
Norrie, Vicki, F-O-R-T-U-N-E Personnel Consultants of Boise (R), ID, *70*
O'Reilly, William E., Management Recruiters of Cincinnati/Sharonville, Inc. (C), OH, *457*
Parker, Murray B., The Borton Wallace Co. (R), NC, *19*
Rose, V. Thomas, F-O-R-T-U-N-E Personnel Consultants of Boise (R), ID, *70*
Schwartz, Alan M., Selective Management Services, Inc. (C), FL, *578*
Sexton, Lynn, Engineering Placement Specialists (C), WI, *330*
Shearer, Gary F., Management Recruiters of Bonita Springs, Inc. (C), FL, *443*
Siegrist, Jeffrey M., Foster Partners (R), NC, *71*
Steel, Mark D., Selective Management Services, Inc. (C), FL, *578*
Sturgess, Don, Wood West & Partners Inc. (C), BC, *624*
Tippel, Fred C., Fred C. Tippel & Assoc. (C), OH, *607*
Vague, Mark, F-O-R-T-U-N-E of West Portland (C), OR, *348*
Valmore, Kim, Professions, Inc. (C), OH, *523*
Wheeler, Ray B., RBW Assoc. Inc. (C), OR, *531*
Wynn, John, Cook Assoc.,® Inc. (R), IL, *40*
Young, Paula G., Career Counseling Inc. (CCI) (C), KY, *282*

PeopleSoft

Christ, Celeste, Quality Consulting Group, Inc. (C), WI, *526*
Cognac, Michael, Retained Search Assoc. (R), NC, *176*
Davis Wolfe, Kathryn, HDB Incorporated (C), MO, *371*
Geiman, Barry, Leader Institute, Inc. (C), GA, *414*
Gerlach, Mary, Quality Consulting Group, Inc. (C), WI, *526*
Harmon, Jerry, Delta Resource Group, Ltd. (C), GA, *311*
Hulme, Doug, Leader Institute, Inc. (C), GA, *414*
Huntley, David E., Huntley Associates (Dallas), Inc. (C), TX, *386*
Mesina, Roman, The Consulting Group of North America, Inc. (C), VA, *297*
Perkins, Yvonne, Leader Institute, Inc. (C), GA, *414*
Plavin, Avery, The Consulting Group of North America, Inc. (C), VA, *297*
Robbins, Mark, Search Solutions Inc. (C), CA, *576*
Sprouse, Laurie, Tech-Net (C), TX, *601*
Swami, Pad N., Fortuna Technologies Inc. (C), CA, *343*
Vlahos, Ben, Leader Institute, Inc. (C), GA, *414*
Zabor, Richard, Leader Institute, Inc. (C), GA, *414*

Pesticides

Molliver, Marshall E., National Search, Inc. (R), NC, *151*

Pet food

Howell, Jeff, Whittaker & Assoc., Inc. (C), GA, *620*
Smith, Charles D., Smith & Laue Search (R), OR, *193*
Smith, Martin, Hughes & Company (R), VA, *98*
Whittaker, Arnold G., Whittaker & Assoc., Inc. (C), GA, *620*

Petrochemical

Collier, Gordon L., R. C. Services (C), TX, *528*
Dexter, Peter, Search Research Assoc., Inc. (R), MA, *187*
Hughes, Tim, Hughes & Assoc. Int'l. Inc. (C), AL, *383*
McClain, Jack, PIC Executive Search (C), GA, *511*
Morgan, Richard, Morgan Samuels Co. (R), CA, *147*
Schlect, Nancy, Morgan Samuels Co. (R), CA, *147*
Scott, Sabrina, Professional Search, Inc. Int'l. (C), TX, *523*
Walhof, Chris, Management Recruiters of Boise (C), ID, *446*

Pharmaceutical

Adams, Lauren, Fortune Group Int'l., Inc. (R), PA, *70*
Agriesti, Kay, Agriesti & Assoc. (C), CA, *243*
Akre, Suzanne, Healthcare Recruiters Int'l. Phoenix (C), AZ, *372*
Archie, Otis, Kuhn Med-Tech (C), CA, *409*
Arnold, Jerome M., Houtz•Strawn & Arnold, Inc. (R), TX, *96*
Arsenault, Alfred J., Insight Consulting Co. (C), NY, *389*
Artze, Angeles, A. Artze Assoc.-Personnel Consultants (C), PR, *253*
Banister, John, Delta ProSearch (C), PA, *311*
Barkley, Keith, The Mackenzie Group (R), MD, *133*
Baron, Annette S., Eagle Research, Inc. (C), NJ, *325*
Bauer, Robert, Sampson Medical Search (C), AZ, *564*
Bauman, Ina, The Bauman Group (R), CA, *14*
Benkwitt, Barbara, The Brentwood Group, Inc. (R), NJ, *22*
Bever, Hugh, Kingsley Quinn/USA (R), NJ, *115*
Bilinski, Kalyna, Coe & Co. Int'l. Inc./EMA Partners Int'l. (R), AB, *37*
Blakslee, Jan H., J: Blakslee Int'l., Ltd. (R), CA, *18*
Blank, Paula, Lewis & Blank Int'l. (R), CA, *129*
Boccuzi, Joseph H., SpencerStuart (R), NY, *196*
Boje, Bruce A., Westfields Int'l., Inc. (C), NY, *619*
Bormann, David C., Yungner & Bormann (R), MN, *226*
Bouchard, Rena Roberts, Strategic Resources Biotechnology & Medical Group (C), WA, *595*
Briggs, Farris R., Staff Resources, Inc. (C), SC, *590*

RECRUITER SPECIALTIES

Brissenden, Hoke, Brissenden, McFarland, Fuccella & Reynolds, Inc. (R), NJ, *23*
Bunker, Ralph, Management Recruiters of San Luis Obispo (C), CA, *439*
Burkey, Julie V., J. Burkey Assoc. (R), NJ, *25*
Campbell, Sandra, Management Recruiters of Milford Inc. (C), CT, *442*
Caplan, John, The Caplan-Taylor Group (R), CA, *28*
Caplan, Shellie, Caplan Assoc., Inc. (R), NJ, *28*
Christopher, Rosemarie, Med Exec Int'l. (C), CA, *476*
Chrzan, Phyllis, Brethet, Barnum & Assoc., Inc. (C), ON, *273*
Ciari, Kate Regan, Fortune Personnel Consultants (C), MT, *347*
Cimicata, Richard, National Search Assoc. (C), CA, *490*
Clark, Ellen H., Clark Executive Search (C), NY, *292*
Clark, Elliot, Raymond Karsan Assoc. (C), NJ, *530*
Cobb, Lynn A., Management Recruiters of Springfield, Inc. (C), IL, *447*
Coghan, Tom, The Yaiser Group (C), NJ, *625*
Collins, Steve L., S L Collins Assoc. (C), NC, *294*
Conedera, Joanne, Icon Recruiters, LLC (C), CA, *387*
Cooper, Bill, Management Recruiters of Chattanooga-Brainerd, Inc. (C), TN, *461*
Cooper, Larry, Management Recruiters of Atlanta (C), GA, *445*
Cracknell, Jo Anne, NCC Executive Search Consultants (C), CA, *490*
Crossman, Chuck, The Stewart Group (C), FL, *593*
Crumpley, Jim, Jim Crumpley & Assoc. (C), MO, *304*
Curry, Michael J., Curry, Telleri Group, Inc. (R), NJ, *44*
DeMan, Denise, Bench Int'l. Search, Inc. (R), CA, *15*
Dietrich, Sandra, Fortune Personnel Consultants of Hilton Head (C), SC, *349*
Dimke, Tom, Raymond Karsan Assoc. (C), PA, *530*
Eastwood, Gary, Beck/Eastwood Recruitment Solutions (C), CA, *261*
Elizondo, Jennifer, Management Recruiters of Fresno (C), CA, *440*
Feerst, James E., James Feerst & Assoc., Inc. (C), AZ, *339*
Fisher, Jack Stuart, Jack Stuart Fisher Assoc. (C), NJ, *341*
Froelich, K., Murphy Partners Int'l. (R), IL, *150*
Gallagher, Michael, Mankuta Gallagher & Assoc., Inc. (C), FL, *468*
Gasbarre, John, The Haystack Group, Inc. (R), ME, *88*
Gladstone, Athur, Roth Young Executive Search (C), TX, *546*
Gostin, Howard I., Sanford Rose Assoc. - Columbia, MD (C), MD, *567*
Greenberg, Louise, Ruderfer & Co., Inc. (C), NJ, *548*
Hardbrod, Herbert, Management Recruiters of Middlesex County NJ (C), NJ, *454*
Haverty, Carol, Iona Partners (C), CA, *394*
Hebel, Robert W., R. W. Hebel Assoc. (R), TX, *89*
Hetzel, Ben W., Sales Consultants of Chester County, PA (C), PA, *562*
Hill, Ted, Culver Personnel Services (C), CA, *304*
Hirschbein, Don, Management Recruiters Peninsula (C), CA, *439*
Hoffman, Mark, Management Recruiters of Emeryville (C), CA, *440*
Hoffman, Theresa E., Wellington Management Group (R), PA, *217*
Hogan, Ann B., The Hogan Group (C), OH, *380*
Howard, Linda J., Doleman Enterprises (R), VA, *53*
Hurley, Michael, Century Assoc., Inc. (C), PA, *287*
Irwin, Bill, Southern Recruiters & Consultants, Inc. (C), SC, *587*
Jeffers, Robert, Allen-Jeffers Assoc. (C), CA, *245*
Johnson, Mark, Sampson Medical Search (C), CA, *564*
Johnson, Ron L., Management Recruiters of Fresno (C), CA, *440*
Johnson, Sean M., Healthcare Recruiters Int'l. - Alabama (C), AL, *372*
Johnston, J. Reid, Hughes & Company (R), VA, *98*
Jones, Michael A., The Century Group (C), KS, *287*
Jose, William, Management Recruiters of Woodbury Inc. (C), NY, *455*
Jurenovich, Gary S., The Stewart Group (C), FL, *593*
Kaiser, Joe, Fortune Personnel Consultants of Anderson, Inc. (C), SC, *349*
Kasten, Marc, Fortune Personnel Consultants (C), CA, *344*
Kazan, J. Neil, Kazan International, Inc. (R), NJ, *110*
Klein, Howard G., F-O-R-T-U-N-E Personnel Consultants of Bergen County Inc. (C), NJ, *347*
Kleinman, Victor, The Stevenson Group, Inc. (R), FL, *200*
Kress, Daryl, Fortune Personnel Consultants of Anderson, Inc. (C), SC, *349*
Kuhl, William R., Place Mart Personnel Service (C), NJ, *513*
Labrecque, B. F., Ray & Berndtson/Laurendeau Labrecque (R), QE, *172*
Lareau, Belle, The Hampton Group (C), NY, *368*
Layton, Bernard, Morgan Int'l., Inc. (R), IL, *147*
LeBow, Joanne, Harbrowe, Inc. (C), NY, *368*
Lee, Albert G., Albert G. Lee Assoc. (C), RI, *415*
Leech, David M., Houtz•Strawn & Arnold, Inc. (R), TX, *96*
Leinen, Rebecca, Management Recruiters - Piedmont (C), VA, *464*
Len, Ronald D., Healthcare Recruiters International-NY/NJ (C), NJ, *373*
Lennon, Bill, Hall Management Group, Inc. (C), GA, *367*
Lerner, Joel S., Sanford Rose Assoc. - Louisville (C), KY, *567*
Levin, Becky, Levin & Company, Inc. (R), MA, *128*
Lewis, Daphne V., Lewis & Blank Int'l. (R), CA, *129*
Licata, Pat, Pat Licata & Assoc. (C), NC, *417*
Long, Helga, Horton Int'l. Inc. (R), NY, *96*
Lord, J. Scott, J. S. Lord & Company, Inc. (R), MA, *131*
Lurier, Amy B., TechFind, Inc. (R), MA, *207*
Lybrook, David, Lybrook Assoc., Inc. (C), RI, *421*
Majczan, Robert, Ken Clark Int'l. (R), NJ, *36*
Mankuta, Eric G., EGM Consulting, Inc. (R), FL, *57*
Maslan, Neal L., LAI Ward Howell (R), CA, *123*
Matteson, Scott, Horizon Medical Search of NH (C), NH, *381*
McCann, Mary Ellen, Wellington Management Group (R), PA, *217*
McGeehan, Gayle A., Management Recruiters of Bethlehem, PA (C), PA, *458*
McGrath, Robert E., Robert E. McGrath & Assoc. (R), CT, *141*
Meltser, Thomas, Patriot Assoc. (C), PA, *505*
Mero, Kevin J., innovativestaffsearch (C), TX, *389*
Mero, Kevin J., innovativestaffsearch (C), WI, *389*
Miller, Judith E., James Feerst & Assoc., Inc. (C), AZ, *339*
Mitchell, William G., Eagle Consulting Group Inc. (C), TX, *325*
Monroe, Jr., Kenneth R., Sanford Rose Assoc. - Clearwater (C), FL, *566*
Montgomery, Rita, Healthcare Recruiters Int'l. - Los Angeles (C), CA, *372*
Moore, Sandee, Moore Research Assoc. (R), NJ, *147*
Morgan, Paul, Sanford Rose Assoc. - Columbia (C), SC, *570*
Mullen, Maryrose H., Emmett Executive Search, Inc. (C), NY, *330*
Mustin, Joyce, J: Blakslee Int'l., Ltd. (R), CA, *18*
Newell, Carlyle, Management Alliance Group, Inc. (R), NJ, *134*
Norindr, Bev, The Hampton Group (C), NY, *368*
Ornstein, Carole, CSA/Clinical Staffing Assoc., LLC (C), NJ, *304*
Ortman, Jim, Ortman Recruiting Int'l. (C), CA, *500*
Oster, R. Rush, Management Recruiters of Anna Maria Island (C), FL, *443*
Ottke, Robert C., Robert Ottke Assoc. (R), CA, *157*

Pace, Susan A., Horton International Inc. (R), CT, *96*
Pacini, Joseph, Premier Business Advisors (C), PA, *516*
Pagana, Pat, The Brentwood Group, Inc. (R), NJ, *22*
Paine, Donne G., Fortune Personnel Consultants of Hilton Head (C), SC, *349*
Pajak, Michael A., The Danielson Group, Inc. (C), TX, *306*
Peluso, Philip, National Search Assoc. (C), CA, *490*
Pencarski, Robert, Bio-Venture Group (C), RI, *266*
Perlman, Dan, Romac Int'l., Inc. (C), FL, *543*
Perry, Len, The Caplan-Taylor Group (R), CA, *28*
Peskosky, Mike, Prime Search (C), NC, *518*
Pfannenstiel, Roseann, Fortune Group Int'l., Inc. (R), PA, *70*
Piatkiewicz, Mary Lou, Medical Executive Search Assoc., Inc. (C), AZ, *477*
Piatkiewicz, William L., Medical Executive Search Assoc., Inc. (C), AZ, *477*
Pike, Geoff, F-O-R-T-U-N-E Personnel Consultants of Greenwood Village (C), CO, *344*
Piper, William D., W. P. Assoc. (C), CA, *613*
Porada, Stephen D., S.D.P. Contract Recruiters (C), NJ, *550*
Pritchett, Philip H., FORTUNE Personnel Consultants of North Dallas (C), TX, *350*
Remkus, Valerie, The Hampton Group (C), NY, *368*
Reynolds, John H., Brissenden, McFarland, Fuccella & Reynolds, Inc. (R), NJ, *23*
Rimele, J. R., Sales Recruiters of Oklahoma City (C), OK, *564*
Robbins, Melvyn, Healthcare Recruiters of New England (C), MA, *373*
Roe, Sylvia A., Craig Roe & Assoc., LLC (C), MD, *540*
Romanchek, Walter R., Wellington Management Group (R), PA, *217*
Romeo, Paul C., Romeo-Hudgins & Assoc., Ltd. (C), NJ, *545*
Rosenthal, Abbe L., ALW Research Int'l. (R), NJ, *4*
Ross, Ruthie M., Recruitment Resources (C), CA, *532*
Rutkauskas, Patsy A., Sales Consultants of Bangor, Inc. (C), ME, *559*
Sabbio, Kathy, The Brentwood Group, Inc. (R), NJ, *22*
Sampson, Judie, Sampson Medical Search (C), CA, *564*
Sampson, Kellie, Sampson Medical Search (C), CA, *564*
Santamaria, Jay, The Beam Group (R), NY, *14*
Schall, William, The Stevenson Group, Inc. (R), FL, *200*
Scherck, III, Henry J., LAI Ward Howell (R), NY, *123*
Schindel, Kim, Searchworks, Inc. (C), FL, *577*
Schwartz, Raymond, The Partnership Group (R), NJ, *160*
Scott, George, Raymond Karsan Assoc. (C), PA, *530*
Secor, David B., The Search Committee (C), MD, *574*
Sheedy, III, Edward J., Dieckmann & Assoc., Ltd. (R), IL, *51*
Shiell, Donald M., Shiell Personnel (C), LA, *580*
Shiley, Bob, Brethet, Barnum & Assoc., Inc. (C), ON, *273*
Slaton, C. Philip, Icon Recruiters, LLC (C), CA, *387*
Solomon, Phyllis, Phyllis Solomon Executive Search, Inc. (C), NJ, *587*
Spargo, Rick, Personnel Solutions (C), AZ, *509*
Spencer, Norman, FORTUNE Personnel Consultants of North Dallas (C), TX, *350*
Stevens, Jennifer A., Ledbetter/Davidson Int'l., Inc. (R), NY, *127*
Stevenson, Jani, Howard Fischer Assoc. Int'l., Inc. (R), TX, *67*
Stewart, James H., The Stewart Group (C), FL, *593*
Stewart, Tina Hunter, BioPharmMed (C), FL, *267*
Stockton, J. R., Management Catalysts (R), NJ, *134*
Storfer, Paul D., Storfer & Assoc. (C), NY, *595*
Storfer, Paul D., The Dartmouth Group (R), NY, *46*
Strand, Michael G., Fortune Group Int'l., Inc. (R), PA, *70*
Stratman, Sandra, Management Recruiters of Milford Inc. (C), CT, *442*
Strawn, William M., Houtz•Strawn & Arnold, Inc. (R), TX, *96*
Sullivan, Donald S., Executives Worldwide, Inc. (C), OR, *337*
Taylor, John, The Caplan-Taylor Group (R), AZ, *28*
Tomkin, Shelly, Career Counseling Ltd. (C.C.L.) (C), NY, *282*
Travis, John A., Travis & Co., Inc. (R), MA, *210*
Trosin, Walt, Johnson Smith & Knisely (R), NJ, *107*
VanDolah, A. F., Management Recruiters of Lionville, Inc. (C), PA, *459*
Vice, Michael, D.A.I Human Resources Consultants (R), QE, *45*
Visnich, L. Christine, Bason Associates (R), OH, *13*
Weiss, Linda S., Pharmaceutical Recruiters, Inc. (R), NY, *163*
Weston, Joan C., F-O-R-T-U-N-E Personnel Consultants of Wilmington (C), DE, *344*
Weston, Leonard A., F-O-R-T-U-N-E Personnel Consultants of Wilmington (C), DE, *344*
Williams, Kandi, Medical Executive Recruiters (C), CA, *477*
Wonderfund, Vicky, Management Recruiters of Columbia (C), MD, *450*
Yaiser, Richard A., The Yaiser Group (C), NJ, *625*
Young, Florence D., Alexander Enterprises, Inc. (C), PA, *243*
Young, Stephanie, Alexander Enterprises, Inc. (C), PA, *243*
Yungner, Steven J., Yungner & Bormann (R), MN, *226*
Zackrison, Walter, Zackrison Assoc., Inc. (C), FL, *627*
Zaring, David, Management Recruiters of Plant City, Inc. (C), FL, *444*
Zipfel, John, Debbon Recruiting Group, Inc. (C), MO, *310*

PHD's

Boutin, Jean, Pharmaceutical Search Professionals, Inc. (C), PA, *510*
Graham, David, Pharmaceutical Search Professionals, Inc. (C), PA, *510*
Wuko, John D., Pharmaceutical Search Professionals, Inc. (C), PA, *510*

Physical therapy

Corkum, Jennifer, Doherty Healthcare Consultants (C), ME, *313*
Dinino, Sabina, Trillium Human Resources Inc. (C), ON, *609*
Hollander, Heidi, Career Counseling Ltd. (C.C.L.) (C), NY, *282*
Talbot, Lorri, Trillium Human Resources Inc. (C), ON, *609*
Waller, Victoria, Health Search, Inc. (C), KS, *371*
Watson, Diana L., Premier Healthcare Recruiters, Inc. (C), MI, *516*

Physicians

Alexander, Susan M., Manuso, Alexander & Associates, Inc. (R), NY, *135*
Allen, Jay, Jay Allen & Assoc. (C), FL, *244*
Allhands, Kelly, Allhands Placement Consultants (C), IN, *245*
Anderson, Trevor, Kincaid Group Inc. (KGI) (C), TX, *406*
Balsamo, Mike, JPM International (C), CA, *401*
Bariola, Dara, American Medical Recruiting Co. Inc. (C), MS, *248*
Baumann, John, Jacobson Assoc. (C), GA, *396*
Beiter, Sheila M., Pathfinders Int'l. (C), MI, *504*
Bergeon, Eric, Vickers Chambless Managed Search (C), GA, *289*
Bicknell, Helen M., Born & Bicknell, Inc. (C), LA, *270*
Born, Jane E., Born & Bicknell, Inc. (C), FL, *270*
Born, Samuel J., Born & Bicknell, Inc. (C), FL, *270*
Boutin, Jean, Pharmaceutical Search Professionals, Inc. (C), PA, *510*
Brin, Bradley, Concorde Staff Source Inc. (C), WI, *296*

RECRUITER SPECIALTIES

Bruce, Linda, The Whitaker Companies (C), TX, *619*
Burke, Markey, Brandywine Management Group (R), MD, *22*
Carlton, Sara B., Rob Dey Executive Search (R), MD, *49*
Cassandras, Stephanie, Sherriff & Assoc. (C), KS, *580*
Ciancio, Marybeth, Christopher and Long (C), MO, *291*
Cinquina, Jr., V. James, Merlin Int'l. Inc. (C), NJ, *479*
Collingwood, Beryl, Trillium Human Resources Inc. (C), ON, *609*
Conedera, Joanne, Icon Recruiters, LLC (C), CA, *387*
Corkum, Jennifer, Doherty Healthcare Consultants (C), ME, *313*
Cowan, Roberta, Drew Assoc. Int'l. (R), NJ, *54*
Daugherty-Hill, Kimberly J., Hayman Daugherty Assoc., Inc. (C), GA, *370*
DeFranco, Manny, Physician Recruiting Services, Inc. (C), MO, *511*
Dietz, David, MSI Int'l. (C), LA, *487*
Doherty, Shawn, Doherty Healthcare Consultants (C), ME, *313*
DuBois, Anthony G., Horizon Medical Search of NH (C), NH, *381*
DuBois, Jr., Joseph W., Horizon Medical Search of NH (C), NH, *381*
DuBois, Sabine G., Horizon Medical Search of NH (C), NH, *381*
Dye, Carson E., LAI Ward Howell (R), OH, *123*
Eren, Sal, Medserve & Assoc. Inc. (C), MD, *478*
Estelle, Tracy, Kincaid Group Inc. (KGI) (C), TX, *406*
Fineman, David M., Manuso, Alexander & Associates, Inc. (R), NY, *135*
Foster, David, Doherty Healthcare Consultants (C), ME, *313*
Gaudette, Charles L., Medical Recruiters Exchange (C), AZ, *477*
Gibney, Patrick, Medfall Inc. (C), ON, *476*
Glick, Douglas I., MedSearch Resources, Inc. (C), FL, *478*
Grace, Madison, Medicorp, Inc. (C), MO, *477*
Graham, David, Pharmaceutical Search Professionals, Inc. (C), PA, *510*
Grebenschikoff, Jennifer R., Physician Executive Management Center (R), FL, *164*
Harrison, John S., Practice Dynamics, Inc. (C), TX, *515*
Hiesiger, Emile M., Manuso, Alexander & Associates, Inc. (R), NY, *135*
Hochgraber, Kent, Dunhill Personnel Service of Fargo (C), ND, *322*
Hollander, Heidi, Career Counseling Ltd. (C.C.L.) (C), IL, *282*
Hollander, Heidi, Career Counseling Ltd. (C.C.L.) (C), NY, *282*
Howell, Janice Hopkins, Rob Dey Executive Search (R), FL, *49*
Jacobs, Ken, Joseph Goldring & Assoc. Inc. (C), MI, *360*
Jacobs, Phillip E., E. J. Michaels, Ltd. (C), NY, *481*
Johnson, Frank Y., Healthcare Recruiters Int'l. - Alabama (C), AL, *372*
Johnson, Jack, Medicorp, Inc. (C), MO, *477*
Johnson, Lisa M., LJ Networking, Inc. (C), MD, *418*
Johnson, Sean M., Healthcare Recruiters Int'l. - Alabama (C), AL, *372*
Kendall, James C., Kendall & Davis Co., Inc. (C), MO, *405*
Kincaid, Raymond W., Kincaid Group Inc. (KGI) (C), TX, *406*
Kirschman, David R., Physician Executive Management Center (R), FL, *164*
Kirschner, Michael, American Medical Consultants, Inc. (C), FL, *248*
Leighton, Sheldon, Bailey Employment System Inc. (C), CT, *257*
Linney, George, Tyler & Company (R), GA, *212*
Lovett, Karen M., Practice Dynamics, Inc. (C), TX, *515*
Lowderman, William, Loderman & Costello (C), GA, *419*
Lyons, Mary Francis, Witt/Kieffer, Ford, Hadelman & Lloyd (R), MO, *223*
Magic, Michael F., Scott Douglas Inc. (C), CA, *573*
Manuso, James S. J., Manuso, Alexander & Associates, Inc. (R), NY, *135*
McMillan, Chuck, Physician Recruiting Services, Inc. (C), MO, *511*
Mero, Kevin J., innovativestaffsearch (C), TX, *389*
Mero, Kevin J., innovativestaffsearch (C), WI, *389*
Meyer, Verne, Delacore Resources (C), MN, *310*
Osinski, Martin H., American Medical Consultants, Inc. (C), FL, *247*
Perry, Cole, Jay Allen & Assoc. (C), FL, *244*
Pinkerton, Paul, American Medical Recruiting Co. Inc. (C), MS, *248*
Proctor, Richard W., Foley Proctor Yoskowitz (R), NJ, *69*
Prouty, Alden F., Manuso, Alexander & Associates, Inc. (R), NY, *135*
Rachels, John, Southwestern Professional Services (C), VA, *588*
Rae, Fern, Career Counseling Ltd. (C.C.L.) (C), IL, *282*
Scaturro, Mary Ellen, Boone-Scaturro Assoc., Inc. (C), GA, *269*
Shasteen, Martha F., Primary Care Service Corp. (C), GA, *518*
Shasteen, Stephen P., Primary Care Service Corp. (C), GA, *518*
Sherriff, Julie A., Sherriff & Assoc. (C), KS, *580*
Sherriff, William W., Sherriff & Assoc. (C), KS, *580*
Sikes, Charles R., Medical Search of America, Inc. (C), GA, *477*
Sikes, Laurie L., Medical Search of America, Inc. (C), GA, *477*
Skupsky, Lorraine, Skupsky & Assoc. (C), CO, *583*
Slaton, C. Philip, Icon Recruiters, LLC (C), CA, *387*
Socha, Rudy, Advancement Recruiting Services (C), OH, *241*
Stern, Daniel, Daniel Stern & Assoc. (C), PA, *592*
Stoll, Joan, Medfall Inc. (C), ON, *476*
Sullivan, Steve, Jackson & Coker (C), GA, *396*
Valone, Michael, UniQuest Int'l., Inc. (C), FL, *611*
Waldman, Noah W., LAI Ward Howell (R), GA, *123*
Watson, Diana L., Premier Healthcare Recruiters, Inc. (C), MI, *516*
Whitlow, M. Blanton, Manuso, Alexander & Associates, Inc. (R), NY, *135*
Wilkins, Walter K., Walter K. Wilkins & Co. (R), NJ, *221*
Williams, Alexander H., Witt/Kieffer, Ford, Hadelman & Lloyd (R), NY, *223*
Winterburn, Karen, Heartland National Medical Search (C), IL, *374*
Wright, Linda, Acuity Medical Recruitment (C), MS, *239*
Wuko, John D., Pharmaceutical Search Professionals, Inc. (C), PA, *510*
Zahradka, James F., P. J. Murphy & Assoc., Inc. (R), WI, *150*
Ziarko, Jacqueline R., Selective Search Associates (C), OH, *578*
Ziegler, Helen, Helen Ziegler & Assoc., Inc. (C), ON, *627*

Pipe & tube

Fruchtman, Gary, Management Recruiters of Northwest Ohio, Inc. (C), OH, *458*

Pipeline

Cole, Floyd, National Field Service Corp. (C), NY, *489*

Plant

Brown, Ginny, Stewart/Greene & Co. of The Triad, Inc. (C), NC, *594*
Esler, Mike, Strategic Resources (C), WA, *595*
Goldbeck, Henry, Goldbeck Recruiting Inc. (C), BC, *359*
Hetherington, Don, Landon Morgan (C), ON, *412*
Hirsch, Ruth, Ruth Hirsch Assoc., Inc. (C), NY, *379*
Jesberg, Gary H., Michael Latas & Assoc., Inc. (R), MO, *126*
Little, John J., Alpha Executive Search (C), AL, *246*
Martin, Bill, Fortune Personnel Consultants of Greensboro, NC, Inc. (C), NC, *348*
McKinney, Adrienne, Wachendorfer & Assoc. (C), TX, *613*
Mitchell, Lauren, Wachendorfer & Assoc. (C), TX, *613*

Ormond, Mark R., Capstone Consulting, Inc. (R), IL, *29*
Palos, Michael V., Kelly Associates (R), PA, *112*
Roach, Ronald R., Sanford Rose Assoc. - Burlington, NC (C), NC, *569*
Skelton, Brenda, Cumberland Professional Search Inc. (C), TN, *304*
Tomeo, Pat, S-H-S TechStaff (C), PA, *550*

Plastics

Allen, Jim, Southern Chemical & Plastics Search (C), GA, *587*
Andrews, David, Engineering Futures, LLC (C), CT, *330*
Ballou, Jodie, Management Recruiters of the Baltimore Washington Corridor (C), MD, *450*
Bason, Maurice L., Bason Associates (R), OH, *13*
Bauzenberger, III, E. H., The Currier-Winn Co., Inc. (C), NJ, *305*
Beck, Joseph W., National Computerized Employment Service, Inc. (C), PA, *489*
Bell, Lindy, Fortune Personnel Consultants of Huntsville, Inc. (C), AL, *344*
Bethmann, Chris, Southern Recruiters & Consultants, Inc. (C), SC, *587*
Bittner, Greg, NHA Plastics Recruiters (C), FL, *493*
Brown, James D., Northern Consultants Inc. (R), ME, *153*
Cahn, Juliette Lang, Juliette Lang Cahn Executive Search (C), NY, *279*
Clark, Jim, Management Recruiters of Pensacola (C), FL, *444*
Colbourn, Ken, F-O-R-T-U-N-E Personnel Consultants of Knoxville (C), TN, *350*
Compton, Bill, F-O-R-T-U-N-E Personnel Consultants of St. Louis-West County (C), MO, *347*
Creeger, David, Sanford Rose Assoc. - Fairlawn (C), OH, *569*
David, Dave, Executive Resource Assoc. (C), VA, *334*
Dugan, John H., J. H. Dugan & Assoc., Inc. (R), CA, *55*
Duke, Ann, Sanford Rose Assoc. - Fairlawn (C), OH, *569*
Enrico, Jim, Unisearch Search & Recruiting Inc. (C), AZ, *611*
Ford, Travis, Ford & Assoc., Inc. (C), SC, *343*
Fountas, N. G., JLI-Boston (R), MA, *106*
Freeman, Evelyn, Brierwood Group, Inc. (C), IN, *274*
Fremon, Michael W., The Revere Assoc., Inc. (R), OH, *176*
Fruchtman, Gary, Management Recruiters of Northwest Ohio, Inc. (C), OH, *458*
Gerst, Thomas J., Management Recruiters of Akron (C), OH, *457*
Grant, Anthony, Management Recruiters of Columbia (C), MD, *450*
Gros, Dennis, Gros Executive Search, Inc. (C), TN, *363*
Hildebrand, John D., JM & Company (R), PA, *106*
Hiller, Arnie, U.S. Search (C), VA, *610*
Holloway, Roger M., Management Recruiters of Lake Co., Inc. (C), FL, *444*
Johnson, John, HRNI (C), MI, *383*
Just, Debra, Just Management Services Inc. (C), TN, *402*
Just, Susan, Just Management Services Inc. (C), FL, *402*
Kirchgessner, Ken, Management Recruiters of Pensacola (C), FL, *444*
Lane, Andrew J., Overton Consulting (R), WI, *157*
Lawry, William R., W. R. Lawry, Inc. (R), CT, *126*
Lewis, Al, The Stelton Group, Inc. (C), NJ, *592*
Linstead, Rick, Carnegie Resources, Inc. (C), NC, *284*
Lybrook, David, Lybrook Assoc., Inc. (C), RI, *421*
Lyngen, C. J., Construct Management Services (C), MN, *297*
Lyons, Olin, Lyons Pruitt Int'l. (R), PA, *132*
Machi, Michael T., Management Recruiters of Pleasanton (C), CA, *441*
Mathey, Joyce, Mathey Services (C), IL, *472*
Mattocks, Paul, G. P. Mattocks & Associates (C), NC, *473*
May, William M., Management Recruiters of Decatur, LLC (C), AL, *438*
McCall, Tom, Tom McCall Executive Search (C), IL, *473*
McElhaney, Ron, Management Recruiters of Savannah (C), GA, *446*
McElhaney, Jr., Ron, Management Recruiters of Savannah (C), GA, *446*
Murray, Patrick, The Murray Group (C), IL, *487*
O'Reilly, William E., Management Recruiters of Cincinnati/Sharonville, Inc. (C), OH, *457*
Pajak, Michael A., The Danielson Group, Inc. (C), TX, *306*
Paterson, David, Scientific Solutions, Inc. (C), MI, *572*
Paterson, Sharon, Scientific Solutions, Inc. (C), MI, *572*
Pike, Dick, Management Recruiters of Burlington (C), NC, *455*
Presley, Robert L., The Inside Track (C), TX, *389*
Price, Rita A., Human Resources Personnel Agency (R), AR, *99*
Reed, Dave, Management Recruiters - Flint (C), MI, *451*
Richards, Paul E., Executive Directions (R), OH, *62*
Roddy, Jack P., J. P. Roddy Consultants (C), PA, *540*
Roth, Bill, Lou Michaels Assoc., Inc. (C), MI, *481*
Sgro, David J., Midland Consultants (C), OH, *481*
Slate, James E., Fortune Personnel Consultants of Topsfield (C), MA, *346*
Snider, Jr., Les, Bryan & Louis Research (C), OH, *275*
Stobbelaar, Rick, The Icard Group, Inc. (C), MI, *387*
Symanski, Donald G., Tierney Assoc., Inc. (R), PA, *209*
Taylor, Sandi M., Strategic Technologies, Inc. (C), TX, *596*
Telleri, Frank C., Curry, Telleri Group, Inc. (R), NJ, *44*
Tillman, Allen, Hardage Group (C), TN, *369*
Tippel, Fred C., Fred C. Tippel & Assoc. (C), OH, *607*
Toms, Dennis M., National Recruiting Service (C), IN, *489*
Tracey, Jay E., Jay Tracey Assoc. Inc. (C), VT, *608*
Vague, Mark, F-O-R-T-U-N-E of West Portland (C), OR, *348*
Villee, Mark, Management Recruiters of Columbia (C), MD, *450*
Vosika, Duane, Sales Consultants of Omaha, Inc. (C), NE, *560*
Wells, Robert A., R. A. Wells Co. (C), GA, *618*
White, David, W. Robert Eissler & Assoc., Inc. (C), TX, *327*
Wynn, John, Cook Assoc.,® Inc. (R), IL, *40*
Young, Paula G., Career Counseling Inc. (CCI) (C), KY, *282*
Zamjahn, Charles J., River Region Personnel, Inc. (C), LA, *538*

Plywood

Gandee, Joan C., Management Recruiters of Sugar Land Inc. (C), TX, *464*
Gandee, John R., Management Recruiters of Sugar Land Inc. (C), TX, *464*
Hayes, Don, Management Recruiters of Sugar Land Inc. (C), TX, *464*

Polymers

McDowell, Jane, Cook Assoc.,® Inc. (R), IL, *40*
Telem, Peter B., Telem Adhesive Search Corp. (C), MD, *605*
Wonderfund, Vicky, Management Recruiters of Columbia (C), MD, *450*

Polyurethane

Hunt, Leigh, Leigh Hunt & Assoc., Inc. (C), ME, *384*

Portfolio management

Elzweig, Mark, Mark Elzweig Co., Ltd. (C), NY, *329*
Hermsen, Patrick, Capital Markets Resources, Inc. (C), NC, *281*
Jostrom, Karen, The Oxbridge Group, Ltd. (C), MA, *500*
Katz, Martin, Crispi, Wagner & Co., Inc. (R), NY, *43*
McFadden, Ashton S., Johnson Smith & Knisely (R), NY, *107*

RECRUITER SPECIALTIES

Miller, Nancy, Mark Elzweig Co., Ltd. (C), NY, *329*
Weinstock, Michael A., Advisors' Search Group, Inc. (C), NY, *241*
Williamson, Joseph R., Johnson Brown Assoc., Inc. (C), IN, *400*

Poultry

Daffala, Ronald, Merit Professional Search, Inc. (C), TN, *479*
Haggard, Luke, First Search America, Inc. (C), AL, *341*
Howell, Jeff, Whittaker & Assoc., Inc. (C), GA, *620*
Johnson, Ray, First Search America, Inc. (C), AL, *341*
Smitherman, Jim, Merit Professional Search, Inc. (C), TN, *479*

Power

Ambruster, David L., Renaissance Resources, LLC (R), VA, *174*
Berry, Skip, PIC Executive Search (C), GA, *511*
Brentari, Michael, Search Consultants Int'l., Inc. (C), TX, *575*
Devaney, Marie, W. Robert Eissler & Assoc., Inc. (C), TX, *327*
Dillon, Mark E., NaTek Corp. (C), NY, *488*
Donelon, Wayne, WMD inc. (C), NJ, *623*
Fisher, Earl, Management Recruiters of Cass County, NE (C), NE, *453*
Granet, Marc, IDC Executive Search Inc. (C), FL, *387*
Howe, Timothy L., The Resource Group (R), NJ, *175*
Luffman, Danae, IDC Executive Search Inc. (C), FL, *387*
Morris, Kevin, PIC Executive Search (C), GA, *511*
Nickels, Edward L., Michael Latas & Assoc., Inc. (R), MO, *126*
Pellitier, Matt, PIC Executive Search (C), GA, *511*
Ragan, William E., Michael Latas & Assoc., Inc. (R), MO, *126*
Ray, Jr., Harry, Management Recruiters of Kanawha Valley, LLC (C), WV, *465*

Presidents

McFeely, Clarence E., Clarence E. McFeely, Inc. (R), IL, *141*
Southworth, David E., Michigan Consulting Group (R), MI, *144*

Pricing

Farrell, Cathy, Government Contract Solutions, Inc. (C), VA, *361*
Geller, Nicole, Government Contract Solutions, Inc. (C), VA, *361*

Printing

Boule, James P., F-O-R-T-U-N-E Personnel Consultants of Cincinnati (C), OH, *348*
Bridgett, Cal, Sales Consultants of Savannah, GA (C), GA, *557*
Caprio, Jerry, Caprio & Assoc. Inc. (R), IL, *29*
Clark, David A., Sprout/Standish, Inc. (C), NH, *590*
Cossa, Kristen, JM & Company (R), PA, *106*
Covalciuc, Rick, Sales Consultants of Omaha, Inc. (C), NE, *560*
Forbes, Kenneth P., Sanford Rose Assoc. - Evansville (C), IN, *567*
Glancey, Jr., Thomas F., Gordon Wahls Executive Search (C), PA, *613*
Griffin, Al, Gardner-Ross Assoc., Inc. (R), NY, *74*
Grumney, David E., David E. Grumney Co. Inc. (R), WA, *83*
Hemenway, Albert I., Sanford Rose Assoc. - Effingham (C), IL, *566*
Huff, David, Kutt, Inc. (C), CO, *410*
Kingsbury, Scott C., Kingsbury • Wax • Bova (R), MA, *114*
Knapp, Miranda, Cook Assoc.,® Inc. (R), IL, *40*
Maiola, Diana E., Maiola & Co. (C), OH, *423*
Marquez, Paul, Sanford Rose Assoc. - Fairhope (C), AL, *565*
Marriott, Gloria A., Management Recruiters of Franklin, Inc. (C), TN, *461*
Marriott, Roger H., Management Recruiters of Franklin, Inc. (C), TN, *461*
Neighbors, Greg, Kutt, Inc. (C), CO, *410*
Phelps, Grace, Hardage Group (C), TN, *369*
Pulito, Carol M., Maiola & Co. (C), OH, *423*
Ranberg, Carol, Marsteller Wilcox Assoc. (C), IL, *471*
Robison, Margaret H., Robison Humphreys & Assoc., Inc. (R), ON, *180*
Soltan, Steve, S.C.S. & Assoc. (C), NC, *550*
St. Denis, Robert A., Sanford Rose Assoc. - Effingham (C), IL, *566*
Tippel, Fred C., Fred C. Tippel & Assoc. (C), OH, *607*

Process control

Barz, James M., International Management Services Inc. (R), IL, *102*
Daum, Alan N., Alan N. Daum & Assoc., Inc. (C), OH, *308*
Gehle, Frederick P., Dunhill Professional Search of Augusta (C), GA, *320*
McGinnis, William A., National Metal Services Corp. (C), IN, *489*

Procurement

Farrell, Cathy, Government Contract Solutions, Inc. (C), VA, *361*
Geller, Nicole, Government Contract Solutions, Inc. (C), VA, *361*
Gragg, Robert, Montgomery West (R), CA, *146*
Panos, James, The P & L Group (C), NY, *500*
Pleva, Will, Leslie Kavanagh Assoc., Inc. (C), NY, *416*

Produce

Allison, Tom, Tom Allison Assoc. (C), NM, *245*
Heintz, William, MIXTEC Group (R), CA, *145*
Heintz, William, MIXTEC Group (R), CA, *146*
Holford, Jay, MIXTEC Group (R), CA, *145*
Nelson, Christopher, MIXTEC Group (R), CA, *145*

Product development

Greenwood, Katherine, Fortune Personnel Consultants of Plano (C), TX, *350*
Grubb, Peg Iversen, Executive Search Consultants (C), CA, *335*
Holland, Lee, Carnegie Resources, Inc. (C), NC, *284*
King, Michael, Fortune Personnel Consultants of San Antonio, Inc. (C), TX, *350*
Kuhlenbeck, Phillip, Austin Group Int'l./ Marlar Int'l. (R), TX, *9*
Larsen, Ken, Fortune Personnel Consultants of San Antonio, Inc. (C), TX, *350*
Martin, Carol, Medical Innovations (C), NY, *477*
Reed, Kat, Executive Search Consultants (C), CA, *335*
Reyes, Randolph, Management Recruiters of Columbia (C), MD, *450*

Product management

Anderson, Jim, Howard Clark Assoc. (C), NJ, *292*
Berg, Charlie, Management Recruiters of Lake Forest, IL (C), IL, *447*
Buchanan, Christine, Management Recruiters of Bordentown (C), NJ, *454*
Emery, Karlan, Emerging Medical Technologies, Inc. (C), CO, *329*
Gorberg, Richard D., Fortune Personnel Consultants of Raleigh, Inc. (C), NC, *348*
Poole, Don V., Don V. Poole & Assoc., Inc. (C), CO, *514*
Riley, Brian, Austin Group Int'l./Marlar Int'l. (R), TX, *9*
Taylor, Jerry, Executive Recruiters (C), WA, *334*
Wascovich, Tina, Rojek Marketing Group, Inc. (R), OH, *181*

Production

Baehl, Thomas A., World Search (C), OH, *625*

Blevins, David C., David Blevins & Assoc. (C), WA, *268*
Bradley, Mary X., Bradley & Assoc. (C), MN, *272*
Cagan, Randy A., Fortune Personnel Consultants of Raleigh, Inc. (C), NC, *348*
Cruz, Raymond, A-Linko & Assoc. (C), TX, *231*
de La Hoz Ramirez, Armando, OSAGUI S.A. de C.V. (C), MX, *500*
DeJong, Jack, Management Recruiters of Tucson (C), AZ, *439*
Doyle, David, System 1 Search (C), CA, *598*
Goldbeck, Henry, Goldbeck Recruiting Inc. (C), BC, *359*
Helnore, Kim, Partners in Recruiting (C), IL, *504*
Joslin, Robert S., Joslin & Assoc., Ltd. (C), IL, *401*
Keller, Andrea, F-O-R-T-U-N-E Personnel Consultants of Palm Beach (C), FL, *345*
Knox, Dave, APA Employment Agency Inc. (C), OR, *251*
Lay, Jim, A-Linko & Assoc. (C), TX, *231*
Macurda, Bradford, The Energists (R), TX, *59*
Mathias, William J., Preng & Assoc., Inc. (R), TX, *167*
Preston, Alex, The Energists (R), TX, *59*
Skelton, Brenda, Cumberland Professional Search Inc. (C), TN, *304*
Thomason, Ronald, Montgomery, Thomason & Assoc. (C), ON, *484*
Wachendorfer, Tom, Wachendorfer & Assoc. (C), TX, *613*

Professional services

Andrews, Pamela J., LAI Ward Howell (R), IL, *123*
Austn, Annie, Johnson Smith & Knisely (R), NY, *107*
Bliley, Jerry, SpencerStuart (R), ON, *197*
Block, Rochelle, Johnson Smith & Knisely (R), NY, *107*
Brenner, Michael, LAI Ward Howell (R), NY, *122*
Cesafsky, Barry R., LAI Ward Howell (R), IL, *123*
Christoff, Matt, SpencerStuart (R), MN, *197*
Clemens, Bill, SpencerStuart (R), CT, *196*
Colavito, II, Joseph W., LAI Ward Howell (R), GA, *123*
Corey, Michael J., LAI Ward Howell (R), WI, *124*
Corey, Patrick M., LAI Ward Howell (R), WI, *124*
Daubenspeck, Rima, Daubenspeck & Associates, Ltd. (R), IL, *46*
Davison McNicholas, Patricia, LAI Ward Howell (R), TX, *124*
Dorst, Martin, Dorst Information Services, Inc. (C), NY, *314*
Drinkwater, Wendy A., Drinkwater & Assoc. (R), MA, *54*
Eldridge, Charles B., Ray & Berndtson (R), GA, *172*
Eversbush, Helene, Johnson Smith & Knisely (R), GA, *107*
Gardiner, Earl, Austin Park Management Group Inc. (C), ON, *256*
Gorfinkle, Gayle, Executive Search Int'l./Transearch (R), MA, *63*
Greco, Sheila, Sheila Greco Assoc. (C), NY, *362*
Johnson, Peter, ZanExec L.L.C. (R), VA, *226*
Jones-Parker, Janet, Jones-Parker/Starr (R), NC, *108*
Kelley, Randall D., SpencerStuart (R), TX, *197*
Kreisberg, Robert S., Opus Marketing (R), CA, *156*
Laurendeau, J. E., Ray & Berndtson/Laurendeau Labrecque (R), QE, *172*
McGregor, Jock, Reynolds Consulting Int'l. (R), ON, *177*
McKeown, Morgan, Christian & Timbers, Inc. (R), OH, *34*
Neuberth, Jeffrey, Johnson Smith & Knisely (R), NY, *107*
O'Brien, Timothy M., O'Brien & Bell (R), OH, *153*
Pappalardo, Chuck, Christian & Timbers, Inc. (R), OH, *34*
Posselt, Jeffrey, Cook Assoc.,® Inc. (R), IL, *40*
Prince, Howard, Austin Park Management Group Inc. (C), ON, *256*
Rothschild, John S., LAI Ward Howell (R), IL, *123*
Schwartz, Carole, Johnson Smith & Knisely (R), NY, *107*
Shay, David, cFour Partners (R), CA, *32*
Sheehan, Kari, Johnson Smith & Knisely (R), NY, *107*
Shimp, David J., LAI Ward Howell (R), IL, *123*
Smith, Mark L., Korn/Ferry Int'l. (R), MA, *118*
Somers, Scott D., Ray & Berndtson (R), CA, *172*
Starr, Jonathan, Jones-Parker/Starr (R), GA, *108*
Sullivan, Michael J., LAI Ward Howell (R), NY, *123*
Voss, Erik, Sheila Greco Assoc. (C), NY, *362*
Wier, Daniel C., Daniel Wier & Assoc. (R), CA, *220*

Programming

Armstrong, C.J., Dunhill Professional Search of Byram (C), MS, *321*
Arons, Sheldon, Colt Systems Professional Personnel Services (C), CA, *294*
Babicky, Kay, Management Recruiters of Wausau, LLC (C), WI, *466*
Babson, Jay, Dunhill Staffing Systems (C), NC, *321*
Barry, Cheryl, Management Recruiters of Atlanta NE (C), GA, *446*
Capozzi, John, C Assoc. (C), DC, *278*
Cavicchio, Dan, Greenwich Internet (C), CT, *363*
DiLorenzo, Matthew B., The Inside Track (C), TX, *389*
Diorio, Scott, Management Recruiters of Fresno (C), CA, *440*
Fare, Sarah, Management Recruiters-Cedar Rapids, Inc. (C), IA, *448*
Flowers, Terry, Russ Hadick & Assoc. Inc. (C), OH, *365*
Garcia, Abel, Allen Austin Lowe & Powers (R), TX, *3*
Geiman, Barry, Leader Institute, Inc. (C), GA, *414*
Gruszecki, Irene, Management Recruiters of Wausau, LLC (C), WI, *466*
Hawkins, Max, Management Recruiters of Wausau, LLC (C), WI, *466*
Heacock, Barbara, B. D. Wallace & Assoc. (C), MD, *614*
Hochgraber, Kent, Dunhill Personnel Service of Fargo (C), ND, *322*
Hudson, Paul E., The Hudson Group (C), CT, *383*
Hulme, Doug, Leader Institute, Inc. (C), GA, *414*
Lascelle, Donald, Lascelle & Assoc. Inc. (C), ON, *413*
Law, Grace, Software Engineering Solutions, Inc. (C), CA, *587*
Makhani, Thukbir, LCS, Inc. (C), TX, *414*
McAvoy, Edward P., Romano McAvoy Assoc., Inc. (C), NY, *544*
McKee, Edward F., McKee Cyber Search (C), MS, *475*
Michaels, Ben, Ritech Management Inc. (C), NY, *537*
Olesen, Jeannette, Management Recruiters of the Baltimore Washington Corridor (C), MD, *450*
Perkins, Yvonne, Leader Institute, Inc. (C), GA, *414*
Prochnow, Laurie, Management Recruiters of Wausau, LLC (C), WI, *466*
Raj, Amritha, Softrix, Inc. (C), NJ, *586*
Rehmeyer, Kelly, Allen Austin Lowe & Powers (R), TX, *3*
Ross, Larry, The Summit Group (C), CA, *596*
Sabrin, Joe, ManTech Consulting (C), NY, *468*
Sajankila, Raj, Softrix, Inc. (C), NJ, *586*
Salcido, Chris, Protocol Inc. (C), CA, *525*
Sieler, Susan, C Assoc. (C), DC, *278*
Sonne, Bill, PeopleSource Inc. (C), TX, *506*
Stokes, George N., The Inside Track (C), TX, *389*
Suri, Prem, Fortuna Technologies Inc. (C), GA, *343*
Vegas, Carmen, Sofco (C), NY, *586*
Vlahos, Ben, Leader Institute, Inc. (C), GA, *414*
Wachuku, Bobbiette, Management Recruiters-Cedar Rapids, Inc. (C), IA, *448*
Woodward, Lee, Search Assoc., Inc. (C), CA, *574*
Zabor, Richard, Leader Institute, Inc. (C), GA, *414*

RECRUITER SPECIALTIES

Property management

Ames, Mildred S., Ames Assoc. Inc. (C), MD, *249*
Beller, Allen, Michael Latas & Assoc., Inc. (R), MO, *126*
Fox, James P., Michael Latas & Assoc., Inc. (R), MO, *126*
Hoffman, Glenn, Huntress Real Estate Executive Search (R), MO, *100*
Lomax, J. Alan, ADR Accounting Management Recruiters (C), ON, *240*
Moss, Barbara, Moss & Co. (R), WA, *148*
Sprehe, J. Christopher, The Christopher Group (C), NC, *291*
Stoll, Steve, Sharrow & Assoc., Inc. (C), KY, *579*

Public relations

Abrahamson, Susan, SearchCom, Inc. (R), TX, *187*
Ball, Carol, Carol Ball & Co. (C), CT, *258*
Barnes, Gary B., Brigade, Inc. (R), CA, *23*
Brand, Elizabeth, Carol Ball & Co. (C), NJ, *258*
Brownstein, Joan, Julian Assoc., Inc. (C), CT, *401*
Brownstein, Julian, Julian Assoc., Inc. (C), CT, *401*
Burton, Catherine, Innovative Partnerships (R), CA, *101*
Caruthers, Robert D., Caruthers & Co., L.L.C. (R), CT, *31*
Chaloner, Edward H., Chaloner Assoc. (R), MA, *32*
Charet, Sandra, Charet & Assoc. (C), NJ, *289*
Corwen, Leonard, Leonard Corwen Assoc. (C), NY, *302*
Eskew, Martha, Recruiting Options, Inc. (C), GA, *532*
Flesher, Susan, Flesher & Assoc., Inc. (R), CA, *68*
Frank, Neil, Neil Frank & Co. (R), CA, *71*
Fry, John M., The Fry Group, Inc. (C), NY, *353*
Gardner, Brian, Bosch & Assoc., LLC (R), CT, *20*
Greene, Dorcas P., Greene Personnel Consultants (C), RI, *362*
Gregory, Rose, Kay Henry, Inc. (C), PA, *376*
Haggerty, Noreen, K. Russo Assoc. Inc. (C), CT, *548*
Hamilton, Lisa J., Hamilton & Co. (C), OH, *367*
Hammond, Karla, People Management Northeast, Inc. (R), CT, *162*
Hazlett, Kirk, Chaloner Assoc. (R), MA, *32*
Henry, Kay, Kay Henry, Inc. (C), PA, *376*
Huberman, Arnold, Arnold Huberman Assoc., Inc. (R), NY, *97*
Jackson, Laurie, McHale & Assoc. (R), WA, *141*
Kanzer, William F., Kanzer Assoc., Inc. (R), IL, *109*
Kissel, Brian J., Management Recruiters of Northern Palm Beaches (C), FL, *444*
Kissel, James R., Management Recruiters of Northern Palm Beaches (C), FL, *444*
Larsen, Michael G., Barnes & Assoc. Executive Search (C), CA, *259*
Lawson, Trina R., Search Assoc., Inc. (C), NJ, *574*
Lee, Carol Ricci, Ricci Lee Assoc., Inc. (C), CA, *415*
Luden, Ben V., Marketing/Public Relations Research Recruiting (C), CT, *471*
Mahr, Toni, K. Russo Assoc. Inc. (C), CT, *548*
Marshall, Larry, Marshall Consultants, Inc. (R), NY, *137*
McCandless, Hugh, Marshall Consultants, Inc. (R), NY, *137*
Miller, Shelley, Kay Henry, Inc. (C), PA, *376*
Mitchell, Laurie, Laurie Mitchell & Co., Inc. (R), OH, *145*
Morgan, Nancy, K. Russo Assoc. Inc. (C), CT, *548*
Moyer, David S., Moyer, Sherwood Assoc., Inc. (R), NY, *148*
Orton, Linda Sedloff, Intelligent Marketing Solutions, Inc. (C), NY, *390*
Paschal, Carolyn Smith, Carolyn Smith Paschal Int'l. (R), CA, *160*
Quinn, Gail, Marshall Consultants, Inc. (R), NY, *137*
Richards, Sharon, Richards Assoc., Inc. (R), NY, *178*
Romano, Joseph C., Romano McAvoy Assoc., Inc. (C), NY, *544*
Russo, Karen, K. Russo Assoc. Inc. (C), CT, *548*
Schwartz, Rachel, Arnold Huberman Assoc., Inc. (R), NY, *97*
Shea, Michelle, Chaloner Assoc. (R), MA, *32*
Silverman, Marjorie, Marshall Consultants, Inc. (R), NY, *137*
Spring, Dennis, Spring Assoc., Inc. (R), NY, *198*
Warren, Ted, Strategic Resources (C), WA, *595*
Wascovich, Tina, Rojek Marketing Group, Inc. (R), OH, *181*
White, Richard B., SpencerStuart (R), CT, *196*

Public sector

Arnold, Lindy, The Glazin Group (R), BC, *77*
Casey, Mike, David M. Griffith & Assoc., Ltd. (R), IL, *82*
Doupe, S. Scott, Conroy Partners Ltd. (R), AB, *39*
Estrada, Barbara, Montgomery West (R), CA, *146*
Geller, William, Boulware & Assoc. Inc. (R), IL, *20*
Hawkins, Jr., Jack M., First Advisory Services Int'l., Inc. (R), MD, *67*
Murray, Robert W., David M. Griffith & Assoc., Ltd. (R), CA, *82*
Narlock, Renée, David M. Griffith & Assoc., Ltd. (R), FL, *82*
Neumayer, Chuck, David M. Griffith & Assoc., Ltd. (R), CA, *82*
O'Biern, Matt, David M. Griffith & Assoc., Ltd. (R), IL, *82*
Peckham, Bobbi, David M. Griffith & Assoc., Ltd. (R), CA, *82*
Van Leeuwen, Lee, Van Leeuwen Assoc. (R), CA, *213*
Wallace, Clarke, PricewaterhouseCoopers Executive Search (R), ON, *168*
Whitfield, Sue, Avery Assoc. (R), CA, *9*

Publishing

Banach-Osenni, Doris, The Brentwood Group, Inc. (R), NJ, *22*
Berardi, Loretta A., Stentiford & Berardi Assoc. Ltd. (R), NY, *199*
Bishop, Susan, Bishop Partners (R), NY, *17*
Burz, Christina, Bishop Partners (R), NY, *17*
Caprio, Jerry, Caprio & Assoc. Inc. (R), IL, *29*
Collins, Kenneth B., Executive Search Partners (R), NY, *63*
Corwen, Leonard, Leonard Corwen Assoc. (C), NY, *302*
Crawford, Marjorie, Personnel Assoc. (C), CA, *508*
Curtis, Susan J., ProSearch Recruiting (C), CA, *524*
D'Andrea, Albert P., EDMS Solutions (C), TX, *326*
DeLuca, Matthew J., Management Resource Group, Inc. (C), NY, *467*
Dougan, Sally, Bert Davis Publishing Placement Consultants (C), NY, *309*
Ellis, Bennett A., Greenhaven & Assoc., Inc. (R), NY, *81*
Faller, Laura McGrath, Redden & McGrath Assoc., Inc. (R), NY, *173*
Fixler, Eugene, Ariel Recruitment Assoc. (R), NY, *7*
Glancey, Jr., Thomas F., Gordon Wahls Executive Search (C), PA, *613*
Gold, Susan, Stentiford & Berardi Assoc. Ltd. (R), NY, *200*
Goldberg, Risa, Media Recruiting Group, Inc. (C), NY, *476*
Goldberg, Steve, Media Recruiting Group, Inc. (C), NY, *476*
Goldstein, Michael, Goldstein & Co. (C), CA, *360*
Harragan, James K., Management Recruiters of Gramercy, Inc. (C), NY, *455*
Hogan, Sandra M., Larsen, Whitney, Blecksmith & Zilliacus, Inc. (R), CA, *125*
Hoyda, Louis A., Thorndike Deland Assoc. LLC (R), NY, *48*
Hughes, Cathy N., The Ogdon Partnership (R), NY, *155*
Humphreys, William M., Robison Humphreys & Assoc., Inc. (R), ON, *180*
Jones, Geoffrey J., Precision Executive Search (C), AZ, *516*
Kurbatoff, Jerry, The Black Leopard (C), CA, *267*
Lynch, Patrick J., P. J. Lynch Assoc. (R), CT, *132*

Malcom, John W., Johnson Smith & Knisely (R), NY, *107*
Masquelier, Sibyl, Executive Resource Group, Inc. (R), ME, *63*
Munson, Brad, ProSearch Recruiting (C), CA, *524*
Pagana, Pat, The Brentwood Group, Inc. (R), NJ, *22*
Papike, Richard, TriStaff Group (C), CA, *609*
Robison, Margaret H., Robison Humphreys & Assoc., Inc. (R), ON, *180*
Ross, Elsa, Gardner-Ross Assoc., Inc. (R), NY, *74*
Ruttanai-Fanelli, Lynn, Ariel Recruitment Assoc. (R), NY, *7*
Smith, Herbert E., The Enfield Company (C), TX, *330*
Stentiford, Charles M., Stentiford & Berardi Assoc. Ltd. (R), NY, *199*
Wells, Edward, Personnel Assoc. (C), CA, *508*
Wexler, Rona, Ariel Recruitment Assoc. (R), NY, *7*
White, Richard B., SpencerStuart (R), CT, *196*
Wilson, Robert F., Wilson McLeran, Inc. (C), CT, *622*
Zidwick, Christiana, WTW Assoc., Inc. (R), NY, *225*

Pulp

Charron, Maynard G., Paper Industry Recruitment (P.I.R.) (C), ME, *502*
Martin, Wayne, Human Resources Personnel Agency (R), AR, *99*
McCracken, Terri, T E M Assoc. (C), WI, *599*

Pumps

Ortman, Jim, Ortman Recruiting Int'l. (C), CA, *500*

Purchasing

Adzima, Allan G., MARBL Consultants, Inc. (C), WI, *469*
Antonio, Marshall, Fortune of Arlington Heights (C), IL, *346*
Banks, Paul C., Paul C. Banks Assoc. (C), GA, *259*
Beaudin, Elizabeth C., Callan Assoc., Ltd. (R), IL, *27*
Beck, Larry, Synergy Solutions, Ltd. (C), WA, *597*
Brill, Ted, F-O-R-T-U-N-E Personnel Consultants of Tampa (C), FL, *345*
Cousins, John L., Procurement Resources (C), MD, *520*
Dietrich, Sandra, Fortune Personnel Consultants of Hilton Head (C), SC, *349*
Fenimore, Joseph S., F-O-R-T-U-N-E Personnel Consultants of Cincinnati (C), OH, *348*
Ford, Neil, R. Green & Assoc., Inc. (C), OH, *362*
Howell, Jean, Fortune Personnel Consultants of the Virginia Highlands (C), VA, *351*
Jacobs, James W., Callan Assoc., Ltd. (R), IL, *27*
Jordan, Dick, Staff Resources, Inc. (C), SC, *590*
Keller, Andrea, F-O-R-T-U-N-E Personnel Consultants of Palm Beach (C), FL, *345*
Kensinger, John P., Sanford Rose Assoc. - Burlington, NC (C), NC, *569*
Klein, Howard G., F-O-R-T-U-N-E Personnel Consultants of Bergen County Inc. (C), NJ, *347*
Kosteva, David, NDI Services (R), MI, *151*
Lamb, Lynn, Fortune Personnel Consultants of Huntsville, Inc. (C), AL, *344*
Lipe, Jerold L., Compass Group Ltd. (R), MI, *38*
Little, John J., Alpha Executive Search (C), AL, *246*
Malatesta, Roger, Professional Recruiting Consultants, Inc. (C), DE, *521*
Perkins, Arthur, Management Alliance Group, Inc. (R), NJ, *134*
Peterson, Jerry, MARBL Consultants, Inc. (C), WI, *469*
Pompelli, Jean, JAG Group (R), MO, *105*
Portanova, Peter M., ROI Assoc. (R), NY, *181*
Rohan, James, J. P. Canon Assoc. (C), NY, *280*
Singer, David L., Fortune Personnel Consultants of Raleigh, Inc. (C), NC, *348*
Slater, Marjorie, Logistics Management Resources, Inc. (R), NY, *131*
Storfer, Herbert F., The Dartmouth Group (R), NY, *46*
Tutchings, Amy, Strategic Assoc., Inc. (C), TX, *595*
Weiner, Al, Lucas Group (C), NY, *421*
Wells, Lee, F-O-R-T-U-N-E Personnel Consultants of East Seattle (C), WA, *351*

Quality

Abbott, Robert, Pacific Coast Recruiting (C), CA, *501*
Ambruster, David L., Renaissance Resources, LLC (R), VA, *174*
Antonio, Marshall, Fortune of Arlington Heights (C), IL, *346*
Axelrod, Mark H., F-O-R-T-U-N-E Personnel Consultants of Rockland County, Inc. (C), NY, *348*
Baker, Ray, Management Recruiters of Ogden (C), UT, *464*
Berg, Charlie, Management Recruiters of Lake Forest, IL (C), IL, *447*
Berg, Eric M., J.N. Adams & Assoc., Inc. (C), PA, *396*
Berry, Paul, Canyon Consulting, Inc. (C), TX, *281*
Boone, Jr., Joseph E., Premier Search Group (C), IN, *517*
Brandvold, Steven C., Executive Connection (C), OH, *333*
Brookes, Cindy, Technical Employment Consultants (C), PA, *602*
Cagan, Randy A., Fortune Personnel Consultants of Raleigh, Inc. (C), NC, *348*
Ciccone, Beverlee, Fortune Group Int'l., Inc. (R), PA, *70*
Colbourn, Ken, F-O-R-T-U-N-E Personnel Consultants of Knoxville (C), TN, *350*
Cole, Don, Riley Cole (C), CA, *537*
Cracknell, Jo Anne, NCC Executive Search Consultants (C), CA, *490*
Cruz, Raymond, A-Linko & Assoc. (C), TX, *231*
Cunneff, Harry J., Management Recruiters of Lake Forest, IL (C), IL, *447*
Daum, Deborah, Premier Search Group (C), IN, *517*
Davis, Charlie, Dunhill of Ft. Wayne, Inc. (C), IN, *320*
Davis, Ronald, International Management Development Corp. (C), NY, *393*
Deyeaux, Victoria, John Williams & Assoc. (C), TX, *621*
Dmytrow, Eric D., F-O-R-T-U-N-E Personnel Consultants of Palm Beach (C), FL, *345*
Dorfman, Jan, F-O-R-T-U-N-E Personnel Consultants of Denver, Inc. (C), CO, *344*
Doyle, David, System 1 Search (C), CA, *598*
Ducharme, David J., Fortune Personnel Consultants of Hilton Head (C), SC, *349*
Engel, Walter E., F-O-R-T-U-N-E Personnel Consultants of the Tri-Cities, Inc. (C), TN, *350*
English, Robert, RTE Search (C), NJ, *547*
English, Robert, RTE Search (C), VA, *547*
Furioso, Carmine A., F-O-R-T-U-N-E Personnel Consultants of San Diego (C), CA, *344*
Greenwood, Katherine, Fortune Personnel Consultants of Plano (C), TX, *350*
Hanson, Hugh, Fortune Personnel Consultants of Huntsville, Inc. (C), AL, *344*
Harvey, Bob, Mayhall Search Group, Inc. (C), IN, *473*
Helnore, Kim, Partners in Recruiting (C), IL, *504*
Holohan, Jr., Barth A., Holohan Group, Ltd. (R), MO, *95*
Hudson, Judy K., The Hudson Group (C), CT, *383*
Jordan, Dick, Staff Resources, Inc. (C), SC, *590*
Joslin, Robert S., Joslin & Assoc., Ltd. (C), IL, *401*
Keister, Beth, The Stanton Group, Inc. (C), IL, *591*
Kensinger, John P., Sanford Rose Assoc. - Burlington, NC (C), NC, *569*
King, Michael, Fortune Personnel Consultants of San Antonio, Inc. (C), TX, *350*
Krezo, Rich, Premier Recruiting Group (C), MI, *516*
Kush, Max S., Management Recruiters of Easton, PA (C), PA, *458*
Lawry, William R., W. R. Lawry, Inc. (R), CT, *126*
Lay, Jim, A-Linko & Assoc. (C), TX, *231*
Livingston, Hyman, The P & L Group (C), NY, *500*

RECRUITER SPECIALTIES

Lybrook, Christian, Lybrook Assoc., Inc. (C), RI, 421
Manning, Jerry, Management Recruiters of Ogden (C), UT, 464
Maye, Carolyn, Ken Clark Int'l. (R), NJ, 36
McDowell, Ron, Carnegie Resources, Inc. (C), NC, 284
Mitchell, Lauren, Wachendorfer & Assoc. (C), TX, 613
Morin, Paul, F-O-R-T-U-N-E Personnel Consultants of Knoxville (C), TN, 350
Morrisey, Jim, Fortune Personnel Consultants of San Antonio, Inc. (C), TX, 350
Nanney, Brenda, Lou Michaels Assoc., Inc. (C), MI, 481
Oglesby, Tom, F-O-R-T-U-N-E Personnel of Nashville (C), TN, 350
Pepple, Bob, Fortune Personnel Consultants of Jacksonville (C), FL, 345
Petras, Michael, F-O-R-T-U-N-E Personnel Consultants of South Bend (C), IN, 346
Pompelli, Jean, JAG Group (R), MO, 105
Powell, Donald L., Proquest Inc. (C), SC, 524
Price, Rita A., Human Resources Personnel Agency (R), AR, 99
Richards, Carl, Technical Employment Consultants (C), PA, 602
Ross, Larry, The Summit Group (C), CA, 596
Rudnick, Marlene, Marcus & Assoc. (C), NY, 469
Sarver, Dan, F-O-R-T-U-N-E Personnel Consultants of Tampa (C), FL, 345
Schroeder, Tim, F-O-R-T-U-N-E Personnel of Nashville (C), TN, 350
Schwartz, Lou, Technical Employment Consultants (C), PA, 602
Spears, Robert, FORTUNE Personnel Consultants of Charleston, Inc. (C), SC, 349
Suhay, Gary T., Elite Resources Group (R), OH, 58
Tapler, Harold, Ruderfer & Co., Inc. (C), NJ, 548
Terry, Jeff, Southern Recruiters & Consultants, Inc. (C), SC, 587
Urban, Charles V., Quality Control Recruiters (C), CT, 526
Wachendorfer, Nancy, Wachendorfer & Assoc. (C), TX, 613
Walker, Donald G., Executive Search Plus, Inc. (C), IN, 336
Wallace, Mark J., Management Recruiters of Broome County, Inc. (C), NY, 454
Walt, Lee, M H Executive Search Group (C), TX, 422
Weiner, Al, Lucas Group (C), NY, 421
Xagas, Steve, Xagas & Assoc. (R), IL, 226
Zimmermann, Karl, Fortune Personnel Consultants of Bloomfield, Inc. (C), MI, 346

Radio frequency

Anderson, Gregory D., Anderson Industrial Assoc., Inc. (C), GA, 250
Austin, Cami, Cami Austin & Assoc. (C), IL, 256
Du Ket, Holly V., New Venture Development, Inc. (C), CA, 492
Hudson, Paul E., The Hudson Group (C), CT, 383
Kendle, Vernon S., New Venture Development, Inc. (C), CA, 492
Moore, Michael H., The Inside Track (C), TX, 389

Railroad

LaBorde, John, The LaBorde Group (C), CA, 411
Lee, Robert, Management Recruiters, Inc. (C), FL, 443

Re-engineering

Baum, Betty, The Technology Group (R), IL, 208
Chin, Joe, Cornell Group Int'l. Consulting, Inc. (R), NY, 41

Real estate

Adams, Gerald, G. Adams Partners (R), IL, 2
Baron, Robert, Peak Search Assoc. (C), ON, 506
Beaudine, Robert E., Eastman & Beaudine, Inc. (R), TX, 56
Bell, Edward, Edward Bell Assoc. (C), CA, 263
Beller, Allen, Michael Latas & Assoc., Inc. (R), MO, 126
Blecksmith, Edward L., Larsen, Whitney, Blecksmith & Zilliacus, Inc. (R), CA, 125
Bloch, Carla, Lending Personnel Services (C), CA, 416
Bruccoleri, Theodore A., StratfordGroup (R), OH, 203
Canzian, Philip, Crown Advisors, Inc. (R), PA, 43
Caruso, Dennis, Caruso & Assoc., Inc. (R), FL, 31
Cech, Raymond R., Dunhill Executive Search of Los Angeles, Inc. (C), CA, 319
Cigna, John, Crown Advisors, Inc. (R), PA, 43
Clapp, Arlene, Arlene Clapp, Ltd. (R), MN, 35
Cleveland, Anthony, The Talon Group (R), TX, 206
Crystal, Jonathan A., SpencerStuart (R), TX, 197
Dremely, Mark, Richard, Wayne & Roberts (C), TX, 536
Erickson-Pearson, David, Boulware & Assoc. Inc. (R), IL, 20
Feste, Ward P., The Carlyle Group, Ltd. (R), IL, 30
• Flagg, Jessica S., The Consulting Group Ltd. (R), NY, 40
Fox, James P., Michael Latas & Assoc., Inc. (R), MO, 126
Gaines, Donna, Gaines & Assoc. Int'l., Inc. (R), IL, 73
Gilbert, Jr., H. Harry, Gilbert Scott Assoc., LLC (C), MA, 357
Glazin, Lynne, The Glazin Group (R), BC, 77
GoodsonHarrington & O'Brien, Inc. W. Kenneth, DLG Assoc., Inc. (R), NC, 53
Guilford, David J., DLG Assoc., Inc. (R), NC, 53
Hall, Peter V., Argonaut Partners, LLC (R), CA, 6
Hall, Rodney, The Talon Group (R), TX, 205
Hauswirth, Jeffrey M., SpencerStuart (R), ON, 197
Helbling, Thomas J., Helbling & Assoc., Inc. (R), PA, 91
Herbert, Paul, David Blevins & Assoc. (C), WA, 268
Hermsen, Patrick, Capital Markets Resources, Inc. (C), NC, 281
Hess, Robert W., Robert Hess & Assoc., Inc. (C), CO, 377
Highland, Maryjo, Highland & Assoc. (C), CA, 378
Hyland, Kenneth J., Hyland Executive Search (C), AZ, 386
Hyland, Susan L., Hyland Executive Search (C), AZ, 386
Jablo, Steven A., Dieckmann & Assoc., Ltd. (R), IL, 51
James, Chip, Morgan Samuels Co. (R), CA, 147
• Kalus, Lisa, Lisa Kalus & Assoc., Inc. (C), NY, 403
Karel, Stephen A., Karel & Co. (R), CA, 109
• Kaufman, Stuart, Management Recruiters of Great Neck (C), NY, 454
Kimmel, Joe W., Kimmel & Associates, Inc. (C), NC, 406
Kovach, Jerry, The J. Kovach Group (R), PA, 119
• Krauser, H. James, SpencerStuart (R), CT, 196
Lean, Allyn, The Curtiss Group International (R), FL, 44
• Littman, Stephen, Rhodes Associates (R), NY, 177
• LoPinto, Anthony J., Rhodes Associates (R), NY, 177
Loubet, Larry S., The Carlyle Group, Ltd. (R), IL, 30
Lyngen, Trish Construct Management Services (C), MN, 297
• Lyons, Jane, Rhodes Associates (R), NY, 177
Mason, Jean, The Talon Group (R), TX, 206
Maxin, Keith A., K. Maxin & Assoc. (R), PA, 139
McDermott, Bert, Crown Advisors, Inc. (R), PA, 43
McDonald, Louise, Real Estate Executive Search, Inc. (C), CA, 531
• Mitchell, J. Michael, The Consulting Group Ltd. (R), NY, 40
Morbitzer, Tina, Tina Morbitzer & Assoc. (C), FL, 485
Moss, Barbara, Moss & Co. (R), WA, 148
• Nass, Martin D., LAI Ward Howell (R), NY, 122

• Nava, Terri, The Consulting Group Ltd. (R), NY, *40*
Olsen, Robert F., Robert Connelly & Assoc., Inc. (R), MN, *39*
Pais, Lisa A., Gilbert Scott Assoc., LLC (C), MA, *357*
• Phillips, Jr., James L., Highland Search Group, L.L.C. (R), NY, *93*
Piper, Robert A., The Talon Group (R), TX, *205*
Pugrant, Mark A., Grant/Morgan Assoc., Inc. (C), MD, *361*
Rabinowitz, Peter A., P.A.R. Assoc., Inc. (R), MA, *158*
Robinson, Mel, MDR & Associates (C), AR, *476*
Ropes, John, Ropes Associates, Inc. (R), FL, *182*
Saxner, David, David Saxner & Assoc., Inc. (DSA, Inc.) (R), IL, *185*
Scarpino, William A., Allen Austin Lowe & Powers (R), TX, *3*
Schultz, Jon, The Carlyle Group, Ltd. (R), IL, *30*
• Schwartz, Alan, Advice Personnel Inc. (C), NY, *241*
Slepin, Matthew B., Argonaut Partners, LLC (R), CA, *6*
Sloane, Ron, Management Recruiters of Milwaukee-North (C), WI, *466*
Smith, II, Don, Smith, Brown & Jones (C), FL, *585*
Sprehe, J. Christopher, The Christopher Group (C), NC, *291*
Stewart, Harvey, Executive Registry (C), QE, *334*
Stoll, Steve, Sharrow & Assoc., Inc. (C), KY, *579*
Sussman, Patti, Weinman & Assoc. (C), AZ, *617*
• Taylor, Peter R., Peter R. Taylor Assoc., Inc. (C), NY, *600*
• Thompson, Pat, The Alfus Group (R), NY, *3*
• Traynor, Thomas H., Traynor Confidential, Ltd. (C), NY, *609*
Van Leeuwen, Lee, Van Leeuwen Assoc. (R), CA, *213*
Vognsen, Rikke, David Saxner & Assoc., Inc. (DSA, Inc.) (R), IL, *185*
• Wallberg, Marilyn, Stephen Haas Legal Placement (C), NY, *365*
• Welling, Suzanne, IMA Search, Inc. (R), NY, *101*
Wilkson, James, Allen Austin Lowe & Powers (R), TX, *3*
• Zarkin, Norman, The Zarkin Group, Inc. (R), NY, *226*

Recreational vehicles

McGuire, John, Sage Employment Recruiters (C), IN, *550*

Recruiters

Fox, Allis, Intersource, Ltd. (R), GA, *103*
Hangartner, Robin, Intersource, Ltd. (R), GA, *103*
Jones-Parker, Janet, Jones-Parker/Starr (R), NC, *108*
Lessner, Jack, J. E. Lessner Assoc., Inc. (R), MI, *128*
Mitchell, Michael R., Computer Int'l. Consultants, Inc. (C), FL, *295*
Parr, James A., KPMG Executive Search (R), ON, *119*
Sewell, Jerry, Fox-Morris Assoc., Inc. (C), TX, *352*
Starr, Jonathan, Jones-Parker/Starr (R), GA, *108*

Recycling

Charron, Maynard G., Paper Industry Recruitment (P.I.R.) (C), ME, *502*
Donnelly, John J., Management & Human Resources (R), MA, *134*

Refining

Hughes, Tim, Hughes & Assoc. Int'l. Inc. (C), AL, *383*
Johnston, Gail, NJ Solutions (C), CA, *493*
Lasini, Dennis, Genesis Research (C), MO, *356*
McClain, Jack, PIC Executive Search (C), GA, *511*
Williams, Steve, Barton Assoc., Inc. (R), TX, *13*
Zamjahn, Charles J., River Region Personnel, Inc. (C), LA, *538*

Refrigeration

Difatta, Jon, Management Recruiters of Barrington (C), IL, *447*
Polvere, Gary T., Management Recruiters of Barrington (C), IL, *447*

Regulatory

Berry, Paul, Canyon Consulting, Inc. (C), TX, *281*
Bunker, Ralph, Management Recruiters of San Luis Obispo (C), CA, *439*
Ciccone, Beverlee, Fortune Group Int'l., Inc. (R), PA, *70*
Cracknell, Jo Anne, NCC Executive Search Consultants (C), CA, *490*
Cunneff, Harry J., Management Recruiters of Lake Forest, IL (C), IL, *447*
De Mange, Jean M., Wellington Thomas Ltd. (C), FL, *618*
DeRario, Donna, F-O-R-T-U-N-E Personnel Consultants of San Diego (C), CA, *344*
Dorfman, Jan, F-O-R-T-U-N-E Personnel Consultants of Denver, Inc. (C), CO, *344*
Ducharme, David J., Fortune Personnel Consultants of Hilton Head (C), SC, *349*
Emery, Karlan, Emerging Medical Technologies, Inc. (C), CO, *329*
Furioso, Carmine A., F-O-R-T-U-N-E Personnel Consultants of San Diego (C), CA, *344*
Greenwood, Katherine, Fortune Personnel Consultants of Plano (C), TX, *350*
Holohan, Jr., Barth A., Holohan Group, Ltd. (R), MO, *95*
Maye, Carolyn, Ken Clark Int'l. (R), NJ, *36*
Miller, Thomas C., Emerging Medical Technologies, Inc. (C), CO, *329*
Morrisey, Jim, Fortune Personnel Consultants of San Antonio, Inc. (C), TX, *350*
Oppenheim, Norman J., Fortune Personnel Consultants (C), NH, *347*
Powell, Donald L., Proquest Inc. (C), SC, *524*
Ruderfer, Irwin A., Ruderfer & Co., Inc. (C), NJ, *548*
Rudnick, Marlene, Marcus & Assoc. (C), NY, *469*
Stewart, James H., The Stewart Group (C), FL, *593*
Vice, Michael, D.A.I Human Resources Consultants (R), QE, *45*
Welch, Lauren, Management Recruiters of Lake Forest, IL (C), IL, *447*
Woody, Cary, Career Marketing Assoc., Inc. (C), CO, *282*

Rehabilitation

Black, David A., Lake Medical Associates (C), ME, *411*
Carter, Christine, Health Care Dimensions (C), CO, *371*
Hazelton, Lisa, Health Care Dimensions (C), CO, *371*
Howard, Jill, Health Care Dimensions (C), CO, *371*
West, Nancy, Health Care Dimensions (C), CO, *371*

Research

Anderson, Maria, The Ransford Group (R), TX, *171*
Binen, Carol, Thorndike Deland Assoc. LLC (R), NY, *48*
Boltrus, Richard, Sink, Walker, Boltrus Int'l. (R), MA, *192*
Brown, Bonny, Career Marketing Consultants, Inc. (C), GA, *283*
Carr, Denise, Carr Management Services, Inc. (C), PA, *284*
Cowlan, Trudi, Trudi Cowlan (C), NY, *302*
Crowe, Claudeth, A. E. Feldman Assoc., Inc. (C), NY, *339*
Deutschman, Michele, Placements by Jesse Reid Assoc., Inc. (C), NY, *513*
Dodd, Carol, Staff Resources, Inc. (C), SC, *590*
Doleman, Robert J., Doleman Enterprises (R), VA, *53*
Edington, Patti D., Drinkwater & Assoc. (R), MA, *55*
Federman, Jack, W. R. Rosato & Assoc., Inc. (R), NY, *182*
Jostrom, Karen, The Oxbridge Group, Ltd. (C), MA, *500*
Kroll, Gary, General Engineering Tectonics (C), CA, *356*

RECRUITER SPECIALTIES

L'Archevesque, Lee, Sink, Walker, Boltrus Int'l. (R), MA, *192*
Larkin, Dick, Larkin & Co. (R), CA, *125*
Lynne, Robyn, Search Masters, USA (C), FL, *576*
O'Bryant, Morgan, Brad Marks Int'l. (R), CA, *136*
Ornstein, Robert, Trebor Weldon Lawrence, Inc. (R), NY, *210*
Patrick, Janet L., Sanford Rose Assoc. - Norcross (C), GA, *566*
Pautler, Margaret O., Holohan Group, Ltd. (R), MO, *95*
Rowan, Carol, Hunter, Rowan & Crowe (C), WI, *386*
Schneider, Jim, Hunter Douglas Group, Inc. (R), IL, *99*
Spiedel, Julie, MIXTEC Group (R), CA, *145*
Stuart, Carolyn, Joy Reed Belt Search Consultants, Inc. (R), OK, *15*
Thomason, Ronald, Montgomery, Thomason & Assoc. (C), ON, *484*
Tomkin, Shelly, Career Counseling Ltd. (C.C.L.) (C), NY, *282*
Treaster, Valerie D., Davis & Company (R), CA, *47*
Van Campen, Jerry, Gilbert & Van Campen Int'l. (R), NY, *76*
Vento, Rachelle, Barton Assoc., Inc. (R), TX, *12*
Webb, Elliot, E. J. Lance Management Assoc., Inc. (C), NY, *412*
Zaccaria, Jack, Zaccaria Int'l. (C), NJ, *627*

Research & development

Allen, Jr., Lindsay, Mark III Personnel, Inc. (C), NC, *470*
Ambos, Merry, Molecular Solutions, Inc. (C), SC, *484*
Ballou, Jodie, Management Recruiters of the Baltimore Washington Corridor (C), MD, *450*
Beaudin, Elizabeth C., Callan Assoc., Ltd. (R), IL, *27*
Beehler, Lance, Fortune Personnel Consultants of Hilton Head (C), SC, *349*
Berry, Charles D., Management Recruiters of San Marcos (C), TX, *463*
Bradley, Mary X., Bradley & Assoc. (C), MN, *272*
Bunker, Ralph, Management Recruiters of San Luis Obispo (C), CA, *439*
Cegelski, Chris, The H. S. Group, Inc. (C), WI, *365*
Cheng, Karen, Specialty Employment Services, Inc. (C), GA, *589*
Coe, Karen, Coe & Co. Int'l. Inc./EMA Partners Int'l. (R), AB, *37*
Cole, Don, Riley Cole (C), CA, *537*
Cracknell, Jo Anne, NCC Executive Search Consultants (C), CA, *490*
Domann, Jr., William A., The Domann Organization (R), CA, *53*
Dukas, Theodore, Dukas Assoc. (C), MA, *315*
English, Robert, RTE Search (C), NJ, *547*
English, Robert, RTE Search (C), VA, *547*
Fabriele, John, Gallin Associates, Inc. (C), FL, *354*
Gale, Rhoda, Management Recruiters of the Baltimore Washington Corridor (C), MD, *450*
Haupt, Bruce W., Bruce W. Haupt Assoc. (R), DC, *88*
Hoye, Dan, Marcus & Assoc. (C), NY, *469*
Johnson, K. L., Sales Consultants of Chico (C), CA, *556*
Johnson, Karl, K. E. Johnson Assoc. (C), WA, *400*
Jones, Keith, Ken Clark Int'l. (R), NJ, *36*
Joslin, Robert S., Joslin & Assoc., Ltd. (C), IL, *401*
Kaiser, Joe, Fortune Personnel Consultants of Anderson, Inc. (C), SC, *349*
Kaplan, Dean, Marcus & Assoc. (C), NY, *469*
Kuhl, William R., Place Mart Personnel Service (C), NJ, *513*
Kunkle, Denise, D. Kunkle & Assoc. (C), IL, *410*
Lawrence, Ellen B., Holohan Group, Ltd. (R), MO, *95*
Leavy, Renee, Affinity Executive Search (C), FL, *241*
Lee, Albert G., Albert G. Lee Assoc. (C), RI, *415*
Murphy, Cornelius J., Goodrich & Sherwood Assoc., Inc. (R), NY, *80*
Ornstein, Carole, CSA/Clinical Staffing Assoc., LLC (C), NJ, *304*
Otsuka, Fyllis L., Holohan Group, Ltd. (R), MO, *95*
Pelisson, Charles J., Marra Peters & Partners (R), NJ, *136*
Remkus, Valerie, The Hampton Group (C), NY, *368*
Richon, Allen, Molecular Solutions, Inc. (C), SC, *484*
Sacarny, Bonnie, Marcus & Assoc. (C), NY, *469*
Shaw, R. William, Management Recruiters of South Bend (C), IN, *448*
Sherman, Terri, Tom Sloan & Assoc., Inc. (C), WI, *583*
Stanley, Wade, Management Recruiters of Raleigh (C), NC, *456*
Suhay, Gary T., Elite Resources Group (R), OH, *58*
Tapler, Harold, Ruderfer & Co., Inc. (C), NJ, *548*
Wachendorfer, Nancy, Wachendorfer & Assoc. (C), TX, *613*
Willis, Jr., William H., William Willis Worldwide Inc. (R), CT, *221*
Worthing, Ellen, Management Recruiters of the Baltimore Washington Corridor (C), MD, *450*

Resins

McDowell, Jane, Cook Assoc.,® Inc. (R), IL, *40*
Richards, R. Glenn, Executive Directions (R), OH, *62*
Tippel, Fred C., Fred C. Tippel & Assoc. (C), OH, *607*

Resorts

Casey, David, The Alfus Group (R), NY, *3*
Francis, Joseph, Hospitality Int'l. (C), NY, *381*
Gentry, Allen, Hospitality Int'l. (C), AZ, *381*
Pappas, Sewell B., Alpha Resource Group, Inc. (C), TX, *246*
Thieringer, Stephan, Search Int'l. (R), MA, *187*
Wilner, Susan, The Alfus Group (R), NY, *3*

Restaurants

Alfus, Phillip, The Alfus Group (R), NY, *3*
Brown, Beirne, Bennett Search & Consulting Co. (R), FL, *16*
Chitvanni, John W., National Restaurant Search, Inc. (R), GA, *150*
Claybaugh, Brian, Roth Young Executive Search (C), TX, *546*
Damon, Robert A., SpencerStuart (R), NY, *196*
Fedele, Rocco M., Devin Scott Assoc. (C), NJ, *572*
Gray, Mark, Executive Referral Services, Inc. (C), IL, *334*
Kauffman, Christopher C., Chris Kauffman & Company (R), GA, *110*
Kopulos, Judy, Rand-Curtis Resources (C), AZ, *529*
Marino, Frank, Hospitality Int'l. (C), NY, *381*
Marshall, Layne, Executive Referral Services, Inc. (C), IL, *334*
McKay, Bob, Further Management Group (C), MD, *353*
Meagher, III, Edward A., The Woodstone Consulting Company, Inc. (R), CO, *224*
Meagher, Linda J., The Woodstone Consulting Company, Inc. (R), CO, *224*
Morrison, C. Robert, Quetico Corp. (R), TX, *170*
Olsen, Elizabeth Clark, Olsen/Clark (R), WA, *156*
Powers, Robert, Robert Powers & Assoc. (C), CA, *515*
Powers, Susan, Robert Powers & Assoc. (C), CA, *515*
Radice, Joseph A., Hospitality Int'l. (C), NY, *381*
Reda, Pat, P. J. Reda & Assoc., Inc. (C), GA, *533*
Reich, Joshua, The Alfus Group (R), NY, *3*
Rice, Patrice, Patrice & Assoc. (C), MD, *505*
Seabaugh, Kitty, Windsor Consultants, Inc. (C), TX, *622*
White, Clyde, Further Management Group (C), MD, *353*
Wray, Dick, Dick Wray & Consultants, Inc. (R), CA, *225*

Retail

Allgire, Mary, Kenzer Corp. (R), IL, *113*

Amsterdam, Gail, Foster Partners (R), NY, *70*
Andrews, Dan, BR & Assoc. (C), NJ, *271*
Andrews, Robert L., Allen Austin Lowe & Powers (R), TX, *3*
Aquavella, Charles P., Charles P. Aquavella & Assoc. (C), TX, *252*
Arledge, Tom, Allen Austin Lowe & Powers (R), TX, *3*
Arnold, Lindy, The Glazin Group (R), BC, *77*
Baker, Gary M., Cochran, Cochran & Yale, Inc. (R), NY, *36*
Barron, Robert, Johnson Smith & Knisely (R), NY, *107*
Beaudine, Frank R., Eastman & Beaudine, Inc. (R), TX, *56*
Beaudine, Robert E., Eastman & Beaudine, Inc. (R), TX, *56*
Berman, Shirlee J., Retail Recruiters/Spectrum Consultants, Inc. (C), PA, *535*
Black, James L., J.B.A. Assoc. (R), WA, *104*
Blood, Burwood O., D. R. Blood & Assoc. (R), AZ, *18*
Bothereau, Elizabeth, Kenzer Corp. (R), MN, *113*
Bowerman, Rob, Recruiting Specialists (C), MA, *532*
Brauerman, Donna, John Kurosky & Assoc. (R), CA, *122*
Breault, Larry J., Management Recruiters of St. Lucie County, Inc. (C), FL, *444*
Buchholtz, Bruce Barton, Fairfield Int'l. Resources (R), NY, *65*
Butcher, Barbara, The Stevenson Group, Inc. (N.J.) (R), NJ, *200*
Cargill, Jim, Management Recruiters of Lake Tahoe, NV (C), NV, *453*
Carideo, Joseph J., Thorndike Deland Assoc. LLC (R), NY, *48*
Cary, Con, Cary & Assoc. (R), FL, *31*
Chesla, Garry, Executive Referral Services, Inc. (C), IL, *334*
Cooper, Karen, Ashford Management Group, Inc. (R), GA, *8*
Cooper, Michael, Cooper Management Assoc., Inc. (C), NJ, *298*
Corwin, J. Blade, Seitchik Corwin & Seitchik Inc. (R), CA, *188*
Daniel, David S., SpencerStuart (R), NY, *196*
Davis, Ronald, International Management Development Corp. (C), NY, *393*
Davis, III, Samuel, PRAXIS Partners (R), VA, *167*
Dominguez, Connie, Dominguez-Metz & Assoc. (R), CA, *53*
Douglas, Marc, Prestige Inc. (C), WI, *518*
Doutre, Judy, Dumont & Co. (C), BC, *316*
Drinkwater, Wendy A., Drinkwater & Assoc. (R), MA, *54*
Duffy, Kevin, Kensington Int'l., Inc. (R), IL, *113*
Dumont, Brenda, Dumont & Co. (C), BC, *316*
Durica, Daniel, Recruiting Specialists (C), MA, *532*
Eagan, Karen, Management Recruiters of Grass Valley (C), CA, *440*
Eagan, Ridge, Management Recruiters of Grass Valley (C), CA, *440*
Edwards, Greg, Eden & Assoc., Inc. (C), PA, *326*
Elzweig, Mark, Mark Elzweig Co., Ltd. (C), NY, *329*
Ericksen, Linda, MESA International (C), OR, *480*
Erickson, Elaine, Kenzer Corp. (R), NY, *113*
Esecson, Diane P., Drinkwater & Assoc. (R), MA, *55*
Feigenbaum, Irwin J., Professional Resources (C), NY, *522*
Feldman, Abe, A. E. Feldman Assoc., Inc. (C), NY, *339*
FitzGibbon, Michael T., FitzGibbon & Assoc. (R), PA, *68*
Ford, Eileen F., Ford & Ford (C), MA, *343*
Frankovich, John, BRW Search (C), MN, *275*
Freier, Bruce, Executive Referral Services, Inc. (C), IL, *334*
Friedman, Nathan, Retail Recruiters (C), CT, *535*
Fuller, Thomas, Epsen, Fuller & Assoc., LLC (R), NJ, *60*
Gallagher, David W., LAI Ward Howell (R), GA, *123*
George, Alan, Ken Clark Int'l. (R), NJ, *36*
Gernetzke, James, J. Gernetzke & Assoc., Inc. (C), OH, *357*
Goldberg, Sybil, Spectra International LLC (C), AZ, *589*
Gorfinkle, Gayle, Executive Search Int'l./Transearch (R), MA, *63*
Griesedieck, Jr., Joseph E., SpencerStuart (R), CA, *196*
Griffey, Annette, Ashford Management Group, Inc. (R), CA, *8*
Gross, Kathy, Evie Kreisler Assoc. Inc. (C), NY, *409*
Groussman, Maria, Groussman & Assoc., Inc. (R), TX, *82*
Guerrero, Daniel, Kenzer Corp. (R), CA, *113*
Harbaugh, Jr., Paul J., International Management Advisors, Inc. (R), NY, *103*
Harcourt, Judy, Harcourt & Assoc. (C), AB, *368*
Harmeling, Dutch, Harmeling & Associates (C), CA, *369*
Hart, Susan S., SpencerStuart (R), CT, *196*
Hawkins, Michael J., Michael J. Hawkins, Inc. (C), IL, *370*
Henard, John B., LAI Ward Howell (R), FL, *123*
Hirshorn, Richard P., Fairfield Int'l. Resources (R), NY, *65*
Jackowitz, Todd, J. Robert Scott (R), MA, *104*
Jacob, Marilyn, Huntress Real Estate Executive Search (R), MO, *100*
Jones, Donald, Kenzer Corp. (R), TX, *113*
Kanal, David S., Johnson Smith & Knisely (R), NY, *107*
Kaye, Manuel, Retail Executive Search (C), FL, *535*
Kenzer, Robert D., Kenzer Corp. (R), NY, *113*
Kirkendorfer, Laura, The Kingsley Group (R), CA, *115*
Kosmetos, Michael, Michael Kosmetos & Assoc., Inc. (C), OH, *408*
Kreisler, Debbi, Evie Kreisler Assoc. Inc. (C), GA, *409*
Kreisler, Evie, Evie Kreisler Assoc. Inc. (C), CA, *409*
Laba, Marvin, Marvin Laba & Assoc. (R), CA, *122*
Laba, Stuart, Marvin Laba & Assoc. (R), NJ, *122*
Laughlin, Cindy, Recruiting Specialists (C), MA, *532*
Lav, Madeleine, Madeleine Lav & Assoc. (C), CA, *413*
Leavee, Kenneth S., The Alice Groves Co., Inc. (C), CT, *244*
Leavee, Raymond J., The Alice Groves Co., Inc. (C), CT, *244*
Lemming, Jeff, Lemming/LeVan, Inc. (R), GA, *128*
LeVan, Salli, Lemming/LeVan, Inc. (R), GA, *128*
Levine, Alan C., Alan Levine Assoc. (R), MA, *129*
Levine, Harvey, Fairfield Int'l. Resources (R), NY, *65*
MacDowell, Leanna, Madison MacArthur Inc. (R), ON, *133*
Maher, William J., Johnson Smith & Knisely (R), NY, *107*
Martinez, Janis E., Ashford Management Group, Inc. (R), GA, *8*
Martirano, Nancy, Recruiting Specialists (C), MA, *532*
McCarthy, Richard, McCarthy Assoc. National BancSearch, LLC (C), LA, *473*
McIntyre, Jeffrey F., McIntyre Assoc. (R), CT, *141*
Meagher, III, Edward A., The Woodstone Consulting Company, Inc. (R), CO, *224*
Meagher, Linda J., The Woodstone Consulting Company, Inc. (R), CO, *224*
Metz, Nancy, Dominguez-Metz & Assoc. (R), CA, *53*
Milstein, Bonnie, Marvin Laba & Assoc. (R), CA, *122*
Moore, Robert, Management Recruiters of Rockville (C), MD, *450*
Morrison, C. Robert, Quetico Corp. (R), TX, *170*
Moy, Betty, Cook Assoc.,® Inc. (R), IL, *40*
Nelson, Lynn, Ashford Management Group, Inc. (R), GA, *8*
Nemec, Edward C., Craig Affiliates, Inc. (C), TX, *302*
Nicolaas, Gina, Dumont & Co. (C), BC, *316*
O'Dell, Robert, Roth Young Executive Search (C), TX, *546*
Ollinger, Chuck, Ollinger Partners (R), MA, *156*
Penwell, Wayne, Recruiting Specialists (C), MA, *532*

RECRUITER SPECIALTIES

Perlstadt, Douglas, Interactive Search Network (R), CA, *102*
Pezim, Steven G., The Bedford Consulting Group Inc. (R), ON, *15*
Phelps, Grace, Hardage Group (C), TN, *369*
Phillips, David, Matthews & Stephens Assoc., Inc. (C), CT, *472*
Pollin, M. Ellen, LAI Ward Howell (R), FL, *123*
Porter, Nancy, Porter & Assoc., Inc. (C), FL, *514*
Powell, Marie, Kenzer Corp. (R), GA, *113*
Powell, Mike, Marc-Allen Assoc., Inc. (C), FL, *469*
Powers, Robert, Robert Powers & Assoc. (C), CA, *515*
Powers, Susan, Robert Powers & Assoc. (C), CA, *515*
Presser, Janet, N.A.P. Executive Services (Canada) Inc. (C), QE, *488*
Priftis, Tony, Evie Kreisler Assoc. Inc. (C), TX, *409*
Ragaza, Jessica, RitaSue Siegel Resources, Inc. (R), NY, *191*
Reifersen, Ruth F., The Jonathan Stevens Group, Inc. (R), NJ, *108*
Reiser, Ellen, Thorndike Deland Assoc. LLC (R), NY, *48*
Richards-Davy, Penny, Management Recruiters of Rockville (C), MD, *450*
Riley, Jim, Riley Cole (C), CA, *537*
Rohan, James, J. P. Canon Assoc. (C), NY, *280*
Rothstein, Steve, N.A.P. Executive Services (Canada) Inc. (C), ON, *488*
Rotsky, Bernard, BR & Assoc. (C), NJ, *271*
Rotsky, Sally, BR & Assoc. (C), NJ, *271*
Russell, Robin, Kenzer Corp. (R), NY, *113*
Ruthrauff, Debbie, Kelly Associates (R), PA, *112*
Schall, David R., Schall Executive Search Partners (R), MN, *185*
Schorejs, Ray, Roth Young Executive Search (C), TX, *546*
Schwartz, Deborah, Ollinger Partners (R), MA, *156*
Segal, Eric B., Kenzer Corp. (R), NY, *113*
Seitchik, Jack, Seitchik Corwin & Seitchik Inc. (R), CA, *188*
Seitchik, William, Seitchik Corwin & Seitchik Inc. (R), NY, *188*
Shapiro, Lisa, Ellis Career Consultants (C), NJ, *328*
Shulman, Mel, M. Shulman, Inc. (R), CA, *191*
Simpson, Terre, Simpson Associates (C), NY, *582*
Skirbe, Douglas, The Zarkin Group, Inc. (R), NY, *226*
Smith, II, Don, Smith, Brown & Jones (C), FL, *585*
Snyder, Thomas J., SpencerStuart (R), IL, *197*
Spahr, Donald B., Roth Young Executive Recruiters (C), MN, *546*
Spencer, Frank T., DHR Int'l., Inc. (R), NY, *50*
Spiegel, Deborah, Kenzer Corp. (R), NY, *113*
Steinberg, Paul D., IMA Search, Inc. (R), NY, *101*
Stone, Laura, Sales Consultants of Cincinnati (C), OH, *561*
Sullivan, Tami, Culver Personnel Services (C), CA, *304*
Sumurdy, Melinda M., LAI Ward Howell (R), TX, *124*
Suss, Mark J., Executive/Retail Placement Assoc. (C), MD, *337*
Tadda, Wayne, Evie Kreisler Assoc. Inc. (C), IL, *409*
Talabisco, Barbara, Wakefield Talabisco Int'l. (R), NY, *214*
Tambor, Morris, Reynolds Consulting Int'l. (R), ON, *177*
Thaler, Brian D., Scott-Thaler Assoc. Agency, Inc. (C), CA, *573*
Thaller, Carole, Retail Connection, Inc. (C), NJ, *535*
Thiemann, Brian, Christopher and Long (C), MO, *291*
Thomas, Jeffrey, Fairfaxx Corp. (R), CT, *64*
Toole, Thomas J., Management Recruiters of Laguna Hills (C), CA, *440*
Trilling, Dean D., LAI Ward Howell (R), OH, *123*
Valdes, Maria Elena, Korn/Ferry, Int'l., S.A. de C.V. (R), MX, *118*
Vennetti, Carie, Strategic Resources (C), WA, *595*
Walker, Walter G., Walker Group, Inc. (R), MN, *215*
Walsh, Joe, A.J. & Assoc. (C), FL, *232*
Weiss, John J., Executive Placement Services (C), GA, *333*
Wells, Lee, F-O-R-T-U-N-E Personnel Consultants of East Seattle (C), WA, *351*
Wilensky, Joel H., Joel H. Wilensky Assoc., Inc. (C), MA, *620*
Wilson, Donald, Allerton Heneghan & O'Neill (R), IL, *4*
Wolcott, Tracy, Recruiting Specialists (C), MA, *532*
Womack, Chris, MESA International (C), OR, *480*
Wyatt, Robert S., R. S. Wyatt Assoc., Inc. (R), TX, *225*
York, Felecia, Human Resource Dimensions, Inc. (C), TX, *384*
Zaccaria, Fran, Zaccaria Int'l. (C), NJ, *627*
Zaccaria, Jack, Zaccaria Int'l. (C), NJ, *627*
Zarkin, Norman, The Zarkin Group, Inc. (R), NY, *226*

Retirement housing

Carter, Christine, Health Care Dimensions (C), CO, *371*
Clark, Michael, Cornerstone Search Assoc. Inc. (C), MA, *299*
Feingold, Robin, Cornerstone Search Assoc. Inc. (C), MA, *299*
Hazelton, Lisa, Health Care Dimensions (C), CO, *371*
Howard, Jill, Health Care Dimensions (C), CO, *371*
Rosen, Richard, Cornerstone Search Assoc. Inc. (C), MA, *299*
West, Nancy, Health Care Dimensions (C), CO, *371*

Risk management

Anwar, Tarin, Jay Gaines & Company, Inc. (R), NY, *74*
Bayard, Thomas E., Claimsearch (C), CA, *291*
Bergeris, Jim, Bergeris & Co., Inc. (C), NY, *265*
Bonham, Apryl, Claimsearch (C), CA, *291*
Chin, Joe, Cornell Group Int'l. Consulting, Inc. (R), NY, *41*
Ciaramitaro, Joseph, Corporate Search Consultants, Inc. (C), FL, *301*
Davis, Andrew, Smith Hanley Assoc., Inc. (C), CT, *584*
Gogates, Andrew, The Gogates Group, Inc. (R), NY, *79*
Goldbach, Linda J., Beacon Int'l., Inc. (C), VA, *261*
Gunther, James J., Harvard Aimes Group (R), CT, *87*
Hellebusch, Jerry, Morgan Hunter Corp. (C), KS, *485*
Horton, Scott, Capital Markets Resources, Inc. (C), NC, *281*
Mayer, Mary L., Mary L. Mayer, Ltd. (R), MN, *139*
Mehta, Narinder K., Mehta Consulting (C), NJ, *478*
Moore, Connie, C. A. Moore & Assoc., Inc. (C), MN, *484*
Richer, Joyce Eidenberg, W. F. Richer Assoc., Inc. (C), NY, *537*
Richer, William F., W. F. Richer Assoc., Inc. (C), NY, *536*
Rountree, III, John B., Lexington Software Inc. (C), NY, *417*
Russillo, Thomas P., Russillo/Gardner/Spolsino (C), MA, *548*
Ryan, Debra, Bonell Ryan Inc. (R), NY, *19*
Spolsino, Robert J., Russillo/Gardner/Spolsino (C), MA, *548*
Stephens, Susan, Sales Consultants of Chicago South (C), IL, *558*
Watson, David L. B., Pacific Coast Recruiters (C), OR, *501*
Wolfson, Robert H., Mitchell/Wolfson, Assoc. (R), IL, *145*

Rubber

Bell, Lindy, Fortune Personnel Consultants of Huntsville, Inc. (C), AL, *344*
Creeger, David, Sanford Rose Assoc. - Fairlawn (C), OH, *569*
Gerst, Thomas J., Management Recruiters of Akron (C), OH, *457*
Mattocks, Paul, G. P. Mattocks & Associates (C), NC, *473*
Pajak, Michael A., The Danielson Group, Inc. (C), TX, *306*

Roth, Bill, Lou Michaels Assoc., Inc. (C), MI, *481*
Sgro, David J., Midland Consultants (C), OH, *481*
Skelton, Brenda, Cumberland Professional Search Inc. (C), TN, *304*
Symanski, Donald G., Tierney Assoc., Inc. (R), PA, *209*

Safety

Barick, Bradford L., Management Recruiters of Stevens Point, Inc. (C), WI, *466*
Cunningham, Douglas, Staff Resources, Inc. (C), SC, *590*
Fehrenbach, Ray, Southern Recruiters & Consultants, Inc. (C), SC, *587*
Hunkins, Deborah J., Career Images (C), FL, *282*
Mallinson, Robert, Ritta Professional Search Inc. (C), NY, *538*
Newell, Wayne, Management Alliance Group, Inc. (R), NJ, *134*
Palos, Michael V., Kelly Associates (R), PA, *112*
Razuri, Patrick, Management Recruiters of Savannah (C), GA, *446*
Sims, Larry, Reality Group (C), OK, *531*
White, Ken, Management Recruiters of Winston-Salem (C), NC, *457*
Williams, Randy L., Environmental, Health & Safety Search Assoc. (C), FL, *331*

Sales

Adams, Arthur, Arthur Adams & Assoc. (C), OH, *239*
Adams, Robert, Sales Consultants of Dallas (C), TX, *563*
Addison, Mike, Sales Consultants of Dallas (C), TX, *563*
Adler, Louis S., CJA-The Adler Group, Inc. (R), CA, *35*
Aguirrezabal, Angelina, OSAGUI S.A. de C.V. (C), MX, *500*
Alexander, Edward J., EagleView, Inc. (C), MA, *325*
Alexander, Gary, Mark Christian & Assoc., Inc. (C), AZ, *470*
Alexander, Myra, Mark Christian & Assoc., Inc. (C), AZ, *470*
Andrews, Charles, The Borton Wallace Co. (R), TN, *19*
Angell, Tryg R., Tryg R. Angell, Ltd. (C), CT, *250*
Anton, Michael, Michael James & Co. (C), IL, *480*
Aquavella, Charles P., Charles P. Aquavella & Assoc. (C), TX, *252*
Archibald, David E., The Eldridge Group, Ltd. (C), IL, *327*
Aronin, Michael, Fisher-Todd Assoc. (C), NY, *342*
Babka, James, Roth Young of Chicago (C), IL, *546*
Baer, Curtis L., Sales Consultants of Barrington (C), IL, *558*
Baker, Susan F., Diversified Consulting Services, Inc. (C), CO, *313*
Balakonis, Charles L., Lawrence-Balakonis & Assoc., Inc. (C), GA, *414*
Ball, Ronald D., BallResources (C), MO, *258*
Balzen, David, InterNeed (C), TX, *394*
Barick, Linda R., Management Recruiters of Stevens Point, Inc. (C), WI, *466*
Barnes, Gary B., Brigade, Inc. (R), CA, *23*
Barnes, Vern, Capital Consulting Group, Inc. (R), MD, *28*
Baron, Sheldon S., Sales Consultants of Nashua-Manchester (C), NH, *560*
Barrett, Bill, The Barrett Group (C), NH, *260*
Bayer, Richard L., Top Gun Group, Inc. (C), NV, *607*
Beamer, Thomas G., Thomas Lyle & Co. (C), IL, *606*
Beaudin, Elizabeth C., Callan Assoc., Ltd. (R), IL, *27*
Belanger, Richard, Kingsley Allen Partners Inc. (R), ON, *114*
Bender, Alan, Bender Executive Search Management Consulting (R), NY, *16*
Berg, Charlie, Management Recruiters of Lake Forest, IL (C), IL, *447*
Berger, Joel, Midas Management (C), CT, *481*
Bernal, Joan M., Barnes & Assoc. Executive Search (C), CA, *259*
Besso, Sandy, Intersource, Ltd. (R), TX, *103*
Blood, James L., D. R. Blood & Assoc. (R), AZ, *18*
Bolls, Rich, Management Recruiters of Houston (C), TX, *463*
Booker, Calvin, National Affirmative Action Career Network, Inc. (C), CO, *488*
Booth, Sandra, SKB Enterprises (C), NY, *582*
Bosch, Diane, Bosch & Assoc., LLC (R), CT, *20*
Bosch, Eric E., Bosch & Assoc., LLC (R), CT, *20*
Bose, Emile, Fred Hood & Assoc. (C), CA, *380*
Bourque, Jack, Management Recruiters of Winsted, Inc. (C), CT, *442*
Boyle, Lori, JDC Assoc. (C), NY, *397*
Brauninger, John C., AmeriPro Search, Inc. (C), NC, *248*
Brennise, Stacie, Healthcare Recruiters Int'l. Phoenix (C), AZ, *372*
Britten, Albert, Sales Consultants of Scottsdale, Inc. (C), AZ, *556*
Brody, Stuart, R. Green & Assoc., Inc. (C), OH, *362*
Brooks, Debbie, DBC Recruiting Network (C), GA, *309*
Brown, Alan V., Personnel Alliance Group (C), NJ, *508*
Brown, Buzz, Brown, Bernardy, Van Remmen, Inc. (C), CA, *275*
Brown, Gene, Management Recruiters of Atlanta West, Inc. (C), GA, *445*
Bryant, Ed, Kiley, Owen & McGovern, Inc. (R), NJ, *114*
Buckley, Daniel, The Buckley Group (C), FL, *276*
Burgess, III, William H., The Burgess Group-Corporate Recruiters Int'l., Inc. (R), NY, *25*
Burns, Patrick J., Career Alternatives Executive Search (C), MI, *281*
Buteau, R. N., Datamatics Management Services, Inc. (C), NJ, *308*
Cain, Douglas, Sales Recruiting Network (C), PA, *564*
Cain, Randy, Career Counseling Inc. (CCI) (C), KY, *282*
Campbell, Brian H., Venpro Consulting Inc. (C), ON, *612*
Capanna, Patricia A., Management Recruiters of Madison, Inc. (C), WI, *466*
Carlson, Mark, MetroVantage Personnel Systems (C), CA, *480*
Carpenter, Edward, Executive Search of America, Inc. (C), OH, *336*
Cech, Raymond R., Dunhill Executive Search of Los Angeles, Inc. (C), CA, *319*
Christine, Rich, R. Christine Assoc. (C), PA, *290*
Chrzan, Phyllis, Brethet, Barnum & Assoc., Inc. (C), ON, *273*
Ciak, Rosemarie, Ken Clark Int'l. (R), NJ, *36*
Clark, David A., Sprout/Standish, Inc. (C), NH, *590*
Clark, Donna, StratfordGroup (R), CA, *203*
Clark, Larry A., The Clark Group (C), MI, *292*
Clarke, Brian G., Kensington Int'l., Inc. (R), IL, *113*
Clinton, Omari, Clinton, Charles, Wise & Co. (C), FL, *293*
Coco, Jr., Carl, Professions, Inc. (C), OH, *523*
Cole, Christopher, Tech-Net (C), TX, *601*
Collins, Victoria, Sales Consultants of Dallas (C), TX, *563*
Conner, Chuck, Strauss Personnel Service (C), PA, *596*
Cook, Clifford L., CEO Consulting (C), FL, *287*
Cooper, Michael, Chad Management Group (C), ON, *288*
Cotton, Peter C., Sales Consultants of Rhode Island, Inc. (C), RI, *562*
Crane, Mary, International Pro Sourcing, Inc. (C), PA, *393*
Credidio, Thomas J., The DataFinders Group, Inc. (C), NJ, *307*
Crosby, Kimberly A., Fast Switch, Ltd. (C), OH, *338*
Curtis, Susan J., ProSearch Recruiting (C), CA, *524*
Damon, Richard E., Damon & Assoc., Inc. (C), TX, *306*
Dant, Wendy A., Hire Authority, Inc. (C), MI, *379*
Davis, Glenn S., Next Step Recruiting (C), CA, *493*
DeClouet, J. Michael, The J. B. Search Group (C), CA, *395*
DeRose, Rick, Telecom Executive Group (C), NJ, *605*
Despres, Raoul, Despres & Associates (C), IL, *311*

RECRUITER SPECIALTIES

Deutschman, Michele, Placements by Jesse Reid Assoc., Inc. (C), NY, *513*
Devlin, Jack, The Devlin Search Group, Inc. (C), MA, *312*
Devoto, Andrea, Devoto & Assoc. (C), CA, *312*
Dickson, Elaine, Management Recruiters of Milwaukee - Downtown (C), WI, *466*
Dolphin, Barbara, Harbrowe, Inc. (C), NY, *368*
Donnelly, Dan, The Donnelly Group-Sales Recruiters, Inc. (C), MO, *314*
Doyle, Don, Bosch & Assoc., LLC (R), CT, *20*
Dukas, Theodore, Dukas Assoc. (C), MA, *315*
Dunlap, Thomas, Charles Dahl Group, Inc. (C), MN, *306*
Durning, Charles, The Pollack Group (C), ON, *514*
Dussick, Vince, Dussick Management Assoc. (C), CT, *323*
Duval, Dick, B. D. Wallace & Assoc. (C), MD, *614*
Dykes, Mimi, Staffing Edge, Inc. (C), TX, *591*
Edelberg, Frank, Management One Consultants (C), ON, *425*
Edwards, Greg, Eden & Assoc., Inc. (C), PA, *326*
Edwards, Lisa, Edwards & Assoc. (C), GA, *327*
Edwards, Verba Lee, Wing Tips & Pumps, Inc. (C), MI, *623*
Ellis, Bill, Interspace Interactive, Inc. (C), NY, *394*
Elrick, Bill, Mayhall Search Group, Inc. (C), IN, *473*
Emery, Karlan, Emerging Medical Technologies, Inc. (C), CO, *329*
Finley, Margot E., Avondale Search Int'l., Inc. (R), FL, *9*
Fisher, Iris L., Healthcare Recruiters International-NY/NJ (C), NJ, *373*
Fitzgibbons, David, International Executive Recruiters (C), OH, *393*
Flannery, Michael, Redwood Partners Ltd. (R), NY, *173*
Foster, William A., Bridgecreek Personnel Agency (C), CA, *273*
Franz, Ronald, Fisher-Todd Assoc. (C), NY, *342*
Fraser, William, Windsor Consultants, Inc. (C), TX, *622*
Frishman, Robert, Greenwich Search Partners, LLC (C), CT, *363*
Fumano, Gary W., Chapman & Assoc. (C), BC, *289*
Furman, Matt, MJF Assoc. (C), CT, *483*
Gale, Rhoda, Management Recruiters of the Baltimore Washington Corridor (C), MD, *450*
Gallagher, Joan, International Pro Sourcing, Inc. (C), PA, *393*
Gallagher, Kelly, International Pro Sourcing, Inc. (C), PA, *393*
Gardner, Brian, Bosch & Assoc., LLC (R), CT, *20*
Garfinkle, Benson D., MetroVantage Personnel Systems (C), CA, *480*
Garrett, Kelly, Management Recruiters - Indianapolis (C), IN, *448*
Gehn, Valerie, Harbrowe, Inc. (C), NY, *368*
Gerarde, Paul S., Keena Staffing Services (C), NY, *404*
Gideon, Mark, Eagle Search Assoc. (C), CA, *325*
Gilbert, Brian, Sales Consultants of Dallas (C), TX, *563*
Gilchrist, Robert J., Horton International Inc. (R), CT, *96*
Gildersleeve, John, Snelling & Snelling, Inc. (C), FL, *585*
Giles, Kenn, Dick Williams & Assoc. (C), CA, *621*
Gilson, Linda L., Key Resources Int'l. (C), CA, *406*
Glassberg, Bob, Sales Search (C), ON, *564*
Gleason, Helen, Management Recruiters of Clearwater (C), FL, *443*
Gleason, James P., J. P. Gleason Assoc., Inc. (R), IL, *77*
Glosser, Elizabeth B., Executive Exchange Corp. (C), NJ, *333*
Goldman, Jeff, Global 1000 Int'l. Services (C), CA, *358*
Gray, Leanne P., Career Profiles (C), NH, *283*
Gray, Norman G., Career Profiles (C), NH, *283*
Greenberg, Jordan A., The Pinnacle Source, Inc. (C), CO, *512*
Griffin, Deana A., Souder & Assoc. (R), VA, *195*
Grimes, Matthew, Angel Group Int'l. (C), KY, *250*
Gross, Jerry, Creative HR Solutions (C), GA, *303*
Gross, Philip, Professions, Inc. (C), OH, *523*
Gungle, Theresa, Gowdy Consultants (C), TX, *361*
Hailey, H. M., Damon & Assoc., Inc. (C), TX, *306*
Hakim, Ronald J., The GlobalSearch Group (C), TX, *359*
Haller, Thomas, International Executive Recruiters (C), OH, *393*
Hamel, Ed, Sales Consultants of Dallas (C), TX, *563*
Hanssen, Barbara, Executive Search Team (C), MI, *336*
Harris, Ann, International Pro Sourcing, Inc. (C), PA, *393*
Heller, Phillip, Heller Kil Assoc., Inc. (C), FL, *375*
Hendricks, II, Stanley M., National Recruiting Service (C), IN, *489*
Herlihy, Jack, J. J. Herlihy & Assoc., Inc. (C), CA, *376*
Hertz, Al, Carter/MacKay (C), NC, *285*
Hickman, Fred, Carnegie Partners, Inc. (R), IL, *30*
Hill, Ted, Culver Personnel Services (C), CA, *304*
Hoffenberg, Elliot, H. J. Elliot, Inc. (R), IL, *58*
Hoglund, Gerald C., Hoglund & Assoc., Inc. (R), IL, *94*
Hughes, Donald J., Hughes & Company (R), VA, *98*
Hughes, Susan F., Opus Marketing (R), MN, *157*
Humay, Gene, E. F. Humay Assoc. (C), PA, *384*
Humay, Jane, E. F. Humay Assoc. (C), PA, *384*
Humphreys, Scott W., Robison Humphreys & Assoc., Inc. (R), ON, *180*
Humphreys, William M., Robison Humphreys & Assoc., Inc. (R), ON, *180*
Hurley, Michael, Century Assoc., Inc. (C), PA, *287*
Israel, Sheldon, Sales Professionals Personnel Services (C), CA, *564*
Jackson, Cindy, CJSI-Cindy Jackson Search Int'l. (C), CA, *291*
Jackson, Eric, ProFinders, Inc. (C), FL, *523*
Jacobs, David M., Jacobs & Co. (R), CT, *105*
James, Carolyn, J. Joseph & Assoc. (C), OH, *395*
Johnson, Glen, Sales Recruiters of Oklahoma City (C), OK, *564*
Johnson, Greg, Sales Recruiters of Oklahoma City (C), OK, *564*
Johnson, Robert J., Quality Search Inc. (C), OH, *526*
Johnson, Ron L., Management Recruiters of Fresno (C), CA, *440*
Jones, M. Susan, Greenwich Search Partners, LLC (C), CT, *363*
Joseph, Allen F., CBA Companies (C), CA, *286*
Jurenovich, Gary S., The Stewart Group (C), FL, *593*
Kallfelz, Paul F., A. G. Fishkin & Assoc., Inc. (R), MD, *68*
Katz, Martin, Crispi, Wagner & Co., Inc. (R), NY, *43*
Kaufman, Susan, Kaufman Assoc. (R), CA, *110*
Kay, Heidi, Kay Concepts, Inc. (C), FL, *404*
Keefe, Steve, The Search America Group Inc. (C), OH, *573*
Kelly, Rory, The Ellsworth Group (C), NY, *329*
Keyser, James M., Career +Plus (C), NY, *281*
Kimball, Dex, Lanken-Kimball-Therrell & Assoc. (C), GA, *412*
Kindig, Becky, Management Recruiters-Cedar Rapids, Inc. (C), IA, *448*
King, J. C., A H Justice Search Consultants (C), TX, *402*
King, Jack, Newman-Johnson-King, Inc. (C), TX, *492*
Kinney, Carol, Dussick Management Assoc. (C), CT, *323*
Kirkbride, Robert, Kirkbride Assoc., Inc. (C), WA, *407*
Kissel, James R., Management Recruiters of Northern Palm Beaches (C), FL, *444*

Knight, Lene M., The Professional Sales Search Co., Inc. (C), WA, *522*
Koch, Gail Kleinberg, CAS Comsearch Inc. (C), NY, *286*
Koller, Jr., Edward R., The Howard-Sloan-Koller Group (R), NY, *97*
Komorner, Paul, The Whitney Group (C), GA, *620*
Konrad, William, ISC of Atlanta, Inc. (C), GA, *394*
Kool, Joan, Professional Recruiters, Inc. (C), PA, *521*
Koppes, Jenny, Future Employment Service, Inc. (C), IA, *354*
Kreisberg, Robert S., Opus Marketing (R), CA, *156*
Kressenberg, Sammye Jo, Kressenberg Assoc. (C), TX, *409*
Krezo, Rich, Michigan Consulting Group (R), MI, *144*
Krezo, Rich, Premier Recruiting Group (C), MI, *516*
Kuhlenbeck, Phillip, Austin Group Int'l./Marlar Int'l. (R), TX, *9*
Kuntz, William A., Sales Consultants of Indianapolis (C), IN, *559*
Kuschnov, Janice, Charles Dahl Group, Inc. (C), MN, *306*
Laite, Joseph, Search Int'l. (R), MA, *187*
Langley, Mark, Southwestern Professional Services (C), FL, *588*
Lanken, Joel, Lanken-Kimball-Therrell & Assoc. (C), GA, *412*
Lantz, Delores, A C Personnel Services, Inc. (C), OK, *231*
Larsen, Michael G., Barnes & Assoc. Executive Search (C), CA, *259*
Larson, Ray, Larson Assoc. (R), CA, *125*
Lasee, Jeff, The H. S. Group, Inc. (C), WI, *365*
Lawrence, Gina, Micro Staff Solutions, Inc. (C), TX, *481*
Lawson, Trina R., Search Assoc., Inc. (C), NJ, *574*
Lear, Daniel, Omega Systems, LLC (C), VA, *498*
Lee, Barbara A., Management Recruiters, Inc. (C), FL, *443*
Leggett, Amy, APA Employment Agency Inc. (C), WA, *251*
Leininger, Dennis, Staffing Edge, Inc. (C), IA, *590*
Lenobel, Stephen, Professional Recruiters, Inc. (C), PA, *521*
Lessner, Mark, J. E. Lessner Assoc., Inc. (R), MI, *128*
Letts, Douglas R., The Professional Sales Search Co., Inc. (C), WA, *522*
Levin, Phillip, Executive Search Team (C), MI, *336*
Liles, Cheryl, Snelling Search Recruiters (C), NC, *586*
Lippincott, Roger, Dunhill Professional Search of Ramsey (C), NJ, *321*
Little, John J., Alpha Executive Search (C), AL, *246*
Logie, Richard, Kirkbride Assoc., Inc. (C), WA, *407*
Lombardi, Helen T., Pearce & Assoc. (C), FL, *506*
Longshaw, Dawn A., Holloway Schulz & Partners (C), BC, *380*
Louis, Gregory, Louis Search Group, Inc. (C), NJ, *420*
Lowery, Bruce N., Bruce Lowery & Assoc. (C), MI, *420*
Lynch, Jack, Michigan Consulting Group (R), MI, *144*
Lynch, Jack, Premier Recruiting Group (C), MI, *516*
MacKenzie, Bruce J., Chapman & Assoc. (C), BC, *289*
Madden, Heather, Bosch & Assoc., LLC (R), CT, *20*
Manning, Roger, Executive Search Team (C), MI, *336*
Martin, Robert A., Phoenix Partners, Inc. (C), GA, *511*
Mason, Ron, Professional Recruiters (C), UT, *522*
Mathias, Kathy A., Stone, Murphy & Olson (R), MN, *201*
Matthews, Alyce, The Matthews Group, Inc. (C), NJ, *472*
Maun, Fran, Roth Young of Tampa (C), FL, *546*
Mayhall, Dale, Mayhall Search Group, Inc. (C), IN, *473*
McAndrew, Cindy, Aries Search Group (C), GA, *252*
McCartt, Sandra, Professional Search, Inc. Int'l. (C), TX, *523*
McElmeel, Joseph J., Brooke Chase Assoc., Inc. (R), IL, *24*
McFadden, James, PSP Agency (C), NY, *525*
McGlawn, Walter, Corporate Plus, Ltd. (C), GA, *300*
McGoldrick, Joe, J. Joseph & Assoc. (C), OH, *395*
McHale, John P., McHale & Assoc. (R), WA, *141*
McIvor, Mike, Christmas, McIvor & Assoc. Inc. (C), ON, *290*
McKee, Edward F., McKee Cyber Search (C), MS, *475*
McKersie, Edward S., ProSearch, Inc. (C), ME, *524*
McLean, Andrew, The Pollack Group (C), ON, *514*
Medley, Jerry, The Medley Group (C), CA, *477*
Mehta, Narinder K., Mehta Consulting (C), NJ, *478*
Menefee, Shawn, Corporate Plus, Ltd. (C), GA, *300*
Milne, Danette, Danette Milne Corporate Search Inc. (C), ON, *482*
Milne, Evette, Danette Milne Corporate Search Inc. (C), ON, *482*
Mitchell, John, Fred Hood & Assoc. (C), CA, *380*
Mitchell, Sheri, ProFinders, Inc. (C), FL, *523*
Moere, Linda A., Michaels & Moere (C), WI, *481*
Molkentine, Jon, Dunhill Search of Arlington (C), TX, *322*
Molnar, David, National Register Columbus Inc. (C), OH, *490*
Mols, Jeff, Aurora Tech Search (C), ON, *256*
Monset, Rachel, NCC Executive Search Consultants (C), CA, *490*
Montijo, Alicia, NCC Executive Search Consultants (C), CA, *491*
Moore, Michael, RCI Employment Solutions (C), FL, *531*
Moore, Michael H., The Inside Track (C), TX, *389*
Moran, Gayle, Dussick Management Assoc. (C), CT, *323*
Mueller, William, Noll Human Resource Services (C), MO, *494*
Nanney, Jerry, Lou Michaels Assoc., Inc. (C), MI, *481*
Narita, Art, Essential Solutions, Inc. (C), CA, *331*
Natowitz, Robert, DeMatteo Associates (C), NY, *311*
Nicklas, Kirk, The Ellsworth Group (C), NY, *329*
Nigro, Marci Yacker, Telecom Executive Group (C), NY, *605*
Nimmo, Richard, AmeriResource Group Inc. (C), OK, *248*
Normann, Amy, Robert M. Flanagan & Assoc., Ltd. (R), NY, *68*
Northrop, Michael S., Management Resource Group (C), MN, *467*
Noyes, Jim, Sales Consultants - Bristol County (C), MA, *559*
O'Neal, Jane, Austin Group Int'l./Marlar Int'l. (R), TX, *9*
Oberman, Heidi, Medical Recruiters Inc. (C), MO, *477*
Olesen, Jeannette, Management Recruiters of the Baltimore Washington Corridor (C), MD, *450*
Pallman-David, Cynthia, Bonnell Assoc. Ltd. (R), CT, *19*
Palmer, Connie, The Touchstone Group (C), MA, *607*
Pann, Arthur J., Arthur Pann Assoc., Inc. (C), NY, *502*
Pappas, Linda, Barclay Consultants, Inc. (C), NJ, *259*
Parisien, Simon, Yves Elkas Inc. (R), QE, *58*
Parker, Susan, Parker-Worthington, Inc. (C), TX, *503*
Patchin, Rory J., R2 Services, LLC (C), IL, *528*
Payette, Angela, Greene Personnel Consultants (C), RI, *362*
Peskosky, Mike, Prime Search (C), NC, *518*
Peterson, Greg, Sales Consultants of Ft. Lauderdale, Inc. (C), FL, *557*
Peterson, Michael T., BayResearch Group, Inc. (R), IL, *14*
Petry, Georgia M., Placements by Jesse Reid Assoc., Inc. (C), NY, *513*
Piccione, Mike, Dussick Management Assoc. (C), CT, *323*

Polyzos, Ginia M., Management Advisors Int'l., Inc. (C), NC, *424*
Poole, Don V., Don V. Poole & Assoc., Inc. (C), CO, *514*
Poutouves, Paul, Martha Ward Executive Search, Inc. (C), NY, *615*
Presley, Philip E., Presley Consultants, Inc. (C), CA, *517*
Price, Lynn M., Alan J. Price Assoc., Inc. (C), RI, *518*
Price, Velinda Hodge, Price & Assoc., Inc. (C), VA, *518*
Pukita, Mark, Fast Switch, Ltd. (C), OH, *338*
Putman, Joseph, Snelling Search (C), AL, *585*
Quinn, Thomas H., Weterrings & Agnew, Inc. (C), NY, *619*
Rachels, John, Southwestern Professional Services (C), VA, *588*
Raymont, Scott, J. Joseph & Assoc. (C), OH, *395*
Rexroad, Nancy, Strauss Personnel Service (C), PA, *596*
Richner, George A., Search Assoc., Inc. (C), NJ, *574*
Richter, Rick, Chad Management Group (C), ON, *288*
Riely, James A., Brownstone Sales & Marketing Group, Inc. (C), NY, *275*
Riendeau, Russell, Thomas Lyle & Co. (C), IL, *606*
Riley, Brian, Austin Group Int'l./Marlar Int'l. (R), TX, *9*
Rimele, J. R., Sales Recruiters of Oklahoma City (C), OK, *564*
Robins, Jeri N., Nagler, Robins & Poe, Inc. (R), MA, *150*
Robinson, Scott, Kensington Int'l., Inc. (R), IL, *113*
Rockwell, Sr., Richard B., Applied Search Assoc., Inc. (C), GA, *252*
Romaniw, Michael J., A la Carte Int'l., Inc. (R), VA, *1*
Roodvoets, Jan, J. E. Lessner Assoc., Inc. (R), MI, *128*
Rossi, Donna, Rossi & Assoc. Inc. (C), BC, *545*
Rowe, K. Michael, Management Resource Group (C), MN, *467*
Rowell, Mike, Carter/MacKay (C), MA, *285*
Sabrin, Joe, ManTech Consulting (C), NY, *468*
Salzberg, David, Roth Young Seattle (C), WA, *546*
Saracen, Robert R., The Libra Group Inc. (C), CT, *417*
Satterfield, Jr., Richard W., Satterfield & Assoc., Inc. (R), OH, *184*
Schmeh, Sandy, Sales Solutions (C), CA, *564*
Schrenzel, Steven N., The Governance Group, Inc. (R), NJ, *80*
Schwarz, Meredith Barnes, Barnes & Assoc. Executive Search (C), CA, *259*
Scoggins, Tim, Jackson Resources (R), TX, *105*
Seymour, Janice F., Baldwin & Assoc. (C), OH, *258*
Sharp, Paul S., Management Recruiters of Roanoke (C), VA, *465*
Shehan, Paul, Sales Consultants of Dallas (C), TX, *563*
Sherman, Terri, Tom Sloan & Assoc., Inc. (C), WI, *583*
Siegel, Michael, Specialty Employment Services, Inc. (C), GA, *589*
Silberger, Gary, Key Employment (C), NJ, *405*
Silverman, Jules, Barclay Consultants, Inc. (C), NJ, *259*
Singel, Jo, Jonathan Lawrence Assoc. (C), NJ, *400*
Skrypuch, Roman M., Financial Plus Management Solutions Inc. (R), ON, *66*
Slusser, Christine M., Lawrence Glaser Assoc., Inc. (C), NJ, *358*
Smith, Dan, Healthcare Resources Group (C), OK, *374*
Smith, Randall E., R2 Services, LLC (C), IL, *528*
Snow, Thomas J., The Search America Group Inc. (C), OH, *573*
Souder, Jr., E. G., Souder & Assoc. (R), VA, *195*
Southworth, David E., Michigan Consulting Group (R), MI, *144*
Spadaro, Raymond, David Perry Assoc. (C), NJ, *308*
Sparks, Michele Benum, Micro Staff Solutions, Inc. (C), TX, *481*
Sparks, Michele Benum, The Alternatives Group, Inc. (C), TX, *246*
Speciale, Pamela, Austin Group Int'l./Marlar Int'l. (R), TX, *9*
Stacey, Bryce A., Chapman & Assoc. (C), BC, *289*
Stanley, Wade, Management Recruiters of Raleigh (C), NC, *456*
Sted, Eric, The Search America Group Inc. (C), OH, *573*
Steiner, Judy, Future Employment Service, Inc. (C), IA, *354*
Sterenfeld, David, Corporate Dynamix (C), AZ, *300*
Stevenson, Alex, Search Masters, USA (C), FL, *576*
Stewart, Larry, American Resources Corp. (C), IL, *248*
Stroud, Toni, Management Recruiters of the Baltimore Washington Corridor (C), MD, *450*
Suchomski, Larry, The Montgomery Group, Inc. (C), TN, *484*
Sullivan, Mary, Sales Consultants of Chicago South (C), IL, *558*
Sullivan, Tami, Culver Personnel Services (C), CA, *304*
Talan, Marv, Executive Search Team (C), MI, *336*
Tamayo, Roland, Management Recruiters of Fresno (C), CA, *440*
Taylor, Jeffrey A., Sales Consultants of Ft. Lauderdale, Inc. (C), FL, *557*
Therizien, Greg, The Devlin Search Group, Inc. (C), MA, *312*
Therrell, Brock, Lanken-Kimball-Therrell & Assoc. (C), GA, *412*
Tinker, J. Jay, Management Recruiters of the Baltimore Washington Corridor (C), MD, *450*
Tomkin, Shelly, Career Counseling Ltd. (C.C.L.) (C), NY, *282*
Toms, Dennis M., National Recruiting Service (C), IN, *489*
Toole, Mary, Management Recruiters of Laguna Hills (C), CA, *440*
Townsend, James C., Future Employment Service, Inc. (C), IA, *353*
Trapani, Chris, ExecuSource Consultants, Inc. (C), TX, *332*
Trapani, Delores, ExecuSource Consultants, Inc. (C), TX, *332*
Unger, Don, Harcourt & Assoc. (C), AB, *368*
Valmore, Kim, Professions, Inc. (C), OH, *523*
Van Beek, Mel, Dunhill Personnel Service of Fargo (C), ND, *322*
Van Remmen, Roger, Brown, Bernardy, Van Remmen, Inc. (C), CA, *275*
Vaughan, David B., Vaughan & Co. (C), CA, *612*
Vegas, Carmen, Sofco (C), NY, *586*
Vozekas, James P., The Touchstone Group (C), MA, *607*
Walmsley, Scott, Association for Sales Force Management (C), WA, *254*
Walsh, Joe, A.J. & Assoc. (C), FL, *232*
Ward, Gayle E., Ward-Hoffman & Assoc. (C), ID, *615*
Warns, Peter, The DataFinders Group, Inc. (C), NJ, *307*
Weaver, John, Culver Personnel Services (C), CA, *304*
Welker, Henry A., Henry Welker & Assoc. (C), MI, *618*
Williams, Dick, Dick Williams & Assoc. (C), CA, *621*
Williamson, Bob, Grossberg & Assoc. (R), IL, *82*
Wise, Annette C., Clinton, Charles, Wise & Co. (C), FL, *293*
Wise, Craig D., Clinton, Charles, Wise & Co. (C), FL, *293*
Wisnewski, Edward J., Wisnewski & Assoc. (R), CA, *223*
Worthing, Ellen, Management Recruiters of the Baltimore Washington Corridor (C), MD, *450*
Wottowa, Denise, Medical Recruiters Inc. (C), MO, *477*
Wright, J. Robert, Bob Wright Recruiting, Inc. (C), CT, *625*
Yakimishyn, Michael, Zen Zen Int'l. Inc. (C), MB, *627*
Young, Wayne T., Management Recruiters of Morris County, NJ (C), NJ, *453*
Zeif, Kenneth, Newport Management (C), NY, *492*
Zillifro, Keith, Management Recruiters of Roanoke (C), VA, *465*

Management

Bond, Ann F., Ann Bond Assoc. Inc. (C), MD, *269*
Bond, Robert S., Ann Bond Assoc. Inc. (C), MD, *269*
Smith, Gregory K., Global Technologies Group Inc. (C), NC, *359*
Vito, Joseph, Multi Processing, Inc. (R), NH, *149*

Sales & marketing

Agriesti, Kay, Agriesti & Assoc. (C), CA, *243*
Alexander, Richard J., Alexander Associates (R), NJ, *2*
Allen, Marla, Allen & Assoc. (C), NV, *244*
Ammirati, Greg, Sales Consultants of Western McHenry County (C), IL, *558*
Andrews, Robert L., Allen Austin Lowe & Powers (R), TX, *3*
Anthony, Fred, Fred Anthony Assoc. (C), WI, *251*
Arnold, Chris, Sales Consultants of Laurel Park, Inc. (C), MI, *560*
Ascher, Daniel, D.A.I Human Resources Consultants (R), QE, *45*
Aswell, Judy, Management Recruiters of San Marcos (C), TX, *463*
Austin, Cami, Cami Austin & Assoc. (C), IL, *256*
Bailey, Edward L., The Patience Motivation Belief Group, Inc. (C), GA, *505*
Baker, Kim, Sales Advantage (C), FL, *551*
Bakken, Roger, J. Rodgers & Associates (C), IL, *540*
Barca, Anthony J., Ross Personnel Consultants, Inc. (C), CT, *545*
Barnes, Vern, Capital Consulting Group, Inc. (R), MD, *28*
Barr, Charly, Barr Assoc. (C), PA, *259*
Bassett, Mark, Hobson Assoc. (C), CT, *379*
Beck, Steven, Beck/Eastwood Recruitment Solutions (C), CA, *261*
Beech, Robert, Robert Beech West Inc. (C), CA, *262*
Bennett, Marilyn, Brentwood Int'l. (R), CA, *23*
Berry, Charles D., Management Recruiters of San Marcos (C), TX, *463*
Besso, Thom, Intersource, Ltd. (R), TX, *103*
Bilinski, Kalyna, Coe & Co. Int'l. Inc./EMA Partners Int'l. (R), AB, *37*
Bivona, Ernest, Sales Consultants of Morris County, Inc. (C), NJ, *561*
Blair, Jane, Management Recruiters - Indianapolis (C), IN, *448*
Blaney, John A., Blaney Executive Search (R), MA, *18*
Bogle, Tom, Tom Bogle & Assoc. (C), CA, *269*
Bogue, Randall L., TBC, Inc. (C), KY, *600*
Bontempo, David M., Dunhill Professional Search of Bucks-Mont., Inc. (C), PA, *322*
Boucher, Greg, Southwestern Professional Services (C), TN, *588*
Brennan, Vincent, Clayman & Co. (R), MA, *36*
Brest, Dan, Capital Consulting Group, Inc. (R), MD, *28*
Briggs, Farris R., Staff Resources, Inc. (C), SC, *590*
Britten, Albert, Sales Consultants of Scottsdale, Inc. (C), AZ, *556*
Burns, Susan, The Technology Group (R), IL, *208*
Burwell, Jr., Frank, PSP Agency (C), NY, *525*
Caplan, Deborah, PricewaterhouseCoopers Executive Search (R), ON, *168*
Caracciolo, Peter, Management Recruiters of Nassau, Inc. (R), NY, *134*
Carieri, Carl R., American Executive Search (C), FL, *247*
Carni, April, Snelling Search (C), AL, *585*
Catherman, H. O., Lectra Search (C), GA, *415*
Cavicchio, Dan, Greenwich Internet (C), CT, *363*
Cebrowski, John W., Sales Builders, Inc. (R), VA, *183*
Cegelski, Chris, The H. S. Group, Inc. (C), WI, *365*
Champion, Dale, The Marathon Group (C), GA, *469*
Chisum, Jeanne, Executive Sales Search (C), CO, *335*
Ciari, Kate Regan, Fortune Personnel Consultants (C), MT, *347*
Cizynski, Katherine W., James Mead & Co. (R), CT, *142*
Clark, Howard L., Howard Clark Assoc. (C), NJ, *292*
Clark, Lisa, Cooper Assoc., Inc. (C), NY, *298*
Clarke, Karen, HEC Group (C), ON, *375*
Clayman, Steven G., Clayman & Co. (R), MA, *36*
Clingan, Robert H., Management Recruiters of Broome County, Inc. (C), NY, *454*
Coffey, Michael O., The Langford Search, Inc. (C), AL, *412*
Combs, Stephen, StratfordGroup (R), CA, *203*
Connelly, Amy Reece, Johnson Brown Assoc., Inc. (C), IN, *400*
Cook, Daniel P., Alpha Resources (C), IL, *246*
Cook, John S., C. J. Vincent Assoc., LLC (C), MD, *612*
Cooper, Ron, High Tech Opportunities, Inc. (C), NH, *377*
Crabtree, G. A., Roger Dietsch & Assoc. (C), MN, *312*
Crawford, John H., Clayman & Co. (R), MA, *36*
Crittenden, John M., Dunhill Professional Search of Miami (C), FL, *320*
Crowe, Thomas H., Hunter, Rowan & Crowe (C), FL, *386*
Cucuzzella, Vincent J., C. J. Vincent Assoc., LLC (C), MD, *612*
Culbertson, Beth, Sales Consultants of Milwaukee (C), WI, *563*
DeLany, Donald F., Resource Perspectives, Inc. (R), CA, *175*
DeMatteo, Robena, DeMatteo Associates (C), NY, *311*
Denman, Anna Marie, AMD & Associates (C), GA, *247*
Denton, Randolph, The Executive Tree (R), FL, *64*
Désilets, Georges H., Yves Plouffe & Assoc. (R), QE, *165*
Dexter, Peter, Search Research Assoc., Inc. (R), MA, *187*
Diefenbach, John C., Hreshko Consulting Group (C), NJ, *382*
Dietsch, Roger A., Roger Dietsch & Assoc. (C), MN, *312*
Donovan, Jerry, Management Recruiters of Arlington (C), VA, *464*
Dotson, M. Ileen, Dotson & Assoc. (R), NY, *54*
Eastwood, Gary, Beck/Eastwood Recruitment Solutions (C), CA, *261*
Eden, Dianne, Steeple Resources & Consulting (R), NJ, *199*
Edmond, Bruce, Corporate Recruiters Ltd. (C), BC, *300*
Ehrenreich, Lisa C., Greenhaven & Assoc., Inc. (R), NY, *81*
Ellis, James, Sanford Rose Assoc. - Lake St. Louis (C), MO, *568*
Ellis, Mitch, Sanford Rose Assoc. - Lake St. Louis (C), MO, *568*
Embrey, Boe E., Sales Consultants of Auburn Hills (C), MI, *559*
Enochs, Steve, Buckman/Enochs & Assoc., Inc. (C), OH, *276*
Fair, Carolyn, Dunhill Executive Search of Los Angeles, Inc. (C), CA, *319*
Farro, Jerry, VZ Int'l., Inc. (C), AZ, *613*
Faulkner, LaCarole A., L&L Assoc. Global Search (C), PA, *411*
Fisher, Mel V., The Fisher Group (R), AB, *67*
Fitzgerald, Matthew A., Telecom Recruiters, Inc. (C), VA, *605*
Flanagan, Greg, Marcus & Assoc. (C), NY, *469*
Flanagan, Robert M., Robert M. Flanagan & Assoc., Ltd. (R), NY, *68*
Fockler, David B., David Fockler & Assoc., Inc. (C), CA, *342*
Frankovich, John, BRW Search (C), MN, *275*
Fried, Steve, Management Recruiters of Chicago-North Shore (C), IL, *447*
Fried, Steven L., Sales Consultants (C), IL, *558*
Gaffney, William M., Teknon Employment Resources, Inc. (C), OH, *604*
Gardner, Scott, Chesapeake Group (C), CT, *290*
Gauger, Dianne, Dianne Gauger & Assoc. (C), CA, *355*
Gebler, Stephen, Systems Research Group (C), CA, *598*
Gerard, William, Fox-Morris Assoc., Inc. (C), CA, *352*
Gertler, Richard, Prairie Resource Group, Inc. (R), IL, *166*
Gilmore, Howard A., Howard Gilmore & Assoc. (R), OH, *77*

RECRUITER SPECIALTIES

Glaser, Larry, Lawrence Glaser Assoc., Inc. (C), NJ, *358*
Goldbeck, Henry, Goldbeck Recruiting Inc. (C), BC, *359*
Goldberg, Sybil, Spectra International LLC (C), AZ, *589*
Gonedes, James T., Business Solutions Worldwide, Inc. (C), NJ, *277*
Goodere, Greg, Montgomery West (R), CA, *146*
Gowdy, Olga M., Gowdy Consultants (C), TX, *361*
Graham, Alexander J., Alexander Graham Assoc. (C), NJ, *361*
Grant, Daniel M., Sales Consultants of Western McHenry County (C), IL, *558*
Greene, Jr., W. Luke, Broward-Dobbs, Inc. (C), GA, *274*
Grillo, Scott, Professional Recruiting Network (C), CA, *521*
Gross, Alan H., Marketing & Sales Resources, Inc. (C), FL, *470*
Gugler, Wolf, Wolf Gugler & Assoc. Ltd. (R), ON, *83*
Gunning, Phill, TBC, Inc. (C), KY, *600*
Gurney, Darrell W., A Permanent Success Employment Services (C), CA, *231*
Hammer, Amy, Sales Advantage (C), FL, *551*
Hanna, Jr., M. A. Jack, The Hanna Group (C), OH, *368*
Harlan, James, Management Recruiters of Franktown (C), CO, *442*
Hill, Tom, Hill & Assoc. (C), CA, *378*
Hills, Glen, G. H. Enterprises (C), AZ, *354*
Hinds, Susan, Job Link, Inc. (C), CA, *399*
Hochwalt, Mike, M H Executive Search Group (C), TX, *422*
Holley, Ray, Austin Group Int'l./Marlar Int'l. (R), TX, *9*
Hood, Fred L., Fred Hood & Assoc. (C), CA, *380*
Hucko, Donald, Jonas, Walters & Assoc., Inc. (R), WI, *108*
Huff, Margaret L., Huff Assoc. (R), NJ, *98*
Huff, William Z., Huff Assoc. (R), NJ, *98*
Hughes, Tom, Fox-Morris Assoc., Inc. (C), NJ, *352*
Ingram, Meredith, Meredith Ingram, Ltd. (C), IL, *388*
Jackson, Carolyn, Sales Consultants of Orangeburg (C), SC, *562*
Jackson, Jennifer, Jackson Resources (R), TX, *105*
Jackson, Richard, Sales Consultants of Orangeburg (C), SC, *562*
Johnson, Bill, Global Consulting Group Inc. (C), ON, *358*
Johnson, Paul, Johnson, Kemper & Assoc. (C), TX, *400*
Kader, Richard H., Richard Kader & Assoc. (C), OH, *403*
Kanzer, William F., Kanzer Assoc., Inc. (R), IL, *109*
Kaufman, Matthew, Sales Advantage (C), FL, *551*
Kearney, John, The Buckley Group (C), TX, *276*
Keefe, John, Kelly Associates (R), PA, *112*
Kelley, Kathy, Straube Associates (R), MA, *203*
Kiken, Mark E., COBA Executive Search (R), CO, *36*
King, Karl, Capital Consulting Group, Inc. (R), MD, *28*
Kohn, Steven, Affinity Executive Search (C), FL, *241*
Koller, Jr., Edward R., Howard-Sloan Assoc. (C), NY, *381*
Kotloski, Dennis, Management Recruiters of Chicago-North Shore (C), IL, *447*
Kranak, Karen, Professions, Inc. (C), OH, *523*
Lace, Hayley, C.T.E.W. Executive Personnel Services Inc. (C), BC, *278*
Lasini, Dennis, Genesis Research (C), MO, *356*
Legal, Dale, Capital Consulting Group, Inc. (R), MD, *28*
Leinen, Rebecca, Management Recruiters - Piedmont (C), VA, *464*
LePatner, Steve, Dunhill Executive Search of Los Angeles, Inc. (C), CA, *319*
Levy, Warren, The Gabriel Group (C), PA, *354*
Levy, William M., Sherbrooke Assoc., Inc. (C), NJ, *580*
Lipsky, Marla J., Lipsky Group, Inc. (R), CA, *129*
Lockton, Kathy, StratfordGroup (R), CA, *203*
Loewenstein, Ron, Loewenstein & Assoc., Inc. (R), TX, *131*
Ludwig, Bob, Ludwig & Assoc., Inc. (C), VA, *421*
Luzar, James, Sales Consultants of Milwaukee (C), WI, *563*
Lybrook, Christian, Lybrook Assoc., Inc. (C), RI, *421*
Lynch, J. F., Management Recruiters of Lionville, Inc. (C), PA, *459*
Lyness, Cindy, Management Recruiters-Cedar Rapids, Inc. (C), IA, *448*
Lynne, Robyn, Search Masters, USA (C), FL, *576*
MacArthur, Ian, Madison MacArthur Inc. (R), ON, *133*
Mahoney, Michael, Carol Maden Group (C), VA, *422*
Martin, Donovan, Donovan Martin & Assoc. (R), CA, *137*
Martin, Suzanne, The Beam Group (R), PA, *14*
Mason, Christopher, KM Associates (C), MA, *407*
Matras, Debbie, Sales Consultants of Milwaukee (C), WI, *563*
May, Peter, MIXTEC Group (R), CA, *145*
Mayer, Mary L., Mary L. Mayer, Ltd. (R), MN, *139*
McDermott, Jeffrey T., Vlcek & Company, Inc. (R), CA, *214*
McGovern, Sheila M., Kiley, Owen & McGovern, Inc. (R), NJ, *114*
McGrath, Steven L., McGrath & Assoc., Inc. (R), NJ, *141*
McKinnon, Greg, The McKinnon Management Group Inc. (C), ON, *475*
Mead, James D., James Mead & Co. (R), CT, *142*
Meissner, Bob, Management Recruiters of Milwaukee-North (C), WI, *466*
Miggins, Bob, Brad Marks Int'l. (R), CA, *136*
Miglio, Dusty, Premier Recruiting Group (C), MI, *516*
Miller, William, V. Robinson & Co., Inc. (C), MO, *539*
Miners, Richard A., Sedlar & Miners (R), NY, *188*
Moore, Michael, The Marathon Group (C), FL, *469*
Morency, Marcia, Morency Assoc. (C), MA, *485*
Mott, Alex, Headden Assoc. (R), WA, *88*
Moyer, Laurene F., OmniSearch, Inc. (C), FL, *499*
Moyer, Samuel, OmniSearch, Inc. (C), FL, *499*
Mullen, Maryrose H., Emmett Executive Search, Inc. (C), NY, *330*
Murphy, Irene, StratfordGroup (R), CA, *203*
Musso, Connie, Consumer Search Inc. (C), MA, *298*
Nalley, Ed, Executive Search Int'l. (C), TX, *336*
Nalley, Jeff, Executive Search Int'l. (C), TX, *336*
Nelson, David G., The Personnel Group, Inc. (R), MN, *163*
Nicolosi, Charles, CN Associates (C), CA, *293*
O'Brien, Frank E., Austin Michaels, Ltd., Inc. (C), AZ, *256*
O'Keefe, Frank, The Marathon Group (C), FL, *469*
Olson, Judy A., Management Recruiters of Woodbury (C), MN, *430*
Olson, Judy A., Management Recruiters of Woodbury (C), MN, *452*
Oppedisano, Edward, Oppedisano & Co., Inc. (R), NY, *156*
Ormond, Mark R., Capstone Consulting, Inc. (R), IL, *29*
Ortega de Diego, Estela, Dunhill Professional Search of Miami (C), FL, *320*
Osborn, Ted, Paladin Group, Inc. (C), CO, *502*
Owen, Jamie, Management Recruiters of Seattle (C), WA, *465*
Owen, Ralph, Kiley, Owen & McGovern, Inc. (R), NJ, *114*
Oxenham, Roger, Madison MacArthur Inc. (R), ON, *133*
Pailin, Sr., David L., The Pailin Group Professional Search Consultants (R), TX, *158*
Palumbo, Robert F., The Recruitment Group, Inc. (C), NY, *532*
Park, Tammy, Robert Larned Assoc., Inc. (C), VA, *413*
Parker, Roberta, R. Parker & Assoc., Inc. (R), NY, *159*
Parr, Thomas A., Holland & Assoc., Inc. (R), MI, *94*

Patrick, Donald R., Sanford Rose Assoc. - Norcross (C), GA, *566*
Payne, Joe, Van Treadaway Assoc., Inc. (R), GA, *210*
Pearce, Lois, Pearce & Assoc. (C), FL, *506*
Pearson, A. B., Sales Consultants of Concord (C), NC, *554*
Pearson, Anna Lee, Sales Consultants of Concord (C), NC, *554*
Perkins, Arthur, Management Alliance Group, Inc. (R), NJ, *134*
Perl, Eric, BR & Assoc. (C), NJ, *271*
Peters, Peter Louis, Success Seekers Connection (C), FL, *596*
Pezim, Steven G., The Bedford Consulting Group Inc. (R), ON, *15*
Plouffe, Yves J., Yves Plouffe & Assoc. (R), QE, *165*
Plyley, Jr., C. Ace, The Stelton Group, Inc. (C), NJ, *592*
Pollack, Jonathan, Executive Sales Search (C), CO, *335*
Presley, Jason T., Presley Consultants, Inc. (C), MT, *517*
Rafferty, Mark, Management Recruiters of Chicago-North Shore (C), IL, *447*
Reed, Alec, The Argus Group Corp. (C), ON, *252*
Reifersen, Ruth F., The Jonathan Stevens Group, Inc. (R), NJ, *108*
Reilly, Toni Marie, Fox-Morris Assoc., Inc. (C), NC, *352*
Reinitz, Robert, Professional Recruiters Inc. (C), MN, *521*
Reitzamer, Elizabeth P., Dunhill Professional Search of Miami (C), FL, *320*
Riddle, James E., Riddle & McGrath LLC (R), GA, *178*
Riley, Jim, Riley Cole (C), CA, *537*
Roberts, Carl R., Southwestern Professional Services (C), TN, *588*
Roberts, Libby, Global Consulting Group Inc. (C), ON, *358*
Robinson, Verneda, V. Robinson & Co., Inc. (C), KS, *539*
Robinson, Verneda, V. Robinson & Co., Inc. (C), MO, *539*
Rodd, Mamie, Richard Kader & Assoc. (C), OH, *403*
Rodriguez, George L., InteliSearch, Inc. (R), CT, *102*
Roe, Craig T., Craig Roe & Assoc., LLC (C), MD, *540*
Roe, Sylvia A., Craig Roe & Assoc., LLC (C), MD, *540*
Romano, Joseph C., Romano McAvoy Assoc., Inc. (C), NY, *544*
Ross, Andrew, DARE Personnel Inc. (C), ON, *307*
Ross, Heather, Management Recruiters-Cedar Rapids, Inc. (C), IA, *448*
Ross, Robert F., Bertrand, Ross & Assoc., Inc. (C), IL, *266*
Rubin, Ron, Geddes & Rubin Management Inc. (R), ON, *76*
Russo, Antonella, The Zarkin Group, Inc. (R), NY, *226*
Ryan, David, The Recruitment Group, Inc. (C), NY, *532*
Salloway, Andrew N., A. N. Salloway Executive Search & Consulting, L.L.C. (C), MA, *564*
Salway, Clancy, Sales Management Resources (C), CA, *563*
Samuels, Jonathan, Boston Professional Search, Inc. (C), MA, *270*
Santamaria, Jay, The Beam Group (R), NY, *14*
Sattler, John E., Impact Source, Inc. (C), FL, *387*
Schiff, Arlene D., A.D. Schiff & Assoc., Ltd. (C), IL, *572*
Schmeh, Bill, Sales Solutions (C), CA, *564*
Schoellkopf, Karl, K. Jaeger & Assoc. (C), MA, *396*
Schoff, Diane L., The Edge Resource Group (C), PA, *326*
Schwartz, Michael, Synapse Human Resource Consulting Group (R), TX, *205*
Sedlar, Jeri L., Sedlar & Miners (R), NY, *188*
Shackleton, Dora Lee, Carpenter, Shackleton & Company (R), IL, *30*
Shaw, R. William, Management Recruiters of South Bend (C), IN, *448*
Shifrin, Brad, Shifrin-Fischer Group, Inc. (C), NJ, *580*
Sloat, Robert L., Executive Search of New England, Inc. (C), ME, *336*
Smith, Robert, Fox-Morris Assoc., Inc. (C), GA, *352*
Soodsma, William, Sales Consultants of Northern Jersey, Inc. (C), NJ, *560*
Steele, Kevin, Winter, Wyman & Co. (C), MA, *623*
Steffensrud, Dick, Staff Extension Int'l. (C), TX, *590*
Stevens, Jennifer A., Ledbetter/Davidson Int'l., Inc. (R), NY, *127*
Stevens, Wayne J., Stevens Assoc. (C), MA, *593*
Stokes, Carolyn, Corporate Dynamix (C), CA, *300*
Stoller, Richard S., Heath/Norton Assoc., Inc. (R), NY, *89*
Stubberfield, Lee, Management Recruiters of the Baltimore Washington Corridor (C), MD, *450*
Tang, Cliff, Wood West & Partners Inc. (C), BC, *624*
Tann, Robert, Staff Extension, Int'l. (C), TX, *590*
Tavens, Lester, Marvel Consultants, Inc. (C), OH, *472*
Taylor, Jerry, Executive Recruiters (C), WA, *334*
Tewes, Steve, Management Recruiters of Milwaukee - Downtown (C), WI, *466*
Thomason, Nancy, Montgomery, Thomason & Assoc. (C), ON, *484*
Trapp, Ed, Management Recruiters of Reno (C), NV, *453*
Tumbiolo, Lisa, Agriesti & Assoc. (C), CA, *243*
Van Zanten, William, VZ Int'l., Inc. (C), AZ, *613*
Verriez, Paul M., The Verriez Group Inc. (R), ON, *213*
Wachendorfer, Tom, Wachendorfer & Assoc. (C), TX, *613*
Wagner, Susan J., EDI/Executive Dynamics Inc. (C), NJ, *326*
Wallace, William J., Wallace Management Co. (R), TN, *215*
Watson, David L. B., Pacific Coast Recruiters (C), OR, *501*
Webster, Bruce, Sales Consultants of Milwaukee (C), WI, *563*
Webster, Doug, The Buckley Group (C), NJ, *276*
Weiss, John P., Star Search Consultants (C), ON, *591*
Whitney, Jr., Kenneth L., K. L. Whitney Company (R), NJ, *219*
Willner, Nathaniel, N. Willner & Co., Inc. (R), NJ, *221*
Wilson, Jeffrey M., Sales Consultants of Western McHenry County (C), IL, *558*
Witt, Gerald E., The Witt Group (C), FL, *623*
Wittlin, Brian D., Brian Assoc., Inc. (C), NY, *273*
Wojcik, Raymond F., Management Recruiters The Delta Group, Inc. (C), TN, *461*
Wolf, Lisa, Lawrence Glaser Assoc., Inc. (C), NJ, *358*
Woo, Aaron C., Essential Solutions, Inc. (C), CA, *331*
Wood, Bill, Search Plus Int'l.-Ohio (C), OH, *576*
Wood, Ron, Wood West & Partners Inc. (C), BC, *624*
Wooller, Edmund A. M., Windsor International (R), GA, *222*
Zonka, Thomas J., Thomas & Assoc. of Michigan (C), MI, *606*
Zukerman, Claire, Corporate Search, Inc. (C), NY, *301*

Sanitation

Egan, David C., D. C. Egan & Assoc. (C), GA, *327*
English, Robert, RTE Search (C), NJ, *547*
English, Robert, RTE Search (C), VA, *547*

SAP

Anderson, Murray, MIS Computer Professionals, Inc. (C), KS, *482*
Becker, John, Becker Project Resources, Inc. (C), OR, *262*
Brauninger, John C., AmeriPro Search, Inc. (C), NC, *248*
Capps, Norm, MIS Computer Professionals, Inc. (C), KS, *482*
Christ, Celeste, Quality Consulting Group, Inc. (C), WI, *526*
Davis Wolfe, Kathryn, HDB Incorporated (C), MO, *371*
Eastmer, Gregory, Professional Support Inc. (C), NY, *523*
Gerlach, Mary, Quality Consulting Group, Inc. (C), WI, *526*
Huntley, David E., Huntley Associates (Dallas), Inc. (C), TX, *386*

RECRUITER SPECIALTIES

Mesina, Roman, The Consulting Group of North America, Inc. (C), VA, *297*
Plavin, Avery, The Consulting Group of North America, Inc. (C), VA, *297*
Robbins, Mark, Search Solutions Inc. (C), CA, *576*
Salvatore, Philip A., LAS Management Consulting Group, Inc. (R), NJ, *125*
Swami, Pad N., Fortuna Technologies Inc. (C), CA, *343*

Satellites

Cook, Clifford L., CEO Consulting (C), FL, *287*
Gibson, Jan, Advanced Corporate Search (C), CA, *240*
Hebert, Chris, Management Recruiters of Nassau, Inc. (R), NY, *134*
King, Karl, Capital Consulting Group, Inc. (R), MD, *28*
Legal, Dale, Capital Consulting Group, Inc. (R), MD, *28*

Sawmill

Waschuk, Bill, Forest People Int'l. Search Ltd. (C), BC, *343*

Science

Allen, James R., Continental Search Assoc. (C), OH, *298*
Anderson, Jim, Howard Clark Assoc. (C), NJ, *292*
Boltrus, Richard, Sink, Walker, Boltrus Int'l. (R), MA, *192*
Boyce, Kevin, Laboratory Resource Group (C), MA, *411*
Brakel, H. R., ProTech Nationwide Staffing, Inc. (C), NY, *525*
Burchell, Robert A., Fernow Assoc. (C), PA, *340*
Chambers, Judy, Global Consulting Group Inc. (C), ON, *358*
Dahl, Charles, Charles Dahl Group, Inc. (C), MN, *306*
Danielsen, Annemarie T., Astro Executive Search Firm (C), LA, *254*
Dishaw, Raymond J., R. J. Dishaw & Assoc. (R), TX, *52*
Dorfman, Jan, F-O-R-T-U-N-E Personnel Consultants of Denver, Inc. (C), CO, *344*
Feightner, Ted, BioTech Research Recruiters Inc. (C), CA, *267*
Fernow, Charles S., Fernow Assoc. (C), PA, *340*
Fiore, Richard, Search Consultants Int'l., Inc. (C), TX, *575*
Harelick, Arthur S., Ashway Ltd. Agency (C), NY, *253*
Hennessy, Robert, Ken Clark Int'l. (R), NJ, *36*
Hershman, Arnold, Holohan Group, Ltd. (R), MO, *95*
Holtz, Richard D., Technical Resource Assoc. (C), TN, *602*
Johnson, Karl, K. E. Johnson Assoc. (C), WA, *400*
Johnson, Randall, Inter Regional Executive Search, Inc. (IRES, Inc.) (C), NJ, *391*
Kagan, Philip, Strategic Resources (C), WA, *595*
Kaiser, Joe, Fortune Personnel Consultants of Anderson, Inc. (C), SC, *349*
King, Steven, Ashway Ltd. Agency (C), NY, *253*
L'Archevesque, Lee, Sink, Walker, Boltrus Int'l. (R), MA, *192*
Lawrence, Ellen B., Holohan Group, Ltd. (R), MO, *95*
Lybrook, Karen, Lybrook Assoc., Inc. (C), RI, *421*
MacBean, Paul, Technical Skills Consulting Inc. (R), ON, *207*
MacKinnon, Helen, Technical Connections, Inc. (C), CA, *602*
Mars, Roxanne, Technical Skills Consulting Inc. (R), ON, *207*
McPoyle, Jr., Thomas C., TCM Enterprises (C), MD, *600*
Otsuka, Fyllis L., Holohan Group, Ltd. (R), MO, *95*
Petruzzi, Vincent J., Petruzzi Assoc. (C), NJ, *509*
Poster, Lawrence D., Catalyx Group (R), NY, *31*
Ratts, K. Wayne, Holohan Group, Ltd. (R), MO, *95*
Rueppel, Melvin L., Holohan Group, Ltd. (R), MO, *95*
Sendler, Peter A., International Consulting Services, Inc. (C), IL, *392*
Slusser, Cindy L., The Stelton Group, Inc. (C), NJ, *592*
Steinbach, David M., Steinbach & Co. (C), MA, *592*
Weinpel, Charles J., Weinpel Search, Inc. (C), NJ, *617*
Winter, Peter, Catalyx Group - Canada (R), ON, *31*
Zaring, David, Management Recruiters of Plant City, Inc. (C), FL, *444*

Seafood

Howell, Jeff, Whittaker & Assoc., Inc. (C), GA, *620*

Security

Albertson, Rob, Dick Williams & Assoc. (C), CA, *621*
Brandon, Irwin, Hadley Lockwood, Inc. (R), NY, *84*
Caliguiri, Edward, Response Staffing Services (C), NY, *535*
Carey, Cameron, Computer Security Placement Service (C), MA, *296*
Ciaramitaro, Paul, Corporate Search Consultants, Inc. (C), FL, *301*
Coleman, Tracy A., West Coast Recruiting (C), CA, *619*
Connolly, Claire E., CEC Associates (R), MA, *32*
de Cholnoky, Andrea, SpencerStuart (R), NY, *196*
Esler, Mike, Strategic Resources (C), WA, *595*
Flagg, Jessica S., The Consulting Group Ltd. (R), NY, *40*
Fossett, Gary J., John Michael Assoc. (R), DC, *106*
Frost, Edward W., Mortgage Search Network (C), AZ, *486*
Glass, Robert, McGrath & Assoc., Inc. (R), NJ, *141*
Goldsmith, Jerry, The Primary Group, Inc. (R), FL, *168*
Hart, David, Hadley Lockwood, Inc. (R), NY, *84*
Hill, Michelle, The Alfus Group (R), NY, *3*
Misarti, Paul R., Paul Misarti Inc. (C), NY, *483*
Mitchell, J. Michael, The Consulting Group Ltd. (R), NY, *40*
Mussato, Ray, Dick Williams & Assoc. (C), CA, *621*
Nava, Terri, The Consulting Group Ltd. (R), NY, *40*
Nini, Steven B., West Coast Recruiting (C), CA, *619*
Paetzhold, Jerry, Davis & James, Inc. (C), MO, *308*
Press, Fredrick R., Adept Tech Recruiting, Inc. (C), NY, *240*
Richard, David A., Financial Connections Company (C), VA, *340*
Richey, Nancy, The Stonebridge Group (C), PA, *594*
Selbach, Barbara, SpencerStuart (R), NY, *196*
Trendl, Joseph, J. R. Scott & Assoc., Ltd. (C), IL, *395*

Semiconductors

Amara, Edmund, SpencerSearch, Inc. (C), TX, *589*
Ansara, Peter, Ansara, Bickford & Fiske (C), MA, *251*
Ashton, Barbara L., Ashton Computer Professionals, Inc. (C), BC, *253*
Barr, Charly, Barr Assoc. (C), PA, *259*
Barr, Sharon A., Barr Assoc. (C), PA, *259*
Belsjoe, Robert, Robert Belsjoe (C), TX, *528*
Boltrus, Richard, Sink, Walker, Boltrus Int'l. (R), MA, *192*
Bower, Richard, Bower & Associates (C), TX, *271*
Cook, Clifford L., CEO Consulting (C), FL, *287*
Donahue, Jack, Dunhill of Ft. Collins, Inc. (C), CO, *319*
Farro, Jerry, VZ Int'l., Inc. (C), AZ, *613*
Flott, Stan, General Engineering Tectonics (C), CA, *356*
Giles, Kenn, Dick Williams & Assoc. (C), CA, *621*
Harrison, Sally, Brandywine Management Group (R), MD, *22*
Hollands, Rachel, PSD Group, Inc. (C), CA, *525*

Keifer, Kevin A. P., Dunhill Professional Search of San Jose (C), CA, *319*
Kelly, Sean, Iona Partners (C), CA, *394*
Keyser, Rich, VZ Int'l., Inc. (C), PA, *613*
Kressenberg, Sammye Jo, Kressenberg Assoc. (C), TX, *409*
Ku, Theresa, Sanford Rose Assoc. - Anaheim (C), CA, *566*
L'Archevesque, Lee, Sink, Walker, Boltrus Int'l. (R), MA, *192*
Lechtenberg, Richard C., Dick Berg & Assoc. (C), CA, *264*
Marks, Ira Alan, J. M. Meredith & Assoc. Inc. (C), CA, *479*
McDermitt, Tom, Professional Recruiting Consultants (C), FL, *521*
Ozoroski, Tom, Barr Assoc. (C), PA, *259*
Poole, Don V., Don V. Poole & Assoc., Inc. (C), CO, *514*
Reichardt, Karl J., R & K Associates, Inc. (C), AZ, *528*
Roethlein, John, Management Recruiters Tucson-Foothills, Inc. (C), AZ, *439*
Roethlein, Lorian E., Management Recruiters Tucson-Foothills, Inc. (C), AZ, *439*
Rudzinsky, Howard, Louis Rudzinsky Assoc., Inc. (C), MA, *548*
Shinn, Michael, Shinn & Assoc. (R), CA, *189*
Sink, Clifton W., Sink, Walker, Boltrus Int'l. (R), TX, *192*
Spencer, Dan R., SpencerSearch, Inc. (C), CO, *589*
Spragge, Patrick, Sanford Rose Assoc. - Sunnyvale (C), CA, *566*
Stepler, Paul, Gallin Associates of Naples, FL (C), FL, *354*
Stiles, Jack D., Sanford Rose Assoc. - Portland (C), OR, *570*
Tracey, Jay E., Jay Tracey Assoc. Inc. (C), VT, *608*
Van Zanten, William, VZ Int'l., Inc. (C), AZ, *613*
Williams, Dick, Dick Williams & Assoc. (C), CA, *621*
Zabeli, Agim, Barr Assoc. (C), PA, *259*
Zeiger, David Barkin, Zeiger Assoc. L.L.C. (C), CA, *627*
Zheng, Rui, PSD Group, Inc. (C), CA, *525*

Senior management

Abbott, Peter D., The Abbott Group, Inc. (R), MD, *1*
Aldana, Manny, Bor-Maq Assoc. (C), TX, *269*
Alexander, Susan M., Manuso, Alexander & Associates, Inc. (R), NY, *135*
Allen, Michael, Allen/Associates (R), OH, *4*
Ambra, Glenn P., J. R. Phillip & Assoc., Inc. (R), CA, *164*
Ammirati, Greg, Sales Consultants of Western McHenry County (C), IL, *558*
Amy, Rupert R., Careers/Inc. (C), PR, *284*
Arcara, Gwen O., Executive Dimensions (R), NY, *62*
Ariail, Randolph C., Ariail & Assoc. (R), NC, *7*
Arons, Sheldon, Colt Systems Professional Personnel Services (C), CA, *294*
Banach-Osenni, Doris, The Brentwood Group, Inc. (R), NJ, *22*
Barger, H. Carter, Barger & Sargeant, Inc. (R), NH, *11*
Barkauskas, Richard T., The Corporate Advisory Group (R), NJ, *41*
Barth, David K., Barth Smith Company (R), IL, *12*
Barus, Daniel P., Lloyd Prescott & Churchill, Inc. (R), IL, *130*
Barus, Daniel P., Lloyd Prescott Assoc., Inc. (C), IL, *419*
Battson, A. R., The Washington Firm, Ltd. (R), WA, *216*
Beck, Larry, Synergy Solutions, Ltd. (C), WA, *597*
Beecher, Arthur P., J. Nicholas Arthur (R), MA, *104*
Beeson, William B., Lawrence-Leiter & Co. (R), KS, *126*
Behm, Susan M., The Human Resource Consulting Group, Inc. (R), CO, *98*
Belt, Joy Reed, Joy Reed Belt Search Consultants, Inc. (R), OK, *15*
Bernard, Harry, Colton Bernard Inc. (R), CA, *37*
Besen, Douglas, Besen Assoc. Inc. (C), NJ, *266*
Best, G. Tim, BEST/World Assoc. Inc. (R), TX, *16*
Birnbaum, Richard, R. J. Associates (C), NY, *528*
Bogard, Nicholas C., J. Nicholas Arthur (R), MA, *104*
Boguski, Ronald T., The Hamilton Group (R), MD, *85*
Bowman, Daniel P., Bowman & Assoc. (C), CA, *271*
Boyle, Mike, Boyle/Ogata Executive Search (R), CA, *21*
Bregman, Mark, Boyle/Ogata Executive Search (R), CA, *21*
Brien, Richard H., Creative Input, Inc. (C), RI, *303*
Brooks, Harvey, Fox-Morris Assoc., Inc. (C), PA, *352*
Bucci, Michael T., The Partnership Group (R), NJ, *160*
Buck, Jr., Charles A., Charles Buck & Assoc., Inc. (R), NY, *24*
Burnette, Dennis W., Sanford Rose Assoc. - Atlanta North (C), GA, *566*
Cantor, Daniel D., The Human Resource Consulting Group, Inc. (R), MA, *98*
Caplan, John, The Caplan-Taylor Group (R), CA, *28*
Capo, John, Carter McKenzie, Inc. (C), NJ, *285*
Carrigan, Denise, Management Recruiters of San Antonio (C), TX, *463*
Christian, Jeffrey E., Christian & Timbers, Inc. (R), OH, *34*
Clarke, Brian G., Kensington Int'l., Inc. (R), IL, *113*
Clement, Laura K., Stroman Int'l., Inc. (R), CO, *204*
Cobb, Mark A., Management Recruiters of Springfield, Inc. (C), IL, *447*
Cobb-West, Rosemary G., West & West (R), CA, *218*
Cochran, Corinne, Early Cochran & Olson (R), IL, *56*
Colasanto, Frank M., W. R. Rosato & Assoc., Inc. (R), NY, *182*
Colton, Roy C., Colton Bernard Inc. (R), CA, *37*
Comparetto, Gino, Lloyd Prescott & Churchill, Inc. (R), NY, *130*
Comparetto, Gino, Lloyd Prescott Assoc., Inc. (C), NY, *419*
Cook, P. Gene, P. G. Cook Assoc. (R), TN, *40*
Cooke, Jeffrey R., The Cooke Group (R), WI, *40*
Cooper, B. V., QVS Int'l. (R), GA, *170*
Cowall, Frank A., Altec/HRC (C), MI, *246*
Curtis, Susan J., ProSearch Recruiting (C), CA, *524*
Dato, Thomas J., Lloyd Prescott & Churchill, Inc. (R), IL, *130*
Dato, Thomas J., Lloyd Prescott Assoc., Inc. (C), IL, *419*
Davidson, Shawn, GAAP Inc. (R), QE, *73*
Daxon, Corey, Feldman Gray & Assoc. Inc. (C), ON, *339*
Delaney, Patrick J., Sensible Solutions, Inc. (R), IL, *188*
DeMoss, J. V., Careers/Inc. (C), PR, *284*
Desgrosellier, Gary P., Personnel Unlimited/Executive Search (C), WA, *509*
Dise, Jr., Ralph A., Dise & Co. (R), OH, *52*
Doering, Louis, Doering & Assoc. (C), CA, *313*
Donald, R.J., Feldman Gray & Assoc. Inc. (C), ON, *339*
Douglas, Calvin H., Cal Douglas Executive Search, Inc. (R), PA, *54*
Dumont, Brenda, Dumont & Co. (C), BC, *316*
Early, Bert H., Early Cochran & Olson (R), IL, *56*
Eden, Brooks D., Eden & Assoc., Inc. (C), PA, *326*
Edman, Silas E. G., The Partnership Group (R), NJ, *160*
Eisele, Steven M., Lloyd Prescott & Churchill, Inc. (R), NY, *130*
Eisele, Steven M., Lloyd Prescott Assoc., Inc. (C), NY, *419*
Elkas, Yves, Yves Elkas Inc. (R), QE, *58*
Erder, Debra, Canny, Bowen Inc. (R), NY, *28*
Ericksen, Bruce, MESA International (C), OR, *480*
Erickson, Mary R., Mary R. Erickson & Assoc. (R), MN, *60*
Eyler, Richard N., Eyler Assoc., Inc. (R), IA, *64*
Fagan, III, Charles A., Fagan & Company (R), PA, *64*
Farley, Leon A., Leon A. Farley Assoc. (R), CA, *65*
Fawcett, Marcia A., The Fawcett Group (R), MA, *65*

RECRUITER SPECIALTIES

Fell, Robert M., Fell & Nicholson Technology Resources (R), CA, *65*
Fergus, Colin, Fergus Legal Search & Consulting, Inc. (C), NY, *339*
Fergus, Jean M. H., Fergus Legal Search & Consulting, Inc. (C), NY, *339*
Fineman, David M., Manuso, Alexander & Associates, Inc. (R), NY, *135*
Fischetti, Tony M., Pharmaceutical Search Professionals, Inc. (C), PA, *510*
Fisher, Mel V., The Fisher Group (R), AB, *67*
Fitzgerald, Jon K., Health Industry Consultants, Inc. (R), CO, *89*
Flynn, Jerry, J. G. Flynn & Assoc. Inc. (R), BC, *69*
Foley, Thomas J., Foley Proctor Yoskowitz (R), NY, *69*
Forbes, Kathy, The Forbes Group (R), GA, *69*
Frank, Jr., William E., The Curtiss Group International (R), FL, *44*
Fredericks, Ward A., MIXTEC Group (R), CA, *145*
Froehlich, Peter, Peter Froehlich & Co. (C), TX, *353*
Gabriel, Alan L., Lloyd Prescott & Churchill, Inc. (R), OH, *130*
Gabriel, Alan L., Lloyd Prescott Assoc., Inc. (C), OH, *419*
Gahan, Thomas M., Gahan Assoc. (R), NY, *73*
Gale, Rhoda, Management Recruiters of the Baltimore Washington Corridor (C), MD, *450*
Gasga, Pedro Salinas, Michigan Consulting Group (R), MI, *144*
Gates, Becky, Primus Assoc., L.C. (R), TX, *169*
Gaudette, Charles L., Medical Recruiters Exchange (C), AZ, *477*
Gay, Martha, Salzmann Gay Assoc., Inc. (R), PA, *184*
George, Richard, Kensington Int'l., Inc. (R), IL, *113*
Gerald, C. Richard, C. R. Gerald & Assoc. (C), ON, *356*
Gerstl, Ronald, Maxecon Executive Search Consultants (R), FL, *138*
Getzug, Richard F., Lloyd Prescott & Churchill, Inc. (R), PA, *130*
Getzug, Richard F., Lloyd Prescott Assoc., Inc. (C), PA, *419*
Gibson, Bruce, Gibson & Co., Inc. (R), WI, *76*
Ginsberg, Sheldon M., Lloyd Prescott & Churchill, Inc. (R), FL, *130*
Ginsberg, Sheldon M., Lloyd Prescott Assoc., Inc. (C), FL, *419*
Glicksman, Russell A., The Beam Group (R), PA, *14*
Glynn, Thomas J., Fox-Morris Assoc., Inc. (C), PA, *352*
Gobbell, John J., The Gobbell Co. (R), CA, *78*
Goehring, Hal, H. L. Goehring & Assoc., Inc. (C), OH, *359*
Goldman, Jeff, Global 1000 Int'l. Services (C), CA, *358*
Gordon, Manuel F., Lloyd Prescott & Churchill, Inc. (R), FL, *130*
Gordon, Manuel F., Lloyd Prescott Assoc., Inc. (C), FL, *419*
Grant, Daniel M., Sales Consultants of Western McHenry County (C), IL, *558*
Grantham, John D., Grantham & Co., Inc. (R), NC, *81*
Gray, Frank, Feldman Gray & Assoc. Inc. (C), ON, *339*
Greenland, Gregory L., MedXec USA, Inc. (C), FL, *478*
Gregg, Larry, The Lear Group, Inc. (R), OH, *127*
Gregg, Paul J., Dunhill Professional Search of Miami (C), FL, *320*
Hahn, Loel G., Fergason Assoc., Inc. (C), IL, *339*
Hale, Maureen D., Hale Assoc. (R), IL, *84*
Halyburton, Robert R., The Halyburton Co., Inc. (R), NC, *85*
Hamilton, Denman, Synergy 2000 (C), DC, *597*
Handelsman, Simon, Anderson & Schwab, Inc. (R), NY, *6*
Hansen, David G., Ott & Hansen, Inc. (R), CA, *157*
Hardison, Richard L., Hardison & Company (R), TX, *86*
Harrison, John S., Chase Partners (R), ON, *33*
Harrison, Sally, Brandywine Management Group (R), NJ, *22*
Hauck, Fred P., The Cassie Group (R), NJ, *31*
Havener, D. Clarke, The Abbott Group, Inc. (R), MD, *1*
Hawley, Robert E., Hayden Group, Inc. (R), MA, *88*
Hay, William E., William E. Hay & Co. (R), IL, *88*
Healy, Thomas C., Resource Inc. (R), MA, *175*
Heffelfinger, Thomas V., Heffelfinger Assoc., Inc. (R), MA, *89*
Heisser, Robert, MRI, The Sequel Group, LLC (C), CO, *486*
Hensge, Bill, The Hensge Co. (R), IL, *91*
Herrmann, Gerlinde, The Herrmann Group Ltd. (R), ON, *92*
Herz, Stanley, Stanley Herz & Co. (R), NY, *92*
Hewett, Martin J., McCray, Shriver, Eckdahl & Assoc., Inc. (R), CA, *140*
Hiesiger, Emile M., Manuso, Alexander & Associates, Inc. (R), NY, *135*
Hofmeister, Mark, Winston Search, Inc. (R), MD, *222*
Hogg, Ronald J., Forest People Int'l. Search Ltd. (C), BC, *343*
Hogya, Nicholas, Interim Management Resources Inc. (C), ON, *392*
Hornbuckle, R. Michael, BCG Search, Inc. (R), FL, *14*
Hughes, Emerson, GAAP Inc. (R), QE, *73*
Hunt, Joseph B., The Hunt Group, Inc. (R), NC, *99*
Hunter, Durant A., Pendleton James Assoc., Inc. (R), MA, *105*
Hussey, John, GAAP Inc. (R), QE, *73*
Jackson, Ronald N., Lloyd Prescott & Churchill, Inc. (R), NC, *130*
Jackson, Ronald N., Lloyd Prescott Assoc., Inc. (C), NC, *419*
Jacobs, David M., Jacobs & Co. (R), CT, *105*
Jakobs, Frederick H., Jakobs & Assoc. Int'l. (R), NY, *105*
Johnson, Gil, Snelling Search (C), LA, *586*
Johnstone, Steve, GAAP Inc. (R), QE, *73*
Kane, John F., The Human Resource Consulting Group, Inc. (R), CO, *98*
Kash, Gene R., Lloyd Prescott & Churchill, Inc. (R), GA, *130*
Kash, Gene R., Lloyd Prescott Assoc., Inc. (C), GA, *419*
Kaulius-Barry, Aldonna, Aldonna Barry Personnel & Management (C), ON, *260*
King, Margaret, Christian & Timbers, Inc. (R), OH, *34*
King, Roger M., Tech Search (C), CA, *601*
Knapp, Karen Gordon, Tarnow Int'l. (R), NJ, *206*
Knose, II, Joseph M., Corporate Image Group (C), TN, *300*
Kraemer, Katherine R., Katherine R. Kraemer (R), CA, *120*
Krezo, Rich, Premier Recruiting Group (C), MI, *516*
Kris, John R., Organization Resources Inc. (R), MA, *157*
Kulper, Keith D., Kulper & Co., L.L.C. (R), NJ, *121*
Kurosky, John, John Kurosky & Assoc. (R), CA, *122*
Ladzinski, Terri, The Human Resource Consulting Group, Inc. (R), WI, *98*
Langley, Carol M., Langley & Associates, Inc. (Executive Search Consultants) (R), CO, *124*
Lawrence, J. Robert, Lawrence-Balakonis & Assoc., Inc. (C), GA, *414*
Leadford, Charles, Primus Assoc., L.C. (R), TX, *169*
Leduc, Lauren, GAAP Inc. (R), ON, *73*
Lekan, Dennis, Lekan & Assoc., Inc. (R), OH, *128*
LeMar, Bruce R., Early Cochran & Olson (R), IL, *56*
Levine, Alan M., MB Inc. Executive Search (C), NY, *473*
Linde, Roger W., Graphic Search Assoc. Inc. (C), PA, *362*
Lionas, James, The Hunter Group, Inc. (C), MI, *385*
Lipsky, Marla J., Lipsky Group, Inc. (R), CA, *129*
Lovas, W. Carl, Ray & Berndtson/Lovas Stanley (R), ON, *172*
Lucht, John, The John Lucht Consultancy Inc. (R), NY, *132*
Lutostanski, Frank, Selectis Corp. (C), IL, *578*
Lybrook, Karen, Lybrook Assoc., Inc. (C), RI, *421*
Lynch, Jack, Michigan Consulting Group (R), MI, *144*

Lynch, Jack, Premier Recruiting Group (C), MI, *516*
Maher, Peter T., The Partnership Group (R), NJ, *160*
Manuso, James S. J., Manuso, Alexander & Associates, Inc. (R), NY, *135*
Marcus, Alvin B., Marcus & Assoc. (C), NY, *469*
Mazziota, Daniel R., Ruth Sklar Assoc., Inc. (RSA Executive Search) (R), NY, *192*
McCooe, John J., McCooe & Assoc., Inc. (R), NJ, *140*
McCooe, Sean J., McCooe & Assoc., Inc. (R), NJ, *140*
McCormick, Harry B., Hayden Group, Inc. (R), MA, *88*
McCormick, Jim, McCormick Search Inc. (C), IL, *474*
McCray, Harold C., McCray, Shriver, Eckdahl & Assoc., Inc. (R), CA, *140*
McIvor, Jim, Christmas, McIvor & Assoc. Inc. (C), ON, *290*
McNichol, Jr., John, McNichol Assoc. (R), PA, *142*
McTaggart, Joseph J., Joseph J. McTaggart (C), CA, *476*
Meyers, Ron, Feldman Gray & Assoc. Inc. (C), ON, *339*
Milius, Kent, Management Recruiters of Colorado, Inc. (C), CO, *442*
Miller, Diane, Wilcox Bertoux & Miller (R), CA, *220*
Miller, Sharon, The Elmhurst Group (C), CA, *329*
Miller, Thomas C., Emerging Medical Technologies, Inc. (C), CO, *329*
Miner, David B., The Curtiss Group International (R), FL, *44*
Mittenthal, Robert H., David Gomez & Assoc., Inc. (R), IL, *79*
Molloy, Thomas, Molloy Partners (R), NY, *146*
Morgan, Richard, Ray & Berndtson/Lovas Stanley (R), ON, *172*
Morgan, Richard, Ray & Berndtson/Lovas Stanley (R), ON, *173*
Moris, Kristina, The Washington Firm, Ltd. (R), WA, *216*
Morse, Jeffrey A., Brandywine Management Group (R), MD, *22*
Murphy, Bob, Murphy Partners Int'l. (R), IL, *150*
Murray, David, Ray & Berndtson/Lovas Stanley (R), ON, *172*
Murray, David, Ray & Berndtson/Lovas Stanley (R), ON, *173*
Myers, Richard L., MedXec USA, Inc. (C), FL, *478*
Myers, Thomas, Careers Plus (R), CA, *29*
Naegle, Brad, KABL Ability Network (C), CA, *402*
Needham, Mary, Reserve Technology Institute (R), TX, *175*
Newell, Donald Pierce, Newell Assoc. (R), NY, *151*
Nicholson, Jack F., Fell & Nicholson Technology Resources (R), CA, *65*
Norwine, James O., ExecuGroup, Inc. (R), PA, *61*
Nunn, Roy M., The Corporate Advisory Group (R), FL, *41*
O'Brien, Jr., James J., O'Brien Consulting Services (R), MA, *153*
O'Keefe, Michael, Ray & Berndtson/Lovas Stanley (R), ON, *172*
O'Keefe, Michael, Ray & Berndtson/Lovas Stanley (R), ON, *173*
O'Neill, Kevin R., Performance Resources, Inc. (C), RI, *507*
Ogata, Keith, Boyle/Ogata Executive Search (R), CA, *21*
Olson, B. Tucker, Early Cochran & Olson (R), IL, *56*
Ormond, Mark R., Capstone Consulting, Inc. (R), IL, *29*
Ott, George W., Ott & Hansen, Inc. (R), CA, *157*
Otto, Christopher P., Lloyd Prescott & Churchill, Inc. (R), MO, *130*
Otto, Christopher P., Lloyd Prescott Assoc., Inc. (C), MO, *419*
Page, Stephen J. L., Page-Wheatcroft & Co., Ltd. (R), TX, *158*
Palazzolo, Kathy, Michigan Consulting Group (R), MI, *144*
Pamenter, Fred, Pamenter, Pamenter, Brezer & Deganis Ltd. (R), ON, *159*
Parker, Michele, Management Alliance Group, Inc. (R), NY, *134*
Parsons, Charles E., Dunhill Professional Search of Miami (C), FL, *320*
Pauling, John, C. J. Stafford & Assoc. (C), ON, *591*
Peasback, David R., Canny, Bowen Inc. (R), NY, *28*
Pedelty, Lori K., Capstone Consulting, Inc. (R), IL, *29*
Pergal, Donald, Resource Networking Inc. (C), IN, *534*
Perlmutter, Martin, Hook-Up! (C), CA, *380*
Perras, Paul, KPMG Executive Search (R), ON, *119*
Perry, Brandon, Software Engineering Solutions, Inc. (C), CA, *587*
Perry, David, Perry-Martel Int'l., Inc. (R), ON, *163*
Peterson, John S., Greger/Peterson Assoc., Inc. (R), CA, *81*
Pezim, Howard J., The Bedford Consulting Group Inc. (R), ON, *15*
Phillip, John R., J. R. Phillip & Assoc., Inc. (R), CA, *164*
Pierce, Matthew J., Pierce & Assoc. (C), CA, *512*
Powell, Donald L., Proquest Inc. (C), SC, *524*
Prouty, Alden F., Manuso, Alexander & Associates, Inc. (R), NY, *135*
Raggio, Matthew G., Oak Assoc. (R), CA, *155*
Raheja, Marc C., CanMed Consultants Inc. (C), ON, *280*
Ralles, Vickie, Feldman Gray & Assoc. Inc. (C), ON, *339*
Ray, Robert T., ExecuGroup, Inc. (R), MS, *61*
Ray, William D., Lloyd Prescott & Churchill, Inc. (R), CO, *130*
Ray, William D., Lloyd Prescott Assoc., Inc. (C), CO, *419*
Rice, Gene, Rice Cohen Int'l. (R), PA, *178*
Rich, Mark E., Page-Wheatcroft & Co., Ltd. (R), TX, *158*
Robinson, Scott, Kensington Int'l., Inc. (R), IL, *113*
Robyn, Eric W., QVS Int'l. (R), GA, *170*
Rodriguez, George L., InteliSearch, Inc. (R), CT, *102*
Roher, Howard F., Franklin Allen Consultants, Ltd. (R), NY, *71*
Rojek, Lorraine, Rojek Marketing Group, Inc. (R), OH, *181*
Rolfe, Pamela, Career Specialists, Inc. (R), WA, *29*
Rosato, William R., W. R. Rosato & Assoc., Inc. (R), NY, *182*
Rosenbaum, Bette, Healthcare Executive Recruiters, Inc. (C), CA, *372*
Rosenow, Richard, Heath/Norton Assoc., Inc. (R), NY, *89*
Ross, Cheryl Molliver, Thomas, Whelan Assoc., Inc. (C), DC, *606*
Scheye, Klaus G., Anderson & Schwab, Inc. (R), NY, *6*
Schmidt, Frank B., F. B. Schmidt Int'l. (R), CA, *185*
Schoales, Gloria, Schoales & Assoc. Inc. (C), ON, *572*
Schoales, Michael, Schoales & Assoc. Inc. (C), ON, *572*
Schoon, Richard G., The Partnership Group (R), NJ, *160*
Schuyler, Lambert, Schuyler Assoc., Ltd. (R), GA, *185*
Schwab, Jr., Frank, Anderson & Schwab, Inc. (R), NY, *6*
Schwartz, Michael, Synapse Human Resource Consulting Group (R), TX, *205*
Schwartz, Raymond, The Partnership Group (R), NJ, *160*
Schweiger, Michael, Search Int'l. (R), MA, *187*
Selman, Gary L., Careerfit, Inc. (C), TX, *283*
Shakes, Joe, Fell & Nicholson Technology Resources (R), CA, *66*
Shattuck, M. B., M. B. Shattuck & Assoc., Inc. (R), CA, *189*
Sheweloff, William J., McCray, Shriver, Eckdahl & Assoc., Inc. (R), CA, *140*
Shipherd, John T., The Cassie Group (R), NC, *31*
Silverman, Gary, GWS Partners (R), CA, *84*
Silverman, Gary, GWS Partners (R), IL, *84*
Skewes, Gail, Reid Ellis Assoc. Inc. (C), ON, *533*
Smith, Charles D., Smith & Laue Search (R), OR, *193*
Smith, Colin, Anderson & Schwab, Inc. (R), NY, *6*
Smith, Dickson, The Kinlin Co., Inc. (R), MA, *115*
Smith, Gregory L., G. L. Smith Assoc. (C), CA, *584*
Southworth, David E., Premier Recruiting Group (C), MI, *516*

RECRUITER SPECIALTIES

Spangenberg, J. Brand, The Brand Co., Inc. (R), FL, *22*
Spatt, Jonathan M., Hospitality Executive Search, Inc. (R), MA, *96*
Spence, Bob, Creative-Leadership, Inc. (R), CA, *42*
Stanley, Paul R. A., Ray & Berndtson/Lovas Stanley (R), ON, *172*
Stanton, Stan, Huntress Real Estate Executive Search (R), MO, *100*
Stein, Neil A., R. H. Perry & Assoc., Inc. (R), DC, *162*
Stiles, Linford E., Linford E. Stiles & Assoc., L.L.C. (R), NH, *201*
Stroman, III, Alfred L., Stroman Int'l., Inc. (R), CO, *204*
Stubberfield, Lee, Management Recruiters of the Baltimore Washington Corridor (C), MD, *450*
Sur, William K., Canny, Bowen Inc. (R), NY, *28*
Surrette, Mark J., Robertson-Surrette Ltd. (R), NS, *179*
Taylor, John, The Caplan-Taylor Group (R), AZ, *28*
Taylor, Rachel, Harcor Quest & Assoc. (R), OH, *86*
Tingley, Harleigh V. S., Anderson & Schwab, Inc. (R), NY, *6*
Tinker, J. Jay, Management Recruiters of the Baltimore Washington Corridor (C), MD, *450*
Trapani, Chris, ExecuSource Consultants, Inc. (C), TX, *332*
Turnblacer, John, The Gabriel Group (C), PA, *354*
van Biesen, Jacques A. H., Search Group Inc. (R), AB, *186*
Van Hevelingen, Nicholaas, AM & G Certified Public Accountants & Consultants (R), IL, *4*
Vice, Michael, D.A.I Human Resources Consultants (R), QE, *45*
Vito, Joseph, Multi Processing, Inc. (R), NH, *149*
Vogel, Emil, Tarnow Int'l. (R), NJ, *206*
Wascovich, Tina, Rojek Marketing Group, Inc. (R), OH, *181*
Watkins, Robert J., R. J. Watkins & Co., Ltd. (R), CA, *216*
Wayne, Vici, Christian & Timbers, Inc. (R), OH, *34*
Weiner, Al, Lucas Group (C), NY, *421*
Weiss, John J., Executive Placement Services (C), GA, *333*
West, Paul A., West & West (R), CA, *218*
Whitlow, M. Blanton, Manuso, Alexander & Associates, Inc. (R), NY, *135*
Wilensky, Ivy S., Anderson & Schwab, Inc. (R), NY, *6*
Wilson, Donald, Allerton Heneghan & O'Neill (R), IL, *4*
Wilson, Gordon, Ray & Berndtson/Lovas Stanley (R), ON, *172*
Wilson, Jeffrey M., Sales Consultants of Western McHenry County (C), IL, *558*
Wilson, Patricia L., Leon A. Farley Assoc. (R), CA, *65*
Winitz, Joel M., GSW Consulting Group, Inc. (R), CA, *83*
Winston, Thomas, Winston Search, Inc. (R), MD, *222*
Wolkensperg, G. Michael, Rushmore • Judge Inc. (R), ON, *183*
Yoskowitz, Reggie, Foley Proctor Yoskowitz (R), NJ, *69*
Zaccaro, Joseph L., The Human Resource Consulting Group, Inc. (R), CO, *98*
Zambrana, Fernando, Conasa de Mexico, S.C. (R), MX, *39*
Zink, Al, The Human Resource Consulting Group, Inc. (R), MA, *98*

Service industry

Adams, Robert, Sales Consultants of Dallas (C), TX, *563*
Andersen, Phil, Blackhawk Advantage, Inc. (C), CA, *267*
Barnes, Roanne L., Barnes Development Group, LLC (R), WI, *11*
DeLalla, Barbara, DeLalla - Fried Assoc. (C), NY, *310*
Fried, Ann, DeLalla - Fried Assoc. (C), NY, *310*
Gilbert, Brian, Sales Consultants of Dallas (C), TX, *563*
Higbee, Joan, Thorndike Deland Assoc. LLC (R), NY, *48*
Hill, Michelle, The Alfus Group (R), NY, *3*
Maher, Peter T., The Partnership Group (R), NJ, *160*
Mass, Angela, Focus Executive Search (C), MN, *343*
Meagher, III, Edward A., The Woodstone Consulting Company, Inc. (R), CO, *224*
Meagher, Linda J., The Woodstone Consulting Company, Inc. (R), CO, *224*
Stafford, Peter B., Stafford Consulting Group (R), CA, *198*
Van Leeuwen, Lee, Van Leeuwen Assoc. (R), CA, *213*
Wenzel, Dawn, Partners in Recruiting (C), IL, *504*

Shopping centers

Morbitzer, Tina, Tina Morbitzer & Assoc. (C), FL, *485*
Poline, Bob, Bob Poline Assoc. Inc. (C), CA, *514*
Poline, Rich, Bob Poline Assoc. Inc. (C), GA, *514*

Social services

Henderson, Etta Ish, Boulware & Assoc. Inc. (R), IL, *20*
Zweifler, Rhyan, Boulware & Assoc. Inc. (R), IL, *20*

Software

Albertson, Rob, Dick Williams & Assoc. (C), CA, *621*
Allen, David, Century Assoc., Inc. (C), PA, *287*
Allen, Debbie, Hall Kinion (C), CA, *366*
Allen, Martin, Rice Cohen Int'l. (R), PA, *178*
Alman, Paul D., Holland & Assoc., Inc. (R), MI, *94*
Ammirati, Greg, Sales Consultants of Western McHenry County (C), IL, *558*
Arnone, Patrick J., Patrick Arnone & Assoc. Inc. (R), VA, *7*
Atkinson, Arthur, Atkinson Search & Placement, Inc. (C), IA, *255*
Auriema, Mark H., Jay Tracey Assoc. Inc. (C), VT, *608*
Austin, Larry, Lucas Assoc. (C), TX, *421*
Baer, Curtis L., Sales Consultants of Barrington (C), IL, *558*
Bakehorn, Thomas, Martin Stevens Tamaren & Assoc., Inc. (R), CA, *206*
Barker, Thomas E., EBA Group (R), NJ, *56*
Bauzenberger, III, E. H., The Currier-Winn Co., Inc. (C), NJ, *305*
Baxley, Eric, McCoy Ltd. (C), CA, *474*
Becker, Ralph L., Automation Technology Search (C), CA, *256*
Bell, Dixie Lee, MIS Computer Professionals, Inc. (C), KS, *482*
Bogue, Randall L., TBC, Inc. (C), KY, *600*
Booth, Sandra, SKB Enterprises (C), NY, *582*
Bornholdt, John, Bornholdt Shivas & Friends Executive Recruiters (C), NY, *270*
Bradley, Mark, The Landstone Group (C), NY, *412*
Brandle, James, McCoy Ltd. (C), CA, *474*
Brei, Randy, Brei & Assoc., Inc. (C), IA, *272*
Buckley, Michael, High Tech Opportunities, Inc. (C), NH, *377*
Buehler, Brad, The Goodman Group (R), CA, *79*
Cadwell, Larry, F. P. Lennon Assoc. (C), FL, *416*
Campbell, Brian H., Venpro Consulting Inc. (C), ON, *612*
Chan, Elsie, Elsie Chan & Assoc. (C), CA, *289*
Christian, Jeffrey E., Christian & Timbers, Inc. (R), OH, *34*
Cleary, Jeanne, The Rossi Search Group (C), PA, *545*
Corey, Richard F., Weterrings & Agnew, Inc. (C), NY, *619*
Corrales, Shaun, cFour Partners (R), CA, *32*
Cunningham, John, Medical Executive Recruiters (C), CA, *477*
Curry, Joseph, MediaCOM Talent Group (C), MA, *477*
Davis, Glenn S., Next Step Recruiting (C), CA, *493*
Deckelbaum, Stan, Fortune Personnel Consultants of Raleigh, Inc. (C), NC, *348*
DeCorrevont, James, DeCorrevont & Assoc. (C), IL, *310*
Dermady, Timothy J., ExecutiveFit (C), NY, *337*

DiLorenzo, Matthew B., The Inside Track (C), TX, *389*
DiMauro, Paula, Sales Consultants of Omaha, Inc. (C), NE, *560*
Dorst, Martin, Dorst Information Services, Inc. (C), NY, *314*
Earle, Holland R., Executive Strategies, Inc. (C), GA, *337*
Eckler, Geoffrey N., Eckler Personnel Network (C), VT, *326*
Endres, Devlin, Allstaff, Inc. (C), IL, *245*
Ertaud, Wilfrid, MediaCOM Talent Group (C), MA, *477*
Fafard, Lina, Montgomery West (R), CA, *146*
Fair, Carolyn, Dunhill Executive Search of Los Angeles, Inc. (C), CA, *319*
Fare, Sarah, Management Recruiters-Cedar Rapids, Inc. (C), IA, *448*
Feinberg, Erika, Pearson & Assoc., Inc. (C), AZ, *506*
Fowler, Gary, Analog Solutions (C), NY, *249*
Frankian, Joseph R., Allstaff, Inc. (C), IL, *245*
Franklin, Gary, FAI (C), CO, *338*
Frazer, Mel, Mel Frazer Consultant (C), CA, *352*
Gawitt, Dan, Management Recruiters of the Baltimore Washington Corridor (C), MD, *450*
Gertler, Richard, Prairie Resource Group, Inc. (R), IL, *166*
Gilson, Linda L., Key Resources Int'l. (C), CA, *406*
Grant, Daniel M., Sales Consultants of Western McHenry County (C), IL, *558*
Guerin, Michael R., Michael R. Guerin Co. (C), CA, *364*
Guld, Allison, Jenex Technology Placement Inc. (C), BC, *398*
Haberman, Rebecca Powers, Norman Powers Assoc., Inc. (C), MA, *515*
Hall, Charles, Butterfield & Co. Int'l., Inc. (C), NC, *277*
Hancock, Jason, Hall Kinion (C), CA, *366*
Hannas, Jeanine K., Executive Business Solutions, Inc. (C), WA, *332*
Harmon, Jerry, Delta Resource Group, Ltd. (C), GA, *311*
Hay, Jennifer, The Pollack Group (C), ON, *514*
Hebert, Chris, Management Recruiters of Nassau, Inc. (R), NY, *134*
Heisser, Robert, MRI, The Sequel Group, LLC (C), CO, *486*
Henson, Jeff, Henson Partners (C), AZ, *376*
Ho, John, Management Recruiters of Chanhassen (C), MN, *452*
Howlett, Tracy A., Ross Personnel Consultants, Inc. (C), CT, *545*
Hudson, Judy K., The Hudson Group (C), CT, *383*
Huff, Margaret L., Huff Assoc. (R), NJ, *98*
Huff, William Z., Huff Assoc. (R), NJ, *98*
Jacobs, Bob, StratfordGroup (R), CA, *203*
Johnson, Walt, Pacific Crossing (C), CA, *501*
Joseph, Allen F., CBA Companies (C), CA, *286*
Joyce, Mark, Louis Rudzinsky Assoc., Inc. (C), MA, *548*
Joyce, William J., The Guild Corp. (C), VA, *364*
Kahn, Beverly A., New Dimensions in Technology, Inc. (C), MA, *492*
Karkow, Drew, David Weinfeld Group (C), NC, *617*
Karson, Allan, Allan Karson Assoc., Inc. (R), NJ, *110*
Kennedy, Mike, MK & Assoc. (R), CA, *146*
Kennedy, Sharon, MK & Assoc. (R), CA, *146*
Kierstead, Robert, High Tech Opportunities, Inc. (C), NH, *377*
Kiken, Mark E., COBA Executive Search (R), CO, *36*
King, Margaret, Christian & Timbers, Inc. (R), OH, *34*
Kohonoski, Michael M., The Guild Corp. (C), VA, *364*
Kossuth, David, Kossuth & Assoc., Inc. (R), WA, *119*
Kossuth, Jane, Kossuth & Assoc., Inc. (R), WA, *119*
Kraemer, Katherine R., Katherine R. Kraemer (R), CA, *120*
Kreutz, Gary L., Kreutz Consulting Group, Inc. (R), IL, *121*
Landay, Mark, Dynamic Synergy Corp. (R), CA, *56*
Landwerb, Sandy, Capital Consulting Group, Inc. (R), MD, *28*
Lane, Douglas, Management Recruiters of Milwaukee - Downtown (C), WI, *466*
Lapat, Aaron, J. Robert Scott (R), MA, *104*
Lawrence, James B., The Hamilton Group (R), VA, *85*
Lehrman, Peter A., Emerging Technology Search (C), GA, *329*
LePatner, Steve, Dunhill Executive Search of Los Angeles, Inc. (C), CA, *319*
Levitt, Peter, Sales Consultants King of Prussia (C), PA, *562*
Litras, Steve, F. P. Lennon Assoc. (C), GA, *416*
Loftus, Daniel P., McCoy Ltd. (C), CA, *474*
Love, Jon R., JL & Co. (C), CA, *399*
Mader, Stephen P., Christian & Timbers, Inc. (R), MA, *34*
Mader, Steve, Christian & Timbers, Inc. (R), OH, *34*
Mancini, Deborah, Mancini Technical Recruiting (C), VA, *468*
Marseline, Tracy, CJSI-Cindy Jackson Search Int'l. (C), CA, *291*
Matson, Marshall, General Engineering Tectonics (C), CA, *356*
McCabe, William, Allstaff, Inc. (C), IL, *245*
McMann, Dean E., The Ransford Group (R), TX, *171*
McNally, John R., McCoy Ltd. (C), CA, *474*
Mihalka, Laura, NCC Executive Search Consultants (C), CA, *490*
Mordue, Michael J., Mordue, Allen, Roberts, Bonney Ltd. (C), WA, *485*
Mulcahy, Patrick, Mulcahy Co. (C), WI, *487*
Mulvey, James E., SilverSands Int'l. (C), FL, *582*
Murphy, Dan, The Pollack Group (C), ON, *514*
Mussato, Ray, Dick Williams & Assoc. (C), CA, *621*
Navickas, Sophia, Lynx, Inc. (C), MA, *421*
Nelson, Len, Len Nelson & Assoc., Inc. (C), TX, *491*
Nelson, Richard, Pacific Crossing (C), CA, *501*
Nicolosi, Charles, CN Associates (C), CA, *293*
O'Keefe, Ian, O'Keefe & Assoc. (C), AR, *498*
O'Keefe, John P., O'Keefe & Assoc. (C), TX, *498*
Pappalardo, Chuck, Christian & Timbers, Inc. (R), OH, *34*
Patronella, Larry, W. Robert Eissler & Assoc., Inc. (C), TX, *327*
Peden, Ann, Peden & Assoc. (C), CA, *506*
Pickens, Gregory D., Gregory D. Pickens (C), TX, *512*
Powers, Norman S., Norman Powers Assoc., Inc. (C), MA, *515*
Radzely, Larry, Adel-Lawrence Assoc., Inc. (C), NJ, *240*
Raggio, Matthew G., Oak Assoc. (R), CA, *155*
Ray, Marianne C., Callan Assoc., Ltd. (R), IL, *27*
Renwick, David, John Kurosky & Assoc. (R), CA, *122*
Rigal, Jennifer, Jenex Technology Placement Inc. (C), BC, *398*
Rivera, Monica, NCC Executive Search Consultants (C), CA, *491*
Romstein, Christina, cFour Partners (R), CA, *32*
Rowland, John R., Rowland Assoc. (C), CA, *547*
Rudzinsky, Jeff, Louis Rudzinsky Assoc., Inc. (C), MA, *548*
Russell, Steven, Nyborg•Dow Assoc., Inc. (C), CA, *497*
Rystrom, R. L., R. L. Rystrom & Assoc., Inc. (C), MN, *549*
Sarchett, A. Wayne, Systems Careers (C), CA, *598*
Schaefer, John, Professional Employment Group (C), MD, *520*
Schindel, Kim, Searchworks, Inc. (C), FL, *577*
Schmidt, Susan, David Weinfeld Group (C), NC, *617*
Schoenfeld, Jack, Dunhill of Manchester Inc. (C), NH, *321*
Schultz, William A., Sales Consultants of Madison (C), WI, *563*
Selker, Gregory, Christian & Timbers, Inc. (R), OH, *34*

RECRUITER SPECIALTIES

Shinn, Michael, Shinn & Assoc. (R), CA, *189*
Shue, Colleen, Bennett Search & Consulting Co. (R), FL, *16*
Siker, Paul W., The Guild Corp. (C), VA, *364*
Sill, Igor M., Geneva Group Int'l. (R), CA, *76*
Silver, Lee, L. A. Silver Assoc., Inc. (R), MA, *191*
Silverman, Craig, Hall Kinion (C), CA, *366*
Starling, Dick, ProNet, Inc. (C), NC, *524*
Sterenfeld, David, Corporate Dynamix (C), AZ, *300*
Stevens, Brett M., Sales Consultants of Cherokee (C), GA, *558*
Stevens, Martin, Martin Stevens Tamaren & Assoc., Inc. (R), CA, *206*
Stone, Susan L., Stone Enterprises Ltd. (C), IL, *594*
Stroud, Toni, Management Recruiters of the Baltimore Washington Corridor (C), MD, *450*
Swimley, E. Scott, Lautz, Grotte, Engler & Swimley (R), CA, *126*
Tackett, Lynn, National Recruiters (C), OK, *489*
Talman, Ilya, Roy Talman & Assoc. (C), IL, *599*
Taylor, Jerry, Executive Recruiters (C), WA, *334*
Tracey, Jay E., Jay Tracey Assoc. Inc. (C), VT, *608*
Turner, Linda, Kuhn Med-Tech (C), CA, *409*
Vandegrift, Tom, Kiley, Owen & McGovern, Inc. (R), NJ, *114*
Veblan, Jennifer, NCC Executive Search Consultants (C), CA, *490*
Vento, Joseph P., Vento Assoc. (C), TN, *612*
Vick, Bill, Vick & Assoc. (R), TX, *214*
Waldrip, Jennifer, Hall Kinion (C), CA, *366*
Walker, Bob, McCoy Ltd. (C), CA, *474*
Watkins, Robert J., R. J. Watkins & Co., Ltd. (R), CA, *216*
Weaver, John, Culver Personnel Services (C), CA, *304*
Weinfeld, David C., David Weinfeld Group (C), NC, *617*
Weinpel, Charles J., Weinpel Search, Inc. (C), NJ, *617*
Whitehead, Elizabeth S., Whitehead & Assoc., Inc. (C), MO, *620*
Wichansky, Carole, Tele-Solutions of Arizona, Inc. (C), AZ, *604*
Woodward, Lee, Search Assoc., Inc. (C), CA, *574*
Young, Philip M., Ross Personnel Consultants, Inc. (C), CT, *545*
Ziarko, Michael E., Selective Search Associates (C), OH, *578*

Speech

Collingwood, Beryl, Trillium Human Resources Inc. (C), ON, *609*
Waller, Victoria, Health Search, Inc. (C), KS, *371*

Sports

Bailey, III, Joseph A., Russell Reynolds Assoc., Inc. (R), TX, *177*
Beaudine, Frank R., Eastman & Beaudine, Inc. (R), TX, *56*
Beaudine, Robert E., Eastman & Beaudine, Inc. (R), TX, *56*
Blood, James L., D. R. Blood & Assoc. (R), AZ, *18*
Capanna, Patricia A., Management Recruiters of Madison, Inc. (C), WI, *466*
Clayman, Stan, CMS, Inc. (C), NH, *293*
Damon, Robert A., SpencerStuart (R), NY, *196*
Gielow, Curtis C., Gielow Assoc., Inc. (R), WI, *76*
Hughes, Don, ProLinks Inc. (R), VA, *170*
Hughes, Jr., John E., LAI Ward Howell (R), PA, *123*
Lee, Amy T., Sanford Rose Assoc. - Salt Lake City (C), UT, *571*
Lee, Rodger A., Sanford Rose Assoc. - Salt Lake City (C), UT, *571*
Padwa, Danielle, The Alfus Group (R), NY, *3*
Pickering, Dorothy C., Livingston, Robert & Co. (R), CT, *130*
Porter, Lindsay, HCI Corp. (C), IL, *371*
Stefan, David E., ChaseAmerica, Inc. (R), FL, *33*
Tudi, Mark, DHR Int'l., Inc. (R), AZ, *49*
White, Joseph A., Sports Group Int'l. (R), NC, *198*
Whiting, Frank, Cook Assoc.,® Inc. (R), IL, *40*
Zender, Mark, Strategic Resources (C), WA, *595*

Staffing

Austin, Suzanne, Flexible Resources, Inc. (C), MA, *342*
Babcock, James A., The Premier Staffing Group (C), OH, *517*
Bayer, Cathy, Electronic Search, Inc. (C), IL, *328*
Blakemore, Linda, Atlantic Pacific Group (C), CA, *255*
Campbell, J. S., Sterling Int'l. Management Recruitment, Ltd. Inc. (C), NC, *592*
Campbell, K. J., Sterling Int'l. Management Recruitment, Ltd. Inc. (C), NC, *592*
Clovis, Jr., James R., Handy HRM (R), NY, *86*
Cronin, Dolores, Corporate Careers, Inc. (C), CA, *299*
Glasspiegel, Susan, Flexible Resources, Inc. (C), CT, *342*
Handler, Marilyn, MedXec USA, Inc. (C), FL, *478*
Hart, Jessica, Synergistech Communications (C), CA, *597*
Hogan, Karen, Davis-Smith, Inc. (C), MI, *309*
Hughes, R. Kevin, Handy HRM (R), NY, *86*
Katzman, Sheri B., Rosenfeld & Co., Inc. (C), MI, *545*
Mee, Robin, Mee Derby & Co. (C), DC, *478*
Mockler, Nadine, Flexible Resources, Inc. (C), CT, *342*
Morrical, Michael, Carnegie Partners, Inc. (R), IL, *30*
Patrick, Donald R., Sanford Rose Assoc. - Norcross (C), GA, *566*
Peters, Alec, Alec Peters Assoc. Inc./DLR (R), GA, *163*
Putiri, Vincent, Asheville Search & Consulting (C), NC, *253*
Rietano-Davey, Susan, Flexible Resources, Inc. (C), CT, *342*
Rivers, Janeen, H.I. Hunt & Co., Ltd. (R), MA, *99*
Ross, Terri, Soderlund Assoc. Inc. (R), OH, *195*
Sutkamp, Paige, Soderlund Assoc. Inc. (R), OH, *195*
Walters, Roy, H.I. Hunt & Co., Ltd. (R), MA, *99*
Whelan, Kim, Flexible Resources, Inc. (C), MA, *342*
Wood, N. Lloyd, Corporate Careers, Inc. (C), CA, *299*
Young, Laurie, Flexible Resources, Inc. (C), CT, *342*
Young, Roy, Flexible Resources, Inc. (C), CA, *342*

Start-up companies

Herbert, Paul, David Blevins & Assoc. (C), WA, *268*
Kaplan, Alan J., Kaplan & Assoc., Inc. (R), PA, *109*

Steel

Fruchtman, Gary, Management Recruiters of Northwest Ohio, Inc. (C), OH, *458*
Lasini, Dennis, Genesis Research (C), MO, *356*
Leader, D. June, Leader Network (C), PA, *414*
Mayberry, Karen Sue, Singleton & Assoc. (C), VA, *582*
Oster, R. Rush, Management Recruiters of Anna Maria Island (C), FL, *443*
Singleton, Steven L., Singleton & Assoc. (C), VA, *582*

Strategic Planning

Bacher, Judith, SpencerStuart (R), NY, *196*
Brindisi, Thomas J., Brindisi Search (R), MD, *23*
Fox, Glenn M., Strategic Search, LLC (C), CA, *595*
Hoffman, Tala R., TRH Assoc., Inc. (R), NY, *210*
Kip, Luanne S., Kip Williams, Inc. (R), NY, *115*

Peterson, Michael T., BayResearch Group, Inc. (R), IL, *14*

Subacute Healthcare

Carter, Christine, Health Care Dimensions (C), CO, *371*
Clark, Michael, Cornerstone Search Assoc. Inc. (C), MA, *299*
Feingold, Robin, Cornerstone Search Assoc. Inc. (C), MA, *299*
Hazelton, Lisa, Health Care Dimensions (C), CO, *371*
Howard, Jill, Health Care Dimensions (C), CO, *371*
Rosen, Richard, Cornerstone Search Assoc. Inc. (C), MA, *299*
West, Nancy, Health Care Dimensions (C), CO, *371*

Superconductivity

Adams, Frank S., Thomson, Sponar & Adams, Inc. (C), WA, *606*

Supermarkets

Arledge, Tom, Allen Austin Lowe & Powers (R), TX, *3*
Hebert, Larry, Lawrence James Assoc. (C), NJ, *414*
McDaniel, Paul, The Paul McDaniel Co. (C), TN, *474*
Okyn, Leonard, Lawrence James Assoc. of Florida, Inc. (C), FL, *414*

Suppliers

Alvey, Frank, Sage Employment Recruiters (C), IN, *550*
Gugler, Wolf, Wolf Gugler & Assoc. Ltd. (R), ON, *83*

Surgery

Allhands, Kelly, Allhands Placement Consultants (C), IN, *245*

Surgical

Faas, Vicki L., Healthcare Recruiters of the Rockies, Inc. (C), CO, *372*

Systems

Baert, Yvonne, Personnel Management Group (C), MB, *508*
Barbosa, Franklin J., Skott/Edwards Consultants (R), NJ, *192*
Berger, Jay, Pathway Executive Search, Inc. (C), NY, *505*
Brody, Steve, Executive Resource Systems (C), CA, *335*
Campbell, Brian H., Venpro Consulting Inc. (C), ON, *612*
Capps, Linda, MIS Computer Professionals, Inc. (C), KS, *482*
Colman, Michael, Executive Placement Consultants (C), IL, *333*
Critchley, Walter, Cochran, Cochran & Yale, Inc. (R), NY, *37*
Dangerfield, Chris, Technology Search Int'l. (C), CA, *603*
de La Hoz Ramirez, Armando, OSAGUI S.A. de C.V. (C), MX, *500*
Duval, Dick, B. D. Wallace & Assoc. (C), MD, *614*
Dyson, Steve, Technology Search Int'l. (C), CA, *603*
Geiman, Barry, Leader Institute, Inc. (C), GA, *414*
Heisser, Robert, MRI, The Sequel Group, LLC (C), CO, *486*
Hulme, Doug, Leader Institute, Inc. (C), GA, *414*
Jacobs, Gilbert B., Focus Consulting Services, Inc. (C), VA, *343*
Kelso, Pat, Barton Assoc., Inc. (R), TX, *12*
Kohn, Adam, Christian & Timbers, Inc. (R), OH, *34*
Kraemer, Katherine R., Katherine R. Kraemer (R), CA, *120*
Kurtz, Sheldon I., Kurtz Pro-Search, Inc. (C), NJ, *410*
Law, Grace, Software Engineering Solutions, Inc. (C), CA, *587*
May, Donald C., Allied Search, Inc. (C), CA, *245*
Mygatt, Marlena, Software Engineering Solutions, Inc. (C), CA, *587*
Patronella, Larry, W. Robert Eissler & Assoc., Inc. (C), TX, *327*
Perkins, Yvonne, Leader Institute, Inc. (C), GA, *414*
Perry, Brandon, Software Engineering Solutions, Inc. (C), CA, *587*
Powers, Janet, Powers Consultants, Inc. (R), MO, *166*
Rogers, Roc, Dynamic Computer Consultants, Inc. (C), AZ, *324*
Ross, Cheryl Molliver, Thomas, Whelan Assoc., Inc. (C), DC, *606*
Rudzinsky, Jeff, Louis Rudzinsky Assoc., Inc. (C), MA, *548*
Sabrin, Joe, ManTech Consulting (C), NY, *468*
Schlatter, Craig, Schlatter & Assoc. (C), CA, *572*
Shapiro, Alan, Technology Search Int'l. (C), CA, *603*
Sirey, Don, Technology Search Int'l. (C), CA, *603*
Stelika, Kit, Southport Int'l. Assoc. Inc. (C), FL, *588*
Talarico, Joseph, Hreshko Consulting Group (C), NJ, *382*
Vlahos, Ben, Leader Institute, Inc. (C), GA, *414*
Waldman, Noah W., LAI Ward Howell (R), GA, *123*
Young, Susan M., Management Recruiters of Morris County, NJ (C), NJ, *453*
Zabor, Richard, Leader Institute, Inc. (C), GA, *414*

Tax

Bynum, Sam, TaxSearch Inc. (R), OK, *207*
Ciaramitaro, Anthony, Corporate Search Consultants, Inc. (C), FL, *301*
Cowling, John W., Professional Resources (C), OK, *522*
Curle, Suzanne, E T Search Inc. (C), CA, *324*
Davidson, Julie, Drinkwater & Assoc. (R), MA, *55*
Davis, Guy, Kane & Assoc. (C), TX, *403*
Fink, Allen, PMJ & Assoc. (C), ON, *513*
Glaser, David, ECG Resources, Inc. (C), NY, *326*
Greco, Sheila, Sheila Greco Assoc. (C), NY, *362*
Grue, Douglas Harrison, Harrison Consulting Group, Inc. (C), CA, *369*
Habelmann, Gerald B., Habelmann & Assoc. (R), MI, *84*
Heino, Jay, Jay Heino Company, LLC (C), NY, *375*
Hermann, George A., Hermann & Westmore (R), NY, *92*
Hunter, Steven, Diamond Tax Recruiting (C), NY, *312*
Krueger, Todd L., Todd L. Krueger & Assoc. (C), WA, *409*
Kutcher, Howard, Kutcher Tax Careers, Inc. (C), NY, *410*
Laguzza, John, Laguzza Assoc., Ltd. (R), NY, *122*
Lee, Joseph J., Larsen & Lee, Inc. (R), MD, *125*
Leff, Lisa A., Berger & Leff (C), CA, *264*
Lieff, Shelley, Advice Personnel Inc. (C), NY, *241*
Marino, Mike, Tax Network Resources, Inc. (C), NY, *600*
Musick, Diana, Musick & Assoc. (C), CA, *487*
Musick, Stephen, Musick & Assoc. (C), CA, *487*
Neuharth, Kathleen, E T Search Inc. (C), CA, *324*
Pann, Arthur J., Arthur Pann Assoc., Inc. (C), NY, *502*
Rosenblatt, Michael F., The Quest Organization (C), NY, *527*
Santiago, Anthony, TaxSearch Inc. (R), OK, *207*
Thunberg, Richard A., Jeff Rich Assoc. (C), NJ, *536*
Voss, Erik, Sheila Greco Assoc. (C), NY, *362*
Wayne, Cary S., ProSearch, Inc. (C), OH, *524*
Westmore, Robert J., Hermann & Westmore (R), CA, *92*

Technical

Adler, David, Don Allan Assoc., Inc. (C), CA, *313*
Agnello, Frank, Systems Research Inc. (SRI) (C), IL, *598*
Alexander, Myra, Mark Christian & Assoc., Inc. (C), AZ, *470*

RECRUITER SPECIALTIES

Allen, Debbie, Hall Kinion (C), CA, *366*
Allen, Jr., Lindsay, Mark III Personnel, Inc. (C), NC, *470*
Anderson, Douglas L., Quantum Int'l., Ltd. (R), FL, *170*
Angell, Tryg R., Tryg R. Angell, Ltd. (C), CT, *250*
Anton, Michael, Michael James & Co. (C), IL, *480*
Ashworth, Kevin, Impact Technical Staffing (C), OR, *387*
Baldwin, W. Keith, Baldwin & Assoc. (C), OH, *258*
Barkan, Stacey, Current Resource Group, Inc. (C), GA, *305*
Barr, Sharon A., Barr Assoc. (C), PA, *259*
Batista, Daniel T., Careerfit, Inc. (C), TX, *283*
Bourque, Jack, Management Recruiters of Winsted, Inc. (C), CT, *442*
Bouzan, Paul X., The Executive Group, Inc. (R), CA, *62*
Boyce, Kevin, Laboratory Resource Group (C), MA, *411*
Brakel, H. R., ProTech Nationwide Staffing, Inc. (C), NY, *525*
Braxton, Jonathan J., Brian Assoc., Inc. (C), NY, *273*
Brecciaroli, Diane, DiTech Resources (C), CT, *313*
Brittingham, R. P., Search & Recruit Int'l. (C), VA, *573*
Burke, Alan, The BMW Group, Inc. (C), NY, *268*
Carter, Carolyn, Thomas Mangum Co. (R), CA, *208*
Chadwell, Rebecca A., Chadwell & Assoc., Inc. (C), MI, *288*
Cherney, Steven D., Resource Perspectives, Inc. (R), CA, *175*
Christopher, Rosemarie, Med Exec Int'l. (C), CA, *476*
Christy, Tim, The Partnership Group (R), NJ, *160*
Clark, John Edward, Management Recruiters of Altamonte (C), FL, *442*
Cobb-West, Rosemary G., West & West (R), CA, *218*
Cole, Christopher, Tech-Net (C), TX, *601*
Cook, P. Gene, P. G. Cook Assoc. (R), TN, *40*
Cook, Stephen G., Cook Assoc. Int'l., Inc. (C), TN, *298*
Cooper, Bill, Management Recruiters of Chattanooga-Brainerd, Inc. (C), TN, *461*
Cowall, Frank A., Altec/HRC (C), MI, *246*
Dagneau, Thierry, Personnel Tangent Inc. (C), QE, *509*
Dahl, Stan, C.T.E.W. Executive Personnel Services Inc. (C), BC, *278*
Daugherty-Hill, Kimberly J., Hayman Daugherty Assoc., Inc. (C), GA, *370*
Davis, Andrew, Synergistech Communications (C), CA, *597*
DeLany, Donald F., Resource Perspectives, Inc. (R), CA, *175*
Desiderio, Anthony J., Dunhill Professional Search of Wilkes-Barre/Scranton, Inc. (C), PA, *322*
Dimick, Don, Impact Technical Staffing (C), OR, *387*
Doro, Chip, Career Marketing Assoc., Inc. (C), CO, *282*
Doyle, David, System 1 Search (C), CA, *598*
Dunbar, Meg, M. Dunbar & Assoc. (C), TX, *316*
Dusome, Terry, Holloway Schulz & Partners (C), BC, *380*
Duval, Dick, B. D. Wallace & Assoc. (C), MD, *614*
Eason, Larry E., JRL Executive Recruiters (C), MO, *401*
Eden, Don, Management Recruiters of Livonia (C), MI, *451*
Empey, David, Management Recruiters of Franktown (C), CO, *442*
Farro, Jerry, VZ Int'l., Inc. (C), AZ, *613*
Fisher, Iris L., Healthcare Recruiters International-NY/NJ (C), NJ, *373*
Fitzgerald, Thomas L., Telecom Recruiters, Inc. (C), VA, *605*
Fosnot, Michael, Management Recruiters of McMurray, Inc. (C), PA, *459*
Foster, Barton T., The Barton Group, Inc. (C), MI, *260*
Fought, Jay D., Fought, Jameson Assoc. (C), IL, *351*
Furman, Matt, MJF Assoc. (C), CT, *483*
Garfinkle, Benson D., MetroVantage Personnel Systems (C), CA, *480*
Garland, R. Darryl, Garland Assoc. Int'l. (C), CA, *355*
Gavin, David R., Northland Employment Services Inc. (C), MN, *496*
Gaw, F. William, Brandywine Management Group (R), MD, *22*
Gerald, C. Richard, C. R. Gerald & Assoc. (C), ON, *356*
Gilliam, Jon, LCS, Inc. (C), TX, *414*
Gold, Alan, L & L Assoc. (C), CA, *410*
Gold, Walter, Proven Edge (C), CA, *525*
Goldstein, Barry, Interim Financial Solutions (C), VA, *392*
Gonzer, Lawrence J., L. J. Gonzer Assoc. (C), NJ, *360*
Gowetski, K. Michael, Nationwide Personnel Placement, Inc. (C), OH, *490*
Grauss, Bryan J., Grauss & Co. (C), CA, *362*
Greenberg, Jordan A., The Pinnacle Source, Inc. (C), CO, *512*
Griffin, Deana A., Souder & Assoc. (R), VA, *195*
Grim, Gene, Sales Consultants of Cherry Hill (C), NJ, *560*
Gruszecki, Irene, Management Recruiters of Wausau, LLC (C), WI, *466*
Guerrier, Alain M., PersoNet, Inc. (C), FL, *507*
Hall, Scott, Advancement, Inc. (C), IL, *241*
Hancock, Jason, Hall Kinion (C), CA, *366*
Handelsman, Simon, Anderson & Schwab, Inc. (R), NY, *6*
Harris, Michael, A. E. Feldman Assoc., Inc. (C), NY, *339*
Heasley, Franklin A., The Franklin Search Group, Inc./Medzilla (R), WA, *71*
Helfer, Frederick W., Helfer Executive Consultants (R), TN, *91*
Helnore, Diann, Partners in Recruiting (C), IL, *504*
Hendricks, II, Stanley M., National Recruiting Service (C), IN, *489*
Herlihy, Jack, J. J. Herlihy & Assoc., Inc. (C), CA, *376*
Hetherington, Don, Landon Morgan (C), ON, *412*
Hicks, Albert M., Phillips Resource Group (C), SC, *510*
Hinds, Susan, Job Link, Inc. (C), CA, *399*
Holtz, Richard D., Technical Resource Assoc. (C), TN, *602*
Huddleston, Linda, Huddleston Assoc. (C), OK, *383*
Huddleston, Victor, Huddleston Assoc. (C), OK, *383*
Hughes, Susan F., Opus Marketing (R), MN, *157*
Hummel, D. Linda, Careerfit, Inc. (C), TX, *283*
Hurley, Art, Systems Research Inc. (SRI) (C), IL, *598*
Hursh, John, National Corporate Consultants, Inc. (C), IN, *489*
Isenberg, H. Peter, Management Recruiters of Noblesville, Inc. (C), IN, *448*
Jameson, Brad M., Fought, Jameson Assoc. (C), IL, *351*
Johnson, Cheri, Johnson & Assoc., Inc. (R), CA, *106*
Johnson, Lee, Kincaid Group Inc. (KGI) (C), TX, *406*
Johnson, Robert J., Quality Search Inc. (C), OH, *526*
Joseph, Allen F., CBA Companies (C), CA, *286*
Kane, Rich, Systems Research Inc. (SRI) (C), IL, *598*
Kapetan, Nicholas, Barrett Partners (C), IL, *260*
Keller, Lorraine, Management Recruiters of North West Austin (C), TX, *462*
Kennedy, Louis, S-H-S Int'l. of Cherry Hill (C), NJ, *549*
Kirchgessner, Ken, Management Recruiters of Pensacola (C), FL, *444*
Kirkbride, Robert, Kirkbride Assoc., Inc. (C), WA, *407*
Kleven, Robert, The Kleven Group, Inc. (C), MA, *407*
Koenig, Jerrold, P R Management Consultants, Inc. (C), NJ, *500*
Kotloski, Dennis, Management Recruiters of Chicago-North Shore (C), IL, *447*
Kreisberg, Robert S., Opus Marketing (R), CA, *156*
Kuesis, Dan, Systems Research Inc. (SRI) (C), IL, *598*
Kwapisz, Arthur, ISC of Atlanta, Inc. (C), GA, *394*
Lalagos, Dee, DEL Technical Services, Inc. (C), IL, *310*
Law, Grace, Software Engineering Solutions, Inc. (C), CA, *587*
Leader, D. June, Leader Network (C), PA, *414*

Lechtenberg, Leda, Dick Berg & Assoc. (C), CA, *264*
Lee, Albert G., Albert G. Lee Assoc. (C), RI, *415*
Leek, Robert, HEC Group (C), ON, *375*
Levine, Donald, Sharp Placement Professionals, Inc. (C), NY, *579*
Levine, Eileen, Williamsburg Group (C), NJ, *621*
Lewis, Richard, Cole, Warren & Long, Inc. (R), PA, *37*
Logie, Richard, Kirkbride Assoc., Inc. (C), WA, *407*
Longo, Roger, Longo Associates (C), CA, *420*
Makhani, Thukbir, LCS, Inc. (C), TX, *414*
Manning, Jerry, Management Recruiters of Ogden (C), UT, *464*
Mantel, Michael, The BMW Group, Inc. (C), NY, *268*
Marentez, Frank, Marentz & Co. (C), TX, *469*
Marsh, Robin, MetroVantage Personnel Systems (C), CA, *480*
McAvoy, Edward P., Romano McAvoy Assoc., Inc. (C), NY, *544*
McKinney, Pat, Prichard Kymen Inc. (R), AB, *168*
McNear, Jeffrey, Barrett Partners (C), IL, *260*
Mendrala, Karen, Lab Market Specialists (C), UT, *411*
Metzger, Susan, Techstaff Inc. (C), WI, *603*
Mihalka, Laura, NCC Executive Search Consultants (C), CA, *490*
Miller, Curt, A-L Assoc., Inc. (R), NY, *1*
Milman, Olga, A. E. Feldman Assoc., Inc. (C), NY, *339*
Mirsky, Al, The Barton Group, Inc. (C), MI, *260*
Montgomery, Thomas, Techstaff Inc. (C), WI, *603*
Morris, Joseph, Lekan & Assoc., Inc. (R), OH, *128*
Morse, Jeffrey A., Brandywine Management Group (R), MD, *22*
Muhlfelder, Daniel J., L. J. Gonzer Assoc. (C), NJ, *360*
Muir, Sherry, The Hunter Group, Inc. (C), MI, *385*
Mullen, Maryrose H., Emmett Executive Search, Inc. (C), NY, *330*
Mygatt, Marlena, Software Engineering Solutions, Inc. (C), CA, *587*
Nelson, C J, Lekan & Assoc., Inc. (R), OH, *128*
Nelson, Paul, London Executive Consultants Inc. (C), ON, *420*
Neubauer, Robert, E O Technical (C), CT, *324*
Newell, Wayne, Management Alliance Group, Inc. (R), NJ, *134*
Newman, Caleene Jones, Unlimited Staffing Solutions, Inc. (C), MI, *611*
Norman, Marcie, Management Recruiters of Franktown (C), CO, *442*
O'Dell, Krista, Impact Technical Staffing (C), OR, *387*
O'Neal, Jane, Austin Group Int'l./Marlar Int'l. (R), TX, *9*
Pappas, Linda, Barclay Consultants, Inc. (C), NJ, *259*
Paterson, David, Scientific Solutions, Inc. (C), MI, *572*
Paterson, Sharon, Scientific Solutions, Inc. (C), MI, *572*
Pelle, Michael A., M. A. Pelle Assoc., Inc. (C), NY, *506*
Pencarski, Robert, Bio-Venture Group (C), RI, *266*
Perlmutter, Martin, Hook-Up! (C), CA, *380*
Perry, Lisa Lepore, Aminex Corp. (C), MA, *249*
Petroski, Gary, E O Technical (C), CT, *324*
Putman, Joseph, Snelling Search (C), AL, *585*
Radzely, Larry, Adel-Lawrence Assoc., Inc. (C), NJ, *240*
Reed, Dave, Management Recruiters - Flint (C), MI, *451*
Refi, Thomas, Robert Harkins Assoc., Inc. (C), PA, *369*
Rivera, Monica, NCC Executive Search Consultants (C), CA, *491*
Roberts, Bryan, MetroVantage Personnel Systems (C), CA, *480*
Sall, Ron, Interim Financial Solutions (C), VA, *392*
Sargis, Scott R., Strategic Search Corp. (R), IL, *202*
Schapira, Kenneth, Wilson Personnel, Inc. (C), NC, *622*
Schick, Jon, Schick Professional Search, Inc. (C), OH, *572*
Schick, Rex, Schick Professional Search, Inc. (C), OH, *572*
Schneider, Paul J., Prime Resource Assoc. (C), WI, *518*
Schwartz, Stewart, Brandywine Management Group (R), MD, *22*
Schwarz, Meredith Barnes, Barnes & Assoc. Executive Search (C), CA, *259*
Scrivens, Dan, Snelling Search (C), AL, *585*
Sears, Kirk P., The Wilmington Group (C), NC, *622*
Sewell, Jerry, Fox-Morris Assoc., Inc. (C), TX, *352*
Sharp, Paul S., Management Recruiters of Roanoke (C), VA, *465*
Sherman, Terri, Tom Sloan & Assoc., Inc. (C), WI, *583*
Sherwood, Robert F., Sherwood Lehman Massucco, Inc. (R), CA, *189*
Sherwood, Rose-Marie, DARE Personnel Inc. (C), ON, *307*
Siegel, Michael, Specialty Employment Services, Inc. (C), GA, *589*
Silverman, Craig, Hall Kinion (C), CA, *366*
Silverman, Jules, Barclay Consultants, Inc. (C), NJ, *259*
Sinks, Lucius F., Aminex Corp. (C), MA, *249*
Skelton, Brenda, Cumberland Professional Search Inc. (C), TN, *304*
Skewes, Gail, Reid Ellis Assoc. Inc. (C), ON, *533*
Small, Carol D., Quantum Int'l., Ltd. (R), FL, *170*
Smith, Colin, Anderson & Schwab, Inc. (R), NY, *6*
Smith, Craig, Impact Technical Staffing (C), OR, *387*
Somershoe, Judy, Management Recruiters of Livonia (C), MI, *451*
Sotelo, Henry, Dunhill Professional Search of Hawaii (C), HI, *320*
Souder, Jr., E. G., Souder & Assoc. (R), VA, *195*
Speciale, Pamela, Austin Group Int'l./Marlar Int'l. (R), TX, *9*
Spremulli, Paul L., PKS Assoc., Inc. (C), RI, *513*
Stanley, Wade, Management Recruiters of Raleigh (C), NC, *456*
Stevens, Ron, Ron Stevens & Assoc., Inc. (C), FL, *593*
Stollenmaier, Nadine, Dunhill Professional Search of Hawaii (C), HI, *320*
Stoneburner, Dwight T., Stoneburner Assoc., Inc. (C), KS, *594*
Suhay, Gary T., Elite Resources Group (R), OH, *58*
Susleck, Matthew M., ESS (Executive Search Services) (R), CA, *61*
Suvak, Miranda, Huddleston Assoc. (C), OK, *383*
Talbot, Norman, Management Recruiters of Medford, N.J. (C), NJ, *453*
Tapler, Harold, Ruderfer & Co., Inc. (C), NJ, *548*
Tashima, Spencer S., Essential Solutions, Inc. (C), CA, *331*
Thomason, Nancy, Montgomery, Thomason & Assoc. (C), ON, *484*
Thomason, Ronald, Montgomery, Thomason & Assoc. (C), ON, *484*
Tolstrup, Rick, Aminex Corp. (C), MA, *249*
Toms, Dennis M., National Recruiting Service (C), IN, *489*
Trainor, James F., Trainor/Frank & Assoc. Inc. (C), WI, *608*
Unger, Don, Harcourt & Assoc. (C), AB, *368*
Van Wick, Mike, Management Recruiters of Rankin Co. (C), MS, *452*
Van Zanten, William, VZ Int'l., Inc. (C), AZ, *613*
Vlasek, Ray, Management Recruiters of LBJ Park/Dallas (C), TX, *462*
Wade, Alan, Data-AxIS Corp. (C), FL, *307*
Wainwright, Nancy, Locus Inc. (C), WV, *419*
Waldrip, Jennifer, Hall Kinion (C), CA, *366*
Weglarz, Patrick, Jim Kay & Assoc. (C), IL, *404*
Weiner, Arlene, Sanford Rose Assoc. - Athens (C), GA, *566*
Weiner, Art, Sanford Rose Assoc. - Athens (C), GA, *566*
Weiss, John P., Star Search Consultants (C), ON, *591*
Weiss, Linda, Prichard Kymen Inc. (R), AB, *168*

RECRUITER SPECIALTIES

Weiss, Ronald, The BMW Group, Inc. (C), NY, *268*
West, Paul A., West & West (R), CA, *218*
Wilder, Ben, A. E. Feldman Assoc., Inc. (C), NY, *339*
Willden, Vincent G. B., Coast Personnel Services Ltd. (C), BC, *293*
Winnewisser, William E., Accounting & Computer Personnel (C), NY, *238*
Witt, Gerald E., The Witt Group (C), FL, *623*
Wittlin, Brian D., Brian Assoc., Inc. (C), NY, *273*
Wylie, John L., John Wylie Assoc., Inc. (C), OK, *625*
Young, Wayne T., Management Recruiters of Morris County, NJ (C), NJ, *453*
Zilliacus, Patrick W., Larsen, Whitney, Blecksmith & Zilliacus, Inc. (R), CA, *125*
Zillifro, Keith, Management Recruiters of Roanoke (C), VA, *465*

Technicians

Cole, Floyd, National Field Service Corp. (C), NY, *489*
Hayward, Robert M., National Field Service Corp. (C), NY, *489*
Hirnikel, L. J., Orion Int'l. Consulting Group, Inc. (C), OH, *500*
Lalagos, Dee, DEL Technical Services, Inc. (C), IL, *310*
Nelson, Randy, Orion Int'l. Consulting Group, Inc. (C), NC, *499*
Price, Velinda Hodge, Price & Assoc., Inc. (C), VA, *518*
Raney, Albert, Dunhill Personnel Service of Fargo (C), ND, *322*
Simkanin, Christine, Michael J. Hall & Co. (R), WA, *85*

Technology

Anderson, Dean, Corporate Resources Professional Placement (C), MN, *301*
Anderson, Gregory D., Anderson Industrial Assoc., Inc. (C), GA, *250*
Andrews, Pamela J., LAI Ward Howell (R), IL, *123*
Ardi, Dana B., LAI Ward Howell (R), CA, *123*
Ayers, Jr., William L., The Ayers Group, Inc. (R), NY, *10*
Baker, Jake A., Allen Austin Lowe & Powers (R), TX, *3*
Ballach, Allen, Allen Ballach Assoc. Inc. (R), ON, *10*
Barrett, Barbara, Access Assoc. Inc. (C), MD, *233*
Bass, Rebecca, Johnson Smith & Knisely (R), GA, *107*
Bell, Nancy, Professional Recruiters (C), UT, *522*
Bellano, Robert W., cFour Partners (R), CA, *32*
Birarda, Richard W., JSG Group Management Consultants (R), ON, *109*
Brian, Brad, Professional Recruiters (C), UT, *522*
Brian, Waylon, Professional Recruiters (C), UT, *522*
Bussey, Sharon, The Center for Career Advancement, LLC (C), NJ, *287*
Butterfield, N. Blair, Butterfield & Co. Int'l., Inc. (C), HI, *277*
Cahill, Peter, Cahill Assoc. (C), CT, *279*
Cantus, Jane-Scott, Christian & Timbers, Inc. (R), VA, *34*
Cesafsky, Barry R., LAI Ward Howell (R), IL, *123*
Champion, Geoffrey, Korn/Ferry Int'l. (R), CA, *117*
Clemons, Jani, Robert Shields & Assoc. (C), TX, *538*
Conlin, Edward T., Allen Austin Lowe & Powers (R), TX, *3*
Corey, Patrick M., LAI Ward Howell (R), WI, *124*
Corrales, Shaun, cFour Partners (R), CA, *32*
Courtney, Brendan, Interim Financial Solutions - Mid-Atlantic Region (C), MD, *392*
Craig, Randy H., J. Fielding Nelson & Assoc., Inc. (R), UT, *151*
Crane, Howard C., LAI Ward Howell (R), CA, *123*
Davidson, Julie, Drinkwater & Assoc. (R), MA, *55*
Desmond, Mike, Newcomb-Desmond & Assoc., Inc. (C), OH, *492*
Dillon, Larry, Johnson Smith & Knisely (R), CA, *107*
Drinkwater, Wendy A., Drinkwater & Assoc. (R), MA, *54*
Duncan, Gail, Careers First, Inc. (C), NJ, *283*
Edwards, Charles R., LAI Ward Howell (R), GA, *123*
Ehrenzeller, Tony, Management Recruiters of Fairfax, VA (C), VA, *464*
Eidelberg, Larry, Bert Davis Publishing Placement Consultants (C), NY, *309*
Eisenborg, Franci, Professional Recruiters (C), UT, *522*
Epstein, Kathy J., LAI Ward Howell (R), MA, *123*
Erikson, Theodore J., Erikson Consulting Assoc., Inc. (R), NY, *60*
Esecson, Diane P., Drinkwater & Assoc. (R), MA, *55*
Fitzpatrick, Susan, Management Recruiters of Milwaukee - Downtown (C), WI, *466*
Forbes, Kathy, The Forbes Group (R), GA, *69*
Fox, Allis, Intersource, Ltd. (R), GA, *103*
Frankovich, John, BRW Search (C), MN, *275*
Gallagher, Kelly, K2 Resources, L.P. (C), CT, *402*
Gamboa, Victor, Quest Worldwide Executive Search Corp. (C), CA, *527*
Garcia, Abel, Allen Austin Lowe & Powers (R), TX, *3*
Gauger, Dianne, Dianne Gauger & Assoc. (C), CA, *355*
Goldsmith, Fred J., Fred J. Goldsmith Assoc. (R), CA, *79*
Hangartner, Robin, Intersource, Ltd. (R), GA, *103*
Heath, Jeffrey A., The Landstone Group (C), NY, *412*
Heffelfinger, Thomas V., Heffelfinger Assoc., Inc. (R), MA, *89*
Hershman, Arnold, Holohan Group, Ltd. (R), MO, *95*
Hockett, Bill, Hockett Associates, Inc. (R), CA, *94*
Houchins, William C. Buster, Christian & Timbers, Inc. (R), MD, *34*
Hoyda, Louis A., Thorndike Deland Assoc. LLC (R), NY, *48*
Ingram, Spencer, Johnson Smith & Knisely (R), CT, *107*
Jenkins, Virginia L., The Center for Career Advancement (C), MD, *287*
Jordan, Lewis James, The Executive Tree (R), FL, *64*
Kaplan, Alan J., Kaplan & Assoc., Inc. (R), PA, *109*
Kaplan, Bittian, Brentwood Int'l. (R), CA, *23*
Kaufman, Susan, Kaufman Assoc. (R), CA, *110*
Kendrick, M. Steven, LAI Ward Howell (R), TX, *124*
Knotts, Jerry, MIXTEC Group (R), CA, *145*
Konstans, Gregory C., LAI Ward Howell (R), TX, *124*
Kooyman, Dave, Professional Recruiters (C), UT, *522*
Kors, Paul, cFour Partners (R), TX, *32*
Kurtz, Sheldon I., Kurtz Pro-Search, Inc. (C), NJ, *410*
Lambert, Judith A., EDI, Inc. (C), MD, *326*
Lanctot, Bill, Corporate Resources Professional Placement (C), MN, *301*
Landon, Susan J., LAI Ward Howell (R), NY, *122*
Langley, Ted, Jaeger Int'l., Inc. (C), OH, *396*
Larkin, Dick, Larkin & Co. (R), CA, *125*
Latini, Anthony A., Princeton Search Partners, Inc. (R), NJ, *169*
Lawrence, Ellen B., Holohan Group, Ltd. (R), MO, *95*
Ledbetter, Charlene, Ledbetter/Davidson Int'l., Inc. (R), NY, *127*
Lewis, Marc D., Handy HRM (R), NY, *86*
Lombardo, Steve, Search America, Inc. (C), MA, *574*
Macaluso, Kelly, K2 Resources, L.P. (C), CT, *402*
MacBean, Paul, Technical Skills Consulting Inc. (R), ON, *207*
Mars, Roxanne, Technical Skills Consulting Inc. (R), ON, *207*
Martin, Suzanne, The Beam Group (R), PA, *14*
Matson, Erik W., LAI Ward Howell (R), NY, *122*
McCloskey, Frank, DHR Int'l., Inc. (R), IL, *49*

McCormick, Gregg J., Retained Search Assoc. (R), NC, *176*
McElroy, Brian, Drinkwater & Assoc. (R), MA, *55*
McNahan, Rod, Foster Partners (R), TX, *71*
Mock, Lora Lea, Professional Recruiters (C), UT, *522*
Moore, Lynda, Professional Recruiters (C), UT, *522*
Moreno, Melissa, Johnson Smith & Knisely (R), CT, *107*
Morganti, Ray, Romac Int'l., Inc. (C), FL, *543*
Moses, Brad, Information Systems Professionals (C), NC, *388*
Nehring, Sara, Johnson Smith & Knisely (R), IL, *107*
Neiman, Jennifer, Brentwood Int'l. (R), CA, *23*
Nitchke, Howard, Johnson Smith & Knisely (R), CA, *107*
Nosky, Richard E., LAI Ward Howell (R), AZ, *123*
Obrand, Barry, Russell Reynolds Assoc., Inc. (R), CA, *176*
Otsuka, Fyllis L., Holohan Group, Ltd. (R), MO, *95*
Pallman-David, Cynthia, Bonnell Assoc. Ltd. (R), CT, *19*
Palmlund, III, David W., LAI Ward Howell (R), TX, *124*
Papayanopulos, Manuel, Korn/Ferry, Int'l., S.A. de C.V. (R), MX, *118*
Parenica, Jim, Parenica & Co. (R), NC, *159*
Pezim, Steven G., The Bedford Consulting Group Inc. (R), ON, *15*
Picard, Daniel A., Picard Int'l., Ltd. (R), NY, *164*
Poe, James B., Nagler, Robins & Poe, Inc. (R), MA, *150*
Price, Alan J., Alan J. Price Assoc., Inc. (C), RI, *518*
Pryor, Carrie Looms, LAI Ward Howell (R), NY, *123*
Ratts, K. Wayne, Holohan Group, Ltd. (R), MO, *95*
Reiser, Ellen, Thorndike Deland Assoc. LLC (R), NY, *48*
Ribeiro, Claudia, Ledbetter/Davidson Int'l., Inc. (R), NY, *127*
Rossi, Alfred F., The Rossi Search Group (C), PA, *545*
Rothschild, John S., LAI Ward Howell (R), IL, *123*
Rotter, Stephen, RSMR, Inc. (R), IL, *182*
Rueppel, Melvin L., Holohan Group, Ltd. (R), MO, *95*
Salottolo, Al, Tactical Alternatives (R), CA, *205*
Santamaria, Jay, The Beam Group (R), NY, *14*
Schneider, Steven A., Schneider, Hill & Spangler, Inc. (R), PA, *185*
Schrenzel, Steven N., The Governance Group, Inc. (R), NJ, *80*
Schwartz, Vince, Johnson Smith & Knisely (R), IL, *107*
Searing, James M., Korn/Ferry Int'l. (R), VA, *118*
Setford, George, Setford-Shaw-Najarian Assoc. (C), NY, *579*
Settles, Barbara Z., LAI Ward Howell (R), TX, *124*
Shay, David, cFour Partners (R), CA, *32*
Sheiko, Michele, The Park Group & Assoc., Inc. (C), MD, *503*
Shimp, David J., LAI Ward Howell (R), IL, *123*
Shulman, Mel, M. Shulman, Inc. (R), CA, *191*
Simon, Robert, Johnson Smith & Knisely (R), CT, *107*
Stepler, Paul, Gallin Associates of Naples, FL (C), FL, *354*
Stow, Ralph P., Page-Wheatcroft & Co., Ltd. (R), TX, *158*
Swann, Al, The Beam Group (R), NY, *14*
Swartz, William K., Swartz & Assoc., Inc. (R), AZ, *204*
Sweet, Robert J., Atlanta Executive Partners, Inc. (R), MA, *8*
Tambor, Morris, Reynolds Consulting Int'l. (R), ON, *177*
Tazzia, Ed, Gundersen Partners, L.L.C. (R), MI, *83*
Thompson, Kelvin, Norman Broadbent Int'l., Inc. (R), CA, *152*
Trowbridge, Robert L., Trowbridge & Co., Inc. (R), MA, *211*
Uhrig, Scott, LAI Ward Howell (R), TX, *124*
Ullstein, Ashley B., Drinkwater & Assoc. (R), MA, *55*
Venable, William, Thorndike Deland Assoc. LLC (R), NY, *48*
Watkins, Jeffrey P., LAI Ward Howell (R), GA, *123*
Watson, Jim, MSI Int'l. (C), GA, *487*
Wayne, Vici, Christian & Timbers, Inc. (R), OH, *34*
Willbanks, Bret, TTG/Sterling Services (C), CA, *610*
Williams, Bob, Information Systems Professionals (C), NC, *388*
Wilson, Denver, Sales Consultants of Northwest Arkansas, Inc. (C), AR, *556*
Yackel, Doug, Management Recruiters of Spokane (C), WA, *465*
Zinn, Michael D., Michael D. Zinn & Assoc., Inc. (R), NJ, *227*

Telecommunications

Ames, George C., Ames-O'Neill Assoc., Inc. (C), NY, *249*
Ansara, Peter, Ansara, Bickford & Fiske (C), MA, *251*
Arcand, Arthur J., Tech 2000 (C), FL, *601*
Ashton, Barbara L., Ashton Computer Professionals, Inc. (C), BC, *253*
Ashton, Neil K., Sales Consultants of Bangor, Inc. (C), ME, *559*
Austin, Cami, Cami Austin & Assoc. (C), IL, *256*
Baez, Ana Luisa, Sales Consultants of Ft. Myers, Inc. (C), FL, *557*
Bailey, Jerald W., Dunhill Professional Search of Greater New Orleans (C), LA, *321*
Bakehorn, Thomas, Martin Stevens Tamaren & Assoc., Inc. (R), CA, *206*
Baker, Charles D., Corporate Staffing Group, Inc. (C), PA, *301*
Baker, Chet, Diversified Consulting Services, Inc. (C), CO, *313*
Baker, Lynette, Management Recruiters Int'l.-The Woodlands (C), TX, *464*
Barker, Thomas E., EBA Group (R), NJ, *56*
Barr, Sharon A., Barr Assoc. (C), PA, *259*
Barrow, Dan J., The Regency Group, Ltd. (C), NE, *533*
Bartchak, Thomas, Telequest Communications, Inc. (C), NJ, *605*
Bavli, Mark, Tech Consulting (C), FL, *601*
Bishop, Susan, Bishop Partners (R), NY, *17*
Boate, Mike, Tanner & Assoc., Inc. (R), TX, *206*
Bogue, Randall L., TBC, Inc. (C), KY, *600*
Borkenhagen, Christine, Morgan Samuels Co. (R), CA, *147*
Born, Al, Electronic Search, Inc. (C), IL, *328*
Bornholdt, John, Bornholdt Shivas & Friends Executive Recruiters (C), NY, *270*
Bratland, A. J., Bratland & Assoc. (C), IL, *272*
Brodersen, Mark K., Sales Consultants of Omaha, Inc. (C), NE, *560*
Buckwald, Brett, The Worth Group (C), GA, *625*
Buonavita, Tina, Adam-Bryce Inc. (C), NY, *239*
Burgess, Rick, Human Resource Dimensions, Inc. (C), TX, *384*
Calder, Darryl, The Silicon Network (C), ON, *581*
Campbell, Robert Scott, Wellington Management Group (R), PA, *217*
Cantus, Jane-Scott, Christian & Timbers, Inc. (R), VA, *34*
Capanna, Patricia A., Management Recruiters of Madison, Inc. (C), WI, *466*
Carey, Cameron, Computer Security Placement Service (C), MA, *296*
Carey, Laurie B., Corporate Staffing Group, Inc. (C), PA, *301*
Carpenter, Edward, Executive Search of America, Inc. (C), OH, *336*
Cepull, Janeen, Elite Consultants, Inc. (C), FL, *328*
Chaffin, Denise M., Professional Team Search, Inc. (R), AZ, *169*
Cimino, Ron, Paul-Tittle Assoc., Inc. (R), VA, *161*
Clancey, Darcie, Broadband Resource Group (C), CA, *274*
Clancey, Mark, Broadband Resource Group (C), CA, *274*
Clark, John Edward, Management Recruiters of Altamonte (C), FL, *442*
Clarke, Debra, NMC & Kay Int'l. (R), CO, *152*
Coe, Karen, Coe & Co. Int'l. Inc./EMA Partners Int'l. (R), AB, *37*

RECRUITER SPECIALTIES

Coltrane, Mike, Richard, Wayne & Roberts (C), AZ, *536*
Connelly, Laura, Management Recruiters of Pittsburgh (C), PA, *459*
Cooper, Larry, Management Recruiters of Atlanta (C), GA, *445*
Cooper, Liz, The Beardsley Group Inc. (C), CT, *261*
Corrales, Shaun, cFour Partners (R), CA, *32*
Cowlishaw, Ronnette, Sales Consultants of Denver (C), CO, *557*
Crane, Howard C., LAI Ward Howell (R), CA, *123*
Crigler, James, Management Recruiters of Winona (C), MN, *452*
Cropp, Wes, Management Recruiters of Franktown (C), CO, *442*
Crowell, Kimberly D., Grant/Morgan Assoc., Inc. (C), MD, *361*
Crowley, David G., DSR-Search & Recruitment (C), TX, *315*
Curry, Joseph, MediaCOM Talent Group (C), MA, *477*
Daniels, Donna, Jonas, Walters & Assoc., Inc. (R), WI, *108*
Dansky, Ellen, Telequest Communications, Inc. (C), NJ, *605*
deMartino, Cathy, Lucas Assoc. (C), GA, *421*
DePhillipo, William R., Tele-Media Int'l. Inc. (C), PA, *604*
Dermady, Timothy J., ExecutiveFit (C), NY, *337*
DeRose, Rick, Telecom Executive Group (C), NJ, *605*
Dicicco, Benjamin, McCoy Ltd. (C), CA, *474*
Dietrich, Sandra, Fortune Personnel Consultants of Hilton Head (C), SC, *349*
DiLorenzo, Matthew B., The Inside Track (C), TX, *389*
Donovan, Jerry, Management Recruiters of Arlington (C), VA, *464*
Dorst, Martin, Dorst Information Services, Inc. (C), NY, *314*
Dreier, John S., Dreier Consulting (C), NJ, *315*
Dromeshauser, Peter, Dromeshauser Assoc. (R), MA, *55*
Du Ket, David R., New Venture Development, Inc. (C), CA, *492*
Duncan, Laura, Management Recruiters - Indianapolis (C), IN, *448*
Ehrenreich, Lisa C., Greenhaven & Assoc., Inc. (R), NY, *81*
Ellis, James, Sanford Rose Assoc. - Lake St. Louis (C), MO, *568*
Ellis, James P., Ellis & Associates (C), HI, *328*
Ellis, Mitch, Sanford Rose Assoc. - Lake St. Louis (C), MO, *568*
Endres, Devlin, Allstaff, Inc. (C), IL, *245*
Engler, Christine, CEO Consulting (C), FL, *287*
Epstein, Robert G., RGE (C), VA, *535*
Ertaud, Wilfrid, MediaCOM Talent Group (C), MA, *477*
Everett, Jim, EA Plus, Inc. (C), TX, *325*
Faucher, Cornel, Sink, Walker, Boltrus Int'l. (R), MA, *192*
Feldman, Mitchell, A. E. Feldman Assoc., Inc. (C), NY, *339*
Fell, III, John R., Howe & Assoc. (R), PA, *97*
Fischer, Howard, Howard Fischer Assoc. Int'l., Inc. (R), PA, *67*
Fischer, Howard, Howard Fischer Assoc. Int'l., Inc. (R), TX, *67*
Fisher, Neal, PPS Information Systems Staffing (C), MD, *515*
Fishkin, Anita, A. G. Fishkin & Assoc., Inc. (R), MD, *68*
Fitzgerald, Matthew A., Telecom Recruiters, Inc. (C), VA, *605*
Fitzgerald, Thomas L., Telecom Recruiters, Inc. (C), VA, *605*
Fitzpatrick, John, Newport Strategic Search LLC (C), CA, *492*
Forbes, Catherine M., StratfordGroup (R), CO, *203*
Fossett, Gary J., John Michael Assoc. (R), DC, *106*
Gaffney, William M., Teknon Employment Resources, Inc. (C), OH, *604*
Gilson, Dirk S., Key Resources Int'l. (C), CA, *406*
Gorberg, Richard D., Fortune Personnel Consultants of Raleigh, Inc. (C), NC, *348*
Gordon, Dave, Cemco, Ltd. (C), IL, *287*
Goyette, Marc, ROI International, Inc. (R), WA, *181*
Goyette, Margo, ROI International, Inc. (R), WA, *181*
Graham, Lesley, JPM International (C), CA, *401*
Gray, Russell, Johnson Smith & Knisely (R), GA, *107*
Griesedieck, Jr., Joseph E., SpencerStuart (R), CA, *196*
Griffith, Doug, Caywood Partners, Ltd. (R), CA, *32*
Gross, Jerry, Creative HR Solutions (C), GA, *303*
Guerin, Michael R., Michael R. Guerin Co. (C), CA, *364*
Hall, Elizabeth, Bason Associates (R), OH, *13*
Hall, Scott, Advancement, Inc. (C), IL, *241*
Harlan, James, Management Recruiters of Franktown (C), CO, *442*
Harmon, Jerry, Delta Resource Group, Ltd. (C), GA, *311*
Harper, Deborah, Harper Hewes, Inc. (C), NY, *369*
Harris, T. J., Sales Consultants of Ft. Myers, Inc. (C), FL, *557*
Harris, Thomas E., Sales Consultants of Ft. Myers, Inc. (C), FL, *557*
Harvey, Arnold D., PSP Agency (C), NY, *525*
Hawksworth, A. Dwight, A. D. & Assoc. Executive Search, Inc. (C), GA, *231*
Headden, Jr., William P., Headden Assoc. (R), WA, *88*
Hebert, Chris, Management Recruiters of Nassau, Inc. (R), NY, *134*
Hechkoff, Robert B., Hechkoff/Work Executive Search Inc. (R), NY, *89*
Heinschel, Phil, Phillips Personnel/Search (C), CO, *510*
Hendelman, Peter R., P.R.H. Management, Inc. (R), CT, *158*
Hertz, Al, Carter/MacKay (C), NC, *285*
Hilles, Jeffrey W., Williams & Delmore, Inc. (C), NC, *621*
Hinkle, Alfred, Renaissance Resources, LLC (R), VA, *174*
Ho, John, Management Recruiters of Chanhassen (C), MN, *452*
Hoffman, Adele, The Beardsley Group Inc. (C), CT, *261*
Hoffman, Brian, Sales Consultants of Rockville, MD (C), MD, *559*
Hoffman, Theresa E., Wellington Management Group (R), PA, *217*
Hurtubise, Jean Pierre, Reynolds Consulting Int'l. (R), QE, *177*
Jacobson, Priscilla, Tech Connector Group (C), CA, *601*
James, Chip, Morgan Samuels Co. (R), CA, *147*
Jensen, Christine, John Kurosky & Assoc. (R), CA, *122*
Johnson, Jennifer, JenKim Int'l. Ltd., Inc. (C), FL, *398*
Jones, Roberta, Tech 2000 (C), FL, *601*
Junker, Sherry, Bolton Group (C), CA, *269*
Kaplan, Alan J., Kaplan & Assoc., Inc. (R), PA, *109*
Karkow, Drew, David Weinfeld Group (C), NC, *617*
Karson, Allan, Allan Karson Assoc., Inc. (R), NJ, *110*
Kelly, Elizabeth Ann, Wellington Management Group (R), PA, *217*
King, Gail, Management Recruiters of Tampa North (C), FL, *444*
King, Gary, Sales Consultants of Tampa North, Inc. (C), FL, *557*
King, Karl, Capital Consulting Group, Inc. (R), MD, *28*
Kinney, Sandy, Executive Search Consultants Corp. (C), IL, *335*
Kling, Constance W., LAI Ward Howell (R), IL, *123*
Koch, Gail Kleinberg, CAS Comsearch Inc. (C), NY, *286*
Koellhoffer, Thomas J., T. J. Koellhoffer & Assoc. (R), NJ, *116*
Kors, Paul, cFour Partners (R), TX, *32*
Krautler, William, Krautler Personnel Recruitment (C), FL, *409*
Kreutz, Gary L., Kreutz Consulting Group, Inc. (R), IL, *121*
Krochenski, Caren, Management Recruiters Int'l.-The Woodlands (C), TX, *464*
Ku, Theresa, Sanford Rose Assoc. - Anaheim (C), CA, *566*
Kulper, Keith D., Kulper & Co., L.L.C. (R), NJ, *121*
LaBarge-Wilson, Cynthia, Largent Parks & Partners (C), TX, *503*
Labrecque, B. F., Ray & Berndtson/Laurendeau Labrecque (R), QE, *172*

LaCosta, Paul, LaCosta & Assoc. Int'l. Inc. (C), CA, *411*

Laks, Naomi, Adam-Bryce Inc. (C), NY, *239*

Lane, Douglas, Management Recruiters of Milwaukee - Downtown (C), WI, *466*

Laresen, Rolph, The Silicon Network (C), ON, *581*

Larry, Melvin P., ExecuSource Assoc., Inc. (C), GA, *332*

Laub, Stuart R., Abraham & London Ltd. (C), CT, *232*

Laufersweiler, Steve, PIC Executive Search (C), GA, *511*

Lawrence, Gina, Micro Staff Solutions, Inc. (C), TX, *481*

Lawrence, James B., The Hamilton Group (R), VA, *85*

Lawry, William R., W. R. Lawry, Inc. (R), CT, *126*

Lechtenberg, Richard C., Dick Berg & Assoc. (C), CA, *264*

Lee, Barbara A., Management Recruiters, Inc. (C), FL, *443*

Legal, Dale, Capital Consulting Group, Inc. (R), MD, *28*

Leone, Joan, The Beardsley Group Inc. (C), CT, *261*

Levitt, Peter, Sales Consultants King of Prussia (C), PA, *562*

Lewis, Marc, Christian & Timbers, Inc. (R), OH, *34*

Licht, Marilyn, Management Recruiters - Indianapolis (C), IN, *448*

Lynch, J. F., Management Recruiters of Lionville, Inc. (C), PA, *459*

Mader, Stephen P., Christian & Timbers, Inc. (R), MA, *34*

Mader, Steve, Christian & Timbers, Inc. (R), OH, *34*

Maher, Kevin, TBC, Inc. (C), KY, *600*

Manni, Tom, Electronic Search, Inc. (C), NJ, *328*

Marentez, Frank, Marentz & Co. (C), TX, *469*

Marshall, Dennis, L O R (R), NJ, *122*

Marshall, E. Leigh, Johnson Smith & Knisely (R), NJ, *107*

Marshall, Paul M., Management Recruiters of Stevens Point, Inc. (C), WI, *466*

Mason, Maurice, McCray, Shriver, Eckdahl & Assoc., Inc. (R), CA, *140*

Mather, David, Christian & Timbers, Inc. (R), OH, *34*

Mather, David R., Christian & Timbers, Inc. (R), CA, *34*

McCabe, William, Allstaff, Inc. (C), IL, *245*

McCann, Mary Ellen, Wellington Management Group (R), PA, *217*

McCormack, Kathy, The Beardsley Group Inc. (C), CT, *261*

McDowell, John, McDowell & Co., Recruiters (C), TX, *474*

McGinty, Kevin, The Silicon Network (C), ON, *581*

McIntyre, Jeffrey F., McIntyre Assoc. (R), CT, *141*

McMillan, Dwight, Management Recruiters of Atlanta NE (C), GA, *446*

Mielcarek, Kevin, The NEIS Corp., Inc. (C), FL, *491*

Miller, John, Electronic Search, Inc. (C), CA, *328*

Milton, Charles E., Smith James Group, Inc. (R), GA, *194*

Mogul, Gene, Mogul Consultants, Inc. (C), NY, *483*

Mole, Norman, DSR-Search & Recruitment (C), TX, *315*

Morse, Mary K., Travis & Co., Inc. (R), MA, *210*

Moses, Brad, Information Systems Professionals (C), NC, *388*

Mott, Alex, Headden Assoc. (R), WA, *88*

Nelson, Len, Len Nelson & Assoc., Inc. (C), TX, *491*

Newell, Beverly, The Beardsley Group Inc. (C), CT, *261*

Newman, Keith, W. Robert Eissler & Assoc., Inc. (C), TX, *327*

Nickels, Edward L., Michael Latas & Assoc., Inc. (R), MO, *126*

Nicolosi, Charles, CN Associates (C), CA, *293*

Niedbalski, Michael, Executive Search Plus, Inc. (C), IN, *336*

Nigro, Marci Yacker, Telecom Executive Group (C), NY, *605*

Norman, Paul W., Paul Winston Norman & Assoc. (R), IL, *152*

Norton, Kim, JenKim Int'l. Ltd., Inc. (C), FL, *398*

Norton, Robert W., JenKim Int'l. Ltd., Inc. (C), FL, *398*

O'Maley, Kimberlee, SpencerStuart (R), CA, *196*

Orr, George H., Telecom Connections, Inc. (C), TX, *604*

Ozoroski, Tom, Barr Assoc. (C), PA, *259*

Panchella, Joseph J., Wellington Management Group (R), PA, *217*

Parenica, Jim, Parenica & Co. (R), NC, *159*

Patterson, Brenda, Management Recruiters - Indianapolis (C), IN, *448*

Pearson, A. B., Sales Consultants of Concord (C), NC, *554*

Pearson, Anna Lee, Sales Consultants of Concord (C), NC, *554*

Pearson, Robert L., LAI Ward Howell (R), TX, *124*

Perry, James A., Strategic Executives, Inc. (R), IL, *202*

Piché, Jérôme, SpencerStuart (R), QE, *197*

Plappert, James F., Sales Consultants of Newtown, Inc. (C), PA, *562*

Poole, Don V., Don V. Poole & Assoc., Inc. (C), CO, *514*

Poriotis, Wesley, Wesley Brown & Bartle Co., Inc. (R), NY, *218*

Prencipe, Michael, Raymond Karsan Assoc. (C), VA, *530*

Putnam, Denise, Elite Consultants, Inc. (C), FL, *328*

Ragan, William E., Michael Latas & Assoc., Inc. (R), MO, *126*

Rana, Julie B., HR Advantage, Inc. (C), VA, *382*

Ranta, Ed, J. E. Ranta Assoc. (C), MA, *529*

Ratliff, Steve, GateSource Partners (C), VA, *355*

Reiss, Phyllis, Adam-Bryce Inc. (C), NY, *239*

Richards, Christos, Stanton Chase Int'l. (R), CA, *199*

Richman, Jack, Jack Richman & Assoc. (C), FL, *537*

Robertson, Janice, Tele-Solutions of Arizona, Inc. (C), AZ, *604*

Rodriguez, Steven, SpencerStuart (R), CA, *196*

Rolland, Guy, Rolland Ressources Humaines Inc. (R), QE, *181*

Rooney, Joseph J., Rooney Assoc., Inc. (R), IL, *181*

Roscoe, Harry, The Beardsley Group Inc. (C), CT, *261*

Rosenblum, Al, The Worth Group (C), NY, *625*

Ross, Larry, The Summit Group (C), CA, *596*

Rowell, Mike, Carter/MacKay (C), MA, *285*

Rubin, Nadine, Adam-Bryce Inc. (C), NY, *239*

Rudolph, Lee, Management Recruiters of Franktown (C), CO, *442*

Salfi, James P., Ritta Professional Search Inc. (C), NY, *538*

Schene, Philip, A. E. Feldman Assoc., Inc. (C), NY, *339*

Schlesinger, Dawn, The Quantum Group (C), NJ, *527*

Schmidt, Susan, David Weinfeld Group (C), NC, *617*

Schneider, Thomas P., WTW Assoc., Inc. (R), NY, *225*

Schoff, Frank J., Management Recruiters of Cedar Mountain (C), NC, *455*

Schwam, Carol, A. E. Feldman Assoc., Inc. (C), NY, *339*

Schwartz, Raymond, The Partnership Group (R), NJ, *160*

Scott, E. Ann, Scott Executive Search, Inc. (R), NY, *186*

Searing, James M., Korn/Ferry Int'l. (R), VA, *118*

Shelton, L., American Executive Management, Inc. (R), MA, *5*

Sheth, Pinakini, Software Resource Consultants (C), TN, *587*

Shinn, Michael, Shinn & Assoc. (R), CA, *189*

Shufelt, Douglas G., Sink, Walker, Boltrus Int'l. (R), MA, *192*

Sink, Clifton W., Sink, Walker, Boltrus Int'l. (R), TX, *192*

Smith, David P., HRS, Inc. (R), PA, *97*

Smith, Gregory K., Global Technologies Group Inc. (C), NC, *359*

Smith, Stacy, Smith James Group, Inc. (R), GA, *194*

Smith, Wilton, The Stark Wilton Group (R), MI, *199*

RECRUITER SPECIALTIES

Snow, Christine, C. Snow & Assoc. (C), ON, *586*
Sparks, Michele Benum, Micro Staff Solutions, Inc. (C), TX, *481*
Sparks, Michele Benum, The Alternatives Group, Inc. (C), TX, *246*
Sparks, Jr., R. Thomas, Sparks, McDonough & Assoc., Inc. (C), MO, *588*
Stefunek, Paul C., StratfordGroup (R), OH, *203*
Stelika, Kit, Southport Int'l. Assoc. Inc. (C), FL, *588*
Stepler, Paul, Gallin Associates of Naples, FL (C), FL, *354*
Steuer, Ira, Cemco, Ltd. (C), MO, *287*
Stevens, Martin, Martin Stevens Tamaren & Assoc., Inc. (R), CA, *206*
Stewart, F. Colleen, Johnson Smith & Knisely (R), GA, *107*
Stone, Susan L., Stone Enterprises Ltd. (C), IL, *594*
Stover, Bruce, StratfordGroup (R), CO, *203*
Sweet, Robert J., Atlanta Executive Partners, Inc. (R), MA, *8*
Tang, Cliff, Wood West & Partners Inc. (C), BC, *624*
Tarquinio, Alfred, Sales Consultants of Butler County (C), PA, *561*
Taylor, Patricia, Smartsource Inc. (C), CA, *583*
Thibault, Elaine, Adam-Bryce Inc. (C), NY, *239*
Timoney, Laura, Bishop Partners (R), NY, *17*
Trapani, Chris, ExecuSource Consultants, Inc. (C), TX, *332*
Trapani, Delores, ExecuSource Consultants, Inc. (C), TX, *332*
Treadaway, Van, Van Treadaway Assoc., Inc. (R), GA, *210*
Upton, Noreen, The Beardsley Group Inc. (C), CT, *261*
Vandegrift, Tom, Kiley, Owen & McGovern, Inc. (R), NJ, *114*
Vann, Dianne, Button Group (C), TX, *277*
Venditti, Paul, The Stewart Group (C), FL, *593*
Vermillion, Michael, Management Recruiters of Des Moines (C), IA, *449*
Walsh, John, J. D. Walsh & Co. (R), CT, *215*
Walsh, Patty, Abraham & London Ltd. (C), CT, *232*
Walters, William F., Jonas, Walters & Assoc., Inc. (R), WI, *107*
Walton, Craig, Management Recruiters of San Marcos (C), TX, *463*
Waltz, B., Ki Technologies, Inc. (C), UT, *406*
Warren, Deborah, Management Recruiters of Lubbock (C), TX, *463*
Wasserman, Harvey, Churchill & Affiliates, Inc. (R), PA, *35*
Weber, Janette, Management Recruiters of Des Moines (C), IA, *449*
Webster, Bruce, Sales Consultants of Milwaukee (C), WI, *563*
Weinfeld, David C., David Weinfeld Group (C), NC, *617*
West, Fred, Wood West & Partners Inc. (C), BC, *624*
Wichansky, Carole, Tele-Solutions of Arizona, Inc. (C), AZ, *604*
Wilkson, James, Allen Austin Lowe & Powers (R), TX, *3*
Williams, Bob, Information Systems Professionals (C), NC, *388*
Wimmer, Walter, The Silicon Network (C), ON, *581*
Wisnewski, Edward J., Wisnewski & Assoc. (R), CA, *223*
Wood, Ron, Wood West & Partners Inc. (C), BC, *624*
Woods, Bruce Gilbert, Bruce G. Woods Executive Search (R), TX, *224*
Wysocki, Robert, Cornell Group Int'l. Consulting, Inc. (R), NY, *41*
York, Felecia, Human Resource Dimensions, Inc. (C), TX, *384*
Young, Dennis F., Tell/Com Recruiters (C), PA, *605*
Young, Susan M., Management Recruiters of Morris County, NJ (C), NJ, *453*
Young, William H., Bill Young & Assoc. (C), VA, *626*
Zabeli, Agim, Barr Assoc. (C), PA, *259*

Telemarketing

Caroli, Connie, TeleManagement Search (C), NY, *605*
Harragan, James K., Management Recruiters of Gramercy, Inc. (C), NY, *455*
Peragine, Ralph, The Resource Group (R), CT, *175*
Peragine, Ralph P., The Resource Group (R), CT, *175*

Telephony

Bell, Dixie Lee, MIS Computer Professionals, Inc. (C), KS, *482*
Capps, Norm, MIS Computer Professionals, Inc. (C), KS, *482*
Chalmers, Lynda, Delta Management Group Ltd. (C), ON, *310*
Cropp, Wes, Management Recruiters of Franktown (C), CO, *442*
Kohn, Adam, Christian & Timbers, Inc. (R), OH, *34*
LaCosta, Paul, LaCosta & Assoc. Int'l. Inc. (C), CA, *411*
Madison, T. Dean, Warren, Morris & Madison, Ltd. (C), VA, *616*
Ratliff, Steve, GateSource Partners (C), VA, *355*

Television

Bege, Lorraine, Hands-on Broadcast (R), NY, *86*
DeLuca, Matthew J., Management Resource Group, Inc. (C), NY, *467*
Faller, Laura McGrath, Redden & McGrath Assoc., Inc. (R), NY, *173*
Saracen, Robert R., The Libra Group Inc. (C), CT, *417*

Temporary

Anderson, Jeff, Raymond Karsan Assoc. (C), PA, *530*
Atkinson, S. Graham, Raymond Karsan Assoc. (C), NY, *530*
Berger, Joel, Meridian Legal Search/Legal Temps (C), NY, *479*
Cohen, Jeff, Rice Cohen Int'l. (R), PA, *178*
Croasdale, J. Scott, Raymond Karsan Assoc. (C), CO, *530*
McCarthy, Debra, Becker Personnel (C), FL, *262*
Pye, Susan, Prescott Legal Search, Inc. (C), TX, *517*
Taraso, Julie, Christmas, McIvor & Assoc. Inc. (C), ON, *290*
Voigt, John A., Partners Resource Group (C), VA, *504*

Test

Deckelbaum, Stan, Fortune Personnel Consultants of Raleigh, Inc. (C), NC, *348*
Kendle, Vernon S., New Venture Development, Inc. (C), CA, *492*

Textiles

Brien, Richard H., Creative Input, Inc. (C), RI, *303*
Chavons, Crawford, Phillips Resource Group (C), SC, *510*
Corwin, J. Blade, Seitchik Corwin & Seitchik Inc. (R), CA, *188*
Glynn, Mary Anne, E. A. Hughes & Co., Inc. (R), NY, *98*
Harshman, Donald, The Stevenson Group, Inc. (N.J.) (R), NJ, *200*
Hill, III, Gabe C., S. P. Assoc., Inc. (C), NC, *550*
Hughes, Elaine A., E. A. Hughes & Co., Inc. (R), NY, *98*
Just, Susan, Just Management Services Inc. (C), FL, *402*
Lord, Marvin, E. A. Hughes & Co., Inc. (R), NY, *98*
Margolin, Robert, Kenn Spinrad Inc. (C), PA, *589*
McIntyre, Joel, Phillips Resource Group (C), NC, *511*
McNeil, Janet, Cook Assoc.,® Inc. (R), IL, *40*
Phillips, Jr., Sam B., Phillips Resource Group (C), SC, *510*
Phillips, Walter, Phillips Int'l., Inc. (C), SC, *510*
Plunkett, Mike, Phillips Resource Group (C), NC, *511*
Presser, Janet, N.A.P. Executive Services (Canada) Inc. (C), QE, *488*
Rothstein, Steve, N.A.P. Executive Services (Canada) Inc. (C), ON, *488*
Sawyer, Pierce, Phillips Resource Group (C), NC, *511*
Seitchik, Jack, Seitchik Corwin & Seitchik Inc. (R), CA, *188*

Seitchik, William, Seitchik Corwin & Seitchik Inc. (R), NY, *188*
Thaler, Brian D., Scott-Thaler Assoc. Agency, Inc. (C), CA, *573*
Tillman, Allen, Hardage Group (C), TN, *369*
Wilson, Wayne, Wilson & Assoc. Int'l. Inc. (C), FL, *622*

Thermoforming

Reyes, Renee, Management Recruiters of Columbia (C), MD, *450*
Wynn, John, Cook Assoc.,® Inc. (R), IL, *40*

Tooling

Grant, Anthony, Management Recruiters of Columbia (C), MD, *450*
Guarniere, John W., RCE Assoc. (R), NJ, *173*

Tourism

O'Malley, Chris, Travel Personnel (C), OH, *609*
Rubin, Karen, Travel Executive Search (C), NY, *608*

Toxicology

Leyden, Terry, Career Marketing Assoc., Inc. (C), CO, *282*

Toys

Boyer, Adrienne, Cook Assoc.,® Inc. (R), IL, *40*
Keoughan, Thomas, The C.P.R. Group (C), NJ, *278*
Lee, Rodger A., Sanford Rose Assoc. - Salt Lake City (C), UT, *571*
Porter, Lindsay, HCI Corp. (C), IL, *371*

Trading

Federman, Jack, W. R. Rosato & Assoc., Inc. (R), NY, *182*
Ray, Jr., Harry, Management Recruiters of Kanawha Valley, LLC (C), WV, *465*

Traffic

McDorman, Terrence, American Logistics Consultants, Inc. (C), IL, *247*

Training

Capecci, Eileen, Rice Cohen Int'l. (R), PA, *178*
Eagar, Brian, Search Int'l. (R), MA, *187*
Kurke, David S., Starbridge Group Inc. (C), VA, *591*
Saunders, Wayne, Lanken-Kimball-Therrell & Assoc. (C), GA, *412*
Vujeec, John, Executive Search, Ltd. (C), OH, *336*

Transportation

Ahrensdorf, Lee, Ahrensdorf & Assoc. (R), PA, *2*
Alvey, Frank, Sage Employment Recruiters (C), IN, *550*
Bailey, David C., Management Recruiters of Lake Tahoe, NV (C), NV, *453*
Bailey, Tom, Snelling Search - Transportation Division (C), AR, *585*
Bauman, Martin H., Martin H. Bauman Assoc., Inc. (R), NY, *13*
Berlet, William, KPMG Executive Search (R), ON, *119*
Brenowitz, Larry, Fortune Personnel Consultants of Greensboro, NC, Inc. (C), NC, *348*
Calale, Paul, Halbrecht & Co. (C), CT, *365*
Collins, Phil, Claremont-Branan, Inc. (C), GA, *292*
Drury, III, James J., SpencerStuart (R), IL, *197*
Erickson-Pearson, David, Boulware & Assoc. Inc. (R), IL, *20*
Evans, Ray, Evans Transportation Search (C), ON, *331*
Harding, Michael W., Shey-Harding Assoc. Inc. (C), CA, *580*
Harlson, Howard, Snelling Search - Transportation Division (C), AR, *585*
Herring, Bill, Herring & Assoc. (C), AR, *376*
Hood, Fred L., Fred Hood & Assoc. (C), CA, *380*
Horne, Tony, Herring & Assoc. (C), AR, *376*
Huebner, Mary C., Hire Authority, Inc. (C), MI, *378*
Kelly, Jim, The LaBorde Group (C), CA, *411*
Kensington, Holland, Kensington International (R), CA, *113*
Kirkendorfer, Laura, The Kingsley Group (R), CA, *115*
Kressenberg, Sammye Jo, Kressenberg Assoc. (C), TX, *409*
LaBorde, John, The LaBorde Group (C), CA, *411*
Larry, Melvin P., ExecuSource Assoc., Inc. (C), GA, *332*
McDorman, Terrence, American Logistics Consultants, Inc. (C), IL, *247*
McGrath, Patrick, Riddle & McGrath LLC (R), GA, *178*
McNamara, Timothy C., Horton Int'l. Inc. (R), MD, *96*
Orlich, Joseph, Hughes & Wilden Assoc. (C), PA, *383*
Parham, Jim, Jim Parham & Assoc., Inc. (R), FL, *159*
Provost, Ed L., Management Recruiters Dana Point (C), CA, *440*
Provost, Todd, Management Recruiters Dana Point (C), CA, *440*
Rollins, Joan E., Rollins & Assoc. (C), CA, *541*
Rubin, Karen, Travel Executive Search (C), NY, *608*
Schroeder, John W., SpencerStuart (R), TX, *197*
Schumann, Robert, Reinecke & Assoc. (C), NJ, *533*
Shey-Harding, Deborah, Shey-Harding Assoc. Inc. (C), CA, *580*
Smirnoff, Olga, Management Recruiters of Fresno (C), CA, *440*
Springer, Neil A., Springer Souder & Assoc. L.L.C. (R), IL, *198*
Suhay, Gary T., Elite Resources Group (R), OH, *58*
Sulkowski, Roger, Hughes & Wilden Assoc. (C), PA, *383*
Uhlich, Jeff, KPMG Executive Search (R), AB, *119*
Van Opstal, Lori, Your Advantage Staffing Consultants Inc. (C), ON, *626*
Wharton, Cynthia, Personnel Management Group (C), MB, *508*
Wilkins, Diana, Lanken-Kimball-Therrell & Assoc. (C), GA, *412*

Travel

Hering, Robyn, Yours In Travel Personnel Agency, Inc. (C), NJ, *627*
King, P. Jason, Yours In Travel Personnel Agency, Inc. (C), NY, *626*
Koenig, Barbara, Royal Assoc. (C), CA, *547*
Kurzrok, Jeanie, Yours In Travel Personnel Agency, Inc. (C), VA, *627*
O'Malley, Chris, Travel Personnel (C), OH, *609*
Pagana, Pat, The Brentwood Group, Inc. (R), NJ, *22*
Rubin, Karen, Travel Executive Search (C), NY, *608*
Steinberg, Paul D., IMA Search, Inc. (R), NY, *101*

Treasury

Belvedere, Tina, Wesley Brown & Bartle Co., Inc. (R), NY, *218*
Chappell, Peter C., Robertson & Assoc. (C), IL, *539*
Christie, Stephen G., Marsar & Co., Inc. (C), FL, *471*
Ciaramitaro, Anthony, Corporate Search Consultants, Inc. (C), FL, *301*
Marsar, Kevin P., Marsar & Co., Inc. (C), FL, *471*
Myers, Deedee, DDJ Myers, Ltd. (R), AZ, *150*
Myers, John, DDJ Myers, Ltd. (R), MA, *150*
Steinfield, David, Steinfield & Assoc. (C), TX, *592*

Trust

Andersen, Phil, Blackhawk Advantage, Inc. (C), CA, *267*

RECRUITER SPECIALTIES

Ciaramitaro, Anthony, Corporate Search Consultants, Inc. (C), FL, *301*
Glaser, David, ECG Resources, Inc. (C), NY, *326*
Graff, Thomas D. B., The Hanover Consulting Group (C), MD, *368*
Jaspersen, Kenneth A., Dunhill Professional Search of Omaha, Inc. (C), NE, *321*
Lassiter, P. Frank, Dunhill Professional Search of Richmond (C), VA, *323*
McCulla, Herb, Dunhill of Ft. Collins, Inc. (C), CO, *319*
Williston, Nada D., Active Search & Placement Inc. (C), CA, *239*

Underwriting

Buchanan, Christine, Management Recruiters of Bordentown (C), NJ, *454*
Curry, Donna, Don Neal & Assoc. (C), OK, *491*
DeMatteo, Robena, DeMatteo Associates (C), NY, *311*
Haugen, Audrey D., Roger Dietsch & Assoc. (C), MN, *312*
Hugley, Trey, QuestPro, Inc. (C), TX, *527*
Lear, Roger R., Lear & Assoc., Inc. (C), FL, *415*
Levinson, Lauren, QuestPro, Inc. (C), TX, *527*
Neal, Don, Don Neal & Assoc. (C), OK, *491*
Ramey, Pamela R., Lear & Assoc., Inc. (C), FL, *415*
Rank, Christy L., Mortgage Search Network (C), AZ, *486*
Svetic, Mark, Lear & Assoc., Inc. (C), FL, *415*
Watson, David L. B., Pacific Coast Recruiters (C), OR, *501*

Unix

Bell, Dixie Lee, MIS Computer Professionals, Inc. (C), KS, *482*
Bouchard, Rodney, Management Recruiters of Winsted, Inc. (C), CT, *442*
Capozzi, John, C Assoc. (C), DC, *278*
Ciaramitaro, Paul, Corporate Search Consultants, Inc. (C), FL, *301*
Sieler, Susan, C Assoc. (C), DC, *278*
Wachuku, Bobbiette, Management Recruiters-Cedar Rapids, Inc. (C), IA, *448*

Utilities

Bailey, Jerald W., Dunhill Professional Search of Greater New Orleans (C), LA, *321*
Block, Bonny, Power Recruiting Group (C), TX, *515*
Bodnar, Robert J., Sales Consultants of Princeton, Inc. (C), NJ, *561*
Colling, Douglas, KPMG Executive Search (R), ON, *119*
Cooke, Gerald W., STM Assoc. (R), UT, *201*
Cutler, Robert, Brissenden, McFarland, Fuccella & Reynolds, Inc. (R), WI, *23*
Dexter, Peter, Search Research Assoc., Inc. (R), MA, *187*
Edwards, J. Michael, Power Recruiting Group (C), TX, *515*
Fuccella, Carl J., Brissenden, McFarland, Fuccella & Reynolds, Inc. (R), NJ, *23*
Gunning, Phill, TBC, Inc. (C), KY, *600*
Haentzler, Robert A, Michael Latas & Assoc., Inc. (R), MO, *126*
Langley, Carol M., Langley & Associates, Inc. (Executive Search Consultants) (R), CO, *124*
Miller, Paul McG., LAI Ward Howell (R), IL, *123*
Milton, Charles E., Smith James Group, Inc. (R), GA, *194*
Morgan, Richard, Morgan Samuels Co. (R), CA, *147*
Palumbo, Michael J., Michael Latas & Assoc., Inc. (R), MO, *126*
Raben, Steven, Ray & Berndtson (R), TX, *172*
Ray, Breck, Ray & Berndtson (R), TX, *172*
Reynolds, John H., Brissenden, McFarland, Fuccella & Reynolds, Inc. (R), NJ, *23*
Robinson, Rodney L., Michael Latas & Assoc., Inc. (R), MO, *126*
Robinson, Verneda, V. Robinson & Co., Inc. (C), KS, *539*
Robinson, Verneda, V. Robinson & Co., Inc. (C), MO, *539*
Roylance, Robert L., STM Assoc. (R), UT, *201*
Ruschak, Randy R., Management Recruiters of Bordentown (C), NJ, *454*
Samuels, Lew, Morgan Samuels Co. (R), CA, *147*
Schlect, Nancy, Morgan Samuels Co. (R), CA, *147*
Searing, James M., Korn/Ferry Int'l. (R), VA, *118*
Sharpe, Charles, C. J. Stafford & Assoc. (C), ON, *591*
Shields, Robert G., SpencerStuart (R), IL, *197*
Simpson, Cathy G., Conroy Partners Ltd. (R), AB, *39*
Stanewick, B. David, Stanewick, Hart & Assoc., Inc. (C), FL, *591*
Swan, Christopher, RSMR, Inc. (R), IL, *182*
Walker, Kelly, Kelly Walker Assoc. (C), TX, *614*
Waller, Jody W., Michael Latas & Assoc., Inc. (R), MO, *126*
Watson, Hanan S., Watson Int'l., Inc. (R), NY, *216*

Valves

Eissler, W. Robert, W. Robert Eissler & Assoc., Inc. (C), TX, *327*

Van conversion

McGuire, John, Sage Employment Recruiters (C), IN, *550*

Venture capital

Bartholdi, Sr., Theodore G., Bartholdi & Co., Inc. (R), AZ, *12*
Bauman, Martin H., Martin H. Bauman Assoc., Inc. (R), NY, *13*
Beaudine, Robert E., Eastman & Beaudine, Inc. (R), TX, *56*
Bellano, Robert W., cFour Partners (R), CA, *32*
Blank, Paula, Lewis & Blank Int'l. (R), CA, *129*
Bowman, Mary, Healthcare Management Resources, Inc. (R), GA, *89*
Clement, Laura K., Stroman Int'l., Inc. (R), CO, *204*
Combs, Stephen, StratfordGroup (R), CA, *203*
Davis, III, Samuel, PRAXIS Partners (R), VA, *167*
Epstein, Joel P., StratfordGroup (R), OH, *203*
Esposito, Mark, Christian & Timbers, Inc. (R), OH, *34*
Holodnak, William A., J. Robert Scott (R), MA, *104*
Kip, Luanne S., Kip Williams, Inc. (R), NY, *115*
Kuhn, Larry A., Kuhn Med-Tech (C), CA, *409*
Levy, Stefan, Management Search, Inc. (C), IL, *467*
Lewis, Daphne V., Lewis & Blank Int'l. (R), CA, *129*
Ogdon, Thomas H., The Ogdon Partnership (R), NY, *155*
Sawhill, Louise, Healthcare Management Resources, Inc. (R), GA, *89*
Stroman, III, Alfred L., Stroman Int'l., Inc. (R), CO, *204*
Visnich, L. Christine, Bason Associates (R), OH, *13*
Westmore, Diane, Healthcare Management Resources, Inc. (R), GA, *89*

Veterinary

Noebel, Todd R., The Noebel Search Group, Inc. (C), TX, *494*

Vice president

Britten, Albert, Sales Consultants of Scottsdale, Inc. (C), AZ, *556*
Laguzza, John, Laguzza Assoc., Ltd. (R), NY, *122*
Rooney, Joseph J., Rooney Assoc., Inc. (R), IL, *181*
Surrette, Mark J., Robertson-Surrette Ltd. (R), NS, *179*

Virtual reality

Wheel, Eric, Management Recruiters of Northern California (C), CA, *440*

Vision

Auriema, Mark H., Jay Tracey Assoc. Inc. (C), VT, *608*
Tracey, Jay E., Jay Tracey Assoc. Inc. (C), VT, *608*

VSAT

Du Ket, Holly V., New Venture Development, Inc. (C), CA, *492*
Gibson, Jan, Advanced Corporate Search (C), CA, *240*

Wall Street

Donnelly, John P., J P Donnelly Assoc., Inc. (C), NY, *314*
Kelly, John, Rand Thompson Executive Search Consultants (C), NY, *528*

WAN's

Bouchard, Rodney, Management Recruiters of Winsted, Inc. (C), CT, *442*
Gionta, Michael, Management Recruiters of Colchester (C), CT, *442*
Griffith, Doug, Caywood Partners, Ltd. (R), CA, *32*

Waste water

Ortman, Jim, Ortman Recruiting Int'l. (C), CA, *500*

Watches

Feldman, Abe, A. E. Feldman Assoc., Inc. (C), NY, *339*

Welding

Donahue, Timothy J., Kelly Associates (R), PA, *112*

Wholesale

Buchholtz, Bruce Barton, Fairfield Int'l. Resources (R), NY, *65*
Cary, Con, Cary & Assoc. (R), FL, *31*
Goldman, Irwin, Michael Wayne Recruiters (C), IL, *481*
Gross, Kathy, Evie Kreisler Assoc. Inc. (C), NY, *409*
Hirshorn, Richard P., Fairfield Int'l. Resources (R), NY, *65*
Kreisler, Debbi, Evie Kreisler Assoc. Inc. (C), GA, *409*
Kreisler, Evie, Evie Kreisler Assoc. Inc. (C), CA, *409*
Levine, Harvey, Fairfield Int'l. Resources (R), NY, *65*
Mazzola, Richard J., Futures, Inc. (C), NH, *354*
McDaniel, Paul, The Paul McDaniel Co. (C), TN, *474*
Moy, Betty, Cook Assoc.,® Inc. (R), IL, *40*
Nemec, Edward C., Craig Affiliates, Inc. (C), TX, *302*
Priftis, Tony, Evie Kreisler Assoc. Inc. (C), TX, *409*
Schorejs, Ray, Roth Young Executive Search (C), TX, *546*
Stillings, Bob, Alpha Search (C), FL, *246*
Tadda, Wayne, Evie Kreisler Assoc. Inc. (C), IL, *409*

Wireless

Austin, Cami, Cami Austin & Assoc. (C), IL, *256*
Ellis, James, Sanford Rose Assoc. - Lake St. Louis (C), MO, *568*
Ellis, Mitch, Sanford Rose Assoc. - Lake St. Louis (C), MO, *568*
Gorberg, Richard D., Fortune Personnel Consultants of Raleigh, Inc. (C), NC, *348*
Kossuth, David, Kossuth & Assoc., Inc. (R), WA, *119*
Kossuth, Jane, Kossuth & Assoc., Inc. (R), WA, *119*
LaCosta, Paul, LaCosta & Assoc. Int'l. Inc. (C), CA, *411*
McCain, Barbara, Tele-Solutions of Arizona, Inc. (C), AZ, *604*
McIntyre, Jeffrey F., McIntyre Assoc. (R), CT, *141*
Rudolph, Lee, Management Recruiters of Franktown (C), CO, *442*
Shindler, Stanley L., Franklin Int'l. Search, Inc. (C), MA, *352*
Warren, Scott C., Warren, Morris & Madison, Ltd. (C), NH, *616*

Women

Bennett, Delora, Genesis Personnel Service, Inc. (C), OH, *356*
High, Claude, Action Managment Corp. (C), VA, *239*
Hyde, Anne P., The Hyde Group, Inc. (R), CT, *101*
June, Valerie L., Action Management Corp. (C), MI, *239*

Wood

Brown, Bob, Management Recruiters of Sandy Springs (C), GA, *446*
Corder, Eutha, RBW Assoc. Inc. (C), AR, *531*
Greene, William, Stewart/Greene & Co. of The Triad, Inc. (C), NC, *594*
Ibsen, John, Stewart/Greene & Co. of The Triad, Inc. (C), NC, *594*
Irwin, Bill, Southern Recruiters & Consultants, Inc. (C), SC, *587*
Martin, Wayne, Human Resources Personnel Agency (R), AR, *99*
Parker, Joan, Management Recruiters of Sandy Springs (C), GA, *446*
Stewart, Tom, Stewart/Greene & Company of the Triad, Inc. (C), NC, *594*

World Wide Web

Capozzi, John, C Assoc. (C), DC, *278*
Dyson, Steve, Technology Search Int'l. (C), CA, *603*
Kratimenos, Peter, Ansara, Bickford & Fiske (C), MA, *251*
Van Campen, Jerry, Gilbert & Van Campen Int'l. (R), NY, *76*
Wheel, Eric, Management Recruiters of Northern California (C), CA, *440*

Worldwide

Hernandez, Jr., Luis A., Independent Power Consultants (C), TX, *387*

Year 2000

Devlin, Jack, The Devlin Search Group, Inc. (C), MA, *312*
Lynch, William E., Fortuna Technologies Inc. (C), CA, *343*
Nair, Sanjay, Fortuna Technologies Inc. (C), NJ, *343*
Suri, Prem, Fortuna Technologies Inc. (C), GA, *343*
Therizien, Greg, The Devlin Search Group, Inc. (C), MA, *312*

RECRUITER SPECIALTIES

Key Principals Index

Firms with (R) are from the Retainer Section, which begins on page 1.
Firms with (C) are from the Contingency Section, which begins on page 231.

Aaron, Lauren - Bert Davis Executive Search, Inc. (R), NY, *47*
Aavik, Karl - Egon Zehnder Int'l. Inc. (R), IL, *227*
Abbott, Brenda L. - Abbott Associates (R), CA, *1*
Abbott, Charles J. - Specialty Consultants Inc. (R), PA, *196*
Abbott, Peter D. - The Abbott Group, Inc. (R), MD, *1*
Abbott, Robert - Pacific Coast Recruiting (C), CA, *501*
Abdulla, Jennifer - AES Search (C), NJ, *241*
Abécassis, Pauline P. - Abécassis Conseil (R), QE, *1*
Abeln, Kenneth E. - Abeln, Magy & Assoc., Inc. (R), MN, *1*
Abeln, Mary - Abeln, Magy & Assoc., Inc. (R), MN, *1*
Abelson, Cathy B. - Cathy Abelson Legal Search (C), PA, *232*
Abert, Janice - Johnson Smith & Knisely (R), NY, *107*
Abkin, Stephen J. - Millennium Search Group, Inc. (R), CA, *144*
Abrahamson, Susan - SearchCom, Inc. (R), TX, *187*
Abramowicz, Andrew - DHR Int'l., Inc. (R), CA, *49*
Abrams, Burton J. - B. J. Abrams & Assoc. Inc. (C), IL, *233*
Abramson, Daniel - Dunhill Staffing Systems, Inc. (C), NY, *316*
Abruzzo, James - A.T. Kearney Executive Search (R), NY, *111*
Acosta, Guillermo - CEO Consulting (C), FL, *287*
Acosta, Jeanette - Fresquez & Assoc. (C), CA, *353*
Acridge, Charles W. - CRI Professional Search (C), CA, *303*
Adair, Connie - Taylor Winfield (R), TX, *207*
Adair, Sharon - Creative Management Strategies, Ltd. (R), NY, *42*
Adams, Amy - Richard, Wayne & Roberts (C), TX, *536*
Adams, Arthur - Arthur Adams & Assoc. (C), OH, *239*
Adams, Chris - Fortune Group Int'l., Inc. (R), PA, *70*
Adams, David - Accountants On Call (C), WA, *237*
Adams, David - Accountants On Call (C), OR, *237*
Adams, Frank S. - Thomson, Sponar & Adams, Inc. (C), WA, *606*
Adams, Gary - Management Recruiters of Omaha (C), NE, *431*
Adams, Gerald - G. Adams Partners (R), IL, *2*
Adams, James - DHR Int'l., Inc. (R), FL, *50*
Adams, Lauren - Fortune Group Int'l., Inc. (R), PA, *70*
Adams, Len - KPA Assoc., Inc. (C), NY, *408*
Adams, Oscar - Shore Asociados Ejecutivos, S. A. de C.V. (R), MX, *190*
Adams, Robert - Sales Consultants of Dallas (C), TX, *563*
Adams, Vicki - Management Recruiters of Morgantown (C), WV, *437*
Adamson, C. Lynn - Levison Search Assoc. (R), CA, *129*
Addison, Mike - Sales Consultants of Dallas (C), TX, *563*
Adelman, Don - Joel H. Paul & Assoc., Inc. (C), NY, *505*
Adler, David - Don Allan Assoc., Inc. (C), CA, *313*
Adler, Jack E. - Adler Management, Inc. (R), NJ, *2*
Adler, Louis S. - CJA-The Adler Group, Inc. (R), CA, *35*
Adler, Rita - Discovery, The Staffing Specialists, Inc. (C), CA, *312*
Adzima, Allan G. - MARBL Consultants, Inc. (C), WI, *469*
Aeziman, Alicia - Stone, Murphy & Olson (R), MN, *201*
Africa, Martha Fay - Major, Hagen & Africa (C), CA, *423*
Agius, Leslie - Sales Consultant of Franklin (C), NJ, *554*
Aglinsky, William E. - Management Recruiters International, Inc. (MRI) (C), OH, *425*
Aglinsky, William E. - Sales Consultants (C), OH, *551*
Agnello, Frank - Systems Research Inc. (SRI) (C), IL, *598*
Agnew, Gary R. - Canadian Career Partners (R), AB, *27*
Agnos, Stacy - TSI Group/TSI Staffing Services (C), ON, *610*
Agriesti, Kay - Agriesti & Assoc. (C), CA, *243*
Aguirre, Doris - DCA Professional Search (C), TX, *309*
Aguirrezabal, Angelina - OSAGUI S.A. de C.V. (C), MX, *500*
Ahearn, Mary - Charles Luntz & Assoc., Inc. (R), MO, *132*
Ahearn, Mike - TASA International (R), MA, *206*
Ahrensdorf, Lee - Ahrensdorf & Assoc. (R), PA, *2*
Aiken, David - Commonwealth Consultants (C), GA, *294*
Aitken, Carol - Information Technology Search (C), PA, *388*
Akin, Gary K. - Management Recruiters of Champions (C), TX, *462*
Akin, J. R. - J. R. Akin & Co. (R), MA, *2*
Akin, Nicola - Management Recruiters of Champions (C), TX, *462*
Akre, Suzanne - Healthcare Recruiters Int'l. Phoenix (C), AZ, *372*
Albanese, Matt J. - Management Recruiters of Glendora (C), CA, *425*
Albergato, Vincent - Raymond Karsan Assoc. (C), MA, *530*
Albers, Joan - Carver Search Consultants (C), CA, *285*
Albertini, Nancy L. - Taylor Winfield (R), TX, *207*
Albertson, Rob - Dick Williams & Assoc. (C), CA, *621*
Albisua, Francisco - TASA International (R), MX, *206*
Albrecht, Franke M. - Albrecht & Assoc., Executive Search Consultants (C), TX, *243*
Albus, John P. - Lord & Albus Co. (C), TX, *420*
Alcott, Michael - Accountants On Call (C), RI, *237*
Aldana, Manny - Bor-Maq Assoc. (C), TX, *269*
Alexander, Craig A. - Sales Consultants of Boise (C), ID, *552*
Alexander, Craig R. - Management Recruiters of Boise (C), ID, *446*
Alexander, David - Elite Medical Search (C), GA, *328*
Alexander, Edward J. - EagleView, Inc. (C), MA, *325*
Alexander, Gary - Mark Christian & Assoc., Inc. (C), AZ, *470*
Alexander, Karen Vacheron - BT&A, LLC (R), CT, *24*
Alexander, Myra - Mark Christian & Assoc., Inc. (C), AZ, *470*
Alexander, Penelope - Alexander & Co. (C), CA, *243*
Alexander, Richard J. - Alexander Associates (R), NJ, *2*
Alexander, Susan M. - Manuso, Alexander & Associates, Inc. (R), NY, *135*
Alexanderson, John L. - DHR Int'l., Inc. (R), MA, *50*
Alfus, Phillip - The Alfus Group (R), NY, *3*
Ali, Iqbal E. - Petro Staff Int'l. (C), AB, *509*
Ali, T. - Petro Staff Int'l. (C), AB, *509*
Alisbrook, William - Fortune Personnel Consultants of Chattanooga Inc. (C), TN, *349*
Al-Jo, Sue - Bright Search/Professional Staffing (C), MN, *274*
Allard, Susan - Allard Associates (C), CA, *244*
Allen, Barbara A. - Allen & Assoc. (C), NV, *244*
Allen, Cynthia Y. - Reinecke & Assoc. (C), IL, *533*
Allen, David - Baker Scott & Co. (C), NJ, *258*
Allen, David - Century Assoc., Inc. (C), PA, *287*
Allen, Debbie - Hall Kinion (C), CA, *366*
Allen, Don - D. S. Allen Assoc. (C), NJ, *244*
Allen, Douglas - Sullivan & Assoc. (R), MI, *204*
Allen, Frank - Frank E. Allen & Assoc. (C), NJ, *244*
Allen, James R. - Continental Search Assoc. (C), OH, *298*
Allen, Jamieson - DHR Int'l., Inc. (R), CA, *49*

PRINCIPALS

Allen, Jay - Jay Allen & Assoc. (C), FL, *244*
Allen, Jean E. - LAI Ward Howell (R), NY, *122*
Allen, Jim - Southern Chemical & Plastics Search (C), GA, *587*
Allen, Leslie - Straube Associates (R), MA, *203*
Allen, Jr., Lindsay - Mark III Personnel, Inc. (C), NC, *470*
Allen, Mark - Frank E. Allen & Assoc. (C), NJ, *244*
Allen, Mark - Computer Professionals Unlimited (C), TX, *295*
Allen, Marla - Allen & Assoc. (C), NV, *244*
Allen, Martin - Rice Cohen Int'l. (R), PA, *178*
Allen, Michael - Allen/Associates (R), OH, *4*
Allen, Paul - Berkana Int'l., Inc. (C), WA, *265*
Allen, Rita - Gatti & Assoc. (C), MA, *355*
Allen, Rolly - Ward Liebelt Assoc. Inc. (R), CT, *215*
Allen, Thomas R. - Allen Consulting Group, Inc. (C), MO, *244*
Allen, Wade H. - Cendea Connection Int'l. (R), TX, *32*
Allen, William F. - Techaid Inc. (C), QE, *601*
Allen-Oberbillig, Debbie - Hall Kinion (C), NY, *367*
Aller, Joan - L O R (R), NJ, *122*
Allerton, Donald - Allerton Heneghan & O'Neill (R), IL, *4*
Alley, Glenwood - Management Recruiters of St. Louis-West County (C), MO, *431*
Allgire, Mary - Kenzer Corp. (R), IL, *113*
Allhands, Kelly - Allhands Placement Consultants (C), IN, *245*
Allison, Tom - Tom Allison Assoc. (C), NM, *245*
Allman, Steven L. - Allman & Co., Inc. (C), NC, *245*
Allred, J. Michael - SpencerStuart (R), GA, *197*
Alman, Paul D. - Holland & Assoc., Inc. (R), MI, *94*
Almour, Chloe - Kramer Executive Resources, Inc. (C), NY, *409*
Alpern, Eric - Accountants On Call (C), NJ, *236*
Alstrin, Robert W. - Roth Young Executive Search of Milwaukee (C), WI, *547*
Altieri, Robert J. - StratfordGroup (R), PA, *203*
Altreuter, Ken - The Altco Group (C), NJ, *246*
Altschule, Abe - Logic Assoc., Inc. (C), NY, *419*
Altschuler, Joseph - Management Recruiters of Gramercy, Inc. (C), NY, *455*
Alvarez, E. Linda - RJN Consulting (R), NY, *179*
Alvarez, Elizabeth - DHR Int'l., Inc. (R), NY, *50*
Alvear, Clemente - Brandywine Retained Ventures, Inc. (R), CT, *22*
Alves, Manuel J. - M/J/A Partners (R), IL, *133*
Alvey, Frank - Sage Employment Recruiters (C), IN, *550*
Amara, Edmund - SpencerSearch, Inc. (C), TX, *589*
Amato, Bobbi - Amato & Associates Insurance Recruiters (C), PA, *247*
Amato, George - Faro Consultants Int'l. (C), VA, *338*
Amato, Joseph D. - Amato & Assoc., Inc. (C), CA, *246*
Ambler, Peter W. - Peter W. Ambler Co. (R), TX, *5*
Ambos, Merry - Molecular Solutions, Inc. (C), SC, *484*
Ambra, Glenn P. - J. R. Phillip & Assoc., Inc. (R), CA, *164*
Ambrosio, Trish - Pennington Consulting Group (C), NJ, *506*
Ambruster, David L. - Renaissance Resources, LLC (R), VA, *174*
Amcis, Lillian - Joel H. Paul & Assoc., Inc. (C), NY, *505*
Ameen, Edward N. - Management Recruiters of New Orleans (C), LA, *429*
Ameen, Edward N. - Sales Consultants of New Orleans (C), LA, *553*
Ames, A. P. - Ames & Ames (R), CA, *5*
Ames, George C. - Ames-O'Neill Assoc., Inc. (C), NY, *249*
Ames, Mildred S. - Ames Assoc. Inc. (C), MD, *249*
Amicci, Bruno C. - Triad Technology Group (C), OR, *609*
Amici, Michelle - DHR Int'l., Inc. (R), CA, *49*
Ammann, Elisabeth - The Stevenson Group, Inc. (N.J.) (R), NJ, *200*
Ammirati, Greg - Sales Consultants of Western McHenry County (C), IL, *558*
Amore, Lisa - Branthover Assoc. (C), NY, *272*
Amsterdam, Gail - Foster Partners (R), NY, *70*
Amy, Rupert R. - Careers/Inc. (C), PR, *284*
Ancona, Don - Management Recruiters of The Sandias (C), NM, *454*
Anderer, Albert M. - Managed Care Consultants (C), AZ, *424*
Andersen, Phil - Blackhawk Advantage, Inc. (C), CA, *267*
Anderson, Annette - Advanced Executive Resources (R), MI, *2*
Anderson, Ashlee - Management Solutions, Inc. (C), WA, *468*
Anderson, Barbara - Blackshaw, Olmstead, Lynch & Koenig (R), GA, *18*
Anderson, Christian A. - Effective Search, Inc. (R), IL, *57*
Anderson, David C. - Heidrick & Struggles, Inc. (R), TX, *90*
Anderson, Dean - Corporate Resources Professional Placement (C), MN, *301*
Anderson, Doris - Management Recruiters of Ft. Myers, FL. (C), FL, *443*
Anderson, Douglas K. - Anderson & Associates (R), NC, *5*
Anderson, Douglas L. - Quantum Int'l., Ltd. (R), FL, *170*
Anderson, George Wright - Gans, Gans & Assoc., Inc. (R), IL, *74*
Anderson, Jr., Glenn G. - LAI Ward Howell (R), OH, *123*
Anderson, Gregory D. - Anderson Industrial Assoc., Inc. (C), GA, *250*
Anderson, Harry - Andex Executive Search (C), CT, *250*
Anderson, Jeff - Raymond Karsan Assoc. (C), PA, *530*
Anderson, Jim - Howard Clark Assoc. (C), NJ, *292*
Anderson, Jim L. - Management Recruiters of Fremont (C), CA, *425*
Anderson, Kevin - Stanton Chase Int'l. (R), TX, *199*
Anderson, Kristine M. - Rollo Assoc. (R), CA, *181*
Anderson, Lauren - Robert William James & Assoc. (C), CA, *539*
Anderson, Maria - The Ransford Group (R), TX, *171*
Anderson, Mary - Romac Int'l., Inc. (C), CA, *542*
Anderson, Murray - MIS Computer Professionals, Inc. (C), KS, *482*
Anderson, Richard L. - Grant Cooper & Assoc., Inc. (R), MO, *81*
Anderson, Robert T. - Hanzel & Co., Inc. (R), NY, *86*
Anderson, Robert W. - Anderson Bradshaw Assoc., Inc. (R), TX, *6*
Anderson, Roger J. - BioQuest Inc. (R), CA, *17*
Anderson, Trevor - Kincaid Group Inc. (KGI) (C), TX, *406*
Anderson, Vince - HRCS (R), CA, *97*
Anderson, Wayne F. - Anderson Network Group (C), OH, *250*
Andrews, Charles - The Borton Wallace Co. (R), TN, *19*
Andrews, Dan - BR & Assoc. (C), NJ, *271*
Andrews, David - Engineering Futures, LLC (C), CT, *330*
Andrews, Dwight L. - Andrews & Assoc. (C), NC, *250*
Andrews, J. Douglas - Clarey & Andrews, Inc. (R), IL, *35*
Andrews, Liz - Human Resource Dimensions, Inc. (C), TX, *384*
Andrews, Pamela J. - LAI Ward Howell (R), IL, *123*
Andrews, Robert L. - Allen Austin Lowe & Powers (R), TX, *3*
Angel, Steve - Angel Group Int'l. (C), KY, *250*
Angel, Steve - Sales Consultants of Louisville (C), KY, *553*
Angel, Steven R. - Management Recruiters of Louisville (C), KY, *429*
Angelini, Cynthia - Diedre Moire Corp., Inc. (C), NJ, *483*
Angell, Robert A. - Management Recruiters International, Inc. (MRI) (C), OH, *425*
Angell, Robert A. - Sales Consultants (C), OH, *551*

Angell, Tryg R. - Tryg R. Angell, Ltd. (C), CT, *250*
Anger, Gerry - Sales Consultant of Bloomfield Hills (C), MI, *553*
Angott, Mark - Management Recruiters of North Oakland County, Inc. (C), MI, *452*
Angowitz, Anne - Preferred Placement, Inc. (C), NY, *516*
Angowitz, Stuart - Preferred Placement, Inc. (C), NY, *516*
Angus, Thomas R. - The Angus Group, Ltd. (C), OH, *251*
Ankeney, Dan R. - Management Recruiters of Norfolk (C), NE, *431*
Annesi, Jerry - Management Recruiters of Rochester (C), NY, *432*
Annesi, Jerry - Sales Consultants of Rochester (C), NY, *554*
Ansara, Peter - Ansara, Bickford & Fiske (C), MA, *251*
Anson, Alice J. - Deborah Snow Walsh, Inc. (R), IL, *215*
Anter, Edna J. - Mangement Recruiters of Brecksville (C), OH, *433*
Anterasian, Cathy - Egon Zehnder Int'l. Inc. (R), CA, *227*
Anthony, Fred - Fred Anthony Assoc. (C), WI, *251*
Anton, Michael - Michael James & Co. (C), IL, *480*
Antoniak, Peggy - The Executive Tree (R), MD, *64*
Antoniazzi, Marie - Neail Behringer Consultants Inc. (R), NY, *15*
Antonio, Marshall - Fortune of Arlington Heights (C), IL, *346*
Antonochi, Pat - Cypress Int'l., Inc. (R), FL, *45*
Anwar, Tarin - Jay Gaines & Company, Inc. (R), NY, *74*
Aplin, David - David Aplin & Assoc. (C), AB, *251*
Aplin, Jeff - David Aplin & Assoc. (C), AB, *251*
Apostle, George - Search Dynamics, Inc. (C), IL, *575*
Apple, Richard W. - R. W. Apple & Assoc. (C), NJ, *251*
Appleton, Diane - Management Recruiters of Plano-East (C), TX, *436*
Aquavella, Charles P. - Charles P. Aquavella & Assoc. (C), TX, *252*
Aral, Stephanie - Henrietta's Personnel & Executive Search, Inc. (C), FL, *376*
Arcand, Arthur J. - Tech 2000 (C), FL, *601*
Arcara, Gwen O. - Executive Dimensions (R), NY, *62*
Arceri, John Mark - John Ryan Assoc., LLC. (C), NY, *399*
Archer, Helen - Executive Search Consultants (R), CA, *63*
Archibald, David E. - The Eldridge Group, Ltd. (C), IL, *327*
Archibald, Lace - Accountants On Call (C), TX, *237*
Archie, Otis - Kuhn Med-Tech (C), CA, *409*
Ardi, Dana B. - LAI Ward Howell (R), CA, *123*
Arend, Lewis - McKinley•Arend Int'l. (R), TX, *141*
Argenio, Paul J. - Tierney Assoc., Inc. (R), PA, *209*
Ariail, Randolph C. - Ariail & Assoc. (R), NC, *7*
Arias, Jr., Victor - DHR Int'l., Inc. (R), TX, *51*
Arledge, Tom - Allen Austin Lowe & Powers (R), TX, *3*
Armitage, John D. - Armitage Associates Ltd. (R), ON, *7*
Armstrong, Anna Marie - Major, Hagen & Africa (C), CA, *423*
Armstrong, C.J. - Dunhill Professional Search of Byram (C), MS, *321*
Armstrong, Don - Dunhill Professional Search of Byram (C), MS, *321*
Arnautovic, Zora - Consulpro (R), ON, *39*
Arndt, Greg - Management Recruiters of Boise (C), ID, *446*
Arnette, Tom - Team One Partners, Inc. (C), GA, *600*
Arnold, Chris - Sales Consultants of Laurel Park, Inc. (C), MI, *560*
Arnold, Dave - Markent Personnel (C), WI, *470*
Arnold, David - Management Solutions, Inc. (C), CA, *468*
Arnold, Janet N. - R & J Arnold & Assoc., Inc. (C), CO, *253*
Arnold, Janet N. - Management Recruiters of Broomfield (C), CO, *426*
Arnold, Jay - Staffing Edge, Inc. (C), KS, *590*
Arnold, Jerome M. - Houtz•Strawn & Arnold, Inc. (R), TX, *96*
Arnold, Lindy - The Glazin Group (R), BC, *77*
Arnold, Patrick A. - Attorneys at Work (C), GA, *256*
Arnold, Robert W. - R & J Arnold & Assoc., Inc. (C), CO, *253*
Arnold, Sheridan J. - William B. Arnold Assoc., Inc. (R), CO, *7*
Arnold, William B. - William B. Arnold Assoc., Inc. (R), CO, *7*
Arnone, Patrick J. - Patrick Arnone & Assoc. Inc. (R), VA, *7*
Aronin, Michael - Fisher-Todd Assoc. (C), NY, *342*
Aronow, Lawrence E. - Aronow Assoc., Inc. (C), FL, *253*
Arons, Richard - Korn/Ferry Int'l. (R), NJ, *118*
Arons, Sheldon - Colt Systems Professional Personnel Services (C), CA, *294*
Arrants, Becky - F-O-R-T-U-N-E Personnel Consultants of Knoxville (C), TN, *350*
Arredondo, Fred - SpectraWest (C), CA, *589*
Arsenault, Alfred J. - Insight Consulting Co. (C), NY, *389*
Artis, Robert E. - Sales Consultants of Buffalo (C), NY, *554*
Artze, Angeles - A. Artze Assoc.-Personnel Consultants (C), PR, *253*
Aruza, Al - Cornell Group Int'l. Consulting, Inc. (R), NY, *41*
Ascher, Daniel - D.A.I Human Resources Consultants (R), QE, *45*
Ascher, Susan - The Ascher Group (R), NJ, *7*
Ash, Robert I. - Ashworth Consultants, Inc. (R), MA, *8*
Ashby, Sarah R. - Secura/Burnett Partners (R), CA, *187*
Ashok, T. C. - Fortuna Technologies Inc. (C), CA, *343*
Ashton, Barbara L. - Ashton Computer Professionals, Inc. (C), BC, *253*
Ashton, Edward J. - E. J. Ashton & Assoc., Ltd. (C), IL, *253*
Ashton, Neil K. - Sales Consultants of Bangor, Inc. (C), ME, *559*
Ashton, Steve - Robertson-Surrette Ltd. (R), NS, *179*
Ashworth, Kevin - Impact Technical Staffing (C), OR, *387*
Aslaksen, James S. - LAI Ward Howell (R), IL, *123*
Aspell, Tim - New Venture Development, Inc. (C), CA, *492*
Ast, Steven T. - AST/BRYANT (R), CT, *8*
Aswell, Judy - Management Recruiters of San Marcos (C), TX, *463*
Atchison, Ann G. - W. R. Atchison & Assoc., Inc. (C), NC, *255*
Atchison, W. R. - W. R. Atchison & Assoc., Inc. (C), NC, *255*
Aten, Herb - DHR Int'l., Inc. (R), MO, *50*
Atkinson, Arthur - Atkinson Search & Placement, Inc. (C), IA, *255*
Atkinson, Faith - Lamon + Stuart + Michaels Inc. (R), ON, *124*
Atkinson, Patrick J. - Waterford Executive Group Ltd. (C), IL, *616*
Atkinson, S. Graham - Raymond Karsan Assoc. (C), NY, *530*
Atley, David - Joe L. Giles & Assoc. (C), MI, *357*
Attea, William - Hazard, Young, Attea & Assoc., Ltd. (C), IL, *371*
Attewell, Brad J. - Dise & Co. (R), OH, *52*
Atwood, Barrie - The Abbott Group, Inc. (R), MD, *1*
Atwood, Bob - Canyon Consulting, Inc. (C), TX, *281*
Aubin, Richard E. - Aubin Int'l. Inc. (R), MA, *8*
Auerbach, Judith A. - Auerbach Associates, Inc. (R), MA, *9*
Auman, Patrick A. - Executive Solutions (R), MN, *64*
Auriema, Mark H. - Jay Tracey Assoc. Inc. (C), VT, *608*
Auster, A. Marc - A. M. Auster Associates (R), FL, *9*
Austin, Cami - Cami Austin & Assoc. (C), IL, *256*
Austin, Carrie - Management Recruiters of Boise (C), ID, *446*
Austin, Larry - Lucas Assoc. (C), TX, *421*

Austin, Mark - Yankee Hospitality Search (C), CT, *626*
Austin, Peter T. - Organization Resources Inc. (R), MA, *157*
Austin, Suzanne - Flexible Resources, Inc. (C), MA, *342*
Austn, Annie - Johnson Smith & Knisely (R), NY, *107*
Avazian, Mary Ann - National Field Service Corp. (C), NY, *489*
Avazian, Richard W. - National Field Service Corp. (C), NY, *489*
Avestruz, Alner - Avestruz & Assoc. (C), CA, *257*
Axelrod, Mark H. - F-O-R-T-U-N-E Personnel Consultants of Rockland County, Inc. (C), NY, *348*
Axne, Glen A. - Access Data Personnel, Inc. (C), NH, *233*
Aydelotte, G. Thomas - Ingram & Aydelotte, Inc. (R), NY, *101*
Ayers, Joseph - Hollander Horizon Int'l. (R), MN, *95*
Ayers, Jr., William L. - The Ayers Group, Inc. (R), NY, *10*
Ayling, Michael L. - MLA Resources, Inc. (C), OK, *483*
Aylsworth, Robert J. - DHR Int'l., Inc. (R), IL, *49*
Aylward, John - Hemingway Personnel, Inc. (C), CA, *375*
Babashan, Bruce - DHR Int'l., Inc. (R), DC, *50*
Babchick, Don - Weatherby Healthcare (C), IL, *617*
Babcock, James A. - The Premier Staffing Group (C), OH, *517*
Babic, Val - The Garms Group (R), IL, *75*
Babicky, Kay - Management Recruiters of Wausau, LLC (C), WI, *466*
Babka, James - Roth Young of Chicago (C), IL, *546*
Babson, Jay - Dunhill Staffing Systems (C), NC, *321*
Babson, Lelia - Dunhill Staffing Systems (C), NC, *321*
Baces, Steve - Healthcare Recruiters of Indiana (C), IN, *372*
Bacher, Judith - SpencerStuart (R), NY, *196*
Bachhuber, Thomas - Management Alliance Group, Inc. (R), NJ, *134*
Bacigalupo, Terry - Management Recruiters of Lake St. Louis (C), MO, *431*
Back, Bobbie - National Bank & Finance Executive Search (C), CA, *488*
Bacon, Michael - Management Recruiters of Bedford (C), NH, *431*
Bader, Sam - Bader Research Corp. (C), NY, *257*
Badger, Carole - Tuft & Assoc., Inc. (R), IL, *212*
Badger, Fred H. - The Badger Group (R), CA, *10*
Badgley, Rick - Elliot Assoc. Inc. (R), OH, *58*
Baehl, Thomas A. - World Search (C), OH, *625*
Baer, Curtis L. - Sales Consultants of Barrington (C), IL, *558*
Baert, Robert A. - Personnel Management Group (C), MB, *508*
Baert, Yvonne - Personnel Management Group (C), MB, *508*
Baez, Ana Luisa - Sales Consultants of Ft. Myers, Inc. (C), FL, *557*
Bagg, Keith - Keith Bagg & Assoc., Inc. (C), ON, *257*
Bagg, Mary - Keith Bagg & Assoc., Inc. (C), ON, *257*
Baggott, Richard - Executive Search Placements, Inc. (C), CO, *336*
Bagileo, Jean - David Powell, Inc. (R), CA, *166*
Bagley, James M. - Russell Reynolds Assoc., Inc. (R), NY, *177*
Bagley, Rass - Marketing Recruiters, Inc. (C), NC, *470*
Bahr, Bob - Dunhill Professional Search of Crystal City (C), MO, *317*
Bailey, Dan - Johnson Smith & Knisely (R), GA, *107*
Bailey, David C. - Management Recruiters of Lake Tahoe, NV (C), NV, *453*
Bailey, Edward L. - The Patience Motivation Belief Group, Inc. (C), GA, *505*
Bailey, Evelyn - HeartBeat Medical, Inc. (C), OR, *374*
Bailey, Jerald - Dunhill Professional Search of Greater New Orleans (C), LA, *317*
Bailey, Jerald W. - Dunhill Professional Search of Greater New Orleans (C), LA, *321*
Bailey, III, Joseph A. - Russell Reynolds Assoc., Inc. (R), TX, *177*
Bailey, III, Joseph A. - Russell Reynolds Assoc., Inc. (R), TX, *177*
Bailey, Paul - Preston-Hunter, Inc. (R), IL, *167*
Bailey, Ralph - Ridgefield Search Int'l. (C), CT, *537*
Bailey, Scott - HeartBeat Medical, Inc. (C), OR, *374*
Bailey, Tom - Snelling Search - Transportation Division (C), AR, *585*
Bailin, Fred - Asset Resource, Inc. (C), CA, *254*
Baillie, Jamie - Robertson-Surrette Ltd. (R), NS, *179*
Baine, Mike - California Search Agency, Inc. (C), CA, *279*
Baird, Blaine T. - Physicians Search®, Inc. (C), CA, *511*
Baird, David W. - D. W. Baird & Associates (C), MD, *257*
Bajc, Sarah J. H. - Innovative Search Group, Inc. (R), GA, *102*
Bakehorn, Thomas - Ki Technologies, Inc. (C), UT, *406*
Bakehorn, Thomas - Martin Stevens Tamaren & Assoc., Inc. (R), CA, *206*
Baker, Bill - Kaye/Bassman Int'l. Corp. (R), TX, *110*
Baker, Charles D. - Corporate Staffing Group, Inc. (C), PA, *301*
Baker, Chet - Diversified Consulting Services, Inc. (C), CO, *313*
Baker, Craig - JM & Company (R), PA, *106*
Baker, Gary M. - Cochran, Cochran & Yale, Inc. (R), NY, *36*
Baker, George - Dunhill of Chicago (C), IL, *317*
Baker, Gerry - A.T. Kearney Executive Search (R), ON, *111*
Baker, Howard - The Johnson Group, Unlimited (C), NY, *400*
Baker, Jake - Allen Austin Lowe & Powers (R), CA, *4*
Baker, Jake A. - Allen Austin Lowe & Powers (R), TX, *3*
Baker, Jerry H. - Schuyler, Baker & Parker, Inc. (R), GA, *185*
Baker, Jr., Joseph N. - JNB Assoc., Inc. (C), MA, *399*
Baker, Judith M. - Search Consultants Int'l., Inc. (C), TX, *575*
Baker, Kim - Sales Advantage (C), FL, *551*
Baker, Lynette - Management Recruiters Int'l.-The Woodlands (C), TX, *464*
Baker, Ray - Management Recruiters of Ogden (C), UT, *464*
Baker, S. Joseph - Search Consultants Int'l., Inc. (C), TX, *575*
Baker, Sharon - Boyle/Ogata Executive Search (R), CA, *21*
Baker, Sharon I. - Baker, Nelms & Montgomery (C), IL, *258*
Baker, Susan F. - Diversified Consulting Services, Inc. (C), CO, *313*
Baker, Walter U. - LAI Ward Howell (R), FL, *123*
Baker, Wendy - Bert Davis Publishing Placement Consultants (C), NY, *309*
Baker, William W. - Baker, Nelms & Montgomery (C), IL, *258*
Bakken, Roger - J. Rodgers & Associates (C), IL, *540*
Bakker, Robert E. - Management Recruiters of Holland (C), MI, *430*
Balakonis, Charles L. - Lawrence-Balakonis & Assoc., Inc. (C), GA, *414*
Balchumas, Charlie - Romac Int'l., Inc. (C), AZ, *542*
Baldwin, II, Arthur D. - Artgo, Inc. (R), OH, *7*
Baldwin, Keith R. - The Baldwin Group (R), IL, *10*
Baldwin, Stephen - SearchCorp International (C), AB, *577*
Baldwin, W. Keith - Baldwin & Assoc. (C), OH, *258*
Bales, L. Patrick - Donahue/Bales Assoc. (R), IL, *54*
Bales, Sally - The Bales-Waugh Group (C), FL, *258*
Balian, Christina L. - Compass Group Ltd. (R), MI, *38*
Balistreri, Bonnie - DHR Int'l., Inc. (R), NE, *50*
Balistreri, Ted - DHR Int'l., Inc. (R), NE, *50*

Balk, Gregorius K. - Healthcare Search Associates (C), CA, *374*
Balk, Gregorius K. - Healthcare Search Associates (C), CA, *374*
Ball, Benny - Dick Wray & Consultants, Inc. (R), TN, *225*
Ball, Carol - Carol Ball & Co. (C), CT, *258*
Ball, Ronald D. - BallResources (C), MO, *258*
Ballach, Allen - Allen Ballach Assoc. Inc. (R), ON, *10*
Ballantyne, Tom - Ballantyne & Assoc. (R), CA, *10*
Ballein, Kathleen - Witt/Kieffer, Ford, Hadelman & Lloyd (R), IL, *223*
Ballos, Constantine J. - Ballos & Co., Inc. (R), NJ, *11*
Ballos, H. P. - Ballos & Co., Inc. (R), NJ, *11*
Ballou, Jodie - Management Recruiters of the Baltimore Washington Corridor (C), MD, *450*
Balogh, Steve - David Powell, Inc. (R), CA, *166*
Balsamo, Carol M. - Rurak & Assoc., Inc (R), DC, *183*
Balsamo, Mike - JPM International (C), CA, *401*
Balzen, David - InterNeed (C), TX, *394*
Bamford, Charles R. - Rockwood Assoc. (C), NY, *540*
Banach-Osenni, Doris - The Brentwood Group, Inc. (R), NJ, *22*
Bandzerewicz, Deborah - Management Recruiters of Washington, DC Inc. (C), MD, *450*
Bangert, James - James Bangert & Assoc., Inc. (R), MN, *11*
Baniqued, Douglas J. - CompuPro (C), IL, *295*
Banister, John - Delta ProSearch (C), PA, *311*
Banker, Judith - Gatti & Assoc. (C), MA, *355*
Banks, Crystal - DS&A (Doug Sears & Assoc.) (C), GA, *315*
Banks, Merrill - Lloyd Staffing (C), NY, *419*
Banks, Paul C. - Paul C. Banks Assoc. (C), GA, *259*
Banks, Renate - Management Recruiters of North Alabama (C), AL, *425*
Banks, Robert - Empire International (R), PA, *59*
Bannister, Robert - World Search (C), OH, *625*
Bannister, Sherry - World Search (C), OH, *625*
Barack, Brianne - The Barack Group, Inc. (R), NY, *11*
Barad, Joel I. - Curran Partners, Inc. (R), CT, *44*
Baraniuk, Reg - Pro Tec Technical Services (C), ON, *519*
Baranski, David J. - Management Recruiters of Chicago-Downtown (C), IL, *428*
Baranski, Glenda A. - Management Recruiters of Chicago-Downtown (C), IL, *428*
Barbeau, Tom - Dunhill Professional Search of N. Charlotte (C), NC, *318*
Barber, Barbara R. - Barber & Assoc. (C), KY, *259*
Barber, Bill C. - Barber & Assoc. (C), KY, *259*
Barber, Darrell B. - Sales Consultant of The Bluegrass (C), KY, *553*
Barbieri, Ellen - Stanton Chase Int'l./ Botrie Assoc. (R), ON, *199*
Barbosa, Franklin J. - Skott/Edwards Consultants (R), NJ, *192*
Barbour, Mary Beth - Tully/Woodmansee Int'l., Inc. (R), WA, *212*
Barca, Anthony J. - Ross Personnel Consultants, Inc. (C), CT, *545*
Barch, Sherrie L. - Furst Group/MPI (R), IL, *72*
Bard, Ann - Management Recruiters of St. Augustine (C), FL, *444*
Bard, Cliff - Management Recruiters of St. Augustine (C), FL, *444*
Bard, Justin - Management Recruiters of St. Augustine (C), FL, *444*
Bardol, Hank - L. J. Gonzer Assoc. (C), MA, *360*
Barefield, Ernest - Gans, Gans & Assoc., Inc. (R), PA, *74*
Barefield, Simone Gans - Gans, Gans & Assoc., Inc. (R), FL, *74*
Barger, H. Carter - Barger & Sargeant, Inc. (R), NH, *11*
Bargholz, Harry L. - Management Recruiters of Wilmington (C), NC, *457*
Barham, Andrew - Dunhill Staffing Systems (C), TX, *318*
Barick, Bradford L. - Management Recruiters of Stevens Point, Inc. (C), WI, *466*
Barick, Linda R. - Management Recruiters of Stevens Point, Inc. (C), WI, *466*
Barillas, Nick - Management Recruiters of Atlanta-Alpharetta (C), GA, *427*
Bariola, Dara - American Medical Recruiting Co. Inc. (C), MS, *248*
Barkan, Stacey - Current Resource Group, Inc. (C), GA, *305*
Barkauskas, Richard T. - The Corporate Advisory Group (R), NJ, *41*
Barker, Carol - Telecom Executive Group (C), OH, *605*
Barker, Mary J. - Management Recruiters of Traverse City (C), MI, *430*
Barker, Steve - Insurance Recruiting Specialists (C), OH, *390*
Barker, Thomas E. - EBA Group (R), NJ, *56*
Barkley, James - Management Recruiters of Champions (C), TX, *462*
Barkley, Keith - The Mackenzie Group (R), MD, *133*
Barkocy, Andrew B. - Princeton Executive Search (C), NJ, *518*
Barley, Kerstin - Brown Venture Assoc. (R), CA, *24*
Barleycorn, James W. - J. W. Barleycorn, Renard & Assoc., Inc. (R), OH, *11*
Barnard, Carl - Accountants On Call (C), IL, *235*
Barnes, Bruce P. - Sales Consultants of Greensboro (C), NC, *554*
Barnes, David - Johnson Smith & Knisely (R), NY, *107*
Barnes, Gary B. - Brigade, Inc. (R), CA, *23*
Barnes, Richard E. - Barnes Development Group, LLC (R), WI, *11*
Barnes, Roanne L. - Barnes Development Group, LLC (R), WI, *11*
Barnes, Sheryl - Blane, Stevens & Kellogg (C), FL, *268*
Barnes, Sheryl - Blane, Stevens & Kellogg (C), GA, *268*
Barnes, Vern - Capital Consulting Group, Inc. (R), MD, *28*
Barnett, Barney O. - Management Recruiters of Shelbyville (C), KY, *429*
Barnett, Dan - J. B. Brown & Assoc., Inc. (C), OH, *275*
Barnett, Kim M. - Management Recruiters of Cleveland-SE (C), OH, *434*
Barnette, Fred A. - Fred A. Barnette & Assoc. (R), NC, *11*
Barnette, Fred A. - Fred A. Barnette & Assoc. (R), NJ, *11*
Barnette, Fred A. - Hartman & Barnette (R), NC, *87*
Barnhart, David - Lechner & Assoc., Inc. (C), FL, *415*
Barnum, Toni M. - Stone, Murphy & Olson (R), MN, *201*
Baron, Annette S. - Eagle Research, Inc. (C), NJ, *325*
Baron, Harvey J. - Management Recruiters of San Diego (C), CA, *426*
Baron, Harvey J. - Sales Consultant of San Diego (C), CA, *551*
Baron, Robert - Peak Search Assoc. (C), ON, *506*
Baron, Sheldon S. - Sales Consultants of Nashua-Manchester (C), NH, *560*
Barone, Marialice - Barone-O'Hara Assoc., Inc. (R), NJ, *11*
Baroness, Anita - Prime Management Group Inc. (C), ON, *518*
Barowsky, Diane M. - LAI Ward Howell (R), IL, *123*
Barr, Charly - Barr Assoc. (C), PA, *259*
Barr, Jamie - Barr Associates (C), NY, *260*
Barr, Kelly - Barr Associates (C), NY, *260*
Barr, Linda - Brentwood Int'l. (R), CA, *23*
Barr, Sharon A. - Barr Assoc. (C), PA, *259*
Barranco, Leticia - Leaders-Trust Int'l./ Carce y Asociados, S.C. (R), MX, *127*
Barrett, Barbara - Access Assoc. Inc. (C), MD, *233*
Barrett, Bill - The Barrett Group (C), NH, *260*
Barrett, Dan - Management Recruiters of Forsyth County (C), GA, *445*
Barrett, Leigh - Krautler Personnel Recruitment (C), FL, *409*

PRINCIPALS

Barrett, Molly - Focus Executive Search (C), MN, *343*
Barrett, Peter - Barrett Hospitality Search (R), CA, *12*
Barron, Robert - Johnson Smith & Knisely (R), NY, *107*
Barrow, Dan J. - The Regency Group, Ltd. (C), NE, *533*
Barry, Cheryl - Management Recruiters of Atlanta NE (C), GA, *446*
Barry, James - CFR Executive Search, Inc. (C), IL, *288*
Barry, Nathan - Nathan Barry Assoc., Inc. (R), MA, *12*
Barsher, Brian - S.C.S. & Assoc. (C), NY, *550*
Barsuglia, Barry - Management Recruiters of Chico (C), CA, *425*
Bartchak, Thomas - Telequest Communications, Inc. (C), NJ, *605*
Bartell, Barbara L. - BLB Consulting (C), NY, *268*
Bartesch, Heinz - Professional Consulting Network, Inc. (C), CA, *520*
Barth, David K. - Barth Smith Company (R), IL, *12*
Bartholdi, Jr., Theodore G. - Bartholdi & Co., Inc. (R), NH, *12*
Bartholdi, Sr., Theodore G. - Bartholdi & Co., Inc. (R), AZ, *12*
Bartholomew, Catherine - C. Berger And Company (R), IL, *16*
Bartl, Frank - Bartl & Evins (C), NY, *260*
Bartle, Tom - Wesley Brown & Bartle Co., Inc. (R), NY, *218*
Bartlett, Phil - P. J. Lynch Assoc. (R), CT, *132*
Bartlett, Stephen P. - DHR Int'l., Inc. (R), RI, *51*
Barton, Gary - Barton Assoc., Inc. (R), TX, *12*
Bartz, Douglas - Bartz Rogers & Partners (C), MN, *261*
Barus, Daniel P. - Lloyd Prescott & Churchill, Inc. (R), IL, *130*
Barus, Daniel P. - Lloyd Prescott Assoc., Inc. (C), IL, *419*
Barz, James M. - International Management Services Inc. (R), IL, *102*
Bascom, Janet - Pro-Tech Search, Inc. (C), IL, *519*
Bascom, Shirley R. - Management Recruiters - North Canton, Inc. (C), OH, *458*
Basel, Larry - Accountants On Call (C), NC, *236*
Bashor, Terry W. - Legal Search Assoc. (C), KS, *416*
Basil, Marvin B. - Marvel Consultants, Inc. (C), OH, *472*
Baskin, Peter J. - Personnel Assoc. Inc. (C), NY, *508*
Baskowski, Stephen A. - Matthews & Stephens Assoc., Inc. (C), CT, *472*
Bason, Maurice L. - Bason Associates (R), OH, *13*
Bass, Harvey C. - Sales Consultant of Sparta (C), NJ, *554*
Bass, Mary - SpencerStuart (R), TX, *197*
Bass, Nate - J.J. & H., Ltd. (R), PA, *105*
Bass, Nate - Jacobson Assoc. (C), PA, *396*
Bass, Rebecca - Johnson Smith & Knisely (R), GA, *107*
Bass, Stanley - Spectrum Consultants (R), CA, *196*
Bassett, Mark - Hobson Assoc. (C), CT, *379*
Bassett, Martyn - Bassett Laudi Partners (C), ON, *261*
Bassman, Bob - Kaye/Bassman Int'l. Corp. (R), TX, *110*
Bassman, Sandy - Kaye/Bassman Int'l. Corp. (R), TX, *110*
Bast, Larry C. - Bast & Assoc., Inc. (C), CA, *261*
Bast, Sue E. - Bast & Assoc., Inc. (C), CA, *261*
Bastian, Mike - Munroe, Curry & Bond Assoc. (R), NJ, *149*
Bastoky, Bruce M. - January Management Group (R), OH, *105*
Bateman, Don - Executive Alliance (R), MA, *62*
Bates, Diane - Alan Davis & Assoc. Inc. (R), QE, *47*
Bates, Nina - Allard Associates (C), CA, *244*
Bates, Ron - StratfordGroup (R), CA, *203*
Bates, Scott W. - Kittleman & Assoc.,LLC (R), IL, *115*
Batista, Daniel T. - Careerfit, Inc. (C), TX, *283*
Batozech, Jeff - IR Search (R), CA, *103*
Battalin, Laurence H. - L. Battalin & Co. (C), FL, *261*
Battan, Pierre - Robertson-Surrette Ltd. (R), NB, *180*
Battipaglia, Vincent - Winthrop Partners, Inc. (R), NY, *222*
Battson, A. R. - The Washington Firm, Ltd. (R), WA, *216*
Baty, R. Gaines - R. Gaines Baty Assoc., Inc. (R), TX, *13*
Bauer, Benjamin - Rob Dey Executive Search (R), FL, *49*
Bauer, Bob - Management Recruiters of Will County (C), IL, *428*
Bauer, Noelle - Youngblood Assoc. (C), NC, *626*
Bauer, Robert - Sampson Medical Search (C), AZ, *564*
Bauer, Steve - Techstaff Inc. (C), IL, *603*
Bauly, Ted - John Kurosky & Assoc. (R), CA, *122*
Baum, Betty - The Technology Group (R), IL, *208*
Bauman, Bobbi - BJB Assoc. (C), VA, *267*
Bauman, Ina - The Bauman Group (R), CA, *14*
Bauman, Martin H. - Martin H. Bauman Assoc., Inc. (R), NY, *13*
Baumann, John - J.J. & H., Ltd. (R), GA, *105*
Baumann, John - Jacobson Assoc. (C), GA, *396*
Baumgaertel, Ingrid - Hedlund Corp. (C), IL, *375*
Bauzenberger, III, E. H. - The Currier-Winn Co., Inc. (C), NJ, *305*
Bavli, Mark - Tech Consulting (C), FL, *601*
Bawza, Leo F. - Chelsea Resources, Inc. (C), CT, *290*
Baxley, Eric - McCoy Ltd. (C), CA, *474*
Baxter, Peter - ISG Informatics Search Group (C), ON, *395*
Baxter, Sheryl - Vincent Lee Assoc. (C), NY, *415*
Bayard, Thomas E. - Claimsearch (C), CA, *291*
Bayer, Cathy - Electronic Search, Inc. (C), IL, *328*
Bayer, Richard L. - Top Gun Group, Inc. (C), NV, *607*
Bayrd, Linda - Wood, Franchot Inc. (R), PA, *224*
Beach, William L. - Beach Executive Search Inc. (R), FL, *14*
Beakey, Lelia G. - Personnel Resources Organization (C), PA, *509*
Beall, Charles P. - G. E. McFarland & Co. (R), GA, *140*
Beals, Calvin - Management Recruiters of Ft. Myers, FL. (C), FL, *443*
Beamer, Thomas G. - Thomas Lyle & Co. (C), IL, *606*
Bean, Marjean - EDP Staffing Solutions, Inc. (C), AR, *327*
Bean, Jr., Robert L. - Management Recruiters of Charleston (C), SC, *435*
Beard, Barbara - Angel Group Int'l. (C), KY, *250*
Bearman, Marvin - Dunhill of Atlanta (C), GA, *317*
Beaton, Carrie - Strategic Assoc., Inc. (C), TX, *595*
Beatty, Richard H. - Brandywine Consulting Group (R), PA, *22*
Beatty, Jr., Robert L. - The Curtiss Group International (R), FL, *44*
Beaudin, Elizabeth C. - Callan Assoc., Ltd. (R), IL, *27*
Beaudine, Jr., Frank R. - Eastman & Beaudine, Inc. (R), GA, *56*
Beaudine, Frank R. - Eastman & Beaudine, Inc. (R), TX, *56*
Beaudine, Robert E. - Eastman & Beaudine, Inc. (R), TX, *56*
Beaupre, Joe - Price Waterhouse Executive Search (R), QE, *168*
Beaver, Ben - The Onstott Group (R), MA, *156*
Bechard, Lori - Lascelle & Assoc. Inc. (C), ON, *413*
Bechtold, Terry - Management Recruiters of Houston-SW (C), TX, *436*
Beck, Joseph W. - National Computerized Employment Service, Inc. (C), PA, *489*
Beck, Larry - Synergy Solutions, Ltd. (C), WA, *597*
Beck, Steven - Beck/Eastwood Recruitment Solutions (C), CA, *261*
Becker, John - Becker Project Resources, Inc. (C), OR, *262*
Becker, Matthew - Becker Personnel (C), FL, *262*

Becker, Ralph L. - Automation Technology Search (C), CA, *256*
Becker, Robert C. - Becker, Norton & Co. (R), PA, *14*
Beckerat, Michael - Michael Thomas, Inc. (C), OH, *480*
Beckley, Preston - The Alexander Group (R), NJ, *3*
Beckman, Susan R. - Beckman & Assoc. Legal Search (C), OH, *262*
Beckvold, John B. - Atlantic Search Group, Inc. (C), MA, *255*
Beckwith, Randy - Seltzer Fontaine Beckwith (C), CA, *579*
Bedard, Felix - Applied Technology Solutions Inc. (C), ON, *252*
Bedard, Felix - Groupe PCA Inc. (C), ON, *364*
Bedingfield, Ray N. - Woodmoor Group (C), CO, *624*
Beech, Arleen - Robert Beech West Inc. (C), CA, *262*
Beech, Robert - Robert Beech West Inc. (C), CA, *262*
Beech, Robert - Robert Beech West Inc. (C), CA, *262*
Beecher, Arthur P. - J. Nicholas Arthur (R), MA, *104*
Beechey, Lynn - Connors, Lovell & Assoc. Inc. (C), ON, *296*
Beed, David J. - The Search Alliance, Inc. (R), FL, *186*
Beed, David J. - The Search Alliance, Inc. (R), CT, *186*
Beehler, Lance - Fortune Personnel Consultants of Hilton Head (C), SC, *349*
Beeson, William B. - Lawrence-Leiter & Co. (R), KS, *126*
Bege, Lorraine - Hands-on Broadcast (R), NY, *86*
Begun, Mike - Search West, Inc. (C), CA, *577*
Behm, Susan M. - The Human Resource Consulting Group, Inc. (R), CO, *98*
Behrens, Mark - Interim Accounting Professionals (C), CA, *391*
Behrens, Rick - Behrens and Company (C), WA, *262*
Behringer, Neail - Neail Behringer Consultants Inc. (R), NY, *15*
Behringer, Neail - Neail Behringer Consultants Inc. (R), NY, *15*
Beilin, Marcia - Marcia Beilin, Inc. (C), NY, *262*
Beiter, Sheila M. - Pathfinders Int'l. (C), MI, *504*
Belaiche, Marc - Creative Financial Staffing Inc. (C), ON, *303*
Belanger, Richard - Kingsley Allen Partners Inc. (R), ON, *114*
Belanger, Rick - Belanger Partners Ltd. (C), ON, *262*
Belastock, Gary - The Retail Network (C), MA, *535*
Belcher, Bob - Sales Consultants of Overland Park (C), KS, *553*
Belcher, Ed - Dunhill Professional Search of Greenville (C), NC, *318*
Beldon, Richard - Professional Support Inc. (C), OH, *523*
Belen, Linda A. - DNPitchon Assoc. (R), NJ, *165*
Bell, Andy - Norrell Financial Staffing (C), TN, *495*
Bell, Catherine - Search Group Inc. (R), AB, *186*
Bell, Cathy - Management Recruiters of Ellicott City (C), MD, *430*
Bell, Danny - Management Recruiters of Ellicott City (C), MD, *430*
Bell, Dixie Lee - MIS Computer Professionals, Inc. (C), KS, *482*
Bell, Edward - Edward Bell Assoc. (C), CA, *263*
Bell, Euris - Innovative Search Group, Inc. (R), GA, *102*
Bell, Gary S. - Gary S. Bell Assoc., Inc. (C), NJ, *263*
Bell, Greg - Cook Assoc. Int'l., Inc. (C), TN, *298*
Bell, Jeff - SpencerStuart (R), PA, *197*
Bell, Lindy - Fortune Personnel Consultants of Huntsville, Inc. (C), AL, *344*
Bell, Michael - SpencerStuart (R), FL, *197*
Bell, Mike - Western Management Consultants (R), ON, *218*
Bell, Nancy - Professional Recruiters (C), UT, *522*
Bell, Nelson C. - Bell Wishingrad Partners Inc. (R), NY, *15*
Bell, Peter P. - Goldman+Bell, LLC (C), NY, *360*
Bell, Thomas D. - John J. Davis & Assoc., Inc. (R), NY, *47*
Bellamy, William J. - Bellamy & Assoc. (C), GA, *263*
Bellano, Robert W. - cFour Partners (R), CA, *32*
Belle Isle, Bill - F-O-R-T-U-N-E Search Consultants (C), MO, *347*
Belle Isle, Patrice - F-O-R-T-U-N-E Search Consultants (C), MO, *347*
Beller, Allen - Michael Latas & Assoc., Inc. (R), MO, *126*
Beller, Rick - CMS Management Services LLC (C), TN, *293*
Beller, Robert - T. H. Hunter, Inc. (C), MN, *599*
Belletieri, Nancy - Probe Technology (C), PA, *519*
Belletieri, Thomas F. - Probe Technology (C), PA, *519*
Bellin, Jean - Boyden (R), FL, *21*
Bellontine, Joanne - Brandywine Retained Ventures, Inc. (R), CT, *22*
Bellview, Allen - Yankee Hospitality Search (C), CT, *626*
Bellview, Louis - Management Recruiters - Friendswood (C), TX, *462*
Bellview, Sibyl - Management Recruiters - Friendswood (C), TX, *462*
Belochi, Michael - Parker & Lynch (C), CA, *503*
Belous, Rhonda - Consulting Rhonda (C), ON, *297*
Belsjoe, Robert - Robert Belsjoe (C), TX, *528*
Belt, Cynthia - Columbia Consulting Group (R), MD, *38*
Belt, Joy Reed - Joy Reed Belt Search Consultants, Inc. (R), OK, *15*
Beltz, Donald R. - SHS of Louisville, KY (C), KY, *580*
Belvedere, Tina - Wesley Brown & Bartle Co., Inc. (R), NY, *218*
Benamati, Nancy - Benamati & Assoc. (C), CO, *263*
Bencik, James P. - J. P. Bencik Assoc. (C), MI, *263*
Bencin, Richard L. - Richard L. Bencin & Assoc. (C), OH, *264*
Bender, Alan - Bender Executive Search Management Consulting (R), NY, *16*
Benedict, James - RLM Assoc., Ltd. (R), NY, *179*
Benedict, Steve - Hayden & Assoc., Inc. (C), MN, *370*
Benefield, Dotson - Summit Group Int'l., Inc. (R), GA, *204*
Benford, Edward A. - Benford & Assoc., Inc. (C), MI, *264*
Benjamin, Judy D. - LAI Ward Howell (R), GA, *123*
Benke, Norman L. - N. L. Benke & Assoc., Inc. (C), OH, *264*
Benkwitt, Barbara - The Brentwood Group, Inc. (R), NJ, *22*
Bennett, Bob - ISC of Houston, Inc. (C), TX, *394*
Bennett, Delora - Genesis Personnel Service, Inc. (C), OH, *356*
Bennett, Joan - Adams & Assoc. Int'l. (R), IL, *1*
Bennett, Linda E. - Bennett & Co. Consulting Group (C), CA, *264*
Bennett, M.D. - The Bennett Group, Inc. (R), IN, *16*
Bennett, Marilyn - Brentwood Int'l. (R), CA, *23*
Bennett, Mark - Bennett & Associates (C), TX, *264*
Bennett, Neysa - Wheelless Group (R), IL, *219*
Bennett, Paul - HEC Group (C), ON, *375*
Bennett, Jr., Robert C. - Bennett Search & Consulting Co. (R), FL, *16*
Benson, Kate - Herbert Mines Assoc., Inc. (R), NY, *145*
Bentley, Lynn H. - The Curtiss Group International (R), FL, *44*
Bentley, Mark - The Thomas Tucker Co. (R), CA, *212*
Berack, Caryn - Keystone Consulting Group (C), GA, *406*
Beran, Helena - Michael J. Cavanagh & Assoc. Inc. (R), ON, *31*
Berardi, Loretta A. - Stentiford & Berardi Assoc. Ltd. (R), NY, *199*
Bereck, Brian - Abacus Group LLC (C), NY, *232*
Berenblum, Marvin B. - Heidrick & Struggles, Inc. (R), CT, *90*
Berg, Charlie - Management Recruiters of Lake Forest, IL (C), IL, *447*
Berg, Eric M. - J.N. Adams & Assoc., Inc. (C), PA, *396*

PRINCIPALS

Bergeon, Eric - Vickers Chambless Managed Search (C), GA, *289*
Berger, Carol A. - C. Berger And Company (R), IL, *16*
Berger, Jay - Pathway Executive Search, Inc. (C), NY, *505*
Berger, Jay V. - Morris & Berger (R), CA, *147*
Berger, Jerry - ACC Consultants, Inc. (C), NM, *233*
Berger, Joel - Meridian Legal Search/Legal Temps (C), NY, *479*
Berger, Joel - Midas Management (C), CT, *481*
Berger, Judith E. - MDR Associates, Inc. (C), FL, *476*
Berger, Mitchell L. - Howard-Sloan Legal Search, Inc. (C), NY, *382*
Bergeris, Jim - Bergeris & Co., Inc. (C), NY, *265*
Berglund, Sharon - Berglund Int'l. Resources, Inc. (C), TX, *265*
Bergman, Jeffrey - Boyden (R), DC, *21*
Berke, Carl E. - The Cassie Group (R), PA, *31*
Berke, Michael J. - LAI Ward Howell (R), IL, *123*
Berkhemer-Credaire, Betsy - Berkhemer/Clayton, Inc. (R), CA, *16*
Berkowitz, Edwin - Wesley Brown & Bartle Co., Inc. (R), NY, *218*
Berlet, William - KPMG Executive Search (R), ON, *119*
Berlin, Norton H. - Magellan Int'l., L.P. (C), TX, *422*
Berlin, Stephen - Corporate Recruiters Inc. (C), PA, *300*
Berlowe, Katharine - Bert Davis Executive Search, Inc. (R), NY, *47*
Berman, Lynn - Goodkind Assoc. Inc. (C), NY, *360*
Berman, Mitchell - The Carlyle Group, Ltd. (R), IL, *30*
Berman, Shirlee J. - Retail Recruiters/Spectrum Consultants, Inc. (C), PA, *535*
Bernal, Joan M. - Barnes & Assoc. Executive Search (C), CA, *259*
Bernard, Harry - Colton Bernard Inc. (R), CA, *37*
Bernhart, Jerry - Bernhart Assoc. (C), MN, *265*
Berntsen, Mary - Accountants On Call (C), NJ, *236*
Berquist, Gailmarie - American Medical Recruiters (C), CO, *248*
Berry, Charles D. - Management Recruiters of San Marcos (C), TX, *463*
Berry, Harold B. - The Hindman Co. (R), KY, *94*
Berry, Paul - Canyon Consulting, Inc. (C), TX, *281*
Berry, Paul S. - Target Search, Inc. (C), PA, *600*
Berry, Skip - PIC Executive Search (C), GA, *511*
Bertchy, Christopher - Meder & Assoc., Inc. (R), IL, *142*
Bertok, Ken - The Wentworth Co., Inc. (R), CA, *217*
Bertolas, Ed - Ed Bertolas Assoc., Inc. (C), CA, *265*
Bertoux, Michael P. - Wilcox Bertoux & Miller (R), CA, *220*
Bertram, John J. - Jack Bertram, Executive Recruiter (C), PA, *265*
Bertsch, Gary D. - Sanford Rose Assoc. - Flemington (C), NJ, *568*
Bertsch, Phil L. - Management Recruiters of St. Louis-Westport (C), MO, *431*
Besen, Douglas - Besen Assoc. Inc. (C), NJ, *266*
Besso, Sandy - Intersource, Ltd. (R), TX, *103*
Besso, Thom - Intersource, Ltd. (R), TX, *103*
Best, G. Tim - BEST/World Assoc. Inc. (R), TX, *16*
Best, Robert - Best, Coleman & Co., Inc. (R), MA, *16*
Beste, Kevin M. - Andrews & Assoc. (C), NC, *250*
Bethmann, Chris - Southern Recruiters & Consultants, Inc. (C), SC, *587*
Bever, Hugh - Kingsley Quinn/USA (R), NJ, *115*
Bevivino, Sal - Questor Consultants, Inc. (C), PA, *527*
Bewsey, Darrell L. - Management Recruiters of Chicago-South (C), IL, *428*
Bhandari, Parul - Tarbex (C), DC, *599*
Bhutani, Praveen - The Options Group, Inc. (C), NY, *499*
Bialecki, Linda - Bialecki Inc. (R), NY, *17*
Bialkin, Joan - Federal Placement Services (C), NY, *339*
Bialla, Vito - Bialla & Assoc. Inc. (R), CA, *17*
Bickerstaff, John - Synagent Inc. (C), ON, *597*
Bickerton, Brion - Bickerton & Gordon LLC (C), MA, *266*
Bicknell, Helen M. - Born & Bicknell, Inc. (C), LA, *270*
Bielecki, Mark - Sales Consultant of Kalamazoo (C), MI, *553*
Bierschwal, Joseph J. - Management Recruiters of Fairfield (C), OH, *434*
Biestek, Paul J. - Paul J. Biestek Assoc., Inc. (R), IL, *17*
Bilbao, Mia - Accountants On Call (C), CA, *235*
Bilinski, Kalyna - Coe & Co. Int'l. Inc./EMA Partners Int'l. (R), AB, *37*
Billingsley, Dennis - Joseph Michaels (C), CA, *401*
Billington, Brian J. - Billington & Assoc. (R), CA, *17*
Billington, William H. - Spriggs & Co., Inc. (R), IL, *198*
Bilotta, Chris - Effective Search, Inc. (R), PA, *57*
Binder, Kenneth K. - Binder Hospitality Group (C), KY, *266*
Bindrim, Melissa - Accountants On Call (C), NY, *236*
Binen, Carol - Thorndike Deland Assoc. LLC (R), NY, *48*
Bingham, Rick - Briant Assoc., Inc. (R), IL, *23*
Bingle, John R. - Capital Consulting & Research, Inc. (R), CT, *28*
Binke, Brian - Management Recruiters of Birmingham (C), MI, *451*
Binke, Brian - Sales Consultants of Birmingham (C), MI, *559*
Binke, Elle - Sales Consultants of Birmingham (C), MI, *559*
Binney, David - NMC & Kay Int'l. (R), CO, *152*
Birarda, Richard W. - JSG Group Management Consultants (R), ON, *109*
Birch, Jerry - Birch & Associes (C), QE, *267*
Birch, Stanley - Birch & Associes (C), QE, *267*
Bird, Len - Management Recruiters of Clear Lake (C), TX, *436*
Birdie, Khurshed F. - NorthStar Technologies, Inc. (C), NY, *496*
Birnbaum, Richard - R. J. Associates (C), NY, *528*
Bishop, Anne - Johnson Smith & Knisely (R), IL, *107*
Bishop, Deborah - Deborah Bishop & Assoc. (R), CA, *17*
Bishop, Don - Sales Consultants of Honolulu (C), HI, *558*
Bishop, James F. - Burke, O'Brien & Bishop Assoc., Inc. (R), NJ, *25*
Bishop, Larry R. - HR Consultants (C), GA, *382*
Bishop, Sandra K. - F-O-R-T-U-N-E Personnel Consultants of Boise (R), ID, *70*
Bishop, Sandy - Management Recruiters of Delaware County (C), PA, *459*
Bishop, Susan - Bishop Partners (R), NY, *17*
Bissell, John - Gundersen Partners, L.L.C. (R), MI, *83*
Bitar, Ed - Boyden (R), DC, *21*
Bittner, Greg - NHA Plastics Recruiters (C), FL, *493*
Bittner, Susan E. - NHA Plastics Recruiters (C), FL, *493*
Bivona, Ernest - Sales Consultants of Morris County, Inc. (C), NJ, *561*
Bizick, Ron - Management Recruiters of Royal Palm Beach (C), FL, *427*
Bizzano, Allison - DHR Int'l., Inc. (R), WA, *51*
Bjong, Mary - The Lawson Group, Inc. (C), SC, *414*
Blabolil, Marie - Engineering & Scientific Search Assoc. (ESSA) (C), NJ, *330*
Black, Amber - United Personnel Services (C), MA, *611*
Black, David A. - Lake Medical Associates (C), ME, *411*
Black, Dean A. - TPS Staffing Solutions (C), IN, *608*
Black, Dennis - Action Executive Personnel Consulting Inc. (C), ON, *239*
Black, Jr., Frank S. - Management Recruiters of Washington, DC Inc. (C), MD, *450*

Black, George - Robert Shields & Assoc. (C), TX, *538*
Black, James L. - DHR Int'l., Inc. (R), WA, *51*
Black, James L. - J.B.A. Assoc. (R), WA, *104*
Blackshaw, Brian - Blackshaw, Olmstead, Lynch & Koenig (R), GA, *18*
Blair, Jane - Management Recruiters - Indianapolis (C), IN, *448*
Blair, Juliet - Johnson Smith & Knisely (R), NY, *107*
Blair, Kelly A. - The Caldwell Partners Amrop International (R), ON, *26*
Blair, Patrick - Creative Management Strategies, Ltd. (R), NY, *42*
Blake, Barbara - Ron Sunshine & Assoc. (C), IL, *597*
Blake, Stacia Foster - SFB Legal Search (C), NY, *579*
Blakemore, Linda - Atlantic Pacific Group (C), CA, *255*
Blakslee, Jan H. - J: Blakslee Int'l., Ltd. (R), CA, *18*
Blanchard, Jeb - Healthcare Recruiters of Midsouth (C), TN, *373*
Blanchard, Sr., Richard E. - C. M. Management Services, Inc. (R), KY, *26*
Blaney, John A. - Blaney Executive Search (R), MA, *18*
Blank, Paula - Lewis & Blank Int'l. (R), CA, *129*
Blanton, Julia - Blanton & Co. (C), AL, *268*
Blanton, Thomas - Blanton & Co. (C), AL, *268*
Blaushild, Eric - AutoPeople (C), VT, *257*
Blaushild, Eric - AutoPeople (C), TX, *257*
Bleau, Donn E. - Global Resources Group (R), CA, *78*
Blecksmith, Edward L. - Larsen, Whitney, Blecksmith & Zilliacus, Inc. (R), CA, *125*
Blender, Dennis - Plante & Moran, LLP (R), MI, *165*
Blessing, Marc L. - Management Recruiters International, Inc. (MRI) (C), OH, *425*
Blessing, Marc L. - Sales Consultants (C), OH, *551*
Blevins, David C. - David Blevins & Assoc. (C), WA, *268*
Bliley, Jerry - SpencerStuart (R), ON, *197*
Bliss, Barbara P. - Lamay Assoc., Inc. (R), CT, *124*
Bloch, Carla - Lending Personnel Services (C), CA, *416*
Bloch, Thomas L. - Southern Research Services (R), FL, *195*
Block, Bonny - Power Recruiting Group (C), TX, *515*
Block, David J. - H. Hertner Assoc., Inc. (C), FL, *377*
Block, Randall T. - Block & Assoc. (R), CA, *18*
Block, Rochelle - Johnson Smith & Knisely (R), NY, *107*
Blom, Ed - Hall Kinion (C), CA, *366*
Blonsky, Lorena M. - LMB Assoc. (C), IL, *419*
Blood, Burwood O. - D. R. Blood & Assoc. (R), AZ, *18*
Blood, Dennis R. - D. R. Blood & Assoc. (R), AZ, *18*
Blood, James L. - D. R. Blood & Assoc. (R), AZ, *18*
Bloodworth, Traci - Cook Assoc. Int'l., Inc. (C), TN, *298*
Bloom, Howard - The Howard C. Bloom Co. (C), TX, *268*
Bloom, Joyce - The Howard C. Bloom Co. (C), TX, *268*
Bloom, Mary - Robert Bennett Assoc. (C), NY, *264*
Bloomer, James E. - L. W. Foote Co. (R), WA, *69*
Bloomfield, Mary - Gatti & Assoc. (C), MA, *355*
Blount, K. Michael - The Maroon Group (R), CT, *136*
Blue, C. David - Management Recruiters of Lynchburg (C), VA, *437*
Bluhm, Claudia Cole - Schweichler Assoc., Inc. (R), CA, *186*
Blum, D. L. Buzz - Blum & Co. (R), WI, *19*
Blum-Rothman, Dena - HVS Executive Search (R), NY, *100*
Blumenstein, LeAnn - Corporate Builders, Inc. (C), OR, *299*
Blumenthal, Joan H. - Lauer, Sbarbaro Assoc., EMA Partners Int'l. (R), IL, *126*
Blumenthal, Paula - J. P. Canon Assoc. (C), NY, *280*
Blust, Ed - Accountants On Call (C), NJ, *235*
Blythe, Thomas J. - Halo Insurance Service (C), AL, *367*
Boag, John - Norm Sanders Assoc., Inc. (R), NJ, *184*
Boal, Robert A. - Management Recruiters of Cleveland-SW (C), OH, *433*
Boase, Stacy - Accountants On Call (C), AZ, *235*
Boate, Mike - Tanner & Assoc., Inc. (R), TX, *206*
Boatman, Millie A. - Whittaker & Assoc., Inc. (C), GA, *620*
Boccuzi, Joseph H. - SpencerStuart (R), NY, *196*
Bodin, Thomas H. - The Personnel Group, Inc. (R), MN, *163*
Bodine, Christine - C. Berger And Company (R), IL, *16*
Bodle, Barbara - Nationwide Personnel Recruiting & Consulting, Inc. (C), OR, *490*
Bodle, Darryl - Nationwide Personnel Recruiting & Consulting, Inc. (C), OR, *490*
Bodnar, Beverly H. - Management Recruiters of Princeton (C), NJ, *454*
Bodnar, Beverly H. - Sales Consultants of Princeton, Inc. (C), NJ, *561*
Bodnar, Robert J. - Management Recruiters of Princeton (C), NJ, *454*
Bodnar, Robert J. - Sales Consultants of Princeton, Inc. (C), NJ, *561*
Bodnaryk, David - The Grant Search Group, Inc. (C), ON, *361*
Bodner, Marilyn S. - Bodner Inc. (C), NY, *269*
Boehm, Maureen - Management Recruiters of Fairfield (C), IA, *449*
Boesch, Thomas R.B. - Pearson, Caldwell & Farnsworth (R), CA, *161*
Boettcher, Jack W. - Boettcher Assoc. (R), WI, *19*
Bogard, Nicholas C. - J. Nicholas Arthur (R), MA, *104*
Bogart, James - The Bankers Register (C), NY, *259*
Bogdajewicz, John J. - Executive Solutions (R), MO, *64*
Boggus, Francis O. - Sales Consultants of Omaha, Inc. (C), NE, *560*
Bogle, Tom - Tom Bogle & Assoc. (C), CA, *269*
Bogue, Randall L. - TBC, Inc. (C), KY, *600*
Boguski, Ronald T. - The Hamilton Group (R), MD, *85*
Bohlke, Sherri - Accountants On Call (C), CA, *235*
Bois, Steven J. - The Furst Group, Inc. (R), IL, *72*
Boje, Bruce A. - Westfields Int'l., Inc. (C), NY, *619*
Bole, John Jeffrey - William J. Christopher Assoc., Inc. (R), PA, *34*
Bolger, Thomas J. - Waveland Int'l. (R), AZ, *216*
Bolger, Thomas J. - Waveland Int'l. (R), NY, *216*
Bolls, Rich - Management Recruiters of Houston (C), TX, *463*
Bolno, Mark - Mark Bolno & Assoc. (C), FL, *269*
Bolt, Kathryn - Robert Half Canada Inc. (C), ON, *366*
Boltrus, Dick - Sink, Walker, Boltrus Int'l. (R), CA, *192*
Boltrus, Richard - Sink, Walker, Boltrus Int'l. (R), MA, *192*
Bommarito, Bob - Management Recruiters of St. Clair County (C), MI, *430*
Bond, Ann F. - Ann Bond Assoc. Inc. (C), MD, *269*
Bond, Delores - Munroe, Curry & Bond Assoc. (R), NJ, *149*
Bond, James - People Management Northeast, Inc. (R), CT, *162*
Bond, Robert S. - Ann Bond Assoc. Inc. (C), MD, *269*
Bondi, Nikki C. - Advantage Partners, Inc. (R), OH, *2*
Bone, Gilda - Selective Recruiting Assoc., Inc. (C), MI, *578*
Bonewell, David - Career Strategies, Inc. (C), AZ, *283*
Bongiovanni, Vincent - ESA (R), CT, *60*
Bonham, Apryl - Claimsearch (C), CA, *291*
Bonnell, William R. - Bonnell Assoc. Ltd. (R), CT, *19*

PRINCIPALS

(R) = Retainer; (C) = Contingency

Bonner, Rodney D. - Management Recruiters of Denver-Golden Hill (C), CO, *426*
Bono, Jeffrey D. - Michael Latas & Assoc., Inc. (R), MO, *126*
Bontempo, David M. - Dunhill Professional Search of Bucks-Mont., Inc. (C), PA, *322*
Bontempo, Mary F. - Dunhill Professional Search of Bucks-Mont., Inc. (C), PA, *322*
Booker, Calvin - National Affirmative Action Career Network, Inc. (C), CO, *488*
Boone, Charles C. - Boone-Scaturro Assoc., Inc. (C), GA, *269*
Boone, James E. - Korn/Ferry Int'l. (R), GA, *118*
Boone, John C. - John C. Boone & Co. (R), IL, *19*
Boone, Jr., Joseph E. - Premier Search Group (C), IN, *517*
Booth, David - Kane & Assoc. (C), TX, *403*
Booth, III, Otis - A.T. Kearney Executive Search (R), CA, *111*
Booth, Sandra - SKB Enterprises (C), NY, *582*
Borchert, Gregory L. - Borchert Assoc. (C), TX, *269*
Borden, Stuart S. - M. A. Churchill & Assoc., Inc. (R), PA, *35*
Borel, David P. - Management Recruiters of Smyrna (C), GA, *427*
Boren, Susan - SpencerStuart (R), MN, *197*
Borenstine, Alvin J. - Synergistics Assoc. Ltd. (R), IL, *205*
Borkenhagen, Christine - Morgan Samuels Co. (R), CA, *147*
Borkin, Andrew - Strategic Advancement Inc. (R), NJ, *202*
Borkin, Andrew - Stratin Assoc. (C), NJ, *596*
Borland, Joyce - Hall Kinion (C), CA, *366*
Borman, Theodore H. - LAI Ward Howell (R), NY, *122*
Bormann, David C. - Yungner & Bormann (R), MN, *226*
Born, Al - Electronic Search, Inc. (C), IL, *328*
Born, Jane E. - Born & Bicknell, Inc. (C), FL, *270*
Born, Samuel J. - Born & Bicknell, Inc. (C), FL, *270*
Borne, Lynn H. - Lynn Borne & Co. (C), CA, *270*
Bornholdt, John - Bornholdt Shivas & Friends Executive Recruiters (C), NY, *270*
Boruff, Doug - Dunhill Personnel of Boulder (C), CO, *319*
Boruff, Fran - Dunhill Personnel of Boulder (C), CO, *319*
Bos, John - Bos Business Consultants (C), NY, *270*
Boscacci, Gene - IR Search (R), CA, *104*
Bosch, Diane - Bosch & Assoc., LLC (R), CT, *20*
Bosch, Eric E. - Bosch & Assoc., LLC (R), CT, *20*
Bose, Emile - Fred Hood & Assoc. (C), CA, *380*
Bosland, Richard - Bosland Gray Assoc. (R), NJ, *20*
Bosworth, Tim J. - Sales Consultants of Lexington (C), KY, *553*
Bothereau, Elizabeth - Kenzer Corp. (R), MN, *113*
Botrie, Jim - Stanton Chase Int'l./ Botrie Assoc. (R), ON, *199*
Bottero, Paul - ISG Informatics Search Group (C), ON, *395*
Bouchard, Rena Roberts - Strategic Resources Biotechnology & Medical Group (C), WA, *595*
Bouchard, Rodney - Management Recruiters of Winsted, Inc. (C), CT, *442*
Boucher, Betsy - Romac Int'l., Inc. (C), MA, *543*
Boucher, Greg - Southwestern Professional Services (C), TN, *588*
Bouer, Judy - Baker Scott & Co. (C), NJ, *258*
Boujemaa, Ben - Hunt Patton & Brazeal, Inc. (C), TX, *385*
Boule, James P. - F-O-R-T-U-N-E Personnel Consultants of Cincinnati (C), OH, *348*
Boulware, Christine - Boulware & Assoc. Inc. (R), IL, *20*
Bourbeau, Paul J. - Boyden (R), QE, *21*
Bourque, Jack - Management Recruiters of Winsted, Inc. (C), CT, *442*
Boutin, Jean - Pharmaceutical Search Professionals, Inc. (C), PA, *510*
Bouzan, Paul X. - The Executive Group, Inc. (R), CA, *62*
Bova, Barry A. - Kingsbury • Wax • Bova (R), NY, *114*
Bovich, Maryann C. - Higdon Prince Inc. (R), NY, *93*
Bowden, II, Otis H. - BowdenGlobal, Ltd. (R), OH, *20*
Bowen, Howard - Howard Bowen Consulting (C), FL, *270*
Bower, Richard - Bower & Associates (C), TX, *271*
Bowerman, Rob - Recruiting Specialists (C), MA, *532*
Bowers, Bob - Claremont-Branan, Inc. (C), GA, *292*
Bowie, Andrew - Bowie & Associates, Inc. (C), MD, *271*
Bowles, Mary - RMA Search (R), TN, *179*
Bowling, Ellen E. - RMA Search (R), TN, *179*
Bowman, Carole - Jordon & Jordon, Inc. (R), PA, *108*
Bowman, Daniel P. - Bowman & Assoc. (C), CA, *271*
Bowman, David - TTG/Sterling Services (C), CA, *610*
Bowman, Mary - Healthcare Management Resources, Inc. (R), GA, *89*
Bowman, Susan C. - Managed Care Resources (C), TX, *424*
Boxberger, Michael - Korn/Ferry Int'l. (R), NY, *117*
Boxer, Harry - The Century Group (C), CA, *287*
Boxer, Kay S. - Roth Young Executive Search of Milwaukee (C), WI, *547*
Boyce, Kevin - Laboratory Resource Group (C), MA, *411*
Boyd, John T. - Onsite Staffing Solutions (R), IL, *156*
Boyd, Lew - Coastal Int'l., Inc. (R), MA, *36*
Boyd, N. O. - Management Catalysts (R), NJ, *134*
Boyd, Sara - Accountants On Call (C), CA, *235*
Boyd, Sara - Accountants On Call (C), UT, *237*
Boyer, Adrienne - Cook Assoc.,® Inc. (R), IL, *40*
Boykin, Steven H. - Page-Wheatcroft & Co., Ltd. (R), TX, *158*
Boyle, Angelique - Management Recruiters - Indianapolis (C), IN, *448*
Boyle, Elizabeth - Infovia (C), CA, *388*
Boyle, Lori - JDC Assoc. (C), NY, *397*
Boyle, Mike - Boyle/Ogata Executive Search (R), CA, *21*
Boyle, Russell E. - Egon Zehnder Int'l. Inc. (R), NY, *227*
Boynton, Richard N. - Wilcoxen, Blackwell, Niven & Assoc. (R), FL, *220*
Bozell, Jeanna - Professional Resource Group, Inc. (C), IN, *522*
Bozman, Bob - Taylor Winfield (R), TX, *207*
Bozza, Gary - Management Recruiters of Chicago-North West (C), IL, *428*
Brace, Betsy - Bertrand, Ross & Assoc., Inc. (C), IL, *266*
Brace, Betsy - International Management Services Inc. (R), IL, *102*
Bradbury, Jr., Paul W. - The Bradbury Management Group, Inc. (R), CA, *21*
Bradford, Carl - CJA-The Adler Group, Inc. (R), TX, *35*
Bradford, Karen - Phillips Resource Group (C), SC, *510*
Bradford, Philip - Major, Hagen & Africa (C), NY, *423*
Bradley, Dalena - Woodworth Int'l. Group (R), OR, *225*
Bradley, Mark - The Landstone Group (C), NY, *412*
Bradley, Mary X. - Bradley & Assoc. (C), MN, *272*
Bradley, Richard - Dynamic Staffing Network (C), IL, *324*
Bradley, Robert - Management Recruiters of Research Triangle Park (C), NC, *433*
Bradley, Sandy - MTA Partners (R), TX, *148*
Bradley, T. John - Bradley & Assoc. (C), MN, *272*
Bradley, Virgina - Fell & Nicholson Technology Resources (R), CA, *66*
Bradshaw, Chris - The McKinnon Management Group Inc. (C), ON, *475*
Bradshaw, Dave - Transportation Recruiting Services, Inc. (C), MS, *608*

Bradshaw, Jack W. - StratfordGroup (R), TX, *203*
Bradshaw, Patrick M. - The Patience Motivation Belief Group, Inc. (C), GA, *505*
Brady, Colin - Johnson Smith & Knisely (R), GA, *107*
Brady, Eileen - Systems Search Group, Inc. (C), NC, *599*
Brady, Marty - The Oxbridge Group, Ltd. (C), PA, *500*
Braile, Jr., Frank - Sales Consultant of Coral Springs (C), FL, *552*
Brakel, H. R. - ProTech Nationwide Staffing, Inc. (C), NY, *525*
Bramblett, Jeanette - Dunhill Personnel of St. Andrews (C), SC, *322*
Bramblett, Richard V. - Dunhill Personnel of St. Andrews (C), SC, *322*
Bramel, Dick - Romac Int'l., Inc. (C), FL, *542*
Branch, Len - Advanced Recruiting, Inc. (C), OK, *240*
Branch, Minnie - M. F. Branch Assoc., Inc. (C), NC, *272*
Brand, Elizabeth - Carol Ball & Co. (C), NJ, *258*
Brand, John E. - Management Recruiters of Santa Rosa (C), FL, *427*
Brand, Karen M. - Management Recruiters of Santa Rosa (C), FL, *427*
Brandeis, Rich - C.P.S., Inc. (C), IL, *278*
Brandenburg, David - Right/McKee Consulting Group (C), TX, *537*
Brandjes, Michael - Brandjes Assoc. (C), MD, *272*
Brandle, James - McCoy Ltd. (C), CA, *474*
Brandon, Irwin - Hadley Lockwood, Inc. (R), NY, *84*
Brandt, Aaron - Career +Plus (C), NY, *281*
Brandt, William E. - Brandt Associates (C), PA, *272*
Brandvold, Steven C. - Executive Connection (C), OH, *333*
Brann, Rudy - Executive Search Group, Inc. (C), CT, *335*
Brannon, Vince - Current Resource Group, Inc. (C), GA, *305*
Branston, Bill - Rushmore • Judge Inc. (R), ON, *183*
Branthover, Jeanne - Branthover Assoc. (C), NY, *272*
Bratches, Howard - Thorndike Deland Assoc. LLC (R), NY, *48*
Bratland, A. J. - Bratland & Assoc. (C), IL, *272*
Brauerman, Donna - John Kurosky & Assoc. (R), CA, *122*
Brault, J. P. - Brault & Assoc., Ltd. (R), VA, *22*
Braun, Jerold - Jerold Braun & Assoc. (C), CA, *272*
Braun, Steven R. - Sales Consultant of Baltimore-Downtown (C), MD, *553*
Brauninger, Elaine - AmeriPro Search, Inc. (C), NC, *248*
Brauninger, John C. - AmeriPro Search, Inc. (C), NC, *248*
Braxton, Jonathan J. - Brian Assoc., Inc. (C), NY, *273*
Bray, A. D. - Rodzik & Assoc., Inc. (R), NC, *180*
Bray, Robert C. - Organization Resources Inc. (R), MA, *157*
Breadon, Peggy - Managed Care Consultants (C), AZ, *424*
Breaks, Nick - The Levton Group Inc. (R), ON, *129*
Breault, Larry J. - Management Recruiters of St. Lucie County, Inc. (C), FL, *444*
Brecciaroli, Diane - DiTech Resources (C), CT, *313*
Bredeson, D. A. - Bredeson Executive Recruitment, LLC (R), TX, *22*
Bredeson, Sheri - Bredeson Executive Recruitment, LLC (R), TX, *22*
Breen, Bill - Personnel, Inc. (C), AL, *508*
Breen, Lupe J. - Dunhill of Buffalo Agency, Ltd. (C), NY, *318*
Breen, Susan V. - GFI Professional Staffing Services (C), NH, *357*
Bregman, Barry I. - Sullivan & Company (R), NY, *204*
Bregman, Mark - Boyle/Ogata Executive Search (R), CA, *21*
Brei, Randy - Brei & Assoc., Inc. (C), IA, *272*
Bremer, Michael - Woodmoor Group (C), CO, *624*
Bremer, Rich - Fortune Personnel Consultants of Greensboro, NC, Inc. (C), NC, *348*
Brennan, Patrick - Handy HRM (R), NY, *86*
Brennan, Vincent - Clayman & Co. (R), MA, *36*
Brennecke, R. C. - Sales Consultants of Greenville, Inc. (C), SC, *562*
Brenneman, Thomas E. - Roth Young Executive Search of Milwaukee (C), WI, *547*
Brennen, Richard J. - SpencerStuart (R), IL, *197*
Brenner, Judy - Branthover Assoc. (C), NY, *272*
Brenner, Michael - LAI Ward Howell (R), NY, *122*
Brenner, Richard - Somerset Group, Inc. (C), CT, *587*
Brennise, Stacie - Healthcare Recruiters Int'l. Phoenix (C), AZ, *372*
Brenowitz, Larry - Fortune Personnel Consultants of Greensboro, NC, Inc. (C), NC, *348*
Brentari, Michael - Search Consultants Int'l., Inc. (C), TX, *575*
Brescher, Frank - The E & K Group (C), NJ, *324*
Brest, Dan - Capital Consulting Group, Inc. (R), MD, *28*
Brian, Brad - Professional Recruiters (C), UT, *522*
Brian, Waylon - Professional Recruiters (C), UT, *522*
Brickner, William J. - Princeton Search Partners, Inc. (R), NJ, *169*
Bridgett, Cal - Sales Consultants of Savannah, GA (C), GA, *557*
Bridgett, Gloria - Sales Consultants of Savannah, GA (C), GA, *557*
Brieger, Steven M. - Thorne, Brieger Assoc., Inc. (R), NY, *209*
Brien, Jason - Kane & Assoc. (C), TX, *403*
Brien, Richard H. - Creative Input, Inc. (C), RI, *303*
Briggs, Farris R. - Staff Resources, Inc. (C), SC, *590*
Bright, Develous A. - The Urban Placement Service (C), TX, *611*
Bright, Jr., James J. - Bristol Assoc., Inc. (C), CA, *274*
Bright, Leo D. - Bright Search/Professional Staffing (C), MN, *274*
Bright, William - The Perkins Group (R), NC, *162*
Bright, Willie S. - The Urban Placement Service (C), TX, *611*
Brill, Michael - F-O-R-T-U-N-E Personnel Consultants of Tampa (C), FL, *345*
Brill, Ted - F-O-R-T-U-N-E Personnel Consultants of Tampa (C), FL, *345*
Brin, Bradley - Concorde Staff Source Inc. (C), WI, *296*
Brindise, Michael J. - Dynamic Search Systems, Inc. (C), IL, *324*
Brindisi, Thomas J. - Brindisi Search (R), MD, *23*
Brink, James - Noble & Assoc., Inc. (C), NY, *494*
Brinkerhoff, David W. - Abbott Smith Assoc., Inc. (R), NY, *193*
Brinkley, Thomas M. - Coleman Lew & Assoc., Inc. (R), NC, *37*
Briody, Steve - Management Recruiters of Arlington Heights (C), IL, *428*
Briody, Steve - Sales Consultants of Arlington Heights (C), IL, *552*
Brissenden, Hoke - Brissenden, McFarland, Fuccella & Reynolds, Inc. (R), NJ, *23*
Britt, Karen - Pennington Consulting Group (C), NJ, *506*
Britten, Albert - Sales Consultants of Scottsdale, Inc. (C), AZ, *556*
Brittingham, R. P. - Search & Recruit Int'l. (C), VA, *573*
Brizendine, Raymond E. - The Alexander Group (R), CA, *3*
Broadhurst, Jr., Austin - LAI Ward Howell (R), CT, *123*
Broadway, David - Ryman, Bell, Green & Michaels, Inc. (C), TX, *549*
Brocard, Vivian C. - Gustin Partners, Ltd. (R), MA, *83*
Brock, John - Korn/Ferry Int'l. (R), TX, *118*
Brock, Rufus C. - Management Recruiters of Mobile Co., Inc. (C), AL, *438*
Brock, T. Michael - DHR Int'l., Inc. (R), IL, *49*
Brockman, Dan B. - Dan B. Brockman (C), IL, *274*
Brod, Walt - MSI Int'l. (C), VA, *487*

PRINCIPALS

Brodersen, Mark K. - Sales Consultants of Omaha, Inc. (C), NE, *560*
Brody, Ilana - Edward Bell Assoc. (C), CA, *263*
Brody, Steve - Executive Resource Systems (C), CA, *335*
Brody, Stuart - R. Green & Assoc., Inc. (C), OH, *362*
Brogan, Pat - Human Resource Bureau (C), CA, *384*
Brolin, Lawrence E. - DLB Assoc. (R), NY, *53*
Bronder, Stephanie L. - Fagan & Company (R), PA, *64*
Bronson, Daniel B. - Lasher Assoc. (R), FL, *125*
Brook, Marsha - C. M. Management Services, Inc. (R), KY, *26*
Brookes, Cindy - Technical Employment Consultants (C), PA, *602*
Brookes, Michael T. - Executive Access Inc. (R), NY, *62*
Brookins, Jackson A. - Selected Executives, Inc. (C), MA, *578*
Brookman, Geoffrey - Brookman Associates (C), NY, *274*
Brooks, Bernard E. - Bernard E. Brooks & Assoc., Inc. (R), SC, *24*
Brooks, Debbie - DBC Recruiting Network (C), GA, *309*
Brooks, Fred - Management Recruiters of Glenview/Northfield (C), IL, *429*
Brooks, Harvey - Fox-Morris Assoc., Inc. (C), PA, *352*
Brooks, Jan - The Personnel Network, Inc. (C), NC, *509*
Brooks, Natalie - Raymond Karsan Assoc. (C), NJ, *530*
Brooks, Peter - Phillips Resource Group (C), SC, *510*
Brophy, Melissa - Maximum Management Corp. (C), NY, *473*
Brother, Joy - Charles Luntz & Assoc., Inc. (R), MO, *132*
Brown, Alan V. - Personnel Alliance Group (C), NJ, *508*
Brown, Anthony T. - Egon Zehnder Int'l. Inc. (R), NY, *227*
Brown, Arlene - Management Recruiters of Orlando-Downtown (C), FL, *427*
Brown, Arlene - Sales Consultant of Orlando (C), FL, *552*
Brown, Ashley - Premier Search Group (C), IL, *517*
Brown, Beirne - Bennett Search & Consulting Co. (R), FL, *16*
Brown, Billye - Tuft & Assoc., Inc. (R), IL, *212*
Brown, Bob - Management Recruiters of Sandy Springs (C), GA, *446*
Brown, Bob - Smith, Brown & Jones (C), KS, *585*
Brown, Bobbi - Management Recruiters of Charlotte (C), NC, *432*
Brown, Bobby - Sales Consultant of Charlotte (C), NC, *554*
Brown, Bonny - Career Marketing Consultants, Inc. (C), GA, *283*
Brown, Buzz - Brown, Bernardy, Van Remmen, Inc. (C), CA, *275*
Brown, C.C. Jay - Fortune Personnel Consultants of Raleigh, Inc. (C), NC, *348*
Brown, Charlene N. - Accent On Achievement, Inc. (C), MI, *233*
Brown, Daniel P. - Johnson Brown Assoc., Inc. (C), IN, *400*
Brown, David - Snelling Search (C), AL, *585*
Brown, David F. - ETI Search Int'l. (R), GA, *61*
Brown, Dennis S. - D. Brown & Assoc., Inc. (C), OR, *275*
Brown, Dudley G. - BridgeGate LLC (C), CA, *273*
Brown, Franklin Key - Handy HRM (R), NY, *86*
Brown, Franklin Key - Horton Int'l. Inc. (R), NY, *96*
Brown, Gene - Management Recruiters of Atlanta West, Inc. (C), GA, *445*
Brown, Gina R. - Strategic Alliance Network, Ltd. (C), OH, *595*
Brown, Ginny - Stewart/Greene & Co. of The Triad, Inc. (C), NC, *594*
Brown, Jr., Hobson - Russell Reynolds Assoc., Inc. (R), NY, *176*
Brown, Ian - SearchCorp International (C), AB, *577*
Brown, James D. - Northern Consultants Inc. (R), ME, *153*
Brown, Jeffrey B. - J. B. Brown & Assoc., Inc. (C), OH, *275*
Brown, Jeffrey W. - Comprehensive Search (C), GA, *295*
Brown, Jennifer - Johnson Smith & Knisely (R), NY, *107*
Brown, Jerry - Brown Venture Assoc. (R), CA, *24*
Brown, Kenneth - ISC of Cincinnati Inc. (C), OH, *394*
Brown, Kevin - Raymond Karsan Assoc. (C), PA, *530*
Brown, Larry - Horton International Inc. (R), CT, *96*
Brown, Michael - Management Recruiters of Shakopee (C), MN, *430*
Brown, Pat - Corporate Suite, Ltd. (C), IA, *301*
Brown, Richard E. - O'Connor, O'Connor, Lordi, Ltd. (R), PA, *154*
Brown, S. Ross - Egon Zehnder Int'l. Inc. (R), CA, *227*
Brown, S. Ross - Egon Zehnder Int'l. Inc. (R), CA, *227*
Brown, S. Ross - Egon Zehnder Int'l. Inc. (R), CA, *227*
Brown, Steffen - Woodworth Int'l. Group (R), OR, *225*
Brown, Thomas - Sales Consultant of Orlando (C), FL, *552*
Brown, Timothy A. - LAI Ward Howell (R), TX, *124*
Brown, Tom - Management Recruiters of Orlando-Downtown (C), FL, *427*
Brown, Wanda - Cyberna Assoc. Ltd. (C), QE, *305*
Brown, William Thomas - Overton Consulting (R), WI, *157*
Brown-Alcala, Sheila - Michael J. Hall & Co. (R), WA, *85*
Browne, David - Personnel Tangent Inc. (C), QE, *509*
Browning, Ed - HeartBeat Medical, Inc. (C), OR, *374*
Brownstein, Joan - Julian Assoc., Inc. (C), CT, *401*
Brownstein, Julian - Julian Assoc., Inc. (C), CT, *401*
Brubaker, Denny - Fortune Personnel Consultants of San Antonio, Inc. (C), TX, *350*
Bruccoleri, Theodore A. - StratfordGroup (R), OH, *203*
Bruce, Dick - The Badger Group (R), CA, *10*
Bruce, Linda - The Whitaker Companies (C), TX, *619*
Bruce, Michael C. - SpencerStuart (R), CA, *196*
Bruder, Dan - CS Dowling Executive Services (R), NJ, *54*
Bruder, William E. - Argus National, Inc. (R), CT, *6*
Brudno, Robert J. - Savoy Partners, Ltd. (R), DC, *185*
Brugh, Amy - Management Recruiters - Indianapolis (C), IN, *448*
Brunelle, Francis W. H. - The Caldwell Partners Amrop International (R), ON, *26*
Bruner, Barbara - Elan Pratzer & Partners Inc. (R), ON, *167*
Bruno, David A. - DHR Int'l., Inc. (R), AZ, *49*
Bruno, Deborah F. - The Hindman Co. (R), KY, *94*
Bruns, Matthew - The North Peak Group (C), OH, *496*
Brunschwig, John M. - Technical Search Assoc. (C), OH, *602*
Brust, Sharon - Pro-Tech Search, Inc. (C), IL, *519*
Bruton, Bob - Sanford Rose Assoc. - Charlotte (C), NC, *568*
Bryan, Amber - Premier Search Group (C), IN, *517*
Bryan, Paula - Angel Group Int'l. (C), KY, *250*
Bryan, Rickie - Bryan, Jason & Assoc. Inc. (C), ON, *275*
Bryant, Christopher P. - AST/BRYANT (R), CA, *8*
Bryant, Ed - Kiley, Owen & McGovern, Inc. (R), NJ, *114*
Bryant, Lori - Renaissance Resources, LLC (R), VA, *174*
Bryant, Mike - Sales Consultant of Los Angeles-Culver City (C), CA, *551*
Bryant, Robert L. - Renaissance Resources, LLC (R), VA, *174*
Bryant, Tom - Bryant Research (C), NJ, *276*
Bryza, Robert M. - Robert Lowell Int'l. (R), TX, *179*

Brzezinski, Ronald T. - Callan Assoc., Ltd. (R), IL, *27*
Bucci, Michael T. - The Partnership Group (R), NJ, *160*
Buchanan, Christine - Management Recruiters of Bordentown (C), NJ, *454*
Buchanan, Martha - Wilson McLeran, Inc. (C), CT, *622*
Buchholtz, Bruce Barton - Fairfield Int'l. Resources (R), NY, *65*
Buchholtz, Bruce Barton - Fairfield Int'l. Resources (R), CA, *65*
Buchsbaum, Debbie - Accountants On Call (C), NJ, *235*
Buck, Jr., Charles A. - Charles Buck & Assoc., Inc. (R), NY, *24*
Buck, James Beau - ASI (C), CA, *254*
Buckingham, Derrick R. - The Hollins Group, Inc. (R), IL, *95*
Buckingham, Ian D. - Anderson & Schwab, Inc. (R), NY, *6*
Buckland, G. Russell - The Bedford Consulting Group Inc. (R), ON, *15*
Buckley, Daniel - The Buckley Group (C), FL, *276*
Buckley, Michael - High Tech Opportunities, Inc. (C), NH, *377*
Buckman, Bob - Hunt Patton & Brazeal, Inc. (C), TX, *385*
Buckman, Jim - Buckman/Enochs & Assoc., Inc. (C), KY, *276*
Buckner, Carol - Mruk & E.M.A. Partners (R), NY, *148*
Buckwald, Brett - The Worth Group (C), GA, *625*
Buda, Jr., Danny - Management Recruiters of Overland Park (C), KS, *429*
Buda, Danny - Sales Consultants of Overland Park (C), KS, *553*
Buehler, Brad - The Goodman Group (R), CA, *79*
Bueschel, David A. - Shepherd Bueschel & Provus, Inc. (R), IL, *189*
Buffey, Gail - Global Consulting Group Inc. (C), ON, *358*
Bufkin, E. Ralph - BFW, Inc. (C), GA, *266*
Buggy, Linda - Bonnell Assoc. Ltd. (R), CT, *19*
Bui, Allison - Accountancies (C), CA, *234*
Bujold, Joseph M. - The Curtiss Group International (R), FL, *44*
Buller, Juergen E. - Sales Consultants of Boca Raton, Inc. (C), FL, *557*
Bullis, Richard J. - Bullis & Co., Inc. (R), CA, *25*
Bullock, David - Columbia Consulting Group (R), NY, *38*
Bulmer, Robert E. - Alaska Executive Search, Inc. (C), AK, *243*
Bumgarner, Robin - Accountants On Call (C), AZ, *235*
Bump, Gerald J. - Foster Partners (R), GA, *70*
Bunce, David C. - Sales Consultants of Raleigh-Durham-RTP (C), NC, *561*
Bunce, David S. - Summit Search Specialists (C), TX, *596*
Bunges, Colin - BT&A, LLC (R), CT, *24*
Bunker, Ralph - Management Recruiters of San Luis Obispo (C), CA, *439*
Bunting, David F. - Crane, Reed & Co., Inc. (C), NH, *302*
Bunton, III, Tom - Sales Consultant of High Point (C), NC, *554*
Buntrock, George - Management Recruiters Dallas North (MRDN) (C), TX, *462*
Buonavita, Tina - Adam-Bryce Inc. (C), NY, *239*
Buono, Angelo - Raymond Karsan Assoc. (C), MA, *530*
Burchell, Robert A. - Fernow Assoc. (C), PA, *340*
Burchill, Barbara E. - BGB Assoc., Inc. (C), IL, *266*
Burchill, Gregory J. - BGB Assoc., Inc. (C), IL, *266*
Burden, W. Gene - The Cherbonnier Group, Inc. (R), WA, *33*
Burfield, Elaine - Skott/Edwards Consultants (R), NY, *192*
Burford, Kevin - DHR Int'l., Inc. (R), MO, *50*
Burgess, Jr., Carter L. - Egon Zehnder Int'l. Inc. (R), NY, *227*
Burgess, Rick - DHR Int'l., Inc. (R), TX, *51*
Burgess, Rick - Human Resource Dimensions, Inc. (C), TX, *384*
Burgess, III, William H. - The Burgess Group-Corporate Recruiters Int'l., Inc. (R), NY, *25*
Burgess, III, William H. - The Burgess Group-Corporate Recruiters Int'l., Inc. (R), CT, *25*
Burgman, Deanna - The Consulting Group of North America, Inc. (C), PA, *297*
Burke, Alan - The BMW Group, Inc. (C), NY, *268*
Burke, Karen - ISC of Houston, Inc. (C), TX, *394*
Burke, Kathleen - The Fourbes Group, Inc. (C), NJ, *351*
Burke, Kaye - J. Burke & Assoc., Inc. (C), TX, *276*
Burke, Lori M. - The Furst Group, Inc. (R), IL, *72*
Burke, Markey - Brandywine Management Group (R), MD, *22*
Burke, Sally - Chaloner Assoc. (R), MA, *32*
Burke, Stoney - J. Burke & Assoc., Inc. (C), TX, *276*
Burke, T. Michael - Burke & Assoc./The Westfield Group (C), CT, *276*
Burkey, Julie V. - J. Burkey Assoc. (R), NJ, *25*
Burkhill, J. L. - The Talley Group (R), VA, *205*
Burkholder, John - Burkholder & Assoc., Inc. (C), TX, *276*
Burkholder, John - Management Recruiters of Addison (C), TX, *436*
Burkland, Skott B. - Skott/Edwards Consultants (R), NY, *192*
Burnaugh, Reg - Management Recruiters of Ogden (C), UT, *464*
Burneikis, Monica - Dunhill Professional Search of San Jose (C), CA, *319*
Burnett, Brendan G. - Sullivan & Company (R), NY, *204*
Burnett, Glenn - WestPacific National Search, Inc. (C), CA, *619*
Burnett, Joan Cooper - Pathways Int'l. (C), CT, *505*
Burnett, Louis C. - Secura/Burnett Partners (R), CA, *187*
Burnette, Dennis W. - Sanford Rose Assoc. - Atlanta North (C), GA, *566*
Burns, Alan - The Enns Partners Inc. (R), ON, *59*
Burns, Donita - Norrell Financial Staffing (C), PA, *495*
Burns, Gale - Snelling Search Recruiters (C), NC, *586*
Burns, Joseph R. - Joseph R. Burns & Assoc., Inc. (R), NJ, *25*
Burns, P. - Hunt Patton & Brazeal, Inc. (C), CO, *385*
Burns, Patricia - Flexible Resources, Inc. (C), NY, *342*
Burns, Patrick - Tekworx, Inc. (C), TX, *604*
Burns, Patrick J. - Career Alternatives Executive Search (C), MI, *281*
Burns, Susan - The Technology Group (R), IL, *208*
Burns, Terry - Foster Partners (R), IL, *70*
Burns, Vicki - The Premier Staffing Group (C), OH, *517*
Burns, Vicki - The Premier Staffing Group (C), OH, *517*
Burny, Holly - Hedlund Corp. (C), IL, *375*
Burr, Jr., Robert E. - Anthony Michael & Co. (C), MA, *251*
Burridge, Jeff - Management Recruiters of Reading (C), PA, *435*
Burt, David S. - David S. Burt Assoc. (C), MT, *276*
Burt, James M. - Sales Consultants of Stamford-Darien (C), CT, *557*
Burtch, Linda - Smith Hanley Assoc., Inc. (C), IL, *584*
Burton, Catherine - Innovative Partnerships (R), CA, *101*
Burton, Linda A. - Management Recruiters of Baltimore (C), MD, *451*
Burton, Linda A. - Sales Consultants of Baltimore (C), MD, *559*
Burton, Rob - Interim Accounting Professionals (C), CA, *391*
Burtt, Christine - J. L. Mark Assoc., Inc. (R), CO, *135*
Burwell, Jr., Frank - PSP Agency (C), NY, *525*
Burz, Christina - Bishop Partners (R), NY, *17*
Busch, Jack - Busch International (R), CA, *25*
Bush, Allison - Boyden (R), NY, *21*
Bush, Debbie - Hall Kinion (C), NC, *367*
Bushee, Robert J. - Corporate Management Services (C), PA, *300*
Bushnell, Sandy - J. L. Mark Assoc., Inc. (R), CO, *135*

PRINCIPALS

Bushong, Suzanne - Austin Group Int'l./ Marlar Int'l. (R), TX, *9*
Buss, Martin - A. Herndon & Assoc., Inc. (R), TX, *92*
Busser-Andersen, Phyllis - Blackhawk Advantage, Inc. (C), CA, *267*
Bussey, Sharon - The Center for Career Advancement, LLC (C), NJ, *287*
Butcher, Barbara - The Stevenson Group, Inc. (N.J.) (R), NJ, *200*
Buteau, R. N. - Datamatics Management Services, Inc. (C), NJ, *308*
Butler, Carol - Leonard Corwen Assoc. (C), NY, *302*
Butler, Daniel - Hreshko Consulting Group (C), NJ, *382*
Butler, Dennis - Management Recruiters - Indianapolis (C), IN, *448*
Butler, Donald W. - Management Recruiters of Milwaukee - Downtown (C), WI, *466*
Butler, Kevin - SpencerStuart (R), CT, *197*
Butler, Jr., Kirby B. - The Butlers Co. Insurance Recruiters (C), FL, *277*
Butler, Lisa - Rushmore • Judge Inc. (R), ON, *183*
Butler, Martha - The Butlers Co. Insurance Recruiters (C), FL, *277*
Butler, Robert J. - Smith, Roth & Squires (R), AZ, *194*
Butler, S. Marcella - Egon Zehnder Int'l. Inc. (R), NY, *227*
Butler, T. Christopher - SpencerStuart (R), CA, *196*
Butler, Vandy - Management Recruiters of Ogden (C), UT, *464*
Butterfass, Stanley W. - Butterfass, Pepe & MacCallan Inc. (R), NJ, *25*
Butterfield, N. Blair - Butterfield & Co. Int'l., Inc. (C), HI, *277*
Button, David R. - Button Group (C), TX, *277*
Butts, Catherine P. - Major, Hagen & Africa (C), GA, *423*
Butz, Richard R. - Career Consultants (R), IN, *29*
Buxton, Carolyn J. - Sinclair & Co. Inc. (R), FL, *192*
Buzhardt, J. F. - Buzhardt Assoc. (R), MS, *25*
Bye, Randy - Elinvar (C), NC, *328*
Byer, Kris - Watring & Assoc., Inc. (C), CA, *616*
Byington, S. John - Page-Wheatcroft & Co., Ltd. (R), TX, *158*
Byington, S. John - Page-Wheatcroft & Co., Ltd. (R), VA, *158*
Bynum, Sam - TaxSearch Inc. (R), OK, *207*
Byrd, Chantel - Performance Resources, Inc. (C), RI, *507*
Byrd, Osborne - Dunhill Staffing Systems of Fort Myers (C), FL, *317*
Byrne, Carolyn M. - The TGA Company (C), TX, *606*
Byrne, Jill - Snelling Search (C), AL, *585*
Byrnes, Tom - The Search Alliance, Inc. (R), FL, *186*
Cabaldon, Larry - DHR Int'l., Inc. (R), CA, *49*
Cabell, Randy - Mercedes & Co., Inc. (R), MA, *143*
Cabugos, Ted - NCC Executive Search Consultants (C), CA, *490*
Cacho, Patick - Dunhill Profesisonal Search of North San Francisco Bay (C), CA, *316*
Cadwell, Larry - F. P. Lennon Assoc. (C), FL, *416*
Cagan, Randy A. - Fortune Personnel Consultants of Raleigh, Inc. (C), NC, *348*
Cage, Jack H. - Sullivan & Company (R), NY, *204*
Caggiano, Anthony - Accountants On Call (C), NC, *236*
Cahan, Edward T. - Sales Consultants of Cape Cod (C), MA, *553*
Cahill, Danny - Hobson Assoc. (C), CT, *379*
Cahill, Peter - Cahill Assoc. (C), CT, *279*
Cahn, Jeff - Gundersen Partners, L.L.C. (R), NY, *83*
Cahn, Juliette Lang - Juliette Lang Cahn Executive Search (C), NY, *279*
Cain, Douglas - Sales Recruiting Network (C), PA, *564*
Cain, John A. - Effective Search, Inc. (R), IL, *57*
Cain, Randy - Career Counseling Inc. (CCI) (C), KY, *282*
Calale, Paul - Halbrecht & Co. (C), CT, *365*
Calcaterra, Thomas M. - Romac Int'l., Inc. (C), FL, *542*
Caldemeyer, Marjorie L. - Management Recruiters of Evansville (C), IN, *429*
Caldemeyer, Marjorie L. - Sales Consultants of Evansville (C), IN, *552*
Calder, Darryl - The Silicon Network (C), ON, *581*
Calderon, Alfonso - Shore Asociados Ejecutivos, S. A. de C.V. (R), NL, *190*
Calderone, Mary Ellen - JT Assoc. (C), CT, *401*
Caldwell, C. Douglas - The Caldwell Partners Amrop International (R), ON, *26*
Caldwell, Clarke - Carnegie Partners, Inc. (R), IL, *30*
Caldwell, Kate - Caldwell Legal Recruiting Consultants (C), ME, *279*
Caldwell, Robert - Robert Caldwell & Assoc. (R), CA, *26*
Caldwell, William R. - Pearson, Caldwell & Farnsworth (R), CA, *161*
Calhoon, Lee - Lee Calhoon & Co., Inc. (R), PA, *26*
Calhoun, Dave - Selective Recruiting Assoc., Inc. (C), MI, *578*
Caliguiri, Edward - Response Staffing Services (C), NY, *535*
Calkins, Quentin D. - Major, Hagen & Africa (C), IL, *423*
Callahan, Tom - Crown Advisors, Inc. (R), PA, *43*
Callan, Robert M. - Callan Assoc., Ltd. (R), IL, *27*
Callicott, Robin D. - Perfect Search, Inc. (C), FL, *507*
Callos, John G. - Callos Personnel Services (C), OH, *279*
Calzaretta, Frank - Abbott Smith Assoc., Inc. (R), IL, *193*
Cameron, James W. - Cameron Consulting Group (R), CA, *27*
Cammarota, Stephen - The Kennett Group, Inc. (R), PA, *112*
Camp, David K. - Management Recruiters of Charlotte-South (C), NC, *433*
Campa, Carl - Campa & Assoc. (R), ON, *27*
Campbell, Brian H. - Venpro Consulting Inc. (C), ON, *612*
Campbell, Carole - Stanton Chase Int'l. (R), TX, *199*
Campbell, Carolyn - Custom Resources (C), AL, *305*
Campbell, Elizabeth - The Bradbury Management Group, Inc. (R), CA, *21*
Campbell, Ellen C. - Reinecke & Assoc. (C), CA, *533*
Campbell, Gary - Management Recruiters of Champaign (C), IL, *429*
Campbell, J. S. - Sterling Int'l. Management Recruitment, Ltd. Inc. (C), NC, *592*
Campbell, James - Executive Alliance (R), MA, *62*
Campbell, Joanna Williams - Sterling Int'l. Management Recruitment, Ltd. Inc. (C), NC, *592*
Campbell, K. J. - Sterling Int'l. Management Recruitment, Ltd. Inc. (C), NC, *592*
Campbell, Margaret - Pricewaterhouse-Coopers Executive Search (R), ON, *168*
Campbell, Patricia - The Onstott Group (R), MA, *156*
Campbell, Robert Scott - Wellington Management Group (R), PA, *217*
Campbell, Sandra - Management Recruiters of Milford Inc. (C), CT, *442*
Campbell, Stephen P. - DHR Int'l., Inc. (R), IL, *49*
Campbell, Terri - T. M. Campbell Co. (R), WA, *27*
Campbell, Vicki - Management Solutions, Inc. (C), WA, *468*
Campeas, David - Management Recruiters of Cherry Hill (C), PA, *459*
Campos, Lily - Marentz & Co. (C), TX, *469*
Camus, Louis - Quantum EDP Recruiting Services (C), QE, *526*
Canady, Sonja - Cook Assoc. Int'l., Inc. (C), TN, *298*
Canala-Parola, Daniel - Allen Davis & Assoc. (C), MA, *308*
Canavan, Patricia - United Personnel Services (C), MA, *611*
Cannavino, John - Financial Resource Assoc., Inc. (C), FL, *340*
Cannavo, Louise M. - The Whitney Group (R), NY, *219*
Cannon, Alexis - Richard, Wayne & Roberts (C), TX, *536*
Cantor, Daniel D. - The Human Resource Consulting Group, Inc. (R), MA, *98*

Cantus, Jane-Scott - Christian & Timbers, Inc. (R), VA, *34*
Canzian, Philip - Crown Advisors, Inc. (R), PA, *43*
Capanna, Cindy L. - Management Recruiters of El Paso (C), TX, *436*
Capanna, Patricia A. - Management Recruiters of Madison, Inc. (C), WI, *466*
Capecci, Eileen - Rice Cohen Int'l. (R), PA, *178*
Capel, Rob - Research Personnel Consultants (C), ON, *534*
Capello, Christa A. - Carnegie Partners, Inc. (R), IL, *30*
Capello, Christa A. - Carnegie Partners, Inc. (R), PA, *30*
Caplan, Deborah - PricewaterhouseCoopers Executive Search (R), ON, *168*
Caplan, John - The Caplan-Taylor Group (R), CA, *28*
Caplan, Sally - Sally Caplan & Assoc. (C), WA, *281*
Caplan, Shellie - Caplan Assoc., Inc. (R), NJ, *28*
Caple, Robert - Coe & Co. Int'l. Inc./EMA Partners Int'l. (R), AB, *37*
Capo, John - Carter McKenzie, Inc. (C), NJ, *285*
Capodice, Peter - Franstaff Inc. (C), FL, *352*
Capozzi, John - C Assoc. (C), DC, *278*
Cappe, Richard R. - Roberts Ryan & Bentley, Inc. (R), MD, *179*
Cappellini, Gloria - Lemming/LeVan, Inc. (R), NY, *128*
Capps, Linda - MIS Computer Professionals, Inc. (C), KS, *482*
Capps, Norm - MIS Computer Professionals, Inc. (C), KS, *482*
Capra, Jamie V. - Warren, Morris & Madison, Ltd. (C), NH, *616*
Caprio, Jerry - Caprio & Assoc. Inc. (R), IL, *29*
Carabelli, Paula - Witt/Kieffer, Ford, Hadelman & Lloyd (R), CA, *223*
Caracciolo, Peter - Management Recruiters of Nassau, Inc. (R), NY, *134*
Caram, Cristina - Litchfield & Willis, Inc. (R), TX, *130*
Caravello, Cindy - Desktop Staffing, Inc. (C), IL, *311*
Cardwell, Jean - Cardwell Enterprises Inc. (R), IL, *29*
Carey, Brenda - The Carey Company (C), NC, *284*
Carey, Cameron - Computer Security Placement Service (C), MA, *296*
Carey, Dennis C. - SpencerStuart (R), PA, *197*
Carey, Harvey - Carion Resource Group Inc. (C), ON, *284*
Carey, Laurie B. - Corporate Staffing Group, Inc. (C), PA, *301*
Carey, Robert - Romac Int'l., Inc. (C), TX, *544*
Cargill, Jim - Management Recruiters of Lake Tahoe, NV (C), NV, *453*
Carideo, Joseph J. - Thorndike Deland Assoc. LLC (R), NY, *48*
Carieri, Carl R. - American Executive Search (C), FL, *247*
Carleton, Bob - Fristoe & Carleton, Inc. (C), OH, *353*
Carlsen, Ann R. - Carlsen Resources, Inc. (R), CO, *29*
Carlson, Eric - Romac Int'l., Inc. (C), WA, *544*
Carlson, Eric - Romac Int'l., Inc. (C), OR, *544*
Carlson, Gregory P. - Carlson & Czeswik (R), IA, *30*
Carlson, Jane E. - Dean M. Coe Assoc. (R), MA, *37*
Carlson, LuAnn - Houser, Martin, Morris (C), WA, *381*
Carlson, Mark - MetroVantage Personnel Systems (C), CA, *480*
Carlson, Pam - Focus Executive Search (C), MN, *343*
Carlton, Sara B. - Rob Dey Executive Search (R), MD, *49*
Carmena, Jane - SpencerStuart (R), CA, *196*
Carmichael, Wayne F. - G. E. McFarland & Co. (R), GA, *140*
Carni, April - Snelling Search (C), AL, *585*
Carol, Barbara - Health Search (C), CA, *371*
Caroli, Connie - TeleManagement Search (C), NY, *605*
Carow, James A. - Management Recruiters of Northdale (C), FL, *427*
Carpenter, Dave - Smith Hanley Assoc., Inc. (C), PA, *584*
Carpenter, Edward - Executive Search of America, Inc. (C), OH, *336*
Carpenter, Elsie - Carpenter & Assoc. (C), TX, *284*
Carpenter, Eric G. - Carpenter, Shackleton & Company (R), IL, *30*
Carpenter, Judi - Carpenter Assoc., Inc. (R), IL, *30*
Carpenter, Lori J. - Carpenter Legal Search (C), PA, *284*
Carpenter, Traci - Transportation Recruiting Services, Inc. (C), MS, *608*
Carper, L. S. - Management Recruiters of Kiawah Island (C), SC, *435*
Carr, Denise - Carr Management Services, Inc. (C), PA, *284*
Carr, Vicki - Searchforce, Inc. (R), FL, *187*
Carr, III, W. Lyles - The McCormick Group (C), VA, *474*
Carrese, Frank - Schwab-Carrese Assoc., Inc. Executive Search (R), NC, *185*
Carrick, Jr., Kenneth D. - Coleman Lew & Assoc., Inc. (R), NC, *37*
Carrigan, Denise - Management Recruiters of San Antonio (C), TX, *463*
Carrillo, Jose G. - Amrop International (R), NL, *5*
Carrillo, Michael - Sales Management Resources (C), CA, *564*
Carrington, Marian H. - Carrington & Carrington, Ltd. (R), IL, *30*
Carrington, Willie E. - Carrington & Carrington, Ltd. (R), IL, *30*
Carris, S. Joseph - Carris, Jackowitz Assoc. (R), NY, *30*
Carro, Carl R. - Executive Search Consultants International, Inc. (R), NY, *63*
Carroll, Kathy - K. Carroll & Assoc. (C), IL, *284*
Carroll, Richard J. - HMO Executive Search (C), IN, *379*
Carrott, Gregory T. - Egon Zehnder Int'l. Inc. (R), ON, *227*
Carson, Sandra - Carson-Thomas & Assoc. (C), CA, *284*
Carson, Sonja - Berkana Int'l., Inc. (C), WA, *265*
Cartella, Janet - Management Recruiters of Laurie (C), MO, *431*
Cartella, Mike - Management Recruiters of Laurie (C), MO, *431*
Carter, Carolyn - Thomas Mangum Co. (R), CA, *208*
Carter, Christine - Health Care Dimensions (C), CO, *371*
Carter, D. Michael - Management Recruiters of Cherry Valley (C), IL, *428*
Carter, Guy W. - Management Recruiters of Travelers Rest, Inc. (C), SC, *461*
Carter, James D. - Bennett Search & Consulting Co. (R), FL, *16*
Carter, Jane - Bennett Search & Consulting Co. (R), FL, *16*
Carter, Jeffrey M. - Carter-Evdemon & Assoc. (C), FL, *285*
Carter, Jon F. - Egon Zehnder Int'l. Inc. (R), CA, *227*
Carter, Keith - Procom (C), ON, *520*
Carter, Kitte H. - Management Recruiters of Tallahassee (C), FL, *427*
Carter, Traci - Accountants On Call (C), CA, *235*
Carter, Wayne A. - The Personnel Group, Inc. (R), MN, *163*
Caruso, Dennis - Caruso & Assoc., Inc. (R), FL, *31*
Caruthers, Robert D. - Caruthers & Co., L.L.C. (R), CT, *31*
Carver, Graham - Cambridge Management Planning (R), ON, *27*
Cary, Con - Cary & Assoc. (R), FL, *31*
Cary, John - Cornerstone Resources, Inc. (C), GA, *299*
Casano, Stephen - Diedre Moire Corp., Inc. (C), NJ, *483*
Casanova, Laura - Hemingway Personnel, Inc. (C), CA, *376*
Casati, Christine - China Human Resources Group (R), NJ, *33*
Case, David R. - Case Executive Search (C), MI, *286*
Case, Mike - Management Recruiters of Cleveland-Client Services (C), OH, *433*
Casey, Carol M. - Casey & Assoc., Inc. (C), TX, *286*
Casey, Daniel J. - Creative Financial Staffing (C), PA, *303*
Casey, Darren M. - Management Solutions, Inc. (C), WA, *468*

PRINCIPALS

Casey, David - The Alfus Group (R), NY, *3*
Casey, Mike - David M. Griffith & Assoc., Ltd. (R), IL, *82*
Casey, Steve - Orion Int'l. Consulting Group, Inc. (C), TX, *500*
Cashen, Anthony B. - LAI Ward Howell (R), NY, *122*
Casillo, Robert - Razzino-Claymore Assoc. (C), NJ, *530*
Cason, Lyn - Brad Marks Int'l. (R), CA, *136*
Cass, Rosemary - Rosemary Cass Ltd. (R), CT, *31*
Cassady, Pat - Michael Shirley Assoc. Inc. (R), KS, *190*
Cassandras, Stephanie - Sherriff & Assoc. (C), KS, *580*
Cassie, Ronald L. - The Cassie Group (R), NJ, *31*
Castanet, Emile - Don Hall & Assoc. (C), GA, *366*
Castell, Jr., William J. - Management Advisors Int'l., Inc. (C), NC, *424*
Castellano-Mattran, Rose - Sales Consultants of Sarasota (C), FL, *552*
Castine, Michael P. - Highland Search Group, L.L.C. (R), NY, *93*
Castriota, Dominic - Rhodes Associates (R), NY, *177*
Catherman, H. O. - Lectra Search (C), GA, *415*
Catt, Steve - Commercial Programming Systems, Inc. (C), CA, *294*
Catton, Chris Lea - Zweig White & Assoc., Inc. (R), CA, *228*
Cauallo, Vincent L. - Behavioral Science Assoc., Inc. (R), AZ, *15*
Cavanagh, Michael - Michael J. Cavanagh & Assoc. Inc. (R), ON, *31*
Cavarretta, Joann - Career Strategies, Inc. (C), CA, *283*
Caven, Peter - Stanton Chase Int'l./ Botrie Assoc. (R), ON, *199*
Cavicchio, Dan - Greenwich Internet (C), CT, *363*
Cavolina, Michael - Carver Search Consultants (C), CA, *285*
Cavoto, Bob - Cook Assoc.,® Inc. (R), IL, *40*
Cebak, William - Entelechy Group Ltd. (R), MD, *60*
Cebrowski, John W. - Sales Builders, Inc. (R), VA, *183*
Cech, Raymond R. - Dunhill Executive Search of Los Angeles, Inc. (C), CA, *319*
Cecilio, Cesca - Montgomery West (R), CA, *146*
Cederquist, Malin - Malin Cederquist, Esq. (C), NY, *286*
Cegelski, Chris - The H. S. Group, Inc. (C), WI, *365*
Cejka, Susan - Cejka Healthcare Executive Search Services (CHESS) (R), MO, *32*
Cepull, Janeen - Elite Consultants, Inc. (C), FL, *328*
Ceresi, Carole - Management Recruiters of Bay Head (C), NJ, *453*
Ceresi, Robert P. - Management Recruiters of Bay Head (C), NJ, *453*
Cerra, Ken - William Bell Assoc., Inc. (C), NJ, *263*
Cerreta, DeAnne - Hintz Associates (C), NY, *378*
Ceryak, George V. - Management Recruiters of Indianapolis-North (C), IN, *448*
Ceryak, George V. - Sales Consultants of Indianapolis-North (C), IN, *558*
Cesafsky, Barry R. - LAI Ward Howell (R), IL, *123*
Cesare, Joan - Personnel Resources Organization (C), PA, *509*
Cesare, Lawrence - Personnel Resources Organization (C), PA, *509*
Chacra, Steven - Chacra, Belliveau & Assoc. Inc. (C), QE, *288*
Chad, Rick A. - Chad Management Group (C), ON, *288*
Chadick, Susan L. - Gould, McCoy & Chadick, Inc. (R), NY, *80*
Chadwell, Rebecca A. - Chadwell & Assoc., Inc. (C), MI, *288*
Chaffin, Denise M. - Professional Team Search, Inc. (R), AZ, *169*
Chaifetz, Marc - Management Recruiters of Chicago-Far West (C), IL, *429*
Chaifetz, Sherri - Management Recruiters of Chicago-Far West (C), IL, *429*
Chalmers, Lynda - Delta Management Group Ltd. (C), ON, *310*
Chaloner, Edward H. - Chaloner Assoc. (R), MA, *32*
Chamberlain, Ann H. - Keeley Consulting Inc. (C), ON, *404*
Chamberlain, Inga - Chamberlain Assoc. (C), GA, *288*
Chamberlain, Wayne - Wayne S. Chamberlain & Assoc. (C), CA, *288*
Chamberland, Roland - Management Recruiters of Sonoma (C), CA, *441*
Chambers, Cindy - Entelechy Group Ltd. (R), MD, *60*
Chambers, David E. - David Chambers & Assoc., Inc. (R), CT, *32*
Chambers, Jere - Sales Consultants of Cherry Hill (C), NJ, *560*
Chambers, Judy - Global Consulting Group Inc. (C), ON, *358*
Chambers, Patricia - Global Consulting Group Inc. (C), ON, *358*
Chambers, III, William - ETI Search Int'l. (R), GA, *61*
Chambless, Vickers - Vickers Chambless Managed Search (C), GA, *289*
Champagne, Richard - Koll-Fairfield LLC (C), CT, *408*
Champion, Dale - The Marathon Group (C), GA, *469*
Champion, Geoffrey - Korn/Ferry Int'l. (R), CA, *117*
Chan, Elsie - Elsie Chan & Assoc. (C), CA, *289*
Chan, Margaret - Webb, Johnson Assoc., Inc. (R), NY, *216*
Chandler, Brad J. - Furst Group/MPI (R), MN, *72*
Chandler, Carole A. - StratfordGroup (R), OH, *203*
Chandler, Joseph J. - Joseph Chandler & Assoc., Inc. (R), IL, *33*
Chandler, Robert C. - LAI Ward Howell (R), GA, *123*
Chanko, Jim - Chanko-Ward, Ltd. (R), NY, *33*
Chanski, Vern - Hobson Assoc. (C), CT, *379*
Chapa, Victor - Victor White Int'l. (C), CA, *612*
Chapas, Kristyn - Cook Assoc.,® Inc. (R), IL, *40*
Chapman, Jeff H. - The Chapman Group, Inc. (C), AZ, *289*
Chappell, Peter - The Bankers Group (C), IL, *258*
Chappell, Peter - Sales & Management Search, Inc. (C), IL, *551*
Chappell, Peter C. - Robertson & Assoc. (C), IL, *539*
Chappelle, Wanda - Warren Executive Services (C), GA, *616*
Charet, Sandra - Charet & Assoc. (C), NJ, *289*
Charette, Anne - The Burke Group (C), ON, *276*
Charles, Kamal - Clinton, Charles, Wise & Co. (C), FL, *293*
Charles, Rebecca - Matrix Consultants, Inc. (C), NC, *472*
Charles, Ronald D. - The Caldwell Partners Amrop International (R), ON, *26*
Charon, Robert L. - Robert L. Charon (C), TX, *289*
Charron, Maynard G. - Paper Industry Recruitment (P.I.R.) (C), ME, *502*
Chartrand, Pierre - Groupe PCA Inc. (C), QE, *363*
Chase, Alta L. - Northern Consultants Inc. (R), ME, *153*
Chauvin, Ralph A. - The Caldwell Partners Amrop International (R), ON, *26*
Chaves-Gregg, Cecilia - Dunhill Professional Search of Miami (C), FL, *320*
Chavoen, James E. - Mannard & Assoc., Inc. (R), IL, *135*
Chavons, Crawford - Phillips Resource Group (C), SC, *510*
Chazen, Jennifer - Sanford Rose Assoc. - Amherst, NY (C), NY, *568*
Check, Andrew D. - A. D. Check Assoc., Inc. (R), PA, *33*
Chelsom, Judith - The Executive Source (C), SA, *337*
Chelston, Joseph - SoftSearch Inc. (C), NJ, *586*
Cheney, Timothy W. - Cheney Associates (C), CT, *290*
Cheng, Karen - Specialty Employment Services, Inc. (C), GA, *589*
Chenoweth, Lori - Agra Placements, Ltd. (C), IA, *242*
Cherbonnier, L. Michael - The Cherbonnier Group, Inc. (R), TX, *33*
Chermak, Carolyn A. - Management Recruiters of Orange County, N.Y., Inc. (C), NJ, *453*

Cherney, Lynn K. - Martin Partners, L.L.C. (R), IL, *137*
Cherney, Steven D. - Resource Perspectives, Inc. (R), CA, *175*
Chertkof, Robert - Fallstaff Search (C), MD, *338*
Chesla, Garry - Executive Referral Services, Inc. (C), IL, *334*
Chesney, Kimberley - Prime Management Group Inc. (C), ON, *518*
Chester, Frank G. - The Libra Group (C), NC, *417*
Chewning, Jr., Ed - Management Recruiters of Orangeburg (C), SC, *435*
Chiaravallo, Laurenc - Diedre Moire Corp., Inc. (C), NJ, *483*
Chin, Daniel - F-O-R-T-U-N-E Personnel Consultants of East Seattle (C), WA, *351*
Chin, Joe - Cornell Group Int'l. Consulting, Inc. (R), NY, *41*
Chisholm, Robert D. - Ashlar-Stone Management Consultants Inc. (R), ON, *8*
Chisum, Jeanne - Executive Sales Search (C), CO, *335*
Chitvanni, John W. - National Restaurant Search, Inc. (R), GA, *150*
Choi, Helen - Pioneer Consulting Group (C), CA, *512*
Choi, Julie A. - McCann, Choi & Associates, LLC (R), NY, *139*
Chrisman, Timothy - Chrisman & Co. Inc. (R), CA, *34*
Christ, Celeste - Quality Consulting Group, Inc. (C), WI, *526*
Christensen, Garn - F-O-R-T-U-N-E Personnel Consultants of Boise (R), ID, *70*
Christensen, Lois - Management Recruiters of Albion (C), IL, *428*
Christensen, Tom - Management Recruiters of Albion (C), IL, *428*
Christenson, H. Alan - Christenson Hutchison McDowell, LLC (R), NJ, *34*
Christian, Jeffrey E. - Christian & Timbers, Inc. (R), OH, *34*
Christiansen, G. W. - Spectrum Consultants (R), CA, *196*
Christiansen, H. Douglas - C.P.S., Inc. (C), IL, *278*
Christidis, Aurora - Brad Marks Int'l. (R), CA, *136*
Christie, Stephen G. - Marsar & Co., Inc. (C), FL, *471*
Christine, Rich - R. Christine Assoc. (C), PA, *290*
Christoff, Matt - SpencerStuart (R), MN, *197*
Christopher, David W. - Resources for Management (R), PA, *176*
Christopher, Rosemarie - Med Exec Int'l. (C), CA, *476*
Christy, Tim - The Partnership Group (R), NJ, *160*
Chrobak, John J. - Pro Tec Technical Services (C), ON, *519*
Chrzan, Phyllis - Brethet, Barnum & Assoc., Inc. (C), ON, *273*
Chung, Glen - Pioneer Consulting Group (C), CA, *512*
Church, Jim - J. F. Church Associates (C), WA, *291*
Chyla, David - DHR Int'l., Inc. (R), IL, *49*
Ciak, Rosemarie - Ken Clark Int'l. (R), NJ, *36*
Cianchetti, Frank - HCI Corp. (C), IL, *371*
Ciancio, Marybeth - Christopher and Long (C), MO, *291*
Cianciolo, Joan - The Sager Co. (R), OH, *183*
Ciaramitaro, Anthony - Corporate Search Consultants, Inc. (C), FL, *301*
Ciaramitaro, Joseph - Corporate Search Consultants, Inc. (C), FL, *301*
Ciaramitaro, Paul - Corporate Search Consultants, Inc. (C), FL, *301*
Ciari, Kate Regan - Fortune Personnel Consultants (C), MT, *347*
Cicchino, William M. - LAI Ward Howell (R), NY, *122*
Cicci, Mary - Squires Resources Inc. (C), ON, *590*
Ciccone, Beverlee - Fortune Group Int'l., Inc. (R), PA, *70*
Cigna, John - Crown Advisors, Inc. (R), PA, *43*
Cimicata, Richard - National Search Assoc. (C), CA, *490*
Cimino, James J. - Executive Search, Ltd. (C), OH, *336*
Cimino, Ron - Paul-Tittle Assoc., Inc. (R), VA, *161*
Cimino, Terry - Executive Search, Ltd. (C), OH, *336*
Cinco, Lawrence K. - Management Recruiters of Melbourne, Inc. (C), FL, *443*
Cinco, Sue K. - Management Recruiters of Melbourne, Inc. (C), FL, *443*
Cinquina, Jr., V. James - Merlin Int'l. Inc. (C), NJ, *479*
Cioffoletti, Anthony - Gahan Assoc. (R), NY, *73*
Cipriani, Sr., Jim - Systems Personnel, Inc. (C), NY, *598*
Cipriani, Jr., Jim - Systems Personnel, Inc. (C), NY, *598*
Citarella, Richard A. - A.T. Kearney Executive Search (R), GA, *111*
Citrin, James M. - SpencerStuart (R), CT, *196*
Citron, Barry - Logic Assoc., Inc. (C), NY, *419*
Cizek, John T. - Cizek Assoc., Inc. (R), IL, *35*
Cizek, Marti J. - Cizek Assoc., Inc. (R), AZ, *35*
Cizynski, Katherine W. - James Mead & Co. (R), CT, *142*
Clancey, Darcie - Broadband Resource Group (C), CA, *274*
Clancey, Mark - Broadband Resource Group (C), CA, *274*
Clanton, Diane - Clanton & Co. (C), CA, *292*
Clapp, Arlene - Arlene Clapp, Ltd. (R), MN, *35*
Clarey, Jack R. - Clarey & Andrews, Inc. (R), IL, *35*
Clarey, II, William A. - Clarey/Napier Int'l., L.C. (R), TX, *35*
Clark, Charles B. - Dahl-Morrow Int'l. (R), VA, *45*
Clark, David A. - Sprout/Standish, Inc. (C), NH, *590*
Clark, Donald B. - Ray & Berndtson (R), IL, *172*
Clark, Donna - Clark Personnel Service, Inc. (C), AL, *292*
Clark, Donna - StratfordGroup (R), CA, *203*
Clark, Ellen H. - Clark Executive Search (C), NY, *292*
Clark, Elliot - Raymond Karsan Assoc. (C), NJ, *530*
Clark, Howard L. - Howard Clark Assoc. (C), NJ, *292*
Clark, J. Arthur - Barrett Rose & Lee, Inc. (C), ON, *260*
Clark, Jerry - Executive Solutions (R), MN, *64*
Clark, Jim - C.P.S., Inc. (C), IL, *278*
Clark, Jim - Management Recruiters of Pensacola (C), FL, *444*
Clark, John A. - Healthcare Recruiters of Indiana (C), IN, *372*
Clark, John Edward - Management Recruiters of Altamonte (C), FL, *442*
Clark, Kenneth - Ken Clark Int'l. (R), NJ, *36*
Clark, Larry A. - The Clark Group (C), MI, *292*
Clark, Lisa - Cooper Assoc., Inc. (C), NY, *298*
Clark, Michael - Cornerstone Search Assoc. Inc. (C), MA, *299*
Clark, Peggy - Dunhill Staffing Systems (C), AL, *316*
Clark, Ronda - Management Recruiters of Seattle (C), WA, *465*
Clark, Steven M. - D. A. Kreuter Assoc., Inc. (R), PA, *121*
Clark, Suzanne - Kaye/Bassman Int'l. Corp. (R), TX, *110*
Clark, Toby - Toby Clark Assoc. Inc. (C), NY, *292*
Clarke, Brian G. - Kensington Int'l., Inc. (R), IL, *113*
Clarke, Debra - NMC & Kay Int'l. (R), CO, *152*
Clarke, J. Robert - Furst Group/MPI (R), IL, *72*
Clarke, Karen - HEC Group (C), ON, *375*
Clarke, Murray W. - Derhak Ireland & Partners Ltd. (R), ON, *48*
Clarke, Richard - Richard Clarke Assoc., Inc. (R), NY, *36*
Clarke, Terry M. - LAI Ward Howell (R), WI, *124*
Clarkson, Dave - Lamon + Stuart + Michaels Inc. (R), ON, *124*
Clarkson, Roger - SpencerStuart (R), ON, *197*
Claudio, Lizzette - DHR Int'l., Inc. (R), NY, *50*
Clauhsen, Elizabeth - Savoy Partners, Ltd. (R), DC, *185*

PRINCIPALS

Clawson, Bob - Romac Int'l., Inc. (C), IL, *543*
Clawson, Bob - Romac Int'l., Inc. (C), IL, *543*
Clawson, Kathy - Mayhall Search Group, Inc. (C), IN, *473*
Claybaugh, Brian - Roth Young Executive Search (C), TX, *546*
Clayman, Stan - CMS, Inc. (C), NH, *293*
Clayman, Steven G. - Clayman & Co. (R), MA, *36*
Clayton, Frank - Executive Search Consultants (R), CA, *63*
Clayton, Fred J. - Berkhemer/Clayton, Inc. (R), CA, *16*
Clayton, John - F-O-R-T-U-N-E Personnel Consultants of Palm Beach (C), FL, *345*
Cleary, Jeanne - The Rossi Search Group (C), PA, *545*
Clegg, James J. - Sanford Rose Assoc. - Charlotte (C), NC, *568*
Clemens, Bill - SpencerStuart (R), CT, *196*
Clemens, Frederick R. - Dorothy W. Farnath & Assoc., Inc. (C), NJ, *338*
Clemens, Jeannette - Kremple & Meade, Inc. (R), CA, *120*
Clement, Laura K. - Stroman Int'l., Inc. (R), CO, *204*
Clements, Denise - Marcus & Assoc. (C), NY, *469*
Clements, Paulette - Probus Executive Search (C), CA, *519*
Clemons, Jani - Robert Shields & Assoc. (C), TX, *538*
Cleveland, Anthony - The Talon Group (R), TX, *206*
Cline, Richard T. - NPS of Atlanta, Inc. (C), GA, *496*
Clingan, Robert H. - Management Recruiters of Broome County, Inc. (C), NY, *454*
Clinton, Omari - Clinton, Charles, Wise & Co. (C), FL, *293*
Clos, Barbara - Carr Management Services, Inc. (C), PA, *284*
Close, Jr., E. Wade - Boyden (R), PA, *21*
Cloutier, E. J. - American Executive Management, Inc. (R), MA, *5*
Clovis, Jr., James R. - Handy HRM (R), NY, *86*
Cobb, Kimberly - Interim Financial Solutions - Mid-Atlantic Region (C), MD, *392*
Cobb, Lynn A. - Management Recruiters of Springfield, Inc. (C), IL, *447*
Cobb, Mark A. - Management Recruiters of Springfield, Inc. (C), IL, *447*
Cobb-West, Rosemary G. - West & West (R), CA, *218*
Cochlan, Paul T. - PC Assoc. (C), CO, *505*
Cochran, Corinne - Early Cochran & Olson (R), IL, *56*
Cochran, Ginny - Romac Int'l., Inc. (C), TX, *544*
Cochran, Mayumi - Corporate Select Int'l., Ltd. (C), IL, *301*
Coco, Jr., Carl - Professions, Inc. (C), OH, *523*
Cody-Quinn, Amy - Management Recruiters of Kona (C), HI, *428*
Coe, Ann - Ann Coe & Assoc. (C), IL, *294*
Coe, Karen - Coe & Co. Int'l. Inc./EMA Partners Int'l. (R), AB, *37*
Coello, Jorge - Shore Asociados Ejecutivos, S. A. de C.V. (R), JAL, *190*
Coelyn, Ronald H. - The Coelyn Group (R), CA, *37*
Coff, Scott - Johnson Smith & Knisely (R), NY, *107*
Coffee, Michael - Franstaff Inc. (C), FL, *352*
Coffey, Michael O. - The Langford Search, Inc. (C), AL, *412*
Coffin, Susan M. - The Heidrick Partners, Inc. (R), IL, *90*
Cogavin, Lynn - Accountants On Call (C), MA, *236*
Coghan, Tom - The Yaiser Group (C), NJ, *625*
Cognac, Michael - Retained Search Assoc. (R), NC, *176*
Cohen, Barry - Response Staffing Services (C), NY, *535*
CoHen, Debra - Accountants On Call (C), MO, *236*
Cohen, Diane - Michael Levine Search Consultants (R), NY, *129*
Cohen, Eve - Aster Search Group (R), NY, *8*
Cohen, Harris J. - Sales Consultants of Melville (C), NY, *554*
Cohen, Irwin - Benson Associates (C), NY, *264*
Cohen, Jeff - Rice Cohen Int'l. (R), PA, *178*
Cohen, Kenneth R. - The Synergy Organization (R), PA, *205*
Cohen, Lawrence J. - Norgate Technology, Inc. (C), NY, *494*
Cohen, Michael R. - Intech Summit Group, Inc. (R), CA, *102*
Cohen, Pamela S. - Topaz Int'l., Inc., Attorney Search (C), NJ, *607*
Cohen, Richard - Management Recruiters of Manhattan on Broadway (C), NY, *455*
Cohen, Robert C. - Intech Summit Group, Inc. (R), CA, *102*
Cohen, Samuel N. - Professions, Inc. (C), OH, *523*
Cohen, Stephanie - Johnson Smith & Knisely (R), NY, *107*
Cokins, Nicholas - The Hiring Authority, Inc. (C), FL, *379*
Colacchio, Thomas P. - Futures, Inc. (C), NH, *354*
Colacci, Gary - Carnegie Partners, Inc. (R), CA, *30*
Colasanto, Frank M. - W. R. Rosato & Assoc., Inc. (R), NY, *182*
Colavito, II, Joseph W. - LAI Ward Howell (R), GA, *123*
Colbourn, Ken - F-O-R-T-U-N-E Personnel Consultants of Knoxville (C), TN, *350*
Cole, Christopher - Tech-Net (C), TX, *601*
Cole, Don - Riley Cole (C), CA, *537*
Cole, Floyd - National Field Service Corp. (C), NY, *489*
Cole, James - Systems Research Group (C), OH, *598*
Cole, John P. - Creative Management Strategies, Ltd. (R), NY, *42*
Cole, Leslie C. - Management Recruiters of Middlesex (C), CT, *442*
Cole, Ronald - Cole, Warren & Long, Inc. (R), PA, *37*
Cole-Hill, Susan - Brentwood Int'l. (R), CA, *23*
Coleman, Claudia A. - Best, Coleman & Co., Inc. (R), MA, *16*
Coleman, Greg - Strategic Assoc., Inc. (C), TX, *595*
Coleman, J. Kevin - J. Kevin Coleman & Assoc., Inc. (R), CA, *37*
Coleman, John A. - Boardroom Consultants/Kenny Kindler Tholke (R), NY, *19*
Coleman, Michael M. - Coleman Legal Search Consultants (C), NJ, *294*
Coleman, Michael M. - Coleman Legal Search Consultants (C), PA, *294*
Coleman, Neil F. - Management Recruiters of Statesville (C), NC, *433*
Coleman, Tracy A. - West Coast Recruiting (C), CA, *619*
Coleman, William - Stephens Assoc. Ltd., Inc. (R), OH, *200*
Coletti, Diane - Prestonwood Assoc. (R), MA, *168*
Collard, Joseph A. - SpencerStuart (R), TX, *197*
Collier, Carmen Anne - William-Johns Co., Inc. (C), CA, *621*
Collier, Gordon L. - R. C. Services (C), TX, *528*
Colling, Douglas - KPMG Executive Search (R), ON, *119*
Collingwood, Beryl - Trillium Human Resources Inc. (C), ON, *609*
Collins, Bart - Computer Placements Unlimited Inc. (C), NY, *295*
Collins, Judy - Sales Consultants of Chicago South (C), IL, *558*
Collins, Kenneth B. - Executive Search Partners (R), NY, *63*
Collins, Lynn - Computer Placements Unlimited Inc. (C), NY, *295*
Collins, Phil - Claremont-Branan, Inc. (C), GA, *292*
Collins, Philip M. - Collins & Associates (C), MI, *294*
Collins, Robert J. - Financial Search Corp. (C), IL, *340*
Collins, Sara E. - Alexander & Collins (C), CA, *243*
Collins, Sean - DHR Int'l., Inc. (R), FL, *50*
Collins, Steve - The Johnson Group, Unlimited (C), NY, *400*
Collins, Steve L. - S L Collins Assoc. (C), NC, *294*
Collins, Susan - Creative-Leadership, Inc. (R), CA, *42*
Collins, Victoria - Sales Consultants of Dallas (C), TX, *563*
Collis, Marty - E. L. Shore & Assoc. (R), ON, *190*

Colman, Michael - Executive Placement Consultants (C), IL, *333*
Colton, Roy C. - Colton Bernard Inc. (R), CA, *37*
Colton, Scott C. - The Colton Partnership, Inc. (R), NY, *38*
Colton, W. Hoyt - The Colton Partnership, Inc. (R), NY, *38*
Coltrane, Mike - Richard, Wayne & Roberts (C), AZ, *536*
Colucci, Bart A. - Colucci, Blendow & Johnson (R), CA, *38*
Coman, Michael J. - The Human Resource Group, Inc. (R), OH, *98*
Combe, II, Charles V. - Empire International (R), PA, *59*
Combs, Stephen - StratfordGroup (R), CA, *203*
Comer, Patricia - Accountants On Call (C), NC, *236*
Comparetto, Gino - Lloyd Prescott & Churchill, Inc. (R), NY, *130*
Comparetto, Gino - Lloyd Prescott Assoc., Inc. (C), NY, *419*
Compton, Bill - F-O-R-T-U-N-E Personnel Consultants of St. Louis-West County (C), MO, *347*
Comstock, Roger - Johnson Smith & Knisely (R), CA, *107*
Conant, Harold B. - Healthcare Recruiters International-NY/NJ (C), NJ, *373*
Conard, Rodney J. - Conard Associates, Inc. (R), NH, *39*
Concannon, Bob - StratfordGroup (R), CA, *203*
Cone, Dan P. - Management Recruiters of Rocky Mount (C), NC, *432*
Conedera, Joanne - Icon Recruiters, LLC (C), CA, *387*
Conley, Kevin E. - LAI Ward Howell (R), MA, *123*
Conley, Laura - United Personnel Services (C), CT, *611*
Conlin, Ed - Allen Austin Lowe & Powers (R), TX, *4*
Conlin, Edward T. - Allen Austin Lowe & Powers (R), TX, *3*
Connelly, Amy Reece - Johnson Brown Assoc., Inc. (C), IN, *400*
Connelly, Heather - The Caldwell Partners Amrop International (R), ON, *26*
Connelly, III, Joseph H. - CS Associates, LLC (C), AZ, *304*
Connelly, Kevin M. - SpencerStuart (R), IL, *197*
Connelly, Laura - Management Recruiters of Pittsburgh (C), PA, *459*
Connelly, Susan D. - CS Associates, LLC (C), AZ, *304*
Conner, Chuck - Strauss Personnel Service (C), PA, *596*
Conner, Marlene L. - M. L. Conner (C), FL, *296*
Conners, Jeffrey - Jeffrey Allan Co., Inc. (C), CA, *398*
Conners, Norma - Jeffrey Allan Co., Inc. (C), CA, *398*
Connolly, Claire E. - CEC Associates (R), MA, *32*
Connor, Jean - Management Recruiters - Indianapolis (C), IN, *448*
Connors, Barry - Conors, Lovell & Assoc., Inc. (C), ON, *296*
Connors, Brian J. - S. Tanner & Assoc. Inc. (C), ON, *599*
Conover, Jo Carol - TASA International (R), CA, *206*
Conroy, Daniel J. - Michael Latas & Assoc., Inc. (R), MO, *126*
Conroy, M. J. - Conroy Partners Ltd. (R), AB, *39*
Conroy, Martin - T. H. Hunter, Inc. (C), MN, *599*
Constant, Rene - Milrod Assoc. (C), NJ, *482*
Converse, Wendy - DHR Int'l., Inc. (R), NY, *50*
Conville, RJ (Kip) - The Park Group & Assoc., Inc. (C), MD, *503*
Conway, Maureen - Conway & Assoc. (R), IL, *40*
Conway, Philip A. - Philip Conway Management (R), IL, *40*
Conway, Thomas - Technology Consultants Int'l. (C), CA, *603*
Conyngham, Beth - Excalibur Human Resources, Inc. (R), NJ, *61*
Cook, Amanda - Partnervision Consulting Group Inc. (R), ON, *160*
Cook, Clifford L. - CEO Consulting (C), FL, *287*
Cook, Daniel P. - Alpha Resources (C), IL, *246*
Cook, Dennis F. - MESA, Inc. (R), CO, *143*
Cook, Gene - Cook Assoc. Int'l., Inc. (C), TN, *298*
Cook, John S. - C. J. Vincent Assoc., LLC (C), MD, *612*
Cook, Leslie - Kirk Palmer & Assoc., Inc. (R), MA, *158*
Cook, Martin E. - Cook Assoc. Int'l., Inc. (C), TN, *298*
Cook, P. Gene - P. G. Cook Assoc. (R), TN, *40*
Cook, Robin - Impact Search & Strategies (C), PA, *387*
Cook, Stephen G. - Cook Assoc. Int'l., Inc. (C), TN, *298*
Cook, Thomas - Cypress Int'l., Inc. (R), FL, *45*
Cooke, Gerald W. - STM Assoc. (R), UT, *201*
Cooke, Jeffrey R. - The Cooke Group (R), WI, *40*
Cooke, Katherine H. - Horton International Inc. (R), CT, *96*
Cooksey, Ben - Management Recruiters of Clear Lake (C), TX, *436*
Cooper, B. V. - QVS Int'l. (R), GA, *170*
Cooper, Bill - Management Recruiters of Chattanooga-Brainerd, Inc. (C), TN, *461*
Cooper, Bill - Sales Consultants of Chattanooga-Brainerd (C), TN, *555*
Cooper, David C. - David C. Cooper & Assoc. Financial Search (C), GA, *298*
Cooper, Elizabeth - Creative-Leadership, Inc. (R), CA, *42*
Cooper, Jesse - DHR Int'l., Inc. (R), MA, *50*
Cooper, Jill - DHR Int'l., Inc. (R), MA, *50*
Cooper, Karen - Ashford Management Group, Inc. (R), GA, *8*
Cooper, Larry - Management Recruiters of Atlanta (C), GA, *445*
Cooper, Larry W. - Sales Consultants of Atlanta (C), GA, *552*
Cooper, Linda - BG & Assoc. (C), MD, *266*
Cooper, Liz - The Beardsley Group Inc. (C), CT, *261*
Cooper, Michael - Chad Management Group (C), ON, *288*
Cooper, Michael - Cooper Management Assoc., Inc. (C), NJ, *298*
Cooper, Norman T. - Cooper Assoc., Inc. (C), NY, *298*
Cooper, Robert M. - The Cooper Executive Search Group Inc. (R), WI, *41*
Cooper, Ron - High Tech Opportunities, Inc. (C), NH, *377*
Copeland, Dawn - Descheneaux Recruitment Services Ltd. (C), BC, *311*
Copeland, Gates - Management Recruiters of Houston-Northeast (C), TX, *463*
Copeland, Linda - Management Recruiters of Houston-Northeast (C), TX, *463*
Copp, Bob - Adirect Recruiting Corp. (C), ON, *240*
Coppola, Anna - The Flagship Group (R), MA, *68*
Corabelli, Paula - EMN/Witt/Kieffer (R), CA, *59*
Corbett, Charles C. - Davis-Smith, Inc. (C), MI, *309*
Corbin, Earl - Corbin Packaging Professionals (C), MO, *299*
Corcoran, Gary - Southern Chemical & Plastics Search (C), GA, *587*
Cordell, Cindy Andrew - Corporate Resources (C), OH, *301*
Corder, Eutha - RBW Assoc. Inc. (C), AR, *531*
Corey, Joe - Industry Consultants, Inc. (C), AZ, *388*
Corey, Michael J. - LAI Ward Howell (R), WI, *124*
Corey, Michael J. - Witt/Kieffer, Ford, Hadelman & Lloyd (R), IL, *223*
Corey, Patrick M. - LAI Ward Howell (R), WI, *124*
Corey, Richard F. - Weterrings & Agnew, Inc. (C), NY, *619*
Corkum, Jennifer - Doherty Healthcare Consultants (C), ME, *313*
Cormier, Don - National Executive (C), ON, *489*
Cornehlsen, James H. - Skott/Edwards Consultants (R), NY, *192*
Cornelison, Mike - M.C. Executive Search (C), CA, *422*
Cornell, Don - Consultant Recruiters (C), WI, *297*
Cornell, Rich - Hitchens & Foster, Inc. (C), MO, *379*
Cornett, Kristine - Management Recruiters of Boone (C), NC, *456*

PRINCIPALS

(R) = Retainer; (C) = Contingency

Cornfoot, James L. - Management Recruiters of San Antonio (C), TX, *463*
Corporon, Charles E. - Quirk-Corporon & Assoc., Inc. (C), WI, *527*
Corrales, Shaun - cFour Partners (R), CA, *32*
Corrao, Laura S. - Corrao, Miller, Rush & Wiesenthal (C), NY, *301*
Corrao, Michele - The Garvis Group, Inc. (C), LA, *355*
Correia, Linda Mercedes - Mercedes & Co., Inc. (R), MA, *143*
Corriero, Mike - RCI Employment Solutions (C), FL, *531*
Corrigan, Jr., George T. - Howe & Assoc. (R), PA, *97*
Corrigan, Gerald F. - The Corrigan Group (R), CA, *42*
Corso, Glen S. - LAI Ward Howell (R), CA, *123*
Corso, John J. - Corso, Mizgala + French (R), ON, *42*
Cortez, Roger B. - TASA International (R), TX, *206*
Corwen, Leonard - Leonard Corwen Assoc. (C), NY, *302*
Corwin, J. Blade - Seitchik Corwin & Seitchik Inc. (R), CA, *188*
Corya, James E. - National Corporate Consultants, Inc. (C), IN, *489*
Cosier, Brian - Cosier & Assoc. (C), AB, *302*
Cossa, Kristen - JM & Company (R), PA, *106*
Costa, Karen - The Kinlin Co., Inc. (R), MA, *115*
Costabile, Lou - Business Systems of America, Inc. (C), IL, *277*
Costas, John - Management Consultants Corporate Recruiters (C), AZ, *424*
Costello, Lynda - Coe & Co. Int'l. Inc./EMA Partners Int'l. (R), AB, *37*
Costick, Kathryn J. - John Sibbald Assoc., Inc. (R), MO, *191*
Cote, John J. - Sales Consultant of Hooksett (C), NH, *553*
Cotter, Dan - J. D. Cotter Search Inc. (C), OH, *302*
Cotter, Joe - J. D. Cotter Search Inc. (C), OH, *302*
Cotterell, Dirk A. - Management Recruiters of Salt Lake City (C), UT, *464*
Cotton, Peter C. - Sales Consultants of Rhode Island, Inc. (C), RI, *562*
Coughlin, Linda - Partners in Recruiting (C), IL, *504*
Cougle, Nancy - Advanced Recruitment, Inc. (C), TN, *240*
Counts, Robert L. - Granger, Counts & Assoc. (R), OH, *81*
Courbat, Thomas - Bartholdi & Co., Inc. (R), CA, *12*
Courtney, Brendan - Interim Financial Solutions - Mid-Atlantic Region (C), MD, *392*
Courtney-Couch, Terri - DHR Int'l., Inc. (R), WI, *51*
Courtright, Robert J. - Courtright & Assoc., Inc. (R), PA, *42*
Cousins, John L. - Procurement Resources (C), MD, *520*
Covalciuc, Rick - Sales Consultants of Omaha, Inc. (C), NE, *560*
Cowall, Frank A. - Altec/HRC (C), MI, *246*
Cowan, Bruce - Synergy Systems (C), ON, *598*
Cowan, Gordon - Tittemore Cowan Assoc. (C), AB, *607*
Cowan, Lawrence G. - Search West, Inc. (C), CA, *576*
Cowan, Robert A. - Search West, Inc. (C), CA, *576*
Cowan, Roberta - Drew Assoc. Int'l. (R), NJ, *54*
Cowell, Roy A. - Cowell & Associates, Ltd. (R), IL, *42*
Cowin, David M. - Cowin Assoc. (R), NY, *42*
Cowlan, Trudi - Trudi Cowlan (C), NY, *302*
Cowling, John W. - Professional Resources (C), OK, *522*
Cowlishaw, Ronnette - Sales Consultants of Denver (C), CO, *557*
Cox, James O. - MES Search Co. (C), GA, *479*
Cox, Joan - The Pailin Group Professional Search Consultants (R), TX, *158*
Cox, Larry - Human Resource Solutions (R), TX, *99*
Cox, Patti - O'Rourke Companies, Inc. (R), TX, *154*
Cox, William R. - Cox, Darrow & Owens, Inc. (C), NJ, *302*
Cozzens, Robert W. - Wayne Assoc., Inc. (C), VA, *616*
Cozzillio, Larry - The Andre Group, Inc. (R), PA, *6*
Crabtree, G. A. - Roger Dietsch & Assoc. (C), MN, *312*
Cracknell, Jo Anne - NCC Executive Search Consultants (C), CA, *490*
Craig, Lynn - The Riverbend Group (C), MO, *538*
Craig, Michael C. - Magellan Int'l., L.P. (C), TX, *422*
Craig, Randy H. - J. Fielding Nelson & Assoc., Inc. (R), UT, *151*
Cram, Noel - Barone Assoc. (C), NJ, *259*
Cramer, Paul J. - C/R Associates (C), NY, *278*
Crane, Don - California Search Agency, Inc. (C), CA, *279*
Crane, Howard C. - LAI Ward Howell (R), CA, *123*
Crane, Mary - International Pro Sourcing, Inc. (C), PA, *393*
Crass, Dorothea - Corporate Management Services (C), PA, *300*
Crath, Paul F. - PricewaterhouseCoopers Executive Search (R), ON, *168*
Crawford, Arlen - PIC Executive Search (C), GA, *511*
Crawford, Dick B. - Management Recruiters of Orangeburg (C), SC, *435*
Crawford, Ed - Romac Int'l., Inc. (C), FL, *542*
Crawford, Ed - Romac Int'l., Inc. (C), FL, *542*
Crawford, Ed - Romac Int'l., Inc. (C), FL, *543*
Crawford, Jacqueline - Graphic Arts Marketing Assoc., Inc. (C), MI, *361*
Crawford, John D. - Boyden (R), ON, *21*
Crawford, John H. - Clayman & Co. (R), MA, *36*
Crawford, Marjorie - Personnel Assoc. (C), CA, *508*
Crawford, Roger - Graphic Arts Marketing Assoc., Inc. (C), MI, *361*
Crawford, Tom - The Crawford Group (C), GA, *303*
Creasy, Nancy - Michael Latas & Assoc., Inc. (R), MO, *126*
Crecos, Gregory P. - Gregory Michaels & Assoc., Inc. (R), IL, *82*
Credaire, Cris - Berkhemer/Clayton, Inc. (R), CA, *16*
Credidio, Thomas J. - The DataFinders Group, Inc. (C), NJ, *307*
Creech, Bud - McCarthy Assoc. National BancSearch, LLC (C), LA, *473*
Creeger, David - Sanford Rose Assoc. - Fairlawn (C), OH, *569*
Cresci, Joseph - Yankee Hospitality Search (C), CT, *626*
Cresci, Joseph - Yankee Hospitality Search (C), MA, *626*
Crigler, James - Management Recruiters of Winona (C), MN, *452*
Cripe, Joyce - MIXTEC Group (R), CA, *145*
Cris, Jan - The Cris Group, Inc. (R), NY, *43*
Crispi, Nicholas - Crispi, Wagner & Co., Inc. (R), NY, *43*
Crist, Athan - O'Keefe & Assoc., Inc. (R), CT, *154*
Crist, Peter D. - Crist Partners, Ltd. (R), IL, *43*
Critchfield, Marlene - Marlene Critchfield Co. (C), CA, *303*
Critchley, Walter - Cochran, Cochran & Yale, Inc. (R), NY, *37*
Critchley, Walter Y. - Cochran, Cochran & Yale, Inc. (R), NY, *36*
Crittenden, John M. - Dunhill Professional Search of Miami (C), FL, *320*
Croasdale, J. Scott - Raymond Karsan Assoc. (C), CO, *530*
Crone, Russell - Maczkov-Biosciences, Inc. (R), CA, *133*
Cronin, Dolores - Corporate Careers, Inc. (C), CA, *299*
Cronin, Kathleen A. - Hodge-Cronin & Assoc., Inc. (R), IL, *94*
Cronin, Richard J. - Hodge-Cronin & Assoc., Inc. (R), IL, *94*
Cropp, Wes - Management Recruiters of Franktown (C), CO, *442*
Crosbie, D. C. - Interim Management Resources Inc. (C), ON, *392*
Crosby, Georgann - Family-Business Roundtable, Inc. (R), AZ, *65*
Crosby, Kimberly A. - Fast Switch, Ltd. (C), OH, *338*

Crossman, Chuck - The Stewart Group (C), FL, *593*
Croteau, Paul - KPMG Executive Search (R), MB, *119*
Crow, Dennis - Pierce & Crow (R), CA, *164*
Crowder, Edward W. - Crowder & Company (R), MI, *43*
Crowe, Claudeth - A. E. Feldman Assoc., Inc. (C), NY, *339*
Crowe, Thomas H. - Hunter, Rowan & Crowe (C), FL, *386*
Crowe, Jr., Timothy D. - Timothy D. Crowe, Jr. (R), MA, *43*
Crowell, Kimberly D. - Grant/Morgan Assoc., Inc. (C), MD, *361*
Crowley, David G. - DSR-Search & Recruitment (C), TX, *315*
Crumbaker, Robert H. - LAI Ward Howell (R), OH, *123*
Crumpley, Jim - Jim Crumpley & Assoc. (C), MO, *304*
Cruse, O. D. - SpencerStuart (R), TX, *197*
Crusit, Francis - Sanford Rose Assoc. - Santa Barbara (C), CA, *565*
Cruz, Raymond - A-Linko & Assoc. (C), TX, *231*
Crystal, Jonathan A. - SpencerStuart (R), TX, *197*
Csorba, Les - A.T. Kearney Executive Search (R), TX, *111*
Cucuzzella, Vincent J. - C. J. Vincent Assoc., LLC (C), MD, *612*
Cuddy, Brian C. - Romac Int'l. Inc. (R), MA, *181*
Cuddy, Brian C. - Romac Int'l., Inc. (C), FL, *542*
Cuellar, Paulina Robles - Ray & Berndtson (R), MX, *172*
Cuenca, Christine - mfg/Search, Inc. (C), IN, *480*
Culbertson, Beth - Sales Consultants of Milwaukee (C), WI, *563*
Culbreth, Carolyn - The Corporate Source Group, Inc. (R), NY, *42*
Cullen, Andrew - The Pennmor Group (C), NJ, *506*
Culli, Ray - Christopher and Long (C), MO, *291*
Culver, Timothy J. - Culver Personnel Services (C), CA, *304*
Cundick, Jeff L. - Management Recruiters of Pleasant Hill (C), CA, *426*
Cunneff, Harry J. - Management Recruiters of Lake Forest, IL (C), IL, *447*
Cunningham, Douglas - Staff Resources, Inc. (C), SC, *590*
Cunningham, Jack - Cypress Int'l., Inc. (R), FL, *45*
Cunningham, John - Medical Executive Recruiters (C), CA, *477*
Cunningham, Sheila - Adams & Assoc. Int'l. (R), IL, *1*
Cunningham, Tanya R. - Hughes & Sloan, Inc. (C), GA, *383*
Cuomo, Frank - Frank Cuomo & Assoc., Inc. (C), NY, *305*
Cupp, C. A. - Austin - Allen Co. (C), TN, *256*
Curci, Ronald L. - ARI Int'l. (R), CA, *6*
Curle, Suzanne - E T Search Inc. (C), CA, *324*
Curran, Ann - Lewis Companies Inc. (R), ON, *129*
Curran, Martin - M. J. Curran & Assoc., Inc. (R), MA, *43*
Curran, Michael N. - Curran Partners, Inc. (R), CT, *44*
Curran, Nick - Management Recruiters of Milwaukee-North (C), WI, *466*
Curry, Donna - Don Neal & Assoc. (C), OK, *491*
Curry, Gerald - Munroe, Curry & Bond Assoc. (R), NJ, *149*
Curry, Joseph - MediaCOM Talent Group (C), MA, *477*
Curry, Lynn C. - Shelton, Wiseman & Leon (R), CA, *189*
Curry, Michael J. - Curry, Telleri Group, Inc. (R), NJ, *44*
Curry, Robert - KPMG Executive Search (R), ON, *119*
Curtin, Michelle - Brentwood Int'l. (R), CA, *23*
Curtis, Howard - Tony Curtis & Associates (C), ON, *305*
Curtis, Ron - Fortune Personnel Consultants of Colorado Springs (C), CO, *344*
Curtis, Shari - Goodwin & Co. (R), DC, *80*
Curtis, Susan J. - ProSearch Recruiting (C), CA, *524*
Curtis, Tony - Tony Curtis & Associates (C), ON, *305*
Curtiss, Chris N. - Dunhill of San Francisco, Inc. (C), CA, *319*
Curtiss, George R. - Dunhill of San Francisco, Inc. (C), CA, *319*
Curtiss, Michael R. - Dunhill of San Francisco, Inc. (C), CA, *319*
Curzi, Anjanette - Kelly Associates (R), PA, *112*
Cusack, Peter - Cusack Consulting (R), NY, *44*
Cushing, P. Barry - Roth Young of Tampa (C), FL, *546*
Cushman, Judith - Judith Cushman & Assoc. (R), WA, *44*
Custer, B.W. - The Custer Group, Inc. (R), TN, *44*
Custer, George - Dynamic Staffing Network (C), IL, *324*
Custer, J. Dwight - The Custer Group, Inc. (R), TN, *44*
Cuthbert, Bruce - McKavis Assoc. (C), CA, *475*
Cutler, Robert - Brissenden, McFarland, Fuccella & Reynolds, Inc. (R), WI, *23*
Cutshaw, Robert - F-O-R-T-U-N-E Personnel Consultants of Knoxville (C), TN, *350*
Cygan, H. - American Executive Management, Inc. (R), MA, *5*
Cyphers, Amy - HDB Incorporated (C), TX, *371*
Cyphers, Ralph - Strategic Assoc., Inc. (C), TX, *595*
Cyr, Maury N. - Cyr Associates, Inc. (C), MA, *306*
Czajkowski, John - Management Recruiters of Annapolis (C), MD, *429*
Czamanske, Paul - Compass Group Ltd. (R), MI, *38*
Czamanske, Peter M. - Compass Group Ltd. (R), MI, *38*
Czeswik, Frederick R. - Carlson & Czeswik (R), MN, *30*
D'Alessio, Gary A. - Chicago Legal Search, Ltd. (C), IL, *290*
D'Amora, Jim - Eastridge Infotech (C), NV, *326*
D'Andrea, Albert P. - EDMS Solutions (C), TX, *326*
D'Angelo, Ron E. - Management Recruiters of Baltimore City (C), MD, *430*
D'Eramo, Tony P. - Management Recruiters of Cincinnati (C), OH, *433*
Dabich, Thomas M. - Robert Harkins Assoc., Inc. (C), PA, *369*
Dach, Brad - Management Recruiters of Spencer (C), IA, *448*
Daffala, Ronald - Merit Professional Search, Inc. (C), TN, *479*
Daggett, James W. - Daggett & Kvistad (R), CA, *45*
Dagneau, Thierry - Personnel Tangent Inc. (C), QE, *509*
Dahl, Charles - Charles Dahl Group, Inc. (C), MN, *306*
Dahl, Stan - C.T.E.W. Executive Personnel Services Inc. (C), BC, *278*
Daigneault, Claude - Price Waterhouse Executive Search (R), QE, *168*
Dailey, Linda - Allen Austin Lowe & Powers (R), TX, *3*
Dailey, Monika - Southern Recruiters & Consultants, Inc. (C), SC, *587*
Daily, John - Christian & Timbers, Inc. (R), OH, *34*
Daily, John C. - Handy HRM (R), NY, *86*
Dale, Dick - Tully/Woodmansee Int'l., Inc. (R), MO, *212*
Dalenberg, David D. - Abbott Smith Assoc., Inc. (R), IL, *193*
Dalton, Bret - Robert W. Dingman Co., Inc. (R), CA, *52*
Dalton, Evonne - Dalton Management Consultants, Ltd. (C), NJ, *306*
Dalton, Joseph - Florapersonnel, Inc. (R), FL, *68*
Daly, Mark R. - Sales Consultant of Ocean (C), NJ, *554*
Daly, Shauna - Schwab-Carrese Assoc., Inc. Executive Search (R), NC, *185*
Dalyan, Catrayl - Genesis Consulting Partners (R), PA, *76*
Damon, Richard E. - Damon & Assoc., Inc. (C), TX, *306*
Damon, Robert A. - SpencerStuart (R), NY, *196*
Danford, Dan - Neail Behringer Consultants Inc. (R), NY, *15*
Danforth, Andrea - Ethos Consulting, Inc. (R), CA, *61*
Danforth, W. Michael - Hyde Danforth & Co. (R), TX, *100*

PRINCIPALS

Dangerfield, Chris - Technology Search Int'l. (C), CA, *603*
Daniel, Beverly R. - Foy, Schneid & Daniel, Inc. (R), NY, *71*
Daniel, David S. - SpencerStuart (R), NY, *196*
Daniels, Alfred - Alfred Daniels & Assoc., Inc. (R), CA, *46*
Daniels, Donna - Jonas, Walters & Assoc., Inc. (R), WI, *108*
Daniels, E. Gene - Hunt Patton & Brazeal, Inc. (C), CO, *385*
Danielsen, Annemarie T. - Astro Executive Search Firm (C), LA, *254*
Dankowski, Eden - Professional Healthcare Search & Consultants, Inc. (C), CA, *520*
Dankowski, Tom - Dankowski & Assoc., Inc. (C), OH, *307*
Dannenberg, Richard A. - Roberts Ryan & Bentley, Inc. (R), MD, *179*
Danner, David - Combined Resources Inc. (R), OH, *38*
Danoff, Richard - Tschudin Inc. (R), NJ, *211*
Dansky, Ellen - Telequest Communications, Inc. (C), NJ, *605*
Dant, Wendy A. - Hire Authority, Inc. (C), MI, *379*
Danziger, Karen - Howard-Sloan Assoc. (C), NY, *381*
Danziger, Karen - The Howard-Sloan-Koller Group (R), NY, *97*
Darcy, Dawn - Direct Marketing Resources (C), NC, *312*
Darling, Alan - Alan Darling Consulting (R), VT, *46*
Darrow, Robert J. - Cox, Darrow & Owens, Inc. (C), NJ, *302*
Darter, Steven - People Management Northeast, Inc. (R), CT, *162*
Darwin, Susan - Egon Zehnder Int'l. Inc. (R), CA, *227*
Dato, Thomas J. - Lloyd Prescott & Churchill, Inc. (R), IL, *130*
Dato, Thomas J. - Lloyd Prescott Assoc., Inc. (C), IL, *419*
Daubenspeck, Kenneth - Daubenspeck & Associates, Ltd. (R), IL, *46*
Daubenspeck, Rima - Daubenspeck & Associates, Ltd. (R), IL, *46*
Daudlin, Paul T. - Daudlin, De Beaupre & Co., Inc. (R), MI, *46*
Daudt, Jack - Triad Consultants, Inc. (C), NJ, *609*
Daugbjerg, Ray J. - LAI Ward Howell (R), TX, *124*
Daugenti, Gary - Gent & Assoc. (C), CA, *356*
Daugherty, Gary L. - Schuyler, Baker & Parker, Inc. (R), GA, *185*
Daugherty, Hal - Management Recruiters of Dallas-NW (C), TX, *436*
Daugherty, Judy - Management Recruiters of Dallas-NW (C), TX, *436*
Daugherty, Sue - Allard Associates (C), CA, *244*
Daugherty-Hill, Kimberly J. - Hayman Daugherty Assoc., Inc. (C), GA, *370*
Daum, Alan N. - Alan N. Daum & Assoc., Inc. (C), OH, *308*
Daum, Deborah - Premier Search Group (C), IN, *517*
Daum, Julie H. - SpencerStuart (R), NY, *196*
Davenport, Charles - S-H-S TechStaff (C), PA, *550*
David, Dave - Executive Resource Assoc. (C), VA, *334*
David, Dodie C. - Sullivan & Assoc. (R), MI, *204*
Davidson, Arthur J. - LAI Ward Howell (R), IL, *123*
Davidson, Julie - Drinkwater & Assoc. (R), MA, *55*
Davidson, Mary Anne - KPMG Executive Search (R), SA, *120*
Davidson, Shawn - GAAP Inc. (R), QE, *73*
Davies, A. Gerry - Davies, Park (R), AB, *46*
Davis, Alan - Alan Davis & Assoc. Inc. (R), QE, *47*
Davis, Allen - Allen Davis & Assoc. (C), MA, *308*
Davis, Andrew - Smith Hanley Assoc., Inc. (C), CT, *584*
Davis, Andrew - Synergistech Communications (C), CA, *597*
Davis, Barry - Martin Grant Assoc. Inc., Insurance Personnel (C), MA, *472*
Davis, Carolyn - Carolyn Davis Assoc., Inc. (C), NY, *309*
Davis, Charlie - Dunhill of Ft. Wayne, Inc. (C), IN, *320*
Davis, Colette - ExeConnex, LLC (R), GA, *61*
Davis, Donna - Donna Davis Assoc. (C), NJ, *309*
Davis, Evelyn C. - EFL Assoc. (R), KS, *57*
Davis, Frank - Bertrand, Ross & Assoc., Inc. (C), IL, *266*
Davis, G. Gordon - Davis & Company (R), CA, *47*
Davis, George - Egon Zehnder Int'l. Inc. (R), IL, *227*
Davis, Glenn S. - Next Step Recruiting (C), CA, *493*
Davis, Guy - Kane & Assoc. (C), TX, *403*
Davis, Jack - John J. Davis & Assoc., Inc. (R), NY, *47*
Davis, Jeff - DataPro Personnel Consultants (C), TX, *308*
Davis, John J. - John J. Davis & Assoc., Inc. (R), NY, *47*
Davis, Joseph A. - Joseph A. Davis Consultants, Inc. (R), NY, *47*
Davis, Joyce - Jerold Braun & Assoc. (C), CA, *272*
Davis, Kenneth R. - Management Recruiters of Baltimore (C), MD, *451*
Davis, Kenneth R. - Sales Consultants of Baltimore (C), MD, *559*
Davis, Linda - Sanford Rose Assoc. - Youngstown (C), NC, *569*
Davis, Melanie F. - The Heidrick Partners, Inc. (R), IL, *90*
Davis, Peter E. - Zurick, Davis & Co., Inc. (R), MA, *227*
Davis, Ronald - International Management Development Corp. (C), NY, *393*
Davis, III, Samuel - PRAXIS Partners (R), VA, *167*
Davis, Sharon - Toby Clark Assoc. Inc. (C), NY, *292*
Davis, Stephanie - Morgan Samuels Co. (R), CA, *147*
Davis, Steven M. - Sullivan & Company (R), NY, *204*
Davis, T. Nancy - Dorothy W. Farnath & Assoc., Inc. (C), NJ, *338*
Davis, Theresa - Management Recruiters of Milwaukee - Downtown (C), WI, *466*
Davis, Troy M. - Davis & Company (R), CA, *47*
Davis, Winifred R. - Joseph A. Davis Consultants, Inc. (R), NY, *47*
Davis Wolfe, Kathryn - HDB Incorporated (C), MO, *371*
Davison McNicholas, Patricia - LAI Ward Howell (R), TX, *124*
Dawson, Keith - Management Recruiters of Johnson City (C), TN, *436*
Daxon, Corey - Feldman Gray & Assoc. Inc. (C), ON, *339*
Day, J. Kevin - Nadzam, Lusk, Horgan & Assoc., Inc. (R), CA, *150*
Day, Rice - Management Recruiters of Chapel Hill (C), NC, *432*
De Beaupre, Mary Anne - Daudlin, De Beaupre & Co., Inc. (R), MI, *46*
de Cholnoky, Andrea - SpencerStuart (R), NY, *196*
De Cordova, Fernando Fernandez - Shore Asociados Ejecutivos, S. A. de C.V. (R), MX, *190*
de Funiak, William S. - De Funiak & Edwards (R), IN, *47*
De Kesel, Herman - TASA International (R), CA, *206*
de La Hoz Ramirez, Armando - OS-AGUI S.A. de C.V. (C), MX, *500*
de Lottinville, Brian L. - Trans-United Consultants Ltd. (C), ON, *608*
De Mange, Jean M. - Wellington Thomas Ltd. (C), FL, *618*
de Munnik, Lynne - Boyden (R), ON, *21*
De Palacios, Jeannette C. - J. Palacios & Assoc., Inc. (R), PR, *158*
De Riviera, Sandra - Parker Page Group (C), TX, *503*
de Wilde, David - LAI Ward Howell (R), CA, *123*
Deakmann, Richard - Management Decision Systems, Inc. (MDSI) (C), NJ, *425*
Deal, Chuck - Management Recruiters of Gastonia (C), NC, *456*
Deal, Michael T. - AGRI-associates (C), GA, *242*
Dean, Bruce - Recruiting/Solutions (C), CA, *532*
Dean, Bruce A. - Recruiting Resources Int'l. (C), CA, *532*
Dean, David - DHR Int'l., Inc. (R), CA, *49*
Dean, Jr., Eric W. - Management Recruiters of Pittsburgh-USC (C), PA, *435*
Dean, James L. - Dean-Dzierzawiec Assoc. (C), NJ, *309*

Dean, Richard - DHR Int'l., Inc. (R), GA, *50*
Deason, Ellen - Accountants On Call (C), CA, *235*
Deavours, James M. - F-O-R-T-U-N-E Personnel Consultants of Atlanta, Inc. (C), GA, *345*
DeBaugh, David H. - PRAXIS Partners (R), VA, *167*
deBerry, Marian Alexander - Boulware & Assoc. Inc. (R), IL, *20*
DeBourcy, Tom - Professional Research Services, Inc. (R), IL, *169*
Debry, Monica - Benford & Assoc., Inc. (C), MI, *264*
DeCaster, Paul - DeCaster Assoc. (C), WI, *310*
Deck, Jack - Romac Int'l., Inc. (C), MO, *543*
Deckelbaum, Rick - Fortune Personnel Consultants of Raleigh, Inc. (C), NC, *348*
Deckelbaum, Stan - Fortune Personnel Consultants of Raleigh, Inc. (C), NC, *348*
Decker, Robert - Ray & Assoc., Inc. (C), IA, *529*
DeClouet, J. Michael - The J. B. Search Group (C), CA, *395*
DeCorrevont, James - DeCorrevont & Assoc. (C), IL, *310*
DeCristoforo, Ralph B. - DHR Int'l., Inc. (R), CT, *49*
Dee, Vincent W. - Hartsfield Group, Inc. (R), GA, *87*
Deehring, Walt - Management Recruiters of Peoria (C), IL, *429*
Deerwester, Dave - Snelling Search (C), AL, *585*
Deffler, Karin E. - Med-Ex Services (C), OH, *476*
DeForest, Jim - Sales Consultants of Houston (C), TX, *563*
DeForrest, Liz - Rice Cohen Int'l. (R), PA, *178*
DeFranco, Manny - Physician Recruiting Services, Inc. (C), MO, *511*
Degges, Victoria - Impact Search & Strategies (C), PA, *387*
DeGioia, Joseph - JDG Assoc., Ltd. (C), MD, *397*
DeGrasse, Bob - SignatureSoft Inc. (C), CA, *581*
deGreve, Alexander - Accountants On Call (C), NJ, *235*
DeHart, Donna - Tower Consultants, Ltd. (R), PA, *210*
Deibert, Nicole - Accountants On Call (C), IL, *235*
Deighen, Roderick P. - Dean-MacDonald (R), OH, *47*
Deissig, Robert - The Ayers Group, Inc. (R), NY, *10*
DeJong, Jack - Management Recruiters of Tucson (C), AZ, *439*
Del Chiaro, Michael - Management Recruiters of Ft. Scott (C), KS, *429*
Del Valle, Pedro Cortina - Ray & Berndtson (R), MX, *172*
DeLalla, Barbara - DeLalla - Fried Assoc. (C), NY, *310*
DeLaney, Patricia - Jude M. Werra & Assoc. (R), WI, *218*
Delaney, Patrick J. - Sensible Solutions, Inc. (R), IL, *188*
Delano, Steven W. - S. W. Delano & Co. (R), CT, *48*
DeLany, Donald F. - Resource Perspectives, Inc. (R), CA, *175*
deLemos, Susanne - Heyman Assoc., Inc. (R), NY, *93*
DeLena, Robert - Boston Professional Search, Inc. (C), MA, *270*
Delisle, Pierre H. - PHD Conseil en Ressources Humaines Inc. (C), QE, *510*
Dell'Aquilla, Joseph - Allen Austin Lowe & Powers (R), TX, *3*
Delmotte, James - Daudlin, De Beaupre & Co., Inc. (R), MI, *46*
DelNegro, Anthony T. - DHR Int'l., Inc. (R), CT, *49*
DelPrete, Karen - Gilbert Tweed Assoc. Inc. (R), NY, *76*
Delray, Victor - Management Decision Systems, Inc. (MDSI) (C), NJ, *425*
DeLuca, Matthew J. - Management Resource Group, Inc. (C), NY, *467*
DeMan, Denise - Bench Int'l. Search, Inc. (R), CA, *15*
Demarest, Gretchen - Sanford Rose Assoc. - Charlotte (C), NC, *568*
DeMaria, Deborah - DHR Int'l., Inc. (R), NY, *50*
DeMario, William - Accountants On Call (C), CA, *235*
DeMarlie, Gary P. - LAI Ward Howell (R), WI, *124*
deMartino, Cathy - Lucas Assoc. (C), GA, *421*
DeMatteo, Robena - DeMatteo Associates (C), NY, *311*
Demchak, James P. - TASA International (R), TX, *206*
Dement, James W. - Franstaff Inc. (C), FL, *352*
Deming, David W. - Munroe, Curry & Bond Assoc. (R), NJ, *149*
DeMoss, J. V. - Careers/Inc. (C), PR, *284*
DeneDale, Mark - Staffing Edge, Inc. (C), IA, *590*
Denis, Liz - Brentwood Int'l. (R), CA, *23*
Denis, McReginald H. - PersoNet, Inc. (C), FL, *507*
Denison, Susan - Johnson Smith & Knisely (R), NY, *107*
Denker, Robert - Carpenter, Shackleton & Company (R), IL, *30*
Denman, Anna Marie - AMD & Associates (C), GA, *247*
Denn, Paula - Norrell Financial Staffing (C), TX, *495*
Dennehy, Kristin - Herbert Mines Assoc., Inc. (R), NY, *145*
Denney, Christopher - Goodkind Assoc. Inc. (C), NY, *360*
Denson, Steve - Sales Consultant of Bradenton (C), FL, *552*
Dent, Vickie - Recruiters Professional Network - Fairview (C), MO, *531*
Denton, Randolph - The Executive Tree (R), FL, *64*
DePhillipo, William R. - Tele-Media Int'l. Inc. (C), PA, *604*
DePiero, Randy - Stanton Chase Int'l./ Botrie Assoc. (R), ON, *199*
DePuydt, Daniel G. - Triumph Consulting, Inc. (R), IA, *210*
DeRario, Donna - F-O-R-T-U-N-E Personnel Consultants of San Diego (C), CA, *344*
DerAris, Neal - A. E. Feldman Assoc., Inc. (C), NY, *339*
Derhak, Allen R. - Derhak Ireland & Partners Ltd. (R), ON, *48*
Derhak, William M. - Derhak Ireland & Partners Ltd. (R), ON, *48*
Dermady, Timothy J. - ExecutiveFit (C), NY, *337*
Dermott, Paula - Dan P. McLean Assoc., Inc. (C), ON, *475*
deRoode, Robert - Hitchens & Foster, Inc. (C), MO, *379*
DeRose, Rick - Telecom Executive Group (C), NJ, *605*
Derr, David - Orion Int'l. Consulting Group, Inc. (C), WA, *500*
Desai, Sushila A. - Sink, Walker, Boltrus Int'l. (R), MA, *192*
DeSantis, Rich - Dunhill Staffing Systems, Inc. (C), NY, *316*
Deschamps, Becky - F-O-R-T-U-N-E Personnel Consultants of East Seattle (C), WA, *351*
Deschamps, Martine - Boyden (R), QE, *21*
Descheneaux, Pat - Descheneaux Recruitment Services Ltd. (C), BC, *311*
Desgrosellier, Gary P. - Personnel Unlimited/Executive Search (C), WA, *509*
Desgrosellier, Shawn - Personnel Unlimited/Executive Search (C), WA, *509*
DeShano, Kristen - DHR Int'l., Inc. (R), UT, *51*
Desiderio, Anthony J. - Dunhill Professional Search of Wilkes-Barre/Scranton, Inc. (C), PA, *322*
Désilets, Georges H. - Yves Plouffe & Assoc. (R), QE, *165*
Desley, Carolyn M. - Erlanger Assoc. (R), CT, *60*
Desmond, Dennis A. - G. E. McFarland & Co. (R), GA, *140*
Desmond, Mike - Newcomb-Desmond & Assoc., Inc. (C), OH, *492*
Despres, Raoul - Despres & Associates (C), IL, *311*
Despres, Suzzett - Despres & Associates (C), IL, *311*
DesRosiers, Kathleen - Marshall Consultants, Inc. (R), CA, *137*
Detling, John - Executive Search, Ltd. (C), OH, *336*
Detore, Robert R. - Drew Assoc. Int'l. (R), NJ, *54*
Dettra, Arthur C. - Dunhill Professional Search of Bucks-Mont., Inc. (C), PA, *322*
Deuel, Stacy N. - Kaplan & Assoc., Inc. (R), PA, *109*

PRINCIPALS

Deutsch, Barry A. - CJA-The Adler Group, Inc. (R), CA, *35*
Deutscher, Todd - Empowered Solutions Corp. (C), GA, *330*
Deutschman, Michele - Placements by Jesse Reid Assoc., Inc. (C), NY, *513*
Devaney, Marie - W. Robert Eissler & Assoc., Inc. (C), TX, *327*
Devlin, Jack - The Devlin Search Group, Inc. (C), MA, *312*
Devoto, Andrea - Devoto & Assoc. (C), CA, *312*
deVry, Kim - Tower Consultants, Ltd. (R), PA, *210*
Dework, Frank M. - Kingsley Quinn/USA (R), NJ, *115*
Dexter, Hilary - Deborah Snow Walsh, Inc. (R), IL, *215*
Dexter, Peter - Search Research Assoc., Inc. (R), MA, *187*
Dey, Irene - Rob Dey Executive Search (R), FL, *49*
Dey, Robert L. - Rob Dey Executive Search (R), FL, *49*
Deyeaux, Victoria - John Williams & Assoc. (C), TX, *621*
DeZara, Max - The Carlyle Group, Ltd. (R), IL, *30*
Diaz, Del - Management Recruiters of Miami-North (C), FL, *444*
Diaz, Norm - The Canon Group (C), CA, *280*
Diblasi, Joseph J. - First Advisory Services Int'l., Inc. (R), MD, *67*
Dicicco, Benjamin - McCoy Ltd. (C), CA, *474*
Dick, John G. - Sales Consultants of Charleston (C), SC, *555*
Dickens, Marcia - R. Gaines Baty Assoc., Inc. (R), GA, *13*
Dicker, Barry L. - ESA (R), CT, *60*
Dickerhoff, Tracy - Romac Int'l., Inc. (C), GA, *543*
Dickerson, Elizabeth A. - Management Recruiters of Los Gatos (C), CA, *426*
Dickerson, Joseph A. - Penn Associates (R), PA, *162*
Dickerson, Ken - Management Recruiters of Des Moines (C), IA, *449*
Dickey, Avis D. - Innovative Healthcare Services, Inc. (C), GA, *389*
Dickey, Chester W. - Bowden & Co., Inc. (R), OH, *20*
Dickin, Noranne - Reynolds Consulting Int'l. (R), BC, *177*
Dickin, Noranne - Reynolds Consulting Int'l. (R), AB, *177*
Dickson, David W. - Fortune Personnel Consultants of Chattanooga Inc. (C), TN, *349*
Dickson, Elaine - Management Recruiters of Milwaukee - Downtown (C), WI, *466*
Dickson Parigi, Maria - Prescott Legal Search (C), TX, *517*
Dickstein, Joel - Management Recruiters of Ft. Lauderdale (C), FL, *427*
Diduca, Tom A. - Management Recruiters of Prospect Heights (C), IL, *428*
Dieck, Daniel W. - DieckMueller Group (R), WI, *51*
Dieckmann, Ralph E. - Dieckmann & Assoc., Ltd. (R), IL, *51*
Diefenbach, John C. - Hreshko Consulting Group (C), NJ, *382*
Diersing, Joe - Executive Search, Ltd. (C), OH, *336*
Dietrich, Sandra - Fortune Personnel Consultants of Hilton Head (C), SC, *349*
Dietsch, Roger A. - Roger Dietsch & Assoc. (C), MN, *312*
Dietz, David - MSI Int'l. (C), LA, *487*
Difatta, Jon - Management Recruiters of Barrington (C), IL, *447*
Dillon, Larry - Johnson Smith & Knisely (R), CA, *107*
Dillon, Larry A. - Predictor Systems Corp. (R), CA, *167*
Dillon, Mark E. - NaTek Corp. (C), NY, *488*
DiLorenzo, Matthew B. - The Inside Track (C), TX, *389*
Dilworth, Lawrence A. - StratfordGroup (R), VA, *203*
Dilworth, Lawrence A. - StratfordGroup (R), MD, *203*
DiMaggio, Dorothy - Hintz Associates (C), NY, *378*
DiMarchi, Paul - DiMarchi Partners (R), CO, *51*
DiMauro, Paula - Sales Consultants of Omaha, Inc. (C), NE, *560*
Dimick, Don - Impact Technical Staffing (C), OR, *387*
Dimke, Tom - Raymond Karsan Assoc. (C), PA, *530*
DiMucchio, Joe - The Jotorok Group (C), RI, *401*
Dinerstein, Jan - J. Dinerstein & Co., Inc. (R), NY, *51*
Dingman, Bruce - Robert W. Dingman Co., Inc. (R), CA, *52*
Dingman, Robert W. - Robert W. Dingman Co., Inc. (R), CA, *52*
Dinino, Sabina - Trillium Human Resources Inc. (C), ON, *609*
Dinklage, Kenneth T. - Selected Executives, Inc. (C), MA, *578*
Dinse, Elizabeth - Management Recruiters of Sacramento North (C), CA, *441*
Dinse, Karl - Management Recruiters of Sacramento North (C), CA, *441*
Dinte, Paul - Dinte Resources, Inc. (R), VA, *52*
Dion, Frank - The Barrett Group (C), NH, *260*
Dionne, Bert - Insurance Search (C), TX, *390*
Diorio, Scott - Management Recruiters of Fresno (C), CA, *440*
DiPalo, Al - Searchforce, Inc. (R), FL, *187*
Dipaolo, Jeff - Management Recruiters of Cleveland-Airport (C), OH, *433*
DiPaolo, Jeff - Management Recruiters of Cleveland (C), OH, *457*
Dipaolo, Jeff - Sales Consultants of Cleveland-Airport (C), OH, *555*
DiPiazza, Joseph - Boyden (R), NJ, *21*
DiSalvo, Fred - The Cambridge Group Ltd. (C), VA, *280*
DiSalvo, Fred - Cambridge Group Ltd.-Exec. Search Div. (C), VA, *280*
DiSanti, Joseph R. - Specialty Consultants Inc. (R), PA, *196*
Dise, Jr., Ralph A. - Dise & Co. (R), OH, *52*
Dishaw, Raymond J. - R. J. Dishaw & Assoc. (R), TX, *52*
Dittmann, Courtney - Raymond Karsan Assoc. (C), NY, *530*
Ditzel, C. Russell - J. M. Joseph Assoc. (R), NJ, *109*
Divine, Robert S. - O'Shea, Divine & Co., Inc. (R), CA, *154*
Dix, Bradley - Interim Management Resources Inc. (C), ON, *392*
Dixon, Anita - Cook Assoc. Int'l., Inc. (C), TN, *298*
Dixon, Glenda - Search Assoc. (C), KY, *574*
Dixon, Jim L. - MESA International (C), CA, *480*
Dixon, Sayre - Employr (C), PA, *330*
Dixon, Susan K. - Matthews Professional Employment Specialists, Inc. (C), IL, *472*
Dixon, Violet - Opalka Dixon Consultants to Management (R), VA, *156*
Dmytrow, Eric D. - F-O-R-T-U-N-E Personnel Consultants of Palm Beach (C), FL, *345*
Doan, James - DHR Int'l., Inc. (R), IN, *50*
Dobbs, Wesley Q. - Major, Hagen & Africa (C), GA, *423*
Dobson, Karin - Kenneth Murphy & Assoc. (C), NS, *487*
Docker, William - Raymond Karsan Assoc. (C), MA, *530*
Dodd, Carol - Staff Resources, Inc. (C), SC, *590*
Dodd Perry, Dena - The Hollins Group, Inc. (R), IL, *95*
Doddridge, James H. - Atlantic West Int'l. (C), UT, *255*
Dodson, Ellen - ADECCO Employment Services (C), VA, *240*
Doele, Don - Goodrich & Sherwood Assoc., Inc. (R), NJ, *80*
Doering, Louis - Doering & Assoc. (C), CA, *313*
Doherty, Brian - Sales Consultant (C), OH, *554*
Doherty, John J. - Doherty Int'l., Inc. (R), IL, *53*
Doherty, Leonard J. - L. J. Doherty & Assoc. (R), MA, *53*
Doherty, Shawn - Doherty Healthcare Consultants (C), ME, *313*
Doino, Dene - Thorndike Deland Assoc. LLC (R), NY, *48*
Dolan-Brady, Nancy - NDB Assoc., Inc. (C), PA, *491*
Doleman, Robert J. - Doleman Enterprises (R), VA, *53*
Dollaway, Renee - Brown, Bernardy, Van Remmen, Inc. (C), CA, *275*

Dolphin, Barbara - Harbrowe, Inc. (C), NY, *368*
Domann, Jr., William A. - The Domann Organization (R), CA, *53*
Dombeck, Diane - Kennedy & Co. (R), IL, *112*
Domby, Samuel F. - eXsource Inc. (C), SC, *337*
Dominguez, Connie - Dominguez-Metz & Assoc. (R), CA, *53*
Domres, Terry A. - Domres Professional Search (R), WI, *53*
Dona, Christopher - DHR Int'l., Inc. (R), MA, *50*
Donahue, E. M. Mick - Donahue/Bales Assoc. (R), IL, *54*
Donahue, Jack - Dunhill of Ft. Collins, Inc. (C), CO, *319*
Donahue, Patrick D. - Winguth, Grant & Donahue (R), CA, *222*
Donahue, Timothy J. - Kelly Associates (R), PA, *112*
Donald, R.J. - Feldman Gray & Assoc. Inc. (C), ON, *339*
Donelon, Wayne - WMD inc. (C), NJ, *623*
Dong, Steven - Executive Search, Ltd. (C), OH, *336*
Donini, Jerry P. - Donini Assoc. (R), VA, *54*
Donini, Patricia - Donini Assoc. (R), VA, *54*
Donnellan, Shaun K. - Glass & Assoc., Inc. (C), OH, *358*
Donnelly, Christopher - Christopher-Westmont & Assoc., Inc. (R), OH, *35*
Donnelly, Dan - The Donnelly Group-Sales Recruiters, Inc. (C), MO, *314*
Donnelly, George J. - SpencerStuart (R), TX, *197*
Donnelly, John - MIXTEC Group (R), CA, *145*
Donnelly, John J. - Management & Human Resources (R), MA, *134*
Donnelly, John P. - J P Donnelly Assoc., Inc. (C), NY, *314*
Donnelly, John P. - J P Donnelly Assoc., Inc. (C), NY, *314*
Donnelly, John R. - Christopher-Westmont & Assoc., Inc. (R), OH, *35*
Donnelly, Patrick - Christopher-Westmont & Assoc., Inc. (R), OH, *35*
Donovan, Jerry - Management Recruiters of Arlington (C), VA, *464*
Donovan, John - Human Capital Resources, Inc. (C), FL, *384*
Doody, Michael F. - Witt/Kieffer, Ford, Hadelman & Lloyd (R), IL, *223*
Dooley, James L. - Management Recruiters of Mt. Pleasant (C), SC, *435*
Dorfman, Ellen S. - Krauthamer & Assoc. (R), MD, *120*
Dorfman, Jan - F-O-R-T-U-N-E Personnel Consultants of Denver, Inc. (C), CO, *344*
Dorfman, Kim - Rice Cohen Int'l. (R), PA, *178*
Dorfman, Todd - Krauthamer & Assoc. (R), MD, *120*
Dority, Thomas - The Mercer Group, Inc. (R), MI, *143*
Dorman, Reuel A. - The McLeod Group, Inc. (R), CT, *141*
Doro, Chip - Career Marketing Assoc., Inc. (C), CO, *282*
Doroba, Carol - Impact Search & Strategies (C), PA, *387*
Dorsi, Carolyn - Handy HRM (R), NY, *86*
Dorst, Martin - Dorst Information Services, Inc. (C), NY, *314*
Dose, Vikki L. - O'Rourke Companies, Inc. (R), TX, *154*
Dostal, Kris - Sales Consultants of Omaha, Inc. (C), NE, *560*
Dotson, M. Ileen - Dotson & Assoc. (R), NY, *54*
Doty, Eleanor C. - The Doty Group (C), TX, *314*
Dougan, Sally - Bert Davis Publishing Placement Consultants (C), NY, *309*
Dougherty, Carolyn - IntelliSource, inc. (C), PA, *391*
Dougherty, Larry J. - Sales Consultant of Cobb County (C), GA, *552*
Dougherty, Lawrence J. - Management Recruiters Cobb County (C), GA, *428*
Dougherty, Robert E. - Dougherty & Assoc. (C), TN, *314*
Douglas, Bob - Hunter Douglas Group, Inc. (R), IL, *99*
Douglas, Calvin H. - Cal Douglas Executive Search, Inc. (R), PA, *54*
Douglas, Courtney - Norrell Financial Staffing (C), CA, *495*
Douglas, Marc - Prestige Inc. (C), WI, *518*
Douglass, Suzanne - Harris Heery & Assoc., Inc. (R), CT, *87*
Doupe, S. Scott - Conroy Partners Ltd. (R), AB, *39*
Doutre, Judy - Dumont & Co. (C), BC, *316*
Dow, Ian James - Dow Consultants Int'l. (C), NY, *314*
Dow, Lori - Davidson, Laird & Assoc. (C), MI, *308*
Dow, R. Steven - Scott-Wayne Assoc., Inc. (C), MA, *573*
Dowell, Mary K. - Professional Search Assoc. (C), CA, *522*
Dowell, Pat - M.C. Executive Search (C), CA, *422*
Downing, Gus - Downing & Downing, Inc. (C), OH, *314*
Downing, Jack W. - Sales Consultant of Chicago-Downtown (C), IL, *552*
Downing, Jacqueline - Downing & Downing, Inc. (C), OH, *314*
Downing, Judi - Peck & Assoc., Ltd. (R), WI, *161*
Downs, Diann C. - Sanford Rose Assoc. - Charlotte (C), NC, *568*
Downs, Greg - Executive Recruiters Agency, Inc. (C), AR, *333*
Downs, James L. - Sanford Rose Assoc. - Charlotte (C), NC, *568*
Doyen, Mike - Greenfields Engineering Search (C), MO, *363*
Doyle, Christopher K. - Brownstone Sales & Marketing Group, Inc. (C), NY, *275*
Doyle, David - System 1 Search (C), CA, *598*
Doyle, Don - Bosch & Assoc., LLC (R), CT, *20*
Doyle, James W. - Executive Search Consultants International, Inc. (R), NY, *63*
Doyle, Jennifer L. - Phillips Resource Group (C), SC, *510*
Doyle, John - Search Research Assoc., Inc. (R), MA, *187*
Doyle, William J. - Kingsley Quinn/USA (R), NY, *115*
Drake, Nancy - G. E. McFarland & Co. (R), GA, *140*
Dralle, Robert D. - Odell & Assoc., Inc. (C), TX, *498*
Draper, Gary - Heritage Pacific Corp. (C), CA, *376*
Draper, Michael P. - Blane, Stevens & Kellogg (C), FL, *268*
Dreier, John S. - Dreier Consulting (C), NJ, *315*
Dremely, Mark - Richard, Wayne & Roberts (C), TX, *536*
Dresner, Rhonda - Recruiting Specialists (C), MA, *532*
Dressen, Ronald - Romac Int'l., Inc. (C), MN, *543*
Dressler, Carol F. - Haley Associates (R), CA, *85*
Drexler, Robert C. - Robert Drexler Assoc., Inc. (R), NJ, *54*
Dreyfus, Rita - Cypress Int'l., Inc. (R), FL, *45*
Drinkwater, Wendy A. - Drinkwater & Assoc. (R), MA, *54*
Driscoll, Anne - Meder & Assoc., Inc. (R), IL, *142*
Driscoll, Donald L. - Management Recruiters of Boone (C), NC, *456*
Drohan, Robert - American Heritage Group, Inc. (C), MI, *247*
Dromeshauser, Peter - Dromeshauser Assoc. (R), MA, *55*
Dromsky, James V. - Orion Consulting, Inc. (R), NJ, *157*
Drown, Peggy - Management Recruiters of Bellaire (C), TX, *436*
Drury, III, James J. - SpencerStuart (R), IL, *197*
Drury, Robert - Hughes & Sloan, Inc. (C), GA, *383*
Dryer, Laura - Michael Shirley Assoc. Inc. (R), KS, *190*
Drysdale, Sally - Procom (C), AB, *519*
Du Ket, David R. - New Venture Development, Inc. (C), CA, *492*
Du Ket, Holly V. - New Venture Development, Inc. (C), CA, *492*
Dubbs, Bill - Williams Executive Search, Inc. (R), MN, *221*
Dubeck, Michael - F-O-R-T-U-N-E Personnel Consultants of Troy, Inc. (C), MI, *347*
Dubin, Scott M. - Major, Hagen & Africa (C), CA, *423*

PRINCIPALS

DuBois, Anthony G. - Horizon Medical Search of NH (C), NH, *381*
Dubois, Denis R. - Networking Unlimited of NH, Inc. (C), NH, *491*
DuBois, Jr., Joseph W. - Horizon Medical Search of NH (C), NH, *381*
DuBois, Sabine G. - Horizon Medical Search of NH (C), NH, *381*
Dubrow, Richard M. - R/K International Inc. (R), CT, *171*
DuBrul, Donald C. - DuBrul Management Co. (C), NY, *315*
Dubuque, Bill - Christopher and Long (C), MO, *291*
Ducharme, David J. - Fortune Personnel Consultants of Hilton Head (C), SC, *349*
Duckett, Tim - Creative HR Solutions (C), GA, *303*
Duckworth, Donald R. - Johnson Smith & Knisely (R), GA, *107*
Dudasik, Patrick - David Gomez & Assoc., Inc. (R), IL, *79*
Dudley, Craig J. - Ray & Berndtson (R), MX, *172*
Dudley, John P. - Woodworth Int'l. Group (R), OR, *225*
Dudley, Robert R. - Sanford Rose Assoc. - Laguna Beach (C), CA, *565*
Duff, Michael - West Coast Recruiting (C), CA, *619*
Duffy, Kevin - Kensington Int'l., Inc. (R), IL, *113*
Duffy, Sue - Techstaff Inc. (C), CA, *603*
Dugan, John H. - J. H. Dugan & Assoc., Inc. (R), CA, *55*
Duggan, Lou - Armor Personnel (C), ON, *253*
Duggan, Lynette - Robert William James & Assoc. (C), OR, *539*
Dukas, Theodore - Dukas Assoc. (C), MA, *315*
Duke, Ann - Sanford Rose Assoc. - Fairlawn (C), OH, *569*
Duke, Lawrence - Management Recruiters of Charlotte - North, Inc. (C), NC, *456*
Dumanis, Kathryn Hale - K. C. Hale, Inc. (R), CT, *85*
Dumas, Sergio Albores - Management Recruiters of Mexico City-South (C), MX, *438*
Dummer, Charles F. - Charles & Associates, Inc. (C), NE, *289*
Dummer, Jeffry J. - Charles & Associates, Inc. (C), NE, *289*
Dumont, Brenda - Dumont & Co. (C), BC, *316*
Dunbar, Meg - M. Dunbar & Assoc. (C), TX, *316*
Duncan, Bill - Management Recruiters of Forest Acres (C), SC, *435*
Duncan, Gail - Careers First, Inc. (C), NJ, *283*
Duncan, James W. - Sanford Rose Assoc. - Lake Forest (R), IL, *184*
Duncan, Laura - Management Recruiters - Indianapolis (C), IN, *448*
Duncan, Robin - Weinman & Assoc. (C), AZ, *617*
Dunkel, David L. - Romac Int'l., Inc. (C), FL, *542*
Dunlap, Richard A. - Dunlap & Sullivan Assoc. (R), MI, *55*
Dunlap, Stanley R. - Dunlap & Sullivan Assoc. (R), MI, *55*
Dunlap, Thomas - Charles Dahl Group, Inc. (C), MN, *306*
Dunn, David - RMA Search (R), TN, *179*
Dunn, John G. - Management Dimensions Ltd. (R), ON, *134*
Dunn, Margaret A. - Dunn Associates (R), PA, *55*
Dunn, Markay - Sales Consultant of Alexandria (C), LA, *553*
Dunn, Peter - Korn/Ferry Int'l. (R), NY, *117*
Dunn, Sharon M. - The Morley Group (C), IN, *486*
Dupilka, John M. - Michael Latas & Assoc., Inc. (R), MO, *126*
Duquette, Edmond J. - Schattle & Duquette (C), RI, *571*
Durakis, Sr., Charles A. - C. A. Durakis Assoc., Inc. (R), FL, *55*
Durakis, Jr., Charles A. - C. A. Durakis Assoc., Inc. (R), MD, *55*
Durante, Arthur J. - Sales Consultants of Wellesley, Inc. (C), MA, *559*
Durica, Daniel - Recruiting Specialists (C), MA, *532*
Durning, Charles - The Pollack Group (C), ON, *514*
Dusome, Terry - Holloway Schulz & Partners (C), BC, *380*
Dussick, Vince - Dussick Management Assoc. (C), CT, *323*
Dussling, Kate - Cook Assoc.,® Inc. (R), IL, *40*
Duval, Dick - B. D. Wallace & Assoc. (C), MD, *614*
Dvorak, Donald F. - Donald F. Dvorak & Co. (R), IL, *55*
Dwyer, Gilbert E. - Dwyer Consulting Group, Inc. (R), WV, *56*
Dycus, Gwen - Gwen Dycus & Assoc. (C), FL, *323*
Dye, Bill - Bruce Henry Assoc. Inc. (R), TX, *91*
Dye, Carson E. - LAI Ward Howell (R), OH, *123*
Dyer, John - Pacific Finance Search, Inc. (C), CA, *501*
Dyer, Mark - Snelling Search (C), IL, *586*
Dykeman, James J. - Management Recruiters of Mercer Island (C), WA, *437*
Dykes, Larry L. - Personnel Consultants (C), WA, *508*
Dykes, Mimi - Staffing Edge, Inc. (C), TX, *591*
Dykes, Mimi - Staffing Edge, Inc. (C), TX, *591*
Dykes, Mimi - Staffing Edge, Inc. (C), TX, *591*
Dykes, Mimi - Staffing Edge, Inc. (C), TX, *591*
Dykstra, Gene L. - G. L. Dykstra Assoc., Inc. (C), MI, *323*
Dykstra, Glenda M. - G. L. Dykstra Assoc., Inc. (C), MI, *323*
Dyson, Steve - Technology Search Int'l. (C), CA, *603*
Dzierzawiec, Kenneth J. - Dean-Dzierzawiec Assoc. (C), NJ, *309*
Eagan, Karen - Management Recruiters of Grass Valley (C), CA, *440*
Eagan, Ridge - Management Recruiters of Grass Valley (C), CA, *440*
Eagar, Brian - Search Int'l. (R), MA, *187*
Earhart, Bill - Sanford Rose Assoc. - Columbus North (C), OH, *570*
Earle, Holland R. - Executive Strategies, Inc. (C), GA, *337*
Earle, Paul W. - SpencerStuart (R), IL, *197*
Early, Bert H. - Early Cochran & Olson (R), IL, *56*
Eason, James M. - JRL Executive Recruiters (C), GA, *401*
Eason, Jan - Summit Group Int'l., Inc. (R), GA, *204*
Eason, Larry E. - JRL Executive Recruiters (C), MO, *401*
Easterling, Yvonne - A First Resource (C), NC, *231*
Eastham, Marvene - Witt/Kieffer, Ford, Hadelman & Lloyd (R), TX, *223*
Eastmer, Gregory - Professional Support Inc. (C), NY, *523*
Eastmer, Paul H. - Professional Support Inc. (C), NY, *523*
Easton, Bill - Management Recruiters of Irving-North (C), TX, *436*
Eastwood, Gary - Beck/Eastwood Recruitment Solutions (C), CA, *261*
Eatman, Fred - Management Recruiters of New Bern (C), NC, *433*
Eaton, Bob - PricewaterhouseCoopers Executive Search (R), ON, *168*
Eazle, Julie - Management Recruiters of Oklahoma City-South (C), OK, *434*
Ebeling, John - Gilbert Tweed Assoc. Inc. (R), NJ, *77*
Eckert, III, E. J. - Sales Consultants of Traverse City (C), MI, *553*
Eckhart, Kenneth V. - SpencerStuart (R), FL, *197*
Eckler, Geoffrey N. - Eckler Personnel Network (C), VT, *326*
Eckley, Barbara - Pinnacle Executive Group Inc. (C), MO, *512*
Eckley, Scott - Pinnacle Executive Group Inc. (C), MO, *512*
Ector, John - Insurance Personnel Resources, Inc. (C), GA, *390*
Edahl, A. J. - S. P. Assoc., Inc. (C), NC, *550*
Eddington, Steve - Electronic Search, Inc. (C), IL, *328*
Edelberg, Frank - Management One Consultants (C), ON, *425*
Edell, David - Development Resource Group (R), DC, *48*
Edelman, Diane - Stephen Haas Legal Placement (C), NY, *365*
Eden, Brooks D. - Eden & Assoc., Inc. (C), PA, *326*

Eden, Darren - DHR Int'l., Inc. (R), MO, *50*
Eden, Dianne - Steeple Resources & Consulting (R), NJ, *199*
Eden, Don - Management Recruiters of Livonia (C), MI, *451*
Eden, Earl M. - Eden & Assoc., Inc. (C), PA, *326*
Edgerton, Paul - The Cassie Group (R), PA, *31*
Edington, Patti D. - Drinkwater & Assoc. (R), MA, *55*
Edman, Silas E. G. - The Partnership Group (R), NJ, *160*
Edmond, Bruce - Corporate Recruiters Ltd. (C), BC, *300*
Edwards, Charles R. - LAI Ward Howell (R), GA, *123*
Edwards, Chris - Business Systems of America, Inc. (C), IL, *277*
Edwards, Doug - Fortune Personnel Consultants of Greensboro, NC, Inc. (C), NC, *348*
Edwards, Douglas W. - Egon Zehnder Int'l. Inc. (R), GA, *227*
Edwards, Edward C. P. - Ingram & Aydelotte, Inc. (R), NY, *101*
Edwards, Greg - Eden & Assoc., Inc. (C), PA, *326*
Edwards, J. Michael - Power Recruiting Group (C), TX, *515*
Edwards, Jack O. - Sales Consultant of Bloomington (C), IL, *552*
Edwards, Jim - Cornerstone Resources, Inc. (C), OK, *299*
Edwards, John W. - The Bedford Group (R), RI, *15*
Edwards, Leslie - DHR Int'l., Inc. (R), TN, *51*
Edwards, Lillian E. - The Bedford Group (R), RI, *15*
Edwards, Lisa - Edwards & Assoc. (C), GA, *327*
Edwards, Lyn M. - Sales Consultant of Bloomington (C), IL, *552*
Edwards, Lynda - Hughes & Sloan, Inc. (C), GA, *383*
Edwards, Peter G. - Conroy Partners Ltd. (R), AB, *39*
Edwards, Randolph J. - De Funiak & Edwards (R), MD, *47*
Edwards, S. Bruce - Bruce Edwards & Associates, Inc. (R), NC, *56*
Edwards, Tom - Southern Chemical & Plastics Search (C), FL, *587*
Edwards, Verba Lee - Wing Tips & Pumps, Inc. (C), MI, *623*
Egan, Daniel K. - Egan & Assoc. (R), WI, *57*
Egan, David C. - D. C. Egan & Assoc. (C), GA, *327*
Egan, John - Egan Search Group (R), NY, *57*
Egan, Patrick J. - Schenck & Assoc. SC (C), WI, *572*
Egan, Jr., Stephen D. - The Mercer Group, Inc. (R), GA, *143*
Egeland, Karen - Peter Froehlich & Co. (C), TX, *353*
Egeland, Noel - Peter Froehlich & Co. (C), TX, *353*
Eggers, J. W. - Eggers Consulting Co., Inc. (C), NE, *327*
Eggers, James W. - Eggers Consulting Co., Inc. (C), NE, *327*
Ehman, John - Executive Placement Services (C), MD, *333*
Ehrenreich, L. Catherine - Greenhaven & Assoc., Inc. (R), NY, *81*
Ehrenzeller, Tony - Management Recruiters of Fairfax, VA (C), VA, *464*
Eibeler, Charles J. - Amherst Personnel Group Inc. (C), NY, *249*
Eichbaum, June - Major, Hagen & Africa (C), NY, *423*
Eicher, Bob - Management Recruiters of Julington Creek (C), FL, *427*
Eicher, Donna - Management Recruiters of Julington Creek (C), FL, *427*
Eickenhorst, Richard - Richard Wright Co. (C), CT, *536*
Eickhoff, Mike - Management Recruiters - Indianapolis (C), IN, *448*
Eidelberg, Larry - Bert Davis Publishing Placement Consultants (C), NY, *309*
Eilertson, Douglas R. - Sanford Rose Assoc. (C), OH, *565*
Einsel, A. Ray - Grant Cooper & Assoc., Inc. (R), MO, *81*
Eisele, Lucy - The HRM Group, Inc. (C), AL, *383*
Eisele, Steven M. - Lloyd Prescott & Churchill, Inc. (R), NY, 130
Eisele, Steven M. - Lloyd Prescott Assoc., Inc. (C), NY, *419*
Eiseman, Joe - Romac Int'l., Inc. (C), NJ, *543*
Eiseman, Joe - Romac Int'l., Inc. (C), NJ, *543*
Eiseman, Joe - Romac Int'l., Inc. (C), NJ, *543*
Eiseman, Joe - Romac Int'l., Inc. (C), NJ, *543*
Eiseman, Joe - Romac Int'l., Inc. (C), NY, *544*
Eiseman, Joe - Romac Int'l., Inc. (C), NY, *544*
Eisenborg, Franci - Professional Recruiters (C), UT, *522*
Eisert, Robert M. - Sanford Rose Assoc. - Doylestown (C), PA, *570*
Eissler, W. Robert - W. Robert Eissler & Assoc., Inc. (C), TX, *327*
Elam, Bill J. - Management Recruiters of Lincoln (C), NE, *431*
Elam, Robert W. - Wheeler, Moore & Elam Co. (R), TX, *219*
Elam, Jr., William J. - William J. Elam & Assoc. (R), NE, *58*
Eldredge, Peter - Johnson Smith & Knisely (R), NY, *107*
Eldridge, Charles B. - Ray & Berndtson (R), GA, *172*
Elias, Julius - Perez-Arton Consultants, Inc. (R), NY, *162*
Elinski, Mike - Human Resources Management Hawaii, Inc. (C), HI, *384*
Elizando, Rudy - Allen Austin Lowe & Powers (R), TX, *3*
Elizondo, Jennifer - Management Recruiters of Fresno (C), CA, *440*
Elkas, Yves - Yves Elkas Inc. (R), QE, *58*
Ellefson, Gene - Gene Ellefson & Assoc. Inc. (C), MI, *328*
Elliot, Alice - Elliot Assoc. Inc. (R), NY, *58*
Elliott, C. J. - Health Network USA (C), TX, *371*
Elliott, David J. - Health Network USA (C), TX, *371*
Elliott, Gene - The Whyte Group, Inc. (R), MD, *220*
Elliott, Mark P. - LAI Ward Howell (R), OH, *123*
Elliott, Roger S. - The Elliott Company (R), MA, *58*
Ellis, Bennett A. - Greenhaven & Assoc., Inc. (R), NY, *81*
Ellis, Bill - Interspace Interactive, Inc. (C), NY, *394*
Ellis, James - Sanford Rose Assoc. - Lake St. Louis (C), MO, *568*
Ellis, James P. - Ellis & Associates (C), HI, *328*
Ellis, Kristin - Romac Int'l., Inc. (C), FL, *543*
Ellis, Mary - Sanford Rose Assoc. - Lake St. Louis (C), MO, *568*
Ellis, Milton H. - Accountants On Call (C), TN, *237*
Ellis, Mitch - Sanford Rose Assoc. - Lake St. Louis (C), MO, *568*
Ellis, Ronald A. - Management Recruiters of Jupiter (C), FL, *427*
Ellis, Sandra - R. H. Perry & Assoc., Inc. (R), DC, *162*
Ellis, Steve - Steve Ellis (C), CA, *328*
Ellis, Ted K. - The Hindman Co. (R), VA, *94*
Ellis, Walter - Packaging Personnel Co., Ltd. (C), WI, *502*
Ellis-Kirk, Matrice - SpencerStuart (R), TX, *197*
Ellison, Richard H. - Sanford Rose Assoc. - Youngstown (C), OH, *569*
Ellner, David M. - David M. Ellner Assoc. (R), NY, *59*
Elnaggar, Hani - StratfordGroup (R), CA, *203*
Elrick, Bill - Mayhall Search Group, Inc. (C), IN, *473*
Elsom, Jr., Kendall A. - Genesis Consulting Partners (R), PA, *76*
Elston, William - DHR Int'l., Inc. (R), FL, *50*
Elwell, Richard F. - Elwell & Assoc., Inc. (R), MI, *59*
Elwell, Stephen R. - Elwell & Assoc., Inc. (R), MI, *59*
Ely, Jim - Management Recruiters of Visalia (C), CA, *426*
Elzweig, Mark - Mark Elzweig Co., Ltd. (C), NY, *329*
Embrey, Boe E. - Sales Consultants of Auburn Hills (C), MI, *559*

PRINCIPALS

Emerick, Sylvia E. - Amherst Human Resource Group, Ltd. (C), IL, *249*
Emerson, Annette - Dunhill Staffing Systems (C), NJ, *317*
Emerson, Jr., Bill - Dunhill Staffing Systems (C), NJ, *317*
Emerson, Randy - Romac Int'l., Inc. (C), IN, *543*
Emerson, Randy - Romac Int'l., Inc. (C), IN, *543*
Emerson, William - Dunhill Staffing Systems (C), NJ, *317*
Emery, Jodie A. - LAI Ward Howell (R), CT, *123*
Emery, Karlan - Emerging Medical Technologies, Inc. (C), CO, *329*
Emerzian, Jennifer - Johnson Smith & Knisely (R), NY, *107*
Emmott, Carol B. - SpencerStuart (R), CA, *196*
Emory, Vaughn - BayResearch Group, Inc. (R), IL, *14*
Empey, David - Management Recruiters of Franktown (C), CO, *442*
Endres, Devlin - Allstaff, Inc. (C), IL, *245*
Engel, Walter E. - F-O-R-T-U-N-E Personnel Consultants of the Tri-Cities, Inc. (C), TN, *350*
Engelgau, Elvita - Sales Consultants of Portland (C), OR, *555*
Engelgau, Elvita B. - Management Recruiters of Portland (C), OR, *434*
Engelgau, Larry - Sales Consultants of Portland (C), OR, *555*
Engelgau, Larry P. - Management Recruiters of Portland (C), OR, *434*
England, Marc - Austin-McGregor Int'l. (R), TX, *9*
Engler, Christine - CEO Consulting (C), FL, *287*
Engler, Peter G. - Lautz, Grotte, Engler & Swimley (R), CA, *126*
English, Michael R. - The Human Resource Group, Inc. (R), OH, *98*
English, Robert - RTE Search (C), VA, *547*
English, Robert - RTE Search (C), NJ, *547*
English Jones, Suzanne - Vera L. Rast Partners Inc. (C), IL, *529*
Enns, George - The Enns Partners Inc. (R), ON, *59*
Enochs, Steve - Buckman/Enochs & Assoc., Inc. (C), OH, *276*
Enrico, Jim - Unisearch Search & Recruiting Inc. (C), AZ, *611*
Ensing, Pat - Chicago Research Group, Inc. (R), IL, *33*
Ensminger, Chub - Management Recruiters of Chattanooga-North (C), TN, *436*
Epstein, Bess - Accountants On Call (C), NJ, *236*
Epstein, Harvey - Ferrari Search Group (C), OH, *340*
Epstein, Joel P. - StratfordGroup (R), OH, *203*
Epstein, Kathy J. - LAI Ward Howell (R), MA, *123*
Epstein, Robert G. - RGE (C), VA, *535*
Erb, Troy - Elliot Assoc. Inc. (R), TX, *58*
Erbach, Rachel - American Resources Corp. (C), IL, *248*
Erbe, H. Pete - Dunhill Staffing Systems, Inc. (C), NY, *316*
Erder, Debra - Canny, Bowen Inc. (R), NY, *28*
Eren, Sal - Medserve & Assoc. Inc. (C), MD, *478*
Ergas, Patricia - Unisearch Search & Recruiting Inc. (C), CA, *611*
Erhard, Donna - Dunhill Staffing Systems (C), NJ, *317*
Ericksen, Bruce - MESA International (C), OR, *480*
Ericksen, Linda - MESA International (C), OR, *480*
Erickson, Bill - Raymond Karsan Assoc. (C), NE, *530*
Erickson, Cara - Johnson Smith & Knisely (R), NY, *107*
Erickson, Elaine - Kenzer Corp. (R), NY, *113*
Erickson, Keith - Executives Worldwide, Inc. (C), OR, *337*
Erickson, Mary R. - Mary R. Erickson & Assoc. (R), MN, *60*
Erickson, Mike - Orion Int'l. Consulting Group, Inc. (C), VA, *500*
Erickson, Tom - Diedre Moire Corp., Inc. (C), NJ, *483*
Erickson-Pearson, David - Boulware & Assoc. Inc. (R), IL, *20*
Ericson, Pam - Major Search (C), NJ, *423*
Erikson, Theodore J. - Erikson Consulting Assoc., Inc. (R), NY, *60*
Erlanger, Richard A. - Erlanger Assoc. (R), CT, *60*
Ertaud, Wilfrid - MediaCOM Talent Group (C), MA, *477*
Erwin, Ronald R. - Erwin Assoc. (R), IL, *60*
Erwin, Susan - J. W. Barleycorn, Renard & Assoc., Inc. (R), OH, *11*
Escandon, Rafael - SpencerStuart (R), MX, *197*
Escher, W. Jon - Major, Hagen & Africa (C), CA, *423*
Esecson, Diane P. - Drinkwater & Assoc. (R), MA, *55*
Eskew, Martha - Recruiting Options, Inc. (C), GA, *532*
Eskra, Michael D. - Sanford Rose Assoc. - Port Washington (C), WI, *571*
Eskudt, Rita - The Enns Partners Inc. (R), ON, *59*
Esler, Mike - Strategic Resources (C), WA, *595*
Esposito, Kathy - Vincent Lee Assoc. (C), NY, *415*
Esposito, Mark - Christian & Timbers, Inc. (R), OH, *34*
Estelle, Tracy - Kincaid Group Inc. (KGI) (C), TX, *406*
Estes, Gregory A. - The Lawson Group, Inc. (C), SC, *414*
Estes, S. - The Talley Group (R), VA, *205*
Estes, Susan - The Associates, HR Search Executives, Inc. (C), OK, *254*
Estok, Patricia - Tuft & Assoc., Inc. (R), IL, *212*
Estrada, Barbara - Montgomery West (R), CA, *146*
Esty, Gregory C. - Management Recruiters of Park City (C), UT, *437*
Esty, Janet S. - Management Recruiters of Park City (C), UT, *437*
Ethington, Steve - DHR Int'l., Inc. (R), IL, *49*
Etlinger, Alan C. - Resource Recruiting (C), NH, *534*
Etter, Duane - Accounting & Bookkeeping Personnel, Inc. (C), AZ, *238*
Ettlinger, Lisa - Sales & Marketing Search, Inc. (C), MA, *551*
Evan-Cook, James - Cook Assoc.,® Inc. (R), IL, *40*
Evans, Chester P. - Greenhaven & Assoc., Inc. (R), NY, *81*
Evans, Jeffrey A. - Sullivan & Assoc. (R), MI, *204*
Evans, Patrick - The Evans McDonnell Co. (C), TX, *331*
Evans, Ray - Evans Transportation Search (C), ON, *331*
Evans, Ronald R. - The Evans Search Group (R), CT, *61*
Evans, Roy - American Resources Corp. (C), WI, *248*
Evdemon, II, Michael S. - Carter-Evdemon & Assoc. (C), FL, *285*
Everett, Jim - EA Plus, Inc. (C), TX, *325*
Eversbush, Helene - Johnson Smith & Knisely (R), GA, *107*
Evins, Susan - Bartl & Evins (C), NY, *260*
Extract, Raymond L. - Raymond L. Extract & Assoc. (R), CA, *64*
Eyler, Richard N. - Eyler Assoc., Inc. (R), IA, *64*
Faas, Vicki L. - Healthcare Recruiters of the Rockies, Inc. (C), CO, *372*
Faber, Jill S. - A.T. Kearney Executive Search (R), AZ, *111*
Faber, William - O'Brien & Bell (R), OH, *153*
Fabian, Jeanne - Fabian Assoc. Inc. (C), NY, *338*
Fabian, Kristina - Networking Unlimited of NH, Inc. (C), FL, *491*
Fabriele, John - Gallin Associates, Inc. (C), FL, *354*
Faerber, Cathleen - The Wellesley Group, Inc. (R), IL, *217*
Fafard, Lina - Montgomery West (R), CA, *146*
Fafard, Lina - The Partners, LLC (C), CA, *504*
Fagan, III, Charles A. - Fagan & Company (R), PA, *64*
Fagan, Mark - Management Recruiters of Greer (C), SC, *435*
Fagin, Charles D. - Beckman & Assoc. Legal Search (C), CO, *262*
Fahey, Michael T. - NorTech Resources (C), NY, *496*
Fair, Carolyn - Dunhill Executive Search of Los Angeles, Inc. (C), CA, *319*

Fairlie, Suzanne F. - ProSearch, Inc. (C), PA, *524*
Falcon, Elizabeth - Leaders-Trust Int'l./ Carce y Asociados, S.C. (R), MX, *127*
Falcon, Fritz - Dunhill of Baton Rouge, Inc. (C), LA, *317*
Falcone, Jr., Paul S. - Paul Falcone Assoc. (R), NJ, *65*
Falk, John - D. S. Allen Assoc. (C), OH, *244*
Faller, Laura McGrath - Redden & McGrath Assoc., Inc. (R), NY, *173*
Fandel, Arthur J. - Parsons, Anderson & Gee, Inc. (C), NY, *503*
Fanning, Jr., Charles J. - Major, Hagen & Africa (C), CA, *423*
Farabee, Randy L. - A.M.C.R., Inc. (C), FL, *232*
Farah, James C. - The S C Group LLC (R), NY, *183*
Fare, Sarah - Management Recruiters-Cedar Rapids, Inc. (C), IA, *448*
Farias, Juan Manuel - TASA International (R), MX, *206*
Farkas, Denny P. - Management Recruiters of Lehigh County (C), PA, *435*
Farler, Wiley - Romac Int'l., Inc. (C), PA, *544*
Farler, Wiley - Romac Int'l., Inc. (C), OH, *544*
Farley, Leon A. - Leon A. Farley Assoc. (R), CA, *65*
Farmer, David W. - Whitney Smith Co. (C), TX, *620*
Farnath, Dorothy W. - Dorothy W. Farnath & Assoc., Inc. (C), NJ, *338*
Farnsworth, John A. - Pearson, Caldwell & Farnsworth (R), CA, *161*
Farrar, Carolyn - Sanford Rose Assoc. - Springfield (C), MO, *568*
Farrar, Gary - Sanford Rose Assoc. - Springfield (C), MO, *568*
Farrell, Cathy - Government Contract Solutions, Inc. (C), VA, *361*
Farrell, Hugh - Organization Consulting Ltd. (R), ON, *157*
Farrell, John A. - The Curtiss Group International (R), FL, *44*
Farrell, John A. - The Curtiss Group, Int'l (R), FL, *44*
Farrell, III, Joseph E. - D.A.L. Associates, Inc. (R), CT, *45*
Farris, James W. - James Farris Assoc. (R), OK, *65*
Farro, Jerry - VZ Int'l., Inc. (C), AZ, *613*
Farrow, Jerry M. - McCormack & Farrow (R), CA, *140*
Faso, Nancy - Management Recruiters of Chicago West (C), IL, *447*
Fasola, Mary Lou - International Research Group (R), CA, *103*
Faubert, Denis - DARE Personnel Inc. (C), ON, *307*
Faucher, Cornel - Sink, Walker, Boltrus Int'l. (R), MA, *192*
Faulkner, LaCarole A. - L&L Assoc. Global Search (C), PA, *411*
Faulkner, Len - L&L Assoc. Global Search (C), PA, *411*
Fausett, A. Smith - Alynco, Inc. (C), AR, *246*
Favero, Luigi - Edward Bell Assoc. (C), CA, *263*
Fawcett, Anne M. - The Caldwell Partners Amrop International (R), ON, *26*
Fawcett, Marcia A. - The Fawcett Group (R), MA, *65*
Fawkes, Gary S. - Kennison & Assoc. Inc. (C), MO, *405*
Fazio, Joe - JT Assoc. (C), CT, *401*
Fedele, Rocco M. - Devin Scott Assoc. (C), NJ, *572*
Feder, Gwen L. - Egon Zehnder Int'l. Inc. (R), NY, *227*
Federman, Jack - W. R. Rosato & Assoc., Inc. (R), NY, *182*
Fee, J. Curtis - SpencerStuart (R), IL, *197*
Feerst, James E. - James Feerst & Assoc., Inc. (C), AZ, *339*
Fehrenbach, Ray - Southern Recruiters & Consultants, Inc. (C), SC, *587*
Feigenbaum, Irwin J. - Professional Resources (C), NY, *522*
Feightner, Ted - BioTech Research Recruiters Inc. (C), CA, *267*
Feimster, Alan - Management Recruiters of Florence (C), SC, *460*
Feinberg, Bernard A. - The Kay Group of 5th Ave. (C), NY, *404*
Feinberg, Erika - Pearson & Assoc., Inc. (C), AZ, *506*
Feingold, Marilyn - MedPro Personnel, Inc. (C), GA, *478*
Feingold, Robin - Cornerstone Search Assoc. Inc. (C), MA, *299*
Feinson, Milton M. - Sales Consultants of Brockton, Inc. (C), MA, *559*
Felactu, Odessa J. - The Odessa Group (R), CA, *155*
Feldman, Abe - A. E. Feldman Assoc., Inc. (C), NY, *339*
Feldman, Mitchell - A. E. Feldman Assoc., Inc. (C), NY, *339*
Fell, David W. - LAI Ward Howell (R), OH, *123*
Fell, Gregory L. - Sales Consultants of Baton Rouge (C), LA, *553*
Fell, III, John R. - Howe & Assoc. (R), PA, *97*
Fell, Robert M. - Fell & Nicholson Technology Resources (R), CA, *65*
Fells, Norman - EFCO Consultants, Inc. (C), NY, *327*
Fenimore, Joseph S. - F-O-R-T-U-N-E Personnel Consultants of Cincinnati (C), OH, *348*
Fennell, P. J. - Korn/Ferry Int'l. (R), ON, *118*
Fenton, Steve - Interim Accounting Professionals (C), TX, *392*
Fenwick, J. Brett - Sales Builders, Inc. (R), VA, *184*
Fenyves, Leslie - James Moore & Assoc. (C), CA, *397*
Fergus, Colin - Fergus Legal Search & Consulting, Inc. (C), NY, *339*
Fergus, Jean M. H. - Fergus Legal Search & Consulting, Inc. (C), NY, *339*
Ferguson, Cindy - The Canon Group (C), CA, *280*
Fernandez, Lynn - The Madison Group (R), NY, *133*
Fernandez, Michael - The Silicon Network (C), ON, *581*
Ferneborg, Jay W. - Ferneborg & Assoc., Inc. (R), CA, *66*
Ferneborg, John R. - Ferneborg & Assoc., Inc. (R), CA, *66*
Fernow, Charles S. - Fernow Assoc. (C), PA, *340*
Ferrante, Peter - National Executive (C), ON, *489*
Ferrante, Robert L. - Heyman Assoc., Inc. (R), NY, *93*
Ferrara, David K. - David Anthony Personnel Assoc., Inc. (C), NJ, *308*
Ferrara, David M. - Millennium Search Group, Inc. (R), CA, *144*
Ferrari, S. Jay - Ferrari Search Group (C), OH, *340*
Ferrel, James L. - Career Marketing Consultants, Inc. (C), GA, *283*
Ferrell, Randy - Romac Int'l., Inc. (C), FL, *543*
Ferry, Richard - Korn/Ferry Int'l. (R), NY, *117*
Feste, Ward P. - The Carlyle Group, Ltd. (R), IL, *30*
Fetridge, Guild - Guild Fetridge Acoustical Search, Inc. (C), NY, *340*
Fiala, Joanne C. - Burke & Assoc./The Westfield Group (C), CT, *276*
Fiala, Joanne C. - The Westfield Group (C), CT, *619*
Fidelle, Thomas P. - ExecuTech (C), IN, *332*
Fidlow, Darlene - Sales Search Specialist (C), IL, *564*
Fidlow, Elliott - Sales Search Specialist (C), IL, *564*
Fields, Fredric L. - C. A. Durakis Assoc., Inc. (R), MD, *55*
Fields, Sharon K. - Career Development Associates (C), NV, *282*
Fienberg, Chester A. - Drummond Assoc., Inc. (C), NY, *315*
Fifield, George C. - Egon Zehnder Int'l. Inc. (R), CA, *227*
Filippelli, Frank J. - The Glenwood Group (C), IL, *358*
Filko, Gary - Management Recruiters of Allentown-South (C), PA, *434*
Fill, Clifford G. - Dixie Search Assoc. (C), GA, *313*
Fill, Ellyn H. - Dixie Search Assoc. (C), GA, *313*
Finch, Dan - Management Recruiters of Addison Central (C), TX, *436*
Finch, Dianne - Management Recruiters of Addison Central (C), TX, *436*
Finch, John Juanito - Resolve Assoc. Int'l. (R), FL, *175*
Fincher, Richard P. - Phase II Management (R), CT, *164*
Fineman, David M. - Manuso, Alexander & Associates, Inc. (R), NY, *135*

Fingers, Dave - Bradford & Galt, Inc. (C), TX, *271*
Fink, Allen - PMJ & Assoc. (C), ON, *513*
Fink, Don J. - Technical Staffing Solutions (C), TX, *602*
Fink, Neil - Neil Fink Assoc. (R), CA, *66*
Fink, Ronald L. - Sales Consultant of New Haven (C), CT, *552*
Fink, Sarah S. - Sales Consultant of New Haven (C), CT, *552*
Finkel, Leslie - Caliber Associates (R), PA, *27*
Finkle, Linda - LG Brand, Inc. (C), MD, *417*
Finley, Heather - C. D. Warner & Assoc. (C), MD, *615*
Finley, Kerry - Recruiting Services Group, Inc. (C), TN, *532*
Finley, Margot E. - Avondale Search Int'l., Inc. (R), FL, *9*
Finn, Eileen - Eileen Finn & Assoc., Inc. (C), NY, *341*
Finn, Eileen - The MVP Group (C), NY, *487*
Finn, Jacquelyn - Finn & Schneider Assoc., Inc. (C), DC, *341*
Finn, James N. - The Garret Group (R), FL, *75*
Finnegan, Gerald F. - Finnegan & Assoc. (R), CA, *67*
Finnegan, Richard - Finnegan & Assoc. (R), CA, *67*
Finnell, Anne-Marie - TASA International (R), NY, *206*
Finnigan Werra, Nora - Jude M. Werra & Assoc. (R), WI, *218*
Finocchiaro, Jim - Sales Consultant of Riverside (C), IA, *552*
Finseth, Carl L. - Meng, Finseth & Assoc., Inc. (R), CA, *143*
Fiore, Richard - Search Consultants Int'l., Inc. (C), TX, *575*
Fiorentino, Patricia - Barr Associates (C), NY, *260*
Fippinger, Stephanie - PLA, Inc. (C), NJ, *513*
Fippinger, Steve - PLA, Inc. (C), NJ, *513*
Fischer, Howard - Howard Fischer Assoc. Int'l., Inc. (R), PA, *67*
Fischer, Howard - Howard Fischer Assoc. Int'l., Inc. (R), TX, *67*
Fischer, Janet L. - Boyden (R), IL, *21*
Fischer, John C. - Horton Int'l. Inc. (R), NY, *96*
Fischer, Judith - RJ Associates (C), CA, *538*
Fischer, Karl W. - Dunhill Search of Medford (C), NJ, *321*
Fischer, Robert - Thor, Inc. (C), CA, *606*
Fischer, Ronald - RJ Associates (C), CA, *538*
Fischer, Sabine - Linford E. Stiles & Assoc., L.L.C. (R), NH, *201*
Fischer, Sherwin J. - J. R. Scott & Assoc., Ltd. (C), IL, *395*
Fischetti, Tony M. - Pharmaceutical Search Professionals, Inc. (C), PA, *510*
Fischler, Nick P. - NPF Assoc. Ltd. Inc. (R), FL, *153*
Fish, Donald - Bruce Edwards & Associates, Inc. (R), NC, *57*
Fishback, Joren - Derek Associates, Inc. (C), MA, *311*
Fishel, Richard A. - Fishel HR Assoc., Inc. (C), AZ, *341*
Fisher, Earl - Management Recruiters of Cass County, NE (C), NE, *453*
Fisher, Gary E. - Fisher & Assoc. (R), CA, *67*
Fisher, Iris L. - Healthcare Recruiters International-NY/NJ (C), NJ, *373*
Fisher, Jack Stuart - Jack Stuart Fisher Assoc. (C), NJ, *341*
Fisher, Lawrence C. - Mullen Assoc., Inc. (R), NC, *149*
Fisher, Mel V. - The Fisher Group (R), AB, *67*
Fisher, Neal - Fisher Personnel Management Services (R), CA, *68*
Fisher, Neal - PPS Information Systems Staffing (C), MD, *515*
Fisher, Richard - Richard A. Eisner & Co., LLP (R), NY, *57*
Fisher, Suzanne - Quality Control (C), MI, *526*
Fishkin, Anita - A. G. Fishkin & Assoc., Inc. (R), MD, *68*
Fishman, Judy - Vintage Resources, Inc. (C), NY, *613*
Fishman, Perry - Vintage Resources, Inc. (C), NY, *613*
Fisk, James L. - James L. Fisk & Assoc. (C), MO, *342*
Fitzgerald, Diane - Fitzgerald Associates (R), MA, *68*
Fitzgerald, Don - Elliot Assoc. Inc. (R), CA, *58*
Fitzgerald, Geoffrey - Fitzgerald Associates (R), MA, *68*
Fitzgerald, Jon K. - Health Industry Consultants, Inc. (R), CO, *89*
Fitzgerald, Matthew A. - Telecom Recruiters, Inc. (C), VA, *605*
Fitzgerald, Ted - Accountants On Call (C), NJ, *236*
Fitzgerald, Thomas L. - Telecom Recruiters, Inc. (C), VA, *605*
FitzGibbon, Michael T. - FitzGibbon & Assoc. (R), PA, *68*
Fitzgibbons, David - International Executive Recruiters (C), OH, *393*
Fitzmorris, Robert - DHR Int'l., Inc. (R), FL, *50*
Fitzpatrick, Alan - Merlin Int'l. Inc. (C), NJ, *479*
Fitzpatrick, John - Newport Strategic Search LLC (C), CA, *492*
Fitzpatrick, Susan - Management Recruiters of Milwaukee - Downtown (C), WI, *466*
Fitzsimmons, Doris J. - Accountants On Call (C), NJ, *235*
Fixler, Eugene - Ariel Recruitment Assoc. (R), NY, *7*
Flagg, Jessica S. - The Consulting Group Ltd. (R), NY, *40*
Flam, Rick M. - LAI Ward Howell (R), CA, *123*
Flamer, Michael - The Dorfman Group (C), AZ, *314*
Flanagan, Dale M. - LAI Ward Howell (R), NY, *122*
Flanagan, Greg - Marcus & Assoc. (C), NY, *469*
Flanagan, Robert M. - Robert M. Flanagan & Assoc., Ltd. (R), NY, *68*
Flannery, Michael - Redwood Partners Ltd. (R), NY, *173*
Flannery, Peter - Jonas, Walters & Assoc., Inc. (R), WI, *108*
Flannery, Thomas T. - Resources for Management (R), PA, *176*
Flash, James - Richard Kader & Assoc. (C), OH, *403*
Flatt, Ryan - DeMatteo Associates (C), NY, *311*
Flax, Robin - Alan Davis & Assoc. (R), QE, *47*
Flax, Robin - Alan Davis & Assoc. Inc. (R), QE, *47*
Fleischer, Susan - Healthcare Executive Recruiters, Inc. (C), CA, *372*
Fleischman, Edward - The Execu/Search Group (C), NY, *332*
Fleishman, William M. - First Advisory Services Int'l., Inc. (R), MD, *67*
Fleming, Michael - Sanford Rose Assoc. - Cedar Rapids (C), IA, *567*
Fleming, Richard - Gatti & Assoc. (C), MA, *355*
Fleming, Richard L. - TASA International (R), FL, *206*
Fleming, Robert - Accountants On Call (C), PA, *237*
Flesher, Susan - Flesher & Assoc., Inc. (R), CA, *68*
Fletcher, Susan - Susan Fletcher Attorney Employment Services (C), PA, *342*
Fligel, Robert - The Execu/Search Group (C), NY, *332*
Flood, Michael - Norman Broadbent Int'l., Inc. (R), NY, *152*
Florence, Kathy - Pryor & Associates (C), CA, *525*
Flores, Laura Chávez - Pricewaterhouse-Coopers Executive Search (R), MX, *168*
Flott, Stan - General Engineering Tectonics (C), CA, *356*
Flowers, John - Empire International (R), PA, *59*
Flowers, Terry - Russ Hadick & Assoc. Inc. (C), OH, *365*
Fludd, Virgil L. - The CARVIR Group, Inc. (C), GA, *285*
Flynn, Jack - Executive Search Consultants Corp. (C), IL, *335*
Flynn, Jerry - J. G. Flynn & Assoc. Inc. (R), BC, *69*
Flynn, Joanne T. - Pinnacle Group Int'l. (C), AZ, *512*
Flynn, Peter - Partnervision Consulting Group Inc. (R), ON, *160*
Flynn, Stephen F. - Pinnacle Group Int'l. (C), AZ, *512*
Fockler, David B. - David Fockler & Assoc., Inc. (C), CA, *342*

Fodge, Robert - Management Recruiters of Washington, DC Inc. (C), MD, *450*
Fodge, Robert C. - Skipping Stone Inc. (C), VA, *582*
Fogec, Thomas G. - Fogec Consultants, Inc. (R), WI, *69*
Fogle, Aimee - Stanton Chase Int'l. (R), TX, *199*
Foley, Susan - DHR Int'l., Inc. (R), WI, *51*
Foley, Thomas J. - Foley Proctor Yoskowitz (R), NY, *69*
Folletta, Wallamena - Action Executive Personnel Consulting Inc. (C), ON, *239*
Folts, Richard W. - Battalia Winston Int'l./The Euram Consultants Group (R), IL, *13*
Foltz, T. J. - Capital Markets Resources, Inc. (C), NC, *281*
Fonfa, Ann E. - S. R. Wolman Assoc., Inc. (R), NY, *224*
Fontaine, Valerie A. - Seltzer Fontaine Beckwith (C), CA, *579*
Fooce, Denise - Stephens Assoc. Ltd., Inc. (R), OH, *200*
Foote, Leland W. - L. W. Foote Co. (R), WA, *69*
Forbes, Catherine M. - StratfordGroup (R), CO, *203*
Forbes, Kathy - The Forbes Group (R), GA, *69*
Forbes, Kay Koob - Sanford Rose Assoc. - Evansville (C), IN, *567*
Forbes, Kenneth P. - Sanford Rose Assoc. - Evansville (C), IN, *567*
Ford, Eileen F. - Ford & Ford (C), MA, *343*
Ford, J. Daniel - Witt/Kieffer, Ford, Hadelman & Lloyd (R), IL, *223*
Ford, Merlin B. - Ford & Assoc., Inc. (C), SC, *343*
Ford, Neil - R. Green & Assoc., Inc. (C), OH, *362*
Ford, Sandra D. - The Ford Group, Inc. (R), PA, *69*
Ford, Travis - Ford & Assoc., Inc. (C), SC, *343*
Foreman, David C. - Koontz, Jeffries & Assoc., Inc. (R), FL, *117*
Forest, Adam - McCormack & Assoc. (R), CA, *140*
Forest, Gilbert - Egon Zehnder Int'l. Inc. (R), QE, *227*
Forman, Margaret M. - National Field Service Corp. (C), NY, *489*
Forman, Phil - Ryman, Bell, Green & Michaels, Inc. (C), TX, *549*
Fornabaio, Thomas A. - Biomedical Search Consultants (R), CT, *17*
Fornino, Rita M. - Garrison-Randall, Inc. (R), CA, *75*
Fornino, Rita M. - Garrison-Randall, Inc. (R), CA, *75*
Forray, Karen - Forray Assoc., Inc. (R), NY, *70*
Forrest, Casey - Pinton Forrest & Madden/EMA Partners Int'l. (R), BC, *165*
Fortin-Menendez, Joanne - Avion International Technology Inc. (C), ON, *257*
Fosnot, Michael - Management Recruiters of McMurray, Inc. (C), PA, *459*
Foss, Gregory - Diedre Moire Corp., Inc. (C), NJ, *483*
Fossett, Gary J. - John Michael Assoc. (R), DC, *106*
Foster, Andrew B. - Management Recruiters of Brentwood (C), TN, *436*
Foster, Barton T. - The Barton Group, Inc. (C), MI, *260*
Foster, David - Doherty Healthcare Consultants (C), ME, *313*
Foster, Dennis J. - Major Legal Services, Inc. (C), OH, *423*
Foster, Donald J. - Foster Associates (C), NJ, *351*
Foster, Dwight E. - Foster Partners (R), NY, *70*
Foster, Holly - A First Resource (C), NC, *231*
Foster, Kathie - Michael Latas & Assoc., Inc. (R), MO, *126*
Foster, Nancy - Baldwin & Assoc. (C), OH, *258*
Foster, Jr., Torrey N. - Lynch Miller Moore Partners, Inc. (R), IL, *132*
Foster, William A. - Bridgecreek Personnel Agency (C), CA, *273*
Fought, Jay D. - Fought, Jameson Assoc. (C), IL, *351*
Fountain, Ray - Management Recruiters of North Charleston (C), SC, *460*
Fountas, N. G. - JLI-Boston (R), MA, *106*
Fousie, Duane - Staffing Edge, Inc. (C), TX, *591*
Fowler, Gary - Analog Solutions (C), NY, *249*
Fowler, Jim - First Search America, Inc. (C), TN, *341*
Fowler, Thomas A. - The Hindman Co. (R), TX, *94*
Fox, Allis - Intersource, Ltd. (R), GA, *103*
Fox, Candy - D. R. Blood & Assoc. (R), AZ, *18*
Fox, Gary - F-O-R-T-U-N-E Personnel Consultants of Southwest Indiana (C), IN, *346*
Fox, Glenn M. - Strategic Search, LLC (C), CA, *595*
Fox, James P. - Michael Latas & Assoc., Inc. (R), MO, *126*
Fox, Lucie - Allard Associates (C), CA, *244*
Fox, Michael L. - Management Recruiters of Woodbury (C), MN, *430*
Fox, Michael L. - Management Recruiters of Woodbury (C), MN, *452*
Fox, Susan - Adirect Recruiting Corp. (C), ON, *240*
Foxman, Marty - Pierce & Assoc. (C), CA, *512*
Foy, James C. - Foy, Schneid & Daniel, Inc. (R), NY, *71*
Foy, Richard - Boyden (R), NY, *20*
Foy, Richard - Boyden (R), NY, *20*
Frabetti, Alton J. - Applied Resources (C), MA, *252*
Franchot, Douglas W. - Wood, Franchot Inc. (R), MN, *224*
Francis, Brad - Romac Int'l., Inc. (C), CO, *542*
Francis, Dwaine - Francis & Assoc. (R), IA, *71*
Francis, John - Zwell Int'l. (R), CA, *228*
Francis, Joseph - Hospitality Int'l. (C), NY, *381*
Francis, N. Kay - Francis & Assoc. (R), IA, *71*
Franco, Virginia - Shore Asociados Ejecutivos, S. A. de C.V. (R), MX, *190*
Frank, Dale A. - New Directions, Inc. (C), IL, *492*
Frank, Joel - Trainor/Frank & Assoc. Inc. (C), WI, *608*
Frank, Miriam J. - Major, Hagen & Africa (C), IL, *423*
Frank, Neil - Neil Frank & Co. (R), CA, *71*
Frank, Sheila - Accountants On Call (C), NY, *236*
Frank, Valerie S. - Norman Roberts & Assoc., Inc. (R), CA, *179*
Frank, Jr., William E. - The Curtiss Group International (R), FL, *44*
Frankel, Howard - Recruit Xpress (C), TX, *531*
Frankel, Len - Abacus Group LLC (C), NY, *232*
Frankel, Marcia - Recruit Xpress (C), TX, *531*
Frankel, Miriam - PMJ & Assoc. (C), ON, *513*
Frankian, Joseph R. - Allstaff, Inc. (C), IL, *245*
Franklin, Gary - FAI (C), CO, *338*
Franklin, Michael - Hreshko Consulting Group (C), NJ, *382*
Frankovich, John - BRW Search (C), MN, *275*
Franquemont, Jeffrey D. - EFL Int'l. (R), AZ, *57*
Franquemont, William R. - EFL Int'l. (R), AZ, *57*
Frantz, Sally - Martin Partners, L.L.C. (R), IL, *137*
Franz, Bill - Cornerstone Resources, Inc. (C), OK, *299*
Franz, Ronald - Fisher-Todd Assoc. (C), NY, *342*
Franzel, Jerry - DHR Int'l., Inc. (R), GA, *50*
Franzino, Michael - TASA International (R), NY, *206*
Frary, Kevin S. - KS Frary & Assoc. (R), MA, *71*
Fraser, Lawrence J. - Secura/Burnett Partners (R), NY, *188*
Fraser, William - Windsor Consultants, Inc. (C), TX, *622*
Frazer, Mel - Mel Frazer Consultant (C), CA, *352*
Frazier, Donna - Management Recruiters of Austin (C), TX, *462*
Frazier, Scott - Ron Sunshine & Assoc. (C), IL, *597*
Frazier, Steven M. - Sanford Rose Assoc. - Philadelphia North (C), PA, *570*

PRINCIPALS

Frease, Don - Management Recruiters The Delta Group, Inc. (C), TN, *461*
Freda, Louis A. - Waveland Int'l. (R), TX, *216*
Fredericks, Ward A. - MIXTEC Group (R), CA, *145*
Freeh, Tom - Romac Int'l., Inc. (C), GA, *543*
Freeman, Evelyn - Brierwood Group, Inc. (C), IN, *274*
Freeman, Mark - ESA (R), CT, *60*
Freese, Hal - Dunhill of Greenwood (C), SC, *318*
Freier, Bruce - Executive Referral Services, Inc. (C), IL, *334*
Fremon, Michael W. - The Revere Assoc., Inc. (R), OH, *176*
French, Guy P. - Corso, Mizgala + French (R), ON, *42*
French, Peter N. - P. N. French Assoc., Inc. (R), MA, *72*
French, William G. - Preng & Assoc., Inc. (R), TX, *167*
Fresquez, Ernesto - Fresquez & Assoc. (C), CA, *353*
Fretz, William - The 500 Granary Inc. (C), ON, *231*
Frey, Florence - Frey & Sher Assoc., Inc. (C), VA, *353*
Frey, Steve - National Corporate Consultants, Inc. (C), IN, *489*
Fridley, Patricia - Carol Maden Group (C), VA, *422*
Fried, Ann - DeLalla - Fried Assoc. (C), NY, *310*
Fried, Steve - Management Recruiters of Chicago-North Shore (C), IL, *447*
Fried, Steven L. - Sales Consultants (C), IL, *558*
Friedland, Robert J. - Secura/Burnett Partners (R), NY, *188*
Friedman, Donna L. - Tower Consultants, Ltd. (R), FL, *210*
Friedman, Helen E. - McCormack & Farrow (R), CA, *140*
Friedman, Ken - The Primary Group, Inc. (R), FL, *168*
Friedman, Nathan - Retail Recruiters (C), CT, *535*
Friedman, Wendy - DHR Int'l., Inc. (R), NY, *50*
Frigon, Bernard - Bernard Frigon & Assoc. Inc. (C), QE, *353*
Frisch, Gerald - Gerald Frisch Assoc., Inc. (R), NY, *72*
Frischman, Timothy - Furst Group/MPI (R), MN, *72*
Frishman, Robert - Greenwich Search Partners, LLC (C), CT, *363*
Frishman, Robin - Allen Austin Lowe & Powers (R), TX, *3*
Fristoe, Jack - Fristoe & Carleton, Inc. (C), OH, *353*
Frock, Suzanne - Brandjes Assoc. (C), MD, *272*
Froehlich, Peter - Peter Froehlich & Co. (C), TX, *353*
Froelich, K. - Murphy Partners Int'l. (R), IL, *150*
Froelich, Kris - Norrell Financial Staffing (C), PA, *495*
Fronteras, Helene - The Shorr Group (R), IL, *190*
Frost, Edward W. - Mortgage Search Network (C), AZ, *486*
Fruchtman, Gary - Management Recruiters of Northwest Ohio, Inc. (C), OH, *458*
Frumess, Gregory - Foster Partners (R), NY, *70*
Fry, Don - Dunhill of Corpus Christi, Inc. (C), TX, *323*
Fry, John M. - The Fry Group, Inc. (C), NY, *353*
Fuccella, Carl J. - Brissenden, McFarland, Fuccella & Reynolds, Inc. (R), NJ, *23*
Fulgham-MacCarthy, Ann - Columbia Consulting Group (R), NY, *38*
Fuller, Craig - Korn/Ferry Int'l. (R), DC, *118*
Fuller, Thomas - Epsen, Fuller & Assoc., LLC (R), NJ, *60*
Fullerton, Kimberly - Major, Hagen & Africa (C), CA, *423*
Fullerton, Murray - The Churchill Group (C), ON, *291*
Fumano, Gary W. - Chapman & Assoc. (C), BC, *289*
Funk, Bill - Korn/Ferry Int'l. (R), TX, *118*
Funk, Terry L. - International Technical Resources (C), FL, *394*
Furioso, Carmine A. - F-O-R-T-U-N-E Personnel Consultants of San Diego (C), CA, *344*
Furlong, James W. - Furlong Search, Inc. (R), OR, *72*
Furlong, James W. - Furlong Search, Inc. (R), CA, *72*
Furlong, James W. - Furlong Search, Inc. (R), CA, *72*
Furman, Matt - MJF Assoc. (C), CT, *483*
Furr, C. Franklin - C. F. Furr & Co. (R), NC, *72*
Furst, Stephen - Strategic Resources (C), WA, *595*
Furst, Thomas C. - The Furst Group, Inc. (R), IL, *72*
Gabel, Greg - Canny, Bowen Inc. (R), NY, *28*
Gable, Jacqueline S. - Gable Healthcare Group, Inc. (R), FL, *73*
Gabor, Robert A. - Kehn & Gabor, Inc. (C), OH, *405*
Gabriel, Alan L. - Lloyd Prescott & Churchill, Inc. (R), OH, *130*
Gabriel, Alan L. - Lloyd Prescott Assoc., Inc. (C), OH, *419*
Gabriele, Leslie - Gabriele & Company (C), MA, *354*
Gaffney, David L. - Profit Pros, Inc. (C), CA, *523*
Gaffney, Keith - Gaffney Management Consultants (R), IL, *73*
Gaffney, William - Gaffney Management Consultants (R), IL, *73*
Gaffney, William M. - Teknon Employment Resources, Inc. (C), OH, *604*
Gagan, Joan - Gilbert Tweed Assoc. Inc. (R), NY, *76*
Gagan, Joan - Ward Liebelt Assoc. Inc. (R), CT, *215*
Gaggiano, William - DHR Int'l., Inc. (R), DC, *50*
Gagliano, Chris - DHR Int'l., Inc. (R), MO, *50*
Gagola, J. - American Executive Management, Inc. (R), MA, *5*
Gahan, Ann M. - Gahan Assoc. (R), NY, *73*
Gahan, Carolyn M. - Gahan Assoc. (R), NY, *73*
Gahan, Thomas M. - Gahan Assoc. (R), NY, *73*
Gaillard, Bill - Management Recruiters of Hickory (C), NC, *433*
Gaines, Donna - Gaines & Assoc. Int'l., Inc. (R), IL, *73*
Gaines, Jay - Jay Gaines & Company, Inc. (R), NY, *74*
Gaines, Ronni L. - Topaz Int'l., Inc., Attorney Search (C), NJ, *607*
Galante, Suzanne - Vlcek & Company, Inc. (R), CA, *214*
Galbraith, Deborah M. - StratfordGroup (R), OH, *203*
Gale, Joseph E. - DHR Int'l., Inc. (R), IL, *49*
Gale, Michael - Professional Healthcare Search & Consultants, Inc. (C), CA, *520*
Gale, Rhoda - Management Recruiters of the Baltimore Washington Corridor (C), MD, *450*
Galitzine, Gai - Global Research Partnership Inc. (R), NY, *78*
Galka, John - Huntley Associates (Dallas), Inc. (C), TX, *386*
Gallagher, Alice - Synergistech Communications (C), CA, *597*
Gallagher, David A. - Sweeney Harbert & Mummert, Inc. (R), FL, *205*
Gallagher, David W. - LAI Ward Howell (R), GA, *123*
Gallagher, Dennis - Multisearch Recruiters (C), CA, *487*
Gallagher, Jim - Management Recruiters of Pittsburgh-Airport (C), PA, *435*
Gallagher, Joan - International Pro Sourcing, Inc. (C), PA, *393*
Gallagher, Kelly - International Pro Sourcing, Inc. (C), PA, *393*
Gallagher, Kelly - K2 Resources, L.P. (C), CT, *402*
Gallagher, Michael - Mankuta Gallagher & Assoc., Inc. (C), FL, *468*
Gallagher, Sallie - Management Recruiters of Pittsburgh-Airport (C), PA, *435*
Gallagher, Susan - Accountants On Call (C), VA, *237*
Gallagher, Terence M. - Battalia Winston Int'l./The Euram Consultants Group (R), NJ, *13*
Gallagher, Terence M. - Battalia Winston Int'l./The Euram Consultants Group (R), NY, *13*
Galliano, Lynda - Accountants On Call (C), CA, *235*
Galliano, Lynda - Accountants On Call (C), CA, *235*

Gallin, Lawrence - Gallin Associates, Inc. (C), FL, *354*
Gallman, LaVerne - Tuft & Assoc., Inc. (R), IL, *212*
Gallo, John - Logic Assoc., Inc. (C), NY, *419*
Galloway, Gayle - Management Recruiters of Highland Park (C), IL, *428*
Gamache, Valerie - Joe L. Giles & Assoc. (C), MI, *357*
Gamboa, Mark - Solomon-Page Healthcare Group (R), CA, *195*
Gamboa, Victor - Quest Worldwide Executive Search Corp. (C), CA, *527*
Gammel, Matthew C. - Wilder, Gammel Partners, Ltd. (R), CA, *220*
Gammill, Robert A. - The Gammill Group, Inc. (C), OH, *354*
Gandal, Robert - Management Recruiters International, Inc. (MRI) (C), OH, *425*
Gandal, Robert - Sales Consultants (C), OH, *551*
Gandee, Bob - Management Recruiters of Cleveland-Airport (C), OH, *433*
Gandee, Bob - Sales Consultants of Cleveland-Central (C), OH, *555*
Gandee, Bob - Sales Consultants of Cleveland-Airport (C), OH, *555*
Gandee, Brad - Management Recruiters of Sugar Land Inc. (C), TX, *464*
Gandee, Joan C. - Management Recruiters of Sugar Land Inc. (C), TX, *464*
Gandee, John R. - Management Recruiters of Sugar Land Inc. (C), TX, *464*
Gandee, Robert - Management Recruiters of Cleveland (C), OH, *457*
Gansser, Bill - Techstaff Inc. (C), MI, *603*
Garb, Sheila - Garb & Assoc., Legal Placement (C), CA, *354*
Garbarini, William N. - W. N. Garbarini & Assoc. (R), NJ, *74*
Garbutt, Mimi - Harcourt & Assoc. (C), AB, *368*
Garcia, Abel - Allen Austin Lowe & Powers (R), TX, *3*
Garcia, Chris - Management Recruiters of Reston (C), VA, *437*
Garcia, Joseph - Management Recruiters of Nogales (C), AZ, *425*
Garcia, Linda - Management Recruiters of Reston (C), VA, *437*
Garcia, Lourdes - AES Search (C), NJ, *241*
Gardella, Richard - The Whyte Group, Inc. (R), MD, *220*
Gardiner, E. Nicholas P. - Gardiner, Townsend & Assoc. (R), NY, *74*
Gardiner, Earl - Austin Park Management Group Inc. (C), ON, *256*
Gardiner, Gary - Management Recruiters of Cleveland (C), OH, *457*
Gardner, Brian - Bosch & Assoc., LLC (R), CT, *20*
Gardner, Glen - Sanford Rose Assoc. - Columbus North (C), OH, *570*
Gardner, J. W. - Management Recruiters of Jackson (C), MS, *430*
Gardner, Marvin - Gardner-Ross Assoc., Inc. (R), NY, *74*
Gardner, Richard E. - Russillo/Gardner/Spolsino (C), MA, *548*
Gardner, Scott - Chesapeake Group (C), CT, *290*
Gardner, Sidney - Chase-Gardner Executive Search Associates, Inc. (C), FL, *289*
Gardner, Stan - Management Recruiters of El Dorado Hills (C), CA, *425*
Garfield, Patricia - Healthcare Recruiters Int'l. Bay Area (C), CA, *372*
Garfinkle, Benson D. - MetroVantage Personnel Systems (C), CA, *480*
Garfinkle, Steven M. - Battalia Winston Int'l./The Euram Consultants Group (R), MA, *13*
Garland, David C. - Healthcare Recruiters - Northwest (C), WA, *374*
Garland, Dick - Dick Garland Consultants (R), NY, *74*
Garland, Dick - Dick Garland Consultants (R), NY, *74*
Garland, Mike - Raymond Thomas & Assoc. (C), FL, *530*
Garland, R. Darryl - Garland Assoc. Int'l. (C), CA, *355*
Garman, Herb - Management Recruiters of Tucson (C), AZ, *439*
Garms, Daniel S. - The Garms Group (R), IL, *75*
Garner, Ann - Accountants On Call (C), CA, *235*
Garner, Ron - Accountants On Call (C), CA, *235*
Garofolo, Frank A. - StratfordGroup (R), PA, *203*
Garoufalis, Byron T. - International Management Services Inc. (R), IL, *102*
Garren, Gayle - MetroVantage Personnel Systems (C), CA, *480*
Garrett, Donald L. - Garrett Assoc. Inc. (R), GA, *75*
Garrett, Kelly - Management Recruiters - Indianapolis (C), IN, *448*
Garrett, Linda M. - Garrett Assoc. Inc. (R), GA, *75*
Garrett, William R. - Sales Consultant of St. Petersburg (C), FL, *552*
Garrison, Ed - The Garrison Organization (R), IA, *75*
Garrison, Jeff - Management Recruiters of Blue Bell (C), PA, *434*
Garrison, Randall - The Garrison Organization (R), CO, *75*
Garrity, Irene - Management Recruiters of Westborough (C), MA, *430*
Garrote, L. Ignacio - Phoenix Search (R), MX, *164*
Garton, Dennis - Dunhill Professional Search of Oklahoma City (C), OK, *318*
Garzone, Dolores - M. A. Churchill & Assoc., Inc. (R), PA, *35*
Gasbarre, John - The Haystack Group, Inc. (R), ME, *88*
Gasga, Pedro Salinas - Michigan Consulting Group (R), MI, *144*
Gaspar, Adam - Aggressive Corporation (C), IL, *242*
Gasperini, Peter - Peter Gasperini & Assoc., Inc. (R), NY, *75*
Gassett, Sam - Primus Assoc., L.C. (R), TX, *169*
Gates, Becky - Primus Assoc., L.C. (R), TX, *169*
Gates, Will - Morgan Samuels Co. (R), CA, *147*
Gatti, Robert D. - Gatti & Assoc. (C), MA, *355*
Gaudette, Charles L. - Medical Recruiters Exchange (C), AZ, *477*
Gaudreau, Betsy - Sales & Marketing Search, Inc. (C), MA, *551*
Gaudry, Jean - Gaudry, Shink, Levasseur (R), QE, *75*
Gauger, Dianne - Dianne Gauger & Assoc. (C), CA, *355*
Gaulden, David G. - Sales Consultant of Pleasanton (C), CA, *551*
Gauss, James - Witt/Kieffer, Ford, Hadelman & Lloyd (R), CA, *223*
Gauthier, Robert C. - Columbia Consulting Group (R), MD, *38*
Gavigan, Colleen - Petrie Partners, Inc. (R), FL, *163*
Gavin, David - The Comwell Company, Inc. (C), NJ, *296*
Gavin, David R. - Northland Employment Services Inc. (C), MN, *496*
Gavura, Nicholas J. - Michael Latas & Assoc., Inc. (R), MO, *126*
Gaw, F. William - Brandywine Management Group (R), MD, *22*
Gawitt, Dan - Management Recruiters of the Baltimore Washington Corridor (C), MD, *450*
Gay, Martha - Salzmann Gay Assoc., Inc. (R), PA, *184*
Gay, Richard C. - IprGroup, Inc. (C), GA, *394*
Gazzolo, Diana - Martin Grant Assoc. Inc., Insurance Personnel (C), MA, *472*
Gebler, Stephen - Systems Research Group (C), CA, *598*
Geddes, Murray - Geddes & Rubin Management Inc. (R), ON, *76*
Gehle, Frederick P. - Dunhill Professional Search of Augusta (C), GA, *320*
Gehn, Valerie - Harbrowe, Inc. (C), NY, *368*
Geiman, Barry - Leader Institute, Inc. (C), GA, *414*
Geiser, Diane - The York Group (C), CA, *626*
Gelatka, Charles T. - The Bennett Group, Inc. (R), IN, *16*
Gelbard, William - DHR Int'l., Inc. (R), DC, *50*
Gélinas, Normand - Yves Plouffe & Assoc. (R), QE, *165*
Geller, Nicole - Government Contract Solutions, Inc. (C), VA, *361*
Geller, William - Boulware & Assoc. Inc. (R), IL, *20*
Gelpi, Gerry - Gelpi & Assoc. (C), LA, *355*
Genel, George - Genel Associates (C), CA, *356*
Gennawey, Robert - Romac Int'l., Inc. (C), CA, *542*

Gensch, Marie - Marra Peters & Partners (R), FL, *136*
Genser, Elaina Spitaels - Witt/Kieffer, Ford, Hadelman & Lloyd (R), CA, *223*
Gentry, Alison - Accountants On Call (C), IL, *235*
Gentry, Allen - Hospitality Int'l. (C), AZ, *381*
George, Alan - Ken Clark Int'l. (R), NJ, *36*
George, Bethany W. - Rollo Assoc. (R), CA, *181*
George, Delores F. - Delores F. George, C.P.C. (C), MA, *356*
George, Richard - Kensington Int'l., Inc. (R), IL, *113*
Georgian, Bruce - Wallace Assoc. (C), MA, *614*
Gerald, C. Richard - C. R. Gerald & Assoc. (C), ON, *356*
Gerard, William - Fox-Morris Assoc., Inc. (C), CA, *352*
Gerarde, Paul S. - Keena Staffing Services (C), NY, *404*
Gerlach, Mary - Quality Consulting Group, Inc. (C), WI, *526*
Germain, Valerie - Jay Gaines & Company, Inc. (R), NY, *74*
Germaine, Debra - Fenwick Partners (R), MA, *66*
Gerner, Jeri - Rovner Gerner & Assoc. (R), CA, *182*
Gernetzke, James - J. Gernetzke & Assoc., Inc. (C), OH, *357*
Gersin, Harvey - Sales Consultants of Farmington Hills (C), MI, *560*
Gerson, Fred - Affordable Executive Recruiters (C), CA, *241*
Gerst, Thomas J. - Management Recruiters of Akron (C), OH, *457*
Gerstl, Ronald - Maxecon Executive Search Consultants (R), FL, *138*
Gertler, Richard - Prairie Resource Group, Inc. (R), IL, *166*
Gesing, Rand W. - Rand Assoc. (R), ME, *171*
Gettys, James R. - International Staffing Consultants, Inc. (C), CA, *393*
Getzug, Richard F. - Lloyd Prescott & Churchill, Inc. (R), PA, *130*
Getzug, Richard F. - Lloyd Prescott Assoc., Inc. (C), PA, *419*
Giacalone, Louis - Allard Associates (C), NY, *244*
Giacoponello, Thomas V. - Search America, Inc. (C), PA, *573*
Giallombardo, Gary - Central Executive Search, Inc. (C), OH, *287*
Giannerini, Roxanne - Recruitment Specialists, Inc. (C), MD, *532*
Giannino, Richard - Elliot Assoc. Inc. (R), MA, *58*
Gibbons, Betsy - The Caldwell Partners Amrop International (R), ON, *26*
Gibbons, Ronald L. - Flynn, Hannock, Inc. (R), CT, *69*
Gibeault, Joe - Cornerstone Resources, Inc. (C), OK, *299*
Gibney, Patrick - Medfall Inc. (C), ON, *476*
Gibson, Bruce - Gibson & Co., Inc. (R), WI, *76*
Gibson, Holli - Sales Consultants of Dallas (C), TX, *563*
Gibson, Jan - Advanced Corporate Search (C), CA, *240*
Gideon, Mark - Eagle Search Assoc. (C), CA, *325*
Gielow, Curtis C. - Gielow Assoc., Inc. (R), WI, *76*
Giesen, Al - Stone, Murphy & Olson (R), MN, *201*
Gilbert, Brian - Sales Consultants of Dallas (C), TX, *563*
Gilbert, Elaine - Herbert Mines Assoc., Inc. (R), NY, *145*
Gilbert, Jr., H. Harry - Gilbert Scott Assoc., LLC (C), MA, *357*
Gilbert, Jacqueline - GAAP Inc. (R), QE, *73*
Gilbert, James - Dynamic Staffing Network (C), IL, *324*
Gilbert, Jerry - Gilbert & Van Campen Int'l. (R), NY, *76*
Gilbert, John - John Gilbert Co. (C), TX, *357*
Gilbert, Keith A. - Management Recruiters of Pismo Beach (C), CA, *426*
Gilbert, Mark - Sales Consultants of Farmington Hills (C), MI, *560*
Gilbert, Mary - Management Recruiters of Pismo Beach (C), CA, *426*
Gilbert, Patricia G. - Lynch Miller Moore Partners, Inc. (R), IL, *132*
Gilchrist, Carl - SpencerStuart (R), GA, *197*
Gilchrist, Robert J. - Horton International Inc. (R), CT, *96*
Gildea, Catherine T. - The Whyte Group, Inc. (R), MD, *220*
Gildea, Catherine T. - The Whyte Group, Inc. (R), MA, *220*
Gildersleeve, John - Snelling & Snelling, Inc. (C), FL, *585*
Giles, Joe L. - Joe L. Giles & Assoc. (C), MI, *357*
Giles, Kenn - Dick Williams & Assoc. (C), CA, *621*
Gill, Karine - The IMC Group, Miami, Florida (R), FL, *101*
Gill, Susan - Plummer & Associates, Inc. (R), GA, *166*
Gill, Trish - Columbia Consulting Group (R), NY, *38*
Gillard, Cheryl A. - Gillard Assoc. Legal Search (C), MA, *357*
Gillard, Elizabeth A. - Gillard Assoc. Legal Search (C), MA, *357*
Gillenwater, Patti - Elinvar (C), NC, *328*
Gillespie, David - The Kennett Group, Inc. (R), PA, *112*
Gilliam, Dale - Management Recruiters of Spokane (C), WA, *465*
Gilliam, Jon - LCS, Inc. (C), TX, *414*
Gillin, Samuel Shay - Empire International (R), PA, *59*
Gills, Bob - Sales Consultant of Boulder (C), CO, *552*
Gilmore, David A. - Elwell & Assoc., Inc. (R), MI, *59*
Gilmore, Howard A. - Howard Gilmore & Assoc. (R), OH, *77*
Gilmore, Jerry - Management Recruiters of Loudoun County South (C), VA, *465*
Gilmore, Roger - Gilmore & Assoc. (C), CA, *357*
Gilmour, Ian - NMC & Kay Int'l. (R), CO, *152*
Gilreath, Diane C. - Gilreath Weatherby Inc. (R), MA, *77*
Gilreath, James M. - Gilreath Weatherby Inc. (R), MA, *77*
Gilson, Dirk S. - Key Resources Int'l. (C), CA, *406*
Gilson, Linda L. - Key Resources Int'l. (C), CA, *406*
Gimbel, Mike - Gimbel & Assoc. (C), FL, *357*
Ginsberg, Sheldon M. - Lloyd Prescott & Churchill, Inc. (R), FL, *130*
Ginsberg, Sheldon M. - Lloyd Prescott Assoc., Inc. (C), FL, *419*
Gionta, Michael - Management Recruiters of Colchester (C), CT, *442*
Giordano, Louis P. - L. Patrick Group (R), NJ, *122*
Giorgetti, Richard - Management Solutions, Inc. (C), CA, *468*
Gipson, Jeff - Bradford & Galt, Inc. (C), IL, *271*
Giries, Juliet - Barton Assoc., Inc. (R), TX, *12*
Gist, Carl - Dunhill Personnel Service of San Antonio (C), TX, *318*
Gitlin, Bernardo - Boyden Latin America S.A. de C.V. (R), MX, *21*
Givens, Steve - Chesapeake Group (C), CT, *290*
Gladstone, Athur - Roth Young Executive Search (C), TX, *546*
Gladstone, Elaine - Roth Young Executive Search (C), TX, *546*
Gladstone, Robert - Roth Young Executive Search (C), TX, *546*
Gladwell, Don - ProLink (C), NC, *524*
Glancey, Jr., Thomas F. - Gordon Wahls Executive Search (C), PA, *613*
Glandon, Stephanie - Management Recruiters of Kanawha Valley, LLC (C), WV, *465*
Glaser, David - ECG Resources, Inc. (C), NY, *326*
Glaser, Larry - Lawrence Glaser Assoc., Inc. (C), NJ, *358*
Glass, Robert - McGrath & Assoc., Inc. (R), NJ, *141*
Glassberg, Bob - Sales Search (C), ON, *564*
Glassick, Charles E. - Jon McRae & Associates, Inc. (R), GA, *142*
Glasspiegel, Susan - Flexible Resources, Inc. (C), CT, *342*
Glatman, Marcia - HRD Consultants, Inc. (R), NJ, *97*
Glatzer, Neil - Management Solutions, Inc. (C), CA, *468*

Glavin, James E. - Wood-Glavin, Inc. (R), KS, *224*
Glaza, Ron - Management Recruiters of Morro Bay (C), CA, *426*
Glazin, Lynne - The Glazin Group (R), BC, *77*
Gleason, Helen - Management Recruiters of Clearwater (C), FL, *443*
Gleason, James P. - J. P. Gleason Assoc., Inc. (R), IL, *77*
Gleckman, Mark - Winter, Wyman & Co. (C), MA, *623*
Glennon, Tony - GSP International (C), NJ, *364*
Glick, Douglas I. - MedSearch Resources, Inc. (C), FL, *478*
Glickman, Kenneth S. - Harvey Hohauser & Assoc. (R), MI, *87*
Glicksman, Russell A. - The Beam Group (R), PA, *14*
Glines, Larry - Glines Assoc., Inc. (R), IL, *77*
Glomski, Jane - Management Recruiters of Rochester (C), MN, *452*
Gloss, Fred C. - F. Gloss Int'l. (R), VA, *78*
Glosser, Elizabeth B. - Executive Exchange Corp. (C), NJ, *333*
Glou, Alan - Glou Int'l., Inc. (R), MA, *78*
Glover, Tracy - The Tracy Glover Co. (R), TX, *78*
Glymph, Tina - Michael J. Hall & Co. (R), WA, *85*
Glynn, Mary Anne - E. A. Hughes & Co., Inc. (R), NY, *98*
Glynn, Thomas J. - Fox-Morris Assoc., Inc. (C), PA, *352*
Gmutza, Al - F-O-R-T-U-N-E Personnel Consultants of Southwest Indiana (C), IN, *346*
Gnodde, R. Dirk - Gnodde Assoc. (C), IL, *359*
Goar, Duane R. - TASA International (R), TX, *206*
Gobbell, John J. - The Gobbell Co. (R), CA, *78*
Gobdel, Bruce - Creative Financial Staffing (C), MA, *303*
Godat, Stacy - DHR Int'l., Inc. (R), MO, *50*
Godfrey, James R. - Godfrey Personnel, Inc. (C), IL, *359*
Godfrey, Robert G. - Robert G. Godfrey Assoc. Ltd. (R), IL, *79*
Goehring, Hal - H. L. Goehring & Assoc., Inc. (C), OH, *359*
Goehring, Robert E. - Management Recruiters of Northern Monmouth County (C), NJ, *432*
Goehring, Susan - STAT Search (C), NH, *592*
Goerss, Ronald - Boyden (R), CA, *20*
Goff, Debbie - J. L. Nixon Consulting (C), IL, *493*
Gogates, Andrew - The Gogates Group, Inc. (R), NY, *79*
Goheen, Joyce - Meads & Assoc. (R), FL, *142*
Goich, S. George - Fernow Assoc. (C), PA, *340*
Goicoechea, Lydia - Management Recruiters of San Antonio-NW (C), TX, *436*
Goicoechea, Sam - Management Recruiters of San Antonio-NW (C), TX, *436*
Gold, Alan - L & L Assoc. (C), CA, *410*
Gold, Barry M. - Barry M. Gold & Co. (C), CA, *359*
Gold, Don - Executive Search, Ltd. (C), OH, *336*
Gold, Leslie - Major, Hagen & Africa (C), NY, *423*
Gold, Lisa - Strategic Advancement Inc. (R), NJ, *202*
Gold, Lisa - Stratin Assoc. (C), NJ, *596*
Gold, Ruth - The Madison Group (R), NY, *133*
Gold, Susan - Stentiford & Berardi Assoc. Ltd. (R), NY, *200*
Gold, Walter - Proven Edge (C), CA, *525*
Goldbach, Linda J. - Beacon Int'l., Inc. (C), VA, *261*
Goldbeck, Henry - Goldbeck Recruiting Inc. (C), BC, *359*
Goldberg, Barry - Barry Goldberg & Assoc., Inc. (C), CA, *360*
Goldberg, Risa - Media Recruiting Group, Inc. (C), NY, *476*
Goldberg, Steve - Media Recruiting Group, Inc. (C), NY, *476*
Goldberg, Sybil - Spectra International LLC (C), AZ, *589*
Goldenberg, Susan T. - Grant Cooper & Assoc., Inc. (R), MO, *81*
GoldFarb, Abbe S. - TASA International (R), NY, *206*
Golding, Michael S. - Michael Assoc. (R), IL, *144*
Golding, Rob - Korn/Ferry Int'l. (R), TX, *118*
Goldman, Donald L. - Management Recruiters International, Inc. (MRI) (C), OH, *425*
Goldman, Donald L. - Sales Consultants (C), OH, *551*
Goldman, Elaine - The Goldman Group Inc. (R), NY, *79*
Goldman, Elaine - Goldman+Bell, LLC (C), NY, *360*
Goldman, Elaine - Phyllis Hawkins & Assoc., Inc. (C), AZ, *370*
Goldman, Howard - Management Assoc. (C), CA, *424*
Goldman, Irwin - Michael Wayne Recruiters (C), IL, *481*
Goldman, Jeff - Global 1000 Int'l. Services (C), CA, *358*
Goldman, M. - Hunt Patton & Brazeal, Inc. (C), CO, *385*
Goldman, Michael L. - Strategic Assoc., Inc. (C), TX, *595*
Goldrick, John R. - Spriggs & Co., Inc. (R), IL, *198*
Goldring, Joe - Joseph Goldring & Assoc. Inc. (C), MI, *360*
Goldshore, Steven - Winthrop Partners, Inc. (R), NY, *222*
Goldsmith, Fred J. - Fred J. Goldsmith Assoc. (R), CA, *79*
Goldsmith, Jerry - The Primary Group, Inc. (R), FL, *168*
Goldsmith, Joseph B. - Higdon Prince Inc. (R), NY, *93*
Goldstein, Barry - Interim Financial Solutions (C), VA, *392*
Goldstein, Don - JAG Group (R), MO, *105*
Goldstein, Gary S. - The Whitney Group (R), NY, *219*
Goldstein, Lory - Omni Search, Inc. (C), CA, *499*
Goldstein, Michael - AES Search (C), NJ, *241*
Goldstein, Michael - Goldstein & Co. (C), CA, *360*
Goldstein, Peggy - Goldstein & Co. (C), CA, *360*
Goldstein, Steve - Forum Personnel Inc. (C), NY, *351*
Goldstein, Steven G. - The Jonathan Stevens Group, Inc. (R), NJ, *108*
Golenberke, Michael - Accountants On Call (C), OH, *236*
Gomez, Christina - StratfordGroup (R), CA, *203*
Gomez, David P. - David Gomez & Assoc., Inc. (R), IL, *79*
Gomez, Margie - Bor-Maq Assoc. (C), TX, *269*
Gomez, Miguel - Gomez Fregoso y Asociados (C), JAL, *360*
Gomez, Veronica - Engineering Futures, LLC (C), CT, *330*
Gonedes, James T. - Business Solutions Worldwide, Inc. (C), NJ, *277*
Gongloff, Jr., William J. - Sanford Rose Assoc. - Rochester (C), MI, *568*
Gonye, Peter K. - Egon Zehnder Int'l. Inc. (R), NY, *227*
Gonzalez, Cecelia - Brystol Cove Assoc. (R), CA, *24*
Gonzalez, Denise - FCI, Inc. (R), NJ, *65*
Gonzalez, Eric - Sales Consultant of Middletown (C), NJ, *554*
Gonzalez, Joe - Brystol Cove Assoc. (R), CA, *24*
Gonzalez, Romulo - Korn/Ferry Int'l. (R), NL, *118*
Gonzalez, Romulo - Korn/Ferry, Int'l., S.A. de C.V. (R), NL, *118*
Gonzalez-Miller, Laura - Management Recruiters of Avon (Indianapolis-West) (C), IN, *429*
Gonzer, Lawrence J. - L. J. Gonzer Assoc. (C), NJ, *360*
Gooch, Raymond B. - Teknon Employment Resources, Inc. (C), OH, *604*
Good, David J. - Management Recruiters of Sioux Falls, LLP (C), SD, *461*
Good, Robert B. - Management Recruiters of Sioux Falls, LLP (C), SD, *461*
Goodall, Rhys - C. J. Stafford & Assoc. (C), ON, *591*
Goode, Laura K. - Kiradjieff & Goode, Inc. (R), MA, *115*
Goode, Jr., Richard W. - Kiradjieff & Goode, Inc. (R), MA, *115*
Goodere, Greg - Montgomery West (R), CA, *146*

PRINCIPALS

Goodkind, Peter - Goodkind Assoc. Inc. (C), NY, *360*
Goodman, Goody - Harvard Group Int'l. (R), CO, *87*
Goodman, Lion - The Goodman Group (R), CA, *79*
Goodman-Brolin, Dorothy - DLB Assoc. (R), NY, *53*
Goodrich, III, Dana C. - First Advisory Services Int'l., Inc. (R), MD, *67*
Goodson, Jr., W. Kenneth - DLG Assoc., Inc. (R), NC, *53*
Goodspeed, Peter - Witt/Kieffer, Ford, Hadelman & Lloyd (R), TX, *223*
Goodwin, Joe D. - LAI Ward Howell (R), GA, *123*
Goodwin, Martha - Page-Wheatcroft & Co., Ltd. (R), TX, *158*
Goodwin, Tom - Goodwin & Co. (R), DC, *80*
Gorberg, Richard D. - Fortune Personnel Consultants of Raleigh, Inc. (C), NC, *348*
Gordon, Alan - The Healthsearch Group, Inc. (C), NY, *374*
Gordon, Dave - Cemco, Ltd. (C), IL, *287*
Gordon, Donald E. - Interim Management Resources Inc. (C), ON, *392*
Gordon, Elliot - Korn/Ferry Int'l. (R), CA, *117*
Gordon, Gregory - Wallace Assoc. (C), CT, *614*
Gordon, Jeff - The Healthsearch Group, Inc. (C), NY, *374*
Gordon, Libby - Elliot Assoc. Inc. (R), AZ, *58*
Gordon, Manuel F. - Lloyd Prescott & Churchill, Inc. (R), FL, *130*
Gordon, Manuel F. - Lloyd Prescott Assoc., Inc. (C), FL, *419*
Gordon, Richards - Bickerton & Gordon LLC (C), MA, *266*
Gordon, Susan - Lynne Palmer Executive Recruitment, Inc. (C), NY, *421*
Gordon, Trina D. - Boyden (R), IL, *21*
Gordy, Thomas - Harvard Group Int'l. (R), GA, *87*
Gore, Les - Executive Search Int'l./ Transearch (R), MA, *63*
Gorfinkle, Gayle - Executive Search Int'l./ Transearch (R), MA, *63*
Gorry, John E. - Cella Assoc. (C), GA, *286*
Gossage, Wayne - Gossage Regan Assoc. (R), NY, *80*
Gostin, Howard I. - Sanford Rose Assoc. - Columbia, MD (C), MD, *567*
Gostyla, Rick - SpencerStuart (R), CA, *196*
Gotheif, Julie - Retained Search Assoc. (R), NC, *176*
Gottenberg, Norbert - SpencerStuart (R), NY, *196*
Gottesfeld, Sheldon - Cross Country Consultants, Inc. (C), MD, *304*
Gottlieb, Ira N. - Creative Management Strategies, Ltd. (R), NY, *42*
Goulbourne, Lance M. - Milo Research (R), NY, *145*
Gould, Cotter Ray - Executives Worldwide, Inc. (C), OR, *337*
Gould, Nanci - National Search, Inc.r (C), FL, *490*
Gould, William E. - Gould, McCoy & Chadick, Inc. (R), NY, *80*
Gouran, Marc S. - Solomon-Page Healthcare Group (R), NY, *195*
Govig, Dick A. - Management Recruiters of Scottsdale (C), AZ, *425*
Govig, Todd - Management Recruiters of Scottsdale (C), AZ, *425*
Gow, Roderick C. - LAI Ward Howell (R), NY, *122*
Gowdy, Olga M. - Gowdy Consultants (C), TX, *361*
Gowetski, K. Michael - Nationwide Personnel Placement, Inc. (C), OH, *490*
Goyette, Marc - ROI International, Inc. (R), WA, *181*
Goyette, Marc L. - Management Recruiters of Seattle-South (C), WA, *437*
Goyette, Margo - ROI International, Inc. (R), WA, *181*
Grace, Madison - Medicorp, Inc. (C), MO, *477*
Grace, Patty - Management Recruiters of Siouxland (C), IA, *449*
Gracin, Ada - Computer Placements Unlimited Inc. (C), NY, *295*
Grady, April - BEST/World Assoc. Inc. (R), TX, *16*
Grady, Jerry - The Ward Group (R), MA, *215*
Grady, Richard F. - Drew Assoc. Int'l. (R), NJ, *54*
Grady, William A. - Romac Int'l. Inc. (R), MA, *181*
Graf, Adrienne - McCormack & Assoc. (R), CA, *140*
Graff, Thomas D. B. - The Hanover Consulting Group (C), MD, *368*
Gragg, Bryan L. - Millennium Search Group, Inc. (R), CA, *144*
Gragg, Robert - Montgomery West (R), CA, *146*
Graham, Alexander J. - Alexander Graham Assoc. (C), NJ, *361*
Graham, Dale - C.P.S., Inc. (C), IL, *278*
Graham, David - Pharmaceutical Search Professionals, Inc. (C), PA, *510*
Graham, Don - H.Q. Search, Inc. (C), IL, *365*
Graham, Lesley - JPM International (C), CA, *401*
Graham, Pat - Milrod Assoc. (C), NJ, *482*
Graham, Robert - Cambridge Management Planning (R), ON, *27*
Graham, Robert - Michael J. Hall & Co. (R), WA, *85*
Graham, Robert E. - Fortune Personnel Consultants of Allentown, Inc. (C), PA, *348*
Graham, Robert W. - Robert Graham Assoc. (R), RI, *81*
Graham, Sara L. - Fortune Personnel Consultants of Allentown, Inc. (C), PA, *348*
Graham, Tony - Executives Worldwide, Inc. (C), OR, *337*
Graham, Tony - Synergy Systems (C), ON, *598*
Graham-Bryce, Robert - PSD Group, Inc. (C), CA, *525*
Grand, Alissa - Accountants On Call (C), CA, *235*
Grandin, Valerie J. - H. Hertner Assoc., Inc. (C), FL, *377*
Granet, Marc - IDC Executive Search Inc. (C), FL, *387*
Granger, John - Romac Int'l., Inc. (C), MA, *543*
Grant, Anthony - Management Recruiters of Columbia (C), MD, *450*
Grant, Dan - Marsteller Wilcox Assoc. (C), IL, *471*
Grant, Daniel M. - Sales Consultants of Western McHenry County (C), IL, *558*
Grant, Lee - Grant-Franks & Assoc. (C), NJ, *361*
Grant, Robert - Robert Grant Assoc., Inc. (C), CA, *361*
Grant, Susan G. - Winguth, Grant & Donahue (R), CA, *222*
Grantham, John D. - Grantham & Co., Inc. (R), NC, *81*
Grantham, Phil - Columbia Consulting Group (R), MD, *38*
Grassl, Peter - Bowman & Marshall, Inc. (C), KS, *271*
Grauss, Bryan J. - Grauss & Co. (C), CA, *362*
Grauss, Debra M. - Grauss & Co. (C), CA, *362*
Gravelle, Paul F. - Bert Davis Executive Search, Inc. (R), NY, *47*
Graver, Patricia - Excalibur Human Resources, Inc. (R), NJ, *61*
Graves, Ron - Management Recruiters of McRae (C), GA, *428*
Gray, Andrew - Bosland Gray Assoc. (R), NJ, *20*
Gray, Annie - Annie Gray Assoc., Inc. (R), MO, *81*
Gray, Betty - Accent On Achievement, Inc. (C), MI, *233*
Gray, Brian A. - BG & Assoc. (C), MD, *266*
Gray, Frank - Feldman Gray & Assoc. Inc. (C), ON, *339*
Gray, Kent - Romac Int'l. - San Francisco (C), CA, *541*
Gray, Leanne P. - Career Profiles (C), NH, *283*
Gray, Mark - Executive Referral Services, Inc. (C), IL, *334*
Gray, Norman G. - Career Profiles (C), NH, *283*
Gray, Russell - Johnson Smith & Knisely (R), GA, *107*
Grayem, Tim - The Canon Group (C), CA, *280*
Grayson, Donna - ETI Search Int'l. (R), GA, *61*
Grayson, E. C. - SpencerStuart (R), CA, *196*
Grayson, George - Health Search (C), CA, *371*

Graziano, Rosemarie - Engineering & Scientific Search Assoc. (ESSA) (C), NJ, *330*
Graziano, Toni - Central Executive Search, Inc. (C), OH, *287*
Greaney, Francis J. - Corporate Leadership Strategies, Inc. (R), NH, *41*
Greathouse, Lesa - Premier Search Group (C), IN, *517*
Grebenschikoff, Jennifer R. - Physician Executive Management Center (R), FL, *164*
Grebenstein, Charles R. - Skott/Edwards Consultants (R), NJ, *192*
Greco, Ben - Ben Greco Assoc., Inc. (C), CA, *362*
Greco, Sheila - Sheila Greco Assoc. (C), NY, *362*
Greebe, Neil - Preferred Professional Recruiters (C), OH, *516*
Green, Bruce - Canadian Career Partners (R), AB, *27*
Green, Bruce - Carter/MacKay (C), NJ, *285*
Green, Heide - JAG Group (R), MO, *105*
Green, Jane - Phillips Resource Group (C), SC, *510*
Green, John A. - JAG Group (R), MO, *105*
Green, Judith - Dunhill Professional Search (C), OH, *318*
Green, Larry A. - Winston & Green (C), IL, *623*
Green, Lucille K. - Attorney Search Global, Inc. (C), IL, *255*
Green, Lynn - Nuance Personnel Search, Inc. (C), NC, *497*
Green, Mark - Rice Cohen Int'l. (R), PA, *178*
Green, Rita - R. Green & Assoc., Inc. (C), OH, *362*
Green, Thomas R. - The TGA Company (C), TX, *606*
Greenberg, Herb - HG & Assoc. (R), IL, *93*
Greenberg, Jordan A. - The Pinnacle Source, Inc. (C), CO, *512*
Greenberg, Louise - Ruderfer & Co., Inc. (C), NJ, *548*
Greenblatt, Stephanie - The Bauman Group (R), CA, *14*
Greene, Dorcas P. - Greene Personnel Consultants (C), RI, *362*
Greene, Frederick J. - Boyden (R), CA, *20*
Greene, Jeff - Wesley Brown & Bartle Co., Inc. (R), NY, *218*
Greene, Karin L. - Greene-Levin-Snyder LLC (C), NY, *362*
Greene, Pervis - Sales Consultant of High Point (C), NC, *554*
Greene, Sharon - Stewart/Greene & Co. of The Triad, Inc. (C), NC, *594*
Greene, Timothy G. - Greene & Co. (C), MA, *362*
Greene, Jr., W. Luke - Broward-Dobbs, Inc. (C), GA, *274*
Greene, William - Stewart/Greene & Co. of The Triad, Inc. (C), NC, *594*
Greene, Zina L. - Hartman Greene & Wells (C), DC, *370*
Greenfader, David - Management Recruiters of Los Angeles-Encino (C), CA, *425*
Greenfader, David - Sales Consultant of Los Angeles-Encino (C), CA, *551*
Greenfield, Art - Management Recruiters of Boston (C), MA, *430*
Greenfield, Marci - DHR Int'l., Inc. (R), DC, *50*
Greenland, Gregory L. - MedXec USA, Inc. (C), FL, *478*
Greenspan, Phillip D. - Waveland Int'l. (R), IL, *216*
Greenwald, Anita - Concorde Search Assoc. (C), NY, *296*
Greenwald, Jane - Gilbert Tweed Assoc. Inc. (R), NJ, *77*
Greenwood, Harry - The Partners, LLC (C), CA, *504*
Greenwood, Katherine - Fortune Personnel Consultants of Plano (C), TX, *350*
Greger, Kenneth R. - Greger/Peterson Assoc., Inc. (R), OR, *82*
Gregg, Larry - Christopher-Westmont & Assoc., Inc. (R), OH, *35*
Gregg, Larry - The Lear Group, Inc. (R), OH, *127*
Gregg, Paul - Dunhill Professional Search of Miami (C), FL, *317*
Gregg, Paul J. - Dunhill Professional Search of Miami (C), FL, *320*
Gregor, Joie A. - Heidrick & Struggles, Inc. (R), NY, *90*
Gregorius, Stephanie - DHR Int'l., Inc. (R), MO, *50*
Gregory, Elaine - Dunhill Staffing Systems of Orlando (C), FL, *317*
Gregory, Mark - Accountants On Call (C), NC, *236*
Gregory, Ron - Dunhill Staffing Systems of Orlando (C), FL, *317*
Gregory, Rose - Kay Henry, Inc. (C), PA, *376*
Gres, Ed - Pioneer Executive Consultants (C), ON, *512*
Gresham, James G. - Executive Search Inc. (R), MN, *63*
Gresosky, Thomas - Romac Int'l., Inc. (C), FL, *543*
Greven, Gregg A. - Corporate Search Consultants (C), IN, *301*
Griesedieck, Jr., Joseph E. - SpencerStuart (R), CA, *196*
Griffey, Annette - Ashford Management Group, Inc. (R), CA, *8*
Griffey, Gail A. - Romac Int'l., Inc. (C), FL, *543*
Griffin, Al - Gardner-Ross Assoc., Inc. (R), NY, *74*
Griffin, Cathy - A.T. Kearney Executive Search (R), OR, *111*
Griffin, Deana A. - Souder & Assoc. (R), VA, *195*
Griffin, H. S. Skip - Right/McKee Consulting Group (C), TX, *537*
Griffin, Helen - Major, Hagen & Africa (C), NY, *423*
Griffith, David B. - F-O-R-T-U-N-E Personnel Consultants of Charlotte (C), NC, *348*
Griffith, Doug - Caywood Partners, Ltd. (R), CA, *32*
Griffith, Sandra - F-O-R-T-U-N-E Personnel Consultants of Charlotte (C), NC, *348*
Griffith, III, Warland - Griffith & Werner, Inc. (R), FL, *82*
Griffiths, William J. - Romac Int'l. Inc. (R), MA, *181*
Grillo, Scott - Professional Recruiting Network (C), CA, *521*
Grim, Gene - Sales Consultants of Cherry Hill (C), NJ, *560*
Grimes, Amanda - TASA International (R), GA, *206*
Grimes, G. D. - Management Recruiters of Warren County, KY (C), KY, *449*
Grimes, Matthew - Angel Group Int'l. (C), KY, *250*
Grimes, Nancy C. - Management Recruiters of Warren County, KY (C), KY, *449*
Grimes, Richard D. - Management Recruiters of Warren County, KY (C), KY, *449*
Grimm, Peter G. - Nordeman Grimm, Inc. (R), NY, *152*
Grindlinger, Arthur R. - Fortune Personnel Consultants of Sarasota Inc. (C), FL, *345*
Groban, Jack L. - A.T. Kearney Executive Search (R), CA, *111*
Groenekamp, William A. - Groenekamp & Assoc. (C), CA, *363*
Grokas, George - StaffWriters Plus (C), NY, *591*
Groner, James B. - J. B. Groner Executive Search, Inc. (C), DE, *363*
Groom, Charles C. - C. G. & Assoc. (R), PA, *26*
Gros, Dennis - Gros Executive Search, Inc. (C), TN, *363*
Gross, Alan H. - Marketing & Sales Resources, Inc. (C), FL, *470*
Gross, Dean - Becker Personnel (C), FL, *262*
Gross, Dean - Becker Personnel (C), FL, *262*
Gross, Howard - Herbert Mines Assoc., Inc. (R), NY, *145*
Gross, Jerry - Creative HR Solutions (C), GA, *303*
Gross, Joe - V.I.P. Resources, Inc. (C), NY, *611*
Gross, Kathy - Evie Kreisler Assoc. Inc. (C), NY, *409*
Gross, Ken - Data Search Network, Inc. (C), FL, *307*
Gross, Philip - Professions, Inc. (C), OH, *523*
Gross, Richard - Robert Shields & Assoc. (C), TX, *538*
Grossberg, Robert M. - Grossberg & Assoc. (R), IL, *82*
Grossman, Allan D. - A. Davis Grant & Co. (R), NJ, *81*

PRINCIPALS

Grossman, Barbara - Pathway Executive Search, Inc. (C), NY, *505*
Grossman, Gary - The Execu/Search Group (C), NY, *332*
Grotte, Lawrence C. - Lautz, Grotte, Engler & Swimley (R), CA, *126*
Groussman, Maria - Groussman & Assoc., Inc. (R), TX, *82*
Grovenstein, Gerald - Sales Consultant of Mobile (C), AL, *551*
Grover, James R. - Grover & Assoc. (R), OH, *82*
Groves, Jane - MSA Executive Search (R), MO, *148*
Growick, Philip - Jerry Fields Assoc. (C), NY, *340*
Grubb, Peg Iversen - Executive Search Consultants (C), CA, *335*
Grue, Douglas Harrison - Harrison Consulting Group, Inc. (C), CA, *369*
Gruen, Constance - Argus National, Inc. (R), CT, *6*
Grumney, David E. - David E. Grumney Co. Inc. (R), WA, *83*
Grushkin, Joel T. - DHR Int'l., Inc. (R), CA, *49*
Gruszecki, Irene - Management Recruiters of Wausau, LLC (C), WI, *466*
Gualtieri, Jill - Raymond Karsan Assoc. (C), NJ, *530*
Guardiani, Janet - Edward Bell Assoc. (C), CA, *263*
Guarino, Alan - Cornell Group Int'l. Consulting, Inc. (R), NY, *41*
Guarino, Kathleen - Cornell Group Int'l. Consulting, Inc. (R), NY, *41*
Guarniere, John W. - RCE Assoc. (R), NJ, *173*
Guber, Nadine B. - Nadine Guber & Assoc., Inc. (C), NY, *364*
Gude, John S. - Boyden (R), IL, *21*
Guerin, Michael R. - Michael R. Guerin Co. (C), CA, *364*
Guerrero, Daniel - Kenzer Corp. (R), CA, *113*
Guerrier, Alain M. - PersoNet, Inc. (C), FL, *507*
Guest, Denise - Jones Management Co. (R), CT, *108*
Guevara, Charles - The Colton Partnership, Inc. (R), NY, *38*
Gugler, Wolf - Wolf Gugler & Assoc. Ltd. (R), ON, *83*
Guidarelli, Shelley - Guidarelli Assoc., Inc. (R), MI, *83*
Guido, Ronald J. - Argus National, Inc. (R), CT, *6*
Guidroz, Ken - Management Recruiters of San Marcos (C), TX, *463*
Guidry, Jim - Guidry & East Healthcare Search Consultants (R), TX, *83*
Guilford, David J. - DLG Assoc., Inc. (R), NC, *53*
Guinn, Andrea - ISG Informatics Search Group (C), ON, *395*
Guld, Allison - Jenex Technology Placement Inc. (C), BC, *398*
Gulden, Stacy L. - Management Recruiters of Orlando/Winter Park (C), FL, *427*
Gulian, Randolph S. - Strategic Executives, Inc. (R), CT, *202*
Gumbinner, Paul S. - Gumbinner/Haubenstock, Inc. (C), NY, *364*
Gundersen, Jeff - Gundersen Partners, L.L.C. (R), NY, *83*
Gundersen, Steven G. - Gundersen Partners, L.L.C. (R), NY, *83*
Gungle, Theresa - Gowdy Consultants (C), TX, *361*
Gunkel, Keith J. - KGA Inc. (C), WI, *406*
Gunning, Phill - TBC, Inc. (C), KY, *600*
Gunther, Greg - Raymond Karsan Assoc. (C), NJ, *530*
Gunther, James J. - Harvard Aimes Group (R), CT, *87*
Gurley, Herschel - Management Recruiters of Martinsville (C), VA, *437*
Gurliacci, Lisa - Johnson Smith & Knisely (R), NY, *107*
Gurney, Darrell W. - A Permanent Success Employment Services (C), CA, *231*
Gurr, Roger - Boyden (R), BC, *21*
Gurrola, Jose D. - J.D.G. y Asociados, S.A. de C.V. (R), SO, *104*
Gustafson, Dale - Management Recruiters of Bloomington (C), MN, *452*
Gustafson, Terry - Matthews & Stephens Assoc., Inc. (C), CT, *472*
Gustin, Charles A. - Gustin Partners, Ltd. (R), MA, *83*
Gutierrez, Mary Rose - Job Link, Inc. (C), CA, *399*
Gutterman, Allen - Response Staffing Services (C), NY, *535*
Guy, C. William - William Guy & Assoc., Inc. (R), CA, *84*
Guzzetta, Christy - GES Services, Inc. (R), NY, *76*
Habelmann, Gerald B. - Habelmann & Assoc. (R), MI, *84*
Haber, Erica - AES Search (C), NJ, *241*
Haberman, Meyer - Interquest, Inc. (R), NY, *103*
Haberman, Rebecca Powers - Norman Powers Assoc., Inc. (C), MA, *515*
Hacker, Russell - RHAssoc. Inc. (C), KS, *535*
Hackett, Carrie - Cejka Healthcare Executive Search Services (CHESS) (R), MO, *32*
Hackett, Donald F. - Management Recruiters of Mt. Airy (C), NC, *456*
Haddad, Charles G. - Gateway Group Personnel, LLC (C), TN, *355*
Haddad, Ronald J. - Haddad Assoc. (R), FL, *84*
Hadelman, Jordan M. - Witt/Kieffer, Ford, Hadelman & Lloyd (R), IL, *223*
Hadick, Russ - Russ Hadick & Assoc. Inc. (C), OH, *365*
Hadley, Thomas M. - Hadley Associates, Inc. (C), NJ, *365*
Haentzler, Robert A - Michael Latas & Assoc., Inc. (R), MO, *126*
Hagedorn, Jens - Management Recruiters of Cuernavaca (C), MX, *438*
Hageman, Jr., Leo - HR Inc. (C), NC, *382*
Hagen, Laura J. - Major, Hagen & Africa (C), IL, *423*
Hager, Eve - Eastridge Infotech (C), CA, *326*
Haggard, Jr., John H. - Growth Consultants of America (R), MI, *82*
Haggard, Luke - First Search America, Inc. (C), AL, *341*
Haggard, Melissa M. - MarketPro, Inc. (C), GA, *471*
Haggard, Robin - Lee Weil Assoc., Inc. (C), CA, *617*
Haggerty, Noreen - K. Russo Assoc. Inc. (C), CT, *548*
Haggith, Marvin - M. A. Haggith Consultants Ltd. (R), ON, *84*
Hagglund, Karl - D. J. Simpson Assoc. Inc. (R), ON, *191*
Hagler, Carlos - MSI Int'l. (C), GA, *487*
Hagy, J. Ronald - The Corporate Source Group, Inc. (R), PA, *42*
Hahn, Kenneth R. - Hahn & Assoc., Inc. (C), OH, *365*
Hahn, Loel G. - Fergason Assoc., Inc. (C), IL, *339*
Hailey, H. M. - Damon & Assoc., Inc. (C), TX, *306*
Hailey, Susan L. - Egon Zehnder Int'l. Inc. (R), CA, *227*
Haines, Linda - Human Resource Solutions (R), TX, *99*
Hajek, Kathleen Lehman - Martin Partners, L.L.C. (R), IL, *137*
Hakim, Ronald J. - The GlobalSearch Group (C), TX, *359*
Halbrich, Mitch - Interim Financial Solutions - Mid-Atlantic Region (C), MD, *392*
Halbrich, Mitch - Interim Financial Solutions (C), MD, *392*
Halding, Jennifer L. - Brian Assoc., Inc. (C), NY, *273*
Hale, Dillon - Cemco, Ltd. (C), IL, *286*
Hale, Don - Management Recruiters of Midland (C), TX, *436*
Hale, Maureen D. - Hale Assoc. (R), IL, *84*
Hale, Michele J. - First Choice Search (R), WA, *67*
Hale, Pam - Management Recruiters of Midland (C), TX, *436*
Halek, Frederick D. - Sanford Rose Assoc. - Gastonia (C), NC, *568*
Hall, Charles - Butterfield & Co. Int'l., Inc. (C), NC, *277*
Hall, Debbie - Management Recruiters of Lexington (C), SC, *435*
Hall, Don - Don Hall & Assoc. (C), TX, *366*
Hall, Donald L. - Higley, Hall & Co., Inc. (R), MA, *93*
Hall, Doug - Accountants On Call (C), TX, *237*
Hall, Dwight - The Landstone Group (C), NY, *412*
Hall, Earl R. - Management Recruiters of Little Rock (C), AR, *439*
Hall, Elizabeth - Bason Associates (R), OH, *13*

Hall, James E. - The Duncan-O'Dell Group Inc. (C), TX, *316*
Hall, Joann - Don Hall & Assoc. (C), TX, *366*
Hall, John - Synergy Systems (C), ON, *598*
Hall, Keith - E. L. Shore & Assoc. (R), ON, *190*
Hall, Larry D. - Miller-Hall HRISearch (C), CA, *482*
Hall, Marcia - Larson, Katz & Young, Inc. (C), VA, *413*
Hall, Michael J. - Michael J. Hall & Co. (R), WA, *85*
Hall, Nancy L. - Hallman Group, Inc. (C), MI, *367*
Hall, Nancy M. - The Hollins Group, Inc. (R), GA, *95*
Hall, Noel K. - Management Recruiters of Little Rock (C), AR, *439*
Hall, Peter V. - Argonaut Partners, LLC (R), CA, *6*
Hall, Rodney - The Talon Group (R), TX, *205*
Hall, Roger - Management Recruiters of Lexington (C), SC, *435*
Hall, Scott - Advancement, Inc. (C), IL, *241*
Hall, Shannon Kelly - Sampson Medical Search (C), CA, *564*
Hall, Sharon - SpencerStuart (R), GA, *197*
Hall, Susan - Susan Hall Executive Search (C), TX, *366*
Hall, Todd - Romac Int'l., Inc. (C), CA, *542*
Halladay, Patti - Intersource, Ltd. (R), TX, *103*
Hallam, Andy J. - Management Recruiters of Pittsburgh-South Hills (C), PA, *435*
Haller, Thomas - International Executive Recruiters (C), OH, *393*
Halmy, Alexis - AKH Executive Search (C), OR, *243*
Halper, Harlan R. - Strategic Executives, Inc. (R), NY, *202*
Halstead, Frederick A. - LAI Ward Howell (R), TX, *124*
Halstead, Richard - CMS Management Services LLC (C), IN, *293*
Halvorsen, Jeanne M. - Kittleman & Assoc.,LLC (R), IL, *115*
Halyburton, Robert R. - The Halyburton Co., Inc. (R), NC, *85*
Hamara, Ron - Harris McCully Assoc., Inc. (C), NY, *369*
Hamburg, Jennifer P. - Ledbetter/Davidson Int'l., Inc. (R), NY, *127*
Hamel, Ed - Sales Consultants of Dallas (C), TX, *563*
Hamer, Thurston R. - Korn/Ferry, Int'l., S.A. de C.V. (R), MX, *118*
Hamer, Thurston R. - Korn/Ferry, Int'l., S.A. de C.V. (R), MX, *118*
Hamilius, Raymond - Eggers Consulting Co., Inc. (C), NE, *327*
Hamill, Robert W. - Robert Howe & Assoc. (R), GA, *97*
Hamilton, Casey - Crowe Chizek & Co. (C), IN, *304*
Hamilton, Denman - Synergy 2000 (C), DC, *597*
Hamilton, Dianne - The Barton Group, Inc. (C), MI, *260*
Hamilton, Frank - Gwen Dycus & Assoc. (C), FL, *323*
Hamilton, Lisa J. - Hamilton & Co. (C), OH, *367*
Hamilton, Marilyn - Fisher Personnel Management Services (R), CA, *68*
Hamilton, Melanie - Strategic Resources (C), WA, *595*
Hamilton, Peter - Dunhill Professional Search of Vancouver (C), BC, *318*
Hamilton, Rich - Hall Kinion (C), TX, *367*
Hamilton, Timothy J. - The Caldwell Partners Amrop International (R), ON, *26*
Hamlin, Rachel - Johnson Smith & Knisely (R), NY, *107*
Hamm, Gary - Witt/Kieffer, Ford, Hadelman & Lloyd (R), CA, *223*
Hammer, Amy - Sales Advantage (C), FL, *551*
Hammes-Briggs, Renee - Templeton & Assoc. (C), MN, *605*
Hammond, Anna - Management Recruiters of Fresno (C), CA, *440*
Hammond, Cynthia C. - DHR Int'l., Inc. (R), UT, *51*
Hammond, Karla - People Management Northeast, Inc. (R), CT, *162*
Hammrick, Jennifer - Mayhall Search Group, Inc. (C), IN, *473*
Hampford, Kate - Carlsen Resources, Inc. (R), CO, *29*
Hampshire, Kay - Allard Associates (C), CA, *244*
Hancock, Anna - Schwab-Carrese Assoc., Inc. Executive Search (R), NC, *185*
Hancock, Jason - Hall Kinion (C), CA, *366*
Hand, Jean - Management Recruiters of Seminole (C), FL, *427*
Handel, Jr., Richard C. - R. C. Handel Assoc. Inc. (R), CT, *85*
Handelsman, Simon - Anderson & Schwab, Inc. (R), NY, *6*
Handler, Marilyn - MedXec USA, Inc. (C), FL, *478*
Handler, William L. - W. L. Handler & Assoc. (R), GA, *86*
Handley, Bill - Management Recruiters of Apollo Beach (C), FL, *426*
Handy, Linda - Management Recruiters - Indianapolis (C), IN, *448*
Hangartner, Robin - Intersource, Ltd. (R), GA, *103*
Hankins, George - First Advisory Services Int'l., Inc. (R), MD, *67*
Hankins, George - Management Assoc. (C), MD, *424*
Hanley, Alan P. - Williams, Roth & Krueger, Inc. (R), IL, *221*
Hanley, Dorothy - Hanley & Assoc. (R), FL, *86*
Hanna, Dwight - Cadillac Assoc. (C), CA, *278*
Hanna, Jr., M. A. Jack - The Hanna Group (C), OH, *368*
Hanna, U. T. - The Hanna Group (C), OH, *368*
Hannafin, James D. - JDH & Assoc. (C), CA, *398*
Hannas, Jeanine K. - Executive Business Solutions, Inc. (C), WA, *332*
Hannes, Suzy - Allen Austin Lowe & Powers (R), TX, *3*
Hannigan, Melissa - JPM International (C), CA, *401*
Hannock, III, Elwin W. - Flynn, Hannock, Inc. (R), CT, *69*
Hanrahan, Kevin - Crist Partners, Ltd. (R), IL, *43*
Hansen, Arthur E. - Ritta Professional Search Inc. (C), NY, *538*
Hansen, Bente K. - DHR Int'l., Inc. (R), CA, *49*
Hansen, Charles A. - Management Recruiters of Jacksonville-South (C), FL, *427*
Hansen, Dana - AGRI-associates (C), MN, *242*
Hansen, David G. - Ott & Hansen, Inc. (R), CA, *157*
Hansen, James P. - Hansen Executive Search, Inc. (C), NE, *368*
Hansen, Ty E. - Blake/Hansen Ltd. (R), FL, *18*
Hanses, Louis - Accountants On Call (C), MO, *236*
Hanson, Darlene - Healthcare Recruiters Int'l. Phoenix (C), AZ, *372*
Hanson, Harry - Datamatics Management Services, Inc. (C), NJ, *308*
Hanson, Hugh - Fortune Personnel Consultants of Huntsville, Inc. (C), AL, *344*
Hanson, Paul David - LAI Ward Howell (R), WI, *124*
Hanson, Paul L. - LAI Ward Howell (R), WI, *124*
Hanson, Ralph - Massey-Horton Int'l. (R), ON, *138*
Hanson, Richard - Dunhill Staffing Systems, Inc. (C), NJ, *317*
Hanson, Russell V. - Management Recruiters of Appleton (C), WI, *465*
Hanssen, Barbara - Executive Search Team (C), MI, *336*
Hanzel, Bruce S. - Hanzel & Co., Inc. (R), NY, *86*
Happillon, Jennifer - cFour Partners (R), CA, *32*
Harants, George A. - Management Recruiters of Bartlett (C), TN, *436*
Harbaugh, Jr., Paul J. - International Management Advisors, Inc. (R), NY, *103*
Harbert, David O. - Sweeney Harbert & Mummert, Inc. (R), FL, *205*
Harberth, Janet - Janet Harberth & Assoc., Inc. (C), GA, *368*
Harbin, Steve - Dunhill Personnel of St. Andrews (C), SC, *322*
Harcourt, Judy - Harcourt & Assoc. (C), AB, *368*
Harcourt, Peter - Harcourt & Assoc. (C), AB, *368*
Hardage, Phillip - Hardage Group (C), TN, *369*

PRINCIPALS

Hardbrod, Herbert - Management Recruiters of Middlesex County NJ (C), NJ, *454*
Hardesty, Jack - Sales Consultant of Minneapolis (C), MN, *553*
Hardesty, Kelly - Phillips Resource Group (C), SC, *510*
Harding, Michael W. - Shey-Harding Assoc. Inc. (C), CA, *580*
Harding, III, Price P. - Bell Oaks Co., Inc. (C), GA, *263*
Hardison, Richard L. - Hardison & Company (R), TX, *86*
Hardwick, Michael - Management Recruiters of Aiken (C), SC, *460*
Hardy, Thomas G. - SpencerStuart (R), NY, *196*
Hare, Beth C. - Fidelity Search Group, Inc. (R), PA, *66*
Harelick, Arthur S. - Ashway Ltd. Agency (C), NY, *253*
Harfenist, Harry - Parker Page Group (C), FL, *503*
Hargrave, Michael - Health Care Plus, Inc. (C), MD, *371*
Hargrave, Susan - Health Care Plus, Inc. (C), MD, *371*
Harkins, Archie - Consolidated Management Services (C), ON, *296*
Harkins, Michael P. - Munroe, Curry & Bond Assoc. (R), NJ, *149*
Harkins, Robert E. - Robert Harkins Assoc., Inc. (C), PA, *369*
Harlan, James - Management Recruiters of Franktown (C), CO, *442*
Harlson, Howard - Snelling Search - Transportation Division (C), AR, *585*
Harmeling, Dutch - Harmeling & Associates (C), CA, *369*
Harmon, Jerry - Delta Resource Group, Ltd. (C), GA, *311*
Harper, Deborah - Harper Hewes, Inc. (C), NY, *369*
Harper, Rosa - Dunhill Staffing Systems of Columbia (C), MD, *317*
Harragan, James K. - Management Recruiters of Gramercy, Inc. (C), NY, *455*
Harrell, Philip - Allen Austin Lowe & Powers (R), TX, *3*
Harrell, Stephen G. - The Personnel Network, Inc. (C), SC, *508*
Harrington, Cherie - Human Resources Personnel Agency (R), AR, *99*
Harrington, Chip - Management Recruiters of Spartanburg (C), SC, *435*
Harrington, Christopher Patrick - Harrington & O'Brien, Inc. (C), NH, *369*
Harrington, Robert C. - Resource Recruiting (C), NH, *534*
Harrington, Robert J. - Sanford Rose Assoc. - Greensboro (C), NC, *569*
Harrington, Tamzen - Romac Int'l., Inc. (C), PA, *544*
Harris, Alan - Harris McCully Assoc., Inc. (C), NY, *369*
Harris, Andrew S. - Harris Heery & Assoc., Inc. (R), CT, *87*
Harris, Ann - International Pro Sourcing, Inc. (C), PA, *393*
Harris, Bea - Exec Tech, Inc. (C), IL, *332*
Harris, David P. - Egon Zehnder Int'l. Inc. (R), ON, *227*
Harris, Gerry - Management Recruiters of Columbus-Downtown (C), OH, *434*
Harris, Gerry E. - Sales Consultants of Columbus Downtown (C), OH, *555*
Harris, Heather - DHR Int'l., Inc. (R), GA, *50*
Harris, Jack L. - Management Recruiters of North Central (C), MI, *430*
Harris, Jeff - Moss & Co. (R), WA, *148*
Harris, Jerry - Sales Consultant of La Costa (C), CA, *551*
Harris, Joan - The Ryan Charles Group, Inc. (C), FL, *549*
Harris, John - Management Recruiters of Rochester (C), MN, *452*
Harris, Julia - The Whitney Group (R), NY, *219*
Harris, Maria - Barton Assoc., Inc. (R), TX, *12*
Harris, Michael - A. E. Feldman Assoc., Inc. (C), NY, *339*
Harris, Nancy - AGRI-associates (C), TX, *242*
Harris, T. J. - Sales Consultants of Ft. Myers, Inc. (C), FL, *557*
Harris, Thomas E. - Sales Consultants of Ft. Myers, Inc. (C), FL, *557*
Harris, Vicki M. - Management Recruiters of North Central (C), MI, *430*
Harris, Victoria - Houser, Martin, Morris (C), WA, *381*
Harrison, C.A. - Chad Management Group (C), ON, *288*
Harrison, Harold M. - InfoTech Search (C), TX, *388*
Harrison, Joel - D. A. Kreuter Assoc., Inc. (R), PA, *121*
Harrison, John S. - Chase Partners (R), ON, *33*
Harrison, John S. - Practice Dynamics, Inc. (C), TX, *515*
Harrison, Priscilla - Phillips Resource Group (C), SC, *510*
Harrison, Sally - Brandywine Management Group (R), MD, *22*
Harrison, Sally - Brandywine Management Group (R), NJ, *22*
Harshman, Donald - The Stevenson Group, Inc. (N.J.) (R), NJ, *200*
Hart, David - Hadley Lockwood, Inc. (R), NY, *84*
Hart, Gerry - Hart & Co. (C), NY, *370*
Hart, Jessica - Synergistech Communications (C), CA, *597*
Hart, Robert T. - Foster Partners (R), NY, *70*
Hart, Susan S. - SpencerStuart (R), CT, *196*
Hartig, Dave - The Angus Group, Ltd. (C), OH, *251*
Hartley, Sherry - Custom Resources (C), AL, *305*
Hartman, Beverly - Management Assoc. (C), MD, *424*
Hartman, Caroline - Avion International Technology Inc. (C), ON, *257*
Hartman, Robert J. - Hartman & Barnette (R), VA, *87*
Hartwell, Jenifer H. - Secura/Burnett Partners (R), CA, *187*
Harvey, Arnold D. - PSP Agency (C), NY, *525*
Harvey, Bob - Mayhall Search Group, Inc. (C), IN, *473*
Harvey, E. Graeme - Sales Consultants of Appleton (C), WI, *563*
Harvey, John K. - Management Recruiters of North Fulton (C), GA, *445*
Harvey, Michael D. - Advanced Executive Resources (R), MI, *2*
Harvey, Rick - Western Management Consultants (R), AB, *218*
Harvey, Stephen W. - Matthews & Stephens Assoc., Inc. (C), CT, *472*
Harvey, Susan - Bradford & Galt, Inc. (C), IL, *271*
Harvey, Warren - Management Recruiters of Nassau, Inc. (R), NY, *134*
Harvill, Jon - Dunhill Search of West Atlanta (C), GA, *320*
Hase, Susan - O'Shea, Divine & Co., Inc. (R), CA, *154*
Hassel, Elizabeth - Cook Assoc.,® Inc. (R), IL, *40*
Hastings, W. Jeff - Bialla & Assoc. Inc. (R), CA, *17*
Hatch, Michael - The Kinlin Co., Inc. (R), MA, *115*
Hatcher, Eddy - Management Recruiters of Cordova (C), TN, *436*
Hatcher, Jennifer L. - DHR Int'l., Inc. (R), MA, *50*
Haubenstock, Eileen - Gumbinner/Haubenstock, Inc. (C), NY, *364*
Hauck, Fred P. - The Cassie Group (R), NJ, *31*
Haugen, Audrey D. - Roger Dietsch & Assoc. (C), MN, *312*
Haupert, Thomas J. - MCS Assoc. (R), CA, *142*
Haupt, Bruce W. - Bruce W. Haupt Assoc. (R), DC, *88*
Hauser, Herb - Dunhill Search of Vermont (C), VT, *323*
Hausherr, Mark - The Corporate Source Group, Inc. (R), FL, *41*
Hauswirth, Jeffrey M. - SpencerStuart (R), ON, *197*
Havener, D. Clarke - The Abbott Group, Inc. (R), MD, *1*
Havens, J. A. - Real Estate Executive Search, Inc. (C), CA, *531*
Haverty, Carol - Iona Partners (C), CA, *394*
Hawfield, III, Sam G. - Management Recruiters of Cornelius & Davidson (C), NC, *433*
Hawke, Marjorie - Becker Personnel (C), FL, *262*
Hawkins, Jr., Jack M. - First Advisory Services Int'l., Inc. (R), MD, *67*
Hawkins, Kirk - Management Recruiters of Topeka, Inc. (C), KS, *449*
Hawkins, Max - Management Recruiters of Wausau, LLC (C), WI, *466*

Hawkins, Michael J. - Michael J. Hawkins, Inc. (C), IL, *370*
Hawkins, Phyllis - Phyllis Hawkins & Assoc., Inc. (C), AZ, *370*
Hawkins, William D. - The Hawkins Co. (R), CA, *88*
Hawks, Robert L. - Sales Consultants of Salt Lake City (C), UT, *555*
Hawksworth, A. Dwight - A. D. & Assoc. Executive Search, Inc. (C), GA, *231*
Hawley, Robert E. - Hayden Group, Inc. (R), MA, *88*
Hawley, Sheila R. - Ryan-Allen & Assoc., Inc. (C), CA, *549*
Hawthorne, Christine - Search Int'l. (R), MA, *187*
Hay, Elaine - Campbell, Edgar Inc. (C), BC, *280*
Hay, Jennifer - The Pollack Group (C), ON, *514*
Hay, William E. - William E. Hay & Co. (R), IL, *88*
Hayden, Dale - Sanford Rose Assoc. - Pittsburgh North (C), PA, *570*
Hayden, Lynn - Erlanger Assoc. (R), FL, *60*
Haydon, Meredith - Haydon Legal Search (C), IL, *370*
Hayek, Kim - Norrell Financial Staffing (C), VA, *495*
Hayes, Don - Management Recruiters of Sugar Land Inc. (C), TX, *464*
Hayes, Jerry - Holden & Harlan Assoc., Inc. (C), IL, *380*
Hayes, Jim - Orion Int'l. Consulting Group, Inc. (C), OH, *499*
Hayes, Mara - Holden & Harlan Assoc., Inc. (C), IL, *380*
Hayes, Stephen A. - DHR Int'l., Inc. (R), DC, *50*
Hayes, William - The Ransford Group (R), TX, *171*
Hayman, Thomas C. - Hayman & Co. (R), TX, *88*
Haynie, Duke - Dunhill of Greenville (C), SC, *318*
Hays, Brenda - Fortune Personnel Consultants of Chattanooga Inc. (C), TN, *349*
Hayward, Robert M. - National Field Service Corp. (C), NY, *489*
Haywood, Joy - Pasona Canada, Inc. (C), ON, *504*
Hazan, Lynn - Beverly von Winckler & Assoc. (C), IL, *613*
Hazelton, Lisa - Health Care Dimensions (C), CO, *371*
Hazlett, Kirk - Chaloner Assoc. (R), MA, *32*
Hazlett, Thomas M. - Hazlett Associates (R), IL, *88*
Heacock, Barbara - B. D. Wallace & Assoc. (C), MD, *614*
Headden, Jr., William P. - Headden Assoc. (R), WA, *88*
Heagy, Linda - Heidrick & Struggles, Inc. (R), IL, *90*
Healey, David - Healey Executive Search, Inc. (R), MN, *88*
Healy, Frank P. - F. P. Healy & Co., Inc. (R), NY, *89*
Healy, Richard P. - F. P. Healy & Co., Inc. (R), NY, *89*
Healy, Thomas C. - Resource Inc. (R), MA, *175*
Healy, William C. - Management Recruiters of Milwaukee-West (C), WI, *465*
Hearne, Shannan - Sanford Rose Assoc. - Charlotte (C), NC, *568*
Heasley, Franklin A. - The Franklin Search Group, Inc./Medzilla (R), WA, *71*
Heath, Grant - Gaines & Assoc. Int'l., Inc. (R), GA, *73*
Heath, Jeffrey A. - The Landstone Group (C), NY, *412*
Heath, Jeffrey A. - Management Recruiters of Manhattan at Madison Avenue (C), NY, *432*
Heath, Pamela A. - The Winn Group, Inc. (C), KS, *623*
Heath, Thomas A. - The Winn Group, Inc. (C), KS, *623*
Hebel, Robert W. - R. W. Hebel Assoc. (R), TX, *89*
Hebert, Buy - The Caldwell Partners Amrop International (R), QE, *26*
Hebert, Chris - Management Recruiters of Nassau, Inc. (R), NY, *134*
Hebert, Guy - The Caldwell Partners Amrop International (R), ON, *26*
Hebert, Larry - Lawrence James Assoc. (C), NJ, *414*
Hebert, Lise - Groupe Ranger Inc. (C), QE, *364*
Hebert, Robert R. - Austin Michaels, Ltd., Inc. (C), AZ, *256*
Hebert, Sylvain - Groupe PCA Inc. (C), QE, *363*
Hechkoff, Robert B. - Hechkoff/Work Executive Search Inc. (R), NY, *89*
Hecker, Henry C. - O'Brien & Bell (R), OH, *153*
Hedberg, Cindy - Executive Solutions (R), MN, *64*
Hedefine, Thomas E. - Thomas E. Hedefine Assoc. (C), ON, *375*
Hedlund, David - Hedlund Corp. (C), IL, *375*
Hedman, Kent R. - Hedman & Assoc. (R), TX, *89*
Heery, William J. - Harris Heery & Assoc., Inc. (R), CT, *87*
Heffelfinger, Thomas V. - Heffelfinger Assoc., Inc. (R), MA, *89*
Heideman, Mary Marren - Tryon & Heideman, LLC (R), MO, *211*
Heidrick, Gardner W. - The Heidrick Partners, Inc. (R), IL, *90*
Heidrick, Robert L. - The Heidrick Partners, Inc. (R), IL, *90*
Heineman, James W. - Management Resources (C), TX, *467*
Heinemann, H. Peter - Barrett Rose & Lee, Inc. (C), ON, *260*
Heinle, Jr., Norman C. - Datamatics Management Services, Inc. (C), NJ, *308*
Heinle, R. Kevin - Datamatics Management Services, Inc. (C), NJ, *308*
Heino, Jay - Jay Heino Company, LLC (C), NY, *375*
Heinschel, Phil - Phillips Personnel/Search (C), CO, *510*
Heintz, William - MIXTEC Group (R), CA, *145*
Heintz, William - MIXTEC Group (R), CA, *146*
Heinze, David - Heinze & Assoc. Inc. (R), MN, *91*
Heise, Paul - Human Capital Resources, Inc. (C), FL, *384*
Heissan, Arlene - P. J. Lynch Assoc. (R), CT, *132*
Heisser, Robert - MRI, The Sequel Group, LLC (C), CO, *486*
Helbling, Thomas J. - Helbling & Assoc., Inc. (R), PA, *91*
Helfenbein, Sr., Robert J. - Snelling Search Recruiters (C), NC, *586*
Helfer, Frederick W. - Helfer Executive Consultants (R), TN, *91*
Helffrich, Jr., Alan B. - Helffrich Int'l. (C), FL, *375*
Helffrich, Henrietta - Helffrich Int'l. (C), FL, *375*
Helffrich, Michael D. - Helffrich Int'l. (C), FL, *375*
Helgeson, Burton H. - Norm Sanders Assoc., Inc. (R), NJ, *184*
Hellebusch, Jerry - Morgan Hunter Corp. (C), KS, *485*
Heller, Gary A. - Heller Assoc., Ltd. (R), IL, *91*
Heller, Jason - Norrell Financial Staffing (C), NC, *495*
Heller, Paul M. - Cromwell Partners, Inc. (R), NY, *43*
Heller, Phillip - Heller Kil Assoc., Inc. (C), FL, *375*
Heller, Shelly - Ira Z. Nitzberg (C), NY, *493*
Heller, Steven A. - Martin H. Bauman Assoc., Inc. (R), NY, *13*
Hellinger, Audrey - Martin H. Bauman Assoc., Inc. (R), IL, *14*
Helmer, Michael - OEI, Inc. (C), NJ, *498*
Helms, Mary P. - The Helms Int'l. Group (R), VA, *91*
Helnore, Diann - Partners in Recruiting (C), IL, *504*
Helnore, Douglas - Partners in Recruiting (C), IL, *504*
Helnore, Kim - Partners in Recruiting (C), IL, *504*
Helt, Wally A. - Management Recruiters of Montoursville (C), PA, *435*
Hembertt, Ellen - Eggers Consulting Co., Inc. (C), NE, *327*
Hemenway, Albert I. - Sanford Rose Assoc. - Effingham (C), IL, *566*
Hemer, Craig - Ray & Berndtson/Tanton Mitchell (R), BC, *172*
Hemer, Craig - Ray & Berndtson/Tanton Mitchell (R), BC, *173*
Hemmings, Jackie - S-H-S TechStaff (C), PA, *550*
Henard, John B. - LAI Ward Howell (R), FL, *123*

PRINCIPALS

(R) = Retainer; (C) = Contingency

Hendelman, Peter R. - P.R.H. Management, Inc. (R), CT, *158*
Hendershot, Janie - Dunhill Professional Search of Wilkes-Barre/Scranton, Inc. (C), PA, *322*
Henderson, Cathy - Management Recruiters of Aptos (C), CA, *439*
Henderson, Etta Ish - Boulware & Assoc. Inc. (R), IL, *20*
Henderson, J. Fred - Bartholdi & Co., Inc. (R), CO, *12*
Henderson, John - Staffing Edge, Inc. (C), AZ, *590*
Henderson, Kaaren Liz - The Search Network (C), CA, *576*
Hendricks, II, Stanley M. - National Recruiting Service (C), IN, *489*
Hendrickson, Gary - Management Recruiters of Clovis (C), CA, *440*
Hendrickson, Jill - Johnson Smith & Knisely (R), IL, *107*
Hendriks, Jr., Warren K. - DHR Int'l., Inc. (R), IL, *49*
Hendrix, John A. - Sockwell & Assoc. (R), NC, *194*
Heneghan, Donald A. - Allerton Heneghan & O'Neill (R), IL, *4*
Henkel, John J. - Management Recruiters of Milwaukee-South (C), WI, *438*
Henkel, John J. - Management Recruiters of Racine (C), WI, *438*
Henkel, John J. - Sales Consultants of Racine (C), WI, *555*
Henley, Mark D. J. - Smythe Masterson & Judd, Inc. (C), NY, *585*
Henn, Jr., George W. - G. W. Henn & Co. (R), OH, *91*
Hennessy, Robert - Ken Clark Int'l. (R), NJ, *36*
Henry, Bruce - Bruce Henry Assoc. Inc. (R), CA, *91*
Henry, Jeannette A. - Huntington Personnel Consultants, Inc. (C), NY, *386*
Henry, Jeremy - A First Resource (C), NC, *231*
Henry, Jim - MTA Partners (R), TX, *148*
Henry, Kay - Kay Henry, Inc. (C), PA, *376*
Henry, Pat - Fortune Personnel Consultants of Huntsville, Inc. (C), AL, *343*
Henry, Shelley - Taylor Winfield (R), TX, *207*
Hensge, Bill - The Hensge Co. (R), IL, *91*
Henshaw, Andrew - Fortune Personnel Consultants of Huntsville, Inc. (C), AL, *343*
Henshaw, Bob - Fortune Personnel Consultants of Huntsville, Inc. (C), AL, *343*
Hensley, Bert C. - Morgan Samuels Co. (R), CA, *147*
Hensley, Gayla K. - Atlantic Search Group, Inc. (C), MA, *255*
Henson, Jeff - Henson Partners (C), AZ, *376*
Henton, Sara - Management Recruiters-Cedar Rapids, Inc. (C), IA, *448*
Henzlik, Laura - Meder & Assoc., Inc. (R), IL, *142*
Herb, Jerome B. - Meder & Assoc., Inc. (R), IL, *142*
Herbeck, J. Brad - Herbeck Kline & Assoc. (R), IL, *92*
Herbert, Kevin - Pacific Finance Search, Inc. (C), CA, *501*
Herbert, Paul - David Blevins & Assoc. (C), WA, *268*
Herbert, Raymond - American Resources Corp. (C), MI, *248*
Herbert, Stacey - Central Executive Search, Inc. (C), OH, *287*
Herbruck, Gretchen S. - The Baer Group (R), OH, *10*
Herbst, jody - Management Recruiters of Milwaukee - Downtown (C), WI, *466*
Herbst, Mary Ann - The Abbott Group, Inc. (R), MD, *1*
Herbst, Mary Ann - The Abbott Group, Inc. (R), VA, *1*
Heres, Bart - Sales Consultants of Cherokee (C), GA, *558*
Hergenrather, Edmund R. - Hergenrather & Co. (R), WA, *92*
Hergenrather, Richard A. - Hergenrather & Co. (R), WA, *92*
Herget, James P. - Harcourt Group Ltd. (R), OH, *86*
Herget, Jane K. - Harcourt Group Ltd. (R), OH, *86*
Hering, Robyn - Yours In Travel Personnel Agency, Inc. (C), NJ, *627*
Herlihy, Jack - J. J. Herlihy & Assoc., Inc. (C), CA, *376*
Herman, Eugene - Earley Kielty & Assoc., Inc. (R), NY, *56*
Herman, Joyce Ralph - Management Assoc. (C), MD, *424*
Hermann, George A. - Hermann & Westmore (R), NY, *92*
Hermsen, Patrick - Capital Markets Resources, Inc. (C), NC, *281*
Hermsmeyer, Rex - Hitchens & Foster, Inc. (C), MO, *379*
Hernandez, Jr., Luis A. - Independent Power Consultants (C), TX, *387*
Hernandez, Rafael E. - SearchCorp (C), FL, *577*
Herndon, Angela - A. Herndon & Assoc., Inc. (R), TX, *92*
Herrerias, Paul - Herrerias & Assoc. (R), CA, *92*
Herrin, Jill T. - J & D Resources Inc. (C), TN, *395*
Herring, Bill - Herring & Assoc. (C), AR, *376*
Herrmann, Gerlinde - The Herrmann Group Ltd. (R), ON, *92*
Herrmann, Jerry C. - Management Recruiters of Quad Cities (C), IA, *429*
Herrod, Vicki - Accountants On Call (C), MI, *236*
Herrod, Vicki - Accountants On Call (C), IN, *236*
Herrod, Vicki - Accountants On Call (C), MI, *236*
Hersey, Jeffrey D. - J. D. Hersey & Assoc. (C), OH, *377*
Hersher, Betsy S. - Hersher Assoc., Ltd. (R), IL, *92*
Hershman, Arnold - Holohan Group, Ltd. (R), MO, *95*
Hershman, Robert B. - AutoPeople (C), MA, *257*
Hertan, Richard L. - Executive Manning Corp. (R), FL, *63*
Hertlein, James N. J. - Boyden (R), TX, *21*
Hertner, Herbert H. - H. Hertner Assoc., Inc. (C), FL, *377*
Hertner, Pamela R. - H. Hertner Assoc., Inc. (C), FL, *377*
Hertz, Al - Carter/MacKay (C), NC, *285*
Herz, Jr., Ralph - American Group Practice, Inc. (R), NY, *5*
Herz, Stanley - Stanley Herz & Co. (R), NY, *92*
Hess, Cherie - Romac Int'l., Inc. (C), FL, *542*
Hess, Robert W. - Robert Hess & Assoc., Inc. (C), CO, *377*
Hessel, Jeffrey J. - Hessel Assoc., Inc. (C), NY, *377*
Hesselgrave, Katherine - Insurance People (C), IN, *390*
Hester, Teresa - Romac Int'l., Inc. (C), CA, *542*
Hetherington, Don - Landon Morgan (C), ON, *412*
Hetherington, Holly - The Executive Source (C), SA, *337*
Hetzel, Ben W. - Sales Consultants of Chester County, PA (C), PA, *562*
Hetzel, Mark W. - Sales Consultants of Chester County, PA (C), PA, *562*
Hetzel, Terrie - Sales Consultants of Chester County, PA (C), PA, *562*
Hetzel, William G. - The Hetzel Group, Inc. (R), IL, *93*
Hewett, Martin J. - McCray, Shriver, Eckdahl & Assoc., Inc. (R), CA, *140*
Hewitt, Diane - AmeriResource Group Inc. (C), OK, *249*
Hewitt, Rives D. - The Dalley Hewitt Co. (R), GA, *45*
Heybroek, Eric J. - Sanford Rose Assoc. - Rockville (C), MD, *568*
Heyman, William C. - Heyman Assoc., Inc. (R), NY, *93*
Hickel, Stephen - mfg/Search, Inc. (C), MI, *480*
Hickman, Fred - Carnegie Partners, Inc. (R), IL, *30*
Hicks, Albert M. - Phillips Resource Group (C), SC, *510*
Hicks, Bill - R.A.N. Assoc., Inc. (C), OH, *528*
Hicks, Jr., Donald R. - Sales Consultants of Winston-Salem (C), NC, *554*
Hiesiger, Emile M. - Manuso, Alexander & Associates, Inc. (R), NY, *135*
Higbee, Joan - Thorndike Deland Assoc. LLC (R), NY, *48*
Higbee, R. W. - Higbee Assoc., Inc. (C), CT, *377*
Higdon, Henry G. - Higdon Prince Inc. (R), NY, *93*
Higgins, Bruce W. - B. W. Higgins, Inc. (C), IN, *377*

Higgins, David - DHR Int'l., Inc. (R), TN, *51*
Higgins, David J. - Warren, Morris & Madison, Ltd. (C), NH, *616*
Higgins, John B. - Higgins Assoc., Inc. (R), IL, *93*
Higgins, Susan - The Rogan Group, Inc. (C), CA, *541*
High, Claude - Action Managment Corp. (C), VA, *239*
Highfill, Steven B. - Blane, Stevens & Kellogg (C), FL, *268*
Highland, Maryjo - Highland & Assoc. (C), CA, *378*
Hildebrand, John D. - JM & Company (R), PA, *106*
Hildner, Jack - DHR Int'l., Inc. (R), MD, *50*
Hildner, Jack F. - DHR Int'l., Inc. (R), MD, *50*
Hildy, Edward V. - Systems One Ltd. (C), IL, *598*
Hill, Emery - MSI Int'l. (C), NC, *487*
Hill, Frank P. - Frank P. Hill (R), MX, *93*
Hill, III, Gabe C. - S. P. Assoc., Inc. (C), NC, *550*
Hill, Jennifer - Lamon + Stuart + Michaels Inc. (R), ON, *124*
Hill, Jerry R. - Management Recruiters International, Inc. (MRI) (C), OH, *425*
Hill, Jerry R. - Sales Consultants (C), OH, *551*
Hill, Michael G. - Austin, Hill & Assoc. (C), MD, *256*
Hill, Michelle - The Alfus Group (R), NY, *3*
Hill, Mike - Tyler & Company (R), TX, *212*
Hill, Paul - Cypress Int'l., Inc. (R), FL, *45*
Hill, Ted - Culver Personnel Services (C), CA, *304*
Hill, Tom - Hill & Assoc. (C), CA, *378*
Hillen, Skip - The McCormick Group (C), MA, *474*
Hiller, Arnie - U.S. Search (C), VA, *610*
Hilles, Jeffrey W. - Williams & Delmore, Inc. (C), NC, *621*
Hilliker, Alan D. - Egon Zehnder Int'l. Inc. (R), NY, *227*
Hillner, Jill - Continental Research Search, Inc. (C), WI, *298*
Hills, Glen - G. H. Enterprises (C), AZ, *354*
Hind, Catherine - Frank E. Allen & Assoc. (C), NJ, *244*
Hind, Ronald W. - DHR Int'l., Inc. (R), MO, *50*
Hindman, Jeffrey J. - The Hindman Group, Inc. (C), CA, *378*
Hindman, Neil C. - The Hindman Co. (R), KY, *94*
Hinds, Susan - Job Link, Inc. (C), CA, *399*
Hinebough, William R. - A.M.C.R., Inc. (C), OH, *232*
Hinkle, Alfred - Renaissance Resources, LLC (R), VA, *174*
Hintz, George - Hintz Associates (C), NY, *378*
Hirnikel, L. J. - Orion Int'l. Consulting Group, Inc. (C), OH, *500*
Hirsch, Julia C. - Boyden (R), CA, *20*
Hirsch, Neal - Richard, Wayne & Roberts (C), TX, *536*
Hirsch, Ruth - Ruth Hirsch Assoc., Inc. (C), NY, *379*
Hirsch, Tom - InSearch (C), CO, *389*
Hirschbein, Don - Management Recruiters Peninsula (C), CA, *439*
Hirschbein, Donald - Sales Consultants Peninsula, Inc. (C), CA, *556*
Hirschel, Jerry S. - Professional Search Centre, Ltd. (C), IL, *522*
Hirshman, Kenneth A. - McGrath & Assoc., Inc. (R), NJ, *141*
Hirshorn, Richard P. - Fairfield Int'l. Resources (R), NY, *65*
Hite, Dick - Sales Consultants of Toledo (C), OH, *555*
Hite, Lynn - Sales Consultants of Toledo (C), OH, *555*
Hite, III, William A. - Hite Executive Search (R), OH, *94*
Ho, John - Management Recruiters of Chanhassen (C), MN, *452*
Hobbins, Elaine K. - Barnes & Assoc. Executive Search (C), CA, *259*
Hobbs, Mike - Culver Personnel Services (C), CA, *304*
Hochberg, Brian M. - M. A. Churchill & Assoc., Inc. (R), PA, *35*
Hochberg, Steven P. - Caliber Associates (R), PA, *27*
Hochgraber, Kent - Dunhill Personnel Service of Fargo (C), ND, *322*
Hochman, Judi - Hochman & Assoc. (C), CA, *379*
Hochwalt, Mike - M H Executive Search Group (C), TX, *422*
Hockett, Bill - Hockett Associates, Inc. (R), CA, *94*
Hodde, Fred - Heritage Search Group, Inc. (C), CT, *376*
Hodge, Jeff - Heidrick & Struggles, Inc. (R), CA, *90*
Hodges, Linda B. - Hersher Assoc., Ltd. (R), IL, *92*
Hodges, Wanda - Insurance Search (C), TX, *390*
Hodges, Whitney - Recruiting Services Group, Inc. (C), TN, *532*
Hodgson, Judy H. - Management Recruiters of Camdenton (C), MO, *431*
Hodgson, Robert D. - Management Recruiters of Camdenton (C), MO, *431*
Hoehne, Rebecca - Advanced Resources, Inc. (C), MO, *241*
Hoene, Patrick - Management Recruiters of St. Louis-Earth City (C), MO, *431*
Hoene, Patrick - Sales Consultants of St. Louis-Earth City (C), MO, *553*
Hoevel, Michael J. - Poirier, Hoevel & Co. (R), CA, *166*
Hoffenberg, Elliot - H. J. Elliot, Inc. (R), IL, *58*
Hoffman, Adele - The Beardsley Group Inc. (C), CT, *261*
Hoffman, Bradley D. - Hoffman Partnership Group Inc. (C), NY, *379*
Hoffman, Brian - Sales Consultants of Rockville, MD (C), MD, *559*
Hoffman, Cherri - Brandywine Retained Ventures, Inc. (R), NM, *22*
Hoffman, Ed - NaTek Corp. (C), NY, *488*
Hoffman, Eli - Richard A. Eisner & Co., LLP (R), NJ, *58*
Hoffman, Glenn - Huntress Real Estate Executive Search (R), MO, *100*
Hoffman, Judd A. - Hoffman Recruiters (C), MA, *380*
Hoffman, Laurie - Columbia Consulting Group (R), MD, *38*
Hoffman, Linda - The Mallard Group (C), IN, *423*
Hoffman, Lisa M. - Hoffman Partnership Group Inc. (C), NY, *379*
Hoffman, Mark - Management Recruiters of Emeryville (C), CA, *440*
Hoffman, Mark S. - Hoffman Recruiters (C), MA, *380*
Hoffman, Robert - The Mallard Group (C), IN, *423*
Hoffman, Tala R. - TRH Assoc., Inc. (R), NY, *210*
Hoffman, Theresa E. - Wellington Management Group (R), PA, *217*
Hoffmann, David H. - DHR Int'l., Inc. (R), IL, *49*
Hoffmeir, Patty - Tyler & Company (R), PA, *212*
Hofmeister, Mark - Winston Search, Inc. (R), MD, *222*
Hofner, Kevin E. - LAI Ward Howell (R), TX, *124*
Hogan, Ann B. - The Hogan Group (C), OH, *380*
Hogan, Karen - Davis-Smith, Inc. (C), MI, *309*
Hogan, Kevin B. - Computer Professionals (R), IL, *38*
Hogan, Sandra M. - Larsen, Whitney, Blecksmith & Zilliacus, Inc. (R), CA, *125*
Hogg, Jr., James G. - Whittlesey & Assoc., Inc. (R), PA, *220*
Hogg, Ronald J. - Forest People Int'l. Search Ltd. (C), BC, *343*
Hoglund, Gerald C. - Hoglund & Assoc., Inc. (R), IL, *94*
Hogya, Nicholas - Interim Management Resources Inc. (C), ON, *392*
Hohauser, Harvey - Harvey Hohauser & Assoc., LLC (R), MI, *87*
Hohlstein, Jeff - Management Recruiters of Round Rock (C), TX, *463*
Hohlstein, Jodi - Management Recruiters of Round Rock (C), TX, *463*
Hohman, Daniel G. - Bosco-Hubert & Assoc. (C), KS, *270*
Hoinacki, Mark - DHR Int'l., Inc. (R), CA, *49*
Hokanson, Mark D. - Crowder & Company (R), MI, *43*
Holbrook, Richard D. - Richard D. Holbrook Assoc. (R), MA, *94*

PRINCIPALS

Holder, Lee - Gowdy Consultants (C), TX, *361*
Holder, Robin - The Donnelly Group-Sales Recruiters, Inc. (C), MO, *314*
Holert, Robert - Houser, Martin, Morris (C), WA, *381*
Holford, Jay - MIXTEC Group (R), CA, *145*
Holford, Jay - MIXTEC Group (R), FL, *146*
Holland, Daniel O. - Holland & Assoc., Inc. (R), WI, *95*
Holland, Dave G. - Management Recruiters of Shelby (C), NC, *432*
Holland, Jamie - Search South, Inc. (C), AL, *576*
Holland, John A. - Ray & Berndtson, Inc. (R), CA, *172*
Holland, John H. - Sloan & Assoc., Inc. (C), VA, *583*
Holland, Kyle R. - Holland Rusk & Assoc. (R), IL, *95*
Holland, Lee - Carnegie Resources, Inc. (C), NC, *284*
Holland, Richard G. - Management Recruiters of Atlanta-Vinings (C), GA, *427*
Holland, Rose Mary - Price Waterhouse Executive Search (R), AB, *168*
Holland, Stacey M. - Resources for Management (R), PA, *176*
Holland, Susan R. - Holland Rusk & Assoc. (R), IL, *95*
Hollander, Fred - Tyler & Company (R), PA, *212*
Hollander, Heidi - Career Counseling Ltd. (C.C.L.) (C), IL, *282*
Hollander, Heidi - Career Counseling Ltd. (C.C.L.) (C), NY, *282*
Hollander, Michael - Hollander Horizon Int'l. (R), NJ, *95*
Hollander, Paula - Accountants On Call (C), BC, *237*
Hollands, Rachel - PSD Group, Inc. (C), CA, *525*
Holley, Ray - Austin Group Int'l./Marlar Int'l. (R), TX, *9*
Holliday, John - American Heritage Group, Inc. (C), MI, *247*
Holliday, John - American Heritage Group, Inc. (C), MI, *247*
Hollins, Lawrence I. - The Hollins Group, Inc. (R), NY, *95*
Hollins, Lawrence I. - The Hollins Group, Inc. (R), IL, *95*
Hollis, Betsy - Robert Shields & Assoc. (C), TX, *539*
Hollis, Robert W. - Carnegie Partners, Inc. (R), IL, *30*
Hollis, Ron - Management Recruiters of Windy Hill (C), GA, *428*
Holloway, Clive - Holloway Schulz & Partners (C), BC, *380*
Holloway, Roger M. - Management Recruiters of Lake Co., Inc. (C), FL, *444*
Holly, Beth - Wyndham Mills Int'l., Inc. (R), NC, *226*
Holmes, Cory T. - Columbia Consulting Group (R), MD, *38*
Holmes, Dave - Hreshko Consulting Group (C), NJ, *382*
Holmes, Jeff - Hreshko Consulting Group (C), NJ, *382*
Holmes, Lawrence J. - Columbia Consulting Group (R), MD, *38*
Holmes, Len - Management Recruiters of Lakewood/Tacoma (C), WA, *437*
Holmes, Peter - O'Brien & Bell (R), OH, *153*
Holodnak, William A. - J. Robert Scott (R), MA, *104*
Holohan, Jr., Barth A. - Holohan Group, Ltd. (R), MO, *95*
Holohan, Marie Falbo - Holohan Group, Ltd. (R), MO, *95*
Holsopple, Ben V. - ACSYS Resources, Inc. (C), NJ, *238*
Holsopple, Ben V. - ACSYS Resources, Inc. (C), NJ, *238*
Holt, Carol - Bartholdi & Co., Inc. (R), VA, *12*
Holt, Douglas - Management Recruiters of Columbia, Tennessee (C), TN, *461*
Holt, Elaine - Norrell Financial Staffing (C), CO, *495*
Holton, David - PSD Group, Inc. (C), CA, *525*
Holtz, Richard D. - Technical Resource Assoc. (C), TN, *602*
Holtzman, Gene - Mitchell Martin Inc. (C), NY, *483*
Holupka, Gary F. - Management Recruiters of Pittsburgh-North Allegheny (C), PA, *435*
Holupka, Patricia L. - Management Recruiters of Pittsburgh-North Allegheny (C), PA, *435*
Holzberger, Georges L. - Highland Search Group, L.L.C. (R), NY, *93*
Holzheimer, Robert - Exclusive Search Consultants (C), OH, *331*
Holzman, Alfred J. - Summit Executive Search Consultants, Inc. (R), FL, *204*
Homer, Judy B. - J. B. Homer Assoc. Inc. (R), NY, *95*
Homrich, Patricia J. - David C. Cooper & Assoc. Financial Search (C), GA, *298*
Honey, W. Michael M. - O'Callaghan Honey/Ray & Berndtson Inc. (R), AB, *153*
Honey, W. Michael M. - O'Callaghan Honey/Ray & Berndtson Inc. (R), AB, *172*
Honquest, Richard W. - Quest Enterprises, Ltd. (C), IL, *527*
Hood, Dennis - DHR Int'l., Inc. (R), WI, *51*
Hood, Fred L. - Fred Hood & Assoc. (C), CA, *380*
Hood, Joyce G. - J. G. Hood Assoc. (C), CT, *380*
Hoover, Catherine B. - J. L. Mark Assoc., Inc. (R), CO, *135*
Hoover, Donna - J. H. Lindell & Co. (C), CA, *418*
Hopard, Stuart M. - Olympian Recruitment, Ltd. (C), NY, *498*
Hope, Elizabeth - Search Consultants, LLC (C), VA, *575*
Hopkins, Chester A. - Handy HRM (R), NY, *86*
Hopp, Lorrie A. - Gregory Michaels & Assoc., Inc. (R), IL, *82*
Hopson, Bradford J. - IntelliSearch (C), TX, *391*
Horan, Robert - Barone Assoc. (C), NJ, *259*
Horgan, Thomas F. - Nadzam, Lusk, Horgan & Assoc., Inc. (R), CA, *150*
Horn, David C. - David C. Horn Executive Search (C), TX, *381*
Hornberger, Jr., Frederick C. - Hornberger Management Company (R), DE, *96*
Hornbuckle, R. Michael - BCG Search, Inc. (R), FL, *14*
Horne, Tony - Herring & Assoc. (C), AR, *376*
Horton, Jim - Creative-Leadership, Inc. (R), CA, *42*
Horton, Robert H. - Horton Int'l. Inc. (R), NY, *96*
Horton, Scott - Capital Markets Resources, Inc. (C), NC, *281*
Hosey, Debra - The Pailin Group Professional Search Consultants (R), TX, *158*
Hoskins, Charles R. - Heidrick & Struggles, Inc. (R), FL, *90*
Hotchkiss, Jay - John Jay & Co. (C), ME, *399*
Houchins, Buster - Christian & Timbers, Inc. (R), OH, *34*
Houchins, Jr., Eugene E. - Management Recruiters of Atlanta-Buckhead (C), GA, *427*
Houchins, Todd - The Abbott Group, Inc. (R), MD, *1*
Houchins, William C. Buster - Christian & Timbers, Inc. (R), MD, *34*
Houck, Paula - Search Consultants, LLC (C), MD, *575*
Houze, Geoffry Clayton - William C. Houze & Co. (R), CA, *96*
Houze, William C. - William C. Houze & Co. (R), CA, *96*
Hovey, Dick - Management Recruiters of Centerville (C), IA, *429*
Howard, Brian E. - Management Recruiters of Leawood (C), KS, *429*
Howard, Carole - Villasenor & Assoc. (C), CA, *612*
Howard, George - Howard/Williams Assoc. (C), FL, *382*
Howard, Grazell R. - The Libra Group (C), NC, *417*
Howard, Jill - Health Care Dimensions (C), CO, *371*
Howard, Kathleen S. - Management Recruiters of Leawood (C), KS, *429*
Howard, Lee Ann - LAI Ward Howell (R), CT, *123*
Howard, Linda J. - Doleman Enterprises (R), VA, *53*
Howard, Marybeth - Accounting & Bookkeeping Personnel, Inc. (C), AZ, *238*

Howard, Michael - Allen Austin Lowe & Powers (R), TX, *3*
Howard, Randall C. - Randall Howard & Assoc., Inc. (R), TN, *97*
Howard, Richard H. - Management Recruiters of Berkeley (C), CA, *439*
Howard, Tracy L. - Brush Creek Partners (R), MO, *24*
Howard, Valerie - Peter Froehlich & Co. (C), TX, *353*
Howe, Jr., Edward R. - Howe & Assoc. (R), PA, *97*
Howe, Phillip T. - Management Recruiters of Sedona (C), AZ, *438*
Howe, Timothy L. - The Resource Group (R), NJ, *175*
Howe, Vance A. - LAI Ward Howell (R), AZ, *123*
Howe, W. Lawrence - C. R. Krafski & Assoc., Inc. (R), IL, *120*
Howe, William S. - Hunt & Howe Inc. (R), NY, *99*
Howell, Janice Hopkins - Rob Dey Executive Search (R), FL, *49*
Howell, Jean - Fortune Personnel Consultants of the Virginia Highlands (C), VA, *351*
Howell, Jeff - Whittaker & Assoc., Inc. (C), GA, *620*
Howell, Tom - Mayhall Search Group, Inc. (C), IN, *473*
Howland, Ellen - EDP Staffing Solutions, Inc. (C), AR, *327*
Howlett, Grant - CountryHouse Hotels Executive Search (C), VA, *302*
Howlett, Tracy A. - Ross Personnel Consultants, Inc. (C), CT, *545*
Howze, Jane S. - The Alexander Group (R), TX, *3*
Hoy, Thomas J. - Sales Consultant of Detroit (C), MI, *553*
Hoyda, Louis A. - Thorndike Deland Assoc. LLC (R), NY, *48*
Hoye, Dan - Marcus & Assoc. (C), NY, *469*
Hreshko, Frank M. - Hreshko Consulting Group (C), NJ, *382*
Hruska, Thomas - The Search Group (C), MD, *575*
Hubbard, Anna Marie - Accountants On Call (C), ON, *237*
Hubbard, Ted L. - KS Frary & Assoc. (R), MA, *71*
Hubble, Joanna - DHR Int'l., Inc. (R), CO, *49*
Huberman, Arnold - Arnold Huberman Assoc., Inc. (R), NY, *97*
Hucko, Donald - Jonas, Walters & Assoc., Inc. (R), WI, *108*
Huddleston, Linda - Huddleston Assoc. (C), OK, *383*
Huddleston, Linda - Hunt Patton & Brazeal, Inc. (C), OK, *385*
Huddleston, Linda - Tekworx, Inc. (C), OK, *604*
Huddleston, Victor - Huddleston Assoc. (C), OK, *383*
Hudson, Betty - SpencerStuart (R), NY, *196*
Hudson, Bill - Sage Employment Recruiters (C), IN, *550*
Hudson, George A. - Hudson Assoc. Inc. (C), IN, *383*
Hudson, Judith S. - The Alexander Group (R), CA, *3*
Hudson, Judy K. - The Hudson Group (C), CT, *383*
Hudson, Karen - The Corporate Source Group, Inc. (R), CA, *41*
Hudson, Kevin - Raymond Karsan Assoc. (C), PA, *530*
Hudson, Kevin - Raymond Karsan Assoc. (C), TX, *530*
Hudson, Kevin - Romac Int'l., Inc. (C), FL, *543*
Hudson, Paul E. - The Hudson Group (C), CT, *383*
Hudson, Reginald M. - Search Bureau Int'l. (C), IL, *574*
Huebner, Mary C. - Hire Authority, Inc. (C), MI, *378*
Huegel, Ray - Raymond Thomas & Assoc. (C), FL, *530*
Huettl, Robin - Packaging Personnel Co., Ltd. (C), WI, *501*
Huff, David - Kutt, Inc. (C), CO, *410*
Huff, Margaret L. - Huff Assoc. (R), NJ, *98*
Huff, William Z. - Huff Assoc. (R), NJ, *98*
Huffman, Richard B. - Professional Engineering Technical Personnel Consultants (C), NC, *520*
Hughes, Cathy N. - The Ogdon Partnership (R), NY, *155*
Hughes, Don - ProLinks Inc. (R), VA, *170*
Hughes, Donald J. - Hughes & Company (R), VA, *98*
Hughes, Elaine A. - E. A. Hughes & Co., Inc. (R), NY, *98*
Hughes, Emerson - GAAP Inc. (R), QE, *73*
Hughes, J. Reilly - ProLinks Inc. (R), VA, *170*
Hughes, Jr., John E. - LAI Ward Howell (R), PA, *123*
Hughes, Ken - Hughes & Assoc. (C), TX, *383*
Hughes, Louis B. - Norm Sanders Assoc., Inc. (R), NJ, *184*
Hughes, Melba N. G. - Hughes & Sloan, Inc. (C), GA, *383*
Hughes, R. Kevin - Handy HRM (R), NY, *86*
Hughes, Robert J. - Worlco Computer Resources, Inc (C), NJ, *625*
Hughes, Susan F. - Opus Marketing (R), MN, *157*
Hughes, Tim - Hughes & Assoc. Int'l. Inc. (C), AL, *383*
Hughes, Tom - Fox-Morris Assoc., Inc. (C), NJ, *352*
Hughes, Warren B. - RepFinders USA (C), PA, *534*
Hugley, Trey - QuestPro, Inc. (C), TX, *527*
Hugsman, Rob - Russ Hadick & Assoc. Inc. (C), OH, *365*
Huitt, Joy - Management Recruiters of Fresno (C), CA, *440*
Hulme, Doug - Leader Institute, Inc. (C), GA, *414*
Hulse, Jeanne - Richmond Assoc. (C), NY, *537*
Humay, Gene - E. F. Humay Assoc. (C), PA, *384*
Humay, Jane - E. F. Humay Assoc. (C), PA, *384*
Humes, James - Management Recruiters of Nassau, Inc. (R), NY, *134*
Hummel, D. Linda - Careerfit, Inc. (C), TX, *283*
Hummel, Thomas F. - Sales Consultants of Prince Georges County (C), MD, *553*
Humphreys, Scott W. - Robison Humphreys & Assoc., Inc. (R), ON, *180*
Humphreys, William M. - Robison Humphreys & Assoc., Inc. (R), ON, *180*
Hunegnaw, David B. - Hunegnaw Executive Search (C), OH, *384*
Hunkins, Deborah J. - Career Images (C), FL, *282*
Hunsaker, Floyd - Woodworth Int'l. Group (R), OR, *225*
Hunt, Bridgford H. - The Hunt Co. (R), NY, *99*
Hunt, III, Herbert I. - H.I. Hunt & Co., Ltd. (R), MA, *99*
Hunt, James E. - Hunt & Howe Inc. (R), NY, *99*
Hunt, Jeff - Plummer & Assoc., Inc. (R), CT, *166*
Hunt, Joseph B. - The Hunt Group, Inc. (R), NC, *99*
Hunt, Leigh - Leigh Hunt & Assoc., Inc. (C), ME, *384*
Hunt, Ron S. - King ComputerSearch, Inc. (C), TX, *407*
Hunter, David - Stanewick, Hart & Assoc., Inc. (C), FL, *591*
Hunter, Debra - F-O-R-T-U-N-E Personnel Consultants of Troy, Inc. (C), MI, *347*
Hunter, Durant A. - Pendleton James Assoc., Inc. (R), MA, *105*
Hunter, Helen - The Wabash Group (C), IN, *613*
Hunter, Jr., John B. - John Sibbald Assoc., Inc. (R), MO, *191*
Hunter, Juliette - Prime Management Group Inc. (C), ON, *518*
Hunter, Sharon W. - Management Recruiters of Boulder (C), CO, *426*
Hunter, Steven - Diamond Tax Recruiting (C), NY, *312*
Huntley, David E. - Huntley Associates (Dallas), Inc. (C), TX, *386*
Huntley, Dean R. - Huntley Associates (Dallas), Inc. (C), TX, *386*
Hunzeker, Brenda - Accountants On Call (C), MO, *236*
Hurd, J. Nicholas - Russell Reynolds Assoc., Inc. (R), MA, *177*
Hurd, Jane - Rollo Assoc. (R), CA, *181*
Hurd, Philip J. - Lynx, Inc. (C), MA, *421*
Hurley, Art - Systems Research Inc. (SRI) (C), IL, *598*
Hurley, Gerard F. - Association Executive Resources Group (R), MD, *8*

PRINCIPALS

Hurley, Helen G. - Management Recruiters of Siouxland (C), IA, *449*
Hurley, Michael - Century Assoc., Inc. (C), PA, *287*
Hurley, Paula B. - Auerbach Associates, Inc. (R), MA, *9*
Hursey, Bruce - Management Recruiters of Monroe, Inc. (C), LA, *450*
Hursh, John - National Corporate Consultants, Inc. (C), IN, *489*
Hurt, Thomas E. - Management Recruiters of Milwaukee-South (C), WI, *438*
Hurt, Thomas E. - Management Recruiters of Racine (C), WI, *438*
Hurt, Thomas E. - Sales Consultants of Racine (C), WI, *555*
Hurtubise, Jean Pierre - Reynolds Consulting Int'l. (R), QE, *177*
Hussar, Andrew - DHR Int'l., Inc. (R), NY, *50*
Hussey, John - GAAP Inc. (R), QE, *73*
Hussey, Wayne - Krecklo Executive Search Inc. (R), ON, *120*
Hutchinson, Vicki - Snelling & Snelling, Inc. (C), FL, *585*
Hutchison, Richard H. - Rurak & Assoc., Inc (R), DC, *183*
Hutchison, Robert - Overton Consulting (R), WI, *157*
Hutchison, William K. - Christenson Hutchison McDowell, LLC (R), NJ, *34*
Hutt, Gayle - W. Hutt Management Resources Ltd. (R), ON, *100*
Hutt, Wayne - W. Hutt Management Resources Ltd. (R), ON, *100*
Hutton, M. Joan - The Hutton Group, Inc. (C), FL, *386*
Hutton, Thomas J. - Hutton Merrill & Assoc. (R), CA, *100*
Hutts, Mark - InTech Services, Inc. (C), GA, *390*
Hwang, Anthony T. - Lindsey & Co., Inc. (R), CT, *129*
Hyde, Anne P. - The Hyde Group, Inc. (R), CT, *101*
Hyde, Tom G. - Management Recruiters of Murfreesboro (C), TN, *436*
Hyde, Tonda - Prescott Legal Search, Inc. (C), TX, *517*
Hyde, W. Jerry - Hyde Danforth & Co. (R), TX, *100*
Hykes, Don - A.T. Kearney Executive Search (R), MN, *111*
Hyland, Kenneth J. - Hyland Executive Search (C), AZ, *386*
Hyland, Susan L. - Hyland Executive Search (C), AZ, *386*
Hyman, Derry - Hyman & Assoc. (C), TX, *386*
Hyman, Jean W. - Management Search Assoc., Inc. (C), GA, *467*
Hynes, Kathryn - The Wallace Law Registry (C), CT, *614*
Hypes, Jr., Richard G. - Lynch Miller Moore Partners, Inc. (R), IL, *132*
Hytowitz, Allan - Southern Chemical & Plastics Search (C), GA, *587*
Ianni, Robert - The Sager Co. (R), OH, *183*
Iaquinto, Rachelle - Accountants On Call (C), MI, *236*
Ibsen, John - Stewart/Greene & Co. of The Triad, Inc. (C), NC, *594*
Icard, Sr., Bob - The Icard Group, Inc. (C), MI, *387*
Icard, Jr., Robert - The Icard Group, Inc. (C), MI, *387*
Ikle, A. Donald - LAI Ward Howell (R), NY, *123*
Imber, John - John Imber Assoc., Ltd. (R), IL, *101*
Imely, Larry S. - StratfordGroup (R), OH, *203*
Imler-Diskin, Lydia - David Rowe & Assoc., Inc. (R), IL, *182*
Incitti, Lance M. - Management Recruiters of Sparta (C), NJ, *432*
Infanti, Diana - Robert Half Canada Inc. (C), BC, *366*
Ingala, Thomas A. - Direct Marketing Solutions (C), KY, *312*
Ingalise, James - Sales Consultants of Omaha, Inc. (C), NE, *560*
Ingram, D. John - Ingram & Aydelotte, Inc. (R), NY, *101*
Ingram, Meredith - Meredith Ingram, Ltd. (C), IL, *388*
Ingram, Spencer - Johnson Smith & Knisely (R), CT, *107*
Insinger, Kathy - Allen Austin Lowe & Powers (R), TX, *3*
Irving, Jeffrey J. - Jeffrey Irving Assoc., Inc. (R), VA, *104*
Irwin, Bill - Southern Recruiters & Consultants, Inc. (C), SC, *587*
Isaacs, Rhoda - R. I. James, Inc. (C), NY, *397*
Isaacson, Ira - Egon Zehnder Int'l. Inc. (R), GA, *227*
Isaacson, John - Isaacson, Miller (R), MA, *104*
Isacco, Robert J. - DHR Int'l., Inc. (R), NY, *50*
Isacco, Tim - Orion Int'l. Consulting Group, Inc. (C), CA, *499*
Isbister, Joan - Joan Isbister Consultants (C), NY, *394*
Isenberg, H. Peter - Management Recruiters of Noblesville, Inc. (C), IN, *448*
Iserson, Michael - Ward Liebelt Assoc. Inc. (R), CT, *215*
Israel, Ann M. - Ann Israel & Assoc., Inc. (C), NY, *395*
Israel, Ehud - Search Innovations, Inc. (R), PA, *187*
Israel, Sheldon - Sales Professionals Personnel Services (C), CA, *564*
Ives, Phyllis E. - Ives & Associates, Inc. (C), OH, *395*
Ives, Richard K. - Wilkinson & Ives (R), CA, *221*
Ivey, Wayne - Data Bank Executive Search (R), OH, *46*
Izzo, Thomas - Innovative Resource Group, LLC (C), GA, *389*
Izzo, Thomas M. - Spear-Izzo Assoc., LLC (C), GA, *589*
Jablo, Steven A. - Dieckmann & Assoc., Ltd. (R), IL, *51*
Jackley, Brian D. - Jackley Search Consultants (C), MN, *396*
Jackowitz, Ronald N. - Carris, Jackowitz Assoc. (R), NY, *30*
Jackowitz, Ronald N. - Carris, Jackowitz Assoc. (R), NJ, *31*
Jackowitz, Todd - J. Robert Scott (R), MA, *104*
Jackson, Angie - Alan Davis & Assoc. Inc. (R), QE, *47*
Jackson, Carolyn - Sales Consultants of Orangeburg (C), SC, *562*
Jackson, Cindy - CJSI-Cindy Jackson Search Int'l. (C), CA, *291*
Jackson, Clarke H. - The Caldwell Partners Amrop International (R), ON, *26*
Jackson, David - The Oxford Group (C), TX, *500*
Jackson, Eric - ProFinders, Inc. (C), FL, *523*
Jackson, George E. - Jackson Group Int'l. (C), CO, *396*
Jackson, Jennifer - Jackson Resources (R), TX, *105*
Jackson, Laurie - McHale & Assoc. (R), WA, *141*
Jackson, Noel - Sanford Rose Assoc. - Mobile (C), AL, *565*
Jackson, Randy - Sales Consultants of Omaha, Inc. (C), NE, *560*
Jackson, Richard - Sales Consultants of Orangeburg (C), SC, *562*
Jackson, Ron - Ron Jackson & Assoc. (C), GA, *396*
Jackson, Ronald N. - Lloyd Prescott & Churchill, Inc. (R), NC, *130*
Jackson, Ronald N. - Lloyd Prescott Assoc., Inc. (C), NC, *419*
Jacob, Don C. - Management Recruiters of Preston Park (C), TX, *436*
Jacob, Marilyn - Huntress Real Estate Executive Search (R), MO, *100*
Jacob, Thomas - Slayton Int'l., Inc. (R), IL, *192*
Jacobs, Bob - StratfordGroup (R), CA, *203*
Jacobs, David M. - Jacobs & Co. (R), CT, *105*
Jacobs, Gilbert B. - Focus Consulting Services, Inc. (C), VA, *343*
Jacobs, James F. - Sales Consultants of Nassau (C), NY, *554*
Jacobs, James W. - Callan Assoc., Ltd. (R), IL, *27*
Jacobs, Judith - The Rubicon Group (C), AZ, *547*
Jacobs, Karen S. - A.M.C.R., Inc. (C), OH, *232*
Jacobs, Ken - Joseph Goldring & Assoc. Inc. (C), MI, *360*
Jacobs, Klaus - TASA International (R), NY, *206*
Jacobs, Martin - The Rubicon Group (C), AZ, *547*
Jacobs, Mike - Thorne, Brieger Assoc., Inc. (R), NY, *209*
Jacobs, Phillip E. - E. J. Michaels, Ltd. (C), NY, *481*

Jacobsen, Carolyn - The Abbott Group, Inc. (R), MD, *1*
Jacobsen, Patricia - D. W. Simpson & Co. (C), IL, *582*
Jacobson, David - Jacobson Assoc. (C), IL, *396*
Jacobson, David N. - J.J. & H., Ltd. (R), IL, *104*
Jacobson, Donald - Hunt Ltd. (C), NJ, *385*
Jacobson, Eric K. - Management Recruiters of Las Colinas (C), TX, *436*
Jacobson, Gregory - Jacobson Assoc. (C), GA, *396*
Jacobson, Gregory P. - J.J. & H., Ltd. (R), GA, *105*
Jacobson, Phil - The Century Group (C), CA, *287*
Jacobson, Priscilla - Tech Connector Group (C), CA, *601*
Jacobson, Rick - The Windham Group (R), OH, *222*
Jacobson, Robert E. - Management Recruiters of Cleveland-South (C), OH, *433*
Jadewald, James - Tekworx, Inc. (C), CO, *604*
Jaffe, Mark - Wyatt & Jaffe (R), MN, *225*
Jagielo, Thomas A. - Martin Partners, L.L.C. (R), IL, *137*
Jakobs, Frederick H. - Jakobs & Assoc. Int'l. (R), NY, *105*
Jalbert, Michael - Sales & Marketing Search, Inc. (C), MA, *551*
James, Carolyn - J. Joseph & Assoc. (C), OH, *395*
James, Chip - Morgan Samuels Co. (R), CA, *147*
James, Cindy - Discovery, The Staffing Specialists, Inc. (C), DE, *312*
James, David - David James Search (C), CA, *397*
James, E. Pendleton - Pendleton James Assoc., Inc. (R), NY, *105*
James, Ed - Staffing Edge, Inc. (C), IA, *590*
James, Maryellen - Capital Consulting & Research, Inc. (R), CT, *28*
James, Michael - Lee Koehn Assoc., Inc. (R), OR, *116*
James, Richard - Criterion Executive Search, Inc. (C), FL, *303*
Jameson, Brad M. - Fought, Jameson Assoc. (C), IL, *351*
Jameson, John B. - The Jameson Group (C), CA, *397*
Janecek, Robert - Management Recruiters of Milwaukee-Central (C), WI, *438*
Janik, Bradley - DHR Int'l., Inc. (R), CA, *49*
Janis, Laurence - Integrated Search Solutions Group, LLC (ISSG) (R), NY, *102*
Jankinson, Andrez M. - Sanford Rose Assoc. - Austin (C), TX, *570*
Jansen, Carl - Search North America, Inc. (C), OR, *576*
Jansen, Douglas L. - Search Northwest Assoc. (C), OR, *576*
Jansen, John F. - Delta Services (R), TX, *48*
Jante, Ellen L. - Sales Consultants of Racine (C), WI, *555*
Jarrell, Jay K. - Strauss Personnel Service (C), PA, *596*
Jarvis, Daniel G. - Boyden (R), NY, *21*
Jason, Bonnie - Bryan, Jason & Assoc. Inc. (C), ON, *275*
Jaspersen, Kenneth A. - Dunhill Professional Search of Omaha, Inc. (C), NE, *321*
Jay, John C. - Organization Resources Inc. (R), MA, *157*
Jay, Robert - The Fourbes Group, Inc. (C), NJ, *351*
Jayroe, Laurie - The Canon Group (C), CA, *280*
Jayroe, Tom - Management Recruiters of Atlanta-Downtown (C), GA, *428*
Jazylo, John V. - Secura/Burnett Partners (R), NY, *188*
Jebens, Harry - Markent Personnel (C), MN, *470*
Jefferies, George - Hintz Associates (C), NY, *378*
Jeffers, Richard B. - Dieckmann & Assoc., Ltd. (R), IL, *51*
Jeffers, Robert - Allen-Jeffers Assoc. (C), CA, *245*
Jender, Jesse - Jender & Company (R), IL, *105*
Jenkins, Virginia L. - The Center for Career Advancement (C), MD, *287*
Jenne, Suzanne - Raymond Karsan Assoc. (C), CA, *529*
Jennings, Allison - The Personnel Network, Inc. (C), SC, *509*
Jennings, Kirsten - Moss & Co. (R), WA, *148*
Jensen, Brad - The Conrad Lee Co. Inc. (R), FL, *127*
Jensen, Christine - John Kurosky & Assoc. (R), CA, *122*
Jensen, David G. - Search Masters Int'l. (R), AZ, *187*
Jensen, Don - J. Gernetzke & Assoc., Inc. (C), OH, *357*
Jerabek, Kim - Michael Shirley Assoc. Inc. (R), KS, *190*
Jernigan, Susan N. - Sockwell & Assoc. (R), NC, *194*
Jerome, Gerald E. - Jerome & Co. (C), CA, *398*
Jesberg, Gary H. - Michael Latas & Assoc., Inc. (R), MO, *126*
Jeselnick, James L. - Quality Search (C), IN, *526*
Jespersen, Brent - The Diestel Group (R), UT, *51*
Jester, Jillian - Major, Hagen & Africa (C), IL, *423*
Jewell, Jessica - DHR Int'l., Inc. (R), AZ, *49*
Jewell, Trish - Avondale Search Int'l., Inc. (R), FL, *9*
Jilka, Dan - Management Recruiters of Seattle (C), WA, *465*
Jimenez, Gil C. - Management Recruiters of San Antonio-Crossroads (C), TX, *436*
Jochems, Julie A. - StratfordGroup (R), OH, *203*
Jock, Lawrence M. - Professional Search, Inc. (C), CO, *522*
Jocke, John - Management Recruiters of Boise (C), ID, *446*
Joffe, Barry - Bason Associates (R), OH, *13*
Joffe, Jon - Meridian Resources (C), OH, *479*
Johasky, Tom K. - Management Recruiters of Palm Beach (C), FL, *427*
John, Harold A. - John & Powers, Inc. (R), MO, *106*
Johns, Joel - Brandywine Retained Ventures, Inc. (R), CT, *22*
Johnsen, Scott - Romac Int'l., Inc. (C), IL, *543*
Johnson, Al - Management Recruiters of Fridley (C), MN, *430*
Johnson, Amy M. - Capstone Inc. (R), NY, *29*
Johnson, Bill - Global Consulting Group Inc. (C), ON, *358*
Johnson, Carl - International Management Services,Inc. (R), FL, *102*
Johnson, Carl A. - Bertrand, Ross & Assoc., Inc. (C), IL, *266*
Johnson, Carl A. - International Management Services Inc. (R), IL, *102*
Johnson, Carol - Sales Consultants of Chico (C), CA, *556*
Johnson, Cheri - Johnson & Assoc., Inc. (R), CA, *106*
Johnson, Dan - Johnson Smith & Knisely (R), NY, *107*
Johnson, Daniel - Morgan Samuels Co. (R), CA, *147*
Johnson, Dennis R. - Management Recruiters of Tacoma (C), WA, *437*
Johnson, Donna - Management Recruiters of Fresno (C), CA, *440*
Johnson, Eileen R. - Empowered Solutions Corp. (C), GA, *330*
Johnson, Frank Y. - Healthcare Recruiters Int'l. - Alabama (C), AL, *372*
Johnson, Gil - Snelling Search (C), LA, *586*
Johnson, Glen - Sales Recruiters of Oklahoma City (C), OK, *564*
Johnson, Glenn W. - Roster Inc. (C), IN, *545*
Johnson, Greg - Sales Recruiters of Oklahoma City (C), OK, *564*
Johnson, Harold E. - LAI Ward Howell (R), NY, *122*
Johnson, Jack - Medicorp, Inc. (C), MO, *477*
Johnson, Jane - The Stevenson Group, Inc. (N.J.) (R), NJ, *200*
Johnson, Jennifer - JenKim Int'l. Ltd., Inc. (C), FL, *398*
Johnson, Jerry A. - Sanford Rose Assoc. - Charlotte (C), NC, *568*
Johnson, Joan - Corporate Builders, Inc. (C), OR, *299*
Johnson, Joe - Business Partners, Inc. (C), FL, *277*
Johnson, John - HRNI (C), MI, *383*

PRINCIPALS

Johnson, John F. - LAI Ward Howell (R), OH, *123*
Johnson, John H. - John H. Johnson & Assoc., Inc. (R), IL, *106*
Johnson, John Kimbrough - Johnson Brown Assoc., Inc. (C), IN, *400*
Johnson, Jr., John W. - Webb, Johnson Assoc., Inc. (R), NY, *216*
Johnson, Joseph P. - Columbia Consulting Group (R), NY, *38*
Johnson, Joseph P. - Columbia Consulting Group (R), AZ, *38*
Johnson, Justyna M. - J. M. Johnson & Assoc. (C), MN, *399*
Johnson, K. L. - Sales Consultants of Chico (C), CA, *556*
Johnson, Karl - K. E. Johnson Assoc. (C), WA, *400*
Johnson, Kathleen - Barton Assoc., Inc. (R), TX, *12*
Johnson, Kathleen N. - The Repovich-Reynolds Group (TRRG, Inc.) (R), CA, *175*
Johnson, Krissa - Rurak & Assoc., Inc (R), DC, *183*
Johnson, L. J. - L. J. Johnson & Co. (R), MI, *106*
Johnson, Lee - Kincaid Group Inc. (KGI) (C), TX, *406*
Johnson, Lisa M. - LJ Networking, Inc. (C), MD, *418*
Johnson, Maria - Search Int'l. (R), MA, *187*
Johnson, Mark - Sampson Medical Search (C), CA, *564*
Johnson, Mike - The 500 Granary Inc. (C), ON, *231*
Johnson, Mike - The Wabash Group (C), IN, *613*
Johnson, Paul - Johnson, Kemper & Assoc. (C), TX, *400*
Johnson, Peggy - Gaines & Assoc. Int'l., Inc. (R), GA, *73*
Johnson, Peter - ZanExec L.L.C. (R), VA, *226*
Johnson, Priscilla - The Johnson Group, Unlimited (C), NY, *400*
Johnson, R. W. - Leader Search Inc. (R), AB, *127*
Johnson, Randall - Inter Regional Executive Search, Inc. (IRES, Inc.) (C), NJ, *391*
Johnson, Ray - First Search America, Inc. (C), AL, *341*
Johnson, Robert - A.T. Kearney Executive Search (R), TX, *111*
Johnson, Robert J. - Quality Search Inc. (C), OH, *526*
Johnson, Ron L. - Management Recruiters of Fresno (C), CA, *440*
Johnson, Ron L. - Sales Consulant of Fresno (C), CA, *551*
Johnson, Ronald S. - Ronald S. Johnson Assoc., Inc. (R), CA, *107*
Johnson, S. Hope - Boyden (R), DC, *21*
Johnson, Scott - Johnson Assoc., Inc. (C), IL, *399*
Johnson, Sean M. - Healthcare Recruiters Int'l. - Alabama (C), AL, *372*
Johnson, Stanley C. - Johnson & Company (R), CT, *107*
Johnson, Steve - Management Recruiters of Woodland Park (C), CO, *426*
Johnson, Suzanne M. - Miller/Davis & Assoc., Inc. (C), NY, *482*
Johnson, T.M. - Robert E. McGrath & Assoc. (R), CT, *141*
Johnson, Timothy W. - Magellan Int'l., L.P. (C), TX, *422*
Johnson, Walt - Pacific Crossing (C), CA, *501*
Johnson, William - Columbia Consulting Group (R), NY, *38*
Johnston, Brian - Roye Johnston Assoc., Inc. (C), CA, *400*
Johnston, Cindy - Management Recruiters of Shaker Heights (C), OH, *434*
Johnston, Debbie - Harcourt & Associates (C), AB, *369*
Johnston, Gail - NJ Solutions (C), CA, *493*
Johnston, J. Reid - Hughes & Company (R), VA, *98*
Johnston, James E. - Computer Search Group, Ltd. (R), IL, *39*
Johnston, Phil - SpencerStuart (R), CA, *196*
Johnston, Robert - Organization Consulting Ltd. (R), ON, *157*
Johnston, Roye - Roye Johnston Assoc., Inc. (C), CA, *400*
Johnston, Tom - Sales Consultants of Shaker Heights (C), OH, *555*
Johnstone, Bill - Search Assoc. (C), KY, *574*
Johnstone, Debra J. - Canadian Career Partners (R), AB, *27*
Johnstone, Steve - GAAP Inc. (R), QE, *73*
Jolly, Janine - The Hampton Group (C), NY, *368*
Joly, Richard - The Caldwell Partners Amrop International (R), ON, *26*
Jones, Bonita - Global Career Services, Inc. (C), NY, *358*
Jones, Bonnie - Jones Management Co. (R), NY, *108*
Jones, Courtney A. - The Hollins Group, Inc. (R), IL, *95*
Jones, Dale E. - LAI Ward Howell (R), GA, *123*
Jones, Daniel F. - Atlantic Search Group, Inc. (C), MA, *255*
Jones, Donald - Kenzer Corp. (R), TX, *113*
Jones, Francis E. - Jones Management Co. (R), CT, *108*
Jones, Frank - Global Career Services, Inc. (C), NY, *358*
Jones, Gary - BGB Assoc., Inc. (C), IL, *266*
Jones, Geoffrey J. - Precision Executive Search (C), AZ, *516*
Jones, Herschel - Korn/Ferry Int'l. (R), WA, *118*
Jones, James A. - Jones Consulting Executive Search (C), GA, *400*
Jones, Jeff - Management Recruiters of Atlanta (C), GA, *445*
Jones, Jeffrey - AJM Professional Services (C), MI, *243*
Jones, Judy - Management Recruiters of Winston-Salem (C), NC, *457*
Jones, Keith - Ken Clark Int'l. (R), NJ, *36*
Jones, Kenneth D. - O'Shea, Divine & Co., Inc. (R), CA, *154*
Jones, Kevin - Crown Advisors, Inc. (R), PA, *43*
Jones, M. Susan - Greenwich Search Partners, LLC (C), CT, *363*
Jones, Madeline G. - Eastern Executive Assoc. (C), NJ, *325*
Jones, Mark - RHS Assoc. (C), AL, *536*
Jones, Michael A. - The Century Group (C), KS, *287*
Jones, Mike - Management Recruiters of Winston-Salem (C), NC, *457*
Jones, Pamela K. - Jones and Jones (R), OR, *108*
Jones, Paul M. - The Marlow Group (R), MA, *136*
Jones, PJ - Sales Consultants of Pittsburgh (C), PA, *562*
Jones, Quinn - Dunhill Professional Search of Greater New Orleans (C), LA, *321*
Jones, Roberta - Tech 2000 (C), FL, *601*
Jones, Ronald T. - ARJay & Assoc. (C), NC, *252*
Jones, Yvonne - T. Page & Assoc. (C), TX, *502*
Jones-Parker, Janet - Jones-Parker/Starr (R), NC, *108*
Jordan, Bill - Matrix Consultants, Inc. (C), NC, *472*
Jordan, Dick - Phillips Resource Group (C), NC, *511*
Jordan, Dick - Staff Resources, Inc. (C), SC, *590*
Jordan, Jean - Accountants On Call (C), VA, *237*
Jordan, Lewis James - The Executive Tree (R), FL, *64*
Jordeth, Lola - Systems Research Group (C), CA, *598*
Jordon, Bud - Jordon & Jordon, Inc. (R), PA, *108*
Jorgensen, T. C. - The Talley Group (R), VA, *205*
Jose, Bill O. - Management Recruiters of The Hamptons (C), NY, *432*
Jose, William - Management Recruiters of Woodbury Inc. (C), NY, *455*
Joseph, Allen F. - CBA Companies (C), CA, *286*
Joseph, Craig - Management Assoc. (C), MD, *424*
Joseph, Jacob - Dunhill Staffing Systems of Irving (C), TX, *318*
Joseph, Patti D. - CBA Companies (C), CA, *286*
Joseph, Surette - Marsteller Wilcox Assoc. (C), IL, *471*
Josephson, Martha - Egon Zehnder Int'l. Inc. (R), CA, *227*
Joslin, Robert S. - Joslin & Assoc., Ltd. (C), IL, *401*
Jostrom, Karen - The Oxbridge Group, Ltd. (C), MA, *500*

Joswick, Thomas - Michael Thomas, Inc. (C), OH, *480*
Joure, Sylvia A. - Frye/Joure & Assoc., Inc. (C), TN, *353*
Joy, Kevin - HCI Corp. (C), IL, *371*
Joyce, Janet - Management Recruiters of Stanhope (C), NJ, *432*
Joyce, Mark - Louis Rudzinsky Assoc., Inc. (C), MA, *548*
Joyce, Sheila M. - Verkamp-Joyce Assoc., Inc. (R), IL, *213*
Joyce, William J. - The Guild Corp. (C), VA, *364*
Jozwik, Peter - Professional Consulting Network, Inc. (C), CA, *520*
Juarez, Lyn A. - Stoopen Asociados, S.C./ EMA Partners Int'l. (R), MX, *202*
Juarez, Ma. Elena - Amrop International (R), MX, *5*
Judd, Heidi - Judd Associates (R), NJ, *109*
Judge, Alfred - Cambridge Group Ltd. - Exec. Search Div. (C), CT, *279*
Judge, Alfred - The Cambridge Group Ltd. (C), CT, *280*
Judge, Stephen E. - Management Search of R.I. Inc. (R), RI, *135*
Juelis, John J. - Peeney Assoc., Inc. (R), NJ, *161*
June, Valerie L. - Action Management Corp. (C), MI, *239*
Jung, Justin - Pioneer Consulting Group (C), CA, *512*
Junker, Sherry - Bolton Group (C), CA, *269*
Jurenovich, Gary S. - The Stewart Group (C), FL, *593*
Juska, Frank A. - Rusher, Loscavio & LoPresto (R), CA, *183*
Just, Debra - Just Management Services Inc. (C), TN, *402*
Just, Jim - Just Management Services Inc. (C), FL, *402*
Just, Susan - Just Management Services Inc. (C), FL, *402*
Justiss, Ted - David C. Cooper & Assoc. Financial Search (C), GA, *298*
Justus, Janet - Dunhill Executive Search of Los Angeles, Inc. (C), CA, *319*
Kaas, Linda M. - Kaas Employment Services (C), IA, *402*
Kabanuk, James Allen - Kabana Corp. (C), MI, *402*
Kabanuk, Steven E. - Kabana Corp. (C), MI, *402*
Kacedan, Arliss - Slayton Int'l., Inc. (R), IL, *192*
Kacevich, Jr., Joseph B. - Kacevich, Lewis & Brown, Inc. (R), MA, *109*
Kacyn, Louis - Egon Zehnder Int'l. Inc. (R), IL, *227*
Kaczanowski, Rosemary - The Search Company (R), ON, *186*
Kaczmar, Michael A. - Kaczmar & Assoc. (C), PA, *403*
Kader, Richard H. - Richard Kader & Assoc. (C), OH, *403*
Kaestner, Bob - Robert Kaestner & Assoc. (C), FL, *403*
Kaffke, Cas - Major Search (C), NJ, *423*
Kagan, Philip - Strategic Resources (C), WA, *595*
Kagee, Raymond J. - Aggressive Corporation (C), IL, *242*
Kahn, Beverly A. - New Dimensions in Technology, Inc. (C), MA, *492*
Kahn, Chris - Techstaff Inc. (C), WI, *603*
Kahn, R. J. - Techstaff Inc. (C), WI, *603*
Kahng, Alex - C.T.E.W. Executive Personnel Services Inc. (C), BC, *278*
Kain, Dennis J. - Longshore + Simmons (R), PA, *131*
Kaiser, Donald - Dunhill Personnel of New Haven (C), CT, *316*
Kaiser, Greg - Execu-Tech Search Inc. (C), MN, *332*
Kaiser, Joe - Fortune Personnel Consultants of Anderson, Inc. (C), SC, *349*
Kaiser, Marv - Execu-Tech Search Inc. (C), MN, *332*
Kalas, John - The Tidewater Group Inc. (C), CT, *607*
Kalember, Jr., Robert J. - Fortune Personnel Consultants of Hinsdale, IL (C), IL, *346*
Kalesnik, Larry - Dunhill Staffing Systems (C), OK, *318*
Kaleta, Victoria - Accountants On Call (C), CA, *235*
Kalinski, Jr., Felix - Baeder Kalinski Int'l. Group, Inc. (R), NH, *10*
Kallfelz, Paul F. - A. G. Fishkin & Assoc., Inc. (R), MD, *68*
Kalus, Lisa - Lisa Kalus & Assoc., Inc. (C), NY, *403*
Kalyna, Adrianne - Martin Partners, L.L.C. (R), IL, *137*
Kam, Connie - Major, Hagen & Africa (C), NY, *423*
Kames, Robert - Kames & Assoc. (C), MD, *403*
Kammerer, Robert J. - Baldwin Associates, LLC (R), CT, *10*
Kampmann, Sara - Johnson Smith & Knisely (R), CA, *107*
Kanal, David S. - Johnson Smith & Knisely (R), NY, *107*
Kandall, Hazel S. - Marley Group Ltd. (C), NY, *471*
Kane, Bernie - Kane & Assoc. (C), TX, *403*
Kane, J. Michael - Sanford Rose Assoc. - Orland Park (C), IL, *567*
Kane, John F. - The Human Resource Consulting Group, Inc. (R), CO, *98*
Kane, Michael - Kane & Assoc. (C), TX, *403*
Kane, Rich - Systems Research Inc. (SRI) (C), IL, *598*
Kane, Steve - Sanford Rose Assoc. - Charlotte (C), NC, *568*
Kanoff, Nan - Ruderfer & Co., Inc. (C), NJ, *548*
Kanovsky, Gerald - Career Consulting Group, Inc. (C), CT, *281*
Kanovsky, Marlene - Career Consulting Group, Inc. (C), CT, *281*
Kanter, Troy - Raymond Karsan Assoc. (C), NE, *530*
Kanuit, Cathie - Brown, Bernardy, Van Remmen, Inc. (C), CA, *275*
Kanzer, William F. - Kanzer Assoc., Inc. (R), IL, *109*
Kapetan, Nicholas - Barrett Partners (C), IL, *260*
Kaplan, Alan J. - Kaplan & Assoc., Inc. (R), PA, *109*
Kaplan, Bittian - Brentwood Int'l. (R), CA, *23*
Kaplan, Dean - Marcus & Assoc. (C), NY, *469*
Kaplan, Gary - Gary Kaplan & Assoc. (R), CA, *109*
Kaplan, Robert - The Executive Group, Inc. (R), CA, *62*
Kapral, Shannon M. - Sanford Rose Assoc. - Philadelphia North (C), PA, *570*
Karel, Stephen A. - Karel & Co. (R), CA, *109*
Karkow, Drew - David Weinfeld Group (C), NC, *617*
Karp, Linda S. - Karp & Assoc. (C), FL, *403*
Karp, Michael - The Options Group, Inc. (C), NY, *499*
Karr, Cynthia - Howard Karr & Assoc., Inc. (R), CA, *110*
Karr, Howard L. - Howard Karr & Assoc., Inc. (R), CA, *110*
Karr, Liz - Howard Karr & Assoc., Inc. (R), CA, *110*
Karras, Bill - Karras Personnel, Inc. (C), NJ, *403*
Karsan, Nooruddin S. - Raymond Karsan Assoc. (C), PA, *529*
Karson, Allan - Allan Karson Assoc., Inc. (R), NJ, *110*
Kartin, Martin C. - Martin Kartin & Co., Inc. (R), NY, *110*
Kasbaum, David J. - The Ransford Group (R), TX, *171*
Kase, Philip - Re-Mark Assoc. Inc. (C), NJ, *531*
Kash, Gene R. - Lloyd Prescott & Churchill, Inc. (R), GA, *130*
Kash, Gene R. - Lloyd Prescott Assoc., Inc. (C), GA, *419*
Kashinsky, Richard J. - Management Recruiters of Monterey (C), CA, *441*
Kasperski, Leon - Rice Cohen Int'l. (R), PA, *178*
Kass, Roberta - Seltzer Fontaine Beckwith (C), CA, *579*
Kasten, Marc - Fortune Personnel Consultants (C), CA, *344*
Katz, Allen M. - First Search Inc. (C), IL, *341*
Katz, Arthur - Management Recruiters of Atlanta North, Inc. (C), GA, *446*
Katz, Martin - Crispi, Wagner & Co., Inc. (R), NY, *43*
Katz, Norman - MCS Assoc. (R), CA, *142*
Katzman, Daniel D. - Lloyd Prescott & Churchill, Inc. (R), FL, *130*
Katzman, Melissa - Melissa Katzman, Executive Search (C), NY, *404*
Katzman, Sheri B. - Rosenfeld & Co., Inc. (C), MI, *545*

PRINCIPALS

Kauffman, Christopher C. - Chris Kauffman & Company (R), GA, *110*
Kaufman, Matthew - Sales Advantage (C), FL, *551*
Kaufman, Stuart - Management Recruiters of Great Neck (C), NY, *454*
Kaufman, Susan - Kaufman Assoc. (R), CA, *110*
Kaufmann, Anita D. - A-K-A (Anita Kaufmann Assoc.) (C), NY, *231*
Kaufmann, Robert E. - SpencerStuart (R), CT, *197*
Kaulius-Barry, Aldonna - Aldonna Barry Personnel & Management (C), ON, *260*
Kausch, Rolf H. - Priority Executive Search (C), FL, *518*
Kawahara, Wade - HCI Corp. (C), IL, *371*
Kay, Bill - Madison Executive Search, Inc. (C), NJ, *422*
Kay, Elizabeth - E. J. Lance Management Assoc., Inc. (C), NY, *412*
Kay, Heidi - Kay Concepts, Inc. (C), FL, *404*
Kay, Jerry L. - LAI Ward Howell (R), CA, *123*
Kay, Jim - Jim Kay & Assoc. (C), IL, *404*
Kay, Joseph H. - The Kay Group of 5th Ave. (C), NY, *404*
Kay, Peter - NMC & Kay Int'l. (R), CO, *152*
Kay, Phyllis - William Bell Assoc., Inc. (C), NJ, *263*
Kay, Tom - L & K Assoc. (C), NJ, *410*
Kayajian, Bob - Management Recruiters of Colonie (C), NY, *432*
Kaye, Edward - GSP International (C), NJ, *364*
Kaye, Francine C. - MedSearch Resources, Inc. (C), FL, *478*
Kaye, Jeff - Kaye/Bassman Int'l. Corp. (R), TX, *110*
Kaye, Manuel - Retail Executive Search (C), FL, *535*
Kaye, Pat - Robert Kaestner & Assoc. (C), FL, *403*
Kaye, Shelley - Cassell & Kaye (C), NY, *286*
Kazan, J. Neil - Kazan International, Inc. (R), NJ, *110*
Kean, Marjorie - Korn/Ferry Int'l. (R), FL, *118*
Kean, Richard W. - Dunhill Staffing Systems, Inc. (C), NY, *316*
Keane, Kevin - Keane Assoc. (R), MA, *110*
Kearney, Frank - ProSearch, Inc. (C), MA, *524*
Kearney, John - The Buckley Group (C), TX, *276*
Keating, Kevin - O'Keefe & Assoc., Inc. (R), CT, *154*
Keefe, John - Kelly Associates (R), PA, *112*
Keefe, Steve - The Search America Group Inc. (C), OH, *573*
Keegan, Kenneth W. - Management Recruiters of Los Gatos (C), CA, *426*
Keegan, Kira lee - Management Recruiters of Los Gatos (C), CA, *426*
Keeley, Lawrence W. Pete - AGRI-associates (C), TX, *242*
Keeley, Stephanie Brooks - Keeley Consulting Inc. (C), ON, *404*
Keeley, Timothy J. - Keeley Consulting Inc. (C), ON, *404*
Keen, Jr., Robert - Management Recruiters of Columbia (C), SC, *435*
Keenan, James - Brentwood Int'l. (R), CA, *23*
Keenan, Mike - Schwab-Carrese Assoc., Inc. Executive Search (R), NC, *185*
Keesom, W. H. Peter - TASA International (R), GA, *206*
Kefgen, Keith - HVS Executive Search (R), NY, *100*
Kehn, Elizabeth R. - Kehn & Gabor, Inc. (C), OH, *405*
Keifer, Danna - Dunhill Professional Search of San Jose (C), CA, *319*
Keifer, Kevin A. P. - Dunhill Professional Search of San Jose (C), CA, *319*
Keister, Beth - The Stanton Group, Inc. (C), IL, *591*
Keister, John - The Stanton Group, Inc. (C), IL, *591*
Keith-Murray, M. - The Keith-Murray Partnership (R), ON, *112*
Keljo, Judith - Larsen Int'l., Inc. (R), TX, *125*
Kelleher, Patricia C. - Fenwick Partners (R), MA, *66*
Keller, Andrea - F-O-R-T-U-N-E Personnel Consultants of Palm Beach (C), FL, *345*
Keller, Barbara - Barton Assoc., Inc. (R), TX, *12*
Keller, Jason - GCO (C), CA, *355*
Keller, Lorraine - Management Recruiters of North West Austin (C), TX, *462*
Kellerhals, Gloria - Management Recruiters of Westminster (C), CO, *426*
Kellett, Jr., Samuel B. - Attorneys at Work (C), GA, *256*
Kelley, Carolyn - The CARVIR Group, Inc. (C), GA, *285*
Kelley, Ed - Korn/Ferry Int'l. (R), NY, *117*
Kelley, Kathy - Straube Associates (R), MA, *203*
Kelley, Randall D. - SpencerStuart (R), TX, *197*
Kelley, Tom A. - Thomas A. Kelley & Assoc. (R), CA, *112*
Kelley, Verne - Kelley & Keller, Inc. (C), FL, *405*
Kelly, Claudia L. - SpencerStuart (R), CT, *196*
Kelly, Donna - Accountants On Call (C), NV, *236*
Kelly, Elizabeth Ann - Wellington Management Group (R), PA, *217*
Kelly, Jeanine P. - Integrated Management Solutions (C), NY, *390*
Kelly, Jim - The LaBorde Group (C), CA, *411*
Kelly, John - Rand Thompson Executive Search Consultants (C), NY, *528*
Kelly, Mary K. - Kelly Assoc. (R), WI, *112*
Kelly, Peter W. - Rollo Assoc. (R), CA, *181*
Kelly, Ron - Hunter Int'l., Inc. (R), CT, *100*
Kelly, Ronald - Kelly Assoc. (R), WI, *112*
Kelly, Rory - The Ellsworth Group (C), NY, *329*
Kelly, Roy P. - Management Recruiters of Haddonfield (C), NJ, *431*
Kelly, Sean - Iona Partners (C), CA, *394*
Kelly, Susan D. - S. D. Kelly & Assoc., Inc. (R), MA, *112*
Kelly, Sussannah - Herman Smith Executive Initiatives Inc. (R), ON, *193*
Kelly, William W. - Jon McRae & Associates, Inc. (R), GA, *142*
Kelso, Pat - Barton Assoc., Inc. (R), TX, *12*
Kempf, Cathie - Gaines & Assoc. Int'l., Inc. (R), NM, *73*
Kendall, James C. - Kendall & Davis Co., Inc. (C), MO, *405*
Kendall, Steven W. - Management Recruiters of Atlanta West, Inc. (C), GA, *445*
Kendle, Vernon S. - New Venture Development, Inc. (C), CA, *492*
Kendrick, M. Steven - LAI Ward Howell (R), TX, *124*
Kennedy, Bradford M. - Tecmark Associates Inc. (C), NY, *604*
Kennedy, David - David Warwick Kennedy & Assoc. (R), BC, *112*
Kennedy, IV, Joseph W. - Quest Enterprises, Ltd. (C), IL, *527*
Kennedy, Louis - S-H-S Int'l. of Cherry Hill (C), NJ, *549*
Kennedy, Lynn - NPS of Atlanta, Inc. (C), GA, *496*
Kennedy, Michael - The Danbrook Group, Inc. (C), TX, *306*
Kennedy, Mike - MK & Assoc. (R), CA, *146*
Kennedy, Sharon - MK & Assoc. (R), CA, *146*
Kennedy, Walt - Romac Int'l., Inc. (C), MN, *543*
Kennedy, Walt - Romac Int'l., Inc. (C), MN, *543*
Kenney, George T. - Search Research Assoc., Inc. (R), MA, *187*
Kenney, William - William W. Kenney (C), CT, *405*
Kennison, Victoria - Kennison & Assoc. Inc. (C), MO, *405*
Kenny, Eugene F. - OEI, Inc. (C), NJ, *498*
Kenny, J. Thomas - Moriarty/Fox, Inc. (R), IL, *147*
Kenny, Mary R. - OEI, Inc. (C), NJ, *498*
Kenny, Megan - Partners Resource Group (C), MD, *504*
Kenny, Peter J. - Rob Dey Executive Search (R), FL, *49*
Kenny, Roger M. - Boardroom Consultants/Kenny Kindler Tholke (R), NY, *19*
Kensinger, John P. - Sanford Rose Assoc. - Burlington, NC (C), NC, *569*
Kensington, Holland - Kensington International (R), CA, *113*

Kent, Melvin - Kent & Assoc. (R), OH, *113*
Kenton, Dianne - Partnervision Consulting Group Inc. (R), ON, *160*
Kenzer, Robert D. - Kenzer Corp. (R), NY, *113*
Keogh, James - Sanford Rose Assoc. - Oak Brook (C), IL, *567*
Keoughan, Thomas - The C.P.R. Group (C), NJ, *278*
Kerber, Maureen - Hall Kinion (C), WA, *367*
Keremelevich, Les - International Business Partners (C), ON, *392*
Keren, Yardena - Search Group (C), CA, *575*
Kern, Tina - R. Green & Assoc., Inc. (C), OH, *362*
Kerner, Barbara - Barbara Kerner Consultants (C), NY, *405*
Kerrigan, Geoffrey M. - ESA (R), CT, *60*
Kershaw, Blair - Blair Kershaw Assoc., Inc. (C), PA, *405*
Kershner, Bruce - Kershner & Co. (R), DC, *113*
Kerstein, Daniel J. - Daniel J. Kerstein, Consultant to Management (R), CO, *114*
Kessler, Roy - J. B. Linde & Assoc. (C), MO, *395*
Kessler, Timothy - Romac Int'l., Inc. (C), NC, *544*
Kessler, Vivian - Search Innovations, Inc. (R), PA, *187*
Kesten, Howard - APA Search, Inc. (R), NY, *6*
Ketner, Michael L. - Michael L. Ketner & Assoc., Inc. (R), PA, *114*
Keymer, Robert J. - H R Solutions, Inc. (C), MO, *365*
Keyser, Amy L. - Major, Hagen & Africa (C), CA, *423*
Keyser, James M. - Career +Plus (C), NY, *281*
Keyser, Rich - VZ Int'l., Inc. (C), PA, *613*
Kezerli, Veronique - Claude Vezina, Conseil en recherche de cadres inc. (R), QE, *213*
Khan, Nick - NorthStar Technologies, Inc. (C), NY, *496*
Kiburz, Megan - Romac Int'l., Inc. (C), GA, *543*
Kick, James - The Prairie Group (C), IL, *515*
Kidd, Bobby - Phillips Resource Group (C), NC, *511*
Kielty, III, John L. - Earley Kielty & Assoc., Inc. (R), NY, *56*
Kien-Jersey, Tammy - SpencerStuart (R), CT, *197*
Kier, Mary - Cook Assoc.,® Inc. (R), IL, *40*
Kierstead, Robert - High Tech Opportunities, Inc. (C), NH, *377*
Kiken, Mark E. - COBA Executive Search (R), CO, *36*
Kilcoyne, Pat - C.P.S., Inc. (C), IL, *278*
Kilcoyne, Richard - Carter McKenzie, Inc. (C), NJ, *285*
Kile, Robert W. - Rusher, Loscavio & Lo-Presto (R), CA, *183*
Kilian, Walter D. - Availability Personnel Consultants (C), NH, *257*
Kilinski, Donald M. - Heidrick & Struggles, Inc. (R), IL, *90*
Kilkenney, Tom - Sales Consultant of Bloomfield Hills (C), MI, *553*
Killman, Kenneth - Hallman Group, Inc. (C), MI, *367*
Kilman, Paul H. - The Kilman Advisory Group (R), CT, *114*
Kim, Brandon - Pioneer Consulting Group (C), CA, *512*
Kimball, Dex - Lanken-Kimball-Therrell & Assoc. (C), GA, *412*
Kimmel, Joe W. - Kimmel & Associates, Inc. (C), NC, *406*
Kimura, Paul - Avery Assoc. (R), CA, *9*
Kincaid, Lynn - Kincaid Group Inc. (KGI) (C), TX, *407*
Kincaid, Raymond W. - Kincaid Group Inc. (KGI) (C), TX, *406*
Kincannon, Kelly - Kincannon & Reed (R), VA, *114*
Kinderis, Paul - Kinderis & Loercher Group (C), IL, *407*
Kindig, Becky - Management Recruiters-Cedar Rapids, Inc. (C), IA, *448*
Kindler, Peter A. - Boardroom Consultants/Kenny Kindler Tholke (R), NY, *19*
Kiner, Linda - Insurance Career Center, Inc. (C), CT, *390*
King, Barbara - Walter K. Wilkins & Co. (R), NJ, *221*
King, Byron L. - Management Recruiters of Bethlehem (C), NC, *433*
King, Damon - The Canon Group (C), CA, *280*
King, Gail - Management Recruiters of Tampa North (C), FL, *444*
King, Gary - Management Recruiters of Tampa North (C), FL, *444*
King, Gary - Sales Consultants of Tampa North, Inc. (C), FL, *557*
King, Gregory - Somerset Group, Inc. (C), CT, *587*
King, J. C. - A H Justice Search Consultants (C), TX, *402*
King, Jack - Newman-Johnson-King, Inc. (C), TX, *492*
King, James B. - The Westminster Group, Inc. (R), RI, *218*
King, Jeremy C. - DHR Int'l., Inc. (R), GA, *50*
King, Jim - Career Strategies, Inc. (C), CA, *283*
King, John - Roster Inc. (C), IN, *545*
King, Karl - Capital Consulting Group, Inc. (R), MD, *28*
King, Liz - Newman-Johnson-King, Inc. (C), TX, *492*
King, Margaret - Christian & Timbers, Inc. (R), OH, *34*
King, Michael - Fortune Personnel Consultants of San Antonio, Inc. (C), TX, *350*
King, Neil - Procom (C), TX, *519*
King, P. Jason - Yours In Travel Personnel Agency, Inc. (C), NY, *626*
King, Richard M. - Kittleman & Assoc.,LLC (R), IL, *115*
King, Robert E. - Behavioral Science Assoc., Inc. (R), AZ, *15*
King, Roger M. - Tech Search (C), CA, *601*
King, Sally - King ComputerSearch, Inc. (C), TX, *407*
King, Steven - Ashway Ltd. Agency (C), NY, *253*
Kingdom, Scott - Korn/Ferry Int'l. (R), IL, *118*
Kingsbury, Scott C. - Kingsbury • Wax • Bova (R), MA, *114*
Kingwergs, Carlos - Management Recruiters of Cuernavaca (C), MX, *438*
Kinkopf, Lesley - Major Legal Services, Inc. (C), OH, *423*
Kinley, Kathy - Intech Summit Group (R), CA, *102*
Kinley, R. David - The Caldwell Partners Amrop International (R), ON, *26*
Kinlin, Ellen C. - The Kinlin Co., Inc. (R), MA, *115*
Kinney, Carol - Dussick Management Assoc. (C), CT, *323*
Kinney, Diane C. - The Stewart Group (C), FL, *593*
Kinney, Linda - Prospective Personnel Service, Inc. (C), OK, *524*
Kinney, Sandy - Executive Search Consultants Corp. (C), IL, *335*
Kins, Arnie - Cook Assoc.,® Inc. (R), IL, *40*
Kins, John - Cook Assoc.,® Inc. (R), IL, *40*
Kinser, Richard - Richard Kinser & Assoc. (R), NY, *115*
Kinsey, Joanne - Eastridge Infotech (C), CA, *326*
Kinzie, George - Franchise Recruiters Ltd. (R), ON, *71*
Kip, Luanne S. - Kip Williams, Inc. (R), NY, *115*
Kirby, James E. - Management Recruiters of Marietta, Inc. (C), GA, *446*
Kirby, William P. - Kirby Assoc. (R), PA, *115*
Kirchgessner, Ken - Management Recruiters of Pensacola (C), FL, *444*
Kirk, Ruth - Campbell, Edgar Inc. (C), BC, *280*
Kirk, Ruth - Campbell, Edgar Inc. (C), AB, *280*
Kirkbride, Robert - Kirkbride Assoc., Inc. (C), WA, *407*
Kirkendorfer, Laura - The Kingsley Group (R), CA, *115*
Kirkman, Angie - MTA Partners (R), TX, *148*
Kirkman, Michael - Korn/Ferry Int'l. (R), DC, *118*
Kirkpatrick, Robert L. - Reese Assoc. (R), PA, *174*
Kirkwood, Vincent - Executive Connection (C), OH, *333*

PRINCIPALS

Kirschman, David R. - Physician Executive Management Center (R), FL, *164*
Kirschner, John - Management Recruiters of Denver-Downtown (C), CO, *426*
Kirschner, Michael - American Medical Consultants, Inc. (C), FL, *248*
Kirschner, Richard - Marley Group Ltd. (C), NY, *471*
Kirschner, Stephan W. - The Regis Group, Ltd. (R), GA, *174*
Kissel, Brian J. - Management Recruiters of Northern Palm Beaches (C), FL, *444*
Kissel, James R. - Management Recruiters of Northern Palm Beaches (C), FL, *444*
Kissel, Rosemary - Eastbourne Assoc. Inc. (R), NY, *56*
Kitt, James - Searchforce, Inc. (R), FL, *187*
Kivler, Peggy - MGA Executive Search (C), FL, *480*
Klages, Constance W. - International Management Advisors, Inc. (R), NY, *103*
Klaus, Stephanie - DHR Int'l., Inc. (R), KS, *50*
Klavins, Larissa R. - Briant Assoc., Inc. (R), IL, *23*
Kleames, Jerry - Genesis Recruiting (C), CA, *356*
Klebanoff, Elizabeth - Johnson Smith & Knisely (R), NY, *107*
Klebba, Arthur - Morgan & Assoc. (C), MA, *485*
Kleber, Deb - Kleber & Assoc. (C), WA, *407*
Klegman, Hal - Roy Talman & Assoc. (C), IL, *599*
Kleiman, Howard - Derhak Ireland & Partners Ltd. (R), ON, *48*
Klein, Ariel - AKH Executive Search (C), OR, *243*
Klein, Gary Ethan - Klein, Landau & Romm (C), DC, *407*
Klein, Howard G. - F-O-R-T-U-N-E Personnel Consultants of Bergen County Inc. (C), NJ, *347*
Klein, Lynn M. - Riotto-Jones Assoc. (R), NY, *179*
Klein, Matthew - DHR Int'l., Inc. (R), GA, *50*
Klein, Mel Stewart - Stewart/Laurence Assoc., Inc. (R), NJ, *201*
Klein, Nancy A. - Marley Group Ltd. (C), NY, *471*
Klein, Robert - Allen Evans Assoc. (R), NY, *4*
Kleinman, Robert C. - Marketing & Sales Resources, Inc. (C), FL, *470*
Kleinman, Victor - The Stevenson Group, Inc. (R), FL, *200*
Kleinstein, Jonah A. - The Kleinstein Group, Inc. (R), NJ, *116*
Klemmer, Raymond J. - Raymond J. Klemmer & Assoc. (R), NY, *116*
Kleven, Robert - The Kleven Group, Inc. - Executive Search Division (R), MA, *116*
Kleven, Robert - The Kleven Group, Inc. (C), MA, *407*
Klimaski, Remus J. - Sales Consultants of Summit (C), NJ, *554*
Kline, Dennis - Herbeck Kline & Assoc. (R), IL, *92*
Kline, James O. - Management Recruiters of Knoxville (C), TN, *436*
Kline, Keith - Marcus & Assoc. (C), NY, *469*
Kling, Constance W. - LAI Ward Howell (R), IL, *123*
Klingensmith, Steve - The Hunter Group, Inc. (C), MI, *385*
Kloppman, David - Williams Recruiting, Inc. (C), WA, *621*
Klos, Larry - MSI Int'l. (C), TX, *487*
Kluck, Darlene - Accountants On Call (C), MN, *236*
Klus, Chris - KPMG Executive Search (R), ON, *119*
Kmet, Jeremy - Procom (C), CA, *519*
Knapp, Karen Gordon - Tarnow Int'l. (R), NJ, *206*
Knapp, Miranda - Cook Assoc.,® Inc. (R), IL, *40*
Knapp, Ronald A. - Knapp Consultants (R), CT, *116*
Knauf, Shirley - Managed Care Resources (C), TX, *424*
Knauff, Joyce C. - Joyce C. Knauff & Assoc. (C), IL, *408*
Knauss, Steve - Management Recruiters of Durham (C), NC, *433*
Kneen, Linda - General Engineering Tectonics (C), CA, *356*
Knight, Lene M. - The Professional Sales Search Co., Inc. (C), WA, *522*
Knighton, Krisnne - Keystone Consulting Group (C), NC, *406*
Knisely, Gary - Johnson Smith & Knisely (R), NY, *107*
Knopik, Robert - Boyden (R), IL, *21*
Knose, II, Joseph M. - Corporate Image Group (C), TN, *300*
Knotts, Jerry - MIXTEC Group (R), CA, *145*
Knowles, Jr., James H. - Resources for Management (R), PA, *176*
Knowles, Scott - Management Recruiters of Georgetown (C), SC, *461*
Knowlson, Maureen - M. K. & Assoc. (C), PA, *422*
Knox, Dave - APA Employment Agency Inc. (C), OR, *251*
Knutson, David A. - North American Recruiters, Inc. (R), MN, *153*
Ko, Jane - Phillips Resource Group (C), SC, *510*
Koblentz, Joel M. - Egon Zehnder Int'l. Inc. (R), GA, *227*
Koch, Gail Kleinberg - CAS Comsearch Inc. (C), NY, *286*
Kochmer, Sheila - Management Recruiters of Scranton (C), PA, *434*
Kochmer, Victor - Management Recruiters of Scranton (C), PA, *434*
Koehler, Frank R. - The Koehler Group (C), PA, *408*
Koehler, Jack - Koehler & Co. (R), WI, *116*
Koehn, Lee - Lee Koehn Assoc., Inc. (R), OR, *116*
Koeller, Michael J. - Waveland Int'l. (R), NY, *216*
Koellhoffer, Thomas J. - T. J. Koellhoffer & Assoc. (R), NJ, *116*
Koenig, Allen E. - R. H. Perry & Assoc., Inc. (R), OH, *162*
Koenig, Barbara - Royal Assoc. (C), CA, *547*
Koenig, Jerrold - P R Management Consultants, Inc. (C), NJ, *500*
Koenig, Joel S. - Blackshaw, Olmstead, Lynch & Koenig (R), GA, *18*
Koerner, Pam L. - Koerner & Assoc., Inc. (C), TN, *408*
Koers, Trina - TRS Staffing Solutions Inc. (C), OH, *610*
Koester, Diana - Accountants On Call (C), IN, *236*
Koff, Patty - American Medical Recruiters (C), CO, *248*
Koff, Patty - American Medical Recruiters (C), CO, *248*
Koffler, Fred - Fred Koffler Assoc. (R), NY, *116*
Kohlbry, Cynthia J. - Grant Cooper & Assoc., Inc. (R), MO, *81*
Kohn, Adam - Christian & Timbers, Inc. (R), OH, *34*
Kohn, Steven - Affinity Executive Search (C), FL, *241*
Kohonoski, Michael M. - The Guild Corp. (C), VA, *364*
Kolacia, V. - Murphy Partners Int'l. (R), IL, *150*
Kolburne, Barbara - Foster Partners (R), NY, *70*
Koletic, Rudy E. - Management Recruiters of Tampa-Palma Ceia (C), FL, *427*
Kolh, Barbara - Executive Solutions (R), MN, *64*
Kollaritsch, Lynn - DataPro Personnel Consultants (C), TX, *308*
Koller, Jr., Edward R. - Jerry Fields Assoc. (C), NY, *340*
Koller, Jr., Edward R. - Howard-Sloan Assoc. (C), NY, *381*
Koller, Jr., Edward R. - The Howard-Sloan-Koller Group (R), NY, *97*
Koltnow, Emily - Koltnow & Company (R), NY, *117*
Komorner, Paul - The Whitney Group (C), GA, *620*
Konefsky, Gary - M. A. Churchill & Assoc., Inc. (R), PA, *35*
Konrad, William - ISC of Atlanta, Inc. (C), GA, *394*
Konstans, Gregory C. - LAI Ward Howell (R), TX, *124*
Kool, Joan - Professional Recruiters, Inc. (C), PA, *521*
Koontz, Donald N. - Koontz, Jeffries & Assoc., Inc. (R), FL, *117*
Kooyman, Dave - Professional Recruiters (C), UT, *522*
Kopelan, Rolfe I. - Boyden (R), NY, *21*
Kopff, Fred - META/MAT, Ltd. (R), NJ, *144*
Koppelman, William - Kingsley Quinn/USA (R), NJ, *115*

Koppes, Jenny - Future Employment Service, Inc. (C), IA, *354*
Kopplin, Richard M. - Kopplin Search, Inc. (R), CA, *117*
Kopsick, Joseph M. - SpencerStuart (R), IL, *197*
Kopulos, Judy - Rand-Curtis Resources (C), AZ, *529*
Kopyt, Leon - The Consortium (C), NY, *296*
Korban, Richard O. - Korban Associates (R), PA, *117*
Kordus, Benedict N. - Kordus Consulting Group (C), WI, *408*
Kordus, Lee Walther - Kordus Consulting Group (C), WI, *408*
Koren, Michael - Koren, Rogers Assoc. Inc. (R), NY, *117*
Korkuch, Sandy - The Addison Consulting Group (C), NJ, *239*
Kornacki, Stephan J. - Groton Planning Group (R), ME, *82*
Kornfeld, Warren - Management Recruiters of Woodbury Inc. (C), NY, *455*
Kors, Paul - cFour Partners (R), TX, *32*
Kors, R. Paul - Kors Montgomery Int'l. (R), TX, *118*
Kortjohn, Dick - Robert William James & Assoc. (C), OH, *539*
Korytko, Lesia - COBA Executive Search (R), CO, *36*
Koslow, Esther - Marley Group Ltd. (C), NY, *471*
Kosmetos, Michael - Michael Kosmetos & Assoc., Inc. (C), OH, *408*
Koss, Kendra - Leader Search Inc. (R), AB, *127*
Kossuth, David - Kossuth & Assoc., Inc. (R), WA, *119*
Kossuth, Jane - Kossuth & Assoc., Inc. (R), WA, *119*
Kost, Harold - Rand Thompson Executive Search Consultants (C), NY, *528*
Kostadinova, Kosta - The Search Committee, Inc. (C), FL, *575*
Kosteva, David - NDI Services (R), MI, *151*
Kostiuk, Richard - Dick Wray & Consultants, Inc. (R), PA, *225*
Kostmayer, John B. - Kostmayer Assoc., Inc. (R), NY, *119*
Kostmayer, Roger C. - Kostmayer Assoc., Inc. (R), MD, *119*
Kostrub, Todd - Diedre Moire Corp., Inc. (C), NJ, *483*
Kotler, Gerald R. - Management Recruiters of Dayton, Inc. (C), OH, *457*
Kotler, Jerry R. - Sales Consultants (C), OH, *555*
Kotloski, Dennis - Management Recruiters of Chicago-North Shore (C), IL, *447*
Kovach, Jerry - The J. Kovach Group (R), PA, *119*
Kowalski, Joseph J. - Capitol Management Consulting, Inc. (C), NJ, *281*
Kozachok, Peter D. - Executive Solutions (R), MN, *64*
Kozlin, Jeffrey M. - Kozlin Assoc., Inc. (C), NY, *408*
Kraemer, Katherine R. - Katherine R. Kraemer (R), CA, *120*
Krafski, Charlene - C. R. Krafski & Assoc., Inc. (R), IL, *120*
Kraft, M. Katherine - Princeton Search Partners, Inc. (R), NJ, *169*
Kraftson, Ann - The Oxbridge Group, Ltd. (C), NY, *500*
Krainen, Cindy - Harper Associates (C), MI, *369*
Krakower, Bernard H. - Krakower Group, Inc. (R), CA, *120*
Kramer, Alan L. - Kramer Executive Resources, Inc. (C), NY, *409*
Kramer, Desni C. - Management Recruiters of Lewisville (C), TX, *463*
Kramer, Donald J. - Dunhill Professional Search of Tampa (C), FL, *320*
Kramer, Kim - Million & Assoc., Inc. (R), OH, *145*
Kramer, Mitchel - Interim Accounting Professionals (C), FL, *392*
Kramer, Mona - Dunhill Professional Search of Tampa (C), FL, *320*
Kramer, Peter - Dunhill Professional Search of Tampa (C), FL, *320*
Kranak, Karen - Professions, Inc. (C), OH, *523*
Krasnow, Arthur L. - Atomic Personnel, Inc. (C), PA, *255*
Kratimenos, Peter - Ansara, Bickford & Fiske (C), MA, *251*
Kratz, Stephen J. - Tyler & Company (R), GA, *212*
Krauser, H. James - SpencerStuart (R), CT, *196*
Krauss, Jack - J. Krauss Assoc. (R), FL, *120*
Krauthamer, Gary L. - Krauthamer & Assoc. (R), MD, *120*
Krautler, William - Krautler Personnel Recruitment (C), FL, *409*
Kravetz, Gary - NCC Executive Search Consultants (C), CA, *490*
Krawetz, Ben - National Career Search (C), AZ, *489*
Krecklo, Brian D. - Krecklo & Assoc., Inc. (R), QE, *120*
Krecklo, Brian D. - Krecklo Executive Search Inc. (R), ON, *120*
Kreisberg, Robert S. - Opus Marketing (R), CA, *156*
Kreisler, Debbi - Evie Kreisler Assoc. Inc. (C), GA, *409*
Kreisler, Evie - Evie Kreisler Assoc. Inc. (C), CA, *409*
Kreiss, John P. - Zweig White & Assoc., Inc. (R), MA, *228*
Krejci, Stanley - Boyden (R), DC, *21*
Krell, Barry - Cosier & Assoc. (C), AB, *302*
Krell, Richard B. - Russell Reynolds Assoc., Inc. (R), CA, *176*
Kremer, Erica - Brigade, Inc. (R), CA, *23*
Kremple, Jeffrey J. - Kremple Consulting Group (R), CA, *120*
Kremple, Robert J. - Kremple Consulting Group (R), CA, *120*
Krenz, Ron - MESA International (C), CA, *480*
Kreps, Charles D. - The Normyle/Erstling Health Search Group (C), NJ, *494*
Kresich, William J. - William-Johns Co., Inc. (C), CA, *621*
Kress, Daryl - Fortune Personnel Consultants of Anderson, Inc. (C), SC, *349*
Kressenberg, Sammye Jo - Kressenberg Assoc. (C), TX, *409*
Kreuter, Daniel A. - D. A. Kreuter Assoc., Inc. (R), PA, *121*
Kreutz, Gary L. - Kreutz Consulting Group, Inc. (R), IL, *121*
Kreuzberger, Neil L. - Accounting Additions (C), CA, *238*
Krezo, Rich - Michigan Consulting Group (R), MI, *144*
Krezo, Rich - Premier Recruiting Group (C), MI, *516*
Krick, Terry L. - Financial Resource Assoc., Inc. (C), FL, *340*
Krieger, Dennis F. - Seiden Krieger Assoc., Inc. (R), NY, *188*
Krienke, Paul G. - C and P Marketing, Ltd. (C), OK, *278*
Krier, Michael S. - Overton Consulting (R), WI, *157*
Kriesel, David W. - Management Recruiters of Woodbury (C), MN, *430*
Kriesel, David W. - Management Recruiters of Woodbury (C), MN, *452*
Kring, Kenneth L. - Heidrick & Struggles, Inc. (R), PA, *90*
Kris, John R. - Organization Resources Inc. (R), MA, *157*
Kriste, Pat - Ronald S. Johnson Assoc., Inc. (R), CA, *107*
Kristufek, Arthur N. - Magnum Search (C), IL, *422*
Kristy, Michael T. - Heidrick & Struggles, Inc. (R), CA, *90*
Krochenski, Caren - Management Recruiters Int'l.-The Woodlands (C), TX, *464*
Kroll, Gary - General Engineering Tectonics (C), CA, *356*
Krueger, Kurt - Krueger Assoc. (R), IL, *121*
Krueger, Todd L. - Todd L. Krueger & Assoc. (C), WA, *409*
Krumel, Richard - The Perkins Group (R), NC, *162*
Krumel, Richard G. - The Perkins Group (R), NC, *162*
Krumenacker, Elizabeth - Heyman Assoc., Inc. (R), NY, *93*
Krumholz, Jill - KL Consultants (C), NJ, *407*
Kruse, Kevin - Raymond Karsan Assoc. (C), NJ, *530*
Krutzsch, Linda - Accountants On Call (C), NJ, *235*
Ku, Theresa - Sanford Rose Assoc. - Anaheim (C), CA, *566*
Kubiak, Thomas J. - Halbrecht & Co. (C), CT, *365*
Kuehnling, William - Sanford Rose Assoc. - Canton (C), OH, *569*

PRINCIPALS

Kuesis, Dan - Systems Research Inc. (SRI) (C), IL, *598*
Kuhl, William R. - Place Mart Personnel Service (C), NJ, *513*
Kuhlenbeck, Phillip - Austin Group Int'l./ Marlar Int'l. (R), TX, *9*
Kuhn, John J. - John Kuhn & Assoc., Inc. (R), WI, *121*
Kuhn, Larry A. - Kuhn Med-Tech (C), CA, *409*
Kuhnmuench, R. G. - K & C Assoc. (C), CA, *402*
Kukoy, Stephen J. - Kukoy Associates (R), CO, *121*
Kulesza, Michael - Anthony Michael & Co. (C), MA, *251*
Kull, Paul - Paul Kull & Co. (R), NJ, *121*
Kulper, Keith D. - Kulper & Co., L.L.C. (R), NJ, *121*
Kundtz, Robb - David Powell, Inc. (R), CA, *166*
Kunke, Russ - Dunhill Professional Search of Rolling Meadows (C), IL, *320*
Kunkel, Thomas J. - Bayland Assoc. (C), CA, *261*
Kunkle, Denise - D. Kunkle & Assoc. (C), IL, *410*
Kuntz, William A. - Management Recruiters of Indianapolis (C), IN, *448*
Kuntz, William A. - Sales Consultants of Indianapolis (C), IN, *559*
Kunzer, Diane S. - Kunzer Assoc., Ltd. (R), IL, *121*
Kunzer, William J. - Kunzer Assoc., Ltd. (R), IL, *121*
Kupchik, Allen B. - Franklin Allen Consultants, Ltd. (R), NY, *71*
Kurbatoff, Jerry - The Black Leopard (C), CA, *267*
Kurbatoff, Lauren - The Black Leopard (C), CA, *267*
Kurbe, Joe - Procom (C), QE, *520*
Kurdziel, John F. - Nuessle, Kurdziel & Weiss, Inc. (R), PA, *153*
Kuric, Mary J. - Juno Systems, Inc. (C), NY, *402*
Kurke, David S. - Starbridge Group Inc. (C), VA, *591*
Kurkowski, A. R. - Koontz, Jeffries & Assoc., Inc. (R), FL, *117*
Kurosky, John - John Kurosky & Assoc. (R), CA, *122*
Kurth, Dick - Jay Gaines & Company, Inc. (R), NY, *74*
Kurtz, Leonard A. - Executive Search Consultants, Inc. (C), FL, *335*
Kurtz, Michael E. - MDR Associates, Inc. (C), VA, *476*
Kurtz, Sheldon I. - Kurtz Pro-Search, Inc. (C), NJ, *410*
Kurtzman, Jerry - Corporate Advisors, Inc. (C), FL, *299*
Kurz, Richard A. - Management Recruiters of O'Hare (C), IL, *428*
Kurz-Shorr, Carol - The Shorr Group (R), IL, *190*
Kurzrok, Jeanie - Yours In Travel Personnel Agency, Inc. (C), VA, *627*
Kuschnov, Janice - Charles Dahl Group, Inc. (C), MN, *306*
Kush, Max S. - Management Recruiters of Easton, PA (C), PA, *458*
Kushan, Dave - Management Recruiters of Davis (C), CA, *425*
Kushell, Douglas T. - Franchise Search, Inc. (C), NY, *352*
Kusnetz, Ellen G. - Business Solutions Worldwide, Inc. (C), NJ, *277*
Kussner, Janice N. - Herman Smith Executive Initiatives Inc. (R), ON, *193*
Kutcher, Howard - Kutcher Tax Careers, Inc. (C), NY, *410*
Kuypers, Arnold - LAI Ward Howell (R), TX, *124*
Kuypers, Marcia L. - Hire Authority, Inc. (C), MI, *378*
Kuzmick, John - Accountants On Call (C), AZ, *235*
Kvistad, Niles K. - Daggett & Kvistad (R), CA, *45*
Kvring, Richard - Procom (C), NC, *519*
Kwapisz, Arthur - ISC of Atlanta, Inc. (C), GA, *394*
Kyle, Donald - Kyle Assoc. (C), NY, *410*
L'Archevesque, Lee - Sink, Walker, Boltrus Int'l. (R), MA, *192*
L'Hote, Jeffrey R. - LAI Ward Howell (R), NY, *122*
La Iond, Anne - Carlsen Resources, Inc. (R), CO, *29*
Laake, Patrick B. - CMS Management Services LLC (C), IN, *293*
Laba, Marvin - Marvin Laba & Assoc. (R), CA, *122*
Laba, Stuart - Marvin Laba & Assoc. (R), NJ, *122*
Labadie, Ernie - Management Recruiters of Boca Raton (C), FL, *443*
LaBarge-Wilson, Cynthia - Largent Parks & Partners (C), TX, *503*
LaBorde, John - The LaBorde Group (C), CA, *411*
LaBorde, Michael - The LaBorde Group (C), CA, *411*
Labrecque, B. F. - Ray & Berndtson/Laurendeau Labrecque (R), QE, *172*
Labrecque, B. F. - Ray & Berndtson/Laurendeau Labrecque (R), QE, *172*
Lace, Hayley - C.T.E.W. Executive Personnel Services Inc. (C), BC, *278*
Lachance, Roger - Ray & Berndtson/Laurendeau Labrecque (R), QE, *172*
Lachance, Roger - Ray & Berndtson/Laurendeau Labrecque (R), QE, *172*
LaCosta, Paul - LaCosta & Assoc. Int'l. Inc. (C), CA, *411*
Lacoste, Daniel - The Caldwell Partners Amrop International (R), ON, *26*
Lacy, Ann - IM Independent Management Recruiters (R), TN, *101*
Lacy-Higgins, Lynda - B. W. Higgins, Inc. (C), IN, *377*
Laderman, David - ACSYS Resources, Inc. (C), PA, *239*
Ladzinski, Terri - The Human Resource Consulting Group, Inc. (R), WI, *98*
Lafferty, John - DHR Int'l., Inc. (R), IL, *49*
LaFlamme, Rene - Rene LaFlamme & Associes (R), QE, *122*
Lageman, Regis - Management Recruiters of Orangepark (C), FL, *427*
LaGrow, Ronald E. - DHR Int'l., Inc. (R), CA, *49*
Laguzza, John - Laguzza Assoc., Ltd. (R), NY, *122*
Laguzza, John - Laguzza Assoc., Ltd. (R), NY, *122*
Lai, Karen - C.T.E.W. Executive Personnel Services Inc. (C), BC, *278*
Laird, Cheryl - C.P.S., Inc. (C), IL, *278*
Laird, Meri - Davidson, Laird & Assoc. (C), MI, *308*
Laite, Joseph - Search Int'l. (R), MA, *187*
Lajous, Luz - Russell Reynolds Assoc., Inc. (R), MX, *177*
Laka, Gregory - Gregory Laka & Co. (C), IL, *411*
Lake, Courtney F. - Lee Calhoon & Co., Inc. (R), CT, *26*
Laks, Naomi - Adam-Bryce Inc. (C), NY, *239*
Lalagos, Dee - DEL Technical Services, Inc. (C), IL, *310*
Laliberte, Marie A. - TASA International (R), MA, *206*
Lalonde, Joel - Management Recruiters of Las Vegas (C), NV, *431*
Lam, Pat - Physician Associates (C), HI, *511*
Lamar, John C. - The Alexander Group (R), TX, *3*
Lamb, Angus - Raymond Karsan Assoc. (C), PA, *530*
Lamb, Lynn - Fortune Personnel Consultants of Huntsville, Inc. (C), AL, *344*
Lamb, Peter - Executive Resource Inc. (C), WI, *334*
Lambert, Judith A. - EDI, Inc. (C), MD, *326*
Lambre, Glenn C. - McCooe & Assoc., Inc. (R), NJ, *140*
Lambrecht, Pat - Lam Assoc. (C), HI, *411*
Lamon, Wayne - Lamon + Stuart + Michaels Inc. (R), ON, *124*
Lamond, Elizabeth - The Whyte Group, Inc. (R), MD, *220*
Lamontagne, Manon - Groupe Ranger Inc. (C), QE, *364*
LaMorte, Brian A. - Pascale & LaMorte, LLC (C), CT, *504*
LaMotta, Steve - Human Resource Solutions (R), TX, *98*
Lampert, Bill - Michael Stern Assoc., Inc./ Euram (R), ON, *200*
Lampl, Joni - Management Recruiters of Pittsburgh-North, Inc. (C), PA, *460*
Lampl, Richard - Management Recruiters of Pittsburgh-North, Inc. (C), PA, *460*
Lampl, Tom - Management Recruiters of Sun Valley (C), ID, *447*
Lancaster, Jr., Raymond F. - Lancaster Assoc., Inc. (C), NJ, *412*
Lanctot, Bill - Corporate Resources Professional Placement (C), MN, *301*

Lanctot, Dominique - Matte Consulting Group Inc. (R), QE, *138*
Landau, David - Klein, Landau & Romm (C), DC, *407*
Landay, Mark - Dynamic Synergy Corp. (R), CA, *56*
Landon, Susan J. - LAI Ward Howell (R), NY, *122*
Landsman, Jeffrey B. - Roth Young Personnel Services of Washington, DC (C), MD, *546*
Landwerb, Sandy - Capital Consulting Group, Inc. (R), MD, *28*
Lane, Andrew J. - Overton Consulting (R), WI, *157*
Lane, Douglas - Management Recruiters of Milwaukee - Downtown (C), WI, *466*
Lane, Douglas W. - Management Recruiters of Jensen Beach (C), FL, *427*
Lane, Thomas J. - Aggressive Corporation (C), IL, *242*
Lane-Dodge, Lori - PersoNet, Inc. (C), FL, *507*
Lang, Joyce - DHR Int'l., Inc. (R), CA, *49*
Lang, Joyce - DHR Int'l., Inc. (R), CA, *49*
Lang, Nick - Technical Recruiting Services (C), OH, *602*
Langdon, Ashley P. - Hughes & Sloan, Inc. (C), GA, *383*
Lange, Jack - Lange & Assoc., Inc. (C), IN, *412*
Lange, Jack - National Corporate Consultants, Inc. (C), IN, *489*
Lange, Jim - Lange & Assoc., Inc. (C), IN, *412*
Lange, William R. - Sevcor Int'l., Inc. (R), IL, *188*
Langford, Ann S. - The Langford Search, Inc. (C), AL, *412*
Langford, Bob - Fortune Personnel Consultants of Huntsville, Inc. (C), AL, *343*
Langford, Judy - Fortune Personnel Consultants of Huntsville, Inc. (C), AL, *343*
Langford, K. R. Dick - The Langford Search, Inc. (C), AL, *412*
Langford, Matt - Fortune Personnel Consultants of Huntsville, Inc. (C), AL, *344*
Langley, Carol M. - Langley & Associates, Inc. (Executive Search Consultants) (R), CO, *124*
Langley, Mark - Southwestern Professional Services (C), FL, *588*
Langley, Ted - Jaeger Int'l., Inc. (C), OH, *396*
Langlois, Peter - Dick Wray & Consultants, Inc. (R), TX, *225*
Laniel, Richard - Claude Vezina, Conseil en recherche de cadres inc. (R), QE, *213*
Lanken, Joel - Lanken-Kimball-Therrell & Assoc. (C), GA, *412*
Lankenau, Gene - L & K Assoc. (C), NJ, *410*
Lantz, Delores - A C Personnel Services, Inc. (C), OK, *231*
Lanum, Monica - Executive Referral Services, Inc. (C), IL, *334*
Lapat, Aaron - J. Robert Scott (R), MA, *104*
Lapham, Lawrence L. - Lawrence L. Lapham, Inc. (R), NY, *124*
LaPolice, Denis - Resource Management Group (C), CT, *534*
Lara, Dolores - Hemingway Personnel, Inc. (C), CA, *375*
Laramee, Stephen - Stephen Laramee & Assoc. Inc. (C), ON, *413*
Lardner, Lucy - Tully/Woodmansee Int'l., Inc. (R), NJ, *212*
Lareau, Belle - The Hampton Group (C), NY, *368*
Lareau, Belle - Management Recruiters of The Hamptons (C), NY, *432*
Lareau, Gerard A. - The Hampton Group (C), NY, *368*
Lareau, Jerry A. - Management Recruiters of The Hamptons (C), NY, *432*
Laresen, Rolph - The Silicon Network (C), ON, *581*
Larkin, Dick - Larkin & Co. (R), CA, *125*
Larkin, Ward - Management Recruiters of O'Hare (C), IL, *428*
Larned, Robert T. - Robert Larned Assoc., Inc. (C), VA, *413*
Larrea, Antonio - TASA International (R), MX, *206*
Larry, Melvin P. - ExecuSource Assoc., Inc. (C), GA, *332*
Larsen, C. Lars - The Personnel Network, Inc. (C), SC, *508*
Larsen, Charles L. - The Personnel Network, Inc. (C), SC, *508*
Larsen, Donald J. - Larsen Int'l., Inc. (R), TX, *125*
Larsen, Jack B. - Jack B. Larsen & Assoc., Inc. (C), PA, *413*
Larsen, James K. - The Personnel Network, Inc. (C), SC, *508*
Larsen, Ken - Fortune Personnel Consultants of San Antonio, Inc. (C), TX, *350*
Larsen, Merlyne T. - The Personnel Network, Inc. (C), SC, *508*
Larsen, Michael G. - Barnes & Assoc. Executive Search (C), CA, *259*
Larsen, Richard F. - Larsen, Whitney, Blecksmith & Zilliacus, Inc. (R), CA, *125*
Larsen, Robert H. - R. H. Larsen & Assoc., Inc. (R), FL, *125*
Larson, Ila - i.j. & assoc., inc. (C), CO, *387*
Larson, Ray - Larson Assoc. (R), CA, *125*
Larson, Robert - Berman & Larson (C), NJ, *265*
Larson, Robert L. - RML Assoc. (C), PA, *538*
Lascelle, Donald - Lascelle & Assoc. Inc. (C), ON, *413*
Lasee, Jeff - The H. S. Group, Inc. (C), WI, *365*
Lasher, Charles M. - Lasher Assoc. (R), FL, *125*
Lasini, Dennis - Genesis Research (C), MO, *356*
Lasker, Bob - Sales Consultant of Scottsdale-Metro (C), AZ, *551*
Lasko, Mary - DHR Int'l., Inc. (R), CA, *49*
Laskowski, Peter R. - Goodrich & Sherwood Assoc., Inc. (R), MX, *80*
Lasse, Daniel C. - Management Recruiters of St. Charles (C), IL, *447*
Lassiter, P. Frank - Dunhill Professional Search of Richmond (C), VA, *323*
Latas, Michael - Michael Latas & Assoc., Inc. (R), MO, *126*
Latas, Richard L. - Michael Latas & Assoc., Inc. (R), MO, *126*
Latimer, Dick - Technical Recruiting Consultants (C), IL, *602*
Latini, Anthony A. - Princeton Search Partners, Inc. (R), NJ, *169*
Latona, Catherine - Management Recruiters of Fresno (C), CA, *440*
Latondresse, Heather G. - Holloway Schulz & Partners (C), BC, *380*
Latterell, Jeffrey D. - HRS, Inc. (R), PA, *97*
Lau, Hayley - C.T.E.W. Executive Personnel Services Inc. (C), ON, *278*
Laub, Stuart R. - Abraham & London Ltd. (C), CT, *232*
Lauber, Mark - Management Recruiters of Sugar Land Inc. (C), TX, *464*
Laubitz, Christopher J. - The Caldwell Partners Amrop International (R), ON, *26*
Lauchiere, Linda - W. N. Garbarini & Assoc. (R), NJ, *74*
Lauderback, David R. - A.T. Kearney Executive Search (R), OH, *111*
Laudi, Mario - Bassett Laudi Partners (C), ON, *261*
Laue, Elizabeth - Smith & Laue Search (R), OR, *193*
Lauerman, Fred J. - Development Search Specialists (R), MN, *49*
Laufersweiler, Steve - PIC Executive Search (C), GA, *511*
Laughlin, Bill - Orion Int'l. Consulting Group, Inc. (C), NC, *499*
Laughlin, Cindy - Recruiting Specialists (C), MA, *532*
Laurence, David - Forest People Int'l. Search Ltd. (C), BC, *343*
Laurendeau, J. E. - Ray & Berndtson/Laurendeau Labrecque (R), QE, *172*
Laurendeau, J. E. - Ray & Berndtson/Laurendeau Labrecque (R), QE, *172*
Lautz, Lindsay A. - Lautz, Grotte, Engler & Swimley (R), CA, *126*
Laux, Frank J. - StratfordGroup (R), TX, *203*
Lav, Madeleine - Madeleine Lav & Assoc. (C), CA, *413*
LaVallee, Michael J. - LaVallee & Associates (C), NC, *413*
Lavender, Steven M. - Morgan/Webber, Inc. (R), NY, *147*
Lavoie, Gille - The 500 Granary Inc. (C), QE, *231*
Lavoie, Leo R. - Carter, Lavoie Associates (C), RI, *285*
Law, Grace - Software Engineering Solutions, Inc. (C), CA, *587*
Lawler, Tim - Sales Consultants of Milwaukee (C), WI, *563*

PRINCIPALS

Lawler, III, Timothy M. - Management Recruiters of Milwaukee-North (C), WI, *466*
Lawrence, Ellen B. - Holohan Group, Ltd. (R), MO, *95*
Lawrence, Gina - The Alternatives Group, Inc. (C), TX, *246*
Lawrence, Gina - Micro Staff Solutions, Inc. (C), TX, *481*
Lawrence, J. Robert - Lawrence-Balakonis & Assoc., Inc. (C), GA, *414*
Lawrence, James B. - The Hamilton Group (R), VA, *85*
Lawrence, Kent L. - Michael Latas & Assoc., Inc. (R), MO, *126*
Lawry, William R. - W. R. Lawry, Inc. (R), CT, *126*
Lawson, Carol - Columbia Consulting Group (R), NY, *38*
Lawson, Debra - Management Recruiters of Detroit & Farmington Hills (C), MI, *451*
Lawson, James W. - The Lawson Group, Inc. (C), SC, *414*
Lawson, Ron S. - Management Recruiters of Richmond (C), KY, *449*
Lawson, Trina R. - Search Assoc., Inc. (C), NJ, *574*
Lawton, Christopher - Raymond Karsan Assoc. (C), NJ, *530*
Laxgang, Thomas - DHR Int'l., Inc. (R), CO, *49*
Lay, Jim - A-Linko & Assoc. (C), TX, *231*
Layhee, Pat - Norrell Financial Staffing (C), GA, *495*
Layton, Barbara - Bradford & Galt, Inc. (C), MO, *271*
Layton, Bernard - Morgan Int'l., Inc. (R), IL, *147*
Layton, Bradford - Bradford & Galt, Inc. (C), MO, *271*
Layton, Marni - Forray Assoc., Inc. (R), NY, *70*
Lazaro, Alicia C. - The Whitney Group (R), NY, *219*
Lazinsk, Mal - Sanders Management Assoc., Inc. (C), NJ, *565*
Leace, Elyse - Impact Search & Strategies (C), PA, *387*
Leader, D. June - Leader Network (C), PA, *414*
Leadford, Charles - Primus Assoc., L.C. (R), TX, *169*
Leal, Shannon - Romac Int'l., Inc. (C), CA, *542*
Lean, Allyn - The Curtiss Group International (R), FL, *44*
Lear, Daniel - Omega Systems, LLC (C), VA, *498*
Lear, Roger R. - Lear & Assoc., Inc. (C), FL, *415*
Leask, Kimberly A. - Douglas-Allen, Inc. (R), MA, *54*
Leavee, Kenneth S. - The Alice Groves Co., Inc. (C), CT, *244*
Leavee, Raymond J. - The Alice Groves Co., Inc. (C), CT, *244*
Leavy, Renee - Affinity Executive Search (C), FL, *241*
LeBoeuf, Michel - Robert Half Canada Inc. (C), QE, *366*
LeBoeuf, William G. - Physicians Search®, Inc. (C), CA, *511*
Lebovits, Neil - Accountants On Call (C), NJ, *236*
Lebow, Allan J. - RHS Assoc. (C), AL, *536*
LeBow, Joanne - Harbrowe, Inc. (C), NY, *368*
Lebus, Reynolds - Reynolds Lebus Assoc. (C), AZ, *415*
Lechner, David B. - Lechner & Assoc., Inc. (C), FL, *415*
Lechner, David B. - Management Recruiters of Sarasota (C), FL, *427*
Lechtenberg, Leda - Dick Berg & Assoc. (C), CA, *264*
Lechtenberg, Richard C. - Dick Berg & Assoc. (C), CA, *264*
LeComte, Andre - Egon Zehnder Int'l. Inc. (R), QE, *227*
Ledbetter, Charlene - Ledbetter/Davidson Int'l., Inc. (R), NY, *127*
Ledbetter, Steven G. - Cendea Connection Int'l. (R), TX, *32*
Ledingham, Lorene M. - Management Recruiters of St. Simons Island (C), GA, *428*
Leduc, Lauren - GAAP Inc. (R), ON, *73*
Leduc, Normand - Groupe Ranger Inc. (C), QE, *364*
Lee, Albert G. - Albert G. Lee Assoc. (C), RI, *415*
Lee, Amy T. - Sanford Rose Assoc. - Salt Lake City (C), UT, *571*
Lee, Barbara - Lee Management Group Inc. (C), NJ, *416*
Lee, Barbara A. - Management Recruiters, Inc. (C), FL, *443*
Lee, Brian - Vincent Lee Assoc. (C), NY, *415*
Lee, Carol Ricci - Ricci Lee Assoc., Inc. (C), CA, *415*
Lee, Conrad P. - The Conrad Lee Co. Inc. (R), FL, *127*
Lee, Deborah - Stanton Chase Int'l./ Botrie Assoc. (R), ON, *199*
Lee, Donna N. - Kincannon & Reed (R), VA, *114*
Lee, Jacquelene - Royal Assoc. (C), CA, *547*
Lee, Jacquelene R. - Healthcare Search Associates (C), CA, *374*
Lee, James - Sanford Rose Assoc. - Charlotte (C), NC, *568*
Lee, Jay - Pioneer Consulting Group (C), CA, *512*
Lee, Jess J. - Management Search Int'l. (C), CA, *467*
Lee, Joseph J. - Larsen & Lee, Inc. (R), MD, *125*
Lee, Judy - JCL & Assoc. (C), FL, *397*
Lee, Kenneth D. - The Regis Group, Ltd. (R), GA, *174*
Lee, Kenneth D. - Special Markets Group, Inc. (R), GA, *195*
Lee, Molly - The Kinlin Co., Inc. (R), MA, *115*
Lee, Robert - Management Recruiters, Inc. (C), FL, *443*
Lee, Rodger A. - Sanford Rose Assoc. - Salt Lake City (C), UT, *571*
Lee, Roger A. - Montgomery Resources, Inc. (C), CA, *484*
Lee, Vincent - Vincent Lee Assoc. (C), NY, *415*
Leech, David M. - Houtz•Strawn & Arnold, Inc. (R), TX, *96*
Leeds, Gerald I. - Leeds and Leeds (C), TN, *416*
Leek, Robert - HEC Group (C), ON, *375*
Leetma, Imbi - Stanton Chase Int'l. (R), CA, *199*
Leety, Murray - Fox-Morris Assoc., Inc. (C), PA, *352*
Leevy, Daniel - DNA Search, Inc. (C), CA, *313*
Lefebvre, Lynn - Partnervision Consulting Group Inc. (R), ON, *160*
Leff, Ilene J. - Richard A. Eisner & Co., LLP (R), NY, *57*
Leff, Lisa A. - Berger & Leff (C), CA, *264*
Leffer, Gary - Re-Mark Assoc. Inc. (C), NJ, *531*
Lefier, Deborah D. - Strategic Search, LLC (C), CA, *595*
Legal, Dale - Capital Consulting Group, Inc. (R), MD, *28*
Legate, Brian - Corporate Builders, Inc. (C), OR, *299*
Leggett, Amy - APA Employment Agency Inc. (C), WA, *251*
Lehman, Jan A. - Lehman McLeskey (R), TX, *128*
Lehman, Neal G. - Sherwood Lehman Massucco, Inc. (R), CA, *189*
Lehman, Victor J. - V. J. Lehman & Assoc., Inc. (R), CO, *127*
Lehn, Mallory - Vickers Chambless Managed Search (C), GA, *289*
Lehnst, John J. - Management Recruiters of Williamsburg (C), IA, *449*
Lehrman, Laura M. - Emerging Technology Search (C), GA, *329*
Lehrman, Peter A. - Emerging Technology Search (C), GA, *329*
Leib, Bruce - The Ryan Charles Group, Inc. (C), FL, *549*
Leighton, Nina - The Ogdon Partnership (R), NY, *155*
Leighton, Sheldon - Bailey Employment System Inc. (C), CT, *257*
Leimpeter, Peter - Goldstein & Co. (C), CA, *360*
Leinen, Rebecca - Management Recruiters - Piedmont (C), VA, *464*
Leinen, Rebecca R. - Sales Consultant of Genesee (C), MI, *553*
Leininger, Dennis - Staffing Edge, Inc. (C), IA, *590*
Leinwetter, Theresa - Michael Shirley Assoc. Inc. (R), KS, *190*
Lekan, Dennis - Lekan & Assoc., Inc. (R), OH, *128*
LeMar, Bruce R. - Early Cochran & Olson (R), IL, *56*

LeMay, Steven E. - Saber Group, Inc. (C), TX, *550*
Lemiuex, Maureen - Leader Search Inc. (R), AB, *127*
Lemke, Peter K. - EFL Assoc. (R), KS, *57*
Lemming, Jeff - Lemming/LeVan, Inc. (R), GA, *128*
Lemon, Kay - Management Recruiters of North Fresno (C), CA, *425*
LeMon, Monet M. - The Repovich-Reynolds Group (TRRG, Inc.) (R), CA, *175*
Lempicke, Martha - The Hunter Group (C), NC, *385*
Lempicke, Todd - The Hunter Group (C), NC, *385*
Len, Ronald D. - Healthcare Recruiters International-NY/NJ (C), NJ, *373*
Lencioni, Dennis - The Oldani Group (R), WA, *155*
Lennon, Bill - Hall Management Group, Inc. (C), GA, *367*
Lennon, Frank P. - F. P. Lennon Assoc. (C), PA, *416*
Lennox, Allan - AG Lennox & Assoc. (R), AB, *128*
Lennox, Charles - PricewaterhouseCoopers Executive Search (R), ON, *168*
Lenobel, Stephen - Professional Recruiters, Inc. (C), PA, *521*
Lentz, Ina - Management Recruiters of Valley Forge (C), PA, *459*
Lentz, James - Management Recruiters of Valley Forge (C), PA, *459*
Lenz, Kathryn - Major Legal Services, Inc. (C), OH, *423*
Leo, Steve - DHR Int'l., Inc. (R), DC, *50*
Leofsky, Peter J. - Dapexs Consultants, Inc. (C), NY, *307*
Leon-Shelton, Diana - Shelton, Wiseman & Leon (R), CA, *189*
Leonard, Linda - Harris Heery & Assoc., Inc. (R), CT, *87*
Leonard, Mell D. - International Recruiting Services (C), FL, *393*
Leonard, Tom - The Jotorok Group (C), RI, *401*
Leonard, William C. - Michael Latas & Assoc., Inc. (R), MO, *126*
Leone, Joan - The Beardsley Group Inc. (C), CT, *261*
Leone, Nicholas A. - Conex Inc./InterSearch (R), NY, *39*
Leone, Nick - Earley Kielty & Assoc., Inc. (R), NY, *56*
LePage, Jacques - Jacques LePage Executive Search Inc. (R), QE, *128*
LePatner, Steve - Dunhill Executive Search of Los Angeles, Inc. (C), CA, *319*
Lerch, Brent - Insurance Personnel Resources, Inc. (C), GA, *390*
Lerner, Joel S. - Sanford Rose Assoc. - Louisville (C), KY, *567*
Leslie, C.C. - Johnson Smith & Knisely (R), NY, *107*
Leslie, Doug - Raymond Karsan Assoc. (C), WI, *530*
Leslie, William H. - Boyden (R), GA, *21*
Lessmeister, George - Accountants On Call (C), IL, *235*
Lessner, Jack - J. E. Lessner Assoc., Inc. (R), MI, *128*
Lessner, Mark - J. E. Lessner Assoc., Inc. (R), MI, *128*
Lessner, Mary Ann - J. E. Lessner Assoc., Inc. (R), MI, *128*
Letcher, Harvey D. - TASA International (R), TX, *206*
LeTourneau, Buddy - Schwab-Carrese Assoc., Inc. Executive Search (R), NC, *185*
Letson, Susan - KPMG Executive Search (R), NS, *119*
Letts, Douglas R. - The Professional Sales Search Co., Inc. (C), WA, *522*
LeVan, Salli - Lemming/LeVan, Inc. (R), GA, *128*
Levasseur, Marc - Gaudry, Shink, Levasseur (R), QE, *75*
Leverette, James - The Broadmoor Group, L.L.C. (R), TX, *24*
Levi, Haskel - Boulware & Assoc. Inc. (R), IL, *20*
Levin, Alisa F. - Greene-Levin-Snyder LLC (C), NY, *362*
Levin, Becky - Levin & Company, Inc. (R), MA, *128*
Levin, Phillip - Executive Search Team (C), MI, *336*
Levine, Alan C. - Alan Levine Assoc. (R), MA, *129*
Levine, Alan M. - MB Inc. Executive Search (C), NY, *473*
Levine, Donald - Sharp Placement Professionals, Inc. (C), NY, *579*
Levine, Eileen - Williamsburg Group (C), NJ, *621*
Levine, Harvey - Fairfield Int'l. Resources (R), NY, *65*
Levine, Jamie - TRS Staffing Solutions Inc. (C), OH, *610*
Levine, Lawrence - Trebor Weldon Lawrence, Inc. (R), NY, *210*
Levine, Michael - Michael Levine Search Consultants (R), NY, *129*
Levine, Tracey - Herbert Mines Assoc., Inc. (R), NY, *145*
Levinson, Lauren - QuestPro, Inc. (C), TX, *527*
Levison, Michael - Levison Search Assoc. (R), CA, *129*
Levison, Regina - Levison Search Assoc. (R), CA, *129*
Levitt, Bob - Management Recruiters of Melville (C), NY, *432*
Levitt, Bob - Sales Consultants of Suffolk County-North (C), NY, *554*
Levitt, Jeff - Stanton Chase Int'l. (R), IL, *199*
Levitt, Muriel - D. S. Allen Assoc. (C), CA, *244*
Levitt, Peter - Sales Consultants King of Prussia (C), PA, *562*
Levy, Eve - Hal Levy & Assoc. (C), NY, *417*
Levy, Hal - Hal Levy & Assoc. (C), NY, *417*
Levy, Richard - Ruderfer & Co., Inc. (C), NJ, *548*
Levy, Stefan - Management Search, Inc. (C), IL, *467*
Levy, Warren - The Gabriel Group (C), PA, *354*
Levy, William M. - Sherbrooke Assoc., Inc. (C), NJ, *580*
Lew, Charles E. - Coleman Lew & Assoc., Inc. (R), NC, *37*
Lew, Edwin - LanSo Int'l., Inc. (C), NY, *413*
Lewis, Al - The Stelton Group, Inc. (C), NJ, *592*
Lewis, Bill - Adams & Assoc. Int'l. (R), IL, *1*
Lewis, Bryn - Systems Research Group (C), OH, *598*
Lewis, Christina - General Engineering Tectonics (C), CA, *356*
Lewis, Daphne V. - Lewis & Blank Int'l. (R), CA, *129*
Lewis, Don - Merrick & Moore (C), FL, *479*
Lewis, Donnie - Lewis Consulting Service (C), IL, *417*
Lewis, Jon A. - TASA International (R), TX, *206*
Lewis, K. Jane - Selected Executives, Inc. (C), MA, *578*
Lewis, Lorraine - Lewis Companies Inc. (R), ON, *129*
Lewis, Lynn - A. Davis Grant & Co. (R), NJ, *81*
Lewis, Marc - Christian & Timbers, Inc. (R), OH, *34*
Lewis, Marc D. - Handy HRM (R), NY, *86*
Lewis, Mark E. - Management Recruiters of Myrtle Beach, Inc. (C), SC, *460*
Lewis, Nancy - Merrick & Moore (C), FL, *479*
Lewis, Richard - Cole, Warren & Long, Inc. (R), PA, *37*
Lewis, Stephany - Keystone Consulting Group (C), GA, *406*
Lewisohn, Dina K. S. - LAI Ward Howell (R), NY, *122*
Lewke, Reynold H. - Egon Zehnder Int'l. Inc. (R), CA, *227*
Leyden, Terry - Career Marketing Assoc., Inc. (C), CO, *282*
Lezama, Luis - Ray & Berndtson (R), MX, *172*
Lheureau, J. Randall - Spear-Izzo Assoc., LLC (C), PA, *589*
Liberatore, Joe - Romac Int'l., Inc. (C), FL, *543*
Libes, Dory - Accountants On Call (C), NJ, *235*
Libes, Mark S. - Accountants Executive Search (C), PA, *234*
Libes, Mark S. - Accountants On Call (C), PA, *237*
Libes, Stewart C. - Accountants On Call (C), NJ, *235*
Licata, Pat - Pat Licata & Assoc. (C), NC, *417*
Licht, Marilyn - Management Recruiters - Indianapolis (C), IN, *448*
Lichtenauer, William E. - Britt Assoc., Inc. (C), IL, *274*

PRINCIPALS

Lichtenstein, Ben - Alexander Ross & Co. (R), NY, *3*
Lickteig, Mark - Dunhill Staffing Systems (C), MO, *317*
Lieberman, Beverly - Halbrecht Lieberman Assoc., Inc. (R), CT, *84*
Lieberman, Howard - Howard Lieberman & Assoc., Inc. (C), MN, *417*
Liebesny, Claudia B. - TASA International (R), MA, *206*
Lieblich, Michele - DHR Int'l., Inc. (R), NY, *50*
Liebman, Linda - Steven Michaels & Assoc. (C), NY, *593*
Liebowitz, Michael - Highland Search Group, L.L.C. (R), NY, *93*
Lieff, Shelley - Advice Personnel Inc. (C), NY, *241*
Lifter, Barbara - Lifter & Assoc. (C), CA, *418*
Lifter, Jay - Lifter & Assoc. (C), CA, *418*
Liggett, Dwight - The Garrison Organization (R), IA, *75*
Liggett, Wilson M. - Michael/Merrill (C), KS, *481*
Lightner Jr., Ralph H. - Stanton Chase Int'l. (R), MD, *199*
Lihan, Dana L. - MedXec USA, Inc. (C), FL, *478*
Liles, Cheryl - Snelling Search Recruiters (C), NC, *586*
Liles, James - Management Recruiters of Emerald Isle (C), NC, *433*
Lilienthal, Russ - Working Relationships, Inc. (C), MN, *624*
Lilja, Raymond - American Logistics Consultants, Inc. (C), IL, *247*
Lilja, Raymond - American Services Group (C), IL, *248*
Lincoln, M. - JLI-Boston (R), MA, *106*
Lindal, Bruce G. - Linden Group, Inc. (C), NC, *418*
Lindauer, Lois L. - Lois L. Lindauer Searches (C), MA, *418*
Lindberg, Eric J. - MSI Int'l. (C), GA, *486*
Lindberg, Gillis - Wells, Bradley & Assoc., Inc. (C), MN, *618*
Linde, Roger W. - Graphic Search Assoc. Inc. (C), PA, *362*
Lindell, John H. - J. H. Lindell & Co. (C), CA, *418*
Lindell, Leslie S. - J. H. Lindell & Co. (C), CA, *418*
Lindeman, Lee - DHR Int'l., Inc. (R), ME, *50*
Lindholst, Kai - Egon Zehnder Int'l. Inc. (R), IL, *227*
Lindsay, Lynn - Dunhill Staffing Systems of London, Ltd. (C), ON, *318*
Lindsey, Ginger - Ginger Lindsey & Assoc., Inc. (C), TX, *418*
Lindsey, Jonathan - Major, Hagen & Africa (C), NY, *423*
Lindsey, Lary L. - Lindsey & Co., Inc. (R), CT, *129*
Lindsey, Mary M. - Norm Sanders Assoc., Inc. (R), NJ, *184*
Lineal, Lisa - Lineal Recruiting Services (C), CT, *418*
Lineback, Pam - Management Recruiter of Dallas (C), TX, *436*
Lineback, Robert - Management Recruiter of Dallas (C), TX, *436*
Lingle, Bruce - ContactBridge, Inc. (R), IL, *40*
Linney, George - Tyler & Company (R), GA, *212*
Lins, Peter T. - McGrath & Assoc., Inc. (R), NJ, *141*
Linstead, Rick - Carnegie Resources, Inc. (C), NC, *284*
Linton, Leonard M. - Byron Leonard Int'l., Inc. (R), CA, *26*
Lionas, James - The Hunter Group, Inc. (C), MI, *385*
Lipe, Jerold L. - Compass Group Ltd. (R), IL, *38*
Lipe, Jerold L. - Compass Group Ltd. (R), MI, *38*
Lipinski, Edmund - E. J. Ashton & Assoc., Ltd. (C), IL, *253*
Lippe, John L. - Dunhill Professional Search of Englewood, Inc. (C), CO, *319*
Lippens, Susan - Major Legal Services, Inc. (C), OH, *423*
Lippincott, Roger - Dunhill Professional Search of Ramsey (C), NJ, *321*
Lipsky, Marla J. - Lipsky Group, Inc. (R), CA, *129*
Lipson, Harriet L. - Lipson & Co. (R), CA, *130*
Lipson, Howard R. - Lipson & Co. (R), CA, *130*
Lipton, Pat - PLA, Inc. (C), FL, *513*
Lipton, Robert J. - Lipton Assoc., Inc. (R), NY, *130*
List, Michael - Cheney Associates (C), CT, *290*
Litchfield, Barbara H. - Litchfield & Willis, Inc. (R), TX, *130*
Litras, Steve - F. P. Lennon Assoc. (C), GA, *416*
Little, Bradley J. - Egon Zehnder Int'l. Inc. (R), CA, *227*
Little, John J. - Alpha Executive Search (C), AL, *246*
Littman, Cheryl L. - The Penn Partners, Inc. (R), PA, *162*
Littman, Stephen - Rhodes Associates (R), NY, *177*
Litvin, Bruce - Windsor Consultants, Inc. (C), TX, *622*
Livingston, Hyman - The P & L Group (C), NY, *500*
Livingston, Peter R. - Livingston, Robert & Co. (R), CT, *130*
Livolsi, Sebastian F. - Management Recruiters of Suffolk (C), NY, *432*
Llaguno, Juan - Korn/Ferry Int'l. (R), NL, *118*
Llaguno, Juan F. - Korn/Ferry, Int'l., S.A. de C.V. (R), NL, *118*
Lloyd, Carolyn T. - Lloyd Associates (R), GA, *130*
Lloyd, John S. - Witt/Kieffer, Ford, Hadelman & Lloyd (R), IL, *223*
Locher, Rodger - Central Executive Search, Inc. (C), OH, *287*
Locke, Jr., M. Fred - Locke & Assoc. (R), NC, *131*
Lockleer, Julia - EA Plus, Inc. (C), TX, *325*
Lockton, Kathy - StratfordGroup (R), CA, *203*
Loeb, Stephen H. - Grant Cooper & Assoc., Inc. (R), MO, *81*
Loewenstein, Ron - Loewenstein & Assoc., Inc. (R), TX, *131*
Loewenstein, Victor H. - Egon Zehnder Int'l. Inc. (R), NY, *227*
Loftus, Anne - Herbert Mines Assoc., Inc. (R), NY, *145*
Loftus, Daniel P. - McCoy Ltd. (C), CA, *474*
Loftus, Mary - Romac Int'l., Inc. (C), MA, *543*
Loftus, Michael G. - Interim Executive Recruiting (C), GA, *392*
Logan, III, James P. - J. P. Logan & Co., Inc. (R), NY, *131*
Logan, Joseph - Pinnacle Group Int'l. (C), NY, *512*
Logie, Richard - Kirkbride Assoc., Inc. (C), WA, *407*
Logue, Kenneth F. - Logue & Rice Inc. (C), VA, *420*
Lohkamp, Richard - Longshore + Simmons (R), PA, *131*
Loiacano, Michael - DHR Int'l., Inc. (R), MA, *50*
Lomax, J. Alan - ADR Accounting Management Recruiters (C), ON, *240*
Lombardi, Helen T. - Pearce & Assoc. (C), FL, *506*
Lombardi, Nancy - WTW Assoc., Inc. (R), NY, *225*
Lombardo, Steve - Search America, Inc. (C), MA, *574*
London, Anne - London & Company (C), NY, *420*
Long, Benjamin H. - Travaille Executive Search (R), DC, *210*
Long, Dave - Procom (C), GA, *519*
Long, David B. - DBL Associates (C), CA, *309*
Long, Helga - Horton Int'l. Inc. (R), NY, *96*
Long, Jack P. - John J. Davis & Assoc., Inc. (R), NY, *47*
Long, Janet R. - Integrity Search, Inc. (R), PA, *102*
Long, Keith A. - Christopher and Long (C), MO, *291*
Long, Thomas E. - Egon Zehnder Int'l. Inc. (R), ON, *227*
Long, William G. - McDonald, Long & Assoc., Inc. (R), NY, *140*
Longo, Roger - Longo Associates (C), CA, *420*
Longshaw, Dawn A. - Holloway Schulz & Partners (C), BC, *380*
Longshore, George F. - Longshore + Simmons (R), PA, *131*
Lopez, Christina - Conex Inc./InterSearch (R), NY, *39*
Lopez, Manney C. - Management Recruiters of Bend (C), OR, *434*

LoPinto, Anthony J. - Rhodes Associates (R), NY, *177*
LoPresto, Robert L. - Rusher, Loscavio & LoPresto (R), CA, *183*
Loprete, Lawrence D. - Kenmore Executives Inc. (C), FL, *405*
LoPrete, Steven - Kenmore Executives Inc. (C), FL, *405*
Lord, Anthony W. G. - LAI Ward Howell (R), NY, *123*
Lord, J. Scott - J. S. Lord & Company, Inc. (R), MA, *131*
Lord, Marvin - E. A. Hughes & Co., Inc. (R), NY, *98*
Lord, Patricia - Romac Int'l., Inc. (C), PA, *544*
Loria, Frank - Accounting Personnel & Engineering Personnel Consultants (C), LA, *238*
Loscavio, J. Michael - Rusher, Loscavio & LoPresto (R), CA, *183*
Loser, Jim - Advanced Executive Resources (R), MI, *2*
Losner, Ingram - Romac Int'l., Inc. (C), CA, *542*
Lotufo, Donald A. - D.A.L. Associates, Inc. (R), CT, *45*
Loubet, Larry S. - The Carlyle Group, Ltd. (R), IL, *30*
Loughlin, Timothy M. - Bankers Search, L.L.C. (C), CT, *259*
Louis, Anne - Focus Consulting Services, Inc. (C), FL, *342*
Louis, Gregory - Louis Search Group, Inc. (C), NJ, *420*
Lovas, W. Carl - Ray & Berndtson/Lovas Stanley (R), ON, *172*
Lovas, W. Carl - Ray & Berndtson/Lovas Stanley (R), ON, *172*
Love, Cindi M. - Michael Latas & Assoc., Inc. (R), MO, *126*
Love, Jon R. - JL & Co. (C), CA, *399*
Love, Scott T. - Scott Love Assoc., Inc. (C), AZ, *420*
Lovell, Andrée - Connors, Lovell & Assoc. Inc. (C), ON, *296*
Lovett, Karen M. - Practice Dynamics, Inc. (C), TX, *515*
Loving, Vikki - Intersource, Ltd. (R), GA, *103*
Low, Linda - Development Resource Group (R), NY, *48*
Lowderman, William - Loderman & Costello (C), GA, *419*
Lowe, Daniel M. - Daniel Marks Company (C), OH, *306*
Lowery, Andrew - Search Int'l. (R), MA, *187*
Lowery, Bruce N. - Bruce Lowery & Assoc. (C), MI, *420*
Lowery, Gene - Management Recruiters of Harrison County (C), MS, *431*
Lowery, John - Quality Control (C), AZ, *526*
Lowrance, Bob - Global Employer's Network, Inc. (R), TX, *77*
Lowrie, Jim - Hanley & Assoc. (R), FL, *86*
Lowry, James - Carr Management Services, Inc. (C), PA, *284*
Lowy, Gary - NaviSearch (C), GA, *490*
Lubaroff, Beth - Impact Search & Strategies (C), PA, *387*
Lubin, Aaron - Executive Recruiters Agency, Inc. (C), AR, *333*
Lucarelli, Joan - The Onstott Group (R), MA, *156*
Lucas, III, Charles C. - The McAulay Firm (R), NC, *139*
Lucas, Kelly J. - Protocol Inc. (C), CA, *525*
Lucas, Thomas A. - Management Recruiters of Philadelphia (C), PA, *435*
Luce, Dan - Romac Int'l., Inc. (C), TX, *544*
Luce, Paul M. - Management Recruiters of New Orleans (C), LA, *429*
Luce, Paul M. - Sales Consultants of New Orleans (C), LA, *553*
Lucht, John - The John Lucht Consultancy Inc. (R), NY, *132*
Luciani, Thomas G. - The Luciani Group (R), CA, *132*
Lucifero, Lisa - ACSYS Resources, Inc. (C), NJ, *238*
Luckey, Horace - Sales Consultants of Daphne (C), AL, *556*
Luckey, Janet - Sales Consultants of Daphne (C), AL, *556*
Lucy, Christine - Robert Half Canada Inc. (C), ON, *366*
Luden, Ben V. - Marketing/Public Relations Research Recruiting (C), CT, *471*
Ludlow, Elizabeth - Pennington Consulting Group (C), NJ, *506*
Ludwig, Bob - Ludwig & Assoc., Inc. (C), VA, *421*
Ludwig, Curtis - Interim Accounting Professionals (C), TX, *392*
Luffman, Danae - IDC Executive Search Inc. (C), FL, *387*
Luisi, Francis J. - Fran Luisi Assoc. (R), NJ, *132*
Luke, A. Wayne - Heidrick & Struggles, Inc. (R), GA, *90*
Lummus, Victoria A. - Management Recruiters of El Paso (C), TX, *436*
Lumsby, George - Boyden (R), NY, *21*
Lumsby, George N. - International Management Advisors, Inc. (R), NY, *103*
Lundy, Jim - The Enns Partners Inc. (R), ON, *59*
Lunn, Jerry D. - Brush Creek Partners (R), MO, *24*
Luntz, Charles E. - Charles Luntz & Assoc., Inc. (R), MO, *132*
Luntz, Michael C. - Charles Luntz & Assoc., Inc. (R), MO, *132*
Lupton, Joseph - DHR Int'l., Inc. (R), GA, *50*
Lurier, Amy B. - TechFind, Inc. (R), MA, *207*
Lusk, Jack - Gilbert Tweed Assoc. Inc. (R), NY, *77*
Lussier, Grant - SpencerStuart (R), MX, *197*
Luther, Paul T. - Financial Search Group, Inc. (R), MA, *66*
Lutostanski, Frank - Selectis Corp. (C), IL, *578*
Lutz, Allen - Lutz Associates (C), CT, *421*
Luzar, James - Sales Consultants of Milwaukee (C), WI, *563*
Lybrook, Christian - Lybrook Assoc., Inc. (C), RI, *421*
Lybrook, David - Lybrook Assoc., Inc. (C), RI, *421*
Lybrook, Karen - Lybrook Assoc., Inc. (C), RI, *421*
Lyman, Craig S. - Management Recruiters of Edmond (C), OK, *434*
Lyman, David M. - Schall Executive Search Partners (R), MN, *185*
Lynch, Helen - Healthcare Recruiters Int'l. - Pittsburgh (C), PA, *373*
Lynch, J. F. - Management Recruiters of Lionville, Inc. (C), PA, *459*
Lynch, Jack - Michigan Consulting Group (R), MI, *144*
Lynch, Jack - Premier Recruiting Group (C), MI, *516*
Lynch, Joanne A. - Willmott & Assoc. (C), MA, *622*
Lynch, III, John P. - Blackshaw, Olmstead, Lynch & Koenig (R), CT, *18*
Lynch, Michael C. - Lynch Miller Moore Partners, Inc. (R), IL, *132*
Lynch, Patrick J. - P. J. Lynch Assoc. (R), CT, *132*
Lynch, Sean - Raymond Karsan Assoc. (C), PA, *529*
Lynch, William E. - Fortuna Technologies Inc. (C), CA, *343*
Lyness, Cindy - Management Recruiters-Cedar Rapids, Inc. (C), IA, *448*
Lynge, R. J. - Management Recruiters of Ft. Myers, FL. (C), FL, *443*
Lyngen, C. J. - Construct Management Services (C), MN, *297*
Lyngen, Robert - Construct Management Services (C), MN, *297*
Lyngen, Trish - Construct Management Services (C), MN, *297*
Lynn, Audrey - Latham International, Ltd. (R), NJ, *126*
Lynne, Robyn - Search Masters, USA (C), FL, *576*
Lyon, Jenny K. - Marra Peters & Partners (R), NC, *136*
Lyons, Barbara L. - Whittlesey & Assoc., Inc. (R), PA, *220*
Lyons, Bonnie - The Whitaker Companies (C), TX, *619*
Lyons, Denis B. K. - SpencerStuart (R), NY, *196*
Lyons, J. David - Aubin Int'l. Inc. (R), MA, *8*
Lyons, Jane - Rhodes Associates (R), NY, *177*
Lyons, Jerold - Dunhill of Ft. Collins, Inc. (C), CO, *319*
Lyons, Kent T. - Lyons & Assoc., Inc. (C), IL, *422*
Lyons, M. Don - L O R (R), NJ, *122*
Lyons, Mary Francis - Witt/Kieffer, Ford, Hadelman & Lloyd (R), MO, *223*
Lyons, Olin - Lyons Pruitt Int'l. (R), PA, *132*

PRINCIPALS

Lyons, Scott - Lyons Pruitt Int'l. (R), PA, *132*
Lyons, Sean J. - Lyons Assoc. (R), NY, *132*
Lysaght, Evan J. - The Moran Group (C), IL, *484*
Lysenko, Lisa - A.L.S. Group (C), NJ, *232*
Lysenko, Scott - A.L.S. Group (C), NJ, *232*
Lyttle, Jordene - KPMG Executive Search (R), ON, *119*
Macaluso, Kelly - K2 Resources, L.P. (C), CT, *402*
MacArthur, Ian - Madison MacArthur Inc. (R), ON, *133*
MacArthur, Sylvia - Madison MacArthur Inc. (R), ON, *133*
MacBean, Paul - Technical Skills Consulting Inc. (R), ON, *207*
MacCallan, Deirdre - Butterfass, Pepe & MacCallan Inc. (R), NJ, *25*
MacCarthy, Dave - Michael Stern Assoc., Inc./Euram (R), ON, *200*
MacCarthy, Thomas - Empire International (R), PA, *59*
Macdonald, Craig - Houser, Martin, Morris (C), WA, *381*
Macdonald, G. William - The Macdonald Group, Inc. (R), NJ, *133*
Macdonald, Jr., Robert W. - Russell Reynolds Assoc., Inc. (R), MN, *177*
MacDougall, Andrew J. - SpencerStuart (R), ON, *197*
MacDougall, Audrey - Robert Half Canada Inc. (C), AB, *366*
MacDowell, Leanna - Madison MacArthur Inc. (R), ON, *133*
MacEachern, David - SpencerStuart (R), ON, *197*
MacGorman, Terry - Organization Consulting Ltd. (R), ON, *157*
MacGregor, Malcolm - Boyden (R), PA, *21*
Machi, Michael T. - Management Recruiters of Pleasanton (C), CA, *441*
Mack, Linda - Johnson Smith & Knisely (R), IL, *107*
Mackenna, Kathy - Plummer & Assoc., Inc. (R), CT, *166*
MacKenzie, Bruce J. - Chapman & Assoc. (C), BC, *289*
Mackenzie, Robert A. - Management Recruiters of Kingston (C), NY, *432*
MacKinnon, Helen - Technical Connections, Inc. (C), CA, *602*
MacKinnon, Peter - Technical Connections, Inc. (C), CA, *602*
MacLean, Andy - Romac Int'l., Inc. (C), VA, *544*
MacLean, Veroushka - Becker Personnel (C), FL, *262*
MacNaughton, Sperry - MacNaughton Assoc. (R), CA, *133*
Macomber, Keith S. - Sullivan & Company (R), NY, *204*
MacRaild, Clive L. - Canadian Career Partners (R), AB, *27*
MacTadyen, David - Sharrow & Assoc., Inc. (C), IN, *579*
Macurda, Bradford - The Energists (R), TX, *59*
Maczkov, Nicholas - Maczkov-Biosciences, Inc. (R), CA, *133*
Madden, George - Pinton Forrest & Madden/EMA Partners Int'l. (R), BC, *165*
Madden, Heather - Bosch & Assoc., LLC (R), CT, *20*
Maddox, Julie - Career Strategies, Inc. (C), CA, *283*
Maden, Carol - Carol Maden Group (C), VA, *422*
Mader, Stephen P. - Christian & Timbers, Inc. (R), MA, *34*
Mader, Steve - Christian & Timbers, Inc. (R), OH, *34*
Madison, T. Dean - Warren, Morris & Madison, Ltd. (C), VA, *616*
Madrigal, Debbie - William Bell Assoc., Inc. (C), NJ, *263*
Mae, Bonita - TE, Inc. (C), IL, *600*
Magee, Charles - Management Recruiters of Shreveport (C), LA, *429*
Magee, Charles R. - DieckMueller Group (R), WI, *51*
Magee, Gerri - Management Recruiters of Shreveport (C), LA, *429*
Magee, Harrison R. - Bowden & Co., Inc. (R), OH, *20*
Magennis, Sean - Kingsley Allen Partners Inc. (R), ON, *114*
Maggs, Richard - Lechner & Assoc., Inc. (C), FL, *415*
Magic, Michael F. - Scott Douglas Inc. (C), CA, *573*
Maglio, Charles J. - Maglio & Co., Inc. (R), WI, *134*
Magnani, Susan M. - The Search Center Inc. (C), TX, *574*
Magnusen, Henry F. - Management Recruiters of North Warren Inc. (C), NJ, *453*
Maguire, Declan - DHR Int'l., Inc. (R), NY, *50*
Magy, David S. - Abeln, Magy & Assoc., Inc. (R), MN, *1*
Mahan, Donna - Accountants On Call (C), NJ, *236*
Maher, Kevin - TBC, Inc. (C), KY, *600*
Maher, Peter T. - The Partnership Group (R), NJ, *160*
Maher, William J. - Johnson Smith & Knisely (R), NY, *107*
Mahfood, Teresa - DHR Int'l., Inc. (R), CA, *49*
Mahnke, Dottie - Accountants On Call (C), WI, *237*
Mahoney, Brian - Management Decision Systems, Inc. (MDSI) (C), NJ, *425*
Mahoney, Kevin - Sullivan & Assoc. (R), MI, *204*
Mahoney, Michael - Carol Maden Group (C), VA, *422*
Mahoney, Molly - McCarthy Assoc. National BancSearch, LLC (C), LA, *473*
Mahr, Toni - K. Russo Assoc. Inc. (C), CT, *548*
Maiola, Diana E. - Maiola & Co. (C), OH, *423*
Maiorino, Robert V. - Maiorino & Weston Assoc., Inc. (R), CT, *134*
Maire, Mark - Management Recruiters of Calhoun County (C), MI, *430*
Maire, Renee - Management Recruiters of Calhoun County (C), MI, *430*
Maitland, Thomas C. - DHR Int'l., Inc. (R), CO, *49*
Majczan, Robert - Ken Clark Int'l. (R), NJ, *36*
Major, Jr., Robert A. - Major, Hagen & Africa (C), CA, *423*
Major, Sue - A.T. Kearney Executive Search (R), CA, *111*
Makhani, Thukbir - LCS, Inc. (C), TX, *414*
Makrianes, Jr., James K. - Webb, Johnson Assoc., Inc. (R), NY, *216*
Malatesta, Roger - Professional Recruiting Consultants, Inc. (C), DE, *521*
Malcolm, Doug C. - Management Recruiters of Smyrna (C), GA, *427*
Malcom, John W. - Johnson Smith & Knisely (R), NY, *107*
Malek, L. - Professional Search Consultants (PSC) (C), TX, *523*
Malfetti, Jim L. - Management Recruiters of Union County (C), NJ, *431*
Malfetti, Rosemary - Management Recruiters of Union County (C), NJ, *431*
Malinski, Mark - The Ransford Group (R), TX, *171*
Mallinson, Robert - Ritta Professional Search Inc. (C), NY, *538*
Malloy, James K. - Sales Consultants of Middlesex County, Inc. (C), NJ, *561*
Malone, Mary Beth - Kittleman & Assoc.,LLC (R), IL, *115*
Malouf, Terry - Bartholdi & Co., Inc. (R), CO, *12*
Malouin, Etienne - The Pollack Group (C), ON, *514*
Maltby, Thomas J. - Halbrecht & Co. (C), VA, *365*
Manassero, Henri J. P. - International Management Advisors, Inc. (R), NY, *103*
Manatine, Tony - Career Search Group (C), FL, *283*
Mancini, Deborah - Mancini Technical Recruiting (C), VA, *468*
Mancini, Jennifer - Maschal/Connors Inc. (R), NJ, *137*
Mancino, Gene - Blau Mancino Schroeder (R), NJ, *18*
Mand, Tammy - Norrell Financial Staffing (C), IL, *495*
Mangiafico, Jane - Largent Parks & Partners (C), TX, *503*
Mangieri, Chris - Mangieri/Solutions LLC (C), CT, *468*
Mangum, Maria - Thomas Mangum Co. (R), CA, *208*
Mangum, Stacy - Thomas Mangum Co. (R), WA, *209*
Mangum, William T. - Thomas Mangum Co. (R), CA, *208*
Mangum, William T. - Thomas Mangum Co. (R), CA, *208*

Manheim, Gene S. - Sullivan & Company (R), NY, *204*
Mankuta, Eric G. - EGM Consulting, Inc. (R), FL, *57*
Manly, Jo - Management Recruiters of Round Rock (C), TX, *463*
Mann, Douglas G. - LAI Ward Howell (R), WI, *124*
Mann, Stacey - S. R. Wolman Assoc., Inc. (R), NY, *224*
Mannard, Thomas B. - Mannard & Assoc., Inc. (R), IL, *135*
Manni, Tom - Electronic Search, Inc. (C), NJ, *328*
Manning, Bob - Management Recruiters of Rocky Mount - Southwest (C), NC, *456*
Manning, Dianne - Manning Lloyd Assoc. Ltd. (C), NY, *468*
Manning, Jerry - Management Recruiters of Ogden (C), UT, *464*
Manning, Jr., Joseph R. - Blue Chip Law Consulting, Inc. (C), CA, *268*
Manning, Roger - Executive Search Team (C), MI, *336*
Manning, Sheila - O'Neill Group (C), NJ, *498*
Mannix, Francis L. - F. L. Mannix & Co. (R), MA, *135*
Mannix, Sandra G. - Cathy Abelson Legal Search (C), PA, *232*
Manns, Suzanne - HRCS (R), CA, *97*
Manson, Phyllis - BG & Assoc. (C), MD, *266*
Mantel, Michael - The BMW Group, Inc. (C), NY, *268*
Manthey, Merv - KPMG Executive Search (R), AB, *119*
Manuso, James S. J. - Manuso, Alexander & Associates, Inc. (R), NY, *135*
Manzo, Romero - The Prairie Group (C), IL, *515*
Maphet, Harriet - The Stevenson Group, Inc. (N.J.) (R), NJ, *200*
Marcantel, Angelle - David Weinfeld Group (C), NC, *617*
Marcello, Joe - Executive Search Consultants Corp. (C), IL, *335*
Marchetti, James - International Market Recruiters (C), NC, *393*
Marcovich, Carol - CMC Search Consultants (C), IL, *293*
Marcus, Alvin B. - Marcus & Assoc. (C), NY, *469*
Marcus, Elton - The Hiring Authority, Inc. (C), FL, *379*
Marenger, Christine - Yves Plouffe & Assoc. (R), QE, *165*
Marentez, Frank - Marentz & Co. (C), TX, *469*
Margolin, Efraim - Margolin Consultants, Inc. (C), NY, *469*
Margolin, Robert - Kenn Spinrad Inc. (C), PA, *589*
Marin, Natalie - Campbell, Edgar Inc. (C), BC, *280*
Marini, Larry - Management Recruiters of Northern Palm Beaches (C), FL, *444*
Marino, Chet - Cochran, Cochran & Yale, Inc. (R), CO, *37*
Marino, Frank - Hospitality Int'l. (C), NY, *381*
Marino, Jory J. - Sullivan & Company (R), NY, *204*
Marino, Mike - Tax Network Resources, Inc. (C), NY, *600*
Marino, Mike - Tax Network Resources, Inc. (C), NY, *600*
Marion, Bradford B. - LAI Ward Howell (R), IL, *123*
Marion, Joe - Matrix Consultants, Inc. (C), NC, *472*
Mark, John L. - J. L. Mark Assoc., Inc. (R), CO, *135*
Mark, Lynne B. - J. L. Mark Assoc., Inc. (R), CO, *135*
Markessinis, Barbara - Berkshire Search Assoc. (C), MA, *265*
Markoff, Janet - Major, Hagen & Africa (C), NY, *423*
Marks, Brad - Brad Marks Int'l. (R), CA, *136*
Marks, Ira Alan - J. M. Meredith & Assoc. Inc. (C), CA, *479*
Marks, Ira M. - Strategic Alternatives (R), CA, *202*
Marks, Paula F. - Paula Marks Inc. (R), NY, *136*
Marks, Jr., Russell E. - Webb, Johnson Assoc., Inc. (R), NY, *216*
Marks, Sarah J. - The Executive Source Inc. (R), NY, *64*
Marks, Sharon - Marks & Co., Inc. (R), CT, *136*
Markt, John H. - The Human Resource Group, Inc. (R), OH, *98*
Marling, Richard A. - R M Associates (R), OH, *171*
Marlow, Bill - Straube Associates (R), MA, *203*
Marquez, Paul - Sanford Rose Assoc. - Fairhope (C), AL, *565*
Marra, Jr., John - Marra Peters & Partners (R), NJ, *136*
Marra, John - Marra Peters & Partners (R), FL, *136*
Marrin, Rick - Finney-Taylor Personnel & Management Consultants Ltd. (C), AB, *341*
Marriott, Gloria A. - Management Recruiters of Franklin, Inc. (C), TN, *461*
Marriott, Roger H. - Management Recruiters of Franklin, Inc. (C), TN, *461*
Mars, Roxanne - Technical Skills Consulting Inc. (R), ON, *207*
Marsar, Kevin P. - Marsar & Co., Inc. (C), FL, *471*
Marsden, Jonathan - QD Legal (C), ON, *526*
Marseline, Tracy - CJSI-Cindy Jackson Search Int'l. (C), CA, *291*
Marsh, Norman R. - California Management Search (C), CA, *279*
Marsh, Robin - MetroVantage Personnel Systems (C), CA, *480*
Marshall, Deborah - Chicago Research Group, Inc. (R), NC, *33*
Marshall, Dennis - L O R (R), NJ, *122*
Marshall, Dennis - Karen Marshall Assoc. (C), KY, *471*
Marshall, Don - The Marshall Group (R), IL, *137*
Marshall, Donald - Raymond Karsan Assoc. (C), MA, *530*
Marshall, E. Leigh - Johnson Smith & Knisely (R), NJ, *107*
Marshall, John C. - JM & Company (R), PA, *106*
Marshall, John L. - Fishel HR Assoc., Inc. (C), AZ, *341*
Marshall, Karen - Karen Marshall Assoc. (C), KY, *471*
Marshall, Larry - Marshall Consultants, Inc. (R), NY, *137*
Marshall, Larry - Marshall Consultants, Inc. (R), CA, *137*
Marshall, Layne - Executive Referral Services, Inc. (C), IL, *334*
Marshall, P. William - Dise & Co. (R), OH, *52*
Marshall, Paul M. - Management Recruiters of Stevens Point, Inc. (C), WI, *466*
Marsteller, Franklin D. - SpencerStuart (R), PA, *197*
Marsteller, Linda - Marsteller Wilcox Assoc. (C), IL, *471*
Martel, Anita - Perry-Martel Int'l., Inc. (R), ON, *163*
Martens, Maxine - Herbert Mines Assoc., Inc. (R), NY, *145*
Marth, David L. - Management Recruiters International, Inc. (MRI) (C), OH, *425*
Marti, Lydia S. - Major, Hagen & Africa (C), IL, *423*
Martin, Bill - Fortune Personnel Consultants of Greensboro, NC, Inc. (C), NC, *348*
Martin, Bob - The LaBorde Group (C), CA, *411*
Martin, Carol - Medical Innovations (C), NY, *477*
Martin, Charles E. - Management Recruiters of Birmingham-South, Inc. (C), AL, *438*
Martin, Donovan - Donovan Martin & Assoc. (R), CA, *137*
Martin, Geary D. - Boyden (R), GA, *21*
Martin, George R. - George R. Martin (R), PA, *137*
Martin, James - DHR Int'l., Inc. (R), DC, *50*
Martin, Jean M. - The Ultimate Source (R), CA, *212*
Martin, Jon N. G. - Egon Zehnder Int'l. Inc. (R), ON, *227*
Martin, Judy R. - J. Martin & Assoc. (R), CA, *137*
Martin, Leslie - Donna Davis Assoc. (C), NJ, *309*
Martin, Lois G. - The Martin Group (R), CA, *137*
Martin, Lynne Koll - Boyden (R), CA, *20*
Martin, Mary Lou - Neail Behringer Consultants Inc. (R), NY, *15*
Martin, Maureen - DHR Int'l., Inc. (R), IL, *49*
Martin, Michael - HRCS (R), CA, *97*

Martin, Michael - HRCS (R), NY, *97*
Martin, Nancy A. - EMN/Witt/Kieffer (R), MA, *59*
Martin, Patricia - Management Recruiters of Birmingham-South, Inc. (C), AL, *438*
Martin, Randall - John Sibbald Assoc., Inc. (R), MO, *191*
Martin, Rande L. - Management Recruiters of Richmond (C), IN, *429*
Martin, Sr., Robert - The Pailin Group Professional Search Consultants (R), TX, *158*
Martin, Robert A. - Phoenix Partners, Inc. (C), GA, *511*
Martin, Roz - STAT Search (C), MA, *592*
Martin, Susan - Howard/Williams Assoc. (C), FL, *382*
Martin, Suzanne - The Beam Group (R), PA, *14*
Martin, Suzanne S. - Selected Executives, Inc. (C), MA, *578*
Martin, Jr., Theodore B. - Martin Partners, L.L.C. (R), IL, *137*
Martin, Timothy P. - The Martin Group (R), CA, *137*
Martin, Vicki - Janou Pakter, Inc. (C), NY, *502*
Martin, Wayne - Human Resources Personnel Agency (R), AR, *99*
Martineau, Bill - Dunhill Professional Search of Winston-Salem (C), NC, *322*
Martineau, Bob - Dunhill Professional Search of Winston-Salem (C), NC, *322*
Martineau, Dan - Dunhill Professional Search of Winston-Salem (C), NC, *322*
Martinez, Janis E. - Ashford Management Group, Inc. (R), GA, *8*
Martinez, Roberto - Strategic Resources (C), WA, *595*
Martinez, Stephen A. - Stephens Assoc. Ltd., Inc. (R), OH, *200*
Martinolich, Michael - Tennyson Advisors (R), NY, *208*
Martirano, Nancy - Recruiting Specialists (C), MA, *532*
Martire, Nick - AmeriResource Group Inc. (C), OK, *248*
Martwick, Gail - The Martwick Group, Inc. (C), OR, *472*
Marumoto, William H. - Boyden (R), DC, *21*
Marunick, Kevin - Fortune Personnel Consultants of Chattanooga Inc. (C), TN, *349*
Marvin, Cindy - Romac Int'l., Inc. (C), FL, *543*
Maschal, Chuck - Maschal/Connors Inc. (R), NJ, *137*
Mashack, Michael - Management Recruiters of Bucks County (C), PA, *435*
Mashack, Ted M. - Management Recruiters of Bucks County (C), PA, *435*
Maslan, Neal L. - LAI Ward Howell (R), CA, *123*
Mason, Christopher - KM Associates (C), MA, *407*
Mason, Eileen - Management Recruiters of Kansas City (C), MO, *431*
Mason, Jean - The Talon Group (R), TX, *206*
Mason, Kimball L. - KM Associates (C), MA, *407*
Mason, Marlene - Richard Kader & Assoc. (C), OH, *403*
Mason, Maurice - McCray, Shriver, Eckdahl & Assoc., Inc. (R), CA, *140*
Mason, Morgan - Mason & Nicastri Ltd. (R), CA, *138*
Mason, Ron - Professional Recruiters (C), UT, *522*
Mason, William E. - Battalia Winston Int'l./The Euram Consultants Group (R), CA, *13*
Masquelier, Sibyl - Executive Resource Group, Inc. (R), ME, *63*
Mass, Angela - Focus Executive Search (C), MN, *343*
Massar, Joy V. - Egan & Assoc. (R), WI, *57*
Massarsky, Alan - Marshall-Alan Assoc., Inc. (C), NY, *471*
Masserman, Bruce - Masserman & Assoc., Inc. (R), NY, *138*
Massey, Bruce - Massey-Horton Int'l. (R), ON, *138*
Massey, III, H. Heath - Robison & Associates (R), NC, *180*
Massitti, Pat - Leader Search Inc. (R), AB, *127*
Masson, Thomas E. - TEMCO-The Executive Management Consulting Organization (R), WI, *208*
Massucco, Harry A. - Sherwood Lehman Massucco, Inc. (R), CA, *189*
Massung, Larry J. - Management Recruiters of Provo (C), UT, *437*
Mastandrea, Pat - Johnson Smith & Knisely (R), NY, *107*
Masters, Meri - MESA International (C), CA, *480*
Masterson, Louis T. - Louis Thomas Masterson & Co. (R), OH, *138*
Masterson, Paul - Gerald Walsh & Co. Inc. (C), NB, *615*
Mastripolito, Mary - Harvey Hohauser & Assoc., LLC (R), MI, *87*
Masuga, James - Heyman Assoc., Inc. (R), NY, *93*
Mather, David - Christian & Timbers, Inc. (R), OH, *34*
Mather, David R. - Christian & Timbers, Inc. (R), CA, *34*
Mather, Richard L. - Richard L. Mather & Assoc. (C), CT, *472*
Mathes, Tricia - NPS of Atlanta, Inc. (C), GA, *496*
Mathews, Barry C. - Corporate Image Group (C), TN, *300*
Mathews, Sherry - Human Resource Dimensions, Inc. (C), TX, *384*
Mathey, Joyce - Mathey Services (C), IL, *472*
Mathias, Kathy A. - Stone, Murphy & Olson (R), MN, *201*
Mathias, William J. - Preng & Assoc., Inc. (R), TX, *167*
Matras, Debbie - Sales Consultants of Milwaukee (C), WI, *563*
Matson, Erik W. - LAI Ward Howell (R), NY, *122*
Matson, Marshall - General Engineering Tectonics (C), CA, *356*
Matte, Richard - Matte Consulting Group Inc. (R), QE, *138*
Matté, Norman E. - Matté & Company, Inc. (R), CT, *138*
Mattes, Jr., Edward C. - The Ogdon Partnership (R), NY, *155*
Matteson, Larry - The Rubinic Consulting Group (C), OH, *548*
Matteson, Scott - Horizon Medical Search of NH (C), NH, *381*
Matthews, Alyce - The Matthews Group, Inc. (C), NJ, *472*
Matthews, G. L. - Robert William James & Assoc. (C), IL, *539*
Matthews, James M. - Stanton Chase Int'l. (R), MD, *199*
Matthews, John C. - Management Recruiters of Henry County (C), VA, *437*
Matthews, Laurie - Accountants On Call (C), CA, *235*
Mattingly, Kathy - Romac Int'l., Inc. (C), KY, *543*
Mattis, Tim - Ensearch Management Consultants (C), CA, *331*
Mattison, Elaine - DHR Int'l., Inc. (R), MO, *50*
Mattocks, Paul - G. P. Mattocks & Associates (C), NC, *473*
Mattox, Robert D. - SpencerStuart (R), GA, *197*
Mattran, Donald A. - Sales Consultants of Sarasota (C), FL, *552*
Matucan, Ariel B. - Search Advisors Int'l. Corp. (R), FL, *186*
Mauck, Laura B. - The Oxbridge Group, Ltd. (C), MA, *500*
Maude, Elaine - The Burke Group (C), ON, *276*
Mauk, Gary - Evergreen & Co. (C), MA, *331*
Mauk, Patricia - Evergreen & Co. (C), MA, *331*
Maul, Lisa M. - Professional Persons Career Services (C), NY, *521*
Maun, Fran - Roth Young of Tampa (C), FL, *546*
Mauriello, Linda Marie - HLR Consulting (C), NY, *379*
Maurina, Kate - Victor White Int'l. (C), CA, *612*
Maurizio, Michael - Management Recruiters of Mohawk Valley (C), NY, *432*
Maximo, Anita - The Gabriel Group (C), PA, *354*
Maxin, Keith A. - Michael L. Ketner & Assoc., Inc. (R), PA, *114*
Maxin, Keith A. - K. Maxin & Assoc. (R), PA, *139*
Maxwell, R. Patrick - Templeton & Assoc. (C), MN, *605*
May, Donald C. - Allied Search, Inc. (C), CA, *245*
May, Donald C. - Allied Search, Inc. (C), CA, *245*

May, Patricia - Johnson Smith & Knisely (R), NY, *107*
May, Paul - Paul May & Assoc. (C), IL, *473*
May, Peter - MIXTEC Group (R), CA, *145*
May, Russell H. - The Harris Consulting Corp. (R), MB, *87*
May, William M. - Management Recruiters of Decatur, LLC (C), AL, *438*
Mayberry, Karen Sue - Singleton & Assoc. (C), VA, *582*
Maye, Carolyn - Ken Clark Int'l. (R), NJ, *36*
Mayer, Mary L. - Mary L. Mayer, Ltd. (R), MN, *139*
Mayer, Robert - Kennedy & Co. (R), IL, *112*
Mayers, Lawrence S. - Lamay Assoc., Inc. (R), CT, *124*
Mayes, Abby - The Mayes Group, Ltd. (R), PA, *139*
Mayes, Kay H. - John Shell Assoc., Inc. (C), SC, *580*
Mayfield, Barbara L. - Prescott Legal Search, Inc. (C), TX, *517*
Mayhall, Dale - Mayhall Search Group, Inc. (C), IN, *473*
Mayo, Buz - TeamBuilders (C), GA, *601*
Mazziota, Daniel R. - Ruth Sklar Assoc., Inc. (RSA Executive Search) (R), NY, *192*
Mazzitelli, Teresa - The Mazzitelli Group, Ltd. (R), MN, *139*
Mazzola, Richard J. - Futures, Inc. (C), NH, *354*
Mazzuckelli, Katie - Tyler & Company (R), GA, *212*
McAleavy, Steve - Search Consultants Int'l., Inc. (C), TX, *575*
McAllister, Jim - O'Rourke Companies, Inc. (R), TX, *154*
McAllister, Lon - Search Consultants Int'l., Inc. (C), TX, *575*
McAloon, Justin - Norrell Financial Staffing (C), RI, *495*
McAlpine, Bruce - Keith Bagg & Assoc., Inc. (C), ON, *257*
McAndrew, Cindy - Aries Search Group (C), GA, *252*
McAndrew, Michael - Tyler & Company (R), TX, *212*
McAnney, Michael - S-H-S TechStaff (C), PA, *550*
McAteer, Thomas K. - Montgomery Resources, Inc. (C), CA, *484*
McAulay, Jr., Albert L. - The McAulay Firm (R), NC, *139*
McAvoy, Edward P. - Romano McAvoy Assoc., Inc. (C), NY, *544*
McBride, Dee - Deeco Int'l. (C), UT, *310*
McBride, Jonathan E. - McBride Assoc., Inc. (R), DC, *139*
McBryde, Marnie - SpencerStuart (R), NY, *196*
McBurney, Kevin - The Caldwell Partners Amrop International (R), ON, *26*
McBurney, Kevin - The Caldwell Partners Amrop International (R), BC, *26*
McCabe, William - Allstaff, Inc. (C), IL, *245*
McCafferty, Dee - Sales Consultants of Southampton (C), PA, *555*
McCafferty, George - Sales Consultants of Southampton (C), PA, *555*
McCain, Barbara - Tele-Solutions of Arizona, Inc. (C), AZ, *604*
McCall, Tom - Tom McCall Executive Search (C), IL, *473*
McCallister, Richard A. - Boyden (R), IL, *21*
McCammon, Betsy - Rogish Assoc., Inc. (C), OH, *541*
McCandless, Hugh - Marshall Consultants, Inc. (R), NY, *137*
McCann, Connie B. - SpencerStuart (R), PA, *197*
McCann, Jim - Dunhill Professional Search of Madison (C), WI, *318*
McCann, III, Joseph H. - McCann, Choi & Associates, LLC (R), NY, *139*
McCann, Mary Ellen - Wellington Management Group (R), PA, *217*
McCartan, Charles P. - McCartan Assoc. (R), NJ, *139*
McCarter, John - Sanford Rose Assoc. - Charlotte (C), NC, *568*
McCarthy, Charles - Sanford Rose Assoc. - Santa Ana (C), CA, *565*
McCarthy, Deborah - The Whyte Group, Inc. (R), MD, *220*
McCarthy, Debra - Becker Personnel (C), FL, *262*
McCarthy, Dennis - Sales Consultant of Miami-Coral Gables (C), FL, *552*
McCarthy, Frank X. - Xavier Associates, Inc. (R), MA, *226*
McCarthy, Kathleen A. - Meder & Assoc., Inc. (R), IL, *142*
McCarthy, Kevin E. - K. E. McCarthy & Assoc. (R), CA, *139*
McCarthy, Maureen - Management Recruiters of Fresno (C), CA, *440*
McCarthy, Richard - McCarthy Assoc. National BancSearch, LLC (C), LA, *473*
McCarthy, Richard J. - J. Robert Scott (R), MA, *104*
McCartt, IV, E. J. - Professional Search, Inc. Int'l. (C), TX, *523*
McCartt, Sandra - Professional Search, Inc. Int'l. (C), TX, *523*
McCauley, Eileen - Earley Kielty & Assoc., Inc. (R), NY, *56*
McClain, Duane - Construction Search Specialists, Inc. (C), WI, *297*
McClain, Jack - PIC Executive Search (C), GA, *511*
McClain, Michael - Battalia Winston Int'l./The Euram Consultants Group (R), CA, *13*
McClearen, Bruce - Tyler & Company (R), GA, *212*
McClendon, III, Sidney - Allen Austin Lowe & Powers (R), TX, *3*
McClimans, Robert M. - NRI Staffing Resources (C), DC, *497*
McCloskey, Frank - DHR Int'l., Inc. (R), IL, *49*
McClosky, Evan - Open Concepts (C), CA, *499*
McClosky, John - John Kurosky & Assoc. (R), CA, *122*
McClosky, John - Open Concepts (C), CA, *499*
McClosky, Linda - Open Concepts (C), CA, *499*
McCollum, Ken - MESA International (C), CA, *480*
McConnell, Greg - Winter, Wyman & Co. (C), GA, *623*
McCooe, John J. - McCooe & Assoc., Inc. (R), NJ, *140*
McCooe, Sean J. - McCooe & Assoc., Inc. (R), NJ, *140*
McCool, Anne G. - Sullivan & Company (R), NY, *204*
McCorkle, Sam B. - Morton, McCorkle & Assoc. Inc. (R), MO, *147*
McCormack, Joseph A. - McCormack & Assoc. (R), CA, *140*
McCormack, Kathleen M. - K. C. Hale, Inc. (R), CT, *85*
McCormack, Kathy - The Beardsley Group Inc. (C), CT, *261*
McCormick, Brian D. - The McCormick Group (C), VA, *474*
McCormick, Brian D. - The McCormick Group (C), VA, *474*
McCormick, Gregg J. - Retained Search Assoc. (R), NC, *176*
McCormick, Harry B. - Hayden Group, Inc. (R), MA, *88*
McCormick, Jim - McCormick Search Inc. (C), IL, *474*
McCormick, Pat - Barrett Hospitality Search (R), CA, *12*
McCormick, William J. - The McCormick Group (C), VA, *474*
McCormick-Kelch, Anna - Johnson Smith & Knisely (R), IL, *107*
McCosh, Michelle - Abraxas Technologies, Inc. (C), FL, *233*
McCowan, Elle - Management Recruiters of Birmingham (C), MI, *451*
McCoy, Denise - Dunhill Personnel of St. Andrews (C), SC, *322*
McCoy, Horacio - Korn/Ferry Int'l. (R), NY, *117*
McCoy, Horacio - Korn/Ferry, Int'l., S.A. de C.V. (R), MX, *118*
McCoy, Horacio - Korn/Ferry, Int'l., S.A. de C.V. (R), MX, *118*
McCoy, Karl - Pro-Tech Search, Inc. (C), IL, *519*
McCoy, Millington F. - Gould, McCoy & Chadick, Inc. (R), NY, *80*
McCracken, Terri - T E M Assoc. (C), WI, *599*
McCracken, Wes - Sales Consultant of Clemmons (C), NC, *554*
McCray, Harold C. - McCray, Shriver, Eckdahl & Assoc., Inc. (R), CA, *140*
McCrea, Frank - Procom (C), ON, *519*
McCrea, Joan I. - Nursing Technomics (R), PA, *153*
McCreary, Charles - Austin-McGregor Int'l. (R), TX, *9*

PRINCIPALS

McCulla, Herb - Dunhill of Ft. Collins, Inc. (C), CO, *319*
McCullough, Joe - Management Recruiters of Cincinnati (C), OH, *433*
McCutcheon, Pat - Iona Partners (C), CA, *394*
McCutcheon, Scott - John Kurosky & Assoc. (R), CA, *122*
McDaniel, James - H R Solutions, Inc. (C), MO, *365*
McDaniel, Paul - The Paul McDaniel Co. (C), TN, *474*
McDannel, Marilyn - Southwest Search & Consulting, Inc. (C), AZ, *588*
McDermid, Earl - Earl L. McDermid & Assoc. (C), IL, *474*
McDermitt, Tom - Professional Recruiting Consultants (C), FL, *521*
McDermott, Bert - Crown Advisors, Inc. (R), PA, *43*
McDermott, Jeffrey T. - Vlcek & Company, Inc. (R), CA, *214*
McDermott, Tom - Corporate Environment Ltd. (R), IL, *41*
McDonald, Elizabeth A. - R. H. Larsen & Assoc., Inc. (R), FL, *125*
McDonald, John R. - TSS Consulting, Ltd. (C), AZ, *610*
McDonald, Louise - Real Estate Executive Search, Inc. (C), CA, *531*
McDonald, Stanleigh B. - McDonald Assoc. Int'l. (R), IL, *140*
McDonald, Thomas W. - Mengel & McDonald Ltd. (C), IL, *479*
McDorman, Terrence - American Logistics Consultants, Inc. (C), IL, *247*
McDowell, Jane - Cook Assoc.,® Inc. (R), IL, *40*
McDowell, John - McDowell & Co., Recruiters (C), TX, *474*
McDowell, Robert N. - Christenson Hutchison McDowell, LLC (R), NJ, *34*
McDowell, Ron - Carnegie Resources, Inc. (C), NC, *284*
McDowell, Sally A. - Professional Selection Services (R), GA, *169*
McElhaney, Ron - Management Recruiters of Savannah (C), GA, *446*
McElhaney, Jr., Ron - Management Recruiters of Savannah (C), GA, *446*
McElhearn, Scott S. - Scott Sibley Assoc. (C), NY, *573*
McElhearn, Scott S. - Scott Sibley Assoc. (C), NY, *573*
McElmeel, Joseph J. - Brooke Chase Assoc., Inc. (R), IL, *24*
McElroy, Brian - Drinkwater & Assoc. (R), MA, *55*
McElroy, John - Management Recruiters of Everett (C), WA, *437*
McEwen, Al - Management Recruiters of Rogers (C), AR, *425*
McFadden, Ashton S. - Johnson Smith & Knisely (R), NY, *107*
McFadden, James - Parker, McFadden & Assoc. (C), GA, *503*
McFadden, James - PSP Agency (C), NY, *525*
McFadzean, James A. - Ray & Berndtson, Inc. (R), CA, *172*
McFarlan, Cydney - Discovery, The Staffing Specialists, Inc. (C), CA, *312*
McFarland, Jerry - Stanton Chase Int'l. (R), TX, *199*
McFaul, William - Management Assoc. (C), MD, *424*
McFeely, Clarence E. - Clarence E. McFeely, Inc. (R), IL, *141*
McGahan, Michael E. - Prior/Martech Assoc., Inc. (R), WA, *169*
McGavern, David O. - The Yorkshire Group, Ltd. (C), MA, *626*
McGee, Jerry - Joseph Consulting, Inc. (C), FL, *401*
McGee, Tom - Lucas Assoc. (C), GA, *421*
McGeehan, Gayle A. - Management Recruiters of Bethlehem, PA (C), PA, *458*
McGill, Robert - The Caldwell Partners Amrop International (R), ON, *26*
McGinnis, A. Ashley - Wilcoxen, Blackwell, Niven & Assoc. (R), FL, *220*
McGinnis, W. John - Earl L. McDermid & Assoc. (C), IL, *474*
McGinnis, William A. - National Metal Services Corp. (C), IN, *489*
McGinty, Kevin - The Silicon Network (C), ON, *581*
McGlawn, Walter - Corporate Plus, Ltd. (C), GA, *300*
McGoldrick, Joe - J. Joseph & Assoc. (C), OH, *395*
McGonigle, Kevin - Egon Zehnder Int'l. Inc. (R), GA, *227*
McGovern, Sheila M. - Kiley, Owen & McGovern, Inc. (R), NJ, *114*
McGovern, Terence P. - Korn/Ferry Int'l. (R), CT, *118*
McGowan, Malcolm - Holloway Schulz & Partners (C), BC, *380*
McGowan, Matt - Career Strategies, Inc. (C), CA, *283*
McGranaham, Pam - Stanton Chase Int'l. (R), CA, *199*
McGrath, Patrick - Riddle & McGrath LLC (R), GA, *178*
McGrath, Robert E. - Robert E. McGrath & Assoc. (R), CT, *141*
McGrath, Steven L. - McGrath & Assoc., Inc. (R), NJ, *141*
McGrath, Tom - Spriggs & Co., Inc. (R), IL, *198*
McGraw, John - The Rogan Group, Inc. (C), CA, *541*
McGraw, T. Jeff - Strauss Personnel Service (C), PA, *596*
McGregor, Jill E. - AGRI-associates (C), OH, *242*
McGregor, Jock - Reynolds Consulting Int'l. (R), ON, *177*
McGuigan, Walter J. - Norm Sanders Assoc., Inc. (R), NJ, *184*
McGuire, Dawn - Bradford & Galt, Inc. (C), KS, *271*
McGuire, John - Sage Employment Recruiters (C), IN, *550*
McGurk, Stacey - The Luciani Group (R), CA, *132*
McGurn, Sharman - B. J. Abrams & Assoc. Inc. (C), IL, *233*
McHale, John P. - McHale & Assoc. (R), WA, *141*
McInerney, Thomas K. - Lindsey & Co., Inc. (R), CT, *129*
McIntire, Richard - DHR Int'l., Inc. (R), IL, *49*
McIntosh, James - DHR Int'l., Inc. (R), NJ, *50*
McInturff, Robert E. - McInturff & Assoc., Inc. (C), MA, *474*
McIntyre, Jeffrey F. - McIntyre Assoc. (R), CT, *141*
McIntyre, Joel - Phillips Resource Group (C), NC, *511*
McIntyre, Marlene - McIntyre Management Resources (C), ON, *475*
McIvor, Jim - Christmas, McIvor & Assoc. Inc. (C), ON, *290*
McIvor, Mike - Christmas, McIvor & Assoc. Inc. (C), ON, *290*
McKavis, Adel - McKavis Assoc. (C), CA, *475*
McKay, Bob - Further Management Group (C), MD, *353*
McKay, Kim - The Network Corporate Search Personnel Inc. (C), AB, *491*
McKay, Lynda Moore - Deborah Snow Walsh, Inc. (R), IL, *215*
McKay, W. John - O'Callaghan Honey/Ray & Berndtson Inc. (R), AB, *153*
McKay, W. John - O'Callaghan Honey/Ray & Berndtson Inc. (R), AB, *172*
McKee, Edward F. - McKee Cyber Search (C), MS, *475*
McKeen, J. J. - McKeen & Company (R), TX, *141*
McKenna, Brian - The Pollack Group (C), ON, *514*
McKenna, Catherine - Marcus & Assoc. (C), NY, *469*
McKenna, Elaine - Weterrings & Agnew, Inc. (C), NY, *619*
McKenna, Scott - The Beam Group (R), PA, *14*
McKenzie, George - Professional Search (R), MI, *169*
McKenzie, Ingrid - Professional Search (R), MI, *169*
McKeown, Morgan - Christian & Timbers, Inc. (R), NY, *34*
McKeown, Morgan - Christian & Timbers, Inc. (R), OH, *34*
McKeown, Patricia - DiMarchi Partners (R), CO, *51*
McKersie, Edward S. - ProSearch, Inc. (C), ME, *524*
McKinley, James M. - McKinley•Arend Int'l. (R), TX, *141*
McKinney, Adrienne - Wachendorfer & Assoc. (C), TX, *613*
McKinney, Danny L. - J & D Resources Inc. (C), TN, *395*
McKinney, Pat - Prichard Kymen Inc. (R), AB, *168*
McKinnon, Greg - The McKinnon Management Group Inc. (C), ON, *475*

McKnight, Vincent J. - Derhak Ireland & Partners Ltd. (R), ON, *48*
McLafferty, Tim - Focus Executive Search (C), MN, *343*
McLane, Bradford - Egon Zehnder Int'l. Inc. (R), IL, *227*
McLaughlin, Brad - Meridian Resources (C), OH, *479*
McLaughlin, John - Romac Int'l. - San Francisco (C), CA, *541*
Mclaughlin, John - TASA International (R), NY, *206*
McLaughlin, John F. - William K. McLaughlin Assoc., Inc. (C), NY, *475*
McLaughlin, Patricia A. - William K. McLaughlin Assoc., Inc. (C), CO, *475*
McLaughlin, William K. - William K. McLaughlin Assoc., Inc. (C), NY, *475*
McLean, Andrew - The Pollack Group (C), ON, *514*
McLean, B. Keith - PricewaterhouseCoopers Executive Search (R), ON, *168*
McLean, Barbara - The Corporate Source Group, Inc. (R), IL, *41*
McLean, Chris - Chaloner Assoc. (R), MA, *32*
McLean, Dan P. - Dan P. McLean Assoc., Inc. (C), ON, *475*
McLean, E. Peter - SpencerStuart (R), NY, *196*
McLean, Luella - Dan P. McLean Assoc., Inc. (C), ON, *475*
McLean, Robert T. - Tecmark Associates Inc. (C), MA, *604*
McLellan, Ed - Polson & Co., Inc. (R), MN, *166*
McLeskey, Penny - Lehman McLeskey (R), TX, *128*
McLey, Curt - Harrison Moore Inc. (C), NE, *370*
McMahan, Steve - Romac Int'l., Inc. (C), MA, *543*
McMahan, Steve - Romac Int'l., Inc. (C), MA, *543*
McMahan, Steve - Romac Int'l., Inc. (C), MA, *543*
McMahan, Steve - Romac Int'l., Inc. (C), NH, *543*
McMahon, Jean Anne - The Quantum Group (C), NJ, *527*
McMahon, Marguerite A. - Sullivan & Company (R), NY, *204*
McMahon, Mark J. - A.T. Kearney Executive Search (R), CT, *111*
McMahon, Norman - Romac Int'l., Inc. (C), PA, *544*
McMahon, Thomas J. - Columbia Consulting Group (R), MD, *38*
McMalton, Jean Anne - The Quantum Group (C), NJ, *527*
McManamon, Tim - Rogers - McManamon Executive Search (R), CA, *180*
McMann, Dean E. - The Ransford Group (R), TX, *171*
McManners, Donald E. - McManners Assoc., Inc. (R), CA, *142*
McManus, Robert J. - Whittlesey & Assoc., Inc. (R), PA, *220*
McMath, George R. - Insurance People (C), IN, *390*
McMillan, Chuck - Physician Recruiting Services, Inc. (C), MO, *511*
McMillan, Dwight - Management Recruiters of Atlanta NE (C), GA, *446*
McMillin, Michael - TASA International (R), TX, *206*
McMillin, Robert - Price Waterhouse Executive Search (R), BC, *168*
McMullan, Don - The Associates, HR Search Executives, Inc. (C), OK, *254*
McNahan, Rod - Foster Partners (R), TX, *71*
McNair, Tracy - Gaines & Assoc. Int'l., Inc. (R), NY, *73*
McNally, Glenna Q. - Cusack Consulting (R), NY, *44*
McNally, John R. - McCoy Ltd. (C), CA, *474*
McNamara, Michael - Sales Consultant (C), CO, *552*
McNamara, Robert - Global Career Services, Inc. (C), NY, *358*
McNamara, Timothy C. - Horton Int'l. Inc. (R), MD, *96*
McNeal, Jack - Probus Executive Search (C), CA, *519*
McNear, Jeffrey - Barrett Partners (C), IL, *260*
McNeil, Janet - Cook Assoc.,® Inc. (R), IL, *40*
McNerney, Kevin A. - Heidrick & Struggles, Inc. (R), VA, *90*
McNichol, Jr., John - McNichol Assoc. (R), PA, *142*
McNicholas, John - Boyden (R), IL, *21*
McNichols, Walter B. - Gary Kaplan & Assoc. (R), CA, *109*
McNitt, Dean - Healthcare Recruiters of New York, Inc. (C), NY, *373*
McNulty, Kelly L. - Gregory Michaels & Assoc., Inc. (R), IL, *82*
McNulty, Neil P. - Management Recruiters of Suffolk (C), VA, *437*
McPherson, Ron - National Bank & Finance Executive Search (C), CA, *488*
McPherson, Stephen M. - LAI Ward Howell (R), NY, *123*
McPolin, James B. - Advantage Partners, Inc. (R), OH, *2*
McPoyle, Jr., Thomas C. - TCM Enterprises (C), MD, *600*
McQuiddy, Brian - Woodmoor Group (C), CO, *624*
McRae, Keith - Dunhill of Chicago (C), IL, *317*
McRae, O. Jon - Jon McRae & Associates, Inc. (R), GA, *142*
McRobbie, Jason - Forest People Int'l. Search Ltd. (C), BC, *343*
McRoberts, C. F. - McRoberts & Assoc. (C), OH, *475*
McRoberts, Dana L. - Management Recruiters of Plano-East (C), TX, *436*
McShane, Keith - Chesapeake Group (C), CT, *290*
McSherry, James F. - Battalia Winston Int'l./The Euram Consultants Group (R), IL, *13*
McSherry, Terry - Johnson Smith & Knisely (R), IL, *107*
McSpadden, Stephen - First Advisory Services Int'l., Inc. (R), MD, *67*
McSweeney, Arlene - The Chatham Group, Ltd. (C), CT, *289*
McSweeney, Marilyn - Comprehensive Search (C), GA, *295*
McTaggart, Joseph J. - Joseph J. McTaggart (C), CA, *476*
McWilliams, Sara P. - Abbott Smith Assoc., Inc. (R), NY, *193*
Mead, James D. - James Mead & Co. (R), CT, *142*
Meade, Thomas M. - Kremple & Meade, Inc. (R), CA, *120*
Meadley, Ron - The Clayton Edward Group (C), MI, *292*
Meadley, Ronald J. - Management Recruiters of Grand Rapids (C), MI, *430*
Meadows, C. David - Right/McKee Consulting Group (C), TX, *537*
Meads, Walter F. - Meads & Assoc. (R), FL, *142*
Meagher, Daniel J. - Willmott & Assoc. (C), MA, *622*
Meagher, III, Edward A. - The Woodstone Consulting Company, Inc. (R), CO, *224*
Meagher, Linda J. - The Woodstone Consulting Company, Inc. (R), CO, *224*
Meagher-Clare, Patricia - SpencerStuart (R), IL, *197*
Mealia, John - Elan Pratzer & Partners Inc. (R), ON, *167*
Means, Wallace - Management Recruiters of Charlotte SW (C), NC, *432*
Meany, Brian - Herbert Mines Assoc., Inc. (R), NY, *145*
Mears, Jack - Kelly Walker Assoc. (C), TX, *614*
Meder, Peter F. - Meder & Assoc., Inc. (R), IL, *142*
Medina-Haro, Adolfo - Heidrick & Struggles, Inc. (R), MX, *90*
Medley, Jerry - The Medley Group (C), CA, *477*
Medoff, Lynn - C. A. Durakis Assoc., Inc. (R), CT, *55*
Medtlie, Peder - Management Recruiters of Milwaukee-West (C), WI, *465*
Mee, Robin - Mee Derby & Co. (C), DC, *478*
Meehling, Catherine E. - First Advisory Services Int'l., Inc. (R), MD, *67*
Meehling, Catherine E. - Management Assoc. (C), MD, *424*
Mega, Ed - Romac Int'l., Inc. (C), PA, *544*
Mehta, Narinder K. - Mehta Consulting (C), NJ, *478*
Meier, J. Dale - Grant Cooper & Assoc., Inc. (R), MO, *81*
Meiland, A. Daniel - Egon Zehnder Int'l. Inc. (R), NY, *227*
Meints, Ron - Computer Personnel, Inc. (C), WA, *295*

PRINCIPALS

Meisel, Martin H. - Martin H. Meisel Assoc., Inc. (R), NY, *143*
Meisels, Greer - DHR Int'l., Inc. (R), NY, *50*
Meissner, Bob - Management Recruiters of Milwaukee-North (C), WI, *466*
Meister, Verle - Management Recruiters of Cheyenne (C), WY, *466*
Meitz, Robert - Management Recruiters of West Chester, Inc. (C), PA, *460*
Meixner, Robert - Accountants On Call (C), NJ, *236*
Melancon, Robert M. - Melancon & Co. (R), TX, *143*
Meller, John - Keystone Consulting Group (C), OH, *406*
Meller, Peggy - Hedlund Corp. (C), IL, *375*
Mellilo, Joe - Dunhill Professional Search of huntington (C), NY, *318*
Mellos, James S. - Ki Technologies, Inc. (C), UT, *406*
Melmet, Dee Dee - Smartsource Inc. (C), CA, *583*
Melrose, Susan - Templeton & Assoc. (C), MN, *606*
Meltser, Thomas - Patriot Assoc. (C), PA, *505*
Menda, Issac - Management Recruiters of Bellevue (C), WA, *437*
Mendez, Larry W. - Layne-Mendez & Co. (R), TX, *127*
Mendez-Tucker, Barbara - Wesley Brown & Bartle Co., Inc. (R), NY, *218*
Mendrala, Karen - Lab Market Specialists (C), UT, *411*
Menefee, Juan F. - Juan Menefee & Assoc. (C), IL, *478*
Menefee, Shawn - Corporate Plus, Ltd. (C), GA, *300*
Meneghetti, Mauro - Western Management Consultants (R), AB, *218*
Meng, Cameron E. - Meng, Finseth & Assoc., Inc. (R), CA, *143*
Meng, Charles M. - Meng, Finseth & Assoc., Inc. (R), CA, *143*
Menk, Carl W. - Canny, Bowen Inc. (R), NY, *28*
Menner, Shauna - Accountants On Call (C), WA, *237*
Mercer, James L. - The Mercer Group, Inc. (R), NM, *143*
Mercer, James L. - The Mercer Group, Inc. (R), GA, *143*
Mercer, Julie - Columbia Consulting Group (R), MD, *38*
Merjos, Susan - The Beam Group (R), NY, *14*
Mero, Kevin J. - innovativestaffsearch (C), TX, *389*
Mero, Kevin J. - innovativestaffsearch (C), WI, *389*
Merrell, Randy - Management Solutions, Inc. (C), CA, *468*
Merrick, George - Pacific Finance Search, Inc. (C), CA, *501*
Merrifield, Gary - Accountants On Call (C), OH, *236*
Merrigan, Eileen M. - LAI Ward Howell (R), NY, *122*
Merrill, Barbara - Hutton Merrill & Assoc. (R), CA, *100*
Merriman, Clint - DHR Int'l., Inc. (R), WA, *51*
Merriman, Jack - Management Recruiters of Colorado Springs (C), CO, *441*
Merriman, Mark - Management Recruiters of Colorado Springs (C), CO, *441*
Merz, Monte - Accountants On Call (C), CO, *235*
Meschke, Jason M. - EFL Assoc. (R), KS, *57*
Meschke, Linda - Accountants On Call (C), RI, *237*
Mesger, Robin - RJN Consulting (R), NY, *179*
Mesina, Roman - The Consulting Group of North America, Inc. (C), VA, *297*
Messett, III, William J. - Messett Assoc., Inc. (R), FL, *143*
Messina, Angelo - Management Decision Systems, Inc. (MDSI) (C), NJ, *425*
Messina, Chris - Chesapeake Group (C), CT, *290*
Mestepey, John T. - A.T. Kearney Executive Search (R), FL, *111*
Metcalf, Virgil L. - Sales Consultant of Naples (C), FL, *552*
Mettler, Renate - William-Johns Co., Inc. (C), CA, *621*
Metz, Alex - Hunt Ltd. (C), NJ, *385*
Metz, Nancy - Dominguez-Metz & Assoc. (R), CA, *53*
Metzgar, Jim - Management Recruiters of Charlottesville (C), VA, *437*
Metzger, Norman - Martin H. Meisel Assoc., Inc. (R), NY, *143*
Metzger, Pete - Foster Partners (R), DC, *70*
Metzger, Susan - Techstaff Inc. (C), WI, *603*
Meyer, Dan - Tuttle Venture Group, Inc. (R), TX, *212*
Meyer, Fred R. - Management Recruiters of Bethlehem, PA (C), PA, *458*
Meyer, Henry F. - Glass & Assoc., Inc. (C), OH, *358*
Meyer, James L. - Management Search of R.I. Inc. (R), RI, *135*
Meyer, Lenore - Kennedy & Co. (R), IL, *112*
Meyer, Michael F. - Witt/Kieffer, Ford, Hadelman & Lloyd (R), AZ, *223*
Meyer, Paul R. - Prior/Martech Assoc., Inc. (R), WA, *169*
Meyer, Rick M. - Meyer Assoc., Inc. (R), GA, *144*
Meyer, Tom - CCI - Career Consultants Int'l. (C), CA, *286*
Meyer, Verne - Delacore Resources (C), MN, *310*
Meyer, Walter E. - Walter Meyer & Assoc. (R), NY, *144*
Meyers, James - Techstaff Inc. (C), AZ, *603*
Meyers, Maurice R. - Management Recruiters, Inland Empire Agency (C), CA, *441*
Meyers, Ron - Feldman Gray & Assoc. Inc. (C), ON, *339*
Meyers, Stuart - Management Recruiters of Washington, DC Inc. (C), MD, *450*
Meysing, Larry E. - Corporate Builders, Inc. (C), OR, *299*
Meysing, William C. - Corporate Builders, Inc. (C), OR, *299*
Michaels, Ben - Ritech Management Inc. (C), NY, *537*
Michaels, Ellen - Shupack & Michaels Inc. (C), NY, *581*
Michaels, Lou - Lou Michaels Assoc., Inc. (C), MI, *481*
Michaels, Lynda - Cypress Int'l., Inc. (R), FL, *45*
Michaels, Randy - Lou Michaels Assoc., Inc. (C), MI, *481*
Michaels, Stewart - Topaz Int'l., Inc., Attorney Search (C), NJ, *607*
Michaels, Vincent - ISG Informatics Search Group (C), ON, *395*
Michalisin, Jr., Nicholas J. - S-H-S TechStaff (C), PA, *550*
Michaud, Daryl-Lynn - Sales & Marketing Search, Inc. (C), MA, *551*
Middlebrook, C. Jay - Sales Consultants of Austin, Inc. (C), TX, *562*
Middlebrook, Linda - Sales Consultants of Austin, Inc. (C), TX, *562*
Middleton, Alfred - The Neil Michael Group, Inc./Global Partners (R), NY, *151*
Mielcarek, Kevin - The NEIS Corp., Inc. (C), FL, *491*
Migdol, Kenneth - Ramm Search (C), NY, *528*
Miggins, Bob - Brad Marks Int'l. (R), CA, *136*
Miglio, Dusty - Premier Recruiting Group (C), MI, *516*
Mihalka, Laura - NCC Executive Search Consultants (C), CA, *490*
Mikula, Linda - Schweichler Assoc., Inc. (R), CA, *186*
Milanese, Diane - Management Recruiters of Sidney (C), OH, *458*
Milar, John F. - Fenzel Milar Assoc. (C), OH, *339*
Mildrew, Dave - McCormack & Farrow (R), CA, *140*
Miles, Cynthia - Quantum EDP Recruiting Services (C), QE, *526*
Miles, Cynthia - Quantum Management Services Limited (C), NB, *526*
Miletti, Carol - Interim Accounting Professionals (C), MN, *392*
Milius, Kent - Management Recruiters of Colorado, Inc. (C), CO, *442*
Milkint, Margaret Resce - J.J. & H., Ltd. (R), IL, *104*
Millar, James G. - Millar Walker & Gay (R), ON, *144*
Miller, Andrew S. - Management Recruiters of New Providence (C), NJ, *454*
Miller, Arnie - Isaacson, Miller (R), MA, *104*

Miller, Bert E. - Management Recruiters of Avon (Indianapolis-West) (C), IN, *429*
Miller, Bill - Management Recruiters of Santa Fe (C), NM, *432*
Miller, Carol - Systems Research Inc. (SRI) (C), IL, *598*
Miller, Curt - A-L Assoc., Inc. (R), NY, *1*
Miller, Darryl - Management Alliance Group, Inc. (R), NJ, *134*
Miller, David - Global Executive Search Group (C), MA, *358*
Miller, Diane - Wilcox Bertoux & Miller (R), CA, *220*
Miller, Dixie - Miller & Assoc. (C), FL, *481*
Miller, Donna - Object Resources Int'l., Inc. (C), CT, *498*
Miller, Eric L. - Miller Denver (C), CO, *482*
Miller, Gordon - Comprehensive Search (C), GA, *295*
Miller, Howard - Doleman Enterprises (R), VA, *53*
Miller, Jennifer - Romac Int'l., Inc. (C), CA, *542*
Miller, John - Electronic Search, Inc. (C), CA, *328*
Miller, Judith E. - James Feerst & Assoc., Inc.(C), AZ, *339*
Miller, Kenneth - Computer Network Resources, Inc. (C), CA, *295*
Miller, L. D. - Eggers Consulting Co., Inc. (C), NE, *327*
Miller, Marc S. - Miller-Hall HRISearch (C), NY, *482*
Miller, Marlene - Management Recruiters-Cedar Rapids, Inc. (C), IA, *448*
Miller, Matt - HeartBeat Medical, Inc. (C), OR, *374*
Miller, Michael R. - Lynch Miller Moore Partners, Inc. (R), IL, *132*
Miller, Nancy - Mark Elzweig Co., Ltd. (C), NY, *329*
Miller, Paul McG. - LAI Ward Howell (R), IL, *123*
Miller, Randy - Raymond Karsan Assoc. (C), TX, *530*
Miller, Robin S. - Corrao, Miller, Rush & Wiesenthal (C), NY, *301*
Miller, Roger - Ryan, Miller & Assoc. (C), CA, *549*
Miller, Roxxanne - The Pailin Group Professional Search Consultants (R), TX, *158*
Miller, Roy - The Enns Partners Inc. (R), ON, *59*
Miller, Russ - Sales Consultant of Orange (C), CA, *551*
Miller, Russell E. - ARJay & Assoc. (C), NC, *252*
Miller, Russell H. - DHR Int'l., Inc. (R), FL, *50*
Miller, Scott - Gerald Walsh & Co. Inc. (C), NS, *614*
Miller, Sharon - The Elmhurst Group (C), CA, *329*
Miller, Shelley - Kay Henry, Inc. (C), PA, *376*
Miller, Shirley - Miller + Miller (C), WA, *482*
Miller, Susan C. - Susan C. Miller Assoc., Inc. (C), DC, *482*
Miller, Sylvia - Interquest, Inc. (R), NY, *103*
Miller, Thomas C. - Emerging Medical Technologies, Inc. (C), CO, *329*
Miller, Tom - First Union Executive Search (R), NC, *67*
Miller, William - V. Robinson & Co., Inc. (C), MO, *539*
Million, Ken - Million & Assoc., Inc. (R), OH, *145*
Millonzi, Joel C. - Johnson Smith & Knisely (R), NY, *107*
Mills, Aaron - Hall Kinion (C), CO, *367*
Mills, Joseph - Select Services (C), IL, *578*
Milman, Olga - A. E. Feldman Assoc., Inc. (C), NY, *339*
Milne, Carole - Danette Milne Corporate Search Inc. (C), ON, *482*
Milne, Danette - Danette Milne Corporate Search Inc. (C), ON, *482*
Milne, Evette - Danette Milne Corporate Search Inc. (C), ON, *482*
Milne, Robert P. - TASA International (R), GA, *206*
Milnes, M. Louise - Munroe, Curry & Bond Assoc. (R), NJ, *149*
Milo, Bill - Management Recruiters of Harrisburg (C), PA, *434*
Milo, J. Raymond - Siger & Assoc., LLC (C), CT, *581*
Milo, William P. - The Stonebridge Group (C), PA, *594*
Milrod, Jane - Milrod Assoc. (C), NJ, *482*
Milstead, Robert - Allen Austin Lowe & Powers (R), TX, *3*
Milstein, Bonnie - Marvin Laba & Assoc. (R), CA, *122*
Milton, Charles E. - Smith James Group, Inc. (R), GA, *194*
Mims, Stephen S. - Mims & Associates (R), TX, *145*
Mincy, Jim - Corporate Image Group (C), GA, *300*
Mindlin, Freda - Opportunity Resources, Inc. (R), NY, *156*
Miner, David B. - The Curtiss Group International (R), FL, *44*
Miners, Richard A. - Sedlar & Miners (R), NY, *188*
Mines, Herbert - Herbert Mines Assoc., Inc. (R), NY, *145*
Mingle, Larry D. - Columbia Consulting Group (R), FL, *38*
Minor, Anne - Susan C. Miller Assoc., Inc. (C), DC, *482*
Minso, Eugene A. - Sanford Rose Assoc. - Burlington, NC (C), NC, *569*
Mintzer, Anna - The Goldman Group Inc. (R), NY, *79*
Mirsky, Al - The Barton Group, Inc. (C), MI, *260*
Mirtz, P. John - Mirtz Morice, Inc. (R), CT, *145*
Misarti, Paul R. - Paul Misarti Inc. (C), NY, *483*
Misita, Robert - Hall Kinion (C), MA, *367*
Missirlian, Barbara - Dunhill Staffing Systems (C), NY, *318*
Missirlian, Philip - Dunhill Staffing Systems (C), NY, *318*
Mistura, Dan - Professional Personnel Consultants, Inc. (C), MI, *521*
Mitchell, J. Michael - The Consulting Group Ltd. (R), NY, *40*
Mitchell, John - Fred Hood & Assoc. (C), CA, *380*
Mitchell, Jr., John R. - Management Recruiters of Muskegon (C), MI, *451*
Mitchell, Judith - Stephens Assoc. Ltd., Inc. (R), OH, *200*
Mitchell, Kyle - Ray & Berndtson/Tanton Mitchell (R), BC, *172*
Mitchell, Kyle - Ray & Berndtson/Tanton Mitchell (R), BC, *173*
Mitchell, Lauren - Wachendorfer & Assoc. (C), TX, *613*
Mitchell, Laurie - Laurie Mitchell & Co., Inc. (R), OH, *145*
Mitchell, Linda M. - Computer Int'l. Consultants, Inc. (C), FL, *295*
Mitchell, Michael R. - Computer Int'l. Consultants, Inc. (C), FL, *295*
Mitchell, Robert A. - The Alexander Group (R), MA, *3*
Mitchell, Sheri - ProFinders, Inc. (C), FL, *523*
Mitchell, Susan J. - Major, Hagen & Africa (C), IL, *423*
Mitchell, Thomas M. - Heidrick & Struggles, Inc. (R), CA, *90*
Mitchell, William G. - Eagle Consulting Group Inc. (C), TX, *325*
Mitroff, Norm - Thomas Resource Group (R), CA, *209*
Mittenthal, Robert H. - David Gomez & Assoc., Inc. (R), IL, *79*
Mitton, William H. - Executive Resource Inc. (C), WI, *334*
Mitzmacher, Michael - Edward Bell Assoc. (C), CA, *263*
Mizel, Lynn - Weinman & Assoc. (C), AZ, *617*
Mizgala, Anthony B. - Corso, Mizgala + French (R), ON, *42*
Mochwart, Donald - Drummond Assoc., Inc. (C), NY, *315*
Mock, Lora Lea - Professional Recruiters (C), UT, *522*
Mockler, Nadine - Flexible Resources, Inc. (C), CT, *342*
Moe, Susan Lee - Faro Consultants Int'l. (C), VA, *338*
Moeller, Ed - Sales Consultant of Troy (C), MI, *553*
Moeller, Ed J. - Management Recruiters (C), MI, *430*
Moerbe, Ed H. - Stanton Chase Int'l. (R), TX, *199*
Moere, Linda A. - Michaels & Moere (C), WI, *481*
Moffat, Lori - The Caldwell Partners Amrop International (R), ON, *26*
Moffitt, Timothy D. - Moffitt Int'l., Inc. (R), NC, *146*

PRINCIPALS

Mogg, Dennis - Partnervision Consulting Group Inc. (R), ON, *160*
Mogilner, Myra - Joel H. Paul & Assoc., Inc. (C), NY, *505*
Mogul, Gene - Mogul Consultants, Inc. (C), NY, *483*
Mohan, Jack - Management Recruiters of Boston (C), MA, *430*
Mohan, Jack - Management Recruiters of Springfield (C), MA, *430*
Mojek, Chuck - American Resources Corp. (C), IL, *248*
Mole, Norman - DSR-Search & Recruitment (C), TX, *315*
Molina, Dominique - Winthrop Partners, Inc. (R), NY, *222*
Molitor, John L. - Barrett Partners (C), IL, *260*
Molkentine, Jon - Dunhill Search of Arlington (C), TX, *322*
Molliver, Marshall E. - National Search, Inc. (R), NC, *151*
Molloy, Harry - Data Bank Executive Search (R), OH, *46*
Molloy, Thomas - Molloy Partners (R), NY, *146*
Molnar, David - National Register Columbus Inc. (C), OH, *490*
Molovinsky, Gale - DHR Int'l., Inc. (R), DC, *50*
Mols, Jeff - Aurora Tech Search (C), ON, *256*
Momberger, Lynn M. - The Furst Group, Inc. (R), IL, *72*
Monahan, Edward - Engineering & Scientific Search Assoc. (ESSA) (C), NJ, *330*
Monahan, Stephen C. - Management Recruiters - Towne Lake (C), GA, *446*
Monroe, Jr., Kenneth R. - Sanford Rose Assoc. - Clearwater (C), FL, *566*
Monset, Rachel - NCC Executive Search Consultants (C), CA, *490*
Montaño, Oscar W. - Oscar Montaño, Inc. (R), CA, *146*
Monte, Linda - Vincent Lee Assoc. (C), NY, *415*
Montgomery, Denis - Healthcare Recruiters of New England (C), MA, *373*
Montgomery, Rita - Healthcare Recruiters Int'l. - Los Angeles (C), CA, *372*
Montgomery, Scott - Rojek Marketing Group, Inc. (R), OH, *181*
Montgomery, Thomas - Techstaff Inc. (C), WI, *603*
Montigny, Paul F. - Management Recruiters of Cleveland-South (C), OH, *433*
Montijo, Alicia - NCC Executive Search Consultants (C), CA, *491*
Montville, Bruce A. - EXETER 2100 (C), NH, *337*
Moon, Thomas A. - Power Search (C), TX, *515*
Mooney, Jill - STAT Search (C), NH, *592*
Mooney, Midge - AES Search (C), NJ, *241*
Mooney, Penny - Christian & Timbers, Inc. (R), OH, *34*
Mooney, Penny - Christian & Timbers, Inc. (R), CT, *34*
Moore, Allen - PRAXIS Partners (R), VA, *167*
Moore, Ann M. - Healthcare Recruiters International-NY/NJ (C), NJ, *373*
Moore, Anne - KPMG Executive Search (R), BC, *119*
Moore, Bill - Marc Nichols Assoc., Inc. (C), NY, *493*
Moore, Bob - Computer Recruiters, Inc. (C), CA, *295*
Moore, Brian P. - Bradford Executives Int'l. (C), VA, *272*
Moore, Connie - C. A. Moore & Assoc., Inc. (C), MN, *484*
Moore, David S. - Lynch Miller Moore Partners, Inc. (R), IL, *132*
Moore, Denise - DHR Int'l., Inc. (R), WI, *51*
Moore, Larry W. - Larry Moore & Assoc. (C), CA, *484*
Moore, Lynda - Professional Recruiters (C), UT, *522*
Moore, Mark H. - Wheeler, Moore & Elam Co. (R), TX, *219*
Moore, Meredith - StratfordGroup (R), CA, *203*
Moore, Michael - The Marathon Group (C), FL, *469*
Moore, Michael - RCI Employment Solutions (C), FL, *531*
Moore, Michael H. - The Inside Track (C), TX, *389*
Moore, Richard - Healthcare Recruiters of the Rockies, Inc. (C), CO, *372*
Moore, Richard C. E. - Russell Reynolds Assoc., Inc. (R), ON, *177*
Moore, Robert - Management Recruiters of Rockville (C), MD, *450*
Moore, Sandee - Moore Research Assoc. (R), NJ, *147*
Moore, Sherrie - The Alfus Group (R), NY, *3*
Moore, Stuart K.J. - Ashlar-Stone Management Consultants Inc. (R), ON, *8*
Moore, Susan - O'Keefe & Assoc., Inc. (R), CT, *154*
Moore, Ted J. - The Human Resource Group, Inc. (R), OH, *98*
Moore, Thomas D. - Management Recruiters of West View (C), PA, *435*
Moore, Thomas R. - Thomas R. Moore Executive Search (R), TX, *146*
Moore, Tina - Gundersen Partners, L.L.C. (R), NY, *83*
Morack, Merle - Management Recruiters of Lake Wisconsin (C), WI, *438*
Moran, Andrea - DHR Int'l., Inc. (R), IL, *49*
Moran, Gayle - Dussick Management Assoc. (C), CT, *323*
Moran, Linda - Health Care Plus, Inc. (C), MD, *371*
Moran, Marilyn - RitaSue Siegel Resources, Inc. (R), NY, *191*
Moran, Mike - Techstaff Inc. (C), CA, *603*
Moran, Norm - Management Recruiters of Summerville (C), SC, *435*
Moran, Paul - Fenwick Partners (R), MA, *66*
Moran, Rion J. - Bowman & Assoc. (C), CA, *271*
Moran, Thomas F. - LAI Ward Howell (R), WI, *124*
Moran, Thomas J. - Kennedy & Co. (R), IL, *112*
Morbitzer, Tina - Tina Morbitzer & Assoc. (C), FL, *485*
Mordue, Michael J. - Mordue, Allen, Roberts, Bonney Ltd. (C), WA, *485*
Morency, Marcia - Morency Assoc. (C), MA, *485*
Moreno, Melissa - Johnson Smith & Knisely (R), CT, *107*
Morgan, David G. - Morgan Stampfl, Inc. (C), NY, *485*
Morgan, Diane R. - Morgan & Assoc. (C), MA, *485*
Morgan, Hillary A. - Lindsey & Co., Inc. (R), CT, *129*
Morgan, Joseph - Jaral Consultants, Inc. (C), NJ, *397*
Morgan, Joyce - People Management Mid-South, LLC (R), TN, *162*
Morgan, Kay - Accountants On Call (C), TX, *237*
Morgan, Laura K. - The Oxbridge Group, Ltd. (C), MA, *500*
Morgan, Nancy - K. Russo Assoc. Inc. (C), CT, *548*
Morgan, Paul - Sanford Rose Assoc. - Columbia (C), SC, *570*
Morgan, Richard - Morgan Samuels Co. (R), CA, *147*
Morgan, Richard - Ray & Berndtson/Lovas Stanley (R), ON, *172*
Morgan, Richard - Ray & Berndtson/Lovas Stanley (R), ON, *172*
Morgan, Richard - Ray & Berndtson/Lovas Stanley (R), ON, *173*
Morgan, Richard - Ray & Berndtson/Lovas Stanley (R), ON, *173*
Morgan, Vincent - Bishop Partners (R), NY, *17*
Morganti, Ray - Romac Int'l., Inc. (C), FL, *543*
Morgenstern, Richard L. - Morgenstern Int'l., Inc. (C), CA, *485*
Morgenstern, Richard L. - Morgenstern Int'l., Inc. (C), FL, *485*
Moriarty, Philip S. J. - Moriarty/Fox, Inc. (R), IL, *147*
Morice, James L. - Mirtz Morice, Inc. (R), CT, *145*
Morin, Gail - Comprehensive Search (C), GA, *295*
Morin, Michelle - SpencerStuart (R), ON, *197*
Morin, Paul - F-O-R-T-U-N-E Personnel Consultants of Knoxville (C), TN, *350*
Moris, Kristina - The Washington Firm, Ltd. (R), WA, *216*
Morley, Michael A. - The Morley Group (C), IN, *486*
Morreale, Stephen S. - Diversified Health Search (R), PA, *52*
Morreale, Stephen S. - Diversified Search, Inc. (R), PA, *52*

Morrical, Michael - Carnegie Partners, Inc. (R), IL, *30*
Morrill, Cary - Executive Alliance (R), MA, *62*
Morris, Barbara - Chad Management Group (C), ON, *288*
Morris, Charles C. - Warren, Morris & Madison, Ltd. (C), CA, *616*
Morris, David A. - Heidrick & Struggles, Inc. (R), TX, *90*
Morris, David W. - WTW Assoc., Inc. (R), NY, *225*
Morris, Delia - DHR Int'l., Inc. (R), DC, *50*
Morris, Gary - Management Resources (C), TX, *467*
Morris, Jay - Dunhill Professional Search of Peoria (C), IL, *317*
Morris, Joseph - Lekan & Assoc., Inc. (R), OH, *128*
Morris, Kevin - PIC Executive Search (C), GA, *511*
Morris, Kristine A. - Morris & Berger (R), CA, *147*
Morris, Lana - Dunhill Professional Search of Mansfield (C), TX, *318*
Morris, Leonard - Specialized Search Assoc. (C), FL, *589*
Morris, Paul T. - The Morris Group (C), PA, *486*
Morris, Robert J. - Dunhill Staffing Systems, Inc. (C), NY, *318*
Morris, Sunny - Human Resource Dimensions, Inc. (C), TX, *384*
Morrisey, Jim - Fortune Personnel Consultants of San Antonio, Inc. (C), TX, *350*
Morrison, Brian M. - Western Management Consultants (R), BC, *218*
Morrison, C. Robert - Quetico Corp. (R), TX, *170*
Morrison, Janis - Garrett Assoc. Inc. (R), GA, *75*
Morrison, Stephen - Lewis Companies Inc. (R), ON, *129*
Morrison, Susan S. - Quetico Corp. (R), TX, *170*
Morrison, William - Longshore + Simmons (R), PA, *131*
Morrow, Michael - RSMR, Inc. (R), IL, *182*
Morse, Aaron - Management Recruiters of South Central Alaska (C), AK, *425*
Morse, James A. - Sales Consultants of Honolulu (C), HI, *558*
Morse, Jeannine - Management Recruiters of South Central Alaska (C), AK, *425*
Morse, Jeffrey A. - Brandywine Management Group (R), MD, *22*
Morse, Mary K. - Travis & Co., Inc. (R), MA, *210*
Morse, Stephen W. - Management Recruiters of Braintree (C), MA, *430*
Morse, Stephen W. - Management Recruiters of Providence (C), RI, *435*
Morse, Sy - Sofco (C), NY, *586*
Mortensen, Kenneth A. - Kingsley Quinn/USA (R), NJ, *115*
Morton, Dudley - DHR Int'l., Inc. (R), IL, *49*
Morton, John M. - New Directions, Inc. (C), IL, *492*
Morton, Nancy J. - Robert T. Morton Assoc., Inc. (C), MA, *486*
Morton, R. C. - Morton, McCorkle & Assoc. Inc. (R), MO, *147*
Morton, Robert T. - Robert T. Morton Assoc., Inc. (C), MA, *486*
Morton, Sam - Sloan & Assoc., Inc. (C), VA, *583*
Mosca, Bob - Management Recruiters of Adirondacks (C), NY, *432*
Moscow, Frank - The Brentwood Group Ltd. (R), OR, *23*
Moser, Amy - TriStaff Group (C), CA, *609*
Moses, Brad - Information Systems Professionals (C), NC, *388*
Moses, Jerry - J. M. Eagle Partners Ltd. (C), WI, *325*
Mosholder, Rick - Robert William James & Assoc. (C), OH, *539*
Moson, Carol L. - The Coelyn Group (R), CA, *37*
Moss, Barbara - Moss & Co. (R), WA, *148*
Moss, Rich - Quest Enterprises, Ltd. (C), IL, *527*
Mossman, John G. - M. K. & Assoc. (C), PA, *422*
Mostow, David - SHS of Allentown (C), PA, *580*
Mott, Alex - Headden Assoc. (R), WA, *88*
Mouchet, Marcus - Commonwealth Consultants (C), GA, *294*
Mountain, Russell D. - Rowland Mountain & Assoc. (C), GA, *547*
Mowatt, Ginny - SpencerStuart (R), IL, *197*
Moy, Betty - Cook Assoc.,® Inc. (R), IL, *40*
Moyer, David S. - Moyer, Sherwood Assoc., Inc. (R), NY, *148*
Moyer, Laurene F. - OmniSearch, Inc. (C), FL, *499*
Moyer, Samuel - OmniSearch, Inc. (C), FL, *499*
Moynihan, Susan - Orion Int'l. Consulting Group, Inc. (C), HI, *499*
Moyse, Richard G. - Thorndike Deland Assoc. LLC (R), NY, *48*
Mroczek, Darlene - Wheelless Group (R), IL, *219*
Mrozek, Joe - Moffitt Int'l., Inc. (R), NJ, *146*
Mruk, Edwin S. - Mruk & E.M.A. Partners (R), NY, *148*
Much, Isaac - Much & Co. (R), NY, *148*
Muecke, Heidi - DHR Int'l., Inc. (R), IL, *49*
Mueller, Howard - mfg/Search, Inc. (C), IN, *480*
Mueller, Michael S. - DieckMueller Group (R), WI, *51*
Mueller, William - Noll Human Resource Services (C), MO, *494*
Mueller-Maerki, Fortunat F. - Egon Zehnder Int'l. Inc. (R), NY, *227*
Muendel, H. Edward - Stanton Chase Int'l. (R), MD, *199*
Muhlfelder, Daniel J. - L. J. Gonzer Assoc. (C), NJ, *360*
Muir, Sherry - The Hunter Group, Inc. (C), MI, *385*
Mulberger, Robert D. - NRI Staffing Resources (C), DC, *497*
Mulcahey, Bob T. - Management Recruiters of Albany (C), NY, *432*
Mulcahy, Patrick - Mulcahy Co. (C), WI, *487*
Mullen, James J. - Mullen Assoc., Inc. (R), NC, *149*
Mullen, Maryrose H. - Emmett Executive Search, Inc. (C), NY, *330*
Mullenhoff, James A. - Rob Dey Executive Search (R), FL, *49*
Muller, Charles A. - AJM Professional Services (C), MI, *243*
Muller, Michael - Financialjobs.com (C), CA, *340*
Muller, Russell M. - Management Recruiters of Orange (C), CA, *426*
Mulligan, Judy - Emerald Legal Search (C), NH, *329*
Mulligan, Pamela L. - Pamela L. Mulligan, Inc. (R), NH, *149*
Mulliken, Ken - Human Resource Dimensions, Inc. (C), MO, *384*
Mullings, Joe S. - Management Recruiters of Delray Beach (C), FL, *427*
Mullins, Bob H. - Effective Search, Inc. (R), IL, *57*
Mulshine, Michael A. - The Mulshine Co., Inc. (R), NJ, *149*
Mulshine, Michael G. - The Mulshine Company, Ltd. (R), NY, *149*
Mulvaney, Ronald F. - R. F. Mulvaney & Assoc., Inc. (R), MO, *149*
Mulvey, James E. - SilverSands Int'l. (C), FL, *582*
Mulvey, Scott - SilverSands Int'l. (C), PA, *582*
Mummert, Dennis D. - Sweeney Harbert & Mummert, Inc. (R), FL, *205*
Munger, Donald - Berkshire Search Assoc. (C), MA, *265*
Munn, Bill - RHS Assoc. (C), AL, *536*
Muñoz, Francisco Noriega - PricewaterhouseCoopers Executive Search (R), MX, *168*
Munro, Jennifer - Jennifer Munro & Partners, Inc. (R), SC, *149*
Munroe, Michael - Munroe, Curry & Bond Assoc. (R), NJ, *149*
Munson, Brad - ProSearch Recruiting (C), CA, *524*
Munson, Larry - DHR Int'l., Inc. (R), MO, *50*
Murawski, Joseph S. - Teknon Employment Resources, Inc. (C), OH, *604*
Murff, Pamela - Dunhilkl Staffing Systems of Oakland/Macomb (C), MI, *317*
Murlas, Kim - DHR Int'l., Inc. (R), IL, *49*
Murphey, James F. - Management Recruiters of Virginia Beach (C), VA, *437*
Murphey, James F. - Sales Consultants of Virginia Beach (C), VA, *555*

PRINCIPALS

Murphy, Bob - Murphy Partners Int'l. (R), IL, *150*
Murphy, Clarke - Russell Reynolds Assoc., Inc. (R), NY, *177*
Murphy, Cornelius J. - Goodrich & Sherwood Assoc., Inc. (R), NY, *80*
Murphy, Dan - The Pollack Group (C), ON, *514*
Murphy, Dan - Dick Wray & Consultants, Inc. (R), UT, *225*
Murphy, Darlene R. - Gateway Group Personnel, LLC (C), TN, *355*
Murphy, Gary J. - Stone, Murphy & Olson (R), MN, *201*
Murphy, Irene - StratfordGroup (R), CA, *203*
Murphy, James - MSI Int'l. (C), GA, *487*
Murphy, Ken - Kenneth Murphy & Assoc. (C), NS, *487*
Murphy, Marsha - MTA Partners (R), TX, *148*
Murphy, Pat - Robert William James & Assoc. (C), OR, *539*
Murphy, Patrick J. - P. J. Murphy & Assoc., Inc. (R), WI, *150*
Murphy, Robert - Cypress Int'l., Inc. (R), FL, *45*
Murphy, Susan - Onsite Staffing Solutions (R), IL, *156*
Murray, David - Ray & Berndtson/Lovas Stanley (R), ON, *172*
Murray, David - Ray & Berndtson/Lovas Stanley (R), ON, *173*
Murray, Jeanette M. - The Murray Group (C), IL, *487*
Murray, John - Cypress Int'l., Inc. (R), FL, *45*
Murray, Matthew - Management Recruiters of Boone (C), NC, *456*
Murray, Megan - The Mayes Group, Ltd. (R), PA, *139*
Murray, Patrick - The Murray Group (C), IL, *487*
Murray, Robert W. - David M. Griffith & Assoc., Ltd. (R), CA, *82*
Murrell, James O. - Professionals in Recruiting Co. (C), TN, *523*
Murrell, Maxine W. - Professionals in Recruiting Co. (C), TN, *523*
Musick, Diana - Musick & Assoc. (C), CA, *487*
Musick, Stephen - Musick & Assoc. (C), CA, *487*
Mussato, Ray - Dick Williams & Assoc. (C), CA, *621*
Musso, Connie - Consumer Search Inc. (C), MA, *298*
Mustin, Joyce - J: Blakslee Int'l., Ltd. (R), CA, *18*
Muthersbaugh, Jeff - Brandywine Retained Ventures, Inc. (R), CT, *22*
Myatt, Jr., James S. - Sanford Rose Assoc. - Santa Barbara (C), CA, *565*
Mycoff, Carl A. - Mycoff & Assoc. (R), CO, *150*
Mydlach, Renee - C.P.S., Inc. (C), IL, *278*
Myer, Rusty - RLM Assoc., Ltd. (R), NY, *179*
Myeroff, Sheldon - Direct Recruiters, Inc. (C), OH, *312*
Myers, Bonnie - Myers Career Assoc., Inc. (C), CA, *488*
Myers, Deedee - DDJ Myers, Ltd. (R), AZ, *150*
Myers, Ed - D.P. Specialists, Inc. (C), CA, *306*
Myers, IV, F. Scott - Corporate Search Consultants (C), IN, *301*
Myers, Hal - Fortune Personnel Consultants of Huntsville, Inc. (C), AL, *344*
Myers, Jamie - Management Recruiters of Houston-Northeast (C), TX, *463*
Myers, John - DDJ Myers, Ltd. (R), MA, *150*
Myers, Michael L. - ISC of Cincinnati Inc. (C), OH, *394*
Myers, Richard L. - MedXec USA, Inc. (C), FL, *478*
Myers, Roy - National Career Search (C), AZ, *489*
Myers, Terry - Boyden (R), NJ, *21*
Myers, Thomas - Careers Plus (R), CA, *29*
Myers, William A. - Tarnow Int'l. (R), NJ, *206*
Mygatt, Marlena - Software Engineering Solutions, Inc. (C), CA, *587*
Nachman, Philip S. - Nachman Biomedical (C), MA, *488*
Nadeau, Robert - KPMG Executive Search (R), QE, *120*
Nadel, R. J. - ACCESS Technology (C), CA, *234*
Naderi, Fred - Executive Direction, Inc. (C), CA, *333*
Nadherny, Christopher C. - SpencerStuart (R), IL, *197*
Nadherny, Pete - The Angus Group, Ltd. (C), OH, *251*
Nadzam, Richard J. - Nadzam, Lusk, Horgan & Assoc., Inc. (R), CA, *150*
Naegle, Brad - KABL Ability Network (C), CA, *402*
Naff, Bud - Management Recruiters of Lynnwood (C), WA, *465*
Nagata, Lorene - QD Legal (C), ON, *526*
Nagle, Chip - Tyler & Company (R), GA, *212*
Nagler, Leon G. - Nagler, Robins & Poe, Inc. (R), MA, *150*
Nagy, Lou - The Ward Group (R), MA, *215*
Nahas, Caroline - Korn/Ferry Int'l. (R), CA, *117*
Nahas, Robert - Herbert Mines Assoc., Inc. (R), NY, *145*
Nails, Clarence - DHR Int'l., Inc. (R), IL, *49*
Nair, Sanjay - Fortuna Technologies Inc. (C), NJ, *343*
Nalepa, Jim - DHR Int'l., Inc. (R), IL, *49*
Nalley, Ed - Executive Search Int'l. (C), TX, *336*
Nalley, Ginger - Executive Search Int'l. (C), TX, *336*
Nalley, Jeff - Executive Search Int'l. (C), TX, *336*
Nanney, Brenda - Lou Michaels Assoc., Inc. (C), MI, *481*
Nanney, Jerry - Lou Michaels Assoc., Inc. (C), MI, *481*
Napier, Ginger L. - Clarey/Napier Int'l., L.C. (R), TX, *36*
Naples, Len Di - Roth Young of Pittsburgh (C), PA, *546*
Narita, Art - Essential Solutions, Inc. (C), CA, *331*
Narlock, Renée - David M. Griffith & Assoc., Ltd. (R), FL, *82*
Narsh, Daniel - Windsor Consultants, Inc. (C), TX, *622*
Nash, James - The Gammill Group, Inc. (C), OH, *354*
Nash, Lisa - Alliance Executive Search, Inc. (R), MA, *4*
Nashleanas, Richard P. - Monarch Technology Management LLC (C), CO, *484*
Nason, Dennis H. - Nason & Nason (C), FL, *488*
Nason-Robson, Nayda - Nason & Nason (C), FL, *488*
Nass, Martin D. - LAI Ward Howell (R), NY, *122*
Nassar, Richard D. - Sales Consultant of Syracuse (C), NY, *554*
Natdone, II, Dominick M. - Saviar, Inc. (C), AZ, *571*
Nathan, Catherine R. - LAI Ward Howell (R), NY, *123*
Nathan, Edward - Systems Search (C), IL, *599*
Nathasingh, Steve - Growth Strategies, Inc. (R), FL, *83*
Natowitz, Robert - DeMatteo Associates (C), NY, *311*
Natvig, Diane - Meng, Finseth & Assoc., Inc. (R), CA, *143*
Naud, Renee L. - Compass Group Ltd. (R), MI, *38*
Naughton, James - Dunhill Professional Search of Virginia Beach (C), VA, *318*
Naulty, Sharon - Koltnow & Company (R), NY, *117*
Nava, Terri - The Consulting Group Ltd. (R), NY, *40*
Navickas, Sophia - Lynx, Inc. (C), MA, *421*
Neal, Denton M. - Sales Consultants of Chattanooga-East (C), TN, *555*
Neal, Don - Don Neal & Assoc. (C), OK, *491*
Neal, Randall - The Broadmoor Group, L.L.C. (R), TX, *24*
Near, Thomas - Sales Consultant of Charlotte-SE (C), NC, *554*
Needham, Mary - Reserve Technology Institute (R), TX, *175*
Neelin, Sharon - The Caldwell Partners Amrop International (R), ON, *26*
Neely, Bob E. - Sales Consultants (C), GA, *552*
Neenan, Ed - Technology Consultants Int'l. (C), OH, *603*
Neff, Thomas J. - SpencerStuart (R), NY, *196*

Negus, Suzie - Norrell Financial Staffing (C), GA, *495*
Nehiley, Jack J. - Management Recruiters of Boston (C), MA, *430*
Nehring, Sara - Johnson Smith & Knisely (R), IL, *107*
Neidenberg, Steven - William Bell Assoc., Inc. (C), NJ, *263*
Neidhart, Craig C. - TNS Partners, Inc. (R), TX, *209*
Neighbors, Betty - Personnel Assoc. (C), NC, *508*
Neighbors, Cliff - Personnel Assoc. (C), NC, *508*
Neighbors, Greg - Kutt, Inc. (C), CO, *410*
Neiman, Jennifer - Brentwood Int'l. (R), CA, *23*
Nein, Lawrence F. - LAI Ward Howell (R), IL, *123*
Neir, Karla - Southwest Selective Search, Inc. (C), TX, *588*
Neir, Paul - Southwest Selective Search, Inc. (C), TX, *588*
Nelms, Debra - Baker, Nelms & Montgomery (C), IL, *258*
Nelson, Allan C. - Davies, Park (R), AB, *47*
Nelson, Beverly M. - Beverly Nelson & Assoc. Inc. (C), CA, *491*
Nelson, C J - Lekan & Assoc., Inc. (R), OH, *128*
Nelson, Christopher - MIXTEC Group (R), CA, *145*
Nelson, David G. - The Personnel Group, Inc. (R), MN, *163*
Nelson, Jane Ann - Taylor Winfield (R), TX, *207*
Nelson, Len - Len Nelson & Assoc., Inc. (C), TX, *491*
Nelson, Lynn - Ashford Management Group, Inc. (R), GA, *8*
Nelson, Nancy - Howard Lieberman & Assoc., Inc. (C), MN, *417*
Nelson, Paul - London Executive Consultants Inc. (C), ON, *420*
Nelson, Randy - Orion Int'l. Consulting Group, Inc. (C), NC, *499*
Nelson, Richard - Pacific Crossing (C), CA, *501*
Nelson, Richard D. - Heidrick & Struggles, Inc. (R), IL, *90*
Nemec, Edward C. - Craig Affiliates, Inc. (C), TX, *302*
Nepovadny, John A. - The Langford Search, Inc. (C), AL, *412*
Nepple, Rosemarie - Management Recruiters of Upper Westchester (C), NY, *454*
Nepple, Vern D. - Management Recruiters of Upper Westchester (C), NY, *454*
Nestor, Kristin C. - Crowder & Company (R), MI, *43*
Neubauer, Robert - E O Technical (C), CT, *324*
Neuberth, Jeffrey - Johnson Smith & Knisely (R), NY, *107*
Neufeld, Max - Partners In Human Resources Int'l., Inc. (R), NY, *160*
Neuharth, Kathleen - E T Search Inc. (C), CA, *324*
Neumann, Joan - Gossage Regan Assoc. (R), NY, *80*
Neumann, Pete - Management Recruiters of Evergreen (C), CO, *426*
Neumann, Vicki A. - Management Recruiters of Evergreen (C), CO, *426*
Neumayer, Chuck - David M. Griffith & Assoc., Ltd. (R), CA, *82*
Neuweiler, Mark - Saber Group, Inc. (C), TX, *550*
Neves, Trever - TriStaff Group (C), CA, *609*
Nevins, Phyllis S. - Morgenstern Int'l., Inc. (C), FL, *485*
Newberry, Joyce - Human Resource Bureau (C), CA, *384*
Newby, Neville I. - Dunhill Staffing Systems (C), NY, *318*
Newcomb, Carol A. - Tierney Assoc., Inc. (R), PA, *209*
Newcomb, Janet - Accountants On Call (C), KY, *236*
Newcorn, Andrew R. - The Neil Michael Group, Inc./Global Partners (R), NY, *151*
Newell, Beverly - The Beardsley Group Inc. (C), CT, *261*
Newell, Carlyle - Management Alliance Group, Inc. (R), NJ, *134*
Newell, Donald Pierce - Newell Assoc. (R), NY, *151*
Newell, Wayne - Management Alliance Group, Inc. (R), NJ, *134*
Newhart, Tal - DHR Int'l., Inc. (R), IL, *49*
Newman, Caleene Jones - Unlimited Staffing Solutions, Inc. (C), MI, *611*
Newman, Edgar F. - ENI (R), CT, *59*
Newman, Gloria - Jack Richman & Assoc. (C), FL, *537*
Newman, Keith - W. Robert Eissler & Assoc., Inc. (C), TX, *327*
Newman, Richard J. - RJN Consulting (R), NY, *179*
Newpoff, Brad L. - Furst Group/MPI (R), IL, *72*
Newpoff, Brad L. - Global HealthCare Partners (R), IL, *78*
Newton, Marje - Perry • Newton Assoc. (C), MD, *507*
Newton, Scott - DHR Int'l., Inc. (R), RI, *51*
Nguyen, Hanh - Huntley Associates (Dallas), Inc. (C), TX, *386*
Nicastri, Diane - Mason & Nicrasti Ltd. (R), CA, *138*
Nichipor, Michael A. - Sanford Rose Assoc. - Carmel, IN (C), IN, *567*
Nicholaou, Jean - Nicholaou & Co. (R), IL, *151*
Nicholas, Jack - DHR Int'l., Inc. (R), PA, *51*
Nicholas, Tara J. - Creative Management Strategies, Ltd. (R), NY, *42*
Nicholls, R. J. - Interim Management Resources Inc. (C), ON, *392*
Nichols, Charles H. - Nichols & Company (R), CO, *151*
Nichols, E. Diane - Nichols Brown Int'l. (R), NY, *151*
Nichols, Gary - Koontz, Jeffries & Assoc., Inc. (R), FL, *117*
Nichols, Marc - Marc Nichols Assoc., Inc. (C), NY, *493*
Nicholson, Jack F. - Fell & Nicholson Technology Resources (R), CA, *65*
Nicholson, Joy - Hughes & Sloan, Inc. (C), GA, *383*
Nicholson, Philip J. - P. J. Nicholson & Assoc. (C), IL, *493*
Nickels, Edward L. - Michael Latas & Assoc., Inc. (R), MO, *126*
Nickerson, Dennis - Survival Systems Staffing, Inc. (C), CA, *597*
Nickerson, Jeanette - Survival Systems Staffing, Inc. (C), CA, *597*
Nicklas, Kirk - The Ellsworth Group (C), NY, *329*
Nickley, Sandy - Executive Search, Ltd. (C), OH, *336*
Nicolaas, Gina - Dumont & Co. (C), BC, *316*
Nicolai, Linda - Brad Marks Int'l. (R), CA, *136*
Nicoll, Marty - Management Recruiters of Short Hills (C), NJ, *431*
Nicolosi, Charles - CN Associates (C), CA, *293*
Niedbalski, Michael - Executive Search Plus, Inc. (C), IN, *336*
Niemond, Nancy A. - The Niemond Corp. (R), CA, *152*
Niemond, Wesley E. - The Niemond Corp. (R), CA, *152*
Niermann, Richard - NPS of Atlanta, Inc. (C), GA, *496*
Nigbor, Jeannie - Healthcare Recruiters of Indiana (C), IN, *372*
Nigg, Daniel - Slayton Int'l., Inc. (R), IL, *192*
Nigro, Marci Yacker - Telecom Executive Group (C), NY, *605*
Niles, Charles K. - The Human Resource Department Ltd. (R), OH, *98*
Nimmo, Richard - AmeriResource Group Inc. (C), OK, *248*
Nini, Steven B. - West Coast Recruiting (C), CA, *619*
Nino, Jr., Reyes - Nino Recruiting & Staffing, Inc. (C), TX, *493*
Nirenberg, David - Stanton Chase Int'l./Botrie Assoc. (R), ON, *199*
Nishimoto, Lynn S. - The Coelyn Group (R), CA, *37*
Nitchke, Howard - Johnson Smith & Knisely (R), CA, *107*
Nitzberg, Ira Z. - Ira Z. Nitzberg (C), NY, *493*
Nix Gilmore, Pamela - Management Recruiters of Loudoun County South (C), VA, *465*
Nixon, Barbara - PricewaterhouseCoopers Executive Search (R), ON, *168*
Nixon, Jeffrey L. - J. L. Nixon Consulting (C), TX, *493*
Nixon, Ted - TechNix Inc. (C), ON, *602*
Noble, Donald - Noble & Assoc., Inc. (C), NY, *494*
Noble, Jeffrey M. - Management Recruiters of Dayton, Inc. (C), OH, *457*

PRINCIPALS

Noble, Jeffrey M. - Sales Consultants (C), OH, *555*
Nocifora, David - Christian & Timbers, Inc. (R), OH, *34*
Noebel, Todd R. - The Noebel Search Group, Inc. (C), TX, *494*
Noeske, Nancy R. - Overton Consulting (R), WI, *157*
Nolan, Michael - Accounting & Bookkeeping Personnel, Inc. (C), AZ, *238*
Nolan, Nancy C. - The Nolan Group (C), CA, *494*
Nolan, Raymond P. - Mangement Recruiters of Summerlin (C), NV, *431*
Nolan, Thomas P. - The Nolan Group (C), CA, *494*
Noland, Amy - Accountants On Call (C), GA, *235*
Noll, William T. - Noll Human Resource Services (C), NE, *494*
Nolte, Jr., William D. - W. D. Nolte & Company (R), CT, *152*
Noonan, Michael A. - Management Association Network (C), WI, *424*
Noone, Christine - Cook Assoc.,® Inc. (R), IL, *40*
Noorani, Frank - Management Recruiters of Edison (C), NJ, *431*
Nord, Steve - Techstaff Inc. (C), IA, *603*
Nordeman, Jacques C. - Nordeman Grimm, Inc. (R), NY, *152*
Norindr, Bev - The Hampton Group (C), NY, *368*
Norman, Allen G. - Pursuant Legal Consultants (R), WA, *170*
Norman, Marcie - Management Recruiters of Franktown (C), CO, *442*
Norman, Paul W. - Paul Winston Norman & Assoc. (R), IL, *152*
Normann, Amy - Robert M. Flanagan & Assoc., Ltd. (R), NY, *68*
Norrie, Vicki - F-O-R-T-U-N-E Personnel Consultants of Boise (R), ID, *70*
Norris, Abby J. - GES Services, Inc. (R), NY, *76*
Norris, Cathy A. - Norris Agency (C), TX, *496*
Norris, Dan - Management Recruiters of Boone (C), NC, *456*
Norris, Daniel F. - Allen, Wayne & Co. LLC (C), TX, *245*
Norris, John B. - John B. Norris & Assoc., Inc. (C), MD, *495*
Norris, Kris - Interim Accounting Professionals (C), CA, *391*
Norris, Ronald - Ronald Norris & Assoc. (C), IL, *495*
Norris, Terry - Creative-Leadership, Inc. (R), CA, *42*
North, Barbara - Herbert Mines Assoc., Inc. (R), NY, *145*
Northrop, Michael S. - Management Resource Group (C), MN, *467*
Norton, Greg - Norton & Assoc. (C), IL, *496*
Norton, III, James B. - LAI Ward Howell (R), GA, *123*
Norton, Kim - JenKim Int'l. Ltd., Inc. (C), FL, *398*
Norton, Paul - Romac Int'l., Inc. (C), MA, *543*
Norton, Robert W. - JenKim Int'l. Ltd., Inc. (C), FL, *398*
Norwine, James O. - ExecuGroup, Inc. (R), PA, *61*
Norwood, Donna - Robert Half Canada Inc. (C), AB, *366*
Nosal, David - Korn/Ferry Int'l. (R), CA, *117*
Nosky, Richard E. - LAI Ward Howell (R), AZ, *123*
Noto, Joseph A. - CMS Management Services LLC (C), IN, *293*
Nour, Naz - Med-Ex Services (C), OH, *476*
Novak, Karen - Francis & Assoc. (R), IA, *71*
Nowakowski, Mark R. - Global Engineers Inc. (C), ME, *358*
Noyes, Jim - Sales Consultants - Bristol County (C), MA, *559*
Nuessle, Warren G. - Nuessle, Kurdziel & Weiss, Inc. (R), PA, *153*
Nugent, Randolph L. - Management Recruiters of Roswell-West (C), GA, *428*
Nunn, Roy M. - The Corporate Advisory Group (R), FL, *41*
Nunziata, Fred A. - Eden & Assoc., Inc. (C), PA, *326*
Nyborg, Marilyn - Nyborg•Dow Assoc., Inc. (C), CA, *497*
Nyhan, Alan - Management Recruiters of Burlington (C), VT, *437*
Nymark, John - NYCOR Search, Inc. (C), MN, *497*
Nyvall, S. L. - McKeen & Company (R), TX, *141*
O'Biern, Matt - David M. Griffith & Assoc., Ltd. (R), IL, *82*
O'Brien, Brent - Executive Search Consultants Corp. (C), IL, *335*
O'Brien, David - Finney-Taylor Personnel & Management Consultants Ltd. (C), AB, *341*
O'Brien, Debbie A. - Management Recruiters of Bernardsville (C), NJ, *431*
O'Brien, Frank E. - Austin Michaels, Ltd., Inc. (C), AZ, *256*
O'Brien, Jr., James J. - O'Brien Consulting Services (R), MA, *153*
O'Brien, Justus J. - Egon Zehnder Int'l. Inc. (R), NY, *227*
O'Brien, Katy - Telecom Executive Group (C), VA, *605*
O'Brien, Lindy - O'Brien and Roof (C), OH, *497*
O'Brien, Marlon W. - Management Recruiters of Bernardsville (C), NJ, *431*
O'Brien, Michael Joseph - Harrington & O'Brien, Inc. (C), NH, *369*
O'Brien, Timothy M. - O'Brien & Bell (R), OH, *153*
O'Bryant, Morgan - Brad Marks Int'l. (R), CA, *136*
O'Callaghan, Terry K. - O'Callaghan Honey/Ray & Berndtson Inc. (R), AB, *153*
O'Callaghan, Terry K. - O'Callaghan Honey/Ray & Berndtson Inc. (R), AB, *172*
O'Callaghan, William - Ken Clark Int'l. (R), NJ, *36*
O'Connell, Brian M. - O'Connell Group Inc. (C), CT, *497*
O'Connell, Bridget - Accountants On Call (C), IL, *235*
O'Connell, Michael - Ryan, Miller & Assoc. (C), CA, *549*
O'Connor, Fred - F-O-R-T-U-N-E Consultants of Memphis (C), TN, *349*
O'Connor, John R. - John R. O'Connor & Assoc. (C), IL, *497*
O'Connor, Kerry - Fell & Nicholson Technology Resources (R), CA, *66*
O'Connor, Rod - O'Connor Resources (C), TX, *497*
O'Connor, Thomas F. - O'Connor, O'Connor, Lordi, Ltd. (R), PA, *154*
O'Connor, William M. - Kennedy & Co. (R), IL, *112*
O'Daniel, Beverly W. - The Elsworth Group (C), TX, *329*
O'Daniel, James E. - The Elsworth Group (C), TX, *329*
O'Dell, Krista - Impact Technical Staffing (C), OR, *387*
O'Dell, Robert - Roth Young Executive Search (C), TX, *546*
O'Donnell, M. Theresa - Grant/Morgan Assoc., Inc. (C), MD, *361*
O'Donnell, Margaret L. - Moyer, Sherwood Assoc., Inc. (R), CT, *148*
O'Donnell, Tim - Johnson Smith & Knisely (R), IL, *107*
O'Gorman, David J. - DHR Int'l., Inc. (R), IL, *49*
O'Halloran, Terry - Dick Wray & Consultants, Inc. (R), NY, *225*
O'Hara, Daniel M. - Lynch Miller Moore Partners, Inc. (R), IL, *132*
O'Hara, James J. - Barone-O'Hara Assoc., Inc. (R), NJ, *11*
O'Hara, Kelly - Goodkind Assoc. Inc. (C), NY, *360*
O'Hearn, Tierney E. - Marley Group Ltd. (C), NY, *471*
O'Keefe, Frank - The Marathon Group (C), FL, *469*
O'Keefe, Ian - O'Keefe & Assoc. (C), AR, *498*
O'Keefe, Jack - John O'Keefe & Assoc., Inc. (R), WA, *154*
O'Keefe, John - O'Keefe & Assoc., Inc. (R), CT, *154*
O'Keefe, John P. - O'Keefe & Assoc. (C), TX, *498*
O'Keefe, Kathy - O'Keefe & Assoc., Inc. (R), CT, *154*
O'Keefe, Kelly - O'Keefe & Assoc., Inc. (R), CT, *154*
O'Keefe, Mary E. - Johnson Smith & Knisely (R), NY, *107*
O'Keefe, Michael - Ray & Berndtson/Lovas Stanley (R), ON, *172*
O'Keefe, Michael - Ray & Berndtson/Lovas Stanley (R), ON, *173*

O'Leary, James - The Brentwood Group Ltd. (R), OR, *23*
O'Maley, Kimberlee - SpencerStuart (R), CA, *196*
O'Malley, Chris - Travel Personnel (C), OH, *609*
O'Meally, Diane - Accountants On Call (C), NJ, *235*
O'Neal, Jane - Austin Group Int'l./Marlar Int'l. (R), TX, *9*
O'Neill, James P. - Battalia Winston Int'l./The Euram Consultants Group (R), IL, *13*
O'Neill, Kathleen A. - RIC Corp. (R), FL, *177*
O'Neill, Kevin - J. B. Brown & Assoc., Inc. (C), OH, *275*
O'Neill, Kevin R. - Performance Resources, Inc. (C), RI, *507*
O'Neill, Sean - Waterford Executive Group Ltd. (C), IL, *616*
O'Neill, Stephen A. - O'Neill & Co. (R), CT, *154*
O'Neill, Ted - Russ Hadick & Assoc. Inc. (C), OH, *365*
O'Pray, James - Management Recruiters of Port St. Lucie (C), FL, *426*
O'Reilly, John D. - StratfordGroup (R), OH, *203*
O'Reilly, William E. - Management Recruiters of Cincinnati/Sharonville, Inc. (C), OH, *457*
O'Rourke, Bart - Abacus Group LLC (C), NY, *232*
O'Rourke, Dennis M. - O'Rourke Companies, Inc. (R), TX, *154*
O'Rourke, Kevin - Ward Assoc. (C), ON, *615*
O'Rourke, Kevin - Ward Assoc. (C), QE, *615*
O'Rourke, Rachel - O'Rourke Companies, Inc. (R), TX, *154*
O'Shaughnessy, John - Boyden (R), CA, *20*
O'Shea, Bree - DHR Int'l., Inc. (R), CA, *49*
O'Steen, Gloria - American Professional Search, Inc. (C), TN, *248*
O'Steen, Ray - American Professional Search, Inc. (C), TN, *248*
O'Sullivan, Kathleen - O'Sullivan Search Inc. (C), ON, *498*
O'Toole, Dennis P. - Dennis P. O'Toole & Assoc. Inc. (R), NY, *154*
O'Toole, Nancy L. - O'Toole & Company, Inc. (R), IL, *154*
O'Toole, William R. - O'Toole & Company, Inc. (R), IL, *154*
Oakley, Jr., Mitch - Management Recruiters of Greensboro (C), NC, *433*
Oakley-Lowe, Carolyn - DHR Int'l., Inc. (R), IL, *49*
Ober, Lynn W. - Ober & Company (R), CA, *155*
Oberlander, Howard I. - Oberlander & Co., Inc. (R), IL, *155*
Oberlander, James - Major, Hagen & Africa (C), IL, *423*
Oberman, Heidi - Medical Recruiters Inc. (C), MO, *477*
Oberting, Dave - Sales Consultants (C), OH, *551*
Oberting, Dave W. - Management Recruiters of Charlotte-West (C), NC, *432*
Oberting, David - Management Recruiters International, Inc. (MRI) (C), OH, *425*
Obledo, Oscar - DHR Int'l., Inc. (R), CA, *49*
Obrand, Barry - Russell Reynolds Assoc., Inc. (R), CA, *176*
Occhiboi, Emil - Romac Int'l., Inc. (C), PA, *544*
Occhiboi, Emil - Romac Int'l., Inc. (C), PA, *544*
Ocon, Olga - Busch International (R), CA, *25*
Oda, Lynn - The Hollins Group, Inc. (R), IL, *95*
Odell, Steve N. - Odell & Assoc., Inc. (C), TX, *498*
Odia, Frank Michael - High Tech Staffing Group (C), OR, *377*
Offutt, Brian - SpencerStuart (R), NY, *196*
Ogata, Keith - Boyle/Ogata Executive Search (R), CA, *21*
Ogden, Dayton - SpencerStuart (R), CT, *196*
Ogdon, Thomas H. - The Ogdon Partnership (R), NY, *155*
Oglesby, Peggy - F-O-R-T-U-N-E Personnel of Nashville (C), TN, *350*
Oglesby, Tom - F-O-R-T-U-N-E Personnel of Nashville (C), TN, *350*
Ojeda, Frank - Harbor Consultants Int'l., Inc. (C), VA, *368*
Okyn, Leonard - Lawrence James Assoc. of Florida, Inc. (C), FL, *414*
Oldani, Jerrold - The Oldani Group (R), WA, *155*
Oldani, Jerry - The Oldani Group (R), WA, *155*
Oldfield, Theresa L. - Strategic Alliance Network, Ltd. (C), OH, *595*
Olenick, John G. - Partners Resource Group (C), VA, *504*
Olesen, Jeannette - Management Recruiters of the Baltimore Washington Corridor (C), MD, *450*
Oliveira, Beatriz J. - Priority Executive Search (C), FL, *518*
Oliverio, Anthony P. - Management Recruiters of Charleston (C), WV, *437*
Oliveros, Nancy P. - New Dawn Employment Search (C), CA, *491*
Ollinger, Chuck - Ollinger Partners (R), MA, *156*
Olman, Robert - COR Management Services, Ltd. (C), NY, *298*
Olmstead, George T. - Blackshaw, Olmstead, Lynch & Koenig (R), GA, *18*
Olsen, Carl M. - A.T. Kearney Executive Search (R), CA, *111*
Olsen, David G. - Handy HRM (R), NY, *86*
Olsen, Elizabeth Clark - Olsen/Clark (R), WA, *156*
Olsen, Rex - Olsen/Clark (R), WA, *156*
Olsen, Robert F. - Robert Connelly & Assoc., Inc. (R), MN, *39*
Olson, B. Tucker - Early Cochran & Olson (R), IL, *56*
Olson, Jr., Harold - Elsie Chan & Assoc. (C), CA, *289*
Olson, John - Cook Assoc.,® Inc. (R), IL, *40*
Olson, John - Dunhill of Sarasota (C), FL, *317*
Olson, Judy A. - Management Recruiters of Woodbury (C), MN, *430*
Olson, Judy A. - Management Recruiters of Woodbury (C), MN, *452*
Olszewski, Larry D. - PRAXIS Partners (R), VA, *167*
Ongirski, Richard P. - Raymond Karsan Assoc. (C), PA, *529*
Onizuka, Sayoko - Pasona Canada, Inc. (C), ON, *504*
Onstott, Joe - The Onstott Group (R), MA, *156*
Oppedisano, Edward - Oppedisano & Co., Inc. (R), NY, *156*
Oppenheim, Norman J. - Fortune Personnel Consultants (C), NH, *347*
Oppenheimer, A. M. - M. L. Conner (C), FL, *296*
Oppenheimer, Toni - M. L. Conner (C), FL, *296*
Orange, Crystal - Fortune Personnel Consultants of Huntsville, Inc. (C), AL, *344*
Orbach, Larry - Carter/MacKay (C), NY, *285*
Orceyre, Mike - Dunhill Staffing Systems, Inc. (C), CO, *316*
Orceyre, Mike - Dunhill Professional (C), FL, *317*
Orchant, Edward - A-L Assoc., Inc. (R), NY, *1*
Ordini, Lou - Major Search (C), NJ, *423*
Orkin, Ralph - Sanford Rose Assoc. - Euclid (C), OH, *569*
Orkin, Sheilah - Sanford Rose Assoc. - Euclid (C), OH, *569*
Orlich, Joseph - Hughes & Wilden Assoc. (C), PA, *383*
Ormond, Mark R. - Capstone Consulting, Inc. (R), IL, *29*
Ormson, Gilbert E. - Executive Recruiters, Inc. (C), WI, *334*
Ornstein, Carole - CSA/Clinical Staffing Assoc., LLC (C), NJ, *304*
Ornstein, Robert - Trebor Weldon Lawrence, Inc. (R), NY, *210*
Orr, George H. - Telecom Connections, Inc. (C), TX, *604*
Orr, Kenneth B. - Jon McRae & Associates, Inc. (R), GA, *142*
Orr, Marilyn - Kenmore Executives Inc. (C), FL, *405*
Orr, Steve - Management Recruiters of Kansas City (C), MO, *431*
Ortega de Diego, Estela - Dunhill Professional Search of Miami (C), FL, *320*
Ortman, Jim - Ortman Recruiting Int'l. (C), CA, *500*
Orton, Linda Sedloff - Intelligent Marketing Solutions, Inc. (C), NY, *390*
Oruche, Osita - American Resources Corp. (C), IL, *248*

PRINCIPALS

Orwig, David L. - Management Search, Inc. (C), OK, *468*
Osborn, Jim - Dick Wray & Consultants, Inc. (R), FL, *225*
Osborn, Ted - Paladin Group, Inc. (C), CO, *502*
Osborne, Julie - Rogish Assoc., Inc. (C), OH, *541*
Osinski, Martin H. - American Medical Consultants, Inc. (C), FL, *247*
Ossow, Kitty - K. Ossow & Co. (C), NY, *500*
Ostarticki-Sanchez, Karen - STAT Search (C), FL, *592*
Oster, R. Rush - Management Recruiters of Anna Maria Island (C), FL, *443*
Ostroff, Stephen R. - Triangle Assoc. (C), PA, *609*
Otsuka, Fyllis L. - Holohan Group, Ltd. (R), MO, *95*
Ott, George W. - Ott & Hansen, Inc. (R), CA, *157*
Ott, Robert S. - Global Telecommunications, Inc. (C), TX, *359*
Ottke, Robert C. - Robert Ottke Assoc. (R), CA, *157*
Otto, Christopher P. - Lloyd Prescott & Churchill, Inc. (R), MO, *130*
Otto, Christopher P. - Lloyd Prescott Assoc., Inc. (C), MO, *419*
Otto, Karen - Witt/Kieffer, Ford, Hadelman & Lloyd (R), IL, *223*
Otto, Robert W. - Onsite Staffing Solutions (R), IL, *156*
Ouellet, Jacques E. - Yves Elkas Inc. (R), QE, *58*
Outman, Timothy J. - CTR (R), CA, *43*
Ovca, Jr., William J. - Ovca Assoc. Inc. (R), KY, *157*
Overson, Donna - Michael Shirley Assoc. Inc. (R), KS, *190*
Owen, Jamie - Management Recruiters of Seattle (C), WA, *465*
Owen, Ralph - Kiley, Owen & McGovern, Inc. (R), NJ, *114*
Owens, LaMonte - LaMonte Owens, Inc. (R), PA, *158*
Owens, Lynn - Advanced Recruiting, Inc. (C), CO, *240*
Owens, Reggie - The Gabriel Group (C), PA, *354*
Owens, Robyn - Sanford Rose Assoc. - Norcross (C), GA, *566*
Oxenham, Roger - Madison MacArthur Inc. (R), ON, *133*
Ozoroski, Tom - Barr Assoc. (C), PA, *259*
Pace, Jill - Templeton & Assoc. (C), IL, *605*
Pace, Susan A. - Horton International Inc. (R), CT, *96*
Pacheco, John - DHR Int'l., Inc. (R), CA, *49*
Pacheco, Ricardo - Amrop International (R), NL, *5*
Pacini, Joseph - Premier Business Advisors (C), PA, *516*
Pacini, Lauren R. - Hite Executive Search (R), OH, *94*
Packer, Brent - Hall Kinion (C), UT, *367*
Paddock, Jeff - Management Recruiters The Delta Group, Inc. (C), TN, *461*
Padilla, Jose Sanchez - Egon Zehnder Int'l. Inc. (R), MX, *227*
Padilla, Juan - Raymond Karsan Assoc. (C), PR, *530*
Padwa, Danielle - The Alfus Group (R), NY, *3*
Paetzhold, Jerry - Davis & James, Inc. (C), MO, *308*
Pagan, Rod - Management Recruiters of Anderson (C), SC, *435*
Pagana, Pat - The Brentwood Group, Inc. (R), NJ, *22*
Page, Bonnie L. - Hite Executive Search (R), OH, *94*
Page, Stephen J. L. - Page-Wheatcroft & Co., Ltd. (R), TX, *158*
Page, Susan - John Kurosky & Assoc. (R), CA, *122*
Page, Theresa - T. Page & Assoc. (C), TX, *502*
Pahls, Jud - Management Recruiters of Altamonte (C), FL, *442*
Paige, Jacqueline - Smith Hanley Assoc., Inc. (C), CT, *584*
Pailin, Cheryl - The Pailin Group Professional Search Consultants (R), TX, *158*
Pailin, Sr., David L. - The Pailin Group Professional Search Consultants (R), TX, *158*
Paine, Donne G. - Fortune Personnel Consultants of Hilton Head (C), SC, *349*
Paine, Leah - Dunhill Staffing Systems (C), IN, *317*
Pais, Lisa A. - Gilbert Scott Assoc., LLC (C), MA, *357*
Pajak, Michael A. - The Danielson Group, Inc. (C), TX, *306*
Paju, John - Worldwide Medical Services (C), CA, *625*
Pakter, Janou - Janou Pakter, Inc. (C), NY, *502*
Palazola, Vic - Healthcare Recruiters of New Orleans (C), LA, *373*
Palazzolo, Kathy - Michigan Consulting Group (R), MI, *144*
Palazzolo, Kathy - Premier Recruiting Group (C), MI, *516*
Palermo, Nicholas J. - AES Search (C), NJ, *241*
Pallman-David, Cynthia - Bonnell Assoc. Ltd. (R), CT, *19*
Palma, Frank R. - Goodrich & Sherwood Assoc., Inc. (R), NJ, *80*
Palmer, Adrian - Western Management Consultants (R), BC, *218*
Palmer, Carleton A. - G. E. McFarland & Co. (R), GA, *140*
Palmer, Connie - The Touchstone Group (C), MA, *607*
Palmer, Greg - Elliot Assoc. Inc. (R), PA, *58*
Palmer, James H. - The Hindman Co. (R), KY, *94*
Palmer, John A. - Intelegra, Inc. (C), NJ, *390*
Palmer, Kirk - Kirk Palmer & Assoc., Inc. (R), NY, *158*
Palmlund, III, David W. - LAI Ward Howell (R), TX, *124*
Palos, Michael V. - Kelly Associates (R), PA, *112*
Palubiak, Sandy - Keystone Consulting Group (C), MO, *406*
Palumbo, Michael J. - Michael Latas & Assoc., Inc. (R), MO, *126*
Palumbo, Robert F. - The Recruitment Group, Inc. (C), NY, *532*
Pamenter, Craig - Pamenter, Pamenter, Brezer & Deganis Ltd. (R), ON, *159*
Pamenter, Fred - Pamenter, Pamenter, Brezer & Deganis Ltd. (R), ON, *159*
Panchella, Joseph J. - Wellington Management Group (R), PA, *217*
Panetta, Tim - Commonwealth Consultants (C), GA, *294*
Pang, Christopher - QD Legal (C), ON, *526*
Pankratz, Dennis L. - Furst Group/MPI (R), IL, *72*
Pann, Arthur J. - Arthur Pann Assoc., Inc. (C), NY, *502*
Panos, James - The P & L Group (C), NY, *500*
Papasadero, Kathleen - Woodworth Int'l. Group (R), OR, *225*
Papayanopulos, Manuel - Korn/Ferry, Int'l., S.A. de C.V. (R), MX, *118*
Papayanopulos, Manuel - Korn/Ferry, Int'l., S.A. de C.V. (R), MX, *118*
Pape, Florence - Florence Pape Legal Search, Inc. (C), NJ, *502*
Papike, Richard - TriStaff Group (C), CA, *609*
Pappalardo, Chuck - Christian & Timbers, Inc. (R), OH, *34*
Pappas, James - PCD Partners (R), PA, *161*
Pappas, James C. - Search Dynamics, Inc. (C), IL, *575*
Pappas, Linda - Barclay Consultants, Inc. (C), NJ, *259*
Pappas, Sewell B. - Alpha Resource Group, Inc. (C), TX, *246*
Pappas, Timothy C. - Jude M. Werra & Assoc. (R), WI, *218*
Paquet, Marc - MPA Executive Search Inc. (R), QE, *148*
Parato, Lisa - DHR Int'l., Inc. (R), MA, *50*
Parbs, Michael - Accountants On Call (C), VA, *237*
Pardo, Maria Elena - Smith Search, S.C. (R), MX, *194*
Paredes, Patricia - Brystol Cove Assoc. (R), CA, *24*
Parekh, Dinesh V. - Sanford Rose Assoc. - Amherst, NY (C), NY, *568*
Parenica, Jim - Parenica & Co. (R), NC, *159*
Parfitt, Bill - Management Solutions, Inc. (C), WA, *468*
Parfitt, Jan - Management Solutions, Inc. (C), WA, *468*
Parham, Jim - Jim Parham & Assoc., Inc. (R), FL, *159*
Parillo, Frank - Frank Parillo & Assoc. (R), CA, *159*

Paris, Eileen - Romac Int'l., Inc. (C), GA, *543*
Parisi, Frank - Worlco Computer Resources, Inc. (C), PA, *624*
Parisien, Simon - Yves Elkas Inc. (R), QE, *58*
Park, Carol - Carol Park (C), MO, *502*
Park, Cleve A. - Management Recruiters of Birmingham (C), AL, *438*
Park, Cleve A. - Management Recruiters of Birmingham, Inc. (C), AL, *438*
Park, Cleve A. - Sales Consultants of Birmingham (C), AL, *556*
Park, Dabney G. - Mark Stanley & Co./ EMA Partners International (R), FL, *136*
Park, K. Darwin - Davies, Park (R), AB, *46*
Park, Tammy - Robert Larned Assoc., Inc. (C), VA, *413*
Parker, Sr., Daniel F. - Schuyler, Baker & Parker, Inc. (R), GA, *185*
Parker, David P. - D. P. Parker & Assoc., Inc. (R), MA, *159*
Parker, Gayle W. - Trebor Weldon Lawrence, Inc. (R), NY, *210*
Parker, Joan - Management Recruiters of Sandy Springs (C), GA, *446*
Parker, John - Marley Group Ltd. (C), NY, *471*
Parker, Kenneth - Parker, McFadden & Assoc. (C), GA, *503*
Parker, Michele - Management Alliance Group, Inc. (R), NY, *134*
Parker, Montie - Parker & Lynch (C), CA, *503*
Parker, Murray B. - The Borton Wallace Co. (R), NC, *19*
Parker, Murray B. - Merrick & Moore (C), NC, *479*
Parker, P. Grant - Raymond Karsan Assoc. (C), PA, *529*
Parker, P. Grant - Raymond Karsan Assoc. (C), NY, *530*
Parker, Rael - Accountancies (C), CA, *234*
Parker, Roberta - R. Parker & Assoc., Inc. (R), NY, *159*
Parker, Susan - Parker-Worthington, Inc. (C), TX, *503*
Parker, Susan - Parker-Worthington, Inc. (C), TX, *503*
Parker, Thomas - Anderson & Schwab, Inc. (R), NY, *6*
Parker, Thomas - Anderson & Schwab, Inc. (R), CO, *6*
Parnes, Leon - Dunhill Search of Denver South (C), CO, *316*
Parnes, Sandy - Dunhill Search of Denver South (C), CO, *316*
Parr, James A. - KPMG Executive Search (R), ON, *119*
Parr, Thomas A. - Holland & Assoc., Inc. (R), MI, *94*
Parres, Mike - Michael W. Parres & Assoc. (R), MI, *159*
Parris, Jr., Ed - Management Recruiters of Pickens County (C), SC, *435*
Parry, William H. - Horton Int'l. Inc. (R), CA, *96*
Parsons, Allison - Barton Assoc., Inc. (R), TX, *12*
Parsons, Charles E. - Dunhill Professional Search of Miami (C), FL, *320*
Parsons, Crystal - Management Recruiters Peninsula (C), CA, *439*
Parsons, Crystal - Sales Consultants Peninsula, Inc. (C), CA, *556*
Parsons, Gerald - DHR Int'l., Inc. (R), CA, *49*
Parsons, Sue N. - Parsons Assoc. Inc. (R), IL, *159*
Partridge, Robert J. - Partridge Assoc., Inc. (R), MA, *160*
Pasahow, David R. - Heidrick & Struggles, Inc. (R), ON, *90*
Pascal, Rick - Rick Pascal & Assoc., Inc. (C), NJ, *504*
Pascale, Paul M. - Management Recruiters of Wilton (C), CT, *426*
Pascale, Ron - Pascale & LaMorte, LLC (C), CT, *504*
Paschal, Carolyn Smith - Carolyn Smith Paschal Int'l. (R), CA, *160*
Pask, Mike - Peter Froehlich & Co. (C), TX, *353*
Pasquale, Thomas S. O. - Spear-Izzo Assoc., LLC (C), PA, *589*
Passon, Steven A. - Teamsearch, Inc. (C), MI, *601*
Pastrana, Dario - Egon Zehnder Int'l. Inc. (R), MX, *227*
Patch, Terry - Andre David & Assoc., Inc. (R), TX, *6*
Patchin, Rory J. - R2 Services, LLC (C), IL, *528*
Patenge, David W. - Handy HRM (R), NY, *86*
Paterson, David - Scientific Solutions, Inc. (C), MI, *572*
Paterson, Sharon - Scientific Solutions, Inc. (C), MI, *572*
Patlovich, Michael J. - Witt/Kieffer, Ford, Hadelman & Lloyd (R), MA, *223*
Patrick, Donald R. - Sanford Rose Assoc. - Norcross (C), GA, *566*
Patrick, Janet L. - Sanford Rose Assoc. - Norcross (C), GA, *566*
Patronella, Larry - W. Robert Eissler & Assoc., Inc. (C), TX, *327*
Patterson, Brenda - Management Recruiters - Indianapolis (C), IN, *448*
Patterson, John H. - Michael Latas & Assoc., Inc. (R), MO, *126*
Patton, Gary - Career Marketing Assoc., Inc. (C), CO, *282*
Patton, M. Pat - Tekworx, Inc. (C), OK, *604*
Patton, Michael - Hunt Patton & Brazeal, Inc. (C), OK, *385*
Patton, Pat - Hunt Patton & Brazeal, Inc. (C), CO, *385*
Patton, Pat - Tekworx, Inc. (C), CO, *604*
Paufeta, Robert J. - Creative Management Strategies, Ltd. (R), NY, *42*
Paul, Joel H. - Joel H. Paul & Assoc., Inc. (C), NY, *505*
Paul, Linda - Gilbert Tweed Assoc. Inc. (R), NJ, *77*
Paul, Mari - Levin & Company, Inc. (R), CA, *128*
Paul, Mary - Premier Search Group (C), IL, *517*
Paules, Paul E. - Paules Associates (C), CA, *505*
Pauling, John - C. J. Stafford & Assoc. (C), ON, *591*
Pautler, Margaret O. - Holohan Group, Ltd. (R), MO, *95*
Pawelczyk, Art - Cook Assoc.,® Inc. (R), IL, *40*
Pawlik, Bernadette - Pawlik/Dorman Partners (R), IL, *161*
Paxton, James W. - Stanton Chase Int'l. (R), MD, *199*
Payette, Angela - Greene Personnel Consultants (C), RI, *362*
Payette, Pierre - Egon Zehnder Int'l. Inc. (R), QE, *227*
Payne, Dennis - Roster Inc. (C), IN, *545*
Payne, Joe - Van Treadaway Assoc., Inc. (R), GA, *210*
Payton, Andrew J. - Professional Search Consultants (C), KY, *522*
Pearce, Frank - Pearce & Assoc. (C), FL, *506*
Pearce, Lois - Pearce & Assoc. (C), FL, *506*
Pearl, David A. - Sales Consultants of Richmond Hill (C), GA, *552*
Pearson, A. B. - Sales Consultants of Concord (C), NC, *554*
Pearson, Anna Lee - Sales Consultants of Concord (C), NC, *554*
Pearson, Brian - Roth Young Executive Search (C), TX, *546*
Pearson, Chuck - Pearson & Assoc., Inc. (C), AZ, *506*
Pearson, John R. - Pearson, Caldwell & Farnsworth (R), CA, *161*
Pearson, Keith D. - TASA International (R), TX, *206*
Pearson, Robert L. - LAI Ward Howell (R), TX, *124*
Peart, Carolyn - Cook Assoc.,® Inc. (R), IL, *40*
Peasback, David R. - Canny, Bowen Inc. (R), NY, *28*
Peat, Daniel A. - Innovative Search Group, Inc. (R), GA, *102*
Peck, James - Peggy Shea & Assoc. (R), CA, *189*
Peckenpaugh, Ann - Schweichler Assoc., Inc. (R), CA, *186*
Peckham, Bobbi - David M. Griffith & Assoc., Ltd. (R), CA, *82*
Pecot, Jack L. - Management Recruiters of St. Tammany (C), LA, *429*
Pedelty, Lori K. - Capstone Consulting, Inc. (R), IL, *29*
Peden, Ann - Peden & Assoc. (C), CA, *506*
Peebles, Elisabeth - Bradford Executives Int'l. (C), VA, *272*
Peeney, James D. - Peeney Assoc., Inc. (R), NJ, *161*
Peet, John - Management Recruiters of Boone (C), NC, *456*

Pelayo, Joe - Joseph Michaels (C), CA, *401*
Pelegrino, John - Kuhn Med-Tech (C), CA, *409*
Pelisson, Charles J. - Marra Peters & Partners (R), NJ, *136*
Pell, Maria - The Goldman Group Inc. (R), NY, *79*
Pelland, Paul S. - Paul S. Pelland, P.C. (R), SC, *161*
Pelle, Michael A. - M. A. Pelle Assoc., Inc. (C), NY, *506*
Pellitier, Matt - PIC Executive Search (C), GA, *511*
Pelton, Margaret - PricewaterhouseCoopers Executive Search (R), ON, *168*
Pelusi, Tiziana - Synagent Inc. (C), ON, *597*
Peluso, Philip - National Search Assoc. (C), CA, *490*
Pencarski, Robert - Bio-Venture Group (C), RI, *266*
Pendergast, Joseph - Weatherby Healthcare (C), CT, *617*
Pendergast, Michael - Weatherby Healthcare (C), FL, *617*
Peniche, Pedro - Amrop International (R), MX, *5*
Penley, Jeffrey M. - Highlander Search (C), NC, *378*
Penn, Scott - NaviSearch (C), GA, *490*
Pennella, Neil - Brad Marks Int'l. (R), CA, *136*
Penney, Robert J. - Sales Consultants of Westchester-South, Inc. (C), NY, *561*
Penrod, John V. - National Metal Services Corp. (C), IN, *489*
Penwell, Wayne - Recruiting Specialists (C), MA, *532*
Pepe, Leonida R. - Butterfass, Pepe & MacCallan Inc. (R), NJ, *25*
Pepin, J. Lawrence - The Morgan/Geoffries Group (C), CA, *485*
Pepper, Marci - Johnson Smith & Knisely (R), NY, *107*
Pepple, Bob - Fortune Personnel Consultants of Jacksonville (C), FL, *345*
Peragine, Ralph - The Resource Group (R), CT, *175*
Peragine, Ralph P. - The Resource Group (R), CT, *175*
Percifield, J. Michael - Management Recruiters of Columbus (C), IN, *429*
Percival, Chris - Chicago Legal Search, Ltd. (C), IL, *290*
Perea, Cheryl - Tele-Solutions of Arizona, Inc. (C), AZ, *604*
Perelson, Jill - The Diestel Group (R), UT, *51*
Perez, Gale - Perez & Assoc. (C), MI, *507*
Perez, Maria M. - Perez-Arton Consultants, Inc. (R), NY, *162*
Pergal, Donald - Resource Networking Inc. (C), IN, *534*
Perkins, Arthur - Management Alliance Group, Inc. (R), NJ, *134*
Perkins, Barbara - Harcourt & Assoc. (C), AB, *368*
Perkins, R. Patrick - The Perkins Group (R), NC, *162*
Perkins, Yvonne - Leader Institute, Inc. (C), GA, *414*
Perl, Eric - BR & Assoc. (C), NJ, *271*
Perler, Andy - Raymond Karsan Assoc. (C), IL, *530*
Perlman, Dan - Romac Int'l., Inc. (C), FL, *543*
Perlmutter, Martin - Hook-Up! (C), CA, *380*
Perlstadt, Douglas - Interactive Search Network (R), CA, *102*
Perog, Walter - Search Consultants, Inc. (C), NJ, *575*
Perras, Paul - KPMG Executive Search (R), ON, *119*
Perron, Daniel - Accountants On Call (C), FL, *235*
Perry, Bill - Logic Assoc., Inc. (C), NY, *419*
Perry, Brandon - Software Engineering Solutions, Inc. (C), CA, *587*
Perry, Cole - Jay Allen & Assoc. (C), FL, *244*
Perry, Jr., Darrell L. - Management Recruiters of Louisburg (C), NC, *433*
Perry, David - Perry-Martel Int'l., Inc. (R), ON, *163*
Perry, Dick - Perry • Newton Assoc. (C), MD, *507*
Perry, Fred - Fred Perry Assoc. (C), TX, *507*
Perry, James A. - Strategic Executives, Inc. (R), IL, *202*
Perry, Len - The Caplan-Taylor Group (R), CA, *28*
Perry, Len - Perry-D'Amico & Assoc. (R), CA, *163*
Perry, Lisa Lepore - Aminex Corp. (C), MA, *249*
Perry, Marcus - Perry Search Assoc. (C), CA, *507*
Perry, Philip - Lindsey & Co., Inc. (R), OH, *129*
Perry, R. H. - R. H. Perry & Assoc., Inc. (R), DC, *162*
Perry, Virginia - Perry-D'Amico & Assoc. (R), CA, *163*
Persico, Victor J. - Management Recruiters of Chicago-Southwest (C), IL, *428*
Persky, Barry - Barry Persky & Co., Inc. (R), CT, *163*
Person, Glenn J. - AGRI-associates (C), MO, *242*
Perunovich, Lise - The Park Group & Assoc., Inc. (C), MD, *503*
Pesco, Michelle - Chatham Search Assoc., Inc. (C), NJ, *290*
Peskosky, Mike - Prime Search (C), NC, *518*
Peterman, James R. - J. R. Peterman Assoc., Inc. (C), VT, *509*
Peters, Alec - Alec Peters Assoc. Inc./DLR (R), GA, *163*
Peters, Deborah L. - Major Legal Services, Inc. (C), OH, *423*
Peters, James - TNS Partners, Inc. (R), TX, *209*
Peters, Peter Louis - Success Seekers Connection (C), FL, *596*
Peters, Ray - J. Stroll Assoc., Inc. (R), CT, *204*
Petersen, Laraine - W. A. Rutledge & Assoc. (R), CT, *183*
Peterson, David A. - Management Recruiters of Vero Beach (C), FL, *445*
Peterson, Diana K. - Management Recruiters of Vero Beach (C), FL, *445*
Peterson, Eric N. - StratfordGroup (R), OH, *203*
Peterson, Greg - Sales Consultants of Ft. Lauderdale, Inc. (C), FL, *557*
Peterson, Jerry - MARBL Consultants, Inc. (C), WI, *469*
Peterson, John A. - Management Recruiters of Lansing (C), MI, *430*
Peterson, John S. - Greger/Peterson Assoc., Inc. (R), CA, *81*
Peterson, Kevin E. - Management Recruiters of Cleveland-Client Services (C), OH, *433*
Peterson, Michael T. - BayResearch Group, Inc. (R), IL, *14*
Peterson, Priscilla J. - Management Recruiters of Lansing (C), MI, *430*
Peterson, Richard A. - Richard Peterson & Assoc., Inc. (R), GA, *163*
Peterson, Roger J. - D. L. Weiss & Assoc. (R), CA, *217*
Peterson, Vicki - Maglio & Co., Inc. (R), WI, *134*
Petras, Michael - F-O-R-T-U-N-E Personnel Consultants of South Bend (C), IN, *346*
Petrello-Pray, Gina - Direct Recruiters, Inc. (C), OH, *312*
Petrie, Christopher J. - Petrie Partners, Inc. (R), FL, *163*
Petroski, Gary - E O Technical (C), CT, *324*
Petrucci, Charlie - Norrell Financial Staffing (C), NC, *495*
Petruzzi, Vincent J. - Petruzzi Assoc. (C), NJ, *509*
Petry, Georgia M. - Placements by Jesse Reid Assoc., Inc. (C), NY, *513*
Pettengill, Maurice A. - Associated Recruiters (C), WI, *254*
Pettersson, Tara L. - LAI Ward Howell (R), TX, *124*
Pettibone, Linda - Herbert Mines Assoc., Inc. (R), NY, *145*
Pettigrew, Reece - Ray & Berndtson (R), TX, *171*
Pettway, Samuel H. - SpencerStuart (R), GA, *197*
Peyser, Robert E. - Peyser Assoc., Inc. (R), FL, *163*
Pezim, Howard J. - The Bedford Consulting Group Inc. (R), ON, *15*
Pezim, Steven G. - The Bedford Consulting Group Inc. (R), ON, *15*
Pfaendler, Robert E. - Robert E. Pfaendler & Assoc., Inc. (C), OR, *510*
Pfannenstiel, Roseann - Fortune Group Int'l., Inc. (R), PA, *70*

Pfannkuche, Anthony V. - SpencerStuart (R), CA, *196*
Pfeiffer, Irene - Price Waterhouse Executive Search (R), AB, *168*
Pfeiffer, Joseph - Insurance Personnel Resources, Inc. (C), NC, *390*
Phaneuf, Don - Technical Skills Consulting Inc. (R), ON, *207*
Pharr, Thomas - Baldwin & Assoc. (C), OH, *258*
Phelps, Gene - McCormack & Farrow (R), CA, *140*
Phelps, Gene - McCormack & Farrow (R), AZ, *140*
Phelps, Grace - Hardage Group (C), TN, *369*
Phelps, Ronald A. - Phelps Personnel Assoc., Inc. (C), SC, *510*
Philipp-Edmonds, Tom - Avondale Search Int'l., Inc. (R), FL, *9*
Phillip, John R. - J. R. Phillip & Assoc., Inc. (R), CA, *164*
Phillips, Anna W. - Witt/Kieffer, Ford, Hadelman & Lloyd (R), MD, *223*
Phillips, Annamarie - Schwab-Carrese Assoc., Inc. Executive Search (R), NC, *185*
Phillips, Catherine - C. P. Consulting (R), PA, *26*
Phillips, Daniel J. - Phillips & Assoc. (R), MA, *164*
Phillips, David - Matthews & Stephens Assoc., Inc. (C), CT, *472*
Phillips, Don - Accountants On Call (C), FL, *235*
Phillips, Jr., James L. - Highland Search Group, L.L.C. (R), NY, *93*
Phillips, Jim - Executive Search, Ltd. (C), OH, *336*
Phillips, Jonathan H. - Magellan Int'l., L.P. (C), TX, *422*
Phillips, K. Jerry - Snelling & Snelling, Inc. (C), FL, *585*
Phillips, Mike - FORTUNE Personnel Consultants of Charleston, Inc. (C), SC, *349*
Phillips, Mimi - Snelling Search Recruiters (C), NC, *586*
Phillips, Richard K. - Handy HRM (R), NY, *86*
Phillips, Jr., Sam B. - Phillips Resource Group (C), SC, *510*
Phillips, Sharin - Rice Cohen Int'l. (R), PA, *178*
Phillips, Veronica - Phillips Assoc. (C), FL, *510*
Phillips, Walter - Phillips Int'l., Inc. (C), SC, *510*
Phillips, William M. - Hunter Int'l. LLC (C), MA, *385*
Philo, Dave - Philo & Associates (C), GA, *511*
Phipps, Peggy - Woodworth Int'l. Group (R), OR, *225*
Piatkiewicz, Mary Lou - Medical Executive Search Assoc., Inc. (C), AZ, *477*
Piatkiewicz, William L. - Medical Executive Search Assoc., Inc. (C), AZ, *477*
Piatoff, Barry - Goldman+Bell, LLC (C), NY, *360*
Picard, Daniel A. - Picard Int'l., Ltd. (R), NY, *164*
Picarella, Greg - Gregory, Kyle & Assoc. (C), NC, *363*
Piccione, Mike - Dussick Management Assoc. (C), CT, *323*
Piché, Jérôme - SpencerStuart (R), QE, *197*
Pickens, Barbara - Johnson Smith & Knisely (R), NY, *107*
Pickens, Gregory D. - Gregory D. Pickens (C), TX, *512*
Pickering, Dale - Agri-Tech Personnel, Inc. (C), MO, *242*
Pickering, Dorothy C. - Livingston, Robert & Co. (R), CT, *130*
Pierce, Charlotte - IM Independent Management Recruiters (R), TN, *101*
Pierce, Jonathan - Pro-Tech Search, Inc. (C), IL, *519*
Pierce, Matthew J. - Pierce & Assoc. (C), CA, *512*
Pierce, Richard - Pierce & Crow (R), CA, *164*
Pierce, Sharon S. - Pierce & Assoc. (C), CA, *512*
Pierson, Edward J. - Johnson Smith & Knisely (R), NY, *107*
Pierson, Kevin - ACC Technical Services (C), OH, *233*
Pigott, A. Daniel - ESA (R), NC, *60*
Pike, Dick - Management Recruiters of Burlington (C), NC, *455*
Pike, Geoff - F-O-R-T-U-N-E Personnel Consultants of Greenwood Village (C), CO, *344*
Pilcher, James P. - F-O-R-T-U-N-E Personnel Consultants of Cincinnati (C), OH, *348*
Pilley, Lyn - Michael Shirley Assoc. Inc. (R), KS, *190*
Pilz, Alfred N. - Fagan & Company (R), PA, *64*
Pimental, Jane - Tondorf & Assoc. Inc. (C), MA, *607*
Pinato, Randy - Management Recruiters of Mayfield Heights (C), OH, *434*
Pinedo, Mario - Bor-Maq Assoc. (C), TX, *269*
Pinger, Earl - Systems Research Group (C), CA, *598*
Pinkerton, Paul - American Medical Recruiting Co. Inc. (C), MS, *248*
Pinsker, Richard J. - Pinsker and Company, Inc. (R), CA, *164*
Pinson, Stephanie - Gilbert Tweed Assoc. Inc. (R), NY, *76*
Pinto, David - Nason & Nason (C), FL, *488*
Pinton, Garth - Pinton Forrest & Madden/ EMA Partners Int'l. (R), BC, *165*
Piper, Jr., James R. - Stanton Chase Int'l. (R), IL, *199*
Piper, Robert A. - The Talon Group (R), TX, *205*
Piper, William D. - W. P. Assoc. (C), CA, *613*
Pirnack, Margaret - McKavis Assoc. (C), CA, *475*
Pirocanac, Paul - Matthews Professional Employment Specialists, Inc. (C), IL, *473*
Pirre, Ray - GSP International (C), NJ, *364*
Pirro, Anthony S. - Cornwall Stockton & Co., Inc. (C), TX, *299*
Pisano, Robert - Rand Thompson Executive Search Consultants (C), NY, *528*
Pistentis, Jean - Dunn Associates (R), PA, *55*
Pitcher, Geoff J. - Sales Consultants of Stroudsburg (C), PA, *555*
Pitcher, Nancy J. - Sales Consultants of Stroudsburg (C), PA, *555*
Pitchford, Gavin - Delta Management Group Ltd. (C), ON, *310*
Pitchford, Jim J. - Management Recruiters of Olympia (C), WA, *437*
Pitchon, Daniel N. - DNPitchon Assoc. (R), NJ, *165*
Pitman, P. - American Executive Management, Inc. (R), MA, *5*
Pittard, Patrick S. - Heidrick & Struggles, Inc. (R), IL, *90*
Pittard, Patrick S. - Heidrick & Struggles, Inc. (R), GA, *90*
Pittarelli, Tony - Quantum EDP Recruiting Services (C), NY, *526*
Pittleman, Linda - Pittleman & Assoc. (C), NY, *513*
Pittleman, Steven - Pittleman & Assoc. (C), NY, *513*
Pitz, Judy A. - Sales Consultant of Manatee County (C), FL, *552*
Pitzer, Steve - Barrett Hospitality Search (R), CA, *12*
Pizzariello, Ann Marie - Conex Inc./InterSearch (R), NY, *39*
Pizzi, Donald - Mark Adam Assoc. (R), NJ, *135*
Plagge, Cheryl L. - Management Recruiters of Mason City (C), IA, *429*
Plappert, James F. - Sales Consultants of Newtown, Inc. (C), PA, *562*
Plattenburg, Ted W. - Bason Associates (R), OH, *13*
Plavin, Avery - The Consulting Group of North America, Inc. (C), VA, *297*
Plazza, Richard C. - The Executive Source Inc. (R), NY, *64*
Plemmons, Patrick F. - Plemmons Assoc., Inc. (R), GA, *165*
Plessner, Rene - Rene Plessner Assoc., Inc. (R), NY, *165*
Pletkin, Michelle - Accountants On Call (C), CA, *235*
Pletkin, Michelle - Romac Int'l., Inc. (C), CA, *542*
Pleva, Will - Leslie Kavanagh Assoc., Inc. (C), NY, *416*
Plimpton, Ralph L. - R. L. Plimpton Assoc., Inc. (R), CO, *165*
Pliszka, Donald J. - PRAXIS Partners (R), VA, *167*
Plock, Gerald R. - The PAR Group - Paul A. Reaume, Ltd. (R), IL, *159*
Plotner, George A. - Management Recruiters of Middletown (C), OH, *434*

PRINCIPALS

(R) = Retainer; (C) = Contingency

Plouffe, Yves J. - Yves Plouffe & Assoc. (R), QE, *165*
Plummer, Cyril - The McKinnon Management Group Inc. (C), ON, *475*
Plummer, Heidi - Plummer & Assoc., Inc. (R), CT, *166*
Plummer, John - Plummer & Assoc., Inc. (R), CT, *166*
Plunkett, Mike - Phillips Resource Group (C), NC, *511*
Plyley, Jr., C. Ace - The Stelton Group, Inc. (C), NJ, *592*
Poach, Sr., Joseph M. - Management Recruiters of Broomall (C), PA, *434*
Poach, Shauna L. - Management Recruiters of Broomall (C), PA, *434*
Pober, Andrew - Interim Accounting Professionals (C), FL, *391*
Pocs, Martin M. - DHR Int'l., Inc. (R), CO, *49*
Poe, James B. - Nagler, Robins & Poe, Inc. (R), MA, *150*
Poeppelmeier, David J. - ISC of Cincinnati Inc. (C), OH, *394*
Poindexter, Cabell M. - Wyndham Mills Int'l., Inc. (R), GA, *225*
Poirier, Roland L. - Poirier, Hoevel & Co. (R), CA, *166*
Poitras, Sandy - Squires Resources Inc. (C), ON, *590*
Poklemba, Dale - STAT Search (C), NH, *592*
Polacek, Frank - Search Enterprises, Inc. (C), FL, *575*
Polachi, Jr., Charles A. - Fenwick Partners (R), MA, *66*
Polachi, Peter V. - Fenwick Partners (R), MA, *66*
Polak, Traci - Landon Morgan (C), ON, *412*
Polaski, Fern - Gordon/Tyler (R), PA, *80*
Polen, Jerry B. - The Polen Group (C), PA, *514*
Polhill, Ray L. - Ray Polhill & Assoc. (R), NC, *166*
Poline, Bob - Bob Poline Assoc. Inc. (C), CA, *514*
Poline, Rich - Bob Poline Assoc. Inc. (C), GA, *514*
Polk, Nancy - The Evans Search Group (R), TX, *61*
Pollack, Jonathan - Executive Sales Search (C), CO, *335*
Pollack, Marcy L. - Business Solutions Worldwide, Inc. (C), NJ, *277*
Pollack, Paul - The Pollack Group (C), ON, *514*
Pollan, Arthur - Snelling & Snelling, Inc. (C), FL, *585*
Pollin, M. Ellen - LAI Ward Howell (R), FL, *123*
Pollock, Peter - Dunhill Personnel of North York (C), ON, *318*
Poloni, James A. - Management Recruiters of Vancouver-Downtown (C), WA, *437*
Polson, Christopher C. - Polson & Co., Inc. (R), MN, *166*
Polvere, Gary T. - Management Recruiters of Barrington (C), IL, *447*
Polyzos, Ginia M. - Management Advisors Int'l., Inc. (C), NC, *424*
Pomerance, Mark - C.P.S., Inc. (C), IL, *278*
Pomeroy, II, T. Lee - Egon Zehnder Int'l. Inc. (R), NY, *227*
Pompelli, Jean - JAG Group (R), MO, *105*
Ponaman, Albert L. - Al Ponaman Company, Inc. (C), CA, *514*
Poole, Don V. - Don V. Poole & Assoc., Inc. (C), CO, *514*
Poole, Kenneth - The Harris Consulting Corp. (R), MB, *87*
Poole-Ferrari, Kathryn - Ferrari Search Group (C), OH, *340*
Poore, Larry D. - LAI Ward Howell (R), IL, *123*
Pope, Carla - Straube Associates (R), MA, *203*
Pope, John S. - DHR Int'l., Inc. (R), IL, *49*
Pope, W. E. Gene - AGRI-associates (C), FL, *242*
Popham, Harold C. - Emerson & Co. (C), GA, *329*
Popp, Diana - Management Recruiters of Germantown (C), WI, *437*
Poracky, John W. - M. Wood Company (R), IL, *224*
Porada, Stephen D. - S.D.P. Contract Recruiters (C), NJ, *550*
Porges, John M. - Nason & Nason (C), FL, *488*
Poriotis, Wesley - Wesley Brown & Bartle Co., Inc. (R), NY, *218*
Porrello, Joy M. - Dunhill Personnel of Northeast Tulsa, Inc. (C), OK, *322*
Portanova, Peter M. - ROI Assoc. (R), NY, *181*
Porter, Carlton - Windsor Consultants, Inc. (C), TX, *622*
Porter, Donald - Amherst Personnel Group Inc. (C), NY, *249*
Porter, Gale - Techstaff Inc. (C), FL, *603*
Porter, Jack - Jack Porter Assoc., Inc. (C), WA, *514*
Porter, James H. - TPG & Assoc. (C), TX, *608*
Porter, Lindsay - HCI Corp. (C), IL, *371*
Porter, Mary C. - TPG & Assoc. (C), TX, *608*
Porter, Nanci - Eastridge Infotech (C), CA, *326*
Porter, Nancy - Porter & Assoc., Inc. (C), FL, *514*
Portes, Daniel H. - Management Resource Group, Ltd. (C), IA, *467*
Posner, Gary J. - EMN/Witt/Kieffer (R), TN, *59*
Posselt, Jeffrey - Cook Assoc.,® Inc. (R), IL, *40*
Poster, Lawrence D. - Catalyx Group (R), NY, *31*
Posthes, Doris W. - Longshore + Simmons (R), PA, *131*
Postlethwaite, John - Edward Bell Assoc. (C), CA, *263*
Potter, Aggie - Management Solutions, Inc. (C), CA, *468*
Potter, Douglas C. - Stanton Chase Int'l. (R), TX, *199*
Potter, Steven B. - Highland Search Group, L.L.C. (R), NY, *93*
Poutouves, Paul - Martha Ward Executive Search, Inc. (C), NY, *615*
Powell, Aleesa - Hemingway Personnel, Inc. (C), CA, *376*
Powell, Curtis - Burkholder & Assoc., Inc. (C), TX, *276*
Powell, David - David Powell, Inc. (R), CA, *166*
Powell, Jr., David - David Powell, Inc. (R), CA, *166*
Powell, Donald L. - Proquest Inc. (C), SC, *524*
Powell, Lloyd - KPMG Executive Search (R), NF, *119*
Powell, Marie - Kenzer Corp. (R), GA, *113*
Powell, Mike - Marc-Allen Assoc., Inc. (C), FL, *469*
Powell-Florip, Kathy - Alliance Search Management Inc. (R), TX, *4*
Power, Alex G. - H.I. Hunt & Co., Ltd. (R), MA, *99*
Powers, Gordon - Dunhill of Rockville (C), MD, *317*
Powers, Janet - Powers Consultants, Inc. (R), MO, *166*
Powers, Keith - Baldwin & Assoc. (C), OH, *258*
Powers, Norman S. - Norman Powers Assoc., Inc. (C), MA, *515*
Powers, Robert - Robert Powers & Assoc. (C), CA, *515*
Powers, Susan - Robert Powers & Assoc. (C), CA, *515*
Powers, William D. - Powers Consultants, Inc. (R), MO, *166*
Poyck, Walter S. - Stewart Assoc. (C), PA, *593*
Pradarelli, Dennis J. - MARBL Consultants, Inc. (C), WI, *469*
Prager, Paul Gershon - P. G. Prager Search Assoc., Ltd. (C), NY, *515*
Pratt, Andy - Sales Consultant of Wilton-Westport (C), CT, *552*
Pratt, Brian - Western Management Consultants (R), SA, *218*
Pratt, Tyler P. - Furst Group/MPI (R), IL, *72*
Pratz, Robert P. - The Park Group & Assoc., Inc. (C), MD, *503*
Pratzer, Elan - Elan Pratzer & Partners Inc. (R), ON, *167*
Preger, G. A. - George Preger & Associates Inc. (R), ON, *167*
Prehogan, Avalee - Robert Half Canada Inc. (C), ON, *366*
Prencipe, Michael - Raymond Karsan Assoc. (C), VA, *530*
Preng, David E. - Preng & Assoc., Inc. (R), TX, *167*
Preng, Richard J. - SpencerStuart (R), TX, *197*
Prentiss, Michael C. - Management Recruiters of Bethesda (C), MD, *430*

Prescott, Larry W. - Prescott Legal Search, Inc. (C), TX, *517*
Prescott, Lauren Eaton - Prescott Legal Search, Inc. (C), TX, *517*
Presley, Jason T. - Presley Consultants, Inc. (C), CA, *517*
Presley, Jason T. - Presley Consultants, Inc. (C), MT, *517*
Presley, Linda C. - Presley Consultants, Inc. (C), CA, *517*
Presley, Philip E. - Presley Consultants, Inc. (C), CA, *517*
Presley, Robert L. - The Inside Track (C), TX, *389*
Presley-Cannon, Judy - Corporate Image Group (C), TN, *300*
Press, Fredrick R. - Adept Tech Recruiting, Inc. (C), NY, *240*
Presser, Janet - N.A.P. Executive Search (Canada) Inc. (C), QE, *488*
Presser, Janet - N.A.P. Executive Services (Canada) Inc. (C), QE, *488*
Preston, Alex - The Energists (R), TX, *59*
Preston, Joe - Preston & Co. (R), NJ, *167*
Preston, Ron - DHR Int'l., Inc. (R), FL, *50*
Price, Alan J. - Alan J. Price Assoc., Inc. (C), RI, *518*
Price, Andrew - The Thomas Tucker Co. (R), CA, *211*
Price, Daniel - Gavin Forbes & Price (R), CA, *75*
Price, Debra J. - UniQuest Int'l., Inc. (C), FL, *611*
Price, Linda - Accelerated Data Decision, Inc. (C), NJ, *233*
Price, Lynn M. - Alan J. Price Assoc., Inc. (C), RI, *518*
Price, P. Anthony - Russell Reynolds Assoc., Inc. (R), CA, *176*
Price, Rita A. - Human Resources Personnel Agency (R), AR, *99*
Price, Velinda Hodge - Price & Assoc., Inc. (C), VA, *518*
Price, William G. - Engineering Profiles (C), FL, *330*
Priem, Windle B. - Korn/Ferry Int'l. (R), NY, *117*
Priftis, Tony - Evie Kreisler Assoc. Inc. (C), TX, *409*
Prince, Howard - Austin Park Management Group Inc. (C), ON, *256*
Prince, Marylin L. - Higdon Prince Inc. (R), NY, *93*
Prior, Donald - The Caldwell Partners Amrop International (R), ON, *26*
Priseler, Michael - IR Search (R), CA, *103*
Pritchett, Jami - DHR Int'l., Inc. (R), MO, *50*
Pritchett, Philip H. - FORTUNE Personnel Consultants of North Dallas (C), TX, *350*
Prochnow, Laurie - Management Recruiters of Wausau, LLC (C), WI, *466*
Procopio, Vince - Paragon Recruiting Officials Inc. (C), OH, *502*
Proct, Nina - Martin H. Bauman Assoc., Inc. (R), NY, *13*
Proctor, Richard W. - Foley Proctor Yoskowitz (R), NJ, *69*
Proul, Ron - The Century Group (C), CA, *287*
Prouty, Alden F. - Manuso, Alexander & Associates, Inc. (R), NY, *135*
Provda, Peter - F-O-R-T-U-N-E Personnel Consultants of Menlo Park, Inc. (C), NJ, *347*
Provost, Ed L. - Management Recruiters Dana Point (C), CA, *440*
Provost, Todd - Management Recruiters Dana Point (C), CA, *440*
Provus, Barbara L. - Shepherd Bueschel & Provus, Inc. (R), IL, *189*
Prufeta, John R. - Creative Management Strategies, Ltd. (R), NY, *42*
Pruitt, Diane - MARBL Consultants, Inc. (C), WI, *469*
Pruitt, Glen O. - Locke & Assoc. (R), AL, *131*
Pruitt, Jim - Lyons Pruitt Int'l. (R), PA, *132*
Prusak, Conrad E. - Ethos Consulting, Inc. (R), CA, *61*
Prusak, Julie J. - Ethos Consulting, Inc. (R), CA, *61*
Pryde, Marcia P. - A.T. Kearney Executive Search (R), CO, *111*
Pryor, Carrie Looms - LAI Ward Howell (R), NY, *123*
Pryor, Jo-Ann - Pryor & Associates (C), CA, *525*
Pryor, William L. - Cendea Connection Int'l. (R), TX, *32*
Psaceas, Phil - Romac Int'l., Inc. (C), MA, *543*
Pschirrer, Martin E. - The Furst Group, Inc. (R), IL, *72*
Puckett, William E. - Searchline Services, Inc. (C), OH, *577*
Puente, Fred J. - Management Recruiters of Eastern Shore (C), MD, *430*
Puestow, Michael - The Beam Group (R), IL, *14*
Pufahl, John P. - Avalon Health Group, Inc. (R), NY, *9*
Pugrant, Mark A. - Grant/Morgan Assoc., Inc. (C), MD, *361*
Puisis, John - Egon Zehnder Int'l. Inc. (R), IL, *227*
Pukita, Mark - Fast Switch, Ltd. (C), OH, *338*
Pulito, Carol M. - Maiola & Co. (C), OH, *423*
Purcell, Carol - The Executive Tree (R), FL, *64*
Purcell, Kathryn - The Executive Tree (R), FL, *64*
Purvis, Iain - Pro Tec Technical Services (C), ON, *519*
Putiri, Vincent - Asheville Search & Consulting (C), NC, *253*
Putman, Joseph - Snelling Search (C), AL, *585*
Putnam, A.E. - ISC of Cincinnati Inc. (C), OH, *394*
Putnam, Denise - Elite Consultants, Inc. (C), FL, *328*
Putrim, Thomas G. - LAI Ward Howell (R), IL, *123*
Pye, Susan - Prescott Legal Search, Inc. (C), TX, *517*
Quarin, Randy - Partners Executive Search Consultants Inc. (R), ON, *160*
Quesnell, Donald A. - Allen, Wayne & Co. LLC (C), TX, *245*
Quick, Roger A. - Norman Broadbent Int'l., Inc. (R), IL, *153*
Quigley, Jack - Quigley Assoc. (R), MD, *170*
Quinlin, Carolyn - Descheneaux Recruitment Services Ltd. (C), BC, *311*
Quinn, Frank A. - Management Recruiters of Charlotte-East (C), NC, *432*
Quinn, Gail - Marshall Consultants, Inc. (R), NY, *137*
Quinn, Joseph P. - Sales Consultant of La Jolla (C), CA, *551*
Quinn, L. J. - L. J. Quinn & Assoc., Inc. (R), NY, *170*
Quinn, Leonard J. - L. J. Quinn & Assoc., Inc. (R), CA, *170*
Quinn, Peggy - Management Recruiters of Charlotte-East (C), NC, *432*
Quinn, Pierre - Quantum EDP Recruiting Services (C), ON, *526*
Quinn, Thomas H. - Weterrings & Agnew, Inc. (C), NY, *619*
Quiring, Patti L. - Quiring Assoc., Inc. (C), IN, *527*
Quirk, Therese M. - Quirk-Corporon & Assoc., Inc. (C), WI, *527*
Quiros, Vince - CV Associates (C), NY, *305*
Quitel, Scott - Impact Search & Strategies (C), PA, *387*
Quitel, Scott M. - Management Recruiters of Manayunk/Chestnut Hill (C), PA, *435*
Qureshi, Julie - Major, Hagen & Africa (C), CA, *423*
Raab, Julie - Vaughan & Co. (C), CA, *612*
Rabe, William - Sales Executives, Inc. (C), MI, *563*
Raben, Steven - Ray & Berndtson (R), TX, *172*
Rabinowitz, Peter A. - P.A.R. Assoc., Inc. (R), MA, *158*
Rach, Walter - Cook Assoc.,® Inc. (R), IL, *40*
Rachels, John - Southwestern Professional Services (C), VA, *588*
Racht, Janet G. - Crowe Chizek & Co. (C), IN, *304*
Rackley, Eugene M. - Heidrick & Struggles, Inc. (R), NC, *90*
Raczkowski, Waldemar - RemTech Business Solutions, Inc. (C), MI, *534*
Radice, Joseph A. - Hospitality Int'l. (C), NY, *381*
Rado, Darin - Career Strategies, Inc. (C), CA, *283*
Radosevic, Frank - Radosevic Assoc. (R), CA, *171*
Radosevic, Tanya C. - Radosevic Assoc. (R), CA, *171*
Radzely, Larry - Adel-Lawrence Assoc., Inc. (C), NJ, *240*
Rae, Fern - Career Counseling Ltd. (C.C.L.) (C), IL, *282*

PRINCIPALS

Raemer-Rodriguez, Susan - Friedman Eisenstein Raemer & Schwartz, LLP (R), IL, *72*
Rafey, Andrew - Gustin Partners, Ltd. (R), MA, *84*
Rafferty, Mark - Management Recruiters of Chicago-North Shore (C), IL, *447*
Rafferty, Marlene M. - Meng, Finseth & Assoc., Inc. (R), CA, *143*
Raffin, Robert P. - Management Recruiters of St. Petersburg (C), FL, *427*
Ragan, William E. - Michael Latas & Assoc., Inc. (R), MO, *126*
Ragaza, Jessica - RitaSue Siegel Resources, Inc. (R), NY, *191*
Raggio, Matthew G. - Oak Assoc. (R), CA, *155*
Ragnoli, John - Sales Consultants of Hartland (C), MI, *553*
Rahaim, Richard D. - Howard/Williams Assoc. (C), FL, *382*
Raheja, Marc C. - CanMed Consultants Inc. (C), ON, *280*
Rahmn, Barbara - Pacific Coast Recruiting (C), CA, *501*
Raia, Carol - Healthcare Recruiters Int'l. Orange County (C), CA, *372*
Raia, Tony - Healthcare Recruiters Int'l. Orange County (C), CA, *372*
Raiber, Laurie - The IMC Group of Companies (R), NY, *101*
Railey, J. Larry - Railey & Assoc. (C), TX, *528*
Raines, Bruce R. - Raines Int'l. Inc. (R), NY, *171*
Rainone, Maryanne B. - Heyman Assoc., Inc. (R), NY, *93*
Raj, Amritha - Softrix, Inc. (C), NJ, *586*
Raley, Frederick O. - Sales Consultant of Hartford (C), CT, *552*
Rallerty, James - Wilder & Assoc. (C), VA, *620*
Ralles, Vickie - Feldman Gray & Assoc. Inc. (C), ON, *339*
Ralley, P. Neil - E.P. Int'l. (C), NY, *324*
Ralley, P. Neil - E.P. Int'l. (C), NJ, *325*
Rallis, Justin - Carlsen Resources, Inc. (R), CO, *29*
Ralphs, Allyson - DHR Int'l., Inc. (R), UT, *51*
Ralston, Doug O. - Management Recruiters of Woodstock (C), GA, *428*
Ramey, Pamela R. - Lear & Assoc., Inc. (C), FL, *415*
Ramirez, Joe - Joseph Chris & Assoc. (C), TX, *400*
Ramirez, Richard - Marentz & Co. (C), TX, *469*
Ramming, George - Ramming & Assoc., Inc. (C), NJ, *528*
Rampey, Wayne - Acclaim Services, Inc. (C), TX, *234*
Ramsey, Donald M. - RHI Consulting (C), VA, *536*
Ramsey, John H. - Mark Stanley & Co. (R), DC, *136*
Ramsey, John H. - Mark Stanley & Co./ EMA Partners International (R), FL, *136*
Rana, Julie B. - HR Advantage, Inc. (C), VA, *382*
Ranberg, Carol - Marsteller Wilcox Assoc. (C), IL, *471*
Rand, Arnold - KPMG Executive Search (R), AB, *119*
Rand, Chris - Accounting Additions (C), CA, *238*
Randall, Craig E. - DHR Int'l., Inc. (R), IL, *49*
Randell, Candace - Management Recruiters of Boone (C), NC, *456*
Randels, Michael J. - The TBI Group (R), PA, *207*
Randolph, Bob - Career Counseling Inc. (CCI) (C), KY, *282*
Randolph, John - Romac Int'l., Inc. (C), TX, *544*
Randolph, Lea - Lea Randolph & Assoc., Inc. (C), TX, *529*
Randolph, Troy - Lea Randolph & Assoc., Inc. (C), TX, *529*
Raney, Albert - Dunhill Personnel Service of Fargo (C), ND, *322*
Range, Mary Jane - Bishop Partners (R), NY, *17*
Ranger, Jean-Jacques - Groupe Ranger Inc. (C), QE, *364*
Raniere, Rich - Romac Int'l., Inc. (C), FL, *542*
Raniere, Rich - Romac Int'l., Inc. (C), FL, *542*
Rank, Christy L. - Mortgage Search Network (C), AZ, *486*
Rankin, Ed - Human Resource Solutions (R), TX, *98*
Rankin, Jeffrey A. - The Rankin Group, Ltd. (R), WI, *171*
Rankin, M. J. - The Rankin Group, Ltd. (R), WI, *171*
Ranta, Ed - J. E. Ranta Assoc. (C), MA, *529*
Raperto, Marie T. - The Cantor Concern, Inc. (R), NY, *28*
Rapp, Harold L. - Harold L. Rapp Assoc. (C), NY, *529*
Rardin, Ed - Brentwood Int'l. (R), CA, *23*
Rascher, Linda - Bert Davis Publishing Placement Consultants (C), NY, *309*
Raskin, John - Healthcare Search Associates (C), CA, *374*
Rasmussen, Traci - Skipping Stone Inc. (C), TX, *582*
Rast, Vera L. - Vera L. Rast Partners Inc. (C), IL, *529*
Ratajczak, Paul - Romac Int'l., Inc. (C), CA, *542*
Ratanasin, Nick - Joy Reed Belt Search Consultants, Inc. (R), OK, *15*
Rathborne, Kenneth J. - Blair/Tech Recruiters, Inc. (C), NJ, *268*
Ratliff, Steve - GateSource Partners (C), VA, *355*
Ratner, Joanne E. - Joanne E. Ratner Search (C), NY, *529*
Ratts, K. Wayne - Holohan Group, Ltd. (R), MO, *95*
Raub, Bonnie - Kelly Associates (R), PA, *112*
Rauba, Frank R. - AGRI-associates (C), PA, *242*
Rauch, Carl W. - Physicians Search®, Inc. (C), CA, *511*
Rauch, Clifford W. - Physicians Search®, Inc. (C), CA, *511*
Raulerson, Derek - Search South, Inc. (C), AL, *576*
Raven, Joel - DHR Int'l., Inc. (R), NY, *50*
Raver, Miki - Hook-Up! (C), CA, *380*
Ray, Breck - Ray & Berndtson (R), TX, *172*
Ray, Breck - Ray & Berndtson (R), TX, *172*
Ray, Gary L. - Ray & Assoc., Inc. (C), IA, *529*
Ray, Jr., Harry - Management Recruiters of Kanawha Valley, LLC (C), WV, *465*
Ray, Heather - Accountants On Call (C), OH, *236*
Ray, Joan - Elliot Assoc. Inc. (R), GA, *58*
Ray, Marianne C. - Callan Assoc., Ltd. (R), IL, *27*
Ray, Jr., Paul R. - Ray & Berndtson (R), TX, *171*
Ray, Sr., Paul R. - Ray & Berndtson (R), TX, *171*
Ray, Robert T. - ExecuGroup, Inc. (R), MS, *61*
Ray, William D. - Lloyd Prescott & Churchill, Inc. (R), CO, *130*
Ray, William D. - Lloyd Prescott Assoc., Inc. (C), CO, *419*
Raymond, Allan H. - Korn/Ferry Int'l. (R), MN, *118*
Raymond, Barry - Raymond Karsan Assoc. (C), NH, *530*
Raymont, Scott - J. Joseph & Assoc. (C), OH, *395*
Raz, Daniel - Analytic Recruiting, Inc. (C), NY, *249*
Raz, Rita - Analytic Recruiting, Inc. (C), NY, *249*
Razuri, Patrick - Management Recruiters of Savannah (C), GA, *446*
Razzino, Janelle - Razzino-Claymore Assoc. (C), NJ, *530*
Reagan, P. W. - Delphi Systems, Ltd. (R), MO, *48*
Reagan, Paul W. - Management Recruiters of Hilo (C), HI, *428*
Real, Toffee - Eastridge Infotech (C), CA, *326*
Reardanz, Eileen - AGRI-associates (C), CA, *242*
Reardanz, Les E. - AGRI-associates (C), CA, *242*
Reaume, Paul A. - The PAR Group - Paul A. Reaume, Ltd. (R), IL, *159*
Recsetar, Steven - Waveland Int'l. (R), IL, *216*
Rector-Gable, Mary - Mary Rector & Assoc., Inc. (C), IL, *533*
Reda, Pat - P. J. Reda & Assoc., Inc. (C), GA, *533*
Redden, Daniel J. - Redden-Shaffer Group (R), CA, *173*
Redden, Mary - Redden & McGrath Assoc., Inc. (R), NY, *173*

Reddick, David C. - Horton Int'l. Inc. (R), GA, *96*
Reddicks, Nate - Search West, Inc. (C), CA, *577*
Redeker, Judy - Taylor Winfield (R), OH, *207*
Redell, John - Redell Search, Inc. (C), IL, *533*
Redgrove, Peter J. - Kass/Abell & Assoc., Inc. (C), CA, *404*
Redmond, Andrea - Russell Reynolds Assoc., Inc. (R), IL, *176*
Rednick, Mark - Sales Consultants of Houston (C), TX, *563*
Rednick, Mark B. - Sales Consultants of Dallas (C), TX, *563*
Redwood, Derek - Rushmore • Judge Inc. (R), ON, *183*
Redwood, Guy W. - Massey-Horton Int'l. (R), ON, *138*
Reece, Christopher S. - Reece & Mruk Partners/EMA Partners Int'l. (R), MA, *173*
Reed, Alec - The Argus Group Corp. (C), ON, *252*
Reed, Bob - The Options Group, Inc. (C), NY, *499*
Reed, Dave - Management Recruiters - Flint (C), MI, *451*
Reed, Fred - Stanton Chase Int'l. (R), TX, *199*
Reed, Kat - Executive Search Consultants (C), CA, *335*
Reed, Jr., Richard W. - Resources for Management (R), PA, *176*
Reed, Rick - Management Recruiters - Flint (C), MI, *451*
Reeder, Kirk - Sales Consultants of Omaha, Inc. (C), NE, *560*
Reeder, Michael S. - Reeder & Assoc., Ltd. (R), GA, *173*
Reek, Don - DHR Int'l., Inc. (R), FL, *50*
Reen, Brendan - DHR Int'l., Inc. (R), MA, *50*
Reep, Walt - Data Bank Executive Search (R), OH, *46*
Reese, Cedric - Cedric L. Reese Inc. (C), CA, *533*
Reese, Jr., Charles D. - Reese Assoc. (R), PA, *174*
Reese, Whitney - Marks & Co., Inc. (R), CT, *136*
Reeve, Philip - Reeve & Assoc. (C), CT, *533*
Reeves, Ron C. - Management Recruiters of Elgin (C), IL, *428*
Reeves, William B. - SpencerStuart (R), GA, *197*
Refi, Thomas - Robert Harkins Assoc., Inc. (C), PA, *369*
Regan, Ray - Fortune Personnel Consultants (C), MT, *347*
Regan, Thomas J. - Tower Consultants, Ltd. (R), FL, *210*
Regehly, Herbert - The IMC Group of Companies (R), NY, *101*
Regina, Aida - Brigade, Inc. (R), CA, *23*
Regush, Catherine - Ambridge Management Corp. (C), ON, *247*
Rehmeyer, Kelly - Allen Austin Lowe & Powers (R), TX, *3*
Rehner, Leonard - R & L Assoc., Ltd. (R), NY, *170*
Reich, Joshua - The Alfus Group (R), NY, *3*
Reichardt, Karl J. - R & K Associates, Inc. (C), AZ, *528*
Reid, Carol - Headden Assoc. (R), WA, *88*
Reid, Ellen T. - Lynch Miller Moore Partners, Inc. (R), IL, *132*
Reid, Gary - KPMG Executive Search (R), ON, *119*
Reid, Michael J. - Michael James Reid & Co. (R), CA, *174*
Reifel, Laurie L. - Reifel & Assoc. (R), IL, *174*
Reifersen, Ruth F. - The Jonathan Stevens Group, Inc. (R), NJ, *108*
Reiff, Jonathan - Romac Int'l., Inc. (C), PA, *544*
Reight, Gene - Brett Personnel Specialists (C), NJ, *273*
Reilly, Hayes - DHR Int'l., Inc. (R), OH, *51*
Reilly, Jr., Robert E. - DHR Int'l., Inc. (R), IL, *49*
Reilly, Toni Marie - Fox-Morris Assoc., Inc. (C), NC, *352*
Reimer, Marvin - Management Recruiters of Wichita (C), KS, *429*
Reimer, Marvin - Sales Consultants of Wichita (C), KS, *553*
Rein, David - Rein & Co., Inc. (R), NJ, *174*
Rein, Steve - Rein & Co., Inc. (R), NJ, *174*
Reinecke, G. - Reinecke & Assoc. (C), NJ, *533*
Reinecke, Mark - Tyler & Company (R), GA, *212*
Reiner, Linda - D.A.L. Associates, Inc. (R), CT, *45*
Reinhart, Jeaneen - Accountants On Call (C), WA, *237*
Reinitz, Robert - Professional Recruiters Inc. (C), MN, *521*
Reiser, Ellen - Thorndike Deland Assoc. LLC (R), NY, *48*
Reisfeld, Lynn Scullion - Alfred Daniels & Assoc., Inc. (R), CA, *46*
Reiss, Phyllis - Adam-Bryce Inc. (C), NY, *239*
Reiter, Douglas - The Douglas Reiter Co., Inc. (R), OR, *174*
Reiter, Harold - Herbert Mines Assoc., Inc. (R), NY, *145*
Reiter, Steve - Romac Int'l. - San Francisco (C), CA, *541*
Reitkopp, Ellen - Management Recruiters of McLean (C), VA, *437*
Reitkopp, Howard H. - Management Recruiters of McLean (C), VA, *437*
Reitman, Harriet - Bert Davis Executive Search, Inc. (R), CA, *47*
Reitz, Doris - The Rossi Search Group (C), PA, *545*
Reitzamer, Elizabeth P. - Dunhill Professional Search of Miami (C), FL, *320*
Reliford, David - Management Recruiters of Massillon (C), OH, *434*
Rembisz, Laura - RemTech Business Solutions, Inc. (C), MI, *534*
Remillard, Brad M. - CJA-The Adler Group, Inc. (R), CA, *35*
Remkus, Valerie - The Hampton Group (C), NY, *368*
Renard, James A. - J. W. Barleycorn, Renard & Assoc., Inc. (R), OH, *11*
Renwick, David - John Kurosky & Assoc. (R), CA, *122*
Resch, Linda - The Kennett Group, Inc. (R), PA, *112*
Ressler, Dan R. - Management Recruiters of Naples (C), FL, *427*
Resto, Jose - Raymond Karsan Assoc. (C), PR, *530*
Reszotko, Leonard J. - L. J. Reszotko & Assoc. (C), IL, *535*
Retis, Lillian - Retis Assoc., Inc. (C), IL, *535*
Reuning, Stephen M. - Diedre Moire Corp., Inc. (C), NJ, *483*
Reusser, Mary - Michael Shirley Assoc. Inc. (R), KS, *190*
Rexroad, Nancy - Strauss Personnel Service (C), PA, *596*
Reyes, Randolph - Management Recruiters of Columbia (C), MD, *450*
Reyes, Renee - Management Recruiters of Columbia (C), MD, *450*
Reyman, Susan - S. Reyman & Assoc., Ltd. (R), IL, *176*
Reynes, Tony - Tesar-Reynes, Inc. (R), IL, *208*
Reynolds, Arlen - Executive Dimensions (R), AL, *62*
Reynolds, Bud O. - Management Recruiters of Colorado Springs-Pikes Peak (C), CO, *426*
Reynolds, Gregory - Roberts Ryan & Bentley, Inc. (R), MD, *179*
Reynolds, John H. - Brissenden, McFarland, Fuccella & Reynolds, Inc. (R), NJ, *23*
Reynolds, Juli - Hall Kinion (C), FL, *367*
Reynolds, Smooch S. - The Repovich-Reynolds Group (TRRG, Inc.) (R), CA, *175*
Reynolds, Sydney - Reynolds Partners (R), NY, *177*
Reynolds, Tom - Koll-Fairfield LLC (C), CT, *408*
Rhodes, Eugene - Dunhill of Memphis, Inc. (C), TN, *318*
Ribeiro, Claudia - Ledbetter/Davidson Int'l., Inc. (R), NY, *127*
Rice, Jr., Booker - DHR Int'l., Inc. (R), NY, *50*
Rice, Doug - Agra Placements, Ltd. (C), IN, *242*
Rice, Gene - Rice Cohen Int'l. (R), PA, *178*
Rice, Inge - Automation Technology Search (C), CA, *257*
Rice, Jim K. - Management Recruiters of New Braunfels (C), TX, *436*
Rice, Joel - Recruiting/Solutions (C), CA, *532*

Rice, Marie - Jay Gaines & Company, Inc. (R), NY, *74*
Rice, Marshall T. - Marshall Rice Assoc. (R), RI, *178*
Rice, Patrice - Patrice & Assoc. (C), MD, *505*
Rice, Raymond D. - Logue & Rice Inc. (C), VA, *420*
Rich, Kenneth M. - Ray & Berndtson (R), NY, *172*
Rich, Lyttleton - Sockwell & Assoc. (R), NC, *194*
Rich, Mark E. - Page-Wheatcroft & Co., Ltd. (R), TX, *158*
Richard, David A. - Financial Connections Company (C), VA, *340*
Richards, Carl - Technical Employment Consultants (C), PA, *602*
Richards, Christos - Stanton Chase Int'l. (R), CA, *199*
Richards, Christos - Stanton Chase Int'l. (R), CA, *199*
Richards, Claire - Sales & Marketing Search, Inc. (C), MA, *551*
Richards, David P. - Insight Personnel Group, Inc. (C), TX, *389*
Richards, Don - Dunhill of Shreveport, Inc. (C), LA, *317*
Richards, Joni K. - Insight Personnel Group, Inc. (C), TX, *389*
Richards, Paul E. - Executive Directions (R), OH, *62*
Richards, R. Glenn - Executive Directions (R), OH, *62*
Richards, Jr., Robert A. - Sloan & Assoc., Inc. (C), VA, *583*
Richards, Sharon - Richards Assoc., Inc. (R), NY, *178*
Richards, Suzanne - Fortune Consultants (C), VA, *349*
Richards, Suzanne S. - Fortune Consultants of Ft. Washington (C), PA, *349*
Richards, Terry - Terry Richards (C), OH, *536*
Richards, Vivian - The Bankers Register (C), NY, *259*
Richards, Wesley D. - Heidrick & Struggles, Inc. (R), CA, *90*
Richards-Davy, Penny - Management Recruiters of Rockville (C), MD, *450*
Richardson, David M. - DHR Int'l., Inc. (R), NJ, *50*
Richardson, J. Rick - SpencerStuart (R), CT, *196*
Richardson, Karrie - Management Recruiters of Round Rock (C), TX, *463*
Richardson, Tony R. - Management Recruiters of Traverse City (C), MI, *430*
Richer, Joyce Eidenberg - W. F. Richer Assoc., Inc. (C), NY, *537*
Richer, William F. - W. F. Richer Assoc., Inc. (C), NY, *536*
Richey, Nancy - The Stonebridge Group (C), PA, *594*
Richman, Jack - Jack Richman & Assoc. (C), FL, *537*
Richner, George A. - Search Assoc., Inc. (C), NJ, *574*
Richon, Allen - Molecular Solutions, Inc. (C), SC, *484*
Richter, Earl - The Wabash Group (C), IN, *613*
Richter, Heidi - Career Counseling Ltd. (C.C.L.) (C), IL, *282*
Richter, Michael - Career Counseling Ltd. (C.C.L.) (C), FL, *282*
Richter, Michael - Career Counseling Ltd. (C.C.L.) (C), NY, *282*
Richter, Rick - Chad Management Group (C), ON, *288*
Richter, Ryan - John Ryan Assoc., LLC. (C), NY, *399*
Riddell, Pat - The Network Corporate Search Personnel Inc. (C), AB, *491*
Riddle, James E. - Riddle & McGrath LLC (R), GA, *178*
Ridenour, Suzanne S. - Ridenour & Assoc. (R), IL, *178*
Rieger, Louis J. - SpencerStuart (R), TX, *197*
Riehl, Nancy J. - Dynamic Choices Inc. (C), MO, *324*
Riely, James A. - Brownstone Sales & Marketing Group, Inc. (C), NY, *275*
Rien, David - Jeffrey Meryl Assoc., Inc. (C), NJ, *398*
Riendeau, Russell - Thomas Lyle & Co. (C), IL, *606*
Rieser, John D. - Rieser & Assoc., Inc. (R), MO, *178*
Rietano-Davey, Susan - Flexible Resources, Inc. (C), CT, *342*
Rigal, Jennifer - Jenex Technology Placement Inc. (C), BC, *398*
Riggs, David - Management Recruiters of Duluth (C), GA, *445*
Rigter, Joe D. - Sales Consultants of Mt. Pleasant (C), SC, *555*
Rigter, Kay H. - Sales Consultants of Mt. Pleasant (C), SC, *555*
Rijke, R. Fred - TASA International (R), NY, *206*
Riles, Wilson - Wilson Riles & Assoc., Inc. (R), CA, *178*
Riley, Brian - Austin Group Int'l./Marlar Int'l. (R), TX, *9*
Riley, Jim - Riley Cole (C), CA, *537*
Riley, Kathy - Romac Int'l., Inc. (C), TX, *544*
Rimele, J. R. - Sales Recruiters of Oklahoma City (C), OK, *564*
Rimmel, James E. - The Hindman Co. (R), OH, *94*
Rimmele, Mike - Hall Kinion (C), IL, *367*
Rio, Monica - Management Recruiters of Cleveland-Independence (C), OH, *434*
Rios, Dyann - Career Development Associates (C), NV, *282*
Rios, Lorena Zuñiga - Pricewaterhouse-Coopers Executive Search (R), MX, *168*
Riotto, Anthony R. - Riotto-Jones Assoc. (R), NY, *179*
Ripp, Dan L. - Sales Consultant of New Orleans Northshore (C), LA, *553*
Risalvato, Frank G. - Inter Regional Executive Search, Inc. (IRES, Inc.) (C), NJ, *391*
Risher, Carolyn - Dise & Co. (R), OH, *52*
Risma, Bill E. - Management Recruiters of Salem Corner (C), MN, *430*
Ritchey, Toni J. - Whittlesey & Assoc., Inc. (R), PA, *220*
Ritchings, David - David Allen Assoc. (R), NJ, *3*
Ritt, Arthur - Ritt-Ritt & Assoc., Inc. (C), IL, *537*
Rivard, Richard L. - Management Recruiters of Atlanta NE (C), GA, *446*
Rivas, Alberto F. - Boyden Latin America S.A. de C.V. (R), MX, *21*
Rivera, Al - Rivera Legal Search, Inc. (C), CA, *538*
Rivera, Monica - NCC Executive Search Consultants (C), CA, *491*
Rivera-Lopez, Elba - Raymond Karsan Assoc. (C), PA, *529*
Rivers, Janeen - H.I. Hunt & Co., Ltd. (R), MA, *99*
Rizk, Nayla - SpencerStuart (R), CA, *196*
Rizzo, Deborah M. - Brian Assoc., Inc. (C), NY, *273*
Rizzo, L. Donald - Barone Assoc. (C), NJ, *259*
Roach, Janet L. - Sanford Rose Assoc. - Burlington, NC (C), NC, *569*
Roach, Ronald R. - Sanford Rose Assoc. - Burlington, NC (C), NC, *569*
Robbins, Jeffrey - Health Search (C), CA, *371*
Robbins, Mark - Search Solutions Inc. (C), CA, *576*
Robbins, Melvyn - Healthcare Recruiters of New England (C), MA, *373*
Roberson, Sandra - Interim Accounting Professionals (C), GA, *392*
Roberts, Brian M. - Sales Consultants of Buffalo Grove (C), IL, *552*
Roberts, Bryan - MetroVantage Personnel Systems (C), CA, *480*
Roberts, Carl R. - Southwestern Professional Services (C), TN, *588*
Roberts, Keith - Boyden (R), NY, *21*
Roberts, Ken - PERI Corp/Professional Executive Recruiters, Inc. (C), TX, *507*
Roberts, Libby - Global Consulting Group Inc. (C), ON, *358*
Roberts, Luke - The Retail Network (C), MA, *535*
Roberts, Marc - Action Executive Personnel Consulting Inc. (C), ON, *239*
Roberts, Marc - The Stevenson Group, Inc. (N.J.) (R), NJ, *200*
Roberts, Nick - Pacific Search Group, Inc. (C), CA, *501*
Roberts, Norman C. - Norman Roberts & Assoc., Inc. (R), CA, *179*
Roberts, Paul - Kirkbride Assoc., Inc. (C), WA, *407*
Roberts, Richard F. - Management Recruiters of Santa Monica (C), CA, *426*
Roberts, Scott - Jonas, Walters & Assoc., Inc. (R), WI, *108*
Roberts, Warren H. - White, Roberts & Stratton, Inc. (C), IL, *619*
Robertson, Bruce J. - LAI Ward Howell (R), NY, *122*

Robertson, Janice - Tele-Solutions of Arizona, Inc. (C), AZ, *604*
Robertson, R. Vic - Sanford Rose Assoc. - Chicago (C), IL, *566*
Robertson, Richard W. - AGRI-associates (C), NE, *242*
Robertson, Ron - Robertson-Surrette Ltd. (R), ON, *180*
Robertson, William R. - LAI Ward Howell (R), GA, *123*
Robinow, Larry - Health Search (C), CA, *371*
Robins, Jeri N. - Nagler, Robins & Poe, Inc. (R), MA, *150*
Robinson, Adrienne - R. L. Plimpton Assoc., Inc. (R), CO, *165*
Robinson, Bruce - Bruce Robinson Assoc. (R), NJ, *180*
Robinson, Bunny - Robinson-Robinson & Assoc., Inc. (C), MN, *539*
Robinson, Donald Alan - The Robinson Group, D.A., Ltd. (C), IL, *539*
Robinson, Eric - Bruce Robinson Assoc. (R), NJ, *180*
Robinson, Joanne - The 500 Granary Inc. (C), ON, *231*
Robinson, John - Bruce Robinson Assoc. (R), NJ, *180*
Robinson, Mel - MDR & Associates (C), AR, *476*
Robinson, Michael - Management Recruiters of Atlanta (C), GA, *445*
Robinson, P. Andrew - Consulting Resource Group, Inc. (C), GA, *297*
Robinson, Rodney L. - Michael Latas & Assoc., Inc. (R), MO, *126*
Robinson, Sam - Robinson-Robinson & Assoc., Inc. (C), MN, *539*
Robinson, Scott - Kensington Int'l., Inc. (R), IL, *113*
Robinson, Stephen - Robinson, Fraser Group Ltd. (R), ON, *180*
Robinson, Steve - Marsteller Wilcox Assoc. (C), IL, *471*
Robinson, Tom - Sanford Rose Assoc. - Norcross (C), GA, *566*
Robinson, Verneda - V. Robinson & Co., Inc. (C), MO, *539*
Robinson, Verneda - V. Robinson & Co., Inc. (C), KS, *539*
Robison, John H. - Robison & Associates (R), NC, *180*
Robison, Margaret H. - Robison Humphreys & Assoc., Inc. (R), ON, *180*
Robley, Robb - Team One Partners, Inc. (C), GA, *600*
Robohm, Peter - Baldwin Associates, LLC (R), CT, *10*
Robsham, Beverly H. - Robsham & Assoc., Inc. (R), MA, *180*
Roby, Joan - Management Recruiters of Georgetown (C), SC, *461*
Robyn, Eric W. - QVS Int'l. (R), GA, *170*
Roche, Gerard R. - Heidrick & Struggles, Inc. (R), IL, *90*
Rock, Kramer - Dunhill Staffing Systems (C), WI, *318*
Rockow, Gary - David Powell, Inc. (R), CA, *166*
Rockwell, Bruce - Romac Int'l., Inc. (C), OH, *544*
Rockwell, Bruce - Romac Int'l., Inc. (C), OH, *544*
Rockwell, Bruce - Romac Int'l., Inc. (C), OH, *544*
Rockwell, Bruce - Romac Int'l., Inc. (C), OH, *544*
Rockwell, Sr., Richard B. - Applied Search Assoc., Inc. (C), GA, *252*
Rodd, Mamie - Richard Kader & Assoc. (C), OH, *403*
Roddy, Jack P. - J. P. Roddy Consultants (C), PA, *540*
Rodebaugh, Karen - Management Recruiters of Lancaster (C), PA, *434*
Rodebaugh, Jr., Thomas L. - Management Recruiters of Lancaster (C), PA, *434*
Rodgers, Gayle - Rodgers, Ramsey, Inc. (C), TX, *540*
Rodgers, Sandy - Raymond Karsan Assoc. (C), VA, *530*
Rodgers, Sarah J. - Management Recruiters of North Hunterdon County (C), NJ, *431*
Rodriguez, Andrew - A.J. & Assoc. (C), FL, *232*
Rodriguez, Carlos R. - Management Recruiters of Puerto Rico (C), PR, *460*
Rodriguez, Dan - Romac Int'l., Inc. (C), FL, *543*
Rodriguez, George L. - InteliSearch, Inc. (R), CT, *102*
Rodriguez, Janet - T. Page & Assoc. (C), TX, *502*
Rodriguez, Larry - Marentz & Co. (C), TX, *469*
Rodriguez, Louise - Carpenter, Shackleton & Company (R), IL, *30*
Rodriguez, Steven - SpencerStuart (R), CA, *196*
Rodriguez Smithson, Raquel - R. A. Rodriguez & Assoc., Inc. (C), TX, *540*
Rodzik, C. L. - Rodzik & Assoc., Inc. (R), NC, *180*
Rodzik, Gerald F. - Rodzik & Assoc., Inc. (R), NC, *180*
Rodzik, T. A. - Rodzik & Assoc., Inc. (R), NC, *180*
Roe, Craig T. - Craig Roe & Assoc., LLC (C), MD, *540*
Roe, Sylvia A. - Craig Roe & Assoc., LLC (C), MD, *540*
Roeder, James V. - Snelling Search (C), IL, *585*
Roethlein, John - Management Recruiters Tucson-Foothills, Inc. (C), AZ, *439*
Roethlein, Lorian E. - Management Recruiters Tucson-Foothills, Inc. (C), AZ, *439*
Rogan, Daniel - The Rogan Group, Inc. (C), CA, *541*
Rogers, Gay - Rogers - McManamon Executive Search (R), CA, *180*
Rogers, George W. - Dunhill Executive Search of Brown County (C), IN, *321*
Rogers, Leah - Dinte Resources, Inc. (R), VA, *52*
Rogers, Linda - Executive Search Int'l. (C), TX, *336*
Rogers, Paul - Management Recruiters of Oakton (C), VA, *437*
Rogers, Roc - Dynamic Computer Consultants, Inc. (C), AZ, *324*
Rogers, S. L. - Dunhill Executive Search of Brown County (C), IN, *321*
Rogers, Scott - Bartz Rogers & Partners (C), MN, *261*
Rogish, Nick - Rogish Assoc., Inc. (C), OH, *541*
Rohan, James - J. P. Canon Assoc. (C), NY, *280*
Roher, Howard F. - Franklin Allen Consultants, Ltd. (R), NY, *71*
Rohrer, Ramona - Preferred Professional Recruiters (C), TX, *516*
Rojas, Carlos A. - Amrop International (R), MX, *5*
Rojek, Lorraine - Rojek Marketing Group, Inc. (R), OH, *181*
Rokey, Michael - Recruiting Assoc. of Amarillo (C), TX, *531*
Rolfe, Pamela - Career Specialists, Inc. (R), WA, *29*
Roll, Bill - Management Recruiters of Dallas-West (C), TX, *436*
Roll, M. A. - Roll International (C), TX, *541*
Rolland, Guy - Rolland Ressources Humaines Inc. (R), QE, *181*
Rollins, James - Modis (C), MD, *483*
Rollins, Jay M. - Rollins Search Group, Inc. (C), GA, *541*
Rollins, Joan E. - Rollins & Assoc. (C), CA, *541*
Rollins, Scott - S. C. Int'l., Ltd. (C), IL, *550*
Rollo, Robert S. - Rollo Assoc. (R), CA, *181*
Romanchek, Walter R. - Wellington Management Group (R), PA, *217*
Romanello, Daniel P. - SpencerStuart (R), CT, *196*
Romaniw, Michael J. - A la Carte Int'l., Inc. (R), VA, *1*
Romano, Joseph C. - Romano McAvoy Assoc., Inc. (C), NY, *544*
Romano, Lee - C.P.S., Inc. (C), IL, *278*
Romeo, Paul C. - Romeo-Hudgins & Assoc., Ltd. (C), NJ, *545*
Romm, Barry - Klein, Landau & Romm (C), DC, *407*
Romo, Dorothy E. - Physicians Search®, Inc. (C), CA, *511*
Romstein, Christina - cFour Partners (R), CA, *32*
Roodvoets, Jan - J. E. Lessner Assoc., Inc. (R), MI, *128*
Roof, Howard - O'Brien and Roof (C), OH, *497*
Rooney, Joseph J. - Rooney Assoc., Inc. (R), IL, *181*
Root, Leslie A. - The Wright Group (C), TX, *625*
Ropella, Patrick B. - Ropella & Assoc. (R), FL, *181*

PRINCIPALS

Roper, Joanne - The Shorr Group (R), IL, *190*
Ropes, John - Ropes Associates, Inc. (R), FL, *182*
Rosamilia, Frank - Healthcare Recruiters Int'l. Philadelphia (C), NJ, *373*
Rosato, William R. - W. R. Rosato & Assoc., Inc. (R), NY, *182*
Roscoe, Harry - The Beardsley Group Inc. (C), CT, *261*
Rose, Author - Sofco (C), NY, *586*
Rose, Emery - Emery A. Rose & Assoc. (C), WA, *545*
Rose, Greta - Access Assoc. Inc. (C), MD, *233*
Rose, James L. - Unisearch Search & Recruiting Inc. (C), CA, *611*
Rose, John M. - The Curtiss Group International (R), FL, *44*
Rose, Sanford M. - Sanford Rose Assoc. - Akron (C), OH, *569*
Rose, V. Thomas - F-O-R-T-U-N-E Personnel Consultants of Boise (R), ID, *70*
Roseman, Bonnie - Ruderfer & Co., Inc. (C), NJ, *548*
Rosemarin, Gloria J. - Barrington Hart, Inc. (R), IL, *12*
Rosen, Elayne - Noble & Assoc., Inc. (C), NY, *494*
Rosen, Richard - Cornerstone Search Assoc. Inc. (C), MA, *299*
Rosenbaum, Bette - Healthcare Executive Recruiters, Inc. (C), CA, *372*
Rosenberg, John - Management Recruiters of Springfield (C), VA, *437*
Rosenberg, Kevin M. - BridgeGate LLC (C), CA, *273*
Rosenberger, Jim - The Rose Search Group, Inc. (C), NC, *545*
Rosenblatt, Michael F. - The Quest Organization (C), NY, *527*
Rosenblum, Al - The Worth Group (C), NY, *625*
Rosenfeld, Martin J. - Rosenfeld & Co., Inc. (C), MI, *545*
Rosenow, Richard - Heath/Norton Assoc., Inc. (R), NY, *89*
Rosenthal, Abbe L. - ALW Research Int'l. (R), NJ, *4*
Rosenthal, Nathan - Pioneer Placement, Inc. (C), MA, *512*
Rosica, John - Management Recruiters Inc. of Silicon Valley (C), CA, *441*
Rosica, John - Sales Consultants of Silicon Valley (C), CA, *556*
Rosner, David - Dunhill Professional Search of San Jose (C), CA, *319*
Ross, Allison - Major, Hagen & Africa (C), NY, *423*
Ross, Andrew - DARE Personnel Inc. (C), ON, *307*
Ross, Cheryl Molliver - Thomas, Whelan Assoc., Inc. (C), DC, *606*
Ross, Craig - Norrell Financial Staffing (C), GA, *495*
Ross, Elsa - Gardner-Ross Assoc., Inc. (R), NY, *74*
Ross, Garland E. - Management Recruiters of Green Bay (C), WI, *438*
Ross, Garland E. - Sales Consultants of Green Bay (C), WI, *555*
Ross, H. Lawrence - Ross & Company, Inc. (R), CT, *182*
Ross, Heather - Management Recruiters-Cedar Rapids, Inc. (C), IA, *448*
Ross, Irene - New World Healthcare Solutions, Inc. (R), NY, *151*
Ross, Karen M. - The Hetzel Group, Inc. (R), IL, *93*
Ross, Larry - The Summit Group (C), CA, *596*
Ross, Marc A. - Flowers & Assoc. (C), OH, *342*
Ross, Marty - LAI Ward Howell (R), CA, *123*
Ross, Robert - Chicago Research Group, Inc. (R), NC, *33*
Ross, Robert F. - Bertrand, Ross & Assoc., Inc. (C), IL, *266*
Ross, Ruthie M. - Recruitment Resources (C), CA, *532*
Ross, Terri - Soderlund Assoc. Inc. (R), OH, *195*
Ross, Wanda - Moss & Co. (R), WA, *148*
Ross, William J. - Flowers & Assoc. (C), OH, *342*
Rossen, Michael - Direct Recruiters, Inc. (C), OH, *312*
Rossi, Alfred F. - The Rossi Search Group (C), PA, *545*
Rossi, Donna - Rossi & Assoc. Inc. (C), BC, *545*
Rossi, George A. - Heidrick & Struggles, Inc. (R), MA, *90*
Rossi, Larry - The Executive Group, Inc. (R), CA, *62*
Rossman, Paul R. - Management Recruiters of Pittsburgh-South Hills (C), PA, *435*
Rossow, Bob - E/Search Int'l. (C), CT, *325*
Rotella, Marshall W. - The Corporate Connection, Ltd. (C), VA, *300*
Roth, Bill - Lou Michaels Assoc., Inc. (C), MI, *481*
Roth, Jim - Management Recruiters of Des Moines (C), IA, *449*
Roth, Mark - AMS Int'l. (R), VA, *5*
Roth, Patricia - Patricia Roth Int'l. (C), FL, *545*
Roth, Robert J. - Williams, Roth & Krueger, Inc. (R), IL, *221*
Roth, Ronald P. - Smith, Roth & Squires (R), NY, *194*
Rothenbush, Chuck - Romac Int'l., Inc. (C), OH, *544*
Rothman, Judith L. - Royal Assoc. (C), CA, *547*
Rothrock, Jr., T. Hardy - Rothrock Associates, Inc. (C), NC, *547*
Rothschild, John S. - LAI Ward Howell (R), IL, *123*
Rothstein, Steve - N.A.P. Executive Services (Canada) Inc. (C), ON, *488*
Rotsky, Bernard - BR & Assoc. (C), NJ, *271*
Rotsky, Sally - BR & Assoc. (C), NJ, *271*
Rotter, E. Joseph - Search Assoc., Inc. (C), NJ, *574*
Rotter, Stephen - RSMR, Inc. (R), IL, *182*
Rotundo, F. J. - Management Resources Int'l. (R), NY, *135*
Rouleau, Gilles - Lamon + Stuart + Michaels Inc. (R), QE, *124*
Rountree, III, John B. - Lexington Software Inc. (C), NY, *417*
Routh, Maria - The Kleven Group, Inc. (C), MA, *407*
Rovner, Bettyann - Rovner & Assoc., Inc. (R), IL, *182*
Rovner, Louis - Rovner Gerner & Assoc. (R), CA, *182*
Rowan, Carol - Hunter, Rowan & Crowe (C), WI, *386*
Rowe, David E. - David Rowe & Assoc., Inc. (R), IL, *182*
Rowe, K. Michael - Management Resource Group (C), MN, *467*
Rowe, Mark - Dunhill Technical Staffing (C), IN, *320*
Rowe, William - Foster Partners (R), TX, *71*
Rowell, Mike - Carter/MacKay (C), MA, *285*
Rowenhorst, Brenda - The Bren Group (C), AZ, *273*
Rowland, John R. - Rowland Assoc. (C), CA, *547*
Rowls, Gene - E. J. Ashton & Assoc., Ltd. (C), IL, *253*
Roy, Gary P. - Management Recruiters of Oklahoma City (C), OK, *458*
Roy, Ruth - Lois L. Lindauer Searches (C), MA, *418*
Royer, Dade - The Stonebridge Group (C), PA, *594*
Royfe, Dan - D.R. Assoc. (R), CA, *45*
Roylance, Robert L. - STM Assoc. (R), UT, *201*
Rozenboom, Carol E. - David Rowe & Assoc., Inc. (R), IL, *182*
Rozner, Burton L. - Oliver & Rozner Assoc., Inc. (R), NY, *155*
Rubenstein, Alan J. - Chicago Legal Search, Ltd. (C), IL, *290*
Rubin, David S. - Sales Consultants of Columbia (C), MD, *553*
Rubin, Howard - Ferrari Search Group (C), OH, *340*
Rubin, Karen - Travel Executive Search (C), NY, *608*
Rubin, Lauren H. - Morgenstern Int'l., Inc. (C), NY, *486*
Rubin, Nadine - Adam-Bryce Inc. (C), NY, *239*
Rubin, Ron - Geddes & Rubin Management Inc. (R), ON, *76*
Rubin, Stephanie - Amherst Human Resource Group, Ltd. (C), IL, *249*
Rubinic, Michael - The Rubinic Consulting Group (C), OH, *548*
Rubinic, Roxanna - The Rubinic Consulting Group (C), OH, *548*
Ruden, Shauna - Dunhill Professional Search of San Jose (C), CA, *319*
Ruderfer, Irwin A. - Ruderfer & Co., Inc. (C), NJ, *548*

Rudich, Susan - Susan Rudich (C), NY, *548*
Rudin, Harold - Management Recruiters of Greater Ft. Wayne (C), IN, *429*
Rudin, Myra - Management Recruiters of Greater Ft. Wayne (C), IN, *429*
Rudnick, Marlene - Marcus & Assoc. (C), NY, *469*
Rudolph, Arlyn B. - Management Recruiters of Springfield (C), MO, *431*
Rudolph, Lee - Management Recruiters of Franktown (C), CO, *442*
Rudolph, Mary Ellen - Perez-Arton Consultants, Inc. (R), NY, *162*
Rudy, Camille - Meder & Assoc., Inc. (R), IL, *142*
Rudzinsky, Howard - Louis Rudzinsky Assoc., Inc. (C), MA, *548*
Rudzinsky, Jeff - Louis Rudzinsky Assoc., Inc. (C), MA, *548*
Ruebusch, Pamela - TSI Group/TSI Staffing Services (C), ON, *610*
Rueppel, Melvin L. - Holohan Group, Ltd. (R), MO, *95*
Ruf, Ines - Stoopen Asociados, S.C./EMA Partners Int'l. (R), MX, *202*
Ruggeri, Chris - DHR Int'l., Inc. (R), NY, *50*
Ruhmann, John D. - J. D. Ruhmann & Assoc. (C), MO, *548*
Rumbarger, Charles D. - Association Executive Resources Group (R), MD, *8*
Rumson, Barbara A. - Management Recruiters of Asheville, Inc. (C), NC, *455*
Rumson, Paul M. - Management Recruiters of Asheville, Inc. (C), NC, *455*
Rumson, Paul Michael - Management Recruiters of Asheville, Inc. (C), NC, *455*
Runquist, U. W. - Webb, Johnson Assoc., Inc. (R), NY, *216*
Rupar, Kathy - Marc-Allen Assoc., Inc. (C), FL, *469*
Rupert, James A. - Management Recruiters of Siouxland (C), IA, *449*
Rupp, Jane M. - MRF Enterprises, Inc. (C), TX, *486*
Rupp, Sandra - Johnson Smith & Knisely (R), NY, *107*
Ruppert, Eleanora T. - Ruppert Comann Assoc., Inc. (R), CO, *182*
Ruppert, William J. - Ruppert Comann Assoc., Inc. (R), CO, *182*
Rurak, Zbigniew T. - Rurak & Assoc., Inc (R), DC, *183*
Ruschak, Randy R. - Management Recruiters of Bordentown (C), NJ, *454*
Rush, Michael E. - D.A.L. Associates, Inc. (R), CT, *45*
Rush, Renee Berliner - Corrao, Miller, Rush & Wiesenthal (C), NY, *301*
Rusher, Jr., William H. - Rusher, Loscavio & LoPresto (R), CA, *183*
Rushmore, Stephen - HVS Executive Search (R), NY, *100*
Rusnov, Samuel - Michael Latas & Assoc., Inc. (R), OH, *126*
Russel, Grant - Management Recruiters of Findlay (C), OH, *434*
Russell, Robin - Kenzer Corp. (R), NY, *113*
Russell, Ronald G. - McPherson Square Assoc., Inc. (C), DC, *475*
Russell, Steven - Nyborg•Dow Assoc., Inc. (C), CA, *497*
Russillo, Thomas P. - Russillo/Gardner/Spolsino (C), MA, *548*
Russo, Antonella - The Zarkin Group, Inc. (R), NY, *226*
Russo, Joseph E. - Hamilton-Chase & Assoc., Inc. (R), MA, *85*
Russo, Joseph E. - Hamilton-Chase & Assoc., Inc. (R), MA, *85*
Russo, Karen - K. Russo Assoc. Inc. (C), CT, *548*
Rust, John R. - Rust & Assoc., Inc. (R), IL, *183*
Rutherford, Frank H. - Gaming Consultants, Inc. (R), LA, *74*
Ruthrauff, Debbie - Kelly Associates (R), PA, *112*
Rutkauskas, Patsy A. - Sales Consultants of Bangor, Inc. (C), ME, *559*
Rutkovsky, Laurence - Benson Associates (C), NY, *264*
Rutledge, Andy - Management Recruiters - Indianapolis (C), IN, *448*
Rutledge, William A. - W. A. Rutledge & Assoc. (R), CT, *183*
Ruttanai-Fanelli, Lynn - Ariel Recruitment Assoc. (R), NY, *7*
Rutter, David - Romac Int'l., Inc. (C), MA, *543*
Ryan, Bernard J. - Brissenden, McFarland, Fuccella & Reynolds, Inc. (R), NJ, *23*
Ryan, Brian - The Logan Group, Inc. (R), MO, *131*
Ryan, David - The Recruitment Group, Inc. (C), NY, *532*
Ryan, Debra - Bonell Ryan Inc. (R), NY, *19*
Ryan, Elisabeth A. - Heyman Assoc., Inc. (R), NY, *93*
Ryan, J. Barry - The Winchester Group (R), CA, *222*
Ryan, James A. - The Gullgroup (C), TX, *364*
Ryan, John - RSMR, Inc. (R), IL, *182*
Ryan, Katherine - The Park Group & Assoc., Inc. (C), MD, *503*
Ryan, Lee - Ryan, Miller & Assoc. (C), CA, *549*
Ryan, Martin - Accountants On Call (C), OR, *237*
Ryan, Nancy - Health Search (C), CA, *371*
Ryan-Ulyatt, Theresa - Chatham Search Assoc., Inc. (C), NJ, *290*
Ryder, Elvira F. - Webb, Johnson Assoc., Inc. (R), NY, *216*
Ryder, John - Accountants On Call (C), MD, *236*
Ryder Stone, Robert - LAI Ward Howell (R), CT, *123*
Rystrom, R. L. - R. L. Rystrom & Assoc., Inc. (C), MN, *549*
Sabbio, Kathy - The Brentwood Group, Inc. (R), NJ, *22*
Sabrin, Joe - ManTech Consulting (C), NY, *468*
Sacarny, Bonnie - Marcus & Assoc. (C), NY, *469*
Sacchetti, Lisa - The Renaissance Network (C), MA, *534*
Sacerdote, John - Raymond Karsan Assoc. (C), MA, *530*
Sachs, Susan - Johnson Smith & Knisely (R), NY, *107*
Sackmary, Marcia T. - Sanford Rose Assoc. - Austin (C), TX, *570*
Sackmary, Stephen M. - Sanford Rose Assoc. - Austin (C), TX, *570*
Sadaka, Steve - Steven Douglas Assoc. (C), FL, *593*
Sadlier, Darbi - APA Employment Agency Inc. (C), OR, *251*
Sadlier, Darbi - APA Employment Agency Inc. (C), OR, *251*
Sadovnick, Mark - Steven Douglas Assoc. (C), FL, *593*
Sadow, Raymond - R. S. Sadow Assoc. (C), NJ, *550*
Saenger, Gary - R.J. Watkins & Co., Ltd. (R), CA, *216*
Sahagian, John - The Search Alliance, Inc. (R), RI, *186*
Sajankila, Raj - Softrix, Inc. (C), NJ, *586*
Sakuru, Anita - Raymond Karsan Assoc. (C), MA, *530*
Sakuru, Raghu - Raymond Karsan Assoc. (C), MA, *530*
Salcido, Chris - Protocol Inc. (C), CA, *525*
Salfi, James P. - Ritta Professional Search Inc. (C), NY, *538*
Salikof, Allen B. - Management Recruiters International, Inc. (MRI) (C), OH, *425*
Salikof, Kaye - Management Recruiters of Cherry Hill (C), PA, *459*
Salinas, Pedro - Premier Recruiting Group (C), MI, *516*
Salisbury, Darla - Sales Consultants of Oklahoma City (C), OK, *555*
Sall, Ron - Interim Financial Solutions (C), VA, *392*
Salloway, Andrew N. - A. N. Salloway Executive Search & Consulting, L.L.C. (C), MA, *564*
Salls, David - Schwab-Carrese Assoc., Inc. Executive Search (R), NC, *185*
Salmela, Alexander K. - A.K.S. Assoc., Ltd. (R), MA, *1*
Salmon, C. Scott - DHR Int'l., Inc. (R), MO, *50*
Salottolo, Al - Tactical Alternatives (R), CA, *205*
Saloukas, Bill I. - Broad Waverly & Assoc. (C), NJ, *274*
Salter, Michelle - APA Employment Agency Inc. (C), WA, *251*
Saltzman, Larry - Accountants On Call (C), NJ, *235*
Salvagno, Michael - Cambridge Group Ltd. - Exec. Search Div. (C), CT, *279*
Salvagno, Mike - The Cambridge Group Ltd. (C), CT, *280*
Salvatore, Philip A. - LAS Management Consulting Group, Inc. (R), NJ, *125*

PRINCIPALS

Salveson, John - Salveson Stetson Group, Inc. (R), PA, *184*
Salway, Clancy - Sales Management Resources (C), CA, *563*
Salzberg, David - Roth Young Seattle (C), WA, *546*
Salzer, Sally - Management Recruiters of Highland Park (C), IL, *428*
Salzman, John W. - Dunhill Staffing Systems, Inc. (C), OH, *318*
Samet, Saul - Fisher-Todd Assoc. (C), NY, *342*
Sammons, James A. - Prestige Inc. (C), WI, *517*
Sampson, Judie - Sampson Medical Search (C), CA, *564*
Sampson, Kellie - Sampson Medical Search (C), CA, *564*
Sampson, Paul - O'Keefe & Assoc., Inc. (R), CT, *154*
Sampson, Ron - Market Niche Consulting (C), AZ, *470*
Samuels, Ivan R. - George D. Sandel Assoc. (C), MA, *565*
Samuels, Jonathan - Boston Professional Search, Inc. (C), MA, *270*
Samuels, Lew - Morgan Samuels Co. (R), CA, *147*
Samuels, Steve - CountryHouse Hotels Executive Search (C), VA, *302*
Sanborn, Jr., Lee R. - Selected Executives, Inc. (C), MA, *578*
Sanchez, Jorge - Interim Accounting Professionals (C), FL, *392*
Sanders, David - Management Recruiters of Roseville (C), CA, *441*
Sanders, Gail - Discovery, The Staffing Specialists, Inc. (C), IL, *312*
Sanders, Jason - Sanders Management Assoc., Inc. (C), NJ, *565*
Sanders, Karen M. - Norm Sanders Assoc., Inc. (R), NJ, *184*
Sanders, Marlaine - Shell Technology Group (C), CA, *580*
Sanders, Melba - Berkhemer/Clayton, Inc. (R), CA, *16*
Sanders, Norman D. - Norm Sanders Assoc., Inc. (R), NJ, *184*
Sanders, Roy - Sanders Management Assoc., Inc. (C), NJ, *565*
Sanders, Todd A. - Norm Sanders Assoc., Inc. (R), NJ, *184*
Sanderson, Dean - Management Recruiters of Delavan (C), WI, *437*
Sandor, Richard - Flynn, Hannock, Inc. (R), CT, *69*
Sands, Tony - Healthcare Search Associates (C), CA, *374*
Sandusky, Dave - DHR Int'l., Inc. (R), CO, *49*
Sandusky, Edward - Professional Support Inc. (C), NY, *523*
Sangster, Jeffrey A. - F-O-R-T-U-N-E Personnel Consultants of Manatee County (C), FL, *345*
Santamaria, Jay - The Beam Group (R), NY, *14*
Santangelo, Richard - Santangelo Consultants Inc. (C), NY, *571*
Santarelli, Richard L. - New Directions, Inc. (C), IL, *492*
Santiago, Anthony - TaxSearch Inc. (R), OK, *207*
Saporito, Richard P. - Circuit Search (C), NH, *291*
Sarabosing, Sal - Barrett Hospitality Search (R), CA, *12*
Saracen, Robert R. - The Libra Group Inc. (C), CT, *417*
Sarafa, Sam N. - Management Recruiters of Ann Arbor (C), MI, *430*
Sarantino, Tina - Management Recruiters of Fresno (C), CA, *440*
Sarchett, A. Wayne - Systems Careers (C), CA, *598*
Sargent, Robert A. - JM & Company (R), PA, *106*
Sargis, Scott R. - Strategic Search Corp. (R), IL, *202*
Sarkis, Stephen - Stone & Youngblood (C), MA, *594*
Sarn, Allan G. - Allan Sarn Assoc., Inc. (R), NY, *184*
Sarver, Catherine J. - Sarver & Carruth Assoc. (C), OK, *571*
Sarver, Dan - F-O-R-T-U-N-E Personnel Consultants of Tampa (C), FL, *345*
Saso, Maria - Dunhill Professional Search of San Jose (C), CA, *319*
Satenstein, Sloan - Higdon Prince Inc. (R), NY, *93*
Sathe, Mark - Sathe & Associates, Inc. (R), MN, *184*
Sather, Jan - Career Marketing Assoc., Inc. (C), CO, *282*
Satterfield, Jr., Richard W. - Satterfield & Assoc., Inc. (R), OH, *184*
Sattler, John E. - Impact Source, Inc. (C), FL, *387*
Sauer, Andrea Garcia - Frank P. Hill (R), MX, *93*
Sauer, Harry - ACSYS Resources, Inc. (C), PA, *239*
Saunders, Wayne - Lanken-Kimball-Therrell & Assoc. (C), GA, *412*
Savage, Edward J. - Stanton Chase Int'l. (R), CA, *199*
Savalli, Frank - Savalli & Assoc., Inc. (C), MI, *571*
Savard, Jr., Robert F. - Horton International Inc. (R), CT, *96*
Savior, Rick - RLM Assoc., Ltd. (R), NY, *179*
Savoy, Michelle - SpencerStuart (R), ON, *197*
Savransky, Alan - Home Health & Hospital Recruiters, Inc. (C), GA, *380*
Savransky, Barry P. - Home Health & Hospital Recruiters, Inc. (C), GA, *380*
Sawhill, Louise - Healthcare Management Resources, Inc. (R), GA, *89*
Sawyer, Patricia L. - Smith & Sawyer, Inc. (R), NY, *193*
Sawyer, Pierce - Phillips Resource Group (C), NC, *511*
Sawyer, Scott J. - Management Search Int'l. (C), CA, *467*
Sawyer, Whitney A. - Curran Partners, Inc. (R), CT, *44*
Saxe, Ray - Advanced Executive Resources (R), MI, *2*
Saxner, David - David Saxner & Assoc., Inc. (DSA, Inc.) (R), IL, *185*
Saxon, Alexa - Woodworth Int'l. Group (R), CA, *225*
Saylor, Bill E. - Management Recruiters of North Tacoma (C), WA, *437*
Sbarbaro, Richard D. - Lauer, Sbarbaro Assoc., EMA Partners Int'l. (R), IL, *126*
Scalamera, Tom - C.P.S., Inc. (C), IL, *278*
Scanlon, Carol-Anne - The 500 Granary Inc. (C), ON, *231*
Scanlon, James D. - Sherbrooke Assoc., Inc. (C), NJ, *580*
Scaparotti, Jim - Fox-Morris Assoc., Inc. (C), OH, *352*
Scarcele, Robert - Diedre Moire Corp., Inc. (C), NJ, *483*
Scardifield, David - Omnisearch Assoc. (C), CA, *499*
Scarpino, William A. - Allen Austin Lowe & Powers (R), TX, *3*
Scassellati, Cheryl - Accountants On Call (C), IL, *235*
Scaturro, Leonard - Boone-Scaturro Assoc., Inc. (C), GA, *269*
Scaturro, Mary Ellen - Boone-Scaturro Assoc., Inc. (C), GA, *269*
Schaack, Mike - Carlsen Resources, Inc. (R), CO, *29*
Schachter, Laura J. - Professional Placement Assoc., Inc. (C), NY, *521*
Schaefer, Jr., Frederick M. - Stratford-Group (R), CO, *203*
Schaefer, John - Professional Employment Group (C), MD, *520*
Schaeffer, Ella - Sage Employment Recruiters (C), IN, *550*
Schalk, Julie - Account Ability Now (C), MI, *234*
Schall, David R. - Schall Executive Search Partners (R), MN, *185*
Schall, William - The Stevenson Group, Inc. (R), FL, *200*
Schaller, Susan - Jay Gaines & Company, Inc. (R), NY, *74*
Schapira, Kenneth - Wilson Personnel, Inc. (C), NC, *622*
Schappell, Marc P. - Egon Zehnder Int'l. Inc. (R), NY, *227*
Scharringhausen, Michael C. - Saber Group, Inc. (C), TX, *550*
Schattle, Donald J. - Schattle & Duquette (C), RI, *571*
Schatz, Jr., William G. - The Schatz Company (C), MO, *571*
Schaul, Mark - Staffing Edge, Inc. (C), IA, *590*
Schechter, Phil - Management Recruiters of Atlanta (C), GA, *445*
Scheetz, James - DHR Int'l., Inc. (R), OR, *51*
Schegg, John P. - Goodrich & Sherwood Assoc., Inc. (R), CT, *80*
Scheibel, Scott - Accountants On Call (C), MO, *236*

Schemo, Nate - Sales Consultant of Sandy Springs (C), GA, *552*
Schenck, Anthony N. - The McLeod Group, Inc. (R), CT, *141*
Schenck, Kurt - Management Recruiters of North Charleston (C), SC, *460*
Schene, Philip - A. E. Feldman Assoc., Inc. (C), NY, *339*
Schepman, Susan - DHR Int'l., Inc. (R), AZ, *49*
Scher, Mark G. - LAI Ward Howell (R), NY, *123*
Scherck, III, Henry J. - LAI Ward Howell (R), NY, *123*
Schere, Ivan - National Search, Inc.r (C), FL, *490*
Scheye, Klaus G. - Anderson & Schwab, Inc. (R), NY, *6*
Schiavone, Mary Rose - Canny, Bowen Inc. (R), NY, *28*
Schibli, Peter - H.I. Hunt & Co., Ltd. (R), MA, *99*
Schichtle, Nick - Accountants Executive Search (C), CA, *237*
Schick, Jon - Schick Professional Search, Inc. (C), OH, *572*
Schick, Rex - Schick Professional Search, Inc. (C), OH, *572*
Schiel, John M. - Western Management Consultants (R), AB, *218*
Schiff, Arlene D. - A.D. Schiff & Assoc., Ltd. (C), IL, *572*
Schiller, Christian - Cook Assoc.,® Inc. (R), IL, *40*
Schindel, Kim - Searchworks, Inc. (C), FL, *577*
Schinke, Brenda - HCI Corp. (C), IL, *371*
Schlabach, Charles F. - Carnegie Partners, Inc. (R), IL, *30*
Schlanger, Ruth - Richard, Wayne & Roberts (C), TX, *536*
Schlarmann, Erika - The Partners, LLC (C), CA, *504*
Schlatter, Craig - Schlatter & Assoc. (C), CA, *572*
Schlect, Nancy - Morgan Samuels Co. (R), CA, *147*
Schlender, Lesly - Rovner & Assoc., Inc. (R), IL, *182*
Schlesinger, Dawn - The Quantum Group (C), NJ, *527*
Schlesinger, Michael - The Quantum Group (C), NJ, *527*
Schlifke, Richard B. - New Directions, Inc. (C), IL, *492*
Schluter, Rob - Sales Consultants of Bend (C), OR, *555*
Schlutow, Debra - Harvey Hohauser & Assoc., LLC (R), MI, *87*
Schmeh, Bill - Sales Solutions (C), CA, *564*
Schmeh, Sandy - Sales Solutions (C), CA, *564*
Schmidt, Frank B. - F. B. Schmidt Int'l. (R), CA, *185*
Schmidt, James - Cejka Healthcare Executive Search Services (CHESS) (R), MO, *32*
Schmidt, Jeri E. - Blake/Hansen & Schmidt, Ltd. (R), NY, *18*
Schmidt, Paul W. - LAI Ward Howell (R), IL, *123*
Schmidt, Peter R. - Boyden (R), NJ, *21*
Schmidt, Robert C. - Management Recruiters of Norwalk (C), CT, *426*
Schmidt, Susan - David Weinfeld Group (C), NC, *617*
Schmidtke, Kent - DHR Int'l., Inc. (R), AZ, *49*
Schneekluth, Mark J. - PRO, Inc./Professional Recruiting Offices, Inc. (C), CA, *519*
Schneider, Jim - Hunter Douglas Group, Inc. (R), IL, *99*
Schneider, Jim - Professional Consulting Network, Inc. (C), CA, *520*
Schneider, Paul J. - Prime Resource Assoc. (C), WI, *518*
Schneider, Perry M. - Agra Placements, Ltd. (C), IL, *242*
Schneider, Skip W. - Schneider, Hill & Spangler, Inc. (R), PA, *185*
Schneider, Steven A. - Schneider, Hill & Spangler, Inc. (R), PA, *185*
Schneider, Susan - Finn & Schneider Assoc., Inc. (C), DC, *341*
Schneider, Ted - HealthSearch Assoc. (C), MD, *374*
Schneider, Thomas P. - WTW Assoc., Inc. (R), NY, *225*
Schneider, Tom J. - Management Recruiters of Albuquerque (C), NM, *432*
Schneiderman, Gerald - Management Resource Assoc., Inc. (C), FL, *467*
Schneiderman, Sheila - Management Resource Assoc., Inc. (C), FL, *467*
Schoales, Gloria - Schoales & Assoc. Inc. (C), ON, *572*
Schoales, Michael - Schoales & Assoc. Inc. (C), ON, *572*
Schoeling, Beverly - Tom McCall Executive Search (C), IL, *473*
Schoellkopf, Karl - K. Jaeger & Assoc. (C), MA, *396*
Schoen, Stephen G. - MDR Associates, Inc. (C), FL, *476*
Schoenfeld, Jack - Dunhill of Manchester Inc. (C), NH, *321*
Schoenfeld, Marian - Dunhill of Manchester Inc. (C), NH, *321*
Schoenfeld, Randy - Redwood Partners Ltd. (R), NY, *173*
Schoenwetter, Carrie - Management Recruiters of Minneapolis (C), MN, *430*
Schoff, Diane L. - The Edge Resource Group (C), PA, *326*
Schoff, Frank J. - Management Recruiters of Cedar Mountain (C), NC, *455*
Schonberg, Alan R. - Management Recruiters International, Inc. (MRI) (C), OH, *425*
Schonberg, Alan R. - Sales Consultants (C), OH, *551*
Schoon, Richard G. - The Partnership Group (R), RI, *160*
Schoon, Richard G. - The Partnership Group (R), NJ, *160*
Schoonmaker, John - Creative Management Strategies, Ltd. (R), NY, *42*
Schorejs, Ray - Roth Young Executive Search (C), TX, *546*
Schorle, Randall W. - Onsite Staffing Solutions (R), IL, *156*
Schraeter, Jack M. - Lake Medical Associates (C), ME, *411*
Schrandt, Fred - Rice Cohen Int'l. (R), PA, *178*
Schreiber, Sandy - Survival Systems Staffing, Inc. (C), CA, *597*
Schrenzel, Steven N. - The Governance Group, Inc. (R), NJ, *80*
Schrepferman, William W. - Baldwin & Assoc. (C), OH, *258*
Schriber, Floyd - F-O-R-T-U-N-E Consultants of Memphis (C), TN, *349*
Schroeder, John W. - SpencerStuart (R), TX, *197*
Schroeder, Lee - Blau Mancino Schroeder (R), NE, *18*
Schroeder, Steven J. - Blau Mancino Schroeder (R), NM, *18*
Schroeder, Tim - F-O-R-T-U-N-E Personnel of Nashville (C), TN, *350*
Schuback, Donna - DataPro Personnel Consultants (C), TX, *308*
Schuckman, Dalon W. - Joy Reed Belt Search Consultants, Inc. (R), OK, *15*
Schuckman, Louis - Accountants On Call (C), NJ, *236*
Schueneman, Dave - C.P.S., Inc. (C), IL, *278*
Schuessler, Mary Ann - Drake & Assoc. (C), CA, *315*
Schuhmacher, Daniel - Management Recruiters of Round Rock (C), TX, *463*
Schulenburg, Neil P. - Schulenburg & Assoc. (C), GA, *572*
Schuller, Eric K. - TE, Inc. (C), IL, *600*
Schulman, Michael - Search West, Inc. (C), CA, *576*
Schultz, Bob - Wegner & Assoc. (C), WI, *617*
Schultz, Craig - F-O-R-T-U-N-E Personnel Consultants of St. Louis-West County (C), MO, *347*
Schultz, Helen - Predictor Systems Corp. (R), CA, *167*
Schultz, Jon - The Carlyle Group, Ltd. (R), IL, *30*
Schultz, Robert E. - TSW Assoc., LLC (R), CT, *211*
Schultz, Roger C. - Management Recruiters of Hartford-South (C), CT, *426*
Schultz, Sandy - F-O-R-T-U-N-E Personnel Consultants of St. Louis-West County (C), MO, *347*
Schultz, Sheila A. - Mordue, Allen, Roberts, Bonney Ltd. (C), WA, *485*
Schultz, Tim - Focus Executive Search (C), MN, *343*
Schultz, William A. - Sales Consultants of Madison (C), WI, *563*
Schulz, Bill - Holloway Schulz & Partners (C), BC, *380*
Schulz, Chris - Wilson Assoc. Inc. (R), NS, *222*

PRINCIPALS

Schumann, Robert - Reinecke & Assoc. (C), NJ, *533*
Schumer, Marvin - R & L Assoc., Ltd. (R), NY, *170*
Schumer, Rochelle - R & L Assoc., Ltd. (R), NY, *170*
Schutz, Andrea - Ken Clark Int'l. (R), NJ, *36*
Schuyler, Lambert - Schuyler Assoc., Ltd. (R), GA, *185*
Schuyler, Lambert - Schuyler, Baker & Parker, Inc. (R), GA, *185*
Schwab, Jr., Frank - Anderson & Schwab, Inc. (R), NY, *6*
Schwab, James K. - Schwab-Carrese Assoc., Inc. Executive Search (R), NC, *185*
Schwam, Carol - A. E. Feldman Assoc., Inc. (C), NY, *339*
Schwan, John - The Technology Group (R), IL, *208*
Schwartz, Alan - Advice Personnel Inc. (C), NY, *241*
Schwartz, Alan M. - Selective Management Services, Inc. (C), FL, *578*
Schwartz, Bennett - Harper Associates (C), MI, *369*
Schwartz, Beth O. - G. L. Schwartz & Assoc., Inc. (C), GA, *572*
Schwartz, Carole - Johnson Smith & Knisely (R), NY, *107*
Schwartz, Deborah - Ollinger Partners (R), MA, *156*
Schwartz, Gary L. - G. L. Schwartz & Assoc., Inc. (C), GA, *572*
Schwartz, Jay S. - Management Recruiters of Richmond (C), VA, *437*
Schwartz, Jay S. - Sales Consultants of Richmond (C), VA, *555*
Schwartz, Kenneth - John Kurosky & Assoc. (R), CA, *122*
Schwartz, Lou - Technical Employment Consultants (C), PA, *602*
Schwartz, Margot - Sterling Int'l. (R), NJ, *200*
Schwartz, Mark L. - F-o-r-t-u-n-e Personnel Consultants of Detroit, Inc. (C), MI, *346*
Schwartz, Michael - Synapse Human Resource Consulting Group (R), TX, *205*
Schwartz, Rachel - Arnold Huberman Assoc., Inc. (R), NY, *97*
Schwartz, Raymond - The Partnership Group (R), NJ, *160*
Schwartz, Stephen D. - Management Recruiters of Gramercy, Inc. (C), NY, *455*
Schwartz, Stewart - Brandywine Management Group (R), MD, *22*
Schwartz, Vince - Johnson Smith & Knisely (R), IL, *107*
Schwarz, Meredith Barnes - Barnes & Assoc. Executive Search (C), CA, *259*
Schweichler, Lee - Schweichler Assoc., Inc. (R), CA, *186*
Schweiger, Michael - Search Int'l. (R), MA, *187*
Schwimmer, Samuel - The Wayne Group, Ltd. (C), NY, *617*
Scodius, Joseph J. - Gregory Michaels & Assoc., Inc. (R), IL, *82*
Scofield, Larry J. - Management Recruiters of Tampa-Bayside (C), FL, *427*
Scofield, Nancy A. - Management Recruiters of Tampa-Bayside (C), FL, *427*
Scoggins, Tim - Jackson Resources (R), TX, *105*
Scorce, Kristin - Bishop Partners (R), NY, *17*
Scott, Bob - Robert Scott Assoc. (C), NJ, *573*
Scott, Corwyn J. - Warren, Morris & Madison, Ltd. (C), NH, *616*
Scott, Douglas W. - New Directions, Inc. (C), IL, *492*
Scott, E. Ann - Scott Executive Search, Inc. (R), NY, *186*
Scott, Evan - Howard Fischer Assoc. Int'l., Inc. (R), PA, *67*
Scott, George - Raymond Karsan Assoc. (C), PA, *530*
Scott, Gordon - Search Advisors Int'l. Corp. (R), FL, *186*
Scott, Gordon S. - Search Research Assoc., Inc. (R), MA, *187*
Scott, Harold - Graham & Co. (R), NJ, *80*
Scott, Mark - The Prairie Group (C), IL, *515*
Scott, Melissa F. - Dorothy W. Farnath & Assoc., Inc. (C), NJ, *338*
Scott, Nat - C. J. Stafford & Assoc. (C), ON, *591*
Scott, Nicky - Management Recruiters of St. Lawrence County (C), NY, *432*
Scott, Robin - Stanton Chase Int'l. (R), MD, *199*
Scott, Ronald - Richard Kader & Assoc. (C), OH, *403*
Scott, Sabrina - Professional Search, Inc. Int'l. (C), TX, *523*
Scrivens, Dan - Snelling Search (C), AL, *585*
Scrivines, Hank - Search Northwest Assoc. (C), OR, *576*
Scullion, Terry - Quantum EDP Recruiting Services (C), ON, *526*
Seabaugh, Kitty - Windsor Consultants, Inc. (C), TX, *622*
Seaholts, J. Mark - Executech (R), OH, *62*
Seal, Jock - The H. S. Group, Inc. (C), WI, *365*
Searboro, M.D. - Management Recruiters of Greenville (C), SC, *460*
Searing, James M. - Korn/Ferry Int'l. (R), VA, *118*
Sears, J. Douglas - DS&A (Doug Sears & Assoc.) (C), FL, *315*
Sears, Jerry - Sears & Associates (C), CA, *577*
Sears, Keith - Edward Bell Assoc. (C), CA, *263*
Sears, Kirk - Management Recruiters of Wilmington-North (C), NC, *433*
Sears, Kirk P. - The Wilmington Group (C), NC, *622*
Sears, Richard G. - The Wilmington Group (C), NC, *622*
Seco, William M. - Seco & Zetto Assoc., Inc. (C), NJ, *577*
Secor, David B. - The Search Committee (C), MD, *574*
Secrist, Nancy - Norrell Financial Staffing (C), TX, *495*
Sedak, George - Curry, Telleri Group, Inc. (R), NJ, *44*
Sedlar, Jeri L. - Sedlar & Miners (R), NY, *188*
Seebinger, Larry - ACC Consultants, Inc. (C), NM, *233*
Seebinger, Virginia - ACC Consultants, Inc. (C), NM, *233*
Seehusen, Joseph R. - J. R. Seehusen Assoc., Inc. (R), IA, *188*
Segal, Eric B. - Kenzer Corp. (R), NY, *113*
Segal, Laura - Major, Hagen & Africa (C), NY, *423*
Segal, Sheila - Segal & Assoc. (C), GA, *578*
Segil, Annette R. - Executive Careers (R), CA, *62*
Segovia, Barbara - KPMG Executive Search (R), BC, *119*
Seidel, James - Holloway Schulz & Partners (C), BC, *380*
Seiden, Steven A. - Seiden Krieger Assoc., Inc. (R), NY, *188*
Seitchik, Jack - Seitchik Corwin & Seitchik Inc. (R), CA, *188*
Seitchik, William - Seitchik Corwin & Seitchik Inc. (R), NY, *188*
Seitz, Charles - Neail Behringer Consultants Inc. (R), NY, *15*
Seitz, Christopher R. - DHR Int'l., Inc. (R), MA, *50*
Sekera, Roger I. - A.T. Kearney Executive Search (R), VA, *111*
Selbach, Barbara - SpencerStuart (R), NY, *196*
Selig, Robert J. - Selig Executive Search (C), NH, *579*
Seligson, Gary - Bell Oaks Co., Inc. (C), MA, *263*
Selker, Gregory - Christian & Timbers, Inc. (R), OH, *34*
Sellery, Jr., Robert A. - Robert Sellery Assoc., Ltd. (R), DC, *188*
Sells, Jack - Sales Consultants of Brentwood (C), TN, *555*
Selman, Gary L. - Careerfit, Inc. (C), TX, *283*
Seltzer, Madeleine E. - Seltzer Fontaine Beckwith (C), CA, *579*
Seminerio, Charles - Sales Consultant of Essex County (C), NJ, *554*
Seminerio, Debbie - Sales Consultant of Essex County (C), NJ, *554*
Semmes, John R. - Management Recruiters of Fayetteville (C), NC, *455*
Semyan, John K. - TNS Partners, Inc. (R), TX, *209*
Sendler, Peter A. - International Consulting Services, Inc. (C), IL, *392*
Server, Pauline - Matthews Professional Employment Specialists, Inc. (C), IL, *473*
Serviss, Ken - Norrell Financial Staffing (C), NJ, *495*

Sessa, Vincent J. - Integrated Search Solutions Group, LLC (ISSG) (R), NY, *102*
Setford, George - Setford-Shaw-Najarian Assoc. (C), NY, *579*
Settles, Barbara Z. - LAI Ward Howell (R), TX, *124*
Setze, Michael - DHR Int'l., Inc. (R), IL, *50*
Severinsen, J. Randy - Sevcor Int'l., Inc. (R), IL, *188*
Sewell, Danny J. - Management Recruiters of Rocky Mount-West (C), NC, *433*
Sewell, Jerry - Fox-Morris Assoc., Inc. (C), TX, *352*
Seweloh, Theodore W. - The Heidrick Partners, Inc. (R), IL, *90*
Sexton, Joseph - CFR Executive Search, Inc. (C), IL, *288*
Sexton, Lynn - Engineering Placement Specialists (C), WI, *330*
Seymour, Holly - Executive Partners Inc. (C), CT, *333*
Seymour, Janice F. - Baldwin & Assoc. (C), OH, *258*
Sezonov, Tim - New Directions, Inc. (C), IL, *492*
Sgro, David J. - Midland Consultants (C), OH, *481*
Shabot, David - Korn/Ferry Int'l. (R), PA, *118*
Shackleton, Dora Lee - Carpenter, Shackleton & Company (R), IL, *30*
Shackleton, George M. - Carpenter, Shackleton & Company (R), IL, *30*
Shackleton, Michael - Carpenter, Shackleton & Company (R), IL, *30*
Shaffer, Bradford W. - Redden-Shaffer Group (R), CA, *173*
Shaffer, Michael - Management Recruiters Peninsula (C), CA, *439*
Shaffer, Michael T. - Sales Consultants Peninsula, Inc. (C), CA, *556*
Shake, Samuel - DHR Int'l., Inc. (R), FL, *50*
Shakes, Joe - Fell & Nicholson Technology Resources (R), CA, *66*
Shalet, Lisa - Blackshaw, Olmstead, Lynch & Koenig (R), GA, *18*
Shalinsky, John - Rice Cohen Int'l. (R), PA, *178*
Shandler, Donald - First Advisory Services Int'l., Inc. (R), MD, *67*
Shankwalkar, Sundeep - Ken Clark Int'l. (R), FL, *36*
Shanley, Robert M. - F-O-R-T-U-N-E Personnel Consultants of Houston, Inc. (C), TX, *350*
Shanley, Suzanne M. - F-O-R-T-U-N-E Personnel Consultants of Houston, Inc. (C), TX, *350*
Shannahan, Peter - Shannahan & Co., Inc. (R), CA, *189*
Shannon, Emily - Herbert Mines Assoc., Inc. (R), NY, *145*
Shannon, Marsha L. - Baldwin Associates, LLC (R), CT, *10*
Shapiro, Alan - Technology Search Int'l. (C), CA, *603*
Shapiro, Eve - Hedlund Corp. (C), IL, *375*
Shapiro, Ira E. - New World Healthcare Solutions, Inc. (R), NY, *151*
Shapiro, Larry - Heller Kil Assoc., Inc. (C), IL, *375*
Shapiro, Lisa - Ellis Career Consultants (C), NJ, *328*
Shapiro, Liz - Cathy Abelson Legal Search (C), PA, *232*
Shapiro, Steve - Accountants On Call (C), CA, *235*
Sharf, Bernard - Search Assoc., Inc. (C), CA, *574*
Shariff, Hassan - The Johnson Group, Unlimited (C), NY, *400*
Sharp, Lee - DHR Int'l., Inc. (R), CA, *49*
Sharp, Megan - J. L. Mark Assoc., Inc. (R), CO, *135*
Sharp, Paul S. - Management Recruiters of Roanoke (C), VA, *465*
Sharpe, Charles - C. J. Stafford & Assoc. (C), ON, *591*
Sharpe, Jocelyn - Dunhill Professional Search of Winston-Salem (C), NC, *322*
Sharrow, Beth S. - Sharrow & Assoc., Inc. (C), MI, *579*
Shasteen, Martha F. - Primary Care Service Corp. (C), GA, *518*
Shasteen, Stephen P. - Primary Care Service Corp. (C), GA, *518*
Shattuck, M. B. - M. B. Shattuck & Assoc., Inc. (R), CA, *189*
Shaughnessy, Betty - Alliance Executive Search, Inc. (R), MA, *4*
Shaw, Darryl C. - Management Recruiters of Highlands Ranch (C), CO, *426*
Shaw, R. William - Management Recruiters of South Bend (C), IN, *448*
Shay, David - cFour Partners (R), CA, *32*
Shea, Bryan - Empire International (R), PA, *59*
Shea, Christopher J. - Ingram & Aydelotte, Inc. (R), NY, *101*
Shea, John - The Altco Group (C), NJ, *246*
Shea, Kathleen M. - The Penn Partners, Inc. (R), PA, *162*
Shea, Kathleen P. - Thomas E. Hedefine Assoc. (C), ON, *375*
Shea, Michelle - Chaloner Assoc. (R), MA, *32*
Shea, Peggy - Peggy Shea & Assoc. (R), CA, *189*
Shearer, Edie - R. L. Plimpton Assoc., Inc. (R), CO, *165*
Shearer, Gary F. - Management Recruiters of Bonita Springs, Inc. (C), FL, *443*
Shearer, Thomas - Carnegie Resources, Inc. (C), NC, *284*
Shedroff, Michael - ACSYS Resources, Inc. (C), NJ, *238*
Sheedy, III, Edward J. - Dieckmann & Assoc., Ltd. (R), IL, *51*
Sheedy, Joseph D. - Marketing Resources (C), MA, *470*
Sheehan, Kari - Johnson Smith & Knisely (R), NY, *107*
Sheehan, Thomas L. - Managed Care Resources (C), TX, *424*
Sheehan-Armstrong, Jennifer - J. S. Armstrong & Assoc., Inc. (R), CA, *7*
Sheeran, Douglas L. - FCI, Inc. (R), NJ, *65*
Sheets, Russell - Accountants On Call (C), OH, *236*
Shehan, Paul - Sales Consultants of Dallas (C), TX, *563*
Sheiko, Michele - The Park Group & Assoc., Inc. (C), MD, *503*
Shell, III, John C. - John Shell Assoc., Inc. (C), SC, *580*
Shelley, Pete - Pacific Finance Search, Inc. (C), CA, *501*
Shelton, Frederick L. - Shelton, Wiseman & Leon (R), CA, *189*
Shelton, L. - American Executive Management, Inc. (R), MA, *5*
Shelton, Merritt S. - Comprehensive Search (C), GA, *295*
Shen, Eugene Y. - The Whitney Group (R), NY, *219*
Shenton, Jr., Joseph W. - DHR Int'l., Inc. (R), IL, *49*
Shepherd, Daniel M. - Shepherd Bueschel & Provus, Inc. (R), IL, *189*
Shepherd, Linda - Electronic Search, Inc. (C), IL, *328*
Shepherd, Ronald G. - ProStar Systems, Inc. (C), MD, *525*
Sheppard, Jerry - Don Hall & Assoc. (C), CA, *366*
Sher, Eileen - Frey & Sher Assoc., Inc. (C), VA, *353*
Sher, Jared - Susan C. Miller Assoc., Inc. (C), DC, *482*
Sher, Lawrence - M. A. Churchill & Assoc., Inc. (R), PA, *35*
Sheridan, James J. - Executive Search Consultants (R), CA, *63*
Sheridan, John A. - Sheridan Search (R), IL, *189*
Sheridan, Lynda - The Goodman Group (R), CA, *79*
Sheridan, Scott - Sales Consultant of Jacksonville (C), FL, *552*
Sherman, Dan - Goodwin & Co. (R), DC, *80*
Sherman, Gilbert - Combined Resources Inc. (R), OH, *38*
Sherman, John - Adler Management, Inc. (R), NJ, *2*
Sherman, Robert - Mortgage & Financial Personnel Services (C), CA, *486*
Sherman, Susan - Mortgage & Financial Personnel Services (C), CA, *486*
Sherman, Terri - Tom Sloan & Assoc., Inc. (C), WI, *583*
Sherriff, Julie A. - Sherriff & Assoc. (C), KS, *580*
Sherriff, William W. - Sherriff & Assoc. (C), KS, *580*
Sherrill, Lee S. - Management Recruiters of Shelby (C), NC, *432*
Sherwin, Gordon K. - Ambridge Management Corp. (C), ON, *247*
Sherwood, Andrew - Goodrich & Sherwood Assoc., Inc. (R), NY, *79*
Sherwood, Robert F. - Sherwood Lehman Massucco, Inc. (R), CA, *189*

PRINCIPALS

Sherwood, Rose-Marie - DARE Personnel Inc. (C), ON, *307*
Sheth, Pinakini - Software Resource Consultants (C), TN, *587*
Shetler, James W. - Professional Personnel Services (C), IA, *520*
Shetler, Patricia A. - Professional Personnel Services (C), IA, *520*
Sheweloff, William J. - McCray, Shriver, Eckdahl & Assoc., Inc. (R), CA, *140*
Shey-Harding, Deborah - Shey-Harding Assoc. Inc. (C), CA, *580*
Shield, Nancy - Maximum Management Corp. (C), NY, *473*
Shields, Robert G. - SpencerStuart (R), IL, *197*
Shiell, Donald M. - Shiell Personnel (C), LA, *580*
Shifrin, Brad - Shifrin-Fischer Group, Inc. (C), NJ, *580*
Shiley, Bob - Brethet, Barnum & Assoc., Inc. (C), ON, *273*
Shimp, David J. - LAI Ward Howell (R), IL, *123*
Shindler, Stanley L. - Franklin Int'l. Search, Inc. (C), MA, *352*
Shink, Gilles - Gaudry, Shink, Levasseur (R), QE, *75*
Shinn, Michael - Shinn & Assoc. (R), CA, *189*
Shipherd, John T. - The Cassie Group (R), NC, *31*
Shirley, Michael R. - Michael Shirley Assoc. Inc. (R), KS, *190*
Shneider, Vic - Accountants On Call (C), CA, *235*
Shoemaker, Larry - Shoemaker & Assoc. (R), GA, *190*
Shoemaker, Richard - IR Search (R), CA, *103*
Shooshan, Daniel M. - Hunter Assoc. (C), MA, *385*
Shor, Hillary - Interim Accounting Professionals (C), CA, *391*
Shore, Earl - E. L. Shore & Assoc. (R), ON, *190*
Shore, Linda - Shore Asociados Ejecutivos, S. A. de C.V. (R), MX, *190*
Shore, Susan - Shore Asociados Ejecutivos, S. A. de C.V. (R), MX, *190*
Shore, Susan - Shore Asociados Ejecutivos, S. A. de C.V. (R), MX, *190*
Shorr, Karen - The Shorr Group (R), IL, *190*
Short, Mary Sue - Placement Solutions (C), WI, *513*
Shotland, David R. - The Shotland Group (R), CA, *190*
Shue, Colleen - Bennett Search & Consulting Co. (R), FL, *16*
Shufelt, Douglas G. - Sink, Walker, Boltrus Int'l. (R), MA, *192*
Shuherk, Marty - Fament, Inc. (C), OH, *338*
Shulman, Fran - Asset Resource, Inc. (C), CA, *254*
Shulman, Leo - Christian & Timbers, Inc. (R), OH, *34*
Shulman, Mel - M. Shulman, Inc. (R), CA, *191*
Shultz, Susan F. - SSA Executive Search Int'l. (R), AZ, *198*
Shupack, Joseph - Shupack & Michaels Inc. (C), NY, *581*
Shute, Randall - Executive Recruitment Services, Inc. (ERS, Inc.) (C), GA, *334*
Sibbald, John R. - John Sibbald Assoc., Inc. (R), MO, *191*
Sibul, Shelly Remen - Chicago Legal Search, Ltd. (C), IL, *290*
Siburt, Karen L. - A First Resource (C), NC, *231*
Sicilia, John - GSP International (C), NJ, *364*
Siciliano, Gene - Western Management Assoc. (R), CA, *218*
Siebenmorgen, John - SearchOne, Inc. (C), AR, *577*
Siebenmorgen, Vickie H. - SearchOne, Inc. (C), AR, *577*
Siedlecki, Pamela - FCI, Inc. (R), NJ, *65*
Siegel, Alec - Halbrecht & Co. (C), VA, *365*
Siegel, Brigid Oliveri - Fenwick Partners (R), MA, *66*
Siegel, Carl W. - Winfield Assoc., Inc. (C), MA, *623*
Siegel, Fred - Conex Inc./InterSearch (R), NY, *39*
Siegel, Larry - Larry Siegel & Assoc. (R), WA, *191*
Siegel, Michael - Specialty Employment Services, Inc. (C), GA, *589*
Siegel, Peter A. - Peter Siegel & Co. (C), MA, *581*
Siegel, RitaSue - RitaSue Siegel Resources, Inc. (R), NY, *191*
Siegrist, Jeffrey M. - Foster Partners (R), NC, *71*
Sieler, Susan - C Assoc. (C), DC, *278*
Sierra, Rafael A. - LAI Ward Howell (R), GA, *123*
Siker, Paul W. - The Guild Corp. (C), VA, *364*
Sikes, Charles R. - Medical Search of America, Inc. (C), GA, *477*
Sikes, Laurie L. - Medical Search of America, Inc. (C), GA, *477*
Sikora, Keda - Management Recruiters - Indianapolis (C), IN, *448*
Sikorski, Hank - Diedre Moire Corp., Inc. (C), NJ, *483*
Silbar, Adam - Pathfinders (C), CA, *504*
Silber, Mike - Professional Research Services, Inc. (R), IL, *169*
Silberger, Gary - Key Employment (C), NJ, *405*
Silberman, Allen - Global HealthCare Partners (R), PA, *78*
Silcott, Marvin L. - Marvin L. Silcott & Assoc., Inc. (C), TX, *581*
Silivanch, Garry - Global Data Services, Inc. (R), NY, *77*
Sill, Darrell E. - Sill Technical Assoc., Inc. (C), PA, *581*
Sill, Igor M. - Geneva Group Int'l. (R), CA, *76*
Sillery, Charles H. - Executive Career Search (C), VA, *332*
Silvas, Stephen D. - Roberson & Co. (C), AZ, *538*
Silver, Barbara - Management Recruiters of Washington, DC Inc. (C), MD, *450*
Silver, Lee - L. A. Silver Assoc., Inc. (R), MA, *191*
Silver, Susan - Silver Associates (C), CA, *581*
Silverman, Craig - Hall Kinion (C), CA, *366*
Silverman, Gary - GWS Partners (R), IL, *84*
Silverman, Gary - GWS Partners (R), CA, *84*
Silverman, Jules - Barclay Consultants, Inc. (C), NJ, *259*
Silverman, Marjorie - Marshall Consultants, Inc. (R), NY, *137*
Silverstein, Daniel A. - Daniel A. Silverstein Assoc. Inc. (R), FL, *191*
Silverstein, Michael L. - Management Recruiters of Columbus, Inc. (C), GA, *445*
Silverstein, Rita - Accountants On Call (C), NJ, *236*
Simkanin, Christine - Michael J. Hall & Co. (R), WA, *85*
Simmeman, Daneene - Keystone Consulting Group (C), FL, *406*
Simmerman, Jeff - Management Recruiters of Des Moines (C), IA, *449*
Simmons, Anneta - Fortune Personnel Consultants of Huntsville, Inc. (C), AL, *344*
Simmons, Daniel C. - Continental Search & Outplacement, Inc. (C), MD, *298*
Simmons, George - Fox-Morris Assoc., Inc. (C), MD, *352*
Simmons, H. J. - Longshore + Simmons (R), PA, *131*
Simmons, J. Gerald - Handy HRM (R), NY, *86*
Simmons, Lynn D. - Management Recruiters of Boone (C), NC, *456*
Simmons, Noel A. - The Simmons Group (C), CA, *582*
Simmons, Sandra - IR Search (R), CA, *103*
Simmons, Thomas M. - SpencerStuart (R), TX, *197*
Simon, Bernard - Accountants Executive Search (C), CT, *234*
Simon, Bernard M. - Accountants On Call (C), NY, *236*
Simon, Joan Blum - SFB Legal Search (C), NY, *579*
Simon, John D. - John J. Davis & Assoc., Inc. (R), NY, *47*
Simon, Lisa - Tierney Assoc., Inc. (R), PA, *209*
Simon, Mary K. - Gregory Michaels & Assoc., Inc. (R), IL, *82*
Simon, Robert - Johnson Smith & Knisely (R), CT, *107*
Simpkins, Marsha - Dunhill Professional Search of West Virginia (C), WV, *318*
Simpson, Cathy G. - Conroy Partners Ltd. (R), AB, *39*

Simpson, Clair - Professional Recruiters (C), UT, *522*
Simpson, David - D. W. Simpson & Co. (C), IL, *582*
Simpson, David - D. J. Simpson Assoc. Inc. (R), ON, *191*
Simpson, Kent T. - Management Recruiters of Lexington (C), KY, *429*
Simpson, Mae - NPS of Atlanta, Inc. (C), GA, *496*
Simpson, Terre - Simpson Associates (C), NY, *582*
Sims, John - Management Recruiters of Iowa City (C), IA, *429*
Sims, Larry - Reality Group (C), OK, *531*
Sinay, Richard K. - Sales Consultants of Hudson County (C), NJ, *554*
Sinclair, Douglas L. - Sinclair & Co., Inc. (R), MA, *192*
Sinclair, Kathleen A. - Executive Recruiters Int'l. (C), MI, *333*
Sinclair, Paul - Pioneer Executive Consultants (C), ON, *512*
Sinclair, Rachel - Management Recruiters of Fresno (C), CA, *440*
Sinclair, Tom - PricewaterhouseCoopers Executive Search (R), ON, *168*
Sinden, Peter - Attorneys at Work (C), GA, *256*
Singel, Don - Jonathan Lawrence Assoc. (C), NJ, *400*
Singel, Jo - Jonathan Lawrence Assoc. (C), NJ, *400*
Singer, David L. - Fortune Personnel Consultants of Raleigh, Inc. (C), NC, *348*
Singer, Jon A. - C & H Personnel (C), PA, *277*
Singer, Lloyd - Romac Int'l., Inc. (C), IL, *543*
Singer, Lloyd R. - Romac Int'l. (C), IL, *542*
Singer, Suzanne - GFI Professional Staffing Services (C), VT, *357*
Singerman, Lowell - Hayden & Assoc., Inc. (C), MN, *370*
Singleton, Robin - Tyler & Company (R), GA, *212*
Singleton, Steven L. - Singleton & Assoc. (C), VA, *582*
Sinisi, Vinny - W. Robert Eissler & Assoc., Inc. (C), TX, *327*
Sink, Clifton W. - Sink, Walker, Boltrus Int'l. (R), TX, *192*
Sinks, Lucius F. - Aminex Corp. (C), MA, *249*
Sirena, Evelyn - Winthrop Partners, Inc. (R), NY, *222*
Sirey, Don - Technology Search Int'l. (C), CA, *603*
Sistek, Walter J. - First Advisory Services Int'l., Inc. (R), MD, *67*
Sistek, Walter J. - Management Assoc. (C), MD, *424*
Sitter, Vikki - Management Recruiters of Johnson City (C), TN, *436*
Sitter, William P. - Jordan-Sitter Assoc. (R), TX, *108*
Sjogren, Denny - Agra Placements, Ltd. (C), MN, *242*
Skaar, Mirlam - Engineering & Scientific Search Assoc. (ESSA) (C), NJ, *330*
Skaar, Steve - Engineering & Scientific Search Assoc. (ESSA) (C), NJ, *330*
Skalet, Ira - A. E. Feldman Assoc., Inc. (C), NY, *339*
Skeegan, Samuel - Roth Young Personnel Service of Detroit, Inc. (C), MI, *546*
Skelton, Brenda - Cumberland Professional Search Inc. (C), TN, *304*
Skewes, Gail - Reid Ellis Assoc. Inc. (C), ON, *533*
Skiba, Jeff - Management Recruiters of Lake Tahoe, NV (C), NV, *453*
Skillern, Steve - Management Recruiters - Indianapolis (C), IN, *448*
Skirbe, Douglas - The Zarkin Group, Inc. (R), NY, *226*
Sklar, Ruth - Ruth Sklar Assoc., Inc. (RSA Executive Search) (R), NY, *192*
Sklarski, Kevin - The Jotorok Group (C), RI, *401*
Sklut, Eric - Executive Recruitment Specialists, Inc. (R), NC, *63*
Skode, David - Finney-Taylor Personnel & Management Consultants Ltd. (C), AB, *341*
Skorupski, JoAnn - Data Search Network, Inc. (C), NJ, *307*
Skrypuch, Roman M. - Financial Plus Management Solutions Inc. (R), ON, *66*
Skupsky, Lorraine - Skupsky & Assoc. (C), CO, *583*
Sladky, Jackie - The Norland Group (C), CA, *494*
Slate, James E. - Fortune Personnel Consultants of Topsfield (C), MA, *346*
Slater, Marjorie - Logistics Management Resources, Inc. (R), NY, *131*
Slaton, C. Philip - Icon Recruiters, LLC (C), CA, *387*
Slaughter, Katherine T. - Compass Group Ltd. (R), MI, *38*
Slayton, Richard C. - Slayton Int'l., Inc. (R), IL, *192*
Slayton, Richard S. - Slayton Int'l., Inc. (R), IL, *192*
Slepin, Matthew B. - Argonaut Partners, LLC (R), CA, *6*
Sloan, Michael D. - Sloan & Assoc., Inc. (C), VA, *583*
Sloan, Tom - Tom Sloan & Assoc., Inc. (C), WI, *583*
Sloan-Young, Linda - Hughes & Sloan, Inc. (C), GA, *383*
Sloane, Ron - Management Recruiters of Milwaukee-North (C), WI, *466*
Sloat, Robert L. - Executive Search of New England, Inc. (C), ME, *336*
Slosar, John - Boyden (R), MI, *21*
Slusser, Christine M. - Lawrence Glaser Assoc., Inc. (C), NJ, *358*
Slusser, Cindy L. - The Stelton Group, Inc. (C), NJ, *592*
Small, Carol D. - Quantum Int'l., Ltd. (R), FL, *170*
Small, Jane - Selective Staffing (C), CA, *579*
Small, Jim - J. L. Small Assoc. (C), AL, *583*
Small, Lynn - DHR Int'l., Inc. (R), IL, *49*
Smallhorn, Christopher - Christopher Smallhorn Executive Recruiting, Inc. (R), MA, *193*
Smirnoff, Olga - Management Recruiters of Fresno (C), CA, *440*
Smith, Aaron - Staffing Edge, Inc. (C), CO, *590*
Smith, Adam M. - AMS Int'l. (R), VA, *5*
Smith, Ana Luz - Smith Search, S.C. (R), MX, *194*
Smith, Andrew - Search Excellence (R), CA, *186*
Smith, Barry - Sales Consultants Bridgewater, Inc. (C), NJ, *560*
Smith, Barry S. - Management Recruiters of Bridgewater (C), NJ, *431*
Smith, Bob - Sales Consultants of Danbury (C), CT, *557*
Smith, Brant R. - Smith Hanley Assoc., Inc. (C), NY, *584*
Smith, Carroll V. - Management Recruiters of Janesville, Inc. (C), WI, *466*
Smith, Charles - The Smith Group, Inc. (C), NC, *584*
Smith, Charles D. - Smith & Laue Search (R), OR, *193*
Smith, Clark W. - F-O-R-T-U-N-E Personnel Consultants of Savannah, Inc. (C), GA, *345*
Smith, Colin - Anderson & Schwab, Inc. (R), NY, *6*
Smith, Craig - Impact Technical Staffing (C), OR, *387*
Smith, Dan - Healthcare Resources Group (C), OK, *374*
Smith, Dan - Sales Consultants of Tampa (C), FL, *552*
Smith, Darrell G. - Smith & Assoc. (C), CA, *583*
Smith, David P. - HRS, Inc. (R), PA, *97*
Smith, Dickson - The Kinlin Co., Inc. (R), MA, *115*
Smith, II, Don - Smith, Brown & Jones (C), FL, *585*
Smith, Donald L. - Smith, Brown & Jones (C), KS, *585*
Smith, Douglas M. - LAI Ward Howell (R), IL, *123*
Smith, Dwight - Consolidated Management Services (C), ON, *296*
Smith, Eric - Dunhill Technical Staffing (C), IN, *320*
Smith, F. Clawson - LAI Ward Howell (R), CT, *123*
Smith, Gayle - J. Burke & Assoc., Inc. (C), TX, *276*
Smith, George D. - Bruce Edwards & Associates, Inc. (R), NC, *57*
Smith, Gin-Nie - Management Recruiters of High Point (C), NC, *433*
Smith, Glen - Healthcare Recruiters Int'l. - Los Angeles (C), CA, *372*
Smith, Grant - Price Waterhouse Executive Search (R), BC, *168*
Smith, Gregory K. - Global Technologies Group Inc. (C), NC, *359*

PRINCIPALS

Smith, Gregory L. - G. L. Smith Assoc. (C), CA, *584*
Smith, Herbert C. - H. C. Smith Ltd. (R), OH, *194*
Smith, Herbert E. - The Enfield Company (C), TX, *330*
Smith, Jr., Herman D. - Management Recruiters of Rock Hill (C), SC, *435*
Smith, Herman M. - Herman Smith Executive Initiatives Inc. (R), ON, *193*
Smith, Howard O. - The Johnson Group, Unlimited (C), NY, *400*
Smith, Howard W. - Howard W. Smith Assoc. (R), CT, *193*
Smith, James F. - James F. Smith & Assoc. (C), GA, *583*
Smith, James H. - J. Harrington Smith Assoc. (C), IN, *584*
Smith, Jamie - Kaye/Bassman Int'l. Corp. (R), TX, *110*
Smith, Jill - ACSYS Resources, Inc. (C), PA, *239*
Smith, Jr., John E. - Smith Search, S.C. (R), MX, *194*
Smith, John F. - The Penn Partners, Inc. (R), PA, *162*
Smith, Joseph E. - Smith & Syberg, Inc. (R), IN, *193*
Smith, Judy - JPM International (C), CA, *401*
Smith, Ken - Smith Assoc. (C), IA, *584*
Smith, Kirsten - The Thomas Tucker Co. (R), CA, *212*
Smith, Kristine - Carlsen Resources, Inc. (R), CO, *29*
Smith, Kyle A. - MedXec USA, Inc. (C), OH, *478*
Smith, L. J. - Management Recruiters of Shelby-Uptown (C), NC, *433*
Smith, Mark - Cornerstone Resources, Inc. (C), OK, *299*
Smith, Mark L. - Korn/Ferry Int'l. (R), MA, *118*
Smith, Martin - Hughes & Company (R), VA, *98*
Smith, Marvin E. - Management Solutions, Inc. (C), WA, *468*
Smith, Michael - Sales Consultant of Chaska (C), MN, *553*
Smith, Michael - Smith James Group, Inc. (R), GA, *194*
Smith, Michael R. - Michaels & Moere (C), WI, *481*
Smith, Michael W. - Management Recruiters of Danville (C), KY, *449*
Smith, Patrick - Smith & Syberg, Inc. (R), IN, *193*
Smith, Patti - Discovery, The Staffing Specialists, Inc. (C), TX, *313*
Smith, Paul C. - Barth Smith Company (R), IL, *12*
Smith, Perry - Noll Human Resource Services (C), TX, *494*
Smith, Peter A. - Peter A. Smith & Assoc. (C), OR, *584*
Smith, Phyllis E. - ISC of Cincinnati Inc. (C), OH, *394*
Smith, Ralph E. - Ralph Smith & Assoc. (C), IL, *584*
Smith, Randall E. - R2 Services, LLC (C), IL, *528*
Smith, Rebecca Ruben - H. C. Smith Ltd. (R), OH, *194*
Smith, Richard - HCI Corp. (C), IL, *371*
Smith, Robert - Fox-Morris Assoc., Inc. (C), GA, *352*
Smith, Robert - Sales Consultants of Omaha, Inc. (C), NE, *560*
Smith, Robert L. - Smith & Sawyer, Inc. (R), NY, *193*
Smith, Rod - Management Recruiters of Peoria (C), IL, *429*
Smith, Russell L. - Sales & Marketing Search, Inc. (C), MA, *551*
Smith, S. - American Executive Management, Inc. (R), MA, *5*
Smith, Sally - Smith, Brown & Jones (C), KS, *585*
Smith, Sam - Romac Int'l., Inc. (C), KY, *543*
Smith, Sandra - DNA Search, Inc. (C), CA, *313*
Smith, Scott B. - LAI Ward Howell (R), WI, *124*
Smith, Stacy - Smith James Group, Inc. (R), GA, *194*
Smith, Steve - Management Recruiters of High Point (C), NC, *433*
Smith, Steven B. - The McAulay Firm (R), NC, *139*
Smith, Susan P. - Smith Professional Search (C), MI, *585*
Smith, Sylvia - Smith & Assoc. (C), FL, *583*
Smith, Thomas W. - The Ransford Group (R), TX, *171*
Smith, Tim - Stanton Chase Int'l. (R), CA, *199*
Smith, Toni S. - SpencerStuart (R), IL, *197*
Smith, Wilton - The Stark Wilton Group (R), MI, *199*
Smitherman, Jim - Merit Professional Search, Inc. (C), TN, *479*
Smithson, Fred - R. A. Rodriguez & Assoc., Inc. (C), TX, *540*
Smitter, Janet - Carol Maden Group (C), VA, *422*
Smolizer, Carole E. - Marketing Consultants (C), WI, *470*
Smyth, William - A. William Smyth, Inc. (R), CA, *194*
Snart, Allen - Western Management Consultants (R), AB, *218*
Snedden, Alan - Management Recruiters of Bloomington (C), IL, *429*
Snellbaker, Mary W. - Management Recruiters of Southeastern Michigan (C), MI, *451*
Snider, Jr., George R. - Sanford Rose Assoc. (C), OH, *565*
Snider, Jr., Les - Bryan & Louis Research (C), OH, *275*
Snoddy, Jr., Mark F. - Peachtree Executive Search (R), GA, *161*
Snodgrass, Stephen E. - Defrain Mayer (R), KS, *48*
Snook, Maria P. - Management Recruiters of Enfield (C), NC, *433*
Snook, Marvin G. - Management Recruiters of Enfield (C), NC, *433*
Snow, Christine - C. Snow & Assoc. (C), ON, *586*
Snow, Thomas J. - The Search America Group Inc. (C), OH, *573*
Snow Walsh, Deborah - Deborah Snow Walsh, Inc. (R), IL, *215*
Snowden, Debra - Mortgage & Financial Personnel Services (C), CA, *486*
Snyder, Amy - Southern Recruiters & Consultants, Inc. (C), SC, *587*
Snyder, C. Edward - Horton International Inc. (R), CT, *96*
Snyder, Gary - F-O-R-T-U-N-E Personnel Consultants (C), MI, *346*
Snyder, Jr., James F. - Snyder & Co. (R), CT, *194*
Snyder, Susan Kurz - Greene-Levin-Snyder LLC (C), NY, *362*
Snyder, Suzanne - Wilkinson & Ives (R), CA, *221*
Snyder, Thomas J. - SpencerStuart (R), IL, *197*
Sobecki, John F. - The Comwell Company, Inc. (C), NJ, *296*
Sobel, Andrea - Andrea Sobel & Assoc., Inc. (C), CA, *586*
Socha, Rudy - Advancement Recruiting Services (C), OH, *241*
Sockwell, J. Edgar - Sockwell & Assoc. (R), NC, *194*
Soderlind, Isabel - Judith Cushman & Associates (R), WA, *44*
Soderlund, Eric - Soderlund Assoc. Inc. (R), OH, *195*
Sokol, Herbert - Eastbourne Assoc. Inc. (R), NY, *56*
Solhjou, Candace - Romac Int'l., Inc. (C), VA, *544*
Soll, John - DHR Int'l., Inc. (R), MN, *50*
Sollman, Robert - Robert Sollman & Assoc. (C), FL, *587*
Solomon, Bruce - Management Recruiters of Menlo Park (C), CA, *426*
Solomon, Neil M. - The Neil Michael Group, Inc./Global Partners (R), NY, *151*
Solomon, Phyllis - Phyllis Solomon Executive Search, Inc. (C), NJ, *587*
Soloway, David - The Madison Group (R), NY, *133*
Soltan, Steve - S.C.S. & Assoc. (C), NC, *550*
Soltis, Charles W. - Soltis Management Services (R), PA, *195*
Soltwedel, Michelle - TPS Staffing Solutions (C), IN, *608*
Somers, Donald A. - Management Recruiters of Youngstown (C), OH, *458*
Somers, Scott D. - Ray & Berndtson (R), CA, *172*
Somershoe, Judy - Management Recruiters of Livonia (C), MI, *451*
Sondhi, Rick - Human Resource Technologies, Inc. (R), IL, *99*
Sondhi, Rick - Raymond Karsan Assoc. (C), IL, *530*
Sonis, Stephen M. - Stephen M. Sonis Assoc. (R), MA, *195*

Sonne, Bill - PeopleSource Inc. (C), TX, *506*
Soo Hoo, Patrick J. - Chelsea Resources, Inc. (C), CT, *290*
Soodsma, William - Sales Consultants of Northern Jersey, Inc. (C), NJ, *560*
Soper, Gracemarie - The Shorr Group (R), IL, *190*
Soren, Robin - SpencerStuart (R), NY, *196*
Sorey, Jr., Hilmon - Management Recruiters of Evanston (C), IL, *428*
Sotelo, Henry - Dunhill Professional Search of Hawaii (C), HI, *320*
Soth, Mark - Management Recruiters of Fairfield (C), IA, *449*
Souder, Jr., E. G. - Souder & Assoc. (R), VA, *195*
Souder, Elizabeth W. - Springer Souder & Assoc. L.L.C. (R), IL, *198*
Souder, Linda - Dunhill Staffing Systems (C), NJ, *317*
Southerland, Keith - Witt/Kieffer, Ford, Hadelman & Lloyd (R), TX, *223*
Southwell, Mary - Lynne Palmer Executive Recruitment, Inc. (C), MN, *421*
Southworth, David E. - Michigan Consulting Group (R), MI, *144*
Southworth, David E. - Premier Recruiting Group (C), MI, *516*
Soutouras, James - Smith James Group, Inc. (R), GA, *194*
Sowers, John - Marvel Consultants, Inc. (C), OH, *472*
Spadaro, Raymond - David Perry Assoc. (C), NJ, *308*
Spahr, Donald B. - Roth Young Executive Recruiters (C), MN, *546*
Spangenberg, J. Brand - The Brand Co., Inc. (R), FL, *22*
Spangler, Jeffrey - Next Step Recruiting (C), CA, *493*
Spangler, Kristi - Keystone Consulting Group (C), AL, *406*
Spann, Richard E. - Goodrich & Sherwood Assoc., Inc. (R), CT, *80*
Sparber, Karin - DHR Int'l., Inc. (R), AZ, *49*
Spargo, Rick - Personnel Solutions (C), AZ, *509*
Sparks, Francine - Willmott & Assoc. (C), MA, *622*
Sparks, Michele Benum - The Alternatives Group, Inc. (C), TX, *246*
Sparks, Michele Benum - Micro Staff Solutions, Inc. (C), TX, *481*
Sparks, Jr., R. Thomas - Sparks, McDonough & Assoc., Inc. (C), MO, *588*
Sparks, Robert W. - Protocol Inc. (C), CA, *525*
Spatt, Jonathan M. - Hospitality Executive Search, Inc. (R), MA, *96*
Spear, Ken - Innovative Resource Group, LLC (C), PA, *389*
Spear, Kenneth T. - Spear-Izzo Assoc., LLC (C), PA, *589*
Spears, Robert - FORTUNE Personnel Consultants of Charleston, Inc. (C), SC, *349*
Speciale, Pamela - Austin Group Int'l./Marlar Int'l. (R), TX, *9*
Spellacy, James P. - Management Recruiters of Lorain County (C), OH, *434*
Spellacy, James P. - Sales Consultants of Lorain County (C), OH, *555*
Spellisex, Peter - Boyden (R), ON, *21*
Spence, Bob - Creative-Leadership, Inc. (R), CA, *42*
Spence, Jr., Joseph T. - Russell Reynolds Assoc., Inc. (R), GA, *176*
Spencer, Dan R. - SpencerSearch, Inc. (C), CO, *589*
Spencer, Frank T. - DHR Int'l., Inc. (R), NY, *50*
Spencer, Gene - American Resources Corp. (C), IL, *248*
Spencer, Glenda - HR Inc. (C), NC, *382*
Spencer, John - Romac Int'l., Inc. (C), CA, *542*
Spencer, John - Romac Int'l., Inc. (C), CA, *542*
Spencer, John - Romac Int'l., Inc. (C), NV, *543*
Spencer, Norman - FORTUNE Personnel Consultants of North Dallas (C), TX, *350*
Spencer, Randall W. - Management Recruiters of San Antonio - North (C), TX, *463*
Spengler, Silas - Webb, Johnson Assoc., Inc. (R), NY, *216*
Speth, Don - Independent Resource Systems (C), CA, *388*
Spicer, Merrilyn - Search West, Inc. (C), CA, *577*
Spicher, John H. - M. A. Churchill & Assoc., Inc. (R), PA, *35*
Spiedel, Julie - MIXTEC Group (R), CA, *145*
Spiegel, Deborah - Kenzer Corp. (R), NY, *113*
Spiegel, Gayle - The Spiegel Group (R), MA, *197*
Spielman, Sharon - Jerry Fields Assoc. (C), NY, *340*
Spilman, Mary P. - Spilman & Assoc. (R), TX, *197*
Spinale, Mark - DHR Int'l., Inc. (R), TN, *51*
Spindel, Howard - Integrated Management Solutions (C), NY, *390*
Spinn, Mark - LCS, Inc. (C), TX, *414*
Spinner, Jill - DHR Int'l., Inc. (R), CO, *49*
Spinrad, Kenn - Kenn Spinrad Inc. (C), PA, *589*
Spinrad, Sharon - Kenn Spinrad Inc. (C), PA, *589*
Spitz, L. Grant - The Caldwell Partners Amrop International (R), ON, *26*
Spitzer, Erin - Accountants On Call (C), CA, *235*
Splaine, Charles - Splaine & Assoc., Inc. (R), CA, *198*
Spolsino, Robert J. - Russillo/Gardner/Spolsino (C), MA, *548*
Sponseller, Vern - Richard Kader & Assoc. (C), OH, *403*
Spotswood, Mel - Consulpro (R), ON, *39*
Spragge, Patrick - Sanford Rose Assoc. - Sunnyvale (C), CA, *566*
Sprankle, Kathryn - Zweig White & Assoc., Inc. (R), MA, *228*
Sprankle, Kathryn - Zweig White & Assoc., Inc. (R), DC, *228*
Sprawson, Barrie - Cambridge Management Planning (R), ON, *27*
Sprehe, J. Christopher - The Christopher Group (C), NC, *291*
Spremulli, Paul L. - PKS Assoc., Inc. (C), RI, *513*
Spriggs, Martha - Polson & Co., Inc. (R), MN, *166*
Spriggs, Robert D. - Spriggs & Co., Inc. (R), IL, *198*
Spring, Dennis - Spring Assoc., Inc. (R), NY, *198*
Springer, Mark H. - M. H. Springer & Assoc. (R), CA, *198*
Springer, Neil A. - Springer Souder & Assoc. L.L.C. (R), IL, *198*
Springstein, Bob - Dan P. McLean Assoc., Inc. (C), ON, *475*
Sprouse, Laurie - Tech-Net (C), TX, *601*
Sprowls, Linda - Allard Associates (C), CA, *244*
Squires, Frank - Squires Resources Inc. (C), ON, *590*
Squires, R. James - Smith, Roth & Squires (R), NY, *194*
Sroka, John - The Riverbend Group (C), MO, *538*
Srolis, Robert B. - Raymond Karsan Assoc. (C), PA, *529*
St. Clair, Alan R. - TNS Partners, Inc. (R), TX, *209*
St. Denis, Robert A. - Sanford Rose Assoc. - Effingham (C), IL, *566*
St. Denis, Sherry A. - Sanford Rose Assoc. - Effingham (C), IL, *566*
St. Jean, N. - The Ryan Charles Group, Inc. (C), IL, *549*
St. Jean, Norman D. - The Ryan Charles Group, Inc. (C), FL, *549*
Stacey, Bryce A. - Chapman & Assoc. (C), BC, *289*
Stack, James K. - Boyden (R), CA, *20*
Stack, Kevin M. - Circuit Search (C), NY, *291*
Stackhouse, Cathy - Strauss Personnel Service (C), PA, *596*
Stafford, Chris - C. J. Stafford & Assoc. (C), ON, *591*
Stafford, Chris - Stafford Consulting Group (R), CA, *198*
Stafford, Norma - Stafford Consulting Group (R), CA, *198*
Stafford, Peter B. - Stafford Consulting Group (R), CA, *198*
Stafford, Susan P. - Hospitality Int'l. (C), NY, *381*
Staggemeier, Debbie - Executive Solutions (R), MO, *64*
Stahl, Nancellen - The Conrad Lee Co. Inc. (R), FL, *127*
Staley, Marilyn - Management Recruiters of Washington, DC Inc. (C), MD, *450*

PRINCIPALS

Stalowicz, Bruce - Koll-Fairfield LLC (C), CT, *408*
Stampfl, Eric - Morgan Stampfl, Inc. (C), NY, *485*
Standard, Gail W. - Comprehensive Search (C), GA, *295*
Stanewick, B. David - Stanewick, Hart & Assoc., Inc. (C), FL, *591*
Stanford, M. J. - Empire International (R), PA, *59*
Stang, Frederick W. - Ackerman Johnson Inc. (C), TX, *238*
Stanislaw, Robert W. - DHR Int'l., Inc. (R), WI, *51*
Stankievech, Kathy - Leader Search Inc. (R), AB, *127*
Stanley, Harry - Whittaker & Assoc., Inc. (C), GA, *620*
Stanley, John - Search Int'l. (R), MA, *187*
Stanley, Paul R. A. - Ray & Berndtson/Lovas Stanley (R), ON, *172*
Stanley, Paul R. A. - Ray & Berndtson/Lovas Stanley (R), ON, *172*
Stanley, Wade - Management Recruiters of Raleigh (C), NC, *456*
Stannard, Lee - Dunhill of Iowa City (C), IA, *317*
Stanton, Grant - TSC Management Services Group, Inc. (C), IL, *610*
Stanton, John - StratfordGroup (R), TX, *203*
Stanton, Robert G. - TSC Management Services Group, Inc. (C), IL, *610*
Stanton, Stan - Huntress Real Estate Executive Search (R), MO, *100*
Staples, Marcia - Keystone Consulting Group (C), NC, *406*
Starecheski, Edward - Alliance Executive Search, Inc. (R), MA, *4*
Starich, Mike - Orion Int'l. Consulting Group, Inc. (C), CA, *499*
Stark, James - Management Recruiters of Ft. Scott (C), KS, *429*
Stark, Jeffrey M. - Thorne, Brieger Assoc., Inc. (R), NY, *209*
Stark, Mary - The Stark Wilton Group (R), MI, *199*
Stark, Mary - The Stark Wilton Group (R), MI, *199*
Starling, Dick - ProNet, Inc. (C), NC, *524*
Starman, Jane - Robert William James & Assoc. (C), MN, *539*
Starner, William S. - Fenwick Partners (R), MA, *66*
Starr, Jeffrey - Accountancies (C), CA, *234*
Starr, Jonathan - Jones-Parker/Starr (R), GA, *108*
Statson, Dale E. - Sales Executives, Inc. (C), MI, *563*
Staub, Robert A. - Staub, Warmbold & Assoc., Inc. (R), NY, *199*
Stauffer, Joseph K. - Rylan Forbes Consulting Group, Inc. (C), NJ, *549*
Steadman, Reyn - Vickers Chambless Managed Search (C), GA, *289*
Stecker, Bernd - The Garret Group (R), NJ, *75*
Stecker, Lori - Management Recruiters of Williamsburg (C), IA, *449*
Sted, Eric - The Search America Group Inc. (C), OH, *573*
Steel, Mark D. - Selective Management Services, Inc. (C), FL, *578*
Steele, Dolores M. - Dunhill Professional Search, Inc. of McAllen (C), TX, *323*
Steele, Kevin - Winter, Wyman & Co. (C), MA, *623*
Steele, Lloyd F. - Dunhill Professional Search, Inc. of McAllen (C), TX, *323*
Stefan, David E. - ChaseAmerica, Inc. (R), FL, *33*
Steffensen, John E. - Western Management Consultants (R), AB, *218*
Steffensrud, Dick - Staff Extension Int'l. (C), TX, *590*
Steffke, Sandra - D. W. Simpson & Co. (C), IL, *582*
Stefunek, Paul C. - StratfordGroup (R), OH, *203*
Stein, Jodi - Tom McCall Executive Search (C), IL, *473*
Stein, Neil A. - R. H. Perry & Assoc., Inc. (R), DC, *162*
Stein, Richard - Futures Int'l. (R), CT, *73*
Stein, Terry W. - Stewart, Stein & Scott, Ltd. (R), MN, *200*
Steinau, Peter B. - International Management Services Inc. (R), IL, *102*
Steinbach, David M. - Steinbach & Co. (C), MA, *592*
Steinberg, Joan - Marshall-Alan Assoc., Inc. (C), NY, *471*
Steinberg, Paul D. - IMA Search, Inc. (R), NY, *101*
Steinem, Andy - Dahl-Morrow Int'l. (R), VA, *45*
Steinem, Barbara - Dahl-Morrow Int'l. (R), VA, *45*
Steiner, Bruce - Technifind Int'l. (C), TX, *602*
Steiner, Judy - Future Employment Service, Inc. (C), IA, *354*
Steinfield, David - Steinfield & Assoc. (C), TX, *592*
Steinman, Richard - Career Marketing Assoc., Inc. (C), CO, *282*
Steinman, Stephen M. - The Stevenson Group, Inc. (N.J.) (R), NJ, *200*
Stelika, Kit - Southport Int'l. Assoc. Inc. (C), FL, *588*
Stenfors, Lyle - Thomas Lyle & Co. (C), IL, *606*
Stenholm, Gilbert R. - SpencerStuart (R), IL, *197*
Stenhouse, Judy - Phillips Resource Group (C), SC, *510*
Stentiford, Charles M. - Stentiford & Berardi Assoc. Ltd. (R), NY, *199*
Stephens, Ken - Leader Resources Group (C), GA, *415*
Stephens, Susan - Sales Consultants of Chicago South (C), IL, *558*
Stephens, Teresa - Leader Resources Group (C), GA, *415*
Stephenson, E. A. - Phoenix BioSearch, Inc. (C), NJ, *511*
Stephenson, Harold - C. R. Assoc. (C), CA, *278*
Stephenson, Jay - JG Consultants, Inc. (R), TX, *106*
Stephenson, Phil - Executive Search Group LLC (C), CA, *335*
Stepler, Paul - Gallin Associates, Inc. (C), FL, *354*
Stepler, Paul - Gallin Associates of Naples, FL (C), FL, *354*
Stepp, Paulette - Zingaro & Company (R), TX, *227*
Sterenfeld, David - Corporate Dynamix (C), AZ, *300*
Sterling, Cheryl - Management Recruiters of Mentor, Inc. (C), OH, *458*
Sterling, Jay - Earley Kielty & Assoc., Inc. (R), NY, *56*
Sterling, Peter D. - Peter Sterling & Co. (C), TX, *592*
Sterling, Ronald - Management Recruiters of Mentor, Inc. (C), OH, *458*
Sterling, Shawn - Raymond Karsan Assoc. (C), NE, *530*
Stern, Daniel - Daniel Stern & Assoc. (C), PA, *592*
Stern, Leslie W. - Sullivan & Company (R), NY, *204*
Stern, Michael - Michael Stern Assoc., Inc./Euram (R), ON, *200*
Stern, Scott - Creative Management Strategies, Ltd. (R), NY, *42*
Sternlicht, Marvin - Accountants Executive Search (C), CT, *234*
Stetson, Sally - Salveson Stetson Group, Inc. (R), PA, *184*
Steuer, Ira - Cemco, Ltd. (C), MO, *287*
Stevens, Brett M. - Sales Consultants of Cherokee (C), GA, *558*
Stevens, Chris - BCG Search, Inc. (R), MD, *14*
Stevens, III, David S. - Johnson Smith & Knisely (R), NY, *107*
Stevens, James D. - J. H. Lindell & Co. (C), CA, *418*
Stevens, Jennifer A. - Ledbetter/Davidson Int'l., Inc. (R), NY, *127*
Stevens, Ken G. - The Stevens Group (R), TX, *200*
Stevens, Leonard W. - Stevens, Valentine & McKeever (C), NJ, *593*
Stevens, Mal - The Dayton Group, Ltd. (C), NY, *309*
Stevens, Martha - The Stevens Group (C), CA, *593*
Stevens, Martin - Martin Stevens Tamaren & Assoc., Inc. (R), CA, *206*
Stevens, Paul - AES Search (C), NJ, *241*
Stevens, Ralph - Preng & Assoc., Inc. (R), TX, *167*
Stevens, Robert D. - Douglas-Allen, Inc. (R), MA, *54*
Stevens, Ron - Ron Stevens & Assoc., Inc. (C), FL, *593*
Stevens, Wayne J. - Stevens Assoc. (C), MA, *593*
Stevenson, Alex - Search Masters, USA (C), FL, *576*

Stevenson, Jani - Howard Fischer Assoc. Int'l., Inc. (R), TX, *67*
Stevenson, Terry - Bartholdi & Co., Inc. (R), CO, *12*
Stevick, Marianne - Management Recruiters of Columbia, Tennessee (C), TN, *461*
Stewart, Dana - Management One Consultants (C), ON, *425*
Stewart, Evan - Angus Employment Ltd. (C), ON, *250*
Stewart, F. Colleen - Johnson Smith & Knisely (R), GA, *107*
Stewart, Harvey - Executive Registry (C), QE, *334*
Stewart, James H. - The Stewart Group (C), FL, *593*
Stewart, Jan J. - Egon Zehnder Int'l. Inc. (R), ON, *227*
Stewart, Jeffrey O. - Stewart, Stein & Scott, Ltd. (R), MN, *200*
Stewart, Joe - Creative Input, Inc. (C), RI, *303*
Stewart, Larry - American Resources Corp. (C), IL, *248*
Stewart, Lawrence D. - Weatherby Healthcare (C), CT, *617*
Stewart, Robyn - Independent Power Consultants (C), TX, *387*
Stewart, Tina Hunter - BioPharmMed (C), FL, *267*
Stewart, Tom - Stewart/Greene & Company of the Triad, Inc. (C), NC, *594*
Stewart, Wilfred C. - KPMG Executive Search (R), ON, *119*
Stickler, IV, Charles W. - Charles Stickler Assoc. (R), PA, *201*
Stickler, III, Charles W. - Charles Stickler Assoc. (R), PA, *201*
Stieglitz, Eric - Conspectus, Inc. (C), NY, *297*
Stieglitz, John - Conspectus, Inc. (C), NY, *297*
Stiles, Jr., Cortland - Fenwick Partners (R), MA, *66*
Stiles, Jack D. - Sanford Rose Assoc. - Portland (C), OR, *570*
Stiles, Jake - Linford E. Stiles & Assoc., L.L.C. (R), NH, *201*
Stiles, Judy - MedQuest Assoc. (C), CO, *478*
Stiles, Linford E. - Linford E. Stiles & Assoc., L.L.C. (R), NH, *201*
Stiles, Timothy W. - Sanford Rose Assoc. - Portland (C), OR, *570*
Stillinger, Regina V. - Stillinger & Assoc. (R), CA, *201*
Stillinger, Scott R. - Stillinger & Assoc. (R), CA, *201*
Stillinger, Skip - Stillinger & Assoc. (R), CA, *201*
Stillings, Bob - Alpha Search (C), FL, *246*
Stillings, Eleanor - Alpha Search (C), FL, *246*
Stirn, Bradley A. - SpencerStuart (R), CA, *196*
Stoa, Gordon - PERC, Ltd. (C), AZ, *506*
Stoa, Jackie - PERC, Ltd. (C), AZ, *506*
Stobbe, David - D & M Associates (C), PA, *306*
Stobbe, Mickey - D & M Associates (C), PA, *306*
Stobbelaar, Rick - The Icard Group, Inc. (C), MI, *387*
Stockard, Robert G. - Sales Consultant of Boston (C), MA, *553*
Stockman, Ronald F. - National Restaurant Search, Inc. (R), IL, *150*
Stockton, J. R. - Management Catalysts (R), NJ, *134*
Stockwell, Kye - Gateway Management Resources (C), IL, *355*
Stoessel, Robert J. - Management Recruiters of Arlington (C), TX, *462*
Stofflet, Mary Jo - Dunhill Professional Search of Lehigh Valley (C), PA, *318*
Stokes, Carolyn - Corporate Dynamix (C), CA, *300*
Stokes, George N. - The Inside Track (C), TX, *389*
Stolee, Allan J. - Allan Stolee Inc. (R), FL, *201*
Stoll, Joan - Medfall Inc. (C), ON, *476*
Stoll, Steve - Sharrow & Assoc., Inc. (C), KY, *579*
Stollenmaier, James - Dunhill Professional Search of Hawaii (C), HI, *320*
Stollenmaier, Nadine - Dunhill Professional Search of Hawaii (C), HI, *320*
Stoller, Richard S. - Heath/Norton Assoc., Inc. (R), NY, *89*
Stoller, William H. - Robert William James & Assoc. (C), OR, *539*
Stoltz, Richard - Management Recruiters of Columbus (C), OH, *457*
Stone, Dave M. - DM Stone Personnel Services (C), CA, *594*
Stone, Laura - Sales Consultants of Cincinnati (C), OH, *561*
Stone, Richard - Stone Assoc. LLC (C), MI, *594*
Stone, Susan L. - Stone Enterprises Ltd. (C), IL, *594*
Stoneburner, Dwight T. - Stoneburner Assoc., Inc. (C), KS, *594*
Stoopen, Josefina - Stoopen Asociados, S.C./EMA Partners Int'l. (R), MX, *202*
Storer, Steve - Executive Search, Ltd. (C), OH, *336*
Storfer, Herbert F. - The Dartmouth Group (R), NY, *46*
Storfer, Herbert F. - Storfer & Assoc. (C), NY, *595*
Storfer, Paul D. - The Dartmouth Group (R), NY, *46*
Storfer, Paul D. - Storfer & Assoc. (C), NY, *595*
Stork, Jennifer - Goodkind Assoc. Inc. (C), NY, *360*
Stotz, Tara - The Corporate Source Group, Inc. (R), MD, *41*
Stout, Terry D. - Management Recruiters of Greensboro (C), NC, *433*
Stovall, Jaye - Boulware & Assoc. Inc. (R), IL, *20*
Stover, Bruce - StratfordGroup (R), CO, *203*
Stow, Ralph P. - Page-Wheatcroft & Co., Ltd. (R), TX, *158*
Stowers, James - Sales Consultants of High Point West (C), NC, *554*
Stoy, Jr., Roger W. - Heidrick & Struggles, Inc. (R), DC, *90*
Straat, Kent L. - Object Resources Int'l., Inc. (C), CT, *498*
Straight, Gary R. - Straight & Co. (R), GA, *202*
Strain, Stephen R. - SpencerStuart (R), CA, *196*
Stranberg, James R. - Callan Assoc., Ltd. (R), IL, *27*
Stranberg, Mark - Mark Stranberg & Assoc. Inc. (R), MA, *202*
Strand, Michael G. - Fortune Group Int'l., Inc. (R), PA, *70*
Strassner, Wendy A. - Hughes & Sloan, Inc. (C), GA, *383*
Strathmann, Winfried R. - W. R. Strathmann Assoc. (R), NY, *203*
Stratman, Sandra - Management Recruiters of Milford Inc. (C), CT, *442*
Stratton, Cary - Coastal Int'l., Inc. (R), MA, *36*
Stratton, Scott - LifeWork, Inc. (C), TX, *418*
Stratton, William F. - White, Roberts & Stratton, Inc. (C), IL, *619*
Straube, Stan - Straube Associates (R), MA, *203*
Strawn, William M. - Houtz•Strawn & Arnold, Inc. (R), TX, *96*
Strayhorn, Larry - Management Recruiters of Chicago West (C), IL, *447*
Strayhorn, Patricia - Management Recruiters of Chicago West (C), IL, *447*
Strickland, Sherry - Management Recruiters of Rocky Mount - Southwest (C), NC, *456*
Strieker, Mike - Healthcare Recruiters Int'l. Phoenix (C), AZ, *372*
Stringer, Dann P. - Foster Partners (R), DC, *70*
Stroble, Chuck - Earley Kielty & Assoc., Inc. (R), CT, *56*
Strobo, Ray S. - Management Recruiters of Lenoir City (C), TN, *436*
Stroll, Joseph - J. Stroll Assoc., Inc. (R), CT, *204*
Strom, Justin V. - Overton Consulting (R), WI, *157*
Strom, Mark N. - Search Advisors Int'l. Corp. (R), FL, *186*
Stroman, III, Alfred L. - Stroman Int'l., Inc. (R), CO, *204*
Strong, Alan - Commercial Programming Systems, Inc. (C), CA, *294*
Strong, Duane - Executive Resource Inc. (C), WI, *334*
Stroud, Robert - Industry Consultants, Inc. (C), GA, *388*
Stroud, Toni - Management Recruiters of the Baltimore Washington Corridor (C), MD, *450*
Stroup, Jonathan - Egon Zehnder Int'l. Inc. (R), GA, *227*
Strzelczyk, Robert R. - Strelcheck & Assoc., Inc. (R), WI, *203*

PRINCIPALS

(R) = Retainer; (C) = Contingency

Stuart, Bob - Lamon + Stuart + Michaels Inc. (R), ON, *124*
Stuart, Carolyn - Joy Reed Belt Search Consultants, Inc. (R), OK, *15*
Stubberfield, Lee - Management Recruiters of the Baltimore Washington Corridor (C), MD, *450*
Stubblefield, Janine - Angel Group Int'l. (C), KY, *250*
Stubbs, Judy N. - LAI Ward Howell (R), TX, *124*
Stupay, Michael E. - Integrated Management Solutions (C), NY, *390*
Sturgess, Bob - Michael Stern Assoc., Inc./ Euram (R), ON, *200*
Sturgess, Don - Wood West & Partners Inc. (C), BC, *624*
Sturgill, Vicki Hayes - Professional Careers, Inc. (C), NC, *520*
Sturgis, Miles - Management Recruiters of Plantation (C), FL, *427*
Sturtz, James W. - Compass Group Ltd. (R), MI, *38*
Stynetski, Bill - Largent Parks & Partners (C), TX, *503*
Suchesk, Lisa - PSD Group, Inc. (C), CA, *525*
Suchomski, Larry - The Montgomery Group, Inc. (C), TN, *484*
Sudina, Chuck - Sudina Search, Inc. (C), MD, *596*
Suhay, Gary T. - Elite Resources Group (R), OH, *58*
Sulkowski, Roger - Hughes & Wilden Assoc. (C), PA, *383*
Sullivan, Brian M. - Sullivan & Company (R), NY, *204*
Sullivan, Dan - Direct Marketing Resources (C), NC, *312*
Sullivan, Dennis B. - Sullivan & Assoc. (R), MI, *204*
Sullivan, Donald S. - Executives Worldwide, Inc. (C), OR, *337*
Sullivan, G. Kay - Rusher, Loscavio & LoPresto (R), CA, *183*
Sullivan, John P. - Dunlap & Sullivan Assoc. (R), MI, *55*
Sullivan, Jr., Joseph J. - Joe Sullivan & Assoc., Inc. (R), NY, *204*
Sullivan, Joseph M. - International Market Recruiters (C), NY, *393*
Sullivan, Mary - Sales Consultants of Chicago South (C), IL, *558*
Sullivan, Michael J. - LAI Ward Howell (R), NY, *123*
Sullivan, Peggy - Tuft & Assoc., Inc. (R), IL, *212*
Sullivan, Steve - Jackson & Coker (C), GA, *396*
Sullivan, Tami - Culver Personnel Services (C), CA, *304*
Sullivan, Tom - Brandywine Retained Ventures, Inc. (R), CT, *22*
Sullivan, Walter M. - Accelerated Data Decision, Inc. (C), NJ, *233*
Summerfield-Beall, Dotty - Summerfield Assoc., Inc. (C), TN, *596*
Summerlin, Gerald - Management Recruiters of Rockingham County (C), NC, *433*
Summers, Tom - Elan Pratzer & Partners Inc. (R), ON, *167*
Sumurdy, Melinda M. - LAI Ward Howell (R), TX, *124*
Sunshine, Ron - Ron Sunshine & Assoc. (C), IL, *597*
Sur, William K. - Canny, Bowen Inc. (R), NY, *28*
Suri, Prem - Fortuna Technologies Inc. (C), GA, *343*
Surrette, Mark J. - Robertson-Surrette Ltd. (R), NS, *179*
Susleck, Matthew M. - ESS (Executive Search Services) (R), CA, *61*
Suss, Mark J. - Executive/Retail Placement Assoc. (C), MD, *337*
Sussman, Patti - Weinman & Assoc. (C), AZ, *617*
Sutherland, Dana - Keystone Consulting Group (C), VA, *406*
Sutherland, Grant - C.T.E.W. Executive Personnel Services Inc. (C), BC, *278*
Sutherland, Matthew - Alliance Executive Search, Inc. (R), MA, *4*
Sutkamp, Paige - Soderlund Assoc. Inc. (R), OH, *195*
Sutter, Howard W. - Romac Int'l., Inc. (C), FL, *542*
Sutton, Eric - Callos Personnel Services (C), OH, *279*
Sutton, Robert J. - The Caldwell Partners Amrop International (R), ON, *26*
Sutton, Robert J. - The Caldwell Partners Amrop International (R), AB, *26*
Sutton, Robert P. - Sampson Medical Search (C), CA, *564*
Sutton, Stark - F-O-R-T-U-N-E Personnel Consultants of Savannah, Inc. (C), GA, *345*
Suvak, Miranda - Huddleston Assoc. (C), OK, *383*
Sveinbjornson, Lynn - The Verriez Group Inc. (R), ON, *213*
Svetic, Mark - Lear & Assoc., Inc. (C), FL, *415*
Swaak, Rick A. - Frank E. Allen & Assoc. (C), NJ, *244*
Swami, Pad N. - Fortuna Technologies Inc. (C), CA, *343*
Swan, Barbara - Lancaster Assoc., Inc. (C), NJ, *412*
Swan, Christopher - RSMR, Inc. (R), IL, *182*
Swan, Richard A. - Witt/Kieffer, Ford, Hadelman & Lloyd (R), CA, *223*
Swan, Steve - David Fockler & Assoc., Inc. (C), IL, *342*
Swann, Al - The Beam Group (R), NY, *14*
Swanson, Dick - Raymond Karsan Assoc. (C), MA, *530*
Swanson, Les - APA Employment Agency Inc. (C), OR, *251*
Swanson, Les - APA Employment Agency Inc. (C), OR, *251*
Swanson, Pat - Technical Employment Consultants (C), PA, *602*
Swanson, Scott - Gregory Laka & Co. (C), IL, *411*
Swartz, James D. - Romac Int'l., Inc. (C), FL, *542*
Swartz, Karen M. - The Penn Partners, Inc. (R), PA, *162*
Swartz, Pamela L. - Swartz & Assoc., Inc. (R), AZ, *204*
Swartz, William K. - Swartz & Assoc., Inc. (R), AZ, *204*
Swearingen, Gene - The Mercer Group, Inc. (R), VA, *143*
Sweeney, Diane - O'Keefe & Assoc., Inc. (R), CT, *154*
Sweeney, James W. - Sweeney Harbert & Mummert, Inc. (R), FL, *205*
Sweeney, Patrick B. - The Kennett Group, Inc. (R), PA, *112*
Sweet, Charles W. - A.T. Kearney Executive Search (R), IL, *111*
Sweet, Eleanor Anne - The Remington Group (R), IL, *174*
Sweet, Robert J. - Atlanta Executive Partners, Inc. (R), MA, *8*
Swidler, J. Robert - Egon Zehnder Int'l. Inc. (R), QE, *227*
Swiff, Jeffrey G. - Thorndike Deland Assoc. LLC (R), NY, *48*
Swift, Catherine - Swift & Assoc. (C), ME, *597*
Swift, Nina E. - The Oxbridge Group, Ltd. (C), PA, *500*
Swimley, E. Scott - Lautz, Grotte, Engler & Swimley (R), CA, *126*
Switzer, L. - Petro Staff Int'l. (C), AB, *509*
Swystun, Karen - Price Waterhouse Executive Search (R), MB, *168*
Syberg, Keith A. - Smith & Syberg, Inc. (R), IN, *193*
Sykes, Hugh L. - Management Recruiters of Mooresville (C), NC, *433*
Symanski, Donald G. - Tierney Assoc., Inc. (R), PA, *209*
Symcox, Jim - SPC Symcox Personnel Consultants (C), TX, *588*
Sypher, Patty - Gerald Walsh & Co. Inc. (C), NS, *614*
Szabad, C. - The Talley Group (R), VA, *205*
Szajkovics, Charles - First Search Inc. (C), IL, *341*
Szesny, Jim - Lechner & Assoc., Inc. (C), FL, *415*
Szewczuk, Louisa - Leith & Assoc., Inc. (C), OH, *416*
Szymanski, C. - The Hanna Group (C), OH, *368*
Tabb, Roosevelt - Tabb & Assoc. (R), OH, *205*
Tabbert, Mark - Sales Consultant of Irvine (C), CA, *551*
Tabisz, Susanne - Executive Referral Services, Inc. (C), IL, *334*
Tabler, Tracy - Phyllis Hawkins & Assoc., Inc. (C), AZ, *370*
Tabor, Gary - Careers On Track (C), NJ, *283*
Tackett, Lynn - National Recruiters (C), OK, *489*

Tadda, Wayne - Evie Kreisler Assoc. Inc. (C), IL, *409*
Tadewald, J. - Hunt Patton & Brazeal, Inc. (C), CO, *385*
Taft, David G. - Techsearch Services Inc. (C), CT, *603*
Tague, Maureen - The Moran Group (C), IL, *484*
Takacs, Gloria - Gilbert & Van Campen Int'l. (R), NJ, *76*
Talabisco, Barbara - Wakefield Talabisco Int'l. (R), NY, *214*
Talan, Marv - Executive Search Team (C), MI, *336*
Talarico, Joseph - Hreshko Consulting Group (C), NJ, *382*
Talbot, Lorri - Trillium Human Resources Inc. (C), ON, *609*
Talbot, Matt - Management Recruiters of Medford, N.J. (C), NJ, *453*
Talbot, Norman - Management Recruiters of Medford, N.J. (C), NJ, *453*
Talbott Creed, Pamela - The Hollins Group, Inc. (R), IL, *95*
Talio, John - Romac Int'l., Inc. (C), ON, *544*
Tallino, Paul R. - HRI Services, Inc. (C), MA, *382*
Tallino, Jr., Paul R. - HRI Services, Inc. (C), MA, *382*
Talman, Ilya - Roy Talman & Assoc. (C), IL, *599*
Tamayo, Roland - Management Recruiters of Fresno (C), CA, *440*
Tambor, Morris - Reynolds Consulting Int'l. (R), ON, *177*
Tames, Rodolfo - Amrop International (R), MX, *5*
Tanaka, Jun - Premier Recruiting Group (C), MI, *516*
Tanenbaum, Wendy - Marshall Consultants, Inc. (R), CA, *137*
Tang, Cliff - Wood West & Partners Inc. (C), BC, *624*
Tann, Robert - Staff Extension, Int'l. (C), TX, *590*
Tanner, Jack - Dunhill Staffing Systems (C), NY, *318*
Tanner, Joanne - S. Tanner & Assoc. Inc. (C), ON, *599*
Tanner, Steve - S. Tanner & Assoc. Inc. (C), ON, *599*
Tannura, Robert P. - Tannura & Assoc., Inc. (R), IL, *206*
Tansey, Char - Management Recruiters of Rochester (C), MN, *452*
Tansill, Bob - Romac Int'l., Inc. (C), CA, *542*
Tanton, John - Ray & Berndtson/Tanton Mitchell (R), BC, *172*
Tanton, John - Ray & Berndtson/Tanton Mitchell (R), BC, *173*
Tapler, Harold - Ruderfer & Co., Inc. (C), NJ, *548*
Tappan, Michael A. - LAI Ward Howell (R), NY, *123*
Taraso, Julie - Christmas, McIvor & Assoc. Inc. (C), ON, *290*
Tardugno, Carl - Management Recruiters of Utica/Rome (C), NY, *432*
Tarquinio, Alfred - Sales Consultants of Butler County (C), PA, *561*
Tashima, Spencer S. - Essential Solutions, Inc. (C), CA, *331*
Tasler, Sheryl - Robert William James & Assoc. (C), MN, *539*
Tatar, Steven M. - Magellan Int'l., L.P. (C), TX, *422*
Tate, Andrew - Tate Consulting, Inc. (R), FL, *207*
Tate, Gene M. - Tate & Assoc., Inc. (R), NJ, *207*
Tattersfield, Roberto E. - Frank P. Hill (R), MX, *93*
Tavens, Lester - Marvel Consultants, Inc. (C), OH, *472*
Tavin, Jerry - Janou Pakter, Inc. (C), NY, *502*
Tawney, Mel - M. L. Tawney & Assoc. (C), TX, *600*
Taylor, Carl J. - Carl J. Taylor & Co. (R), TX, *207*
Taylor, Charles E. - LAI Ward Howell (R), GA, *123*
Taylor, Dick - Packaging Personnel Co., Ltd. (C), WI, *501*
Taylor, Ernest A. - LAI Ward Howell (R), GA, *123*
Taylor, H. Gordon - F-O-R-T-U-N-E Consultants of Memphis (C), TN, *349*
Taylor, Jane A. - Paul S. Pelland, P.C. (R), SC, *161*
Taylor, Jared - Hall Kinion (C), AZ, *366*
Taylor, Jeffrey A. - Sales Consultants of Ft. Lauderdale, Inc. (C), FL, *557*
Taylor, Jerry - Executive Recruiters (C), WA, *334*
Taylor, Jim - The HRM Group, Inc. (C), AL, *382*
Taylor, John - The Caplan-Taylor Group (R), AZ, *28*
Taylor, Kenneth W. - Egon Zehnder Int'l. Inc. (R), IL, *227*
Taylor, M. Kent - Prairie Resource Group, Inc. (R), IL, *166*
Taylor, Michael - Cejka Healthcare Executive Search Services (CHESS) (R), MO, *32*
Taylor, Patricia - Smartsource Inc. (C), CA, *583*
Taylor, Peter R. - Peter R. Taylor Assoc., Inc. (C), NY, *600*
Taylor, Rachel - Harcor Quest & Assoc. (R), OH, *86*
Taylor, Sandi M. - Strategic Technologies, Inc. (C), TX, *596*
Taylor, Staci - Interim Accounting Professionals (C), CA, *391*
Taylor, Stuart - Career Enterprises (C), OH, *282*
Taylor, Walter W. - Management Recruiters of Venice, Inc. (C), FL, *445*
Taylor, Winifred C. - Management Recruiters of Venice, Inc. (C), FL, *445*
Tazzia, Ed - Gundersen Partners, L.L.C. (R), MI, *83*
Tedla, Solomon - Creative HR Solutions (C), GA, *303*
Teicher, Arthur - Smith's Fifth Avenue (C), NY, *585*
Teichman, Mark - Management Recruiters of Montco (C), PA, *434*
Telem, Peter B. - Telem Adhesive Search Corp. (C), MD, *605*
Telford, Daniel W. - CadTech Staffing Services (C), GA, *279*
Telford, Jr., John H. - Telford, Adams & Alexander (R), CA, *208*
Teller, Jr., Charles H. - DHR Int'l., Inc. (R), GA, *50*
Telleri, Frank C. - Curry, Telleri Group, Inc. (R), NJ, *44*
Tello, Fernando - Korn/Ferry, Int'l., S.A. de C.V. (R), MX, *118*
Tello, Fernando - Korn/Ferry, Int'l., S.A. de C.V. (R), MX, *118*
Templeton, Denise - Templeton & Assoc. (C), MN, *605*
Terada, Hideki - Pacific Advisory Service, Inc. (C), IL, *501*
Teresko, Dorothy A. - Bowden & Co., Inc. (R), OH, *20*
Terkovich, Branko A. - Engineering Resource Group, Inc. (C), NJ, *331*
Terkovich, James Z. - Engineering Resource Group, Inc. (C), NJ, *331*
Terlizzi, Antony R. - Bryan & Louis Research (C), OH, *275*
Terlizzi, R. Louis - Bryan & Louis Research (C), OH, *275*
Terry, J. - Management Recruiters of Oklahoma City-South (C), OK, *434*
Terry, J. - Sales Consultant of Albuquerque (C), NM, *554*
Terry, Jeff - Southern Recruiters & Consultants, Inc. (C), SC, *587*
Tesar, Bob - Tesar-Reynes, Inc. (R), IL, *208*
Tesoriero, Philip - The Madison Group (R), NY, *133*
Tessin, Cy - Management Recruiters of Kalamazoo (C), MI, *430*
Tessman, Russ - Management Recruiters of Des Moines (C), IA, *449*
Testart, Marion - Placement Testart Inc. (C), QE, *513*
Teter, Sandra - The Danbrook Group, Inc. (C), TX, *306*
Tewes, Steve - Management Recruiters of Milwaukee - Downtown (C), WI, *466*
Textor, Jack T. - Personnel Incorporated (C), IA, *508*
Thaler, Brian D. - Scott-Thaler Assoc. Agency, Inc. (C), CA, *573*
Thaller, Carole - Retail Connection, Inc. (C), NJ, *535*
Thayer, Robert T. - Executive Search of New England, Inc. (C), ME, *336*
Therizien, Greg - The Devlin Search Group, Inc. (C), MA, *312*
Therrell, Brock - Lanken-Kimball-Therrell & Assoc. (C), GA, *412*
Therrell, Brock - Lanken-Therrell & Assoc. (C), GA, *412*

Thibault, Elaine - Adam-Bryce Inc. (C), NY, *239*
Thibault, Raymond - Career Advisors, Inc. (C), FL, *281*
Thielman, Joseph - Barrett Partners (C), IL, *260*
Thiemann, Brian - Christopher and Long (C), MO, *291*
Thieme, Sue - The Riverbend Group (C), MO, *538*
Thieringer, Stephan - Search Int'l. (R), MA, *187*
Thiras, Ted - MIXTEC Group (R), CA, *145*
Tholke, William E. - Boardroom Consultants/Kenny Kindler Tholke (R), NY, *19*
Thomas, Barbara - Unlimited Staffing Solutions, Inc. (C), TN, *611*
Thomas, Betty J. - Tuft & Assoc., Inc. (R), IL, *212*
Thomas, Bill - The Search Alliance, Inc. (R), CT, *186*
Thomas, Bill E. - Management Recruiters of Kinston (C), NC, *456*
Thomas, Bonnie - The Premier Staffing Group (C), OH, *517*
Thomas, Bruce - Angel Group Int'l. (C), KY, *250*
Thomas, C. - Petro Staff Int'l. (C), AB, *509*
Thomas, Frank - Carson-Thomas & Assoc. (C), CA, *284*
Thomas, G. Alan - IPR, Inc. (R), VA, *103*
Thomas, Gina R. - Hughes & Sloan, Inc. (C), GA, *383*
Thomas, Gordon K. - IPR, Inc. (R), VA, *103*
Thomas, Ian A. - International Staffing Consultants, Inc. (C), CA, *393*
Thomas, Jeffrey - Fairfaxx Corp. (R), CT, *64*
Thomas, Kurt J. - P. J. Murphy & Assoc., Inc. (R), WI, *150*
Thomas, Lori - J. E. Lessner Assoc., Inc. (R), MI, *128*
Thomas, Norman A. - R.A.N. Assoc., Inc. (C), OH, *528*
Thomas, Pat Bowers - BowersThomas (C), CA, *271*
Thomas, Roger C. - Innovative Resource Group, LLC (C), NC, *389*
Thomas, Sharon - Management Recruiters of Williamsburg (C), IA, *449*
Thomas, Terry - Thomas Resource Group (R), CA, *209*
Thomas, Tommy - People Management Mid-South, LLC (R), TN, *162*
Thomas, Tracy - Barrett Hospitality Search (R), CA, *12*
Thomas III, William - William-Johns Co., Inc. (C), CA, *621*
Thomaschek, Charles F. - North Coast Meridian (C), NY, *496*
Thomason, Nancy - Montgomery, Thomason & Assoc. (C), ON, *484*
Thomason, Penny - F-O-R-T-U-N-E Personnel Consultants of East Seattle (C), WA, *351*
Thomason, Ronald - Montgomery, Thomason & Assoc. (C), ON, *484*
Thompson, Carlton W. - SpencerStuart (R), CT, *196*
Thompson, Dave - Battalia Winston Int'l./The Euram Consultants Group (R), CA, *13*
Thompson, Dennis - Thompson Assoc. (C), CA, *606*
Thompson, John T. - Heidrick & Struggles, Inc. (R), IL, *90*
Thompson, Judy - Judy Thompson & Assoc., Inc. (C), CA, *606*
Thompson, Kelvin - Norman Broadbent Int'l., Inc. (R), CA, *152*
Thompson, Ken - Allen & Assoc. (C), NV, *244*
Thompson, Kenneth L. - McCormack & Farrow (R), CA, *140*
Thompson, Pat - The Alfus Group (R), NY, *3*
Thompson, Richard - Accountants On Call (C), TX, *237*
Thompson, Richard E. - AGRI-associates (C), TN, *242*
Thompson, Richard P. - Richard Thompson Assoc., Inc. (R), MN, *209*
Thompson, Tammy - Connors, Lovell & Assoc. Inc. (C), ON, *296*
Thompson, Teri - Moss & Co. (R), WA, *148*
Thompson, Terri - Carlsen Resources, Inc. (R), CO, *29*
Thomson, H. Scott - Bialla & Assoc. Inc. (R), CA, *17*
Thomson, Steve - Roevin Technical People (C), ON, *540*
Thorlakson, Alan - The Harris Consulting Corp. (R), MB, *87*
Thormodsgaard, Terry - Thor, Inc. (C), CA, *606*
Thornton, Bill - C. M. Management Services, Inc. (R), KY, *26*
Thornton, Jennifer - Herring & Assoc. (C), TN, *376*
Thornton, John M. - StratfordGroup (R), OH, *203*
Thorpe, James - Kenn Spinrad Inc. (C), PA, *589*
Thrapp, Mark S. - Executive Search Consultants International, Inc. (R), NY, *63*
Thrower, Tom - Sales Consultants Int'l. of Oakland (C), CA, *556*
Thrower, Tom S. - Management Recruiters of Oakland (C), CA, *426*
Thunberg, Richard A. - Jeff Rich Assoc. (C), NJ, *536*
Thurber, Raymond N. - Overton Consulting (R), WI, *157*
Tierney, Eileen - The Whitney Group (R), NY, *219*
Tierney, George F. - Tierney Assoc., Inc. (R), PA, *209*
Tierney, John F. - Dunhill Professional Search of Oakland (C), CA, *319*
Tierney, Linda - Avalon Health Group, Inc. (R), NY, *9*
Tilley, Kyle - Romac Int'l., Inc. (C), KS, *543*
Tillman, Allen - Hardage Group (C), TN, *369*
Tillman, Rob - Crist Partners, Ltd. (R), IL, *43*
Timm, Spencer L. - TSW Assoc., LLC (R), CT, *211*
Timoney, Laura - Bishop Partners (R), NY, *17*
Tincu, John C. - Ferneborg & Assoc., Inc. (R), CA, *66*
Tindall, Chasity - Personnel Assoc. (C), NC, *508*
Tingley, Harleigh V. S. - Anderson & Schwab, Inc. (R), NY, *6*
Tinker, J. Jay - Management Recruiters of the Baltimore Washington Corridor (C), MD, *450*
Tippel, Fred C. - Fred C. Tippel & Assoc. (C), OH, *607*
Tirocchi, Fred - Tirocchi, Wright, Inc. (R), CA, *209*
Tittle, David M. - Paul-Tittle Assoc., Inc. (R), VA, *161*
Tittlemore, Jim - Tittemore Cowan Assoc. (C), AB, *607*
Titus, Dave - Management Recruiters of Bartow (C), FL, *426*
Tlustos, Mitch - Synergy Solutions, Ltd. (C), WA, *597*
Tobin, Kathryn - Norrell Financial Staffing (C), AZ, *495*
Toedtman, Craig B. - Effective Search, Inc. (R), OH, *57*
Tohill, Bill - O'Keefe & Assoc., Inc. (R), CT, *154*
Toke, Ron - Russ Hadick & Assoc. Inc. (C), OH, *365*
Tolette, Skip - Skip Tolette Executive Search Consulting (R), NJ, *209*
Tolle, David W. - Management Recruiters of Mattoon (C), IL, *428*
Tolman, Dan - Yankee Hospitality Search (C), CT, *626*
Tolstrup, Rick - Aminex Corp. (C), MA, *249*
Tomack, Arthur - Koll-Fairfield LLC (C), CT, *408*
Tomaras, David - Willmott & Assoc. (C), MA, *622*
Tomasco, Raymond - Boehmer, Tomasco & Alexander (R), CT, *24*
Tomasco, Raymond - BT&A, LLC (R), CT, *24*
Tomasco, Raymond - Huntington Group (R), CT, *100*
Tomei, Ted - Waterford Executive Group Ltd. (C), IL, *616*
Tomeo, Pat - S-H-S TechStaff (C), PA, *550*
Tomita, Betty Wong - Global Research Partnership Inc. (R), NY, *78*
Tomkin, Shelly - Career Counseling Ltd. (C.C.L.) (C), NY, *282*
Tomko, Jeffrey M. - Searchline Services, Inc. (C), OH, *577*
Tomlinson, Betsy - Tomlinson Assoc. Inc. (C), IL, *607*
Tommarello, Tony - Lucas Assoc. (C), CA, *421*
Tompkins, Donald - Raymond Karsan Assoc. (C), NJ, *530*

Toms, Dennis M. - National Recruiting Service (C), IN, *489*
Tondorf, Jr., Paul - Tondorf & Assoc. Inc. (C), MA, *607*
Toner, George - Western Management Consultants (R), ON, *218*
Toney, Roger - MTA Partners (R), TX, *148*
Toole, Mary - Management Recruiters of Laguna Hills (C), CA, *440*
Toole, Thomas J. - Management Recruiters of Laguna Hills (C), CA, *440*
Toomey, Pat - Target Search, Inc. (C), PA, *600*
Tootsey, Mark - Interim Financial Solutions (C), DC, *392*
Tootsey, Mark A. - Interim Financial Solutions (C), MD, *392*
Tornesello, Michael P. - The Yorkshire Group, Ltd. (C), MA, *626*
Torseth, Theresa - Moss & Co. (R), WA, *148*
Totah, Tamara - The Oxbridge Group, Ltd. (C), NY, *500*
Tourish, Abigail - Neil Fink Assoc. (R), TX, *67*
Townsend, Carol A. - Future Employment Service, Inc. (C), IA, *353*
Townsend, James C. - Future Employment Service, Inc. (C), IA, *353*
Townsend, John W. - Gardiner, Townsend & Assoc. (R), NY, *74*
Toy, Arlene - Advanced Executive Resources (R), MI, *2*
Tracey, Jay E. - Jay Tracey Assoc. Inc. (C), VT, *608*
Trachtenberg, Mort - Techno-Trac Systems, Inc. (C), NY, *603*
Tracy, Patricia - USA Medical Placement Inc. (C), TX, *611*
Tracy, Ronald O. - Egon Zehnder Int'l. Inc. (R), IL, *227*
Tracy, Susan - Wheeler Assoc. (R), CT, *219*
Trafer, Eduardo - Korn/Ferry, Int'l., S.A. de C.V. (R), NL, *118*
Trager, Alan - Dunhill Professional Search of Main Line (C), NY, *317*
Train, John L. - Trans-United Consultants Ltd. (C), ON, *608*
Trainor, James F. - Trainor/Frank & Assoc. Inc. (C), WI, *608*
Trainor, Joseph - Resource Services, Inc. (C), NY, *534*
Trainor, Mary Ann - Resource Services, Inc. (C), NY, *534*
Trambley, J. Brian - Trambley the Recruiter (C), NM, *608*
Trammell, Kay - Kressenberg Assoc. (C), TX, *409*
Trapani, Chris - ExecuSource Consultants, Inc. (C), TX, *332*
Trapani, Delores - ExecuSource Consultants, Inc. (C), TX, *332*
Trapp, Ed - Management Recruiters of Reno (C), NV, *453*
Trappen, Andrew - Dunhill Professional Search of San Jose (C), CA, *319*
Trasatti, Anthony - The Pennmor Group (C), NJ, *506*
Travis, Carl D. - Management Recruiters of Chesterfield (C), MO, *431*
Travis, Edward - Management Recruiters of St. Louis-West County (C), MO, *431*
Travis, John A. - Travis & Co., Inc. (R), MA, *210*
Travis, Michael J. - Travis & Co., Inc. (R), MA, *210*
Travis, Robert - Boyden (R), AB, *21*
Travis, Sam - Boyden (R), AB, *21*
Traylor, M. Ben - Human Resources Personnel Agency (R), AR, *99*
Traynor, Thomas H. - Traynor Confidential, Ltd. (C), NY, *609*
Treadaway, Van - Van Treadaway Assoc., Inc. (R), GA, *210*
Treaster, Valerie D. - Davis & Company (R), CA, *47*
Trendl, Joseph - J. R. Scott & Assoc., Ltd. (C), IL, *395*
Treney, Sue - Norrell Financial Staffing (C), FL, *495*
Trent, Alex - Vera L. Rast Partners Inc. (C), IL, *529*
Trent, Wendell C. - Larson & Trent Assoc. (C), TN, *413*
Trepton, Dave - Management Recruiters of Johnson Creek (C), WI, *438*
Trewhella, Michael - Romac Int'l., Inc. (C), MI, *543*
Trewhella, Michael - Romac Int'l., Inc. (C), MI, *543*
Tribbett, III, Charles A. - Russell Reynolds Assoc., Inc. (R), IL, *176*
Trilling, Dean D. - LAI Ward Howell (R), OH, *123*
Trimarchi, Steve - Roster Inc. (C), IN, *545*
Tringle, Terry - Sanford Rose Assoc. - Nashville (C), TN, *570*
Tripician, Philip - Heritage Search Group, Inc. (C), FL, *376*
Tripp, William J. - Management Recruiters of Dearborn, Inc. (C), MI, *451*
Trocina, Linda - Intersource, Ltd. (R), GA, *103*
Trombadore, Sheila - David Powell, Inc. (R), CA, *166*
Trosin, Walt - Johnson Smith & Knisely (R), NJ, *107*
Trott, Kathryn - Allard Associates (C), CA, *244*
Trout, Dan - Sterling Int'l. (R), NJ, *200*
Trout, Thomas L. - Trout & Assoc. Inc. (R), UT, *211*
Trowbridge, Robert L. - Trowbridge & Co., Inc. (R), MA, *211*
Troyanos, Dennis - Gundersen Partners, L.L.C. (R), NY, *83*
Trueb, Dick - Strategic Resources (C), WA, *595*
Trueba, Lucia - Stoopen Asociados, S.C./ EMA Partners Int'l. (R), MX, *202*
Truesdell, Michael - Ethos Consulting, Inc. (R), CA, *61*
Truex, John F. - Morton, McCorkle & Assoc. Inc. (R), MO, *147*
Truitt, Tom - Southwestern Professional Services (C), TN, *588*
Truman, Robert P. - The Truman Agency (C), CA, *610*
Tryon, Katey - Tryon & Heideman, LLC (R), MO, *211*
Tschudin, Hugo - Tschudin Inc. (R), NJ, *211*
Tschudin, Ruth - Tschudin Inc. (R), NJ, *211*
Tucci, Joseph - Fairfaxx Corp. (R), CT, *64*
Tucker, Angela - Accountants On Call (C), SC, *237*
Tucker, Guy - Ask Guy Tucker (C), GA, *254*
Tucker, John J. - Tucker Assoc. (R), NJ, *211*
Tucker, Merlene K. - Tucker Assoc. (R), NJ, *211*
Tucker, Michael - MTA Partners (R), TX, *148*
Tucker, Thomas A. - The Thomas Tucker Co. (R), CA, *211*
Tucker, Tonay - DHR Int'l., Inc. (R), IL, *49*
Tucker, Weida G. - W. G. Tucker & Assoc. (R), PA, *211*
Tudi, Mark - DHR Int'l., Inc. (R), AZ, *49*
Tufenkjian, Richard - C. A. Durakis Assoc., Inc. (R), MA, *55*
Tuft, Mary Ann - Tuft & Assoc., Inc. (R), IL, *212*
Tully, Jim - Orion Int'l. Consulting Group, Inc. (C), NC, *499*
Tully, Margo L. - Tully/Woodmansee Int'l. Inc. (R), FL, *212*
Tumbiolo, Lisa - Agriesti & Assoc. (C), CA, *243*
Tunis, R. - Petro Staff Int'l. (C), AB, *509*
Tunney, Jr., William - Grant Cooper & Assoc., Inc. (R), MO, *81*
Turczyn, Charlene - CMW & Associates, Inc. (C), IL, *293*
Turczyn, Charlene - CMW & Associates, Inc. (C), MO, *293*
Turk, Jeffrey M. - Omega Search, Inc. (C), NC, *498*
Turkal, Terry - Advanced Recruitment, Inc. (C), TN, *240*
Turnblacer, John - The Gabriel Group (C), PA, *354*
Turnbull, B. Harrison - Sockwell & Assoc. (R), NC, *194*
Turner, Alvan - SpencerStuart (R), IL, *197*
Turner, Bill - DHR Int'l., Inc. (R), GA, *50*
Turner, Kim - Barton Assoc., Inc. (R), TX, *12*
Turner, Linda - Kuhn Med-Tech (C), CA, *409*
Turner, Michael - Rocky Mountain Recruiters, Inc. (C), CO, *540*
Turner, Ray - Romac Int'l., Inc. (C), CT, *542*
Turner, Ray - Romac Int'l., Inc. (C), CT, *542*
Turner, Tami - Robert Half Canada Inc. (C), ON, *366*
Tuschman, Joe D. - JDavid Assoc., Inc. (R), CT, *105*

PRINCIPALS

(R) = Retainer; (C) = Contingency

Tutchings, Amy - Strategic Assoc., Inc. (C), TX, *595*
Tuttle, Donald E. - Tuttle Venture Group, Inc. (R), TX, *212*
Tweed, Janet - Gilbert Tweed Assoc. Inc. (R), NY, *76*
Twiste, Craig - Raymond Karsan Assoc. (C), GA, *530*
Tyler, J. Larry - Tyler & Company (R), GA, *212*
Tyson, Richard L. - Bonifield Assoc. (C), NJ, *269*
Udulutch, Mark - Markent Personnel, Inc. (C), WI, *470*
Udulutch, Thomas L. - Markent Personnel, Inc. (C), WI, *470*
Uhl, Jack N. - Management Recruiters of Green Tree (C), PA, *435*
Uhlich, Jeff - KPMG Executive Search (R), AB, *119*
Uhrig, Scott - LAI Ward Howell (R), TX, *124*
Ullstein, Ashley B. - Drinkwater & Assoc. (R), MA, *55*
Ulrich, Mary Ann - D. S. Allen Assoc. (C), NJ, *244*
Underwood, David L. - Sales Consultants of Grand Rapids (C), MI, *560*
Underwood, Stephaine J. - Longshore + Simmons (R), PA, *131*
Unger, Don - Harcourt & Assoc. (C), AB, *368*
Unger, Mike A. - Management Recruiters of Southern Monmouth County (C), NJ, *432*
Unger, Mike A. - Sales Consultant of Monmouth County (C), NJ, *554*
Uniacke, Keith J. - Management Recruiters of Sidney (C), OH, *458*
Upham, Suzanne - Snelling & Snelling, Inc. (C), FL, *585*
Upton, Noreen - The Beardsley Group Inc. (C), CT, *261*
Urban, Charles V. - Quality Control Recruiters (C), CT, *526*
Ursin, Kathleen - Johnson Smith & Knisely (R), CA, *107*
Utroska, Donald R. - LAI Ward Howell (R), IL, *123*
Utterson, Marshall - O'Rourke Companies, Inc. (R), TX, *154*
Vacca, Domenic L. - ACSYS Resources, Inc. (C), DE, *238*
Vacca, Domenic L. - ACSYS Resources, Inc. (C), DE, *238*
Vaccaro, George - The Advisory Group, Inc. (R), CA, *2*
Vacheron Alexander, Karen - Huntington Group (R), CT, *100*
Vachon-Vierra, Ronald - The Madeira Group (R), PA, *133*
Vague, Mark - F-O-R-T-U-N-E of West Portland (C), OR, *348*
Vahn, Martin - Sanford Rose Assoc. - Charlotte (C), NC, *568*
Valdes, Maria Elena - Korn/Ferry, Int'l., S.A. de C.V. (R), MX, *118*
Valdes, Maria Elena - Korn/Ferry, Int'l., S.A. de C.V. (R), MX, *118*
Valencia-Icard, Cheryl - The Icard Group, Inc. (C), MI, *387*
Valente, Joseph - Management Recruiters of Batavia (C), IL, *447*
Valenti, Joe - The MVP Group (C), NY, *487*
Valenti, Richard W. - Atlantic West Int'l. (C), NC, *255*
Valentine, Donald R. - Tecmark Associates Inc. (C), NY, *604*
Valentine, James P. - Valentine & Assoc. (C), IL, *611*
Valentine, Linda S. - Valentine & Assoc. (C), IL, *611*
Valkarcel, Beth - Hall Kinion (C), TX, *367*
Valkarcel, Beth - Hall Kinion (C), TX, *367*
Valle, Javier - A.T. Kearney Executive Search (R), MX, *111*
Valmore, Kim - Professions, Inc. (C), OH, *523*
Valone, Anthony F. - UniQuest Int'l., Inc. (C), FL, *611*
Valone, Judith - UniQuest Int'l., Inc. (C), FL, *611*
Valone, Michael - UniQuest Int'l., Inc. (C), FL, *611*
Van Alstine, Catherine - Ray & Berndtson/Tanton Mitchell (R), BC, *172*
Van Alstine, Catherine - Ray & Berndtson/Tanton Mitchell (R), BC, *173*
Van Beek, Mel - Dunhill Personnel Service of Fargo (C), ND, *322*
van Biesen, Coby - Search Group Inc. (R), AB, *186*
van Biesen, Jacques A. H. - Search Group Inc. (R), AB, *186*
Van Boven, Kathleen - Secura/Burnett Partners (R), CA, *187*
Van Buskirk, Bruce - Horizons Unlimited (C), CA, *381*
Van Campen, Jerry - Gilbert & Van Campen Int'l. (R), NY, *76*
Van Campen, Stephen B. - Gilbert & Van Campen Int'l. (R), NY, *76*
Van Dyke, Roger - Van Dyke Assoc. (R), IL, *212*
Van Eaton, Jim - Management Recruiters of Barrington (C), IL, *447*
van Eik, Gary - TriStaff Group (C), CA, *609*
Van Gyseghem, Marc - Stone Assoc. LLC (C), MI, *594*
Van Hevelingen, Nicholaas - AM & G Certified Public Accountants & Consultants (R), IL, *4*
Van Leer, Peter - Peter Van Leer & Assoc. (R), MN, *213*
Van Leeuwen, Lee - Van Leeuwen Assoc. (R), CA, *213*
Van Nostrand, Mara - Barton Assoc., Inc. (R), TX, *12*
Van Opstal, Lori - Your Advantage Staffing Consultants Inc. (C), ON, *626*
Van Remmen, Roger - Brown, Bernardy, Van Remmen, Inc. (C), CA, *275*
Van Schaik, David E. - Derhak Ireland & Partners Ltd. (R), ON, *48*
Van Weelde, Ron - ATS Executive Recruitment (C), GA, *255*
Van Wick, Mike - Management Recruiters of Rankin Co. (C), MS, *452*
Van Zandt, Eric - Prescott Legal Search, Inc. (C), TX, *517*
Van Zanten, William - VZ Int'l., Inc. (C), AZ, *613*
Vance, D. - Ki Technologies, Inc. (C), UT, *406*
Vance, Joe - F-o-r-t-u-n-e of Owensboro, Inc. (C), KY, *346*
Vande Water, Katie E. - J. Robert Scott (R), MA, *104*
Vande Woude, John - NorthStar Technologies, Inc. (C), NY, *496*
Vandegrift, Tom - Kiley, Owen & McGovern, Inc. (R), NJ, *114*
Vanden Hul, Marinus - Dunhill Professional Search of Colorado Springs (C), CO, *316*
Vanderleeuw, Jim - Connors, Lovell & Assoc. Inc. (C), ON, *296*
VanDolah, A. F. - Management Recruiters of Lionville, Inc. (C), PA, *459*
VanEs, Judith - mfg/Search, Inc. (C), IN, *480*
Vang, Karen - Accountants On Call (C), TX, *237*
Vangel, Joan - Access/Resources, Inc. (C), MI, *234*
Vangel, Peter V. - Access/Resources, Inc. (C), MA, *234*
VanMaldegiam, Norman E. - VanMaldegiam Assoc., Inc. (R), IL, *213*
Vann, Dianne - Button Group (C), TX, *277*
VanNus, Rob - Price Waterhouse Executive Search (R), BC, *168*
VanReypen, Robert D. - VanReypen Enterprises, Ltd. (R), NY, *213*
VanReypen, Shirley - VanReypen Enterprises, Ltd. (R), NY, *213*
VanSlyke, Dayton - Search By Design (C), AZ, *574*
Vant, Randy - Landon Morgan (C), ON, *412*
Vardaris, Richard - Lekan & Assoc., Inc. (R), OH, *128*
Varney, Rudy - J. L. Nixon Consulting (C), TX, *493*
Varrichio, Mike - Romac Int'l., Inc. (C), TX, *544*
Varrichio, Mike - Romac Int'l., Inc. (C), TX, *544*
Varrichio, Mike - Romac Int'l., Inc. (C), TX, *544*
Vasu, George - CCI - Career Consultants Int'l. (C), CA, *286*
Vaughan, David - Dunhill Professional Search of irvine/Newport (C), CA, *316*
Vaughan, David B. - Vaughan & Co. (C), CA, *612*
Vaughn, Emmett - American Resources Corp. (C), IL, *248*
Vautour, Eric L. - Russell Reynolds Assoc., Inc. (R), DC, *176*
Vazquez, Monica - Gomez Fregoso y Asociados (C), JAL, *360*

Veblan, Jennifer - NCC Executive Search Consultants (C), CA, *490*
Vegas, Carmen - Sofco (C), NY, *586*
Velten, Mark - Boyden (R), NJ, *21*
Venable, William - Thorndike Deland Assoc. LLC (R), NY, *48*
Vendetti, Lisa - The Alfus Group (R), NY, *3*
Venditti, Christine - TASA International (R), CA, *206*
Venditti, Paul - The Stewart Group (C), FL, *593*
Venekotter, Mike - UniQuest Int'l., Inc. (C), FL, *611*
Vennat, Manon - SpencerStuart (R), QE, *197*
Vennetti, Carie - Strategic Resources (C), WA, *595*
Vento, Joseph P. - Vento Assoc. (C), TN, *612*
Vento, Rachelle - Barton Assoc., Inc. (R), TX, *12*
Verchot, Hinky - Solutions Group (R), AL, *195*
Vergara, Gail H. - SpencerStuart (R), IL, *197*
Vergari, Jane - Herbert Mines Assoc., Inc. (R), NY, *145*
Verkamp, J. Frank - Verkamp-Joyce Assoc., Inc. (R), IL, *213*
Vermillion, Michael - Management Recruiters of Des Moines (C), IA, *449*
Verner, Josef - Houser, Martin, Morris (C), WA, *381*
Vernon, Howard - Aggressive Corporation (C), IL, *242*
Verriez, Paul M. - The Verriez Group Inc. (R), ON, *213*
Verros, Jill Hodgins - Daudlin, De Beaupre & Co., Inc. (R), MI, *46*
Vezan, Henry D. - Vezan Assoc. (C), CT, *612*
Vezina, Claude - Claude Vezina, Conseil en recherche de cadres inc. (R), QE, *213*
Vezina, Donald A. - Sales Consultant of Westlake Village (C), CA, *551*
Viall, Peter - Boyden (R), MI, *21*
Vialosky, John - Brandywine Retained Ventures, Inc. (R), CT, *22*
Vice, Michael - D.A.I Human Resources Consultants (R), QE, *45*
Vick, Bill - Vick & Assoc. (R), TX, *214*
Vickers, Jane - Robert William James & Assoc. (C), ON, *539*
Vickers, Jane - Robert William James & Assoc. (C), ON, *539*
Victor, Johnathon - The Executive Tree (R), FL, *64*
Vida, Tim - Technifind Int'l. (C), TX, *602*
Vierkant, Nona E. - Management Recruiters of Rochester (C), MN, *452*
Vierkant, Robert - Management Recruiters of Rochester (C), MN, *452*
Viescas, Diana - Professional Recruiters (C), UT, *522*
Viglino, Victor P. - DHR Int'l., Inc. (R), FL, *50*
Viglione, Donna L. - Lamay Assoc., Inc. (R), CT, *124*
Vigneault, Lucie - Groupe PCA Inc. (C), FL, *364*
Vignet, Gayle Hill - Hill Allyn Assoc. (C), CA, *378*
Vignuolo, Olga - Hreshko Consulting Group (C), NJ, *382*
Villano, George - Carter/MacKay (C), NJ, *285*
Villareal, Morey J. - Villareal & Assoc., Inc. (R), OK, *214*
Villareal, Victoria - Conasa de Mexico, S.C. (R), MX, *39*
Villasenor, Hector - Villasenor & Assoc. (C), CA, *612*
Villee, Mark - Management Recruiters of Columbia (C), MD, *450*
Villella, Paul - Romac Int'l., Inc. (C), DC, *542*
Villella, Paul - Romac Int'l., Inc. (C), MD, *543*
Villella, Paul F. - Romac Int'l., Inc. (C), VA, *544*
Vincenty, Lorraine - Vincenty & Co. (C), OH, *612*
Vinzenz, Michael S. - AGRI-associates (C), IA, *242*
Violette, Brad - Accountants On Call (C), NJ, *235*
Virchaux, Jean-Dominique - Heidrick & Struggles, Inc. (R), FL, *90*
Virgili, Franca - Johnson Smith & Knisely (R), CA, *107*
Visayan, Kavita - Boulware & Assoc. Inc. (R), IL, *20*
Viscusi, Stephen P. - The Viscusi Group, Inc. (R), NY, *214*
Visnich, L. Christine - Bason Associates (R), OH, *13*
Vissers, Robert - JFW Associates, LLC (C), CT, *398*
Vita, Eileen - O'Keefe & Assoc., Inc. (R), CT, *154*
Vitale, Joseph - Accountants On Call (C), OH, *236*
Vitanza, Jocelyne - DARE Personnel Inc. (C), ON, *307*
Vito, Joseph - Multi Processing, Inc. (R), NH, *149*
Vittorioso, Antonio - KPA Assoc., Inc. (C), NY, *408*
Viviano, Ralph - Sales Consultants of Pittsburgh-Southpointe (C), PA, *555*
Vlahos, Ben - Leader Institute, Inc. (C), GA, *414*
Vlasek, Ray - Management Recruiters of LBJ Park/Dallas (C), TX, *462*
Vlcek, Thomas J. - Vlcek & Company, Inc. (R), CA, *214*
Vlock, Evelyn - Romac Int'l., Inc. (C), FL, *543*
Vockley, James - Moffitt Int'l., Inc. (R), NC, *146*
Voelker, Larry - mfg/Search, Inc. (C), MI, *480*
Vogel, Don - Dunhill Professional Search (C), MO, *321*
Vogel, Emil - Tarnow Int'l. (R), NJ, *206*
Vogel, Michael S. - Vogel Assoc. (C), PA, *613*
Vogel, Ruth - Sales Consultants of Westchester-South, Inc. (C), NY, *561*
Vognsen, Rikke - David Saxner & Assoc., Inc. (DSA, Inc.) (R), IL, *185*
Vogus, Jerry - Cumberland Group Inc. (C), IL, *304*
Voigt, Jeff - APA Employment Agency Inc. (C), OR, *251*
Voigt, John A. - Partners Resource Group (C), VA, *504*
Voigt, Raymond R. - Voigt Assoc. (R), IL, *214*
Vojta, Marilyn B. - Lindsey & Co., Inc. (R), CT, *129*
Voketz, Dennis W. - Dunhill Personnel of Lansing (C), MI, *317*
Volk, Donald - Raymond Karsan Assoc. (C), PA, *529*
Volpe, Louis - Fox, White & Assoc. (C), FL, *351*
Volz, Scott - Management Recruiters of Hickory (C), NC, *433*
von Baillou, Astrid - Richard Kinser & Assoc. (R), NY, *115*
Von Recklinghausen, Renate - Dunhill Search of Vermont (C), VT, *323*
von Seldeneck, Judith M. - Diversified Health Search (R), PA, *52*
von Seldeneck, Judith M. - Diversified Search, Inc. (R), PA, *52*
von Stein, William - Johnson Smith & Knisely (R), CA, *107*
Von Villas, Lynne - Employment Solutions, Inc. (C), TX, *330*
Vosika, Duane - Sales Consultants of Omaha, Inc. (C), NE, *560*
Voss, Erik - Sheila Greco Assoc. (C), NY, *362*
Vourakis, Zan - ZanExec L.L.C. (R), VA, *226*
Vozekas, James P. - The Touchstone Group (C), MA, *607*
Vrabel, Frank - ISG Informatics Search Group (C), ON, *395*
Vroom, Cynthia D. - Cyntal Int'l. Ltd. (R), NY, *44*
Vucicevic, Andy - General Engineering Tectonics (C), CA, *356*
Vujeec, John - Executive Search, Ltd. (C), OH, *336*
Waanders, Patricia J. - ExecuQuest, Inc. (R), MI, *61*
Waanders, William L. - ExecuQuest, Inc. (R), MI, *61*
Wachendorfer, Nancy - Wachendorfer & Assoc. (C), TX, *613*
Wachendorfer, Tom - Wachendorfer & Assoc. (C), TX, *613*
Wachuku, Bobbiette - Management Recruiters-Cedar Rapids, Inc. (C), IA, *448*
Wackerle, Frederick W. - Fred Wackerle, Inc. (R), IL, *214*
Wada, Fumie - Pasona Canada, Inc. (C), ON, *504*
Wade, Alan - Data-AxIS Corp. (C), FL, *307*
Wade, Bridgette - Norrell Financial Staffing (C), CA, *495*
Wade, Elliott - Search Int'l. (R), MA, *187*

PRINCIPALS

Wade, Jim - McCormack & Farrow (R), CA, *140*
Wadsworth, Robert H. - Robert H. Wadsworth & Assoc., Inc. (R), AZ, *214*
Wagaman, Randy - Accountants On Call (C), CA, *235*
Wagenknecht, Jason - H R Solutions, Inc. (C), MO, *365*
Wagner, Deborah - Romac Int'l. (C), PA, *542*
Wagner, R. J. - TSC Management Services Group, Inc. (C), IL, *610*
Wagner, Susan J. - EDI/Executive Dynamics Inc. (C), NJ, *326*
Wainwright, Nancy - Locus Inc. (C), WV, *419*
Waite, Thomas M. - Sales Consultants of Harrisburg (C), PA, *561*
Wakefield, J. Alvin - Wakefield Talabisco Int'l. (R), VT, *214*
Walch, Hutch - Working Relationships, Inc. (C), MN, *624*
Wald, E. Steven - Andrews & Wald Group (C), FL, *250*
Waldman, Noah W. - LAI Ward Howell (R), GA, *123*
Waldon, Jeffrey - Accountants On Call (C), FL, *237*
Waldon, Maita - Accountants On Call (C), FL, *237*
Waldorf, Michael - Waldorf Associates, Inc. (C), CA, *614*
Waldrip, Jennifer - Hall Kinion (C), CA, *366*
Waldron, Charlie W. - Magellan Int'l., L.P. (C), TX, *422*
Walhof, Chris - Management Recruiters of Boise (C), ID, *446*
Walker, Bob - McCoy Ltd. (C), CA, *474*
Walker, Cheryl - Corporate Builders, Inc. (C), OR, *299*
Walker, Craig - Interim Financial Solutions - Mid-Atlantic Region (C), MD, *392*
Walker, David - Accountants On Call (C), CA, *235*
Walker, David - Accountants On Call (C), CA, *235*
Walker, David - Accountants On Call (C), CA, *235*
Walker, Donald G. - Executive Search Plus, Inc. (C), IN, *336*
Walker, Douglas G. - Sink, Walker, Boltrus Int'l. (R), MA, *192*
Walker, Jr., J. Ewing - LAI Ward Howell (R), TX, *124*
Walker, Jim - Dick Wray & Consultants, Inc. (R), CA, *225*
Walker, Karen K. - K. K. Walker Professional Recruitment (C), CA, *614*
Walker, Kelly - Kelly Walker Assoc. (C), TX, *614*
Walker, Linda G. - Walker Personnel, Inc. (C), LA, *614*
Walker, Walter G. - Walker Group, Inc. (R), MN, *215*
Walker, Warren T. - Millar Walker & Gay (R), ON, *144*
Wall, Christine - Quantum EDP Recruiting Services (C), ON, *526*
Wallace, Alec - Ray & Berndtson/Tanton Mitchell (R), BC, *172*
Wallace, Alec - Ray & Berndtson/Tanton Mitchell (R), BC, *173*
Wallace, Jr., Charles E. - Heidrick & Struggles, Inc. (R), OH, *90*
Wallace, Clarke - PricewaterhouseCoopers Executive Search (R), ON, *168*
Wallace, Dennis M. - Sanford Rose Assoc. - Rockford (C), IL, *567*
Wallace, Marilyn - Delta Medical Search Assoc. (C), OH, *311*
Wallace, Mark J. - Management Recruiters of Broome County, Inc. (C), NY, *454*
Wallace, Robert - O'Keefe & Assoc., Inc. (R), CA, *154*
Wallace, William J. - Wallace Management Co. (R), TN, *215*
Wallberg, Marilyn - Stephen Haas Legal Placement (C), NY, *365*
Wallens, Charles N. - Allen, Wayne & Co. LLC (C), WI, *245*
Waller, Jody W. - Michael Latas & Assoc., Inc. (R), MO, *126*
Waller, Victoria - Health Search, Inc. (C), KS, *371*
Walley, Kimberly - DHR Int'l., Inc. (R), IL, *49*
Walling, Robert - Management Recruiters of Windsor (C), NJ, *431*
Wallis, Ginger - Intersource, Ltd. (R), GA, *103*
Walmsley, Scott - Association for Sales Force Management (C), WA, *254*
Walsh, Edmund J. - Weston Consultants, Inc. (R), MA, *219*
Walsh, Gerald - Gerald Walsh & Co. Inc. (C), NS, *614*
Walsh, Joe - A.J. & Assoc. (C), FL, *232*
Walsh, John - J. D. Walsh & Co. (R), CT, *215*
Walsh, Kenneth A. - R/K International Inc. (R), CT, *171*
Walsh, Patty - Abraham & London Ltd. (C), CT, *232*
Walsh, Richard - The Gabriel Group (C), PA, *354*
Walsh, Thomas - Callos Personnel Services (C), OH, *279*
Walt, Lee - M H Executive Search Group (C), TX, *422*
Walter, Linda - Linda Walter & Associes (C), QE, *615*
Walter, MaryAnn - SpencerStuart (R), CA, *196*
Walters, C. Scott - DiMarchi Partners (R), CO, *51*
Walters, Roy - H.I. Hunt & Co., Ltd. (R), MA, *99*
Walters, Tom - Bor-Maq Assoc. (C), TX, *269*
Walters, William F. - Jonas, Walters & Assoc., Inc. (R), WI, *107*
Walton, Craig - Management Recruiters of San Marcos (C), TX, *463*
Walton, Lee H. - Lee H. Walton & Assoc. (R), NY, *215*
Waltz, B. - Ki Technologies, Inc. (C), UT, *406*
Wampole, Carole - Legal Network Inc. (C), CA, *416*
Wampole, Daniel - Legal Network Inc. (C), CA, *416*
Wanger, Karen - Karen Wanger & Assoc., Inc. (C), IL, *615*
Ward, Al L. - Ward-Hoffman & Assoc. (C), ID, *615*
Ward, Anthony C. - Ward Liebelt Assoc. Inc. (R), CT, *215*
Ward, Catherine M. - Blue Chip Law Consulting, Inc. (C), CA, *268*
Ward, Dick - Chanko-Ward, Ltd. (R), NY, *33*
Ward, Gayle E. - Ward-Hoffman & Assoc. (C), ID, *615*
Ward, Glenda M. - Christopher and Long (C), MO, *291*
Ward, James M. - The Ward Group (R), MA, *215*
Ward, Jennifer - David Aplin & Assoc. (C), AB, *251*
Ward, Madeleine - L T M Assoc. (C), IL, *410*
Ward, Martha - Martha Ward Executive Search, Inc. (C), NY, *615*
Ward, Peter - Ward Assoc. (C), ON, *615*
Warden, Shannon - Peggy Shea & Assoc. (R), CA, *189*
Ware, Ginny - Healthcare Recruiters of Indiana (C), IN, *372*
Ware, John - SpencerStuart (R), CA, *196*
Warmbold, Herman P. - Staub, Warmbold & Assoc., Inc. (R), NY, *199*
Warner, C. Douglas - C. D. Warner & Assoc. (C), PA, *615*
Warner, Susan C. - C. D. Warner & Assoc. (C), PA, *615*
Warner, Thomas P. - Warner & Assoc., Inc. (C), OH, *615*
Warns, Peter - The DataFinders Group, Inc. (C), NJ, *307*
Warren, Deborah - Management Recruiters of Lubbock (C), TX, *463*
Warren, Lester - Management Recruiters of Lubbock (C), TX, *463*
Warren, Pamela A. - Egon Zehnder Int'l. Inc. (R), ON, *227*
Warren, Richard - Cole, Warren & Long, Inc. (R), PA, *37*
Warren, Rick - Cantrell & Assoc. (C), FL, *280*
Warren, Robert - Warren Int'l. (R), NY, *215*
Warren, Robert L. - Warren Executive Services (C), GA, *616*
Warren, Scott C. - Warren, Morris & Madison, Ltd. (C), NH, *616*
Warren, Susan - Human Resource Dimensions, Inc. (C), TX, *384*
Warren, Ted - Strategic Resources (C), WA, *595*
Warren, Tom S. - F.L.A.G. (C), OH, *338*
Warriner, Bob - Job-Born Candidate Selection Bureau (C), ON, *399*
Warriner, Mary Ann - Job-Born Candidate Selection Bureau (C), ON, *399*

Warring, J. T. - Warring & Assoc. (R), CA, *215*
Waschuk, Bill - Forest People Int'l. Search Ltd. (C), BC, *343*
Wascovich, Tina - Rojek Marketing Group, Inc. (R), OH, *181*
Washatka, Robert - Dunhill Personnel of Topeka, Inc. (C), KS, *317*
Washburn, Natalie - Smith Hanley Assoc., Inc. (C), GA, *584*
Washburn, Ron - Elite Medical Search (C), GA, *328*
Wasiele, Brian D. - Carnegie Partners, Inc. (R), IL, *30*
Wasley, John - DHR Int'l., Inc. (R), CA, *49*
Wasmuth, Doug - Accountancies (C), CA, *234*
Wasp, Jr., Warren T. - WTW Assoc., Inc. (R), NY, *225*
Wasserman, Harvey - Churchill & Affiliates, Inc. (R), PA, *35*
Wasserman, Stan - Wasserman Assoc. Inc. (C), MD, *616*
Wasson, David K. - The Oldani Group (R), TX, *155*
Wasson, Thomas W. - SpencerStuart (R), CT, *196*
Watkins, Chris - Management Recruiters of Delaware County (C), OH, *434*
Watkins, Edwin - RHS Assoc. (C), AL, *536*
Watkins, Greg - Management Recruiters of Delaware County (C), OH, *434*
Watkins, Jean T. - The Repovich-Reynolds Group (TRRG, Inc.) (R), CA, *175*
Watkins, Jeff - Norrell Financial Staffing (C), GA, *495*
Watkins, Jeffrey P. - LAI Ward Howell (R), GA, *123*
Watkins, Melissa - Michael Shirley Assoc. Inc. (R), KS, *190*
Watkins, Robert J. - R. J. Watkins & Co., Ltd. (R), CA, *216*
Watkins, III, Thomas M. - LAI Ward Howell (R), TX, *124*
Watkinson, Jim - The Badger Group (R), CA, *10*
Watring, Bernie - Watring & Assoc., Inc. (C), IL, *616*
Watson, Barbara A. - Sales Consultants of Ann Arbor (C), MI, *553*
Watson, David - Accountants On Call (C), MD, *236*
Watson, David L. B. - Pacific Coast Recruiters (C), OR, *501*
Watson, Diana L. - Premier Healthcare Recruiters, Inc. (C), MI, *516*
Watson, Hanan S. - Watson Int'l., Inc. (R), NY, *216*
Watson, Jim - MSI Int'l. (C), GA, *487*
Watson, Lisa - mfg/Search, Inc. (C), IN, *480*
Watson, Lynn - Joy Reed Belt Search Consultants, Inc. (R), OK, *15*
Watson, Martha - Scott Watson & Assoc., Inc. (R), FL, *216*
Watson, Scott - Scott Watson & Assoc., Inc. (R), FL, *216*
Watson, Stacey - Romac Int'l., Inc. (C), KY, *543*
Watson, Wally - Management Recruiters of Memphis, TN (C), TN, *462*
Watt, Charlie - TASA International (R), MA, *206*
Watters, John T. - DHR Int'l., Inc. (R), FL, *50*
Watters, Tamara - Construction Search Specialists, Inc. (C), WI, *297*
Waugh, Chris - The Bales-Waugh Group (C), FL, *258*
Wawrzeniak, Mark M. - Management Recruiters of Pittsburgh-Airport (C), PA, *435*
Wax, Robert M. - Kingsbury • Wax • Bova (R), MA, *114*
Wayne, Cary S. - ProSearch, Inc. (C), OH, *524*
Wayne, Vici - Christian & Timbers, Inc. (R), OH, *34*
Weatherstone, William - Executive Search Consultants Corp. (C), IL, *335*
Weaver, John - Culver Personnel Services (C), CA, *304*
Weaver, John T. - C. R. Krafski & Assoc., Inc. (R), IL, *120*
Webb, Donald W. - Management Recruiters of Dalton (C), GA, *428*
Webb, Elliot - E. J. Lance Management Assoc., Inc. (C), NY, *412*
Webb, Jr., George H. - Webb, Johnson Assoc., Inc. (R), NY, *216*
Webb, John R. - Dunhill Personnel Service of San Antonio (C), TX, *318*
Webb, Melissa - Circlewood Search Group, Inc. (C), MI, *291*
Webb, Pat - Management Recruiters of Frederick, Inc. (C), MD, *450*
Webb, Shirley - Robert William James & Assoc. (C), OK, *539*
Webb, Verna F. - Management Recruiters of Dalton (C), GA, *428*
Webb, Vincent J. - Management Recruiters International, Inc. (MRI) (C), OH, *425*
Webb, Vincent J. - Sales Consultants (C), OH, *551*
Webber, Mary Ann - Shiloh Careers Int'l., Inc. (C), TN, *580*
Weber, Fran - Marley Group Ltd. (C), NY, *471*
Weber, H. Jurgen - BioQuest Inc. (R), CA, *17*
Weber, James K. - Management Recruiters of Coral Gables (C), FL, *427*
Weber, Janette - Management Recruiters of Des Moines (C), IA, *449*
Weber, L. Lee - TASA International (R), GA, *206*
Weber, Ronald R. - Weber Executive Search (R), NY, *216*
Webster, Bruce - Sales Consultants of Milwaukee (C), WI, *563*
Webster, Doug - The Buckley Group (C), NJ, *276*
Webster, Larry - Technology Management Partners (R), CA, *208*
Webster, William L. - S. B. Webster & Associates (R), MA, *217*
Weddell, Dave - Management Recruiters of Rocky Mount - Southwest (C), NC, *456*
Wedderien, Wayne - National Bank & Finance Executive Search (C), CA, *488*
Wegesin, Mark - Accountants On Call (C), TX, *237*
Weglarz, Patrick - Jim Kay & Assoc. (C), IL, *404*
Wegner, Carl - Wegner & Assoc. (C), WI, *617*
Weil, Lee - Lee Weil Assoc., Inc. (C), IL, *617*
Weil, Richard - LCS, Inc. (C), TX, *414*
Weiler, Wendy C. - Rhodes Associates (R), NY, *177*
Wein, Michael S. - Media Management Resources, Inc. (R), CO, *142*
Wein, William - Media Management Resources, Inc. (R), FL, *143*
Weiner, Al - Lucas Group (C), NY, *421*
Weiner, Arlene - Sanford Rose Assoc. - Athens (C), GA, *566*
Weiner, Art - Sanford Rose Assoc. - Athens (C), GA, *566*
Weiner, Ken - Sanford Rose Assoc. - Athens (C), GA, *566*
Weiner, Linda - Sterling Int'l. (R), NJ, *200*
Weinfeld, David C. - David Weinfeld Group (C), NC, *617*
Weinhold, Jean - LCC Companies (C), AZ, *414*
Weinhold, Ray - LCC Companies (C), AZ, *414*
Weinman, Mary - Weinman & Assoc. (C), AZ, *617*
Weinpel, Charles J. - Weinpel Search, Inc. (C), NJ, *617*
Weinrauch, Kathleen - Mannard & Assoc., Inc. (R), IL, *135*
Weinstein, Bruce - Western Technical Resources (C), CA, *619*
Weinstein, Lewis R. - Weinstein & Co. (R), MA, *217*
Weinstein, Stanley E. - S.E. Weinstein Co. (R), IL, *217*
Weinstock, Michael A. - Advisors' Search Group, Inc. (C), NY, *241*
Weir, David G. - Intercontinental Executive Group (C), PA, *391*
Weis, Robert - CFOs 2 Go (C), CA, *288*
Weisinger, Ronald J. - The Oldani Group (R), MD, *155*
Weiss, Cathy - C. Weiss Assoc., Inc. (C), NY, *618*
Weiss, David L. - D. L. Weiss & Assoc. (R), CA, *217*
Weiss, Dick - Richard, Wayne & Roberts (C), TX, *536*
Weiss, Gerald E. - Nuessle, Kurdziel & Weiss, Inc. (R), PA, *153*
Weiss, John J. - Executive Placement Services (C), GA, *333*
Weiss, John P. - Star Search Consultants (C), ON, *591*
Weiss, Karen - Foster Partners (R), NY, *70*
Weiss, Linda - Prichard Kymen Inc. (R), AB, *168*

PRINCIPALS

(R) = Retainer; (C) = Contingency

Weiss, Linda S. - Pharmaceutical Recruiters, Inc. (R), NY, *163*
Weiss, Michael G. - Applied Resources, Inc. (C), MN, *252*
Weiss, Ronald - The BMW Group, Inc. (C), NY, *268*
Weitzel, Freda - Management Recruiters of Winston-Salem (C), NC, *457*
Welch, Lauren - Management Recruiters of Lake Forest, IL (C), IL, *447*
Welch, R. Thomas - RIC Corp. (R), FL, *177*
Welch, Roger - Western Management Consultants (R), BC, *218*
Weliver, Billie S. - Weliver & Assoc. (C), MI, *618*
Weliver, Edward A. - Weliver & Assoc. (C), MI, *618*
Welker, Henry A. - Henry Welker & Assoc. (C), MI, *618*
Weller, Paul S. - Mark Stanley & Co. (R), DC, *136*
Welles, Christopher - The Oxbridge Group, Ltd. (C), MA, *500*
Welling, Suzanne - IMA Search, Inc. (R), NY, *101*
Wellman, Michael - Korn/Ferry Int'l. (R), NY, *117*
Wells, Edward - Personnel Assoc. (C), CA, *508*
Wells, Juli C. - Cook Assoc. Int'l., Inc. (C), TN, *298*
Wells, Lee - F-O-R-T-U-N-E Personnel Consultants of East Seattle (C), WA, *351*
Wells, Patricia - Fortune Group Int'l., Inc. (R), PA, *70*
Wells, Robert A. - R. A. Wells Co. (C), GA, *618*
Welti, Rene - Direct Marketing Resources (C), NC, *312*
Welzig, Frank E. - Welzig, Lowe & Assoc. (C), CO, *618*
Wendeln, Bert - Management Recruiters of Carlisle (C), PA, *434*
Wendler, Kambrea R. - Gregory Michaels & Assoc., Inc. (R), IL, *82*
Wenom, Carol Dibb - The Whitaker Companies (C), TX, *619*
Wentworth, John - The Wentworth Co., Inc. (R), CA, *217*
Wentz, Terry M. - Management Recruiters of Perry (C), GA, *428*
Wenzel, Dawn - Partners in Recruiting (C), IL, *504*
Wenzel, Tim - Accountancies (C), CA, *234*
Wenzel, Tim - DM Stone Personnel Services (C), CA, *594*
Werbin, Susan - Werbin Assoc. Executive Search, Inc. (C), NY, *618*
Werlin, Paul A. - Human Capital Resources, Inc. (C), FL, *384*
Werner, Vivian - Smith's Fifth Avenue (C), NY, *585*
Werra, Jude M. - Jude M. Werra & Assoc. (R), WI, *218*
Wesley, Donald - Spear-Izzo Assoc., LLC (C), PA, *589*
Wesley, Terry R. - Management Recruiters of Mayfield Village (C), OH, *434*
Wesolich, Elizabeth S. - Executive Solutions (R), MO, *64*
West, Al - West & Assoc. (C), IL, *618*
West, Fred - Wood West & Partners Inc. (C), BC, *624*
West, Nancy - Health Care Dimensions (C), CO, *371*
West, Paul A. - West & West (R), CA, *218*
Westerberg, Kevin - Romac Int'l., Inc. (C), MA, *543*
Westerfield, Dick - Russ Hadick & Assoc. Inc. (C), OH, *365*
Westerfield, Putney - Boyden (R), CA, *20*
Westfall, Ed - Zwell Int'l. (R), IL, *228*
Westhoff, Clifford - RHAssoc. Inc. (C), KS, *535*
Westmore, Diane - Healthcare Management Resources, Inc. (R), GA, *89*
Westmore, Robert J. - Hermann & Westmore (R), CA, *92*
Weston, Corinne - D. A. Kreuter Assoc., Inc. (R), PA, *121*
Weston, Joan C. - F-O-R-T-U-N-E Personnel Consultants of Wilmington (C), DE, *344*
Weston, Leonard A. - F-O-R-T-U-N-E Personnel Consultants of Wilmington (C), DE, *344*
Westphal, Birgit - Reynolds Consulting Int'l. (R), ON, *177*
Wetterman, Bill - Management Recruiters of Tulsa (C), OK, *434*
Wexler, Jo Ann - The Oldani Group (R), CA, *155*
Wexler, Rona - Ariel Recruitment Assoc. (R), NY, *7*
Wexler, Suzanne - S. J. Wexler Assoc., Inc. (R), NY, *219*
Whaley, Robert B. - TASA International (R), NY, *206*
Wharton, Cynthia - Personnel Management Group (C), MB, *508*
Wharton, John P. - The Garret Group (R), NJ, *75*
Wheel, Eric - Management Recruiters of Northern California (C), CA, *440*
Wheeler, Bruce - Cypress Int'l., Inc. (R), FL, *45*
Wheeler, Ray B. - RBW Assoc. Inc. (C), OR, *531*
Wheelless, Pat - Wheelless Group (R), IL, *219*
Whelan, David - Ethos Consulting, Inc. (R), CA, *61*
Whelan, Fred - StratfordGroup (R), CA, *203*
Whelan, Kim - Flexible Resources, Inc. (C), MA, *342*
Wheless, Michael - Solutions Group (R), AL, *195*
Whetstone-Smith, B. K. - Allen Austin Lowe & Powers (R), TX, *3*
Whicker, Rex - Management Recruiters of Shelby-Uptown (C), NC, *433*
Whitaker, Bruce - The Whitaker Companies (C), TX, *619*
Whitaker, Bryan - Data Bank Executive Search (R), OH, *46*
Whitaker, Geraldine - Rusher, Loscavio & LoPresto (R), CA, *183*
Whitbeck, Elizabeth C. - Whitbeck & Assoc. (R), MN, *219*
White, Clyde - Further Management Group (C), MD, *353*
White, David - W. Robert Eissler & Assoc., Inc. (C), TX, *327*
White, Edward - Katelyn Partners (C), FL, *404*
White, Evelyne F. - Fox, White & Assoc. (C), FL, *351*
White, Evelyne F. - Fox, White & Assoc. (C), PA, *351*
White, Gordon - DHR Int'l., Inc. (R), MI, *50*
White, J.W. - Schneider, Hill & Spangler, Inc. (R), PA, *185*
White, Jonathan O. - SpencerStuart (R), CA, *196*
White, Joseph A. - Sports Group Int'l. (R), NC, *198*
White, Ken - Management Recruiters of Winston-Salem (C), NC, *457*
White, Lenny - The Brentwood Group Ltd. (R), OR, *23*
White, Lindsay - David Powell, Inc. (R), CA, *166*
White, Marc P. - White, Roberts & Stratton, Inc. (C), IL, *619*
White, Michele - The Kleven Group, Inc. - Executive Search Division (R), MA, *116*
White, Michele - The Kleven Group, Inc. (C), MA, *407*
White, Richard B. - SpencerStuart (R), CT, *196*
White, Robert B. - Pennington Consulting Group (C), NJ, *506*
White, Scott M. - Triumph Consulting, Inc. (R), IA, *210*
White, William C. - Venture Resources, Inc. (R), CA, *213*
Whiteford, Scott - Modis (C), MD, *483*
Whitehead, III, Arch S. - Arch S. Whitehead Assoc. Inc. (ASWA) (R), NY, *219*
Whitehead, Elizabeth S. - Whitehead & Assoc., Inc. (C), MO, *620*
Whitehead, Robert S. - Whitehead & Assoc., Inc. (C), MO, *620*
Whitehurst, James - Katelyn Partners (C), FL, *404*
Whitfield, Sue - Avery Assoc. (R), CA, *9*
Whiting, Anthony - Johnson Smith & Knisely (R), NY, *107*
Whiting, Frank - Cook Assoc.,® Inc. (R), IL, *40*
Whitley, Sue Ann - Roberts Ryan & Bentley, Inc. (R), FL, *179*
Whitley, T. H. - Management Recruiters - Kannapolis (C), NC, *456*
Whitlock, Ann N. - Coleman Lew & Assoc., Inc. (R), NC, *37*
Whitlow, M. Blanton - Manuso, Alexander & Associates, Inc. (R), NY, *135*
Whitney, Jr., Kenneth L. - K. L. Whitney Company (R), NJ, *219*
Whitney, Ron - Sales Consultants of Sacramento (C), CA, *556*

Whitney, William A. - Larsen, Whitney, Blecksmith & Zilliacus, Inc. (R), CA, *125*
Whittaker, Arnold G. - Whittaker & Assoc., Inc. (C), GA, *620*
Whittaker, Cynthia - Brentwood Int'l. (R), CA, *23*
Whittaker-Jhaveri, Michelle A. - The Whittaker Group (C), MI, *620*
Whittier, Richard - The Ransford Group (R), TX, *171*
Whitton, Paula L. - Pearson, Caldwell & Farnsworth (R), NY, *161*
Whyte, Roger J. - The Whyte Group, Inc. (R), MD, *220*
Wichansky, Carole - Tele-Solutions of Arizona, Inc. (C), AZ, *604*
Wicker, David J. - Agri-Personnel (C), GA, *242*
Wieder, Thomas - Management Recruiters of Nassau, Inc. (R), NY, *134*
Wier, Daniel C. - Daniel Wier & Assoc. (R), CA, *220*
Wierichs, Jeffrey C. - TASA International (R), NY, *206*
Wiesenthal, Lauren M. - Corrao, Miller, Rush & Wiesenthal (C), NY, *301*
Wigder, T. Harvey - The Enterprise Group (R), MA, *60*
Wilborn, Missy - Litchfield & Willis, Inc. (R), TX, *130*
Wilbur, John - JFW Associates, LLC (C), CT, *398*
Wilcox, Alex B. - The Bridge (C), CO, *273*
Wilcox, Fred T. - Wilcox Bertoux & Miller (R), CA, *220*
Wilcox, Greg - Orion Int'l. Consulting Group, Inc. (C), NY, *499*
Wilcox, Mark - Marsteller Wilcox Assoc. (C), IL, *471*
Wilcoxen, C. E. - Wilcoxen, Blackwell, Niven & Assoc. (R), FL, *220*
Wilczynski, Tom - O'Keefe & Assoc., Inc. (R), CT, *154*
Wilder, Barry S. - Wilder, Gammel Partners, Ltd. (R), CA, *220*
Wilder, Ben - A. E. Feldman Assoc., Inc. (C), NY, *339*
Wilder, Bruce - Wilder & Assoc. (C), VA, *620*
Wilder, Diana - Wilder & Assoc. (C), VA, *620*
Wilder, Diane - Wilder & Assoc. (C), VA, *620*
Wilder, Mark - International Research Group (R), CA, *103*
Wilensky, Ivy S. - Anderson & Schwab, Inc. (R), NY, *6*
Wilensky, Joel H. - Joel H. Wilensky Assoc., Inc. (C), MA, *620*
Wilfong, Jean - Johnson Brown Assoc., Inc. (C), IN, *400*
Wilkenson, Charles R. - Tecmark Associates Inc. (C), CA, *604*
Wilkerson, Jerry C. - Franchise Recruiters Ltd. (R), IL, *71*
Wilkie, Glenn A. - The Wilkie Group Int'l. (R), ON, *220*
Wilkin, Terry - Management Recruiters - Indianapolis (C), IN, *448*
Wilkins, A. M. - International Research Group (R), CA, *103*
Wilkins, Diana - Lanken-Kimball-Therrell & Assoc. (C), GA, *412*
Wilkins, Sherrie - International Research Group (R), CA, *103*
Wilkins, Sid - International Research Group (R), CA, *103*
Wilkins, Walter K. - Walter K. Wilkins & Co. (R), NJ, *221*
Wilkinson, Ann Trego - Wilkinson SoftSearch, Inc. (C), VA, *621*
Wilkinson, Charla - Norrell Financial Staffing (C), FL, *495*
Wilkinson, Charles - The HRM Group, Inc. (C), AL, *382*
Wilkinson, Frank M. - TSW Assoc., LLC (R), CT, *211*
Wilkinson, Kurt A. - Wilkinson SoftSearch, Inc. (C), VA, *620*
Wilkson, James - Allen Austin Lowe & Powers (R), TX, *3*
Wilkson, James C. - Allen Austin Lowe & Powers (R), FL, *4*
Willbanks, Bret - TTG/Sterling Services (C), CA, *610*
Willcocks, Roy - Dan P. McLean Assoc., Inc. (C), ON, *475*
Willcox, David R. - Senior Careers (R), NY, *188*
Willden, Vincent G. B. - Coast Personnel Services Ltd. (C), BC, *293*
Williams, Aaron - Aaron Consulting, Inc. (C), MO, *232*
Williams, Alexander H. - Witt/Kieffer, Ford, Hadelman & Lloyd (R), NY, *223*
Williams, April M. - The Hollins Group, Inc. (R), IL, *95*
Williams, Bill - Executive Search Consultants Corp. (C), IL, *335*
Williams, Bob - Information Systems Professionals (C), NC, *388*
Williams, Clement W. - High-Tech Recruiters (C), CT, *378*
Williams, Dick - Dick Williams & Assoc. (C), CA, *621*
Williams, Ellen - Search West, Inc. (C), CA, *577*
Williams, Gail - Williams Recruiting, Inc. (C), WA, *621*
Williams, Gary P. - Management Recruiters International, Inc. (MRI) (C), OH, *425*
Williams, Gary P. - Sales Consultants (C), OH, *551*
Williams, Jack R. - Staff Extension Int'l. (C), TX, *590*
Williams, John - Howard/Williams Assoc. (C), FL, *382*
Williams, John G. - John Williams & Assoc. (C), TX, *621*
Williams, John R. - John R. Williams & Assoc., Inc. (C), NC, *621*
Williams, Kandi - Medical Executive Recruiters (C), CA, *477*
Williams, Kenneth C. - Management Recruiters of Champaign (C), IL, *429*
Williams, Larry - Raymond Karsan Assoc. (C), MD, *530*
Williams, Laurelle - MSI Int'l. (C), LA, *487*
Williams, Lee - Woodmoor Group (C), CO, *624*
Williams, Parm - David Powell, Inc. (R), CA, *166*
Williams, Randy L. - Environmental, Health & Safety Search Assoc. (C), FL, *331*
Williams, Richard - Dunhill of St. Petersburg (C), FL, *317*
Williams, Richard - Management Solutions, Inc. (C), CA, *468*
Williams, Roger K. - Williams, Roth & Krueger, Inc. (R), IL, *221*
Williams, Steve - Barton Assoc., Inc. (R), TX, *13*
Williams, Steve - Cypress Int'l., Inc. (R), FL, *45*
Williams, Todd - Management Recruiters of Columbus-Downtown (C), OH, *434*
Williams, Todd - Sales Consultants of Columbus Downtown (C), OH, *555*
Williams, Trish - Interim Accounting Professionals (C), CA, *391*
Williams, Walter E. - LAI Ward Howell (R), MA, *123*
Williams, Wayne - Sales Consultants of Memphis-East (C), TN, *555*
Williams Badanes, Anne - Marketing Search Inc. (C), OH, *471*
Williamson, Bob - Grossberg & Assoc. (R), IL, *82*
Williamson, Frank - Management Recruiters of Westmoreland County, Inc. (C), PA, *459*
Williamson, Joseph R. - Johnson Brown Assoc., Inc. (C), IN, *400*
Willis, Dana - The Corporate Source Group, Inc. (R), MA, *41*
Willis, Francille - Willis & Assoc. (R), OH, *221*
Willis, Jr., William H. - William Willis Worldwide Inc. (R), CT, *221*
Williston, Nada D. - Active Search & Placement Inc. (C), CA, *239*
Willmott, D. Clark - Willmott & Assoc. (C), MA, *622*
Willner, Nannette - S. R. Wolman Assoc., Inc. (R), NY, *224*
Willner, Nathaniel - N. Willner & Co., Inc. (R), NJ, *221*
Wills, James C. - Wills Consulting Assoc. Inc. (R), CT, *222*
Wilmot, Tracey - Bert Davis Executive Search, Inc. (R), NY, *47*
Wilner, Susan - The Alfus Group (R), NY, *3*
Wilson, Akira - Largent Parks & Partners (C), TX, *503*
Wilson, Bill - Tyler & Company (R), PA, *212*
Wilson, Charles K. - Wilson Personnel, Inc. (C), NC, *622*
Wilson, Deborah - Healthcare Recruiters Int'l. - Los Angeles (C), CA, *372*

PRINCIPALS

Wilson, Denver - Sales Consultants of Northwest Arkansas, Inc. (C), AR, *556*
Wilson, Dick - Fox-Morris Assoc., Inc. (C), PA, *352*
Wilson, Donald - Allerton Heneghan & O'Neill (R), IL, *4*
Wilson, Edward - Search Advisors Int'l. Corp. (R), FL, *186*
Wilson, G.H. - Wilson Assoc. Inc. (R), NS, *222*
Wilson, Gordon - Ray & Berndtson/Lovas Stanley (R), ON, *172*
Wilson, Gordon - Ray & Berndtson/Lovas Stanley (R), ON, *172*
Wilson, Harry W. - First Union Executive Search (R), NC, *67*
Wilson, Jeffrey M. - Sales Consultants of Western McHenry County (C), IL, *558*
Wilson, Jim - Wilson Assoc. Inc. (R), NS, *222*
Wilson, Jim - Wilson Assoc. Inc. (R), NF, *222*
Wilson, John T. - Wilson-Douglas-Jordan (C), IL, *622*
Wilson, Mary - Matthews & Stephens Assoc., Inc. (C), CT, *472*
Wilson, Pamela J. - SR Wilson, Inc. (C), CA, *590*
Wilson, Patricia - Global Technologies Group Inc. (C), NC, *359*
Wilson, Patricia L. - Leon A. Farley Assoc. (R), CA, *65*
Wilson, Paul - NorthStar Technologies, Inc. (C), NY, *496*
Wilson, Robert F. - Wilson McLeran, Inc. (C), CT, *622*
Wilson, Steven - Herman Smith Executive Initiatives Inc. (R), ON, *193*
Wilson, Stoney - SR Wilson, Inc. (C), CA, *590*
Wilson, Thomas H. - LAI Ward Howell (R), TX, *124*
Wilson, Wayne - Wilson & Assoc. Int'l. Inc. (C), FL, *622*
Wimberly, Jim - Healthcare Recruiters of Dallas (C), TX, *374*
Wimmer, Walter - The Silicon Network (C), ON, *581*
Winarsky, David - Place Mart Personnel Service (C), NJ, *513*
Wingard, David - Kresin Wingard (C), IL, *409*
Winitsky, Larry - The Richards Group (C), PA, *536*
Winitz, Joel M. - GSW Consulting Group, Inc. (R), CA, *83*
Wink, Cheryl - Sanford Rose Assoc. - Salt Lake City (C), UT, *571*
Winkler, Brad - Whittaker & Assoc., Inc. (C), GA, *620*
Winn, James G. - The Winn Group, Inc. (C), KS, *623*
Winnewisser, William E. - Accounting & Computer Personnel (C), NY, *238*
Winslow, Lawrence J. - DHR Int'l., Inc. (R), CO, *49*
Winston, Dale - Battalia Winston Int'l./The Euram Consultants Group (R), NY, *13*
Winston, Thomas - Winston Search, Inc. (R), MD, *222*
Winter, Peter - Catalyx Group - Canada (R), ON, *31*
Winterburn, Karen - Heartland National Medical Search (C), IL, *374*
Winters, Angela - The Hollins Group, Inc. (R), IL, *95*
Winters, Rebecca - Staffing Edge, Inc. (C), TX, *591*
Winters, Rebecca - Staffing Edge, Inc. (C), TX, *591*
Wisdom, T. J. - Management Recruiters of Fresno (C), CA, *440*
Wise, Annette C. - Clinton, Charles, Wise & Co. (C), FL, *293*
Wise, Craig D. - Clinton, Charles, Wise & Co. (C), FL, *293*
Wise, David E. - Management Recruiters of Hunt Valley (C), MD, *430*
Wise, J. Herbert - TASA International (R), TX, *206*
Wise, Richard - Romac Int'l., Inc. (C), MA, *543*
Wise, Ronald L. - Management Recruiters of Atlanta-South (C), GA, *428*
Wishingrad, Vivian - Bell Wishingrad Partners Inc. (R), NY, *15*
Wishingrad, Vivian - Bell Wishingrad Partners Inc. (R), CT, *15*
Wismar, Daniel - Callos Personnel Services (C), OH, *279*
Wisnewski, Edward J. - Wisnewski & Assoc. (R), CA, *223*
Wissman, Jack P. - LAI Ward Howell (R), FL, *123*
Witt, Gerald E. - The Witt Group (C), FL, *623*
Witt, Stan - Fortune Personnel Consultants of San Antonio, Inc. (C), TX, *350*
Witte, David L. - LAI Ward Howell (R), TX, *124*
Wittebort, Bob - DHR Int'l., Inc. (R), IL, *49*
Wittlin, Brian D. - Brian Assoc., Inc. (C), NY, *273*
Wittner, Jean - Hedlund Corp. (C), IL, *375*
Wlodawsky, Wayne - Romac Int'l., Inc. (C), TX, *544*
Wnek, Ron - The Jotorok Group (C), RI, *401*
Wohl, Sheldon - Sales Consultant of Livingston (C), NJ, *554*
Wojcik, Raymond F. - Management Recruiters The Delta Group, Inc. (C), TN, *461*
Wojdula, Andrew G. - Wojdula & Assoc., Ltd. (R), WI, *223*
Wojdula, Donna - Wojdula & Assoc., Ltd. (R), WI, *223*
Wojdula, Donna M. - Wojdula & Assoc., Ltd. (R), WI, *223*
Wojeik, Christine - Johnson Smith & Knisely (R), IL, *107*
Wolchansky, Beth - Largent Parks & Partners (C), TX, *503*
Wolcott, Tracy - Recruiting Specialists (C), MA, *532*
Wolf, David A. - D. S. Wolf Assoc., Inc. (R), NY, *223*
Wolf, Lisa - Lawrence Glaser Assoc., Inc. (C), NJ, *358*
Wolf, Stephen M. - Byron Leonard Int'l., Inc. (R), CA, *26*
Wolf, Stephen M. - Montenido Assoc. (R), CA, *146*
Wolfe, John R. - Korban Associates (R), PA, *117*
Wolfe, Peter W. - Management Recruiters of Tampa (C), FL, *427*
Wolfram, David A. - EFL Assoc. (R), KS, *57*
Wolfson, Gary M. - The Blackman Kallick Search Division (C), IL, *267*
Wolfson, Robert H. - Mitchell/Wolfson, Assoc. (R), IL, *145*
Wolkensperg, G. Michael - Rushmore • Judge Inc. (R), ON, *183*
Wolman, Steve - S. R. Wolman Assoc., Inc. (R), NY, *224*
Wolohan, Sarah - Cook Assoc.,® Inc. (R), IL, *40*
Wolowicz, Frank - Diversified Management Resources (C), IL, *313*
Wolters, Anthony A. - Management Recruiters of Tulsa (C), OK, *434*
Wolters, Tony A. - Sales Consultants of Tulsa (C), OK, *555*
Woltz, Kenneth A. - Woltz & Assoc., Inc. (R), IL, *224*
Womack, Chris - MESA International (C), OR, *480*
Womak, Joseph - The Bankers Group (C), IL, *258*
Womble, O. J. - Matrix Consultants, Inc. (C), NC, *472*
Wonderfund, Vicky - Management Recruiters of Columbia (C), MD, *450*
Wonderling, Susan - Susan L. Wonderling Recruiting (C), PA, *623*
Wong, Douglas - International Market Recruiters (C), PA, *393*
Wong, Ed - Campbell, Edgar Inc. (C), BC, *280*
Wong, Vera - Hutton Merrill & Assoc. (R), CA, *100*
Woo, Aaron C. - Essential Solutions, Inc. (C), CA, *331*
Wood, Bill - Search Plus Int'l.-Ohio (C), OH, *576*
Wood, Harold - Dunhill of Wichita, Inc. (C), KS, *317*
Wood, John - SpencerStuart (R), NY, *196*
Wood, Karen - Armitage Associates Ltd. (R), ON, *7*
Wood, Louise - Louise Wood & Assoc. (C), NY, *624*
Wood, Martin F. - LAI Ward Howell (R), TX, *124*
Wood, Michael D. - Wood, Franchot Inc. (R), MN, *224*
Wood, Milo - Wood & Assoc./Executive Search Consultants (C), CA, *624*
Wood, Milton M. - M. Wood Company (R), IL, *224*
Wood, N. Lloyd - Corporate Careers, Inc. (C), CA, *299*

Wood, Ray - Management Recruiters of Morgantown (C), WV, *437*
Wood, Ron - Wood West & Partners Inc. (C), BC, *624*
Wood, Steven N. - DHR Int'l., Inc. (R), MO, *50*
Wood, Thomas C. - Trac One (R), NJ, *210*
Wood, William M. - Wood-Glavin, Inc. (R), KS, *224*
Woodard, Angella - Dunhill of New Braunfels (C), TX, *318*
Woodmansee, Bruce - Tully/Woodmansee Int'l., Inc. (R), OH, *212*
Woodruff, Mark S. - Management Recruiters of Paragould (C), AR, *425*
Woods, Bruce Gilbert - Bruce G. Woods Executive Search (R), TX, *224*
Woods, Deborah T. - LAI Ward Howell (R), TX, *124*
Woods, Eleanor - National Metal Services Corp. (C), IN, *489*
Woods, Jacques - Ray & Berndtson/Laurendeau Labrecque (R), QE, *172*
Woods, Jacques - Ray & Berndtson/Laurendeau Labrecque (R), QE, *172*
Woodson, Benjamin N. - Warring & Assoc. (R), TX, *216*
Woodson, Jim - Jim Woodson & Assoc., Inc. (C), MS, *624*
Woodward, Lee - Search Assoc., Inc. (C), CA, *574*
Woodworth, Gail L. - Woodworth Int'l. Group (R), OR, *225*
Woody, Cary - Career Marketing Assoc., Inc. (C), CO, *282*
Wooller, Edmund A. M. - Windsor International (R), GA, *222*
Woolley, Dennis R. - The Wentworth Co., Inc. (R), MI, *217*
Work, Alan J. - Hechkoff/Work Executive Search Inc. (R), NY, *89*
Worrell, Connie - Robert William James & Assoc. (C), OR, *539*
Worth, Anita S. - Prescott Legal Search (C), TX, *517*
Worthing, Ellen - Management Recruiters of the Baltimore Washington Corridor (C), MD, *450*
Worton, Craig - Rylan Forbes Consulting Group, Inc. (C), PA, *549*
Wottowa, Denise - Medical Recruiters Inc. (C), MO, *477*
Wozny, Joy - The Premier Staffing Group (C), OH, *517*
Wozny, Joy - The Premier Staffing Group (C), OH, *517*
Wraith, Bill - David Powell, Inc. (R), CA, *166*
Wray, Dick - Dick Wray & Consultants, Inc. (R), CA, *225*
Wren, Jay - Jay Wren & Assoc. (C), CA, *625*
Wren, Shelly - Sloan & Assoc., Inc. (C), VA, *583*
Wright, Anne B. - Management Recruiters of Pinehurst (C), NC, *433*
Wright, Carl A. J. - Interim Financial Solutions - Mid-Atlantic Region (C), MD, *392*
Wright, Doug - Management Recruiters of Pinehurst (C), NC, *433*
Wright, J. Robert - Bob Wright Recruiting, Inc. (C), CT, *625*
Wright, Jay - The Wright Group (C), TX, *625*
Wright, John - Corporate Image Group (C), TN, *300*
Wright, Leslie - The Stevenson Group, Inc. (N.J.) (R), NJ, *200*
Wright, Linda - Acuity Medical Recruitment (C), MS, *239*
Wright, Paula G. - Tirocchi, Wright, Inc. (R), CA, *209*
Wright, William - Meder & Assoc., Inc. (R), IL, *142*
Wuko, John D. - Pharmaceutical Search Professionals, Inc. (C), PA, *510*
Wyatt, James R. - Wyatt & Jaffe (R), MN, *225*
Wyatt, Robert S. - R. S. Wyatt Assoc., Inc. (R), TX, *225*
Wyche, Ellen Adair - Jon McRae & Associates, Inc. (R), GA, *142*
Wylie, John L. - John Wylie Assoc., Inc. (C), OK, *625*
Wylie, Pamela A. - M. A. Churchill & Assoc., Inc. (R), PA, *35*
Wyman, Michael B. - Martin Partners, L.L.C. (R), IL, *137*
Wynkoop, Mary - Tyler & Company (R), GA, *212*
Wynn, Dennis N. - Dennis Wynn Assoc., Inc. (C), FL, *625*
Wynn, Jean - Dennis Wynn Assoc., Inc. (C), FL, *625*
Wynn, John - Cook Assoc.,® Inc. (R), IL, *40*
Wysocki, Robert - Cornell Group Int'l. Consulting, Inc. (R), NY, *41*
Wysocki, Robert A. - Cornell Group Int'l. (R), CT, *41*
Xagas, Steve - Xagas & Assoc. (R), IL, *226*
Yackel, Doug - Management Recruiters of Spokane (C), WA, *465*
Yacullo, William J. - Lauer, Sbarbaro Assoc., EMA Partners Int'l. (R), IL, *126*
Yaeger, Don - The Century Group (C), CA, *287*
Yager, Jim A. - Sales Consultant of La Costa (C), CA, *551*
Yaiser, Richard A. - The Yaiser Group (C), NJ, *625*
Yakimishyn, Michael - Zen Zen Int'l. Inc. (C), MB, *627*
Yanagi, Hanako - Management Recruiters of Palo Alto (C), CA, *426*
Yarwood, Samantha - Madison MacArthur Inc. (R), ON, *133*
Yeager, Jeffrey A. - Sales Consultants of Lansing-West (C), MI, *553*
Yelverton, Jack R. - Yelverton Executive Search (R), CA, *226*
Yenhana, Kim - Keystone Consulting Group (C), TX, *406*
Yerzik, Rik - Romac Int'l., Inc. (C), UT, *544*
Yorba, Anissa - Professional Healthcare Search & Consultants, Inc. (C), CA, *520*
York, Felecia - Human Resource Dimensions, Inc. (C), TX, *384*
York, Karen - The York Group (C), CA, *626*
Yormak, Stuart I. - Yormak & Assoc. (C), CA, *626*
Yoskowitz, Reggie - Foley Proctor Yoskowitz (R), NJ, *69*
Yossem, Sheila - Bishop Partners (R), NY, *17*
Young, Arthur - Management Recruiters of Stanhope (C), NJ, *432*
Young, Arthur L. - Search South, Inc. (C), AL, *576*
Young, Dennis F. - Tell/Com Recruiters (C), PA, *605*
Young, Doug - Management Recruiters International, Inc. (MRI) (C), OH, *425*
Young, Doug - Sales Consultants (C), OH, *551*
Young, Florence D. - Alexander Enterprises, Inc. (C), PA, *243*
Young, Laurie - Flexible Resources, Inc. (C), CT, *342*
Young, Mark E. - Foster Partners (R), FL, *70*
Young, Monique S. - Blane, Stevens & Kellogg (C), FL, *268*
Young, Monique S. - Blane, Stevens & Kellogg (C), GA, *268*
Young, Nicholas - SpencerStuart (R), NY, *196*
Young, Paula G. - Career Counseling Inc. (CCI) (C), KY, *282*
Young, Philip M. - Ross Personnel Consultants, Inc. (C), CT, *545*
Young, Rich - Chaloner Assoc. (R), MA, *32*
Young, Roy - Flexible Resources, Inc. (C), CA, *342*
Young, Stephanie - Alexander Enterprises, Inc. (C), PA, *243*
Young, Steven J. - Career Counseling Inc. (CCI) (C), KY, *282*
Young, Susan M. - Management Recruiters of Morris County, NJ (C), NJ, *453*
Young, Wayne T. - Management Recruiters of Morris County, NJ (C), NJ, *453*
Young, William H. - Bill Young & Assoc. (C), VA, *626*
Youngberg, Dave - Romac Int'l., Inc. (C), WI, *544*
Youngblood, Ava D. - Deborah Snow Walsh, Inc. (R), IL, *215*
Youngblood, Robert S. - Youngblood Assoc. (C), NC, *626*
Yuhara, Gary - Dunhill Staffing Systems of Santo Clara County (C), CA, *316*
Yungerberg, Steven A. - Steven Yungerberg Assoc., Inc. (R), MN, *226*
Yungner, Steven J. - Healthcare Recruiters Int'l - Minnesota, Inc. (C), MN, *373*
Yungner, Steven J. - Yungner & Bormann (R), MN, *226*
Zabeli, Agim - Barr Assoc. (C), PA, *259*
Zabor, Richard - Leader Institute, Inc. (C), GA, *414*

PRINCIPALS

Zaccaria, Fran - Zaccaria Int'l. (C), NJ, *627*
Zaccaria, Jack - Zaccaria Int'l. (C), NJ, *627*
Zaccaro, Joseph L. - The Human Resource Consulting Group, Inc. (R), CO, *98*
Zackrison, Walter - Zackrison Assoc., Inc. (C), FL, *627*
Zadek, Kate - Johnson Smith & Knisely (R), NY, *107*
Zadfar, Maryanne - The Thomas Tucker Co. (R), CA, *211*
Zaffrann, Craig S. - P. J. Murphy & Assoc., Inc. (R), WI, *150*
Zaharek, John - Management Recruiters of Winsted, Inc. (C), CT, *442*
Zahariades, Didi - Hall Kinion (C), WA, *367*
Zaher, Richard - Fox-Morris Assoc., Inc. (C), NY, *352*
Zahra, Robert F. - Florapersonnel, Inc. (R), FL, *68*
Zahradka, James F. - P. J. Murphy & Assoc., Inc. (R), WI, *150*
Zak, Adam - Horton Int'l. Inc. (R), IL, *96*
Zaleta, Andy R. - A.T. Kearney Executive Search (R), MA, *111*
Zalman, Andrew - Interim Accounting Professionals (C), FL, *392*
Zambito, John - Sales Consultants of Columbus Downtown (C), OH, *555*
Zambito, John R. - Management Recruiters of Columbus-Downtown (C), OH, *434*
Zamborsky, George - Boyden (R), MO, *21*
Zambrana, Fernando - Conasa de Mexico, S.C. (R), MX, *39*
Zambrano, Tony - Accountants On Call (C), DC, *235*
Zamjahn, Charles J. - River Region Personnel, Inc. (C), LA, *538*
Zammataro, Frank - The Zammataro Company (R), OH, *226*
Zander, Craig - Jefferson-Ross Assoc. Inc. (C), PA, *398*
Zanotti, Les V. - Management Recruiters of Omaha (C), NE, *431*
Zapotocky, V. J. - Computer Professionals Unlimited (C), TX, *295*
Zaremski, Michael V. - Romac Int'l. (C), GA, *541*
Zaring, David - Management Recruiters of Plant City, Inc. (C), FL, *444*
Zaring, Judy - Management Recruiters of Plant City, Inc. (C), FL, *444*
Zarkin, Norman - The Zarkin Group, Inc. (R), NY, *226*
Zarnek, Michael R. - First Search Inc. (C), IL, *341*
Zaslav, Debra M. - Telford, Adams & Alexander (R), CA, *208*
Zaslav, Debra M. - Telford, Adams & Alexander (R), CA, *208*
Zawicki, David - Management Recruiters of Passaic County-North (C), NJ, *431*
Zay, Thomas C. - Boyden (R), GA, *21*
Zay, Jr., Thomas C. - Boyden (R), TX, *21*
Zeefe, Herrick A. - Morgenstern Int'l., Inc. (C), FL, *485*
Zegas, Jeffrey M. - Zurick, Davis & Co., Inc. (R), MA, *227*
Zehner, Donna - Dunhill Professional Search of Wilkes-Barre/Scranton, Inc. (C), PA, *322*
Zeif, Kenneth - Newport Management (C), NY, *492*
Zeiger, David Barkin - Zeiger Assoc. L.L.C. (C), CA, *627*
Zeiger, Stephen A. - Zeiger Assoc. L.L.C. (C), CA, *627*
Zeigler, Mark - The Gammill Group, Inc. (C), OH, *354*
Zelezny, Susan - Thomas A. Kelley & Assoc. (R), CA, *112*
Zell, David M. - Logix, Inc. (C), MA, *420*
Zell, David M. - Logix West (C), CA, *420*
Zellerbach, Charles R. - Leon A. Farley Assoc. (R), CA, *65*
Zemper, Ted - Raymond Karsan Assoc. (C), IL, *530*
Zender, Mark - Strategic Resources (C), WA, *595*
Zenner, Teri E. - Zenner Consulting Group (C), IL, *627*
Zenzer, Anne - Witt/Kieffer, Ford, Hadelman & Lloyd (R), IL, *223*
Zera, Ronald J. - SpencerStuart (R), TX, *197*
Zerkle, Sr., John P. - Interactive Search Assoc. (C), PA, *391*
Zetto, Kathryn - Seco & Zetto Assoc., Inc. (C), NJ, *577*
Zevy, Dov - Elan Pratzer & Partners Inc. (R), ON, *167*
Zheng, Rui - PSD Group, Inc. (C), CA, *525*
Ziarko, Jacqueline R. - Selective Search Associates (C), OH, *578*
Ziarko, Michael E. - Selective Search Associates (C), OH, *578*
Ziccardi, Joseph - Cromwell Partners, Inc. (R), NY, *43*
Zickerman, Donna - DRZ Medical Recruiters (C), CO, *315*
Zidwick, Christiana - WTW Assoc., Inc. (R), NY, *225*
Ziegler, Edwin - Hunter Adams (C), NC, *385*
Ziegler, Helen - Helen Ziegler & Assoc., Inc. (C), ON, *627*
Zielazny, William A. - mfg/Search, Inc. (C), OH, *480*
Zier, Patricia D. - P. D. Zier Assoc. (C), CT, *627*
Zilliacus, Patrick W. - Larsen, Whitney, Blecksmith & Zilliacus, Inc. (R), CA, *125*
Zillifro, Keith - Management Recruiters of Roanoke (C), VA, *465*
Ziluck, Scott W. - Management Recruiters of Voorhees (C), NJ, *431*
Zimbehl, Jeanne - D. A. Kreuter Assoc., Inc. (R), PA, *121*
Zimering, Chuck - Chuck Zimering Advertising Recruitment (CZAR) (C), NY, *627*
Zimmer, Walt - Polytechnical Consultants, Inc. (C), IL, *514*
Zimmerman, Arnold - Hollander Horizon Int'l. (R), CA, *95*
Zimmermann, Karl - Fortune Personnel Consultants of Bloomfield, Inc. (C), MI, *346*
Zincavage, David - Cybernautic Corp. (C), CT, *305*
Zingaro, Joe - Preferred Professional Recruiters (C), TX, *516*
Zingaro, Ron - Zingaro & Company (R), TX, *227*
Zinger, Juliana A. - Egon Zehnder Int'l. Inc. (R), NY, *227*
Zink, Al - The Human Resource Consulting Group, Inc. (R), MA, *98*
Zinn, Michael D. - Michael D. Zinn & Assoc., Inc. (R), NY, *227*
Zinn, Michael D. - Michael D. Zinn & Assoc., Inc. (R), NJ, *227*
Zipfel, John - Debbon Recruiting Group, Inc. (C), MO, *310*
Zito, David - Willmott & Assoc. (C), RI, *622*
Zivic, Janis M. - SpencerStuart (R), CA, *196*
Zoldos, Darb - Staffing Edge, Inc. (C), TX, *591*
Zoldos, Darb - Staffing Edge, Inc. (C), TX, *591*
Zona, Henry F. - Zona & Assoc., Inc. (C), NY, *628*
Zonka, Thomas J. - Thomas & Assoc. of Michigan (C), MI, *606*
Zuckerman, Harvey - HLR Consulting (C), NY, *379*
Zukerman, Claire - Corporate Search, Inc. (C), NY, *301*
Zulpo, Darcy - Quest Enterprises, Ltd. (C), IL, *527*
Zuzack, Robert T. - DHR Int'l., Inc. (R), MA, *50*
Zweifler, Rhyan - Boulware & Assoc. Inc. (R), IL, *20*
Zweighaft, Stuart - AES Search (C), NJ, *241*
Zwell, Michael - Zwell Int'l. (R), IL, *228*

Geographical Index

Firms with (R) are from the Retainer Section, which begins on page 1.
Firms with (C) are from the Contingency Section, which begins on page 231.

UNITED STATES

Alabama

Anniston
Search South, Inc. (C), *576*

Athens
First Search America, Inc. (C), *341*

Birmingham
Blanton & Co. (C), *268*
Custom Resources (C), *305*
Dunhill Staffing Systems (C), *316*
Executive Dimensions (R), *62*
Healthcare Recruiters Int'l. - Alabama (C), *372*
The HRM Group, Inc. (C), *382*
Keystone Consulting Group (C), *406*
The Langford Search, Inc. (C), *412*
Management Recruiters of Birmingham (C), *438*
Management Recruiters of Birmingham, Inc. (C), *438*
Management Recruiters of Birmingham-South, Inc. (C), *438*
RHS Assoc. (C), *536*
Sales Consultants of Birmingham (C), *555*
J. L. Small Assoc. (C), *583*
Solutions Group (R), *195*

Daphne
Sales Consultants of Daphne (C), *556*

Decatur
First Search America, Inc. (C), *341*
Management Recruiters of Decatur, LLC (C), *438*

Fairhope
Sanford Rose Assoc. - Fairhope (C), *565*

Huntsville
Fortune Personnel Consultants of Huntsville, Inc. (C), *343*
The HRM Group, Inc. (C), *383*
Management Recruiters of North Alabama (C), *425*
Personnel, Inc. (C), *508*
Snelling Search (C), *585*

Mobile
Clark Personnel Service, Inc. (C), *292*
Halo Insurance Service (C), *367*
Hughes & Assoc. Int'l. Inc. (C), *383*
Management Recruiters of Mobile Co., Inc. (C), *438*
Sales Consultant of Mobile (C), *551*
Sanford Rose Assoc. - Mobile (C), *565*

Montgomery
Locke & Assoc. (R), *131*

Pointe Clear
Alpha Executive Search (C), *245*

Wetumpka
RHS Assoc. (C), *536*

Alaska

Anchorage
Alaska Executive Search, Inc. (C), *243*

Kenai
Management Recruiters of South Central Alaska (C), *425*

Arizona

Carefree
Pinnacle Group Int'l. (C), *512*

Chandler
Mortgage Search Network (C), *486*

Flagstaff
Columbia Consulting Group (R), *38*

Fountain Hills
Rand-Curtis Resources (C), *529*

Glendale
Elliot Assoc. Inc. (R), *58*

Goodyear
Sampson Medical Search (C), *564*

Green Valley
Medical Recruiters Exchange (C), *477*

Lake Havasu City
Search By Design (C), *574*
Unisearch Search & Recruiting Inc. (C), *611*

Mesa
Accountants On Call (C), *235*
Behavioral Science Assoc., Inc. (R), *15*
Hall Kinion (C), *366*
Precision Executive Search (C), *516*

Nogales
Management Recruiters of Nogales (C), *425*

Peoria
McCormack & Farrow (R), *140*

Phoenix
Accountants On Call (C), *235*
Accounting & Bookkeeping Personnel, Inc. (C), *237*
Career Strategies, Inc. (C), *283*
Cizek Assoc., Inc. (R), *35*
DHR Int'l., Inc. (R), *49*
Family-Business Roundtable, Inc. (R), *65*
Fishel HR Assoc., Inc. (C), *341*
G. H. Enterprises (C), *354*
Phyllis Hawkins & Assoc., Inc. (C), *370*
Healthcare Recruiters Int'l. Phoenix (C), *372*
Henson Partners (C), *376*
Hyland Executive Search (C), *386*
A.T. Kearney Executive Search (R), *111*
LAI Ward Howell (R), *123*
Market Niche Consulting (C), *470*
DDJ Myers, Ltd. (R), *150*
Norrell Financial Staffing (C), *495*
PERC, Ltd. (C), *506*
Personnel Solutions (C), *509*
Professional Team Search, Inc. (R), *169*
Romac Int'l., Inc. (C), *542*
SSA Executive Search Int'l. (R), *198*
Staffing Edge, Inc. (C), *590*
Techstaff Inc. (C), *603*
TSS Consulting, Ltd. (C), *610*
Robert H. Wadsworth & Assoc., Inc. (R), *214*
Waveland Int'l. (R), *216*
Witt/Kieffer, Ford, Hadelman & Lloyd (R), *223*

Scottsdale
Austin Michaels, Ltd., Inc. (C), *256*
Bartholdi & Co., Inc. (R), *12*
D. R. Blood & Assoc. (R), *18*
The Bren Group (C), *273*
The Chapman Group, Inc. (C), *289*
Corporate Dynamix (C), *300*
The Dorfman Group (C), *314*
Dynamic Computer Consultants, Inc. (C), *324*
EFL Int'l. (R), *57*
Hospitality Int'l. (C), *381*
LCC Companies (C), *414*
Reynolds Lebus Assoc. (C), *415*
Scott Love Assoc., Inc. (C), *420*
Managed Care Consultants (C), *423*
Managed Care Consultants (C), *424*
Management Consultants Corporate Recruiters (C), *424*
Management Recruiters of Scottsdale (C), *425*
Mark Christian & Assoc., Inc. (C), *469*
National Career Search (C), *489*
Pearson & Assoc., Inc. (C), *506*
Roberson & Co. (C), *538*
The Rubicon Group (C), *547*
Sales Consultant of Scottsdale-Metro (C), *551*
Sales Consultants of Scottsdale, Inc. (C), *556*
Saviar, Inc. (C), *571*
Spectra International LLC (C), *589*
Swartz & Assoc., Inc. (R), *204*
Tele-Solutions of Arizona, Inc. (C), *604*
VZ Int'l., Inc. (C), *613*
Weinman & Assoc. (C), *617*

Sedona
Management Recruiters of Sedona (C), *438*
Search Masters Int'l. (R), *187*

Show Low
Quality Search (C), *526*

Tempe
R & K Associates, Inc. (C), *527*
Richard, Wayne & Roberts (C), *536*
Southwest Search & Consulting, Inc. (C), *588*

Tucson
Accounting & Bookkeeping Personnel, Inc. (C), *238*
The Caplan-Taylor Group (R), *28*
CS Associates, LLC (C), *304*
James Feerst & Assoc., Inc. (C), *339*
Industry Consultants, Inc. (C), *388*

GEOGRAPHICAL

Management Recruiters Tucson-Foothills, Inc. (C), *439*
Management Recruiters of Tucson (C), *439*
Medical Executive Search Assoc., Inc. (C), *477*
Smith, Roth & Squires (R), *194*

Arkansas

Bentonville
Snelling Search - Transportation Division (C), *585*

Fayetteville
Sales Consultants of Northwest Arkansas, Inc. (C), *556*

Hot Springs Village
MDR & Associates (C), *476*
RBW Assoc. Inc. (C), *531*

Jasper
O'Keefe & Assoc. (C), *498*

Little Rock
Alynco, Inc. (C), *246*
EDP Staffing Solutions, Inc. (C), *327*
Executive Recruiters Agency, Inc. (C), *333*
Human Resources Personnel Agency (R), *99*
Management Recruiters of Little Rock (C), *439*
SearchOne, Inc. (C), *577*

Maumelle
Herring & Assoc. (C), *376*

Paragould
Management Recruiters of Paragould (C), *425*

Rogers
Management Recruiters of Rogers (C), *425*

California

Agoura Hills
F. B. Schmidt Int'l. (R), *185*

Alameda
Deborah Bishop & Assoc. (R), *17*

Alhambra
D.R. Assoc. (R), *45*

Alturas
Bolton Group (C), *269*

Anaheim
Health Search (C), *371*

Anaheim Hills
Warring & Assoc. (R), *215*

Aptos
Management Recruiters of Aptos (C), *439*

Arcadia
K & C Assoc. (C), *402*

Atascadero
Management Recruiters of San Luis Obispo (C), *439*

Ballico
Multisearch Recruiters (C), *487*

Belmont
The Simmons Group (C), *582*

Benicia
Dunhill Profesisonal Search of North San Francisco Bay (C), *316*

Berkeley
Management Recruiters of Berkeley (C), *439*

Beverly Hills
Allied Search, Inc. (C), *245*
Blue Chip Law Consulting, Inc. (C), *268*
Elliot Assoc. Inc. (R), *58*
Fairfield Int'l. Resources (R), *65*
Global 1000 Int'l. Services (C), *358*
Groenekamp & Assoc. (C), *363*
Morgan Samuels Co. (R), *147*

Boulder Creek
Key Resources Int'l. (C), *405*

Brea
L & L Assoc. (C), *410*
Larson Assoc. (R), *125*

Buena Park
Dianne Gauger & Assoc. (C), *355*

Burbank
Accountants On Call (C), *235*
West Coast Recruiting (C), *619*

Burlingame
Management Recruiters Peninsula (C), *439*
Sales Consultants Peninsula, Inc. (C), *556*

Calabasas
Fred Hood & Assoc. (C), *380*
Montenido Assoc. (R), *146*
Mortgage & Financial Personnel Services (C), *486*
Profit Pros, Inc. (C), *523*
Zeiger Assoc. L.L.C. (C), *627*

Campbell
The Bradbury Management Group, Inc. (R), *21*
Dunhill Staffing Systems of Santo Clara County (C), *316*
Dunhill Professional Search of San Jose (C), *319*
Essential Solutions, Inc. (C), *331*

Canoga Park
Independent Resource Systems (C), *388*

Capistrano Beach
Executive Resource Systems (C), *335*

Capitola
Hall Kinion (C), *366*

Carlsbad
Accountants On Call (C), *235*
Fell & Nicholson Technology Resources (R), *66*
Intech Summit Group (R), *102*
McKavis Assoc. (C), *475*
National Search Assoc. (C), *490*
Robert Beech West Inc. (C), *262*
Sales Consultant of La Costa (C), *551*
Technology Consultants Int'l. (C), *603*

Carmel
J. H. Dugan & Assoc., Inc. (R), *55*

Castro Valley
M.C. Executive Search (C), *422*

Chatsworth
Hermann & Westmore (R), *92*
Lifter & Assoc. (C), *418*
Al Ponaman Company, Inc. (C), *514*

Chico
Management Recruiters of Chico (C), *425*
Sales Consultants of Chico (C), *556*

Chino
Professional Healthcare Search & Consultants, Inc. (C), *520*

Citrus Heights
IR Search (R), *103*
MESA International (C), *480*

City of Industry
Accountants On Call (C), *235*
The Truman Agency (C), *610*

Clovis
Carver Search Consultants (C), *285*
Management Recruiters of North Fresno (C), *425*
Management Recruiters of Clovis (C), *440*

Coarsegold
International Research Group (R), *103*

Corte Madera
Schweichler Assoc., Inc. (R), *186*

Costa Mesa
CBA Companies (C), *286*
McCormack & Farrow (R), *140*
Norrell Financial Staffing (C), *495*
Pacific Crossing (C), *501*
Resource Perspectives, Inc. (R), *175*
The Rogan Group, Inc. (C), *541*
G. L. Smith Assoc. (C), *584*
Telford, Adams & Alexander (R), *208*
Telford, Adams & Alexander (R), *208*
Lee Weil Assoc., Inc. (C), *617*

Culver City
Management Recruiters of Los Angeles-Culver City (C), *425*
Norrell Financial Staffing (C), *495*
Sales Consultant of Los Angeles-Culver City (C), *551*

Cupertino
Brigade, Inc. (R), *23*
Christian & Timbers, Inc. (R), *34*
Hall Kinion (C), *366*
Tecmark Associates Inc. (C), *604*

Dana Point
Management Recruiters Dana Point (C), *440*

Danville
The Badger Group (R), *10*
The Hindman Group, Inc. (C), *378*

Davis
Abbott Associates (R), *1*
Management Recruiters of Davis (C), *425*

Del Mar
Jeffrey Allan Co., Inc. (C), *398*
Carolyn Smith Paschal Int'l. (R), *160*
Warren, Morris & Madison, Ltd. (C), *616*

El Dorado Hills
Management Recruiters of El Dorado Hills (C), *425*

El Segundo
D.P. Specialists, Inc. (C), *306*

Emeryville
Management Recruiters of Emeryville (C), *440*
Witt/Kieffer, Ford, Hadelman & Lloyd (R), *223*

Encinitas
Elsie Chan & Assoc. (C), *289*
F-O-R-T-U-N-E Personnel Consultants of San Diego (C), *344*
Systems Research Group (C), *598*
Woodworth Int'l. Group (R), *225*

Encino
DNA Search, Inc. (C), *313*
Healthcare Executive Recruiters, Inc. (C), *372*
LAI Ward Howell (R), *123*
Management Recruiters of Los Angeles-Encino (C), *425*
Sales Consultant of Los Angeles-Encino (C), *551*
The Shotland Group (R), *190*

Fair Oaks
Rowland Assoc. (C), *547*
K. K. Walker Professional Recruitment (C), *614*

Foster City
Omnisearch Assoc. (C), *499*

Freedom
Doering & Assoc. (C), *313*

Fremont
Allen Austin Lowe & Powers (R), *4*
Edward Bell Assoc. (C), *263*
Johnson Smith & Knisely (R), *107*
Management Recruiters of Fremont (C), *425*
McCoy Ltd. (C), *474*
The Oldani Group (R), *155*
SpectraWest (C), *589*

Fresno
Management Recruiters of Fresno (C), *440*
Cedric L. Reese Inc. (C), *533*
Sales Consulant of Fresno (C), *551*

Selective Staffing (C), *579*
Sherwood Lehman Massucco, Inc. (R), *189*

Ft. Bragg
Claimsearch (C), *291*

Fullerton
The J. B. Search Group (C), *395*
Paules Associates (C), *505*

Garden Grove
Bridgecreek Personnel Agency (C), *273*

Gardena
Romac Int'l., Inc. (C), *542*

Glen Ellen
The Domann Organization (R), *53*

Glendale
Med Exec Int'l. (C), *476*

Glendora
Management Recruiters of Glendora (C), *425*
Oscar Montaño, Inc. (R), *146*

Granite Bay
The Elmhurst Group (C), *329*
Genesis Recruiting (C), *356*

Grass Valley
Management Recruiters of Grass Valley (C), *440*
Nyborg•Dow Assoc., Inc. (C), *497*

Greenbrae
Eagle Search Assoc. (C), *325*
Ethos Consulting, Inc. (R), *61*
Pierce & Crow (R), *164*

Half Moon Bay
Colucci, Blendow & Johnson (R), *38*
Perry-D'Amico & Assoc. (R), *162*

Hermosa Beach
Fortune Personnel Consultants (C), *344*
Raymond Karsan Assoc. (C), *529*

Huntington Beach
Commercial Programming Systems, Inc. (C), *294*
Mason & Nicrasti Ltd. (R), *138*
NJ Solutions (C), *493*
Watring & Assoc., Inc. (C), *616*

Inglewood
The Century Group (C), *287*

Irvine
ACCESS Technology (C), *234*
Active Search & Placement Inc. (C), *239*
Asset Resource, Inc. (C), *254*
Avestruz & Assoc. (C), *257*
Blue Chip Law Consulting, Inc. (C), *268*
Tom Bogle & Assoc. (C), *269*
Boyle/Ogata Executive Search (R), *21*
BridgeGate LLC (C), *273*
California Search Agency, Inc. (C), *279*
Career Strategies, Inc. (C), *283*
The Century Group (C), *287*
The Coelyn Group (R), *37*
DHR Int'l., Inc. (R), *49*

Dunhill Professional Search of irvine/Newport (C), *316*
EMN/Witt/Kieffer (R), *59*
Barry M. Gold & Co. (C), *359*
Heidrick & Struggles, Inc. (R), *90*
Heritage Pacific Corp. (C), *376*
Human Resource Bureau (C), *384*
Interim Accounting Professionals (C), *391*
International Staffing Consultants, Inc. (C), *393*
Korn/Ferry Int'l. (R), *117*
John Kurosky & Assoc. (R), *122*
Legal Network Inc. (C), *416*
J. H. Lindell & Co. (C), *418*
Lucas Assoc. (C), *421*
Management Search Int'l. (C), *467*
MCS Assoc. (R), *142*
Pacific Finance Search, Inc. (C), *501*
Pierce & Assoc. (C), *512*
Romac Int'l., Inc. (C), *542*
Sales Consultant of Irvine (C), *551*
TriStaff Group (C), *609*
Vaughan & Co. (C), *612*
D. L. Weiss & Assoc. (R), *217*
Witt/Kieffer, Ford, Hadelman & Lloyd (R), *223*

Kelseyville
Horizons Unlimited (C), *381*

Kenwood
Levison Search Assoc. (R), *129*

La Jolla
Alfred Daniels & Assoc., Inc. (R), *46*
Don Allan Assoc., Inc. (C), *313*
E T Search Inc. (C), *324*

La Palma
Accountants On Call (C), *235*

La Quinta
The Black Leopard (C), *267*
William C. Houze & Co. (R), *96*
Kopplin Search, Inc. (R), *117*
O'Keefe & Assoc., Inc. (R), *154*

Lafayette
Dunhill Professional Search of Oakland (C), *319*

Laguna Beach
Atlantic Pacific Group (C), *255*
Sanford Rose Assoc. - Laguna Beach (C), *565*

Laguna Hills
Management Recruiters of Laguna Hills (C), *440*
Newport Strategic Search LLC (C), *492*
Opus Marketing (R), *156*
Martin Stevens Tamaren & Assoc., Inc. (R), *206*
Victor White Int'l. (C), *612*
WestPacific National Search, Inc. (C), *619*

Laguna Niguel
D. S. Allen Assoc. (C), *244*
Allen-Jeffers Assoc. (C), *245*
MetroVantage Personnel Systems (C), *480*

GEOGRAPHICAL

Lake Forest
Barrett Hospitality Search (R), *12*

Lakeport
California Management Search (C), *279*

Lakewood
Rollins & Assoc. (C), *541*

Larkspur
Wood & Assoc./Executive Search Consultants (C), *624*

Livermore
Automation Technology Search (C), *257*

Lomita
Wayne S. Chamberlain & Assoc. (C), *288*

Long Beach
Yormak & Assoc. (C), *626*

Los Altos
The Bauman Group (R), *14*
Busch International (R), *25*
The Caplan-Taylor Group (R), *28*
Flesher & Assoc., Inc. (R), *68*
Furlong Search, Inc. (R), *72*
Hockett Associates, Inc. (R), *94*
Johnson & Assoc., Inc. (R), *106*
Katherine R. Kraemer (R), *120*
Probus Executive Search (C), *519*
Technology Management Partners (R), *208*

Los Angeles
A Permanent Success Employment Services (C), *231*
Accountants On Call (C), *235*
Alexander & Collins (C), *243*
ASI (C), *254*
Bast & Assoc., Inc. (C), *261*
Battalia Winston Int'l./The Euram Consultants Group (R), *13*
Bench Int'l. Search, Inc. (R), *15*
Berkhemer/Clayton, Inc. (R), *16*
Billington & Assoc. (R), *17*
BowersThomas (C), *271*
Jerold Braun & Assoc. (C), *272*
Brentwood Int'l. (R), *23*
BridgeGate LLC (C), *273*
Bristol Assoc., Inc. (C), *274*
Brown, Bernardy, Van Remmen, Inc. (C), *275*
Cadillac Assoc. (C), *279*
Robert Caldwell & Assoc. (R), *26*
Career Strategies, Inc. (C), *283*
Career Strategies, Inc. (C), *283*
Carson-Thomas & Assoc. (C), *284*
Chrisman & Co. Inc. (R), *33*
CJA-The Adler Group, Inc. (R), *35*
Colt Systems Professional Personnel Services (C), *294*
Commercial Programming Systems, Inc. (C), *294*
Corporate Dynamix (C), *300*
The Corporate Source Group, Inc. (R), *41*
DHR Int'l., Inc. (R), *49*
Discovery, The Staffing Specialists, Inc. (C), *312*
Dunhill Executive Search of Los Angeles, Inc. (C), *319*
Executive Careers (R), *62*
Flexible Resources, Inc. (C), *342*
Barry Goldberg & Assoc., Inc. (C), *360*
Ben Greco Assoc., Inc. (C), *362*
The Hawkins Co. (R), *88*
Healthcare Search Associates (C), *374*
Heidrick & Struggles, Inc. (R), *90*
Hochman & Assoc. (C), *379*
HRCS (R), *97*
The Jameson Group (C), *397*
Ronald S. Johnson Assoc., Inc. (R), *107*
Johnson Smith & Knisely (R), *107*
Kass/Abell & Assoc., Inc. (C), *404*
A.T. Kearney Executive Search (R), *111*
Kenzer Corp. (R), *113*
Korn/Ferry Int'l. (R), *117*
Evie Kreisler Assoc. Inc. (C), *409*
Marvin Laba & Assoc. (R), *122*
The LaBorde Group (C), *411*
LAI Ward Howell (R), *123*
Larsen, Whitney, Blecksmith & Zilliacus, Inc. (R), *125*
Lipson & Co. (R), *130*
Management Recruiters of Santa Monica (C), *426*
Brad Marks Int'l. (R), *136*
J. Martin & Assoc. (R), *137*
K. E. McCarthy & Assoc. (R), *139*
McCormack & Assoc. (R), *140*
McCray, Shriver, Eckdahl & Assoc., Inc. (R), *140*
The Medley Group (C), *477*
Ober & Company (R), *155*
The Odessa Group (R), *155*
Pacific Search Group, Inc. (C), *501*
Pioneer Consulting Group (C), *512*
Poirier, Hoevel & Co. (R), *166*
Ray & Berndtson (R), *172*
Russell Reynolds Assoc., Inc. (R), *176*
Rivera Legal Search, Inc. (C), *538*
Norman Roberts & Assoc., Inc. (R), *179*
Rollo Assoc. (R), *181*
Romac Int'l., Inc. (C), *542*
Ryan, Miller & Assoc. (C), *549*
Search Group (C), *575*
Search West, Inc. (C), *576*
Seltzer Fontaine Beckwith (C), *579*
Silver Associates (C), *581*
Smith & Assoc. (C), *583*
Andrea Sobel & Assoc., Inc. (C), *586*
SpencerStuart (R), *196*
Stanton Chase Int'l. (R), *199*
Technical Connections, Inc. (C), *601*
TTG/Sterling Services (C), *610*
Van Leeuwen Assoc. (R), *213*
Villasenor & Assoc. (C), *612*
Waldorf Associates, Inc. (C), *614*
Western Management Assoc. (R), *218*
Daniel Wier & Assoc. (R), *220*
Wilder, Gammel Partners, Ltd. (R), *220*
Egon Zehnder Int'l. Inc. (R), *227*

Los Gatos
The Advisory Group, Inc. (R), *2*
Avery Assoc. (R), *9*
Management Recruiters of Los Gatos (C), *426*
Splaine & Assoc., Inc. (R), *198*
Western Technical Resources (C), *619*
Dick Wray & Consultants, Inc. (R), *225*
Yelverton Executive Search (R), *226*

Malibu
Careers Plus (R), *29*
Marshall Consultants, Inc. (R), *137*
Musick & Assoc. (C), *487*
The York Group (C), *626*

Manhattan Beach
DBL Associates (C), *309*
Fisher Personnel Management Services (R), *68*
Greger/Peterson Assoc., Inc. (R), *81*
Thor, Inc. (C), *606*

Menlo Park
Ames & Ames (R), *5*
Brown Venture Assoc. (R), *24*
Heidrick & Struggles, Inc. (R), *90*
Thomas A. Kelley & Assoc. (R), *112*
Management Recruiters of Menlo Park (C), *426*
Russell Reynolds Assoc., Inc. (R), *176*
SpencerStuart (R), *196*
The Ultimate Source (R), *212*

Mill Valley
J: Blakslee Int'l., Ltd. (R), *18*
Block & Assoc. (R), *18*
Management Recruiters of Northern California (C), *440*
MK & Assoc. (R), *146*
Shannahan & Co., Inc. (R), *189*
Wilkinson & Ives (R), *221*

Milpitas
Hall Kinion (C), *366*

Mission Viejo
Computer Network Resources, Inc. (C), *295*
Healthcare Recruiters Int'l. Orange County (C), *372*
JPM International (C), *401*

Modesto
Automation Technology Search (C), *256*
Ortman Recruiting Int'l. (C), *500*

Monarch Beach
Sales Management Resources (C), *563*

Monterey
David Fockler & Assoc., Inc. (C), *342*
Management Recruiters of Monterey (C), *441*

Morro Bay
Management Recruiters of Morro Bay (C), *426*

Moss Beach
Ballantyne & Assoc. (R), *10*

Mountain View
Hall Kinion (C), *366*
Software Engineering Solutions, Inc. (C), *586*

Murrieta
Bartholdi & Co., Inc. (R), *12*

Napa
Perry Search Assoc. (C), *507*

Nevada City
Kremple Consulting Group (R), *120*

Newhall
McCoy Ltd. (C), *474*

Newport Beach
Accountants On Call (C), *235*
Barnes & Assoc. Executive Search (C), *259*
CCI - Career Consultants Int'l. (C), *286*
Corporate Careers, Inc. (C), *299*
Davis & Company (R), *47*
Drake & Assoc. (C), *315*
The Gobbell Co. (R), *78*
Hemingway Personnel, Inc. (C), *375*
Lipsky Group, Inc. (R), *129*
Miller-Hall HRISearch (C), *482*
O'Shea, Divine & Co., Inc. (R), *154*
Robert Ottke Assoc. (R), *157*
Romac Int'l., Inc. (C), *542*
Vlcek & Company, Inc. (R), *214*
Dick Wray & Consultants, Inc. (R), *225*

Norco
Presley Consultants, Inc. (C), *517*

Northridge
AGRI-associates (C), *242*
Furlong Search, Inc. (R), *72*
Healthcare Search Associates (C), *374*
J. J. Herlihy & Assoc., Inc. (C), *376*

Novato
Maczkov-Biosciences, Inc. (R), *133*
Search Solutions Inc. (C), *576*

Oakland
Accountants On Call (C), *235*
Bennett & Co. Consulting Group (C), *264*
CRI Professional Search (C), *303*
Fresquez & Assoc. (C), *352*
Infovia (C), *388*
Management Recruiters of Oakland (C), *426*
Riley Cole (C), *537*
Sales Consultants Int'l. of Oakland (C), *556*

Ojai
Financialjobs.com (C), *340*

Ontario
Search West, Inc. (C), *577*

Orange
Clanton & Co. (C), *292*
Discovery, The Staffing Specialists, Inc. (C), *312*
Fox-Morris Assoc., Inc. (C), *352*
Management Recruiters of Orange (C), *426*
Frank Parillo & Assoc. (R), *159*
Physicians Search®, Inc. (C), *511*
Professional Search Assoc. (C), *522*
Recruitment Resources (C), *532*
Sales Consultant of Orange (C), *551*
Search West, Inc. (C), *577*
Unisearch Search & Recruiting Inc. (C), *611*

Oxnard
Techstaff Inc. (C), *603*

Pacific Grove
Cameron Consulting Group (R), *27*
Stillinger & Assoc. (R), *201*

Pacific Palisades
Hill & Assoc. (C), *378*
Kremple & Meade, Inc. (R), *120*

Palm Canyon
Robert Beech West Inc. (C), *262*

Palm Desert
Shey-Harding Assoc. Inc. (C), *580*

Palm Springs
Cadillac Assoc. (C), *278*
Thomas Mangum Co. (R), *208*

Palo Alto
Accountants On Call (C), *235*
C. R. Assoc. (C), *278*
DHR Int'l., Inc. (R), *49*
Fell & Nicholson Technology Resources (R), *65*
Gent & Assoc. (C), *356*
Haley Associates (R), *85*
Hutton Merrill & Assoc. (R), *100*
International Research Group (R), *103*
Kaufman Assoc. (R), *110*
Major, Hagen & Africa (C), *423*
Management Recruiters of Palo Alto (C), *426*
Donovan Martin & Assoc. (R), *137*
Ray & Berndtson, Inc. (R), *172*
Rusher, Loscavio & LoPresto (R), *183*
TASA International (R), *206*
The Thomas Tucker Co. (R), *212*
Egon Zehnder Int'l. Inc. (R), *227*

Palos Verdes Estates
Finnegan & Assoc. (R), *67*

Pasadena
Gary Kaplan & Assoc. (R), *109*
Morris & Berger (R), *147*
Ott & Hansen, Inc. (R), *157*
Protocol Inc. (C), *525*
L. J. Quinn & Assoc., Inc. (R), *170*
The Repovich-Reynolds Group (TRRG, Inc.) (R), *175*
Ryan, Miller & Assoc. (C), *549*
Sales Management Resources (C), *563*
Thomas Mangum Co. (R), *208*

Petaluma
Ensearch Management Consultants (C), *331*
Executive Search Consultants (C), *335*
Management Recruiters of Sonoma (C), *441*

Pismo Beach
Management Recruiters of Pismo Beach (C), *426*

Placentia
Robert Powers & Assoc. (C), *515*

Playa Del Rey
Jerome & Co. (C), *398*

Pleasant Hill
Management Recruiters of Pleasant Hill (C), *426*

Pleasanton
Accountants On Call (C), *235*
Daggett & Kvistad (R), *45*
Management Recruiters of Pleasanton (C), *441*
Predictor Systems Corp. (R), *167*
Sales Consultant of Pleasanton (C), *551*
Thompson Assoc. (C), *606*
Dick Williams & Assoc. (C), *621*

Portola Valley
Strategic Alternatives (R), *202*
Strategic Alternatives (R), *202*

Poway
Agriesti & Assoc. (C), *243*

Ramona
Scott Douglas Inc. (C), *573*

Rancho Cordova
Smartsource Inc. (C), *583*

Rancho Mirage
GWS Partners (R), *84*

Redlands
Management Recruiters, Inland Empire Agency (C), *441*

Redondo Beach
Neil Frank & Co. (R), *71*
Hollander Horizon Int'l. (R), *95*
Morgenstern Int'l., Inc. (C), *485*
Professional Recruiting Network (C), *521*
Quest Worldwide Executive Search Corp. (C), *527*

Redwood City
Korn/Ferry Int'l. (R), *117*
Peden & Assoc. (C), *506*
J. R. Phillip & Assoc., Inc. (R), *164*
Romac Int'l., Inc. (C), *542*

Redwood Shores
A.T. Kearney Executive Search (R), *111*

Reseda
Lynn Borne & Co. (C), *270*

Riverside
Accountants On Call (C), *235*
MacNaughton Assoc. (R), *133*
W. P. Assoc. (C), *613*

Roseville
Management Recruiters of Roseville (C), *441*
Medical Executive Recruiters (C), *477*
Tirocchi, Wright, Inc. (R), *209*

Ross
A. William Smyth, Inc. (R), *194*

Sacramento
Accountants On Call (C), *235*

Ashford Management Group, Inc. (R), *8*
David M. Griffith & Assoc., Ltd. (R), *82*
Management Recruiters of Sacramento North (C), *441*
New Dawn Employment Search (C), *491*
Wilson Riles & Assoc., Inc. (R), *178*
Sales Consultants of Sacramento (C), *556*
Wilcox Bertoux & Miller (R), *220*
Jay Wren & Assoc. (C), *625*

Salinas
Marlene Critchfield Co. (C), *303*
MIXTEC Group (R), *146*
Larry Moore & Assoc. (C), *484*

San Anselmo
Herrerias & Assoc. (R), *92*
Oak Assoc. (R), *155*

San Bruno
Logix West (C), *420*

San Carlos
Devoto & Assoc. (C), *312*
The Norland Group (C), *494*

San Clemente
Open Concepts (C), *499*
Personnel Assoc. (C), *508*
Strategic Search, LLC (C), *595*

San Diego
Accountants On Call (C), *235*
The Alexander Group (R), *3*
Dick Berg & Assoc. (C), *264*
Brystol Cove Assoc. (R), *24*
Creative-Leadership, Inc. (R), *42*
Culver Personnel Services (C), *304*
DHR Int'l., Inc. (R), *49*
Eastridge Infotech (C), *326*
The Executive Group, Inc. (R), *62*
Gavin Forbes & Price (R), *75*
Global Resources Group (R), *78*
GSW Consulting Group, Inc. (R), *83*
Michael R. Guerin Co. (C), *364*
Harmeling & Associates (C), *369*
Highland & Assoc. (C), *378*
Icon Recruiters, LLC (C), *387*
Innovative Partnerships (R), *101*
Intech Summit Group, Inc. (R), *102*
Interim Accounting Professionals (C), *391*
Job Link, Inc. (C), *399*
Roye Johnston Assoc., Inc. (C), *400*
A.T. Kearney Executive Search (R), *111*
LaCosta & Assoc. Int'l. Inc. (C), *411*
Management Recruiters of San Diego (C), *426*
Millennium Search Group, Inc. (R), *144*
Myers Career Assoc., Inc. (C), *488*
Beverly Nelson & Assoc. Inc. (C), *491*
Orion Int'l. Consulting Group, Inc. (C), *499*
Bob Poline Assoc. Inc. (C), *514*
PRO, Inc./Professional Recruiting Offices, Inc. (C), *519*
Proven Edge (C), *525*
Radosevic Assoc. (R), *171*
Romac Int'l., Inc. (C), *542*
Ryan-Allen & Assoc., Inc. (C), *549*
Sales Consultant of La Jolla (C), *551*
Sales Consultant of San Diego (C), *551*
The Search Network (C), *576*
Sears & Associates (C), *577*
Shelton, Wiseman & Leon (R), *189*
SignatureSoft Inc. (C), *581*
Spectrum Consultants (R), *196*
Stafford Consulting Group (R), *198*
Stanton Chase Int'l. (R), *199*
Judy Thompson & Assoc., Inc. (C), *606*
TriStaff Group (C), *609*
R. J. Watkins & Co., Ltd. (R), *216*
West & West (R), *218*

San Francisco
Accountancies (C), *234*
Accountants On Call (C), *235*
Accounting Additions (C), *238*
Alexander & Co. (C), *243*
The Alexander Group (R), *3*
Allard Associates (C), *244*
Allied Search, Inc. (C), *245*
Amato & Assoc., Inc. (C), *246*
Argonaut Partners, LLC (R), *6*
J. S. Armstrong & Assoc., Inc. (R), *7*
Battalia Winston Int'l./The Euram Consultants Group (R), *13*
Edward Bell Assoc. (C), *263*
Berger & Leff (C), *264*
BioQuest Inc. (R), *17*
Boyden (R), *20*
Bullis & Co., Inc. (R), *25*
Colton Bernard Inc. (R), *37*
Columbia Consulting Group (R), *38*
Bert Davis Executive Search, Inc. (R), *47*
DHR Int'l., Inc. (R), *49*
Dominguez-Metz & Assoc. (R), *53*
Dunhill of San Francisco, Inc. (C), *319*
Eastridge Infotech (C), *326*
Executive Direction, Inc. (C), *333*
Leon A. Farley Assoc. (R), *65*
Neil Fink Assoc. (R), *66*
Garrison-Randall, Inc. (R), *75*
Garrison-Randall, Inc. (R), *75*
Geneva Group Int'l. (R), *76*
Robert Grant Assoc., Inc. (C), *361*
Grauss & Co. (C), *362*
Heidrick & Struggles, Inc. (R), *90*
Bruce Henry Assoc. Inc. (R), *91*
Hill Allyn Assoc. (C), *378*
Hook-Up! (C), *380*
Interactive Search Network (R), *102*
Interim Accounting Professionals (C), *391*
Iona Partners (C), *394*
IR Search (R), *104*
James Moore & Assoc. (C), *397*
Johnson Smith & Knisely (R), *107*
Joseph Michaels (C), *401*
Kensington International (R), *113*
The Kingsley Group (R), *114*
Korn/Ferry Int'l. (R), *117*
LAI Ward Howell (R), *123*
Larkin & Co. (R), *124*
Lautz, Grotte, Engler & Swimley (R), *126*
Ricci Lee Assoc., Inc. (C), *415*
Levin & Company, Inc. (R), *128*
Major, Hagen & Africa (C), *423*
McCormack & Assoc. (R), *140*
Montgomery Resources, Inc. (C), *484*
Montgomery West (R), *146*
Orion Int'l. Consulting Group, Inc. (C), *499*
Parker & Lynch (C), *503*
Pearson, Caldwell & Farnsworth (R), *161*
Professional Consulting Network, Inc. (C), *520*
Pryor & Associates (C), *525*
PSD Group, Inc. (C), *525*
Michael James Reid & Co. (R), *174*
Russell Reynolds Assoc., Inc. (R), *176*
Robert Beech West Inc. (C), *262*
Romac Int'l. - San Francisco (C), *541*
Romac Int'l., Inc. (C), *542*
Rusher, Loscavio & LoPresto (R), *183*
Sales Professionals Personnel Services (C), *564*
Schlatter & Assoc. (C), *572*
Search West, Inc. (C), *577*
Secura/Burnett Partners (R), *187*
Seitchik Corwin & Seitchik Inc. (R), *188*
M. B. Shattuck & Assoc., Inc. (R), *189*
Shinn & Assoc. (R), *189*
M. Shulman, Inc. (R), *191*
SpencerStuart (R), *196*
DM Stone Personnel Services (C), *594*
StratfordGroup (R), *203*
StratfordGroup (R), *203*
Systems Careers (C), *598*
The Thomas Tucker Co. (R), *211*
Winguth, Grant & Donahue (R), *222*
Egon Zehnder Int'l. Inc. (R), *227*
Zweig White & Assoc., Inc. (R), *228*
Zwell Int'l. (R), *228*

San Jose
Accountants Executive Search (C), *237*
CJSI-Cindy Jackson Search Int'l. (C), *291*
Corporate Careers, Inc. (C), *299*
Fisher & Assoc. (R), *67*
Interim Accounting Professionals (C), *391*
Management Recruiters Inc. of Silicon Valley (C), *441*
Management Solutions, Inc. (C), *468*
McManners Assoc., Inc. (R), *142*
Joseph J. McTaggart (C), *476*
Montgomery West (R), *146*
Parker & Lynch (C), *503*
Romac Int'l. - San Francisco (C), *541*
Romac Int'l., Inc. (C), *542*
Romac Int'l., Inc. (C), *542*
Sales Consultants of Silicon Valley (C), *556*
Sink, Walker, Boltrus Int'l. (R), *192*
StratfordGroup (R), *203*
Technology Search Int'l. (C), *603*
Tirocchi, Wright, Inc. (R), *209*

San Juan Capistrano
Broadband Resource Group (C), *274*
Kuhn Med-Tech (C), *409*
Rogers - McManamon Executive Search (R), *180*

San Luis Obispo
Shell Technology Group (C), *580*

San Marcos
The Niemond Corp. (R), *152*

San Mateo
Bowman & Assoc. (C), *271*
Ferneborg & Assoc., Inc. (R), *66*
Hall Kinion (C), *366*
Howard Karr & Assoc., Inc. (R), *110*
Lewis & Blank Int'l. (R), *129*

Next Step Recruiting (C), *493*
Norman Broadbent Int'l., Inc. (R), *152*
Procom (C), *519*
Synergistech Communications (C), *597*
The Winchester Group (R), *222*

San Pedro
The Wentworth Co., Inc. (R), *217*

San Rafael
Accounting Additions (C), *238*
Bayland Assoc. (C), *261*
CN Associates (C), *293*
The Goodman Group (R), *79*
Longo Associates (C), *420*

San Ramon
Tactical Alternatives (R), *205*

Santa Ana
Carnegie Partners, Inc. (R), *30*
Lending Personnel Services (C), *416*
Sanford Rose Assoc. - Santa Ana (C), *565*
Scott-Thaler Assoc. Agency, Inc. (C), *573*

Santa Barbara
Garland Assoc. Int'l. (C), *355*
KABL Ability Network (C), *402*
Krakower Group, Inc. (R), *120*
NCC Executive Search Consultants (C), *490*
Sanford Rose Assoc. - Santa Barbara (C), *565*

Santa Clara
CTR (R), *43*
Management Assoc. (C), *424*
Nadzam, Lusk, Horgan & Assoc., Inc. (R), *150*
Wisnewski & Assoc. (R), *223*

Santa Clarita
The Canon Group (C), *280*
Horton Int'l. Inc. (R), *96*
R.J. Watkins & Co., Ltd. (R), *216*

Santa Cruz
Robert William James & Assoc. (C), *539*

Santa Monica
AST/BRYANT (R), *8*
cFour Partners (R), *32*
The Corrigan Group (R), *42*
Dynamic Synergy Corp. (R), *56*
Steve Ellis (C), *328*
ESS (Executive Search Services) (R), *61*
Executive Search Group LLC (C), *335*
Garb & Assoc., Legal Placement (C), *354*
Mason & Nicastri Ltd. (R), *138*

Santa Rosa
Pacific Coast Recruiting (C), *501*
Real Estate Executive Search, Inc. (C), *531*
SR Wilson, Inc. (C), *590*

Saratoga
Pinsker and Company, Inc. (R), *164*

Sausalito
Bialla & Assoc. Inc. (R), *17*
JL & Co. (C), *399*
The Luciani Group (R), *132*

Tech Search (C), *601*

Seal Beach
ARI Int'l. (R), *6*

Sherman Oaks
Affordable Executive Recruiters (C), *241*
Fred J. Goldsmith Assoc. (R), *79*
William Guy & Assoc., Inc. (R), *84*
Healthcare Recruiters Int'l. - Los Angeles (C), *372*
Romac Int'l., Inc. (C), *542*
Royal Assoc. (C), *547*
Search Assoc., Inc. (C), *574*

Simi Valley
Advanced Corporate Search (C), *240*

Solana Beach
Ed Bertolas Assoc., Inc. (C), *265*
Electronic Search, Inc. (C), *328*
McCoy Ltd. (C), *474*
Solomon-Page Healthcare Group (R), *195*

Sonoma
J. H. Lindell & Co. (C), *418*

Soquel
J. M. Meredith & Assoc. Inc. (C), *479*

South Pasadena
J. Kevin Coleman & Assoc., Inc. (R), *37*

St. Helena
Caywood Partners, Ltd. (R), *32*

Stockton
General Engineering Tectonics (C), *356*

Sun City
Executive Search Consultants (R), *63*

Sunnyvale
Accountancies (C), *234*
Fortuna Technologies Inc. (C), *343*
Romac Int'l., Inc. (C), *542*
Sanford Rose Assoc. - Sunnyvale (C), *566*
DM Stone Personnel Services (C), *594*

Tahoma
Stillinger & Assoc. (R), *201*

Tarzana
Pathfinders (C), *504*

Temecula
David James Search (C), *397*

Thousand Oaks
Genel Associates (C), *356*
New Venture Development, Inc. (C), *492*
Search Excellence (R), *186*
The Summit Group (C), *596*
Techstaff Inc. (C), *603*

Tiburon
Thomas Resource Group (R), *209*

Topanga
Gilmore & Assoc. (C), *357*

Torrance
Accountants On Call (C), *235*
GCO (C), *355*

Goldstein & Co. (C), *360*
Healthcare Search Associates (C), *374*
Meng, Finseth & Assoc., Inc. (R), *143*
The Partners, LLC (C), *504*
Reinecke & Assoc. (C), *533*
Sampson Medical Search (C), *564*

Tustin
Blackhawk Advantage, Inc. (C), *267*
CJA-The Adler Group, Inc. (R), *35*
Don Hall & Assoc. (C), *366*
William-Johns Co., Inc. (C), *621*

Ukiah
Worldwide Medical Services (C), *625*

Valencia
Beck/Eastwood Recruitment Solutions (C), *261*

Van Nuys
Karel & Co. (R), *109*

Ventura
NCC Executive Search Consultants (C), *490*
Redden-Shaffer Group (R), *173*
Survival Systems Staffing, Inc. (C), *597*

Villa Park
Sanford Rose Assoc. - Anaheim (C), *566*

Visalia
Management Recruiters of Visalia (C), *426*

Vista
National Bank & Finance Executive Search (C), *488*

Walnut Creek
Accountants On Call (C), *235*
CFOs 2 Go (C), *288*
Goldstein & Co. (C), *360*
Healthcare Recruiters Int'l. Bay Area (C), *372*
Interim Accounting Professionals (C), *391*
The Martin Group (R), *137*
The Nolan Group (C), *494*
Romac Int'l., Inc. (C), *542*
Sales Solutions (C), *564*
Smartsource Inc. (C), *583*
System 1 Search (C), *598*

West Hills
Raymond L. Extract & Assoc. (R), *64*

West Los Angeles
Hemingway Personnel, Inc. (C), *375*

Westlake Village
BioTech Research Recruiters Inc. (C), *267*
Byron Leonard Int'l., Inc. (R), *25*
Robert W. Dingman Co., Inc. (R), *52*
JDH & Assoc. (C), *397*
MIXTEC Group (R), *145*
Omni Search, Inc. (C), *499*
ProSearch Recruiting (C), *524*
Protocol Inc. (C), *525*
Recruiting Resources Int'l. (C), *532*
Recruiting/Solutions (C), *532*
Royal Assoc. (C), *547*

Sales Consultant of Westlake Village (C), *551*
Search West, Inc. (C), *577*
Peggy Shea & Assoc. (R), *189*
Tech Connector Group (C), *601*
Venture Resources, Inc. (R), *213*

Woodland
Allard Associates (C), *244*

Woodland Hills
Accountants On Call (C), *235*
Career Strategies, Inc. (C), *283*
Computer Recruiters, Inc. (C), *295*
Mel Frazer Consultant (C), *352*
Harrison Consulting Group, Inc. (C), *369*
Madeleine Lav & Assoc. (C), *413*
The Morgan/Geoffries Group (C), *485*
RJ Associates (C), *538*
Rovner Gerner & Assoc. (R), *182*
M. H. Springer & Assoc. (R), *198*
The Stevens Group (C), *593*

Woodside
David Powell, Inc. (R), *166*

Colorado

Angelwood
Staffing Edge, Inc. (C), *590*

Arvada
The Bridge (C), *273*

Aspen
Beckman & Assoc. Legal Search (C), *262*
InSearch (C), *389*

Aurora
Benamati & Assoc. (C), *263*
COBA Executive Search (R), *36*
National Affirmative Action Career Network, Inc. (C), *488*

Boulder
R & J Arnold & Assoc., Inc. (C), *253*
Bartholdi & Co., Inc. (R), *12*
Executive Search Placements, Inc. (C), *336*
Kutt, Inc. (C), *410*
Management Recruiters of Boulder (C), *426*
Management Recruiters of Broomfield (C), *426*
William K. McLaughlin Assoc., Inc. (C), *475*
Nichols & Company (R), *151*
Paladin Group, Inc. (C), *502*
Sales Consultant of Boulder (C), *552*

Castle Rock
Miller Denver (C), *482*

Colorado Springs
American Medical Recruiters (C), *248*
Dunhill Professional Search of Colorado Springs (C), *316*
Fortune Personnel Consultants of Colorado Springs (C), *344*
Harvard Group Int'l. (R), *87*
Management Recruiters of Colorado Springs-Pikes Peak (C), *426*
Management Recruiters of Colorado Springs (C), *441*
Monarch Technology Management LLC (C), *484*

Conifer
Mycoff & Assoc. (R), *150*

Denver
Accountants On Call (C), *235*
American Medical Recruiters (C), *248*
Anderson & Schwab, Inc. (R), *6*
William B. Arnold Assoc., Inc. (R), *7*
Bartholdi & Co., Inc. (R), *12*
DHR Int'l., Inc. (R), *49*
DHR Int'l., Inc. (R), *49*
Dunhill Staffing Systems, Inc. (C), *316*
FAI (C), *338*
The Garrison Organization (R), *75*
Hunt Patton & Brazeal, Inc. (C), *385*
Jackson Group Int'l. (C), *396*
A.T. Kearney Executive Search (R), *111*
Daniel J. Kerstein, Consultant to Management (R), *114*
V. J. Lehman & Assoc., Inc. (R), *127*
Management Recruiters of Denver-Downtown (C), *426*
J. L. Mark Assoc., Inc. (R), *135*
Norrell Financial Staffing (C), *495*
Phillips Personnel/Search (C), *510*
The Pinnacle Source, Inc. (C), *512*
Rocky Mountain Recruiters, Inc. (C), *540*
StratfordGroup (R), *203*
Tekworx, Inc. (C), *604*

Dillon
Robert Hess & Assoc., Inc. (C), *377*

Englewood
Dunhill Search of Denver South (C), *316*
Dunhill Professional Search of Englewood, Inc. (C), *319*
Emerging Medical Technologies, Inc. (C), *329*
Hall Kinion (C), *367*
Health Industry Consultants, Inc. (R), *89*
Healthcare Recruiters of the Rockies, Inc. (C), *372*
Management Recruiters of Highlands Ranch (C), *426*
Management Recruiters of Colorado, Inc. (C), *442*
Media Management Resources, Inc. (R), *142*
MedQuest Assoc. (C), *478*
MRI, The Sequel Group, LLC (C), *486*
NMC & Kay Int'l. (R), *152*
Professional Search, Inc. (C), *522*
Romac Int'l., Inc. (C), *542*
Sales Consultants of Denver (C), *557*
Stroman Int'l., Inc. (R), *204*

Evergreen
Diversified Consulting Services, Inc. (C), *313*
Kukoy Associates (R), *121*
Management Recruiters of Evergreen (C), *426*
SpencerSearch, Inc. (C), *589*

Franktown
Management Recruiters of Franktown (C), *442*

Ft. Collins
Dunhill of Ft. Collins, Inc. (C), *319*

Golden
Raymond Karsan Assoc. (C), *530*

Grand Junction
Carlsen Resources, Inc. (R), *29*

Greenwood Village
Career Marketing Assoc., Inc. (C), *282*
F-O-R-T-U-N-E Personnel Consultants of Greenwood Village (C), *344*
R. L. Plimpton Assoc., Inc. (R), *165*
Skupsky & Assoc. (C), *582*

Highlands Ranch
Langley & Associates, Inc. (Executive Search Consultants) (R), *124*

Lakewood
Advanced Recruiting, Inc. (C), *240*
The Human Resource Consulting Group, Inc. (R), *98*
i.j. & assoc., inc. (C), *386*
Management Recruiters of Denver-Golden Hill (C), *426*
PC Assoc. (C), *505*
Sales Consultant (C), *552*

Leadville
Bartholdi & Co., Inc. (R), *12*

Littleton
DRZ Medical Recruiters (C), *315*
Executive Sales Search (C), *335*
F-O-R-T-U-N-E Personnel Consultants of Denver, Inc. (C), *344*
Don V. Poole & Assoc., Inc. (C), *514*
Ruppert Comann Assoc., Inc. (R), *182*

Louisville
Welzig, Lowe & Assoc. (C), *618*

Manitau Springs
Health Care Dimensions (C), *371*

Monument
Woodmoor Group (C), *624*

Niwot
DiMarchi Partners (R), *51*
Dunhill Personnel of Boulder (C), *319*

Parker
MESA, Inc. (R), *143*

Steamboat Springs
The Woodstone Consulting Company, Inc. (R), *224*

Westminster
Cochran, Cochran & Yale, Inc. (R), *37*
Lloyd Prescott & Churchill, Inc. (R), *130*
Lloyd Prescott Assoc., Inc. (C), *419*
Management Recruiters of Westminster (C), *426*

Woodland Park
Management Recruiters of Woodland Park (C), *426*

Connecticut

Avon
The Evans Search Group (R), *61*
K. C. Hale, Inc. (R), *85*
Horton International Inc. (R), *96*
People Management Northeast, Inc. (R), *162*
Snyder & Co. (R), *194*

Bloomfield
Insurance Career Center, Inc. (C), *389*
Pathways Int'l. (C), *505*

Branford
DiTech Resources (C), *313*

Bristol
Quality Control Recruiters (C), *526*

Brookfield
Cornell Group Int'l. (R), *41*

Canton Center
Richard Wright Co. (C), *536*

Cheshire
Hobson Assoc. (C), *379*

Colchester
Executive Search Group, Inc. (C), *335*

Cos Cob
Flexible Resources, Inc. (C), *342*
The Hyde Group, Inc. (R), *101*

Cromwell
Management Recruiters of Middlesex (C), *442*

Danbury
Abraham & London Ltd. (C), *232*
Argus National, Inc. (R), *6*
Biomedical Search Consultants (R), *17*
Dunhill Staffing Systems of Danbury (C), *316*
E O Technical (C), *324*

Darien
Koll-Fairfield LLC (C), *408*
Lindsey & Co., Inc. (R), *129*
W. D. Nolte & Company (R), *152*

East Hartford
Dunhill Stafifng Systems of East Hartford (C), *316*
Romac Int'l., Inc. (C), *542*

East Windsor
Dunhill Staffing Systems of East Windsor (C), *316*

Fairfield
Somerset Group, Inc. (C), *587*

Farmington
Dunhill Staffing Systems of Farmington (C), *316*
The Kilman Advisory Group (R), *114*
McIntyre Assoc. (R), *141*
Yankee Hospitality Search (C), *626*

Glastonbury
Executive Partners Inc. (C), *333*
R. C. Handel Assoc. Inc. (R), *85*
Management Recruiters of Colchester (C), *442*
Richard L. Mather & Assoc. (C), *472*

Greens Farms
Bosch & Assoc., LLC (R), *19*

Greenwich
Blackshaw, Olmstead, Lynch & Koenig (R), *18*
David Chambers & Assoc., Inc. (R), *32*
Earley Kielty & Assoc., Inc. (R), *56*
Erlanger Assoc. (R), *60*
Greenwich Internet (C), *363*
Greenwich Search Partners, LLC (C), *363*
Heidrick & Struggles, Inc. (R), *90*
K2 Resources, L.P. (C), *402*
Livingston, Robert & Co. (R), *130*
Matté & Company, Inc. (R), *138*
K. Russo Assoc. Inc. (C), *548*
William Willis Worldwide Inc. (R), *221*
Wills Consulting Assoc. Inc. (R), *221*

Guilford
JFW Associates, LLC (C), *398*
The Resource Group (R), *175*

Hamden
Cheney Associates (C), *290*

Hartford
S. W. Delano & Co. (R), *48*
High-Tech Recruiters (C), *378*
Howard W. Smith Assoc. (R), *193*
United Personnel Services (C), *611*
The Wallace Law Registry (C), *614*

Lakeville
Jacobs & Co. (R), *105*

Litchfield
The Maroon Group (R), *136*

Madison
Bankers Search, L.L.C. (C), *259*
Dussick Management Assoc. (C), *323*
ESA (R), *60*
JDavid Assoc., Inc. (R), *105*
Techsearch Services Inc. (C), *603*

Manchester
Engineering Futures, LLC (C), *330*
Lutz Associates (C), *421*

Meriden
Johnson Smith & Knisely (R), *107*

Milford
Andex Executive Search (C), *250*
Management Recruiters of Milford Inc. (C), *442*
Sales Consultant of New Haven (C), *552*

Monroe
Mangieri/Solutions LLC (C), *468*
The Tidewater Group Inc. (C), *607*

New Canaan
Baldwin Associates, LLC (R), *10*
Capital Consulting & Research, Inc. (R), *28*
JT Assoc. (C), *401*
J. D. Walsh & Co. (R), *215*

New Fairfield
The Burgess Group-Corporate Recruiters Int'l., Inc. (R), *25*

New Haven
Dunhill Personnel of New Haven (C), *316*
Wilson McLeran, Inc. (C), *622*

Newington
Julian Assoc., Inc. (C), *401*

Newtown
Cybernautic Corp. (C), *305*

Nichols
Tryg R. Angell, Ltd. (C), *250*

Norwalk
Dunhill Staffing Systems of Norwalk (C), *316*
Fairfaxx Corp. (R), *64*
Goodrich & Sherwood Assoc., Inc. (R), *79*
Harris Heery & Assoc., Inc. (R), *87*
William W. Kenney (C), *405*
The Libra Group Inc. (C), *417*
Marks & Co., Inc. (R), *136*
O'Neill & Co. (R), *154*
The Resource Group (R), *175*
Ross Personnel Consultants, Inc. (C), *545*
TSW Assoc., LLC (R), *211*
Weatherby Healthcare (C), *617*

Norwich
Chelsea Resources, Inc. (C), *290*

Old Greenwich
Halbrecht & Co. (C), *365*

Redding Ridge
Lee Calhoon & Co., Inc. (R), *26*

Ridgefield
The Chatham Group, Ltd. (C), *289*
P. J. Lynch Assoc. (R), *132*
Maiorino & Weston Assoc., Inc. (R), *134*
Ridgefield Search Int'l. (C), *537*

Riverside
Lamay Assoc., Inc. (R), *124*

Rocky Hill
Management Recruiters of Hartford-South (C), *426*
Matthews & Stephens Assoc., Inc. (C), *472*
Retail Recruiters (C), *535*
Sales Consultant of Hartford (C), *552*

Rowayton
Higbee Assoc., Inc. (C), *377*
Plummer & Assoc., Inc. (R), *166*

Sandy Hook
Brandywine Retained Ventures, Inc. (R), *22*
Sales Consultants of Danbury (C), *557*

Shelton
The Beardsley Group Inc. (C), *261*
Goodrich & Sherwood Assoc., Inc. (R), *80*
Romac Int'l., Inc. (C), *542*

Simsbury
Flexible Resources, Inc. (C), *342*
The Hudson Group (C), *383*
W. R. Lawry, Inc. (R), *126*

Southbury
DHR Int'l., Inc. (R), *49*
Hunter Int'l., Inc. (R), *100*

Southington
Cahill Assoc. (C), *279*

Southport
Bonnell Assoc. Ltd. (R), *19*
E O Technical (C), *324*
O'Keefe & Assoc., Inc. (R), *154*
Ross & Company, Inc. (R), *182*
Smith Hanley Assoc., Inc. (C), *584*

Stamford
Accountants Executive Search (C), *234*
The Alice Groves Co., Inc. (C), *244*
AST/BRYANT (R), *8*
Bell Wishingrad Partners Inc. (R), *15*
Boehmer, Tomasco & Alexander (R), *24*
Burke & Assoc./The Westfield Group (C), *276*
Career Consulting Group, Inc. (C), *281*
Curran Partners, Inc. (R), *44*
D.A.L. Associates, Inc. (R), *45*
Flynn, Hannock, Inc. (R), *69*
Halbrecht Lieberman Assoc., Inc. (R), *84*
Huntington Group (R), *100*
InteliSearch, Inc. (R), *102*
Jones Management Co. (R), *108*
A.T. Kearney Executive Search (R), *111*
Korn/Ferry Int'l. (R), *118*
LAI Ward Howell (R), *123*
Mirtz Morice, Inc. (R), *145*
Moyer, Sherwood Assoc., Inc. (R), *148*
Object Resources Int'l., Inc. (C), *498*
P.R.H. Management, Inc. (R), *158*
Pascale & LaMorte, LLC (C), *504*
Reeve & Assoc. (C), *533*
Resource Management Group (C), *534*
Sales Consultants of Stamford-Darien (C), *557*
Siger & Assoc., LLC (C), *581*
SpencerStuart (R), *196*
Strategic Executives, Inc. (R), *202*
The Westfield Group (C), *619*

Stratford
Chesapeake Group (C), *290*

Trumbull
BT&A, LLC (R), *24*
Huntington Group (R), *100*
Lineal Recruiting Services (C), *418*
P. D. Zier Assoc. (C), *627*

Wallingford
Dunhill Staffing Systems of Wallingford (C), *316*
MJF Assoc. (C), *483*

Waterbury
Dunhill Staffing Systems of Waterbury (C), *316*
Heritage Search Group, Inc. (C), *376*
Wallace Assoc. (C), *614*

West Hartford
Flynn, Hannock, Inc. (R), *69*
The Search Alliance, Inc. (R), *186*
Vezan Assoc. (C), *612*

West Haven
Harvard Aimes Group (R), *87*

West Suffield
E/Search Int'l. (C), *325*

Westport
Bailey Employment System Inc. (C), *257*
Cambridge Group Ltd. - Exec. Search Div. (C), *279*
The Cambridge Group Ltd. (C), *280*
Caruthers & Co., L.L.C. (R), *31*
Rosemary Cass Ltd. (R), *31*
Christian & Timbers, Inc. (R), *34*
C. A. Durakis Assoc., Inc. (R), *55*
Futures Int'l. (R), *73*
J. G. Hood Assoc. (C), *380*
Marketing/Public Relations Research Recruiting (C), *471*
Robert E. McGrath & Assoc. (R), *141*
The McLeod Group, Inc. (R), *141*
James Mead & Co. (R), *142*
Midas Management (C), *481*
Barry Persky & Co., Inc. (R), *163*
Phase II Management (R), *164*
R/K International Inc. (R), *171*
J. Stroll Assoc., Inc. (R), *203*
Ward Liebelt Assoc. Inc. (R), *215*
Wheeler Assoc. (R), *219*

Wilton
Abraham & London Ltd. (C), *232*
Carol Ball & Co. (C), *258*
ENI (R), *59*
Johnson & Company (R), *107*
Knapp Consultants (R), *116*
Management Recruiters of Wilton (C), *426*
Management Recruiters of Norwalk (C), *426*
O'Connell Group Inc. (C), *497*
Sales Consultant of Wilton-Westport (C), *552*
Bob Wright Recruiting, Inc. (C), *625*

Winsted
Management Recruiters of Winsted, Inc. (C), *442*

Woodbury
W. A. Rutledge & Assoc. (R), *183*

Delaware

Claymont
J. B. Groner Executive Search, Inc. (C), *363*

Newark
F-O-R-T-U-N-E Personnel Consultants of Wilmington (C), *344*

Wilmington
ACSYS Resources, Inc. (C), *238*
ACSYS Resources, Inc. (C), *238*
Discovery, The Staffing Specialists, Inc. (C), *312*
Hornberger Management Company (R), *95*
Professional Recruiting Consultants, Inc. (C), *521*

District of Columbia

Washington
Accountants On Call (C), *235*
Boyden (R), *20*
C Assoc. (C), *278*
Development Resource Group (R), *48*
DHR Int'l., Inc. (R), *50*
Finn & Schneider Assoc., Inc. (C), *341*
Foster Partners (R), *70*
Goodwin & Co. (R), *80*
Hartman Greene & Wells (C), *370*
Bruce W. Haupt Assoc. (R), *88*
Heidrick & Struggles, Inc. (R), *90*
Interim Financial Solutions (C), *392*
John Michael Assoc. (R), *106*
Kershner & Co. (R), *113*
Klein, Landau & Romm (C), *407*
Korn/Ferry Int'l. (R), *118*
Mark Stanley & Co. (R), *136*
McBride Assoc., Inc. (R), *139*
McPherson Square Assoc., Inc. (C), *475*
Mee Derby & Co. (C), *478*
Susan C. Miller Assoc., Inc. (C), *482*
NRI Staffing Resources (C), *496*
R. H. Perry & Assoc., Inc. (R), *162*
Russell Reynolds Assoc., Inc. (R), *176*
Romac Int'l., Inc. (C), *542*
Rurak & Assoc., Inc (R), *182*
Savoy Partners, Ltd. (R), *184*
Robert Sellery Assoc., Ltd. (R), *188*
Synergy 2000 (C), *597*
Tarbex (C), *599*
Thomas, Whelan Assoc., Inc. (C), *606*
Travaille Executive Search (R), *210*
Zweig White & Assoc., Inc. (R), *228*

Florida

Altamonte Springs
A. M. Auster Associates (R), *9*
Howard Bowen Consulting (C), *270*
Clinton, Charles, Wise & Co. (C), *293*
Financial Resource Assoc., Inc. (C), *340*
Karp & Assoc. (C), *403*
Management Recruiters of Altamonte (C), *442*

Apollo Beach
Management Recruiters of Apollo Beach (C), *426*
Wellington Thomas Ltd. (C), *618*

Apopka
Robert Sollman & Assoc. (C), *587*

Atlantic Beach
Dick Wray & Consultants, Inc. (R), *225*

Aventura
Growth Strategies, Inc. (R), *83*
Henrietta's Personnel & Executive Search, Inc. (C), *376*

Belleair Bluffs
Searchforce, Inc. (R), *187*

Boca Raton
Born & Bicknell, Inc. (C), *270*
The Buckley Group (C), *276*
Career Counseling Ltd. (C.C.L.) (C), *282*
The Curtiss Group International (R), *44*
Data Search Network, Inc. (C), *307*
Data-AxIS Corp. (C), *307*
Interim Accounting Professionals (C), *391*
JenKim Int'l. Ltd., Inc. (C), *398*
Kenmore Executives Inc. (C), *405*
The Conrad Lee Co. Inc. (R), *127*
Management Recruiters of Boca Raton (C), *443*
Management Resource Assoc., Inc. (C), *467*
Marra Peters & Partners (R), *136*
MedSearch Resources, Inc. (C), *478*
Morgenstern Int'l., Inc. (C), *485*
Perfect Search, Inc. (C), *507*
Sales Consultants of Boca Raton, Inc. (C), *557*
SearchCorp (C), *577*
Daniel A. Silverstein Assoc. Inc. (R), *191*
The Stevenson Group, Inc. (R), *200*
Tate Consulting, Inc. (R), *207*

Bonita Springs
Hunter, Rowan & Crowe (C), *386*
J. Krauss Assoc. (R), *120*
Management Recruiters of Bonita Springs, Inc. (C), *443*

Boynton Beach
Aronow Assoc., Inc. (C), *253*

Bradenton
Mark Bolno & Assoc. (C), *269*
Gwen Dycus & Assoc. (C), *323*
Management Recruiters of Anna Maria Island (C), *443*
Sales Consultant of Bradenton (C), *552*
Sales Consultant of Manatee County (C), *552*
Ron Stevens & Assoc., Inc. (C), *593*

Brandon
Management Recruiters of Bartow (C), *426*
Smith & Assoc. (C), *583*

Clearwater
The Butlers Co. Insurance Recruiters (C), *277*
F-O-R-T-U-N-E Personnel Consultants of Tampa (C), *344*
Management Recruiters of Clearwater (C), *443*
Merrick & Moore (C), *479*
MGA Executive Search (C), *480*
Roberts Ryan & Bentley, Inc. (R), *179*
Sanford Rose Assoc. - Clearwater (C), *566*
Tech Consulting (C), *601*
Wilson & Assoc. Int'l. Inc. (C), *622*

Cooper City
Management Recruiters of Port St. Lucie (C), *426*

Coral Gables
Accountants On Call (C), *235*
Ken Clark Int'l. (R), *36*
The IMC Group, Miami, Florida (R), *101*
Interim Accounting Professionals (C), *392*
Management Recruiters of Coral Gables (C), *426*
Mark Stanley & Co./EMA Partners International (R), *136*
Sales Consultant of Miami-Coral Gables (C), *552*
SpencerStuart (R), *197*

Coral Springs
Beach Executive Search Inc. (R), *14*
National Search, Inc.r (C), *490*
NPF Assoc. Ltd. Inc. (R), *153*
Sales Consultant of Coral Springs (C), *552*
Search Enterprises, Inc. (C), *575*
Searchworks, Inc. (C), *577*

Dania
Norrell Financial Staffing (C), *495*

Daytona Beach
Heller Kil Assoc., Inc. (C), *375*

Deerfield Beach
F. P. Lennon Assoc. (C), *416*
MedXec USA, Inc. (C), *478*
The Ryan Charles Group, Inc. (C), *548*

Deland
Alpha Search (C), *246*

Delray Beach
Andrews & Wald Group (C), *250*
Management Recruiters of Delray Beach (C), *427*
Marketing & Sales Resources, Inc. (C), *470*
Phillips Assoc. (C), *510*
Southport Int'l. Assoc. Inc. (C), *588*
Specialized Search Assoc. (C), *589*

Destin
Porter & Assoc., Inc. (C), *514*

Dunnellon
Zackrison Assoc., Inc. (C), *627*

Englewood
Blake/Hansen Ltd. (R), *18*
The Garret Group (R), *75*

Fernandina Beach
The Search Alliance, Inc. (R), *186*

Ft. Lauderdale
American Executive Search (C), *247*
American Medical Consultants, Inc. (C), *248*
Becker Personnel (C), *262*
Boyden (R), *21*
M. L. Conner (C), *296*
DHR Int'l., Inc. (R), *50*
DHR Int'l., Inc. (R), *50*
Executive Manning Corp. (R), *63*
Gimbel & Assoc. (C), *357*
Groupe PCA Inc. (C), *364*
Interim Accounting Professionals (C), *392*
Kelley & Keller, Inc. (C), *405*
R. H. Larsen & Assoc., Inc. (R), *125*
Lasher Assoc. (R), *125*
Lawrence James Assoc. of Florida, Inc. (C), *414*
Management Recruiters of Ft. Lauderdale (C), *427*
Management Recruiters of Palm Beach (C), *427*
Marc-Allen Assoc., Inc. (C), *469*
Retail Executive Search (C), *535*
Romac Int'l., Inc. (C), *542*
Romac Int'l., Inc. (C), *542*
Ropes Associates, Inc. (R), *182*
Sales Advantage (C), *551*
Sales Consultants of Ft. Lauderdale, Inc. (C), *557*
Snelling & Snelling, Inc. (C), *585*
Allan Stolee Inc. (R), *201*
Weatherby Healthcare (C), *617*

Ft. Myers
Dunhill Staffing Systems of Fort Myers (C), *316*
Management Recruiters of Ft. Myers, FL. (C), *443*
The NEIS Corp., Inc. (C), *491*
Sales Consultants of Ft. Myers, Inc. (C), *557*

Gainesville
AGRI-associates (C), *242*

Gulf Breeze
Media Management Resources, Inc. (R), *143*

Holiday
Success Seekers Connection (C), *596*

Hollywood
PersoNet, Inc. (C), *507*
Wilcoxen, Blackwell, Niven & Assoc. (R), *220*

Howey in the Hills
NHA Plastics Recruiters (C), *493*

Indialantic
Management Recruiters of Melbourne, Inc. (C), *443*

Islamorada
CEO Consulting (C), *287*

Jacksonville
Avondale Search Int'l., Inc. (R), *9*
The Bales-Waugh Group (C), *258*
Blane, Stevens & Kellogg (C), *268*
DS&A (Doug Sears & Assoc.) (C), *315*
Fortune Personnel Consultants of Jacksonville (C), *345*
Heidrick & Struggles, Inc. (R), *90*
Keystone Consulting Group (C), *406*
Management Recruiters of Julington Creek (C), *427*
Management Recruiters of Jacksonville-South (C), *427*

GEOGRAPHICAL

Management Recruiters, Inc. (C), *443*
Pearce & Assoc. (C), *506*
Sales Consultant of Jacksonville (C), *552*
Southwestern Professional Services (C), *588*

Jacksonville Beach
The Marathon Group (C), *469*

Jensen Beach
Management Recruiters of Jensen Beach (C), *427*

Jupiter
Columbia Consulting Group (R), *38*
International Technical Resources (C), *393*
Management Recruiters of Jupiter (C), *427*

Key Biscayne
Dunhill Professional Search of Miami (C), *317*

Lake Placid
Tully/Woodmansee Int'l. Inc. (R), *212*

Lake Worth
PLA, Inc. (C), *513*

Lakeland
Meads & Assoc. (R), *142*
Jim Parham & Assoc., Inc. (R), *159*

Land O' Lakes
Robert Kaestner & Assoc. (C), *403*

Largo
Career Search Group (C), *283*
Dunhill of St. Petersburg (C), *317*
Quantum Int'l., Ltd. (R), *170*

Lighthouse Point
Executive Search Consultants, Inc. (C), *335*
Gable Healthcare Group, Inc. (R), *73*

Longwood
Elite Consultants, Inc. (C), *328*
The Primary Group, Inc. (R), *168*
Raymond Thomas & Assoc. (C), *530*
The Witt Group (C), *623*

Lutz
Business Partners, Inc. (C), *277*

Maitland
Dunhill Staffing Systems of Orlando (C), *317*
Management Recruiters of Orlando-Downtown (C), *427*
Tina Morbitzer & Assoc. (C), *485*
Norrell Financial Staffing (C), *495*
Sales Consultant of Orlando (C), *552*

Miami
American Medical Consultants, Inc. (C), *247*
Becker Personnel (C), *262*
Corporate Advisors, Inc. (C), *299*
Dunhill Professional Search of Miami (C), *319*
Foster Partners (R), *70*
Griffith & Werner, Inc. (R), *82*
Heidrick & Struggles, Inc. (R), *90*
H. Hertner Assoc., Inc. (C), *377*
A.T. Kearney Executive Search (R), *111*
Korn/Ferry Int'l. (R), *118*
Management Recruiters of Miami-North (C), *443*
Maxecon Executive Search Consultants (R), *138*
MDR Associates, Inc. (C), *476*
Messett Assoc., Inc. (R), *143*
Nason & Nason (C), *488*
Parker Page Group (C), *503*
Peyser Assoc., Inc. (R), *163*

Miami Beach
Summit Executive Search Consultants, Inc. (R), *204*

Miami Lakes
Career Advisors, Inc. (C), *281*
Interim Accounting Professionals (C), *392*
Romac Int'l., Inc. (C), *542*
Romac Int'l., Inc. (C), *542*

Milton
Management Recruiters of Santa Rosa (C), *427*
Ropella & Assoc. (R), *181*

Mt. Dora
Management Recruiters of Lake Co., Inc. (C), *444*

Naples
Bennett Search & Consulting Co. (R), *16*
C. A. Durakis Assoc., Inc. (R), *55*
Gallin Associates of Naples, FL (C), *354*
Hanley & Assoc. (R), *86*
International Management Services,Inc. (R), *102*
Management Recruiters of Naples (C), *427*
Sales Consultant of Naples (C), *552*
Smith, Brown & Jones (C), *585*

New Smyrna Beach
Sinclair & Co. Inc. (R), *192*

North Miami
Patricia Roth Int'l. (C), *545*

North Miami Beach
Affinity Executive Search (C), *241*

Oldsmar
Katelyn Partners (C), *404*

Orangepark
Management Recruiters of Orangepark (C), *427*

Orlando
BCG Search, Inc. (R), *14*
Corporate Search Consultants, Inc. (C), *301*
Rob Dey Executive Search (R), *49*
International Recruiting Services (C), *393*
Petrie Partners, Inc. (R), *163*
ProFinders, Inc. (C), *523*
Romac Int'l., Inc. (C), *542*

Oviedo
Abraxas Technologies, Inc. (C), *233*

Palm Beach
The Executive Tree (R), *64*
Nason & Nason (C), *488*

Palm Beach Gardens
L. Battalin & Co. (C), *261*
ChaseAmerica, Inc. (R), *33*
F-O-R-T-U-N-E Personnel Consultants of Palm Beach (C), *345*
Management Recruiters of Northern Palm Beaches (C), *444*

Palm Harbor
Career Images (C), *282*
Chase-Gardner Executive Search Associates, Inc. (C), *289*
Environmental, Health & Safety Search Assoc. (C), *331*
Impact Source, Inc. (C), *387*
Kay Concepts, Inc. (C), *404*
OmniSearch, Inc. (C), *499*

Palmetto
F-O-R-T-U-N-E Personnel Consultants of Manatee County (C), *345*

Panama City
JCL & Assoc. (C), *397*

Pensacola
Engineering Profiles (C), *330*
Management Recruiters of Pensacola (C), *444*

Pierson
M. L. Conner (C), *296*

Plant City
Management Recruiters of Plant City, Inc. (C), *444*

Plantation
Jay Allen & Assoc. (C), *244*
Focus Consulting Services, Inc. (C), *342*
Management Recruiters of Plantation (C), *427*
Networking Unlimited of NH, Inc. (C), *491*

Pompano Beach
Dunhill Professional (C), *317*
Resolve Assoc. Int'l. (R), *175*

Ponte Vedra Beach
DHR Int'l., Inc. (R), *50*
DHR Int'l., Inc. (R), *50*
The Marathon Group (C), *469*
The Stewart Group (C), *593*

Port Orange
A.M.C.R., Inc. (C), *232*

Port St. Lucie
Heritage Search Group, Inc. (C), *376*
Management Recruiters of St. Lucie County, Inc. (C), *444*

Royal Palm Beach
Management Recruiters of Royal Palm Beach (C), *427*

Safety Harbor
Gallin Associates, Inc. (C), *354*
Helffrich Int'l. (C), *375*
Just Management Services Inc. (C), *402*

Sanford
Florapersonnel, Inc. (R), *68*

Sarasota
Dunhill of Sarasota (C), *317*
Fortune Personnel Consultants of Sarasota Inc. (C), *345*
Franstaff Inc. (C), *352*
Koontz, Jeffries & Assoc., Inc. (R), *117*
Lechner & Assoc., Inc. (C), *415*
Management Recruiters of Sarasota (C), *427*
Professional Recruiting Consultants (C), *521*
Sales Consultants of Sarasota (C), *552*
Search Masters, USA (C), *576*
Selective Management Services, Inc. (C), *578*
TASA International (R), *206*

St. Augustine
Management Recruiters of St. Augustine (C), *444*

St. Petersburg
A.J. & Assoc. (C), *232*
Human Capital Resources, Inc. (C), *384*
IDC Executive Search Inc. (C), *387*
Krautler Personnel Recruitment (C), *409*
Management Recruiters of Seminole (C), *427*
Management Recruiters of St. Petersburg (C), *427*
Scott Watson & Assoc., Inc. (R), *216*
Dennis Wynn Assoc., Inc. (C), *625*

Stuart
Fox, White & Assoc. (C), *351*
RIC Corp. (R), *177*
Tower Consultants, Ltd. (R), *210*

Sugarloaf Key
The Corporate Advisory Group (R), *41*

Sunrise
STAT Search (C), *592*

Tallahassee
Cantrell & Assoc. (C), *280*
David M. Griffith & Assoc., Ltd. (R), *82*
Management Recruiters of Tallahassee (C), *427*
The Search Committee, Inc. (C), *575*
Stanewick, Hart & Assoc., Inc. (C), *591*

Tamarac
EGM Consulting, Inc. (R), *57*
Mankuta Gallagher & Assoc., Inc. (C), *468*
Jack Richman & Assoc. (C), *537*

Tampa
Accountants On Call (C), *237*
Allen Austin Lowe & Powers (R), *4*
BioPharmMed (C), *267*
Carter-Evdemon & Assoc. (C), *285*
Computer Int'l. Consultants, Inc. (C), *295*
The Corporate Source Group, Inc. (R), *41*
Criterion Executive Search, Inc. (C), *303*
The Curtiss Group, Int'l (R), *44*
Cypress Int'l., Inc. (R), *45*
DHR Int'l., Inc. (R), *50*
DHR Int'l., Inc. (R), *50*
Dunhill Professional Search of Tampa (C), *320*
Gans, Gans & Assoc., Inc. (R), *74*
Hall Kinion (C), *367*
The Hiring Authority, Inc. (C), *379*
LAI Ward Howell (R), *123*
LAI Ward Howell (R), *123*
Lloyd Prescott & Churchill, Inc. (R), *130*
Lloyd Prescott Assoc., Inc. (C), *418*
Management Recruiters of Northdale (C), *427*
Management Recruiters of Tampa-Bayside (C), *427*
Management Recruiters of Tampa-Palma Ceia (C), *427*
Management Recruiters of Tampa (C), *427*
Management Recruiters of Tampa North (C), *444*
Marsar & Co., Inc. (C), *471*
Miller & Assoc. (C), *481*
Physician Executive Management Center (R), *164*
Priority Executive Search (C), *518*
Romac Int'l., Inc. (C), *542*
Romac Int'l., Inc. (C), *543*
Romac Int'l., Inc. (C), *543*
Romac Int'l., Inc. (C), *543*
Roth Young of Tampa (C), *546*
Sales Consultants of Tampa (C), *552*
Sales Consultants of Tampa North, Inc. (C), *557*
Search Advisors Int'l. Corp. (R), *186*
Southern Research Services (R), *195*
Sweeney Harbert & Mummert, Inc. (R), *205*
Techstaff Inc. (C), *603*
UniQuest Int'l., Inc. (C), *610*

Tarpon Springs
Haddad Assoc. (R), *84*

Treasure Island
Sales Consultant of St. Petersburg (C), *552*

University Park
Southern Chemical & Plastics Search (C), *587*

Valrico
Tech 2000 (C), *601*

Venice
Management Recruiters of Venice, Inc. (C), *445*

Vero Beach
The Brand Co., Inc. (R), *22*
The Hutton Group, Inc. (C), *386*
Management Recruiters of Vero Beach (C), *445*
MIXTEC Group (R), *146*

West Palm Beach
Caruso & Assoc., Inc. (R), *31*
Erlanger Assoc. (R), *60*
Howard/Williams Assoc. (C), *382*
RCI Employment Solutions (C), *531*

Weston
Steven Douglas Assoc. (C), *593*

Winter Park
Accountants On Call (C), *235*
Cary & Assoc. (R), *31*
Joseph Consulting, Inc. (C), *401*
Lear & Assoc., Inc. (C), *415*
Management Recruiters of Orlando/Winter Park (C), *427*

Winter Springs
SilverSands Int'l. (C), *582*

Georgia

Acworth
DS&A (Doug Sears & Assoc.) (C), *315*

Alpharetta
AGRI-associates (C), *242*
Aries Search Group (C), *252*
Current Resource Group, Inc. (C), *305*
Elliot Assoc. Inc. (R), *58*
Management Recruiters of Atlanta-Alpharetta (C), *427*
Management Recruiters of North Fulton (C), *445*
Philo & Associates (C), *511*
Sales Consultants (C), *552*
Sanford Rose Assoc. - Norcross (C), *566*
Specialty Employment Services, Inc. (C), *589*
Straight & Co. (R), *202*

Athens
Sanford Rose Assoc. - Athens (C), *566*
Smith Hanley Assoc., Inc. (C), *584*

Atlanta
A. D. & Assoc. Executive Search, Inc. (C), *231*
Accountants On Call (C), *235*
Agri-Personnel (C), *242*
Ashford Management Group, Inc. (R), *7*
Ask Guy Tucker (C), *254*
Attorneys at Work (C), *255*
R. Gaines Baty Assoc., Inc. (R), *13*
Bell Oaks Co., Inc. (C), *263*
Blackshaw, Olmstead, Lynch & Koenig (R), *18*
Blane, Stevens & Kellogg (C), *268*
Boone-Scaturro Assoc., Inc. (C), *269*
Boyden (R), *21*
Broward-Dobbs, Inc. (C), *274*
Vickers Chambless Managed Search (C), *288*
Commonwealth Consultants (C), *294*
Consulting Resource Group, Inc. (C), *297*
David C. Cooper & Assoc. Financial Search (C), *298*
Cornerstone Resources, Inc. (C), *299*
The Crawford Group (C), *303*
The Dalley Hewitt Co. (R), *45*
DHR Int'l., Inc. (R), *50*
Dunhill of Atlanta (C), *317*
Dunhill Search of West Atlanta (C), *320*
Eastman & Beaudine, Inc. (R), *56*
D. C. Egan & Assoc. (C), *327*
ETI Search Int'l. (R), *61*
ExecuSource Assoc., Inc. (C), *332*
Executive Placement Services (C), *333*
The Forbes Group (R), *69*
Foster Partners (R), *70*
Fox-Morris Assoc., Inc. (C), *352*

GEOGRAPHICAL

Gaines & Assoc. Int'l., Inc. (R), *73*
Garrett Assoc. Inc. (R), *75*
W. L. Handler & Assoc. (R), *85*
Hartsfield Group, Inc. (R), *87*
Harvard Group Int'l. (R), *87*
Healthcare Management Resources, Inc. (R), *89*
Heidrick & Struggles, Inc. (R), *90*
The Hollins Group, Inc. (R), *95*
Robert Howe & Assoc. (R), *97*
Hughes & Sloan, Inc. (C), *383*
Innovative Search Group, Inc. (R), *102*
Insurance Personnel Resources, Inc. (C), *390*
Interim Accounting Professionals (C), *392*
Interim Executive Recruiting (C), *392*
IprGroup, Inc. (C), *394*
ISC of Atlanta, Inc. (C), *394*
J.J. & H., Ltd. (R), *105*
Jackson & Coker (C), *396*
Jacobson Assoc. (C), *396*
Johnson Smith & Knisely (R), *107*
Chris Kauffman & Company (R), *110*
A.T. Kearney Executive Search (R), *111*
Kenzer Corp. (R), *113*
Keystone Consulting Group (C), *406*
Keystone Consulting Group (C), *406*
Korn/Ferry Int'l. (R), *118*
Evie Kreisler Assoc. Inc. (C), *409*
LAI Ward Howell (R), *123*
Lawrence-Balakonis & Assoc., Inc. (C), *414*
Leader Institute, Inc. (C), *414*
Lectra Search (C), *415*
Lemming/LeVan, Inc. (R), *128*
Lloyd Associates (R), *130*
Lloyd Prescott & Churchill, Inc. (R), *130*
Lloyd Prescott Assoc., Inc. (C), *419*
Lucas Assoc. (C), *421*
Major, Hagen & Africa (C), *423*
Management Recruiters of Atlanta-Vinings (C), *427*
Management Recruiters of Smyrna (C), *427*
Management Recruiters of Atlanta-Buckhead (C), *427*
Management Recruiters of Atlanta-Downtown (C), *428*
Management Recruiters of Atlanta (C), *445*
Management Search Assoc., Inc. (C), *467*
Jon McRae & Associates, Inc. (R), *142*
MedPro Personnel, Inc. (C), *478*
The Mercer Group, Inc. (R), *143*
MSI Int'l. (C), *486*
MSI Int'l. (C), *487*
MSI Int'l. (C), *487*
MSI Int'l. (C), *487*
Norrell Financial Staffing (C), *495*
Norrell Financial Staffing (C), *495*
NPS of Atlanta, Inc. (C), *496*
Parker, McFadden & Assoc. (C), *503*
The Patience Motivation Belief Group, Inc. (C), *505*
Alec Peters Assoc. Inc./DLR (R), *163*
Richard Peterson & Assoc., Inc. (R), *163*
Phoenix Partners, Inc. (C), *511*
Bob Poline Assoc. Inc. (C), *514*
Procom (C), *519*
Professional Selection Services (R), *169*
Ray & Berndtson (R), *172*
Recruiting Options, Inc. (C), *531*
P. J. Reda & Assoc., Inc. (C), *533*
Russell Reynolds Assoc., Inc. (R), *176*
Riddle & McGrath LLC (R), *178*
Romac Int'l. (C), *541*
Romac Int'l., Inc. (C), *543*
Romac Int'l., Inc. (C), *543*
Rowland Mountain & Assoc. (C), *547*
Sales Consultant of Sandy Springs (C), *552*
Sales Consultants of Atlanta (C), *552*
Schulenburg & Assoc. (C), *572*
Schuyler Assoc., Ltd. (R), *185*
Schuyler, Baker & Parker, Inc. (R), *185*
Segal & Assoc. (C), *578*
Shoemaker & Assoc. (R), *190*
James F. Smith & Assoc. (C), *583*
SpencerStuart (R), *197*
TASA International (R), *206*
Tyler & Company (R), *212*
Whittaker & Assoc., Inc. (C), *620*
Windsor International (R), *222*
Winter, Wyman & Co. (C), *623*
Egon Zehnder Int'l. Inc. (R), *227*

Augusta
Dunhill Professional Search of Augusta (C), *320*
Edwards & Assoc. (C), *327*

Clarkston
Innovative Healthcare Services, Inc. (C), *389*

Columbus
Management Recruiters of Columbus, Inc. (C), *445*

Cumming
Anderson Industrial Assoc., Inc. (C), *250*
Management Recruiters of Forsyth County (C), *445*

Dalton
Management Recruiters of Dalton (C), *428*

Dawsonville
Applied Search Assoc., Inc. (C), *252*

Duluth
AMD & Associates (C), *247*
Executive Recruitment Services, Inc. (ERS, Inc.) (C), *334*
Industry Consultants, Inc. (C), *388*
JRL Executive Recruiters (C), *401*
Management Recruiters of Duluth (C), *445*
Medical Search of America, Inc. (C), *477*

Dunwoody
A. D. & Assoc. Executive Search, Inc. (C), *232*
Fortuna Technologies Inc. (C), *343*
InTech Services, Inc. (C), *390*
Raymond Karsan Assoc. (C), *530*

Fayetteville
The CARVIR Group, Inc. (C), *285*

Gainesville
Hall Management Group, Inc. (C), *367*

Jasper
Insurance Personnel Resources, Inc. (C), *390*

Kennesaw
R. A. Wells Co. (C), *618*
Wyndham Mills Int'l., Inc. (R), *225*

LaGrange
Comprehensive Search (C), *294*

Lawrenceville
Janet Harberth & Assoc., Inc. (C), *368*

Lilburn
Emerson & Co. (C), *329*
Warren Executive Services (C), *616*

Lithia Springs
Management Recruiters of Atlanta West, Inc. (C), *445*

Marietta
Paul C. Banks Assoc. (C), *259*
CadTech Staffing Services (C), *279*
Chamberlain Assoc. (C), *288*
Corporate Image Group (C), *300*
Delta Resource Group, Ltd. (C), *311*
Dixie Search Assoc. (C), *313*
Home Health & Hospital Recruiters, Inc. (C), *380*
Lanken-Kimball-Therrell & Assoc. (C), *412*
Loderman & Costello (C), *419*
Management Recruiters of Windy Hill (C), *428*
Management Recruiters Cobb County (C), *428*
Management Recruiters of Marietta, Inc. (C), *446*
The Marathon Group (C), *469*
MarketPro, Inc. (C), *471*
Meyer Assoc., Inc. (R), *144*
PIC Executive Search (C), *511*
Plummer & Associates, Inc. (R), *166*
Primary Care Service Corp. (C), *518*
The Regis Group, Ltd. (R), *174*
Sales Consultant of Cobb County (C), *552*
Team One Partners, Inc. (C), *600*
Van Treadaway Assoc., Inc. (R), *210*
The Whitney Group (C), *620*

McDonough
Leader Resources Group (C), *415*

McRae
Management Recruiters of McRae (C), *428*

Norcross
Cella Assoc. (C), *286*
DBC Recruiting Network (C), *309*
Don Hall & Assoc. (C), *366*
F-O-R-T-U-N-E Personnel Consultants of Atlanta, Inc. (C), *345*
Innovative Resource Group, LLC (C), *389*
Jones Consulting Executive Search (C), *400*
Management Recruiters of Atlanta NE (C), *446*
F. P. Lennon Assoc. (C), *416*
Southern Chemical & Plastics Search (C), *587*

Spear-Izzo Assoc., LLC (C), *589*
TeamBuilders (C), *600*
The Worth Group (C), *625*

Peachtree City
Jones-Parker/Starr (R), *108*
Management Recruiters of Atlanta-South (C), *428*
Southern Chemical & Plastics Search (C), *587*

Perry
Management Recruiters of Perry (C), *428*

Richmond Hill
Sales Consultants of Richmond Hill (C), *552*

Roswell
ATS Executive Recruitment (C), *255*
Bellamy & Assoc. (C), *263*
Career Marketing Consultants, Inc. (C), *282*
Emerging Technology Search (C), *329*
Empowered Solutions Corp. (C), *330*
ExeConnex, LLC (R), *61*
Executive Strategies, Inc. (C), *337*
Hayman Daugherty Assoc., Inc. (C), *370*
Horton Int'l. Inc. (R), *96*
Intersource, Ltd. (R), *103*
Management Recruiters of Roswell-West (C), *428*
Management Recruiters of Atlanta North, Inc. (C), *446*
G. E. McFarland & Co. (R), *140*
National Restaurant Search, Inc. (R), *150*
Peachtree Executive Search (R), *161*
Plemmons Assoc., Inc. (R), *165*
Reeder & Assoc., Ltd. (R), *173*
Sanford Rose Assoc. - Atlanta North (C), *566*
G. L. Schwartz & Assoc., Inc. (C), *572*
Smith James Group, Inc. (R), *194*

Sandy Springs
Management Recruiters of Sandy Springs (C), *446*

Savannah
F-O-R-T-U-N-E Personnel Consultants of Savannah, Inc. (C), *345*
Management Recruiters of Savannah (C), *446*
QVS Int'l. (R), *170*
Sales Consultants of Savannah, GA (C), *557*

Smyrna
MES Search Co. (C), *479*

Snellville
ARJay & Assoc. (C), *253*
HR Consultants (C), *382*
Lanken-Therrell & Assoc. (C), *412*
Summit Group Int'l., Inc. (R), *204*

St. Simons Island
BFW, Inc. (C), *266*
Management Recruiters of St. Simons Island (C), *428*

Stone Mountain
Claremont-Branan, Inc. (C), *292*
Creative HR Solutions (C), *303*
Special Markets Group, Inc. (R), *195*

Suwanee
NaviSearch (C), *490*

Tucker
Corporate Plus, Ltd. (C), *300*
Elite Medical Search (C), *328*

Union City
Ron Jackson & Assoc. (C), *396*

Woodstock
Management Recruiters of Woodstock (C), *428*
Management Recruiters - Towne Lake (C), *446*
Rollins Search Group, Inc. (C), *541*
Sales Consultants of Cherokee (C), *558*

Hawaii

Hilo
Management Recruiters of Hilo (C), *428*

Honolulu
Dunhill Professional Search of Hawaii (C), *320*
Ellis & Associates (C), *328*
Human Resources Management Hawaii, Inc. (C), *384*
Lam Assoc. (C), *411*
Orion Int'l. Consulting Group, Inc. (C), *499*
Physician Associates (C), *511*
Sales Consultants of Honolulu (C), *558*

Kamuela
Management Recruiters of Kona (C), *428*

Koloa
Butterfield & Co. Int'l., Inc. (C), *277*

Idaho

Boise
F-O-R-T-U-N-E Personnel Consultants of Boise (R), *70*

Boise
Management Recruiters of Boise (C), *446*
Sales Consultants of Boise (C), *552*

Coeur d'Alene
Ward-Hoffman & Assoc. (C), *615*

Ketchum
Management Recruiters of Sun Valley (C), *447*

Illinois

Albion
Management Recruiters of Albion (C), *428*

Algonquin
Roth Young of Chicago (C), *546*

Arlington Heights
Allstaff, Inc. (C), *245*
The Baldwin Group (R), *10*
Dynamic Search Systems, Inc. (C), *324*
Fortune of Arlington Heights (C), *345*
Management Recruiters of Arlington Heights (C), *428*
Sales Consultants of Arlington Heights (C), *552*
Systems Search (C), *599*

Aurora
Management Recruiters of Chicago West (C), *447*

Barrington
Adams & Assoc. Int'l. (R), *1*
The Beam Group (R), *14*
Dan B. Brockman (C), *274*
Carpenter, Shackleton & Company (R), *30*
Despres & Associates (C), *311*
The Garms Group (R), *74*
Horton Int'l. Inc. (R), *96*
Joslin & Assoc., Ltd. (C), *401*
C. R. Krafski & Assoc., Inc. (R), *120*
D. Kunkle & Assoc. (C), *410*
LAI Ward Howell (R), *123*
Management Recruiters of Barrington (C), *447*
Management Search, Inc. (C), *467*
Murphy Partners Int'l. (R), *150*
The Remington Group (R), *174*
Sales Consultants of Barrington (C), *558*
Sensible Solutions, Inc. (R), *188*
TSC Management Services Group, Inc. (C), *610*

Batavia
Management Recruiters of Batavia (C), *447*

Bloomington
Sales Consultant of Bloomington (C), *552*

Broadview
Abbott Smith Assoc., Inc. (R), *193*

Brookfield
David Rowe & Assoc., Inc. (R), *182*

Buffalo Grove
Career Counseling Ltd. (C.C.L.) (C), *282*
HG & Assoc. (R), *93*
International Consulting Services, Inc. (C), *392*
Earl L. McDermid & Assoc. (C), *474*

Carol Stream
C. Berger And Company (R), *16*

Cary
J. P. Gleason Assoc., Inc. (R), *77*

Chatham
Pro-Tech Search, Inc. (C), *519*

Cherry Valley
Management Recruiters of Cherry Valley (C), *428*

GEOGRAPHICAL

Chicago

Accountants On Call (C), *235*
G. Adams Partners (R), *2*
Allerton Heneghan & O'Neill (R), *4*
AM & G Certified Public Accountants & Consultants (R), *4*
American Resources Corp. (C), *248*
Amherst Human Resource Group, Ltd. (C), *249*
Attorney Search Global, Inc. (C), *255*
Baker, Nelms & Montgomery (C), *258*
The Bankers Group (C), *258*
Barrett Partners (C), *260*
Barrington Hart, Inc. (R), *12*
Battalia Winston Int'l./The Euram Consultants Group (R), *13*
Martin H. Bauman Assoc., Inc. (R), *14*
The Blackman Kallick Search Division (C), *267*
Boulware & Assoc. Inc. (R), *20*
Boyden (R), *21*
Briant Assoc., Inc. (R), *23*
Brooke Chase Assoc., Inc. (R), *24*
Business Systems of America, Inc. (C), *277*
Capstone Consulting, Inc. (R), *29*
Cardwell Enterprises Inc. (R), *29*
The Carlyle Group, Ltd. (R), *30*
Carpenter Assoc., Inc. (R), *30*
Carpenter, Shackleton & Company (R), *30*
Carrington & Carrington, Ltd. (R), *30*
Cemco, Ltd. (C), *286*
CFR Executive Search, Inc. (C), *288*
Chicago Legal Search, Ltd. (C), *290*
CMC Search Consultants (C), *293*
Computer Search Group, Ltd. (R), *39*
Cook Assoc.,® Inc. (R), *40*
Corporate Select Int'l., Ltd. (C), *301*
The Corporate Source Group, Inc. (R), *41*
Crist Partners, Ltd. (R), *43*
Daubenspeck & Associates, Ltd. (R), *46*
DHR Int'l., Inc. (R), *49*
Dieckmann & Assoc., Ltd. (R), *51*
Discovery, The Staffing Specialists, Inc. (C), *312*
Doherty Int'l., Inc. (R), *53*
Donahue/Bales Assoc. (R), *54*
Dunhill of Chicago (C), *317*
Early Cochran & Olson (R), *56*
Executive Referral Services, Inc. (C), *334*
Executive Search Consultants Corp. (C), *335*
Fergason Assoc., Inc. (C), *339*
First Search Inc. (C), *341*
Foster Partners (R), *70*
Fought, Jameson Assoc. (C), *351*
Friedman Eisenstein Raemer & Schwartz, LLP (R), *72*
Gaines & Assoc. Int'l., Inc. (R), *73*
Gans, Gans & Assoc., Inc. (R), *74*
Glines Assoc., Inc. (R), *77*
Godfrey Personnel, Inc. (C), *359*
David Gomez & Assoc., Inc. (R), *79*
Gregory Laka & Co. (C), *411*
Gregory Michaels & Assoc., Inc. (R), *82*
GWS Partners (R), *84*
Hale Assoc. (R), *84*
Hall Kinion (C), *367*
William E. Hay & Co. (R), *88*
Hedlund Corp. (C), *375*
Heidrick & Struggles, Inc. (R), *90*
Heidrick & Struggles, Inc. (R), *90*
The Heidrick Partners, Inc. (R), *90*
Hoglund & Assoc., Inc. (R), *94*
Holland Rusk & Assoc. (R), *95*
The Hollins Group, Inc. (R), *95*
Hunter Douglas Group, Inc. (R), *99*
Meredith Ingram, Ltd. (C), *388*
J. R. Scott & Assoc., Ltd. (C), *395*
J.J. & H., Ltd. (R), *104*
Jacobson Assoc. (C), *396*
John H. Johnson & Assoc., Inc. (R), *106*
Johnson Smith & Knisely (R), *107*
Kanzer Assoc., Inc. (R), *109*
A.T. Kearney Executive Search (R), *111*
Kennedy & Co. (R), *112*
Kenzer Corp. (R), *113*
Kittleman & Assoc.,LLC (R), *115*
Korn/Ferry Int'l. (R), *118*
Evie Kreisler Assoc. Inc. (C), *409*
Kresin Wingard (C), *409*
LAI Ward Howell (R), *123*
Lauer, Sbarbaro Assoc., EMA Partners Int'l. (R), *126*
Lloyd Prescott & Churchill, Inc. (R), *130*
Lloyd Prescott Assoc., Inc. (C), *419*
Lynch Miller Moore Partners, Inc. (R), *132*
Major, Hagen & Africa (C), *423*
Management Recruiters of Chicago-Downtown (C), *428*
Martin Partners, L.L.C. (R), *137*
Paul May & Assoc. (C), *473*
Clarence E. McFeely, Inc. (R), *141*
Mengel & McDonald Ltd. (C), *479*
Moriarty/Fox, Inc. (R), *147*
Paul Winston Norman & Assoc. (R), *152*
Norman Broadbent Int'l., Inc. (R), *152*
Norrell Financial Staffing (C), *495*
John R. O'Connor & Assoc. (C), *497*
Onsite Staffing Solutions (R), *156*
Pacific Advisory Service, Inc. (C), *501*
Pawlik/Dorman Partners (R), *161*
Vera L. Rast Partners Inc. (C), *529*
Ray & Berndtson (R), *172*
Redell Search, Inc. (C), *533*
S. Reyman & Assoc., Ltd. (R), *176*
Russell Reynolds Assoc., Inc. (R), *176*
Ridenour & Assoc. (R), *178*
Robertson & Assoc. (C), *539*
Romac Int'l. (C), *541*
Romac Int'l., Inc. (C), *543*
Rovner & Assoc., Inc. (R), *182*
RSMR, Inc. (R), *182*
Sales & Management Search, Inc. (C), *551*
Sales Consultant of Chicago-Downtown (C), *552*
Sanford Rose Assoc. - Chicago (C), *566*
David Saxner & Assoc., Inc. (DSA, Inc.) (R), *185*
Search Bureau Int'l. (C), *574*
Search Dynamics, Inc. (C), *575*
Shepherd Bueschel & Provus, Inc. (R), *189*
Sheridan Search (R), *189*
The Shorr Group (R), *190*
D. W. Simpson & Co. (C), *582*
Slayton Int'l., Inc. (R), *192*
Smith Hanley Assoc., Inc. (C), *584*
SpencerStuart (R), *197*
Springer Souder & Assoc. L.L.C. (R), *198*
Stanton Chase Int'l. (R), *199*
Stone Enterprises Ltd. (C), *594*
Strategic Executives, Inc. (R), *202*
Strategic Search Corp. (R), *202*
Ron Sunshine & Assoc. (C), *597*
Synergistics Assoc. Ltd. (R), *205*
Roy Talman & Assoc. (C), *599*
Templeton & Assoc. (C), *605*
Tesar-Reynes, Inc. (R), *208*
Tomlinson Assoc. Inc. (C), *607*
Tuft & Assoc., Inc. (R), *212*
Beverly von Winckler & Assoc. (C), *613*
Fred Wackerle, Inc. (R), *214*
Waveland Int'l. (R), *216*
Lee Weil Assoc., Inc. (C), *617*
Wheelless Group (R), *219*
White, Roberts & Stratton, Inc. (C), *619*
Williams, Roth & Krueger, Inc. (R), *221*
Wilson-Douglas-Jordan (C), *622*
Winston & Green (C), *623*
M. Wood Company (R), *224*
Egon Zehnder Int'l. Inc. (R), *227*
Zenner Consulting Group (C), *627*
Zwell Int'l. (R), *228*

Countryside

The Glenwood Group (C), *358*

Crete

Franchise Recruiters Ltd. (R), *71*

Crystal Lake

Corporate Environment Ltd. (R), *41*
Kinderis & Loercher Group (C), *407*
Lyons & Assoc., Inc. (C), *422*

Decatur

Premier Search Group (C), *517*

Deerfield

Diversified Management Resources (C), *313*
Meder & Assoc., Inc. (R), *142*

Des Plaines

Executive Placement Consultants (C), *333*
Financial Search Corp. (C), *340*
Human Resource Technologies, Inc. (R), *99*
Management Recruiters of O'Hare (C), *428*
Raymond Karsan Assoc. (C), *530*
Ritt-Ritt & Assoc., Inc. (C), *537*
Selectis Corp. (C), *578*

Downers Grove

S. C. Int'l., Ltd. (C), *550*

Dundee

Norton & Assoc. (C), *496*

Effingham

Sanford Rose Assoc. - Effingham (C), *566*

Elgin

Lewis Consulting Service (C), *417*
Management Recruiters of Elgin (C), *428*
The Technology Group (R), *208*

Elmhurst

Michael Assoc. (R), *144*
J. L. Nixon Consulting (C), *493*

Evanston
Ann Coe & Assoc. (C), *294*
Conway & Assoc. (R), *40*
Haydon Legal Search (C), *370*
Hazlett Associates (R), *88*
Management Recruiters of Evanston (C), *428*

Flossmoor
Gateway Management Resources (C), *355*
Holden & Harlan Assoc., Inc. (C), *380*

Frankfort
Management Recruiters of Will County (C), *428*

Geneva
Oberlander & Co., Inc. (R), *155*
Xagas & Assoc. (R), *226*

Glen Ellyn
Marsteller Wilcox Assoc. (C), *471*
Parsons Assoc. Inc. (R), *159*
Reifel & Assoc. (R), *174*
Rooney Assoc., Inc. (R), *181*

Glendale Heights
Gaffney Management Consultants (R), *73*

Glenview
John C. Boone & Co. (R), *19*
Heartland National Medical Search (C), *374*
Retis Assoc., Inc. (C), *535*
Sales Search Specialist (C), *564*
Spriggs & Co., Inc. (R), *198*

Gurnee
Advancement, Inc. (C), *241*
H. J. Elliot, Inc. (R), *58*

Highland Park
LMB Assoc. (C), *419*
Management Recruiters of Highland Park (C), *428*
Michael Wayne Recruiters (C), *480*
Mitchell/Wolfson, Assoc. (R), *145*

Hinsdale
Philip Conway Management (R), *40*
Fortune Personnel Consultants of Hinsdale, IL (C), *346*
Gnodde Assoc. (C), *359*
The Murray Group (C), *487*

Hoffman Estates
R2 Services, LLC (C), *528*

Homewood
Gregory Laka & Co. (C), *411*
Management Recruiters of Chicago-South (C), *428*

Inverness
Michael J. Hawkins, Inc. (C), *370*
The Hetzel Group, Inc. (R), *92*

Itasca
BGB Assoc., Inc. (C), *266*
Sevcor Int'l., Inc. (R), *188*
VanMaldegiam Assoc., Inc. (R), *213*

Joliet
Britt Assoc., Inc. (C), *274*

La Grange Park
Joseph Chandler & Assoc., Inc. (R), *33*

Lake Bluff
The PAR Group - Paul A. Reaume, Ltd. (R), *159*
Sanford Rose Assoc. - Lake Forest (R), *184*

Lake Forest
Chicago Research Group, Inc. (R), *33*
The Eldridge Group, Ltd. (C), *327*
Kreutz Consulting Group, Inc. (R), *121*
Management Recruiters of Lake Forest, IL (C), *447*
McDonald Assoc. Int'l. (R), *140*
Morgan Int'l., Inc. (R), *147*

Lake Zurich
E. J. Ashton & Assoc., Ltd. (C), *253*
Management Recruiters of Chicago-North West (C), *428*
The Stanton Group, Inc. (C), *591*
The Wellesley Group, Inc. (R), *217*

Libertyville
CompuPro (C), *295*
Matthews Professional Employment Specialists, Inc. (C), *473*
Rust & Assoc., Inc. (R), *183*

Lincoln
Agra Placements, Ltd. (C), *242*

Lincolnshire
The Marshall Group (R), *137*

Lisle
Aggressive Corporation (C), *242*
Verkamp-Joyce Assoc., Inc. (R), *213*

Lockport
Management Recruiters of Chicago-Southwest (C), *428*

Lombard
Onsite Staffing Solutions (R), *156*

Marion
Cami Austin & Assoc. (C), *256*

Mattoon
Management Recruiters of Mattoon (C), *428*
Preston-Hunter, Inc. (R), *167*

McHenry
Bratland & Assoc. (C), *272*

Mokena
Sanford Rose Assoc. - Orland Park (C), *567*

Moline
Snelling Search (C), *585*

Mt. Prospect
Exec Tech, Inc. (C), *332*
Magnum Search (C), *422*
Management Recruiters of Prospect Heights (C), *428*
L. J. Reszotko & Assoc. (C), *535*

Technical Recruiting Consultants (C), *602*

Naperville
Carnegie Partners, Inc. (R), *30*
Cumberland Group Inc. (C), *304*
David Fockler & Assoc., Inc. (C), *342*
H.Q. Search, Inc. (C), *365*
Jender & Company (R), *105*
L T M Assoc. (C), *410*
Management Recruiters of Chicago-Far West (C), *429*
J. Rodgers & Associates (C), *540*

Niles
Polytechnical Consultants, Inc. (C), *514*

Normal
Heller Kil Assoc., Inc. (C), *375*
Management Recruiters of Bloomington (C), *429*

Northbrook
Accountants On Call (C), *235*
K. Carroll & Assoc. (C), *284*
Clarey & Andrews, Inc. (R), *35*
David M. Griffith & Assoc., Ltd. (R), *82*
Hersher Assoc., Ltd. (R), *92*
Higgins Assoc., Inc. (R), *93*
Management Recruiters of Chicago-North Shore (C), *447*
Sales Consultants (C), *558*
Voigt Assoc. (R), *214*
Deborah Snow Walsh, Inc. (R), *215*
Karen Wanger & Assoc., Inc. (C), *615*

Northfield
B. J. Abrams & Assoc. Inc. (C), *233*
Hazard, Young, Attea & Assoc., Ltd. (C), *371*
Heller Assoc., Ltd. (R), *91*
Management Recruiters of Glenview/Northfield (C), *429*
Ralph Smith & Assoc. (C), *584*

Oak Brook
American Logistics Consultants, Inc. (C), *247*
American Services Group (C), *248*
Bradford & Galt, Inc. (C), *271*
Callan Assoc., Ltd. (R), *27*
Cemco, Ltd. (C), *287*
Cizek Assoc., Inc. (R), *35*
Dynamic Staffing Network (C), *324*
Erwin Assoc. (R), *60*
Grossberg & Assoc. (R), *82*
Kensington Int'l., Inc. (R), *113*
Kunzer Assoc., Ltd. (R), *121*
M/J/A Partners (R), *133*
P. J. Nicholson & Assoc. (C), *493*
Romac Int'l., Inc. (C), *543*
The Ryan Charles Group, Inc. (C), *549*
Snelling Search (C), *586*
TE, Inc. (C), *600*
Witt/Kieffer, Ford, Hadelman & Lloyd (R), *223*
Witt/Kieffer, Ford, Hadelman & Lloyd (R), *223*

Oak Park
Cowell & Associates, Ltd. (R), *42*
DeCorrevont & Assoc. (C), *310*

GEOGRAPHICAL

Robert G. Godfrey Assoc. Ltd. (R), 78
Juan Menefee & Assoc. (C), 478
O'Toole & Company, Inc. (R), 154
Prairie Resource Group, Inc. (R), 166

Oakbrook Terrace
Accountants On Call (C), 235
Alpha Resources (C), 246
Compass Group Ltd. (R), 38
Tannura & Assoc., Inc. (R), 206

Olympia Fields
Tom McCall Executive Search (C), 473

Palatine
The Robinson Group, D.A., Ltd. (C), 539
Sales Consultants of Buffalo Grove (C), 552
Thomas Lyle & Co. (C), 606

Palos Heights
Sales Consultants of Chicago South (C), 558

Palos Park
Reinecke & Assoc. (C), 533

Peoria
Bradford & Galt, Inc. (C), 271
Dunhill Professional Search of Peoria (C), 317
Management Recruiters of Peoria (C), 429

Rock Island
S. E. Weinstein Co. (R), 217

Rockford
The Furst Group, Inc. (R), 72
Furst Group/MPI (R), 72
Global HealthCare Partners (R), 78
Partners in Recruiting (C), 503
Sanford Rose Assoc. - Rockford (C), 567

Rolling Meadows
Computer Professionals (R), 38
Dunhill Professional Search of Rolling Meadows (C), 320
Electronic Search, Inc. (C), 327
John Imber Assoc., Ltd. (R), 101
Mannard & Assoc., Inc. (R), 135
Romac Int'l., Inc. (C), 543

Roscoe
Effective Search, Inc. (R), 57

Roselle
Mary Rector & Assoc., Inc. (C), 533

Rosemont
Bertrand, Ross & Assoc., Inc. (C), 266
Paul J. Biestek Assoc., Inc. (R), 17
Hodge-Cronin & Assoc., Inc. (R), 94
International Management Services Inc. (R), 102
Techstaff Inc. (C), 603
Weatherby Healthcare (C), 617

Schaumburg
Accountants On Call (C), 235
BayResearch Group, Inc. (R), 14
ContactBridge, Inc. (R), 40
Desktop Staffing, Inc. (C), 311
DHR Int'l., Inc. (R), 50
Hali Kinion (C), 367
Jim Kay & Assoc. (C), 404
McCormick Search Inc. (C), 474
Professional Research Services, Inc. (R), 169
Professional Search Centre, Ltd. (C), 522
Systems One Ltd. (C), 598
Systems Research Inc. (SRI) (C), 598
Valentine & Assoc. (C), 611
West & Assoc. (C), 618

Skokie
Ronald Norris & Assoc. (C), 495

Springfield
CMW & Associates, Inc. (C), 293
Management Recruiters of Springfield, Inc. (C), 447
Robert William James & Assoc. (C), 539

St. Charles
Management Recruiters of St. Charles (C), 447
Michael James & Co. (C), 480
National Restaurant Search, Inc. (R), 150
Select Services (C), 578

Sycamore
Mathey Services (C), 472

Tuscola
Management Recruiters of Champaign (C), 429

Union
Sales Consultants of Western McHenry County (C), 558

Vernon Hills
Herbeck Kline & Assoc. (R), 92
A.D. Schiff & Assoc., Ltd. (C), 572

Villa Park
Caprio & Assoc. Inc. (R), 29

Warrenville
HCI Corp. (C), 371

Waukegan
Matthews Professional Employment Specialists, Inc. (C), 472

West Dundee
Woltz & Assoc., Inc. (R), 224

Westchester
C.P.S., Inc. (C), 278
The Prairie Group (C), 515

Westmont
Nicholaou & Co. (R), 151

Wheaton
DEL Technical Services, Inc. (C), 310
The Hensge Co. (R), 91
Johnson Assoc., Inc. (C), 399
New Directions, Inc. (C), 492
Quest Enterprises, Ltd. (C), 527
Sanford Rose Assoc. - Oak Brook (C), 567
Van Dyke Assoc. (R), 212
Watring & Assoc., Inc. (C), 616

Wheeling
Matthews Professional Employment Specialists, Inc. (C), 473
The Moran Group (C), 484

Wilmette
Barth Smith Company (R), 12
Donald F. Dvorak & Co. (R), 55
Joyce C. Knauff & Assoc. (C), 408
Krueger Assoc. (R), 121

Winfield
Waterford Executive Group Ltd. (C), 616

Indiana

Anderson
Hudson Assoc. Inc. (C), 383

Angola
Sharrow & Assoc., Inc. (C), 579

Avon
Management Recruiters of Avon (Indianapolis-West) (C), 429

Carmel
Healthcare Recruiters of Indiana (C), 372
Management Recruiters of Indianapolis-North (C), 448
Sales Consultants of Indianapolis-North (C), 558
Sanford Rose Assoc. - Carmel, IN (C), 567

Chesterton
Quality Search (C), 526

Columbus
Management Recruiters of Columbus (C), 429
Smith & Syberg, Inc. (R), 193

Dyer
National Metal Services Corp. (C), 489
National Recruiting Service (C), 489

Elkhart
Sage Employment Recruiters (C), 550

Evansville
Management Recruiters of Evansville (C), 429
Sales Consultants of Evansville (C), 552

Ft. Wayne
Brierwood Group, Inc. (C), 273
Dunhill of Ft. Wayne, Inc. (C), 320
The Mallard Group (C), 423
Management Recruiters of Greater Ft. Wayne (C), 429
Mayhall Search Group, Inc. (C), 473
National Corporate Consultants, Inc. (C), 489
Roster Inc. (C), 545

Greencastle
Premier Search Group (C), 517

Greenwood
Dunhill Staffing Systems (C), 317

Indianapolis
Accountants On Call (C), *236*
The Bennett Group, Inc. (R), *16*
Career Consultants (R), *29*
CMS Management Services LLC (C), *293*
DHR Int'l., Inc. (R), *50*
Dunhill Staffing Systems of Indianapolis Northeast (C), *317*
Dunhill Staffing Systems of Indianapolis NW (C), *317*
Dunhill Staffing Systems of Indianapolis West (C), *317*
Dunhill Technical Staffing (C), *320*
B. W. Higgins, Inc. (C), *377*
HMO Executive Search (C), *379*
Insurance People (C), *390*
Johnson Brown Assoc., Inc. (C), *400*
Management Recruiters - Indianapolis (C), *448*
Management Recruiters of Indianapolis (C), *448*
The Morley Group (C), *486*
Quiring Assoc., Inc. (C), *527*
Resource Networking Inc. (C), *534*
Romac Int'l., Inc. (C), *543*
Romac Int'l., Inc. (C), *543*
Sales Consultants of Indianapolis (C), *558*
J. Harrington Smith Assoc. (C), *584*

Lafayette
Allhands Placement Consultants (C), *245*
The Wabash Group (C), *613*

Long Beach
De Funiak & Edwards (R), *47*

Mt. Vernon
F-O-R-T-U-N-E Personnel Consultants of Southwest Indiana (C), *346*

Muncie
Professional Resource Group, Inc. (C), *522*

Nashville
Dunhill Executive Search of Brown County (C), *321*

Newburgh
Sanford Rose Assoc. - Evansville (C), *567*

Noblesville
Management Recruiters of Noblesville, Inc. (C), *448*
TPS Staffing Solutions (C), *608*

Peru
Agra Placements, Ltd. (C), *242*

Richmond
Management Recruiters of Richmond (C), *429*

South Bend
CMS Management Services LLC (C), *293*
Crowe Chizek & Co. (C), *304*
Executive Search Plus, Inc. (C), *336*
F-O-R-T-U-N-E Personnel Consultants of South Bend (C), *346*
Management Recruiters of South Bend (C), *448*
mfg/Search, Inc. (C), *480*

Terre Haute
Corporate Search Consultants (C), *301*

Wabash
Lange & Assoc., Inc. (C), *412*

West Lafayette
ExecuTech (C), *332*

Iowa

Arnolds Park
Management Recruiters of Spencer (C), *448*

Bettendorf
AGRI-associates (C), *242*
Management Recruiters of Quad Cities (C), *429*
Techstaff Inc. (C), *603*
Triumph Consulting, Inc. (R), *210*

Cedar Rapids
Future Employment Service, Inc. (C), *354*
Kaas Employment Services (C), *402*
Management Recruiters-Cedar Rapids, Inc. (C), *448*
Ray & Assoc., Inc. (C), *529*
Sanford Rose Assoc. - Cedar Rapids (C), *567*

Centerville
Management Recruiters of Centerville (C), *429*

Coralville
Management Recruiters of Iowa City (C), *429*

Council Bluffs
Sales Consultant of Riverside (C), *552*

Davenport
Management Resource Group, Ltd. (C), *467*
Professional Personnel Services (C), *520*

Des Moines
Carlson & Czeswik (R), *30*
Corporate Suite, Ltd. (C), *301*
Eyler Assoc., Inc. (R), *64*
The Garrison Organization (R), *75*
Management Recruiters of Des Moines (C), *449*
Personnel Incorporated (C), *508*

Dubuque
Future Employment Service, Inc. (C), *353*

Fairfield
Atkinson Search & Placement, Inc. (C), *255*
Management Recruiters of Fairfield (C), *449*
J. R. Seehusen Assoc., Inc. (R), *188*
Smith Assoc. (C), *584*

Iowa City
Dunhill of Iowa City (C), *317*

Maquoketa
Future Employment Service, Inc. (C), *354*

Marion
Brei & Assoc., Inc. (C), *272*

Mason City
Management Recruiters of Mason City (C), *429*

Sioux City
Management Recruiters of Siouxland (C), *449*

West Des Moines
Agra Placements, Ltd. (C), *242*
Francis & Assoc. (R), *71*
Staffing Edge, Inc. (C), *590*

Williamsburg
Management Recruiters of Williamsburg (C), *449*

Kansas

Fairway
Staffing Edge, Inc. (C), *590*

Ft. Scott
Management Recruiters of Ft. Scott (C), *429*

Kansas City
V. Robinson & Co., Inc. (C), *539*

Lawrence
The Winn Group, Inc. (C), *623*

Mission
MIS Computer Professionals, Inc. (C), *482*

Overland Park
Bowman & Marshall, Inc. (C), *271*
Bradford & Galt, Inc. (C), *271*
The Century Group (C), *287*
Defrain Mayer (R), *48*
DHR Int'l., Inc. (R), *50*
EFL Assoc. (R), *57*
Legal Search Assoc. (C), *416*
Management Recruiters of Overland Park (C), *429*
Management Recruiters of Leawood (C), *429*
Morgan Hunter Corp. (C), *485*
RHAssoc. Inc. (C), *535*
Romac Int'l., Inc. (C), *543*
Sales Consultants of Overland Park (C), *553*
Sherriff & Assoc. (C), *580*
Michael Shirley Assoc. Inc. (R), *190*
Wood-Glavin, Inc. (R), *224*

Shawnee Mission
The Christopher Group (C), *291*
Lawrence-Leiter & Co. (R), *126*
Michael/Merrill (C), *481*
Smith, Brown & Jones (C), *585*
Stoneburner Assoc., Inc. (C), *594*

St. Marys
Bosco-Hubert & Assoc. (C), *270*

Topeka
Dunhill Personnel of Topeka, Inc. (C), *317*
Management Recruiters of Topeka, Inc. (C), *449*

Wichita
Dunhill of Wichita, Inc. (C), *317*
Health Search, Inc. (C), *371*
Management Recruiters of Wichita (C), *429*
Sales Consultants of Wichita (C), *553*

Kentucky

Bardstown
Buckman/Enochs & Assoc., Inc. (C), *276*

Bowling Green
Management Recruiters of Warren County, KY (C), *449*

Danville
Binder Hospitality Group (C), *266*
Management Recruiters of Danville (C), *449*

Eastwood
Search Assoc. (C), *574*

Florence
Sharrow & Assoc., Inc. (C), *579*

Georgetown
Barber & Assoc. (C), *259*

Lexington
C. M. Management Services, Inc. (R), *26*
Management Recruiters of Lexington (C), *429*
Sales Consultant of The Bluegrass (C), *553*
Sales Consultants of Lexington (C), *553*
TBC, Inc. (C), *600*

Louisville
Accountants On Call (C), *236*
Angel Group Int'l. (C), *250*
The Hindman Co. (R), *94*
Management Recruiters of Louisville (C), *429*
Ovca Assoc. Inc. (R), *157*
Professional Search Consultants (C), *522*
Romac Int'l., Inc. (C), *543*
Romac Int'l., Inc. (C), *543*
Sales Consultants of Louisville (C), *553*
Sanford Rose Assoc. - Louisville (C), *567*
SHS of Louisville, KY (C), *580*

Owensboro
Career Counseling Inc. (CCI) (C), *282*
F-o-r-t-u-n-e of Owensboro, Inc. (C), *346*

Prospect
Karen Marshall Assoc. (C), *471*

Richmond
Management Recruiters of Richmond (C), *449*

Salem
Direct Marketing Solutions (C), *312*

Shelbyville
Management Recruiters of Shelbyville (C), *429*

Louisiana

Alexandria
Sales Consultant of Alexandria (C), *553*

Baton Rouge
Astro Executive Search Firm (C), *254*
Dunhill of Baton Rouge, Inc. (C), *317*
Sales Consultants of Baton Rouge (C), *553*

Harahan
Gelpi & Assoc. (C), *355*

Kenner
Gaming Consultants, Inc. (R), *74*

Mandeville
Dunhill Professional Search of Greater New Orleans (C), *317*
The Garvis Group, Inc. (C), *355*
Sales Consultant of New Orleans Northshore (C), *553*
Shiell Personnel (C), *580*

Metairie
Dunhill Professional Search of Greater New Orleans (C), *321*
Healthcare Recruiters of New Orleans (C), *373*
Management Recruiters of New Orleans (C), *429*
River Region Personnel, Inc. (C), *538*
Sales Consultants of New Orleans (C), *553*
Walker Personnel, Inc. (C), *614*

Monroe
Management Recruiters of Monroe, Inc. (C), *450*
MSI Int'l. (C), *487*
Snelling Search (C), *586*

New Orleans
Accounting Personnel & Engineering Personnel Consultants (C), *238*
McCarthy Assoc. National BancSearch, LLC (C), *473*
MSI Int'l. (C), *487*

Ruston
Born & Bicknell, Inc. (C), *270*

Shreveport
Dunhill of Shreveport, Inc. (C), *317*
Management Recruiters of Shreveport (C), *429*

Slidell
Management Recruiters of St. Tammany (C), *429*

Maine

Bailey Island
Global Engineers Inc. (C), *358*

Brewer
Sales Consultants of Bangor, Inc. (C), *559*

Brunswick
DHR Int'l., Inc. (R), *50*
Leigh Hunt & Assoc., Inc. (C), *384*

Cape Elizabeth
Executive Resource Group, Inc. (R), *63*

Gorham
Lake Medical Associates (C), *411*
Paper Industry Recruitment (P.I.R.) (C), *502*

Hampden
Northern Consultants Inc. (R), *153*

Kennebunk
Rand Assoc. (R), *171*

Northport
Caldwell Legal Recruiting Consultants (C), *279*

Portland
Doherty Healthcare Consultants (C), *313*
John Jay & Co. (C), *399*
ProSearch, Inc. (C), *524*
Swift & Assoc. (C), *597*

South Portland
Executive Search of New England, Inc. (C), *336*

Vinalhaven
The Haystack Group, Inc. (R), *88*

Wiscasset
Groton Planning Group (R), *82*

Maryland

Annapolis
The Abbott Group, Inc. (R), *1*
Ann Bond Assoc. Inc. (C), *269*
DHR Int'l., Inc. (R), *50*
Kames & Assoc. (C), *403*
Management Recruiters of Annapolis (C), *429*
The Oldani Group (R), *155*
B. D. Wallace & Assoc. (C), *614*

Arnold
The Park Group & Assoc., Inc. (C), *502*

Baltimore
Accountants On Call (C), *236*
D. W. Baird & Associates (C), *257*
Bowie & Associates, Inc. (C), *271*
Brandjes Assoc. (C), *272*
Columbia Consulting Group (R), *38*
Columbia Consulting Group (R), *38*
Continental Search & Outplacement, Inc. (C), *298*
Rob Dey Executive Search (R), *49*
EDI, Inc. (C), *326*
The Executive Tree (R), *64*
First Advisory Services Int'l., Inc. (R), *67*
Fox-Morris Assoc., Inc. (C), *352*
Horton Int'l. Inc. (R), *96*

Interim Financial Solutions - Mid-Atlantic Region (C), *392*
Kostmayer Assoc., Inc. (R), *119*
Management Assoc. (C), *424*
Management Recruiters of Baltimore City (C), *430*
Partners Resource Group (C), *504*
Professional Employment Group (C), *520*
Roberts Ryan & Bentley, Inc. (R), *179*
Romac Int'l., Inc. (C), *543*
Sales Consultant of Baltimore-Downtown (C), *553*
Stanton Chase Int'l. (R), *198*

Berlin
Brandywine Management Group (R), *22*

Bethesda
BG & Assoc. (C), *266*
A. G. Fishkin & Assoc., Inc. (R), *68*
Further Management Group (C), *353*
Grant/Morgan Assoc., Inc. (C), *361*
The Hamilton Group (R), *85*
Interim Financial Solutions (C), *392*
Larsen & Lee, Inc. (R), *125*
LG Brand, Inc. (C), *417*
Management Recruiters of Bethesda (C), *430*
Raymond Karsan Assoc. (C), *530*
Roberts Ryan & Bentley, Inc. (R), *179*
StratfordGroup (R), *203*
The Whyte Group, Inc. (R), *220*
Witt/Kieffer, Ford, Hadelman & Lloyd (R), *223*

Chevy Chase
Ames Assoc. Inc. (C), *249*
Krauthamer & Assoc. (R), *120*

Columbia
Christian & Timbers, Inc. (R), *34*
Dunhill Staffing Systems of Columbia (C), *317*
C. A. Durakis Assoc., Inc. (R), *55*
Health Care Plus, Inc. (C), *371*
Interim Financial Solutions (C), *392*
Management Recruiters of Columbia (C), *450*
Sales Consultants of Columbia (C), *553*
Sanford Rose Assoc. - Columbia, MD (C), *567*
Search Consultants, LLC (C), *575*
The Search Group (C), *575*
C. J. Vincent Assoc., LLC (C), *612*

Crownsville
DHR Int'l., Inc. (R), *50*

Dunkirk
ProStar Systems, Inc. (C), *525*

Ellicott City
Austin, Hill & Assoc. (C), *256*
Management Recruiters of Ellicott City (C), *430*

Finksburg
Procurement Resources (C), *520*

Forest Hill
C. D. Warner & Assoc. (C), *615*

Frederick
Management Recruiters of Frederick, Inc. (C), *450*

Gaithersburg
Association Executive Resources Group (R), *8*
HealthSearch Assoc. (C), *374*

Hanover
Management Recruiters of the Baltimore Washington Corridor (C), *450*

Havre de Grace
The Mackenzie Group (R), *133*

Hunt Valley
Cross Country Consultants, Inc. (C), *304*
Fallstaff Search (C), *338*
The Hanover Consulting Group (C), *368*
Management Recruiters of Hunt Valley (C), *430*

Hyattsville
Sales Consultants of Prince Georges County (C), *553*

Kensington
Management Recruiters of Rockville (C), *450*

Laurel
Capital Consulting Group, Inc. (R), *28*
Modis (C), *483*

Leonardtown
De Funiak & Edwards (R), *47*

Lutherville
Brindisi Search (R), *23*
The Search Committee (C), *574*

North Potomac
Roth Young Personnel Services of Washington, DC (C), *546*

Owings Mills
Craig Roe & Assoc., LLC (C), *540*
Telem Adhesive Search Corp. (C), *605*

Pasadena
Patrice & Assoc. (C), *505*

Reisterstown
Wasserman Assoc. Inc. (C), *616*

Rockville
Accountants On Call (C), *236*
The Corporate Source Group, Inc. (R), *41*
Dunhill of Rockville (C), *317*
Executive/Retail Placement Assoc. (C), *337*
JDG Assoc., Ltd. (C), *397*
Perry • Newton Assoc. (C), *507*
Sales Consultants of Rockville, MD (C), *559*
Sanford Rose Assoc. - Rockville (C), *567*

Salisbury
Management Recruiters of Eastern Shore (C), *430*

Severna Park
Medserve & Assoc. Inc. (C), *478*

Silver Spring
Management Recruiters of Washington, DC Inc. (C), *450*

Smithsburg
LJ Networking, Inc. (C), *418*

Timonium
BCG Search, Inc. (R), *14*
Management Recruiters of Baltimore (C), *451*
Sales Consultants of Baltimore (C), *559*
Sudina Search, Inc. (C), *596*
TCM Enterprises (C), *600*
Winston Search, Inc. (R), *222*

Towson
Access Assoc. Inc. (C), *233*
The Center for Career Advancement (C), *287*
PPS Information Systems Staffing (C), *515*
Quigley Assoc. (R), *170*
Recruitment Specialists, Inc. (C), *532*

Waldorf
Executive Placement Services (C), *333*

Westminster
Entelechy Group Ltd. (R), *59*
John B. Norris & Assoc., Inc. (C), *495*

Massachusetts

Acton
Management & Human Resources (R), *134*

Amesbury
Wallace Assoc. (C), *614*

Amherst
Allen Davis & Assoc. (C), *308*

Andover
Sales Consultant of Boston (C), *553*

Becket
Berkshire Search Assoc. (C), *265*

Bedford
Gabriele & Company (C), *354*

Belmont
Cornerstone Search Assoc. Inc. (C), *299*
Dukas Assoc. (C), *315*

Beverly
Sales & Marketing Search, Inc. (C), *551*

Beverly Farms
Drinkwater & Assoc. (R), *54*

Boston
Accountants On Call (C), *236*
The Alexander Group (R), *3*
Aminex Corp. (C), *249*
Ashworth Consultants, Inc. (R), *8*
Atlantic Search Group, Inc. (C), *255*
Aubin Int'l. Inc. (R), *8*
Auerbach Associates, Inc. (R), *9*
Nathan Barry Assoc., Inc. (R), *12*
Best, Coleman & Co. (R), *16*
Bickerton & Gordon LLC (C), *266*

GEOGRAPHICAL

Boston Professional Search, Inc. (C), 270
Chaloner Assoc. (R), 32
Clayman & Co. (R), 36
Dean M. Coe Assoc. (R), 37
Creative Financial Staffing (C), 303
M. J. Curran & Assoc., Inc. (R), 43
DHR Int'l., Inc. (R), 50
The Flagship Group (R), 68
Hayden Group, Inc. (R), 88
Heidrick & Struggles, Inc. (R), 90
Hospitality Executive Search, Inc. (R), 96
H.I. Hunt & Co., Ltd. (R), 99
Hunter Int'l. LLC (C), 385
Isaacson, Miller (R), 104
J. Nicholas Arthur (R), 104
J. Robert Scott (R), 104
Pendleton James Assoc., Inc. (R), 105
JLI-Boston (R), 106
A.T. Kearney Executive Search (R), 111
The Kinlin Co., Inc. (R), 115
Korn/Ferry Int'l. (R), 118
LAI Ward Howell (R), 123
Lois L. Lindauer Searches (C), 418
Management Recruiters of Boston (C), 430
Management Recruiters of Boston (C), 430
Martin Grant Assoc. Inc., Insurance Personnel (C), 472
Mercedes & Co., Inc. (R), 143
DDJ Myers, Ltd. (R), 150
Organization Resources Inc. (R), 157
The Oxbridge Group, Ltd. (C), 500
P.A.R. Assoc., Inc. (R), 158
Raymond Karsan Assoc. (C), 530
The Renaissance Network (C), 534
Russell Reynolds Assoc., Inc. (R), 176
Robsham & Assoc., Inc. (R), 180
Romac Int'l. Inc. (R), 181
Romac Int'l., Inc. (C), 543
Romac Int'l., Inc. (C), 543
Russillo/Gardner/Spolsino (C), 548
A. N. Salloway Executive Search & Consulting, L.L.C. (C), 564
Scott-Wayne Assoc., Inc. (C), 573
Christopher Smallhorn Executive Recruiting, Inc. (R), 193
Stone & Youngblood (C), 594
Willmott & Assoc. (C), 622
Winter, Wyman & Co. (C), 623

Braintree
Management Recruiters of Braintree (C), 430
The Retail Network (C), 535

Brockton
Sales Consultants of Brockton, Inc. (C), 559
Xavier Associates, Inc. (R), 226

Burlington
Christian & Timbers, Inc. (R), 34
The Elliott Company (R), 58
Hall Kinion (C), 367
Romac Int'l., Inc. (C), 543
Romac Int'l., Inc. (C), 543
Witt/Kieffer, Ford, Hadelman & Lloyd (R), 223

Cambridge
Allen Davis & Assoc. (C), 308
Bell Oaks Co., Inc. (C), 263
C. A. Durakis Assoc., Inc. (R), 55
Kingsbury • Wax • Bova (R), 114
Levin & Company, Inc. (R), 128
Nachman Biomedical (C), 488

Canton
Laboratory Resource Group (C), 411
Alan Levine Assoc. (R), 129
Stephen M. Sonis Assoc. (R), 195

Carlisle
P. N. French Assoc., Inc. (R), 72

Chelmsford
Timothy D. Crowe, Jr. (R), 43
Marketing Resources (C), 470
ProSearch, Inc. (C), 524

Chestnut Hill
Flexible Resources, Inc. (C), 342

Concord
Blaney Executive Search (R), 18
DHR Int'l., Inc. (R), 50
K. Jaeger & Assoc. (C), 396

Danvers
Morency Assoc. (C), 485

Dedham
Gillard Assoc. Legal Search (C), 357
JNB Assoc., Inc. (C), 399
S. D. Kelly & Assoc., Inc. (R), 112
Recruiting Specialists (C), 532

Duxbury
Ollinger Partners (R), 156
S. B. Webster & Associates (R), 217

Easthampton
United Personnel Services (C), 611

Framingham
Carter/MacKay (C), 285
Franklin Int'l. Search, Inc. (C), 352
Norman Powers Assoc., Inc. (C), 515
L. A. Silver Assoc., Inc. (R), 191
Tecmark Associates Inc. (C), 604
Yankee Hospitality Search (C), 626

Gloucester
Hamilton-Chase & Assoc., Inc. (R), 85

Granby
Morgan & Assoc. (C), 485

Hamilton
Kirk Palmer & Assoc., Inc. (R), 158

Hanover
Search America, Inc. (C), 574

Hingham
A.K.S. Assoc., Ltd. (R), 1
Phillips & Assoc. (R), 164

Lexington
The Corporate Source Group, Inc. (R), 41
Fenwick Partners (R), 66
Fitzgerald Associates (R), 68
Hamilton-Chase & Assoc., Inc. (R), 85
The Kleven Group, Inc. - Executive Search Division (R), 116
The Kleven Group, Inc. (C), 407
Lynx, Inc. (C), 421
Louis Rudzinsky Assoc., Inc. (C), 548
TASA International (R), 206
Willmott & Assoc. (C), 622

Manchester by the Sea
Gilreath Weatherby Inc. (R), 77

Mansfield
Sales Consultants - Bristol County (C), 559

Marblehead
Richard D. Holbrook Assoc. (R), 94
New Dimensions in Technology, Inc. (C), 492
J. E. Ranta Assoc. (C), 529

Marlborough
Executive Alliance (R), 62

Marshfield
Stevens Assoc. (C), 593

Marshfield Hills
Resource Inc. (R), 175

Maynard
Steinbach & Co. (C), 592

Medfield
Gatti & Assoc. (C), 355
J. S. Lord & Company, Inc. (R), 131
Prestonwood Assoc. (R), 168

Medford
Applied Resources (C), 252

Mendon
Derek Associates, Inc. (C), 311

Nantucket
EMN/Witt/Kieffer (R), 59

Natick
McInturff & Assoc., Inc. (C), 474
TechFind, Inc. (R), 207
Weinstein & Co. (R), 217
The Yorkshire Group, Ltd. (C), 626
Zweig White & Assoc., Inc. (R), 228

Needham
Ford & Ford (C), 343
Glou Int'l., Inc. (R), 78
Reece & Mruk Partners/EMA Partners Int'l. (R), 173
Peter Siegel & Co. (C), 581
Trowbridge & Co., Inc. (R), 211

New Seabury
The Whyte Group, Inc. (R), 220

Newbury
Coastal Int'l., Inc. (R), 36

Newburyport
Elliot Assoc. Inc. (R), 58
Search Int'l. (R), 187

Newton
Keane Assoc. (R), 110
The Spiegel Group (R), 197

Newton Centre
Sinclair & Co., Inc. (R), *192*

Newton Lower Falls
Gustin Partners, Ltd. (R), *83*

North Andover
The Devlin Search Group, Inc. (C), *311*
Financial Search Group, Inc. (R), *66*
The Human Resource Consulting Group, Inc. (R), *98*
Straube Associates (R), *203*

North Falmouth
Alliance Executive Search, Inc. (R), *4*

Northborough
Computer Security Placement Service (C), *296*
Consumer Search Inc. (C), *298*
Kacevich, Lewis & Brown, Inc. (R), *109*

Norwell
CEC Associates (R), *32*
Tondorf & Assoc. Inc. (C), *607*

Norwood
Heffelfinger Assoc., Inc. (R), *89*

Osterville
Access/Resources, Inc. (C), *234*
The Kinlin Co., Inc. (R), *115*

Peabody
Healthcare Recruiters of New England (C), *373*

Reading
L. J. Gonzer Assoc. (C), *360*

Rockland
Anthony Michael & Co. (C), *251*

Sagamore Beach
Sales Consultants of Cape Cod (C), *553*

Salem
American Executive Management, Inc. (R), *5*
KS Frary & Assoc. (R), *71*

Sharon
AutoPeople (C), *257*
Partridge Assoc., Inc. (R), *160*

Sherborn
Greene & Co. (C), *362*

South Hamilton
J. R. Akin & Co. (R), *2*

Springfield
Douglas-Allen, Inc. (R), *54*
Management Recruiters of Springfield (C), *430*
United Personnel Services (C), *611*

Sudbury
L. J. Doherty & Assoc. (R), *53*
Mark Stranberg & Assoc. Inc. (R), *202*
Travis & Co., Inc. (R), *210*
Joel H. Wilensky Assoc., Inc. (C), *620*

Swampscott
The Fawcett Group (R), *65*

Teaticket
Atlanta Executive Partners, Inc. (R), *8*

Topsfield
Fortune Personnel Consultants of Topsfield (C), *346*

Walpole
Hoffman Recruiters (C), *380*

Waltham
EagleView, Inc. (C), *325*
Global Executive Search Group (C), *358*
Logix, Inc. (C), *420*
George D. Sandel Assoc. (C), *565*
Winter, Wyman & Co. (C), *623*

Wellesley
Dromeshauser Assoc. (R), *55*
Executive Search Int'l./Transearch (R), *63*
Kiradjieff & Goode, Inc. (R), *115*
The Marlow Group (R), *136*
Nagler, Robins & Poe, Inc. (R), *150*
The Onstott Group (R), *156*
D. P. Parker & Assoc., Inc. (R), *159*
Sales Consultants of Wellesley, Inc. (C), *559*

Wellesley Hills
Battalia Winston Int'l./The Euram Consultants Group (R), *13*
Cyr Associates, Inc. (C), *306*
The McCormick Group (C), *474*
Sink, Walker, Boltrus Int'l. (R), *192*

West Newton
The Enterprise Group (R), *60*

West Springfield
Ansara, Bickford & Fiske (C), *251*
Dunhill Staffing Systems of Springfield (C), *317*
Hunter Assoc. (C), *385*

Westborough
Higley, Hall & Co., Inc. (R), *93*
Management Recruiters of Westborough (C), *430*
Romac Int'l., Inc. (C), *543*
STAT Search (C), *592*

Westfield
Pioneer Placement, Inc. (C), *512*

Weston
KM Associates (C), *407*
F. L. Mannix & Co. (R), *135*
Robert T. Morton Assoc., Inc. (C), *486*
Weston Consultants, Inc. (R), *219*

Westport
Evergreen & Co. (C), *331*

Westwood
HRI Services, Inc. (C), *382*

Weymouth
Winfield Assoc., Inc. (C), *623*

Winchester
O'Brien Consulting Services (R), *153*

Woburn
Gatti & Assoc. (C), *355*
Gilbert Scott Assoc., LLC (C), *357*
Raymond Karsan Assoc. (C), *530*
Search Research Assoc., Inc. (R), *187*
Selected Executives, Inc. (C), *578*
The Ward Group (R), *215*
Zurick, Davis & Co., Inc. (R), *227*

Worcester
Delores F. George, C.P.C. (C), *356*
The Touchstone Group (C), *607*

Wrentham
MediaCOM Talent Group (C), *476*

Michigan

Ada
Bruce Lowery & Assoc. (C), *420*
The Wentworth Co., Inc. (R), *217*

Ann Arbor
Elwell & Assoc., Inc. (R), *59*
HRNI (C), *383*
L. J. Johnson & Co. (R), *106*
Management Recruiters of Ann Arbor (C), *430*
Sales Consultants of Ann Arbor (C), *553*
Selective Recruiting Assoc., Inc. (C), *578*
Weliver & Assoc. (C), *618*

Auburn Hills
Sales Consultants of Auburn Hills (C), *559*

Battle Creek
Management Recruiters of Calhoun County (C), *430*
Lou Michaels Assoc., Inc. (C), *481*
Savalli & Assoc., Inc. (C), *571*

Bingham Farms
Management Recruiters of Birmingham (C), *451*
Sales Consultants of Birmingham (C), *559*

Birmingham
Compass Group Ltd. (R), *38*
Habelmann & Assoc. (R), *84*
Smith Professional Search (C), *584*
Sullivan & Assoc. (R), *204*
The Whittaker Group (C), *620*

Blissfield
Management Recruiters of Southeastern Michigan (C), *451*

Bloomfield Hills
Boyden (R), *21*
Crowder & Company (R), *43*
Dunlap & Sullivan Assoc. (R), *55*
Fortune Personnel Consultants of Bloomfield, Inc. (C), *346*
Gundersen Partners, L.L.C. (R), *83*
The Hunter Group, Inc. (C), *385*
Sales Consultant of Bloomfield Hills (C), *553*
Unlimited Staffing Solutions, Inc. (C), *611*

Brownstown
American Resources Corp. (C), *248*

Center Line
Sharrow & Assoc., Inc. (C), *579*

Chelsea
Holland & Assoc., Inc. (R), *94*

Dearborn
Gene Ellefson & Assoc. Inc. (C), *328*
Hire Authority, Inc. (C), *379*
Management Recruiters of Dearborn, Inc. (C), *451*
Perez & Assoc. (C), *507*
Premier Healthcare Recruiters, Inc. (C), *516*

Detroit
Executive Recruiters Int'l. (C), *333*
Management Recruiters of Detroit & Farmington Hills (C), *451*

East Lansing
The Mercer Group, Inc. (R), *143*
The Stark Wilton Group (R), *199*

Farmington
RemTech Business Solutions, Inc. (C), *534*

Farmington Hills
Executive Search Team (C), *336*
F-O-R-T-U-N-E Personnel Consultants (C), *346*
Joseph Goldring & Assoc. Inc. (C), *360*
Harper Associates (C), *369*
Professional Personnel Consultants, Inc. (C), *521*
Roth Young Personnel Service of Detroit, Inc. (C), *546*
Sales Consultants of Farmington Hills (C), *560*
Teamsearch, Inc. (C), *601*

Flint
Action Management Corp. (C), *239*
Management Recruiters - Flint (C), *451*

Grand Blanc
Growth Consultants of America (R), *82*
Sales Consultant of Genesee (C), *553*

Grand Rapids
Account Ability Now (C), *234*
Advanced Executive Resources (R), *2*
The Clayton Edward Group (C), *292*
Dunlap & Sullivan Assoc. (R), *55*
ExecuQuest, Inc. (R), *61*
Management Recruiters of Grand Rapids (C), *430*
mfg/Search, Inc. (C), *480*
Romac Int'l., Inc. (C), *543*
Sales Consultants of Grand Rapids (C), *560*
Techstaff Inc. (C), *603*

Grosse Pointe Farms
Daudlin, De Beaupre & Co., Inc. (R), *46*
Michael W. Parres & Assoc. (R), *159*

Grosse Pointe Park
Case Executive Search (C), *286*

Harbor Springs
Career Alternatives Executive Search (C), *281*
The Clark Group (C), *292*

Hartland
Sales Consultants of Hartland (C), *553*

Holland
G. L. Dykstra Assoc., Inc. (C), *323*
Management Recruiters of Holland (C), *430*

Holt
Management Recruiters of Lansing (C), *430*

Houghton Lake
Management Recruiters of North Central (C), *430*

Kalamazoo
Circlewood Search Group, Inc. (C), *291*
Collins & Associates (C), *294*
Hallman Group, Inc. (C), *367*
Management Recruiters of Kalamazoo (C), *430*
Sales Consultant of Kalamazoo (C), *553*

Lambertville
Graphic Arts Marketing Assoc., Inc. (C), *361*

Lansing
DHR Int'l., Inc. (R), *50*
Dunhill Personnel of Lansing (C), *317*
Sales Consultants of Lansing-West (C), *553*

Lapeer
J. E. Lessner Assoc., Inc. (R), *128*

Livonia
Access/Resources, Inc. (C), *234*
The Barton Group, Inc. (C), *260*
Management Recruiters of Livonia (C), *451*
mfg/Search, Inc. (C), *480*
Sales Consultants of Laurel Park, Inc. (C), *560*
Henry Welker & Assoc. (C), *618*

Madison Heights
American Heritage Group, Inc. (C), *247*

Marine City
Management Recruiters of St. Clair County (C), *430*

Muskegon
Management Recruiters of Muskegon (C), *451*
Professional Search (R), *169*

Novi
NDI Services (R), *151*

Oak Park
Rosenfeld & Co., Inc. (C), *545*

Okemos
Harvey Hohauser & Assoc. (R), *87*

Portage
Chadwell & Assoc., Inc. (C), *288*

Rochester
Sanford Rose Assoc. - Rochester (C), *568*

Rochester Hills
J. P. Bencik Assoc. (C), *263*
Management Recruiters of North Oakland County, Inc. (C), *452*
Pathfinders Int'l. (C), *504*

Royal Oak
Hire Authority, Inc. (C), *378*
Michigan Consulting Group (R), *144*
Premier Recruiting Group (C), *516*
Stone Assoc. LLC (C), *594*

Saginaw
The Stark Wilton Group (R), *199*

Saline
Scientific Solutions, Inc. (C), *572*

Southfield
Accountants On Call (C), *236*
Benford & Assoc., Inc. (C), *264*
Davidson, Laird & Assoc. (C), *308*
Davis-Smith, Inc. (C), *309*
Dunhilkl Staffing Systems of Oakland/Macomb (C), *317*
F-o-r-t-u-n-e Personnel Consultants of Detroit, Inc. (C), *346*
Joe L. Giles & Assoc. (C), *357*
Plante & Moran, LLP (R), *165*
Romac Int'l., Inc. (C), *543*
Sales Consultant of Detroit (C), *553*

St. Joseph
The Icard Group, Inc. (C), *387*

Stevensville
Guidarelli Assoc., Inc. (R), *83*

Traverse City
The Icard Group, Inc. (C), *387*
Management Recruiters of Traverse City (C), *430*
Sales Consultants of Traverse City (C), *553*

Troy
Accent On Achievement, Inc. (C), *233*
Accountants On Call (C), *236*
AJM Professional Services (C), *243*
Altec/HRC (C), *246*
American Heritage Group, Inc. (C), *247*
F-O-R-T-U-N-E Personnel Consultants of Troy, Inc. (C), *347*
Harvey Hohauser & Assoc., LLC (R), *87*
Management Recruiters (C), *430*
Sales Consultant of Troy (C), *553*
Sales Executives, Inc. (C), *563*
Wing Tips & Pumps, Inc. (C), *623*

Union Pier
Thomas & Assoc. of Michigan (C), *606*

Wixom
Kabana Corp. (C), *402*

Wyoming
Quality Search (C), *526*

Minnesota

Bloomington
AGRI-associates (C), *242*
Bradley & Assoc. (C), *272*
A.T. Kearney Executive Search (R), *111*
Lynne Palmer Executive Recruitment, Inc. (C), *421*
Management Recruiters of Bloomington (C), *452*
Romac Int'l., Inc. (C), *543*

Brooklyn Park
Markent Personnel (C), *470*

Burnsville
Jackley Search Consultants (C), *396*

Chanhassen
Management Recruiters of Chanhassen (C), *452*

Eden Prairie
Healthcare Recruiters Int'l - Minnesota, Inc. (C), *373*
Opus Marketing (R), *157*
Robinson-Robinson & Assoc., Inc. (C), *539*
Yungner & Bormann (R), *226*

Fridley
Management Recruiters of Fridley (C), *430*

Golden Valley
North American Recruiters, Inc. (R), *153*

Hutchinson
Delacore Resources (C), *310*

Lake Elmo
Wells, Bradley & Assoc., Inc. (C), *618*

Lakeville
Professional Recruiters Inc. (C), *521*
R. L. Rystrom & Assoc., Inc. (C), *549*

Maple Grove
Applied Resources, Inc. (C), *252*
Construct Management Services (C), *297*
Roger Dietsch & Assoc. (C), *312*

Medina
Mary L. Mayer, Ltd. (R), *139*

Minneapolis
Accountants On Call (C), *236*
Bartz Rogers & Partners (C), *260*
Bright Search/Professional Staffing (C), *274*
Carlson & Czeswik (R), *30*
Arlene Clapp, Ltd. (R), *35*
Robert Connelly & Assoc., Inc. (R), *39*
Corporate Resources Professional Placement (C), *300*
Charles Dahl Group, Inc. (C), *306*
Mary R. Erickson & Assoc. (R), *60*
Execu-Tech Search Inc. (C), *332*
Executive Search Inc. (R), *63*
Executive Solutions (R), *64*
Focus Executive Search (C), *343*
Furst Group/MPI (R), *72*
Hayden & Assoc., Inc. (C), *370*
Healey Executive Search, Inc. (R), *88*
Interim Accounting Professionals (C), *392*
Kenzer Corp. (R), *113*
Korn/Ferry Int'l. (R), *118*
Howard Lieberman & Assoc., Inc. (C), *417*
Management Recruiters of Minneapolis (C), *430*
Management Resource Group (C), *467*
Northland Employment Services Inc. (C), *496*
NYCOR Search, Inc. (C), *497*
The Personnel Group, Inc. (R), *163*
Polson & Co., Inc. (R), *166*
Russell Reynolds Assoc., Inc. (R), *177*
Romac Int'l., Inc. (C), *543*
Romac Int'l., Inc. (C), *543*
Roth Young Executive Recruiters (C), *546*
Sales Consultant of Minneapolis (C), *553*
Sathe & Associates, Inc. (R), *184*
Schall Executive Search Partners (R), *185*
SpencerStuart (R), *197*
Stewart, Stein & Scott, Ltd. (R), *200*
Stone, Murphy & Olson (R), *201*
T. H. Hunter, Inc. (C), *599*
Templeton & Assoc. (C), *605*
Templeton & Assoc. (C), *605*
Richard Thompson Assoc., Inc. (R), *209*
Walker Group, Inc. (R), *215*
Williams Executive Search, Inc. (R), *221*
Wood, Franchot Inc. (R), *224*
Working Relationships, Inc. (C), *624*
Steven Yungerberg Assoc., Inc. (R), *226*

Minnetonka
BRW Search (C), *275*
Heinze & Assoc. Inc. (R), *91*
Wyatt & Jaffe (R), *225*

New Ulm
Agra Placements, Ltd. (C), *242*

Owatonna
Bernhart Assoc. (C), *265*
Robert William James & Assoc, (C), *539*

Richfield
DHR Int'l., Inc. (R), *50*

Robbinsdale
Hollander Horizon Int'l. (R), *95*

Rochester
Management Recruiters of Salem Corner (C), *430*
Management Recruiters of Rochester (C), *452*
Robert William James & Assoc. (C), *539*

Shakopee
Management Recruiters of Shakopee (C), *430*
Sales Consultant of Chaska (C), *553*

St. Paul
Development Search Specialists (R), *49*
J. M. Johnson & Assoc. (C), *399*

Stillwater
Whitbeck & Assoc. (R), *219*

Wayzata
Abeln, Magy & Assoc., Inc. (R), *1*
James Bangert & Assoc., Inc. (R), *11*
The Mazzitelli Group, Ltd. (R), *139*
C. A. Moore & Assoc., Inc. (C), *484*
Peter Van Leer & Assoc. (R), *213*

Winona
Management Recruiters of Winona (C), *452*

Woodbury
Management Recruiters of Woodbury (C), *430*
Management Recruiters of Woodbury (C), *452*

Mississippi

Bolton
Buzhardt Assoc. (R), *25*

Brandon
Transportation Recruiting Services, Inc. (C), *608*

Goodman
Acuity Medical Recruitment (C), *239*

Grenada
ExecuGroup, Inc. (R), *61*

Jackson
American Medical Recruiting Co. Inc. (C), *248*
Dunhill Professional Search of Byram (C), *321*
Management Recruiters of Jackson (C), *430*
Management Recruiters of Rankin Co. (C), *452*
Jim Woodson & Assoc., Inc. (C), *624*

Long Beach
Management Recruiters of Harrison County (C), *431*

Pascagoula
McKee Cyber Search (C), *475*

Missouri

Ballwin
Dunhill Professional Search (C), *321*

Ballwin
Tully/Woodmansee Int'l., Inc. (R), *212*

Camdenton
Management Recruiters of Camdenton (C), *431*

Chesterfield
Davis & James, Inc. (C), *308*
Dynamic Choices Inc. (C), *323*
James L. Fisk & Assoc. (C), *342*
F-O-R-T-U-N-E Personnel Consultants of St. Louis-West County (C), *347*
J. B. Linde & Assoc. (C), *395*
Charles Luntz & Assoc., Inc. (R), *132*
The Riverbend Group (C), *538*

GEOGRAPHICAL

Clayton
DHR Int'l., Inc. (R), *50*

Fairview
Recruiters Professional Network - Fairview (C), *531*

Fenton
Management Recruiters of St. Louis-West County (C), *431*

Festus
Dunhill Professional Search of Crystal City (C), *317*

Independence
Human Resource Dimensions, Inc. (C), *384*
MSA Executive Search (R), *148*

Joplin
Dunhill Staffing Systems (C), *317*

Kansas City
Accountants On Call (C), *236*
AGRI-associates (C), *242*
Agri-Tech Personnel, Inc. (C), *242*
BallResources (C), *258*
Brush Creek Partners (R), *24*
Delphi Systems, Ltd. (R), *48*
Huntress Real Estate Executive Search (R), *100*
Kennison & Assoc. Inc. (C), *405*
Management Recruiters of Kansas City (C), *431*
Carol Park (C), *502*
V. Robinson & Co., Inc. (C), *539*
Tryon & Heideman, LLC (R), *211*

Ladue
Powers Consultants, Inc. (R), *166*

Lake Ozark
Whitehead & Assoc., Inc. (C), *620*

Lake St. Louis
Management Recruiters of Lake St. Louis (C), *431*
Medicorp, Inc. (C), *477*
Sanford Rose Assoc. - Lake St. Louis (C), *568*

Laurie
Management Recruiters of Laurie (C), *431*

Lees Summit
Brush Creek Partners (R), *24*
Pinnacle Executive Group Inc. (C), *512*

Manchester
Management Recruiters of Chesterfield (C), *431*

Maryland Heights
Christopher and Long (C), *291*

North Kansas City
JRL Executive Recruiters (C), *401*

Rolla
Greenfields Engineering Search (C), *363*

Springfield
Jim Crumpley & Assoc. (C), *304*
F-O-R-T-U-N-E Search Consultants (C), *347*
Management Recruiters of Springfield (C), *431*
Sanford Rose Assoc. - Springfield (C), *568*

St. Ann
Dunhill Personnel of Brentwood (C), *317*

St. Charles
J. D. Ruhmann & Assoc. (C), *548*

St. Louis
Aaron Consulting, Inc. (C), *232*
Accountants On Call (C), *236*
Advanced Resources, Inc. (C), *241*
Allen Consulting Group, Inc. (C), *244*
Boyden (R), *21*
Bradford & Galt, Inc. (C), *271*
Cejka Healthcare Executive Search Services (CHESS) (R), *32*
Cemco, Ltd. (C), *287*
CMW & Associates, Inc. (C), *293*
Corbin Packaging Professionals (C), *299*
Debbon Recruiting Group, Inc. (C), *310*
The Donnelly Group-Sales Recruiters, Inc. (C), *314*
Dunhill Staffing Systems of St. Louis (C), *317*
Executive Solutions (R), *64*
Grant Cooper & Assoc., Inc. (R), *81*
Annie Gray Assoc., Inc. (R), *81*
HDB Incorporated (C), *371*
The Hindman Group,Inc. (C), *378*
Hitchens & Foster, Inc. (C), *379*
Holohan Group, Ltd. (R), *95*
JAG Group (R), *105*
John & Powers, Inc. (R), *106*
Kendall & Davis Co., Inc. (C), *405*
Keystone Consulting Group (C), *406*
Michael Latas & Assoc., Inc. (R), *125*
Lloyd Prescott & Churchill, Inc. (R), *130*
Lloyd Prescott Assoc., Inc. (C), *419*
The Logan Group, Inc. (R), *131*
Management Recruiters of St. Louis-Westport (C), *431*
Management Recruiters of St. Louis-Earth City (C), *431*
Medical Recruiters Inc. (C), *477*
Morton, McCorkle & Assoc. Inc. (R), *147*
R. F. Mulvaney & Assoc., Inc. (R), *149*
Noll Human Resource Services (C), *494*
Physician Recruiting Services, Inc. (C), *511*
Powers Consultants, Inc. (R), *166*
Rieser & Assoc., Inc. (R), *178*
Romac Int'l., Inc. (C), *543*
Sales Consultants of St. Louis-Earth City (C), *553*
The Schatz Company (C), *571*
John Sibbald Assoc., Inc. (R), *191*
Sparks, McDonough & Assoc., Inc. (C), *588*
Witt/Kieffer, Ford, Hadelman & Lloyd (R), *223*

St. Peters
H R Solutions, Inc. (C), *365*

Sunset Hills
Accountants On Call (C), *236*

Westport
Accountants On Call (C), *236*

Wildwood
Genesis Research (C), *356*

Montana

Billings
David S. Burt Assoc. (C), *276*
Presley Consultants, Inc. (C), *517*

Bozeman
Fortune Personnel Consultants (C), *347*

Nebraska

Kearney
Charles & Associates, Inc. (C), *289*

Lincoln
Blau Mancino Schroeder (R), *18*
DHR Int'l., Inc. (R), *50*
William J. Elam & Assoc. (R), *58*
Management Recruiters of Lincoln (C), *431*
Raymond Karsan Assoc. (C), *530*

Norfolk
Management Recruiters of Norfolk (C), *431*

Omaha
AGRI-associates (C), *242*
Dunhill Professional Search of Omaha, Inc. (C), *321*
Eggers Consulting Co., Inc. (C), *327*
Hansen Executive Search, Inc. (C), *368*
Harrison Moore Inc. (C), *370*
Management Recruiters of Omaha (C), *431*
Management Recruiters of Cass County, NE (C), *452*
Noll Human Resource Services (C), *494*
The Regency Group, Ltd. (C), *533*
Sales Consultants of Omaha, Inc. (C), *560*

Nevada

Las Vegas
Accountants On Call (C), *236*
Allen & Assoc. (C), *244*
Career Development Associates (C), *282*
Eastridge Infotech (C), *326*
Management Recruiters of Las Vegas (C), *431*
Mangement Recruiters of Summerlin (C), *431*
Romac Int'l., Inc. (C), *543*
Top Gun Group, Inc. (C), *607*

Reno
Management Recruiters of Reno (C), *453*

Stateline
Management Recruiters of Lake Tahoe, NV (C), *453*

New Hampshire

Atkinson
Multi Processing, Inc. (R), *149*

Bedford
Availability Personnel Consultants (C), *257*
Baeder Kalinski Int'l. Group, Inc. (R), *10*
Corporate Leadership Strategies, Inc. (R), *41*
Emerald Legal Search (C), *329*
Management Recruiters of Bedford (C), *431*
Sprout/Standish, Inc. (C), *589*
STAT Search (C), *592*

Center Harbor
Barger & Sargeant, Inc. (R), *11*
Crane, Reed & Co., Inc. (C), *302*

Concord
Raymond Karsan Assoc. (C), *530*

Derry
Circuit Search (C), *291*

Durham
Warren, Morris & Madison, Ltd. (C), *616*

Exeter
Bartholdi & Co., Inc. (R), *12*
Futures, Inc. (C), *354*

Hampton
EXETER 2100 (C), *337*

Hooksett
Sales Consultant of Hooksett (C), *553*

Hopkinton
Pamela L. Mulligan, Inc. (R), *149*

Keene
GFI Professional Staffing Services (C), *357*
Harrington & O'Brien, Inc. (C), *369*
Networking Unlimited of NH, Inc. (C), *491*

Laconia
Selig Executive Search (C), *579*

Manchester
Access Data Personnel, Inc. (C), *233*
CMS, Inc. (C), *293*
Dunhill of Manchester Inc. (C), *321*

Merrimack
Sales Consultants of Nashua-Manchester (C), *560*

Nashua
Conard Associates, Inc. (R), *39*
Fortune Personnel Consultants (C), *347*
Horizon Medical Search of NH (C), *381*
Resource Recruiting (C), *534*
Romac Int'l., Inc. (C), *543*

New London
Linford E. Stiles & Assoc., L.L.C. (R), *201*

Portsmouth
Career Profiles (C), *283*
Warren, Morris & Madison, Ltd. (C), *616*

Salem
The Barrett Group (C), *260*
High Tech Opportunities, Inc. (C), *377*

New Jersey

Aberdeen
Adel-Lawrence Assoc., Inc. (C), *240*
Re-Mark Assoc. Inc. (C), *531*

Allenwood
Barone Assoc. (C), *259*

Andover
Carris, Jackowitz Assoc. (R), *30*

Augusta
Accelerated Data Decision, Inc. (C), *233*

Avenel
The Fourbes Group, Inc. (C), *351*

Basking Ridge
Fran Luisi Assoc. (R), *132*
OEI, Inc. (C), *498*

Bay Head
Management Recruiters of Bay Head (C), *453*

Beach Haven
Maschal/Connors Inc. (R), *137*

Bellmawr
Howard Clark Assoc. (C), *292*

Belvidere
Gilbert & Van Campen Int'l. (R), *76*

Bernardsville
Management Recruiters of Bernardsville (C), *431*

Blackwood
Kiley, Owen & McGovern, Inc. (R), *114*

Bradley Beach
Electronic Search, Inc. (C), *328*

Bridgewater
The Cassie Group (R), *31*
T. J. Koellhoffer & Assoc. (R), *116*
Management Recruiters of Bridgewater (C), *431*
Sales Consultants Bridgewater, Inc. (C), *560*

Brielle
Barclay Consultants, Inc. (C), *259*
The Yaiser Group (C), *625*

Califon
Management Recruiters of North Hunterdon County (C), *431*

Cedar Grove
Ruderfer & Co., Inc. (C), *548*

Cedar Knolls
Paul Falcone Assoc. (R), *65*

Chatham
ALW Research Int'l. (R), *4*
Christenson Hutchison McDowell, LLC (R), *34*

Cherry Hill
ACSYS Resources, Inc. (C), *238*
The Currier-Winn Co., Inc. (C), *305*
Dunhill Staffing Systems (C), *317*
Dorothy W. Farnath & Assoc., Inc. (C), *338*
Grant-Franks & Assoc. (C), *361*
Management Recruiters of Voorhees (C), *431*
Ramming & Assoc., Inc. (C), *528*
Romeo-Hudgins & Assoc., Ltd. (C), *544*
S-H-S Int'l. of Cherry Hill (C), *549*
Sales Consultants of Cherry Hill (C), *560*
Worlco Computer Resources, Inc (C), *624*

Cinnaminson
Careers First, Inc. (C), *283*

Clark
D. S. Allen Assoc. (C), *244*
HRD Consultants, Inc. (R), *97*
Jeff Rich Assoc. (C), *536*
Sherbrooke Assoc., Inc. (C), *580*

Cliffside Park
BR & Assoc. (C), *271*

Cranbury
Management Recruiters of Windsor (C), *431*

Cranford
Moffitt Int'l., Inc. (R), *146*
Shifrin-Fischer Group, Inc. (C), *580*

Cresskill
Charet & Assoc. (C), *289*

Dayton
Softrix, Inc. (C), *586*

Denville
The E & K Group (C), *324*
Management Recruiters of Orange County, N.Y., Inc. (C), *453*

East Brunswick
Blair/Tech Recruiters, Inc. (C), *268*
Curry, Telleri Group, Inc. (R), *44*
Williamsburg Group (C), *621*

East Windsor
Personnel Alliance Group (C), *507*

Edison
Accountants On Call (C), *236*
ACSYS Resources, Inc. (C), *238*
The Altco Group (C), *246*
A. Davis Grant & Co. (R), *81*
Jeffrey Meryl Assoc., Inc. (C), *398*

Emerson
Bryant Research (C), *275*
Data Search Network, Inc. (C), *307*

Englewood Cliffs
Phyllis Solomon Executive Search, Inc. (C), *587*
The Stevenson Group, Inc. (N.J.) (R), *200*

GEOGRAPHICAL

Englishtown
Stewart/Laurence Assoc., Inc. (R), *201*

Fair Lawn
Rick Pascal & Assoc., Inc. (C), *504*

Fairfield
Eagle Research, Inc. (C), *325*
Razzino-Claymore Assoc. (C), *530*
Retail Connection, Inc. (C), *535*
Sales Consultant of Essex County (C), *554*
Sterling Int'l. (R), *200*

Fanwood
Engineering & Scientific Search Assoc. (ESSA) (C), *330*
Peeney Assoc., Inc. (R), *161*

Far Hills
Intelegra, Inc. (C), *390*

Flanders
The Comwell Company, Inc. (C), *296*

Flemington
Sanford Rose Assoc. - Flemington (C), *568*

Florham Park
Frank E. Allen & Assoc. (C), *244*
Chatham Search Assoc., Inc. (C), *290*
The Corporate Advisory Group (R), *41*
Richard A. Eisner & Co., LLP (R), *58*
Hadley Associates, Inc. (C), *365*
Marvin Laba & Assoc. (R), *122*
Management Recruiters of Morris County, NJ (C), *453*

Fords
Datamatics Management Services, Inc. (C), *307*

Franklin
Sales Consultant of Franklin (C), *554*

Freehold
Dunhill Staffing Systems, Inc. (C), *317*

Ft. Lee
Cooper Management Assoc., Inc. (C), *298*
Donna Davis Assoc. (C), *309*
The Matthews Group, Inc. (C), *472*
Devin Scott Assoc. (C), *572*

Gibbsboro
Cox, Darrow & Owens, Inc. (C), *302*
RTE Search (C), *547*

Glen Rock
Gary S. Bell Assoc., Inc. (C), *263*
Healthcare Recruiters International-NY/NJ (C), *373*
Sales Consultants of Northern Jersey, Inc. (C), *560*

Green Brook
Trac One (R), *210*

Hackensack
Robert Drexler Assoc., Inc. (R), *54*

Haddonfield
David Allen Assoc. (R), *3*
Management Recruiters of Haddonfield (C), *431*
The Pennmor Group (C), *506*
The Quantum Group (C), *527*
Stevens, Valentine & McKeever (C), *593*

Harrington Park
Seco & Zetto Assoc., Inc. (C), *577*

Hasbrouck Heights
Carter/MacKay (C), *285*

Hazlet
Sales Consultant of Middletown (C), *554*
Norm Sanders Assoc., Inc. (R), *184*

High Bridge
J. M. Joseph Assoc. (R), *109*

Hoboken
Florence Pape Legal Search, Inc. (C), *502*
Sales Consultants of Hudson County (C), *554*

Hope
Management Recruiters of North Warren Inc. (C), *453*

Hopewell
Capitol Management Consulting, Inc. (C), *281*

Howell
William Bell Assoc., Inc. (C), *263*

Iselin
ACSYS Resources, Inc. (C), *238*
Battalia Winston Int'l./The Euram Consultants Group (R), *13*
Coleman Legal Search Consultants (C), *294*
Fortuna Technologies Inc. (C), *343*
The Kleinstein Group, Inc. (R), *116*

Jersey City
Accountants On Call (C), *236*
The Center for Career Advancement, LLC (C), *287*
Dalton Management Consultants, Ltd. (C), *306*

Kinnelon
The Brentwood Group, Inc. (R), *22*

Lake Hopatcong
O'Neill Group (C), *498*

Lakehurst
EBA Group (R), *56*

Lakewood
Jack Stuart Fisher Assoc. (C), *341*
Rein & Co., Inc. (R), *174*

Lawrenceville
Alexander Associates (R), *2*
McGrath & Assoc., Inc. (R), *141*
Moore Research Assoc. (R), *147*
PLA, Inc. (C), *513*

Little Silver
Graham & Co. (R), *80*

Livingston
Accountants On Call (C), *236*
Sales Consultant of Livingston (C), *554*

Lyndhurst
Fox-Morris Assoc., Inc. (C), *352*
Hunt Ltd. (C), *385*

Madison
Joseph R. Burns & Assoc., Inc. (R), *25*
Karras Personnel, Inc. (C), *403*

Mahwah
Butterfass, Pepe & MacCallan Inc. (R), *25*
EDI/Executive Dynamics Inc. (C), *326*
Telequest Communications, Inc. (C), *605*

Manalapan
Latham International, Ltd. (R), *126*

Manasquan
R. W. Apple & Assoc. (C), *251*
Executive Exchange Corp. (C), *333*
The Mulshine Co., Inc. (R), *149*
Sales Consultant of Ocean (C), *554*

Mantoloking
Mehta Consulting (C), *478*

Marlton
Bonifield Assoc. (C), *269*
David Perry Assoc. (C), *308*
Healthcare Recruiters Int'l. Philadelphia (C), *373*
Telecom Executive Group (C), *605*

Matawan
N. Willner & Co., Inc. (R), *221*

Maywood
The DataFinders Group, Inc. (C), *307*

Medford
The Addison Consulting Group (C), *239*
Dunhill Search of Medford (C), *321*
Management Recruiters of Medford, N.J. (C), *453*
McCartan Assoc. (R), *139*
Munroe, Curry & Bond Assoc. (R), *149*

Mendham
Kazan International, Inc. (R), *110*

Metuchen
CSA/Clinical Staffing Assoc., LLC (C), *304*
F-O-R-T-U-N-E Personnel Consultants of Menlo Park, Inc. (C), *347*
Management Recruiters of Edison (C), *431*

Milford
A.L.S. Group (C), *232*

Millburn
Management Recruiters of Short Hills (C), *431*
Marra Peters & Partners (R), *136*

Monmouth Beach
Fred A. Barnette & Assoc. (R), *11*

Montclair
The C.P.R. Group (C), *278*

Epsen, Fuller & Assoc., LLC (R), *60*

Montville
Search Assoc., Inc. (C), *574*

Moorestown
Lawrence Glaser Assoc., Inc. (C), *357*

Morganville
Judd Associates (R), *109*
LAS Management Consulting Group, Inc. (R), *125*

Morris Plains
Engineering Resource Group, Inc. (C), *331*

Morristown
Ballos & Co., Inc. (R), *10*
Boyden (R), *21*
Foley Proctor Yoskowitz (R), *69*
Jonathan Lawrence Assoc. (C), *400*
Kulper & Co., L.L.C. (R), *121*
Skott/Edwards Consultants (R), *192*

Mountain Lakes
Besen Assoc. Inc. (C), *266*
Brandywine Management Group (R), *22*
Orion Consulting, Inc. (R), *157*

Mountainside
Management Recruiters of Union County (C), *431*

Mt. Laurel
Alexander Graham Assoc. (C), *361*
Management Recruiters of Bordentown (C), *454*

Murray Hill
Raymond Karsan Assoc. (C), *530*

New Brunswick
Place Mart Personnel Service (C), *513*

New Providence
Management Recruiters of New Providence (C), *454*

Newark
L. J. Gonzer Assoc. (C), *360*
Norrell Financial Staffing (C), *495*

North Bergen
Allan Karson Assoc., Inc. (R), *110*
KL Consultants (C), *407*

North Brunswick
Hreshko Consulting Group (C), *382*
Key Employment (C), *405*

North Caldwell
Eastern Executive Assoc. (C), *325*
K. L. Whitney Company (R), *219*

Oakland
Dunhill Professional Search of Ramsey (C), *321*

Ocean City
Huff Assoc. (R), *98*

Oradell
Management Decision Systems, Inc. (MDSI) (C), *424*

Paramus
Accountants On Call (C), *236*
AES Search (C), *241*
Berman & Larson (C), *265*
David Anthony Personnel Assoc., Inc. (C), *308*
Romac Int'l., Inc. (C), *543*
Search Consultants, Inc. (C), *575*

Parlin
Management Recruiters of Middlesex County NJ (C), *454*

Parsippany
Baker Scott & Co. (C), *258*
Bosland Gray Assoc. (R), *20*
The Garret Group (R), *75*
Goodrich & Sherwood Assoc., Inc. (R), *80*
Romac Int'l., Inc. (C), *543*
Sales Consultants of Morris County, Inc. (C), *561*
Sanders Management Assoc., Inc. (C), *565*

Pennington
Pennington Consulting Group (C), *506*

Piscataway
Sales Consultants of Middlesex County, Inc. (C), *561*
Strategic Advancement Inc. (R), *202*
Stratin Assoc. (C), *596*

Pitman
The Buckley Group (C), *276*

Pittstown
Preston & Co. (R), *167*
WMD inc. (C), *623*

Pompton Lakes
Inter Regional Executive Search, Inc. (IRES, Inc.) (C), *391*
Management Recruiters of Passaic County-North (C), *431*

Princeton
Accountants On Call (C), *236*
ACSYS Resources, Inc. (C), *238*
Adler Management, Inc. (R), *2*
Barone-O'Hara Assoc., Inc. (R), *11*
Blau Mancino Schroeder (R), *18*
Burke, O'Brien & Bishop Assoc., Inc. (R), *25*
China Human Resources Group (R), *33*
Ken Clark Int'l. (R), *36*
Dunhill Staffing Systems of Princeton (C), *317*
Excalibur Human Resources, Inc. (R), *61*
Goodrich & Sherwood Assoc., Inc. (R), *80*
Hollander Horizon Int'l. (R), *95*
The Jonathan Stevens Group, Inc. (R), *108*
Korn/Ferry Int'l. (R), *118*
L O R (R), *122*
Milrod Assoc. (C), *482*
P R Management Consultants, Inc. (C), *500*
Princeton Executive Search (C), *518*
Princeton Search Partners, Inc. (R), *169*
Raymond Karsan Assoc. (C), *530*
Romac Int'l., Inc. (C), *543*
Rylan Forbes Consulting Group, Inc. (C), *549*

Tucker Assoc. (R), *211*
Michael D. Zinn & Assoc., Inc. (R), *227*

Ramsey
Dreier Consulting (C), *315*
Major Search (C), *423*
Merlin Int'l. Inc. (C), *479*

Rancocas
Robert Scott Assoc. (C), *573*

Randolph
Paul Kull & Co. (R), *121*

Raritan
Brissenden, McFarland, Fuccella & Reynolds, Inc. (R), *23*

Red Bank
Broad Waverly & Assoc. (C), *274*
Management Recruiters of Southern Monmouth County (C), *432*
The Resource Group (R), *175*
Sales Consultant of Monmouth County (C), *554*

Ridgewood
McCooe & Assoc., Inc. (R), *140*
DNPitchon Assoc. (R), *165*

River Edge
J. Burkey Assoc. (R), *25*

River Vale
Tschudin Inc. (R), *211*

Riverdale
Weinpel Search, Inc. (C), *617*

Robbinsville
Diedre Moire Corp., Inc. (C), *483*

Rochelle Park
F-O-R-T-U-N-E Personnel Consultants of Bergen County Inc. (C), *347*
The Normyle/Erstling Health Search Group (C), *494*

Roseland
The Ascher Group (R), *7*
The Partnership Group (R), *160*

Rutherford
Caplan Assoc., Inc. (R), *28*
The Macdonald Group, Inc. (R), *133*
Yours In Travel Personnel Agency, Inc. (C), *627*

Saddle Brook
Accountants On Call (C), *234*

Salem
L & K Assoc. (C), *410*

Sayreville
Louis Search Group, Inc. (C), *420*

Scotch Plains
Petruzzi Assoc. (C), *509*

Sea Girt
Zaccaria Int'l. (C), *627*

Secaucus
Accountants On Call (C), *236*
Curry, Telleri Group, Inc. (R), *44*
Reinecke & Assoc. (C), *533*
Bruce Robinson Assoc. (R), *180*

Ship Bottom
Management Catalysts (R), *134*

Short Hills
The Governance Group, Inc. (R), *80*

Shrewsbury
FCI, Inc. (R), *65*

Skillman
Business Solutions Worldwide, Inc. (C), *277*
RCE Assoc. (R), *173*

Somerset
Lawrence James Assoc. (C), *414*
R. S. Sadow Assoc. (C), *550*

Somerville
Dean-Dzierzawiec Assoc. (C), *309*
Lancaster Assoc., Inc. (C), *411*

South Orange
Walter K. Wilkins & Co. (R), *221*

South Plainfield
The Stelton Group, Inc. (C), *592*

Sparta
Madison Executive Search, Inc. (C), *422*
Management Recruiters of Sparta (C), *432*
Sales Consultant of Sparta (C), *554*
Tully/Woodmansee Int'l., Inc. (R), *212*

Springfield
Jaral Consultants, Inc. (C), *397*
Kingsley Quinn/USA (R), *115*
Tarnow Int'l. (R), *206*

Stanhope
Management Recruiters of Stanhope (C), *432*

Summit
DHR Int'l., Inc. (R), *50*
Management Alliance Group, Inc. (R), *134*
Sales Consultants of Summit (C), *554*
Search Assoc., Inc. (C), *574*

Tenafly
Careers On Track (C), *283*

Tennent
S.D.P. Contract Recruiters (C), *550*

Toms River
The Cassie Group (R), *31*

Turnersville
SoftSearch Inc. (C), *586*

Union
Brett Personnel Specialists (C), *273*

Upper Montclair
DHR Int'l., Inc. (R), *50*
Foster Associates (C), *351*
The Quantum Group (C), *526*

Upper Saddle River
META/MAT, Ltd. (R), *144*
Skip Tolette Executive Search Consulting (R), *209*

Verona
Drew Assoc. Int'l. (R), *54*
E.P. Int'l. (C), *324*

Vineland
Lee Management Group Inc. (C), *416*

Warren
Kurtz Pro-Search, Inc. (C), *410*

Wayne
CS Dowling Executive Services (R), *54*

West Berlin
The Alexander Group (R), *3*

West Caldwell
Phoenix BioSearch, Inc. (C), *511*
Triad Consultants, Inc. (C), *609*

West Long Branch
Ellis Career Consultants (C), *328*
Management Recruiters of Northern Monmouth County (C), *432*

West Orange
Carter McKenzie, Inc. (C), *285*
Gilbert Tweed Assoc. Inc. (R), *77*
L. Patrick Group (R), *122*
Steeple Resources & Consulting (R), *199*
Topaz Int'l., Inc., Attorney Search (C), *607*

West Trenton
Management Recruiters of Princeton (C), *454*
Sales Consultants of Princeton, Inc. (C), *561*

Westfield
W. N. Garbarini & Assoc. (R), *74*
Johnson Smith & Knisely (R), *107*
Mark Adam Assoc. (R), *135*
Tate & Assoc., Inc. (R), *207*

Woodbridge
GSP International (C), *364*
Romac Int'l., Inc. (C), *543*

Wyckoff
Carol Ball & Co. (C), *258*

New Mexico

Albuquerque
ACC Consultants, Inc. (C), *233*
Tom Allison Assoc. (C), *245*
Blau Mancino Schroeder (R), *18*
Brandywine Retained Ventures, Inc. (R), *22*
Gaines & Assoc. Int'l., Inc. (R), *73*
Management Recruiters of Albuquerque (C), *432*
Management Recruiters of The Sandias (C), *454*
Sales Consultant of Albuquerque (C), *554*
Trambley the Recruiter (C), *608*

Santa Fe
Management Recruiters of Santa Fe (C), *432*
The Mercer Group, Inc. (R), *143*

New York

Albany
DeMatteo Associates (C), *311*
Management Recruiters of Colonie (C), *432*
Management Recruiters of Albany (C), *432*
Ritta Professional Search Inc. (C), *538*

Amagansett
Martha Ward Executive Search, Inc. (C), *615*

Amherst
Executive Dimensions (R), *62*

Amsterdam
Sheila Greco Assoc. (C), *362*

Ardmore
Dunhill Professional Search of Main Line (C), *317*

Armonk
LanSo Int'l., Inc. (C), *413*
Olympian Recruitment, Ltd. (C), *498*

Babylon
IMA Search, Inc. (R), *101*

Baldwin
Management Recruiters of Nassau, Inc. (R), *134*

Baldwinsville
Orion Int'l. Consulting Group, Inc. (C), *499*

Bedford Hills
HLR Consulting (C), *379*

Bellmore
J P Donnelly Assoc., Inc. (C), *314*

Bellport
International Management Development Corp. (C), *393*

Bemus Point
Westfields Int'l., Inc. (C), *619*

Binghamton
Management Recruiters of Broome County, Inc. (C), *454*

Bronxville
Manuso, Alexander & Associates, Inc. (R), *135*

Brooklyn
Brian Assoc., Inc. (C), *273*
The Ellsworth Group (C), *329*
PSP Agency (C), *525*

Buffalo
C/R Associates (C), *278*
Dunhill of Buffalo Agency, Ltd. (C), *317*
Sales Consultants of Buffalo (C), *554*

Camillus
Dapexs Consultants, Inc. (C), *307*

Carle Place
Cowin Assoc. (R), *42*

Chappaqua
Raymond J. Klemmer & Assoc. (R), *116*

Clarence
Kozlin Assoc., Inc. (C), *408*

Commack
StaffWriters Plus (C), *591*

Cooperstown
Richmond Assoc. (C), *537*

Cortland
Hospitality Int'l. (C), *381*

Croton-on-Hudson
Cusack Consulting (R), *44*
Laguzza Assoc., Ltd. (R), *122*

Delmar
NorTech Resources (C), *496*

Dewitt
Sales Consultant of Syracuse (C), *554*

East Islip
Dick Wray & Consultants, Inc. (R), *225*

East Northport
Shupack & Michaels Inc. (C), *580*

East Norwich
Insight Consulting Co. (C), *389*

East Williston
Peter R. Taylor Assoc., Inc. (C), *600*

Eden
Professional Persons Career Services (C), *521*

Elmont
Vincent Lee Assoc. (C), *415*

Fairport
Parsons, Anderson & Gee, Inc. (C), *503*
Scott Sibley Assoc. (C), *573*

Fayetteville
Raymond Karsan Assoc. (C), *530*

Garden City
Dorst Information Services, Inc. (C), *314*
Franklin Allen Consultants, Ltd. (R), *71*
Paul Misarti Inc. (C), *483*
P. G. Prager Search Assoc., Ltd. (C), *515*

Glens Falls
Keena Staffing Services (C), *404*

Granite Springs
Ira Z. Nitzberg (C), *493*

Great Neck
Bender Executive Search Management Consulting (R), *16*
A. E. Feldman Assoc., Inc. (C), *339*
Interquest, Inc. (R), *103*
Management Recruiters of Great Neck (C), *454*
Travel Executive Search (C), *608*

Harrison
The Zarkin Group, Inc. (R), *226*

Hartsdale
Newport Management (C), *492*

Hauppauge
Ames-O'Neill Assoc., Inc. (C), *249*
Dunhill Staffing Systems, Inc. (C), *316*
Eastbourne Assoc. Inc. (R), *56*
JDC Assoc. (C), *397*
Lloyd Prescott & Churchill, Inc. (R), *130*
Lloyd Prescott Assoc., Inc. (C), *419*

Hawthorne
Sales Consultants of Westchester-South, Inc. (C), *561*

Hicksville
Amherst Personnel Group Inc. (C), *249*
Tax Network Resources, Inc. (C), *600*

Huntington
Dunhill Professional Search of huntington (C), *318*
Huntington Personnel Consultants, Inc. (C), *386*
M. A. Pelle Assoc., Inc. (C), *506*
Weber Executive Search (R), *216*

Huntington Station
Management Recruiters of Melville (C), *432*
Sales Consultants of Suffolk County-North (C), *554*

Irvington
Media Recruiting Group, Inc. (C), *476*

Jericho
Accountants On Call (C), *236*
Bartl & Evins (C), *260*
Mogul Consultants, Inc. (C), *483*
The P & L Group (C), *500*

Lake Success
Carter/MacKay (C), *285*

Larchmont
Bergeris & Co., Inc. (C), *265*
Hermann & Westmore (R), *92*
E. J. Michaels, Ltd. (C), *481*
Dennis P. O'Toole & Assoc. Inc. (R), *154*

Little Neck
Robert Bennett Assoc. (C), *264*

Liverpool
Healthcare Recruiters of New York, Inc. (C), *373*

Long Island City
SKB Enterprises (C), *582*

Madrid
Management Recruiters of St. Lawrence County (C), *432*

Malverne
Gahan Assoc. (R), *73*
Sales Consultants of Nassau (C), *554*

Mamaroneck
APA Search, Inc. (R), *6*
Oliver & Rozner Assoc., Inc. (R), *155*

Massapequa
Dunhill Staffing Systems (C), *318*
Morgan/Webber, Inc. (R), *147*

Massapequa Park
ROI Assoc. (R), *180*

Melville
Lloyd Staffing (C), *419*
Ramm Search (C), *528*
Sales Consultants of Melville (C), *554*

Millbrook
Abbott Smith Assoc., Inc. (R), *193*

Millwood
Marcus & Assoc. (C), *469*

Mineola
HVS Executive Search (R), *100*
Norgate Technology, Inc. (C), *494*

Mt. Kisco
Management Recruiters of Upper Westchester (C), *454*

New City
Adam-Bryce Inc. (C), *239*
Career Counseling Ltd. (C.C.L.) (C), *282*
Jakobs & Assoc. Int'l. (R), *105*
Professional Resources (C), *522*

New Hampton
Brown, Bernardy, Van Remmen, Inc. (C), *275*

New Rochelle
Miller-Hall HRISearch (C), *482*
Newell Assoc. (R), *151*

New York
A-K-A (Anita Kaufmann Assoc.) (C), *231*
A-L Assoc., Inc. (R), *1*
Abacus Group LLC (C), *232*
Accountants On Call (C), *236*
Advice Personnel Inc. (C), *241*
Advisors' Search Group, Inc. (C), *241*
Alexander Ross & Co. (R), *3*
The Alfus Group (R), *3*
Allard Associates (C), *244*
Allen Evans Assoc. (R), *4*
American Group Practice, Inc. (R), *5*
Analytic Recruiting, Inc. (C), *249*
Anderson & Schwab, Inc. (R), *5*
Ariel Recruitment Assoc. (R), *7*
Ashway Ltd. Agency (C), *253*
Aster Search Group (R), *8*
Avalon Health Group, Inc. (R), *9*
The Ayers Group, Inc. (R), *9*
Bader Research Corp. (C), *257*
The Bankers Register (C), *259*
The Barack Group, Inc. (R), *11*
Barr Associates (C), *260*

GEOGRAPHICAL

Battalia Winston Int'l./The Euram Consultants Group (R), *13*
Martin H. Bauman Assoc., Inc. (R), *13*
The Beam Group (R), *14*
Neail Behringer Consultants Inc. (R), *15*
Marcia Beilin, Inc. (C), *262*
Bell Wishingrad Partners Inc. (R), *15*
Benson Associates (C), *264*
Bialecki Inc. (R), *17*
Bishop Partners (R), *17*
Blake/Hansen & Schmidt, Ltd. (R), *18*
BLB Consulting (C), *268*
The BMW Group, Inc. (C), *268*
Boardroom Consultants/Kenny Kindler Tholke (R), *19*
Bodner Inc. (C), *268*
Bonell Ryan Inc. (R), *19*
Bornholdt Shivas & Friends Executive Recruiters (C), *270*
Boyden (R), *20*
Boyden (R), *20*
Boyden (R), *21*
Branthover Assoc. (C), *272*
Brookman Associates (C), *274*
Brownstone Sales & Marketing Group, Inc. (C), *275*
Charles Buck & Assoc., Inc. (R), *24*
The Burgess Group-Corporate Recruiters Int'l., Inc. (R), *25*
Juliette Lang Cahn Executive Search (C), *279*
Canny, Bowen Inc. (R), *27*
J. P. Canon Assoc. (C), *280*
The Cantor Concern, Inc. (R), *28*
Carris, Jackowitz Assoc. (R), *30*
CAS Comsearch Inc. (C), *285*
Cassell & Kaye (C), *286*
Catalyx Group (R), *31*
Malin Cederquist, Esq. (C), *286*
Chanko-Ward, Ltd. (R), *33*
Christian & Timbers, Inc. (R), *34*
Toby Clark Assoc. Inc. (C), *292*
Richard Clarke Assoc., Inc. (R), *36*
The Colton Partnership, Inc. (R), *38*
Columbia Consulting Group (R), *38*
Conex Inc./InterSearch (R), *39*
The Consortium (C), *296*
The Consulting Group Ltd. (R), *40*
COR Management Services, Ltd. (C), *298*
The Corporate Source Group, Inc. (R), *42*
Corrao, Miller, Rush & Wiesenthal (C), *301*
Leonard Corwen Assoc. (C), *302*
Trudi Cowlan (C), *302*
Creative Management Strategies, Ltd. (R), *42*
The Cris Group, Inc. (R), *42*
Crispi, Wagner & Co., Inc. (R), *43*
Cromwell Partners, Inc. (R), *43*
Cyntal Int'l. Ltd. (R), *44*
The Dartmouth Group (R), *46*
John J. Davis & Assoc., Inc. (R), *47*
Joseph A. Davis Consultants, Inc. (R), *47*
Bert Davis Executive Search, Inc. (R), *47*
Bert Davis Publishing Placement Consultants (C), *309*
The Dayton Group, Ltd. (C), *309*
DeLalla - Fried Assoc. (C), *310*
Thorndike Deland Assoc. LLC (R), *48*
Development Resource Group (R), *48*
DHR Int'l., Inc. (R), *50*
Diamond Tax Recruiting (C), *312*
J. Dinerstein & Co., Inc. (R), *51*
DLB Assoc. (R), *53*
J P Donnelly Assoc., Inc. (C), *314*
Dotson & Assoc. (R), *54*
Dow Consultants Int'l. (C), *314*
Drummond Assoc., Inc. (C), *315*
E.P. Int'l. (C), *324*
Earley Kielty & Assoc., Inc. (R), *56*
Egan Search Group (R), *57*
Richard A. Eisner & Co., LLP (R), *57*
David M. Ellner Assoc. (R), *59*
Mark Elzweig Co., Ltd. (C), *329*
Erikson Consulting Assoc., Inc. (R), *60*
The Execu/Search Group (C), *332*
Executive Access Inc. (R), *62*
Executive Search Consultants International, Inc. (R), *63*
Executive Search Partners (R), *63*
The Executive Source Inc. (R), *64*
Fabian Assoc. Inc. (C), *338*
Fairfield Int'l. Resources (R), *65*
Fergus Legal Search & Consulting, Inc. (C), *339*
Jerry Fields Assoc. (C), *340*
Eileen Finn & Assoc., Inc. (C), *341*
Fisher-Todd Assoc. (C), *341*
Flexible Resources, Inc. (C), *342*
Foley Proctor Yoskowitz (R), *69*
Forray Assoc., Inc. (R), *70*
Forum Personnel Inc. (C), *351*
Foster Partners (R), *70*
Fox-Morris Assoc., Inc. (C), *352*
Foy, Schneid & Daniel, Inc. (R), *71*
Gerald Frisch Assoc., Inc. (R), *72*
The Fry Group, Inc. (C), *353*
Gaines & Assoc. Int'l., Inc. (R), *73*
Jay Gaines & Company, Inc. (R), *73*
Gardiner, Townsend & Assoc. (R), *74*
Gardner-Ross Assoc., Inc. (R), *74*
Dick Garland Consultants (R), *74*
GES Services, Inc. (R), *76*
Gilbert & Van Campen Int'l. (R), *76*
Gilbert Tweed Assoc. Inc. (R), *76*
Global Career Services, Inc. (C), *358*
The Gogates Group, Inc. (R), *79*
The Goldman Group Inc. (R), *79*
Goldman+Bell, LLC (C), *360*
Goodkind Assoc. Inc. (C), *360*
Goodrich & Sherwood Assoc., Inc. (R), *79*
Gossage Regan Assoc. (R), *80*
Gould, McCoy & Chadick, Inc. (R), *80*
Greene-Levin-Snyder LLC (C), *362*
Greenhaven & Assoc., Inc. (R), *81*
Nadine Guber & Assoc., Inc. (C), *364*
Gumbinner/Haubenstock, Inc. (C), *364*
Gundersen Partners, L.L.C. (R), *83*
Stephen Haas Legal Placement (C), *365*
Hadley Lockwood, Inc. (R), *84*
Hall Kinion (C), *367*
Hands-on Broadcast (R), *86*
Handy HRM (R), *86*
Hanzel & Co., Inc. (R), *86*
Harris McCully Assoc., Inc. (C), *369*
Hart & Co. (C), *370*
F. P. Healy & Co., Inc. (R), *89*
Heath/Norton Assoc., Inc. (R), *89*
Hechkoff/Work Executive Search Inc. (R), *89*
Heidrick & Struggles, Inc. (R), *90*
Jay Heino Company, LLC (C), *375*
Hessel Assoc., Inc. (C), *377*
Heyman Assoc., Inc. (R), *93*
Higdon Prince Inc. (R), *93*
Highland Search Group, L.L.C. (R), *93*
Ruth Hirsch Assoc., Inc. (C), *379*
The Hollins Group, Inc. (R), *95*
J. B. Homer Assoc. Inc. (R), *95*
Horton Int'l. Inc. (R), *96*
Hospitality Int'l. (C), *381*
Howard-Sloan Assoc. (C), *381*
Howard-Sloan Legal Search, Inc. (C), *382*
The Howard-Sloan-Koller Group (R), *97*
HRCS (R), *97*
Arnold Huberman Assoc., Inc. (R), *97*
E. A. Hughes & Co., Inc. (R), *98*
Hunt & Howe Inc. (R), *99*
The Hunt Co. (R), *99*
The IMC Group of Companies (R), *101*
Ingram & Aydelotte, Inc. (R), *101*
Integrated Management Solutions (C), *390*
Intelligent Marketing Solutions, Inc. (C), *390*
International Management Advisors, Inc. (R), *103*
International Market Recruiters (C), *393*
Interquest, Inc. (R), *103*
Interspace Interactive, Inc. (C), *394*
Joan Isbister Consultants (C), *394*
Ann Israel & Assoc., Inc. (C), *395*
Pendleton James Assoc., Inc. (R), *105*
R. I. James, Inc. (C), *397*
John Ryan Assoc., LLC. (C), *399*
The Johnson Group, Unlimited (C), *400*
Johnson Smith & Knisely (R), *107*
Jones Management Co. (R), *108*
Juno Systems, Inc. (C), *402*
Lisa Kalus & Assoc., Inc. (C), *403*
Martin Kartin & Co., Inc. (R), *110*
The Kay Group of 5th Ave. (C), *404*
A.T. Kearney Executive Search (R), *111*
Kenzer Corp. (R), *113*
Barbara Kerner Consultants (C), *405*
Kingsbury • Wax • Bova (R), *114*
Richard Kinser & Assoc. (R), *115*
Kip Williams, Inc. (R), *115*
Koltnow & Company (R), *117*
Korn/Ferry Int'l. (R), *117*
Kostmayer Assoc., Inc. (R), *119*
KPA Assoc., Inc. (C), *408*
Kramer Executive Resources, Inc. (C), *409*
Evie Kreisler Assoc. Inc. (C), *409*
Laguzza Assoc., Ltd. (R), *122*
LAI Ward Howell (R), *122*
LAI Ward Howell (R), *123*
E. J. Lance Management Assoc., Inc. (C), *412*
The Landstone Group (C), *412*
Lawrence L. Lapham, Inc. (R), *124*
Ledbetter/Davidson Int'l., Inc. (R), *127*
Lemming/LeVan, Inc. (R), *128*
Leslie Kavanagh Assoc., Inc. (C), *416*
Michael Levine Search Consultants (R), *129*
Hal Levy & Assoc. (C), *417*
Lexington Software Inc. (C), *417*

Lipton Assoc., Inc. (R), *130*
J. P. Logan & Co., Inc. (R), *131*
Logic Assoc., Inc. (C), *419*
Logistics Management Resources, Inc. (R), *131*
London & Company (C), *420*
The John Lucht Consultancy Inc. (R), *131*
Lynne Palmer Executive Recruitment, Inc. (C), *421*
The Madison Group (R), *133*
Major, Hagen & Africa (C), *423*
Management Alliance Group, Inc. (R), *134*
Management Recruiters of Manhattan at Madison Avenue (C), *432*
Management Recruiters of Gramercy, Inc. (C), *455*
Management Recruiters of Manhattan on Broadway (C), *455*
Management Resource Group, Inc. (C), *467*
Management Resources Int'l. (R), *135*
ManTech Consulting (C), *468*
Margolin Consultants, Inc. (C), *469*
Paula Marks Inc. (R), *136*
Marley Group Ltd. (C), *471*
Marshall Consultants, Inc. (R), *137*
Marshall-Alan Assoc., Inc. (C), *471*
Maximum Management Corp. (C), *473*
MB Inc. Executive Search (C), *473*
McCann, Choi & Associates, LLC (R), *139*
Martin H. Meisel Assoc., Inc. (R), *143*
Meridian Legal Search/Legal Temps (C), *479*
Miller/Davis & Assoc., Inc. (C), *482*
Milo Research (R), *145*
Herbert Mines Assoc., Inc. (R), *145*
Mitchell Martin Inc. (C), *483*
Morgan Stampfl, Inc. (C), *485*
Morgenstern Int'l., Inc. (C), *486*
Moyer, Sherwood Assoc., Inc. (R), *148*
Mruk & E.M.A. Partners (R), *148*
Much & Co. (R), *148*
The MVP Group (C), *487*
The Neil Michael Group, Inc./Global Partners (R), *151*
New World Healthcare Solutions, Inc. (R), *151*
Marc Nichols Assoc., Inc. (C), *493*
Nichols Brown Int'l. (R), *151*
Noble & Assoc., Inc. (C), *494*
Nordeman Grimm, Inc. (R), *152*
Norman Broadbent Int'l., Inc. (R), *152*
NorthStar Technologies, Inc. (C), *496*
The Ogdon Partnership (R), *155*
Oppedisano & Co., Inc. (R), *156*
Opportunity Resources, Inc. (R), *156*
The Options Group, Inc. (C), *499*
K. Ossow & Co. (C), *500*
The Oxbridge Group, Ltd. (C), *500*
Janou Pakter, Inc. (C), *502*
Kirk Palmer & Assoc., Inc. (R), *158*
R. Parker & Assoc., Inc. (R), *159*
Partners In Human Resources Int'l., Inc. (R), *160*
Pathway Executive Search, Inc. (C), *505*
Joel H. Paul & Assoc., Inc. (C), *505*
Pearson, Caldwell & Farnsworth (R), *161*
Pharmaceutical Recruiters, Inc. (R), *163*
Picard Int'l., Ltd. (R), *164*
Pinnacle Group Int'l. (C), *512*
Pittleman & Assoc. (C), *512*
Placements by Jesse Reid Assoc., Inc. (C), *513*
Rene Plessner Assoc., Inc. (R), *165*
Preferred Placement, Inc. (C), *516*
ProTech Nationwide Staffing, Inc. (C), *525*
Quantum EDP Recruiting Services (C), *526*
The Quest Organization (C), *527*
L. J. Quinn & Assoc., Inc. (R), *170*
R & L Assoc., Ltd. (R), *170*
Raines Int'l. Inc. (R), *171*
Rand Thompson Executive Search Consultants (C), *528*
Joanne E. Ratner Search (C), *529*
Ray & Berndtson (R), *172*
Raymond Karsan Assoc. (C), *530*
Redwood Partners Ltd. (R), *173*
Response Staffing Services (C), *534*
Russell Reynolds Assoc., Inc. (R), *176*
Russell Reynolds Assoc., Inc. (R), *177*
Reynolds Partners (R), *177*
Rhodes Associates (R), *177*
Richards Assoc., Inc. (R), *178*
Riotto-Jones Assoc. (R), *178*
Ritech Management Inc. (C), *537*
RJN Consulting (R), *179*
RLM Assoc., Ltd. (R), *179*
Rockwood Assoc. (C), *540*
Romac Int'l., Inc. (C), *544*
W. R. Rosato & Assoc., Inc. (R), *182*
Susan Rudich (C), *548*
The S C Group LLC (R), *183*
S.C.S. & Assoc. (C), *550*
Santangelo Consultants Inc. (C), *571*
Allan Sarn Assoc., Inc. (R), *184*
Secura/Burnett Partners (R), *188*
Sedlar & Miners (R), *188*
Seiden Krieger Assoc., Inc. (R), *188*
Seitchik Corwin & Seitchik Inc. (R), *188*
Senior Careers (R), *188*
Setford-Shaw-Najarian Assoc. (C), *579*
SFB Legal Search (C), *579*
RitaSue Siegel Resources, Inc. (R), *191*
Simpson Associates (C), *582*
Ruth Sklar Assoc., Inc. (RSA Executive Search) (R), *192*
Skott/Edwards Consultants (R), *192*
Smith & Sawyer, Inc. (R), *193*
Smith Hanley Assoc., Inc. (C), *584*
Smith, Roth & Squires (R), *194*
Smith's Fifth Avenue (C), *585*
Smythe Masterson & Judd, Inc. (C), *585*
Sofco (C), *586*
Solomon-Page Healthcare Group (R), *195*
SpencerStuart (R), *196*
Spring Assoc., Inc. (R), *198*
Staub, Warmbold & Assoc., Inc. (R), *199*
Stentiford & Berardi Assoc. Ltd. (R), *199*
Steven Michaels & Assoc. (C), *593*
Storfer & Assoc. (C), *595*
Strategic Executives, Inc. (R), *202*
W. R. Strathmann Assoc. (R), *203*
Sullivan & Company (R), *204*
TASA International (R), *206*
Tax Network Resources, Inc. (C), *600*
Techno-Trac Systems, Inc. (C), *603*
Telecom Executive Group (C), *605*
TeleManagement Search (C), *605*
Tennyson Advisors (R), *208*
Thorne, Brieger Assoc., Inc. (R), *209*
Trebor Weldon Lawrence, Inc. (R), *210*
TRH Assoc., Inc. (R), *210*
V.I.P. Resources, Inc. (C), *611*
Vintage Resources, Inc. (C), *613*
The Viscusi Group, Inc. (R), *214*
Wakefield Talabisco Int'l. (R), *214*
Warren Int'l. (R), *215*
Watson Int'l., Inc. (R), *216*
The Wayne Group, Ltd. (C), *616*
Webb, Johnson Assoc., Inc. (R), *216*
C. Weiss Assoc., Inc. (C), *618*
Werbin Assoc. Executive Search, Inc. (C), *618*
Wesley Brown & Bartle Co., Inc. (R), *218*
S. J. Wexler Assoc., Inc. (R), *219*
The Whitney Group (R), *219*
Witt/Kieffer, Ford, Hadelman & Lloyd (R), *223*
D. S. Wolf Assoc., Inc. (R), *223*
S. R. Wolman Assoc., Inc. (R), *224*
Louise Wood & Assoc. (C), *624*
The Worth Group (C), *625*
WTW Assoc., Inc. (R), *225*
Yours In Travel Personnel Agency, Inc. (C), *626*
Egon Zehnder Int'l. Inc. (R), *227*
Chuck Zimering Advertising Recruitment (CZAR) (C), *627*
Michael D. Zinn & Assoc., Inc. (R), *227*
Zona & Assoc., Inc. (C), *628*

Newburgh
Cornell Group Int'l. Consulting, Inc. (R), *41*

North Salem
Robert M. Flanagan & Assoc., Ltd. (R), *68*

Northport
Global Data Services, Inc. (R), *77*
Management Recruiters of Suffolk (C), *432*

Nyack
CV Associates (C), *305*

Old Forge
Career +Plus (C), *281*

Orchard Park
Bos Business Consultants (C), *270*
Walter Meyer & Assoc. (R), *144*
Systems Personnel, Inc. (C), *598*

Orient
Medical Innovations (C), *477*

Ossining
The Healthsearch Group, Inc. (C), *374*

Ossining-on-Hudson
Perez-Arton Consultants, Inc. (R), *162*

Patchogue
ECG Resources, Inc. (C), *326*

Peekskill
Melissa Katzman, Executive Search (C), *404*

Pine Bush
North Coast Meridian (C), *496*

GEOGRAPHICAL

Pittsford
Dunhill Staffing Systems (C), *318*
Harper Hewes, Inc. (C), *369*
Traynor Confidential, Ltd. (C), *609*

Plainview
Computer Placements Unlimited Inc. (C), *295*

Pleasantville
Redden & McGrath Assoc., Inc. (R), *173*
W. F. Richer Assoc., Inc. (C), *536*

Port Washington
Dunhill Staffing Systems (C), *318*
Integrated Search Solutions Group, LLC (ISSG) (R), *102*
Tecmark Associates Inc. (C), *604*

Purchase
Waveland Int'l. (R), *216*
Winthrop Partners, Inc. (R), *222*

Queensbury
The Mulshine Company, Ltd. (R), *149*

Quogue
EFCO Consultants, Inc. (C), *327*

Red Hook
Circuit Search (C), *291*

Rochester
Analog Solutions (C), *249*
Career +Plus (C), *281*
Cochran, Cochran & Yale, Inc. (R), *36*
Goodrich & Sherwood Assoc., Inc. (R), *80*
Lloyd Prescott & Churchill, Inc. (R), *130*
Lloyd Prescott Assoc., Inc. (C), *419*
Management Recruiters of Rochester (C), *432*
William K. McLaughlin Assoc., Inc. (C), *475*
Professional Support Inc. (C), *523*
Sales Consultants of Rochester (C), *554*
Scott Executive Search, Inc. (R), *186*
Scott Sibley Assoc. (C), *573*
Weterrings & Agnew, Inc. (C), *619*

Rockville Centre
Manning Lloyd Assoc. Ltd. (C), *468*

Rome
Management Recruiters of Adirondacks (C), *432*
Management Recruiters of Utica/Rome (C), *432*

Roslyn
Harold L. Rapp Assoc. (C), *529*

Rye
Conspectus, Inc. (C), *297*
Cooper Assoc., Inc. (C), *298*

Rye Brook
Dunhill Staffing Systems, Inc. (C), *318*
Professional Placement Assoc., Inc. (C), *521*

Sag Harbor
Arch S. Whitehead Assoc. Inc. (ASWA) (R), *219*

Saratoga Springs
Molloy Partners (R), *146*
NaTek Corp. (C), *488*

Scarsdale
Adept Tech Recruiting, Inc. (C), *240*
Frank Cuomo & Assoc., Inc. (C), *305*
Peter Gasperini & Assoc., Inc. (R), *75*
Global Research Partnership Inc. (R), *78*
Kyle Assoc. (C), *410*
McDonald, Long & Assoc., Inc. (R), *140*
SFB Legal Search (C), *579*

Sea Cliff
Franchise Search, Inc. (C), *352*

Shelter Island
Clark Executive Search (C), *292*

Somers
Stanley Herz & Co. (R), *92*

Southampton
The Hampton Group (C), *367*
Management Recruiters of The Hamptons (C), *432*

Southold
Joe Sullivan & Assoc., Inc. (R), *204*

Spring Valley
F-O-R-T-U-N-E Personnel Consultants of Rockland County, Inc. (C), *348*

Springwater
Kingsley Quinn/USA (R), *115*

St. James
Romano McAvoy Assoc., Inc. (C), *544*

Stone Ridge
Management Recruiters of Kingston (C), *432*

Suffern
Federal Placement Services (C), *339*
National Field Service Corp. (C), *489*

Syosset
Corporate Search, Inc. (C), *301*
Lucas Group (C), *421*

Syracuse
Accounting & Computer Personnel (C), *238*
ExecutiveFit (C), *337*
Personnel Assoc. Inc. (C), *508*

Tarrytown
DuBrul Management Co. (C), *315*
Elliot Assoc. Inc. (R), *58*
Guild Fetridge Acoustical Search, Inc. (C), *340*
Kutcher Tax Careers, Inc. (C), *410*

Troy
Capstone Inc. (R), *29*
Lyons Assoc. (R), *132*

Valhalla
Hintz Associates (C), *378*

Valley Cottage
Lee H. Walton & Assoc. (R), *215*

Walworth
VanReypen Enterprises, Ltd. (R), *213*

West Amherst
Professional Support Inc. (C), *523*

West Islip
Neail Behringer Consultants Inc. (R), *15*

Westbury
Sharp Placement Professionals, Inc. (C), *579*

White Plains
Concorde Search Assoc. (C), *296*
Carolyn Davis Assoc., Inc. (C), *309*
Dick Garland Consultants (R), *74*
Harbrowe, Inc. (C), *368*
Koren, Rogers Assoc. Inc. (R), *117*
Masserman & Assoc., Inc. (R), *138*
Arthur Pann Assoc., Inc. (C), *502*
R. J. Associates (C), *528*
Romac Int'l., Inc. (C), *544*

Whitesboro
Management Recruiters of Mohawk Valley (C), *432*

Williamsville
Cochran, Cochran & Yale, Inc. (R), *37*
Hoffman Partnership Group Inc. (C), *379*
The Recruitment Group, Inc. (C), *532*
Sanford Rose Assoc. - Amherst, NY (C), *568*

Woodbury
Management Recruiters of Woodbury Inc. (C), *455*
Resource Services, Inc. (C), *534*

Woodmere
Fred Koffler Assoc. (R), *116*

Yonkers
Emmett Executive Search, Inc. (C), *330*

North Carolina

Apex
Professional Engineering Technical Personnel Consultants (C), *520*

Arden
Asheville Search & Consulting (C), *253*

Asheboro
Marketing Recruiters, Inc. (C), *470*

Asheville
The Borton Wallace Co. (R), *19*
M. F. Branch Assoc., Inc. (C), *272*
Kimmel & Associates, Inc. (C), *406*
Management Recruiters of Asheville, Inc. (C), *455*
Merrick & Moore (C), *479*
Moffitt Int'l., Inc. (R), *146*
Wilson Personnel, Inc. (C), *622*

Belmont
HR Inc. (C), *382*

Boiling Springs
Management Recruiters of Shelby (C), *432*

Boone
Butterfield & Co. Int'l., Inc. (C), *277*

Bunn
Management Recruiters of Rocky Mount (C), *432*

Burlington
Management Recruiters of Burlington (C), *455*

Cary
ARJay & Assoc. (C), *252*
Carter/MacKay (C), *285*
Dunhill Staffing Systems (C), *321*
Pat Licata & Assoc. (C), *417*
The Personnel Network, Inc. (C), *509*
Rothrock Associates, Inc. (C), *547*
Sales Consultants of Raleigh-Durham-RTP (C), *561*

Cedar Mountain
Management Recruiters of Cedar Mountain (C), *455*

Chapel Hill
Atlantic West Int'l. (C), *255*
Chicago Research Group, Inc. (R), *33*
Grantham & Co., Inc. (R), *81*
Insurance Personnel Resources, Inc. (C), *390*
Jones-Parker/Starr (R), *108*
Management Recruiters of Chapel Hill (C), *432*
S.C.S. & Assoc. (C), *550*

Charlotte
Accountants On Call (C), *236*
Anderson & Associates (R), *5*
Andrews & Assoc. (C), *250*
Capital Markets Resources, Inc. (C), *281*
Carnegie Resources, Inc. (C), *284*
Coleman Lew & Assoc., Inc. (R), *37*
S L Collins Assoc. (C), *294*
Direct Marketing Resources (C), *312*
DLG Assoc., Inc. (R), *53*
Executive Recruitment Specialists, Inc. (R), *63*
First Union Executive Search (R), *67*
F-O-R-T-U-N-E Personnel Consultants of Charlotte (C), *348*
Foster Partners (R), *71*
Fox-Morris Assoc., Inc. (C), *352*
C. F. Furr & Co. (R), *72*
Global Technologies Group Inc. (C), *359*
The Halyburton Co., Inc. (R), *85*
Heidrick & Struggles, Inc. (R), *90*
Hunter Adams (C), *385*
International Market Recruiters (C), *393*
Keystone Consulting Group (C), *406*
The Libra Group (C), *417*
Linden Group, Inc. (C), *418*
Lloyd Prescott & Churchill, Inc. (R), *130*
Lloyd Prescott Assoc., Inc. (C), *419*
Locke & Assoc. (R), *131*
Management Advisors Int'l., Inc. (C), *424*
Management Recruiters of Charlotte-East (C), *432*
Management Recruiters of Charlotte SW (C), *432*
Management Recruiters of Charlotte (C), *432*
Management Recruiters of Charlotte-West (C), *432*
Mark III Personnel, Inc. (C), *470*
Marra Peters & Partners (R), *136*
The McAulay Firm (R), *139*
MSI Int'l. (C), *487*
Norrell Financial Staffing (C), *495*
Omega Search, Inc. (C), *498*
The Perkins Group (R), *162*
Phillips Resource Group (C), *511*
Ray Polhill & Assoc. (R), *166*
Prime Search (C), *518*
Retained Search Assoc. (R), *176*
Robison & Associates (R), *180*
Romac Int'l., Inc. (C), *544*
The Rose Search Group, Inc. (C), *545*
S. P. Assoc., Inc. (C), *550*
Sales Consultant of Charlotte-SE (C), *554*
Sales Consultant of Charlotte (C), *554*
Sanford Rose Assoc. - Charlotte (C), *568*
Schwab-Carrese Assoc., Inc. Executive Search (R), *185*
Sockwell & Assoc. (R), *194*

Cherryville
Personnel Assoc. (C), *508*

Clemmons
Sales Consultant of Clemmons (C), *554*

Concord
Gregory, Kyle & Assoc. (C), *363*
Sales Consultants of Concord (C), *554*

Cornelius
AmeriPro Search, Inc. (C), *248*
The Hunt Group, Inc. (R), *99*
Management Recruiters of Cornelius & Davidson (C), *433*
Parenica & Co. (R), *159*

Cove City
Management Recruiters of New Bern (C), *433*

Durham
Bruce Edwards & Associates, Inc. (R), *56*
Hall Kinion (C), *367*
Management Recruiters of Research Triangle Park (C), *433*
Management Recruiters of Durham (C), *433*
Procom (C), *519*

Emerald Isle
Management Recruiters of Emerald Isle (C), *433*

Enfield
Management Recruiters of Enfield (C), *433*

Fayetteville
Management Recruiters of Fayetteville (C), *455*
Professional Careers, Inc. (C), *520*

Gastonia
Management Recruiters of Gastonia (C), *456*
Sanford Rose Assoc. - Gastonia (C), *568*

Graham
The Carey Company (C), *284*
Sanford Rose Assoc. - Burlington, NC (C), *569*

Greensboro
Accountants On Call (C), *236*
Ariail & Assoc. (R), *7*
W. R. Atchison & Assoc., Inc. (C), *254*
Fortune Personnel Consultants of Greensboro, NC, Inc. (C), *348*
Highlander Search (C), *378*
Management Recruiters of Greensboro (C), *433*
Phillips Resource Group (C), *511*
Sales Consultants of Greensboro (C), *554*
Sanford Rose Assoc. - Greensboro (C), *569*
Sterling Int'l. Management Recruitment, Ltd. Inc. (C), *592*
John R. Williams & Assoc., Inc. (C), *621*
Wyndham Mills Int'l., Inc. (R), *226*

Greenville
Dunhill Professional Search of Greenville (C), *318*

Hendersonville
Youngblood Assoc. (C), *626*

Hickory
Management Advisors Int'l., Inc. (C), *424*
Management Recruiters of Hickory (C), *433*
Management Recruiters of Bethlehem (C), *433*
Stewart/Greene & Company of the Triad, Inc. (C), *594*

High Point
Management Recruiters of High Point (C), *433*
Sales Consultant of High Point (C), *554*
Sales Consultants of High Point West (C), *554*

Huntersville
Management Recruiters of Charlotte - North, Inc. (C), *456*
Systems Search Group, Inc. (C), *599*

Kannapolis
Management Recruiters - Kannapolis (C), *456*

Kernersville
Dunhill Professional Search of Winston-Salem (C), *322*

Kinston
Management Recruiters of Kinston (C), *456*

Littleton
ESA (R), *60*

GEOGRAPHICAL

Louisburg
Management Recruiters of Louisburg (C), *433*

Madison
Management Recruiters of Rockingham County (C), *433*

Matthews
Management Recruiters of Charlotte-South (C), *433*

Mooresville
Management Recruiters of Mooresville (C), *433*
Nuance Personnel Search, Inc. (C), *497*
The Perkins Group (R), *162*

Mt. Airy
Management Recruiters of Mt. Airy (C), *456*

New Bern
The Cassie Group (R), *31*

Pinehurst
Management Recruiters of Pinehurst (C), *433*
Mullen Assoc., Inc. (R), *148*

Pleasant Garden
Stewart/Greene & Co. of The Triad, Inc. (C), *594*

Raleigh
Accountants On Call (C), *236*
The Christopher Group (C), *291*
Elinvar (C), *328*
Fortune Personnel Consultants of Raleigh, Inc. (C), *348*
The Hunter Group (C), *385*
Information Systems Professionals (C), *388*
Management Recruiters of Raleigh (C), *456*
National Search, Inc. (R), *150*
National Search, Inc. (R), *150*
Norrell Financial Staffing (C), *495*
Orion Int'l. Consulting Group, Inc. (C), *499*
ProNet, Inc. (C), *524*
Rodzik & Assoc., Inc. (R), *180*
Snelling Search Recruiters (C), *586*
Sports Group Int'l. (R), *198*
David Weinfeld Group (C), *617*
Williams & Delmore, Inc. (C), *621*

Rocky Mount
Management Recruiters of Rocky Mount-West (C), *433*
Management Recruiters of Rocky Mount - Southwest (C), *456*
ProLink (C), *524*

Shelby
Management Recruiters of Shelby-Uptown (C), *433*

Sherrills Ford
Dunhill Professional Search of N. Charlotte (C), *318*

Southern Pines
Innovative Resource Group, LLC (C), *389*

Statesville
Management Recruiters of Statesville (C), *433*

Valle Crucis
Management Recruiters of Boone (C), *456*

Wake Forest
Sanford Rose Assoc. - Youngstown (C), *569*

Wilmington
Allman & Co., Inc. (C), *245*
Fred A. Barnette & Assoc. (R), *11*
Hartman & Barnette (R), *87*
Management Recruiters of Wilmington-North (C), *433*
Management Recruiters of Wilmington (C), *457*
The Smith Group, Inc. (C), *584*
The Wilmington Group (C), *622*

Wilson
G. P. Mattocks & Associates (C), *473*

Winston-Salem
A First Resource (C), *231*
Keystone Consulting Group (C), *406*
LaVallee & Associates (C), *413*
Management Recruiters of Winston-Salem (C), *457*
Sales Consultants of Winston-Salem (C), *554*

Wrightsville Beach
Matrix Consultants, Inc. (C), *472*

North Dakota

Fargo
Dunhill Personnel Service of Fargo (C), *322*

Ohio

Akron
A.M.C.R., Inc. (C), *232*
ACC Technical Services (C), *233*
Callos Personnel Services (C), *279*
International Executive Recruiters (C), *393*
Management Recruiters of Akron (C), *457*
Sanford Rose Assoc. (C), *565*
Sanford Rose Assoc. - Akron (C), *569*

Avon
Advancement Recruiting Services (C), *241*
McRoberts & Assoc. (C), *475*

Bath
The Revere Assoc., Inc. (R), *176*

Bay Village
Rojek Marketing Group, Inc. (R), *181*

Beachwood
D. S. Allen Assoc. (C), *244*
Dean-MacDonald (R), *47*
Direct Recruiters, Inc. (C), *312*
Howard Gilmore & Assoc. (R), *77*

Beavercreek
Data Bank Executive Search (R), *46*

Berea
Effective Search, Inc. (R), *57*

Brecksville
Richard L. Bencin & Assoc. (C), *264*
Executive Connection (C), *333*
Professional Support Inc. (C), *523*

Broadview Heights
Mangement Recruiters of Brecksville (C), *433*
Sales Consultant (C), *554*

Brooklyn
Midland Consultants (C), *481*

Brunswick
Management Recruiters of Cleveland-SW (C), *433*

Canfield
The Hindman Co. (R), *94*
Sanford Rose Assoc. - Youngstown (C), *569*

Canton
Executive Directions (R), *62*
Glass & Assoc., Inc. (C), *358*
The Premier Staffing Group (C), *517*
Sanford Rose Assoc. - Canton (C), *569*

Centerville
Russ Hadick & Assoc. Inc. (C), *365*

Chesterland
The Hanna Group (C), *368*

Cincinnati
Accountants On Call (C), *236*
Accountants On Call (C), *236*
Allen/Associates (R), *4*
The Angus Group, Ltd. (C), *251*
Baldwin & Assoc. (C), *258*
Bason Associates (R), *13*
Beckman & Assoc. Legal Search (C), *262*
Corporate Resources (C), *301*
Data Bank Executive Search (R), *46*
Dunhill Professional Search (C), *318*
Elliot Assoc. Inc. (R), *58*
Executive Search, Ltd. (C), *336*
F-O-R-T-U-N-E Personnel Consultants of Cincinnati (C), *348*
Genesis Personnel Service, Inc. (C), *356*
ISC of Cincinnati Inc. (C), *394*
Management Recruiters of Cincinnati (C), *433*
Management Recruiters of Cincinnati/Sharonville, Inc. (C), *457*
Marketing Search Inc. (C), *471*
Million & Assoc., Inc. (R), *144*
Professions, Inc. (C), *523*
Romac Int'l., Inc. (C), *544*
Romac Int'l., Inc. (C), *544*
Sales Consultants of Cincinnati (C), *561*
Satterfield & Assoc., Inc. (R), *184*
Soderlund Assoc. Inc. (R), *194*
Strategic Alliance Network, Ltd. (C), *595*
Systems Research Group (C), *598*
Technology Consultants Int'l. (C), *603*

Travel Personnel (C), *609*
TRS Staffing Solutions Inc. (C), *610*

Cleveland
Advantage Partners, Inc. (R), *2*
Artgo, Inc. (R), *7*
The Baer Group (R), *10*
N. L. Benke & Assoc., Inc. (C), *264*
Bowden & Co., Inc. (R), *20*
BowdenGlobal, Ltd. (R), *20*
J. B. Brown & Assoc., Inc. (C), *275*
Bryan & Louis Research (C), *275*
Bryan & Louis Research (C), *275*
Christian & Timbers, Inc. (R), *34*
Christopher-Westmont & Assoc., Inc. (R), *34*
Executive Search of America, Inc. (C), *336*
Ferrari Search Group (C), *340*
Fox-Morris Assoc., Inc. (C), *352*
Harcor Quest & Assoc. (R), *86*
Heidrick & Struggles, Inc. (R), *90*
Hite Executive Search (R), *94*
The Hogan Group (C), *380*
The Human Resource Department Ltd. (R), *98*
The Human Resource Group, Inc. (R), *98*
Richard Kader & Assoc. (C), *403*
A.T. Kearney Executive Search (R), *111*
Michael Kosmetos & Assoc., Inc. (C), *408*
LAI Ward Howell (R), *123*
The Lear Group, Inc. (R), *127*
Lekan & Assoc., Inc. (R), *128*
Maiola & Co. (C), *423*
Major Legal Services, Inc. (C), *423*
Management Recruiters International, Inc. (MRI) (C), *425*
Management Recruiters of Cleveland-Airport (C), *433*
Management Recruiters of Cleveland-Client Services (C), *433*
Management Recruiters of Cleveland-South (C), *433*
Management Recruiters of Cleveland (C), *457*
Management Recruiters of Cleveland (C), *457*
Management Recruiters of Cleveland (C), *457*
Marvel Consultants, Inc. (C), *472*
Louis Thomas Masterson & Co. (R), *138*
Laurie Mitchell & Co., Inc. (R), *145*
The North Peak Group (C), *496*
O'Brien & Bell (R), *153*
R.A.N. Assoc., Inc. (C), *528*
The Sager Co. (R), *183*
Sales Consultants (C), *551*
Sales Consultants of Cleveland-Airport (C), *554*
Sales Consultants of Cleveland-Central (C), *555*
Search Plus Int'l.-Ohio (C), *576*
Searchline Services, Inc. (C), *577*
StratfordGroup (R), *203*

Cleveland Heights
Harcourt Group Ltd. (R), *86*

Columbus
Accountants On Call (C), *236*
AGRI-associates (C), *242*
Buckman/Enochs & Assoc., Inc. (C), *276*
J. D. Cotter Search Inc. (C), *302*
Daniel Marks Company (C), *306*
Delta Medical Search Assoc. (C), *310*
DHR Int'l., Inc. (R), *51*
Dunhill Staffing Systems, Inc. (C), *318*
Fament, Inc. (C), *338*
The Gammill Group, Inc. (C), *354*
J. Gernetzke & Assoc., Inc. (C), *357*
G. W. Henn & Co. (R), *91*
J. D. Hersey & Assoc. (C), *376*
Hunegnaw Executive Search (C), *384*
Ives & Associates, Inc. (C), *395*
Jaeger Int'l., Inc. (C), *396*
January Management Group (R), *105*
Keystone Consulting Group (C), *406*
Lloyd Prescott & Churchill, Inc. (R), *130*
Lloyd Prescott Assoc., Inc. (C), *419*
Management Recruiters of Columbus-Downtown (C), *434*
Management Recruiters of Columbus (C), *457*
Meridian Resources (C), *479*
National Register Columbus Inc. (C), *490*
O'Brien and Roof (C), *497*
Paragon Recruiting Officials Inc. (C), *502*
R. H. Perry & Assoc., Inc. (R), *162*
Romac Int'l., Inc. (C), *544*
Sales Consultants of Columbus Downtown (C), *555*
Stephens Assoc. Ltd., Inc. (R), *200*
Tabb & Assoc. (R), *205*
Taylor Winfield (R), *207*
Tully/Woodmansee Int'l., Inc. (R), *212*

Concord
Downing & Downing, Inc. (C), *314*

Cuyahoga Falls
The Premier Staffing Group (C), *517*

Dayton
Anderson Network Group (C), *250*
H. L. Goehring & Assoc., Inc. (C), *359*
Hahn & Assoc., Inc. (C), *365*
Management Recruiters of Dayton, Inc. (C), *457*
mfg/Search, Inc. (C), *480*
Quality Search Inc. (C), *526*
Robert William James & Assoc. (C), *539*
Romac Int'l., Inc. (C), *544*
Romac Int'l., Inc. (C), *544*
Sales Consultants (C), *555*
Teknon Employment Resources, Inc. (C), *604*
World Search (C), *625*

Dublin
Alan N. Daum & Assoc., Inc. (C), *308*
Fast Switch, Ltd. (C), *338*
Grover & Assoc. (R), *82*
Hamilton & Co. (C), *367*
Kent & Assoc. (R), *113*
R M Associates (R), *171*
Vincenty & Co. (C), *612*

Elyria
Med-Ex Services (C), *476*

Euclid
Exclusive Search Consultants (C), *331*
Sanford Rose Assoc. - Euclid (C), *569*

Fairfield
Management Recruiters of Fairfield (C), *434*

Fairlawn
Elite Resources Group (R), *58*
Sanford Rose Assoc. - Fairlawn (C), *569*
The Windham Group (R), *222*

Findlay
Management Recruiters of Findlay (C), *434*

Highland Heights
Central Executive Search, Inc. (C), *287*

Hilliard
The Rubinic Consulting Group (C), *548*

Hudson
Career Enterprises (C), *282*
Fristoe & Carleton, Inc. (C), *353*
Kehn & Gabor, Inc. (C), *405*
The Zammataro Company (R), *226*

Independence
Accountants On Call (C), *236*
Management Recruiters of Cleveland-Independence (C), *434*
Med-Ex Services (C), *476*
Romac Int'l., Inc. (C), *544*

Ironton
Fenzel Milar Assoc. (C), *339*

Kent
Executech (R), *62*
Executech (R), *62*

Lancaster
MedXec USA, Inc. (C), *478*

Loveland
Nationwide Personnel Placement, Inc. (C), *490*

Lyndhurst
Willis & Assoc. (R), *221*

Mansfield
The Premier Staffing Group (C), *517*

Marietta
Fred C. Tippel & Assoc. (C), *607*

Mason
Orion Int'l. Consulting Group, Inc. (C), *499*
Orion Int'l. Consulting Group, Inc. (C), *499*

Massillon
Management Recruiters of Massillon (C), *434*
The Premier Staffing Group (C), *517*

Maumee
Preferred Professional Recruiters (C), *516*
StratfordGroup (R), *203*

Mayfield Heights
Management Recruiters of Mayfield Heights (C), *434*

GEOGRAPHICAL

Mayfield Village
Management Recruiters of Mayfield Village (C), *434*

Mentor
Management Recruiters of Mentor, Inc. (C), *458*

Miamisburg
StratfordGroup (R), *203*

Middletown
Management Recruiters of Middletown (C), *434*

Milford
Newcomb-Desmond & Assoc., Inc. (C), *492*

North Canton
Management Recruiters - North Canton, Inc. (C), *458*
Selective Search Associates (C), *578*

North Lima
Schick Professional Search, Inc. (C), *572*

North Olmsted
Combined Resources Inc. (R), *38*

North Ridgeville
Dankowski & Assoc., Inc. (C), *307*
Management Recruiters of Lorain County (C), *434*
Sales Consultants of Lorain County (C), *555*

Pickerington
Continental Search Assoc. (C), *298*
Insurance Recruiting Specialists (C), *390*
Technical Recruiting Services (C), *602*

Powell
Management Recruiters of Delaware County (C), *434*

Reynoldsburg
J. W. Barleycorn, Renard & Assoc., Inc. (R), *11*

Rocky River
Technical Search Assoc. (C), *602*

Sagamore Hills
Telecom Executive Group (C), *605*

Shaker Heights
Dise & Co. (R), *52*
Management Recruiters of Shaker Heights (C), *434*
Sales Consultants of Shaker Heights (C), *555*
H. C. Smith Ltd. (R), *194*

Sidney
Management Recruiters of Sidney (C), *458*

Solon
Management Recruiters of Cleveland-SE (C), *434*

Springfield
F.L.A.G. (C), *338*
Robert William James & Assoc. (C), *539*

Stow
J. Joseph & Assoc. (C), *395*

Strongsville
The Search America Group Inc. (C), *573*

Sylvania
Sales Consultants of Toledo (C), *555*

Toledo
Flowers & Assoc. (C), *342*
R. Green & Assoc., Inc. (C), *362*
Management Recruiters of Northwest Ohio, Inc. (C), *458*

Troy
Granger, Counts & Assoc. (R), *81*

Wadsworth
The Premier Staffing Group (C), *517*

Westerville
Rogish Assoc., Inc. (C), *541*
Sanford Rose Assoc. - Columbus North (C), *569*
Warner & Assoc., Inc. (C), *615*

Westlake
Leith & Assoc., Inc. (C), *416*

Willoughby
Terry Richards (C), *536*

Willoughby Hills
ProSearch, Inc. (C), *524*

Wooster
The Premier Staffing Group (C), *517*

Worthington
Arthur Adams & Assoc. (C), *239*
Lindsey & Co., Inc. (R), *129*
Michael Thomas, Inc. (C), *480*

Youngstown
Callos Personnel Services (C), *279*
Michael Latas & Assoc., Inc. (R), *126*
Management Recruiters of Youngstown (C), *458*

Oklahoma

Ardmore
Dunhill Staffing Systems (C), *318*
National Recruiters (C), *489*

Broken Arrow
Reality Group (C), *531*

Del City
Healthcare Resources Group (C), *374*

Durant
Sarver & Carruth Assoc. (C), *571*

Edmond
Dunhill Professional Search of Oklahoma City (C), *318*
Management Recruiters of Edmond (C), *434*

Enid
C and P Marketing, Ltd. (C), *278*

Oklahoma City
A C Personnel Services, Inc. (C), *231*
Advanced Recruiting, Inc. (C), *240*
AmeriResource Group Inc. (C), *248*
The Associates, HR Search Executives, Inc. (C), *254*
Joy Reed Belt Search Consultants, Inc. (R), *15*
Cornerstone Resources, Inc. (C), *299*
James Farris Assoc. (R), *65*
Management Recruiters of Oklahoma City-South (C), *434*
Management Recruiters of Oklahoma City (C), *458*
Management Search, Inc. (C), *468*
Robert William James & Assoc. (C), *539*
Sales Consultants of Oklahoma City (C), *555*
Sales Recruiters of Oklahoma City (C), *564*

Stroud
Don Neal & Assoc. (C), *491*

Tulsa
AmeriResource Group Inc. (C), *249*
Joy Reed Belt Search Consultants, Inc. (R), *15*
Dunhill Personnel of Northeast Tulsa, Inc. (C), *322*
Huddleston Assoc. (C), *383*
Hunt Patton & Brazeal, Inc. (C), *385*
Management Recruiters of Tulsa (C), *434*
MLA Resources, Inc. (C), *483*
Professional Resources (C), *522*
Prospective Personnel Service, Inc. (C), *524*
Sales Consultants of Tulsa (C), *555*
TaxSearch Inc. (R), *207*
Tekworx, Inc. (C), *604*
Villareal & Assoc., Inc. (R), *214*
John Wylie Assoc., Inc. (C), *625*

Oregon

Beaverton
APA Employment Agency Inc. (C), *251*

Bend
Executives Worldwide, Inc. (C), *337*
Management Recruiters of Bend (C), *434*
Robert William James & Assoc. (C), *539*
Sales Consultants of Bend (C), *555*

Clackamas
Search Northwest Assoc. (C), *576*

Corvallis
HeartBeat Medical, Inc. (C), *374*

Eugene
Pacific Coast Recruiters (C), *501*
Peter A. Smith & Assoc. (C), *584*

Hillsboro
Furlong Search, Inc. (R), *72*

Junction City
RBW Assoc. Inc. (C), *531*

Lake Oswego
The Brentwood Group Ltd. (R), *23*
DHR Int'l., Inc. (R), *51*
F-O-R-T-U-N-E of West Portland (C), *348*
Greger/Peterson Assoc., Inc. (R), *82*

Portland
Accountants On Call (C), *237*
AKH Executive Search (C), *243*
APA Employment Agency Inc. (C), *251*
Becker Project Resources, Inc. (C), *262*
D. Brown & Assoc., Inc. (C), *275*
Corporate Builders, Inc. (C), *299*
Hall Kinion (C), *367*
High Tech Staffing Group (C), *377*
Impact Technical Staffing (C), *387*
Jones and Jones (R), *108*
A.T. Kearney Executive Search (R), *111*
Lee Koehn Assoc., Inc. (R), *116*
Management Recruiters of Portland (C), *434*
The Martwick Group, Inc. (C), *472*
The Douglas Reiter Co., Inc. (R), *174*
Robert William James & Assoc. (C), *539*
Romac Int'l., Inc. (C), *544*
Sales Consultants of Portland (C), *555*
Sanford Rose Assoc. - Portland (C), *570*
Smith & Laue Search (R), *193*
Triad Technology Group (C), *609*
Woodworth Int'l. Group (R), *224*

Springfield
Robert William James & Assoc. (C), *539*

Sunriver
Search North America, Inc. (C), *576*

Tigard
Robert E. Pfaendler & Assoc., Inc. (C), *509*

Tualatin
Nationwide Personnel Recruiting & Consulting, Inc. (C), *490*

Warrenton
MESA International (C), *480*

Pennsylvania

Allentown
Lyons Pruitt Int'l. (R), *132*
Management Recruiters of Allentown-South (C), *434*
SHS of Allentown (C), *580*

Allison Park
Becker, Norton & Co. (R), *14*
Cal Douglas Executive Search, Inc. (R), *54*

Bala Cynwyd
Fernow Assoc. (C), *339*
Professional Recruiters, Inc. (C), *521*
Retail Recruiters/Spectrum Consultants, Inc. (C), *535*

Bensalem
L&L Assoc. Global Search (C), *411*
The Synergy Organization (R), *205*

Berwyn
Empire International (R), *59*
F. P. Lennon Assoc. (C), *416*

Bethlehem
Dunhill Professional Search of Lehigh Valley (C), *318*
ExecuGroup, Inc. (R), *61*
Fortune Personnel Consultants of Allentown, Inc. (C), *348*
Kelly Associates (R), *112*
Management Recruiters of Bethlehem, PA (C), *458*

Birchrunville
Lee Calhoon & Co., Inc. (R), *26*

Blue Bell
Effective Search, Inc. (R), *57*
Management Recruiters of Blue Bell (C), *434*

Bridgeville
Elliot Assoc. Inc. (R), *58*

Broomall
Management Recruiters of Broomall (C), *434*

Bryn Mawr
The Morris Group (C), *486*
Tele-Media Int'l. Inc. (C), *604*

Buckingham
Sanford Rose Assoc. - Doylestown (C), *570*

Butler
M. K. & Assoc. (C), *422*

Camp Hill
Sales Consultants of Harrisburg (C), *561*

Carlisle
Management Recruiters of Carlisle (C), *434*

Center Square
Alexander Enterprises, Inc. (C), *243*

Chadds Ford
Carr Management Services, Inc. (C), *284*
Information Technology Search (C), *388*
Tyler & Company (R), *212*

Chesterbrook
The TBI Group (R), *207*

Chinchilla
Management Recruiters of Scranton (C), *434*

Clarks Summit
Brandt Associates (C), *272*
Courtright & Assoc., Inc. (R), *42*

Collegeville
Kirby Assoc. (R), *115*

Colmar
Questor Consultants, Inc. (C), *527*

Conshohocken
D. A. Kreuter Assoc., Inc. (R), *121*
Longshore + Simmons (R), *131*

Cranberry Township
Sales Consultants of Butler County (C), *561*

Delta
Delta ProSearch (C), *311*

Downingtown
C. D. Warner & Assoc. (C), *615*

Doylestown
The Cassie Group (R), *31*
Corporate Staffing Group, Inc. (C), *301*
Kaczmar & Assoc. (C), *403*
George R. Martin (R), *137*
SilverSands Int'l. (C), *582*

Drexel Hill
Search America, Inc. (C), *573*

East Stroudsburg
NDB Assoc., Inc. (C), *491*

Easton
Management Recruiters of Easton, PA (C), *458*

Ephrata
Robert Harkins Assoc., Inc. (C), *369*

Erie
Blair Kershaw Assoc., Inc. (C), *405*
Jack B. Larsen & Assoc., Inc. (C), *413*
National Computerized Employment Service, Inc. (C), *489*

Exton
Management Recruiters of Lionville, Inc. (C), *459*

Fairview Village
E. F. Humay Assoc. (C), *384*

Feasterville
Churchill & Affiliates, Inc. (R), *35*
Dunhill Professional Search of Bucks-Mont., Inc. (C), *322*
Kay Henry, Inc. (C), *376*

Flourtown
Corporate Recruiters Inc. (C), *300*

Ft. Washington
Fortune Consultants of Ft. Washington (C), *349*
Management Recruiters of Montco (C), *434*
Salzmann Gay Assoc., Inc. (R), *184*

Greensburg
Dunn Associates (R), *55*
The Edge Resource Group (C), *326*

Harrisburg
Management Recruiters of Harrisburg (C), *434*
The Stonebridge Group (C), *594*

Havertown
PCD Partners (R), *161*

Huntingdon Valley
Vogel Assoc. (C), *613*

Irvine
Susan L. Wonderling Recruiting (C), *623*

Jenkintown
Jordon & Jordon, Inc. (R), *108*

Kennett Square
Korban Associates (R), *117*

King of Prussia
Accountants On Call (C), *237*
The Andre Group, Inc. (R), *6*
Norrell Financial Staffing (C), *495*
Probe Technology (C), *519*
Romac Int'l., Inc. (C), *544*

Lake Ariel
C. P. Consulting (R), *26*

Lancaster
ACSYS Resources, Inc. (C), *239*
AGRI-associates (C), *242*
C & H Personnel (C), *277*
Management Recruiters of Lancaster (C), *434*
The Rossi Search Group (C), *545*
Stewart Assoc. (C), *593*
Charles Stickler Assoc. (R), *201*

Langhorne
International Pro Sourcing, Inc. (C), *393*
Tell/Com Recruiters (C), *605*

Ligonier
Fagan & Company (R), *64*

Malvern
Brandywine Consulting Group (R), *22*
Brandywine Consulting Group (R), *22*
Management Recruiters of Valley Forge (C), *459*
Sales Consultants of Chester County, PA (C), *562*
Tower Consultants, Ltd. (R), *209*

McMurray
Management Recruiters of McMurray, Inc. (C), *459*

Mechanicsburg
Carnegie Partners, Inc. (R), *30*
Sill Technical Assoc., Inc. (C), *581*
Dick Wray & Consultants, Inc. (R), *225*

Media
R. Christine Assoc. (C), *290*
Employr (C), *330*
FitzGibbon & Assoc. (R), *68*
The Kennett Group, Inc. (R), *112*
RepFinders USA (C), *534*
Schneider, Hill & Spangler, Inc. (R), *185*
Gordon Wahls Executive Search (C), *613*

Montoursville
Management Recruiters of Montoursville (C), *434*

Moscow
The Madeira Group (R), *133*

Murrysville
Hughes & Wilden Assoc. (C), *383*
Management Recruiters of Westmoreland County, Inc. (C), *459*
Roth Young of Pittsburgh (C), *546*

Narberth
IntelliSource, inc. (C), *391*

Newtown
Sales Consultants of Newtown, Inc. (C), *562*

Newtown Square
Graphic Search Assoc. Inc. (C), *362*
Management Recruiters of Delaware County (C), *459*

North Wales
Pharmaceutical Search Professionals, Inc. (C), *510*

Paoli
Eden & Assoc., Inc. (C), *326*
Target Search, Inc. (C), *600*

Philadelphia
Cathy Abelson Legal Search (C), *232*
Accountants Executive Search (C), *234*
ACSYS Resources, Inc. (C), *239*
Atomic Personnel, Inc. (C), *255*
The Beam Group (R), *14*
Century Assoc., Inc. (C), *287*
Cole, Warren & Long, Inc. (R), *37*
Coleman Legal Search Consultants (C), *294*
Creative Financial Staffing (C), *303*
Diversified Health Search (R), *52*
Diversified Search, Inc. (R), *52*
Howard Fischer Assoc. Int'l., Inc. (R), *67*
Fox-Morris Assoc., Inc. (C), *351*
The Gabriel Group (C), *354*
Gans, Gans & Assoc., Inc. (R), *74*
Genesis Consulting Partners (R), *76*
Gordon/Tyler (R), *80*
Heidrick & Struggles, Inc. (R), *90*
Impact Search & Strategies (C), *387*
International Market Recruiters (C), *393*
Jefferson-Ross Assoc. Inc. (C), *398*
The Koehler Group (C), *408*
Korn/Ferry Int'l. (R), *118*
Management Recruiters of Manayunk/Chestnut Hill (C), *435*
Management Recruiters of Philadelphia (C), *435*
Management Recruiters of Cherry Hill (C), *459*
McNichol Assoc. (R), *142*
Norrell Financial Staffing (C), *495*
Nuessle, Kurdziel & Weiss, Inc. (R), *153*
LaMonte Owens, Inc. (R), *157*
The Oxbridge Group, Ltd. (C), *500*
Penn Associates (R), *161*
The Penn Partners, Inc. (R), *162*
Personnel Resources Organization (C), *509*
The Richards Group (C), *536*
J. P. Roddy Consultants (C), *540*
Romac Int'l., Inc. (C), *544*
Romac Int'l., Inc. (C), *544*
Rylan Forbes Consulting Group, Inc. (C), *549*
SpencerStuart (R), *197*
Wellington Management Group (R), *217*
Wood, Franchot Inc. (R), *224*

Pittsburgh
Accountants On Call (C), *237*
Boyden (R), *21*
C. G. & Assoc. (R), *26*
Carpenter Legal Search (C), *284*
Corporate Management Services (C), *300*
The Corporate Source Group, Inc. (R), *42*
Crown Advisors, Inc. (R), *43*
D & M Associates (C), *306*
DHR Int'l., Inc. (R), *51*
Susan Fletcher Attorney Employment Services (C), *342*
Fox, White & Assoc. (C), *351*
Fox-Morris Assoc., Inc. (C), *352*
Healthcare Recruiters Int'l. - Pittsburgh (C), *373*
HRS, Inc. (R), *97*
Innovative Resource Group, LLC (C), *389*
Michael L. Ketner & Assoc., Inc. (R), *114*
The J. Kovach Group (R), *119*
LAI Ward Howell (R), *123*
Lloyd Prescott & Churchill, Inc. (R), *130*
Lloyd Prescott & Assoc., Inc. (C), *419*
Management Recruiters of Pittsburgh-USC (C), *435*
Management Recruiters of West View (C), *435*
Management Recruiters of Pittsburgh-North Allegheny (C), *435*
Management Recruiters of Pittsburgh-South Hills (C), *435*
Management Recruiters of Pittsburgh-Airport (C), *435*
Management Recruiters of Pittsburgh (C), *459*
K. Maxin & Assoc. (R), *139*
O'Connor, O'Connor, Lordi, Ltd. (R), *154*
Resources for Management (R), *175*
Romac Int'l. (C), *542*
Romac Int'l., Inc. (C), *544*
Sales Consultants of Pittsburgh-Southpointe (C), *555*
Sales Consultants of Pittsburgh (C), *562*
Spear-Izzo Assoc., LLC (C), *588*
Specialty Consultants Inc. (R), *195*
Daniel Stern & Assoc. (C), *592*
Strauss Personnel Service (C), *596*
W. G. Tucker & Assoc. (R), *211*

Plymouth Meeting
ProSearch, Inc. (C), *524*
StratfordGroup (R), *203*

Quakertown
Barr Assoc. (C), *259*

Radnor
Howe & Assoc. (R), *97*
Soltis Management Services (R), *195*

Reading
Management Recruiters of Reading (C), *435*
Kenn Spinrad Inc. (C), *589*

Richboro
Sanford Rose Assoc. - Philadelphia North (C), *570*

Sewickley
Management Recruiters of Pittsburgh-North, Inc. (C), *460*

Southampton
M. A. Churchill & Assoc., Inc. (R), *35*
Sales Consultants of Southampton (C), *555*
Technical Employment Consultants (C), *602*

Southeastern
Interactive Search Assoc. (C), *391*

Springfield
Ahrensdorf & Assoc. (R), *2*
Integrity Search, Inc. (R), *102*

St. Peters
The Mayes Group, Ltd. (R), *139*

State College
Fox-Morris Assoc., Inc. (C), *352*
J.N. Adams & Assoc., Inc. (C), *396*

Stroudsburg
Sales Consultants of Stroudsburg (C), *555*

Swarthmore
Premier Business Advisors (C), *516*

Tarentum
Sales Recruiting Network (C), *564*

Trevose
J.J. & H., Ltd. (R), *105*
Jacobson Assoc. (C), *396*

Unionville
Global HealthCare Partners (R), *78*

Upper St. Clair
Management Recruiters of Green Tree (C), *435*

Warminster
Fortune Group Int'l., Inc. (R), *70*
Intercontinental Executive Group (C), *391*
Management Recruiters of Bucks County (C), *435*
VZ Int'l., Inc. (C), *613*

Warren
RML Assoc. (C), *538*

Warrington
Triangle Assoc. (C), *609*

Washington
The Polen Group (C), *514*

Wayne
ACSYS Resources, Inc. (C), *239*
Caliber Associates (R), *27*
Fidelity Search Group, Inc. (R), *66*
The Ford Group, Inc. (R), *69*
JM & Company (R), *106*
Patriot Assoc. (C), *505*
Raymond Karsan Assoc. (C), *529*
Raymond Karsan Assoc. (C), *530*
Sales Consultants King of Prussia (C), *562*
Salveson Stetson Group, Inc. (R), *184*
Smith Hanley Assoc., Inc. (C), *584*
Worlco Computer Resources, Inc. (C), *624*

West Chester
Jack Bertram, Executive Recruiter (C), *265*
William J. Christopher Assoc., Inc. (R), *34*
Management Recruiters of West Chester, Inc. (C), *460*
Nursing Technomics (R), *153*
Search Innovations, Inc. (R), *187*
Whittlesey & Assoc., Inc. (R), *220*

West Mifflin
The Consulting Group of North America, Inc. (C), *297*

Wexford
Helbling & Assoc., Inc. (R), *91*
Reese Assoc. (R), *174*
Sanford Rose Assoc. - Pittsburgh North (C), *570*

Whitehall
Management Recruiters of Lehigh County (C), *435*

Wilkes-Barre
A. D. Check Assoc., Inc. (R), *33*
Dunhill Professional Search of Wilkes-Barre/Scranton, Inc. (C), *322*
S-H-S TechStaff (C), *549*
Tierney Assoc., Inc. (R), *209*

Wynnewood
Amato & Associates Insurance Recruiters (C), *247*
Kaplan & Assoc., Inc. (R), *109*

Yardley
Rice Cohen Int'l. (R), *178*

York
Leader Network (C), *414*

Puerto Rico

Hato Rey
Careers/Inc. (C), *284*

San Juan
A. Artze Assoc.-Personnel Consultants (C), *253*
Management Recruiters of Puerto Rico (C), *460*
J. Palacios & Assoc., Inc. (R), *158*
Raymond Karsan Assoc. (C), *530*

Rhode Island

Charlestown
Marshall Rice Assoc. (R), *177*

Coventry
PKS Assoc., Inc. (C), *513*

Cranston
Greene Personnel Consultants (C), *362*
Willmott & Assoc. (C), *622*

East Greenwich
Creative Input, Inc. (C), *303*
DHR Int'l., Inc. (R), *51*

Hope Valley
Carter, Lavoie Associates (C), *285*

Jamestown
Performance Resources, Inc. (C), *507*

Lincoln
Bio-Venture Group (C), *266*

Little Compton
The Bedford Group (R), *15*

Newport
Lybrook Assoc., Inc. (C), *421*

North Kingstown
Schattle & Duquette (C), *571*

Pawtucket
Alan J. Price Assoc., Inc. (C), *518*

Providence
Accountants On Call (C), *237*
Robert Graham Assoc. (R), *81*
The Jotorok Group (C), *401*
Management Recruiters of Providence (C), *435*
Management Search of R.I. Inc. (R), *135*
Norrell Financial Staffing (C), *495*
The Partnership Group (R), *160*
Performance Resources, Inc. (C), *507*
The Search Alliance, Inc. (R), *186*
The Westminster Group, Inc. (R), *218*

Rumford
Albert G. Lee Assoc. (C), *415*

Warwick
Sales Consultants of Rhode Island, Inc. (C), *562*

South Carolina

Aiken
Management Recruiters of Aiken (C), *460*
Southern Recruiters & Consultants, Inc. (C), *587*

Anderson
Fortune Personnel Consultants of Anderson, Inc. (C), *349*
Management Recruiters of Anderson (C), *435*

Beaufort
eXsource Inc. (C), *337*

Charleston
Management Recruiters of Kiawah Island (C), *435*
Management Recruiters of Charleston (C), *435*

Columbia
Dunhill Personnel of St. Andrews (C), *322*
Management Recruiters of Forest Acres (C), *435*
Management Recruiters of Columbia (C), *435*
Management Recruiters of Lexington (C), *435*

John Shell Assoc., Inc. (C), *579*

Florence
Management Recruiters of Florence (C), *460*

Greenville
Accountants On Call (C), *237*
Dunhill of Greenville (C), *318*
Management Recruiters of Greenville (C), *460*
Jennifer Munro & Partners, Inc. (R), *149*
Phelps Personnel Assoc., Inc. (C), *510*
Phillips Int'l., Inc. (C), *510*
Phillips Resource Group (C), *510*
Proquest Inc. (C), *524*
Sales Consultants of Greenville, Inc. (C), *562*

Greenwood
Dunhill of Greenwood (C), *318*

Greer
Management Recruiters of Greer (C), *435*

Hilton Head Island
Fortune Personnel Consultants of Hilton Head (C), *349*
The Lawson Group, Inc. (C), *414*

Irmo
The Personnel Network, Inc. (C), *508*

Isle of Palms
Molecular Solutions, Inc. (C), *483*

Johns Island
Paul S. Pelland, P.C. (R), *161*

Lexington
Sanford Rose Assoc. - Columbia (C), *570*

Mt. Pleasant
FORTUNE Personnel Consultants of Charleston, Inc. (C), *349*
Management Recruiters of Mt. Pleasant (C), *435*
Sales Consultants of Mt. Pleasant (C), *555*

Murrells Inlet
The Personnel Network, Inc. (C), *509*

Myrtle Beach
Ford & Assoc., Inc. (C), *343*
Management Recruiters of Myrtle Beach, Inc. (C), *460*

North Charleston
Management Recruiters of North Charleston (C), *460*

Orangeburg
Management Recruiters of Orangeburg (C), *435*
Sales Consultants of Orangeburg (C), *562*

Pawleys Island
Management Recruiters of Georgetown (C), *461*

Pickens
Management Recruiters of Pickens County (C), *435*

Rock Hill
Management Recruiters of Rock Hill (C), *435*
Staff Resources, Inc. (C), *590*

Spartanburg
Bernard E. Brooks & Assoc., Inc. (R), *24*
Management Recruiters of Spartanburg (C), *435*

Summerville
Management Recruiters of Summerville (C), *435*
Sales Consultants of Charleston (C), *555*

Travelers Rest
Management Recruiters of Travelers Rest, Inc. (C), *461*

South Dakota

Sioux Falls
Management Recruiters of Sioux Falls, LLP (C), *461*

Tennessee

Ardmore
First Search America, Inc. (C), *341*
Merit Professional Search, Inc. (C), *479*

Bartlett
Advanced Recruitment, Inc. (C), *240*
Herring & Assoc. (C), *376*

Brentwood
CMS Management Services LLC (C), *293*
Cook Assoc. Int'l., Inc. (C), *298*
P. G. Cook Assoc. (R), *40*
The Custer Group, Inc. (R), *44*
Gros Executive Search, Inc. (C), *363*
Koerner & Assoc., Inc. (C), *408*
Leeds and Leeds (C), *416*
Management Recruiters of Brentwood (C), *436*
RMA Search (R), *179*
Sales Consultants of Brentwood (C), *555*
Sanford Rose Assoc. - Nashville (C), *570*
Shiloh Careers Int'l., Inc. (C), *580*
Dick Wray & Consultants, Inc. (R), *225*

Chattanooga
The Borton Wallace Co. (R), *19*
Dougherty & Assoc. (C), *314*
Fortune Personnel Consultants of Chattanooga Inc. (C), *349*
IM Independent Management Recruiters (R), *101*
Management Recruiters of Chattanooga-North (C), *436*
Management Recruiters of Chattanooga-Brainerd, Inc. (C), *461*
Sales Consultants of Chattanooga-East (C), *555*
Sales Consultants of Chattanooga-Brainerd (C), *555*

College Grove
American Professional Search, Inc. (C), *248*

Collierville
Healthcare Recruiters of Midsouth (C), *373*

Columbia
Management Recruiters of Columbia, Tennessee (C), *461*

Cordova
Austin - Allen Co. (C), *256*
F-O-R-T-U-N-E Consultants of Memphis (C), *349*
Management Recruiters of Cordova (C), *436*

Dandridge
Larson & Trent Assoc. (C), *413*

Dyersburg
Hardage Group (C), *369*

Franklin
Management Recruiters of Franklin, Inc. (C), *461*

Gallatin
Cumberland Professional Search Inc. (C), *304*

Hendersonville
Technical Resource Assoc. (C), *602*

Jefferson City
Just Management Services Inc. (C), *402*

Johnson City
F-O-R-T-U-N-E Personnel Consultants of the Tri-Cities, Inc. (C), *350*
Management Recruiters of Johnson City (C), *436*

Knoxville
F-O-R-T-U-N-E Personnel Consultants of Knoxville (C), *350*
Management Recruiters of Knoxville (C), *436*
The Montgomery Group, Inc. (C), *484*
RMA Search (R), *179*
Vento Assoc. (C), *612*

Lenoir City
Management Recruiters of Lenoir City (C), *436*

Memphis
AGRI-associates (C), *242*
Corporate Image Group (C), *300*
Dunhill of Memphis, Inc. (C), *318*
Frye/Joure & Assoc., Inc. (C), *353*
Gateway Group Personnel, LLC (C), *355*
Randall Howard & Assoc., Inc. (R), *96*
J & D Resources Inc. (C), *395*
Management Recruiters of Bartlett (C), *436*
Management Recruiters The Delta Group, Inc. (C), *461*
Management Recruiters of Memphis, TN (C), *462*
The Paul McDaniel Co. (C), *474*
Norrell Financial Staffing (C), *495*
Professionals in Recruiting Co. (C), *523*

Recruiting Services Group, Inc. (C), *532*
RMA Search (R), *179*
Sales Consultants of Memphis-East (C), *555*
Software Resource Consultants (C), *587*
Summerfield Assoc., Inc. (C), *596*

Murfreesboro
Management Recruiters of Murfreesboro (C), *436*

Nashville
Accountants On Call (C), *237*
DHR Int'l., Inc. (R), *51*
EMN/Witt/Kieffer (R), *59*
F-O-R-T-U-N-E Personnel of Nashville (C), *350*
Helfer Executive Consultants (R), *91*
People Management Mid-South, LLC (R), *162*
Southwestern Professional Services (C), *588*
Unlimited Staffing Solutions, Inc. (C), *611*
Wallace Management Co. (R), *215*

Texas

Amarillo
Professional Search, Inc. Int'l. (C), *523*
Recruiting Assoc. of Amarillo (C), *531*

Arlington
BEST/World Assoc. Inc. (R), *16*
J. Burke & Assoc., Inc. (C), *276*
Dunhill Search of Arlington (C), *322*
Hedman & Assoc. (R), *89*
Human Resource Dimensions, Inc. (C), *384*
Management Recruiters of Arlington (C), *462*
Thomas R. Moore Executive Search (R), *146*
The Stevens Group (R), *200*
Tyler & Company (R), *212*

Austin
Accountants On Call (C), *237*
Allen Austin Lowe & Powers (R), *4*
Austin Group Int'l./Marlar Int'l. (R), *9*
Bredeson Executive Recruitment, LLC (R), *22*
Cendea Connection Int'l. (R), *32*
EDMS Solutions (C), *326*
Elliot Assoc. Inc. (R), *58*
The Enfield Company (C), *330*
Neil Fink Assoc. (R), *67*
Hall Kinion (C), *367*
Hall Kinion (C), *367*
R. W. Hebel Assoc. (R), *89*
Houtz•Strawn & Arnold, Inc. (R), *96*
Human Resource Solutions (R), *99*
Intersource, Ltd. (R), *103*
Jackson Resources (R), *105*
Korn/Ferry Int'l. (R), *118*
LAI Ward Howell (R), *124*
Lehman McLeskey (R), *128*
Management Recruiters of North West Austin (C), *462*
Management Recruiters of Austin (C), *462*
O'Keefe & Assoc. (C), *497*
Orion Int'l. Consulting Group, Inc. (C), *500*
T. Page & Assoc. (C), *502*
Power Recruiting Group (C), *515*
Preferred Professional Recruiters (C), *516*
Prescott Legal Search, Inc. (C), *517*
Primus Assoc., L.C. (R), *169*
Romac Int'l., Inc. (C), *544*
Sales Consultants of Austin, Inc. (C), *562*
Sanford Rose Assoc. - Austin (C), *570*
Strategic Assoc., Inc. (C), *595*
Telecom Connections, Inc. (C), *604*
Zingaro & Company (R), *227*

Bedford
Bower & Associates (C), *271*
CJA-The Adler Group, Inc. (R), *35*
Southwest Selective Search, Inc. (C), *588*

Bellaire
Management Recruiters of Bellaire (C), *436*
Recruit Xpress (C), *531*

Boerne
Bruce Henry Assoc. Inc. (R), *91*

Carrollton
Management Recruiters of Addison Central (C), *436*

Celeste
J. L. Nixon Consulting (C), *493*

Coppell
Managed Care Resources (C), *424*

Corpus Christi
Dunhill of Corpus Christi, Inc. (C), *323*

Dallas
Acclaim Services, Inc. (C), *234*
Accountants On Call (C), *237*
Accountants On Call (C), *237*
The Alternatives Group, Inc. (C), *246*
Peter W. Ambler Co. (R), *5*
Andre David & Assoc., Inc. (R), *6*
Austin-McGregor Int'l. (R), *9*
AutoPeople (C), *257*
R. Gaines Baty Assoc., Inc. (R), *13*
The Howard C. Bloom Co. (C), *268*
Borchert Assoc. (C), *269*
The Broadmoor Group, L.L.C. (R), *23*
The Buckley Group (C), *276*
Burkholder & Assoc., Inc. (C), *276*
Carpenter & Assoc. (C), *284*
Casey & Assoc., Inc. (C), *286*
Computer Professionals Unlimited (C), *295*
Cornwall Stockton & Co., Inc. (C), *299*
Damon & Assoc., Inc. (C), *306*
The Danbrook Group, Inc. (C), *306*
DataPro Personnel Consultants (C), *308*
Discovery, The Staffing Specialists, Inc. (C), *313*
R. J. Dishaw & Assoc. (R), *52*
The Doty Group (C), *314*
Eagle Consulting Group Inc. (C), *325*
Eastman & Beaudine, Inc. (R), *56*
The Evans Search Group (R), *61*
FORTUNE Personnel Consultants of North Dallas (C), *350*
Foster Partners (R), *71*
Fox-Morris Assoc., Inc. (C), *352*
Global Employer's Network, Inc. (R), *77*
Groussman & Assoc., Inc. (R), *82*
Hayman & Co. (R), *88*
Health Network USA (C), *371*
Healthcare Recruiters of Dallas (C), *374*
Heidrick & Struggles, Inc. (R), *90*
David C. Horn Executive Search (C), *381*
Hyde Danforth & Co. (R), *100*
InfoTech Search (C), *388*
IntelliSearch (C), *391*
Interim Accounting Professionals (C), *392*
JG Consultants, Inc. (R), *106*
Johnson, Kemper & Assoc. (C), *400*
Kaye/Bassman Int'l. Corp. (R), *110*
A.T. Kearney Executive Search (R), *111*
Kenzer Corp. (R), *113*
Keystone Consulting Group (C), *406*
King ComputerSearch, Inc. (C), *407*
Korn/Ferry Int'l. (R), *118*
Evie Kreisler Assoc. Inc. (C), *409*
Kressenberg Assoc. (C), *409*
LAI Ward Howell (R), *124*
Larsen Int'l., Inc. (R), *125*
Management Recruiter of Dallas (C), *436*
Management Recruiters of Dallas-NW (C), *436*
Management Recruiters of Addison (C), *436*
Management Recruiters of LBJ Park/Dallas (C), *462*
Management Recruiters Dallas North (MRDN) (C), *462*
McDowell & Co., Recruiters (C), *474*
Micro Staff Solutions, Inc. (C), *481*
The Noebel Search Group, Inc. (C), *494*
Noll Human Resource Services (C), *494*
Norris Agency (C), *495*
Odell & Assoc., Inc. (C), *498*
The Oxford Group (C), *500*
Page-Wheatcroft & Co., Ltd. (R), *158*
The Pailin Group Professional Search Consultants (R), *158*
Parker-Worthington, Inc. (C), *503*
Largent Parks & Partners (C), *503*
Prescott Legal Search (C), *517*
QuestPro, Inc. (C), *527*
Lea Randolph & Assoc., Inc. (C), *529*
Ray & Berndtson (R), *172*
Russell Reynolds Assoc., Inc. (R), *177*
Robert Lowell Int'l. (R), *179*
Roll International (C), *541*
Romac Int'l., Inc. (C), *544*
Romac Int'l., Inc. (C), *544*
Sales Consultants of Dallas (C), *563*
SearchCom, Inc. (R), *187*
Marvin L. Silcott & Assoc., Inc. (C), *581*
Sink, Walker, Boltrus Int'l. (R), *192*
SpencerStuart (R), *197*
Spilman & Assoc. (R), *197*
Staff Extension Int'l. (C), *590*
Staffing Edge, Inc. (C), *590*
Staffing Edge, Inc. (C), *591*
Stanton Chase Int'l. (R), *199*
Steinfield & Assoc. (C), *592*
StratfordGroup (R), *203*
Synapse Human Resource Consulting Group (R), *205*
The Talon Group (R), *205*

GEOGRAPHICAL

Tanner & Assoc., Inc. (R), *206*
TASA International (R), *206*
Carl J. Taylor & Co. (R), *207*
Taylor Winfield (R), *207*
Tech-Net (C), *601*
Technical Staffing Solutions (C), *602*
TNS Partners, Inc. (R), *209*
Tuttle Venture Group, Inc. (R), *212*
Wachendorfer & Assoc. (C), *613*
Kelly Walker Assoc. (C), *614*
Waveland Int'l. (R), *216*
Wheeler, Moore & Elam Co. (R), *219*
Witt/Kieffer, Ford, Hadelman & Lloyd (R), *223*
Bruce G. Woods Executive Search (R), *224*
The Wright Group (C), *625*
The Wright Group (C), *625*

Denton
The Danielson Group, Inc. (C), *306*

El Paso
Bor-Maq Assoc. (C), *269*
Management Recruiters of El Paso (C), *436*
R. A. Rodriguez & Assoc., Inc. (C), *540*
Technifind Int'l. (C), *602*

Friendswood
Management Recruiters - Friendswood (C), *462*
Robert Shields & Assoc. (C), *538*

Frisco
The Tracy Glover Co. (R), *78*

Ft. Worth
Accountants On Call (C), *237*
EA Plus, Inc. (C), *325*
Hughes & Assoc. (C), *383*
Human Resource Solutions (R), *99*
O'Rourke Companies, Inc. (R), *154*
Ray & Berndtson (R), *171*
Ray & Berndtson (R), *172*
Romac Int'l., Inc. (C), *544*
Staffing Edge, Inc. (C), *591*
Staffing Edge, Inc. (C), *591*
The TGA Company (C), *606*
Whitney Smith Co. (C), *620*

Houston
Accountants On Call (C), *237*
Ackerman Johnson Inc. (C), *238*
Albrecht & Assoc., Executive Search Consultants (C), *243*
The Alexander Group (R), *3*
Allen Austin Lowe & Powers (R), *3*
Allen, Wayne & Co. LLC (C), *245*
Anderson Bradshaw Assoc., Inc. (R), *6*
Barton Assoc., Inc. (R), *12*
Berglund Int'l. Resources, Inc. (C), *265*
Boyden (R), *21*
Careerfit, Inc. (C), *283*
cFour Partners (R), *32*
The Cherbonnier Group, Inc. (R), *33*
Clarey/Napier Int'l., L.C. (R), *35*
The Energists (R), *59*
The Evans McDonnell Co. (C), *331*
ExecuSource Consultants, Inc. (C), *332*
F-O-R-T-U-N-E Personnel Consultants of Houston, Inc. (C), *350*
The GlobalSearch Group (C), *359*
Hall Kinion (C), *367*
Heidrick & Struggles, Inc. (R), *90*
A. Herndon & Assoc., Inc. (R), *92*
Hunt Patton & Brazeal, Inc. (C), *385*
Independent Power Consultants (C), *387*
Insight Personnel Group, Inc. (C), *389*
Interim Accounting Professionals (C), *392*
InterNeed (C), *394*
Intersource, Ltd. (R), *103*
ISC of Houston, Inc. (C), *394*
A H Justice Search Consultants (C), *402*
Kane & Assoc. (C), *403*
A.T. Kearney Executive Search (R), *111*
Korn/Ferry Int'l. (R), *118*
Kors Montgomery Int'l. (R), *118*
LAI Ward Howell (R), *124*
Litchfield & Willis, Inc. (R), *130*
Loewenstein & Assoc., Inc. (R), *131*
Lord & Albus Co. (C), *420*
Lucas Assoc. (C), *421*
Magellan Int'l., L.P. (C), *422*
Management Recruiters of Houston-SW (C), *436*
Management Recruiters of Clear Lake (C), *436*
Management Recruiters of Clear Lake (C), *436*
Management Recruiters of Houston (C), *462*
Management Recruiters of Champions (C), *462*
McKinley•Arend Int'l. (R), *141*
Mims & Associates (R), *145*
Newman-Johnson-King, Inc. (C), *492*
Norrell Financial Staffing (C), *495*
O'Connor Resources (C), *497*
The Oldani Group (R), *155*
Parker Page Group (C), *503*
PeopleSource Inc. (C), *506*
Fred Perry Assoc. (C), *507*
Practice Dynamics, Inc. (C), *515*
Preng & Assoc., Inc. (R), *167*
Prescott Legal Search, Inc. (C), *517*
Professional Search Consultants (PSC) (C), *523*
Railey & Assoc. (C), *528*
The Ransford Group (R), *171*
Ray & Berndtson (R), *172*
Raymond Karsan Assoc. (C), *530*
Reserve Technology Institute (R), *175*
Russell Reynolds Assoc., Inc. (R), *177*
Richard, Wayne & Roberts (C), *536*
Right/McKee Consulting Group (C), *537*
Robert Shields & Assoc. (C), *538*
Rodgers, Ramsey, Inc. (C), *540*
Romac Int'l., Inc. (C), *544*
Romac Int'l., Inc. (C), *544*
Roth Young Executive Search (C), *546*
Ryman, Bell, Green & Michaels, Inc. (C), *549*
Saber Group, Inc. (C), *550*
Sales Consultants of Houston (C), *563*
Sales Consultants of Houston (C), *563*
The Search Center Inc. (C), *574*
Search Consultants Int'l., Inc. (C), *575*
Skipping Stone Inc. (C), *582*
SpencerStuart (R), *197*
Staff Extension, Int'l. (C), *590*
Staffing Edge, Inc. (C), *591*
Staffing Edge, Inc. (C), *591*
Peter Sterling & Co. (C), *592*
StratfordGroup (R), *203*
Summit Search Specialists (C), *596*
M. L. Tawney & Assoc. (C), *600*
Tekworx, Inc. (C), *604*
TPG & Assoc. (C), *608*
The Urban Placement Service (C), *611*
Warring & Assoc. (R), *216*
The Whitaker Companies (C), *619*
Windsor Consultants, Inc. (C), *622*
Witt/Kieffer, Ford, Hadelman & Lloyd (R), *223*
Dick Wray & Consultants, Inc. (R), *225*

Hurst
Dunhill Staffing Systems (C), *318*

Irving
Bradford & Galt, Inc. (C), *271*
DHR Int'l., Inc. (R), *51*
Dunhill Staffing Systems of Irving (C), *318*
The Hindman Co. (R), *94*
Human Resource Solutions (R), *98*
Layne-Mendez & Co. (R), *127*
LifeWork, Inc. (C), *418*
Ginger Lindsey & Assoc., Inc. (C), *418*
Management Recruiters of Irving-North (C), *436*
Management Recruiters of Las Colinas (C), *436*
Management Recruiters of Dallas-West (C), *436*
MSI Int'l. (C), *487*
Norrell Financial Staffing (C), *495*
Quetico Corp. (R), *170*
Staffing Edge, Inc. (C), *591*

Kingwood
Joseph Chris & Assoc. (C), *400*
Management Recruiters of Houston-Northeast (C), *463*

La Porte
The Duncan-O'Dell Group Inc. (C), *316*

Lewisville
AGRI-associates (C), *242*
DCA Professional Search (C), *309*
Employment Solutions, Inc. (C), *330*
Management Recruiters of Lewisville (C), *463*
R. C. Services (C), *528*

Lubbock
Management Recruiters of Lubbock (C), *463*

Mansfield
Dunhill Professional Search of Mansfield (C), *318*

McAllen
Dunhill Professional Search, Inc. of McAllen (C), *323*
USA Medical Placement Inc. (C), *611*

McKinney
Melancon & Co. (R), *143*

Midland
Management Recruiters of Midland (C), *436*

Mineral Wells
Management Resources (C), *467*

New Braunfels
Canyon Consulting, Inc. (C), *281*
Management Recruiters of New Braunfels (C), *436*

Oak Point
Charles P. Aquavella & Assoc. (C), *252*

Odessa
Bennett & Associates (C), *264*

Pearland
Guidry & East Healthcare Search Consultants (R), *83*

Pflugerville
John Williams & Assoc. (C), *621*

Plano
Alpha Resource Group, Inc. (C), *246*
Button Group (C), *277*
Executive Search Int'l. (C), *335*
Fortune Personnel Consultants of Plano (C), *350*
Susan Hall Executive Search (C), *366*
Hardison & Company (R), *86*
Huntley Associates (Dallas), Inc. (C), *386*
M H Executive Search Group (C), *422*
Management Recruiters of Plano-East (C), *436*
Management Recruiters of Preston Park (C), *436*
MTA Partners (R), *148*
J. L. Nixon Consulting (C), *493*
SpencerSearch, Inc. (C), *589*
Vick & Assoc. (R), *214*

Richardson
Robert L. Charon (C), *289*
Craig Affiliates, Inc. (C), *302*
DSR-Search & Recruitment (C), *315*
McKeen & Company (R), *141*
PERI Corp/Professional Executive Recruiters, Inc. (C), *507*
Procom (C), *519*
Strategic Technologies, Inc. (C), *596*

Rockwall
The Gullgroup (C), *364*
Power Search (C), *515*

Round Rock
LCS, Inc. (C), *414*
Management Recruiters of Round Rock (C), *463*

San Antonio
A-Linko & Assoc. (C), *231*
Allen, Wayne & Co. LLC (C), *245*
Robert Belsjoe (C), *528*
Dunhill Personnel Service of San Antonio (C), *318*
Dunhill of New Braunfels (C), *318*
The Elsworth Group (C), *329*
Howard Fischer Assoc. Int'l., Inc. (R), *67*
Fortune Personnel Consultants of San Antonio, Inc. (C), *350*
Global Telecommunications, Inc. (C), *359*
Gowdy Consultants (C), *361*
innovativestaffsearch (C), *389*
Jordan-Sitter Assoc. (R), *108*
Kincaid Group Inc. (KGI) (C), *406*
Kincaid Group Inc. (KGI) (C), *407*
Management Recruiters of San Antonio-NW (C), *436*
Management Recruiters of San Antonio-Crossroads (C), *436*
Management Recruiters of San Antonio (C), *463*
Management Recruiters of San Antonio - North (C), *463*
MRF Enterprises, Inc. (C), *486*
Len Nelson & Assoc., Inc. (C), *491*
Nino Recruiting & Staffing, Inc. (C), *493*
Parker-Worthington, Inc. (C), *503*
SPC Symcox Personnel Consultants (C), *588*
Staffing Edge, Inc. (C), *591*

San Marcos
Management Recruiters of San Marcos (C), *463*

Southlake
R. S. Wyatt Assoc., Inc. (R), *225*

Spring
HDB Incorporated (C), *371*

Stafford
Management Recruiters of Sugar Land Inc. (C), *464*

Sugar Land
Delta Services (R), *48*
M. Dunbar & Assoc. (C), *316*

The Woodlands
Alliance Search Management Inc. (R), *4*
W. Robert Eissler & Assoc., Inc. (C), *327*
John Gilbert Co. (C), *357*
Hyman & Assoc. (C), *386*
Insurance Search (C), *390*
Management Recruiters Int'l.-The Woodlands (C), *464*
Marentz & Co. (C), *469*
Raymond Karsan Assoc. (C), *530*

Waco
Don Hall & Assoc. (C), *366*

Weatherford
Peter Froehlich & Co. (C), *353*
The Inside Track (C), *389*

Wylie
Gregory D. Pickens (C), *511*

Utah

Brighton
Dick Wray & Consultants, Inc. (R), *225*

Farmington
Ki Technologies, Inc. (C), *406*

Layton
J. Fielding Nelson & Assoc., Inc. (R), *151*

Ogden
Management Recruiters of Ogden (C), *464*

Park City
Management Recruiters of Park City (C), *436*
Sanford Rose Assoc. - Salt Lake City (C), *571*

Provo
Management Recruiters of Provo (C), *437*

Salt Lake City
Accountants On Call (C), *237*
Atlantic West Int'l. (C), *255*
Deeco Int'l. (C), *310*
DHR Int'l., Inc. (R), *51*
The Diestel Group (R), *51*
Hall Kinion (C), *367*
Management Recruiters of Salt Lake City (C), *464*
Professional Recruiters (C), *521*
Romac Int'l., Inc. (C), *544*
Sales Consultants of Salt Lake City (C), *555*
STM Assoc. (R), *201*

Sandy
Lab Market Specialists (C), *411*
Trout & Assoc. Inc. (R), *211*

Vermont

Brattleboro
AutoPeople (C), *257*
GFI Professional Staffing Services (C), *357*

Bridgewater
Jay Tracey Assoc. Inc. (C), *608*

Burlington
Management Recruiters of Burlington (C), *437*

Mendon
Wakefield Talabisco Int'l. (R), *214*

South Newfane
Alan Darling Consulting (R), *46*

Stowe
J. R. Peterman Assoc., Inc. (C), *509*

Warren
Dunhill Search of Vermont (C), *323*

Woodstock
Eckler Personnel Network (C), *326*

Virginia

Alexandria
Hughes & Company (R), *98*

Alexandria
Jeffrey Irving Assoc., Inc. (R), *104*
A.T. Kearney Executive Search (R), *111*

GEOGRAPHICAL

Page-Wheatcroft & Co., Ltd. (R), *158*
ProLinks Inc. (R), *170*
Raymond Karsan Assoc. (C), *530*

Annandale
Financial Connections Company (C), *340*

Arlington
Action Managment Corp. (C), *239*
BJB Assoc. (C), *267*
Frey & Sher Assoc., Inc. (C), *353*
Management Recruiters of Arlington (C), *464*
Mancini Technical Recruiting (C), *468*
The McCormick Group (C), *474*
Partners Resource Group (C), *504*
RHI Consulting (C), *536*
Wilder & Assoc. (C), *620*
Yours In Travel Personnel Agency, Inc. (C), *627*

Bridgewater
Souder & Assoc. (R), *195*

Bristol
The Hindman Co. (R), *94*

Burke
HR Advantage, Inc. (C), *382*

Centerville
The Mercer Group, Inc. (R), *143*

Chantilly
GateSource Partners (C), *355*
Harbor Consultants Int'l., Inc. (C), *368*
Larson, Katz & Young, Inc. (C), *413*

Charlottesville
CountryHouse Hotels Executive Search (C), *302*
Hartman & Barnette (R), *87*
Management Recruiters of Charlottesville (C), *437*

Chesapeake
Ludwig & Assoc., Inc. (C), *421*

Edinburg
Wilder & Assoc. (C), *620*

Fairfax
AMS Int'l. (R), *5*
Halbrecht & Co. (C), *365*
Management Recruiters of Reston (C), *437*
Management Recruiters of Fairfax, VA (C), *464*
Romac Int'l., Inc. (C), *544*
Sales Builders, Inc. (R), *183*
Starbridge Group Inc. (C), *591*
Telecom Recruiters, Inc. (C), *605*
Wilkinson SoftSearch, Inc. (C), *620*

Falls Church
Bradford Executives Int'l. (C), *271*
U.S. Search (C), *610*

Fredericksburg
The McCormick Group (C), *473*

Great Falls
Brault & Assoc., Ltd. (R), *22*
The Hamilton Group (R), *85*

Hampton
Carol Maden Group (C), *422*

Herndon
MDR Associates, Inc. (C), *476*
Raymond Karsan Assoc. (C), *530*

Lightfoot
Executive Career Search (C), *332*

Lynchburg
ADECCO Employment Services (C), *240*
Management Recruiters of Lynchburg (C), *437*
Singleton & Assoc. (C), *582*

Martinsville
Management Recruiters of Martinsville (C), *437*
Management Recruiters of Henry County (C), *437*

McLean
The Abbott Group, Inc. (R), *1*
Dinte Resources, Inc. (R), *52*
Donini Assoc. (R), *54*
Government Contract Solutions, Inc. (C), *360*
The Guild Corp. (C), *364*
Management Recruiters of McLean (C), *437*
Paul-Tittle Assoc., Inc. (R), *161*
Search Consultants, LLC (C), *575*
Wilkinson SoftSearch, Inc. (C), *621*

Millboro
Fortune Personnel Consultants of the Virginia Highlands (C), *351*

Nellysford
Bill Young & Assoc. (C), *626*

Oakton
Management Recruiters of Oakton (C), *437*

Palmyra
Management Recruiters - Piedmont (C), *464*

Reston
Patrick Arnone & Assoc. Inc. (R), *7*
Bartholdi & Co., Inc. (R), *12*
Dahl-Morrow Int'l. (R), *45*
Doleman Enterprises (R), *53*
IPR, Inc. (R), *103*
MSI Int'l. (C), *487*
Norrell Financial Staffing (C), *495*

Richmond
Accountants On Call (C), *237*
The Corporate Connection, Ltd. (C), *299*
Dunhill Professional Search of Richmond (C), *323*
Keystone Consulting Group (C), *406*
Management Recruiters of Richmond (C), *437*
Opalka Dixon Consultants to Management (R), *156*
PRAXIS Partners (R), *167*
Recruiting Specialists (C), *532*
Renaissance Resources, LLC (R), *174*
RTE Search (C), *547*
Sales Consultants of Richmond (C), *555*

Roanoke
Management Recruiters of Roanoke (C), *465*

Springfield
Management Recruiters of Springfield (C), *437*

Staunton
The Talley Group (R), *205*

Sterling
Management Recruiters of Loudoun County South (C), *465*

Suffolk
Management Recruiters of Suffolk (C), *437*

Vienna
Accountants On Call (C), *237*
Beacon Int'l., Inc. (C), *261*
Christian & Timbers, Inc. (R), *34*
The Consulting Group of North America, Inc. (C), *297*
Faro Consultants Int'l. (C), *338*
Focus Consulting Services, Inc. (C), *343*
Fortune Consultants (C), *349*
F. Gloss Int'l. (R), *78*
Heidrick & Struggles, Inc. (R), *90*
The Helms Int'l. Group (R), *91*
Interim Financial Solutions (C), *392*
Kincannon & Reed (R), *114*
Korn/Ferry Int'l. (R), *118*
Logue & Rice Inc. (C), *420*
RGE (C), *535*
Romac Int'l., Inc. (C), *544*
Skipping Stone Inc. (C), *582*
StratfordGroup (R), *203*
Telecom Executive Group (C), *605*
ZanExec L.L.C. (R), *226*

Virginia Beach
A la Carte Int'l., Inc. (R), *1*
Dunhill Professional Search of Virginia Beach (C), *318*
Executive Resource Assoc. (C), *334*
Robert Larned Assoc., Inc. (C), *413*
Management Recruiters of Virginia Beach (C), *437*
Omega Systems, LLC (C), *498*
Orion Int'l. Consulting Group, Inc. (C), *500*
Price & Assoc., Inc. (C), *518*
Sales Consultants of Virginia Beach (C), *555*
Search & Recruit Int'l. (C), *573*
Southwestern Professional Services (C), *588*
Warren, Morris & Madison, Ltd. (C), *616*
Wayne Assoc., Inc. (C), *616*

Williamsburg
Cambridge Group Ltd.-Exec. Search Div. (C), *280*
The Cambridge Group Ltd. (C), *280*
Sloan & Assoc., Inc. (C), *583*

Washington

Bainbridge Island
Moss & Co. (R), *148*
Moss & Co. (R), *148*
Olsen/Clark (R), *156*

Bellevue
Accountants On Call (C), *237*
Career Specialists, Inc. (R), *29*
The Cherbonnier Group, Inc. (R), *33*
J. F. Church Associates (C), *291*
Executive Recruiters (C), *334*
L. W. Foote Co. (R), *69*
F-O-R-T-U-N-E Personnel Consultants of East Seattle (C), *351*
Hall Kinion (C), *367*
Headden Assoc. (R), *88*
Houser, Martin, Morris (C), *381*
Kirkbride Assoc., Inc. (C), *407*
Kossuth & Assoc., Inc. (R), *119*
Management Recruiters of Bellevue (C), *437*
Management Solutions, Inc. (C), *468*
The Oldani Group (R), *155*
The Oldani Group (R), *155*
Personnel Consultants (C), *508*
Romac Int'l., Inc. (C), *544*
Roth Young Seattle (C), *546*
Strategic Resources Biotechnology & Medical Group (C), *595*
Strategic Resources (C), *595*

Bellingham
Synergy Solutions, Ltd. (C), *597*

Bothell
Executive Business Solutions, Inc. (C), *332*

Easton
Behrens and Company (C), *262*

Eastsound
David E. Grumney Co. Inc. (R), *83*

Edmonds
The Franklin Search Group, Inc./Medzilla (R), *71*

Everett
Management Recruiters of Everett (C), *437*

Gig Harbor
Management Recruiters of Tacoma (C), *437*
Mordue, Allen, Roberts, Bonney Ltd. (C), *485*
Orion Int'l. Consulting Group, Inc. (C), *500*
The Professional Sales Search Co., Inc. (C), *522*

Issaquah
Sally Caplan & Assoc. (C), *281*
Judith Cushman & Assoc. (R), *44*
DHR Int'l., Inc. (R), *51*
J.B.A. Assoc. (R), *104*
K. E. Johnson Assoc. (C), *399*
Jack Porter Assoc., Inc. (C), *514*

Kenmore
Moss & Co. (R), *148*

Kirkland
Healthcare Recruiters - Northwest (C), *374*
Miller + Miller (C), *482*

Lakewood
Management Recruiters of Lakewood/Tacoma (C), *437*
Thomson, Sponar & Adams, Inc. (C), *606*

Lynnwood
Management Recruiters of Lynnwood (C), *465*

Mercer Island
Management Recruiters of Mercer Island (C), *437*
John O'Keefe & Assoc., Inc. (R), *154*

Olympia
Management Recruiters of Olympia (C), *437*
Emery A. Rose & Assoc. (C), *545*

Poulsbo
Michael J. Hall & Co. (R), *85*

Redmond
Moss & Co. (R), *148*
Thomas Mangum Co. (R), *208*
Williams Recruiting, Inc. (C), *621*

Seattle
Accountants On Call (C), *237*
Association for Sales Force Management (C), *254*
Berkana Int'l., Inc. (C), *265*
David Blevins & Assoc. (C), *268*
T. M. Campbell Co. (R), *27*
Computer Personnel, Inc. (C), *295*
First Choice Search (R), *67*
Hall Kinion (C), *367*
Judith Cushman & Associates (R), *44*
Kleber & Assoc. (C), *407*
Korn/Ferry Int'l. (R), *118*
Todd L. Krueger & Assoc. (C), *409*
Management Recruiters of Seattle-South (C), *437*
Management Recruiters of Seattle (C), *465*
McHale & Assoc. (R), *141*
Moss & Co. (R), *148*
Prior/Martech Assoc., Inc. (R), *169*
Pursuant Legal Consultants (R), *170*
ROI International, Inc. (R), *181*
Larry Siegel & Assoc. (R), *191*
Tully/Woodmansee Int'l., Inc. (R), *212*
The Washington Firm, Ltd. (R), *216*

Spokane
Hergenrather & Co. (R), *92*
Management Recruiters of Spokane (C), *465*
Personnel Unlimited/Executive Search (C), *509*

Tacoma
Management Recruiters of North Tacoma (C), *437*

Vancouver
APA Employment Agency Inc. (C), *251*
Management Recruiters of Vancouver-Downtown (C), *437*

Vashon
Moss & Co. (R), *148*

West Virginia

Charleston
Dunhill Professional Search of West Virginia (C), *318*
Management Recruiters of Charleston (C), *437*

Hurricane
Management Recruiters of Kanawha Valley, LLC (C), *465*

Morgantown
Management Recruiters of Morgantown (C), *437*

New Haven
Locus Inc. (C), *419*

Wheeling
Dwyer Consulting Group, Inc. (R), *56*

Wisconsin

Appleton
DieckMueller Group (R), *51*
Management Recruiters of Appleton (C), *465*
Sales Consultants of Appleton (C), *563*
Schenck & Assoc. SC (C), *572*

Brookfield
Boettcher Assoc. (R), *19*
DHR Int'l., Inc. (R), *51*
Gibson & Co., Inc. (R), *76*
KGA Inc. (C), *406*
Maglio & Co., Inc. (R), *134*
Prime Resource Assoc. (C), *518*
Jude M. Werra & Assoc. (R), *218*

Coleman
Domres Professional Search (R), *53*

De Pere
T E M Assoc. (C), *599*

Delavan
Management Recruiters of Delavan (C), *437*

Elcho
Engineering Placement Specialists (C), *330*

Elkhart Lake
Hunter, Rowan & Crowe (C), *386*

Elm Grove
Koehler & Co. (R), *116*
Management Recruiters of Milwaukee-West (C), *465*

Fond Du Lac
Quality Consulting Group, Inc. (C), *526*

Germantown
Management Recruiters of Germantown (C), *437*

Glendale
Allen, Wayne & Co. LLC (C), *245*

Grafton
Mulcahy Co. (C), *487*

Green Bay
DeCaster Assoc. (C), *310*
Dunhill Staffing Systems (C), *318*
The H. S. Group, Inc. (C), *365*
Management Recruiters of Green Bay (C), *438*
Packaging Personnel Co., Ltd. (C), *501*
Sales Consultants of Green Bay (C), *555*
Techstaff Inc. (C), *603*

Hales Corners
Management Recruiters of Milwaukee-South (C), *438*

Hartland
Executive Resource Inc. (C), *334*

Jackson
Michaels & Moere (C), *481*

Janesville
Management Recruiters of Janesville, Inc. (C), *466*

Johnson Creek
Management Recruiters of Johnson Creek (C), *438*

LaCrosse
Construction Search Specialists, Inc. (C), *297*

Lake Geneva
Fred Anthony Assoc. (C), *251*
Continental Research Search, Inc. (C), *298*
LAI Ward Howell (R), *124*
The Rankin Group, Ltd. (R), *171*

LaValle
Prestige Inc. (C), *518*

Lodi
Management Recruiters of Lake Wisconsin (C), *438*

Madison
Executive Recruiters, Inc. (C), *334*
innovativestaffsearch (C), *389*
Kelly Assoc. (R), *112*
Raymond Karsan Assoc. (C), *530*
Wojdula & Assoc., Ltd. (R), *223*

Menomonee Falls
Trainor/Frank & Assoc. Inc. (C), *608*

Mequon
Barnes Development Group, LLC (R), *11*
The Cooke Group (R), *40*
J. M. Eagle Partners Ltd. (C), *325*
Overton Consulting (R), *157*
Sales Consultants of Milwaukee (C), *563*
Strelcheck & Assoc., Inc. (R), *203*

Middleton
Management Recruiters of Madison, Inc. (C), *466*
Sales Consultants of Madison (C), *563*

Milwaukee
Accountants On Call (C), *237*
American Resources Corp. (C), *248*
Associated Recruiters (C), *254*
Brissenden, McFarland, Fuccella & Reynolds, Inc. (R), *23*
Concorde Staff Source Inc. (C), *296*
Consultant Recruiters (C), *297*
Fogec Consultants, Inc. (R), *69*
Gielow Assoc., Inc. (R), *76*
Jonas, Walters & Assoc., Inc. (R), *107*
Kordus Consulting Group (C), *408*
Management Association Network (C), *424*
Management Recruiters of Milwaukee-Central (C), *438*
Management Recruiters of Milwaukee-North (C), *466*
Management Recruiters of Milwaukee - Downtown (C), *466*
MARBL Consultants, Inc. (C), *469*
Marketing Consultants (C), *470*
P. J. Murphy & Assoc., Inc. (R), *150*
Quirk-Corporon & Assoc., Inc. (C), *527*
Romac Int'l., Inc. (C), *544*
Roth Young Executive Search of Milwaukee (C), *547*
Techstaff Inc. (C), *603*
Wegner & Assoc. (C), *617*

Mosinee
Management Recruiters of Stevens Point, Inc. (C), *466*

Necedah
Markent Personnel (C), *470*

Oconomowoc
Blum & Co. (R), *19*
TEMCO-The Executive Management Consulting Organization (R), *208*

Oostburg
Packaging Personnel Co., Ltd. (C), *501*

Plover
Holland & Assoc., Inc. (R), *95*

Port Washington
Sanford Rose Assoc. - Port Washington (C), *571*

Racine
The Human Resource Consulting Group, Inc. (R), *98*
Management Recruiters of Racine (C), *438*
Sales Consultants of Racine (C), *555*

Reedsburg
Prestige Inc. (C), *517*

Sheboygan Falls
John Kuhn & Assoc., Inc. (R), *121*

Sun Prairie
Dunhill Professional Search of Madison (C), *318*

Thiensville
Peck & Assoc., Ltd. (R), *161*

Wales
The Cooper Executive Search Group Inc. (R), *41*

Watertown
Tom Sloan & Assoc., Inc. (C), *583*

Waukesha
Placement Solutions (C), *513*

Wausau
Management Recruiters of Wausau, LLC (C), *466*

Wauwatosa
Dunhill Staffing Systems of Milwaukee (C), *318*

West Bend
Egan & Assoc. (R), *57*

Whitewater
Wojdula & Assoc., Ltd. (R), *223*

Wisconsin Dells
Markent Personnel, Inc. (C), *470*

Wyoming

Cheyenne
Management Recruiters of Cheyenne (C), *466*

CANADA

Alberta

Calgary
Boyden (R), *21*
The Caldwell Partners Amrop International (R), *26*
Canadian Career Partners (R), *27*
Coe & Co. Int'l. Inc./EMA Partners Int'l. (R), *37*
Conroy Partners Ltd. (R), *39*
Cosier & Assoc. (C), *302*
Davies, Park (R), *47*
Finney-Taylor Personnel & Management Consultants Ltd. (C), *341*
The Fisher Group (R), *67*
Robert Half Canada Inc. (C), *366*
Harcourt & Associates (C), *369*
KPMG Executive Search (R), *119*
Leader Search Inc. (R), *127*
AG Lennox & Assoc. (R), *128*
The Network Corporate Search Personnel Inc. (C), *491*
O'Callaghan Honey/Ray & Berndtson Inc. (R), *153*
O'Callaghan Honey/Ray & Berndtson Inc. (R), *172*
Petro Staff Int'l. (C), *509*
Price Waterhouse Executive Search (R), *168*
Procom (C), *519*
Reynolds Consulting Int'l. (R), *177*
Search Group Inc. (R), *186*

SearchCorp International (C), *577*
Tittemore Cowan Assoc. (C), *607*
Western Management Consultants (R), *218*

Edmonton
David Aplin & Assoc. (C), *251*
Campbell, Edgar Inc. (C), *280*
Davies, Park (R), *46*
Robert Half Canada Inc. (C), *366*
Harcourt & Assoc. (C), *368*
KPMG Executive Search (R), *119*
Price Waterhouse Executive Search (R), *168*
Prichard Kymen Inc. (R), *168*
Western Management Consultants (R), *218*

British Columbia

Coquitlam
Boyden (R), *21*

Delta
Campbell, Edgar Inc. (C), *280*

Nanaimo
Coast Personnel Services Ltd. (C), *293*

North Vancouver
Ashton Computer Professionals, Inc. (C), *253*

Richmond
Campbell, Edgar Inc. (C), *280*

Vancouver
Accountants On Call (C), *237*
C.T.E.W. Executive Personnel Services Inc. (C), *278*
The Caldwell Partners Amrop International (R), *26*
Chapman & Assoc. (C), *289*
Corporate Recruiters Ltd. (C), *300*
Descheneaux Recruitment Services Ltd. (C), *311*
Dumont & Co. (C), *316*
Dunhill Professional Search of Vancouver (C), *318*
J. G. Flynn & Assoc. Inc. (R), *69*
Forest People Int'l. Search Ltd. (C), *343*
The Glazin Group (R), *77*
Goldbeck Recruiting Inc. (C), *359*
Robert Half Canada Inc. (C), *366*
Holloway Schulz & Partners (C), *380*
Jenex Technology Placement Inc. (C), *398*
David Warwick Kennedy & Assoc. (R), *112*
KPMG Executive Search (R), *119*
Pinton Forrest & Madden/EMA Partners Int'l. (R), *165*
Price Waterhouse Executive Search (R), *168*
Ray & Berndtson/Tanton Mitchell (R), *172*
Ray & Berndtson/Tanton Mitchell (R), *173*
Reynolds Consulting Int'l. (R), *177*
Rossi & Assoc. Inc. (C), *545*
Western Management Consultants (R), *218*
Wood West & Partners Inc. (C), *624*

Manitoba

Winnipeg
The Harris Consulting Corp. (R), *87*
KPMG Executive Search (R), *119*
Personnel Management Group (C), *508*
Price Waterhouse Executive Search (R), *168*
Zen Zen Int'l. Inc. (C), *627*

New Brunswick

Fredericton
Quantum Management Services Limited (C), *526*
Gerald Walsh & Co. Inc. (C), *615*

Moncton
Robertson-Surrette Ltd. (R), *180*

Newfoundland

St. John's
KPMG Executive Search (R), *119*
Wilson Assoc. Inc. (R), *222*

Nova Scotia

Halifax
KPMG Executive Search (R), *119*
Kenneth Murphy & Assoc. (C), *487*
Robertson-Surrette Ltd. (R), *179*
Gerald Walsh & Co. Inc. (C), *614*
Wilson Assoc. Inc. (R), *222*

Ontario

Alliston
Squires Resources Inc. (C), *590*

Ancaster
HEC Group (C), *375*

Ayr
Trillium Human Resources Inc. (C), *609*
Your Advantage Staffing Consultants Inc. (C), *626*

Bolton
Aldonna Barry Personnel & Management (C), *260*

Brampton
Armor Personnel (C), *253*

Burlington
Angus Employment Ltd. (C), *250*
W. Hutt Management Resources Ltd. (R), *100*
Trans-United Consultants Ltd. (C), *608*

Cambridge
Conors, Lovell & Assoc., Inc. (C), *296*
Prime Management Group Inc. (C), *518*

Etobicoke
Brethet, Barnum & Assoc., Inc. (C), *273*
Pamenter, Pamenter, Brezer & Deganis Ltd. (R), *159*
Pioneer Executive Consultants (C), *512*
Robison Humphreys & Assoc., Inc. (R), *180*

Hamilton
Job-Born Candidate Selection Bureau (C), *399*
McIntyre Management Resources (C), *474*

Kitchener
Robert William James & Assoc. (C), *539*

London
The 500 Granary Inc. (C), *231*
Dunhill Staffing Systems of London, Ltd. (C), *318*
London Executive Consultants Inc. (C), *420*
Prime Management Group Inc. (C), *518*
Robert William James & Assoc. (C), *539*
The Verriez Group Inc. (R), *213*

Markham
Global Consulting Group Inc. (C), *358*
Danette Milne Corporate Search Inc. (C), *482*

Mississauga
The 500 Granary Inc. (C), *231*
Ashlar-Stone Management Consultants Inc. (R), *8*
Avion International Technology Inc. (C), *257*
CanMed Consultants Inc. (C), *280*
Carion Resource Group Inc. (C), *284*
Christmas, McIvor & Assoc. Inc. (C), *290*
Connors, Lovell & Assoc. Inc. (C), *296*
Consolidated Management Services (C), *296*
Groupe PCA Inc. (C), *364*
Robert Half Canada Inc. (C), *366*
Interim Management Resources Inc. (C), *392*
ISG Informatics Search Group (C), *395*
Stephen Laramee & Assoc. Inc. (C), *413*
Montgomery, Thomason & Assoc. (C), *484*
D. J. Simpson Assoc. Inc. (R), *191*
TSI Group/TSI Staffing Services (C), *610*

Nepean
Catalyx Group - Canada (R), *31*

Niagara Falls
Medfall Inc. (C), *476*

North York
Tony Curtis & Associates (C), *305*
Dunhill Personnel of North York (C), *318*
M. A. Haggith Consultants Ltd. (R), *84*
Robert Half Canada Inc. (C), *366*
The McKinnon Management Group Inc. (C), *475*
Romac Int'l., Inc. (C), *544*
Synergy Systems (C), *598*
TechNix Inc. (C), *602*
Venpro Consulting Inc. (C), *612*

Oakville
The 500 Granary Inc. (C), *231*
GAAP Inc. (R), *73*
Reid Ellis Assoc. Inc. (C), *533*
S. Tanner & Assoc. Inc. (C), *599*

Ottawa
The 500 Granary Inc. (C), *231*
Consulpro (R), *39*
DARE Personnel Inc. (C), *307*
Robert Half Canada Inc. (C), *366*
KPMG Executive Search (R), *119*
Perry-Martel Int'l., Inc. (R), *163*
The Pollack Group (C), *514*
Procom (C), *519*
Quantum EDP Recruiting Services (C), *526*
Ray & Berndtson/Lovas Stanley (R), *172*
Ray & Berndtson/Lovas Stanley (R), *172*
Ray & Berndtson/Lovas Stanley (R), *173*
Ray & Berndtson/Lovas Stanley (R), *173*
Robertson-Surrette Ltd. (R), *180*
Synagent Inc. (C), *597*
Ward Assoc. (C), *615*

Owen Sound
Aurora Tech Search (C), *256*

Sarnia
Roevin Technical People (C), *540*

St. Catharines
The Burke Group (C), *276*

Thornhill
Management Dimensions Ltd. (R), *134*

Thorold
Landon Morgan (C), *412*

Toronto
Accountants On Call (C), *237*
Action Executive Personnel Consulting Inc. (C), *239*
Adirect Recruiting Corp. (C), *240*
ADR Accounting Management Recruiters (C), *240*
Ambridge Management Corp. (C), *247*
Applied Technology Solutions Inc. (C), *252*
The Argus Group Corp. (C), *252*
Armitage Associates Ltd. (R), *7*
Austin Park Management Group Inc. (C), *256*
Keith Bagg & Assoc., Inc. (C), *257*
Barrett Rose & Lee, Inc. (C), *260*
Bassett Laudi Partners (C), *261*
The Bedford Consulting Group Inc. (R), *14*
Boyden (R), *21*
Bryan, Jason & Assoc. Inc. (C), *275*
C.T.E.W. Executive Personnel Services Inc. (C), *278*
The Caldwell Partners Amrop International (R), *26*
Cambridge Management Planning (R), *27*
Campa & Assoc. (R), *27*
Michael J. Cavanagh & Assoc. Inc. (R), *31*
Chad Management Group (C), *288*
Chase Partners (R), *33*
The Churchill Group (C), *291*
Consulting Rhonda (C), *297*
Corso, Mizgala + French (R), *42*
Creative Financial Staffing Inc. (C), *303*
Delta Management Group Ltd. (C), *310*
Derhak Ireland & Partners Ltd. (R), *48*
The Enns Partners Inc. (R), *59*
Feldman Gray & Assoc. Inc. (C), *339*
Financial Plus Management Solutions Inc. (R), *66*
Franchise Recruiters Ltd. (R), *71*
Geddes & Rubin Management Inc. (R), *76*
The Grant Search Group, Inc. (C), *361*
Wolf Gugler & Assoc. Ltd. (R), *83*
Robert Half Canada Inc. (C), *366*
Thomas E. Hedefine Assoc. (C), *375*
Heidrick & Struggles, Inc. (R), *90*
The Herrmann Group Ltd. (R), *92*
International Business Partners (C), *392*
A.T. Kearney Executive Search (R), *111*
Keeley Consulting Inc. (C), *404*
The Keith-Murray Partnership (R), *112*
Kingsley Allen Partners Inc. (R), *114*
Korn/Ferry Int'l. (R), *118*
KPMG Executive Search (R), *119*
Krecklo Executive Search Inc. (R), *120*
Lamon + Stuart + Michaels Inc. (R), *124*
Lascelle & Assoc. Inc. (C), *413*
The Levton Group Inc. (R), *129*
Lewis Companies Inc. (R), *129*
Madison MacArthur Inc. (R), *133*
Management One Consultants (C), *425*
Massey-Horton Int'l. (R), *138*
Millar Walker & Gay (R), *144*
N.A.P. Executive Services (Canada) Inc. (C), *488*
National Executive (C), *489*
O'Sullivan Search Inc. (C), *498*
Organization Consulting Ltd. (R), *157*
Partners Executive Search Consultants Inc. (R), *160*
Partnervision Consulting Group Inc. (R), *160*
Pasona Canada, Inc. (C), *504*
Peak Search Assoc. (C), *506*
PMJ & Assoc. (C), *513*
Elan Pratzer & Partners Inc. (R), *167*
George Preger & Associates Inc. (R), *167*
PricewaterhouseCoopers Executive Search (R), *168*
Procom (C), *519*
QD Legal (C), *525*
Quantum EDP Recruiting Services (C), *526*
Ray & Berndtson/Lovas Stanley (R), *172*
Ray & Berndtson/Lovas Stanley (R), *172*
Research Personnel Consultants (C), *534*
Russell Reynolds Assoc., Inc. (R), *177*
Reynolds Consulting Int'l. (R), *177*
Robinson, Fraser Group Ltd. (R), *180*
Rushmore • Judge Inc. (R), *183*
Sales Search (C), *564*
Schoales & Assoc. Inc. (C), *572*
The Search Company (R), *186*
E. L. Shore & Assoc. (R), *190*
The Silicon Network (C), *581*
Herman Smith Executive Initiatives Inc. (R), *193*
C. Snow & Assoc. (C), *586*
SpencerStuart (R), *197*
C. J. Stafford & Assoc. (C), *591*
Stanton Chase Int'l./ Botrie Assoc. (R), *199*
Michael Stern Assoc., Inc./Euram (R), *200*
Michael Stern Assoc., Inc./Euram (R), *200*
Michael Stern Assoc., Inc./Euram (R), *200*
Technical Skills Consulting Inc. (R), *207*
Ward Assoc. (C), *615*
Western Management Consultants (R), *218*
The Wilkie Group Int'l. (R), *220*
Egon Zehnder Int'l. Inc. (R), *227*
Helen Ziegler & Assoc., Inc. (C), *627*

Tottenham
Dan P. McLean Assoc., Inc. (C), *475*

Unionville
JSG Group Management Consultants (R), *109*

Uxbridge
C. R. Gerald & Assoc. (C), *356*

Waterloo
KPMG Executive Search (R), *119*

Whitby
Allen Ballach Assoc. Inc. (R), *10*

Willowdale
Belanger Partners Ltd. (C), *262*
Evans Transportation Search (C), *331*
Pro Tec Technical Services (C), *519*
Star Search Consultants (C), *591*

Quebec

Brossard
MPA Executive Search Inc. (R), *148*

Hudson Heights
Alan Davis & Assoc. Inc. (R), *47*

Ile Perrot
Linda Walter & Associes (C), *615*

Longueuil
Rene LaFlamme & Associes (R), *122*

Montreal
The 500 Granary Inc. (C), *231*
Abécassis Conseil (R), *1*
Birch & Associes (C), *267*
Boyden (R), *21*
The Caldwell Partners Amrop International (R), *26*
Chacra, Belliveau & Assoc. Inc. (C), *288*
Cyberna Assoc. Ltd. (C), *305*
D.A.I Human Resources Consultants (R), *45*
Alan Davis & Assoc. (R), *47*
Yves Elkas Inc. (R), *58*
Executive Registry (C), *334*
Bernard Frigon & Assoc. Inc. (C), *353*
GAAP Inc. (R), *73*
Gaudry, Shink, Levasseur (R), *75*
Groupe PCA Inc. (C), *363*
Groupe Ranger Inc. (C), *364*
Robert Half Canada Inc. (C), *366*
KPMG Executive Search (R), *119*
Krecklo & Assoc., Inc. (R), *120*
Lamon + Stuart + Michaels Inc. (R), *124*
Jacques LePage Executive Search Inc. (R), *128*
Matte Consulting Group Inc. (R), *138*

N.A.P. Executive Services (Canada) Inc. (C), 488
N.A.P. Executive Search (Canada) Inc. (C), 488
PHD Conseil en Ressources Humaines Inc. (C), 510
Placement Testart Inc. (C), 513
Price Waterhouse Executive Search (R), 168
Quantum EDP Recruiting Services (C), 526
Ray & Berndtson/Laurendeau Labrecque (R), 172
Ray & Berndtson/Laurendeau Labrecque (R), 172
Reynolds Consulting Int'l. (R), 177
Rolland Ressources Humaines Inc. (R), 181
SpencerStuart (R), 197
Techaid Inc. (C), 601
Claude Vezina, Conseil en recherche de cadres inc. (R), 213
Ward Assoc. (C), 615
Egon Zehnder Int'l. Inc. (R), 227

Quebec
Quantum EDP Recruiting Services (C), 526

Rouyn-Noranda
Yves Plouffe & Assoc. (R), 165

Ville Mont Royal
Procom (C), 520

Westmount
Personnel Tangent Inc. (C), 509

Saskatchewan

Regina
The Executive Source (C), 337
KPMG Executive Search (R), 120

Saskatoon
Western Management Consultants (R), 218

MEXICO

Jalisco

Guadalajara
Gomez Fregoso y Asociados (C), 360
Shore Asociados Ejecutivos, S. A. de C.V. (R), 190

Zapopan
Fresquez & Assoc. (C), 353

Mexico

Cuernavaca Moreios
Management Recruiters of Cuernavaca (C), 438

Mexico City
Amrop International (R), 5
Boyden Latin America S.A. de C.V. (R), 21
Conasa de Mexico, S.C. (R), 39
Goodrich & Sherwood Assoc., Inc. (R), 80
Heidrick & Struggles, Inc. (R), 90
Frank P. Hill (R), 93
A.T. Kearney Executive Search (R), 111
Korn/Ferry, Int'l., S.A. de C.V. (R), 118
Korn/Ferry, Int'l., S.A. de C.V. (R), 118
Leaders-Trust Int'l./Carce y Asociados, S.C. (R), 127
Management Recruiters of Mexico City-South (C), 438
OSAGUI S.A. de C.V. (C), 500
Phoenix Search (R), 164
PricewaterhouseCoopers Executive Search (R), 168
Ray & Berndtson (R), 172
Russell Reynolds Assoc., Inc. (R), 177
Roll International (C), 541
Shore Asociados Ejecutivos, S. A. de C.V. (R), 190
Smith Search, S.C. (R), 194
SpencerStuart (R), 197
Stoopen Asociados, S.C./EMA Partners Int'l. (R), 202
TASA International (R), 206
Egon Zehnder Int'l. Inc. (R), 227

Naucalpan
Shore Asociados Ejecutivos, S. A. de C.V. (R), 190

Nuevo Leon

Garza Garcia
Amrop International (R), 5

Monterrey
Korn/Ferry Int'l. (R), 118
Korn/Ferry, Int'l., S.A. de C.V. (R), 118
Shore Asociados Ejecutivos, S. A. de C.V. (R), 190

Sonora

Hermosillo
J.D.G. y Asociados, S.A. de C.V. (R), 104

Firms Index

Firms with (R) are from the Retainer Section, which begins on page 1.
Firms with (C) are from the Contingency Section, which begins on page 231.

The 500 Granary Inc. (C), ON, *231*
A C Personnel Services, Inc. (C), OK, *231*
A First Resource (C), NC, *231*
A la Carte Int'l., Inc. (R), VA, *1*
A Permanent Success Employment Services (C), CA, *231*
A-K-A (Anita Kaufmann Assoc.) (C), NY, *231*
A-L Assoc., Inc. (R), NY, *1*
A-Linko & Assoc. (C), TX, *231*
A. D. & Assoc. Executive Search, Inc. (C), GA, *231*
A.J. & Assoc. (C), FL, *232*
A.K.S. Assoc., Ltd. (R), MA, *1*
A.L.S. Group (C), NJ, *232*
A.M.C.R., Inc. (C), OH, *232*
Aaron Consulting, Inc. (C), MO, *232*
Abacus Group LLC (C), NY, *232*
Abbott Associates (R), CA, *1*
The Abbott Group, Inc. (R), MD, *1*
Abécassis Conseil (R), QE, *1*
Abeln, Magy & Assoc., Inc. (R), MN, *1*
Cathy Abelson Legal Search (C), PA, *232*
Abraham & London Ltd. (C), CT, *232*
B. J. Abrams & Assoc. Inc. (C), IL, *233*
Abraxas Technologies, Inc. (C), FL, *233*
ACC Consultants, Inc. (C), NM, *233*
ACC Technical Services (C), OH, *233*
Accelerated Data Decision, Inc. (C), NJ, *233*
Accent On Achievement, Inc. (C), MI, *233*
Access Assoc. Inc. (C), MD, *233*
Access Data Personnel, Inc. (C), NH, *233*
ACCESS Technology (C), CA, *234*
Access/Resources, Inc. (C), MA, *234*
Acclaim Services, Inc. (C), TX, *234*
Account Ability Now (C), MI, *234*
Accountancies (C), CA, *234*
Accountants Executive Search (C), CT, *234*
Accountants Executive Search (C), PA, *234*
Accountants On Call (C), NJ, *234*
Accountants On Call (C), TN, *237*
Accountants On Call (C), FL, *237*
Accountants Executive Search (C), CA, *237*
Accounting & Bookkeeping Personnel, Inc. (C), AZ, *237*
Accounting & Computer Personnel (C), NY, *238*
Accounting Additions (C), CA, *238*
Accounting Personnel & Engineering Personnel Consultants (C), LA, *238*
Ackerman Johnson Inc. (C), TX, *238*
ACSYS Resources, Inc. (C), DE, *238*
Action Executive Personnel Consulting Inc. (C), ON, *239*
Action Management Corp. (C), MI, *239*
Active Search & Placement Inc. (C), CA, *239*
Acuity Medical Recruitment (C), MS, *239*
Adam-Bryce Inc. (C), NY, *239*
Arthur Adams & Assoc. (C), OH, *239*
Adams & Assoc. Int'l. (R), IL, *1*
G. Adams Partners (R), IL, *2*
The Addison Consulting Group (C), NJ, *239*
ADECCO Employment Services (C), VA, *240*
Adel-Lawrence Assoc., Inc. (C), NJ, *240*
Adept Tech Recruiting, Inc. (C), NY, *240*
Adirect Recruiting Corp. (C), ON, *240*
Adler Management, Inc. (R), NJ, *2*
ADR Accounting Management Recruiters (C), ON, *240*
Advanced Corporate Search (C), CA, *240*
Advanced Executive Resources (R), MI, *2*
Advanced Recruiting, Inc. (C), OK, *240*
Advanced Recruitment, Inc. (C), TN, *240*
Advanced Resources, Inc. (C), MO, *241*
Advancement Recruiting Services (C), OH, *241*
Advancement, Inc. (C), IL, *241*
Advantage Partners, Inc. (R), OH, *2*
Advice Personnel Inc. (C), NY, *241*
Advisors' Search Group, Inc. (C), NY, *241*
The Advisory Group, Inc. (R), CA, *2*
AES Search (C), NJ, *241*
Affinity Executive Search (C), FL, *241*
Affordable Executive Recruiters (C), CA, *241*
Aggressive Corporation (C), IL, *242*
Agra Placements, Ltd. (C), IA, *242*
AGRI-associates (C), MO, *242*
Agri-Personnel (C), GA, *242*
Agri-Tech Personnel, Inc. (C), MO, *242*
Agriesti & Assoc. (C), CA, *243*
Ahrensdorf & Assoc. (R), PA, *2*
AJM Professional Services (C), MI, *243*
AKH Executive Search (C), OR, *243*
J. R. Akin & Co. (R), MA, *2*
Alaska Executive Search, Inc. (C), AK, *243*
Albrecht & Assoc., Executive Search Consultants (C), TX, *243*
Alexander & Co. (C), CA, *243*
Alexander & Collins (C), CA, *243*
Alexander Associates (R), NJ, *2*
Alexander Enterprises, Inc. (C), PA, *243*
The Alexander Group (R), TX, *3*
The Alexander Group (R), NJ, *3*
Alexander Ross & Co. (R), NY, *3*
The Alfus Group (R), NY, *3*
The Alice Groves Co., Inc. (C), CT, *244*
Allard Associates (C), CA, *244*
Allen & Assoc. (C), NV, *244*
Frank E. Allen & Assoc. (C), NJ, *244*
Jay Allen & Assoc. (C), FL, *244*
D. S. Allen Assoc. (C), NJ, *244*
David Allen Assoc. (R), NJ, *3*
Allen Austin Lowe & Powers (R), TX, *3*
Allen Consulting Group, Inc. (C), MO, *244*
Allen Evans Assoc. (R), NY, *4*
Allen, Wayne & Co. LLC (C), WI, *245*
Allen-Jeffers Assoc. (C), CA, *245*
Allen/Associates (R), OH, *4*
Allerton Heneghan & O'Neill (R), IL, *4*
Allhands Placement Consultants (C), IN, *245*
Alliance Executive Search, Inc. (R), MA, *4*
Alliance Search Management Inc. (R), TX, *4*
Allied Search, Inc. (C), CA, *245*
Tom Allison Assoc. (C), NM, *245*
Allman & Co., Inc. (C), NC, *245*
Allstaff, Inc. (C), IL, *245*
Alpha Executive Search (C), AL, *245*
Alpha Resource Group, Inc. (C), TX, *246*
Alpha Resources (C), IL, *246*
Alpha Search (C), FL, *246*
The Altco Group (C), NJ, *246*
Altec/HRC (C), MI, *246*
The Alternatives Group, Inc. (C), TX, *246*
ALW Research Int'l. (R), NJ, *4*
Alynco, Inc. (C), AR, *246*
AM & G Certified Public Accountants & Consultants (R), IL, *4*
Amato & Assoc., Inc. (C), CA, *246*
Amato & Associates Insurance Recruiters (C), PA, *247*
Peter W. Ambler Co. (R), TX, *5*
Ambridge Management Corp. (C), ON, *247*
AMD & Associates (C), GA, *247*
American Executive Management, Inc. (R), MA, *5*
American Executive Search (C), FL, *247*
American Group Practice, Inc. (R), NY, *5*
American Heritage Group, Inc. (C), MI, *247*
American Logistics Consultants, Inc. (C), IL, *247*
American Medical Consultants, Inc. (C), FL, *247*
American Medical Recruiters (C), CO, *248*
American Medical Recruiting Co. Inc. (C), MS, *248*
American Professional Search, Inc. (C), TN, *248*
American Resources Corp. (C), IL, *248*
American Services Group (C), IL, *248*
AmeriPro Search, Inc. (C), NC, *248*
AmeriResource Group Inc. (C), OK, *248*
Ames & Ames (R), CA, *5*
Ames Assoc. Inc. (C), MD, *249*
Ames-O'Neill Assoc., Inc. (C), NY, *249*
Amherst Human Resource Group, Ltd. (C), IL, *249*
Amherst Personnel Group Inc. (C), NY, *249*
Aminex Corp. (C), MA, *249*
Amrop International (R), MX, *5*
AMS Int'l. (R), VA, *5*
Analog Solutions (C), NY, *249*
Analytic Recruiting, Inc. (C), NY, *249*
Anderson & Associates (R), NC, *5*
Anderson & Schwab, Inc. (R), NY, *5*
Anderson Bradshaw Assoc., Inc. (R), TX, *6*
Anderson Industrial Assoc., Inc. (C), GA, *250*
Anderson Network Group (C), OH, *250*
Andex Executive Search (C), CT, *250*
Andre David & Assoc., Inc. (R), TX, *6*
The Andre Group, Inc. (R), PA, *6*
Andrews & Assoc. (C), NC, *250*
Andrews & Wald Group (C), FL, *250*
Angel Group Int'l. (C), KY, *250*
Tryg R. Angell, Ltd. (C), CT, *250*
Angus Employment Ltd. (C), ON, *250*
The Angus Group, Ltd. (C), OH, *251*
Ansara, Bickford & Fiske (C), MA, *251*
Fred Anthony Assoc. (C), WI, *251*
Anthony Michael & Co. (C), MA, *251*
APA Employment Agency Inc. (C), OR, *251*
APA Search, Inc. (R), NY, *6*
David Aplin & Assoc. (C), AB, *251*
R. W. Apple & Assoc. (C), NJ, *251*
Applied Resources (C), MA, *252*
Applied Resources, Inc. (C), MN, *252*

(R) = Retainer; (C) = Contingency

Applied Search Assoc., Inc. (C), GA, *252*
Applied Technology Solutions Inc. (C), ON, *252*
Charles P. Aquavella & Assoc. (C), TX, *252*
Argonaut Partners, LLC (R), CA, *6*
The Argus Group Corp. (C), ON, *252*
Argus National, Inc. (R), CT, *6*
ARI Int'l. (R), CA, *6*
Ariail & Assoc. (R), NC, *7*
Ariel Recruitment Assoc. (R), NY, *7*
Aries Search Group (C), GA, *252*
ARJay & Assoc. (C), NC, *252*
Armitage Associates Ltd. (R), ON, *7*
Armor Personnel (C), ON, *253*
J. S. Armstrong & Assoc., Inc. (R), CA, *7*
R & J Arnold & Assoc., Inc. (C), CO, *253*
William B. Arnold Assoc., Inc. (R), CO, *7*
Patrick Arnone & Assoc. Inc. (R), VA, *7*
Aronow Assoc., Inc. (C), FL, *253*
Artgo, Inc. (R), OH, *7*
A. Artze Assoc.-Personnel Consultants (C), PR, *253*
The Ascher Group (R), NJ, *7*
Asheville Search & Consulting (C), NC, *253*
Ashford Management Group, Inc. (R), GA, *7*
Ashlar-Stone Management Consultants Inc. (R), ON, *8*
E. J. Ashton & Assoc., Ltd. (C), IL, *253*
Ashton Computer Professionals, Inc. (C), BC, *253*
Ashway Ltd. Agency (C), NY, *253*
Ashworth Consultants, Inc. (R), MA, *8*
ASI (C), CA, *254*
Ask Guy Tucker (C), GA, *254*
Asset Resource, Inc. (C), CA, *254*
Associated Recruiters (C), WI, *254*
The Associates, HR Search Executives, Inc. (C), OK, *254*
Association Executive Resources Group (R), MD, *8*
Association for Sales Force Management (C), WA, *254*
AST/BRYANT (R), CT, *8*
Aster Search Group (R), NY, *8*
Astro Executive Search Firm (C), LA, *254*
W. R. Atchison & Assoc., Inc. (C), NC, *254*
Atkinson Search & Placement, Inc. (C), IA, *255*
Atlanta Executive Partners, Inc. (R), MA, *8*
Atlantic Pacific Group (C), CA, *255*
Atlantic Search Group, Inc. (C), MA, *255*
Atlantic West Int'l. (C), NC, *255*
Atomic Personnel, Inc. (C), PA, *255*
ATS Executive Recruitment (C), GA, *255*
Attorney Search Global, Inc. (C), IL, *255*
Attorneys at Work (C), GA, *255*
Aubin Int'l. Inc. (R), MA, *8*
Auerbach Associates, Inc. (R), MA, *9*
Aurora Tech Search (C), ON, *256*
A. M. Auster Associates (R), FL, *9*
Cami Austin & Assoc. (C), IL, *256*
Austin - Allen Co. (C), TN, *256*
Austin Group Int'l./Marlar Int'l. (R), TX, *9*
Austin Michaels, Ltd., Inc. (C), AZ, *256*
Austin Park Management Group Inc. (C), ON, *256*
Austin, Hill & Assoc. (C), MD, *256*
Austin-McGregor Int'l. (R), TX, *9*
Automation Technology Search (C), CA, *256*
AutoPeople (C), VT, *257*
Availability Personnel Consultants (C), NH, *257*
Avalon Health Group, Inc. (R), NY, *9*
Avery Assoc. (R), CA, *9*
Avestruz & Assoc. (C), CA, *257*
Avion International Technology Inc. (C), ON, *257*
Avondale Search Int'l., Inc. (R), FL, *9*
The Ayers Group, Inc. (R), NY, *9*
Bader Research Corp. (C), NY, *257*
The Badger Group (R), CA, *10*
Baeder Kalinski Int'l. Group, Inc. (R), NH, *10*
The Baer Group (R), OH, *10*
Keith Bagg & Assoc., Inc. (C), ON, *257*
Bailey Employment System Inc. (C), CT, *257*
D. W. Baird & Associates (C), MD, *257*
Baker Scott & Co. (C), NJ, *258*
Baker, Nelms & Montgomery (C), IL, *258*
Baldwin & Assoc. (C), OH, *258*
Baldwin Associates, LLC (R), CT, *10*
The Baldwin Group (R), IL, *10*
The Bales-Waugh Group (C), FL, *258*
Carol Ball & Co. (C), CT, *258*
Allen Ballach Assoc. Inc. (R), ON, *10*
Ballantyne & Assoc. (R), CA, *10*
Ballos & Co., Inc. (R), NJ, *10*
BallResources (C), MO, *258*
James Bangert & Assoc., Inc. (R), MN, *11*
The Bankers Group (C), IL, *258*
The Bankers Register (C), NY, *259*
Bankers Search, L.L.C. (C), CT, *259*
Paul C. Banks Assoc. (C), GA, *259*
The Barack Group, Inc. (R), NY, *11*
Barber & Assoc. (C), KY, *259*
Barclay Consultants, Inc. (C), NJ, *259*
Barger & Sargeant, Inc. (R), NH, *11*
J. W. Barleycorn, Renard & Assoc., Inc. (R), OH, *11*
Barnes & Assoc. Executive Search (C), CA, *259*
Barnes Development Group, LLC (R), WI, *11*
Fred A. Barnette & Assoc. (R), NC, *11*
Barone Assoc. (C), NJ, *259*
Barone-O'Hara Assoc., Inc. (R), NJ, *11*
Barr Assoc. (C), PA, *259*
Barr Associates (C), NY, *260*
The Barrett Group (C), NH, *260*
Barrett Hospitality Search (R), CA, *12*
Barrett Partners (C), IL, *260*
Barrett Rose & Lee, Inc. (C), ON, *260*
Barrington Hart, Inc. (R), IL, *12*
Nathan Barry Assoc., Inc. (R), MA, *12*
Aldonna Barry Personnel & Management (C), ON, *260*
Barth Smith Company (R), IL, *12*
Bartholdi & Co., Inc. (R), CO, *12*
Bartl & Evins (C), NY, *260*
Barton Assoc., Inc. (R), TX, *12*
The Barton Group, Inc. (C), MI, *260*
Bartz Rogers & Partners (C), MN, *260*
Bason Associates (R), OH, *13*
Bassett Laudi Partners (C), ON, *261*
Bast & Assoc., Inc. (C), CA, *261*
Battalia Winston Int'l./The Euram Consultants Group (R), NY, *13*
L. Battalin & Co. (C), FL, *261*
R. Gaines Baty Assoc., Inc. (R), TX, *13*
Martin H. Bauman Assoc., Inc. (R), NY, *13*
The Bauman Group (R), CA, *14*
Bayland Assoc. (C), CA, *261*
BayResearch Group, Inc. (R), IL, *14*
BCG Search, Inc. (R), FL, *14*
Beach Executive Search Inc. (R), FL, *14*
Beacon Int'l., Inc. (C), VA, *261*
The Beam Group (R), PA, *14*
The Beardsley Group Inc. (C), CT, *261*
Beck/Eastwood Recruitment Solutions (C), CA, *261*
Becker, Norton & Co. (R), PA, *14*
Becker Personnel (C), FL, *262*
Becker Project Resources, Inc. (C), OR, *262*
Beckman & Assoc. Legal Search (C), OH, *262*
The Bedford Consulting Group Inc. (R), ON, *14*
The Bedford Group (R), RI, *15*
Robert Beech West Inc. (C), CA, *262*
Behavioral Science Assoc., Inc. (R), AZ, *15*
Behrens and Company (C), WA, *262*
Neail Behringer Consultants Inc. (R), NY, *15*
Marcia Beilin, Inc. (C), NY, *262*
Belanger Partners Ltd. (C), ON, *262*
Edward Bell Assoc. (C), CA, *263*
Gary S. Bell Assoc., Inc. (C), NJ, *263*
William Bell Assoc., Inc. (C), NJ, *263*
Bell Oaks Co., Inc. (C), GA, *263*
Bell Wishingrad Partners Inc. (R), NY, *15*
Bellamy & Assoc. (C), GA, *263*
Joy Reed Belt Search Consultants, Inc. (R), OK, *15*
Benamati & Assoc. (C), CO, *263*
Bench Int'l. Search, Inc. (R), CA, *15*
J. P. Bencik Assoc. (C), MI, *263*
Richard L. Bencin & Assoc. (C), OH, *264*
Bender Executive Search Management Consulting (R), NY, *16*
Benford & Assoc., Inc. (C), MI, *264*
N. L. Benke & Assoc., Inc. (C), OH, *264*
Bennett & Associates (C), TX, *264*
Bennett & Co. Consulting Group (C), CA, *264*
Robert Bennett Assoc. (C), NY, *264*
The Bennett Group, Inc. (R), IN, *16*
Bennett Search & Consulting Co. (R), FL, *16*
Benson Associates (C), NY, *264*
Dick Berg & Assoc. (C), CA, *264*
Berger & Leff (C), CA, *264*
C. Berger And Company (R), IL, *16*
Bergeris & Co., Inc. (C), NY, *265*
Berglund Int'l. Resources, Inc. (C), TX, *265*
Berkana Int'l., Inc. (C), WA, *265*
Berkhemer/Clayton, Inc. (R), CA, *16*
Berkshire Search Assoc. (C), MA, *265*
Berman & Larson (C), NJ, *265*
Bernhart Assoc. (C), MN, *265*

Ed Bertolas Assoc., Inc. (C), CA, *265*
Jack Bertram, Executive Recruiter (C), PA, *265*
Bertrand, Ross & Assoc., Inc. (C), IL, *266*
Besen Assoc. Inc. (C), NJ, *266*
Best, Coleman & Co., Inc. (R), MA, *16*
BEST/World Assoc. Inc. (R), TX, *16*
BFW, Inc. (C), GA, *266*
BG & Assoc. (C), MD, *266*
BGB Assoc., Inc. (C), IL, *266*
Bialecki Inc. (R), NY, *17*
Bialla & Assoc. Inc. (R), CA, *17*
Bickerton & Gordon LLC (C), MA, *266*
Paul J. Biestek Assoc., Inc. (R), IL, *17*
Billington & Assoc. (R), CA, *17*
Binder Hospitality Group (C), KY, *266*
Bio-Venture Group (C), RI, *266*
Biomedical Search Consultants (R), CT, *17*
BioPharmMed (C), FL, *267*
BioQuest Inc. (R), CA, *17*
BioTech Research Recruiters Inc. (C), CA, *267*
Birch & Associes (C), QE, *267*
Deborah Bishop & Assoc. (R), CA, *17*
Bishop Partners (R), NY, *17*
BJB Assoc. (C), VA, *267*
The Black Leopard (C), CA, *267*
Blackhawk Advantage, Inc. (C), CA, *267*
The Blackman Kallick Search Division (C), IL, *267*
Blackshaw, Olmstead, Lynch & Koenig (R), GA, *18*
Blair/Tech Recruiters, Inc. (C), NJ, *268*
Blake/Hansen Ltd. (R), FL, *18*
J: Blakslee Int'l., Ltd. (R), CA, *18*
Blane, Stevens & Kellogg (C), FL, *268*
Blaney Executive Search (R), MA, *18*
Blanton & Co. (C), AL, *268*
Blau Mancino Schroeder (R), NJ, *18*
BLB Consulting (C), NY, *268*
David Blevins & Assoc. (C), WA, *268*
Block & Assoc. (R), CA, *18*
D. R. Blood & Assoc. (R), AZ, *18*
The Howard C. Bloom Co. (C), TX, *268*
Blue Chip Law Consulting, Inc. (C), CA, *268*
Blum & Co. (R), WI, *19*
The BMW Group, Inc. (C), NY, *268*
Boardroom Consultants/Kenny Kindler Tholke (R), NY, *19*
Bodner Inc. (C), NY, *268*
Boettcher Assoc. (R), WI, *19*
Tom Bogle & Assoc. (C), CA, *269*
Mark Bolno & Assoc. (C), FL, *269*
Bolton Group (C), CA, *269*
Ann Bond Assoc. Inc. (C), MD, *269*
Bonell Ryan Inc. (R), NY, *19*
Bonifield Assoc. (C), NJ, *269*
Bonnell Assoc. Ltd. (R), CT, *19*
John C. Boone & Co. (R), IL, *19*
Boone-Scaturro Assoc., Inc. (C), GA, *269*
Bor-Maq Assoc. (C), TX, *269*
Borchert Assoc. (C), TX, *269*
Born & Bicknell, Inc. (C), FL, *270*
Lynn Borne & Co. (C), CA, *270*
Bornholdt Shivas & Friends Executive Recruiters (C), NY, *270*
The Borton Wallace Co. (R), NC, *19*
Bos Business Consultants (C), NY, *270*
Bosch & Assoc., LLC (R), CT, *19*
Bosco-Hubert & Assoc. (C), KS, *270*
Bosland Gray Assoc. (R), NJ, *20*
Boston Professional Search, Inc. (C), MA, *270*
Boulware & Assoc. Inc. (R), IL, *20*
Bowden & Co., Inc. (R), OH, *20*
BowdenGlobal, Ltd. (R), OH, *20*
Howard Bowen Consulting (C), FL, *270*
Bower & Associates (C), TX, *271*
BowersThomas (C), CA, *271*
Bowie & Associates, Inc. (C), MD, *271*
Bowman & Assoc. (C), CA, *271*
Bowman & Marshall, Inc. (C), KS, *271*
Boyden (R), NY, *20*
Boyle/Ogata Executive Search (R), CA, *21*
BR & Assoc. (C), NJ, *271*
The Bradbury Management Group, Inc. (R), CA, *21*
Bradford & Galt, Inc. (C), MO, *271*
Bradford Executives Int'l. (C), VA, *271*
Bradley & Assoc. (C), MN, *272*
M. F. Branch Assoc., Inc. (C), NC, *272*
The Brand Co., Inc. (R), FL, *22*
Brandjes Assoc. (C), MD, *272*
Brandt Associates (C), PA, *272*
Brandywine Consulting Group (R), PA, *22*
Brandywine Management Group (R), MD, *22*
Brandywine Retained Ventures, Inc. (R), CT, *22*
Branthover Assoc. (C), NY, *272*
Bratland & Assoc. (C), IL, *272*
Brault & Assoc., Ltd. (R), VA, *22*
Jerold Braun & Assoc. (C), CA, *272*
Bredeson Executive Recruitment, LLC (R), TX, *22*
Brei & Assoc., Inc. (C), IA, *272*
The Bren Group (C), AZ, *273*
The Brentwood Group, Inc. (R), NJ, *22*
The Brentwood Group Ltd. (R), OR, *23*
Brentwood Int'l. (R), CA, *23*
Brethet, Barnum & Assoc., Inc. (C), ON, *273*
Brett Personnel Specialists (C), NJ, *273*
Brian Assoc., Inc. (C), NY, *273*
Briant Assoc., Inc. (R), IL, *23*
The Bridge (C), CO, *273*
Bridgecreek Personnel Agency (C), CA, *273*
BridgeGate LLC (C), CA, *273*
Brierwood Group, Inc. (C), IN, *273*
Brigade, Inc. (R), CA, *23*
Bright Search/Professional Staffing (C), MN, *274*
Brindisi Search (R), MD, *23*
Brissenden, McFarland, Fuccella & Reynolds, Inc. (R), NJ, *23*
Bristol Assoc., Inc. (C), CA, *274*
Britt Assoc., Inc. (C), IL, *274*
Broad Waverly & Assoc. (C), NJ, *274*
Broadband Resource Group (C), CA, *274*
The Broadmoor Group, L.L.C. (R), TX, *23*
Dan B. Brockman (C), IL, *274*
Brooke Chase Assoc., Inc. (R), IL, *24*
Brookman Associates (C), NY, *274*
Bernard E. Brooks & Assoc., Inc. (R), SC, *24*
Broward-Dobbs, Inc. (C), GA, *274*
D. Brown & Assoc., Inc. (C), OR, *275*
J. B. Brown & Assoc., Inc. (C), OH, *275*
Brown, Bernardy, Van Remmen, Inc. (C), CA, *275*
Brown Venture Assoc. (R), CA, *24*
Brownstone Sales & Marketing Group, Inc. (C), NY, *275*
Brush Creek Partners (R), MO, *24*
BRW Search (C), MN, *275*
Bryan & Louis Research (C), OH, *275*
Bryan, Jason & Assoc. Inc. (C), ON, *275*
Bryant Research (C), NJ, *275*
Brystol Cove Assoc. (R), CA, *24*
BT&A, LLC (R), CT, *24*
Charles Buck & Assoc., Inc. (R), NY, *24*
The Buckley Group (C), FL, *276*
Buckman/Enochs & Assoc., Inc. (C), OH, *276*
Bullis & Co., Inc. (R), CA, *25*
The Burgess Group-Corporate Recruiters Int'l., Inc. (R), NY, *25*
J. Burke & Assoc., Inc. (C), TX, *276*
Burke & Assoc./The Westfield Group (C), CT, *276*
The Burke Group (C), ON, *276*
Burke, O'Brien & Bishop Assoc., Inc. (R), NJ, *25*
J. Burkey Assoc. (R), NJ, *25*
Burkholder & Assoc., Inc. (C), TX, *276*
Joseph R. Burns & Assoc., Inc. (R), NJ, *25*
David S. Burt Assoc. (C), MT, *276*
Busch International (R), CA, *25*
Business Partners, Inc. (C), FL, *277*
Business Solutions Worldwide, Inc. (C), NJ, *277*
Business Systems of America, Inc. (C), IL, *277*
The Butlers Co. Insurance Recruiters (C), FL, *277*
Butterfass, Pepe & MacCallan Inc. (R), NJ, *25*
Butterfield & Co. Int'l., Inc. (C), HI, *277*
Button Group (C), TX, *277*
Buzhardt Assoc. (R), MS, *25*
Byron Leonard Int'l., Inc. (R), CA, *25*
C & H Personnel (C), PA, *277*
C and P Marketing, Ltd. (C), OK, *278*
C Assoc. (C), DC, *278*
C. G. & Assoc. (R), PA, *26*
C. M. Management Services, Inc. (R), KY, *26*
C. P. Consulting (R), PA, *26*
C. R. Assoc. (C), CA, *278*
The C.P.R. Group (C), NJ, *278*
C.P.S., Inc. (C), IL, *278*
C.T.E.W. Executive Personnel Services Inc. (C), BC, *278*
C/R Associates (C), NY, *278*
Cadillac Assoc. (C), CA, *278*
CadTech Staffing Services (C), GA, *279*
Cahill Assoc. (C), CT, *279*
Juliette Lang Cahn Executive Search (C), NY, *279*
Robert Caldwell & Assoc. (R), CA, *26*
Caldwell Legal Recruiting Consultants (C), ME, *279*
The Caldwell Partners Amrop International (R), ON, *26*
Lee Calhoon & Co., Inc. (R), PA, *26*

Caliber Associates (R), PA, *27*
California Management Search (C), CA, *279*
California Search Agency, Inc. (C), CA, *279*
Callan Assoc., Ltd. (R), IL, *27*
Callos Personnel Services (C), OH, *279*
Cambridge Group Ltd. - Exec. Search Div. (C), CT, *279*
The Cambridge Group Ltd. (C), CT, *280*
Cambridge Management Planning (R), ON, *27*
Cameron Consulting Group (R), CA, *27*
Campa & Assoc. (R), ON, *27*
T. M. Campbell Co. (R), WA, *27*
Campbell, Edgar Inc. (C), BC, *280*
Canadian Career Partners (R), AB, *27*
CanMed Consultants Inc. (C), ON, *280*
Canny, Bowen Inc. (R), NY, *27*
J. P. Canon Assoc. (C), NY, *280*
The Canon Group (C), CA, *280*
The Cantor Concern, Inc. (R), NY, *28*
Cantrell & Assoc. (C), FL, *280*
Canyon Consulting, Inc. (C), TX, *281*
Capital Consulting & Research, Inc. (R), CT, *28*
Capital Consulting Group, Inc. (R), MD, *28*
Capital Markets Resources, Inc. (C), NC, *281*
Capitol Management Consulting, Inc. (C), NJ, *281*
Sally Caplan & Assoc. (C), WA, *281*
Caplan Assoc., Inc. (R), NJ, *28*
The Caplan-Taylor Group (R), CA, *28*
Caprio & Assoc. Inc. (R), IL, *29*
Capstone Consulting, Inc. (R), IL, *29*
Capstone Inc. (R), NY, *29*
Cardwell Enterprises Inc. (R), IL, *29*
Career +Plus (C), NY, *281*
Career Advisors, Inc. (C), FL, *281*
Career Alternatives Executive Search (C), MI, *281*
Career Consultants (R), IN, *29*
Career Consulting Group, Inc. (C), CT, *281*
Career Counseling Inc. (CCI) (C), KY, *282*
Career Counseling Ltd. (C.C.L.) (C), NY, *282*
Career Development Associates (C), NV, *282*
Career Enterprises (C), OH, *282*
Career Images (C), FL, *282*
Career Marketing Assoc., Inc. (C), CO, *282*
Career Marketing Consultants, Inc. (C), GA, *282*
Career Profiles (C), NH, *283*
Career Search Group (C), FL, *283*
Career Specialists, Inc. (R), WA, *29*
Career Strategies, Inc. (C), CA, *283*
Careerfit, Inc. (C), TX, *283*
Careers First, Inc. (C), NJ, *283*
Careers On Track (C), NJ, *283*
Careers Plus (R), CA, *29*
Careers/Inc. (C), PR, *284*
The Carey Company (C), NC, *284*
Carion Resource Group Inc. (C), ON, *284*
Carlsen Resources, Inc. (R), CO, *29*
Carlson & Czeswik (R), MN, *30*
The Carlyle Group, Ltd. (R), IL, *30*
Carnegie Partners, Inc. (R), IL, *30*
Carnegie Resources, Inc. (C), NC, *284*
Carpenter & Assoc. (C), TX, *284*
Carpenter Assoc., Inc. (R), IL, *30*
Carpenter Legal Search (C), PA, *284*
Carpenter, Shackleton & Company (R), IL, *30*
Carr Management Services, Inc. (C), PA, *284*
Carrington & Carrington, Ltd. (R), IL, *30*
Carris, Jackowitz Assoc. (R), NY, *30*
K. Carroll & Assoc. (C), IL, *284*
Carson-Thomas & Assoc. (C), CA, *284*
Carter, Lavoie Associates (C), RI, *285*
Carter McKenzie, Inc. (C), NJ, *285*
Carter-Evdemon & Assoc. (C), FL, *285*
Carter/MacKay (C), NJ, *285*
Caruso & Assoc., Inc. (R), FL, *31*
Caruthers & Co., L.L.C. (R), CT, *31*
Carver Search Consultants (C), CA, *285*
The CARVIR Group, Inc. (C), GA, *285*
Cary & Assoc. (R), FL, *31*
CAS Comsearch Inc. (C), NY, *285*
Case Executive Search (C), MI, *286*
Casey & Assoc., Inc. (C), TX, *286*
Rosemary Cass Ltd. (R), CT, *31*
Cassell & Kaye (C), NY, *286*
The Cassie Group (R), NJ, *31*
Catalyx Group (R), NY, *31*
Michael J. Cavanagh & Assoc. Inc. (R), ON, *31*
Caywood Partners, Ltd. (R), CA, *32*
CBA Companies (C), CA, *286*
CCI - Career Consultants Int'l. (C), CA, *286*
CEC Associates (R), MA, *32*
Malin Cederquist, Esq. (C), NY, *286*
Cejka Healthcare Executive Search Services (CHESS) (R), MO, *32*
Cella Assoc. (C), GA, *286*
Cemco, Ltd. (C), IL, *286*
Cendea Connection Int'l. (R), TX, *32*
The Center for Career Advancement, LLC (C), NJ, *287*
Central Executive Search, Inc. (C), OH, *287*
Century Assoc., Inc. (C), PA, *287*
The Century Group (C), CA, *287*
The Century Group (C), KS, *287*
CEO Consulting (C), FL, *287*
CFOs 2 Go (C), CA, *288*
cFour Partners (R), CA, *32*
CFR Executive Search, Inc. (C), IL, *288*
Chacra, Belliveau & Assoc. Inc. (C), QE, *288*
Chad Management Group (C), ON, *288*
Chadwell & Assoc., Inc. (C), MI, *288*
Chaloner Assoc. (R), MA, *32*
Wayne S. Chamberlain & Assoc. (C), CA, *288*
Chamberlain Assoc. (C), GA, *288*
David Chambers & Assoc., Inc. (R), CT, *32*
Vickers Chambless Managed Search (C), GA, *288*
Elsie Chan & Assoc. (C), CA, *289*
Joseph Chandler & Assoc., Inc. (R), IL, *33*
Chanko-Ward, Ltd. (R), NY, *33*
Chapman & Assoc. (C), BC, *289*
The Chapman Group, Inc. (C), AZ, *289*
Charet & Assoc. (C), NJ, *289*
Charles & Associates, Inc. (C), NE, *289*
Robert L. Charon (C), TX, *289*
Chase Partners (R), ON, *33*
Chase-Gardner Executive Search Associates, Inc. (C), FL, *289*
ChaseAmerica, Inc. (R), FL, *33*
The Chatham Group, Ltd. (C), CT, *289*
Chatham Search Assoc., Inc. (C), NJ, *290*
A. D. Check Assoc., Inc. (R), PA, *33*
Chelsea Resources, Inc. (C), CT, *290*
Cheney Associates (C), CT, *290*
The Cherbonnier Group, Inc. (R), TX, *33*
Chesapeake Group (C), CT, *290*
Chicago Legal Search, Ltd. (C), IL, *290*
Chicago Research Group, Inc. (R), NC, *33*
China Human Resources Group (R), NJ, *33*
Chrisman & Co. Inc. (R), CA, *33*
Christenson Hutchison McDowell, LLC (R), NJ, *34*
Christian & Timbers, Inc. (R), OH, *34*
R. Christine Assoc. (C), PA, *290*
Christmas, McIvor & Assoc. Inc. (C), ON, *290*
Christopher and Long (C), MO, *291*
William J. Christopher Assoc., Inc. (R), PA, *34*
The Christopher Group (C), NC, *291*
Christopher-Westmont & Assoc., Inc. (R), OH, *34*
J. F. Church Associates (C), WA, *291*
Churchill & Affiliates, Inc. (R), PA, *35*
M. A. Churchill & Assoc., Inc. (R), PA, *35*
The Churchill Group (C), ON, *291*
Circlewood Search Group, Inc. (C), MI, *291*
Circuit Search (C), NY, *291*
Cizek Assoc., Inc. (R), AZ, *35*
CJA-The Adler Group, Inc. (R), CA, *35*
CJSI-Cindy Jackson Search Int'l. (C), CA, *291*
Claimsearch (C), CA, *291*
Clanton & Co. (C), CA, *292*
Arlene Clapp, Ltd. (R), MN, *35*
Claremont-Branan, Inc. (C), GA, *292*
Clarey & Andrews, Inc. (R), IL, *35*
Clarey/Napier Int'l., L.C. (R), TX, *35*
Howard Clark Assoc. (C), NJ, *292*
Toby Clark Assoc. Inc. (C), NY, *292*
Clark Executive Search (C), NY, *292*
The Clark Group (C), MI, *292*
Ken Clark Int'l. (R), NJ, *36*
Clark Personnel Service, Inc. (C), AL, *292*
Richard Clarke Assoc., Inc. (R), NY, *36*
Clayman & Co. (R), MA, *36*
The Clayton Edward Group (C), MI, *292*
Clinton, Charles, Wise & Co. (C), FL, *293*
CMC Search Consultants (C), IL, *293*
CMS, Inc. (C), NH, *293*
CMS Management Services LLC (C), IN, *293*
CMW & Associates, Inc. (C), IL, *293*
CN Associates (C), CA, *293*
Coast Personnel Services Ltd. (C), BC, *293*
Coastal Int'l., Inc. (R), MA, *36*
COBA Executive Search (R), CO, *36*
Cochran, Cochran & Yale, Inc. (R), NY, *36*
Ann Coe & Assoc. (C), IL, *294*
Coe & Co. Int'l. Inc./EMA Partners Int'l. (R), AB, *37*

Dean M. Coe Assoc. (R), MA, *37*
The Coelyn Group (R), CA, *37*
Cole, Warren & Long, Inc. (R), PA, *37*
J. Kevin Coleman & Assoc., Inc. (R), CA, *37*
Coleman Legal Search Consultants (C), PA, *294*
Coleman Lew & Assoc., Inc. (R), NC, *37*
Collins & Associates (C), MI, *294*
S L Collins Assoc. (C), NC, *294*
Colt Systems Professional Personnel Services (C), CA, *294*
Colton Bernard Inc. (R), CA, *37*
The Colton Partnership, Inc. (R), NY, *38*
Colucci, Blendow & Johnson (R), CA, *38*
Columbia Consulting Group (R), MD, *38*
Combined Resources Inc. (R), OH, *38*
Commercial Programming Systems, Inc. (C), CA, *294*
Commonwealth Consultants (C), GA, *294*
Compass Group Ltd. (R), MI, *38*
Comprehensive Search (C), GA, *294*
CompuPro (C), IL, *295*
Computer Int'l. Consultants, Inc. (C), FL, *295*
Computer Network Resources, Inc. (C), CA, *295*
Computer Personnel, Inc. (C), WA, *295*
Computer Placements Unlimited Inc. (C), NY, *295*
Computer Professionals (R), IL, *38*
Computer Professionals Unlimited (C), TX, *295*
Computer Recruiters, Inc. (C), CA, *295*
Computer Search Group, Ltd. (R), IL, *39*
Computer Security Placement Service (C), MA, *296*
The Comwell Company, Inc. (C), NJ, *296*
Conard Associates, Inc. (R), NH, *39*
Conasa de Mexico, S.C. (R), MX, *39*
Concorde Search Assoc. (C), NY, *296*
Concorde Staff Source Inc. (C), WI, *296*
Conex Inc./InterSearch (R), NY, *39*
Robert Connelly & Assoc., Inc. (R), MN, *39*
M. L. Conner (C), FL, *296*
Connors, Lovell & Assoc. Inc. (C), ON, *296*
Conroy Partners Ltd. (R), AB, *39*
Consolidated Management Services (C), ON, *296*
The Consortium (C), NY, *296*
Conspectus, Inc. (C), NY, *297*
Construct Management Services (C), MN, *297*
Construction Search Specialists, Inc. (C), WI, *297*
Consulpro (R), ON, *39*
Consultant Recruiters (C), WI, *297*
The Consulting Group Ltd. (R), NY, *40*
The Consulting Group of North America, Inc. (C), VA, *297*
Consulting Resource Group, Inc. (C), GA, *297*
Consulting Rhonda (C), ON, *297*
Consumer Search Inc. (C), MA, *298*
ContactBridge, Inc. (R), IL, *40*
Continental Research Search, Inc. (C), WI, *298*
Continental Search & Outplacement, Inc. (C), MD, *298*
Continental Search Assoc. (C), OH, *298*
Conway & Assoc. (R), IL, *40*
Philip Conway Management (R), IL, *40*
Cook Assoc. Int'l., Inc. (C), TN, *298*
P. G. Cook Assoc. (R), TN, *40*
Cook Assoc.,® Inc. (R), IL, *40*
The Cooke Group (R), WI, *40*
David C. Cooper & Assoc. Financial Search (C), GA, *298*
Cooper Assoc., Inc. (C), NY, *298*
The Cooper Executive Search Group Inc. (R), WI, *41*
Cooper Management Assoc., Inc. (C), NJ, *298*
COR Management Services, Ltd. (C), NY, *298*
Corbin Packaging Professionals (C), MO, *299*
Cornell Group Int'l. Consulting, Inc. (R), NY, *41*
Cornerstone Resources, Inc. (C), OK, *299*
Cornerstone Search Assoc. Inc. (C), MA, *299*
Cornwall Stockton & Co., Inc. (C), TX, *299*
Corporate Advisors, Inc. (C), FL, *299*
The Corporate Advisory Group (R), NJ, *41*
Corporate Builders, Inc. (C), OR, *299*
Corporate Careers, Inc. (C), CA, *299*
The Corporate Connection, Ltd. (C), VA, *299*
Corporate Dynamix (C), AZ, *300*
Corporate Environment Ltd. (R), IL, *41*
Corporate Image Group (C), TN, *300*
Corporate Leadership Strategies, Inc. (R), NH, *41*
Corporate Management Services (C), PA, *300*
Corporate Plus, Ltd. (C), GA, *300*
Corporate Recruiters Inc. (C), PA, *300*
Corporate Recruiters Ltd. (C), BC, *300*
Corporate Resources Professional Placement (C), MN, *300*
Corporate Resources (C), OH, *301*
Corporate Search Consultants, Inc. (C), FL, *301*
Corporate Search Consultants (C), IN, *301*
Corporate Search, Inc. (C), NY, *301*
Corporate Select Int'l., Ltd. (C), IL, *301*
The Corporate Source Group, Inc. (R), MA, *41*
Corporate Staffing Group, Inc. (C), PA, *301*
Corporate Suite, Ltd. (C), IA, *301*
Corrao, Miller, Rush & Wiesenthal (C), NY, *301*
The Corrigan Group (R), CA, *42*
Corso, Mizgala + French (R), ON, *42*
Leonard Corwen Assoc. (C), NY, *302*
Cosier & Assoc. (C), AB, *302*
J. D. Cotter Search Inc. (C), OH, *302*
CountryHouse Hotels Executive Search (C), VA, *302*
Courtright & Assoc., Inc. (R), PA, *42*
Cowell & Associates, Ltd. (R), IL, *42*
Cowin Assoc. (R), NY, *42*
Trudi Cowlan (C), NY, *302*
Cox, Darrow & Owens, Inc. (C), NJ, *302*
Craig Affiliates, Inc. (C), TX, *302*
Crane, Reed & Co., Inc. (C), NH, *302*
The Crawford Group (C), GA, *303*
Creative Financial Staffing Inc. (C), ON, *303*
Creative Financial Staffing (C), MA, *303*
Creative HR Solutions (C), GA, *303*
Creative Input, Inc. (C), RI, *303*
Creative Management Strategies, Ltd. (R), NY, *42*
Creative-Leadership, Inc. (R), CA, *42*
CRI Professional Search (C), CA, *303*
The Cris Group, Inc. (R), NY, *42*
Crispi, Wagner & Co., Inc. (R), NY, *43*
Crist Partners, Ltd. (R), IL, *43*
Marlene Critchfield Co. (C), CA, *303*
Criterion Executive Search, Inc. (C), FL, *303*
Cromwell Partners, Inc. (R), NY, *43*
Cross Country Consultants, Inc. (C), MD, *304*
Crowder & Company (R), MI, *43*
Crowe Chizek & Co. (C), IN, *304*
Timothy D. Crowe, Jr. (R), MA, *43*
Crown Advisors, Inc. (R), PA, *43*
Jim Crumpley & Assoc. (C), MO, *304*
CS Associates, LLC (C), AZ, *304*
CSA/Clinical Staffing Assoc., LLC (C), NJ, *304*
CTR (R), CA, *43*
Culver Personnel Services (C), CA, *304*
Cumberland Group Inc. (C), IL, *304*
Cumberland Professional Search Inc. (C), TN, *304*
Frank Cuomo & Assoc., Inc. (C), NY, *305*
M. J. Curran & Assoc., Inc. (R), MA, *43*
Curran Partners, Inc. (R), CT, *44*
Current Resource Group, Inc. (C), GA, *305*
The Currier-Winn Co., Inc. (C), NJ, *305*
Curry, Telleri Group, Inc. (R), NJ, *44*
Tony Curtis & Associates (C), ON, *305*
The Curtiss Group International (R), FL, *44*
Cusack Consulting (R), NY, *44*
Judith Cushman & Assoc. (R), WA, *44*
The Custer Group, Inc. (R), TN, *44*
Custom Resources (C), AL, *305*
CV Associates (C), NY, *305*
Cyberna Assoc. Ltd. (C), QE, *305*
Cybernautic Corp. (C), CT, *305*
Cyntal Int'l. Ltd. (R), NY, *44*
Cypress Int'l., Inc. (R), FL, *45*
Cyr Associates, Inc. (C), MA, *306*
D & M Associates (C), PA, *306*
D.A.I Human Resources Consultants (R), QE, *45*
D.A.L. Associates, Inc. (R), CT, *45*
D.P. Specialists, Inc. (C), CA, *306*
D.R. Assoc. (R), CA, *45*
Daggett & Kvistad (R), CA, *45*
Charles Dahl Group, Inc. (C), MN, *306*
Dahl-Morrow Int'l. (R), VA, *45*
The Dalley Hewitt Co. (R), GA, *45*
Dalton Management Consultants, Ltd. (C), NJ, *306*
Damon & Assoc., Inc. (C), TX, *306*
The Danbrook Group, Inc. (C), TX, *306*
Daniel Marks Company (C), OH, *306*
Alfred Daniels & Assoc., Inc. (R), CA, *46*

The Danielson Group, Inc. (C), TX, *306*
Dankowski & Assoc., Inc. (C), OH, *307*
Dapexs Consultants, Inc. (C), NY, *307*
DARE Personnel Inc. (C), ON, *307*
Alan Darling Consulting (R), VT, *46*
The Dartmouth Group (R), NY, *46*
Data Bank Executive Search (R), OH, *46*
Data Search Network, Inc. (C), FL, *307*
Data-AxIS Corp. (C), FL, *307*
The DataFinders Group, Inc. (C), NJ, *307*
Datamatics Management Services, Inc. (C), NJ, *307*
DataPro Personnel Consultants (C), TX, *308*
Daubenspeck & Associates, Ltd. (R), IL, *46*
Daudlin, De Beaupre & Co., Inc. (R), MI, *46*
Alan N. Daum & Assoc., Inc. (C), OH, *308*
David Anthony Personnel Assoc., Inc. (C), NJ, *308*
David Perry Assoc. (C), NJ, *308*
Davidson, Laird & Assoc. (C), MI, *308*
Davies, Park (R), AB, *46*
Allen Davis & Assoc. (C), MA, *308*
Alan Davis & Assoc. Inc. (R), QE, *47*
John J. Davis & Assoc., Inc. (R), NY, *47*
Davis & Company (R), CA, *47*
Davis & James, Inc. (C), MO, *308*
Donna Davis Assoc. (C), NJ, *309*
Carolyn Davis Assoc., Inc. (C), NY, *309*
Joseph A. Davis Consultants, Inc. (R), NY, *47*
Bert Davis Executive Search, Inc. (R), NY, *47*
Bert Davis Publishing Placement Consultants (C), NY, *309*
Davis-Smith, Inc. (C), MI, *309*
The Dayton Group, Ltd. (C), NY, *309*
DBC Recruiting Network (C), GA, *309*
DBL Associates (C), CA, *309*
DCA Professional Search (C), TX, *309*
De Funiak & Edwards (R), IN, *47*
Dean-Dzierzawiec Assoc. (C), NJ, *309*
Dean-MacDonald (R), OH, *47*
Debbon Recruiting Group, Inc. (C), MO, *310*
DeCaster Assoc. (C), WI, *310*
DeCorrevont & Assoc. (C), IL, *310*
Deeco Int'l. (C), UT, *310*
Defrain Mayer (R), KS, *48*
DEL Technical Services, Inc. (C), IL, *310*
Delacore Resources (C), MN, *310*
DeLalla - Fried Assoc. (C), NY, *310*
Thorndike Deland Assoc. LLC (R), NY, *48*
S. W. Delano & Co. (R), CT, *48*
Delphi Systems, Ltd. (R), MO, *48*
Delta Management Group Ltd. (C), ON, *310*
Delta Medical Search Assoc. (C), OH, *310*
Delta ProSearch (C), PA, *311*
Delta Resource Group, Ltd. (C), GA, *311*
Delta Services (R), TX, *48*
DeMatteo Associates (C), NY, *311*
Derek Associates, Inc. (C), MA, *311*
Derhak Ireland & Partners Ltd. (R), ON, *48*
Descheneaux Recruitment Services Ltd. (C), BC, *311*
Desktop Staffing, Inc. (C), IL, *311*
Despres & Associates (C), IL, *311*
Development Resource Group (R), NY, *48*
Development Search Specialists (R), MN, *49*
The Devlin Search Group, Inc. (C), MA, *311*
Devoto & Assoc. (C), CA, *312*
Rob Dey Executive Search (R), FL, *49*
DHR Int'l., Inc. (R), IL, *49*
Diamond Tax Recruiting (C), NY, *312*
Dieckmann & Assoc., Ltd. (R), IL, *51*
DieckMueller Group (R), WI, *51*
The Diestel Group (R), UT, *51*
Roger Dietsch & Assoc. (C), MN, *312*
DiMarchi Partners (R), CO, *51*
J. Dinerstein & Co., Inc. (R), NY, *51*
Robert W. Dingman Co., Inc. (R), CA, *52*
Dinte Resources, Inc. (R), VA, *52*
Direct Marketing Resources (C), NC, *312*
Direct Marketing Solutions (C), KY, *312*
Direct Recruiters, Inc. (C), OH, *312*
Discovery, The Staffing Specialists, Inc. (C), IL, *312*
Dise & Co. (R), OH, *52*
R. J. Dishaw & Assoc. (R), TX, *52*
DiTech Resources (C), CT, *313*
Diversified Consulting Services, Inc. (C), CO, *313*
Diversified Health Search (R), PA, *52*
Diversified Management Resources (C), IL, *313*
Diversified Search, Inc. (R), PA, *52*
Dixie Search Assoc. (C), GA, *313*
DLB Assoc. (R), NY, *53*
DLG Assoc., Inc. (R), NC, *53*
DNA Search, Inc. (C), CA, *313*
Doering & Assoc. (C), CA, *313*
L. J. Doherty & Assoc. (R), MA, *53*
Doherty Healthcare Consultants (C), ME, *313*
Doherty Int'l., Inc. (R), IL, *53*
Doleman Enterprises (R), VA, *53*
The Domann Organization (R), CA, *53*
Dominguez-Metz & Assoc. (R), CA, *53*
Domres Professional Search (R), WI, *53*
Don Allan Assoc., Inc. (C), CA, *313*
Donahue/Bales Assoc. (R), IL, *54*
Donini Assoc. (R), VA, *54*
J P Donnelly Assoc., Inc. (C), NY, *314*
The Donnelly Group-Sales Recruiters, Inc. (C), MO, *314*
The Dorfman Group (C), AZ, *314*
Dorst Information Services, Inc. (C), NY, *314*
Dotson & Assoc. (R), NY, *54*
The Doty Group (C), TX, *314*
Dougherty & Assoc. (C), TN, *314*
Cal Douglas Executive Search, Inc. (R), PA, *54*
Douglas-Allen, Inc. (R), MA, *54*
Dow Consultants Int'l. (C), NY, *314*
CS Dowling Executive Services (R), NJ, *54*
Downing & Downing, Inc. (C), OH, *314*
Drake & Assoc. (C), CA, *315*
Dreier Consulting (C), NJ, *315*
Drew Assoc. Int'l. (R), NJ, *54*
Robert Drexler Assoc., Inc. (R), NJ, *54*
Drinkwater & Assoc. (R), MA, *54*
Dromeshauser Assoc. (R), MA, *55*
Drummond Assoc., Inc. (C), NY, *315*
DRZ Medical Recruiters (C), CO, *315*
DS&A (Doug Sears & Assoc.) (C), FL, *315*
DSR-Search & Recruitment (C), TX, *315*
DuBrul Management Co. (C), NY, *315*
J. H. Dugan & Assoc., Inc. (R), CA, *55*
Dukas Assoc. (C), MA, *315*
Dumont & Co. (C), BC, *316*
M. Dunbar & Assoc. (C), TX, *316*
The Duncan-O'Dell Group Inc. (C), TX, *316*
Dunhill Staffing Systems, Inc. (C), NY, *316*
Dunhill of Ft. Collins, Inc. (C), CO, *319*
Dunhill Professional Search of San Jose (C), CA, *319*
Dunhill Professional Search of Oakland (C), CA, *319*
Dunhill Executive Search of Los Angeles, Inc. (C), CA, *319*
Dunhill Professional Search of Englewood, Inc. (C), CO, *319*
Dunhill Personnel of Boulder (C), CO, *319*
Dunhill Professional Search of Miami (C), FL, *319*
Dunhill of San Francisco, Inc. (C), CA, *319*
Dunhill of Ft. Wayne, Inc. (C), IN, *320*
Dunhill Professional Search of Tampa (C), FL, *320*
Dunhill Technical Staffing (C), IN, *320*
Dunhill Search of West Atlanta (C), GA, *320*
Dunhill Professional Search of Augusta (C), GA, *320*
Dunhill Professional Search of Hawaii (C), HI, *320*
Dunhill Professional Search of Rolling Meadows (C), IL, *320*
Dunhill Professional Search of Byram (C), MS, *321*
Dunhill Professional Search of Omaha, Inc. (C), NE, *321*
Dunhill Search of Medford (C), NJ, *321*
Dunhill Professional Search of Ramsey (C), NJ, *321*
Dunhill Staffing Systems (C), NC, *321*
Dunhill Professional Search of Greater New Orleans (C), LA, *321*
Dunhill Executive Search of Brown County (C), IN, *321*
Dunhill Professional Search (C), MO, *321*
Dunhill of Manchester Inc. (C), NH, *321*
Dunhill Search of Arlington (C), TX, *322*
Dunhill Professional Search of Winston-Salem (C), NC, *322*
Dunhill Personnel Service of Fargo (C), ND, *322*
Dunhill Personnel of Northeast Tulsa, Inc. (C), OK, *322*
Dunhill Professional Search of Bucks-Mont., Inc. (C), PA, *322*
Dunhill Professional Search of Wilkes-Barre/Scranton, Inc. (C), PA, *322*
Dunhill Personnel of St. Andrews (C), SC, *322*
Dunhill Search of Vermont (C), VT, *323*
Dunhill Professional Search of Richmond (C), VA, *323*
Dunhill Professional Search, Inc. of McAllen (C), TX, *323*

Dunhill of Corpus Christi, Inc. (C), TX, *323*
Dunlap & Sullivan Assoc. (R), MI, *55*
Dunn Associates (R), PA, *55*
C. A. Durakis Assoc., Inc. (R), MD, *55*
Dussick Management Assoc. (C), CT, *323*
Donald F. Dvorak & Co. (R), IL, *55*
Dwyer Consulting Group, Inc. (R), WV, *56*
Gwen Dycus & Assoc. (C), FL, *323*
G. L. Dykstra Assoc., Inc. (C), MI, *323*
Dynamic Choices Inc. (C), MO, *323*
Dynamic Computer Consultants, Inc. (C), AZ, *324*
Dynamic Search Systems, Inc. (C), IL, *324*
Dynamic Staffing Network (C), IL, *324*
Dynamic Synergy Corp. (R), CA, *56*
The E & K Group (C), NJ, *324*
E O Technical (C), CT, *324*
E T Search Inc. (C), CA, *324*
E.P. Int'l. (C), NY, *324*
E/Search Int'l. (C), CT, *325*
EA Plus, Inc. (C), TX, *325*
Eagle Consulting Group Inc. (C), TX, *325*
J. M. Eagle Partners Ltd. (C), WI, *325*
Eagle Research, Inc. (C), NJ, *325*
Eagle Search Assoc. (C), CA, *325*
EagleView, Inc. (C), MA, *325*
Earley Kielty & Assoc., Inc. (R), NY, *56*
Early Cochran & Olson (R), IL, *56*
Eastbourne Assoc. Inc. (R), NY, *56*
Eastern Executive Assoc. (C), NJ, *325*
Eastman & Beaudine, Inc. (R), TX, *56*
Eastridge Infotech (C), CA, *326*
EBA Group (R), NJ, *56*
ECG Resources, Inc. (C), NY, *326*
Eckler Personnel Network (C), VT, *326*
Eden & Assoc., Inc. (C), PA, *326*
The Edge Resource Group (C), PA, *326*
EDI, Inc. (C), MD, *326*
EDI/Executive Dynamics Inc. (C), NJ, *326*
EDMS Solutions (C), TX, *326*
EDP Staffing Solutions, Inc. (C), AR, *327*
Edwards & Assoc. (C), GA, *327*
Bruce Edwards & Associates, Inc. (R), NC, *56*
EFCO Consultants, Inc. (C), NY, *327*
Effective Search, Inc. (R), IL, *57*
EFL Assoc. (R), KS, *57*
EFL Int'l. (R), AZ, *57*
Egan & Assoc. (R), WI, *57*
D. C. Egan & Assoc. (C), GA, *327*
Egan Search Group (R), NY, *57*
Eggers Consulting Co., Inc. (C), NE, *327*
EGM Consulting, Inc. (R), FL, *57*
Richard A. Eisner & Co., LLP (R), NY, *57*
W. Robert Eissler & Assoc., Inc. (C), TX, *327*
William J. Elam & Assoc. (R), NE, *58*
The Eldridge Group, Ltd. (C), IL, *327*
Electronic Search, Inc. (C), IL, *327*
Elinvar (C), NC, *328*
Elite Consultants, Inc. (C), FL, *328*
Elite Medical Search (C), GA, *328*
Elite Resources Group (R), OH, *58*
Yves Elkas Inc. (R), QE, *58*
Gene Ellefson & Assoc. Inc. (C), MI, *328*
Elliot Assoc. Inc. (R), NY, *58*
H. J. Elliot, Inc. (R), IL, *58*
The Elliott Company (R), MA, *58*
Ellis & Associates (C), HI, *328*
Ellis Career Consultants (C), NJ, *328*
Steve Ellis (C), CA, *328*
David M. Ellner Assoc. (R), NY, *59*
The Ellsworth Group (C), NY, *329*
The Elmhurst Group (C), CA, *329*
The Elsworth Group (C), TX, *329*
Elwell & Assoc., Inc. (R), MI, *59*
Mark Elzweig Co., Ltd. (C), NY, *329*
Emerald Legal Search (C), NH, *329*
Emerging Medical Technologies, Inc. (C), CO, *329*
Emerging Technology Search (C), GA, *329*
Emerson & Co. (C), GA, *329*
Emmett Executive Search, Inc. (C), NY, *330*
EMN/Witt/Kieffer (R), MA, *59*
Empire International (R), PA, *59*
Employ® (C), PA, *330*
Employment Solutions, Inc. (C), TX, *330*
Empowered Solutions Corp. (C), GA, *330*
The Energists (R), TX, *59*
The Enfield Company (C), TX, *330*
Engineering & Scientific Search Assoc. (ESSA) (C), NJ, *330*
Engineering Futures, LLC (C), CT, *330*
Engineering Placement Specialists (C), WI, *330*
Engineering Profiles (C), FL, *330*
Engineering Resource Group, Inc. (C), NJ, *331*
ENI (R), CT, *59*
The Enns Partners Inc. (R), ON, *59*
Ensearch Management Consultants (C), CA, *331*
Entelechy Group Ltd. (R), MD, *59*
The Enterprise Group (R), MA, *60*
Environmental, Health & Safety Search Assoc. (C), FL, *331*
Epsen, Fuller & Assoc., LLC (R), NJ, *60*
Mary R. Erickson & Assoc. (R), MN, *60*
Erikson Consulting Assoc., Inc. (R), NY, *60*
Erlanger Assoc. (R), CT, *60*
Erwin Assoc. (R), IL, *60*
ESA (R), CT, *60*
ESS (Executive Search Services) (R), CA, *61*
Essential Solutions, Inc. (C), CA, *331*
Ethos Consulting, Inc. (R), CA, *61*
ETI Search Int'l. (R), GA, *61*
The Evans McDonnell Co. (C), TX, *331*
The Evans Search Group (R), CT, *61*
Evans Transportation Search (C), ON, *331*
Evergreen & Co. (C), MA, *331*
Excalibur Human Resources, Inc. (R), NJ, *61*
Exclusive Search Consultants (C), OH, *331*
Exec Tech, Inc. (C), IL, *332*
ExeConnex, LLC (R), GA, *61*
Execu-Tech Search Inc. (C), MN, *332*
The Execu/Search Group (C), NY, *332*
ExecuGroup, Inc. (R), MS, *61*
ExecuQuest, Inc. (R), MI, *61*
ExecuSource Assoc., Inc. (C), GA, *332*
ExecuSource Consultants, Inc. (C), TX, *332*
Executech (R), OH, *62*
ExecuTech (C), IN, *332*
Executive Access Inc. (R), NY, *62*
Executive Alliance (R), MA, *62*
Executive Business Solutions, Inc. (C), WA, *332*
Executive Career Search (C), VA, *332*
Executive Careers (R), CA, *62*
Executive Connection (C), OH, *333*
Executive Dimensions (R), NY, *62*
Executive Direction, Inc. (C), CA, *333*
Executive Directions (R), OH, *62*
Executive Exchange Corp. (C), NJ, *333*
The Executive Group, Inc. (R), CA, *62*
Executive Manning Corp. (R), FL, *63*
Executive Partners Inc. (C), CT, *333*
Executive Placement Consultants (C), IL, *333*
Executive Placement Services (C), GA, *333*
Executive Recruiters Agency, Inc. (C), AR, *333*
Executive Recruiters Int'l. (C), MI, *333*
Executive Recruiters, Inc. (C), WI, *334*
Executive Recruiters (C), WA, *334*
Executive Recruitment Specialists, Inc. (R), NC, *63*
Executive Recruitment Services, Inc. (ERS, Inc.) (C), GA, *334*
Executive Referral Services, Inc. (C), IL, *334*
Executive Registry (C), QE, *334*
Executive Resource Assoc. (C), VA, *334*
Executive Resource Group, Inc. (R), ME, *63*
Executive Resource Inc. (C), WI, *334*
Executive Resource Systems (C), CA, *335*
Executive Sales Search (C), CO, *335*
Executive Search Consultants International, Inc. (R), NY, *63*
Executive Search Consultants (R), CA, *63*
Executive Search Consultants (C), CA, *335*
Executive Search Consultants, Inc. (C), FL, *335*
Executive Search Consultants Corp. (C), IL, *335*
Executive Search Group, Inc. (C), CT, *335*
Executive Search Group LLC (C), CA, *335*
Executive Search Inc. (R), MN, *63*
Executive Search Int'l./Transearch (R), MA, *63*
Executive Search Int'l. (C), TX, *335*
Executive Search, Ltd. (C), OH, *336*
Executive Search of New England, Inc. (C), ME, *336*
Executive Search of America, Inc. (C), OH, *336*
Executive Search Partners (R), NY, *63*
Executive Search Placements, Inc. (C), CO, *336*
Executive Search Plus, Inc. (C), IN, *336*
Executive Search Team (C), MI, *336*
Executive Solutions (R), MN, *64*
The Executive Source Inc. (R), NY, *64*
The Executive Source (C), SA, *337*
Executive Strategies, Inc. (C), GA, *337*
The Executive Tree (R), FL, *64*
Executive/Retail Placement Assoc. (C), MD, *337*
ExecutiveFit (C), NY, *337*
Executives Worldwide, Inc. (C), OR, *337*
EXETER 2100 (C), NH, *337*

eXsource Inc. (C), SC, *337*
Raymond L. Extract & Assoc. (R), CA, *64*
Eyler Assoc., Inc. (R), IA, *64*
F.L.A.G. (C), OH, *338*
Fabian Assoc. Inc. (C), NY, *338*
Fagan & Company (R), PA, *64*
FAI (C), CO, *338*
Fairfaxx Corp. (R), CT, *64*
Fairfield Int'l. Resources (R), NY, *65*
Paul Falcone Assoc. (R), NJ, *65*
Fallstaff Search (C), MD, *338*
Fament, Inc. (C), OH, *338*
Family-Business Roundtable, Inc. (R), AZ, *65*
Leon A. Farley Assoc. (R), CA, *65*
Dorothy W. Farnath & Assoc., Inc. (C), NJ, *338*
Faro Consultants Int'l. (C), VA, *338*
James Farris Assoc. (R), OK, *65*
Fast Switch, Ltd. (C), OH, *338*
The Fawcett Group (R), MA, *65*
FCI, Inc. (R), NJ, *65*
Federal Placement Services (C), NY, *339*
James Feerst & Assoc., Inc. (C), AZ, *339*
A. E. Feldman Assoc., Inc. (C), NY, *339*
Feldman Gray & Assoc. Inc. (C), ON, *339*
Fell & Nicholson Technology Resources (R), CA, *65*
Fenwick Partners (R), MA, *66*
Fenzel Milar Assoc. (C), OH, *339*
Fergason Assoc., Inc. (C), IL, *339*
Fergus Legal Search & Consulting, Inc. (C), NY, *339*
Ferneborg & Assoc., Inc. (R), CA, *66*
Fernow Assoc. (C), PA, *339*
Ferrari Search Group (C), OH, *340*
Guild Fetridge Acoustical Search, Inc. (C), NY, *340*
Fidelity Search Group, Inc. (R), PA, *66*
Jerry Fields Assoc. (C), NY, *340*
Financial Connections Company (C), VA, *340*
Financial Plus Management Solutions Inc. (R), ON, *66*
Financial Resource Assoc., Inc. (C), FL, *340*
Financial Search Corp. (C), IL, *340*
Financial Search Group, Inc. (R), MA, *66*
Financialjobs.com (C), CA, *340*
Neil Fink Assoc. (R), CA, *66*
Eileen Finn & Assoc., Inc. (C), NY, *341*
Finn & Schneider Assoc., Inc. (C), DC, *341*
Finnegan & Assoc. (R), CA, *67*
Finney-Taylor Personnel & Management Consultants Ltd. (C), AB, *341*
First Advisory Services Int'l., Inc. (R), MD, *67*
First Choice Search (R), WA, *67*
First Search America, Inc. (C), TN, *341*
First Search Inc. (C), IL, *341*
First Union Executive Search (R), NC, *67*
Howard Fischer Assoc. Int'l., Inc. (R), PA, *67*
Fishel HR Assoc., Inc. (C), AZ, *341*
Fisher & Assoc. (R), CA, *67*
Jack Stuart Fisher Assoc. (C), NJ, *341*
The Fisher Group (R), AB, *67*
Fisher Personnel Management Services (R), CA, *68*
Fisher-Todd Assoc. (C), NY, *341*
A. G. Fishkin & Assoc., Inc. (R), MD, *68*
James L. Fisk & Assoc. (C), MO, *342*
Fitzgerald Associates (R), MA, *68*
FitzGibbon & Assoc. (R), PA, *68*
The Flagship Group (R), MA, *68*
Robert M. Flanagan & Assoc., Ltd. (R), NY, *68*
Flesher & Assoc., Inc. (R), CA, *68*
Susan Fletcher Attorney Employment Services (C), PA, *342*
Flexible Resources, Inc. (C), CT, *342*
Florapersonnel, Inc. (R), FL, *68*
Flowers & Assoc. (C), OH, *342*
J. G. Flynn & Assoc. Inc. (R), BC, *69*
Flynn, Hannock, Inc. (R), CT, *69*
David Fockler & Assoc., Inc. (C), CA, *342*
Focus Consulting Services, Inc. (C), FL, *342*
Focus Executive Search (C), MN, *343*
Fogec Consultants, Inc. (R), WI, *69*
Foley Proctor Yoskowitz (R), NJ, *69*
L. W. Foote Co. (R), WA, *69*
The Forbes Group (R), GA, *69*
Ford & Assoc., Inc. (C), SC, *343*
Ford & Ford (C), MA, *343*
The Ford Group, Inc. (R), PA, *69*
Forest People Int'l. Search Ltd. (C), BC, *343*
Forray Assoc., Inc. (R), NY, *70*
Fortuna Technologies Inc. (C), CA, *343*
F-O-R-T-U-N-E Personnel Consultants of Boise (R), ID, *70*
Fortune Group Int'l., Inc. (R), PA, *70*
Fortune Personnel Consultants of Huntsville, Inc. (C), AL, *343*
F-O-R-T-U-N-E Personnel Consultants of Denver, Inc. (C), CO, *344*
F-O-R-T-U-N-E Personnel Consultants of San Diego (C), CA, *344*
Fortune Personnel Consultants (C), CA, *344*
F-O-R-T-U-N-E Personnel Consultants of Greenwood Village (C), CO, *344*
F-O-R-T-U-N-E Personnel Consultants of Wilmington (C), DE, *344*
F-O-R-T-U-N-E Personnel Consultants of Tampa (C), FL, *344*
Fortune Personnel Consultants of Colorado Springs (C), CO, *344*
Fortune Personnel Consultants of Jacksonville (C), FL, *345*
F-O-R-T-U-N-E Personnel Consultants of Palm Beach (C), FL, *345*
F-O-R-T-U-N-E Personnel Consultants of Manatee County (C), FL, *345*
Fortune Personnel Consultants of Sarasota Inc. (C), FL, *345*
F-O-R-T-U-N-E Personnel Consultants of Atlanta, Inc. (C), GA, *345*
F-O-R-T-U-N-E Personnel Consultants of Savannah, Inc. (C), GA, *345*
Fortune of Arlington Heights (C), IL, *345*
Fortune Personnel Consultants of Topsfield (C), MA, *346*
F-o-r-t-u-n-e Personnel Consultants of Detroit, Inc. (C), MI, *346*
Fortune Personnel Consultants of Bloomfield, Inc. (C), MI, *346*
F-o-r-t-u-n-e of Owensboro, Inc. (C), KY, *346*
F-O-R-T-U-N-E Personnel Consultants of Southwest Indiana (C), IN, *346*
F-O-R-T-U-N-E Personnel Consultants (C), MI, *346*
Fortune Personnel Consultants of Hinsdale, IL (C), IL, *346*
F-O-R-T-U-N-E Personnel Consultants of South Bend (C), IN, *346*
F-O-R-T-U-N-E Search Consultants (C), MO, *347*
F-O-R-T-U-N-E Personnel Consultants of Menlo Park, Inc. (C), NJ, *347*
Fortune Personnel Consultants (C), MT, *347*
F-O-R-T-U-N-E Personnel Consultants of St. Louis-West County (C), MO, *347*
F-O-R-T-U-N-E Personnel Consultants of Troy, Inc. (C), MI, *347*
F-O-R-T-U-N-E Personnel Consultants of Bergen County Inc. (C), NJ, *347*
Fortune Personnel Consultants (C), NH, *347*
Fortune Personnel Consultants of Allentown, Inc. (C), PA, *348*
F-O-R-T-U-N-E Personnel Consultants of Charlotte (C), NC, *348*
Fortune Personnel Consultants of Greensboro, NC, Inc. (C), NC, *348*
Fortune Personnel Consultants of Raleigh, Inc. (C), NC, *348*
F-O-R-T-U-N-E Personnel Consultants of Cincinnati (C), OH, *348*
F-O-R-T-U-N-E of West Portland (C), OR, *348*
F-O-R-T-U-N-E Personnel Consultants of Rockland County, Inc. (C), NY, *348*
Fortune Personnel Consultants of Chattanooga Inc. (C), TN, *349*
Fortune Consultants of Ft. Washington (C), PA, *349*
Fortune Personnel Consultants of Anderson, Inc. (C), SC, *349*
FORTUNE Personnel Consultants of Charleston, Inc. (C), SC, *349*
F-O-R-T-U-N-E Consultants of Memphis (C), TN, *349*
Fortune Personnel Consultants of Hilton Head (C), SC, *349*
Fortune Personnel Consultants of Plano (C), TX, *350*
F-O-R-T-U-N-E Personnel Consultants of the Tri-Cities, Inc. (C), TN, *350*
F-O-R-T-U-N-E Personnel Consultants of Knoxville (C), TN, *350*
F-O-R-T-U-N-E Personnel of Nashville (C), TN, *350*
F-O-R-T-U-N-E Personnel Consultants of Houston, Inc. (C), TX, *350*
Fortune Personnel Consultants of San Antonio, Inc. (C), TX, *350*
FORTUNE Personnel Consultants of North Dallas (C), TX, *350*
F-O-R-T-U-N-E Personnel Consultants of East Seattle (C), WA, *351*
Fortune Personnel Consultants of the Virginia Highlands (C), VA, *351*
Forum Personnel Inc. (C), NY, *351*

Foster Associates (C), NJ, *351*
Foster Partners (R), NY, *70*
Fought, Jameson Assoc. (C), IL, *351*
The Fourbes Group, Inc. (C), NJ, *351*
Fox, White & Assoc. (C), FL, *351*
Fox-Morris Assoc., Inc. (C), PA, *351*
Foy, Schneid & Daniel, Inc. (R), NY, *71*
Franchise Recruiters Ltd. (R), IL, *71*
Franchise Search, Inc. (C), NY, *352*
Francis & Assoc. (R), IA, *71*
Neil Frank & Co. (R), CA, *71*
Franklin Allen Consultants, Ltd. (R), NY, *71*
Franklin Int'l. Search, Inc. (C), MA, *352*
The Franklin Search Group, Inc./Medzilla (R), WA, *71*
Franstaff Inc. (C), FL, *352*
KS Frary & Assoc. (R), MA, *71*
Mel Frazer Consultant (C), CA, *352*
P. N. French Assoc., Inc. (R), MA, *72*
Fresquez & Assoc. (C), CA, *352*
Frey & Sher Assoc., Inc. (C), VA, *353*
Friedman Eisenstein Raemer & Schwartz, LLP (R), IL, *72*
Bernard Frigon & Assoc. Inc. (C), QE, *353*
Gerald Frisch Assoc., Inc. (R), NY, *72*
Fristoe & Carleton, Inc. (C), OH, *353*
Peter Froehlich & Co. (C), TX, *353*
The Fry Group, Inc. (C), NY, *353*
Frye/Joure & Assoc., Inc. (C), TN, *353*
Furlong Search, Inc. (R), CA, *72*
C. F. Furr & Co. (R), NC, *72*
The Furst Group, Inc. (R), IL, *72*
Furst Group/MPI (R), IL, *72*
Further Management Group (C), MD, *353*
Future Employment Service, Inc. (C), IA, *353*
Futures, Inc. (C), NH, *354*
Futures Int'l. (R), CT, *73*
G. H. Enterprises (C), AZ, *354*
GAAP Inc. (R), QE, *73*
Gable Healthcare Group, Inc. (R), FL, *73*
The Gabriel Group (C), PA, *354*
Gabriele & Company (C), MA, *354*
Gaffney Management Consultants (R), IL, *73*
Gahan Assoc. (R), NY, *73*
Gaines & Assoc. Int'l., Inc. (R), IL, *73*
Jay Gaines & Company, Inc. (R), NY, *73*
Gallin Associates, Inc. (C), FL, *354*
Gaming Consultants, Inc. (R), LA, *74*
The Gammill Group, Inc. (C), OH, *354*
Gans, Gans & Assoc., Inc. (R), FL, *74*
Garb & Assoc., Legal Placement (C), CA, *354*
W. N. Garbarini & Assoc. (R), NJ, *74*
Gardiner, Townsend & Assoc. (R), NY, *74*
Gardner-Ross Assoc., Inc. (R), NY, *74*
Garland Assoc. Int'l. (C), CA, *355*
Dick Garland Consultants (R), NY, *74*
The Garms Group (R), IL, *74*
The Garret Group (R), NJ, *75*
Garrett Assoc. Inc. (R), GA, *75*
The Garrison Organization (R), IA, *75*
Garrison-Randall, Inc. (R), CA, *75*
The Garvis Group, Inc. (C), LA, *355*
Peter Gasperini & Assoc., Inc. (R), NY, *75*
GateSource Partners (C), VA, *355*
Gateway Group Personnel, LLC (C), TN, *355*
Gateway Management Resources (C), IL, *355*
Gatti & Assoc. (C), MA, *355*
Gaudry, Shink, Levasseur (R), QE, *75*
Dianne Gauger & Assoc. (C), CA, *355*
Gavin Forbes & Price (R), CA, *75*
GCO (C), CA, *355*
Geddes & Rubin Management Inc. (R), ON, *76*
Gelpi & Assoc. (C), LA, *355*
Genel Associates (C), CA, *356*
General Engineering Tectonics (C), CA, *356*
Genesis Consulting Partners (R), PA, *76*
Genesis Personnel Service, Inc. (C), OH, *356*
Genesis Recruiting (C), CA, *356*
Genesis Research (C), MO, *356*
Geneva Group Int'l. (R), CA, *76*
Gent & Assoc. (C), CA, *356*
Delores F. George, C.P.C. (C), MA, *356*
C. R. Gerald & Assoc. (C), ON, *356*
J. Gernetzke & Assoc., Inc. (C), OH, *357*
GES Services, Inc. (R), NY, *76*
GFI Professional Staffing Services (C), NH, *357*
Gibson & Co., Inc. (R), WI, *76*
Gielow Assoc., Inc. (R), WI, *76*
Gilbert & Van Campen Int'l. (R), NY, *76*
John Gilbert Co. (C), TX, *357*
Gilbert Scott Assoc., LLC (C), MA, *357*
Gilbert Tweed Assoc. Inc. (R), NY, *76*
Joe L. Giles & Assoc. (C), MI, *357*
Gillard Assoc. Legal Search (C), MA, *357*
Gilmore & Assoc. (C), CA, *357*
Howard Gilmore & Assoc. (R), OH, *77*
Gilreath Weatherby Inc. (R), MA, *77*
Gimbel & Assoc. (C), FL, *357*
Lawrence Glaser Assoc., Inc. (C), NJ, *357*
Glass & Assoc., Inc. (C), OH, *358*
The Glazin Group (R), BC, *77*
J. P. Gleason Assoc., Inc. (R), IL, *77*
The Glenwood Group (C), IL, *358*
Glines Assoc., Inc. (R), IL, *77*
Global 1000 Int'l. Services (C), CA, *358*
Global Career Services, Inc. (C), NY, *358*
Global Consulting Group Inc. (C), ON, *358*
Global Data Services, Inc. (R), NY, *77*
Global Employer's Network, Inc. (R), TX, *77*
Global Engineers Inc. (C), ME, *358*
Global Executive Search Group (C), MA, *358*
Global HealthCare Partners (R), IL, *78*
Global Research Partnership Inc. (R), NY, *78*
Global Resources Group (R), CA, *78*
Global Technologies Group Inc. (C), NC, *359*
Global Telecommunications, Inc. (C), TX, *359*
The GlobalSearch Group (C), TX, *359*
F. Gloss Int'l. (R), VA, *78*
Glou Int'l., Inc. (R), MA, *78*
The Tracy Glover Co. (R), TX, *78*
Gnodde Assoc. (C), IL, *359*
The Gobbell Co. (R), CA, *78*
Robert G. Godfrey Assoc. Ltd. (R), IL, *78*
Godfrey Personnel, Inc. (C), IL, *359*
H. L. Goehring & Assoc., Inc. (C), OH, *359*
The Gogates Group, Inc. (R), NY, *79*
Barry M. Gold & Co. (C), CA, *359*
Goldbeck Recruiting Inc. (C), BC, *359*
Barry Goldberg & Assoc., Inc. (C), CA, *360*
The Goldman Group Inc. (R), NY, *79*
Goldman+Bell, LLC (C), NY, *360*
Joseph Goldring & Assoc. Inc. (C), MI, *360*
Fred J. Goldsmith Assoc. (R), CA, *79*
Goldstein & Co. (C), CA, *360*
David Gomez & Assoc., Inc. (R), IL, *79*
Gomez Fregoso y Asociados (C), JAL, *360*
L. J. Gonzer Assoc. (C), NJ, *360*
Goodkind Assoc. Inc. (C), NY, *360*
The Goodman Group (R), CA, *79*
Goodrich & Sherwood Assoc., Inc. (R), NY, *79*
Goodwin & Co. (R), DC, *80*
Gordon/Tyler (R), PA, *80*
Gossage Regan Assoc. (R), NY, *80*
Gould, McCoy & Chadick, Inc. (R), NY, *80*
The Governance Group, Inc. (R), NJ, *80*
Government Contract Solutions, Inc. (C), VA, *360*
Gowdy Consultants (C), TX, *361*
Graham & Co. (R), NJ, *80*
Alexander Graham Assoc. (C), NJ, *361*
Robert Graham Assoc. (R), RI, *81*
Granger, Counts & Assoc. (R), OH, *81*
A. Davis Grant & Co. (R), NJ, *81*
Robert Grant Assoc., Inc. (C), CA, *361*
Grant Cooper & Assoc., Inc. (R), MO, *81*
The Grant Search Group, Inc. (C), ON, *361*
Grant-Franks & Assoc. (C), NJ, *361*
Grant/Morgan Assoc., Inc. (C), MD, *361*
Grantham & Co., Inc. (R), NC, *81*
Graphic Arts Marketing Assoc., Inc. (C), MI, *361*
Graphic Search Assoc. Inc. (C), PA, *362*
Grauss & Co. (C), CA, *362*
Annie Gray Assoc., Inc. (R), MO, *81*
Ben Greco Assoc., Inc. (C), CA, *362*
Sheila Greco Assoc. (C), NY, *362*
R. Green & Assoc., Inc. (C), OH, *362*
Greene & Co. (C), MA, *362*
Greene Personnel Consultants (C), RI, *362*
Greene-Levin-Snyder LLC (C), NY, *362*
Greenfields Engineering Search (C), MO, *363*
Greenhaven & Assoc., Inc. (R), NY, *81*
Greenwich Internet (C), CT, *363*
Greenwich Search Partners, LLC (C), CT, *363*
Greger/Peterson Assoc., Inc. (R), CA, *81*
Gregory, Kyle & Assoc. (C), NC, *363*
Gregory Michaels & Assoc., Inc. (R), IL, *82*
David M. Griffith & Assoc., Ltd. (R), CA, *82*
Griffith & Werner, Inc. (R), FL, *82*
Groenekamp & Assoc. (C), CA, *363*
J. B. Groner Executive Search, Inc. (C), DE, *363*
Gros Executive Search, Inc. (C), TN, *363*
Grossberg & Assoc. (R), IL, *82*

Groton Planning Group (R), ME, *82*
Groupe PCA Inc. (C), QE, *363*
Groupe Ranger Inc. (C), QE, *364*
Groussman & Assoc., Inc. (R), TX, *82*
Grover & Assoc. (R), OH, *82*
Growth Consultants of America (R), MI, *82*
Growth Strategies, Inc. (R), FL, *83*
David E. Grumney Co. Inc. (R), WA, *83*
GSP International (C), NJ, *364*
GSW Consulting Group, Inc. (R), CA, *83*
Nadine Guber & Assoc., Inc. (C), NY, *364*
Michael R. Guerin Co. (C), CA, *364*
Wolf Gugler & Assoc. Ltd. (R), ON, *83*
Guidarelli Assoc., Inc. (R), MI, *83*
Guidry & East Healthcare Search Consultants (R), TX, *83*
The Guild Corp. (C), VA, *364*
The Gullgroup (C), TX, *364*
Gumbinner/Haubenstock, Inc. (C), NY, *364*
Gundersen Partners, L.L.C. (R), NY, *83*
Gustin Partners, Ltd. (R), MA, *83*
William Guy & Assoc., Inc. (R), CA, *84*
GWS Partners (R), IL, *84*
H R Solutions, Inc. (C), MO, *365*
The H. S. Group, Inc. (C), WI, *365*
H.Q. Search, Inc. (C), IL, *365*
Stephen Haas Legal Placement (C), NY, *365*
Habelmann & Assoc. (R), MI, *84*
Haddad Assoc. (R), FL, *84*
Russ Hadick & Assoc. Inc. (C), OH, *365*
Hadley Associates, Inc. (C), NJ, *365*
Hadley Lockwood, Inc. (R), NY, *84*
M. A. Haggith Consultants Ltd. (R), ON, *84*
Hahn & Assoc., Inc. (C), OH, *365*
Halbrecht & Co. (C), VA, *365*
Halbrecht Lieberman Assoc., Inc. (R), CT, *84*
Hale Assoc. (R), IL, *84*
K. C. Hale, Inc. (R), CT, *85*
Haley Associates (R), CA, *85*
Robert Half Canada Inc. (C), ON, *366*
Don Hall & Assoc. (C), TX, *366*
Michael J. Hall & Co. (R), WA, *85*
Susan Hall Executive Search (C), TX, *366*
Hall Kinion (C), CA, *366*
Hall Management Group, Inc. (C), GA, *367*
Hallman Group, Inc. (C), MI, *367*
Halo Insurance Service (C), AL, *367*
The Halyburton Co., Inc. (R), NC, *85*
Hamilton & Co. (C), OH, *367*
The Hamilton Group (R), MD, *85*
Hamilton-Chase & Assoc., Inc. (R), MA, *85*
The Hampton Group (C), NY, *367*
R. C. Handel Assoc. Inc. (R), CT, *85*
W. L. Handler & Assoc. (R), GA, *85*
Hands-on Broadcast (R), NY, *86*
Handy HRM (R), NY, *86*
Hanley & Assoc. (R), FL, *86*
The Hanna Group (C), OH, *368*
The Hanover Consulting Group (C), MD, *368*
Hansen Executive Search, Inc. (C), NE, *368*
Hanzel & Co., Inc. (R), NY, *86*
Janet Harberth & Assoc., Inc. (C), GA, *368*
Harbor Consultants Int'l., Inc. (C), VA, *368*
Harbrowe, Inc. (C), NY, *368*
Harcor Quest & Assoc. (R), OH, *86*
Harcourt & Assoc. (C), AB, *368*
Harcourt Group Ltd. (R), OH, *86*
Hardage Group (C), TN, *369*
Hardison & Company (R), TX, *86*
Robert Harkins Assoc., Inc. (C), PA, *369*
Harmeling & Associates (C), CA, *369*
Harper Associates (C), MI, *369*
Harper Hewes, Inc. (C), NY, *369*
Harrington & O'Brien, Inc. (C), NH, *369*
The Harris Consulting Corp. (R), MB, *87*
Harris Heery & Assoc., Inc. (R), CT, *87*
Harris McCully Assoc., Inc. (C), NY, *369*
Harrison Consulting Group, Inc. (C), CA, *369*
Harrison Moore Inc. (C), NE, *370*
Hart & Co. (C), NY, *370*
Hartman & Barnette (R), VA, *87*
Hartman Greene & Wells (C), DC, *370*
Hartsfield Group, Inc. (R), GA, *87*
Harvard Aimes Group (R), CT, *87*
Harvard Group Int'l. (R), GA, *87*
Harvey Hohauser & Assoc., LLC (R), MI, *87*
Bruce W. Haupt Assoc. (R), DC, *88*
Phyllis Hawkins & Assoc., Inc. (C), AZ, *370*
The Hawkins Co. (R), CA, *88*
Michael J. Hawkins, Inc. (C), IL, *370*
William E. Hay & Co. (R), IL, *88*
Hayden & Assoc., Inc. (C), MN, *370*
Hayden Group, Inc. (R), MA, *88*
Haydon Legal Search (C), IL, *370*
Hayman & Co. (R), TX, *88*
Hayman Daugherty Assoc., Inc. (C), GA, *370*
The Haystack Group, Inc. (R), ME, *88*
Hazard, Young, Attea & Assoc., Ltd. (C), IL, *371*
Hazlett Associates (R), IL, *88*
HCI Corp. (C), IL, *371*
HDB Incorporated (C), MO, *371*
Headden Assoc. (R), WA, *88*
Healey Executive Search, Inc. (R), MN, *88*
Health Care Dimensions (C), CO, *371*
Health Care Plus, Inc. (C), MD, *371*
Health Industry Consultants, Inc. (R), CO, *89*
Health Network USA (C), TX, *371*
Health Search (C), CA, *371*
Health Search, Inc. (C), KS, *371*
Healthcare Executive Recruiters, Inc. (C), CA, *372*
Healthcare Management Resources, Inc. (R), GA, *89*
Healthcare Recruiters Int'l. Orange County (C), CA, *372*
Healthcare Recruiters of Indiana (C), IN, *372*
Healthcare Recruiters of the Rockies, Inc. (C), CO, *372*
Healthcare Recruiters Int'l. Bay Area (C), CA, *372*
Healthcare Recruiters Int'l. Phoenix (C), AZ, *372*
Healthcare Recruiters Int'l. - Alabama (C), AL, *372*
Healthcare Recruiters Int'l. - Los Angeles (C), CA, *372*
Healthcare Recruiters of New Orleans (C), LA, *373*
Healthcare Recruiters of New England (C), MA, *373*
Healthcare Recruiters Int'l - Minnesota, Inc. (C), MN, *373*
Healthcare Recruiters International-NY/NJ (C), NJ, *373*
Healthcare Recruiters Int'l. Philadelphia (C), NJ, *373*
Healthcare Recruiters of New York, Inc. (C), NY, *373*
Healthcare Recruiters Int'l. - Pittsburgh (C), PA, *373*
Healthcare Recruiters of Midsouth (C), TN, *373*
Healthcare Recruiters - Northwest (C), WA, *374*
Healthcare Recruiters of Dallas (C), TX, *374*
Healthcare Resources Group (C), OK, *374*
Healthcare Search Associates (C), CA, *374*
HealthSearch Assoc. (C), MD, *374*
The Healthsearch Group, Inc. (C), NY, *374*
F. P. Healy & Co., Inc. (R), NY, *89*
HeartBeat Medical, Inc. (C), OR, *374*
Heartland National Medical Search (C), IL, *374*
Heath/Norton Assoc., Inc. (R), NY, *89*
R. W. Hebel Assoc. (R), TX, *89*
HEC Group (C), ON, *375*
Hechkoff/Work Executive Search Inc. (R), NY, *89*
Thomas E. Hedefine Assoc. (C), ON, *375*
Hedlund Corp. (C), IL, *375*
Hedman & Assoc. (R), TX, *89*
Heffelfinger Assoc., Inc. (R), MA, *89*
Heidrick & Struggles, Inc. (R), IL, *90*
The Heidrick Partners, Inc. (R), IL, *90*
Jay Heino Company, LLC (C), NY, *375*
Heinze & Assoc. Inc. (R), MN, *91*
Helbling & Assoc., Inc. (R), PA, *91*
Helfer Executive Consultants (R), TN, *91*
Helffrich Int'l. (C), FL, *375*
Heller Assoc., Ltd. (R), IL, *91*
Heller Kil Assoc., Inc. (C), FL, *375*
The Helms Int'l. Group (R), VA, *91*
Hemingway Personnel, Inc. (C), CA, *375*
G. W. Henn & Co. (R), OH, *91*
Henrietta's Personnel & Executive Search, Inc. (C), FL, *376*
Bruce Henry Assoc. Inc. (R), CA, *91*
Kay Henry, Inc. (C), PA, *376*
The Hensge Co. (R), IL, *91*
Henson Partners (C), AZ, *376*
Herbeck Kline & Assoc. (R), IL, *92*
Hergenrather & Co. (R), WA, *92*
Heritage Pacific Corp. (C), CA, *376*
Heritage Search Group, Inc. (C), FL, *376*
J. J. Herlihy & Assoc., Inc. (C), CA, *376*
Hermann & Westmore (R), CA, *92*
A. Herndon & Assoc., Inc. (R), TX, *92*
Herrerias & Assoc. (R), CA, *92*
Herring & Assoc. (C), AR, *376*
The Herrmann Group Ltd. (R), ON, *92*
J. D. Hersey & Assoc. (C), OH, *376*
Hersher Assoc., Ltd. (R), IL, *92*

H. Hertner Assoc., Inc. (C), FL, *377*
Stanley Herz & Co. (R), NY, *92*
Robert Hess & Assoc., Inc. (C), CO, *377*
Hessel Assoc., Inc. (C), NY, *377*
The Hetzel Group, Inc. (R), IL, *92*
Heyman Assoc., Inc. (R), NY, *93*
HG & Assoc. (R), IL, *93*
Higbee Assoc., Inc. (C), CT, *377*
Higdon Prince Inc. (R), NY, *93*
Higgins Assoc., Inc. (R), IL, *93*
B. W. Higgins, Inc. (C), IN, *377*
High Tech Opportunities, Inc. (C), NH, *377*
High Tech Staffing Group (C), OR, *377*
High-Tech Recruiters (C), CT, *378*
Highland & Assoc. (C), CA, *378*
Highland Search Group, L.L.C. (R), NY, *93*
Highlander Search (C), NC, *378*
Higley, Hall & Co., Inc. (R), MA, *93*
Hill & Assoc. (C), CA, *378*
Hill Allyn Assoc. (C), CA, *378*
Frank P. Hill (R), MX, *93*
The Hindman Co. (R), KY, *94*
The Hindman Group, Inc. (C), CA, *378*
Hintz Associates (C), NY, *378*
Hire Authority, Inc. (C), MI, *378*
The Hiring Authority, Inc. (C), FL, *379*
Ruth Hirsch Assoc., Inc. (C), NY, *379*
Hitchens & Foster, Inc. (C), MO, *379*
Hite Executive Search (R), OH, *94*
HLR Consulting (C), NY, *379*
HMO Executive Search (C), IN, *379*
Hobson Assoc. (C), CT, *379*
Hochman & Assoc. (C), CA, *379*
Hockett Associates, Inc. (R), CA, *94*
Hodge-Cronin & Assoc., Inc. (R), IL, *94*
Hoffman Partnership Group Inc. (C), NY, *379*
Hoffman Recruiters (C), MA, *380*
The Hogan Group (C), OH, *380*
Hoglund & Assoc., Inc. (R), IL, *94*
Richard D. Holbrook Assoc. (R), MA, *94*
Holden & Harlan Assoc., Inc. (C), IL, *380*
Holland & Assoc., Inc. (R), MI, *94*
Holland Rusk & Assoc. (R), IL, *95*
Hollander Horizon Int'l. (R), CA, *95*
The Hollins Group, Inc. (R), IL, *95*
Holloway Schulz & Partners (C), BC, *380*
Holohan Group, Ltd. (R), MO, *95*
Home Health & Hospital Recruiters, Inc. (C), GA, *380*
J. B. Homer Assoc. Inc. (R), NY, *95*
Fred Hood & Assoc. (C), CA, *380*
J. G. Hood Assoc. (C), CT, *380*
Hook-Up! (C), CA, *380*
Horizon Medical Search of NH (C), NH, *381*
Horizons Unlimited (C), CA, *381*
David C. Horn Executive Search (C), TX, *381*
Hornberger Management Company (R), DE, *95*
Horton Int'l. Inc. (R), NY, *96*
Hospitality Executive Search, Inc. (R), MA, *96*
Hospitality Int'l. (C), NY, *381*
Houser, Martin, Morris (C), WA, *381*
Houtz•Strawn & Arnold, Inc. (R), TX, *96*
William C. Houze & Co. (R), CA, *96*
Randall Howard & Assoc., Inc. (R), TN, *96*
Howard-Sloan Assoc. (C), NY, *381*
Howard-Sloan Legal Search, Inc. (C), NY, *382*
The Howard-Sloan-Koller Group (R), NY, *97*
Howard/Williams Assoc. (C), FL, *382*
Howe & Assoc. (R), PA, *97*
Robert Howe & Assoc. (R), GA, *97*
HR Advantage, Inc. (C), VA, *382*
HR Consultants (C), GA, *382*
HR Inc. (C), NC, *382*
HRCS (R), CA, *97*
HRD Consultants, Inc. (R), NJ, *97*
Hreshko Consulting Group (C), NJ, *382*
HRI Services, Inc. (C), MA, *382*
The HRM Group, Inc. (C), AL, *382*
HRNI (C), MI, *383*
HRS, Inc. (R), PA, *97*
Arnold Huberman Assoc., Inc. (R), NY, *97*
Huddleston Assoc. (C), OK, *383*
Hudson Assoc. Inc. (C), IN, *383*
The Hudson Group (C), CT, *383*
Huff Assoc. (R), NJ, *98*
Hughes & Assoc. (C), TX, *383*
Hughes & Assoc. Int'l. Inc. (C), AL, *383*
E. A. Hughes & Co., Inc. (R), NY, *98*
Hughes & Company (R), VA, *98*
Hughes & Sloan, Inc. (C), GA, *383*
Hughes & Wilden Assoc. (C), PA, *383*
Human Capital Resources, Inc. (C), FL, *384*
Human Resource Bureau (C), CA, *384*
The Human Resource Consulting Group, Inc. (R), CO, *98*
The Human Resource Department Ltd. (R), OH, *98*
Human Resource Dimensions, Inc. (C), TX, *384*
The Human Resource Group, Inc. (R), OH, *98*
Human Resource Solutions (R), TX, *98*
Human Resource Technologies, Inc. (R), IL, *99*
Human Resources Management Hawaii, Inc. (C), HI, *384*
Human Resources Personnel Agency (R), AR, *99*
E. F. Humay Assoc. (C), PA, *384*
Hunegnaw Executive Search (C), OH, *384*
Leigh Hunt & Assoc., Inc. (C), ME, *384*
H.I. Hunt & Co., Ltd. (R), MA, *99*
Hunt & Howe Inc. (R), NY, *99*
The Hunt Co. (R), NY, *99*
The Hunt Group, Inc. (R), NC, *99*
Hunt Ltd. (C), NJ, *385*
Hunt Patton & Brazeal, Inc. (C), OK, *385*
Hunter Adams (C), NC, *385*
Hunter Assoc. (C), MA, *385*
Hunter Douglas Group, Inc. (R), IL, *99*
The Hunter Group, Inc. (C), MI, *385*
The Hunter Group (C), NC, *385*
Hunter Int'l., Inc. (R), CT, *100*
Hunter Int'l. LLC (C), MA, *385*
Hunter, Rowan & Crowe (C), FL, *386*
Huntington Group (R), CT, *100*
Huntington Personnel Consultants, Inc. (C), NY, *386*
Huntley Associates (Dallas), Inc. (C), TX, *386*
Huntress Real Estate Executive Search (R), MO, *100*
W. Hutt Management Resources Ltd. (R), ON, *100*
The Hutton Group, Inc. (C), FL, *386*
Hutton Merrill & Assoc. (R), CA, *100*
HVS Executive Search (R), NY, *100*
Hyde Danforth & Co. (R), TX, *100*
The Hyde Group, Inc. (R), CT, *101*
Hyland Executive Search (C), AZ, *386*
Hyman & Assoc. (C), TX, *386*
i.j. & assoc., inc. (C), CO, *386*
The Icard Group, Inc. (C), MI, *387*
Icon Recruiters, LLC (C), CA, *387*
IDC Executive Search Inc. (C), FL, *387*
IM Independent Management Recruiters (R), TN, *101*
IMA Search, Inc. (R), NY, *101*
John Imber Assoc., Ltd. (R), IL, *101*
The IMC Group of Companies (R), NY, *101*
Impact Search & Strategies (C), PA, *387*
Impact Source, Inc. (C), FL, *387*
Impact Technical Staffing (C), OR, *387*
Independent Power Consultants (C), TX, *387*
Independent Resource Systems (C), CA, *388*
Industry Consultants, Inc. (C), GA, *388*
Information Systems Professionals (C), NC, *388*
Information Technology Search (C), PA, *388*
InfoTech Search (C), TX, *388*
Infovia (C), CA, *388*
Ingram & Aydelotte, Inc. (R), NY, *101*
Meredith Ingram, Ltd. (C), IL, *388*
Innovative Healthcare Services, Inc. (C), GA, *389*
Innovative Partnerships (R), CA, *101*
Innovative Resource Group, LLC (C), NC, *389*
Innovative Search Group, Inc. (R), GA, *102*
innovativestaffsearch (C), TX, *389*
InSearch (C), CO, *389*
The Inside Track (C), TX, *389*
Insight Consulting Co. (C), NY, *389*
Insight Personnel Group, Inc. (C), TX, *389*
Insurance Career Center, Inc. (C), CT, *389*
Insurance People (C), IN, *390*
Insurance Personnel Resources, Inc. (C), GA, *390*
Insurance Recruiting Specialists (C), OH, *390*
Insurance Search (C), TX, *390*
InTech Services, Inc. (C), GA, *390*
Intech Summit Group, Inc. (R), CA, *102*
Integrated Management Solutions (C), NY, *390*
Integrated Search Solutions Group, LLC (ISSG) (R), NY, *102*
Integrity Search, Inc. (R), PA, *102*
Intelegra, Inc. (C), NJ, *390*
InteliSearch, Inc. (R), CT, *102*
Intelligent Marketing Solutions, Inc. (C), NY, *390*
IntelliSearch (C), TX, *391*

(R) = Retainer; (C) = Contingency

IntelliSource, inc. (C), PA, *391*
Inter Regional Executive Search, Inc. (IRES, Inc.) (C), NJ, *391*
Interactive Search Assoc. (C), PA, *391*
Interactive Search Network (R), CA, *102*
Intercontinental Executive Group (C), PA, *391*
Interim Accounting Professionals (C), CA, *391*
Interim Executive Recruiting (C), GA, *392*
Interim Financial Solutions - Mid-Atlantic Region (C), MD, *392*
Interim Management Resources Inc. (C), ON, *392*
International Business Partners (C), ON, *392*
International Consulting Services, Inc. (C), IL, *392*
International Executive Recruiters (C), OH, *393*
International Management Services Inc. (R), IL, *102*
International Management Advisors, Inc. (R), NY, *103*
International Management Development Corp. (C), NY, *393*
International Market Recruiters (C), NY, *393*
International Pro Sourcing, Inc. (C), PA, *393*
International Recruiting Services (C), FL, *393*
International Research Group (R), CA, *103*
International Staffing Consultants, Inc. (C), CA, *393*
International Technical Resources (C), FL, *393*
InterNeed (C), TX, *394*
Interquest, Inc. (R), NY, *103*
Intersource, Ltd. (R), GA, *103*
Interspace Interactive, Inc. (C), NY, *394*
Iona Partners (C), CA, *394*
IPR, Inc. (R), VA, *103*
IprGroup, Inc. (C), GA, *394*
IR Search (R), CA, *103*
Jeffrey Irving Assoc., Inc. (R), VA, *104*
Isaacson, Miller (R), MA, *104*
Joan Isbister Consultants (C), NY, *394*
ISC of Atlanta, Inc. (C), GA, *394*
ISC of Cincinnati Inc. (C), OH, *394*
ISC of Houston, Inc. (C), TX, *394*
ISG Informatics Search Group (C), ON, *395*
Ann Israel & Assoc., Inc. (C), NY, *395*
Ives & Associates, Inc. (C), OH, *395*
J & D Resources Inc. (C), TN, *395*
J. B. Linde & Assoc. (C), MO, *395*
The J. B. Search Group (C), CA, *395*
J. Joseph & Assoc. (C), OH, *395*
J. Nicholas Arthur (R), MA, *104*
J. R. Scott & Assoc., Ltd. (C), IL, *395*
J. Robert Scott (R), MA, *104*
J.B.A. Assoc. (R), WA, *104*
J.D.G. y Asociados, S.A. de C.V. (R), SO, *104*
J.J. & H., Ltd. (R), IL, *104*
J.N. Adams & Assoc., Inc. (C), PA, *396*
Jackley Search Consultants (C), MN, *396*
Ron Jackson & Assoc. (C), GA, *396*
Jackson & Coker (C), GA, *396*
Jackson Group Int'l. (C), CO, *396*
Jackson Resources (R), TX, *105*
Jacobs & Co. (R), CT, *105*
Jacobson Assoc. (C), IL, *396*
K. Jaeger & Assoc. (C), MA, *396*
Jaeger Int'l., Inc. (C), OH, *396*
JAG Group (R), MO, *105*
Jakobs & Assoc. Int'l. (R), NY, *105*
Pendleton James Assoc., Inc. (R), NY, *105*
R. I. James, Inc. (C), NY, *397*
James Moore & Assoc. (C), CA, *397*
David James Search (C), CA, *397*
The Jameson Group (C), CA, *397*
January Management Group (R), OH, *105*
Jaral Consultants, Inc. (C), NJ, *397*
JCL & Assoc. (C), FL, *397*
JDavid Assoc., Inc. (R), CT, *105*
JDC Assoc. (C), NY, *397*
JDG Assoc., Ltd. (C), MD, *397*
JDH & Assoc. (C), CA, *397*
Jefferson-Ross Assoc. Inc. (C), PA, *398*
Jeffrey Allan Co., Inc. (C), CA, *398*
Jeffrey Meryl Assoc., Inc. (C), NJ, *398*
Jender & Company (R), IL, *105*
Jenex Technology Placement Inc. (C), BC, *398*
JenKim Int'l. Ltd., Inc. (C), FL, *398*
Jerome & Co. (C), CA, *398*
JFW Associates, LLC (C), CT, *398*
JG Consultants, Inc. (R), TX, *106*
JL & Co. (C), CA, *399*
JLI-Boston (R), MA, *106*
JM & Company (R), PA, *106*
JNB Assoc., Inc. (C), MA, *399*
Job Link, Inc. (C), CA, *399*
Job-Born Candidate Selection Bureau (C), ON, *399*
John & Powers, Inc. (R), MO, *106*
John Jay & Co. (C), ME, *399*
John Michael Assoc. (R), DC, *106*
John Ryan Assoc., LLC. (C), NY, *399*
Johnson & Assoc., Inc. (R), CA, *106*
John H. Johnson & Assoc., Inc. (R), IL, *106*
J. M. Johnson & Assoc. (C), MN, *399*
L. J. Johnson & Co. (R), MI, *106*
Johnson & Company (R), CT, *107*
Ronald S. Johnson Assoc., Inc. (R), CA, *107*
Johnson Assoc., Inc. (C), IL, *399*
K. E. Johnson Assoc. (C), WA, *399*
Johnson Brown Assoc., Inc. (C), IN, *400*
The Johnson Group, Unlimited (C), NY, *400*
Johnson, Kemper & Assoc. (C), TX, *400*
Johnson Smith & Knisely (R), NY, *107*
Roye Johnston Assoc., Inc. (C), CA, *400*
Jonas, Walters & Assoc., Inc. (R), WI, *107*
Jonathan Lawrence Assoc. (C), NJ, *400*
The Jonathan Stevens Group, Inc. (R), NJ, *108*
Jones and Jones (R), OR, *108*
Jones Consulting Executive Search (C), GA, *400*
Jones Management Co. (R), CT, *108*
Jones-Parker/Starr (R), NC, *108*
Jordan-Sitter Assoc. (R), TX, *108*
Jordon & Jordon, Inc. (R), PA, *108*
J. M. Joseph Assoc. (R), NJ, *109*
Joseph Chris & Assoc. (C), TX, *400*
Joseph Consulting, Inc. (C), FL, *401*
Joseph Michaels (C), CA, *401*
Joslin & Assoc., Ltd. (C), IL, *401*
The Jotorok Group (C), RI, *401*
JPM International (C), CA, *401*
JRL Executive Recruiters (C), MO, *401*
JSG Group Management Consultants (R), ON, *109*
JT Assoc. (C), CT, *401*
Judd Associates (R), NJ, *109*
Julian Assoc., Inc. (C), CT, *401*
Juno Systems, Inc. (C), NY, *402*
Just Management Services Inc. (C), FL, *402*
A H Justice Search Consultants (C), TX, *402*
K & C Assoc. (C), CA, *402*
K2 Resources, L.P. (C), CT, *402*
Kaas Employment Services (C), IA, *402*
Kabana Corp. (C), MI, *402*
KABL Ability Network (C), CA, *402*
Kacevich, Lewis & Brown, Inc. (R), MA, *109*
Kaczmar & Assoc. (C), PA, *403*
Richard Kader & Assoc. (C), OH, *403*
Robert Kaestner & Assoc. (C), FL, *403*
Lisa Kalus & Assoc., Inc. (C), NY, *403*
Kames & Assoc. (C), MD, *403*
Kane & Assoc. (C), TX, *403*
Kanzer Assoc., Inc. (R), IL, *109*
Gary Kaplan & Assoc. (R), CA, *109*
Kaplan & Assoc., Inc. (R), PA, *109*
Karel & Co. (R), CA, *109*
Karp & Assoc. (C), FL, *403*
Howard Karr & Assoc., Inc. (R), CA, *110*
Karras Personnel, Inc. (C), NJ, *403*
Allan Karson Assoc., Inc. (R), NJ, *110*
Martin Kartin & Co., Inc. (R), NY, *110*
Kass/Abell & Assoc., Inc. (C), CA, *404*
Katelyn Partners (C), FL, *404*
Melissa Katzman, Executive Search (C), NY, *404*
Chris Kauffman & Company (R), GA, *110*
Kaufman Assoc. (R), CA, *110*
Jim Kay & Assoc. (C), IL, *404*
Kay Concepts, Inc. (C), FL, *404*
The Kay Group of 5th Ave. (C), NY, *404*
Kaye/Bassman Int'l. Corp. (R), TX, *110*
Kazan International, Inc. (R), NJ, *110*
Keane Assoc. (R), MA, *110*
A.T. Kearney Executive Search (R), IL, *111*
Keeley Consulting Inc. (C), ON, *404*
Keena Staffing Services (C), NY, *404*
Kehn & Gabor, Inc. (C), OH, *405*
The Keith-Murray Partnership (R), ON, *112*
Thomas A. Kelley & Assoc. (R), CA, *112*
Kelley & Keller, Inc. (C), FL, *405*
S. D. Kelly & Assoc., Inc. (R), MA, *112*
Kelly Assoc. (R), WI, *112*
Kelly Associates (R), PA, *112*
Kendall & Davis Co., Inc. (C), MO, *405*
Kenmore Executives Inc. (C), FL, *405*
David Warwick Kennedy & Assoc. (R), BC, *112*
Kennedy & Co. (R), IL, *112*

The Kennett Group, Inc. (R), PA, *112*
William W. Kenney (C), CT, *405*
Kennison & Assoc. Inc. (C), MO, *405*
Kensington Int'l., Inc. (R), IL, *113*
Kensington International (R), CA, *113*
Kent & Assoc. (R), OH, *113*
Kenzer Corp. (R), NY, *113*
Barbara Kerner Consultants (C), NY, *405*
Blair Kershaw Assoc., Inc. (C), PA, *405*
Kershner & Co. (R), DC, *113*
Daniel J. Kerstein, Consultant to Management (R), CO, *114*
Michael L. Ketner & Assoc., Inc. (R), PA, *114*
Key Employment (C), NJ, *405*
Key Resources Int'l. (C), CA, *405*
Keystone Consulting Group (C), GA, *406*
KGA Inc. (C), WI, *406*
Ki Technologies, Inc. (C), UT, *406*
Kiley, Owen & McGovern, Inc. (R), NJ, *114*
The Kilman Advisory Group (R), CT, *114*
Kimmel & Associates, Inc. (C), NC, *406*
Kincaid Group Inc. (KGI) (C), TX, *406*
Kincannon & Reed (R), VA, *114*
Kinderis & Loercher Group (C), IL, *407*
King ComputerSearch, Inc. (C), TX, *407*
Kingsbury • Wax • Bova (R), MA, *114*
Kingsley Allen Partners Inc. (R), ON, *114*
The Kingsley Group (R), CA, *114*
Kingsley Quinn/USA (R), NJ, *115*
The Kinlin Co., Inc. (R), MA, *115*
Richard Kinser & Assoc. (R), NY, *115*
Kip Williams, Inc. (R), NY, *115*
Kiradjieff & Goode, Inc. (R), MA, *115*
Kirby Assoc. (R), PA, *115*
Kirkbride Assoc., Inc. (C), WA, *407*
Kittleman & Assoc.,LLC (R), IL, *115*
KL Consultants (C), NJ, *407*
Kleber & Assoc. (C), WA, *407*
Klein, Landau & Romm (C), DC, *407*
The Kleinstein Group, Inc. (R), NJ, *116*
Raymond J. Klemmer & Assoc. (R), NY, *116*
The Kleven Group, Inc. - Executive Search Division (R), MA, *116*
The Kleven Group, Inc. (C), MA, *407*
KM Associates (C), MA, *407*
Knapp Consultants (R), CT, *116*
Joyce C. Knauff & Assoc. (C), IL, *408*
Koehler & Co. (R), WI, *116*
The Koehler Group (C), PA, *408*
Lee Koehn Assoc., Inc. (R), OR, *116*
T. J. Koellhoffer & Assoc. (R), NJ, *116*
Koerner & Assoc., Inc. (C), TN, *408*
Fred Koffler Assoc. (R), NY, *116*
Koll-Fairfield LLC (C), CT, *408*
Koltnow & Company (R), NY, *117*
Koontz, Jeffries & Assoc., Inc. (R), FL, *117*
Kopplin Search, Inc. (R), CA, *117*
Korban Associates (R), PA, *117*
Kordus Consulting Group (C), WI, *408*
Koren, Rogers Assoc. Inc. (R), NY, *117*
Korn/Ferry Int'l. (R), NY, *117*
Korn/Ferry, Int'l., S.A. de C.V. (R), MX, *118*
Kors Montgomery Int'l. (R), TX, *118*
Michael Kosmetos & Assoc., Inc. (C), OH, *408*
Kossuth & Assoc., Inc. (R), WA, *119*
Kostmayer Assoc., Inc. (R), MD, *119*
The J. Kovach Group (R), PA, *119*
Kozlin Assoc., Inc. (C), NY, *408*
KPA Assoc., Inc. (C), NY, *408*
KPMG Executive Search (R), ON, *119*
Katherine R. Kraemer (R), CA, *120*
C. R. Krafski & Assoc., Inc. (R), IL, *120*
Krakower Group, Inc. (R), CA, *120*
Kramer Executive Resources, Inc. (C), NY, *409*
J. Krauss Assoc. (R), FL, *120*
Krauthamer & Assoc. (R), MD, *120*
Krautler Personnel Recruitment (C), FL, *409*
Krecklo Executive Search Inc. (R), ON, *120*
Evie Kreisler Assoc. Inc. (C), CA, *409*
Kremple & Meade, Inc. (R), CA, *120*
Kremple Consulting Group (R), CA, *120*
Kresin Wingard (C), IL, *409*
Kressenberg Assoc. (C), TX, *409*
D. A. Kreuter Assoc., Inc. (R), PA, *121*
Kreutz Consulting Group, Inc. (R), IL, *121*
Todd L. Krueger & Assoc. (C), WA, *409*
Krueger Assoc. (R), IL, *121*
John Kuhn & Assoc., Inc. (R), WI, *121*
Kuhn Med-Tech (C), CA, *409*
Kukoy Associates (R), CO, *121*
Paul Kull & Co. (R), NJ, *121*
Kulper & Co., L.L.C. (R), NJ, *121*
D. Kunkle & Assoc. (C), IL, *410*
Kunzer Assoc., Ltd. (R), IL, *121*
John Kurosky & Assoc. (R), CA, *122*
Kurtz Pro-Search, Inc. (C), NJ, *410*
Kutcher Tax Careers, Inc. (C), NY, *410*
Kutt, Inc. (C), CO, *410*
Kyle Assoc. (C), NY, *410*
L & K Assoc. (C), NJ, *410*
L & L Assoc. (C), CA, *410*
L O R (R), NJ, *122*
L T M Assoc. (C), IL, *410*
L&L Assoc. Global Search (C), PA, *411*
L. Patrick Group (R), NJ, *122*
Lab Market Specialists (C), UT, *411*
Marvin Laba & Assoc. (R), CA, *122*
Laboratory Resource Group (C), MA, *411*
The LaBorde Group (C), CA, *411*
LaCosta & Assoc. Int'l. Inc. (C), CA, *411*
Rene LaFlamme & Associes (R), QE, *122*
Laguzza Assoc., Ltd. (R), NY, *122*
LAI Ward Howell (R), NY, *122*
Gregory Laka & Co. (C), IL, *411*
Lake Medical Associates (C), ME, *411*
Lam Assoc. (C), HI, *411*
Lamay Assoc., Inc. (R), CT, *124*
Lamon + Stuart + Michaels Inc. (R), ON, *124*
Lancaster Assoc., Inc. (C), NJ, *411*
E. J. Lance Management Assoc., Inc. (C), NY, *412*
Landon Morgan (C), ON, *412*
The Landstone Group (C), NY, *412*
Lange & Assoc., Inc. (C), IN, *412*
The Langford Search, Inc. (C), AL, *412*
Langley & Associates, Inc. (Executive Search Consultants) (R), CO, *124*
Lanken-Kimball-Therrell & Assoc. (C), GA, *412*
LanSo Int'l., Inc. (C), NY, *413*
Lawrence L. Lapham, Inc. (R), NY, *124*
Stephen Laramee & Assoc. Inc. (C), ON, *413*
Larkin & Co. (R), CA, *124*
Robert Larned Assoc., Inc. (C), VA, *413*
R. H. Larsen & Assoc., Inc. (R), FL, *125*
Jack B. Larsen & Assoc., Inc. (C), PA, *413*
Larsen & Lee, Inc. (R), MD, *125*
Larsen Int'l., Inc. (R), TX, *125*
Larsen, Whitney, Blecksmith & Zilliacus, Inc. (R), CA, *125*
Larson & Trent Assoc. (C), TN, *413*
Larson Assoc. (R), CA, *125*
Larson, Katz & Young, Inc. (C), VA, *413*
LAS Management Consulting Group, Inc. (R), NJ, *125*
Lascelle & Assoc. Inc. (C), ON, *413*
Lasher Assoc. (R), FL, *125*
Michael Latas & Assoc., Inc. (R), MO, *125*
Latham International, Ltd. (R), NJ, *126*
Lauer, Sbarbaro Assoc., EMA Partners Int'l. (R), IL, *126*
Lautz, Grotte, Engler & Swimley (R), CA, *126*
Madeleine Lav & Assoc. (C), CA, *413*
LaVallee & Associates (C), NC, *413*
Lawrence James Assoc. of Florida, Inc. (C), FL, *414*
Lawrence-Balakonis & Assoc., Inc. (C), GA, *414*
Lawrence-Leiter & Co. (R), KS, *126*
W. R. Lawry, Inc. (R), CT, *126*
The Lawson Group, Inc. (C), SC, *414*
Layne-Mendez & Co. (R), TX, *127*
LCC Companies (C), AZ, *414*
LCS, Inc. (C), TX, *414*
Leader Institute, Inc. (C), GA, *414*
Leader Network (C), PA, *414*
Leader Resources Group (C), GA, *415*
Leader Search Inc. (R), AB, *127*
Leaders-Trust Int'l./Carce y Asociados, S.C. (R), MX, *127*
Lear & Assoc., Inc. (C), FL, *415*
The Lear Group, Inc. (R), OH, *127*
Reynolds Lebus Assoc. (C), AZ, *415*
Lechner & Assoc., Inc. (C), FL, *415*
Lectra Search (C), GA, *415*
Ledbetter/Davidson Int'l., Inc. (R), NY, *127*
Albert G. Lee Assoc. (C), RI, *415*
Ricci Lee Assoc., Inc. (C), CA, *415*
Vincent Lee Assoc. (C), NY, *415*
The Conrad Lee Co. Inc. (R), FL, *127*
Lee Management Group Inc. (C), NJ, *416*
Leeds and Leeds (C), TN, *416*
Legal Network Inc. (C), CA, *416*
Legal Search Assoc. (C), KS, *416*
V. J. Lehman & Assoc., Inc. (R), CO, *127*
Lehman McLeskey (R), TX, *128*
Leith & Assoc., Inc. (C), OH, *416*
Lekan & Assoc., Inc. (R), OH, *128*
Lemming/LeVan, Inc. (R), GA, *128*
Lending Personnel Services (C), CA, *416*
F. P. Lennon Assoc. (C), PA, *416*
AG Lennox & Assoc. (R), AB, *128*
Jacques LePage Executive Search Inc. (R), QE, *128*
Leslie Kavanagh Assoc., Inc. (C), NY, *416*
J. E. Lessner Assoc., Inc. (R), MI, *128*

Levin & Company, Inc. (R), MA, *128*
Alan Levine Assoc. (R), MA, *129*
Michael Levine Search Consultants (R), NY, *129*
Levison Search Assoc. (R), CA, *129*
The Levton Group Inc. (R), ON, *129*
Hal Levy & Assoc. (C), NY, *417*
Lewis & Blank Int'l. (R), CA, *129*
Lewis Companies Inc. (R), ON, *129*
Lewis Consulting Service (C), IL, *417*
Lexington Software Inc. (C), NY, *417*
LG Brand, Inc. (C), MD, *417*
The Libra Group Inc. (C), CT, *417*
The Libra Group (C), NC, *417*
Pat Licata & Assoc. (C), NC, *417*
Howard Lieberman & Assoc., Inc. (C), MN, *417*
LifeWork, Inc. (C), TX, *418*
Lifter & Assoc. (C), CA, *418*
Lois L. Lindauer Searches (C), MA, *418*
J. H. Lindell & Co. (C), CA, *418*
Linden Group, Inc. (C), NC, *418*
Ginger Lindsey & Assoc., Inc. (C), TX, *418*
Lindsey & Co., Inc. (R), CT, *129*
Lineal Recruiting Services (C), CT, *418*
Lipsky Group, Inc. (R), CA, *129*
Lipson & Co. (R), CA, *130*
Lipton Assoc., Inc. (R), NY, *130*
Litchfield & Willis, Inc. (R), TX, *130*
Livingston, Robert & Co. (R), CT, *130*
LJ Networking, Inc. (C), MD, *418*
Lloyd Associates (R), GA, *130*
Lloyd Prescott & Churchill, Inc. (R), FL, *130*
Lloyd Prescott Assoc., Inc. (C), FL, *418*
Lloyd Staffing (C), NY, *419*
LMB Assoc. (C), IL, *419*
Locke & Assoc. (R), NC, *131*
Locus Inc. (C), WV, *419*
Loderman & Costello (C), GA, *419*
Loewenstein & Assoc., Inc. (R), TX, *131*
J. P. Logan & Co., Inc. (R), NY, *131*
The Logan Group, Inc. (R), MO, *131*
Logic Assoc., Inc. (C), NY, *419*
Logistics Management Resources, Inc. (R), NY, *131*
Logix, Inc. (C), MA, *420*
Logue & Rice Inc. (C), VA, *420*
London & Company (C), NY, *420*
London Executive Consultants Inc. (C), ON, *420*
Longo Associates (C), CA, *420*
Longshore + Simmons (R), PA, *131*
Lord & Albus Co. (C), TX, *420*
J. S. Lord & Company, Inc. (R), MA, *131*
Louis Search Group, Inc. (C), NJ, *420*
Scott Love Assoc., Inc. (C), AZ, *420*
Bruce Lowery & Assoc. (C), MI, *420*
Lucas Assoc. (C), GA, *421*
Lucas Group (C), NY, *421*
The John Lucht Consultancy Inc. (R), NY, *131*
The Luciani Group (R), CA, *132*
Ludwig & Assoc., Inc. (C), VA, *421*
Fran Luisi Assoc. (R), NJ, *132*
Charles Luntz & Assoc., Inc. (R), MO, *132*
Lutz Associates (C), CT, *421*
Lybrook Assoc., Inc. (C), RI, *421*
P. J. Lynch Assoc. (R), CT, *132*
Lynch Miller Moore Partners, Inc. (R), IL, *132*
Lynne Palmer Executive Recruitment, Inc. (C), NY, *421*
Lynx, Inc. (C), MA, *421*
Lyons & Assoc., Inc. (C), IL, *422*
Lyons Assoc. (R), NY, *132*
Lyons Pruitt Int'l. (R), PA, *132*
M H Executive Search Group (C), TX, *422*
M. K. & Assoc. (C), PA, *422*
M.C. Executive Search (C), CA, *422*
M/J/A Partners (R), IL, *133*
The Macdonald Group, Inc. (R), NJ, *133*
The Mackenzie Group (R), MD, *133*
MacNaughton Assoc. (R), CA, *133*
Maczkov-Biosciences, Inc. (R), CA, *133*
The Madeira Group (R), PA, *133*
Carol Maden Group (C), VA, *422*
Madison Executive Search, Inc. (C), NJ, *422*
The Madison Group (R), NY, *133*
Madison MacArthur Inc. (R), ON, *133*
Magellan Int'l., L.P. (C), TX, *422*
Maglio & Co., Inc. (R), WI, *134*
Magnum Search (C), IL, *422*
Maiola & Co. (C), OH, *423*
Maiorino & Weston Assoc., Inc. (R), CT, *134*
Major, Hagen & Africa (C), CA, *423*
Major Legal Services, Inc. (C), OH, *423*
Major Search (C), NJ, *423*
The Mallard Group (C), IN, *423*
Managed Care Consultants (C), AZ, *423*
Managed Care Resources (C), TX, *424*
Management & Human Resources (R), MA, *134*
Management Advisors Int'l., Inc. (C), NC, *424*
Management Alliance Group, Inc. (R), NJ, *134*
Management Assoc. (C), CA, *424*
Management Assoc. (C), MD, *424*
Management Association Network (C), WI, *424*
Management Catalysts (R), NJ, *134*
Management Consultants Corporate Recruiters (C), AZ, *424*
Management Decision Systems, Inc. (MDSI) (C), NJ, *424*
Management Dimensions Ltd. (R), ON, *134*
Management One Consultants (C), ON, *425*
Management Recruiters of Nassau, Inc. (R), NY, *134*
Management Recruiters International, Inc. (MRI) (C), OH, *425*
Management Recruiters of Birmingham, Inc. (C), AL, *438*
Management Recruiters of Sedona (C), AZ, *438*
Management Recruiters of Mobile Co., Inc. (C), AL, *438*
Management Recruiters of Decatur, LLC (C), AL, *438*
Management Recruiters of Birmingham (C), AL, *438*
Management Recruiters of Birmingham-South, Inc. (C), AL, *438*
Management Recruiters Tucson-Foothills, Inc. (C), AZ, *439*
Management Recruiters of Tucson (C), AZ, *439*
Management Recruiters of Little Rock (C), AR, *439*
Management Recruiters of Aptos (C), CA, *439*
Management Recruiters of San Luis Obispo (C), CA, *439*
Management Recruiters of Berkeley (C), CA, *439*
Management Recruiters Peninsula (C), CA, *439*
Management Recruiters of Fresno (C), CA, *440*
Management Recruiters of Northern California (C), CA, *440*
Management Recruiters of Grass Valley (C), CA, *440*
Management Recruiters of Emeryville (C), CA, *440*
Management Recruiters Dana Point (C), CA, *440*
Management Recruiters of Clovis (C), CA, *440*
Management Recruiters of Laguna Hills (C), CA, *440*
Management Recruiters of Monterey (C), CA, *441*
Management Recruiters of Sonoma (C), CA, *441*
Management Recruiters of Pleasanton (C), CA, *441*
Management Recruiters, Inland Empire Agency (C), CA, *441*
Management Recruiters of Roseville (C), CA, *441*
Management Recruiters of Sacramento North (C), CA, *441*
Management Recruiters Inc. of Silicon Valley (C), CA, *441*
Management Recruiters of Colorado Springs (C), CO, *441*
Management Recruiters of Colchester (C), CT, *442*
Management Recruiters of Milford Inc. (C), CT, *442*
Management Recruiters of Altamonte (C), FL, *442*
Management Recruiters of Middlesex (C), CT, *442*
Management Recruiters of Colorado, Inc. (C), CO, *442*
Management Recruiters of Franktown (C), CO, *442*
Management Recruiters of Winsted, Inc. (C), CT, *442*
Management Recruiters of Boca Raton (C), FL, *443*
Management Recruiters of Bonita Springs, Inc. (C), FL, *443*
Management Recruiters of Anna Maria Island (C), FL, *443*
Management Recruiters of Clearwater (C), FL, *443*
Management Recruiters of Ft. Myers, FL. (C), FL, *443*

Management Recruiters of Melbourne, Inc. (C), FL, *443*
Management Recruiters, Inc. (C), FL, *443*
Management Recruiters of Miami-North (C), FL, *443*
Management Recruiters of Pensacola (C), FL, *444*
Management Recruiters of Tampa North (C), FL, *444*
Management Recruiters of St. Augustine (C), FL, *444*
Management Recruiters of Plant City, Inc. (C), FL, *444*
Management Recruiters of Northern Palm Beaches (C), FL, *444*
Management Recruiters of Lake Co., Inc. (C), FL, *444*
Management Recruiters of St. Lucie County, Inc. (C), FL, *444*
Management Recruiters of Venice, Inc. (C), FL, *445*
Management Recruiters of Vero Beach (C), FL, *445*
Management Recruiters of North Fulton (C), GA, *445*
Management Recruiters of Atlanta (C), GA, *445*
Management Recruiters of Columbus, Inc. (C), GA, *445*
Management Recruiters of Forsyth County (C), GA, *445*
Management Recruiters of Duluth (C), GA, *445*
Management Recruiters of Atlanta West, Inc. (C), GA, *445*
Management Recruiters of Sandy Springs (C), GA, *446*
Management Recruiters of Savannah (C), GA, *446*
Management Recruiters of Boise (C), ID, *446*
Management Recruiters of Atlanta North, Inc. (C), GA, *446*
Management Recruiters of Marietta, Inc. (C), GA, *446*
Management Recruiters of Atlanta NE (C), GA, *446*
Management Recruiters - Towne Lake (C), GA, *446*
Management Recruiters of Sun Valley (C), ID, *447*
Management Recruiters of Chicago West (C), IL, *447*
Management Recruiters of Barrington (C), IL, *447*
Management Recruiters of Batavia (C), IL, *447*
Management Recruiters of Lake Forest, IL (C), IL, *447*
Management Recruiters of Chicago-North Shore (C), IL, *447*
Management Recruiters of Springfield, Inc. (C), IL, *447*
Management Recruiters of St. Charles (C), IL, *447*
Management Recruiters - Indianapolis (C), IN, *448*
Management Recruiters-Cedar Rapids, Inc. (C), IA, *448*
Management Recruiters of Spencer (C), IA, *448*
Management Recruiters of Noblesville, Inc. (C), IN, *448*
Management Recruiters of Indianapolis (C), IN, *448*
Management Recruiters of Indianapolis-North (C), IN, *448*
Management Recruiters of South Bend (C), IN, *448*
Management Recruiters of Des Moines (C), IA, *449*
Management Recruiters of Fairfield (C), IA, *449*
Management Recruiters of Siouxland (C), IA, *449*
Management Recruiters of Williamsburg (C), IA, *449*
Management Recruiters of Topeka, Inc. (C), KS, *449*
Management Recruiters of Warren County, KY (C), KY, *449*
Management Recruiters of Danville (C), KY, *449*
Management Recruiters of Richmond (C), KY, *449*
Management Recruiters of the Baltimore Washington Corridor (C), MD, *450*
Management Recruiters of Frederick, Inc. (C), MD, *450*
Management Recruiters of Washington, DC Inc. (C), MD, *450*
Management Recruiters of Columbia (C), MD, *450*
Management Recruiters of Monroe, Inc. (C), LA, *450*
Management Recruiters of Rockville (C), MD, *450*
Management Recruiters of Baltimore (C), MD, *451*
Management Recruiters of Birmingham (C), MI, *451*
Management Recruiters of Southeastern Michigan (C), MI, *451*
Management Recruiters of Dearborn, Inc. (C), MI, *451*
Management Recruiters of Detroit & Farmington Hills (C), MI, *451*
Management Recruiters - Flint (C), MI, *451*
Management Recruiters of Livonia (C), MI, *451*
Management Recruiters of Muskegon (C), MI, *451*
Management Recruiters of Rochester (C), MN, *452*
Management Recruiters of Cass County, NE (C), NE, *452*
Management Recruiters of Rankin Co. (C), MS, *452*
Management Recruiters of Winona (C), MN, *452*
Management Recruiters of Chanhassen (C), MN, *452*
Management Recruiters of Bloomington (C), MN, *452*
Management Recruiters of North Oakland County, Inc. (C), MI, *452*
Management Recruiters of Woodbury (C), MN, *452*
Management Recruiters of Medford, N.J. (C), NJ, *453*
Management Recruiters of Reno (C), NV, *453*
Management Recruiters of Lake Tahoe, NV (C), NV, *453*
Management Recruiters of Bay Head (C), NJ, *453*
Management Recruiters of Orange County, N.Y., Inc. (C), NJ, *453*
Management Recruiters of Morris County, NJ (C), NJ, *453*
Management Recruiters of North Warren Inc. (C), NJ, *453*
Management Recruiters of Upper Westchester (C), NY, *454*
Management Recruiters of Great Neck (C), NY, *454*
Management Recruiters of The Sandias (C), NM, *454*
Management Recruiters of Broome County, Inc. (C), NY, *454*
Management Recruiters of Middlesex County NJ (C), NJ, *454*
Management Recruiters of Bordentown (C), NJ, *454*
Management Recruiters of New Providence (C), NJ, *454*
Management Recruiters of Princeton (C), NJ, *454*
Management Recruiters of Fayetteville (C), NC, *455*
Management Recruiters of Gramercy, Inc. (C), NY, *455*
Management Recruiters of Manhattan on Broadway (C), NY, *455*
Management Recruiters of Woodbury Inc. (C), NY, *455*
Management Recruiters of Asheville, Inc. (C), NC, *455*
Management Recruiters of Burlington (C), NC, *455*
Management Recruiters of Cedar Mountain (C), NC, *455*
Management Recruiters of Boone (C), NC, *456*
Management Recruiters of Rocky Mount - Southwest (C), NC, *456*
Management Recruiters of Raleigh (C), NC, *456*
Management Recruiters of Mt. Airy (C), NC, *456*
Management Recruiters of Kinston (C), NC, *456*
Management Recruiters - Kannapolis (C), NC, *456*
Management Recruiters of Gastonia (C), NC, *456*
Management Recruiters of Charlotte - North, Inc. (C), NC, *456*
Management Recruiters of Cleveland (C), OH, *457*
Management Recruiters of Columbus (C), OH, *457*
Management Recruiters of Dayton, Inc. (C), OH, *457*
Management Recruiters of Cleveland (C), OH, *457*

Management Recruiters of Akron (C), OH, *457*
Management Recruiters of Wilmington (C), NC, *457*
Management Recruiters of Winston-Salem (C), NC, *457*
Management Recruiters of Cincinnati/ Sharonville, Inc. (C), OH, *457*
Management Recruiters - North Canton, Inc. (C), OH, *458*
Management Recruiters of Sidney (C), OH, *458*
Management Recruiters of Northwest Ohio, Inc. (C), OH, *458*
Management Recruiters of Youngstown (C), OH, *458*
Management Recruiters of Oklahoma City (C), OK, *458*
Management Recruiters of Bethlehem, PA (C), PA, *458*
Management Recruiters of Easton, PA (C), PA, *458*
Management Recruiters of Mentor, Inc. (C), OH, *458*
Management Recruiters of McMurray, Inc. (C), PA, *459*
Management Recruiters of Pittsburgh (C), PA, *459*
Management Recruiters of Cherry Hill (C), PA, *459*
Management Recruiters of Westmoreland County, Inc. (C), PA, *459*
Management Recruiters of Valley Forge (C), PA, *459*
Management Recruiters of Lionville, Inc. (C), PA, *459*
Management Recruiters of Delaware County (C), PA, *459*
Management Recruiters of Pittsburgh-North, Inc. (C), PA, *460*
Management Recruiters of West Chester, Inc. (C), PA, *460*
Management Recruiters of Puerto Rico (C), PR, *460*
Management Recruiters of Aiken (C), SC, *460*
Management Recruiters of Florence (C), SC, *460*
Management Recruiters of Greenville (C), SC, *460*
Management Recruiters of Myrtle Beach, Inc. (C), SC, *460*
Management Recruiters of North Charleston (C), SC, *460*
Management Recruiters of Chattanooga-Brainerd, Inc. (C), TN, *461*
Management Recruiters of Franklin, Inc. (C), TN, *461*
Management Recruiters of Columbia, Tennessee (C), TN, *461*
Management Recruiters of Travelers Rest, Inc. (C), SC, *461*
Management Recruiters of Georgetown (C), SC, *461*
Management Recruiters of Sioux Falls, LLP (C), SD, *461*
Management Recruiters The Delta Group, Inc. (C), TN, *461*
Management Recruiters of North West Austin (C), TX, *462*
Management Recruiters of Houston (C), TX, *462*
Management Recruiters of Champions (C), TX, *462*
Management Recruiters - Friendswood (C), TX, *462*
Management Recruiters Dallas North (MRDN) (C), TX, *462*
Management Recruiters of Austin (C), TX, *462*
Management Recruiters of Arlington (C), TX, *462*
Management Recruiters of Memphis, TN (C), TN, *462*
Management Recruiters of LBJ Park/Dallas (C), TX, *462*
Management Recruiters of Lewisville (C), TX, *463*
Management Recruiters of San Marcos (C), TX, *463*
Management Recruiters of San Antonio - North (C), TX, *463*
Management Recruiters of San Antonio (C), TX, *463*
Management Recruiters of Lubbock (C), TX, *463*
Management Recruiters of Houston-Northeast (C), TX, *463*
Management Recruiters of Round Rock (C), TX, *463*
Management Recruiters of Sugar Land Inc. (C), TX, *464*
Management Recruiters Int'l.-The Woodlands (C), TX, *464*
Management Recruiters of Ogden (C), UT, *464*
Management Recruiters of Salt Lake City (C), UT, *464*
Management Recruiters of Arlington (C), VA, *464*
Management Recruiters of Fairfax, VA (C), VA, *464*
Management Recruiters - Piedmont (C), VA, *464*
Management Recruiters of Loudoun County South (C), VA, *465*
Management Recruiters of Appleton (C), WI, *465*
Management Recruiters of Milwaukee-West (C), WI, *465*
Management Recruiters of Kanawha Valley, LLC (C), WV, *465*
Management Recruiters of Lynnwood (C), WA, *465*
Management Recruiters of Roanoke (C), VA, *465*
Management Recruiters of Seattle (C), WA, *465*
Management Recruiters of Spokane (C), WA, *465*
Management Recruiters of Janesville, Inc. (C), WI, *466*
Management Recruiters of Madison, Inc. (C), WI, *466*
Management Recruiters of Milwaukee-North (C), WI, *466*
Management Recruiters of Milwaukee - Downtown (C), WI, *466*
Management Recruiters of Stevens Point, Inc. (C), WI, *466*
Management Recruiters of Wausau, LLC (C), WI, *466*
Management Recruiters of Cheyenne (C), WY, *466*
Management Resource Group, Ltd. (C), IA, *467*
Management Resource Group (C), MN, *467*
Management Resource Assoc., Inc. (C), FL, *467*
Management Resource Group, Inc. (C), NY, *467*
Management Resources Int'l. (R), NY, *135*
Management Resources (C), TX, *467*
Management Search Assoc., Inc. (C), GA, *467*
Management Search Int'l. (C), CA, *467*
Management Search, Inc. (C), IL, *467*
Management Search, Inc. (C), OK, *468*
Management Search of R.I. Inc. (R), RI, *135*
Management Solutions, Inc. (C), CA, *468*
Management Solutions, Inc. (C), WA, *468*
Mancini Technical Recruiting (C), VA, *468*
Mangieri/Solutions LLC (C), CT, *468*
Mankuta Gallagher & Assoc., Inc. (C), FL, *468*
Mannard & Assoc., Inc. (R), IL, *135*
Manning Lloyd Assoc. Ltd. (C), NY, *468*
F. L. Mannix & Co. (R), MA, *135*
ManTech Consulting (C), NY, *468*
Manuso, Alexander & Associates, Inc. (R), NY, *135*
The Marathon Group (C), FL, *469*
MARBL Consultants, Inc. (C), WI, *469*
Marc-Allen Assoc., Inc. (C), FL, *469*
Marcus & Assoc. (C), NY, *469*
Marentz & Co. (C), TX, *469*
Margolin Consultants, Inc. (C), NY, *469*
Mark Adam Assoc. (R), NJ, *135*
J. L. Mark Assoc., Inc. (R), CO, *135*
Mark Christian & Assoc., Inc. (C), AZ, *469*
Mark III Personnel, Inc. (C), NC, *470*
Mark Stanley & Co./EMA Partners International (R), FL, *136*
Markent Personnel, Inc. (C), WI, *470*
Market Niche Consulting (C), AZ, *470*
Marketing & Sales Resources, Inc. (C), FL, *470*
Marketing Consultants (C), WI, *470*
Marketing Recruiters, Inc. (C), NC, *470*
Marketing Resources (C), MA, *470*
Marketing Search Inc. (C), OH, *471*
Marketing/Public Relations Research Recruiting (C), CT, *471*
MarketPro, Inc. (C), GA, *471*
Marks & Co., Inc. (R), CT, *136*
Paula Marks Inc. (R), NY, *136*
Brad Marks Int'l. (R), CA, *136*
Marley Group Ltd. (C), NY, *471*
The Marlow Group (R), MA, *136*
The Maroon Group (R), CT, *136*
Marra Peters & Partners (R), NJ, *136*
Marsar & Co., Inc. (C), FL, *471*
Karen Marshall Assoc. (C), KY, *471*

Marshall Consultants, Inc. (R), NY, *137*
The Marshall Group (R), IL, *137*
Marshall-Alan Assoc., Inc. (C), NY, *471*
Marsteller Wilcox Assoc. (C), IL, *471*
Donovan Martin & Assoc. (R), CA, *137*
J. Martin & Assoc. (R), CA, *137*
George R. Martin (R), PA, *137*
Martin Grant Assoc. Inc., Insurance Personnel (C), MA, *472*
The Martin Group (R), CA, *137*
Martin Partners, L.L.C. (R), IL, *137*
The Martwick Group, Inc. (C), OR, *472*
Marvel Consultants, Inc. (C), OH, *472*
Maschal/Connors Inc. (R), NJ, *137*
Mason & Nicastri Ltd. (R), CA, *138*
Masserman & Assoc., Inc. (R), NY, *138*
Massey-Horton Int'l. (R), ON, *138*
Louis Thomas Masterson & Co. (R), OH, *138*
Richard L. Mather & Assoc. (C), CT, *472*
Mathey Services (C), IL, *472*
Matrix Consultants, Inc. (C), NC, *472*
Matté & Company, Inc. (R), CT, *138*
Matte Consulting Group Inc. (R), QE, *138*
Matthews & Stephens Assoc., Inc. (C), CT, *472*
The Matthews Group, Inc. (C), NJ, *472*
Matthews Professional Employment Specialists, Inc. (C), IL, *472*
G. P. Mattocks & Associates (C), NC, *473*
Maxecon Executive Search Consultants (R), FL, *138*
Maximum Management Corp. (C), NY, *473*
K. Maxin & Assoc. (R), PA, *139*
Paul May & Assoc. (C), IL, *473*
Mary L. Mayer, Ltd. (R), MN, *139*
The Mayes Group, Ltd. (R), PA, *139*
Mayhall Search Group, Inc. (C), IN, *473*
The Mazzitelli Group, Ltd. (R), MN, *139*
MB Inc. Executive Search (C), NY, *473*
The McAulay Firm (R), NC, *139*
McBride Assoc., Inc. (R), DC, *139*
Tom McCall Executive Search (C), IL, *473*
McCann, Choi & Associates, LLC (R), NY, *139*
McCartan Assoc. (R), NJ, *139*
K. E. McCarthy & Assoc. (R), CA, *139*
McCarthy Assoc. National BancSearch, LLC (C), LA, *473*
McCooe & Assoc., Inc. (R), NJ, *140*
McCormack & Assoc. (R), CA, *140*
McCormack & Farrow (R), CA, *140*
The McCormick Group (C), VA, *473*
McCormick Search Inc. (C), IL, *474*
McCoy Ltd. (C), CA, *474*
McCray, Shriver, Eckdahl & Assoc., Inc. (R), CA, *140*
The Paul McDaniel Co. (C), TN, *474*
Earl L. McDermid & Assoc. (C), IL, *474*
McDonald Assoc. Int'l. (R), IL, *140*
McDonald, Long & Assoc., Inc. (R), NY, *140*
McDowell & Co., Recruiters (C), TX, *474*
G. E. McFarland & Co. (R), GA, *140*
Clarence E. McFeely, Inc. (R), IL, *141*
Robert E. McGrath & Assoc. (R), CT, *141*
McGrath & Assoc., Inc. (R), NJ, *141*
McHale & Assoc. (R), WA, *141*
McInturff & Assoc., Inc. (C), MA, *474*
McIntyre Assoc. (R), CT, *141*
McIntyre Management Resources (C), ON, *474*
McKavis Assoc. (C), CA, *475*
McKee Cyber Search (C), MS, *475*
McKeen & Company (R), TX, *141*
McKinley•Arend Int'l. (R), TX, *141*
The McKinnon Management Group Inc. (C), ON, *475*
William K. McLaughlin Assoc., Inc. (C), NY, *475*
Dan P. McLean Assoc., Inc. (C), ON, *475*
The McLeod Group, Inc. (R), CT, *141*
McManners Assoc., Inc. (R), CA, *142*
McNichol Assoc. (R), PA, *142*
McPherson Square Assoc., Inc. (C), DC, *475*
Jon McRae & Associates, Inc. (R), GA, *142*
McRoberts & Assoc. (C), OH, *475*
MCS Assoc. (R), CA, *142*
Joseph J. McTaggart (C), CA, *476*
MDR & Associates (C), AR, *476*
MDR Associates, Inc. (C), FL, *476*
James Mead & Co. (R), CT, *142*
Meads & Assoc. (R), FL, *142*
Med Exec Int'l. (C), CA, *476*
Med-Ex Services (C), OH, *476*
Meder & Assoc., Inc. (R), IL, *142*
Medfall Inc. (C), ON, *476*
Media Management Resources, Inc. (R), CO, *142*
Media Recruiting Group, Inc. (C), NY, *476*
MediaCOM Talent Group (C), MA, *476*
Medical Executive Recruiters (C), CA, *477*
Medical Executive Search Assoc., Inc. (C), AZ, *477*
Medical Innovations (C), NY, *477*
Medical Recruiters Exchange (C), AZ, *477*
Medical Recruiters Inc. (C), MO, *477*
Medical Search of America, Inc. (C), GA, *477*
Medicorp, Inc. (C), MO, *477*
The Medley Group (C), CA, *477*
MedPro Personnel, Inc. (C), GA, *478*
MedQuest Assoc. (C), CO, *478*
MedSearch Resources, Inc. (C), FL, *478*
Medserve & Assoc. Inc. (C), MD, *478*
MedXec USA, Inc. (C), FL, *478*
Mee Derby & Co. (C), DC, *478*
Mehta Consulting (C), NJ, *478*
Martin H. Meisel Assoc., Inc. (R), NY, *143*
Melancon & Co. (R), TX, *143*
Juan Menefee & Assoc. (C), IL, *478*
Meng, Finseth & Assoc., Inc. (R), CA, *143*
Mengel & McDonald Ltd. (C), IL, *479*
Mercedes & Co., Inc. (R), MA, *143*
The Mercer Group, Inc. (R), NM, *143*
J. M. Meredith & Assoc. Inc. (C), CA, *479*
Meridian Legal Search/Legal Temps (C), NY, *479*
Meridian Resources (C), OH, *479*
Merit Professional Search, Inc. (C), TN, *479*
Merlin Int'l. Inc. (C), NJ, *479*
Merrick & Moore (C), NC, *479*
MES Search Co. (C), GA, *479*
MESA, Inc. (R), CO, *143*
MESA International (C), CA, *480*
Messett Assoc., Inc. (R), FL, *143*
META/MAT, Ltd. (R), NJ, *144*
MetroVantage Personnel Systems (C), CA, *480*
Walter Meyer & Assoc. (R), NY, *144*
Meyer Assoc., Inc. (R), GA, *144*
mfg/Search, Inc. (C), IN, *480*
MGA Executive Search (C), FL, *480*
Michael Assoc. (R), IL, *144*
Michael James & Co. (C), IL, *480*
Michael Thomas, Inc. (C), OH, *480*
Michael Wayne Recruiters (C), IL, *480*
Michael/Merrill (C), KS, *481*
Michaels & Moere (C), WI, *481*
Lou Michaels Assoc., Inc. (C), MI, *481*
E. J. Michaels, Ltd. (C), NY, *481*
Michigan Consulting Group (R), MI, *144*
Micro Staff Solutions, Inc. (C), TX, *481*
Midas Management (C), CT, *481*
Midland Consultants (C), OH, *481*
Millar Walker & Gay (R), ON, *144*
Millennium Search Group, Inc. (R), CA, *144*
Miller & Assoc. (C), FL, *481*
Miller + Miller (C), WA, *482*
Susan C. Miller Assoc., Inc. (C), DC, *482*
Miller Denver (C), CO, *482*
Miller-Hall HRISearch (C), NY, *482*
Miller/Davis & Assoc., Inc. (C), NY, *482*
Million & Assoc., Inc. (R), OH, *144*
Danette Milne Corporate Search Inc. (C), ON, *482*
Milo Research (R), NY, *145*
Milrod Assoc. (C), NJ, *482*
Mims & Associates (R), TX, *145*
Herbert Mines Assoc., Inc. (R), NY, *145*
Mirtz Morice, Inc. (R), CT, *145*
MIS Computer Professionals, Inc. (C), KS, *482*
Paul Misarti Inc. (C), NY, *483*
Laurie Mitchell & Co., Inc. (R), OH, *145*
Mitchell Martin Inc. (C), NY, *483*
Mitchell/Wolfson, Assoc. (R), IL, *145*
MIXTEC Group (R), CA, *145*
MJF Assoc. (C), CT, *483*
MK & Assoc. (R), CA, *146*
MLA Resources, Inc. (C), OK, *483*
Modis (C), MD, *483*
Moffitt Int'l., Inc. (R), NC, *146*
Mogul Consultants, Inc. (C), NY, *483*
Diedre Moire Corp., Inc. (C), NJ, *483*
Molecular Solutions, Inc. (C), SC, *483*
Molloy Partners (R), NY, *146*
Monarch Technology Management LLC (C), CO, *484*
Oscar Montaño, Inc. (R), CA, *146*
Montenido Assoc. (R), CA, *146*
The Montgomery Group, Inc. (C), TN, *484*
Montgomery Resources, Inc. (C), CA, *484*
Montgomery West (R), CA, *146*
Montgomery, Thomason & Assoc. (C), ON, *484*
C. A. Moore & Assoc., Inc. (C), MN, *484*
Larry Moore & Assoc. (C), CA, *484*
Thomas R. Moore Executive Search (R), TX, *146*
Moore Research Assoc. (R), NJ, *147*
The Moran Group (C), IL, *484*
Tina Morbitzer & Assoc. (C), FL, *485*

(R) = Retainer; (C) = Contingency

Mordue, Allen, Roberts, Bonney Ltd. (C), WA, *485*
Morency Assoc. (C), MA, *485*
Morgan & Assoc. (C), MA, *485*
Morgan Hunter Corp. (C), KS, *485*
Morgan Int'l., Inc. (R), IL, *147*
Morgan Samuels Co. (R), CA, *147*
Morgan Stampfl, Inc. (C), NY, *485*
The Morgan/Geoffries Group (C), CA, *485*
Morgan/Webber, Inc. (R), NY, *147*
Morgenstern Int'l., Inc. (C), FL, *485*
Moriarty/Fox, Inc. (R), IL, *147*
The Morley Group (C), IN, *486*
Morris & Berger (R), CA, *147*
The Morris Group (C), PA, *486*
Mortgage & Financial Personnel Services (C), CA, *486*
Mortgage Search Network (C), AZ, *486*
Robert T. Morton Assoc., Inc. (C), MA, *486*
Morton, McCorkle & Assoc. Inc. (R), MO, *147*
Moss & Co. (R), WA, *148*
Moyer, Sherwood Assoc., Inc. (R), NY, *148*
MPA Executive Search Inc. (R), QE, *148*
MRF Enterprises, Inc. (C), TX, *486*
MRI, The Sequel Group, LLC (C), CO, *486*
Mruk & E.M.A. Partners (R), NY, *148*
MSA Executive Search (R), MO, *148*
MSI Int'l. (C), GA, *486*
MTA Partners (R), TX, *148*
Much & Co. (R), NY, *148*
Mulcahy Co. (C), WI, *487*
Mullen Assoc., Inc. (R), NC, *148*
Pamela L. Mulligan, Inc. (R), NH, *149*
The Mulshine Co., Inc. (R), NJ, *149*
The Mulshine Company, Ltd. (R), NY, *149*
Multi Processing, Inc. (R), NH, *149*
Multisearch Recruiters (C), CA, *487*
R. F. Mulvaney & Assoc., Inc. (R), MO, *149*
Jennifer Munro & Partners, Inc. (R), SC, *149*
Munroe, Curry & Bond Assoc. (R), NJ, *149*
P. J. Murphy & Assoc., Inc. (R), WI, *150*
Kenneth Murphy & Assoc. (C), NS, *487*
Murphy Partners Int'l. (R), IL, *150*
The Murray Group (C), IL, *487*
Musick & Assoc. (C), CA, *487*
The MVP Group (C), NY, *487*
Mycoff & Assoc. (R), CO, *150*
Myers Career Assoc., Inc. (C), CA, *488*
DDJ Myers, Ltd. (R), AZ, *150*
N.A.P. Executive Services (Canada) Inc. (C), ON, *488*
Nachman Biomedical (C), MA, *488*
Nadzam, Lusk, Horgan & Assoc., Inc. (R), CA, *150*
Nagler, Robins & Poe, Inc. (R), MA, *150*
Nason & Nason (C), FL, *488*
NaTek Corp. (C), NY, *488*
National Affirmative Action Career Network, Inc. (C), CO, *488*
National Bank & Finance Executive Search (C), CA, *488*
National Career Search (C), AZ, *489*
National Computerized Employment Service, Inc. (C), PA, *489*
National Corporate Consultants, Inc. (C), IN, *489*
National Executive (C), ON, *489*
National Field Service Corp. (C), NY, *489*
National Metal Services Corp. (C), IN, *489*
National Recruiters (C), OK, *489*
National Recruiting Service (C), IN, *489*
National Register Columbus Inc. (C), OH, *490*
National Restaurant Search, Inc. (R), GA, *150*
National Search Assoc. (C), CA, *490*
National Search, Inc. (R), NC, *150*
National Search, Inc.® (C), FL, *490*
Nationwide Personnel Placement, Inc. (C), OH, *490*
Nationwide Personnel Recruiting & Consulting, Inc. (C), OR, *490*
NaviSearch (C), GA, *490*
NCC Executive Search Consultants (C), CA, *490*
NDB Assoc., Inc. (C), PA, *491*
NDI Services (R), MI, *151*
Don Neal & Assoc. (C), OK, *491*
The Neil Michael Group, Inc./Global Partners (R), NY, *151*
The NEIS Corp., Inc. (C), FL, *491*
J. Fielding Nelson & Assoc., Inc. (R), UT, *151*
Beverly Nelson & Assoc. Inc. (C), CA, *491*
Len Nelson & Assoc., Inc. (C), TX, *491*
The Network Corporate Search Personnel Inc. (C), AB, *491*
Networking Unlimited of NH, Inc. (C), NH, *491*
New Dawn Employment Search (C), CA, *491*
New Dimensions in Technology, Inc. (C), MA, *492*
New Directions, Inc. (C), IL, *492*
New Venture Development, Inc. (C), CA, *492*
New World Healthcare Solutions, Inc. (R), NY, *151*
Newcomb-Desmond & Assoc., Inc. (C), OH, *492*
Newell Assoc. (R), NY, *151*
Newman-Johnson-King, Inc. (C), TX, *492*
Newport Management (C), NY, *492*
Newport Strategic Search LLC (C), CA, *492*
Next Step Recruiting (C), CA, *493*
NHA Plastics Recruiters (C), FL, *493*
Nicholaou & Co. (R), IL, *151*
Nichols & Company (R), CO, *151*
Marc Nichols Assoc., Inc. (C), NY, *493*
Nichols Brown Int'l. (R), NY, *151*
P. J. Nicholson & Assoc. (C), IL, *493*
The Niemond Corp. (R), CA, *152*
Nino Recruiting & Staffing, Inc. (C), TX, *493*
Ira Z. Nitzberg (C), NY, *493*
J. L. Nixon Consulting (C), TX, *493*
NJ Solutions (C), CA, *493*
NMC & Kay Int'l. (R), CO, *152*
Noble & Assoc., Inc. (C), NY, *494*
The Noebel Search Group, Inc. (C), TX, *494*
The Nolan Group (C), CA, *494*
Noll Human Resource Services (C), NE, *494*
W. D. Nolte & Company (R), CT, *152*
Nordeman Grimm, Inc. (R), NY, *152*
Norgate Technology, Inc. (C), NY, *494*
The Norland Group (C), CA, *494*
Paul Winston Norman & Assoc. (R), IL, *152*
Norman Broadbent Int'l., Inc. (R), NY, *152*
The Normyle/Erstling Health Search Group (C), NJ, *494*
Norrell Financial Staffing (C), GA, *495*
John B. Norris & Assoc., Inc. (C), MD, *495*
Ronald Norris & Assoc. (C), IL, *495*
Norris Agency (C), TX, *495*
NorTech Resources (C), NY, *496*
North American Recruiters, Inc. (R), MN, *153*
North Coast Meridian (C), NY, *496*
The North Peak Group (C), OH, *496*
Northern Consultants Inc. (R), ME, *153*
Northland Employment Services Inc. (C), MN, *496*
NorthStar Technologies, Inc. (C), NY, *496*
Norton & Assoc. (C), IL, *496*
NPF Assoc. Ltd. Inc. (R), FL, *153*
NPS of Atlanta, Inc. (C), GA, *496*
NRI Staffing Resources (C), DC, *496*
Nuance Personnel Search, Inc. (C), NC, *497*
Nuessle, Kurdziel & Weiss, Inc. (R), PA, *153*
Nursing Technomics (R), PA, *153*
Nyborg•Dow Assoc., Inc. (C), CA, *497*
NYCOR Search, Inc. (C), MN, *497*
O'Brien & Bell (R), OH, *153*
O'Brien and Roof (C), OH, *497*
O'Brien Consulting Services (R), MA, *153*
O'Callaghan Honey/Ray & Berndtson Inc. (R), AB, *153*
O'Connell Group Inc. (C), CT, *497*
John R. O'Connor & Assoc. (C), IL, *497*
O'Connor, O'Connor, Lordi, Ltd. (R), PA, *154*
O'Connor Resources (C), TX, *497*
O'Keefe & Assoc. (C), TX, *497*
O'Keefe & Assoc., Inc. (R), CT, *154*
O'Neill & Co. (R), CT, *154*
O'Neill Group (C), NJ, *498*
O'Rourke Companies, Inc. (R), TX, *154*
O'Shea, Divine & Co., Inc. (R), CA, *154*
O'Sullivan Search Inc. (C), ON, *498*
Dennis P. O'Toole & Assoc. Inc. (R), NY, *154*
O'Toole & Company, Inc. (R), IL, *154*
Oak Assoc. (R), CA, *155*
Ober & Company (R), CA, *155*
Oberlander & Co., Inc. (R), IL, *155*
Object Resources Int'l., Inc. (C), CT, *498*
Odell & Assoc., Inc. (C), TX, *498*
The Odessa Group (R), CA, *155*
OEI, Inc. (C), NJ, *498*
The Ogdon Partnership (R), NY, *155*
The Oldani Group (R), WA, *155*
Oliver & Rozner Assoc., Inc. (R), NY, *155*
Ollinger Partners (R), MA, *156*
Olsen/Clark (R), WA, *156*
Olympian Recruitment, Ltd. (C), NY, *498*
Omega Search, Inc. (C), NC, *498*

Omega Systems, LLC (C), VA, *498*
Omni Search, Inc. (C), CA, *499*
Omnisearch Assoc. (C), CA, *499*
OmniSearch, Inc. (C), FL, *499*
Onsite Staffing Solutions (R), IL, *156*
The Onstott Group (R), MA, *156*
Opalka Dixon Consultants to Management (R), VA, *156*
Open Concepts (C), CA, *499*
Oppedisano & Co., Inc. (R), NY, *156*
Opportunity Resources, Inc. (R), NY, *156*
The Options Group, Inc. (C), NY, *499*
Opus Marketing (R), CA, *156*
Organization Consulting Ltd. (R), ON, *157*
Organization Resources Inc. (R), MA, *157*
Orion Consulting, Inc. (R), NJ, *157*
Orion Int'l. Consulting Group, Inc. (C), NC, *499*
Ortman Recruiting Int'l. (C), CA, *500*
OSAGUI S.A. de C.V. (C), MX, *500*
K. Ossow & Co. (C), NY, *500*
Ott & Hansen, Inc. (R), CA, *157*
Robert Ottke Assoc. (R), CA, *157*
Ovca Assoc. Inc. (R), KY, *157*
Overton Consulting (R), WI, *157*
LaMonte Owens, Inc. (R), PA, *157*
The Oxbridge Group, Ltd. (C), PA, *500*
The Oxford Group (C), TX, *500*
The P & L Group (C), NY, *500*
P R Management Consultants, Inc. (C), NJ, *500*
P.A.R. Assoc., Inc. (R), MA, *158*
P.R.H. Management, Inc. (R), CT, *158*
Pacific Advisory Service, Inc. (C), IL, *501*
Pacific Coast Recruiting (C), CA, *501*
Pacific Coast Recruiters (C), OR, *501*
Pacific Crossing (C), CA, *501*
Pacific Finance Search, Inc. (C), CA, *501*
Pacific Search Group, Inc. (C), CA, *501*
Packaging Personnel Co., Ltd. (C), WI, *501*
T. Page & Assoc. (C), TX, *502*
Page-Wheatcroft & Co., Ltd. (R), TX, *158*
The Pailin Group Professional Search Consultants (R), TX, *158*
Janou Pakter, Inc. (C), NY, *502*
J. Palacios & Assoc., Inc. (R), PR, *158*
Paladin Group, Inc. (C), CO, *502*
Kirk Palmer & Assoc., Inc. (R), NY, *158*
Pamenter, Pamenter, Brezer & Deganis Ltd. (R), ON, *159*
Arthur Pann Assoc., Inc. (C), NY, *502*
Florence Pape Legal Search, Inc. (C), NJ, *502*
Paper Industry Recruitment (P.I.R.) (C), ME, *502*
The PAR Group - Paul A. Reaume, Ltd. (R), IL, *159*
Paragon Recruiting Officials Inc. (C), OH, *502*
Parenica & Co. (R), NC, *159*
Jim Parham & Assoc., Inc. (R), FL, *159*
Frank Parillo & Assoc. (R), CA, *159*
Carol Park (C), MO, *502*
The Park Group & Assoc., Inc. (C), MD, *502*
D. P. Parker & Assoc., Inc. (R), MA, *159*
R. Parker & Assoc., Inc. (R), NY, *159*
Parker & Lynch (C), CA, *503*
Parker, McFadden & Assoc. (C), GA, *503*
Parker Page Group (C), FL, *503*
Parker-Worthington, Inc. (C), TX, *503*
Largent Parks & Partners (C), TX, *503*
Michael W. Parres & Assoc. (R), MI, *159*
Parsons, Anderson & Gee, Inc. (C), NY, *503*
Parsons Assoc. Inc. (R), IL, *159*
Partners Executive Search Consultants Inc. (R), ON, *160*
Partners In Human Resources Int'l., Inc. (R), NY, *160*
Partners in Recruiting (C), IL, *503*
The Partners, LLC (C), CA, *504*
Partners Resource Group (C), VA, *504*
The Partnership Group (R), NJ, *160*
Partnervision Consulting Group Inc. (R), ON, *160*
Partridge Assoc., Inc. (R), MA, *160*
Rick Pascal & Assoc., Inc. (C), NJ, *504*
Pascale & LaMorte, LLC (C), CT, *504*
Carolyn Smith Paschal Int'l. (R), CA, *160*
Pasona Canada, Inc. (C), ON, *504*
Pathfinders (C), CA, *504*
Pathfinders Int'l. (C), MI, *504*
Pathway Executive Search, Inc. (C), NY, *505*
Pathways Int'l. (C), CT, *505*
The Patience Motivation Belief Group, Inc. (C), GA, *505*
Patrice & Assoc. (C), MD, *505*
Patriot Assoc. (C), PA, *505*
Joel H. Paul & Assoc., Inc. (C), NY, *505*
Paul-Tittle Assoc., Inc. (R), VA, *161*
Paules Associates (C), CA, *505*
Pawlik/Dorman Partners (R), IL, *161*
PC Assoc. (C), CO, *505*
PCD Partners (R), PA, *161*
Peachtree Executive Search (R), GA, *161*
Peak Search Assoc. (C), ON, *506*
Pearce & Assoc. (C), FL, *506*
Pearson & Assoc., Inc. (C), AZ, *506*
Pearson, Caldwell & Farnsworth (R), CA, *161*
Peck & Assoc., Ltd. (R), WI, *161*
Peden & Assoc. (C), CA, *506*
Peeney Assoc., Inc. (R), NJ, *161*
Paul S. Pelland, P.C. (R), SC, *161*
M. A. Pelle Assoc., Inc. (C), NY, *506*
Penn Associates (R), PA, *161*
The Penn Partners, Inc. (R), PA, *162*
Pennington Consulting Group (C), NJ, *506*
The Pennmor Group (C), NJ, *506*
People Management Mid-South, LLC (R), TN, *162*
People Management Northeast, Inc. (R), CT, *162*
PeopleSource Inc. (C), TX, *506*
PERC, Ltd. (C), AZ, *506*
Perez & Assoc. (C), MI, *507*
Perez-Arton Consultants, Inc. (R), NY, *162*
Perfect Search, Inc. (C), FL, *507*
Performance Resources, Inc. (C), RI, *507*
PERI Corp/Professional Executive Recruiters, Inc. (C), TX, *507*
The Perkins Group (R), NC, *162*
R. H. Perry & Assoc., Inc. (R), DC, *162*
Perry • Newton Assoc. (C), MD, *507*
Fred Perry Assoc. (C), TX, *507*
Perry Search Assoc. (C), CA, *507*
Perry-D'Amico & Assoc. (R), CA, *162*
Perry-Martel Int'l., Inc. (R), ON, *163*
Barry Persky & Co., Inc. (R), CT, *163*
PersoNet, Inc. (C), FL, *507*
Personnel Alliance Group (C), NJ, *507*
Personnel Assoc. (C), CA, *508*
Personnel Assoc. (C), NC, *508*
Personnel Assoc. Inc. (C), NY, *508*
Personnel Consultants (C), WA, *508*
The Personnel Group, Inc. (R), MN, *163*
Personnel, Inc. (C), AL, *508*
Personnel Incorporated (C), IA, *508*
Personnel Management Group (C), MB, *508*
The Personnel Network, Inc. (C), SC, *508*
Personnel Resources Organization (C), PA, *509*
Personnel Solutions (C), AZ, *509*
Personnel Tangent Inc. (C), QE, *509*
Personnel Unlimited/Executive Search (C), WA, *509*
J. R. Peterman Assoc., Inc. (C), VT, *509*
Alec Peters Assoc. Inc./DLR (R), GA, *163*
Richard Peterson & Assoc., Inc. (R), GA, *163*
Petrie Partners, Inc. (R), FL, *163*
Petro Staff Int'l. (C), AB, *509*
Petruzzi Assoc. (C), NJ, *509*
Peyser Assoc., Inc. (R), FL, *163*
Robert E. Pfaendler & Assoc., Inc. (C), OR, *509*
Pharmaceutical Recruiters, Inc. (R), NY, *163*
Pharmaceutical Search Professionals, Inc. (C), PA, *510*
Phase II Management (R), CT, *164*
PHD Conseil en Ressources Humaines Inc. (C), QE, *510*
Phelps Personnel Assoc., Inc. (C), SC, *510*
J. R. Phillip & Assoc., Inc. (R), CA, *164*
Phillips & Assoc. (R), MA, *164*
Phillips Assoc. (C), FL, *510*
Phillips Int'l., Inc. (C), SC, *510*
Phillips Personnel/Search (C), CO, *510*
Phillips Resource Group (C), SC, *510*
Philo & Associates (C), GA, *511*
Phoenix BioSearch, Inc. (C), NJ, *511*
Phoenix Partners, Inc. (C), GA, *511*
Phoenix Search (R), MX, *164*
Physician Associates (C), HI, *511*
Physician Executive Management Center (R), FL, *164*
Physician Recruiting Services, Inc. (C), MO, *511*
Physicians Search® Inc. (C), CA, *511*
PIC Executive Search (C), GA, *511*
Picard Int'l., Ltd. (R), NY, *164*
Gregory D. Pickens (C), TX, *511*
Pierce & Assoc. (C), CA, *512*
Pierce & Crow (R), CA, *164*
Pinnacle Executive Group Inc. (C), MO, *512*
Pinnacle Group Int'l. (C), AZ, *512*
The Pinnacle Source, Inc. (C), CO, *512*
Pinsker and Company, Inc. (R), CA, *164*
Pinton Forrest & Madden/EMA Partners Int'l. (R), BC, *165*
Pioneer Consulting Group (C), CA, *512*

(R) = Retainer; (C) = Contingency

Pioneer Executive Consultants (C), ON, *512*
Pioneer Placement, Inc. (C), MA, *512*
DNPitchon Assoc. (R), NJ, *165*
Pittleman & Assoc. (C), NY, *512*
PKS Assoc., Inc. (C), RI, *513*
PLA, Inc. (C), NJ, *513*
Place Mart Personnel Service (C), NJ, *513*
Placement Solutions (C), WI, *513*
Placement Testart Inc. (C), QE, *513*
Placements by Jesse Reid Assoc., Inc. (C), NY, *513*
Plante & Moran, LLP (R), MI, *165*
Plemmons Assoc., Inc. (R), GA, *165*
Rene Plessner Assoc., Inc. (R), NY, *165*
R. L. Plimpton Assoc., Inc. (R), CO, *165*
Yves Plouffe & Assoc. (R), QE, *165*
Plummer & Assoc., Inc. (R), CT, *166*
PMJ & Assoc. (C), ON, *513*
Poirier, Hoevel & Co. (R), CA, *166*
The Polen Group (C), PA, *514*
Ray Polhill & Assoc. (R), NC, *166*
Bob Poline Assoc. Inc. (C), CA, *514*
The Pollack Group (C), ON, *514*
Polson & Co., Inc. (R), MN, *166*
Polytechnical Consultants, Inc. (C), IL, *514*
Al Ponaman Company, Inc. (C), CA, *514*
Don V. Poole & Assoc., Inc. (C), CO, *514*
Porter & Assoc., Inc. (C), FL, *514*
Jack Porter Assoc., Inc. (C), WA, *514*
David Powell, Inc. (R), CA, *166*
Power Recruiting Group (C), TX, *515*
Power Search (C), TX, *515*
Robert Powers & Assoc. (C), CA, *515*
Norman Powers Assoc., Inc. (C), MA, *515*
Powers Consultants, Inc. (R), MO, *166*
PPS Information Systems Staffing (C), MD, *515*
Practice Dynamics, Inc. (C), TX, *515*
P. G. Prager Search Assoc., Ltd. (C), NY, *515*
The Prairie Group (C), IL, *515*
Prairie Resource Group, Inc. (R), IL, *166*
Elan Pratzer & Partners Inc. (R), ON, *167*
PRAXIS Partners (R), VA, *167*
Precision Executive Search (C), AZ, *516*
Predictor Systems Corp. (R), CA, *167*
Preferred Placement, Inc. (C), NY, *516*
Preferred Professional Recruiters (C), OH, *516*
Preferred Professional Recruiters (C), TX, *516*
George Preger & Associates Inc. (R), ON, *167*
Premier Business Advisors (C), PA, *516*
Premier Healthcare Recruiters, Inc. (C), MI, *516*
Premier Recruiting Group (C), MI, *516*
Premier Search Group (C), IN, *517*
The Premier Staffing Group (C), OH, *517*
Preng & Assoc., Inc. (R), TX, *167*
Prescott Legal Search, Inc. (C), TX, *517*
Presley Consultants, Inc. (C), CA, *517*
Prestige Inc. (C), WI, *517*
Preston & Co. (R), NJ, *167*
Preston-Hunter, Inc. (R), IL, *167*
Prestonwood Assoc. (R), MA, *168*
Price & Assoc., Inc. (C), VA, *518*
Alan J. Price Assoc., Inc. (C), RI, *518*
PricewaterhouseCoopers Executive Search (R), ON, *168*
PricewaterhouseCoopers Executive Search (R), MX, *168*
Prichard Kymen Inc. (R), AB, *168*
Primary Care Service Corp. (C), GA, *518*
The Primary Group, Inc. (R), FL, *168*
Prime Management Group Inc. (C), ON, *518*
Prime Resource Assoc. (C), WI, *518*
Prime Search (C), NC, *518*
Primus Assoc., L.C. (R), TX, *169*
Princeton Executive Search (C), NJ, *518*
Princeton Search Partners, Inc. (R), NJ, *169*
Prior/Martech Assoc., Inc. (R), WA, *169*
Priority Executive Search (C), FL, *518*
PRO, Inc./Professional Recruiting Offices, Inc. (C), CA, *519*
Pro Tec Technical Services (C), ON, *519*
Pro-Tech Search, Inc. (C), IL, *519*
Probe Technology (C), PA, *519*
Probus Executive Search (C), CA, *519*
Procom (C), ON, *519*
Procurement Resources (C), MD, *520*
Professional Careers, Inc. (C), NC, *520*
Professional Consulting Network, Inc. (C), CA, *520*
Professional Employment Group (C), MD, *520*
Professional Engineering Technical Personnel Consultants (C), NC, *520*
Professional Healthcare Search & Consultants, Inc. (C), CA, *520*
Professional Personnel Services (C), IA, *520*
Professional Personnel Consultants, Inc. (C), MI, *521*
Professional Persons Career Services (C), NY, *521*
Professional Placement Assoc., Inc. (C), NY, *521*
Professional Recruiting Network (C), CA, *521*
Professional Recruiting Consultants, Inc. (C), DE, *521*
Professional Recruiting Consultants (C), FL, *521*
Professional Recruiters Inc. (C), MN, *521*
Professional Recruiters, Inc. (C), PA, *521*
Professional Recruiters (C), UT, *521*
Professional Research Services, Inc. (R), IL, *169*
Professional Resource Group, Inc. (C), IN, *522*
Professional Resources (C), NY, *522*
Professional Resources (C), OK, *522*
The Professional Sales Search Co., Inc. (C), WA, *522*
Professional Search (R), MI, *169*
Professional Search Consultants (C), KY, *522*
Professional Search Centre, Ltd. (C), IL, *522*
Professional Search, Inc. (C), CO, *522*
Professional Search Assoc. (C), CA, *522*
Professional Search, Inc. Int'l. (C), TX, *523*
Professional Search Consultants (PSC) (C), TX, *523*
Professional Selection Services (R), GA, *169*
Professional Support Inc. (C), NY, *523*
Professional Team Search, Inc. (R), AZ, *169*
Professionals in Recruiting Co. (C), TN, *523*
Professions, Inc. (C), OH, *523*
ProFinders, Inc. (C), FL, *523*
Profit Pros, Inc. (C), CA, *523*
ProLink (C), NC, *524*
ProLinks Inc. (R), VA, *170*
ProNet, Inc. (C), NC, *524*
Proquest Inc. (C), SC, *524*
ProSearch Recruiting (C), CA, *524*
ProSearch, Inc. (C), ME, *524*
ProSearch, Inc. (C), OH, *524*
ProSearch, Inc. (C), PA, *524*
Prospective Personnel Service, Inc. (C), OK, *524*
ProStar Systems, Inc. (C), MD, *525*
ProTech Nationwide Staffing, Inc. (C), NY, *525*
Protocol Inc. (C), CA, *525*
Proven Edge (C), CA, *525*
Pryor & Associates (C), CA, *525*
PSD Group, Inc. (C), CA, *525*
PSP Agency (C), NY, *525*
Pursuant Legal Consultants (R), WA, *170*
QD Legal (C), ON, *525*
Quality Consulting Group, Inc. (C), WI, *526*
Quality Control Recruiters (C), CT, *526*
Quality Search (C), IN, *526*
Quality Search Inc. (C), OH, *526*
Quantum EDP Recruiting Services (C), QE, *526*
The Quantum Group (C), NJ, *526*
Quantum Int'l., Ltd. (R), FL, *170*
Quest Enterprises, Ltd. (C), IL, *527*
The Quest Organization (C), NY, *527*
Quest Worldwide Executive Search Corp. (C), CA, *527*
Questor Consultants, Inc. (C), PA, *527*
QuestPro, Inc. (C), TX, *527*
Quetico Corp. (R), TX, *170*
Quigley Assoc. (R), MD, *170*
L. J. Quinn & Assoc., Inc. (R), CA, *170*
Quiring Assoc., Inc. (C), IN, *527*
Quirk-Corporon & Assoc., Inc. (C), WI, *527*
QVS Int'l. (R), GA, *170*
R & K Associates, Inc. (C), AZ, *527*
R & L Assoc., Ltd. (R), NY, *170*
R M Associates (R), OH, *171*
R. C. Services (C), TX, *528*
R. J. Associates (C), NY, *528*
R.A.N. Assoc., Inc. (C), OH, *528*
R/K International Inc. (R), CT, *171*
R2 Services, LLC (C), IL, *528*
Radosevic Assoc. (R), CA, *171*
Railey & Assoc. (C), TX, *528*
Raines Int'l. Inc. (R), NY, *171*
Ramm Search (C), NY, *528*
Ramming & Assoc., Inc. (C), NJ, *528*
Rand Assoc. (R), ME, *171*
Rand Thompson Executive Search Consultants (C), NY, *528*
Rand-Curtis Resources (C), AZ, *529*

Lea Randolph & Assoc., Inc. (C), TX, *529*
The Rankin Group, Ltd. (R), WI, *171*
The Ransford Group (R), TX, *171*
J. E. Ranta Assoc. (C), MA, *529*
Harold L. Rapp Assoc. (C), NY, *529*
Vera L. Rast Partners Inc. (C), IL, *529*
Joanne E. Ratner Search (C), NY, *529*
Ray & Assoc., Inc. (C), IA, *529*
Ray & Berndtson (R), TX, *171*
Ray & Berndtson/Laurendeau Labrecque (R), QE, *172*
Ray & Berndtson/Lovas Stanley (R), ON, *172*
Ray & Berndtson/Tanton Mitchell (R), BC, *173*
Raymond Karsan Assoc. (C), PA, *529*
Raymond Thomas & Assoc. (C), FL, *530*
Razzino-Claymore Assoc. (C), NJ, *530*
RBW Assoc. Inc. (C), OR, *531*
RCE Assoc. (R), NJ, *173*
RCI Employment Solutions (C), FL, *531*
Re-Mark Assoc. Inc. (C), NJ, *531*
Real Estate Executive Search, Inc. (C), CA, *531*
Reality Group (C), OK, *531*
Recruit Xpress (C), TX, *531*
Recruiters Professional Network - Fairview (C), MO, *531*
Recruiting Assoc. of Amarillo (C), TX, *531*
Recruiting Options, Inc. (C), GA, *531*
Recruiting Resources Int'l. (C), CA, *532*
Recruiting Services Group, Inc. (C), TN, *532*
Recruiting Specialists (C), MA, *532*
Recruiting/Solutions (C), CA, *532*
The Recruitment Group, Inc. (C), NY, *532*
Recruitment Resources (C), CA, *532*
Recruitment Specialists, Inc. (C), MD, *532*
Mary Rector & Assoc., Inc. (C), IL, *533*
P. J. Reda & Assoc., Inc. (C), GA, *533*
Redden & McGrath Assoc., Inc. (R), NY, *173*
Redden-Shaffer Group (R), CA, *173*
Redell Search, Inc. (C), IL, *533*
Redwood Partners Ltd. (R), NY, *173*
Reece & Mruk Partners/EMA Partners Int'l. (R), MA, *173*
Reeder & Assoc., Ltd. (R), GA, *173*
Reese Assoc. (R), PA, *174*
Cedric L. Reese Inc. (C), CA, *533*
Reeve & Assoc. (C), CT, *533*
The Regency Group, Ltd. (C), NE, *533*
The Regis Group, Ltd. (R), GA, *174*
Michael James Reid & Co. (R), CA, *174*
Reid Ellis Assoc. Inc. (C), ON, *533*
Reifel & Assoc. (R), IL, *174*
Rein & Co., Inc. (R), NJ, *174*
Reinecke & Assoc. (C), NJ, *533*
The Douglas Reiter Co., Inc. (R), OR, *174*
The Remington Group (R), IL, *174*
RemTech Business Solutions, Inc. (C), MI, *534*
The Renaissance Network (C), MA, *534*
Renaissance Resources, LLC (R), VA, *174*
RepFinders USA (C), PA, *534*
The Repovich-Reynolds Group (TRRG, Inc.) (R), CA, *175*
Research Personnel Consultants (C), ON, *534*
Reserve Technology Institute (R), TX, *175*
Resolve Assoc. Int'l. (R), FL, *175*
The Resource Group (R), NJ, *175*
The Resource Group (R), CT, *175*
Resource Inc. (R), MA, *175*
Resource Management Group (C), CT, *534*
Resource Networking Inc. (C), IN, *534*
Resource Perspectives, Inc. (R), CA, *175*
Resource Recruiting (C), NH, *534*
Resource Services, Inc. (C), NY, *534*
Resources for Management (R), PA, *175*
Response Staffing Services (C), NY, *534*
L. J. Reszotko & Assoc. (C), IL, *535*
Retail Connection, Inc. (C), NJ, *535*
Retail Executive Search (C), FL, *535*
The Retail Network (C), MA, *535*
Retail Recruiters (C), CT, *535*
Retail Recruiters/Spectrum Consultants, Inc. (C), PA, *535*
Retained Search Assoc. (R), NC, *176*
Retis Assoc., Inc. (C), IL, *535*
The Revere Assoc., Inc. (R), OH, *176*
S. Reyman & Assoc., Ltd. (R), IL, *176*
Russell Reynolds Assoc., Inc. (R), NY, *176*
Reynolds Consulting Int'l. (R), ON, *177*
Reynolds Partners (R), NY, *177*
RGE (C), VA, *535*
RHAssoc. Inc. (C), KS, *535*
RHI Consulting (C), VA, *536*
Rhodes Associates (R), NY, *177*
RHS Assoc. (C), AL, *536*
RIC Corp. (R), FL, *177*
Marshall Rice Assoc. (R), RI, *177*
Rice Cohen Int'l. (R), PA, *178*
Jeff Rich Assoc. (C), NJ, *536*
Richard, Wayne & Roberts (C), TX, *536*
Richard Wright Co. (C), CT, *536*
Richards Assoc., Inc. (R), NY, *178*
The Richards Group (C), PA, *536*
Terry Richards (C), OH, *536*
W. F. Richer Assoc., Inc. (C), NY, *536*
Jack Richman & Assoc. (C), FL, *537*
Richmond Assoc. (C), NY, *537*
Riddle & McGrath LLC (R), GA, *178*
Ridenour & Assoc. (R), IL, *178*
Ridgefield Search Int'l. (C), CT, *537*
Rieser & Assoc., Inc. (R), MO, *178*
Right/McKee Consulting Group (C), TX, *537*
Wilson Riles & Assoc., Inc. (R), CA, *178*
Riley Cole (C), CA, *537*
Riotto-Jones Assoc. (R), NY, *178*
Ritech Management Inc. (C), NY, *537*
Ritt-Ritt & Assoc., Inc. (C), IL, *537*
Ritta Professional Search Inc. (C), NY, *538*
River Region Personnel, Inc. (C), LA, *538*
Rivera Legal Search, Inc. (C), CA, *538*
The Riverbend Group (C), MO, *538*
RJ Associates (C), CA, *538*
RJN Consulting (R), NY, *179*
RLM Assoc., Ltd. (R), NY, *179*
RMA Search (R), TN, *179*
RML Assoc. (C), PA, *538*
Roberson & Co. (C), AZ, *538*
Robert Lowell Int'l. (R), TX, *179*
Robert Shields & Assoc. (C), TX, *538*
Robert William James & Assoc. (C), OR, *539*
Norman Roberts & Assoc., Inc. (R), CA, *179*
Roberts Ryan & Bentley, Inc. (R), MD, *179*
Robertson & Assoc. (C), IL, *539*
Robertson-Surrette Ltd. (R), NS, *179*
V. Robinson & Co., Inc. (C), MO, *539*
Bruce Robinson Assoc. (R), NJ, *180*
The Robinson Group, D.A., Ltd. (C), IL, *539*
Robinson, Fraser Group Ltd. (R), ON, *180*
Robinson-Robinson & Assoc., Inc. (C), MN, *539*
Robison & Associates (R), NC, *180*
Robison Humphreys & Assoc., Inc. (R), ON, *180*
Robsham & Assoc., Inc. (R), MA, *180*
Rockwood Assoc. (C), NY, *540*
Rocky Mountain Recruiters, Inc. (C), CO, *540*
J. P. Roddy Consultants (C), PA, *540*
J. Rodgers & Associates (C), IL, *540*
Rodgers, Ramsey, Inc. (C), TX, *540*
R. A. Rodriguez & Assoc., Inc. (C), TX, *540*
Rodzik & Assoc., Inc. (R), NC, *180*
Craig Roe & Assoc., LLC (C), MD, *540*
Roevin Technical People (C), ON, *540*
The Rogan Group, Inc. (C), CA, *541*
Rogers - McManamon Executive Search (R), CA, *180*
Rogish Assoc., Inc. (C), OH, *541*
ROI Assoc. (R), NY, *180*
ROI International, Inc. (R), WA, *181*
Rojek Marketing Group, Inc. (R), OH, *181*
Roll International (C), TX, *541*
Rolland Ressources Humaines Inc. (R), QE, *181*
Rollins & Assoc. (C), CA, *541*
Rollins Search Group, Inc. (C), GA, *541*
Rollo Assoc. (R), CA, *181*
Romac Int'l. (C), IL, *541*
Romac Int'l. - San Francisco (C), CA, *541*
Romac Int'l. (C), GA, *541*
Romac Int'l. (C), PA, *542*
Romac Int'l. Inc. (R), MA, *181*
Romac Int'l., Inc. (C), FL, *542*
Romano McAvoy Assoc., Inc. (C), NY, *544*
Romeo-Hudgins & Assoc., Ltd. (C), NJ, *544*
Rooney Assoc., Inc. (R), IL, *181*
Ropella & Assoc. (R), FL, *181*
Ropes Associates, Inc. (R), FL, *182*
W. R. Rosato & Assoc., Inc. (R), NY, *182*
Emery A. Rose & Assoc. (C), WA, *545*
The Rose Search Group, Inc. (C), NC, *545*
Rosenfeld & Co., Inc. (C), MI, *545*
Ross & Company, Inc. (R), CT, *182*
Ross Personnel Consultants, Inc. (C), CT, *545*
Rossi & Assoc. Inc. (C), BC, *545*
The Rossi Search Group (C), PA, *545*
Roster Inc. (C), IN, *545*
Patricia Roth Int'l. (C), FL, *545*
Roth Young of Chicago (C), IL, *546*
Roth Young Executive Search (C), TX, *546*
Roth Young Seattle (C), WA, *546*
Roth Young of Pittsburgh (C), PA, *546*

(R) = Retainer; (C) = Contingency

Roth Young Executive Recruiters (C), MN, *546*
Roth Young Personnel Services of Washington, DC (C), MD, *546*
Roth Young of Tampa (C), FL, *546*
Roth Young Personnel Service of Detroit, Inc. (C), MI, *546*
Roth Young Executive Search of Milwaukee (C), WI, *547*
Rothrock Associates, Inc. (C), NC, *547*
Rovner & Assoc., Inc. (R), IL, *182*
Rovner Gerner & Assoc. (R), CA, *182*
David Rowe & Assoc., Inc. (R), IL, *182*
Rowland Assoc. (C), CA, *547*
Rowland Mountain & Assoc. (C), GA, *547*
Royal Assoc. (C), CA, *547*
RSMR, Inc. (R), IL, *182*
RTE Search (C), NJ, *547*
The Rubicon Group (C), AZ, *547*
The Rubinic Consulting Group (C), OH, *548*
Ruderfer & Co., Inc. (C), NJ, *548*
Susan Rudich (C), NY, *548*
Louis Rudzinsky Assoc., Inc. (C), MA, *548*
J. D. Ruhmann & Assoc. (C), MO, *548*
Ruppert Comann Assoc., Inc. (R), CO, *182*
Rurak & Assoc., Inc (R), DC, *182*
Rusher, Loscavio & LoPresto (R), CA, *183*
Rushmore • Judge Inc. (R), ON, *183*
Russillo/Gardner/Spolsino (C), MA, *548*
K. Russo Assoc. Inc. (C), CT, *548*
Rust & Assoc., Inc. (R), IL, *183*
W. A. Rutledge & Assoc. (R), CT, *183*
The Ryan Charles Group, Inc. (C), FL, *548*
Ryan, Miller & Assoc. (C), CA, *549*
Ryan-Allen & Assoc., Inc. (C), CA, *549*
Rylan Forbes Consulting Group, Inc. (C), NJ, *549*
Ryman, Bell, Green & Michaels, Inc. (C), TX, *549*
R. L. Rystrom & Assoc., Inc. (C), MN, *549*
The S C Group LLC (R), NY, *183*
S-H-S Int'l. of Cherry Hill (C), NJ, *549*
S-H-S TechStaff (C), PA, *549*
S. C. Int'l., Ltd. (C), IL, *550*
S. P. Assoc., Inc. (C), NC, *550*
S.C.S. & Assoc. (C), NC, *550*
S.D.P. Contract Recruiters (C), NJ, *550*
Saber Group, Inc. (C), TX, *550*
R. S. Sadow Assoc. (C), NJ, *550*
Sage Employment Recruiters (C), IN, *550*
The Sager Co. (R), OH, *183*
Sales & Management Search, Inc. (C), IL, *551*
Sales & Marketing Search, Inc. (C), MA, *551*
Sales Advantage (C), FL, *551*
Sales Builders, Inc. (R), VA, *183*
Sales Consultants (C), OH, *551*
Sales Consultants of Birmingham (C), AL, *555*
Sales Consultants Int'l. of Oakland (C), CA, *556*
Sales Consultants of Chico (C), CA, *556*
Sales Consultants of Silicon Valley (C), CA, *556*
Sales Consultants of Daphne (C), AL, *556*
Sales Consultants of Northwest Arkansas, Inc. (C), AR, *556*
Sales Consultants Peninsula, Inc. (C), CA, *556*
Sales Consultants of Scottsdale, Inc. (C), AZ, *556*
Sales Consultants of Sacramento (C), CA, *556*
Sales Consultants of Stamford-Darien (C), CT, *557*
Sales Consultants of Savannah, GA (C), GA, *557*
Sales Consultants of Tampa North, Inc. (C), FL, *557*
Sales Consultants of Ft. Myers, Inc. (C), FL, *557*
Sales Consultants of Boca Raton, Inc. (C), FL, *557*
Sales Consultants of Danbury (C), CT, *557*
Sales Consultants of Denver (C), CO, *557*
Sales Consultants of Ft. Lauderdale, Inc. (C), FL, *557*
Sales Consultants of Barrington (C), IL, *558*
Sales Consultants of Indianapolis-North (C), IN, *558*
Sales Consultants of Western McHenry County (C), IL, *558*
Sales Consultants of Indianapolis (C), IN, *558*
Sales Consultants of Honolulu (C), HI, *558*
Sales Consultants of Cherokee (C), GA, *558*
Sales Consultants of Chicago South (C), IL, *558*
Sales Consultants (C), IL, *558*
Sales Consultants of Brockton, Inc. (C), MA, *559*
Sales Consultants of Birmingham (C), MI, *559*
Sales Consultants of Auburn Hills (C), MI, *559*
Sales Consultants - Bristol County (C), MA, *559*
Sales Consultants of Baltimore (C), MD, *559*
Sales Consultants of Rockville, MD (C), MD, *559*
Sales Consultants of Bangor, Inc. (C), ME, *559*
Sales Consultants of Wellesley, Inc. (C), MA, *559*
Sales Consultants Bridgewater, Inc. (C), NJ, *560*
Sales Consultants of Farmington Hills (C), MI, *560*
Sales Consultants of Cherry Hill (C), NJ, *560*
Sales Consultants of Northern Jersey, Inc. (C), NJ, *560*
Sales Consultants of Omaha, Inc. (C), NE, *560*
Sales Consultants of Grand Rapids (C), MI, *560*
Sales Consultants of Laurel Park, Inc. (C), MI, *560*
Sales Consultants of Nashua-Manchester (C), NH, *560*
Sales Consultants of Westchester-South, Inc. (C), NY, *561*
Sales Consultants of Butler County (C), PA, *561*
Sales Consultants of Harrisburg (C), PA, *561*
Sales Consultants of Raleigh-Durham-RTP (C), NC, *561*
Sales Consultants of Princeton, Inc. (C), NJ, *561*
Sales Consultants of Middlesex County, Inc. (C), NJ, *561*
Sales Consultants of Morris County, Inc. (C), NJ, *561*
Sales Consultants of Cincinnati (C), OH, *561*
Sales Consultants of Chester County, PA (C), PA, *562*
Sales Consultants of Greenville, Inc. (C), SC, *562*
Sales Consultants of Austin, Inc. (C), TX, *562*
Sales Consultants of Orangeburg (C), SC, *562*
Sales Consultants of Rhode Island, Inc. (C), RI, *562*
Sales Consultants King of Prussia (C), PA, *562*
Sales Consultants of Newtown, Inc. (C), PA, *562*
Sales Consultants of Pittsburgh (C), PA, *562*
Sales Consultants of Dallas (C), TX, *563*
Sales Consultants of Houston (C), TX, *563*
Sales Consultants of Appleton (C), WI, *563*
Sales Consultants of Milwaukee (C), WI, *563*
Sales Consultants of Madison (C), WI, *563*
Sales Executives, Inc. (C), MI, *563*
Sales Management Resources (C), CA, *563*
Sales Professionals Personnel Services (C), CA, *564*
Sales Recruiters of Oklahoma City (C), OK, *564*
Sales Recruiting Network (C), PA, *564*
Sales Search (C), ON, *564*
Sales Search Specialist (C), IL, *564*
Sales Solutions (C), CA, *564*
A. N. Salloway Executive Search & Consulting, L.L.C. (C), MA, *564*
Salveson Stetson Group, Inc. (R), PA, *184*
Salzmann Gay Assoc., Inc. (R), PA, *184*
Sampson Medical Search (C), CA, *564*
George D. Sandel Assoc. (C), MA, *565*
Norm Sanders Assoc., Inc. (R), NJ, *184*
Sanders Management Assoc., Inc. (C), NJ, *565*
Sanford Rose Assoc. - Lake Forest (R), IL, *184*
Sanford Rose Assoc. - Laguna Beach (C), CA, *565*
Sanford Rose Assoc. - Santa Ana (C), CA, *565*
Sanford Rose Assoc. - Fairhope (C), AL, *565*
Sanford Rose Assoc. (C), OH, *565*
Sanford Rose Assoc. - Santa Barbara (C), CA, *565*
Sanford Rose Assoc. - Mobile (C), AL, *565*
Sanford Rose Assoc. - Norcross (C), GA, *566*

Sanford Rose Assoc. - Effingham (C), IL, *566*
Sanford Rose Assoc. - Chicago (C), IL, *566*
Sanford Rose Assoc. - Athens (C), GA, *566*
Sanford Rose Assoc. - Clearwater (C), FL, *566*
Sanford Rose Assoc. - Anaheim (C), CA, *566*
Sanford Rose Assoc. - Sunnyvale (C), CA, *566*
Sanford Rose Assoc. - Atlanta North (C), GA, *566*
Sanford Rose Assoc. - Cedar Rapids (C), IA, *567*
Sanford Rose Assoc. - Columbia, MD (C), MD, *567*
Sanford Rose Assoc. - Rockville (C), MD, *567*
Sanford Rose Assoc. - Louisville (C), KY, *567*
Sanford Rose Assoc. - Carmel, IN (C), IN, *567*
Sanford Rose Assoc. - Oak Brook (C), IL, *567*
Sanford Rose Assoc. - Orland Park (C), IL, *567*
Sanford Rose Assoc. - Rockford (C), IL, *567*
Sanford Rose Assoc. - Evansville (C), IN, *567*
Sanford Rose Assoc. - Springfield (C), MO, *568*
Sanford Rose Assoc. - Gastonia (C), NC, *568*
Sanford Rose Assoc. - Charlotte (C), NC, *568*
Sanford Rose Assoc. - Flemington (C), NJ, *568*
Sanford Rose Assoc. - Lake St. Louis (C), MO, *568*
Sanford Rose Assoc. - Rochester (C), MI, *568*
Sanford Rose Assoc. - Amherst, NY (C), NY, *568*
Sanford Rose Assoc. - Greensboro (C), NC, *569*
Sanford Rose Assoc. - Columbus North (C), OH, *569*
Sanford Rose Assoc. - Fairlawn (C), OH, *569*
Sanford Rose Assoc. - Euclid (C), OH, *569*
Sanford Rose Assoc. - Canton (C), OH, *569*
Sanford Rose Assoc. - Akron (C), OH, *569*
Sanford Rose Assoc. - Burlington, NC (C), NC, *569*
Sanford Rose Assoc. - Youngstown (C), OH, *569*
Sanford Rose Assoc. - Portland (C), OR, *570*
Sanford Rose Assoc. - Doylestown (C), PA, *570*
Sanford Rose Assoc. - Philadelphia North (C), PA, *570*
Sanford Rose Assoc. - Pittsburgh North (C), PA, *570*
Sanford Rose Assoc. - Columbia (C), SC, *570*
Sanford Rose Assoc. - Nashville (C), TN, *570*
Sanford Rose Assoc. - Austin (C), TX, *570*
Sanford Rose Assoc. - Salt Lake City (C), UT, *571*
Sanford Rose Assoc. - Port Washington (C), WI, *571*
Santangelo Consultants Inc. (C), NY, *571*
Allan Sarn Assoc., Inc. (R), NY, *184*
Sarver & Carruth Assoc. (C), OK, *571*
Sathe & Associates, Inc. (R), MN, *184*
Satterfield & Assoc., Inc. (R), OH, *184*
Savalli & Assoc., Inc. (C), MI, *571*
Saviar, Inc. (C), AZ, *571*
Savoy Partners, Ltd. (R), DC, *184*
David Saxner & Assoc., Inc. (DSA, Inc.) (R), IL, *185*
Schall Executive Search Partners (R), MN, *185*
Schattle & Duquette (C), RI, *571*
The Schatz Company (C), MO, *571*
Schenck & Assoc. SC (C), WI, *572*
Schick Professional Search, Inc. (C), OH, *572*
A.D. Schiff & Assoc., Ltd. (C), IL, *572*
Schlatter & Assoc. (C), CA, *572*
F. B. Schmidt Int'l. (R), CA, *185*
Schneider, Hill & Spangler, Inc. (R), PA, *185*
Schoales & Assoc. Inc. (C), ON, *572*
Schulenburg & Assoc. (C), GA, *572*
Schuyler Assoc., Ltd. (R), GA, *185*
Schuyler, Baker & Parker, Inc. (R), GA, *185*
Schwab-Carrese Assoc., Inc. Executive Search (R), NC, *185*
G. L. Schwartz & Assoc., Inc. (C), GA, *572*
Schweichler Assoc., Inc. (R), CA, *186*
Scientific Solutions, Inc. (C), MI, *572*
Devin Scott Assoc. (C), NJ, *572*
Robert Scott Assoc. (C), NJ, *573*
Scott Douglas Inc. (C), CA, *573*
Scott Executive Search, Inc. (R), NY, *186*
Scott Sibley Assoc. (C), NY, *573*
Scott-Thaler Assoc. Agency, Inc. (C), CA, *573*
Scott-Wayne Assoc., Inc. (C), MA, *573*
Search & Recruit Int'l. (C), VA, *573*
Search Advisors Int'l. Corp. (R), FL, *186*
The Search Alliance, Inc. (R), FL, *186*
The Search America Group Inc. (C), OH, *573*
Search America, Inc. (C), PA, *573*
Search America, Inc. (C), MA, *574*
Search Assoc. (C), KY, *574*
Search Assoc., Inc. (C), NJ, *574*
Search Assoc., Inc. (C), CA, *574*
Search Bureau Int'l. (C), IL, *574*
Search By Design (C), AZ, *574*
The Search Center Inc. (C), TX, *574*
The Search Committee (C), MD, *574*
The Search Company (R), ON, *186*
Search Consultants, Inc. (C), NJ, *575*
Search Consultants Int'l., Inc. (C), TX, *575*
Search Consultants, LLC (C), MD, *575*
Search Dynamics, Inc. (C), IL, *575*
Search Enterprises, Inc. (C), FL, *575*
Search Excellence (R), CA, *186*
Search Group (C), CA, *575*
Search Group Inc. (R), AB, *186*
The Search Group (C), MD, *575*
Search Innovations, Inc. (R), PA, *187*
Search Int'l. (R), MA, *187*
Search Masters Int'l. (R), AZ, *187*
Search Masters, USA (C), FL, *576*
The Search Network (C), CA, *576*
Search North America, Inc. (C), OR, *576*
Search Northwest Assoc. (C), OR, *576*
Search Plus Int'l.-Ohio (C), OH, *576*
Search Research Assoc., Inc. (R), MA, *187*
Search Solutions Inc. (C), CA, *576*
Search South, Inc. (C), AL, *576*
Search West, Inc. (C), CA, *576*
SearchCom, Inc. (R), TX, *187*
SearchCorp (C), FL, *577*
SearchCorp International (C), AB, *577*
Searchforce, Inc. (R), FL, *187*
Searchline Services, Inc. (C), OH, *577*
SearchOne, Inc. (C), AR, *577*
Searchworks, Inc. (C), FL, *577*
Sears & Associates (C), CA, *577*
Seco & Zetto Assoc., Inc. (C), NJ, *577*
Secura/Burnett Partners (R), CA, *187*
Sedlar & Miners (R), NY, *188*
J. R. Seehusen Assoc., Inc. (R), IA, *188*
Segal & Assoc. (C), GA, *578*
Seiden Krieger Assoc., Inc. (R), NY, *188*
Seitchik Corwin & Seitchik Inc. (R), CA, *188*
Select Services (C), IL, *578*
Selected Executives, Inc. (C), MA, *578*
Selectis Corp. (C), IL, *578*
Selective Management Services, Inc. (C), FL, *578*
Selective Recruiting Assoc., Inc. (C), MI, *578*
Selective Search Associates (C), OH, *578*
Selective Staffing (C), CA, *579*
Selig Executive Search (C), NH, *579*
Robert Sellery Assoc., Ltd. (R), DC, *188*
Seltzer Fontaine Beckwith (C), CA, *579*
Senior Careers (R), NY, *188*
Sensible Solutions, Inc. (R), IL, *188*
Setford-Shaw-Najarian Assoc. (C), NY, *579*
Sevcor Int'l., Inc. (R), IL, *188*
SFB Legal Search (C), NY, *579*
Shannahan & Co., Inc. (R), CA, *189*
Sharp Placement Professionals, Inc. (C), NY, *579*
Sharrow & Assoc., Inc. (C), MI, *579*
M. B. Shattuck & Assoc., Inc. (R), CA, *189*
Peggy Shea & Assoc. (R), CA, *189*
John Shell Assoc., Inc. (C), SC, *579*
Shell Technology Group (C), CA, *580*
Shelton, Wiseman & Leon (R), CA, *189*
Shepherd Bueschel & Provus, Inc. (R), IL, *189*
Sherbrooke Assoc., Inc. (C), NJ, *580*
Sheridan Search (R), IL, *189*
Sherriff & Assoc. (C), KS, *580*
Sherwood Lehman Massucco, Inc. (R), CA, *189*
Shey-Harding Assoc. Inc. (C), CA, *580*
Shiell Personnel (C), LA, *580*
Shifrin-Fischer Group, Inc. (C), NJ, *580*
Shiloh Careers Int'l., Inc. (C), TN, *580*
Shinn & Assoc. (R), CA, *189*
Michael Shirley Assoc. Inc. (R), KS, *190*
Shoemaker & Assoc. (R), GA, *190*

E. L. Shore & Assoc. (R), ON, *190*
Shore Asociados Ejecutivos, S. A. de C.V. (R), MX, *190*
The Shorr Group (R), IL, *190*
The Shotland Group (R), CA, *190*
SHS of Allentown (C), PA, *580*
M. Shulman, Inc. (R), CA, *191*
Shupack & Michaels Inc. (C), NY, *580*
John Sibbald Assoc., Inc. (R), MO, *191*
Larry Siegel & Assoc. (R), WA, *191*
Peter Siegel & Co. (C), MA, *581*
RitaSue Siegel Resources, Inc. (R), NY, *191*
Siger & Assoc., LLC (C), CT, *581*
SignatureSoft Inc. (C), CA, *581*
Marvin L. Silcott & Assoc., Inc. (C), TX, *581*
The Silicon Network (C), ON, *581*
Sill Technical Assoc., Inc. (C), PA, *581*
L. A. Silver Assoc., Inc. (R), MA, *191*
Silver Associates (C), CA, *581*
SilverSands Int'l. (C), FL, *582*
Daniel A. Silverstein Assoc. Inc. (R), FL, *191*
The Simmons Group (C), CA, *582*
D. W. Simpson & Co. (C), IL, *582*
D. J. Simpson Assoc. Inc. (R), ON, *191*
Simpson Associates (C), NY, *582*
Sinclair & Co., Inc. (R), MA, *192*
Singleton & Assoc. (C), VA, *582*
Sink, Walker, Boltrus Int'l. (R), MA, *192*
SKB Enterprises (C), NY, *582*
Skipping Stone Inc. (C), VA, *582*
Ruth Sklar Assoc., Inc. (RSA Executive Search) (R), NY, *192*
Skott/Edwards Consultants (R), NY, *192*
Skupsky & Assoc. (C), CO, *582*
Slayton Int'l., Inc. (R), IL, *192*
Sloan & Assoc., Inc. (C), VA, *583*
Tom Sloan & Assoc., Inc. (C), WI, *583*
J. L. Small Assoc. (C), AL, *583*
Christopher Smallhorn Executive Recruiting, Inc. (R), MA, *193*
Smartsource Inc. (C), CA, *583*
Smith & Assoc. (C), FL, *583*
Smith & Assoc. (C), CA, *583*
James F. Smith & Assoc. (C), GA, *583*
Peter A. Smith & Assoc. (C), OR, *584*
Ralph Smith & Assoc. (C), IL, *584*
Smith & Laue Search (R), OR, *193*
Smith & Sawyer, Inc. (R), NY, *193*
Smith & Syberg, Inc. (R), IN, *193*
Smith Assoc. (C), IA, *584*
G. L. Smith Assoc. (C), CA, *584*
Howard W. Smith Assoc. (R), CT, *193*
Abbott Smith Assoc., Inc. (R), NY, *193*
J. Harrington Smith Assoc. (C), IN, *584*
Herman Smith Executive Initiatives Inc. (R), ON, *193*
The Smith Group, Inc. (C), NC, *584*
Smith Hanley Assoc., Inc. (C), NY, *584*
Smith James Group, Inc. (R), GA, *194*
H. C. Smith Ltd. (R), OH, *194*
Smith Professional Search (C), MI, *584*
Smith, Roth & Squires (R), NY, *194*
Smith Search, S.C. (R), MX, *194*
Smith's Fifth Avenue (C), NY, *585*
Smith, Brown & Jones (C), KS, *585*
A. William Smyth, Inc. (R), CA, *194*
Smythe Masterson & Judd, Inc. (C), NY, *585*
Snelling & Snelling, Inc. (C), FL, *585*
Snelling Search (C), AL, *585*
Snelling Search (C), IL, *585*
Snelling Search - Transportation Division (C), AR, *585*
Snelling Search (C), IL, *586*
Snelling Search (C), LA, *586*
Snelling Search Recruiters (C), NC, *586*
C. Snow & Assoc. (C), ON, *586*
Snyder & Co. (R), CT, *194*
Andrea Sobel & Assoc., Inc. (C), CA, *586*
Sockwell & Assoc. (R), NC, *194*
Soderlund Assoc. Inc. (R), OH, *194*
Sofco (C), NY, *586*
Softrix, Inc. (C), NJ, *586*
SoftSearch Inc. (C), NJ, *586*
Software Engineering Solutions, Inc. (C), CA, *586*
Software Resource Consultants (C), TN, *587*
Robert Sollman & Assoc. (C), FL, *587*
Phyllis Solomon Executive Search, Inc. (C), NJ, *587*
Solomon-Page Healthcare Group (R), NY, *195*
Soltis Management Services (R), PA, *195*
Solutions Group (R), AL, *195*
Somerset Group, Inc. (C), CT, *587*
Stephen M. Sonis Assoc. (R), MA, *195*
Souder & Assoc. (R), VA, *195*
Southern Chemical & Plastics Search (C), GA, *587*
Southern Recruiters & Consultants, Inc. (C), SC, *587*
Southern Research Services (R), FL, *195*
Southport Int'l. Assoc. Inc. (C), FL, *588*
Southwest Search & Consulting, Inc. (C), AZ, *588*
Southwest Selective Search, Inc. (C), TX, *588*
Southwestern Professional Services (C), TN, *588*
Sparks, McDonough & Assoc., Inc. (C), MO, *588*
SPC Symcox Personnel Consultants (C), TX, *588*
Spear-Izzo Assoc., LLC (C), PA, *588*
Special Markets Group, Inc. (R), GA, *195*
Specialized Search Assoc. (C), FL, *589*
Specialty Consultants Inc. (R), PA, *195*
Specialty Employment Services, Inc. (C), GA, *589*
Spectra International LLC (C), AZ, *589*
SpectraWest (C), CA, *589*
Spectrum Consultants (R), CA, *196*
SpencerSearch, Inc. (C), CO, *589*
SpencerStuart (R), NY, *196*
The Spiegel Group (R), MA, *197*
Spilman & Assoc. (R), TX, *197*
Kenn Spinrad Inc. (C), PA, *589*
Splaine & Assoc., Inc. (R), CA, *198*
Sports Group Int'l. (R), NC, *198*
Spriggs & Co., Inc. (R), IL, *198*
Spring Assoc., Inc. (R), NY, *198*
M. H. Springer & Assoc. (R), CA, *198*
Springer Souder & Assoc. L.L.C. (R), IL, *198*
Sprout/Standish, Inc. (C), NH, *589*
Squires Resources Inc. (C), ON, *590*
SR Wilson, Inc. (C), CA, *590*
SSA Executive Search Int'l. (R), AZ, *198*
Staff Extension Int'l. (C), TX, *590*
Staff Resources, Inc. (C), SC, *590*
Staffing Edge, Inc. (C), IA, *590*
C. J. Stafford & Assoc. (C), ON, *591*
Stafford Consulting Group (R), CA, *198*
StaffWriters Plus (C), NY, *591*
Stanewick, Hart & Assoc., Inc. (C), FL, *591*
Stanton Chase Int'l. (R), MD, *198*
The Stanton Group, Inc. (C), IL, *591*
Star Search Consultants (C), ON, *591*
Starbridge Group Inc. (C), VA, *591*
The Stark Wilton Group (R), MI, *199*
STAT Search (C), NH, *592*
Staub, Warmbold & Assoc., Inc. (R), NY, *199*
Steeple Resources & Consulting (R), NJ, *199*
Steinbach & Co. (C), MA, *592*
Steinfield & Assoc. (C), TX, *592*
The Stelton Group, Inc. (C), NJ, *592*
Stentiford & Berardi Assoc. Ltd. (R), NY, *199*
Stephens Assoc. Ltd., Inc. (R), OH, *200*
Peter Sterling & Co. (C), TX, *592*
Sterling Int'l. (R), NJ, *200*
Sterling Int'l. Management Recruitment, Ltd. Inc. (C), NC, *592*
Daniel Stern & Assoc. (C), PA, *592*
Michael Stern Assoc., Inc./Euram (R), ON, *200*
Steven Douglas Assoc. (C), FL, *593*
Steven Michaels & Assoc. (C), NY, *593*
Ron Stevens & Assoc., Inc. (C), FL, *593*
Stevens Assoc. (C), MA, *593*
The Stevens Group (R), TX, *200*
The Stevens Group (C), CA, *593*
Stevens, Valentine & McKeever (C), NJ, *593*
The Stevenson Group, Inc. (N.J.) (R), NJ, *200*
Stewart Assoc. (C), PA, *593*
The Stewart Group (C), FL, *593*
Stewart, Stein & Scott, Ltd. (R), MN, *200*
Stewart/Greene & Co. of The Triad, Inc. (C), NC, *594*
Stewart/Laurence Assoc., Inc. (R), NJ, *201*
Charles Stickler Assoc. (R), PA, *201*
Linford E. Stiles & Assoc., L.L.C. (R), NH, *201*
Stillinger & Assoc. (R), CA, *201*
STM Assoc. (R), UT, *201*
Allan Stolee Inc. (R), FL, *201*
Stone & Youngblood (C), MA, *594*
Stone Assoc. LLC (C), MI, *594*
Stone Enterprises Ltd. (C), IL, *594*
Stone, Murphy & Olson (R), MN, *201*
DM Stone Personnel Services (C), CA, *594*
The Stonebridge Group (C), PA, *594*
Stoneburner Assoc., Inc. (C), KS, *594*
Stoopen Asociados, S.C./EMA Partners Int'l. (R), MX, *202*
Storfer & Assoc. (C), NY, *595*
Straight & Co. (R), GA, *202*

Mark Stranberg & Assoc. Inc. (R), MA, *202*
Strategic Advancement Inc. (R), NJ, *202*
Strategic Alliance Network, Ltd. (C), OH, *595*
Strategic Alternatives (R), CA, *202*
Strategic Assoc., Inc. (C), TX, *595*
Strategic Executives, Inc. (R), CT, *202*
Strategic Resources Biotechnology & Medical Group (C), WA, *595*
Strategic Resources (C), WA, *595*
Strategic Search Corp. (R), IL, *202*
Strategic Search, LLC (C), CA, *595*
Strategic Technologies, Inc. (C), TX, *596*
StratfordGroup (R), OH, *203*
W. R. Strathmann Assoc. (R), NY, *203*
Stratin Assoc. (C), NJ, *596*
Straube Associates (R), MA, *203*
Strauss Personnel Service (C), PA, *596*
Strelcheck & Assoc., Inc. (R), WI, *203*
J. Stroll Assoc., Inc. (R), CT, *203*
Stroman Int'l., Inc. (R), CO, *204*
Success Seekers Connection (C), FL, *596*
Sudina Search, Inc. (C), MD, *596*
Sullivan & Assoc. (R), MI, *204*
Joe Sullivan & Assoc., Inc. (R), NY, *204*
Sullivan & Company (R), NY, *204*
Summerfield Assoc., Inc. (C), TN, *596*
Summit Executive Search Consultants, Inc. (R), FL, *204*
Summit Group Int'l., Inc. (R), GA, *204*
The Summit Group (C), CA, *596*
Summit Search Specialists (C), TX, *596*
Ron Sunshine & Assoc. (C), IL, *597*
Survival Systems Staffing, Inc. (C), CA, *597*
Swartz & Assoc., Inc. (R), AZ, *204*
Sweeney Harbert & Mummert, Inc. (R), FL, *205*
Swift & Assoc. (C), ME, *597*
Synagent Inc. (C), ON, *597*
Synapse Human Resource Consulting Group (R), TX, *205*
Synergistech Communications (C), CA, *597*
Synergistics Assoc. Ltd. (R), IL, *205*
Synergy 2000 (C), DC, *597*
The Synergy Organization (R), PA, *205*
Synergy Solutions, Ltd. (C), WA, *597*
Synergy Systems (C), ON, *598*
System 1 Search (C), CA, *598*
Systems Careers (C), CA, *598*
Systems One Ltd. (C), IL, *598*
Systems Personnel, Inc. (C), NY, *598*
Systems Research Group (C), CA, *598*
Systems Research Group (C), OH, *598*
Systems Research Inc. (SRI) (C), IL, *598*
Systems Search (C), IL, *599*
Systems Search Group, Inc. (C), NC, *599*
T E M Assoc. (C), WI, *599*
T. H. Hunter, Inc. (C), MN, *599*
Tabb & Assoc. (R), OH, *205*
Tactical Alternatives (R), CA, *205*
The Talley Group (R), VA, *205*
Roy Talman & Assoc. (C), IL, *599*
The Talon Group (R), TX, *205*
Martin Stevens Tamaren & Assoc., Inc. (R), CA, *206*
S. Tanner & Assoc. Inc. (C), ON, *599*
Tanner & Assoc., Inc. (R), TX, *206*
Tannura & Assoc., Inc. (R), IL, *206*
Tarbex (C), DC, *599*
Target Search, Inc. (C), PA, *600*
Tarnow Int'l. (R), NJ, *206*
TASA International (R), NY, *206*
Tate & Assoc., Inc. (R), NJ, *207*
Tate Consulting, Inc. (R), FL, *207*
M. L. Tawney & Assoc. (C), TX, *600*
Tax Network Resources, Inc. (C), NY, *600*
TaxSearch Inc. (R), OK, *207*
Carl J. Taylor & Co. (R), TX, *207*
Peter R. Taylor Assoc., Inc. (C), NY, *600*
Taylor Winfield (R), TX, *207*
TBC, Inc. (C), KY, *600*
The TBI Group (R), PA, *207*
TCM Enterprises (C), MD, *600*
TE, Inc. (C), IL, *600*
Team One Partners, Inc. (C), GA, *600*
TeamBuilders (C), GA, *600*
Teamsearch, Inc. (C), MI, *601*
Tech 2000 (C), FL, *601*
Tech Connector Group (C), CA, *601*
Tech Consulting (C), FL, *601*
Tech Search (C), CA, *601*
Tech-Net (C), TX, *601*
Techaid Inc. (C), QE, *601*
TechFind, Inc. (R), MA, *207*
Technical Connections, Inc. (C), CA, *601*
Technical Employment Consultants (C), PA, *602*
Technical Recruiting Consultants (C), IL, *602*
Technical Recruiting Services (C), OH, *602*
Technical Resource Assoc. (C), TN, *602*
Technical Search Assoc. (C), OH, *602*
Technical Skills Consulting Inc. (R), ON, *207*
Technical Staffing Solutions (C), TX, *602*
Technifind Int'l. (C), TX, *602*
TechNix Inc. (C), ON, *602*
Techno-Trac Systems, Inc. (C), NY, *603*
Technology Consultants Int'l. (C), CA, *603*
The Technology Group (R), IL, *208*
Technology Management Partners (R), CA, *208*
Technology Search Int'l. (C), CA, *603*
Techsearch Services Inc. (C), CT, *603*
Techstaff Inc. (C), WI, *603*
Tecmark Associates Inc. (C), NY, *604*
Teknon Employment Resources, Inc. (C), OH, *604*
Tekworx, Inc. (C), OK, *604*
Tele-Media Int'l. Inc. (C), PA, *604*
Tele-Solutions of Arizona, Inc. (C), AZ, *604*
Telecom Connections, Inc. (C), TX, *604*
Telecom Executive Group (C), NJ, *605*
Telecom Recruiters, Inc. (C), VA, *605*
Telem Adhesive Search Corp. (C), MD, *605*
TeleManagement Search (C), NY, *605*
Telequest Communications, Inc. (C), NJ, *605*
Telford, Adams & Alexander (R), CA, *208*
Tell/Com Recruiters (C), PA, *605*
TEMCO-The Executive Management Consulting Organization (R), WI, *208*
Templeton & Assoc. (C), MN, *605*
Tennyson Advisors (R), NY, *208*
Tesar-Reynes, Inc. (R), IL, *208*
The TGA Company (C), TX, *606*
Thomas & Assoc. of Michigan (C), MI, *606*
Thomas Lyle & Co. (C), IL, *606*
Thomas Mangum Co. (R), CA, *208*
Thomas Resource Group (R), CA, *209*
Thomas, Whelan Assoc., Inc. (C), DC, *606*
Judy Thompson & Assoc., Inc. (C), CA, *606*
Thompson Assoc. (C), CA, *606*
Richard Thompson Assoc., Inc. (R), MN, *209*
Thomson, Sponar & Adams, Inc. (C), WA, *606*
Thor, Inc. (C), CA, *606*
Thorne, Brieger Assoc., Inc. (R), NY, *209*
The Tidewater Group Inc. (C), CT, *607*
Tierney Assoc., Inc. (R), PA, *209*
Fred C. Tippel & Assoc. (C), OH, *607*
Tirocchi, Wright, Inc. (R), CA, *209*
Tittemore Cowan Assoc. (C), AB, *607*
TNS Partners, Inc. (R), TX, *209*
Skip Tolette Executive Search Consulting (R), NJ, *209*
Tomlinson Assoc. Inc. (C), IL, *607*
Tondorf & Assoc. Inc. (C), MA, *607*
Top Gun Group, Inc. (C), NV, *607*
Topaz Int'l., Inc., Attorney Search (C), NJ, *607*
The Touchstone Group (C), MA, *607*
Tower Consultants, Ltd. (R), PA, *209*
TPG & Assoc. (C), TX, *608*
TPS Staffing Solutions (C), IN, *608*
Trac One (R), NJ, *210*
Jay Tracey Assoc. Inc. (C), VT, *608*
Trainor/Frank & Assoc. Inc. (C), WI, *608*
Trambley the Recruiter (C), NM, *608*
Trans-United Consultants Ltd. (C), ON, *608*
Transportation Recruiting Services, Inc. (C), MS, *608*
Travaille Executive Search (R), DC, *210*
Travel Executive Search (C), NY, *608*
Travel Personnel (C), OH, *609*
Travis & Co., Inc. (R), MA, *210*
Traynor Confidential, Ltd. (C), NY, *609*
Van Treadaway Assoc., Inc. (R), GA, *210*
Trebor Weldon Lawrence, Inc. (R), NY, *210*
TRH Assoc., Inc. (R), NY, *210*
Triad Consultants, Inc. (C), NJ, *609*
Triad Technology Group (C), OR, *609*
Triangle Assoc. (C), PA, *609*
Trillium Human Resources Inc. (C), ON, *609*
TriStaff Group (C), CA, *609*
Triumph Consulting, Inc. (R), IA, *210*
Trout & Assoc. Inc. (R), UT, *211*
Trowbridge & Co., Inc. (R), MA, *211*
TRS Staffing Solutions Inc. (C), OH, *610*
The Truman Agency (C), CA, *610*
Tryon & Heideman, LLC (R), MO, *211*
TSC Management Services Group, Inc. (C), IL, *610*
Tschudin Inc. (R), NJ, *211*
TSI Group/TSI Staffing Services (C), ON, *610*

TSS Consulting, Ltd. (C), AZ, *610*
TSW Assoc., LLC (R), CT, *211*
TTG/Sterling Services (C), CA, *610*
W. G. Tucker & Assoc. (R), PA, *211*
Tucker Assoc. (R), NJ, *211*
The Thomas Tucker Co. (R), CA, *211*
Tuft & Assoc., Inc. (R), IL, *212*
Tully/Woodmansee Int'l. Inc. (R), FL, *212*
Tuttle Venture Group, Inc. (R), TX, *212*
Tyler & Company (R), GA, *212*
U.S. Search (C), VA, *610*
The Ultimate Source (R), CA, *212*
UniQuest Int'l., Inc. (C), FL, *610*
Unisearch Search & Recruiting Inc. (C), CA, *611*
United Personnel Services (C), MA, *611*
Unlimited Staffing Solutions, Inc. (C), MI, *611*
The Urban Placement Service (C), TX, *611*
USA Medical Placement Inc. (C), TX, *611*
V.I.P. Resources, Inc. (C), NY, *611*
Valentine & Assoc. (C), IL, *611*
Van Dyke Assoc. (R), IL, *212*
Peter Van Leer & Assoc. (R), MN, *213*
Van Leeuwen Assoc. (R), CA, *213*
VanMaldegiam Assoc., Inc. (R), IL, *213*
VanReypen Enterprises, Ltd. (R), NY, *213*
Vaughan & Co. (C), CA, *612*
Venpro Consulting Inc. (C), ON, *612*
Vento Assoc. (C), TN, *612*
Venture Resources, Inc. (R), CA, *213*
Verkamp-Joyce Assoc., Inc. (R), IL, *213*
The Verriez Group Inc. (R), ON, *213*
Vezan Assoc. (C), CT, *612*
Claude Vezina, Conseil en recherche de cadres inc. (R), QE, *213*
Vick & Assoc. (R), TX, *214*
Victor White Int'l. (C), CA, *612*
Villareal & Assoc., Inc. (R), OK, *214*
Villasenor & Assoc. (C), CA, *612*
C. J. Vincent Assoc., LLC (C), MD, *612*
Vincenty & Co. (C), OH, *612*
Vintage Resources, Inc. (C), NY, *613*
The Viscusi Group, Inc. (R), NY, *214*
Vlcek & Company, Inc. (R), CA, *214*
Vogel Assoc. (C), PA, *613*
Voigt Assoc. (R), IL, *214*
Beverly von Winckler & Assoc. (C), IL, *613*
VZ Int'l., Inc. (C), AZ, *613*
W. P. Assoc. (C), CA, *613*
The Wabash Group (C), IN, *613*
Wachendorfer & Assoc. (C), TX, *613*
Fred Wackerle, Inc. (R), IL, *214*
Robert H. Wadsworth & Assoc., Inc. (R), AZ, *214*
Gordon Wahls Executive Search (C), PA, *613*
Wakefield Talabisco Int'l. (R), NY, *214*
Waldorf Associates, Inc. (C), CA, *614*
Kelly Walker Assoc. (C), TX, *614*
Walker Group, Inc. (R), MN, *215*
Walker Personnel, Inc. (C), LA, *614*
K. K. Walker Professional Recruitment (C), CA, *614*
B. D. Wallace & Assoc. (C), MD, *614*
Wallace Assoc. (C), CT, *614*
Wallace Assoc. (C), MA, *614*
The Wallace Law Registry (C), CT, *614*
Wallace Management Co. (R), TN, *215*
Gerald Walsh & Co. Inc. (C), NS, *614*
J. D. Walsh & Co. (R), CT, *215*
Deborah Snow Walsh, Inc. (R), IL, *215*
Linda Walter & Associes (C), QE, *615*
Lee H. Walton & Assoc. (R), NY, *215*
Karen Wanger & Assoc., Inc. (C), IL, *615*
Ward Assoc. (C), ON, *615*
Martha Ward Executive Search, Inc. (C), NY, *615*
The Ward Group (R), MA, *215*
Ward Liebelt Assoc. Inc. (R), CT, *215*
Ward-Hoffman & Assoc. (C), ID, *615*
C. D. Warner & Assoc. (C), PA, *615*
Warner & Assoc., Inc. (C), OH, *615*
Warren Executive Services (C), GA, *616*
Warren Int'l. (R), NY, *215*
Warren, Morris & Madison, Ltd. (C), CA, *616*
Warring & Assoc. (R), CA, *215*
The Washington Firm, Ltd. (R), WA, *216*
Wasserman Assoc. Inc. (C), MD, *616*
Waterford Executive Group Ltd. (C), IL, *616*
R. J. Watkins & Co., Ltd. (R), CA, *216*
Watring & Assoc., Inc. (C), IL, *616*
Scott Watson & Assoc., Inc. (R), FL, *216*
Watson Int'l., Inc. (R), NY, *216*
Waveland Int'l. (R), IL, *216*
Wayne Assoc., Inc. (C), VA, *616*
The Wayne Group, Ltd. (C), NY, *616*
Weatherby Healthcare (C), CT, *617*
Webb, Johnson Assoc., Inc. (R), NY, *216*
Weber Executive Search (R), NY, *216*
S. B. Webster & Associates (R), MA, *217*
Wegner & Assoc. (C), WI, *617*
Lee Weil Assoc., Inc. (C), IL, *617*
David Weinfeld Group (C), NC, *617*
Weinman & Assoc. (C), AZ, *617*
Weinpel Search, Inc. (C), NJ, *617*
Weinstein & Co. (R), MA, *217*
S. E. Weinstein Co. (R), IL, *217*
D. L. Weiss & Assoc. (R), CA, *217*
C. Weiss Assoc., Inc. (C), NY, *618*
Weliver & Assoc. (C), MI, *618*
Henry Welker & Assoc. (C), MI, *618*
The Wellesley Group, Inc. (R), IL, *217*
Wellington Management Group (R), PA, *217*
Wellington Thomas Ltd. (C), FL, *618*
Wells, Bradley & Assoc., Inc. (C), MN, *618*
R. A. Wells Co. (C), GA, *618*
Welzig, Lowe & Assoc. (C), CO, *618*
The Wentworth Co., Inc. (R), CA, *217*
Werbin Assoc. Executive Search, Inc. (C), NY, *618*
Jude M. Werra & Assoc. (R), WI, *218*
Wesley Brown & Bartle Co., Inc. (R), NY, *218*
West & Assoc. (C), IL, *618*
West & West (R), CA, *218*
West Coast Recruiting (C), CA, *619*
Western Management Assoc. (R), CA, *218*
Western Management Consultants (R), BC, *218*
Western Technical Resources (C), CA, *619*
The Westfield Group (C), CT, *619*
Westfields Int'l., Inc. (C), NY, *619*
The Westminster Group, Inc. (R), RI, *218*
Weston Consultants, Inc. (R), MA, *219*
WestPacific National Search, Inc. (C), CA, *619*
Weterrings & Agnew, Inc. (C), NY, *619*
S. J. Wexler Assoc., Inc. (R), NY, *219*
Wheeler Assoc. (R), CT, *219*
Wheeler, Moore & Elam Co. (R), TX, *219*
Wheelless Group (R), IL, *219*
The Whitaker Companies (C), TX, *619*
Whitbeck & Assoc. (R), MN, *219*
White, Roberts & Stratton, Inc. (C), IL, *619*
Whitehead & Assoc., Inc. (C), MO, *620*
Arch S. Whitehead Assoc. Inc. (ASWA) (R), NY, *219*
K. L. Whitney Company (R), NJ, *219*
The Whitney Group (R), NY, *219*
The Whitney Group (C), GA, *620*
Whitney Smith Co. (C), TX, *620*
Whittaker & Assoc., Inc. (C), GA, *620*
The Whittaker Group (C), MI, *620*
Whittlesey & Assoc., Inc. (R), PA, *220*
The Whyte Group, Inc. (R), MD, *220*
Daniel Wier & Assoc. (R), CA, *220*
Wilcox Bertoux & Miller (R), CA, *220*
Wilcoxen, Blackwell, Niven & Assoc. (R), FL, *220*
Wilder & Assoc. (C), VA, *620*
Wilder, Gammel Partners, Ltd. (R), CA, *220*
Joel H. Wilensky Assoc., Inc. (C), MA, *620*
The Wilkie Group Int'l. (R), ON, *220*
Walter K. Wilkins & Co. (R), NJ, *221*
Wilkinson & Ives (R), CA, *221*
Wilkinson SoftSearch, Inc. (C), VA, *620*
William-Johns Co., Inc. (C), CA, *621*
Dick Williams & Assoc. (C), CA, *621*
John R. Williams & Assoc., Inc. (C), NC, *621*
John Williams & Assoc. (C), TX, *621*
Williams & Delmore, Inc. (C), NC, *621*
Williams Executive Search, Inc. (R), MN, *221*
Williams Recruiting, Inc. (C), WA, *621*
Williams, Roth & Krueger, Inc. (R), IL, *221*
Williamsburg Group (C), NJ, *621*
Willis & Assoc. (R), OH, *221*
William Willis Worldwide Inc. (R), CT, *221*
Willmott & Assoc. (C), MA, *622*
N. Willner & Co., Inc. (R), NJ, *221*
Wills Consulting Assoc. Inc. (R), CT, *221*
The Wilmington Group (C), NC, *622*
Wilson & Assoc. Int'l. Inc. (C), FL, *622*
Wilson Assoc. Inc. (R), NS, *222*
Wilson McLeran, Inc. (C), CT, *622*
Wilson Personnel, Inc. (C), NC, *622*
Wilson-Douglas-Jordan (C), IL, *622*
The Winchester Group (R), CA, *222*
The Windham Group (R), OH, *222*
Windsor Consultants, Inc. (C), TX, *622*
Windsor International (R), GA, *222*
Winfield Assoc., Inc. (C), MA, *623*
Wing Tips & Pumps, Inc. (C), MI, *623*
Winguth, Grant & Donahue (R), CA, *222*
The Winn Group, Inc. (C), KS, *623*
Winston & Green (C), IL, *623*
Winston Search, Inc. (R), MD, *222*

Winter, Wyman & Co. (C), MA, *623*
Winthrop Partners, Inc. (R), NY, *222*
Wisnewski & Assoc. (R), CA, *223*
The Witt Group (C), FL, *623*
Witt/Kieffer, Ford, Hadelman & Lloyd (R), IL, *223*
WMD inc. (C), NJ, *623*
Wojdula & Assoc., Ltd. (R), WI, *223*
D. S. Wolf Assoc., Inc. (R), NY, *223*
S. R. Wolman Assoc., Inc. (R), NY, *224*
Woltz & Assoc., Inc. (R), IL, *224*
Susan L. Wonderling Recruiting (C), PA, *623*
Louise Wood & Assoc. (C), NY, *624*
Wood & Assoc./Executive Search Consultants (C), CA, *624*
M. Wood Company (R), IL, *224*
Wood, Franchot Inc. (R), MN, *224*
Wood West & Partners Inc. (C), BC, *624*
Wood-Glavin, Inc. (R), KS, *224*
Woodmoor Group (C), CO, *624*
Bruce G. Woods Executive Search (R), TX, *224*
Jim Woodson & Assoc., Inc. (C), MS, *624*
The Woodstone Consulting Company, Inc. (R), CO, *224*
Woodworth Int'l. Group (R), OR, *224*
Working Relationships, Inc. (C), MN, *624*
Worlco Computer Resources, Inc. (C), PA, *624*
World Search (C), OH, *625*
Worldwide Medical Services (C), CA, *625*
The Worth Group (C), GA, *625*
Dick Wray & Consultants, Inc. (R), CA, *225*
Jay Wren & Assoc. (C), CA, *625*
The Wright Group (C), TX, *625*
Bob Wright Recruiting, Inc. (C), CT, *625*
WTW Assoc., Inc. (R), NY, *225*
Wyatt & Jaffe (R), MN, *225*
R. S. Wyatt Assoc., Inc. (R), TX, *225*
John Wylie Assoc., Inc. (C), OK, *625*
Wyndham Mills Int'l., Inc. (R), GA, *225*
Dennis Wynn Assoc., Inc. (C), FL, *625*
Xagas & Assoc. (R), IL, *226*
Xavier Associates, Inc. (R), MA, *226*
The Yaiser Group (C), NJ, *625*
Yankee Hospitality Search (C), CT, *626*
Yelverton Executive Search (R), CA, *226*
The York Group (C), CA, *626*
The Yorkshire Group, Ltd. (C), MA, *626*
Yormak & Assoc. (C), CA, *626*
Bill Young & Assoc. (C), VA, *626*
Youngblood Assoc. (C), NC, *626*
Your Advantage Staffing Consultants Inc. (C), ON, *626*
Yours In Travel Personnel Agency, Inc. (C), NY, *626*
Steven Yungerberg Assoc., Inc. (R), MN, *226*
Yungner & Bormann (R), MN, *226*
Zaccaria Int'l. (C), NJ, *627*
Zackrison Assoc., Inc. (C), FL, *627*
The Zammataro Company (R), OH, *226*
ZanExec L.L.C. (R), VA, *226*
The Zarkin Group, Inc. (R), NY, *226*
Egon Zehnder Int'l. Inc. (R), NY, *227*
Zeiger Assoc. L.L.C. (C), CA, *627*
Zen Zen Int'l. Inc. (C), MB, *627*
Zenner Consulting Group (C), IL, *627*
Helen Ziegler & Assoc., Inc. (C), ON, *627*
P. D. Zier Assoc. (C), CT, *627*
Chuck Zimering Advertising Recruitment (CZAR) (C), NY, *627*
Zingaro & Company (R), TX, *227*
Michael D. Zinn & Assoc., Inc. (R), NJ, *227*
Zona & Assoc., Inc. (C), NY, *628*
Zurick, Davis & Co., Inc. (R), MA, *227*
Zweig White & Assoc., Inc. (R), MA, *228*
Zwell Int'l. (R), IL, *228*

Other Useful Recruiter Resources

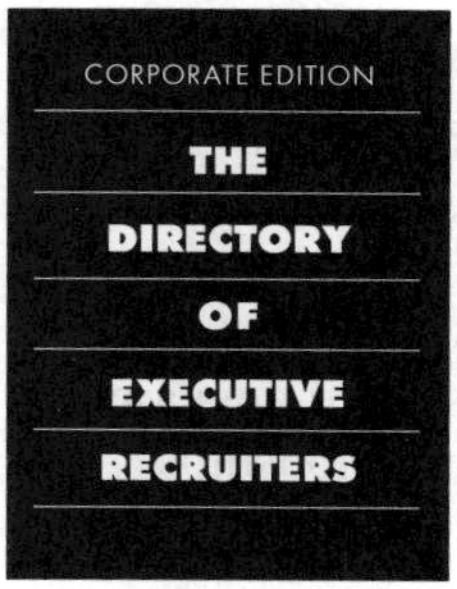

THE DIRECTORY OF EXECUTIVE RECRUITERS: CORPORATE EDITION (2 volume set)

Deluxe hardcover version designed for corporate executives and other users of executive search services. Over 1,500 pages, including expanded information on each firm.

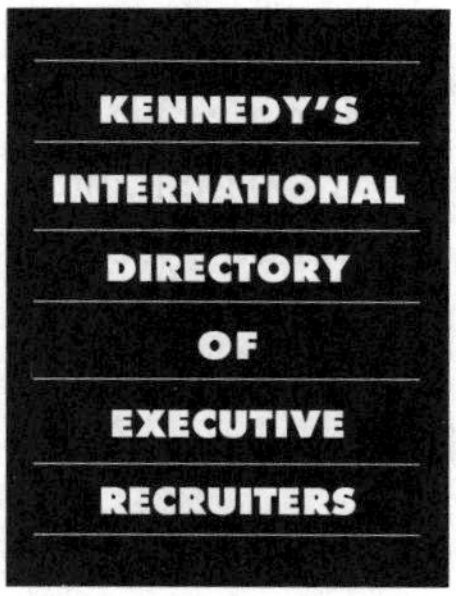

KENNEDY'S INTERNATIONAL DIRECTORY OF EXECUTIVE RECRUITERS

This directory is arranged by country and indexed by functions, industries, firm names and key principals. Includes 2,508 individual recruiters in 59 countries. Introductory articles are written by industry leaders.

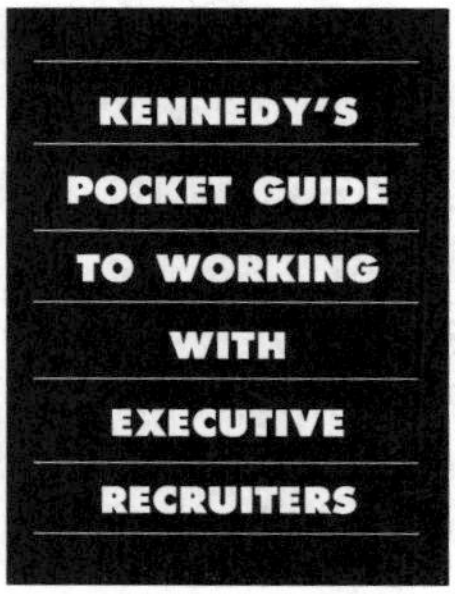

KENNEDY'S POCKET GUIDE TO WORKING WITH EXECUTIVE RECRUITERS

Highly recommended as a companion to *The Directory of Executive Recruiters, Kennedy's Pocket Guide to Working with Executive Recruiters* contains 30 chapters written by the experts themselves. Contains all the information you need to know when working with an executive recruiter.

Monthly Intelligence

EXECUTIVE RECRUITER NEWS

This monthly newsletter presents search firm rankings, eye-opening profiles of interesting firms, exclusive interviews with recruiters and clients, trends, valuable statistics on the changing size and shape of the executive search profession, and updates on management techniques for staff development, compensation, marketing and client relationships.

RECRUITING TRENDS

The monthly newsletter that provides strategies and tactics for creating and maintaining a competitive workforce. Practical guidance on college recruiting, finding 'in demand' talent, interviewing, diversity, legal issues, reference checking, managing cost-per-hire expenses and much more.

Executive Temporary Placement

KENNEDY'S DIRECTORY OF TEMPORARY PLACEMENT FIRMS, FOR EXECUTIVES MANAGERS AND PROFESSIONALS

This directory combines an analysis of the burgeoning exec temp market with the most comprehensive listings of executive, managerial and professional-level specialists available.

KENNEDY INFORMATION 800-531-0007 603-585-6544 FAX:603-585-9555 bookstore@kennedyinfo.com

Fax Back Order Form 603-585-9555

❑ **THE DIRECTORY OF EXECUTIVE RECRUITERS: PAPERBACK EDITION** $44.95 +$4.95 p&h

❑ **THE DIRECTORY OF EXECUTIVE RECRUITERS: CORPORATE EDITION (2 volume set)** $179.95 +$10.95 p&h

❑ **KENNEDY'S INTERNATIONAL DIRECTORY OF EXECUTIVE RECRUITERS** $149.95 +$10.95 p&h

❑ **KENNEDY'S POCKET GUIDE TO WORKING WITH EXECUTIVE RECRUITERS** $9.95 +$4.95 p&h

❑ **EXECUTIVE RECRUITER NEWS** $187.00/year, 12 monthly issues

❑ **RECRUITING TRENDS** $155.00/year, 12 monthly issues

❑ **KENNEDY'S DIRECTORY OF TEMPORARY PLACEMENT FIRMS FOR EXECUTIVES MANAGERS AND PROFESSIONALS** $39.95 +$4.95 p&h

❑ **SEARCHSELECT® FOR WINDOWS SINGLE COPY** $195.00

❑ **SEARCHSELECT® FOR WINDOWS ANNUAL SUBSCRIPTION (includes 4 updates)** $595.00

Or, let us create a customized list just for you on PC discs or mailing labels:
Please phone for counts & costs.

Name: ______________________

Company: ______________________

Address: ______________________

City, State, Zip: ______________________

Phone: ______________________

Orders must be pre-paid by check, money order or credit card. Orders are shipped within 24 hours.

Amount of order $ ________ Charge my: ❑ VISA ❑ MasterCard ❑ ❑ Check enclosed

Card # ______________________ Exp. ________ Signature: ______________________